THE
HARPER CONNELLY
OMNIBUS

Grave Sight
Grave Surprise
An Ice Cold Grave
Grave Secret

Charlaine Harris

First published in Great Britain in 2013 by
Gollancz
An imprint of the Orion Publishing Group
Orion House, 5 Upper St Martin's Lane,
London WC2H 9EA
An Hachette UK Company

1 3 5 7 9 10 8 6 4 2

A CIP catalogue record for this book
is available from the British Library

ISBN 978 0 575 09219 8

Typeset at The Spartan Press Ltd,
Lymington, Hants

Printed and bound by CPI Group (UK) Ltd,
Croydon, CRO 4YY

The Orion Publishing Group's policy is to use papers
that are natural, renewable and recyclable products and
made from wood grown in sustainable forests. The logging
and manufacturing processes are expected to conform to
the environmental regulations of the country of origin.

www.charlaineharris.com
www.orionbooks.co.uk
www.gollancz.co.uk

CONTENTS

GRAVE SIGHT

The silent witnesses lie everywhere, passing from one form of matter to another, gradually becoming unrecognizable to their nearest and dearest. Their bodies are rolled into gullies, shut in the trunks of abandoned cars, harnessed to cement blocks and thrown down to the bottom of lakes. Those more hastily discarded are tossed on the side of the highway – so that life, having swerved away, can swiftly pass them by without pausing to look.

Sometimes I dream I am an eagle. I soar above them, noting their remains, bearing testimony to their disposal. I spy the man who went hunting with his enemy – there, under that tree, in that thicket. I spot the bones of the waitress who served the wrong man – there, under the collapsed roof of an old shack. I detect the final destination of the teenage boy who drank too much in the wrong company – a shallow grave in the piney woods. Often, their spirits hover, clinging to the mortal remnants that housed them. Their spirits do not become angels. They were not believers during life, why should they be angels now? Even average people, people you think of as 'good,' can be foolish or venal or jealous.

My sister Cameron lies somewhere among them. In some drainage pipe or under some foundation folded into the rusted trunk of an abandoned car or strewn across a forest floor, Cameron molders. Perhaps her spirit is clinging to what is left of her body, as she waits to be discovered, as she waits for her story to be told.

Perhaps that's all they desire, all of the silent witnesses.

1

The sheriff didn't want me there. That made me wonder who'd initiated the process of finding me and asking me to come to Sarne. It had to be one of the civilians standing awkwardly in his office – all of them well dressed and well fed, obviously people used to shedding authority all around them. I looked from one to the other. The sheriff, Harvey Branscom, had a lined, red face with a bisecting white mustache and close-cropped white hair. He was at least in his mid fifties, maybe older. Dressed in a tight khaki uniform, Branscom was sitting in the swivel chair behind the desk. He looked disgusted. The man standing to Branscom's right was younger by at least ten years, and darker, and much thinner, and his narrow face was clean-shaven. His name was Paul Edwards, and he was a lawyer.

The woman with whom he was arguing, a woman somewhat younger with expensively dyed blonde hair, was Sybil Teague. She was a widow, and my brother's research had shown that she had inherited a great deal of the town of Sarne. Beside her was another man, Terence Vale, who had a round face scantily topped with thin no-color hair, wire-rimmed glasses, and one of those stick-on name-tags. He'd come from a City Council open house, he'd said when he bustled in. His stick-on tag read, 'Hi! I'm TERRY, the MAYOR.'

Since Mayor Vale and Sheriff Branscom were so put out by my presence, I figured I'd been summoned by Edwards or Teague. I swiveled my gaze from one to the other. Teague, I decided. I crossed my legs and slumped down in the uncomfortable chair. I swung my free foot, watching the toe of my black leather loafer get closer and closer to the front of the sheriff's desk. They were shooting accusations back and forth, like I wasn't in the room. I wondered if Tolliver could hear them from the waiting room.

'You all want to hash this out while we go back to the hotel?' I asked, cutting through the arguments.

They all stopped and looked at me.

'I think we brought you here under the wrong impression,' Branscom said. His voice sounded as though he were trying to be courteous, but his face looked like he wanted me the hell away. His hands were clenched on the top of his desk.

'And that wrong impression was . . . ?' I rubbed my eyes. I'd come directly from another site, and I was tired.

'Terry here misled us somewhat as to your credentials.'

'Okay, you all decide, while I get me some sleep,' I said, abruptly giving up. I pulled myself to my feet, feeling as old as the hills, or at least far older than my actual age of twenty-four. 'There's another job waiting for me in Ashdown. I'd just as soon leave here early in the morning. You'll owe us travel money, at the least. We drove here from Tulsa. Ask my brother how much that'll be.'

Without waiting for anyone to speak, I left Harvey Branscom's office and went down a corridor and through a door into the reception area. I ignored the dispatcher behind the desk, though she was looking at me curiously. No doubt she'd been aiming the same curiosity at Tolliver until I'd redirected her attention.

Tolliver tossed down the aged magazine he'd been riffling through. He pushed himself up from the fake-leather chair. Tolliver's twenty-seven. His mustache has a reddish cast; otherwise, his hair is as black as mine.

'Ready?' he asked. He could tell I was exasperated. He looked down at me, his eyebrows raised questioningly. Tolliver's at least four inches above my five foot seven. I shook my head, to tell him I'd fill him in later. He held open the glass door for me. We went out into the chilly night. I felt the cold in my bones. The seat on the Malibu was adjusted for my legs, since I'd driven last, so I slid back behind the wheel.

The police department was on one side of the town square, facing the courthouse, which stood in the center. The courthouse was a massive building erected during the twenties, the kind of edifice that would feature marble and high vaulted ceilings; impossible to heat or cool to modern standards, but impressive nonetheless. The grounds around the old building were beautifully kept, even now that all the foliage was dying back. There were still tourists parked in the premium town square parking spots. This time of year, Sarne's visitors were middle-aged to old white people, with rubber-soled shoes and windbreakers. They walked slowly and carefully, and curbs required negotiation. They tended to drive exactly the same way.

We had to navigate around the square twice before I could get in the correct lane to go east to the motel. I had a feeling that all roads in Sarne led to the square. The stores on the square and those immediately off of it were the dressed-up part of the town, the part primed for public consumption. Even the streetlights were picturesque – curving lines of metal painted a dull green and decorated with curlicues and leaves. The sidewalks were smooth and wheelchair accessible, and there were plenty of garbage bins carefully disguised to look like cute little houses. All the storefronts on the square had been remodeled to coordinate, and they all had wooden facades with 'old-timey' signs in antique lettering: Aunt Hattie's Ice Cream Parlor, Jeb's Sit-a-Spell, Jn. Banks Dry Goods and General Store, Ozark Annie's Candy. There was a heavy wooden bench outside each one. Through the bright store windows, I caught a glimpse of one or two of the shopkeepers; they were all in costume, wearing turn-of-the-century clothing.

It was past five o'clock when we finally left the square. In late October, on an overcast day, the sky was almost completely dark.

Sarne was an ugly place once you left the tourist-oriented area centered around the courthouse. Businesses like Mountain Karl's Kountry Krafts gave way to more pedestrian necessities, like First National Bank and Reynolds Appliances. The further away I drove from the square on these side streets, the more frequently I noticed occasional empty storefronts, one or two with shattered windows. The traffic was nearly nonexistent. This was the private part of Sarne, for locals. Tourist season would be over, the mayor had told me, when the leaves fell; Sarne was about to roll up its carpets – and its hospitality – for the winter months.

I was irritated with our wasted time and mileage. But I hadn't given up hope yet, and when I felt the unmistakable pull at a four-way stop five blocks east of the square, I was almost happy. It came from my left, about six yards away.

'Recent?' Tolliver asked, seeing my head jerk. I always look, even if there's no way I'll see a thing with my physical eyes.

'Very.' We weren't passing a cemetery, and I wasn't getting the feel of a newly embalmed corpse, which might indicate a funeral home. This impression was too fresh, the pull too strong.

They want to be found, you know.

Instead of going straight, which would've gotten us to the motel, I turned left, following the mental 'scent.' I pulled over into the parking lot of a small gas station. My head jerked again as I listened to the voice calling to me from the overgrown lot on the other side of the street. I say 'scent' and 'voice,' but what draws me is not really something as clear-cut as those words indicate.

About three yards into the lot was the facade of a building. From what I could read of the scorched and dangling sign, this was the former site of Evercleen Laundromat. Judging by the state of the remains of the building, Evercleen had burned halfway to the ground some years before.

'In the ruin, over there,' I told Tolliver.

'Want me to check?'

'Nah. I'll call Branscom when I get in the room.' We gave each other brief smiles. There's nothing like a concrete example to establish my bona fides. Tolliver gave me an approving nod.

I put the car into drive again. This time we reached our motel and checked into our respective rooms with no interruption. We need a break from each other after being together all day; that's the reason for the separate rooms. I don't think either of us is excessively modest.

My room was like all the others I've slept in over the past few years. The bedspread was green and quilted and slick, and the picture above the bed was a bridge somewhere in Europe, looked like. Other than those little identifiers, I could have been in any cheap motel room, anywhere in America. At least it smelled clean. I pulled out my makeup-and-medicine bag and put it in the little bathroom. Then I went and sat on the bed, leaning over to peer at the dial-out instructions on the ancient telephone. After I'd looked up the right number in the little area phone book, I called the law enforcement building and asked for the sheriff. Branscom's voice came on in less than a minute, and he was clearly less than happy to talk to me a second time. He started in again on how I'd been misrepresented – as if I'd had anything to do with that – and I interrupted him.

'I thought you'd like to know that a dead man named something like Chess, or Chester, is in the burned laundromat on Florida Street, about five blocks off the square.'

'What?' There was a long moment of silence while Harvey Branscom let that soak in. 'Darryl Chesswood? He's at home in his daughter's house. They added on a room for him last year when he began to forget where he lived. How dare you say such a thing?' He sounded honestly, righteously, offended.

'That's what I do,' I said, and laid the receiver gently on its cradle.

The town of Sarne had just gotten a freebie.

I lay back on the slippery green bedspread and crossed my hands over my ribs. I didn't need to be a psychic to predict what would happen now. The sheriff would call Chesswood's daughter. She would go to check on her dad, and she'd find he was gone. The sheriff would probably go to the site himself, since he'd be embarrassed to send a deputy on such an errand. He'd find Darryl Chesswood's body.

The old man had died of natural causes – a cerebral hemorrhage, I thought.

It was always refreshing to find someone who hadn't been murdered.

The next morning, when Tolliver and I entered the coffee shop (Kountry Good Eats) that was conveniently by the motel, the whole group was there, ensconced in a little private room. The doors to the room were open, so they couldn't miss our entrance. The dirty plates on the table in front of them, the two empty chairs, and the pot of coffee all indicated we were anticipated. Tolliver nudged me, and we exchanged looks.

I was glad I'd already put on my makeup. Usually, I don't bother until I've had my coffee.

It would have been too coy to pick another table, so I led the way to the open doors of the meeting room, the newspaper I'd bought from a vending machine tucked under my arm. The cramped room was almost filled with a big round table. Sarne's movers and shakers sat around that table, staring at us. I tried to remember if I'd combed my hair that morning. Tolliver would've told me if I'd looked really bed-headed, I told myself. I keep my hair short. It has lots of body, and it's curly, so if I let it grow, I have a black bush to deal with. Tolliver is lucky; his is straight, and he lets it grow until he can tie it back. Then he'll get tired of it and whack it off. Right now, it was short.

'Sheriff,' I said, nodding. 'Mr Edwards, Ms Teague, Mr Vale. How are you all this morning?' Tolliver held out my chair and I sat. This was an extra, for-show courtesy. He figures the more honor he shows me publicly, the more the public will feel I'm entitled to. Sometimes it works that way.

The waitress had filled my coffee cup and I'd taken my first swallow before the sheriff spoke. I tore my gaze away from my paper, still folded by my plate. I really, really like to read the paper while I drink my coffee.

'He was there,' Harvey Branscom said heavily. The man's face was ten years older than it'd been the night before, and there was white stubble on his cheeks.

'Mr Chesswood, you mean.' I ordered the fruit plate and some yogurt from a waitress who seemed to think that was a strange choice. Tolliver got French toast and bacon and a flirtatious look. He's hell on waitresses.

'Yeah,' the sheriff said. 'Mr Chesswood. Darryl Chesswood. He was a good friend of my father's.' He said this with a heavy emphasis, as if the fact that I'd told him where the old man's body was had laid the responsibility for the death at my door.

'Sorry for your loss,' Tolliver said, as a matter of form. I nodded. After that, I let the silence expand. With a gesture, Tolliver offered to refill my coffee cup, but I raised my hand to show him how steady it was today. I took another deep sip gratefully, and I topped the cup off. I touched Tolliver's mug to ask if he was ready for more, but he shook his head.

Under the furtive scrutiny of all those eyes, I wasn't able to open the newspaper I had folded in front of me. I had to wait on these yahoos to make up their minds to something they'd already agreed to do. I'd felt optimistic when I'd seen them waiting for us, but that optimism was rapidly deteriorating.

A lot of eye signaling was going on among the Sarnites (Sarnians?). Paul Edwards leaned forward to deliver the result of all this conferencing. He was a handsome man, and he was used to being noticed.

'How did Mr Chesswood die?' he asked, as if it were the bonus question.

'Cerebral hemorrhage.' God, these people. I looked at my paper longingly.

Edwards leaned back as though I'd socked him in the mouth. They all did some more eye signaling. My fruit arrived – sliced cantaloupe that was hard and tasteless, canned pineapple, a banana in the peel, and some grapes. Well, after all, it was fall. When Tolliver had been served his eggs and toast, we began to eat.

'We're sorry there may have been some hesitation last night,' Sybil

Teague said. 'Especially since it seems you, ah, interpreted it as us backing out on our agreement.'

'Yes, I did take it that way. Tolliver?'

'I took it that way, too,' he said solemnly. Tolliver has acne-scarred cheeks and dark eyes and a deep, resonant voice. Whatever he says sounds significant.

'I just got cold feet, I guess.' She tried to look charmingly apologetic, but it didn't work for me. 'When Terry told me what he'd heard about you, and Harvey agreed to contact you, we had no idea what we were getting into. Hiring someone like you is not something I've ever done before.'

'There is no one like Harper,' Tolliver said flatly. He was looking up from his plate, meeting their eyes.

He'd thrown Sylvia Teague off her stride. She had to pause and regroup. 'I am sure you're right,' she said insincerely. 'Now, Miss Connelly, to get back to the job we're all hoping you'll do.'

'First of all,' Tolliver said, patting his mustache with his napkin, 'Who's paying Harper?'

They stared at him as if that were a foreign concept.

'You all are obviously the town officials, though I'm not real sure what Mr Edwards here does. Ms Teague, are you paying Harper privately, or is she on the town payroll?'

'I'm paying Miss Connelly,' Sybil Teague said. There was a lot more starch in her voice now that money had been mentioned. 'Paul's here as my lawyer. Harvey's my brother.' Evidently, Terry Vale wasn't her anything. 'Now, let me tell you what I want you to do.' Sybil met my eyes.

I glanced back at my plate while I took the grapes off the stem. 'You want me to look for a missing person,' I said flatly. 'Like always.' They like it better when you say 'missing person' rather than the more accurate 'missing corpse.'

'Yes, but she was a wild girl. Maybe she ran away. We're not entirely sure . . . not all of us are sure . . . that she is actually dead.'

As if I hadn't heard *that* before. 'Then we have a problem.'

'And that is?' She was getting impatient – not used to much discussion of her agenda, I figured.

'I only find dead people.'

*

'They knew that,' I told Tolliver in an undertone, as we walked back to our rooms. 'They *knew* that. I don't find live people. I can't.'

I was getting upset, and that was dumb.

'Sure, they know,' he said calmly. 'Maybe they just don't want to admit she's dead. People are funny like that. It's like – if they pretend there's hope, there *is* hope.'

'It's a waste of my time – hope,' I said.

'I know it is,' Tolliver said. 'They can't help it, though.'

Round three.

Paul Edwards, Sybil Teague's attorney, had drawn the short straw. So here he was in my room. The others, I assumed, had scattered to step back into their daily routine.

Tolliver and I had gotten settled into the two chairs at the standard cheap-motel table. I had finally begun reading the paper. Tolliver was working on a science fiction sword-and-sorcery paperback he'd found discarded in the last motel. We glanced at each other when we heard the knock at the door.

'My money's on Edwards,' I said.

'Branscom,' Tolliver said.

I grinned at him from behind the lawyer's back as I shut the door.

'If you would agree, after all our discussion,' the lawyer said apologetically, 'I've been asked to take you to the site.' I glanced at the clock. It was now nine o'clock. They'd taken about forty-five minutes to arrive at a consensus.

'And this is the site of . . . ?' I let my words hang in the air.

'The probable murder of Teenie – Monteen – Hopkins. The murder, or maybe suicide, of Dell Teague, Sybil's son.'

'Am I supposed to be finding one body, or two?' Two would cost them more.

'We know where Dell is,' Edwards said, startled. 'He's in the cemetery. You just need to find Teenie.'

'Are we talking woods? What kind of terrain?' Tolliver asked practically.

'Woods. Steep terrain, in places.'

Knowing we were on our way to the Ozarks, we'd brought the right gear. I changed to my hiking boots, put on a bright blue padded jacket, and stuck a candy bar, a compass, a small bottle of water, and a fully charged cell phone in my pockets. Tolliver went through the connecting door into his own room, and when he returned he was togged out in a similar manner. Paul Edwards watched us with a peculiar fascination. He was interested enough to forget how handsome he was, just for a few minutes.

'I guess you do this all the time,' he said.

I tightened my bootlaces to the right degree of snugness. I doubleknotted them. I grabbed a pair of gloves. 'Yep,' I said. 'That's what I do.' I tossed a bright red knitted scarf around my neck. I'd tuck it in properly when I got really cold. The scarf was not only warm, but highly visible. I glanced in the mirror. Good enough.

'Don't you find it depressing?' Edwards asked, as if he just couldn't help himself. There was a subtle warmth in his eyes that hadn't been there before. He'd remembered he was handsome, and that I was a young woman.

I almost said, 'No, I find it lucrative.' But I know people find my earning method distasteful, and that would have been only partly the truth, anyway.

'It's a service I can perform for the dead,' I said finally, and that was equally true.

Edwards nodded, as if I'd said something profound. He wanted all three of us to go in his Outback, but we took our own car. We always did. (This practice dates from the time a client left us in the woods nineteen miles from town, upset at my failure to find his brother's body. I'd been pretty sure the body lay somewhere to the west of the area he'd had me target, but he didn't want to pay for a longer search. It wasn't my fault his brother had lived long enough to stagger toward the stream. Anyway, it had been a long, long walk back into town.)

I let my mind go blank as we followed Edwards northwest, farther into the Ozarks. The foliage was beautiful this time of year, and that beauty drew a fair amount of tourists. The twisting, climbing road was dotted with stands for selling rocks and crystals – 'genuine Ozark crafts' – and all sorts of homemade jellies and jams. All the stands touted some version of the hillbilly theme, a marketing strategy that I found incomprehensible. 'We were sure ignorant and toothless and picturesque! Stop to see if we still are!'

I stared into the woods as we drove, into their chilly and brilliant depths. All along the way, I got 'hits' of varying intensity.

There are dead people everywhere, of course. The older the death, the less of a buzz I get.

It's hard to describe the feeling – but of course, that's what everyone wants to know, what it feels like to sense a dead person. It's a little like hearing a bee droning inside your head, or maybe the pop of a Geiger counter – a persistent and irregular noise, increasing in strength the closer I get to the body. There's something electric about it, too; I can feel this buzzing all through my body. I guess that's not too surprising.

We passed three cemeteries (one quite small, very old) and one hidden Indian burial site, a mound or barrow that had been reshaped by time until it just resembled another rolling hill. That ancient site signaled very faintly; it was like hearing a cloud of mosquitoes, very far away.

I was tuned in to the forest and the earth by the time Paul Edwards pulled to the shoulder of the road. The woods encroached so nearly that there was hardly room to park the vehicles and still leave room for other cars to pass. I figured Tolliver had to be worried someone would come along too fast and clip the Malibu. But he didn't say anything.

'Tell me what happened,' I said to the dark-haired man.

'Can't you just go look? Why do you need to know?' He was suspicious.

'If I have a little knowledge about the circumstances, I can look for her more intelligently,' I said.

'Okay. Well. Last spring, Teenie came out here with Mrs Teague's son, who was also Sheriff Branscom's nephew – Sybil and Harvey are brother and sister. Sybil's son was named Dell. Dell was Teenie's boyfriend, had been for two years, off and on. They were both seventeen. A hunter found Dell's body. He'd been shot, or he'd shot himself. They never found Teenie.'

'How was their location discovered?' Tolliver asked, pointing at the patch of ground on which we stood.

'Car parked right where we're parked now. See that half-fallen pine? Supported by two other trees? Makes a good marker to remember the spot by. Dell'd been missing less than four hours when one of the families that live out this way gave Sybil a call about the car. There were folks out searching soon after that, but like I say, it was another few hours before Dell was found. Right after that, it started raining, and it rained for hours. Wiped out the tracking scent, so the bloodhounds weren't any use.'

'Why wasn't anyone looking for Teenie?'

'No one knew Teenie was with Dell. Her mom didn't realize Teenie was missing for almost twenty hours, maybe longer. She didn't know about Dell, and she delayed calling the police.'

'How long ago was this?'

'Maybe six months ago.'

Hmm. Something fishy, here. 'How come we're just being called out now?'

'Because half the town thinks that Teenie was killed and buried by Dell, and then he committed suicide. It's making Sybil crazy. Teenie's mom's hard up. Even if she thought of calling you in, she couldn't afford you. Sybil decided to fund this, after she heard about you through Terry, who went to some mayor's conference and talked to the head honcho of some little town in the Arklatex.' I glanced over at Tolliver. 'El Dorado,' he murmured, and I nodded after a second, remembering. Paul Edwards said, 'Sybil can't stand the shame of the suspicion. She liked Teenie, no matter how wild the girl was. Sybil really assumed she'd be part of their family some day.'

'No Mister Teague?' I asked. 'She's a widow, right?'

'Yes, Sybil's a fairly recent widow. She's got a daughter, too, Mary Nell, who's seventeen.'

'So why were Teenie and Dell out here?'

He shrugged, with a half smile. 'That's a question no one ever asked; I mean, hell, seventeen, in the woods in spring . . . I guess we all thought it was a little obvious.'

'But they parked up by the road.' That was what was obvious, but apparently not to Paul Edwards. 'Kids wanting to have sex, they're going to hide their car better than that. Small town kids know how easy it is to be caught out.'

Edwards looked surprised, his lean dark face shutting down on sudden and unwelcome thoughts. 'Not much traffic out on this road,' he said, but without much conviction.

I put on my dark glasses. Edwards again looked at me askance. It was an overcast day. I nodded to Tolliver.

'Lay on, Macduff,' Tolliver said, to Paul Edwards's confusion. Edwards's high school must have done *Julius Caesar* instead of *Macbeth*. Tolliver gestured to the woods, and Edwards, looking relieved to understand his mission, began to lead us downhill.

It was steep going. Tolliver stayed by my side, as he always did; I was abstracted, and he knew I might fall. It had happened before.

After twenty minutes of careful, slow, downhill hiking, made even trickier by the slippery leaves and pine needles blanketing the steep slope, we came to a large fallen oak piled with leaves, branches, and other detritus. It was easy to see that a heavy rainfall would sweep debris downslope, to lodge against the tree.

'This is where Dell was found,' Paul Edwards said. He pointed to the downslope side of the fallen oak. I wasn't surprised it had taken two days to find Dell Teague's body, even in the spring; but I was startled at the location of the corpse. I was glad I'd put on the dark glasses.

'On that side of the log?' I asked, pointing to make sure I had it right.

'Yes,' Edwards said.

'And he had a gun? It was by his body?'

'Well, no.'

'But the theory was that he'd shot himself?'

'Yeah, that's what the sheriff's office said.'

'Obvious problem there.'

'The sheriff thought maybe the gun could've been grabbed by a hunter who didn't report what he found. Or maybe one of the guys who actually did find Dell lifted the gun. After all, guns are expensive and almost everyone here uses firearms of some kind.' Edwards shrugged. 'Or, if Dell shot himself on the upslope side of the log and fell over it, the gun could have slid down the hill quite a distance, gotten hidden like that.'

'So the wounds – how many were there?'

'Two. One, a graze to the side of his head, was counted as a . . . sort of a first try. Then, through the eye.'

'So the two wounds were counted as suicide wounds, one unsuccessful and one not, and no gun was found. And he was on the downslope side of the log.'

'Yes, ma'am.' The lawyer took off his hat, slapped it against his leg.

This was all wrong. Well, maybe . . . 'How was he lying? What position?'

'What, you want me to show you?'

'Yes. Did you see him?'

'Yes, ma'am, I sure did. I came out to identify him. Didn't want his mom to see him like that. Sybil and I have been friends for years.'

'Then just humor me by assuming the position Dell was in, okay?'

Edwards looked as if he wished he were elsewhere. He knelt on the ground, reluctance in every line of his body. He was facing the fallen tree. Putting out a hand to steady himself, he sank down to the ground. His legs were bent at the knees and he was on his right side.

Tolliver moved behind me. 'This ain't right,' he whispered in my ear.

I nodded agreement. 'Okay, thanks,' I said out loud. Paul Edwards scrambled to his feet.

'I don't see why you needed to see where Dell was, anyway,' he said, trying his best not to sound accusatory. 'We're looking for Teenie.'

'What's her last name?' Not that it mattered for search purposes, but I'd forgotten; and it showed respect, to know the name.

'Teenie Hopkins. Monteen Hopkins.'

I was still upslope of the fallen tree, and I began making my way to the right. It felt appropriate, and it was as good a way to begin as any.

'You might as well go back up to your SUV,' I heard Tolliver telling our reluctant escort.

'You might need help,' Edwards said.

'We do, I'll come get you.'

I didn't worry about us getting lost. Tolliver's job was to prevent that, and he'd never failed me; except for once, in the desert, and I'd teased him about that for so long that he'd about gone crazy. Of course, since we'd nearly died, it was a lesson worth reinforcing.

It was best if I could walk with my eyes closed, but on this terrain that would be dangerous. The dark glasses helped, blocking out some of the color and life around me.

For the first thirty minutes of struggling across the steep slope, all I felt were the faint *pings* of ancient deaths. The world is sure full of dead people.

When I was convinced that no matter how stealthily he might be able to move, Paul Edwards could not have followed us, I paused at a rocky outcrop and took off my dark glasses. I looked at Tolliver.

'Bullshit,' he said.

'No kidding.'

'The gun's missing, but it's suicide? Shot twice, and it's suicide? I could swallow one of those, but not both. And anyone who's going to kill himself, he's going to sit on the log and think about it. He's not going to stand downhill of a landmark like that. Suicides go *up*.' We'd had experience.

'Besides,' I said, 'he fell on the hand that would've been holding the gun. If by some weird chance that should have happened, I feel pretty confident that no one would be reaching under the corpse to steal the gun.'

'Only someone with a cast-iron stomach.'

'And through the eye! Have you ever heard of anyone shooting himself like that?'

Tolliver shook his head.

'Someone done killed that boy,' he said. Some days Tolliver is more country than others.

'Damn straight,' I said.

We thought about that for a minute. 'But we better keep on looking for the girl,' I said. Tolliver would expect me to make up my own mind about that.

He nodded. 'She's out here, too,' he said, a little question in his voice.

'Most likely.' I cocked my head to one side while I considered. 'Unless the boy was killed trying to stop someone from taking her.' We started walking again, and the ground became easier going; certainly not a flat surface, but not so steep.

There are worse ways to spend a fall day than walking through the woods while the leaves are brilliant, the sun dappling the ground from time to time when the clouds shifted. I felt out with all my senses. We tracked a *ping* that, upon attaining, proved too old by a decade to be the girl. When I was standing a foot from the site, I knew the body to be that of a black male who had died of exposure. He had become naturally buried under leaves, branches, and dirt that had washed downhill over the course of the past decade. What you could see was blackened ribs with tattered cloth and bits of muscle still clinging to the bones.

I took one of the red cloth strips I keep in my jacket pocket, and Tolliver took a whippy length of wire from a supply he kept stashed in a long pocket on his pants leg. I tied a strip to one end of the wire while Tolliver ran the other end into the ground. We'd walked maybe a quarter of a mile southwest from the fallen tree, and I jotted that down.

'Hunting accident,' Tolliver suggested. I nodded. I can't always pin it down exactly, but the moment of death had that feel: panic, solitude. Long-suffering. I was certain he'd fallen out of his deer stand, breaking his back. He'd lain there until the elements claimed him. There were a few pieces of wood still nailed way up in the tree. Named Bright? Mark Bright? Something like that.

Well, he wasn't part of my paycheck. This man was my second freebie for the town of Sarne. Time to earn some money.

We started off again. I began working my way to the east, but I felt uneasy. After we'd proceeded maybe sixty feet from the hunter's bones, I got a welcome, sharp buzz from the north. Uphill, which was slightly odd. But then I realized that we had to go uphill to get to the road. The closer to the road I climbed, the closer I approached the remains of Teenie Hopkins – or some young white girl. The buzzing turned into a continuous drone, and I fell to my knees in the leaves. She was there. Not all of her, but enough. Some big branches had been thrown across her for concealment, but now they were dead and dry. Teenie Hopkins had spent a long, hot summer under those branches. But she still made more of a corpse than the hunter, despite insects, animals, and a few months of weather.

Tolliver knelt by me, one arm around me.

'Bad?' he asked. Though my eyes were closed, I could feel the movements of his body as his head turned, checking in all directions. Once we'd been surprised at the dumpsite by the killer returning with another body. Talk about your irony.

This was the hard part. This was the worst part. Normally, finding a corpse simply indicated I'd been successful. The manner of its becoming a corpse did not particularly affect me. This was my job. All people had to die somehow or other. But this rotting thing in the leaves . . . she'd been running, running, breath whistling in and out, reduced from a person to a panicked organism, and then the bullet had entered her back and then another one had . . .

I fainted.

Tolliver was holding me in his lap. We were among the leaves – oak and gum and sassafras and maple – a ruffle of gold and brown and red. He had his back to a big old gum tree, and I was sure he was uncomfortable with all the gum-balls that must be pressing into his butt.

'Come on, baby, wake up,' he was telling me, and from the sound of his voice, it wasn't the first time he'd said it.

'I'm awake,' I said, hating how weak my voice came out.

'Jesus, Harper. Don't do that.'

'Sorry.'

I leaned my face against his chest for one more minute, sighed, and reasserted myself by scrambling to my feet. I wavered back and forth for a second until I got stabilized.

'What killed her?' he asked.

'Shot in the back, twice.'

He waited to see if I'd add more.

'She was running,' I explained. So he would understand her terror and her desperation, in the last moments of her life.

Last minutes are hardly ever that bad.

Of course, my standard is probably different from most people's.

Paul Edwards was waiting by his gleaming silver Outback when we emerged from the woods. His whole face was a question, but our first report should be to our client. Tolliver asked the lawyer to start back to town to assemble the committee, if that was what Ms Teague wanted. We drove silently back to Sarne, stopping only once at a convenience store. Tolliver went in to get me a Coke, one with real sugar in it. I always crave sugar after finding a body.

'You need to drink about four of these, gain some weight,' Tolliver muttered, as he often did.

I ignored him, as I always did, and drank the Coke. I felt better after ten minutes. Until I'd discovered the sugar remedy, I'd sometimes had to go to bed for a day following a successful recovery.

The same group would be gathered in the sheriff's office, and I sat in the car and stared at the glass doors for a second, reluctant to begin this segment of the job.

'You want me to wait in the lobby?'

'No, I want you to come in with me,' I said, and Tolliver nodded. I paused, one hand on the car door. 'They're not gonna like this,' I said.

He nodded again.

This time, we were in a conference room. It was a tight fit, with Branscom, Edwards, Teague, and Vale, plus Tolliver and me.

'The map,' I said to Tolliver. He spread it out. I laid everything I wanted to say out in a line ahead of me, so I could reach my goal, which was to get out of this office and this town with a check in my hands.

'Before we get into the main subject,' I said, 'let me point out that we also found the body of a black male, dead about ten years, at this site.' I indicated the red mark we'd made first. 'He died of exposure.'

The sheriff seemed to be thinking back. 'That might be Marcus Allbright,' he said slowly. 'I was a deputy back then. His wife thought he'd run off. My God. I'll go collect what's left.'

I shrugged. Nothing to do with me. 'Now, for Teenie Hopkins.' They all tensed, and Paul Edwards even leaned closer. 'She was shot twice in the back, and her remains are right here.' I touched a spot with my fingertip.

There was an audible gasp from the people seated at the table.

'You saw her?' Hi, I'm TERRY, the MAYOR asked. His eyes were wide behind his wire-rimmed glasses. Mr Mayor was on the verge of crying.

'Saw what's left,' I said, and then reflected that a nod would have been sufficient.

'You mean,' the Teague woman said incredulously, 'you left her out there?' Harvey Branscom gave her a look of sheer amazement.

I stared back at her with much the same expression. 'It's a crime scene,' I said. 'And I don't do body retrieval. I leave that to qualified people. You go get her, if you don't want the sheriff to investigate.' Then I took a deep breath. This was the client. 'Two shots in the back, so we still don't know how it happened. If your son was shot first, then Teenie was killed by the same person. Of course, if it was your son who shot her, he then killed himself afterward. But I doubt he committed suicide.'

That shut her up, at least temporarily. I had the complete and utter attention of everyone in the room. 'Oh my God,' whispered Sybil.

'So how do you *know*?' the sheriff asked.

'How do I find bodies in the first place? I just do. When I find 'em, I know what killed 'em. Believe me, don't believe me. It's up to you, now. You wanted me to find Teenie Hopkins, I found what's left of her. There might be a bone or two missing. Animals.'

Sybil Teague was staring at me with an extraordinary expression on her face. She didn't know whether to praise me or be disgusted by me.

But at least I believed her son Dell had not committed suicide. She ran her hands over her golden-brown pants suit, over and over, smoothing the front of the light jacket, then the material over her thighs.

'Call Hollis,' the sheriff said into his intercom, and we sat in frozen silence until a man in a deputy's uniform came in. He was in his late twenties, sturdy and blond and blue-eyed and curious as hell about what had been going on in the sheriff's office. He gave Tolliver and me a comprehensive stare. He'd know us again. He looked pretty good in the uniform.

'Ms Connelly,' the sheriff said. 'You go out with Hollis here, show him where the body is.'

Hollis looked startled as he took in the sense of what was more an order than a request.

'Which one?' I asked, and his eyes widened.

'I'll go,' Tolliver said. 'Harper needs to rest.'

'No, Ms Connelly is the one who found her, she needs to go.'

Tolliver glared at the sheriff and he glared right back. I was betting the sheriff wanted to make sure I earned every penny of my fee. I made myself stir. 'I'll go,' I said. I put my hand on Tolliver's arm. 'It'll be okay.' My fingers curled around the material of his jacket, holding on to him for a long moment. Then I let go. I jerked my head at the blond deputy. 'He'll bring me right back,' I said over my shoulder, because I wanted Tolliver to stay there while I was gone. He nodded, and the door closed behind me, and I lost sight of him.

The deputy led the way out to his patrol car. 'My name is Hollis Boxleitner,' he said, by way of introduction.

'Harper Connelly,' I said.

'That your husband in there?'

'My brother. Tolliver Lang.'

'Different names.'

'Yeah.'

'Where we goin'?'

'Drive out Highway 19, going northwest.'

'Out where—'

'The boy was shot,' I said.

'Killed himself,' Hollis Boxleitner corrected, but with little conviction.

'Hmmph,' I said contemptuously.

'How do you find them?' he asked.

'The sheriff tell you I was coming?'

'I overheard him on the phone. He thought Sybil was crazy for asking you to come. He was mad at Terry Vale for telling her what he'd heard about you.'

'I got struck by lightning,' I said, 'When I was about fifteen.'

He seemed to be groping for questions to ask. 'Were you at your house?'

'Yes,' I said. 'Me, and Tolliver, and my sister Cameron . . . we were at home alone. My two younger half-sisters were singing in some special program. My mother actually went to the pre-school to watch.' The state my mother was in by that time, it was amazing she remembered she had children. 'And the storm come up, about four in the afternoon. I was in the bathroom. The sink was next to the window, and the window was open. I was standing at the sink so I could look in the mirror while I used my electric hair curler. It came in the window. Next thing I knew, I was on the floor looking up at the ceiling, and my hair was smoking, and my shoes were off my feet. Tolliver gave me CPR. Then the ambulance came.'

This was babbling, for me. I decided to shut up.

Hollis Boxleitner didn't seem to have any more questions, which was wonderful and puzzling. For most people, that would just have scratched the surface of what they wanted to know. I hugged my jacket to my chest, imagining how good it would be when I could get in the bed at the motel. I would pile on the covers. I would have hot soup for supper. I closed my eyes for a few minutes. When I opened them, I felt better. We were close to the site.

I instructed the deputy to pull over when I calculated, by the pull I felt, that we were at the bit of road closest to the body. Now that I knew where she was, the body was easier to locate on my mental map. We got out for the hike downhill, a much easier one than our earlier descent to the death site of the boy. As we moved carefully downslope, Boxleitner said, 'So now you find dead people for your living.'

'Yep,' I said. 'That's what I do.' I also had very bad headaches, shaky hands, and a strange spiderweb pattern on my right leg, which was weaker than my left. Though I run regularly to keep the muscles strong, making my way up and down steep slopes today had made that leg feel wobbly. I leaned against a tree as I pointed to the pile of debris that concealed what was left of Teenie Hopkins.

After he looked under the branches, Boxleitner threw up. He

seemed embarrassed by that, but I thought nothing of it. You have to see that kind of thing real often to be unimpressed by the havoc time and nature can wreck on our bodies. I had a feeling small town policemen didn't see old bodies very often. And he'd probably known the girl.

'It's worst when they're in-between,' I offered.

He understood what I meant, and he nodded vehemently. I started back to the patrol car, leaving him alone to collect himself and do whatever official stuff he had to do.

I was leaning against the car door when Hollis Boxleitner struggled up the slope, wiping at his mouth with the back of his hand. To mark the spot, he tied an orange strip of plastic to the tree nearest the road and the car. He gestured toward the car door, indicating I should get in, and he drove back to the town in grim silence. 'Teenie Hopkins was my sister-in-law,' he said as we parked.

There wasn't anything for me to say.

I let him precede me into the police station. We had only been gone forty-five minutes or so, and the crew was still assembled. The tightness in Tolliver's jaw told me that they'd been grilling him about me – maybe about my success rate – and he'd had to do some explaining. He hated that.

All the faces turned toward us, questioning: the mayor's looked only curious, the lawyer's cautious, the sheriff's angry. Tolliver was relieved. Sybil Teague was tense and miserable.

'Body's there,' Hollis said briefly.

'You're sure it's Teenie?' Mrs Teague sounded . . . somewhere between stunned and grief-stricken.

'No, ma'am,' Boxleitner said. 'No, ma'am, I'm not sure at all. The dentist will be able to tell us. I'll give Dr Kerry a call. That'll be good enough for an unofficial identification. We'll have to send the remains to Little Rock.'

I was sure the body was Teenie Hopkins, of course, but Sybil Teague wouldn't thank me for saying so again. In fact, she was looking at me with some distaste. It was an attitude I'd run across many times before. She'd hired me, and she would pay me a very tidy sum of money, but she didn't want to believe me. She'd actually be happy if I was wrong. And I certainly wasn't her favorite person, though I'd brought her the information for which she'd asked . . . the information she'd gone to so much trouble to bring me to Sarne to deliver.

Maybe, when I'd first started out in my business, I was able to sympathize with this perverse attitude: but I couldn't any longer. It just made me feel tired.

2

No one wanted to talk to us, or needed to talk to us, any longer. In fact, the very sight of me was giving Mayor Terry Vale a serious case of the cold creepies. He was the least connected to the case, and in fact I couldn't figure out his continued presence, but the others appeared to be worried about his peace of mind, so Tolliver and I took our leave.

A series of phone calls had revealed that Teenie's dentist, Dr Kerry, was out of town for the next four days. The body could only be identified in Little Rock. Sheriff Branscom had called the state crime lab, and they'd said as soon as they got the body they'd confirm the identification first thing, before they did their full work-up. Since the Arkansas crime lab is notoriously behind, that was a good concession. Branscom had a copy of Teenie's dental records to send down with the body.

We wouldn't get a check from Sybil until the body was declared to be that of Teenie Hopkins, so it looked like we'd be stuck in Sarne at least twenty-four hours. Twenty-four hours with nothing to do. We spend a lot of time waiting, but it's not easy.

'The motel's got HBO,' Tolliver said. 'Maybe we can catch a movie we haven't seen.'

But after we'd reviewed the movie list and discovered we'd already seen the ones we were at all interested in seeing, Tolliver left to pursue the waitress from the diner. Not that he spelled it out for me, but I figured.

I was too restless to read, and I'd warmed up enough to discard the crawling-into-bed plan. I've gotten into doing my fingernails and toenails, just to have a hobby. So I got out my manicure kit, and I was painting my toenails a deep, almost golden red, when Hollis Boxleitner knocked on my door.

'Can I come in?' he asked. I leaned sideways to look past him, checking to make sure he wasn't in a police car. Nope. Though he was still in his uniform, he was driving his own vehicle, an electric-blue Ford pickup.

'I guess,' I said. I left the door open to the beautiful day, and the big deputy didn't protest. Hollis Boxleitner sat in one of the two chairs. I took the other one, after offering him a can of Fresca that was chilly and wet from the ice chest. He popped the tab and took a gulp. I propped my foot up on the edge of the table and continued my pedicure.

'You want to go down to the restaurant, have some chicken-fried steak?' he asked.

'No thanks.' It was a little past one o'clock, so I should eat something, but I wasn't feeling too hungry.

'Not the calories, is it? You could use some more flesh on your bones.'

'No, not the calories.' I stroked the brush very carefully from base to end of my big toenail.

'Your brother's already down there. He's having a conversation with Janine.'

I shrugged.

'What about the Sonic?' I darted a glance at him, but he only looked mildly inquiring.

'What do you want?' I asked. I don't like being maneuvered.

He looked at me, put the can of soda down. 'I just want to talk to you a little bit about Monteen Hopkins. My sister-in-law. The girl you think we found today.'

'I don't need to know anything else about her.' It was better not to. I knew enough. I knew about her last moments on earth. That was as personal as you could get. 'And I guarantee,' I added, since I have professional pride, 'the body we found is Monteen Hopkins.'

He looked at his empty hands, big hands with golden hair on the backs. 'I was afraid you'd say that,' he said, falling quiet for a minute. 'Come on, let's get a milk shake. I was the one who threw up at the site, and even my stomach is saying it needs something. So I know yours has got to be ready.'

I looked at him for a long moment, trying to figure him out. But he was a closed door to me, since he was among the living. Finally, I nodded.

My toenails weren't quite dry, so despite the autumn bite in the air, I stepped into his truck barefoot. He seemed to find that amusing. Hollis Boxleitner was a husky man with a crooked nose, a broad face, and a smile full of gleaming white teeth, though at the moment he was far from smiling. His pale blond hair was smooth as glass.

'You always lived here in Sarne?' I asked, after we'd parked at the Sonic and he'd pressed the button to order two chocolate shakes.

'For ten years,' he said. 'I moved here my last two years of high school, and I stayed. I had a couple years of community college, but I commuted to class after the first year.'

'Been married? Was that how Teenie was your sister-in-law?'

'Yes.'

I nodded acknowledgment. 'Kids?'

'No.'

Maybe he'd known the marriage wouldn't last.

'My wife was Monteen's older sister,' he said. 'My wife is dead.'

That was a shocker. I sighed. While Hollis paid for the shakes, I reflected that I was going to learn about Teenie Hopkins, whether I wanted to or not.

'I met Monteen when she was thirteen. I picked her up from outside a juke joint way out in the county, while I was on patrol. It was so obvious she was underage and had no business being there. She made a pass at me in the police car. She was totally out of hand. I met Sally when I took Monteen home to her mom's house that night.' He was silent for a moment, remembering. 'I liked Sally a lot, the first time I laid eyes on her. She was a regular girl, with a lot of sweetness in her. Teenie was wild as a razorback.'

'So the Teagues couldn't have been that happy about their son dating her.'

'You could say that. Teenie got it from her mom. At that time, Helen was drinking a lot, and not too particular about who she brought home. But Helen managed to change, finally quit drinking. When Teenie's mom settled down, Teenie did, too.'

That wasn't how Sybil had tried to make it appear, at our second meeting. I filed that fact for future reference.

'How do you get hired?' he asked.

I sucked hard on the straw, thinking over the abrupt change in subject. It was a good milk shake, but it had been a mistake to get a cold drink on a brisk day when I was barefoot. I shivered.

'Lots of word of mouth. That's how I got hired here; Terry Vale heard something about me at a city government conference. Law enforcement people talk to each other, at conventions and by email. And there've been stories in a professional magazine or two.'

He nodded. 'I guess you couldn't advertise.'

'Sometimes, we do. Hard to get the wording right.'

'I can see that.' He smiled reluctantly. Then he reverted to just being intense. 'You just . . . feel them?'

I nodded. 'I see the last moments. Like a tiny clip of a video. Can you please turn on the heater?'

'Yes, we'll ride.' A minute later, we'd left Sonic and were cruising what there was of Sarne.

'How big is the police force here?' I was trying to be polite. There was an undercurrent here, and the water in it was moving faster and faster.

'Full-time, besides me? The sheriff, two other deputies right now.'

'Stretched pretty thin.'

'Not during this season. Now, we've just got leaf people. Come to see the colors change. They're pretty peaceable.' Hollis shook his head over people taking time off from life to look at a bunch of leaves. 'Summer tourist season, we take on six part-time people. Traffic control and so on.'

Hollis Boxleitner's income would be small. He was a youngish man, and he seemed both capable and intelligent. What was he doing, stuck in Sarne? Okay, not my business: but I was curious.

'I inherited my parents' house here,' he said, as if he were answering my unspoken question. 'They got killed when a logging truck hit their car.' He nodded in acknowledgment when I told him I was sorry. He didn't want to talk about their deaths, and that was a good thing. 'I like the hunting and the fishing, and the people. In the summer, I get some hours in helping my brother-in-law; he's got a rafting business, rents 'em out to the tourists. I pretty much work around the clock for three months, but it helps me build up my bank account. What does your brother do, when he's not helping you?'

'He's always with me.'

Hollis looked as if he were politely swallowing scorn. 'That's all he does?'

'It's enough.' The thought of managing by myself made me shiver.

'So, how much do you charge for your services?' he asked, his eyes on the road ahead of him.

I hoped there wasn't an implication there. I kept silent.

It took a while to make Hollis uncomfortable, longer than it took for most people.

'I want to hire you,' he said, by way of explanation.

I hadn't expected that, 'I charge five thousand dollars,' I told him. 'Payable on a positive identification of the body.'

'What if the location of the body is known? You can tell the cause of death, too, right?'

'Yes. Of course I charge less if I don't have to find the body.' Sometimes the family wants an independent suggestion about the cause of death.

'You ever been wrong?'

'Not that I know of.' I looked out the window at the passing town. 'When I can locate the body, that is. I don't always find it. Sometimes, there's just not enough information available to tell me where to search. Like the Morgenstern girl.' I was referring to a case that had made headlines the year before. Tabitha Morgenstern had been grabbed off a suburban road in Nashville, and she'd never been seen since that day. 'Just knowing the point where someone vanished isn't enough. She might have been dumped anywhere, in Tennessee or Mississippi or Kentucky. Not enough information. I had to tell her parents I couldn't do it.'

Though the cemetery wasn't yet visible, I knew we were approaching one. I could tell by the buzzing along my skin. 'How old is the cemetery?' I asked. 'It's the newest one, I guess?'

He pulled over to the side of the road so abruptly I almost lost my grip on my milk shake. He glared at me, his face flushed. I'd spooked him.

'How the hell – did you and your brother drive by here earlier?'

'Nope.' We were pretty far off any streets that tourists or casual visitors would take, a bit out in the countryside and away from any tourist amenities. 'Just what I do.'

'It's the new cemetery,' Hollis said, his voice jerky. 'The old one's . . .'

I turned my head from side to side, estimating. 'South-west of here. About four miles.'

'Jesus, woman, you're creepy.'

I shrugged. It didn't seem creepy to me.

He said, 'I can give you three thousand. Will you do something for me?'

'Yes, I'll do it. Since we haven't run a credit check on you, I need the money in advance.'

'You're businesslike.' His tone was not admiring.

'No, I'm not. That's why Tolliver usually does this part.' I finished my milk shake, making a loud slurping noise.

Hollis did a U-turn to head back to town. He went through the drive-through at the bank. The teller did her best not to act surprised when he sent his withdrawal slip over to her, and she also tried not to peer too obviously at me. I wanted to tell Hollis that if I were performing any other service, he wouldn't be sitting there all huffy; if I cleaned houses, he wouldn't be asking me to go clean his for free, right? My lips parted, but I clamped them shut. I refused to justify myself.

He thrust the money, still in its bank envelope, into my hand. I slid the envelope into my jacket pocket without comment. We drove back to the turn-off that led to the cemetery. We were parked on a gravel path winding among the tombstones, when he turned off the engine. 'Come on,' he said. 'The grave is over here.' The day had cleared up, turned bright, and I watched big sycamore leaves turn cartwheels in the wind across the dying grass.

'Embalming mutes the effect,' I warned him.

His eyes lit up. He was thinking I'd faked my results before, somehow, and that now he'd unmask me. And he'd get his money back. He had about a ton of ambiguity resting on his shoulders.

I stepped gingerly onto the nearest grave, the ground chilly under my bare feet. Since a cemetery is so full of death, I have difficulty getting a clear reading. When you add the competing emanations from the corpses to the effects of the embalming process, you have to get as close as you can. 'Middle-aged white man, died of . . . a massive coronary,' I said, my eyes closed. The name was Matthews, something like that.

There was a silence while Hollis read the headstone. Then Hollis growled, 'Yes.' He caught his breath jaggedly. 'We're going to walk now. Keep your eyes shut.' I felt his big hand take mine, lead me carefully to another patch of ground. I reached down deep with that inner sense that had never yet failed me. 'Very old man.' I shook my head. 'I think he just ran down.' I was led to yet another grave, this one farther away. 'Woman, sixties, car accident. Named Turner, Turnage? A drunk, I think.'

We went back in our original direction, and I knew by the tension in his body that this was the grave he'd been aiming for all along. When he guided me onto the grave, I knelt. This was death by violence, I knew at once. I took a deep breath and reached below me. 'Oh,' I said sharply. I realized dimly that because Hollis was thinking of this dead person so strongly, it was helping me to reach her. I could hear the water running in the bathtub. House was hot, window was open. Breeze coming in the high frosted window of the bathroom. Suddenly . . . 'Let go!' she said, but it was as if I were the woman, and I was saying it, too. And then her/my head was under water, and we were looking up at the stippled ceiling, and we couldn't breathe, and we drowned.

'Someone had ahold of her ankles,' I said, and I was all by myself in my skin, and I was alive. 'Someone pulled her under.'

After a long moment, I opened my eyes, looked down at the headstone in front of me. *Sally Boxleitner*, it read. *Beloved Wife of Hollis.*

'Coroner always said he couldn't figure it out. I sent her for an autopsy,' the deputy said. 'The results were inconclusive. She might have fainted and slipped under the water, fallen asleep in the tub or something. I couldn't understand why she couldn't save herself. But there wasn't any evidence either way.'

I just watched him. Grieving people can be unpredictable.

'Vagal shock,' I murmured. 'Or maybe it's called vagal inhibition. People can't even struggle, if it's sudden.'

'You've seen this before?' There were tears in his eyes, angry tears.

'I've seen everything.'

'Someone murdered her.'

'Yes.'

'You can't see who.'

'No. I don't see who. I see how, when I find the body. I know it's not you. If you were the murderer, and you were right by your victim, I might be able to tell.' Which I hadn't intended to say: this was exactly why I really needed Tolliver to speak for me. I began to miss him, which was ridiculous. 'Can you take me back to the motel, please?'

He nodded, still lost in his own thoughts. We began to make our way between the headstones. The sun was still shining and the leaves were still fluttering across the browning lawn, but the spark had gone out of the day. I was trembling with a fine small movement as my bare feet moved through the short cool grass. On the way back to Hollis's electric-blue truck, I paused to read the name on the largest monument in the cemetery. There were at least eight graves in the plot marked *Teague*.

Good. I carefully stepped onto the one marked Dell. He was there, buried not too deeply in the rocky soil of the Ozarks. I spared a second to think that I was lucky that connecting with the embalmed dead was never as dramatic as connecting with a corpse; Hollis would never have thought to provide me with the support Tolliver did. I reached down again with that extra sense of mine, trying not to assume what I'd find when my lightning-sparked gift touched the body of Dell Teague.

Suicide, my ass, was my instant, and silent, reaction. Why hadn't Sybil hired me to come out here to read his grave first, instead of sending me to the woods to find Teenie? Of course this boy hadn't shot himself. Dell Teague had been murdered, just like his wild girlfriend. I opened my eyes. Hollis Boxleitner had swung around to check on what I was doing. I looked into the intent face of the deputy. 'No suicide here,' I said.

In the long pause that followed, I looked off to the west and saw a bank of dark clouds approaching in a hurry. The break in the weather was over. Hollis looked, too. I saw a shaft of brightness split through the distant clouds.

'Come on,' Hollis said. 'You just carry hard luck around with you.' He shook his head.

We climbed into the truck. On the way back into Sarne, neither of us broke the silence. While he was looking at the road, I slipped his money out of my pocket and put it on the seat between us. At the motel, I scrambled out of the truck real quick, slamming the truck door behind me and unlocking my room almost in one motion. Hollis drove away without a word. I guess he had a lot to think about.

I put my ear to the wall and heard a buzz. Tolliver was home. He must have had the television on. But I waited a minute, since I'd made similar assumptions before and paid for them with my own embarrassment. It was a good thing I hesitated, because after a second I realized that Tolliver had company. I was willing to bet it was Janine, the waitress from the diner. Evidence suggested that Tolliver was much more appealing to women than I was to men. Sometimes that pissed me off. I didn't think the difference was in our looks, exactly; I thought it lay in our baggage. I sighed, feeling like sticking out my tongue or kicking the wall – something childish.

I'd imagined for a few minutes that Hollis Boxleitner was really attracted to me, but what he had wanted was what I had to offer professionally, not personally.

And there was a storm coming on.

I picked up my novel and tried to read. The darkness was thickening outside, and within ten minutes I had to turn on a lamp. From not too far off, there was a deep rumble. Thunder.

I made myself read a couple of sentences. I really, really wanted to lose awareness of the here and now. The best way for me to do that was bury myself in a book.

We keep a box of secondhand paperbacks in the backseat of the car. When each book has been read, we leave it where someone else can pick it up. If the book's in very good shape we keep it to trade. We stop at every secondhand bookstore we see to restock. I've read a lot of things I hadn't planned on reading, due to the selection at these stores. And I've read a lot of books years after they were bestsellers, which doesn't bother me a bit.

Tolliver's not quite as omnivorous as I am. He draws the line at romances (he thinks they're too predictable) and spy novels (he finds them ludicrous), but he'll read just about anything else. Westerns, mysteries, science fiction, even some non-fiction – almost any book is grist for our mill. Right now I was reading a tattered copy of Richard Preston's *The Hot Zone*. It was one of the most frightening things I'd ever read – but I'd rather be afraid of Preston's account of the origin and spread of the Ebola virus than think about the rumble of the thunder.

Before I tried to re-immerse myself in Preston's exploration of a cave in Africa, I glanced at the clock. I estimated that the waitress would leave the room next door in about an hour. Maybe by the time the storm got here, Tolliver would be alone.

With the book weighted open in front of me on the cheap table, I turned on my cordless curler and used it. Then I brushed my hair. From time to time I glanced up at the mirror. I looked okay, I thought. Not too bad. Frail and pale, though.

My brother and I didn't look anything alike, aside from the similarity in our coloring – black hair, brown eyes. Tolliver looked tough, secretive, a little forbidding. His scarred cheeks and wide, bony shoulders made him seem very male.

But it was me who frightened people.

Thunder rumbled again, much closer. Not even the Ebola virus could hold my attention now. I tried to distract myself. The sheriff would have gotten Teenie Hopkins' body out of the woods by now, and it would be on its way to Little Rock. I bet he was glad he'd gotten her out before the rain. It couldn't have taken long, since there wouldn't exactly be a crime scene to secure. Of course, even the most lax police officer would search the area. I wondered if Hollis had been part of the search. I wondered if they'd found anything. I should have asked Hollis questions while I was in his truck. Maybe he was out in the woods, right at this moment.

But what difference did it make, really? I would be gone before anyone was brought to justice. I tapped my fingernails against the table in an anxious rhythm, my feet patting along to an inaudible beat. I switched off the lamp and the light in the bathroom.

I was going to conquer this. This time, it would not get the best of me.

A boom of thunder was followed by a brilliant bolt of lightning. I jumped about a foot. Though the curler was cordless, I turned it off. I unplugged the television and went to sit on the foot of my bed, on the shiny, green, slick motel bedspread. More thunder, and another crack of lightning outside the window. I shivered, my arms crossed over my abdomen. The rain pounded down outside the motel room, drumming on the roof of our car, splashing violently against the pavement. Another lightning bolt. I made a little noise, involuntarily.

The door between the rooms opened and Tolliver came in, a towel wrapped around his waist, his hair still wet from the shower. I saw a flicker of movement in his room; the waitress, pulling on her clothes, her face angry.

He sat on the end of the bed by me, his arm around my shoulders. He didn't say a word. Neither did I. I shivered and shook until the lightning was past.

3

Sarne seemed like a complicated little town. I would be glad when we left it. We were supposed to show up in Ashdown within the next couple of days, and I wanted to keep the appointment. I try to be as professional as my odd calling will permit.

There were times we sat in our apartment in St Louis for two weeks at a stretch. Then the phone would ring steadily, one call right after another. With my work schedule so unpredictable, we had to be ready to get on the road at any time. The dead could wait forever, but the living were always urgent.

The sheriff called me the next morning right before seven. Normally, I would've been out for a run, but the day after I both find a body and get through a storm is going to be a slow day. I peered at the clock before I lifted the receiver. 'The body's Teenie, the lab in Little Rock said,' he told me. He sounded tired, though it was early and he should just have risen from a night's sleep. 'Go pick up your check at Paul Edwards's office.' He hung up. He didn't say, 'And never come here again,' but the words were hanging in the air.

Tolliver had just come in, dressed and ready for breakfast, his favorite meal. He looked at my face as I hung up the room phone.

'Blaming the messenger,' he said. 'I guess it was a positive ID?'

I nodded. 'I never understand that. You know, they ask me here to find the body. I find the body. Then they're pissed at me, and they give me the check like I should have done the whole thing for free.'

He shrugged. 'I guess we would do it for free if we could get a government grant or something.'

'Oh, sure, the government just loves me.' Paying taxes was excruciating – not because I minded giving the devil his due, but because accounting for my income was very difficult. I called myself a consultant. So far, I'd flown under the radar, but that would change sooner or later.

Tolliver grinned while I pulled on a T-shirt and a sweater. Since I'd planned today as a traveling day, I was wearing jeans. I don't care much about clothes, except my blue jeans. I'm particular about them. This was my favorite pair, and they were worn thin in spots.

'We'll stop by Edwards's office and get the check on our way out of town.'

'We better cash it quick,' I said, speaking from bitter experience.

The motel phone rang again. We looked at each other. I picked it up.

'Miss Connelly,' said a woman. 'Harper Connelly?'

'Yes?'

'This is Helen Hopkins. I'm Sally and Teenie's momma. Can you come talk to me?' Hollis's mother-in-law: Had he told her what I'd found at the cemetery?

I closed my eyes. I *so* didn't want to do this. But this woman was the mother of two murdered women. 'Yes ma'am, I guess so.'

She gave me her address and asked if I could come in a half hour. I told her it'd be an hour, but we'd be there.

It actually took us a bit over an hour, because after we'd checked out of the motel and loaded our bags and gone into the restaurant, Janine, the waitress Tolliver had entertained the afternoon before, dragged her feet serving us. She'd glare at me, try to touch him – a performance both obvious and painful. Did she think I was forcing my brother to stay with me, dragging Tolliver all around the United States in my wake? Did she imagine that if I relaxed my grip on him, he'd stay here in Sarne and get a job at the grocery store, make her an honest woman?

Sometimes I teased him about his conquests, but this wasn't one of those times. His cheeks were flushed when we left, and he didn't say a word as we drove to Paul Edwards's downtown office. It was housed in an old home right off the town square, a home which had been painted in lime green and light blue, a whimsical combination I'm sure the original builders would have deplored. Paul Edwards was fitting into the image Sarne was trying to sell the tourists, that of a fun-house antique town with something interesting around every corner.

Tolliver said, 'I'll wait in the car.'

I'd assumed the lawyer would have left the check in an envelope at the reception desk, but Edwards himself came out when I told his secretary my name. He shook my hand while the parched and dyed blonde watched his every move with fascination. I could see why. Paul Edwards was a man with charm.

He ushered me back into his office.

'What can I do for you?' I asked reluctantly. I was ready to go. I sat in the leather visitor's chair, while he leaned against the edge of his huge desk.

'You're a remarkable woman,' he said, shaking his head at the phenomenon of my remarkableness. I didn't know whether to laugh sardonically or blush. In the end, I raised an eyebrow, remained silent, and waited for his next move.

'In one day, you've made a tremendous difference in the lives of two of my clients.'

'How would that be?'

'Helen Hopkins is grateful that her Teenie's body has been found. Now she can have closure. And Sybil Teague is so relieved that poor Dell won't be the victim of these foolish and false accusations people have been making since Teenie's disappearance.'

I digested this silently, wondering what he really wanted to say to me.

'If you're going to be in Sarne for a while, I was hoping for the chance to take you out to dinner and find out more about you,' Paul Edwards said. I looked at his good suit and white shirt, his gleaming shoes. His hair was groomed and well-cut, his shave had been close, and his brown eyes were glowing with sincerity.

'As a matter of fact,' I said slowly, 'my brother and I are leaving Sarne in an hour or so. We're just dropping by Helen Hopkins' place first, at her request. Then we're outta here.'

'Oh, that's too bad,' he said. 'I've missed my opportunity. Maybe someday if you have business close to here, you'll give me a call?' He tucked a business card into my hand.

'Thanks,' I said noncommittally, and after some more hand clasping and eye-to-eye contact, I got out the front door with the check in my hand.

I tried to tell Tolliver about the odd interview I'd just had, but I guess he was miffed at the long wait he'd had outside the lawyer's office. In fact, Tolliver was mighty quiet while he searched for the Hopkins house, which turned out to be a humble box-like building on a humble street.

Hollis Boxleitner had said some pretty bad things about his wife's mother's past, and I had formed a negative picture of Helen Hopkins. When she answered the door I was surprised to see a tidy, thin woman with wispy brown hair and popping blue eyes. She had once been pretty, in a waif-like way. Now she seemed more like a dried shell. She was wearing a flowered T-shirt and khakis, and her face was about as wide as my thin hand.

'I'm Harper Connelly,' I said. 'This here's my brother, Tolliver Lang.'

'Helen Hopkins. God bless you for coming to meet me,' she said rapidly. 'Please come in and sit down.' She gestured around the tiny living room. It was jammed with furniture and so cluttered that it took me a moment to realize the room was nonetheless extremely clean. There was a shelf mounted on the wall, full of a display of Avon carnival glass. A huge Bible was centered on the cheap coffee table. Flanking it were two starched crocheted doilies, and in the exact center of each one was a glass candlestick holding a white candle.

I knew a shrine when I saw one.

And the pictures; two brunette girls were duplicated over and over around the room. There was an age progression beginning on the north wall. Sally and Teenie were born, went to grade school, trick-or-treated, danced, graduated from grade school and junior high, went to proms, and in Sally's case, got married. This room was a panorama of the lives of two girls, both of them murdered. The last picture in the progression was a bleak shot of a white casket covered with a pall of carnations resting on a bier at the front of a church. This final picture, surely taken at Sally's funeral, had a bare spot next to it; this would be where the picture of Teenie's casket would hang. I swallowed hard.

'I been sober now for thirty-two months,' Helen Hopkins said, gesturing to us to take the two armchairs squeezed together opposite the sofa, where she perched on the edge of a cushion.

'Congratulations, I'm glad to hear it,' I said.

'If you've been in this town for more than ten minutes, someone will have told you something bad about me. I drank and fornicated for many years. But I'm sober now, by the grace of God and some damn hard work.'

Tolliver nodded, to show we were registering her words.

'Both my girls are dead,' Helen Hopkins continued. Her voice was absolutely steady and harsh, but the muscles in her jaw were taut with agony. 'I ain't had a husband in years. No one here to help me but me, myself, and I. I want to know who brought you here, and what you are, and what you done out in the woods to find my girl. I didn't know anything about this till yesterday, when Hollis called me.'

You couldn't get more straightforward than that. Tolliver and I looked at each other, asking a silent question. This woman was a lot like our mother – well, my mother, Tolliver's stepmother – except my mother had gone to law school, and she'd never gotten sober. Tolliver gave a shrug that couldn't have been seen by anyone but me, and I returned an infinitesimal nod.

'I find bodies, Mrs Hopkins. I got hit by lightning when I was a girl, and that's what happened to me afterward. I found out I just knew when I came close to a dead person. And I knew what had killed that person – though not who, if the person was murdered.' I wanted to be real clear about that. 'What I know is how the person died.'

'Sybil Teague hired you?'

'Yes.'

'How'd she know about you?'

'I believe through Terry Vale.'

'Are you always right?'

'Yes, ma'am.'

'You think the Lord likes what you're doing?'

'I wonder about it all the time,' I said.

'So, Sybil asked you to come here and find Monteen. She say why?'

'The sheriff told me that everyone was thinking her son had killed Teenie, and she wanted to find Teenie's body to disprove that.'

'And you found Teenie.'

'Yes, that's what Sheriff Branscom told me. I'm sorry for your loss.'

'I knew she was dead,' Helen said, eyes dry. 'I been knowing since she vanished, that Teenie had passed over.'

'How?' If she could be blunt, I could, too.

'She would've come home, otherwise.'

According to Hollis, Teenie had been as out of control as her mother at one time. I doubted Helen Hopkins was speaking realistically. Her next words echoed my doubts so closely that I wondered if the woman was psychic.

'She'd been a wild girl,' Helen Hopkins said slowly, 'acting out because she could get away with it, because I was a drunk. But when I sobered up, she began to come around, too.'

She gave me a wisp of a smile, and I tried to smile back. This dried-out husk of a woman had once had a jaunty charm not too many years ago. You could see the traces of it in her face and posture.

'I liked Dell Teague just fine,' Helen said. Her voice was slow, as if she was thinking out what she was saying very carefully. 'I didn't ever think that he'd killed my girl. I liked him, and I think Sybil's okay. But the kids wanted to get married, and I didn't want Teenie to marry early, the way Sally did. Not that Sally made a bad marriage. Hollis is a fine man, and I don't blame him for not caring for me none. He had enough reasons. But Teenie . . . she didn't need to be getting so tight with Dell Teague, so young. I just wanted Teenie to have some choices. It was good of Sybil to pay you to look for my girl, though . . .'

'Hollis tell you we went out to the cemetery?' I was trying to make sense of this flow of thoughts.

'Yes. He come by yesterday, the first time I've talked to him in a long time. He told me that you said Sally had been killed, that it wasn't no accident.' I saw Tolliver stiffen. He shot me a look. He didn't like me going off with someone, he didn't like me doing freebies, and he didn't like me not telling him everything.

'How do you do it?' she asked. 'How can you tell? How can I trust you?'

These were all good questions, questions I'd been asked before.

'You don't have to believe a thing I say,' I told Helen Hopkins. 'I see what I see.'

'You think God gave you this gift? Or the devil?'

I wasn't about to tell this woman what I really thought. 'You believe what you want,' I said.

'I believe that you saw both my daughters get murdered,' Helen Hopkins said. Her huge brown eyes seemed to get even bigger and rounder. 'I believe God sent you to find out who did this to them.'

'No,' I said immediately. 'I am not a lie detector. I can find bodies. I can tell what killed 'em. But who, or why, that's beyond me.'

'How did they die?'

'You don't want to hear this,' Tolliver said.

'Shut up, mister. This is my right.'

She was little, but persistent. *Like a mosquito*, I thought.

'Your daughter Sally was drowned in her bathtub. She was grabbed by the ankles, so that her head went under the water. Your daughter Teenie was shot in the back.'

All the strength seeped out of Helen Hopkins as we watched.

'My poor girls,' she said. 'My poor girls.'

She looked over at us, without really seeing us. 'I thank you for coming,' she said stiffly. 'I thank you. I'm in your debt. I'll tell the girls' fathers what you've said.'

Tolliver and I got up. Helen didn't speak again.

'Now we leave,' Tolliver said, when we were outside. And after we stopped by the bank to cash Sybil Teague's check, we got in our car and drove south out of Sarne.

We pulled into our motel in Ashdown a few silent hours later. Tolliver sat in the chair in my room after we'd eaten supper, and I perched on the foot of the bed.

'Tell me about going out with the trooper,' he said. His voice was mild, but I knew that was deceptive. I'd been waiting for that shoe to drop all day.

'He came by while you were gone flirting with that waitress,' I said. 'He wanted me to take a ride with him.' Tolliver snorted, but I decided to ignore that. 'Anyway, he talked, and he talked, and we got a milk shake, and then I realized that he just wanted to take me out to the cemetery and get me to tell him what happened to his wife.'

I could hardly bear to look at Tolliver's face, but I sneaked a peek. To my relief, he wasn't full of anger. He hated it when people took advantage of me, and he hated it more when the person was a man. But he didn't want me to feel bad, either.

'Don't you think he liked what he saw, and that's why he came by the motel?'

I ducked my head. Tolliver's hand smoothed my hair.

'No,' I said. 'I think all along he planned on getting me there to his wife's grave. I told him I had to be paid, Tolliver. So he took me by the bank and got the money.' I didn't tell Tolliver it hadn't been the full amount. 'But I left it in the truck, because I felt so bad about the whole thing.' Bad and mad and guilty and hurt.

'You did the right thing,' he said, at last. 'Next time, don't go anywhere without telling me, okay?'

'You going to follow me?' I asked, feeling a little spark of anger. 'What should I do when *you* go off without *me*? Make the woman promise to bring you back by ten? Take her picture so I can track her down when you're late?'

Tolliver counted to ten. I could tell by the tiny movements of his head. 'No,' he said. 'But I worry about you. You're a strong woman, but a strong woman still isn't as strong as most men.' This was one of those simple biological truths that made me wonder what God had been thinking. 'If he hadn't taken you to the cemetery, he could have taken you anywhere else. I would have been looking for you, like we track other people.'

'If anyone in this world is aware that she might be killed at any moment, Tolliver Lang, that person is me.' I pointed at my own chest, my finger rigid. 'Amazingly, every day millions of women go out with men who have no ulterior motive whatsoever. Amazingly, almost all of them come home perfectly all right!'

'I don't care about them. I care about you. How you could ever trust anyone when what we see, so many times a year, is murder . . .'

'And yet, you have no problem inviting a woman you just met into your room!'

He threw up his hands. 'Okay, forget it! Forget I said anything! All I want is to know where you are, and for you to be safe!' He stomped out of my room into his, which required going outside; no connecting doors in this cut-rate motel.

I heard the television come on in the next room. What had we been quarrelling about? Did Tolliver really want me to sit in my room while he had fun? Did he really want me to turn down every invitation that came my way, in the name of safety?

I was pretty sure the answer, if you asked him, would be yes.

During the night, the phone by Tolliver's bed rang. I could hear it through the thin walls. After a moment, it stopped. I tried to imagine who could know where we were and what we were doing, and in the middle of imagining, I fell back to sleep. I ran the next morning, and in the cold crisp air it felt great. The hot shower felt even better. While I was dressing, Tolliver knocked on my door. After I let him in, I finished buttoning my blouse. I was wearing better clothes since we would be meeting the Ashdown client for the first time. This would be a cemetery job, and I wouldn't have to change. A quick in-and-out.

'The call last night,' he said.

'Yeah, who was that?' I'd almost forgotten.

'It was the police in Sarne.'

'Who in the police?'

'Harvey Branscom, the sheriff.'

I waited, hairbrush in hand.

'We have to go back.'

'Not until we do this job. Why, what happened?'

'Last night, someone went into Helen Hopkins' house and beat her to death.'

I stared at Tolliver for a minute. I was so used to death that it was hard to produce a normal reaction to news like this.

'Well,' I said finally, 'I hope it was quick.'

'I told them we'd have to finish our business here first, then we'd drive back up there.'

'I'm ready.' I tucked my blouse in my gray slacks. I pulled on my matching blazer.

'Hey, the jacket matches your eyes,' Tolliver said.

'That was my intent,' I said dryly. Tolliver always seemed to think that if I looked good, it was a happy accident. The blouse I wore with the gray suit was light green, with a kind of bamboo pattern on it. I put on a gold chain that Tolliver had given me the previous Christmas, and slid into black pumps. I fluffed my hair, checked my makeup, and told Tolliver I was ready. He was wearing a long-sleeved cotton pullover sweater in a dark red. He looked very good in it. I'd given it to him.

We met the client and her lawyer at the designated cemetery, one of those modern ones with flat headstones. They're cheaper, and more convenient for the mower. Though not atmospheric, the 'park' look does make for easier walking.

The lawyer, a woman in her sixties, made it clear she thought I was in the business of defrauding the desperate and grief stricken. I was getting a lot of red flags, not only from the lawyer's attitude, but from the twitchiness of the client. Following our standard procedure when I got vibes like those, I endorsed the check and handed it to Tolliver, indicating he should go to the bank while I did the 'reading.' The situation was showing all the indicators of a bad transaction.

The client, a heavy, peevish woman in her forties, wanted her husband to have died of something more dramatic than a radio falling into his bathtub. (Bathtubs had been big this month. Sometimes I got such a run of one cause of death that it made even me nervous. Last year, I had a streak of accidental drownings – five in a row. Made me scared to go swimming for a couple of months.) Geneva Roller, the client, had her own elaborate conspiracy theory about how the radio came to be in the bathtub. Her theory involved Mr Roller's first wife and his best friend.

I love it when the location of the body is known. It was a little treat when the client led me directly to her husband's grave. Geneva Roller was a brisk walker, and I could feel the heels of my pumps sinking into the soft dirt. The lawyer was right behind me, as if I'd cut and run unless I was blocked in.

We stopped by a headstone reading *Farley Roller*. To give Geneva her emotional money's worth, I stepped onto the grave and crouched, my hand resting on the headstone. *Farley*, I thought, *what the hell happened to you?* And then I saw it, as I always did. To let Geneva know what was going on, I said, 'He is in the tub. He has – um, he's uncircumcised.' That was unusual.

This convinced my client I was the real deal. Geneva Roller gasped, her hand going up to her chest. Her bright red lips formed an O. The lawyer, Patsy Bolton, snorted. 'Anyone could know that, Geneva,' she said.

Right, that was the first thing I asked guys.

'He's whistling,' I said. I couldn't hear what Farley Roller was whistling, unfortunately. I could see the counter in the bathroom. 'There's a radio on the counter,' I said. 'I think he's whistling along with the music.' This was one of the times when I saw more than the moment of death. This was not the norm.

'He did that when he bathed,' Geneva breathed. 'He did, Patsy!' The lawyer looked less skeptical and more spooked.

I said. 'There's the cat. On the bathroom counter. A marmalade color cat.'

'Patpaws,' said Geneva, smiling. I was willing to bet the lawyer wasn't smiling.

'The cat's bracing to leap over the tub to the open window.'

'The window *was* open,' Geneva said. She wasn't smiling anymore.

'The cat knocked the radio into the water,' I said.

Then the cat leaped out of the window and into the yard while Mr Roller came to his end. The bathtub was an old one, an unusual shade of avocado green. 'You have a green tub,' I said, shaking my head in puzzlement. 'Can that be right?'

Patsy the lawyer was gaping at me. 'You're for real,' she said. 'I actually believe you. Their tub is avocado.'

I got to my feet, dusting off my knees. I ignored Patsy Bolton. 'I'm

so sorry, Ms Roller. Your cat killed your husband in a freak accident,'
I said. I assumed this would be good news.

'NO!' Geneva Roller yelled, and even the lawyer looked astonished.

'Geneva, this is a reasonable explanation,' Patsy Bolton began,
giving her client a formidable stare, but Geneva Roller had no emotional restraints.

'It was his first wife, that Angela. It was her, I know it! She went in
the house while I was at the store, and she murdered him. Angela did
it. Not my little Patpaws!'

I'd had disbelieving reactions before, of course, though most often
these came when I'd discovered the death was a suicide. So it sure
wasn't the first time I'd found that people invest a lot in their theories.
In a Jack Nicholson moment, I very nearly told Geneva Roller that she
couldn't handle the truth.

'I'll take my check back. I won't pay you a dime,' she hissed. I was
glad I'd sent Tolliver to the bank.

Looking over Geneva's shoulder, I could see our car turning into
the cemetery. Relief gave me courage.

'Ms Roller, your cat caused an accident, quite innocently. Your
husband wasn't murdered. There's no one to blame,' I said.

She launched herself at me, and the lawyer caught her by the
shoulders. 'Geneva, recall who you are,' Patsy Bolton said. Her cheeks
were red, and her brown-and-gray streaked hair had become a mess in
the breeze that had sprung up. 'Don't embarrass yourself like this.'

With excellent timing, Tolliver pulled up beside me. Trying not to
hurry, I climbed into the car while saying, 'I'm so sorry for your loss,
Ms Roller.' We sped out of the cemetery while Geneva Roller
screamed at us.

'Got the money?' I asked.

'Yep. Good thing?'

'Yeah, she didn't want it to be an accident. I guess she was hoping
for an A and E documentary. "Murder in Ashdown," or something.' I
deepened my voice. ' "The widow, however, suspected from the beginning that Farley Roller's death was a "not what it appeared to be,"
kind of thing. Instead, all she has to blame is her stupid cat. Kind of a
letdown, I guess.'

'It's a lot more interesting to be the wife of a murder victim than the
owner of a killer cat,' Tolliver said, but I had to wonder about that.

4

We'd already checked out of the Ashdown motel, so we drove straight to Sarne. Tolliver went directly to the sheriff's office, and seconds after we sat down in the chairs in front of his desk, the sheriff came in, yanking his hat off and tossing it on a table behind him.

'I hear you went to visit with Helen Hopkins yesterday,' Harvey Branscom said. He bent over and switched on the intercom. 'Reba, send Hollis in,' he said. A squawk came back, and in a minute Hollis Boxleitner came in, carrying a mug of steaming coffee. I could smell it from my chair, but I didn't ask for any, nor did I look him in the face. Beside me, Tolliver stiffened.

'Mr Lang, I want you to go with Deputy Boxleitner here. I'd like to talk to Miss, Ms Connelly.'

I turned to look at Tolliver, trying not to let my anxiety show on my face. He knew I would hate for him to say anything out loud. I like to keep my fears to myself. He gave me a very steady look, and I relaxed just a little. Without a word, he stood and left the room with Hollis.

'How'd you make contact with Helen?' the sheriff asked me. His face was set in harsh lines. I could see the shadow of white whiskers on his face, as though his cheeks had been frostbitten. Lack of sleep made the lines across his forehead even deeper.

'She called us,' I said, biting off any color commentary. Tolliver had always advised me not to answer any extra when I talked to the police.

'What did she want?' asked the sheriff, with an air of elaborate patience.

'Us to come visit her.' I read the expression on Branscom's face correctly. 'She wanted to know who'd hired me, and why.'

'Sybil hadn't told her you all were coming?' Branscom himself seemed surprised, and he was Sybil Teague's brother.

'Evidently not.'

'Was she angry about that?'

We looked at each other for a long second. 'Not that she said,' I answered.

'What else did you talk about?'

I spoke very carefully. 'She told us she'd had a bad life for a while, but that she'd been sober for thirty-two months. She talked about her daughters. She was proud of both of them.'

'Did she ask you about their deaths?'

'Sure. She wanted to know how I knew, if I were sure how they were killed. She said she would tell their fathers.'

Harvey Branscom had been lifting his mug to his mouth as I spoke. Now the mug was lowered back to the desk. 'Say what?' he asked.

'She said she would tell the girls' fathers what I'd said.'

'The fathers of the girls. Both of them. *Plural*.'

I nodded.

'She never would tell anyone who Teenie's dad was. I always thought she just didn't know. And Sally's dad Jay left years ago, after she put the restraining order on him. Did Helen mention any names?'

'No.' I was in the clear on that one.

'What else did she talk about?' the sheriff asked. 'Be sure you tell me everything.'

'She wanted to know how I do what I do, if I thought my gift had come from God or the devil. She wanted to be convinced I knew what I was talking about.'

'What did you tell her?' He seemed genuinely interested to know.

'I didn't tell her anything. She made up the answer she wanted to hear, all on her own.' My voice might have been a little dry.

'What time did you leave her house?'

I'd thought about that, of course. 'We left about nine thirty,' I said. 'We went by the bank on the way out of town. We got to Ashdown and checked into the motel about two, two thirty.'

He wrote that down, and the name of the motel. I handed him the receipt that I'd tucked in my purse. He copied it and made some more entries in his notebook.

'What time did she die?' I asked.

He looked up at me. 'Sometime before noon,' he said. 'Hollis went over there on his lunch hour to talk to her about Teenies funeral. He'd spoken to her for the first time in a year or two, when he went over to tell her what you'd told him about Sally. Which, by the way, I don't believe. I think you're just trying to mine for gold here, and I'm telling you, Hollis ain't a rich man.'

I was puzzled. 'He gave me money, but I left it in his truck. He didn't tell you that?' Maybe Hollis just hadn't wanted to tell his superior I'd asked for it in the first place – though why, I don't know. Sheriff Branscom didn't think much of me, and it wouldn't have surprised him at all that I'd wanted to be paid (for something I do for my living!). It would have confirmed his poor opinion. Yes, I expect even poor people who want my services to pay me. So does everyone else.

'No,' the sheriff said, easing back into his creaking chair. He rubbed a hand over his stubbled jowls. 'No, he didn't mention that. Maybe he was embarrassed at giving money to someone like you in the first place.'

Sometimes you just can't win. Sheriff Branscom would never join my fan club. It's lucky I'm used to meeting people like that, or I might slip and get my feelings hurt.

'Where's Tolliver?' I asked, my tolerance all used up.

'He'll be in here directly,' the sheriff said. 'I guess Hollis ain't finished up his questions yet.'

I fidgeted. 'I really need to go to the motel and lie down,' I said. 'I really need Tolliver to take me there.'

'You've got some car keys,' the sheriff observed. 'Hollis'll bring him over when they're done.'

'No,' I said. 'I need my brother.'

'Don't you raise your voice to me, young woman. He'll be through in a minute.' But there was the faintest look of alarm on the round soft face.

'Now,' I said. 'I need him *now*.' I let my eyes go wide so the white showed all around the irises. My hands wrung together, over and over.

'I'll check,' said the sheriff, and he could hardly get up from behind his desk fast enough.

Most places, I would've gotten thrown in the cage or taken to the hospital, but I had gauged this man correctly. Within four minutes, Tolliver came in, moving quickly. Because Hollis was watching, he knelt at my feet and took both my hands. 'I'm here, honey,' he said. 'Don't be scared.'

I let tears flow down my cheeks. 'I need to go, Tolliver,' I said softly. 'Please take me to the motel.' I threw my arms around his neck. I loved hugging Tolliver, who was bony and hard and warm. I loved to listen to the air going in and out of his lungs, the swoosh of his heart.

He raised me up out of the chair and walked me to the front door, one arm wrapped around my shoulders. The few people in the outer office eyed us curiously as we made our way to the door.

When we were safely back in the car and on our way, Tolliver said, 'Thanks.'

'Was it going bad for you?' I asked, taking my hands from my face and straightening in my seat. 'The sheriff thinks I made up everything I said, but the motel receipt was pretty conclusive.'

'Hollis Boxleitner has a thing for you,' Tolliver said. 'He can't decide if he wants to go to bed with you or slap you around, and he's full of anger like a volcano's full of lava.'

'Because of his wife getting killed.'

'Yep. He believes in you, but that makes him mad, too.'

'He's gonna burn himself up,' I said.

'Yes,' Tolliver agreed.

'Did he tell you anything about Helen Hopkins' murder?'

'He said he found her. He said she'd been hit on the head.'

'With something there, something already in the house?'

'Candlestick.'

I remembered the glass candlesticks flanking the Bible on the coffee table.

'Was she standing when she was hit?'

'No,' he said, 'I think she was sitting on the couch.'

'So the killer was standing in front of her.'

Tolliver thought about it. 'That makes sense,' he said. 'But the deputy didn't say one way or another.'

'Being suspected of a murder isn't going to help business,' I said.

'No, we need to get out of here as soon as possible.' He parked in front of the motel and went in to get our rooms.

I really did want to lie down by the time we were in our rooms, and I was glad when Tolliver came through the connecting door and turned on my television. I propped up on the pillows while he slouched in the chair, and we watched the Game Show Network. He beat me at *Jeopardy!* I beat him at *Wheel of Fortune*. Of course, I would rather have won at *Jeopardy!*, but Tolliver had always been better at remembering facts than I was.

Our parents were brilliant people, once upon a time; before they became alcoholic, drug-addicted disbarred attorneys. And before they'd decided their clients' criminal lifestyles were more appealing and adventuresome than their own. My mother and Tolliver's dad found each other on their way down the drain, having shed their original spouses. My sister Cameron and I had gone from living in a four-bedroom suburban home in east Memphis to a rental house with a hole in the bathroom floor in Texarkana, Arkansas. This hadn't happened all at once; we'd experienced many degrees of degradation. Tolliver had fallen from a lower height, but he and his brother had descended with his father, too. He'd been our companion in that hole in Texarkana. That's where we'd been when the lightning struck.

My mother and Tolliver's dad had had two more children together, Mariella and Gracie. Tolliver and I watched out for them as best we could. Mariella and Gracie had no memory of anything better than the life we were living.

What had happened to our other parents: my father and Tolliver's mother? Why didn't they save us from the terrifying turn our lives had taken? Well, by that time, my real dad had gone to jail for a long string of white-collar crimes, and Tolliver's mother had died of cancer – leaving our at-large parents to complete their own downward passage, dragging us and their own children behind them.

So here we were, Tolliver and I, in a run-down motel in a seedy Ozarks tourist town in the off-season, hoping to dodge being charged with murder.

But by golly, we were smart.

We were playing Scrabble when we heard a knock at the door.

It was my room, so I asked, 'Who is it?'

'Hollis.'

I opened the door. Hollis saw Tolliver behind me and said, 'May I come in?'

I shrugged and moved back. Hollis stepped in far enough to allow me to shut the door behind him.

'You're here to apologize, I assume,' I said in the coldest voice I could summon. It was pretty damn cold.

'Apologize! For what?' He sounded genuinely bewildered.

'For telling the sheriff I took your money. For implying I cheated you.'

'You did take my money.'

'I left it on the seat of the truck. I felt bad for you.' I was so angry I was almost spitting; I'd gone from cold to hot in less than five seconds.

'It wasn't on the seat of the truck.'

'Yes. It was.'

He fished his keys out of his pocket. 'Show me.'

'No, you look yourself, so you can't accuse me of planting it.'

Tolliver and I followed Hollis back outside. The sky was gray, and the trees around the motel were beginning to whip in the wind. I was cold without my coat, but I wasn't going back in to put it on. Tolliver put his arm around me. Hollis opened the passenger door of his truck, began thrusting his fingers in the crack at the back of the seat, and in about ten seconds he came up with the bank envelope, still fat with money.

He stared at it in his hand, flushed red, and then went white. After a moment or two, he met our eyes. 'You told Harvey the truth,' he said. 'I'm sorry.'

'There now,' I said. 'Are we all clear about this?'

He nodded.

'Okay, then,' I said. I spun and walked into my room. Tolliver stayed outside for a bit. Then he came in, too.

We finished our game of Scrabble. I won.

We drove to a little town just five miles away to eat supper. Tolliver didn't seem keen on going back to the motel diner, and I didn't tease him about the waitress. We had country-fried steak, mashed potatoes, and lima beans at a near-duplicated Kountry Good Eats, and it was actually very tasty. The ambience was familiar: Formica-topped tables, cracked linoleum floor, two tired waitresses, and a man behind the counter, the manager. The iced tea was good, too.

'You know someone followed us here,' Tolliver said, as the waitress took our plates and strode toward the kitchen. He fished out his wallet to pay our tab.

'A girl,' I said. 'In a Honda.'

'Yeah. I guess she's a deputy, too? She looks awful young. Or maybe they just deputized her for this.'

'She's probably cold sitting out there in that little Honda.'

'Well, that's her job.'

We paid, tipped, and left. The threatened rain was finally upon us, and Tolliver and I ran to the car. He'd clicked it unlocked as we left the restaurant, and I dove inside as fast as I could. I hate being wet. I hate storms. I won't talk on the phone when it's raining hard.

At least there was no thunder this time.

'I don't understand,' Tolliver had said once, exasperated at not being able to call me when he was a few miles away. 'Why? The worst has already happened. You've already been hit by lightning. What are the odds of that happening twice?'

'What were the odds of it happening once?' I countered, though my real reasons were probably not what he supposed.

We drove slowly, and the red Honda stuck with us. The roads around Sarne were narrow and flanked by some steep terrain, and there was the ever-present possibility a deer would dash across the road.

When we got to the motel, we had a debate about whether to stop and let the unknown girl see where we were staying (which she'd already know if she was a cop) or keep riding around until she tired of following us. Going to the police station, we agreed, felt silly. After all, she hadn't threatened us or done anything other than ride behind us.

It was my bladder that determined our course of action. We pulled in, I dashed into my room, and by the time I came out, Tolliver reported, 'She's trying to make up her mind to come over and knock on the door.' He was concealed behind the curtains, and he hadn't turned on a light in the room.

I joined him, and it was like watching a pantomime. The girl's car was clearly lit up by the lights in the parking lot, and she was recognizable; that is, I'd be able to pick her out in a police lineup now, though her features weren't crystal clear. She had short brown hair worn in a longer version of a standard boys' haircut, which looked cute on her, since she was a petite thing. She was maybe seventeen, maybe younger, and she had a pouting lower lip. She was wearing enough eye makeup for three ordinary women. Her small face had that look so common in teenage girls from homes where all is not well – part defiant, part vulnerable, all wary.

Cameron had worn that expression on her face all too often.

'How much are you willing to put down on this? I think she'll give up and drive away. We're too scary for her.' Tolliver put his hand on my shoulder and squeezed it.

'Nah, she's coming in,' I said with assurance. 'I'd be taking your money too easily. See? She's daring herself.'

Rain began to pelt down again as she made up her mind to brave us. She launched herself from the car and dashed for my door. She pounded on it twice.

Tolliver turned on the lamp beside the bed as I answered her summons.

She glared at me. 'You the woman that finds bodies?'

'You know I am, or you wouldn't have been following us. I'm Harper Connelly. Come in.' I stepped back, and, shooting me a suspicious look, she entered the room. She looked around carefully. Tolliver was sitting in the chair trying to look harmless. 'This is my brother Tolliver Lang,' I said. 'He travels with me. You want a Diet Coke?'

'Sure,' she said, as if turning down a soft drink was unthinkable. Tolliver got one out of the ice chest and handed it to her. She took it with her arm extended as far as she could reach, to keep her distance from him. I pushed the other chair out to indicate she should use it, and I perched on the side of the bed.

'Can I help you?' I asked.

'You can tell me what happened to my brother. I'm not saying I think what you're doing is okay, or even morally defensible.' She glared at me. 'But I want to know what you think.'

I thought she had a good civics teacher.

'Okay,' I said slowly. 'Maybe first you could tell me who your brother is?'

She flushed red. She was accustomed to being a notable fish in a very small pond. 'I'm Nell,' she said, clipping off the words. 'Mary Nell Teague. Dell was my brother.'

'You can't be much younger than he was.'

'We were ten months apart.'

Tolliver and I looked at each other briefly. This girl was not only a minor, but the sister of a murder victim. And I was willing to bet she'd never been out of Sarne for more than a two-week vacation.

'Morally defensible,' Tolliver repeated, as struck by the phrase as I'd been. He rolled the words over his tongue as if he was testing the taste of them.

'I mean, I think it's wrong, all right? Telling people what happened to their dead relatives. No offense, but you could be making all this up, right?'

No offense, my ass. I was sick of people telling me I was evil. 'Listen, Nell,' I said, trying my best to keep my voice under strict control. 'I make my living the best way I know how. For you to assume I'm not honest *is* an offense to me. There's no way it couldn't be.'

Maybe she wasn't used to her words being taken seriously. 'Um, well, okay,' she muttered, clearly taken aback. 'But listen, can you tell me? What you told my mom?'

'You're a minor. I don't want to get into trouble,' I said.

Tolliver looked as if he were mulling it over.

'Listen, I may be a kid, you know, but he was my brother! And I should know what happened to my brother!' There was a very real anguish behind her words.

We gave each other tiny nods.

'I don't believe he killed himself,' I said.

'I knew it,' she said. 'I knew it.'

For someone who'd been so sure I was a fraud, she was taking my word without a second thought.

'So if he didn't kill himself,' she said, talking faster and faster, 'then he didn't kill Teenie, and if he didn't kill Teenie, then he didn't . . .' She stopped with an almost comic expression of panic, her eyes popping wide and her mouth clamped together to block the crucial word in, whatever it might have been.

A pounding at the door startled Tolliver and me; we'd been staring at Nell Teague as if we could pry the end of the sentence out of her with our eyes.

'Wonderful,' I said after I looked through the peephole. 'It's Sybil Teague, Tolliver.'

'Ohmigod,' said our visitor, who suddenly looked even younger than her age.

I cursed very thoroughly but silently, wishing that Sybil had arrived five minutes earlier. I had a fleeting idea that we could sneak Nell out through Tolliver's room, but as sure as we tried that, we'd be caught. After all, we hadn't done anything wrong. I opened the door, and Sybil came in like a well-groomed goddess of wrath.

'Is my child here?' she demanded, though we were making no move to conceal Nell, who was sitting in plain view. It was like she'd preplanned the moment.

'Right here,' Tolliver said gently, with an edge of sarcasm to his voice. Sybil flushed, her natural color warring with the carefully applied tints of rose and cream.

Sybil took in the sight of Nell sitting in the chair, unmolested and with a Diet Coke clutched in her hand, and she seemed to deflate. 'Where have you been, young lady?' she asked, rallying almost instantly. 'I expected you home two hours ago.'

Fortunately for us, Nell decided to come clean. 'I followed them. They went to Flo and Jo's for supper,' the teenager told her mother. 'They took their time. I followed them here, and then I asked them if I could come in.'

'You drove back in the rain from that place, with the roads slick, in the dark?' Sybil Teague's face went even paler. 'I'm glad I didn't know about it.'

'Mom, I've driven in rain plenty of times.'

'Oh, yes, in the two years you've been driving. You have nowhere near enough experience . . .' Sybil took a deep breath and made herself relax. 'All right, Nell, I know you wanted to talk about what happened to your brother. God knows, I've wanted to find out, too. And I thought this woman would give me answers. I just have more questions than I started out with, now.'

'This woman' felt like throwing up her hands in exasperation. 'This woman' did not like being spoken of as though she weren't there.

Paul Edwards appeared in the doorway behind Sybil. His hair was dark with rain. He put his hand on Sybil's shoulder, I thought to move her farther into the room so he could get out of the weather. I also thought it would be nice if they shut the door, since the wind was gusting in. Sybil stepped forward reluctantly, but his hand stayed on her shoulder.

For the first time, it occurred to me that there might be more between the two than attorney-client privilege. I'm just not as sharp about the living as I am the dead.

Nell's face shut down completely when she saw Paul Edwards. All the youth slid out of her mouth and eyes, and she looked like a hooker with her heavy eye makeup and tight clothes, instead of a cute kid trying on her personality.

'Hello, Miss Connelly, Mr Lang,' Edwards said. He focused on Nell. 'I'm glad we caught up with you, young lady.'

I wondered if Edwards was related to Sybil Teague's deceased husband. His ears were the same shape as Nell's, though otherwise she looked more like her mother.

'Right,' Nell said, in a voice as expressionless as they come. 'Thanks for coming out to look for me, Mr Edwards.' You could have cut the sarcasm with a chain saw.

'Your mother doesn't need anything else to worry about, Nell,' he said, with so much gentle reproof in his voice that I wanted to deck him. I had no doubt that Sybil Teague had suffered over the loss of her son, but I was pretty sure Dell's little sister had been missing him, too. If anything happened to Tolliver, I'd . . . I found I couldn't even imagine it.

I'd rather have been out doing 'cause of death' for a whole cemetery than be standing in that room right then.

'Goodbye,' I said, making a hostess gesture toward the door. I was sure no hostess actually indicated her guests should leave, but this was my room, and I could behave as I chose. Everyone looked astonished except Tolliver, who smiled, just a twitch of the lips. I smiled myself, and out of habit they all responded, though uncertainly.

'Yes, of course. I'm sure you're tired,' Sybil said. Like a true lady, she was providing a reason for my discourtesy.

I opened my mouth to disagree, but Tolliver beat me to it. 'We've had a long day,' he said with a smile. Mary Nell Teague suddenly looked at him with more interest. When Tolliver smiles, it's so unexpected it gives you a pleasant surprise.

Within a minute, the mother and daughter and lawyer were on the other side of the door, which was exactly where I wanted them.

'Harper,' Tolliver said, in a reproving way.

'I know, I know,' I acknowledged, without any regret. 'What do you think she was really here for?'

'I'm trying to figure it out. Wait a minute, which "she" do you mean?'

'I mean the mother.'

'Good. Me, too. You think she was here to find out what Nell was saying to us? Or to keep us from telling Nell anything?'

'Maybe we should be wondering why Nell was so determined to talk to us. You think she might actually know something about her brother's death?'

'We're getting too wrapped up in this. We need to get out of Sarne.'

'I agree. But I don't think the sheriff will let us leave.' I drooped on the end of the bed, trying not to look at myself in the mirror opposite after one quick glance. I looked too pale and even a little haggard. I looked like a woman who needed a big mug of hot chocolate and about ten hours' sleep.

I could do something about that. I always carry powdered hot chocolate with me, and there was a little coffeepot in the room. After making sure Tolliver didn't want any, I had a steaming mug in hand. I scooted up against the headboard, pillows stuffed behind my back, and looked at Tolliver, who had slid down in the chair so that his long legs were fully extended. 'What's our next appointment?' I asked.

'Memphis, in a week,' he said. 'Occult Studies at some university.'

'A lecture?' I tried not to act as dismayed as I felt. I hated going back to Memphis, where I'd had the only easy part of life I could recall.

'Reading a small cemetery. I think they know the COD for most of the inhabitants.' Cause of death. 'It's a test. I could hear the professor gloating over exposing you, over the phone. Patronizing as hell. Is he going to be surprised or what?'

'Jerk,' I said scornfully. 'They paying us?'

'A nominal amount. But we should do it, because I figure the word-of-mouth on this one is gonna be great, and it's a private university, so some of the parents have money. Plus, we have an appointment in Millington the day after, which is real close.'

Tolliver had arranged things very well. 'Thanks, brother,' I said, and I meant it with my heart.

He waved a hand to discount my gratitude. 'Hey, what else would I be doing?' he asked. 'Herding carts at Wal-Mart? Running a forklift in some warehouse?'

'Married with a couple of kids in a three-bedroom ranch, stable and happy,' I almost said; but then I clenched my teeth over the words.

Some things I was scared to say out loud.

5

We had no purpose the next day, which again dawned sunny and crisp. I went out for a run right after I got up, and I saw Tolliver trotting down the street in the opposite direction when I was almost back at the motel. After I'd showered, and he'd returned and cleaned up, we ate at a different diner.

About midmorning, I was so bored I got Tolliver to take me out to the older cemetery, the one I'd noticed the morning I'd found Teenie. I found it with my other sense, instead of asking for directions. This cemetery had graves over a hundred and fifty years old – well established, at least in American terms. The presence of so many old dead produced a constant, mellow reverberation, almost soothing; like giant ancient drums in the distance. Though the grounds were well tended, in the oldest section I spied a few overturned headstones with writing that time had obscured. These stones would belong to families who had died out; there were no living descendants to tend the plots. I amused myself by going from grave to grave, reaching deep to pull from each collection of bones what information I could garner. The glimpses I caught of these faces were often blurred or obscured, as if the dead themselves had forgotten who they'd been. Every now and then I saw the features clearly, heard a name, caught a longer glimpse of death in the past.

'Childbirth,' I called to Tolliver, who was sitting half-in half-out of the car while he worked a crossword puzzle.

'Another one,' he said, hardly raising his eyes from the page. It was the third childbirth death I'd found.

'Kind of scary.' I stepped to the next grave. Since this was simply to pass the time and keep in practice, I'd left my shoes on. It was a nippy day, and I didn't want to catch a cold, especially since I was just messing around. 'You know, Tolliver, men didn't used to die of heart attacks.'

'That so?'

'That's what I heard on the news the other day. Oh! This guy was crushed by a tree he was cutting down.'

Tolliver didn't bother to look up. 'Um,' he said, so I gathered he wasn't listening. I moved to my right. 'Asthma attack,' I muttered. 'Blood poisoning from a knife cut. Scarlet fever. Smallpox. Flu. Pneumonia.' I shook my head. So many of these things could be cured, or at least eased, now. I couldn't fathom people who longed for the past. They weren't thinking about the absence of antibiotics, that was for sure.

The next grave was one of the oldest. The tombstone had broken in half, and someone had tried to set it back together. I couldn't read the name.

'Hey, gunshot wound,' I called to Tolliver.

'That's Lieutenant Pleasant Early,' Hollis Boxleitner said, from about a yard behind me. 'He was shot during the Civil War.'

If there'd been an open grave, I would've jumped into it. Tolliver looked up sharply and lay down the clipboard. 'Where'd you come from?' he asked, in no very friendly tone.

'I was weeding my great-grandmother's grave over there.' Hollis inclined his head toward the north side of the cemetery; sure enough, there was a bucket full of weeds and a trowel beside a grave with a leaning headstone.

'During a murder investigation, you have time to weed?' Tolliver's voice was sharper than necessary.

'It relaxes me.' Hollis's broad face remained calm. 'And the state guys are in town.'

A gust of wind blew dry leaves across the graves. As they crossed the graveled drive that wended through the cemetery, they made a hissing sound. I liked it.

'So, is this kind of . . . recreation, for you?' Hollis asked, indicating the graves around us.

'Yes. Just kind of keeping my hand in.' People always expect me to be embarrassed by what I do. Why?

'Have you ever been to a really old graveyard? Like in England?'

I ducked my head. 'Not often. There are the Indian mounds, of course, and even more ancient people. Those are pretty interesting. And we went to a very early American one. In Massachusetts.'

'Was it the same? Does the length of time they've been dead make a difference?'

I was pleased at the question. Not many people want to know too much about what I do. 'Yes, it does,' I said. 'I get fainter pictures, less exact knowledge. Someday I want us to go to Westminster Abbey. And Stonehenge.' Lots of ancient dead people there, for sure.

'You think you could get any more information by going back to Helen Hopkins' house?' The policeman had switched back to the here and now, putting an end to our conversation.

'No,' I said. 'I have to be with the body.' I didn't want to go through that, not at all. It was very unpleasant, seeing the death of someone you'd known.

'The state police have taken over the investigation,' Hollis said, after he'd retrieved his bucket of weeds. 'I just answer the phones on my shift. There's a hot line number.'

It took me a second to understand that he'd been banished from the investigation.

'That sucks,' I offered. I've met enough cops to know that the best of them like to be in charge. The best ones have that confidence.

He shrugged. 'In a way. I'm just a part-time cop, it's true.'

'She was your mother-in-law.'

'Yes,' he said heavily. 'They're waiting for you.'

For a second, since I was standing on a grave, I was sure he meant all the dead people; and I already knew they were. Then I realized his meaning was much more mundane. The lawyer, Paul Edwards, and a uniformed man I'd never seen, were standing by the car talking to Tolliver. I was glad I'd left my shoes on. I took a breath and began walking toward the men.

'Good luck,' said Hollis, and I nodded. I knew he was watching, and he would see.

We had a dismal time at the police station. The state police thought I was a blood-sucking leech. I'd anticipated their attitude as we drove into town, but it wore me out anyway. The male faces followed each other in slow succession. Thin, heavy, white, black, intelligent, dense; they all shared an opinion of me they didn't take any pains to hide. I guess they thought Tolliver was the enabler of the blood-sucking leech.

I don't like being treated like a confidence trickster, and I'm sure Tolliver likes it even less. I retreat inside myself, and I don't let them touch my quick. Tolliver tries to do that, too, but he is less successful. He gets very upset when people impugn our honor.

'We looked into your file,' said a thin man with a greyhound face and cold, narrow eyes. The interrogation room was small and beige. They'd taken Tolliver into the one next door.

I breathed in, breathed out, looked at the wall behind his ear.

'You and your "brother" have been questioned lots of times,' he said. His name tag read, *Green*. He waited to make sure I'd heard he'd put 'brother' in quotes.

Since there was nothing to respond to, I did some of my own waiting.

'No one's ever put you behind bars,' he said.

This was another indisputable fact, and I did some more waiting.

'Of course, they should've.'

Opinion. Didn't call for a response. My parents hadn't been lawyers for nothing.

'You know what they say about people from this neck of the woods,' Green said. 'The kind of people who go to family reunions to get a date?'

Green was from somewhere else, I assumed. I slid lower in the plastic chair.

'I figure you and your brother are people like that,' he said, with a most unpleasant smile.

Another opinion, and one he knew was based on incorrect information.

'He's not really your brother, is he?'

'Stepbrother,' I said.

He was taken aback. 'But you introduce him as your brother.'

'Simplification,' I said. I crossed my legs the other way, just to have a change. I was ready to eat lunch. Tolliver and I would go to a restaurant, or we'd get something at the grocery store to heat up in the little microwave we carried with us and plugged in at motel rooms. We'd talked about buying a little house outside of Dallas. We would have a bigger microwave there, or maybe I'd learn to cook. I liked to clean; that is, I didn't exactly love the process, but I did love the result. I might subscribe to a magazine, something it had never been practical for me to do. Maybe *National Geographic*. The December after we moved into the house, Tolliver and I would buy a Christmas tree. I hadn't had a Christmas tree in ten years.

'. . . hearing a word I say?' Greyhound Green's face was drawn with anger.

'No, I haven't. I'm ready to go now. You know I didn't kill that poor woman. You know Tolliver didn't, either. There's not a reason in the world we'd want to do anything to her. You just don't like me. But you can't put me in jail because you don't like me.'

'You prey on the grief of others.'

'How?'

He glared at me. 'They're grieving, wanting closure, and you and your brother turn up like crows to pick at the carcass.'

'Not so,' I said briskly. I was on sure ground, here. 'I find the body. Then they have closure. They're happier.' I got to my feet, feeling my legs prickle after sitting so long in the same chair. 'We'll stay in town as long as you want. But we didn't hurt Helen Hopkins. You know it.'

He stood, too, and tried to think of something to say that would stop me from leaving, convict me of some crime. But there was nothing, and he had to watch me leave. I knocked on the door of the next room. 'Tolliver,' I called. 'Let's us go.'

After a pause, Tolliver opened the door and stepped out. I looked up at him, and saw his eyes were filled with rage. I gently put my hand on his cheek, and when a moment had passed, he relaxed. Together, we walked out of the tiny Sarne police station and over to the car. The grass around the courthouse was starting to brown, and the big silver maple leaves cartwheeled across it exuberantly.

Following the path of one leaf, my eyes lit on Mary Nell Teague. She was waiting for us, her face eager. No, she was waiting for Tolliver. I was clearly a shadow walking beside him, in her eyes. She'd parked her little car right by ours, which must have been difficult. It was a Saturday, and the town was busy.

A group of teenage boys was clustered around the war memorial. They could have been teenagers from anywhere in the United States – jeans, T-shirts, sneakers. Maybe their haircuts weren't cutting edge, but that wouldn't bother anyone here. I wouldn't have had a second look at them if I hadn't realized they were watching us. They didn't look friendly. The tallest one was glaring from Nell to Tolliver.

'Hmm,' I said, wanting to be sure Tolliver had noticed the boys.

'Psychics are all crap,' the tallest boy said, loud enough for us to hear. Of course, that was his purpose. He was probably on the football team, probably class president. He was the alpha wolf.

Handsome and brawny, he was wearing sneakers that had cost more than every stitch I was wearing added together. 'The devil is in people who say they talk to the dead,' he said even louder. Mary Nell was probably too far away to hear him, but she was glancing back and forth from the pack of boys to us, and she looked, in turn, indignant, horrified, and excited. I thought we had us a little love triangle going on here: Alpha Boy, Mary Nell, and Tolliver. Only, Tolliver didn't know about it.

I was becoming antsier by the second. The boys were moving to intercept us. Tolliver had gotten the keys out of his pocket and pressed the pad to unlock the doors.

Mary Nell, moving swiftly, intercepted us just before the boys did. 'Hey, Tolliver!' she said brightly, taking his arm. 'Oh . . . hi, Harper.' I tried not to smile at my second-class status. It was easier not to smile when I saw there was no way to avoid some kind of confrontation with the boys. Alpha Boy laid his hand on Nell's shoulder, halting her progress, and therefore ours.

'You shouldn't be hanging around with these people,' he said to Mary Nell. I could tell from his voice he had known Nell for a long time, and had a proprietary interest in her.

Alpha Boy might have known her for a long time, but he hadn't known her well. Her little face tightened with anger. He'd embarrassed her in front of her newest fixation, an exotic out-of-town older man. 'Scotty, you don't have any say over me,' she said. 'Tolliver, let's us go to the Sonic and have a Coke.'

Tolliver was caught between a rock and a hard place, and I waited to see what he'd do to get out of it. While he squirmed, I looked from young male face to young male face, trying to meet each set of eyes and smile, the squeaky non-sexual smile of a newscaster. Only two of them made the effort to nod to me; the others either evaded my gaze or scowled at me. This was not good.

'Mary Nell, I'd like to, but Harper and I have to go back to the motel and make some phone calls,' Tolliver said. I could see him casting around for something to say that would simultaneously salvage her pride, get him off the hook, and mollify the angry columns of testosterone that were glowering at us. There was nothing that would serve all three functions.

'Maybe Mary Nell would like to have supper with us tonight,' I said unwillingly. It was not so much that I was trying to show the girl some mercy; if she got angry with us, her anger would give the boys permission to attack.

I saw the conflict on Mary Nell's face pass in a flash; it was I who had asked, which negated the value of the invitation, but it did save her face, to some extent. 'That would be wonderful,' she said, giving me the barest glance. 'I'll see you at six at the Ozark Valley Inn.'

I had no idea where that was, but I said, 'See you then,' and Nell walked away to her car very quickly, her head held high. Just as quickly, Tolliver and I got in our car and drove away, stopping at the next light to buckle our seat belts.

Tolliver looked angry and embarrassed. 'Too bad you don't want to be in a boy band,' I said, after a minute of riding in silence. 'You've obviously got the charisma.'

'Oh, shut up!' he said. 'How about you? You gonna be one of the Babes of Law Enforcement?'

'Well, at least Hollis is legal age . . .' I began, but then I couldn't help smiling.

Tolliver managed a small upcurve of the lips. 'Where the hell is the Ozark Valley Inn?' he said.

'I have no idea, but we better find it by six o'clock. Gosh, I have a headache. I sure hope it doesn't get so bad that I have to bow out of the dinner . . .'

'You do and you die.'

We picked up salads for lunch, and took them back to the motel. The phone rang just as we were settling down to read. We were in my room, so I answered.

'This is Hollis. Do you want to go to supper with me?'

We could double-date with Mary Nell and Tolliver! Wouldn't that be fun? I bit my lip to suppress the idea. 'I'm busy for supper,' I said hesitantly, knowing I should turn him down flat, but tempted none-theless.

'A drink afterward?'

'Yes,' I said cautiously, after I'd thought about it.

'I'll pick you up at the motel. Eight o'clock?'

'Okay, see you then.'

'All right. Goodbye.'

I said goodbye, too, and hung up. Tolliver was eyeing me sardonic-ally. 'Let me guess, Cop Boy?'

I nodded. 'We're going to have a drink together tonight at eight, so we'll have to cut short our romantic rendezvous with Mary Nell. I'm sure you don't want to be unchaperoned.'

'If there's anywhere here it would take two hours to eat, I'd be very astonished,' Tolliver said, at his driest.

I agreed, and re-opened my book. But for a few minutes, I read the same page over and over.

When we stopped by the motel office to ask for directions to the Ozark Valley Inn, we noticed that the older man who ran the place was not too happy about helping us. We'd learned his name was Vernon, and he wore overalls and had the worn and wrinkled face of a basset. Vernon had been pleasant enough up to now, though we hadn't seen much of him. But tonight he was distant, his gaze disapproving. 'You planning on moving your bags over there?' he asked, almost hopefully.

'No,' I said, surprised. 'We're just meeting someone for dinner in the restaurant at the inn.'

' 'Cause I been meaning to tell you, I'm going to need those rooms pretty soon. Hope you two wasn't planning on staying very long.'

'I'm sure you have tons of business coming in,' I agreed, maybe a little coldly. 'And we won't stay a minute longer than we have to.'

'Glad to hear it.'

'I guess no one's going to ask us to judge the floats in the homecoming parade,' I said to Tolliver when we were in the car.

He smiled, but it was a small smile. 'The sooner we can get out of Sarne, the better,' he said.

Mary Nell came in seven minutes after we were seated at a table in the inn, which was on the southern side of the town. Her face was flushed and her cell phone was in her hand. I was willing to bet she'd lied to her mother about where she was going and whom she was going to be with. I almost hated the girl at that moment, for the trouble she might get us into.

'Sorry I'm late,' Mary Nell said, as she took a chair. 'I had some things I had to do at home. My mom is so paranoid.'

'She lost your brother,' I said. 'I'm sure that's made her more protective.' I wouldn't have thought even a self-absorbed teenager could have missed that point.

The girl flushed deep red. 'Of course,' she said stiffly. 'I just mean, she doesn't seem to know how old I am.' She'd dressed with care, in new low riders with a tight green T-shirt. She wore a soft fuzzy cardigan sweater and boots.

'That's a common thing with mothers,' I said. My own mother had forgotten how old I was, after she'd started chasing the drugs with alcohol. She'd decided I was much older and needed a boyfriend. She picked a doping buddy of hers who was willing to give her free samples for the privilege of being my first 'date.' Tolliver had gone off to college by then, and I'd had to spend a day locked in my room. I had known that eventually they'd go to sleep and I'd be able to get out of the house, but I was hungry and thirsty and had no access to a bathroom. After that, I kept bottled water and a box of crackers and an old cooking pot in my room.

'Have you lived in Sarne all your life?' Tolliver asked Mary Nell.

She flushed when he spoke directly to her. 'Yes,' she said. 'My dad's parents were born here, too. Dad died just before Dell.' I was startled. When Edwards had told me Sybil was a recent widow, I hadn't realized how recent. 'Dell, he really missed Dad . . . He was closer to Dad than me.' She sounded vaguely resentful.

'I want to ask you a question, Mary Nell,' I said. 'I don't want to upset you any more than I have to, but when you were talking to us the other night, you paused after you said one sentence. You said something like, "I knew he wouldn't kill Teenie and . . ." and then you stopped. What were you going to say?'

Mary Nell eyed me. You could tell her feelings were conflicted. 'Please tell us, Nell,' Tolliver said, and she crumbled when she looked into his dark brown eyes. He'd called her something special.

'Okay,' she said, leaning across the table to share her big secret. 'Dell told me, the week before he and Teenie . . . the week before they died, that Teenie was gonna have a baby.' Her heavily made-up eyes were as big and round as a raccoon's. The girl was clearly shocked that her brother had been having sex with his girlfriend, and she just as clearly considered the pregnancy top-secret knowledge.

'No one knew?'

'He sure didn't tell my mom. She would've killed him.' Then, as she realized what she'd said, Mary Nell turned red as a brick, and tears filled her eyes.

'That's okay,' I said hastily, 'we know your mom wouldn't really do that.'

'Well, Mom never has liked Teenie's mom too much. I don't know why. Miss Helen used to work for us a few years ago, and I thought she was great. Always singing.'

And I could tell that she suddenly remembered that Helen Hopkins had been murdered, too. There was a look on her face, a lost look, like she was drowning.

'If I'd killed everyone I didn't like, I'd be able to dress in their scalps,' Tolliver said.

Mary Nell gave a startled giggle and covered her mouth with her small hand.

After all this time, could an autopsy establish Teenie's pregnancy?

'Dell didn't tell anyone but you?' I asked.

'No one knew but me,' Mary Nell said proudly.

Mary Nell was sure her brother hadn't told anyone about the baby, but what about Teenie? Had she told someone? Her mother, maybe?

Her mother, who was . . . gee, let me think . . . dead.

6

After Tolliver and I had exchanged glances, we steered off the subject quickly. Mary Nell's sad, tearful face had already attracted some attention from the sparse clientele. Her coloring cleared up and her demeanor brightened as she talked about happier topics, addressing her conversation almost exclusively to my brother. Tolliver found out that Nell planned to go to the University of Arkansas the next year, that she wanted to be a physical therapist so she could help people, that she was a cheerleader and didn't like algebra. Her cheerleading sponsor was totally cool.

I was free to think my own thoughts. Mary Nell didn't seem much different from any of the girls I'd known in high school, the girls with sober parents, the girls who had enough money to ward off worry and homelessness. She was bright but not brilliant, virginal but not saintly. The loss of her sibling had left her drifting, searching for a new identity when her old one had been shaken at its core. I could see the knowledge of her brother's secret life with Teenie had disturbed Mary Nell deeply, until that shock had been smothered by the greater trauma of Dell's death. Clearly, sharing her brother's secret had relieved the knot of tension deep inside Mary Nell Teague. It didn't seem to make a difference to Mary Nell that the people she'd shared it with were strangers.

The girl was fascinated with Tolliver. Since she was popular, pretty, and a teenager, Mary Nell was sure Tolliver would find her equally fascinating. I observed Mary Nell flounder through the conversation, trying to find the key to cajoling my brother into noticing she was a woman. Mary Nell would begin an anecdote about her homeroom teacher, realize that was a kid topic, and make a huge effort to switch to some conversational gambit she believed would appeal to an older man.

'Did you go to college?' she asked Tolliver.

'I went two years,' he said. 'Then I worked for a while. After that, Harper and I started our traveling.'

'How come you don't get a regular job and stay somewhere?' Like real people do.

Tolliver looked at me. I looked back. 'Good question,' he said. I looked at him askance, determined not to answer. She hadn't asked *me*.

'Harper helps people,' he said. 'She's one of a kind.'

'But she gets paid for it,' Nell said, outraged.

'Sure,' Tolliver said. 'Why not? When you get to be a therapist, you'll get paid.'

Mary Nell ignored this royally.

'And she can do that by herself. Does she have to have help?'

Hey, sitting right here! Listening! I spread my hands, palms up. Only Tolliver noticed the gesture.

'It's not that she has to have my help. It's that I want to give it to her,' Tolliver said gently. I looked straight down at my plate. Mary Nell abruptly excused herself to go to the ladies' room. I had no intention of accompanying her – I would not be welcome – so Tolliver and I silently picked at the remnants of our food until she returned, her eyes red and her head held high.

'Thanks for dinner,' she said stiffly. We'd insisted on treating her. 'I enjoyed it.' Then, holding her eyes wide and unblinking, she strode out of the dining room.

I watched her car pull out of the dark parking lot. I was a little surprised to find myself actually concerned about the girl. Her life was crashing in ruins around her, and that could make her careless. Too many things can happen to girls who don't watch where they're going. I find their corpses every year.

We got back to our motel in plenty of time for me to brush my hair and spray on a little perfume for my date. Tolliver watched without comment, his face harsh in the shadowy light of the room. 'You got your cell phone?' he asked. 'I'll leave mine on.'

'Okay,' I said. Tolliver went into his room, shutting the door behind him very gently.

Hollis knocked on my door right on time. When I opened it, he said, 'You look pretty,' sounding unflatteringly surprised. I was wearing jeans and a black blouse and some black heels. I wore a gold chain with a jade pendant, a gift from me to me after I'd gotten a bonus from a distraught husband who'd been looking for his wife's body for four years.

Hollis looked pretty good himself, solid and blond in a new pair of jeans and a gold-and-brown plaid shirt. He'd shaved, and he smelled of some cologne. He'd made an effort. Maybe this was a bit more of a date than I'd imagined.

We went to a small dive a little north of town. It was built of dark wood and had plastic banners on long ropes tied from the building to the trees and lamp poles around the graveled lot. If the brightly colored triangles had been fluttering in some breeze, possibly the effect would have been cheerful and festive. In the chilly, still night air, the banners were simply depressing, forlorn reminders of failed festivity.

The interior looked better than I'd imagined, given the exterior. The bar itself was polished wood and the floor had been redone recently in that fake oak flooring that actually looks pretty good. The tables and booths were clean. The decor was definitely Hunting Lodge, with deer heads and large fish mounted on the walls, interspersed with mirrors and old license plates. The jukebox was wailing country and western.

I was pleased with the place, and I smiled. Hollis asked if I wanted one of the small booths or a table, and I picked a booth. He asked me what I wanted to drink, and when I said a Coors would be fine, he went to the bar and returned with two longnecks. He also brought two napkins, one of which he solemnly placed on the heavily polyurethaned wood in front of me before he put my mug on it. I suppressed a smile.

So much for the preliminaries.

'What do you like to do?' he asked. 'While you're traveling around the country?'

Not the opening I'd expected. 'I like to read,' I said. 'Sometimes, we try to catch a movie. I run. I watch television. I like to watch the WNBA games, since I played a little basketball in high school. I plan my dream house.'

'Tell me about your dream house,' Hollis said, smiling.

'Okay,' I said, slowly. This was something I didn't talk about too often. 'It will have to be off the beaten road, of course. I want it to look like a log cabin, but without the inconveniences of a real log cabin. I found a plan on the Internet, and I bought it. But of course, I want to alter it a little.'

'Of course,' he said, taking a sip of beer.

'It would be two bedrooms and a study, with a family room. There'd be a kitchen here, with the washroom right off of it.' I was looking down at the table, drawing with my finger. 'Around back, there'd be a *porte cochere* for the cars, so you could carry groceries right into the kitchen without getting wet. There's a deck off the right side of the kitchen, see? Or maybe I'd put it off the family room. That's where the fireplace will be, and you could keep your firewood on the deck. And you could put your gas grill on the deck. For steaks.'

'Who lives in that house with you?'

I looked up at him, startled. 'Well, of course—' I began. Then I shut my mouth.

'Surely your brother will get married somewhere along the line?' Hollis asked gently, his eyes steady and his face calm. 'You might want to marry, yourself. Cut down on your traveling, some.'

'Yes, that might happen,' I said after a moment. 'What about you?'

'I'll stay here,' he said, almost sadly. 'Maybe I'll feel like trying something permanent again, who knows? I haven't been the man I was since Sally died. And before I met Sally, I was married for about ten minutes when I was just a kid. It might be hard to get some sweet thing to spend time with me.'

'I don't think that'll be the issue,' I said. Some women might be put off by Hollis, but it was hardly his fault that his second wife had been murdered. 'Was being married . . . was it good? Living with someone full-time?'

He gave it some thought, staring down at his beer. Then he looked at me.

'The first time, it was heaven for two months. Then it was hell,' he said, his mouth turning up wryly. 'What a mistake that was. The only thing I can say, she was as eager to make that mistake as I was. We wanted each other so bad I couldn't sleep nights. At the time we married, we looked on it as a license to screw. And boy, did we. We didn't realize there'd be a lot more to it. We found out, right quick. When we split up, it would be a toss-up as to which of us was the more relieved.'

After raising an inquiring eyebrow at me, he fetched us two more beers. 'Sally, she was different,' he said. 'She was as sweet as her mom and her sister were wild. She wanted to get away from them, but she felt responsible for raising her sister, since her mom was such a lush. Then Helen kind of took a deep breath and got sober.' He shook his head from side to side. 'Now they're all gone, it don't make a difference, does it? Helen might as well have kept on drinking.'

'Did the autopsy results come back on Teenie?' I asked.

His face became more guarded, cautious. 'I can't talk to you about that.' He looked at me for a long minute. 'Why?'

It wasn't up to me to reveal the dead couple's secret. And I suddenly wondered why I even cared. I found bodies, and then I walked away. People died, died all the time, some in bed, some in the woods, some with a gun in their mouths. The end result was always the same. Why was this time different from any other?

'What is the worst case you've ever had?' Hollis asked me out of the blue.

I wondered if some expression crossing my face had triggered the question. 'Oh, the tornado one,' I said without even having to consider.

'Where was this tornado?'

'In Texas,' I said. 'Went right down the main street of this little town. I can't remember if the siren had gone off or not – or if it just came so suddenly there wasn't a chance to sound the siren. For whatever reason, this woman, her name was Molly Mathers, was running from her business to her car with her baby in one of those plastic carrying things with a handle. Little bitty baby.'

'Storm took the baby?'

I nodded. 'Snatched the carrier right out of Molly's hand.'

We kept a moment of silence together.

'Everyone was sure the baby hadn't survived, of course, but the mom just couldn't let go of the idea that the baby was still in the carrier, maybe in some field, and was going hungry.' I said this very evenly, because it was a hard thing to think of, a hard memory to carry around with me.

'You find the baby?'

I nodded, my lips pressed hard together.

'Deceased?'

'Sure. Up in a tree. She was still in the carrier.'

'God.'

I nodded again. Nothing you could say about that. 'But mostly it's not so bad,' I said, after a long moment of allowing the memory to dissipate. 'Mostly it's girls who don't come home, or older people who wander away. Sometimes abducted kids – not too often, because if someone picked them up in a vehicle, of course there's no way to guess where the body would be.'

'So you take cases where the body location is known?'

'Well, if it can be pinned down to a reasonable area. You couldn't say, "Hey, he was hiking somewhere in the Mojave Desert," and expect me to find anything. Unless you had unlimited money for the amount of time it'd take me.'

'What's it like?'

'What?'

'The feeling, when a body's close.'

'It's like a buzzing. A humming. In my bones, in my brain. It almost hurts. The closer I get, the more intense it gets. And when I'm close, when I'm in the body's presence, I see the death.'

'How much of the death?'

'I see the few seconds before it. But the only person I see is the one who died. Not any other people around. At the same time, I'm in that person, feeling it. So it can be pretty . . . unpleasant.'

'That seems like an understatement.' He took a long sip of his beer.

I nodded. 'I wish I could see the face of the murderer, but I never do.'

'Couldn't prosecute on your word alone, anyway.'

'Yeah, I get that, but still.' I shrugged. 'I'd be more useful.'

'You look on your job as useful?'

'Sure. Everyone needs closure, right? Uncertainty eats at you; well, I meant "you" in the general sense, but didn't it make you feel better when you knew what had happened to your wife? Plus, if people believe me, I can save lots of money. Like, "Don't dredge that pond or send in divers. No body there." Or, "You don't need to search through the landfill." Stuff like that.'

'If people believe you.'

'Yeah. Lots don't.'

'How do you handle that?'

'I've learned to let it go and walk away.'

'It must be tough.'

'At first it was. Not now. What about your job?'

'Oh about what you'd expect. Drunk drivers, mostly. Neighbor disputes. Sometimes some shoplifting. Burglary. Not too much that's mysterious or even very serious. Every now and then a wife-beater, or someone with a gun on a Saturday night. I never get to see anyone at their best.' He gave me a crooked half-smile.

I'd wondered what we could possibly find to talk about, but the next couple of hours went easier than I'd anticipated. He talked about deer hunting, and told me about the time he'd fallen out of his shooting stand and gotten nothing worse than a sprained ankle, the same year his friend John Harley had fallen from a stand and broken his back. I had once hurt my back playing basketball. He had played basketball in high school. He'd had a great time in high school, but never wanted to revisit those days. I didn't either. I had spent my high school years trying to keep my head down and my mouth shut so no one would find out how truly weird my life was. Because of my mother and my stepfather, I didn't want to bring anyone home with me. I'd managed pretty well until Cameron vanished. Her disappearance had been so spectacular, so media-saturated, that it had drawn a lot of unwanted attention to me.

'Seems like I remember that,' Hollis said thoughtfully. He was on his third beer. I was still nursing my second. 'Wasn't she taken by a man in a blue pickup?'

I nodded. 'Grabbed on her way home. She'd been decorating the gym for some dance. I'd walked home earlier, so she was alone. This guy took her right off the street. There were witnesses. But no one ever found her.'

'I'm sorry,' he said.

I nodded in acknowledgment. 'Someday I'll find her,' I said. 'Someday it'll be her, when I feel that buzz. And we'll know what happened to her.'

'Are your parents still alive?'

'My father is, I think. My mother died last year.' Her addictions had finally succeeded in eating up her body.

'What's your connection with Tolliver?'

'Tolliver's dad married my mother. We were brought up as family, after that.' If we'd been 'brought up' at all, I added to myself. Mostly, we'd fended for ourselves. After a while, we'd become good at presenting a facade to the authorities who might separate us. Tolliver watched over Cameron and me, I watched over the two littler girls, Mariella and Gracie. Tolliver's older brother Mark stopped by on a regular basis to make sure we were eating. If we weren't, Mark would bring groceries. Tolliver got a job at a restaurant as soon as he was old enough, and he brought home all the food he could.

Sometimes our parents were both working, sometimes we got government assistance. But mostly the money went down their throats or into their veins.

We learned to survive on very little, and we learned how to pick clothes at the thrift store and at yard sales, clothes that wouldn't give away our situation. Mark would lecture us on how important it was to make good grades. 'As long as you keep clean and neat, don't skip school, and make at least average grades, social services won't come by,' he'd taught us, and he'd been right. Until Cameron vanished.

I tried explaining those years to Hollis.

'That sounds horrible,' Hollis said. His face looked sad, sad for the girl I had been, God bless him. 'Did they hit you?'

'No,' I said. 'Neglect was the key to their parenting system, even for Mariella and Gracie. My mom tried to take care of them when they were babies, but after that, it was kind of up to Cameron and me, mostly me. It was hard for us not to go down the same drain.' I had clung to my memory of what life had been like before – before my mother had begun using drugs, before my father had gone to jail. I'd promised myself I could have that life again. My two younger sisters hadn't had as hard a time; they had no memory of anything better.

The tension of maintaining the status quo had almost killed me. But we'd managed, until Cameron got snatched.

'What happened then?' Hollis asked.

I fidgeted, looked anywhere else. 'Let's talk about something else,' I said. 'The summary is that I spent my senior year living with a foster family, and my little half-sisters stayed with my aunt and uncle.'

'How was the foster family?'

'They were decent people,' I said. 'Not child molesters, not slave-drivers. As long as I did my assigned chores and finished my home-work, I wasn't unhappy.' It had been an acute pleasure to live in a household that valued order and cleanliness.

'Any trace of your sister ever found?'

'Her purse. Her backpack.' I shifted my right leg, which tended to numb if I didn't move it around.

'Tough.'

'Yeah, I'd say we've both had lives that had a few bumps.'

Hollis nodded. 'Here's to trying to live a better life,' he said, and we bumped glasses.

We went to his small house later, gaining a little comfort and warmth from each other. But I wouldn't spend the night, though he wanted me to stay. About three in the morning, I kissed him good-bye at the door to my motel room, and we held each other for a long minute. I went inside by myself, cold to my bones.

7

It was a good morning for running: the third clear day in a row, chilly, with the promise of brilliance in the early sky. I ran a brush through my hair and put on my dogtag engraved with my name and Tolliver's cell phone number. I dressed in a sports bra and three-quarter length Lycra running pants. An old 'Race for the Cure' T-shirt covered the little canister of pepper spray clipped to my pants. I'd found a plastic slotted cover with a hole punched in one end, and I slipped my room key in it and put it on the same chain with my dogtag.

After some warm-up stretches, I decided I'd run from the motel until I'd reached the Kroger that was at the other end of town. I didn't want to follow the main drag; even in Sarne, there'd be traffic, and I hated inhaling truck exhaust fumes. I had picked out a route that involved backstreets lined with small businesses and homes. With an inner feeling of release, I began running.

When I was able to pick up my pace, it was possible to think of something other than the act of running. A little to my surprise, I felt better than I had expected: relaxed, not guilty. Though I was fairly inexperienced, Hollis had seemed a tender and considerate lover. He'd also seemed to need the contact, the basic act of joining flesh, as much as I had. So, I told myself, *that was actually an okay thing to do.*

Absorbed in my thoughts, I gradually realized a pickup was moving just behind me. The growl of the motor had been chewing at the edge of my awareness for a minute or two. My heart began pounding with an unpleasant desperation when I realized the driver was definitely dogging me. The dark shadow in the corner of my left eye turned into a rumbling presence. Though I kept running at a steady pace, all my attention was focused on the truck creeping along like a lion through high grass, waiting for my inattention to prove fatal. I flipped open the little holster and eased the canister of pepper spray out of it. Was Arkansas one of the states where the spray was legal? I couldn't remember, and at the moment I decided that was the least of my worries. I was at least half a mile from the motel, and there were few cars stirring in the streets. I couldn't count on any help. The little canister was almost completely concealed in my hand.

I was in front of a little strip of businesses that hadn't yet opened; a laundry, a jewelry store, an insurance agency. No cars, no passersby. The tension roiled under my skin as I waited for whoever was in the pickup to act. If they would just wait until we were closer to the main street, or if I could angle through the downtown buildings to the police station . . . but then the suspense was over.

The pickup swerved to pull across the sidewalk, blocking my path, and three young men hopped out. Of course! Alpha male, the high school boy Mary Nell had called Scotty. He had his two buddies with him, naturally.

I stopped, and they ranged themselves in front of me, their faces ugly with tension. Incongruously, the three were wearing high school football jackets. Scotty was in the middle, and a smaller black-haired boy was on my right. There was a husky brown-haired boy, uniformly thick through the chest and middle, on my left. They didn't have weapons, at first glance. But they all had clenched fists.

'Hey bitch, we told you to leave town,' Scotty said. His words' ugliness twisted his face. The three were suppressing so much excitement they were literally shifting from foot to foot, shoulders moving restlessly.

My eyes went from face to face as I wondered who would charge first. They were cocked and primed and ready to fire.

'You guys thinking of raping me?' I asked, wanting to have it clear in my mind.

They looked shocked. *Shocked.* The two followers looked at the alpha, so he could answer for them. Or maybe they needed to find out what they wanted to do.

'We don't want any part of you, you skanky ho,' Scotty said, trying to sound scornful, to square his lack of rape aspiration with his need to assert his manhood. Of course, real men should be ready to have any sort of sex, any time. So if they didn't want to rape me, I must not be desirable.

'That's good,' I said, and then I saw that the black-haired boy on my right had gotten too tense to hold back any longer. His arm had gone back to hit me. Stupid to telegraph like that. I sprayed him right in the face, and he turned red and began clawing at his eyes and shrieking.

'It's burning! I can't see!' he screamed. While his two buddies were staring at him with their mouths open, I sprayed them, too, though Scotty tried to dodge at the last minute, and I didn't get his eyes.

The blip of a police siren scared me out of what wits I had left. When I'd recovered from the shock, I was delighted to see the police car, and even more delighted to see that the driver was Sheriff Harvey Branscom.

He was not as glad to see me as I was to see him.

'What happened here?' he asked, surveying the young men with disgust. They were crying and moaning, and the black-haired boy was actually on the ground.

'They swerved in front of me and got out of the truck to threaten me,' I said.

'No, Sheriff,' wailed the black-haired boy who'd swung his fist first. 'It was her! She—'

'She pulled your truck over to the sidewalk, dragged you out, and made you stand in a row in front of her so she could squirt you with pepper spray?' Harvey Branscom would have loved a credible reason to blame me, but he was honest enough not to manufacture one. 'You three make me sick. Scot, if I see you even cast a glance at my niece after this little incident, I'll find a way to stick you in jail, and you won't like it one little bit.'

I wasn't sure if Scot was absorbing any of Sheriff Branscom's threats, since he was doubled over rubbing at his burning face. That was exactly the wrong thing to do, according to the booklet that came with the pepper spray. Sheriff Branscom sighed heavily and pulled a six-pack of Ozark Mountain bottled water out of the police car. 'Lucky I ride around with this,' he muttered. He opened a bottle and made the boys stand still while he poured it over their faces.

'I hope you're all ashamed of yourselves. Not only were you on the edge of committing a felony, you were three big guys about to beat up a lone woman. Not only *that*, but you're tardy for school, and that means you're all going to be in detention this afternoon, which means you're going to miss football practice. I'm going to be interested to hear what the coach puts you through after I call him and explain the reason. And I will call him.' Harvey raised his eyebrows at me. 'That is, unless this lady wants to bring charges against you? If she does, you ain't going to get to school anytime today.'

I knew a cue when I heard one. I hesitated. Then I nodded, and I saw the tension leave the sheriff's shoulders. 'If you call their football coach, and you're sure he can give them a good punishment, I'll be satisfied with that. After all,' I said pointedly, 'if I bring charges against them, they'll be off the team, at least for a while.'

Harvey looked relieved. 'Yes, they would be off the team. And of course, their parents would know all about this little fiasco. I figure a felony arrest would sure screw up their college applications, huh? Your dad would love to hear your explanation for this, Scot, especially since he just had to pay for three new mailboxes on Bainbridge Road. Justin, I know your mama had a hard time buying that football jacket.' Justin was weeping too hard to reply, but he did look a little more miserable. 'Cody, what do you think your grandmother would have to say about you attacking a woman?'

'We just wanted her to leave town,' Cody muttered. I must not have aimed well when I sprayed him.

My heart was still thumping like a rabbit's when it hears the dog in the bushes. It was an unpleasant and humiliating feeling, being this frightened. If I hadn't had my pepper spray, or if the sheriff hadn't intervened, by this time I'd have a broken jaw, or some fractured ribs. Three big boys/men, only a few years younger than I . . . they might have killed me by sheer stupid accident.

Harvey Branscom was as good as his word. He whipped out his cell phone and called the football coach at the high school, and without spelling out what the boys had almost done, he let the coach know they deserved the worst punishment the coach could hand out. I knew a football coach could hand out plenty, especially in season. I wasn't dissatisfied with the bargain I'd struck with the sheriff. I thought that in Sarne it was the best I would manage.

When he thought Scot could see well enough to drive his pickup, Branscom sent the boys on their way to school. After they'd driven out of sight, and my heart had calmed down to a normal rate, Sheriff Branscom said, 'Miss Connelly, I guess you aren't popular here in Sarne.' I sure wasn't popular with the elder law enforcement segment. His face was hard with repressed distaste. 'I'm sorry that happened to you. Scot's had it bad for Mary Nell since they were in the first grade together.'

I was still bouncing on the balls of my feet with adrenaline. 'And he shows it by beating up another woman?'

'No, the idiot shows it by defending my niece against someone he imagines is going to hurt her,' Branscom said heavily. He leaned against his car. At this moment, he looked far older than his years. 'People around here just can't understand you or what you do, Ms Connelly. It makes it worse that you're for real, I think. You did find Teenie, sure enough. But we're not closer to finding out who killed her, and there's still no way to prove Dale didn't. Somehow, finding Teenie has led to Helen getting killed, too. In fact, I guess we'll be burying Teenie and her mother at the same time, side by side, right in the plot with Sally. According to what you told Hollis, that's three murder victims in the same family. I wish that bolt of lightning had struck you a little harder. Maybe you would have seen enough to straighten out this mess.'

Or maybe, his unspoken thought continued, I would have been killed and none of this would be a problem. I was swept with a wave of overwhelming disbelief. 'You've had months and months to solve any mystery surrounding Dell's death and Teenie's disappearance,' I said, almost whispering in an effort not to shout. 'You have a police force and a police lab at your service in solving Helen's murder. I'm *one woman* who can find bodies, and I never claimed to be more. Don't you dare try to shift any of the blame for this whole mess to me.'

Another police car pulled up behind the sheriff's. Hollis, creaking and heavily laden in his cop gear, was out of the car and beside us before I could make my mouth try to smile at him.

'Are you all right?' he asked, his hand cupping the curve of my shoulder. He leaned down to look in my face. What he saw there made him angry. 'I stopped the Briscoe boy over by the high school for speeding, and he looked so bad I asked what happened to him. He told me everything, didn't understand why I didn't applaud.'

I felt old. In the chilly breeze, my running clothes seemed inadequate, and the only warmth in the world was my skin under Hollis's hand. 'I'm all right,' I said steadily. 'I think I'll finish my run and get back to the motel.'

'Where's your brother? You want me to go get him and bring him here?'

Suddenly, my head felt as light as a balloon. I realized that the combination of intense fear followed by intense relief – and then equally intense anger – had just made me numb. And it was something, you know . . . hearing Hollis be intuitive enough to hit on the one thing I found I wanted above all else. But I wasn't going to ask him for it.

'I appreciate your concern,' I said very softly. 'But I'm just going to run, now.'

I don't know if he understood or not; I hope he did grasp my sincerity. Since we were on the side of a public road, I didn't want to hug him. Even if we'd been in a more private situation, I'm not sure I'd have hugged him. But I tried to smile at him as I began to jog down the road. I moved very slowly, because my body chemistry was all screwed up; my muscles didn't know if they were cold from inactivity or warm from adrenaline, and my mind was scurrying around many different corners, but focused on one thing – finishing this run, out of pride.

I got back to the motel with no further incident. I had completed my self-assigned distance. I was walking around the parking lot outside my room, cooling down, trying hard to put the fear behind me. Stupid. I was stupid, stupid, stupid.

My brother came down the road, finishing up his own run. I hastily went to my own door and slid in the plastic card.

'No, you don't!' he called out. 'You stay right there.'

Shit. I kept my back to him.

He spun me around by one shoulder. He looked me up and down.

'Are you all right?' he asked.

He'd run into one of the lawmen.

'Yes,' I said, trying not to sound sullen. 'I'm fine. Who told you?'

'I saw Hollis Boxleitner,' he said. 'That where you were last night?'

I nodded, not meeting Tolliver's eyes.

'We have to get out of this place,' he said. 'We could go if they found out who did this.'

'Maybe it would do some good if I could get to Helen's body,' I said. 'I might pick up something.'

'Hollis said she got a phone call after we'd left her place that morning. The lawyer called her. Paul Edwards.'

'What about?'

'Hollis didn't say. I don't guess he mentioned it last night?'

'No.' I could feel my face heating up.

'But the sheriff still doesn't want us to go, because he still thinks we must know something.'

'We could just leave anyway,' I said. 'There's no legal way he can keep us here, right?'

'I don't think so,' Tolliver said. He'd been gripping my arms, and when he let go, I got that tingly feeling as blood rushed back through the veins and arteries. 'But you know one bad word from law enforcement will mean we'll lose a lot of jobs.'

That was true enough. The last time a chief of police had been dissatisfied with me – he'd been convinced I had some prior knowledge of the body's location, that I was in direct communication with the killer and out to feather my own nest – I'd had almost no income for six months. It had been a hard time, and I'd had enough hard times. I didn't want any more, ever.

'Your boyfriend'll give us a good word,' Tolliver said teasingly, trying to lift my spirits.

I didn't even protest over Tolliver's use of the term 'boyfriend.' I knew he didn't believe that Hollis was anything to me. As usual, he was both right and wrong.

8

Gleason and Sons Mortuary was a place of heavy carpeting and dark corners. It was picturesquely located in an old Victorian-style home, and it was landscaped outside and painted a serene blue inside, with stained-glass windows that must have cost a small fortune. The restored Victorian held the two viewing rooms, an office where the families could select – and pay – for caskets and other services, and a kitchen to brew the constant stream of coffee consumed by mourners. A low, discreet modern addition in the rear held the grimmer rooms where the actual functions of the funeral home were conducted.

Elijah Gleason showed us the more public part before we went to the modern addition. He was proud of his accomplishments as the third Gleason in the funeral business in Sarne, and I had respect for following an honorable tradition. He was a short, stout man in his late thirties with slicked thick black hair and a wide, thin-lipped mouth.

'This is my wife Laura,' he said as we passed an open door. The woman inside waved. She had very short brown hair and a rounded figure. 'She does my books in the winter, and in the summer she's Aunt Hattie at Aunt Hattie's Ice Cream Parlor.' The woman smiled and nodded in an abstract way and returned her attention to the computer screen before her. From the coatrack in the corner hung a soft, flowered bonnet and a matching long apron. I hoped Aunt Hattie's was air conditioned.

'I guess your business is pretty constant, rather than seasonal,' I said, for lack of some better response.

Elijah Gleason said, 'You'd be surprised. We get at least two deaths a summer from the tourists. Of course, those are usually just getting the remains ready to send to their home mortuary, but it all adds up.'

I could think of nothing to say to that, so I just nodded. I reminded myself to stay away from Sarne in the summer. It was somehow embarrassing to think of these people dressing up to imitate a past that was hotter, smellier, more ignorant, and chock-full of deaths that nowadays could be easily prevented. Women in childbirth, kids with polio, babies with conflicting Rh factors, men whose fingers turned septic after little accidents with a saw . . . I'd seen all these during my little outing at the cemetery. Most people didn't think about this aspect of living in the past when they tried to imagine how it must have been. They saw the absence of what they perceived as modern ills: abortion, homosexuality, television, divorce. They saw the past in terms of Friday evening fiddling with the neighbors on the front porch, shoofly pie, gospel singing, long happy marriages.

I saw sudden, needless death.

Soon enough we were in the new part of the funeral home, and the director was showing us Helen. Hollis had asked him to do it, after assuring Gleason I wouldn't faint or throw up at the sight of the body. I like funeral homes. I like the attempt to make death presentable and palatable. It's a cushion to life. It's like the pretty padded lining to the coffin. The dead sure don't care, but makes the living feel better.

The buzzing in my head steadily increased as we grew closer to the room with the closed door. It reached a high drone when I stepped into the bright white sterility of the modern embalming room.

'I haven't started on her yet,' Elijah Gleason said. 'I just got her back from the state crime lab. It'll take them months to finish the toxicology, they told me, they're hundreds of cases behind.'

'Would you stay outside?' Tolliver asked. 'It's just that my sister has a pretty startling reaction sometimes, and it might alarm you.'

'Sorry,' Gleason said firmly. 'Helen's body's under my care, and I'm staying with her.'

Well, I hadn't expected much different. I nodded, all my attention focused on the form on the tilted table. I held up a hand to ask the two men not to speak.

I approached Helen. From her neck down, she was covered by a sheet. Her hair had been brushed. The hum of her presence filled my head. Her soul was still there. That was very unexpected. I jerked with surprise. For the soul to linger three days after death, especially when the body had been found, was almost unprecedented. I knew I would get more information since she was still intact. But I felt full of pity. My neck muscles began to jerk, almost imperceptibly, because I wasn't trying to search for her, she was right in front of me. And she was intact.

The funeral home director was eyeing me with ill-concealed disgust. 'She's there,' I said very softly, and I saw Gleason's face go slack with horror. I glanced at Tolliver, and he nodded, understanding. 'I'm just going to touch her,' I explained to Gleason. 'With respect.'

I stared down at Helen's battered face, my neck and facial muscles relaxing finally. All the bruising made her look as if someone had painted her in shades of dark. Under the edge of the sheet, my fingertips made contact with the skin of her shoulder.

From a distance, I could hear myself gasp – a deep, throaty, alarmed sound. I could see the arm upraised, the arm that held a candlestick. I was crouching down, trying to avoid the blow. The arm was a man's, in a long sleeve. An overwhelming sense of betrayal and shock. The glimpse of the descending arm. Pain and disillusionment, bitterness, the hope of resurrection, a terrifying blend of final emotions. And then nothing, nothing, nothing.

'I know,' I whispered. 'You can go, now.'

And the soul of Helen Hopkins left her body.

This had only happened to me once before. I hadn't known what to do then, had only stumbled on the presence of the dead person by accident. This is what leads to the stories of haunting. The soul wants some acknowledgment of its struggle; the agony involved in the death of the body, and the emotional turmoil of being killed, somehow adhere the soul to the body. If not addressed before burial, this adhesion leads to hauntings.

I'd laid Helen Hopkins to rest before she was even buried. I had done something good.

But I'd endured her final moment with her, and the aftermath settled in. I was very shaky, and I felt Tolliver take my arm and lead me to a metal chair. What was in front of me finally registered in my brain, and I realized that Elijah Gleason was staring at me, mouth agape, eyes narrowed. I knew that look. It was a witch-burning look.

'Helen is at rest with our Lord,' I said immediately, and I managed to smile. They like that.

Gleason looked a smidge less horrified. 'You can tell?' he asked, at last.

'Yes,' I said, my voice firm. 'She is in heaven with all the saints, in eternal glory.'

This toeing of the line always impressed them and got them off my back. It was a card I hated to play. I'm not saying I'm an unbeliever. Nor am I an agnostic. But I have to talk to other people about God in ways they'll understand, because my God doesn't seem to be anything like theirs. Even if they don't believe – really, truly – themselves, they're always reassured to hear the terms of fundamental Christianity. In fact, coming from me, it shakes their half-concealed disbelief.

And it keeps me safe. Tolliver, too.

Gleason flung the sheet over Helen's face, and I looked at the length of flesh draped in the bleached cotton. It was empty now, and it was just a collection of cells that would accelerate its dissolution now that it had served its purpose.

When we were back in the cool sunshine again, I asked Tolliver if we could track down a friend of Helen's. After a phone call to Hollis, who said Helen's best friend was Annie Gibson, we consulted a Sarne directory. Five minutes later we were sitting in a front room that was nearly a clone of Helen Hopkins'. The photographs of children as they aged, the big family Bible on the coffee table, the crowded clean furniture and the smell of cooking . . . it was all familiar. The only touch that differentiated the house was the set of newer pictures: Annie Gibson had grandchildren. There was a basket of toys in the corner, waiting for little hands to strew them around the small room.

Annie Gibson herself was nothing like Helen Hopkins, no matter if they shared the same concept of interior arrangement. Annie was fat, and her hair was short and curly. She wore glasses with blue plastic rims, and she breathed heavily. There was nothing stupid about Annie Gibson. She wouldn't let us sit down in her shabby house until we'd shown her our driver's licenses, and she offered us coffee in a way that let us know it was automatic courtesy and not heartfelt.

'Helen told me about your visit,' Annie Gibson said. 'I don't know if you're good people or not. But she spoke well of you, and that'll have to be good enough for me. I'm going to miss Helen. We had coffee together every other day, just about, and we went shopping in Little Rock together twice a year. We sent each other birthday cards.' Tears began running down her plump cheeks, and Annie reached for the box of tissues on the table before her. She patted the tears and blew her nose, unselfconsciously. 'Our mamas were best friends, and they had us the same month.'

I tried to imagine having the same person as a friend for so long. Annie Gibson was probably in her late thirties. I tried to imagine having grandchildren, but I couldn't even project how it would feel to have a child. Having a friend for as long as Annie had had Helen – that was something equally unimaginable.

I would be lucky to live that long, I thought. I watched the tail end of that thought trail out of sight and wondered where it had come from. At the moment, I had to pay attention to this woman across from me.

'I have to talk to you about something you may not like,' I said. This was a direct woman, and I sensed it would be better to approach her head-on.

'You have to run it by me before I decide.' Her face might be soft physically, but there was nothing soft about her will. 'Some things ought to be secret.'

'I agree,' I said. I leaned forward, my elbows on my knees. 'Ms Gibson, Helen herself told us she had a bad time when she was drinking.'

Annie Gibson nodded, her eyes not leaving my face. 'That's so,' she said.

'With Teenie being murdered, Helen was real upset when she asked us to come by to talk to her,' I said, going so slowly, so carefully. 'When I told her about Teenie and Sally, she said, "I'll have to call their fathers." What I want to know from you is, Who was Teenie's father?'

Annie Gibson shook her head. The brown curls moved with her, as if they'd been fixed in place with spray. Maybe they had. 'I promised Helen I'd never tell,' she said. 'She told me not to tell even if Teenie came and asked me.'

'And did she?' I asked. I blessed my brother for his silence.

'Yes,' Annie said without hesitation. 'Yes, she did. Right before she died.'

'So, it seems like that was a pretty crucial secret,' I said. 'You see? She asked, and she died. Helen tells me she's going to call Teenie's father, and she dies.'

Annie Gibson looked startled, as though she'd finally put two and two together. 'But that can't be,' she said. 'He'd have no reason to.'

'He must have,' I said. I tried to keep my voice gentle and reasonable. 'I told Helen that Hollis's wife Sally was murdered, too. All three members of that family are gone now. And they all knew who Teenie's father was.'

'Not Teenie,' Annie Gibson said. 'Teenie never knew. I didn't tell her. I promised Helen I wouldn't. And I knew she'd asked Helen, many a time, after she began to suspect it wasn't Jay.'

'Jay?' Tolliver asked.

'Helen's husband. Sally's father. He's coming back for the funeral. He may have been divorced from Helen, but I guess he inherits the house now. He called me this morning.'

'Where is he staying?' I wondered if he would have a few words with us.

'He's at the motel where ya'll are at. But don't expect to get much sense out of him. Helen may have quit drinking, but Jay ain't. She had to take out a restraining order on him, I guess a year or two after Sally was born. Jay used to be a nice-looking man, and he had sweet folks, but he ain't worth a tinker's damn.'

'We've had experience in dealing with drunks,' I said.

'Oh, like that, huh?' She looked at me, with level eyes. 'I thought I seen the mark on you.'

'The mark?'

'Kids raised by drunks. They all got the same mark. I can see it. Not everyone can.'

I was certainly not the only person walking this earth possessed of a weird little talent.

Tolliver and I rose to our feet, and Annie wiggled forward on her chair to rise with us. I looked around the small house, and I noticed she had good locks on the doors. And it was obvious a drove of friends and family came in and out all the time. The phone had rung twice while we were there, and she'd let her answering machine take the call. Annie seemed fairly well protected.

'If I were you,' I said, very carefully, 'I'd go to Little Rock for a couple of days to go shopping, or something like that.'

'Are you threatening me?' she said right back at me.

'No ma'am, I am not. I liked Helen, the little I knew of her. And I saw her after she died. I don't want you to be as scared as she was.'

'Sounds to me like you *are* threatening me,' Annie Gibson said. Her jaw hardened, and she looked like a very determined pug.

'I swear I am not,' I said, as earnestly as I could. 'I'm just worried about you.' She wasn't going to listen to a word I said, so I might as well save my breath. From now on, anything Tolliver and I told her would go straight to feed her conviction that we meant her ill.

'You all need to go to the gospel singing tonight, get some good thoughts in your head,' she concluded, shutting the door behind us.

'I thought Helen was a tough nut to crack,' I muttered. 'I just hadn't met Annie Gibson.'

We ate lunch at a McDonald's, which showed we were at the bottom of our spirits. Our parents had fed us from the fast-food place so often when we were little that we could hardly bear the smell of one now. When my mother had been married to my father, and we'd had the nice home in Memphis, we had a maid I'd been fond of. Her name was Marilyn Coachman. She was a stern black woman, you didn't back talk her, and when she told you to do something, you did it. The minute she'd realized my mother was using drugs, Marilyn quit. I wondered where Marilyn was now.

I looked down at the French fries in their grease-marked cardboard sleeve and shoved them away. She was a great cook.

'We need vegetables,' I said.

Tolliver said, 'Potatoes are a vegetable. And ketchup is made from tomatoes. I know technically they're a fruit, but I always think of them as vegetables.'

'Very funny. I mean it. You know I have to avoid this shit. We need a place where we can live. I'll learn to cook.'

'You mean it?'

'I do.'

'You want to buy a house.'

'We've talked about it before.'

'But I didn't . . . You were serious, huh?'

'Yes.' I was deeply hurt. 'I guess you weren't.'

He put down his Big Mac. He wiped his fingers on the paper napkin. A very young mother went by, carrying one child on her hip. The other hand held a tray full of food and drinks. A boy, maybe five, followed close on her heels. She put the tray down on a nearby table and began getting the children into their places and sorting out the food. She looked harried. Her bra strap kept falling down her arm; both her arms were bare. She was wearing a sleeveless tank top despite the chilly day.

Tolliver was giving me all his attention, now. 'You're still thinking Dallas?'

'Or thereabouts. 'We could find a nice small house, maybe in Longview or even closer to Dallas, to the north. That'd be more central than the Atlanta area, which was the other place we'd discussed.'

His dark eyes searched mine. 'Dallas is close to Mariella and Grace.'

'Maybe they won't always feel the same.'

'Maybe they will. There's no point banging our heads against that wall.'

'Someday they'll change.'

'You think those people will let us see them?' Mariella and Grace now lived with my stepfather's sister and her husband. Tolliver's aunt Iona had never intervened to save me and Cameron, or her blood kin Tolliver and Mark. But when the end came, when Human Services discovered after Cameron's abduction how bad things were in our household and I'd been farmed out to a foster family and Tolliver had gone to his brother, Iona and Hank had swooped down to save poor precious Mariella and baby Grace, in a hail of publicity and denials of all knowledge of how low my mother had sunk.

After living with Iona and Hank two months, our little sisters had gone from regarding us as their saviors and defenders to reacting as if we had visible plague sores.

Out of many painful memories of that short era, the picture of Grace screaming, 'I don't want to see you ever again!' when I'd gone to pick her up was the most shattering.

'It couldn't be them,' I said for maybe the hundredth time to Tolliver, as we sat surrounded by the smell of cooking oil and lots of primary colors. 'They loved us.' He nodded, as he had every other time.

'Iona and Hank have convinced them we had something to do with how that household was run,' he said.

'Or not run. How it was bungled,' I said, out of the deep well of bitterness that separated me from other people.

'She's dead now,' he said, very quietly. 'He might as well be.'

'I know, I know. I'm sorry.' I waved a hand in front of my face, to dispel the recurrence of anger. 'I just can't help but hope that someday the little girls will be grown up enough to understand.'

'It won't ever be the same.' Tolliver was my oracle, and he knew. He almost always said the things I was scared to even think. He was right.

'I guess not. But someday they'll need a sister and a brother, and they'll call us.'

He bent back to his food. 'Some days, I hope not,' he said very quietly, and I couldn't think of anything to say.

I knew what he meant. We had no one to answer to. We had no one to take care of. We only had each other. After years of desperately plastering the cracks in our family so no one could see in, just watching out for each other in the here and now seemed relatively simple and even soothing.

Hollis sat down at our table, his meal in a bag in his hand. 'I hope I'm not interrupting anything,' he said. 'I was going through the drive-through and I saw you two in here. You looked mighty serious.'

Tolliver gave the policeman a sharp glance. Hollis was in uniform. He looked good in it. I smiled down at what was left of my lunch.

'We're ready to leave this town,' Tolliver said. 'But we can't go until the sheriff gives us the nod.'

'What happened at the funeral home?' Hollis wisely ignored Tolliver.

I told him that Helen had been killed by someone she knew and trusted, which was no revelation. Her little house had been as neat as a house can be that's the site of a violent murder. No one had broken into it. No one had rifled it.

'Someone wearing long sleeves, not a uniform.' I knew that.

'That's all you got?'

'*No, I released Helen's soul to heaven,*' I wanted to say. But there are a lot of things that are better left unsaid, and this was definitely one of them. 'Tell me, Hollis . . . someone told me that Helen had taken out a restraining order on her first husband, Jay. Is that so?'

'Yeah, Jay was a drunk like Helen was, at least at the time. He was drunk at Sally's and my wedding, for sure. My uncle had to take him out of the church because he was getting loud. It embarrassed Sally real bad.' Hollis shook his head at the recollection. 'He's back in town, I hear. Evidently, Helen had made a will. Jay inherits the house and what little Helen had in the bank.'

'Why would Helen leave what she had to a man who abused her so badly?' That hadn't fit the Helen Hopkins I'd met, however briefly.

Hollis cleared his throat. 'Ah, well, she might have been grateful that he was willing to acknowledge Teenie as his.'

'No one knows for sure who Teenie's dad was?'

'No, but there must have been at least a chance that Jay was. They never had a DNA test, though. Jay acted like she was his, and Helen put his name on forms, so—'

'Why would he agree to that?' Tolliver asked, his eyes still focused on the food wrappers. He was crushing them into balls and putting each ball on our tray.

'If he said she wasn't, he'd have been admitting his wife wasn't satisfied with him,' Hollis explained, as if the answer were self-evident.

'He'd rather acknowledge a bastard than admit his wife had slept with someone else?' Tolliver was openly skeptical.

'And it was the gentlemanly thing to do.' Hollis did some staring in another direction himself this time. He was looking at me, and I could feel the heat rising in my face. 'Sometimes men do the right thing,' Hollis said, very seriously.

'But if Teenie wasn't his, he was denying another man the chance to do the right thing,' I said.

'Weren't a lot of men clamoring for the honor of claiming the baby,' Hollis said.

I remembered high school all too clearly. There was something that had baffled me from the start, and now seemed as good a time as any to ask Hollis about it. 'There's something I don't understand. Dell Teague didn't mind dating a girl with such a bad reputation? He's from the best family in town, right? Or at least the one with the most money. And yet . . . he's dating a girl who has an alcoholic mother and an absent father, a poor girl, a wild girl.' I waited, with my eyebrow cocked, for Hollis to comment.

Hollis ruminated for a minute or two. 'They didn't run with the same crowd, until Helen started working for Sybil. She'd have Teenie come over there, after school, and do her homework. They were drawn to each other from that time, is all I know to tell you. When Teenie got into trouble after that, it was when Dell's parents decided to interfere between them, or when Helen was on a tear. If Teenie couldn't go out with Dell, she'd raise hell.'

That was interesting. It didn't lead anywhere, but it was interesting.

I folded my own wrappers neatly and put them on the same tray with Tolliver's.

'Before Helen had to get a restraining order against Jay, was their relationship violent? Did the cops have to go there every weekend? Or did something specific spark that episode?'

Hollis looked thoughtful. 'If it came to that, it was before my time on the force. You'd have to ask one of the older guys about that. One of 'em runs the hotel where you're staying at, Vernon McCluskey? He'd know about that.'

We weren't exactly popular with Vernon McCluskey, if he was the skinny older guy in overalls that was usually behind the motel counter, the one who'd hinted broadly that we weren't welcome anymore.

Tolliver got up to dump the trash from the tray into the garbage bin. One of the uniformed workers, a woman about twenty-five, watched him from her spot at one of the cash registers, an avid look in her eyes. She was short and dumpy and the McDonald's uniform didn't suit her. I'll give her this, she had outstandingly beautiful skin, something Tolliver's a real sucker for, maybe because of his own scarred face. I don't think it would occur to Tolliver to list 'good skin' if someone asked him to make a list of things he found attractive, but I'd noticed that everyone he hit on had a clear complexion.

Today, this woman longed in vain, because Tolliver never once glanced her way. He went to the men's room, and while he was gone, Hollis asked me if I would see him again that night. 'We can go to the gospel singing on the lawn at the courthouse. It's the last of the season. There won't be many tourists there, and you might enjoy it.'

'I might, huh?' I thought about Annie Gibson's recommendation, and his big hand covered mine.

'Please,' he said. 'I want to see you again.'

There were a lot of things I almost told him, but I didn't say them.

'All right,' I finally said. 'What time?'

'I'll take you out to eat first, okay? See you at the motel at six thirty,' he said. His radio squawked, and he rose hastily, telling me goodbye at the same time he was taking his own tray to the stand by the door. As he pushed open the glass door, he was talking into his shoulder set.

Tolliver came back, swinging his hands in an exaggerated arc. 'I hate those damn hot-air dryers,' he said. 'I like paper towels.' I'd heard him complain about hot-air dryers maybe three hundred times, and I gave him an exasperated look.

'Rub your hands on your jeans,' I said.

'Well, you got another date with lover-boy?'

'Oh, shut up,' I said, mildly irritated. 'Yes, as a matter of fact, I do.'

'Maybe he's talking his boss into keeping us here so he can have another date with you.'

Tolliver sounded so serious that I actually considered the idea for a minute, before I caught my brother's smirk. I smacked him lightly and got up, hanging my purse on my shoulder. 'Jerk,' I said, smiling.

'You two gonna go watch the sidewalks roll up?'

'No, we're going to a gospel singing on the courthouse lawn, evidently.' When Tolliver raised his eyebrows, I said seriously, 'It's the last one of the season.' He laughed out loud.

I felt a little ashamed of myself, though, and when we were going back to the motel I said, 'He's a nice guy, Tolliver. I like him.'

'I know,' he said. 'I know you do.'

9

We talked about approaching Vernon McCluskey when we were back at the motel. I was redoing my fingernails in a deep brown, and Tolliver was working a puzzle in a *New York Times* Sunday crossword collection. I knew what I was getting Tolliver for Christmas: some book containing the Hebrew alphabet. The Hebrew alphabet was a major feature of crossword puzzles, at least according to Tolliver, and he was totally ignorant about it. I might get him a world atlas, too. That way, if the question was 'river in Siberia' he could damn well look it up, instead of asking me.

'Why are we talking to this asshole?' Tolliver asked. 'He's made it clear he wants us out of here. Do we really need to find out about Helen Hopkins' relationship to her ex-husband? Why don't we just lie low until the sheriff lets us go? How long can he actually keep us here? Not long. One phone call to a lawyer, and we're out of here.'

I looked at Tolliver, the polish brush suspended over my little fingernail. 'We don't want to be remembered here as people who were released because they couldn't find anything to pin on us, do we? You know how we operate. People will be calling Branscom to find out what kind of job we did. They'll ask him how cooperative we were. We need to look as though we're taking him seriously, that we're trying to get to the bottom of these deaths, too. That we care.'

'Do we care?' He tossed his pencil on top of the crossword puzzle book. 'I think you do.'

I hesitated, taken aback by what sounded very much like an accusation. 'It bothers you?'

'That depends on what you care about.'

'I kind of liked Helen Hopkins,' I said at last, very carefully. 'So, yeah, I'm upset that someone cracked her skull. I care that two young people were shot, that they died out in the woods, that people think the boy killed her and then himself. That's not what happened.'

'Do you feel like they're asking you to investigate?'

'They?'

'The dead people.'

I felt a big light bursting behind my eyeballs. 'No,' I said. 'Not at all. Nobody knows better than I do that dead is dead. They're not wanting anything. Well, maybe Helen Hopkins was, but now she's released.'

'You don't feel an obligation?'

I polished my little fingernail. 'Nope. We did what we were paid for. I don't like thinking about someone getting away with murder, but I'm not a cop, either.' I wished immediately that I hadn't added the last phrase.

Tolliver got to his feet, suddenly in a hurry. 'I'm going to go wash the car. I'm pretty sure there's an Easy Klean right off Main Street. But I'll stop by the office to ask the McCluskey guy for the location. It'll give me an excuse to talk to him. I'll be gone about an hour, more or less.'

'Sure, that sounds good. You don't want me to talk to McCluskey?'

'No. He thinks you're the great Satan, remember? I'm just Satan's assistant.'

I smiled at him. 'Okay, thanks. You want me to tell Hollis you're coming with us, tonight?'

'No, Harper. You go enjoy being a girl for a while.'

He didn't sound like he meant it. 'What's that supposed to mean?'

'Did you ever stop to think we could settle down in a town like this? We could quit what we're doing? We could get regular jobs?'

Of course I'd thought of it. 'No,' I said. 'It's never crossed my mind.'

'Liar. You could date some guy like Hollis for real. You could work in a department store, or in an office. Somewhere with live people.'

I looked away from his face. 'You could date a hundred Janines, or even wait for Mary Nell Teague to grow up,' I countered. 'You could get a job at a Home Depot. You'd be manager in no time.'

'Could we do that?' he asked. He didn't mean, could we do it if we had the option; we had the option, all right. He meant, was it possible for us to settle down to being regular citizens.

'It would be pretty hard,' I said, after a pause, in a noncommittal voice.

'Getting a house might be the first step,' he said.

I shrugged. 'Could be.'

He shut the door behind him very quietly.

We didn't talk much about the future.

Of course, I'd had plenty of opportunities to think about it. We spent a lot of time driving. Though we listened to audiobooks and the radio, inevitably there were long periods of silence.

Though I didn't want to tell Tolliver this, I thought way too much about our past. I tried not to dwell on the squalor of daily life in that house in Texarkana. Maybe if I hadn't been raised so gently to start with, it wouldn't have bothered me quite so much. But the descent from pampered princess to virgin pussy peddled for drug money had been too shocking, too abrupt. I hadn't seasoned slowly enough. I'd acquired a hard brittle shell instead of toughening all the way through.

'Bullshit,' I said out loud. 'To hell with this.' I pushed introspection right out of my brain and turned on the television. My nails were beautiful by the time I finished with them.

Tolliver returned about four o'clock, a lot later than I'd expected. When he came in, I smelled a whiff of beer and sex. Okay, I told myself. Steady. Tolliver almost never drank much, and he wasn't drunk now. But the fact that he'd had a beer during the day, and the fact that he'd stayed away to have sex when he knew I'd be anxious – those were significant facts.

'Well, the car is clean,' he said, 'and I talked to former police officer McCluskey, who is without a doubt one of the most repellent people I've ever had a conversation with.'

'That's good, about the car,' I said. I was pleased with how level my voice was. 'What did McCluskey have to say? Anything interesting?'

'It took me forever to get him soothed down and to the point,' Tolliver said.

'This is part of your build-up, to let me know what a tedious job I gave you?'

'Damn straight. I worked for this information.'

'Um-hmmm.'

'And I expect you to appreciate that.'

'Oh, believe me, I do.'

'Do I hear some sarcasm in your voice?'

'God forbid.'

'Then I'll finish what I was saying.'

'Please do.'

Tolliver sprawled on my bed, lying on his back with his arms flung out on either side.

'McCluskey – did I mention how nasty the man is? McCluskey's decided I'm your bodyguard, and he wanted to know how I managed to stay around you, since surely you were marked by the devil.'

'Oh, yeah? And I thought I'd showered real well.'

'You probably missed some Satan behind the ears.'

'Sorry about that.'

'Well, he thinks anything to do with contacting the dead, or seeing the dead, is a big church no-no, and anyone who claims to be able to do that is—'

'Let me guess – Evil?'

'How'd you know? Amazing! You're right!'

'Just lucky.'

'Anyway.' Tolliver yawned. 'He heard about the boys this morning, and though he thought young men shouldn't hurt women, he also thought putting a scare in you was a good thing.'

'Oh, gee, thanks.'

'I told him it wasn't.' Tolliver sounded suddenly sincere. 'I told him if anything happened like that again, I'd be forced to display some of my amazing bodyguard skills, learned at the Special Forces camp.'

'What Special Forces camp?'

'Obviously, the one that exists to train specially vicious and lethal bodyguards.'

'Oh, that one.'

'Right. Anyway, he swallowed some of that story, and he said that he was sure nothing else like that would happen to you here in Sarne, since Sheriff Branscom was so put out about your being threatened.'

'Well, actually, that's nice to know.'

'That's what I thought. Do you think it's safe for you to go out tonight?'

I stopped looking at my fingernails and started looking at Tolliver.

'I'm not trying to stop you,' he said hastily. 'You go on with Officer Friendly, if you want to. I'm just reminding you, this is a fundament-alist community and they don't admire your ability.'

I held my tongue for a long minute, trying to think through Tolliver's advice. But I heard myself saying, 'It's okay for you to go out and get laid while you're getting the car washed, and it's not okay for me to go to a gospel singing?'

Tolliver's skin reddened. 'I just don't want anything to happen to you,' he said steadily. 'You remember what happened in West Virginia.'

In West Virginia, the entire populace of a tiny hamlet had thrown rocks at our car.

'I remember,' I said. 'But it was a smaller place, and it had a strong leader who hated the whole idea of me.'

'You're saying there's no united front here in Sarne?'

I nodded.

'You may be right,' he said, after a long moment. 'But I just hate that anything . . .' his voice trailed off.

'I don't want to be the target of any kind of attack,' I said, after a pause. 'I do *not*. But I also don't want to cower in this hotel room.'

'And you want to see Hollis again.'

'Yes.'

He looked away for a second. 'Okay.' He made himself nod. 'It'll be good to go to something different. Have a good time.'

I definitely didn't want to stand out, but I also thought it might be disrespectful to under-dress. I had a hard time imagining what you'd wear to an al fresco gospel concert. I picked what I thought of as neutral clothes: good slacks, a sweater set, loafers. I snatched up a heavier jacket when Hollis picked me up. He was wearing new jeans and a corduroy shirt – the softest narrow-wale corduroy I'd ever seen. He had a jacket, too. And he was wearing cowboy boots, which surprised me.

'Nice footwear,' I said.

He looked down, as if he'd never seen his boots before. 'I used to do a little riding,' he said. 'I got to like 'em.'

He asked me how I was feeling after the incident of the morning, and I told him I was fine. That wasn't entirely accurate, but close enough. I didn't want to think about it anymore, and *that* was the truth.

There were cars parked all around the square, and the pretty streetlights that had been put up for the tourists lent the area an air of prosperity and quaintness. The broad courthouse lawn was strewn with folding chairs of all kinds. Little children were dashing through the gathering crowd, shrieking and excited in the chill evening air. Since I was an outsider, I couldn't tell the leafers from the locals, but Hollis told me the ratio was about forty to sixty.

The stage that had been thrown up at the base of the old courthouse was not very high, and it was crowded with the equipment of the first group to perform. A woman in a long full skirt and a wide turquoise belt was tuning a guitar. Her gray hair fell to her waist, and her face was deeply lined, intent and calm. The men behind her were in their forties and fifties, and they all shared her air of professionalism.

'This here's Roberta Moore and her Sons of Grace,' Hollis said. 'They're from over to Mountain Home.'

'How many groups will play?'

'We just see who shows up,' he said. 'Sometimes six or seven, but tonight I only see three others. Bobby Tatum, he sings by himself.' Bobby Tatum was a very young man in a cowboy hat and a very elaborate cowboy shirt and boots. His jacket was Western-tailored, of course, and his clean-shaven face gleamed with eagerness. He was chatting with a cluster of girls who looked about Mary Nell's age, and they were giggling at everything he said.

The other entertainers seemed to be groups like Roberta Moore's. I eyed the amount of expensive equipment piled up behind the stage and was taken aback. This wasn't slapdash and amateurish. These people knew their stuff.

As the darkness gathered closer, Hollis got a blanket from the truck and moved his chair right by mine so we could share its warmth. Terry Vale, the mayor, made some public service announcements. He was far from the anxious man I'd met at the sheriff's office. He was happy, relaxed. 'The tan Chevy Venture blocking the driveway to Martin's Pharmacy, be advised you've blocked Jeb Martin in, and he sure wants to go home. Unless you want him to call the tow truck, you better get over there with an apology on your lips,' Terry Vale said, and the crowd laughed. A very young man with a sparse mustache got up, abashed, and headed for the pharmacy. After a couple more public service announcements, including a reminder to pick up trash when the concert was over, Terry Vale introduced Roberta Moore and the Sons of Grace to a big round of applause. The gray-haired woman nodded absently at the crowd and continued tuning her guitar. When she felt she was ready, Roberta Moore gave her band a signal, and she began to sing.

It was just great. I was sure these people were pharmacists and pest control sprayers and farmers by day, but by night they were talented musicians, and I was enthralled. I didn't know any of the songs, though I had a vague feeling that when I was very young I'd heard one or two of the spirituals. The voices, twangy and plangent, rose through the clear night air. From time to time, one of the singers would say, 'Now we're gonna do an old favorite, and if you know it, you sing along.' But it was not an old favorite of mine or my parents, or even my grandparents, as far as I knew, and I realized how ignorant I was. It wasn't the first time I'd reflected on that, and it wouldn't be the last.

Hollis sang along with 'The Old Rugged Cross.' To my surprise he had a nice baritone.

Just when I was thinking I was getting too cold to enjoy any more singing, Hollis produced a thermos of hot chocolate, and I was glad to drink some. I felt so relaxed. No one was paying me any attention, and that was just fine. Hollis's hand was warm and dry when he held mine, and the hot chocolate was good.

The singing drew to an end after a couple of hours, and people began to pack up their blankets and chairs. Children were carried to cars, their sleeping heads resting on parental shoulders. I gathered up the blanket and the thermos while Hollis toted the chairs. I was surprised to cross the path of Sybil Teague. She was doing exactly the same thing; the man in charge of her chairs was Paul Edwards.

It was a draw as to which one of us was the more astonished. 'I didn't know you were in town,' Sybil said. She looked a bit more expensive than anyone else in the crowd. So did Paul, for that matter.

'The sheriff doesn't want us to go just yet,' I said. I thought Sybil had certainly known we were in town. I thought Sybil had to have heard about the incident this morning, especially since the boy who was the ringleader was such a follower of Mary Nell's. I thought Sybil was just surprised to see me here on the courthouse lawn. Paul Edwards didn't make any effort to charm or greet me, he just stood behind Sybil with their two chairs slung across his back.

'I don't understand why,' Sybil said. 'I'm sorry you're being, ah, inconvenienced this way.' She looked at me as if she had no idea how to end the encounter, and I was petty enough to leave her in the lurch. 'Why don't you come to lunch with me tomorrow?' she suggested, I guess since she couldn't think of anything else to say. 'You and your brother. Noon okay? Do you know how to get to my house?'

'Thanks. I expect we can find it.' I gave her a very small smile and nod, and then Hollis and I moved on to his pickup.

Hollis made a choked noise, and I realized he was trying not to laugh out loud. 'What's up with you?' I asked, smiling a little myself.

'She couldn't get out of that one,' he said.

'Nope. She feels obliged to the hired help.'

'You could have helped her out some,' he said, but not as if he were too worried about Sybil's social dilemma.

'Nah. I figured she'd come up with an idea. And she did.'

We deposited our burdens in the bed of the pickup and climbed into the cab. Hollis put his hands on my waist and gave me an unnecessary but pleasant boost.

When we got to the motel, I asked him in.

He said, 'I always did want to make love to someone in a motel.'

'That's my goal . . . expanding your horizons.'

The motel bed was much nicer with someone else in it.

10

Hollis slipped out at five o'clock. He whispered that he had to go home, shower, and get to work. He kissed me, and I hugged him close for a long moment, wishing he didn't have to go. Though finesse would never be Hollis's trademark, either in making love or conversation, that wasn't a bad thing. He was warm and big, and he had a delicate snore that made me feel all cozy. It was like being in bed with a giant, enthusiastic teddy bear.

I would not mind being with him for lots of nights.

That thought woke me up completely.

I almost never had sex. One reason I picked a sex partner so rarely was the sure brevity of the connection. One-night stands were about scratching an itch, and I'd rather do that by myself than enlist a human dildo. Oh yeah, I knew consenting adults could give and take a little of themselves in one night. I knew it didn't have to be tawdry and cheap. But most often it was; and it left me feeling a little nauseous and dissatisfied with myself, no matter how satisfying the physical act had been.

This was the other downside. Now, I'd been with Hollis two nights, and already I found myself wanting extended time with him. But I knew damn good and well that the nature of my life precluded more.

It seemed so much easier for Tolliver. He made eye contact with a woman, she agreed to have sex, they did it, and she left. She knew he was leaving town, of course, as suddenly as he'd blown into it. Or did some of these women think, 'It'll be so good, he'll like me so much, he'll send his sister away by herself and he'll stay with me for a while.' Since I didn't have any women friends, hadn't had for years, I couldn't say what other women thought. But maybe, some day, that would happen.

Despite that niggling worry, I dozed back to sleep, but by seven I was in the shower. I was dressed when Tolliver knocked carefully on the outer door to my room.

He looked around quickly when I let him in and relaxed when he saw we were alone. 'How was the gospel singing?' he asked.

'Really good. You would have enjoyed it.' I didn't ask him what he'd done instead. 'You ready for breakfast?'

'Yeah. Let's go to the Denny's.'

Maybe Denny's fruit plate would be better. Like many lightning-strike survivors, I have trouble with terrible headaches, and my right leg is much weaker than my left. I can lessen those symptoms by avoiding fried food and starches. Our lunch at McDonald's the day before had been a serious fall from grace, and my leg had twitched all night. Luckily, Hollis hadn't noticed. But I'd been too uncertain on my feet to run this morning.

'Oh, we've been invited to lunch,' I told Tolliver as we buckled our seat belts. The day was cloudy and chilly. Soon there'd be a rainstorm with high winds, and it would whip all the beautiful leaves off the trees – oak and maple and gum. Sarne would roll up the few sidewalks it had left out for the leafers. Its people would put away their hillbilly costumes and close their fruit and crystal stands, and Sarne would be alone for the winter.

'Where?' Tolliver asked, drawing me back into the present.

'At Sybil Teague's.' I told him about running into Sybil and Paul the night before.

'That's interesting,' he said. 'Before we go in the restaurant, let me tell you what I learned from Janine last night. Paul Edwards was the lawyer Helen hired to get her restraining order and then her divorce from Jay Hopkins. And he'd represented Jay and Helen before, in a lawsuit they brought against Terry Vale.'

'What'd they sue the mayor for?'

'Maybe he wasn't the mayor then. He owns the local furniture and carpet sales company. Jay Hopkins said the carpet Terry sold them wasn't stain resistant, and Terry wouldn't make good on the warranty.'

'Hmm,' I said. 'I'm not sure what that all means.' And I needed a cup of coffee before I even began to figure it out.

'It means,' Tolliver said, 'that Paul Edwards is in a position to know all the secrets of both families.'

'Like?'

'Who Teenie's father really was, for one.'

'Oh.'

'And maybe he knows why Teenie and Dell were out in the woods that day. What could have made them go out to that place, on land that neither family owned, to be killed?'

'Who does own that land?'

'I guess we don't know.'

'Could we find that out this morning?'

'Sure. We can go to the county clerk's office. But why should we go to the effort?'

'I'd rather have something to do than go back to the motel room and work crossword puzzles.'

'Yeah, me, too.' We worked out a plan for the day.

First thing after breakfast, we did our laundry in the Sudsy Kleen Laundromat, owned by (not to our surprise) Terry Vale. His representative at the Laundromat was a seamed old woman with a walker who dispensed correct change for the washers and dryers. She also sold little boxes of detergent and dryer sheets from behind a dilapidated desk. We learned by observation that the old woman also washed and folded laundry upon request. Sudsy Kleen did a great drop-off business.

This stout old woman performed a great service and did a good job, we decided, but she was determined to be as unpleasant as possible while she did it.

Initially, the fluffy white hair and the crocheted white sweater suckered me into believing I should be gently polite with this old bat. But when I asked for change for a dollar bill so I could feed the dryer, she drew in her breath as if I'd made a nasty suggestion. I stood transfixed, trying to figure out what I'd done. Dumbly, I held out the money. Granny Grump fumblingly took the dollar from my hand and examined it, since I was obviously a counterfeiter, I guess. Then she very slowly counted out the correct change, casting quick glances at me all the while as if she suspected I was going to snatch the money box and run. Her glasses glinted with every glance, just a quick flash in the overhead lights, as if she had bionic eyes. When I took the coins to my brother, I was half amused and half angry.

'She's charming, you need to go meet her,' I said, in a conversational tone, dumping the quarters into the slots on the machine.

Tolliver glanced her way, started to say something, tried not to smile.

'I mean, it's just adorable when she glowers,' I told him. 'What a character! You just can't find old ladies like that anymore!'

'Shh,' he said, but not as if he meant it.

I wasn't sure if she'd heard me or not – her expression of extreme disgust never changed. Was there something personal about us that she loathed? Or did she distrust us simply because we weren't from Sarne? Hard to tell. I wasn't sure I cared.

We finished washing and folding our clothes pretty quickly, since the Laundromat had few customers early in the morning. Maybe the dragon had driven all the self-serve customers away.

Our next stop was closer to the center of town. The county clerk's office was in the old courthouse in the square. It was the first time we'd actually entered the building. The ceilings were just as high as I'd imagined, and the windows just as huge; obviously this building predated the widespread use of air-conditioning. The room we entered was so disproportional, the distance from floor to ceiling so much more than from wall to wall, that I felt a little uneasy. I couldn't imagine working in such a room.

The two women who did work there were definitely surprised to see strangers come in, but the older of the two, a very round woman with dyed brown hair, immediately rose from her desk and came to the counter. When we asked to see a map of the county, she pointed silently to the wall behind us.

'Snake,' I muttered to Tolliver after we turned around. There was a huge map of Colleton County right there. He nodded, understanding that I'd meant, 'If it had been a snake, it would have bit us.' I tried to orient myself by following the two main roads that formed a waggly X through Sarne, but I was still working it out when Tolliver pinpointed the area where we'd gotten out of our car when we'd been searching for Teenie's body.

After some cross-referencing, we decided which parcel of land that was, and the clerk handed us the appropriate ledger. According to the ledger, Colleton County Land Development was the owner of the property, and of several other parcels on both sides of that road. I couldn't see that we were any further along than we had been. Tolliver asked the county clerk if she knew who was actually behind Colleton County Land Development.

'Oh,' she said, smiling. 'That's Paul Edwards, Terence Vale, and Dick Teague. They bought up quite a bit of property over the years, thinking that someday we'd become another Branson. I don't think that's ever going to happen.'

'The same names keep showing up over and over,' I said when we were alone in the car.

'That's going to happen in a small town with a long history,' Tolliver said, logically enough. 'I'm not sure it means anything. Where next?'

We got to the newspaper office about nine forty-five, where we discovered that all the past issues of the *Colleton Mountain Gazette* (at least for the past ten years) were on computer. We were free to look through the computer archives, all we wanted, right there at the newspaper. This unexpectedly enthusiastic reception was due to a woman about my age, a brand-new reporter, who hoped we might be good for some kind of story. She was plump and dark-haired and wearing a color I'd call mustard. I am no clotheshorse, and fashion trends aren't of much interest to me, but even I could tell it was maybe the worst color she could have picked. But she was a person who liked bright things, as attested by her gold chain and gold bracelet and shiny bronze lipstick, so maybe the mustard was part of the same syndrome. Her name was Dinah Trout, according to the plate on her desk. She offered us coffee, she strode past us about eleven more times than was necessary, and she eavesdropped on every word we said to each other. Today was our day for meeting challenging women.

In self-defense, Tolliver and I took turns sitting at the computer. The one who was not reading had the job of deflecting the extremely curious Ms Trout. If some of the people of Sarne knew about my unusual career, they apparently hadn't shared it with Ms Trout, and I was really grateful.

In about an hour, I was sure we'd read every article that dealt with the death of Dell Teague, the disappearance of Teenie Hopkins, and the 'tragic accident' of Sally Hopkins Boxleitner. I was fascinated by pictures of the Hopkins sisters. It was a shock to see them living.

I'd been so overwhelmed by the multiplicity of pictures in Helen's living room that I hadn't taken any time to examine the subjects.

The sisters didn't look alike. Sally, Hollis's wife, had been light in coloring, with reddish-blonde hair and freckles. She had a broad face and broad shoulders and a pleasant look about her. I couldn't see anything lurking in her eyes – no hidden misery in her stance, nothing that hinted she knew she was going to die. I tracked down her wedding picture (it was eerie to see a much younger Hollis feeding her wedding cake) and an employee photograph taken at Wal-Mart, where she'd been the manager of the baby department.

Her younger sister Teenie was shown in her school picture, the saddest accompaniment to an obituary. She'd been a little over made-up for the occasion, and her hair was dramatically combed in two solid falls of darkness on either side of her face. She had her mother's narrow features and small build, and she had a sharp nose, perfectly straight. It was hard to extrapolate anything about her character from a class picture. She was smiling, of course, but it was just an arrangement of her lips. There wasn't anything genuinely happy about it. She was a deep well, and I wasn't surprised Dell Teague had been intrigued.

Dell Teague was blond like his mother. I found a shot of Dell on an old sports page, where he was shown dressed in his football uniform. It was enough to break your heart – even my heart – seeing the young man standing there smiling at the camera, full of youth and pride and strength. I wondered if he'd known what was happening to him, or if the shot had been a complete surprise – if he'd had a chance to worry about his girlfriend's fate. The feeling I'd gotten, while I stood on his grave, was that he had known what was happening. I felt sorry for that.

I looked at Dell's picture, then back at Teenie's. Then again. They shared something, these two. I checked the years the pictures had been taken. Teenie's had been taken earlier in the fall, so had Dell's. Too early for Teenie to think she might be pregnant. What secret was it they shared? I wanted to print out the articles and take them with me. Then I realized I was getting too caught up in the lives of these two teenagers who were dead and buried.

While I was getting so much good stuff, I searched the computer for any stories or pictures including Mary Nell Teague. Mary Nell was in lots of pictures; she was a cheerleader (no surprise there), she was her class president, she'd been on the homecoming court. I even took a second to look at a picture of Dick Teague, the deceased husband of Sybil. He was a medium man; medium stature, medium brown hair, light complexion, narrow shoulders, and a tentative smile, at least in the newspaper pictures. He had a definite overbite, a generous nose, and he'd died of a sudden heart attack in his home.

Nonetheless, it was sad to hear that such an abrupt end had come to a man who'd done a lot for the community, at least according to his obituary. Dick Teague had been a county judge. He'd been in the Lion's Club and the Rotary. He'd been a member of the Chamber of Commerce, and he'd been on the Board of the Boys and Girls Club. He'd even been a local leader for Habitat for Humanity. I wondered if Sybil was upholding his banner in the civic department. Somehow I doubted it.

Speaking of Sybil . . . I glanced at my watch.

'We need to go,' I murmured to Tolliver, who was smiling at Dinah, maybe dazzled by the gleam off her many polished surfaces. 'Could we print out these articles?' I asked, trying to be charming.

'Sure, for twenty-five cents a page,' she said. Guess I wasn't charming enough. 'We don't mind doing it, but we have to pay for the ink cartridges, of course.' I could understand that, and I tried to maintain a pleasant expression as the printer slowly spit out the pages I'd designated.

Dinah Trout urged us to come back any time, which I didn't think was likely. She was wearing a wedding ring, so I knew Tolliver wouldn't ask her out, even if she sent a clear signal she would be willing.

Seeing we were slipping from her grasp, Dinah thought of a few more questions to ask us, and we dodged them more or less politely. 'The Ozarks breed women of strong character,' I told Tolliver. He nodded a little grimly.

The most unremarkable woman I'd talked to all day was Sybil Teague, and she was no slouch in the grooming and looks department. She was wearing a skirt and sweater set in red and white, and she looked really good. I wondered if she was the kind of mother who scoured her deceased child's room, or if she was the kind of mother who kept that room intact as a shrine. I would have put money on her being a scourer, but I was wrong. When I slipped into Dell's room after lunch, excusing myself to use the bathroom, I found it was probably neater and cleaner than a teenage boy would leave it. But the dead boy's clothes were hanging in the closet, and though he didn't have a bulletin board of pathetic souvenirs as Teenie had, a framed picture of the girl sat on his computer desk. I thought the better of Sybil that she had left it there.

It had taken some maneuvering to get a look at the house, but fortunately Sybil was egotistical enough to take my gap-mouthed admiration at face value. Tolliver and I got a tour the minute I showed interest; no 'it's not in its best shape' protestations from Sybil, no 'please excuse the mess.' The house was in perfect order, and probably always was. Even Mary Nell's room was spick and span – no clothes tossed on the floor, no unmade bed. The bathroom was scrubbed and there were clean towels out. If Mary Nell married a local boy, he'd have a hard act to follow.

There was a maid, of course, whom I had to credit with all this cleanliness and order. She was a gaunt older woman in a snagged knit shirt and baggy stretch pants. Sybil didn't introduce her, but the woman gave us an openly curious look as we strolled through the kitchen. Through glimpses of the backyard I caught at various windows, I spotted a man raking and burning the fallen leaves. I couldn't discern his features – that was how far it was to the back fence. This was a mansion, or as close to a mansion as Sarne could offer.

I wondered again how Sybil must have felt when Dell had picked a girl from the bottom stratum of local society. Having seen her house, I knew her talk of having accepted Teenie as a potential daughter-in-law was pure bullshit. I wondered how far she would go to prevent Dell from being trapped in that relationship by fathering a child on the girl; because I was pretty sure that was how Sybil would see it. Whatever part she'd played in the death of Teenie Hopkins, Sybil had surely loved her son Dell.

Mary Nell came home while we were sitting at the dining table. She dashed in, calling, 'Mom? Mom? Look at my skirt!' Mary Nell turned red when she saw us in her home. I didn't know if that was because she was upset at seeing Tolliver, or because she was appalled at facing me after what her admirer had done to get me to leave town. Maybe both.

'Mary Nell, what are you doing home?' Sybil asked, obviously surprised.

'Stupid Heather spilled her stupid drink on my skirt,' Mary Nell said, after a second's pause. She held her leg out to show the splotch on her denim skirt. 'I asked Mrs Markham if I could sign out for thirty minutes and run home to change.'

'Mrs Markham is the cheerleader sponsor,' Sybil explained to us, as though we cared. 'Well, go change, honey,' she said to Nell. She might as well have said 'Shoo!' and flapped her hands. Nell darted away, her cheeks flushed. In five minutes she was back, dressed in a dark blue long-sleeved T-shirt and a khaki skirt. I was willing to bet her previous outfit was on the floor of her room. 'I'm gone, Mom!' she called as she went down the hall to the kitchen. The kitchen had a door leading into the garage, and I was sure that Nell had her own car. Sure enough, within a minute I saw a Dodge Dart zipping down the graveled driveway.

'She's so active in her school,' Sybil said.

'And what year is she?' I asked politely.

'Oh, I'll have her for one more year,' Sybil said. 'Then it'll just be me rattling around in this big empty house.'

'You might remarry,' I said, in a completely neutral voice.

Sybil looked startled, maybe at my offering a suggestion about a subject that was clearly none of my business. 'Well, I suppose that's possible,' she said stiffly. 'I hadn't thought about it.'

I didn't believe that for a minute. From the way the maid cut her eyes toward Sybil (she was carrying out the used plates), she didn't, either. We'd had iced tea with our salad and our chicken divan served over rice, but I'd only had one refill. I wanted to get into Nell's room, but I could hardly say I had to use the bathroom again. That would just be too suspicious. There was no way I could tell Tolliver what I needed, and he was not very good at sneaking, anyway.

A picture presided over the dining room, and I assumed the portrait was of Sybil's dead husband. I was seated opposite it, so I had forty-five minutes to stare at the painted features and look for their traces in the pictures of Dell and Mary Nell that were hanging on either side.

'Your husband?' I offered, nodding toward the picture. I thought it had been painted from a snapshot, but it was interesting. The eyes looked alive, and the tension of the seated body suggested that Teague was going to leap up at any moment.

She turned her head to look at the picture, as if she'd forgotten it was there. 'He was a good man,' she said softly. 'He was just nuts about the kids, of course. He'd had pneumonia, one of those strains that's resistant to antibiotics, so he'd been in the hospital in Little Rock. He'd had a little heart trouble, but the doctors kept telling us it wasn't much, not to worry. They were going to do more about it when he got over the pneumonia, you see. But one afternoon, while he was recuperating, he was in his study with all the medical records from the past year. He wasn't satisfied with our insurance, or he thought that they should have paid more on his doctor bill, or something. I don't even remember now. But it had been a big year medically, you have those sometimes, I guess. Mary Nell had had a tonsillectomy, and Dell was the passenger in a car that had a little accident. The driver had a broken leg, and Dell had a little knock on the head and some stitches. Bloody, but really after it was cleaned up, he wasn't hurt too badly. And I'd had high cholesterol. So Dick had this pile of papers he was going through, and sometime in the afternoon he just . . . passed. When I went in to get him for supper, he had his head on the desk.'

'I'm so sorry,' I said. Sybil had had a lot to bear in her life, and I had to respect that, no matter how cold I found her.

'I'm curious, Sybil,' my brother said, sounding as if going from one subject to another was simply logical. Sybil blinked and refocused on Tolliver. 'Why didn't you ask Harper to come to Sarne earlier?'

'I'm sorry?' Sybil's attractive face was blank.

'Why didn't you ask Harper right after Teenie went missing?'

'I . . . well, I . . . of course, at first I was shocked by my son's death, and I just couldn't think about Teenie. Frankly, I just . . . didn't care, in the face of my own loss.' Sybil gave us a noble face, telling us she was ashamed of that, but so what?

'Of course,' I said. 'Of course.' This was just noise, to get her to continue.

'But when I heard all the rumors that were going around town, about how there was only justice for the rich, and why wasn't anyone looking for Teenie, and people seemed so sure that Dell had done something terrible to her . . . I was talking to Terry at Sunday lunch at the country club, and he told me what he'd heard about you. Paul was dead set against it, but I just couldn't leave a stone unturned. There had to be something I could do besides get out there and search the woods myself. You know, they should have brought in tracking dogs right away. But no one knew Teenie was out there with Dell. When he got found, it was assumed he was a suicide. By the time Helen realized Teenie was missing, too, it was late at night. It rained real heavy. When they resumed the search the next day, the scent was gone, I guess. I don't remember any of that, at all. I was far from worrying about Teenie.'

'No cadaver dogs?' I asked.

'They're different from trackers, right? No, I guess not. After Helen thought about it, she said she was sure Teenie would turn up somewhere alive, and bringing in the cadaver dogs would be like saying she was dead. I thought for sure she'd back down on that one, but she said everyone was telling her it was not the right thing to do.' Sybil shook her head. 'Terry thought it would give the town a bad name, too, but the hell with that. If a young one's missing, you got to look for 'em. Maybe if Jay had been around . . . Oh, he wants you to come by the house, by the way. He called here this morning to find out more about you. Anyway, Jay and Helen's relationship wasn't all bad. Helen was more of a woman after she lay off the alcohol, you understand, but she had more backbone altogether when she was with Jay. She'd just listen to this one and that one and end up all confused after she separated from Jay.'

That was totally not the impression I'd gotten of Helen Hopkins. It sounded as though Sybil and Helen hadn't communicated face to face at all.

As if she'd heard my inner comment, Sybil said, 'She never wanted to sit down and talk to me, so we could work out what to do. I'd call and get someone else. I'd send a message, and she wouldn't respond.' Sybil shook her head. 'And now it's too late,' she said dramatically, able to be insincere now that she was no longer talking about the tragedy of her son. 'Poor Helen. But at least she was spared the burial of her daughter. Harvey will catch the one who did it. The son of a bitch'll try to sell something he stole from Helen, or he'll get drunk in a bar and tell some buddy of his. Harvey says that's the way it works.'

Sybil Teague herself would never know how things worked, I thought. In some way I had yet to define, she was so far from the truth she wouldn't know it if it bit her in the ass.

11

'Why aren't you one of those computer hackers?' I asked Tolliver. 'Then I could tell you all this, and you'd have some brilliant idea, and you'd hack into the law enforcement system, or the Teagues' home computer, and find out some critical information, and I'd put it to brilliant use.'

'You need to stop reading mysteries for a while,' Tolliver said, braking gently for one of the town's numerous four-way stops. 'Or get a new sidekick.'

'Sidekick?'

'Yeah, if you're the brilliant sleuth, I must be the slightly denser but brilliant-in-my-own-useful-way sidekick, right?'

'Yes, Watson.'

'More like Sharona,' he muttered.

'That'd make me Monk?'

'If the shoe fits.'

Actually, that hurt a little bit, the way a joke does when it's just a tad too close to the truth.

'Of course, you're a lot cuter,' he said in a judicious voice, and I felt better. A little.

'Listen, did that sound like Helen Hopkins to you, all those things Sybil said?'

'No,' he said promptly. 'By the way, where are we going?'

'To Helen Hopkins' house. Jay Hopkins wants to meet with us.'

'Why?'

'I have no idea.'

'Well, it sounded like neither of them really wanted to make the effort to talk to each other, despite the fact that one was the mother of a dead teenager, and the other was the mom of a missing teenager. And those two kids loved each other. But it must have drenched them with a bucket of ice water, finding out Teenie was pregnant.'

'Yeah. And evidently, she hadn't told her mom. And Dell hadn't told Sybil, that's for sure. But he had told his little sister. Don't you think that's strange?'

'No. I'd tell you anything before I'd tell my dad or your mother.'

I felt warmer immediately. 'But those were our circumstances. These two were brought up normal.'

'Normal? Helen was an alcoholic, and she divorced her husband because he drank and beat her. Sybil Teague is one of the coldest women I ever met, and if she didn't marry that poor guy to get his money . . . well, it seems to me that what she loves is one, her son Dell, two, herself, and running a long third, Mary Nell.'

'Okay,' I said. 'Okay.' Sometimes Tolliver astonished me, and this was one of those times.

We drove around town, taking in the limited sights and sounds of Sarne. With the weekend over, the town had returned to its own pre-occupation with battening down for the winter. The banners were being taken down from the ornamental streetlights. No one was wearing a cute costume. Aunt Sally's had a 'Closed for the Winter' sign in the window. The horses and carriages were gone from the square.

Our cell phone rang as we made our way once again to the little house on Freedom Street. I answered it since Tolliver was driving.

'Hello,' I said, and a remote voice asked, 'Harper?'

'Yes?'

'It's Iona. Tolliver's aunt.'

'Iona,' I whispered to Tolliver. I put my mouth back to the receiver. 'Yes, what do you want?'

'Your sister's run off.'

'Which one?'

'Mariella.'

Mariella had just turned eleven. Tolliver and I had sent a card, enclosing money. Of course, we hadn't gotten a thank-you of any kind, and when we'd called – okay, I'd called – on the actual day, Iona had told me Mariella was out. I'd been sure I heard her in the background, though.

This seemed horribly like Cameron's history. I made myself say, 'Did she run off with someone, or did she just disappear?'

'She ran off with a little boy who's thirteen. Some delinquent named Craig.'

'And?'

'We want you to come back and look for her.'

I held the phone away to give it the look of incredulous amazement her statement deserved.

'You told her for years how awful Tolliver and I were,' I said to my aunt Iona. 'She wouldn't come back with me if I found her. She'd run the other way. Besides, I only find dead people. You look for her. Call the police, of course. I bet you haven't.' I pressed the button to end the conversation, if you could call it that.

'What?' Tolliver asked. I recounted Iona's words.

'Don't you think you were a little hasty?' His words were mild, but they stung me.

'We're due in Memphis and Millington, and we've been delayed here already. There's no telling where Mariella is, or this Craig either. How far could they be? They can't drive. They're right down the road from Iona, I bet. She hasn't gone to the police because she's too proud to let them know Mariella's run away.'

'You remember what Cameron was like at eleven?' Tolliver asked. 'I didn't know her then. But I bet she ran off, too, huh?'

'No,' I said. 'We were still safe when Cameron was eleven.' Though probably the signs of our parents' dissolution had been there by then, we'd just been too young to interpret them. We'd still been cocooned in upper middle class assurances. 'Maybe Mariella and her friend went to join the circus,' I suggested. 'Or travel with a rock band.'

'I think you're being old-fashioned,' Tolliver said. 'Girls now want to be fashion designers or supermodels.'

'Well, Mariella will never make it,' I said. The last time we'd seen our sister Mariella, she'd been on the short and plump side, and models notoriously aren't. It was a little early for her to have gotten her growth spurt.

'They'll call Mark next,' Tolliver said. His older brother lived not too far from Will and Iona.

'Poor Mark,' I said. He always helped other people, and he needed a break himself. His first marriage had failed spectacularly and quickly, and he'd been dating a string of losers ever since. Mark was a nice guy, and he deserved better, but he always sought worse. 'We should call him tonight.'

'Good idea. Well, here we are again.'

The little house seemed drenched in gloom today. Jay Hopkins might have a hard time selling the place, though the paint was fresh and the yard in good condition.

Jay Hopkins was as thin as his ex-wife had been. I had a fleeting image of their skeletons clacking together during sex, an image I was quick to banish from my mind. He was sitting on the front steps, so I was able to get a good look as we crossed the yard. Helen's ex had the malnourished face of a longtime drinker, and he could have passed for anywhere between his probable age – which would be in his early forties – and sixty. His hair was sparse and silver-blond, and he smoked with quick jerks of his hand.

'Thank you all for coming by,' he said. 'You must be the psychic lady.'

'I'm not psychic,' I explained, for maybe the thousandth time. I started to add I wasn't a lady, either, but that would become evident, and the topic bored me. 'I just find bodies.'

'I'm Tolliver Lang, Harper's brother.' Tolliver extended his hand. 'I'm sorry for your loss.'

'My whole family is dead now,' Jay Hopkins said, matter-of-factly. 'Both my daughters, and my wife. You couldn't get a much bigger loss than that.'

I groped around mentally for something to say, but came up speechless. Maybe there just wasn't anything.

'Have a seat,' Jay said, when the pause became painful.

'Before I do,' I said abruptly, 'I have a question for you. Did your wife leave Teenie's room just like it was?'

'Yes, because she always expected her to come back,' he said unsteadily. 'Sally and Teenie shared that room until Sally married Hollis, and then Teenie had it all to herself. What are you wanting to know?'

'May I see it?'

'You said you weren't psychic. What are you hoping to find out?' Jay Hopkins was sharper than I'd given him credit for. Maybe he hadn't started drinking for the day.

I hesitated. 'I want to see if some of her hair is left in her hairbrush,' I said finally.

'For what reason?' He lit another cigarette. It was his house, I reminded myself.

'I want to have it tested,' I said.

'To find out what?'

Now he'd asked one question too many.

'I think you know,' Tolliver said unexpectedly. 'I think you wonder, too.'

Jay stubbed out the cigarette with vicious jabs. 'What're you talking about, mister?'

'You wonder who her father was.'

Jay froze in position, I guess amazed that someone had actually been rude enough to say it out loud. 'She was my daughter,' he said finally, in a final voice.

'Yes, in every way that mattered. But we need to know whose daughter she was in the biological way,' Tolliver said.

'Why? I'm burying that child. You can't take that away from me.' This was the voice of a man who had lost many things, though I was sure he'd tossed some of it away himself.

'If her father hasn't made a sound toward claiming her yet, he's not going to now,' I said reasonably.

'There's every chance I could be Teenie's father. I don't want anyone thinking bad of Helen.'

Too late for that. 'I think everyone knows Helen was human,' I said gently. 'I think the shame would be on the father, for not owning up to his responsibility.' I was thinking, Tolliver can hold him down and I'll run back to the room . . .

'All right, then,' Jay Hopkins said. He sounded defeated, beaten down, and I knew caving in to my request was one more item in a line of items that marked his unmanning. But at the moment, his sense of self was not too high on my list of things to preserve. I doubted he had much self left, anyway.

'What'll you do with her hair?' he asked.

'Send it to a lab, have it tested for her DNA.'

'How?'

I shrugged. 'Via UPS, I guess.'

'Her room's on the left.' His elbows were propped on his bony knees, and he bent his head over his clasped hands. There was something smug about him, now. I should have been warned.

The house was so small there was little question of which room he meant. It still held twin beds, with a nightstand jammed between them. The walls were covered with posters and memorabilia. There were dried corsages and party invitations, notes from friends and buttons with cute sayings, a big straw hat and a napkin from Dairy

Queen. Little things like that would only evoke a memory for the one who saved them; and now those memories did not exist anymore. I was willing to bet that all Sally's memorabilia had come down when she married. All these items were Teenie's. There wasn't any hair in the brush on the shelf under the small mirror. I wondered if the police had taken it when she'd vanished, to get a DNA sample. I spied a purse was on top of the battered chest of drawers. I dumped it out on the nearest bed and was rewarded with a smaller hairbrush choked with Teenie's dark hair. I put the brush into a brown envelope I'd brought with me and glanced around the crowded space. I was sure various people had already searched this room thoroughly – the police and Helen, of course. I would search my daughter's room if she went missing. I would tear up the floorboards. There didn't seem to be any point in me combing it for clues.

I got a hair sample from Jay Hopkins, who made a wry joke about how little of it he had to spare. Now I had hair samples from both Teenie and Jay, and a fat lot of good it would do me. But I would send them in, nonetheless.

Tolliver had a friend in a big private lab in Dallas. He could get things done that I couldn't. His friend was a woman, and he had to give her a certain amount of sweet talk, but that never killed anyone. Well, it made my stomach clench, but I wouldn't die of it.

I was anxious to leave, but Jay wanted to know about our last talk with Helen, and I felt obliged to recount it just as I had to the police. He gave me permission to get hair from Helen's brush, too, and he suddenly seemed more interested than upset by the idea that now he could find out if he was Teenie's biological father.

'And you're paying for this?' Tolliver asked as we drove away. We went to the UPS pickup spot, which was in an auto parts store many blocks from the square. Small businesses in Sarne – in the south in general – had to diversify, but I was used to that and kind of enjoyed it. I got some mailers and followed the advice of Tolliver's friend at the lab in packing the samples I had.

'Yes, I am,' I said. 'I'm paying for this.'

'Why, in God's name, are you doing this?'

'I don't really know. I want to leave. I want justice done. I feel terrible that Helen lost both her daughters to a murderer.'

'Or is this all about Hollis?' Tolliver asked, his voice sharp. 'Is this about you wanting to impress a law man?'

I felt like slapping Tolliver, or screaming. But I stared up at him and did neither of those things. After a long moment, he said, 'Okay, I'm sorry.'

'She said it would take three days to get a preliminary answer?' I responded.

'Yes. Longer for a definitive answer, but three days for a quick yes or no. Since it's from hair follicles, and not blood samples.'

We were leaving the store when a patrol car pulled up beside ours. A deputy got out, a man I hadn't seen before. He was tall, thin, and middle-aged, his colorless hair shaved close to his head. He wore ugly glasses and he was tense as a coiled snake. He stalked to the rear of the car and looked at our Texas license plate like it was in German.

'I run your license plate,' he said. 'You got a warrant out for your arrest in Montana.'

'No we don't,' I said, but Tolliver gripped my arm.

'And you got a busted out taillight back here.' He pointed, but I wasn't fool enough to get close to him to look. He waited for a reaction from us, seemed a little disappointed when he didn't get one. 'You, sir, you're the legal owner of this car?'

'Yes,' Tolliver said carefully.

'Lean up against your car with your hands on the hood. I'm going to have to take you in.'

I felt a humming start up in my head, just a distant little humming. I stood frozen while my brother silently, almost casually, complied. Tolliver had seen the tension in the deputy's body, too.

'What . . .' I had to clear my throat. 'What are you doing?'

'Outstanding warrants, he's got to go to jail while I clear this up.'

'What?' I couldn't understand him because the humming felt louder.

'Judge'll come to town soon. If there's any mistake, he'll be out quick as a New York minute.'

'What?'

'Ain't you understanding me?' the tall man said. 'Can't you speak English, woman?'

'You're arresting my brother,' I said.

'You got it.'

'Because you say there's a Montana warrant out for him.'

'Yes'm.'

'But that's not true. The charges were dismissed.'

'That's not what the computer says. And, ma'am, aside from that, there's the matter of the taillight.' And he pointed. While Tolliver stayed where he was, I edged carefully around the car, keeping a safe distance from the deputy. The taillight was smashed.

'It was okay when we went in the store,' I said.

'You'll excuse us if we can't take your word for it,' the deputy said, smirking. He walked around the end of the car, taking care to stay as far from me as I wanted to be from him, and he patted Tolliver down. I could see shiny pieces of the broken light scattered on the street.

'When can I get him out?' I asked, pretending with all my might that the deputy didn't exist. This was sheer bullshit, but there was nothing I could do about it.

'After the judge sets the fine for the taillight, and we get this warrant thing settled,' the deputy said. 'We don't have a sitting judge here; have to wait for the judge to come around.'

I gasped. I couldn't help it. Every fearful reaction I gave fed the deputy's sense of power and gloating, but there was nothing I could do about it. I was on the teetering edge of panic, and I was scrabbling around in my head for some way to put this right, *right now*.

'What's your name?' I asked.

'Bledsoe,' he answered, not too happily.

'Harper,' my brother said. He was handcuffed now, and the humming level rose higher and higher as I looked at the metal around his wrists. The deputy was looking at me uneasily. He'd quit grinning. 'Just call Art. He'll recommend someone.' Art Barfield was our lawyer. His office was in Atlanta, which was where we'd been the first time we needed an attorney.

The deputy looked even more jittery as he absorbed the implication that we had a high-powered lawyer at our backs (which wasn't exactly true), and he began to say something. Suddenly he thought the better of it and stopped, a word half out of his mouth. Then he made up his mind again. 'Don't go crazy about this, young lady. Nothing's going to happen to your brother in our jail.'

I hadn't even thought about that. My focus had been on my own selfish need for Tolliver, my panic for fear of how I'd manage without him. I had been frightened of the wrong thing, I saw immediately. I realized Tolliver would be in the hands of this deputy, who was a fool with power.

Tolliver began trying to make his way around the car to me, and the deputy yanked him back by his cuffed wrists.

I had to pull myself together. I concentrated, completely, on pushing the terrified child inside me back into her hole. I breathed slowly, deeply. I had to focus on Tolliver now, not myself and my trembling hands. My brain began to function again; maybe not well, but it began to produce thoughts.

I looked directly into Bledsoe's eyes. 'If anything happens to Tolliver in your jail, it would be very, very unfortunate.' That wasn't a threat, was it? I didn't want to give him any excuse to lock me up, too.

'I'm going to get our cell phone from my brother, now. It's in his pocket,' I said, in a voice barely above a whisper. I put my purse on the hood of the car so that I was obviously unarmed and unencumbered. No one moved as I held up my hands and walked very slowly over to Tolliver. I wanted the deputy to die. I wanted to stand on his grave. I never lowered my stare from his eyes, which were narrow and watery blue. His lids fluttered, and he looked away at his patrol car, pretending to be fascinated by the querulous voice coming over the radio.

I slid my hand in Tolliver's pocket, pulled out the phone.

'Proud of you,' he murmured, and I smiled up at him, as much of a smile as I could manage. I lay my head against his shoulder for a second, and then I straightened, widening the smile as much as I could, while the deputy shoved Tolliver into the back of the patrol car. The policeman climbed in, and while I watched him, he backed out and drove Tolliver away.

I stood there until the man inside the auto parts store came out to ask me if I was all right.

12

I drove back to the motel very slowly and carefully. I felt like my right hand had been amputated, or one of my feet. I felt exposed and as vulnerable as if a target were attached to my back, as conspicuous as a giraffe would be if it wandered down the streets of Sarne.

When I was back in my room, with the door locked, I felt how close I was to the edge. My right leg, damaged by the lightning all those years ago, was trembling and would barely take my weight. But I got a grip, if only by my fingernails. I stared into the mirror over the sink. 'I'm going to hold on,' I told myself out loud. 'I'm going to hold on, because I'm the only one Tolliver has to get him out of this.' I felt better after I'd stared at myself for a minute and seen my own resolve. I looked like a person who could cope.

I called Art Barfield. Art was not a nationally famous lawyer, nor was he a member of a huge firm. He was well respected in the south for his old and wealthy family, and well known in Atlanta for his eccentricity. He was in a partnership with two other lawyers, lawyers only a bit more traditional than Art.

His secretary was a straight arrow, and she was not amused to hear me demand to be put straight through to Art. But after she checked with her boss, I heard his booming southern voice, and the dreadful tension that had gripped me eased off a fraction.

'Where are you, honeychild?' Art asked.

'Sarne, Arkansas.'

'My God almighty, what the hell are you doing there?'

I almost smiled. 'We had a case here. But there were complications. When we came out of the auto parts store, there was this asshole deputy waiting to arrest Tolliver.' I explained about the open warrants and the broken taillight.

'Hmmm. So, Tolliver is in jail?'

'Yes.' That was way too close to a whine. I gripped the cell phone so tightly my fingers were white.

'You're there all by yourself, darlin'?'

'Yes.'

'That's not good. Of course Tolliver's not wanted in Montana. We got that all cleared up. He couldn't be arrested for a broken taillight, so the cop trumped up something else for some reason.'

That really wasn't the point I'd make if I were defending Tolliver, but I was glad to talk to someone who took Tolliver's innocence for granted.

'Are you going to be able to handle this, sweet thing?' Art's voice was very gentle, but also brisk, as if he expected a quick answer.

'Yes, I'll be fine,' I said, pretty sure I was lying.

'That means you're going to try real hard,' Art translated.

'Yep.'

'Good for you, darlin'. Tell you what, I know a lawyer in Little Rock who can drive up there and steer you through this. Her name is Phyllis Folliette. Write that down, now.'

There was nothing wrong with my memory, but I did write it down, along with the lawyer's phone number.

'I'm calling her as soon as I hang up the phone with you, and she'll be in touch with you right away, or at least very soon.'

'That's good,' I said. 'That's real good. Listen, Art? They can't open packages we were sending via UPS, can they?'

'No,' he said. 'I guess they'd have to have a warrant to do that.' Then he told me to call him if I needed anything more and hung up.

I was hoping that Bledsoe didn't know what we were doing at the auto parts store; he hadn't gone inside to enquire while I was standing there, and he hadn't asked me. So maybe sending off the hair samples hadn't been the trigger for Tolliver's arrest. Maybe there had been something else.

Harvey Branscom, while not my favorite guy, had seemed like a pretty independent fellow to me, and one who knew his business. Why would he consent to be part of the charade outside the auto parts store? Who could influence him so heavily? He had to know what his deputy was doing.

What was gained by having Tolliver in jail? That was the crucial question. What was the result of his incarceration?

Well, the first thing to pop up in my mind was that we'd have to stay in Sarne longer now. But I couldn't understand why that would be to anyone's advantage. A wild thought crossed my mind, and I made myself consider it. Could Hollis have become so nuts about me in such a short time that he was willing to frame Tolliver to keep me here? I just couldn't swallow that. Actually, it was somewhat easier to believe a scenario in which Mary Nell sprung the same trap on Tolliver, because the phony warrant and the broken taillight seemed like such desperate and amateurish steps. But it seemed very unlikely that Mary Nell would even know we'd been in trouble in Montana once upon a time, and even if she'd learned about the episode some-how, she wouldn't be able to go on the police computer network and somehow enter a false incident.

I tried to imagine a credible progression of cause and effect, opportunity and motive, sitting in my lonely hotel room. When my mind remained persistently blank, I opened the door to Tolliver's room and went and sat there. The maid had done the beds and put fresh towels out, so there wasn't even a trace of Tolliver in his room, at least to my eyes. For a little while, though, being there made me feel a tad better; but after a bit, I felt foolish, and then I felt like an intruder, so I went back.

There was a knock at the door, and I nearly jumped out of my skin. I glanced down at my watch. I'd been sitting there, with my thoughts scurrying around like hamsters in an exercise wheel, for over an hour.

At the door, Hollis said, 'I'm sorry.'

'Did you . . . you didn't have anything to do with this, right?'

'No,' he said, not sounding offended. He sounded almost too gentle, the way you sound when you're afraid a dog might turn on you. 'Marv Bledsoe and Jay Hopkins, they used to drink together.'

I remembered the smug look on Jay Hopkins' face, and I felt sure he'd called Marv and told him where to catch hold of us. No wonder he hadn't minded us getting the hair samples. He hadn't believed we'd have time to get them in the mail.

'I've never trusted Jay, or Marv for that matter. Unfortunately, Harvey does, or at least he acts like he does. And the state guys are gone. They went off to check out another teen date murder they think might be related to Teenie's and Dell's. So there's no brakes on Marv, like there ought to be.'

'So, have you seen this warrant?'

'No, not me. I gather there was some problem in Montana while you worked up there, last year?'

'Yeah, but it was all resolved. There's no warrant for Tolliver's arrest. I'd know for sure. And we didn't have a busted light this morning when we got up.'

'Did you see him do it?'

'No, we didn't.'

'If Marv made all this up, he would have some way to stop you,' Hollis said, sitting down heavily on the foot of my bed. He caught my eyes, and said hesitantly, 'I thought I better stop by to see how you were doing. I got the impression you depend a lot on your brother.'

'I do,' I said simply. 'But I'm going to be okay. I've already called a lawyer in Little Rock. She's going to call me back.'

'That's good,' Hollis said heartily. 'You're doing real good.' Again, the encouragement was too overdone.

I was well aware that I wasn't, you know, Miss Stability. But there's a difference between knowing you have a flaw and seeing other people reacting to it. 'You can't hide how weird you are,' was the unspoken message. 'You require special handling and careful treatment.' I began to tense up all over again.

'Hollis,' I said, hearing my voice come out as a growl. 'You make sure nothing happens to Tolliver in that jail. You hear me?'

I could see his resentment at the implication, but at the moment, that wasn't important to me. What mattered to me was that I see in his face the assurance that nothing could happen to my brother in that jail, that he would be treated fairly and guarded well.

I could not find that in Hollis's expression.

'Hollis, you listen to me,' I said, in the quietest voice I could manage. 'I know you love this town and you love the life you have here. But something's going on in Sarne, there's a rotten apple somewhere spoiling things. There's a lot we don't know about these deaths. Someone you know murdered Dell Teague and Teenie Hopkins. Someone you know killed your wife Sally and beat Helen Hopkins to death. And someone you know doesn't want my brother and me to leave, for some reason. Now, we have to find out who that someone is. I came here, and I did my job, and I did it quick and I did it right. Now, Tolliver and I should be able to leave you all to solve your own damn problems.'

'You were beginning to care about me until this happened,' Hollis said, completely to my surprise. It seemed more like the kind of thing men expect women to say; if life were like a sitcom, that would have been my line.

'Yes,' I said. 'I was.'

'I know someone is responsible for all the deaths,' he said. 'I know that. And I realize it's someone I know. But I can't imagine why. Sally was a good woman, a nice woman, and I loved her.' Hollis was apparently having as hard a time keeping his thoughts on track as I was.

'She knew something,' I said intently. 'She knew a secret, a big secret. She died first.'

We thought about that for a second.

'Can you remember anything about her, in the days before she died? Was she excited, upset, worried?'

Hollis looked profoundly depressed. I wanted to touch his hair, stroke it, but I kept my hands locked together in my lap. 'She seemed like someone who had a secret,' he said heavily. 'She would talk to me about almost anything, but some things about her family and the mess her mother had gotten into – I guess it's not too surprising that she didn't want to talk about their drinking and fighting and their divorce, or her mom's and dad's . . . well . . . infidelities.'

I worked my way through that sentence. 'So, she'd be open and honest with you about almost anything except her family,' I said.

He hesitated. 'Yes,' he said finally, firmly. 'Anything but her family.'

'Do you think she had a secret because she had just figured something out – like, "Oho! Eureka!" or because her mom or Teenie had confided in her?'

Hollis tried hard to remember, while I tried hard not to be impatient. I was sorry he had to go through even more pain, but I thought it was necessary. Actually, part of me was asking, 'Why didn't he do all this before?' Of course, he'd thought his wife had died accidentally. Now that he knew she'd been murdered, though, surely he'd been turning that time over in his head?

'I think she'd figured out something,' he said. 'It's almost impossible to say what was going through someone's mind, you know? And I've been thinking maybe I didn't know Sally as well as I thought I did. If we'd been married longer, trusted each other more, she would have told me what she was worried about, thinking of. We could have worked on it together. We just hadn't been married that long. We hadn't been tested.'

This wasn't getting us anywhere. 'Did anything happen right before she died?' I asked, realizing I might sound callous. 'Anything that might have triggered her death?'

'Only Dick Teague dying,' Hollis said.

'When did he die?' I asked. I'd seen the newspaper stories, but I hadn't noted the date.

'I think in February. That sounds right,' Hollis said, after a moment's thought. 'When Sybil found him, she couldn't cope with cleaning up everything for the funeral, so she hired Helen and Sally to clean the house. Did you know Sybil used to have Helen clean her house, before Helen began drinking so bad and all? Sybil hired Barb Happ after that. I didn't much want Sally cleaning for anyone, but Sally really enjoyed cleaning and she said she might as well do it on her day off from Wal-Mart, not only because she felt sorry for Sybil, but because she wanted some extra money for Christmas. Sally came home that day feeling real concerned about something.'

'But she didn't give you any hints?' I'd been assuming that Sally had discovered her sister's pregnancy, but Sally had died months before the event.

'Of course, I asked her how the job went. She said she cleaned the downstairs while her mom took the upstairs, and that's about all she said. The study was just like it had been when Dick fell over dead, and that made her feel a little funny, she said. But that night, she searched out one of her high school textbooks. The school system discontinued this book, so the students could keep it if they wanted to, and she did. Sally was interested in some things that surprised me.'

'What book was it?'

'She had several. I can't even remember now. I only recall it because she seemed so . . . like she was thinking real hard about something else, and then when Sally found the book, she studied over it for the longest time. That was unusual.'

'So, do you think you could remember?'

'Maybe. I'll look this evening, see if I can find it. Seems like I remember it had a red back cover . . .' Hollis looked distant, as if his eyes were seeing a distant scene, and I guess they were.

The phone rang. I jumped about a foot. 'Hello?' I said.

'Ms Connelly?' It was a woman's voice, heavily southern and somehow really smart.

'Yes.'

'This is Phyllis Folliette? With Huff, Moon, and Greene?'

'Right. Oh, good.' Hollis was pointing at the door, indicating he needed to leave, and I nodded and waved before returning my attention to the lawyer.

'Okay,' she said, and her voice became carefully soothing. 'I hear you're in kind of a jam, over in Sarne.'

'Yes.'

'I just wanted to tell you, I called the sheriff's office and they said your brother wouldn't be arraigned for two more days. I can't bail him out until the judge sets the bail, you understand?'

'Yes, I understand.'

'And the judge won't be there until the day after tomorrow.'

Okay, I wasn't dumb. 'I understand that two days means the day after tomorrow,' I said clearly.

'Um. I get that . . . Sorry if I was talking down,' the lawyer apologized. 'Occupational hazard.'

'Umm.'

'So, I'll be there in Sarne, day after tomorrow, to get your brother out of jail,' she said. 'These charges sound like a bunch of crap, but I'm calling Montana first thing in the morning to get this straightened out. In the meantime, don't do anything rash, and don't worry. Art especially charged me to tell you that. Okay?'

'Yes.'

'Okay. Now I'm going to switch you over to our financial office, so you can take care of that part of it.'

Everyone wants to be paid, even me – especially me, since I figure at any moment my gift could be taken from me. I want to use it while I have it, and it's really my only marketable skill. It should support me, I figure. It robbed me of a normal life.

After I fixed things with the financial office, I hung up and tried to figure out what I should do next. I packed up Tolliver's stuff and stowed it in my room, then I walked up to the motel office and told horrible old Vernon McCluskey that we wouldn't be using the second room for now. He said he was about ready for me to check out, and I said I had to stay in Sarne a few more days. He couldn't throw me out, not legally – though today I'd had a big hint that the legal system in Sarne wasn't exactly on the up and up. If he did somehow make me leave, I'd just go to the next town, which was in a different county.

While I ran through all these contingencies, I returned to the room. I found myself shaking my hands vigorously in the air like in a children's exercise, to refocus my mind. It was time to eat, and I opened a granola bar. I needed more than that, better food, but I didn't want to go out by myself. It was one thing when I knew Tolliver was waiting for me back at the motel, or that he was somewhere in the same town: it was entirely another thing when Tolliver was locked away in a jail. I wondered what they'd fed him for supper, and when I could see him. I wondered if he had a cellmate. I wondered how ruthless his cellmate was.

The most important person I knew in Sarne, aside from the sheriff, was Sybil Teague. I didn't know if she'd even care, and I doubted she'd help, but I called her anyway.

'My brother's in jail on a trumped-up charge, Sybil,' I said, after she'd told me she was glad to hear from me.

'Paul Edwards mentioned that to me this afternoon,' Sybil said, in her cool rich-woman's voice. 'I'm so sorry for your trouble.'

This didn't sound promising. 'Tolliver isn't wanted by police anywhere,' I said, as calmly as I could.

'I know my brother's the sheriff, but you must realize that I can't interfere with legal matters,' Sybil said, and her voice was frosty rather than cool.

'Tolliver is my brother, and your brother's deputy set him up, for reasons best known to himself.'

'Which deputy?' Sybil said, and that did surprise me.

'The one named Bledsoe. Some coincidence, right?' I wanted Sybil to confess that she'd sicced the deputy on to me, so I'd know who my enemy was.

'That would be Marv,' she said slowly, and now she sounded distinctly unhappy, whether because I'd tried to involve her or for some other reason. 'Paul's second cousin. But that doesn't mean anything.'

Was everyone involved in this case related?

Sybil wasn't willing to do a thing to help me, and I wasn't even sure I could think of anything concrete for her to do. She wasn't happy, and I definitely got the feeling she didn't think Tolliver was guilty of anything. But she also couldn't or wouldn't intercede with the sheriff. We hung up, equally unhappy with each other.

I thought long and hard. Then I called Mary Nell Teague on her cell phone. She'd given the number to Tolliver, and I'd fished it out of his jacket pocket when I packed up his stuff. She'd drawn a little curlicue under 'Nell.'

Mary Nell wasn't happy at hearing my voice on the other end of the line.

'Tolliver himself can't call you,' I said, 'since your uncle Harvey put him in jail.' This was not entirely accurate, but I wasn't interested in being fair.

She shrieked and carried on for a full minute while I waited patiently on the other end of the line.

'Of course, he isn't wanted by the police in Montana,' she said. 'That's just crazy.'

Though Mary Nell was just basing her opinion on her sexual attraction to Tolliver rather than any factual basis, it was nice to hear someone so positively on his side. To set the outspoken teenager on the right track, I told her that her mother had refused to help. I didn't put it as bluntly as that, but I made sure the picture got transferred. This would ensure that Sybil's life would be irritating and unpleasant for at least twenty-four hours, which was no more than she deserved. I'm not above being petty.

I called Hollis next, and got no answer. Considering his earlier exit, as if he urgently needed to be somewhere else, I wondered if he'd had to return to patrol. Or maybe he was just being a cowardly rat bastard? Possibly the sheriff had told him to stay away from me if he wanted to keep his job? Hollis probably did want to keep his job badly enough for that. I tried not to blame him, but I was miserable enough to think that it made him a rat bastard, anyway.

I considered my next course of action. The likelihood that I'd break down crying lurked just over the horizon, trembling and shivering. But that would be counterproductive, and there must be something I could do besides sit in the damn hotel room. I could go beat up Bledsoe; and at the moment I felt like I could dig out his liver with my fingernails. But surely there was something more constructive . . . I considered everything I knew, and then I had it. I called Hollis again and left a message on his machine.

'If you aren't picking up because you don't want to talk to me, that's okay, but know this: I'm going to your house right now, and I'm going to want to search your bookshelves.' I was sorry I'd been honorable enough to return his money, since I could have used that as an extra incentive if I'd kept hold of it.

I ran to Hollis's house, since I needed the exercise. It might help keep me calm for a while longer. The leg faltered a couple of times, but didn't give out utterly. There was no truck parked under the carport. I had planned on getting in whether Hollis was home or not, so I didn't care. But I didn't want to be arrested while doing it. Fortunately, the back door was fairly well screened from the neighboring small houses by thick bushes. Since it was a working day, quite possibly the neighbors were gone.

For a policeman, he sure had lousy security. I found his spare key in the third place I looked – hanging from a little nail in the roof over the porch. It was in a dark corner, and partially hidden from view, but my fingers patted around until they felt the nail, and in a second the key was in my hand. I was glad to find it; it would spare me from breaking one of the panes of glass in the back door – also a security risk, as any cop should know.

Since the day was once again gloomy and overcast, I switched on a lamp in the living room. I'd only passed through on my way to the bedroom the last time I'd been here, so I wasn't familiar with the layout. The little room was comfortable and . . . cozy, with an over-stuffed love seat and matching recliner. There was the usual coffee table in front of the love seat, and an occasional table cluttered with a lamp, some magazines, and a book, plus various remotes by the recliner. Within arm's reach was a particle-board bookcase crammed with books, mostly romantic suspense-type paperbacks by Jayne Anne Krentz, Sandra Brown, Nora Roberts, and the like. There were a few adventure/mystery paperbacks – Lee Child and Thomas Cook – which more likely belonged to Hollis.

I did a quick tour of the house to make sure I was looking in the right place. The bedroom didn't have any bookshelves, and the second bedroom (used as a computer room/storeroom now) held only computer manuals and video game guides. The kitchen had a couple of cookbooks, and the bathroom a wicker basket of magazines. Back in the living room, I squatted by the jammed shelves.

Hollis had told me his wife had gotten out one of her old school textbooks. I was willing to bet he hadn't packed them away yet, and I was right. Sally Hopkins Boxleitner had kept a book of British poetry, a copy each of *Julius Caesar* and *The Merchant of Venice*, and an American history textbook. There was a basic biology textbook, too, much battered and torn.

According to Hollis, the book had had a red cover. Both the history text and the biology text were predominately red, at least on their spines.

'What the hell are you doing in here?' I guess part of me had absorbed the small sounds of Hollis arriving home, because I didn't jump. He sounded pretty mad.

'I'm looking for whatever Sally was thinking about that night,' I said. 'I found your spare key in less than two minutes. Here. Here's the history book. Is this the one she had?'

'Why didn't you just wait for me to get home?' Maybe he sounded a tad bit less angry.

'I thought you were avoiding me, and I figured you wouldn't let me in.'

'So you decided right away to just break in my house? You know that's illegal?'

'So's putting a man in jail on trumped-up evidence. Is this the book she had?'

'It might be,' he said, distracted. 'Is there another red one?'

'Yes, the biology book, here.'

'That might be it, too.'

'Okay. You look at the history, I'll look at the biology.'

I turned the book upside down and shook it, and a piece of paper fell out. I figured I'd discovered an old grocery list or a note she'd written the boy who sat beside her in fourth period in high school. I found it was something much less straightforward.

It was half a sheet of blank paper, and on it was written, 'SO, MO, DA, NO.'

'If you'd left it in there, we'd know which section it fell from,' Hollis pointed out.

'You're absolutely right,' I said absently. 'I messed up. Does this mean anything to you?'

'No, not at first glance. But that's her handwriting . . . Sally's.'

There was a new note in his voice that penetrated even my over-loaded emotional system.

'I'm sorry,' I said, making a great effort. 'I know this is dredging up stuff for you that you're trying to put behind you.'

'No, I'm not trying to put Sally behind me,' he said. 'But I am trying to think about the rest of my life. And the ideas of the last few days, the idea that Sally was murdered, that the son of bitch who did it has been walking around this town, talking to me, free, has been curdling my gut. And the fact that every time I see you, I want to screw you so bad it hurts. You practically break in my house, my damn house, and I want to fuck you right here on the floor.'

'Yeah?'

'Yeah.'

It was like he'd flipped a switch. Suddenly, I was thinking about it, too, thinking that it would feel good to forget about my problems for a few minutes, and I rolled over on my back and pulled my shirt over my head.

It was short and violent and the most exciting encounter I'd ever experienced. Nails and teeth, slick skin against slick skin, the thud of body against body. Afterward, he lay beside me on the floor in the small space we'd had available and said, 'I need to vacuum.' He was panting heavily, and the words came out slowly.

'A few dust bunnies,' I agreed. 'But they were good company.'

He wheezed as he laughed, and I pulled my bra back up because there was a draft along the floor. I rolled to my side and propped up on one elbow.

'I made your back bleed,' I said, looking from the scratches to my fingernails. 'I'm sorry.'

'It felt good when it happened,' he said, and he was beginning to drift off to sleep. 'I don't mind.'

While he dozed, I rolled onto my stomach and flipped through the biology book. It was a very basic text, with chapters on plant cells and reproduction, the human nervous system, how eyes work, and . . .

I glanced at the scratches on Hollis's shoulder and shook my head. I looked back down at the graph on the page.

I pulled my jeans back on.

'Hollis,' I said, very quietly.

'Mmph?' he said, opening his eyes.

'I have to go.'

'What? Wait a minute. Where's your car?'

'I ran from the motel to your house. I'll walk back.'

'No, just wait a minute, I'll run you to the motel. Or you can stay here. I know you don't like to be alone.'

It wasn't being alone that made me so antsy. It was being without my brother. But I didn't want to explain that. 'I need to go back to the motel,' I said, as regretfully as I could manage. 'I think the lawyer may call me.' Okay, that was a lie, but I was trying to spare his feelings. I had a few things I needed to do, and I'd have free rein to do them when I wasn't around Hollis, the lawman. He pulled on his uniform swiftly.

'Have you eaten?' Hollis asked practically, as we drove down Main.

'Ah . . . no, I guess not.' I hadn't even finished the granola bar.

'Then at least let me take you to Subway to get something.'

'That would be good,' I agreed, suddenly aware that I was hungry.

The truck filled with the good smell of the hot chicken sub; my mouth was watering.

When Hollis pulled into the slot in front of my room I hopped out of the truck with the bag containing my sandwich; I wanted to use the glare of his headlights to help me fit the key in the lock. The motel was anything but well-lit. Hollis began backing up as I pushed the door open. I turned to wave at him with one hand while the other hand clutched my bag of food. I could vaguely see Hollis's arm move as he switched gears to pull out of the lot.

Suddenly, from inside the room there was a grip on my upper arm that spun me around, then I was stumbling into the room and meeting the rug with a speed that was terrifying.

I rolled to my feet and launched myself at my attacker, pushing him right back out the open door. Never let yourself get cornered. You have to fight instantly, I'd found as a teenager, or your opponent has the upper hand; your injuries hurt too much, or you get scared. And you have to go with it with every fiber of your being. Pull, bite, strike, scratch, squeeze; let go completely. If you're dedicated to hurting someone else, it doesn't register so much when they hurt you. I hardly felt the two pounding blows the man got in on my ribs before I grabbed his testicles and clamped down, and then I bit him on the neck as hard as I could. He was shrieking and trying to pry me off when Hollis separated us.

I sat back against the wall of the motel, sobbing and shaking with the aftermath of unleashing all that, and stared at my assailant, whom Hollis handcuffed with a few economical motions. It was Scot, of course, the teenage admirer of Mary Nell; Scot, who'd tried to attack me before. He was whimpering now, little snot-nose bastard.

'Are you crazy?' Hollis yelled at him. 'Are you nuts? What are you doing, attacking a woman like that?'

'She's the one who's crazy,' Scot said. He spit out a little blood. 'Did you see her?'

'Scot, what the hell made you decide to do this?' I could see that Hollis was absolutely stunned. 'Who let you in her room?' He shook the boy.

The teenager stayed silent, glaring up at Hollis.

Vernon McCluskey hobbled out of the office and down the sidewalk to where we were poised in our strange tableau.

'Vernon, did you let this boy into Harper's room?' Hollis bellowed.

'Naw,' Vernon said. He looked down at the boy contemptuously. I knew it wasn't because the boy had been poised to attack a smaller woman, but because the boy had failed to attack hard enough, and at the wrong time. 'I rented him a room, the room this lady's brother was in earlier. If she happened to leave the adjoining door unlocked, ain't my fault. I had no idea Scot would do anything like this.' Vernon shook his head with insincere regret.

Son of a bitch.

If I was feeling paranoid, it was with some justification.

'Get up, Scot,' Hollis said. 'You're going to jail. Harper, you're going to press charges?'

'Oh, you bet.' I needed a hand up, but Hollis was escorting Scot to his truck, and I wouldn't have asked Vernon for a place to spit on the sidewalk. Shakily, I worked my way to my feet. My thigh muscles were trembling, and I felt weak and sick. I hated pretty nearly everyone. 'I may have to wait until tomorrow, but I'm definitely going to press charges. I was willing to forgive the first time, when he looked to be a teenager driven nuts by jealousy, but this is above and beyond.'

What on earth could have induced this boy, who'd been so scared of his parents and his coach, to attempt something like this? What had he been ordered to do? Kill me, or beat me up?

'Paid,' I said. Hollis stopped, halfway through pushing the handcuffed boy up into his truck. 'I'll bet someone paid him to do this.'

And I saw by Scot's face that I'd struck oil. 'Were you supposed to break some bones?' I asked him, conversationally. 'Or kill me?'

'Shut up,' he said, turning his face away from me. 'Just don't talk to me anymore.'

'Coward,' I said, and I remembered that Harvey Branscom had called him the same thing the morning before. Harvey had been right.

'Burn in hell,' Scot said, and then Hollis slammed the door on him.

Vernon was still standing there when they pulled away.

'You do anything but take my key when I leave, I'll slap you with a lawsuit that will bankrupt this motel,' I said. I knew damn good and well I'd locked the interconnecting door. 'If any harm comes to me, my brother will see to it. Any harm comes to him, our lawyer will do it.'

He didn't say anything, but he watched me with old, hostile eyes while I shut and locked my door. I picked up the bag of food from Subway. Luckily, I hadn't gotten a drink, since I had bottled drinks in the ice chest in my room. Vernon probably would have had me arrested for defacing his property if I'd spilled a Coke on his green carpet.

I shoved a chair under the doorknob and moved the ice chest against the connecting door. It wouldn't hold the door, but it would slow down an entrance and provide noise. I used my cell phone to call Art in Atlanta, and I left a detailed account of what had just happened on his answering machine. Just for the record.

I was so lonely I cried.

Then I ate the food in the bag, not because I wanted it (it was nasty and cold by that time), but because I had to have fuel. I peeled off my clothes with shaking fingers. I was a mess; I'd had sex and a fight in the same evening, and I needed a shower. I looked at myself in the mirror over the sink. My ribs were already turning blue on my left side where Scot had gotten in the two good punches. I breathed deeply, trying to decide if I had any broken ribs. I didn't think I did, after a few experimental movements.

It gave me some satisfaction to think that if it had been a bad day for me, it had been a worse day for Scot. He'd turned from being football team quarterback and suitor for Mary Nell Teague into a soon-to-be felon. Hurt pride had done it; that, and a bribe, I figured. I could conjecture he'd felt embarrassed after the morning incident. The coach had probably made him feel like a fool, after the sheriff had called him a coward. Instead of taking their words to heart, he'd gotten angry, and when he'd been offered money, he'd jumped at the chance to recoup his self-esteem. It was one of those situations where you learn what you're made of. Unfortunately for Scot, it turned out he was made of lesser things.

Hollis called after he'd booked Scot into the jail. He wanted to find out how I was and to reassure me that nothing would disturb my night. 'We'll figure out what the initials mean,' he said. 'I knew my wife, and I'll understand it sooner or later.'

I didn't think we had 'later,' and I didn't know if understanding Sally would help or not. She'd known exactly what she meant, and she'd been referring to something simple and obvious. With all due respect to Sally, if a girl who'd graduated from Sarne High could make some significant discovery after a glance at her biology textbook, then I should be able to figure it out. So should any number of people, and that was what had me worried. 'SO MO DA NO' I wrote on the little pad of paper kept by the phone. I wrote it as one word. I wrote it backwards. I tried to make a word out of the letters. I fell asleep with the pencil clutched in my hand.

13

A pounding on the door woke me up. I rolled an eye toward the clock on the bedside table. It was seven in the morning.

'Who is it?' I asked cautiously, when I'd stumbled over to the door.

'Mary Nell.'

Oh, wonderful. I moved the chair to open the door, and she strode in. 'We've got to get him out,' she said dramatically, and I felt like smacking her.

'Yes,' I said. 'I want him out, too.' If there was a little sarcasm in my voice, it was lost on Nell Teague.

'What have you done about it?'

I blinked, sat on the side of the bed. 'I've hired a lawyer, who'll be here tomorrow,' I said.

'Oh,' she said, somewhat deflated. 'Well, I called Toby Buckell, but he just laughed at me. Said he wouldn't take a case unless a grown-up called him.'

I could just imagine. 'I'm sorry he treated you with disrespect,' I said, trying hard to sound like I meant it. 'I appreciate your effort. But Tolliver is my brother, and I have to be the one who works on this.' I wanted to be nice to this girl, whose only fault was that she was sixteen, but she was wearing me out. Talk about drama. Then I reminded myself she'd lost her brother and her father in a very short period, and I forced myself into a more hospitable mode.

'Would you like some coffee, or a soda?' I asked.

'Sure,' she said, going over to the ice chest and pulling out a Coke. I brewed a little pot of coffee from the motel coffeemaker, and poor coffee it was, but it was hot and contained caffeine. I looked at my visitor. Mary Nell's face was bare of makeup, and her hair was pulled back into a very short ponytail. She looked her age, no more. She should be at home working on her English composition paper, or on the phone with one of her friends about last night's date, rather than in a motel room with a woman like me.

'You said you called another lawyer,' I said. 'Why not Paul Edwards?'

She said suddenly, 'I think my mom might marry Mr Edwards.'

'You don't like him?' I was groping around for what to say.

'We get along okay,' Mary Nell said. 'He's always been around. He and my dad were friends, and my mom always got his opinion on everything. Dell never liked Mr Edwards much, and they had a big argument before Dell died.'

'What was that about?' I asked, trying to sound casual.

'I don't know. Dell wouldn't tell me. He'd found out something, and he went to Mr Edwards to talk about it, but Dell didn't like whatever Mr Edwards said.'

'Something he'd found out about Paul?'

'I don't know if it was about Mr Edwards, or someone else. Dell just thought Mr Edwards would be able to help him out with it, give him an answer.'

'Oh.' None of the letters had been a P or an E, assuming the letters Sally had written referred to a person. Damn, why didn't people just write what they meant? To hell with shorthand.

'I thought you and Dell were so close,' I said, which was tactless and stupid. 'I'm surprised he didn't tell you what he was mad about.'

She gave me an outraged stare. 'Well, for brother and sister we were close.'

'What does that mean?'

'There's stuff brothers and sisters don't talk about,' she said, as if she'd been requested to explain snow to an Eskimo. 'I mean, there's stuff you and Tolliver don't talk about, right? Oh, I forgot. You're not *really* his sister. So you wouldn't know.'

Touché.

'Brothers and sisters don't talk about sex, I bet not even when they're grown up,' she instructed me. I remembered how shocked she'd been when she'd told me her brother had said Teenie was pregnant. 'Brothers and sisters don't talk about which of their friends are doing it, either. But other stuff, that's what they talk about.'

'Did you and Scot talk about him coming here to beat me up?' I asked.

She flinched. 'What are you talking about?'

So the Sarne grapevine hadn't gotten in gear yet, and she didn't know. 'Someone paid Scot to come here and hide in my room last night. He was supposed to beat me up. It was just like the other morning, except this time he was by himself. If Hollis Boxleitner hadn't been with me, I could be in the hospital by now.'

'I didn't know,' she said, and again I felt guilty. But there's no gentle way to tell someone a tale like that. And I couldn't minimize it any more than I had. 'What's happening to our town? We were okay until you came!'

That was a fine turnaround. 'Your mother invited me,' I reminded her. 'All I did was find Teenie's body, like I was supposed to.'

'It would have been better if you'd never found her,' Nell said childishly, as if I could have predicted this outcome.

'That was my job. She shouldn't have been lying out there in the woods, waiting to be found. I did my job, and it was the right thing to do.' I said this as calmly as I could.

'Then why is all this happening?' she asked, like I was supposed to supply her with an answer. 'What's going on?'

I shook my head. I had no idea. When I got one, one that would release my brother, I was never going to put foot in Sarne again.

Nell left to go to school, looking stunned and very young.

I stopped in the police station to give a statement about the incident of the night before and ask when I could see Tolliver. I was almost scared to ask the desk clerk, the round woman who'd been there the first time I'd come in the week before. I was scared that once they found out I wanted to see him, they'd find some way to keep me from him. And I didn't even know who 'they' were.

'Visiting hours are from two to three on Tuesday and Friday,' she said, looking away from me as if I were too loathsome for her eyes to behold.

Since it was Tuesday, I could see him that afternoon. The relief was enormous. But until two o'clock, I didn't have anything to do. I was sick to death of that motel room.

I went out to the cemetery, the newer one. I wanted to have another visit with the rest of the Teagues, the deceased side of the family. This time I was able to park very close to the Teague plot, and I was bundled up pretty heavily, because the temperature was dropping. This was Arkansas in early November, so snow wasn't too likely; but in the Ozarks, it also wasn't out of the question. I had a red scarf wrapped around my neck and wore my red gloves. I was wearing a puffy bright blue jacket. I like to be visible, especially in Arkansas in hunting season. It was the first time I'd wrapped up quite so much this fall, and I felt as padded as a child being sent out to play in the snow for the first time.

I looked around me at the people-empty landscape. Across the county road, to the west, was a stand of forest. There was a small group of houses, perhaps twenty, to the north; they had half-acre lawns and sundecks and gas grills outside their sliding glass doors. No visible cars; everyone worked to maintain that slice of suburbia. The cemetery stretched south over the swell of a steep hill, part of a line that also blocked the view to the east. This was a peaceful place.

It was easy to locate the Teague plot. There was a large monument on a plinth in the center, with TEAGUE carved on it twice, once to the north and once to the south.

I moved through the Teagues, slowly working my way from grave to grave. They were not a family that had long lives, as a whole. Dell's grandfather had lived only until he was fifty-two, when he'd had a massive heart attack. Two of Grandfather's sibs were there, dead in infancy. Dell's grandmother had come from hardier stock. She'd been seventy-two, and she'd died just two years ago – of pneumonia, basically. I gave Dell a hello; his gunshot death brought the average down sharply, of course. I did the subtraction on his father's tomb-stone and found that Dell's dad had only been forty-seven when Sybil found him facedown on his desk.

Of course, Dick Teague had been my goal all along. When I stepped onto his final resting place, I felt an edge of anticipation, like you feel before you bite into a gourmet dessert. Down through the rocky soil my special sense went, making contact with the body below me. I examined Dick Teague with the careful attention he deserved. But I found the barrier of shoes and dirt and coffin were muffling my response. I needed more contact. I sank down in front of the head-stone to lay my hands on the earth. Just as I did so, there was a cracking noise from the woods to the west of the cemetery, and something stung my face sharply enough to make me cry out.

I put my gloved hand to my cheek, and it came away with blood on it. My blood was a different red than the cheerful scarlet of the glove, and I looked at it with some bewilderment. I heard the same crack again, and suddenly I realized that someone was shooting at me.

I launched myself from squatting to prone in one galvanic motion. Thank God I wasn't in the Delta, where the land was so flat I wouldn't have been able to conceal myself from a fly. I crawled to take cover on the east side of the big monument in the middle of the plot. It wasn't as wide as me, but it was the best I could do.

For a miracle, I'd put my phone in my pocket, and I stripped off one glove and called 911. I could tell the person who answered was the woman I'd just talked to at the desk at the police station. 'I'm at the cemetery off 314, and someone's firing at me from the woods,' I said. 'Two shots.'

'Have you been hit?'

'Just by a piece of granite. But I'm scared to move.' I'd started crying from sheer terror, and it was an effort to keep my voice level.

'Okay, I'll have someone out there right away,' she said. 'Do you want to stay on the phone?' She turned away for a minute, and I heard her ordering a patrol car to my location. 'Probably just a hunter making a mistake,' she offered.

'Only if deer here are bright blue.'

'Have you heard any more shots?'

'No,' I said. 'But I'm behind the Teague monument.'

'Do you hear the car coming yet?'

'Yes, I hear the siren.' It wasn't the first time I'd been glad to hear a police siren in Sarne. I wiped my face with the clean glove. A police car pulled to a screeching halt behind my car, and Bledsoe, the deputy who'd arrested Tolliver, stepped out of it. He sauntered over to the spot where I crouched.

'You say someone's firing at you?' he asked. I could tell that for two cents he'd whip out his own gun and take a shot.

I got up slowly, fighting a tendency on the part of my legs to stay collapsed. I leaned against the granite monument, thinking a few deep breaths would have me back up to walking speed.

He looked at my face. His demeanor became a lot more business-like. 'Where'd you say these shots came from?'

I pointed to the woods across the road to the west, the closest cover to the cemetery. 'See, look at Dick Teague's tombstone,' I said, pointing to the jagged little white scar where a chunk had been blown off the edge.

Suddenly, Bledsoe was scanning the woods with narrow eyes. His hand went to his holster.

'What's the blood from?' he asked. 'Were you hit?'

'It was the chip from the stone,' I said, and I wasn't happy with how uneven my voice was. 'The bullet was that close. The chip hit me in the cheek.'

I spotted it on the ground, picked it up and handed it to him.

'Course, you coulda done it yourself,' he said, with no conviction.

'I don't care what you think,' I told him. 'I don't care what report you write up. As long as you showed up and stopped him shooting at me, I don't care.'

'You say "him" for a reason?' he asked.

'No reason at all.' My breathing was about normal by now. As I adjusted to the fact that no one was going to try to kill me in the next second or so, I reverted to my former opinion of the deputy.

'What were you doing out here, anyway?' He, too, was reverting to hostility.

'Just visiting.'

He looked disgusted. 'You're some piece of work, you know that?'

'I could say the same. Listen, I'm leaving while you're standing here, because I don't want to die in this town. Thanks for coming. At least . . .' I stopped before I finished with, 'At least the police here aren't totally corrupt.' I figured that would be less than tactful, especially since the deputy wasn't standing there pointing at me and yelling, 'You can go on and shoot her!'

He gave me a curt nod. As I was shutting my door, he said, 'You were standing on Dick Teague's grave?'

I nodded.

'You wanted to know what killed him?'

I nodded again.

'Well, what was it? According to you?'

'Heart attack, just like his dad.' I looked at the deputy, making sure my face was smooth and sincere.

'So, the doctor was right?'

'Yes.'

He nodded, rather smugly. I started my engine and turned the heater up. When I stopped at the turnoff from the cemetery onto the county road, I glanced in the rearview mirror. Deputy Bledsoe was right behind me. I realized at the same time that I needed to stop by the motel before I went to see Tolliver, unless I wanted to give him his own heart attack. My cheek was spotted with drying blood, and some had spattered on my coat, too.

I hated the motel by this time, but (since no attacker leaped out at me when I unlocked the door) I had to admit it felt safer than the streets. Sarne was beginning to represent one big danger zone to me. With the dead bolt and the chain employed on the door, I washed my face and put on some makeup, including bright lipstick. I didn't want to look like a ghost when I went to visit Tolliver. Possibly the little butterfly strips I put across the cut on my cheekbone detracted from the effect, but I had to use them. I put the blood-spotted jacket and glove in the bathtub to soak in cold water and I got out a black leather jacket.

On the drive to the jail, I caught myself checking my surroundings every few seconds. I tried not to feel ridiculous. No one was going to try to kill me in broad daylight in a busy town, I told myself. But then, I'd thought I'd seen the last of Scot, too; that he was a basically harmless teenage lunk whose punishment I could safely leave to his football coach. Ha.

I'd visited jails before. Being searched and having to let the jailer keep my purse was nothing new or extraordinary. It was far from pleasant, though. The sudden movements I'd made at the cemetery had reawakened the painful bruises from the night before. I was just a mass of misery, and I hated being so needy.

Seeing Tolliver enter the room in an orange jail jumpsuit made my brain flicker. When a jailer ushered him in, I had to cover my mouth with my hand. Two other prisoners entered the room with him (neither of them Scot), and they went to their visitors at their little separate tables. The rules at the Sarne jail were: Keep your hands on the table so they're visible at all times. Do not pass anything to the inmates unless you'd had it cleared with the jailers first. Do not speak loudly or rise suddenly from your chair until the prisoners have left the room.

Tolliver took my hands. We looked at each other. Finally, he said, 'You've been hurt.'

'Yes,' I said.

His face was rigid. 'Your face. Did one of them hit you?'

'No, no.' I hadn't prepared a story for him. It would be stupid to try to conceal what had happened to me since he'd been in jail. I couldn't think of a lie that would cover everything, not even for Tolliver's peace of mind. 'Someone shot at me from the woods,' I said flatly. 'I wasn't hurt, except for this scratch. I won't go back to the cemetery.'

'What's going on in this town?' Tolliver was having a hard time controlling his voice. 'What's wrong with these people?'

'Have you seen Scot?' I asked, trying to put a little perkiness in my voice.

'Scot the kid?'

'Yeah.'

'They brought someone in last night, someone I haven't seen yet. What's he in for?'

'He was in my motel room when Hollis brought me back last night, and he . . .'

The expression on Tolliver's face stopped me.

'You have to calm down,' I said, very quietly and intently, holding on to his hands as if they were lifelines and I was drowning. Or he was. 'You have to. You just have to. You can't get into trouble in here, or they'll keep you. Now you listen, I'm going to be okay. I've called the lawyers, and a lady, Phyllis Folliette, from Little Rock, is coming tomorrow for your arraignment. She's a friend of Art's, so she's good. You'll get out, and we'll be okay.' I adjusted my position in the hard chair, suppressing a wince.

'That Scot's a rat bastard,' Tolliver said. His voice was misleadingly calm.

'Yeah,' I said, and gave a little snort of laughter. 'Yeah, that's what he is, all right. But I think someone paid him to be more of a rat bastard than he actually is.'

I told Tolliver about the death of Dick Teague, the fact that Sally had been hired to clean the study, the fact that she'd seen something on Dick Teague's desk that had aroused her curiosity or her interest, so much so that she'd come home and consulted her textbook about what she'd noticed. 'SO MO DA NO' didn't mean anything to Tolliver, either.

'Maybe an anagram?' he asked.

'I haven't been able to make a word of it, if so,' I said. 'And those aren't anyone's initials. I tried writing it backwards. I tried assigning numbers. I tried moving the letters one forward in the alphabet, and one backward. I don't think Sally Boxleitner was up to a more complex code than that.'

Tolliver thought for a minute. Under my fingers, I felt his pulse, steady and vital.

'And what was on his desk?' Tolliver asked.

'Insurance forms.'

'Whose?'

'According to Sybil, he was reviewing the family's medical bills for the year.'

'And he really had a heart attack?'

'Yeah, that was what I was checking at the cemetery. He really did. It runs in his family; at least, Dick's father died the same way, real early – though not as early as Dick.'

'I can sure give it a lot of thought, since I don't have anything else to do,' Tolliver said, trying hard not to sound bitter.

I cleared my throat. 'I brought one of your books. They're searching it for hidden messages, I guess, and they'll pass it on to you when you go back to your cell.'

'Oh, thanks.' There was a pause while he struggled not to say anything, but he lost. 'You know, I ended up in here so I can't stop someone when they try to hurt you.'

'I know.'

'I feel as angry as I've ever felt in my life.'

'I got that.'

'But we have to know who wanted me in here so bad.'

'Surely . . . surely it must be Jay Hopkins?'

'What's your figuring on that?'

'Marv Bledsoe is a good buddy of Jay Hopkins. And Marv's a cousin of Paul Edwards. Or else it was Harvey the sheriff, himself, who told Marv to arrest you.'

'Of the three, I'd rather this be Jay's doing.'

I nodded. Jay was the weakest of the three.

'Time's up,' the jailer said, and the other two visitors stood. Tolliver and I looked at each other. I was making a huge effort not to look as anxious as I felt. I suspected Tolliver was doing the same.

'I'll see you tomorrow in the courtroom,' he said, when the jailer showed signs of impatience. I let go of his hands and pushed back the chair.

Five minutes later, I was standing out in the cold, bright day, wondering what I should do next. I couldn't stop myself from wondering if anyone was looking at me, and if that anyone had a rifle in his hands. I wondered if I would live long enough to get Tolliver out of jail. I despised myself for my fear, because at least I was free; my brother was not. He was probably not any safer in jail than I was walking around, especially if our enemy turned out to be the sheriff.

I could see from the traffic that school had let out for the day. So I wasn't surprised when my new best friend, Mary Nell Teague, pulled up in her little car. 'Come for a ride,' she called, and I climbed in the front seat. I was surprised she was by herself, and I was also surprised that she would want to approach me so publicly.

'Have you seen him?' she asked, backing out and driving away at what I could only think was a reckless speed.

'Yes.'

'They wouldn't let me, since I'm not family or a spouse.' She said this with sullen amazement, as if it was extraordinarily bull-headed of the jailers not to let a lovesick teenage girl visit a prisoner. I was getting so tired of this girl, with her burdensome crush and her sense of privilege. But I also felt a certain amount of pity for her, and I hoped she could still be useful in helping us figure out what was really happening in Sarne.

And she needed to start doing that now. 'Mary Nell, what do you know about Jay Hopkins?'

'He used to be Miss Helen's husband,' she said, 'you know that.'

'Did he have any contact with Dell?'

'What difference does that make? I don't think about trashy people like him.'

'This isn't going to be easy, but it's time for you to grow up a little.'

'Like I haven't, this past year?'

'You've had some tragedy this year, but as far as I can tell, it hasn't matured you any.'

She pulled to the side of the road, tears in her eyes. 'I can't believe you,' she said chokingly. 'You're so mean! Tolliver deserves a better sister than you.'

'I agree. But I'm what he's got, and I have to do everything I can for him. He's all I've got, too.' I noticed she still hadn't answered my question. But I figured that was a kind of answer in itself.

She wiped her face with a tissue and blew her nose. 'So why do you keep asking me about people?'

'Someone took a shot at me today. Someone paid your teenage admirer to beat me up, and someone let him into my room. I don't think he thought of that on his own, do you?'

She shook her head. 'When I talked to Scot yesterday, he was mad at me, and mad at you, but he was going to stay away from you. Mr Random, the football coach, he got onto Scot in front of the entire team and gave him twenty bleachers, and then Scot's dad grounded him from television or the telephone for a month.'

'So what could have happened in the meantime, to make him hide in my room like he did?' Running up the bleachers and back twenty times, and no TV or telephone. Glad to know terrorizing me came with a stiff penalty.

'Did you ever think it might have been your *lover-boy*, Hollis, who asked him?' Mary Nell had decided to counterattack.

'No, I never did. Why do you suggest that?' Mary Nell was trying to make me angry, and she was pretty close to succeeding, but I made myself hold on to my temper with a ferocious effort.

'Well, just maybe Hollis wanted the chance to save you from something bad, so he could look like a big hero? And maybe he shot at you, too, which I have only your word for – that it ever happened, I mean.'

'Why would he shoot at me?'

'To make you need him,' she said. 'To make you hold on to him. Now that your brother's out of the way, you need an ally, right? So maybe Hollis even got Tolliver arrested.'

I was impressed with Mary Nell. This was deep and indirect thinking from a seventeen-year-old. What she said made sense, sort of. I didn't want to believe her theory about Hollis, and I don't think I really did believe it, but I had to consider her idea for a second or two. It made as much sense as any of my theories, and maybe more than some of them. I remembered having sex with Hollis the night before, and I had a bleak, black moment of wondering if he might have betrayed me from the start. Then I realized, more rationally, that Mary Nell was striking back at me for many reasons, most of all for having a closer relationship with my brother than she would ever have.

Silly girl. But looking at her, as she mopped at her face and then brushed her hair, I realized that she was only seven years younger than I. Mary Nell's life had been no picnic, of course, but probably it had been better than mine. By the time I was Mary Nell's age, even aside from the lightning strike, my life had changed forever. I had watched adults I knew and loved, as they threw their futures away. Then I had lost my sister Cameron; literally, lost her.

'Don't look at me like that,' Mary Nell said, her voice quavering. 'Do you even know where you are? God, stop it!'

I blinked. I hadn't realized I'd been staring.

'Sorry,' I said automatically. 'Your mother says you had a tonsil-lectomy this past year?'

'You are so weird. So fucking weird,' she said, daring to say the bad word in front of me, daring me to admonish her.

I didn't give her any reaction. 'Answer me,' I said, after a pause.

'Yes, I did,' she said, sullenly.

'You were in the hospital here?'

'In the next town, Mount Parnassus. Our little hospital closed two years ago.'

'Dell was in the same hospital when he had to have stitches?' I was dredging up Sybil's conversation from when we'd seen her house. It was hard going. I wasn't sure what I was probing for; maybe I'd know it when I heard it. 'He had a broken leg, or was that someone else?'

'That was the boy who was driving the car. Dell had stitches in his head. At first the emergency doctor thought he might have other problems, and he was unconscious for a little while, but they just kept him overnight.'

'And your dad was in the hospital, too.' I was trying to make something out of nothing.

'Yes, he had pneumonia.' Mary Nell's face grew sad. 'He had a bad heart, and the pneumonia just weakened him. I told him he'd get better, but the day before he died, he said, "Nelly, I'm just not the man I was before I caught that bug."'

'He called you Nelly?'

'Yeah, or Nell. He liked me and my brother being Nell and Dell.' The teenager's little face collapsed as I watched her. 'I don't have a brother or a father. Probably nobody'll call me that again in my whole life.'

'Sure someone will,' I said, trying to figure out what had rung a bell in my head. 'You're a pretty girl, Mary Nell, and you have a lot of spirit. Someone will come along who'll call you anything you want him to.'

She brightened, happy to hear this even from someone she thought she despised. What she actually felt toward me was probably some-thing closer to envy.

'You think so?'

'Yes, I think so.'

'Harper,' she said, and I realized she'd never spoken my name before, 'what's going to happen to Tolliver?'

'Like I said, I called our lawyer. He gave me the name of an Arkansas attorney. She'll be here tomorrow. She's coming from Little Rock. She's going to appear at Tolliver's arraignment. I know she'll get him out.'

'You fixed that up yourself?'

I nodded. 'Sure.'

'I couldn't do that,' she said, subdued. 'I wouldn't know how to begin.'

I didn't want to sound like Ozark Granny Wisewoman, but I said, 'You'll know when you need to.'

'I liked Miss Helen,' Mary Nell said, surprising me yet again.

'You told me that before,' I said mildly. 'I did, too. How well did you know her?'

'Well, she worked for us for a while. That's how Dell got to know Teenie. I mean, he knew who she was from school, because we all know each other, right? But he probably never would have spent time with her if Miss Helen hadn't worked at our house. That's how he got to know what she was really like. Then Miss Helen got to drinking so much she didn't get to work on time, and Mom had to let her go, and hired Mrs Happ to help. But Dell and Teenie were sneaking off to see each other by then.'

I'd heard pretty much the same thing from Hollis.

'Then Mr Jay, Jay Hopkins, he beat Miss Helen up, and I heard my mom and Uncle Paul arguing about whether we should get Miss Helen back to work in the house. Uncle Paul said Miss Helen was sober and deserved a second chance, and Mom said after what she knew now, she wouldn't have Helen back in the house for love nor money. Especially love, she said.'

'What do you think she meant by that?' I asked. With Mary Nell around, you wouldn't need a tape recorder.

'I have no idea,' the girl answered. 'I never did understand. I think my mom thought Miss Helen took something from her. But they wouldn't tell me.' Familiar bitterness tinged her voice: the teenager vs. the adult world.

'Mary Nell, could you drop me back by my car?'

She sounded a little hurt when she told me she could.

I'd been too abrupt; but I had to think, and I knew Mary Nell would keep on talking as long as I was available to be her audience.

Once I was by myself, I felt both visible and vulnerable. I drove to my motel by the most direct route and shut myself in the damn room with the damn green bedspread. I had no messages. I couldn't decide if that was a good thing or a bad thing. My leg was tingling, as it sometimes did, and I peeled off my jeans and rubbed the skin, with its fine tracery of purple spiderwebs. Cameron had called me Spider-woman for a while, before we'd figured out that the branching lines weren't going away. My stepfather had been fond of ordering me to show the leg to his friends.

Hollis never mentioned it. Maybe he didn't understand it was lightning-related. Maybe he thought it was a birthmark of some kind and didn't want to hurt my feelings.

I lay down on the bed. SO MO DA NO, I thought. It might almost be the chorus to a Caribbean song. Okay. Reverse it. ON AD OM OS. NO DA MO SO. Dams, moon, soon, mad, mono, moans, nomad. Damon, doom, moods. Amos. Samoa? Nope, only one A. Why one A? Every other phrase ended with O.

Okay, what if the second letter was some . . . condition? What if the first letters stood for names? S could be for Sybil, D for Dell, N for . . . oh, Mary Nell had said her dad had called her Nelly. That could be N. But then, who was M? No one's name started with M, that I could recall. D could be for Dick Teague, if not Dell.

For the first time, I wished that I could ask questions of the dead. I could only take what they gave me. They gave me a picture of their deaths. They gave me what they'd been feeling at the moment. But they never told me why, or who, just how.

A bullet in my back . . . an infection in my lungs . . . my heart stuttered and quit pumping . . . I was just too old and worn out . . . the car hit so hard . . . the fall was from too high . . . I picked up the razor blade . . . I couldn't breathe, couldn't breathe, my inhaler was too far away . . . the meat lodged in my throat . . . the virus traveled through me and laid waste to my body . . . the knife traveled through my liver, then my stomach, then . . .

The dead all had stories, but they never explained or condemned. I'd heard, on odd little message boards that I visited, that some others like me – people who'd been French-kissed by electricity – could see the dead, could even communicate with them. No one else had confessed to having my truncated sort of relationship with those in their graves. There were lightning-struck people who could see the future, who now walked with a limp, who were blind in one eye. One woman had said no one in her family would help her right after she'd been hit because they were convinced she was charged with electricity. On a more private board, a board with far fewer members, a man in Colorado Springs posted that he was accompanied everywhere he went by his dead brother, who'd been killed by the same lightning bolt. No one else could see the brother, of course; his family had even had him committed for a time.

I stayed in my room all night. I ordered a delivery pizza. Hollis called to tell me he was working that night, all night, and to remind me to call him if I needed anything. I got one heavy-breathing anonymous call, a call I figured came from one of the teenage boys who'd confronted me. Paul Edwards called to tell me he was sorry about my brother's 'situation,' and he offered to help me in any way he could.

Since it was his cousin who had arrested my brother, I was pretty sure there would be a conflict of interest there, but I thanked him politely. He hinted that he wanted to come over and hang around with me. I turned him down, much less tactfully.

He was handsome, and he was a lawyer, and I could probably use a handsome lawyer friend, but Paul Edwards didn't offer to come hang around with a woman for no reason at all. He wanted something, and maybe it wasn't sex. He didn't seem to be a constant lover. The relationship between the lawyer and Sybil Teague wasn't clandestine, yet here he was with his ulterior motives.

I got a few hours' sleep that night, which was more than I expected. I drank coffee in the room. It wasn't good, but I didn't have to face anyone to drink it. I couldn't have eaten anything, so a restaurant was a waste of time.

I'd arranged to meet Phyllis Folliette at the courthouse. I didn't know what the lawyer would look like, but she proved to be very easy to pick out. The second I saw her I knew she wasn't from Sarne. Phyllis Folliette was a tall woman in a dark green suit and bronze silk blouse, with beautiful cordovan leather pumps that matched her bag and her briefcase . . . even her hair. Somewhere in her forties, Folliette exuded confidence and intelligence. That was what we needed.

I felt almost embarrassed to approach someone who was so

obviously a star. I think few women would feel very well groomed or attractive when they looked at this woman, and I was no exception. I was all too aware of my messy hair and my wrinkled pantsuit. I'd made the effort to pull 'meet the client' clothes out of my suitcase, but I'd lacked the energy to iron them. With Phyllis Folliette so ably making a great impression, I regretted not having stuck with jeans.

'I'm glad to meet you,' she said. 'You've impressed Art Barfield, and that's saying something.' She shook my hand and began to tell me what she'd learned in talking to the law enforcement people in Sarne. 'I've been over to the jail,' she said. 'Something is up. For one thing, if they were taking the story about Montana warrants seriously, Mr Lang would be appearing before a different court. I don't know how much you know about the legal system in Arkansas.' She raised her eyebrows.

'Assume I'm ignorant,' I said, which was pretty much the truth.

'They would never have arrested him for a broken taillight unless he did something else, like shove a cop or try to evade arrest, something like that. What gave the patrolman the juice to arrest Tolliver was the allegation that he had open warrants in Montana.' That's what Art had said, too. 'Now, if they were sticking by that story, your brother would be appearing in circuit court. But he's not. He's going to appear in the Sarne District Court, which only handles misdemeanors. You'll see when we get in there. We'll have to wait our turn, so you'll listen to lots of other charges against other people.' Her brown eyes summed me up while she spoke.

'Harper, honey, you're very wired up,' she said after a moment or two. 'You need to try to relax.'

'You don't know how bogus this is!' I whispered. I was trying hard to keep my voice down, because we were in a public hallway and the people who went by were eyeing us curiously, but I was so anxious I thought my frayed nerves would snap. 'Are you telling me that the Montana thing is just going to go away?'

She glanced down at her watch. 'I think it just might. We have a while before they bring him in. Let's find a quiet place. I think you need to tell me the whole story.'

I didn't think it would be possible to tell Phyllis Folliette everything that had happened in Sarne, but I did manage to arrange enough of it in a coherent narrative to bring it to a conclusion with Tolliver's arrest.

'It's definite that some force in this town is against you,' she said, after a silence. 'It's evident you're being hounded. No matter what I think of the way you make your living, Miss Connelly, what's being done to you is wrong. And your brother is apparently being held to reinforce the message that you're unwelcome here. I'll do my best to get him out. He was actually arrested in Montana last year, right?'

'Well, yes. This guy threw a rock at me. Tolliver got upset. Of course.'

'Of course,' she said, as if she routinely spoke to clients who'd been literally stoned. 'Tolliver was upset enough to put the man in the hospital?'

'Hey, those charges were dismissed.'

'Um-hm. I think you had some luck with the judge on that one.'

'You have a sister?'

'Uh . . . yes.'

'Someone throws a rock at her, you'd go after the rock-thrower, right?'

'I think I'd probably be taking care of my sister. I'd let the cops arrest the rock-thrower.'

'Look at it from the guy point of view.'

'Okay, I see your drift.'

'You talked to Tolliver about this, right?'

'Yes, they let me see him this morning. He mentioned the incident, but didn't give any details.'

I smiled. 'That's Tolliver.'

'You two are close,' she observed. 'Why the different names? You've been married?'

'No,' I said. 'His father married my mother when we were both in our teens.' I didn't like explaining this.

She nodded, giving me a sideways look. She excused herself to go to the ladies' room, and I stared at my feet for a while. When Phyllis emerged, she did a lot of meeting and greeting on her way back to our bench, in particular with a man with graying hair, probably in his early fifties, who was wearing glasses and a nice suit.

After he went into the courtroom, Phyllis Folliette made her way back to me, giving me a brisk nod. 'Time to go in or we won't get a seat,' she said, and we joined a stream of people passing through massive double doors to the courtroom.

The ceiling was somewhere in the clouds over our heads. There was no telling how many words were buzzing around under that high ceiling, trapped there over the years. Phyllis and I sat quietly, and people began filing in. The jailers brought a line of prisoners in, and I got to see Tolliver.

I stood up, so he could see me right away, and he gave me a serious look. I sat down in the folding wooden seat. 'He looks all right,' I said to the lawyer, trying to reassure myself. 'Don't you think he looks all right?'

'He does,' she agreed. 'I don't think orange is his color, though.'

'No,' I said. 'No, it isn't.'

As all the people in the courtroom seemed to be sorting themselves out, Phyllis said, 'While we have a minute, I'm just curious. Are you any relation to the Cameron Connelly who was abducted in Texas a few years ago? I'm only asking because when Art Barfield called me, he said you had grown up in Texas and you and the girl who vanished both have what could be last names for your first name. If that makes sense.'

'Yes, it makes sense,' I said, though I can't say I was totally focused on the conversation. 'I was named for my father's mother's family, Cameron for my mother's mother's family. She was my sister.'

'I notice you use the past tense. Was she ever found? Once the media stopped covering it . . .'

'No. But someday I'll find her body.'

'Ah . . . okay.'

After a beat, I noticed the peculiar tone to the lawyer's voice. 'You know,' I said more directly, 'that when people are gone that long, they're dead.'

'There was that girl in Utah, Elizabeth Smart.'

'Yes. There was that girl in Utah. She turned up alive. But mostly, when people have been gone for more than a couple of days, and no ransom's been asked, they're dead. Or they wanted to go. I know Cameron didn't want to leave. So she's dead.'

'You hold no hope?' She sounded incredulous.

'I hold no false hope.' I knew my business.

The bailiff told us the judge was coming in, and we rose. A spare gray-haired man (in a suit, instead of a robe) took his seat before us. I wasn't surprised to recognize the man with whom Phyllis had been chatting earlier. The city attorney (at least I guessed that was what he was) was already in his seat facing the judge, a huge pile of files in front of him, and the proceedings began.

I'd been in court before, for this or that, so it no longer surprised me that it wasn't like *Perry Mason* reruns or the more recent *Judge Judy*. People wandered in and out. Prisoners were removed and brought in. Between cases, there was a low buzz of conversation. There was no reverential air, and there were very few dramatics. Justice was conducted as business-as-usual.

When their name was called, people went up to the podium in front of the judge's bench. The judge read out the offense, asked if the plaintiff had anything to state, then (after discussion) told the plaintiff what his fine was.

'Isn't this more like traffic court, or something? This doesn't seem serious enough,' I whispered to Phyllis. She'd been listening to the judge carefully, getting his measure.

'Those warrants were bullshit,' she said, just as quietly. 'He's just going up for the taillight. This is unbelievable.'

It took an hour for the judge to work down the list to Tolliver. Tolliver looked tired. Every now and then he'd look toward me, and he tried to smile, but I could tell it was an effort.

Finally, the clerk called, 'Tolliver Lang.'

Tolliver wasn't handcuffed or shackled, thank God. He went up to the podium, with one of the jail guards accompanying him.

'Mr Lang, I see here that you were initially charged with outstanding warrants from Montana, and that you had a problem with a rear taillight.' The judge didn't seem to expect Tolliver to answer. The judge had a frown on his narrow face. 'But the officer who gave you the ticket for the taillight – Officer Bledsoe? Is he here?'

'No, your honor,' answered the clerk. 'He's on patrol today.'

'Amazing. He says now he made a mistake about the warrants?'

'Yes, your honor,' said the city attorney. 'He apologizes for the mistake.'

'This is a very serious error,' said the judge. He frowned at the papers some more. 'And very strange. What about the taillight?'

'He stands by the taillight, your honor,' said the attorney, with a straight face.

'How long was this man in jail?'

'Two nights.'

'In jail two nights for a broken taillight.'

'Uh, yes, sir.'

'You didn't resist arrest?' For the first time, the judge addressed Tolliver directly. I could see Tolliver's back straighten.

'No, sir,' Tolliver said.

'Have you ever been arrested in Montana?'

'Yes, sir, but the charges were dismissed.'

'That's a matter of public record.'

'Yes, sir. And it was over a year ago.'

'Mr Lang, do you want to bring charges against Officer Bledsoe?'

'No, sir. I just want out of the jail.'

'And I can understand that. You'll be released, no bail, just pay the fine for the taillight. You don't contest that, I guess?'

Tolliver was silent. I was sure he was debating about telling the judge that Bledsoe had broken it with his nightstick.

'No, your honor.'

'Okay, broken taillight, one hundred fifty dollar fine,' the judge said, and that was that. The jailer led Tolliver back through the side door where he'd entered, I assumed to return him to the jail and start the release paperwork. 'Someone here to pay the fine?'

I held up my hand.

The judge barely glanced at me. 'Through the door behind the clerk,' he said, inclining his head in the right direction. On shaky legs, I made my way to the back of the court and through the door, where I was faced by a phlegmatic woman in khakis and a T-shirt, and an armed Hollis in full uniform. The woman was sitting behind a small table holding a cash box. I guess she needed Hollis to guard the money and make sure someone angry about paying a fine didn't decide to take it out on her.

'It all came out all right, then?' Hollis asked, looking genuinely relieved.

'Yes,' I said, handing over the papers the clerk had given me, along with one hundred fifty dollars in cash. She filed the money and stamped 'PAID' on the papers, handing them right back to me. I wanted to say something else to Hollis, but I couldn't figure out what, and there was someone right behind me waiting to make her own payment. So I smiled at him, happy for the first time in days, and went back through the courtroom, which looked just as full as it had when the morning began. The lawyer was waiting for me outside in the cavernous hall.

'Thanks, Phyllis,' I said, and I pumped her hand.

Phyllis smiled at me. 'All I did was show up and let the court know I was here,' she said. 'If you were to ask me what happened, it sounds like someone told Bledsoe to back off, not to make an issue of what he'd done.'

'Maybe he did it on impulse, thinking he'd please someone, and then found out he hadn't.'

Maybe it was his cousin Paul. Maybe it was his boss, the sheriff. Maybe it was the lady who owned half the town, Sybil. Maybe . . .

'Let's go over to the jail,' Phyllis said. 'I saw the van leave. I'll wait with you until they process him out, just to make sure.'

We went into the jail again, and I asked the woman behind the counter where to wait. She pointed at the chairs in the same reception area where I'd waited so nervously to see Tolliver the day before.

It took a long time to process out a prisoner, and Phyllis Folliette stayed with me faithfully. Of course, I knew she was billing me for her time, but most lawyers would have given me a pat on the back and sped on their way to their office. She pulled something out of her briefcase to study when I showed I'd rather be silent. I sat with my eyes closed, letting the world go by, and I thought about all the people I'd met in Sarne, how closely they all seemed connected, how the repugnant stereotype of uneducated, inbred, unsophisticated-but-surprisingly wise hillbilly was both mined for tourist money and denigrated by the people who lived here. What had begun as a way of life determined by geographic isolation and poverty had become simplified and mythologized and made fun of for the world's consumption. And all of the people we'd been dealing with had been living in this town for several generations, except Hollis.

I let the incidents of the past week flow through my mind, not trying to sort them out. I thought it might help to make a list. That would be our program for tonight, maybe.

Then I heard footsteps I knew, and I opened my eyes. Tolliver was coming toward me, and I jumped up. We hugged, hard and fast, before I introduced him to Phyllis, who was looking at him with some curiosity. Tolliver thanked her, and she again protested that she hadn't done anything at all other than show up.

'But you called the sheriff yesterday,' Tolliver said. I was eyeing him anxiously, but he only looked tired and in need of a shower.

'Yes, I did that,' she said, smiling slightly. 'I figured it couldn't hurt for the sheriff's department to know that someone from out of town was keeping an eye on the situation, someone with a little legal clout. Don't worry, you'll be billed for it.'

'It was worth the money,' I said, and after shaking our hands, Phyllis got back into her BMW and left Sarne. Lucky Phyllis.

While we drove to the motel, I explained to Tolliver about his room, and he said, 'I don't care. I'm going to have a shower and some decent food, and then I think I'll sleep for a few hours. Then I'll get up and shower again and eat more decent food and sleep again.'

'And this, after being in jail all of thirty-six hours! What if you'd had to stay in all week?'

He made a big production of shuddering. 'You wouldn't believe how bad that jail is. I think they're trying to feed the prisoners on a dime a day, or something.'

'You've been in jail before,' I said, a little puzzled by his violent reaction.

'I wasn't worried about you getting hurt then, and I wasn't worried the whole town was in on some kind of conspiracy.'

'You feel that?'

'I would have felt better if the most prominent lawyer in town and the sheriff hadn't been big buddies, and both involved in the deal that brought us up here. I couldn't sleep in the jail; the guy in the cell with me was brought in extremely drunk, and he snored and stank. I lay awake so long I convinced myself that something would happen to me in there, and they'd say I'd slipped on a bar of soap and banged my head, or accidentally tripped with my head in a noose. And then they'd get you.'

'Phyllis says we don't have to stay in Sarne.'

'Then we're leaving in the morning.'

'That's fine with me.'

Tolliver rummaged around in his suitcase for clean clothes and stalked off to the bathroom. I went out to get him some food. I even went through the drive-through so I wouldn't have to get out of the car. My paranoia was running high; although I had to admit that I had gotten nothing but good treatment from the people of Sarne I'd run into in impersonal capacities. The drive-through girl was polite and cheerful, the woman who took my money at the gas station was civil, and the judge had been businesslike and brisk. No question but that I was getting a skewed picture of Sarne and its people.

So be it, I thought. *We're outta here.*

I ate the food I'd gotten for myself with a better appetite than I'd had in days. Then I lay down and snoozed. I distantly heard the water shut off and then Tolliver eating. The paper bags made rustling noises, no matter how quiet he tried to be. Just as I was really drifting away to sleep, I heard the creak of bedsprings as he lay down on the other bed. Then there was peaceful silence, underlined by the drone of the heating unit.

I didn't nap as long as my brother, because I'd had some sleep the night before. I parted the curtains to peer outside and looked at the sky, gray with impending rain. It was about four in the afternoon, but it would be full dark within an hour. I brushed my teeth and hair and put my shoes on, and then I sat at the little table with a sheet of motel paper and a pencil. I like to make lists, but there's seldom any need for me to do so; I don't go to the grocery store much, and most of our errands are undertaken on the road.

I decided to list all the facts I could recall and see what shook out.

1. Sybil and the sheriff were brother and sister.
2. Sybil and Paul Edwards were lovers.
3. Sybil's son had been murdered.
4. Sybil's son's girlfriend had been murdered at the same time.
5. The girlfriend, Teenie Hopkins, was sister to the murdered wife of Deputy Hollis Boxleitner.
6. Sally (murdered wife) had been killed after she cleaned the study of . . .
7. Sybil's husband, victim of an untimely heart attack, while he was examining . . .
8. Medical records of his son (at that time alive) and daughter and himself.
9. Also murdered – Helen Hopkins, mother of Teenie Hopkins and Hollis Boxleitner's wife.
10. Helen had been the cleaning woman for Sybil's family for years, until she began drinking heavily and had an episode of violence with her ex-husband, Jay Hopkins.
11. Her attorney in the case against her ex-husband, and her attorney in the much earlier divorce, was Paul Edwards, also Sybil's attorney and lover.
12. Terry Vale recommended my services to Sybil.

13. Hollis had wanted to know for sure what had happened to his wife.
14. Paul Edwards had been glad to pay us.
15. Someone inflamed teenager Scot to the point where he accepted money (or maybe just followed the suggestion) that he lie in wait for me and beat me up.
16. That same someone, or possibly someone different, took a shot at me in the Sarne cemetery.
17. My brother went to jail on trumped-up charges; possibly to leave a shooter free to make a try at me, possibly just to shake us up enough that we would leave no matter what the sheriff had told us.

Tolliver stretched and yawned and came to look over my shoulder.

'Whats this for?' he asked.

'We've got to understand what's happening. That's the only way we can get out of here.'

'We're leaving in the morning. I don't care if they put a roadblock across the highway, we're getting out of this town.'

14

I had to smile, even while I shook two Tylenol out of the bottle and swallowed them down.

He went to the windows to look outside. 'Ah-oh,' he said. 'It's coming up a storm.'

'*That's* why my head's beginning to hurt.'

'Maybe, too, you're hungry?' he asked mildly.

'I ate a few hours ago.'

'It has been a while.'

'You ate half a sandwich. Let's drive to Mount Parnassus. We don't want to get into any more trouble.'

'Sounds good. But you know, we could just pack up our stuff and start driving now,' I said.

'Not with a storm coming on.'

It was because of me we couldn't drive during storms, because sometimes I had a very bad reaction; another weakness on my part.

'We'll go to Mount Parnassus,' he said. 'It's just twelve miles north.'

It was dark already, at least in part because of the oncoming storm. Tolliver was driving because of my headache, so I answered the cell phone when it rang. It was Tolliver's older brother, Mark.

'Hi,' I said. 'How are you?'

'Well, I been better,' he said. 'Tolliver there?'

I silently handed Tolliver the phone. He disliked driving and talking at the same time, so he pulled over to the side of the road. Mark Lang had been nearly old enough to leave home by the time my mother and his father started living together and eventually got married. He hadn't liked my mother, hadn't liked the situation in his home, and had gotten out as soon as possible. For Tolliver's sake, he'd checked in at the house about every two weeks. He'd also helped to feed and clothe us, and he'd gotten us medical help when we'd needed it and the adults had been too strung out to provide it. And Mark had been especially fond of Cameron, as Tolliver had been of me. The little girls just represented two more sets of needs and wants, to Mark. I could imagine how unhappy he was at being called about Mariella's disappearance, and I was sure that was his reason for calling Tolliver now.

'He found her,' Tolliver told me now, leaning away from the phone briefly. 'Took him an hour.'

That wasn't bad. I had a few questions, of course, but I decided to let the conversation run itself to a halt before I asked them.

Tolliver hung up soon enough. 'They were hiding in Craig's Sunday school building,' he said briefly.

'What – where is she now?'

'She went home. Craig had run out of food, anyway, so there wasn't any more fun in it for her.'

We fell silent. There wasn't any more to say about Mariella. Mariella had seen too much as a kid to ever be innocent, and she'd probably go down the same path as our mother as fast as could be, despite all the Sunday school lessons and hours in Iona's church, despite the moral teachings and the days of school. So their lives wouldn't be all work and no play, Tolliver and I had sent funds for extras for Mariella and Gracie: dance lessons, voice lessons, art lessons. All this was a familiar litany in my head, as I tried again to figure out what else we could have done. The court would never have left the girls' upbringing to Tolliver and me.

My head pounded harder, and I looked at the sky ahead of us anxiously. I knew soon I would see a flicker of lightning.

We turned on the radio to listen to the weather. Storms were predicted, with heavy downpour and thunder and lightning. What a surprise. Flash flood warnings – which you had to take seriously in a terrain that included roads that dipped so deeply before rising again – in an area where all the streams and ponds were already full from plentiful rainfall earlier in the season.

We reached a little chain restaurant within ten minutes and went in, taking our raincoats with us. Inside, there was an older couple sitting close to the kitchen door; there was a single guy reading a newspaper, a dirty plate shoved across the table. A young couple, in their early twenties, sat with their two children in a booth by the big window. They were pale and fat, both wearing sweats from Wal-Mart. He wore a gimme cap with his. Her hair was pulled back into a curly ponytail, and her eyelids were blue with makeup. The little boy, maybe six, was wearing camo and carrying a plastic gun. The little girl was a pretty thing, with lots of light brown hair like her mothers, and a sweet and vacant face. She was coloring.

A waitress in jeans and a blouse strolled over to take our order. Her hair was dressed in a formidable bleached bubble, and she was chewing gum. She told us she was pleased to help us, but I doubted her sincerity. After we'd looked at the menus for a minute, she took our orders and strolled over to the window to the kitchen to turn them in.

After she'd gotten our iced tea, she vanished.

The couple started arguing about whether or not to enter their daughter in the next beauty pageant. It cost quite a bit to enter a child in a pageant, I learned, and to rent a dress and take time off from work to do the girl's hair and makeup cost even more.

I raised my eyebrows at Tolliver, who suppressed a smile. My mother had tried to get Cameron to do the pageant circuit. At the very first one, Cameron had told the judges she thought the pageant system was very close to white slavery. She had accused the judges of many unpleasant perversions. Needless to say, that had ended Cameron's career as a beauty contestant. Of course, Cameron was fourteen at the time. The little girl across the room was maybe eight and didn't look like she'd say boo to a goose.

Our cell rang again, and this time Tolliver answered it.

'Hello?' He paused and listened for a moment. 'Hey, Sascha. What's the word?' Ah. The hair samples. The DNA test.

He listened for a few moments, then turned to me.

'No match,' he said. 'The male is not the father. Female One is the mother of Female Two.' That was the way I'd marked the samples.

'Thanks, Sascha. I owe you,' he said.

He'd no sooner put down the phone than the phone rang again. We looked at each other, exasperated and I answered it.

'Harper Connelly,' said a strained voice.

'Yes. Who is this?' I asked.

'Sybil.'

I never would have known this was my former client. Her voice was so tense, her enunciation so jerky.

'What's wrong, Sybil?' I tried to keep my voice level.

'You need to come here, tonight.'

'Why?'

'I need to see you.'

'Why?'

'There's something I need to tell you.'

'You don't need to talk to us,' I said. 'We've finished our transaction.' I struggled to keep myself calm and firm. 'I did what you paid me to do, and Tolliver and I are going to get out of town as soon as we can.'

'No, I want to see you tonight.'

'Then you'll just have to want.'

There was a desperate pause. 'It's about Mary Nell,' Sybil said, abruptly. 'It's about her obsession with your brother. I need to talk to both of you, and if you're leaving town tomorrow, it's got to be tonight. Mary Nell's talking about killing herself.'

I held the phone away to stare at it for a minute. This sounded wildly unlikely. In my limited experience of Mary Nell Teague, she'd be more apt to be thinking of taking Tolliver hostage and bombarding him with love until he yielded to her. 'Okay, Sybil,' I said warily. 'We'll be there in about an hour.'

'Sooner, if you can,' she said, sounding almost breathless with relief.

The waitress brought our food as I was relaying the conversation to Tolliver, who'd been able to hear most of it, anyway.

He made a face.

I wrote SO MO DA NO on an extra napkin with a tine of my fork. I looked at it while I picked at my salad, which was about what you'd expect at a diner in the middle of nowhere. I tried to think myself into the scenario. Okay, Dick's been making notes to himself while he goes through the family's medical records for the year, getting ready for tax time. Four separate notations. Four members of the family.

S could be Sybil, M could be Mary Nell, D could be Dell, then N could be . . . who? I'd already gone over the fact that Dick Teague had called his daughter Nelly. But if that took care of the N, what about the M? I stared down at the napkin, thinking about making little notes about myself and my family . . .

Oh, for God's sake! The M was for Me!

I put the fork down.

'Harper?' Tolliver said.

'Blood types,' I said. 'Stupid, stupid, stupid me.'

'Harper?'

'It's *blood types*, Tolliver. Dick Teague was saying, "I have type O, Sybil has type O, Mary Nell has type O, but Dell has type A." That was what Sally Boxleitner was looking up in her high school science textbook. She suspected right away when she found the note Dick left on the medical records right before his heart attack. Dick had discovered he could not have been Dell's dad. Two O's can't have an A.'

'I can see where that might trigger a heart attack,' Tolliver said slowly. He put down his own fork, patted his lips with his napkin. 'But why would that lead to Dell and Teenie getting shot?'

'I'm thinking,' I said.

The family of four had cleared out while we were eating, with the topic of the beauty pageant still unresolved. I would put money on the mother winning. The older couple ate in a leisurely way, and just as slowly paid and took their leave, exchanging pleasantries with the waitress. The single man was still reading the paper, and every now and then the waitress would top off his coffee cup. Tolliver paid our bill while I stared into space, trying to imagine what had happened next in the Teague family drama.

Okay, next Hollis's wife had been killed. Sally had figured out that Dell wasn't Dick's son. Who would she tell? She would be more likely to tell a woman.

I thought she would tell her mother. But there must be something else . . .

We were in the car going back toward Sarne when I told Tolliver what I was thinking. 'Why wouldn't she tell Hollis?' he asked. 'It would be natural to tell your husband.'

'Hollis told me she didn't like to talk about her family troubles,' I said. 'I think to Sally, Dell's parentage would fall into that category. So, Sally told her mother. Her mother, rather than Teenie, because Sally was closer to her mother. Besides, the secret was about Dell, and Teenie would've told him.'

'So what happened next?' Tolliver asked, as though I would surely know.

I did try to puzzle it out. 'Helen,' I muttered. 'What would Helen do? Why would she care whose kid Dell was?'

Why, indeed?

Say Teenie and Dell don't know anything about this. And then Sally dies. Sally dies because . . . she told. Because she told her mother. But I remembered Helen's overwhelming grief, and I didn't think Helen had known why Sally died. Until I came along and told Hollis and Helen differently, they'd thought her death was an accident. As far as I knew, Helen had never questioned that. And she'd believed Dell shot Teenie. Why? Over Teenie's pregnancy, of course! And then, unable to face what he'd done, Helen believed that Dell had shot himself.

Only then, to clear his name, Sybil had hired me, and I'd told Helen that Dell hadn't shot Teenie. I'd told Helen that both her daughters had been murdered by someone else.

I didn't exactly feel like all these deaths were my fault, but I didn't feel good about them, either. I'd done what I'd been hired to do, with no idea what the consequences might be in a confused place like Sarne. I believed after she found out they'd been killed, Helen must have realized who would have wanted both her daughters to die. I believed she would have arranged to confront that person to verify her suspicions, and during that confrontation that person had killed her, watched by all those pictures of two dead girls, in the little box-like house.

'I don't believe Sybil,' I said abruptly.

Tolliver looked over at me briefly before turning his attention back to the rain-slick road. There was a distant rumble. I shivered.

'Why?'

'I don't believe Mary Nell would ever threaten to kill herself,' I said. 'I don't believe she would resort to tactics like this to win your interest. I think she's too proud.'

'She's sixteen.'

'Yeah, but she's got her backbone in straight.'

'So, why are we going?'

'Because Sybil wants us there badly enough to lie about it, and I want to know why.'

'I don't know, maybe we should just go back to the motel. It's thundering, and you know there may be lightning.'

'I got that.' As a matter of fact, the Tylenol hadn't prevented the ferocious headache building behind my eyes. 'But I think we should go to Sybil's.' Something was pushing me, and I had a bad feeling it wasn't something smart.

I spotted a flash of lightning out of the corner of my eye and tried not to flinch. I was safe, in a car, and when I got out, I'd be very careful not to step into a downed electrical wire or hold a golf club or stand under a tree or do any of the myriad things people did that increased their chances of being electrocuted by lightning, either directly or indirectly. But I couldn't help ducking and hiding my face.

'You can't do this,' Tolliver said. 'We need to get inside.'

'Go to the Teagues' house,' I yelled. I was terrified, but I was driven.

He didn't say anything else, but turned in the right direction. I was ashamed of myself for yelling at my brother, but I was also strangely light-headed and focused on what lay ahead. A little part of my brain was still gnawing at the problem: Why would Dell and Teenie have to die, if Dell wasn't Dick Teague's son? What secret was so important that all those people had to die, the people who could reveal it?

The Teague house was mostly dark when we pulled up to it. I'd imagined it would be blazing with light, but only one window glowed through the darkness. None of the outside lights were on, which I thought was strange. If I'd been Sybil, I'd have turned on all the outside lights once I'd made sure company was coming, especially on an evening when bad weather was obviously imminent.

'This is bad,' Tolliver said slowly. He didn't elaborate. He didn't need to. We parked at the front of the house. The rain drummed on the roof of the car. 'I think you better call your cop buddy,' he said to me. 'I think we better stay out of that house until we have someone with authority here.' He switched on the dome light.

'I can't count on him being the one on call,' I said, but I dialed his home number on the chance that Hollis was snug and warm and dry in his little house. No answer. I tried the sheriff's office. The dispatcher answered. She sounded distracted. I could hear the radio squawking in the background. 'Is Hollis on patrol?' I asked.

'No, he's answering a call about a tree being across the road on County Road 212,' she snapped. 'And I got a three-car accident on Marley Street.' I could see that a personal call to a busy officer would not be priority.

'Tell him to come to the Teagues' house as soon as he can,' I said. 'Tell him it's very important. I think a crime's been committed there.'

'Someone'll come as soon as they can get free from the ones we're sure about,' she said, and she hung up the phone.

'Okay, we're on our own,' I told Tolliver. He switched off the light, leaving us in a dark island of dry warmth. The cold rain was pelting down, drenching the lawn and rinsing off the car. The flashes of lightning were only occasional. I could stand it, I told myself. We'd parked at the end of the sidewalk that led directly to the main doors. The garage, with its door into the kitchen, was to our left on the west side of the house.

'I'll go in the front, you go in the garage door,' I said. By the distant glow of the streetlights, I could see Tolliver open his mouth to protest, then close it again.

'All right,' he said. 'On the count of three. One, two, three!'

We leapt from our respective sides of the car and took off for our separate goals. I reached mine first, without being hit by anything except leaves and twigs snapped from a tree by the high winds.

The front door wasn't locked. That might not mean anything. I was pretty sure that in Sarne no one locked up until they turned in for the night. But the hair on my neck prickled. I pushed it open, but only a foot.

The door opened directly into the large formal living room, which was unlit and shadowy. The rain running down the big picture window and the streetlight shining through it made the room seem underwater in the glimpse I had before I crouched and rolled as I pushed the door wide open. A shot whistled past and above me. I scrambled to take cover behind a big chair. I'd never held a gun in my life, but I was regretting my lack of firepower at this instant.

There was a scream from somewhere else in the big house. I thought it came from the back, maybe from the family room.

Where was Tolliver? But he'd have heard the shot. He'd be careful.

For an unbearably long moment, nothing more happened. I wondered how many people were hiding from each other in these rooms, and I wondered if I'd survive to find out.

Gradually, my eyes became used to the faint and watery light. Though the drapes had been partially drawn, I could identify the furniture by shape.

There was another doorway directly opposite the front entrance, and I was pretty sure that was where the shot had come from. I took a deep breath and rolled from the armchair to a coffee table. Next step, the couch. That would put me within a few feet of the other doorway, which was the only way into the rest of the house, if I was remembering the layout correctly.

'Nell!' I yelled, hoping to distract the shooter from Tolliver's progress, wherever he was. 'Sybil!'

There was an answering shriek from the second floor. I didn't know which one of them was yelling, and I didn't know the location or number of people in the house, but I did know all of them were alive. Not a buzz in my head.

I'd been feeling very determined, but now the storm kicked up a notch. The rain began lashing harder at the window and soaking the carpet through the open front door. The rumble of thunder became almost continuous, and the crack of lightning followed right after. I felt as though I was pinned on a map and the lightning could see me, was tracking me, getting closer and closer until it could hit me again. Then I'd lose everything. The unimaginable pain would arc through me for the second time, and I'd lose my sight or my memory or the use of my leg, or something else irreplaceable. I moaned in fear, covering my eyes, and when I took my hands away, a man was standing over me with a gun in his hand.

In a desperate attempt to save my life, I dove at him, grabbing him around the knees and bringing him down. The gun went off; he'd had his finger on the trigger, oh God oh God. But if I was hit I didn't know it yet, and when he swung the gun at my head I grabbed his wrist with both hands and clung to it, literally for dear life.

Maybe my intense fear made me stronger than usual, because I was able to keep my hold on him though he hit at me with his other arm and thrashed around to shake me off. He was trying to bring the gun to bear on me, trying to force his arm into a straight line so he could fire at me, and as we rolled around in a snarling heap I saw my chance and sank my teeth into the fleshy heel of his hand and bit down with all my might. He gave a cry of pain – *yay!* – and let go of the gun. I would like to say that had been my intent, but if it was, I'd made the decision on a level I'd never tapped consciously.

Then the lights came on in the room, blinding me, and a shape I thought was Tolliver leaped forward. All three of us were in the melee on the floor, crashing into tables and sending heavy lamps toppling to the pale carpet.

'Stop!' screamed a new voice. 'I've got a gun!'

We all froze. I still had my teeth in the man's hand, and Tolliver had raised a heavy glass ornament shaped like an apple to bash in his head. For the first time, I unclenched my teeth and looked up at the man's face. Paul Edwards. He was a far cry from the suave lawyer I'd met in the sheriff's office. He was wearing a flannel shirt and khakis and sneakers, and his hair was completely disheveled. He was panting heavily, and blood was streaming from his hand where I'd bitten him. Most striking of all was the absence of that calm assurance he'd had, the certainly that his little world was his to rule and order. He looked more like a raccoon that had been treed – bared teeth and glinting eyes and hissing noises.

'Oh my God, Paul,' Sybil said, the gun wavering in her hand. Dammit, why does everyone have a gun? Sybil's was smaller, but looked just as lethal. 'Oh, my God.' She was as struck by the transformation as I was, probably more. 'How could you do this?'

I hoped she was asking him, not us. At least the light had made the storm retreat in my forest of fears. Tolliver gently set the glass apple on a table by the kitchen doorway.

'Sybil, I couldn't let them know.' He was trying to sound reasonable, but it just came out weak.

'That's what you said before, when you made me call them. I still don't understand.'

Tolliver and I might as well not have been in the room.

I noticed for the first time that Sybil had a scarf tied to one wrist, and the other wrist was deeply scored with a red line. He'd had her tied up.

'Where's Nell?' I croaked, but neither of them answered. They were so focused on each other, we weren't even on the same planet. I noticed that Tolliver silently bent to retrieve Paul's gun where it lay against the baseboard. The gun looked horribly functional in the expensive, feminine room, which right now was not looking its orderly best. Tolliver slid the gun under the skirt of the couch. Good.

'Sybil, we were together for so long,' Paul said. 'So long. You'd never divorce him. You'd never even agree to quit sleeping with him.'

'He was my *husband*, for God's sake!' she said harshly.

'So when Helen divorced that bastard Jay, she . . .' Paul looked at the carpet as if it covered a secret he needed to know. 'We got close.'

'You had an affair with her,' Sybil said, absolutely stunned. 'With that low-class drunken slut. After you denied it to my face! Harvey was right.'

I risked a look at Tolliver. He met my eyes and we exchanged looks.

'I knew Dell was really my son,' Paul said. 'But Teenie was mine, too.'

'No,' said Sybil, shaking her head from side to side. 'No.'

'Yes,' he said. But his eyes were straying now and again to the gun. Sybil was holding it pretty steady, for now. Tolliver and I had edged away from Paul, naturally, not wanting to be in the line of fire, but now I wondered if we shouldn't have kept hold of him, and possibly

Tolliver should have bashed him with the glass apple, just to be sure. The lawyer was getting his spirit back, the longer Sybil talked to him without shooting him.

'You could have just told them,' she said. 'You could have just told them.'

'I did tell them,' he said. 'That day they died. I did tell them.' His voice was unsteady, as shaky as Sybil's.

'You killed them? Why'd you kill your son, our son?' Tears were running down her cheeks, but she wasn't ready to crumple yet. I'd been right when I'd pegged her as stoic.

'Because Teenie was pregnant, you stupid cow,' he said, retreating to a more comfortable emotion, anger. 'Teenie was pregnant, and she wouldn't have an abortion! Said it was wrong! And your son, our son, wouldn't make her!'

'Pregnant! Oh! Oh, my God. How did you find out?'

'From me.' A bedraggled Nell stood in the doorway. She had a letter opener in her hands, and her wrists held the same red marks that her mother's showed. 'I'm the most stupid person in the world, Mama. I was so worried about Teenie being pregnant that when Dell told me, I thought I'd ask Paul to talk to her, tell her to give it up for adoption. Dell was too young to get married, Mama, and I just didn't want to be Teenie Hopkins' sister-in-law. So they died! He killed them, Mama, and it's all my fault!'

'Don't you ever think that, Mary Nell. It's *his* fault.' Sybil gestured with the gun toward her longtime lover.

It seemed to me it was sort of Sybil's fault, too, but I wasn't going to raise any issues as long as she was holding the gun. While I was being ignored, I wanted to put a safer distance between me and Paul Edwards, so I was edging back to the far end of the couch. On Edwards's other side, Tolliver was shifting himself a little closer to the two women, but he was careful to keep the line of fire between Sybil and Paul free and clear.

'Yes, it's my fault,' Paul gabbled. He was looking around the floor surreptitiously. He was looking for his gun. Paul Edwards was not down for the count.

'You need to tie him up,' Tolliver suggested. 'Call the police.'

Nell began to move back through the doorway, presumably to go into the kitchen to call the police, but Paul made a sudden move and she stilled.

'No, don't call,' Paul said. 'Mary Nell, I'm your dad, too. Don't give me up.'

Poor Nell couldn't have looked more horrified if he'd said he'd made an offer for her hand.

'No,' Sybil hissed. 'Don't listen, Mary Nell. It's not true.'

'She's right,' I said, very quietly. But no one paid attention. My brother and I were definitely the audience. The innocent bystanders. You know what happens to innocent bystanders.

'Did you kill my dad, somehow?' she asked Paul. 'My real dad?'

'No,' I said. 'Your dad died of a heart attack, Nell. He really did.' I didn't see any need to throw in the circumstances.

'You . . . you . . . asshole,' she said to Paul Edwards.

Her mother opened her mouth to reprimand Mary Nell, then had the good sense to close it.

'You killed my son,' Sybil said instead. 'You killed my son. You killed his baby. You killed his girlfriend. You killed . . . who else did you kill? Helen, I guess. The mother of your *daughter*.'

'You have yourself to blame for that,' he said sullenly. 'It was you hiring Helen, you having her around here cleaning that gave Dell and Teenie a chance to get to know each other.'

'Gave you a chance to see Helen again, too, I guess,' Sybil said in a very ugly voice. 'Who else did you kill, Paul?'

'Sally Boxleitner?' I suggested.

Edwards gaped at me as if I'd sprouted another head. 'Why do you . . . ?' he began, then trailed off, apparently at a loss.

'She figured it out, didn't she?' I asked. 'Did she call you?'

'She called me,' he admitted. 'She said she, she . . .'

'What did my wife tell you?' Hollis asked from the open front door.

I wondered if Tolliver and I could just creep out through the kitchen and be gone. We could go back to the motel and grab our stuff, leave this town forever. I caught Tolliver's eye and tilted my head toward the doorway into the rest of the house. He shook his head slightly. We were just spectators at the showdown at the OK Corral, but that still meant some injudicious move might get us killed in the cross fire.

Hollis didn't look like the stoical cop I'd met when I'd come to Sarne, and he didn't look like the lover I'd joined in bed. His eyes were showing a lot of white. He was wearing a long shiny waterproof slicker, and his uniform hat had a plastic bag on it. His face was wet with rain, and his slicker dripped onto the carpet. He was wearing rubber boots over his heavy cop shoes, and he had a glove on his left hand. His right hand was bare, holding his own gun in a very business-like way.

I wondered if Mary Nell had a firearm tucked in a pocket.

'I didn't kill her,' Paul said. 'She called me, told me she had some questions about blood types. I agreed to meet her, though at the time I didn't know what she was talking about.'

'You killed Dell,' Mary Nell said. 'You killed Teenie, and the baby, and Miss Helen. How can we believe you didn't kill Sally, too?'

'Sybil,' I whispered.

Only Tolliver heard me. His eyes widened.

'You can't pin that one on me,' Paul Edwards said, beginning to pull himself to his knees. I thought it was strange that the charge would make him indignant enough to be defiant, with all that he'd admitted. 'I think you can understand why I didn't want Teenie to bring a child into the world with a bloodline like that,' and he half-smiled in a parody of a reasonable expression. 'But I never laid a hand on Sally. Sally was a good girl. And definitely not mine, of course.'

'Good,' Hollis growled.

'But you know, since I thought she'd drowned in the tub by accident, like the coroner said, I'd never stopped to think. Sybil, I told you that Sally called me, said she had something to tell me about Dick's death. At the time, I thought Sally might be priming up to tell me a tale for some kind of blackmail. But when she died, too, it didn't seem to make any difference. Sybil, did you go talk to Sally?'

Mary Nell gave a choked laugh. 'Don't you try to go blame that on her, you murderer! Mama, tell him . . .' The girl's voice trailed off when she saw her mother's face. 'Mama?' She sounded lost. Gone for good.

'She said she'd looked up blood typing, and she knew Dell wasn't really a Teague,' Sybil said dully. 'She wanted me to ask Harvey to resign early. Sally wanted Hollis to have Harvey's job. She was scared Hollis would get restless without it, that he wasn't happy piecing together a living in a little town like this.'

Hollis looked like someone had hit him in the head. His hand was wavering. He didn't know who he wanted to shoot most. I understood the feeling.

Sybil gulped. Her own gun was falling down to her side. 'I couldn't do that. And I couldn't stand her lying like that. I made myself believe it was a lie. So I went by one afternoon. She'd left the door unlocked, which I figured, and I walked in with this gun, but she was in the tub, singing away.'

Hollis looked sick.

'And I just stepped in the bathroom and I grabbed her heels and pulled,' Sybil went on. 'And after a minute, she stopped trying to get up.' Sybil stood there, lost in the memory, the gun down by her side.

Mary Nell screamed in horror. Paul Edwards launched himself at Sybil's gun, and Tolliver leaped over to knock me down behind the couch, his arms wrapped around me. Of course, a bullet could pass through the couch like it could pass through butter, but at least we were out of sight and mind.

A gun fired, and there were more screams – I was pretty sure Mary Nell's was one of them. When there was a little period of silence, we stuck our heads around the end of the couch.

'You can get up,' Hollis said, his voice heavy and about a million years old. Tolliver straightened first and helped me up. My bad leg refused to lock for a minute, leaving me wobbly.

Paul Edwards was on his knees, clutching his shoulder. Behind him there was a dent in the wall, and pieces of glass glinted on the carpet. Mary Nell was standing as if she'd been turned into stone, glaring at Paul. Sybil was looking at her daughter.

'You dislocated my shoulder,' Paul wheezed, 'you little bitch.'

'I hit him,' Mary Nell said in a disconcertingly childish voice. 'I threw the glass apple and hit him.'

'Were you trying to hit him in the head?' Hollis asked. 'I wish you'd aimed higher.'

Horribly, she laughed.

'Why don't you shoot me, Hollis?' Sybil's voice was deep and throbbing. 'Come on, you know you want to. I'd rather you shot me now than go through a trial and sentencing.'

'You're the selfish bitch,' Hollis said. 'Sure. I'm going to shoot you in front of your daughter. Hell of a way to give her another great memory, don't you think? Take a moment to think of someone besides yourself, why don't you?'

After a second, he said in a voice much closer to sane, 'Tolliver, please call the sheriff's office.' My brother patted his pocket. No cell. He slipped past the little group into the kitchen, and I could hear him punching buttons and speaking. The storm had stopped; the only traces of it were heard in the drip, drip, drip of water from the eaves.

I felt like I was looking at them through the wrong end of the telescope. These four miserable people. They looked far away, small, but clear-cut in their distress.

'Everything's lost, for you,' I said to Paul Edwards. His eyes widened as he looked at me. 'I'm not sorry. Besides all the other, more horrible things you've done, you had my brother thrown in jail – though you had a lot of help doing that. You shot at me in the cemetery, and I have to believe that was you all by yourself, right? Now, your life is over.'

'What are you now, a seer?' Sybil said bitterly. 'I wish I'd never asked you here, never tried to find out what happened to the girl.'

'Then I'm glad you already paid me.' It was all I could think of to say. She laughed, but not as if she really found it humorous. Her daughter was still looking from Sybil to Paul, from her mother to the man who'd been her mother's lover, and she looked sick and young and defenseless.

'You're going to be a great woman,' I said to Mary Nell. She didn't look at me; I don't think she was any fonder of me at that moment than was her mother or Paul. Even as my brother came back in the room, we heard sirens approaching, and lights began to flash up and down the soaking suburban street.

'Why'd you do all that to me?' I asked Paul. 'I don't understand.'

'The baby,' he said. 'I never thought you'd find Teenie. When you did, I was sure you knew about the baby. I thought if I kept you scared, you wouldn't figure it out.'

But the baby had left no bones. If Paul had left us alone, we'd have departed Sarne without a second thought.

We didn't get away until perhaps three in the morning. We had to tell many, many people what we'd seen and heard. We were too wired to sleep for an hour after we got back to our room, but once we did, we slept until noon.

We had our bags in the car an hour later. We settled with the front desk, and the odious Vernon practically did the macarena when he found out we were really going. I felt empty, hollow; but I wanted to leave Sarne so badly I pushed myself to do all the right things toward that end. We got gas and swung by the police station as we'd been told.

Hollis was there again, or maybe was still there. Harvey Branscom's office was empty, the door wide open. I was sure he'd been having a terrible night and a bad day since his sister was in the pokey for murder. I studied Hollis's face. He looked somehow younger, as if the solving of his wife's death had erased a couple of years and some lines of tension.

'You all shoving off?' he asked.

'Yes,' Tolliver said.

'We've got your numbers and your lawyer's address, just in case?'

'Yes,' I said. I knew Hollis would never call my number.

'Okay, then. We appreciate all your help.' He was trying to keep this as brisk and impersonal as possible. But I could see Tolliver bristling for my sake. I put my hand on his arm.

'No problem,' I said. 'No problem.'

'Well, then.'

We both nodded at him, and he gave us a curt nod back, and we went out the swinging glass doors for the last time, I hoped to God.

Tolliver was driving, and after we'd put on our seat belts and picked a radio station, he took the car through the streets of Sarne to the highway that would take us east.

'Think we could make Memphis before tonight?' I asked.

'I'm sure of it,' he said. 'Will you – are you okay with saying goodbye like that?'

'Yes. What's the point of a sentimental parting?'

He seemed to acknowledge this with a tilt of his head. 'But you liked him.'

'Yeah, sure. But, you know, it just wasn't meant to be.'

'Someday . . .' he began, and let the idea trail off.

'You know what, Tolliver? You remember when we did *Romeo and Juliet* in high school?' We might have studied it years apart, but our high school stuck to its course of study religiously.

'Yeah. And?'

'There was that line that Mercutio says, when he gets killed in the feud between the Montagues and the Capulets. He says it in his dying speech. You remember?'

'No,' he said. 'Tell me.'

'He says, "A plague on both your houses." And then he dies.'

' "A plague on both your houses," ' Tolliver repeated. 'That about sums it up.'

I had a thought. 'But of course, Paul Edwards had a foot in both houses – the Hopkins house and the Teague house.'

'Somehow that seems like the right thing to say, anyway.'

We were quiet for a minute. Then, as the last of Sarne fell behind us and we headed from the mountains to the delta, the flatlands that stretched on and on, I said, 'You know, I keep thinking about Teenie, lying out there in the woods, all alone. No matter what happened, I did a good thing.'

'Never doubt it. It was a good thing.' He hesitated. 'Do you think they know? When they've been found?'

'Oh, yes. They know,' I said, and the miles to Memphis opened ahead of us.

GRAVE SURPRISE

This book is dedicated to a tiny minority of the American population: people who have survived a lightning strike. Members of a small and exclusive club, some of these survivors spend the rest of their lives trying to convince doctors of the validity of the myriad of ongoing problems plaguing them. The other survivors simply try to go on with their lives, though they're invariably altered by the experience. I wish you all freedom from pain and anxiety, and I thank you for letting me share your experiences.

1

I didn't like Clyde Nunley the first time I met him face-to-face in the old cemetery. There was nothing wrong with the exterior of the man: he was dressed like a regular person would dress for the mild winter weather of southern Tennessee, especially considering the task at hand. His old blue jeans, work boots, shapeless hat, flannel shirt, and down vest were reasonable attire. But Dr Nunley had a smug, smooth, air about him that said that he'd brought me here to be an object of derision, said he'd never believed I was anything but a fraud.

He shook my hand, standing right in front of me. He was having a great time, scanning the faces of my brother and me, as we waited side by side for his directions.

Offered under the aegis of the anthropology department of Bingham College, the course Dr Clyde Nunley taught was titled 'An Open Mind: Experiences Outside the Box.' I noted the irony.

'Last week we had a medium,' he said.

'For lunch?' I asked, and got a scowl for my reward.

I glanced sideways at Tolliver. His eyes narrowed slightly, letting me know he was amused but warning me to play nice.

If it hadn't been for the presence of that asshole of a professor, I would have been brimming with anticipation. I drew in a deep breath as I glanced past Dr Nunley at the tombstones, worn and weathered. This was my kind of place.

By American standards, the cemetery was an old one. The trees had had nearly two centuries to mature. Some of these hardwoods could have been saplings when the denizens of St Margaret's churchyard had been laid to rest. Now they were tall, with thick branches; in the summer, their shade would be a blessing. Right now, in November, the branches were bare, and the grass was bleached and strewn with dead leaves. The sky was that chill, leaden gray that makes the heart sad.

I would have been as subdued as the rest of the people gathered there if I hadn't had a treat in store. The headstones still upright were uneven, both in lodgment and in color. Below them, the dead waited for me.

It hadn't rained in a week or two, so I was wearing Pumas rather than boots. I would have better contact if I took the Pumas off, but the students and the professor would doubtless interpret that as further evidence of my eccentricity. Also, it was a bit too cold for going around barefoot.

Nunley's students were there to watch my 'demonstration.' That was the point. Of the twenty or so in the group, two were older; one, a woman, was in her forties. I was willing to bet she'd arrived in the minivan now sitting frumpily among the other vehicles pulled up to the wire strung between white posts to separate the gravel parking lot from the grass of the churchyard. Her face was open and curious as she evaluated me.

The other 'nontraditional' class member was a man I placed in his early thirties, who was dressed in cords and a heathery sweater. The thirties man was the shining Colorado pickup. Clyde Nunley would be the ancient Toyota. The four other cars, battered and small, would be those of the traditional students who formed the bulk of the little crowd here to watch. Though St Margaret's was actually on the campus grounds, the old church was tucked far back into the reaches of Bingham College, beyond the little stadium, the tennis courts, the soccer field – so it wasn't surprising that the students who could, had driven, especially in the chilly weather. The kids were in the typical college eighteen-to-twenty-one age bracket, and with an odd jolt I realized that made them only a bit younger than me. They were wearing the usual uniform of blue jeans, sneakers, and padded jackets – more or less what Tolliver and I were wearing.

Tolliver's jacket was from Lands' End, bright red with a blue lining. Red looked good with his black hair, and the jacket was warm enough for most situations in the South. I was wearing my bright blue padded jacket, because it made me feel safe and soft, and because Tolliver had given it to me.

We were spots of color in the overall grayness. The trees that surrounded the old church, its yard, and its cemetery gave us a feeling of privacy, as if we'd been marooned at the back of the Bingham campus.

'Miss Connelly, we're all anxious to see your demonstration,' Dr Nunley said, practically laughing in my face. He made an elaborate sweeping gesture with his arm that encompassed the gaggle of head-stones. The students didn't look anxious. They looked cold, bored, or mildly curious. I wondered who the medium had been. There weren't many with genuine gifts.

I glanced at Tolliver again. *Fuck him*, his eyes said, and I smiled.

They all had clipboards, all the students. And all the clipboards had diagrams of the old graveyard, with the gravesites neatly drawn in and labeled. Though this information wasn't on their clipboards, I knew there was a detailed record of the burials in this particular graveyard, a record containing the cause of death of most of the bodies buried in it. The parish priest had kept this record for the forty years he'd served St Margaret's church, keeping up the custom of his predecessor. But Dr Nunley had informed me that no one had been buried here for fifty years.

The St Margaret records had been discovered three months ago in a box in the most remote storeroom of the Bingham College library. So there was no way I could have found out the information the registers contained beforehand. Dr Nunley, who had originated the occult studies class, had heard of me somehow. He wouldn't say exactly how my name had come to his attention, but that didn't surprise me. There are websites that connect to websites that connect to other websites; and in a very subterranean circle, I'm famous.

Clyde Nunley thought he was paying me to be exposed in front of the 'An Open Mind' class. He thought I considered myself some form of psychic, or maybe a Wiccan.

Of course, that made no sense. Nothing I did was occult. I didn't pray to any god before I got in touch with the dead. I do believe in God, but I don't consider my little talent a gift from Him.

I got it from a bolt of lightning. So if you think God causes natural disasters, then I suppose God is responsible.

When I was fifteen, I was struck through an open window of the trailer where we lived. At that time, my mother was married to Tolliver's father, Matt Lang, and they had had two children, Gracie and Mariella. Crowded into the trailer (besides that lovely nuclear family) were the rest of us – me, my sister Cameron, Tolliver, and his brother Mark. I don't remember how long Mark was actually in residence. He's several years older than Tolliver. Anyway, Mark wasn't at the trailer that afternoon.

It was Tolliver who performed CPR until the ambulance got there.

My stepfather gave Cameron hell for calling the ambulance. It was expensive, and of course, we didn't have any insurance. The doctor who wanted to keep me overnight for observation got an earful. I never saw him again, or any other doctor. But from the Internet list I'm on, a list for lightning strike survivors, I've gathered it wouldn't have done me a lot of good, anyway.

I recovered – more or less. I have a strange spiderweb pattern of red on my torso and right leg. That leg has episodes of weakness. Sometimes my right hand shakes. I have headaches. I have many fears. And I can find dead people. If their location is known, I can diagnose the cause of death.

That was the part that interested the professor. He had a record of the cause of death of almost every person in this cemetery, a record to which I'd had no access. This was his idea of a perfect test, a test that would expose me for the fraud I was. With an almost jaunty air, he led our little party through the dilapidated iron fence that had guarded the cemetery for so many decades.

'Where would you like me to begin?' I asked, with perfect courtesy. I had been raised well, until my parents started using drugs.

Clyde Nunley smirked at his students. 'Why, this one would be fine,' he said, gesturing to the grave to his right. Of course, there was no mound, probably hadn't been in a hundred and seventy years. The headstone was indecipherable, at least to my unaided eyes. If I bent down with a flashlight, maybe I could read it. But they didn't care about that part of it; they wanted to know what I would say about the cause of death.

The faint tremor, the vibration I'd been feeling since I'd neared the cemetery, increased in frequency as I stepped onto the grave. I'd been feeling the hum in the air even before I'd passed through the rusted gate, and now it increased in intensity, vibrating just below the surface of my skin. It was like getting closer and closer to a hive of bees.

I shut my eyes, because it was easier to concentrate that way. The bones were directly underneath me, waiting for me. I sent that extra sense down into the ground under my feet, and the knowledge entered me with the familiarity of a lover.

'Cart fell on him,' I said. 'This is a man, I think in his thirties. Ephraim? Something like that? His leg was crushed, and he went into shock. He bled out.'

There was a long silence. I opened my eyes. The professor had stopped smirking. The students were busily making notations on their clipboards. One girl's eyes were wide as she looked at me.

'All right,' said Dr Clyde Nunley, his voice suddenly a lot less scornful. 'Let's try another one.'

Gotcha, I thought.

The next grave was Ephraim's wife. The bones didn't tell me that; I deduced her identity from the similar headstone positioned side by side with Ephraim's. 'Isabelle,' I said with certainty. 'Isabelle. Oh, she died in childbirth.' My hand grazed my lower stomach. Isabelle must have been pregnant when her husband met with his accident. Hard luck. 'Wait a minute,' I said. I wanted to interpret that faint echo I was picking up underneath Isabelle's. To hell with what they thought. I pulled off my shoes, but kept my socks on in a compromise with the cold weather. 'The baby's in there with her,' I told them. 'Poor little thing,' I added very softly. There was no pain in the baby's death.

I opened my eyes.

The group had shifted its configuration. They stood closer to each other, but farther from me.

'Next?' I asked.

Clyde Nunley, his mouth compressed into a straight line, gestured toward a grave so old its headstone had split and fallen. The marble had been white when it had been situated.

As Tolliver and I went over to the next body, his hand on my back, one of the students said, 'He should stand somewhere else. What if he's somehow feeding her information?'

It was the older male student, the guy in his thirties. He had brown hair, a thread or two of gray mixed in. He had a narrow face and the broad shoulders of a swimmer. He didn't sound as if he actually suspected me. He sounded objective.

'Good point, Rick. Mr Lang, if you'd stand out of Miss Connelly's sight?'

I felt a tiny flutter of anxiety. But I made myself nod at Tolliver in a calm way. He went back to lean against our car, parked outside what remained of the cemetery fence. While I watched him, another car pulled up, and a young black man with a camera got out. It was a dilapidated car, dented and scraped, but clean.

'Hey, y'all,' the newcomer called, and several of the younger students waved at him. 'Sorry I'm late.'

The professor said, 'Miss Connelly, this is Clark. I forgot to tell you that the student newspaper wanted to get a few shots.'

I didn't think he'd forgotten. He just didn't care if I objected or not.

I considered for a moment. I really didn't care. I was ready to have a good fight with Clyde Nunley, but not a frivolous one. I shrugged. 'I don't mind,' I said. I stepped onto the grave, close to the headstone, and focused my whole attention on ground below me. This one was hard to decipher. It was very old, and the bones were scattered; the coffin had disintegrated. I hardly felt my right hand begin to twitch, or my head begin to turn from side to side. My facial muscles danced beneath my skin.

'Kidneys,' I said, at last. 'Something with his kidneys.' The ache in my back swelled to a level of pain that was almost unbearable, and then it was gone. I opened my eyes and took a deep breath. I fought the impulse to turn to look at my brother.

One of the youngest of the students was white as a sheet. I'd spooked her good. I smiled at her, trying to look friendly and reassuring. I don't think I achieved it. She took another step away from me. I sighed and turned my attention back to my job.

Next, I found a woman who'd died of pneumonia; a child who'd died of an infected appendix; a baby who'd had a heart malformation; a baby who'd had a blood problem – I suspected he was the second child of a couple with conflicting Rh factors – and a pre-teen boy who'd had one of the fevers, scarlet, maybe. Every now and then I heard the photographer snap a picture, but it really didn't bother me. I don't care much about my physical appearance when I'm working.

After thirty or forty minutes, Nunley seemed almost won over. He pointed to a grave in the corner of the cemetery farthest from the gate. The plot he indicated lay right by the fence, which had collapsed almost completely in that area. The headstone was partially obscured by the overhanging branches of a live oak, and the light was especially bad. This is a draining process, so I was beginning to get tired. At first I attributed my extraordinary reading to that. I opened my eyes, frowned.

'It's a girl,' I said.

'Ha!' Nunley chose to regard himself as vindicated. He kind of overdid his glee, he was so happy to be proved right. 'Wrong!' he said. Mr Open Mind.

'I'm not wrong,' I said, though I really wasn't thinking about him, or the students, or even Tolliver. I was thinking about the puzzle under the ground. I was thinking about solving it.

I took off my socks. My feet felt fragile in the chilly air. I stepped back onto the dead grass in line with the headstone to get a fresh outlook. For the first time, I noticed that though an attempt had been made to level this grave – it bore the flattened spots that blows with a shovel on soft dirt would have produced – the earth had been recently turned.

Well, well, well. I stood still for a moment, the implications working their way through my brain. I had the ominous creeping feeling you get when you just know something's right outside your realm of knowledge – a bad piece of future poised to jump out from behind a door and scream in your face.

Though the kids were muttering to each other and the two older students were having a low-voiced conversation, I squatted down to decipher the headstone. It read, JOSIAH POUNDSTONE, 1839–1858, REST IN PEACE BELOVED BROTHER. No mention of a wife, or a twin, or . . .

Okay, maybe the ground had shifted a bit and the body buried next to Josiah's had sort of wandered over.

I stepped back onto the grave, and I squatted. Distantly, I heard the click of the camera, but it was not relevant. I laid my hand on the turned earth. I was as connected as I could be without lying full length on the ground.

I glanced over at Tolliver. 'Something's wrong here,' I said, loudly enough for him to hear. He started over.

'A problem, Miss Connelly?' Dr Nunley asked, scorn lending his voice fiery edges. This was a man who loved to be right.

'Yes.' I stepped off the grave, shook myself, and tried again. Standing right above Josiah Poundstone, I reached down again.

Same result.

'There are two bodies here, not one,' I said.

Nunley made the predictable attempts to find an explanation. 'A coffin gave way in the next grave,' he said impatiently. 'Or something like that.'

'No, the body that's lower is in an intact coffin.' I took a deep breath. 'And the upper body isn't. It's much newer. This ground has been turned over recently.'

Finally interested, the students quieted down. Dr Nunley consulted his papers. 'Who do you . . . see . . . in there?'

'The lower body, the older one . . .' I closed my eyes, trying to peer through one body to another. I'd never done this before. 'Is a young man named Josiah, like the headstone says. By the way, he died of blood poisoning from a cut.' I could tell from Nunley's face that I was right. However the priest had described Josiah's death, modern knowledge could recognize the symptoms. What the priest may not have known, however, is that the cut had come from a stab wound, inflicted in a fight. I could see the knife sliding into the young man's flesh, feel him staunch the blood. But the infection had carried him off.

'The upper body, the newer one, is a young girl.'

There was sudden and absolute silence. I could hear the traffic rushing by on busy roads just yards away from the old graveyard.

'How recent is the second body?' Tolliver asked.

'Two years at the most,' I said. I tilted my head from side to side, to get the most accurate 'reading' I could. On the age of the bones, I mostly go by the intensity of the vibration and the feel of it. I never said I was a scientist. But I'm right.

'Oh, my God,' whispered one of the female students, finally understanding the implication.

'She's a murder victim,' I said. 'Her name was . . . Tabitha.' As I heard what my voice was saying, an awful sense of doom flowed over me. The boogeyman jumped out from behind the door and screamed in my face.

My brother moved across the intervening ground like a quarterback who could see the end zone. He stopped just short of the grave, but he was close enough to take my hand. Our eyes met. His echoed the dismay in mine.

'Tell me it's not,' Tolliver said. His dark brown eyes were steady on mine.

'It is,' I said. 'We finally found Tabitha Morgenstern.'

After a moment, in which the younger people in the group turned to look at each other with inquiring faces, Clyde Nunley said, 'You mean . . . the girl who was abducted from Nashville?'

'Yes,' I said. 'That's who I mean.'

2

I'd been standing on two murder victims, one ancient (at least to me), and one modern. There were differences in the reading I got from the older one, in addition to the shock of finding Tabitha. I stowed Josiah Poundstone away to ponder later. No one here in St Margaret's cemetery was concerned with him today.

'You got some explaining to do,' the detective said. He was putting it mildly. We were at Homicide, and the carpeted partitions and the ringing phones and the flag tacked to the wall made the floor seem more like a modest company with a burgeoning business than a cop facility.

Sometimes I faint when I find a body that has passed in a violent way. It would have been good if I'd fainted this time. But I hadn't. I'd been all too conscious of the disbelief and outrage on the faces of the police, uniformed and plainclothes. The initial skepticism and anger on the part of the two uniforms who'd rolled up on the scene had been understandable and predictable. They didn't imagine anyone would dig up a centuries-old grave on the say-so of a lunatic woman who made her living as a con artist.

But the more Clyde Nunley explained, the more they began to look uneasy. After a lot of comparison of the grave's surface with the others around it, the larger black cop finally radioed in, calling a detective to the scene.

We'd gone over the whole sequence of events again. This took a lot of time. Tolliver and I were leaning against our car, getting progressively colder and wearier, while the slow and repetitive questioning went on and on. Everyone was angry with us. Everyone thought we were frauds. Clyde Nunley grew more defensive and loud with each amazed reaction he got from the cops. Yes, he conducted a course during which students 'experienced' people who claimed they could communicate with the dead: ghost hunters, mediums, psychics, tarot readers, and other paranormal practitioners. Yes, people actually sent their kids to college to learn stuff like that, and yes, they paid

a rather high tuition for it. Yes, the papers about the old cemetery had
been kept quite secure, and Harper Connelly had had no chance to
examine them. Yes, the box containing the papers had been sealed
when the library staff had discovered it. No, neither Tolliver nor I had
ever been a student at the college. (We had to smile when we heard
that one.)

To no one's surprise, we were 'asked' to come to the police station.
And there we sat, answering all the same questions over and over
again, until we were left to vegetate in an interview room. The garbage
can was full of snack wrappers and stained Styrofoam coffee cups, and
the walls needed a new coat of paint. In the past, someone had thrown
the chair I was sitting on. I could tell, because one of the metal legs
was slightly bowed. At least the room was warm enough. I'd gotten
chilled down to my bones in the cemetery.

'You think it would look bad if I read?' Tolliver asked. Tolliver is
twenty-eight now, and he likes to grow his black hair out, wear it long
for a while, and then cut it drastically. At the moment, it was long
enough to pull back into a short ponytail. He has a mustache and
acne-scarred cheeks. He's a runner, like me. We spend a lot of hours in
cars, and running is a good way to counteract that.

'Yes, I think it would look callous,' I said. He glowered at me.
'Well, you asked me,' I said. We sat in dreary silence for a minute or
two.

'I wonder if we'll have to see the Morgensterns again?' I said.

'You know we will,' he said. 'I bet they've already called them, and
they're driving over from Nashville right now.'

His cell phone rang.

He checked who was calling, looked as blank as a man can look,
and answered it. 'Hey,' he said. 'Yeah, it's true. Yes, we're here in
Memphis. I was going to call you tonight. I'm sure we'll see each
other. Yes. Yes. All right, goodbye.'

He didn't look happy as he snapped the phone shut. Of course I
wanted to know who his caller had been, but I didn't say anything. If
anything could have made me gloomier, it was the idea that sooner or
later we'd have to see Joel and Diane Morgenstern again.

When I'd realized whom the bones belonged to, my dismay was
more overwhelming than my feeling of triumph. I'd failed the Morgensterns eighteen months ago, though I'd tried as hard as I could to

find their daughter. Now I'd finally come through for them, but the success was bitter.

'How'd she die?' Tolliver asked very quietly. You never knew who was listening, in a police station. I guess we're the suspicious sort.

'Suffocated,' I said. Another silence. 'With a blue pillow.' We'd seen so many pictures of Tabitha alive: on the news broadcasts, pinned to the walls of her room, in her parents' hands, blown up to illustrate the fliers they'd given us. She'd been a very average girl of eleven, to everyone but her parents. Tabitha had had bushy reddish-brown hair she hadn't yet learned to deal with. She'd had big brown eyes, and braces, and she hadn't begun to mature physically. She'd liked gymnastics, and art lessons, and she'd hated making her bed and taking out the trash. I remembered all this from talking to her parents; or more accurately, listening to their monologues. Joel and Diane had seemed to believe that if they made Tabitha real to me, I would work harder at finding her.

'You think she's been down there since she was missing?' Tolliver asked, finally.

It had been the spring of the preceding year when we'd been summoned to Nashville by the Morgenstern family. By then, Tabitha had been gone a month. The police had just cut back on their search, since they'd looked everywhere they could. The FBI had scaled back its presence, also. The extra equipment that had been installed to trace phone calls had been removed, because there hadn't been any ransom demands. By then, no one was expecting such a demand.

'No,' I said. 'The ground was too freshly disturbed. But I think she's been dead the whole time. I really hope so.' The only thing more awful than a murdered child was a murdered child who'd been subjected to prolonged torture or sexual abuse.

'There was no way you could have found her,' Tolliver said. 'Back then.'

'No,' I agreed. 'There wasn't.'

But it hadn't been for lack of trying. The Morgensterns had called me when they'd exhausted all the traditional methods of finding their lost child.

Yes, I had failed; but I had given it my all. I'd been over the house, the yard, the neighborhood, into the yards of anyone with a police record who lived in the surrounding area. Some I'd done at night because the homeowner wouldn't consent. Not only was I risking arrest, but injury. A dog had almost gotten me the second night.

I'd toured nearby junkyards, ponds, parks, landfills, and cemeteries, in the process finding one other murder victim in the trunk of a junked car (a freebie for the Nashville police – they'd been so pleased to have another murder victim on the books), and one natural death, a homeless man in a park. But I hadn't found any eleven-year-old girls. For nine days I'd searched, until the time came when I'd had to tell Diane and Joel Morgenstern that I could not find their child.

Tabitha had been snatched from her yard in an upscale Nashville suburb while she was watering the flowers in the beds around the front door of the house on a warm morning during spring break. When Diane had come out to go to the grocery, she'd discovered Tabitha was nowhere to be found. The hose was still running.

Daughter of a senior accountant with a firm that handled lots of Nashville singers and record people, Tabitha had had a blessed childhood. Though she had a stepbrother because Joel had been married and widowed previously, Tabitha had obviously enjoyed a well-regulated home life centered on maintaining her health and happiness, and incidentally that of Victor, her half sib.

My childhood, and Tolliver's, had not been like that – at least, after a certain point. That was the point where our lawyer parents began using drugs and drinking with their clients. After a while, the clients had ceased to be clients, and had become peers. That downward slide had brought me to the moment in time when I'd been standing in the bathroom in that trailer in Texarkana and the lightning had come through the window.

Trips down memory lane aren't happy jaunts for me.

I was almost glad when the detective – Corbett Lacey was his name – came back with cups of coffee for both of us. He was trying the soft approach. Sooner or later (probably later) someone else would try the hard approach.

'Tell me how you came to be here this morning,' suggested Corbett Lacey. He was a burly man with receding blond hair, a large belly, and quick blue eyes like restless marbles.

'We were invited by Dr Nunley to come to the old cemetery. I was supposed to show the students what I do.'

'What exactly do you do?' He looked so sincere, as if he would believe any answer I gave him.

'I find the dead.'

'You track people?'

'No, I find corpses. People call me in, and I find the bodies of those who've passed on.' That was my favorite euphemism. I have quite a repertoire. 'If the location of the corpse is already known, I can tell you the cause of death. That was what I was doing at the cemetery today.'

'What's your success rate?'

Okay, that was unexpected. I'd assumed he'd sneer, at this point. 'If the relatives or the police can give me a bead on the location, I can find the body,' I said matter-of-factly. 'When I find the body, I know the cause of death. In the case of Tabitha Morgenstern, when the family called me in, I could never find her. She'd been taken from her yard and put in a car pretty quick, I guess, and her corpse just wasn't there for me to sense.'

'How does this work?'

Another unexpected question. 'I feel them, like a buzz in my head,' I said. 'The closer I get, the more intense the buzz, the vibration, is. When I'm on top of them, I can reach down and tell how they died. I'm not a psychic. I'm not a precognate, or a telepath. I don't see who killed them. I only see the death when I'm near the bones.'

He hadn't expected such a matter-of-fact reply. He looked at me, leaning forward on the other side of the table. His own cup of coffee was forgotten in front of him. 'Why would anyone believe that?' Lacey asked wonderingly.

'Because I produce results,' I said.

'Don't you think it's quite a coincidence? That you were called in by the Morgensterns when they were looking for their little girl, and now, months later, in a different city, you say you've found her? How do you think those poor folks are going to feel when the area's dug and there's nothing there? You should be ashamed of yourself.' The detective regarded me with profound disgust.

'That's not going to happen.' I shrugged. 'I'm not ashamed of anything. She's there.' I glanced at my watch. 'They should have reached her by now.'

Detective Lacey's cell phone rang. He answered, 'Yeah?' As he listened, his face changed. He looked harder and older. His eyes fell on me with a look I've seen often – a stare compounded of distaste, fear, and a dawning belief.

'They've reached some bones in a garbage bag,' he said heavily. 'Too small to be an adult's.'

I tried very hard to look neutral.

'A foot below the garbage bag bones, there are wood remnants. Probably a coffin. So there may be another set of bones.' He breathed heavily. 'There's no trace of a coffin around the upper bones.'

I nodded. Tolliver squeezed my hand.

'We'll get a very preliminary identification in a couple hours, if it's the Morgenstern girl. The dental records have been faxed from Nashville. Of course, a solid ID will have to wait on a full exam of the body. Well, what's left of the body.' Detective Lacey set his own personal coffee mug on the battered table with unnecessary force. 'Nashville police are sending the X-rays by car, and the car should be here in a couple of hours. The local FBI office is sending someone to witness the full autopsy. The Fibbies are offering their lab for the trace stuff. You are not to say anything about this to anyone until we've talked to the family.'

I nodded again.

'Good,' Tolliver said, just to goose the silence.

Corbett Lacey gave us a steady glare. 'We've had to call her parents, and if this isn't her, I don't even like to think about what they'll feel. If you hadn't broadcast her name to the whole group standing there, we could have kept this quiet until we had something solid to tell them. Now, we've had to talk to them because it looks like the damn television will have it on the air soon.'

'I'm sorry about that. I just wasn't thinking.' I should have kept my mouth shut. He had a good point.

'Why do you even do this, anyway?' He gave me a puzzled face, as if he really couldn't figure me out. I didn't think he was completely sincere, but I was.

'It's always better to know. That's why I do it.'

'You seem to make quite a bit of money, too,' Corbett Lacey observed.

'I have to make a living, same as anybody else.' I wasn't going to act ashamed of that. But, truly, I sometimes wished I worked at Wal-Mart, or Starbucks, and let the dead lie unfound.

'So, I guess Joel and Diane started out right away,' Tolliver said. He was right; a change of subject was in order. 'It'll take them how long to get here?'

Detective Lacey looked puzzled.

'The Morgensterns. How long a drive is it, Nashville to Memphis?' I said.

He gave us an unreadable look. 'Like you didn't know.'

Okay, I wasn't getting this at all. 'Know . . . ?' I looked at Tolliver. He shrugged, as bewildered as I was. A possibility occurred to me. 'Tell me they're not dead!' I said. I'd liked them, and I didn't often have feelings for clients.

It was Lacey's turn to look uncertain. 'You really don't know?'

'We don't understand what you're talking about,' Tolliver said. 'Just tell us.'

'The Morgensterns left Nashville about a year after the little girl was abducted,' Lacey said. He ran a hand over his thinning blond hair. 'They live here in Memphis now. He manages the Memphis branch of the same accounting firm, and his wife's pregnant again. Maybe you didn't know that he and his first wife were both from Memphis, and since Diane Morgensterns family lives overseas, back here was where they needed to be if they wanted the support of family during the pregnancy and birth.'

I suspected my mouth was hanging open, but for the moment I didn't care. I had so many thoughts I couldn't process them all at once. The Morgensterns being here turned everything upside down. If I'd thought we were placed in a bad situation, ours was nothing compared to theirs. It looked so bad for them, Tabitha's body being found here. And their presence here in Memphis made the fact that I'd been the one to finally find her even fishier, since they'd employed me before.

I simply couldn't think of any explanation that cleared the couple of some involvement in their daughter's death.

My stunned reaction struck true to the detective, and Tolliver's was even more obvious. Lacey nodded sharply, as if he were reluctantly convinced of something.

After that, there weren't any more questions. We were released to go back to our motel, an absolutely typical airport motel in a medium-range chain that we'd picked because it was right off the interstate and not too far from the college. On our way back, we'd gone through a Wendy's drive-through to pick up sandwiches, and before we went up to our room we each pulled a soft drink from the ice chest in the back seat. Our room was wonderfully quiet and warm. I gulped my soda down right away, because I needed the sugar after our experience in the cemetery. (We've found, by trial and error, that sugar really helps get me up and running after a job.) Sure enough, after the sugar hit me, I was able to eat my sandwich at a calm pace. I felt much better. After we'd cleared away the debris, Tolliver stood and looked down from our second-story window.

'There are reporters already gathering,' Tolliver said, after a minute. 'It's only a matter of time before they come up to the room and knock on the door.'

I should have thought of that already. 'This will generate a lot of publicity,' I said, and the ambivalence was clear in Tolliver's face, as I'm sure it was in mine.

'You think we need to call Art?' Art Barfield was our attorney, and his firm was based in Atlanta.

'That might be a good idea,' I said. 'Would you talk to him?'

'Sure.' Tolliver pulled out his cell phone and dialed, while I went to the sink to wash my face. After I turned off the water, I could hear him talking. I was combing my hair in the mirror – my hair was almost as dark as Tolliver's – when he hung up.

'His secretary says he's with a client, but he'll call soonest possible. Of course, he'll charge an arm and a leg if we ask him to come. That is, if he can get away.'

'He'll come, or he'll recommend someone local. We've only asked him once before, and we're his most . . . lurid clients,' I said practically. 'If he doesn't come, we'll be swamped.'

Art called us back about an hour later. From Tolliver's end of the conversation, you could tell Art was not too excited about the prospect of leaving home – Art was not young, and he liked his home comforts – but when Tolliver told Art about the reporters gathered at the police station, the lawyer allowed himself to be persuaded to get on a plane right away.

'Corinne'll call you with my plane information,' Art said to Tolliver, but I could hear him clearly. Art has one of those carrying voices, which is really useful if you're a trial lawyer.

Art likes publicity almost as much as he loves his remote control and his wife's cooking. He's had a taste of it since he became our lawyer, and his practice has increased exponentially. His secretary, the middle-aged Corinne, called us within minutes to give us Art's flight number and his ETA.

'I don't think we'd better meet Art at the airport,' I told Corinne. I watched another news van enter the parking lot. 'I think we're going to have to go to a hotel, one with more security than this.'

'You'd better make the change now, and I'll book Mr Barfield a room at the same place,' Corinne said practically. 'I'll call him on his cell when he lands. In fact, I'll make a phone call or two, find the right place, and book the reservation for all of you. One room or two, for you and Mr Lang?'

The hotel was sure to be very expensive. Normally I'd be inclined to share one room with Tolliver, as we were doing now. But if the newspapers were checking, better to err on the side of the Goddess of Rightness.

'Two,' I said. 'Adjacent. Or if we can get a suite, that would be good.'

'I'll do some quick research, and then I'll confirm with you,' the efficient Corinne said.

She called back to tell us we were booked into the Cleveland. It was, as I'd feared, way too expensive for my taste, but I'd pay the money to ensure the privacy. I didn't like being on television. Publicity was good for business, but only the right kind of publicity.

We left our motel, as disguised as we could be without looking ludicrous. Before strolling out one of the side doors and making a beeline to our car, we had bundled to the teeth. Because we looked so humble, Tolliver lugging the ice chest and me carrying our overnight bags, we managed to escape the attention of the news crew until we were pulling out of the parking lot. The newswoman, whose lips were so shiny they looked polyurethaned, made a flying leap to land right beside the driver's window. Tolliver couldn't see to turn left into the traffic flowing the way we needed to go, so we were more or less trapped. He rolled down the window and put on an agreeable smile.

'Shellie Quail from Channel Thirteen,' the shiny woman said. She was the color of hot chocolate, and her black hair gleamed like it had been polished. It was in a smooth helmet style. Shellie Quail's makeup was equally warlike, lots of bright colors and definite lines. I wondered how long it took her to get ready to leave her house in the morning. She was wearing a tight pantsuit in a brownish, tweedy material, flecked with orange. The little flecks made her skin glow. 'Mr Lang, are you Miss Connelly's manager? Have I got that right?' the shining woman said.

'Yes, you do,' Tolliver said agreeably. I knew the camera was rolling. But I had faith in my brother. He has a lot of charm when the occasion arises, especially if it arises in the presence of a pretty woman.

'Can you comment on this morning's happenings in the old St Margaret's cemetery at Bingham College?' she asked. The microphone she'd been clutching was thrust at Tolliver's chin in what I considered a very aggressive way.

'Yes,' he said. 'We're waiting to hear if the body we discovered can be identified.' I admired the way he kept his voice so level and calm – but serious, and worthy of being taken seriously.

'Is it true the police are considering the possibility that the skeleton may be that of Tabitha Morgenstern?'

Well, that hadn't taken long to leak out.

'Our thoughts and our prayers are with the Morgenstern family. Of course, like everyone else here, we're very anxious to hear some news,' Tolliver said neutrally.

'Mr Lang, is it true your sister stated that the body just exhumed from the cemetery is *definitely* that of the missing girl?'

We weren't going to get by with anything. 'We believe that to be true,' he said, indirectly.

'How do you explain the coincidence?'

'What coincidence?' Tolliver asked, which I thought was maybe a little over the top.

Even Shellie Quail looked disconcerted. But she got back on her roll. 'That your sister was hired to look for Tabitha Morgenstern months ago in Nashville, and then hired to look at the graves in the old St Margaret's cemetery here in Memphis. And that a body reported to be that of Tabitha Morgenstern is found in that cemetery.'

'We have no idea how this came about, and we're looking forward to hearing the explanation,' Tolliver said sternly, as if we'd been mightily put-upon. Baffled, Shellie Quail paused to think of another question, and we took the opportunity to make our left turn.

3

The Cleveland was beautiful. The Cleveland was discreet. I was not going to want to see our credit card bill when it came next month.

A valet took our car, and we rolled into the lobby in a flurry of baggage and desperation, anxious to get away from the reporters who'd actually followed us to the new hotel. The staff was as courteous as if we'd stayed at the Cleveland four times a year. We were upstairs and out of reach of anyone in the twinkling of an eye. I was so glad to have time to regroup in relative safety and privacy, I could have cried.

The suite had a central living room with a bedroom on each side. Going directly to the bedroom on the right, I took off my shoes, lay down on my very own king-size bed, and surrounded myself with pillows. That's something I love about really good hotels: the abundance of pillows. Once I was padded and quiet and warm, I closed my eyes and let my thoughts drift. Of course, they drifted right to the little girl I'd found in the cemetery.

I'd assumed Tabitha was dead from the moment I'd read about her disappearance, weeks before the Morgensterns had asked me to find her body. Based on the information in the newspaper accounts and even more on my own experience, that was a logical assumption. In fact, I'd been fairly sure the child had been dead since scant hours after her disappearance.

That didn't mean I was happy to be right. I'm not callous about death; at least I don't think I am. I think of myself as more . . . matter-of-fact. And I'd seen the Morgensterns' anguish first-hand. Because of my sympathy for them, I'd persisted longer in the search than I'd thought was reasonable, and certainly long enough to cut into our profit very severely. Tolliver didn't even charge them the full amount; he didn't say anything to me, but when I went over our profits and expenses at the end of the year, I'd noticed.

Since Tabitha had been dead all this time, I thought it would be better for Joel and Diane to know what had happened to their daughter.

I could only hope that the sentiment I'd sprouted so glibly to the detective was valid. I could only hope that knowing for sure what had happened to Tabitha gave the Morgensterns some relief. At least they would know she wasn't in the hands of some madman, actively suffering.

I found myself wishing I'd had longer with the body. I'd been so startled at the identity of the grave's unauthorized inhabitant that I hadn't spent enough energy evaluating the girl's last moments. I'd only seen the blue cushion, a flash of the long seconds as Tabitha slipped into unconsciousness and then passed away – as she passed from the imitation of death to death itself.

I don't believe that death and life are two sides of the same coin. I think that's bullshit. I'm not going to say Tabitha was at peace with God, because God hasn't let me know on that one. And there'd been a strange feeling to my connection with the body; a sensation I'd seldom experienced before. I tried to analyze the difference, but I didn't come up with anything. That would bother me until I understood it.

I have seen a lot of death – a *lot*. I know death the way most people know sleep, or eating. Death is a fundamental human necessity, a solitary passage into the unknown. But Tabitha had made her passage years too early, at the end of a painful and frightening ordeal. I was sorry for the manner of her death. And something about it had marked her during that transition, in a way I had yet to understand. I filed it away to consider later; maybe another trip to the cemetery would help. It was hardly likely I'd be in contact with the body again.

I turned onto my side and stretched back to prop a pillow against my shoulders. I turned my thoughts down a mental path so familiar that it had ruts worn in it. That path led to my sister Cameron. Her face was fuzzy in my memory now, or it took on the contours of her last school picture, which I carried in my wallet.

Somehow, discovering Tabitha's corpse in such an indirect and unexpected way gave me hope that someday I might find my sister Cameron's remains.

Cameron has been gone for six years. Like Tabitha, she was snatched out of the stream of her life, leaving her backpack behind on the shore as witness to her departure. When Cameron had become way overdue at home that day, I started looking for her. I'd roused my mother enough to feel she could watch Mariella and Gracie for at least a little while, and I'd trudged through the sweltering heat, following the route Cameron took when she walked home from the high school. It was getting to be twilight by then. Cameron had stayed at school later than I because she was helping to decorate for a dance; the senior prom, I think.

I'd found her backpack, fully loaded with the school-books, note-books, notes passed to her in class, broken pencils, and small change. And that was all that was left of Cameron. The police had kept it for a long time, gone through its compartments, asked me about the content of every note. Then we'd asked for its return. Today, we carried that backpack in the trunk of our car.

When Tolliver came in, I was still lying on my bed. I'd rotated again, to lie flat on my back as I gazed at the ceiling, thinking about my sister.

'The car from the hotel's going to pick up Art at the airport,' he said. 'I got it all arranged.'

'Thanks,' I said, moving over to give him room. He lay on the other half of the vast king bed, shoes properly off. I let him have a pillow. Then I gave him another one.

'Looking back on the cemetery thing this morning,' he began, and gave me a moment to fix my attention back on the nearer past.

'Okay,' I said, to let him know I was ready to listen.

'Did you notice that man mixed in with the kids?'

'Yes, the guy who looked to be about thirty-five or so?'

'Dark brown hair, five ten, medium build.'

'Right. Yes, of course I noticed him. He stood out.'

'You think there was something fishy about him?'

'There was another older student,' I said, not really protesting Tolliver's direction, but testing it out.

'Yeah, but she was a regular person. There was something off about this guy; he was there for a purpose, not because he had to be. You think he was some kind of professional debunker? There to spot how we did it, and expose us?'

'Well, I think that was Clyde Nunley's goal in teaching the course, don't you? Not an inquiry to stimulate students' minds to seriously consider spiritualism and the people who practice it, but to prove that it's all claptrap.'

'But not as . . . I don't know, this guy seemed to have an agenda. He was purposeful.'

'I know what you mean,' I said.

'You think we've been set up?'

'Yes, I sure do think so. Unless this is the most amazing coincidence in the history of coincidences.'

'But why?' Tolliver turned his head to look at me.

'And who?' I countered.

The worry in his face mirrored my own.

My business would die without word of mouth. But it has to be a quiet word. If I brought a trail of newspaper and television reporters with me, half the people who use my services wouldn't want to see me coming. There are a few who'd love nothing better, but only a few. Most clients are embarrassed at hiring me at all, because they don't want to seem gullible. Some are desperate enough to be just that. But very few of them want any outside scrutiny.

So restrained coverage from time to time is okay. Once, a really good reporter wrote a story on me for a law enforcement journal, and I still get business from that exposure. Lots of officers clipped that story; when all else fails, they may get in touch with me through my website. My prices scare off some of the people who apply for my services. I'm not a lawyer, and no one asks me to do pro bono work.

Well, that's not true. People do. But I refuse.

However, I've never left a body unreported. If I find one in the course of a job, I'll report it, and I never ask for extra money for that.

If I got into the news too much, I'd be absolutely grabbing at pro bono work, just to get the good press. I didn't want to have to do that.

'Who do you think would hire such a person? Someone I didn't satisfy?' I asked the ceiling.

'We've found everyone since Tabitha,' Tolliver said.

Yes, I'd had a long string of successes: cases with enough information to go on and enough persistence on my part. Bodies found, causes of death confirmed. Money in the bank.

'Maybe someone connected with the college who wanted to check on what the class was being exposed to?' I guessed.

'Could be. Or someone connected with St Margaret's, who felt the cemetery was being used in some irreligious way.'

We both fell silent, puzzled and unhappy about too many things at once.

'I'm glad I found her, though,' I said. 'No matter what.'

My brother, who had followed my thoughts as he often did, said, 'Yeah.'

'Nice people,' I said.

'You never thought what the police suspected—?'

'No,' I said. 'I never believed Joel did it. These days, everyone looks at the dad first. Did he molest her?' I did my television announcer voice. 'Were there dark secrets in the house that seemed so normal?' I smiled with a twist of my mouth. People sure loved believing there were dark secrets – they love discovering happy normal families are anything but. Truly, sometimes there were plenty of secrets, more than enough to go around. But Joel and Diane Morgenstern had struck me as truly devoted parents, and I'd seen enough of the kind of parents who weren't to recognize the ones who were.

'I never believed it,' I repeated. 'But – here they are. In Memphis.' We looked at each other. 'How the hell could it have happened that her body turned up here, the city where her parents are living now? Unless there's a connection.'

There was a tap at our suite door.

'The troops are here,' Tolliver said.

'Well. The troop.'

Art was missing a lot of his hair. What remained was curly and white. He was very heavy, but he dressed very well. So he looked like an eminently respectable, sweet-natured grandpa – which just goes to show how deceptive appearances can be.

Art maintains the fiction that he is my father substitute.

'Harper!' he cried, throwing open his arms. I stepped in, gave him a light hug, and backed away when I could. Tolliver got a clap on the shoulder and a handshake.

We asked about his wife, and he told us what (but not how) Johanna was doing: taking art classes, keeping the grandchildren, remaining active in their church and several charities.

Not that we'd ever met Johanna.

I watched Art grope, trying to think of someone he could ask us about in return. He could hardly ask about our parents: my mother had died the previous year, in jail, of AIDS. Tolliver's mother had died years ago, of breast cancer, before we'd even met Art. Tolliver's dad, my stepfather, was in the wind since he'd gotten out of jail, having served his time on drug charges. My own father was still in big-boy prison, and would be for maybe five more years. He'd taken some money from his clients to support the drug habit he and my mother had developed. We never saw our little half sisters, Gracie and Mariella, because my Aunt Iona, my mom's sister, had poisoned the girls against us. Tolliver's brother, Mark, had his own life, and didn't much approve of ours, but we called him at least once a month.

And of course, there was never any news about Cameron.

'It's great to see you two looking so healthy,' Art said in his heartiest voice. 'Now, let's order some room service, and you can tell me all about this.' Art loved it when we ate together. Not only did it make the meal billable, but it also reassured Art that Tolliver and I were normal people and not some kind of vampires. After all, we ate and drank like the rest of the world.

'It should be up in a minute,' Tolliver said, and Art had to go on and on about how amazed he was that Tolliver had been so farseeing.

Actually, I was pretty impressed myself.

Art made notes throughout the meal as we told him everything we remembered about our previous search for Tabitha Morgenstern. My brother got out his laptop and checked our records to be sure of how much the Morgensterns had paid us for our fruitless search. We assured Art that we had no intention of charging them anything for finding her today – in fact, the idea made me sick. Art looked kind of relieved when I told him that.

'There's no way we can leave here without seeing the Morgensterns or talking to the police?' I asked, knowing I sounded cowardly.

'No way in the world,' Art said. For once, he sounded as hard as he actually was. 'In fact, the sooner you talk to them, the better. And you have to issue a press statement.'

'Why?' Tolliver asked.

'Silence is suspicious. You have to say clearly that you had no idea that you would find Tabitha's body, that you're shocked and saddened, and that you are praying for the Morgensterns.'

'We already told Channel Thirteen that.'

'You need to tell everyone.'

'You'll do that for us?'

'Yes. We need to write a statement. I'll read it on-camera for you. I'll take a few questions from the press, just enough to establish who you are. After that, I think questions will just muddy the water, especially since I won't be able to answer them.'

I looked at Art, perhaps with a certain skepticism; he gave me big hurt eyes. 'Harper, you know I wouldn't put you all in a spot hotter than the one you're in already. But we have to set the record straight while we can.'

'You think we're going to be arrested?'

'Not necessarily. I didn't say that. I meant, highly unlikely.' Art was backpedaling to firmer ground. 'I'm saying this is our chance to get in our licks with the public, while we can.'

Tolliver looked at Art for a minute. 'All right,' he said, when he reached his conclusion. 'Art, you stay here while Harper and I go in the other room and write the press statement. Then you can look it over.'

Leaving our lawyer no chance to offer another plan, we retreated to Tolliver's room, with his laptop to act as our secretary.

Tolliver settled at the desk, while I flung myself across the bed. 'Dr Nunley never said anything to you, did he, about Tabitha? When he asked us to come here?' I asked.

'Not a word. I would have told you,' Tolliver said. 'He just talked about the old cemetery, about how it would be a true test, since you really had no idea who was buried there and there was no way you could find out. He wanted to know if you'd be comfortable with that. Of course, he thought I'd make some excuse for you, trying to back out. Nunley was really surprised when I emailed him back, told him to expect us. He'd just had Xylda Bernardo, the psychic. She lives in this area, remember?'

I'd met Xylda once or twice, in the line of duty. 'How'd she do?' I asked, out of sheer professional curiosity. Xylda, a colorful woman in her fifties, likes to dress in the traditional stage-gypsy style – lots of jewelry and scarves, long messy hair – which immediately makes people distrust her. But Xylda has a true gift. Unfortunately, like most commercial psychics, she embellishes that nugget of talent with a lot of theatrics and made-up flourishes, which she thinks lend her visions credibility.

Psychics – honest psychics – do receive a lot of information when they touch something a crime victim owned. The bad part is, quite often they receive information so vague it's almost useless ('The body's buried in the middle of an empty field'), unless you have a good idea what you're looking for to begin with. Even if there are a few psychics who can see a clear picture of, say, the house where a child's being held hostage, unless the psychic can also see the address, and the police find an identifiable suspect lives in that house, the building's appearance is almost irrelevant. There are even some psychics who can achieve all that, but then they have to get the police to believe them . . . since I've never met a single psychic who was also up on SWAT tactics.

'Oh, according to Nunley, Xylda did her usual,' Tolliver said. 'Vague stuff that sounded really good, like "Your grandmother says to look for something unexpected in the attic, something that will make you very happy," or "Be careful of the dark man who comes unexpectedly, for he is not trustworthy," and that's flexible enough to cover a lot of circumstances. The members of the class were pretty weirded out, since Xylda insists on touching the people she's reading. The students didn't want Xylda holding their hands. But that's the way it's done; for Xylda, touch is everything. You think she's for real?'

'I think most of what Xylda tells clients is bullshit. But I also think she actually has a few moments when she knows stuff.'

Every now and then, I wonder: if the lightning had hit me a little harder, if I'd gotten a few more volts – would I have become able to see *who* caused the deaths of the people I find? Sometimes I think such a condition would be wonderful, a truly valuable gift. Sometimes it seems like my worst nightmare.

What if the lightning had entered through my foot, or my head, instead of jumping from the sink to the electric hair curler I held in my hands . . . what would have happened then? I probably wouldn't be around to know. My heart would have stopped for good, instead of for a few seconds. The CPR wouldn't have worked.

By now, Tolliver might be married to some nice girl who liked to be pregnant, the kind of girl who enjoyed going to home decoration parties.

Carrying this stream of supposition to an extreme length – if I'd died that day, maybe, somehow, Cameron would not have been on the road on that day at that hour, and she would not have been taken.

It's stupid and profitless, thinking like that, of course. So I don't indulge in it very often. Right at this moment, I needed to force myself to throw off this train of thought. Instead of daydreaming, I needed to concentrate on helping Tolliver compose the press release. What he'd said to Shellie Quail had been the gist of our public policy. We began embroidering on that. It was hard to imagine that anyone would believe us; after all, what were the odds that the same people who had failed to find the body in Nashville would find it in Memphis? But we had to try.

We'd just finished printing out our statement when I had to answer the phone. The manager said, 'Ms Connelly, there are some people down here who want to come up to talk to you and Mr Lang. Are you receiving guests?'

'Who are they, please?'

'The Morgensterns. And another lady.'

Diane and Joel. My heart sank, but this had to be done. 'Yes, send them up, please.'

Tolliver stepped into the living room to update Art while I printed out the statement. Art read it and made a few minor changes while we waited. In two or three minutes a hand rapped on our door.

I took a deep breath and opened it, and received yet another shock in a day that had already been full of them. Detective Lacey had told us Diane was expecting another baby, but I hadn't gotten a visual with that fact. Seeing her now, there was no mistaking it. Diane Morgenstern was really, really pregnant – seven months along, at the least.

She was still beautiful. Her bitter-chocolate hair was smooth and short, and her big dark eyes owed nothing to makeup. Diane had a small mouth and a small nose. She looked like a really pretty lemur of some kind. Just at the moment, though, her expression was simply blank with shock.

Her husband, Joel, was maybe five foot ten and stocky, powerful looking. He'd been a wrestler in college. I remembered the trophies in his study in their Nashville house. He had light red hair and bright blue eyes, a ruddy complexion, and a square face with a nose like a knife blade. How did all this add to up to a man women could not ignore? I don't have the faintest idea. Joel Morgenstern was the kind of man who focused on the person to whom he was speaking, which might have been the secret of the magnetism he exuded. To Joel's credit, he didn't seem to be aware of this; or maybe he took it so for granted that he didn't even think of the effect he had on women.

In Nashville, even under the circumstances I'd noticed how the female representatives of the media clustered around him. Maybe they'd been thinking the father is always a likely suspect, maybe they'd been trying to pick holes in his story, but they'd hovered around him like hummingbirds at a big red blossom. Not too surprisingly, the police had checked over and over to see if Joel was having an affair. They hadn't found a trace of such a thing; in fact, everyone who knew Joel commented on how devoted he was to Diane. For that matter, it was universal knowledge how caring he'd been during his first wife's terminal illness.

Maybe because lightning had fried my brain, maybe because my standards of judgment were completely different, Joel just didn't affect me like he did most women.

Felicia Hart, whose sister had been Joel's first wife, trailed in after Diane and Joel. I remembered Felicia from my first encounter with the family. She had been trying hard to be a good aunt to Victor, the son that first marriage had produced. She'd been aware that Victor was a suspect in Tabitha's disappearance, and she'd been at the house constantly, perhaps imagining that the loss of their daughter had meant that Diane and Joel would not be able to focus on Victor's needs and on his legal position.

'You found her,' Joel said, taking my hand and pumping it ferociously. 'God bless you, you found her. The medical examiner says there's a long way to go before an official identification, but the dental charts do match. We have to keep this to ourselves, but Dr Frierson was kind enough to let us know in person. Thank God, we can have some peace.'

This was such a different reaction from the one I'd expected that I was unable to respond. Luckily, Tolliver was more collected.

'Please, Diane, Joel, sit down,' he said. Tolliver is very reverent toward pregnant women.

Diane had always seemed the frailer partner in the couple, even when she wasn't so obviously carrying a child.

'Let me hug you first,' she said in her soft voice, and she wrapped her arms around me. I felt her distended belly pressing against my flat one, and I felt something wiggle while she was hugging me. After a second, I realized it was the baby, kicking against her stomach. Something deep inside me clenched in a mixture of horror and longing. I let Diane go and backed away, trying to smile at her.

Felicia Hart was no hugger, to my relief. She gave me a firm handshake, though she did put her arms around Tolliver. In fact, she muttered something in his ear. I blinked at that. 'Glad to see you,' she said a bit loudly, addressing an area somewhere between us. Felicia was a single woman. I placed her in her early thirties. She had jaw-length glossy brown hair that curved forward, and her expertly cut bangs stayed where they were supposed to be. As a professional woman on her own, she could spend all her money on herself, and her clothes and makeup showed it. If I remembered correctly, Felicia was a financial adviser employed by a national company. Though I hadn't talked to her at any length, I knew Felicia would have to be both intelligent and bold to hold down so responsible a job with such success.

When we were all seated, Joel and Diane on the love seat, Felicia perched on one arm of it by Diane, and Tolliver and I in wing chairs on the other side of the coffee table, with Art settled uncomfortably on a chair set a bit aside, I realized I had to somehow proceed with a conversation.

'I'm so sorry,' I said finally, since that was the truth. 'I'm sorry I found her so late, and I'm sorry the circumstances make life even more difficult for you.' It made life a hell of a lot more difficult for us, too, but this didn't seem like the moment to dwell on it.

'You're right, this doesn't look good for us,' Joel said. He took Diane's hand. 'We were already under suspicion. Not Felicia, of course, but Diane and I and Victor, and now that . . .' He had trouble going on. 'Now that her body has been found here – of all the places on earth – I think the police are going to decide it was one of us all along. I almost don't blame them. It just looks bad. If I didn't know how much we loved Tabitha . . .' He sighed heavily. 'Maybe they think we conspired together to kill our daughter. They're paid to be suspicious. They can't know it's the last thing in the world we'd do. But as long as they're focusing on us, they won't be looking for the son of a bitch who actually took her.'

'Exactly,' Diane said, and her hand rubbed her stomach in a circular motion. I yanked my gaze away.

'How long have the police suspected you?' Tolliver asked. When we'd been there, Tabitha had been missing for several weeks, and the police hadn't been around so much any more. But we'd been impressed at how cordial the relationship that had formed between Detective Haines, who'd been the Last Man Standing on the case, and the Morgensterns had seemed. I should have realized that the other cops might have developed other suspicions. Haines had actually gotten to know the Morgensterns a lot better than her associates.

'From the get-go,' Joel said, his voice resigned. 'After nosing around Vic for a while, they got the idea that Diane was guilty.'

I could almost see why they'd suspect Joel, even Victor. But Diane?

'How could that be?' I said incautiously, and she flushed. 'I'm sorry,' I said instantly. 'I'm not trying to dredge up bad memories. I was sure, always, that you and Joel were telling the truth.'

'Tabitha and I had a fight that morning,' Diane said. Big fat tears ran down her cheeks. 'I was mad because we'd just given her a cell phone for her birthday, and she'd already exceeded her minutes. I took her cell away from her, and then I told her to go outside to water the plants around the front door, just to get her out of the house because I was so angry. She was furious, too. Spring break, and no way to communicate with her three hundred best friends. She was just into that "Mo-THER!" stage, the eye-rolling thing.' Diane wiped her face with Joel's handkerchief. 'I didn't think we'd get to that until she was fifteen, and here she was, eleven years old, giving me the whole routine.' She smiled in a watery sort of way. 'I hated to tell the police about this really trivial conversation, but one of my neighbors overheard us arguing when she came over to ask if we were through with our paper. So then I had to relate the whole thing to the police, and they turned hostile so quickly, as if I'd been withholding important evidence from them!'

Of course, to the police, this was important evidence. The fact that Diane couldn't see that only proved what I'd suspected about her when I'd met her: Diane Morgenstern was no rocket scientist. I was willing to bet that she never read crime fiction, either. If she had, she'd have known that any such revelation would make the police suspicious.

All the incident really proved was that Diane was out of touch with popular culture, in the reading-and-television-watching category.

'When did you move to Memphis?' Tolliver asked.

'About a year ago,' Joel said. 'We couldn't wait there, in that house, any longer.' He sat up a little straighter, and as if he were reciting a credo, he said, 'We had to accept the fact that our daughter was gone, and we had to leave that house ourselves. It wouldn't be fair to the new family we're starting, to have the baby there. I actually grew up in Memphis, so it felt like coming home, to me. My parents are here. And Felicia was here, along with her parents, my first in-laws. She and

Victor are very close, and we figured the move would be a good thing for him. He's had a very tough time.'

So everyone was happy here, except possibly Diane. It hadn't been coming home for her. It had been a move to a strange city that held many memories for her husband, memories of his first wife.

'We'd had a lot of therapy, the whole family,' Diane said softly.

'We all went, Diane and I and Victor,' Joel said. 'Even Felicia drove over to Nashville from Memphis to go to some of the sessions.'

I'd been to therapy, too.

The high school guidance counselor had been horrified when Cameron's disappearance had exposed the conditions under which we lived. 'Why didn't you come to me?' she'd asked, more than once. And one time she'd shaken her head and said, 'I should have noticed.' I didn't blame her for not noticing; after all, we'd gone to great efforts to conceal our home life, so we could stay together. Maybe a part of me had hoped that our substandard parents would be taken away and we would be given good parents, instead; but that hadn't happened.

'When is the new baby due?' Art asked in the cheerful voice parents used when they weren't going to be having any more babies themselves.

'In five weeks,' Diane said, an involuntary smile curving her lips even under the circumstances. 'A healthy boy, the doctor says.'

'That's great,' Tolliver and I said, more or less in unison. I eyed Felicia Hart, who'd risen to stand behind the love seat. Felicia was looking less than ecstatic, perhaps even impatient. Maybe she thought the new baby would mean even more attention was diverted from Victor. It was also possible the childless Felicia was even more creeped out by pregnant women than I was.

'Today, we have to deal with Tabitha,' Diane said, to give us an easement back into the grim reality of the body in the cemetery. 'How . . . you know how she died?'

'She was suffocated,' I said, not knowing any other way to say it. Severely deprived of air? Terminally oxygenless? I wasn't trying to tell myself jokes, but there are only so many ways to talk about the COD of any individual, even a child, especially to the mother.

The couple did their best to take the news on the chin, but Diane couldn't suppress a moan of horror. Felicia looked away, her face a hard mask concealing deep emotion.

There were many worse ways to die, but that would hardly be a consolation. Suffocation was bad enough. 'It would be over in seconds,' I said, as gently as I could. 'She would be unconscious, after a tiny bit.' This was an exaggeration, but I thought Diane's condition called for as much cushioning as possible. I was terrified that she would go into labor right in front of us.

Art had the strangest expression as he looked at me. It was like he'd never seen me before; like the reality of me, of what I did, had just hit him in the portly belly he carried in front of him like an announcement of his own importance.

'We should call Vic,' Joel said, in his warm voice. 'Excuse me for a moment.' He brushed at his eyes and groped in his pocket for his cell phone. Vic, Joel's son by his first marriage, had been a sullen fifteen-year-old at the time of Tabitha's abduction. I'd glimpsed him trying hard to be tough and contained in the face of an overwhelming situation.

Diane, who had seemed very fond of the boy and in fact had largely raised him – she'd married Joel when Victor was very young – said, 'If he needs to talk to me, I'm okay,' as Joel rose to walk a few feet away, his back to the room, to punch in the number.

'How's Victor done here in Memphis?' I asked Felicia, just to be saying something. Victor and I had shared a strange moment when I'd been trying to find his half sister. The boy had come into the living room of the Morgenstern home and begun to curse a blue streak, evidently thinking he was by himself. When I'd moved, he'd clutched me, crying on my shoulder, having to bend a little to do so. People weren't given to touching me, and I'd been startled. But I knew grief, and I knew release, and I'd held him until he was through. When he'd done crying and my blouse was a blotched mess, Victor had drawn back, appalled at his breakdown. Anything I said would have been wrong, so I'd just given him a nod. He'd nodded back, and fled.

Felicia was giving a surprised look. I supposed she was astonished that I remembered Victor at all. 'He's done . . . middling,' she said. 'Diane and Joel have sent him to a private school. I help them out a little. He's such a fragile kid, hanging in the balance. At that age, they can go either way, you feel, at any moment. And with this new baby coming . . .' Her voice trailed off, as if she couldn't imagine how to finish the sentence without criticizing Joel and Diane for their ill-timed fertility.

Joel came back and sat down by his wife, and he was frowning.

'Victor isn't holding together very well,' he said to us in general. Diane's face simply looked exhausted, as if she had no energy to spare for maintaining someone else's spirits when her own were so fraught with misery. 'He came home from school early, after we called. We didn't want anyone to see it on the news at noon and tell him when they got back to campus,' he explained.

We all nodded wisely, but my mind was on something entirely different.

'We never knew you moved,' I said, wanting to get that absolutely clear, 'so we were astonished when the police said they were contacting you. You don't have anything to do with the faculty at Bingham, do you? You're not an alumna, Diane?'

'No, I went to Vanderbilt, and Joel did, too,' she said, bewildered. 'Felicia, didn't you go to Bingham? With David?'

Felicia said, 'More years ago than I care to remember. Yes, David was in my class. I don't believe you met him in Nashville, Harper. Joel's brother.'

'Felicia's parents are here in Memphis, too,' Diane said. 'They both went to Bingham. And so did Joel's. It was quite a scandal when he decided to go to Vanderbilt. Why are you asking?'

'Just trying to think of some connection between you and the school. Someone put Tabitha's . . . Tabitha there, and someone made sure we were hired for this job.'

The couple sat and looked at me wide-eyed. I had the uncharitable thought that this increased Diane's resemblance to a lemur. Though the pregnant woman looked as though she were about to bolt, Joel was alert and intense. The man had an overabundance of energy, and it boiled around him, even under these circumstances. Behind them, Felicia was staring at me with an incredulous face.

'Surely it's just a coincidence,' Felicia said, finally, looking at me as though I were delusional. 'You don't think . . . you can't imagine that someone created such an elaborate plot? How could someone have put Tabitha there, and then find you, get you here, make sure you found Tabitha? That's just incredible.'

We all spent a second or two staring at each other. Art was looking from me to Felicia, as if we were playing Ping-Pong.

'I agree,' I said. 'But I can't make sense out of any other scenario. Actually, there's not much sense in that one.'

'We have to issue some kind of statement to the press,' Art said, when he realized the conversation had reached a stalemate. 'It has to be a statement that treads a fine line. We can't rule anything out, like Diane just did. We can't make any fantastic claims, like Harper did. We have to regret everything and admit nothing about our personal feelings about what might have happened.'

Tolliver was the only one who nodded his head in agreement.

'You know, our own lawyer is downstairs,' Diane murmured.

At the same moment Joel erupted. 'No!' he said. 'No! We have to condemn whoever did this to our daughter in the strongest possible terms!' Diane and Felicia both nodded their agreement.

'Oh, of course,' Art said. 'Naturally, that, too.'

4

We turned on the television in the living room of the suite to watch Art meet the news cameras. There were three stations in Memphis, and all three had sent representatives to the press conference, which was held on the sidewalk outside the Cleveland. By that time, the Morgenstern family lawyer, a chic fortyish woman named Blythe Benson, had arrived on the scene. Joel and Diane had told us that Benson had insisted on the Morgenstern family issuing their own separate-but-equal statement. The local lawyer and Art made an impressive duo. Art had that older-man gravitas thing going, and Blythe was cool and blond and WASP-y to the nth degree.

Blythe had consulted with the Morgensterns at their home about what she was going to say on their behalf, Diane told us. Felicia shot me a glance as Diane said this, and I wondered what was coming. Felicia Hart, as I've said, seemed way smarter than Diane. It made me wonder what Felicia's sister, Joel's first wife, had been like.

Downstairs and outside, Blythe Benson prepared to make the first statement. The family was most important, we had all agreed.

'Diane and Joel Morgenstern are devastated at the news that the body that may be that of their child, Tabitha, has been found in St Margaret's cemetery. Though closure is something they have sought for many months, Diane and Joel Morgenstern had hoped that closure would come with the return of their living daughter. Instead, they have recovered what may well be her body.' The blonde lawyer paused for effect. The newscasters were fairly quivering with the desire to ask questions, but Blythe plowed on. 'The Morgenstern family would like to urge anyone who may have knowledge of the disappearance of Tabitha to come forward at this time. Though the reward for the discovery of her body is most likely out of consideration now, there is still a reward standing for the submission of facts about Tabitha's abduction.'

I wasn't sure what that meant. I hadn't known there was a reward, since we hadn't maintained contact with the Morgensterns (naturally) after our failure to locate their daughter in Nashville.

Thinking that was the end of the statement, I'd turned to look at Tolliver to get his reaction when I heard Blythe Benson's precise voice continue. I looked back at the screen.

'As to what police have termed an "amazing coincidence" – that the psychic Diane and Joel Morgenstern hired to find Tabitha's body actually did find the body, though in a different location . . .'

She's losing control of that sentence, I thought.

'The fact remains that there are coincidences in life, and this is one of them. Diane and Joel Morgenstern did not hire Harper Connelly to come to Memphis. They have not seen her or her manager since Miss Connelly arrived in Memphis. They did not know that Miss Connelly was scheduled to give a demonstration at the old cemetery of St Margaret's this morning. Neither of the Morgensterns attended Bingham College. Neither has ever been connected with the college department that arranged Harper Connelly's visit to St Margaret's cemetery. In fact, no member of the Morgenstern family has contacted Harper Connelly or her brother and manager, Tolliver Lang, since her unsuccessful attempt to find Tabitha over eighteen months ago. Thank you.'

Though Art hadn't moved physically, the cameras caught him staring at Blythe Benson as though she'd just sprouted horns, and I didn't blame him for the look.

Just for openers, Benson's voice had emphasized 'psychic' and 'giving a demonstration' as if they were words for something far nastier and more disreputable. Then she'd gone on to sever her clients from us in every possible way. She'd all but said we were implicated somehow in the death of the girl.

We'd been hung out to dry.

As one, Tolliver and I turned to look at the couple on the couch. The Morgensterns seemed oblivious to the implications of the speech Blythe Benson had just read. They were staring at the television, waiting for Art's speech, in a kind of numb silence. Behind them, Felicia gave us a significant look that meant, 'Ha! I told you so!' I exchanged a look with Tolliver, a look of sheer incredulity. He half-opened his mouth, and I reached over to touch his arm. 'Not now,' I said, very quietly.

I wasn't sure why I chose to be quiet, rather than confront Joel and

Diane. God knows, even Diane was smart enough to realize that they'd just dumped us publicly, while sitting in our very own (temporarily) living room. They'd said, in effect, 'Whatever these people claim, we're not responsible for it. We don't know them, we haven't seen them, we'd never collaborate with them, and they failed the first time we asked them to find our child.'

Art took his place before the microphones. It's just strange seeing someone you know on television, not that it's an experience I've had often. The fact that the person who was just in the room with you is now on-camera, for the moment an icon, is weird and unsettling. It's as if they've become translated by the screen into another being – someone less flawed and more knowledgeable, someone smoother and smarter.

Art had our statement, the one Tolliver and I had written, but he was doing yet another rewrite in his head at just this minute; a hasty and public one. I could see it in the long downward focus of his eyes before he began speaking.

'My client, Harper Connelly, is astounded and grieved by the events of the day. At this moment Ms Connelly is with Tabitha's parents, who came here to thank Harper, from their hearts, for her part in the discovery of a body we believe to be that of their missing daughter.'

Ha! Ball in your court, Blythe!

'Ms Connelly is deeply saddened by the tragic end to her search for Tabitha Morgenstern. Though she did not maintain any contact whatsoever with the family during the months since her original employment, and though she had no knowledge that the Morgenstern family had moved to Memphis, Ms Connelly is glad that circumstances brought about the discovery of the long-lost child the Morgensterns have been seeking. Perhaps, thanks to my client, the Morgensterns' long time of uncertainty has come to an end.'

'When will Harper Connelly meet with us?' said a reporter, in a voice that was not awfully loud, but extremely piercing.

Art gave the reporter a wonderful look; it combined reproof with resignation. 'Ms Connelly does not talk to reporters,' he said, as if that were a well-known fact. 'Ms Connelly lives a very private life.'

'Is it true . . .' began a familiar voice, and the camera swung around to frame the shining Shellie Quail.

'For God's sake,' I said. 'She's everywhere.'

Tolliver smiled. He thought the reporter's doggedness was a little funny, maybe even admirable.

'. . . that Miss Connelly charges a fee for finding bodies?'

'Ms Connelly is a professional woman with an unusual gift,' Art said. 'She does not like to be in the spotlight of media attention, something she has never sought.'

That's true enough, I thought. *Evasive, but true.*

'Is it true that your client will be claiming the reward for finding Tabitha's body?' asked Shellie Quail, and Tolliver's smile vanished in the blink of my eye.

'That's not a subject we've discussed,' Art concluded. 'I have no more to say at this time. Thank you for coming.' And he turned to pace back inside the Cleveland's front door. The Morgensterns' lawyer was nowhere to be seen. Blythe Benson had slipped away in the preceding moments, apparently.

I hoped she didn't plan on coming up to the suite.

The cameras cut back to the scheduled program, and in a moment Art returned to the room, in actual reality. Again, I felt that curious jolt.

'That went well,' Joel said without a touch of irony. Tolliver and I had to struggle to keep our faces neutral. 'And of course, you'll get the reward.' Joel got up, checked his watch. 'Diane, we have to get home. We have people to call. I wonder how long it will take for them to be sure they've got . . . Tabitha's remains. When we can have them.'

Felicia picked up her purse and Diane's, ready to help the pregnant woman return to their car.

With a heave, Diane got to her feet. She was absently rubbing her hand across her gravid stomach, as if to keep its contents calm. I remembered my own mother's pregnancies with Mariella and Gracie. I also couldn't help recalling *Rosemary's Baby*; Tolliver and I had watched it the week before on an old-movie channel.

'Thanks, Felicia,' Diane said.

'Let us know how Victor's doing,' Tolliver asked out of the clear blue sky.

'What?' Felicia turned, and her eyes pinned Tolliver to the wall. 'Why, of course.' There was a bite to her voice that I simply didn't understand. I looked from her to Tolliver, but didn't get an explanation.

'This has been harder on Victor than just about anyone,' Joel said. 'Kids can be so cruel.'

'Victor's what, now? Sixteen?' I asked brightly, trying to ease the atmosphere. I don't know why. I should have stood in absolute silence until the party left.

'He's just turned seventeen,' Diane said. Suddenly her face lost its Madonna-like sweetness. She had struck me, even when I'd first met her after the abduction, as a woman fed up to the teeth with her stepson's moody teenage behavior, and now her jaw had a certain set that gave her simple words a real edge. 'I love that boy, but everything they say about teenagers is true, as far as Vic's concerned: he's been secretive and sullen or talking back for the past three years. When Tabitha began to show signs she was entering the same phase, I just wasn't ready for it. I overreacted.'

Victor had been a spotty – but athletic and attractive – boy eighteen months before. I remembered him always skulking on the edge of any group of adults in the Morgenstern home, his face tight with suppressed – rage? Fear? I hoped for the boy's sake that his complexion and his attitude had cleared up now. I was willing to believe Victor had feelings and thoughts that were complicated and dealt with something besides himself, but only because I tried to believe that of all people.

'How can you say that, Diane?' Felicia asked, but without much real indignation. 'He's been yours since he was a baby. You have to love him, like I do.'

'I do love him,' Diane said, sounding as surprised as an emotionally exhausted pregnant woman can. 'I've always loved him, at first for his mother's sake, but then because I raised him as my son. You, of all people, should know that. Even if he were my own biological child, I'd be having a hard time with him right now. It's not him, it's his stage of life.'

'He doesn't like school here very much,' Joel said. He sounded just as tired as his wife, as if dealing with Victor wore him out. 'But he's great on the tennis team.'

'Poor Victor,' my brother said, somewhat to my surprise.

'Yes, the whole thing's been very hard on him, too,' Joel said. 'Of course, he was sure he was going to be arrested and executed instantly, the drastic way teenagers decide things, when the police questioned him very . . . persistently.'

'They thought he might resent his little sister, the attention she got as the child of the second marriage.' Then Diane went absolutely still, and I had a moment of panic, thinking something was happening with the baby. But it was just one of the moments when anguish comes sweeping down like an eagle from the air, to tear at you with cruel talons.

'Oh, Tabitha,' Diane said, in a low voice that contained profound grief. 'Oh, my girl.' Large tears began to roll from her beautiful dark eyes.

Her husband put his arm around her and together they left to return to their new home. Felicia trailed after them, her face heavy with unhappiness.

I looked at the closed door a few minutes after they'd passed through it. I wondered if the baby's room was ready yet. I wondered what they'd done with all Tabitha's things.

With their departure, the tension eased out of the room. Art, Tolliver, and I looked at each other with some relief.

'That's great news, about the reward. Last I heard, it was up to twenty-five thousand dollars. Before taxes, of course.' Art was reviewing the afternoon mentally, I could tell from the way he was drumming his fingers on the occasional table. 'I'm glad I went second, after all,' Art said next. 'I've heard of Blythe Benson. She said a few things I took issue with.'

'Yeah, we noticed.' Tolliver got a crossword puzzle book out of his laptop bag and began rummaging around in the bottom of the pocket for his pencil.

Art looked irritated. 'You think I could have handled it differently, Tolliver, you say so.'

Tolliver looked up, apparently surprised. 'No, Art, no problem. You, Harper?'

'I noticed you didn't say Tolliver was your client, too, Art,' I said.

Art did his best to seem surprised; though I thought his only real surprise was that we'd noticed the omission. 'Tolliver's name hadn't been brought into the mix at that point, I was just trying to keep it that way,' he said. 'You want me to call all the reporters and correct myself?'

'No, Art, that's fine,' I said. 'Just, for future reference, be more thorough and include that little detail.'

'Message received,' Art said brightly. 'It's been a long day for an old man, kids. I'm going to my room, call the office, catch up on my work.'

'Sure, Art,' Tolliver said, his attention on the puzzle open before him. 'If you're not flying back to Atlanta until tomorrow, you'll have to join us for dinner.'

'Thanks, we'll see how much work I have to do tonight. I may just get room service. But give me a call when you're ready to head out.'

'See you later,' I said.

When he was safely gone, I said, 'What do you think he's heard?'

'I was trying to figure it out. Maybe the police think I had Tabitha's body all this time and moved it into the cemetery to prove you were a genuine sensitive.'

I gaped at him and then laughed. It was just too ridiculous.

Tolliver put down his pencil and focused on me. 'Yeah, right. I don't know where I'm supposed to have stowed the poor girl's body for eighteen months, or whatever.'

'The trunk,' I said, deadpan, and after a second he smiled at me. It was a real smile, something he didn't give me that often, and I enjoyed seeing it. Tolliver hadn't been struck by lightning, and his mom hadn't tried to sell him to one of her drug buddies for sexual use, it's true, but Tolliver has his own scars, and he's not any more fond of talking about them than I am.

'Tabitha was somewhere for eighteen months,' Tolliver pointed out. 'That is, her body was either in that grave, or in some other hiding place.'

'Was she there all the time?' I asked, but I was just thinking out loud. 'I don't think so. The earth was disturbed. The rest of the ground in the cemetery was smooth, but this ground had an uneven feeling, and there wasn't any grass on the grave.'

'Well, we know she was buried somewhere during the last eighteen months,' Tolliver pointed out reasonably.

'No, she could have been alive for part of that time. Or she could have been dead in a freezer, or a meat locker, or a morgue. Or buried somewhere else, as you say.' I thought about the possibilities I'd raised. 'But I don't think so. I still believe she's been dead since she was abducted, or very nearly the whole time. But she wasn't lying in St Margaret's all that time. I just don't understand why she was put there, and how it happened that I was the one to find her. It's so strange.'

'In fact, it's almost . . . unbelievable,' Tolliver said, his voice quiet and thoughtful.

5

The morning didn't start on any more of a positive note. I turned on CNN while I drank my morning coffee, the complimentary newspaper folded open to the page that featured an old picture of Tabitha, a recent shot of the Morgensterns, and a picture of me taken when I was at a crime scene about two years ago.

The TV coverage was just as hyper as the newspaper article. The FBI had definitely had a presence at the initial crime of Tabitha's kidnapping. Now, they'd put their expertise at the service of the Memphis police, including the resources of their lab.

'We are confident in the ability of the Memphis police to conduct this investigation,' said an agent who looked like he ate nails for breakfast. 'We'll have an agent in place who participated in the investigation of Tabitha's abduction, and he'll make available any service he can offer to local officials. All we want is to get justice for this little girl and her family.'

I wondered if we'd be allowed to leave for our apartment in St Louis – though it would be better yet if we could slip away to some unexpected destination, so we'd be harder to track. We weren't in residence at our apartment often, true, but it was our address of record, and the news media would definitely find us there.

I didn't remember what the next job on our list was, or even if we had one. Tolliver managed that side of our lives. I was already restless and bored, having finished the one book I'd brought in from our car. Ordinarily, I'd go out for a run.

There was no point whatsoever in trying to run today. Though I still felt a bit shaky from yesterday's discovery, I was definitely in the mood to get in a couple of miles, or more. But if I ran today, I'd be followed, and that was no fun.

Tolliver knocked at the connecting door, and I called to him to come in. He was toweling the wetness out of his hair.

'I went running on the treadmill in the health club,' he said, in answer to my unspoken question. 'It was better than nothing.'

I hate running on treadmills. It just makes me feel stupid. I'm not really going anywhere. But this morning I was willing, since I needed activity in the worst kind of way. While he poured his own cup of coffee, I was on the elevator in my running shoes and my shorts and my T-shirt.

There were several treadmills. One was already occupied by a man who was probably in his forties, dark hair just beginning to turn silvery at the edges. He was pounding along, his face set and remote. He gave me an absent nod, which I barely returned.

I studied the control panel and the instructions, since I couldn't imagine anything that would make me feel stupider than flying off the back of a treadmill. When I was confident I understood what I was doing, I started off slow, getting used to the feel of the rubber under my feet. I thought of nothing, just the feeling of my shoes hitting the treadmill, and then I reached down and pressed the control to increase the speed. Soon I was going at a good clip – and though I was indoors and not going anywhere and the damn scenery never changed, I was content. I began sweating, and gradually I began to feel that welcome exhaustion that tells you you've gone just about your limit. I slowed the pace a bit, and then slowed again, and finally I walked for about five minutes.

I'd been vaguely aware Mr Silvertip was still in the room, moving from weight station to weight station, one of the hotel towels around his neck. I headed for the stack on a table by the door as soon as I was through, and while I was patting my face dry, a voice said, 'It's good to run in the mornings, isn't it? Helps you to start your day on a good note.'

I lowered the towel to appraise the speaker.

'FBI?' I asked.

He couldn't control his jerk of surprise. 'You're really psychic,' he said pleasantly after a moment.

'No, I'm not,' I said. 'Or only in the most limited way. Were you down here when Tolliver ran, too?'

He had dark blue eyes, and he examined me with them very carefully. I was exasperated. He'd had plenty of time to look me over while I was running. This wasn't about him deciding I was a hunkette of burning love. This was about something else.

'I decided you were more approachable,' he said. 'And you're the more interesting, of the two of you.'

'You're wrong there,' I said.

He looked down at my right leg. The top part of the leg is marked with a fine spider's web of red lines. My Lycra running shorts stopped at mid-thigh, and the web was clearly visible if you looked at the right leg with attention. That's the leg that gives out, every now and then. That's another reason I need to run, to keep that leg strong.

'What happened to you?' he asked. 'I've never seen marks like that.' He was quite clinical.

'I was hit by lightning,' I said.

He made an impatient movement, as if he'd read that and just recalled it. Or maybe he simply didn't believe me. 'How'd it come about?' he asked.

I explained the circumstances. 'I was doing my hair. I had a date,' I said, remotely remembering that detail. 'Of course, I never went out with that boy. The blast blew my shoe off and stopped my heart.'

'What saved you?'

'My brother, Tolliver. Gave me CPR.'

'I've never met anyone before who was hit by lightning and lived to tell about it.'

'There are plenty of us around,' I said, and I went out the glass door, towel still clutched in my hand.

'Wait,' he said behind me. 'I'd like to talk to you, if I may.'

I turned to face him. A woman stepped past us, ready for her own workout. She was wearing old shorts and a T-shirt dingy with age. She glanced at us curiously. I found myself glad to have a witness.

'What about?'

'I was there, in Nashville, for a while. That's why I got this assignment.'

I waited.

'I really want to know how you knew ahead of time that Tabitha was in the graveyard.'

'I didn't.'

'But you did.'

'If you're not in charge of the investigation, I don't have to talk to you, do I? And I can't think of any reason I'd want to.'

'I'm Agent Seth Koenig.' He said that as if I should have heard the name.

'I don't care.' And I got into the elevator before he could, pressed

the door close button, and smiled as he took a surprised step toward
me, realizing I was actually leaving.

After I showered, I knocked on the door to Tolliver's room and told
him what had happened.

'That bastard. That was an ambush,' Tolliver said.

'That's putting it a little strong. It was more like a strategic approach,' I said.

Tolliver recognized my description of Seth Koenig. The agent had
been in the exercise room when he was, sure enough. 'He thought you
would recognize his name, huh?' Tolliver said thoughtfully. 'Well,
let's see.' Tolliver's laptop was already plugged in. He Googled the
name and got several hits. Seth Koenig had been present at a few hunts
for serial killers. Seth Koenig had been a heavy hitter.

'But all those are in the past,' I said, reading the dates. 'Nothing in
the last four years or so.'

'That's true,' Tolliver said. 'I wonder what happened to his career?'

'And I wonder why he's here. I haven't heard any suggestion that
Tabitha's abduction and death was part of any serial killer's pattern.
And I think I'd remember if another girl had shown up buried in a
cemetery, miles away from her abduction site, buried on top of somebody else, right?' I thought that over. 'Actually, other than her burial,
there's nothing distinctive about Tabitha's case. That in itself is pretty
awful, when you think about it.'

Tolliver wasn't in the mood to discuss the degeneration of American society as exemplified by the emergence of the serial killer as
common occurrence. He just nodded.

'He's different,' I said. 'Seth Koenig.'

'Define.'

I shook my head. 'He's pretty intense, pretty deep. Not your regular
law enforcement type.'

'You hot for him?'

I laughed. 'Nah. He's too old for me.'

'How old?'

'Probably in his early forties.'

'But in good shape, you said.'

There are times when I just don't appreciate Tolliver's teasing. 'I'm
not talking about his body. I'm talking about his head.'

'Can you pin that down a little?'

'I think . . .' I hesitated for a long moment, uneasy about putting my idea into words. 'I think he's more than professionally interested. Maybe obsessed.'

'With you,' Tolliver said, very levelly.

'No, with Tabitha. Not her personally.' I struggled to express what I felt. 'He's obsessed with the puzzle of it. You know, how some people spend a large part of their lives rehashing the Lizzie Borden case? How futile that is, because all the people involved are dead and gone? But there are still books appearing all the time about it. I think that's how Seth Koenig is about Tabitha Morgenstern. Look at his work record. He hasn't done anything newsworthy since he worked her case. And here he is, Johnny-on-the-spot, when she's found. Not because of Tabitha as a person, or because of Joel and Diane, but because of the mystery of it. Like some of the law enforcement people in Colorado are about that little girl who was killed in her own home.'

'The little beauty queen. You think Seth is as fascinated with Tabitha as some people are with her?'

'Yes, I think that's possible. And I think it's dangerous,' I said.

I sat beside him on the end of his bed and found myself looking at the picture he'd stuck in the mirror frame, a picture he carried with him on the road. It was a snapshot of Cameron, Mark, Tolliver, and me. We're all smiling, but not genuinely. Mark's looking down a little, his stout build and round face distinguishing him from the rest of us. Cameron's to my left, in profile, looking away. Her light hair is pulled up in a ponytail. Tolliver and I are in the center, and his arm is around my shoulders. At first glance, you might assume that Tolliver and I were the brother and sister; we're both dark-headed and pale and slim. But if you spend any time with us, you notice that my face is longer and narrower than Tolliver's, which is practically square. And his eyes are a rich dark brown. Mine, though also dark and often mistaken for brown (since people see what they expect to see), are actually gray. Tolliver's mouth is thin and fine-lipped; mine is full. Tolliver had acne as a teen that went untreated, and he has scars on his cheeks as a result. My skin is smooth and fine. Tolliver has a lot of attraction for the opposite sex, and I don't seem to have much of that.

'You just scare them,' Tolliver said quietly.

'Was I talking out loud?'

'No, I could just follow what you were thinking,' he said. 'You're the only psychic in this family.' He put his arm around me and gave me a hug.

'You know I don't like to be called psychic,' I said, but I wasn't really angry.

'I know, but what else would you call it?'

We'd had this discussion before. 'I am a corpse-finder,' I said, with mock hauteur. 'I'm the Human Geiger-Counter.'

'You need a superhero outfit. You'd look good in gray and red,' Tolliver said. 'Tights and a cape, maybe some red gloves, high red boots?' I smiled at the picture. 'After this media hoopla is over, we can go to the apartment for about a week,' Tolliver said. 'We can catch up on our laundry and our sleep.'

The apartment in St Louis wasn't great, but it beat living in a hotel, no matter how fancy. We could open our mail (what little we got), wash our clothes, cook a little.

The constant travel was getting increasingly old. We'd been at it for five years now, at first making almost nothing; in fact, we'd gone into debt. But the past three years, as the word spread, business had started becoming regular, and we'd even turned down a job or two. We'd paid back what we owed, and we'd saved a lot.

Someday, we wanted to buy a house, maybe in Texas, so we wouldn't be too far from our little sisters – though the chances were slim that we'd get to visit with them much, thanks to my aunt Iona and her husband. But we would be on hand when we were needed, and maybe seeing us from time to time would waken better memories for Mariella and Gracie.

When we had a house, we would buy a lawn mower, and I would mow every week. I would have a big planter, one of those that looked like a truncated barrel, and I'd fill it with flowers. Butterflies would perch on them, and bees would lumber in and out. I wanted one of those big Rubbermaid mailboxes, too. You could get them at Wal-Mart.

'Harper?'

'What?'

'You had that dazed look again. What's up?'

'Thinking about a house,' I admitted.

'Well, maybe next year,' Tolliver said.

'Really?'

'Yeah, our bank account is healthy. If we don't have any catastrophes . . .'

I sobered immediately. Of course, health insurance is hard to get for people like us, since we don't have what you'd call regular jobs, and the lightning strike was always classified as a pre-existing condition. That meant I couldn't claim coverage for anything that the insurance people could classify as resulting from the lightning strike. We had to pay an outrageous amount for the most basic policy. It made me angry every time I thought about it. I did everything I could to keep healthy.

'Okay, we won't wreck the car or break a bone or get sued,' I said. We did a lot of doctoring on each other for the everyday sprains and cuts, and we'd spent a week in a motel in Montana when Tolliver had had the flu. But the only persistent health issues facing us were my continuing problems from the lightning strike.

You'd think after you'd recovered from the initial effects, that would be it. Most doctors believe that, too. But that's not the truth. I talk to other strike survivors on the Internet. Memory loss, severe headaches, depression, burning sensations in the feet, ringing in the ears, loss of mobility, and a host of other effects can manifest in the years afterward. Whether these are a result of the neuroses of the victims – which is what most doctors say – or a result of the mysterious reaction of the body to an almost unimaginable jolt of electricity . . . well, opinions vary.

I have my own set of problems, and luckily for me they're pretty consistent.

As far as I know, there is no other strike survivor who has become able to find dead people.

I'd had plenty of time to shower and dress and wonder what we were going to do with our day, when that problem was solved for us. The police came by again, to ask more questions.

Detective Lacey had a chaperone this time, another detective named Brittany Young. Detective Young was in her thirties, and she was a narrow-faced woman with short tousled brown hair and glasses. She had a huge handbag and comfortable shoes, clothes that were no higher-end than Sears, and a gold band on her left hand. She looked around the hotel room curiously, and then she examined me with even more curiosity.

'Do you always travel in this kind of style?' she asked, while Detective Lacey was talking to Tolliver. I sensed they had a plan. Why, gee, what could it be?

'Not hardly,' I said. 'We're more Holiday Inn or Motel 6 people. But we had to have the security.'

She nodded, as if she really understood that and didn't think we were pretentious. Detective Brittany Young was establishing a rapport with me. She grinned at me. I grinned back. I'd done this dance before with other partners.

'We really need all the information you can give us,' she said earnestly, still with the smile. 'It's very important to our investigation to figure out how the body got here and how you came to find it.'

No shit. I tried not to look like I thought she was an idiot. I said, 'Well, I'll be glad to tell you everything I know. But I believe I covered it all yesterday.' I added more sincerely, 'I'm really sorry for the Morgensterns.'

'Would you consider, say, that you and your brother are religious?'

Now she had actually surprised me. 'That's a very personal question, and one I can't answer for my brother,' I said.

'But you would describe yourself as Christians?'

'We were raised Christian.' Cameron and I had been, at least; I didn't know what kind of faith education had taken place in the Lang household. Certainly by the time Tolliver's dad had married my mother, religious training for their children had not been a high priority. In fact, toward the end of our life as a family, my mother hardly knew when it was Sunday. While we'd thought of taking Gracie and Mariella to Sunday school – though they were very young – the thought of what the sharp-eyed church ladies might be able to tell about our home life had stopped us.

We tried so hard to stay together. It had all been for nothing.

'Did your parents have some reason to be prejudiced against Jews?'

'*What?*' Where had that come from?

'Some Christians don't like Jews,' Brittany Young said, as if that would be news to me. But she was making a huge effort to keep her voice neutral. She didn't want to scare me off from offering her my true opinion, just in case I was a closet anti-Semite.

'I'm aware of that,' I said, as mildly as I could. 'But I really don't care what people are.' Then everything clicked. 'So the Morgensterns are Jewish?' I said, genuinely surprised. I just hadn't thought about it, but now I recalled seeing one of those special candleholders in their home in Nashville. I might have missed a lot more symbols and signs. I don't know much about Judaism. The few Jewish kids I'd known in high school hadn't been interested in parading their differences in a Bible-belt area.

Detective Young gave me a look that was full of so much skepticism it almost stood and walked by itself.

'Yes,' she said, as if I was funning with her. 'As you know, the Morgensterns are Jewish.'

'I guess I was too busy wondering where their child was to think about their religion,' I said. 'Probably I had my values backward.'

Okay, maybe I'd overdone the sarcasm, or I was coming off as self-righteous. Detective Young eyed me with scorn. Or, that was the pose she was adopting, to see if it got a rise out of me.

I glanced around for Tolliver, and found that Detective Lacey had maneuvered him over to the other side of the room.

'Hey, Tolliver,' I said. 'Detective Young says the Morgensterns are Jewish! Did you know that?'

'I figured they were,' he said, drifting over to us. 'One of the men I met at their house in Nashville – I'm not sure you met him, you were talking to Joel – I think his name was Feldman . . . anyway, Feldman introduced himself as the Morgensterns' rabbi. So I knew they must be Jewish.'

'I don't remember him.' I really didn't. I still didn't get the relevance of the Morgensterns' faith. Then the lightbulb in my brain clicked on. 'Oh,' I said, 'does that make it worse? That she was buried in a Christian cemetery? The St Margaret's cemetery was Catholic or Episcopal, right?' All I knew about Jewish burial customs was that Jews were supposed to be buried quicker than Christians traditionally were interred. I didn't know why.

Both the officers looked startled, as if their original baseline for questioning had been completely misinterpreted.

'I would think,' Tolliver said, 'that the fact that it really was Tabitha would kind of overwhelm the religious consideration, but maybe not.' He shrugged. 'That's more important to some people than others. Are the Morgensterns really religious? Because I've got to say, they've never mentioned anything about Judaism to us. Have they, Harper? Said anything to you?'

'No. All they said to me was, "Please find my child." They never said, "Please find my *Jewish* child." '

Tolliver sat by me on the love seat, and we presented a united front to Young and Lacey.

'Our lawyer is right next door,' I remarked. 'Do you think we should call Art in here, Tolliver?'

'Do you feel you need protection?' Detective Lacey asked quickly. 'Have you received any unusual messages or phone calls? Do you feel threatened?'

I raised my eyebrows, looked at my brother. 'You scared, Tolliver?'

'I don't think I am,' he said, as if he were surprised by the discovery. 'Seriously,' he said to Detective Young, as if we'd just been playing up till then, 'Has there been any kind of anti-Semitic demonstration against the Morgensterns? I guess I kind of thought society was past that. I love the South, don't get me wrong; but it does lag behind the times in social developments. I'm sure I could be mistaken.' We waited for her to answer, but she just looked at us, an all-too-familiar expression of deep skepticism on her narrow face. Lacey looked more disgusted than anything else.

'Detectives,' I said, getting tired of the dance, 'let me point some things out.' We were on the love seat the Morgensterns had used yesterday, and the two detectives were in the wing chairs we'd occupied. Though Brittany Young was at least ten years younger than Lacey, and a woman, at the moment her expression was identical to his. I took a deep breath. 'The Morgensterns hired me after their daughter had been missing for several weeks. Though I'd read the newspaper stories about Tabitha, I'd never met Diane or Joel or any other member of the family. I had no idea they'd call me to work for them. I couldn't have had anything to do with her disappearance, it stands to reason.'

I thought the atmosphere eased a little.

Detective Lacey took the lead. 'Who, specifically, called you? Felicia Hart? Or Joel Morgenstern's brother, David? Or maybe Joel's father? None of them will claim responsibility.'

The direct question stopped me short.

'Tolliver?' I never talked to clients directly until we got to the site. Tolliver thought it added to my mystique. I thought it made me very anxious.

'That was a while ago,' Tolliver said. He went into his room, came back with a three-hole binder filled with computer printout pages. He'd been messing around with his computer more in the evenings, I'd noticed, and he'd designed some forms for our little business, Connelly Lang Recoveries. He'd been going back and entering all our past 'cases' into the new format. This notebook was labeled 'Case Files

2004' and the first page in each file (a green page) was headed 'First Contact.'

He scanned the page, refreshing his memory. 'Okay. Mr Morgenstern senior called us, at the request of his wife, Hannah Morgenstern. Mr Morgenstern . . .' Tolliver read the page for a couple of minutes, then looked up to tell the cops that the older Mr Morgenstern had told Tolliver about his missing granddaughter, and had asked Tolliver if he thought his sister could help.

'I explained what Harper does, and he got kind of angry and hung up,' Tolliver said. 'Then, the next day, the sister-in-law called.'

'You're saying Felicia Hart called you?'

Tolliver checked the name on the page, quite unnecessarily. 'Yes, that's who called me.' He looked blank – deliberately blank. 'She said no one else would face the truth, but she was sure that her niece was dead, and she wanted Harper to find Tabitha's body so the family could find some closure.'

'And what did you think of that?'

'I thought she was probably right.'

'In your experience, are families often willing to admit that they think their missing loved one is dead?' This was addressed to me. Detective Young seemed to be simply curious.

'This may surprise you, but yes. By the time they call me in, quite a few of them are. They have to have reached some kind of realistic place to even think about hiring me; because that's what I do, I find dead people. No point asking me to come if you think your loved one's alive. Call in the tracking dogs or the private detectives, not me.' I lifted my shoulders. 'That's common sense.'

I can't say the detectives looked horrified. It would take a lot more than that to horrify a homicide detective, I would think. But they did look just that little bit harder around the eyes.

'Of course,' Tolliver chimed in, 'when people's loved ones are missing, most often the family isn't exactly navigating on common sense.'

'Of course,' I echoed, seeing that Tolliver was trying to dilute the bad taste I'd put in their mouths.

'Don't you care?' Detective Young blurted. She leaned forward, her hands clasped, her elbows on her knees, her face intent.

That was a difficult question. 'I feel a lot of different ways about finding a body,' I said, trying to be truthful. 'I'm always glad to find one I've been looking for, because I've done my job if I locate it.'

'And then you get paid,' said Detective Lacey, an edge to his voice.

'I like getting paid,' I said. 'I'm not ashamed of that. I deliver a service for the money. And I give the dead some relief.' The two detectives looked blank. 'They want to be found, you know.'

It seemed so evident to me. But judging by their expressions, it didn't seem so obvious to Lacey and Young.

'You seem so normal, and then you say something just totally nuts,' Young muttered, and her older partner gave her a stare that snapped her into the here-and-now.

'I beg your pardon,' she said formally. 'This is a subject I don't believe I've ever discussed with anyone, and it . . . strikes me as peculiar, I guess.'

'It's not the first time I've heard that, Detective,' I said matter-of-factly.

'No, I guess not.'

'We'll be going now,' said Detective Lacey, running his hand over his short hair in an absent gesture, as if he were polishing a favorite ornament. 'Oh, wait, I have one more question.'

Tolliver and I looked up at him. Tolliver put his hand on my shoulder and exerted a slight pressure. But it wasn't necessary; I knew this was the crucial question.

'Have you talked to any family member since you were in Nashville to search for the Morgenstern girl? *Any* phone conversations?'

I didn't even have to think about it. 'Not me,' I said, and turned to look at Tolliver, fully expecting him to echo my words.

'Yeah, I talked to Felicia Hart a couple of times,' he said, and I used all my self-control to keep my face and body still.

'So, you had conversations with Felicia Hart besides the initial one when she asked you to come to Nashville to look for her niece.'

'Yes, I did.'

I was going to kill him.

'What was the nature of these calls?'

'Personal,' Tolliver said calmly.

'Is it true that you and Felicia Hart had a relationship?'

'No,' Tolliver said.

'Then why the phone calls?'

'We'd had sex,' he said. 'She's called a couple of times after that, while my sister and I were on the road.'

I could feel my fingers curl into fists, and I made them straighten out, made my face remain calm. If it was also sort of fixed and rigid, well, I couldn't help that. I was doing my best.

Tolliver had a lot of appeal, and though we hadn't ever discussed it, he obviously enjoyed sex, judging from the way he tracked down opportunities to do it. I did, too, but I was *way* pickier than Tolliver when it came to selecting a partner. Tolliver viewed sex, as far as I could tell, as a sport he could play well, with any number of the people on his team. I thought of sex a little more personally. You revealed a lot of yourself during sex. I wasn't willing to let many people see that much of me, literally and figuratively.

Maybe these were typical male-versus-female attitudes about sex.

'So what did she want to talk about?' Detective Young asked. She had a narrow-eyed look that I didn't like, as if she felt she'd caught Tolliver out in a guilty secret.

'She wanted to blow off steam about the family situation, about Tabitha's being missing for so long, about how the stress was affecting Victor,' Tolliver said easily, and I thought, *You're lying.* I looked down so my face wouldn't be so easy to read.

I thought of acting strange and making the detectives so nervous that they would leave, but I was really angry with Tolliver. He could make his way out of the tangle as best he could.

'What did she say in these conversations?'

He shrugged. 'I don't recall specifics. After all, it's been months, and it wasn't that memorable.' Aware he sounded less than gallant, Tolliver amended that to, 'I didn't know I'd have to be telling anyone what she'd said. She was worried, of course, and not just about Victor. She was concerned about Diane and Joel, and about her own parents. After all, they're Victor's grandparents, even if they're not Joel's in-laws anymore. And – let's see – she said kids at school were accusing Victor of having something to do with Tabitha's disappearance, because a couple of times he'd mouthed off to his friends about his dad preferring Tabitha to him because Tabitha was Diane's daughter, and he wasn't Diane's son.'

'What was your response?'

'I didn't have much of a response,' Tolliver said. 'I wasn't on the spot, and I didn't know the people involved that well. I felt she mainly wanted to vent to someone who didn't have a vested interest, and I happened to come along at the right time.'

'Did she want you to return to Nashville?'

'We couldn't,' Tolliver said. 'We had a schedule to stick to, and any downtime we have we spend at our apartment in St Louis. We're on the road pretty much year-round.'

'You have that much business?' Detective Young said. He seemed startled.

I nodded. 'We stay pretty busy,' I said. I noticed that Tolliver had dodged answering their original question, but I sure wasn't going to point that out. I was ready for them to be on their way.

Lacey and Young gave each other a look, and a communication seemed to pass between them. The middle-aged man and the younger woman made good partners, somehow. They'd had a meeting of the minds somewhere back in their professional history, and they'd made it work for them. Until this moment, I'd thought Tolliver and I had had the same thing working for us.

'We may need to ask a few more follow-up questions,' Detective Lacey said, making an effort to sound pleasant and as though any further questions would be inconsequential – no problem, no sweat, don't worry, be happy.

'So, you'll be here?' Young asked, pointing at the floor to indicate she meant *right here at this hotel, don't leave town.*

'Yes, I suppose we will,' I said.

'Of course, you'll want to go to the funeral,' Young said, as if something she should have known was just now popping into her head.

'No,' I said.

She cocked her head as if she couldn't have heard me correctly. 'Say what?'

'I don't go to funerals,' I said.

'Not ever?'

'Not ever.'

'What about your mother's? We heard she died last year.'

They'd been making phone calls. 'I didn't go.' I didn't want to feel her presence again, not ever, not even from the grave. 'Goodbye,' I said, standing and smiling at them. They were definitely disconcerted, now, and exchanged one of their glances again, without the certainty.

'So you'll stay in town until we contact you again,' Detective Young said, tucking her hair behind her ear in a gesture oddly reminiscent of that of her partner.

'I think we've established that,' I said, keeping my voice sweet and even.

'Of course we will,' Tolliver said, without a trace of irony.

6

After the departure of the police, the silence that fell was the noisiest silence we'd ever shared. I didn't even want to look at my brother, much less discuss what had just happened. We didn't move. Finally, I threw my hands up in the air, made a sound that came out 'Arrrr,' and stomped into my bedroom, slamming the door behind me. It immediately opened, and Tolliver strode in.

'All right, what did you want me to say?' he said. 'Did you want me to lie?'

I'd thrown myself down on my bed, and Tolliver chose to loom over me, his hands on his hips.

'I didn't want you to say anything,' I said, in as neutral a voice as I could manage. But then I bounced to my feet to glare at him. 'I didn't want you to say *anything* today. What I would have wanted, if I could have had it, was for you to have shown a little discretion, a little common sense, months ago! What were you thinking? Was your upper brain involved in this process at all?'

'You just . . . can't you cut me some slack?'

'No! No! A waitress here or there, well, ick, but okay! You meet someone in a bar, well, okay! We all have needs. But to have a relationship with a client, someone involved in a case . . . come *on*, Tolliver. You should keep your pants zipped! Or can you?'

Since Tolliver was so in the wrong, he got even angrier. 'She was just a woman. She isn't even a member of the family, at least not the direct family!'

'Just a woman. Okay, I'm seeing it now. Just a hole for you to sink into, is that what you're saying? So much for being selective. So much for thinking every time you have sex, "Is this the woman I choose to have a baby with?" Because that's what it means, Tolliver!'

'Was that what you were thinking when you screwed that cop in Sarne? How you wanted to have his baby?'

There was another silence, this one charged with other tensions.

'Hey,' he said, 'I'm sorry I said that.' The anger drained away.

'I don't know if I'm sorry or not,' I said. 'You know you did a wrong thing. Can't you just say it? Do you have to justify it?'

'Do you have to ask me to?'

'Yes, I think I do. Because this wasn't only personal, this was business, too. You've never done that before.' Okay, at least I didn't think he had.

'Felicia wasn't paying us. She's not really a member of the family.'

'But still.'

'Yeah, yeah,' he said, crumbling at last. 'You're right. She was too close to the action. I shouldn't have.' He smiled, that rare, radiant smile that almost made me smile in return. Almost. 'But she made a real pass at me, and I guess I was too weak to turn it down. She was offering, she was pretty, and I couldn't think of a real reason why not.'

I tried to think of something to say, but I couldn't. Actually, why not? Exactly for this reason, that's why not – because this time, Tolliver's sex life had backfired on us. I thought we were in even more trouble than we'd been before, and that hadn't been inconsiderable.

Tolliver hugged me. 'I'm sorry,' he said, and his voice was quiet and sincere. I hugged him back, inhaling the familiar smell of him, laying my cheek against his hard chest. We stood like that for a long minute, with the dust motes floating in the sun coming through the hotel window. Then his arms loosened, and I stepped back.

'This is what the detectives should have asked you: who called you about the cemetery?' I asked.

'Dr Nunley. And in Detective Lacey's defense, he did ask me that at the station.'

'Did Nunley say who'd asked him to call? Or did you get the impression it was just his idea?' I went back out into the living room area to get a drink. Tolliver trailed after me, lost in thought.

'I thought someone had drawn you to his attention, because he asked a lot of questions. If he'd been the one who'd originated the invitation, he would have known more about you. That's my opinion.'

'Okay. So we need to talk to him.' I sympathized when Tolliver made a face. 'Yeah, me, too. He's a jerk, all right.' Tolliver pulled his cell phone out of his pocket and checked a number on a folded piece of paper. Tolliver always has bits of paper in his pockets, and if he didn't do his own laundry I'd have to be searching his pants all the time. He finally found the right piece of paper and the right number and punched it in. From his stance, I could see that he was listening to the phone ringing on the other end. Finally, a recorded message came on, and when the beep sounded, Tolliver left a message. 'Dr Nunley, this is Tolliver Lang,' he said briskly. 'Harper and I need to talk to you. There are some things left unresolved after yesterday's unexpected discoveries. You have my cell number.'

'Now he'll think we want our money.'

Tolliver considered this. 'Yes, and he'll call back about that,' he said finally. 'Come to think of it, if he doesn't pay us, we won't get anything for this. I can't help but be glad we're getting the Morgenstern reward money.'

'I don't really want to have earned it, you know?' He patted me on the shoulder; he knew exactly what I meant. Of course, he also knew that we would take it. We sure deserved it. 'I can't help feeling that we've been yanked into this. I just hope we haven't been shoved right under a ladder or some other bad luck thing. I'm scared we might end up taking someone else's fall for this.'

'Not if I can help it,' Tolliver said. 'I know I've slipped up, but you can be sure I'll do everything in my power from now on out to make sure no one can connect us with the Morgensterns' mess. And it's a simple fact that we didn't take Tabitha, a provable fact. In fact, what date was she taken?' We looked it up on the Internet. Tolliver checked our previous year's schedule. God bless computers. 'We were in Schenectady then,' he said, relief in his voice, and I laughed.

'That's plenty far enough,' I said. 'I'm glad you keep such good records. I guess we've got receipts to back that up?'

'Yes, on file at the apartment,' he said.

'Not just another pretty face,' I said, and cupped his chin in my hand for a second to hold him still while I gave him a kiss on the cheek. But my happy moment didn't last longer than a few seconds. 'Tolliver, who could have done this? Killed the girl, and put her there? Can it possibly be true that it's a massive coincidence?'

He shook his head. 'I don't think that's even remotely likely.'

'You and I both know that massive coincidences usually aren't. But I just can't imagine a conspiracy so elaborate.'

'I can't either,' he said.

Oddly enough, the next person we heard from was Xylda Bernardo.

We'd just finished lunch. It was an uneasy meal. Art had shared it with us, and since he ate a completely different kind of meal from us (he had a major lunch, and we like a light lunch), and he liked to talk business while he ate, I can't say we enjoyed it a whole lot. Art was about to catch a flight back to Atlanta, since he couldn't think of anything else to do in Memphis. The police weren't prepared to charge us with anything that he could discover; and he'd made many, many phone calls to everyone he knew in the justice system in Memphis to try to find out. We'd basically paid a whole hell of a lot for Art to fly over here first class to stay at a great hotel, make a lot of phone calls, and hold one press conference; but we'd known it had been a gamble when we'd called him.

Our lawyer was downing a huge salad, garlic bread, and veal ravioli, while Tolliver and I were having soup and salad on a smaller scale. I was watching Art chew hunks of bread and trying to remember my CPR lessons. Art was explaining what we should expect.

'You'll probably need to produce a record of your travels during the time since you met the Morgensterns,' Art said.

I glanced at Tolliver and he nodded. We were covered on all that. During the years we'd been traveling, Tolliver and I had learned to keep every single receipt, every single credit card slip, every single piece of paper that crossed our paths. This past year, we'd been especially diligent. We had a cheap accordion file that was always on hand in the back seat of the car, and the laptop; we kept good records. We sent off regular packets to our accountant, Sandy Dierdoff, who was based in St Louis. She was a broadly curvy blonde in her forties. She'd only raised her eyebrows and given a bark of laughter when we'd explained what we did for a living. She'd seemed to enjoy our unusual lifestyle. In fact, she'd given us more good advice in our meetings with her than Art had ever even thought of sharing. Sandy had already emailed us about making our annual appointment; fall was fast turning into winter.

I was thinking about Sandy, and by extension our apartment in St Louis, while I said goodbye to Art. We saw him leave with a mutual feeling of relief. Art was kind of proud of having us as clients, as if we were show business people; but at the same time, he wasn't at his easiest or most relaxed when he was alone with us.

After he left, and the staff had removed the lunch things, I asked Tolliver if he thought we could go out for a walk. I still hadn't forgiven Tolliver his huge error in judgment, but I was willing to put it on the back burner until I'd calmed down. A good walk might restore our sense of companionship.

Tolliver was shaking his head before the sentence even got out of my mouth. 'We ran this morning in the gym,' he reminded me. 'I know you don't want to be cooped up in this hotel, but if we go anywhere, someone'll spot us and want a statement.'

I called down to the front desk to ask if there were still reporters waiting outside the hotel. The deskman replied that he couldn't be sure, but that he suspected some of the people loitering in the coffee shop across the street were members of the press. I hung up.

'Crap,' I said.

'Listen, put on your dark glasses and a hat and we'll go to the movies,' he said. He found the complimentary *Commercial Appeal* we'd gotten that morning and looked up movie times. I found myself looking at my own picture on the front page of the Metro section. I'd only looked at the front section this morning, on purpose. There I was: thin, dark-headed, with big deep-set eyes and an erect posture, arms wrapped across each other under my breasts. I thought the picture made me look quite a bit more than twenty-four and that made me a little shivery. Tolliver, right beside me in the photo, was taller, darker, and more solid.

We both looked desperately troubled. We looked like refugees from middle Europe, refugees who'd fled some kind of persecution, leaving behind all they held of value.

'Want to read it?' Tolliver asked, extending the paper. He knew I didn't like reading the few stories in the press about us, but since I'd been staring at the picture, he offered it to me.

I put out my own hand in a 'stop' gesture.

He handed me the movie section instead, and I began scanning the ads. We liked space movies and action movies. We liked movies with happy families. If they got threatened with danger, we liked them to get out of it more or less intact, maybe shooting a couple of bad guys in the process. We didn't like movies about miserable people who became more miserable, no matter how brilliant they were. We didn't like chick flicks. We didn't like foreign movies. I didn't want to go to the movies to learn a damn thing about human nature or the state of the world. I knew as much as I wanted to know about both those things.

There was a movie that fit our profile, which wasn't too surprising, I guess.

I put on a knit cap and my jacket and my dark glasses, and Tolliver bundled up, too. We got the doorman to call a cab instead of bringing our car around. We actually got a silent cab driver, my favorite kind. He could drive well, too, and he got us to the multiplex in time to buy our tickets and walk right in.

I love going to big multiplexes. I love the anonymity, and all the possibilities. I loved the teenagers who kept it clean, in their bright matching shirts and silly hats. Tolliver had had a night job in such a place in Texarkana, and he used to slip me in so I could hide in the darkened theater for a while, forgetting what waited for me at our home.

When the previews started running, I was as content as I could be. We sat together in the dark, passing the popcorn (no butter, light on the salt) back and forth.

We watched our pretty-pathologist-in-danger movie quite happily, knowing that everything would be okay in the end (more or less). We poked each other in the ribs when she was having a lot of trouble determining the cause of death of a very handsome guy. 'You could have told her in a second,' Tolliver said, in a whisper only someone as close as I could have deciphered. The theater wasn't empty, but there was plenty of room at this weekday afternoon showing. No one was talking out loud, and no child was crying, so it was a good experience.

When the movie was over, the bad guy killed several different ways after we thought he was dead initially, we strolled outside, chatting about the special effects and the probable future of the main characters. That was our favorite game. What would happen to them after the action of the movie was over?

'She'll go back to work, even if she said she wouldn't,' I told Tolliver. 'Staying at home will be too boring after all that shooting and chasing. After all, she bashed that guy in the head with her iron.'

'Nah, I think she'll marry the cop, stay home, and devote herself to making her family supper every single night,' Tolliver said. 'She'll never order Chinese takeout again. Remember, she tore down the menu that was tacked to the wall by the phone?'

'She'll probably just order pizza instead.'

He laughed and fished the receipt from the cab out of his pocket so he could call for another one to take us back to the hotel.

Suddenly, my left arm was seized in a strong grip. To say I got a scare would be a large understatement. I turned to stare at a woman holding me. She was wearing a voluminous coat with a loud plaid pattern. She had dyed red hair pulled up on one side of her head to cascade over to the other side in a waterfall of curls. Her lipstick was not exactly within the lines of her actual lips, and her earrings were huge chandeliers with glittery stones that caught the afternoon sun.

Tolliver had swung around and his free hand was heading for her throat.

'I just have to talk to you,' she said, in a hurried, abstracted way.

'Hi, Xylda,' I said, trying for that calm, level voice you use when you're talking to someone you know is over the edge.

'Xylda,' Tolliver said, almost in a growl. He'd been ready for action, and now he had to be tolerant. With more force than necessary, he shoved his phone back into his pocket. 'What can we do for you today? How'd you come to be here?'

'You're in such danger,' she said. 'Such terrible danger. I felt I had to warn you. You're so young, dear. You can't know how terrible this world can be.'

Actually, I thought I had a pretty good idea. 'Tolliver and I aren't young in experience, Xylda,' I said, trying to keep my voice gentle. 'Look, there's a restaurant over there. Shall we go have a cup of hot chocolate, or some coffee? Maybe they have tea?'

'That would be good, really good,' she said. Xylda was as different from me as she could be: shorter, bulkier, and at least thirty years older. She'd been in the psychic business ever since she'd quit prostitution, which had been her first profession. Xylda's husband, Robert, had been her handler, and his death the year before had thrown Xylda for a real loop. I didn't know how she was going to survive unless someone else took her in hand. She sure didn't look or behave like someone I'd want to employ if I were in the market for a psychic. Then again, maybe I was overestimating the public. Some clients actually believed that Xylda's odd manner and dress reinforced the fact that she was a living, breathing psychic.

I disagreed. I knew that a lot of psychics, both real and fake, were also emotionally unstable or out-and-out mentally ill. If you're born psychic, you're going to pay a price, a high one. It's a terrible gift.

Only two of the psychics I'd met managed to live just like ordinary people, but those two were exceptions. And neither of them was Xylda, of course.

Looking gloomy but resigned, Tolliver led Xylda into the cafe and helped her take her awful coat off. He left to get our drinks, while I settled Xylda in at a little table as far from other patrons as I could manage, given that the coffee shop wasn't a large business. I took a deep breath and tried to fix an understanding smile on my face.

Xylda clutched my hand, and I had to bite my lower lip to keep from yanking it away. Casual touching is not comfortable for me, and she'd already held onto me twice; but I reminded myself that Xylda must have a reason for the deliberate contact. As I knew from her own account at a previous meeting, Xylda was being bombarded with images from me. She'd explained it to me once when she'd been having a good day, back when Robert had been alive. 'It's like watching a very fast slide show,' she'd said. 'I see pictures, pictures of the life of the person I'm touching, some from the past and some from the future and some . . .' She'd fallen silent and shaken her head.

'Do they all come true?' I'd asked.

'I have no way of knowing. I know they *might* come true.'

Xylda looked at me now, and her blue eyes really saw me. 'In the time of ice, you'll be so happy,' she said.

'Good,' I said, having no idea what she was talking about. But that was the way of conversations with Xylda, if you could call this a conversation.

'You can't keep lying,' Xylda said gently. 'You have to stop doing that. It won't hurt anyone.'

'I think I'm truthful,' I said, surprised. Many things I could be accused of, and my accuser would be right. But not this.

'Oh, you're truthful about the things that don't matter.'

'Did someone come to Memphis with you, Xylda?'

'Yes, Manfred did.'

'Where is Manfred?' I wasn't completely sure who Manfred was, but learning someone had charge of Xylda was a relief.

'He's parking the car. There wasn't a space.'

'Oh, good,' I said, relieved to hear such a prosaic explanation. Tolliver arrived at the table with our drinks. Xylda seemed glad to get the coffee, which was redolent of vanilla and sugar, and she swirled in even more sugar with the little brown plastic stirrer. Mine was regular coffee, and Tolliver had gotten hot chocolate. 'Tolliver, Xylda says Manfred is with her.'

He raised his eyebrows in query, so he didn't know who that was, either. I shrugged. 'She says he's out parking the car.'

Tolliver stood and stared out the glass windows, then began waving vigorously to someone. 'I think I spotted him,' he said, sinking back into his chair. 'He's coming in.' Tolliver was smiling broadly.

'He's a good boy,' Xylda said. She smiled at us. 'Listen, I hear you found the Morgenstern girl.' Suddenly, she sounded completely practical and all present and accounted for, mentally.

'Yes,' I said.

'You know, they called me in.'

'Yeah?'

'It wasn't the boy,' Xylda said. 'There was passion involved. But there was no sex with the little girl.'

'Okay,' I said. 'Then why was she killed?'

'I don't know,' Xylda said. She looked down into her coffee cup.

See what I mean about psychics being very little help?

'But I know you'll find out,' Xylda said, and she looked up at me very sharply. 'I won't be there to see it, but you'll find out.'

'Are you going to a different city? Have you got another booking?'

'Yes,' she said quite definitely. 'I have another booking. You know, I'm the real thing, and people know that when they meet me.'

'Yes, they do,' Tolliver agreed, and then a thin young man came up to us, dressed all in black. This was Manfred, I assumed.

'I saw her surprise you,' Manfred said cheerfully. 'Sorry about that. Are you her friends? She said she had to meet some friends here.'

Amazing. Xylda's psychic ability had led her to meet with us outside a Cineplex. Manfred was a narrow-shouldered young man in his late teens or early twenties. He had a narrow face and slicked-back peroxided hair, a matching goatee, and at least one tattoo visible on the side of his neck. He had a face decorated with many piercings and his hands were covered with silver rings.

He matched Xylda, in an odd sort of way.

'I'm Tolliver Lang and this is Harper Connelly,' Tolliver said. 'Are you related to Xylda?'

'This is my grandson,' Xylda said proudly.

I was willing to bet that few grandmothers would be able to look at Manfred's extreme facial embellishment without wincing, much less with Xylda's simple pride. There was much to Manfred that met the eye, and quite a lot that didn't – and his grandmother was certainly psychic enough to sense that.

We told the young man we were pleased to meet him, and we explained that we crossed paths with Xylda professionally from time to time.

'She jumped up this morning, right at the breakfast table,' Manfred said. 'She said we had to go to Memphis. So we got in the car, and here we are.' He seemed proud of having taken his grandmother so seriously, of having gotten her here on time to keep her self-appointed rendezvous.

'You know the body was found,' I said to Xylda, who'd finished her coffee before the rest of us had begun to sip at ours.

'Yes, and I knew it was going to be found in a graveyard,' Xylda said. 'I just didn't know which one. I'm glad you found the girl. She's been dead a long time.'

'Since the day she vanished?' I asked.

'No, not quite,' Xylda said. 'She lived a few hours. Not more than that.'

I was actually relieved to hear this. 'That's what I thought. Thanks for telling me,' I said. I wondered if I should relay this bit of information to the police or to Tabitha's family. After a moment's consideration, I realized that was a very bad idea. If it had been hard for the police to believe me, it would be impossible for them to give Xylda any credence. If you could say *anyone* looked like an ex-hooker turned professional psychic, Xylda would be the picture you'd come up with. Police aren't inclined to trust either one, and Xylda reinforced that distrust with every sentence she uttered.

'I Saw it,' Xylda said. I could hear the capital letter in her voice. Her grandson Manfred smiled at his grandmother, the epitome of pride. It was obvious Manfred simply didn't care that almost everyone in the shop had taken a moment or two to stare at our little group. I thought that was extraordinary, especially for a young man hardly out of his teens, if indeed he was. I realized that Manfred and Victor Morgenstern were very close in age. I wondered what the two would make of each other, and found the idea of their conversation almost unimaginable.

'Xylda, have you caught a glimpse of who took her?' Tolliver asked. He spoke very quietly, almost inaudibly, because there was no doubt people were listening.

'It was for love,' Xylda said. 'For love!' Xylda spoke right out.

She smiled at each of us, a distinct and separate look, and then she told Manfred it was time for her nap.

'Sure, Granny,' he said. He stood and pulled her chair back for her. I hadn't seen a man do that in years. As Xylda picked up her purse and began to shuffle toward the door, the fascinated gaze of the other patrons following the progress of the enormous plaid coat, Manfred bent to take my hand. 'A pleasure to see you,' he said, and he suddenly sounded older than his years. 'If you ever need a buddy to hang with, Harper, I'm willing to jump in there.'

The look in his eyes told me that no matter how old Manfred was chronologically, biologically he was a fully developed male. Suddenly I felt very self-conscious and ridiculously flattered.

'I hear you,' I said, and Manfred kissed my hand. Because of the piercings, the effect was strange. I felt a little tongue, a little brush of soft hair from the goatee, and surely a cold metallic touch from a stud in his mouth. I didn't know whether to laugh, or shriek, or pant.

'Just think of the kids we would have,' Manfred said, and I opted for smiling.

'That's a step too far, there,' I said. 'You were doing great, up until the kids.'

'I'll remember,' he said, smiling back. 'Next time I won't make the same mistake.'

When they left, I turned to Tolliver to ask him what he'd gotten out of Xylda's tangled contribution. Tolliver was staring after Manfred with no friendly face.

'Oh, get real,' I said. 'Tolliver! He's years younger than me!'

'Right, maybe three,' Tolliver said, and I remembered that Tolliver was three years older. 'He's got balls, I'll give him that.'

'Probably pierced ones,' I said, and Tolliver gave me a startled look and an unwilling laugh.

'What would you say if I got a tattoo and a ring through my eyebrow?' he said.

'I'd definitely want to watch,' I said. 'And it would be interesting to see what kind of tattoo you picked.' I looked at him for a moment, trying to imagine Tolliver with a silver hoop in his eyebrow or nostril, and I grinned. 'And where you put it.'

'Oh, if I ever got one, I'd get it on my lower back,' he said. 'So I could cover it up almost all the time.'

'You've put thought into this.'

'Yeah. A little.'

'Hmmm. You've picked out the tattoo?'

'Sure.'

'What?'

'A lightning bolt,' he said, and I couldn't tell if he was serious or not.

7

During our cab ride back from the suburban Cineplex to the downtown hotel, I had a little time to think. Xylda was nuts, but she was a true psychic. If she said Tabitha had lived a few hours after the abduction, I believed her. I should have asked different questions, I realized. I should have asked Xylda *why* Tabitha's abductor had kept her alive for that long. A sexual reason? Some other purpose?

'Did it seem to you that Xylda was nuttier than usual?' Tolliver asked, echoing my thoughts to an eerie degree.

'Yes,' I said. 'The kind of nutty that made me wonder how old she really is.'

'She couldn't be over sixty, right?'

'I would have said younger, but today . . .'

'She looked okay.'

'As okay as Xylda ever looks.'

'True. But she seemed to walk just fine, and maneuver all right physically.'

'But mentally, she was quite a bit more off . . . so vague. "In the time of ice, you'll be happy." What the hell does that mean?'

'Yeah, that was weird. And the part about being truthful.'

I nodded. ' "The time of ice." She could have told us things that would have been a hell of a lot more to the point. Maybe it's the loss of Robert that's thrown her for such a loop? Not that she was ever Miss Stability. At least Manfred seems to be taking good care of her, and he respects her talent.'

'Think we should mention that guy we met in San Francisco to the Morgensterns? Think they'd be open to a clairvoyant?'

'Nah,' I said instantly. 'Tom will make something up if he doesn't get a genuine reading.'

'So would Xylda.'

'But only when it didn't matter, Tolliver.' He looked at me as if he couldn't see the difference.

'Like if it was some teenager visiting her on a dare, wanting to know if she'd be happy in the future, Xylda might make up stuff so the kid would leave confident and cheerful. That kind of thing, that can't hurt. But if a lot depended on it, if the client took her seriously, Xylda wouldn't say, "Oh yes, your missing son is really alive," unless she got a true vision. Tom will tell you something under any circumstances, whether or not he really knows anything. He'll just make it up.'

'Then I won't mention him,' Tolliver said, though he sounded a little huffy. 'I was trying to think of some way to help them get through this, and I think the only way they're going to come out the other side of it is to find out who did kill Tabitha. That is, if it really *wasn't* one of them.'

'I know,' I said, surprised at his irritation.

'What did you get from her yesterday? When you were standing on the grave?'

I was very reluctant to return to that moment. But then I thought of the faces of Diane and Joel Morgenstern, and the cloud of suspicion surrounding them, and I knew I had to return to Tabitha's last resting place.

'You think we could go back to the site?' I asked. 'I know there's no physical remains there, but it might help.'

Tolliver never questioned my professional judgment. 'Then we'll go,' he said. 'But I think we better go tonight, so no one'll follow us. We won't want to be in a cab for that.'

I agreed, especially after I caught our current cabbie's curious look in the rearview mirror.

'You want him to drop us off on Beale?' Tolliver asked. 'Maybe we could go listen to some music before supper?'

I glanced at my watch. It seemed unlikely that there would be good blues playing at five in the afternoon. 'Why don't you go?' I suggested. 'I'll go back to the hotel and take a nap.'

So Tolliver got out at B.B. King's Blues Club on legendary Beale Street, and reminded the cabbie where he was to drop me off. The cabbie made a face, said, 'Sure, man, I remember,' and drove me right to the Cleveland. 'He's a little on the protective side,' the man said when I was paying him. 'Your man is a worrier.'

'Yes,' I said. 'My brother.'

'Your *brother*?' The cabbie looked at me, half-smiling, sure I was pulling his leg.

I told him to keep the change because I was kind of rattled, and I scrambled out of the cab and into the hotel without looking around me, which was stupid.

For the second time that day, someone seized hold of me. But this time it was a man, an angry man. He grabbed me as I walked into the lobby, and he marched me over to a chair before I could even be sure who he was.

Dr Clyde Nunley was slightly better dressed than he had been the morning before. This afternoon he looked like a typical college professor in his sport jacket and dark slacks. His shoes needed shining.

'How'd you do it?' he asked me, still gripping my arm.

'What?'

'You've made a fool out of me. I was standing right there. Those records were sealed. I watched over them. No one else had read them. How did you do it? You make me look like an idiot in front of the students, and then your damn pimp calls me to ask me for my money.'

I was disgusted, and I realized Dr Nunley had been drinking.

I tried to yank my arm away. He'd scared me, so now I was proportionately angrier.

'Drop my arm and stand away from me,' I said, and I said it sharply and loudly.

Out of the corner of my eye, I saw that the three (very young) staff members at the counter were buzzing around nervously, unsure of what to do. I was so glad when someone else stepped forward and clamped a hand on Dr Nunley's shoulder.

'Let go of the lady,' said the man who'd been in the class the day before. He had that stillness about him that says, 'I know what I'm doing and no one messes with me.'

'What?' Clyde Nunley was very confused by the interruption of his bullying session. His grip on me didn't loosen. I had a wild impulse to grab the arm of Mr Student, so we'd all be standing there holding on to one another. We must look ridiculous.

'Dr Nunley, let go of me or I'll break your fucking fingers,' I said, and that worked like a charm. He looked startled, as if I'd finally become a real person to him. Mr Student kept hold of the inebriated professor, and his mouth moved in a very small smile.

By that time, one of the staff members had hustled around the desk and was striding over to us, trying to hurry without looking like he was hurrying. It was the pleasant-faced man in his twenties who'd checked us in. 'Problem, Ms Connelly?'

'Don't say a word,' hissed Dr Nunley, as though that would be sure to shut me up. He must normally deal with the well-mannered children of the privileged.

'Yes, there is a problem,' I said to the young man, and Clyde Nunleys face twisted with surprise. He just didn't think I'd complain about him; I don't know why. 'This man grabbed me when I came into the lobby, and he won't leave me alone. If this gentleman hadn't helped me out, he might have hit me.' Of course, I didn't know that, but Dr Nunley had definitely been spoiling for a confrontation, and if he thought I was going to forget he'd called my brother a pimp, he had another thought coming.

'Do you know him, Ms Connelly?'

'I don't know him,' I said firmly. In an existential sense, this was the truth. Do any of us know each other, really? I was sure the staff would back me up with no qualms if they thought Dr Nunley was a stranger off the street, out to harass me. The minute I said the words 'Doctor' and 'Bingham College' I'd lose some of my own stature as a wronged female.

My new assistant, Mr Student, said, 'In that case, mister, I think you should leave. And in view of the fact that you seem drunk, I'd call a cab if I were you.'

The clerk made a courteous gesture toward the door, as if Dr Nunley were an honored guest. 'One of our bellmen will be happy to call a cab for you,' the clerk said in a sunny voice. 'Right this way.'

And before Dr Nunley could regroup, he was out onto the sidewalk and under the watchful eye of the two bellmen who stood there waiting for cars to pull up.

'Thanks,' I said to Mr Student. 'I didn't get your name yesterday.'

'Rick Goldman.'

'Harper Connelly,' I said, with a little nod. I shook his hand, though my own was not steady. 'How did you come to be on the right spot at the right moment, Mr Goldman?'

'Rick, please. "Mr Goldman" makes me feel even older than I am. Would you care to sit and talk for a minute?' There were two brocaded wing chairs at a comfortable angle and distance for conversation.

I hesitated, tempted. I wasn't as calm and steady as I was making out. In fact, I was still shaking. I'd been taken by surprise, and in a bad kind of way. 'For a minute,' I said carefully, and sank down as gracefully as I could manage. I didn't want Rick Goldman to know exactly how shaky I was.

He sat opposite me, his square dark face carefully blank. 'I'm an alumnus of Bingham,' he said.

That told me absolutely nothing. 'So are lots of other people, but I don't see them here now,' I said. 'What's your point?'

'I was a cop on the Memphis force for years. Now I'm a private investigator.'

'Okay.' I wished he'd cut the circling around and arrive at the point.

'The board of trustees is pretty sharply divided right now,' Rick Goldman said. Okay, I was getting bored. I raised my eyebrows and nodded encouragingly.

'There's a liberal majority and a conservative minority. That minority is very concerned with Bingham's public profile. When that conservative faction of the board found out what Clyde was doing in his class, they asked if I would oversee the visiting speakers.'

'Keep your fingers on the pulse,' I said.

'Keep my ear to the ground,' he confirmed.

He seemed quite serious. I had a feeling Rick Goldman was a serious kind of guy. 'Clyde didn't suspect you?'

'I paid my money and signed up for the class,' Rick Goldman said. 'Nothing he could do about it.'

'The older lady in the class, she a monitor, too?'

'Nah, she just likes to take anthropology classes.'

I thought about this for a second. 'So, you just happened to be standing in the lobby here this evening?'

'No, not exactly.'

'Following Clyde, were you?'

'No. He's boring. You're a lot more interesting.'

I wasn't exactly sure how the private detective meant that.

'So have you been following me and my brother?'

'No. But I have been waiting here for you. I wanted to ask you some questions, after watching you in action yesterday.'

I owed him the Q&A, after his timely intervention in the Clyde Nunley incident. 'I'll listen,' I said, which was more than I usually did.

'How'd you do it?' He leaned forward, his eyes fixed on my face. If the circumstances had been different it might have been a flattering moment. But I was afraid I knew what he meant, and that wasn't flattering at all.

I looked back at him with the same intensity. 'You know I couldn't have learned any of that ahead of time,' I said. 'You *know* that, right?'

'Were you in cahoots with Clyde? And now you've had a falling out?'

'No, Mr Goldman. I'm not in cahoots with anyone. I don't think I've ever heard anyone even say that phrase out loud, by the way.' I broke eye contact, sighed. 'I'm the real thing. You may not want to believe it, but eventually you'll have to. Thanks again.' I got up and walked very carefully over to the elevators. My leg was still not steady, and it would be too embarrassing if I fell down.

I punched the up button with a quick stab of my finger. The elevator obligingly opened, and I stepped in, punching our floor number with a quick sideways motion of my hand. I stood with my back to the door so I wouldn't have to see him again.

I was ashamed that I had needed help. If I were as tough as I wanted to be, I could have thrown Clyde Nunley to the floor and kicked him. But that might have been a slight overreaction. I found myself smiling at the back wall of the elevator. I guess I'm the kind of woman who smiles when she thinks about kicking a man when he's down; at least, that man.

I told myself to stiffen my spine. After all, I'd handled that okay. I hadn't screamed or cried or lost my dignity. *I'm not a weak person*, I told myself. *I just get rattled sometimes*. And then there was the physical stuff left over from the lightning strike. One of those symptoms struck now, a headache so vicious I had trouble fitting my plastic key into the slot and getting into my room.

I opened my medicine bag and took a handful of Advil, and then I yanked off my shoes. I knew from experience how comfortable the bed was, and I knew in ten minutes I would feel better. I promised myself that. Actually, it took more like twenty minutes before the pain subsided to a bearable level, and then I looked at the ceiling and thought about Dr Nunley and his temper until I fell asleep.

Tolliver woke me up a couple of hours later. 'Hey,' he said gently. 'How are you? They told me when I came in that you'd had a problem with a man in the lobby, and some knight in corduroy had shown up to rescue you.'

'Yeah.' It was taking me a minute to gather up my senses. Tolliver had turned on my bathroom light, and he was a silhouette sitting on the edge of my mattress. 'Nunley was waiting for me, and he was all

"How did you do this, you imp of Satan?" and so on. Well, he didn't go into the evil stuff so much. He just thought I was dishonest. But he clearly thought I was a big fraud, and he was mad you'd called him, and he wasn't nice about it.'

'Did he hurt you?'

'Nah, grabbed my arm, but that's all. You remember that older man in the class, the one we were wondering about? He was in the lobby, too, waiting for me to come back. He stopped Nunley, and the guy from the desk sent him on his way. Then he told me some interesting information. The only thing is, after that I got a hell of a headache, so I took some medicine and dropped.'

'How's the leg?'

One problem often triggered another. We'd been to maybe ten doctors, and they all said that my problems were psychological – whether or not we told them about the body-finding thing. 'The effects of a lightning strike are over when you leave the hospital afterward,' one particularly pompous jackass had told me. 'There are no well-documented long-term effects.' Sadly, the problems I had with the medical community were common among lightning strike survivors. Very few doctors knew what to do with us. For some of us it was much harder – the ones who couldn't go back to work and were trying to get workmen's comp or disability payments, for example.

At least I didn't have tinnitus, which affected so many survivors, and at least I hadn't lost my sense of taste, another common problem.

'The leg's a little shaky,' I admitted, feeling the muscle weakness as I tried to achieve a leg lift. Only the left leg rose. The right one just quivered with the effort. Tolliver began to massage it, as he often did on the bad days.

'So, tell me the interesting information about the man from the class.'

'He's a private detective,' I began, and Tolliver's hands stopped moving for a second.

'Not good,' he said. 'At least, depending on his goal.'

I tried to recall everything Rick Goldman had said to me, and Tolliver listened to it all with absolute attention.

'I don't think this really has anything to do with us,' Tolliver said. 'He may not believe you're a genuine talent, but since when did that matter? Lots of people don't. He just hasn't needed you yet. As far as the board of trustees, or whatever, you've already been paid a retainer by the college. It wasn't much, anyway. This was more for the good buzz than anything else.'

'So you don't think Goldman can hurt us?'

'No. And why would he?'

'He didn't seem really angry or upset,' I admitted. 'But he might think we were defrauding the college.'

'So, what's he gonna do about it? He's not the guy who writes the checks. We were hired to do something, we did it.'

I felt a little better about Rick Goldman after that, and I decided not to think about Clyde Nunley any more, though I knew Tolliver had a slow burn going about the professor being rough with me. Maybe we wouldn't run into him again. To change the subject, I asked Tolliver how his Beale Street jaunt had gone.

While his long fingers worked on my leg muscles, he told me about Beale Street, and his conversation with a bartender about the famous people who'd come to the bar to hear the blues. I grew more relaxed by the moment, and I was laughing when there was a knock at the door. Tolliver looked at me, surprised, and I shrugged. I wasn't expecting anything or anyone.

A bellman was there, holding a vase of flowers. 'These came for you, Ms Connelly,' he said.

Who doesn't like to get flowers? 'Put them on the table, please,' I said, and glanced at Tolliver to see if he had the tip. He fished out his wallet, gave me a nod, and handed the bellman some bills. The flowers were snapdragons, and I didn't think anyone had ever sent me snapdragons. Actually, I didn't think anyone had ever sent me flowers before, unless you counted a corsage or two when I was in high school. I said as much to Tolliver. He pulled the little envelope from the plastic prongs in the foliage and handed it to me, no expression on his face.

The card read, 'You have given us peace,' and it was signed 'Joel and Diane Morgenstern.'

'They're very pretty,' I said. I touched one blossom lightly.

'Nice of Diane to think of them,' Tolliver said.

'No, this was Joel's idea.'

'Why do you say that?'

'He's the kind of man who thinks of flowers,' I said positively. 'And she's the kind of woman who doesn't.'

Tolliver thought this was foolishness.

'Really, Tolliver, you've got to take my word on this,' I said. 'Joel is the kind of guy who *thinks* about women.'

'I think about women. I think about them all the time.'

'No, that's not what I mean.' I tried to think of how to put it. 'He doesn't just think about wanting to fuck women, when he looks at them. I'm not saying he's gay,' I added hastily, since Tolliver was looking incredulous. 'I'm saying that he thinks about what women like.' That still wasn't quite it, but it was as close as I could come. 'He likes to please women,' I said, but that wasn't exactly right, either.

The phone rang and Tolliver picked it up. 'Yes,' he said. 'Hello, Diane. Harper just got the flowers; she says she loves them. You really shouldn't have done it. Oh, he did? Well, thank him, then.' Tolliver made a face at me, and I grinned. He listened for a few moments. 'Tomorrow? Oh, no thanks, we'd feel like we were intruding . . .' Tolliver looked acutely uncomfortable. 'That's too much trouble,' he said next. His tone was carefully patient. He listened. 'Then, all right,' he said reluctantly. 'We'll be there.'

He hung up and made a face. 'The Morgensterns want us to come to their house tomorrow for lunch,' he said. 'They've had a lot of people bringing food by, they can't eat it all, and they're feeling guilty that we're stuck in Memphis because of them. There'll be other people there,' he assured me when he saw my face. 'The focus won't be on us.'

'Okay, good. That would have crossed a line, after the flowers. There's such a thing as overdoing the gratitude. After all, it was an accident. And we're getting the reward. Joel said so. You should have asked me before you said yes. I really don't want to do that.'

'But you see that we pretty much have to.'

'Yes, I see that,' I said, trying not to sound resentful. I thought that my brother wanted to see Felicia Hart again.

Tolliver nodded, a sharp gesture to close the subject. I wasn't quite sure I was through whining, but he was right. No point in discussing it any longer. 'You ready to go back to the cemetery?' he asked.

'Yes. How cold is it?' I stood up, experimentally stretched the leg. Better.

'The temperature's dropping.'

When we were all bundled up, I called downstairs to have our car brought around. A few minutes later, we were making our way back to St Margaret's. The weekday nighttime traffic in downtown

Memphis was not heavy. Nothing was going on at the Pyramid, and Ellis Auditorium looked dark, too. We drove east through depressed areas, shopping areas, and old residential areas until we got to the streets around Bingham College. The few people on foot were bundled up like urban mummies.

I began to recognize a few landmarks from the morning before. This time we didn't take the main drive through the college, as we had previously. Tolliver drove around the campus to reach a small road at the back of the college property. It had those white barriers that you pull back across the entrance, and yesterday they'd been pulled shut but unlocked, he'd noticed.

The same was true tonight. Rick Goldman, private eye, should tell Bingham their security had a few holes in it.

We passed between the open barriers. The crunch of gravel under our tires sounded especially loud. After a short stretch of landscaped lawn all around us, we entered the wooded corner of the campus. Though the city lay all around us, it felt like we were miles from nowhere. We drove slowly through the trees surrounding the old site, our headlights catching on the branches and trunks as we passed. Nothing moved in the cold stillness. We reached the clearing of the church and its yard. In the small graveled parking lot, we drove up to the low posts connected with wire that kept cars from pulling onto the grass. There was a security light on a high pole at the rear of the church, and one on the far side. They provided just enough light to make the shadow of the dilapidated iron-railing fence obscure the graveyard.

'If this was a horror movie, one of us would be a goner,' I commented.

Tolliver didn't respond, but he wasn't looking any too happy. 'I thought the lighting would be better than this,' he said. We made sure our coats were buttoned and zipped, gloves on, flashlights ready. Tolliver loaded some extra batteries into his pockets, and I did, too.

There was not even a night-light on in the old church.

When we shut the car doors behind us, the slams sounded loud as gunshots. Tolliver shone his flashlight on the wire so I could step over it, and I returned the favor. Then we opened the gate, which creaked loudly in approved horror-movie fashion.

'Just great,' Tolliver muttered. I found myself smiling.

The ground, which had seemed fairly level in the daylight, was rough walking at night. At least, it was for me. I negotiated it slowly, worried about my faltering right leg. But I didn't ask Tolliver for help. I could manage.

From the entrance gate, we needed to work our way southeast to reach the secluded corner where I'd found Tabitha in Josiah Pound-stone's grave. Of course, that was the darkest place in the whole cemetery.

'It feels bigger tonight,' Tolliver said. His voice was just one step up from whispering. I almost asked him why. Then I realized I didn't want to talk out loud, either. As we neared the open grave, I wondered if they'd dug up poor Josiah, too – and if so, what they'd done with him. The familiar vibrations of the dead began to sound louder and louder in my head.

'Have we ever been to a cemetery at night?' I asked, trying to shake off the uneasy, prickling feeling that was riding my shoulders. There was no definite reason for me to feel anxious. In fact, I usually felt alive, alert, and happy in graveyards.

Certainly, no one else was around. The cemetery was surrounded on two sides by thick stands of trees, on the third side by the parking area (beyond which were more trees), and on the fourth by the old church. It wasn't too far off a busy, modern street, but I'd noticed on our previous visit how isolated the graveyard felt. Bugs and birds had sense enough to keep silent and lay low.

'There was that time the couple in Wisconsin wanted you to do a reading at midnight on their son's grave,' Tolliver said in my ear. It had been so long since I'd spoken, I had to recall the question I'd asked.

I was immediately sorry to be reminded about Wisconsin. I'd been trying to forget, to stuff that night into the closet where I kept horrors. Just to add to the weirdness of the couple and their request, they'd requested Halloween night. Plus, they'd invited about thirty best friends. I guess they'd figured if they were going to pay us that much money, they were going to get some mileage out of the event. They'd been mistaken about what I could do, though I'd never tried to mislead them. Right out there, in front of all their friends, I'd blurted out what had really happened to the child. I shuddered, remembering. Then I made myself shake off the memory. *Focus on this night, this dead girl, this grave*, I told myself. I took a deep breath, let it out. Then another.

'I know the body is gone,' I said, almost in a whisper. 'The body's always been my connection, but I'm going to try to recreate what I got from her yesterday.'

'We're in an isolated graveyard in the dark,' Tolliver muttered. 'At least you're not wearing a long white nightgown, and at least we're together. And believe me, my cell phone battery is fully charged.'

I almost smiled. Usually, I felt most comfortable in a cemetery; but not this one, not this night. I stumbled again. Cemeteries are tricky going, especially the older ones. So many of the new ones have the flat headstones. But in the older ones, there are broken headstones in the grass, which is often uneven and tufted with weeds. In more secluded cemeteries, the living often leave trash on top of the dead – broken liquor bottles and crushed beer cans, condoms, food wrappers, all kinds of stuff. I can't count the times I've found underpants suitable to both sexes, and once I found a top hat set jauntily upright on a stone.

St Margaret's graveyard was free from debris of that sort. It had been mowed and trimmed at the end of the summer, so the grass was fairly low. Our flashlights bobbed through the darkness like playful fireflies, sometimes crossing their beams and then floating away.

The still air was cold, a cold that bit through my gloves and made me shiver. I had on a knit cap and scarf, but my nose felt especially chilled. Tolliver, some steps ahead of me and to my left, made the beam of his flashlight dance as he rubbed his hands together.

The night had a thick, waiting quality that made the hair on the back of my neck prickle. I tried to identify the swoosh of the traffic on the road off through the trees, but there was an absolute silence. I felt a stab of alarm. Surely, at night, I should be able to see the lights of those cars, even through the trees? I slowed down, feeling suddenly disoriented. The flashlight beams seemed dimmer. I was very close to the right spot, but somehow I couldn't pick it out. The buzzing of the bodies around me seemed extraordinarily clear and strong for such old corpses. I started to say my brother's name, but I couldn't speak. Suddenly, Tolliver gripped my lower arm with both hands, very tightly, bringing me to a complete standstill. 'Look at your feet,' he said in a very strange voice. I shone the light directly downward.

In one more step I would have fallen into the open grave.

'Ohmygod. That was close. Thank you. Do you hear anything?' I whispered. One hand slid down to mine, squeezed it, and released it. There was something odd about the feel of that bony hand.

And then I realized Tolliver's flashlight was shining at me from the other side of the grave, with Tolliver holding it.

My heart pounded so fast I thought the vibrations might tear my chest apart. I sank down to my knees on the soft, freshly turned earth.

'See?' said the voice, though I couldn't have said where it had come from. With an increasing sense of dread, I directed my flashlight down into the grave.

There was another body in it.

8

Tolliver didn't seem to be able to move from his side of the open grave, and we both shone our flashlights down at the body.

'At least I didn't fall in,' I managed to say, and my voice sounded hoarse and strange to my own ears.

'He stopped you,' Tolliver said.

'You saw him? Clearly?'

'Just his silhouette,' he said, and even Tolliver's voice was strained and breathless. 'A small man. With a beard.'

This was the first time such a thing had happened to us. It was like being an accountant for five years, and then suddenly being presented with a set of alien numerals that had to be balanced in five minutes.

Tolliver stumbled around the grave to kneel beside me, put both his arms around me, and we held each other fiercely. We were shivering, shivering intensely – not from the cold, but from the nearness of the unknown. I made a little noise that was horribly like a whimper. Tolliver said, 'Don't be scared,' and I turned my head a little to tell him I wasn't any more scared than he was; which was to say, quite a lot. He kissed me, and I was glad for his warmth.

I said, 'This is a thin place.'

'What's that?'

'A place where the other world is very close to this world, separated only by a thin membrane.'

'You've been reading Stephen King again.'

'It felt strange from the moment we got here tonight.'

'Did you feel anything different when we were here the first time? Yesterday?'

'The old ones always feel a little different from the new ones. Maybe I saw the dead more clearly, with more detail.' I held him tighter. Now that I'd gotten over my startled reaction to the ghost, I had plenty of other fears to cope with. We had a situation on our hands. 'What will we do about the body, Tolliver? We shouldn't call the police, right? We're already under enough suspicion.'

My feelings about the law were, at best, ambiguous. I couldn't blame the Texarkana PD for not knowing what was going on in our household when I was a teenager. After all, we'd struggled so hard to conceal it. I hardly blamed them for not finding Cameron; I, of all people, knew how hard it could be to find a dead person. But now that I was grown, the thing I valued most was the ability to shape my life as I wanted. The law could take that away from me in a New York minute.

'No one knows we came here,' Tolliver said, as if thinking out loud. 'No one's come out here since we got here. I bet we could leave and not get caught. But someone's got to get this body out of the grave. We can't just leave him.'

I was beginning to feel calmer. 'Who is it?' I asked, and my voice was steadier. After all, bodies were my area of expertise. I was not at all worried about being this close to a corpse. I was worried about the police suspecting I'd made him a corpse.

'I'm not sure.' Tolliver sounded a little surprised, as if he should have known who was in the hole from the brief glimpse we'd had.

'Let's look again,' I said practically. I was feeling a little more like myself.

We pulled apart then, and deployed our flashlights.

If my heart could sink any lower, it did. Since the body was on its stomach, I couldn't identify its face, but the clothes were familiar.

'Crap. It's Dr Nunley,' I said. 'He's still wearing the clothes he had on when he grabbed me at the hotel.' I pressed the button on my watch, and the dial illuminated. It looked as though I had a fairy perched on my wrist. 'It's been three hours since that happened. Just three hours. The lobby staff had to talk to Dr Nunley to get him to leave, and they'll remember it. This couldn't be worse.'

'Not for him, anyway,' my brother said, his voice dry. But he had a slight smile on his face. I could just see the edge of his mouth in the cast-back light. I felt like punching him in the arm, but I wasn't sure I had enough muscle control to manage it. 'And it's not so good for us, you're right,' Tolliver admitted.

'Have we left footprints? Has it rained since we got here yesterday?'

'No, but the dirt here around the grave has been turned over, and I'm sure we've left traces somewhere. On the other hand, so many people have come through the cemetery since you found Tabitha . . . and we're both wearing the same shoes we wore out here yesterday.'

'But there wasn't this loose dirt then. I don't know how we would explain coming out here tonight. Oh, I'm so sorry I got you into this.'

'Bullshit,' he said briskly. 'We were doing what we do. You wanted to see if you could get some other bit of information from the grave. Well, we found out more than we wanted to know, huh? But it's not your fault.' He hesitated. 'Do you want to try to talk to him, the – the ghost? And what about getting a reading from the body?'

Tolliver's suggestion was as bracing as that brisk slap detectives give hysterical women in old movies. 'Yes,' I said. 'Sure.' Of course, I should have thought of that. I had to calm myself first, and center myself. Not too easy, since I was already buzzing like crazy just from being so close to a fresh body.

The closest I could get to Clyde Nunley's corpse without climbing down into the grave – which might have destroyed or damaged evidence – was to hang over the edge with my hand extended to him. I lay down on the ground and wriggled forward. Tolliver held on to my legs. The hole wasn't so deep, and I managed to touch the shirt on Dr Nunley's back.

His death was so recent it was like a continuous droning in my head, almost drowning my reason, and I had to wait for that to subside before I got a sense of his passing. 'Hit on the head,' I mumbled, caught up in the sheer astonishment he'd felt. 'On the back of the head. So surprised.' The shock of it was still lingering around him. He absolutely had not expected the attack.

'Here?'

'Yes,' I said, straining to extract the pictures of the end of his life. He was so fresh, so recently translated into this lump of flesh that could neither act nor reason. I saw the darkness around him, the tombstones, everything like it was now: the cold, the rough ground, the upturned earth. 'Oh, it hurts! Oh, it hurts! My head!' And the hole coming at me, couldn't throw out my hands to take the fall, grayness . . . blackness.

I was close to that blackness myself when Tolliver hauled me up and braced me against him.

'Here, open your mouth,' he said, and then he repeated it. 'Open!'

I parted my lips, and he pushed a piece of peppermint into my mouth.

'Come on, you have to have some sugar,' he said, and his voice was sharp and commanding.

He was right. We'd found that out, by trial and error. I made myself suck on the candy, and in a few minutes I felt better. Next came a butterscotch.

'It's never been this bad,' I said, my voice weak. 'I guess it's because he's so new.' I was worried I couldn't make it across the cemetery back to our car without a lot of help from Tolliver.

'He's absolutely gone, right? That . . . who stopped you – wasn't him? I did think I saw a beard.'

Every now and then, we'd found a soul attached to a body. That was rare, and until this night I had thought that would be the eeriest thing we could find. Now we knew there was more.

'Clyde Nunley's soul's gone,' I said, not willing to commit myself further than that. 'And we should be, too.' I gathered myself to make the attempt.

'Yeah,' Tolliver said. 'We got to get out of here.'

I paused, halfway to my feet. 'But we'll be leaving him by himself.'

'He's been by himself for a hundred years,' Tolliver said, not pretending he didn't understand. 'He'll have to be by himself for a while longer. For all we know, maybe he's got company.'

'Does this qualify as the strangest conversation we've ever had?'

'I think so.'

'I couldn't have anyone else but you here, no one else would understand,' I said. 'I'm so glad you saw him, too.'

'And that's never happened before, right? You've never mentioned anything like that.'

'Never. I've known when souls were still attached to the body, and I've wondered if those would be ghosts if they didn't detach. I've always wondered if I would see a ghost sometime. I've always been a little disappointed that I haven't, in a way. Oh my God, Tolliver. He saved me from falling right into that grave on top of the corpse. The first time I see a ghost, and he saved me.'

'Were you scared?'

'Not that he would hurt me. But I was afraid because it was spooky and I didn't know what to do for him. I don't know why he can't or won't go on, I don't know how he experiences time, I don't know his purpose. And now all his people are gone, I guess. No one could visit him or . . .' I shut up, afraid of sounding maudlin.

They all want to be found, you know. That's all they want. Not vengeance, or forgiveness. They want to be found. At least, that's what I'd always thought.

But Josiah Poundstone – I was sure he was the ghost – had been firmly located since the moment of his death. Someone had erected the 'Beloved Brother' headstone. And someone had murdered him, if that was part of his awareness. When I'd stood on his grave in the daylight, I'd felt only the faintest flutter from him, so overwhelmed had I been with the thrumming from the most recent corpse. I'd assumed Josiah Poundstone was gone for good.

Apparently, I'd been wrong.

9

We made our way back to the car, taking our time. I had to hold on to Tolliver here and there, and I don't think he was sorry to hold onto me. We dusted dirt off my jacket, and stomped our feet to remove bits of soil.

'If there were an emergency room for psychological shocks, we could go there,' he said, unlocking the car.

'I've never left a body unreported,' I said, remembering how proud I'd been of that fact only a day before. 'Never.' I shuddered. 'I wish I could put my brain in a warm bath of something scented,' I said. 'And give my nervous system some aromatherapy.'

'That mental picture is just disgusting,' Tolliver said.

He was right, but that didn't stop me from wanting some way to soothe my emotional self. I took a deep breath and tried to put the frivolous thoughts on the back burner. We still had decisions to make, and they wouldn't be easy ones.

'Did you get anything from the . . . did you get anything?' Tolliver asked.

'Yeah,' I said. 'Yeah, Dr Nunley was really taken by surprise. I don't know why he was out there, but he never expected the person with him had any evil intent.'

'Do ordinary people expect to be attacked, ever?' Tolliver asked reasonably.

I gave him a disgusted look. 'No, they don't, smart aleck, and that's not what I meant. What I mean is – he wasn't with a stranger. He was with someone he knew, and he had no idea that the other guy wished him ill.'

'You just using "guy" for the ease of it?'

'Right.'

'We can't tell the police.'

'Sure we can, but they won't believe us. I don't know what else we can do. And I absolutely don't think we should tell them we were at the grave site again.'

We argued back and forth all the way to the hotel – and with time out for discretion in front of the staff, resumed our argument when we were alone in the elevator.

When we stepped out, we were struck speechless to see Agent Seth Koenig waiting outside our room.

If the management had cast glances at us on our way through the lobby, we'd been too engrossed in our own problems to pick up on it. *Certainly not a psychic*, I thought ruefully. *If I ever claim to be one, strike me dead.* We were completely taken by surprise.

As one, we stopped in our tracks and stared at him.

We weren't alone in the staring department. He was laying one on us.

'What have you two been up to?' he asked.

'I don't believe we need to talk to you,' Tolliver said. 'My sister tells me you're an FBI agent, and we don't know anything of interest to you.'

'Where have you been?' Koenig asked, as though we would be compelled to tell him.

'We went to the movies,' I said.

'Just now,' he said. 'Where were you just now?'

Tolliver took my hand and led me past the agent, who was surely persistent.

I repeated what Tolliver had said. 'We don't have to talk to you.'

'If it was anything to do with Tabitha Morgenstern, I need to know it.' His voice was rough and hard.

'Fuck off,' I said. Tolliver gave me a startled look. That's not my usual style. But I wanted to get away from this guy. Tolliver got the door unlocked and whisked me inside at top speed. We slammed the door behind us.

'He's obsessed with his failure,' I said, as I began to shed all my outerwear. I noticed my shoes were stained with dirt from the cemetery, despite my efforts. I reminded myself that I had to clean them later. At the moment, I couldn't summon the energy. I felt awful: exhausted, weak, upset. 'I have to shower and go to bed. I'm sorry I'm not more help.'

'Don't say that,' Tolliver said. He hated it when I apologized.

I often thought, and sometimes said, that Tolliver would be better off if he hadn't undertaken the role of my backbone. But when I tried to imagine myself going on the road alone, I felt a huge hole in my middle that refused to fill with anything. I tried to keep myself fit and did everything I could to ensure my health, but the fact remained that sometimes I was just overcome by the physical problems that plagued me. And the job itself drained me, though I loved it.

What Tolliver got out of accompanying me, I wasn't able to figure. But he did seem to want to do it, and he accused me of self-pity when I tried to get him to do something he might find more fulfilling.

In the meantime, we shared everything: the money was our money, and the car was our car, and the planning and execution of the itinerary was ours.

'Come on,' Tolliver said, putting an arm around me helping me to my room. 'Hold up your arms.' Like a child, I held my arms up and he pulled off my sweater. 'Sit on the bed.' I did, and he pulled off my shoes and socks. I stood, and he unzipped my jeans.

'I'm good,' I said. 'I got it from here.'

'Sure? Need candy? Need a drink?'

'No, just a shower and bed. I'll be okay after some sleep.'

Tolliver said, 'Call if you need me,' and went back out to the living room. I heard him turn on the television. I couldn't even remember what night it was, so I didn't know if one of his shows was on. We could never count on being able to keep up with episodes, and we'd discussed learning more about TiVo for the set in our apartment.

I thought I heard Tolliver's cell phone ring while I was in the tub, but I simply didn't care who was calling. I soaked in hot, scented water, then scrubbed myself bright pink. After I dried off and put on my pajamas, I was disgusted to find out I still hadn't unwound enough to sleep. I turned on my own television to have background noise while I painted my nails. I decided on a nice dark red, which looked autumnal, and I had a lovely peaceful half hour to myself. You can't be said to have any worries if your fingernails are the center of your universe, and it gave me time to decompress.

I couldn't settle down to read when that was done, though Tolliver had brought a box of paperbacks up with us. We pick them up here and there, and leave them for other people when we're done. We love secondhand bookstores, and we'll go a mile or two out of our way if we've heard of a good one in the area. I'd been reading a biography of Catherine the Great, who may have become an empress but also managed to have a messy life. Maybe all empresses did. I just couldn't get into her tonight, and I was still jangling too much inside to get in the bed. I wandered into the common living room to see what Tolliver was up to.

He was fuming; there was no other word for it.

'The TV screen is going to break if you keep glaring at it like that,' I said. 'What's up?' Tolliver didn't do a lot of brooding and mulling, so I never thought twice about asking.

'Personal,' snapped Tolliver.

I was shocked for a minute, and then gave myself a piece of good advice. Treat this casually, and don't get all tearful and hurt.

'Okay,' I said calmly. 'What's the score in the game?' Tolliver was watching football, which I couldn't care less about, but the question did knock him out of his funk and redirect his irritation. He was off and running on the failure of his favorite team, the Miami Dolphins, to get a first down. Since I know about as much about football as I do about quantum physics, I tried to look sympathetic while keeping my mouth shut. Sleep was out of the question until this was resolved, one way or another.

'We could use some food,' I said, and called room service. I got a hamburger for Tolliver, and a grilled chicken sandwich for me.

By the time I'd done that, Tolliver had calmed down and was wearing his usual expression of good humor. 'That phone call was from Felicia Hart,' he said.

I tried to keep my face still and receptive. I tried very hard not to twitch.

'I've told you I'm sorry for being . . . for starting something with her,' he said. 'I'm not going to say it again.'

'I didn't ask you to,' I pointed out.

'Right.' He shook his head. 'Residual guilt,' he said, by way of explanation. 'She wants to see me again. I said it wasn't a good time.'

'She saw you today, and she was reminded of how fine you are,' I said, careful to be smiling when I said that. 'I bet she wants to start up again.'

He shook his head. 'That seems really unlikely.'

'I wonder if she'll be at the lunch tomorrow,' I said, trying to sound innocent. 'I'll run interference for you if you need me to. She'll probably try to get you by yourself.'

'I don't think so,' he said, refusing to be drawn.

'She's very protective of Victor,' he said after a long pause. I wondered if he'd seen any of the action on the television screen. 'Do you remember what Victor's alibi was when Tabitha was abducted?'

'Well, it was spring break, so he wouldn't have been at school,' I said. 'Nope, I don't recall. Why don't we look it up?'

Tolliver set up his laptop and hooked up to the hotel's Internet service. We began to do a little research into the crime that had led to us being in this room at this moment.

I sat by Tolliver, my arm around his shoulders, as he brought up the familiar story and the images from eighteen months ago. I had forgotten some of the details, and now that I knew all of the people involved, the pictures had much more impact.

What I noticed, first of all, was how many pictures included Agent Seth Koenig. He was in the background of most of the pictures that had appeared in relation to the disappearance. In all of the pictures, whether he was in the foreground or talking to someone in the background, his face was absolutely serious. He was a man absorbed in his mission.

It was shocking to see how much the Morgensterns had aged since Tabitha's abduction. Even Victor looked more adult now – though at his age, that was maybe only to be expected. In the pictures, Diane looked more like five years younger, and Joel looked . . . lighter. He was still charismatic and handsome now, but he walked more heavily, as if he were carrying a burden on his shoulders. I hated to sound all corny about it – but it was true.

We combed through the stories, refreshing our memories.

On that warm spring morning in Nashville, only Diane had been home with Tabitha. Joel had gone to work two hours before. Spring is always a busy time for accountants, and Joel went in most Saturdays until after the tax deadline. That Saturday, he'd gotten in to work so early that no one had seen him arrive. Joel told the police that several other accountants had come into the office after he'd been there an hour. Though he hadn't been under continuous surveillance from the time the other workers had begun arriving until after Tabitha's abduction, he'd been seen at fairly frequent intervals. That time frame made it seem unlikely he could have managed the crime, but it was a possibility.

As for Diane, she'd told us what she'd been doing – arguing with her daughter, talking on the phone, getting ready to go to the store. She'd been unobserved for most of that time.

So much for the parents.

Tabitha's stepbrother Victor had also gotten up early that morning. Victor had driven to his tennis club for an 8:00 A.M. lesson, which had lasted an hour. And then, Victor said, he'd just stayed around the tennis courts to bat some balls against the wall and talk to some of his friends. The friends, apparently, had remembered seeing Victor, but they weren't sure what time that had been. After that, Victor said, he'd stopped at a gas station to fill his car and buy a Gatorade. The gas station cashier had verified the episode. Victor had arrived home about 11:00 A.M. to find his house exploding with the beginnings of panic. Again, there was no way to pin down times more accurately. If Victor had planned ahead, he could have abducted his half sister.

According to one of his friends, Victor hadn't been especially fond of Tabitha. But this 'friend' couldn't think of anything specific Victor had ever said about Tabitha, just that Victor thought she was a spoiled brat.

That seemed like a perfectly ordinary thing for a big brother to say about his sister, whether she was his full sister or his half sister. On the other hand, Victor was at a volatile age.

Were there other suspects? Sure. The articles we read brought up the fact that Joel was a CPA for Huff Taichert Killough, a firm that handled accounts for lots of music industry people. This fact opened the door to vague allusions to shady record company accounting, as if Joel was possibly mixed up in some dubious financial dealings that might have earned him some enemies. But no facts were ever produced to back up that intriguing possibility. And, in fact, Joel continued to work for the same firm. Now he worked for the Memphis branch instead of the Nashville branch, but of course the newspapers didn't specify whether the change of locale had included a change of job description, or not. If some money-laundering scheme had become an investigative reality, I was sure the reporters would have caught wind of it, since they were all over the abduction like white on rice.

I studied the pictures that had been included with the articles: Victor, looking sullen and lost; Diane, looking wasted; Joel, his face bleached of feeling. There was Felicia, looking angry and fierce, her arm around Victor, and by her side was Seth Koenig, the FBI agent who'd been waiting in the hall for us this evening. Hmmm. He was saying something to her in the picture, caught forever in mid-sentence, his face serious behind a pair of dark glasses. The caption read, 'Felicia Hart, aunt of the missing girl, comforts her nephew, Victor

Morgenstern, as she discusses the case with an FBI agent. The FBI offered their lab facilities or any other assistance the local police might deem necessary.'

'Look,' said Tolliver, sounding amused. The next picture was one of us. We both had on dark glasses, too, and I had my head turned away. That was a habit of mine when I saw cameras. I don't mind being photographed, but that doesn't mean I like it, either.

There was a brother of Joel's, too, a near-clone but a bit older, named David. I didn't recall seeing him at the Morgenstern house, but maybe by the time we'd been called in, he'd returned to his work and his life. People had started drifting back into their normal orbits about that time, when it seemed as if the situation was not going to be resolved quickly.

'I don't think we know a damn thing more,' I complained.

'No, probably not,' Tolliver said. 'We haven't called the police, either.'

'They'll find out it's us calling, if we do,' I said. 'They'll find him. He'll be missed soon. I don't think we can risk it.' Okay, that might seem the last word in callousness from me, and believe me, I wasn't happy about it. I was very aware that Clyde Nunley was lying out there dead in the dark and the cold. But you know, the dead don't feel a thing. They're just waiting.

If he wasn't found the next day, maybe I could 'find' him a second time. No one would be surprised if we happened to go out to the old cemetery the next day, I figured. It was our choosing to go there in the middle of the night that would seem extraordinary; and now that I came to think of it, it *had* been an extraordinary thing to do. And foolish, too.

But now we were stuck with it, and we'd have to take the consequences if our presence was discovered.

As I climbed into my bed that night, I was more confused about what had happened to Tabitha Morgenstern than I'd been before I found her bones. And the presence of the ghost at the grave site was forcing me to rethink all my suppositions about the dead. I had plenty to worry about; but my body was exhausted, and before I knew it, I was asleep.

I don't dream much, but that night I dreamed of holding hands that had been reduced to bones. I wasn't frightened in my dream. But I knew it wasn't right.

*

The next morning, there was a knocking at the door while Tolliver and I sat over breakfast, reading the morning paper. Tolliver was working the crossword. I'd reread everything I could find on the abduction of Tabitha, and I'd worked my way up chronologically to the new articles about the recovery of a body that might be hers. I'd reached the stories that were wringing the dregs out of the discovery of the child's body. This included an article on the main subject – the very tentative positive identification based on dental work – plus a rehash of the abduction, the family's plans for a memorial service the following week, quotes from the grieving grandparents; a companion story about Memphis's 'hidden' cemeteries; and an article about child abduction in general, with statistics on the number of children found alive, the number found dead, and the number of those who were never found. Cameron had plenty of company.

There's not much that's more frightening than the idea of a child vanishing, gone for good. I thought of my little sisters, and shivered. Mariella and Gracie were pretty formidable kids when I'd lived with them in the trailer. I didn't know what they were like now, since my aunt and her husband kept telling us the girls didn't want to see us. That might or might not be true, but if it was so, Iona and Hank had been feeding them a load of untruths about us that I wanted a chance to rectify. The girls might not love me, but I loved them.

My mind had wandered, but the knock recalled me to the here and now.

We looked at each other. Tolliver rose. He looked through the peephole.

'It's the FBI guy again,' he said.

'Shit,' I murmured. I was wearing a hotel bathrobe and nothing else, since I'd showered again this morning after doing my time on the hotel treadmill.

'You'd better let me in, I've got news for you,' the voice on the other side of the door said.

Tolliver glanced back at me.

We considered.

'Okay,' I said. 'Better find out what he wants.'

Tolliver opened the door, and Seth Koenig stepped in at once and closed the door. His eyes flashed to my legs, and then away. 'I taped the news this morning, since I thought you two might not have seen it,' he said. He waited for us to respond, and we both shook our heads. We don't turn on the television as a matter of course. From the expression on his face, I felt pretty bad about what was coming.

He strode over to our television and popped the tape in the hotel player. He used the remote to turn on the set. After a moment of sports scores, Shellie Quail filled the camera. She looked resplendent in a bright fall suit and her usual gleaming makeup. Shellie had on her sober newscaster face. Clearly, she was going to deliver Grim Tidings.

'A groundskeeper at Bingham College made a shocking discovery early this morning. Dennis Cuthbert was sent to the site of the old St Margaret's church and cemetery to make sure the garbage had been picked up after the discovery, two days ago, of Tabitha Morgenstern's remains interred in an ancient grave in the cemetery. What Cuthbert found was just as shocking. Inside that same grave, he found *another* body.'

They sure did love the word 'shocking.'

The camera cut to a husky black man wearing a dark blue uniform. Dennis Cuthbert looked mighty upset. 'I got here, and I see the car parked in the parking lot,' he said. 'Wasn't anyone supposed to be here, so I began looking around a little.'

'Did you think at that point that there was anything *wrong?*' Shellie asked, her face in a sober mask.

'Yeah, I did wonder,' said Dennis Cuthbert. 'Anyway, I started walking around, and soon I notice that the grave look a little different.'

'How?'

'The edge look a little collapsed. So I go over there and look down, and there he was.'

Good. He'd walked over the area where I'd lain to touch the corpse.

The camera swung back to Shellie, who said, 'Inside that grave, Cuthbert found the body of a man, tentatively identified as Bingham College professor Dr Clyde Nunley; Dr Nunley was *dead.*'

Switch to the outside of an older home probably dating from the 1940s, the kind yuppies bought and restored. 'Dr Nunley's wife, Anne, told the police that her husband had left their home for the second time between six and seven o'clock last night to check something out, he said. He didn't give any details. When he hadn't returned home at his usual time, she went to bed. When she woke this morning and found him still missing from the home, she called police.'

Evidently, Anne Nunley had declined to be interviewed, because she didn't appear on the screen. Smart woman.

Close-up of the gleaming Shellie. 'Police aren't saying *how* Dr Nunley died. But a source close to the investigation said his death could have been an accident, or could have been *murder*. Apparently suicide has been ruled out. Back to you, Chip.'

The picture turned into gray lint right after that.

I didn't dare to look at Tolliver. I didn't want to look at Seth Koenig, either. He stepped forward to turn off the machine, and then he faced me. 'What do you make of that, Miss Connelly?'

'I think it's very strange, Agent Koenig.'

'Please call me Seth.' He waited a beat to see if I'd return the courtesy, but I didn't. I wondered what to do now. I wanted the agent to leave with a fervent desperation, because I needed to discuss this very puzzling development with Tolliver.

'The groundskeeper noticed a car in the parking lot,' Seth Koenig said. He waited for us to respond.

'That's what the reporter said,' Tolliver said. He sounded as cool as ice. I envied my brother his composure and wished I could match it.

Of course, there'd been no other car there when we'd parked in the parking lot. Dr Nunley hadn't committed suicide, and he hadn't died by accident. He'd been murdered. We knew it without a doubt.

'There were rocks in the grave,' Seth Koenig said.

I did look up then, and met his eyes. 'What kind of rocks?' I said.

'Big ones. They'd been aimed at his head.'

'But . . .' My voice trailed off as I thought that through. Granted, we hadn't had sunlight or much time or inclination to examine the inside of the grave. But I was sure the 'big rocks' hadn't been there. This might be a clumsy attempt to make the death look accidental; the scenario would be that Dr Nunley somehow slipped and fell into the open grave, hitting his head on the rocks that lay in the bottom. The killer wanted the police to think it was such an accident; or in an alternative version, that Dr Nunley had indeed been murdered, but there at the site, by someone who got him to climb down into the grave and then pelted him with large rocks until he expired. Oh, *that* sounded likely.

Seth Koenig sat on the coffee table in front of me. His eyes met mine. His were a peaty brown, warm with a golden undertone. His whole face was craggy and lined and attractive, and right at the moment, he was concentrated on me.

'I don't know what kind of person you are,' he said. 'But I know you have a gift. Right now, I want you to use that gift. I want you to go see Clyde Nunley's body in the morgue, and I want you to tell me what happened to him. Something tells me you'll let me know.'

Now here was a poser. What could I say?

'Why are you here?' Tolliver said. He stood behind me, leaning over so his elbows were resting on the back of the couch right by my head. 'What is your involvement with this case? I know the FBI is no longer actively involved. But you're offering your lab facilities to the police, right?'

'Right,' Koenig said. His eyes had turned their high-beam stare on Tolliver, which was a relief to me. 'But I'm also here to lend whatever help and support they need, and I'm staying until . . .'

He couldn't finish the sentence.

'You were called in at the beginning,' I said, making my voice gentle. 'You were in Nashville.'

He took a deep breath. 'Yes, I was. Our paths never crossed there, but I was sent there when Tabitha was first missing. I talked to the mother, the father, the brother, the aunt, the uncle, the grandparents. I talked to the crossing guard who'd admonished Tabitha about jaywalking, I talked to the teacher who'd threatened to send a note to her parents about Tabitha's talking in class, and I talked to the lawn man who'd told her dad that Tabitha was going to grow up to be real pretty.' He took a deep breath. 'I went with the police to talk to the moms who drove in the car pool with Diane, I talked to Victor and his friends, I talked to Victor's ex-girlfriend who'd sworn she was going to get even with him, and I talked to the maid who said Tabitha hated to pick up her room.' He sat silent for a long moment. 'I never learned a thing from any of them. I never discovered a single reason anyone would want the girl out of the way. She wasn't perfect. Even people who loved her had a problem with her every now and then. So, Tabitha wasn't all sweetness and light. No kid is, especially no kid in that in-between age. But as far as I can tell, her mom and dad loved her no matter what she did or said. As far as I can tell, they were trying hard to be good parents. As far as I can tell, they didn't deserve what happened to them because of Tabitha's disappearance.'

'Why Tabitha? Why are you so wrapped up in this? You must have investigated other disappearances,' I said. 'Some of them children, I'm sure.'

He rubbed his face with both hands, hard, like he wanted to erase some of the lines in his flesh. 'Lots of sevens,' he said. 'Too many.'

Tolliver and I glanced at each other. Tolliver didn't understand the reference, either.

'Sevens?' I tried to keep my voice very quiet. This man was going through a lot, and I didn't want to sway his balance.

'Kidnapping. That's the program designation for kidnapping,' Koenig said.

'There was never a ransom demand for Tabitha,' Tolliver said. He was leaning forward, his elbows on his knees. 'The FBI can come in even when there's no crossing of state lines? When there's no ransom demand?'

The agent nodded.

'Any suspicious disappearance of a child under eleven,' he said. 'We've offered all our facilities to the Nashville police and the Memphis police. We've got forensic experts examining the body. Our guys already went over the grave. Thank God whoever killed Nunley didn't dump him there before our team had finished. And the same team has been all over the grave this morning since the body was found.'

I shut my eyes and leaned back in my chair.

'Of course, Nunley was here last night grabbing you by the arm, Ms Connelly. But we know he left after that. He wouldn't let the hotel staff call him a cab. They saw him get in his car and leave. Did he contact you again last night?'

'No,' I said. 'He didn't.'

'Why was he so angry?'

'He thought I'd cheated somehow. He was having trouble accepting my ability as real. He was trying to find a rational explanation for something that's just unexplainable.' I wondered if I needed to call Art Barfield.

Seth Koenig looked thoughtful, as if he was making a very large mental note.

'And where were you, Mr Lang?' Koenig asked.

'I was walking down Beale Street, trying to find some good blues to listen to. Doing a tourist thing.'

'What time did you get back to the hotel?'

'About seven, I think. Harper had been asleep.'

'I was upset after the little scene with Dr Nunley,' I explained. 'I had a terrible headache. I took some medicine and lay down.'

'Did anyone see you here during that time?'

'I didn't have room service, and no one called.' Dammit.

'And you, Mr Lang?'

'It's possible someone will remember me in some of the places I stopped in on Beale.' Tolliver listed the places he'd visited, and told Agent Koenig he'd had a beer at one bar. 'It's also possible no one will recall me. The street wasn't crammed with people, but it was busy enough.'

'And you were on foot?'

'Yes, we took a cab to the movies.'

'You saw what movie?'

We went all through our afternoon, including our meeting with Xylda Bernardo and her grandson Manfred.

'I've met Ms Bernardo,' Koenig said, a slight smile on his lips. It was the first time I'd seen him smile, and it looked good on him.

He stayed another hour, taking us over the afternoon and evening over and over. Just when I was beginning to think we were home free, Koenig said, 'And now we come to an interesting point. Who was the man in the lobby with you last night, the man who sent Dr Nunley on his way?'

I'd wondered when he was going to get around to Rick Goldman. 'His name is Rick Goldman. He's a private detective, he told me,' I said carefully. 'He was in the class at the cemetery, so he was there two mornings ago. According to him, he signed up for Occult Studies because the – well, a faction of the governing board, whatever it's called – was a little uneasy about Dr Nunley's class. According to him, they'd asked him to take the courses, observe what happened, and report back to them.'

'You got his card?'

'We aren't on those terms.'

Koenig snorted. He'd taken a couple of notes. Now he put his little notebook back into his pocket. I was a bit surprised that he didn't use something higher-tech, like a BlackBerry.

'One more question,' he said, wanting me to relax so he could spring something on me. I refused to take his unspoken invitation to breathe easier. 'When you two went out last night, why'd you return to the St Margaret's cemetery?'

10

I'd been waiting, like a cartoon character with a piano hoisted over its head, for the big collapse of the conversation, and here it was.

Tolliver and I glanced at each other. We had a choice to make. Did Koenig know we'd been there because he had solid evidence of our presence? Was this sheer conjecture, a stab in the dark to see if he hit a nerve? Or did he only know we'd taken our car out?

Tolliver tilted his head slightly. *Up to you*, he was saying.

'We went for a long drive. We had cabin fever,' I said. 'We just looked at Memphis. We've never been here before. But we avoided anywhere we might be recognized. We don't want any more media attention. We want to be out of here, and out of the public eye.'

'You're one of the few people I could hear say those words without wanting to laugh in their face,' Koenig said. He passed a hand over his crisp dark hair. 'And I can't impress on you how lucky you are that it's me investigating this case, instead of . . .'

'One of your colleagues who wouldn't believe I can do what I can do?' I said.

His mouth snapped shut. After a second, he nodded.

'No one knows, right? Where you work? That you're a believer.'

He nodded again.

'How long have you realized there's more to this world?'

'My grandmother could see spirits,' he said.

'You have a big advantage over people whose minds are closed,' Tolliver said.

'Most days I don't think so,' the agent admitted. 'Most days, I'd be happy to be like the other people I work with. Then I could just dismiss you people, all of you. But I believe you have exceptional abilities. That being said, I don't think you're telling me the truth. In fact, I think you're lying.' Koenig looked at us with a kind of profound disappointment. I almost felt guilty.

'We didn't kill him,' I said. That was the important truth. 'We don't know who killed him, or why.'

'Do you think the Morgensterns killed Clyde Nunley? Do you think they killed their daughter?'

'I don't know,' I said. 'I hope to God they didn't.' I hadn't realized how much I hoped that the Morgensterns were innocent of their daughter's death. And if they hadn't killed Tabitha, I couldn't imagine why they would kill Clyde Nunley. I was assuming that the same person or persons had killed both victims.

That assumption might not be true. 'Tolliver and I have been invited to their home for lunch today,' I said, just to change the subject. 'We'll see more of the family then, I guess.'

'Do you want to see what you can get from the body?' Koenig asked as casually as if I'd been a fiber expert or a pathologist. 'That is, if I can arrange it.'

This was kind of exciting, being taken seriously by a law enforcement professional.

'I'll do Nunley if you let me do Tabitha,' I said.

He looked genuinely surprised. 'But you've already, uh, "done" Tabitha.'

I didn't really want to review Nunley. Been there, done that. I'd do it, though, if I could have another chance at the little girl. 'That day, I was so upset and shocked when I realized there really were two sets of bones in the grave. Maybe I could get more.'

'It may take some time, but I'll see what I can do,' Koenig said. I couldn't help but notice his eyes flicked over my bare legs again. Well, he was a male, after all. I didn't think Koenig was particularly interested in the person who used those legs.

'It drains her to touch a body,' Tolliver said, trying to force Agent Koenig to acknowledge that I was making a generous offer.

'Interesting,' he said, and that was his only comment. 'Let me know when you return from the Morgensterns' house, would you? Maybe you'll pick up some impressions from someone there.'

'Hey, once again, not psychic. The only time I get impressions is when I touch a corpse, and I'm not planning on there being any at the Morgensterns' house. In fact, I'd just as soon this case get solved quickly so I wouldn't have to locate another body until we travel to our next job.'

'Assuming you get to,' Koenig said pleasantly.

There was a significant pause, while Tolliver and I absorbed the threat.

'If push comes to shove, we once did a favor for the governor,' I said, very quietly. I was very willing to shove.

I loved the expression on Koenig's face. I'd really surprised him, and that was a true pleasure. Childish, I know, but I never said I was adult all the way through. I don't ever reveal who my clients have been, but in this case, I felt that I had to take a stand.

'You mean you can call the governor of this state, maybe get him to come down on me or on the Memphis police, let you leave Memphis?'

I didn't say anything. I let what I'd said reverberate a bit.

'That's an unexpected threat,' Koenig said. His face had gotten colder and harder. 'Of course, any threat from you two is unexpected. I kind of think you won't be ringing that bell.'

We looked at each other. 'You'd be surprised what we'll do,' I said. Tolliver nodded.

Koenig gave us his best tough-guy stare.

'Whose car was it?' Tolliver asked.

It took Koenig a second to change mental gears.

'Whose car? You mean, the car left at St Margaret's?'

Tolliver nodded.

'Why should I tell you?'

'After all we've shared, and you're not going to let us know?' My tone may have been a wee bit mocking.

'I think we can take it that the car was Dr Nunley's own vehicle,' Tolliver said. 'Just a guess on my part.'

'Yeah,' Koenig admitted. 'It was Nunley's car. It wasn't there at nine last night, but it was there early this morning.'

We tried not to look too startled. We'd been there earlier; the body had been in the grave, but the car hadn't been there, for sure.

'How do you know that?' I asked, and was proud that I sounded so unconcerned.

'The campus police take a turn back there every night about nine, and no one was parked in the St Margaret's parking lot. Since they're campus cops, they just cruise through the lot. They don't even get out of the car, much less check the inside of every grave. The strange thing is, Nunley was probably in the open grave already. The time of death was way earlier than that. He couldn't have died after nine. The body temperature indicates he was dead by seven at the latest, and the stomach contents tend to bear that out. Of course, the lab results aren't back, and there's a lot more to be learned from the body.'

Tolliver and I exchanged a glance. It took all my self-control to keep from covering my eyes with my hand. We hadn't known how lucky we were. If the campus police had caught us there with the corpse, no way in hell would anyone have believed we were innocent.

'So, Agent Koenig, why do you think the killer drove the car away and brought it back?' I asked. 'Let me put on my thinking cap.' I held a finger to my cheek in a parody of concentration.

Actually, I already had a pretty good idea. Or rather, three ideas. One, the killer wanted to get the car cleaned to erase any forensic traces. Two, the killer had to fetch something and take it back to the cemetery to complete the picture he was trying to paint. Three, the killer heard us coming and wanted to get the car out of there while we were approaching, so we wouldn't see who was driving.

Seth Koenig looked from me to Tolliver with a stony face, not amused in the least. He said. 'That man is dead. If you can't take that seriously, you're just not human.'

'Playing the not-human card,' I said to Tolliver.

'As if we hadn't heard that one before,' he said.

'I know what you're doing,' the agent said. 'And you're good at it, I'll give you that. Were the rocks in the grave when you saw the body?'

'We didn't see the body,' I said flatly.

'They were big rocks. Big enough to crack a skull,' Koenig said. 'I think that's why the killer had to come and go. He had to go get a couple of big rocks. He threw them down in the grave so they'd land on Nunley's head – might have taken a couple of tries. The killer wanted the scene to look as though Nunley might have tripped and fallen into the open grave. But we're pretty sure that just didn't happen. Dr Nunley was almost certainly murdered.'

'Dum-dum-*dum*,' I said.

'I know you're not laughing inside about this,' Koenig said. 'I know you want me to leave so you can talk about it. I'm letting you know I'm available for further conversation. And if you remember anything, you're smart enough to realize we need to know about it.' He rose, in an easy motion that made me envious.

'We understand,' Tolliver said, getting up at the same time. He stood between Koenig and me. 'We'll be talking to you.' He hesitated. 'I appreciate that you're doing your best with this case. It's bothered Harper a lot, too.' He looked back at me, and I nodded. Though we were ready, past ready, for Koenig to leave, this had been a much more amicable interview than we usually had with anyone who carried a badge.

When the door shut behind Koenig, Tolliver didn't move for a long moment. Then he turned to me with raised brows.

'That was different,' I agreed.

'The bad thing about him being halfway nice is that I almost don't like lying to him,' my brother said. 'The good thing is, he gave us a lot of useful information.' His face darkened. 'Like the time of death.'

I nodded. 'That's pretty scary, huh? That we got there at just the right moment not to run into the murderer?'

'I wonder if we were that lucky. I wonder if the murderer wasn't parked somewhere, watching us – to see if we'd find the body and call the cops. If we didn't, he'd know he needed to do something different, because there'd be no point in bringing the car back if there'd be a police officer standing there saying, "And what are you doing in the deceased's automobile?"'

I shivered, picturing someone lurking in the dark coldness of the old graveyard, someone watching and waiting to see what we made of our discovery. I'm no good at detecting the presence of living people. But the awful image faded after a moment. That didn't hang together.

'No, no one was there,' I said. 'Because someone did bring the rocks – thought it *was* of use to try to cover up the murder. So it stands to reason that the killer didn't know we'd found the body in the meantime, that we could testify that there wasn't anything in the grave but the corpse when we saw it.'

Tolliver thought that over, nodded. It made sense. 'Assuming we tell anyone. Assuming people believe us,' he muttered.

'Yes, always assuming that.' I stood and stretched. Because of my bad leg, I couldn't stand as smoothly as the FBI agent, who was way older. I tried not to resent that. I moved carefully, loosening the muscles. 'And we just missed the campus cop patrol. We thought it was so deserted out there! They should put in a traffic light.' There was a lot more thinking to do about what Seth Koenig had told us, but we had a social engagement I was dreading. 'I'm going to get ready for the lunch. I guess we have to go.'

Tolliver blew out a deep breath. He was as reluctant as I was, and he had the added complication of Felicia Hart's probable presence. 'I think the Morgensterns feel guilty because we can't leave Memphis,' he said. 'They feel kind of like they're our host and hostess.'

'But their daughter is dead, and they should be free to think about that, concentrate on that.'

'Harper, maybe they don't want to. Maybe we're a welcome distraction.'

I shrugged. 'Then at least we're serving some useful purpose.' But I couldn't even feel good about that. 'I think this is a bad idea.'

'I'm not exactly looking forward to it myself. But we have to do it.'

I held up my hand, because his tone was definitely on the testy side. 'I get that. And I'll stop sulking in a minute. Okay, you shower. I'll get dressed.' I glanced at my watch. 'We've got an hour and a half. Do we have directions?'

'Yeah, I got them over the phone from Joel. I'm sure Felicia is going to be there.' He gave me a stern look. 'Do I have to ask you to be nice?'

'Of course I will be.' I gave him just enough of a smile to make him anxious. We didn't talk much during the long drive across the city. I drove, Tolliver navigated.

The Memphis home of the Morgenstern family was not unlike their Nashville home, though it was located in a somewhat more modest neighborhood. Diane and Joel liked upscale suburbs, not old city neighborhoods. They liked the kind of place where the trees are only partially grown and the lawns were rolled out in strips, where people jog in the early morning and the late evening and there are always service trucks circling the houses like remoras seeking sustenance from sharks.

The Morgenstern house was pale brick with dark red shutters and doors, a yard that would be beautiful in the spring, and a curving doublewide driveway that already contained a few shining cars, including a pearly Lexus, a dark red Buick, a green Navigator, and a candy-apple red Mustang. We parked and got out. I don't know about Tolliver, but I felt I was on alien ground. There were Thanksgiving decorations out at some of the homes, and Diane had put a couple of hay bales in the front yard, topping them with pumpkins and squash and cornstalks and other fall paraphernalia.

Maybe, when we have a house, I'll do the same thing, I thought, and knew right away that was total bullshit. I'd just been trying to tell myself I could live in as nice a place as the Morgensterns and not feel strange and out of place.

Tolliver smiled at me over the top of the car. 'You ready?' he asked. 'You look great today, you know.'

I was wearing a rust-colored long-sleeved sweater over dark brown corduroys and leather high-heeled boots. I had a dark brown suede jacket on. At the last minute, I'd thought about jewelry and added a plain gold chain. I seldom wear jewelry, but this had seemed a good time to add a little gleam. Tolliver had stretched himself to wear a button-up shirt and khakis. I wondered if he had dressed for Felicia Hart's benefit. He said he didn't want her attentions, didn't understand her . . . but I wondered.

I went up the sidewalk, picking up my feet with an effort. I felt more like dragging them. As I rang the doorbell, I noticed a sort of decorated plaque hanging by the right side of the door, brass and turquoise and shiny stones combined in a really interesting way, with etched symbols of doves and Stars of David. I thought it looked as though it was a door, and the depth of the case indicated there might be something inside. I raised my eyebrows at Tolliver, who shrugged. He didn't know what it was, either.

Diane answered the door. She wasn't looking good; I guess that was to be expected. Her pregnancy was laying into her hard, giving her large rings under her eyes, and she'd lost all grace, moving heavily and with ponderous deliberation. But she'd fixed a hostess smile on her face, and she said she was happy we'd come. Joel came next, and shook our hands. He looked in my eyes and told me how glad he was to see me.

Even a non-Joel fan like myself could feel a twinge. And yet, I didn't think there was anything behind his personalization of a commonplace greeting; I didn't imagine he wanted to have an affair with me. It was just his way.

'We're in the family room,' Diane said, her voice limp. 'It's been the nicest quiet morning, with the telephones turned off and the computers shut down. No one's even watched the television.' Her face crumpled for a moment, then came back with a pleasant social smile. 'Come say hello to everyone.'

'Everyone' turned out to be Felicia and her father, Joel's parents, Victor, and Joel's brother, David. Also on hand were a couple of friends of Diane's from Nashville, who'd driven over for the day. The two women were named Samantha and Esther; they were about Diane's age and extremely well groomed, which made me feel sorry for Diane. There was a little conversation going on, of the low-level and subdued variety. Joel waved a hand to gather everyone's attention.

'For those of you who don't know her yet, this is the woman who found Tabitha,' Joel said, and the faces all went absolutely blank.

This was a very strange reaction, one I hadn't foreseen. I'd never been announced like this. The introduction was odd enough; especially considering the dad of the murder victim was doing the introducing. And it was like I'd done them a great and grand favor, instead of being paid for a service that (as far as I was concerned) had borne fruit months too late. Naturally, when I'd worked for them in Nashville, the Morgensterns had paid me for my time. I had a sudden notion: maybe I should turn down the reward money, or donate it to charity, since I'd taken their money before and not given them back the location of their daughter. I put that away to mull over later, but my initial reaction was 'Hell, no.' I never promised anyone I'd find anything; only that if I did, my COD (cause of death) would be accurate. I'd spent days of my time and lots of my energy searching for Tabitha; she just hadn't been there to be found.

I realized another thing as I stood there in the unwanted spotlight. No one in this house knew about the body in the grave in St Margaret's cemetery; the newest body, that is. They'd been incommunicado all morning, by Diane's own testimony. I opened my mouth to share the news, and then I shut it. They would find out soon enough. I glanced at Tolliver, and he nodded. He'd arrived at the same point.

The older Morgensterns, who were only in their mid-fifties, rose to their feet and slowly made their way to me. Mrs Morgenstern was the one needing the help; she had Parkinson's, I could see. Mr Morgenstern looked as strong as his sons, and his handshake was firm. In fact, if he'd been single and he'd asked me out, I'd have thought about accepting, because Mr Morgenstern was as good-looking as his sons, too. 'We're so grateful that we can finally take care of Tabitha,' Mrs Morgenstern said. 'You've performed a great service for our family. Now that they've learned for sure about their girl, maybe Diane and Joel can welcome the little one to come with a clear mind. My name's Judy, and my husband's name is Ben.'

'This is my brother Tolliver,' I said, in turn, having shaken hands with the couple.

'This is Felicia's dad, Victor's grandfather, Fred Hart,' Ben said.

Fred Hart didn't look as hale and hearty as Ben Morgenstern, but again, for a man in his fifties, he looked good: a bit thick around the waist and gray on top, but still a man you'd reckon with. He had a drink in his hand. I was pretty sure it wasn't soda or tea.

'Good to meet you, Fred,' I said, and he shook my hand without comment. Fred Hart's square face was set in an expression I thought must be habitual. He was serious and grim, and his mouth was a compressed flat line that seldom curved in a smile. Of course, he'd lost his daughter to cancer, and he had probably gone through another emotional wringer when his step-granddaughter had been taken. He took another sip from the glass in his hand, and his gaze returned to his living daughter. Maybe he thought she would vanish, too.

The three grandparents were standing in front of built-in shelves that were clogged with framed family pictures and other memorabilia.

'Look, they still have Tabitha's menorah up,' Judy said, pointing to a candlestick. I did recognize that particular symbol of Judaism. There was another menorah right by Tabitha's, but it was radically different in concept.

'Each kid has their own?' I guessed.

'Some families do that,' Judy said in her gentle voice. She pointed with a trembling hand. 'There's Victor's. Of course, his had to be different.' She gave me a conspiratorial smile that said all teenagers were difficult. Victor's menorah was like a little stage or shelf with the eight small candles on it, behind it a little backdrop, a mirror topped with an elaborately worked brass header. If both menorahs hadn't been designed to hold candles, I wouldn't have recognized them as the same religious object.

Fred Hart reached out to point at a picture. His finger was shaking. 'My daughter,' he said, and I obediently looked at the snapshot, which was a happy one. A very attractive woman with short auburn hair and big brown eyes had been photographed sitting on a white-painted wrought iron chair in a garden at the height of its beauty, probably in May, I thought. She was holding a baby on her lap that must be Victor, a little boy in a sailor suit. His hair was fiery, too – not too surprising, with both parents being red-headed – and he was grinning at the camera. I figured he was about two years old, though I'm not good at pegging baby ages. Mr Hart touched the frame of the photo with a kind of stern tenderness, and then he silently turned away to stand at the window, looking out.

Judy and Ben took me over to meet their other son, Joel's brother, David, a slighter, less magnetic version of his brother. I'd seen David in pictures, but the man in the flesh made little impression. David had the same reddish coloring and blue eyes as Joel, but he was built along sleeker lines and his eyes didn't have the draw of Joel's. David Morgenstern didn't seem particularly glad to meet me. From the distant way he touched my hand instead of actually shaking it, I gathered that he couldn't fathom why Tolliver and I should be invited guests in his brother's home.

I was kind of wondering the same thing, so I didn't blame him for his coolness. Oddly enough, on our previous job we'd also been invited to the client's home for a lunch. But that was hardly the normal procedure. Normally, we were in and out of the town as quickly as we could manage. I didn't like this social fraternizing with clients; it seemed to lead to deeper involvement in their problems, and that meant trouble. I promised myself on the spot that I wouldn't do it again.

Though Fred Hart remained aloof from the little crowd, the older Morgensterns had decided I was in their charge. Since Ben and Judy were persistently dragging me (and Tolliver, too) around the room from guest to guest, there was no way I could dodge the next person on the route.

'This is our son Joel's former sister-in-law, Felicia Hart,' Judy said, and her voice had taken on a distinctly cool tone. 'Fred's daughter.'

'Joel's first wife, Whitney, was just a dear,' Ben said, which was one way of saying Whitney's sister was not. There was definitely some bad blood there. I wondered what could have happened to make the older Morgensterns dislike Felicia so heartily.

I said, 'We know Felicia,' at the same moment Felicia said, 'Of course, I saw Tolliver and Harper the other day at their hotel,' and shook hands with us both with perfect aplomb. But her eyes weren't as neutral as her manner. I hadn't expected her to care about seeing me today, but I had expected her to have a strong reaction when she saw Tolliver. I'd expected that it would be a pleasurable reaction.

I'd have to classify it more as smoldering, or maybe volcanic.

Not 'take me in your arms and let's jump into the volcano of love,' but more 'let me push you into the molten lava.'

I began a slow burn. What was up with her? Maybe she imagined Tolliver would refer to their past relationship in front of her father, or maybe, like David, she didn't think we belonged at a family gathering (though surely she didn't have that much claim on Joel's present family). If that was the case, shame on her. If Tolliver was good enough to be her bed partner, he was good enough to break bread with her nearest and dearest. But just as I was tensing up and looking for a moment to say something barbed, Tolliver squeezed my hand. I relaxed. He was sending me a clear message that Felicia was his problem.

After I'd chatted for a brief moment with Diane's friends Esther and Samantha, I tried to find a spot to hole up. Not only were the emotional crosscurrents a little draining, but my leg was hurting. It tingled and felt weak, as though it might decide to give way on a whim.

I found an empty chair right by that of another person who seemed to be feeling like an outsider: Victor, Joel's son by his first marriage. The boy – the young man – was hunched in a chair in a corner, defiantly apart from the rest, and he eyed me with apprehension as I walked over and sank down in the soft chair beside his. Victor gave me a brief look of acknowledgement, then fixed his gaze on his hands.

I was sure that Victor, like me, was remembering our encounter in another living room, in Nashville, and how he'd lost all his restraint and wept on my shoulder. It had made me feel good, actually, to be trusted like that.

For all I knew, Victor was recalling his breakdown with profound regret.

What I *could* be sure of was that Victor thought this gathering sucked. He was trying to get as far away from the grown-ups as he could. He'd had good manners ingrained in his character, and he'd gotten taller and more mature in the past few months – but he was still a teenager; a teenager who would far rather be out with his buds than hanging around with his family on this dismal occasion.

I didn't blame Victor for that, either.

So the room was full of people who didn't particularly want us there; some of them were pretending to be pleased, some of them weren't. Even our host and hostess were acting sheerly out of an imagined obligation.

I could see their point of view. I could even share it. Yet here we were, with no graceful way to get out of this uncomfortable situation. The only exit laid through a blatantly transparent excuse, such as a sudden illness, a phone call summoning us elsewhere, or something equally lame. I couldn't think of how to arrange such a thing without causing even more unhappiness.

In silence, Victor and I watched Samantha carry a glass of iced tea to Joel, watched him accept it with a pleasant nod, watched the woman's eyes as she stood by him hoping for another crumb of his attention.

Victor looked at me and snorted. 'My dad, the babe magnet,' he said derisively, including me in his age bracket so it would be okay to talk to me. Victor didn't sound envious, which I thought would be the case with most teenage boys. He sounded like the babes were the objects of his scorn, right along with his father. Now that he'd overcome his reluctance to speak, he seemed to feel we'd renewed our bond. He leaned closer. Victor said, 'You're not Jewish, are you?'

'No,' I said. That was easy.

'Victor, honey!' Judy Morgenstern called. 'Go out to the Buick and get my cane, please.' The boy looked at me intently. I wondered if there was something specific he wanted to say to me. He gave me a dark glance as he heaved himself up out of his chair and strode off to fetch the cane. I thought I might have a little recovery time, but no. To my surprise, Felicia took his place. I have to admit, I was curious. Not only did I wonder what she wanted to talk about, after her chilly greeting earlier, but also I wanted to discover why Tolliver had ever been attracted to this woman.

At the moment, my brother was talking to David, and he shot me a questioning glance, a little on the concerned side, when Felicia seated herself beside me. But he was too far away to hear our conversation, so I could say what I liked.

'You live here in Memphis, also?' I asked politely. I rubbed my right leg, which was aching, then forced my hand to be still.

'Yes, I have a condo in midtown,' she said. 'Of course, you have to have security there. My dad had a cow when I bought in the Towers. "It's midtown, you're going to get attacked and mugged!" ' She smiled at me in a conspiratorial way, as if the concern of one's parent was a silly thing. 'The parking garage is completely enclosed; you can only get in if you have a sticker. And there's no pedestrian walk-in; entrance only through the building. There's a guard at the car exit, twenty-four/seven. It's expensive, but I couldn't live with my father anymore. Way past the age to move away.' Her dad had a fresh drink in his hands; I'd watched him disappear into the kitchen and return with it. He resumed staring out the window. Felicia followed my gaze and flushed.

'You're very security conscious,' I said, to deflect the moment.

'You have to be, when you're by yourself,' she said. 'Joel is always trying to get me to move out to east Memphis somewhere.' She shook her head with a smile, inviting me to share her amusement with Joel's concern. The implication was that she and Joel were close; I got that. 'And my dad would like me to move back with him. He lives in this huge house, all alone.' Again, message received; her background was stuffed with money. 'But as this family's situation proves, you can be in much more danger in the suburbs than you have to be in midtown, if you take precautions.'

'Of course, they were in Nashville then,' I said.

'Same difference. Everyone feels too safe in the suburbs. They take security for granted.'

Diane, Samantha, and Esther left the room, and I figured they were heading to the kitchen for food preparation. I wondered if I should volunteer, but I decided they'd be much more comfortable with each other if I wasn't there. I turned back to Felicia.

'I'm sure they don't take security for granted anymore,' I said, very quietly, and a shadow crossed Felicia's narrow, elegant face.

'No, not anymore. I'm afraid they'll always be looking over their shoulders, with this baby that's coming. Victor is old enough to take care of himself, at least to some extent. Vic is a typical teenager.' She shook her head, smiling. Typical teenagers, evidently, were stupid. 'They think they're immortal.'

'Victor, of all teenagers, should know that's not true.'

Felicia looked abashed. But she plowed ahead with the conversation. 'It's strange; Victor's physically healthy as a horse, like I am. His mom – my sister, Whitney – she was the sickly one in our family. Whitney had all these allergies when we were kids. My parents would have to sit up with her all night, she'd be wheezing and coughing.' Felicia's face looked grim. I wondered what kind of nurturing Felicia had gotten while Whitney's health crises were front and center in the Hart household. 'She got pneumonia when we were in junior high, and mono, and tonsillitis, and when she was in college she had a ruptured appendix, after she'd started dating Joel. I've never been in a hospital.' She looked over at her former brother-in-law. 'You should have seen the care Joel took of her. He'd hardly let anyone else in the room during the final stages of her last illness. He wanted her all to himself. Second in hovering was my dad.' She looked across the room at Fred Hart, who'd suddenly decided to talk to Joel. I didn't know what the conversation covered, but Joel was looking politely bored.

'I guess Victor was too young to visit the hospital much.'

'Yeah, we didn't want him to remember Whitney like she looked toward the end. I stayed at their house and took care of Victor. He was so little, so cute.'

'He's a handsome young man,' I said politely.

'I still keep an eye on him for my sister's sake. It's been great, having them here in Memphis. Victor stays with me sometimes if things get too tense at home.'

She was dying for me to ask her why things would be tense at home. Surely, the abduction and disappearance of a little girl was reason enough? 'He's lucky to have such a conscientious aunt,' I said, selecting the least weighted of responses.

'I saw your brother a couple of times,' Felicia said suddenly, as though tossing a pebble into a pool to see what happened.

'That's what he told me,' I told her in a completely neutral voice.

She seemed stymied when I didn't continue. After a pause, Felicia said, 'I think he took it a bit hard when the distances between us made me think we'd be better off apart.'

I had no response to that, but I was angry, you can bet on it. This was totally not the story Tolliver had told me. So, of course, she was lying.

'It must be difficult to find someone to date, when you're at that in-between age,' I said.

Her eyes narrowed.

'I mean,' I continued, 'men are either married, or they're on their first divorce, and they may have kids and all kinds of entanglements.'

'I haven't found that a problem,' she said through clenched teeth. 'But I suppose since you travel all the time, it's very hard to meet *eligible* men.'

Oh, ouch – not. If she thought it would bother me to be reminded that I was always in Tolliver's company, she was wrong. Besides, why should I cross swords with this woman? Tolliver was an adult, and he could handle her mixed signals, all on his own.

'Do you know Clyde Nunley?' I said, looking anywhere but at her face.

'Well, we went to Bingham together,' she said, which gave me a jolt. I'd been so sure she'd say she'd never met him. 'He's a couple of years older, but we know each other. Clyde and David are actually fraternity brothers.'

She nodded at David. He looked questioning, and when she smiled at him, he came over, though a bit reluctantly. David Morgenstern would not want to be president of my fan club. But he shook my hand civilly, and when Felicia said, 'Harper was asking about Clyde Nunley.'

David rolled his eyes. 'What an asshole,' he said. 'He was a wild guy in college, lots of fun, but he decided he was the establishment as soon as he became a professor. Smarter than mere mortals, cooler than dry ice. I don't see him socially, but I do catch a glimpse of him at alumni meetings.'

Not any more.

'Look, Diane wants us to come into the dining room,' Felicia said, and I rose to follow the others. David excused himself and went down the hall to a door I assumed was a bathroom's. Tolliver was having a serious talk with the older Morgensterns, but from the few words I caught, he was talking about the Memphis city government. I thought they looked a little relieved, maybe glad not to have to be talking about Tabitha, just for a few minutes. I trailed in the direction Felicia indicated. We were both glad to have an end to our tête-à-tête, I think. I didn't know what Felicia had thought she needed to convey to me, but I'd missed it. 'Why'd you ask about Clyde?' Felicia asked suddenly.

'He came to our hotel last night, kind of irate,' I said, after a moment.

She looked astonished. 'What on earth about?'

'I don't know,' I said, not wanting to talk about it any longer.

Diane had simply made a buffet out of all the food the neighbors had brought over. She and her two Nashville friends had arranged the dishes on a long counter in the spotless kitchen. There was an eat-in area at one end of the room, and the gray winter sky loomed through the large windows around that table in an unpleasant way. There was also a breakfast bar with high stools forming a right angle to one end of the counter, and I'd passed through a formal dining room. This house was focused on eating.

Some of the dishes were hot, some were cold, and there were a lot of casseroles. Some of the flowers and plants the family had received were arranged in with the food and on the two dining tables, formal and informal. This attractive presentation was a talent of Diane's I hadn't expected. I wondered if her friends had done it all, and then chided myself for not giving her enough credit. I'd never seen the unstressed side of the woman.

While the guests were milling around, I eyed the room. The kitchen was simply beautiful, like something that could be photographed for a magazine. White cabinets, dark marble counters, a center island. Beautiful china stacked at the beginning of the spread, and shining silver. The sinks and appliances gleamed with stainless steel – not a fingerprint in sight. If the Morgensterns had a maid, she was invisible. Maybe Diane was the kind of woman who cleaned when she got upset.

At Diane's urging, Joel's parents went through the line first, with Diane herself holding Mrs Morgenstern's plate while the older woman selected what she wanted to eat. Diane got them settled at the table in the formal dining room and told the rest of us to please go ahead. I lined up behind Felicia and David.

As I waited, I watched Fred Hart shake his head when Diane urged him to get in line. Felicia observed the encounter with a curiously blank face, as if she had no emotion left for her father. After a long moment, she went over to him and said something to him in a low voice. He flinched away from her and left the room. As I picked up a plate and silverware, I wondered if I should go out searching for a happy family. Maybe it was my line of work that threw me in the path of so many unhappy ones.

Esther attracted my attention with a little wave of her hand. It was my turn to begin serving myself, and I'd been standing immobile, holding up the line. I gave myself a mental shake.

Some generous soul had brought a thinly sliced roast, but I passed it by, and instead got some broccoli, a fruit casserole baked in some kind of curry sauce, a roll, and a cold three-bean salad. There was the dining table in the dining room, a set of barstools at the kitchen counter, an informal family table, or we could go back in the living room, Diane told us. I got my utensils (rolled up in a bright napkin) and sat at the kitchen counter, since I was spry enough to climb up onto the high stool. When I'd been settled there approximately ten seconds, Esther put a glass of tea by my plate, her bright toothy smile as ferocious as a shark's. 'Unsweetened,' she said. 'Okay?' Her voice hinted that it better be.

'Good, thanks,' I said, and she swam away.

To my surprise, Victor sat beside me. I assumed he'd gotten his grandmother's cane and delivered it. His plate was invisible beneath a truly amazing array of food, very little of it involving vegetables, I noted. He had a can of Coke that he popped open with a defiant hiss.

'So, what you do, it's just weird, right?' was his opening conversational gambit.

'Yes, it is.'

Maybe he'd meant to offend me. If so, my matter-of-fact reply took him off base. I was actually glad to get a dose of sincerity.

'So, you travel all the time?'

'Yeah.'

'Cool.'

'Sometimes. Sometimes I wish I had a nice house like this.'

He glanced around him contemptuously. He could dismiss the value of a beautiful and cared-for home, since he'd never lacked it. 'Yeah, it's okay. But no house is good when you're not happy.'

An interesting and true observation – though in my experience, comfort never hurt whether you were depressed or whether you were cheerful.

'And you're not happy.'

'Not much.'

This was a pretty intense conversation to be having with someone I didn't know at all.

'Because of Tabitha's death?' Since we were being blunt.

'Yeah, and because no one here is happy.'

'Now that she's been found and she can be buried, don't you think things will get better?'

He shook his head doubtfully. He was eating all the while we were having this incredibly doleful conversation. At least he shut his mouth when he chewed. Suddenly I realized I was closer in age to this boy than anyone else in the house, and I knew that was why he'd sought me out.

'Maybe,' he said grudgingly. 'But then we gotta get ready for the baby to come, and it'll cry all night. Tabitha did,' he added, almost inaudibly.

'You really were fond of her,' I said.

'Yeah, she was okay. She bugged me. But she was okay.'

'The police gave you a hard time when she was taken.'

'Oh, yeah. It was intense. They questioned me, Dad had to get me a lawyer.' He was a little proud of that. 'They couldn't get that I wouldn't have anywhere to put her. Why would I take her? Where would I take her? We fought, but even real brothers and sisters fight. You fight with your brother, right?'

'We grew up in the same house,' I said, 'but he's not really my brother. My mom married his dad.' I was surprised at my own words. Sentences just kept coming out of my mouth.

'That would be freaking weird, living in the house with someone your own age you weren't even related to. Especially if you're not the same, you know, sex.'

'It took some getting used to,' I admitted. It hadn't taken long before Cameron and I and Mike and Tolliver had bonded against the common enemy. I took a deep breath. 'Our parents used drugs,' I said. 'They used a lot of cocaine. Weed. Vicodin. Hydros. Whatever they could buy. They used alcohol to fill in the cracks. Did your parents ever have a problem like that?'

His mouth literally dropped open. Not as sophisticated as he'd thought himself, Victor. 'Geez,' he said. 'That's awful. Kids use drugs, not parents.'

If that wasn't the most naïve thing I'd ever heard, it was pretty damn close. But it was kind of nice, too, that he still had illusions like that. I waited for a direct answer.

'No,' he said, having gathered himself. 'My folks would never. Never. Use drugs. I mean, they hardly even drink.'

'That's good,' I said. 'I wish all parents were like that.'

'Yeah, Dad and Mom are okay,' he said, trying to sound tough and careless. But he'd been shaken. 'I mean, you can't tell them stuff. They don't know anything. But they're there when you need them.'

He even called Diane 'Mom,' and that reminded me how young Victor had been when Diane had married Joel.

'You've been around a lot,' Victor said, running a hand through his auburn hair. 'You've had a real life.'

'I've had more than my share of real life,' I said.

'But you would know . . .' His voice trailed off, just when the dialogue was turning in an interesting direction.

I didn't try to prod Victor to pick up the conversational thread. I'd covered all the bases I could with this kid, without getting into the realm of questions too strange to ask him. I hadn't initiated this conversation, but I'd learned a lot from it. I knew, as I watched Victor check out the dishes left on the kitchen counter that he hadn't yet sampled, that this boy had a secret. It might be a big secret, it might be a small one, but I needed to know it, too. I thought maybe he would come to me with it; though teenagers could spin on an emotional dime.

The kitchen had one of those little televisions mounted below the cabinet, presumably so the cook could watch *Ellen* or *Oprah* while she did her job. Though Diane had boasted that televisions were off and phones were off the hook, someone had turned this one on, maybe to catch the weather or some sports scores.

Though the sound was turned down in deference to the occasion, something caught Victor's attention, and he stood squarely in front of it, plate still in hand. The expression on his face grew startled, puzzled, alarmed, all at once.

It wasn't hard to figure out what he was seeing.

Well, we'd known the news would reach the Morgensterns sooner or later, and the moment was now.

'Dad!' said Victor, in a voice that brought his father to his side at a good pace. 'Dad! They found that college guy dead, in Tabitha's grave!'

I sighed, and looked down at my plate. I hadn't thought of it quite that way. After all, it had been Josiah Poundstone's for much longer. It was a much-used grave.

Quite a hubbub ensued, with the big television in the family room getting switched on, and everyone gathering in front, plates still in hand or discarded where the eater had been perching. I consulted Tolliver silently. He looked at the food regretfully, so I guess he hadn't filled up while he could. He nodded. We needed to be gone.

So as not to be hopelessly rude, we quietly thanked Diane, who hardly knew we were speaking to her. That done, we let ourselves out of the house. I wondered if they even realized we'd slipped out.

'If we go back to the hotel, someone'll want to come talk to us,' Tolliver predicted gloomily.

'Let's go to the river.'

I don't know why moving water is soothing, but it is, even on a cold day in November in Tennessee. We went to a riverfront park, and even though I was wearing my high-heeled boots, we enjoyed strolling through the nearly empty area. The Mississippi flowed silently past the Memphis bluffs, as it would do long after the city crumbled, I supposed – if the world didn't get destroyed altogether. Tolliver put his arm around me because it was so chilly, and we didn't talk.

It was good to be silent. It was good to be away from the crowd at the Morgenstern house, and alone with Tolliver. I discounted the two middle-aged homeless guys that passed a bottle back and forth when they didn't think we were looking. They were as happy avoiding us as we were avoiding them.

'That was a strange interlude,' Tolliver said, his voice careful and precise.

'Yes. Pretty house. I loved the kitchen,' I said.

'I had a talk with Fred. He's got an outstanding lease on the Lexus.' Tolliver is jonesing for a new car. Ours is only three years old, but it does have a lot of miles on it. 'Saw you talking to Felicia,' he continued.

'Felicia brought up the fact she'd seen you socially,' I said, which was the nicest way I could put it. 'She seemed to think you all had had a conversation about not seeing each other.'

'Interesting, since she keeps calling me,' he said, after a moment. 'I can't figure her out. No house in the burbs for us.'

Though his voice was light and ironical, I realized he'd been at least taken aback. A woman he'd been to bed with, a woman who'd actively pursued him, had shown no desire to speak to him when she was with her family. Yeah, that would make anyone feel pretty bad, whether or not the relationship was desirable. My ill feeling against Felicia Hart began to congeal into something quite solid. I changed the subject.

'Victor has a secret,' I said.

'Maybe he's got jerk-off magazines under his bed. Babes with big boobs.'

'I don't think that's his secret. At least, not the secret that interests me.'

We walked a moment in silence.

'I think he knows something about one of his family members, something he's trying *not* to connect to the murders.'

'Okay, confused.'

'He's a pretty innocent kid, all things considered,' I said. I was trying hard not to sound overly patient. 'And he's had some big blows in his life.'

'Working hard not to draw parallels, here.'

'Me, too. But the point is, I think Victor can connect some member of that family to . . .'

'What, exactly? His half sister's death? Clyde Nunley?'

'Okay, I don't know. Not exactly. I'm just saying, he knows something, and that's not healthy for him.'

'So what can we do about it? They won't let him hang around with us. They won't believe us. And if he's not talking . . . besides, what if the subject of the secret is one of his parents?'

Another silence, this one a little huffy.

'Speaking of Joel,' Tolliver said, 'how come you're not panting like all the other women?'

'All the other women are panting?'

'Didn't you notice that the woman detective practically drooled whenever she said his name?'

'No,' I said, quite surprised.

'Didn't you see the doe eyes his wife makes at him?'

'Ah . . . no.'

'Even Felicia sits up and takes notice when he speaks. And his own mom looks at him about twice as much as she looks at her other son, David.'

'So, I gather you've been watching Joel pretty closely,' I said cautiously. Understatement.

'Not so much Joel himself, as the way people react to him. Except you.'

'I see that he's a man that women like to be around,' I said, by way of acknowledgment. 'But he doesn't really do anything for me. The snapdragons, I knew those were his idea, and I did tell you then that he was the kind of man who noticed women, who knew how to please them. But I don't think he's really interested in anyone but Diane. I don't think he really understands his own magnetism, to tell you the truth. Or maybe he just accepts it as part of his world, like if he had green eyes or a great singing voice, or something.'

'So, he's got charisma for women that he doesn't use,' Tolliver said.

'More or less.'

'And you're saying it doesn't affect you, like it does other women.' Mr Skeptical.

'I'm saying . . . yes, that's what I'm saying.'

'If he weren't married to Diane, if he asked you out, you wouldn't jump at the chance?'

I gave that more thought than it deserved.

'I don't think so.'

'You're impervious?'

'It's not that. It's that I don't trust men who don't have to work for what they get.'

Tolliver stopped, and turned me to him with a hand on my arm. 'That's ridiculous,' he said. 'You mean a man should have to work for the love of a woman?'

'Maybe,' I said. 'Maybe I'm saying that Joel has probably come to accept this automatic king position as the norm, as his due. Without working for it.'

'You don't think he's a virtuous man?'

'I think he is. I don't think he's a crook, or a secret addict, or a cheater.'

'So, your sole objection is that he doesn't have to work for love?'

'I'm saying, there's something wrong about getting so much invested in you without setting out to earn it.'

Tolliver shrugged. 'I'm still not sure I understand,' he said.

I couldn't explain it any better. I'm not real good at explaining things, especially emotional things. But I knew what I meant. And I didn't entirely trust Joel Morgenstern.

11

When we got back to the hotel, Rick Goldman was waiting for us, sitting in the same chair in the lobby he'd used before.

'I should've figured he'd show up, considering the scene last night,' I told Tolliver. 'I wonder if he's told the cops yet.'

I introduced Rick to Tolliver as politely as if Rick had come to ask us to tea. But there was a muscle jumping in the private detective's jaw, and his whole body was tense.

'Can we have this talk somewhere a little more private?' he growled at me.

Tolliver said, 'That would be best, I think. Come with us.'

The ride up in the elevator was silent and ominous.

The maids had been in, and the room looked clean and welcoming, I was glad to see. There's something kind of seedy in having guests in your hotel room when the evidence of your stay is strewn all around you in disorderly heaps; room service cart, crumpled newspapers, discarded books, a shoe here and there. I'd been enjoying having a sitting room at this hotel, though I never forgot I was paying for it through the nose.

'You didn't have to kill Nunley,' Rick Goldman said. 'I know he was an obnoxious drunk, but he didn't hurt you.' He switched his level gaze to Tolliver. 'Or were you so angry he manhandled your sister that you tracked him down after I left?'

'I might just as well suspect you,' I retorted, not a little pissed off. 'You're the one laid hands on him. You can leave right now if you're going to sit there and accuse us of stuff without having the slightest bit of evidence that we ever saw the man again.'

I took my jacket off and walked over to the door of my room, tossing it inside. Tolliver unbuttoned his more slowly. 'I take it you've been to the police already with your little story about what happened in the lobby,' he said.

'Of course,' said Rick. 'Clyde Nunley was an asshole, but he was a professor at Bingham. He had a family. He deserves to have his murder solved.'

'I saw he was married, on the news,' I said. 'Though, come to think of it, he didn't wear a wedding ring.'

'Lots of men don't,' Rick said.

'Not in my experience,' I said, surprised.

'He had a metal allergy,' Rick said.

'You knew him a little better than I thought.'

'I read his personnel file,' the private detective admitted.

'I'm betting the weird content of Clyde Nunley's classes wasn't the only reason he was being investigated,' Tolliver said. 'I'm betting he had some affairs, maybe with a student or two? And the college decided they'd better check him out. Am I right?'

'There was a certain amount of talk on campus.'

'His wife wasn't so amazed when he didn't come home at night,' I said. 'She didn't even call the police until the next morning.' I sat on the couch and crossed my legs, lacing my fingers together in my lap. Tolliver was still hovering around the room, too restless to perch. Our guest had thrown himself down into one of the wing chairs without waiting for us to ask him to be seated.

'Rick, do you still have a lot of friends on the force?' Tolliver asked.

'Sure.'

'So you won't mind when they ask the staff what they saw last night?'

'Of course not.'

'Even when they tell your former colleagues that they watched you throw a guy out of the lobby, while my sister was absolutely passive?'

I made my eyes look all big and tearful. I look frail anyway, no matter how tough I actually can be.

'I wonder who they'll remember being violent and forceful, you or Harper?'

'Damn. And I was helping her out.' Rick Goldman looked at us as if he could not believe people like us were walking the earth unjudged. 'You people!'

'I did appreciate your helping me, right up until the time you insulted me,' I said. 'But Clyde Nunley was a pest, not a danger. Now he's dead, and I had nothing to do with it. We were just over at the Morgensterns', and they heard the news while we were there. Pretty upsetting.'

'They asked you to their house?' This, again, got a big reaction.

I said, 'Some people don't treat us as if we were frauds and murderers.'

He threw up his hands, as if I'd stepped over a dearly held boundary. 'I give up,' he said.

A little drama on the part of the old Rickster.

'You two are no better than scam artists,' he said. 'It makes me crazy that I can't figure out how you do it. You were right on the money about those deaths, right on the money. How'd you get the documents ahead of time? I really want to know how you did it!'

There's no convincing someone who's not open to reason, or to anything else, for that matter.

'You're not going to believe I'm the real thing, anytime soon,' I said. 'There's no point in talking to you. Besides, the police will be coming, and I want to shower before they get here.' That wasn't true. I'd already showered. I just wanted Rick Goldman to leave, right away.

12

Manfred Bernardo called us from the lobby about three o'clock, asking if he could come up. I smiled when I imagined what the staff was making of Manfred, with his metallic face.

'I wonder what happens when he goes through airport security detectors?' I said to Tolliver. He'd been reading a Robert Crais mystery, one of the earlier ones featuring Elvis Cole, and he'd been smiling to himself from time to time.

'I don't think that's a problem Manfred confronts often,' Tolliver said, but not as if he cared one way or another.

Manfred enjoyed touching people. When I answered the door, I observed that he was perhaps only an inch or two taller than I, but even as I was registering that, he leaned over to give me a kiss on the cheek.

I didn't give him one in return, because casual kissing's not my way. But I think I was smiling as I showed him into the room.

'Hello, Tolliver,' he said, as Tolliver rose to shake his hand. Tolliver just goggled at Manfred for a second. Manfred was wearing all black again; this time he was encased in leather pants, a sheer black T-shirt, and a leather jacket. He was wearing heavy boots and a small fortune in silver on his hands, face, and neck. His platinum hair had been touched up, and his goatee matched. I wondered if all this was for my benefit, or if Manfred just loved looking remarkable for its own sake.

'Please, have a seat. I hope your grandmother's well?' I asked. I sat on the love seat, expecting Manfred to take the wing chair next to Tolliver's, but he sat down beside me.

'She's not doing real good,' Manfred said. His smile faded, and I could see he was worried. 'She's having bad dreams about people in graves they weren't supposed to be in.'

'Have you been watching the news? I don't know how close you live to Memphis, but you get the Memphis news in the evening?'

'We don't watch television,' Manfred said simply. 'Grandma thinks it interferes with her brain waves. If I want to catch a program, I go over to a friend's.'

'Then let us show you what an FBI agent brought us today,' Tolliver suggested, and after he turned on the television, he ran the tape.

Manfred watched silently. He had taken hold of my hand, which was odd, but it didn't seem sexual. It seemed as if he was trying to connect with some emanation I was giving off. The Bernardo family must have some very interesting family reunions if they were all as sensitive as Xylda and Manfred.

'No, we're the only ones,' Manfred said absently, still focused on the television. His many silver rings were just now warming to room temperature after his walk into the hotel.

My eyes widened for a moment, and Tolliver glanced at me as if to ask me what was wrong, but I shook my head. He looked at Manfred's hand on mine, and raised his eyebrows to ask if I was uncomfortable. I shook my head, letting him know it wasn't a problem.

After the tape had run, Manfred said, 'The man in the grave was the man who asked you to come here to do the reading?'

'Yes,' I said.

'So there was an old burial first, when the church was still open, am I right?'

I nodded. Manfred's eyes were very blue, and though they were focused on me, they weren't seeing me.

'And then the little girl was in there?'

'Right.'

'Then you found the man last night, when you were in the cemetery?'

I jumped, but Manfred's hand kept mine prisoner, gently but firmly.

'Yes,' said Tolliver slowly. 'We found him last night.'

'My grandmother was doing a reading for you, at the time you found him, and she knows you saw the visitor,' Manfred said. I had the uncomfortable feeling his eyes were looking right through me.

'Visitor?' I asked.

'That's what she calls ghosts,' Manfred said, and suddenly he was just a very young man again, holding hands with a woman he thought was cute, and giving her a big grin. The stud in his tongue winked at me. 'Grandma uses a lot of her own terminology.'

This was a most interesting boy. He seemed not to have had much experience of the world, and yet he knew some unexpected things. I had the feeling Manfred would not be overawed or even impressed by riches or sophistication.

'Not a boy,' he said, smiling, looking directly into my eyes. The sexual tone was back with a roar. 'I'm definitely a man.'

I didn't know if I was a bit excited, or if I wanted to run screaming into my room. I smiled at him.

'Grandma wanted me to tell you you'll see Tabitha's first grave,' he said. 'I didn't understand when she gave me the message. Her hip is acting up too bad for her to leave home today, so she asked me to come see you. She likes you a lot, you know. She wanted to warn you. Watch out for that grave.'

As he had in the coffee shop, he bent and kissed my hand, making sure I got the gamut of sensations for the second time. He looked up at me from his bent posture. 'Makes you think, doesn't it?' he said softly.

'Thinking isn't doing,' I said practically.

'Not yet,' he said. He stood, shook Tolliver's hand, and left as suddenly as he'd arrived.

'What was all that about?' Tolliver said, looking distinctly suspicious.

'Evidently, when he's touching you, he can read your mind, sort of,' I said, feeling a little uncomfortable that some of my thoughts had been fairly graphic. 'I don't know if that applies to the populace in general, or to people who have some kind of psychic talent, or what.'

'But Xylda is the only one who makes predictions,' Tolliver said. 'And she's added to them today. You'll be happy in the time of ice, whatever that means, and you'll see Tabitha's original grave.'

'I don't think I want to hang around Xylda anymore,' I said. 'And if she reads the cards for me, I don't want to know about it. It just creeps me out.'

'What about Manfred? You want to hang around him?' At least Tolliver was smiling when he said it.

'Oh,' I said deprecatingly. 'You know, he's more than a little different. I mean, you can't help but wonder, when you see someone so extreme . . .' Then I couldn't figure out how to finish the sentence.

Tolliver had mercy on me. 'If I knew a girl with that many piercings, I'd wonder, too,' he said.

'Well, it's already mid-afternoon, and we've had a helluva day. What could we do next that would make it just one round of fun?'

'I could balance the checkbook.'

'Big whoop.'

'We could see what the in-room movie service has to show.'

'I'm sick of this room, and I'm ready to do something a little more active than watch a movie.'

'You got an idea?'

'Yeah. Let's go down to the riverfront park to run.'

'What about the reporter?'

'We'll sneak out the back.'

'It's cold and it looks like rain.'

'Then we better run fast.'

13

We avoided the reporters, but not the Memphis police. Detectives Young and Lacey were less than thrilled at our choice of activity when they tracked us down. I'd been wondering when we'd be hearing from them. I was only surprised they hadn't called the hotel and told us to get our asses down to the station.

They had on their London Fogs, their gloves, and their scarves. Lacey looked morose but resigned. Young looked resentful. Come to find out when we jogged over to them, Young had a cold. In the middle of her narrow face, her reddened nose stood out like a reindeer's, and she had a tissue clutched in the hand not occupied with an umbrella.

'Are you nuts?' she snarled. 'Out here in your skintight whatevers, when it's freezing!' She made a vague gesture toward my running pants. I ran in place for a minute, slowing down gradually. I felt cold and wet, but I also felt exhilarated, as if the chilly damp air had blown away some of the cobwebs in my head.

'I guess you want to talk to us about something?' Tolliver was doing some stretching, and I saw that Detective Young's eyes had strayed to his ass. Lacey said quickly, 'Yes, ma'am, we sure do. Do you two want to come down to the station with us? At least it's dry and warm.'

'I definitely don't want to go to the station,' I said. 'Isn't there a coffee shop somewhere close? Unless you're going to arrest us, going to a cafe would be a lot nicer. Maybe they'd have hot chocolate?' I was deliberately tempting poor Young, who sneezed twice in succession and applied her damp wad of tissues to her raw nose.

'There's that place on Poplar,' she said to her partner, who looked indecisive. 'Remember how good their pie is?' she said, in a heavy-handed attempt at a bribe.

It worked like a charm.

Thirty minutes later we were in a restaurant so warm that the windows were steamy, with coffee in front of the men, hot chocolate in front of Detective Young and me. Lacey was happy as a pig in a wallow with a piece of pecan pie with whipped topping on a plate in front of him, and Young was almost weeping with relief at being indoors.

'Agent Koenig tells us you've heard the news about Clyde Nunley,' she said, her voice sounding nasal but at least human.

We nodded. 'He came by our room this morning and told us,' I said, wanting to be as honest as possible. I always try.

'Rick Goldman came by the station, too,' Lacey said, after he swallowed. He looked blissful. 'Rick was telling us that he had a run-in with Nunley in the lobby of your hotel, Ms Connelly.'

'Yes, that's true. He ended up propelling Dr Nunley out the door. Truthfully, I think Dr Nunley was drunk. He was very belligerent.' I hoped I looked as frank and open as I was trying to be.

'You're not the only person who's commented on that. We'll find out what his blood alcohol level was. What beef did he have with you?' Young asked. Maybe her cold medication was making her blunt, or maybe she was just tired of do-si-doing around.

'He thought that somehow, despite all his precautions, I'd gotten into his precious private records and memorized the COD on all the burials. Goldman accused me of the same thing.'

'And did you do that?'

'No, I don't need to. I'm the real deal.'

There was a moment of silence, while the detectives either thought that over, or dismissed it as another piece of chicanery on my part.

'Did you two go out again last night?' asked Young directly. 'After Mr Lang here came back from wandering Beale Street?' Detective Lacey put down his fork and gave us a look that might have penetrated steel.

'Yes, we did,' Tolliver said. After all, we'd gotten the car from the valet. There was no way we could deny it.

'Where did you go?'

'We drove down to look at Graceland,' Tolliver said. I blinked. What a good lie. Almost any tourist in Memphis would want to at least drive by Elvis's home. And since we'd just told Koenig we'd been looking at the sights of Memphis, this tied right in. Actually, we'd looked up Graceland on the laptop this morning after Koenig had left, so we'd at least have an idea what we were supposed to have seen.

'At night?'

'Yeah, we didn't have anything else to do. And we weren't sure if we'd ever be back this way again. So we drove down to Whitehaven, and we took a couple of passes in front of it. That's some place. You gotta love the gates.'

'And you're not going to go back and see it in the daylight, tour the house?'

'He's buried on-site, right?' I asked.

'Uh . . . yeah. And Vernon and Gladys, his mom and dad, and Minnie May, his grandma.'

'No.' I shook my head definitely. 'I really, really, wouldn't want to do that.'

Detective Young sucked at her teeth. She looked as though she were feeling a bit better, now that she was warm and had finished her hot chocolate. Her short brown hair still looked lank and tired, but her eyes were showing a spark of spirit. Her partner had that happy look that sugar-loving men get after they've had something especially rich. But the pie hadn't made him smarter.

'Why not?' he asked now. 'Why not go see the place they're buried?'

'You know, I connect with bodies. It might kind of ruin the Graceland experience for me.' On the other hand, it might answer a few questions. Tolliver was looking amused.

'So you see why we just drove by,' Tolliver said, picking up the thread of the narrative. 'We'd already cruised around the Pyramid and Beale Street. So, we went back to our hotel.'

I was glad I'd washed my shoes off this morning, and that the hotel laundry had our jeans.

'And the Fibbie came to see you first thing this morning,' Detective Young said. I was glad we'd mentioned it, since it seemed Young already knew about Koenig's visit.

'Yes. He wanted us to know right away about the body found in the grave. I'm guessing he wanted to get our first reaction.'

'And what reaction did he get?'

'Well, of course, we were sorry Clyde Nunley had been killed, or had fallen into the grave and hit his head, or whatever really happened to him. It's never good to hear someone's dead.' Though with some people it's less bad than with others. 'But it's not like we had any reason to want him dead.'

'You might have been a little upset, Mr Lang, him manhandling Ms

Connelly like that. Specially in a public place. Specially since someone else had to help her, since you weren't there.'

Oooh. Low blow. But I thought Tolliver could stand up to it, and he seemed to be coping, if his slight smile was any indicator. 'Harper can take care of herself,' he said, which pleased me. 'Even if Goldman hadn't been there, she would have been okay.'

Since that hadn't worked, Lacey tried something else. 'Agent Koenig says he wants your reading of Nunley's body, and that you would like access to Tabitha's body.'

'That's not exactly what I said,' I told him. 'It wasn't my idea. He thought I might get more of a reading if I tried again, and I agreed that might be so. Of course I don't want to be around the child's body again – but if you have any idea I'd be a help, I have to make myself do that.'

'I have no idea what to believe about you,' Lacey said, his small blue eyes examining me again for maybe the twenty-fifth time. 'I never met anyone like you, and I swear I don't know if you're a fraud or a – I just don't know what you are.'

'Lots of people feel that way,' I said, because he seemed so uncomfortable. 'Don't worry about it. I'm used to it.'

'You two have kids?' Detective Young asked suddenly.

Tolliver and I stared at her blankly.

'Us?' he said, after a long pause.

She seemed to realize she'd put her foot in it. 'Sorry, I just assumed you two . . .'

'We've lived together since we were teenagers,' I said. 'Tolliver's dad married my mother. He's like my . . . brother.' For the first time, I hesitated before I said those words.

'I have two,' she said, obviously wanting to get off the subject as quickly as possible. 'I have a boy and a girl. If my child went missing, I'd want every stone turned to find that child. I'd deal with the devil if I had to. I'll ask the Morgensterns how they feel about you . . . visiting Tabitha's body again. We'll see what they say.'

I wondered what the two cops would say if I told them I'd talked to a ghost the night before. I wondered how fast they'd write us off as charlatans. I thought again of the hard hand gripping my arm, and I had to close my eyes for a minute. How could it be that Josiah Poundstone's ghost was there? I had thought I had the whole thing straight in my mind, the whole life-after-death procedure, but now I stood on shaky ground.

I noticed the traffic outside was getting heavier, and the sky was getting darker. As we sat in the diner with the two detectives, the afternoon had drawn to a close. I had an almost irresistible urge to go back to the cemetery, to see if the ghost was still there, what it was up to. What did ghosts do? Were they there when a human wasn't there to react to them? Did they materialize when they wanted to communicate, or were they always . . .

'Harper,' Tolliver said gently. 'Are you ready to go?'

'Oh, sure,' I said, hastily pulling my jacket back on. The detectives were standing, their coats zipped and buttoned, and from their expressions, they'd been waiting for me to respond for some time.

'Daydreaming,' I said. 'Sorry.' I did my best to look alert and normal, but that's not always my best thing anyway, and I don't think I was very successful. 'Maybe our run tired me more than I thought.'

Given a valid-sounding reason for my distracted state, the two cops looked a bit happier, though Lacey would never be my best friend. 'You need to go back to the hotel and get some rest,' he said. 'Don't go getting into any more trouble while you're here in Memphis. We'll get back with you after we've talked to the Morgensterns.'

'Right, thanks,' Tolliver said. After their car had left, we paid our part of the bill and left the diner. 'What was that all about?' Tolliver asked when we were in the car and trying to make a left turn into traffic to go back to the Cleveland.

I told him the questions I'd been asking myself.

'I can see where that's interesting, and I would like to know the answers, too,' he said. 'But from now on, you should have your thinking sessions when you're safe in bed, or something. You had a pretty strange expression on your face.'

'Did I look weird?' I asked, oddly hurt.

'Not strange-ugly,' he said instantly. 'Strange, as in, "not there."'

'Oh,' I said.

Finally, he took advantage of a hole in the ever-swelling traffic going out of downtown. We were headed back toward the river before I spoke again. 'You know who I'd like to talk to again?'

'Who?'

'Victor. But you talk about peculiar, it would seem real peculiar if we called him and asked him to come to see us.'

'Yeah. No way we can do that.'

'You think since they treated us to a meal, we could invite them to a meal at a restaurant?'

Tolliver thought it over. 'They're in mourning right now, and they've probably got all kinds of arrangements to make. Plus, what reason would we give? Yeah, we could insist we owe them a meal, but what are we gonna talk about? The only connection we have is the death of their daughter. That's just not enough to carry an evening, Sis.'

He hadn't called me that in a long time. I wondered if Young's comment had shaken him up, too.

'Maybe not,' I admitted. 'But as long as we're stuck here, and I guess we are . . . hey, I wonder what would happen if we left?' There was a moment of silence. 'We'd probably get called right back,' I concluded, 'until they've decided what happened to Clyde Nunley. Why would he get killed? I just don't understand. The only thing he knew was – what could he have known?'

'What's the only connection between Clyde Nunley and Tabitha Morgenstern?' Tolliver asked. He was definitely guiding me to a conclusion. I hate it when he does that.

'They shared a grave.'

'I mean, besides that.'

'There was no connection.'

'Yes, there was.'

It was almost full dark now, and the mass of lights in the eastbound lanes was almost bumper-to-bumper. We had much easier going in the westbound lanes. It began to rain again, and Tolliver turned on our windshield wipers.

'Okay, I give.' I threw up my hands in exasperation. 'What was the connection?'

'You.'

14

This hit me with an impact about equal to a bag of cement.

'So you're saying Clyde Nunley was murdered because he knew who had recommended me for this little gig at the college.' I felt cold all over. I may be used to death, and I may know better than anyone how inevitable and ordinary a state it is, but that doesn't mean it's easy to feel you contributed to it. It's like sleet; you know if the atmospheric conditions warrant, there's going to be sleet, but you don't have to be happy about it.

'That's what I think – and I thought about this a lot, last night. I couldn't accept the giant coincidence that Tabitha's body was here. If it wasn't a coincidence, we were steered to find it. We were used. And the person who did that had to be the person who killed Tabitha. Clyde Nunley asked you to read this cemetery. So someone must have whispered your name in Clyde Nunley's ear. I don't know if that person held something over Clyde, or made a friendly suggestion. "Hey, you're having this class about the occult, you have this cemetery just laying there, let's get a weird woman who specializes in finding the dead to come have a look." '

'So, you think that Clyde balked when Tabitha's body was found?'

'I think he did. Or else he couldn't swallow the coincidence any more than we can, and he figured that whoever had talked him into inviting you to Memphis had to have some kind of inside knowledge about the girl's death. Just because he was a jerk doesn't mean he was dumb.'

'True,' I said absently. 'Well, I guess that narrows down the field, right?'

'How do you figure that?'

'Couldn't be Victor.'

'Why not? I'll bet he's pre-enrolled at Bingham. This is his senior year in high school, right?'

'Oh. Well, could be. That seems kind of thin, but okay. What I was thinking – both Felicia and David went to Bingham. And the older

Morgensterns, Judy and Ben, would surely know a lot of people who went there, if they didn't themselves, since they live in the city and paid for David's tuition for four years. I bet the same holds true for Fred Hart.'

After all, the older Morgensterns weren't so darn old. 'Judy has Parkinson's too badly to have gotten Tabitha to the grave, but her husband is really fit,' I said. 'Fred Hart looks pretty strong, too.'

'That would be awful, if it turned out be to the granddad,' Tolliver said.

'It's going to be awful if it's *anybody*,' I said. 'No matter who. Anyone doing that to an eleven-year-old, that's beyond horrible.' I paused to collect myself. 'I was so shocked at finding her, I didn't take as long as I should have to . . . pick through the experience.'

'So you do want to read the body again? If Seth Koenig gets it set up?'

'He wants me to read Clyde Nunley. Of course, he doesn't know that I already have. I don't want to touch Tabitha again. I don't even want to think about it. But I have to be sure I know everything she can tell me.'

'You're a good person,' he said, taking me by surprise.

'I don't think I'm especially good, and there are a lot of people who would argue the other way,' I said, trying to conceal how pleased I was. I looked down at my watch and pressed the button to check the date. Something clicked inside my memory. 'Oh, God, it's about time to call the girls.'

Tolliver said something that would have made my ears turn red if I hadn't heard it a hundred times before. But he didn't protest tonight, though he often argued against this bi-weekly ordeal we put ourselves through.

We waited until we got to our room. I noted with satisfaction that there weren't any reporters outside at all, and no messages waiting. (The first day, there had been twenty or so, and we'd thrown them all away.)

To determine whose turn it would be to dial the number and talk to Iona, we did Rock, Scissors, Paper. As always, I made the wrong choice, which is pretty funny when you come to think of it. If I were actually psychic, as I'm so often accused of being, I think I could manage to win a simple game like that.

I speed-dialed Iona's number. Iona Gorham (née Howe) was my

mother's only sister. She'd been married to Hank Gorham for twelve years, twelve long and childless and God-fearing years. She'd taken charge of Mariella and Gracie when my mother and stepfather went to jail, after the investigation into Cameron's abduction exposed some of their worst faults as parents. I'd had nothing to say about it, because I was underage then. I'd gone into a foster home myself. Iona and Hank hadn't wanted me, which was probably just as well, I guess. At seventeen, they thought my lifelong association with my mother would have irrevocably tainted me. I had a senior year in the high school I'd been attending, a year that was weirdly pleasant despite my shattered emotional system. For the first time since my childhood, I lived in a clean house with regular meals I didn't always have to cook myself. I could do my homework in peace. No one made suggestive comments, no one used drugs, and my foster parents were simple, nice, strict people. You knew where you were. They had two other foster kids, and we got along if we were very careful.

Tolliver, who was twenty then, moved in with his brother, Mark, so he was okay. He came by as often as he could, as often as the Goodmans would let him.

'Hello?' The man's voice yanked me back to the here and now.

'Hank, hello, it's Harper,' I said, making sure that my voice was even and level and uninflected. You had to be Switzerland to talk to Iona and Hank. *Neutral*, I told myself repeatedly. *Neutral*.

'Hello,' he said, with a total lack of welcome or enthusiasm. 'Where are you, Harper?'

'I'm in Memphis, Hank, thanks for asking.'

'I guess Tolliver's with you?'

'Oh, you bet,' I said, cheerful as all get-out. 'It's cold and wet here. How about in Dallas?'

'Oh, can't complain. In the fifties today.'

'Sounds good. I'd like to talk to Mariella, if she's around, and then Gracie.'

'Iona's gone to the store. I'll see if I can track the girls down.'

What a stroke of luck. I held the phone to my chest while I told Tolliver, 'The Wicked Witch isn't there.' Iona had a deep fund of excuses to keep us from talking to the girls. Hank was not as resourceful, or as ruthless.

'Hey,' said Mariella. She was nine now, and she was a lot of trouble. I never told myself she'd be an angel if she lived with us, because I knew better. For their first few years, Mariella and Gracie had never had the care and attention of parents who were in their right minds. I'm not saying my mother and stepfather didn't love their girls, but it wasn't the kind of love that would prompt them to become sober and responsible. At least we older kids had had that, once upon a time. We knew what was right and proper. We knew what parents should be like. We knew about fresh sheets and home-cooked meals and clothes that only we had worn.

'Mariella, it's your sister,' I said, though of course Hank had told her who was on the phone. 'What's happening with you?' I had tried so hard, and so had Cameron and Tolliver. Even Mark had stopped by with food from time to time, when he'd had extra money.

'I got on a basketball team,' Mariella said, 'at the Y.'

'Oh, that's great!' Actually, it was. It was the first time Mariella had given me anything besides a sullen grunt. 'Have you started playing yet, or are you still practicing?'

'We have our first game in a week,' she said. 'If you were here, you could come.'

I widened my eyes at Tolliver to let him know this call was not going as usual. 'We'd love to,' I said. 'We have to check our schedule, but we'd be really glad to watch you play. Is Gracie playing, too?'

'No, she says it's stupid to get out there and sweat like a pig. She says boys don't like girls who sweat. She says everyone will call me a lesbo.'

I heard a shocked exclamation from Hank in the background.

'Gracie's wrong,' I said immediately. 'She just doesn't want to play basketball herself. Maybe you can play basketball a little better than Gracie, huh?'

'You bet,' said Mariella proudly. 'Gracie can't come within a mile of the hoop. I hit it twice last practice.'

'I'm sure there's something Gracie can do that's special to her,' I said, floundering to be diplomatic and yet reinforce the positive stuff that was going on with Mariella.

'Huh,' said Mariella derisively. 'Well, *anyway*.'

'Have you all had your school pictures taken this year?'

'Yeah. They should be back soon.'

'You both save us two, you hear?' I said. 'One for your brother Tolliver to carry in his wallet, and one for me to carry in mine.'

'Okay,' she said. 'Hey, Gracie joined the chorus.'

'No kidding? Is she around?'

'Yeah, she's coming in the kitchen right now.' Sound of a scuffle.

'Yeah?' This was Gracie, all right. Gracie was deep into hating us.

'Gracie, I hear you're in the chorus at school.'

'Yeah, so?'

'Are you a soprano or an alto?'

'I dunno. I sing the melody.'

'Okay, probably a soprano. Listen, we were thinking of coming to one of Mariella's games. Do you think you could sit with us if we did?'

'Well, I might be there with my friends.' Whom she saw at school, every day, and talked to on the phone half the night, if Iona was to be believed.

'I know that's important,' I said, back to being Switzerland, 'but we don't get to see you too often.'

'Okay, I'll think about it,' she said unenthusiastically. 'Stupid basketball. When she runs down the court, her cheeks bounce up and down. Like a hound dog's.'

'You need to be a good sister,' I said, maybe not as neutrally as I could have wished. 'You need to cheer for Mariella.'

'Why should I?'

Okay, not neutral at all. 'Because you're damn lucky to *have* a sister,' I began, my voice hot, and then I heard myself and backed off. I took a deep breath. 'You know why, Gracie? Because it's the right thing to do. Here's your brother.' I handed the phone to Tolliver.

'Gracie, I want to hear you sing,' Tolliver said. That was exactly the right thing to say, and Gracie promised to find out when the chorus would be singing for the first time so Tolliver and I could put the date on the calendar. Then Gracie evidently handed the phone off.

'Iona,' said Tolliver, with the faintest pleasant intonation. 'How are things going? Really? The school called again? Well, you know Gracie isn't stupid, so there must be some other problem. Okay. When's she going for testing? It's good the state's paying for it. But you know we'd . . .' He listened for a while. 'Okay, call us with the results. You know we want to hear.'

After a couple more minutes of listening to this broken conversation, I was delighted when Tolliver finally hung up. 'What's going on?' I asked.

'A couple of things,' he said, frowning. 'That was almost a good conversation with Iona. Gracie's teacher thinks Gracie may have

ADD. She recommended testing, and Iona's taking her this week. The state will pay for the testing, evidently.'

'I don't know anything about that,' I said, as if I could have been prepared for this. 'We'll have to look it up on the net.'

'She would have to take the drugs if she's got it, Iona says.'

'What are the side effects?'

'There are some, but Iona was more concentrating on the benefits. Evidently, Gracie's been pretty disruptive at school, and Iona wants some peace.'

'Don't we all. But if the side effects . . .'

We spent the rest of the evening on the Internet, reading articles about Attention Deficit Disorder and the drugs used to treat it. If this seems excessive or odd, consider this: Tolliver and Cameron and I had raised those girls from birth. My mother had been roused to try to take care of them when they were infants, but if it hadn't been for us, Mariella and Gracie wouldn't have eaten, or been changed, or learned how to count, or been read to. When Cameron had been snatched, Mariella had been only three and Gracie had been five. They'd gone to a preschool together for a few mornings a week, because we'd enrolled them and then told my mother they had to go. We'd gotten them to the preschool before we went to our own school, and all Mom had to do was remember to pick them up, which she usually did if we left her a note.

Here I was remembering, when that was the last thing in the world I wanted to do.

'Enough of this,' Tolliver said after a while, when we felt we knew a little bit about the disorder and the drugs used to treat it. 'We'll learn more when we know if she has it or not.'

I felt like I was drowning. I'd had no idea there were so many things that could go wrong with a child's learning processes. What happened to kids in the years before all these things were identified, and a course of treatment laid out?

'I guess they were labeled slow or difficult,' Tolliver said. 'And that was the end of it.'

That made me feel sad for all the kids who'd never had a fair shake, because their problems hadn't been understood. At the same time, we'd just read two articles about how parents were overmedicating their children for those same problems, so that even children who really did just have some disruptive personality traits were being dosed with drugs that shouldn't have been given them. It was just scary. I wondered if I'd ever have the nerve to have a baby myself. It didn't seem too likely. I'd have to trust my partner completely, to bring his child into the world. The only person I'd ever trusted that much was my brother Tolliver.

And the strangest thing happened as I had that thought. The world seemed to freeze for a minute.

It was like someone had thrown a giant switch in my head. Tolliver was turning away to go to his room, and I was getting up out of the chair I'd pulled over to the desk so I could read the screen on the laptop. I looked at Tolliver's back, and suddenly the world slid sideways and then realigned itself in a new configuration. I opened my mouth to say something, and then I closed it. I didn't know what I wanted to say to him. I didn't think I really wanted him to turn around.

He started to turn, and I bolted for my room.

I shut the door behind me and leaned against it.

'Harper? Is something wrong?' I heard his anxious voice on the other side of the door. I was in a total panic.

'No!'

'But you sound like something's wrong.'

'No! Don't come in!'

Tolliver's voice was a lot chillier the next time he spoke. 'All right.' And he moved away, going to his own room, I supposed.

I sank down to the floor.

I didn't know what to say to myself, how to treat someone as idiotic as me. I was poised in a perfect position to ruin the only thing I had in my life. One word, one wrong act, and it would all be gone. I would be humiliated forever, and I would have nothing.

I had one black moment in which I wondered if I should just go on and kill myself and have done with it. But my strong survival instinct rejected the fleeting notion even as it ran across my brain. If I'd lived through being hit by lightning, I could live through this new knowledge.

He must never know. I crawled across the floor to the bed; pulled myself up, lay prone across it. I planned the next week of my life in a few painful minutes, appalled at my own monstrous selfishness as I did so. Keeping Tolliver with me for one more minute was an awful thing to do.

But I couldn't let go, I argued with myself. If I suddenly shooed him away, he'd suspect something as sure as shooting. I just couldn't do it. In a week or so, when I could figure out the right way. Until then, hold myself carefully; guard my every action.

Life, which had seemed like such a rich crazy quilt laid out before me, suddenly assumed a grayer prospect. I climbed into the hotel bed, as I had climbed into hundreds of hotel beds.

I stared at the ceiling, at the bar of light from somewhere below that crossed it, at the bright red eye of the smoke detector. For hours I tried to remap my life. But I didn't have a clue which direction to go.

15

I was more like a zombie than a person when I came out of my room the next day. Tolliver was eating breakfast, and he poured me a cup of coffee without a word. I went over to the table cautiously, sinking into my chair with as much relief as if I'd negotiated a minefield. He glanced up from his paper, gave me a horrified look.

'Are you sick?' he asked. 'God, you look like something the cat dragged in!'

That actually made me feel much better. If he'd said something sweet, I'd have lost it then and there, grabbed hold of him, and sobbed all over his shirt front.

'I didn't have a good night,' I said, very carefully. 'I didn't sleep.'

'No shit. I can kind of tell. You better get out your makeup.'

'Thanks for the boost, Tolliver.'

'Well, I'm just saying. We don't want the coroner mistaking you for the corpse.'

'Okay, enough.' Somehow, I felt much better after this exchange.

Tolliver had been reading the paper, and he shoved it over to me. He was not going to say anything about my strange behavior of the night before, apparently. 'Not much about Tabitha today. I guess it's getting cold.'

'About time.' I picked up my coffee cup with a shaking hand, managed to get the edge of the cup to my lips without spilling anything. I took a long sip, set the cup down with just as much care. Tolliver had kept the sports section, and he was involved with a basketball story, so he didn't witness this embarrassing weakness. I exhaled, felt some relief, and took a steadier drink. Okay, caffeine was a good thing. I got a croissant out of the basket, knew I'd regret it later, and ate the whole thing in about forty-five seconds.

'Good,' was Tolliver's only comment. 'You could use some body fat.'

'You're just a bundle of compliments this morning,' I said tartly. I felt *much* better now. Suddenly I felt a surge of optimism, with even less ground than I'd felt my deep depression of the night before. I'd been overly dramatic, right? This was okay. We were all right. Everything would be the same.

I ate another croissant. I even buttered it.

'Are you going to run?' Tolliver asked mildly.

'No,' I said.

'You're just a party animal today. Croissants and no running! How's the leg today?'

'Fine. Just fine.'

There was a long pause.

'You were acting kind of weird last night,' he said.

'Ah. Lot to think about,' I said vaguely, waving the last piece of croissant in an arc to indicate the breadth of my thought.

'I hope that worked out for you,' he said. 'You scared me a little.'

'Sorry,' I said, trying to keep my voice light and airy. 'A sudden attack of thoughtfulness will do that to you.'

'Um-hum.' He stared at me, his dark eyes full of his own thoughtfulness.

The cell phone rang when he'd gone back to his newspaper story, and I reached over to answer it. Somehow his hand was there before mine, and I wondered what was happening with him. We were sure being mysterious with each other, these days.

'Tolliver Lang,' he said.

'All right,' he said, after a moment.

'Where is that?' he asked next.

'All right, we'll be there in forty-five minutes,' he said, before folding the phone shut.

He looked at me, somehow harder and sadder than before.

'The family gave permission,' he said. 'We can go see the body now.'

I got up and walked into my room to get dressed without another word.

When I came out twenty minutes later, I was clean and my clothes were fresh, but that was about all I could say. Despite Tolliver's advice, I didn't fool with makeup, and I only ran a brush through my hair. I wore it short, since I couldn't have dealt with a lot of hair to arrange, some days; today was definitely one of those days. I'd pulled on the top sweater in my suitcase, which was cream-colored, and the top pair of jeans, and the top pair of socks. Luckily, I only carry things that can coordinate, because otherwise I would have looked like I'd dressed in the dark.

Tolliver was about on par with me sartorially, and he hugged me when I emerged, ready to go. I was so surprised that I hugged him back for a moment, feeling thankful and grateful for him, as I always did. Then I realized what I was doing, and I froze, every muscle in my body going tense. I could feel the change in him when he realized that something was wrong between us.

'What have I done?' he asked, pulling away, looking down at me. 'What have I done to you?'

I couldn't meet his eyes. 'Nothing,' I muttered. 'Let's just get this over with.'

The car was full of an uneasy silence as we followed the directions Tolliver had been given. Before I had time to calm myself and prepare mentally, we were at the morgue. There were so many dead inside, and they were so fresh, that the vibrations gathered in intensity and strength. When I got out of the car, I was already feeling a little light on my feet. I know we went in, and I know we talked to a few people, but later I remembered nothing. By the time we walked down a corridor I was humming from my head to my toes. I could hardly note my physical surroundings as we followed the very heavy, very young woman leading us to the body we'd come to see. Her big rear swayed in front of me as she walked, and her lank dark hair switched from side to side. She hadn't bothered with makeup, and her clothes were strictly thrift shop. This must be a job that sucked the hope out of you.

The young woman knocked at a door that looked no different from any of the other doors. She must have heard a reply, because she held the door open and we went inside. A sandy-haired man in a lab coat said, 'Hi.' He was standing against the wall. There were two gurneys in the room. The lump on one of them was far bigger than the lump on the other. Tolliver gasped and coughed from the smell. Even through the heavy plastic covering the bodies, the odor was pervasive.

I said, 'Tolliver, you can go,' but I knew he wouldn't.

I introduced myself and Tolliver.

'Dr Lyle Hatton,' the man said. He was very tall and gawky, and he had a way of looking down through his glasses that registered as contemptuous.

His dislike and scorn was something I could ignore in the face of the overwhelming thrumming.

I started to lift the plastic so I could touch Tabitha's body directly, but Lyle Hatton said, 'Gloves!'

He was annoying. I had a mission here, and the vibrations were resounding so loudly that I could hardly comprehend what he wanted. It seemed my choice was either touching her through the plastic sheet, or putting on plastic gloves. I wasn't aware I'd ever thought about the barriers between me and a corpse, and classified them. Cotton would have been better than plastic for my purpose, I knew instinctively.

But I wasn't being given that option. So I lay my hand on the plastic sheet, over the area where her heart should have been; of course, the shape under the sheet was not a full shape anymore, not after eighteen months in the ground. Immediately, I fell into Tabitha's last moments: *woken from sleep, a nap. Seeing a blue cushion, descending. Feeling . . . betrayal, disbelief, horror, NO NO NO NO Mama save me save me save me.*

'Save me,' I whispered. 'Save me.' I wasn't touching her anymore. Tolliver had his arms around me. Tears were streaming down my face.

I put my arms around Tolliver, too; a dangerous indulgence, but I needed him so much. I looked at the masked man in his medical scrubs. 'You collected evidence from the body?' I asked.

'I was there,' Dr Hatton said guardedly.

'Did you find any threads in her nose and mouth? Blue, they would have been.'

'Yes,' he said, after a notable pause. 'Yes, we did.'

'Suffocated,' I said. 'But she fought all the way.'

Dr Hatton made a sudden movement with his hand, as if he was going to show me something, but then he stopped in mid-motion.

'What are you?' he asked, as if he was talking to some interesting hybrid.

'I'm just a woman who got hit by lightning,' I said. 'I wasn't born the way I am.'

'Lightning either kills you or you get over it,' Dr Hatton said impatiently.

'I can tell you've never dealt with a live person who's had the experience,' I said. 'You get hit with a few thousand volts, a few months later you come talk to me about what your life is like.'

'If that many volts hits you directly, you're dead,' he said simply. 'What people survive is the energy discharge from it hitting very nearby.'

I couldn't believe this guy, arguing with me about what had happened to me while Tabitha's body was right here between us.

'Whatever,' I said, and straightened up to show Tolliver I was ready to go. It was hard to pull my arms from around him, but I did it, and his arms loosened around me.

I went over to the second shape, the larger one. I closed my eyes and placed my hand over the body.

My eyes flew open and I glared at Dr Hatton. 'This isn't Clyde Nunley,' I said. 'This is some young man who died of knife wounds.'

Dr Hatton looked at me as though he were seeing a ghost. 'You're right,' he said, as if I weren't standing right there. 'You're right, my God. Okay,' he said, very carefully, as though I might pounce on him, 'let me take you to Dr Nunley.'

Tolliver was furious with Lyle Hatton, and I wasn't far behind him in that. But I was determined to complete my errand. We followed the doctor down the hall to a larger room, a cold room, full of bodies. It was not orderly; the gurneys were not lined up in neat rows. Here and there a hand or foot protruded. The smell was unique, a *bouquet de la mort*. The vibrations in this place were overwhelming. All the dead waited for my attention, from an old woman who'd been murdered in her own home to a baby who'd died of SIDS. But I was only here to call on one corpse, and this time Lyle Hatton led me to him. I was dizzy from being surrounded with all the newly dead, and it took me a long minute to focus on Clyde; then I saw it all again: the surprise, the blow, the fall into the grave. I nodded sharply to Dr Hatton when I was through, and I staggered as I turned away from my final contact with Dr Clyde Nunley.

'You can walk?' Tolliver asked, very low.

'Yes,' I said.

'Wait,' Lyle Hatton said. I looked at him inquiringly. The overhead light winked on his gold-rimmed glasses. 'Since you're here, can I ask you to do one more thing? You were right about the blue threads. You knew when I showed you the wrong body. Maybe you can help me with one more thing.'

Everyone wants a freebie.

'What do you need?' I asked. I wasn't in the mood for finesse.

'This body here . . . I can't determine a cause of death for this woman. She was living at home with her son and daughter-in-law, and she developed stomach symptoms. She might have had any number of things wrong with her, but I've met the couple, and I suspect there's something hinky about her death. What do you think?'

Though Hatton was a jackass, I like to help the dead when I can.

'Tox screen didn't show anything, autopsy turned up nada,' Hatton said coaxingly. 'She lost a lot of weight and had various stomach symptoms before death – diarrhea, nausea, and so on – but she hated going to the doctor and she didn't turn up at a hospital until it was too late.'

'This one?' I asked. I could see a pale hand, though it was not the right color a hand ought to be. I closed my eyes and touched her hand with my finger, a bare contact Hatton made no attempt to block.

'Don't try this on me,' I said, feeling exhausted. 'This is a young woman who died of aplastic anemia.'

Dr Hatton stared at me as if I'd grown another head. He checked the toe-tag. 'I'm sorry,' he said, sounding sincere. 'I really thought that was her. This is.' He double-checked the tag on the body next to the poor young woman.

I sighed heavily. I touched the plastic wrapped around this body. I narrowed my eyes. If he wanted to play, I was up to it.

'Cleona Chatsworth,' I moaned, 'Come forth!'

Out of the corner of my eye, I caught Tolliver ducking his head to hide his smile. Dr Hatton was growing even paler than he'd been before, almost to the point of matching one of his clients. He gasped. I'd heard the name right. Luckily for me, Cleona Chatsworth wanted someone to know what had happened to her, wanted it very badly.

'Cleona was poisoned,' I whispered, my free hand moving in a circle over the corpse. I thought Hatton was going to faint.

'What do I look for?' he croaked.

'Someone gave it to her in salad dressing,' I crooned. 'The selenium.'

I opened my eyes and said, 'This lady was poisoned.'

Lyle Hatton stared at me with glassy eyes.

'We're going now,' I told Tolliver, who was glaring at the doctor, his hands curled into fists.

So we left the room, and we went back down the long hall. The young woman had waited down the hall for us, and as silently as she'd escorted us there, she led us back to the door to the outside. I was profoundly glad to step out into the cold gray day and take a deep breath of air untainted by death. Tolliver and I stood watching the heavy traffic on Madison for maybe five minutes, inhaling and exhaling, happy to be out of the building. The humming had seemed very intense before I'd entered, but it had only been a shadow of what I'd felt when I was actually within the walls.

When I felt more like myself, I said, 'It wasn't Diane who killed her. Tabitha was wanting her mother.'

He absorbed that. 'That's good, then,' he said. 'One down.'

'Don't laugh at me,' I said, though his mouth hadn't twitched. 'I think at least it's a start.'

'Sure,' he said. 'And I'm not doing any laughing.' He gripped my arm so I'd look at him. 'I don't know how you do it and stay sane. I really, really admire you.'

Now was *so* not the time for Tolliver to be all real and sympathetic.

'I want them to name the murderer.' I began walking across the parking lot to our car. 'Usually, I'm more or less accepting of the fact that people murder other people. That's just part of the world, I guess. But I'm really mad about this. I'm really, really angry.'

'You've had children before,' Tolliver said, meaning that I had read their deaths before.

'Oh, sure, I've done children. But this is different. I don't know why. Maybe it's the family, still waiting to find out what happened to her, figuring it's one of them who did it. This has just gotten to me.'

'That's not good. It's tearing you up. I don't want this to happen to you.'

'Well, me either. But I can't seem to stop it, and I can't tell who did it from touching her. And we can't leave for a while, I guess.'

'Do you want to leave?'

I was buckling my seat belt. 'What does that mean?' The tone of his voice had put me on guard.

'You usually can hardly wait to get out of town after we finish up with a client, but you haven't said anything about leaving for a day or two. You want to be here? What's the attraction? Manfred Bernardo? Or Joel Morgenstern? Or Seth Koenig?' He turned the key in the ignition with unnecessary force. He was definitely not looking at me.

'Huh?' I stared at him as if he'd started speaking in Swedish.

Then, as his meaning sunk in, I laughed. It was just too ironic. The thing was, in past times there might have been some basis for his question. I might have been thinking about Manfred, or having secret fantasies about Seth Koenig, or Joel Morgenstern. His wrestler's body was fit and powerful, also good fuel for fantasies – *Ooooh, pin me to the mat, Joel!* But being pinned down was never a fantasy of mine.

And though our age difference was minimal, I regarded Manfred Bernardo as a boy.

'Tolliver, I meant it when I told you I'm not interested in Joel. Plus, he seems happy in his marriage and I've never wanted to be an adulterer. Now Manfred, mmmm.' I smacked my lips. 'That's different. You can't help but wonder what's under all the leather.'

Tolliver gave me an incredulous glance, saw I was smiling, and had the good sense to look embarrassed. 'Okay, okay, I'm sorry,' he said. 'The truth is, I'm in kind of my own situation.'

'What?' I was instantly serious. 'What's up?'

'Felicia has stepped up her phone calls,' he said. We were at a stoplight, and he looked at me steadily.

'Despite the way she acted yesterday? Like she'd never seen you before?'

He nodded. 'Yeah. She's called, like, four times since we left the hotel.'

'You sure you don't want her to call?' I was kind of feeling my way through this, because I couldn't tell what Tolliver was leading up to.

'I definitely don't. You've told me before that sometimes you felt men were dating you because you were so – so different from other women?'

I nodded.

'Well, that's kind of the way I'm feeling.' The light changed, and he turned his eyes to the road ahead. 'We never seemed to have that much in common. She never acted affectionate, or like she wanted to get to know me better. I can't understand her constantly trying to hook up now, again. And then when she actually sees me, she acts like she never was with me. And then she calls me again.'

'You did do the nasty with her. Maybe she really, ah, enjoyed that with you?' I was trying not to sound self-conscious. This was not a frequent topic of conversation between us. Neither of us were kiss-and-discuss types. It was tacky. Plus, not suitable.

'To tell the truth, it was only about average. It was just . . . sex,' he said, with a shrug. He seemed to feel he had lacked gallantry toward a woman he'd bedded. 'She's a pretty woman, and real intense. In fact, maybe a little too intense. And not all that interested in talking.'

I groped for the right thing to say. 'Like she was using you?' I said, making damn sure there wasn't a hint of smile anywhere in my vicinity.

'Exactly,' he said. 'So, I guess I know how women feel when a guy's just using them to masturbate inside.'

Crudely put, but I understood exactly what he was saying. 'And Felicia's calling you all the time, now?' It was hard to reconcile that with the self-contained and sleek young woman I'd met.

'Yeah, after not hearing from her for months and months, she's in a frenzy.'

Maybe seeing Tolliver had reminded her of how good he'd been? Maybe it had been a long time since she'd had sex, and here was a sex partner whose excellence was a known factor, a sex partner who wouldn't entangle her in any relationship talk?

'How are you dealing with it?'

'At first, I thought about doing it,' he said, looking really embarrassed. 'I mean . . .'

'Sex is sex,' I said, trying to sound understanding.

'But something about her puts me off,' he said. 'I can have sex with someone I don't, ah, have a relationship with, and enjoy it. But we have to at least *like* each other.'

'She doesn't like you?' I was hesitant. I'd never heard Tolliver talk about a woman like this, and I have to say, I was a little worried.

'I don't know. I'm not sure I like her, now.'

'Because she's eager?' I wasn't sure I liked the implication.

'No, no. I mean, that's flattering.' He gave a frustrated shrug. 'I'm not one of those guys who only likes women as long as they're hard to get. And I don't think women are sluts if they admit they want sex. It's because Felicia's so . . .' He floundered, looking for the right words. But he couldn't find them.

Finally he said, 'She's too deep for me. It's like swimming in the ocean, when you're used to a pool.'

That was brilliant, and I gazed at Tolliver with admiration and some surprise. He looked a little surprised, himself.

I didn't know what to say, so I took refuge in facetiousness. 'It's all your fault, Tolliver,' I said. He looked at me skeptically. 'You're just so damn magnetic. They can't live without you.'

He gave me an eye roll. 'Cut it out,' he said.

So the subject passed away, but I didn't forget it, and I thought about it while he watched a basketball game on ESPN. He would know I wasn't dismissing his concern, that I'd keep it under my skin until I had an idea about it. In the meantime, I felt like reading. I'd gotten heavily involved in an old mystery, Marjorie Allingham's *A Tiger in the Smoke*, and after a page or two I was in the England of decades ago.

When the room phone rang, I was simply irritated at having to put down my book. I was closest, so I answered it.

A male voice said, 'Hey, can we come up?'

'Who is this?'

'Um. Sorry. This is Victor, you know? Morgenstern?'

I could feel my face wrinkle in a frown. 'Who is "we"?'

'My friend Barney and me.'

I covered the receiver and relayed the request to Tolliver. 'This is weird. I want to talk to him, and here he arrives on our doorstep,' I said. Tolliver was not so pleased. In fact, he looked mildly exasperated. 'Oh, okay,' he said. 'I was thinking about going out for lunch, trying to get some barbecue as long as we're here in Memphis. But we'll see what he wants. You think he's just showing off to his friend or something?'

I shrugged, uncovered the receiver, and gave the boy our room number. After a few minutes, there was a tentative knock on the door.

Tolliver answered it, looking quite grim and intimidating. Actually, he was probably just aggravated at the interruption to his game watching, but Tolliver is a tough-looking guy, and when he's unhappy, he tends to look a little dangerous. If the two teenagers had been dogs, the ruffs on their necks would have been standing up. Like many teenagers, Victor and his friend Barney were strange combinations of tentative and aggressive.

Victor was wearing a tight knit shirt, which allowed us to see just how much he'd been hitting the gym. He didn't have his father's magnetism, but he did have a pair of big blue eyes that worked almost as well. His blond friend Barney was taller, narrower, but still a substantial hunk of immature male. Both were wearing school jackets, jeans, and Pumas. Victor's 'Tommy' polo shirt was green-and-white striped, and Barney's Ralph Lauren was golden brown.

'So, uh, you doing okay?' Victor asked me. 'This is my friend Barney.'

'I'm fine, thank you,' I said. 'Barney, I'm Harper Connelly. This is my brother, Tolliver Lang.'

'Hey,' said Barney. He looked at us furtively, and then back down at his shoes. He and Victor were sitting close together on the love seat, while Tolliver and I were in the chairs.

'Can I get you anything to drink?' I asked politely.

'Oh, no, no thanks. We just had a Coke down in the car,' Victor said.

There was a small, awkward silence.

'Look, dude, I want to talk to your sister,' Victor told Tolliver. He had on the most manly face he could muster.

My mouth twitched, though I did my best to look neutral.

'Go right ahead,' Tolliver said seriously. 'Were you wanting me to leave the room?'

'No, dude,' Victor said anxiously. He looked at his friend Barney, who shook his head, to reinforce Victor's denial. 'No man, stay here.'

The teenager turned his head to me. 'You were in Nashville, so you know how bad that was,' he said. 'I mean, you know that was really awful.'

I nodded.

'So my mom – my stepmom – flipped out for a while.'

'Flipped out how?' I sat forward, focused my attention on the young man. Not completely to my surprise, Barney took Victor's hand. Victor looked startled, but not at having his hand held by another male. He was just surprised Barney felt it was okay to do that in front of us. They looked at each other for a moment, and then Victor squeezed Barney's fingers in a tight grip.

'She was all . . . using pills, you know? She got really strung out. Felicia was having to drive over to Nashville from Memphis all the time to make sure the house was running okay.'

'That must have been really hard,' I said, trying to sound both gentle and encouraging.

'It was,' he said simply. 'My grades went way down, and I was missing my sister, and it was really bad. My dad tried to keep going to work, and my mom would get up and try to clean the house or cook, or just have lunch with friends, but she was crying all the time.'

'The loss of a family member causes all kinds of changes,' I said, which was just about meaningless. It couldn't begin to cover the 'changes' the sudden absence of a sister could cause, as I had good reason to realize. I had no idea where Victor was headed with this, but

I found myself increasingly curious, curious enough to provide conversational lube to keep the talk going.

'Yeah,' he said simply. 'We sure had a bunch.' He seemed to gather himself. 'You know, that morning? The morning she was – gone.'

'Um-hm,' I said.

'My dad was in the neighborhood,' he said in a rush. 'I spotted his car a couple of blocks from the house.'

I didn't sit upright and shriek, 'Oh my God!' but it was definitely an effort to stay in my relaxed position. 'He was?' I said, quite calmly.

'Yeah, because . . . I mean, I did go to tennis practice,' Victor said. 'But after that, my friend I had in Nashville; I mean, it wasn't anything like Barney, but I did, um, have a friend, and he and I hooked up, and then I needed a shower, so I thought I'd run home, but when I went past the house I saw Dad's car at the stoplight two blocks away, and I thought he might notice something. I mean, what was there to notice? But parents, you know.' Victor shrugged. 'So I just went back to the park and hit some balls, met some other friends who'd come to play. The courts were only ten minutes away from home and I even parked in the same spot when I went back, so it was pretty easy for me to say I'd never left.'

We were both shaken by this little account.

'Of course, I couldn't say anything,' Victor said.

'I can see that it would be hard to get into that,' Tolliver said.

'Yeah, you know, one thing would lead to another, and then I'd have to tell them. About me.'

And the world revolved around Victor, of course. 'So they don't know yet,' I said.

'Oh, God, no!' He and Barney rolled their eyes at each other. 'Dad and Mom would freaking flip out.'

'My mom is cool about it, which is awesome,' Barney said. I was glad to confirm he had vocal abilities.

I'd meant that Victor's parents didn't yet know he'd seen the car, but of course Victor had interpreted my question his own way.

'You're sure it was your dad's car?' Tolliver asked. 'Absolutely sure?'

'Yes, I'm sure,' Victor said, as if he had his back against the wall and an army against him. 'Of course, dude. I know my own dad's car.'

I'd never heard anyone call Tolliver 'dude' before, and even under the circumstances, I was kind of enjoying it. 'What's he drive?' I asked Victor.

'He's got a Lexus hybrid,' Victor said. 'A bamboo pearl-colored Lexus with the ivory leather interior. We looked at the website for like a week before we ordered the car.'

Okay, that was distinctive. It couldn't be confused with many other cars, for sure. I was conscious of a bitter disappointment, as if a show dog I'd become fond of had turned and bit me.

'And you never asked him about that,' I said, and I couldn't keep the disbelief out of my voice. 'You're saying your dad could have snatched your sister, and you've known that all along, and yet you've never said anything to anybody about it.'

Victor turned a deep red. Barney looked at me with outright hostility.

'Because,' I went on when they didn't speak, 'you know you're telling us that your father lied about where he was, and you're saying he almost certainly grabbed your half sister, his daughter, and killed her.'

He raised his head, and almost spoke; his mouth moved; and he was so young, so disturbed, it almost hurt to badger him like this, but I had to.

'Leave him alone,' Barney said. His big hands, so smooth and unscarred, had fisted. 'Vic's been through hell over this. He knows his dad couldn't do anything like that. But he saw the car, and he can't forget that. You don't know what it's like.'

Actually, I did, pretty much.

'So, Victor, you gifted us with this information – why? So we could be disturbed, along with you?'

Victor's face couldn't have gotten any redder, and he obviously had to dredge for a reason he'd unburdened himself on us after more than a year of silence. 'I thought,' he said painfully, 'I thought you'd know who killed her. I thought you'd be able to *see* it. I couldn't tell. I already said, then I'd have to say I was home when I said I wasn't, too . . . I was *scared*.'

'How have you been able to live in the house with him for all these months?' I asked, out of sheer curiosity.

'I didn't see him.' Victor struggled with what he wanted to say. 'I saw the car. I didn't see his face, I didn't talk to him, I just saw the car.

There are other Lexuses in the world, like my grandfather's. There are plenty in that neighborhood. We lived in a pretty nice suburb.'

'But you seem convinced that it was your father.'

'Just because it was where it was. So close to our house. And at the time, I thought, "There's Dad." Because of course, Granddad was in Memphis, and we were in Nashville.'

Tolliver sat back in his chair and gave me a quizzical look. What were we supposed to do with this? Something, some small thing, at the time had convinced this wretched boy that he was seeing his father in his father's car. He hadn't doubted it. Now, he was saying he hadn't actually seen the driver. There were other pearl-colored Lexuses – Lexi? – around, of course, as Victor had also pointed out. I almost hated the boy for giving us the burden of useless knowledge.

Victor, however, seemed to be feeling better now that he'd told us the story. I could see by the little gathering motions of his body that Victor was preparing to sweep out with his boyfriend in tow. I felt angry about that, but I struggled against it. After all, I didn't have any right to beat the boy to a pulp because he'd finally revealed a secret he should have told right off.

A sharp knock at the door made me jump. The two boys looked pretty anxious, and I knew for sure that no one in his family knew where Victor was. I was beginning to think that our suite was the home away from home for anyone remotely connected to the disappearance of Tabitha Morgenstern.

Tolliver looked out the peephole, not a normal precaution of his.

'David,' he said briefly. Victor and Barney moved apart as if their inner attraction had suddenly been set on 'repel.' Instead of being a couple, they were transformed into a couple of guilty teenage buddies, caught somewhere they had no reason to be, by an adult who would surely scold them. 'Should I let him in?'

'Why not?' I said, throwing my hands out.

David stepped into the room, his eyes flashing around to all the corners suspiciously. Vindication was written large on his face when he saw his nephew. 'Victor, what the hell are you doing here?' he asked, righteous indignation practically dripping from his voice.

'Hello, David, good to see you again,' I said, and David Morgenstern finally looked at me and turned red.

'You thieving bitch,' he said, and Tolliver hit him.

16

The blow was not premeditated in any way. Tolliver simply drew back his arm and hit David Morgenstern in the stomach as hard as he could. As David collapsed to the carpet, choking and clutching his stomach, Tolliver closed the door so no one in the hall could observe the recovery of our guest. Barney looked scared, and Victor looked about a thousand different things – astonished, envious, and angry being the most identifiable.

Tolliver was rubbing his hand and half-smiling. He stepped away to show me he didn't intend to keep beating on David.

'Did you want something in particular, Mr Morgenstern, or did you just come by to call me names?' I asked as Victor finally crouched by his uncle and tried to help David get up.

'I saw you talking to Victor at the house yesterday,' David said, when he could speak. 'And then, when Victor came up here . . .'

'You followed me?' Victor asked incredulously. 'I don't fucking believe it, Uncle David.'

'Language,' wheezed the man who'd just called me a bitch.

'So, you decided I had a sexual interest in Victor?' I said, with what I thought was remarkable dignity.

'I just wanted to be sure he was okay,' protested David. 'Joel and Diane are so wrapped up in the situation about Tabitha, and Felicia went to work, and my parents are at home . . . my mother's having a bad day . . . so I thought someone should be watching out for what Victor was doing. He doesn't need to be around people like you.'

'And you thought calling me names fell into the category of watching out for Victor?' Tolliver had come to stand beside me, and I felt like kissing the hand that had hit David.

'I thought,' he began, and then he turned so red I thought his blood pressure had soared. He cleared his throat, leaned over so he could clutch the back of a chair for support, and began again. 'I thought the boys had come up here for . . .'

I wasn't going to help him out. Tolliver and I waited obviously and patiently for David to finish his sentence. Barney and Victor exchanged glances that fully expressed how lame this idea had been, and how stupid Uncle David had been to follow Victor. Grown-ups!

'I thought they were going to hang out with you two because they think you're cool,' David said weakly, which was a big fat lie.

'We are,' I said. 'Aren't we, Tolliver?'

'Sure,' he said. He patted my hand with his bruised one.

David finally recovered enough to move around the back of the chair and sit down, though we hadn't asked him.

'Maybe you could tell us why you thought you could call me names, and that would be okay?' I asked, my voice sweet and gentle.

'I am sorry,' he said finally, just when my patience was running out. 'Though I don't know why your brother had to hit me.'

'He's not my brother, but he is my best friend,' I said, to my own amazement. 'And he doesn't like it when people call me names. Wouldn't you want to hit someone who called Diane a thieving bitch?'

'She got some phone calls after Tabitha vanished,' David said unexpectedly. 'People called her all kinds of things. Especially after the story got out about her quarrel with Tabitha that morning. People can be so ugly, you wouldn't believe.'

'Actually, I think I would,' I said.

It took David a minute to get that, but when he did, the red crept over his face and shoulders like a tide rolling in. 'Okay, I'm feeling pretty bad now,' he said. 'I did a stupid thing. I can see Victor's okay, he's got his best bud with him, everything's cool. I know I acted like an idiot. Hey, Barney,' David said, with a pretty pathetic attempt at regaining his superiority. 'How are you, guy?'

Barney looked embarrassed. 'Fine, Mr Morgenstern,' the boy said. 'You?' Then he gasped and choked back a laugh at his automatic question.

'I've been better,' David said, a bit more steadily. 'Victor, why don't you and Barney run along? I've got to talk to Miss Connelly and Mr Lang.'

'Okay, Uncle David, if you're sure you're going to be okay,' Victor said, with false solicitousness.

David gave him such a sharp look I thought Victor would probably end up paying for his moment of fun, but Victor maintained his serious look quite well. 'Come on Barney,' he said. 'The grown-ups want to talk.' They put their letterman jackets back on and left the room, giving each other secret grins as soon as they were out of David's eyesight.

The door closed behind them with a thunk. We might as well leave it open, we were getting so much traffic.

Tolliver and I sat on the love seat and waited for David to flounder ahead.

'Diane says you're getting the reward for finding Tabitha's body,' David said.

We waited.

'Why don't you say something?' he asked, his temper flaring up again. Just when you thought the fire had been stomped out, it popped up again.

'What's to say?' I said.

'You're taking money from my brother and his wife,' David said. 'Money they need.'

'I need it too,' I pointed out reasonably. 'And I earned it. I'll bet not all the money came from Joel and Diane, either.'

He was taken aback. 'Well, there were donations,' he said. 'A lot from Fred, and a chunk from our parents, of course.'

I couldn't have had a better lead-in if I'd ordered it. 'Was your father especially close to Tabitha?'

'Yeah, he was,' David said. His blue eyes were focused on another time, and he said, 'My dad is a great guy. When he and Mom would go to Nashville to visit Diane and Joel, Dad would take Tabitha all the way out to the stables for her riding lessons. He went to her softball games.'

'And your mother went along?'

'No. I'm sure you noticed yesterday that she was too sick to do that much. The Parkinson's is eating her up. Sometimes she'd ride over to Nashville, but she'd just stay at the house with Diane. She's nuts about Diane. Of course, she liked Whitney, too.'

'And your dad has a Lexus like Joel's?'

'Why are you asking me all this?'

I couldn't believe he'd told me this much without asking why. Maybe David was lonely within his own family. As I looked at him, I wondered suddenly if David was the reason Felicia clung so closely to a family that had little connection to hers any more. My brother was looking at me strangely, with an expression I couldn't read.

'What do you do for a living, David?' Tolliver asked. You would never have thought that ten minutes before, he'd socked this guy in the stomach like he wanted his fist to come through the back.

'I work at the *Commercial Appeal*,' David said. 'In the advertising department.'

I didn't know exactly what such a job would consist of, but I was pretty sure David wouldn't make as much money as his brother, Joel. Joel was a CPA with a large firm, and he was obviously doing well at his job if his consumer goods were a reliable yardstick. And Joel had had not one wife, but two; both pretty, if the picture I'd seen the day before at the house hadn't been ridiculously touched up. Joel had a son and he'd had a daughter. I wondered what David had. A huge pile of envy? A case of jealousy?

'You drive your dad's car often, David?' I asked.

'The Buick? Why would I?' he asked.

'Wait, you said he had a Lexus.'

'No I didn't. You asked me if he had a Lexus, and I asked you why you wanted to know.'

Then I remembered Tolliver had said he'd been talking to Fred about his car. I'd misunderstood. And Victor had said his grandfather had a Lexus, but he hadn't specified which grandfather. I'd made a series of assumptions, and had gotten the usual result. Assumptions were dangerous things.

I'd been staring at David while I thought, and he was getting antsy. 'What's up with you?' he asked. 'I made a mistake coming here, and I apologized. I'm leaving now.'

'Were you really following Victor?'

'No one is watching out for him,' David said. 'I need to.'

I noticed that was yet another response that didn't really answer the question: a David Morgenstern specialty, apparently. 'It seems to me that *everyone* says they're watching out for Victor. Certainly Felicia is, and you are. Both of his grandfathers mentioned their concern about him.'

'Oh, Felicia talks about Victor a lot,' David said bitterly. 'But if you ask me, she's using Victor as an excuse to keep hanging around Joel . . . and Diane.' He tacked Diane's name on hastily, as if that would mask what he was implying.

That was an interesting thought, but I stuck to my course. 'Is everyone so worried about Victor because there's reason to think he had something to do with what happened to his sister?' I had caught myself considering, as Victor sat across from me ostensibly spilling his innermost fears, that he could be performing the whole scene as a cover-up for his own guilt.

'We wondered . . . I talked to Joel about this . . . Victor's so secretive. He vanishes and then he won't say where he's been . . . he hangs out with that kid Barney so much, and Barney's parents aren't . . . they're Christian, and they go to one of those churches where people wear Birkenstocks to the service. He locks his door a lot. We'd been wondering if Victor and the boy are into drugs, but his grades are good. He's on the wrestling team, and he's a strong boy, but we worry . . .'

'You sense there's something different and unknown about Victor,' I said.

David nodded. 'Do you know what it is?' he asked me baldly. 'After all, for some reason he came to talk to you. If he didn't come to you for sex . . .'

'It's unthinkable he'd come to me for any other reason,' I said gravely. 'Is that it?'

David looked ashamed all over again.

'I don't have sex with teenagers,' I said. 'Not one of them, not two of them at once. I'm not interested in that.'

Since I kept my voice cool and level, David didn't have any fuel to feed his anger, and he lapsed into his backup emotion, befuddled concern. 'Then why was Victor here?'

'You'll have to ask Victor that,' I said. Considering Victor had spent months thinking his father might have had something to do with Tabitha's disappearance, he was a model of mental health. He'd seemed so relieved to share the burden. He'd also seemed happy to tell someone about his sexual orientation. Victor needed a therapist. I couldn't believe he hadn't been visiting one. I said as much.

'Oh, he went for a while,' David said, anxious to assure me that they'd done their best by the boy. 'But Fred, he's an old-school kind of guy. He thought Victor should suck it up and get on with his life. I guess maybe he talked Joel and Diane around to his point of view, because when Victor moved here from Nashville, they never got him another therapist. Truth be told, Victor did seem a lot better once he was in Memphis.'

'So Fred didn't want him talking to anyone,' I said.

David looked surprised. 'Not to a therapist. He's just an old fashioned man, the kind who thinks you need to keep your problems to yourself and let time heal you.'

I was ready for David to be gone. In fact, I really didn't want to see any more of this extended family. In fact, I wished I'd never heard of Tabitha Morgenstern. I wished I'd never stood on the grave in the corner, but I couldn't help having the idea that I'd been herded toward that grave, I'd been asked to Memphis to find the child, and I'd done exactly what somebody wanted me to. All along, I'd been manipulated.

'Goodbye, David,' Tolliver said, and David actually looked a bit startled that we were ready for him to leave.

'Once again,' he began as he stood up.

'I know. You're sorry,' I said. I felt so tired I thought my flesh might fall off my bones. It wasn't bedtime yet, and I didn't think I'd eaten since a long-ago light breakfast.

Finally David was out the door, and Tolliver said, 'We're getting food right now.' He called room service and placed an order, and though we'd called at a strange time, our food arrived quickly.

As we ate silently, I thought. We have a lot of thinking time, since we're on the road so much. Somehow when we're in a town, when we're not moving, we do anything but think.

I went back over everything I knew.

Tabitha Morgenstern. Eleven. The much-loved child, as far as I could tell, of upper-class professional Jewish parents. Abducted in Nashville, to end up interred in an old Christian cemetery in Memphis. Neither of her parents, the papers had told me, had ever been arrested for anything. Her older half brother, either. But that half brother thought he'd seen his father's car close to the house the day Tabitha had disappeared.

Tabitha had grandparents who lived in Memphis, but had visited in Nashville frequently. Her grandfather and grandmother Morgenstern seemed to adore her. In fact, Victor had told us her grandfather often took her places by himself. Did I have to suspect Ben Morgenstern of fooling with the child? I sighed. And Tabitha had a sort of step-grandfather, Fred Hart, who seemed to have remained close to his former son-in-law. Fred Hart, a Bingham alumnus, owned a pearl Lexus, like the one that Victor had seen in the neighborhood the morning of the abduction. Victor had assumed he was seeing his dad, because it would have been reasonable to see his dad in that location, but what if he'd seen his grandfather's Lexus instead?

Tabitha had a step-aunt, too, Felicia Hart, and an uncle, David Morgenstern. Both had gone to Bingham. David seemed to resent his brother's successes, though as far as I could tell he also seemed to have cared for his niece. The attractive Felicia seemed to have quite an appetite for the male gender. There was nothing wrong with that. She was also very protective of her nephew, and there was nothing wrong with that, either.

I rubbed my face with both hands. There had to be something I could glean from this information, something that would help me lay Tabitha to rest. Being shut up with Tolliver, now that I'd had so many thoughts I shouldn't have had, was becoming intolerable. I dropped my hands to the table and looked over at him. He happened to look up at that moment, and our eyes locked. He put down his fork.

'What are you thinking?' he asked. His voice was very serious. 'Whatever it is, I think you'd better tell me.'

'No,' I said, equally seriously.

'Then what are you willing to talk about?'

'We have to find out who did this, and we have to leave this place,' I said. Movement would bring relief, being on the road again. 'Don't you think a random stranger is completely ruled out?'

'Yes, because of where the body was found,' Tolliver said. 'It's impossible that it was a random act.'

'Do you think I was meant to find the body?'

'Yes, I think that was why you were called here.'

'Then it has to follow that Clyde Nunley was killed because he knew who'd suggested I be the next guest in the series.'

'Maybe,' Tolliver said slowly, 'the key was finding of the priest's records.'

I mulled that over.

'After all, it was the finding of the records that made St Margaret's such a good subject for a reading. It was a controlled experiment.'

'Sure. Dr Nunley had to know if I was getting it right or not, and there was a way to prove that. There usually isn't.'

'So she was put there for me to find. Maybe months ago, when the records were discovered.' I groped my way through the thought. 'Someone wanted her to be found.'

'And that someone had to be the killer.'

I combed over that one, too.

'No,' I said at last. 'Why would that have to follow?'

Tolliver was taken aback. 'Who would know and do nothing?'

'Someone you loved. You might not do anything, if the killer was someone you loved.'

'Not just someone you loved. A member of your family.' Tolliver's face was very grim. 'Your mom or dad or wife or husband or sister or brother . . . that's the only way you'd hide it.'

'So we have a couple of ways to go,' I said. 'We can sit here and wait for the police to work their way around to the solution. They'll probably get it, sooner or later. Or we can skip out on this.'

'Let's try to find out who could have put your name in Clyde Nunley's ear,' Tolliver said.

17

Mrs Clyde Nunley was certainly not Jewish. She was aggressively Christian. There were crosses and crucifixes in every room in the Nunley home, and a painting of a saint on every other wall. Anne Nunley was thin and dry and hollow, and she had few friends. She was even glad to see us.

We thought the professor's widow might not be willing to talk, especially after we saw all the crosses. Anne might not have wanted to talk to another faculty wife, or a neighbor, but she sure wanted to talk to us. Anne was a True Believer in spiritualism.

I've met all kinds of true believers: Christian, Jewish, Wiccan, atheist. I don't think I've ever met an Islamic true believer, because I don't think I've ever met a follower of Islam. What I'm trying to say is, your basic religion doesn't seem to make much of a difference to your belief (or lack of it) in the things that are more in my bailiwick, which is any kind of contact with the dead. You wouldn't think atheists would believe in the spirit surviving death, but some of them do. It's like people just can't help believing in something.

Anne Nunley, it appeared, was an aggressive Christian mystic.

After she'd appeared at the door to greet us, and invited us in, Anne had begged us to be seated. Without asking us, she'd brought in a tray of coffee and cookies. It was about ten in the morning by then, and the day was much brighter than the preceding days had been. It was warmer, too, in the upper fifties. Sunshine poured through the old house's eastern-facing windows. I almost felt I could find a rock and bask like a lizard.

Tolliver and I eyed the laden tray Anne set on the coffee table before us, and I recognized this as sheer overachievement. Anne Nunley was determined to be the best widow in the world. And I also thought Anne Nunley was running on empty. Her husband's sudden and unexpected death had sparked a little explosion in her brain.

'Tell me, do you think Clyde's spirit is at the cemetery still?' she asked in a chatty way. 'I wanted him to be buried on campus; I think it's fitting. I've called the campus board that has St Margaret's under its wing. I don't think I'm asking much, do you? He worked at Bingham for ten years, he died there, and he was practically almost buried there anyway!'

I blinked. 'His spirit is not at the cemetery,' I said, answering her original question. My simple statement was the springboard for a five-minute ramble on Anne's beliefs about life after death, the prevalence of ghosts in Irish folklore (no, I don't remember how that came into the conversation), and the absolute reality of a spirit world. I certainly wasn't going to argue the other way on that one.

Tolliver just sat and listened. Anne wasn't interested in him at all; she saw him as a shadow at my elbow.

'Clyde wasn't faithful to me at all,' Anne said, 'and I had a hard time dealing with that.'

Total disclosure seemed to be the order of the day. 'I'm sorry you had to endure that,' I said carefully.

'You know, men are just pigs,' she said. 'When I married him, I was sure everything would happen the way it was supposed to. We wouldn't have much money, because after all, being a college professor is not the most remunerative of occupations, but we would have lots of respect, because you have to be smart to be a college professor, right? And he had his doctorate. I thought I would have children, and they would get to go to Bingham free, and they would grow up and bring their children home; this house is so big.'

It was a big house, and decorated in just-turned-antique furniture I suspected had come from Anne Nunley's parents, or perhaps Clyde's. Everything was polished and neat, but not fanatically so. Everything was comfortable, and nothing was expensive. It was a good house in an old neighborhood with big trees that had lifted the sidewalks. The big hallway that we'd entered had two large open archways on either side; we'd gone right, into the living room. The other archway revealed another good-size room that appeared to be Clyde's home office.

'But the children didn't come, and Clyde didn't want to be tested, and there was nothing wrong with me. But he was seeing other women. Not students, you know, at least not while they were taking his classes. After they graduated, you know, he might see them.'

She explained this very carefully, as if the exact details were important to me.

'I understand,' I said. And I'd thought we would have trouble getting her to talk to us. The problem was going to be getting her to shut up.

'But of course, he never knew the little girl,' she said. 'His being in her grave is just a terrible . . . invasion. Is she still there?'

The sudden question took me by surprise. 'No,' I said. 'But the man in the grave, the original burial, is still there.'

'Oh, then our Lord wants you to lay him to rest,' she said.

'I believe that's true.'

'Why have you come to see me? Do you need me to be there when you do it?'

Since I had no idea what I could do about Josiah Poundstone's ghost, or essence, or whatever you want to call it, I shook my head. 'No, but I did want to ask you about a few other things.'

She fixed her mad eyes on me. 'All right.'

I felt I was taking advantage of a woman who was not in her right mind. But here I was, and she was eager to talk.

'Did your husband see Felicia Hart or David Morgenstern, socially?'

'Yes, from time to time,' she said, in a surprisingly matter-of-fact way. 'And Clyde and Fred were on a committee together. Fred is active in alumni affairs, you know. His wife was, too, before she died.'

'She died of what?' The women in this family seemed to have extraordinarily bad luck. Joel's first wife had had cancer, his mother had Parkinson's, Tabitha had been abducted . . . it made you wonder about Felicia's and Diane's futures.

'She had a heart attack,' Anne said.

'That's awful,' I said. I really couldn't think of anything else to say.

'Yes,' she agreed. 'Poor woman. It happened when no one was home, about the time Tabitha was taken. She was gone when he found her. What a sad family.'

'Yes, it is.' Though this family seemed to have a lot of tragedy, in Mrs Hart's case, maybe a heart attack was exactly what it had been, and nothing more sinister.

'Do you think Felicia was seeing your husband as a girlfriend?' Tolliver asked. He tried to keep his voice smooth and unobtrusive so he wouldn't stop the flow, but Anne gave him a sharp glance.

'He may have been,' she said, and now her voice was cold and hostile. 'But then again, he may not have been. He didn't tell me names, and I didn't want to know. Felicia was here a time or two for one of our parties. We used to give parties.'

That was too hard for me to imagine, Anne getting the house ready for a party, maybe wondering which of her husband's 'girlfriends' he would invite into their home. Clyde, I knew instinctively, would have been embarrassed by his wife's Christian religious paraphernalia, while Anne would never have considered taking it down for a party. I hoped for her sake that he had simply let it go without comment, but my slight knowledge of Clyde Nunley convinced me he would have made secret sneering comments to his guests.

'Would Clyde have done something for Felicia if she'd asked him?'

'Yes,' Anne said, pouring some more coffee in my cup. Tolliver had quietly been eating the cookies, Keebler's Fudge Stripes, which he loved. 'Clyde liked doing favors for people, if it would give him traction with them. Felicia is pretty and she has a high-profile job, and she's active in the alumni club, so he would have done what she asked. He's been sorry David Morgenstern doesn't seem to be his friend, anymore, too.'

She was slipping into the present tense, I noticed.

'Do you know why they weren't friends anymore?'

'Clyde made some comment about David's nephew not being Bingham material,' Anne said promptly. Maybe there was Sodium Pentothal in the coffee?

'Would you know why he said that? Why he thought Victor wasn't appropriate for Bingham?'

'He'd seen the boy with another young man at a cinema,' Anne explained. 'He was sure they were, you know, in a relationship. Gay,' she elaborated. 'Though of course, they're not. Gay. They're sad, is what they are.'

If Victor was sad, I didn't think his gayness had much to do with it.

'Of course, that made David angry, and he told Clyde if he ever heard Clyde say anything else about Victor, he'd make sure Clyde never opened his mouth again. Clyde was mad about it, but sorry, too. David had been a friend of his, way back. So, he would have done a favor for David, too, to get him back as a friend.'

Had this woman had any illusions about her husband? Surely you needed some?

Anne had found her way back to the original topic like a homing pigeon, when I'd quite lost track of it. 'So,' she said, 'If you're asking me if I'm sure about Felicia, no, I'm not, and I don't want to be judgmental.'

I bit my lip, and Tolliver looked off in another direction entirely. I didn't know if Anne was being one of the most judgmental people I'd ever met, or simply realistic, but I had a terrible impulse to laugh.

'Have you completed the funeral arrangements?' Tolliver asked.

'Oh, yes, part of Clyde's belief system was preparation for your funerary rites,' she said. 'He's got it all written down somewhere. I just have to find the file.' She pointed to a file cabinet across the hall in Clyde's home office. 'It's in there somewhere. Since he was an anthropology professor, he was really into death rituals, and he put a lot of thought into writing down what he wanted. Most funerals involve a church. And a minister of some kind. At one time, Clyde wanted a gathering of the clan elders with a feast and distribution of his goods.'

'The clan elders being?'

'Professors senior to him in the anthropology and sociology departments,' Anne said, as if it were quite evident.

'You would have to provide the feast, I take it?'

'Yes, dammit. Excuse me for swearing. And then all his office stuff to give out! As if anyone wanted his old pencils! But that's what he wanted, the last time I heard. Maybe he changed his mind after that. He liked to play around with ideas.'

I looked across the hall. The file cabinet and desk sat in disarray with all the drawers pulled open, and files were scattered here and there on the floor. For a crazy moment, I wondered if I should offer to help search for the documents containing Clyde's last funerary wishes, but I decided that was too much. I didn't want to know what Clyde's instructions had been about the final disposition of his body and possessions.

I couldn't think of anything else to ask Anne. I glanced at Tolliver and gave a tiny shrug, to show I was finished. Tolliver thanked her for the cookies and the coffee, and then he said, 'Do you know who told your husband that my sister would be a good person to invite for his course?'

'Oh, yes,' she said. 'I know that.'

'Who was it?' I asked, thinking that at least we were getting somewhere.

'Why, it was me,' she said simply. 'After Felicia met you in

Nashville, she talked about you at a party, and I was so interested. She really believed in your powers. So I read about you on-line, and I thought that finally someone would be able to give Clyde some of his own back. He's been teaching that course for two years now, and he just loved exposing all those people as frauds, or at least as less than reliable. It wasn't that Clyde disagreed with their beliefs, either; he just didn't want anyone to be able to do anything different. But you, I knew you were real. I read the articles and I saw some pictures. That day you found the child's body, he was just furious at you. The night he died, he went out once, and then he came back even angrier, and I gathered he'd seen you at your hotel?'

I nodded.

'So then he made a phone call or two on his cell phone, and off he went again,' she said drearily. 'I went to sleep in my room. And that time, he never came home.'

'I'm sorry for your loss,' I said after a moment, when I saw she'd said all she wanted to say. But I wasn't sure she wasn't better off without Clyde Nunley.

Anne remained seated while we showed ourselves out. She was looking down at her hands, and all her manic energy seemed to have faded away, leaving her melancholy. She shook her head when I offered to call a neighbor or friend for her. 'I need to keep looking through Clyde's papers,' she said. 'And that Seth Koenig said he was coming over later. The federal agent.'

We were both quiet for a few minutes after we got in our car.

'He was mean to her,' Tolliver said. 'Surely she'll be better off.'

'Oh, yeah, Clyde was rat poop,' I said. 'But she's going to miss him, anyway.'

I couldn't see any wonderful future for Anne Nunley, but I would have to put that in the file of issues I couldn't do anything about. As we drove, I mentally constructed a future for the widow in which, at Clyde's funeral, she met a wonderful and kind doctor who had a great weakness for thin, needy women who lived in big comfortable houses. He would help her struggle back to emotional health. They would never have parties.

I felt much better after that.

18

We'd learned a lot more about the professor during our strange talk with his widow, but I wasn't sure that what we'd learned would be of much help in narrowing the search for his murderer. Not that I cared a whole lot about who'd killed Nunley – but I did care who'd killed Tabitha.

There was a basketball game I wanted to watch in Texas. I wanted to be free to go to it. I wanted to look for a house in Texas, a house that wasn't too far from where my sisters lived. So I wanted to be free of this situation, both for the sake of the Morgensterns and for my own reasons.

Tolliver was outside tipping the valet as I walked through the Cleveland lobby. I was so lost in thought that I didn't even notice Fred Hart until he called my name.

'Miss Connelly! Miss Connelly!' His heavily southern voice pulled me back into the here and now, though I wasn't happy about it. Maybe the look I gave him wasn't very friendly, because he stopped in his tracks.

'Did you need to see me?' I asked, which was a stupid question, but I had to say something.

'Yes, I'm sorry to disturb you,' he said. 'Joel and Diane asked me to deliver something to you on behalf of the Find Tabitha Fund.'

It took me a few seconds to understand what he was saying, and by that time Tolliver had caught up me and shaken Mr Hart's hand. Standing in the middle of the lobby didn't seem to be a good place for such a conversation. I suggested Mr Hart some up to our room with us. He wasn't very enthusiastic about accepting, but he trailed along after us into the elevator.

The close quarters made me aware that Mr Hart had been lubricating himself with bourbon. I tried not to make a face as the all-too-familiar smell caught at my throat, and I saw Tolliver's face tighten. Tolliver's father had been very fond of bourbon. We both had a great distaste for bourbon.

'I understand that you two met my daughter before,' Mr Hart said. In the mirrored surface of the elevator wall, I stared at a man who seemed to be aging by the minute. Fred Hart was grim and gray.

'Yes,' I said. 'Tolliver dated her for a while.'

I don't know what demon prompted me to add that, but I think I was feeling needled by Fred Hart, by his reluctance to come to our room. I decided that was because he thought there was something distasteful and shoddy about us, and I wanted to get back at him. That was a stupid thing to do.

'Did he now? Felicia is so focused on work . . .' his voice trailed off. He should have finished the sentence by saying 'that I'm glad she found time to go out,' or 'that she seldom seems to date.' Those were the words that would have made sense of the thought. But it was like his heart gave out before he could complete the idea. We both tried hard not to look too startled.

When we finally got into the room, I, for one, was thinking we should maybe call the older man a cab, not let him drive home. I was really concerned. He'd seemed such a nice guy at the Morgensterns' awful luncheon; very serious and sad, true, but also caring and thoughtful. What had happened to Fred Hart?

'Mr Lang, Miss Connelly,' he said ceremoniously, standing in the middle of our little temporary living room, 'Joel asked me to give you this.' He took an envelope out of his inner jacket pocket and handed it over to me.

I stared at the white envelope for a moment before I opened it. There was no way to do this that wasn't awkward. The envelope contained a check for forty thousand dollars. It was the reward money for finding Tabitha's body. With this money added to what we had in savings, we'd be able to buy a house. My eyes filled with tears. I hadn't wanted to earn it this particular way, but I was glad to have it.

'You're shaken, I can see,' Mr Hart said, sounding pretty shaken himself. 'You may not want to accept this, Miss Connelly, but you did the work and you deserve it.'

I did want to accept it, and I had every intention of accepting it. I did deserve it. But somehow his words shamed me, and I felt abruptly sick.

To my horror, I saw a tear trail down Fred Hart's cheek.

'Mr Hart?' I said, in a very small voice. I was not qualified to deal with a weeping man, especially since I didn't know the trigger for his tears.

He sat down heavily in the closest chair, which happened to be one of the wing chairs. Tolliver settled in the other, his face unreadable, and I perched on the edge of the love seat across from them. We had just had a very strange talk with Anne Nunley; now it looked as though we were going to have one with Fred Hart.

Of course, alcohol was playing a major role in opening Fred Hart's emotional conduits.

'How are Joel and Diane?' I asked, another stupid thing to say. I was trying to divert him, since I had no idea what to do.

'Bless them, they're fine,' he said. 'Diane is such a good girl. It was hard to see him marry again, see someone take Whitney's place. Diane should never have married him. I never should have let Whitney marry him. Out of her league, and I knew it.'

'What do you mean? Was he mean to Whitney?'

'Oh, no, he loved her! He was good to her, and he adores Victor, though he doesn't understand him at all. That happens a lot with fathers and sons, though . . . and fathers and daughters, too.'

'You mean Joel didn't understand Tabitha?'

He looked at me with a face that was still wet, but now impatient, too. 'No, of course not. No one "understands" a girl that age, especially the girl herself. No, what I mean is . . . it doesn't make any difference what I mean.'

My heart was pounding fast with anxiety. I felt we were close, so close, to understanding what had happened at the Morgenstern house that spring morning.

'Are you saying Joel molested Tabitha?'

I knew I'd made a terrible mistake the minute his face shut down.

'What a dreadful suggestion. Abominable. I'm sure you see a lot of that kind of thing in your work, but it's not something that's happened in our family, young lady.'

I'm not sure what he was referring to when he said 'my work,' and I'm not sure Fred did, either, but the point was, he now felt entitled to be angry with me, and he was taking full license.

'Something awful did happen in your family, though,' I said, as quietly and gently as a snowflake falling.

His face crumpled for a minute, like tissue paper. 'Yes,' he agreed. 'Yes, it did.' He heaved himself to his feet. 'I have to go.'

'You sure you're okay to drive?' Tolliver asked, in the most neutral voice possible.

'Actually, I don't believe I am,' Fred admitted, much to my surprise. I don't think I'd ever heard a man admit he was incapable of driving, and I have watched scores of men in many states of being high. They all thought they could manage a car, or a truck, or a boat.

'I'll get him home in his car, you follow us,' Tolliver said.

I nodded. I wasn't especially pleased at the prospect of getting the car back out of the hotel garage, but I didn't see anything else we could do.

I stored the check in Tolliver's laptop case for safekeeping while Tolliver called downstairs about the cars. We got Mr Hart up between us, and we went to the elevator. He kept telling us over and over how much he appreciated our help, and how sorry he was he'd spoken to me in an angry way.

I couldn't figure out Victor's grandfather. Finally I stopped trying. It was obvious to me that this man was under a nearly unbearable strain, and the weight of it was crushing him. But why Fred Hart? If our distraught caller had been Joel, I could have understood it better. After all, it was his daughter who was dead, it was his family who was under suspicion, it was his wife who was about to give birth under extremely unhappy circumstances.

With some difficulty, and a little help from the bellboy, we got the older man into the passenger's seat of his car. He was driving his Lexus hybrid, the one like his son-in-law's, and even under the circumstances I could read Tolliver's flush of pleasure at getting to drive the car. I was smiling to myself as I slid into our car, which was very humble in comparison.

Fred had given Tolliver directions, though he was speaking less and less and seemed ready to go to sleep. I followed Tolliver east, again, this time past the Bingham College area to German town. We turned so many times I was worried about Tolliver and me escaping from the suburb after we'd deposited Fred at his home.

When Tolliver pulled into a driveway that led into a large corner lot, I was trying not to be stunned by the obvious richness of the area. Fred Hart's place had been new maybe twenty-five years ago. The whole neighborhood appeared to date from the same era; the homes looked fairly modern in style, but the trees showed a good growth and all the landscaping seemed well-established.

What astonished me so was that all these houses had taken steroids. Not one of them would have less than four bedrooms, and that would only be the beginning of it. I imagined each one of them cost a million, probably way more; this was not the kind of place I planned to look at when Tolliver and I began house hunting. I pulled into the multi-car garage, which could hold two more cars besides the Lexus and ours. Besides being big enough to hold four third-world families, the garage had a large closet at the far right side that must act as a toolshed. And there wasn't a single oil stain.

I jumped out to help Tolliver, who was having trouble getting Fred out of the car.

'He pretty much passed out during the drive,' Tolliver explained. 'At least he'd already given me directions. I hope the house key works. If we're at the wrong house, we're screwed.' We both laughed, but not too merrily. I sure didn't want to have to talk to the police again, for any reason.

Tolliver handed me a key ring he'd extracted from Fred's pocket, and while he resumed pulling Fred out of the car I hurried over to the door. The second key I tried turned in the lock, and his security system, if he had one, wasn't on, because nothing began to tweet or blare when Tolliver got the stumbling man into the house. I moved ahead to find the best place to stow him. I had to stop and gape. I'd thought the Morgenstern house was so pretty and big, but this house was overwhelming. The kitchen we'd entered was huge, just huge. I passed from there into the family room, or den, or living room. I didn't know what to call it. It had exposed beams in the cathedral ceiling, an enormous fireplace, and conversation groupings.

'If I had been brought up here, I would believe I could have anything I wanted,' I said, stunned.

'Where do we go?' Tolliver asked impatiently, not in the mood to listen to sociological reflections. I made my feet move. The master bedroom, I discovered, was downstairs, which was a great relief. Together, Tolliver and I got Fred onto the (of course) king-size bed, got his coat and shoes off, and covered him with a soft afghan that had been thrown artfully over the back of a huge leather chair . . . in front of the master bedroom's very own fireplace and conversational grouping. I didn't know who was supposed to have conversations here, since Fred appeared to live by himself. I predicted I'd find a walk-in closet and a bath with a sunken tub somewhere very close. I opened the closet door, and then the bathroom door. Yep. All that and more.

'Watch out!' a voice called from the bed, and I swung around, startled.

Fred Hart had roused himself to give Tolliver a big caution. He'd grabbed Tolliver's arm while Tolliver was trying to arrange him comfortably.

'You have to watch out. I'll tell you the truth. You just don't know what happened . . .' the older man said, and then he conked out again.

'I know you drank too much,' I muttered.

Tolliver hung up Fred's coat and looked around for any other little thing we should do. 'That's it,' he said. 'Let's go. I feel like I broke in, this is so much not our kind of place.'

I laughed. We left the bedroom, and the sleeping man, and began making our way back to the kitchen. I just had to stop while we were going through the family room. It was so pretty, all dark browns and coppery colors with bright blue touches here and there. I sighed, and turned to look out the huge window into the back yard. I was a bit surprised there wasn't a pool. I decided the lack was due to Fred's gardening habit.

When Ben Morgenstern had told me Fred liked to garden, I had not imagined anything like this. The high red brick wall that enclosed the back yard was covered with vines, carefully pruned and directed. Running all around this wall was a flower bed full with bushes and probably with bulbs that would bloom in the spring and summer. Aside from this, there were groupings of bushes and flowers, much like the groupings of tables and chairs inside the family room. In the more established beds, the bushes were high and thick. There were a couple of beds that looked newer, because the brick edging looked brighter and the plants smaller. I was seeing this garden in November, when it was not flourishing, but I was deeply impressed. Maybe this was why Fred had held on to such a house after the deaths of his wife and daughter.

On a wrought iron table on the flagged patio right outside the windows, I saw gardening gloves, some kind of spray device, and a gardening hat. These things were laid out with precision, and a folded newspaper by them with today's date indicated Fred had been work-ing in his garden this very morning.

Leaning against the table was a spade, covered in dirt. Digging a new flower bed in November? He was enthusiastic. I wondered why he'd left the spade dirty, when everything else was so clean. Maybe he'd intended to finish some job when he'd put it down.

I didn't know much more about gardening than I did about astrophysics. I shrugged. Maybe November was a good time to turn the dirt over so it breathed all winter, or something esoteric like that. To my right, just where the brick wall ran up to the wall of the garage, was a wooden gate. It was placed there so Fred could wheel his gardening stuff back to its place in the tool closet in the carport, I figured.

Tolliver was using our cell phone. 'Hey, Felicia,' he said. 'This is Tolliver. I don't like to leave this as a message on your machine, but I guess I better tell you that your dad is at home, and he could probably use some company. He was feeling kind of sick when he came to see us at the Cleveland, so we brought him home. He seemed pretty upset about something. He's asleep right now.' And with a snap of the phone, Tolliver ended his message without a goodbye.

'Good idea,' I said. 'She should come by and check on him. I wonder if they see each other very much, in the normal course of things. It's quite a drive out here from mid-town, and apparently she has a really high-pressure job.' My voice trailed off. I should shut up.

Tolliver looked at me without expression. He didn't want to talk about Felicia. Okay. I got that.

A final glance around left me feeling more than ever like a ragged orphan in a Dickens novel. We left through the kitchen, locking the back door behind us. Considering the cold weather, it wasn't too surprising that we didn't see a soul as we backed out of the garage and drove to the end of the street to turn right, to get back to more familiar territory.

We had to stop at a Walgreen's to buy a few things, and we filled the car's tank with gas while we were taking care of odds and ends. We'd gotten tired of room service, not only the menu but also the expense, so we had a leisurely meal at a chain restaurant. It was a simple pleasure, doing something so regular and normal. The cell phone didn't ring and there were no messages for us at the front desk or on our voice mail when we finally went back to the Cleveland. The day had sped by.

'You know, now that we've gotten the check, would the police really need us any more?' I asked. 'I don't think so. I know we don't have anything on the schedule until next week, but we could leave Memphis. Stay somewhere cheaper. Maybe get to Texas to see Mariella's basketball game.'

'We should stay here a day or two longer,' Tolliver said. 'Just to see.'

I bit my lip. I'd like to take a big bite out of Felicia Hart, whom I blamed for Tolliver's preference. The bitch was stringing Tolliver along, I just knew it. Now that I'd seen the house she'd grown up in, I was sure. Women like that don't bond with guys like him, not in real life. He'd denied any real attachment to her, but here we were.

Then the cell phone rang.

Tolliver made a big deal out of answering it casually, but I could see that he was tense.

'Hey,' he said. 'Felicia . . . oh, how's he doing? He what? Okay, I'll come.'

He listened for a few seconds. He looked unhappy, puzzled.

I could kill her.

'But she . . .' Tolliver covered the receiver. He looked at me, his face dark and troubled. 'She wants us to come back out to Fred's house,' he said. 'She says she has some questions she wants to ask us about his condition and what happened today.'

'He got here drunk and we took him home,' I said. 'What more is there to say? You can tell her that over the phone. You *are* telling her that over the phone.'

'She seems pretty insistent,' he said.

'I don't want to go. If you have to talk to her, you go.'

'Harper isn't here,' he told the telephone. 'No. She's out on a date. What difference does it make, with who? All right. I'll be there in a little while.' He ended the call, and went to his room to get his coat without a word to me.

I made a face at the mirror by the door.

'Here, keep the cell.' He tossed it onto the table. 'I'll call you from the house if I need to tell you anything. I'll be back before long,' Tolliver said briefly, and he left.

The room felt very empty when the door closed behind him.

I don't often do this, but I cried for a few minutes. Then I washed my face, blew my nose, and slumped on the love seat, my head empty and my heart sore.

Too much had happened to us in the past few days.

I remembered when I'd first searched for Tabitha Morgenstern. I remembered the stale feeling of the Morgenstern family, the feeling that they could feel nothing new, nothing vital.

They'd recovered, to an amazing extent. They'd started a new life. They'd moved to a new location, reestablished ties with Joel's family that had never been weak, since Nashville and Memphis aren't far from each other. Victor had started at a new school and found a new friend, Joel had worked at a new job, Diane had created a lovely home.

Now, what would happen? Of course, Diane would give birth, and maybe this baby would help them to heal. Maybe knowing what had happened to Tabitha would, too. In time, maybe Victor would be able to share his big secret with his parents, and possibly they'd understand.

It must be hard to have a dad like Joel, after all. He was just . . . outstanding. Even if he left me unmoved, I could see that he was handsome, I could see that he was bright, I could see that women adored him. I also saw that he loved one woman in particular, loved her devotedly, but if I hadn't somehow acquired immunity to the Joel mojo, I might not be able to comprehend that. I wondered how often he'd had to fend off serious passes from other women, how many burning glances he'd deflected simply because he seemed ignorant of his attraction.

I tried to remember what Fred, Joel's first father-in-law, had said about Joel that morning. Something about the marriage of Whitney and Joel? He'd said something like, 'I never should have let Whitney marry him. He's out of her league.' He'd also said Diane shouldn't have married Joel. Why would Fred think that? Joel so obviously adored Diane.

I got down on the floor to do some leg lifts, thinking all the while. What was so wrong with Joel, that Fred shouldn't have approved his marriage to Whitney Hart? Did Fred know something bad about Joel, or had it been a bad marriage? But every comment I'd heard and read about Joel's first marriage had emphasized how close the couple had been, how heartbroken he'd been when Whitney died. And then, in less than two years, he'd married Diane. That seemed like a good marriage, too, at least as far as I was any judge. The abduction of Tabitha would have broken up a weak marriage, right? I'd read in several places that the death of a child often caused couples to separate, for a multitude of reasons.

Given the argument Diane had had with her daughter before Tabitha vanished, many husbands in Joel's place would have found reason to blame Diane, to assume the argument had everything to do with Tabitha's disappearance. But Joel was a faithful guy; probably Diane had never thought of leaving Joel. Because women loved Joel.

Women loved Joel. Fred Hart had a Lexus, just like Joel's.

I sat up. I stared at nothing, thinking furiously.

19

It was lucky I remembered the route to Fred Hart's house, because the cab driver didn't know Germantown from shinola. He dropped me off a block away, and I paid him the equivalent of a small fortune. He sped off, probably anxious to get back to the world as he knew it. I was wearing dark clothes and I was using the hood on my jacket, a very reasonable thing to do in the cold weather. I had pulled on my gloves, too.

Away from the main arteries, the night was still and silent. We were way into the burbs, and every soul was shut inside on this freezing night. The huge fireplaces were fired up, the ovens were cooking good meals, hot water was heating the thousands of showers and tubs. Nothing was lacking, inside, to perfect the comfort of the people who inhabited these homes.

And yet, Fred had lost his wife and one daughter, and a step-granddaughter. Nothing could stop tragedy from visiting your home. The angel of death would not pass over, leaving you unscathed, no matter how large your house was.

I crept up to the garage on the side of the house. Our car was there; Fred's car; and another car that must belong to Felicia. I ran silently across the white concrete to the wooden gate in the brick wall. I turned the knob very carefully. It was locked. Sonofabitch.

I looked at the brick wall. It had an occasional gap, part of an openwork design in the bricks. I took a deep breath. I fixed the toe of my right sneaker into the little gap, and I threw myself upward. It didn't work the first time. The weak right leg didn't hold. So I put the left foot in, and with my mouth clenched in determination, I heaved again. This time I clutched the top of the wall with both hands. I pulled myself up while I swung my right leg, and by some miracle I got myself on top of the wall. I was very close to the gate, which was at the angle formed by the house and the wall, and I would only be visible from the family room if someone was standing right up against the window looking outside. It was dark, and this part of the wall did not catch the spill of light from inside. I stayed very still, trying to calm the hammering of my heart. I drew a deep breath. Then another.

I risked moving enough to peer down below me as I lay full-length on the narrow wall. It was hard to make out exactly what was directly underneath, other than that it was vegetation. I figured I was going to have to drop into some rose bushes, but that was just going to have to be their fate.

As it turned out, my landing hurt me more than it did the roses. A thick central stalk jabbed me savagely in the thigh, and I was sure that it had torn my pants and the skin underneath. And I couldn't make a sound. I bit my lip as I extricated myself from the bushes. After a second to collect myself and to let my thigh stop throbbing, I stepped out of the soft earth of the bed, across the neat brick border, and onto the grass. The ground was damp from the previous days' rain, and I knew I was smeared with mud. I crouched and duckwalked over to the huge picture window. The lights were on inside.

Felicia had her back to me, thank God. She was facing Tolliver, who had his hands up.

That wasn't good.

That meant Felicia had a gun in her hand.

It was also bad that Felicia had blood all over her. She was wearing off-white pants and a dark green sweater, and the pants were smeared with dark stains – it was harder to tell what shape the sweater was in.

There was a sliding door in the expanse of glass, but I didn't know if it was unlocked or not. If Fred had gardened that morning, he might have left it open. Or he might have automatically locked it before he started off for our hotel to give us the reward money. I hadn't thought of checking, earlier.

It was locked. Of course, it was locked.

'Why doesn't he love me?' she screamed, her voice so loud I could hear her clearly through the glass. 'Why the hell doesn't he love me?'

She wasn't talking about her father. She meant Joel, of course. This was all about Joel.

'They'll blame you,' she said. 'They'll blame you for this, and I'll have another chance.' And she raised the gun in her hand.

Even if I'd been able to get into the room, there would have been a chair and a table between me and her. There was nothing between Felicia and Tolliver. I saw what I had to do. I pulled one of the bricks out of the border. I tucked it under my arm while I punched in 911.

When a voice answered, I said, 'I'm Harper Connelly, and I'm at Fred Hart's house at 2022 Springsong Valley. Felicia Hart is about to shoot me.' Then I put the phone down on the ground, very gently, and I braced myself. I stood up straight and looked Tolliver in the eyes. He stared over Felicia's shoulder at me, his face full of horror. He shook his head, a tiny shake meant to warn me off.

'Felicia!' I screamed, and I slammed the brick into the glass as hard as I could. A web of cracks began running out from the impact point.

The big noise startled her, and she wheeled around and fired without hesitation.

I saw Tolliver begin to launch himself at her back as the glass shattered in front of my face. I felt the bullet go by my ear. I heard it.

I saw the glass shiver, and I thought it would all rain out on me and I would be sliced open.

Fragments of glass struck me in the cheek, and I felt blood begin to trickle down onto my neck as I leaped backward on the flagstone patio. Before I covered my eyes, I saw Tolliver wrench the gun from Felicia's outstretched hand and bring the butt of it down on her head.

Only once.

Then I was under the patio table, and there were pieces of glass around me and covering the top of the table, and I was shaking all over.

Tolliver unlocked the door from the inside and then he was asking me if I was all right. He was pulling me into the house to drag me into the kitchen where he grabbed up a washcloth and began to dab at my face. There were bits of glass in the cuts on my face, and that hurt quite a bit, as I tried to make clear to him. Then we heard the police sirens, and then he was holding me. And it was all over.

The EMT was doing painful things to my cheek. She was getting the slivers of glass out, and it was hurting, but not as much as getting shot would have hurt. She had pointed that out several times, and I had agreed each time, though with less enthusiasm on every repetition.

The Germantown police had kindly let Detectives Lacey and Young come to the scene of the crime, and they were all listening to Tolliver's story. He'd covered the part about Fred Hart visiting us that morning, and Fred's inebriation.

Then he talked about Felicia's phone call.

'She said she wanted to talk to me here, that she wanted to know all the details about her dad's visit, and so on. I thought she wanted to see me again, because we'd had a . . . we'd hooked up a couple of times. She'd been calling me pretty steadily since. I think she was trying to keep tabs on Harper and me, to know where we were in case she needed us again. Which she did.'

'What did she need you for?' Brittany Young asked. She'd been pulled away from some home activity. Her hair needed a brushing, and she was wearing a sweatsuit and Reeboks.

'She needed us to find Tabitha.' Tolliver took my hand, and I tried to smile.

'You're saying she confessed to taking her,' Detective Lacey said.

'Yes, she did. She knew Tabitha would get in the car with her. She borrowed her father's Lexus, so no one would see her own car. She thought that someone might see the Lexus and report it, and that Joel might be suspected; but she knew he would have an airtight alibi because she called him at work that morning and made sure he was staying put. She thought if Diane suspected Joel, she'd divorce him; or maybe Joel would suspect Diane, and he would divorce her. Felicia thought maybe the stress of the whole thing would rip the marriage apart, even if mutual suspicion didn't. Plus, she didn't like Tabitha. She thought the girl was getting preferential treatment over her own nephew, Victor. And she couldn't just kill Diane, to make way for herself. That hadn't worked when her own sister died.'

'You're saying she had something to do with Whitney's death?'

'I don't see how she could have caused Whitney's cancer. But that kind of opened the door for her, she thought. She made her best play for Joel after her sister died. She came over from Memphis to Nashville a lot, she was as good to Victor as a mother could be, she offered to move in for a while to help Joel out.'

'And he wouldn't bite,' Young said.

'He wouldn't bite,' my brother agreed. 'So Felicia worked on this plan, worked on it for a long time. She took Tabitha back to this house, smothered her there on the couch.'

And then I recognized the cushions. The blue cushions. No wonder they had struck me so much when I'd seen them that afternoon. I hadn't been listening to my inner chimes, and they'd been ringing away.

'And then Felicia buried Tabitha in this garden, wrapped in a black plastic bag. Her dad was putting in a new flower bed, and Felicia put the body in there, deep.'

'Why'd she decide to bring her up?'

'One strategy hadn't worked. And Diane got pregnant, which was a stake in Felicia's heart. It was time to shake things up again. She had her ace in the hole; my sister. Probably, what sparked the whole plan was the discovery of the death records the parish priest had left. She knew Clyde Nunley, and knew he'd do almost anything for her if she worked him right. So she got him to invite Harper to the college, and she waited till her dad was out of town, and she dug up her niece. This was maybe three months ago, she wasn't clear on that.

'And her father caught her in the middle of it. He didn't know what to do. This was his only remaining daughter. So he did what she asked. He helped her take the plastic bag to St Margaret's. They reburied Tabitha.'

I shuddered, and Tolliver's hand tightened on mine. The EMT finished working on my face and put a butterfly bandage on the worst cut. The rest, she dabbed with antiseptic. She wrote down a few instructions and shook her head. 'You're lucky,' she said for maybe the twelfth time, and I nodded. 'You're gonna come out of this much better than the woman who shot at you.'

Felicia was in the emergency room getting her head checked.

Her father was on his way to the morgue. Felicia had killed him every way a daughter could kill her father. All these months, he'd known what his daughter had done. I was surprised he'd lasted this long. Three months' worth of days in this big house, thinking about what Felicia was capable of. It made me shiver just to imagine it.

'So what else did she tell you?' Lacey asked. He was wearing jeans and a cowboy shirt, oddly enough, one with pearl snaps instead of buttons. He had on cowboy boots, too, though I didn't know how he'd seen over his belly to put them on.

'She said that she planned on blaming her father's death on me. She'd kept hold of the shovel they'd used to dig the grave in the St Margaret's cemetery. Today she planted it in the back yard to be found, because it still had dirt on it from the cemetery. When we told her that her dad was here and passed out, she hared out here and hit him in the head with that shovel. She figured he was about to break and give her up. After he was dead, she planned to blame his murder on me, and Tabitha's on him.'

'Why would you kill Fred Hart?'

'I'm sure she would have thought of something,' Tolliver said wearily. 'After all, if a man like me kills a man like Fred Hart, I don't think there'd be too many questions. She would have thrown away her bloody clothes. Maybe if she couldn't figure out how to get blood on me that looked natural, she would have shot me, said she'd caught me in the house after I'd killed him. Who would you have believed?'

The police didn't like that. But I thought my brother was telling the truth.

'What Felicia didn't count on was Harper,' Tolliver said, kissing me on the cheek. 'I was never happier in my life to see anyone, as I was to see you when you popped up by that window.'

'You came out here without a gun or nothing?' asked one of the cops.

'I don't like them,' I said. 'We've never had a gun.'

He shrugged, like I was pretty stupid, and maybe I was.

But if I'd had a gun, I would have shot Felicia until I didn't have any bullets left. As it was, she was alive to stand trial for all the things she'd done.

I got a lot of satisfaction out of that.

20

'You look like a cat attacked you,' Victor said.

I just stared at him.

'Okay, not funny,' he said. 'I'm just really nervous.'

I started to tell him we were, too, but I decided that wouldn't be a calming statement. And Victor really needed to calm down.

I'd figured it might help Victor take his mind off his family situation and at the same time broaden his horizons a bit, so I'd asked him if he wanted to come to the cemetery to help lay Josiah Poundstone's ghost. I was regretting that idea, at the moment. Victor was a little too excited, though he seemed thrilled that I'd asked him. He'd given me a big hug, which surprised the hell out of me and caused Manfred to raise his eyebrows.

I didn't know anything about the business of laying a ghost. So I'd called Xylda Bernardo, and Manfred had brought her. Manfred, resplendent in black leather and silver, had greeted me with a kiss. He'd shaken Victor's hand a little too long. I thought he was trying to get a reading; he wasn't making a pass. Manfred wasn't that diverse. At least, I thought so.

Xylda gazed around the cemetery. 'Tell me about it,' she said.

I explained what I'd seen and felt that night to Xylda, who seemed alert and attentive.

'So, his body is here, and so is his soul. He died of blood poisoning, you think? From a knife cut, given him in a fight.'

'Yes. Really, he was murdered. I don't know who stabbed him, but I suspect it was his Beloved Brother,' I said, because that was something I knew about. 'I think the headstone might indicate guilt. Of course, it could just mean his brother loved him a lot. But I guess that doesn't matter. What really matters is Josiah's ghost being restless, because he wonders why he had to die, and then why his grave was disturbed so often.'

'So, you want his spirit to pass on?'

I didn't even want to consider what other options Xylda could offer me. 'Yes, that's what we want.'

'Good,' Xylda said enigmatically. 'Do you sense him here now?'

It was another cold night, but at least it was clear and not raining. The old cemetery felt just as scary as it had the other time we'd come in the dark. The muted sounds of the city, the uneven ground – but at least the open grave had been filled in. We'd checked that out in the good old daytime, with the sun shining.

I stood once again on this much-used grave and felt downward. I felt Josiah Poundstone's presence not only below me, but around me. 'Yes,' I said. 'He's here.' Victor shivered and looked around as though he expected a murky white figure to approach the grave.

I glanced at my watch. We needed to get a move on. We weren't exactly supposed to be here.

I'd thought about calling the college for permission, but I'd figured it was something they'd never give us. I wanted to get this over with and get off Bingham property before the security guards came by.

Following Xylda's directions, we circled the grave that had held Tabitha's body. We formed a narrow circle around it, and we joined our hands. Manfred's small hand had a strong grip, and his many silver rings pressed into my flesh. Victor had a much lighter grasp on my right hand.

Xylda began saying something in a language I didn't understand. I don't even know if Xylda understood it. But it was effective, whatever it was, because there was a mist forming in front of me, between me and Xylda, and in the mist I could see a face. It was a face I had never seen mobile, animated.

'Jesus,' whispered Manfred, and 'Name of God,' said Victor.

I was not frightened.

'Thank you,' I said. 'Thanks, Josiah.' He'd saved me from falling into the grave, after all. 'No one's going to bother you again. Everyone you knew here has passed on ahead of you. You need to go, too.'

I thought he smiled.

'Don't seek justice, seek peace,' Xylda said, and the face wavered. The eyes turned to Xylda in confusion. And then I saw the lids fall and remain closed. Victor made a gasping sound, and I knew he was weeping as Josiah made his final departure. The face lost its clarity, became less defined, and then the shape of it gradually dispersed. In five minutes, there was no more mist. And the air was clear.

And the cemetery felt empty of anything but us.

I couldn't explain this to anyone, ever.

I'd never believed in anything like this. Souls, I knew; I'd seen them and felt them. But I'd never known one that had lingered for over a hundred years, one that had been strong enough to manifest itself physically. Josiah Poundstone must have been a remarkably vital man, maybe one of the men who charmed everyone, like Joel Morgenstern. Seeing the ghost changed me. Maybe it changed everyone there that night.

I wondered what Fred Hart would have told me if I'd asked him, 'What do you see in your garden at night?'

Detective Lacey told me something interesting. Clyde Nunley's will really had requested a burial at St Margaret's, saying he had loved the college so much he wanted to be on its grounds forever. I thought this was amazing, and I thought Bingham's agreement to this was even more amazing. Detective Lacey didn't have any information on the kind of graveside service Clyde had settled on, and I really didn't want to ask.

Felicia thought so little of Clyde Nunley that his death seemed only incidental to her. Detective Lacey, who had actually developed some respect for me, told me Felicia confessed to killing Clyde almost casually. He was very much an afterthought, a footnote in her grand plan. 'He started acting like he had a claim on me,' she'd said. I suspect he tried to blackmail her; the social-climbing Nunley may have thought of divorcing Anne and marrying Felicia. Perhaps he told her he might tell the police exactly who had suggested that he call me to 'read' the cemetery. If he'd had a true understanding of her character, he would have known he was signing his death warrant.

Felicia had slept with other men only as part of her grand design. Tolliver she'd seduced so she could have a good reason to keep tabs on our whereabouts when she needed to have Clyde call me. It was only a bonus for her when Anne Nunley turned out to be interested in the accounts of me she'd heard, and Anne had also suggested my presence to Clyde when he was discussing the priest's graveyard material he'd found in the archives of the college. Felicia had hooked up with Clyde to have a conduit into the course study, so she could be sure we were brought there. She didn't consider having sex with either Clyde or Tolliver to have any bearing on her love for Joel, which was so much purer, so much finer.

The media feeding frenzy could hardly get enough of the story, right up until the time Diane delivered her son. Joel called us to tell us, and we sent a little gift, though we weren't sure Diane would be glad to get it. We felt obliged. Somehow, their marriage held, even though Diane had to find out that it was for love of Joel that her daughter had died. Diane was evidently a big-hearted woman who could see that none of this was Joel's fault.

At the trial, Joel steadfastly denied giving Felicia any encouragement at all, despite all her attorney's badgering. We had to be there for part of it, and it was as unpleasant as you can imagine. Of course, the women on the jury loved Joel, and I was pretty sure Felicia would be convicted on all counts. The police had come up with some forensic evidence that confirmed some points in the story Felicia had told Tolliver.

Rick Goldman got a ton of business as a result of his small part in the whole thing. Goldman had a way of making a mountain out of a molehill, and his reputation as a private eye soared. He sent us a letter enclosing a brochure and business card with his website address included.

Agent Seth Koenig resigned from the FBI that year and went into private practice. He specializes in tracking down missing children. He sent us a brochure with a business card attached. He doesn't have a website, yet.

So far, Tolliver hasn't talked about Felicia. I hope he didn't love her; I don't think he did. If there's something that needs saying, some day he'll say it.

We made it to Mariella's basketball game, and her team won. She scored twice, and she was elevated to unbelievable heights by this triumph. She was even happy to be in our company for one whole evening. Gracie sang for us, and we managed not to wince. Iona and Hank were half-way civil, which was the best we'd ever gotten.

Sometimes, Manfred calls me. He always keeps the conversation short and teasing. He tells me about his grandmother's doings, and he tells me about any tattoos and piercings he adds to his collection.

'I think he's making those up just to have a reason to talk to you,' Tolliver said one evening in Tucson.

'He's a boy who's got a crush,' I said.

'You know better. He's a guy, and he cares about you. Maybe on a superficial level. But he admires you.'

'I know,' I said with contrition. 'Manfred's not high on my dance card, though.'

'Someday,' Tolliver said, and paused. A knot formed in my belly. 'Someday you're going to meet someone, and you won't want to be on the road with me any more.'

'Then you'll find someone, too,' I said. 'Anyone would be lucky to have you.'

He laughed.

After that, we rode a good ways in silence.

Acknowledgements

There are several people who helped me with information for this book, and though I may not have used it correctly, I want to acknowledge their good intentions and their freely given time. First and foremost is my friend Treva Jackson, who has helped me with details in this book and a few others. Her daughter Miller has chimed in, too, from time to time. My fellow writer Robin Burcell was also a great help, not only in giving me some tips on police procedure but in introducing me to FBI Agent George Fong, who is nothing like the agent in this book. My college pal Ed Uthman also provided some funny reminiscences about his college years in Memphis. Julie Wray Herman and Rochelle Krich straightened out some of my mistaken ideas about the Jewish faith in the kindest way possible. I appreciate you all very much.

AN ICE COLD GRAVE

I'd like to dedicate this book to some people that always make me happy when I see them: Susan McBride, Julie Wray Herman, Dean James, Daniel Hale, Treva Miller, Steve Brewer, Dan Hale, and Elaine Viets. I have some more books to catch up to the ones I've missed!

1

The eastern seaboard is crammed with dead people. When work brings me to that part of America, the whole time I'm there it's like wings of a huge flock of birds are fluttering inside my brain, never coming to rest. That gets old pretty quick.

But I had some jobs in the East, so here I was, driving through South Carolina with my sort-of brother Tolliver in the passenger seat. He was sleeping now, and I glanced over at him, smiling because he couldn't see me and it was okay to smile at him. Tolliver has hair as dark as mine, and if we didn't run and spend quite a bit of time outdoors, we'd both be pale; and we're both on the thin side. Other than that, we're quite different. Tolliver's dad never took him to a skin doctor when Tolliver was a teen, and his cheeks are scarred from acne; his eyes are darker than my murky gray ones, and his cheekbones are high.

When my mother married his dad, it was a case of two yuppies joining together in the hurtling path down the drain. My mother was dead now, and Tolliver's father was somewhere, who knew where? He'd gotten out of jail the previous year. My dad was still in for embezzling and a few other white-collar crimes. We never talked about them.

If you have to be in South Carolina, it's beautiful in the late spring and the early summer. Unfortunately, we were nearly at the end of an especially nasty January. The ground was cold and gray and slushy from the melt of the previous snow, and there was more predicted in a few days. I was driving very carefully because traffic was heavy and the road was not clear. We'd come up from mild and sunny Charleston. A couple there had decided their house was uninhabitable due to ghost activity, and they'd called me in to find out if there were any bodies in the walls or flooring.

The answer was clear: no. But there were bodies in the narrow back yard. There were three of them, all babies. I didn't know what that meant. They'd died so soon after birth that they hadn't had much consciousness for me to tap into, so I hadn't been able to name the cause of death, which is usually quite clear. But the Charleston home-owners had been thrilled with the results, especially after an archae-ologist dug up the meager remains of the tiny bodies. They would dine out on the dead babies for the next decade. They'd handed me a check without hesitation.

That's not always the case.

Tolliver said, 'Where you want to stop to eat?'

I glanced over. He wasn't fully awake. He reached over to pat my shoulder. 'You tired?' he asked.

'I'm okay. We're about thirty miles outside Spartanburg. Too far?'

'Sounds good. Cracker Barrel?'

'You must want some vegetables.'

'Yeah. You know what I look forward to, if we really do buy that house we talk about? Cooking for ourselves.'

'We do okay when we're at home,' I agreed. We had bought a few cookbooks at secondhand bookstores. We picked very simple recipes.

Our apartment in St Louis was hanging in the balance right now. We spent so much time on the road that it was very nearly a waste of money. But we needed a home base, somewhere to collect our mail, a place to call home when we weren't driving around the United States. We'd been saving up to buy a house, probably somewhere in the Dallas area so we'd be close to our aunt and her husband. They had custody of our two little sisters.

We spotted the restaurant sign we'd been looking for after about twenty miles, and I pulled off the interstate. Though it was about two o'clock in the afternoon, the parking lot was crowded. I tried not to grimace. Tolliver just loved Cracker Barrel. He didn't mind wading through all the kitsch in the store part of the building. So after we parked (about a half mile away) we slogged through the slush past the rocking chairs on the porch, stamping our feet on the mat so we wouldn't track the icy mess inside.

The restrooms were clean, and the place was warm. We were seated almost immediately, and the waitress, a very young woman with hair as straight as a horse's tail, was delighted to serve us. Well, Tolliver. Waitresses, barmaids, maids in hotels: serving women love Tolliver. We ordered, and while I was simply enjoying not being in a moving vehicle, Tolliver was thinking about the next job.

'It's a law enforcement invitation,' he warned me.

That meant less money but good buzz. We always wanted law enforcement professionals to give us a good recommendation. About half the referrals we got came from detectives, sheriffs, deputies, and so on. Though they might not believe in me, there'd be pressure on them from somewhere about a particular investigation, and they'd call me in, having heard about me through the law enforcement grapevine. Maybe there was someone influential they wanted to get off their back. Maybe they were stumped about finding someone, or they'd exhausted just about every venue in their search for a missing person. The law didn't pay well. But it paid off.

'What do they want me to do? Cemetery or the search?'

'Search.'

That meant I'd have to go looking for the body. The jobs I got were about fifty-fifty. Since the lightning had snaked through the window of our trailer in Texarkana when I was fifteen, I'd been able to locate corpses. If the body was in its proper grave in the cemetery, the people who hired me wanted to know the cause of death. If the body was in an unknown location, I could track it, if the search was limited in scope. Luckily, the buzz given off by a corpse was less intense as the corpse aged, or I'da been batshit crazy by now. Think about it. Caveman corpses, Native American corpses, the early settlers, the more recently deceased – that's a lot of dead people, and they all let me know where their earthly remains were interred.

I wondered if it would be worthwhile sending my little brochure to archaeological digs, and how Tolliver would go about collecting the address information for such a mailing. Tolliver was much better with our laptop than I was, simply because he was more interested.

It wasn't like he was my servant or anything.

He was the first person I'd told about my strange ability, after I'd recovered from the physical effects of the lightning strike. Though at first he hadn't believed me, he'd been willing to humor me by testing what I could and couldn't do, and as we'd worked out the limits of my odd new power, he'd become a believer. By the time I'd graduated from high school, we had our plan all worked out, and we hit the road. At first, we'd just traveled on weekends; Tolliver had had to work a regular job, too, and I'd picked up money by working in fast-food places. But after two years, he'd been able to quit the day job. We'd been on the road together ever since.

At the moment, Tolliver was playing the peg game that's always on the table at Cracker Barrel. His face looked serious and calm. He didn't look like he was suffering – but then he never did. I knew Tolliver had been having a painful time since the discovery that a woman who'd been pursuing him had had an ulterior motive; even when you're not crazy about someone, even when in fact you're a little repelled by that person, that's got to sting. Tolliver hadn't talked about Memphis much, but it had left its mark on both of us. I watched his long white fingers moving, lost in my own sad place. Things hadn't been as easy between us in the past few weeks. It was my fault . . . all my fault.

The waitress came by to ask if we needed refills on our drinks, managing to smile a little more brightly at Tolliver than at me.

'Where are you all going?' she asked brightly.

'Asheville area,' Tolliver said, glancing up from the game.

'Oh, it's beautiful there,' she said, doing her bit for the tourist board. He gave her an absent smile and bent back over the pegboard. She gave his downturned head a philosophical shrug and hustled off.

'You're staring a hole in me,' Tolliver said, without looking up.

'You're just in my line of sight,' I said. I leaned on my elbows. Where the hell was the food? I folded the paper band that had been around the napkin-rolled tableware.

'Your leg hurting?' he asked. I had a weak right leg.

'Yeah, a little.'

'Want me to massage it tonight?'

'No!'

He looked up then. He raised his eyebrows.

Of course I wanted him to massage my leg. I just didn't know if that would work out. I might do something wrong – wrong for us.

'I think maybe I'll just put some heat on it tonight,' I said. I excused myself and went to the ladies' room, which was filled with a mother and her three daughters, or maybe her daughter had some friends along. They were very young and very loud, and the minute I could get into a stall, I closed the door and pushed the bolt. I stood there for a moment, leaning my head against the wall. Shame and fear, in equal amounts, clogged my throat, and for a second I couldn't breathe. Then I gasped in a long, shuddering breath.

'Mama, I think that lady's crying,' said a child's penetrating voice.

'Shhhh,' said the mother. 'Then we'll just leave her alone.'

And then there was blessed silence.

I actually did have to use the bathroom, and my leg actually was hurting. I eased down my jeans, rubbing the right leg after I'd sat down. There was a faint red spiderweb pattern above my right knee, extending to my upper thigh. I'd had my right side to the window when the lightning came in.

When I rejoined Tolliver, the food had come, and I was able to keep busy eating it. When we went out to the car, Tolliver slid into the driver's seat. It was his turn. I suggested a book on tape; at the last secondhand bookstore we'd visited, I'd gotten three. Unabridged, of course. I popped in a Dana Stabenow novel, leaned back, and walled my brother off. No, I wasn't walling him off; I was walling myself in.

Tolliver had booked one room in the motel in Doraville. At the desk, I could see that he was waiting for me to tell him to ask for another one, since I'd been acting so standoffish.

We'd often shared a room in the past few years of traveling together. At first, we hadn't had enough money for two rooms. Later, sometimes we wanted our privacy, and sometimes we didn't care. It had never been an issue. I wouldn't let it be an issue now, I decided recklessly. I didn't know how long we could trudge on down this dreary road without Tolliver blowing up and demanding an explanation I couldn't give him. So we'd room together, and I'd just have to be uncomfortable in silence. I was getting used to that.

We took in our bags. I always took the bed closest to the bathroom; he got the one by the window. It was a variation on the same room we'd seen over and over again: slick polyester bedspreads, mass-produced chairs and table, television, beige bathroom. Tolliver got busy on his cell phone, while I stretched out on the bed and turned on CNN.

'She wants us to come by at eight tomorrow morning,' he said, getting a pencil out of his bag and folding the morning's newspaper open to the crossword puzzle. Sooner or later, he'd break down and learn how to work sudoku, but he was sticking with his crossword pretty faithfully.

'Then I'd better run now,' I said, and I noticed he didn't move for a few seconds, his pencil poised over the puzzle. We often ran together, though Tolliver usually took off toward the end of our exercise so he could go full-out. 'It'll be too cold in the morning, even if I get up at five.'

'You okay running alone?'

'Yeah, no problem.' I got out my running gear and took off my jeans and sweater. I kept my back to him, but that was normal. While not having any modesty fetish, we tried to keep a boundary there. After all, we were brother and sister.

No, you're not, said my bad self. *He's really not related to you at all.*

I stuck a room key in my pocket and went outside into the cold wet air to run off my unhappiness.

2

'I'm the sheriff of Knott County,' the lean woman said. She was leaning over the counter that divided the front of the station from the back, and she'd been chatting with the dispatcher when we entered. I've never understood how law enforcement people can stand to carry so much equipment around their hips, and this woman was bearing the full complement, too. I never like to stare long enough to identify all the items. I'd had a brief relationship with a deputy, and I should have taken a moment then to examine his cop equipment. I'd been more involved with his other equipment, I guess.

When the sheriff straightened, I saw she was a tall woman. She was in her fifties, with graying brown hair and a comfortable set of wrinkles at the corners of her eyes and mouth. She didn't look like any true believer I'd ever encountered, yet she was the one who'd emailed us.

'I'm Harper Connelly,' I said. 'This is my brother, Tolliver Lang.'

We weren't what she'd expected, either. She gave me a scan up and down.

'You don't look like a dingbat,' she said.

'You don't look like a prejudiced stereotype,' I said.

The dispatcher sucked in her breath. Uh-oh.

Tolliver was right behind me, slightly to my left, and I felt nothing but a calm waiting coming from him. He always had my back.

'Come into my office. We'll talk,' said the tall woman. 'My name is Sandra Rockwell, and I've been sheriff for one year.' Sheriffs are elected in North Carolina. I didn't know how long her term was, but if she'd only been a sheriff a year, she must have plenty to go. Politics might not be as urgent a consideration for Sheriff Rockwell as they would be during election year.

We were in her office by then. It wasn't very big, and it was decorated with pictures of the governor, a state flag, a US flag, and some framed certificates. The only personal thing on Sheriff Rockwell's desk was one of those clear cubes you can fill with pictures. Her cube was full of shots of the same two boys. They were both brown-haired like their mother. One of them, grown, had a wife and child of his own. Nice. The other one had a hunting dog.

'You-all want some coffee?' she asked as she slid into the swivel chair behind the ugly metal desk.

I looked at Tolliver, and we both shook our heads.

'Well, then.' She put her hands flat on the desk. 'I heard about you from a detective in Memphis. Young, her name is.'

I smiled.

'You remember her, then. She's partnered with a guy named Lacey?'

I nodded.

'She seemed like a sensible person. She was no flake. And her clearance rate and reputation are impressive. That's the only reason I'm talking to you, you understand?'

'Yes, I understand.'

She looked a little embarrassed. 'Well, I know I'm sounding rude, and that's not my intention. But you have to understand, this is not something I'd consider doing if you didn't have a track record. I'm not one of these people who listens to that John Edward – not the politician with an s, but the medium – and I'm not one of these who likes to have my palm read, or go to séances, or even read a horoscope.'

'I fully understand,' I said. Maybe my voice was even dryer.

Tolliver smiled. 'We get that you have reservations,' he said.

She smiled back gratefully. 'That's it in a nutshell. I have reservations.'

'So, you must be desperate,' I said.

She gave me an unfriendly look. 'Yes,' she admitted, since she had to. 'Yes, we're desperate.'

'I'm not going to back out,' I said baldly. 'I just want to know what I'm up against.'

She seemed to relax at my frankness. 'Okay, then, cards on the table,' she said. She took a deep breath. 'For the past five years, boys have been going missing in this county. It's up to six boys now. When I say "boys," I mean in the fourteen- to eighteen-year-old range. Now, kids that age are prone to run away, and they're prone to suicide, and they're prone to have fatal car accidents. And if we'd found them, or heard from the runaways, we'd be okay with that, as okay as you can be.'

We nodded.

'But these particular boys, it's just – no one can believe they would run away. And in this time, surely some hunter or bird watcher or hiker would have found a body or two if they'd killed themselves or met with some accident in the woods.'

'So you're thinking that they're buried somewhere.'

'Yes, that's what I'm thinking. I'm sure they're still here, some-where.'

'Then let me ask you a few things,' I said. Tolliver took out his pad and pencil. The sheriff looked surprised, as if the last thing she'd ever expected had been that I would ask her questions.

'Okay, shoot,' Sandra Rockwell said after a brief pause.

'Are there bodies of water in the county?'

'Yes, there's Grunyan's Pond and Pine Landing Lake. And several streams.'

'Have they been searched?'

'Yes. A couple of us dive, and we've searched as well as we can. Nothing's come to the surface, either. Both of those spots are well used, and anything that came up and a lot of things that went down would have been found, if they'd been there to find. And I'm sure the pond's clear. Still, it's possible that there's something in the deepest part of the lake.'

The sheriff clearly believed that wasn't likely.

'What did the missing boys have in common?'

'Besides their age range? Not much, except they're gone.'

'All white?'

'Oh. Yes.'

'All go to the same school?'

'No. Four of them to the local high school, one of them to the junior high, one of them to the private academy, Randolph Prep.'

'The past five years, you said? Do they vanish at the same time of year?'

She looked at a file on her desk, opened it. Flipped over a few pages. 'No,' she said. 'Two in the fall, three in the spring, one in the summer.'

None in the winter, when the conditions would be worst for an outdoor interment – so she was probably right. The boys were buried somewhere.

'You think the same person killed them all,' I said. I was guessing, but it was a good guess.

'Yes,' she said. 'That's what I think.'

It was my turn to take a deep breath. I'd never handled anything like this. I'd never tried to find so many people. 'I don't know a lot about serial killers,' I said, and the two dread words dropped into the room like unwelcome visitors. 'But from what I've read and seen on television, I believe they tend to bury their victims in the same geographic conditions, if not in the exact same location. Like the Green River Killer dumping most of his victims in the river.'

'That's true,' she said. 'Some of them prefer the same location. Then they can visit it over and over. To remember.' She'd done her homework.

'How do you think I can help?'

'Tell me how you work. How do you find bodies?'

'My sister does two things,' Tolliver said, launching into his familiar spiel. 'She can find bodies, and she can determine the cause of death. If we have to search for a body, obviously that's going to take longer than someone taking her to the local cemetery, pointing to a grave, and wanting to know what killed the person in the grave.'

The sheriff nodded. 'It costs more.'

'Yes,' Tolliver said. There was no way to dress that up and make it prettier, so he didn't. Sheriff Rockwell didn't flinch or try to make us feel guilty about earning a living, as some people did. They acted like we were ambulance chasers. This was all I could do, my sole unique ability; and I was determined to bank as much money as I could while it was still operative. Someday, as quickly as it had been given to me, it might be taken away. I imagined I would be glad; but I would also be unemployed.

'How do you decide where to look?' the sheriff asked.

'We get as much information as we can. What did you find after the disappearances?' Tolliver asked. 'Any physical clues?'

The sheriff very sensibly got out a map of the county. After she spread it out over her desk, we all three rose to peer at it. 'Here we are,' she said. 'Here's Doraville. It's the county seat. This is a poor county, rural. We're in the foothills, as you see. There's some hilly land, and there's some steep land, and there's a valley or two with some level acres.'

We nodded. Doraville itself was a town strewn about on many levels.

'Three of them had vehicles of their own,' Sheriff Rockwell said. 'We found Chester Caldwell's old pickup up here, in the parking lot at the head of the hiking trail.'

'He was the first one?' I asked.

'Yes, he was the first one.' Her face tightened all over. 'I was a deputy then. We searched all along that trail for hours and hours. It goes through some steep terrain, and we looked for signs of a fall, or an animal attack. We found nothing. He'd gone missing after football practice, in the middle of September. This was when Abe Madden was sheriff.' She shook her head, trying to shake the bad memories out of it. 'We never found anything. He came from a tough home; mom drinks too much, divorced. His dad was gone and stayed gone.'

She took a deep breath. 'Next gone was Tyler Webb, who was sixteen. Went missing on a Saturday after swimming with friends at Grunyan's Pond, a summer afternoon. We found his car here, at the rest stop off the interstate.' She pointed to the spot, which wasn't too far (as the crow flies) west of Doraville. About as far as the trailhead parking lot was from north Doraville. 'Tyler's stuff was in the car: his driver's license, his towel, his T-shirt. But no one ever saw him again.'

'No other fingerprints?'

'No. A few of Tyler's, a few of his friends', and that's all. None on the wheel or door handle. They were clean.'

'Weren't you wondering by then?'

'I was,' she said. 'Sheriff Madden wasn't.' She shrugged. 'It was pretty easy to believe Chester had run off, though leaving his pickup behind? I didn't think so. But he had a tough time at home, he'd broken up with his girlfriend, and he wasn't doing well in school. So maybe he was a suicide and we simply hadn't found his body. We looked, God knows. Abe figured someone would come across his remains eventually. But Tyler was a whole different kettle of fish. He had a very close family, real devout boy, one of the solid kids. There just didn't seem to be any way he would run off or kill himself, or anything like that. But by then Abe wouldn't hear a word on the subject. He'd found out he had heart trouble by then, and he didn't want to upset himself.'

There was a little moment of silence.

'Then?' I said.

'Then Dylan Lassiter. Dylan didn't have a car. He told his grand-mother he was going to walk over three streets to see a friend, but he never got there. A ball cap that might have been his was found here.' She pointed a finger to a spot on the map. 'That's Shady Grove Cemetery,' she said.

'Okay, a message,' I said.

'Maybe, maybe the wind blew it there. Maybe it wasn't even his, though the hair looked like Dylan's. It was just a Tarheels cap. Eventually, we sent it to SBI, and the DNA was a match for Dylan's. But it didn't do us much good to know that. It just meant wherever he was, he didn't have his hat.'

This was certainly the chronology of a botched investigation. I was no cop and would never be one, but I thought Abe Madden had something for which to answer.

'Hunter Fenwick, a month later,' Rockwell said. 'Hunter was the son of a friend of mine, and he's the reason I ran for sheriff. I respected Sheriff Madden – up to a point – but I knew he was wrong about these missing boys. Hunter . . . well, his car was parked the same place Chester's pickup was found. At the trailhead. And there was a little blood inside – not enough to be able to say for sure that he couldn't have survived losing it. And his wallet was found not a half mile out of town, in a ditch off this road.' She pointed to a meandering county road that led northwest out of Doraville for about twenty miles before heading north and then northeast to the next town, up in the mountains.

'Who next?' Tolliver asked, because the sheriff was getting lost in her own dark thoughts.

'The youngest, Aaron Robertson. Junior high. Fourteen. Too young to drive alone. He stayed at the school to shoot some hoops one afternoon after basketball practice. He always walked home. But we'd had the time change the night before, and it was dark. He never made it to his house. His backpack was never found. No other trace of him.' She pulled a sheet of opaque plastic back from a standing cork-board at one side of her desk. We looked at a row of young faces. Underneath each face was the date of the boy's disappearance. Hearing about it was hard, but seeing their faces was harder.

We all kept a moment of silence. Then Tolliver said, 'The last one?'

'The last one was three months ago. Jeff McGraw. It was because of his grandmother that we called you in. Twyla didn't think we were getting anywhere, and she was right.'

It galled the sheriff to say that, but she said it.

'Twyla Cotton donated a lot of money and raised some more from the families, the ones that could help. And she got some money from some people who just want this to stop, people not related to the missing boys in any way.' Sandra Rockwell shook her head. 'I've never seen anything like the time and energy she put into this. But Jeff was her oldest grandson . . .' Her attention strayed from us to the cube of pictures on her desk. Rockwell was a grandmother, too. Her gaze shifted to the last photograph in the row of faces: a boy with freckles, reddish brown hair, a school sports jacket. Jeff McGraw had lettered in basketball and football. I was willing to bet he'd been a local hero in Doraville. I knew my southern towns.

'So you're like the frontman for this consortium of local people who've donated money to a fund to find the boys,' Tolliver said. 'Since the county, I'm guessing, didn't have the money.'

'Yes,' Sheriff Rockwell said. 'We couldn't spend county money on you, or state money. Had to be private. But I wouldn't have you here unless they let me interview you. And I'm ambivalent about the whole thing.'

Whoa, big words from the sheriff, in more ways than one. I'd never heard a law enforcement professional admit to being doubtful about a course of action involving me. Angry, disapproving, disgusted, yes; doubtful, no.

'I can see how you would be,' I said cautiously. 'I know you've done your best, and it must be, ah, galling to be asked to call in someone like me. I'm sorry about that. But I swear I'll give it my best shot, and I swear I'm not a fraud.'

'You'd better not be,' Sandra Rockwell said. 'And now, I've arranged for you to meet with Twyla Cotton. It only seemed right. After that, we'll pick the place you start to search.'

'Okay,' I said, and that was that.

Twyla Cotton was a very heavy woman. You read about fat people who walk very lightly; she wasn't one of them. She walked ponderously. She answered her door so quickly I figured she'd been standing right inside, since we'd called her to tell her we were on our way from the sheriff's department.

She was wearing jeans and a sweatshirt that read 'Number One Grandma.' Her face was bare of makeup, and her short dark hair had only a few threads of gray. I put her in her midfifties.

After shaking our hands, she led the way through the house. She didn't match the decor. Some designer had worked here, and the result was very pretty – lots of peaches and creams and beiges in the formal living room, dark blues and chocolate browns in the family room – but not very personal. The kitchen was Twyla's natural domain, and that was where she led us. It was full of exposed brick, stainless steel, and gleaming surfaces. It was warm and cozy after the chill gray of the morning. It was the homiest room in the house.

'I was Archie Cotton's cook,' she said. She smiled at me as if she'd been reading my mind.

I'd had a white-collar upbringing for my first decade, but after that my parents had descended pretty quickly through blue collar and down below, so you could say I was a medley. It had been a case of riches to rags. Twyla Cotton had gone the better way, the rags-to-riches way.

'And then he married you,' I said.

'Yep, we got married. Have a seat, hon,' she said to Tolliver, and she pointed at a chair for me. There was also a formal dining room, but this gleaming round table was positioned in a bay window at one end of the kitchen, and the chairs were wide, comfortable, rolling chairs. There was a newspaper and a few magazines, a little pile of bills, handy to the most convenient chair. Tolliver and I both knew not to pick that one. 'Can I get you-all a cup of coffee? Some coffee cake?' our hostess asked.

'I'd like some coffee, if it's already made,' Tolliver said.

'Me, too, please,' I said. I sank into a chair and rolled up under the table.

In short order, we had mugs of coffee, spoons, napkins, and cream and sugar close to hand. It was very good coffee. The morning improved, just a bit.

'Archie had some children, already grown and gone,' Twyla said. 'They didn't come around as much after his wife died. He was lonely, and I'd been working for him for years. It just came natural.'

'Any hard feelings from his children?' Tolliver asked.

'He gave 'em some money, quieted them down,' Twyla said. 'He laid it out to them about the will, and who would get what, in front of two lawyers. Got 'em to sign papers saying they wouldn't contest the will, if I survived him. So I got this house, and a good bit of cash, plus a lot of stock. Archie Junior and Bitsy got their fair shake. They don't exactly love me, but they don't hate me, either.'

'So why did you want us here, Mrs Cotton?'

'I've got a friend you helped a couple of years ago. Linda Barnard, in Kentucky? Wanted to know what had happened to her little grand-baby, the one who was found a mile away from home, no marks on her?'

'I remember.'

'So I thought about calling you in, and Sandra researched you-all. Talked to some policewoman in Memphis.'

'Jeff, your grandson. Is he your son's son? He's sixteen?' Tolliver asked, trying to lead Twyla to the subject we'd come to discuss. Though almost everyone we looked for turned out to be dead, Tolliver and I had learned a long time ago to refer to the missing person in the present tense. It just sounded more respectful and more optimistic.

'He was sixteen. He was the older boy of my son Parker.'

She'd had no hesitation in using the past tense. She read the question in our faces.

'I know he's dead,' Twyla said, her round face rigid with grief. 'He would never run away, like the police say. He would never go this long without letting us hear.'

'He's been gone three months?' I asked. We already knew enough about Jeff McGraw, but I felt it would be indecent not to ask.

'Since October twentieth.'

'No one's heard from him.' I knew the answer, but I had to ask.

'No, and he had no reason to go. He was already playing varsity football; he had a little girlfriend; he and his mom and dad got along good. Parker – Parker McGraw, that was my last name before I married Archie – Parker loved that boy so much. He and Bethalynn have Carson, who's twelve. But you can't replace any child, much less your firstborn. They're all broken up.'

'You understand,' I began carefully, then paused to try to find some other way of saying what I needed to say. 'You understand, I need some idea of where to search, or I might wander around this town forever without getting a location. The sheriff said she had an idea where we should start.' America is so big. You never realize how big, until you're looking for something the size of a corpse.

'Tell me how you work,' she said.

It was great to meet someone so matter-of-fact about it.

'If you have an area you think is more likely than any other, I just start walking around,' I said. 'It may take time. It may take a lot of time. I may never be successful.'

She brushed that aside. 'How will you know it's him?'

'Oh, I'll know. And I've seen his picture. The problem is, there are dead people everywhere. I have to sort through them.'

She looked astonished. After a thoughtful moment, she nodded. Again, not the reaction I was used to.

'If he's in any of the areas you pick for me to search, I'll find him. If he isn't, I'm not going to lie to you – I may never find Jeff. What have you got, in terms of pinning his whereabouts down?'

'His cell phone. It was found on the Madison road. I can show you the exact spot.' She showed me Jeff's picture anyway. It wasn't the same one I'd seen at the police station. It was a posed studio picture of Jeff and his whole family, plus his grandmother. My heart used to break when I saw the image of them alive, cradled in the arms of their nearest and dearest. Now, I just register the features, hoping I'll see them again, even if they're just scattered bones. Because that's how I make our living.

This particular gig in Doraville felt different. Time isn't much of a factor when you're dealing with the dead. They're not going to go anywhere. It's the living who are urgent. But in this case, time was important. If the sheriff was right, we were dealing with a serial killer who might snatch another boy at any moment. His pattern didn't include winter, but who's to say his pattern wouldn't change, that he wouldn't take advantage of this slushy time between snows; plan a final spree before a hard freeze.

I found myself hoping that if I were able to find the missing boys, then something about the way they were buried, something about the location or what was buried with them, would lead to the discovery of their killer. I know better than anyone that death comes to us all. I hate the murderers of the young, because they rob the world of a life that still held potential. This doesn't really make sense, I know; even a dissolute alcoholic seventy-five-year-old can push a woman out of the path of a speeding car, and change a bit of the world forever. But the death of children always carries its own particular horror.

3

Twyla Cotton had a Cadillac, only a year or two old. 'I like a big car,' she said.

We nodded. We liked it, too. We were bundled up for the weather, and Twyla looked like a ball of fudge in her dark brown coat.

'Do your son and his wife know we're here and what we're doing?' I asked cautiously.

'Parker and Bethalynn do know, but they don't believe it will lead to anything. They think I'm wasting my money. But they know it's my money to waste, and if it makes me feel better . . .'

I hoped they were as philosophical about it as Twyla made it sound. Families can give us an awful lot of trouble – which I guess isn't too surprising, since they usually believe we're defrauding their grieving relative. Still, we've had a bellyful of trouble in our lives, and we don't want any that we can avoid. I exchanged a glance with Tolliver, who was in the back seat, and one glance said all this between us.

'Have you ever had a child, Harper?' Twyla asked.

'No, I've never been pregnant,' I said. 'But I know how you feel. My sister has been missing for eight years.'

I didn't normally tell people that. Of course, some of them already knew it. It had made a big splash in the papers when it happened. But I was a high school student then, not a . . . whatever I was now.

'You have other family?'

I said, smiling brightly, 'Well, I have Tolliver. I've got a half brother, Mark, and two half sisters, little ones, Mariella and Gracie. They live in Texas with our aunt and her husband.' Mark wasn't my half brother any more than Tolliver was. He was simply Tolliver's older brother. But I wasn't in the mood to spell it out.

'Oh, I'm so sorry. Your parents already passed?'

'My mother has. My father is still living.' In jail, but living. Tolliver's mother had died before his father met my mom, and Tolliver's father was out of jail and drifting . . . somewhere.

Considering my mom and dad and Tolliver's father had all been attorneys, they'd had a long way to fall. They'd really thrown themselves into it.

Twyla looked a little shocked. 'Well, how awful. I'm so sorry.'

I shrugged. That was just the way it was. 'Thanks,' I said, but I knew I didn't sound sincere. Couldn't help it. When I heard that my mother had died, I was sorry, but not surprised, and not unrelieved.

We were quiet after that until we pulled up by the side of the road. Twyla glanced down at the list she'd taken down during a quick phone call with Sandra Rockwell. Sure enough, Sandra Rockwell had a prioritized list of places to check. This was place number one.

We were behind the high school at the football practice field, a stretch of barren level ground. One of those devices that the boys push around was still sitting by the side of the field, though football season was over. The field house was closed and locked until next year. Basketball would be the sport in play now.

'This is where his truck was,' Twyla said. 'We'd just gotten it for him. It was an old second-hand Dodge.'

Sheriff Rockwell had said less about Jeff than about any of the other boys, perhaps because she'd known we'd be talking to his grandmother. Looking around now, I didn't see anyone. Not a soul. So an abduction at this point wasn't out of the question, though risky. At any moment, someone might come out of the school. But there weren't any houses nearby. The lane behind the practice field was just a bare strip of ground before a steep hill that had been sheared away to build the school.

Though it might be a fair spot for an abduction, I seriously doubted someone had killed the boy on the spot and buried him here, but I wanted to show I was willing. I stepped out, sent out that part of me that made me unique. There was no response. I was getting the tiniest tingle, which meant some incredibly old human remains were somewhere in the area. It was a feeling I'd learned to ignore in my search for modern bodies. Though the range would be almost the same, not enough to make a difference, I walked the length of the property and kept getting the same reading. I shook my head silently and climbed back into the Cadillac. We drove, Twyla pointing out this or that town landmark as we passed it. I didn't listen, concentrating instead on what I was picking up as we moved. The local cemetery provided a huge mass of static, but we had to stop there because that was where Tyler's hat had been found.

Of course there were tons of bodies here, and some of them were very fresh. It was way too cold to pull my shoes off, but I followed my instincts and went to the freshest graves. There was a heart attack, and there was a death by old age. Sometimes, you know, you just give out. Those were the most recent deaths. But Tyler Lassiter had been gone about two years, if I was remembering correctly, so I had to check out a lot more bodies. None of them turned out to be Tyler. They were all exactly who they were supposed to be according to their headstones. I was glad Doraville wasn't bigger, and glad some people were buried in the newer cemetery, which was south of Doraville.

We were now on the western edge of town, and Twyla once more pulled to the side of the road.

'The man that lives there was arrested for attacking a boy,' she said, pointing to a dilapidated white frame house barely visible behind a tangle of vines and young trees. 'He's been questioned over and over.'

I wasn't getting anything from the car. I got out and took a couple of steps forward, closing my eyes. I picked up a buzz from my left, much farther back in the woods, but it was the faint buzz I associated with old cemeteries. I heard Tolliver's window roll down. 'Ask her if there's an old church back there with its own cemetery,' I said.

'Yes,' Twyla called to me. 'Mount Ararat is back there.'

I got back in the car and said, 'Nope.'

Twyla inhaled deeply, as if about to play her last card. She put the car in drive and we pulled out, heading even farther out of the small town of Doraville. We drove northwest, the readout on Twyla's car told me, and the ground began to climb. I looked up at the mountains and I thought that if Jeff's body were up there, I would never find it. I did not want to go hiking in those mountains, especially in this weather. I had a brief selfish thought: Why couldn't Twyla have called me in two months ago? A month, even? I shivered, and thought of the biting cold, the snow that lay in patches on the ground, the predictions of bad weather in a few days. We began to go up, though the pitch of the ground was not so steep here.

And then Twyla stopped again. I noticed how stiffly she sat in the driver's seat, how white she'd gotten.

'This is where the phone was,' Twyla said. She jerked her thumb to the right. 'I put that rock there, to mark where it was exactly, after the sheriff showed me.'

There was a big rock with a blue cross on it, dug into the earth at the side of the road.

'You put it in pretty deep,' Tolliver said.

'The mowers had to pass over it,' she said. 'That was three months ago.'

Practical.

I got out of the Cadillac and looked around, pulling on my gloves as I did so. It was freaking cold up here, no doubt about it. The Madison road rose steeply ahead of us, cut out of the rising mountain to the left. On our side, there was a fairly level narrow strip, perhaps a half acre to an acre of land, before the rolling slope began its rise. In that half acre lay the site of an old home. The house had been abandoned years before. The plot wasn't in a neat rectangle because it followed the contours of the hill. It was long and thin in spots.

We were parked on the shoulder, and if I took a step I'd roll down the slope of a deep ditch. The driveway into the plot ran over a culvert so the flow of rainwater wouldn't be impeded. The remains of this driveway passed through the remains of a fence. Now, with all the leaves fallen, the stands of weeds were golden or brown with winter's death, and the occasional young pine looked startlingly green. The weeds and small trees appeared to be holding up the fence.

The house had been a humble one. The roof wasn't caved in, but there were holes in it, and the porch was sagging. There wasn't any glass in the windows. There was a listing two-car garage off to one side, with wide doors that hung ajar. Once it had been painted white, like the house. The whole thing was southern gothic picturesque decay personified.

The water in the drainage ditch was dark and would be very cold. There'd been a lot of rain the past couple of weeks. And I felt the raw chill of more rain coming.

I could tell from the inclination of Tolliver's head that he expected me to walk down the side of the road to where the hill leveled into the valley. He expected that someone had dumped the body on the more accessible ground and had tossed its accessories off while driving upward into the mountains. And under other circumstances, that's exactly what I would have done.

But there wasn't any need.

The minute my foot had touched the ground, I'd known I was going to have news for Twyla Cotton. The buzzing was intense, increasing as I stepped closer to the eroded driveway. This was not the signal from a single corpse. I began to have a bad feeling, an awful feeling, and I was scared to look at Tolliver. He took my hand, wrapped it around the crook of his elbow. He could tell I'd decided to go into the tangled area that had been the yard of the old house.

'The ground is rough in there. I wish we'd worn our high boots,' he said. But I couldn't register what he was saying. I watched a blue pickup pass, slowing down for the curve, fading away from view. It was the only other vehicle we'd seen on this road.

After the sound of its motor died away, I could hear only the increasingly irrelevant registers of the two live people and the increasingly more compelling signals of the dead. I walked forward, pulling Tolliver with me. Maybe he tried to pull me back a little, but I kept on going, because this was my moment – my connection with the power, or ability, or electrical short, that made me unique.

'You better get the flags,' I said, and he went back to get the lengths of wire topped with red plastic flags.

In the cold damp I stood in the middle of the former yard, between the fence and the ruined house. I turned in a circle, feeling the buzzing rising all around me, as they clamored to be found. That's all they want, you know. They want to be found.

I tried to speak, choked, gasped.

'What's wrong?' Tolliver asked distantly. 'Harper?'

I stumbled to the left a couple of steps. 'Here,' I said.

'My grandson? Jeff's there?' Twyla had forged her way onto the property.

I moved six feet northwest. 'Here, too,' I said.

'He's in *pieces*?'

'There's more than one body,' Tolliver told her.

I held my hands up to sharpen my focus. I turned again, more slowly, my eyes closed, my hands raised, counting. 'Eight,' I said.

'Oh, my Lord in heaven,' Twyla said. She sat down heavily on an old stump. 'I'm going to call the police.'

She must have given Tolliver a glance of sudden misgiving, because he said, 'You can bank on it. Harper's right.' I heard the little beeps as she began punching in numbers.

'What happened to them?' he asked me quietly. He knew I was listening though my eyes were still closed.

I didn't say anything. It was time for me to find out, but I didn't want anyone else to watch while I did it. 'Okay,' I said, to steady myself. 'Tolliver?' I wanted him to be ready.

'I'm here,' he said. 'I've got a hold.' I could feel his grip on my arms.

I stepped directly onto the ground above the corpse, and I looked down through the soil and rocks, caught a glimpse of hell. That was the last thing I remember.

4

'She ever gonna wake up?' The speaker was Sandra Rockwell. I remembered her voice, but she sounded strange and strained.

'Harper?' my brother said. 'Harper?'

I didn't want to do this, but I had to.

'Okay,' I said, and it came out as wobbly as I felt. 'You found them yet?'

'Tell me what to do,' Sheriff Rockwell said. She sounded as if she didn't want to be there.

I had to open my eyes, and I had to look at the anxious brown eyes under the hat. Sheriff Rockwell was in a padded coat that made her look twice as large.

'They're all there,' I said. 'If you can wait a minute, I can tell you who's where. And there are eight of them, not six.'

'How do you know that?'

I was sitting in the back seat of Twyla's car, my head leaning against the cushion.

'Here, eat some sugar,' Tolliver said anxiously, working a piece of candy out of his jeans pocket. He unwrapped it for me, and popped it in my mouth. I knew from experience that I would feel better in a few minutes, especially if I had a Coke.

'You were willing to believe me before I did anything,' I said. 'Have a little more faith. Dig for them.'

'If you're lying, your ass will end up in jail,' she said.

'And I would deserve it.'

With a lot of effort, I turned my head to look out the car window. There were a couple of deputies standing on the site. Twyla was with them. The expression on her face would have made the most jaded con man weep – or maybe not. In our travels, in my line of work, we've met a few con men, and they almost all have no empathy. It's just not in their emotional repertoire.

'Come show me,' Sheriff Rockwell said, and Tolliver helped me out of the car. Slowly we made our way to the place where I'd fainted, and though I was shaking all over because I would have to feel the death again, I stood on the spot where I'd sensed the most recent body.

'Here,' I said, pointing straight down. I knew who it was, too. This was the body of Jeff, Twyla's grandson. Tolliver got out a spiral-bound notebook he had zipped in his jacket. He'd sketched a very rough outline of the site. 'This is Jeff, Jeff McGraw,' I told Tolliver. 'He was strangled.' Tolliver stuck a length of wire in the ground. The red flag flapped a little in the stiff breeze. He put his left arm around me and took my right hand in his. I nodded in the direction we should go, a little uphill and to the north, and I centered myself above another corpse. Tears began rolling down my cheeks . . . I'd never encountered such suffering. 'Here,' I said. 'Chester.' Two yards farther, we had a boy Sheriff Rockwell hadn't mentioned. 'This is someone named something like – Chad, Chad something that begins with a T.' The sheriff was scribbling in her own notebook. The deputies were listening, too, but they were completely skeptical and not a little angry. I couldn't do anything about that. They'd learn soon enough.

I followed the next signal to the rear of the lot, right where the ground began to rise sharply. It was centered behind a clump of bushes. I wiped my face with a handkerchief, said, 'Dylan,' and staggered a bit south. Now I was behind the house. The sheriff and Twyla followed me, and the deputies, too. 'Aaron,' I said. 'Wasn't there an Aaron?' And a few yards south again. This one was harder, for some reason. His horror and panic had short-circuited his brain while he was dying. 'I think this is Tyler,' I said. And then I went to the southernmost grave of all, and I knew it was the oldest, somehow. The vibrations it gave off were just a bit weaker. 'This is the first one,' I told the sheriff, who was keeping pace with us. That wasn't hard, because I was moving very slowly by now, and I was shaking all over. 'His name was . . .' I shook my head slightly, tried to focus more intently. 'His name was James something,' I said. 'James Ray, James Roy, James Robert. I'm not . . . I can't tell his last name. Oh, Tolliver, get me out of here.' There was one more, a boy named Hunter. I could barely stand by the time I had him pinpointed. He'd died of hypothermia. He must have been one of the November abductions.

'Can I take my sister back into town? She needs to lie down,' Tolliver said.

'Nope,' Sandra Rockwell, her jaw clicking shut with a snap. 'Not until we check this out.' If I was lying, Sandra Rockwell wanted me on hand when she discovered the lie. 'You got any advice on which place to check first?' she asked.

I shook my head. 'Any of the places we stuck a flag,' I said.

Twyla had retreated to the Cadillac. I was glad I couldn't tell what live people were thinking, because imagining how she felt couldn't hold a candle to her actual misery. When Tolliver and I climbed in the back seat, she was kind enough to turn the car on so the heater would warm us. For what seemed like a long time, we just huddled there in the car. Not a word was spoken. My head seemed full of a white noise, and I couldn't think about anything. I'd seen horrors.

I didn't turn my head to watch what went on in the old homesite, but Twyla did. Finally, she said, 'They've dug about two feet down, now. It sure is a sloppy day for it. I hope Dave and Harry don't catch a cold. Much less Sandra.'

I thought, *I would have been glad to wait for better weather*, but I didn't say anything.

It was my first mass murder.

A little before eleven o'clock Dave and Harry, the two deputies, uncovered the first bones.

There was a pause, a palpable pause. The three law officers fell still around the hole that had finally gotten deep enough.

I'd been leaning back. I straightened. Tolliver's head rotated, and so did Twyla's.

'My grandson?' she asked. I'd been expecting the question.

'No,' I said. 'They picked the northernmost burial to start at. I'm so sorry. Your grandson is there, Twyla, at the first flag we put in. I wish I could make it better. I wish he wasn't out there.' I didn't know how else to put it.

'You can't be sure.' Her voice was hesitant. I hadn't known Twyla Cotton more than a couple of hours, but I knew that that wasn't her normal attitude.

'No, of course.' I was sure, though. This strange skill is all I have, really. That, and Tolliver, and my two half sisters. So I'm careful of my skill, and I never say anything unless I'm sure. The boy I'd seen in the upslope grave was the same boy in the pictures at Twyla Cotton's house.

'How . . . how did these boys die?'

That was the question I'd been dreading.

'I really can't . . .' I couldn't finish the sentence. 'I really can't,' I said, making it declarative.

Tolliver winced and looked away at the ribbon of road traveling up and around the bend. It didn't take much imagination to know he wished he were traveling that road, getting away from this place. I wished I were, too. I was sick with horror. I had seen so much death I'd thought I was impervious to anything new, but I'd discovered today that was far from the truth.

'You can leave,' Sandra Rockwell said, and I jumped in my seat. She'd come over to the car and pulled open the door. 'Go back to Twyla's, and wait for me there. I'm going to call in SBI, right now.' The State Bureau of Investigation. They would be invaluable to a little force like this, but that's not to say they'd be real welcome. Sandra looked angry, she looked sick, and she looked scared.

Twyla started up the car, and we drove up the mountain a little ways until we got to a turnaround. She made a careful turn, and drove down, past the ruined house and its ghastly yard, down to Doraville. She parked in her garage, and got out of the car slowly, as though she'd added years to her bones while we were gone. Unlocking the house, she led the way ponderously into the kitchen, where we all three stood in awkward silence.

'I think she meant us to stay here, too,' I said. 'I'm sorry. I wish we could go back to the motel and get out of your way. You need some time off.'

'I'll just go upstairs for a little,' Twyla said. 'You all help yourself to the drinks in the refrigerator, and call me if you need anything. If you get hungry, there's ham on the second shelf, and the bread is in the breadbox there.' She pointed, and we nodded, and she went up the stairs slowly, her eyes on the steps in front of her and her face still with grief and unshed tears. After a minute, we heard her voice and realized she was making phone calls.

We sat at the table, not knowing what else to do. Even if we'd been in the mood, we wouldn't have turned on the television or the radio. We read the newspaper, and Tolliver got us each a Coke out of the refrigerator. Tolliver worked the crossword puzzle, and I found a *Reader's Digest* to read.

The kitchen door opened, and a man and woman came in, in a hurry. They stopped at the sight of us, but it was more so they could take a good look than because they were startled. He was very tall and had dark brown hair, and she was very curvy and blond by request.

'Where's my mother?' the man asked, and I said, 'Upstairs.'

Without wasting any more words, up the stairs the couple went. They were both wearing the Doraville winter uniform: heavy coats and jeans, flannel shirts and boots.

'Her son and his wife,' Tolliver said. It seemed like a safe guess. 'Parker and Bethalynn.' He was much better at remembering names than I was.

The phone rang, and was answered upstairs.

To say this was an uncomfortable situation would be putting it mildly.

'We should leave,' Tolliver said. 'I don't care what the cop said. We don't need to be here.'

'At least we could go sit out in our car. That would be better.'

'We can do that.'

We washed the coffee mugs we'd used earlier and put them in the dish drainer. We pulled on our outer gear. As quietly as though we were burglars, we stepped out of the kitchen door into the carport, and got in our car. A big pickup was parked behind Twyla's Cadillac, and I was relieved we weren't blocked in. Tolliver turned on the engine, and the temperature was barely tolerable after five minutes. It wasn't getting any warmer as the day wore on, and the sky was looking grayer and grayer.

After ten minutes, without us exchanging a word, Tolliver backed out of the driveway and we went back to the motel.

Our room was blessedly warm. I fixed us some hot chocolate, and we sat with our hands around the hot mugs, drinking the watery stuff. I got the book I was reading, and stretched out on my bed to try to get lost in it, but it was impossible to get away from the dead boys.

'Eight of them,' Tolliver said. He was sitting in one of the chairs, his feet propped on his bed.

'Yeah,' I said. 'It was really, really awful.'

'Do you want to tell me about it?'

'It's almost too bad to talk about, Tolliver. They were tortured with knives and beatings and all sorts of stuff. They were raped. They were killed slowly. It took a while. I got the impression that there was more than one person there.'

Tolliver looked sick.

'I'm sorry for Twyla, then,' he said. 'This will be worse than just finding him as a skeleton with a broken leg at the bottom of a steep slope.'

'It's going to get even worse before it gets better.' We'd found plenty of accidental deaths – particularly in the mountains. Most people didn't understand that the terrain could kill you, or perhaps they became complacent in a familiar environment. Hunters, especially, grew so used to carrying guns outdoors that they grew lax about the basic safety rules. They carried their rifles carelessly. They let their cell phone batteries die out. They didn't tell anyone where they were going to hunt. They didn't carry any first aid equipment. They didn't have a hunting buddy. They forgot to wear orange.

But these deaths were far from accidental.

'Yes, it'll be a lot worse,' I said again. 'And there'll be someone to blame. Someone around here did this.'

Tolliver stared at me for a minute. 'Right,' he said finally. 'No one but someone local would bury the bodies there. All together.'

'Yeah, no one from out of town would make a trip back to that site to bury a body eight times.' That seemed like a reasonable assumption to me.

'Were they killed there? Do you know?'

'I didn't read all of them,' I said. 'The first one, the first grave – yeah, he died in the old house, or in the shed. Without looking inside, I can't be sure which.'

'He took them in there, did everything?'

I puzzled through the rush of impressions I'd gotten. 'Yeah, I think so,' I said doubtfully. There was something about the feeling of the deaths, something a little off.

'Definitely someone local,' my brother said.

'In a small community like this, how is that possible?' I asked.

'You mean, how could a man conceal from other people the fact that he wanted to torture and kill boys?'

I nodded. 'And how come the people around here haven't been up in arms about the fact that so many boys are missing?'

'I guess, if no bodies are found, it's a little easier to explain away,' Tolliver said.

And then we sat, thinking dark but separate thoughts, pretending from time to time to read, until the early darkness fell. Then Sheriff Rockwell knocked on our door. Tolliver ushered her in. Her dark green uniform pants were covered with stains, and her heavy jacket was smudged, too. 'Me and the SBI guys, we've been digging,' she said. 'You were right. All our boys are there, and even a couple extra.'

5

She sat in one of the two chairs. Tolliver and I sat on the side of his bed facing her. She was already holding a cup of steaming coffee from McDonald's, so I didn't offer her hot chocolate. She didn't bring up our departure from Twyla's. She looked exhausted but wired up.

She said, 'We're going to get a lot of attention in the next few days. The TV stations are already calling the office. They'll be sending crews. The State Bureau of Investigation has taken charge, but they're letting me stay in it. They want me to liaise with you two, since I brought you in. The supervising agent, Pell Klavin, and Special Agent Max Stuart will want to talk to you.

'You know what I wish?' she said, when we didn't speak. 'I wish I could write you your check, and you could just leave town. This thing is going to focus attention on Doraville . . . Well, I guess you-all know what it's like. Not only are we going to look like we were so uncaring we let some maniac kill eight boys before we noticed, but we're going to look credulous in the extreme.'

If the shoe fits, I thought.

'We'd leave now if we could,' Tolliver said, and I nodded. 'We don't want to be around for the circus.' Some media attention was good for my business; a lot of media attention was not.

Sheriff Rockwell sat back in the motel chair, a sudden motion that made us look at her. She was giving us a strange look.

'What?' Tolliver asked.

'I'd never have believed you two'd pass at the chance for free publicity,' she said. 'I think the better of you for it. Are you really ready to go? Maybe I can ask the SBI boys to drive to the next town to talk to you, if you want to switch motels tonight.'

'We'll leave Doraville tonight,' I said. I felt like a huge weight had been shifted off my shoulders. I'd been sure the sheriff would insist we stay. I hate police cases. I like the cemetery bookings. Get to the town, drive out to the cemetery, meet the survivors, stand on the grave, tell the survivors what you saw. Cash the check and leave the town.

Sheriff Rockwell was at least allowing us to get out of the immediate vicinity.

'Let's wait until morning,' Tolliver said. 'You're still pretty shaky.'

'I can rest in the car,' I said. I felt like a rabbit one jump ahead of the greyhounds.

'Okay,' Tolliver said. He looked at me doubtfully. But he was picking up on my almost frantic anxiety to leave Doraville.

'Good,' said the sheriff. She still sounded faintly surprised at our agreement. 'I'm sure Twyla will want to give you a check and talk to you again.'

'We'll talk to her before we leave the area for good. How's the work at the scene going?' he asked as the sheriff pulled herself wearily from the chair and walked to the door.

She had mentally shoved us aside, so she turned back with reluctance. 'We've dug just enough at all the spots to confirm that there are remains there,' she said. 'Tomorrow morning, when the light is good, the forensic guys will be here to supervise the digging. I'm guessing my deputies will do most of the preliminary heavy work. Klavin and Stuart are supposed to keep me in the loop.' She seemed pretty dubious about that.

'That's a good thing, right?' I said, almost babbling in my rush of relief. 'Having the forensic guys in? They'll know how to dig the bodies up without losing any evidence that's there to be found.'

'Yeah, we don't like admitting we need help, but we do.' Sandra Rockwell looked down at her hands for a minute, as if making sure they were her own. 'I've personally gotten phone calls from CNN and two other networks. So you should leave really early in the morning, or take off right now. And call me when you check into another motel. Don't leave the state or anything. Don't forget that you'll have to talk to the SBI guys.'

'We'll do that,' Tolliver said.

She left without further advice, and I grabbed my suitcase. It would take me less than ten minutes to be out of there.

Tolliver got up, too, and began sticking his razor and shaving cream into his valet kit. 'Why are you so anxious to go?' he asked. 'I think you need to sleep.'

'It was so bad, what I saw,' I said. I paused in my packing, a folded sweater in my hands. 'The last thing in the world I want to do is get sucked into this investigation. I'll get the atlas. We better decide which way we want to go.'

Though I was still a little unsteady on my feet, I grabbed our keys off the top of the TV. While Tolliver checked the stock in our ice chest, I stepped out into the dark to open the car. I shut the door behind me. The night was cold and silent. There were lots of lights on in Doraville, including the one right above my head, but that still didn't amount to much. I pulled on my heavy jacket while I looked up at the sky. Though the night was cloudy, I could see the distant glitter of a scattering of stars. I like to look at them, especially when my job gets me down. They're vast and cold and far away; my problems are insignificant compared to their brilliance.

Sometime soon, it would snow. I could almost smell it coming in the air.

I shook off the spell of the night sky, and thought about my more immediate concerns. I clicked the car's keyless entry pad and stepped off the little sidewalk that ran outside our door. Something moved in my peripheral vision and I began to turn my head.

A crushing blow struck my arm just below my elbow. The pain was immediate and intense. I shouted, wordless with alarm, and pressed the panic button on the keypad. The horn began to blare, though in the next instant the keys fell from my numb fingers. I tried to turn to face the danger, trying to throw my hands up to protect myself. The left arm would not obey. I could only make out a man clad in black with a knit hood over his head, and a second blow was already arcing toward the side of my head. Though I launched myself sideways to avoid the full force of the impact, I thought my head would fly off my shoulders when the shovel grazed my skull. I started down to the sidewalk. The last thing I remember is trying to throw my hands out to break my fall, but only one of them answered my command.

'She'll be okay, right?' I heard Tolliver's voice, but it was louder and sharper than usual. 'Harper, Harper, talk to me!'

'She's going to come around in a minute,' said a calm voice. Older man.

'It's cold out here,' Tolliver shouted. 'Get her into the ambulance.'

Oh, shit, we couldn't afford that. Or at least, we shouldn't spend our money this way. 'No,' I said, but it didn't come out coherently.

'*Yes*,' he said. He'd understood me; God bless Tolliver. What if I were by myself in this world? What if he decided . . . Oh, Jesus, my head hurt. Was that blood on my hand?

'Who hit me?' I asked, and Tolliver said, 'Someone hit you? I thought you fainted! Someone hit her! Call the police.'

'Okay, buddy, they'll meet us at the hospital,' said the calm voice again.

My arm hurt worse than anything I'd ever felt. But then, just about every part of my body hurt. I wanted someone to knock me out. This was awful.

'Ready?' asked a new voice.

'One, two, three,' said the calm one, and I was on a gurney and choking on a shriek at the pain of being moved.

'That shouldn't have hurt so much,' New Voice said. New Voice was a woman. 'Does she have another injury? Besides the head?'

'Arm,' I tried to say.

'Maybe you shouldn't move her,' my brother said.

'We've already moved her,' Calm Voice pointed out.

'Is she all right?' asked still another voice. That was a really stupid question, in my opinion.

Then they rolled me to the ambulance; I opened my eyes again, just a crack, to see the flashing red lights. I had another pang of dismay about the money this was going to cost; but then when they slid me in, I had no pangs about anything for a while.

I fluttered up to awareness in the hospital. I saw a man leaning over me, a man with clipped gray hair and gleaming wire-rimmed glasses. His face looked serious but benevolent. Exactly the way a doctor ought to look. I hoped he was a doctor.

'Do you understand me?' he said. 'Can you count my fingers?'

That was two questions. I tried to nod to show I could understand him. That was a big mistake. What fingers?

The next thing I knew, I was in a dim warm room, and I had the impression I was wrapped in swaddling clothes. No room at the inn? I opened my eyes. I appeared to be in a bed, and very snugly wrapped in white cotton blankets. There was a light on over my bed, but it was on low, and there was a hush that told me the night was in its small hours, its weak hours . . . probably about three A.M. There was an orange recliner by the bed, and it was as stretched out as it could get. Tolliver was asleep on it, wrapped in another hospital blanket. There was blood on his shirt. Mine?

I was very thirsty.

A nurse padded in, took my pulse, checked my temperature. She smiled when she saw I was awake and looking at her, but she didn't speak until her tasks were complete.

'Can I get you anything?' she asked in a low voice.

'Water,' I said, hopefully.

She held a straw to my lips and I took a tug or two on the cup of water. I hadn't realized how dry my mouth was until it filled with the refreshing coldness. I was on an IV. I needed to pee.

'I need to go to the bathroom,' I whispered.

'Okay. You can get up, if I help you. We'll take it real slow,' she said.

She let down the side of the bed, and I began to swing upright. That was a real bad idea, and I held still as my head swam. She put an arm around me. Very slowly, I finished straightening. While her arm continued to support me, she spared a hand to lower the bed. I slid off slowly and carefully until my bare feet touched the chilly linoleum, and we shuffled over to the bathroom, rolling the IV along. Getting down on the toilet was tricky, but the relief that followed made the trip worthwhile.

The nurse was right outside the partially open door, and I heard her talking to Tolliver. I was sorry he'd been wakened, but when I was on my journey back to the bed, I couldn't help but feel glad I was looking into his face.

I thanked the nurse, who was the reddish brown of an old penny. 'You push the button if you need me,' she said.

After she left, Tolliver got up to stand by my bedside. He hugged me with as much care as though I were stamped 'Fragile.' He kissed my cheek.

'I thought you'd fallen,' he said. 'I had no idea anyone had hit you. I didn't hear a thing. I thought you'd had – like maybe a flashback, from the crime scene. Or your leg had given way, or something else from the lightning.'

Being struck by lightning is definitely an event that keeps on giving. The year before, out of the blue, I'd had an episode of tinnitus that had finally cleared up; and the only thing I'd ever been able to attribute it to was the lightning strike when I was fifteen. So it wasn't surprising that Tolliver had blamed my old catastrophe when he'd found me on the ground.

'Did you see him?' he asked, and there was guilt in his voice, which was absurd.

'Yes,' I said, and I wasn't happy with the weakness of my voice. 'But not clearly. He was wearing dark clothes and one of those knitted hoods. He came up out of the darkness. He hit me on the shoulder first. And before I could get out of the way, he hit me in the head.' I knew it was lucky I'd been dodging. The blow hadn't landed squarely.

'You have a hairline fracture in your ulna,' Tolliver said. 'You know, one of the bones in your lower arm. And you have a concussion. Not a severe concussion. They had to take some stitches in your scalp, so they had to shave a little of your hair. I swear it doesn't show much,' he said when he saw the look on my face.

I tried not to get upset about a couple of square inches of hair that would grow back. 'I haven't had a broken bone in ten years,' I said. 'And then it was just a toe.' I'd been trying to cook supper for the kids, and my mom had lurched into me when I was taking a nine-by-thirteen glass dish from the oven, which incidentally had been full of baked chicken. My toe had not only been broken, but burned. I was awake enough to realize that the pain I'd experienced then was nothing compared to the pain I'd be feeling now if I weren't heavily drugged.

I wasn't looking forward to those drugs wearing off.

Tolliver was holding my right hand; luckily for me, the broken arm was my left. He was staring off into space. Thinking. Something I was way too foggy to attempt.

'So, it must have been the killer,' he said.

I shuddered. As slow as my brain processes were at the moment, the thought that that person – the one who'd done those unthinkable things to the boys in the ground – had been so close to me, had touched me, had looked at me through the eyes that had enjoyed the sight of so much suffering, was absolutely revolting.

'Can we leave tomorrow?' I asked. I couldn't even draw enough breath for the words to come out in a strong voice.

'No,' he said. 'You're not doing any traveling for a couple of days. You have to get better.'

'But I don't want to stay here,' I said. 'Leaving was a good idea.'

'Yeah, but now we're pinned here for a little while,' he said, trying to sound gentle, but the undertone of anger was clear and strong. 'He

took care of that. The doctor said you were lucky to have a concussion; at first he thought it would be a lot worse.'

'I wonder why he didn't go on and kill me?'

'Because you hit the panic button and I got to the door pretty
quick,' Tolliver said. He got up and began pacing. It made my head
hurt worse. He was very angry, and very worried. 'No, I didn't see a
soul in that parking lot, before you even ask. But I wasn't looking. I
thought you'd fallen. He might have just been a yard away when I
came through that door. And I was moving pretty fast.'

I almost smiled, would have managed the real thing if my head
hadn't been hurting so badly. 'I'll bet,' I whispered.

'You need to sleep,' he said, and I thought it might be a good idea if
I closed my eyes for a minute, sure enough.

The next thing I knew, the sun was coming through the curtains,
and there was a sense of activity all around me; the hospital was
awake. There were voices and footsteps in the hall, and carts rumbling. Nurses came in and did things to me. My breakfast tray came,
laden with coffee and green Jell-O. I discovered I was hungry when I
put a spoonful of the Jell-O in my mouth, surprising even myself.
When I found I'd swallowed the jiggly green stuff with actual pleasure, I realized I couldn't remember the last time I'd eaten. Jell-O was
better than nothing.

'You should eat some breakfast yourself, and go to the hotel and get
a shower,' I said. Tolliver was watching me eat with horrified fascination.

'I'm staying till I talk to the doctor,' he said. 'He'll be by soon, the
nurse says.'

The gray-haired man I remembered from the night before turned
out to be Dr Thomason. He was still up. 'Busy night last night, for
Doraville,' he said. 'I'm on call for the ER three nights a week. I've
never worked as hard.'

'Thanks for taking care of me,' I said politely, though of course it
was his job.

'You're welcome. In case you don't remember, I told you and your
brother last night that you have a hairline fracture of the ulna. It's
cracked, not completely broken through. The soft cast will protect it.
You need to keep it on as close to 24–7 as you can manage. The cast'll
have to stay on for a few weeks. When you check out of the hospital,
you'll have directions on when to get the arm checked. It's going to

hurt for a couple of days. Combined with the head injury, you'll need some pain meds. After that, I think Tylenol will do you.'

'Can I get out of bed and walk a little?'

'If you feel up to it, and if you have someone with you at all times, you can stroll down the hall and back a time or two. Of course if you experience any dizziness, nausea, that kind of thing, it's time to get back in the bed.'

'She's already talking about checking out of the hospital,' Tolliver said. He was trying for a neutral tone, but he fell far short.

The doctor said, 'You know that's not a good idea.' He looked from me to him. I may have looked a little sullen. 'You need to let your brother get some rest, too,' the doctor said. 'He's going to have to take care of you for a few days, young lady. Give him a break. You really need to be here. We need to observe that head of yours. And you've got at least a bit of insurance, I think?'

Of course there was no way I could insist on being released after he'd said that. Only a bad person would refuse to give her brother a break. And I hoped I wasn't such a bad person. Dr Thomason was counting on that. Tolliver was counting on that.

I debated making myself so unpleasant the hospital would be glad to be rid of me. But that would only make Tolliver unhappy. I looked at him, really looked at him, and I saw the circles under his eyes, the slump in his shoulders. He looked older than twenty-eight. 'Tolliver,' I said, regret and self-reproach in my voice. He stepped over and took my good hand. I put his knuckles against my cheek, and the sun came in the window and made a pool of warmth against my face. I loved him more than anything, and he should never know that.

With a sudden briskness, Dr Thomason said, 'Then I'll see you tomorrow morning, at least. You can have a regular diet the rest of the day, I'll tell them at the desk. You take it easy today, and get well.' He was out of the room before I could say anything else, and I let go of Tolliver's hand, guiltily aware I'd held on to him far too long. And I didn't mean holding his hand against my cheek, which was comforting for us both.

He leaned over to kiss my cheek. 'I'm gonna go shower and have breakfast and a nap,' he said. 'Please, don't try to get out of bed by yourself while I'm gone. Promise you'll ring for a nurse.'

'I promise,' I said, wondering why everyone seemed to think I would break the rules as soon as their back was turned. The only odd thing about me was that I'd been struck by lightning. I didn't think of myself as a rebel, a hell-raiser, a rabble-rouser, or anything else exciting or upsetting.

After he left, I found myself at a loss. I didn't have a book; Tolliver had promised to bring me one when he returned. I had doubts about whether my head could tolerate reading anyway. Maybe I'd ask him to bring an audiobook and my little CD player with its headphones.

After ten minutes' boredom, I carefully scrutinized the controls on the side of my hospital bed. I succeeded in turning on the television. The channel that came on was a hospital channel, and I watched people come in and out of the lobby. Even though my boredom threshold was quite high, that palled after ten minutes. I switched to a news channel. As soon as I did, I was sorry.

The quiet, derelict home in its picturesque setting looked a great deal different now from how it looked a day before. I remembered how lonely the site had felt, how isolated. And after all, there'd been enough privacy there to bury eight young men with no one the wiser. Now you couldn't sneeze up there without four people rushing at you with microphones.

I was assuming the film I was seeing was very recent, maybe even live, because the sun looked about in the same position as the sun I could see outside my window. By the way, it was nice to see the sun; I only wished I could be out in it, though from the bundled look of the people I could see on the screen it was still pretty damn cold.

I ignored the commentary and stared instead at the figures behind the newscaster. Some of them were wearing law enforcement uniforms but others were wearing coveralls. Those must be the tech guys from SBI. The two men in suits, they would be Klavin and Stuart. I was proud of myself for remembering their names.

I wondered how long it would be before someone came to see me. I hoped no one from the media would try to call me in the hospital or come in to see me. Maybe I could be released tomorrow and we could follow our plan of getting out of town to keep a little distance between us and the crimes.

I'd been rambling on in my head about this for a few minutes when inevitability knocked at the door.

Two men in suits and ties; exactly what I didn't want to see.

'I'm Pell Klavin, this is Max Stuart,' the shorter man said. He was about forty-five, and he was trim and well dressed. His hair was beginning to show a little gray, and his shoes were gleaming. He wore wire-rimmed glasses. 'We're from the State Bureau of Investigation.' Agent Stuart was a little younger and his hair was a lot lighter, so if he had gray he wasn't showing it. He was just as shipshape as Agent Klavin.

I nodded, and I was immediately sorry. I gingerly touched my bandaged head. Though that head felt like it was going to fall off (and that would be an improvement over how it felt now), the bandage still felt dry and secure. My left arm ached.

'Ms Connelly, we hear you got attacked last night,' Agent Stuart said.

'Yes,' I said. I was angry with myself for sending Tolliver away, and irrationally angry with him for taking me at my word and going.

'We're mighty sorry about that,' Klavin said, exuding so much down-home charm I thought I might throw up. 'Can you tell us why you were attacked?'

'No,' I said. 'I can't. Probably something to do with the graves, though.'

'I'm glad you brought that up,' Stuart said. 'Can you describe how you found those graves? What prior knowledge you had?'

'No prior knowledge,' I said. It seemed they weren't interested in the attack on me anymore, and frankly, I could understand why. I'd lived. Eight other people hadn't.

'And how did you know they were there?' Klavin asked. His eyebrows shot up in a questioning arch. 'Did you know one of the victims?'

'No,' I said. 'I've never been here before.'

I lay back wearily, able to predict the whole conversation. It was so unnecessary. They weren't going to believe, they would try to discover some reason I'd be lying about how I found the bodies, they'd waste time and taxpayer money trying to establish a connection between me and one of the victims, or me and the killer. That connection didn't exist, and no amount of searching would uncover one.

I clutched the covers with my hands, as if they were patience.

'I don't know any of the boys buried in the graves,' I said. 'I don't know who killed them, either. I expect there's a file on me somewhere that you can read, that'll give you the background on me. Can we just assume this conversation is already over?'

'Ah, no, I don't think we can assume that,' Klavin said.

I groaned. 'Oh, come on, guys, give me some rest,' I said. 'I feel terrible, I need to sleep, and I have nothing to do with your investigation. I just find 'em. From now on, it's your job.'

'You're telling us,' Stuart said, sounding as skeptical as a man can sound, 'that you just find corpses at random.'

'Of course it's not at random,' I said. 'That would be nuts.' Then I hated myself for responding. They just wanted to keep me talking, in the hope that I'd finally reveal how I'd found the bodies. They would never accept that I was telling them the truth.

'That would be nuts?' Stuart said. 'You think *that* sounds nuts?'

'And you gentlemen are . . . who?' asked a young man from the doorway.

I could scarcely believe my eyes. 'Manfred?' I said, completely confused. The fluorescent light glinted off Manfred Bernardo's pierced eyebrow (the right), nostril (the left), and ears (both). Manfred had shaved his goatee, I noticed distantly, but his hair was still short, spiky, and platinum.

'Yes, darling, I came as soon as I could,' he said, and if my head hadn't felt so fragile, I would have gaped at him.

He moved to my bedside with the lithe grace of a gymnast and took my free hand, the one without the IV line. He raised it to his lips and kissed it, and I felt the stud in his tongue graze my fingers. Then he held my hand in both his own. 'How are you feeling?' he asked, as if there were no one else in the room. He was looking right into my eyes, and I got the message.

'Not too well,' I said weakly. Unfortunately, I was almost as weak as I sounded. 'I guess Tolliver told you about the concussion? And the broken arm?'

'And these gentlemen are here to talk to you when you're so ill?'

'They don't believe anything I say,' I told him pitifully.

Manfred turned to them and raised his pierced eyebrow.

Stuart and Klavin were regarding my new visitor with a dash of astonishment and a large dollop of distaste. Klavin pushed his glasses up on his nose as if that would make Manfred look better, and Stuart's lips pursed like he'd just bitten a lemon.

'And you would be . . . ?' Stuart said.

'I would be Manfred Bernardo, Harper's dear friend,' he said, and I held my expression with an effort. Resisting the impulse to yank my hand from Manfred's, I squeezed his bottom hand as hard as I could.

'Where are you from, Mr Bernardo?' Klavin asked.

'I'm from Tennessee,' he said. 'I came as soon as I could.' Manfred bent to drop a kiss on my cheek. When he straightened, he said, 'I'm sure Harper is feeling too poorly to be questioned by you gentlemen.' He looked from one of them to the other with an absolutely straight face.

'She seems all right to me,' Stuart said. But he and Klavin glanced at each other.

'I think not,' Manfred said. He was over twenty years younger than Klavin, and smaller than Stuart – Manfred was maybe five foot nine, and slender – but somewhere under all that tattooed and pierced skin was an air of authority and a rigid backbone.

I closed my eyes. I really was exhausted, and I was also not too awfully far from laughing out loud.

'We'll leave you two to catch up,' Klavin said, not sounding happy at all. 'But we're coming back to talk to Ms Connelly again.'

'We'll see you then,' Manfred said courteously.

Feet shuffling . . . the door opening to admit hospital hall noises . . . then the muffling of those noises as the SBI agents carefully pulled the door shut behind them.

I opened my eyes. Manfred was regarding me from maybe five inches away. He was thinking about kissing me. His eyes were bright and blue and hot.

'Nuh-uh, buddy, not so fast,' I said. He withdrew to a safer distance. 'How'd you come to be here? Is your grandmother okay?'

Xylda Bernardo was an old fraud of a psychic who nonetheless had a streak of actual talent. The last time I'd seen her had been in Memphis; she'd been frail enough then, mentally and physically, to necessitate Manfred driving her to Memphis and keeping tabs on her while she talked to us.

'She's at the motel,' Manfred said. 'She insisted on coming with me. We drove in last night. I think we got the last motel room left in Doraville, and maybe the last one in a fifteen-mile radius. One reporter checked out because he got a more comfortable room at a bed and breakfast, and Grandmother had told me to drive to that motel fast and go into the office in a hurry. Every now and then, she comes through in a helpful way.' His face grew somber. 'She doesn't have long.'

'I'm sorry,' I said. I wanted to ask what was wrong, but that was a stupid question. Did it really make a difference? I knew death quite well, and I'd seen it stamped on Xylda's face.

'She doesn't want to be in a hospital,' Manfred said. 'She doesn't want to spend the money, and she hates the ambience.'

I nodded. I could understand that. I wasn't happy about being in one, myself, and I had every prospect of walking out of this one in one piece.

'She's napping now,' Manfred said. 'So I thought I'd drive over to check out how you were doing, and I found the Dynamic Duo asking you questions. I thought they'd listen to me if I said I was your boyfriend. Gives me a little more authority.'

I decided to let that issue ride for the moment. 'What are you-all doing here in the first place?'

'Grandmother said you needed us.' Manfred shrugged, but he believed in her, all right.

'Wouldn't she be more comfortable at home?' It made me feel very guilty to think about the aging and ill Xylda Bernardo dragging herself and her grandson to this little town in the mountains because she thought I needed her.

'Yes, but then she'd be thinking about dying. She said to come – we came.'

'And you knew where we were?'

'I wish I could say Grandmother had seen it in a vision, but there's a website that tracks you.'

'What?' I probably looked as dumbfounded as I felt.

'You've got a website devoted to you and your doings. People email in to report sightings of you.'

I didn't feel any smarter. 'Why?'

'You're one of those people who attracts a following,' Manfred said. 'They want to know where you are and what you've found.'

'That's just weird.' I simply didn't get it.

He shrugged. 'What we do is weird, too.'

'So it's on the Internet? That I'm in Doraville, North Carolina?' I wondered if Tolliver knew about my fan following, too. I wondered why he hadn't told me.

Manfred nodded. 'There are a couple of pictures of you taken here in Doraville, probably with a cell phone,' he said, and I was floored all over again.

'I can hardly believe that,' I said, and shook my head. Ouch.

'Do you want to talk about it?' Manfred asked. 'What happened here?'

'If I'm talking to you and not a website,' I said, and the look on his face made me instantly contrite. 'I'm sorry,' I said. 'I'm just freaked out about the idea that people are following my whereabouts and watching me, and I didn't have a clue about it. I don't think you'd ever do that.'

'Tell me how you came to get hurt,' he said, accepting my apology. Manfred settled into the chair by my bed, the one Tolliver had been snoozing in.

I told Manfred about the graves, about Twyla Cotton and the sheriff, about the dead boys in the cold soil.

'Someone here's been vanishing guys for years, and no one noticed?' Manfred said. 'This is like an Appalachian Gacy, huh?'

'I know it's hard to believe. But when the sheriff explained why there hadn't been a public outcry about the disappearances, it seemed almost reasonable. The boys were all at that runaway age.' There was a silence. I wanted to ask Manfred how old he was.

'Twenty-one,' he said, and I gave a jerk of surprise.

'I have a little talent,' he said, trying for modesty.

'Xylda can be such a fake,' I said, too tired to be tactful. 'But she's the real deal underneath.'

He laughed. 'She can be an old fraud, but when she's on her game, she's outstanding.'

'I can't figure you out,' I said.

'I talk good for a tattooed freak, don't I?'

I smiled. 'You talk good for anybody. And I'm three years older than you.'

'You've lived three years longer, but I guarantee my soul is older than yours.'

It was a distinction too fine for me just at the moment.

'I need to take a nap,' I said and shut my eyes.

I hadn't anticipated that sleep would drag me down before I'd even had a chance to thank Manfred for coming to see me.

Bodies have to have rest to heal, and my body seemed to need more than most. I don't know if that had to do with the lightning that passed through my system or not. A lot of lightning strike victims have trouble sleeping, but that has seldom been my problem. Other survivors I've talked to on the Web have a grab bag of symptoms:

convulsions, loss of hearing, speech problems, blurry vision, uncontrollable rages, weakness of the limbs, ADD. Obviously, any or all of these can lead to further consequences, none of them good. Jobs can be lost, marriages wrecked, money squandered in an attempt to find a cure or at least a palliative.

Maybe I would be in a sheltered workshop somewhere if I hadn't had two huge pieces of luck. The first was that the lightning not only took things away from me, but left me with something I hadn't had before: my strange ability to find bodies. And the second piece of luck was that I had Tolliver, who started my heart beating on the spot; Tolliver, who believed in me and helped me develop a way to make a living from this newfound and unpleasant ability.

I could only have been asleep for thirty minutes or less, but when I woke up, Manfred was gone, Tolliver was back, and the sun had vanished behind clouds. It was nearly eleven thirty, by the big clock on the wall, and I could hear the sound of the lunch cart in the hall.

'Tolliver,' I said, 'do you remember that time we went out to get a Christmas tree?'

'Yeah, that was the year we all moved in together. Your mom was pregnant.'

The trailer had been a tight fit: my older sister, Cameron, and me in one room, Tolliver and his brother, Mark, in another, Tolliver's dad and my pregnant mom in the third. Plus, there was a never-ending flow of the low-life friends of our parents coming in and out. But we kids had decided we had to have a tree, and since our parents simply didn't care, we set out to get one. In the fringe of woods around the trailer park, we'd found a little pine and cut it down. We'd gotten a discarded tree stand from the Dumpster, and Mark had mended it so it would work.

'That was fun,' I said. Mark and Tolliver and Cameron and I had come together during that little expedition, and instead of being kids who lived under the same roof, we became united together against our parents. We became our own support group. We covered for each other, and we lied to keep our family intact, especially after Mariella and Gracie were born.

'They wouldn't have lived if it wasn't for us,' I said.

Tolliver looked blank for a minute, until he caught up with my train of thought. 'No, our parents couldn't take care of them,' he said. 'But that was the best Christmas I'd had. They remembered to go out and get us some presents, I remember? Mark and I would rather have died than say it out loud but we were so glad to have you two, and your mom. She wasn't so bad then. She was trying to be healthy for the baby, when she remembered. And that church group brought by the turkey.'

'We followed the directions. It turned out okay.'

There'd been a cookbook in the house, and Cameron had figured we could read directions as well as anyone. After all, our parents had been lawyers before they fell in love with the lifestyle and vices of the people they defended. We had smart genes in our makeup. Luckily, the cookbook was a thorough one that assumed you were totally ignorant, and the turkey had really been good. The dressing was strictly Stove Top Stuffing, and the cranberry sauce came out of a can. We'd bought a frozen pumpkin pie and opened a can of green beans.

'It turned out better than okay,' he said.

And he was right. It had been wonderful.

Cameron had been so determined that day. My older sister was pretty and smart. We didn't look anything alike. From time to time, I wondered if we really were full sisters, given the way our mom's character had crumbled. You don't suddenly lose all your morals, right? It happens over time. I caught myself wondering if my mother's had started to erode a few years before she and my dad parted. But maybe I'm wrong about that. I sure hope so. When Cameron went missing, it felt like my own life had been cut in half. There was before Cameron, when things were very bad but tolerable, and after Cameron, when everything disintegrated: I went to foster care, my stepfather and my mother went to jail, and Tolliver went to live with Mark. Mariella and Gracie went to Aunt Iona and her husband.

Cameron's backpack, left by the side of the road the day she'd vanished on her way home from school, was still in our trunk. The police had returned it to us after a few years. We took it with us everywhere.

I took a sip of water from my green hospital cup. There wasn't any point in thinking about my sister. I'd resigned myself long since to the fact that she was dead and gone. Someday I'd find her.

Every now and then, I'd glimpse some short girl with long blond hair, some girl with a graceful walk and a straight little nose, and I'd almost call out to her. Of course, if Cameron were alive, she wouldn't be a girl any longer. She'd been gone now – let's see, she'd been taken in the spring of her senior year in high school, when she was eighteen – God, she'd be almost twenty-six. Eight years gone. It seemed impossible to believe.

'I called Mark,' Tolliver said.

'Good. How was he?' Tolliver didn't call Mark as often as he ought to; I didn't know if it was a guy thing, or if there'd been some disagreement.

'He said to tell you to get well soon,' Tolliver said. That didn't really answer my question.

'How's his job going?'

Mark had gotten promoted at work several times. He'd been a busboy, a waiter, a cook, and a manager at a family-style chain restaurant in Dallas. Now he'd been there at least five years. For someone who'd only managed three or four college semesters, he was doing well. He worked long hours.

'He's nearly thirty,' Tolliver said. 'He ought to be settling down.'

I pressed my lips together so I wouldn't say anything. Tolliver was only a couple of years younger, plus a few months.

'Is he dating someone special?' I asked. I was pretty sure I knew the answer.

'If he is, he hasn't said anything.' After a pause, Tolliver said, 'Speaking of dating, I ran into Manfred at the motel.'

I almost asked why that reminded him of dating, but I thought the better of it. 'Yeah, he came by,' I said. 'He told me Xylda had had a vision or something and decided she better come here, too. He told me that Xylda is dying, and I guess he's indulging her as much as he can. He's sure a good grandson.'

Tolliver looked at me skeptically. His eyebrows had risen so far that they looked like part of his hairline. 'Right. And Xylda just happens to have a vision telling her that a woman he wants – he thinks you're hot, don't pretend you don't know that – needs her help. You don't think he had something to do with that?'

Actually, I felt a little shocked. 'No,' I said. 'I think he came because Xylda said to.'

Tolliver practically sneered. I felt a strong dislike for him, just for that moment. He shot to his feet and walked around the little hospital room.

'Probably he can't wait until his grandmother dies. Then he can stop carting her around, and be your agent instead.'

'Tolliver!'

He stopped speaking. Finally.

'That's an awful thing to say,' I said. We'd seen the flawed side of human nature over and over, no doubt about it. But I liked to think we weren't wholly cynical.

'You can't see it,' he said, his voice quiet.

'You're seeing something that isn't there,' I said. 'I'm not an idiot. I know Manfred likes me. I also know he loves his grandmother, and he wouldn't have hauled her out into this cold weather with her failing, unless she told him he had to.'

Tolliver kept his head down, his eyes to himself. I felt I was trembling on the edge of saying something that would push our little barrel over the waterfall, something I'd never be able to take back. And Tolliver was suffering under some burden of his own. I could read the secrets of the dead, but I couldn't tell what my brother was thinking at that moment. I wasn't completely sure I wanted to.

'This past Christmas, just us alone, that was a pretty good Christmas,' he said.

And then the nurse came in to take my temperature and my blood pressure, and the second was gone forever. Tolliver straightened out my blanket, and I lay back on my pillows.

'Raining again,' the nurse remarked, casting a glance out at the gray sky. 'I don't think it'll ever stop.'

Neither of us had anything to say about that.

The sheriff came by that afternoon. She was wearing heavy outdoor clothes and her boots were coated with mud. Not for the first time I reflected that there were worse places to be than this hospital. One of those places was digging through nearly freezing dirt for clues, breathing in the reek of bodies that were in different stages of decay, telling the bad news to families who'd been waiting to hear about their missing boys for weeks, months, years. Yes, indeed. A concussion and a broken arm in the Doraville hospital were far preferable to that.

The sheriff may have been thinking the same thing. She started off angry. 'I'll thank you to keep your media-seeking friends away from here,' she said, biting the words out as if they were sour lemons.

'I'm sorry?'

'Your psychic friend, whatever her name is.'

'Xylda Bernardo,' Tolliver said.

'Yes, she's been down at the station making a scene.'

'What kind of scene?' I asked.

'Telling anyone who'd listen how she'd predicted you'd find these bodies, how she'd sent you up here, how she knew you were going to be hurt.'

'None of that is true,' Tolliver said.

'I didn't think it was. But she's clouding the issue. You know – you show up, of course we're all skeptical, we all think the worst. But then you came through for us somehow. You did find the boys, and we know you couldn't have had prior knowledge of their burial place. Or at least if you did we haven't figured out how.'

I sighed, tried to make it unobtrusive.

'But then she showed up with that weird grandson of hers. She acts out, he just smiles.'

There was nothing else he could do, of course.

'Plus, she looks like she's gonna drop dead any minute. At least you-all are adding to our hospital revenue,' the sheriff added more cheerfully.

There was a cursory knock at the door and it drifted open to show a big man, his fist still raised.

'Hey, Sheriff,' he said, sounding surprised.

'Barney, hey,' she said.

'Am I interrupting?'

'No, come on in, I was just leaving,' Sheriff Rockwell said. 'Back out into the cold and wet.' She stood and began pulling her gloves on. I wondered why she had come by. Complaining about Xylda just didn't seem like a meaningful reason. After all, what could we do about her? 'Have you come by to throw Ms Connelly out?'

'Ha-ha. Nope, this is my courtesy visit. I go around to every patient's room after they've been here a day, make sure things are going okay, listen to complaints – and every now and then maybe even a compliment.' He gave us a big smile. 'Barney Simpson, hospital administrator, so I'm at *your* service. You're Ms Connelly, I take it.' He shook my hand very gently, since I was the sick person. 'And you're . . . ?' He held out his hand to Tolliver.

'I'm her manager, Tolliver Lang.'

I tried not to look as surprised as I felt. I'd never heard my brother introduce himself that way.

'I really shouldn't ask if you two are enjoying your stay in our lovely little town,' Simpson said. He looked as sad as it was in his nature to look. He was a tall man, and thick-bodied, with thick brushy black hair and a big smile that seemed to be his natural expression. 'Our whole community is grieving now, but what a relief and a blessing that these young men have been found.'

There was another knock on the door, and yet another man entered. 'Oh, I'm sorry!' he said. 'I'll come back another time.'

'No, Pastor, come on in, I just dropped by to see if these folks had any questions they wanted to ask about the hospital and the service it's given them, the usual thing,' Barney Simpson said briskly.

I noticed we hadn't had a chance to do any of those usual things.

'I've got to get back out to the site,' Sheriff Rockwell said. There was no need for her to specify which site. In Doraville, there was only one.

'Well, then . . .' The new visitor was as tentative as Simpson was self-assured. He was a small man, about five foot eight, pale and thin, with clear skin and the smile of a happy baby. He shook hands with our two outgoing visitors before he gave his attention to us.

'I'm Pastor Doak Garland,' he said, and we went through the handshaking ritual again. I was getting tired just from greeting people. 'I serve Mount Ida Baptist Church, over on Route 114. I'm on chaplain duty here at the hospital this week. The local ministers take it in turn, and you folks were unlucky enough to get me.' He smiled angelically.

'I'm Tolliver Lang, and I accompany this lady, Harper Connelly. She finds bodies.'

Doak Garland cast a quick glance down at his feet, as if to conceal his reaction to this unusual introduction. What the hell was going on with Tolliver?

'Yes, sir, I heard of you-all,' the preacher said. 'I'm Twyla Cotton's pastor, and she especially asked me to come by. We're going to have a special prayer service tomorrow night, and if you should happen to be out of the hospital by then, we hope you'll attend. This is a special invitation, from our hearts. We are so glad to know what's happened to young Jeff. There comes a point when knowing, whether good or bad, is more important than not knowing.'

I agreed with this completely. I nodded.

'Since you-all were instrumental in finding poor Jeff, we were hoping you would come, if you're well enough. I won't lie and say we don't *wonder* about this special talent you have, and it seems to pass our understanding, but you've used it for the greater glory of God and to comfort our sister Twyla, and Parker, Bethalynn, and little Carson. We want to say thank you.'

On behalf of God? I tried not to smile openly because he was so sincere and seemed so vulnerable. 'I appreciate your taking the time to come by the hospital to invite me,' I said, filling in time while I thought of a way to refuse the invitation.

Tolliver said, 'If the doctor says Harper can leave the hospital tomorrow, you can count on us coming.'

Well, an alien had possessed him. That was the only conclusion I could draw.

Doak Garland seemed a bit surprised, but he said gamely, 'That's just what I wanted to hear. We'll see you at seven o'clock tomorrow night. If you need directions, just give me a call.' He whipped a card out of his pocket in a surprisingly professional way and handed it to Tolliver.

'Thank you,' said Tolliver, and I could only say 'Thanks' myself.

By the time my room cleared out, I was tired again. But I needed to walk, so I got Tolliver to help me out of bed, and hold on to me while I and my IV walked down the hall. No one who passed us paid us any attention, which was a relief. Visitors and patients had their own preoccupations and worries, and one more young woman in a terrible hospital gown wasn't going to rouse them out of their tunnel vision.

'I don't know what to say to you,' I told Tolliver when we reached the end of the hall and paused before we started the journey back to the room. 'Is something wrong? Because you're acting really strange.'

I glanced at him, the quickest sideways look so he wouldn't catch me checking, and I decided Tolliver himself looked like he didn't know what to say.

'I know we need to leave,' he said.

'Then why'd you accept the minister's invitation?'

'Because I don't think the police will let us drive away at this point, and I want us to be around other people anytime we can be. Someone's already tried to kill you once, the police are so wrapped up in the murder investigation that they don't seem to be sparing anyone to try to find out who attacked you, and the best guess I have is that the attacker was the one who killed the boys. Otherwise, why the rage, why take the chance? You ended his fun and games, and he got mad and came by to take a swipe at you if he could. He got his chance. He almost killed you. I don't know if you've considered how lucky you are that you got away with a concussion and a cracked arm.'

This was a long speech for Tolliver, and he delivered it in a low voice in bits and pieces to avoid the attention of the other people. We'd reached my room by the end of it, but I waved my hand down the corridor opposite and we trudged on. I didn't say anything. I was angry, but I didn't know who to aim it at. I believed Tolliver was absolutely right.

We looked out the window at the end of this wing. The rain had turned into a nasty mix of sleet and snow. It rattled when it hit the glass. Oh, joy. The poor searchers. Maybe they would give it up and retreat into the warmth of their vehicles.

I was going very slowly by the time we crossed in front of the nurses' station and neared my room. I still hadn't thought of anything smart to say.

'I think you're right,' I said. 'But . . .' I wanted to say: *that dodges the issue of your hostility to Manfred and his grandmother. Why does his interest in me make you so angry? Why Manfred more than anyone else who's given me a second look?* I didn't say any of these things. And he didn't ask me to finish my thought.

I was glad to see the bed, and I leaned against it heavily as Tolliver arranged the IV stand and line. He helped me sit on the side, pulled off my slippers, and eased me back onto the pillows. We got the covers pulled up and straight.

He'd brought a book for himself and one for me, too, in case my head was feeling better. For an hour or so we read in peace, the snick of the ice against the window the only noise in the room. The whole hospital seemed to be in a lull. I looked up at the wall clock. Soon people would be getting off work, coming by to visit relatives and friends, and for a while the traffic in the hall would pick up. Then the big cart with the supper trays would come around, and the nurse with the medication, and after that a spurt of early evening visitors. Then there would be another lull as everyone who didn't have to stay at the hospital left for the night, and the only ones remaining would be the staff, the patients, and a few dedicated souls who slept in the reclining chairs by their patients' beds.

Tolliver asked me if I wanted him to stay. I was obviously better, and I thought it was touching that he would think of staying in that chair a second night in a row. I was oddly tempted. Maybe I was just better enough to have the energy to spare for fear. I was afraid.

In the end, I couldn't be selfish enough to condemn him to a night in the chair because I was a scaredy-cat. 'You go on back to the motel,' I said. 'There's no reason why you shouldn't be comfortable tonight. I can always ring for the nurse.' Who might come in thirty minutes. This little hospital, like so many others, seemed to be understaffed. Even the cleaners moved briskly because they had so much to do.

'Are you sure?' he asked. 'The motel's so full of reporters that it's quieter here.'

He hadn't mentioned that before. 'Yes, I guess it is,' I said. 'I'm probably lucky I'm here.'

'No doubt about it. As it is, I have to pretend I'm not in the room. One woman knocked for twenty minutes this morning.'

He'd been going through his own problems and I hadn't even asked, I felt guilty. 'I'm sorry,' I said. 'I didn't think about the press.'

'Not your fault,' he said. 'You're getting a lot of publicity out of this, you know. That's another reason . . .' But then his face closed down on the thought. He'd been thinking about Manfred and Xylda again, sure that Xylda was in town to jump on the free ride of publicity the multiple murders would engender. No, I'm not a mind reader. I just know Tolliver very well.

'I'm not above thinking Xylda would cash in under ordinary circumstances,' I said. I was trying to be practical and honest. 'But she's so frail, and Manfred was so reluctant to bring her.'

'He said,' Tolliver pointed out.

'Well, yeah, he said. And you seem to think that Manfred's capable of dragging a sick woman somewhere she doesn't need to be just to satisfy his lust for me, but I don't think that's true.' I gave Tolliver a very level look. After a second, he looked just a bit abashed.

'Okay, I'll agree he really loves the old bat,' he said. 'And he does take her wherever she wants to go, as far as I know.'

That was as much of a concession as I was going to get, but at least it was something. I hated the idea of Tolliver and Manfred meeting up and getting into it with each other.

'Are they at our motel?'

'Yeah. There aren't any rooms anywhere else, I can tell you. The road up the mountain is nearly blocked off to traffic because there are so many news trucks and law enforcement vehicles. There's one lane open with guys with walkie-talkies at either end of the bottleneck.'

Again, I felt a twinge of guilt, as if I were somehow responsible for the disruption of so many peoples' lives. The responsibility, of course, was the murderer's, but I doubt he was staying up worrying about it.

I wondered what he *was* thinking about. He'd vented his rage with me. 'He'll lie low now,' I said. Tolliver didn't have to ask me who I was talking about.

'He'll be cautious,' Tolliver agreed. 'That turning out to try to get you, that was just rage that his games were ended. He'll have cooled off now. He'll be worried about the cops.'

'No time to spare for me.'

'I think not. But this guy has to be a loony, Harper. And you never know what they're thinking. I hope you get out of the hospital tomorrow. Maybe the cops'll be through with questions and we can leave this place. If you feel well enough.'

'I hope so,' I said. I was better, but it would be stretching a point to say I felt good enough to travel.

Tolliver gave me a hug before he left. He would pick up something to eat on his way back to the motel, he said, and stay in the rest of the evening to dodge the reporters. 'Not that there's anywhere to go,' he said. 'Why don't we get more work in cities?'

'I've asked myself that,' I said. 'We had that job in Memphis, and that other one in Nashville.' I didn't want to talk about Tabitha Morgenstern again. 'And before that, we were in St Paul. And that cemetery job in Miami.'

'But most of our calls are from small places.'

'I don't know why. Have we ever done New York?'

'Sure. Remember? But it was really really hard for you, because it was right after 9/11.'

'I guess I was trying to forget,' I said. That had been one of the worst experiences I'd ever had as a professional . . . whatever I was. 'We'll never do that again,' I said.

'Yeah, New York is out.' We looked at each other for a long moment. 'Okay then,' he said. 'I'm gone. Try to eat your supper, and get some sleep. Since you're better, maybe they won't come in so much tonight.'

He fussed around for a minute or two, making sure the rolling table was positioned correctly, clearing it for the supper tray, drawing my attention to the remote control built into the bed rail, moving the phone closer to the edge of the bedside table so I could reach it easily. He put my cell phone in the little drawer beneath the rolling table. 'Call me if you need me,' he said, and then he left.

I dozed off for a little while, until the supper tray came. Tonight I got something more substantial. I'm embarrassed to say that I ate most of the food on my tray. It wasn't awful. And I was really hungry. I hadn't exactly been packing in the calories the last two days.

After that, by way of excitement, a different doctor dropped in to tell me I was making progress and he thought I'd be able to go home in the morning. He didn't appear to care anything about who I was or where home was. He was as overworked as everyone else I'd encountered there at Knott County Memorial Hospital. He wasn't from around these parts, either, judging from his accent. I wondered what had brought him to Doraville. I figured he worked for the same emergency-room-stocking service that employed Dr Thomason.

Barney Simpson's assistant, a very young woman named Heather Sutcliff, came in soon after the doctor's visit.

'Mr Simpson just wanted me to stop by and check with you. Lots of reporters want to see you, but for the peace and privacy of the other patients we've been denying them visiting privileges. And we've screened the calls to your room . . . that was your brother's idea.'

No wonder I'd been able to recover in peace. 'Thanks,' I said. 'That's really a big help.'

'Good. Because it really wouldn't be fair to the other people in this wing, to have all kinds of strangers tromping through.' She gave me a serious look to show she took my reporter problem as a bad thing. And then she slipped out the door, closing it gently behind her.

The most interesting thing that happened after her departure was the tray guy removing my emptied tray. After that surge of excitement, I tried to watch television for a while; but the laugh tracks made my head ache. I read for maybe half an hour. I gradually grew so sleepy that I left the book where it fell on my stomach and just moved my hand enough to switch out the light I could control from my bed rail.

I was awakened by a brilliant flash and the sense of sound and movement very close to me. I cried out, and flailed my good arm to drive the attacker away. In a moment of sense, I punched the button that turned on the light and the one that called the nurse. I was stunned to see there were two men in the room. They were bundled up in coats and they were yelling at me. I couldn't understand a word they said. I punched the nurses button over and over, and I yelled louder, and in about thirty seconds there were more people in my room than it was designed to hold.

The evening nurse was a starchy woman of considerable width. She was tall, too, and she scorned makeup, but she'd met a bottle of red hair dye she was real fond of in the past week or so. I admired her more by the second. She went for those reporters with both guns. Actually, if she'd had guns, the two men would've been dead without a doubt. Hospital Security was there (a man older than my doctor and not nearly as fit), an orderly was there (satisfyingly tall and muscular), and another nurse who added her opinion to that of my big nurse, as I thought of her.

Of course this was a silly episode, and one I should have been able to throw off; and once I considered it, one I should have anticipated. Right at the moment, I couldn't recognize any of those points. I'd been scared very badly, and my heart was thumping like a rabbit's, and my head was hurting as if someone had hit me again, and my arm ached where I'd bumped it when I'd lurched sideways against the railings in my panic.

When it all got sorted out the nurses had given the reporters a first-rate tongue-lashing, the security guard and the orderly were escorting the intruders out, and the two men were trying to hide their smiles.

And I was a mess: frightened, hurting, and lonely.

6

Tolliver was livid when he came in the room the next morning. The nurses had been full of the night's excitement, and they'd been quivering to fill him in on the big event. They'd pounced on him with avidity. The result was that Tolliver was all but breathing fire when he flung open my door.

'I can't believe it,' he said. 'Those bastards! To sneak into a hospital in the night and actually into your room! Jeez, you must have . . . were you asleep? Did they really scare you?' He went from rage to concern in two seconds flat.

I was too tired to put a good face on for him. I'd come awake with a jolt at least three times during the night, sure there was someone else in the room with me.

Tolliver said, 'How'd they even get in here, anyway? The doors are supposed to be locked after nine o'clock. Then you have to punch a big button outside the emergency room door to get in. At least that's what the sign says.'

'So either a door was left open by accident or someone let them in. Might not have known who they were, of course.' I was trying to be fair. I'd really gotten good treatment at this little hospital, and I didn't want to believe any of the staff had been bribed or were malicious enough to simply let reporters in for the hell of it.

Tolliver even sounded off to the doctor about it.

Dr Thomason was back on duty. He seemed both angry and embarrassed, but he also looked as though he'd heard enough about the incident.

I gave Tolliver a look, and he was smart enough to back off.

'You're still going to let me go, right?' I said, trying to smile at the doctor.

'Yeah, I think we'll toss you out. You're recovering well from your injuries. Traveling isn't going to be easy on you, but if you're determined, you can leave. No driving, of course, not until your arm is well.' The doctor hesitated. 'I'm afraid you'll leave our town with a bad impression.'

A serial killer, an attack out of the blue, and a rude awakening . . . why would I get a negative picture of Doraville? But I had manners and sense enough to say, 'Everyone here has been very kind to me, and I couldn't have gotten better treatment in any hospital I've seen.' It was easy to see the relief pass across Dr Thomason's face. Maybe he'd been concerned that I was the kind of person who slapped a lawsuit on anyone who looked at me cross-eyed.

I'd been thinking of the good people I'd met here, and the fact that Manfred and Xylda had come here expressly to see us. That had made me wonder if we shouldn't spend the rest of the day here in town to wind up our loose ends. But after the scare the night before, I was twitching with my desire to get out of this place.

Of course, there was the usual long wait while the paperwork made its way around the hospital, but finally, about eleven o'clock, a nurse came in with the mandated wheelchair, while Tolliver bundled up and went out to pull our car around to the entrance to pick me up. There was another wheelchair waiting just inside the front door. A very young woman, maybe twenty, was perched in it, her arms full of a swaddled bundle. An older woman who had to be her mother was with her. The mother was herding a cart loaded down with pink flower arrangements, a pile of cards that were also predominantly pink, and some gift boxes. There was a pile of pamphlets, too. The top one was titled 'So You're Taking Your Baby Home.'

The new grandmother beamed at me, and she and my nurse began chatting. The young woman in the wheelchair looked over at me. 'Look what I got,' she said happily. 'Man, the last time I was in the hospital I left my appendix. Now I get to leave with a baby.'

'You're lucky,' I said. 'Congratulations. What have you named her?'

'We named her Sparkle,' she said. 'Isn't that cute? No one will ever forget her.'

That was the absolute truth. 'It's unforgettable,' I agreed.

'There's Josh,' the grandmother said and wheeled her daughter and granddaughter through the automatic door.

'Wasn't that the cutest little old girl?' my nurse asked. 'The first grandbaby in that family.' Since the grandmother had been in her late thirties, at the most, I was relieved to hear it.

I wondered if my lightning-fried body could produce a child.

Then it was my turn to be wheeled to the cut-down curb, and Tolliver leaped from the car to hurry around to help me. After I'd carefully eased into the car, he bent over to fasten my seat belt and then rounded the car again to get in the driver's seat.

The nurse leaned down to make sure I was sitting straight with all my bits in so she could close the door. 'Good luck,' she said, smiling. 'Hope we don't see you back here anytime soon.'

I smiled back. I was sure the other departing patient had felt sorry for me, but I felt much better now that I was in our familiar car and Tolliver was with me. I had prescriptions and doctor's instructions, and I was free to leave. That was a great feeling.

We turned right out of the hospital parking lot, and I didn't see any traffic out of the ordinary. No reporters. 'Back to the motel, or can we leave?' I asked.

'We're getting your prescriptions filled and then we're leaving town,' Tolliver said. 'What more could they want from us?'

We stopped at the first pharmacy we saw. It was a couple of blocks from the hospital, and it was a locally owned business. Inside it was a cheerful mixture of smells: candy, medicine, scented candles, potpourri, nickel gum machines. You could get stationery, a picture frame, a Whitman's Sampler, a heating pad, a magazine, paper party plates, or an alarm clock. And at a high counter in the very back, you could actually get your prescriptions filled. There were two plastic chairs arranged in front of that counter, and the young man behind it was moving with such a languid air that I was sure Tolliver and I would have time to find out how comfortable they were.

My only exertion had been getting out of the car and walking into the pharmacy, so it was unpleasant to find how relieved I was to see those plastic chairs. I sat in one while Tolliver surrendered the prescription slips to the young man, whose white coat looked as if it had been bleached and starched – or maybe it was the first one he'd ever worn. I tried to read the date on the framed certificate displayed on the wall behind him, but I couldn't quite manage the small print at that distance.

The young pharmacist was certainly conscientious. 'Ma'am, you understand you have to take these with food,' he said, holding up a brown plastic pill container. 'And these have to be taken twice a day. If you have any of these symptoms listed here on this sheet, you need to call a doctor.' After we'd discussed that for a moment, Tolliver asked where we paid, and the pharmacist pointed to the register at the front of the store. I had to get up to follow Tolliver, and when we got to the checkout clerk, we had to wait for another customer to get her change and have her chat. Then we had to reveal to the clerk that our insurance didn't cover a pharmacy bill and that we were paying cash for the entire amount. She seemed surprised but pleased.

We'd actually stepped outside the store to get back in the car when the sheriff found us. We got so close to being out of Doraville.

'I'm sorry,' she said. 'We need you again.'

It wasn't snowing at the moment, but it was still gray everywhere. I looked up into Tolliver's face, which seemed as pale as the snow.

'What do you need?' I asked, which was probably stupid.

'It's possible there are more,' she said.

We had to renegotiate. The consortium hadn't written me a check for the first successful episode, and I didn't work for free. And the reporters were everywhere. I don't work in front of cameras, not if I can help it.

Since the parking lot at the back of the police station was protected by a high fence topped with razor wire, we got in the back door of the police station without anyone the wiser – anyone among the media, that is. Everyone on duty that wasn't out at the burial site made an opportunity to walk past Sheriff Rockwell's office to have a peek at me. With my arm in a cast and a little bandage on my head, I was something to look at, all right. Tolliver sat at my good side so he could hold my right hand.

'You need to be in bed,' he said. 'I don't know what we're going to do about housing if we stay. I gave up our motel room, and I'm sure it's gone by now.'

I shook my head silently. I was trying to decide if I was up to any more bodies or not. There was always the fact that it was the way I made our living; but there was also the fact that I felt like hell.

'Who do you think the bodies are?' I asked the sheriff. 'I found all the locals that were missing.'

'We went over the missing persons reports for the past five years,' Rockwell said. 'We found two more, somewhat over the age range of the boys in the Davey homesite.'

'The what?'

'That house and garage and yard used to belong to Don Davey and his family. Don was a widower in his eighties. I barely remember him. He died about twelve years ago, and the house has been empty since. The relative who inherited lives in Oregon. She's never come back over here to look at the property. She hasn't made any move at all to dispose of it. She's about eighty herself and very indifferent to the idea of doing anything at all with the land.'

'Did anyone offer to buy it before?'

Rockwell looked surprised. 'No, she didn't mention anything like that.'

'So where is this other place?'

'Inside an old barn. Dirt floor. Hasn't been used in ten years or more, but the owners just left it to fall down.'

'Why do you think there might be more bodies there, specifically?'

'It's actually on the property of a mental health counselor named Tom Almand, who never comes this far back on the property. With all the to-do at the Davey place, the next-door neighbor, a deputy named Rob Tidmarsh, thought he'd check it out because it meets the same criteria as the Davey place: secluded, not in use, easy to dig. The barn floor's mostly dirt. Lo and behold, Rob found some disturbed spots on the floor.'

'Have you checked it out yourself?'

'Not yet. We thought you could point us in the right direction.'

'I don't think so. If the spots are that easy to make out, just sink a rod in and see if smell comes up. Or go for broke and dig a little. The bones won't be that deep, if the surface disturbance is so easy to see. It'll be a lot cheaper, and I can get out of Doraville.'

'They want you. Twyla Cotton said they had money left, since you found the boys in one day.' Sheriff Rockwell gave me a look I couldn't read. 'You don't want the publicity? The press is all over this, as you found last night.'

'I don't want any more to do with this.'

'That's not my call,' she said, with some apparently genuine regret.

I looked down at my lap. I was so sleepy, I was worried I'd drift off while I sat there in the sheriff's office. 'No,' I said. 'I won't do it.'

Tolliver rose right along with me, his face expressionless. The sheriff was staring at us as if she couldn't believe what she was hearing. 'You have to,' she said.

'Why?'

'Because we're telling you to. It's what you can do.'

'I've given you alternatives. I want to leave.'

'Then I'll arrest you.'

'On what grounds?'

'Obstructing an investigation. Something. It won't be hard.'

'So you're trying to blackmail me into staying? What kind of law enforcement officer are you?'

'One who wants these murders solved.'

'Then arrest me,' I said recklessly. 'I won't do it.'

'You're not strong enough to go into jail,' Tolliver said, his voice quiet. I leaned against him, fighting a feeling of terrible weariness. His arms went around me, and I rested my head against his chest. I had a few seconds' peace before I made my brain begin working again.

He was right. With a cracked arm and a head that hadn't healed, I wouldn't have a good time even in a small-town jail like the one in Doraville. And if the town shared a jail with other nearby towns, as was probably the case, I might fare even worse. So I'd have to do what 'they' wanted me to, and I might as well bite the bullet and get it done. But who were 'they'? Did Sheriff Rockwell mean the state police?

I had to pull myself away from Tolliver. I was accepting his support under false pretenses, and sooner or later I'd have to admit it.

'You need to eat,' he said, and I thudded back down to reality.

'Yes,' I said. I did need something to eat, and it would help if we had a place to stay afterwards. I'd need to rest, whether or not the result was a fresh crop of bodies.

'All right then,' I said. 'I'm going to go eat something, and then we'll meet you.'

'Don't think you can get out of town without us seeing you,' she said.

'I really don't like you,' I said.

She looked down. I don't know what expression she wanted to hide. Maybe at the moment she wasn't too fond of herself.

We stole out of the back of the station and finally found a fast-food chain place that looked pretty anonymous. It was too cold to eat in the car. We had to go in. Fortunately, no one in there seemed to read the papers, or else they were simply too polite to accost me. Which meant there weren't any reporters. Either way, I got to eat the food in peace. At least with food this simple, there was nothing Tolliver had to cut up for me. All the aid he had to supply was ripping open the ketchup

444 HARPER CONNELLY OMNIBUS

packets and putting the straw in the drink. I ate slowly because after we finished I'd have to go to the damn barn, and I didn't want to.

'I think this sucks,' I said after I'd eaten half the hamburger. 'Not the food, but the situation.'

'I do, too,' he said. 'But I don't see how we can get out of it without more fuss than doing it will be.'

I started to snap at him, to remind him that it was me that would be doing the unpleasant task; that he would be standing by, as always. Fortunately, I shut my mouth before those awful words came out. I was horrified at how I could have ripped up our relationship based on a moment's peevishness. How many times a week did I thank God that I had Tolliver with me? How many times did I feel grateful that he was there to act as a buffer between me and the world?

'Harper?'

'What?'

'You're looking at me weird. What's the matter?'

'I was just thinking.'

'You must have been thinking some bad thoughts.'

'Yeah.'

'Are you mad at me for some reason? You think I should have argued more with the sheriff?'

'I don't think that would've done any good.'

'Me, either. So why the mad face?'

'I was mad at myself.'

'That's not good. You haven't done anything wrong.'

I tried not to heave a sigh. 'I do wrong things all the time,' I said, and if my voice was morose, well, I just couldn't help it. I knew I wanted more from Tolliver than he could or should give me, and I had to hide that knowledge from everyone, especially from him.

I was definitely on a 'my life sucks' kick, and the sooner I got off of it, the better life would be.

We called Sheriff Rockwell on our way back to the station so she could meet us outside. We parked our car and climbed into hers. 'He doesn't need to come,' she said, nodding her head at Tolliver.

'He comes,' I said. 'That's not a negotiation point. I'd rather talk to the reporters for an hour than go somewhere without him.'

She gave me a very sharp look. Then she shrugged. 'All right,' she said. 'He comes along.'

As she turned out of the parking lot, she turned yet again so she wouldn't drive past the front of the station. I'd wondered if she might be a glory hound, yet she was avoiding the media. I couldn't figure her out at all.

Even though I'd had some food and some time out, by the time we reached our destination at the very edge of town I was realizing my body was far from healed. There were some pain pills in the pharmacy bag back in our car. I wished I'd brought them with us, but I had to admit to myself that I wouldn't have taken one before I worked. I didn't know what would happen if I fiddled with the procedure. For a moment, I entertained myself with a few possibilities, but the fun of that palled pretty quickly. By the time Sheriff Rockwell pulled to a stop, I was leaning my head against the cold glass of the window.

'Are you feeling well enough to do this?' she asked reluctantly.

'Let's get it over with.'

Tolliver helped me out of the car and we walked toward the cluster of men standing at the entrance to a barn that had formerly been red. It wasn't in as bad shape as the garage of the house in the foothills, but there were gaps between the boards, the paint was only clinging to the boards in streaks, and the tin roof seemed to be all that was holding the structure together. I looked around: there was a house a distance away at the front of the property, a house that seemed in much better condition than the barn. So, someone hadn't wanted to farm or keep livestock; they'd just wanted the house and maybe some space around them.

The little knot of men unraveled to show two people standing huddled at its center. One was a man about forty, wearing a heavy coat that he hadn't buttoned. He was a small man, no larger than Doak Garland. The coat engulfed him. I could see a dress shirt and tie underneath. He had his arm around a boy who was possibly twelve. The boy was short, thickset, with long blond hair, and he had a huskier build than his father. At the moment he looked overwhelmed with shock and a kind of anticipatory excitement.

Whatever was in the barn, the boy knew about it.

The sheriff didn't pause as we passed the two, and I let my eyes linger on the boy. *I know you*, I thought, and I knew he could see my recognition. He looked a little frightened.

My connection is with the dead, but every now and then I come in contact with someone who has his or her own preoccupation with the departed. Sometimes these people are quite harmless. Sometimes such a person will decide to work in the funeral industry, or become a morgue worker. This boy was one of those people. I'm sure a lot of times I don't pick up on it – but since the boy didn't have all the mental guards and trip wires of the average adult, I could see it in him. I just didn't know what form this preoccupation had taken.

The barn had an overhead bulb that left more in darkness than it illuminated. It was a fairly large structure, quite open except for three stalls in the back full of moldy hay. They looked like they hadn't been touched in years. There were old tools hanging on the walls, and there was the detritus of a household: an old wheelbarrow, a lawn mower, a few bags of lawn fertilizer, old paint cans stacked in a corner.

The air was very cold, very thick, very unpleasant. Tolliver seemed to be trying to hold his breath. That wasn't going to work.

This was more a job for Xylda Bernardo than me, I could tell already.

I told the sheriff so.

'What, that crazy old woman with the dyed red hair?'

'She looks crazy,' I agreed. 'But she's a true psychic. And what we've got here isn't dead people.'

'Not corpses?' It was hard to say if Rockwell was disappointed or relieved.

'Oh, I think we've got corpses. They're just not human. There's death, but I can't find it. If you don't mind, I'll call her. If she can tell you what's here, you can give her my fee.'

Rockwell stared at me. The cold had bleached the color out of her face. Even her eyes looked paler. 'Done,' she said. 'And if she makes a fool out of you, it's your own fault.'

Xylda and Manfred got there pretty quickly, all things considered. Xylda came into the barn wearing her ratty plaid coat, her long dyed bright red hair wild and tangled around her head. She was a big woman in all ways, and her round face was lavishly decorated with powder and lipstick. She was wearing heavy support hose and loafers. Manfred was a loving grandson; most young men his age would run screaming before they'd appear in public with someone as crazy-looking as Xylda.

Xylda, who was carrying a cane, didn't greet us, or even acknowledge we were there. I couldn't remember if she'd needed one a couple of months ago or not. It gave her a rakish air. I noticed that Manfred

kept his hands lightly on her waist, as if she might topple over all of a
sudden.

She pointed with the cane to one of the slightly mounded areas in
the dirt floor. Then she stood absolutely still. The men who'd come in
with her – everyone who'd been outside, with the addition of the boy
and the man I was sure was his father – had been eyeing her with
derision, and a few of them had made comments not quite softly
enough. But now they were silent, and when Xylda closed her eyes
and appeared to be listening to something no one else could hear, the
level of tension rose almost palpably.

'Tortured animals,' she said crisply. She spun with as much agility
as you can expect from a rather old and hefty woman. She pointed the
cane at the boy. 'You're torturing animals, you little son of a bitch.'

You couldn't accuse Xylda of mincing words.

'They cry out against you,' she said, her voice falling to an eerie
monotone. 'Your future is written in blood.'

The boy looked as if he wanted to break and run when those old
eyes fixed on him. I didn't blame him.

'Son,' said the little man with the big coat. He looked at the boy
with a heartbreaking doubt in his face. 'Is what she says true? Could
you have done something like that?'

'Dad,' the boy said pleadingly, as if his father could stop what
would happen next. 'Don't make me go through this.'

Tolliver's arm tightened around my waist.

The man gave the boy a little shake. 'You have to tell them,' he said.

'It was already hurt,' the boy said, his voice exhausted and dead. 'I
just watched it till it died.'

'Liar,' Xylda said, her voice dripping with disgust.

After that, things really went downhill.

The deputies did their digging and found the aforementioned cat, a
dog, some rabbits – baby rabbits – and a bird or two. They kicked
around the stalls, making dust from the stale hay rise up in thick
clouds. All they discovered was the stalls had bare-board flooring, so
there couldn't be any animal corpses underneath. The father, Tom
Almand, seemed absolutely stunned. Since he was a counselor at the
mental health center, he would know as well as anyone there that one
of the early signs of a developing serial killer was the torture of
animals. I wondered how many kids who tortured animals *didn't*

grow up to be murderers, but I assumed that would be impossible to document. Was it possible to do something so vile and yet become a well-adjusted adult with healthy relationships? Maybe. I hadn't studied the phenomenon, and I sure didn't plan to do any research on it. I saw enough in my day-to-day work life to convince me that people were capable of dreadful things . . . and wonderful things, too. Somehow as I looked at the tear-wet face of Chuck Almand, age thirteen, budding sadist, I couldn't feel optimistic.

I was sure that Sheriff Rockwell would be pleased. We'd kept the locals from making a foolish mistake, we'd uncovered a genuinely disturbed source of future trouble, and I wasn't going to charge a penny on my own behalf for the distress I'd been put through. They did owe Xylda some cash, though, and I wanted to be sure they'd pay it.

The sheriff was not looking sunny, though. In fact, she looked tired, discouraged, and disheartened.

'Why so glum?' I asked her. Tolliver was making conversation with Manfred; he'd forced himself to do the polite thing. Xylda had hold of the arm of one of the officers, and she was giving him an earful of talk. He looked dazed.

'I hoped we'd wrap it up,' she said. She seemed too down to disguise her thoughts and emotions. 'I hoped this would be it. We'd find more bodies here. We'd find evidence – maybe trophies – tying someone, maybe Tom, to all the murders. It would all be over. We would have solved the case ourselves, instead of having to turn it over to the state boys or the FBI.'

Sandra Rockwell was not the clear pool she'd seemed at first.

'There aren't any human corpses here. I'm sorry we can't wave a magic wand and make that come true for you,' I said. And I was sincere. Like most other people, I wanted the bad guys caught, I wanted justice to prevail, and I wanted punishment of the wicked. But so often you didn't get all three at the same time, or in the same degree. 'Can we leave now?' I asked.

The sheriff closed her eyes, just for a second. I had a creepy-crawly feeling in my belly. She said, 'The SBI has asked that you remain on site for another day. They want to question you some more.'

The creepy-crawly feeling resolved into a knot of anxiety. 'I thought we'd get to leave after we did this.' My voice must have gone up, because a lot of people turned to look at us. Even the boy at the heart of this brouhaha turned to look. I stared right into Chuck Almand's face, and for the first time I consciously looked into another human being.

'You might as well shoot him now,' I said. It was an awful feeling. I wondered if this was how Xylda saw things, if this was what had made her so peculiar. I wondered if Manfred would go the same way. It wasn't like free choice had been taken away from the boy, that he was doomed from the beginning by his nature. It was more like I could see what choices he would make. And they were almost all on the side of becoming one of those people who end up as the subject of a documentary on A&E.

Was what I was seeing the truth? Was it inevitable? I hoped not. And I hoped I never experienced it again. Maybe I was able to see inside Chuck Almand only because I was close to two genuine psychics, and their proximity sparked a touch of it in myself. Maybe it was the rumble of thunder far away. That sound always triggered the lightning feelings in me – a jittery combination of fear and agitation. Maybe I had the completely wrong perspective.

'Tolliver,' I said, 'we have to find a place to stay. They're not going to let us leave after all.' We should have taken off from the pharmacy, taken off and never looked back.

My brother was beside me instantly. He looked at Sheriff Rockwell for a long, long moment. 'Then you have to find us a place to stay,' he said. 'We gave up our motel room.'

With unexpected lucidity, Xylda said, 'You can stay with us. It'll be cramped, but it's better than staying in the jail.'

I thought of squeezing in a bed with Xylda while Tolliver and Manfred slept two feet away. I thought of other possible sleeping arrangements. I thought the jail might be better. 'Thanks so much,' I said, 'but I'm sure the sheriff can help us find something.'

'I'm not your travel agent,' Rockwell said. She seemed to be glad to find something to be mad about. 'But I realize you had planned on leaving, and I'll try to think of something. It's your fault the town's this crowded.'

There was a long moment of silence in the barn, as everyone within hearing range stared at her.

'Not exactly your fault,' she said.

'I think not,' I said.

'Everyone in town has rented out every room they've got,' a deputy said. His uniform said he was Tidmarsh – Rob Tidmarsh, the neighbor, then. 'The only place I can think of is Twyla Cotton's lake house.'

The sheriff brightened. 'Give her a call, Rob.' She turned back to us. 'Thanks for coming here, and we'll figure out what to do with the juvenile delinquent here.'

'He won't go to jail?'

'Tom,' the sheriff said, raising her voice, 'you and Chuck come here.'

The two looked relieved that someone was finally talking to them. I didn't want Chuck anywhere close to me, and I took a couple of steps back. I knew he was only thirteen. I knew he wasn't going to hurt me there and then. And I knew that his life was still full of choices and possibilities, and he could change himself if he saw the need to.

Sheriff Rockwell said, 'Tom, we're not going to take Chuck away from you.'

Tom Almand's narrow shoulders slumped in relief. He was such a pleasant-looking man, the kind of guy who'd be glad to accept your UPS package from the carrier or to feed your cat while you were out of town. 'So what will we need to do?' His voice caught on the words as though his mouth were dry.

'There'll be a hearing with the judge. We'll work it all out. What would help is you getting Chuck into some counseling – that should be easy, huh? – even before the hearing. And you gotta keep a watch on your kid.'

Sheriff Rockwell looked down at the boy, so I did, too. For God's sake, he had freckles. There'd never been an *Andy Griffith* episode called 'Opie Skins a Cat.'

Chuck was looking at me with almost equal fascination. I don't know why most young men are so interested in me. I don't mean guys my own age, I mean younger. I sure don't intend to attract them. And I don't look like anybody's mom.

'Chuck, you look at *me*,' the sheriff said.

The boy did look toward Rockwell, with eyes as blue and clear as a mountain lake. 'Yes'm.'

'Chuck, you've been having bad thoughts and doing bad things.'

He looked down hastily.

'Did any of your friends help you, or was this all your doing?'

There was a long pause while Chuck Almand tried to work out which answer would give him some advantage.

'It was just me, Sheriff,' Chuck said. 'I just felt so bad after my mom . . .'

He paused artistically, as if he could not speak the word.

Tolliver and I knew lying when we heard it. We had lied convincingly to everyone in the school system in Texarkana to keep our family together as our parents circled the drain. We knew this boy was not telling the truth. I was ashamed of him hiding behind his mother's death. At least she'd died of something honorable. She hadn't wanted to leave her family.

The boy made the mistake of glancing back at me. He probably thought he could pull any adult female under with that little hitch in his voice. When my eyes met his, he twitched – not quite a flinch, but close.

'Maybe the psychic could tell us more,' Sheriff Rockwell suggested. 'Such as whether he's telling the truth about working alone or not.' I don't think she meant it; I think she was looking for a reaction from the boy that would tell her what she wanted to know. But of course, the psychic in question took her quite seriously.

Xylda said from behind me, 'I'm not going within a yard of the little bastard,' and Tom Almand said desperately, 'This is my *son*. My child.' He put his arm around the boy, who made a visible effort not to throw it off.

I turned to look at the old psychic. Xylda and I exchanged a long gaze. Manfred looked down at his grandmother and shook his head. 'You don't have to, Grandmother,' he said. 'They wouldn't believe you anyway. Not the law.'

'I know.' She looked sadder and older in that moment.

'Lady,' said Chuck Almand. His voice was very young and very urgent, and I found he was talking to me. 'It's true that you can find bodies?'

'Yes.'

'They have to be dead?'

'Yes.'

He nodded, as if confirming a suspicion. 'Thanks for telling me,' he said, and then his father drew him away to talk to a few more people.

After that, the day was out of our hands. After a lot of chatter right out of our range of hearing, Sheriff Rockwell told us that Twyla had said we could use her lake house.

'It's at Pine Landing Lake,' Sandra Rockwell said. 'Parker, Twyla's son, is coming to lead you there.'

It was a huge relief to have a place to stay, though if no one had supplied a bed, they would simply have had to let us leave town. I was definitely feeling just like a person who'd been released from the hospital that morning; not seriously ill, but tired and a little shaky. The police were digging for the animal corpses, I suppose to make sure there weren't any human remains mixed in. We were shunted over to the side of the barn where the earth was clearly undisturbed. Tolliver and I, Manfred, and Xylda stood in a silent row. Every now and then someone in uniform would dart a curious glance in our direction.

By the time Parker McGraw got there to take us to his mother's lake house, the media had discovered the police were at the old barn and were swarming around like flies on a carcass, though they were kept at a distance by the town cops. They were yelling my name from time to time.

After a handshake with Tolliver, Manfred led Xylda out to draw them off us. 'Grandmother loves the photographers,' he said. 'Just watch.' We did. Xylda, her flaming red hair outlining her creased round face like a scarf, strode off across the empty meadow with Manfred in colorful attendance. She paused by her car, with a reluctance so fake it was almost funny, to give the eager reporters a few well-chosen words. 'She's ready for her close-up, Mr DeMille,' Manfred said. He leaned over to kiss my cheek and followed her.

While Xylda was enjoying her moment, Tolliver and I did an end run around the mob to reach Parker's truck. Though I had only a faint recollection of what the truck looked like, Tolliver had admired it when we'd seen it in Twyla's driveway and he led me right to it.

Twyla's son was big and burly, dressed in the usual jeans and flannel shirt and down vest. His boots were huge and streaked with dirt. His mom hadn't had enough money when he was young to take him to the orthodontist.

He shook Tolliver's hand heartily. He was a little more tentative about shaking mine, as if women in his milieu didn't often offer to shake.

'Let's get out of here while the getting's good,' he said, and we slid into his truck as quickly as we could. Tolliver had to give me a boost. We were really jammed in, since Parker had brought his son Carson.

He introduced us, and even under the circumstances, Parker's pride in the boy shone through.

Carson was a dark boy, with a husky build. He was short; he hadn't gotten his growth yet. He had a broad face like his grandmother, and his eyes were clear and brown. He was subdued and silent, which I guess was no wonder, since the body of his brother had been discovered.

'Our car's at the back of the police station,' Tolliver said, and Parker nodded. He seemed friendly enough, but he was a man of few words.

However, once we were clear of the media traffic Parker said, 'I didn't get a chance to thank you the other day. We didn't show you any hospitality, either, but I guess you can understand why.'

'Yes,' I said, and Tolliver nodded. 'Don't think twice about it. We did the job we came here to do.'

'Yes, you did it. You didn't take my mama's money and run for the hills with it. She's a woman who's always done what she thought was right, and she thought calling you two in was right. I don't mind telling you, I disagreed with her real strong, and I told her so. But she knew her own mind, and she was right. Them other two . . .' He shook his head. 'We didn't know how lucky we was with you-all until we saw those two.'

He meant Manfred and Xylda. I glanced to my side to see how Carson was taking all this. He was certainly listening, but he didn't seem upset.

'I'm glad you have a high opinion of us,' I said, struggling to find a way to express myself tactfully. 'But you really can't judge a book by its cover, at least in Xylda Bernardo's case. She's the real deal. I do realize that the way she looks and acts does put some people off.' I hoped I'd been conciliatory enough to coax him into listening to me.

'That was real Christian of you,' Parker McGraw said after he'd thought over my words for a few minutes. Just when I was beginning to think the subject was closed he added, 'But I guess we'll be coming to you for all our supernatural needs.' He had a sense of humor after all. But it went back behind the cloud of his grief as soon as I'd glimpsed it. 'It don't seem right, enjoying anything, when our son is gone from this earth.' In a gesture that just about broke my heart, Carson laid his head on his dad's shoulder just for a second.

'I'm so sorry,' I said. 'I wish I could tell you who did it.'

'Oh, we're going to find out who done it,' he said, without a shadow of a doubt in his voice. 'Me and Bethalynn, we got to. We got Carson here, he deserves to grow up without being afraid.'

Carson's eyes met mine. He didn't seem afraid right now, but he had his dad beside him. The boy's calm eyes told me that Carson had been brought up in the expectation that adults would protect him from harm. Nothing had happened to shake that expectation. Even though his brother had been taken, Carson was sure he would not be. I hoped he was right.

Parker seemed to think that Doraville would be safe if he discovered and eliminated the man who'd killed his son. He seemed to think it would be easy to do this. For a moment, I jeered at him in my head; but then I reminded myself of what this man had gone through. He had a right to any fantasy he chose if it would help him get through this life.

We all have our fantasies.

7

The cabin at the lake had been used by the Cotton family for forty years or more. In recent years, the McGraw family had enjoyed it. Parker said that at first they'd felt like intruders, but the surviving children of Archie Cotton were well into their sixties and had no children of their own living in Doraville any longer. They seemed content to let the children of their dad's wife enjoy the old place.

'Jeff loved it out there,' Parker said. 'Me and Carson, we'll stay out there and go fishing in the spring, won't we, Carson?'

'Sure,' Carson said. 'We'll catch some fish for Mom to clean. She loves to clean fish *so much*.' That startled a smile out of his dad.

The deputy on duty had buzzed us into the fenced parking lot behind the police station. Tolliver and I scrambled out of the truck and got in our car. We followed Parker out of the parking lot.

Pine Landing Lake was about ten miles out of Doraville in a northeastern direction, and those ten miles were up a twisting, narrow two-lane road. We had met light traffic along the way. The lake seemed to be close to a community much smaller than Doraville, a dot on the map called Harmony. We didn't drive all the way around the lake, but at some points I could see its farther shore quite clearly. There were dwellings scattered around the lake, ranging from homes that looked year-round habitable to structures that were little more than open-air pavilions.

'This would be beautiful in summer,' I said, and Tolliver nodded.

We followed Parker's truck at a respectful distance, and when he turned into a narrow driveway we followed, going sharply downhill for a few yards until we could park beside the truck at a broad flat spot by the shore.

The Cotton property was on one of the larger lots. It was a two-story building of very modest size, and you could tell it had been there a lot longer than some of the others because of the huge trees around it. Maybe it had just been built with more landscaping care than the others. Appropriately rustic, with cedar shingles on the roof and cedar siding, it blended into its surroundings better than most of the others we could see.

The bottom level appeared to be a storage area for the boats and other recreational miscellany. There was a heavy padlocked set of doors on this ground-level entrance, facing the lake. Stairs went up the south side of the building to a landing outside the main door. The outer door was screen, of course, the inner a heavy wooden door. Parker unlocked this door and gestured us in.

'Lots of the cabins out here don't have heating or cooling,' he said, 'but this one does. Mr Archie did things right. Now, if the electricity goes off, which it does out here with some regularity, you've got your fireplace there, should be in working order. We had the guy clean it out last month.'

I looked around. The interior was pretty much one big room. There were two double beds set up with their heads against the west wall, and there were several folding beds rolled up against the wall by them, covered with plastic cases. The air in the cabin felt musty, but not unpleasant. The smell of old cedar was strong. The fireplace was in the east wall, and it was faced with natural rock. The walls were unpainted cedar boards, adding to the feel that we were really roughing it. There was a small stove, an ancient refrigerator, and a couple of cabinets by the door where we'd entered, and a walled-off west corner indicated a tiny bathroom. Besides the fireplace, the east wall facing the lake was almost all glass, and through the glass we could see a screened-in porch inhabited by a few heavy wooden rocking chairs.

'Now, the bedding should be in here,' Parker said, opening the cabinet below the sink. 'Yep, right where Bethalynn said it would be.' He pulled out a zippered plastic bag, plopped it on one of the beds. 'Should be enough blankets in there. Sometimes we're out here in the spring and the nights are pretty cold. If you need to start a fire up, the wood is downstairs. You can go directly down to the boat room, now you're inside.' He pointed to a trapdoor in the floor. 'We used to keep the wood outside, but people just aren't as honest as they used to be. They'll take anything we don't lock up, and even then we get broken into every two, three years.'

We all shook our heads over this evidence of modern slack morals.

Parker sighed from the toes of his boots, a gusty sound that was supposed to mask the grief that crossed his face. Carson silently patted his father's shoulder. 'I'll see you two later at the church hall,' he said.

'Mom's got your cell phone number.' And he was gone before we could see him cry. I guess it just got to him every now and then, and I wasn't surprised that was so. I wondered when they would get to bury what was left of their oldest son.

Tolliver opened the trapdoor and descended. 'No windows down here!' he called. I heard a click and the rectangle in the floor illuminated. 'I'm bringing up some firewood,' he said, his voice muffled. While I slung my suitcase on the bed closest to the bathroom, I heard a series of thunks and thuds, and then Tolliver's head appeared, the rest of him following along, his arms loaded with split oak.

I hadn't had much truck with fireplaces. While Tolliver dumped the wood on the hearth, I crouched down and looked up to see if the flue was open. Nope. I found a handle that looked promising and twisted it awkwardly with my good hand. Voila! With a great creak the flue opened and I could see the gray sky. There was a basket of pinecones on the hearth that I'd assumed were for rustic decoration, but Tolliver said he thought they were to help start the fire. Since they were absolutely ordinary pinecones and there were a million more where they came from, I let him put some in the hearth like the former Boy Scout he was. Since neither of us had matches or a lighter, we were relieved to find matches in a Ziploc bag on the mantel, and we were even more relieved when the first one Tolliver struck flared with a tiny flame.

The pinecones caught with gratifying speed, and Tolliver carefully put a few of the logs in the fireplace, crisscrossing them to allow the passage of air, I assumed.

Fire tending seemed to make him feel manly, so I left him to it. I had some granola bars in my suitcase, luckily, and I ate one while he brought up the ice chest, still fairly full of sodas and bottled water.

'We better get some groceries when we go into town tonight,' I said.

'Do you really want to go to the meeting at the church?'

'No, of course not, but if we're going to be here we might as well. I don't want the people here taking against us.' I glanced at my watch. 'We have at least three hours. I'm going to lie down. I'm worn out.'

'You shouldn't have carried that bag upstairs.'

'It was on my good shoulder. No problem.' But I'd taken a pain pill while he was out rummaging in the car, and it was taking effect.

There was a knock on the door, and I jumped a mile. Tolliver jerked in surprise himself, which made me feel a little better. We glanced at each other. We hadn't noticed anyone following us out here, and we'd hoped to dodge the reporters altogether.

'Yes?' Tolliver asked. I moved to stand behind him, peering out from behind his shoulder. Our caller sure didn't look like any reporter I'd ever seen. He was a wizened old man wearing battered cold-weather gear and carrying a casserole dish.

'I'm Ted Hamilton from next door,' the old man said, smiling. 'Me and my wife saw Parker pull up with you-all, and she could hardly wait to send you something. You friends of the family?'

'Please come in,' Tolliver said, because he had to. 'I'm Tolliver Lang; this is my sister Harper.'

'Ms Lang,' Ted Hamilton said, bobbing his head at me. 'Let me just put this down on the counter here.' He set down the dish he'd been carrying.

'Actually, I'm Ms Connelly, but please call me Harper,' I said. 'You and your wife live out here year-round?'

'Yep, since I retired, that's what we do,' he said. The Hamiltons must live in the small white house next door, to the north. I'd seen the Hamiltons' house out the window and noted it was inhabited. Ordinarily the Hamiltons and the McGraws wouldn't really have to see each other a lot, since the McGraw parking was on the south side of the cabin. The Hamiltons' white frame house was a very ordinary little place that just happened to have been put down at the lakeside, with no concession made to setting or locale. It did boast a very nice pier, I'd noted.

'We're just going to be here a couple of days,' I said, pretending to be rueful. 'This was awful nice of Mrs Hamilton.'

'I guess you know Twyla, then?'

He was obviously dying to get the scoop on us, and I was just as determined not to spell it out for him. 'Yes, we know her,' I said. 'A very nice woman.'

'Just for a couple of days? Maybe we can persuade you to stay longer,' Mr Hamilton said. 'Though with the bad weather coming in, you may want to rethink staying out here. You'd be better off with a room in town. It takes them a while to get out here when the electricity goes out.'

'And you think that's gonna happen?'

'Oh, always does when we get a lot of ice and snow like they're predicting for tomorrow night,' Ted Hamilton said. 'Me and the wife have been getting ready for it all day. Went to town, got our groceries, stocked up on water and got oil for our lanterns, and so on. Checked the first aid kit to make sure we can patch up cuts and so on.'

You could tell the oncoming bad weather was a big event for the Hamiltons, and I got the distinct impression they'd enjoyed themselves to the hilt preparing for it.

'We may be on our way tomorrow, with any luck,' I said. 'Please tell your wife we appreciate her fixing us something. We'll get the dish back to you, of course.' We said all this a few more times, and then Ted Hamilton went back down the outside stairs and around our cabin to get back to his. Now that I was listening for it, I could hear his cabin door open and I thought I heard a snatch of his wife's voice raised in eager query.

I took the aluminum foil off the dish to reveal a chicken and rice casserole. I sniffed. Cheese and sour cream, a little onion. 'Gosh,' I said, feeling respect for someone who could whip up a dish like that in the forty-five minutes Tolliver and I had been in residence in the cabin.

'If you had some leftover chicken,' Tolliver said, 'it would only take twenty minutes for the rice to cook.'

'I'm still shocked,' I said. My stomach growled, demanding some of the casserole.

We found plastic forks and spoons and some paper plates, and we ate half the dish on the spot. It wasn't restaurant food. It smelled of home . . . a home, any home. After we'd put the aluminum foil back on and put the remainders in the old refrigerator, I lay down to take a nap, and Tolliver went out exploring. The fire was crackling in a very soothing way, and I wrapped myself in a blanket. We'd made the beds, working together, my rhythm all thrown off by my bad arm. There hadn't been any pillows here – presumably the family brought their own each time they camped out here – but Tolliver and I each had a small pillow in the car, and once I was swaddled in the blanket and warm and full, I drifted off to sleep feeling better than I had in days.

I didn't wake up until almost four o'clock. Tolliver was reading, lying stretched out on his bed. The fire was still going, and he'd brought more wood up. He'd positioned two wooden chairs close to the fire.

There wasn't a sound to be heard: no traffic, no birds, no people. Through the window above my head, I could see the bare branches of an oak tree motionless in the still air. I put my hand to the glass. It was warmer. That wasn't good. The ice would come, I was sure.

'Did you go fish?' I asked Tolliver, after moving around a little to let him know I was awake.

'I don't know if you're supposed to go fishing in the winter,' he said. He hadn't had a bubba upbringing; no hunting and fishing for Tolliver. His dad had been more interested in helping hard men dodge the law, and then in getting high with the same men, than in taking his sons out in the woods for some bonding time. Tolliver and his brother, Mark, had had to learn other skills to prove themselves at school.

'Good, because I have no idea how to clean 'em,' I said.

He rolled off his bed and sat on the edge of mine. 'How's the arm?'

'Pretty good.' I moved it a little. 'And my head feels a lot better.' I moved over to give him room and he stretched out beside me.

He said, 'While you were asleep, I checked our messages on the phone at the apartment.'

'Mm-hm.'

'We had a few. Including one about a job in eastern Pennsylvania.'

'How long a drive from here?'

'I haven't worked it out yet, but I would guess about seven hours.'

'Not too bad. What's the job?'

'A cemetery reading. Parents want to be sure their daughter wasn't murdered. The coroner said the death was an accident. He said the girl slipped down some steps and fell. The parents heard from some friends that, instead, her boyfriend hit her on the head with a beer bottle. The friends are all too scared of the young man to tell the cops.'

'Stupid,' I said. But we encountered stupid people all the time, people who just could not seem to see that elaborate plots almost never worked, that honesty usually was the best policy, and that most people who supposedly died by accident actually *had* died by accident. If the boyfriend was so frightening that a group of young people were too scared to talk about him, there might be a good chance that this girl's 'fall' was an exception.

'Maybe we'll get away from here in time to take it up,' I said. 'They mention any time constraints?'

'The boy's about to leave town – he's joined the army,' Tolliver said. 'They want to know if he's guilty before he goes to basic.'

'They understand, right? That I can't tell them that. I can tell if the girl was hit on the head, but I won't know who did it.'

'I spoke to the parents briefly. They feel that if she was hit on the head, they'll know it was the suspect who did it. And they don't want him to leave before they have a chance to interrogate him again. I said we'd let them know something definite in the next forty-eight hours.'

I hated not being able to tell people yes or no right away, but you have to keep the law happy until their demands become unreasonable. My testimony is no good in court, right? So it's very irksome when the law stops me from leaving town. They don't even believe in me, but they can't seem to let me go.

'Damned if you do, damned if you don't,' I muttered. I remembered my mother's mother saying that: it was one of the few memories I had of her. I remembered her with a child's affection, though she hadn't been one of those sweet cuddly grandmas you see in TV ads. She'd never baked a cookie or knitted a sweater, and as far as dispensing wisdom, the aforementioned saying was about as profound as she'd gotten. She'd vanished as thoroughly as she could when my mother became a predator because of her drug habit. Of course, dodging her needy and dishonest daughter meant she also lost contact with us; but maybe it hadn't been an easy choice.

'You ever hear from your grandmother?' I asked Tolliver. He didn't follow my line of thinking, but he didn't look startled.

'Yeah, every now and then she calls,' he said. 'I try to talk to her once a month.'

'Your dad's mother, right?'

'Yeah, my mother's parents are both gone. She was their youngest, so they were pretty old when she died. It just took the life out of them, my dad said. They both passed away about five years after my mother.'

'We don't have a lot of relatives.' The McGraw-Cotton family seemed pretty united. Parker loved his mom, though she'd remarried. She'd stayed loyal to him instead of going all country club with her accession to money. Twyla had said Archie Cotton's adult children were okay with the marriage.

'Nope.' Tolliver didn't seem concerned. 'We have enough.'

I reached up with my good hand to pat him on the shoulder. 'Damn straight,' I said, with an overly hearty cheer, and he laughed a little.

'Listen, we need to go into town a little early.'

'Why?'

'Well, the computer was down at the hospital this morning, and they wanted to check your bill again.'

'You mean they let me out without you paying the total?'

'I paid it, but they wanted to be sure there weren't any later charges on it. So they asked me to drop by.'

'Okay.'

'You due any medicine?'

We checked, and I took a pill. I decided to take the pain medicine with me in my purse. I was able to use the bathroom by myself, but Tolliver had to help me readjust my clothes; and I let him take a swipe at brushing my hair, too. It was very awkward to attempt that one-handed. We managed to camouflage the bandage a little.

Tolliver went down the steps first, and I came down carefully after him. The gust of relatively warm air that blew in my face was a startling change. It was getting dark fast.

'And there's cold air coming down from the north?' I asked.

'Yeah, late tomorrow,' he said. 'And it'll be this warm here through part of tomorrow. We need to listen to the news on our way into town.'

We did, and the weather prediction was discouraging. Temperatures would remain in the upper forties through tomorrow, and by the evening the hot and the cold air would collide with the strong chance of a resultant ice storm. That sounded terrible. I'd only seen such a thing one other time, in my childhood, but I still remembered the trees down across the road in our trailer park, the bitter cold, and the lack of electricity. It had been a long thirty hours before our power came back on then. I wondered if we could drive out of the area likely to be affected before the storm hit.

The hospital lobby was almost deserted, and the girl on duty at the business window was busy closing out her paperwork. She wasn't too happy to see us, though she was polite. She glanced at a yellow Post-it Note stuck to my file and picked up her telephone. Punching in some numbers, she said, 'Mr Simpson? They're here.' After hanging up, she said, 'Mr Simpson, the administrator, asked to be notified when you came by. He'll be here in just a minute.'

We sat in the padded chairs with the metal legs and stared at the magazines on the low Formica table in front of us. Battered copies of *Field and Stream*, *Parenting*, and *Better Homes and Gardens* were not likely to tempt us, and I closed my eyes and slumped down in my chair. I found myself daydreaming about Christmas trees: white ones with golden ribbon and golden decorations, green ones with red flocked cardinals stuck on the branches, trees covered with big Italian glass ornaments and artificial icicles, dripping with tinsel. It was a shock to open my eyes and see long legs in front of me, legs covered in a dark suiting material. Barney Simpson dropped into a chair opposite us. His hair looked even rougher than it had when he'd come to my hospital room. I wondered if he'd ever tried cream rinse on it, to make it a bit more tameable.

'I have to confess,' he began, 'I put a flag on your statement so Britta would call me when you came in.'

'Why?' Tolliver asked. I sat up and tried not to yawn.

'Because I thought you might bolt without coming to the meeting tonight if I didn't catch you here and remind you to come,' Simpson said with every appearance of frankness. 'Britta told me the computers had been down when you were checking out this morning, so I decided to take advantage of the opportunity.'

'You belong to the same church? Doak Garland's church?'

'Oh, I make an appearance every few Sundays,' he said, not a bit abashed by something most southerners would be ashamed to admit. 'I have to confess that I don't have a great attendance record. I like to sleep in on Sundays, I'm afraid.'

He seemed to expect me to supply him with a comforting reassurance along the lines of 'Don't we all?' or 'We miss a lot of Sundays, too.' But I didn't say anything. This may have been childish on my part. Tolliver and I don't ever go to church. I don't know what Tolliver believes, at least not in detail. I believe in God; I don't believe in church. Churches give me the cold chills. The only reason I'd been in a church in the past five years was to go to a funeral. Having the body that close was very distracting. It buzzed at me during the whole service. If this had been Jeff McGraw's funeral, rather than a kind of memorial service for all the lost boys, I would never have agreed to come to it.

'Abe Madden is due to speak,' Barney Simpson said. 'That should be interesting. Sandra hasn't said much, but it's common knowledge that Abe wouldn't pursue the boys' disappearances with anything like the purpose Sandra wanted when she was a deputy. And it's also no secret that's one reason she was elected sheriff.'

Barney Simpson gave us a serious nod, his big black glasses reflecting the overhead fluorescents.

'Then I guess it should have a little more controversy than the usual memorial service,' Tolliver said. 'Our bill is ready, you said? Your computers are back up and running?'

'Yes. We're backing up everything this evening so we won't lose anything in the upcoming ice storm. I guess you've been listening to the weather, like everyone else around here. Did you-all find a place to stay?'

'Yes, we did,' I said.

'Back in the motel, I guess. You-all were lucky to find somewhere.'

'No,' Tolliver said. 'They were all out of rooms.'

He went over to the window to check on the bill while Barney looked at me expectantly, waiting for me to tell him where we'd found a place to stay – but I didn't. I wasn't sure why I was being so ornery. A bop on the head will only excuse so much. I forced myself to be polite.

'Is there a Mrs Simpson?' I asked, though I simply could not have cared less.

'There was,' he said, regret tingeing his voice with gray. 'We came to a parting of the ways a few years ago, and she and my daughter moved to Greenville.'

'So you get to see your daughter sometimes.'

'Yes, she comes back to stay with me and visit her junior high buddies every so often. Hard to believe she's in college now. Any children for you?'

'No,' I said, shaking my head.

'Well, they're a mixed blessing,' the administrator said in a consoling voice, as if to assure me I didn't have to grieve at not having any.

I stood and moved over to Tolliver, who was getting a receipt from Britta.

'Could I take you two to supper?' Barney Simpson asked, and we tried not to look too astonished.

Tolliver glanced at me quickly to get my reaction to this very unexpected invitation, and he said, 'Thanks, but we already have plans. We appreciate your offer, though.'

'Sure, sure.'

Britta had closed her window and I could see her silhouette behind the glass as she rose and began putting on her coat.

The hospital was as closed as a hospital gets.

We left then, heading out the front door with the receipt and Simpson's goodbyes. 'What a lonely guy,' I said.

'He has a thing for you,' Tolliver said gloomily.

'He does not.' I dismissed the idea without a second glance at it. 'He didn't care about me at all. I didn't represent a woman to him, one little bit.'

'Then why'd he want to be our best friend?'

'I guess it was the newness of us,' I said. 'He may not have the chance to meet that many people. I bet his job pretty much holds him down. We're variety.'

Tolliver shrugged. 'Whatever. Where you want to eat?'

'This is Doraville. What are our choices?'

'It's too cold for Sonic. There's a McDonald's and there's a Satellite Steaks.'

'That'll do.'

Satellite Steaks was very much like Golden Corral or Western Sizzlin'. On this cold night, with the prospect of a memorial service and bad weather to anticipate, everyone in Doraville had had the same idea. There were some easily identifiable strangers who had to be with the news crews, and there were a lot of locals (who probably didn't come in during the summer tourist season), and there were travelers from the interstate. The place was jammed. Manfred and Xylda were at a table for four. Without consulting Tolliver, I went right over to their table and asked if we could share.

'Oh, please,' Xylda said. She had maybe a ton of makeup on. Her encounter with the media at the barn seemed to have galvanized her into going the extra mile. Her eyes were positively Cleopatran, and she'd actually tied a scarf around her head à la a gypsy, with her brilliant red ringlets flying out from under it to form a shocking contrast with her pale, plump, wrinkled face. I sat beside her and got a big whiff of stale perfume. Tolliver had to sit by Manfred, which wouldn't hurt him. And Manfred had to smell better than his grandmother.

'How are you feeling?' Manfred asked. He really looked anxious.

'I'm doing good,' I said. 'My head feels better. The arm is a pain.'

'I heard you two checked out of the motel. I figured you'd be long gone.'

'Tomorrow or the next day,' Tolliver said. 'We're just waiting to see if the state guys have anything else to ask us. Then we'll be on our way. You two?'

'I need to stay until tomorrow afternoon, at least,' Xylda said in a whisper. 'There are more dead people to come. And the time of ice is near.'

Now, that I understood. 'That's what the weather says. There's going to be an ice storm.'

'We're hoping to get out of town ahead of it,' Manfred said quietly. 'Grandma don't need to be away from a big hospital any longer than we can help it. I'll be taking her back home as soon as I can.' I looked at him sideways and read clearly the grief written on his face. It made me want to give him a big hug.

Xylda looked like she was listening to a faraway voice. I was seriously concerned about her. Before, she'd been in the likeable fake category, though she'd always had her moments of true brilliance. They'd just been too few and far between for her to make her living off of them. Now she appeared to be 'on' all the time. The stretches of shrewd reality that had helped her earn a living (if fraudulent) wage seemed to be fewer and farther between.

I wondered what Manfred would do when she was gone. He was very young and he still had all his options open. He could go to college and get a regular job. He could apprentice in a circus. He could assume the hand-to-mouth existence of petty fraud and chicanery that Xylda had led. This wasn't the time or place to quiz him about his future plans, when the big stumbling block to any of them sat beside me spilling salad dressing down her blouse.

Xylda said, 'That boy is going to be a murderer.' Fortunately her voice was quite low. I knew she was talking about Chuck Almand.

Speaking of a young man with options open. 'Not for sure, though. He could still save himself. Maybe his father will find a good therapist for him, and he'll work out all his kinks.' I didn't believe it, but I should at least sound like I thought it was possible.

Manfred shook his head. 'I can't believe they didn't arrest him.'

'He's a minor,' Tolliver said. 'And there aren't any witnesses against him except his own admission. I don't think jail would do him any good, do you? Maybe just the opposite, in fact. Maybe in jail he'd find out how much he enjoyed hurting people.'

'I think in jail he'd be on the other end,' I said. 'I think he'd get hurt a lot, and maybe come out ready to give it back with interest.'

We all mulled it over. The waitress bustled up to take our orders and to ask Manfred and Xylda if they needed more to drink. They both accepted, and it was a few minutes before we could resume our conversation.

'I wonder if there's a kid like that in every community,' Tolliver said. 'One who likes to cause pain, likes to have the power over smaller creatures.'

'There was someone like that in our school in Texarkana?' I asked. I was surprised.

'Yeah. Leon Stipes. Remember him?'

Leon had been six feet tall when he was in the sixth grade. Leon was black, and he was on the football team, and he scared the hell out of the other teams we played. I suspected he'd scared the hell out of most of the players on his own-team, too.

I explained Leon to Xylda and Manfred. 'He liked causing pain?'

'Oh, yeah,' said Tolliver grimly. 'Oh, yeah. He really did. In practice, he'd nail people he didn't have to, just to hear them yelp.'

I shuddered with distaste. With one hand, I opened my purse and pulled out my bottle of vitamins. I pushed it over for Tolliver to deal with. He removed the childproof lid and shook one out. I took it.

'How are you feeling?' Manfred asked. 'The arm hurting?'

I shrugged. 'The pain medicine works pretty well,' I said. 'In fact, I'm wondering if I'll fall asleep in the memorial service.'

'You'll be much better soon,' Xylda said, and I wondered if she was basing that on foresight or on optimism.

'What about you, Xylda?' I looked at her curiously. 'Didn't I hear you were in the hospital last month?' There's an Internet group for those of us who work in the paranormal field. I check it out from time to time.

'Yes,' she said, 'but it's bad for my spirit, the hospital. Too much negative there. Too many desperate people. I won't go in there again.'

I started to protest, caught the warning glance Manfred gave me. I shut up.

'I don't blame you,' Tolliver said. 'Harper's just trailing negative thoughts, and she was only in there for a couple of days.'

I could have kicked him, if I could have summoned the energy. I stuck out my tongue.

Tolliver and Manfred talked about car mileage while we ate, and Xylda and I thought our own thoughts. When Tolliver left to go to the men's room and Manfred was paying their bill, she said, 'I'm going to die soon.'

I was affected enough by the pain medicine to accept this calmly. 'I'm sorry to hear you think so,' I said, which seemed safe enough. 'Are you scared?'

'No,' she said, after a moment's thought, 'I don't believe I am. I've enjoyed my life and I've tried to do good, for the most part. I never took money from anyone who couldn't afford it, and I loved my son and grandson. I believe my soul will enter another body. That's very comforting, knowing the essential part of me won't die.'

'Yes, it must be,' I said, pretty much at a loss as to how to carry my end of the conversation.

'Your questions will all be answered,' she said. 'My sight is clearer the closer I come to the end.'

Then I said something that surprised even myself. 'Will I find my sister, Xylda? Will I find Cameron? She's dead, right?'

'You'll find Cameron,' Xylda said.

I bowed my head.

'I don't know,' Xylda said after a lengthy pause, and I raised my face to stare at her, trying to figure out what she meant. Manfred was coming back to the table to leave a tip. Tolliver was in line at the cash register. We were in a cone of strangeness together. 'But there are more important things for you to think about first,' Xylda continued.

I hardly understood how anything could be more important than finding my sister's body. I slid out of the booth and started struggling into my coat, while Xylda began scooting to the outside. Manfred helped me get my right arm into its coat sleeve and draped the coat over my left shoulder. He bent slightly and gave me a kiss on the neck as he did so. He did this so casually that it seemed churlish to make a big deal out of it. In fact, it wasn't until I saw Tolliver's face that the light kiss really registered on me. Tolliver was absolutely inclined to make a big deal out of it, and I gripped his arm with my good hand and began marching toward the door, forcing him to come along.

'It was nothing,' I said. 'I wasn't even thinking about it. He's just a very young man with a sick grandmother.' I'm not sure what sense that made, but at the moment it just slid right out of my brain and then my mouth. 'We're just going to this meeting now. Come on, or we'll be late.'

Somehow we both ended up in the right car and Tolliver turned on the motor to get the blessed heater started. He pulled my seat belt across me with unnecessary force, and I squeaked because my arm hurt.

'Sorry,' he said, not sounding very sorry at all. 'He rubs me the wrong way. He just crawls around you. All that stuff in his face and God knows where else! Just waiting to touch you.'

Instead of keeping quiet and letting things die down like I ought to have done, I said, 'Isn't it okay that someone likes me?'

'Sure! Just not him!'

Tolliver would rather I got together with Barney Simpson or the Pastor Doak Garland? 'Why not?'

There was a long moment of silence while Tolliver struggled with that question. 'Because he, well, he actually stands a chance with you,' he said. 'Other guys don't because we're always traveling and you aren't going to see them again, but he understands the lifestyle and he has to travel, too, with Xylda.'

I opened my mouth to say, *So you don't want me to have anyone?* But a power beyond me shut my mouth. I didn't say anything. This was closer to the bone than I'd imagined Tolliver would get, and I was scared to take it any further.

'He's younger than me.' I had to say something.

'Not too young,' my brother said. We'd changed sides in the Manfred argument, I realized. Suddenly, I was trying not to smile. I realized the pain pill I'd taken at the cabin was definitely working. I had the blooming warm sense of well-being, the chatty feeling of affection for all mankind. If I ever became addicted to any pharmaceutical, pain pills would be my drug of choice. But I didn't plan on becoming addicted. Once the pain was gone, the pills would be. I had to watch myself, after the example my mother had set me.

'The trick to avoiding these pills is not to get hurt,' I said seriously.

Tolliver had a little trouble catching up to this conversational line, but he got there. 'Yes, you don't want to end up in the hospital again,' he said. 'For one thing, you can't do your share of the driving while you're on them.'

'Oh, yeah, like you care,' I said.

He smiled. I felt better. 'But I do,' he said.

The lot of Mount Ida Baptist Church was already full of cars. One of the local cops was directing the overflow parking. Tolliver asked if he could drop me off right in front of the church, and the cop nodded. I got out of the car awkwardly and stood just inside the vestibule, waiting. As other people passed me and went in, I glimpsed Twyla sitting at a table just inside the door. She had a clear plastic box in front of her, a box with a slot cut in the top.

There was a sign on the front of the box that read 'Please help our families bury their children.' It was already half full of bills and change.

Twyla glimpsed me, too, and made a beckoning gesture. I maneuvered through the doors and went to sit in the vacant folding chair beside her. She leaned over to give me a half hug.

'How you doing, girl?' she asked.

However I was doing, it had to be better than Twyla. Everything wrong with me would heal. Not so, her. 'I'm okay,' I said. 'They've got you working, I see.'

'Yep, they thought it would be more effective if a relative sat here,' she said. 'So here I am. If you say six of the boys were local, we need at least four thousand dollars for each burial, so our goal is twenty-four thousand. We got these up all over town, but this is a poor place. I think we'll be lucky to get six thousand through these collections.'

'How do you expect to make up the rest, or do you think that just won't happen?'

Twyla looked grim. 'I think it won't happen. But we're doing the best we can. Maybe if the poorer families can just make a good down payment on the funerals through these donations, each individual family can pay the rest on time.'

I nodded. 'Good idea.' Emboldened by the pain medication, I said, 'It's too bad the media don't chip in. After all, they're profiting by the deaths as well, aren't they? They should donate something.'

A fire lit in Twyla's eyes. 'That's a good idea,' she said. 'I wonder that I didn't think of it. What happened today at Tom Almand's? I'm hearing some mighty funny things. That boy of his in trouble? Hey, Sarah,' she said, lifting her round face to a woman coming in. 'Thanks for helping,' she added as the older woman dropped a couple of dollars into the slot.

'There are too many people around to talk about it,' I said quietly.

No one had asked me not to discuss the macabre nature of the findings at Tom Almand's, but I didn't want to be broadcasting it. Chuck Almand would be a pariah soon enough. I wouldn't hasten the process. Though some country people tend to be more practical about animals than city people, plenty of the inhabitants of Doraville would be disgusted at the pain inflicted on cats and squirrels and the odd dog . . . especially if the cats and the dog turned out to be somebody's pets. 'But he's not a boy you'd want to have dating your daughter or grand-daughter.'

'The sheriff says we won't get the bodies back for a week at least, maybe longer,' Twyla said. 'It seems hard that we finally discover Jeff, but we can't bury him.'

'At the same time,' I said, 'you want every bit of evidence that can tie his death to the killer.'

'I don't like to think about him getting cut up,' Twyla said. 'I can't think about it.'

I didn't know what to say, and the fuzzy golden goodwill the pill lent me did not give me any inspiration. I decided it was best to keep silent. I looked over the crowd in the pews. Mount Ida was a larger church than I'd imagined from the outside. The pews were gleaming with polish, and the carpet was new, too. At the front of the church were easels with enlarged photographs of the dead boys, each with a spray of flowers at the base. I would have liked to look at them, since I'd touched on each of these young men in my very own way, but going up there would have seemed rude and pushy.

There was a knot of law enforcement uniforms in one of the front pews. I recognized Sheriff Rockwell's hair, and I thought I also saw Deputy Rob Tidmarsh, who'd discovered the animal graves.

Somehow the Bernardos had beat us here. I glimpsed Xylda's unruly red head a few pews up and to the right and Manfred's platinum spikes beside her. From the rear view, the two didn't stand out so much. There was plenty of dyed hair in evidence, and several spiky hairdos.

Tolliver came in, his face pinched with cold. He dropped a twenty into the slot. He was surprised to find me seated by Twyla, but he leaned over to shake her hand and to tell her how sorry he was. 'We appreciate the use of your cabin,' he said. 'It made a big difference, having a place to stay.' I hadn't even thought of thanking her, and I was angry with myself.

'I'm very sorry Harper got hurt,' Twyla said, and I felt better when I realized I wasn't the only one who'd forgotten to mention something fairly major. 'I hope they catch who did it, and I'm sure it was the same bastard who killed our Jeff. This is something else I forgot,' she said, pressing a check into my hands. I nodded and slid it into Tolliver's chest pocket. We started down the aisle to find a place to sit.

We paused by a pew with some free space in the middle, and when the pew's settlers saw my cast, they were kind enough to all shift down to let us sit on the end. I said 'Thank you' several times. It felt good to settle down on the padded pew shoulder to shoulder with Tolliver. We were far enough away from the door to avoid the effects of the constant gusts of cold air with each entrance.

Gradually the murmurs died down and the crowd became silent. The doors didn't open and close anymore. Pastor Garland came out, looking youthful and somehow sweet. But his voice was anything but sweet, or peaceful, as he read the scriptures he'd selected for the occasion. He'd picked a passage from Ecclesiastes, he told us, and he started to read. He began, 'To everything there is a season . . .'

Everyone around me was nodding their heads, though of course Tolliver and I didn't recognize the scripture. We listened with great attention. Was he saying that it had been time for the boys to die? No, maybe his emphasis was on 'a time to mourn.' That was now, for sure. The rest of his readings were from Romans, and the thread that ran through them was about maintaining your own integrity in a world bereft of it. And they were eerily appropriate.

There was no point in saying the murders were events the congregation had to accept philosophically. There was no point in saying the people of Doraville had to turn the other cheek; it wasn't the community's cheek that had been struck. Its children had been stolen. There would be no offering up of other children to be killed, no matter how much scripture was quoted.

No, Doak Garland was smarter than he appeared. He was telling the people of Doraville that they had to endure and trust in God to get them past the bad time, that God would help them in this endeavor. No one could disagree with that message. Not here, not tonight. Not with those faces at the front of the congregation, staring back. As I watched, a deputy ceremoniously added two more easels, but these were left blank. The two boys who were strangers. I felt touched.

'These are the children of our community,' Doak said. He gestured to the faces. Then he pointed to the two blank easels. 'And these are someone else's children, but they were killed and buried right along with ours, and we must pray for them, too.'

One picture was the stern one boys always take for their high school football picture. The scowling boy, looking so very tough . . . I'd seen him in his grave, beaten and cut, tortured beyond his endurance, every vestige of manhood stripped from him. Suddenly the tragedy of it seemed unbearable, and as Doak Garland's voice rose in his sermon, tears flowed out of my eyes. Tolliver fished some Kleenex from his pocket and patted my face. He looked a little bewildered. I'd never reacted like this to a previous case, no matter how horrific.

We sang a hymn or two, we prayed long and loud, and one woman fainted and was helped out into the vestibule. I floated through the service on a cloud of pain medication, every now and then weeping with the emotion that could not be contained. When the usher – the hospital administrator, Barney Simpson – came by with the plate to pass for further donations toward the burials, a man two pews ahead of me turned his head as he handed his neighbor the collection plate, and I saw to my amazement that Tom Almand had come to the service. He had brought his son with him, and that hit me wrong. The counselor should have stayed home with the boy. Chuck was laboring under such a terrible burden, he shouldn't be in a place where the atmosphere was sheer grief and horror. Or did he need to be reminded that other problems were worse than his? I was no counselor. Maybe his dad knew best.

I reached across myself to squeeze Tolliver with my good hand. He looked at me inquiringly. He was restless, and I could tell he wanted to be anywhere but here. I nodded my head to indicate Tom Almand and Chuck, and after scanning the crowd with a blank face, Tolliver gave me a significant look to let me know he'd spotted them. As if he could feel our gazes, Almand turned a bit and looked straight at us. I thought he would look disgusted, or angry, or anguished. What does the father of such a child feel? I didn't have a clue, but I was fairly sure it would be a painful mixture of emotions.

Tom Almand looked blank. I couldn't even be sure he recognized me.

Okay, that was freaky. I would have added forty more dollars to the collection plate if I could have heard what Almand was thinking.

'Huh,' Tolliver said, which put it in a nutshell.

Then the collection was over, and everyone settled back into receptive silence. But a stir went through the crowd when a stubby man in a bad suit rose from the front pew and went to the lectern.

'Those of you don't know me, I'm Abe Madden,' he said, and there was another little ripple of movement. 'I know that some of you blame me for not realizing sooner that those boys were being killed. Maybe, like some of you think, I let what I *wanted* get in the way of what I *should*. I wanted those boys to be okay, just out sowing a few wild oats. I should have been looking harder for them, asking harder questions. Some in my own department told me that.' He might have been looking at the current sheriff when he said that. 'Some in my department thought I was right. Well, we know now I was wrong, and I ask your forgiveness for a great mistake I made. I was your servant while I was in office, and I let you down.' And he went back to his seat.

I'd never heard anything like that before. What it must have cost the man in pride to do that . . . I couldn't even imagine. Tolliver was less impressed. 'Now he's confessed and asked for forgiveness,' he whispered. 'Can't anyone point fingers at him anymore; he's paid his debt.'

A member of each family spoke, some briefly, some at length, but I heard very little fire and brimstone. I expected some homophobic stuff, given the nature of the murders, but I didn't hear any. The anger was directed at the rape, not at the sexual preference of the rapist. Only two family members spoke of vengeance, and then only in terms of the law catching the responsible party. There was no lynch talk, no fist shaking. Grief and relief.

The last speaker said, 'At least now we know this is at an end. No more of our sons will die.' At that, I saw a sudden movement in the Bernardos' pew. Manfred was gripping Xylda by the arm, and her face was turned toward his. She looked angry and urgent. But after a few seconds, she subsided.

We might as well have left then, for all I got out of the rest of the service. I was drowsy and uncomfortable, and I wanted nothing more than to lean my head on Tolliver's shoulder and fall asleep. That would clearly be the wrong thing to do, so I focused on sitting up straight and keeping my eyes open. At last the service was over, and we sang a closing hymn. Then we could go. I stepped out of the pew first since I was on the end, and a grizzled man in overalls took my hand. 'Thank you, young lady,' he said, and then began making his way out of the church without another word. He was the first of many people who made a point of touching me: a light hug, a grip of the hand, a pat on the shoulder. Each contact came with a 'Thank you,' or a 'God bless you and keep you,' and each time I was surprised. This had never happened to me before. I was sure it would never happen again. Doak Garland embraced me when we reached his spot at the door, his white hands light on my shoulders so he wouldn't hurt me. Barney Simpson, towering over me, reached out to give me a light pat. Parker McGraw said, 'Bless you,' and Bethalynn wept, her arms around her remaining son.

No one asked me a single question about how I'd found the boys. The faith of Doraville seemed to hinge on the acceptance of God's mysterious ways and the strange instruments he selects to perform his will.

I was the strange instrument, of course.

8

There were a couple of cars behind us on the long road out to Pine Landing Lake. Of course, the little hamlet of Harmony was past the lake, and there were other people in residence at the lake itself, so I told myself not to be crazy. After we turned off, the other cars continued on their way. Tolliver didn't comment one way or the other, and I didn't want to sound paranoid, so I didn't say anything.

We hadn't left on an outside light – in fact, I wasn't even sure if there was one – and I tried to mark the location of the stairs before Tolliver cut the ignition. We had a few seconds before the headlights turned off, so I hurried as much as I could to start up while I could see my way. There was a noise from the underbrush, and I said, 'What the hell is that?' I had to stop and look, and then I saw a lumbering small shape scoot across the driveway and into the thicket between ours and the next vacant cabin, barely visible through the thick growth of trees and brush.

'Coon,' Tolliver said, relief clear in his voice. Just then the head-lights cut out and we made our way up to the cabin in an anxious silence. Tolliver had gotten the key out, and after some fumbling he managed to turn it the right way. My fingers scrabbled on the wall, trying to find the light switch. Contact! In a split second, we had the miracle of electric light.

The fire had died down in our absence, and Tolliver set about building it back up. He was really into being Frontier Man, and I suspected he was feeling very macho. Not only was his kinswoman wounded (me), requiring his care and attention, but he had to provide fire for me. Soon he would start to draw on the walls about hunting the buffalo. So I was smiling at him when he turned around, and he was startled.

'You ready for bed?' he asked.

'I'm sure ready to put on my pajamas and read,' I said. It was pathetically early, but I was exhausted. He opened my suitcase and got out my flannel sleep pants and the long-sleeved thin top that had come with them. He'd given the set to me for Christmas, and it was dark blue with silver crescent moons on the pants and silver sparkles on the top. I hadn't quite known what to say when I'd opened the box, but I'd grown to like them.

'Are you going to need me to help?' he asked, trying hard to keep any trace of embarrassment out of his voice. We were pretty matter-of-fact about brief glimpses of each other that sometimes occurred when we shared a room, but somehow his assisting me with my clothes was a little more personal.

I ran through the process in my head. 'I'll need help getting my shirt off,' I said, 'and unhooking my bra.' A nurse had helped me get it on that morning.

I went into the very rudimentary bathroom, which was several degrees colder than the main room since it was farthest from the fireplace, and began the unexpectedly complicated task of getting my clothes off and my pajamas on. My socks defeated me, though. We'd put out some towels before we left, and I scrubbed my face, which would just have to do for tonight. After a few groans and some cursing, I had my pajama bottoms on, my shirt half off, and I backed out of the bathroom so Tolliver could help with the rest.

There was a long moment of silence. Then he said, 'There's a lot of bruising on your arms and ribs,' and his voice was tight.

'Yeah, well,' I muttered. 'When someone hits you with something big, that's what happens. Get the bra, okay? I'm freezing.'

I barely felt his fingers as he took care of the hooks. 'Thanks,' I said, and scurried back into the bathroom. When my mission was accomplished, I gathered up my discarded clothes and brought them out with me, shoving my shoes ahead of me with my foot. I'd kept my socks on. It was just too cold to take them off.

Tolliver had turned down my sheets and blankets for me, and propped up the pillows. My book was on the bedside table; but my bad arm would be toward that side. I hadn't thought about that when I'd picked the usual bed.

He held the covers up while I maneuvered myself into bed. Then he covered me up. Oh, even on this lumpy old bed, being on my back felt divine.

'I'm all tucked in,' I said, already feeling sleepier. 'Gonna read me a story?'

'Read your own damn story,' Tolliver said, but he was smiling, and he bent over to give me a kiss. 'You've been a real trouper today, Harper. I'm proud of you.'

I couldn't see what I'd done that day that had been so outstanding. I said so. 'It's just been another day,' I said, my eyelids drifting shut.

He laughed, but if he said anything in response, I missed it.

When I woke up, it was daylight. I hadn't even had to get up to use the bathroom during the night. Tolliver was still asleep in the bed to my left. There weren't any curtains up over the big windows in the cabin – maybe they'd been taken down for the winter, or maybe the family just dispensed with them out here – and I could see trees outside. I turned my head and looked over the hump that was Tolliver to peer out the glass doors onto the big porch outside. Was it a porch, or a balcony? It was on the second floor of the structure . . . I decided it was a porch, and I could see that it was no weather to stand outside on it. The sky was clear and beautiful, and the wind was blowing; it looked cold, somehow. If the weatherman had been correct, this would be the high point of the day.

Maybe we would get to leave today, start up to Pennsylvania. It would be just as cold there, if not colder; but maybe we could dodge the predicted winter storm. I would never see Twyla Cotton again, probably. Maybe I would see Chuck Almand again on the news in a few years, when he got arrested for killing someone. His dad would cry and wonder what he'd done wrong. After we left Doraville, the town would get back to its business of mourning its dead and accommodating its media visitors. The funeral directors would have an unexpected surge in profits. The hotels and restaurants would, too. Sheriff Rockwell would be glad to see the last of the state boys. They'd be glad to leave Doraville and return to wherever they were based.

Manfred and his grandmother would go back to their home in Tennessee. Sometime in the next few months, Xylda would die. Manfred would be on his own, begin his own career of providing psychic insights to the ignorant and the educated. Sometimes he'd be sincere, and sometimes he wouldn't. I thought about Tolliver's surprising paranoia concerning Manfred. I smiled to myself. It was true I found Manfred intriguing, if he wasn't exactly my inner pinup poster. His confidence that he could please me, and his conviction that I was desirable . . . well, what woman doesn't enjoy that? That's pretty potent. But as far as actually following through on it . . . it was probably more fun to flirt with Manfred than actually carry the attraction to the next level. Though I wasn't much older than him in years, in other ways I felt I was way too much his senior.

I really needed to get up to visit the bathroom. With a reluctant sigh, I worked my way out of the covers and sat up. This low bed was not good for such maneuvering, and it was hard keeping quiet, but I wanted to let Tolliver sleep as long as he could. He'd had the harder row to hoe the day before, having to take care of me.

Finally, I was on my feet and heading to the bathroom. That necessary task done, I brushed my hair one-handed, with a very lopsided result, and brushed my teeth a bit more efficiently. I felt better immediately. When I opened the door as quietly as possible, I saw that Tolliver wasn't moving, so I padded over to the fireplace and eyed the remaining embers. Carefully, I added more wood, trying to keep the arrangement tight but with ventilation as Tolliver had done. To my gratification, the fire picked right up. Hah!

'Good job,' said Tolliver, his voice heavy with sleep. I eased into one of the two ancient wooden chairs he'd arranged in front of the fire. Its faded cushion smelled of damp and some long-ago dog. Of course the family would put their castoffs out here. No point buying special furniture for a place where they came to relax, where they'd be coming in wet from swimming. Also, the cabin was pretty vulnerable to theft, and who wants to tempt thieves with something valuable? I told myself how grateful I was to Twyla for letting us stay here, for free and away from the reporters. But at the same time, I admitted to myself that I'd much rather be in the motel, at least from a comfort standpoint.

Tolliver had his cell phone plugged in and charging, and now it rang.

'Crap,' he said, and I agreed with the sentiment. The last thing I wanted to do was talk to anyone.

'Hello,' he said, and after that all I heard was, 'I guess we can,' and 'Okay,' very noncommittal stuff. He hung up and groaned.

'That was the SBI agent, Klavin. He wants us to come into the station in an hour.'

'I have to have coffee before I face any cops,' I said.

'Yeah, no shit.' He got out of bed and stretched. 'You sleep okay?'

'Yeah, I don't think I moved all night.' I did some stretching myself. 'I'll go shower. What are you going to do about that?'

'I'll have to take a sort of sponge bath, I guess. I can't get these bandages wet.' That was another thing that was going to grow old very quickly.

'Okay, I'll hurry.' Tolliver can take the quickest showers of anyone I know, and he was out and toweling his hair while I was still trying to assemble a set of clothes for the day. I managed to get my pajamas off by myself, and I managed to clean myself – more or less – but getting dressed was a real ordeal. I was trying to balance modesty with need, and it wasn't an easy achievement. Putting on my underwear turned out to be literally a pain in the butt, and I had to maneuver endlessly to get my bra up my arms and get my boobs in the cups so Tolliver could hook it.

'Geez, I'm glad I don't have to wear one of these things,' he grumbled. 'Why don't they fasten in front? That would make more sense.'

'There are some that hook in front. I just don't have any.'

'You give me your size, I'll get you some for your birthday.'

'I'd like to see you shopping in Victoria's Secret.'

He grinned.

We had a few extra minutes to go into McDonald's for their alleged pancakes. I pay lip service to hating McDonald's, but the pancakes were good and so was the coffee. And God, it was so warm in there. The windows were steamed up. The place was full of burly men in bulky jackets, mostly in camo patterns. They all wore big boots and had freshly shaved faces. Some of them would be going to work out at the crime scene, and some of them would be going about their usual business. Even the presence of death wouldn't stop life as usual in Doraville. That was a comforting thought, if one I'd had about a million times before. A job like mine makes you a big 'river of life' person.

I hated to leave the homey atmosphere of McDonald's – okay, I guess it's pretty bad if you think McDonald's is homey – for the unpleasant interview ahead. But we wanted to be on time, and we hoped they would let us leave town after. Tolliver had left our stuff at the cabin, though. He said it wouldn't take long to swing back by and throw our stuff into the suitcases if we were allowed to leave. And we'd have to straighten up the cabin a little and return the key.

We ran the gauntlet of the press since we had to park in front that day. There wasn't a friendly officer at the gate to the rear parking lot to let us through, and we hadn't thought about calling ahead. The ranks of the fourth estate seemed a little thin today, and I wondered if the forensic people were still digging at the barn. I got through the remaining light crowd with a few 'No comment's, and they didn't dare follow us into the station.

When we were settled at the table in a conference room, carefully nursing our extra cups of coffee we'd brought with us, we had quite a little wait. Spread out on the table was a big map marked 'Don Davey Property.' The drawing was liberally marked up. From where we sat, Tolliver had a hard time reading the print, but I gave him a superior sneer and read the labels.

'The first grave is marked "Jeff McGraw," and all the others are marked with the name of the boy that was in there,' I said. I caught myself talking in a very low voice, as if I could disturb the dead. 'The two graves where the boys weren't local, they have names on them, too. Maybe there was ID on the bodies. The northernmost one reads "Chad Turner," and the other one is "James Ray Pettijean."' I scooted my chair a little closer to Tolliver's. 'I guess they're all being autopsied now,' I said. It really didn't make any difference what happened to the body after the soul was gone; it was dross. Somehow, there being so many of them gave me the cold grue.

'There wasn't anything *remaining* at the grave site?' Tolliver asked, careful of the fact that ears might be listening.

'No,' I said, just as carefully. No souls, no ghosts; and there's a big difference. I've seen souls lingering around fairly fresh bodies every now and then. I've only seen one ghost.

Pell Klavin and Max Stuart came in just then. The two SBI agents looked very tired. I wondered if there were more agents coming to help them. The two men dragged out chairs and slumped in them, right across from us; between us lay the map.

'What can you tell us that we don't already know?' Stuart said.

I was irritated that he didn't even try to observe a common courtesy, but then I thought of poring over the dead boys' biographies all night, and I excused the two agents. I wouldn't have been inclined to offer meaningless courtesies, either.

'Probably nothing,' I said. 'All I do is find bodies. I'm good at that, but I'm not a detective.'

'We can't keep finding them like this.'

'That's all of them, I think. That's surely all the dead on that piece of property.'

'How do you know he hasn't buried a few somewhere else?'

'I don't. But there's no cutoff date.'

They both leaned forward, eager for an explanation.

'There's a wide spread of death dates,' I said. 'There's years' worth of killing, at least six. And the McGraw boy's only been dead three months. Unless the killer's been active for a very long time, chances seem good that all his victims are there together. He may have an earlier burial ground. He'll start a new one, for sure. But I'm thinking that one probably has all the past few years' victims in it.' I shrugged. Just my opinion.

Stuart and Klavin exchanged glances.

'Oh, and all the ones that are there, they were all killed in the same place,' I said. 'So it seems to me if that's the favored killing spot, all the bodies are there.'

Stuart looked pleased. 'Yes, we think they all died in the old shed there on the property.'

I was glad we hadn't opened the sagging doors while we were there. I didn't want to know what it looked like inside. From my moments with the dead, I had too clear an idea as it was.

'Is . . . is there another site you'd like me to check?' I dreaded them saying yes – but Max Stuart shook his head.

'We don't know how you do what you do,' he said. 'If we hadn't seen the results, we'd never believe you. But we've seen all the bodies, and we've heard how you found them, and no amount of investigation can find any link you ever had with any living soul here. So we have to believe you actually have some uncanny ability. We don't know its dimensions or its limits. Is there anything you can tell us about these boys?'

That must have been incredibly hard for him to say. I started to deny it automatically, but then I thought again. I'd explain as closely as I could. 'I see the moment of death,' I said. 'I see their bodies in the grave. Hold on,' I said, and I shut my eyes, gripping the arm of my chair with my good hand and hugging the bad arm close to me. The clothes had been thrown down into the grave . . .

'Most of them had crosses, right?' I said. Klavin started. Stuart glanced back at the board, as though this was printed right above the boys' names. 'But this is a religious community, and that may be a coincidence.' I looked back at the bodies, staring down into the earth in my memory. Oh, there. 'Broken bones,' I said. 'Some of them have broken bones.'

'Not from the torture?' Tolliver asked me.

'Well, yeah, some fresh ones from the torture. But at some time in the past, at least four of them had broken a bone.' I shrugged.

'Does that mean they were all abused as children? Is that the common thread?' Agent Stuart bent forward, as if he could pull the answer out of my head. 'What did these boys have in common? Why were they picked?'

'I don't know. I see what I see in a total flash: body, emotions, the situation. Once I saw the dead guy's pet, or maybe I just picked up on that from the dying person's thoughts. I don't see the person who caused that death.'

'Just tell us everything you do know,' Klavin said.

I looked from one to the other, suspiciously. They would listen, sure, and then give me those long-suffering looks that said they didn't believe a word I'd said. I'd had investigators tell me that before. 'Oh, please, any little detail will help . . .' Then it was like, 'Oh, that's all you can do? What good is that?'

'We promise we'll be respectful,' Klavin said, interpreting my look correctly. 'We realize you've had trouble with law enforcement agents in the past.'

I thought about it. I thought about the check Twyla Cotton had tucked into my hand the night before, the check that was over and above the amount we'd agreed upon for finding her grandson. I thought about the families crowded into the church, the grief and fear. Balanced against ridicule from men I'd never see again, that ridicule seemed like nothing.

So I took a deep breath, closed my eyes to help me concentrate, and looked into one of the graves again. I picked the one closest to the road. I pointed at it on the drawing. 'This is Tyler,' I said. 'He's been tortured. His skin was cut off in strips. He was raped. Clamps were put on his testicles. He was ready to die and welcomed death, because he knew no help was coming. The cause of death was strangulation. Some time in the recent past, he'd broken his leg.'

There was a quick intake of breath from one of the agents. I didn't open my eyes to see which one. Tolliver took my hand, and I gripped his hard. In my mind, I walked to the next grave. 'Hunter,' I said. 'Whipped, fucked, branded. He thought someone would come, right until the end. Lived for two days. Hypothermia.' Hunter had died in weather like this, cold and damp. The November abduction, I guessed. 'No broken bones. He had . . . scoliosis.' I saw the curve of his spine, shining below me.

It went on, the litany of torture and death. Sex and pain. Young men, used up and discarded. The two transient boys had had no particular bone problems, but the locals had . . . except for Jeff McGraw and Aaron Robertson. So that was fifty percent. The broken bones were a dead end.

They'd died of a variety of reasons. Most of the reasons were oddly passive, like the strangling and hypothermia that had killed Tyler and Hunter.

'Passive?' Klavin sounded indignant. He pulled a white hand-kerchief out of his pocket and patted his nose. He'd caught a cold probing around the killing site. 'Abducted, tortured, raped. That sounds pretty damn active to me.'

'That's not what I'm trying to express,' I said. 'They were let to die. They weren't stabbed or shot or poisoned, something that would cause instant, sure death. Hunter was just left there, and he died. Maybe weather interfered with their visits, maybe he – the killer – was bored with him. The strangulation – well, you can change your mind at the last few seconds on that, too.'

'I see what you mean,' said Stuart. 'Like the death was kind of an afterthought, or an experiment.'

'Like the pleasure didn't come with the death, but with what lay before,' I said. 'The pain was the attraction. And once they were all used up, and there wouldn't be any more reaction from them, they were no good anymore.' But that wasn't quite right. Stuart's comment about it being an experiment was closer to the thought I was trying to express.

Tolliver looked nauseated.

'That's not what we're getting from the other psychic,' Klavin said in challenge. 'She says that the killer sat and watched for the moment of death, taking an "orgasmic" pleasure from it.'

'Then Xylda's probably right,' I said instantly. 'I'm not a psychic, and she is. Or maybe . . .' But then I stopped. Both the agents were looking at me with that expression I knew so well. It said, as clearly as if they'd spoken out loud: *Watch her. She's going to back and fill and try to dovetail her imaginings with the story the other freak told us.*

'Did you ever think,' I said very slowly, very reluctantly, 'that there might be two killers?'

They were both goggling at me. I can't interpret the living nearly as well as I can the dead. I'd done well with the two state agents so far, but I had no idea what their faces were saying now.

'That's all I can tell you,' I said, and I got up to leave. Tolliver hastily got to his feet, too. 'Can we leave town?' I asked. 'Whenever we choose?'

'As long as you let us know how to reach you, you and your brother can hit the road,' Stuart said, in a tone that implied he'd be glad to see the back of us.

'I'm *not* her brother,' Tolliver said. He sounded as angry as if they'd been arguing about it for the previous hour.

Stuart looked surprised. 'All right, then. Whatever,' he said, shrugging. 'You two can go.'

I was so astonished by Tolliver's outburst that I had to fumble to gather up my purse and follow him out. He almost left me in his cloud of dust. He proceeded clear on out of the station, with me trailing behind. With a little awkwardness with the doors, I was slowed down enough that I just reached him when he got to our car. He was standing with his hands on the hood, glaring down at the gray paint. The remaining newspeople were shouting at us, but we completely ignored them.

I had no idea what to say. I just stood there and waited. I would have gotten in the car, but he had the keys in his hand. The mist in the air began to get heavier, become almost-rain. I was miserable.

Finally he straightened up, and without a word to me, he clicked the doors open. I stepped down from the curb to the door on the passenger side, opened it and got in, pulled it closed. Thank God it was my left arm that was out of whack. Still silently, Tolliver leaned over me to pull my seat belt around and click it shut.

'Where?' he said.

'The doctor's office.'

'You hurting?'

'Yes.'

He took a deep breath. He held it for a minute. Let it out. 'I'm sorry,' he said, leaving it open as to what he was sorry about.

'Okay,' I said, not really sure what ground we were walking on. I had a few ideas. Some of them were more frightening than others.

Tolliver had pinpointed the location of the doctor's office earlier on one of his drives to and from the hospital. Dr Thomason's red brick office was small, but the parking lot contained at least six cars. When I went in, I anticipated a long wait. The man who was not my brother went up to the window, told the woman behind it who I was and that I'd seen the doctor at the emergency room.

'We'll have to work her in, hon, it may take a little bit,' she said, reaching up to push her glasses back on her nose. Then she patted her helmet of sprayed hair lightly, to make sure it was still in good shape, I guess. Tolliver was working his old magic. He brought back a clipboard with forms to fill out.

'Apparently, we'll have plenty of time to do this,' he said, for my benefit. I was in a blue molded plastic chair against the far wall, and he came to join me. In the waiting room with us were a young mother and her baby, who was blessedly asleep, an elderly man with a walker parked in front of him, and a very nervous teenage boy, who was one of the tribe of foot jigglers.

A nurse in teal came to the door and called, 'Sallie and Laperla!' The young mother, hardly more than a teenager herself, got up with the infant carrier cradled in her arms.

'I wonder if she knows La Perla is a brand of underwear,' I murmured to Tolliver, but that barely got a smile from him.

The boy scooted down the line of chairs until he was within conversational distance of us. 'You the one found the bodies,' he said.

We both looked at him. I nodded.

Now that he'd told me who I was, he was stumped to think of something else to tell me. 'I knew all them,' he said finally. 'They was good boys. Well, maybe Tyler got into a little trouble now and then. And Chester, he wrecked his dad's new Impala. But we went to youth group together, at Mount Ida.'

'All of you?'

''Cept Dylan, he's a Catholic. They got their own youth group. But the rest of the churches, they all go together at Mount Ida.'

Ordinarily, I'd be bored stiff by this conversation, but I wasn't today.

'Did you read the stories in the paper today?' I asked.

'Yep.'

'You ever met those two boys from out of town?'

He looked surprised. 'No, never,' he said. 'I never heard of 'em. I think they were hitching or something. They were from way far away.'

I hadn't read the whole story. 'Way far away' to this boy might mean Kentucky or Ohio. He meant only that the two out-of-towners weren't from North Carolina.

The young mother came out, her baby crying now. They stopped at the window for a minute, then went out the front door. I could see the rain increasing. She would have to run for her car. The nurse called the old man, who got slowly and carefully to his feet. He shuffled through the door to the inner sanctum preceded by his walker, which had sliced-open tennis balls fixed on the front feet. It gave the walker a jaunty air. As soon as he was through the door, the nurse also called, 'Rory!' Our companion jumped to his feet and hurried back.

Now that we were by ourselves, I thought Tolliver would talk to me, but he leaned back and closed his eyes. He was shutting me out on purpose, and I didn't know what to make of it. If he was just in a snit over some unknown issue, then I could be in a snit right back. If I'd hurt him somehow, or he was harboring some personal grief unknown to me, then I wanted to help him. But if he persisted in being a butt-head, then he could just stew in his own juice.

I leaned my own head against the wall, closed my own eyes.

We probably looked like prize idiots.

After about ten minutes of this, the old man made his way out, and Rory sped past him to hold the door open. 'Allergy shot!' he called to us cheerfully as the old man shuffled past. I didn't know if he was explaining about his own visit or the old man's, but I nodded in acknowledgment.

The nurse opened the door yet again. She was a pretty, trim woman of about forty-five, with dark hair and bright blue eyes. She was so healthy and cheerful that I felt better just looking at her. 'Miss Connelly,' she said, and looked at us curiously.

Tolliver leaped to his feet and reached down to help me get up. This was just plain weird. I took his hand, and he hauled. The nurse showed us back to our designated waiting room. She weighed me and measured me and took my blood pressure, which was just fine. Then she began to ask me questions. It was mostly a repeat of what was on the forms, and the stuff from the hospital.

'So you just wanted to see Dr Thomason today to get him to check up on your injuries?' She sounded a little dubious.

'Yes, I'm having more pain than I'd expected, though that may be because I'm so very, you know, depressed.'

'Oh, I guess in your line of work, that would be . . . under-standable.'

'But surely – excuse me – you must be feeling the same way, here in Dr Thomason's office.'

'Because most of the boys were patients of ours? Yes, it's a sad thing. A sad, sad thing. You never think something like that would happen to anyone you know. And we knew all those boys, though a couple were patients of Dr Whitelaw's.'

'And Jeff's grandmother said he'd been in here recently,' I lied.

'Oh, you must have misunderstood her. Jeff goes to Dr Whitelaw.'

'I must have, sorry.'

'No problem. Let me tell Dr Thomason you're ready.' She sped out on her soft-soled nurse's shoes, and before I could think everything through, Dr Thomason breezed in. 'Hello, young lady. Marcy tells me you're not feeling as well as you'd hoped. You've been out of the hospital – let's see – just since yesterday? That right?' He shook his head, as though keeping track of the passing time was an incredible task. 'Well, let's have a look at you. No fever, blood pressure good,' he muttered, checking what Marcy had written on the chart. He ignored Tolliver as if Tolliver weren't there. Dr Thomason looked and thumped, and felt, and listened. He asked questions very quickly, hardly seeming to give himself time to absorb the answers . . . as if he did not believe I would tell him the truth, or as if he weren't interested in the truth. He came to stand right in front of me. Since I was up on the examining table, his eyes were slightly lower than mine, and as he looked up at my face his eyes looked almost luminous behind his gold-rimmed glasses.

He smiled at me. 'You seem fine to me, Ms Connelly. You're doing well as anyone could hope, after being attacked the way you were. No cause for alarm. You're healing right on schedule. Still got plenty of pain pills, I hope?'

'Oh, yes,' I said.

'Good. If they were all gone, I would worry about you. I think you're good to go. You're simply not going to feel wonderful for a while.'

'Oh. Okay, then, thanks for seeing me.'

'Right. Good luck. You're cleared to travel.' And he strode out, white coat flapping around his legs. He was delighted that I was leaving town, there was no two ways about it. Tolliver came over to help me down from the examining table, and we left in silence, paying on the way out. I glanced at the big filing cabinet in the receptionist's area. If I were a daring detective, I would think of a way to get the receptionist and the nurse out of the way and look through the files of the dead boys. But I wasn't, and there wasn't an excuse on this earth that would get the receptionist, the nurse, and the doctor out of the way long enough for me to do more than roll open the relevant drawers. Women did this all the time in movies and on television. They must have better scriptwriters. Real life didn't afford chances to examine private records unless you just broke in at night and read them, and I wasn't about to do that. My need to know who had done this would only carry me so far. I wouldn't risk going to jail myself.

And, I asked myself, why was I even concerned? The law enforcement people on hand were trained and efficient, and they had all the labs and their own expertise at their beck and call. They would find who'd done this, I had very little doubt. And the deaths would cease. Someone would go to jail after a long and lurid trial.

'There's something nagging me about this,' I said. I had to break the silence or burst. 'There's something wrong about this whole thing.'

'Something wrong, aside from eight dead kids?' Tolliver's voice was level, but his words were edgy.

'Yes. Something wrong.'

'Like what?'

'I just think that someone's in danger.'

'Why?'

'I don't know. There's just . . . where are you going?'

'Back out to the cabin.'

'Are we leaving?'

'The doctor said you were good to go.'

I turned on the car radio. After the warmth of the morning, the temperature was dropping sharply, just as predicted.

'And what's the weather news, Ray?' asked a female voice on one of the local stations.

'In a few words, Candy, the news is . . . stay home! There's an ice storm on the way, and you don't want to get caught in it. The highway patrol is advising all motorists to stay home tonight. Don't try to travel. Wait until the morning, and get another road advisory then.'

'So, Ray, we should bring in a lot of firewood and rent a lot of old movies?'

'Yeah, you can watch 'em until your electricity goes out!' Ray said. 'Get out your board games and flashlights and candles and stock up on water, folks.'

They went on for two more minutes, advising people in the area on how to weather the storm.

Without saying a word, we stopped at the little Wal-Mart.

'Stay in the car,' Tolliver said roughly. 'You'll just get jostled.' It was really crowded, and people were coming out with carts full of emergency stuff, so I didn't argue. We keep a throw blanket in the back of the car all winter, and I pulled it around me as he made his way inside.

Since there were only two of us to provide for and since we didn't plan on staying in the area any longer than we could help, Tolliver didn't have that much shopping to do. Nonetheless, it was at least forty-five minutes before he came out of the store with his buggy.

When we got back to the lake, we parked right by the stairs, about halfway down the steep drive. I decided I could help by moving one thing at a time from the car trunk to the middle of the stairs up to the living quarters, with pretty much a level swing of my arm. Then Tolliver could come down a few steps and get the stuff and put it away. It saved him a little work, and I felt like I was contributing. But I was shaking by the time we finished.

There was one more thing I needed to do. As a last-minute precaution, I backed the car up the sloping driveway and parked it parallel to the road. It wasn't a neat job since I was driving one-handed, but least we wouldn't have to negotiate an iced-over slope. I locked the car and went down the driveway and up the steps, moving carefully. The first licks of moisture were in the air.

Ted Hamilton came over a little later to make sure we'd heard the news about the weather. His wife, Nita, came with him, and she was just as small and slim and spry as her husband. They both seemed pretty excited by the prospect of the oncoming ice storm.

Tolliver had brought up so much wood that I thought we might have to leave Twyla some money to pay for it. The older couple nodded approvingly and settled in for a nice conversation. We unfolded the remaining two chairs, which had been leaning up against the wall. They were cloth spectator chairs, and they smelled a little off, but at least there were chairs. I could only offer the Hamiltons bottled water and a chocolate chip cookie, after we'd thanked Nita for her wonderful casserole, which we planned on finishing up for supper.

'Oh, no, we're fine,' Nita said, speaking for Ted and herself after a glance in his direction. 'You know, we've always been worried about that pine growing behind this cabin.'

'Why?' I asked.

'Pine roots are so shallow, and it overhangs this cabin,' Ted said. 'Pretty poor planning. I said something to Parker about it last summer, but he just laughed. I hope he's not sorry he didn't listen.'

Okay, they were that kind of people.

'We're out here year-round, not like the people who just come here when it's good weather and everything's going well,' Nita said. As if they were the people who really stuck with the poor lake when things weren't going so good. The true friends.

'We'll just have to hope the pine can handle the ice,' Tolliver said. 'Thanks for making us aware of it.' He maybe spoke a little dryly, because Ted's face tightened up a bit.

'I hope it stays up, too,' Ted said. 'Hate for something to happen to you two. Specially since you're visiting.'

'We're lucky to have you two out here,' I said, to smooth over Ted's ruffled feathers. 'I think I'd be scared if we were out here by ourselves.'

That made Ted and Nita both happy. 'We'll be right next door; don't forget to call us if you need us. We got all kinds of emergency gear, anything you might need.'

'That's really good to know,' I said, and they finally, thank God, rose. We kept assuring each other we were so happy to have the other there until they were really down the stairs and on their way back to their own cabin.

We had brought in a radio we kept in the trunk, and we turned it on. The weather news was still the same. The police news was still the same. I guess I'd harbored some wild hope that they'd arrest someone, some secret suspect. Or maybe someone would just walk in to confess, unable to bear the burden of guilt any longer. I said as much to Tolliver.

'A guy that could do this so often, to kids he knew,' Tolliver said, 'he's not going to walk in and say he's sorry unless he craves the attention. He's going to be pissed off that he can't do it again, that he has to relive all his old good times instead of making new ones. And you're the one responsible for that.'

I stared at Tolliver. This was what had been griping him.

'I don't think so,' I said, as calmly as I could. 'I think he came to the motel in a fit of anger, sure enough. But I'd think right now he'd be most concerned about keeping his skin intact and remaining at large. He's not going to do anything that would draw him to police attention. He's going to lie completely low.'

Tolliver thought that over; I'll give him that. 'I hope so,' he said, sounding unconvinced. He went to the window and looked out into the darkness. 'Can you hear it?' he asked.

I went to stand beside him at the window. I could hear a *plink-plink-plink* as the ice hit the glass. In the light that spilled from the window and the big security light, considerately aimed straight down, that the Hamiltons had fixed high on a pole, we could see tiny bits of ice hurtling toward the ground. It was eerily pretty. I had never felt so isolated in my life.

It didn't stop while we got ready for bed. I was tired, but not nearly as achy as I thought I would be. My head was okay now, and my arm was at least much better. I was able to cope with getting undressed and into my pajamas with less help, though Tolliver still had to do the bra-unhooking. We both read for a while; as Tolliver remarked, if we still had electric light we should use it. He was reading an old Harlan Coben, and I was reading Gavin de Becker's *The Gift of Fear*. Finally, I got too sleepy to keep my eyes open, and the bed had gotten warm around me, and I laid down the book and closed my eyes. Some time later, I heard Tolliver snap off the lamp between the beds, and then the only light that came in the room was a faint glow from the Hamiltons' security light. I'd been too exhausted to notice it the night before, and I didn't really think about it now . . . until I woke some time later and that light had vanished. The cabin was in absolute pitch darkness. The wind was howling around the corner of the cabin like a banshee, and I heard an odd sound in the wind.

'What is it?' I asked, and I heard myself sounding terrified.

'It's the frozen branches brushing together,' Tolliver said. 'I woke a few minutes ago and I've been listening. That's what I decided.'

I scare pretty easy where Mother Nature's involved. 'Okay,' I said, but I didn't sound any calmer.

'Come over here, I'm closer to the fire,' Tolliver said. 'Bring some blankets.'

I got out of the bed faster than I would have believed possible. My bare feet thudded on the boards as I yanked the blankets off my bed and brought them over to Tolliver's. I tossed them over the bed awkwardly. I slid in beside him and could hardly wait until the covers settled back over us. My teeth were chattering with cold and fear.

'Here, here,' he said, and put his arms around me. 'You were just out of the covers for a second or two.'

'I know,' I said. 'I'm a chicken. I'm a wuss.' I burrowed into his warmth.

'You're the bravest person I know,' he said, and when I pressed my face into his chest, he said, 'Are you listening to me?'

I pulled away enough to say, 'Yeah, I'm listening.'

'I'm not your brother,' he said, in an entirely different voice.

For a second, I didn't hear the roar of the wind around the cabin or the ominous shaking of the ice-laden branches. 'I know,' I said. 'I know that.'

And he kissed me.

I'd loved him for so long. Though everything might change, would change, I couldn't help but kiss him back.

It was a long kiss, a hard kiss. I'd seen him walk out so many doors with other women, and finally he was with me.

He started to say something, but I said, 'No, don't.' I kissed him again, my own initiation. That seemed to answer his question, if that was what he'd been going to ask. 'It's you,' I said, as he kissed my throat. I had my good hand under his sweatshirt, touching the precious skin of his back, his ribs, the almost flat nipples. I rubbed my face in the hair on his chest and his breath caught in his throat. His hands were not idle, either, and when they found my breasts he made another, altogether different noise. I thought I would weep with joy.

'The shirt's got to come off,' he said, and we worked to do that. 'Your arm?' he asked.

'Okay, don't worry about it,' I whispered. 'Just don't lie on it and it'll be okay.' I felt like I could get hit with a shovel all over again and I wouldn't care right now. My body and my heart were fully engaged for the first time. His hands seemed to know where to go and what to do when they got there. We knew each other so well in every other respect, it seemed only natural that we would easily understand each other's desires in this new activity. We already knew the appearance of each other's bodies, but not the textures or specifics; now we set out to learn those. His phallus was long, not as thick as some I'd encountered. He'd been circumcised. He had a slight upward curve. He was very sensitive around his balls. I loved touching him in places I'd never had the right to touch him before, and he loved being free to touch me between my legs. He loved it, and his fingers could be very clever.

'I wish I could see you,' he said, but I was glad for the dark. It made me a little braver, and I concentrated on my sense of touch, so I didn't have time to think. If I'd had time to think, it wouldn't have gone nearly as wonderfully as it did.

As it was, when we'd finally gotten off enough clothes, when I was sure neither of us was going to back down, when he finally entered me, it was the happiest moment of my life. I let go of my safety, and I said, 'I love you.'

And Tolliver said, 'Always.'

9

'I wish you had some Kleenex,' I murmured. I was resting on his chest. Our clothes were somewhere under the covers with us, or at least most of them were.

'Just use my sweatshirt,' he said in a lazy voice, and I stifled a giggle.

I felt around us, maybe tickling him a little in the process, and located what felt like his sweatshirt. 'I hope you weren't teasing, because I'm going to use it,' I said.

'Go right ahead.' He kissed the top of my head.

So I dried myself off a little, and patted him, too.

'Hey, be careful, that's my favorite body part,' he murmured.

'Mine, too,' I said, and he laughed. I felt his belly heave up and down. It was wonderful.

'I didn't think we'd ever do it,' he said, sounding suddenly serious.

'Me, either. I thought I'd keep on watching you go off with waitresses.'

'Or that cop, the one in Sarne. He really scared me. To say nothing of Manfred.'

'Really?'

'Oh, yeah. I mean, the piercings and the tattoos, that's a lot to put up with, but he's so gone on you. And his grandmother won't live forever. I had a feeling Manfred would say that when Xylda passed away he'd be free to escort you around, and you'd want me to have the normal life you're always trying to shove on me, and you'd dump me and hire Manfred to be your manager, and I'd have to go find a job somewhere away from you.'

'That's not going to happen, right?'

'Not if I have anything to say about it. And I do, right?'

'I believe I remember telling you how I felt about you.'

'I could stand to hear it again.'

'Uh-uh. You first.'

'I love you. I don't love you like I should love a sister. I love you like a man loves a woman. I want to be inside you again, right now. I want to have sex with you over and over.'

I had to stop myself from squeaking, *Really?* I took a deep breath. 'Why?' I said, which might have been worse.

'Because you're beautiful and smart,' he said instantly. 'Because you always try hard, no matter what you're doing. Because you're honest, and because I've wanted to see your boobs for years now, and damn it, it's dark in here and I can't.'

'I got to see your dick one time, when you got out of the shower and the door wasn't shut tight,' I said. 'It was a year ago.'

'Oh, and you been dreaming about it ever since,' he said hopefully.

'Well, actually . . . yes. But don't get a swelled head.'

'That's not the head that's swelling.'

'So I feel.' I licked my thumb and ran it over the lower head.

'Oh, God.'

I did it again.

He just drew in his breath this time. 'Keep doing that,' he said.

So I did, and then he found something to do to me that I liked, and we traded like that until we were ready to join again. This time was even better, and we reached the climax at the same time. I thought we would pound each other into pieces. This time he fell asleep almost as soon as we were through, and after I'd used his sweatshirt again, I did, too.

I was so deeply asleep the huge crash came as a complete surprise to me. In fact, it scared me so much I almost started screaming.

'Tree came down,' said Tolliver. 'It was a tree. Hold on, baby, it wasn't on us.'

We scrambled into all our clothes. Tolliver rejected the sweatshirt with the simple remark 'Damp,' and found his suitcase by patting the area where it was supposed to be. He fished out another one, he told me, and I heard him fumbling around further. I'd gotten out of the bed on the other side and I was feeling the floor for my boots.

With lots of 'Oops' and 'Where are you? I found the flashlight,' we finally connected and went to the window. Tolliver switched the flash on, and we looked outside. It was one of the big searchlight kind, and he'd gotten it at Wal-Mart that afternoon. It showed us that the pine tree the Hamiltons had been so worried about had indeed fallen under the weight of the ice. But due to some force we couldn't fathom, it had fallen at an angle and blocked the Hamiltons' driveway instead. I had an awful feeling their car was under it.

'Does their roof look okay?' I asked. But we couldn't tell.

'I guess I have to go to over and check on them,' Tolliver said.

'I'll come,' I said.

'No, you won't. Not with a broken arm, you're not getting out there to walk around on slick ice. If there's something wrong over there, I'll come back and get you,' he said. 'Hey, how's your arm feeling? We didn't bump it too much?'

'No, it's pretty good.'

'So I'll be back in a few minutes.'

I really couldn't argue with his reasons for wanting me to stay behind. It made sense.

I waited in the cold cabin while Tolliver worked his way down the ice-slick stairs and began a slow progress across the front yard of our cabin and over to the Hamiltons' place. I poked the fire and added a log, and then I pulled a chair over to the window and wrapped myself in a blanket.

Half of me was intent on following the light held in Tolliver's hand, while the other half was standing a little distance apart screaming, 'You just slept with Tolliver! You just slept with Tolliver!' in tones of mingled horror and delight. Only time would tell if we'd just (literally) fucked up the best relationship we'd ever had – or if we'd opened the door to greater happiness.

Even thinking that felt sappy. But God, it might all be okay. I snapped out of this incoherent internal babbling to realize that Tolliver was having a hard time getting to the door of the Hamilton house because of the tree branches.

I opened the window, with a lot of effort. One-handed, it was a bitch.

'You need me to come help?' I called. My voice was startling.

I felt Tolliver was restraining himself from saying that was the last thing in the world he needed. 'No, thanks,' he called back, with wonderful restraint. Even hearing his voice made me catch my breath. There was something different about it, there was. Some tension that had kept him taut and stretched had snapped. I was as moony and dreamy as a girl who'd had her first French kiss, and I made myself enter the here and now.

The Hamiltons' door was opening, and I could see Ted Hamilton.

He was wearing a hat, which looked ridiculous but actually was pretty smart, considering how much of your body heat you lose through your head. He and Tolliver exchanged a few words, and then Tolliver began making his way back over to our temporary home.

I opened the door when he reached the top of the steps, and he propelled himself inside.

'Oh, God, it's cold out there,' he said, and he made a beeline to the fire. He piled on a couple more pieces of wood and stood there for a moment, his face as close to the fire as he could get it without actually singeing his mustache. He closed his eyes with the bliss of the warmth.

'Were they okay?'

'Yeah. Mad. Ted said a few words I think he'd been saving up since the Korean War. I was glad I'm not a member of the McGraw-Cotton family. He actually said he was gonna sue.'

'Wonder if he'd have a chance in court.'

Tolliver held out a hand, tipped it one way then another. 'I want to say that would be ridiculous, but you know how the justice system can be.'

We fell silent, looked at each other.

'Are you sorry?' he asked.

'No. You?'

'We should have done it a long time ago. You kept saying I should leave you. I didn't know if that was what you wanted or not. I finally decided to sink or swim. You were thinking what?'

'I was thinking I loved you so much that I shouldn't keep you around me, because you must not find out I felt that way. I thought you might think it was gross or sick. Or . . . you might feel kind of sorry and responsible for me, which would be worse.'

'As far as I'm concerned, you're the original lemons-into-lemonade girl,' he said. 'You get struck by lightning, and instead of wailing and moaning about it and applying for disability, you discover a usable skill and figure out a way to make it work for you. You've got the brains and the charisma to make it in your very own business.'

'Charisma,' I said scornfully.

'You do, or hadn't you noticed the way men like you?'

'Adolescent boys like me,' I said. 'That's not exactly a big plus.'

'Not just adolescents,' Tolliver said. 'They just don't know how to hide it.'

'You're saying I'm a guy magnet? Get real.'

'Not in the sense that someone like, I don't know, Shakira or Beyonce is. You're not a blond shake-your-booty kind of girl, but you've got your very own attraction, and believe me, men feel it.'

'As long as this man feels it,' I said. I looked up into his face.

'You made me stop breathing there for a minute,' he said.

I looked down and smiled. 'At least you know everything bad about me already.'

'I didn't know you made that sound when you came,' he said, and I did a little not-breathing all my own.

'I didn't know you had that slight curve in your dick,' I countered.

'Yeah . . . ah, how does that . . . I mean, is that okay?'

'Oh, yeah,' I assured him. 'Touches something wonderful inside me.'

'Oh? Hmmm.'

'And I wondered, if you were up for it . . .'

'Yeah?'

'You'd maybe touch it again?'

'I think you could persuade me. If you went to great lengths.'

'Would you like me to go down on you?'

By the light of the flickering fire, I could see his pupils dilate. 'Oh,' he said.

'Lick you? Like this?' I extended my tongue and did a little flickering of my own.

'That would do the trick,' he said hoarsely. 'Jesus, Harper, I don't understand why we don't have guys following us from town to town just to watch you do that.'

'Because I've never done it for anyone but you,' I said. 'You don't think I'd say something like that to anyone else, do you?'

'Please,' he said. 'Please do that for me. And no one else.'

I knelt before him carefully, and pulled down his sweats and the long underwear he'd pulled on before his excursion to the Hamiltons'. Somehow, him still having clothes on seemed to make what I was doing even naughtier.

I looked up to make sure he was looking as I made good on my promise. Oh, yeah. He watched my every move as if I'd hypnotized him.

'Oh, my God,' he said. He reacted in a very gratifying way.

In my limited experience, men were always so glad to get sex, they were pleased with it no matter how inexperienced their partner was. They weren't there to run a critique group. They were there to have an orgasm. Provided you put their penis in the correct hole and made enthusiastic noises, they went away happy. It was like signing up for basic cable. That was what you'd sign up for if you were getting it for a person you didn't know well.

'For you, baby, HBO,' I said, and made him moan.

I woke the next morning to brilliant clear light coming through the bare windows. I blinked and shuddered. I burrowed deeper under the covers, closer to the other body in the bed. Tolliver! I was in bed with Tolliver and we were naked. I sighed with bliss and kissed his neck, which was the easiest thing to reach.

'I guess I have to stop calling you "sis" now,' he said, his voice heavy with sleep.

'Uh-huh.'

'I guess Manfred is shit out of luck.'

'Uh-huh.'

'I guess the chainsaws we hear mean that there are people outside the cabin cutting up the tree, and we don't have any clothes on.'

'Oh . . . no.'

'Yeah, hear 'em?'

I did. Wouldn't you know that even though there were fifty empty cabins and houses around this lake, we'd be in the one that had neighbors? And I was going to have to get out of the warm bed to go to the bathroom, and I'd have to flush it by pouring water in. Yuck. And I definitely needed a sponge bath, for which I'd have to stand naked in the freezing bathroom, since there weren't any curtains on the windows and the stupid Hamiltons were out there trying to free their car from the clutches of the tree.

'I hope their car is a pancake,' I said.

'You don't mean it.'

'No. Yes. Sort of.' I laughed. 'I just don't want to get out of the bed.'

'Do you think they'll stomp up the steps and look in?'

'Oh, yes, any minute.' His hand found mine under the huge pile of blankets and he gripped my fingers tightly.

'I don't want to leave this bed, either,' he said and kissed me. His hand released mine to skim across my ribs. 'But I'm exhausted, too.'

'Oh, poor thing. Did I wear you out?'

'I'm a shadow of myself.'

'That's funny, you feel substantial enough,' I said, rubbing my hand across his (okay, flat and muscular) belly.

'Woman, I need fuel,' he said. 'If I'm going to keep up with your insatiable demands.'

'You haven't even met insatiable yet,' I said. Then I dropped the smile. 'I can't believe we did it, Tolliver. This is all I ever wanted.'

'Me, too. But my metabolism is telling me to eat first and talk later.'

I kissed him. 'So shall it be.' I slid my sweatpants back on and made a dash for the bathroom. Fifteen excruciatingly cold minutes later, I was more or less clean, and I was wearing several layers of clean clothes. I had on two pairs of socks and some rubber boots that Tolliver had pulled off the shelf at Wal-Mart the day before. While Tolliver took his turn in the bathroom, I looked on the shelves above the stove to find a cheap metal pan. I put some water in it and set it on a level place in the large fire. When there was a chance the water was fairly warm, I used Tolliver's folded-over sweatshirt to get the pan off the fire and I poured the hot water into two mugs with powdered hot chocolate in them. We had some Pop-Tarts. Sugar would help restore our energy.

Tolliver smiled when he saw a little steam coming up from the mugs. 'Aw, that's great,' he said. 'Wonder Woman.' We sat in the two chairs closest to the fire and drank and ate while we listened to the battery-powered radio. The roads were in terrible condition, and though the temperature would rise above freezing by the midafternoon, roads wouldn't be clear until the next morning. Even then, they'd be patched with ice. Power crews were out repairing downed power lines, which should be reported, and checking on isolated farms. Citizens were urged to check on their elderly neighbors. I glanced out the window. 'The Hamiltons are okay, Tolliver,' I said.

'Have you tried your cell phone?' he asked.

When I turned it on, I had a few messages.

The first one was from Manfred.

'Hey, Harper, my grandmother got real sick late yesterday, and she's in the hospital here in Doraville,' Manfred said. The second message was from Twyla, hoping we were okay out there at the cabin. The third message was from Manfred. 'It would be great if you and Tolliver would stop by; there are some issues about Grandmother I'd like to talk about,' he said, very much as though he were trying to sound adult but not quite achieving it.

'That sounds bad,' I said. 'That sounds like turning-off-the-machines bad.'

'Do you think we can make it into town?' Tolliver said. 'I'm not even sure we can make it up the driveway.'

'Did you not notice that I moved the car before the storm hit? It's up by the road.'

'Where anyone trying to drive on that narrow road can bash it?'

'Where we won't have to get up an icy slope in it and possibly end up in the lake.' Apparently, happy sex and our altered relationship didn't preclude our occasional squabble.

'Okay, that was a good idea,' he said. 'We'll see if we can get into town around noon, when whatever's going to melt has melted.'

Somehow we never got around to talking further about what had happened between us, and somehow that was okay. Tolliver got restless, which I'd expected, and he bundled up and went outside to help Ted Hamilton for an hour or two. When he came back up the stairs, I could hear him stomping snow and ice off his boots. I was reading by the fire, and I was getting a little stir-crazy. I looked up expectantly, and he came over and bent to give me a casual kiss on the cheek, just as if we'd been married for years.

'Your face is freezing,' I said.

'My face is frozen,' he corrected me. 'Did you call Manfred? We saw a car go by while we were out there working, and they made it okay.'

'I'll call him now,' I said, and found I had to leave a message on Manfred's voice mail.

'Probably has it turned off while he's inside the hospital,' Tolliver said.

I opened my mouth to ask a few questions about our new relationship, and once again I saw the wisdom of closing it. After all, why would Tolliver know any more about it than me?

I relaxed and let the tension drain away. We would make this up as we went along. We didn't have to send out announcements. I did have a sudden awful thought. 'Ah, this new thing we've got may be a little confusing for our sisters,' I said.

I could tell from the expression on Tolliver's face that this hadn't occurred to him. 'Yeah,' he said. 'You know . . . you're right about that. Mariella and Gracie . . . oh, God. Iona.'

Our aunt Iona – well, strictly speaking, my aunt Iona – had gotten guardianship of our two half sisters, who were much younger than us. Iona and her husband were raising the girls in as different a way as possible from the life they'd led with my parents. And in a way, they were absolutely right. It was much better to be brought up as a fundamentalist Christian than as a kid who didn't know what a real meal was, a kid at the mercy of whatever scum our parents let into the trailer. Because that was the way I'd been brought up after my preteen years. Mariella and Gracie were well clothed, well fed, and clean. They had a stable home to come back to every day, and they had rules to follow. These were great things, and if their early years led them to rebel against this regimen now and then, well, so be it. We were trying to build bridges to the girls, but it was uphill work.

Iona's reaction to our new relationship hardly bore thinking about. 'Ah, I guess that's a bridge we'll have to cross when we come to it,' I said.

'We're not hiding anything,' Tolliver said, with sudden firmness. 'I'm not going to even attempt it.'

That had a very nice permanent sound to it. I'd been sure how I felt, but it's always nice to know your partner is feeling the same way. I let out a silent sigh of relief.

'No hiding,' I said.

We ate peanut butter sandwiches for lunch. 'Ted's wife probably whipped up a four-course heart-healthy meal on a woodstove,' I said.

'Hey, you eat heart healthy most of the time.'

My eating habits had gone by the wayside while we stayed in Doraville, for one reason or another. I'd have to resume them soon. With variable health problems like I had, it paid to stave off as much as I could by following good rules.

'How's your leg?' Tolliver asked, following the same train of thought.

'Pretty good,' I said, extending my right leg and rubbing the quads. 'I can tell I haven't been running in a few days, though.'

'When do you get to leave off the cast?'

'Five weeks, the doctor said. We'll have to try to be in St Louis then, so I can check with our doctor there.'

'Great.' Tolliver smiled so broadly that I knew he was thinking of several things that would be much easier when my arm healed.

'Hey, come here,' he said. He was sitting on the floor in front of the fire, leaning back against a chair. He patted the floor between his legs, and I eased myself against him. He put his arms around me. 'I can't believe I can do this now,' he said. If my heart could have wagged its tail, it would have. 'It's okay to touch you. I can touch you as much as I want. I don't have to think twice every time.'

'Were you really thinking twice?'

'I thought I might scare you off.'

'Same here.'

'Idiots.'

'Yeah, but now we're okay.'

We sat there in contentment until Tolliver told me his leg was asleep, and we figured if we were ever going to try to go into town, the time was right.

10

Several times during the trip into town, I was almost sorry I'd turned on my cell phone and gotten Manfred's message. That was the most frightening driving experience I've ever had. Tolliver managed it, but he said every bad word in his vocabulary, even a few I didn't quite understand. We met one other car on our journey, and it was filled with teenage boys, who all have a built-in death wish. As soon as I thought that, I remembered the boys in the frozen ground, and I was sorry.

There were mighty few visitors' cars parked in the hospital parking lot. Snow had covered the sodden yard around the little building, so it looked almost pretty. When we went in, the reception lady was not at her desk, so we wandered back until we found a nurses' station. We inquired there about Xylda Bernardo.

'Oh, the psychic lady,' the nurse said, looking a bit impressed. 'She's in ICU. Her grandson is in the ICU waiting area, if you want to see him.' She gave us directions, and we found Manfred sitting with his head in his hands. He was in one of those waiting areas that's just a little nook lined with chairs and littered with coffee cups and old magazines. It looked as though the hospital cleaning staff hadn't made it in this morning. That wasn't good.

'Manfred,' I said. 'Tell us what's happening with Xylda?'

He raised his head and we could see his eyes were red. His face was tear-stained.

'I don't understand,' he said. 'She was better. She kind of collapsed last night, but this morning she was better. The doctor had been in to see her. The minister came and prayed with us. They were going to move her to a regular room. Then she just – I left just for a minute, just to get some coffee and use the phone – and when I came back she was in a coma.'

'I'm so sorry,' I said. There's really nothing you can say that'll make the situation any better, is there?

'What does the doctor say?' Tolliver asked. I sat beside Manfred and put my hand on his shoulder. Tolliver sat at right angles to us and leaned forward, his elbows on his knees. I looked at his face, so serious, so focused, and I felt a wave of love that almost knocked me over. I had to concentrate to get my mind back on Manfred and Xylda's misfortune.

'It's the same doctor that saw you, Harper,' Manfred said. 'The guy with white hair. He seems okay. He says he doesn't think she's going to wake up. He doesn't know why she took such a turn, but he says he's not surprised. It's all . . . it doesn't seem definite enough. No one's telling me exactly what's happening with her. I thought medicine was sharper than that now.'

'Have you called your other relatives?'

'My mother is on her way. But in the traffic conditions between Tennessee and here, there's no way she'll get here before Grandmother passes away.'

This was awful. 'Your mom's relying on you to make the decisions?'

'Yeah. She says she knows I'll do the right thing.'

What a great thing for a mother to say, but what a huge responsibility.

'I was hoping,' Manfred said after a long moment, 'if you could go in to see her, you'd be able to give me some advice.' He was looking at me when he said this, and he said it very seriously. I understood what he meant, after a moment. He wanted to know if her soul was still there.

Okay. I was cringing inside, but I nodded.

He showed me the door to the ICU unit, which of course was quite small at such a little hospital. I thought Xylda would benefit from going to somewhere larger with more machines – isn't that what it boils down to? – but there was no way to get her there. Nature had overthrown technology once again. That seemed amazing to me, as I looked at all the machines Xylda Bernardo was connected to. They silently recorded everything that was going on inside her; and yet, when Manfred wanted to know something as basic as whether or not his grandmother's soul was still attached to her body, he had to ask me to do it.

I held Xylda's limp hand for a moment, but it wasn't necessary for the task that had been set me. Xylda's soul was still there. I was almost sorry. It would have simplified the decisions ahead for her family if her soul had already departed.

Barney Simpson stuck his head in the door and looked at me quizzically.

'I thought we'd kicked you out,' he said, keeping his voice low out of respect for the quiet figure on the bed.

'You make visits to the patients in the ICU?'

'No, to the families of those patients. I saw someone in here, so I came to check.'

'I'm just standing in for her grandson for a minute,' I said.

'You're a good friend. This is the other lady, right?'

'Xylda Bernardo. The psychic. Yes.'

'She told the law enforcement people about Chuck Almand.'

After a second, I nodded. That was more or less true.

'Yes.'

'What an extraordinary talent,' Simpson said. He ran a hand over his bushy dark hair, trying to tame it, but he didn't have any luck.

'She's definitely out of a different mold,' I said. I took a step toward the door. I wanted to report back to Manfred. Simpson stood back to let me pass. A nurse went by us as she entered Xylda's room. 'You again,' she said to Simpson. 'Can't get rid of you today.'

'Nope. My car's iced in,' he said, smiling.

'Oh, so your stay isn't voluntary,' she said.

'I'd love to go home.'

So would I.

By the time I reached Manfred, Barney Simpson had continued on with his round of visiting.

'She's still intact,' I said. Manfred closed his eyes, whether in dismay or gratitude I couldn't imagine.

'Then I'll wait in there with her,' he said. 'Until she goes.'

'What can we do for you?' Tolliver asked.

Manfred looked at him with an expression that almost broke my heart. 'Nothing,' he said. 'You've claimed her, I can see. But having you two as friends is good, and I'm really grateful you made the effort to get into town to see us. Where are you staying?'

We told him about the lake cottage. He smiled at the story of the Hamiltons. 'When you two leaving?' he asked. 'I guess the cops have cut you loose?'

'I guess we'll leave tomorrow,' I said. 'But we'll come by the hospital to check on you before we go. Sure there's nothing I can get you?'

'Since the hospital still has electricity,' Manfred said, 'the shoe may be on the other foot. You can get hot food here. The cafeteria is open.'

The phrase 'hospital cafeteria' didn't sound very appetizing, but 'hot food' did. We coaxed Manfred into going with us, and we ate hot biscuits with gravy poured over them, and some hamburger steak, and some green beans. I had to swear to myself I'd do double running the next week.

At the last minute, I almost turned back to stay with Manfred. He seemed so alone. But he said, 'There's no point in you staying here, Harper, as much as I appreciate the offer. There's just sitting and waiting here, and I can do that on my own. My mother should be here tomorrow morning, if the roads clear. I'll step out of Grandmother's room from time to time to check my voice mail.'

I gave Manfred a hug, and Tolliver shook his hand. 'We'll come if you need us, man,' he said, and Manfred nodded.

'I don't think she'll last the night,' he said. 'She's tired out. But at least she had a last moment in the sun yesterday. She told me she thought the boy definitely killed the animals, but that something else was going on there, too.'

'Like what?' I'd been moving away, but now I turned back to face Manfred. This was bad news.

He shrugged. 'She never told me. She said the whole property was surrounded by a swamp of evil.'

'Hmmm.' Well, 'swamp of evil' sounded pretty bad. What could Xylda have meant? See, this is what makes me nuts about psychics.

'She used a different word.'

'Than what?'

'Than swamp. She called it a . . . miasma? Is that a word?'

Manfred wasn't stupid, but he wasn't much of a reader, either. 'Yeah, it is. It means, like, a thick unpleasant atmosphere, right, Tolliver?'

Tolliver nodded.

Had I missed something, like a body? Had I made a mistake? The idea was so strong, so shocking, that I hardly noticed the bitter cold as we made our way to our car. 'Tolliver, we've got to go back to that property.'

He looked at me as if I were nuts. 'In this weather, you want to go poke around private property?' he asked, getting all his objections in one sentence.

'I know the weather is wrong for this. But Xylda . . .'

'Half the time Xylda was an old fraud, and you know it.'

'She wouldn't be about this.' A thought occurred to me. 'Do you remember when we were in Memphis, she said, "In the time of ice you'll be so happy?"'

'Yeah,' he said. 'I do remember that. And it is the time of ice and up until you wanted to go trespassing, I was happy.' He didn't look happy. He looked worried. 'As a matter of fact, I wanted to go back to the cabin and stoke up the fire and get happy again.'

I smiled. I couldn't help it. 'Why don't we just ask?' I said.

'Just ask this guy if we can look over his property again? Just ask him if he snuck some bodies in there while we weren't looking? Because there's a miasma of evil around it?'

'Okay, I get your point. I just think we have to do something.'

Tolliver had started the car the minute we got in and the heater was finally working. I bent over a little to let the hot air blow directly on my face.

'We'll go by, have a look,' he said, very reluctantly.

'Then we'll follow your plan about the cabin.'

'Okay, that part sounds good.'

We traced our route of yesterday and alternately slid and bumped our way through the nearly deserted streets to the back of Tom Almand's property. The area where all the police and media vehicles had parked was a churned-up mess, the black mud hardened into a sea filled with black crests. Tolliver parked where it would be very hard to see our car from the house. I got out of the car and moved carefully to the barn. What had I missed there?

Inside the barn, the air was cold and still and stale, and there were several holes in the dirt floor. This was where the sacrificed animals had been exhumed. I thought about the boy, Chuck, but then I banished the picture of his sad eyes from my mind, and I concentrated on opening myself to the vibration that came uniquely from the dead – the human dead.

When I opened my eyes, Chuck Almand was standing in front of me.

'Oh, God, you scared me, boy!' I said, raising a gloved hand to my throat.

He was wearing heavy boots and a heavy coat, a hat and gloves and a scarf, so he was appropriately dressed for the weather, at least.

'What are you doing here?' he asked. 'Did you think you'd missed something?'

'Yes,' I said. I had no reasonable story to tell. 'Yes, I wondered if I'd missed something.'

'You thought there might be dead people here?'

'I was checking.'

'There aren't any. They're all dug up, out at Davey's old farm.'

'You don't know of any others?'

His eyes flickered then, and I heard someone else outside. Thank God.

The door of the barn opened, and my brother came in. 'Hey, Chuck,' he said casually. 'Honey, you finished?'

'Yeah, I think so,' I said. 'Negative results, like we expected.'

Chuck Almand's light, bright eyes were fixed on me. 'Don't be scared of me,' he said.

'I don't believe I am,' I said, trying to smile. And it was true I wasn't exactly frightened of the boy. But I did feel very uncomfortable around him, and I was concerned about him in an impersonal kind of way.

Then I heard another voice calling from outside, 'Chuck! Hey, buddy, you in there? Who's here?' To my bewilderment, Chuck's face changed in the blink of an eye, and the boy punched me in the stomach as hard as he could. His lips moved as he hit; I saw them on my way down to the floor.

'Get out of here!' he screamed as I stared up at him from my kneeling position on the cold dirt. 'Get out! You're trespassing!'

Tom Almand dashed in, the door to the old barn creaking and groaning as it kept moving after he'd shoved it. 'Son, son! Oh, my God, Chuck, what did you do?'

Tolliver was at my side, helping me up. 'You little son of a bitch,' he said to the boy before me. 'Don't touch her again. She wasn't doing anything to you.'

I didn't say anything, I only stared up into his eyes, my good arm across my middle. He might hit me again. I wanted to be ready this time.

But the only thing that happened was a lot of talk. Tom Almand apologized over and over. Tolliver made it clear he wasn't going to let anyone else pound on me. He also made it clear that he didn't want the boy anywhere around me again. Tom thought we shouldn't have been trespassing. Tolliver said the police had been glad to welcome us here to this same spot the day before. Tom informed us that it wasn't the day before and that we needed to get the hell off his property. Tolliver said we'd be glad to, and he was lucky we weren't calling the police to report his son's assault on my person.

I sagged against Tolliver as he helped me out to the car. He was in a complete state. He was trying so hard not to say 'I told you so' that he was practically bursting at the seams. But God bless him, he managed not to say it.

'Tolliver,' I said, when we were safely in the car and on our way back to the cabin.

He stopped in mid rant. 'Yes?'

'Right after he hit me, before he started yelling at me, the boy said, "I'm sorry. Come find me later," ' I said.

'I didn't hear him say that.'

'He said it real low, so you wouldn't hear. So his dad wouldn't hear.'

'He said you should *come find him*?'

'He said he was sorry. Then he told me to come find him later.'

'So is he schizophrenic? Or is he trying to persuade his dad that he is?'

'I think he's trying to persuade his dad of something, I'm not sure what.'

The rest of the drive back to the cabin, we were silent. I don't know what was in Tolliver's head, but mine was busy trying to understand what had just happened.

When we parked at the top of the slope again, we noticed that the Hamiltons' place was silent and still except for the smoke rising from the chimney. Maybe they were taking a nap. That sounded like a good idea.

'I'm not pleased with myself, thinking like a seventy-year-old,' I grumped as we made our way down the drive to the steps up to the door.

'Oh, I bet we'll think of something to do that the Hamiltons aren't doing,' Tolliver said, in such an intimate voice I felt all of my blood rushing to a critical point.

'I don't know; the Hamiltons are pretty hale and hearty for people in their seventies.'

'I think we can give them a run for their money,' Tolliver said.

We started right away, and with pauses to throw some more wood on the fire and lock the door, we managed to make a good effort. I don't know how the Hamiltons' afternoon went, but ours went just fine. And we did eventually get the nap.

That night we made more hot chocolate and ate more peanut butter. We also had some apples. I like to think we would have talked to each other just as much if the electricity had been working, but maybe we wouldn't have. There's an intimacy to being alone together in the near darkness, and every time we made love I felt surer of him, and our new relationship became more solid. Neither of us would have taken the step off the edge of the cliff if we hadn't been after more than yet another one-night stand.

'That last waitress in Sarne,' I said. I gave him a narrow-eyed stare. 'That was the one I really minded, and for a couple of weeks I couldn't figure out why.'

'Well, two things. I was hoping you'd come in on us, clobber the woman, and throw her out and tell me I was your one and only; and barring that, I was horny,' Tolliver said. 'Plus, she offered. Okay, that's three things.'

'I was tempted,' I admitted. 'But I never felt I could risk it. I kept thinking, What if I ask him not to, and he asks me why not? What can I say back to him? No, don't do it, I love you? And you would say, Ohmigod, I can't travel with you anymore.'

'I was thinking you'd say the same thing,' he said. 'You'd say that you couldn't be with someone who wanted to go to bed with you all the time, you had to have a clear head to do your job, and you didn't want to fog it up with dealing with lust. After all, you picked fewer bed partners than me.'

'I'm a woman,' I said. 'I'm not gonna go around sleeping with whoever wants to sleep with me. I need a little bit more than that to go on.'

'Not all women are like that,' he said.

'Yeah, well, lots of them are.'

'Do you hold it against me? Those random women?'

'Not as long as you're disease free. And I know you are.' He got tested as regularly as he could, and he always used a condom.

'So,' he said, 'we're together now.'

He was asking a question. 'Yes,' I said. 'We're together.'

'You're not gonna go with anyone else.'

'I'm not. You?'

'I'm not. You're it.'

'Okay. Good.'

And just like that, we were a couple.

It seemed strange to get ready for bed and then climb into Tolliver's.

'We don't always have to sleep in the same bed,' he said. 'Some beds are going to be narrow and even lumpier than this one. But I want to sleep with you. Really sleep.'

I wanted to really sleep with him, too, and it was easier than I thought. In fact, hearing his breathing beside me seemed to help me doze off faster than I normally did. I hadn't slept in the same bed with anyone for a long time; and maybe not for a whole night since I'd shared a bed with my sister Cameron. When I'd stayed with a guy, I often hadn't made it through till morning.

I did wake up a few times during the night, record my new situation, and fall right back to sleep. On one of these moments of wakefulness, I saw that my phone was vibrating against the floor by the bed. I reached down and scooped it up.

'Hello?' I said quietly, not wanting to wake Tolliver.

'Harper?'

'Yes.'

'She died, Harper.'

'Manfred, I'm so sorry.'

'Harper, maybe someone killed her. I wasn't in the room.'

'Manfred! Don't say that out loud. Don't say that where anyone can hear you. Where are you?'

'I'm standing outside the hospital.'

'Why do you think that?'

'I think that because she was getting better. The nurse even said she thought Grandmother was going to speak. Then she died.'

'Manfred, you need us to come in?'

'Not until morning. It's too bad out there. There's nothing you can do. You stay in bed. I'll see you in the morning. My mother should be here then, too.'

'Manfred, you need to go back to the motel and lock the door.

Don't eat or drink anything at the hospital, all right?' I tried to think of more advice to give him. 'And don't be alone with anyone, okay?'

'I hear you, babe.' He sounded barely conscious. 'I'm getting in the car now, and I'm going to drive to the motel.'

'Hey, call me when you get there.'

He called again within ten minutes to tell me he was safely locked in his room. Furthermore, he'd seen some reporters who were up drinking, and he'd told them someone had been following him. So they were as alert as drinking people could be, and they all professed to be disgusted that someone was following him around on such a sad night. Somehow they all knew already that Xylda had passed. Maybe they were paying one of the hospital staff to be a news clearinghouse.

None of this woke Tolliver, which surprised me until I recalled he'd been outside helping Ted Hamilton earlier. Plus, we'd had our own share of vigorous indoor exercise.

It was after three in the morning when I talked to Manfred the last time. I lay awake praying for him for a few minutes. Since I knew he was safe, and Xylda was beyond my help, I slept again.

11

Sometime during the night, or rather toward the early morning, the electricity came back on. I'm sure it happened after dawn, because it didn't wake us up. I was lying there wondering why the lamp across the room was on, when I realized the miracle of electricity was once again visiting us. I had mixed feelings about electricity, for obvious reasons, but on this day I was glad to see it. I stuck a toe out from under the mound of blankets, and it didn't freeze immediately. I smiled. This was really good. And my arm was much better.

I hauled myself out of bed and went into the bathroom. I brushed and sponged, and changed my clothes, managing to do everything but deal with the bra. That I just left off. It wasn't that noticeable anyway since I was wearing both a tank top and a sweatshirt, so who was going to know?

The police, that's who. Just as I was trying to figure out how to put on clean socks, there was a knock at the door. I realized I'd heard the feet coming up, I'd just been thinking so hard about dressing myself I hadn't paid attention.

I was glad I was awake to answer the door, especially since I'd introduced Tolliver as my brother to the police chief, and she was here right now, and only one bed was in use. It was credible that I could have gotten up first and made my bed, and I just didn't want to have to explain or endure the horrified stare I'd get otherwise.

Sandra Rockwell had bigger fish to fry than worrying about our sleeping arrangements, as it turned out. Tolliver sat up and looked as she pushed past me into the cabin, looking around her as she did so. 'Sheriff,' I said, 'what's up?'

Sandra looked under the beds, in the bathroom, and then she opened the trapdoor and went down in the storage shed underneath. When she came up, she looked more relaxed, if not any happier.

'Okay, I'm not happy with you doing this,' I said, and Tolliver barely bothered turning his back while he pulled off his sleep pants and pulled on his jeans. She gave him a good enough look that I knew she could replay the moment later, and I felt like whaling her one.

'Have you seen Chuck Almand?' she asked.

I was very surprised, which was a massive understatement.

'Not since yesterday. We saw him then. Why would we have seen him? What's happened to him?'

'Can you tell me exactly what happened?'

'Ah. Okay. I wanted to be sure I hadn't overlooked anything in the barn. It just seemed like one of those loose ends, you know? So I went back. I knew it was a stupid thing to do, but I hoped I could just slip in and out without anyone knowing. Chuck came in while I was in there. He got mad at me, and hit me.'

'Hit you?' But she wasn't surprised, not at all. She'd heard all this from Chuck's father, no doubt.

'Yeah, he slugged me in the stomach.'

'I imagine you were pretty angry about that.'

'I wasn't happy.'

'I'll bet your brother wasn't happy, either.'

'I'm right here,' Tolliver said. 'No, I definitely wasn't happy. But his dad came in, and the boy just seemed so disturbed, we left.'

'And you didn't call us to report the whole thing?'

'No, we didn't. We figured you-all had more important things to be doing.' She knew we hadn't called. She was just underscoring all the mistakes we'd made. I felt worse and worse. Going back to the barn had been my fault, my bad decision, and if the boy was gone, maybe that was my fault, too.

'So no one knows where he is?' Tolliver asked. 'Since when?'

'One of the other counselors from the health center came by, maybe an hour after the incident in the barn, as close as I can make out. This is a close friend of Tom's, and he wanted to talk to Chuck to see if he could help.' The sheriff made a face. She didn't believe counseling would make any difference in Chuck's case, it was clear. 'So Tom starts looking for the boy to get him to talk to the counselor, but Chuck wasn't there. So the counselor insisted Tom call the police. He did, and then he began calling Chuck's friends. No one had seen the boy.'

'You haven't had any luck finding someone who saw him around town?'

'No luck. But we thought he might have tried to find you, to finish what he'd started. Or to apologize. With a kid that messed up, who knows what he was going to do.'

Deputy Rob Tidmarsh came in, stomping his feet just like the sheriff had done. 'Didn't see nothing, Sheriff,' he said.

So she'd been distracting us while her minion checked out the property. Well, there was nothing to find, and there was no point getting angry about it. She'd done what she had to do.

'We might need to call our lawyer,' I said.

'I've got him on speed dial,' Tolliver said.

'Or maybe,' Rockwell said, overriding our voices, 'you found Chuck and decided to punch him back.' She was looking at Tolliver as she said this, as if I were accustomed to sending Tolliver to do my punching.

'We were here all night,' Tolliver said. 'We got a phone call at – what time did Manfred call us, Harper?'

'Oh, about three,' I said.

'What evidence is a phone call on a cell phone?' Rockwell asked. 'And did Manfred talk to you?' She was looking at Tolliver with no friendly face.

'He talked to me, but Tolliver was here.'

'He won't say he talked to Tolliver, then.'

'Well, he may have heard him in the background. But he didn't talk to him directly, no.' Calling our lawyer in Atlanta was beginning to seem like a possibility we should bear in mind. Art Barfield had made a mint off us lately, and I was sure he wouldn't mind making a little more.

'I'm not in the habit of abducting boys,' Tolliver said. 'But of course there's someone here in town who is. Why are you looking at me instead of trying to find out who took all the other boys? Isn't it far more likely that that's who's got Chuck Almand? And if that's so, isn't the boy running out of time?'

I figured Sheriff Rockwell was grinding her teeth together in frustration, from the tensed look of her face.

'Do you think we're *not* looking?' she said, almost biting the words out. 'Now that he doesn't have the use of his usual killing ground, where would he have taken the boy? We're searching every shed and barn in the county, but we have to check out all other possibilities. You were one of them, and a pretty likely one at that.'

I didn't think we were so damn likely, but then, we'd had the run-in with Chuck and his dad. There was something more I could tell the law.

'He told me he was sorry,' I said to the sheriff.

'What?'

'The boy said he was sorry. For hitting me. He told me to find him later.'

'Why? Why do you think that was? What sense does that make?' The tall deputy was looking over Rockwell's shoulder at me as though I'd started barking.

'At the time I just thought – I have to say, I thought it was just some kind of mental illness talking. He looked so strange when he said it.'

'And what do you think now?'

'I think . . . I don't know what I think.'

'That's not a hell of a lot of help.'

'I'm not a psychologist, or a profiler, or any kind of law enforcement person,' I said. 'I just find dead people.' *I just find dead people.* Chuck knew that. And he'd said, 'Come find me.'

'Then we should get you out searching, too,' Sandra Rockwell was saying.

I was sitting there in the grip of a horrible idea, wondering how I could have possibly thought only a day ago that the world might be better if someone took Chuck Almand out right now. That was before I'd seen his secret face, the face he wore when he told me he had to hit me.

Tolliver started to say something, stopped. I looked at him. It wasn't the time to remind them that I got paid for this work. His instinct to hold in his words had been a good one. No, I wasn't reading his mind. We just know each other very well.

'Where do you want me to look?' I asked, and my voice was coming from far away.

That stumped her for a moment. 'You'd know if the body was new, right?' she said.

'Yeah.'

'Then we'll just take you everywhere we can think of,' she said.

I thought of Manfred sitting at the hospital, or in his hotel room, hoping we'd show up. I thought of the road out of town, out of this situation. But weighing that against the life of a boy, what could I say? Which Rockwell knew, of course.

'You're ready to go, right? We'll swing back later and pick up Mr Lang here,' the sheriff said.

'No, I think *not*,' I said right back. 'I'm not going anywhere without him.' Though it would be better if Tolliver went to help Manfred, if we had to be separated. But then . . . no. It was better if we stayed together. I was going to be selfish about this.

Tolliver vanished into the little bathroom while I made the sheriff useful by asking her to help me with my shoes. Tidmarsh tried not to snort, but he didn't quite succeed. Sheriff Rockwell was game, and my hiking boots were laced up and tied in a neat bow in no time. I took my pills for the day and picked up the cabin a bit while we waited. I tried to bank the fire so it could be revived. The electricity might be back on, but there was certainly a chance it would go off again. The fireplace was still essential. I had a gloomy feeling we'd be spending another night here.

Manfred would be better than I at solving this problem. Maybe if he went to the house, or to the barn where we'd last seen Chuck, he could trace the boy somehow. On the other hand, it would be inhumane to ask Manfred to work just now. And he might not be up to it. He'd told me several times his psychic sense was weaker than his grandmother's. I thought he was wrong, but that was what he believed.

I called him, since we were waiting, anyway. Manfred sounded sad but collected. I explained the situation to him, and he said that he'd heard from his mother again, that she was making better time now that the roads were clearing up. 'Well see you later,' I said. 'You hang in there, Manfred.'

'I don't trust anyone here,' he said. 'I don't trust the doctor, I don't trust the nurses, I don't think the hospital guy is on the level. Even the minister gives me the creeps. You think I'm being paranoid? You think there's really something wrong here?'

'That's hard to answer at this point,' I said.

'Oh, right, the sheriff's there,' Manfred said dismally. 'I just can't throw the feeling off, Harper. Something's really wrong here.'

'In Doraville? Or specifically at the hospital?'

'I'm just not sharp enough to say,' he said after a long pause. 'I don't have the gift like my grandmother did.'

'I think you're wrong. I think all you need is some experience,' I said. 'I think you do have it in you.'

'You don't know how much that means to me,' he said. 'Listen, I've got to go now. I've got an idea.'

That didn't sound good. That sounded like he was about to do something on his own. Young men on their own in Doraville didn't fare well. I tried to call him back right away.

He did pick up, finally. 'Where are you going?' I asked. Tolliver had come out of the bathroom, finally, clean and dressed. He stood frozen in place by the anxiety in my voice, his dirty clothes in his hands.

'I'm going to look for the boy,' Manfred said.

'No, don't go without someone with you,' I said. 'Tell us where you're going.'

'You might get in trouble again.'

'Hey, we've got the sheriff, remember? Where you going?'

'I'm going to that barn again. That's where I have to go.'

'No, wait for us, okay? Manfred?'

'I'll meet you there.'

But it would take us a lot longer to get there, since we were starting from the lake.

I told the sheriff what the situation was, and she went ballistic. 'We've searched the barn,' she said. 'We've gone over and over it. That dirt floor is empty, the stalls are empty, there's no loft. It's an empty wooden building with walls so thin there couldn't be a hidden space in there. There aren't even any more dead animals, I'm almost a hundred percent sure, and you told us yourself there aren't any bodies there.'

'No dead ones,' I said. Then I said, 'No dead ones . . . at least there weren't any . . . oh, shit. We got to get there.' The feeling of dread that had blossomed in my head now bloomed in full. I didn't speak to anyone again.

We got into the patrol car and onto the road within five minutes. There wasn't much traffic and the roads were a hell of a lot clearer, but it was still a good twenty-minute drive into Doraville, then another ten minutes through the town to the street where the Almands lived.

Instead of creeping up to the barn from the rear of the property as we'd done yesterday, we pulled into the driveway by the aging frame house, and I got out as quickly as I could. My muscles were sorer today than they'd been the previous day, and I was skipping the pain medicine, so I was feeling everything I did.

Tolliver put his arm around my waist to help me along, and we stumbled down the remains of the drive that led beyond the house to the barn. I could catch a glimpse of Manfred's car on the track that ran behind the property.

And I felt the vibration, the stirring in my head. A very fresh body. 'Oh, no,' I said, 'oh no no no.' I began to run, and Tolliver had to grip me under my shoulder to keep me up. The sheriff caught fire when she saw my distress and she and the deputy pulled ahead of us easily. She drew her gun, and I don't even know if she realized she was doing it.

We all screeched to halt when we entered the dilapidated barn.

Tom Almand was standing in front of the stalls at the rear of the barn. He had a shovel in his hands. About three yards in front of him, Manfred was keeping to his feet with great effort. He was bleeding from the head. Manfred had his own weapon, a short-handled spade. It was so shiny and new I suspected Manfred had bought it that very morning, maybe on the way to the barn. He hadn't gotten in a lick yet.

'Tom, put the shovel down,' the sheriff said.

'Tell him first,' Tom Almand said. 'He came in here to attack me.'

'Not true,' Manfred said.

'I mean, look at him, he's a freak,' Tom said. There was a snarl on his narrow face. 'I live here.'

'Tom, put down the shovel. Now.'

'There's a human body here,' I said. 'There's a body here *now*.' I just wanted to be clear they understood. I just wanted them to get that asshole Tom Almand out of the way.

Manfred took two more steps back from Tom, and put his spade on the floor.

And Tom ran at Manfred with his shovel raised to strike.

The deputy shot him first, and missed. Sheriff Rockwell managed to get him in the arm, and he screamed and crumpled.

Tolliver and I stood against the wall while the deputy rushed forward to cover the bleeding counselor, and Manfred fell to his knees, his hands clasped to his head; not to indicate surrender, but because his head was injured.

We started forward to help our friend, but the sheriff said sharply, 'Stay back! Stay out of the scene!' and we did. She was calling for ambulances on her radio, and when the shovel was beyond Tom Almand's reach, she handcuffed him despite his bleeding arm, and searched him very thoroughly. No weapons. She told Tom Almand about his rights, but he didn't respond. His face was as blank as it had been at the church the other night. The small man had gone somewhere else, mentally.

'Do you still feel a body?' she asked when that was done. It took me a second to realize she was talking to me, I was so wrapped up in the tension of what had just happened, the fear that Tom Almand would charge someone again, the possibility of Manfred being critically injured. I didn't worry about Tom's arm wound at all. He might bleed out before the ambulance arrived, and that would be fine with me.

'Yes,' I said. 'There's a very fresh body. Can I show you where?'

'How close do you have to come to this man?'

'I have to go to the first stall.'

'Okay, go.'

I very carefully worked my way around the tableau of bleeding men and law enforcement to get to the opening to the stall. I stepped inside on the old straw and began kicking it aside. It kept falling back into its original position, so I began picking up handfuls and tossing them over the side of the stall. 'Tolliver,' I said. He was at my side immediately, helping. The shovel or the spade would have come in handy, but I knew better than to suggest it. 'Isn't this a latch?' I asked.

Tolliver said, 'I wish we had a flashlight,' and one landed on the floor beside us. Sheriff Rockwell had had one on her belt. Tolliver turned it on and aimed it at the boards at our feet.

'Trapdoor here,' Tolliver said, and the deputy cursed. I guessed he'd been one of the ones who'd searched the barn.

Tom laughed, and I looked out at the tense group of people in the barn. For about a dime, the deputy would have kicked him in the head. His body language spoke loud and clear. I could hear emergency vehicles approaching, and I wanted to open the trapdoor before they got here and there was even more confusion.

Tolliver found the latch quickly. It was very strong, I guess to hold out against battering from below.

We did need a shovel to open it, and without asking Tolliver went across the barn to take Manfred's. We stuck the spade in the little opening and pried. After Tolliver got it up a little, I held the spade with my good hand while Tolliver grasped the edge and swung back the trapdoor. It was very heavy, and we found out why – there was insulation liberally tacked on the underside, which would muffle any sounds from below.

I looked down into a kind of pit, maybe six by six. Probably eight feet deep, it was reachable by a steep wooden ladder. The dead body of Chuck Almand lay at the foot of the ladder. He was staring up at us. The boy had shot himself in the head. What drew the eye first was the terrible damage to Chuck's head.

Behind the corpse there was a naked boy chained to the wall. His mouth was duct-taped shut. He was whimpering behind it, and he was looking over his shoulder and up at us with an expression I never want to see again. He was spattered with Chuck's blood and I suppose some of his own. There were cuts on his body, and the blood there was crusted and black. The cuts were swollen and red with infection. He had no blanket, no jacket, nothing, and he'd been in the pit with the corpse all night.

I ran out of the barn and vomited. One of the ambulance drivers rushing in stopped to check on me, and I just waved my arm to indicate the interior of the barn.

After a few minutes, Tolliver came out. I was leaning against the peeling wood, wishing I were anywhere but here.

'He killed himself so you'd find him,' Tolliver said. 'So you'd find out what his father was doing.'

'So I'd have a corpse to find,' I said. 'Oh, Jesus, he took such a chance. What if I hadn't come back?'

'What if Manfred hadn't decided he had to check the barn again?'

'Do you think Tom Almand's known where Chuck was all this time, since he reported him missing?'

'No, but I guess he didn't have a chance to come out here to check. That other counselor asking to see Chuck made Tom report him missing.' Tolliver shuddered. 'I never want to see anything like that again.'

'He sacrificed himself,' I said. I couldn't get my thoughts together. 'And it was almost – almost – for *nothing*.'

'He wasn't thinking good,' Tolliver said in a massive under-statement. 'And he was just thirteen.'

The stretchers went by, Manfred's first, his face white as death and his eyes open and blank.

'Manfred!' I called, just wanting him to know that someone who knew him was near, knew what he had done. But his face didn't change.

Tom Almand came out next, his eyes closed, his lips in a strange smile. He was now handcuffed to the stretcher by his good arm, and there was a bandage on the arm that had been shot. I hoped he'd been shot good, and I wondered if Sheriff Rockwell had been truly trying to hit his arm. It had been an alarming moment, but then, that was what law enforcement people trained for, right?

Maybe the arm was best. Maybe the people he'd wounded the most, or the survivors he'd wounded most, could get something out of his trial and conviction. Surely he'd be tried and convicted, wouldn't he? We could follow it in the national news. The media loves a serial killer trial, whether the killer being tried is gay or straight, black or white or brown. There's no discrimination in that field.

I realized I was thinking crazy, and I also realized we had no place here. But the two SBI agents were running across the back lane like the barn was on fire with a baby inside, and they weren't about to let us go. Stuart and Klavin weren't out of breath, because they were fit agents, and they stood right in front of us. 'You're here again,' Agent Stuart said. He had on proper gloves and an L.L. Bean heavy outdoor-guy coat, and gleaming boots that went halfway up his calves. If he didn't look like the little mountaineer! Klavin was a bit more down-scale, with a battered waterproof coat that had seen several years of use and a knit cap that had earflaps.

'He killed himself,' I told them. They would want to know.

'Who?' I thought Stuart was going to shake me, he was so anxious to know everything.

'Chuck Almand. He killed himself with a gun.'

Klavin said, 'Who was in the ambulance?'

'Tom Almand and Manfred Bernardo,' Tolliver said.

They looked at each other blankly. 'The kid's dad and the psychic's grandson,' Tolliver said.

'She died last night,' Stuart said.

'Yes, she did. And her grandson almost died today,' I said.

'The last victim is alive,' I said, and they were in the barn so fast you couldn't see them for the smoke.

'Why haven't they brought him out?' Tolliver leaned and looked in, but then he gave up. He didn't want to go in that barn again, and neither did I.

'Maybe they can't get him unlocked,' I said. Tolliver nodded. That seemed reasonable.

'Wonder who he is,' Tolliver said after a long moment. The weather might be much better than it had been, but it was still cold standing out there, and we had nothing to do.

I turned to Tolliver and hugged him. His arms slid around me, and we stood there in the bright cold day, clinging to each other. 'We'll find out,' I said, my lips against his neck. 'It'll be in the papers, or on the news.' The tortured body, slumped against the wall, the blood-stains everywhere. The poor dead boy on the floor of that miserable pit. *Jesus, God. This is not what you intended people for.*

I hadn't thought in Christian terms for a long time, and I was surprised to find myself thinking in them now. And I hadn't rebelled, either, hadn't had the 'Why, God?' thoughts. Those were bad, those were pointless. Of course, I'd never found such atrocities, so closely linked, in adjacent graves.

'Chuck saved that boy's life,' I said numbly. 'He provided a dead body for me to find.'

'Do you think he really cut up those animals?'

'Maybe his dad made Chuck do it, hoping Chuck would follow in his own footsteps. Maybe Tom thought if Chuck was guilty of *something* he'd be less likely to report his dad.'

'Xylda seemed pretty sure Chuck did it.'

'I'd hate to think she was wrong in her last big reading.'

'Me, too.' Tolliver sounded grim. 'You think her loathing of him was what drove Chuck to tie everything up this way? I mean, everyone at the same time looking at him with such disgust, such dislike? And his dad acting right along with them. When he knew better, and the boy knew that.'

'Chuck was a hero. He survived living with a father that killed boys for fun.'

'But he didn't tell anyone.'

'Maybe he didn't know, until the animals were dug up. Maybe then he realized his dad was the one killing the boys, or maybe Tom told him then. Like, "Everyone thinks you're evil and sick now, so I'll show you something really evil and sick! Like it?" '

'Or maybe he knew all along,' Tolliver said, more realistically.

'Maybe he kept silent because he loved his dad, or was scared of his dad, or because he kind of liked torturing the animals and felt he and Tom were two of a kind. Maybe he even helped, with the boys. There must have been times it would have been handy to have an extra pair of hands. Some of the boys were big, and heavy. Football players. Adolescents who'd gotten their growth. Frankly, someone as little as Tom Almand, I don't know how he managed it.'

'But Chuck put a stop to it.' I buried my face in Tolliver's jacket. He ran his fingers through my hair, taking care to avoid the shaved spot on the left side of my head. He patted me. It was intensely comforting.

Finally they brought the last victim out. He was covered with blankets, there was an IV running already, and he was strapped to the gurney. His eyes were closed, and tears were leaking down his filthy face.

'What's your name, son?' Sheriff Rockwell was asking.

'Mel,' the boy whispered. 'Mel Chesney. From Queen's Table, up near Clearstream.'

'Mel, how long have you been down there?' said Klavin, keeping pace on the other side.

'Two days,' he said. 'Two days. I think.'

And then he said, 'I can't talk about it.'

I didn't blame him at all.

The boy had been there yesterday when we'd had our confrontation with Chuck. If Chuck had just told us then . . . but his father had come in, and maybe he simply couldn't. I wondered if Mel Chesney had been in the hole when the police were digging up the animals. Oh, God, that was too bitter to think about.

I was sure every law enforcement person on the scene was wondering the same thing. Mel Chesney had been down there for hours by himself and then with a corpse, thinking all the while he was going to be tortured to death. It was almost a miracle he hadn't died of hypothermia.

No one tried to stop us as we began going to the sheriff's car. But we couldn't go back to the cabin and get our stuff unless someone drove us. The sheriff said, 'Rob, take them to the station.' Rob Tidmarsh raised his forefinger to tell us he'd be one more minute.

Rockwell glared at us as if we were an annoying detail she had to clear off her slate before she turned her attention to more important things, and I think that was exactly the case. 'We got to process this scene, and it's gonna take a while,' she said. 'You two go sit at the station, and when I can spare someone to run you out to the lake, I'll send 'em back to get you.'

'Rob can't take us on out there?'

'Rob's going to pick up more film while he's at the station. The state forensic boys are going to be here as soon as they can get here, but we want our own pictures. Rob'll be coming right back here, and for now, this is the most important spot in Knott County. So you two are gonna have to cool your heels for a while.'

We'd been doing plenty of that.

There was no help for it. No matter how irritated we might feel – and I for one felt plenty irritated – Rob was going to dump us at the station.

'Will they take the boy to the local hospital?' I asked the deputy.

'No, they'll take him on to the bigger hospital in Asheville,' Rob said. 'The SBI guys insisted. We got good doctors here.' He sounded deeply resentful.

'I got good treatment here,' I said. Admittedly, I wanted to be on Rob's good side in case we could get him to take us out to the cabin later. But it was the truth. I was willing to believe, a small town like this, the hospital wouldn't have the big diagnostic machines larger hospitals could acquire, but I seemed to be mending fine, and the nurses had been very kind, if very busy.

Rob relaxed a little.

There's always something strange about riding through town in a cop car when you're seated in the back with a wire mesh between you and the driver. It just makes you feel guilty of something, and you feel awfully conspicuous. When we pulled in back of the station and got out, the media swarmed around the back of the station wanting to know if we'd been arrested. Damn it. I wasn't in the mood to put up with this. I couldn't understand why the vicious swarm hadn't migrated to the old barn.

'We kept radio silence and used our cells,' Rob said when I asked him. He seemed completely open now, and he made a point of walking by my side and holding open the back door to the station, making it clear to the watching reporters that I was in favor.

Inside, there was chaos. The news was spreading in the building and it was only a matter of time before it would flow outward.

Rob looked as if he didn't know what to do with us once we'd gotten to the sheriff's office, so he stuck us in one of the interview rooms, told us where the snack and drink machines were, and said there were some magazines in the waiting area if we wanted to go get them. He was obviously in a tearing hurry to collect the film and get back out to the latest crime scene, so we nodded and he took off.

There ensued several hours of boredom. We could have been on the road getting the hell out of Doraville. We could have been in bed together enjoying our new relationship, an idea that got Tolliver's vote. (I would have enjoyed some aspects of that, but truthfully, I was pretty sore in unexpected places, and my arm had been too busy for a cracked arm.) Or we could have been making money on another job. But instead, we sat in the drab room.

For a change of pace, we made a foray to the station waiting room out front. We commandeered all the magazines, bought junk food from the machines, and tried to stay out of the way.

After four hours, the sheriff came back. She, Klavin, and Stuart came into the room with a couple more chairs, and we went over everything all over again.

'And you really think this boy Chuck killed himself so you'd find the other boy?' Stuart asked for the fifth time.

I shrugged. 'I don't know what was going through his mind.'

'He could have written a note, he could have called us, he could have called you, for that matter, and said, "My dad has put a boy in a hidden room," and that would have solved the problem.'

'That wouldn't have solved the problem for him,' Tolliver said.

'He was an adolescent boy,' I said. 'He was full of drama and horror and guilt and sorrow. I guess he was trying to atone for himself and his father.'

'So what do you think, Ms Connelly? Do you think he tortured the animals willingly?'

'If he did, that enjoyment horrified him.' I didn't think there was a simple explanation of Chuck Almand's behavior. I thought at the end he'd tried to do the right thing, but his thinking processes hadn't foreseen the possibility that he could come out the other side of the horror of his situation, come out and heal and recover. He just hadn't lived long enough to believe that he had a future after his dad's arrest, and he wanted his dad to stop killing. At least, that was the way I interpreted Chuck's actions.

They talked at us for a long time, trying to pry things out of us that weren't there to be gotten. 'And don't tell anyone anything you saw in the barn,' Klavin said. 'Not until we get the case completely locked.'

That was easy to promise. We had no desire to talk about what we'd seen.

I had some doubts that the case was all wrapped up, but I kept them to myself. After all we'd done, they still weren't going to listen to my speculations. But doubt niggled at me, and I had that feeling of incompleteness.

Now we had to find Manfred and his mother, who must be wondering what she'd done in her previous life to merit the punishment she was taking.

I asked the sheriff where Manfred was, and she surprised me by telling me he'd been kept here at the Knott County Hospital. He'd asked to stay here, she said.

'I can understand that,' I said to Tolliver as we climbed into Rob's patrol car again. He'd finally been detailed to take us back to the cabin. 'Otherwise, it would complicate his mom's life so much, and if he can get the care he needs here, that's better than moving him up to Asheville.'

'The doctor said he'd be okay here,' Rob said from the driver's seat.

'Okay, that's good,' I said. Then I remembered that Manfred had suspected someone had killed his grandmother during the night. Maybe it wasn't so good that Manfred was in this hospital after all. Shit. More to worry about.

So when we got back to the cabin, we packed everything – just in case – and put it in the car – just in case. We put out the fire. We hung the cabin key from the rearview mirror so we wouldn't forget to return it to Twyla – just in case. Then we drove back into Doraville. We'd taken the opportunity to freshen up, since we'd had so little time that morning, and we felt better now. My arm was aching because I'd been more active that day than I should, and I took a pain pill. I felt almost ashamed to pop one, there were so many other people who were suffering far worse than I; but the only pain I could ease was my own.

'Can I just keep driving?' Tolliver asked as we came to the major intersection in Doraville. Straight ahead would take us out of town. Turning left would take us to the hospital.

'I wish,' I said. 'But I think we have to make sure Manfred and his mom are okay. Don't we?'

Tolliver looked stubborn. 'I bet Manfred's mom is tough. She'd have to be, with Xylda for a mother. I bet they're fine.'

I gave him a sideways look.

'Yeah, okay,' he said, and took the left turn.

12

Manfred's mother, Rain Bernardo, was a younger version of her mother. The resemblance was only physical, I discovered. Rain was not the least bit psychic, and she hadn't had any special rapport with Xylda. Rain worked in a factory and had risen to management level. She was proud of that. She was proud of being a single mom. She was dismayed that Manfred had followed in Xylda's footsteps and not hers. But she loved her son, and she'd loved her mother, and she was pretty subdued at Manfred's bedside. 'Subdued,' for Rain, meant she only talked fifty words a second instead of a hundred.

She had the family red hair, and she had the curves of her mother, but in Rain's case they weren't nearly as generous. In fact, Rain was a very attractive woman, and I was pretty sure she hadn't seen her fortieth birthday yet.

We were there when the first of the usual callers came in. Barney Simpson was more solemn than I'd ever seen him, and I wondered if he was a friend of Tom Almand's. After Barney had asked his usual questions about his patient's comfort and contentment with the treatment he was receiving in the hospital, he lingered. I wondered if he was admiring Rain. After all, he was a divorced guy.

'I'm very sorry about your mother,' Barney told Rain. 'She was a colorful lady, and I know you'll miss her. She made quite an impression on this little community in the short time she was here. She'll be long remembered.'

That was a model of tact, I thought. Though Manfred was lying there pale and in pain, a twitch of a smile crossed his face.

'I appreciate your saying that,' Rain said, not to be outdone in courtesy. 'Thank you for taking such good care of her. Manfred said you came by to see her. Her health was so poor that both Manfred and I know she was due to go anytime, and we don't blame the hospital for anything.' She cast a quelling look at Manfred, who had closed his eyes, absenting himself from the whole conversation.

'Manfred thinks she should have an autopsy,' Rain said. 'And she hadn't been under a doctor's care here in Doraville. Though of course she had doctors in Tennessee, and she saw her cardiologist right before she left for Doraville. What do you think?'

Dr Thomason came in then, said, 'It's raining outside, folks,' and shook a few droplets off his umbrella. 'Just rain, not ice,' he added reassuringly.

'It's good you came in here now,' Barney said. 'Let me tell you what we've been talking about.' Barney repeated Rain's question. 'What about it, Len?' he asked.

'Depends on what we hear from her doctor in Tennessee,' Len Thomason said, considering. 'If her doctor there is of the opinion that her death was expectable, not a surprise, no questions to be answered about it, then I think it would be reasonable to assume we didn't need an autopsy, and that's what I'll recommend to the coroner. On the other hand,' he went on, raising both his hands to show us 'caution,' 'if that doctor isn't satisfied – and he knew her best – we'll have to check into it.'

Dr Thomason had put it in such a matter-of-fact way that you felt quite sane and reasonable after listening, and you were sure this was the right course. That manner of his must have been invaluable to his practice. It was almost enough to make me ashamed I'd suspected he might have had something to do with the boys' deaths. Now, as I watched him smile gravely at some question of Rain's, I could only imagine all over again how easily Len Thomason could persuade a boy to go with him anywhere. Everyone trusts a doctor. There were a hundred things he could have said to induce a young man to go off with him. Right now I couldn't think of any, but I was sure given time I would.

Even Barney Simpson, who didn't seem like the most lighthearted of individuals, perked up around Dr Thomason. I remembered he'd gone in to talk to Xylda the night before; no, he'd peeked in and gone away. He hadn't even gone into the room.

Doak Garland was across the hall, praying with some relatives outside a room with an 'Oxygen in Use' sign on the door. Anyone would go with him, too. He was so meek and mild, so pink and polite.

Why was I even worried about further suspects? Tom Almand had been arrested. The case was closed. It was hard to believe one man could cause so much misery. Even Almand's own son had died of his evil. There was something about the whole thing that felt – unsealed, uncompleted.

I was sure that Tom had had an accomplice, a partner in crime.

Once I admitted this to myself, the idea wouldn't go away. While Tolliver talked to Barney Simpson, and Rain discussed Manfred's injury with Dr Thomason, I picked out the reasons I suspected this. I had them all in my head when I looked up to meet Manfred's eyes. I felt Manfred connect with me. Suddenly Manfred said, 'Mom.'

Startled, Rain turned to the bed. 'What, honey? You feeling okay?'

'I've been thinking,' he said. 'I won't argue with you about the autopsy if you'll let Harper touch Grandmother and tell us what she sees.'

Rain looked from Manfred to me, and I could tell from her compressed lips that she was trying to hide revulsion. She not only hadn't fully believed in her mother's talent, she had loathed it. 'Oh, Manfred,' she said, really upset, 'that won't be necessary. And I'm sure Harper wouldn't want to do that.'

'I'll know how she died,' I said. 'And I'm sure cheaper and less invasive than an autopsy.'

'Harper,' she said, giving me a face full of disappointment. She struggled with herself for a minute, and I felt sorry for her. Abruptly she swung toward Dr Thomason. 'Would you mind very much, Doctor? If Harper – sees – my mother?'

'No, not at all,' Dr Thomason said. 'We medical people long ago realized that there's more to this earth than we see in our practice. If that would bring comfort to your son, and you're agreeable . . .' He seemed sincere. But then, a sociopath like the one who'd killed the boys would seem very normal, right? Otherwise, people would have spotted him a long time ago.

'Have you heard anything about the boy who was taken to Asheville?' I asked.

'Yes, I have.' Thomason nodded several times. 'He's not talking, not at all. But they don't think his life is in danger. They think he'll recover. Most of his silence is psychological, not physical. That is, his tongue and voice box are in working order. Lungs, too. Well. Miss Connelly, the body is at Sweet Rest Funeral Home on Main. I'll call them after I leave here, and they'll be expecting you.'

I inclined my head. I wasn't looking forward to this, but I did want to know what had taken Xylda into the other world. I owed her that much. And Manfred, too.

'How long do you think Manfred will need to stay in the hospital?' Rain asked.

Dr Thomason, who'd been on the point of leaving the room, turned to give Manfred an assessing look. 'If all his vitals stay good, and he doesn't run any fever or have any other symptoms that scare me, tomorrow should be good,' he said. 'How about you, young lady? Your pain better?' he asked me suddenly.

'I'm doing much better, thank you,' I said. Barney Simpson had been trying to find a break in the conversation to take his leave, and he said 'See you later' to everyone in the room and strode out the door.

Maybe it was the pain, maybe it was the shock to his nerves the past week had been, but out of the blue Manfred said, 'Well, when's the wedding?'

There was instant silence in the room. Dr Thomason completed his own departure in a hurry, and left Rain looking from the bed to Tolliver and me, almost as astonished as we were.

I'd known Manfred wouldn't be happy, but I hadn't thought he'd be angry. I told myself to bear in mind his many shocks of the past few days. Tolliver said, 'We haven't set a date yet,' which was yet another surprise I hadn't wanted.

Now I was mad at everyone. Rain was gaping, Manfred was looking sullen, and Tolliver was really furious.

'I'm sorry,' Rain said in a brittle voice. 'I thought you two were brother and sister. I misunderstood, I guess.'

I took a deep breath. 'We're no relation, but we spent our teen years in the same house,' I said, trying to keep my voice gentle and level. 'Now, I think, Manfred must be tired. We'll just go over to the funeral home. Sweet Rest, I think the doctor said?'

'Yes,' Rain said, 'I think that was it.' She looked confused, and who could blame her?

As we strode out of the hospital, Tolliver said, 'Don't let him spook you, Harper.'

'You think Manfred saying the word "wedding" is going to spook me?' I laughed, but it didn't sound amused. 'I know we're okay. We don't need to take any big jumps. We know that. Right?'

'Right,' he said firmly. 'We've got all the time in the world.'

I wasn't in the habit of feeling so sure about that, since I spent a lot of time with surprised dead people. But I was going to let it slide for now.

This funeral home was one of the one-story brick models, with a parking lot that would fill up way too quickly. I've been in hundreds of funeral homes, since lots of people don't make up their minds until the last minute about asking me in. This would be one of the two-viewing-rooms kind, I was willing to put money on it. After we walked into the lobby, sure enough there were two doors facing us, each with a podium outside with a signing book waiting for mourners. A sign on a stand, the kind with removable white letters that stick into rows of black felt like material, said that the viewing room on the right contained James O. Burris. The one on the left was empty. There were also rooms to our right and left; one of those would be for the owner. The other would be for a co-owner or assistant, or it would maybe be employed as a small reception room for the bereaved family.

And here came the funeral director herself, a comfortably round woman in her fifties. She was wearing a neat pantsuit and comfortable shoes, and her hair and makeup were also on the comfortable side.

'Hello,' she said, with a kind of subdued smile that must be her stock-in-trade. 'Are you Ms Connelly?'

'I am.'

'And you're here to view the remains of Mrs Bernardo?'

'I am.'

'Tolliver Lang,' Tolliver said, and held out his hand.

'Cleda Humphrey,' she said, and shook it heartily. She led us to the back of the building, down a long central hall. There was a rear door, which she unlocked, and we followed her across a bit of parking lot to a large building in the back, which was really a very nice shed that was brick, to match the main building. 'Mrs Bernardo is back here,' she said, 'since she's not going to be buried here. We keep our temporary visitors in a transition room back here.'

'Transition room' turned out to be Cleda Humphrey's comfort-speak for 'refrigerator.' She opened a gleaming stainless steel door and a draft of cold air billowed out. In a black plastic bag on a gurney lay Xylda. 'She's still in her hospital gown, with all the tubes and so on still attached until the autopsy decision is made,' the funeral director said.

Shit, I thought. Tolliver's face went very rigid. 'At least her soul's gone,' I said, and I could have slapped myself when I realized I'd spoken out loud.

'Oh,' said the cheerful, motherly woman. 'You can see 'em, too.'

'Yes,' I said, really startled.

'I thought I might be the only one.'

'I don't think there are many of us,' I said. 'Does it help in your job?'

'When they're gone like they should be,' Cleda said. 'If I see one lingering, I try to call in their pastor to read a prayer. Sometimes that does the trick.'

'I'll have to remember that,' I said faintly. 'All right. Let me do my thing.' I closed my eyes, which wasn't necessary but did help, and to get the best impression possible, I laid my hand on the bag. I could feel the chill flesh under the surface.

I feel so bad, I'm so tired . . . Where's Manfred? What's that man doing here? Looking at me. So tired . . . sleep.

My eyes flew open to meet the funeral director's curious blue gaze.

'Natural death,' I said. It wasn't murder if someone else just stood there and watched. I'd had no sense of touching, or any other kind of contact. Someone, some man, had watched Xylda in her last moments, but that was hardly surprising. It might have been the doctor or a nurse. There was no way to tell. However, the image I got was chilling – someone calmly and dispassionately watching Xylda die. Not aiding, but not preventing, either.

'Oh, good,' Cleda said. 'Well, I'm sure the family will be glad to know that.'

I nodded.

The black bag went back into the transition room.

In a somber silence, we retraced our steps across the parking lot and through the corridor back to the front doors of the funeral home.

'I guess you're braced for a huge amount of business,' Tolliver said. 'When the bodies of the – the young men – are released.' I was sure he'd been going to say 'victims.'

'We're going to be pretty busy, yes, sir,' she said. 'One of those boys was my nephew. His mama, my brother's wife, she can't hardly get out of bed in the morning. It'd be one thing if someone had grabbed him and killed him – that would be bad enough. But to know he lived for a while, and got hurt so bad, and got used so unnatural, that just kills her.'

There was no possible response that would be helpful, because I thought she was exactly right. To know your loved one was cut and burned and raped *would* make the fact of his death much worse, and there was nothing to be done about it. I'd always figured my sister Cameron had been raped before she'd been killed, without ever having proof of either. And just imagining it might have happened was pretty damn awful. I thought the act of rape itself was unnatural, regardless of the gender of the victim. But an emotional time like this was no time to debate the issue.

'We're really sorry,' I said.

'Thank you,' Cleda Humphrey said with dignity, and we let ourselves out.

'She was pretty decent,' Tolliver said as we got into the car. 'Probably the most relaxed funeral home person we've ever dealt with.'

That was certainly true. 'She seemed to take us pretty much in stride,' I said.

'Nice change.'

I nodded.

Pastor Doak Garland pulled into the parking lot in his modest Chevrolet just as Tolliver was putting the keys in the ignition. He approached the car, so Tolliver turned the key and pressed the window button.

'Hello again,' Doak said, bending down to look at us.

'What are you busy doing?' I asked, hoping he wouldn't ask us about our own visit to Sweet Rest.

'Well, one of the bodies is already being released tomorrow, Jeff McGraw's, so I'm here to talk to Cleda about the service. I think we'll need extra traffic control, so I've already been to the sheriff's department, and I think Cleda needs to be prepared for an extra visitation night.'

'This is going to take it out of you,' Tolliver said. 'There are a lot of services coming up.'

'Well, I wasn't the minister for all these boys,' Doak said with a gentle smile. 'But the whole community will turn out for each funeral, so we're all in for a hard time. And maybe we should be. How could this happen in our midst, and we knew nothing?'

That was too big a question for me. 'Wouldn't some of that be due to the former sheriff, Abe, um, Madden?' I said. 'Wouldn't some of that be due to his policy of pretending the boys were runaways instead of missing and in danger? He seemed willing to shoulder his share of the blame at the memorial meeting the other night.'

Doak Garland looked taken aback. 'Maybe we shouldn't be into pointing fingers,' he said, but he didn't say it with any force. It was clear he wasn't thinking about Abe Madden's role in the terrible drama for the first time. 'You really think that had a bearing?' he said.

'Of course,' I said, surprised. I didn't know Abe Madden. I didn't have to be careful of his feelings or his reputation. 'If his attitude toward the vanishing boys was really the one I've heard described, then of course it had a bearing. Possibly if the investigation had gotten under way quicker, we'd have a few more kids walking around alive.'

'But will assigning blame make this any easier?' Doak asked rhetorically.

I decided to take the question literally. 'Yes, it will, for everyone but Abe Madden,' I said. 'Assigning blame does help people feel better, in a lot of ways. At least in my experience. Plus, if you can correct the behavior that led to the problem, the problem might not repeat itself.' I shrugged. Maybe, maybe not.

I'll say this for Doak Garland, he didn't just whip out a platitude, as some men of the cloth were prone to do. He mulled the idea over. 'There's a lot in that,' he said. 'But really, Ms Connelly, that's just assigning a scapegoat to bear the sins of all of us.'

I thought in my turn. 'Okay, there's something to that, too,' I admitted. 'But there is blame to be assigned here, and the former sheriff should shoulder at least some of it.'

'As he did,' Doak Garland said. 'In fact, it would be a good idea if I dropped by to see him. He may be thinking the same way you are.'

I wondered if the pastor was trying to make me feel guilty in turn, but I didn't. I don't like to see people get depressed or shunned, but I knew that in my own experience, you had to assume responsibility for your own actions before you could move along with your life.

We didn't have any more to say, I felt. I raised my eyebrows at Tolliver, and he said, 'Pastor, we've got to be going.' Without further conversation, we rolled up our windows and pulled out of the parking lot.

'Where are we going?' Tolliver asked. 'I mean, I can drive around aimlessly, but since there are still patches of ice . . .'

'I'm hungry, what about you?' I asked, and that was easy to answer. All the businesses in Doraville appeared to be open now, and people were going about their affairs with an air of relief. I felt relieved, too. We could get out of here just about any time now.

'What if we just left?' Tolliver said. 'We could be on the interstate going in the right direction in an hour. We could find twenty restaurants.'

I was surely tempted. We were sitting in the parking lot of the McDonald's again, and I stared at the golden arches, trying to feel something besides resignation.

'We have to return the key,' I said, stalling.

'Yeah, a five-minute delay.'

'Will they let us?'

' "They" being the SBI guys? Sandra Rockwell?'

'Any of the above.'

'What could they want us for?'

'We haven't signed a statement about yesterday.'

'Yeah, true. We might need to stop by the police station for forty-five minutes and do that. Okay, let's go get a burger, and then we'll tie things up.'

I wanted to leave, really I did, but there was something nagging at me, or maybe two or three things nagging at me. But I kept reminding myself I wasn't a police officer, and I wasn't responsible. On the other hand, if I suspected something, I should mention it to someone who'd take me seriously.

I hardly registered standing in line with Tolliver, whom I had to stop thinking of as my brother. We were way past that now. And I realized that now I could touch him in public. Now he knew how I felt. He felt the same way. I didn't have to hide it anymore. It was awful how strong the habit of standing away from him, not touching him, not watching him, had become once I was afraid of losing him if he realized that I loved him. Since the ice storm, I could watch him all I wanted, and he would enjoy it.

'Do you remember us talking yesterday about what Xylda said in Memphis? That in the time of ice, we would be so happy?' I asked him.

'She did say that. We agreed that Xylda wasn't a fraud, at least not all of the time.'

'I think that as she got older, she got closer to the bone,' I said.

'I don't know if that daughter of hers will ever believe it.'

'Rain just wants everything to be normal,' I said. 'Maybe if I'd been

brought up by Xylda, with all her ups and downs and spiritual
moments, I'd be the same way.'

'I think the way we were brought up was bad enough.'

He was right about that. Being raised by Xylda would have been a
cakewalk compared to living in the trailer in Texarkana.

I thought again of the sacrifice Chuck Almand had made as I sat
alone at our table, waiting for Tolliver to bring our order. I'd gathered
the napkins and straws with one hand, transported them, and returned
to get the ketchup packets. I stared down at the table, which was
clean, and wished I never had to go into another fast-food place in my
life, before I returned to the subject of Chuck, niggling at the puzzle of
his behavior.

Tolliver put the tray on the table, and I began taking my food off.
At least I could eat this food one-handed. Without asking, Tolliver
tore open three ketchups for me and squirted them on my French fries.

'Thanks,' I said, and went back to thinking. But this was no place to
tell Tolliver what I was worried about, even if I could put it together –
not here, where every soul in Doraville who wasn't at school or at
work was crowded in together sharing germs and eating food that was
bad for them. I lost my appetite quickly, and piled my trash back on
the tray.

'What's wrong?' Tolliver asked. He did care, but I could hear the
undertone of anxiety, maybe of irritation. He wanted to leave. Doraville gave him the creeps and the deaths of all those young men was
giving him nightmares.

'After we leave here, let's go out to the death site,' I said. 'I'm really,
really sorry,' I added when I saw the expression on his face. 'But I need
to.'

'We found the bodies,' he said, in as low a voice as he could
manage. 'We found them. We did what was required. We got our
money.'

We so seldom disagreed, or at least we hardly ever felt so strongly
about our disagreements. I felt sick.

'I'm sorry,' I said again. 'Can we just leave here, and talk about it?'

In a stiff silence Tolliver dumped our trash into the receptacle and
thumped the tray down on top. He held the door for me when we left,
and unlocked the car and got in the driver's side, of course, but he
didn't start it up. He sat there waiting for an explanation. He'd almost
never done that before. Usually, whatever I said went. But now our

relationship had changed in deep ways, and we didn't yet know the new balance. It had shifted, though. Now I had to explain, and I accepted that. It hadn't always been comfortable, being Queen of the World. I'd gotten a little too used to it, too.

In the past, I would simply have told him I needed to see the site again, and he would have driven me there without asking me any further questions. At least, most of the time. I pulled my left leg up on the seat and twisted so my back was to the passenger door. He was waiting.

'Here's my thinking.' I took a deep breath. 'In the story we've got now, the way it looks, Chuck Almand was helping his dad secure the boys. His dad was bringing him along in the family business by showing him how to kill cats and dogs and other small animals, so Chuck would grow up into a big serial killer like Papa Tom. Right?'

Tolliver nodded.

'But that thinking is wrong,' I said. 'If Chuck was helping his dad, if we accept the idea that it would take more than two people to subdue the boys—'

'Gacy worked alone,' Tolliver said.

That was true. John Wayne Gacy had tortured and killed boys in the Chicago area, and he'd acted alone. Plus, in the pictures I'd seen, he hadn't looked like any really fit guy. 'He got them to put on handcuffs, right?' I said. 'Told them they were trick handcuffs and he'd show them how to take them off, and then they turned out to be real?'

'I think so.'

'So he had a gimmick, and so might Tom,' I said.

'And Dahmer acted by himself.'

'Yeah.'

'So I don't think you're making such a point.'

'I'm thinking there were two people.' It would have been much easier to subdue a healthy adolescent male if there were two abductors. And maybe the boys had been kept alive for a time so two men could enjoy them, each in his own way. 'Maybe one got off on the sex, one on the torture, or each on some personal combination of the two. Or maybe one just enjoyed the death. There are people like that. That's why the boys lived for a while. And we know they did. So the killers could have equal time with their victim.'

'And you're sure about this.'

'I can't say a hundred percent sure. I think so.'

'Based on what?'

'Okay, maybe based on something intangible from their graves,' I said. 'Maybe just my imagination.'

'So – there was Chuck. And Tom made Chuck help him.'

'No. I don't think so. That's where I was going when we started talking about Gacy and Dahmer. See, the animals were pretty fresh. But the boys have been vanishing for five years, right? More or less. The animals, well, none of them had been dead for longer than a year, looked like. Warm summers here, lots of bugs.'

'So what's the bottom line?'

'Tom's helper wasn't Chuck. It was someone else, someone who's still at large.'

Tolliver looked at me with a completely blank face. I had no idea what he was thinking or whether he agreed with me.

I held my hands out, palms up. 'What?' I said.

'I'm thinking,' he said. He turned on the car while he thought, which was good, because it was feeling pretty chilly. Finally he said, 'So, what to do?'

'I have no idea,' I said. 'I need to run in to tell Manfred his grandmother died on her own. Though there was someone there who didn't do anything about it.'

'What?'

'Someone watched her die. Someone didn't call for help. Not that I think it would've done any good. But . . .' I shook my head. 'That's just creepy. She knew someone was standing and watching.'

'But not harming her. And not helping.'

'No,' I said. 'Just watching.'

'Could it have been Manfred himself?'

I snatched at the idea. That would make sense. Manfred wouldn't necessarily have known Xylda was passing. 'No,' I said reluctantly, after I'd thought about my connection with Xylda's last moment in the funeral home cooler. 'No, it wasn't Manfred. At least, if it was, Xylda was beyond recognizing her own grandson, and I didn't get any sense of that much disorientation from our connection.'

Tolliver dropped me off while he went to gas up the car. I strode through the hospital like I worked there, and I got to Manfred's room to find he was by himself. Trying not to look too relieved – Rain was probably a nice woman but she was a lot of work – I went directly to his bedside and touched his hand. Manfred's eyes sprang open, and for a second I thought he was going to yell.

'Oh, thank God it's you,' he said when he'd grasped who I was. 'What did you find out?'

'Your grandmother died of natural causes,' I said. 'Ah – do you remember standing in the doorway to her room and looking at her for any length of time?'

'No. I always went right in and sat in the chair right by her bed. Why?'

'At the moment she died, someone was standing in the doorway watching her.'

'Did they frighten her?'

'Not necessarily. Surprised her. But that didn't cause her death. She was in the process of dying.'

'You're sure.' Manfred didn't know what to do about this random piece of information. Neither did I.

'Yes, I am. She died a natural death.'

'That's great,' he said, much relieved. 'Thanks so much, Harper.' He took my hand, folded it in his warm one. 'You did that for me and it had to be awful. But now we don't need an autopsy, she can rest in peace.'

Xylda's resting in peace had nothing to do with whether or not she had an autopsy, but I decided it was best to let the subject die a natural death, as natural as Xylda's.

'Listen to me,' I said. His face hardened at my tone, which was serious.

'I'm listening,' he said.

'Don't be alone here,' I said. 'Don't be alone in Doraville.'

'But the guy was arrested,' Manfred said. 'It's done.'

'No,' I said. 'No, I don't think it is. I don't think anyone would actually snatch you from the hospital, but if they let you out, you stick right by your mom all the time.'

He could see I was dead serious. He nodded – reluctantly, but he nodded.

And then Manfred's nurse came in the room, and she said it was time for him to get up and walk, aided by her, and I had to go stand out front to wait for Tolliver.

Barney Simpson was on his way to the front of the hospital with a sheaf of papers, and I happened to fall into step beside him.

'I would have thought an administrator would be chained to a desk,' I said. 'You're all around the hospital.'

'If my secretary were well, I would be in my office almost nonstop,' Simpson agreed. 'But she's off. One of the missing boys was a grand-son of hers. And though it's going to be a long time before they get to bury the boy, it just seemed right to let her have a day or two off to be with her daughter.'

'I'm real sorry for all the families.'

'Well, at least there's one happy family. The folks of that boy that was under the stall should sure be having a good day today.'

He gave a nod and veered off into a smaller hall lined with offices. Everyone in Doraville was affected by these crimes, though I guess the severity of the affection was lessened with your emotional distance from ground zero – the killing field above the town.

I felt a little foolish, now that I thought about it. It was nuts, warning Manfred. He was older. But he was small, and attractive, and right now he was vulnerable. He was a stranger, too, and wouldn't be missed as quickly as one of the local boys. It was nuts because if you looked at it logically, there was no way the remaining killer – a killer only I seemed to be worried about – would take another boy. Everyone was watching, everyone was wary, everyone was suspicious. At least, they had been. Now it was another story. The boogeyman was in jail, his tormented son was dead, the last victim was safe in the hospital and going to live. A happy ending for just about everyone. The people I heard talking about it were even not too unhappy about poor Chuck, because he would have been so messed up anyway by his father's death, and all the people assumed he'd had to help his father with the boys and the guilt of it had driven him to sacrifice himself. He'd redeemed himself, maybe.

I thought only part of that was the truth.

But if Chuck were alive, I wouldn't have given a nickel for his life. Because his dad's partner would suspect that Chuck knew his identity, even if the boy hadn't. So someone really was happy Chuck had died, and had good reason for being so.

I thought of all the good things I'd seen in Doraville, and all the nice people I'd met. There was a snake in the grass in this pleasant mountain village, and it was a pretty huge snake. Doraville didn't deserve to be singled out for such horror.

When Tolliver pulled up by me, I got into the car and without saying a word, he drove me up to Davey's old farm, the site of so many cold graves.

Klavin and Stuart were up there, and for once I wasn't displeased to see them. They were measuring the area and making some more pictures of the orientation of the buildings to the road, the surrounding terrain, and whatever else took their fancy. We got out and watched in silence for a few minutes.

They were busy, and disinclined to talk to us. Each couple tried to pretend the other one wasn't there. The wind was blowing up here, and it was chilly, though the beautiful sun took the edge off. I had discarded my heavy coat and put on a blue hoodie, and I pulled the hood up around my face and tucked my hands in my pockets. Tolliver put his arm around me and kissed my cheek.

As if that had been a signal, the two SBI men approached us.

'Have you given your statement at the police station about yesterday?' Klavin said.

'No. We'll do that before we leave town. We just wanted to ask a question, see if you'd answer it,' I said. 'I suppose it'll be a long time before all the tests are finished on those poor boys.'

Stuart nodded. 'What were you wanting to know?' he asked. 'I figure you're entitled to an answer or two, since you found them.'

That was a refreshing point of view, and one with which Klavin didn't necessarily agree.

'I want to know if they were fed and cared for after they were taken,' I said. 'Or maybe they were sedated. I want to know if their lives were extended.'

Both the agents froze. Klavin had been messing with a tiny digital camera, and Stuart had been loading some small machine into the back of their rented SUV. 'Why?' Stuart asked, after they'd resumed moving. 'Why do you want to know that, Ms Connelly?'

'I wonder if there was more than one person involved in torturing these boys,' I said. 'Because I really suspect that Tom Almand wasn't working alone, that he had a killing buddy who helped subdue the poor boys. Some of them were big boys, you know. Tom Almand was a little man. So, did he have some story that made them trust him enough to put themselves into a situation they couldn't get out of? Or did he have a strong right arm that would be sure they got that way?'

The two men looked at each other, and that was enough.

'You gotta tell people,' I said. 'They all think they're safe, and they're not.'

'Look, Ms Connelly,' Stuart said, 'we got half the team in jail. We got their killing floor. We got their dump site. We got their survivor, safe and guarded. We even got their backup place for stashing victims, for whatever reason they had it: maybe they prepared it in case they heard this place was being sold, maybe they realized the road up here might become difficult in the winter. Then they'd use the place in the Almand barn. We figure this because there aren't as many bloodstains at the barn. There isn't all the paraphernalia we found in there.' He nodded toward the old shed to the left of the Davey house.

'We want to catch this other bastard real bad, Harper,' said Klavin. 'You don't know how bad. But we don't figure he's going to be grabbing anyone anytime soon. You see what we're saying?'

No, I was too dumb to understand. 'Yes,' I said, 'I see. And to a certain extent, I agree. It would be crazy for him to grab anyone else. But you see what *I'm* saying? He *is* crazy.'

'But so far, he's managed to maintain a perfect façade,' Stuart said. 'He's clever enough, got enough sense of self-preservation, to keep on doing that.'

'Are you sure about that? Sure enough to risk some boy's life?'

'Listen, the fact is, you don't have anything else to do with this investigation,' Klavin said. He'd reached the end of his patience.

'I know I'm not a cop,' I said. 'I know I usually just come in to a town, do a job, and leave. And I like it that way. If I have to stick around, worse stuff happens. And then we have to stay longer. We want to drive out of Doraville. But we don't want anyone else to die. And until you catch this other killer, there's that possibility.'

'But what can you do to stop it?' Klavin asked reasonably. 'So far as we're concerned, after you give your statement about yesterday, you and your brother can leave. We have your cell phone number, and we know your home address.'

'He's not my brother,' I said. If Tolliver could tell people, I could, too.

'Whatever,' Klavin said. 'Hey, Lang, did you know your dad was in jail in Arizona?'

'No,' Tolliver said. 'I had heard he got out of jail in Texas, though.' If they'd been trying to upset Tolliver, they had gone about it the wrong way.

'You two really got shanked in the parent department,' Klavin said.

'No doubt about it,' I said. He couldn't make me angry like that, either.

He looked a little surprised, maybe a little abashed.

'I can't figure you out,' I said. 'You can be decent when you want to be. But this shit about our parents, you think we haven't heard all this before? You think we don't remember what it was like?'

He hadn't expected me to clear the decks. Klavin clearly had issues.

'You two go on,' he said, while Stuart watched him, a certain guarded look on his face. 'Go back to town. Get your statements entered. Then leave. This case has too much cluttering it up. The psychic. You. Now that you've seen Tom Almand swing a shovel, I guess you know who attacked you. You gonna file charges?'

Oddly enough, I hadn't even thought about it. So much had happened since I'd been attacked that it had been low on my list of mysteries to solve. I took a moment to think about it. Theoretically, I was all in favor of Tom paying for the attack on me. But thinking realistically, how could we prove it was Tom? The only evidence against him was that he'd been known to hit someone else with a shovel, and he'd had reason to want to hit me – if you count the fact that I'd found his victims a reason, and I reckoned it was. I'd stopped his fun. At least, I'd thought so, until the trapdoor had swung open. I saw those boys' faces every time I thought about the trapdoor: the one face covered with blood and lifeless, and the other just as bloody and full of fear and a terrible knowledge.

I'd have to come back here to testify, and there really wasn't any more concrete evidence than there had been.

'No,' I said. 'Is Almand talking?'

'He's not saying one damn word,' Klavin said. 'He was actually pretty shocked about his son, I think, but he kind of shook it off and said the boy had always been weak.'

'That's someone else's influence,' I said. 'Someone else's words.'

'I think so, too,' Stuart told us. He turned his back to us to look out over the acre of land that had yielded such a strange crop. 'He's not going to talk in case he might trip up and expose his fuck buddy.'

I was a little startled at Stuart going crude on us. But if I'd looked at those bodies and examined the inside of that shack as often as Stuart had, I might be pretty deeply upset . . . well, even more upset than I was already.

I wasn't sure why I was here. There were no ghosts, there were no souls, there was nothing left of the bones of the eight young men who had been put in the ground here. There was only the cold air, the gusting wind, and the two angry men who'd spent too much time observing too closely what horrors people could wreak on each other.

'What will you do with the shack?' I asked. Tolliver turned to look at it, along with Stuart.

'We'll have to dismantle it completely and remove it,' Klavin said. 'Otherwise, souvenir hunters will rip it to shreds. You can see the lab techs have removed the most heavily bloodstained areas for the lab's use. And all the instruments that were in there – the manacles, the branding iron, the pincers, the sex toys – they've gone to the lab, too. We brought a bunch of people up here.'

Tolliver's mouth twisted in disgust. 'How could he look in the mirror?' Tolliver said. It was rare for Tolliver to speak when we were in a professional situation like this. But men are less used to the idea of being raped than women are, and it strikes them with a fresh horror. With women, that horror comes right along with the female genitals.

'Because he was enjoying himself,' I said. 'It's easy to look in the mirror when life is fun.'

Stuart turned to look at me, surprised. 'Yes,' he said. 'He was probably happy every morning. Tom Almand pulled the wool over the eyes of almost every member of this community, for years. He's surely been pleased with himself every day of that time. The only person he couldn't fool, eventually, was his own son.'

'So, he fooled everyone else?' I asked.

Tolliver gripped my hand. I squeezed his.

'His colleagues who have worked with him at the mental health center all say they've gotten along with him fine, that he was always on time, conscientious about keeping his appointments, fairly intelligent with his recommendations and referrals, and had only minor complaints by patients in the eight years he's been here.'

I was impressed that they'd gotten together that much information in the limited time they'd had. I wondered if he'd been under suspicion from the beginning. Perhaps they'd gotten a head start on him, from a profile or something similar.

'But what about close friends?' I asked.

'He didn't seem to have any close friends,' Stuart said. 'Oh, he's been on the Hospital Expansion Board for the past six years; and so have Len Thomason and Barney Simpson, which makes sense. They're all health-care professionals, though from different aspects of the field. That minister got elected to the board last year, the one that conducted the memorial service. They've tried to get matching grants, federal money, private money, worked on fund drives, that kind of thing. Knott County really does need a new hospital, as you may have noticed.'

All roads seemed to lead to the hospital. No matter what direction I started out in, I ended up at the front doors of Knott County Memorial.

'Has the boy spoken yet?' I asked, aware that pretty soon Stuart and Klavin would decide not to answer any more questions, just because.

'Not yet.'

'And I know you've got him under very heavy, very careful guard?'

Klavin said, 'You can believe that. Nothing will happen to that boy.'

'His family come forward?'

'Oh, yes, they'd reported him missing the night before. And we found his car on the side of the road about a mile from the Almand house. He had a flat tire, and no spare.'

'Well, that explains that. Considering the weather, he'd be glad to get a ride, no matter how nervous he was.'

'Kids never think anything can happen to them,' Stuart said grimly.

He'd found out different. He'd never be the same.

'Would you consider putting a guard on Manfred Bernardo?' I asked.

'He's older than the other boys,' Stuart said.

'But he's part of the case.'

'He's an adult, and he's in the hospital with plenty of people watching him,' Klavin said gruffly. 'Our budget's shot to hell.'

'It's been interesting talking to you,' I said. 'Thanks.'

'Did you know they were there?' Tolliver asked as we drove back to Doraville.

'No, I had no idea. I just wanted to look at the site again when it was clean.'

'Clean?'

'No bodies. Just dirt and trees.'

We drove in silence for a few minutes. Then I said, 'Tolliver, if you knew you were going to be accused of murder in the next, say, three or four days – you weren't sure when, but you knew it was coming – what would you do?'

'I'd run,' Tolliver said.

'What if you weren't quite sure?'

'If I thought there was a chance I wouldn't be picked out of the lineup, or whatever?'

I nodded.

'If I thought there was a chance I could hold on to my life, I think I'd try to stay around,' Tolliver said, deep in thought. 'Running is getting harder and harder with the rise of computers and the use of debit and credit cards. Cash isn't common, and people who use it are remembered. You have to show your driver's license for almost every-thing. It's hard to stay invisible in the United States, and it's hard to cross a border without a passport. If you're not a career criminal, it would be almost impossible to do either one.'

'I don't think we're dealing with a career criminal here. I think we're dealing with an enthusiastic amateur.'

Tolliver said, 'Let's get out of here.'

He was at the end of indulging me.

We'd had fights before, but they'd never had this element of the personal. But now we were more than manager and talent, more than brother and sister, more than survivors of a common hell.

And he was right. We had no business doing what the police were supposed to do, and God knows there were police enough to do it. But every time I thought of Chuck Almand, dead at thirteen because he wanted to lead me to discover what his life had been like, living with a man who tortured other boys for a pastime . . . Then I told myself, *He succeeded. He got you there, and all the law enforcement people, which was what he surely intended. Let them take the weight of this now.*

'All right,' I said. 'Let's go.'

Tolliver's shoulders relaxed. Up to that moment I hadn't realized how tense he'd been.

He was right.

We had to go to the police station to give our statements, and since there were still plenty of news crews around, we phoned ahead on the cell and asked if we could come in the back. We were denied permis-sion. 'It's already too crowded back there,' the dispatcher said. 'The state boys all have cars there, and a couple of the forensic guys, plus we have deputies working extra shifts. Park in the front, and we'll have someone watching out for you.'

We had to park down the street from the station because of all the media, and we walked briskly through them, looking neither to the right nor the left. Luckily, we'd almost made it to the door by the time we were recognized. As the voices rose in questions I wouldn't answer, I focused on the door. I hoped it would be the last time we'd ever walk into that particular building. Deputy Rob Tidmarsh was standing there ready to swing the door open. He escorted us to what had been an interrogation room. In fact, it was the same one where we'd been such unwilling guests. It was now set up with a laptop computer and a young man who was ready to extract information from us. We gave him our accounts of the happenings in the barn, and he printed them out, and we signed them. All this took about an hour and a half, maybe twice as long as we'd estimated, and we saw Sandra Rockwell pass by about six times, but she didn't feel the need to speak to us.

There must be a lot to do, I thought as Tolliver talked to the young man, who was about our age. Chronologically. In a case of mass murder, there must be a million details to collect and put in order. I couldn't imagine being in charge of that. And then to have other people brought in over my head, people coming into my town and in front of my own employees taking the case away from me, or at least important aspects of it . . . No wonder Rockwell didn't have time to stop to talk to us. Building a case against the man who'd killed eight boys and tried to kill another was way more important than stroking the ego of a woman who'd done her job and been paid for it.

Yes, no matter how connected I felt to the case, it was time for me to go. I'd never stayed as long, or maybe it just hadn't felt as long. I'd never found that many bodies at one event, either. This was a first for all of us.

What I felt like doing was prying open the heads of a few people myself, prying them open and looking inside, trying to locate the guilt I knew was in one of them. My conviction that there was a second murderer remained unshaken. But I couldn't think of a way to discover for sure who it might be, and Tolliver was right. It wasn't my job. I wished, for one deluded minute, that I was telepathic. I could just read a man's mind and fathom his guilt or innocence.

But that wasn't going to happen, and I wouldn't wish telepathy on my worst enemy. If I'd been psychic . . . well, after seeing the havoc even a mild gift had wreaked in Xylda's life, and seeing how isolated Manfred felt, I didn't want that, either. My own talent was so focused, so specific, that its use was very limited. And I'd passed the limit here in this little foothill town.

When we were through, we left out of the same door we'd entered, but in the meantime the newspeople had spotted our car and camped around it. Tolliver put his arm around me and we bulldozed through them. Even though my arm was in a cast and there was a bandage on my head, it was hard to get them to move aside. Maybe we'd been dodging them too much, and it had made them more determined to 'get' us.

I could swear I recognized one newscaster. Then I realized I had seen him on a national news network. 'Have you ever found that many bodies in one place before?' he asked. It was such a pertinent question, and exactly what I'd been thinking about, that I said, 'No, never. I never want to again.'

The others started screaming louder. If I'd answered one question, I might answer more.

But then he made a huge mistake – he asked a 'How did it feel?' question.

Those I won't answer. My feelings are my own.

After a few seconds of struggle to get the door open, of falling inside the car, buckling my seat belt, and locking the door, I was safe from more questions, and then Tolliver tumbled in the driver's door and got himself ready to drive. He put the car in gear and the knot of newspeople relaxed and spread apart to allow us to leave.

It was lucky for us they all stayed close to the police station, hoping for more tidbits from the police or the SBI agents. We were able to get to Twyla's house by ourselves. Twyla's car was the only one in the garage. I wondered how long it would be before she got to bury her grandson. And then there'd be the trial and all the surrounding publicity. Jeff McGraw wouldn't get to rest in peace for years, at least in the minds of his family.

Tolliver pulled in behind Twyla's car, left ours in park with the engine on, and scrambled out with the key to the cabin. He didn't say a word. Maybe he was afraid that if he said something, I would, too; I'd change my mind about leaving.

A car pulled in behind us as I waited. After a second, someone knocked on the window. I pressed the button to roll it down. Pastor Doak Garland stood there, as pink and innocent a man as I'd ever seen.

He said, 'Hello again, Miss Connelly.'

'Hi. I forgot to tell you what a good job you did at the memorial service. I hope you all took up a good bit of money toward the funerals.'

'Praise God, I think we got about twelve thousand dollars together now,' he said.

'That's great!' I was genuinely impressed. That was a huge amount of money in a poor community like Doraville. Divided among the six local boys, that wasn't much, especially when you considered the cost of an average funeral these days. But it would help.

As if he could read my mind, Doak said, 'Three of the boys had burial insurance, so they won't need funds. And we're hoping to bring in at least three thousand more with a raffle. Twyla has very generously offered to match whatever we make for the raffle.'

'That *is* generous.'

'She's a great woman. Can I ask you a question just out of sheer curiosity, Miss Connelly?'

'Ah . . . okay.'

'I'm not sure I've ever been in that old barn behind the Almand house. Where was the poor young man?'

'He was in a kind of – oh, wait, I'm not supposed to talk about it. Sorry, the cops made me promise.'

'Well, you hear all kinds of things, you know,' he said. 'I just wanted to get the facts straight. Where's your companion?'

'He's coming right back out in just a second,' I said. Suddenly I felt very alone, though I was parked in a driveway on a suburban street. I jumped, pretending I'd felt my phone vibrate. 'Hello?' I said, holding it to my ear. 'Oh, hi, Sheriff. Yeah, I'm here at Twyla's, talking to Pastor Garland. He's standing right here, do you need him? No? Okay.' I made an apologetic face at the minister, and he smiled and waved, and started into the house. I kept up the false conversation until he'd gone in the back door.

Half of me felt like a very big idiot, and the other half was simply relieved that he was gone. Where the hell was Tolliver? What was taking him so long?

I turned in my seat and began to undo my seat belt. I'd go in to find out what he was doing. I was really anxious. I had the uneasy feeling I'd overlooked something big.

Something about the ninth boy, the one who'd lived.

I stopped what I was doing and considered. He'd been identified. He was safe in the hospital in Asheville. He might never speak about what had happened to him, but I thought it was probable he would, when he got used to being safer and felt better physically. When he did begin to talk, he would identify the other killer, if in fact there was another one.

But what if he hadn't ever seen the other killer? What if he'd been kept in the stable because it had been Tom Almand, and Almand alone, who'd abducted him? Maybe it had been the first and only time Almand had made his son help him, and that was what had driven Chuck over the edge. Maybe Tom hadn't had a chance to share before he was discovered. So the accomplice had an even better chance of getting away with it.

And Doak Garland was not the man. He'd just asked me where the boy had been kept. If he'd been the other murderer, he would have known. If he'd just been trying to muddy the waters, he could have simply said nothing. It didn't make any difference what I thought. Why should he make such a point of asking me, unless he genuinely didn't know?

But someone had known, someone I'd talked to very recently. Someone had said the boy had been under the floor in the stall, or something to that effect. Who had it been? We'd seen so many people. Obviously, not Rain or Manfred; not any of the law enforcement people, they'd know and that would be okay. All right, who? Who had I talked to? The funeral home lady, Cleda something. No, not her.

I'd been sitting there with the door half-open, one foot out while I thought. With a suddenness that struck me dumb, a big SUV pulled in beside me, the door was ripped from my hands, and my arm was grabbed and I was out of the car. Then a big hand hit me right where the shovel had bashed me a long, long time ago, and then I was out.

13

I was in his vehicle by the time I was conscious enough to understand what was happening, and by then my mouth was taped shut and my hands were bound together. His blitz attack had caught me completely unawares.

Barney Simpson was hunched in the driver's seat, backing out of the driveway and taking off down the road like a maniac. The SUV lurched so violently that I slid to the floor. I had no means to stop myself. I landed on my bad arm, and the pain was excruciating. I would have screamed, but once again, he'd taken care of that.

There's something terrible about being right when being right means you get bitten on the ass.

I'd be lucky if that was all that happened.

He pulled over after five minutes. I still couldn't move, but I was trying to gather my energy. I had no idea where we were. Twyla lived in a suburb, maybe Doraville's only upscale housing development. Five minutes from it would take us almost anywhere: into the older part of Doraville or out into the country. Past Barney's head, I could see ice melting off a pine tree, one of a stand of trees. There are trees all over in North Carolina.

'We had it all,' he said. He was looking down at me, and his big black-framed glasses magnified his eyes, so he was not just looking, but glaring. 'We had it all, until you found them. I'd spot them at the hospital and mark them for the future, or Tom would see them out walking or hitching, and we would pick them up and then we'd just . . . use them up.'

Oh, Jesus, I thought.

'We'd use every bit, all the pain, all the sex, all the fear. We'd consume them. Until they were nothing.'

I was strangling behind the tape, gurgling and gasping.

'We had the second place, the place in the barn, in case we had two boys at the same time. It was like a holding cell. We'd never really had to use it. But I guess Tom just couldn't resist, even though the last thing he should have done was pick up another boy.'

Having made his point, which was that I was the snake in their paradise, he put the SUV in gear and glanced in his rearview mirror. He pulled back onto the road.

'But Tom couldn't give it up, thought it would be his last time, I guess, and a hitchhiker, they're just like apples falling into your lap.'

I couldn't just huddle there on the floorboard and fear. I had to think of something to do. I might manage to open the door and roll out, but the car was going so fast that I didn't think I'd survive. I would save that for a last resort. Dying that way would be better than dying the way the boys had.

Okay, it was time to fight. I kept telling myself that, but I remained so dizzy and disoriented that it was hard to make my muscles agree on an aggressive program. And then it was hard to get in position to make my blows count for something. My legs were free, because Barney hadn't had time to confine them, and also maybe he'd hoped I'd stay unconscious for longer. So I kicked at him, trying to get some force behind my legs, wriggling so that my back was braced against the door. Of course, the SUV swerved and he screamed at me, 'I'm going to pull your skin off!' I knew he meant it literally. He didn't look like a hospital administrator anymore. He looked like what he really was: a man crazed with his own evil.

He struck at me, but he had to drive, so the random swings didn't connect with my legs often. If they did, they didn't have much force behind them because he was having to strain to reach me.

The pain in my arm was constant and increasing. In a way it was good, because it kept me awake and angry, and in a way it was bad, because it was draining my energy and my will. I even caught myself wanting to be careful of the healing injury. But there was no point in keeping the arm from breaking if I died soon after, I told myself stoutly, and I kicked with renewed vigor and rage.

'You crazy bitch!' he screamed. Well, *right back at you, buddy.* I was so pleased I had my hiking boots on.

I'd assumed sooner or later we'd be in the center of Doraville, but he swerved to the right, and I knew we'd turned onto one of the back roads that twisted through the county. We were going up into the mountains. That was the worst possible development.

He leaned way over, till his left hand was barely on the wheel, and he hit me in the face open-handed. I saw gray for a second. He looked very satisfied, when I could focus on his face again. He'd caused pain, and he liked that a lot. Also, I'd quit kicking. He could drive with both hands on the wheel. I debated with myself whether to let him drive safely and not get hit again, or to kick out and get hurt. I rested for a couple of minutes and decided it was time to try again.

I got his knee this time, and there was the familiar swerve, but this time he looked all around and pulled over again. Okay, this was a step for the worse. He flung open his door and dashed around the SUV while I was struggling to change positions so I'd be facing him. But I couldn't manage it, and he popped open the passenger door so suddenly that I fell out. He caught me by my hair, pulling the stitches in my scalp. I made a noise that would have been a scream if I could have opened my mouth. He dragged me out by the hair, out onto the narrow shoulder, gray with ice and snow slush. There was a steep slope down to the forest, patched with white. Beyond the forest, I glimpsed water.

I had to struggle desperately to keep from landing flat on the ground. I got my feet under me somehow, and tried to twist away, and he hit me again, this time with his fist, in the ribs.

Oh, God, it hurt.

Once I got my feet braced I rammed against him, trying to knock him down, but I only made him stagger a foot or two, and then he began beating me in earnest. I thought if I fell down he would kill me, but I didn't think I could stay up for long. I landed a lucky kick to his crotch, but when I brought my foot back down I slipped on the ice by the side of the road, and I toppled over. I rolled through snow and wet grass, down and down to the bottom of the slope.

He was no more dressed than I for something like this; in fact, he was even less prepared, because I was wearing boots and a heavy coat and scarf, and he was wearing a suit and that was it. His shoes went along with the suit, strictly indoor wear. By the time I got to the tree line at the bottom of the slope, he'd begun floundering down after me.

Getting up was very hard with my hands taped, but I was able to struggle to my feet, and I took off. It was terrible, making my way through the heavy brush and trees, with the ground slushy. But I had to put as much distance as I could between him and me.

Would he come down in the trees after me?

Yes, idiot. Of course he will. I heard his inarticulate scream of rage and then the sounds of him thrashing through the trees.

At least he was openly nuts now. At least he wasn't trying to reason. That was the only chance I had, his mental state.

Not that I was thinking. I was just running.

Plan, plan, plan, I needed a plan. The weather and terrain were all against me. If I trod in the patches of snow, all he had to do was follow my tracks. And it was very precarious, trying to hurry and also trying to avoid stepping in the snow. At least there were a few other tracks around; people had ridden their four-wheelers through here, and I could see another set of tracks, vague ones, a few yards away. I leaped between the snow patches, hoping that the ground would not show every print I made simply because it was wet. Maybe he wasn't any more of a woodsman than I was.

I felt the buzz of bones, very close. Instinctively I began tracking the buzz. The dead could not rise up and protect me, which would only have been right . . . but could they hide me? I couldn't have told you exactly what I was thinking, but I was comfortable with the dead.

The sky was darkening and visibility was getting worse even as I ran, bashing into trees and staggering to keep to my feet. I headed for the dead man. If no one had found him, maybe no one would find me. The feeling of him was fairly fresh, and I was so tired. But I kept on scampering, fast as a panicked squirrel.

The dead man was in the thicket right before me, an overgrown patch of short tree saplings, vines, and myrtle. The thicket was surrounded by pines, and there were pinecones littering the ground. I crouched to grab up a couple.

The live man trying to kill me was just a few yards behind me, though I couldn't see him. I could hear him, snorting and pushing through the growth. Half-standing, I threw one pinecone, then another. I threw them as hard as I could with my bound hands, and they made just a bit of noise a few yards away, when they hit the soggy ground. I didn't think Barney Simpson was any Daniel Boone. Maybe he would think he was hearing footsteps. There was a rocky outcropping close, and he might think my next steps had been on the rock surface. The dead man was waiting.

I hunkered down and tried to slow down my breathing. I sounded like a faulty bellows. *Please, Dead Guy,* I begged, *please be a hunter.*

God heard me. Or fate heard me. Or it was just the way it turned out. Dead Guy had a knife. It was in a sheath on his rotting belt. His camo was in shredded rags, stained with the fluids from his body. Some of his bones had been scattered, and the stomach area had been torn open and devoured by something. But Lyle – that was his name, Lyle Worsham – had a knife in that sheath. The Velcro yielded to my fingers, and then with some difficulty, I worked the knife out. It was rusted and pocked, but it was a knife – not the stout hunting knife I'd expected, though. The shape was strange to me. I awkwardly turned it in my fingers and tried to saw through the duct tape with it.

Before I was through, I was glad I had a coat on. My arms would've been a mess. And my first act was to rip the tape off my mouth. No silencing me.

Of course, then I crouched there without making a single noise. Where was he? Was he going to pounce on me any second? Had he given up to go back to the SUV? Was he even now fleeing the county? I didn't mind staying here until I was sure. I was cold and wet and scared, but I could be patient. I had old Lyle here with me. Had Lyle had a gun? He should have, right?

As it turned out, Lyle had been fishing, not hunting. There was a tackle box sitting on its side in two years' worth of downed leaves, and there was a creel that had once contained his catch. So now I knew why this knife had such a strange shape – it must be a filleting knife. He'd been to the lake to fish. Would the surface of the water have iced over? It had gotten above freezing this afternoon, and it had been sunny for a while. Now that the twilight was drawing in, the water might freeze again. I shivered. My vague idea of cutting across the frozen lake surface was simply stupid. My ignorance of the woods was probably equal to Barney Simpson's. Barney preferred indoor sports, like having sex with bound boys. I wonder what the former Mrs Simpson had to say about Barney's sexual kinks.

My mind stopped wandering and focused at the faint noises I was hearing. Barney was trying for stealth, but he was a big man and he was wearing the wrong footwear. The snow crunched under his feet and he was breathing heavily. Me and Lyle, we were really quiet.

The next time I got abducted, I was going to have my gloves on, I promised myself. And a hat.

'Get out here, bitch,' Barney called.

Mr Simpson, I'm not satisfied with my treatment by your staff.

'There aren't any houses around here, and no one's going to come help you,' he called, and he was closer to where I was crouched.

Could he possibly be *lying?* Why, yes, I thought he might be. The same way he'd been lying all along.

The glimpses I'd caught while I was running away had included a brief vista across a body of water, and the glimpse of some cabins; distant, but visible. Reachable. I was pretty sure of my location.

I thought I was very close to the southern shore of Pine Landing Lake. I thought if I struck out through the trees, following the lake line northwest, I might find the cabin again. If I could go up and walk on the road I'd be sure, and walking would be easier and faster.

Now he was right outside the thicket. I bit my lip to keep from letting out my shuddering breath. With my right hand, I held the knife at the ready.

Hold it. Hold it. Don't say anything. And then his feet moved away.

The darkness couldn't fall fast enough to suit me.

He was the one who was in a hurry. Not me.

Lyle, you and me, we can wait forever, right?

And then he howled and pounced but he was howling and pouncing on the wrong shadow, and since I'd held still I was okay, I was okay. My arm was truly broken all the way through now, thanks to the beating by the side of the road, and my scalp was really bleeding, and my head was hurting like someone had dragged me out of a car by my hair, but I was okay. In danger of freezing in this position, though. I'd been in one position for too long, and I needed to move, needed to stretch a little, needed to shift my weight. But I was too scared.

He didn't have a gun, apparently. That was good. He could just shoot at bushes until he hit me; no, that would attract too much attention. Even in the rural South, random shooting will attract a certain amount of notice. But he might risk that, to kill me.

'This is ridiculous,' he said, so close I almost shrieked. 'I mean, after all, you must be nuts to react to a man talking to you that way. Kicking and screaming, fighting and biting. Who could expect anyone in your line of work to be sane, anyway? I was just trying to take you to the hospital when you started having a fit, that's all. Your over-reaction caused me to panic. I took the wrong turn. Now here we are out in the middle of nowhere in very cold weather and you won't let me know where you are so I can get you the help you need.'

The help I need is for someone to come along and shoot you, I thought. Barney was busy building a story, some kind of story that would enable him to hold on to what he had. He was doomed to fail. But then, he'd lasted this long, and it must be hard for him to believe it was the end.

And to think I'd suspected Doak Garland. Well, I shouldn't relax too soon. There might have been *three* of them.

And I really was thinking about that, so you know my mind was wandering. It was the cold and fear that were doing me in. I sharpened back up mentally just in time. I'd almost laughed at the picture of the whole town of Doraville being in on the kidnapping and the murdering. Like a Shirley Jackson short story!

And then he caught me.

14

His big hands grabbed my shoulders, and like so many young men had been, I was now in his power. Except I had a knife in my hand. He pulled me up and up, until I was almost off my feet. In the twilight it was hard to make out details but I could see the white of his shirtfront, where his unbuttoned coat flapped open, and I swung my arm as hard as I could. The knife went into his skin easily enough but skidded along a bone, maybe his rib, and he screamed as the blood welled through his shirt.

He dropped me and I ran. He caught up with me after a second, though; he was quicker to recover from the shock than I expected. He tackled me, and I twisted, coming up on my side and swinging the knife back. This time I got him in the shoulder and it went in much farther. He really did scream, and heaved off of me, scrambling to his feet. We were close to the edge of the lake then, and I saw a sign or two – we were in some sort of public fishing area. I backed up closer to the water because he was coming at me and I didn't have a choice.

He'd done all the talking up till now. 'Come get me, you bastard,' I said. 'Come get me, rapist.'

'They loved it,' he said, amazingly. 'They loved it.'

'Sure,' I said. 'Who doesn't like being chained and burned and sliced before sex?'

'No,' he said, panting, 'not the boys. Tom. Tom and Chuck.'

'Okay, you make me sick,' I said. 'You going to stand there and make me sick some more, asshole?'

And he charged. He can't have been stupid, because he had a good job and he did it well enough to keep it, but he was stupid that night because of the strain and the pain and the freezing temperature, and he did lunge right at me. I leaped to one side and as he shot by I shoved him as hard as I could using both hands, even with the broken arm screaming at me. He landed right at the lake's edge, so I hadn't been close enough, damn it. I'd wanted him to go into the chilly water. But he wasn't getting up, and I took off. All those years of running finally gave me a reward for good behavior.

I was in the trees and working my way around the lake toward the inhabited cabin, the one with lights, which – I was almost certain – was the Hamiltons'.

I thought I heard him a million times. I hid for ten minutes, not moving, at least once; and maybe more than that. I was in too much pain to make sense, too cold to reason. I still had the knife, and though I thought of dropping it, I was scared to be without it in case he caught up with me. When I remembered how it had felt when the knife went into him, I had to stop and throw up. This was a queasy case. I didn't remember ever getting the heaves over any case before. Probably, I thought, I could excuse myself for it over the knifing. But I'd gotten sick outside the barn, too. Maybe it was the torturing, not the knifing?

I knew I wasn't thinking clearly, but knowing that didn't seem to help. I actually shook my head, maybe in the hope that my brains would resettle in a more sensible configuration, but I was really sorry I did that after I got sick yet again. Something was wrong with me, something bad. I needed to go to the hospital! I giggled.

It sure must have been Tom that hit me with that shovel, I thought. *If it had been Barney, he would've killed me.*

I'd forgotten to move for a couple of minutes. I'd just been standing in the dark woods with my mind far, far away. I listened hard, but I couldn't hear anything. That didn't mean it wasn't happening. I didn't trust my senses anymore. But I made myself move, because I couldn't stay out in the cold. I had to reach shelter.

That was the hardest struggle of my life. But I could see the lights and they were getting closer. I was farther from the road, far enough that I could only see lights passing occasionally. And who could tell whose lights they were, anyway?

I finally approached the first cabin. The woods ended, not abruptly, but with a gradual shift from heavy brush and trees, to trees with no brush, to scattered trees, to lawn and cabin. I didn't know anything: where Barney was, if I was for sure at Pine Landing Lake, if Tolliver was even looking for me. How could he not be? But what if he thought I'd gone off voluntarily? We'd been a little irritated with each other. No, that would never happen. He'd never believe I'd leave him.

I was stalling because I was scared to step out into the open. I listened with all my ears and looked with all my eyes. My heart was thudding and my head began pounding in time with it. I was having to fight a terrible desire to lie down on the cold ground and rest there, just for a minute. I took a few deep breaths and braced myself. I stepped out into the darkening evening. The moon would be out and there would be a lot of visibility, but now it was still twilight, the deepest, darkest part.

One step out into the open. Another.

Nothing happened.

I began to move faster, crossing this lawn and going into the next. Saying 'lawn' may give an impression of unbroken sweeps of trimmed grass, but that wasn't exactly accurate. These were summer cabins, or glorified fishing camps, and lawn care was not a big item in the time budget of people who spent weekends at the lake. The lots were not that large, and sometimes there was no division at all between one property and another. Sometimes there was a line of ragged bushes, probably something that flowered in the spring. The ground was often weedy, uneven, and always, it was wet. There were things strewn around: buckets, childrens' toys, boats covered in tarps, even a swing set. One careless cabin owner had left out his deck chairs. I know because I fell over one.

I'd never felt so alone in my life.

I got this feeling that this episode would never end. Forever, for always, I'd be stumbling in the dark through rough territory, with death waiting for me somewhere along the line.

I was actually surprised to find that I had reached the Cotton cabin, where we'd stayed. For the first time I was sure I was at Pine Landing Lake, and the next cabin, the one with lights, was the Hamiltons' place.

But I'd have to step into the bright light to knock on the Hamiltons' door. I might endanger them. Though it seemed to me that Barney Simpson must be heading toward Mexico or Canada in his SUV by now, I couldn't be certain.

I planned it in advance, real carefully. I would run from the shadows of the Cotton cabin, up the slight slope to the Hamiltons' driveway, up the steps to their little deck, across it to the door, *bam bam bam*. Ted would open the door, because it was night. He would let me in. He might not really want to, because I was such a mess and I was bringing trouble with me, but I thought he would.

I gathered myself. Just as I was about to take the step out of the shadows, a large dark shape passed between me and the cottage. It seemed more bear than human, but after a second I was sure I was seeing Barney Simpson – not the kindly hospital administrator, but the beast that had lived within him. He hardly walked like a man. His shoulders were slumped and his left leg was dragging. I was sorry I hadn't hurt him enough to stop him. I thought he was more dangerous now that he'd been wounded.

He stood almost directly outside the Hamiltons' side door, down on the driveway; he didn't mount the steps to the deck. Their security light shone on the top of his head. Barney's hair was full of leaves and twigs. His suit was stained with blood and damp and dirt.

He had a big knife in his right hand. It was really more of a machete than a knife. I wondered if he'd gotten it out of his car, and if so, where it had been during our struggle. He'd been too cocky, then, apparently; he hadn't thought a weapon would be necessary, because he was big and strong.

Okay. I'd just wait until he left.

But Ted Hamilton was on the watch, as always. The door to the cottage opened, and the old man stepped out onto the little deck.

'Is it Mr Simpson from the hospital?' he called. 'Mr Simpson, is that you?'

'Oh, Mr Hamilton,' said Barney. 'Listen, I'm sorry to disturb you. But that young woman that was here to find the bodies, that Harper Connelly, she's having a mental episode and she's somewhere out here running loose.'

'Oh, goodness,' said Mr Hamilton, and it was impossible to tell from his voice what his reaction was.

'I don't suppose you've seen her?' Barney asked, and I wondered if I was the only one who could hear the strain in his voice. Barney was having a hard time sounding and acting like a human.

'No, I haven't,' Ted Hamilton said. 'What do you plan to do when you find her?'

'Why, take her to the hospital,' Barney said.

'Are you planning to cut off her head first? Because that sure is a big knife you've got there.'

'No, Mr Hamilton, watch out!' I jumped out of my hiding place, because I was so scared that Barney would attack the old man and his wife.

But Mr Hamilton was pointing a gun at Barney. He was right on top of the situation, until I'd startled both of them by my sudden appearance.

With a roar, Barney came after me, and I turned to run back to the woods. But then the gun went off behind me.

And Barney wasn't running after me anymore.

15

I stopped and turned around. Barney Simpson was lying in the drive-way, so newly cleaned of tree debris. Now he was getting it dirty again, because he was really bleeding from a hole in his shoulder.

Mr Hamilton had come forward to the edge of the deck, and Nita was behind him. She was wearing another tracksuit, and her short hair looked just as neat in the overhead light as it had in the daytime.

'You think you need to shoot him again?' she asked her husband.

'I think he's done,' Ted Hamilton said. 'You scoot in there and call the police.'

'I'm one step ahead of you, honey, I already did it when I heard his voice outside,' she said. 'Miss Connelly, you want to step around him, real careful, and come inside?'

'Thank you,' I said, in a very shaky voice that didn't sound at all like my own. 'I'd love to be inside. Inside anything.'

'You poor girl, come on in.'

I walked very carefully around Barney Simpson, who was clutching his shoulder and as white as a sheet, though the bright overhead light washed the color out of everything. I went up the stairs very carefully, since nothing in my body seemed to be working exactly right. I was careful not to jostle Ted or come between him and the downed man. I didn't want Barney to get any more like the Terminator than he already had.

When I was close to Nita Hamilton and she got a good look at me, she said, 'We do need to get you inside. Ted, are you good out here?'

'Yes, honey, you take care of the young lady.'

And just like that I was in a warm place. I could have predicted almost everything about the Hamiltons' cottage, from the maple furniture to the crocheted throws folded over the backs of their favorite chairs, from the framed baby pictures to the china rooster on an end table. Nita efficiently threw a towel over the wooden chair by the door, where they probably normally dumped their keys and coats.

After I looked down at myself, I knew that was the only possible place for me to sit.

'You're bleeding,' she said. 'I'm going to get a rag and wipe you off. I know the EMTs will do it right, but you don't want to be sitting there dripping. I know I wouldn't.'

And that was true enough, though I didn't really care that much just at the moment.

She was back with a clean rag and a white enamel basin of warm water in just a couple of minutes, and she began the tedious process of cleaning my face.

'Ted'll keep his distance, don't you worry,' she said quietly, as if shooting men was an everyday occurrence at the lake cottage. 'He won't get too close.'

'When will the police be here?'

'Any moment. Your brother has been looking for you all over town,' Mrs Hamilton said, and my heart felt warm again. 'He called out here and asked us to keep our eyes open, because he saw Barney Simpson's car parked at the other end of the lake. So we were prepared.'

'I hope the police understand,' I said.

'I'm sure they will. Nothing wrong with our sheriff. She's a good one.'

I wasn't as sold on that idea as Nita, but then the sheriff wasn't answerable to me.

'How come your head's bleeding?' Nita asked, as if to make sure I was completely there with her mentally.

'He pulled me out of the car by the hair,' I said, and she looked truly shocked. 'He pulled some stitches out.'

'Well, if Ted knew that, he'd shoot him again,' she said, and that triggered a set of giggles that shook my body in an unpleasant way.

I thought, *Then I wish I'd told him*, but just then we heard an ominous sound outside. It was a deep groan, and it came from right outside the door. Ted Hamilton. Oh, shit.

Quick as a wink, Nita locked the front door, and just barely in time. The knob turned, and when the door wouldn't open to him, Barney threw himself against it.

'Come out,' he bellowed, 'come out here!'

'He's hurt Ted,' Nita said. 'That son of a bitch.'

Even at that moment, I was shocked. But that was only the

beginning. Nita opened a closet on the other side of the front door, pulled out a rifle, and aimed it at the door. 'This is our varmint rifle,' she told me, maybe because I was gaping at her. 'He comes in here, he's dead. I might turn my own cheek, but I ain't offering up yours.'

Barney threw himself against the door. Since I was still sitting to the right of the door, like a fool, I could hear the click in the quiet night. 'Move!' I yelled. 'Move, Nita!' And Barney fired Ted's pistol into the house.

The cabin had a good door, but the bullet came in and passed through the living room and into the kitchen beyond. Nita had moved to the side, and it missed her by a foot or more, but it was pretty shocking. For a moment I thought Nita would falter, that all her courage would drain away, but she raised the rifle and fired right back, and we heard a scream.

After a second of staring at each other, Nita said, 'I have to see about my husband.' Though I thought it was the worst idea in the world for her to open that door, I said 'Of course you do' through stiff lips. I reached up my right hand and unlocked the door, and turned the knob as quietly as I could, though I'm not sure why I was trying to be so quiet at this late date.

The door swung open, and we saw Barney again down and bleeding, and Ted Hamilton crumpled on the deck in a corner, blood running from his shoulder. He was conscious, but only just. Nita said, 'Oh,' and it sounded like she was witnessing the end of the world.

Then she simply stepped over Barney to get to her man, and she knelt down by him, and she put pressure on his shoulder like the sensible woman she was, and I finally managed to subtract myself from the situation by fainting.

16

When I was a little more aware of what was around me, things were better all around. I was being strapped to a gurney and I was willing to bet I was about to get a ride in an ambulance to the Doraville hospital.

'Doraville's not lucky for me,' I said, or at least I thought I was saying that, but I guess I was just mumbling, because the EMT at my head, a plump young woman with an aggressive jaw, said, 'You're gonna be okay, honey, don't you worry.'

'Mr Hamilton?'

'That's nice, your asking about him. We got the bleeding stopped. I think he's gonna be okay, too.'

'Barney?'

'He ain't dead, but I bet he's gonna wish he was.'

'Where's my – where's Tolliver?' *Had* to get out of the habit of calling him my brother.

'Tall, dark, skinny?'

'Mm-hm.'

'Waiting for us to wheel you out.'

And I smiled.

'That's sweet, she's happy to see him,' the young woman said. Her partner, a man in his fifties, said, 'Grace, let's just get her out of here,' and she pouted as they got me down the deck steps.

Tolliver was by me, and he was beside himself. 'He took you right out of the car,' he said, as if I didn't know that. 'I couldn't believe it when I came out and you were gone!'

'Well, you-all can talk all night if you want. Let us get this gal to the hospital,' the older man said.

The ride back to the hospital took a while, and the young woman sat in back with me and chattered the whole time. She took my pulse and checked my temperature and did all kinds of things, including looking at the stitches in my scalp. From the slight face she made, I knew they weren't in good shape.

'Now, I understand you had a cracked ulna a few days ago?' she asked. 'I think you've graduated to a broken arm, but we'll take us an X-ray to be sure.'

'Okay,' I said. We'd have to go into our savings to pay for my Doraville medical bills. That'd be that much longer until we could buy our house. But it was hard for me to worry about that right now, or much of anything else, being in this ambulance felt so blissful compared to my previous three hours of experience.

I felt so safe I actually fell asleep and had to blink my eyes open when we reached the hospital.

The whole hospital experience was déjà vu. I wasn't in the same room – I think Ted Hamilton was in that one. I was down the hall and on the other side.

Sandra Rockwell was my most surprising visitor. After we'd done the 'How are you's and so forth, she said, 'I want to apologize for something.'

I waited.

'I knew whoever attacked you, I knew it had to be the killer. And there wasn't a trace of him. Or his vehicle. Turns out, Tom Almand says he parked over behind Hair Affair and cut across the back parking lots. Then he hid behind the Dumpster behind the motel. He was going to slash your tires, but then you came out, and he'd brought the shovel just on the off chance.'

I tried to remember where Hair Affair was – two doors down from the motel, I thought. It hardly mattered now.

'How's he doing?' I asked.

'Tom?' She sounded surprised. 'Talking his damn head off. But won't mention his son.'

'Maybe Barney will,' I said. Again, I felt as if I hardly cared. Chuck Almand was gone now, and no amount of confession or explanation would bring him back.

Tolliver came in just then. He'd been in the cafeteria getting coffee and breakfast. He'd gotten me some coffee, and though I wasn't sure if I was supposed to have it or not, I planned on drinking it. He bent over to kiss me, and I didn't care, either, what Sandra Rockwell thought about that.

Klavin and Stuart came in then. They both looked exhausted, but they were smiling.

'There's enough pathology between those two to keep the serial-killer writers busy for years,' Klavin said. 'As long as they're behind bars while they're being studied, that's fine with me.'

'The writers are welcome to 'em,' said Stuart. He smoothed his already smooth hair. 'Those two are talking, and that's how we're filling in the cracks.'

Tolliver took my hand.

I sighed.

They began asking me exactly what had happened the afternoon before, and I wasn't really ready to talk about it. But I'd had to do a lot of things I didn't want to do during my stay in Doraville, and this was simply another one of them.

'Did you suspect he was the one?' Stuart asked.

'Yes,' I said, and they all seemed surprised . . . especially Tolliver. 'Because when I was sitting there in the car, I was thinking about the hole under the barn, and I was thinking how strange it was that Barney Simpson knew there was a hole there. He said something about it when I was visiting Manfred here at the hospital. I might not even have thought about it, but when Doak Garland asked me a question about it, it was clear that Doak had no idea there was a pit under the stall. So it was not common knowledge. Yet Barney had known about it. And then I thought about the way so many of the boys had had a trip to the hospital. That would have been a good place for Barney to spot them and mark them for future attention. And he said something to me about that.'

That was what they were anxious to hear, so I tried to remember the way Barney had talked about their methods, and explain about the pit and why it had been built, when the old house out of town was really more isolated.

'They would take turns,' Stuart said. 'Because it was hard to park two cars behind the old house. But sometimes, on weekends, they'd go together. Like double dating.'

I felt sick, and put the coffee down on the rolling table. Tolliver patted me.

'Sometimes the boys would last four or five days, if they gave them food and water,' Klavin said.

'Okay, enough,' Tolliver said, and it was clear he was angry. 'We know as much about this as we want to know.'

'So, we're charging him with attempted homicide on you and Ted Hamilton,' Klavin said, when he'd absorbed the rebuke. 'But with the murders, we got enough to put him away forever. We'll just throw in other charges if there's any way at all he might get off. I mean, you can only give him life so many times.'

'Some of the forensic evidence will tie both of them in, I hope. So it's not just their confessions.'

'There was so much there, some of it's definitely going to come through. For one thing, there are hair matches already. And I'm sure we'll get some DNA matches.'

I nodded. Though these men would eat, breathe, and sleep the case until it came to trial, to me it was at a close.

'How are you doing, by the way?' the sheriff asked. She just wanted to point out that Klavin and Stuart hadn't inquired. They both looked only a tad sheepish.

Tolliver said, 'Her arm is broken all the way through. Her scalp stitches had to be redone and there are more of them now. The scalp wound is infected. She has multiple severe bruises and two loose teeth. You can see the black eye. And now she's got an upper respiratory infection, too.'

Also, a torn fingernail, but he left that out.

Tolliver was glaring at them so indignantly that I expected they would break down and weep, but they just shuffled around un-comfortably until they thought of a good reason to leave. It didn't sound as though I'd have to come back to Doraville, maybe. At least, not anytime soon. That suited me just fine.

Manfred called, but I didn't talk to him. Tolliver did. I was too tired – too emotionally tired – to want to talk to him again.

The only guest I was glad to see was Twyla Cotton. She came in moving even more heavily, it seemed to me. Her face was so serious that it didn't seem she would ever smile again.

'Well,' she said. She was standing right by my bed, and she couldn't meet my eyes. 'They're caught, and my grandson's gone for good.'

I nodded.

'I did the right thing bringing you here, and I'm glad I did. They had to stop what they were doing, even if it was too late for Jeff.'

It had been too late for Jeff by months.

'They'll rot in hell,' Twyla said with absolute conviction. 'And I know Jeff is in heaven. But it's hard for us left here.'

'Yes,' I said, because that was something I knew about. 'It's hard for those left behind.'

'You're thinking of your sister who's missing?'

'Yes, Cameron.'

'Kind of ironic, huh?'

'That I can find everyone else but her? Yes, you could put it that way.'

'Then that's what I'll pray about for you. That you find your sister.'

Looking at Twyla's stricken face, for the first time I wondered if I really wanted to find Cameron. If it would really give me peace. I switched my gaze over to Tolliver. He was looking at Twyla with an unpleasant face. He thought she was making me unhappy, and he didn't think I needed any more unhappiness.

'Thank you, Twyla,' I said. 'I hope . . . I hope your remaining grandson brings you joy.'

She almost smiled. 'He will. Ain't nothing can replace Jeff, but Carson is a good steady boy.'

She left soon after, because we didn't have anything left to say.

Tolliver said, 'Tomorrow, if you don't have a fever, we're leaving this place.'

'Absolutely,' I said. 'Maybe by the time I get to Philadelphia I will have healed enough that I won't scare the clients.'

'We can cancel and go to our apartment and just relax for a couple of weeks.'

'No,' I said. 'Back in the saddle again.' And then I made an effort to smile. 'And when I'm a little better than that, we'll see about *really* getting back in the saddle.' I tried to leer, but the result was so ludicrous that Tolliver had to choke back a laugh.

But I poked him in the ribs, and he let it out.

Back in the saddle again.

Acknowledgements

My heartfelt thanks go to Margaret Maron, who introduced me to Daniel E. Bailey, a chief deputy sheriff in North Carolina. He spent a lot of time answering my questions. I hope I haven't made any huge goof-ups. Molly Weston, a most mysterious woman, helped me with climate questions, and Dr D. P. Lyle, once again, helped me with medical issues. My friend Toni L. P. Kelner gave me some great ideas about improving the book.

GRAVE SECRET

To my son Patrick, simply because I think he's great.

1

'All right,' said the straw-haired woman in the denim jacket. 'Do your thing.' Her accent made the words sound more like 'Dew yore thang.' Her hawklike face was eager, the anticipatory look of someone who is ready to taste an unknown food.

We were standing on a windswept field some miles south of the interstate that runs between Texarkana and Dallas. A car zoomed by on the narrow two-lane blacktop. It was the only other car I'd seen since I'd followed Lizzie Joyce's gleaming black Chevy Kodiak pickup out to the Pioneer Rest Cemetery, which lay outside the tiny town of Clear Creek.

When our little handful of people fell silent, the whistle of the wind scouring the rolling hill was the only sound in the landscape.

There wasn't a fence around the little cemetery. It had been cleared, but not recently. This was an old cemetery, as Texas cemeteries go, established when the live oak in the middle of the graveyard had been only a small tree. A flock of birds was cackling in the oak's branches. Since we were in north Texas, there was grass, but in February it wasn't green. Though the temperature was in the fifties today, the wind was colder than I'd counted on. I zipped up my jacket. I noticed that Lizzie Joyce wasn't wearing one.

The people who lived hereabouts were tough and pragmatic, including the thirtyish blonde who'd invited me here. She was lean and muscular, and she must have tugged up her jeans by greasing her legs. I couldn't imagine how she mounted a horse. But her boots were well-worn, and so was her hat, and if I'd read her belt buckle correctly, she was the previous year's countywide barrel-riding champion. Lizzie Joyce was the real deal.

She also had more money in her bank account than I would ever earn in my life. The diamonds on her hand flashed in the bright sunlight as she waved toward the piece of ground dedicated to the dead. Ms Joyce wanted me to get the show on the road.

I prepared to dew mah thang. Since Lizzie was paying me big bucks

for this, she wanted to get the most out of it. She'd invited her little
entourage, which consisted of her boyfriend, her younger sister, and
her brother, who looked as though he'd rather be anywhere else but in
Pioneer Rest Cemetery.

My brother was leaning against our car, and he wasn't going to stir.
Until I'd done my job, Tolliver wouldn't pay attention to anything but
me.

I still thought of him as my brother, though I was trying to catch
myself when I called him that out loud. We had a much different
relationship, now.

We'd met the Joyces that morning for the first time. We'd driven
down the long, winding driveway leading between wide, fenced-in
fields, following the excellent directions Lizzie had sent to our laptop.

The house at the end of the driveway was very large and very
beautiful, but it wasn't pretentious. It was a house for people who
worked hard. The Latina who'd answered the door had been wearing
nice pants and a blouse, not any kind of uniform, and she'd referred to
her boss as 'Lizzie,' not 'Ms Joyce.' Since every day on a ranch or farm
is a working day, I hadn't been surprised to see that the big house felt
pretty empty, and the only glimpses I caught of other people had been
distant ones. As the housekeeper led us through the house, I'd seen a
Jeep coming up one of the tracks that ran between the huge fields at
the rear of the house.

Lizzie Joyce and her sister, Kate, had been waiting in the gun room.
I was sure they called it the den or the family room, or something else
to indicate it was where they gathered to watch television and play
board games, or whatever really rich people did with their evenings
when they lived way the hell out in the sticks. But to me, it was the
gun room. There were weapons and animal heads all over, and the
décor was supposed to imply this was a rustic hunting lodge. Since the
house had been built by the Joyce grandfather, it reflected his taste, I
guessed, but they could have changed it if they'd objected. He'd been
dead for a while.

Lizzie Joyce looked like the pictures I'd seen of her, but the impression was strictly practical. She was a working woman. Her sister,
Kate, called Katie, was a scaled-down version of her big sister: shorter,
younger, less seasoned. But she seemed just as confident and hard.
Maybe being brought up with gobs of money did that to you.

The gun room had a wall of French doors leading out onto a wide brick porch. There were urns that would be filled with flowers in the spring, but it wasn't time yet. The temperatures still dipped below freezing sometimes at night. I noticed that the Joyces had left their rocking chairs outside during the winter, and I wondered what it would be like to sit out on the roofed brick porch in the morning in the summer, drinking coffee and looking out over all that land.

The Jeep came to a stop at the foot of the gentle slope leading up to the back porch, and two men climbed out and came in.

'Harper, this is the manager of RJ Ranch, Chip Moseley. And this is our brother, Drexell.'

Tolliver and I shook hands with the men.

The manager was rugged, weathered, and skeptical, green eyed and brown haired, and he was as ready to leave as the brother. Both of them were only here because Lizzie wanted them to be. Chip Moseley gave Lizzie a casual kiss on the cheek, and I realized he was her man as well as her manager. That might be awkward.

The brother, Drexell, was the youngest of the Joyces and the most anonymous looking. Lizzie and Katie both had a certain hawk-nosed flamboyance, but Drexell's round face was still a bit babyish. He didn't meet my eyes as his sisters had.

I had a niggling feeling that I'd seen both men somewhere before. Since the huge Joyce ranch wasn't too far from Texarkana, and I'd grown up there, it wasn't beyond the realm of possibility that I'd met Chip and Drexell – but the last thing I wanted to do was bring up my previous life. I hadn't always been the mysterious woman who could find bodies because she'd been fried by lightning.

'I'm so glad you could find time to come here,' Lizzie said.

'My sister likes to collect the unusual,' Katie told Tolliver. She definitely had her eye on him.

'Harper is one of a kind,' he said, and he glanced at me. He looked a little amused.

'Well, you better give Lizzie a good show for her money,' Chip said, his weathered, handsome face giving me a big dose of warning. I looked at him more closely. I didn't want to be seen showing interest in someone else's honey, but there was something for me in Chip Moseley, something that spoke to my special talent. He was moving and breathing, which normally meant disqualification.

My business is with the dead.

Since Lizzie Joyce had found a website that followed my travels, she apparently hadn't been able to rest until she thought of a job for me to do. She'd finally decided she wanted to know what had killed her grandfather, who'd been found far away from the main ranch house, collapsed by the side of his Jeep. Rich Joyce had a skull injury, and the presumption was that he'd slipped and fallen when he was getting into or out of his ride; or maybe the Jeep had hit a rock and tossed him sideways, cracking his skull against the Jeep's frame, though no evidence of such an impact had been found. Anyhow, the Jeep's ignition had been switched off, and Rich Joyce had been dead, and no one else was within miles; so his death had been attributed to heart failure, and he'd been put in the ground years ago. Since Rich's only son and his son's wife had died in a car accident some years before, his three grandchildren had inherited, though not equally. Lizzie was legally in charge of the family's fortunes now, Tolliver's research had indicated, but the other two had shares that were slightly less than a third apiece; just enough to keep Lizzie in the driver's seat. Easy to tell who Rich Joyce had trusted.

I wondered if Rich Joyce had ever known his granddaughter had a streak of mysticism, or maybe simply a love of the unusual. That was why Lizzie had led us to Pioneer Rest Cemetery, and why I was standing waiting for her to give me the go-ahead.

Hardheaded Lizzie wanted value for her money, so she wasn't going to lead me directly to the grave that was her grandfather's. She hadn't even told me the purpose of my search until I'd gotten out of my car thirty minutes before. Of course, I could wander around to read all the headstones until I found one with appropriate dates. There weren't that many Joyces under the dirt and rocks. But I'd spin this out, give her some freebies, because she hadn't flinched at my fee.

I'd taken off my shoes for the reading, though I had to watch where I put my feet. There are thorns hidden in the grass in Texas, no matter how pretty it looks. I cast a final glance across the panorama of rolling ground and trees and emptiness. This little cemetery might as well have been on the moon, the landscape was such a contrast from the thickly clustering housing developments and settled communities we'd seen as we drove to our last job in North Carolina. We'd ended up in a small town, but it hadn't had the isolated feel that I got from the landscape here. There'd always been the awareness that another settlement was within a few minutes' drive.

At least it wasn't as cold here, and at least we could be almost certain there wouldn't be any snow. My feet stung in the chilly air, but nowhere near as much as my whole body had ached in freezing, wet North Carolina.

The Joyces were buried close to the live oak. I could see a large boulder that had been chiseled smooth on one side, and the name JOYCE was carved in it in huge letters. It would have looked willfully naïve to have ignored that clue. I stopped at the first grave I reached in that plot, though it was clearly not the one I'd come to read. But what the hell, I had to start sometime. The tombstone read, *Sarah, Beloved Wife of Paul Joyce*. I took a deep breath, and I stepped on top of it. The connection with the bones beneath my feet was electric and immediate. Sarah was waiting, like all of them, the longtime dead and the recently dead, those buried neatly in graves and those tossed aside like debris. I sent that extra sense I had down into the ground. Connected. Learned.

'Woman in her sixties, aneurysm,' I said. I opened my eyes and stepped to the next grave. This was an older one, much older. 'Hiram Joyce,' I said. I stood there, trying to get a firm fix on the few remaining bones in the ground under my feet. 'Blood poisoning,' I said finally. I walked to the next one, rested for a moment until the buzzing impelled me: that was the call of the bones, the remains. They wanted me to know about them, what had killed them, what their final moments had been like. I looked at the headstone. No point in reinventing the wheel.

This was not a Joyce, though the burial was within the family plot. The date was eight years and a few months before. The carved name was *Mariah Parish*. Though I sensed the two men, waiting under the scanty shade of a twisted tree, were standing much straighter, I was too intent on the connection to wonder about that.

'Oh,' I said, softly. The wind whooshed past, lifting my short dark hair and teasing it. 'Oh, poor thing.'

'What?' asked Lizzie, her harsh voice sounding simply confused. 'That's my grandfather's caregiver. She had a burst appendix or something.'

'She had a hemorrhage, bled out after childbirth,' I said. I put two and two together and glanced over at the two men. Drexell had actually taken a step closer. Chip Moseley was stunned; he was also furious, whether because the information was a shock to him, or because I'd said it out loud, I couldn't say. But whatever they were feeling, it was too late for Mariah. I looked away and stepped over to the right grave, the one I'd been brought to read. It was the biggest headstone in the plot, a double one. Richard Joyce's wife had predeceased him by ten years. Her name had been Cindilynn, and I discovered she'd died of breast cancer. I said so out loud, and I glimpsed Kate and Lizzie look at each other and nod. I stepped to the ground just adjacent, Rich Joyce's side of the headstone. Rich had died eight years ago, not long after his caregiver. I cocked my head as I listened to Richard's bones.

He'd seen something that startled him. I got that, but it took me a few seconds to understand that he'd stopped the Jeep and gotten out because he'd seen someone he knew.

I didn't have a picture of that person in my head. It's not like I'm watching a movie. It's like being inside the person for a moment or two, thinking the person's thoughts, feeling his emotions, in the last seconds of the person's life. So I understood from Rich Joyce that he'd stopped because he'd seen someone. I didn't go through the process of recognizing that person and reasoning that I should stop because he was standing there. As Rich Joyce, I turned off the Jeep, stepped out, and then the snake came flying through the air, the rattlesnake, giving me (Rich Joyce) such a shock that my (his) heart stopped working properly. *So hot no water can't reach phone oh my God to end like this* and then it had all gone black. With my eyes closed to see that scene more clearly, that scene visible only to me, I related what was happening.

When I opened my eyes, the four people in the Joyce party were staring at me as if I'd developed stigmata. Sometimes it grabs people that way, even when they've asked me there to do exactly what I just did.

I creep people out or I fascinate them (not always in a healthy way) . . . or both. However, the fascination thing wasn't going to be a problem today. The boyfriend was looking at me as if I were wearing a straitjacket, and the three Joyces were gaping. Everyone was silent.

'So now you know,' I said briskly.

'You could've made that up,' Lizzie said. 'There was someone there? How'd that happen? No one has said they were there. Are you telling me someone threw a rattlesnake at Granddaddy? And that gave him a heart attack, and then that someone just left him? And you're saying Mariah had a baby? I didn't hire you to tell me lies!'

Okay, that pissed me off. I took a deep breath. From the corner of my eye, I noticed Tolliver had started over to me, the beginnings of alarm evident on his face. Behind them all, Chip Moseley had retreated to the Jeep and was standing with one hand braced on it, doubled over. I realized he was in pain, and I knew he wouldn't thank me if I drew attention to him.

'You brought me here to do this,' I said. I spread my hands. 'There is nothing you can verify, even if you dug your grandfather up. I warned you that might be the case. Of course, you can find out about Mariah Parish, if you really are concerned. There should be a birth record, or some paper trail.'

'That's true,' Lizzie said. Her face was more thoughtful than repulsed now. 'But aside from the issue of what happened to Mariah's baby, if she really had one, it makes me sick that someone would do that to Granddaddy. If you're telling us the truth.'

'Believe me; don't believe me. That's up to you. Did you know about his heart condition?'

'No, he wasn't one for doctors. But he'd had a stroke already. And the last time he went in for a checkup, he came back looking worried.' She'd thought about this many times since her grandfather's death, it was obvious.

'He had a cell phone in his Jeep, right?' I said.

'Yeah,' she said. 'He did.'

'He was trying to reach it.' Some last moments are more informative than others.

I glanced quickly in Tolliver's direction, and then away. The tension was leaving his shoulders. I thought we were going to be okay.

'You believe this stuff?' Chip asked the sisters incredulously. He'd recovered from whatever had ailed him, and he was standing at Lizzie's side. He looked at her as if he'd never seen her before, when I knew from our research that he'd been her escort for the past six years.

Lizzie was too confident to be hurried. She appeared to be thinking hard as she got out a cigarette and lit it. Finally, she tilted her face up to him. 'Yes, I believe it.'

'Shi-it,' Kate Joyce said and pulled off her cowboy hat. She slapped it against her lean thigh. 'You'll be wanting to bring in that John Edward next.'

Lizzie shot her sister a look that was not fond. Drexell said, 'I think she made all of this up, you ask me.'

We had gotten a deposit from Lizzie. We were coming to Texas anyway, but we sure wouldn't have stopped if we hadn't gotten the up-front money. Clients this rich, oddly enough, often change their mind. Poorer people don't. So, though we'd already deposited the first check from RJ Ranch, the balance was due, and a blind man could tell the whole Joyce party was dubious about what I'd accomplished. Before I could get a good start on worrying about it, Lizzie pulled a folded and creased check from her hip pocket and handed it to Tolliver, who'd gotten close enough to slide his arm around me. I was a little shaky. This hadn't been as hard as some readings, because Rich Joyce'd only had a second's surge of fear before he passed over, but direct contact with the dead is draining.

'Need candy?' he asked.

I nodded. He got a Werther's Original out of his pocket and unwrapped it. I opened my mouth and he popped it in. Golden buttery goodness.

'I thought he was your brother,' Kate Joyce said, inclining her head toward Tolliver. Though I knew she had to be in her late twenties, there were more years of experience than that in the way she walked and spoke. I wondered if this was the result of being brought up rich but practical in Texas, or if life in the Joyce household had had other sources of stress.

'He is,' I said.

'Looks more like your boyfriend.' Drexell sniggered.

'I'm her stepbrother and her boyfriend, Drex,' Tolliver said pleasantly. 'We'll be on the road. Thanks for asking us to help you with your problem.' He nodded at them all. He's less than six feet, but not by much, and he's thin, but he has a set of shoulders on him.

I love him more than anything.

The sound of the shower woke me up. We see the inside of so many motel rooms that sometimes I have to spend a second or two recalling where the particular motel room is located. This was one of those mornings.

Texas. After we'd left the Joyces, we had driven most of the previous afternoon to reach this motel off the interstate in Garland, outside of Dallas. This wasn't a business trip; it was personal.

I had that consciousness when I opened my eyes, that grim awareness that I was thinking too much about the old, bad times. Whenever
we visit my aunt and her husband outside of Dallas, the bad memories
resurface.

It's not the fault of the state.

When I'm close to my little sisters, I start remembering the broken
trailer in Texarkana, the one where Tolliver and I lived with his
father, my mother, his brother, my sister, and our two mutual sibs,
who were practically babies at the time that household dissolved.

The delicately balanced deception we older kids had maintained for
several years had collapsed when my older sister, Cameron, vanished.
Our unpleasant home life had been exposed to public view, and our
little sisters had been taken away. Tolliver had gone to live with his
brother, Mark, and I'd gone to a foster home.

The two little girls didn't even remember Cameron. I'd asked them
the last time we saw them. The girls live with Aunt Iona and Uncle
Hank, who don't like us to visit. We do, though; Mariella and Grace
(called Gracie) are our sisters, and we want them to remember they
have family.

I propped up on one elbow to watch Tolliver drying himself off.
He'd left the bathroom door open while he showered, because otherwise the mirror became too foggy for him to use while he shaved.

We don't look unalike; we're both thin and dark haired. Our hair's
even about the same length. His eyes are brown; mine are dark gray.
But Tolliver's complexion is pitted and scarred from acne, because his
dad didn't think of sending him to a dermatologist. His face is
narrower, and he often has a mustache. He hates wearing anything
besides jeans and shirts, but I like to dress up a bit more, and since I'm
the 'talent,' it's more or less expected. Tolliver is my manager, my
consultant, my main support, my companion, and for the past few
weeks he's been my lover.

He turned to look at me, saw I was watching. He smiled and
dropped the towel.

'Come here,' I said.

He was quick to oblige.

'Want to go for a run?' I asked in the afternoon. 'You can take another
shower afterward, with me. So you won't waste water.'

We had our running clothes on in no time, and we took off after we'd stretched. Tolliver's faster than I am. Most often, he pulls away for the last half mile or so, and today was no exception.

We were pleased to find a good place to run. Our motel was on the access road right off the interstate. It was flanked by other hotels and motels, restaurants and gas stations, the usual assortment of services for road warriors. But to the rear of the motel, we found one of those 'business parks': two curving streets with careful, still-small plantings in the flower beds in front of the one-story buildings, each with a parking area. A median ran down the middle of these two streets, wide enough to support a planting of crepe myrtles. There were sidewalks, too, to give the place an inviting and friendly look. Since it was late Friday afternoon, the traffic was minimal among the rows of rectangular buildings chopped up into characterless entities like Great Systems, Inc. and Genesis Distributors, which might conduct business of any sort. Each block was marked off by a driveway running between the buildings, a narrow thing that must lead to a parking lot in back for the employees. There were almost no cars parked in front; customers were gone, the last employees were leaving for the weekend.

In such a place, the last thing I expected to encounter was a dead man. I was thinking of the ache in my right leg, which has flared up from time to time ever since the lightning ran down that side, so I didn't hear his bones calling me at first.

They're everywhere, of course, dead people. I don't hear only the modern dead. I feel the ancient dead, too; even, very rarely, the faint, faint echo of a trace of people who walked the earth before there was writing. But this guy I was connecting with here in the Dallas suburbs was *very* fresh. I ran in place for a moment.

I couldn't be sure unless I got closer to the body, but I was thinking this one felt like a suicide by gun. I pinpointed his location – he was in the back part of an office called Designated Engineering. I shook off his overwhelming misery. I've had practice. Pity him? He'd gotten to choose. If I pitied everyone I met who'd crossed over, I'd be weeping continuously.

No, I wasn't spending my time on emotion. I was trying to decide what to do. I could leave him where he was, and that was my initial impulse. The first person to come into Designated Engineering the next workday would get a rude shock, if the guy's family didn't send the police to check his office tonight when he didn't come home.

It seemed harsh, leaving him there. However, I didn't want to get involved in a long explanation to the police.

Running in place was getting old. I had to make up my mind.

Though I can't agonize over every dead person I find, I don't want to lose my humanity, either.

I looked around for inspiration. I found it in the rocks bordering the ho-hum flower bed at the entrance door. I pulled out the largest rock I could handle and hefted it. After a little experimentation, I decided I could throw it one-handed. I glanced up and down the street; no cars in sight, and no one on foot. Standing a safe distance back, I took a balanced stance and let the rock fly. I had to retrieve the rock and repeat this action twice more before the glass shattered and an alarm began to go off. I took off running. I had to take a metaphorical hat off to the police. I had barely reached the motel parking lot when I saw the patrol car turning off the access road and speeding by the motel to cruise into the business park.

An hour later, I was telling Tolliver what had happened while I put on my makeup. I'd had a long shower, and sure enough, he'd jumped in again to 'help you wash your hair.'

I was leaning my clean self over the sink to peer into the mirror to apply my eyeliner. Though I was only twenty-four, I had to get closer to the mirror now, and I just knew the next time I had an exam, my eye doctor was going to tell me I needed glasses. I'd never considered myself vain, but every time I pictured myself wearing glasses, I felt a pang. Maybe contact lenses? But the thought of sticking anything in my eyes made me shudder.

Every time I thought about this, I worried about the money correcting my vision might cost. We were saving every cent we could to make the down payment on the house we were hoping to buy here in the Dallas area. St Louis was more centrally located from a business point of view, but we could see our sisters more often if Dallas was our home base. Probably Iona and Hank wouldn't care for that, and they might throw a lot of obstacles in our way. They'd formally adopted the girls. But maybe we could persuade them that the girls would benefit from seeing us as much as we would from seeing them.

Tolliver came into the bathroom and paused to kiss my shoulder. I smiled as my eyes met his in the mirror.

'Police activity down the street,' he said. 'You know anything about that?'

'As a matter of fact, I do,' I said, feeling guilty. I hadn't taken the time to explain to Tolliver before I'd gotten in the shower, and he'd distracted me after that. Now I told Tolliver about the dead man, and I explained about the rock and the window.

'The cops have found him by now, so you did the right thing. I have to say, I wish you'd just left him,' Tolliver said.

Pretty much what I'd expected him to say; he was always cautious about being pulled into any situation that we hadn't been paid to deal with. Since I was watching him in the mirror, I saw the subtle changes in his stance that said he was going to switch the subject, and he was going to talk about something serious.

'Do you ever think maybe we should just let go?' Tolliver said.

'Let go?' I finished my right eye and held my mascara wand to the lashes of my left eye. 'Let go of what?'

'Mariella and Gracie.'

I turned to face him. 'I don't understand what you're asking,' I told him, though I was very much afraid that I did.

'Maybe we should only visit once a year. Just send Christmas presents and birthday presents the rest of the time.'

I was shocked. 'Why would we do that?' Wasn't that the whole purpose of saving every cent we could – so we could become a bigger part of their lives, not smaller?

'We're confusing them.' Tolliver stepped a little closer and put his hand on my shoulder. 'The girls may have their problems, but they're doing better with Iona than they would with us. We can't take care of them. We travel too much. Iona and Hank are responsible people, and they don't use alcohol or drugs. They take the girls to church; they make sure they're in school.'

'Are you serious?' I said, though I'd never known Tolliver to be facetious about family topics. I felt blindsided. 'You know I've never thought we should take the girls away, even if we could legally manage it. You seriously think we should keep even our visits to a minimum? See them even less?'

'I do,' he said.

'Explain.'

'When we show up – well, to start with, we come here so . . . irregularly, and we never stay long. We take them out, we try to show them things they don't get to see, we try to interest them in things that're not part of their daily life – and then we vanish, leaving their, well, their "parents," to deal with the result.'

'The result? What result? We're the bad fairies or something?' I was trying very hard not to get angry.

'Iona told me last time – you remember, you took them to the movies – that it usually took her and Hank a week to get the girls back into their routine after one of our visits.'

'But . . .' I didn't know where to start. I shook my head, as if that would arrange my thoughts in order. 'We're supposed to do things for Iona's convenience? We're the girls' brother and sister. We love them. They need to know the whole world isn't like Iona and Hank.' My voice rose.

Tolliver sat down on the bathtub's side. 'Harper, Iona and Hank are raising them. They didn't have to take them in; the state would have taken them if Iona and Hank hadn't volunteered. I can almost guarantee that the court would have kept Mariella and Gracie in a foster home rather than giving them to us. We're lucky Iona and Hank were willing to give it a shot. They're older than most parents of kids that age. They're strict because they're scared the girls will turn out like your mom, or my dad. But they adopted the girls. They're the parents.'

I opened my mouth, closed it. It was like a dam had broken in Tolliver's head, and I was hearing thoughts I'd never heard before, pouring straight out of his mouth.

'Sure, they're limited in their thinking,' he said. 'But they're the ones who have to cope with Gracie and Mariella, day after day. They go to the teacher conferences; they go to the meetings with the principal; they take the girls to get their shots; and they take them to the doctor when they're sick. They enforce the bedtimes and the study times. They buy the clothes. They'll get the braces.' He shrugged. 'All that stuff. We can't do that.'

'So what do you think we ought to do? Instead of what we're doing?' I stepped out of the bathroom and sat down on the edge of the unmade bed. He followed and sat beside me. I braced my hands on my knees. I tried not to cry. 'You think we should abandon our sisters? Almost the only family we've got?' I didn't count Tolliver's father, who'd been in the wind for months.

Tolliver squatted in front of me. 'I think maybe we should come for Thanksgiving and Christmas, or Easter, or the girls' birthdays . . .

expected times. Arranged way in advance. At the most, twice a year. I think we should be more careful about what we say in front of the girls. Gracie told Iona that you said she was too rigid. Except Gracie said "frigid." '

I tried not to smile, but I couldn't help it. 'Okay, you're right about that. Bad-mouthing the people who take care of the girls, that's not cool. I thought I was being so careful.'

'You try,' he said, and he smiled just a little. 'It's the expression on your face rather than your words . . . most of the time.'

'Okay, I get your point. But I thought we would become closer to them if we moved here. Maybe break down some walls between Iona and Hank and us. We'd see the girls more often, and the situation would get more relaxed. Maybe the girls could spend the weekend with us sometimes. Surely Iona and Hank want to be by themselves from time to time.'

Tolliver countered this scenario with his own issue. 'Do you really think Iona will be able to accept *us*? Now that we're together?'

I fell silent. The fact that we'd become a couple would shock my aunt and her husband, and that was putting it mildly. I could understand that point of view, even. After all, Tolliver and I had grown up together in our teen years. We'd lived in the same house. My mother had been married to his father. I'd been introducing him as my brother for years. Sometimes I still referred to him as my brother, because it was the habit of years and because we'd shared an upbringing. Though we weren't blood relations at all, there was a certain ick factor in our sexual relationship, to an outsider's point of view. We'd be fools not to recognize that.

'I don't know,' I said, simply to be argumentative. 'They might just accept it.' I was lying.

'You're lying,' Tolliver said. 'You know both Hank and Iona are going to go ballistic.'

When Iona went ballistic, God got mad. If Iona thought something was morally questionable, God thought so, too. And God, as channeled through Iona, ruled that household.

'But we can't conceal from them what we are to each other,' I said helplessly.

'We shouldn't, and we won't. We'll just have to see what happens.'

I tried to change the subject, because I had to think over everything we'd just said. 'When will we see Mark?' Mark Lang was Tolliver's older brother.

'We're supposed to meet him at the Texas Roadhouse tomorrow night.'

'Oh, good.' I managed a smile, though I'm sure it was a weak one. I'd always liked Mark, though I'd never been as close to him as I'd been to Tolliver. He'd protected all of us as much as he was able. We didn't manage to see Mark every visit to Texas, so I was glad he'd found the time to have supper with us. 'So this evening we're invited to Iona's for a brief visit? And we'll just see what happens. We have no plan?'

'We have no plan,' Tolliver confirmed, and we smiled at each other.

I tried to keep hold of the smile when we got into the car to drive over to the small house in Garland where our sisters lived. Though the weather was clear and bright, I wasn't seeing blue skies ahead.

Iona Gorham (nee Howe) had based her character on being anti-Laurel. Laurel Howe Connelly Lang, my mother, had been Iona's only sibling, and older than Iona by almost ten years. In my mother's teen years and through her twenties, before her drug addiction, she had been fairly attractive, popular, and party loving. She had also made great grades, and she'd gone to law school. She'd married a man she met there, my dad, Cliff Connelly. My mother had been a little wild – well, more than a little – but she'd also been a high achiever.

To compete and contrast, Iona had gone the sweet-and-religious route.

Looking at Iona's face when she answered the door, I wondered when the sweetness had turned sour. Iona had always looked disappointed. Yet today, she seemed a little less sour than usual, and I wondered why. Usually, the arrival of Tolliver and me would make her look like she'd sucked a lemon. I tried to remember how old Iona was, and decided that she must be a little less than forty.

'Well, come on in,' my aunt said, and stepped back into her living room.

I always felt like we were invited to enter only grudgingly, that Iona would have loved to shut the door in our faces. I'm five foot seven, and my aunt is shorter than I am. Iona is pleasantly rounded, and her hair is graying in a pretty way, as though her light brown hair was simply fading a little. Her eyes are dark gray, like mine.

'How are you?' Tolliver asked pleasantly.

'I'm feeling wonderful,' Iona said, and our mouths fell open at the same moment. We'd never heard Iona say anything remotely like that. 'Hank's arthritis is acting up,' she continued, oblivious to our re-action, 'but he can get up and go to work, thank God.' Iona worked at Sam's Club part-time, and Hank was the manager of the meat department at a Wal-Mart Supercenter.

'How have the girls been doing in school?' I asked, my standard fallback question. I was still trying not to look at Tolliver, because I knew he was just as floored as I was. Iona was preceding us into the kitchen, where we usually had our conversations. Iona saved the living room for real company.

'Mariella's been doing pretty good. She's a middle-of-the-road-type student,' Iona said. 'Gracie, they always say she's a little behind where she ought to be. You two want some coffee? I've got the pot on.'

'That would be great,' I said. 'I take it black.'

'I remember,' she said with a sharp edge to her voice, as if I'd accused her of being a bad hostess. That sounded more like the Iona I knew, and I felt a little more comfortable.

'And I take mine with some sugar,' Tolliver said. While her back was to us, he looked at me and raised his eyebrows. Something was up with Iona.

In short order, a mug was in front of him, and a sugar bowl and a spoon and a napkin. I was served second, and I got the plain mug. Iona poured herself some coffee, too, and settled herself in the chair closest to the coffeepot in a way that indicated she was really, really tired. For a minute or two, she didn't speak. She seemed to be thinking hard about something. The table was round, and there was a pile of mail in the middle. I automatically scanned it: phone bill, cable bill, a handwritten letter protruding from its envelope. The handwriting looked sort of familiar in an unpleasant way.

'I'm wore out,' Iona said. 'I been on my feet at work for six hours straight.' Iona was wearing a T-shirt and khakis and sneakers. Clothes had never been a priority for her the way they had been for my mother, until she'd stopped caring about anything at all but the drugs and where they'd come from next. I felt an unexpected flash of sympathy for Iona.

'That's hard on the body,' I said, but she wasn't listening.

'Here come the girls,' she said, and then my ears caught what hers had already registered: the sound of footsteps outside the garage door.

Our sisters burst into the room and tossed their backpacks against the wall right under a coatrack. They hung their jackets on the coatrack and took their shoes off to park beside the backpacks. I wondered how long it had taken Iona to establish those habits.

The next second, I was taken up with examining my sisters. They've always changed when I see them. It takes me a minute to absorb it. Mariella is twelve years old now, and Gracie is just over three years younger.

The girls were surprised to see us, but not startled. I didn't know if Iona had even warned them we were stopping by to see them. Mariella and Gracie hugged us dutifully, but without enthusiasm. I wasn't surprised at that, given how Iona had tried hard to get the girls to regard us as unnecessary and maybe even bad. And since they didn't remember Cameron, I knew their memories of the trailer had to be faint or nonexistent.

For their sakes, I hoped so.

Mariella was starting to look more like a girl and less like a sack of flour. She had brown hair and eyes, and was square-built like her father. Gracie had always been small for her age, and she'd always been moodier than Mariella. She kissed me voluntarily, which was a first.

It's always hard to get comfortable with our sisters. It's uphill work, reestablishing a bond that has always been tenuous. They sat at the table with us and the woman who'd been a mother to them, and they answered questions, and they acted pleased with their little presents. We always got them a book apiece to encourage them to read, a pastime that wasn't the norm in the Gorham household. But we generally got them something else, too, something cute to wear in their hair or little trinkets, something frivolous. It was hard not to light up like a Christmas tree when Mariella said, 'Oh, I read the other two books this lady wrote! Thanks!' I kept my 'You're welcome' down to a pleased smile.

Gracie didn't speak, but she smiled at us. That was the more significant because she's not a smiley girl. She doesn't look a thing like Mariella; but then, my sister and I hadn't looked alike, either. Gracie looks like a little elf: she has greenish eyes, long wispy pale hair, an aggressive little nose, and a cupid's bow mouth.

Maybe I'm not a kid person. I find Gracie more interesting than Mariella, though this confession sounds simply cold. For all I know, real mothers have secret favorites, too. I'm pretty sure I don't show this partiality. I'm waiting for Mariella to do something that interests me, and I was delighted that she was happy about the book. If Mariella turned out to be a reader, I'd find a way to connect with her. Gracie had been so sick, at the same time I'd been sick. It had been the unstable taking care of the weak; I'd been laid low by being struck by lightning, and Gracie had had chronic chest and breathing problems.

'Are you a bad woman, Aunt Harper?' Gracie asked. The question came completely out of the blue.

This 'aunt' business had originated with Iona, who'd thought we were so much older than our sisters that they ought to address us with respect. But that wasn't why I was so dumbfounded. 'I try not to be bad,' I said, to buy some time until I found out what had prompted that question.

Iona made herself mighty busy with her coffee, stirring it with a spoon over and over. I could feel my mouth clamp down in anger, and I was trying to keep the bitter words inside. After a moment, it became clear Iona was going to act like she wasn't involved in the conversation, so I went on. 'I try to be honest with the people I work for,' I said. 'I believe in God.' (Not the same God Iona worshipped, apparently.) 'I work hard and I pay my taxes. I'm the best person I can be.' And this was all true.

'Because if you take money from people and you can't really do what you say you can do, that's bad, right?' Gracie said.

'It sure is,' Tolliver said. 'That's called fraud. And it's something Harper and I would never, never do.' His dark eyes drilled holes in Iona. Gracie looked at her adoptive mother, too. I was sure they were seeing two different people.

Iona was still not meeting our eyes, still stirring the damn coffee.

Hank came in the garage door then, which was good timing. Hank was a big man, with a broad, high-complexioned face and thinning blond hair. He'd been very handsome when he was younger, and he was a good-looking man still, now that he'd reached forty. His waist was barely thicker than it had been when he and Iona had married.

'Harper, Tolliver! Good to see you! We don't see you-all enough.'

Liar.

He kissed the top of Gracie's head and chucked Mariella under the chin. 'Hey, you two!' he said to the girls. 'Mariella, how was that spelling test today?'

Mariella said, 'Hey, Daddy! I got eight out of ten right.'

'That's my girl,' Hank said. He was pouring some Coca-Cola out of a two-liter bottle. He chunked a few ice cubes into the glass and pulled up a folding chair that stood beside the refrigerator. 'Gracie, did you have a good time in chorus today?'

'We sang good,' she said. She seemed relieved to be on familiar conversational ground.

If Hank had noticed the tense atmosphere in the tiny kitchen, he didn't comment on it.

'How are you two doing?' he asked me. 'Find any good bodies lately?' Hank had always talked about our livelihood as if it were a big joke.

I smiled back faintly. 'A few,' I said. Evidently, Hank didn't read the newspapers or watch the news on television. I'd been mentioned more often than I wanted to be in the past month.

'Where you traveled to?' Hank also thought it was amusing that Tolliver and I were always on the road, pursuing this strange living of ours. Hank had been out of Texas when he was in the army, but that was the extent of his traveling experience.

'We were in the mountains of North Carolina,' Tolliver said. He paused to see if either Iona or Hank would pick up on the reference to our last, most notorious, case.

Nope.

'Then we went to another job between here and Texarkana, in Clear Creek. Now here we are in Garland to see you-all.'

'Any big news in the corpse-finding business?' Again with the teasing smile.

'We have other news,' Tolliver said, irritated by Hank's facetiousness. This happened every time. Every damn time. I looked at Tolliver, saw the intent way his eyes were focused on Hank.

Uh-oh, I thought.

'You found you a girlfriend and you're going to settle down!' Hank said jocularly, since Tolliver's lack of a steady girlfriend had long been the subject of many pointed jokes from both Iona and her husband.

'As a matter of fact, I have,' Tolliver said, and the smile on his face made me close my eyes. It was bright and hard.

'Well, listen to that, girls! Your uncle Tolliver has got himself a girl! Who is she, Tol?'

My brother hated it when someone abbreviated his name.

'Harper,' Tolliver said. He reached across the table and took my hand. And we waited.

'Your . . .' Iona almost said 'sister,' but recalled the word in time. 'But . . . you two?' She looked from me to Tolliver. 'That's just not right,' she said hesitantly. 'You two . . .'

'Are not related,' I said, smiling brightly at my aunt.

The girls were looking from one adult to another, confused.

'You're my sister,' Mariella said suddenly.

'Yep,' I said, smiling at her.

'Tolliver is my brother,' she said clearly.

'Also true. But we're not related to each other. You understand that, right? I had a different mom and dad from Tolliver.'

'So,' said Gracie, 'you gonna get married?' She looked pleased. Confused, but pleased.

Tolliver looked across the table at me. His smile gentled. 'I hope so,' he said.

'Oh, boy! Can I be in the wedding?' Mariella said. 'My friend Brianna was in her sister's wedding. Can I wear a long dress? Can I get my hair done? Brianna's mom let her wear lipstick. Can I wear lipstick, Mom?'

'Mariella, we may not have a big wedding,' I said, since I could guarantee that wasn't going to happen. 'We may just go to a justice of the peace. So it might not be in a church, and I wouldn't wear a long white dress.'

'But whatever we do, you can be there, and you can wear whatever you want,' Tolliver said.

'Oh, for goodness' sake!' Iona said, sounding thoroughly disgusted. 'You two got no business getting married! And if you do, which God forbid, Mariella and Gracie sure wouldn't be there!'

'Why not?' Tolliver asked, in that dangerous voice. 'They're our family.'

'It just ain't right,' Hank said, his face serious, giving us the correct and final verdict on our relationship. 'You two was raised too close for comfort.'

'We're not related by blood,' I said, 'and we'll get married when we want to.' Then I realized I'd been sucked into the argument much further than I'd counted on. Tolliver was grinning at me. I closed my eyes.

Apparently Tolliver had just proposed and I had just accepted.

'Well,' said Iona, her lips pursed in the old Iona way, 'we got us some news, too.'

'Oh, what is it?' I was willing to be interested. I was willing to dispel the angry atmosphere that had made my sisters so unhappy. I made myself smile at my aunt to show a decent anticipation.

'Hank and I are gonna have a baby,' Iona said. 'The girls will have a little brother or sister.'

After a long moment of intense struggle not to blurt out, 'After all these years?' I managed to say, 'Oh, what great news! Girls, aren't you excited?'

Tolliver's hand found mine under the table and gripped it hard. We'd never considered that Iona and Hank might have a baby of their own, and, speaking for myself, I'd never been curious about why they didn't have any. In fact, I'd just regarded the two as inconvenient irritants who got in our way when we wanted to see our sisters. However, they were mighty convenient when it came to doing the day-to-day care for those two little girls, who were no walk in the park to deal with.

In a flash of clarity, I realized all this, and I knew we couldn't possibly interfere with Iona and Hank's relationship with the girls now. I looked into Mariella's face and saw the uncertainty there. Neither she nor Gracie needed any other problems to handle at the moment. The girls were trying to feel happy about the baby, but they'd been thrown for a serious loop.

I could sympathize.

2

At the Texas Roadhouse the next night, we'd already put our name on the list for a table when Mark arrived. Mark looks like he's Tolliver's brother, all right; they have the same cheekbones, the same chin, the same brown eyes. But Mark is shorter, thicker, and (an observation I have kept to myself) not nearly as smart as Tolliver.

I had so many great memories of Mark, though, that I knew I'd always be fond of him. Mark had done his best to protect all of us from our parents. Not that our parents had always intended to hurt us . . . but they were addicts. Addicts forget to be parents. They forget to be married. They're only addicted.

Mark had suffered a lot because he had more memories of his dad when his dad was a real person than Tolliver did. Mark remembered a father who'd taken him fishing and hunting, a father who'd gone to teacher conferences and football games and helped him with his arithmetic. Tolliver had told me that he remembered that passage in his own life a little, but the last few years in the trailer had overlaid most of that memory until the hurt had extinguished the flame that kept it alive.

Mark had recently become a manager at JCPenney, and he was wearing navy slacks, a striped shirt, and a pinned-on name tag. When I spotted him entering the restaurant, he looked tired, but his face lit up when he noticed us. Mark had clipped his hair very short and shaved off his mustache, and the cleaner look made him seem older and more confident, somehow.

Tolliver and his brother went through the guy greeting ritual, thumping each other on the back, saying 'Hey, man!' a number of times. I got a more restrained hug. Just at the right moment, we got a buzz to tell us we could be seated. When we were in a booth and supplied with menus, I asked Mark how his job was going.

'We didn't do as well as we should this Christmas,' he said seriously. I noticed how white and even his teeth were, and I felt a stab of resentment on his brother's behalf. Mark had been old enough to get

his teeth aligned, unlike Tolliver. By the time Tolliver should have
been getting his middle-class-American-teen complement of braces
and acne medicine, our parents had started their downward spiral
together. I shook off that unworthy twinge of resentment. Mark had
just been lucky, on that count. 'Our sales weren't as high as they
should've been, and we're going to have to scramble this spring,' he
said.

'So what do you think happened?' Tolliver asked, as if he gave a
rat's ass why the store wasn't performing as well as it ought to have.

Mark rambled on about the store and his responsibilities, and I
tried to show a decent interest. This was a better job than his previous
position managing a restaurant; at least, the hours were better. Mark
had put himself through two years of junior college, and he'd taken
night classes since then. Eventually, he'd earn a degree. I had to
admire that dedication. Neither Tolliver nor I had done that much.

The truth was that though I made sure I looked like I was listening,
and I truly was fond of Mark, I was bored silly. I found myself
remembering a day Mark had knocked down one of my mom's
visitors, a tough guy in his thirties who'd made a blatant pass at
Cameron. Mark hadn't known if the guy was armed (many of our
parents' buddies were), and yet Mark hadn't hesitated a second in his
defense of my sister. This memory made it easy for me to pretend I
was hanging on Mark's every word.

Tolliver was asking relevant questions. Maybe he was more into
this than I'd thought. I wondered, for the hundredth time, if Tolliver
would have enjoyed having a regular life, instead of the one we led.

But I figured he'd pretty much set that fear to rest the day before.

We'd left Iona and Hank's in a very subdued state. We'd been
stunned equally by Iona's news. Though we'd tried to congratulate
her and Hank with enthusiasm, maybe we hadn't sounded excited
enough. We'd been a little shaken by their reaction to our relationship,
and it had been hard to be delighted for their good news since they'd
been so aghast at ours.

Of course the girls had picked up on all the stress and anger. In the
course of a few minutes, they'd gone from being happy for us to being
confused and resentful about all the emotions swirling around. Hank
had retreated to his tiny 'office' to call his pastor and consult with this
unknown man about our relationship, which had made something

tiny in my head explode. He'd taken Tolliver with him, and Tolliver had emerged looking indignant and amused.

Since we'd left Hank and Iona's, we hadn't said another word to each other about the marriage issue, which had popped up like a jack-in-the-box.

Oddly, not talking about it felt . . . okay. We'd gone to the workout room for some treadmill time and then watched a *Law and Order* rerun. We'd been comfortable with each other and relieved to be by ourselves. While we'd been walking on the treadmills, I'd realized that every time we visited our sisters, it was the same emotional wringer. After a short time in that cramped house, we needed to retreat, regroup, and refresh ourselves.

I worried about the bad feelings between my aunt and myself until I reflected that all was well between Tolliver and me, and that was the only relationship I really cared about . . . well, other than the one I was trying to form with my little sisters.

Still, at odd moments during the past evening, I admit that the uncomfortable situation occupied my thoughts. I know it was naïve of me, but I was shocked every time I thought about Iona's pregnancy. I'd lived through my mother's two pregnancies with my sisters, and it still seemed amazing to me that Gracie had been born with all the correct physical attributes and no apparent mental or neurological problems, considering my mother's extensive drug use. She'd had enough will left to restrain herself somewhat during the time she was carrying Mariella, but with Gracie . . . Gracie had been awfully sick when she was born, and many times after that.

I was thinking about those bad days after our treadmill workout the night before. After I'd had a break, I'd taken our hand vacuum out to the car to give the trunk a once-over. I'd taken a shopping bag with me for the trash. When you're in your car as much as we are, it tends to get pretty junky in a short time. While I tossed old receipts and empty cups into the bag, and got all the corners with the vacuum, I worried about my aunt. Iona was healthy, as far as I knew, and she never drank or used drugs. But she was definitely on the older side to be experiencing a first venture into motherhood.

While part of my brain had been trying to remember if I'd seen an oil-change place down the access road, the other part tried to pooh-pooh my own fears. I told myself that lots of women were waiting until later in their lives to start their families. And more power to them, waiting for financial security or a good relationship to form a foundation for child rearing. The problem was, I knew from personal experience how exhausting caring for an infant was. Maybe Iona would be able to quit work.

While I pretended to listen to Mark and sipped the drink our waitress had brought me, I was reliving our little sit-down at Iona's kitchen table. Something I'd seen had troubled me, something I hadn't been able to recall after the hubbub over our family revelations.

As Mark and Tolliver spent way too long discussing retail, I mentally examined every person who'd been sitting around the table. Then I reviewed my memory of the objects on the table. Finally, I succeeded in tracking down the source of my unease. I waited until the brothers fell silent before I obliquely introduced the subject.

'Mark, do you go over to see the girls very often?' I asked.

'No,' he said, ducking his head in a guilty way. 'It's a long drive from my house, and I work horrible hours. Plus, Iona always makes me feel bad about something.' He shrugged. 'To be honest, the girls just aren't that interested in me.'

Mark had left the trailer and started living on his own as soon as he could, which we'd all agreed was the best thing for him to do. He came by when our parents weren't there – or when they were out cold – and he'd (God bless him) brought us supplies whenever he could. But that meant he hadn't been present like we had when the girls were babies, and he hadn't had as much opportunity to bond with them. Cameron and Tolliver and I had taken care of Mariella and Gracie. On the nights when bad memories woke me up and wouldn't let me sleep, I got scared all over again when I thought of what might have happened to the girls if we hadn't been there. That wasn't the girls' concern, though – and it shouldn't be.

'So you haven't talked to Iona lately.' I had to think in the here and now.

'No.' Mark looked at me, a question on his face.

'You know that Iona's heard from your dad?' It was my stepfather's handwriting I'd seen on the letter protruding from the stack of mail.

Mark would never be a successful poker player, because he didn't look anything but guilty. I had to smile at his obvious relief when the waitress picked that moment to take our orders.

But that smile didn't sit on my lips for long. I was scared to look sideways at Tolliver.

When the waitress had bustled off, I opened my hands to Mark, indicating it was time for him to come clean.

'Well, yeah, I was gonna tell you about that,' he said, looking down at his silverware.

'What were you going to tell us, brother?' Tolliver asked, his voice even and pleasant and forced.

'I got a letter from Dad a couple weeks ago,' Mark said. No, he *confessed* it. Then he waited for Tolliver to give him absolution – but Tolliver wasn't about to. We both knew Mark had responded to the letter, or he wouldn't be so hangdog.

'Dad's alive, then,' Tolliver said, and anyone but me would have called his voice neutral.

'Yeah, he's got a job. He's clean and sober, Tol.'

Mark had always had a tender heart for his father. And he'd always been incredibly gullible where his dad was concerned.

'Matthew's been out of jail how long?' I asked, since Tolliver wasn't responding to Mark's assertion. I'd never been able to call Matthew Lang 'Father.'

'Um, a month,' Mark said. He folded the little paper ring that had circled his silverware and napkin. He unfolded it and folded it again. This time he compressed it into a smaller rectangle. 'He got early release for good behavior. After I wrote back, he called me. He wants to reconnect with his family, he says.'

I was sure that (entirely coincidentally) Matthew also wanted money and maybe a place to stay. I wondered if Mark truly believed his father, if he could really be that foolish.

Tolliver didn't say a word.

'Has he been in touch with your uncle Paul or your aunt Miriam?' I asked, struggling to fill the silence.

Mark shrugged. 'I don't know. I never call them.'

While it wasn't technically true that Tolliver and I were each other's only adult family, with the exception of Mark it might as well have been. Matthew Lang's siblings had been hurt and disgusted too often by Matthew to want to maintain any relationship with him, and unfortunately that exclusion had spread outward to include Matthew's kids. Mark and Tolliver could have used help – could have used a *lot* of help – but that would have entailed dealing with Matthew, who had been too difficult and frightening for his more conventional siblings. As a result, Tolliver had cousins he barely knew.

I wasn't sure exactly how he felt about Paul's and Miriam's self-preserving decisions, but he'd never made any attempt to contact them in recent years, when Matthew had been safely behind bars. I guess that spoke for itself.

'What's Dad doing?' Tolliver said. His voice was ominously quiet, but he was holding together.

'He's working at a McDonald's. The drive-through, I think. Or maybe he's cooking.'

I was sure Matthew Lang wasn't the first disbarred lawyer to work the drive-through window at a McDonald's. But given the fact that while I'd lived in the same trailer with the man, I'd never seen him cook beyond popping something in the microwave, and I'd never seen him wash a single dish, that was kind of ironic. Not enough that I'd bust out laughing, though.

'What happened to *your* dad, Harper?' Mark asked. 'Cliff, was that his name?' Mark felt it was time to point out that Matthew wasn't the only bad dad around.

'Last I heard, he was in the prison hospital,' I said. 'I don't think he knows anyone anymore.' I shrugged.

Mark looked shocked. His hands moved involuntarily across the table. 'You don't go see him?' He actually sounded amazed at my heartlessness, which I found almost incredible.

'What?' I said. 'Why would I? He never took care of me. I'm not going to take care of him.'

'Wasn't it okay before he started using drugs? Didn't he give you a good home?'

I understood this wasn't about my father at all, but it was still really irritating. 'Yes,' I agreed. 'He and my mother gave us a nice home. But after they started using, they never thought twice about us.' There were lots of kids who'd had it worse, who hadn't even had a trailer with a hole in the bathroom floor. Hadn't even had siblings who were willing to watch their back. But it had been bad enough. And later, awful things had happened when my mother and Tolliver's father had had their crappy 'friends' over. I remembered one night when all of us kids had slept under the trailer, because we were so scared of what was happening inside.

I shook myself. *No pity.*

'How'd you know to bring up Dad, anyway?' Mark asked. He looked sullen. Mark had always been a transparent sort of guy. It was clear I wasn't his favorite person at the moment.

'I saw a letter from him on Iona's table. It took me a while to remember where I'd seen the handwriting. I wonder why he wrote her. Do you reckon he's trying to get Iona to let him see the girls? Why would he be doing that?'

'Maybe he thinks he ought to see *his daughters*,' Mark said, and he flushed, a sure sign he was angry.

Tolliver and I looked at our brother, and neither of us said a word.

'Okay, okay,' Mark said, rubbing his face with his hands. 'He doesn't deserve to see them. I don't know what he's asking Iona for. When I saw him, he told me he wants to see Tolliver. He doesn't have an address to send Tolliver a letter.'

'There's a reason for that,' Tolliver said.

'He'd seen some website that tracks her,' Mark said, nodding toward me as if I were sitting far away. 'He said you-all's website had an email address, but he didn't want to contact you through her website. Like he was a stranger.'

The waitress came up with our food then, and we took the little ritual of spreading napkins and using salt and pepper to regroup.

'Mark,' Tolliver said, 'is there any reason you can think of that I *ought* to make any effort to include that man in my life? In Harper's life?'

'He's our dad,' Mark said doggedly. 'He's all we've got left.'

'No,' Tolliver said. 'Harper's sitting right here.'

'But she's not *our* family.' Mark looked at me, this time a little apologetically.

'She's *my* family,' Tolliver said.

Mark froze. 'Are you saying I shouldn't have left you-all in that trailer? That I should have stayed there with you? That I let you down?'

'No,' Tolliver said, astonished. We exchanged a quick flicker of a glance. 'I'm saying Harper and I are together.'

'She's your stepsister,' Mark said.

'And she's my girlfriend,' Tolliver said, and I smiled down at my salad. It seemed such an inadequate term.

Mark's mouth hung open as he stared at us. 'What? Is that legal? When did this happen?'

'Recently; yes, it is; and we're happy, thanks for asking.'

'Then I'm glad for you,' Mark said. 'It's good that you have each other.' But he still looked doubtful. 'Isn't it kind of weird, though? I mean, we grew up in the same house.'

'Like you and Cameron,' I said.

'I never felt like that about Cameron,' he said.

'Okay,' I said. 'But this is the way we feel. We didn't start out this way, but it's the way we ended up.' And I smiled at Tolliver, suddenly feeling ridiculously happy.

He smiled back. Our circle closed.

'So what do you want me to tell Dad?' Mark said. There was a little desperation in his voice. I couldn't imagine how Mark had pictured this conversation going, but it had not turned out to his satisfaction, obviously.

'I thought I'd made myself clear. We don't want to see him,' Tolliver said. 'I don't want him to get in touch with me. If he emails us through the website, I won't answer. That last year . . . you were lucky you were out on your own, Mark. I'm glad you were old enough to leave, to start your life. I've never blamed you for leaving, if that's what you're thinking. Even if you'd been in the trailer, you couldn't have stopped anything that happened. And you brought us food and diapers and money when you could. We were glad one of us had made it out into the real world. My job at Taco Bell wouldn't have been enough.'

'You don't think I was just running away?' Mark sawed on his steak, his eyes on his knife.

'No, I think you were saving your life.' Tolliver put down his fork. His face was serious. 'That's what I really believe. And that's what Harper believes.'

Not that Mark was so concerned with my opinion, but I nodded. It had never crossed my mind to think any differently about it.

Mark tried to laugh, but it was a pretty pitiful attempt. He said, 'I never intended this evening to get so intense.'

'It's your dad reappearing. Not your fault.' I smiled at him, trying to will him to lighten up.

But that seemed to be a lost cause. 'You really haven't visited your dad?' he asked me. He was wrestling with my attitude.

'No,' I said. 'Why would I lie about that?'

'What is his illness?'

'I don't know.'

'Has he heard your mom died?'

'I have no idea.'

'He know about Cameron?'

I thought about that for a moment. 'Yeah, because some of the newspeople tracked him down and talked to him when she went missing.'

'He never came to see . . .'

'No. He was incarcerated. He wrote me a few letters. My foster parents gave 'em to me. But I didn't answer. I don't know what happened to him after that. More of the same, I expect. I never heard from him, or about him, until he got so sick. Then the prison chaplain wrote me.'

'And you just . . . didn't answer?'

'I just didn't answer. Tolliver, can I have a bite of your sweet potato?'

'Sure,' he said and slid his plate sideways toward me.

He always orders one when we're at a Texas Roadhouse, and I always have one bite. I swallowed it. It wasn't as good as it usually was, but I didn't think that was the staff's fault. I thought it was Mark's.

He was shaking his head, his eyes turned down to his plate. He looked up, meeting first Tolliver's eyes, then mine. 'I don't know how you two do it,' he said. 'When Dad comes calling, I have to answer. He's my *dad*. If my mother was alive, it'd be the same way.'

'I guess we're just not as good as you, Mark,' I said. What else could I say? *He'll drain you and leech off of you. He'll break his word and your spirit.*

'I don't guess you've heard anything from the police since the last time I talked to you?' Mark said. 'Or from that private eye?'

'You're determined to push all the buttons tonight, Mark,' I said, and now it was a struggle to sound even civil.

'I have to ask. I keep thinking someday there'll be news.'

I let my anger go, because I sometimes thought the same thing. 'There's no news. Someday I'll find her.' I'd said it for years, and it had never happened. But one day, when I least expected it – though on some level I always expected it – I'd feel her nearness, like I'd felt the proximity of so many dead people before. I would find Cameron, and I would know what had happened to her that day.

She'd been walking home alone after helping to decorate the high school gym for the prom. I had become the kind of girl who doesn't do things like that, by that time. The lightning had done its job on me. I was still settling into my new skin, terrified of my new and weird ability, recovering from the physical damage. I was still limping, and I tired easily. I'd gotten one of my terrible headaches that day.

It had been in the spring, and we'd had a cold snap. The night before, the temperature had dropped below forty. That afternoon, it was only in the sixties. Cameron had been wearing black tights and a black and white plaid skirt and a white turtleneck. She looked great. No one would have guessed she'd pieced the outfit together at the thrift store. Her blond hair was long and shiny. My sister Cameron had freckles. She hated them. She made all As.

While Mark and Tolliver made conversation, I tried to imagine what Cameron would look like now. Would she still be blond? Would she have gained weight? She'd been small, shorter than me, with thin arms and legs and a will of iron. She'd run track with some success, though when the paper had called her a 'track star' after she'd vanished, we'd all looked at each other and rolled our eyes.

My sister hadn't been a saint. I'd known Cameron better than anyone else. She was proud. She could keep a secret till it screamed. She was smart. She studied hard. Sometimes she resented our situation, our fall from affluence, with such anger that she screamed out loud. She hated our mother, Laurel, hated her passionately, for dragging us down with her. But Cameron loved our mother, too.

She couldn't stand Matthew, who was Mother's second husband but her hundredth 'boyfriend.' Cameron had had this persistent delusion that our father would return to his pre-drug self, and that he would show up at the dismal trailer someday and take us off with him. We would go back to living in a clean house, and someone else would wash our clothes and cook our meals. Our father would show up at the school for PTA meetings, and he'd talk to us over the supper table about where we might want to go to college.

This was Cameron's fantasy, her happy one. She had some that were darker, much darker. She told me, one morning on our walk to school, that she also dreamed one of our mother's dealers would show up at the trailer while we were gone and kill our mother and stepfather. After they were dead, we'd be put in a nice foster home.

Then, when we'd graduated from high school, we'd get jobs and rent an apartment and work our way through college.

That was as far as Cameron's dream had gone. I wondered what she'd imagined would happen after that. Would we each have found a good and prosperous man, and lived happily ever after? Or maybe instead we'd have continued living together (in our modest but clean apartment), wearing our new clothes (a very important part of Cameron's tale), and eating our good food that we'd learned how to cook.

'Honey?' Tolliver said. I turned to him, startled. He'd never called me that before.

'Do you want dessert?' he asked. I realized that the waitress was waiting, smiling in that pained way that said she was being so, so patient.

I almost never eat dessert. 'No, thanks,' I said. To my irritation, Mark ordered pie, and Tolliver got coffee to keep him company. I was ready to go; I wanted to get away from all this remembrance. I shifted a little to a more comfortable position, stifling a sigh.

When Tolliver and Mark resorted to talking about computers, I was once more free to think about other things.

But all I could think about was Cameron.

3

When we were back in our room, we were both reluctant to start talking about Mark's perfidy in renewing contact with their dad. Tolliver booted up the laptop and went to a fan website that tracks my activities; he monitors it regularly because he's worried that I might acquire a crazy stalker. I never look at it, because there are posts from guys who want to do things with me and to me; and that's scary, not to say repellent. Now, I was worried that Matthew might be reading it at the same moment Tolliver was; he'd be looking for clues on how to find his son.

A nagging pain interrupted my worry session.

I rummaged through my medicine bag to unearth some Icy Hot to rub into my right leg. That's where I feel the long-term effects of getting struck by lightning most of all. I pulled off my shoes and jeans and sat on the bed, stretching out the aching muscles and joints. My right thigh is covered with a tracery of red lines – broken capillaries or something. It's been like that since I got hit, when I was fifteen. It's not pretty.

I worked the cream into my skin for a while in silence. I rubbed hard, trying to get the muscles to give up the discomfort. After a few minutes of massage, I felt some relief. I lay back on the pillows, telling each muscle group to relax in turn. I closed my eyes. 'I'd rather be out in the snow finding a corpse than talking to Iona and Hank, just in general,' I said. 'And sometimes talking to Mark is just as hard.'

'Last night at Iona's . . .' Tolliver said, then paused. When he resumed, he sounded cautious. 'Hank pulled me aside while you were in the bathroom and asked me if I'd gotten you knocked up.'

'He did *not*.'

'Oh, yeah. He did. He was serious, too. He was like, "You gotta marry her if you got her pregnant, boy. If you can't do the time, don't do the crime."'

'Great perspective on marriage and fatherhood.'

Tolliver laughed. 'Well, this is the guy who calls Iona his "ball and chain." '

'Married, not married, I don't care,' I said, before I realized this was a less than tactful way to put it. 'I do care,' I said hastily. 'I mean, I love you and being with you is what I want. I don't care about the marriage part of it. Shit, that wasn't right either.'

'We'll do what's right when the time comes,' Tolliver said, in a voice heavy with elaborate unconcern.

Apparently he *did* want to get married. Why couldn't he just say so? I put my hands over my face, which felt strange because they were tingling from the Icy Hot.

Of course I would marry him, especially if it was a make-or-break issue of our relationship. I would do almost anything to get him to stay.

That wasn't a romantic realization. I lay there thinking, listening to Tolliver's fingers touch the keyboard. I thought, *If anything happens to him, I might as well die.* I wondered if that said a lot for Tolliver – or not much for me.

There was a knock at the door of our room. We looked at each other, puzzled. Tolliver shook his head; he wasn't expecting anyone, either.

He got up and pulled the curtain back a little. He let it drop back into position. 'It's Lizzie Joyce,' he said. 'With her sister. Kate, right?'

'Right.' I was as startled as he was. 'Well,' I said. 'What the hell?' We gave each other little shrugs.

Tolliver, having decided they weren't armed and dangerous, let the Joyce sisters inside. I pulled my jeans back on and rose to greet them.

You'd think they'd never seen a middle-of-the-road motel before. Kate and Lizzie examined the room with nearly identical slow scans. The sisters looked a lot alike. Katie was a little shorter than Lizzie, and maybe two years younger. But she'd colored her hair the same blond as Lizzie's, and her brown eyes were narrow like Lizzie's, and her lean build was the same, too. They were both wearing jeans, boots, and jackets. Lizzie had slicked her hair back into a ponytail at the nape of her neck, while Katie's was loose and bouncy. Between necklaces, earrings, and rings, I figured they each were wearing a couple of thousand dollars' worth of jewelry. (After a subsequent trip to a mall store, I revised that figure upward.)

Katie's eyes were avid as she examined Tolliver. She wasn't so enthusiastic about our paraphernalia: our clothes, his crossword puzzle book, the open laptop, his shoes put neatly by his suitcase.

'Hello, Ms Joyce,' I said, trying to inject my voice with some warmth. 'What can I do for you?'

'You can tell me again what you saw when you stood on Mariah Parish's grave.'

It took me a second to recall. 'Your father's caregiver,' I said. 'The one who had the childbirth problems. The infection.'

'Yeah, why'd you say that? She had complications after her appendectomy,' Lizzie said. She was issuing a very low-level challenge.

Oh, for goodness' sake. This was hardly my fight. 'If that's what you're calling it, okay,' I said. It made no difference to me. Mariah Parish wasn't the one I'd been paid to read, anyway.

'That's what *happened*,' Katie said.

I shrugged. 'All right.'

'What the hell do you mean, "all right"? She either did or she didn't.' The Joyce sisters were not going to let go of this bone.

'Believe what you want to believe. I already told you what she died of.'

'She was a good woman. Why would you make that up?'

'Exactly. Why *would* I make that up?' And what was wrong with a woman having gone through childbirth?

'So who was the father?' Lizzie asked, as abruptly as she'd asked about the death.

'I have no idea.'

'Then . . .' Lizzie floundered to a halt. She was a woman who wasn't used to floundering. She didn't like it. 'Why'd you say it?'

I really had to restrain myself from rolling my eyes. 'I said it because I saw it, and you wanted me to find your grandfather's grave myself,' I said, with fabulous diction. 'To give you your money's worth, I went from grave to grave, as you obviously wanted me to.'

'Everything else you said was right,' Katie said.

'I know.' Had they expected me to be surprised at my own accuracy?

'So why'd you make up that one?'

If they hadn't been so agitated, this would have been boring. My leg hurt, and I wanted to sit down. But I didn't want to invite them to, so I felt obliged to remain standing. 'I didn't. Believe me or not. I don't give a damn.'

'But where's the baby?'

'How should I know?' I'd reached the end of my patience.

'Ladies,' Tolliver said, just in the nick of time, 'my sister finds the dead. The baby was not in the grave she scanned. Either the baby is alive or it's buried somewhere else. Or it might have been miscarried.'

'But if the baby was my granddad's, that baby inherits some of what he left,' Lizzie said, and suddenly their agitation became understandable.

To hell with them. I sank down on the bed, stretching out my aching leg. 'Please have a seat,' I said. 'Do you want a Coke or a 7-Up?'

Tolliver sat by me so the sisters could have the two room chairs. They accepted a drink apiece, and though Katie kept looking at the laptop to see what Tolliver had been up to, they both seemed calmer and less accusatory, which was a relief to me.

'Neither of us had any idea Mariah was pregnant,' Lizzie said. 'That's why we're so shocked. And we didn't realize she was dating anyone. She and my grandfather were pretty good friends, and we're imagining that maybe that became something else. Maybe not. We need to know. Aside from the legal and financial considerations, we owe any child who might be a member of the Joyce family . . . We want to meet that kid. Can I smoke?'

'No, sorry,' Tolliver said.

'The baby must be alive somewhere; there must be some record of its birth,' I said. 'Even if it was born dead, there should still be hospital records. It's knowing who to ask and where to ask. Maybe you can hire a private investigator, someone who can get through the records easily. I only contact the dead, myself.'

'That's a good idea,' Katie said. 'Do you know any?'

'Since you're already here in Garland,' Tolliver said, 'there's a woman a little farther into Dallas who's good. Her name's Victoria Flores. She used to be a cop in Texarkana. And I know there's at least one ex-military guy even closer to your ranch; I think he's based in Longview. His name's Ray Phyfe.'

'There are dozens of big agencies in Dallas, too,' I said, as if that would have been hard for them to figure out.

'We don't want a big agency,' Lizzie said. 'We just want this to be very, very private.'

That was the response I'd been waiting to hear; I'd been curious about their asking us, of all people, for a recommendation. The Joyce empire, of which RJ Ranch was only a part, surely had employed private detectives in the past. Under normal circumstances, I was sure the Joyces would go to an agency they'd used before, where they'd get the deluxe treatment they were used to.

At the moment, I didn't care what they wanted or how they went about it. I wanted to take a lot of Advil and crawl into the bed.

Lizze was talking to Tolliver about Victoria Flores, and he was giving her Victoria's phone number. That name brought back some memories.

'You really saw that?' Katie asked me directly. 'You're not just making this up to jerk us around? No one paid you to play a joke on us?'

'I don't play jokes, in case you missed that about me. I don't take money to make fake pronouncements. Of course I really saw that. It's not a likely thing to make up.'

Lizzie had appropriated our little pad of paper by the telephone and the cheap motel pen to write down Victoria Flores's information.

'She switched locations recently,' Tolliver said. 'This is the right number, though.' I looked down, not wanting my face to reveal how surprised I was.

After more reassurance and more repetition of the things we'd already said, the Joyce sisters were out our door and back on the road. I wondered if they'd spend the night in Dallas or try to make it back to their ranch, which would be quite a drive. They'd stay in some place more palatial if they were lingering in the area, I was sure. Probably had a Dallas apartment.

'So,' I said, when the door had closed behind them and Tolliver had reseated himself at the table to finish his computer work, 'Victoria Flores.'

I didn't need to say anything else.

'I call her from time to time,' Tolliver said. 'Every now and then she hears something new. Every now and then she runs something down. She sends me a bill. I pay her.'

'And you didn't tell me this – because?'

'You get so upset,' he said. 'I just couldn't see what purpose it served. When I used to tell you, every time she called, you'd get all upset. Every time, it would come to nothing. She doesn't call much now, maybe twice a year, and I just couldn't do that to you anymore.'

I took a deep breath. My impulse was to launch into him. It was my business how I reacted to possible news of my sister. It was my right to suffer for her.

Then I had a second thought. On the other hand – Tolliver's hand – did it serve any purpose? Hadn't I been okay, not knowing? Hadn't I been calmer and happier, just waiting to locate Cameron in my own way? Was it not okay to have something done for you, some pain spared you, even if it meant you were ignorant about something that you considered your personal business?

Could that idea have gotten more convoluted?

But I knew what I meant, and I knew what Tolliver meant. And I thought maybe he was right. Or at least, it was okay that he had done that.

I nodded finally. He seemed relieved, because his shoulders relaxed and he blew out a breath. He sat on the bed to pull off his socks, then tossed them into our laundry bag, which reminded me that we were low on detergent.

I had ten little thoughts like this while I got ready for bed. I'd been reading through the novels of Charlie Huston and Duane Swierczynski, but it was like getting a jolt of caffeine if I read either one before bedtime; I definitely didn't need that tonight. Instead, I opened a crossword puzzle book. I crawled into bed in my soft sleep pants and my T, and I lay on my stomach, absorbed in the crossword. Tolliver was better at them than I was, and it was hard not to ask him questions.

Another exciting night in the life of corpse-reader Harper Connelly, I thought. And I was happy that this was so.

4

We were scheduled to take Gracie and Mariella skating that next afternoon, Sunday, but not until two P.M. On Saturday mornings they had to pick up their rooms and do chores before they could go anywhere, and on Sundays they had church and lunch as a family. These were ironclad rules of Iona's. And not bad ones, I thought. I'd run and showered and was about to dress when Tolliver's cell phone rang. He'd been lazy and was still in bed, so I answered it.

'Hey, this must be Harper.'

I recognized the voice. 'Yeah, Tolliver's not up yet, Victoria. How's it going?'

Victoria's great-grandparents had been the immigrants. Victoria, born and bred in Texas, didn't have a trace of an accent. 'It's good to talk to you,' she said. 'Listen, nothing new on your sister, I'm sorry to say. I'm calling about the clients you-all referred to me. The Joyces.'

'They already got in touch?'

'Honey, they already been here in my office and wrote me a check.'

'Oh, good. But I can't take any credit for the referral. Tolliver was the one who told them your name and gave them your phone number.'

'That's what Lizzie said. That woman, she's Texas all the way through, huh? And the sister, Kate? I think she's interested in your brother.'

'He's not my brother,' I said automatically, though I called him that myself about half the time. I took a deep breath. 'In fact, we're engaged,' I said.

Tolliver rolled over and fixed me with a sharp eye.

'Oh . . . well, that's just . . . great. Congratulations to the two of you.' Victoria didn't sound thoroughly delighted. Had she been interested in Tolliver herself?

'Let me know the date of the wedding and where you're registered, okay?' Victoria said, more brightly.

'We haven't planned that far ahead,' I said, thrown off balance and scrambling to get my conversational feet back under me. 'You need to have a word with Tolliver? He's right here.' Tolliver was shaking his head no, but he took the phone from me with a dour look when Victoria told me she'd like to talk to him.

'Victoria, hey. No, I was awake. Yeah, we're together. We haven't set any dates, though. We'll pick a date soon. No hurry.' And he gave me a significant nod, looking right into my eyes.

Okay, got it, Tolliver. No pressure from you. Except who'd told Iona we were getting married in the first place? I turned my back on him and bent to rummage in my suitcase for clothes.

After a second, I felt a finger stroking in a very interesting place. I froze. Stealth-attack sex. This was something new. My body decided that I liked this, and didn't pull away and slap Tolliver's hand. The stroking grew more aggressive, more rhythmic. Oh, oh, oh. I wiggled. Then I felt the warmth of him behind me. Though he was still talking to Victoria, he was sounding more than a little distracted.

'Yeah, I'll call you back,' he said. 'I've got another call coming in.'

The phone snapped shut. Something more substantial replaced the fingers.

'Are you ready?' he asked, his voice hoarse.

'Yeah,' I said, and reached out to brace my palms against the wall. And then the sharp upward curve of his penis pushed into me, and we rocked together.

Tolliver was all about keeping things fresh.

I hadn't been very experienced when we admitted we were interested in each other. But I was learning a lot from him, and the adventure of it was giving me a whole new light on his nature. I'd thought I'd known him so well that he couldn't surprise me. I'd been wrong.

I gave a sharp cry, a sound I was startled to hear coming from my own throat, and he echoed it a second later.

'Why do you think Victoria called?' I asked, when I could talk. We'd collapsed on the bed after disengaging, and we were wrapped around each other in a very happy way. 'It seems a little off base that she'd just call to say thank you. An email or a text would have been more in line.' I kissed his throat.

'She was always fascinated by you,' Tolliver said, and that was completely unexpected.

'Ah . . . that way?'

'No, I don't think she's gay or bi. I think she just finds your ability,

---

and the whole thing with the lightning, really interesting. Maybe even fascinating. Over the past few years, Victoria must have asked me a hundred questions about how you do what you do, what it feels like, what the physical effects are.'

'She's never asked me anything.'

'She told me once that if she asked you questions, you might think she thought you were a freak or had some kind of disability.'

'Like I was in a wheelchair or had a big birthmark on my face? Something I might feel self-conscious about?'

'I think she was showing sensitivity about hurting your feelings or making you feel different. I think Victoria kind of holds you in awe.' Tolliver sounded a little chiding, which maybe I deserved. After all, if Victoria had been trying to spare my feelings, I shouldn't disparage her efforts.

'It just seems strange she wouldn't want to come right to the source.' By which I was hinting that I thought Victoria had wanted reasons to talk to Tolliver, rather than that she was genuinely interested in my little problem.

'Maybe she had both things in mind,' Tolliver said, admitting and giving due credence to my suspicion. 'But I don't think she's ever been very interested in me. It was you. I think Victoria has a kind of mystical streak. I think your ability feeds into that.'

'Like seeing the Virgin Mary on a piece of toast, or something?'

'Something.'

'Hah.' I turned that over in my head. 'Then she should come to a cemetery with us, if she's so interested. See firsthand. She's been a lot of help to us over the years. I wouldn't mind.'

It was Tolliver's turn to be surprised. 'Okay, I'll tell her. I'm sure she'd really get into that.'

He rubbed his chin against the top of my head. I stroked my thumb across one of his flat nipples. He made a little noise of pleasure. I told myself I should get up to shower, since we had to go soon to meet the girls, but I put it off for a few more minutes. We had time. I tried to imagine taking Victoria Flores with us when we went to a cemetery. It would have to be when we didn't have a job set up, when I was visiting to . . . okay, I know this sounds very strange, but if I haven't had a job in a while, I go to a cemetery to keep in shape. With my strange ability.

Having Victoria there would feel funny, but I didn't think her presence would bother me. 'So, she has computer skills, I guess, since most private eyes have to these days,' I said.

'We still talking about Victoria? Yeah, I think so,' Tolliver said. 'She's mentioned a tech guy who works with her part-time.'

I lay there thinking, while Tolliver got up and showered and dressed.

Victoria Flores had suddenly become a lot more interesting to me.

I wondered if she'd find the missing baby, the baby we weren't even sure existed. Whether or not Mariah Parish had borne a living child shouldn't make a bit of difference to me, but I found myself rooting for the Joyces to track down the baby. I suspected that child might not be their grandfather's offspring. On second thought, if the girls had been so ready to believe Richard Joyce had fathered a child with his caregiver, maybe the baby had been his. But Lizzie and Katie hadn't been looking in the direction I'd been looking when I told them what had killed Mariah Parish. I'd been looking at their brother and Lizzie's boyfriend, and they'd looked mighty damn worried. About what, I didn't know, and I might never find out. But I hoped Victoria would.

Maybe they'd both had sex with Rich's caregiver. Maybe one of them had impregnated her. Or maybe they were guilty of helping to bury the baby or put the baby up for adoption.

Whatever the brother – Drexell, his name was – had done, I realized it was no concern of mine, and that the search for the whereabouts of baby Parish was not up to me and not in my area of expertise . . . unless the baby was dead. I thought of proposing I help Victoria look for a dead child. But infants were the hardest. They had so little voice. They registered more strongly when they were buried with their parents.

I abandoned thought of the possible child, possibly dead, in the scramble to get ready to pick up the living children that we were kin to. Both girls ran out to our car when we pulled into the Gorham driveway. They seemed happy, looking forward to the afternoon.

'I got an A on my spelling test last week,' Gracie said. Tolliver told her how good that was, and I smiled. But as I looked into the backseat at her, I noticed Mariella was silent and looked a little dampened.

'What's up, Mariella?' I asked.

'Nothing,' she said, which was obviously untrue.

Gracie said, 'Mariella has to stay after school and do extra work tomorrow.'

'Why, Mariella?' I made my voice matter-of-fact.

'The principal said I caused trouble in class.' Mariella wasn't look-ing at me.

'Did you?'

'It was that Lindsay.'

'Lindsay is a bully,' Gracie said. 'We're not supposed to let people bully us, right? That's bad.' Gracie looked self-consciously righteous.

I wanted Gracie to butt out. 'We'll talk about it later,' I said, and I thought Mariella relaxed a little bit. I wasn't used to problems like this; I wasn't used to children. But I recalled that at Mariella's age, this would have been an all-consuming issue.

When we got to the skating rink, Tolliver gave me a questioning look, and I inclined my head toward Gracie. 'Come on, Gracie, let's go get our skates,' he said, and she hopped out happily and held his hand as they walked to the door.

Mariella got out, too, and we walked more slowly behind them.

'So, tell me,' I prompted.

As I'd expected, it wasn't a huge thing. Lindsay had said something ugly to Mariella about being adopted because her dad was in jail. Mariella had punched Lindsay in the stomach, which from my point of view was the correct and proper response. From the school's perspective, apparently Mariella should have begun crying and gone to her teacher to complain. I liked Mariella's reaction better. This led me to a dilemma. Did I go with my gut, or support the school's position? If I'd been a real parent, I might have known the right answer. As it was, I took a deep breath and began to fumble my way through.

'That was really ugly of Lindsay,' I said. 'You can't help what your birth dad did.'

Mariella nodded, her jaw set in a very familiar way. The image of Matthew, I couldn't help but notice.

'That's what I said to the principal,' Mariella told me. 'That's what Mom told me to say. I guess that's what I should have said to Lindsay. She just made me feel so bad.'

I thought the better of Iona for preparing Mariella for the cruelty of other children. 'I probably would have hit Lindsay, too, in your situation,' I said. 'On the other hand, every time you hit someone you're going to get into trouble.'

'So hitting is wrong?'

'It's not the best way to solve a problem,' I hedged. 'What could you have done instead?' That seemed appropriately touchy-feely.

'I could have told the teacher,' Mariella said. 'But then I'd have to talk to her about my birth dad, and she'd get that funny look on her face.'

'True.' Hmmm.

'I could have walked away, but then Lindsay would have done it again.'

'Also true.' Mariella was more insightful than I'd ever imagined. And she was really enjoying talking to someone who didn't tell her God would solve her problems.

'I could have . . . I can't think of anything else.' My sister waited for my reaction.

'Neither can I. I guess you had an impulse, and you acted on it, and it didn't turn out well for you. What happened to Lindsay?'

'She lost four recesses,' Mariella said. 'For being a bully.'

'So that was good, right?'

'Yeah. But it would have been better if she'd kept her mouth shut in the first place.'

Whoa. Little warrior woman. 'You're right about that. It's not your fault that your birth dad used drugs. You know that. But there are some kids who don't understand what it's like to have parents who do bad things. Those kids are lucky, but they can't seem to get that it's nothing you want to talk about. They just know it'll make you feel bad. So when they want you to feel bad, that's the first thing they're going to throw at you.' I took a deep breath. 'We went through that, too, Mariella. Tolliver and me. When you were really little. Everyone at the school knew how crappy our parents were.'

'Even the teachers?'

'Maybe not the teachers. I don't know how much they guessed. But the other kids, they all knew. Some of them bought drugs at our trailer.'

'So they said mean stuff to you?'

'Yeah, some of them. Others thought we were doing the same bad stuff your mom and dad were. Drugs and stuff.'

'Sex stuff?'

'That, too. But the kids who thought we were the same as our folks? Those were the kids that didn't really know us. We had friends who knew better.' Not too many, but a few.

'So, did you date?'

Whoa! She wasn't even having periods yet. Right? I almost panicked. 'Yes, I dated. And I never went out with a boy who thought I was going to have sex with him right away. The more careful you are, the more reputation you get for being the other way, being very . . .'

'Holding out,' Mariella said knowledgeably.

'Not even that,' I said. 'Because if you say "holding out," that means you're going to give it up someday, that you're just waiting for some boy to say the right thing to unlock your legs. You can't even let that be a *possibility*.' I knew Iona would explode if she could hear this conversation. But that was why my sister was having it with me, not Iona.

'But then no one will date you.'

This was simply awful. 'Then to heck with them,' I said, recalling just in time to rein in my language. 'You don't need to go out with a guy who's sure you're going to give him sex if he goes out with you long enough.'

'Why are they gonna go out with you, then?' she said, looking baffled.

That was nothing compared to the way I felt. 'A boy should go out with you because he likes your company,' I said. 'Because you laugh at the same things, or you're interested in the same things.' At least, that was the theory. Was it ever that way in practice? And it shouldn't even be arising at Mariella's age, which was what? Twelve?

'So he should be your friend.'

'Yes. He should be your friend.'

'Is Tolliver your friend?'

'Yes, he's my best friend.'

'But you're, you know . . .'

She couldn't quite bring herself to say the words, and I could only be thankful for that.

'That's kind of our business,' I said. 'When it's the real thing, it means so much you don't want to talk about it with other people.'

'Oh.' Mariella looked thoughtful. I hoped she was. I hoped I hadn't just committed a colossal blunder. I'd told her not to have sex with the boys she was going to date. Then I hadn't contradicted her assumption that Tolliver and I were doing that very thing. I felt totally inadequate.

I was so glad to see Tolliver and Gracie waiting for us, I found myself hurrying toward them. Tolliver gave me a funny look, but Gracie was simply impatient.

'Let's get our skates!' she said. 'I want to skate!'

After we'd all put on our skates and Tolliver and I'd helped the girls out onto the rink floor, then seen that they were okay when they stuck to the wall railing, we skated off to do a round by ourselves. We held hands and went slowly at first, because it had been a good eight years since either of us had skated. There'd been a rink within walking distance of the trailer, and since it hadn't cost too much at the time, we'd spent hours there.

We enjoyed a few rounds together, and then we went back to our sisters, who were already arguing about who was doing the best. Tolliver took Mariella and I took Gracie, and we got them away from the wall and went around with them, slowly and carefully. I couldn't stop Gracie from falling once, and another time she took me down with her, but she was improving by the time we called it quits. Mariella, who'd played basketball at one of the after-school clubs for kids, had fared a lot better, and she was inclined to brag about it until Tolliver cut her short.

We were coming off the floor, laughing, when I realized someone was watching us: a gray-haired man about five foot eleven, pumped up and muscular. My eyes passed over him once, and then came back to his face. I knew him. I looked right into his dark eyes.

'Hello, Dad,' Tolliver said.

5

Our sisters shrunk closer to us, their eyes fixed on their biological father with – at least on Gracie's part – a mixture of loathing and longing. Mariella seemed more hostile. Her little hands had clenched into fists.

He wasn't *my* father. My feelings were relatively unmixed. 'Matthew,' I said. 'What are you doing here?'

He'd been looking at Tolliver and Mariella, his eyes avid. He glanced at me briefly, without affection. Gracie shrunk behind me. 'I wanted to see my kids,' he said. 'All of them.'

There was a long moment of silence. I digested the fact that his voice was clear: no slurring, coherent. Maybe he wasn't using, as he'd told Mark; though I knew it was only a matter of time before he reverted to his old ways.

'But we don't want to see you,' Tolliver said, keeping his voice carefully hushed. We drew aside, to get out of the way of other skaters. 'We didn't answer the feelers you put out through Mark. I didn't answer your letters. I'm willing to bet Iona hasn't given you permission to see the girls, and she's their legal mom now. Hank's their legal dad.'

'But I'm their real father,' Matthew said.

'You gave them up,' I reminded him, giving each word a lot of weight.

'There was a lot of pressure.' He reached out as if he wanted to stroke Mariella's hair, but she flinched back, still gripping her brother's hand as if she would lose him if she let go.

The rink wasn't really crowded, but people had begun to cast sideways glances at our tense little group. I didn't give a damn about the spectators, but the last thing I wanted was any confrontation, physical or verbal, in front of the girls.

'You need to leave,' I said. 'We're taking the girls back to their home right now. You've ruined our good time. Don't make it any worse.'

'I want to see my children,' he said again.

'You're looking at 'em. You've seen them. Now go.'

'I'm only leaving because of the little ones,' he said, nodding toward Mariella and Gracie, who were confused and miserable. 'I'll see you again soon, Tolliver.' And he turned on his heel and left the rink.

'He followed us,' I said stupidly.

'I guess he was waiting somewhere around Iona's house,' Tolliver said. We stared at each other, silently postponing more discussion. Simultaneously, we took deep breaths. It would have been funny if we hadn't been so jangled.

'Well,' I said to my sisters, trying to sound brisk and upbeat, 'I'm glad that's over. We'll talk to your mom about this, okay, tell her all about it? It won't happen again. We had a good time until this happened, right?' I sounded like an idiot, but at least the girls began stirring, removing their skates. They stopped looking quite so much like deer in headlights.

Our sisters were subdued on the ride back to their house – no big surprise there – and they scrambled out of our car and into the door under the carport as if they were afraid of snipers. Tolliver and I followed more slowly, not eager to relate what had happened to Iona and Hank – though it was no fault of ours.

We weren't too surprised to find our aunt and uncle standing in the kitchen waiting for us.

'What happened?' Iona asked. To my astonishment, she didn't seem angry, only worried.

'My dad showed up at the rink,' Tolliver said, plunging right in. 'I don't know how long he was watching before we knew he was there.' He shrugged. 'He wasn't high; he wasn't hostile. But the girls were shaken up.'

'We were having a good time until we saw him,' I said, realizing that sounded weak. But it was a point I felt obliged to make.

'We got a letter from him last week,' Hank said. 'We didn't answer him. I never thought he'd do this.'

So they were shouldering their own share of guilt, for not warning us they knew Matthew was out of jail.

Though I was reluctant to lose the advantage, I said, 'He's been out of jail for a while. When we had dinner with Mark, he told us that much. But he didn't say any more than that Matthew had a job and was straight.'

'Oh, Mark's in contact with his dad?' Iona frowned and sat heavily in one of the kitchen chairs. Cautiously, we sat down, too. We were surprised that the Gorhams weren't throwing us out and blaming us for the whole incident. 'That Mark, he's too tenderhearted where his dad's concerned,' Iona said.

I secretly agreed. Or maybe not so secretly – Tolliver gave me a look. He could read me almost too easily.

'Could you tell what he wanted?' Iona asked me suddenly.

'What do you mean?'

'With your whatever sense?' Iona waved a hand in front of her like she was waving off a gnat.

'I'm not psychic, Iona, or I'd be glad to uncover what Matthew wants. I wish I knew myself. All I can do is find corpses.' Too late, I saw Mariella over Iona's shoulder. She'd come in from the hall to the bedrooms. Her eyes were open wide. But this couldn't be too big a shock to her, right? What on earth had Iona and Hank been telling her? She spun and ran out of the kitchen.

Well, that just made the day perfect.

'Well, what is that sense telling you?' Iona was nothing if not persistent.

'Nothing helpful, right at the moment,' I said. 'There's not a dead person around here, if that's what you're asking. The nearest corpse is so old it probably predates statehood, and it's way under the soil of your neighbor's front yard. Indian, probably. I'd have to get closer to be sure.'

I had finally shut them up. My aunt and uncle simply gaped at me. This was not moving us forward in our discussion. 'But that doesn't have anything to do with Matthew showing up at the rink today,' I reminded them. 'Should you get a court order against him? I mean, he doesn't have any legal rights over the girls anymore, am I right?'

'That's correct,' Hank said, recovering much more quickly than his wife. 'We've adopted them. He gave up his rights.'

'And I don't want to call the police,' Iona said. 'We've talked to the police enough to last us the rest of our lives.'

'So you want him to show back up again? Scare the girls again?'

'No! But we had enough to do with the police when your sister was taken! We don't want them coming around here again.'

I understood what it felt like to want to glide below the police radar, though most of the law-enforcement people I'd met had simply been human beings trying to do a tough job with less money than they needed. But I also understood that, aside from Iona and Hank's revulsion at the prospect of having police cars parked in front of the house again, my sisters were seriously upset. Maybe seeing the police arrive would make the girls fear they were in more danger than Matthew actually represented. After all, he had no reason to harm Mariella and Gracie. Maybe Iona and Hank were right, though for the wrong reason.

'Then there's nothing else we can do,' Tolliver said, having reached the same conclusion I had. 'We'll be on our way.'

'How long are you going to be in town?' Iona said, sounding a little desperate. 'Do you have another job to go to?'

She'd never been anxious for us to stick around before. In fact, she couldn't get us to leave fast enough, every other time we'd visited.

'We could be here a few more days,' I said, after a glance at Tolliver. As a matter of fact, we didn't have anything on our schedule now, though that could change tomorrow.

'Okay,' she said, nodding as if we had a bargain. 'So we'll call you if he shows up again.'

What were we supposed to do? I opened my mouth to protest, but Tolliver said, 'All right. We'll talk to you again tomorrow, anyway.'

'I'm going to talk to the school principal,' Iona said. 'I hate for them to talk about us, but at least the girls' teachers need to know that Matthew's around.'

That was a relief. I noticed that my aunt was sitting as though she were exhausted, and that Hank was looking worried. I remembered she was pregnant. Hank caught my eye and jerked his head toward the door. I tried not to be exasperated that he thought we didn't have enough intelligence to leave when we needed to.

Tolliver said, 'Talk to you tomorrow, then. 'Bye, girls!' he called down the hall. After a second, I saw the girls peeking out of Mariella's room, and I waved at them. They waved back, a little hesitantly. They were not smiling.

We got into our car in silence. I didn't know what to say.

'We've got to stay a little while, to make sure he's not bothering them,' Tolliver said after we'd gone a block.

'So what's to stop him from waiting a couple of days after we leave and then showing up again?'

Tolliver shook his head as if a bee was buzzing around it. 'Nothing will keep him away if he wants to follow them around. I don't know what to do.'

'He can outwait us, and he will. Besides, what are we, a private army? Why are we suddenly so much protection?'

'I guess they see us as – worldly and much tougher than they are,' Tolliver said, after some thought.

'Well, they're right about that. But that's not saying a whole hell of a lot, huh?'

'He's my dad. I feel like I have to do something.'

'I can see that you feel that way,' I said, which was as tactfully as I could put it. 'And I can see you want to stay a couple more days, and that's fine with me. But we can't stay here forever, camping outside their house, waiting for your dad to approach the girls again. Unless he gets arrested again – and let's face it, he probably will be, because he'll start using again – there's nothing to do about him trying to see them, unless Iona and Hank will go to the police. Even then, the police can't watch the girls all the time.'

'I know.'

Tolliver's tone was abrupt. I snapped my mouth shut on any more words I might have uttered. Neither of us said anything else, all the way back to our motel.

If there's anything that makes me nervous and scattered, it's dissension with my brother. I reminded myself again to stop thinking of Tolliver as my brother, because that was just creepy, but it was a hard habit to break.

When we were in the room, I couldn't settle on an occupation. I didn't want to read, and television is a wasteland on Sunday evening unless you like sports. I couldn't focus on my crossword puzzle. I gathered up our laundry bags. 'I'm going to find a Laundromat,' I said and left the room. If Tolliver said anything, I was out of there too fast to hear it. We needed a break from each other.

I inquired at the motel desk, and the clerk gave me really good directions to a large and clean place about a mile away. We always keep a stock of quarters, and we carry detergent and dryer sheets in the trunk. I was good to go.

There was an attendant in the Laundromat, an older woman with crisp white hair and a comfortable body. She was sitting at a little table, reading, and she glanced up when I came in to give me a nod of acknowledgment. Since it was the weekend, the place was busy, but after a little searching I spotted two empty machines side by side. I found a plastic chair and dragged it over, and after I'd loaded the machines and gotten them started, I sat down and pulled my book out of my purse.

I could read, now that I was away from Tolliver's brooding presence. I don't know why that was so. But it was kind of nice to have bustle and people around me, and it was reassuring to have the achievement of clean clothes.

I was at peace. There weren't any bodies around. For a blissful period, I couldn't hear any buzz at all in my head.

From time to time I looked around me to make sure I wasn't in anyone's way, and I saw a woman about my own age looking at me when I raised my head when the spin cycle was almost over.

'Are you that woman?' she asked. 'Are you the psychic woman who finds bodies?'

'No,' I said instantly. 'I've heard that before, but I work at the mall.'

That's what I always said when I was in an urban area. It had always worked before. There was always a mall, and it provided a reasonable explanation for the questioner to have seen me before.

'Which mall?' the woman asked. She was pretty, even wearing her weekend sloppy clothes, and she was persistent.

'I'm sorry,' I said, with an appropriate smile, 'I don't know you.' I shrugged, which was supposed to mean, *I'm sure you're okay, but I don't want to discuss my personal information with you anymore.*

This gal just didn't pick up on the cue. 'You look just like her,' she said, smiling at me as if that ought to make me happy.

'Okay,' I said, and began pulling clothes out of the washers. I had already appropriated one of the rolling carts.

'If you were her, your brother would be somewhere around,' the woman said. 'I'd sure like to meet him; he looks hot.'

'But I'm not her.' I rolled my cart away with everything else thrown in it along with the wet clothes. I had to stay long enough to dry them. I couldn't leave now. If there was anything in the world I didn't want to do, it was talk to this woman about my life, my activities, and my Tolliver.

The woman watched me the rest of the time I was in the Laundromat, though she didn't approach me again, thank God. I pretended to read while our clothes tumbled, I pretended to be absorbed in folding them when they were dry, and I made up my mind that as far as I was concerned, she simply wasn't there. This technique had worked for me in the past.

By the time I was ready to load the clothes into the car, I figured I'd gotten clean away. But no – here she came, following me out into the parking lot.

'Don't talk to me again,' I said, shaken and at the end of my rope.

'You are her,' she said with a smug nod of her head.

'Leave me alone,' I said, and got in the car and locked the door. I waited to drive away until after she'd reentered the Laundromat. I hoped that someone had stolen her clothes while she'd come out to look at me some more.

At least now I knew she couldn't follow me. But I did look into the rearview mirror a few times, just to be sure, which was how I noticed the car that actually *was* following me. It was hard to be sure, since it was dark by now, but since the area was so urban and well lighted, I was sure I was seeing the same gray Miata in my rearview mirror. I pressed the speed dial number for Tolliver.

'Hey,' he said.

'Someone's following me.'

'Then come straight back here. I'll go outside and wait.'

So I did go straight to the motel, and he was standing in an empty spot right outside our room, to make sure it stayed empty. I parked, leaped from the car, and sped into the room while he waited outside.

After a minute, Tolliver called my name. I checked through the peephole. He wasn't alone.

'It's okay,' he said, but he didn't sound happy.

So I opened the door, and he came in with his father in tow.

Crap.

Tolliver turned to face his dad, standing side by side with me.

'What do you want?' he asked Matthew. 'Why'd you follow Harper here?'

'I just want to talk to you, son.' Matthew glanced at me, tried to look apologetic. 'Alone? This is family stuff, Harper.'

He wanted me to leave my own motel room.

'Not possible,' Tolliver said. He put his arm around me. 'This is my family.'

Matthew's eyes flicked from Tolliver to me, then back again. 'I understand,' he said. 'Listen, I got to apologize to you. I was a terrible father. I let you down, and I let down Laurel's kids, too. And worst of all, I let down our children that we had together.'

Tolliver and I stood together silently, our sides touching. I didn't even need to look up at my brother, because I knew how he felt. Matthew didn't need to tell us who he'd let down. We knew all about it.

And yet, he was obviously waiting for our reaction.

'None of this is news to us,' Tolliver said.

'Laurel and I were addicted,' Matthew said. 'That's not an excuse for our negligence, but a . . . confession, I guess. We did bad things. I'm asking for your forgiveness.'

I wondered if this was something Matthew was obliged to do as a step in some rehabilitation program. If so, he'd gone about it the wrong way entirely. Stalking his children, following me to get to Tolliver, this was not the way to express contrition.

After another moment of silence, I said, 'Do you remember the night Mariella got so sick, and we tried to sneak out of the trailer to take her to the doctor, and you blocked the door and wouldn't let us leave because you didn't want the hospital to call social services? We were willing that night to be separated, if we could just get help for her.'

'She got better!'

'Because we stayed up all night putting her in a cool bath and giving her baby Tylenol!'

Matthew looked blank.

'You don't remember anything about it,' Tolliver said. 'You don't remember the night we had to sleep under the trailer because it was full of your friends. You don't remember when Harper got hit by lightning and you wouldn't call an ambulance.'

'I do remember that.' Matthew looked straight at Tolliver. 'You saved her life that day. You did CPR.'

'And you did nothing,' I said.

'I loved your mother,' he said to me.

'Yeah, I'm really glad you were there for her at the end,' I said. 'When she died alone, and you were in another jail.'

'Were you there?' he said, swift as a striking snake.

'I didn't claim to love her.'

'Did you go to the funeral?'

If he thought he was heaping coals on my head, he could think again. 'No. I don't go to funerals. For obvious reasons.'

Matthew still didn't get it. He'd fried a few of his own brain cells over the course of the past years. He narrowed his eyes at me, asking a question.

'Presence of the dead. It's a real issue for me.'

'Oh, *bullshit*. You don't have to pretend. This is me, here. I know you. You can fool other people, evidently, but not me.' Matthew made a face that was meant to let me know that we were all in a big conspiracy together.

'Leave,' Tolliver said.

'Oh, come on,' Matthew said, incredulous. 'Son, you're not claiming this corpse-finding thing is real. I mean, you can pretend in front of other people, but your sister is anything but some kind of occult witch.'

'She's not my sister, at least not by blood,' Tolliver said. 'We're a couple.'

Matthew's face reddened. He looked like he was going to throw up. 'You make me sick,' he said, and instantly regretted it.

Now nearly everyone we had told had had that reaction, to a greater or lesser degree. If I'd cared about how they felt, I might have been worried about our relationship just about now.

Fortunately, I didn't give a shit.

'Time to go, Matthew,' I said, easing away from Tolliver. 'For a reformed junkie and alcoholic, you're not very tolerant of other people's little differences.' I held open the room door.

Matthew looked from me to his son, waiting for Tolliver to cancel my suggestion. Tolliver jerked his head toward the open door. 'I think you better go before I get any madder than I am,' he said, in a voice with no emotional weight whatsoever.

Matthew gave me a furious look as he walked by me on his way out the door.

I closed it and locked it behind him. I took a step over to Tolliver, hugged him, and looked up at his locked-down face. 'You'd think somebody would be happy for us,' I said, to break the silence. I didn't know what Tolliver was feeling. Was he having second thoughts?

It was now completely dark outside, and the blank window seemed like a big eye looking into the room, especially since we were on the ground floor. Tolliver gave me a little hug and stepped to the window to draw the curtains. I'd feel better when the night was blocked out and Tolliver and I were alone together.

Tolliver was standing in the center of the window, his arms extended to bring the curtains together. I was standing a little to the side and behind him, just about to sit on the bed to unlace my shoes. And then a hundred things happened in tiny layers of seconds. There was a huge noise; my face and chest stung; I was sprinkled with wetness. A gust of cold air blew across my face as Tolliver staggered backward, knocking me down on the bed. He landed on top of me and then slithered to the floor in a boneless way.

I catapulted back to my feet so fast I wobbled, aware that cold air was pouring in the window, inexplicably. I looked down at my cold chest. It was wet – not with rain, but with red spots. My T-shirt was ruined. I don't know why I cared. But I think I screamed, because I already understood on a subterranean level that Tolliver had been shot, that I was cut with glass and covered with blood, and that our world had completely changed in the space of a second.

6

I must have unlocked the door in answer to the pounding, because Matthew was in the room, and I was not being any help to Tolliver because I was standing there looking down at him, my hands held out in front of me because I'd touched my face and my hands were covered with blood. Since my hands were dirty I didn't want to touch Tolliver.

Matthew was on his knees beside his son. I pulled my phone out of my pocket and hit 911, though it required more concentration than anything I'd ever done. I gasped out the motel and its location, and I think I said we needed an ambulance immediately, and I said 'sniper,' because I was thinking of the word.

In a thought that went by so quickly I couldn't catch its trailing ends, I was sorry I'd mentioned a sniper because maybe the ambulance wouldn't come because the driver was scared, and then I tossed that idea overboard and joined Matthew on the carpet, facing him over Tolliver's body.

I'd been shot at through a window before, and it had been frightening. I'd had glass all over me then, too. But this was so much worse, terrible, it was the worst thing that had ever happened to me, because it had happened to Tolliver. That was all I could think of, the eeriness of such a thing happening twice, but I tried to yank myself out of the horror and I tried to help. Matthew was pulling off his shirt and folding it, and he pressed it to the bloodiest spot.

'Hold this, you idiot,' he said, and I put my hands on the pad formed by the shirt. It was soaking through with blood under my fingers.

If he hadn't rushed back to the door so quickly, I would have accused him of doing this to Tolliver, but I just didn't think. It was an idea I definitely would have adopted if it had even occurred to me.

Tolliver's eyes opened. He was pale, bewildered.

'What happened?' he said. 'What happened? Honey, are you okay?'

'Yes, okay,' I said, pressing down with all my might. 'Listen, they're coming, baby.' I couldn't remember ever calling Tolliver 'baby' in all the years we'd known each other. 'They're coming, and they'll fix you up. You're not hurt bad, you're going to be okay.'

'Was there a bomb?' he said. 'Was there an explosion?' His voice faltered. 'Dad, what happened? Harper's hurt.'

'Don't you worry about Harper,' Matthew said. 'She's *fine*. She's going to be okay.' He was examining Tolliver's wounds with his fingers, pulling Tolliver's shirt up to examine the skin.

Then Tolliver's eyes rolled up and his face went slack.

'Oh, *Jesus*!' I almost moved my hands, but even in the panic of the moment I knew I mustn't. I'd held on for what felt like hours. It was no time to let go.

'He's not dead,' Matthew yelled. 'He's not dead.'

But he looked dead to me.

'No,' I said. 'He's not dead. He's not. He can't be. It's his right shoulder, and that's not the heart. He can't die from this.' I knew what a fool I was being, but there was no shame in it right at that moment.

'No, he won't die,' his father said.

I opened my mouth to scream at Matthew, though I don't know what I would have said, and then I clamped my lips together because I heard an ambulance.

There were people crowding in the door to the room, and they were talking and exclaiming, and I heard some of them shouting at the ambulance driver *Come over here, come over here,* and if I turned my head to my left, I could look out the window and see the flashing lights. More than anything else I'd ever wanted, I wanted someone who knew what the hell they were doing to come into this room and take the hell over, someone who could fix my brother and stop this bleeding.

There was more yelling outside, as the police got there right along with the ambulance and began urging everyone to move back, move back, and then the ambulance guys were there inside the room and Matthew and I had to get out of the narrow space so they could work.

The police took me outside, and I could not remember a single face after that night. 'Someone shot him through the window,' I said, to the first face that seemed to be asking me a question. 'I was standing behind him and someone shot him through the window.'

'What relation?' asked the face.

'I'm his sister,' I said automatically. 'This is his dad. Not my dad, but his.' I don't know why I made the distinction, except I'd been making it clear to people for years that I had no kinship to Matthew Lang.

'You need to go to the hospital, too,' said the face. 'You need to get that glass pulled out.'

'What glass?' I said. 'Tolliver got shot.'

'You have glass in your face,' the man said. I could see now that he was a man, that he was an older man in his fifties. I could see that he had brown eyes and deep creases radiating from their corners, and a big mouth and crooked teeth. 'You gotta get that pulled out and cleaned.'

I needed to start wearing safety goggles if I was going to keep on getting glass in my face.

Then I was at the hospital, sitting in a cubicle, and someone had taken my wallet from my purse to get the insurance information. About a hundred people were asking me questions, but I couldn't talk. I was waiting for someone to come to tell me how Tolliver was doing, and there was no point in talking until I knew what had happened to him. The doctor who was removing the glass seemed a little scared of me. She tried to keep talking, maybe thinking I'd relax if her voice kept going.

'You need to look down while I get this piece out,' she said finally, and when I looked down I could feel the tension go out of her body. I must have been staring. I was wishing that I could let go of my body and float down the hall to see what was happening to my brother. If I promised to give him up if he lived, would that help? The bargains you make when you are frightened are probably a true measure of your character. Or maybe just an accurate measure of your primitive nature, what you would be like if you'd never been to a mall or gotten a paycheck or relied on someone else to provide your food.

A woman in a pink smock asked me if there was anyone else she could call for me, anyone who would like to stay with me, and I knew I would start screaming if I saw Iona or Hank, so I said no.

They let his dad go in with him. Not me! I had to get the glass out! I was so angry I thought the top of my head was going to come off when my brain exploded. But I didn't scream. I kept it inside me. When the doctor and the nurse had finished with me, and they'd given me a couple of pills because they thought I'd have an uncomfortable time of it for a while, I nodded to them and went in search of Tolliver. I found Matthew sitting in a waiting room, talking to a policeman.

He looked at me when I came in, and I could see the caution in his face.

'This is Tolliver's stepsister. She was in the room with him, standing behind him,' Matthew said, as if he were the master of ceremonies introducing the lineup.

The policeman was a detective, I guess, since he was in slacks and a shirt and a Windbreaker. He was very tall, and he looked to me like a former football star, which in fact turned out to be the case. Parker Powers had been a famous high school football player from Longview, Texas, who'd gotten injured two years into his contract with the Dallas Cowboys. That made him very nearly a star, certainly a notable. I got all that within ten minutes of meeting him, thanks to Matthew Lang.

Detective Powers was a medium shade of brown and had light blue eyes. His hair was dusty brown and curly and clipped close. He wore a wide wedding ring.

'Who do you think shot at you?' he asked me, which was more direct than I'd expected.

'I can't imagine,' I said. 'I would have said it was Matthew, here, if he hadn't gotten back in the room so quickly.'

'Why his dad?'

'Because who else cares?' I said, realizing that wasn't the most coherent way to make my point. 'Granted, some people don't like what we do, but we're honest and we don't make enemies. At least, not any that I knew of. Obviously, we made at least one.' I don't know how the police made any sense of this, but presumably at some point I had explained what Tolliver and I did. I don't remember.

Detective Powers went through the whole question-and-answer routine about how we made our living, how long we'd been doing it, how much money we made, what our last case had been. I actually had to think for a minute about that, but then I remembered the Joyces' visit and I told him about it. He didn't seem too happy to discover that we were on speaking terms with a wealthy and powerful family.

A doctor came in, an older man with a fringe of hair and a worn-out face. I was on my feet in an instant.

'Mr Lang's family?' He looked from me to Matthew. I could not speak; I was waiting. Matthew nodded.

'I'm Dr Spradling, and I'm an orthopedic surgeon. I've just operated on Mr Lang. Well, good news, on the whole. Mr Lang was shot by a small-caliber bullet, probably from a .22 rifle or a handgun. It went through his clavicle, his collarbone.'

I gasped. I couldn't help it. I was acting like a fool.

'So I've pinned the clavicle. There was no major damage to nerves or blood vessels from the bullet, so he was a lucky man – if you can call anyone who gets shot lucky. He made it through the surgery just fine,' the doctor said. 'And I think he's going to recover without many hitches. As far as what's going to happen next, he'll have to stay in the hospital for two or three days. If everything continues to go well, if no complications come up, he can be released. But he'll probably have to have IV antibiotics for a week after that. We can arrange for a visiting nurse to help with that, but you'll have to remain in the area, and I understand you don't have a residence here.' He aimed his gaze more or less between us, as he waited to see what would develop.

I nodded frantically to assure him I understood. 'Anything you say,' I told Dr Spradling.

'Where do you live, Miss Connelly? I understand he lives with you?'

I caught a glimpse of Matthew's face, and I thought maybe Matthew was about to try to take control of Tolliver's care. A huge fear bobbed to the top of all my other fears. Would they even let me in to see him if Matthew protested? I had to trump Matthew's fatherhood card. I opened my mouth and surprised myself by telling the doctor, totally out of the blue, 'We're common-law married. What you call an informal marriage.' Texas recognized an unmarried union, and I was pretty sure that was what they called it. Common-law wife might beat out stepsister. 'We have an apartment in St Louis. We've been together for six years.'

The doctor couldn't have cared less. He just wanted to let me know what was going to be involved in taking care of Tolliver. He did, however, turn slightly so he was addressing me specifically. 'It would be easier if you could find a place near to the hospital until he's stronger, when we release him. He's not out of the woods yet, but I really think he'll be all right.'

'Okay.' I ran all he'd said back through my mind, hoping I could remember it all. Broken clavicle, small-caliber bullet, no other major damage. Three days in the hospital. IV antibiotics a nurse would administer in the hotel. A closer hotel.

'They can stay with me and their brother if they need to,' Matthew said, and the doctor nodded, clearly uninterested in the details. I could guarantee that wasn't going to happen, but this wasn't the time to settle it.

'As long as he can have someone responsible with him. He needs to be quiet and comfortable, get up and move around several times a day, take his meds on time, avoid alcohol, and eat good food,' the doctor said. 'And again, that's assuming he continues to do well. We'll know more tomorrow.' Dr Spradling wanted to be sure we were sufficiently warned.

I nodded vigorously, shaking with anxiety.

'I'll stay in his room here tonight,' I said, and the doctor, who'd half turned away, made an effort to look sympathetic.

'Since he's just had surgery, he'll be checked on very frequently tonight,' the doctor said. 'And he won't be awake. You'd be much better off going home, cleaning up, and coming back in the morning. If you'll just leave a phone number, they'll contact you if there's any problem at all.'

I looked down at myself. I had blood all over me, and it had dried. I looked . . . horrendous, and now I understood why everyone who walked by me glanced away. And I smelled like blood and fear. And I needed our car. So against my own inclinations, I asked Matthew to take me back to the motel.

The police had finished processing the ruins of our room by then. When I trudged into the lobby to talk to the woman at the front desk, I was greeted by the manager, an African American woman in her fifties with clipped hair and a sympathetic manner. She was anxious to get me out of sight of any guests who might come in, and when we were in the little room in back of the check-in desk, she made me sit down and brought me a cup of coffee, which I didn't remember requesting. Her name tag read *Deneise*.

'Miss Connelly,' she said, very earnestly and sincerely, 'if you'll give your consent, I'll send Cynthia into the room to gather up your clothes and your personal items.'

I wondered where this scene was leading. 'All right, Deneise,' I said. 'That would be very helpful.'

She took a deep breath and said, 'We hope you'll accept our regret that this terrible incident occurred, and we want to make this time as stress free for you as we can. We know you have so many things to think about.'

I finally got it. Deneise was wondering if we considered the motel to blame in the shooting, and she wanted to feel me out about my intentions. And I think she was genuinely shaken up and sorry the whole thing had happened.

After Cynthia had been dispatched to the ruined room to salvage what she could of our stuff – to my relief, Matthew offered to go with her – Deneise got down to terms. 'You may not want to stay here another night, Miss Connelly, but if you do, we'd love to have you.'

I felt that was less than sincere, but I also didn't blame the woman.

'If you do decide to stay, of course we'd be glad to supply you with a comparable room free of charge, to show our regret that you've been . . . inconvenienced.'

I almost smiled. 'That's an understatement,' I said. 'Yes, I'd like to have a room for the rest of the night, but I'll be checking out first thing in the morning. I have to find something closer to the hospital.'

'How is Mr Lang doing?' Deneise asked, and I told her he was going to be all right.

'Oh, that's good news!' She seemed relieved on several different levels, and I didn't blame her a bit.

Now that the motel situation was settled, I was anxious to get into a room and get clean. The manager called Cynthia on her cell phone and told her to take our luggage directly to room 203.

'I thought you might feel better if you weren't on the ground level,' she explained as she hung up.

'You're right,' I said. I thought of the black hole of the window, and I shuddered. My face and shoulders were hurting, I was covered with dried dots and smears of blood, and suddenly I began shivering, now that I had the luxury of time for myself. Now that I thought Tolliver would be all right.

Matthew appeared in the office doorway. 'Your stuff's in your new room, and I don't think anything is missing. Everything seems to be in your purse.'

I didn't like the idea of Matthew having access to my purse, but he had been a real help tonight, and I had to give the devil his due. I told Deneise I was grateful she'd been so thoughtful, and with my new key card in hand, I went out to the lobby with Matthew to get in the elevator.

'Thanks,' I said, as it rumbled up to the open area with snack machines and the ice maker. A couple coming up the stairs glanced at us curiously, and when they'd absorbed my bloody state, they hurried away to their room.

'That's okay,' Matthew said. 'I heard the shot, and I heard you scream. I ran across that parking lot pretty damn fast.' He laughed.

I hadn't even realized I'd screamed.

'You didn't see anyone in the parking lot?'

'Nope. And it makes me nuts, because the shooter had to have been really close to me.'

I stowed that idea away to think over later. 'Well, I guess I'll see you at the hospital tomorrow, if you can get off work,' I said. Abruptly, I wanted to be alone more than anything.

'You want me to call Iona?' Matthew asked.

When I said, 'No!' he laughed, a choky sort of laugh that made him sound like Tolliver for a moment.

'You don't mind me saying so, you're pretty dependent on my son,' Matthew said, chiming in with my thoughts so neatly that I was instantly angry.

'Your son is my lover and my family,' I said. 'We've been together for years. While you were gone.'

'But you need to be able to function on your own,' Matthew said in the righteous tone of someone who's had counseling; and because he was trying to sound gentle, I was even angrier. I may not be your garden-variety person, but I am not as fragile as I seem. Or maybe I am, but that wasn't any of Matthew Lang's business.

'I don't believe you have the right to tell me how I ought to live, how I ought to be,' I said. 'You have no rights over me. You never did. You never will. I appreciate your help tonight. I'm glad you finally did something for your son, though it took him getting shot for you to do it. You need to go now, because I have to shower.' I used the key card, and the door to the new room swung open. The lights were on, and the room was warm. Our suitcases sat on the floor beside the bed.

Matthew nodded to me and walked away without saying one other word, which was a very good thing. I looked at Tolliver's suitcase and began to cry, but I made myself go into the bathroom and shed my blood-speckled clothes. I took a very careful bath, mindful of my scores of cuts and nicks. I put on my pajamas.

I called the hospital again, and found Tolliver was still the same. I reminded them again to call me instantly if there was any change. I put the phone on the charger, and lay in bed, and listened for it to ring.

But it didn't. All night.

The next morning as I went through a McDonald's drive-through, I realized I had to call Iona to tell her what had happened. Otherwise, she might read it in the papers. I didn't expect anything from her, and it was a strange feeling to realize that there was someone I should report to; Tolliver and I are used to being on our own. If we hadn't been in the same urban area, I would never have considered calling Iona about Tolliver's injury. I got to the hospital early, looked into his room to find Tolliver sleeping, and returned to the lobby to use my cell phone. The reception in the lobby wasn't good, so I stepped outside with the smokers. It was a cold, clear day, with a brilliant blue sky.

I checked my watch, felt there was a chance Iona hadn't left for work yet, and called the house. Iona wasn't best pleased to hear from me early in the morning, and she let me know it.

'Tolliver got shot last night,' I said, and she was silent.

'Is he all right?' she asked, even now sounding grudging.

'Yes, he's going to make it,' I said. 'He's in a regular room at God's Mercy Hospital. He had some surgery on his shoulder. He'll be in the hospital for a couple more days, the doctor thinks.'

'Well, I don't believe I need to tell the girls right now,' Iona said. 'Besides, Hank's already taken 'em to school. We'll talk about it when they come home today.'

'Suit yourself,' I said. 'I've got to call Mark.' I clicked the phone shut, angry and disappointed. It wasn't that I wanted my little sisters upset and worried, especially after the skating rink incident yesterday – it was that I knew my interaction with them would always be ruled and regulated by the troll squatting across the drawbridge that led to them. I was being pretty ungrateful to Iona with that comparison. I should be glad *every day* that she and Hank had had the nerve and grace to undertake the raising of two girls from such a damaging background.

But going through her was such an uphill battle.

For the first time, I thought Tolliver might be right. Maybe we should just butt out of our sisters' lives and send them Christmas presents and cards on their birthdays.

Then Mark answered his phone in a drowsy voice, and I had to chuck aside these bad thoughts and deal with the here and now. Mark had worked late the night before so he wasn't too coherent, but I made sure he got the gist of the story and knew the name of the hospital. He promised he'd come by when he could, probably later in the morning.

Then I had nothing else to do but return to the dreary room and watch Tolliver sleep. Of course I had a book in my purse, and I tried to read for a while, but I kept losing track of the narrative. Finally, I put the book away and simply looked at Tolliver.

Tolliver is seldom sick, and he'd never been hurt this seriously. The bandages and the IV and the gray tone of his skin made him seem almost a stranger, as if someone had crept in and usurped his body. I sat staring at him, willing him to sit up, willing the vigor to return to his body.

That worked as well as you'd expect.

I knew I had to be the strong one now. With my brother down, I had to take care of him, of us. It was good that we'd planned on spending a few days in Texas, because I knew we didn't have any other jobs booked that I should be rescheduling. However, I'd have to check the laptop for new messages. I'd have to take care of *everything*. I immediately began to worry that I wouldn't do a good job of it, that I'd forget something critical. But what could I forget that would matter so very much? As long as we didn't miss an engagement, as long as I kept gas in the car so we didn't run out, I would be doing a good job.

Finally, Dr Spradling came in. Tolliver had been moving around a little, so I knew he was about to wake up. Dr Spradling looked even more tired and old today. He gave me a glance and a nod before approaching Tolliver's bed. He said, 'Mr Lang?' in a penetrating voice. Tolliver's eyes flew open. He looked past the doctor, right at me, and relief relaxed the lines of his mouth.

'You okay, baby?' he said, trying to hold out a hand to me.

I stepped past the doctor, circled the bed to the other side. I took his left hand in both my own.

'How are you?' I asked.

Dr Spradling was looking into Tolliver's eyes, reading his chart, and listening to our conversation.

'My shoulder hurts. What happened to you?' he asked. 'The window exploded. Someone throw a brick in? You have cuts on your face.'

'Tolliver, you got shot,' I said. I couldn't think of a tactful way to ease into the subject. 'I only got hit by some of the glass from the window. It's nothing. You're going to be okay.'

Tolliver looked confused. 'I don't remember,' he said. 'I got shot?'

'His memory will clear up,' Dr Spradling said. I looked at him, blinking so I wouldn't cry.

'This is not uncommon,' he told me, and I appreciated his trying to reassure us. 'Mr Lang, I'm going to look at your wound.' A nurse came in, and the next few minutes were really unpleasant. Tolliver looked exhausted by the time he was rebandaged.

'Everything looks fine,' Dr Spradling said briskly. 'Mr Lang, you're coming along just like I'd hoped.'

'I feel so bad,' Tolliver said, not quite complaining, but as though he were worried.

'Being shot is a serious thing,' Dr Spradling said, glancing at me with a slight smile. 'It's not like on television, Mr Lang, when people hop right out of their hospital beds and go chase thieves.'

I don't think Tolliver followed all that, because he was looking at the doctor with an uncertain expression. Spradling turned to me. 'I expect he'll be here tomorrow, and we'll see the next day. He may have to have some physical therapy on that shoulder.'

'But he'll have full use of his arm?' I said, suddenly realizing I hadn't even begun to worry as much as I had reason to.

'If everything continues to go well, that's probable.'

'Oh,' I said, flattened by the lack of certainty. 'What can I do?'

Dr Spradling looked as though he were as much at a loss as Tolliver. The doctor clearly didn't think there would be much I could do for Tolliver except pay his bill. 'It's up to him,' Dr Spradling said. 'Your partner.'

I don't think I would have liked any doctor that day, since a doctor couldn't give me a clear-cut answer. My mind knew Dr Spradling was being logical and realistic, and my mind also told me I should appreciate that. But my mind was taking a backseat to my emotions.

I managed to keep myself under control, and Dr Spradling departed with a cheery wave. Tolliver still looked a little confused, but he drifted back into a doze. His eyelids flickered when there was a sound in the hall, but they never quite opened. I couldn't figure out what to do next. I was standing by the bed, looking down at Tolliver and trying to make a plan, any plan, when Victoria Flores came in after a quick knock on the door.

Victoria was in her late thirties. A former police officer on the Texarkana force, she was both full figured and beautiful. I'd never seen Victoria wearing anything but a suit and heels. She had her own personal dress code. Victoria's dark, coarse hair was smoothed into a shoulder-length pageboy, and heavy gold earrings gave her some bling. Today the suit was a dull red, worn over a cream-colored blouse.

'How is he?' she said, nodding toward the silent figure on the bed. No hug, no handshake, no preliminaries. Victoria went straight to business.

'He's hurt pretty bad,' I said. 'He has a broken bone.' I tapped my own collarbone by way of illustration. 'But the doctor who was just in here, he said Tolliver would be okay if he did physical therapy. If nothing changes.'

Victoria snorted. 'So, what happened?'

I told her.

'What was your last case?' she asked me.

'The Joyces were.'

'I'm meeting with them later this morning.'

I didn't describe the reading I'd gotten at the cemetery, because the Joyces hadn't given me permission, but I did give Victoria an outline of the time we'd spent with them. And she knew they'd visited us at the motel.

'That has to be the most likely cause of the shooting,' Victoria said. 'What about the case before this one?'

'You remember the serial killer, the boys killed in North Carolina? All buried in the same place?'

'That was you – you found them?'

'Yeah. That was awful. Also, we did get a lot of publicity, most of it the wrong kind.' I'd found that quiet word of mouth was better for getting actual paying jobs. Publicity might prompt a flare of interest, but that interest was mostly from people who wanted to explore the unexplained and lurid, not people who wanted to pay a lot of money to have it displayed in their neighborhood.

'So this shooting incident might be a fallout of the North Carolina case?'

'Now that I've said it out loud, that doesn't sound very likely.' Tolliver needed a shave. I should do that, and then I had to comb his hair. I couldn't think of anything else I could do to help him.

He looked so helpless. He *was* so helpless. I was the only defense he had. I had to man up.

'The North Carolina murders really, really upset a lot of people,' Victoria said, her voice thoughtful. She clearly believed Tolliver's shooting must be related to the only case of mass murder we'd ever discovered.

'But the bad guys got caught. Why would anyone want to shoot us because we helped to catch who did it?'

'You sure there weren't any more in on it? The two men were the only killers?'

'I'm sure, and what's more, the police are sure. Believe me, that was one thorough investigation. They haven't gone to trial yet, but the prosecutor's pretty damn sure they're going to get a conviction.'

'Okay.' Victoria looked down at Tolliver for a few seconds. 'Then either you've got a stalker or it's something to do with the Joyces.' She paused for a moment. 'There hasn't been anything new about your sister for a long time. I am assuming the trail's too cold for Cameron's abduction to have any relation to what's happening to you now.'

I nodded. 'I agree. I think the Joyce case is the most likely. If they okay me talking to you, I'll be glad to tell you all about it. There's really not much to tell.'

Victoria whipped out her cell phone and made a call, which I was pretty sure you weren't supposed to do in a hospital. She started talking. A few seconds later, she handed the phone to me.

'Hello,' I said.

'This is Lizzie Joyce.'

'Hi. Did you want me to talk to Victoria?'

'That's real ethical of you. You have my permission.' Did she sound *amused*? I didn't think my morality was funny at all. 'I'm sorry about your manager,' Lizzie continued. 'I understand it happened at that same motel where we visited you. My God! What do you think happened? Was it just a random shooting?'

A memory surfaced. 'One of the cops did tell me there was another shooting a couple of blocks away. So it's possible. But that's pretty hard to believe.'

'Well, I'm real sorry. If there's anything I can do, you just let me know.'

I wondered how sincere the offer was. For one wild minute, I considered saying, 'This hospital stay is going to be really expensive, because our insurance is shitty. Can you take care of the bill? Oh, and pick up the tab for his rehab, too, while you're at it?' But I simply thanked her and handed the phone back to Victoria.

I'd been too preoccupied to think about the financial crunch we were going to face until that moment. I thought unhappy thoughts, while Victoria Flores wound up her conversation with Lizzie Joyce. For the first time, I saw the full scope of the problem in front of me. I realized Tolliver's injury meant the end of our dream of buying a house, at least in the foreseeable future.

It was possible for me to be more depressed, which I would not have believed ten minutes earlier.

I told Victoria about the visit to Pioneer Rest Cemetery. She asked me a lot of questions I couldn't answer, but finally she seemed satisfied that she'd wrung every last bit of knowledge and conjecture out of me.

'I hope I can perform like they want me to,' she said, having her own down moment. 'I can't believe they came to me instead of some big agency, but now that I know the details, I can see why they called someone like me.'

'It's been hard, the move to this area?' I asked.

'Yeah, there's a lot more business, but a lot more competition,' Victoria said. 'It's good to be close to my mother; she helps with my daughter. And the school MariCarmen's in here is better than the one in Texarkana. Plus, the driving distance isn't bad, and I still have business and a lot of contacts back there. It just takes me two and a half, three hours, depending on traffic and weather.'

'We're never going to find Cameron, are we?' I said.

Victoria's mouth opened, as if she was going to tell me something. Then she closed it. 'I wouldn't say that. You never know when a lead will pop up. I wouldn't string you along. You know that's true.'

I nodded.

'It's always in the back of my mind,' Victoria said. 'All those years ago, when I came by your trailer and talked to Tolliver . . . I was just a rookie cop. I thought I could find her quick, and make a name for myself. That didn't happen. But now that I'm out on my own, I still look for her, everywhere I go.'

I closed my eyes. I did, too.

7

After Victoria left, I sat down on the chair next to the hospital bed. My right leg felt wobbly. It's the leg the lightning traveled down that afternoon in the trailer when the thunder was rumbling outside. I'd been getting ready for a date; it was a Saturday, or a Friday. I discovered I no longer remembered all the circumstances, which was a real shock.

I did recall I'd been looking in the bathroom mirror while I used a hair curling rod, which was plugged into the socket by the sink. The lightning came in through the open bathroom window. The next thing I knew, I was flat on my back, half in and half out of the little room, and Tolliver was performing CPR, and the EMTs were taking over, and Matthew was yelling at them in the background. Mark was trying to shut him up.

My mom was passed out in their bedroom. I could see her sprawled across the bed if I turned my head to the left. One of the babies was screaming, probably Mariella. Cameron was standing pressed to the wall in the hall, her face soaked with tears and her expression distraught. There was a strange smell in the air. The hairs on my right arm were little crispy flakes. Nothing about me seemed to work.

'Your brother saved your life,' the older man bending over me said. His voice sounded far away and it buzzed.

I tried to respond, but my mouth wouldn't work. I managed a tiny nod.

'Thank you, Jesus,' Cameron said, the words almost incoherent because she was so choked up.

That scene in the trailer seemed more real to me than this Dallas hospital room. I could picture Cameron so clearly: long straight blond hair, brown eyes like Dad's. We didn't look that much alike, even a quick glance would tell you that; our faces were different shapes and so were our eyes. Cameron had freckles across her nose, and she was shorter, and her build was more compact than mine. Cameron and I both made good grades, but she was more popular. She worked at it.

I think Cameron would have managed much better if she hadn't been able to clearly remember the nice house in Memphis where we'd grown up, before our mom and dad had gone to hell. That memory also made her struggle to keep us up to a standard she held in her head. It made her crazy if we didn't look neat, clean, and prosperous. It made her nuts if anyone even suspected what our home life was like. Sometimes that frantic desire to keep up appearances at school made Cameron a little hard to reason with. To live with, truth be told. But she was absolutely loyal to her siblings, both step and full. She was determined to raise Mariella and Gracie as she deemed fit according to her shadowy memories of our respectable past. Cameron worked constantly to keep the trailer looking clean and orderly, and I was her deputy in that struggle.

Seeing Victoria had raised a lot of ghosts. While Tolliver slept, I remembered the years I'd expected to see my sister everywhere we went. I'd imagined that I'd turn around in a store, and she'd be the clerk who was waiting to ring up my purchases. Or she'd be the prostitute we passed on the street corner at night. Or she'd be the young matron pushing a stroller, the one with the long blond hair.

She hadn't been.

Once I'd even asked someone if she was named Cameron, because I was suddenly convinced that the young woman was my sister, a little aged and worn. I'd frightened her. I'd had to walk away quickly, because I'd known she would call the police if I said one more word.

In all those fantasies, I'd never once explained to myself how Cameron had gotten launched in this second life of hers, or why she hadn't called me or written me in all those years.

At first, I'd been convinced my sister had been abducted by a gang or sold into slavery, something violent and horrible. Later it had occurred to me that maybe she'd simply been fed up with her life: the tawdry parents and the tacky trailer, the sister who limped and looked abstracted, the baby sisters who never seemed to stay clean.

Most days, though, I was sure Cameron was dead.

I was yanked out of my unhappy reverie by the sudden appearance of one of the detectives from the night before. He came into the hospital room very quietly and stood looking down at my brother. Then he said, 'How are you today, Miss Connelly?' in a voice that barely moved the air in the room, it was so hushed and even.

I stood up, because he made me nervous, with his silent entrance and hushed voice. He wasn't especially tall, maybe five foot nine, and he was thickset and had a heavy mustache flecked with gray. He wasn't anything like his partner, Parker Powers. This detective looked like a million other men. I tried to remember his name. Rudy something. Rudy Flemmons.

'I'm fine compared to my brother,' I said, nodding down at the figure on the bed. 'Have you got any ideas about who did this to him?'

'We found some cigarette butts in the parking lot, but they could have come from anyone. However, we bagged them just in case we ever get someone to compare the DNA to. Assuming the lab guys can get DNA.' We did some more looking at the patient. Tolliver opened his eyes, smiled at me very slightly, and went back to sleep.

'Do you think they were really shooting at him?' the detective asked.

'They hit him,' I said, a little confused at the question. Of *course* the shooter had been aiming at Tolliver.

'You think they might have been shooting at you?' Rudy Flemmons asked.

'Why?' That sounded stupid the minute it was out of my lips. 'I mean, why shoot at me? You're saying you think the bullet hitting Tolliver was an accident, that it should have been me?'

'It *might* have been you,' Flemmons said, 'not *should* have been you.'

'You're basing that on . . . what?'

'You're the dominant one in your little group of two,' Flemmons said. 'And your brother is strictly your support staff. You're the talent of the outfit. The chances are much higher of someone taking issue with you, rather than with Mr Lang, here. I understand he doesn't have a girlfriend?'

This was the strangest policeman I'd ever talked to.

I sighed. Here it came again. 'He does,' I said.

'Who is she?' He'd even gotten out his little notebook.

'Me.' Flemmons looked up, his eyes quizzical.

'Come again?' he said.

'He's not my brother by blood, you know.' I was very tired of explaining our relationship.

'Right, you don't share parents,' he said. He'd been doing his research.

'No, we don't. We're partners, in every sense of the word.'

'Okeydokey. I got an interesting phone call this morning,' Flemmons said, throwing the line away. I immediately became more alert.

'Yes? From whom?'

'From a detective on the Texarkana police force. Name of Peter Gresham. He's a friend of mine.'

'What did he tell you?' I said and sighed. I really didn't want to hear yet another rehashing of my sister's disappearance. It had already been a 'grieved about Cameron' day.

'He said there'd been a phone call about your sister.'

'What kind of phone call?' There are more crackpots in the world than you can shake a stick at.

'Someone spotted her at the Texarkana mall.'

I stopped breathing for a second. Then the air surged into my lungs in a choked gasp. 'Cameron? Who saw her? Someone who used to know her?'

'It was an anonymous call. A male, calling from a pay phone.'

'Oh,' I said, feeling as though someone had punched me in the stomach. 'But . . . how can I find out if that's true? Get that person to come forward? Is there any way?'

'You remember Pete Gresham? He was the primary on your sister's case.'

I nodded. I did recall him, but not with much clarity. When I looked back on the bad, bad days immediately following Cameron's vanishing, they seemed like one big blur of anxiety to me. 'He was a big guy,' I said. I added, less certainly, 'Wears cowboy boots all the time? He was losing his hair. He was young to be balding.'

'Yeah, that's him. Pete's bald now. I think he shaves the little he has left in the hair department.'

'So what did he do? About the phone call?'

'He viewed the security tapes.'

'They tape inside the mall?'

'Some, and they tape the parking lot pretty good, Pete said.'

'Was she there?' I thought I would scream if he didn't tell me.

'There was a woman who fits your sister's general description. But there's no clear shot of her face, and there's no real way to know whether or not it's Cameron Connelly.'

'Can I see it?'

'I'll see if that can be arranged. Ordinarily, I guess, you'd want to drive over to Texarkana yourself, but with Mr Lang here, and liable to stay in the hospital for a couple more days, maybe we can let you see them at our office.'

'That would sure be wonderful if you can swing it,' I said. 'The round trip would be a long time to be away from him.' I was trying to force myself to be calm.

Before I could stop myself, I bent over Tolliver and took hold of his hand. It was cold, and I told myself I'd have to ask the nurse for another blanket. 'Hey, you,' I said. 'Did you hear the detective?'

'A little,' Tolliver said. It was more of a mumble, but I could understand him.

'He's going to try to get the mall tapes here for me to see,' I said. 'Maybe we'll finally get a lead.' It seemed incredible that Victoria and I had been discussing this very thing not an hour previously.

'Don't get your hopes up,' Tolliver said, in a clearer voice. 'This has happened before.'

I didn't want to consider all the previous false sightings. 'I understand,' I said. 'But maybe this time will be the charm, huh?'

'She wouldn't be the same,' Tolliver said, his eyes fully open. 'You know that, right? She wouldn't be the same.'

I calmed down in a hurry. 'Yes, I know,' I told him. She would never be the same. Too many years had passed. Too much pain had been felt, too much . . . everything.

'If you need to go to Texarkana . . .' Tolliver began.

'I'm not leaving you,' I said immediately.

'If you need to go, you go,' he said.

'I appreciate that,' I said. 'But I'm not going while you're here in the hospital.' I couldn't believe I said it, even as I listened to my own words. For years I'd been waiting to hear news of my sister. Now there was actually a lead, however odd and unreliable it sounded – and I was telling Tolliver I wasn't going to chase it down immediately.

I sat down in the chair by the bed. I laid my forehead against the cotton blanket that covered my brother. I'd never felt more committed.

Detective Flemmons had listened to our discussion with a blank face. He seemed to be reserving judgment on us, and I appreciated that, too.

He said, 'I'll give you a call when we're ready.'

'Thank you,' I said, feeling a little numb.

When the detective was gone, Tolliver said, 'It's only fair.'

'What?'

'You got shot for me. Now I got shot for you, if he's right. You think the shooter was aiming for you?'

'Huh,' I said. 'The difference is, when I got shot, she almost missed me. I mean, it was just a graze. Whoever shot you did a better job.'

'So,' he said, 'I get shot by more efficient people.'

'I think that pain medication must be pretty damn good.'

'The best,' he said dreamily.

I smiled. It wasn't often Tolliver was so relaxed. I didn't want to think about Cameron anymore, because I didn't know what I wished for.

His dad knocked on the door of the room and stepped in before we could say yes or no. Our peaceful moment was shot all to hell.

Matthew was looking a little ragged, not too surprising considering how late we'd been up the night before; and he'd told me he'd had the morning shift at McDonald's. Clearly he'd taken the time to shower after he'd been at work, because he didn't have the distinctive McDonald's smell.

'Tolliver, your dad helped me while we called for an ambulance,' I said, because I had to give the devil his due. 'And he came to the hospital until they said you were out of danger.'

'You sure he didn't shoot me, too?'

If I hadn't lived with Matthew Lang for several years, I would have been shocked through and through.

Matthew himself gave a good impression of a man hurt to the core. 'Son, how can you believe that?' he asked, simultaneously wounded and angry. 'I know I wasn't the best dad . . .'

'Not the best dad? You remember the time you held a gun to Cameron's head and told me you would blow her brains out if I didn't tell you where I'd hidden your stash?'

Matthew's shoulders slumped. I think he'd managed to forget that little incident.

'And then you ask me how I can believe you'd shoot me.' If Tolliver's voice hadn't been so weak, it would have been hot with sheer rage; as it was, Tolliver's words sounded so sad I could have wept for him. 'It's real easy to believe, *Dad.*'

'But I wouldn't have done it,' Matthew Lang said. 'I loved that girl. I loved all of you. I was just a damn junkie, Tolliver. I was a mess, and

I know it. I'm asking for your forgiveness, now that I'm clean and sober. I won't screw up again, son.'

'It'll take a lot more than words to persuade us,' I said, looking at Tolliver and seeing how exhausted he was after five minutes in his father's presence. 'As long as we're bringing up happy memories, I can sure dredge up a few we haven't reminisced about in a while. You were there last night . . . okay. That was good. But it wasn't a drop in the bucket.'

Matthew looked sad. His brown eyes were like a spaniel's, innocent and liquid with soft feelings.

I didn't believe he'd reformed for a second. And yet, I have to admit, I wanted to believe him. If Tolliver's father could really reform, really try to love Tolliver as he deserved to be loved, respect him as he deserved to be respected, it would be a wonderful thing.

The next second, I cursed myself for being pathetic, for being sucked in to even that extent. Since Tolliver was hurt and weak, I had to be extra vigilant. I was watching out for both of us, not just myself.

'Harper, I know I deserve that,' Matthew said. 'I know it'll take a long time to convince you both that I'm really sorry. I know I fucked up, over and over again. I know I didn't act like a real father. I didn't even act like a responsible adult.'

I looked down at Tolliver to gauge his reaction. All I saw was a young man who'd been shot in the shoulder hours before, a man exhausted by the demands his father was bringing into the room.

'Tolliver doesn't need all this drama now,' I said. 'We shouldn't have gotten into this discussion. Thanks for your help last night. You should leave now.'

To his credit, Matthew said goodbye to Tolliver and turned and walked out of the room.

'Okay, that's over with,' I said, to fill the sudden silence. I'd taken Tolliver's hand, and he squeezed it, but he didn't open his eyes. I didn't know if he was truly asleep, but he needed to act like he was, so that was all right with me. Our stream of visitors seemed to have died out, and we had a few hours of that hospital boredom that I'd anticipated. It was almost a relief to be bored. We watched old movies, and I read a few pages. No one called. No one came to visit.

By the time five o'clock made its appearance on the big clock in his room, Tolliver insisted I needed to leave and check into a hotel, get some rest. After talking to his nurse, I finally agreed. I was almost walking in my sleep, and I wanted to shower again. All the little cuts on my face were sore and itchy.

I was extra careful with my driving as I stopped at a couple of hotels. I checked into one that had a room that was clean and ready and on the third floor. I hauled my bag in and slogged through the lobby and into the elevator, feeling an intense longing for a good bed. I was hungry, too, but the bed was the central item in my little daydream. My cell phone rang. I answered it because I thought it might be the hospital.

Detective Rudy Flemmons said, 'You sound like you're just about asleep on your feet.'

'Yes.'

'We'll have those tapes tomorrow morning. You want to come by the station to watch them?'

'Sure.'

'Okay, then. See you there at nine o'clock, if that suits you.'

'Okay. What's happening with the investigation?'

'We're still canvassing the neighborhood to see if anyone saw anything last night when your brother was shot. The other shooting was on Goodman Street, and it was a case of a falling-out between thieves. It's possible the shooter in that incident was so jacked up after he took care of his buddy that he decided to take a shot at a good target as he drove by the motel. We think we found the spot where the shooter stood.'

'That's good,' I said, unable to drum up more of a reaction. The elevator opened its doors on my floor, and I stepped off and went down the hall to my new room. 'Is that all you need to tell me?' I used the plastic card in the lock.

'I think so,' the detective said. 'Where are you now?'

'I just checked into a Holiday Inn Express,' I said.

'The one on Chisholm?'

'Yeah. Close to the hospital.'

'I'll talk to you later,' Rudy Flemmons said, and I recognized the tone of his voice.

Detective Flemmons was a Believer.

People who meet me in my line of work fall into three categories: those who wouldn't believe me if I produced an affidavit signed by God, those who are open to the idea that there are strange things in this world that they might encounter (the 'Hamlet' people, I call them), and the people who absolutely believe I can do what I do – and furthermore, they *love* that connection I have with the dead.

Believers are likely to watch *Ghost Hunters*, go to séances, and employ psychics like our deceased colleague Xylda Bernardo. If they aren't willing to go quite that far, they're at least open to new experiences. There are not many law enforcement people in the Believer category, not too surprisingly, since law enforcement professionals meet liars every single day.

I'm like catnip to Believers. I'm convincing, because I'm the real deal.

I knew that from now on, Detective Rudy Flemmons would show up more and more often. I was living confirmation of everything he'd ever secretly believed.

And all because I'd gotten struck by lightning.

I wanted to get in the shower, but I pulled off my shoes and lay down on the bed. I called Tolliver to tell him that I had to go by the police department in the morning, and that I'd come by God's Mercy afterward to tell him all about it. He sounded as drowsy as I felt, and instead of getting in the shower after I put my phone on the charger, I shucked off my pants and slid between the sheets.

8

I woke up with a jerk. I lay there for a few seconds, trying to pin down the reason I was so unhappy, and then I remembered that Tolliver was in the hospital. I relived the moment he'd been shot with gruesome clarity.

Since I'd been shot through a window before, I had to wonder what it was with us and windows. If we stayed away from buildings, would we be okay? Though Tolliver had been a Boy Scout and had camped out with them, I didn't remember his particularly enjoying the camping experience, and I knew I wouldn't.

It was four thirty in the morning. I'd slept through the dinner hour and the whole night. Not amazingly, now I was wide awake. I piled up the pillows behind me and turned on the television, keeping the sound very low. Watching the news was out of the question: it's always bad, and I didn't need to witness any more bloodshed and cruelty. I found an old Western. It was phenomenally soothing to watch the good guys win, to see the hardened dance-hall floozies reveal their hearts of gold, and to observe that once upon a time, when people got shot and collapsed to the ground, they didn't bleed. This was a much better world than the one I lived in, and I enjoyed visiting it, especially in the wee hours of the morning.

After an hour, I must have fallen back to sleep, because I woke up again at seven o'clock, and the TV was still on. The remote was clutched loosely in my hand.

When I was showered and dressed and groomed, I went down to the complimentary breakfast buffet. If I didn't eat more regularly, I'd collapse. I had a big bowl of oatmeal and some fruit, and then two cups of coffee. I returned to the room to brush my teeth. Foundation was out of the question since my face was so cut up, but I did manage a little eye shadow and mascara. I made a wry face as I looked at the result in the bathroom mirror. I knew I looked like something the cat dragged in. I might as well give up on trying to improve my appearance.

It was time to go to the police station to watch the videos from the Texarkana mall. My stomach fluttered uneasily with suspense. I'd done my best not to think about the Cameron sighting, but I noticed my hands were shaking as I took my vitamins. I'd called the nurses' station to ask about Tolliver, and the nurse said he'd slept most of the night, so I felt all right about putting off a hospital visit until later.

The rest and food had really helped, and I felt much more like myself, despite my apprehension. The city police department was housed in a one-story edifice that looked like it had started out modest and taken steroids. It had obviously been added onto, and just as obviously it was bursting at the seams. I had a hard time finding a parking spot, and just when I got out of the car, rain came down. At first it was a light sprinkle, but as I hesitated about getting out the umbrella, the downpour started. I whipped out the umbrella and unfolded it in record time, so I wasn't too wet when I got to the lobby.

One way or another, I've spent a lot of time in police stations. New or old, there's a sameness about them; they're just like schools and hospitals, in that respect.

There wasn't a good place to stow my dripping umbrella, so I had to carry it with me. It sprinkled raindrops all over the floor, and I knew the janitor would have a lot to do today. The Latina behind the counter was thin and muscular and all business. She used an intercom to call Detective Flemmons, and I didn't have to wait more than a couple of minutes until he appeared.

'Good morning, Miss Connelly,' he said. 'Come on back.' He led the way into a warren of cubicles created by chest-high partitions, the kind with carpeting on them. As we went past, I noticed that each cubicle had been decorated to suit the person who used it. All the computers were dirty: smudged with fingerprints, their screens so dusty you had to peer at them to read the type. A hum of conversation hung over the bullpen like a cloud of smog.

This was not a happy place. Even though law enforcement people usually thought I was a fraud and a con, which meant that often I didn't get along with them individually, in the abstract I thought it was wonderful that anyone would choose to do this job. 'You have to listen to people lie all the time,' I said, following this line of thought. 'How do you stand it?'

Rudy Flemmons turned to look back at me. 'It's part of the work,' he said. 'Someone's gotta stand between regular people and bad ones.'

I noticed that the detective didn't say 'good' people. If I'd been a cop as long as Flemmons had, I wondered if anyone would seem truly good to me, either.

There was a sort of conference room at the end of the cubicles, with a long table surrounded by battered chairs. Video equipment was set up at one end. Flemmons darkened the lighting after I sat down, then he pressed a button.

I was so tense I felt like the room was humming. I stared at the screen, afraid I would miss something.

In the next minute, I was watching a woman who seemed to be in her late twenties or early thirties walk across a parking lot. Her face was not clearly visible. She was partially turned away. She had long blond hair. She was short. Her build was compact. I put my hand over my mouth so I wouldn't speak until I was sure about what I was going to say.

The scene shifted abruptly to a shot of the same woman walking inside the mall. She was carrying a shopping bag from Buckle. This clip was taken from the front, directly facing the woman. Though the film was grainy and she wasn't on it very long, I closed my eyes and felt my stomach plummet.

'It's not her,' I said. 'That's not my sister.' I thought I would cry – my eyes got that hot feeling – but I didn't. But the shock of the anticipation and my subsequent disappointment (or relief) was immense.

'You're sure?'

'Not completely.' I shrugged. 'How could I be, unless I saw her face-to-face? It's been eight years or more since I saw my sister. But I can tell that this woman's face is rounder, and the way she walks is not the way Cameron walked.'

'Let's watch again, to be completely sure,' Flemmons said in a very neutral voice. I sat up straighter and watched again. This time it was possible to take more notice of the little things.

The woman in the parking lot film was toting a huge purse that I didn't think my sister would ever choose. Granted, people's tastes changed as they grew up and grew older, but I didn't think Cameron's choice of purses would be that drastically different. The shopping woman wore high heels with her dress slacks, and Cameron disdained heels for everyday wear. She could have changed her style in shoes as well as purses, though. I wasn't wearing the same accessories I'd had in high school. But the shape of the woman's face, and the way the woman in the film moved along at a fast clip with her shoulders hunched a little forward . . . no, I was sure this woman wasn't Cameron.

'Definitely not,' I said, after the second viewing. I was a lot calmer now. The shock was over, and the reality of another dashed hope had settled in.

Rudy Flemmons looked down for a minute, and I wondered what expression he was concealing. 'All right,' he said quietly. 'All right. I'll tell Pete Gresham. By the way, he asked me to tell you hello.'

I nodded. Now that I'd seen this film clip, and I knew the woman in it wasn't my sister, I was very curious about the man who'd called it in.

I tried to ask some questions, but Detective Flemmons wasn't spilling any beans. 'I'll let you know if more information comes in,' he said, and I had to be dissatisfied with that.

I redeployed my umbrella and dashed back to the car, feeling the phone in my pocket vibrate as I shook the umbrella off and got into the driver's seat. I tossed the umbrella into the rear, slammed the door, and opened the phone.

'Mariah Parish did have a baby,' Victoria Flores said.

'Should you be telling me that?'

'I've already talked to Lizzie Joyce. I'm tracking down the kid now. Since Lizzie hired me, I've spent hours on the computer, and I've gotten out and done some legwork. This whole thing is weird, I'm telling you. Since she said you could talk to me, I take that to mean I can talk to you, too.' Victoria, who'd always seemed so closemouthed and prosaic, was practically bubbling.

'That doesn't exactly follow, but you know I'm not going to tell anyone.' I admit, I was curious myself.

'Want to have dinner together? I figure you're not getting to chat to too many people since your sweetie's in the hospital.'

'That sounds good.'

'Okay, how about the Outback? There's one close to the hospital.' She gave directions, and I said I'd meet her there at six thirty.

I was not a little surprised that Victoria was being so forthcoming. In fact, her interest in talking to me was almost odd. But the truth was, I was feeling lonely. It felt good to know someone wanted to talk to me. Iona had called exactly once to ask after Tolliver, but that conversation had been brief and dutiful.

Hospitals are all self-contained worlds, and this one was spinning relentlessly along on its own axis. When I got to Tolliver's room, he'd been taken away for tests, but no one could tell me what tests or why he was having them.

I felt oddly forlorn. Even Tolliver, confined to a hospital, wasn't where I thought he'd be. My cell phone rang, and I started guiltily. I wasn't supposed to have it on in the hospital. But I answered it.

'Harper? Are you all right?'

'Manfred! How are you?' I was smiling.

'I got the feeling you were in trouble, and I had to call. Is this a bad time?'

'I'm glad you called,' I said, probably more fervently than I should have.

'Oh, well, then,' he said. 'I'll be on the next plane.' He was only half joking. Manfred Bernardo, developing psychic, was younger than I by three or four years, but he'd never made any bones about how attractive he found me.

'I'm lonely because Tolliver got shot,' I said, and immediately realized how egocentric that sounded. After I'd explained to Manfred what had happened, he got all excited. He was actually serious about coming to Texas to 'give you a shoulder to cry on,' as he put it. I was absurdly touched, and for a crazy minute I considered saying yes. It would be comforting to have Manfred around – piercings, tattoos, and all. Only picturing Tolliver's face as I told him what I'd done stopped me.

By the time Manfred was ready to hang up, I'd promised I'd call him if 'things got any worse,' which was vague enough to satisfy both of us. And he'd sworn he'd check in with me by phone every single day until Tolliver got out of the hospital.

I felt a lot more cheerful when I hung up. To make my day even brighter, an orderly wheeled Tolliver in right after I'd shut my phone. His color was better than it had been the day before, but I could tell he was very weak, just from the way he slumped in the wheelchair. Tolliver was ready to get back into the bed, though he hated to admit it.

After the orderly had made sure Tolliver was settled and comfortable, he left with that quick, quiet walk hospital staff members seem to acquire as part of their job description. Tolliver had had another X-ray to check on his clavicle, he told me, and a neurologist had come in to verify that there hadn't been any nerve damage to the shoulder.

'Have you seen Dr Spradling today?' I asked.

'Yeah, he came by earlier. He said everything looked okay. I kind of expected you an hour ago.' Tolliver had completely forgotten that I'd told him I was going to stop by the police station.

I told him about the film I'd seen, how the woman differed from Cameron.

'I'm sorry,' he said. 'I was ready for it to be someone else, but I guess I've always got a little bit of hope.' That was exactly how I felt.

'It wasn't, and I'm only wondering why someone thought it was her. I mean, who called the police? Who got Pete to look at the tapes? And this woman was close enough in appearance to Cameron to at least make Pete feel I should see the video. Was the anonymous caller someone who went to high school with Cameron and me, someone who was genuinely mistaken? Or was he some creep who just wanted to jerk us around?'

'And why now?' Tolliver said. He looked at me. I didn't have an answer.

'I hardly see how this could have anything to do with Rich Joyce and his caregiver,' I said. 'But the timing is really suspicious, huh?'

We couldn't think of anything else to say about this strange grouping of events. After a while, I found Tolliver's comb in a pocket of his jeans, which were hanging in the closet. They were a little stained. His shirt had been cut off of him. I reminded myself to bring another one to the hospital for the day he was released.

When I began to comb his hair, I found it was dirty, of course, and I tried to think of a way to wash it. With some improvisation, including a clean bedpan, an extra pad that they'd brought in case his shoulder leaked, and the little bottle of shampoo included in his admissions package, I managed. I also helped him shave and brush his teeth, and then I gave him a sponge bath, which turned unexpectedly bawdy.

He was very relaxed and sleepy – and happy – by the time that was over, and he said he felt much better. I combed his damp, dark hair and kissed his smooth cheek. He was going through a clean-shaven phase.

A nurse came in to give him his bath right after I finished, and she shrugged when I told her it was done.

Time in a hospital inevitably drags. Before I had a chance to tell Tolliver about Victoria's phone call, he fell asleep. I hated to wake him when the long day stretched in front of us. I napped myself. I struggled awake when Tolliver's lunch tray came at eleven thirty.

That was another exciting break. I cut up all his food – well, the little that required cutting – and put a straw in his drink for him so that he could eat one-handed. He was so happy to be getting real food instead of liquid that even hospital food was welcome, and he managed pretty well. When I was sure he'd had as much as he wanted, I rolled the table away and handed him the TV remote. I needed to go in search of food myself.

'You don't have to sit here all afternoon, you know,' Tolliver said.

'After I eat, I'll spend the afternoon with you,' I said in a tone that told him not to argue. 'Then I'm meeting Victoria for supper. I probably won't come back after that.'

'Good. You don't need to be cooped up all day. You'll probably want to have a run or try the hotel's weight room or something.'

He was right about that. I'm used to sitting still for long periods, because we're in the car so much, but I'm also used to getting exercise every day, and my muscles were stiff.

I got a salad at a fast-food place, enjoying the bustle and purpose of the people in the restaurant. It felt odd to be alone, though I didn't mind so much after I watched (and listened to) a mother dealing with three preschool-age children at the next table. I wondered if Tolliver wanted to have children. I didn't. I'd already had the care of two babies, my little sisters, and I didn't want to go through that again. And I admitted to myself that while I didn't want to be pushed out of my sisters' lives, I didn't want to be in charge of those lives, either.

Even after I saw the youngest boy give his mother a spontaneous hug and kiss, I didn't warm up to the concept of carrying someone else inside my body. Should I feel guilty about that? Didn't every woman want to have her own child to love?

Not necessarily, I thought. *And God knows there are plenty of children in the world. I don't need to supply another one.*

Tolliver was awake and watching a basketball game when I walked into his room. 'Mark called while you were gone,' he said.

'Oh, gosh, could you reach the phone?'

'It was my big adventure for the day.'

'What did he have to say?'

'Oh, that I'd made my dad feel bad, that he thought I was being an idiot for not welcoming Dad back to the land of the sober, with my arms open wide.'

I debated with myself for a minute before deciding to say what I thought. 'Mark has a real weakness for your dad, Tolliver. You know I love Mark, and I think he's a great guy, but he won't ever really get it, about Matthew.'

'Yeah,' Tolliver said. 'You're right. He was nuts about Mom, and when she died, he kind of transferred that emotion to our dad.'

Tolliver didn't talk about his mother a lot. Her death, from cancer, had to have been completely awful.

'I think Mark believes that Dad has to be good at heart,' Tolliver said slowly. 'Because if Dad isn't good, then he's lost his last parent. And he has to have that relationship.'

'Do you think your dad is good at heart?'

Tolliver really thought about his answer. 'I hope he's got some good left in him,' Tolliver said. 'But honestly, I don't think he'll stay sober, if he's really sober now. He's lied about it before, over and over. He always goes back to the drugs, and you remember that at his worst he'd take whatever anyone offered him. Now, I'm sure he must have been in a lot of emotional pain to need so many drugs to kill it, you know? But he abandoned us to whoever wanted to prey on us, because he had to drug himself. No, I can't trust him,' Tolliver said. 'And I hope I never do, because I'll be disappointed all over again.'

'That was exactly the way I felt about my mother,' I said, understanding completely.

'Yeah, Laurel was a piece of work,' Tolliver said. 'You know she tried to hit on Mark and me?'

I thought I might throw up the food I'd just eaten. 'No,' I said, my voice strangled.

'Yeah. Cameron knew about it. She came in on the, ah, critical moment. I thought Mark was going to die of embarrassment, and I had no idea what to do.'

'So what happened?' I felt a deep and burning shame. I told myself it was none of my concern, but it's hard to believe that when you hear a story about your own flesh and blood that makes you sick to your stomach.

'Well, Cameron dragged her mom into the bedroom and made her put some clothes on,' Tolliver said. 'I don't think Laurel knew where she was or who she was coming on to, Harper, if it makes a difference. Cameron slapped your mom a few times.'

'Jeez,' I said. Sometimes there are no words.

'We're out of it,' Tolliver said, as if he was trying to convince himself.

'Yes,' I said, 'we are. And we have each other.'

'It can't touch us anymore.'

'No,' I said, lying through my teeth. 'It can't.'

9

The restaurant where I met Victoria Flores was crowded, and servers were bustling back and forth. It seemed incredibly lively after the muted sounds of the hospital.

To my surprise, Victoria wasn't by herself. Drexell Joyce, Lizzie and Kate's brother, was sitting at the table with her.

'Hey, girl,' Victoria said, rising to give me a hug. I was surprised, but not enough to pull back. I hadn't known we were on those terms. Somehow, this show was being put on for Drexell Joyce. I'd been picturing a relaxed dinner between two women who found out secrets for a living, not a strategy session with an unknown man.

'Mr Joyce,' I said as I sat down and stowed my purse under the table.

'Oh, please, call me Drex,' he said with a broad grin. He poured a lot of admiration into his look. I didn't believe in his sincerity for a second.

'What are you doing away from the ranch?' I asked, with what I hoped was a disarming smile.

'My sisters asked me to come check with Victoria, here, see what she's found out and how the investigation's going. If we have a little aunt or uncle out there, we want to find that baby and make sure he's brought up right,' Drex said.

'You're simply assuming that Mariah Parish's child was your grandfather's?' I found that astonishing, and I didn't try to hide it.

'Yeah, that's what I'm thinking. He was an old dog, no doubt about it, but he had a few tricks. My granddad liked the ladies, always did.'

'And you think Mariah Parish would have been agreeable to his advances?'

'Well, he had a lot of charisma, and she might have thought her job depended on saying yes. Granddad didn't like to hear "no." '

Charming. I couldn't think of anything to say, so I didn't speak.

'So, how's your brother?' Victoria asked, her voice warm and concerned.

I was disappointed. I was sure now that Victoria had asked me here for some secret purpose of her own. She hadn't simply wanted my company, after all. 'He's doing much better, thanks,' I said. 'I hope he'll be out of the hospital in another day.'

'Where will you go next?'

'Tolliver usually handles our bookings, and I'll have to go over our schedule with him when he feels up to it. We had originally planned on staying here at least a week, so we could see our family.'

'Oh, you got folks in this area?' Drex leaned forward, all interest.

'Yes, our two little sisters live here.'

'Who's bringing 'em up?'

'My aunt and her husband.'

'They live right around here?'

It could be true that Drex was simply fascinated by all things Harper, but I didn't credit his interest as personal. 'Does your family spend a lot of time in Dallas?' I asked. 'I saw your sisters the other day, and now you're here. That's lots of driving.'

'We have an apartment here, and one down in Houston,' Dex said. 'We're on the ranch around ten months out of the year, but we all need to see the bright lights from time to time. 'Cept Chip. He loves running that ranch. But Kate and Lizzie sit on about ten boards apiece, from banks to charities, and those meet in Dallas.'

'Not you?' Victoria asked. 'You don't do charity work?'

Drex laughed, his head thrown back. I suspected that was so we could see his handsome jawline from another angle. I wondered what he would do when he got older and that jawline wasn't quite as firm. I know from my own experience that no one looks pretty in the grave.

'Victoria, I guess most boards are smarter than to ask me to be on 'em,' he said. He had a down-home twinkle in his eye. Just one of the good ol' boy millionaires. 'I'm not too good at sitting still, and I'd go to sleep if I had to listen to all them speeches.'

How could Victoria listen to all this bullshit? She gave every appearance of being genuinely charmed by this asshole.

'But Victoria, to get back to the topic, how's the search going?' Drex asked, with the air of a man who had to abandon his bit of fun to return to grim business.

'Pretty well, I think,' Victoria said, and I went on the alert. Victoria sounded calm and competent, and more than a little cagey. 'I'm working on a complete biography of Mariah, and it's not as easy as I thought it would be. What kind of background check did you run on her before she was hired to help your grandfather?'

'I don't guess Lizzie had that done,' Drex said, sounding genuinely startled. 'I think it was my granddad who did the hiring. Mariah was living in the house by the time we found out about it.'

'But you'd considered hiring a housekeeper for him?' Victoria asked.

'He needed something more than a housekeeper, but less than a registered nurse,' Drex said. 'He needed an assistant. Really, she was like a nanny. Made sure he ate the right food, tried to monitor how much he drank. But he would've smacked us silly if we'd called her that. She took his blood pressure every day, too.'

Victoria pounced on that. 'Mariah had a nursing degree?'

'No, no. I don't think she had a degree at all. She was supposed to make sure he took his medicine, remind him about his appointments, drive him if he didn't feel well, call the doctor if she noticed anything off a list of warning signals they gave her. She was kind of our human Life Alert, at least that was the idea.'

I exchanged a quick glance with Victoria. So I hadn't been the only one to detect a note of resentment in Drex's monologue. By now I wasn't convinced that Victoria was as interested in Drex as she'd appeared at first. Victoria was playing a deeper game than I could plot and execute.

'She saw her role a little differently?' I asked.

'Hell, yes. She saw herself as a watchdog, I guess,' Drex said. He took a big swallow of his beer. He looked around to see if our server was within hailing distance. We'd placed our orders a few minutes before.

'Why did your family pay for her funeral and put her in the family plot?' I asked. It was a subject I'd wondered about a couple of times. 'Where were her people?'

'We looked through all her stuff after she died, and we couldn't find anything with any names and addresses on it,' Drex said. 'Lizzie asked all of us what she'd said about her family, where she came from, and no one could come up with anything. We asked Chip, and none of his kinfolks could remember anything.'

'What about her Social Security Number? As her employer, your granddad had to have that.'

'He paid her under the table.'

It baffled me why a man as rich as Richard Joyce would choose to do that. The Joyces had to have accountants and business people who would jump at the chance to be useful.

Drex said, 'When Lizzie met Mariah, she told Granddad she thought Mariah wouldn't work out. Granddad thought she'd stay, but he could tell we didn't like Mariah that much. He didn't want to go to the trouble of setting something up, only to have to fire Mariah.' He sounded defensive, and I could understand why. I exchanged a long look with Victoria.

'So your granddad hired someone he didn't know, paid her under the table, and didn't know anything about her previous work history, and he had her living in his house with him.' If I sounded incredulous, pardon me. 'Did you say you asked Chip to talk to his family after Mariah died?' I heard thunder and looked over at a window to see rain hitting the glass.

'Yes, they knew her. It was Chip who told us Mariah would be good for the job.'

There was a long silence, while Drex looked around some more for our server and Victoria and I were absorbed in our own thoughts. I didn't know what was going through Victoria's mind, but I was thinking that I hoped my family took better care of me than the Joyces had of their patriarch, Richard.

'How long has Lizzie been seeing Chip?' Victoria asked, as if she was introducing an entirely new topic, a little social side trip.

'Oh, man, years now. They knew each other from the ranch, of course. And they'd see each other when they were both rodeoing. After a few years, and Chip's divorce, they just clicked. He was at a rodeo in Amarillo, calf roping. She was barrel riding. She was having trouble with her trailer hitch, and he came up to help her.'

'So Mariah had worked for Chip's family?'

'They were foster kids in the same house, and when she got out on her own, Chip recommended her to his distant cousin, Arthur Peaden, I think that was his name. The cousin died just around the time the doctors told Granddad that he needed someone at the house all the time. Chip suggested it and sent her to the house, my granddaddy liked her, and that was all she wrote. After we got over the surprise, we felt kind of relieved that we didn't have to interview a lot of people for the job. And Granddad got someone who'd had experience, but she wasn't going around in scrubs all the time making him feel like he was incompetent. She was nice looking, and she was always smiling. She was a great cook, too.'

Drex got his fresh beer, and Victoria asked him some questions designed to get him to talk about himself. Drex was not the brightest guy I'd ever met, and Victoria was a sharp woman, so by simply sitting and listening it became easy to draw a picture of Drex's life. His dad had probably had a hard time accepting that his only son wasn't competent to handle the family affairs, but there was no denying that Lizzie was not only the oldest but the sharpest. Katie, the middle kid, was wilder than either of her siblings. At least Drex thought so.

I was relieved when our food came. I was not a private investigator, and I wasn't being paid to absorb all these long stories about the Joyce family. By the time I'd eaten as much as I wanted, I was tired to death of Drex Joyce, and I wasn't happy at being in league with Victoria to pump this moron for information. However irritating I found her tactics, I could understand why Victoria had decided to include Drex as a guest at dinner. It was easier for us to alternate in the conversation so he didn't seem to understand where it was going, and presumably he told us more than he might have otherwise.

I also thought of a few questions that Victoria didn't.

I decided that Victoria had wanted to give Drex a choice of attractive women, and I was relieved that Drex had decided Victoria was more to his taste than I. I took a malicious pleasure in excusing myself early, before the waitress had asked about coffee and dessert. Victoria looked dismayed for a fleeting second, and then she said she'd talk to me the next day.

I thought not, not if I could avoid it. I dislike feeling used, and I was sure Victoria had deliberately planned the evening before she'd invited me. She could have been honest with me. I couldn't understand why she felt the need to resort to such a thing. Surely, if the Joyce family had hired her, they would cooperate with her in the most extreme way. Why hadn't Victoria gotten all this information already?

I drove back to the hotel feeling disgruntled. Since the rain had stopped, I decided it was time for some activity. I didn't like to run at night, but I really needed to do something physical. I hadn't had time to explore the area in any detail, but a block behind the hotel I'd seen a large high school. Maybe I could run on its track, if the gate was unlocked. If I couldn't get in, there was a big bus yard across the road from the high school.

To my surprise, Parker Powers, the ex–football player turned cop, was sitting in the lobby.

'Were you waiting for me?' I asked, going up to him.

'Yes. Can we talk?' He gave me a very thorough look.

'What do you need?' I asked.

'I wanted to ask you a few more questions about your brother. There was a drive-by a couple of blocks away last night, and we're trying to find out if your brother's shooting was related. I hear he's doing well.'

If he hadn't said that, I wouldn't have bitten. I'd seen that gleam in his eye. But if he was genuinely investigating Tolliver's shooting, I wanted to help him. I wanted to know who'd shot my brother. I wasn't going to talk about it in the public lobby anymore, though, and with that gleam in his eye, I wasn't going to ask him up to my room.

'I'm going for a run,' I said. 'Care to join me?'

'Sure,' he said, with only a brief hesitation. 'I've got running shorts in my car. You know, you really shouldn't be going out by yourself if someone is gunning for your brother. We have no idea why he was shot, yet. Might be related to the drive-by, might not.'

'I'll be back in ten minutes,' I said, and went upstairs to my room. I had a lanyard from which was suspended a clear plastic rectangular holder, and I put my hotel key and my driver's license into it. I put on my running shorts and T-shirt, and my running shoes. I was ready. I tucked the rectangle down into my shirt and bounced up and down on my toes a couple of times to make sure it was secure. I tucked my cell phone into my shorts pocket, zipped the pocket shut, and went back down to the lobby.

Parker was there, wearing ancient shorts and a ragged sweatshirt. I gave him a nod, and we went out to the parking lot and began stretching. I got the impression Parker hadn't run in a long time; probably the shorts and sweatshirt were his gym clothes, because I could see he worked his muscles, though a paunch was gaining ground on his waistline. I could tell he wasn't enthusiastic about the exercise, but he was enjoying watching me.

'Ready?' I asked, and he nodded, his mouth set in a grim line. He looked more like he was going to face the guillotine than a pleasant evening exercise session.

Off we went, down the sidewalk past a block of houses, then another block of houses, then the high school grounds. The outside lights were plentiful, and everyone seemed to be inside tonight. It was chilly, and there were still puddles here and there from the earlier shower. Cars went by with fair frequency, some of them clearly exceeding the speed limit and some of them at a crawl, but with a sidewalk, that didn't present any problem. I wondered if any of the drivers recognized my running partner.

The cold air felt good to me. I went at an easy pace, enjoying the stretch of my legs and the increased rate of my heart. The high school track was surrounded by a high fence, and it was locked, no big surprise. I led my companion across the road to the vast lot filled with school buses. Parker kept up with me, and I glanced sideways to see that he was smiling a little, pleased with himself. I picked up the pace, and the smile faded rapidly. Within four blocks of really running, Parker was wheezing for breath. He kept going because he was fueled by pride.

Even his pride ran out in the next half mile. There were three rows of buses, and we'd run from the road to the end of one row, up the other row, and we were rounding the end by the road to start running the length again. I was really moving and feeling good, but Parker stopped, hands on his knees, chest heaving. I ran in place. He waved a hand at me to tell me to keep on going. 'Stay in sight,' he said, biting each word out in turn.

I waved back at him and began running again. I wasn't half the runner my brother was, but that night I felt as swift and light as a bird, compared to Parker. I zoomed down the silent line of buses, smelling the puddles and the pavement, washed clean by the evening's rain. I glanced over my shoulder to see that Parker was walking after me at a good pace, but I was definitely getting into the 'out of sight' range. With some regret, instead of rounding the bus line and starting up the middle again, I turned and began running back the way I'd come. There must have been another street beyond the bus lot, because from that direction, I could hear a car going slowly. At that moment, car lights came on behind me, shining in Parker's face and casting my own shadow in a long streak in front of me. I felt a jolt of fear, and I slowed down, not sure what to do. The sound behind me was definitely a car engine, idling . . . but it was drawing closer.

The detective, though it was clear his eyes were dazzled, picked up his pace and began trotting toward me. As he drew closer, he pulled up his sweatshirt and drew a gun. I didn't register that for a second, and then I thought he was going to shoot me. My steps faltered, hesitated. The car engine began to get closer.

'*Run,*' he bellowed.

I didn't understand anything, but I began moving faster and faster, my arms sawing the air to build up my momentum. When I reached him, Parker shoved me between two buses and swung to face the oncoming car, his gun at the ready. The car swerved as the driver presumably noticed the gun pointed in his direction, and then, with a screech of tires, accelerated madly, fishtailing out of the parking lot as it sped away.

'What?' I said. 'What?' I jumped out from between the buses to confront my appointed savior, and threw open my arms. '*What?*' I yelled.

'Death threat,' he said. His breathing was still irregular. 'You got a death threat today. Didn't want you going out on your own. Easy target.'

'Why the hell didn't you tell me that? So that's why you agreed to run with me.'

'I didn't know you were a health nut,' he said unfairly. 'I was just supposed to make you aware of the situation, tell you about the drive-by.'

'So instead of . . .' I started to sputter. Then I closed my eyes, gathered myself, and stood up straighter. 'Do you have a name attached to this death threat?'

'No, it was a man's voice. He was saying he thought your work was the work of Satan, and so on. Said he didn't think you ought to be in Texas, and he was going to take care of that the next time he saw you. He mentioned your new hotel by name.'

I was pretty offhand about the phone call until Parker Powers got to the 'he mentioned the hotel' part. That was unnerving, and I knew I had to take this seriously.

'So do you think this car was his, or do you think you just scared the shit out of some teenagers parking back here?' My legs were getting stiff, so I bounced up and down gently on the balls of my feet, then stretched down to touch my toes.

'I don't know,' Parker said, his voice gloomy. 'I got a partial license number, though, and I'll run the plate.'

I suddenly realized, actually understood, that this man had put himself in front of me when he thought someone was going to be shooting at me. The enormity of the act virtually smacked me in the face.

'Thank you,' I said. All of a sudden, my knees were shaking. 'Thank you for doing that.'

'That's what we're supposed to do,' he said. 'We're supposed to protect. Lucky I didn't have to do much protecting. I might have had a heart attack.' He grinned, and I was glad to observe that his chest wasn't heaving anymore.

'So, we should head back, huh? I guess this was pretty much a nonincident?' I didn't want to hurt his feelings, which was pretty absurd.

'No, I guess they left for good.' He seemed relieved about that. 'Let's go back to the hotel.' He holstered his gun.

I knew there was no way I was going to get the policeman back up to a running pace. We were at least walking briskly when we left the bus lot and we passed the high school. Then we were in the residential area, and there was almost no traffic now. Everyone was home from work, no one was going back out tonight. The temperature had dropped a little, and I began to shiver. We had three blocks to go. We were in a little neighborhood where yards were a hobby. Even in the winter, there were trees with leaves, and bushes, and rock gardens decorating the small front yards. Parker Powers was asking me questions designed to calm me down, an inconsequential stream of inquiry about my running history, how long I ran each day, if my brother ran . . .

And just as I recognized that the shadow behind one of the trees was suspiciously man shaped, it began to move. A man stepped out from the tree, and I saw the streetlight glint off a gun. Parker Powers lunged toward me to shove me aside, away from the threat, and the gunman fired right at him and hit him in the chest.

Screaming would have been a waste of time. The only advantage I had was speed, and I jumped onto the tiny grass lawn and took off like a rabbit on meth. I heard footsteps behind me, even on the grass, and I tried to go behind the house and found there was a fenced-in back-yard. It wasn't much of a fence, kind of a swipe at providing security. I grabbed the top of the fence and vaulted it, landing well, then chased across the dead grass and vaulted the other side.

It wasn't until later that I thought of everything that could have made me fall and break my leg.

I found myself in the next backyard, and I had a clear shot at the next street over. There were houses only on one side of the street. The opposite side was a narrow belt of trees with a ravine behind them, as near as I could tell in the spotty pools of light. I began running toward the hotel, running in earnest, flat out. It was much darker back here. I was afraid I would fall, afraid I would get shot, afraid the detective was dead. I knew I was going in the right direction, but I couldn't see the hotel because the street curved. I almost knocked on a door, but then I thought of the danger to the people inside that house, and I ran on. I thought I heard a noise ahead of me, and I dove to the side and crouched behind a car parked in a driveway. I was silent for a mo-ment, listening, though my heart was pounding so loudly it was hard to make out external sounds.

I unzipped my shorts pocket, withdrew the cell phone, and flipped it open, keeping a hand curved around it to dim the light. I punched in 911, and a woman's voice answered. 'I'm hiding in the driveway of a house, in the business park behind the Holiday Inn Express,' I said, keeping my voice as low as I could. 'Detective Parker Powers has been shot. He's lying out on Jacaranda Street. The shooter is after me. Please come quick.'

'Ma'am? Did you say an officer's been shot? Are you wounded?'

'Yes, Detective Powers,' I said. 'I'm not wounded yet. I have to hang up.' I couldn't be talking on the phone. I needed to be listening.

Now that my own breathing had moderated, I was sure I could hear someone else breathing, someone else stepping very quietly through the front yards. Someone who didn't want to be out in the middle of the street. Weren't any of these people aware of what was going on around them? Where were the armed householders with guns when you needed them? I didn't know whether to break and run, or stay where I was and hope he didn't find me.

I found the tension almost intolerable. Waiting crouched beside that car was one of the hardest things I'd ever done. I didn't even know if this quiet street went through. Maybe it dead-ended just around the slight curve. I'd have to plunge back through the yards so I could emerge on Jacaranda Street to get back to the hotel. There might be fences, there might be dogs . . . I could hear one barking now, and it sounded like a big one.

The footsteps, very quiet footsteps, came a little closer and then stopped. Could he see me? Would he shoot me in the next minute?

Then I heard the wail of sirens. God bless the police, God bless their lights and noise and guns. The shadow that had crept almost up to where I crouched made a rapid retreat as the gunman abandoned caution and ran back down the street in the direction I'd come from.

I tried to get up but I couldn't. My legs just wouldn't work. I could see the beam of a large flashlight coming closer and closer, and then it danced over me. It returned to fix me in its glare.

'Lie down with your arms extended!' said a woman's voice.

'Okay,' I said. 'I will.'

At the moment, that seemed a lot better than standing up.

10

In the end, I went back to the hospital and spent the night with Tolliver. I simply didn't want to be by myself, and I felt safer around him even though he had been shot.

Detective Powers was still alive. I was profoundly glad to hear that, profoundly grateful that his courage would be rewarded in this life rather than the next. I had caught snatches of conversation from the cops around me, who'd pretty much treated me as if I weren't there.

'Powers is going to be all right,' the female officer, who'd finally let me get up, had told me. 'He's too tough to kill.'

'All those years playing football, he's got to be tough,' said one of the ambulance attendants who'd been summoned to have a look at me. He was taking his time packing up his stuff, having determined that I was pretty much okay.

'Yeah, those knocks in the head didn't do him any good, though,' said another officer, a young guy with a shaved head. 'Powers played one season too many.'

'Hey, respect the detective,' the older ambulance attendant said. 'He's a good spokesman for the department.'

Reading between the lines, I gathered that Detective Powers had been a recruitment point for the police since he'd been hired, and that had a lot to do with his promotion to detective. People were so thrilled to be questioned by a former football star that they told him things they hadn't planned on spilling, just to keep his attention. So he was not highly regarded because of his cleverness or innate ability, but because he was an asset and was always willing to share the spotlight. Plus, he was regarded as being a genuinely nice guy.

It was a pleasure to tell his cohorts how brave he had been, and a pleasure to see the pride they took in that. The fact that they thought he'd been pretty much of an idiot to go running with me – well, that was left on the back burner.

I had a few speckles of blood on my face, and I went into my hotel room to scrub them off. The female officer, Kerri Sauer, went with me, and she also volunteered to follow me over to God's Mercy, a gesture I appreciated.

'You ever watch Parker play?' she asked, as she watched me scrub his blood off with a washrag.

'No,' I said. 'Did you? You must have been a kid.'

'I was. He was great. Him getting hurt, that was a terrible thing for the team. He did – still does – all kinds of stuff for kids at risk. He's a great guy. You had his location when you called. That saved his life. He's got a chance to make it.'

It seemed counterproductive to point out that Powers probably wouldn't have gotten shot if he hadn't been with me. I nodded and buried my face in a towel so she couldn't read my expression.

After I parked at the hospital and walked to the door, I waved to the patrol car, and it pulled out into the traffic. I had a crazy idea: if I couldn't make money finding bodies anymore, could I be a police officer? I wondered if I could even pass the physical. Usually my right leg was okay, but every now and then it gave me fits. And I got awful headaches. So probably law enforcement wasn't a career option for me. I shook my head and saw the movement reflected in the shiny walls of the elevator. I was just being silly.

I went through the hall on silent feet and opened Tolliver's door carefully. It was dark inside, though the light in the bathroom was on and that door had been left open a crack.

'Harper?' he said, his voice thick with sleep.

'Yeah, it's me. I missed you,' I said, keeping my voice down.

'Come here.'

I went to the bed, and I crouched to take my shoes off. 'I'm going to sleep in the chair,' I said very softly. 'You go back to sleep.'

'Climb in with me, on my good side.'

'Are you sure that'll be comfortable for you? That bed's mighty small.'

'I'm sure. I'd rather be crowded with you than have lots of room without you.'

I felt tears begin to trickle down my cheeks, and I suppressed the sobbing sound that went with them.

'What's wrong?' He put his good arm around me after I'd crawled into the bed. I lay on my side to give him enough room.

'Nothing we need to talk about now,' I said. 'Sleep now. I just didn't want to be by myself.'

'I didn't either,' he said. And he fell back to sleep. After a few minutes, so did I.

The nurse who came in at five thirty in the morning was fairly surprised to find me there, in bed with Tolliver. Once she saw that we were both clothed and she could assume that Tolliver hadn't done anything to hurt his mending shoulder, she relaxed.

Tolliver looked a lot better in the morning light. Being with him had done me good, too. I felt a lot more confident. After he'd been bathed and shaved and he'd eaten breakfast, I told him the story of the night before.

He said instantly, 'I have to get out of here,' and actually began to sit up to get out of the bed.

'No, you aren't,' I said sharply. 'You're going to stay right here, where no one can get at you, until the doctor says you can go.'

Tolliver said, 'You're in danger, baby. We've got to find somewhere to put you, somewhere safe.' He'd abandoned the idea of leaving, I was relieved to see, mostly because the movement had been enough to make him cold and sweaty.

'That sounds good,' I said. 'But I just don't know where that would be.'

'You could leave,' he said, a little wildly. 'You could go up to St Louis, to the apartment.'

'And leave you here by yourself? Not too likely.'

'You could leave the country.'

'Oh, hush. I'm not going to spend the money to fly to Europe or whatever, just because someone shot at guys while I was around.'

'You got a *death threat*,' Tolliver said, as if I was mentally slow or hard of hearing.

'I *know that*,' I said, mimicking his tone accurately. He gave me a narrow-eyed glare. 'Seriously, Tolliver, I think someone's just trying to spook me. I mean, you got shot and then poor Detective Powers. But couldn't that shooter have hit me, just as easily, if I'd been the real target? I'm not so sure anymore that I simply got lucky both times. I'm thinking maybe the shooter is just trying to scare me.'

'I don't particularly like the results of someone trying to scare you any more than I like the idea of someone trying to really kill you,' Tolliver said, indicating his hospital bed pointedly.

'True enough.' It appeared we were at an impasse.

Dr Spradling appeared and asked Tolliver the usual questions. It seemed clear that Tolliver was out of danger, and the doctor talked about dismissing him, provided Tolliver had someone to take care of him at home. I raised my hand, to indicate I was that person.

'What about traveling?' I asked.

'By car?'

'Yes.'

'I wouldn't. He needs to rest for at least two days before you travel. I'm thinking of giving him an antibiotic drip, but if you promise to stick to what I say faithfully, if you promise to keep him in a room and quiet, then I'll make it oral antibiotics and release him tomorrow.'

'Okay,' I said. 'I promise.'

'Then if he continues to improve, doesn't run a fever, tomorrow.'

I was delighted to hear it. Tolliver looked relieved, too. When the doctor had left, I said, 'I guess I'd better go back to the hotel to take a shower and eat something.'

'Can you wait until Mark gets off work? He could go with you.'

'I'll go by myself. I can't stay shut in a room the whole time, Tolliver. I've got to get out and get things done.' I didn't want Mark to get shot, too.

'Who do you think is doing this?'

'I know it sounds ridiculous, but I wondered if it was someone who got obsessed with me on the website, some nut who decided he didn't want me to be around other men. Or maybe it's a coincidence that I was with men both times. Maybe this guy is a really bad shot and was trying to get me. Maybe it's someone who just wants to rattle me and see what I do.'

'Why now? There's got to be a reason.'

'I don't know,' I said, losing patience. 'How would I know? Maybe the police will come up with something. Having one of their own shot is a powerful incentive to find the bad guy. God knows they asked me to tell them every single thing I've done in the past few days, over and over. I'll tell you something else I have to do – I have to go see the detective who got shot.'

Tolliver nodded. He turned his face away from me, to look out the window. The day was cold and clear, the sky so bright a blue that it hurt to look at it. It was an achingly beautiful day. And here we were, shut inside a hospital and peeved with each other.

I stepped over to his bed, took his hand. It was unresponsive in my grasp. 'I have to shower and eat, and I have to go see the detective,' I said. 'After that, I'll be back. If I keep moving, I'll be fine. No one can follow me 24-7. Right?' I hated to sound wheedling, but I did.

'I need to get out of here,' he said.

'Yes, and you will, soon. The doctor said so. Just don't do anything crazy and fall, okay?'

There was a sketchy knock at the door, and as our heads turned, a short man walked in. He was extraordinary looking – all in black, with platinum spiked hair and piercings in his eyebrow, his nose, and (I knew from the past) his tongue. He was younger than me, somewhere around twenty-one, and he was slim and oddly handsome.

'Hello, Manfred,' Tolliver said. 'I never thought I'd say this, but I'm glad to see you.'

11

Manfred seemed a little hurt that I had protested against his coming with me. 'You don't think I can be helpful?' he asked, his blue eyes looking a shade too forlorn.

'Manfred,' I began, exasperated, 'I just don't know what to do with you.'

'I have some very good ideas,' he said. He waggled his eyebrows.

He was making it funny, but he was serious. I never doubted that at my slightest response, Manfred would be booking us into the nearest hotel as fast as he could whip out his wallet.

The thing was, I'd have to pay for the room, because that wallet was probably empty. I didn't know how Manfred was getting by. His grandmother, Xylda Bernardo, had been a colorful old fraud, but she'd had the genuine gift. It just didn't always speak to her when she needed it to, and when she didn't hear the real voice, she'd make one up. She'd made a poor living at it. She had a flare for the dramatic that had led to some pretty unconvincing overacting.

Manfred was much cannier. And he had the gift, too. I didn't know the scope and depth of Manfred's psychic ability, but I had a feeling that as soon as Manfred found his level and honed his gift, he'd be making money. As far as I knew, that hadn't happened yet.

'First,' I told him, ignoring his innuendo, 'I've got to go to my hotel and shower and change. Then we'll go to the other hospital, the one where they took Detective Powers.'

'The Dallas Cowboy? Parker Powers?' Manfred's face lit up in a wonderful way. 'I read an article in *Sports Illustrated* about him, when he became a cop.'

'I would never have guessed you were a football fan,' I said. Life is a process of reevaluation, isn't it?

'Are you kidding? I *love* football. I played in high school.'

I eyed him dubiously.

'Hey, don't let my size fool you,' Manfred said. 'I can run like nobody's business. And it was a little high school, so they didn't have much choice,' he added honestly.

'So what position did you play?'

'I was a tight end.' And he said it absolutely straight. Manfred did not joke about football.

'That's really interesting,' I said, and I meant it. 'Manfred, not to change the subject, but why'd you decide to come all this way after I said I could handle it?'

'I got the feeling you were in trouble,' he said. He looked sideways at me, and then straight out the windshield of his car. We'd decided that if I were being followed (an idea that still seemed incredible to me) taking Manfred's beat-up Camaro might throw my stalker off the trail.

'Really? You saw that?'

'I saw someone shooting at you,' he said. His face was older all of a sudden. 'I saw you fall.'

'Did you . . . You didn't know for sure I was alive when you came into Tolliver's room, did you?'

'Well, I'd watched the news, and I didn't see anything indicating you'd been killed. I did hear that a Garland policeman had been shot. They weren't releasing his name then. I hoped you were okay. But I wanted to see for myself.'

'So you drove all this way.' I shook my head, marveling.

'I wasn't that far away,' Manfred said.

There was a little silence, while I waited for him to continue.

'Okay, I'll bite,' I said. 'Where were you?'

'I was in a motel in Tulsa,' he said. 'I had a job there.'

'You're officially in the business now?'

'Yep. I've got a website, the whole nine yards.'

'How does it work?'

'It's twenty-five dollars for an answer based on one question. Fifty dollars for a consult if they give me their astrological sign and age. And if they want me to travel to them for a private reading, it's . . . a lot more.'

'How are you doing?' I'd definitely been wrong about Manfred's finances.

'Pretty well,' he said, with a slight smile. 'Of course, I'm building on Xylda's reputation. God bless her soul.'

'I know you must miss her.'

'I really, really do. My mother is a very nice woman.' He said that with the air of someone doing his duty. 'But my grandmother gave me more love, and I took care of her as much as I could. My mother had to work all the time, and I don't remember my father, so Xylda was my real . . . she was my home.'

That was a great way to put it.

'Manfred, I'm so sorry about Xylda. I think of her often.'

'Thanks,' he said, his voice lightening in a conscious attempt to brighten the dark conversation. 'She liked you, too. She liked you a lot.'

We were silent for the rest of the ride.

While I showered and changed, Manfred walked down to the place where Parker Powers had been shot the night before. He wanted to see if he could pick up anything there, and he knew I'd be more comfortable if he wasn't in the room while I was cleaning up. I appreciated both ideas. When he knocked on the door, I was dressed, as made up as my healing face would permit, and braced for our next stop. Manfred set his GPS so we could get to the hospital where Parker Powers was a patient. It was called Christian Memorial. I didn't understand why he'd been taken there instead of God's Mercy, where Tolliver was. Tolliver and Parker had both had gunshot wounds, so it couldn't be the level of trauma the emergency room could handle.

I was impressed with Manfred's GPS, and I'd been thinking of getting Tolliver one for his birthday, so we talked about that on the way to Christian Memorial. I didn't want to think about the visit I was about to pay. Fortunately, we had to watch out for everyone else on the road, and that distracted me.

Every city in the world thinks it has the worst traffic. Dallas has grown in such a hurry, and so many people who move to the city haven't driven in an urban area before, that I think Dallas may be right when it claims its traffic is pretty awful. This congestion extends to the dozens of towns that cluster right around Dallas's outskirts. We were maneuvering among those towns now.

When we'd exhausted small talk about the GPS, Manfred asked me about the case we'd been on before we'd come to Dallas. 'Fill me in on your last few days' was the way he put it. 'You know this shooting is related to something you've done recently. I don't see how the Carolina case can be related.'

I agreed with him. Since Manfred was a colleague, I explained to

him about what had happened at Pioneer Rest Cemetery. I wouldn't
have broken my unwritten bond with the Joyces, but I'd come to
believe they were probably involved in what was happening. More
importantly, I knew Manfred would keep it to himself.

'So there are two ways you can go with that,' he said. 'You can
pursue the missing baby, which one of the men you met may have
fathered – though I guess that kid isn't a baby anymore, it'd be in
school – or you can pursue the possibility one of them threw the
rattlesnake at Rich Joyce, startling him into a heart attack.'

'There are those two possibilities,' I said, relieved to be talking
about the whole situation. 'And there's the fact that Tolliver's father
has shown back up, and he's trying to reconnect with Tolliver. And
the girls. And there's the weird thing that after all these years, someone's reported a Cameron sighting.'

I filled Manfred in on our family business.

'So this might have to do with your little sisters, somehow. Or with
your missing sister. What if this has something to do with Cameron?'

I was startled. 'Why would it?'

'There's a caller claiming to have seen Cameron. Then another
caller threatens you. Two anonymous phone calls. Those sure might
be linked, don't you think?'

'Yes,' I said slowly, considering it for the first time. 'Yes, of course
they could.' If I hadn't put this together before, blame it on the fact
that people near me kept getting shot. 'So this might have to do with
Cameron.'

'Or with the caller knowing this was the surest way to get you away
from Tolliver. Maybe he thought you would leave, go to Texarkana.
He couldn't have counted on the police being willing to show you the
tape at the police station.' There was silence for a long minute. 'Uh,
Harper,' Manfred said. 'You sure – for real – that the woman you saw
in the tape wasn't your sister?'

'I'm sure,' I said. 'Her jaw was different, and the way she walked
was different. True, she was blond and she seemed the right height.
True, I don't know why anyone would claim to have seen her when
the case is cold and no one's looking anymore.'

'You're . . . I guess you've always been convinced that Cameron is
dead?'

'Yes, always.' I said that firmly, as if there were no doubt in my mind at all. 'She would never let me worry like this, not for all these years.'

'But you said you two had it real hard at home.'

'Yeah, real hard.' I took a deep breath. 'She wouldn't do that,' I said. I packed my voice full of conviction. 'She loved all of us, all the kids.'

'So your stepdad resurfaces, and suddenly there's a Cameron sighting,' he said, tactfully abandoning the possibility of my sister's voluntary disappearance. 'Isn't that quite a coincidence, too?'

'Yes, it is,' I said. 'And I don't know what to make of it. I've never thought that he killed her. Maybe I should have considered it. But he was visiting a jailbird friend of his, a guy he did business with, and the time frame excluded Matthew.'

'What kind of business?'

'Drugs, and whatever else they could do to raise money.' I had to stop to remember. Crazy. I would have never believed I'd forget any detail of that day. 'That afternoon Renaldo and Matthew were going to take scrap iron to the recycle plant to get some money. But I don't think they ever made it. They started playing pool.'

'What was the friend's full name?'

'Renaldo Simpkins.' I was very unhappy that I had to struggle to recover that memory. 'He was younger than Matthew, and he was a nice-looking man; I remember that.' I tried to picture his face. 'Maybe Tolliver will remember,' I said finally. I felt that in forgetting even the most minute circumstance of that day, I was betraying the memory of my sister. For the first time, I appreciated the records of that day that the police would have, and Victoria Flores, too.

We pulled into the parking lot of yet another hospital. Christian Memorial was maybe a little newer than God's Mercy, though nothing in that area was very old. We walked into the lobby and asked the lady in the pink smock if she could give us directions. She gave us a practiced smile that aimed at being warm and welcoming. 'Detective Powers is up on the fourth floor, but I warn you, it's mighty crowded up there. You may not get to see him.'

'Thanks,' I said, smiling back just as brightly. We made our way across the lobby and into the elevator, where Manfred's facial decorations attracted a certain amount of attention. He seemed oblivious to the startled and fascinated looks that came our way. When the doors opened on the fourth floor, we were confronted by a sea of faces, and the predominant clothing color was blue. There were cops in several different uniforms standing around, and there were men and women who could only be detectives. There was also a football player or two.

Though it hadn't occurred to me to leave Manfred downstairs, I immediately realized I'd made a mistake bringing him up here. He attracted no little attention, and none of it was positive. I stiffened my back. Manfred was my friend, and he had as much right to be here as anyone. A tall woman with broad shoulders and a thick head of brown hair came up to me. She was in charge. She'd be in charge no matter where she was.

'Hello,' she said. 'I'm Beverly Powers, Parker's wife. Can I help you?'

'I hope so,' I said, feeling hesitant. Somehow, I hadn't foreseen this crowd and all these eyes fixed on me. 'I'm Harper Connelly, and Parker was shot when someone tried to kill me. I'd like to thank him. This is my friend Manfred Bernardo, who's driving for me today while my brother's in the hospital.'

'Oh, *you're* the young woman,' Beverly Powers said, looking at me with a lot more interest. 'I'm so glad to meet you. You understand, there are all kinds of stories going around about why you and my husband were out there together, and I very much hope you'll tell me exactly what happened.'

'Of course I will,' I said, surprised. 'There's no big mystery about it.'

She waited, her eyebrows raised to indicate she was ready. I was taken aback, since I realized she meant me to tell her here and now.

Everyone around us was listening, though they were all trying to look like they weren't. Out of the corner of my eye, I saw that Manfred had retreated to a spot against the wall. He was standing with his hands folded together, his eyes on me and his stance alert. He looked like an undercover operative of some kind. I was sure that was his intent. The man was a chameleon.

'My brother had been shot two nights before,' I explained, trying to pick my words carefully. 'And Detective Powers came to the scene then. He and Rudy Flemmons. Detective Flemmons came to see me at my brother's room in the hospital the next day to give me some information, and then last night, when I went back to my hotel, your husband was there. When I told him I was going for a run, since I'd been cooped up with my brother in his hospital room all day, he said he'd run with me, since he wasn't convinced the shooter had actually meant to hit my brother.' There was definitely no point in mentioning Powers's avid eyes. 'He thought the person who shot Tolliver might have been aiming for me, and someone had called in a death threat for me that day. I guess neither one of us took that seriously enough, which was our big mistake – and for that, I'm so sorry. My only excuse is that I've gotten threats before, and they were always nothing. Your husband said he had his running clothes in his trunk, and he changed in his car, and we started out running. He got winded pretty quick – excuse me, he just hadn't run in a long time, I guess.' To my surprise, my audience had relaxed considerably while I was telling Beverly Powers how her husband had come to be shot, and when I described how winded he'd gotten, a few people actually laughed, and a smile flickered across Beverly Powers's face.

I suddenly understood: Mrs Powers and Parker's fellow officers had thought I'd been having an affair with him. My no-frills explanation had dispelled that suspicion. They weren't really amused; they were relieved.

'We were running up and down the aisles of that big bus depot across from the high school on Jacaranda.' I saw some nods out of the corner of my eye. 'We heard a car come into the lot, and Detective Powers and I both thought it was after us, but then it sped away. We decided we better go back to the hotel, and we were walking on the street going back. This guy jumped out from behind some bushes and fired. I don't know if he was trying to hit me or your husband, but Detective Powers shoved me aside real quick. That meant he caught the bullets. I'm really sorry. He was so brave, and I feel awful about him getting hurt so badly. I called 911 as soon as I could.'

'That saved his life,' Beverly said. Her face was round and sweet, but her eyes were another matter. Whatever sport she'd played, this woman had been a ferocious competitor.

I was profoundly glad I hadn't been having an affair with her husband.

'Please, come see him,' Beverly said.

'Is he conscious?'

'No,' she said, and I understood by the way she said that one word that there was a good chance Detective Powers would never be conscious again.

Taking my hand, the tall woman led me to a glass-walled room, and

I looked at her husband. He looked awful, and he was out of it. I didn't know if it was the medication, or if he was in a deep sleep, or if he was maybe in a coma.

'I'm sorry,' I said. He was going to die. I'm not always right – death can hang over people like a shadow without ever descending – but with Detective Powers, I was pretty sure. I hoped I was wrong.

'Thanks for giving me a little longer with him,' she said. We stood for a moment in silence.

'I've got to get back to my brother,' I said. 'I appreciate your talking to me, and letting me see him. Please tell him thanks for what he did for me.'

I patted Beverly's shoulder in an awkward way and eased my way through the crowd over to Manfred, who took my hand and pressed the elevator button. The door opened immediately, and we stepped into an empty elevator. I was praying for the doors to shut out the painful scene.

'I'm glad you came with me,' I said. 'That must have been pretty nerve-wracking for you.'

'Oh, no, I love going into a pen of lions wearing a sign that says *Edible Lamb*.' Now that we were alone, Manfred's bland mask relaxed into a face that was just as relieved as mine must have been.

Our hands were gripping so tightly that I could feel his bones against mine. Even as I realized I was in pain, he eased his hold on me.

'That was an adventure,' he said, in a more normal voice. 'What next? Alligator wrestling?'

'No, I thought we'd go eat lunch. Then I need to go back to Tolliver's room and sit with him.' We were in the car and driving over to the hotel when Manfred asked, 'Did the doctor say when Tolliver would be released?'

'He'll get out tomorrow. I'm sure I'll have to do some nursing. Maybe I should see if I can get a suite at another hotel, instead of the room I've got now. We might be there for a week or so, because the doctor said Tolliver had to stay quiet. He'll be in the bed a lot, and I don't want to bother him.'

'You're definitely settled with Tolliver, then? He's the one?' Manfred asked, his face suddenly serious.

'He's the one,' I said. 'He's been the one since I met him. Of course, you were always my fallback position.' I tried a smile. To my relief, he returned it.

'I'll have to cast my net wider,' he said dramatically. 'Maybe I'll haul in a mermaid.'

'If anyone could find a mermaid, you'd be the one,' I said.

'Speaking of mermaids, are you checking the mirrors for tails? Or are you just scared of my driving?'

'I'm hoping I can tell if someone's following us. That's happened here, and for the life of me, I can't spot anyone. It's good I don't want to be a detective.' Manfred tried to watch, too, but he didn't notice a car that was doing everything we did. In Dallas traffic, that wasn't decisive, but at least I felt a little better.

When we reached the hotel, I collected my stuff and checked out, after first calling another chain hotel down the block to see if they had a suite-type room available. They did, and I booked it under Tolliver's name. The anonymous caller had known I was in this hotel, and though it wouldn't be hard to find me again, I might as well not make it completely easy. I reserved the suite for six nights, figuring I could always check out earlier if Tolliver was doing well enough to leave town. I also called Mark, to tell him where we'd be. Then Manfred drove me to the new hotel and helped me carry in Tolliver's bags as well as mine.

We went out to eat after that, to a family-style restaurant with a long salad bar. It was about time I ate something that wasn't actively bad for me, and I loaded up my plate with salad and fruit. A little to my surprise, Manfred did, too.

My companion was a great believer in conversation. Or at least, he enjoyed talking while I listened. I wondered how well Manfred fitted in with his peers, because he needed to say a lot of things out loud that he maybe hadn't had a chance to say, mostly about Xylda and how much he missed her, the things she'd taught him, the odd items he'd found stored away in her house.

'Thanks for showing up today,' I said when there was a lull in the chatter.

He shrugged. He looked half proud, half uncomfortable. 'I knew you needed me,' he said and found something else to look at.

'I'd like you to meet some of these people and tell me what you get from them,' I said. 'If I can think of a way to make it look natural.'

He looked all too happy about the prospect of doing me a favor.

'Of course, if you need to go home, I'll understand,' I said.

'No,' he said. 'I do a lot of my business on the Web now, and I don't have any readings scheduled for this week. I brought my laptop and my cell; that takes care of me. What am I looking for?' The sense of fun faded from his face, and I was looking at an older person than the Manfred I was used to.

'You're looking for whatever you can tell me about these people,' I said. 'Someone shot Tolliver. Someone shot Detective Powers, though I guess they were trying to hit me. And I think it was one of these people. I want to know why.'

'Not who?'

'Well, of course that, too. But the "why" is pretty important. I need to know if I'm the target or not.'

He nodded. 'I get it.'

We drove back to the hospital, and Manfred dropped me off at a side entrance, the closest to providing concealment that the hospital offered. I scooted inside and made my way to the bank of elevators off the lobby. I didn't think anyone was paying any particular attention to me, and no one seemed to be loitering. Everyone I looked at seemed to have a purpose, and no one spoke to me.

When I got back to Tolliver's room, I found him sitting up in the chair. I felt a wide smile spread across my face.

'Oh, you got adventurous,' I said, beaming at him.

'Hey, I'm no slacker,' he said, but he smiled back. 'Hearing I might get out made me feel better than any of the drugs. How was your trip across the city with the amazing Manfred?'

I told Tolliver about our visit to Detective Powers. 'Once they all understood I wasn't sleeping with him, they were all relieved,' I said.

'When he gets better, you can tell him his fellow officers thought he was a real dog.'

'I don't think he's going to get better,' I said. 'I think he's going to die.'

Tolliver took my hand. 'Harper, that's not up to us. All we can do is hope he pulls through.'

That was such a sweet thing to say; maybe not the words so much as the way Tolliver said it. I could tell he loved me. I cried a little, and he let me without saying anything patronizing, and then I helped him back into bed because he was tired. We should have been talking about who shot him, but at the moment we were simply too flattened.

Mark and Matthew came in together an hour later.

We were watching an old movie, and we were actually enjoying it, but I switched it off to be polite. As they stood together at the foot of the bed, I noticed that Mark and Matthew were much more alike in looks than Tolliver and his dad were. The shorter, thicker build, the square faces . . . All three men had the same coloring, but other than that, Tolliver definitely looked more like his mom. I'd only seen pictures of the first Mrs Lang, but she'd had Tolliver's much narrower face and thinner build.

I wondered if they wanted me to leave.

Tolliver didn't give me any signal one way or the other, and though I half expected Matthew to tell me he wanted to talk to his sons alone, he didn't say a word about it, so I stayed.

After the usual inquiries into Tolliver's recovery and when he'd get out of the hospital, Mark said, 'I wondered if you'd like to come back to stay with me, at my house, I mean. While you get better.'

'Your house,' Tolliver said, as if he'd never heard of such a thing. We'd been to Mark's house exactly once. He'd had us over to dinner, and he'd ordered out. It was an absolutely standard three-bedroom ranch with a fenced-in backyard.

'Yeah, why not? Since you and Harper are . . .' Here he made a kind of indeterminate gesture, meant to indicate that we were sleeping together. 'That means you can share a bed, so there'll be room.'

'So, Dad's staying in the other room now?' Tolliver didn't look at his father as he spoke to Mark. He'd sure picked up on that little indicator.

'Yes, he is,' Mark said. 'It just made sense, since his job doesn't pay a lot, and the bedroom was empty.'

'I already got us a suite at a hotel,' I said. I made sure my voice was both quiet and neutral. I didn't want to make this a confrontation.

But it looked as though I wasn't going to get my wish.

'Listen,' Mark said, flushing up as he did when he was angry, 'you butt out, Harper. This is my brother, and I get to ask him to stay with me. It's his call. We're family.'

Not only was I angry now, too, I was hurt. I didn't care if I ever got called a member of Matthew's family, but Mark and I had shared a lot of woe together. I thought we kids had been our own family. I could feel my own face reddening.

'Mark,' Tolliver said sharply, 'Harper is my family. She's been my family for years now. Yours, too. I *know* you remember how we had to stick together.'

Mark looked down at the floor, conflict making his face really distressing to watch.

'It's okay, Mark,' Matthew said. 'I understand what they're saying. You-all did have to band together. Laurel and I weren't exactly up to making a family work. We were together, but we weren't a real family. Tolliver's right.'

Overkill, I thought.

'Dad,' Mark mumbled, like he was seventeen again. 'You tried to keep us together.'

'I did,' Matthew said. 'But my addictions got in the way.'

I tried very hard not to roll my eyes. Drama 101. Tolliver was watching Matthew confess – yet again – and his face was unreadable. There were still times when I couldn't tell what Tolliver was thinking, and right now was definitely one of those times. He might be softening toward his father, or he might be planning how to kill him. At the moment, I would vote for the killing.

'Please, Tolliver, give me a chance to get to know you again,' Matthew pleaded.

There was a long silence. Mark said, 'Tol, you remember when Gracie got so sick? You remember, Dad took her to the hospital? And the doctors gave her antibiotics and she came home so much better?'

I'd forgotten about that. It had been a long time ago. Gracie had been very little, maybe only four months old. How old had I been? Fifteen? It had been hugely embarrassing to have a baby sister, I remembered, because that was plain evidence that my mother and her husband were actually having sex.

It's amazing what can embarrass you at fifteen.

I knew something about babies by then, because we'd already had the care of Mariella. My mother had been a little better when our first half sister was born, though, and she'd done at least some of the everyday care. We'd been able to leave Mariella with her during the school day, for example. That was out of the question when Gracie was born, underweight and sickly. Why they didn't take Gracie away from Mom in the hospital, I don't know. We had almost prayed that someone would take the baby or that Mom would come to her senses and give Gracie up for adoption.

Neither of those things had come to pass. So Cameron and I had taken turns babysitting for other families, and the boys had earned money, and Matthew had chipped in, too. We'd been able to take the girls to day care while we were out of the house.

Then Gracie, who'd always had trouble with her breathing, had gotten really bad. I couldn't remember much about it, except being scared. We'd been so impressed that Matthew had taken her to the hospital.

'Are you saying I should make friends with Dad because one time, *one time*, he acted like a real father?' Tolliver said, and I let myself exhale. He wasn't fooled.

'Oh, Tolliver.' Matthew shook his head, grief written in big letters on his face. 'I'm trying to stay straight, son. Don't harden your heart against me.'

It took everything I had not to speak, but I was proud that I could hold my tongue. For a second, my heart went to my throat, because I thought I detected a weakening in Tolliver's face. 'Goodbye, Mark. Dad. Thanks for coming by,' he said, and I breathed out a silent sigh of relief.

The two visitors looked at each other, then at me. They obviously wanted me to leave the room, but I wasn't going to do it. After a moment, they could tell I was staying put.

Matthew said, 'If you need our help transferring Tolliver to the hotel, just call Mark's number and leave a message, Harper. We'll be glad to do whatever we can.'

I nodded.

Mark said, 'I'm sorry we can't all . . .' His voice trailed off miserably. 'Jeez, I wish you two could forgive and forget.'

I found this incredible. I had no response to make to my stepbrother, but I had something to say to my stepfather. 'I learned some of the basic lessons of my life under your neglect, Matthew. I don't hate you, but I'm sure not going to forget. That would be under the category of really, really stupid.'

Matthew looked directly at me, and for a second I saw his undisguised dislike before he pulled the repentant mask back over his true face.

'I'm sorry you feel that way, Harper,' he said smoothly. 'Son, you'll be in my prayers.'

Tolliver looked at him silently. Then his father and his brother turned and left the room.

'He hates me,' I said.

'I'm not so sure he feels any different about me,' Tolliver said. 'If I fall down three flights of stairs, don't call them. I love Mark and he's my brother, but he's back under Dad's thumb, and I don't trust him at all.'

12

I left the hospital after dark, and I drove around for a while until I was sure there was no one behind me. I was so new to worrying about being followed that I'm sure there could have been five cars following my trail and I might not have realized it, but I did my best. I parked close to the hotel entrance, and I practically ran into the lobby. The suite was on the second floor, and I waited in the hall until I was sure no one was in sight to watch to see which door I unlocked.

I unpacked and did a little ironing. I optimistically checked over Tolliver's clothes, picking out something he could wear home. I figured he wouldn't be comfortable stretching his arm up to pull on a T-shirt or polo shirt, so I decided on a sports shirt and jeans. I put them in a little bag. I was ready.

After I'd watched the news, I called down for room service. I was glad there was a restaurant attached to the hotel, because I didn't want to go out by myself. I was a little surprised I hadn't gotten a call from Manfred offering to join me for supper, but whether or not I had a companion, I was hungry. I ordered a Caesar salad and some minestrone, figuring that should taste good even if the cook wasn't hugely talented.

I hustled to the door when the expected knock came, but I paused before flinging it open. In my experience, the server knocking at the door always said, 'Room service.' This one hadn't.

With my ear to the door, I listened. I thought someone on the other side might be doing exactly the same thing.

Of course I should look to see who was standing there. But weirdly, I found myself scared to put my eye to the peephole. I was afraid the shooter was standing out there with a gun, and he'd fire through the door if he had proof I was inside. I knew if you were alert you could tell when the person in the room was looking out, and for the life of me, I couldn't make myself do it.

I heard the elevator down the hall, and I heard the ding as it arrived at my floor and the sound of the doors opening. There was the rattle of the cart, a sound I recognized, and I heard someone shift positions right outside my door. Yes, someone was still there. But after a second, my caller walked rapidly away. I put my eye to the peephole, but it was too late. I didn't catch a glimpse of whoever had been at the door.

The next second there was a much firmer knock, and a woman's voice said, 'Room service.' The peephole verified that this was in fact a server with a cart, and I opened the door without hesitation once I saw how bored she seemed.

'Did you see someone walking away from my door?' I asked. I didn't want to seem too paranoid, so I added, 'I was taking a nap, and I thought I heard someone knock right before you did, but by the time I made it to the door, they were gone.'

'There was someone walking the other way,' the woman said, 'but I didn't see his face. Sorry.'

That was the end of that, apparently.

I was pretty angry with myself. I should have looked through the peephole. Maybe I would have discovered it was a stranger who'd gotten the wrong room number. Maybe I would have seen Manfred, who knew I was in this hotel. Or maybe I would have seen the face of my enemy.

Disappointed in my fearful self, I turned on the television set and watched a rerun of *Law and Order* while I had my soup and my salad. The sun never sets on *Law and Order*, and if I'd seen that episode too many times, there was always *CSI* in any of its incarnations. There is plenty of justice on television, but not so much in the real world. Maybe that's why so many of us like television so much.

I ate slowly, and found that I was trying to chew quietly so I could listen for noise at the door. This was silly. I put on the chain and the night bolt, and with that measure of reassurance, I felt better. After I'd eaten, I looked out very carefully before I pushed the cart into the hall, and I retreated into the room and locked up again. There were no doors leading to other rooms, and on the second floor I felt no one could get in the window. But I drew the drapes.

And I stayed isolated in the room until the next morning.

It was no way to live.

Tolliver looked even better the next day, and the doctor said he could check out of the hospital. He gave me a list of instructions. The wound was not supposed to get wet. Tolliver was not supposed to lift anything with his right arm. He was supposed to have some physical therapy on the arm when he got home. (I supposed in our case that would mean when we returned to St Louis.) Of course the discharge process took forever, but eventually we were both in the front seat of our car together, and I'd buckled Tolliver in.

I started to say, 'I wish we could just leave,' but then I thought that might make Tolliver feel bad. We had to follow the doctor's orders, so we had to stay a few more days. I was increasingly eager to leave Texas. I'd thought we might start house hunting this trip, and instead I wanted to pack our stuff into the car and drive like hell.

Tolliver looked out the car window as though he'd been in prison, as though he hadn't seen restaurants and hotels and traffic in years of solitary confinement. He had on the jeans and button-up shirt I'd brought him, and he looked a lot more like himself than he had in the hospital smock.

He caught me looking sideways at him. 'I know I look like hell,' he said, matter-of-factly. 'You don't need to tell me.'

'I was thinking you looked really great,' I said innocently, and he laughed.

'Right,' he said.

'I've never gotten shot before. Not really. Just grazed. Was it really like a big fist hitting you? That's the way they always describe it in books.'

'If the really big fist travels all the way through you, making you bleed and causing some of the worst pain you've ever felt, yeah,' he said. 'It hurt so bad I wanted to die for a minute.'

'Gosh,' I said. I tried to imagine pain that intense. I'd been hurt, and hurt badly, but when the lightning had struck, I hadn't felt anything for a few seconds, except that I was in another world, and then back in this one. After that, I'd pretty much hurt all over. My mother had told me that childbirth was horribly painful, but I'd never experienced that.

'I hope that never happens again,' I said. 'To either of us.'

'Have you heard from anyone?' he asked.

I thought that was an odd way to put it. 'Who, specifically?' I asked.

'Victoria came to the hospital last night,' he said.

I held my tongue for a second. 'Should I be jealous?' I asked when I could manage the appropriately light tone.

'Not any more jealous than I am of Manfred.'

Uh-oh. 'Then you'd better tell me all about it.'

We pulled up at the hotel then, and our talk was postponed while I went around the car to open Tolliver's door. He rotated his feet out, I pulled a little with my hand under his good arm, and out he came. He made a face, and I knew the process had hurt. He moved away from the door, and I shut and locked the car. We went into the hotel slowly. I was more dismayed than I cared to show when I realized just how shaky Tolliver was.

We got through the lobby just fine, then into the elevator. I was trying to keep my eyes on Tolliver in case he needed support, and also trying to watch out for some approaching trouble, so I felt like a demented woman, with my eyes darting here and there and then back to my patient.

When we were actually in our room, I heaved a sigh of sheer relief and helped Tolliver lie down on the bed. I pulled a chair up to the bed, but that felt too much like the hospital, so I lay down beside him and turned on my side so I could look at him.

He took a minute to get settled. Then he turned his head so his eyes would meet mine.

'This is so much better,' he said. 'This is better than anything.'

I agreed that it was. In the spirit of welcoming him back to the nonhospital world, I unzipped his pants and gave him some physical therapy he hadn't expected, which pleased him so much that after kissing me, he fell asleep, and so did I.

We were wakened by a knock at the door. I found myself wishing for a door that I could lock, a door no one could knock on. I should have put out a Do Not Disturb sign. Tolliver stirred, and his eyes opened. I rolled off the bed, straightened myself up and ran a hand through my hair, and went out of the bedroom and through the living room to see who was there. This time, I mustered up my courage and looked through the peephole.

To my astonishment, since I hadn't told anyone in the police department where we were staying now, Rudy Flemmons was outside the door.

'It's the detective,' I said. I'd gone back to the doorway into the bedroom. I was stupid with sleep. 'Rudy Flemmons, not the one that got shot.'

'I'd assumed that,' Tolliver said and yawned. 'I guess you better let him in.' He zipped his jeans and I buttoned them, and we smiled at each other.

I let Detective Flemmons in, and then I helped Tolliver out to the living room to share in the conversation. Tolliver sat carefully on the couch, and Flemmons took the armchair.

'How long have you two been here?' he asked.

I looked at my watch. 'Well, we checked out of the hospital about an hour and a half ago,' I said. 'We came right here and took a nap.'

Tolliver nodded.

Rudy Flemmons said, 'Have you seen your friend Victoria Flores in the past two days?'

'Yes,' Tolliver said right away. 'She came by the hospital last night. Harper wasn't there, she'd already left. I guess Victoria stayed for about forty-five minutes, and then she took off. That must have been about . . . man, I don't know, I was taking a lot of stuff for pain. I think around eight o'clock. I haven't seen her since then.'

'She never came home last night. She'd left her daughter, Mari-Carmen, with her mother, and her mother called the police when Victoria was late picking the child up. Normally, the police wouldn't really think much of that, an adult woman being late picking up her kid, but Victoria used to be on the Texarkana force and some of us know her. She was never late to anything involving her kid, not without calling and explaining. Victoria is a good mother.'

I could tell from his face that he was one of the Garland cops who knew her well. I thought maybe he knew her *very* well. 'Have you found anyone who saw her later than my brother?'

'No,' he said, his voice heavy and depressed. 'I haven't.'

At least no one could imagine that Tolliver had leaped from his hospital bed, subdued Victoria, and stowed her under the bed until he could bribe the janitor to dispose of her body.

'Her mom hasn't heard from her at all?'

The detective shook his head.

'That's awful,' I said. 'I . . . That's awful.'

I remembered Tolliver had been about to tell me a story involving Victoria when we'd gotten to the hotel. I was sitting on the couch beside him, and I turned my head to catch his eyes. I raised my eyebrows in query. Would he bring it up?

He gave an infinitesimal shake of his head. No.

All right.

'What did you two talk about? Did Victoria give any indication of what she was working on, or where she planned to go after she left the hospital?'

'I'm afraid we mostly talked about me,' Tolliver admitted. 'She asked questions about the bullet, about whether the place where the shooter had fired from had been found, if there'd been any other random shootings that night – you-all told Harper there'd been one real close to the motel, right? – how long I was going to have to stay in the hospital, stuff like that.'

'Did she say anything personal?'

'Yes. She said that she'd dated a guy for a while, a guy on the force, and they'd recently broken up. She said she'd reconsidered, and she was going to call him last night.'

I hadn't expected such a dramatic reaction. Detective Flemmons turned white as a sheet. I thought he was going to pass out. 'She said that?' he said, and almost choked on the words.

'Yeah,' Tolliver said, as startled as I was. 'That's almost word for word. I was surprised, because we'd never talked about her love life before. We weren't that close, and she didn't like to talk about personal stuff, either. You know the cop she was seeing?'

'Yes,' Flemmons said. 'It was me.'

Neither of us had anything to say, or any idea how to respond, when we heard that.

Flemmons was there for at least another quarter hour, and he asked Tolliver about twenty more questions, getting every detail of the conversation he'd had with Victoria, but Tolliver never elaborated on what Victoria had told him. I was surprised – and not a little worried – that Tolliver was playing the situation so close to the vest.

I told Rudy Flemmons about the mysterious person at my door the night before, the person who'd knocked before room service came. I didn't really think that person had been Victoria Flores, but I wanted to tell someone that the little incident had occurred.

At last, Detective Flemmons got up to leave. I felt incredibly relieved when I'd shut the door behind him. I waited, listening, and after a moment I heard him go down the hall to the elevators. I heard the ping of the arriving elevator, and then the whoosh of the doors as they opened and shut. I even opened our door and looked around to make sure no one was there.

I was getting paranoid as hell, but I thought I had good reason.

'Tell me,' I said. Though Tolliver was looking very tired and got up laboriously so I could help him back to the bed, I was determined to hear what he'd been about to say when Rudy Flemmons had come to our door.

When he was flat on his back, Tolliver said, 'She asked me if I believed the Joyces really wanted to find the baby Mariah Parish carried, or if I thought they wanted to kill the child.'

'Kill the child,' I said, stunned. Of course, I got the idea right away. 'A Joyce baby would inherit at least a fourth of the estate, I guess. An heir of the body, isn't that the phrase? If the lawyer who drew it up used that phrase, the kid would inherit whether it's legitimate or not. I don't suppose there's any question of Rich Joyce marrying Mariah on the sly?'

Tolliver shook his head. 'No, he would have married her legally, not in some made-up ceremony. He was a four-square kind of guy, according to Victoria. And if the baby was his, he'd own up to it. If he'd known about it.'

'She was sure about that?'

'She was sure because she'd interviewed a lot of people who'd known Rich Joyce, people who'd been close to him. They all told Victoria that Lizzie Joyce is like her granddad, no-nonsense and basically honest, but Kate and Drex are all about the money.'

'What about Chip, the boyfriend?'

'She didn't mention him.'

'Victoria'd found all of this out already?'

'Yeah, she'd been busy.'

'Why'd she tell you all this? I'm guessing it wasn't because she thought you were cute, since she was thinking about getting back together with Rudy Flemmons.'

'Because she thought one of the Joyces had shot me. That's why she told me.'

'Okay, I'm still not following.'

'They all think you know more about Rich Joyce's death than you said at the graveside. They're upset because you identified Mariah's cause of death and raised the question of the existence of a baby at all. They're afraid, I guess, that you'll find the baby's body.'

'Victoria didn't think the baby was alive? She thought someone had killed the baby?'

I felt sick inside. I've seen and heard of bad things, evil things,

because of this 'gift' the lightning left me. In the past, so many babies
died; so many things could go wrong, things that are rare now. I'd
stood on many tiny graves and seen the still, white faces, and it never
failed to be a sad moment. The murder of a child was the worst of
crimes, in my book, the absolute rock bottom of evil.

'That's what she was assuming. She couldn't find any birth record.
So maybe Mariah had the child by herself.'

'Oh, what kind of woman doesn't go to the hospital when she feels
her time's there?'

'Maybe one who can't,' Tolliver said.

I felt my lips compress with disgust and horror. 'You mean someone
wouldn't let her go to the hospital? Or simply allowed her to die of
neglect?' I didn't need to say that was cruel and inhuman. Tolliver
shared my feelings.

'It's possible. That's the best explanation for her having died after
childbirth, and there being no record of the child or a hospital stay for
her.'

'And if it wasn't for me . . .'

'No one would ever have known any of this.'

Put that way, I guess it was no surprise that someone wanted me
dead.

13

I ran in place on the treadmill in the 'exercise room,' the hotel's token nod to fitness. At least it was in an enclosed area, which right now meant 'safe.' I'd woken up early, and I could tell by his breathing that Tolliver was deep in dreamland.

I had a better picture of why all these awful things were happening around me, but I didn't have any idea what to do about it. I had nothing to take to the police, nothing, and the Joyces were rich and connected. I didn't know if all of them were involved, or if the shooter and the murderer (I considered both the deaths of Mariah Parish and Rich Joyce to be murders) were one and the same and acting alone. The three Joyces and the Joyce boyfriend were all capable people with guns, almost undoubtedly. Maybe I was stereotyping, but I didn't think a western rancher like Rich Joyce would teach his granddaughters how to ride rodeo and neglect to teach them how to shoot, and Drex would have to learn as a matter of course. The boyfriend, too. I knew the least about Chip Moseley. He looked like a good match for Lizzie; he was just as lean and weather-beaten, and he looked competent and down-to-earth. He was skeptical of my claims, but he could join most of the people I met in that respect.

I was drenched with sweat when I began my cooldown. I walked for ten more minutes, then I dried my face with a towel and went back to the room. I was beginning to hate hotel rooms. I wouldn't have thought there was much of a domestic gene in me, but I wanted a home, a real home. I wanted a bedspread that wasn't synthetic. I wanted sheets that only I had slept on. I wanted to keep my clothes folded in a drawer; I didn't want to fish them out of a suitcase. I wanted a bookcase, not a cardboard box. We had those things in our apartment, but even the apartment didn't have any air of permanency. It was just a nicer rental than the hotel rooms.

In the elevator, I took a deep breath and shoved all those thoughts into a bucket in the corner of my mind. I put a heavy lid on the bucket and weighted that lid down with a rock. Lots of imagery, but I wanted to be sure I wasn't distracted at this crucial time when someone was gunning for us. I had to be extra strong with Tolliver sidelined.

Rudy Flemmons was standing outside the room, raising his hand to knock.

'Detective,' I called, 'hold on a minute.'

He stayed in position, one hand raised in a fist, and I knew from the way he was standing that something was very wrong.

I came up to him and examined his face, or at least his profile. He didn't turn to look at me.

'Oh, no,' I breathed. 'Listen, let's go in the room.' I reached past him to unlock the door, and we entered. I flicked on the light, hoping I wasn't waking Tolliver, but then I saw that the light was on in the bathroom and I knew he was up. I knocked on the door. 'Hey, you okay in there? We've got company.'

'This early?' he asked, and I knew he'd had a bad night.

'Honey, just get out here,' I said, and hoped he got the message.

He did, and in thirty seconds he'd come out and made his way over to the seating area. I could tell by the way he was moving that he wasn't feeling good. I hurried to bring him some orange juice from the little refrigerator. There wasn't any point in offering some to Rudy Flemmons, who was sunk in a state that I assumed to be misery or extreme apprehension. I didn't know him well enough to tell exactly; I just knew it was bad.

It must have been an unpleasant way for Tolliver to start the day, but he eased back on the couch.

'Tell us why you're here,' Tolliver said.

'I think Victoria's dead,' Rudy Flemmons said. 'Her car was found this morning, in a cemetery in Garland. Her purse was in it.'

'But you haven't found her body?' I said.

'No. I was wondering if you would come take a look.'

This was sad, and it was also professionally awkward. In view of his obvious misery and our friendship with Victoria, I wasn't even thinking about money. I was thinking about the rest of the cops out there who would decide that my arrival on the scene was Rudy Flemmon's anxiety taking an extreme form.

But there wasn't much I could say except, 'Give me ten minutes.'

I jumped into the shower, soaped up and rinsed off, brushed my teeth, and pulled on my clothes. I put on boots; not high-heeled fashion boots, but flat, waterproof Uggs. The weather had been intermittently rainy, and I didn't want to get caught by surprise. Though I hadn't watched the forecast that morning or checked the paper, I noticed Rudy was wearing a heavy jacket, and I bundled up accordingly.

There was no question of Tolliver coming. That idea suddenly hit me in the face when I was ready to go out the door. Sloppy weather, cemetery conditions: not ideal for someone recovering from a gunshot wound.

'I'll be back as soon as I can,' I said, with a terrible pang of anxiety. 'You don't do anything. I mean, get back in bed and watch TV. I'll call you if anything happens, all right?'

Tolliver was as stricken by the belated realization that I was going out on a work call alone as I was. 'Get some candy out of my jacket pocket,' he said, and I did. 'Don't do anything that's going to hurt you,' he said severely.

'Don't worry,' I said, and then I told Rudy Flemmons I was ready to go, though that was far from the truth.

On the ride through the misty rain, in the heavy morning traffic, we were silent. Rudy called someone on the radio to tell them we were on the way, and those were the only words spoken in fifteen minutes.

'I know you charge for this,' he said suddenly, as he pulled in behind a long line of cars on a road through a huge cemetery, the modern kind that forbids headstones. I was being bombarded by the vibrations of the corpses, coming from all directions. They were all intense, since this was a relatively new burial ground. I thought the oldest was maybe twenty years in the ground.

'Not an issue. Please don't mention it again,' I said, and got out of the car. The last thing I wanted to do was debate prices while I was looking for this sad man's girlfriend.

You would think that if I knew the person it would be easier, but it isn't. Otherwise, I would have found my sister long ago. The dead clamor for attention with equal intensity, and if Victoria was out here somewhere, she was simply part of the chorus. It was hard to avoid the graves that called for my attention, and it was incredibly painful to be here without Tolliver. I had no anchor.

Common sense, I told myself. I went as close to the abandoned car as I could. One technician was peering at the tire treads, in a desultory way that told me the major work had been done. There were cops searching the landscaped graveyard, which was on rolling ground. It was a common layout for a modern place: there were areas defined by the tall statue in the middle, like an angel garden or a cross area, to help visitors navigate to the correct gravesite. I had no idea what method was used, whether the plots radiated out from the central sculpture or if you got to pick your site within that area. The place was looking pretty full – lying room only. There was a caretaker's shed in the distance and a chapel in the middle, a sizable marble structure that probably held a mausoleum and a columbarium. Across the width of the grounds I could see a funeral taking place as the search for Victoria Flores went on around me.

Hoping profoundly that no one would notice me, I closed my eyes and reached out. So many signals to sort through, so many clamoring to be recognized; I shuddered, but I persevered.

Freshest. Freshest. I needed something brand spanking new. That is, someone who'd passed over yesterday or even a few hours ago. There, out in front of me. I opened my eyes and walked to a grave still strewn with funeral flowers. I closed my eyes again, reached down.

'No,' I muttered. 'Not her.' I was not surprised to find the detective at my elbow. 'This is Brandon Barstow, who died in a car wreck,' I told him. I reached out again. I felt the pull coming from the caretaker's shed. Very fresh.

'Here we go,' I said, to the air in front of me, and I began walking. I watched my feet, because when I was tracking, it was easy to forget where my feet were going. Rudy Flemmons was right behind me, but he didn't know how to help me. That was okay; I could make it by myself.

The grass was wet and the pine needles made the ground slick in some spots. I knew where I was going; now there was no more uncertainty.

'They looked over here already,' the detective said.

'Someone's here, though,' I said. I already knew the bottom line on this search. 'They're going to try to say I knew this somehow,' I muttered, 'and they'll try to keep me here.'

The body wasn't in the shed itself, or right behind it. The ground behind the shed sloped down to a drainage ditch, where earth and grass thinly covered a culvert. Victoria was in the culvert; her body had been stuffed up inside, and it wasn't visible at all. But I could tell she was there, and I could tell she'd been shot and had bled out.

Rudy looked down uncomprehendingly, and I pointed to the mouth of the culvert. There was nothing for me to say. He scrambled down the slope and fell to his knees. He bent over and peered inside.

And he yelled.

'Here! Here!' he bellowed, and they all came running, every law enforcement person on the scene, including the guy who'd been examining the vehicle. Rudy was thinking, I suppose, that there was a chance she was still alive, but he was just dreaming or staving off the truth. I can't find the living.

I got out of their way, and went back to Victoria's abandoned car.

The trunk was standing open. I found myself staring down into it, trying to look uninterested. There were file folders, lots of loose ones and some in a bundle bound together with a huge rubber band. The top one was labeled *Lizzie Joyce*, and before I could think about what I was doing I picked up the bundle and tossed it in Rudy's car. There were still plenty of file folders left, I told myself – and I also told myself that we owed it to ourselves to find out about our enemies.

I saw afterward that this had been the wrong action to take, incidentally. I should have left things to the police. But at the moment, it seemed a natural, even clever, tactic. That's all I can say in my own defense. One of these people was shooting at us; I had to find out which one was the most likely.

I got into Rudy's car. He had an old jacket tossed into the backseat, and I pulled it into the front and bundled it around me as though I were cold, which wasn't far from the truth. After a few minutes, a uniformed guy came up and said he was supposed to take me back to the hotel. I had put on the jacket and zipped it up with the files inside, by that time. I got out of Rudy's car and climbed into the squad car.

The uniform, a man in his thirties, had a shaven head and a grim face – not too surprising, considering the circumstances. He said exactly one thing to me on our drive. 'As far as we're concerned, we found her during our search,' he said, and he gave me a look that was supposed to make me quake in my boots. It was easy to nod in agreement. I must have looked cowed, because he didn't speak after that.

I made a clumsy job of getting out of the car because of the files. He must have wondered if I was physically disabled in some way, but it didn't soften his attitude any. With my arms wrapped across my middle I strode into the hotel, blessing the automatic doors that allowed me to keep my hands in place, my contraband secure, as I made my way to the elevator.

My hands were cold, and I had a hard time fishing out my plastic key card and putting it in the lock the right way, but the door opened and I almost leaped into the room.

'What happened?' Tolliver called instantly, and I hurried into the bedroom. The maid had been in, and the bed had been made; he was in clean pajamas and lying on top of the bedspread, with the blanket from the foldout couch spread over him. The curtains were open on the dismal gray day. It had begun raining while I was in the elevator. That would complicate things at the cemetery. Raindrops were sliding down the window glass. I went up to the bed, leaned over it, and pulled the bottom of Rudy Flemmons's old jacket open. The files landed on the bedspread with a thud.

'What have you done?' Tolliver asked, not in an accusatory way, but more as if he was simply interested. He clicked off the television and reached out for the bundle, but I was there ahead of him. I pulled off the rubber band, putting it aside for future use, and I handed him the top file, the one labeled *Lizzie Joyce*.

'So she was there,' he said. 'Dammit, she loved her little girl. This is getting worse and worse. Did it take long to find her?'

'Ten minutes,' I said. 'A patrolman brought me back.'

'You stole the files?'

'Yeah. Out of her trunk.'

'How likely are they to come looking?'

'Don't know how hard they'd looked before everyone scrambled to see if she could be revived. Maybe they'd already taken pictures.' I shrugged. I couldn't undo it now.

'What are we looking for?' he asked.

'We're trying to find out which one of these people is most likely to be the one who shot you.'

'Then you have my undivided attention,' he said.

I took off my wet, muddy boots, climbed up on the bed with him, and started in on Kate's file while he tackled Lizzie's.

An hour later I had to take a break and call room service for some coffee and some food. Neither of us had had breakfast, and it was now almost eleven.

We'd learned a lot.

'She was really good,' I said. 'I'd never appreciated Victoria before, but I did now. In a very short time, she'd amassed a lot of information and interviewed quite a few people.

Tolliver was grateful to get a cup of coffee, and he was also glad to get a bran muffin. I slathered it with butter for him, an unusual indulgence. He chewed and swallowed and took another sip of coffee. 'God, that tastes good after hospital food,' he said. 'Lizzie Joyce is a colorful woman, even more colorful than she seemed that day at the cemetery. She really is a barrel-riding champion, several times over, and she's won a lot of other rodeo titles. She was rodeo queen in her teens, all over the state, looks like, and she was also an honor graduate from high school and ranked thirtieth in her class at Baylor.'

I didn't know how many people were in a Baylor class, but that sounded pretty damn good to me. 'What was her major, just out of curiosity?'

'Business,' he said. 'Her dad was already grooming her to take over from him. The Joyces own a huge ranch, but the bulk of his money came from oil in the big boom, and it's since been invested, a lot of it overseas. There is a corps of accountants who just look after Joyce holdings. Victoria says they all keep watch over each other, too, so no one can embezzle; or at least, they won't get away with it if they do. The Joyces also have a big interest in a law firm founded by an uncle.'

'So, what do they do?' I asked.

Tolliver understood what I meant, which was kind of amazing. 'They donate a lot of money to cancer research; that's what took Rich Joyce's wife. They maintain a ranch for disabled children. That's their big charity. It's open five months a year, and the Joyces pay the salaries of the staff, though they accept donations, too. Then they have the main ranch, which the boyfriend, Chip Moseley, is in charge of running. They live there, when they aren't in the Dallas apartment or the Houston apartment. I haven't read the boyfriend's file yet.'

'I'll get to it next,' I said. 'Kate, also known as Katie, is not as smart as her sister. She flunked out of Texas A&M, after majoring in partying, sounds like. In her teens, she had a couple of arrests for driving under the influence, and she smashed the windows on a boyfriend's car when they broke up. Since then, she's grown up a little, apparently. She works on the small ranch set up for the disabled children, she organizes fund-raisers for that ranch, and she shops. Oh, she did a stint as a volunteer at the zoo.'

That just sounded boring.

Chip Moseley was more interesting. He'd come up from the rank and file. His parents had died when he was little, and he'd gone into a foster home, which happened to be on a working ranch. He'd learned to rodeo and made a name for himself. Right out of high school, he'd gotten a job on the Joyce ranch. He'd gotten through one marriage and fell in with Lizzie. He'd worked his way up and taken night courses, and now he managed the cattle operations at the ranch and he'd been 'dating' Lizzie for six years. Aside from a minor brush with the law when he was in his twenties, he was clean. He'd been arrested in a bar brawl in a dive in Texarkana. To my surprise, I recognized the name of the place. My mother and stepfather had gone there from time to time.

I was tired of reading by then. I flopped back on my pillow. Tolliver told me what was in Victoria's file on Drex, though I had surmised most of it after ten minutes in Drex's company. The only male Joyce had been a disappointment all the way around. He'd gotten his high school girlfriend pregnant and they'd had a runaway marriage, followed by a divorce in six months. Drex supported the baby and its mother. Drex had joined the Marines right after he'd turned eighteen (take that, Dad!) and he'd made it through basic until he'd developed ulcers. Or maybe the ulcers he'd already had had gotten worse. Anyway, he'd left the service honorably, and gone on to drift around, doing this and that on his father's big ranch. He'd also worked with the disabled kids from time to time, and he'd worked in one of his dad's friend's businesses for a couple of years in an office job. It wasn't clear exactly what he'd done there.

'Probably not much, and probably not well,' Tolliver said. 'I don't think he's ever gone to college.'

'I feel sorry for him,' I said. I yawned. 'I wonder how old Victoria's mom is. I wonder if she can bring the kid up on her own. Who's the dad? Did Victoria ever say?'

'I wondered if it was my father,' Tolliver said, and I froze in the middle of another yawn.

'You're not kidding,' I said. 'You mean it.'

'Yeah,' he said. 'Victoria was around a lot after Cameron disappeared, you know. But when I figured it out, the timing was wrong. I think he was already in jail by the time the baby was conceived. I never could figure out why women thought he was so attractive.'

'I sure don't,' I said, with absolute sincerity.

'Well, good thing. You like men taller and thinner, right?'

'Oh, you bet, bay-bee. I love those string beans!'

Our hands clasped, and I snuggled closer to Tolliver on the bed. There was a little silence while we watched the rain hit the window of the room. The skies had decided to let go in earnest. I felt sorry for everyone who might still be out at the crime scene, and I decided they should be grateful to me for finding Victoria earlier, in time to get her body out of the culvert. I thought about the Joyce family, the kids who had grown up to be typical rich adults, as far as I could tell. They did some things that were quite good, but it was the bad things I was interested in. I thought it was significant that none of them had managed to sustain a happy marriage – though they were all in the prime age range, and one of them might make it yet. I was just about to shake my head over the truism that being rich didn't mean being happy, when I had the unpleasant realization that Mark, Tolliver, Cameron, and I had hardly turned out to be fulfilled citizens, either. Cameron was in some unknown place, Mark had never had a serious girlfriend that I knew of, and Tolliver and I . . .

'Do you really want to get married?' I asked him.

'Yes, I really do,' he said without a second's hesitation. 'I'd do it tomorrow, if we could. There's no doubt, is there? Do you have any worries about us being right for each other?'

'No,' I said. 'I don't. You're sure far from the commitment-phobic guys in the magazines, Tolliver.'

'You're not anything like the women in the men's magazines, either. And that's a compliment.'

'We sure know each other,' I said. 'We've probably seen the worst of each other. I can't imagine trying to get through life without you. Does that sound too clingy? I can try to be more independent.'

'You are independent. You make a lot of decisions, every day,' he said. 'It's just easier for me to make the practical arrangements. Then you do your specialty. Then we leave, and it's my turn again.'

Somehow that didn't sound completely even.

'Where's Manfred?' he asked, suddenly, as if someone had poked him with a needle.

'Gosh, I don't know. He told me to call him if I needed him. He didn't say where he was going or what he was going to do when he got there.'

'He really has a crush on you.'

'Yeah, I know.'

'How about it? If I was to vanish, would you take up with the Pierced Wonder?'

He said that in a teasing voice, but he wanted a reply. I wasn't foolish enough to actually ponder the question and answer it seriously. 'Are you kidding? That'd be like having hamburger after having steak,' I said loyally. I admitted to myself that there were days when I sure craved a hamburger, and I didn't doubt there would be times when Tolliver eyed other women with appreciation. If he could just keep that urge to the eyeing level, I could do the same. I knew who I loved.

'So, after reading the files, which one do you favor in the role of shooter?' he said more cheerfully.

'Any of them could have done it,' I said. 'It's depressing to think that. But faced with losing a substantial hunk of a fortune, I imagine any of them could have decided hell no. Even Chip Moseley. He's got to have hopes of marrying Lizzie, after all these years of being together. And it wouldn't be human, not to count on all that money. He'd have a better idea of the size of the Joyce estate than most boyfriends might have, since he runs the big ranch. I'll bet he sees a lot of other financial papers, too, on the various Joyce businesses.'

'Yes, I'm sure he does. I'm inclined to dismiss the idea that it's Lizzie, since she was the one who called you in. She had to know that there was a chance you were really able to do what you say you can, so if she was the killer, she'd never have risked it. She'd know that her granddad's death – well, it wasn't an out-and-out murder, but the snake triggered the heart attack and the snake wasn't flying through the air by accident. Someone pitched it at him. Maybe they thought it would bite him, and that would be all she wrote, but instead Rich had a heart attack, which was even better. All the person watching had to do was prevent him from getting to his cell phone. Mission accomplished.'

'That was cold,' I said, 'and the person able to do something like that is really vicious.'

'Do you think that the shooter was aiming at me, or at you?' Tolliver asked. 'I realize there's no real way to know, but that would sure be interesting.'

'Especially for you.'

He laughed, just a little, but it was a sound I'd missed.

A knock at the door interrupted me as I'd started to frame an answer.

We both sighed. 'I'm tired of having people knock at our door and come in to tell us bad stuff,' I said. 'We're sitting targets, here in a hotel.' I didn't know how it'd be any different if we had our own home, but somehow I felt it would be.

I used the peephole, and to my surprise I saw Manfred. Since we'd just been talking about him, I felt a little self-conscious when I opened the door to let him in. And he flashed a very aware look at me, a look that said he knew he was on my mind.

'How's the invalid?' he said. Tolliver came out of the bedroom then, and Manfred said, 'Hey, bro! How's getting shot?'

'Overrated,' Tolliver said. We all sat. I offered Manfred a Coca-Cola or a bottle of water, and he took the Coke.

'I heard about the private eye,' Manfred said. 'She was working for you-all after your sister got taken, right?'

I was surprised that he knew that; I couldn't remember having mentioned it in his hearing. 'Yes,' I said. 'She was. How'd you hear that?'

'It was on the news. About her book.' I looked at him questioningly. 'Did you know Ms Flores was writing a book? She didn't tell you?'

'No,' I said, though Tolliver was silent.

'Yeah, it was going to be called *Private Eye in the Lone Star State,* and she had gotten an offer on it.'

'For real?' I was thunderstruck.

'Yeah, for real. Cameron's case was the one that made her decide to quit the force and become a private eye. Her continuing search for Cameron is the big story in the book.'

I didn't know what to think of that, how to react. There was no real reason I should feel betrayed, but I did. It's particularly unpleasant to think that, for the price of a book, anyone who's inclined is going to be privy to the most agonizing event in your life.

'Did she tell you this last night?' I asked Tolliver.

He nodded. 'I was going to tell you, but then Rudy Flemmons came to get you,' he said.

'You've had time since.'

He hesitated. 'I wasn't sure how you would take it.'

'I wish I'd stolen a manuscript instead of the files,' I said, and Manfred's eyes turned to me with interest.

'What files did you steal? Do the police know you have them? Who are they about?'

'I stole some files out of her trunk,' I said. 'The police would probably make me into mincemeat if they knew I'd taken them. They're about the Joyce family.'

'There's not one on Mariah Parish?'

'No,' Tolliver said. 'Should there be?'

'Actually, no,' Manfred said, 'since I have it right here.' With a typical Bernardo flourish, he opened his jacket and pulled out a file. He'd carried his exactly like I'd carried mine, but he just had the one.

'Where the hell did you get that?' Tolliver sat forward on the couch. He was looking at Manfred as if Manfred had revealed he had a baby hidden in his coat, with a mixture of horror and admiration.

'Late last night, I went by her office, and the door was open,' Manfred said. 'My inner sense had told me it was important to talk to her. But I was too late. I'm assuming this was before she was reported missing. I went inside, and I asked the spirits if there was something there I should find, something that pertained to . . . anyone I know.'

We were both gaping at him by that time, and not because of the 'spirits' reference. 'Victoria's office had been rifled?' I said, thinking that was an unfortunate word to spring to my mind.

'Yes,' he said. 'It had been searched really thoroughly. But not thoroughly enough.' He paused for dramatic effect. 'I was drawn to her couch,' he said, and the moment was somewhat ruined by Tolliver's snort. 'Well, I was,' said Manfred, looking very young for a moment. 'Someone had tossed the cushions off, but it was a sofa bed like the one I slept on at Grandma's, and I pulled it up, and the file was stuck down in there. Like maybe someone had been knocking at the door, and she'd pulled up on the handle just a little and slid the file inside.'

'And I notice you had no trouble making off with it.' Tolliver's voice was so dry it could have been toast.

'No,' Manfred admitted. He had a sunny smile, the only sunny thing about this day.

'We've robbed a dead woman,' I said, abruptly appalled at what I'd done. 'And we've taken some clues away from the police.'

'We're trying to save your life,' Manfred said.

Tolliver gave the psychic a hard, sharp look, and I thought he would say something, but he only nodded. 'The more important question is, who was at her office door?' he said. 'Manfred, can you help us with that?'

Manfred looked smug. 'As it happens, I may be able to. While I was in her office, I took a nail file from her pencil caddy. That's a personal thing, has some skin cells still on it. I'm going to use that for a reading, and see what I can get. May be helpful, may not. You can't count on it; that's why so often those of us in the business are less than honest.'

We didn't disagree. Most 'psychics' were frauds, even the real ones who had a genuine gift. Psychics have to make a living, and if you have to earn your money by sitting in a storefront telling Mrs Sentimental that Fluffy is purring in paradise, that's what you do when your gift is giving you nothing to go on.

'What do you need to do to get ready?' I asked. Every practitioner I've encountered has his or her own process.

'Not much,' he said. 'No loud sounds. Close your eyes for a while, till I get into it.'

That was easy enough. Tolliver and I closed our eyes, and his hand came over to cover mine. It was possible to drift away, wondering where Manfred was in the stream of otherness, the state between waking and sleeping, between this world and the next world. That was the place I inhabited when I looked down at the bones in the earth, and that was the place Manfred was exploring now. It's not too hard to get there, but sometimes it can be hell getting back.

The room was silent except for the low rush of warm air coming from the heating system. After a minute or two, I was sure it was all right to open my eyes. Manfred's head lolled back. He was so relaxed he seemed boneless. I'd never seen Manfred in action. It was interesting and spooky.

'I'm worried,' Manfred said suddenly. I had opened my mouth to tell him everything was okay, when I realized Manfred was not making conversation. He was interpreting Victoria. 'I'm sitting in front of the computer. I've gotten lots of information in a very short time, and it's going to give me enough to go on. I have lots of ideas. If Mariah died by accident, and that's what Harper said, then the baby has a much better chance of being alive. Who would place the baby? Where would that person take a baby? Drop it off at an orphanage? So I'll call all the orphanages in Dallas and Texarkana and in between. I can ask them if they received a baby Doe around Mariah's death date. Maybe I can call a few tonight.'

Wow, Victoria really had been a good investigator.

'I'm worried,' Manfred said, and his head moved restlessly. 'I've talked to all the Joyces and to the boyfriend. I've compiled a list of the rest of the household staff who worked for Rich Joyce while Mariah was there. But I don't know how far I'll get. I can't do any more tonight. I think someone followed me to the office. Rudy?' Manfred pantomimed someone holding a cell phone. 'I hate to leave a message, I haven't talked to you in so long. But I think there's someone following me, and when you're lucky enough to have a cop as your friend, you should call them when you're in a fix like this. I don't want to lead them to my mom's when I pick up MariCarmen. Well . . . 'bye. I'm leaving the office in about ten minutes. I got some phone calls to make.' Half the time Manfred was telling us, though in the first person, what Victoria had been thinking, and half the time he seemed to be speaking as if he were in Victoria's body.

Now Manfred's hands were moving. It was clear he was performing some task, but I couldn't interpret his gestures. I looked at Tolliver and raised my eyebrows in a question. Tolliver pointed at the stack of files on the coffee table. After a moment, I understood. Victoria was tamping papers into a neat stack, then closing them into a folder and stacking it on the others. Then she got a rubber band out of a drawer and worked it around the stack. 'Put this in the trunk,' she whispered. 'Come back, make the calls.' There were slight movements in Manfred's feet and shoulders that suggested Victoria (through Manfred) was going outside, opening the trunk, tossing in the files, shutting the lid, moving back into the office.

This was a very strange experience. Enlightening, but strange.

'Someone's coming,' Victoria/Manfred muttered. 'Huh.'

I understood better, now, why I made people so nervous after they saw me in contact with that other part of the world, the unseen part that was so hard for most people to access. I could feel the tension in Tolliver's hand.

Again, little twitches of Manfred's body suggested that Victoria's movements were happening in his head. He made a definite yanking gesture. I was sure he was pulling open the sleeper couch to insert Mariah's folder. She – no, Manfred – turned her head to look at something, very abruptly, and then Manfred's eyes flew open with a look of complete terror on his face.

'I'm going to die,' he said. 'Oh, my God, I'm going to die tonight.'

14

It took at least fifteen minutes for Manfred to completely come out of walking Victoria through her last moments.

'Who did she see?' Tolliver asked.

'I don't know,' Manfred said. 'I couldn't see them.'

'Well, a hell of a lot of good that did us,' Tolliver said, and I put a hand on his shoulder (his good one, let me point out) and squeezed.

'It did a lot of good,' I said. 'We know what Victoria was thinking, and we know someone did kill her because of the case, or at least we know that's what Victoria thought or she wouldn't have hidden that particular file. She was thinking something might happen to her office, thought someone was after her, so she had already put the other Joyce files in her car to keep them safe. She didn't believe anyone would hurt her personally, but she called her former boyfriend, Rudy Flemmons, to come watch her back. He didn't answer, or he didn't get the message in time, and that's why he's all bent out of shape now.'

'We know those things, but they don't do us any good.' Tolliver was determined to be a butthead.

'Maybe once we look at Mariah's file, they will.'

Manfred was looking tired, and older. He seemed very alone. I felt a pang of pity for him, and then I had to tell myself not to overdo it. Pity and a vague physical attraction were not enough motivation to imperil my relationship with Tolliver. I knew without a doubt that Manfred needed to find someone else.

I found myself wondering what kind of woman would be good for Manfred, and then I realized the answer had to be *Anyone besides me*.

By then it was almost five o'clock, and I called room service and asked them to send up some food and some coffee before I reached down to pick up the file. I opened it to the first page, the fact sheet with Mariah's background information, and read it carefully. Then I passed the fact sheet to Tolliver, and he began studying it. While we looked through the information Victoria had gathered on Mariah, Manfred began reading the Joyce files.

'Mariah Parish wasn't what she seemed,' I said, which was an understatement.

Tolliver shook his head. 'She sure wasn't. If the Joyces had checked her credentials more closely, they wouldn't have hired her.'

It wasn't that Mariah had been deceitful. She'd been an orphan, as she'd said. She'd been taking care of another ill elderly man, Arthur Peaden, before she came to Rich Joyce. She'd done a good job, too, because there were glowing testimonials from Art Peaden's survivors about how kind Mariah had been, how conscientious, while she was taking care of their father.

She'd also been taking college classes over the computer. Eventually, she'd gotten evenings off to attend classes in person. And in the fullness of time, she'd graduated from college with a degree in economics and business.

Mariah had had her own online trading account, and it had been a busy one. At first, she'd lost some money, but more recently, even in the financial downturns the market had taken recently, she'd held steady. The adult babysitter had been profiting from her job to a degree no one would have imagined.

'Wow,' said Tolliver with some admiration. 'She was learning all the tricks of the trade.'

'I guess her "client" talked in front of her, and his friends and family talked in front of her, and she profited by everything she heard.'

'Caregiver by day, stock market trader by night,' Manfred said. 'You gotta admire her nerve and determination.'

'And sneakiness,' I said, wrinkling my nose. 'Isn't that kind of deceptive?'

'I don't know,' Tolliver said after a long pause. 'Is it? She didn't *say* that she was an uneducated, ignorant woman who couldn't get a better job. She let her employers think so, but that's the persona she adopted. She was really smart, and she was determined to put that to use the best way she knew how.'

'Smart,' Manfred said. He sounded approving.

'Two-faced and not really honest.'

'Ah, sour grapes,' Manfred said, smiling. 'You haven't gotten to raid the brains of your dead people to get stock tips.'

'What an opportunity I've missed,' I said, deadpan. 'I need to find a cemetery and look for the grave of a financial wizard, see if he can give me ideas in what I see of the last few moments of his life.'

'That's kind of what Mariah did,' Manfred said.

When I thought about it, he wasn't too far off. 'I wonder if it was a conscious plan or something that just evolved.' I looked at the picture of the young Mariah, who'd had bangs and a chin-length bob. Red hair and freckles, brown eyes, and a cute nose; all she needed was a straw hat, overalls, and an egg basket on one arm. There'd been steel under all that unsophisticated cuteness.

'I bet she talked real country,' Manfred said. 'I bet she made sure she did.'

Deeper and smarter than her surface suggested, Mariah Parish had crafted a way to survive and prosper. And she'd provided good care to those who'd employed her. 'Not bad, Mariah,' I said, toasting her with a coffee cup. Our sandwiches had come, and we were all eating like we'd been starved for days.

'Until she got pregnant,' Tolliver said.

'And I wish we knew the name of the father,' I said. 'That's the million-dollar question.'

'Not so much who the actual dad was,' Manfred corrected, 'as who thought he *might* be the dad.'

'I don't suppose – ?' I gestured at the picture. 'Manfred, do you think you could find out anything about her, your way?'

'Nah, not without something of hers,' he said. 'Since I never met her in life.'

'The dad might have been Rich Joyce himself, or Drexell, or even Chip Moseley.' I was thinking out loud.

'Or anyone else, as long as one of them thought there was a chance he was the dad,' Tolliver said.

'So she had sex with one of these guys, we're assuming. If she had sex with Rich Joyce, think of what a coup it would be if she was going to have his child! Sure, he'd had a stroke, but he had recovered well and he was definitely active and in his right mind. This child would presumably have equal rights with the other kids, and Lizzie, Kate, and Drexell would be out millions of dollars.' I picked up another triangle of club sandwich and bit into it, then had to dust crumbs off my shirt. 'Was Drexell still married nine years ago?'

'Don't remember. I'll have to check his file.' Manfred flipped through some pages. 'Yes, he was. So was Chip.'

'So,' Tolliver said, stretching his legs out in front of him. He propped his feet on the coffee table, now littered with papers and plates and glasses. 'Why now? Why did all this happen now? Mariah and Rich Joyce are both eight years in their graves. Why now?'

'Because Lizzie Joyce started reading Harper's website after the case in North Carolina,' Manfred said, as if the answer was simple. 'She wanted the latest and greatest. And what Lizzie Joyce wants, she makes happen. We don't know how many arguments her family and friends put up against getting Harper here. We don't know how many times they told her she was a fool.'

'If what I saw is any estimate,' Tolliver said, 'she wouldn't take real kindly to that at all. She wanted Harper to come, and she had the money to make it attractive to us. Then came the worst part, her huge mistake. She didn't direct Harper to Rich's grave right away. She let Harper wander and read other graves, and Harper landed on Mariah's. Lizzie either had to believe Harper or disbelieve her, and since she'd spent good money to bring Harper, she decided to believe her. So now Lizzie knew that Mariah had been pregnant, and that her death probably could have been prevented; or at least, the birth took place under circumstances that weren't straightforward and above-board, so she didn't have as good a chance of recovering. And the baby wasn't in the coffin with her, so something happened to it. Also, the death certificate said infection, but not what kind, so I'm wondering if the doctor who signed it was in on the secret.'

'That's something we can look up,' I said. 'We can find him and ask him questions. Is there a copy of the death certificate in Mariah's file?'

Tolliver was looking tired, I realized, and it was Manfred who located the copy of the certificate. 'Dr Tom Bowden,' he said. I called information for the little town next to the Joyce ranch, but he wasn't listed. Next, I tried Texarkana, but no Dr Tom Bowden was there. Manfred went into our bedroom and came back with the huge phone book. He looked up 'Physicians' in the Yellow Pages, and he told us with an air of triumph that there was a Dr Bowden listed.

'We'll have to go see him tomorrow,' I said. 'Tolliver needs to rest.'

'Oh, gosh, sure,' Manfred said, disarmingly apologetic. 'Sorry, Tolliver. I was forgetting you were on the disabled list.'

Tolliver scowled. 'I'll get better every day,' he said.

'Of course,' Manfred reassured him. 'In the meantime, since I still have plenty of energy, I'll track down this doctor's office.'

'Are you sure you ought to do that?' I said. 'Maybe it wouldn't be such a good idea.'

'Ah, I'll just have a look-see,' Manfred said. 'I've got that GPS now, so I better put it to good use. Thanks for supper.' He put the cart out in the hall for me as I helped Tolliver up. For the first time in hours, Tolliver took some pain medication along with his other pills. I chided myself silently for not realizing how tired he was getting.

I helped him with the undressing process, and he was finally settled in bed, covers pulled up, with his pajama bottoms on and a full complement of medicine. I found *Law and Order* and settled in. Tolliver was asleep in ten minutes or less.

My brain was tired. I'd thought about the Joyces, about Mariah Parish, about poor Victoria and her daughter. Other people had filled my head all day, and I had to add Rudy Flemmons's grief on top of that. I didn't want to think anymore, or bear the burden of other people's emotions. It was a sheer relief to go out into the living room area and watch the stupidest movie I could find. I also painted my toenails and fingernails. I called my little sisters and talked to them for twenty minutes, before Iona said they had to get in the bathtub. Iona tried to steer the conversation over to my relationship with Tolliver, but I kept on course and didn't go there. I hung up feeling pleased with myself, a good feeling to have after the unhappy events of the past few days.

Thinking of unhappy events, I called the hospital and asked about Detective Powers. The switchboard connected me to the waiting room, and I asked the man who answered if I could speak to Beverly Powers.

'She can't come to the phone. Parker just died,' said a man's voice, and he hung up the phone. He was crying.

No matter how often I told myself I hadn't killed Parker Powers, I knew he would not have died if he hadn't been trying to protect me.

There was no magic formula that I could use to make this all better. There was no philosophy that would diminish the pain his family and friends were feeling. There was no way I could erase the memory of his collapse, the blood pouring from his wound, the way I'd cowered in the shadow of the car. That was especially galling, that I'd had to hide from the man who'd done such a despicable thing.

That was pride speaking; it only made sense to hide when someone was trying to kill you. Of course it did.

I had this image I needed to conform to, though, maybe culled from the comic books I'd read as a child or the tough-woman fiction I read now. Every female private eye and cop was able to protect citizens without a second thought, able to shoot the evildoer after tracking him down. Every comic-book heroine was able to perform fearlessly, able to commit acts of heroism in the cause of protecting mankind.

I'd let myself be protected by a broken-down, none-too-bright ex–football player, and it had killed him.

He knew he was in danger. He knew that was his job. He was willing to take the risk, my common sense told me.

And I was willing to let him, I had to admit. I tried to think of something else I could have done. If I'd insisted on running by myself, would he still have followed me? Maybe. What if I'd decided to stay in the hotel? Yes, he'd still be alive. I had a terrible responsibility to Parker Powers.

I hoped I would not fail again.

15

I slept that night, but not well. It was reassuring to hear Tolliver's breathing as I tossed and turned. When light crept under the heavy curtains and I permitted myself to get out of bed, I felt used up, exhausted before the day even began. I made myself run on the treadmill again, hoping to drum up some energy with the exercise. That strategy didn't work.

Assuming Manfred had tracked down Tom Bowden's current office, I decided to drop in on Dr Bowden this morning. It would probably be easy to get past the receptionist, because the mirror told me I looked anything but well. Though we hadn't set a definite time the night before, Manfred knocked very quietly on our door just as I finished dressing.

Tolliver, just up, had woken as grouchy as a bear. He was about as much fun to be around as a bear, too. Manfred was petty enough to emphasize Tolliver's invalid status with obnoxious cheerfulness and many wishes for Tolliver's recovery. Manfred was glowing with health and energy. When you added the lights bouncing off his silver piercings, he practically sparkled.

Manfred liked to talk in the morning.

As we drove to the office building Manfred had scouted the night before, he told me that his grandmother's will had left everything to him. That had surprised his mother, who was Xylda's only daughter, but after her initial disappointment, she'd seen the justice in it, since Manfred had taken care of Xylda her last couple of years.

'Xylda had a . . . ?' Then I stopped, embarrassed. I'd been on the verge of expressing amazement that Xylda had had an estate to leave.

'She had a little cash stashed away, and she owned a house,' Manfred said. 'It was my good luck that it was in the downtown area, and the school district needed the ground it stood on to build a new gym. I got a decent price. Like I told you before, I found all kinds of weird shit when I was cleaning out all the accumulated stuff. I put everything I wanted to keep into storage until I decide where to base myself.'

'So you're going to make your living in your grandmother's business, but do most of your work via email and phone?'

'That's the idea. But I'm open to new adventures.' He glanced over at me and waggled his eyebrows.

I laughed, though reluctantly. 'If you can make even a faint pass, given the way I look today, I think you're nuts.'

'Didn't sleep last night?'

'No, not a lot. Detective Powers died.'

Manfred's cheer was wiped off his face as if he'd used an eraser. 'That's crappy. I'm sorry, Harper.'

I shrugged. There wasn't anything to talk about; I'd thought everything there was to think during the course of the night, and Manfred had sense enough to recognize that.

Dr Bowden's office was in a four-story building, an anonymous glass and brick cube that could have held anything from an accounting firm to a crime syndicate. We ran through the pouring rain to reach the sliding glass doors on the south side of the building.

As we entered, I saw a husky gray-haired man leaving the lobby by another set of doors, his jacket held above him to avert the rain. As the automatic doors swooshed shut behind his back, I thought his walk looked familiar. I looked after him for a moment, then shrugged and joined Manfred at the lobby directory. We discovered Dr Bowden was on the third floor. He was listed as a GP.

Dr Bowden had a modest office in that modest building. The waiting room was small, and there was one woman behind the sliding glass panel. Her workstation was messy, almost chaotic. She seemed to be the receptionist, the scheduler, and the insurance clerk, all rolled into one. Her short hair was dyed a deep red, and she wore black glasses that tilted up at the outer corners. Maybe she was aiming for retro.

'Trying to make a fashion statement,' Manfred muttered, I hoped too low for her to hear.

'Excuse me,' I said, when she didn't look up from her computer. She had to know we were standing right there, since there was only one other person in the waiting room, a man in his sixties who was extremely thin. He was reading a *Field and Stream* magazine.

'Excuse me,' I said again, more sharply than I'd intended.

'Oh, sorry,' the receptionist said. She took an earpiece from her ear. 'I didn't hear you.'

'We'd like to see the doctor,' I said.

'Do you have an appointment? Do you have a referral?'

'No,' I said, and smiled.

Nonplussed, she looked past my shoulder at Manfred, as if hoping to find someone who could explain the phenomenon of a person trying to see a doctor without an appointment.

'I'm with her,' he said helpfully. 'We both want to see the doctor. It's about a personal matter.'

'You're not the daughter-in-law – are you?' The red-headed woman was full of delighted, horrified anticipation.

'Sorry, no.' I hated to burst her bubble.

'He won't see you,' she said. She'd switched to a confiding tone. Maybe it was Manfred's facial decoration that had won her heart. She was obviously a woman who liked strong style. 'He's very busy.'

I looked around at the one patient, who was trying to appear oblivious to the interesting conversation we were having. 'That's not the impression I get,' I told her.

'I'll check, though,' she said, as though I hadn't spoken. 'What's your name, please?'

I told her. Before she could ask, I said, 'This is my friend Manfred Bernardo.'

'What's this in reference to?'

She'd never understand the long version. 'It's about a case he had around eight years ago,' I said. 'We want to discuss his findings with him.'

'I'll tell him,' she said, and rose to her feet. 'You'll have to wait your turn.'

We did, and when the thin man had left and no one had taken his place in the waiting room, we waited some more.

Pointy Glasses could tell we weren't going to leave, and apparently the doctor decided against sneaking out without seeing us. When we'd been there forty-five minutes or longer, he appeared at the door into the examining area. Dr Bowden was in his sixties, bald except for a gray fringe. He was one of those anonymous-looking men you'd have trouble describing. You could meet him six times in a row and you'd still have to ask his name.

'All right, I have a moment now,' he said. He preceded us into his office, a small room crowded with bookcases, papers, home-stitched framed needlework ('Doctors leave their patients in stitches'), and photographs of himself with a short, very plump woman and a boy. The boy grew up to be a young man in the photos, and then there was a wedding picture of the grown-up son with his own wife.

He settled himself behind the desk, giving a good impression of a busy and prosperous man who was sparing us a few minutes out of the goodness of his heart.

'My name is Harper Connelly, and this is my friend Manfred Bernardo,' I said. 'I'm here about a death you certified eight years ago, the death of a woman named Mariah Parish.'

'I'd been warned you were coming,' he said, which startled the hell out of me. 'I can't believe you'd have the sheer effrontery to show up here.'

'Why not?' I said, completely at a loss. 'If Mariah Parish was murdered, it completely changes a very complicated situation.'

'Murdered?' He looked as astounded as I was, now. 'But I was told . . . I was told you were alleging that Mariah Parish was still alive.'

'No, I've never said that, and I don't believe it. Who told you that?'

But the doctor didn't answer. He looked very concerned, but not as hostile. 'You aren't here to dispute my filing a death certificate?'

'No. I know Mariah Parish is dead. I'm just wondering why you didn't fill in the cause of death correctly.'

Tom Bowden flushed, and it didn't look good on him. 'Do you represent her family?'

'She didn't have a family,' I said. 'We represent the detective who's looking for her baby.' Which, in a way, was true.

'The baby,' he said, and he aged five years in thirty seconds.

'Yes,' I said, very sternly. 'Tell us about it.'

'You know how influential the Joyces are,' he said. 'They could have ended my career; they could have sent me to jail.'

'But they didn't,' Manfred said, his voice just as severe as mine. 'Tell us.'

We had no idea what was going on, but it was good to look like we did.

'That night, the night she died, of course I was still practicing in Clear Creek,' Dr Bowden said. He swiveled in his chair to look out of his window. 'It was raining that night, pouring, like it is today. I think it was in February. I'd never treated any of the Joyces; they had their own doctors in Texarkana and Dallas and didn't mind driving to go to one of their doctors, miles away.' Bitterness crossed his face and left its tracks. 'I knew who Rich Joyce was, everyone in town knew him. He was one of those rich men who acts like they're just like everyone else, you know? Old pickup truck, Levis? Like he didn't have enough money to drive any vehicle he wanted!' The doctor shook his head at the foibles of someone who could have anything preferring instead to stick with something plain and familiar.

'Was it Rich Joyce who came to your house?'

'Oh, hell, no,' Tom Bowden said. 'It was one of the hands, I think. I don't remember what his name was.' He was lying. 'He said Mr Joyce's housekeeper was sick, needed me, and they'd pay me extra if I'd come out to the house. Of course I went. I didn't want to, but it was my duty, and there was the prospect that I'd get in good with Richard Joyce. I'm not going to pretend I wasn't hoping for that.'

He could have tried to pretend that all day long, and it wouldn't have convinced me. I felt Manfred shift beside me, wondered if he was trying to suppress a laugh.

'What happened?' I asked.

'I went out there in his truck, and we got out in the rain. We went through this big empty house, and we got to a bedroom, and in it was this young woman. She was in bad shape. She had just given birth. Evidently, her labor had started unexpectedly, and from what the man said to me, she hadn't even known she was pregnant.'

I tried to absorb that, couldn't. 'But you went out there knowing that you were going to treat a pregnant woman, right?'

He shook his head. I didn't know if he was trying to say that he hadn't known, or that he didn't want to talk about it. I suspected he didn't want to add to his feeling of guilt by admitting that he'd known he was going out to the Joyce house to treat a patient under conditions he had to know were illegal or pretty damn near.

'What did she say?' I asked.

'She didn't say much of anything. She was having a very hard time. She was very sick, very sick. Her temperature was high; she was sweating, shaking, and very unsteady. Almost incoherent. I couldn't understand why the man hadn't taken her to a hospital, and he told me that she didn't want him to, that she wasn't supposed to be having the baby, it was a real unpleasant family situation. He told me that the baby was the product of incest.' Dr Bowden's mouth folded up in a way that left no doubt as to how uncomfortable the word made him. 'He said she was some kind of favorite of old Mr Joyce, and she wanted to have the baby without him knowing, and then she would go back to her job and give the baby up for adoption. Her memories were too bad for her to want to keep it.'

And you believed this? I wanted to say, but knew I couldn't break the flow of this confession. This was coming more easily than I ever would have believed, and I could only imagine that Tom Bowden had wanted to tell this story for years. I had a fleeting wonder about the kind of background this man must have, to have fallen for any of this. Of course, you had to add in the big dollop of greed that had influenced him.

'She didn't have any family,' Manfred said, and after a second Dr Bowden understood what Manfred was saying. He looked down at his desk fixedly. I could have hit Manfred for his interruption; at the same time, he'd only said what I was thinking.

'I didn't know for sure,' Bowden muttered. 'The man who'd brought me out to the ranch – I thought he was Drexell Joyce – the son. I figured the baby was probably his. Maybe he was ashamed to tell his grandfather that he'd been cheating on his wife; he was wearing a wedding ring, and Ms Parish wasn't.'

'Did she talk to you?' I said.

'What?'

'Mariah. Did she talk to you?' It seemed a simple enough question to me, but Tom Bowden was shifting uneasily in his black leather chair.

'No,' he said, and I sighed. Manfred raised a finger, just at the edge of my vision. He thought the doctor was lying again.

'So what happened?' I said, not seeing how we could get him to be honest unless we started beating on him.

'I cleaned the woman up, with some difficulty,' Dr Bowden said. 'I wanted to call for an ambulance and I told the man so again, but he told me that was out of the question. I went to get my coat to use my cell phone, but he'd taken it out of my coat pocket, and he wouldn't let me have it. I had to treat the patient, and I didn't have time to fight with him about the phone. She was clearly in the end stages. Even if I could've gotten her to a hospital within the hour – and the nearest hospital was that far away, incidentally – she wouldn't have made it. She had a massive infection.'

'You're saying she died that night.'

'Yes. About an hour and a half after I got there, she died. She got to hold the baby.'

We all sat silent for a moment. 'So, what happened then?' Manfred said.

'The man asked me to examine the baby, and I found that she was okay, a little feverish, but nothing serious. Other than that, physically, she was fine.'

'The baby was a girl.'

'Yes, yes, she was. Small, but as far as I could tell she would be okay, if she got the proper course of treatment. He asked if I had the right stuff to give her. He was going to take the baby directly to the adoptive parents. I actually had some antibiotics with me in my bag, samples a salesman had given me. I explained the dosage and administration to him, and he carried the baby out of the room. That was the last I saw of the infant. The mother expired then.'

Expired. 'And what did you do after that?'

He sighed, as if the complexity of relaying his story was too much for him to bear. 'I told the man that we had to call into town. We had to report the death. We had quite an argument. He didn't seem to understand that it was the law, that the law had to be followed.'

Since you'd already bent it so far out of shape, I thought. 'But he let you call, finally?'

'He agreed, as long as I didn't mention the baby. So the funeral home came to get the poor young woman, and I signed the death certificate.' His shoulders slumped. He'd finally told the worst thing, in his view, and now he could relax.

'You said she'd died of . . . ?'

'Massive infection due to a ruptured appendix.'

'And no one questioned that?'

He shrugged. 'No family came forward. The Joyces sent me a check to pay my bill – no more – and after that, if anyone who worked for them got sick, they came to me for treatment.'

It had been very clever of them not to offer Dr Bowden an outright bribe. I was sure the bill he'd sent had been stiff, and they'd paid it just as they would have under normal circumstances. That had reassured the doctor. And since his practice wasn't flourishing, they'd thrown him a big bone.

'With a setup like that, why'd you move to Dallas?' Manfred asked. Again, I wouldn't have gotten into that, but again, I'd underestimated the doctor's elasticity.

'It was my wife. She couldn't stand Clear Creek,' he said. 'And I've got to say, no one there got along with her, either. We were having some real wars at home. About six years ago, I got to talking to a doctor I'd never met before at an AMA meeting. He had a practice in Dallas. He told me his office was coming empty, did I want to take over the lease. It was at the previous price, much lower than new tenants were paying. And he'd throw in the equipment, too, because he was going overseas to a new job at an American consulate in Turkey or somewhere like that.'

Could he really not see how set up that had been? It was like someone attaching a string to a dollar bill and then setting it out on the sidewalk, so he could drag it away and get a passerby to follow the path of the money.

'Jeez Louise,' said Manfred. He almost continued, but fortunately he decided to keep his mouth shut.

'Thanks,' I said, after I'd tried to think of more questions to ask. 'Oh, did someone else come here this morning, asking about Mariah Parish?'

'Ah . . . yes, as a matter of fact.'

Why the hell hadn't I thought to bring pictures of the Joyces with me? I'd done well so far, for someone who didn't know squat about being a detective, but this was a huge mistake I'd made.

'Who was he?'

'Said his name was Ted Bowman.'

Oh, not that that was anything like Tom Bowden, oh, no.

'And he wanted . . .'

Tom Bowden looked troubled, or rather, more troubled. 'He wanted to know the same things you two wanted to know, but not for the same reason.'

'What do you mean?' I asked.

'It was like he already knew the whole story. He just wanted to know how much *I* knew about who was involved.'

'What did you tell him?'

'I told him I had no idea who the man who brought me to the house was, that as far as I could tell, the last time I saw the baby she was fine, and that I'd never talked to anyone else about that night.'

'And he said?'

'He said that was good news; he'd heard the baby had died and he was glad to know that she had survived. He said I better forget about that night, and I told him I hadn't thought about it in years. He warned me that someone else might come asking questions, and he told me whoever came would be someone who was just trying to create trouble by saying Mariah Parish was still alive.'

'What did he tell you to do about that?'

'He told me it would be in my best interest to keep my mouth shut.'

'But you talked to us anyway.'

For the first time, Tom Bowden met my eyes. 'I'm tired of keeping the secret,' he said, and I believed him. 'I got divorced from my wife anyway. My practice isn't doing too well, and my whole life hasn't turned out like I thought it would. I date this downward slide from that night.'

He'd told the truth that time, I was sure. 'And what did this man look like?' I asked.

'He was taller than your friend here' – Dr Bowden nodded condescendingly toward Manfred – 'and a good bit stockier, big muscles and chest. Dark hair, in his forties or fifties. Graying a little.'

'Visible tattoos?'

'No, he was wearing a rain jacket,' Dr Bowden said, in the tone of one pointing out the obvious. His attitude was creeping back. Evidently, crying time was over. I tried to think of more questions to ask him before the well dried up. 'You really don't know the name of the man who took you out to the ranch house?' I found that hard to believe, in a little town like Clear Creek. I said so.

He shrugged. 'I hadn't been in town that long, and the ranch people keep to themselves. This man said he worked for Mr Joyce, and he was driving a ranch truck. He may have given me a name, but I don't remember it. It was a stressful evening. Like I said, I suspected he might be Drexell Joyce. But I'd never met Drexell, so I don't know.'

I'll bet it had been a stressful evening. Especially for Mariah Parish, whose life might have been saved if the ambulance had come for her . . . if anyone had been humane enough to call one.

I was a little surprised that she hadn't been outright murdered, and the baby along with her. At that time Rich Joyce had still been alive,

and maybe the fear of what he'd say and do if his caregiver disappeared in his absence had been the deciding factor. He'd miss
Mariah, even if no one else would. And Rich Joyce wouldn't let go if
he decided something strange was up.

Maybe the child had been stowed in someone's home as a bargain-
ing chip of some kind. Maybe one of the ranch hands was raising her. I
could make up all kinds of stories in my head, but none of them was
more likely than another.

'Where was Rich Joyce that evening?' Manfred asked.

'The man just said he was gone,' Bowden said. 'His truck wasn't
there.'

'He didn't know his caregiver was pregnant? He didn't notice?'

Bowden shrugged. 'That never came up. I don't know what she told
Mr Joyce. Some women just don't show that much, and if she was
trying to hide it . . .'

Manfred and I looked at each other. We didn't have any other
questions.

'Goodbye, Dr Bowden,' I said, standing. He couldn't hide his relief
that we were leaving.

'Are you going to the police?' he asked. 'You know, even if they
exhume poor Ms Parish, they won't be able to tell a thing.' He was
regretting having talked to us. But he was also relieved. This guy had
had a hard time for the past eight years, living inside his own skin. I,
for one, was glad of that.

'I don't know,' Manfred said, very thoughtfully. He'd had the same
reaction. 'We're considering it. If the child came to no harm, it's
possible you may keep your license.'

A horrified Dr Bowden was staring at us as we went down the hall
and out through the waiting room. There were three more patients
there, and I felt sorry for them. I wondered what kind of care the
doctor would give now that he was definitely on the upset side. He'd
had two visits in one day about an event he must have hoped was
buried forever; that would be enough to rattle any man, even one
made of better stuff than Tom Bowden.

'That guy is a human sewer,' Manfred said when we were in the
elevator. He was very angry, his face red with strong emotion.

'I don't know if he's quite that bad,' I said, feeling at least ten years
older than my companion. 'But he's weak. And he's a joke, based on
the standards a doctor ought to uphold.'

'I wouldn't be so surprised if it was the 1930s,' Manfred said, surprising me. 'That sounds like a story you'd read in a collection of old ghost stories. The knock on the door in the middle of the night, the stranger who comes to take you to a mysterious patient in a big house, the dying woman, the baby, the secrecy . . .'

I was goggling at Manfred when the doors opened on the ground floor. That had been exactly what I'd been thinking. 'Do you believe what he told us was the truth? If we both think he was telling us a story that sounds incredible, maybe it is. Maybe it was a pack of lies.'

'I don't think he's a good enough liar,' Manfred said. 'Though some of what he told us was lies, of course. How has he made it this far? Didn't he know that someday, someone would come asking questions? He has to be at least a little smart because he's a doctor, right? Not everybody can make it through med school. And his license was there on the wall, I read it. I'm going to check up on it. Maybe we need another private eye.'

'No, not considering what happened to the last one,' I snapped, and then felt contrite. 'I'm sorry, Manfred. I'm glad you went with me. It's good there was another set of ears listening and another pair of eyes seeing. Did you believe the main outline of his story? You're the psychic.'

'I did believe him,' Manfred said after a perceptible pause. 'I went back over it in my head, and I think he was telling us the truth. Not all the truth; he did know who the man who came to get him was, for example. And I don't think the man hid his phone; I think he told the doctor he absolutely couldn't make a phone call, and I think he told him that in a threatening way. A really good threat would be enough to flatten a guy like Dr Bowden. I also think the guy had warned the doctor what to expect at the house. Doctors don't go out now with big bags, like my grandmother said they did when she was little. I think Dr Bowden knew to take medication for a woman who'd just had a difficult birth, and something for the baby, too.'

That made a lot of sense. 'You're right. So who do you think came into town to get the doctor? Who made that mysterious drive out to the empty big house? Who took the baby? Whoever took Dr Bowden to the ranch, he was wearing a wedding ring.'

'Oh, that's right. Good for you for remembering. Well, we know that Drexell was married for a while, and we know that Chip was, too. Could have been either one, or even someone we haven't met yet.'

We drove back to the hotel, stopping along the way to eat a fast-food lunch. I got a grilled chicken sandwich and didn't eat the fries. I was trying to eat better; I'd feel better if I did. We didn't talk much over the food. I don't know what Manfred was thinking, but I was trying to trace the niggling feeling I'd had when I'd first seen the Joyce party get out of their trucks at the Pioneer Rest Cemetery. I'd thought I'd seen them before, at least the men. Where would I have seen them? Could they have come by the trailer when we were all living there? There had been so many people in and out . . . and I'd tried so hard to dodge them.

I had to put that idea on the back burner when we returned to the hotel to find Tolliver in a real (and rare) snit. He'd tried to take a shower, and during the course of covering his shoulder with a plastic bag, he'd banged it against the wall, and it had hurt, and he was angry because I was gone so long with Manfred. He'd ordered lunch from room service, and then he'd had a hard time managing taking the cover off the drink and unrolling his silverware, with one good hand. Tolliver clearly had a grievance, and though I was prepared to coddle him until he was in a better frame of mind, I got into my own snit when he told me that Matthew had called to check on him, and when he heard Tolliver's tale, Matthew had said he was coming to visit since I'd left Tolliver all by himself.

I was mad at Tolliver, and he was mad at me – though I knew this was all because I'd gone on an errand with someone besides him. Normally, Tolliver is not temperamental, and not irritable, and not unreasonable. Today, he was all those things.

'Oh, Tolliver,' I said, my own voice none too loving. 'Couldn't you just suck it up until I got back?'

He glared at me, but I could tell he was already sorry he'd said anything to his dad. It was too late, though. Apparently, McDonald's was being amazingly forgiving in its work schedule, because in just a few moments Matthew was knocking on the door.

When Matthew came into the living room and walked over to his son while I was still holding the door open, my eyes followed him, and I froze with my hand still on the door. Matthew was the man I'd seen leaving Dr Bowden's office that morning. He'd been going out the doors across the lobby as we'd been entering. Same clothes, same walk, same set of the shoulders.

Manfred's eyes followed mine, and his widened. He asked me a silent question. After a moment, I shook my head. There was no point in having a confrontation – at least, my scrambled head couldn't instantly see any advantage.

If Matthew admitted he'd been there, he'd simply tell us that he was visiting another doctor, or a lawyer, or an accountant, in the same building, for whatever reason. It would be hard to disprove. But his presence in Tom Bowden's building was more coincidence than I could bite off and chew.

It had never occurred to me that Matthew's reappearance in his children's lives had anything to do with the Joyces.

Instead of joining the three men, I went into the bedroom and sat on the side of the bed. I felt as if someone had just slammed a car door on my legs, when I was only half in. I tried hard to focus on one idea out of the dozens that were suddenly percolating in my head. My whole world had shifted, and regaining my balance in that world was almost impossible.

Mariah Parish was dead. She had died in childbirth.

Rich Joyce was dead. He'd been shocked to death, if you could call it that.

Victoria Flores, whom Lizzie Joyce had hired to investigate Mariah's death, was dead, too.

Parker Powers, who'd been investigating the case, was dead.

My stepfather had been to the doctor's office, the doctor who was present when Mariah Parish had died.

And what else had happened only a couple of months after the mysterious birth of the mysterious baby eight years ago?

My sister Cameron had vanished.

16

I went into the bathroom and locked the door. I closed the toilet lid and sat on the toilet. I didn't turn on the light. I didn't want to see my reflection.

Matthew was somehow connected to the Joyces, though I had no idea how. And he was also Cameron's stepfather. And as near as I could ascertain, not that long after Mariah Parish's baby had been born, Cameron had disappeared. It had never, ever occurred to me that anyone in our family had anything to do with Cameron's disappearance. When the police had questioned my mother and Matthew, and Mark and Tolliver and me, I had raged at them because they were wasting time that should be spent tracing the real killer or killers.

I had suspected the boys at our high school, particularly Cameron's last boyfriend, who hadn't taken their breakup with good grace. I'd suspected Laurel and Matthew's druggie friends. I'd suspected a random stranger, any stranger, who'd seen Cameron walking home alone and decided to rob her/rape her/abduct her. I'd suspected the guys who'd sometimes blown wolf whistles at us when we'd been out together. I'd constructed hundreds of scenarios. Some of them were wildly implausible. But they all gave me a possible answer to the terrible mystery of the disappearance of my sister, an answer that didn't involve feeling even more pain from another personal loss.

I felt a deep conviction that even if I couldn't see the connection, even if it seemed incredible, two such incidents could not happen that close together without there being some kind of connection, not if the same man was involved in both incidents.

Was I grossly overreacting? I tried to think, though my brain was cloudy with rage. My stepfather knew something about the Joyces. He knew enough to know the name of the doctor who'd 'treated' Mariah Parish.

He *knew*. And I believed he also knew what had happened to my sister. All these years, he'd kept it from me.

I felt it in my bones.

I couldn't go into the living room and grab him by the neck. He was too strong for me. Tolliver wouldn't let me kill his father. Probably even Manfred, who had no personal stake in the matter, would feel obliged to intervene. But Tolliver was weak and injured, and Manfred would leave sooner or later.

It took all the self-control I could muster to break away from seriously considering how to kill my stepfather.

For one thing, it would be wrong. Maybe. For another thing, a much more important thing, I didn't know enough. I wanted to find my sister's final resting place. I wanted to be sure I knew what had happened to Cameron.

To that end, I had to be prepared to tolerate Matthew's presence.

I worked on it, there alone in the dark. I schooled myself to be strong. And then I got up and turned on the light and washed my face, as if I could wash the new knowledge off of it and return to what had been my happy ignorance.

I went out into the living room, having to move slowly. I felt I'd been kicked in the ribs – fragile, and sore with the suspicion and loathing I carried inside.

I could tell immediately that Matthew wanted Manfred to leave so he could talk to his son alone, and Manfred had not wanted to leave until he spoke to me again. He looked from Matthew to me as I came into the room, and he shuddered. Whatever Manfred saw in me, neither Tolliver nor Matthew could see. That was a good thing.

'Manfred,' I said. 'I'm sorry I flaked out on you. Thanks for going with me today.'

'No problem,' Manfred said, leaping to his feet with an alacrity that told me how anxious he was to get out of this hotel room. 'Would you like to go out and get a cup of coffee with me? Or do you need me to take you to the store? Got enough . . . potato chips?' He was reaching, there. We never ate potato chips. I felt a smile twitch at the corners of my mouth. 'Thanks, Manfred.' I debated quickly inside myself. Manfred wanted to talk to me about what I now realized was our mutual recognition of Matthew, but I didn't know yet what I was going to do. Better to avoid the tête-à-tête until I had made a plan. 'I guess I'll stick around here in case Tolliver needs me.'

I hugged him, acting on an impulse. His bones felt small as my arms circled his body. Somewhat hesitantly, he hugged me back. He was floundering under the psychic image he'd gotten from me. If he could see anything like the way I felt, then he'd seen something awful and murderous. 'Don't do it,' he said into my ear, and I let go of him and stood back.

'Don't worry, we'll be fine,' I said reassuringly. 'I'll call you if I need help, I promise.'

'Well . . . okay. I do have some readings to work on this afternoon. But my cell phone's always charged up and in my pocket. 'Bye, Tolliver. Mr Lang.' And with a last hard look directly into my eyes, Manfred was out the door, walking swiftly down the hall without a backward glance.

'What a flake,' said Matthew. 'Tolliver, you hang out much with people like that? He must be a friend of yours, Harper.'

'He is a friend of mine,' I said. 'His grandmother was, too.' I felt really strange, kind of out of myself. Matthew was sitting beside Tolliver on the couch, so I took the chair. I crossed my legs and wrapped my hands around my top knee. 'It was really messy outside this morning, wasn't it, Matthew?'

He looked surprised. 'Yeah, traffic was a bitch. It always is in Dallas. Raining, too.'

'Did you have errands to run this morning?'

'Oh, a few things I had to do. I have to be at work at two thirty.'

Was he really working at McDonald's? Or was he meeting one of the Joyces? Had he always been in their pay?

And the man I loved most in the world, the only person I truly loved, was this man's son.

That might bother Tolliver, but it didn't make any difference to me. More than most people, I understand the difference between the children and the parents. I had been brought up by the same woman who'd neglected her two little girls so much that her older children had had to take care of them.

I liked to think I'd turned out a little better than my mother.

And yet, if I killed Matthew Lang, would I be any better than my mother?

Well, at least I'd have made my decision with a clear head.

That's hardly true, said my saner self. *Aren't you so choked with hatred that you can't even swallow?*

True. But wasn't it better to kill someone when you really hated them? Was there a virtue to waiting until you were calm and collected?

I'd certainly have a better chance of getting away with it. And of living a life with Tolliver, rather than getting friendly with a bunch of women in prison. That was how my mother had lived out her life . . . and I wasn't like my mother. I wasn't.

I'm sure my expression was strange while I was going through this process, though it wasn't really continuous, but flashing through my head in flickers.

Judging by Tolliver's face, he clearly wanted to ask me if I was all right, but just as clearly he didn't want to do that in front of Matthew. Matthew was sitting turned toward Tolliver so his back was mostly to me, which was a good thing.

I tried to blank out my mind so I could listen to them talk. Matthew was asking Tolliver if he'd ever thought of finishing college, if he'd consider enrolling in one of the many colleges around the Dallas area when we moved here. He thought Tolliver would be able to find a good job if he got his degree, and then he wouldn't need to live off of me anymore.

Trust Matthew to plant a poisonous spin on our relationship. Tolliver looked shocked. 'I don't live off of Harper,' he said.

'You don't have a job other than traveling around with her while she does . . . whatever she does,' his dad said.

'I make sure she gets there to do that job,' Tolliver said. I realized it wasn't the first time he'd had this conversation; it was just that none of the previous times he'd had it were in my hearing. I was almost shocked out of my shell of hatred. 'If I weren't with Harper, she couldn't do that job at all.'

'He's absolutely right,' I said. 'I get sick when I work, and without Tolliver, no telling what would happen to me.' I tried to make my words a simple statement of fact. I didn't want to sound defensive when there was nothing to defend.

'You can tell yourself that,' Matthew said to Tolliver, ignoring me, 'but you know a man's got to make his own way in the world.'

'Like you did?' I said. 'You made your own way by selling drugs, by letting your wife auction me off to the highest bidder? You made your own way by giving up a law practice to go to jail instead?'

Matthew flushed. He couldn't pretend I wasn't there. 'Harper, I'm trying to be a good father. I know it's too late, and I know I did things that make me sick to remember, but I'm trying to mend my relationship with *my son*. I know he "loves" you, but sometimes you just have to butt out and let me talk to him.'

You could hear the quotation marks around 'loves.'

Tolliver said, 'Harper never has to butt out. I do love her. It is too late, and you did things that made all of us sick to our stomachs. You would have let Harper die if I hadn't been there that day when the lightning hit.'

I felt a rush of relief. Some small part of me was frightened that someday Tolliver would listen to his dad, would believe him, would be suckered again.

'Mark, at least, will let me talk to him,' Matthew said, getting up.

He was going to leave, and I still hadn't killed him. I was going to let him walk out.

I had to. I had only my bare hands. And I had to discover what he'd done with Cameron, and why he'd done it. I didn't think he'd wanted to have Cameron sexually. Some of his friends had wanted to have sex with us, but not Matthew. At least, I was fairly sure of that. But there was a reason, and I had to know it. I stood up, my hands clenched at my sides, debating whether or not to hit him.

Matthew picked up on the hostility in the way I was standing. I guess if you spend time in jail, you're on the alert for stuff like that. He edged around me on his path to the door. 'I don't know what's wrong with you today, Harper. I'm just trying to mend fences, here.'

'Not working,' I said through clenched teeth.

'Yeah,' he said, with a nervous laugh. 'I can see that. Son, I'll talk to you later. I hope you're better. Call me if you need me.' And he was out the door and it shut behind him. And he was still alive.

'Sit here,' Tolliver said, his voice so low I almost didn't hear him. 'Sit here, and tell me what's in your head.'

'He was at the doctor's office building,' I said. 'Your father was there, this morning, going out the door across the lobby as we were coming in.'

I stood still until Tolliver processed that. Then he patted the couch beside him again. 'Okay, let's figure it out,' he said, and I could have done handstands and cheered, because he got it completely.

I told Tolliver about Dr Bowden. I related the doctor's story, adding my own commentary. And he listened, God bless him, he listened to every word without interrupting. He abandoned his snit as quickly as he could toss it overboard. I told him how glad I was that Manfred had been there, had heard the same story, because otherwise I'd find it hard to believe it myself.

'So why did that lead to you wanting to disembowel my dad?'

'Because I don't believe in coincidences that huge. What was Matthew doing in that office building? He had to have been seeing Tom Bowden. And why would he know about Tom Bowden? He had to have had a connection with the Joyces, or at least whichever of them wanted to keep Mariah's pregnancy and the birth of the child secret.'

'But did he *have* to?' Tolliver asked. 'I mean, did Dad really have to have been in cahoots with the Joyces, one or all of them? We don't know who it was who took the doctor to the ranch that night. But we do know, from Victoria's files, that Chip Moseley was arrested in Texarkana once, so we can assume he was there pretty often. And we know that the Joyce family had some doctors there, according to Tom Bowden, so they had some connections there, too. That's a slim tie, but it's a tie.'

'And when we met the Joyces, I thought the two men looked familiar. Just a little.'

'Chip and Drex?'

I nodded. 'I know that doesn't seem as conclusive, because I can't place them firmly. But most people I'm that fuzzy on, it's because they came to the trailer, and I hate to remember that time. Plus, I tried not to look, because I knew it was dangerous to know who was buying and selling drugs.'

'Yes,' Tolliver said heavily. 'It was dangerous, every day, to be living there.'

'So all this is why I think your dad is involved. And I'm wondering if he got in touch with Mark so Mark's intervention would lead to your dad's getting to see you.'

Tolliver mulled that over. 'Could be,' he said. 'I would never answer his letters or take his phone calls, so he might have used Mark. He'd know I'd never lose touch with my brother.' There was a little pain in Tolliver's face; even now, he'd had a tiny flicker of hope that his dad was trying to do the right thing, that Matthew had really and truly reformed.

'But what *happened*?' I asked, frustrated. 'Why was he involved with the Joyce family? And how did Cameron get involved in that?'

'Cameron? Why do you think he would hurt Cameron? Not my dad.' Tolliver shook his head. 'He had an alibi, remember. At the time the old woman saw Cameron getting in the truck, Dad was playing pool with that asshole and his girlfriend.'

'I remember that guy,' I said. 'Come on, let's get you into the bed. We can talk about it tomorrow.'

Tolliver was stunned and exhausted. I had to help him climb into the bed. I called room service for some soup and salads for both of us after I got him settled. I sat on the side of the bed while we waited for the food to come.

'I can believe a lot of bad stuff about Matthew,' he said, 'but I don't believe he hurt Cameron.'

'It had never occurred to me, either,' I said. 'Honestly, I don't want to believe it. But if he did have a connection to her disappearance and he's been letting us wonder all these years, I want him to die.' With Tolliver, I wasn't going to worry about how saying such a thing would make him think of me. He knew me. Now he would know me a little better.

Tolliver understood. 'He'd deserve to die, if he hurt Cameron,' he said. 'But there's not one single thing to tie him to Cameron's disappearance, and he had no motive at all. For that matter, we don't have any proof that he's involved in the mess with the Joyce family. We need something more than the sight of a man's back as he walks out of a public building.'

'I understand,' I said – and I really did, even if I hated his logic. 'So we have to figure out a way. We can't go on living our lives unless we get rid of this, one way or another.'

'Yes,' said Tolliver, and then he closed his eyes. Amazingly, he fell asleep.

I ate supper by myself, though I saved his in case he woke up to eat it. After I was through with my salad, I did something I hadn't done in at least a year. I went out to our car, opened the trunk, and got my sister's backpack out of it. Back inside our room, I sat on the couch and unzipped the backpack. We'd thought it was so cute when Cameron picked it out. It was pink with black polka dots. Cameron had gotten a black jacket and black boots, and she'd looked wonderful. No one had to know that everything had come from the second-hand shop.

The police had finally let us have the backpack, after six years. It had been fingerprinted, turned inside out, examined microscopically . . . for all I knew, they'd x-rayed it.

Cameron would be very nearly twenty-six now. She'd been gone for almost eight years.

It was late spring when she'd been taken. She'd been decorating the school gym for the prom. She'd had a date with – oh, God, I couldn't remember. Todd? Yes, Todd Battista. I couldn't remember if I'd had a date or not. Probably not, because following the lightning strike, my popularity had plummeted. My new ability had thrown me completely out of whack, and it had taken me almost a year to adjust to the buzz of dead people. And then I'd had to learn how to conceal my strange ability. During that awful time, I'd earned a well-deserved reputation for being very strange.

She'd been so late that day. And that wasn't like Cameron. I remembered making my mother rouse enough to watch the girls, whom I'd collected from day care. Though it wasn't smart to leave them alone with her, I couldn't take them with me. I hurried down the road, past all the other trailers, following the route we always took coming home.

Tolliver and Mark had been at their respective jobs, and Matthew, as it turned out, had been playing pool in the home of one of his wonderful friends, a junkie named Renaldo Simpkins. The police would never have believed Renaldo, but his girlfriend, Tammy, had been there, too, and she said she'd walked in and out of the room at least five times during the pool game. She was sure that Matthew had never left between around four and six thirty. (The six thirty was firm, because that was when she'd gotten a phone call from a neighbor, telling her that there were police cars all around the Lang trailer, and Matthew better get his ass home.)

Around five thirty, I'd found my sister's backpack – the one now sitting before me on a hotel coffee table – by the side of the street. It was a residential street lined with very small houses. About half of them were abandoned. But there was a woman living in the house across the street from the spot where I'd found Cameron's backpack. Her name was Ida Beaumont.

I'd never talked to Ida Beaumont before, and despite all the times I'd walked past her house, I don't think I'd ever seen her out in her yard. She was afraid of all the teenagers in the neighborhood, and maybe she had good reason. This was a part of town where even police looked over their shoulders. But I met Ida Beaumont that day. I'd walked across the street and knocked on her door.

'Hi, I'm sorry to bother you, but my sister hasn't come home from school and her backpack is there, under that tree.' I pointed over to the bright splotch of color. Ida Beaumont peered at it, her eyes following my finger.

'Yes,' she said cautiously. She was in her early sixties, and the newspaper articles told me later that she was living on some kind of disability check and what remained of her dead husband's pension. I could hear her television going. She was watching a talk show. 'Who's your sister?' she asked. 'Is she that pretty blond girl? I see you two walking home all the time.'

'Yes ma'am. That's her. I'm looking for her. Did you see anything happen over there this afternoon? She would have been coming home sometime within the past hour, I think.'

'I stay at the back of the house, mostly.' Ida seemed to put emphasis on that, because she didn't want to be seen as a busybody. 'But I seen a blue pickup, an old Dodge, about half an hour ago. The man in it was talking to a girl. I couldn't really see her, she was on the other side of the pickup. But she got in, and they took off.'

'Oh.' I tried to make sense of this, tried to remember if anyone we knew had an old blue pickup. But no one popped up in my memory. 'Thanks. That was about half an hour ago?'

'Yes,' she said, very positively. 'Yes, that was when it was.'

'She didn't look like she was . . . like he was making her do it?'

'I couldn't say about that. They talked, she got in, they left.'

'Okay. I appreciate your taking the time to talk to me.' And I turned and walked back across the street. Then I reversed myself. Ida Beaumont was still standing at her doorway.

'Do you have a phone?' I asked. We lived in a neighborhood where you couldn't take that for granted.

'I do.'

'Will you call the police and tell them what I just told you, about my sister? Ask them to come? I'll be standing over there, by the backpack.'

I could see reluctance in Ida's face, knew the older woman was wishing she hadn't come to the door. 'All right,' she said finally, exhaling loudly. 'I'll call 'em.' And without closing the wooden door, *she went to a telephone that was mounted on the wall. I could see her dialing the police, and I could hear her part of the conversation.*

I'll say this for the police: they were there very quickly. Initially, of course, they were doubtful about Cameron really being missing. Teenage girls often found better things to do than go home, especially to a home in this neighborhood. But the abandoned backpack seemed to speak to them, to testify that my sister hadn't been willing to leave.

Finally, I'd broken down crying, explained to them that I had to get home, that my mom couldn't be trusted to take care of my sisters, and that had made everything more serious, right away. They let me call my brothers, who both left work immediately to come home. That neither Mark nor Tolliver was skeptical that Cameron had been abducted also convinced the police that my sister hadn't gone away willingly or intentionally.

Going into the trailer with the cops would have been humiliating under any other circumstances. But I was so frightened by then that I was only glad they were there. They saw that my mother had passed out again on the couch and that the girls were crying. She'd started to put a diaper on Gracie and hadn't finished taping it shut. Mariella was trying to mash some banana for Gracie (who'd just started eating real food) and she was standing on a chair to reach the counter. It was clean, or at least as clean as an old dilapidated trailer could be, but of course we were very crowded in there, and the sheer amount of stuff made it look incredibly cluttered.

'Is it always like this?' asked the younger cop, looking around him.

'Shut up, Ken,' said his partner.

'Cameron and I try,' I said, and I began crying again. My bitterness ran out of me in a stream of explanation. I'd already realized, on some level, that our life there was over, so the pretence was over, too.

While I cried and talked, I was getting Gracie diapered and making a peanut butter sandwich for Mariella. I mashed the banana for Gracie and mixed it with a little formula and put it in a bowl for her. I got her little spoon out of the drainer. My mother never moved, except once. Her hand went out to the spot where Gracie had been, and she patted the air vaguely. I put Gracie in her infant seat and began feeding her, pausing from time to time to wipe my face.

'You take care of your sisters,' the older cop said in a friendly way.

'My brothers make enough to take them to day care while we're at school,' I said. 'We've tried real hard.'

'*I can tell,*' *he said. The younger cop turned away with his mouth pressed together and his eyes hot. '*Where's your daddy?*' *he asked after a minute.*

'*My stepfather,*' *I corrected automatically.* '*I have no idea.*'

When Matthew got home, he acted stunned that the police were there, agonized that Cameron was missing, appalled that his poor wife had slept through such hubbub and turmoil.

This had never happened before, he told the cops. There were several more at the trailer by now. One of them had arrested Matthew before, and he snorted derisively when Matthew finished his performance.

'*Yeah, buddy,*' *the officer said.* '*And where were you this afternoon?*'

Later, Tolliver and I sat together on the couch after my mother had been taken to the hospital. Mark paced, as much as you can pace in a trailer. A woman from Social Services had come to get our sisters. Matthew had been arrested because he had some joints in his car. The drugs were the excuse the cops used; I think they just wanted to arrest him after they saw the trailer and talked to me. Mark and Tolliver had confirmed everything I said: Mark very reluctantly, Tolliver with a matter-of-fact air that said a lot about our lives. But I found Mark crying outside that night, after the police had gone. He was sitting in the lawn chair right at the bottom of the trailer steps, and he had his face in his hands.

'*We tried so hard to stay together,*' *he said, as if he had to explain his distress.*

'*That's all over now,*' *I said.* '*That's all gone, now that Cameron's been taken. There's no more hiding things now.*'

For a month after that, Cameron had been 'seen' numerous times around Texarkana, in Dallas, in Corpus Christi, in Houston, in Little Rock. A teenage panhandler in Los Angeles had been hauled in because she looked like Cameron. But none of those sightings had ever come to anything, and her corpse had never been found. I'd gotten excited about three years after she'd gone, when a hunter had found a girl's body in some woods around Lewisville, Arkansas. The corpse – what there was left of it – was female, and the right size to be Cameron. But after close examination, the bones appeared to be that of a woman somewhat older than my sister, and the DNA wasn't a match. That body had never been identified, though when they'd let me close to her I'd known she'd been a suicide. I didn't share that, because I had limited credibility with the police.

Tolliver and I had started our traveling by then, and we were building up our business. It had taken a long time for word of mouth to get around and for the Internet to pick up on what I was doing. The cops thought I was a scam artist. The first two years were very difficult. After that, my career took on a certain momentum.

But now was not the time to think about my own journey, but about Cameron's. I touched the backpack lovingly, and I took out everything inside. I'd examined every item a hundred times. We'd leafed through every page of the textbooks inside, looking for a message, a clue, anything. All the notes Cameron had been passed by other students were stuffed in a pocket, and we'd pored over them, trying to read something in them that would tell us what had happened to our sister.

Tanya had wanted Cameron to notice how stupid Heather's outfit was, and Tanya had also remarked on the fact that Jerry had said that Heather had had SEX with him when they'd gone out the weekend before. Jennifer thought that Cameron's brother Tolliver was HOT, and was he dating anyone? And wasn't Mr Arden a stupid idiot?

Todd had wondered when he should pick her up for the prom, and would she be getting dressed at Jennifer's house, like she had last time?

(If Cameron could manage it, she got her dates to pick her up somewhere else. I didn't blame her at all.)

There'd been a note from Mr Arden, asking Cameron to tell her parents that one of them needed to come up to the school and explain that they knew the attendance policy. Just bringing a signature back to the school from home wasn't enough. (Mr Arden had told the police that Cameron had missed his class once over the acceptable limit, and he'd wanted to lay eyes on one of Cameron's parents to make sure someone was aware that Cameron couldn't skip any more or she might not graduate.)

She hadn't been skipping the class out of senior giddiness. It was her last class of the day, and sometimes we had to leave early to pick up the girls at day care if Tolliver or Mark couldn't.

Of course, all the teachers we'd had had professed their shock and horror at our living conditions, except Miss Briarly. Miss Briarly had said, 'And what would you have had us do? Call the police so the kids wouldn't have even had each other?'

That was exactly what the press thought Miss Briarly should have done, and she'd gotten reprimanded by the principal. It had made me so angry. Miss Briarly had taught Cameron her favorite class, advanced biology. I remembered how hard Cameron had worked on her senior project about genetics, charting the eye colors of everyone in the neighborhood. She'd gotten an A. Miss Briarly had given me the paper after Cameron's disappearance.

Ida Beaumont had had to tell her story over and over. She'd become such a recluse, as a result, that she'd stopped answering her door and got a church lady to deliver her groceries.

My mother and Tolliver's father had been sentenced to jail on multiple charges of child endangerment and assorted drug offenses.

Tolliver had been given permission to move in with Mark. I'd gone to a foster home, where I'd been treated very decently. It had been marvelous, to me, to be in a home where the floors were solid, where I only had to share a room with one other girl, where everything was clean without me having to clean it personally, and where study time was mandatory. I still sent the Clevelands a Christmas card every year. They'd let Tolliver come to visit me on the Saturdays he wasn't working.

By the time I graduated, we'd developed our plan for using my weird new talent to make our living. We'd spent hours at the cemetery, practicing and exploring the limits of my strange ability. Even weirder than our plan was the fact that this had actually been a very happy time in my life, and I think in Tolliver's, too. The biggest flaw in that new life was the loss of all my sisters. Cameron was gone, and Mariella and Gracie had moved away to live with Iona and Hank.

I opened Cameron's math book. She'd been taking precal; she'd hated it. Cameron had poor math skills. She was good at history, I remembered. She'd liked that. It was easier to study people's lives when they were all dead, their troubles all past. Cameron was a good speller, and she'd enjoyed all her science classes, too, especially the advanced biology class she'd been taking.

The newspapers had gone on and on about the sad condition of the trailer, the depravity of Laurel and Mark, the arrest records of their frequent visitors, the lengths we kids had gone to in our attempt to stay together. Truthfully, I don't think our home was so very unusual.

In the unspoken way kids communicate, we'd learned of a dozen or more kids in our school who had it just as bad or worse.

People often can't help being poor, but they can help being bad. We were unfortunate in having parents who were both.

I flipped open one of my sister's notebooks. Her class notes were still in place. The grubby ruled pages covered in her handwriting were all that I had left of her. Cameron had been the only one, besides me, who could remember the good days – the days when our mom and dad were still married and they hadn't started using. If my dad was still alive, I doubted he'd remember much of anything.

I shook myself. I was not going to get maudlin. But it was necessary to think about the day Cameron had vanished. If she'd gotten into that pickup voluntarily, then I might as well forget about tracing her. Not only would that make her a stranger to me, but there would be no body to sense, unless something had happened to her in the meantime. If Cameron was dead, ironically enough, one of these days I might find her.

I wondered if Ida Beaumont was still alive. I'd been so young then, she'd looked positively tottering on the edge of her grave. Now, I realized she had been no more than sixty-five.

Obeying an impulse I couldn't fathom, I called information in Texarkana and discovered that she still had a listing. My fingers punched in the number before I could even explain to myself why I was doing this.

'Hello?' a creaky voice said suspiciously.

'Mrs Beaumont?'

'Yes, this is Ida Beaumont.'

'You may not remember me,' I said. 'I'm Harper Connelly.'

Dead silence.

'What do you want?' the voice said.

That wasn't exactly the question I'd anticipated.

'Are you still in the same house, Ms Beaumont? I was thinking I might come by to visit you,' I said, making this up on the spot. 'I was thinking I might bring one of my brothers.'

'No,' she said. 'Don't come here. Don't ever come here. The last time you came, I had people knocking on my door all day and night for weeks. And the police still come by. You stay away.'

'We have some questions to ask you,' I said in a voice that I hoped was pitched somewhere between anger and simple determination.

'The police have already asked me plenty of questions,' she snapped, and I knew I'd gone the wrong way. 'I wish I'd never answered the door that day when you come knocking.'

'But then you couldn't have told me about the blue truck,' I said.

'I told you, didn't I, that I didn't see the girl clearly?'

'Yes,' I said, though in my mind, over the years, I'd pretty much disregarded that. I was missing a girl, she'd seen a girl get into a pickup, and Cameron's backpack was there on the spot.

Over the line, I heard a deep sigh. Then Ida Beaumont began speaking. 'A young woman started coming by from Meals on Wheels about six months ago,' she said. 'Those meals, they're never any good, but at least they're free, and sometimes they bring enough to last another day. Her name's Missy Klein.'

'Okay,' I said, since I had no idea what else to say. My heart was sinking into my stomach, because I knew this was going to be bad.

'And she said to me, she says, "Mrs Beaumont, you remember all those years ago when you saw a girl getting into a blue pickup?" And I says, "Yes, sure, and it was a curse to me."'

'All right.' The dark feeling grew inside me.

'So she tells me it was her, getting into the truck with her boyfriend, who she wasn't supposed to be seeing because he was in his twenties.'

'It wasn't my sister.'

'No, it wasn't. It was that Missy Klein, and now she brings me Meals on Wheels.'

'You never saw my sister.'

'No, I didn't. And Missy, she tells me that the backpack was sitting there when she came along and got in his truck.'

I felt like a ton of bricks had fallen on me. 'Have you told the police?' I said finally.

'No, I don't go calling the police. I suppose I should have, but – well, they come by to see me every so often, take me back over that day. Peter Gresham, he comes by. I figured I'd tell him the next time he stopped in.'

'Thank you,' I said. 'I wish I'd known this before. But thank you for telling me.'

'Well, sure. I thought you'd be mad at me,' she said, which I thought was kind of amazing.

'I'm glad I called. Goodbye,' I said. My voice was as numb as my heart. Any minute now, the feeling would come back. I wanted to be off the phone with this woman when that happened.

Ida Beaumont was saying something else about Meals on Wheels when I clicked my phone shut.

Lizzie Joyce called me then, before I could think through the implications of what I'd just heard. 'Oh, my Lord,' she said, 'I can't believe Victoria is dead. You were a friend of hers, right? You-all went way back? Harper, I'm so sorry. What do you think happened to her? You think it had anything to do with looking for the baby?'

'I don't have the slightest idea,' I said, though that wasn't the truth. I didn't think Lizzie Joyce had anything to do with Victoria's murder, but I thought someone close to her was involved. I found myself wondering why she'd called me. Lizzie Joyce, wealthy beyond imagining, didn't have a BFF to call? Where was the sister, and the boyfriend, and the brother? Why didn't she call all the people she sat on boards with, the people who worked for her, the people who did her hair and polished her nails when she was going somewhere fancy, the people who set up the barrels for her competition practice?

After I'd listened for a minute, I realized Lizzie wanted to talk to someone she didn't have to brief, someone who had known Victoria; and I was the person who fit the bill.

'I guess I'm going to the firm of detectives my granddad's company always uses,' she said. 'I thought it would be helpful to talk to a woman out on her own, someone who wasn't up on our business, not involved in the family saga. But I think I caused her death. If I'd gone to our usual firm, she'd still be alive.'

There was no rebuttal to offer on that. 'How come you have a private detective firm on call?' I asked instead.

'Granddaddy started that when he became the head of a big enterprise. More than a rancher. He liked to know who he was hiring, at least for key positions.' Lizzie sounded surprised that I needed to ask.

'So why didn't he get them to check out Mariah Parish?'

'Granddaddy had met her when she worked for the Peadens, and when he needed someone, and she was free, it seemed like a natural fit. I guess he felt like he knew her and didn't need to have her investigated. After all, she wasn't going to be writing checks on our account or anything.'

He wouldn't have trusted her with his checkbook, but he would trust her to cook his food without poisoning him, and he would trust her to clean his house without stealing his possessions. Even suspicious rich people have their blind side. Given what we'd learned about Mariah from reading her file, I found that ironic.

I hadn't known that Rich Joyce had actually met Mariah before she moved into his house. Drexell hadn't mentioned that at our dinner with Victoria. Maybe Rich had seen a good way to sneak a mistress into his house under his kids' eyes. Maybe his friend who'd first employed Mariah had told Rich he'd been bedding her. Nudge nudge, wink wink. Here's a good woman who can cook, count your pills, and warm up your sheets, Rich. And she can stay right there in the house.

'And you didn't even think about investigating her the way you would any other employee?'

'Well,' Lizzie said, clearly uncomfortable, 'she and Granddaddy had everything worked out by the time we knew about it. He was sure in his right mind, so we didn't say anything.'

All the Joyce grandchildren had been scared of the patriarch. 'You didn't have her checked out afterward?'

'Well, he would have known. *That* was when I should have hired an outside source. I gotta tell you the truth, at the time, I didn't think too much about it. That was years ago. I was younger, and less confident, and of course, I expected Granddaddy to live forever.' Lizzie stopped short, probably realizing she'd been oversharing. 'Well, I just wanted to tell you how sorry I am about your friend. And how's your brother doing? This whole thing just keeps getting messier and messier.'

'Do you wish you'd never contacted me?'

A moment of silence. 'Truthfully, yes, that's what I wish,' she said. 'Seems like a lot of people have died and they didn't need to. What's changed? What more do I know? Nothing. My grandfather saw a rattlesnake and died. We don't know if anyone else was there for sure. He's still dead. Mariah's dead, and in my head she's not resting in peace anymore, now that I know she died in childbirth. Where's that baby? Is the baby an aunt or uncle of mine? I still don't know. Maybe I'll never know.'

'Someone's sure trying to make sure you don't,' I said. 'Goodbye, Lizzie.' And I hung up.

Manfred stopped in, and I was glad to see him, but I wasn't in a mood for talking. He asked me about the backpack.

'It's my sister's,' I said. 'She left it the day she vanished.'

I turned away to answer Tolliver's call. He'd woken up briefly and asked for a pain pill. He drifted back to sleep before he even took it.

When I came back in the living room, Manfred was withdrawing his hand from the backpack. He looked sad. 'I'm sorry this happened to you, Harper.'

'Well, thanks for the kind thought, Manfred, but it happened to my sister. I was just caught up in the aftermath.'

'I'll see you soon. Don't worry if I don't call for a couple of days. I've got a job to do.'

'Oh . . . okay, Manfred.' I hadn't thought about worrying. He gave me a peck on the cheek when he left, and I was glad to shut the door behind him. I sat and thought about my sister.

It was a long night. I finally fell asleep after midnight.

18

Tolliver woke up the next morning feeling much better. He'd slept for twelve hours straight, and when he woke me up he let me know that he was full of energy. We had to be careful, but with me on top, sex was doable. Very doable. An absolute delight, in fact. And I thought the top of his head was going to fly off, he enjoyed it so much. He lay there panting afterward, as if he'd done the work, and I collapsed beside him, laughing in a breathless kind of way.

'Now I feel like myself,' he said. 'Somehow it makes you feel even less like a man, when you're bedridden and then you can't even stand the physical part of having sex. Reduces you to a kid.'

'Let's just get in the car and go,' I suggested. 'Let's go to the apartment. We could be in St Louis in a day. You could ride that long, I bet.'

'What about staying here to visit more with the girls? What about finding out if my father was connected to the Joyces and Cameron?'

'Maybe you were right. Maybe we need to leave the girls to Iona and Hank. They're stable, in every sense. We travel so much. We'll never be a constant in their lives. And your dad? He's going to hell anyway. If we drop all this, it'll just take him a little longer. We could be free of him.'

Tolliver looked thoughtful. 'Come here,' he said, and I put my head on his good shoulder. He didn't wince, so that was all right. I stroked the part of his chest not covered with a bandage. Looking back on the time between my discovery that I loved him as a man and the time I found out he felt the same and we acted on it, I wondered how I had survived. We were incredibly lucky, and I knew there was a part of me that I found somewhat scary, the part that would do anything to prevent what we had from being jeopardized.

'You know what we ought to do,' he said.

'What?'

'We ought to take a day trip.'

'Oh, where to?'

'To Texarkana.'

I froze. 'Are you serious?' I said, raising my head to look him in the eyes.

'Yeah, I am. It's time we went back to just look around and let go.'

'Let go.'

'Yeah. We've got to realize that we're not going to find Cameron.'

'I've got some things to tell you about that.'

'Oh?' His voice had an apprehensive edge. If I hadn't liked what he'd said, he was going to dislike what I had to say even more.

'I made some calls yesterday,' I said. 'And I got some calls. While you were asleep. I've got to tell you about them.'

An hour later, Tolliver was saying, 'That woman was wrong? All the time they were looking for the wrong thing? She was just *mixed up*?'

'She never said she saw Cameron clearly, only that the backpack was there after she saw a blond girl get into a blue truck,' I said. 'Who knows? So we're back to square one. In fact . . .' I thought for a second. 'In fact, that throws the whole timeline off. She said Cameron had been picked up thirty minutes before I talked to her, and I set out to look for Cameron almost exactly at five o'clock. But now we can be pretty sure Cameron was picked up by someone even earlier.'

'She left the school at four, right?'

'Right. That's what – oh, her friend, what's her name – Rebecca. That's what Rebecca said. But she also said that maybe the time wasn't on the nose. They'd worked all last period decorating the gym and kept going after school was out. I'd always thought she stood around in the parking lot talking to one of her friends, but now I'm assuming she went straight home. You were at work at the restaurant. Mark was driving between his job at Taco Bell and his job at Super Save-a-Lot.'

'A seven-minute drive,' Tolliver said automatically. We'd talked about it so often.

'Your dad was at Renaldo Simpkins's place from around four to six thirty. My mom was passed out, as usual.'

We looked at each other. With the timeline changed, Matthew's ass wasn't as covered as we'd thought.

'No matter what I think of him, I don't want to believe it,' I said.

'We do need to go to Texarkana.'

'Let's call the doctor's office and see what his nurse says.'

The nurse said no. The nurse said Tolliver needed to stay in the hotel room. No matter how many precautions we said he'd take, she said no. She was glad that he felt much better, but he would tire as the day went on.

Of course we could simply have ignored her strictures and done what we wanted, but I was against that. I suspected she was right to say no, and though I would have been glad if Tolliver had been up to traveling, in all conscience I didn't want to get some hours' drive away from the hospital and have some kind of emergency. Certainly there were doctors in Texarkana, certainly there were hospitals, but common sense said the hospital and doctor who'd treated him initially would be best.

We sat looking at each other. We had few choices: postpone the drive to Texarkana until Tolliver was better, ask Manfred if he was in the area and could go with me, or ask Mark if he could take a day off work to ride with me. 'Here's a novel thought: I could go by myself,' I said. Tolliver shook his head vehemently. 'I know you can, and I know you'd do fine,' he said. 'But when it's about Cameron, we both should go. We'll wait today, and tomorrow, if we have to. Then, no matter what, we go.'

It was good to have a plan of action, excellent to have Tolliver feel up to forming that plan. Iona called and invited us over to supper at their house, if Tolliver was feeling up to the excursion. He nodded, so I told her we'd be glad to come. I didn't ask if we could bring anything, because I couldn't imagine what we could bring and she always turned me down anyway, as though anything I brought into their house would be suspect. The day was boring, restless, and interminable.

Finally we went down to the car, with Tolliver moving very carefully. I drove to Iona and Hank's house with great care, trying to keep the car away from bumps. That's not easy in Dallas, and I was glad we stuck to city streets instead of getting on the interstate in the early evening traffic.

That area on the east side of Dallas is one big suburb. There are all the stores you can find in any suburban area in the country – Bed Bath & Beyond, Home Depot, Staples, Old Navy, Wal-Mart – and after you see one sequence of them, they start to repeat in another area. On the one hand, if you wanted to buy any item you could think of, unless it was too exotic, you could find it. On the other hand . . . we saw these same stores all across America. We traveled a lot, but unless the climate was radically different, it was hard to tell one part of the urban landscape from another, though a thousand miles lay in between.

Architecture was going the same way as the chain stores. We'd seen Iona and Hank's house from Memphis to Tallahassee, from St Louis to Seattle.

Tolliver was telling me all this again as I drove, and I was glad it was such a familiar complaint that I only had to say, 'That's right,' or 'True,' from time to time.

The girls were full of questions about Tolliver's bandage and what had happened to him. Iona had told them he'd been shot by someone who'd been careless and had a gun accident, so she and Hank could impress our sisters with the need for safety. Hank had a gun, he told us, but he kept it locked up and the key hidden. Since they were trying to be the best parents on earth, he and Iona had instructed the girls from an early age in the gun safety rules. I appreciated that, but to me it would have been more to the point to discuss gun *control*. However, that didn't jibe with Hank's ideas about being a true American, so that idea was not one that made an impression on my aunt and uncle.

After Mariella and Gracie had gotten used to having Tolliver around in his sling, they went off to do their usual things. Mariella had homework, Gracie had a song to learn for chorus, and Iona was finishing up the cooking. Tolliver and Hank went into the family room to watch the news, and I offered to help Iona by taking care of the dishes that had accumulated as she cooked. She smiled and nodded, and I rolled up my sleeves and got to work. This is a job I don't mind. I can think while I do it or talk to a Chore Mate or simply take pleasure in a job well done.

'Matthew was by here today.' Iona was stirring a pot on the stove. She'd made chili. 'He did call up several days ago, to ask if he could come by. We thought about it. He scared the girls the other day at the skating rink. We thought maybe if they saw him while we were around, they wouldn't be so worried about it. And maybe he wouldn't try to ambush them again, if he knew we'd be reasonable.'

This showed good sense on the part of Iona. I found myself nodding at her approvingly, not that she cared whether or not I approved of her. 'I'll bet he didn't come just to hang around with the girls and visit with them. What did he want?' Matthew had been a busy bee. I wondered when he found time to work.

'He wanted to take some pictures of the girls. He didn't have any recent ones. We did send him their school pictures, but he said they got taken away in jail. Those men will take anything.'

'Matthew is one of those men.'

She actually laughed. 'Yeah, you're right. Still, if he wants pictures of his daughters, I'm not going to stop him. Though they're our daughters now, and we made sure he knew that.'

'Did he talk to them much?' I asked. I was curious.

'No,' Iona said. She went to the hall, heard that the girls were playing a video game in their room. She returned to her station at the stove. 'That man, I don't understand him. He was blessed with some wonderful children. Tolliver and Mark are both good boys; and he had you and Cameron for stepdaughters, both of you bright and pretty, and no drugs. Then he has these two girls. Mariella's grades are going up. Aside from that one little running-away incident last fall, she's doing good in school. Bless Gracie, she's always a little behind her age group, but she's not a whiner, not a complainer, and she works real hard on her schoolwork. But Matthew don't seem to want to get to know them. He took the pictures, but then he talked to Hank and me. The girls don't know what to make of him.'

'I know they don't remember living in Texarkana.'

'Not really,' Iona said. 'Sometimes they mention it, but they never talk about anything specific. Gracie was just a baby, of course, and Mariella was little more than a toddler.' She shrugged. 'I know there were plenty of times my sister and Matthew weren't there when you needed them.'

That was putting it mildly.

'I never said how glad I was you and Hank were willing to take them in,' I said, surprising even myself. 'It must have been a real shock, going from no kids to two in the blink of an eye.'

Iona stopped stirring and turned from the stove to face me. I was drying the dishes and putting them on the counter for Iona to put away in their designated spots. 'I appreciate you saying that,' she said. 'Though I was glad to have them, and taking them into our home was the right thing to do. We prayed about it. That's the answer we come up with. We love these girls like they were our own. I can't believe we're going to have another baby! At my age! Sometimes I feel like Abraham's wife, seventy years old and with child.'

Until the meal was ready we talked about Iona's startling pregnancy. We talked about her ob/gyn doctor, special tests she might need as an older first-time mother, and all kinds of pregnancy-related topics. Iona was happier than I'd ever seen her, and anything about her interesting condition was fun for her to talk about. I tried to concentrate on looking happy and asking the right questions, but underneath our conversation, I was worried about Matthew's appearance at the house, about his taking pictures of the girls. He didn't want photos of them for his own pleasure or because he was proud of having two such healthy daughters. Matthew never did anything that simple and straightforward.

Tolliver came to the table first, so he could get into position with his paraphernalia, and then Hank. The girls washed their hands and took their places, and Iona and I carried the food to the table. Iona had made chili and cornbread, and I'd grated cheese to sprinkle on the steaming bowls. We said grace before we ate, and then we enjoyed eating. Iona had none of the characteristics I associate with good cooks – she wasn't passionate; she didn't love fresh ingredients like all the chefs on TV; she'd never traveled much and she was suspicious of foreign cuisine. But her chili was wonderful, her cornbread mouthwatering.

Tolliver and I both had more than one bowlful, and Iona looked gratified at our praise. Mariella and Gracie were full of conversation about school and their friends, and I was glad to hear that both of them seemed to get along well with the other children. Gracie was wearing a green top that matched her eyes, so she looked like a little fairy, though her bold little nose hinted that she might not be a benevolent one. She was a funny little thing. She was really 'on' tonight, telling little jokes she'd heard in class, asking Iona if they could have chili dogs the next night if any of the chili was left over. Mariella mentioned Matthew's visit a couple of times, dragging it into the conversation as if it worried her. Each time, Iona or Hank would respond calmly, and I could see Mariella's anxiety abating.

Tolliver and I left soon after we'd eaten, in deference to the girls' evening routine. Our sisters were so excited by a discussion about what to name the baby that the topic of Tolliver and me getting married seemed to have slipped to the backs of their minds, to my relief.

I drove back to the hotel, and Tolliver sat in silence. Now that it was dark, I had to concentrate more on navigating, and we made one false turn before we got back. It was easily corrected, and soon I was helping Tolliver out of the car. I could tell he was tired, but he was moving better.

We were crossing the lobby when he said, 'Hank said Dad took pictures of the girls.'

'That's what Iona told me. I think they were smart to let the girls see Matthew with them both around, so they could kind of put him in perspective.'

'Yeah, that was a smart move,' Tolliver said, but not as though he was giving it any thought. 'But why would he really want pictures of them?'

'I don't think your dad is the kind of guy who puts pictures of his kids on Facebook, do you? So I can't imagine.'

'Oh, I doubt he'd do that,' Tolliver said matter-of-factly. 'Listen, you took care of the girls when they were little.'

'You know I did. Cameron and me. Especially Gracie, she was so frail.' The automatic doors swooshed open and we went into the lobby. The desk clerk was eating a cookie. She glanced up at us, then went back to her book.

'Do you remember when Gracie went to the hospital?' Tolliver said.

'Sure I do. I was scared to death. She was maybe three months old, still real little. Her birth weight was low, remember? She was so sick, and she had been running a temperature for four days. We'd been hassling your dad to take her to the clinic or to the emergency room. Mom was so out of it that she couldn't go. No doctor would have let her leave with a baby in her arms. Your dad was really mad at us, but he got a phone call from some friend of his, and I guess the guy was repaying a loan or paying for some dope or something, because all of a sudden Matthew decided he would take Gracie. We barely had time to change her diaper and remind him how to buckle her in the car seat before he drove off. He took her to Wadley.'

'How do you know that?'

I unlocked the room door and pushed it open. 'What do you mean, how do I know that? He took her to the hospital. He brought her back after a couple of weeks. They'd had her in ICU, so we couldn't see her.

He stayed with her. How could it not have been true? When he brought her back Gracie looked so much better, I could hardly believe it was . . .' I froze.

'You couldn't believe it was Gracie, could you?' Tolliver said after a long silence.

I put my hand over my mouth. Tolliver carefully sat down on the edge of the couch.

When I could move, I sat down on the chair and our eyes met. 'No,' I said. 'I couldn't believe it was Gracie. Her eyes were a hazy blue, but a few weeks after her stay in the hospital, they turned out to be green. So I figured she was older than most babies when their eyes change to their real color. And Matthew said that the doctors told him to put her back on just the bottle, even though she'd started to eat some baby food . . .'

'You took care of Gracie more than Cameron did.'

'Yeah, I did. Cameron was so busy that year, it was her senior year, and I was home more because of the lightning strike.'

'Were you still having trouble with the aftereffects?'

'Oh, yeah, you remember, I had trouble for months. Before I learned to cope. I had terrible headaches, and a lot of pain. But I did my best for Gracie and Mariella,' I said, knowing I sounded defensive.

'Of course you did. You kept all of us going. But my point is, there might have been things you didn't notice because you were having so many physical problems and you were so distracted by sensing the dead people.'

That had certainly been a terrible time in my life. Teenagers are ill equipped to cope with a huge gaping difference between themselves and other teens. 'Your point is that I might not have noticed some changes in the baby? You think Matthew left with one baby and came back with another. You're saying the real Gracie is dead.'

He nodded. 'It was Chip who came to the trailer some,' he said. 'I'm pretty sure I remember him. Maybe Drex, too, but Chip for sure. He had some drug deals with my dad.'

'Oh, my God,' I said. 'I thought they looked a bit familiar. And if one of them took Dr Bowden out to the ranch that night, and they wanted to get rid of a baby without killing it . . .'

'They might have called Matthew, who had a real sick baby that wasn't going to make it.'

'How could they? How could they imagine that Matthew would switch babies? Why would they want to, anyway?'

'If the baby was the biological child of Rich Joyce and Mariah Parish, then she would be literally worth millions.'

I couldn't speak for a minute. 'But why not just kill her, and then the millions would stay where they were? With the three Joyce grandchildren?'

'Maybe they didn't want to murder an infant.'

'They were willing to let Mariah die when she could've been saved.'

'There's a difference between letting someone die and killing someone. And between a grown woman who was pretty unscrupulous and an infant child. More practically, they might not have realized how close to death Mariah was until it was too late.'

I shook my head, dazed. 'So, if this is true, what do you think Matthew did with the real Gracie, his real daughter? Do you think he deliberately left with her that evening and exposed her or something?'

'I have no idea, and I'm not sure I really want to know . . . though I think we have to try to find out,' Tolliver said, and he sounded like an old man. 'But I wonder if he ever really intended to take her to the hospital.'

'The pictures?'

'He wants pictures of Gracie. He just took some of Mariella to give his story some weight,' Tolliver said.

'How did you figure this out?'

'He might have showed up at the skating rink thinking he could take pictures of the girls without us knowing, but we spotted him before he could do it, and the girls were scared of him. He'd already started trying to open communication with Iona and Hank by writing them a letter. When he didn't hear back, he probably thought he could sneak around them. After that didn't work out, he decided to try an open approach, and it worked. Iona and Hank wanted to demystify him so the girls wouldn't be so freaked, so they acted like his visit was normal. They were doing the right thing, but they couldn't imagine what his motives were.'

'What will we do?' I had my elbows resting on my knees, and now I buried my face in my hands. 'I can't wrap my head around all this. How did Cameron fit into all this? Was it just a coincidence that she went missing then?'

'Maybe we made the whole conspiracy up,' Tolliver said. 'Maybe we're as bad as those people who think JFK was shot by Martians.'

'I wish,' I said. 'I *wish*.'

'I wonder if Mark knows anything,' Tolliver said.

'We could call him.'

'Yeah, but Dad's staying there now.'

'Maybe he could meet us somewhere.'

'We'll call him tomorrow. After we go to Texarkana.'

'You sure you're up to that? You're not nearly finished with the antibiotics.'

'I think I'm enough better.'

'Sure, Dr Lang.'

'Hey, there are other things we need besides being super careful about my shoulder.'

'We'll see what the doctor says in the morning,' I told him, and he called me bossy. It felt nice, taking care of him. As upset as I was about the suspicion and the uncertainty surrounding Tolliver's dad, I felt a little proud that I had managed so far. We went to bed after some more rounds of fruitless discussion, and I don't think either of us slept very well that night. When Tolliver did fall asleep, he talked out loud; he only does that when he's really upset.

'*Save her,*' he said.

19

Instead of asking a nurse, I talked to Dr Spradling directly first thing the next morning. To my surprise, he agreed that Tolliver was doing well enough to travel a little, provided he didn't lift anything or exert himself much.

Being able to travel a little made a wonderful change in Tolliver.It was as if he'd been thinking of himself as a sick person because he had to stay still. Now he thought of himself as a well person with temporary problems. I was delighted (and relieved) to see the resolution and decisiveness come back into his face and bearing. But I reminded myself to stay mindful that I had to take care of him.

Since we weren't anchored to the hospital anymore, we checked out of the hotel. We didn't know what would happen during the day or if we'd come back to Garland to spend the night.

It felt so good to drive away from the urban sprawl. We were back on the interstate, together. For an hour we were able to act like we were leaving our problems behind. But the closer we got to Texarkana, the more our questions and uncertainties bore in on us.

We went past the turnoff to Clear Creek, and I said, 'We might have to stop here later.'

Tolliver nodded. We were pretty close to Texarkana by then, and we weren't feeling chatty.

Texarkana straddles the state line, of course, and about fifty thousand people live there. A shopping area has grown up along the interstate passage through the north part of town, a shopping area with all of the usual suspects. We hadn't lived close to that part of town. We'd lived in the raggedy part. Texarkana is not better or worse than any other southern town. Most of our classmates had come from decent homes, and they'd had decent parents. We'd simply drawn the short end of the stick.

The street where we'd lived was lined with trailers. Their virtue was that they weren't packed together in little parks, at least where we'd been. They each had a little lot. Ours had been planted on its lot with the end toward the road, so you pulled into a rutted driveway and swung around to park in the front yard. Well, it was a yard in that it was a space in front of the trailer, but it never had had any grass, and the azaleas that had once been on either side of the concrete steps had been sickly bushes that were hardly worth the trouble.

Seeing it again was strange. We sat in the car, pulled to the side of the road, and looked at it without talking. A Latino walking by stared at us with a hard face. We no longer looked like we belonged here.

'What do you feel?' Tolliver asked.

'I don't feel any bodies,' I said, and the relief made me almost giddy. 'I don't know why I was scared I would. I would've known when we lived here, if – anyone – had been buried here.'

Tolliver closed his eyes for a moment, feeling his own measure of relief. 'Well, that's something,' he said. 'Where do you think we should look next?'

'I'm not sure why we felt like we had to come here,' I said. 'Where should we go next? I guess we should go to Renaldo's place. The chances aren't too good that he and Tammy are still there, but we can try.'

'Do you remember how to get there?'

That was a good question, and it took me ten minutes longer than I'd assumed it would take to find the ratty little rent house that Renaldo and Tammy had lived in when Cameron had been taken.

I wasn't surprised when someone I didn't know answered the door. She was an African American, about my age, and she had two children under school age. They were both busy with safety scissors and an old Penney's catalog, making some kind of art project. 'Just cut out the things you'd want in your house when you build one,' the woman reminded them, before turning back to me. 'What can I do for you?' she asked.

'I'm Harper Connelly, and I used to live a couple of blocks over,' I said. 'My stepfather used to have some friends that lived in this house, and I was wondering if you knew where they live now. Renaldo Simpkins and his girlfriend, Tammy?' I hadn't been able to remember Tammy's last name.

Her face changed. 'Yeah, I know 'em,' she said. 'They live in another house, about six streets over. On Malden. They bad people, you know.'

I nodded. 'I know, but I have to talk to them. They're still to-gether?'

'Yeah, hard to believe anyone would stay with Renaldo. But he had himself an accident, and Tammy, she's taking care of him.' The woman glanced back over her shoulder, and I could tell she was anxious to get back to the kids.

'You know their house number?'

'No, but it's on Malden, and it's a block or two west of this house,' she said. 'It's a brown house with white shutters. Tammy drives a white car.'

'Thanks.'

She nodded and shut her door.

I relayed all this to Tolliver, who'd remained in the car.

With some difficulty, we tracked down a house we thought was the right one. 'Brown' covers a lot of territory. But we suspected a sort of flesh-colored house might fall under the umbrella of brown, and there was a white car in front.

'Tammy,' I said when she answered the door. Tammy – whose last name was Murray, I suddenly remembered – had aged more than the eight years since Cameron had been gone. She had been a full-figured woman of mixed race, with wavy reddish hair and a flamboyant style. Now her hair was cropped very short and slicked to her head with some kind of gel. She had tattoos running down her bare arms. She was gaunt.

'Who are you?' she asked with some curiosity. 'You know me?'

'I'm Harper,' I said. 'Matthew Lang's stepdaughter. My brother is in the car.' I pointed.

'Come in,' she said. 'Tell your brother to come, too.'

I went back to the car and opened the door for Tolliver. 'She wants us to come in,' I said quietly. 'You think that's all right?'

'Should be,' he said, and we walked back to the porch.

'What happened to you, Tolliver?' Tammy said. 'You're all banged up.'

'I got shot,' he said.

This was a place where no one would be surprised by that, and Tammy only said, 'Bad luck, man!' before moving aside so we could enter.

The house was tiny, but since there wasn't much furniture, it didn't feel too crowded. The living room was big enough for a couch, where a figure was lying wrapped up in a blanket, and a battered recliner, clearly Tammy's normal station. It was flanked by an old TV tray laden with a remote control, Kleenex, and a package of cigarettes. Everything smelled like cigarette smoke.

We came around the corner of the couch to look at the man lying on it. If I hadn't known this was Renaldo, I would never have guessed it. Renaldo, who was also of mixed race, had always been light skinned. He'd also had a pencil mustache and worn his hair pulled back in a braid. Now his hair was cut very short. At one time, Renaldo had made what passed for good money in our neighborhood, because he'd been a mechanic at a car dealership, but his drug habit had cost him his job.

His eyes were open, but I couldn't tell if Renaldo was registering our presence or not.

'Hey, honey!' Tammy said. 'Look who's here. Tolliver and his sister, you remember them? Matthew's kids?'

Renaldo's eyelids flickered, and he murmured, 'Sure, I remember.'

'I'm sorry to see you in such bad shape,' Tolliver said, which was honest if not tactful.

'Can't walk,' Renaldo said. I looked around for a wheelchair and glimpsed one leaning against the back door in the kitchen. It almost seemed that since the house was so small, opening up the wheelchair would be a waste of time, but I guess Tammy couldn't lift Renaldo.

'We had a wreck,' Tammy said. 'About three years ago. We've had some bad luck, sure enough. Here, Harper, take this chair and I'll get a couple from the table in the kitchen.'

Tolliver looked frustrated that he couldn't go to get the chairs, but Tammy didn't think anything about doing it herself. She was used to a male that was helpless. I didn't ask any more questions about Renaldo's condition, because I didn't want to know. He looked bad.

'Tammy,' Tolliver said after he and our hostess had wedged themselves into the folding chairs, which barely fit in the room, 'we need to talk about the day my father was here, the day Cameron was taken.'

'Oh, sure, that's all you folks ever want to talk about,' she said, and made a face. 'We're tired of talking about that, ain't we, Renaldo?'

'I'm not tired of it,' he said, in his oddly muffled voice. 'That Cameron was a fine girl; losing her was bad.'

I felt like I'd bitten a lemon, the idea of someone like Renaldo looking at my sister made me feel so sour. But I tried to keep a pleasant expression on my face. 'Can you please tell us again about that day?' I said.

Tammy shrugged. She lit a cigarette, and I tried to hold my breath as long as I could. 'It's been a long time,' she said. 'I can't believe me and Renny been together that long, can you, baby?'

'Good years,' he said, with an effort.

'Yeah, we had some good ones,' she said tolerantly. 'These aren't them, though. Well, that afternoon, your dad called, wanted to do some business with Renny. He told the cops he was going to take some stuff to the recycle with Renny, but that wasn't the truth. We had an overstock on Oxys; your dad had some Ritalin he wanted to swap for it. Your mama, she loved her Oxys.'

'My mom loved everything,' I said.

'That is the truth, child,' Tammy said. 'She loved her pills.'

'And her alcohol,' I said.

'That, too,' Tammy said. She looked at me. 'But you aren't here about your mother. She's dead and gone.'

I shut my mouth.

'So my dad wanted to come over,' Tolliver prompted.

'Yes,' Tammy said, taking a big drag on her cigarette. I was afraid I was going to start coughing. 'He came over about four. Give or take fifteen minutes. It might have been as late as four fifteen, four twenty-five, but it wasn't any later than that, because the TV show I was watching was over at four thirty, and he was at our house by then and in the pool room with Renaldo. They were playing a game. We had a nicer house.' She looked around the tiny room. 'Bigger. I told the police, I think he was here by a few minutes after four. But I wasn't paying too much attention until my program ended, and they called to me to bring them a beer.'

Renaldo laughed, an eerie huh-huh-huh sound. 'We drank us some beer,' he said. 'I won the game. We swapped some pills, made a deal. That was a good time.'

'And he stayed here until he got a phone call?'

'Yeah, he had a cell phone, you know, for business,' Tammy said. 'That guy who lived next door to you-all, he was calling to tell Matthew to get his ass home, the cops were all over the place.'

'Was he surprised?'

'Yeah,' Tammy said, somewhat to my surprise. 'He thought they were there about the drugs, and he flipped out. But he figured he'd better go home rather than run, because he knew your mama couldn't stand up to being questioned.'

'He did?' I was really astonished.

'Oh, yeah,' Tammy said. 'He had big love for Laurel, you know, girl.'

Tolliver and I exchanged glances. If Renaldo and Tammy were right, Matthew hadn't known anything about Cameron's disappearance. Or could he have been acting, to establish an alibi?

'He had a fit,' Renaldo mumbled. 'He didn't want that girl gone. I visited him at the jail. He told me he was sure she run away.'

'Did you believe him?' I leaned forward and looked at Renaldo, which was painful but necessary.

'Yes,' Renaldo said clearly. 'I believed him.'

There wasn't much point staying after that, and we were glad to get out of the reeking little house and away from its hopeless inhabitants.

I could hardly wait for Tolliver to buckle his seat belt. I backed out of the yard without having any idea where we were going. I began to drive back to Texas Boulevard, just to have a direction. 'So, what do you think?' I asked.

'I think Tammy is repeating what my dad told her,' Tolliver said. 'Whether or not he was telling the truth, that's another thing.'

'She believed him.'

Tolliver made a derisive sound, practically a snort. 'Let's see if we can talk to Pete Gresham,' he said, and I headed for the police department. There are two police departments in one building on State Line Avenue, the Texas and the Arkansas police. There are two different police chiefs. I don't know how it all works, or who pays for what.

We found Pete Gresham working at his desk. We'd been given permission to go up to his office, and he was poring over a file on his desk, a file he shut when he saw us standing before him.

'You two! Good to see you! I'm sorry the tape didn't pan out,' he said, standing and leaning over the desk to shake Tolliver's good hand. 'I hear you had a little trouble in Big D.'

'Well, the outskirts of Big D,' I said. 'We were in the neighborhood, and we thought we'd stop by to ask what you knew about the anonymous caller who tipped you off about the woman who looked like Cameron.'

'Male, call came in from a pay phone.' Pete Gresham, a big man who was a little bigger every time I saw him, shrugged. He still didn't wear glasses, but as Rudy Flemmons had told us, there wasn't a hair on Gresham's head. 'Not much to tell.'

'Could we hear it?' Tolliver asked. I turned to look at him. That had come out of nowhere.

'Well, I'll have to track the recording down,' Pete said. He got up and headed toward the elevator, and I said, 'What made you think of that?'

'We might as well,' Tolliver said.

But Pete was back too quickly. I know my bureaucracies, and he couldn't have found the recording that quickly. 'Sorry, you two,' he said. 'The guy who stores all that stuff is off today. He'll be in tomorrow. Can I call you and play it over the phone to you?'

'Sure, that'd be fine,' I said. I gave him my cell phone number.

'You making a good living finding corpses?' he asked.

'Yeah, we do okay,' Tolliver said.

'Hear you stopped a bullet,' Pete said. 'Whose toes did you step on?'

'Hard to say,' Tolliver said, and he smiled. 'Matthew's out of jail, by the way.'

The detective looked a lot more serious. 'I forgot he was due to get out. He turn up in Dallas?'

I nodded.

'Don't let him get you down,' Pete said. 'He's one of the bad ones. I've known guys like him my whole working life, and as a rule, they don't change none.'

'I agree,' I said. 'And we're doing our best to keep away from him.'

'How's those little sisters?' We were walking to the elevator now, and Pete was escorting us.

'They're good. Mariella just turned twelve and Gracie is going on nine.' Maybe she was younger. In fact, I was sure she was younger. It was a strange moment to think it, but I realized that Gracie's being classified as lagging behind in her age group might be an incorrect diagnosis. The lag in her development that we'd attributed to her low birth weight and her persistent bad health might actually have been due to her real birth date being three or four months later than we'd believed.

'I can't imagine them that old.' Pete shook his head at the passage of time, and I pulled myself back into the here and now to say, 'By the way, I talked to Ida the other day.'

'Ida? The woman who saw the blue truck? What did Ida have to say?'

When I told him about Ida's conversation with the Meals on Wheels woman, he cursed a blue streak. Then he apologized. 'Idiots,' he said. 'Now I gotta call the woman and then I'll have to go see Ida again. I swear someday I'm not going to get out of that house. She'll say she don't want any visitors, and once I get there, she'll talk and talk until I think I'm going deaf.'

I tried to smile, but I couldn't squeeze one out. Tolliver just nodded.

'I see what that does to the timeline, Harper. I promise you, any time I get a lead I chase it down. I want to know what happened to your sister about as much as you do. And I'm sorry your asshole of a father ever got out of jail.'

'I am, too,' I said, not sure if I could speak for Tolliver or not. 'But we don't think he took Cameron.'

'I don't either,' Pete said, which surprised me quite a bit. 'I know what you can do, Harper, and I remember seeing you and Tolliver riding around after you graduated from high school. I know you were looking for her. If you didn't find her, I don't think she's here to be found. If Matthew did it, he'd have had to bury her close, real close, and he didn't have much time. You would've found her.'

I nodded. 'We tried,' I said. 'Unless someone took her from the parking lot at the high school and just dumped her bag along the route back to the trailer, which would widen the search area . . .'

'We did think of that,' Pete said mildly.

I flushed. 'I'm not . . .'

'It's okay. You want to find your sister. I do, too.'

'Thanks, Pete,' Tolliver said and shook his hand again.

'You get better now, you hear,' Pete said and turned to walk back to his cubicle.

'We've wasted a lot of time here today,' I said. I was depressed and wondering what to do next.

'I don't know about that,' Tolliver said. 'We've learned a little. You want to drop by to say hello to the Clevelands?'

I thought about it. My foster parents were good people, and I respected them, but I wasn't in the mood for catch-up conversation. 'I guess not,' I said. 'I guess we ought to head back to Garland.'

The cell phone rang. 'Hello,' I said.

'Harper, this is Lizzie.'

She sounded shaky. Though our acquaintance was limited, I'd never heard Lizzie sound less than positive and forceful.

'What's wrong, Lizzie?'

'Oh, gosh, nothing! We were wondering where you were . . . if you could stop by the ranch for a minute.'

Stop by the ranch? When for all they knew, we were two hours' drive away in Garland?

'We're in Texarkana right now,' I said, thinking furiously but not coming up with anything. 'I guess we could come by. What do you need?'

'I just wanted to touch base with you. About poor Victoria, and a couple of other things.'

I relayed all this to Tolliver in fewer words. He looked as taken aback as I felt. 'Do you feel up to this? I can tell her no,' I said.

'We might as well stop by. We're in the area, and they know a lot of people.' The Joyces knew a lot of people with disposable income who might want to have some graves read.

I found myself wondering if we'd see Chip again. There was definitely something about the ranch manager/boyfriend that interested me, and it wasn't a physical attraction. At least not in the 'I want to jump your bones' sense. But bones had something to do with it . . .

We didn't talk much as we drove out of Texarkana. I was puzzled and worried by Lizzie's odd request, and Tolliver was thinking about something that worried him, too. I could tell by the way he sat and the tense muscles of his face. We took the exit off the interstate without any further discussion.

We drove by Pioneer Rest Cemetery and turned off onto the long driveway that ran between wide rolling fields. We could see miles in every direction, even with evening drawing in. Finally, we reached the gate to RJ Ranch, and Tolliver insisted on jumping out to open and then close the gate after I drove through.

I noticed that I couldn't see anyone, anywhere. On our previous visit, we'd been able to see people moving around in the distance.

We pulled up in the large paved parking area in front of the big house. We got out of our car and looked around. Everything seemed still. It was a warm day; in fact, it felt like it was spring. But the hush seemed abnormal. I shook my head doubtfully, but after a shrug, Tolliver led the way up the brick-paved path.

The big front door swung open, and Lizzie stood framed by the rectangle. The entrance hall behind her was shadowy. Talk about abnormal; though she was obviously making a huge effort to smile at us, it seemed more like the grin of a skull. Her eyes were as round as quarters and tension screamed in every muscle.

Red alert. Our steps slowed.

'Hey, you-all, come on in.' All the natural enthusiasm she'd shown when we'd met here the first time had been replaced by an intense anxiety.

'We shouldn't have said we'd come by, we have an appointment in Dallas,' I said. 'Lizzie, can we come back tomorrow? We really can't miss this date we have.'

I saw the relief on Lizzie's narrow face. 'Well, just give me a call tonight,' she said. 'You-all drive on to Dallas.'

'Oh, come in and have a drink,' Chip said from behind her.

She twitched, and her attempt at a smile vanished. 'Get back in the car,' she said, 'Get out!'

'You better not,' Chip said, his voice calm and level. 'You better come on in.' We saw that he had a revolver in his hand. That clarified our choice.

Chip and Lizzie backed up.

'I'm sorry,' she said to me. 'I'm sorry. He said he'd shoot Kate if I didn't call you.'

'I would have done it, too,' Chip said.

'I know you would,' I told him. As we eased past Lizzie and stood in the square foyer, waiting for further directions, I understood what had fascinated me about Chip. His bones. His bones were dead. This was a strange connection, and one I'd never experienced before; or if I had, I hadn't understood its nature.

'Where is everyone?' Tolliver asked. His voice was as calm as Chip's.

'I sent everyone on the payroll to the farthest places on the ranch I could think of, and it's Rosita's day off,' Chip said. He was smiling again, bright and hard, and I sure would have liked to wipe that look off his face. 'It's just me and the family.'

Shit.

Chip herded us all down the hall to the gun room. The light was still streaming in all the French doors, and the view was just as beautiful, but now I was in no mood to admire it.

Drex was standing there. He had a gun, too, which was a surprise. Kate was tied to a chair. They'd released Lizzie to lure us in the house. The ropes were loose around another chair.

'Good to see you again, Harper,' Drex said. 'We had a good time at the Outback, didn't we?'

'It was all right,' I said. 'It was too bad that Victoria was murdered after that. Kind of ruined my memory of the evening.'

He gulped and looked upset, just for a split second. 'Yeah, she was a nice woman,' he said. 'She seemed like a . . . She seemed good at what she did.'

'She worked hard for you-all,' I said.

'You think they'll ever find out who killed her?' Chip said. He smiled some more.

'Did you shoot Tolliver?' I asked him. There didn't seem to be much point in keeping quiet about it.

'Naw,' he said. 'That was my buddy Drex, here. Drex ain't good for much, but he can shoot. I told Drex to shoot *you*, but he seemed reluctant.' He said the word slowly, as if he'd just learned it. 'He didn't want to shoot a woman. Ol' Drex is gallant in his own way. I tried to correct his thinking a few nights later when you were out running, but damn if that cop didn't jump in front of you and take the bullet. I wouldn't have fired if I'd known he was a cop. I thought he looked sort of familiar, and it made me sick when I heard I'd shot a football player.'

'Why shoot us at all?'

'Because you knew about Mariah, and you told. Maybe I could get Lizzie to forget about it if you died, but I knew as long as you lived she'd think about what you said at the cemetery. She'd wonder about her grandfather's death, and she'd ask herself who wanted him dead. Then she'd go looking, if she believed there was a baby. Lizzie would love to have a kid to raise, and she's all about family.' He dug the gun into Lizzie's neck, and he kissed her on the mouth. She spat when he drew away, and he laughed.

'Why would I have to be dead?' I was genuinely curious.

''Cause that's the way my baby is. She pays attention to things when they're right in front of her, but if they're out of sight, they're out of mind.'

That seemed like underrating Lizzie, to me. But he knew her better than I ever would. I understood, after a second's thought. Chip knew that failing to prevent me from coming to Texas was his big mistake. If I died, my death would erase that mistake. Of course that couldn't be done. But it would make him feel better.

'Lizzie, I'm sure someone drew your attention to my website,' I said. 'I'm sure someone pointed you in the right direction, thought it might be interesting to have me here to look at your graveyard.'

'Yeah,' Lizzie said. The sun was shining onto the terrace at an angle; it was about three thirty in the afternoon. 'Yeah, Kate did.'

'How'd you come to think of that, Kate?' I asked.

Kate was clearly in a bad state. Her face was white, her breathing panicky. Her hands were tied to the arms of the chair, and I saw her wrists were chafed raw. It took her a moment to understand the question.

'Drex,' she said, her voice jerky. 'Drex told me that he'd met you once.'

Chip's head whipped around like he was a snake about to strike. 'Drex, thanks to you, we've lost everything,' he said in a deadly voice. 'What were you thinking?'

'It come on the TV when we were watching the news,' Drex whispered. 'About her being in North Carolina, finding those boys' bodies. I told Kate I'd gone to her trailer when she was living in Texarkana, 'cause I knew her stepfather. I'd met her.'

'And you told Lizzie,' I said to Kate.

'She's always looking for something new,' Kate said. 'That's the name of the game, here. Find things for Lizzie, keep her happy.'

Lizzie looked absolutely astounded. If we lived through this day, she would have a lot of mental rearranging to do.

'So it's a TV newscaster that brought me down.' Chip laughed, and it was an awful sound.

'How much of a snake handler are you, Chip?' I asked.

'Oh, now, that's Drex's strong point,' he said, grinning at the man standing beside him.

'Jesus, no!' Lizzie said, shocked out of her senses. 'Drex? Chip, are you saying that *Drex* threw a rattler at Granddaddy?'

'That's what I'm sayin', darlin',' Chip said. His grip on Lizzie's shoulder never wavered.

'Have you gone nuts, man?' Drexell said, and his face looked different now. He didn't look as bewildered and befuddled as he had. He didn't look as weak as he had. He looked craftier and harder. 'Why are you telling my sisters lies?'

'Because we're not going to get away with it,' Chip said. 'You hadn't gotten that yet, I see.' Drexell looked blank. 'There're too many loose ends, fool. We should have killed the doctor. Yes, you asshole, sometime within the past few years we should have moseyed on over to Dallas and taken care of that old idiot. And we knew Matthew was getting out of jail sooner or later. We should have been waiting outside the gate for him with a gun.'

Now there was a sentiment I could agree with.

'You say we're not going to get away with it,' Drex said. 'So why are you doing this hostage thing? I thought you were playing a deeper game. I thought you had a plan. You're just crazy.'

'Yes, I am, and I'll tell you why,' Chip said. He let go of Lizzie's shoulder, and she swung around to face him, taking a step backward, closer to the wall covered with guns. 'I had me an appointment with a much better doctor than Bowden last week, and you know what he told me? I'm eaten up with cancer. At thirty-two! And I don't give a fuck what happens when I'm not on the earth anymore. I don't have long enough to live for you-all to do anything to me. Since I'm not getting away with anything, I sure as hell don't want ol' Drex to.'

His eyes were mean beyond belief when he said this.

'You're going to die?' said Lizzie. 'Well, *good*. I wish Drex had cancer, too. I want you both to die.' She seemed to have shaken off her fear, and I wished I could do the same. I looked at Tolliver, and I thought we would not make it through this. Chip would take us all out, because we were going to live and he wasn't.

With one incredibly fast motion, Lizzie grabbed a rifle off the wall, the one right by one of the doors. It was pointed at Chip in a split second. 'Go on and shoot yourself, since you're going to die anyway!' She meant it, too, and she was ready with that rifle. 'Save me the trouble!'

'I'm not going by myself,' said her lover, and he shot Drexell Joyce in the chest.

Katie shrieked and went over backward in her chair, covered with the mist of her brother's blood, and as we all looked at the falling dead man, the screaming woman, Chip put the gun barrel in his mouth and fired at the same moment Lizzie did.

20

I was so tired after the sheriff's department finished with us that it was hard to focus when I got behind the wheel to drive back to Dallas. In fact, we never did make it to Garland. When I realized there was no real reason why we should, I pulled off at the next exit and got a room. We were just about out in the middle of nowhere, except it was nowhere with an interstate and a motel. It wasn't a very good motel, but we could be pretty sure that no one was going to shoot us through the window.

I was still confused about several things, but both the shooters were dead.

Tolliver took his medicine, and we crawled into the bed. The sheets felt cold and almost damp, and I got back out of bed to turn the heater up. It made the curtains billow in an unpleasant way. I've run into that before, and I keep a big clip in my overnight pack for just such a situation. It came in handy tonight. As I got between the sheets, I realized that Tolliver was already asleep.

When I woke, the sun was up outside. Tolliver was in the bathroom, trying to take a sponge bath, and he was grumbling to himself about it.

'What are you talking about in there?' I asked, sitting and swinging my legs out from under the covers.

'I want to shower,' he said. 'I want to shower more than anything.'

'I'm sorry,' I said, and I was. 'But we can't get the shoulder wet for a few more days.'

'Tonight we'll try taping a garbage bag or a grocery sack over it,' he said. 'If we tape it good, I can shower and be out before the tape starts to give.'

'We'll try,' I said. 'What should we do today?'

He didn't answer.

'Tolliver?'

Silence.

I got up and went into the bathroom. 'Hey, you, what's with the silent treatment?'

'Today,' he said, 'we have to go talk to my dad.'

'We have to,' I said, letting only a hint of a question seep into the words.

'We have to,' he said, absolutely positive.

'And then?'

'We're going to ride off into the sunset,' he said. 'We're going to go back to St Louis and be by ourselves for a while.'

'Oh, that sounds good. I wish we could skip the part about your dad and go right into the "be by ourselves." '

'I thought you'd be straining to get at him.' He'd started working on his stubble, and he paused, one cheek still gleaming with shaving gel.

I'd thought so, too. 'There's a lot I almost don't want to know,' I said. 'I never imagined I'd feel like this. I've waited so long.'

He put his good arm around me and held me close. 'I thought about leaving Texas today,' he said. 'I thought about it. But we can't.'

'No,' I said.

I called Dr Spradling's nurse that morning and told her, as I'd been instructed, that Tolliver wasn't running a temperature, wasn't bleeding, and his wound didn't look red. She reminded me to make sure he took his medicine, and that was that. Despite the shocks of the previous day, Tolliver looked better than he had since the night he was shot, and I was sure he was going to be fine.

The drive into Dallas was easy, with only a few traffic snarls. We had to find Mark's house, which we'd visited only once before. Mark was a solitary man, and I wondered how he and Matthew were getting along together.

To my surprise, Mark's car was parked in the little driveway. His home was smaller than Iona's, which made it mighty small indeed. I automatically noted the buzz around the neighborhood, and it was faint. No dead people here.

There was a narrow raised strip of concrete running from the driveway to the front door. There were cobwebs on the lighting fixtures on either side of the door, and the landscaping was non-existent. It looked like a house that the owner didn't care about.

Mark answered the door. 'Hey, what you two doing over here in my neck of the woods?' he said. 'You come to see Dad?'

'Yes, we have,' Tolliver said. 'He's here?'

'Yeah. Dad,' Mark called. 'Tolliver and Harper are here.' He moved back so we could step inside. He was wearing sweatpants and an old T-shirt. Clearly, he wasn't going in to work today. He caught me looking. 'Sorry,' he said, 'it's my day off. I didn't dress for company.'

'We didn't give you any warning,' I said. The living room was almost as basic as Renaldo's: a big leather couch and matching chair, a big-screen TV, and a coffee table. No lamps for reading. No books. One picture, a framed one of the five of us kids, taken at the trailer. I had forgotten there was one of all of us.

'Who took that?' I asked, surprised.

'Some friend of your mom's,' Mark said. 'Dad packed it away with the other stuff when he went to jail. He just got it out when he got the stuff out of storage.'

I stood looking at the picture, tears in my eyes. Tolliver and Mark were standing side by side. Mark wasn't smiling. Tolliver's lips were turned up slightly, but his eyes were grim. Cameron was by Mark, and she had her arm around him, and she was holding Mariella's hand. Mariella was smiling; like most very little kids, she'd loved to have her picture made. I was holding Gracie, and she was so little! Which Gracie was it? Gracie after the hospital.

'This was taken not long before,' I said.

'Not long before what?'

'You know,' I said, astonished. 'Not long before Cameron was gone.'

He shrugged, as if I might have meant something else.

We were still standing when Matthew came in. He was wearing jeans and a flannel shirt. 'I've got to get to work in an hour, but it's great to see you,' he said to Tolliver, then turned his face so his smile could include me.

Thanks, but no.

'We went to see the Joyces yesterday,' I said. 'Chip and Drex were talking about you.'

I wasn't imagining the alarm that flashed across Matthew's face then. 'Oh, what did they have to say? That's that rich family, right? On the ranch?'

'You know who they are,' Tolliver said. 'You know they came by the trailer.'

Mark looked from his brother to his father. 'Those rich guys?' he said. 'They're who you and Harper went to work for last week?'

'We've had conversations with quite a few people recently,' I said. 'Including Ida, remember her?'

'The old woman who saw your sister getting into a blue truck,' Matthew said.

'Except she didn't,' I said. 'Turns out it wasn't Cameron.'

The surprise on their faces seemed more or less genuine. That is, they were surprised about *something*.

'I saw you at the doctor's office,' I said to Matthew.

He was surprised again. 'I went to see a doctor a couple of days ago,' he said cautiously, 'about this cough I've had since I got out of—'

'Oh, shut up,' I said. 'We know you took Mariah's baby. What we don't know is what happened to the real Gracie.'

There was a long moment of silence; there seemed to be no air in the cramped living room.

'That's crazy talk, Tol,' Mark said. 'Who's this Mariah?'

'Dad knows, Mark,' Tolliver said. 'Tell us all, Dad, who is the little girl living with Hank and Iona?'

'That little girl,' Matthew said, 'is the daughter of Mariah Parish and Chip Moseley.'

This was so not what I'd expected. 'Not Rich Joyce and Mariah,' I said, just to be sure I understood.

'Chip told me old Mr Joyce never had sex with Mariah,' Matthew said. 'Chip said the baby was his.'

Mark was looking from speaker to speaker, and he really didn't seem to know what we were talking about.

'Chip had been buying drugs from me,' Matthew said. 'He and Drex liked to come to our part of town to party. Chip was always smart and hard. He'd been raised in foster homes, and he was determined to make a place for himself with the rich people. So he started work for Rich Joyce, started out low, worked his butt off until Rich really depended on him. After his divorce, he gradually got Lizzie interested in him. He knew Mariah; she was in the foster home with him. Chip helped her get the job with the Peadens, and she learned a lot while she was there. Chip made sure Rich got to know the Peadens well enough that he was able to introduce him to Mariah. Then when old Mr Peaden died, it was natural for Mariah to ask Rich if he had a job for her. He'd had the stroke, and he knew his family wanted him to have someone. It tickled him to have someone as young and pretty as Mariah around, even if he didn't plan on making any moves on her. She knew his heart was weak. She knew he was fond of her. She just hoped he'd leave her some money. She liked the old man.'

'So what happened?' I asked.

'She didn't plan on getting pregnant, but when she did, she put off doing anything about it until it was too late. She wore loose clothes and overalls and such because she didn't want the old man to know she was somebody else's bedmate. And she was afraid he'd find out if she had an abortion. She was tough, but she wasn't tough enough to do that. Chip went nuts when he found out. She was maybe eight months along by then. He came over to Texarkana to get some dope; he wanted to be numb for a while, not think about it. While he was at my place, Drex called on his cell to say that he was all alone in the house with Mariah, and something had gone wrong. Mariah had had the baby all by herself, but she wouldn't stop bleeding. And by the time he'd cut the cord and wrapped up the baby – he'd helped deliver calves and foals – she was near dead. Chip bolted out and the next I heard from him was when he called me about taking the kid off his hands.'

'Chip didn't want her at all.'

'No,' said Matthew. 'He didn't.'

'And you offered to help him out, maybe thinking that someday you might get some money out of the Joyce girls by saying that the baby was their grandfather's.'

'I know it was pretty low,' Matthew said. His deep-set eyes looked shadowed. 'I know that. But you know how I was then. It sounded like a good moneymaking scheme, one I could leave on the back burner, in case we ever needed it.'

'And your own baby was about to die because you hadn't taken her to a doctor,' I said. 'Or was she already dead when Chip called?'

'That's where you got the different baby!' Mark said. I'd never seen so much emotion on his face. 'Dad, why didn't you tell me?'

Now it was Matthew's turn to look confused. 'You knew it wasn't really Gracie?' he said to his son. 'I never worried about you! You were hardly ever around. How'd you know?'

And all of a sudden, everything clicked into place.

'I know how,' I said. 'Cameron told him. She didn't know right away, any more than the rest of us did. It took her a while to figure it out. But when she did her senior biology project, she did it on eye color and genetics. You and my mom couldn't have had a green-eyed child.'

Mark collapsed onto the couch. His legs simply gave out from under him. 'Dad, she was going to call the police,' he said. 'She was going to tell them you'd kidnapped a kid to take Gracie's place, because Gracie had died.'

'It was you, Mark,' I said, feeling that my voice was coming from somewhere very far away. 'It was you. You picked her up when she was on her way back from school. You told her – what did you tell her?'

'I told her that you'd had an accident,' he said. 'I was on my motorbike that day, so I told her to leave the backpack by the road. She didn't ask any questions. She got on. I went toward the hospital, but I pulled off at an empty gas station because I told her something was wrong with my bike. I told her to go around back to see if there was an air pump. I went after her.'

'How did you do it?' I said, very quietly.

He looked up at me with an expression I hope I never see again. He was ashamed, he was horrified, and he was pleased. 'I choked her to death,' he said. 'I have big hands, and she was so small. It didn't take long. I had to leave her there, because I couldn't get her back on the bike. I went later, with Dad's truck. I wanted to leave her there, but I was afraid you'd find her, you freak.'

My head swam and I sat abruptly on the armchair. Tolliver hit Mark with everything he had, and Mark collapsed sideways, bleeding from the mouth. Matthew was standing exactly where he'd been, his mouth literally hanging open.

'I did it for you, Dad,' Mark mumbled. He spat out blood and a tooth. 'Dad, I did it for you.'

'And then they arrested me anyway,' Matthew said, as if that was the important part of the story.

'Where is she, Mark?'

'You and your family,' he said. 'You've been nothing but trouble. First the baby, then Cameron going to call the police on Dad, and now you getting Tolliver to marry you.'

'Where is my sister, Mark?' I wanted to bury her, finally. I wanted to know where her bones were. I wanted to recognize her one last time. Somewhere over in Texarkana, she waited for me. I just wanted a location so I could get in the car and start driving. I could call Pete Gresham and ask him to meet me there.

'I'm not going to tell you,' he said. 'You can't have me arrested unless you find her, and I'm not going to tell you. My dad won't say a word, and my brother won't, either. Our word against yours.'

'*Where is my sister?*'

Matthew was still staring at Mark as if he'd never seen him before.

'Of course I'll tell the police,' Tolliver said. 'Why wouldn't I, Mark?'

'We're family, Tol. If you tell them about Cameron, then we'll have to tell them about Gracie, and she won't belong to anybody but Chip. Iona and Hank would have to give her up. You can imagine what Chip will do with her.'

'Chip's dead, Mark. He killed himself yesterday.'

Mark looked blank for a minute. Then he said, 'So then she'll go to foster care, like Harper had to.'

'You're trying to blackmail me into keeping quiet about my sister's death by threatening my other sister? Mark, you are lower than a snake's belly,' I said. 'I can't imagine you being related to Tolliver.'

'That's the deal,' Mark said, and his mouth set in a mulish way.

There was a knock at the door. Talk about bad timing.

I was the only one who could move, apparently, so I got up and went to the door. It was a relief to be facing away from Mark and Matthew.

I was so numb I wasn't even startled to see Manfred. 'This is a very bad time,' I said, but I waited for him to tell me why he was there.

'He's got a rental shed under another name,' Manfred said. 'He brought her body with him. I know where it is.'

We all froze in place. Finally I said, 'Oh, thank God.' Tears were running down my cheeks.

We called the police. I thought it took them hours to get there, though only a few minutes passed. It was really hard to explain what had happened.

We'd taken Mark's plastic key from his wallet before we climbed into Manfred's car. Tolliver was sitting in the backseat. He'd explained to the patrol car officers that his brother had just confessed to murdering his stepsister, and he was sure his dad would want to stay to be with his son, and then we were out the door. We got into the storage compound by using the key, and when the gate rolled away, we drove in, leaving it open behind us. There was a police car on its way, but we weren't going to wait any longer.

'I knew it was him, after I touched the backpack,' Manfred said, trying to suppress the pride in his voice. 'So I followed him.'

'That's what you've been doing the past couple of days.'

'He came here twice in that time,' Manfred said.

I found that amazing. Did Mark feel so guilty that he had to keep revisiting Cameron's body? Or was he like a squirrel storing something choice for the winter, so afraid someone would steal it that he had to keep checking?

I had never known Mark at all. And if I felt that way, how must his brother feel? I looked back at Tolliver, but I couldn't read his face.

Manfred stopped in front of the garage-style unit numbered 26 and used the key again.

The room wasn't half full. There were things I vaguely recognized as being from the trailer, and I wondered why anyone would save such things. Evidently, Mark had thought Matthew would want them someday. I looked at the clutter, closed my eyes, and began searching.

The buzzing came from a large blanket chest at the back of the unit. There was a box of magazines on top of it, and some pots and pans. I knocked all of them off. I put my hands on the lid. I couldn't open it. I reached inside with my lightning sense and . . .

I found my sister.

21

The legal mess surrounding Gracie – the girl I'd always thought was my sister Gracie – may take some time to unravel. With both her natural parents dead, it's not like her custody was in doubt. After all, Iona and Hank had legally adopted both girls. To them, it was irrelevant that one of the girls wasn't exactly who they'd thought she was. Iona and Hank, after a few minutes of shocked surprise, made up their minds they'd keep Gracie, no matter what. After all, Iona told me, when God had told her to take on the raising of those girls, he hadn't specified what their parentage was. If Gracie had really been the daughter of Rich Joyce, the complications would have been tremendous, and it was really just as well for Gracie that she wasn't. At least, that's what I thought.

Matthew went back to jail, though not for long enough. He hadn't murdered his own baby; not that anyone could prove. The real Gracie's tiny skeleton had vanished from the place where he said he'd buried her, in a public park off the interstate.

His story was that he'd set off to take Gracie to the hospital, but she'd died in the car on the way. He'd buried her and lied to us all about the ICU and the rest because he'd been afraid that my mom would go crazy if she knew Gracie was dead. (Since my mother had already been crazy for years by that time, I didn't believe him.) He's stayed away for a few days to give credence to his story that Gracie was in the hospital in ICU. When Chip called him, Matthew had been more than glad to take a baby whose dubious background he thought might come in handy someday; and of course, producing a healthy girl baby would also keep him from being accused of negligence. We'd expected to get Gracie back from the hospital. Only Cameron suspected that Matthew had sunk low enough to substitute another child.

Cameron's throat was crushed; there was enough left in the trunk to determine her cause of death. Mark confessed that she had shown him the genetic chart she'd made that proved my brown-eyed mother and her brown-eyed husband couldn't have a green-eyed daughter.

Cameron hadn't known whose baby 'Gracie' was, but since she had started with the certainty the child wasn't the same baby, Cameron's realization had explained several puzzling things about Gracie's different behavior since she'd come back 'from the hospital.' After Mark killed Cameron, he'd taken her body to the freezer of the restaurant where he worked and put her in a box at the back of the shelf in the meat locker for a couple of days. Then he'd rented the storage unit in Dallas and driven over there with her in the blanket chest, at the height of the hubbub over her disappearance. There she'd stayed, and he'd tossed in the items from the trailer when he'd moved himself to Dallas. He'd watched over her bones ever since.

Poor Cameron. She'd trusted the wrong person. Mark was the oldest, and steady; it was natural she would turn to him. She'd underestimated his devotion to his father. But she'd been sharp enough to put together all the puzzling things about the green-eyed baby living in our trailer.

I had noticed some puzzling changes, too. After all, I'd taken daily care of Gracie. But it had literally never occurred to me that the baby I was tending to wasn't my sister. I can only attribute that to the stress and strain caused by the lightning strike, and the fact that I couldn't imagine that Matthew would do such a thing, even as low as he got. I do remember marveling at how much Gracie's health had improved. It seems incredible now; I attributed it all to modern medicine.

Mark confessed – what choice did he have, after all. He's doing time now, hard time. I don't think I could stand to ever see him again.

Manfred got a load of free publicity, which I fed with as much fuel as I could. He got the offer of an appearance on one of those ghost-hunting shows, and he looked great on camera. He gets marriage proposals every week.

We never found out who the woman at the Texarkana mall had been. We didn't recognize the voice on the police tape, either. At least from now on, we can ignore any Cameron 'sightings.'

Tolliver and I went back to St Louis and got his shoulder checked out by a doctor there, who found all was well. We were glad to see our apartment. We turned down a job offer or two so we could stay home for a while.

We got married.

The girls might be disappointed because they didn't get to wear pretty dresses and pose in pictures, but we got married all by ourselves in front of a judge. I still call myself Harper Connelly, and Tolliver doesn't seem to mind.

When Cameron's remains were released, I brought them up to St Louis to bury. We bought her a nice headstone. Oddly enough, that didn't make me feel as wonderful as I thought it would. I visited her every day for a while, until I realized that for me, she'd be forever frozen in the moment of her death. I could not move on until I quit going to the grave. Still, at last I know what happened to her.

We'll hit the road again, soon. After all, we have to make some money.

And they're all out there waiting for me. All they want is to be found.

Acknowledgements

My thanks to Ivan Van Laningham, Kerry Hammond, Ashley Mc-Connell, Mary Fitzsimons, Gina and her anonymous friend, Beth Groundwater, my assistant and friend Paula Woldan, Nancy Hayes (my Gun Angel), and Dr Ed Uthman, a college crony, for their assistance in getting the details right. Any mistakes are my own, as much as I would love to blame someone else.

THE HALT PERSPECTIVE

Colonel Charles Irwin Halt

USAF Retired

in collaboration with

Retired UK West Midlands Police Detective

John Hanson

THE HALT PERSPECTIVE

First paperback edition printed 2016 in the United Kingdom.

A catalogue record for this book is available from the British Library.

ISBN 978-0-9574944-9-7

Published by *Haunted Skies Publishing*

Copies of this book will be available on Amazon.com

For any comments please email: johndawn1@sky.com

Telephone: 0121 445 0340

Designed and typeset by Bob Tibbitts ~ (iSET)

Printed in Great Britain

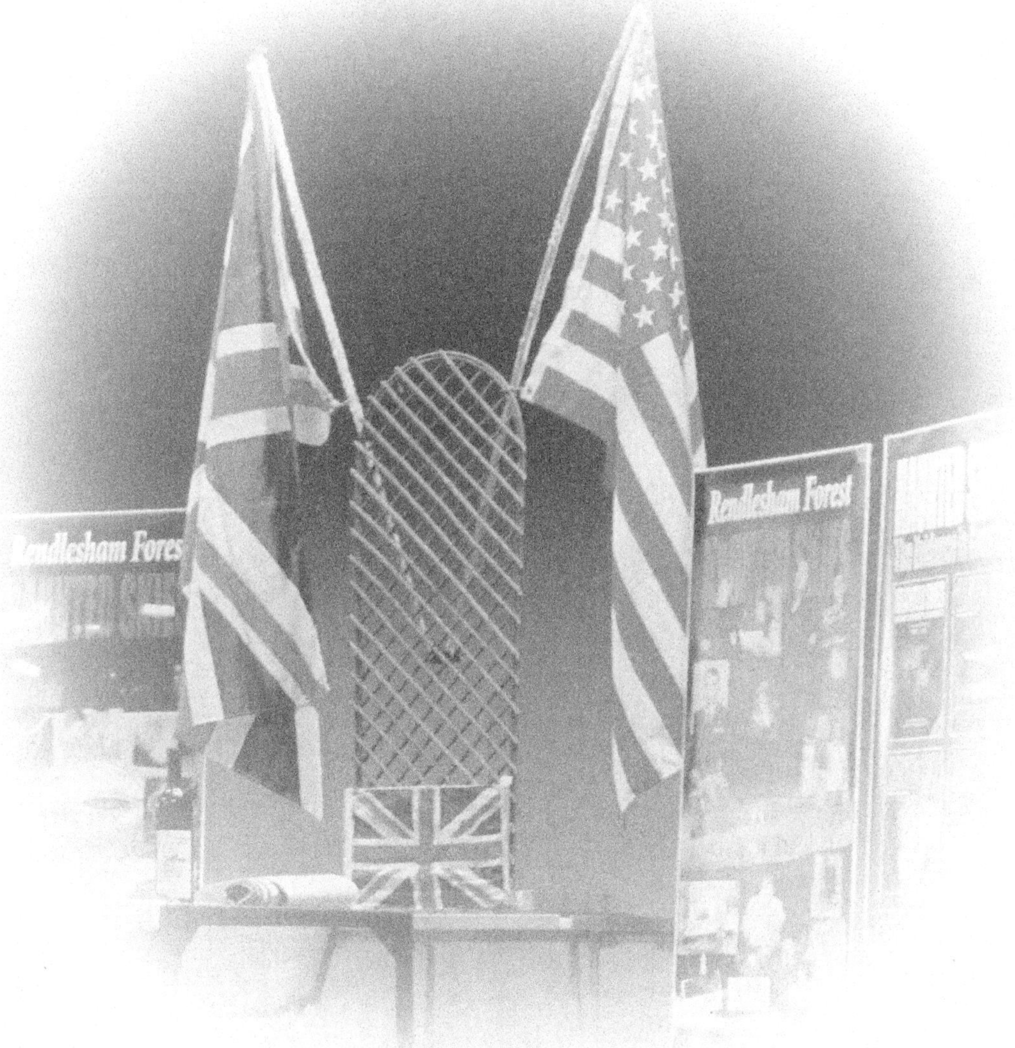

FOREWORD

BY NICK POPE

THE Rendlesham Forest incident is the name given to a series of UFO encounters that occurred over three nights in December 1980, at the twin bases of RAF Bentwaters and RAF Woodbridge – United States Air Force bases in the UK county of Suffolk. In many respects these events are more significant than the infamous Roswell incident that occurred in the New Mexico desert in the summer of 1947.

The Rendlesham Forest incident can truly be regarded as the 'perfect storm' of a UFO case. Every factor on the list of characteristics that enables one to say that a UFO sighting is both compelling and well-evidenced was present here. This was no fleeting 'lights in the sky' sighting, but a series of close encounters that took place over several hours on three consecutive nights. There were dozens of witnesses, many of whom were on-duty USAF personnel. The UFO was tracked on radar. There was a landing, leading to physical trace evidence including indentations in the frozen ground, burn/scorch marks on the trees, and radiation levels that the MoD's Defence Intelligence Staff assessed as being "significantly higher than the average background". Finally, all of these points can be verified by documents in the MoD's own case file, and unlike many controversial documents on this subject, such as the Majestic-12 papers, the provenance of these documents is not disputed: you can read them on the websites of *The National Archives* and the Ministry of Defence.

Now that the last witnesses who had any significant and direct involvement with the Roswell incident have died, the whole saga has effectively passed from living memory into history – or arguably into legend. The situation is very different with the Rendlesham Forest incident, where most – if not all – of the key players are still alive. Many of these people have already spoken out about these events, and indeed I have previously collaborated with two of the main witnesses, John Burroughs and Jim Penniston, teaming up with them to write a book entitled *Encounter In Rendlesham Forest*.

While much information on this case is already in the public domain, arguably the key player in all of this has not had his say until now. Colonel Charles Halt is the central figure in these events for a number of reasons. Firstly, as the Deputy Base Commander, he was in a senior management position and knew most of the other main witnesses. Secondly, and even more importantly, he was both the investigator of these incidents and – as readers will see – a witness himself. As such, he became probably the highest ranking US military officer ever to see and report a UFO while on duty. And while Halt has given the occasional public talk over the years, and has been featured briefly in a number of

THE HALT PERSPECTIVE

TV shows and newspaper articles that have covered these events, this is the first time that he has ever spoken out in detail, finally placing on the record his own detailed account of what took place.

Notwithstanding the above, Colonel Halt was a reluctant player in all of this. His philosophy was the polar opposite of Fox Mulder's "I want to believe". Indeed, when Halt was alerted to the return of the UFO on the third night, he led a team of men out into the forest with the intention of debunking what he regarded as distracting nonsense, and laying the matter to rest, so that normal operations could resume. Even after his attempts to debunk the story were thwarted when he encountered the UFO himself, his reluctance continued. Being labelled 'the UFO Colonel" was hardly likely to get him the promotion he was seeking, and while the affair was to follow him throughout his USAF career (and beyond), he made every effort to shake it off, urging a USAF colleague to burn a document the subsequent release of which was to thrust him into the public eye, dodging the press, and generally shunning the limelight.

Colonel Halt is a colourful character who has led a very full and interesting life. In this book he discusses not just the Rendlesham Forest incident but many other autobiographical details of his life and his 28-year military career – a career that began in Vietnam, with the draft, and ended in the Pentagon. But it's the Rendlesham Forest incident for which he's best-known, and it will be his insights on the case that will be of most interest to the UFO community. His comments are always well-informed and insightful. Halt had the reputation of being an officer who knew every aspect of the base's operation. Part of the job of the Deputy Base Commander was to be the eyes and ears of the Wing Commander, and Halt made it his business to know everything there was to know. One moment he could be found in the kitchens quizzing the cooks, the next he might be out riding with the cops on patrol: no area was off-limits to him, and as often as not, Halt's knowledge came not from carefully-crafted reports delivered by subordinates, but from his own direct observations and interactions.

I've met Charles Halt several times over the years, and he's good company. An officer, a gentleman, and a man of the highest personal integrity, when he tells you something, you can take it to the bank. If his plain speaking has upset some of the other people involved in this story, they should look to their conduct and not his. He doesn't suffer fools gladly and if he thinks somebody is lying or exaggerating, he'll say so. These are qualities that should be commended and not condemned.

I'm pleased that the book includes so many personal anecdotes, and details of some of the funnier and quirkier side of military life. Whether it's SNAFUs or pranks, it adds colour and gives readers an insider's perspective into the politics and the personalities of the story. It puts flesh on the bone and enables readers to see the unfolding events through Halt's eyes, in a way that wouldn't be possible without this insight into his personality.

The Halt Perspective is an extraordinarily important book. Halt's rank, experience and integrity make him an unimpeachable witness, and his key position at the twin bases means that he was perfectly placed to assess and offer informed comments on the events themselves, their aftermath, and all the people involved. Halt has no interest in the politics and personalities of the UFO community and as somebody who stands outside this field, he has no agenda other than telling the truth – and setting the record straight, after the waters have been muddied by a bizarre cast of characters, including wannabees trying to write themselves into the story, and some less-than-honest die-hard debunkers and true believers in the UFO community, who dishonestly twist the facts in order to suit their pre-existing, dogmatic beliefs about UFOs.

Colonel Halt's writing partner on this collaborative work is John Hanson, the retired police officer who – along with his partner Dawn Holloway – have researched and written the highly-respected *Haunted Skies* series of books. John's police background is invaluable here, as he uses his investigative skills to sort through a mass of often conflicting testimony from some of the other characters who are involved – or who claim to have been involved – in these extraordinary events. John also contextualizes the Rendlesham Forest incident by highlighting a wide range of other fascinating UFO sightings that have taken place in this region of the UK over the years, making this a book of extraordinary breadth and depth.

There are a few things that you won't find in this book. When asked about nuclear weapons, Colonel Halt politely declines to comment, or offers the standard "neither confirm nor deny" answer. He may be a man with inside knowledge, but loyalty is important to him, as is his security oath. In a sense, this is what makes this book the real deal. Genuine insiders aren't afraid to say things like "I don't know", or "I can't discuss that", whereas frauds and wannabees have an answer for everything – and it's usually the answer they think people want to hear. So with that in mind, I wholeheartedly endorse *The Halt Perspective*. It gives readers exactly what it says on the front cover: the direct observations, insights and assessments of Colonel Charles Halt, a senior military officer who, having no previous interest or belief in UFOs, found himself at the centre of an event that, in time, will doubtless come to be recognized by the UFO community, the media and the wider public as being bigger than the Roswell incident.

Nick Pope worked for the Ministry of Defence for 21 years. From 1991 to 1994 he was posted to a division where he was responsible for policy, research and investigations in relation to the UFO phenomenon. His final posting was in the Directorate of Defence Security, where he served as an acting Deputy Director. He now lives in the United States.

Nick Pope with Col. Charles Halt, in relaxed mood at a recent event in Los Angeles, USA

1. Early in the morning of 27 Dec 80 (approximately 0300L) two USAF security police patrolmen saw unusual lights outside the back gate at RAF Woodbridge. Thinking an aircraft might have crashed or been forced down, they called for permission to go outside the gate to investigate. The on-duty flight chief responded and allowed three patrolmen to proceed on foot. The individuals reported seeing a strange glowing object in the forest. The object was described as being metallic in appearance and triangular in shape, approximately two to three meters across the base and approximately two meters high. It illuminated the entire forest with a white light. The object itself had a pulsing red light on top and a bank(s) of blue lights underneath. The object was hovering or on legs. As the patrolmen approached the object, it maneuvered through the trees and disappeared. At this time the animals on a nearby farm went into a frenzy. The object was briefly sighted approximately an hour later near the back gate.

2. The next day, three depressions 1.5 inches deep and 7 inches in diameter were found where the object had been sighted on the ground. The following night (29 Dec 80) the area was checked for radiation. Beta/gamma readings of 0.1 milliroentgens were recorded with peak readings in the three depressions and near the center of the triangle formed by the depressions. A nearby tree had moderate (0.05–0.07) readings on the side of the tree toward the depressions.

3. Later in the night a red sun-like light was seen through the trees. It moved about and pulsed. At one point it appeared to throw off glowing particles and then broke into five separate white objects and then disappeared. Immediately thereafter, three star-like objects were noticed in the sky, two objects to the north and one to the south, all of which were about 10 degrees off the horizon. The objects moved rapidly in sharp, angular movements and displayed red, green and blue lights. The objects to the north appeared to be elliptical through an 8-12 power lens. They then turned to full circles. The objects to the north remained in the sky for an hour or more. The object to the south was visible for two or three hours and beamed down a stream of light from time to time. Numerous individuals, including the undersigned, witnessed the activities in paragraphs 2 and 3.

Charles I. Halt, Lt Col, USAF
Deputy Base Commander

NB. The date included in this statement from Col.
Charles Halt is incorrect.
The early morning incident he reports actually
occurred on 26th December, not the 27th.

THE HALT PERSPECTIVE

1940 – USA

Charles Halt ~

I was born in 1940 in Pittsburgh Pennsylvania to a middle class family. My father initially worked in a steel mill, until he joined the Navy and was in training to join the Merchant Marine Fleet. The war ended before he could be assigned so he was sent home. He became a successful insurance salesman and later became a manager. Both my parents were products of the depression- no doubt this was why my mother was always concerned about money and meeting household bills etc., but we always had food on the table.

It was a happy childhood but tight finances meant most of my clothes were quality hand- me-downs as we were fortunate to have several well to do family friends with older boys. When I was nine or 10 years of age I inherited a large, slightly used Erector set for Christmas, from one of those families. It provided countless hours of entertainment and I learned a great deal about engineering principles. It was big step from the mostly homemade toys I had become accustomed to.

When I was nine I inherited a morning paper route with the *Pittsburgh Post Gazette*. The paper bag was so heavy that I had to make several trips around the neighborhood at 5:30 am – this was a bit of a drag but provided an income and I did it until I was 17, by which time I had saved up enough for my first year of college.

The following year I received a hand me down chemistry set for Christmas. I quickly became a budding Chemist. I discovered Fisher Scientific with their major

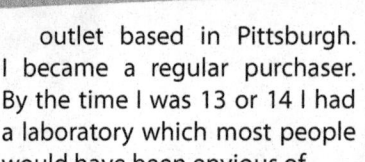

outlet based in Pittsburgh. I became a regular purchaser. By the time I was 13 or 14 I had a laboratory which most people would have been envious of.

One minor problem was I didn't have a hood to remove fumes and on several occasions we had to evacuate the house. I made everything from tear gas to nitro-glycerine. My favourite game was

The Pittsburgh Press

VOLUME 66, No. 311   FRIDAY, MAY 5, 1950   WEATHER—Hot and humid. Showers and cooler tomorrow.

—BASEBALL—
FINAL
CLOSING STOCKS
52 Pages—5 Cents

22 Hurt as Lightning Strikes Trolley

FLASH FLOODS RIP DISTRICT

U. S. Talks Tough

Bristling Note Calls Russia Deliberate Liar

Baltic Plane Incident Dangerous to Peace

WASHINGTON, May 5 (UP) — The United States today accused Russia of deliberately lying about last month's Baltic plane incident and of conducting herself in a manner dangerous to peace.

In one of the most bristling notes of modern times, the State Department charged that Russia has no intention of telling the truth about the April 8 tragedy in which 10 Americans were lost when Soviet fighters shot down an unarmed Navy patrol plane.

Disregard for Law Charged

The language of the note was about as tough as diplomatic usage permits. It accused Russia of...

15-Minute Downpour Brings $500,000 Loss; Bolt Hits Car Downtown

Violent storms across nation injure 45, Page 3.

Damage that may exceed half a million dollars was caused early today when a thunderstorm spread floods and lightning wreckage throughout the Pittsburgh district.

Twenty-five persons were injured — 22 of them when lightning hit a street car at Fourth and Smithfield Sts.

Hardest hit by flash floods were Millvale, Hays and areas in Brentwood and along Route 51 and Sawmill Run.

Nearly two inches of rain fell within 15 minutes, Weather Bureau records show.

Knoxville Trolley Passengers Hurt

Twenty-two persons were injured early today when a bolt of lightning ripped into a Knoxville trolley in front of the old Post Office Bldg. The bolt, which struck at 3:19 a.m., was accompanied by a deafening crash. It shattered windows in the car...

Hays, Brentwood, Millvale Flooded

A crashing thunderstorm flooded the Pittsburgh district early today injuring at least 25 persons.

Damage was estimated in the thousands of dollars. Lightning hit a street car, church, school and many...

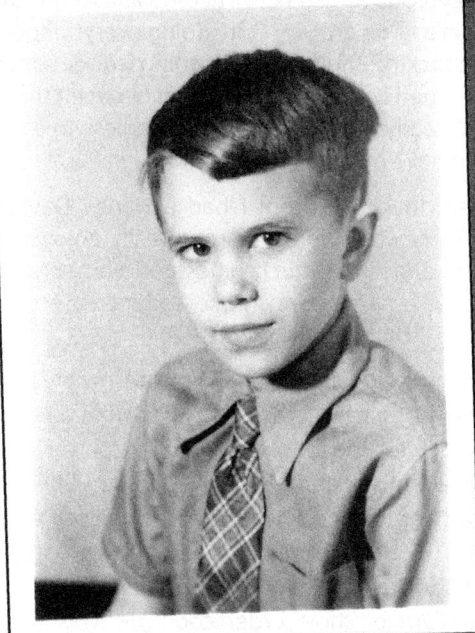

to make nitrogen tri iodine. I would filter it out. When dried it was extremely unstable. The slightest shock would cause a loud report.

I would set it on the window sill with a little sugar and watch it explode when a fly would land on it. Two other budding chemist friends, Paul Cameron and Lynn Weisnerhower and I would make it in the school chemistry lab while the teacher was occupied. We'd then put the results on the hallway floor and then watch the fun when unsuspecting students would step on the paper.

Occasionally we'd torment our homeroom teacher by putting a vial of hydrochloric acid in the supply closet and dropping in some iron sulfide crystals. The resulting gas (hydrogen sulfide), even in small quantity, was overpowering. The chemistry teacher who had the room above always got the blame.

My mother claimed the paper route was causing me to wear out my shoes too quickly so I was required to buy my own shoes. One of the local department stores (Kaufmann's) had a sale on youth shoes and they claimed if you could wear out a pair in less than three months they would replace them with another pair.

I jumped at the offer and paid $7 for a pair. Sure enough, in about a month the heels were worn down. Wanting to get my money's worth I went to G. C. Murphy's and bought a pair of heels. Dad nailed them on for me but they were a little big. He trimmed them with his pocket knife and I wore them for another month or two. I took them back to Kaufman's and they said *"nobody had ever worn them out before"!* The salesman went on to say *"whoever did the heeling did a terrible job".* He was embarrassed when dad admitted he had put the heels on so I could get some more mileage out of them.

At the same time I was working two part time jobs. One was setting pins at the local bowling alley. This was before they installed automatic pin

setters. I usually worked the night men's league and worked two lanes. It was a challenge as most of the bowlers were drinking and thought it funny when I had to dodge early balls. It paid well and I usually got generous tips so I didn't complain. At the same time I was working at a large grocery store doing everything from running a register, stocking shelves to unloading trucks. I did get into a bit of trouble when it was discovered that between the two jobs I was working nearly 40 hours a week. Needless to say my school grades could have been better.

My senior year in high school I had a Harley Davidson motorcycle and a somewhat worn out car. I really enjoyed the Harley. The car took almost as much oil as gas. Someone told me to clean out the engine with Bardall. All that did was make more smoke and increase the oil consumption.

One of my female co-workers at the grocery store was always after me to take her for a ride on the motorcycle. I finally agreed to do it one night after work. She showed up with a small bag and asked to be dropped off at a friend's home. Unknown to me she was running away from home. The next day at work I was quizzed by authorities looking for her and briefly was in a bit of trouble. I finally managed to convince them of my innocence. At the end of my freshman year at college I realized I didn't have enough money for the following year. Thus, I was forced to sell my car and my beloved Harley. Still being short of funds and told that paying for college was my responsibility I took on three part time jobs for the remaining school years. I became a handyman, short order cook, dishwasher and tutor.

I was very active in scouting having early on become an Eagle Scout and was representing my unit at numerous events. I was selected to attend the 1957 National Jamboree at Valley Forge and to represent the US at the International Jamboree at Sutton Park England.

This was the 50th anniversary of scouting and a real privilege. I spent the remainder of the summer travelling in Europe- what an education. When I returned I stayed active in scouting and through scouting made friends with Bob Graham, who was Executive Vice President of US Steel. In those days US Steel was a major corporation. When asked about my future plans and I told him

**SCHOOL DAYS 1953-54
MIFFLIN**

I wanted to be a chemist or chemical engineer. He told me their big library was in Duquesne, PA and not far from my grandparents home and asked if I would be interested in being an intern. I immediately accepted the offer. I learned the routine of all the chemists and filled in for them as they took their summer vacations. Additionally, I worked with the Chief Chemist on a research project trying to find a practical way to extract Germanium from iron ore. I quickly realized that being cooped up in a lab for a career and with luck eventually becoming the Chief Chemist was not what I wanted.

Thus, I changed my major to business/economics with a minor in chemistry. The following summer there were some serious labour issues at the steel mill and the intern position went away. Bob looked out for me and found me a job on the floor running a huge cold saw trimming up steel bars and working as a "hooker" (climbing into rail cars and using a big hook to keep tension on the lowering/hoisting chains). Both jobs were next to the pickling vats where they lowered the red hot steel into acid. The fumes were unbearable so several of us would take turns hanging our heads out the lone small window. I enjoyed it about as much as a trip to the dentist but again it paid well.

The following year I was to come back but there was a strike and the mill shut down. Fortunately, a neighbour worked for Peoples Gas who was doing exploratory work in West Virginia and they needed labourers. Having no other options I signed up for the contractor (Seismograph Service) and was sent to Elkins, West Virginia where I currently have a vacation home. The work involved drilling a 100+ foot hole, packing it with dynamite and recording the explosion at multiple locations. It was hard work but all outdoors and I enjoyed it.

I did have many "interesting" experiences. One that stands out occurred when our shooter (the dynamite guy, Whitey, who wasn't too bright was sent to town to get more drillers mud to pack

the drilling holes. To give you an idea how smart he was he was drinking in the motel bar and mentioned that his truck just outside had almost a ton of dynamite. This resulted in the local sheriff threatening the company and ordering him to move the truck out of town. The driller's mud we were sent to fetch came in 100 pound bags. Another summer hire and I were sent to do the loading. We were told to load the truck while Whitey went for a beer.

We started to load the truck and realized the truck was a ¼ ton pickup and the mud weighted nearly two-and-a-half tons. I spoke to Whitey and explained our misgivings only to be to told to shut up and load the truck. So we loaded the truck and crawled in only to drive 10 feet when both rear tires blew with a huge bang. We then had to unload the truck while Whitey bought new tires. He had a lot of explaining as our delay caused the whole operation to shut down for the day.

Regardless, it was an enjoyable experience and convinced me the property I now own has a significant gas reserve below.

While in college I joined a fraternity and got deep into caving. I even became an early member of the National Speleogical Society. As a result I've caved all over the world from Japan, Belgium, and Thailand to England. While in school in West Virginia we played a scare trick on the fraternity pledges. Several of us sent them across the state on a "hunt" that ended in a cave. We hid on a ledge in the cave and after they past by with their flashlights made noises and jumped down on them. I'm not sure they ever recovered.

About the same time the fraternity house had a problem with a large tree stump in front by the sidewalk. Since I had the brass tools and knowledge of explosives it was decided to blast out the stump. I went to the local hardware store and bought dynamite, fuse and blasting caps. We packed the stump with mud and covered it with an old rug. I sent people up and down the road to stop traffic (this was a major north/ south route thru town) and lit the fuse. The stump barely moved but mud and stone flew up and rained over the entire neighbourhood. About that time a local drunk came staggering up the sidewalk. He saw what we were

doing and commented *"do you know the gas line is under this sidewalk"?* That ended the stump blasting. We put the dynamite in the shed behind the house and forgot about it.

Several months later someone noticed the dynamite was sweating. Knowing that the sweat was nitro glycerine it became urgent to get rid of it. Not having many options we took it several miles out of town to a very rural area and threw a rope over a tree branch, hoisted it, fused it and lit it. We were a good distance away when there was a tremendous explosion. On the way back to town we heard on the local radio station that there had been a large mine explosion and authorities were looking for the source. That was the end of my blasting career.

Military Career

My military career was most enjoyable with most being spent overseas. Two tours in Okinawa/ Japan where I was involved in Planning the return of Naha Air Base to Japan, Removing the gas from the island (*Project Red Hat*), removing the special weapons and eventually the return of Okinawa to Japan – too many stories here to relate.

I was selected as an escort for *Project Home Coming* (the return of our prisoners from North Vietnam). In this capacity I met, debriefed, prepped the returnees for return and delivered them to their awaiting

as we had to recover remains from the wreckage. On one occasion we were transporting the remnants of an F-4 fighter that still was occasionally dripping fuel. As we proceeded through the jungle trail we came across a native complete with loin cloth smoking. It was a real challenge to get him to put out his opium laced smoke. While at Danang RVN we shared the hanger with the Ranch Hands, the C-123 outfit that sprayed 'Agent Orange'. Even today, I have some health issues that are probably related.

Further assignments included Deputy and then Base Commander at RAF Bentwaters, a year with AWAC in Oklahoma City, Base Commander at Kunsan, Korea. This was followed by an assignment opening and simultaneously closing the cruise missile base at Florennes, Belgium. My final assignment was the Director of the Inspection Directorate for the Department of Defense Inspector General. In the latter capacity I was charged with inspection oversight of the entire Department of Defense. In addition to responsibility of the armed forces I directed inspections of many agencies to include NSA and the DIA.

families in the states. It was one of the most rewarding assignments I was given. In Vietnam and Thailand one of my tasks was to recover downed aircraft. On several occasions it was sad

Charles I. Halt

THE HALT PERSPECTIVE

Early trip to Wales

On one of my early trips to Wales I stayed at a bed and breakfast. On the first night after climbing I went to the shared bath for a shower. You can imagine my surprise when I came out of the shower to find no towels. I finally dried on the bath mat. I went downstairs to inquire with Mrs Sutherland and was told I was supposed to bring my own towels. A lesson well learned. I will say she was a good host and her cooking was great. On another occasion we rented a stone cottage in Capel Curig. It turned cold so I foraged and found a bag of coal in the shed. We got the stove going and all was well until my daughter turned on her hair dryer. Suddenly all the lights went out. I accused her of blowing a fuse only to discover the electricity was metered and required coins. A quick trip to the local pub solved that problem. Upon returning home I got a bill for the coal we used. Another lesson learned.

Charles and wife, Yong Ho, in 1986

High Falls Hike, 30-8-2012

I spent two summers in the Alps with the Plas y Brenin crew and climbed most of the major peaks in the western Alps. I also did a winter climb of Ben Nevis with them. The following year I went back to the Alps with my oldest son and two others. We decided to climb the Matterhorn. However, it was too early in the season and there was three feet of snow on the approach. We made our way to the base hut only to find it was still closed.

The next morning we climbed to just short of the summit only to have the weather move in and things got so bad that we couldn't go up or down. The wind and snow were unbelievable and we were stuck. Below the summit there's a small shelter held onto the mountain with a few cables. We spent what probably was the most frightening night of my life not knowing if the cables would hold in the weather.

The weather let up some in the morning so we quickly descended. The following summer we returned to climb Mt Blanc. This time several got altitude sickness just short of the summit.

Discussed, I got some caffeine in them and took them down across the field of crevasses. That brought them around.

Three years later my wife and I went to the summit of Mt. Blanc. The only issue was her face got frost bitten due to the winds. The summit is a challenge as the last 100 meters of the ridge is only a few feet wide and a slip means a fall of several thousand feet.

Several interesting things happened at Plas y Brenin. One evening I was using the class room and went to turn on the light. They had located the glass fire alarm where one would expect to find the light switch. I accidently broke the glass setting off the alarm. It emptied the entire complex. It took them 30+ minutes to find the key to turn off the alarm. I wasn't too popular.

After retiring from the military I found work as a community manager and managed gated communities of up to 7,000 and did that for 15 years. I now travel and spend time at my vacation home in the mountains.

Charles Halt cutting the presentation cake at the 'Halt Briefing', Woodbridge, Suffolk in July 2015

JOHN HANSON

HOW THE 'HALT' BOOK BEGAN

D ESPITE the passing of over 35 years, the public still continue to be fascinated by the UFO events that occurred in Rendlesham Forest, just outside Woodbridge, Suffolk – situated near to the market town of Ipswich – (often referred to by the media as 'Britain's equivalent to Roswell') as can be seen from the colossal number of web entries found on the Internet.

In 2014, following various emails/letters of communication between Charles Halt, John Hanson and Dawn Holloway, the two men met up with Brenda Butler at the *Bull Public House* in Woodbridge, where, during conversation, Charles Halt asked John tentatively if he might be interested in writing up the UFO account from his personal perspective. It was only after his talk that work on the book had begun.

John Hanson

"Following a successful conference arranged on the 11th July 2015, at Woodbridge Community Centre, Suffolk, involving a talk by retired Colonel Charles Irwin Halt, accompanied by his son – Clifford – Charles Halt asked me if I would be interested in publishing a book documenting the facts, rather than inaccuracies.

I agreed, knowing that it would allow him the opportunity to contrast those events with other previously unpublished sightings reported in and around the Suffolk area, if only to show that the airmen were not the only ones to encounter something which was to dramatically change their outlook on the existence of a phenomena which was to affect so many people that we were to come across, over the years."

John Hanson and Dawn Holloway

It was never our intention to 'write-up' a comprehensive account of what had taken place, because much of the wealth of information is already published in various books by people such as Tim Good – ***Above Top Secret,*** Guild Publishing, (1988) – Nick Pope – ***Open Skies, Closed Minds***, Simon & Schuster (1996) – Larry Warren and Pete Robbins – ***Left At East Gate,*** Da Capo Press (1997) – Georgina Bruni – ***You Can't Tell The People,*** Sidgwick and Jackson (2002) – David Clarke, ***The UFO***

Files, The National Archives, (2009) and Nick Pope – *Encounter in Rendlesham Forest,* Thomas Dunne Books, (2014); John Alexandra, Leslie Kean, and a multitude of generals, pilots and Government officials who go on the record.

Is there a 'D' Notice on the books?

During the last five years spent producing the *Haunted Skies* books, we had elicited the help of many high profile figures within the UFO phenomena (who had themselves been the target of debate by the Press) hoping this would attract some interest by the British National Press on our books, bearing in mind they have been sent to the UK Cultural Secretary and the Prime Minster – David Cameron.

We are disappointed that, despite eleven comprehensive Volumes of work, produced at great personal expense, not one National newspaper who asked us for the books to review has ever published anything about our commitment towards preserving what forms part of important British social history!

In July 2015, I (John) met up with Jasper Hamill – an on-line reporter for the *Daily Mirror,* in London. I gave him three Volumes of *Haunted Skies,* after he had promised that he would write an article about our work. At the time of preparing this book (in 2016) the promise, as far as we know, has not come to fruition.

THE HALT PERSPECTIVE

Charles Halt

"John Hanson and Dawn Holloway have undertaken a mammoth task of now documenting British / American / Australian UFO sightings on a day-by-day basis, covering from the early 1940s, right up to the present date. The current Volume 11 of Haunted Skies brings those UFO reports up to 1990, along with an update on other World UFO events from the period 1963 onwards. All of the volumes of Haunted Skies have been produced at considerable personal expense and involve an unbelievable amount of personal time. Not only have John and Dawn been able to sort out the facts but they have had to deal with many misleading and often possible cases of intentional misinformation, quite often self-serving. What happened at Bentwaters is a good example taking into consideration a popular book, published some years ago, which claims to present the facts but is wrong on so many issues. John and I have corresponded at great length and personally met. He and Dawn's work has not always seen the success it merits, despite it clearly laying out the facts requiring further official investigation."

In 2015 Charles Halt points out the correct landing site

Timeline

Woodbridge Airfield

'Prang' or 'Crash Drome'   The Cold War

July 2015 – The exact location pointed out

During a walk in the forest, retracing his footsteps, all of those years ago, Charles Halt pointed out the location of where he had stood with his colleagues overlooking Capel Green – the same location nominated by Larry Warren, although Larry was not there on the first night/early morning of the 26th December 1980.

Tourist attraction

John:

"I was surprised that Charles Halt did not visit the site of a large metal UFO sculpture – situated off track 10, in a clearing a short distance away from the boundary fence – which had been craned into position by the Forestry Commission, some 12 months ago, known locally as the site where Colonel Halt had observed the UFOs. Prior to the 'spaceship' being placed in situ, three posts had been erected, forming a triangle, and the area cleared back. Photographs of the 'craft' which Jim Penniston had encountered were stapled onto the posts, but were misleading and later removed following complaints of copyright issues."

The Rendlesham Forest UFO incident

Christmas 1980 was the time of the UFO sightings during a period of extreme military and political sensitivity owing to the Cold War. The United States Air Force (USAF) leased RAF Woodbridge on the forest's western boundary, with its runway extending into the heart of Rendlesham Forest (point 1 on the UFO Trail and RAF Bentwaters, located four miles north of the forest. The US air force presence was part of the defence network of the North Atlantic Treaty Organisation, more commonly known as NATO.

In the early hours of a cold winter's night on 27 December 1980, two USAF security patrolmen report seeing unusual lights outside the perimeter of RAF Woodbridge. Thinking perhaps an aircraft might have come down they sought permission to leave the base and enter the forest through the East Gate, and on foot, to investigate. They separated in their search.

one described seeing strange lights, the other reports seeing a glowing object that appeared to be metallic and triangular in shape. When he tried to get closer, the object reportedly retreated through the trees and disappeared. Their reports of the incident have caused division of opinion ever since.

Follow the trail to find out more about what these men reported they saw, and try and make up your own mind about what think happened here.

Follow the trail...

US & UK GOVERNMENT COVE
FOR THE TRUTH READ.
'I SIT AT EASTGATE

Charles Halt

"Because it's inaccurate and it didn't look anything like that back in the 1980s, you should remember there weren't even any proper tracks leading into the forest. The area they have cleared bears no resemblance to what it was like and I won't be associated with publicity photographs perpetuating any such claims. This is one of the reasons why I want to clear up things; over the years there have been so many ambiguities and disinformation, its time the record was put straight."

Charles Halt on the UFO subject

"As a teenager growing up into adulthood I never had much interest in the UFO subject, but I can clearly remember reading a book which I came across during a church rummage sale, while assisting my mother, who was organizing the event, entitled The Flying Saucers Are Real, by Donald Keyhoe. This book outlined numerous encounters between USAF fighters, personnel, and other aircraft and UFOs between 1947 and 1950.

Church rummage sales were the forerunner of today's American garage or yard sales – known as car boot, bric-a-brac, garage sales, etc., in the United Kingdom. Most household items could be found for sale – including clothing, kitchen accessories and books. I found Keyhoe's book fascinating but, after reading and putting it aside, forgot all about it.

Memories of it were resurrected in December 1980, when I found myself confronted with an experience I could not explain. The incidents that occurred over a three night period in Rendlesham Forest, Suffolk, left a lasting impression on me and tragically affected the lives of many concerned."

Lives changed for ever

"Without reservation I can say that those involved in the incidents, which occurred on the first night, have never been the same – probably because of a combination of their experience in the forest and then being 'debriefed' afterwards by USAF and British 'spooks' officers, engaged in military intelligence.

Since then I have been privy to hearing of an unbelievable number of first-hand accounts of encounters by very reputable individuals, many occurring in Rendlesham, Suffolk area. I have become firmly convinced that we are not alone. Some type of intelligent life is in our midst, which has the ability to change shape, size, move at phenomenal speed and apparently, significantly affect people who have been witness to the appearance of these objects.

What lies behind the phenomenon is; of course, open to all manner of speculation. My own personal opinion is that whatever it is, it does not normally reside in our known universe unless it's from another dimension."

Swarms of UFOs plague East Anglia and Essex during early years

John Hanson:

"This book will also allow people to see the true picture of the extent of UFO activity, involving 'Z' or 'U' shaped objects tracked by RAF radar installations, during the late 1940s and early 1950s, over East Anglia and the adjacent localities. These 'swarms' of UFOs reappeared in strength during the late 1980s and were the subject of a prolific number of sightings over the Essex, Suffolk, and Norfolk areas.

Ron West

Many of these were documented by the late UFO researcher – Ron West, who is owed a debt of gratitude for his tenacity and determination to preserve the history of something that should be of prime importance to us all. This begs the question, what are they and where do they come from? There are many explanations for their presence; including machines developed by German technology ... the list is endless!"

QUEST INTERNATIONAL
OFFICIAL INVESTIGATOR
Name .... I WEST ....
Signature ....
Authorised by Tony Dodd
Director of Investigations
.........JDodd..........
Date ...I.../..8.../...91...
WORLDWIDE UFO INVESTIGATION
copyright Brenda Butler

Even seen by pilots

In addition both allied and axis pilots, returning home from bombing missions in the Second World War, were puzzled by the appearance of highly unusual objects that flew near the aircraft, which could not be identified as conventional aircraft. On other occasions we learnt of similar objects seen over the capital, caught in the glare of the searchlight beams during the blitz.

GERMAN UFOS

SUNDAY DISPATCH 7·11·54

Six Times In A Few Weeks—

STRANGE SIGHTS IN SKY BAFFLE WAR OFFICE

Picked Up On Many Radar Screens

By Sunday Dispatch Reporter

RADAR operators over a large part of Britain are watching their screens closely for the next appearance of a mystery formation in the sky which has the defence experts baffled.

Six times in the past few weeks a strange pattern of dots—the radar men call them "blips"—have been plotted on their screens, moving from East to West.

—Look-out In Africa—

SOUTH AFRICANS were asked yesterday to report immediately any strange object seen in the sky. The South African Air Force said re-

Neither the War Office, which controls inland radar, nor the Air Ministry can say what these "blips" represent.

A careful check has shown

OSWESTRY AND BORDER COUNTIES ADVERTIZE
13·4·55   20·4·55

THE FLYING SAUCER

Sir,—In his letter to the "Advertiser" of March 2, Mr. Quinn stated that no reliable photograph of a Flying Saucer has ever been taken. The enclosed print was given to me by 16-year-old Harold Cummins, of 24 Stubby Lane, Wednesfield, Wolverhampton, who took it at the end of last year. On December 23, 1954, he was watching the birds on his back lawn from indoors when a black ob-

Supposed Meteor

Sir,—I would be very grateful if any of your readers who saw the supposed meteor which flew over our skies at about 7 p.m. on Thursday, March 24, would get in touch with me, giving details of what they saw, telling me the shape, colour, apparent height and size, angle above the horizon, direction of flight of the object, and also letting me know if it made any sound, and the point where they observed the object.

I understand that the object was widely seen over the Nesscliffe area, so I would be pleased to hear from any reader living in that neighbourhood. I would always be glad to receive details of strange objects seen in the sky, either recently or in the past. If any reader feels more at home in Welsh, he is welcome to write to me in that language, as I understand the ancient tongue.—Yours &c.,
GAVIN GIBBONS,
Glen Severn, The Mount,
Shrewsbury.

BRITISH RADAR sightings

"STRANGE SIGHTS IN SKY BAFFLE WAR OFFICE"

RADAR operators over a large part of Britain are watching their screens closely for the next appearance of a mystery formation in the sky which has the defence experts baffled.

Six times in a few weeks, a strange pattern of "blips" has been plotted on their screens, moving from East to West. Neither the War Office which controls inland radar, nor the Air Ministry can say what these blips represent.

A careful check has shown that they have not been caused by any identifiable aircraft.

TWO MILES UP

The most recent appearance was on November 1st. The blips are said to appear from nowhere, usually about midday, flying at a height of 12,000ft in an East-West direction. First seen by a civilian radar scientist, they have since been plotted by all radar sites in the area. They have been seen both on fine and cloudy mornings, and always in the same formation. A War Office spokesman said:

"We cannot say what they are. They first appear in a 'U' - or badly shapen 'hairpin' formation. After a time they converge into two parallel lines and then take up a 'Z' formation before disappearing. They are invisible to the human eye, but on radar screens they appear as lots and lots of dots, formed by between 40 and 50 echoes. They cover an area in the sky miles long and miles wide.

AREA KEPT SECRET

"Every time they have been seen, they followed the same pattern. It was always around midday. We have checked and found that our sets are not faulty. We are still maintaining a watch. All our sets in the area picked them up".

The "DISPATCH" reporter stated that when he spoke to one man who had seen them, he told him that he had been given very high-level orders to maintain the utmost secrecy as to the area over which these objects are tracked.   (From "Sunday Dispatch" 7/11/54)

Ron West of the Essex UFO group and his extensive library of UFO sightings

Thanks to Essex UFO researcher – Ron West, who laboured long and hard to document the huge number of UFO sightings around the East Anglia and adjacent counties, we are able to show that Colonel Halt and his colleagues were not the only ones to sight UFOs during that period of time.

Ron:

"The majority of people who report seeing UFOs have nothing to gain by their admission; many of them are frightened and upset by their experiences and run the risk of being ridiculed by their family members and friends by speaking about what they have seen. In addition to this we

receive many reports from normally reliable sources, airline pilots, police officers, members of the RAF and USAF. Why would these people make something up and place their reputation in jeopardy if these sightings were not true?"

Ron became actively involved in UFO research during the 1960s, after being demobbed from the Army. He told of having experienced a close encounter with a UFO, while in Malaya.

*"In the past few months – January to March 1988 – we received reports relating to 137 sightings in Norfolk, Suffolk and Essex, with another 192 to investigate. **In the last six months of 1988 we had 489 sightings reported to us; of those, 260 were identified as aircraft, but 229 sightings remain unidentified."** [This is approximately 50%!]*

The sightings contained in this book also relate to accounts by RAF and USAF Officers, mostly of which happened over the Suffolk area, with a small number just over the border into Norfolk – including Thetford Forest – which, like its counterpart at Rendlesham, was to also play host to a number of UFO sightings. In addition to these sightings there was a huge 'wave' of reports around the Essex area (space prevents us including these).

Essex newspapers declined to publish!

We tried to raise some publicity about these incidents during 2015, knowing that the public would be interested in this 'forgotten wave' (which had never been published previously) but the Essex newspapers declined to show any interest and, like the Nationals, declined to publish!

Three separate objects noted

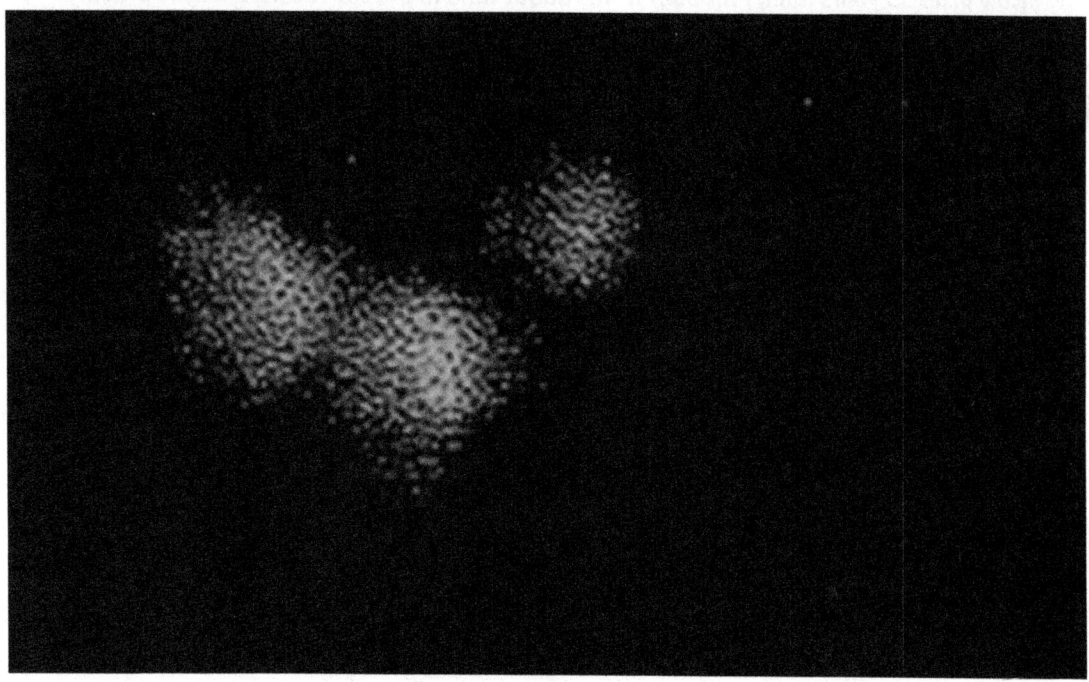

It was interesting to note the number of times when people reported seeing (as did Colonel Halt) *three* separate objects in the sky, sometimes followed by the arrival of something far more structured.

Admittedly evidence of this nature, while not necessarily proving an association with what was seen in the forest outside RAF Bentwaters, at the end of December 1980, surely must be taken into consideration when examining the eye-witness testimonials of people like Charles Halt and his colleagues, rather than accepting carte blanch the ridiculous lighthouse explanation!

While the majority of the UFO sightings documented in this book have taken place in and around the skies of Suffolk, some sightings of importance from adjoining counties will also be brought to the attention of the reader. It would be a travesty of justice not to include them.

Charles Halt – The truth not fiction

*"I never had any real interest in UFOs until what happened at RAF Bentwaters. I did everything I could to keep what was happening from going public. It was not career enhancing and I knew my life would never be the same; despite my efforts my memo and tape were released. Since then I've been stuck out in the public while my former superiors hid. I've tried to get the real story and truth out but every time the media has made it into a sensational story and misrepresented the facts. It really is frustrating. There are very few people that I really trust. One is Leslie Kean, who I assisted with her book. She and Budd Hopkins were trusted friends. There were a few others, such as *Dick Hall who has since passed away. My wife and I made a special trip to attend his memorial service.*

Now after 35 years later, I thought it was about time to put the record straight with my own perspective of what exactly took place, rather than having to constantly read about what other people thought I had seen, which paints a misleading version of events that history should not record!"

*Richard Hall – NICAP

He was born at Christmas, 1930, in Hartford, Connecticut. He graduated from the Gilbert School, Winsted, and in 1949, enlisted in the Air Force. He served on active duty until early in 1951 and then spent six years in the Air Force Reserve. Some of his active duty was spent at Keesler Air Force Base, in Mississippi.

After leaving the military, he attended Tulane University in New Orleans, first as a math major and later as a philosophy major with a minor in math. He spent most of his life in the Washington, D.C. area working for the National Investigations Committee on Aerial Phenomena, one of the first large, international UFO organisations. He worked full-time for NICAP, first as an executive secretary, then an assistant director and, finally, acting director. While there he was largely responsible for the 1964 book, *The UFO Evidence,* which was an examination of the best UFO cases presented at that time. In 2001 he wrote the sequel to *The UFO Evidence*, which covered the period from 1964 to the 1990s.

Later, he served as the chairman of the Fund for UFO Research. He was also, in the late 1970s into the 1980s, the editor of a monthly magazine for MUFON that eventually evolved into the

MUFON UFO Journal. For a number of years he wrote a column for a UFO magazine called *Reality Check.* More recently, he was the chief editor of the *Journal of UFO History,* published six times a year. He had continued to offer advice, criticism and wisdom, to those who asked. He was often the voice of calm in what could sometimes be the very belligerent world of UFO research.

UFO book topped The New York Times best-seller list

Charles Halt on book, *Left At East Gate*

"It's no secret that I continue to criticise the book Left At East Gate, which was written by Larry Warren and Peter Robbins, that in my opinion contains a considerable amount of inaccurate and misleading information. People have had their say and have attacked me time and time again, without allowing me the opportunity of reply – well, its now my opportunity to present not only my side but to show that history should record the facts of what happened, after all I should know I was there!"

> *"I decided to ask John Hanson, who has published a number of accurate books cataloguing all manner of UFO reported activity going back to the 1940s, entitled Haunted Skies, which I have supported, to assist me with his overview of other UFO incidents that had taken place in the Suffolk area, in order to allow the reader the opportunity to see that what happened at Bentwaters was not a one-off case – far from it. I can't specifically associate those reported incidents, however interesting they are, with what we witnessed in the Forest that early morning, but it is of value to recognise that we weren't the only ones to sight UFO activity around the East Anglia area during that period of time."*

John – Larry Warren & Peter Robbins, at Cheltenham, 1995

Dawn and I first met Larry and Peter in Cheltenham, during 1995, to hear them speak following the launch of their book. Fortunately we took a photograph with a Polaroid camera, which dates it perfectly!

John – Dissention among the ranks!

"Over the years, many of the airman participants involved in this incident(s) have continued to openly criticise their colleagues in a never-ending exchange of disagreement of their own individual version of the events that took place there. We have witnessed the fall out of friends and change of 'partners' as time has passed.

Each and every new individual hypothesis is presented as further evidence to explain the source of what was seen. Sometimes I gain an impression that this is not now so much about truth or disclosure, but expanding the parameters of individual egos which fight to attract the attention of an internet-based media, who will always be far more interested in publicising the claims of members of the UFO 'crackpot' fraternity than recognising serious research.

1980s – The onset of the triangular UFO

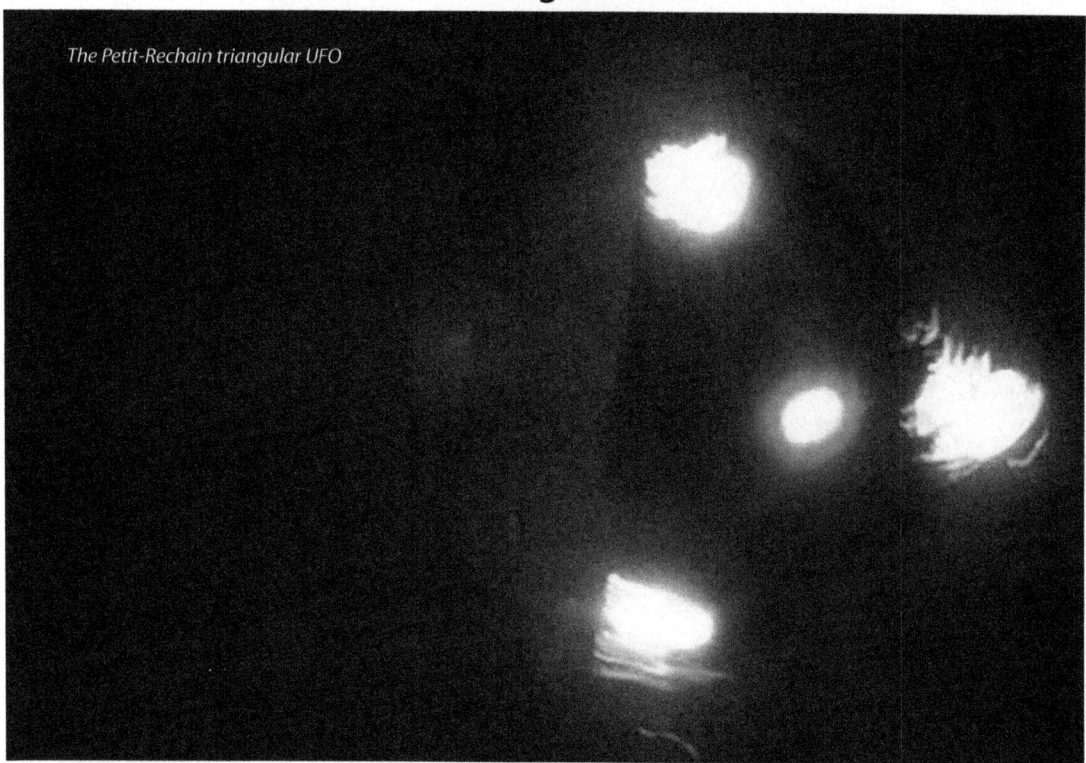

The Petit-Rechain triangular UFO

In the 1980s, there were many reports of triangular objects seen all over Europe – some were chased by the Belgian Air Force.

In addition to this, many people (throughout the years) have sighted three lights (sometimes forming a triangle) moving across the night sky. These appear to dominate the background of UFO history. It is likely there is some connection between what we regard as different classifications of UFOs, and that at the end of the day they all stem from the same source. One should bear this information in mind when reviewing what Charles Halt saw in Rendlesham Forest. The facts, never mind the overwhelming evidence, speak for themselves!

1944

World War Two pilots and 'flying triangles'

During the many years spent researching into worldwide UFO activity, while the majority of UFO sightings involved sightings of cigar or saucer-shaped objects, World War Two pilots also described seeing craft resembling 'triangles' and 'flying Christmas trees' while on their bombing missions over Germany.

On other occasions, black triangular objects were seen in broad daylight. The descriptions of triangular objects, or triangular lights seen moving through the sky, appears to feature quite heavily in the background of so many reports we were to come across through the years.

We spoke to many RAF/USAF pilots during the course of our research. The image of the Lancaster Bomber 'Q' for Queenie was drawn up by David Sankey and approved by ex RAF servicemen Arthur Horton and George Bernard Dye, sadly Arthur and George they have now passed away but their eye witness accounts of the event will be preserved in this and other books. We are proud to have known them and honor their courage; they are real heroes.

Air gunner Bernard Dye (left) and Margaret Madden, his wife-to-be, then an armourer in the WAAF

Bernard Dye

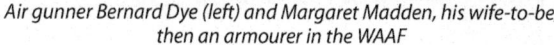

1 Park Place
Park Rd.
Thackley
Bradford
N. Yorks. BD10 0TG
6 4 2000

Tel. 01274 612426.

Dear Mr Hanson,

In answer to your letter of 1.4.2000, I am quite happy to relate for you my version of the phenomenon of the "orange glows" seen by my gunners on the night of 26.4.44.

We were returning from Essen when my gunners reported several "orange glows" coming in toward us from behind - the rear gunner thought that they had a very short stubby wings. I threw the aircraft through all the evasive tactics I knew, only to have the objects follow with apparent ease - it was something entirely new to us - the objects took no offensive action against us, my gunners were asking "shall we fire at them skipper?" my brain - racing - were they magnetic? did they have to touch us? were we expected to fire at them? split second decisions had to be made - I instructed the gunners not to fire - they were not harming us at that point. By now I had the throttles "through the gate" giving excess power to the engines. After crossing the French coast and out to sea, the objects apparently died out.

The whole episode had lasted some ten minutes, we had lost some fourteen thousand feet, and travelled some fifty miles.

On our return to base (Mildenhall - Suffolk) it was reported in our debriefing report, it was made quite a joke for a while. I have a copy of our debriefing report, obtained from the archives at Kew, on which no mention is made of the event.

My Log book just contains the cryptic words - "chased by rockets".

On that particular night, my own navigator having an eye infection, was replaced by F/Lt. A. Nicholl, the station navigator, a man of great experience and many operations, also witnessed the event.

The other witness (now deceased) was my wireless operator, W. White.

In the nose of the aircraft the bomb aimer, my flight engineer, and myself - pilot - were of course unable to actually see the objects, and had to rely on the continuous commentary at the time.

General Data.

Date 26.4.44
A/C Lancaster III LM477
Duration of Flight 4 Hrs 35 Mn

I was born on 18.6.1912

Last occupation (20 years) before retirement :-
Rowntree - York - Production Function - Managerial Status
UFO Sightings - none.

We - the crew - continued our tour of operations to complete our 30 missions, never again seeing - or hearing of - anything like our experience on 26.4.44.

I hope that the above may be of use to you, and wish you well in your investigations.

Yours Sincerely
Arthur Horton

ARTHUR HORTON

FO Arthur Horton

---

1 Park Place
Park Rd
Thackley
Bradford
W. Yorks.
BD10 0TG.

Dear Mr Hanson

Many thanks for your phone call, I enjoyed speaking to you. Enclosed, as promised a photo copy of our debriefing summary obtained from Kew, of our Essen raid on 26.4.44.

Please excuse the blue paper, accidentally in the printer.

Yours sincerely,
Arthur (Horton)

UFO ACTIVITY OVER EAST ANGLIA

1947

UFOs TRACKED ON RADAR OVER THE EAST COAST

DURING the period between January and April 1947, UFOs were plotted by radar on a number of occasions, crossing the East Anglia coast, near Norwich, at estimated speeds of 400mph. Thanks to declassified operational records, previously kept by Eastern RAF Fighter Sector, we learnt of the RAF response behind a number of operations implemented in a bid to identify an 'unidentified flying aircraft', officially designated as X306 but nicknamed by the pilots as 'C' for Charlie.

> '16147 Army commitments were met by 595 Squadron and Meteors of 245 Squadron, operated under Neatishead Control on intercept practice. An unidentified aircraft had been plotted on WC 9585, at 30,000ft, and eastern Sector ops were requested by Group to scramble a Mosquito of 23 Squadron to intercept.'

'Bull's-eye' Exercise

However, as there were no aircraft available with oxygen, an aircraft of 11 Group, which was already airborne on a 'Bull's-eye' Exercise, would try to intercept under Trimley Heath Control. The interception was unsuccessful, owing to engine trouble and the A1 going under. One Mosquito of 23 Squadron, Flight Lt. Kent, was at readiness at RAF Wittering to attempt interception on the unidentified aircraft, which had been plotted several times lately, at 2040 hours.

Flight Lt. William Kent

Flight Lt. Kent:

"The 'bogey' was plotted in WN6038. The plot was at one-time heading south. The Mosquito, which had been brought to standby, was returned to readiness but when the plot again headed into Eastern Sector Area, the Mosquito was scrambled at 2327 hours, although getting within one or two miles, several times, no interception was made of the target, which took violent evasive action. The plot faded at 1.15am, and after patrolling on a north-south line for sometime, the aircraft returned to base."

Was it a burst meteorological balloon?

We contacted Mr William Kent, the pilot of the aircraft (now a retired Group Captain) who had this to say:

"I remember the incident well. At no time, at any height, did I sight anything visual, but one had to understand the extreme care needed to avoid collision by steering a few degrees off centre, when closing on a target at a speed of 10-20 knot's (The following day, I discussed what had happened with the Neatishead Flight Controller and a report was later sent to the Commanding Officer of the Group, who decided the unidentified aircraft was most probably a leaking meteorological balloon – a conclusion assisted by a suggestion made by myself that a burst meteorological balloon was a distinct possibility, deduced from its behaviour. After all, the term 'flying saucers' was unheard of."

Operational Record Book, RAF Wittering

Although the date of the incident is not known, the Operational Record Book kept at RAF Wittering, in the entry for the 17th January, 1947, contained the following information, quote:

'One Meteor of 245 Squadron, at standby from 1300-1600. One Mosquito of 23 Squadron was at standby from 1900 hours. This aircraft was scrambled just before midnight, to intercept an unidentified high-flying object. An interception was made when the aircraft was at 18,000ft, a contact being obtained at 1,500 yards, but the observer was unable to hold it as the target was jerking violently. Further contact was obtained whilst the target lost height to 200ft, when both target and fighter faded going out to sea. The watch was stood down at 0130hours.'

According to the Operational Record Book kept at RAF Coltishall:

An unidentified aircraft [was] sighted at 11.15pm., January 23rd 1947, at 28,000ft, and the readiness aircraft scrambled under Barrington, control handed over to Langtoft and Neatishead in turn. The plot then faded and the aircraft returned to base after an uneventful flight.'

PILOT SIGHTINGS OVER HAMPSHIRE
UFO 'disc-like object' sighted over Hampshire by pilot

On 1st June 1950, the pilot of a Meteor Jet from RAF Tangmere was flying at 20,000ft, on an easterly course over the Portsmouth area, at 2.30pm, when he sighted an object travelling at very high speed on a reciprocal course, 1,000-2,000ft above him and roughly 1,200 yards to starboard. He described it as *"...circular and of bright metallic appearance, moving at an estimated speed of 800 knots for a few seconds".*

Tangmere contacted the radar station at RAF Wartling about the matter and were informed that, at about the same time as the pilot's 'report', the duty controller and three radar operators had observed an unusual response to the PPI, which appeared to be due to a 'target' moving at 1,300-1,650 knots, first approaching and then receding from the station.

RAF – Pilot saw something unusual, no evidence, it wasn't a natural phenomenon!

We discovered the incident had formed the foundation of a Press release by the Air Ministry, in June1950, when it was disclosed, quote:

'The First Officer's report of a 'flying saucer seen over Britain' was being investigated by the Air Ministry, who reported a Meteor jet pilot, flying at 40,000ft,later told the Station Intelligence Officer at RAF Tangmere, near Chichester, Sussex, he had seen: "a shining disc-like object, revolving and travelling at very high speed".

His story could not be shaken under cross-examination. A report of the incident, later sent to Fighter Command H.Q., was checked by Senior Officers and weather experts.

14th August – UFO over Farnborough

Two months later on 14th August 1950, a spectacular sighting took place over RAF Farnborough, involving Stanley Hubbard.

"It was a warm day and unusually quiet for a base that normally resonated with the sound of general noise and aircraft engines.

As I trudged across the runway, heading towards the Mess where I was billeted, I became aware of a strange sound coming from somewhere behind me."

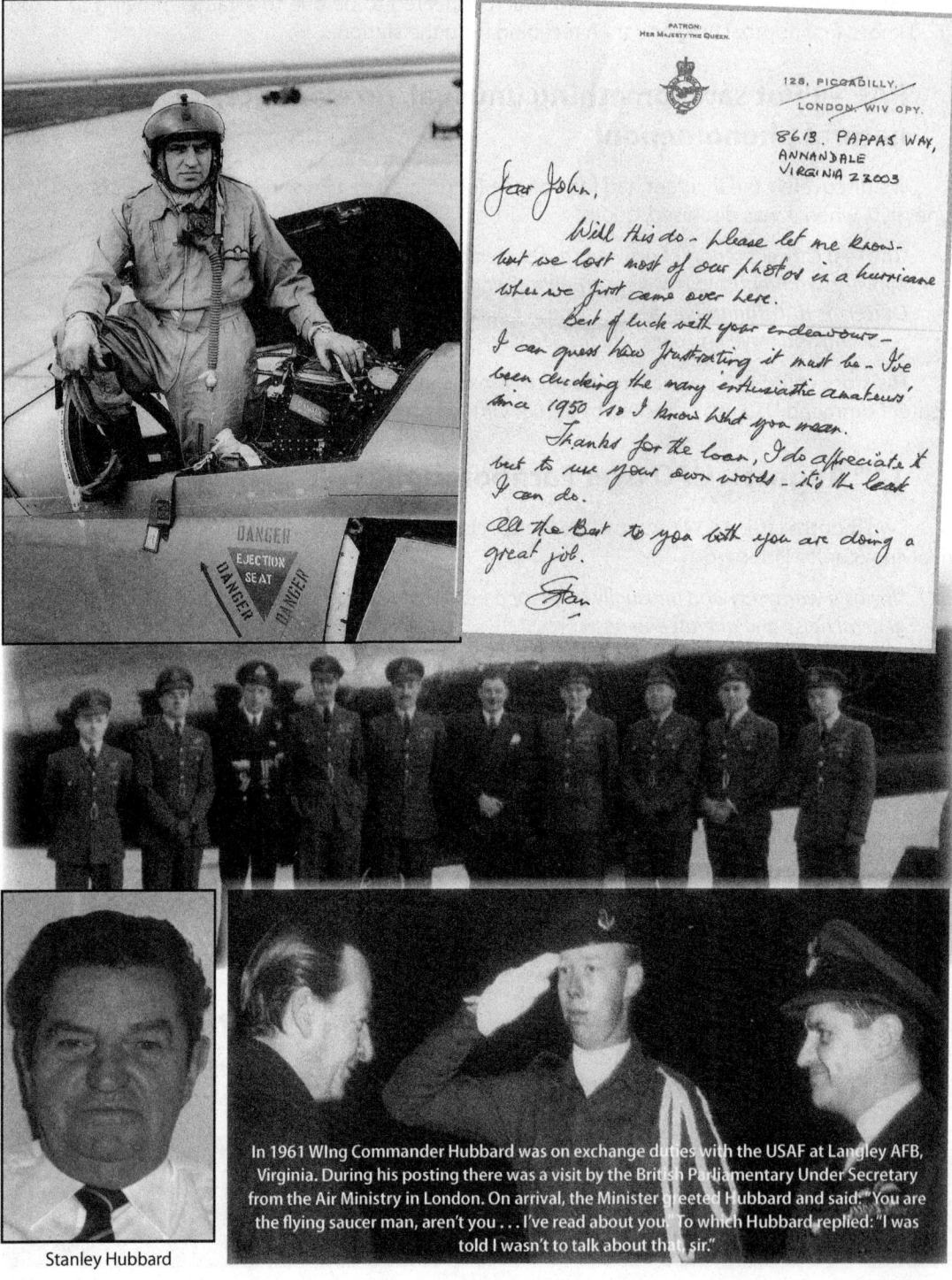

PATRON:
HER MAJESTY THE QUEEN.

128, PICCADILLY,
LONDON. W1V OPY.

8613, PAPPAS WAY,
ANNANDALE
VIRGINIA 22003

Dear John,

Will this do - please let me know-
but we lost most of our photos in a hurricane
when we first came over here.

Best of luck with your endeavours -
I can guess how frustrating it must be - I've
been ducking the many 'enthusiastic amateurs'
since 1950 so I know what you mean.

Thanks for the loan, I do appreciate it
but to use your own words - it's the least
I can do.

All the Best to you both you are doing a
great job.

Stan

DANGER
EJECTION SEAT
DANGER   DANGER

Stanley Hubbard

In 1961 WIng Commander Hubbard was on exchange duties with the USAF at Langley AFB, Virginia. During his posting there was a visit by the British Parliamentary Under Secretary from the Air Ministry in London. On arrival, the Minister greeted Hubbard and said: " You are the flying saucer man, aren't you . . . I've read about you" To which Hubbard replied: "I was told I wasn't to talk about that, sir."

Flying discus UFO

"I stopped and turned around, curious as to the source of this noise, and was very much taken aback to see an object, looking like a 'flying sports discus', rocking from side-to-side in a regular rhythm of movement (approximately 20-25 degrees either side), heading across the sky at about a thousand feet off the ground. I watched as it moved over, noting that the exterior of the craft appeared to be light grey in colour – a bit like mother-of-pearl – blurred, rather than sharply defined.

As it passed overhead, it allowed me to determine it was obviously reflecting light because, as it rocked, it reminded me of a pan lid, rotating segments of light. Around the edges were what looked like tiny crackling, sparkling lights, accompanied by a powerful smell of ozone. The next thing I became aware of was the arrival of the female dispatcher from the radio shack nearby.

She was hysterical. She screamed out my name and said, 'Did you see that horrible thing go over?'

I walked over to the Wing Commander's office and explained what I had seen. He made a telephone call to the Air Ministry, who interviewed me a few hours later, following which I was advised not to make any enquiries about the incident or discuss it with anybody else."

5th September 1950 – UFO visits Farnborough again

Stanley Hubbard was to find himself, once again, sighting something unusual over the same airfield during the afternoon. He was with a group of men watching the sky, near the Flying Control building, waiting for the return of a 'Hawker P108' out on test flight, when he noticed an object in the sky to the south, and grabbed hold of the nearest person – his civilian boss, Jack Spencer, and asked him what he thought the object was.

When he saw it, he shouted *"Oh, my God"* and called for someone to fetch a camera. Nobody moved. He told someone to fetch a pair of binoculars and 'Taffy' Evans came up with a pair, by which time a number of people were gathered watching the performance of this unidentified object as it took off from what appeared to be an unstable hovering position to incredible speeds across the sky, in great angular steps of movement, ranging between 180-330 degrees.

Interviewed by Scientific Intelligence Department – Highly classified

Once again, after bringing the incident to the attention of the Wing Commander, Stanley was interviewed by a group of men from the Scientific Intelligence Department.

"They were very, very specific that I was not to discuss the matter with anybody, because it was highly classified."

Verdict by RAF – Hallucinations, or misidentifications

Over fifty years later, Dr. David Clarke searched declassified documents at the Public Records Office, and found the report into the incidents submitted by Scientific Intelligence. A copy was obtained and shown to Mr Hubbard, who was shocked to discover that both incidents had been explained away as either *"hallucinations, or misidentifications".*

(Source: Personal interviews, 2006)

1951-1952

UFO ACTIVITY OVER EAST ANGLIA & NORFOLK/ LINCOLNSHIRE BORDERS

January – UFOs sighted over Ipswich

Suffolk botanist and ornithologist – Irene Stubbings, from Upland Road, Ipswich, happened to be looking out of her window, one lunchtime in January 1951.

"I saw what looked like two 'silver shillings', one behind the other, travelling high in the sky in a straight line, heading towards the south-west. They didn't appear to be going exceptionally fast, as I had them in view for over a minute."

Strange circular objects tracked on Radar over the coast – RAF scrambled!

We spoke to Jack Baxter – an ex RAF Radar operator, living in Herefordshire – who was quick to point out that while he had never personally seen a UFO, he was convinced they existed after having monitored many radar broadcasts, involving pilots who had been scrambled as part of his National Service between 1949 and 1951, at RAF Wartling, near Pevensey Bay, Eastbourne, Sussex.

"We were divided into crews of four or five airmen, with a pilot officer in charge. Our task was to track and identify all aircraft movement in an area off the south coast. On many occasions, when these flying objects could not be identified, they scrambled Jet Fighters, mostly Meteors, which had a top speed of some 640 knots, from places such as Tangmere and West Malling, to name just a few. Invariably, the pilots would report seeing strange circular objects, which veered away from them as they approached at speeds of 1,100 knots."

Strange *'heat mist'* follows RAF Meteor jets

We also discussed the same matter with Mrs Ena Stevens (now living in Swindon) who was employed at RAF Neatishead as a radar operator.

"UFOs were frequently plotted on the radar scopes as unidentified, rather than 'bogeys' – a term used to identify unidentified aircraft entering the wrong airspace. Contrary to the public's perception now, there was little excitement generated when UFOs were tracked on radar at the Base on one of the four radar scopes, installed in the reposing cabin where I worked at the time.

On one occasion, I was plotting a Squadron of 24 Meteor Jets from RAF Marham, when during a sweep I noticed I was picking up twenty-five returning echoes, the last one being at a height of between five and one hundred-thousand feet. I double-checked the information and then contacted the officer-in-charge, Squadron Leader 'Tiger' Shaw, ex 'Battle of Britain' pilot. After discussing the matter with him I contacted the group leader of the formation by radio and asked him to confirm how many aircraft were operational. He replied, "twenty-four". I then asked one of the pilots at the rear of the formation to obtain a visual image. He radioed back and said he could see what looked like a heat mist rising up and down behind the formation. The aircraft began their landing descent, at which point the 'heat mist' shot off upwards, at a terrific speed, and disappeared off both height radar installations."

June 1951 – Flying Saucer Working Party

The UK's *Flying Saucer Working Party* published its final report in June 1951, which **remained secret for over 50 years.**

The Working Party concluded that all UFO sightings could be explained as misidentifications of ordinary objects or phenomena, optical illusions, psychological misperceptions/aberrations or hoaxes. The report stated: *'We accordingly recommend very strongly that no further investigation of reported mysterious aerial phenomena be undertaken, unless and until some material evidence becomes available.'*

Pilots also reported seeing UFOs over Yorkshire

1952 – UFO sighted over River Deben, Suffolk

Alec White (now living in Felixstowe, Suffolk) wrote to us about what he saw in 1952, whilst plastering the inside of a house at Waldringfield that overlooked the *River Deben*, approximately five miles away from RAF Woodbridge.

"My mates left me to finish off the bathroom, while they went next door to erect some scaffolding. I was plastering around the window but began to feel hot, so I opened the window, glancing across the river, when I noticed this giant black object hovering just above the water. At first, I wondered if it was something dangling on the end of a crane. If this was the case, where were the cables? It then dawned on me that I was looking at something very unusual.

Panicking, I ran next door, ran up one of the ladders and shouted to my mates, 'Quick! Look out of the window'.

All we could see was a giant ring of black smoke. They laughed at me – then a Lancaster Bomber appeared on its landing approach, attracting the comments that what I had seen must have been a flare, which I refused to accept."

(Source: Personal interview)

Dear John Hanson,

thank you for writing to me re UFOs.
==

I have been interested in things that fly all my life, And when i was at
school i could not waite till the end of lessons so that i could walk to
Martlesham Heath Airfield to watch the planes fly, and i saw the first
Spitfire fly which was white.
I built model planes all my life and ended up building and flying radio
controlled models, so i think i know if something strange appears in the
sky.
I think i have had five or six sightings in my life, so i thought you
would like to see my drawings of my most frightening one.
When i was about 26 years old i had a contract for plastering 14 houses
at Waldringfield, overlooking the river Deben. and we started on the first on
My mates left me to finish off the bathroom,and they went next door to put
upthe scaffold to do the ceilings.
While i was plastering round the window i felt hot and opened the windows and
to my suprize right over the river was this giant black object, hovering
just above the water. at first i thought a big crane must be holding it
up but i could not see any cables, then i panicked and ran next door falling
over a heap of rubble itore up the ladder screaming to my mates to look
out of the window,and they said what is it one of those flying saucers
that we heard about on the radio, and i said just look,and we all rushed
to the window, and to my amaizement all we could see was this giant ring
of black smoke, and they both laught,then at that moment a lancaster bomber

was on landing aproach to the airfield,and they said had shot a flare
and i said flares are not as big and black as that and if only you had seen
what i just saw hovering over the water.
they would not accept it, but what i saw is exatley what i have shown
in my drawing , the object looked like the top of a gas ometer, and we
were about half a mile away.
I also have a couple, who had a very frightening experience in Ipswich
And her boyfriend was an American airman from Bentwaters.
Enough for now, please will you return my drawings.
                                        All the best
    Sorry about my bad typing.   Alec F.N.White.
Had to use stickers to cover old address

1953

UFO ACTIVITY OVER EAST ANGLIA & NORFOLK

1953.   1135

Sunday.   From out   S. Victor Yeakes   NT. DIR
                 of the   35, Trefor Jones Court
9 - OCT. 1983.   Unknown. ?   Brookfield Avenue,
                                   Dover, Kent,   •
                                   CT16 2QP U.K
                                   Tel: Dover (0304) 210977

                                                    NEC
                                                    VICTOR 1.

Dear Iain & Keith.
            I have just been reading your
interesting article with reference to UFOs, a
very important interest of mine.
What I have to write here - is the TRUTH and
perhaps I can prove it.
Whilst serving in the R.A.F. at RAF FELIXSTOWE
during 1953 I lived with my wife and son
in married quarters there.
It was on one occasion when they had both gone
to the one and only cinema there - in the centre
of the town.
It was my usual duty to cycle down approx
2 miles into the town centre to meet them coming
out.
It could have been in the region of 9.30 hrs that
evening - a clear star studded sky - azure blue
No Clouds - the moon was not so bright —.
There was no wind - it was a perfect summers evening.
So I cycled through this - then - small town centre
through an avenue of trees - I sensed something
going on in the skies above me.
On looking up - between the avenue of trees - I
could see a dark vague triangle shape of a
flying machine.
It was several thous and feet up - but large-
From its wedge shaped rear yellow and blue
distinct flames were coming away from it in
approx 6 trails.
There was NO NOISE - and wedge shaped jets were
not around in those days.
Due to my RAF knowledge - I sensed - and knew

Spring 1953 – Wedge-shaped 'craft', Felixstowe

RAF Serviceman Sidney Yeakes, stationed at RAF Felixstowe, Norfolk, was cycling towards the town to meet his wife and son from an outing to the local cinema, in spring 1953. A short distance from the cinema he noticed:

"…a dark, wedge-shaped 'craft', trailing six separate yellow and blue flames from its rear, at a height of about 7,000ft – totally unlike any aircraft I had ever seen. Frightened, I dismounted and watched it move over, feeling the hairs on the back of my neck stand on end as the object disappeared in the sky towards the direction of Harwich."

[handwritten letter]

and on top stood up as if electrified and
a tingling feeling came over me – I felt
really and truly scared and stopped the cycle.
On looking around for a witness – a policeman –
anyone – there were NO people about to justify
what I was witnessing – it was one of these
quiet moments in time – only the lights from
houses and shops – No People.
Anyway I watched it gather tremendous
speed as it headed over the town – and
disappeared into the velvet distance.
I was really in a daze when the wife and
son came out and I told them – as at that
time many people were coming out of the cinema
but not when I had needed them most.
I later got in touch with some civilian UFO
observers – and later two of them came to visit
me at another RAF Camp, they asked me
about absolute weather conditions – the colour
of the skie – was there a moon – clouds of any kind
Its estimated height – size – shape – speed – direction
etc etc. I later had a letter from them in which
they agreed with me that what I had seen was
true – and was without doubt an alien machine
as I had told them as it approched – came over
head – and proceeded forwards – there was NO
JET OR ENGINE noises whatsoever – and that
really had shaken me. I have since misplaced
this letter to me, and so have no proof of this
visit either. But if anyone wishes to interview me
at the above address they are welcome to call – I
am at home – mornings – and evenings after 19.00
hours. Hoping you find my recording of some kind
of TRUE interest to your own researches.
                    Yours Sincerely – S V Yeakes. Dover. Kent.

RAF – UFO sighting, autumn, at RAF Waterbeach – film taken

In autumn 1953, Jim – a senior RAF aircraftman – was instructed by RAF Waterbeach control tower to photograph an object picked-up on radar. It was seen to approach the airfield at great speed. It stopped short, about a mile from the end of the runway, at an estimated height of 1,000ft, and 30-35 degrees elevation.

Received burns

Jim obtained several feet of film but, during the procedure, received facial burns and singed hair as an F86 'Super Sabre' (USAF) took off to intercept the object, which immediately fled eastwards at great speed.

On returning to control, the cameras and films were taken and sent away to the Air Ministry. Jim was referred to the airfield hospital for treatment of burns sustained. He had this to say:

"The object was disc-shaped, silver in appearance, and was very prominent in the bright sunlight. The sighting took place roughly around 2.30pm. The UFO was in full view for about five minutes, before the object sped away as the F86 'Super Sabre' Jet took off to intercept it. Air Traffic Control not only picked up this object on radar but saw it in the sky."

Jim also said that the object's size could be compared to holding a five pence piece at arm's length. He has no idea what happened to the film he took. Interestingly, he met the radar operator in the NAAFI, later, who told him *"We've had quite a few of these"*, and showed Jim some UFO files in confidence.

(Source: Gloria Dixon, BUFORA/Malcolm Robinson, SPI)

6th October – 'Flying Saucer' over Norwich

Mr Fred. W. Potter from Norwich (then aged 34) – owner of a local window cleaning business, with over twenty years experience as an amateur astronomer, and member of the British Astronomical Association and the Norwich Astronomical Society – was in the process of leaving his house with his wife to attend a meeting. As the couple stepped out of the house, Mr Potter was the first to see a bright yellow *'star'* moving slowly across the sky, unlike anything he had seen before. The couple rushed back into the house and brought out a three-inch reflecting telescope, which they set up in the back garden. During an observation period, which lasted three and-a-half minutes, they were able to describe the following:

"It had a dark grey hull and a caged dome shape, with the cube of the dome hanging towards the ground, the flat side emitting a pulsating light that was much stronger when the object was stationary but decreased in luminosity when the object moved. In the centre of the caged dome could be seen what looked like a conning tower with eight windows."

Treated with ridicule

As a result of the Potters' publicising what they saw, the couple received scores of insulting letters ridiculing them for having reported the incident, all of them having been written (according to Mr Potter) *'by people without any Scientific training'.*

Our enquiries revealed that a number of other witnesses had also seen this unidentified object over the Norwich area, during the same evening.

7th October – UFO plotted on radar at RAF Neatishead

One is bound to wonder if there was any connection with the saucer-shaped *'craft'* seen by Mr Potter and other inhabitants of Norfolk, when a UFO was plotted on radar by RAF Neatishead, just before dawn the following morning.

According to an unnamed source, a UFO was tracked travelling northwards from Cornwall, at a speed of 36,000mph.

(Source: *Eastern Evening News,* 11.10.1953/*Daily Mail*, 11.2.1954 – 'Was it a 'Saucer' they saw over Norwich?')

3rd November – Pilots sight UFO

On 3rd November 1953, RAF Pilots – Geoffrey Smythe and Terry Johnson – were out on patrol over West Malling, Kent, in their Vampire Jet fighter, at l0am.

Geoffrey Smythe:

"We noticed a bright, circular object, motionless in the sky, at a height of about 20,000ft. Within thirty seconds, it took-off like a rocket, at a fantastic speed, in excess of anything we had seen.

When we landed, we brought the sighting to the attention of our Commanding Officer. The result was electrifying. Rather than dismissing it out-of-hand, he ordered us to go to Fighter HQ, where we were interviewed by a Senior Staff Officer, who actually told us what we had seen could not be explained away as a balloon or aircraft movement.

There was an enormous amount of interest in what we had seen. Prince Philip himself sent out a Squadron Leader (Sir Peter Horsley) to interview us."

(Source: Personal interviews/*Daily Express*, 10.11.1953 – 'Saucers Jet fliers see one from 20,000ft up', Express Air reporter Derek Dempster)

1954

UFO ACTIVITY OVER EAST ANGLIA & PILOT SIGHTING OVER ESSEX

1st March – 'Spinning top' UFO sighted over Lowestoft

Mrs Edith Capes from Lowestoft contacted the local newspaper, *The Eastern Evening News* (2.3.54), after sighting an object looking like a child's spinning top, with a light underneath it, travelling over the town at 7.30pm. Later the same evening, Mr P. Goreham from Norwich reported having seen a spinning *'ball of light'* in the sky, which changed into a 'triangle' as it headed across the sea.

4th – Unusual light seen

At 10.40pm on 4th March 1953, Mrs J.W. Horne of Oulton Road, Lowestoft, was walking along Oulton Road. About 100 yards from the junction with Gorleston Road, she saw what she took to be a bright star travelling in a south-west direction.

"It then came over the village and disappeared in the vicinity of Oulton Broad."

Enquiries made revealed that an identical object was seen two days later, at about the same time.

14th May – UFO sighted – USAF pilots ordered to intercept UFO

At 3.45pm, three USAF fighters (from 91st Fighter Squadron, RAF Bentwaters, in Suffolk) piloted by Captain Kenneth Scott Jnr., Lt. Harry Joseph Eckes, and Lt. David Clarby, were scrambled by GCI Radar type 7 at Bawdsy to intercept a UFO eight miles from their position. It was travelling at 240 knots, and had been sighted visually as a 30ft. in diameter, silver/grey round object, showing a thin silhouette as it turned, at a height estimated to be 50-60,000ft. The pilots were unable to get anywhere near the UFO. What the pilots would not have known is that on the same day, Marine Corps pilots chased a formation of sixteen UFOs, seen moving across the sky near Dallas, Texas.

(Source: NICAP, *The UFO Evidence*, 1964/ Personal interview with Jill Clarby)

14th October 1954 – Three UFOs sighted by RAF pilot

RAF Auxiliary Officer, Flight Lt. James Salandin, MBE, who was stationed at RAF North Weald, Essex, near Epping (then attached to 604 County of Middlesex Squadron) described the mysterious encounter he had while on an air test, climbing towards Southend, Essex, which he said was *"still vivid in my memory, despite it having happened over 50 years ago".*

Flying conditions perfect

Mr Salandin, to whom we had the pleasure of speaking many times over the years, spoke about his service with the Fleet Air Arm and the RAF, having logged 1,800 hours flying time on a variety of aircraft, including 300 hours in the famous Spitfire.

"I took off at about 4.15pm. Flying conditions were perfect. When at a height of some 16,000ft, I noticed a number of contrails in the sky, approximately 30-40,000ft, over North Foreland. Through the middle of these trails I could see three objects, which at first I took to be aircraft, although there was no sign of any vapour trail that one would associate with the movement of an aircraft in high atmosphere. When they reached within a certain distance, two of them went off to my port side; one was gold in colour, the other silver. The third object headed towards me and closed to within a few hundred yards, almost filling the middle of the aircraft windscreen before departing towards my port side. I tried to turn and follow, but it had disappeared from view. The object I saw through the front cockpit of my Meteor 8 jet aircraft was saucer-shaped, with a 'bun' on top and underneath. I didn't see any portholes, windows, or other exterior extrusions that one would associate with the passage of an aircraft."

Bound by Official Secrets Act

"At the time I was bound by the Official Secrets Act and if it hadn't been for leaks, nothing more would have been heard of the incident. I have always said that I know what I saw and my story has never varied over the years – the picture is still clear in my mind. However, I have not at any time given an opinion as to my thoughts on the subject but I feel that now is the moment to do so. Since my wife, Margaret, passed away, I've had plenty of time to reflect and would like to voice my true feelings, as most people appear to be sceptical or just not interested in UFOs.

I was a volunteer in the Fleet Air Arm, from 1943 until demobilization in 1947, my flight training being with the United States Navy, after which I served with 604 County of Middlesex Fighter Squadron 'R' Auxiliary Air Force from 1947 until we were disbanded in 1957. The last five years of my service I was 'B' Flight Commander. During this Decade, 604 were equipped with Spitfires, Vampires, and Gloster Meteors, the Squadron motto being, 'Si vis pacem para bellum', (If you want peace prepare for war!). I mention all of this because I was an experienced pilot and I have never seen, in all the years of my service, anything like I saw on that day."

20.I.2014

To John & Dawn

Well done keep
the Volumes coming!
Happy 2014
Best Wishes
James.

LET'S talk SPACE

WEEK-END PILOT IN NEAR COLLISION WITH FLYING SAUCER

IF Flight-Lieutenant J. R. Salandin, a week-end pilot of No. 604, County of Middlesex Squadron, Royal Auxiliary Air Force, had not been sceptical about Flying Saucers before his near collision with one last October, the Air Ministry might have had one of the first authentic cine records ever taken and been closer to solving the riddle of the unidentified flying objects than ever before.

Reporting for duty after lunch on October 14, Jimmy Salandin climbed into a Meteor Mk. 8 jet fighter and at 4.15 took off from North Weald, Essex.

The sky was blue and cloudless, and as he climbed in a southerly direction towards the Thames Estuary he spotted two Meteors in formation high above him leaving vapour trails behind them.

As his aircraft climbed, Salandin kept his eyes on the two fighters and every now and then checked his instruments and position.

The altimeter was reading

Flight-Lt. J. R. Salandin climbs into his Meteor fighter.

just over 16,000 ft. and Southend was just looming up beneath him when he saw two circular objects streaking between the two Meteors, travelling in the opposite direction.

He watched them until they reached nine o'clock high—a position high on his port beam —when they disappeared beyond his range of vision. Reporting the incident later, Salandin said: "One was silvery and the other gold in colour."

But the shock was yet to come. When he turned to look through his windscreen he was horrified to see another object

coming straight for him at his own level.

"The thing had a bun-shaped top, a flange like two saucers in the middle and a bun underneath," he said, describing it later. "It was silvery in colour and could not have been far off because it overlapped my windscreen."

A Meteor fighter's 37-ft. span wings just fill the windscreen at 150 yards.

As it closed in the object changed direction and passed Salandin on his port side.

"It was travelling at a tremendous speed," he reported and added: "I was so shaken I had to fly around quietly for about ten minutes to recover. I told control over the R/T (radio / telephone) what had happened."

What gripes Jimmy Salandin now is that he did not press his camera-gun button. "The thing was right in my sights," he says wistfully. "Next time I'll be on the ball."

At 150 yards the 37 foot span wings of a Meteor fill the windscreen.

2

Derek Dempster – gone now but not forgotten!

Another man to whom we spoke, also keen to set the record straight, was Derek Dempster M.A, RAF test pilot with the North Weald Squadron from 1948 onwards, and personal friend to James, who inspired his interest in UFOs.

Derek was educated, initially, at the French *Lycee Regnault*, in Tangier, and completed his schooling in England, in 1942, when he then volunteered for the RAF and was sent to Southern Rhodesia for pilot training.

On his commission, after receiving his 'wings', he qualified as a flying instructor. In the mid 1950s he left the RAF and took up a position as air correspondent for the *Daily Express* newspaper. He was then able to sift through reports of UFOs and decide whether further investigations should be carried out.

Book – 'Flying Saucers Have Landed'

He was asked to review a copy of *Flying Saucers Have Landed*, by George Adamski and Desmond Leslie, which increased his curiosity into the UFO subject. Unfortunately, owing to a disagreement with the editor of the newspaper over the grounding of the world's first passenger Jet – the Comet – he left the *Daily Express* and started his new job as first editor of *FSR* at Werner Laurie Publishers, in Doughty Street, London. He was assisted by the following people: Waveney Girvan (publisher), Lewis Barton (Editor of *This Week*, illustrated magazine), The Honourable Brindsley Le Poer Trench – an Accountant at the South African Embassy, Dennis Montgomery (librarian) and Gordon Creighton (Diplomat).

Meetings held near New Scotland Yard

"We held meetings at Westminster, Caxton Hall, near Scotland Yard. We believed these things were coming in from outer space, and we were trying to prove this with science. We had some allies, such as Peter Horsley, who had been Station Commander at North Weald, and was then Equerry to Prince Philip. Also, we received collaboration from Henry Chinnery, who was Horsley's successor.

Both men had a keen interest in keeping the Palace posted on 'flying saucers' and we used to exchange files with them. There was also a shorthand writer for Lord Mountbatten, named Dan Lloyd, who was an ex-Royal Navy man. He was also very interested in 'flying saucer' matters and shared this interest and new research material with Mountbatten. It was said, at the time, that Lord Mountbatten kept lever files of UFO photographs to show visitors on the bridge of the warships when he was at sea. I met George Adamski at this time."

Desmond Leslie (left) with Derek Dempster

Battle of Britain

Derek's literary output includes *The Inhabited Universe* by Kenneth Gatland and Derek Dempster, *Worlds in Creation,* by Kenneth Gatland and Derek Dempster, *The Tale of the Comet,* with Kenneth Gatland, and the award-winning *The Narrow Margin,* with Derek Wood, which served as a source book for the film *Battle of Britain.*

> Derek Dempster M.A. (Cantab)
> 16 Archery Square
> Walmer Deal Kent CT14 7HP
> Tel : 01304 367791
> e-mail : Derek..Dempster @ uwclub.net
>
> Dear John,
> Forgive me for the delay in answering your copious letter - a difficulty caused by rather serious illness. I hope, now, to be on the mend and able to give proper attention to your mammoth task.
>
> First things first, though. I was horrified to see Denis Montgomery's bio about me. Or do I malign the poor bugger ?
>
> I have rewritten the first two paragraphs, which you can integrate with the other introductory matter. I have written a lot more about myself than you need (*yellow copy*) so you have my OK to cut out whatever you want. It's not relevant to UFOs.
>
> Air Marshal
> Sir Peter Horsley's successor at the Palace was Squadron Leader Henry Chinnery, formerly the training officer on my old Squadron (No 604 County of Middlesex) I mention this because he is referred to in Para 5 as **Chilsory.**
>
> I am having trouble finding pictures of Desmond Lesley. I put them away in a safe place, and cannot now find them, Otherwise I enclose one of self.

21st October – RAF pilot sights three objects over the UK

Although admittedly out of the County's jurisdiction, it is of value to make a reference to what Air Commodore Michael Swiney OBE from Norfolk saw on 21st October 1952, when a RAF Flight Lieutenant was stationed at the Central Flying School, Little Rissington, Gloucestershire – if only because it has similarities in description with not only a 'wave' of UFO sightings that was to plague the Essex, Norfolk and Suffolk areas, many years later.

At the time of the incident he was instructing Flight Lt. David Crofts – a naval officer on a high-level exercise.

Air Commodore Michael Swiney OBE

"As we broke cloud cover, I saw what at first I took to be three parachutes in front of the path of the aircraft. Instinctively, I grabbed hold of the control stick and pushed it to one side in an evasive movement, at the same time looking over my left shoulder and directing 'David Crofts' attention to what I had just seen. At this point, I realised the three objects were not parachute flares but two perfect circular objects, with a third object being on edge showing a fuzzy white. I contacted Little Rissington Control Tower by radio and told the Controller, after some deliberation, that we had three UFOs in front of the aircraft, and asked him what action should be taken."

Box Radar Station, Wiltshire

"He replied they would contact the Senior Officer at the Airbase for guidance. A check made with Box Radar Station, Wiltshire, confirmed the objects had been plotted on Radar as three 'blips', which then merged into one echo."

Dear Mr. Hanson.

Thank you for your recent letter; you caught me a bit 'short' over a photo, but I managed to find something which may do for your purpose. It has the merit of being taken over the time of my episode in Oct. 52 when on the staff at CFS; the glass was for purely medicinal reasons, of course!

The Felpham incident was certainly interesting, and it just goes to show that we're not all in it!

With best wishes,
Yours sincerely,
Michael Swiney.

P.S. I should be grateful if you would return the photo in due course.

The pilots made their way to Rissington, flying back through their own contrail in an effort to establish whether they were being followed by the UFOs, bearing in mind the 'blip' on the radar scale had disappeared when the contrails did.

After landing at Little Rissington they were interviewed separately about the incident, but gave identical accounts of what had been seen.

"I can't give any explanation for what we saw. I can't say it was any 'Alien' craft or, indeed, representative of any 'Alien' technology. All I can tell you is what we saw."

Air Marshal Sir Peter Horsley

Air Marshal Sir Peter Horsley – a former Deputy Chief of Strike Command, later Equerry to HM the Queen and HRH Prince Philip – was to take an interest in this matter on behalf of the Prince, whom it is said has always been interested in UFO reports.

*David Croft – UFOs moving at 6,000mph!

We spoke to David Crofts, now living in Hampshire, who corroborated the account given to Mr Swiney, adding:

"After a debriefing with two officers from the Air Ministry, I was told by them the objects were moving at a speed of some 6,000 miles per hour."

In August 2015, we spoke to Michael Swiney. He told us the sad news that David had passed away some weeks ago.

In conversation with Mr Swiney about the version of events as given by Sir Peter Horsley, obtained from their original report, Mr Swiney still felt that while his memory of the event was reasonably accurate, he would have liked to have seen a copy of his original report last seen by him in 1974.

Air Marshal Sir Peter Horsley

Operational Record Book

The ORB (Operational Record Book) kept at the Central Flying School, Little Rissington, contains the following entry, dated 21st October 1952:

"Flight Lieutenant M.I.E. Swiney, Instructor and Lieutenant D. Crofts, Royal Navy Student, sighted three mysterious saucer-shaped objects, travelling at high speed at about 35,000 feet, whilst on a high-level navigation exercise in a Meteor 7. Later A.T.C.C. Gloucester reported radar plots to confirm this, but the Air Ministry discounted any possibility of 'extraterrestrial objects' AAC."

File destroyed

As the years went by, Mr Swiney attempted to obtain sight of his original report but was informed that, in accordance with MOD procedure, all files had been routinely destroyed at five year intervals (this practice was halted in 1967, the earliest records being from 1962), which meant his was no longer available for scrutiny – or at least this was the impression the MOD wanted to give!

In 1974, during a posting to the MOD itself, Mr Swiney, now an Air Commodore, asked for sight of his original UFO report from 1952 and was handed the document, which contained his and David Crofts' account, without any fuss, after being told it had been previously filed in the *Air Intelligence Branch's Blue Book!* After examining them he placed the files into the out-tray and thought no more of it, until retirement in 2002 when he expressed an interest in having sight of the reports again and wrote to the RAF's Air Historical Branch, now based at Bentley Prior. He was advised that UFO reports submitted to Air Ministry Intelligence could have been preserved for transfer to the PRO or, alternatively, marked for destruction – which was suggested to have been the likely fate in this instance.

Letter sent to GCHQ, Cheltenham

Dissatisfied, Mr Swiney wrote to the Director General of GCHQ to enquire if their department had retained a copy of the incident, and was later told that while a search of the archives had failed to find the document, his request had been passed to the MOD. They wrote to him explaining, quote:

"It was generally the case that before 1967, all UFO files were destroyed after 5 years but, since 1967, following an increase in public interest, UFO files are now routinely preserved. Any files from the 1950s and early 1960s are available for examination at the PRO."

Michael Swiney: *"If it was generally the case that before 1967 all UFO reports were destroyed after five years, how was it that I actually saw and read it in1974, some seventeen years later, while serving at the MOD?"*

UFO ACTIVITY OVER EAST ANGLIA

'Flying Saucer' over Lowestoft

At mid-morning on 7th July 1955, Ruth Murray from Beccles, near Lowestoft, was cycling through the town with her young son, Roy, when he pointed upwards into the sky and said:

"Look at the lovely star in the sky".

Mrs Murray looked for herself and saw *'a flat, glistening silver object',* heading silently, at tremendous speed, towards the south-east.

"I was so surprised I very nearly dropped the cycle, with my son in the back seat. It was the most beautiful thing I had ever seen. It couldn't have been an aircraft, nor was there any smoke. I watched it for a few seconds, and then it turned black and disappeared."

(Source: *Lowestoft Journal,* 15.7.55)

'Flying Saucer' sightings are discounted

FLYING SAUCER SIGHTINGS ARE DISCOUNTED

AMERICAN STUDY

FROM OUR OWN CORRESPONDENT
WASHINGTON, Wednesday.

After eight years study of the subject the United States Air Force has concluded that there are no such things as flying saucers.

Last night the Secretary of the Air Force, Mr. Quarles, made public a 316-page booklet based on the investigation of 5,000 reported sightings of flying saucers.

This showed that all but three per cent. of the reports proved to be balloons, aircraft, astronomical bodies, birds or mirages. In some cases other than the three per cent. there has not been enough information to say what gave rise to the reports.

Mr. Quarles at the same time disclosed that the United States Air Force, in co-operation with Avro Ltd. of Canada, is building a disc-shaped aircraft with jet engines that will look rather like the public conception of a flying saucer.

On the basis of the drawing of the model which the Air Force has released, the new plane will look like a round, rather than a flat disc with the pilot's compartment and controls housed in a "bubble" at the centre and with jet engines mounted on the rim. But it is not a real saucer design.

ERA OF THE UNUSUAL

Mr. Quarles said: "Vertical rising aircraft capable of transition to supersonic horizontal flight will be a new phenomenon in our skies, and under certain conditions could give the illusion of the so-called flying saucer."

He noted that the United States was now entering the era when aircraft of unusual configuration and flight characteristics would start appearing. But there would be nothing "supernatural or mysterious" about them.

Mr. Quarles also stated that there is no evidence that any objects mistaken for flying saucers had been of foreign origin. For his part he was sure that, even the three per cent. of the unexplained objects were, in fact, conventional phenomena or illusions.

COSTS OF RESEARCH

As was reported in THE DAILY TELEGRAPH on Aug. 24 from Ottawa, the United States negotiated with Avro Canada to assume the costs of research and construction of this disc plane after the Canadian Government had withdrawn its financial support.

History tends to repeat itself.
appeared in the DAILY TELEGRAPH.
1955.

1956

UFO ACTIVITY OVER EAST ANGLIA & LONDON

Three-domed object seen hovering above Kent Street

On Sunday, 17th July 1955, Margaret Fry – a young housewife, living in Hythe Avenue, Bexleyheath, Kent, was on her way to the doctor's surgery, in King Harold Way, accompanied by the emergency locum, Dr. Thukarta, to collect some medication for her son, Steven, taken ill with suspected sunstroke.

Within minutes into the journey, the 'Austin 7' car was plunged into darkness, as a black shadow fell across it, cutting off the bright sunlight.

"We turned right into Chessington Avenue. The engine of the car began to splutter. The car then came to a halt, near the junction with Ashbourne Road and Whitfield Road."

Light grey elliptical mass above junction

*"Wondering what on earth was going on, we got out of the car, to be confronted by the amazing sight of a light grey elliptical mass with well-defined edges, about 25ft in length, sprawled across the junction, roughly 20ft above our heads; out of the base of this unusual shade of grey-silver pewter coloured object, divided into sections, apparently riveted together, **descended three objects** that resembled huge ball bearing wheels which retracted upwards, followed by a swishing noise as it began to spin.*

After a few minutes it rose slightly off the ground, by which time a group of children had arrived. They shouted, 'flying saucer.'"

Unbelievable sight

"Doctor Thukarta kept saying, 'I don't believe what I'm seeing. It's not happening.' A few minutes later, it tilted at an angle and rose up to about a hundred feet, where it stopped still in the air. A porthole opened. It then immediately moved quickly upwards, making a 'swishing' noise, and rose about another hundred feet, where it began to slowly rock backwards and forwards, before heading away and out-of-sight."

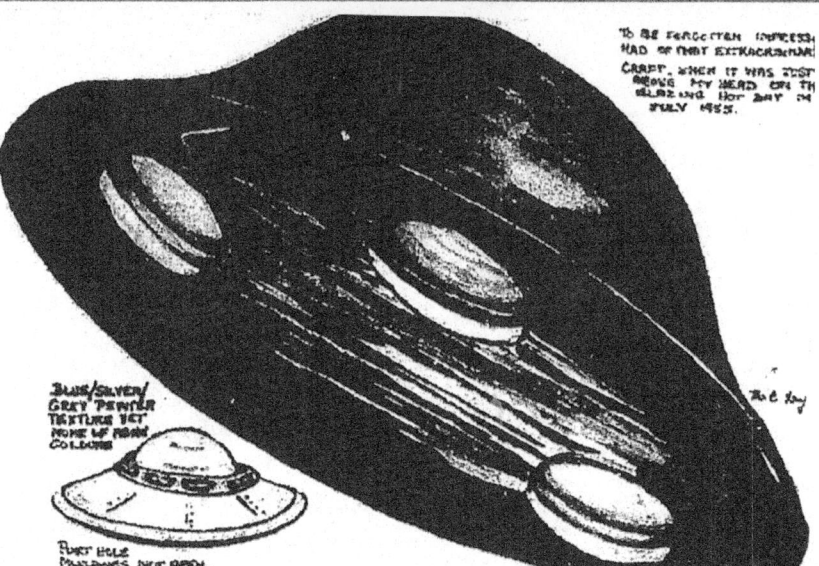

'This (drawing) is the exact impression I had of that extraordinary craft, just 18ft above my head on that blazing hot day in July 1955,' wrote Margaret Fry

Corroboration from another witness

Retired Postman David Philips also contacted us.

"I was living on a council estate in Bexleyheath, during July 1955, about a mile away from your publicised incident at King Harold Way. It was a beautiful hot summer's day, with patchy cloud, when I noticed a 'disc', or saucer-shaped object, hovering a few hundred feet above the ground, about a mile away. Suddenly it tilted, revealing what looked like three ball bearing shaped lumps set into its underside. I was so excited I ran to the house, shouting for my mother and father. As they came running out, whatever it was shot off across the sky – like a black streak of lightning – towards the London area, and was gone."

50 years later Margaret still seeks witnesses!

Margaret pictured here, over 50 years later, was still trying to find the schoolchildren during a visit to the locality. We also spoke to retired Police Constable Jim Streek (who has since passed away). He was on duty and saw what appeared to be an investigation being carried out at the scene of the incident later that day.

It is of value to point out the similarities with what Margaret saw and descriptions noted by other witnesses to the flight of UFOs seen elsewhere in the country. The reader should contrast the sighting at Bexleyheath with another sighting in the Lake District. They appear to be identical. Does this presuppose that we are dealing with just one object, rather than a great number?

PC Jim Streek

---

www.newsshopper.co.uk   *News Shopper (Bexleyheath + Welling) 4 September 2002. 87*   **NEWS**   BW   Septemb

BEXLEYHEATH: *Author appeals for information from 1950s youngsters who saw 'flying saucer'*

UFO kids urged 'phone home'

by **LINDA PIPER**
lpiper@london.newsquest.co.uk

A FORMER policeman who is researching UFO sightings in Britain is trying to trace a group of Bexleyheath children.

John Hanson, who lives in the West Midlands, is writing up a journal of UFO activity between 1941 and 1982.

He believes the children, now well into their 50s and 60s, could have been witnesses to an extraordinary sighting in Bexleyheath in 1955.

The incident took place on July 17 that year, in King Harold Way, when Margaret Fry, who lived in Hythe Avenue, was making her way to her doctor's surgery.

She and the doctor, Dr Thukarta, both saw what she described as an "enormous craft" hovering over the doctor's car.

She described the craft as saucer-shaped with a "blue/silver/grey/pewter texture, yet, none of those colours."

Mrs Fry said it also had what looked like three spheres inset into its base, one of which "flopped out", landing on the ground at the junction of nearby Ashbourne and Whitfield Road.

A group of twelve children who were playing nearby saw it and went over to have a closer look, before it rose up from the ground and into the sky, disappearing from sight after a few minutes.

Dr Thukarta died in 1965 but Mr Hanson has spoken at length to Mrs Fry, who now lives in North Wales, about her experience.

They would both like to know whether anyone else remembers this incident, particularly the children.

If you were one of those children or know anything about the incident, email Mr Hanson at hanson45@btopenworld.com or write to him at PO Box 10467 Kings Norton, Birmingham B30 1WE.

Alternatively, call News Shopper on 01689 885722.

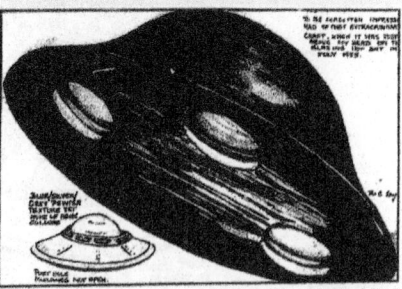

● 'This (drawing) is the exact impression I had of that extraordinary craft, just 18ft above my head on that blazing hot day in July 1955,' wrote Margaret Fry

Did you see the UFO IN 1955?

A WOMAN who claims she stood over a large UFO on a sunny afternoon in Bexleyheath in 1955 returned to the scene last week to search for those who shared the experience with her.

SCOTT SINCLAIR reports...

FOR the first time in two decades Margaret Fry, who now lives in north Wales, stood on the exact spot where, almost 50 years ago, she says she had stared with other excitable residents in bewilderment at the 'pewter coloured object' before her.

Mrs Fry, who used to live in Hythe Avenue, Bexleyheath, is desperate to speak with those children who had shouted: "It's a flying saucer", after it had flipped and landed at the T-junction of Ashbourne Avenue and Chessington Avenue, on Sunday, July 17, 1955.

Researcher

Mrs Fry, who has been a UFO researcher for 38 years as a result of her experience, said: "This is the first opportunity I have had in 22 years to come to Bexleyheath to try and jog the memory of those people who had lived in this area all those years ago.

"There are parts of the event I can not remember but some memories will never leave me.

"That week there had been a heatwave. Temperatures touched 101 degrees. My eldest son had sunstroke and the doctor who came to tend to him suggested we go in his car to King Harold's Way surgery for medication.

"It was about midday. As soon as we left our house, there was

a heavy shadow over our Austin car and the engine stalled. We got out and there was this thing spinning about 18ft above our heads. It just flipped and flopped on to the road.

"I remember there were children playing hopscotch on the pavement and they all came and stood around this craft.

"It was the traditional bell shape, which people may have probably seen on the TV.

"We were all aghast and they were yelling that it was a flying saucer. It stayed perfectly still for about seven minutes. Then it flew upwards and away. It took about another six or seven minutes for it to be out of sight.

"The doctor who was with me did report the incident to the British Medical Board. He was a locum for our GP, Dr Lobo, of Parsonage Manor Way.

"I am trying to trace one of those children who saw this thing with us.

I have tried off and on for the last 49 years to trace them. They must all be in their 50s now.

"Though I understand that this is hardly believable, there are no doubts in my mind that we saw an extra-terrestrial craft that day."

Margaret has now teamed up with UFO researchers John Hanson and Dawn Holloway, who are attempting to help Mrs Fry in her search.

Mr Hanson is writing a book on the subject, compiling the testimonies of dozens of individuals

'There were children playing hopscotch on the pavement and they all came and stood around this craft'

who have made sightings down the years.

He said: "If anybody had told me during my youth that I would be involved in the UFO subject, I would have dismissed this suggestion out-of-hand, believing that flying saucers and UFOs were representative of science-fiction, rather than reality.

"But after researching this subject during the

course of the last nearly 10 years, along with my colleague Dawn Holloway, it is apparent that the UFO phenomena is very much alive."

❉ If you would like to get in touch with Margaret Fry, contact Scott Sinclair at the *Kentish Times* on 020 8269 7000 or e-mail scott.sinclair@archant.co.uk

SEARCHING FOR CLUES: Margaret Fry.   contributed picture

THE HALT PERSPECTIVE

In addition to this, there was a 'wave' of mysterious flying objects showing three lights, set at equilateral distance from each other, that were to plague the Essex and East Anglia areas in the late 1980s, which were to become labelled as examples of the Triangular UFO. Was there a connection? We cannot honestly say, but nevertheless remain intrigued about the similarities in description.

As seen over Betley, Cheshire on 15th August, 1955

Gosport, Hampshire, 1965

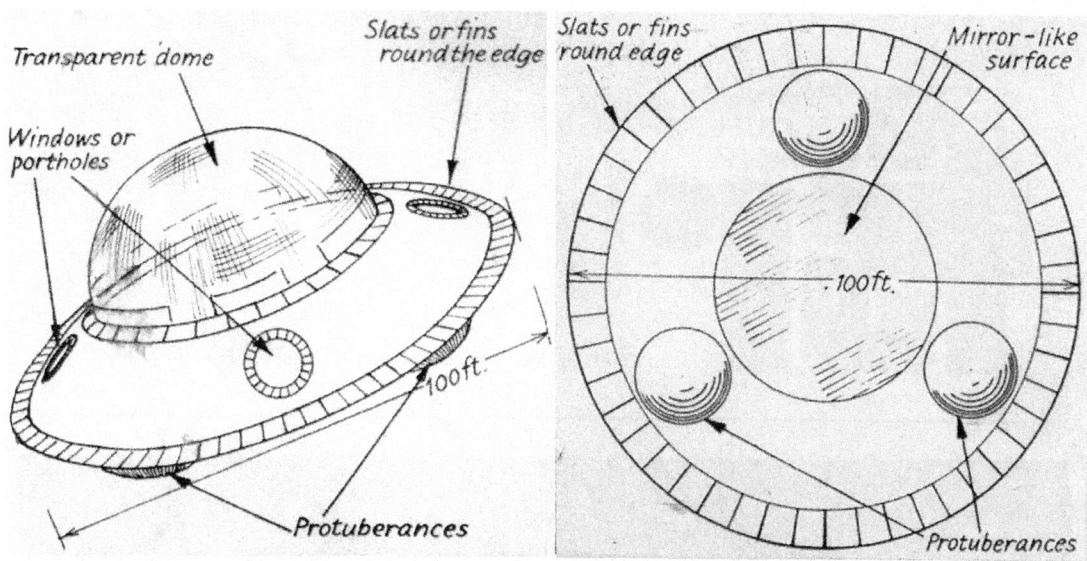

As seen over Staveley, Kendal Cumbria by Harold Threkeld on 19th December 1962

9.30pm on 13th August – Triangular formation tracked on Radar over Lakenheath

At 9.30pm on 13th August, radar operators at RAF Bentwaters and Lakenheath tracked a group of *'dots'* moving in over the East Anglia coast from the direction of Holland. The *'dots',* which could also be seen visually, were then 50 miles distant and closing at nearly 5,000mph – well over the speed of sound but failed to produce any sonic boom. At this point the radar then picked up a number of other 'blips', showing as an irregular group of twelve to fifteen in number, heading north-east at a much slower rate, *"being led by three UFOs, forming a triangular formation".*

At 10pm, a United States Air Force jet was scrambled to intercept but returned to base a short time later, after failing to make contact. Fifty minutes later a UFO, described as *'an oval shaped white light'*, was seen crossing the sky over RAF Bentwaters, at speed – apparently connected with the report of a similarly described object seen hovering over RAF Lakenheath for a short time.

An RAF 'Venom' Night Fighter aircraft, already on patrol over the Bedford area, was instructed to intercept the UFO. After making airborne radar contact, the object began to zigzag behind the jet – both *'vehicles'* being tracked by ground radar. Despite a number of high-speed manoeuvres, the plane was unable to shake off the UFO until another Jet fighter appeared.

Flying Saucer Review

In an edition of *Flying Saucer Review*, dated March/April 1970, Volume 16, Number 2, there is a lengthy article written by James E. McDonald, one of four illustrative reports referred to by him at a symposium on UFOs, held at the 134th Meeting, Boston, Massachusetts, on 29th December 1969. James tells of **three** significant radar sightings made by Bentwaters personnel, prior to their alerting RAF Lakenheath.

FLYING
SAUCER
REVIEW

Vol. 16, No. 2   March/April 1970   Five Shillings

UFO OVER LAKENHEATH
See page 9

Following the 'Venom' suddenly losing the radar 'lock-on' as it neared the unknown target, it was reported that:

'…as the 'Venom' passed the target on radar, the target began a tail chase of the friendly Fighter'.

Ground Controllers asked the pilot to acknowledge this turn of events and he replied:

"I will try to circle and get behind the target".

His attempts to do so proved unsuccessful. The pilot then advised that he was unable to shake the target off his tail and requested assistance. It is then said:

"The 'Venom' pilot tried everything. He climbed, dived, circled, etc., but the UFO acted like it was glued right behind him – always at the same distance, very close, but we had two distinct targets."

The plane returned to Waterbeach Aerodrome being low on fuel.

Observed from the ground

Several people on the ground also observed the objects, which they described as luminous, making dead stops in the sky and reversing back along their course taken. In one instance two white objects merged.

Prophetic words – sadly still the same situation, over 45 years later

James:

"One could easily be enmeshed in a semantic dispute over the meaning of the phrase, 'one genuine UFO', so I shall simply assert that my own position is that the Lakenheath case exemplifies a disturbingly large group of UFO reports in which the apparent degree of scientific inexplicably is so great that instead of being ignored and laughed at, those cases should since 1947, have been drawing the attention of a large body of the World's best scientists. Had the latter occurred, we might now have some answers, some clues to the real nature of the UFO phenomena. But 22 years of inadequate UFO investigations have let this stunning scientific problem out of sight and under a very broad rug called Project Bluebook, whose final termination on December 18th 1969, ought to mark the end of an era and that start of a new one relative to the UFO problem."

According to the Daily Express (22.2.78), quote:

"The UFO was seen to shoot off at right angles and split into two separate objects, before locking onto the tail of the Fighter in a deadly game of hide-and-seek, before eventually disappearing."

Freddie Wimbledon

We contacted Freddie Wimbledon – the flight controller – who was on duty that evening at RAF Neatishead.

"The incident was released into the media by a retired USAF Officer NCO, who wrote his version of what happened, twelve years after the event, which became known as the Lakenheath incident. The article in the Daily Express was full off errors and inaccurate conversations. The

Mr John Hanson   3 Feb. 04
31 Red Lion Street,
Alvechurch
Worcestershire B48 7LG
                                        1409

Dear Mr Hanson,
            Thank you for your letter and all the "bumph". A
bit late in my reply but I only left hospital after a heart attack very
recently. I appreciate that you had the decency to write to me, whereas
so many authors have quoted from printed extracts and bald statements
said to come from me when I have never spoken to them in my life
When I have complained and even threatened litigation, they point out
that legally they are entitled to use anything that appears in press.
Hence I have variously been referred to as "Mr", FLT.LT, SQUADRON LEADR, FLT
CONTROLLER, ATC officer etc etc !

            You must remember (or possibly before your interest was developed)
that the story was "blown" by a retired USAF N.C.O who wrote his
version of what happened 12 years after the event which became known
as the "Lakenheath Incident" and who had "listened in" to the radio
This was pounced upon by the Sunday Times who queried it. but
were told by the M.O.D that they "had no knowledge of this
incident". The American Ambassador was told the same and every
step was taken to deny any knowledge.

            As for people like me who had been involved, we were under
the Official Secrets Act forbidden to mention it. I never even told
my wife!

            Nevertheless, snippets began to emerge and I was pestered by
various organisations, by callers, telephone calls, faxes, letters galore etc
etc, even some people who became rather nasty because I would not
tell them anything!

            I'm afraid I reacted rather hastily and told the Sunday Times
what I thought of them. This didn't help of course, but because of my
anger and the fact, my memory letting me down, I made the mistake
of including one sentence which with later hindsight and contact
with the R.A.F navigator* I have deleted this in the account you
sent me and would ask you to print only the correct version
if you use it at all. Preferably, don't use it !

* which should never have been included.

M.O.D continued to try to squash any reference to the "Incident" but inevitably more revelations occurred when people such as Pilots, Navigators, Sector Controllers and others concerned were found or started to make their own stories available. There was no stopping it, but somebody "high up" in authority issued a statement saying "all the papers in this case have been accidently destroyed" If you believe that, you will believe anything! Undoubtedly this was the most important scientific example of extra terrestrial existence ever known. with witnesses from the ground, from RAF and USAF Radar and the experience of R.A.F personnel in highly equipped aircraft especially designed for that purpose. Is it likely all this would be destroyed?

I am convinced now as much as I was in 1956 that something occurred there was no imagination in the minds of those involved. It happened and that was it. Every logical explanation otherwise has been thoroughly checked and double checked

Yours sincerely,

Freddie Wimbledon

P.S. I did see the Jenny Randles film years ago and thought it complete twaddle! David Clarke I first met about 2½ - 3 years ago but have not heard from him for over a year now.

Many years ago I knew a very learned and serious man who had lived most of his life in Nepal. He was quite convinced that the minds of the, for this letter, call them "orientals" are quite different from ours. and capable of travelling in (again we can call it this) a different world! Personally I do not query this a bit, the brain is a very curious piece of apparatus.

'Venom' was not a single-seater and did not possess the onboard capabilities to apply any gun lock onto the target."

Official Secrets Act

"I can tell you that details of the matter were brought to the attention of the Sunday Times, who contacted the MOD, who denied any knowledge of the incident. Apparently the American ambassador was advised the same. Because of the restrictions of the Official Secrets Act, I wasn't even allowed to discuss what had taken place even with my wife. However, as the years passed and more servicemen came forward to tell what had happened, I became pestered by people who wanted to ask me questions about this incident. They began to get quite nasty towards me."

Memory of the event

"My memory of the event: I was chief controller on duty at RAF Neatishead, East Anglia, on the night of 13th/14th August, 1956. My duties were to monitor the radar picture and scramble the battle flight who were on a 24-hour 'call-out' to intercept any intruder over British airspace not possibly identified in my sector of responsibility."

UFO buzzes USAF Lakenheath Airbase

"I remember Lakenheath United States Air Force Base contacting me, by telephone, to inform me there was something buzzing their airfield. I scrambled a 'Venom' Night Fighter from the battle flight, through sector and my controller."

Interception team takes over

"The interception control team would consist of one fighter controller (an Officer, Corporal, tracker and height reader), consisting of four highly trained personnel, in addition to myself, who could clearly see the object on our radar scopes. After being vectored onto the trail of the object by my interception controller, the pilot called out, 'contact', and continued to close on the target, but after a few seconds and in the space of one or two 'sweeps' of our scopes, the object appeared behind our Fighter. Our pilot called out, 'lost contact – more help.'"

It's behind you!

"He was advised that the target was now behind him and given fresh instructions. I then scrambled second 'Venom', which was vectored towards the area, but before it arrived on the scene, the target had disappeared from our scopes. Although we continued to keep a careful watch, nothing further was seen again. The fact remains that at least nine RAF ground personnel and two RAF crew were conscious of an object, sufficiently solid, to give returns on radar. Following a report made of the incident, a Senior Officer from the Air Ministry came down and interviewed us about what had taken place."

Mr Ivan Logan

Mr Ivan Logan – a retired RAF Navigator from 23 Squadron and one of the pilots involved in the incident – was also anxious to bring to our attention the subsequent exaggerations in the public domain, which included the ridiculous suggestion that one of the 'Venoms' was chased by the UFO.

"At the time we didn't consider the incident to be of any great significance. According to my log book, we took-off at 02.40 hours, on the 14th August1956. My pilot was Ian Fraser-Kerr, and we were airborne for 45 minutes. On this particular night we were the second 'Venom' aircraft used to attempt an intercept and were scrambled at low level, 2-3,000ft, looking for a target near RAF Lakenheath (USAF). Normally we were controlled by RAF Neatishead or Trimmingham GCIS, but on this occasion, we were with RAF Lakenheath Control Approach Radar, who advised us where the 'target' was, rather than controlling us. The difficulty with low altitude operations was the amount of ground clutter produced on the radar when we turned, or scanned.

We had no radar 'lock-on' facility. It was all done manually, moving the scanner by means of a tiny joystick, pointing up if turning towards the target, and down if we were turning away, the amount depending on how much bank the pilot was using. You can imagine the difficulty involved with trying to manually strobe the 'target' and, at the same time, advising the pilot verbally about visual height and target positions.

I remember picking up a contact several times, usually at about three to four miles. It may have been the same one, as it appeared to be virtually stationary. We were unable to turn behind it, as it was closing at high speeds. Eventually, we were forced to return to Base, as fuel was running low."

From: Ivan Logan

[handwritten annotations at top: "MR CHAMBER Ray 1405 / Thoro was a critism... / But was / reminder / on / Visual - / Sen 7 Carpenters you m place"]

Thank you for your letter dated 20 Oct 00.
You will appreciate that my recollection of the events
of 13 Aug 56 are very sketchy not only because it was so
long ago but also, at the time, we did not consider the
incident to be of any great significance. Certainly, we
were not aware then of what was reported earlier at RAF
Bentwaters (USAF).

My log book entry reads: 13 Aug 56. Take-off Time 0240
(Actually it would have been 14 Aug by then) Pilot:
Fg Off Fraser-Ker, Details: 'Scramble', Airborne: 45 mins.

We were normally based at RAF Coltishall in Norfolk but
once or twice a year a squadron was detached to RAF
Waterbeach in Cambridgeshire for QRA (Quick Readiness)
duties. Two aircraft were always on standby with crews
in cockpits to get airborne in two minutes to intercept
unidentified aircraft usually Eastern Block or occasionally
friendly aircraft who may not have filed a flight plan.

On the night in question I believe that we were the second
aircraft scrambled as the first had no success in
intercepting.

Usually when scrambled we climbed to high level for 'trade'
100 miles or so over the North Sea. In this case, we were
at low level 2-3000 feet I think, looking for a target near
RAF Lakenheath (USAF). Normally we were controlled by RAF
Neatishead or Trimmingham GCIs but on this occasion we were
with RAF Lakenheath Approach Control Radar who were simply
telling us where the targets were rather than controlling
us. One difficulty at low altitude was that ground clutter
on the radar tube (AI Mk 21 American Westinghouse kit)
reduced the radar range of pick up. The tubes flooded with
ground returns when we turned or scanned low. We had no
radar 'lock on' facility, it was all done manually moving
the scanner by means a a tiny joystick. Pointing up if
turning towards the target and down if we were turning
away, the amount depending on how much bank the pilot was
using. Having to manually strobe the target and at the same
time talk the pilot into a visual (say 50 yards) position
by means of a standard commentary giving speed, height and
turning orders as well as target position indications.
It was a one armed paper hanger situation.

On the night in question I recall picking up a contact
several times usually at about 3 or 4 miles. It may have
been the same one. As it appeared to be virtually
stationary we could not turn behind it as it was closing
at high speed (our speed) probably 300 kts or so. Our
targets were normally travelling at our speed and when in
behind we synchronised speeds at visual range. In this case
it was impossible. Eventually we returned to base as our
fuel was low, at low altitude fuel consumption is much
higher). We chatted with Dave Chambers & John Brady over
coffee afterwards and compared notes although I don't
remember filing a special report. I think at the time
we thought that it was a met balloon or something similar
and I don't recall considering UFOs neither do I remember
either pilot talking about visual sightings on any lights
although at low level there would have been plenty of lights
to confuse.

I have no idea where Ian Fraser-Ker is today. He was a
South African married and living in the UK. After about
1958 I do not know where he went as he was not my regular
pilot and he is not on the Squadron Association books.
Dave Chambers & John Brady are at the addresses I gave.
Dave left the RAF to become an airline pilot and John
stayed in the RAF retiring as a sqn ldr.

I can't find the Eastern Daily Press cutting I mentioned.
It was sent to me about 6 or 8 years ago by Colin Campbell
Smith who lives near Norwich. It was about the Lakenheath
incident and Colin remembered I was one of the Navs and
sent the cutting. The EDP may well be able to trace the
article.

Finally, I have a couple more cuttings and letters which
I will show you. One American article which you may have
seen is gives an exaggerated account of the whole incident
and quite frankly it is simply not true. It says that one
of the Venoms was actually chased by the UFO!

I hope this is of use.

From: Ivan Logan

18th March 2004

John Hanson
31 Red Lion Street
Alvechurch
B48 7LG

Dear John,

In reply to your letter dated 11th March, I hope the
following will be of some use.

1. I attach a copy of my version of events which I wrote
in Oct 2000. I can't improve on this, however, I will be
happy to answer by telephone any questions which may arise.
For instance , why was I the first contact point on all
this in 1996. With regard to the names mentioned in my
report: Colin Smith died last year, I have no address for
Ian Fraser-Ker (my pilot on the night) but I know Dr David
Clarke had some success. John Brady: 6 Hinshalwood Way,
Costessy, Norwich, Norfolk , NR8 5BN.   Dave Chambers:
10 Sunnymede Avenue, Chesham, Bucks, HP5 3LE. If you need
help in further contacts you can always speak to me first as
I have quite a lot of information on ex- 23 Sqn members.

2. With reference to the reports you sent me, I can only
comment on page 134 and the para ' An RAF Venon single seat
fighter' etc. That says it all, Venom spelt wrongly and
it was a two seater night/all weather fighter. All that
bit is rubbish and I think it is the same piece I refer to
in the final para of my attached report.

3. I enclose some photos which may be of use. I have nothing
suitable from the late fifties.

4. Thanks for the address of the other Ivan Logan. I don't
plan to follow it up.

Yours sincerely,

PS. I would like the large photos back in due course.

From: John Bradley.

Costessey
Norwich
Norfolk

1407

29th April 2004.

John Hanson,
31 Red Lion St,
Alvechurch
Worcestershire
B48 7LG.

Dear John Hanson,

Thank you for your letter of 10th April about the events at Lakenheath on the night 13/14 August 1956.

I was pleased to see Ivan Logan's report and I agree with his comments in his letter. I am sure he will have given you a good insight into the events that night – he and I have discussed these matters in the past. I will just outline for you what I can remember of our flight that night.

At the time, I was a navigator on 23 squadron which was equipped with the de Havilland Venom NF3 night fighter. The squadron was based at Coltishall in Norfolk but was detached to Waterbeach near Cambridge where it provided quick reaction alert to protect the integrity of UK airspace in the area.

Just about an hour or so before we took off my pilot David Chambers, and I were put on 2 minutes readiness. A minute or two before 0200 on 14 Aug, the controller at Neatishead asked for a Venom to investigate a contact for the Americans near their base at Lakenheath. So, we were scrambled and were off at 0200. Neatishead vectored us towards Lakenheath and we were instructed to climb to 7000 feet. Shortly, we were handed over to Lakenheath who gave us indications as to where the contact was positioned. On the

first reach run I saw nothing, but on the subsequent three or four runs I obtained a contact at around 4 miles. However, the contact was not as strong or bright as a contact from a large aircraft but it was quite firm. The approach speed was high and gave the impression that it was stationary but at the same level as our aircraft. The Americans confirmed at one stage that the contact was stationary. Unfortunately, you cannot intercept a target like that and my pilot could see nothing in the dark. The Americans did not offer close control but what they did was sufficient, and our radar – AI 21 – was good enough to obtain a contact. At the end of the fourth or fifth run we heard that another Venom had been scrambled so we returned to Waterbeach, landing at 0255.

At the debrief, Ivan and I agreed that we had obtained good contacts but could not come up with much idea as to what it was. My own belief is that it was probably a met balloon.

Little was made of this incident at the time and it was soon forgotten about although the usual debriefings took place. We certainly had no idea of any other events that night.

I have heard recently that this was the first time an RAF aircraft had been scrambled to intercept a UFO! I have to say that I do not believe in the 'Alien' classes of UFOs but on this night I did have a firm contact.

I doubt that my few words will help you much in your research but I wish you both the best of luck.
                    Yours sincerely,
                    John Bradley.

THE HALT PERSPECTIVE

David Chambers

"After landing, we met up with the other crew – pilot David Chambers and his navigator, John Brady, in order to debrief. I don't remember UFOs being mentioned as the cause of the scramble. There was certainly some conversation about the possibility of it having been a Meteorological balloon, or something similar."

We contacted Mr Chambers about the incident but there was little he could tell us, other than of a faint signal picked up on the corner of the radar screen and that no visual of the object was made.

John Brady

"At the time I was a navigator on 23 Squadron, equipped with the De-Havilland 'Venom' NF3 Night Fighter, based at Coltishall but attached to Waterbeach, near Cambridge, where it provided quick reaction alert to protect the integrity of UK airspace in that area. About an hour or so before we took off, my pilot – David Cambers, and I, were on two minutes readiness."

2am on 14th August

"At about 2am on 14th August, the controller at Neatishead scrambled a 'Venom' Fighter to investigate a contact for the Americans, near their Base at Lakenheath. After scrambling, we were instructed to climb to 7,000ft, where we were handed over to Lakenheath, who gave us indications as to where the contact was positioned. On the first search I saw nothing, but on the subsequent three or four runs, I obtained a contact of around four miles.

However, the contact was not as strong, or bright, as a contact from a large aircraft, but it was quite firm. The approach speed was high and gave the impression it was stationary, but at the same level as our aircraft.

The Americans confirmed, at one stage, the contact was stationary. Unfortunately, you cannot intercept a target like that and my pilot could see nothing in the dark. The Americans didn't offer close control, but what they did was sufficient and our radar AI2I was good enough to obtain a contact; at the end of the fourth or fifth run we heard a 'Venom' had been scrambled so we returned to Waterbeach, landing at 02.55hours. At debrief Ivan and I agreed that we had obtained good contact but could not come up with much idea as to what it was.

My own belief is that it was probably a Meteorological balloon, but little was made of the incident at the time and it was soon forgotten. I heard, recently, this was the first time an RAF aircraft was scrambled to intercept a UFO. Whilst I do not believe in the existence of Alien craft, I did have a firm contact that night."

1957

UFO ACTIVITY OVER EAST ANGLIA

USAF Pilot ordered to open fire on UFO!

We came across details of an incredible story, involving a UFO which was tracked on Radar during one late evening over East Anglia, in May 1957, followed by an order sent to pilots from the USAF-406th FIW (Fighter Interceptor Wing), based at RAF Manston, to intercept and then engage the 'enemy'. We spoke to Milton Torres – now a Professor of Engineering, with over 260 hours spent flying combat missions over Vietnam, to find out what had taken place on that night.

"The 406th FIW (Fighter Interceptor Wing) were committed to Metropolitan Sector (RAF) to have F-86Ds standing by as an operational requirement. I can clearly remember the call to scramble, although I don't remember such specifics as the actual vector to turn after take-off. We were airborne, well within the 5 minutes allocated to us, and basically scrambled to about flight level 310, our vector taking us out over the North Sea. Normally, the other pilot would take the lead. However, for some reason, I was leading pilot. I was advised by GCI (Ground Control Intercept site) that they had been observing, for some considerable time, a 'blip' on radar, orbiting over East Anglia."

Milton – Mysterious 'blip' orbiting Suffolk

"From my conversation with GCI, I was told that all normal procedures of checking with the other controlling agencies had revealed the UFO, with a very unusual flight pattern, was motionless in the sky for long intervals. The instruction came to select the afterburner, to expedite the intercept, and to proceed to a height of 32,000ft. By this time, the aircraft radar was on and I was looking for any sign of the UFO. I was asked to report any visual observation, which would have been highly unlikely – as the weather had closed in, with very poor visibility. I complied with the instructions given to me by Ground Control, containing Information predicted to reach some theoretical point for a lead collision course type rocket release. At this time, the aircraft was travelling at Mach .92, which is as about as fast as the aircraft could travel in a straight and level position."

Milton – Order came to open fire!

"The order then came to fire a full salvo of rockets at the UFO. At that time, I was only a Lieutenant and very much aware of the gravity of the situation. I asked for authentication of the order to fire and received it! This further complicated my difficulty, as the matrix of letters and numbers to find the correct authentication was on a piece of printed paper, about 5x8 inches, with the print not much bigger than normal type, not forgetting that it was totally dark, with the lights down for night flying.

I used my flashlight while trying to watch the radar, which as you will appreciate was no easy task. The authentication was valid and I selected 24 'Mighty Mouse' rockets on salvo. The final turn was given, with instructions to look 30 degrees to port, the UFO exactly where I had been told it would be, at an angle of 30 degrees, 15 miles distance. The 'blip' was 'burning a hole' in the radar with its incredible intensity. It was similar to 'blips' received from B-52 Bombers and seemed to be a magnet of light."

Milton – As big as an aircraft carrier

"What followed next I remember with much clarity. I ran the range gate over the 'blip' and the 'jizzle band' faded, as the marker superimposed over the 'blip'. I had a 'lock-on' that had the proportions of a flying aircraft carrier – by that I mean the radar return was so strong, it could not be overlooked by the fire control system on the F-86D. The larger the aircraft, the easier the 'lock-on' – this almost 'locked-on' by itself. It was one of the best targets I could ever remember having locked onto. I called to the GCI, 'Judy', which signified that I would take all further steering information from my onboard radar computer, rather than depending on instructions from GCI. At this point I was travelling at about 800 knots, with 'dot' centered on my radar screen, requiring only the slightest correction of course."

20 seconds before fire!

"At 20 seconds before launch of the missiles, the circle on the radar screen began to shrink, requiring increased precision to keep the 'dot' centered while keeping the trigger depressed."

10 seconds before fire!

"At 10 seconds from the 'target', I noticed that the overtake position was changing its position. It moved rapidly to 6 o'clock – 3 o'clock, then 12 o'clock, before coming to rest on 11 o'clock position. This indicated a negative overtake of 200 knots.

There was no way of knowing what the actual speed of the UFO was. It could have been travelling at very high Mach numbers and I would only see the 200 knot negative overtake. The circle, now down to about one and-a-half inches in diameter, started to open up rapidly. Within seconds, it was back to three inches in diameter and the 'blip' was visible in the blackened 'jizzle band', moving up the scope."

Now going away

"This meant it was going away from me. I reported this to GCI. They asked me, 'Do you have a tally-ho?' I told them I was still 'in the soup' and could see nothing. By this time, the UFO had broken lock and I saw it leaving my 30 mile range (soon off the radar screen at GCI). Following my return to RAF Manston, I was advised that the mission was considered classified and approached by a civilian in the Squadron operation area. He asked me a number of questions about the mission and told me it was highly classified and not to discuss it with anybody – not even my Commander – threatening me with a National Security breach if I ever breathed a word about it to anyone."

This is an incident which still captivates Milton's attention, who is now actively involved in organising annual RAF Manston reunions. Like us, he wonders on whose authority that order was given and what precedence was in force for allowing the discharge of weapons over civilian airspace.

David Cayton, 2015

Another man who agreed to assist us was well-respected David Cayton, born in March 1937, from Davenport, Cheshire. David has, in the past, sent us some case files relating to his own very professional investigations into reported UFO activity around the mid 1990s. These were much appreciated and will be outlined in a subsequent edition of *Haunted Skies*.

Background

David was conscripted into the RAF in 1955 and served 10 years as a photographer in Cyprus and Germany. He joined British Aerospace in January 1966, and was to become the head of Non Destructive Testing, which involved being responsible for the application of rigorous scientific test procedures on over 20 different civil and military aircraft.

After taking early retirement in 1993, after 27 years service, this highly intelligent man, whom it has always been a pleasure to talk to, joined Quest International as a UFO investigator. He then became interested in researching crop circles and sophisticated animal mutilations, which he believes *"represents physical and tangible phenomenon, which are beyond our current scientific knowledge and capabilities"*.

In a letter sent to the authors in 2015, David Cayton had this to say:

"As an ex RAF man myself, I know 100% that he was shocked to receive the coded signal to fire upon an 'enemy' and would like to bring to the reader's attention the claim that pilots could use their own discretion and judgment in whether to fire upon an unidentified object was not right."

David – Could this have led to an armed conflict starting?

"After all, it was at the height of the Cold War and Soviet aircraft were regularly deliberately flying into our airspace in the North Sea to be provocative – so no pilot, especially one from the USAF, would want to go down in history for being responsible for starting a 'Hot' War........or a full World War Three!

If a pilot did loose off his weapons without the proper 'authority' from the highest Command Centre, such as RAF Fighter Command HQ, at RAF Bentley Priory, he would have been immediately 'grounded' pending a Court Martial, with the added charge of using a lot of expensive ordnance! Remember, this action was also ordered upon Milton's 'wing man', so a total of 48 rockets between them would have been fired, if they had not lost their weapon system 'lock-on' at the last moment!"

"This 1957 UFO case, in my contention, is one of the most important ones ever, because it clearly demonstrates that despite the MODs long-standing claims that they do not and did not investigate UFOs ('Of no Defence significance', etc., etc.) it is a completely hollow statement! Milton's coded 'order' to fire upon his high-speed target would have been generated at a very senior level (Air Commodore rank or above) from the Fighter Control Bunker (known as 'Down the Hole'!) at RAF Fighter HQ, Bentley Priory, Stanmore."

RAF dealt with high-speed unknowns

"An ex-RAF man, who used to work 'Down the Hole', informed me, more recently, that they frequently had high-speed 'unknowns' to deal with! The instruction would have then been passed over to the Cold War secret nuclear bunker at Kelvedon Hatch, in Essex, which at that

time was the Command Unit covering what was known as the 'Metropolitan Sector' and the south-east of England. Milton's temporary Base at RAF Manston was part of that zone. The order to 'scramble' the two 'Sabres' would most probably have come from the 'Metropolitan Sector'. The USAF was taking their turn monitoring that part of the U.K. under the RAF's 'Rotational C&R Scheme', plus the F86D 'Super Sabres' were faster than any RAF jet fighters around, so they stood the best chance of getting to the UFO target!"

"The 'order' would then be passed on the RAF's Signal Unit at Bawdsey Manor, on the Suffolk coast, which was Milton's GCI (Ground Control Instruction) who were always in direct radio contact, but Bawdsey also had radar observations of any targets. When Milton's 'UFO' rapidly pulled away from him, at Mach 10 plus, 10 seconds before he fired, Bawdsey confirmed that the UFO had left their radar screens in just two sweeps and then instructed him to return to Manston and await a debriefing."

Warned not to talk about it!

"Subsequently, an unnamed American NSA official, from London, arrived at Manston to interview Milton and his 'wing man' separately, during which he was warned NOT to talk to anybody about his mission, INCLUDING his Squadron Commander!"

Interestingly, Milton and other pilots had previously been on liaison visits to Kelvedon Hatch and Bawdsey Manor to get to know their respective RAF counterparts, who formed the ground control units and instructed them during any mission sorties, especially when on QRA (Quick Reaction Alert) duties, as they were on the day of the UFO event in 1957! Media debunks story

"Some time later, when this case broke with the media in a big way, I was not surprised to see Dr. David Clarke, as usual, being paraded out on mainstream TV news channels, etc., and trotting out his normal debunking 'explanation' to put the case down. This time his explanation of the incident was that it was merely a deliberately generated false 'ghost' radar 'target' to test the radar systems and mainly to test out the pilots skills in intercepting a target successfully."

Palladium Experimental Radar System

"This was mooted to be an experimental radar system to generate a false return, which was named 'Palladium'. As usual he (or who ever briefed him?) were confident that very few people would check to see if this hypothesis stood up to scrutiny, thus throwing doubt in the minds of the viewing public to the veracity of Milton's personal true account, especially to abolish any concerns that the MOD were seriously involved in the whole claimed incident.

The experimental 'Palladium' system was not actually tested and used until the 1960s and not even used in the UK but only in Cuba, during the 'crisis', and later in Germany, close to the Eastern Soviet border. This, with the intention of confusing the Soviet fighters to waste time and resources chasing 'ghost' radar targets! The bonus of this system was that the CIA/NSA could also evaluate what size of 'target' the enemy could detect, therefore understand how efficient their radar capabilities were!

Having such an up and running system in operation off the Suffolk coast, in May 1957, was complete nonsense and **WHY** would we wish to confuse our own NATO allies flying around to protect the UK at a critical time of the Cold War? As usual no person in the media would check this out with a view of challenging Clarke's spurious story on the spot. Or, maybe they were too lazy, or even complicit in allowing his 'convincing' explanation to go unchallenged to try and 'kill' the story?"

David: Were American pilots ordered to shoot down UFOs in the 1950s?

"It is alleged that many American pilots chasing UFOs, during the 1950s in the USA, were initially ordered to try to shoot them down, and many planes and pilots were lost in attempting to do so, and that eventually this executive 'shoot down order' was rescinded with President Truman's agreement in 1952, as the USAF were losing too many planes at one point, up to one a day! If those allegations were true (and I have to yet see some proof) then this is frightening in its implications!

One has to ponder whether there was some high-level American involvement in the decision to order Milton Torres and his 'wing man', to launch their rockets at the UFO as soon as it was well away from the town of Ipswich (where it had been hovering for some time!) and safely way out over the North Sea? After-all, they WERE American aircraft with USAF crew, so perhaps considered expendable by US top brass? If either pilot had managed to fire upon the UFO, they may have come off worse and lost their lives in the process! In that event, their families and our media would have been informed of an unfortunate airborne collision accident and we all would have been none the wiser! Milton himself expressed some relief that at the eleventh hour, he did not need to fire his rockets!

In response to my FOI request to the MODs Air Historical Branch (RAE) confirmed this to be the RAF's Sector Operational Command Centre cold war bunker, at Kelvedon Hatch, in Essex, responsible for controlling the Military London Metropolitan Sector area, at the time (now open as a privately run museum).

Kelvedon Hatch

This Unit had advised Milton the target 'blip' had entirely gone off the scope in just two sweeps of the GCI, and then instructed him that the mission was considered classified. The next day, he was debriefed by an officer from the National Security Agency. The Commanding Officer, at Kelvedon Hatch, would report up to the ADOC (Air Defence Operations Centre), at Fighter Command HQ, Bentley Priory, Stanmore."

Authorised by Bentley Priory

"I suggest that almost certainly the order to fire would have been authorised by the ADOC, at Bentley Priory. The order would have been issued by the Met. Sector,* Kelvedon Hatch, and then related to the pilots via the GCI Signal Unit, at Bawdsey. I firmly believe this would have been the chain of command. Milton knew for certain that his USAF 406th Fighter Wing was operating under the control of the RAF's control and the USAF would most definitely have not been allowed to independently fire missiles over the UK airspace."

Kelvedon Hatch

Milton was never really sure who the other pilot was. He seemed to think that it might have been Major Dave Robertson, but then rejected that idea. Whether this was because the Officer had chosen not to become involved can only be pure speculation.

Daily Star newspaper article – 'My Dogfight with a UFO!'

However, we did come across an account of the incident published by the *Daily Star* (20.3.1991 – 'How fighter pilot took on a giant alien spaceship – My Dogfight with a UFO!') in which there is a reference by the journalist Dick Durham, quote:

> *'Major Dave Robertson was also alerted that night in his own 'Sabre' Jet. He recalls leaving RAF Manston and then landing at RAF Bentwaters, at Bawdsey, Suffolk, to have his Jet armed with live rockets.'*

Major Dave Robertson:

> *"I was advised that more than one ground control site and multiple UFOs were involved and that the area extended into Scotland. I gave chase to several of the UFOs, but was unable to maintain radar contact long enough to go to 'lock-on.'"*

Harry Harris

Another source of this information was published in *UFO Times*, Number 4, November 1989, by Harry Harris – **'Evidence of a Cover-up – Pilot tells of UFO Intercept'**. Harry tells of meeting Milton at the Cumberland Hotel, London, on 5th June 1988, where he (Harry) was staying overnight to attend a conference the next day. Harry confirms, during conversation with Milton, that he nominated Pilot David Robertson as being involved in the intercept.

David Cayton:

His recollection of that night's event somewhat varies from Milton's as far as where the interception began, but confirms they chased UFOs that evening."

Dave Robertson:

"We were already airborne but unarmed on a training flight, making simulated attack runs on each other, when we were contacted by Ground Control and ordered to land at RAF Bentwaters, where their aircraft were armed with large rockets and scrambled to carry out an intercept. I did get several good radar returns long enough to 'lock-on.'"

Oddly, according to Harry, the name of one of the RAF Ground Controllers was Dick Neville, whose son – Clive Neville – was then employed by the MOD to deal with reported UFO sightings!

Nick Pope, 2015

"The saga of Milton Torres is a reminder of the human cost of UFO secrecy. His loyalty over the years is commendable, and while he set out his story in a sworn affidavit lodged with an attorney and sent to the MOD, he only went public when the MOD itself declassified and released the UFO file containing this affidavit, sending a clear message that Torres was now free to discuss his encounter. Because of my involvement with the initiative to release the MOD's UFO files and make them available at The National Archives, I was able to forewarn Torres that his report was about to be made public. Over the next few days we gave a number of media interviews about his encounter and I was honoured to share the stage with him at a conference in Washington DC some time later. His relief at finally being able to tell his story was palpable, but the strain of having kept the secret for fifty years had clearly taken its toll. I recall seeing this brave man shed tears when he said that he hadn't even told his father what had happened, even though he knew his father would have loved the story. Tragically, his father died before the MOD released the file."

Nick Pope with Milton Torres

DAILY STAR, Wednesday, March 20, 1991

How fighter pilot took on a giant alien space ship

MY DOGFIGHT WITH A UFO!

By DICK DURHAM

TOP GUN fighter pilot Milton Torres has spoken for the first time about how he came within seconds of zapping a massive UFO over British airspace.

TOP GUN: Pilot Torres and his Sabre Picture by Gerald Davey/Colorific

John Hanson and Dawn Holloway
31 Red Lion Street,
Alvechurch,
Worcestershire,
B48 7LG
UNITED KINGDOM

Dear John Hanson and Dawn Holloway,
 Having read your literature I must bring you up to date quickly for you to understand the incident in question. Your request to tell Dave Roberson about your interest will meet with minimum interest from him as I am convinced I approached the wrong man. I am trying as hard as I can to find out who is the correct man that flew my wing that eventful evening is now my primary goal. I have talked to Dave on several occasions and I am absolutely sure he is not the man and the mission he described is another of those light in the sky that we ended up chasing. Since Dave Roberson and I flew so much together that when I was searching for the data that correlated to the things that occurred that I called him and both of us with our form 5's checked for night weather time and we came up with a flight of the same duration with the majority of the NW time as we were running on fumes by the time we reached Manston. This seemed like the correct flight so we both accepted it as fact.

As I stated David and I frequently flew together but in retrospect not this night! While I was talking to him he didn't recall the order to fire (we selected 24 rockets) nor him being with me on his own intercept. Too many discrepancies existed and much too important to mistake. I am certain he recollects another flight that we did have. He did not recall that in the in place turn the Met sector people swapped out positions in order to facilitate the intercept.. He normally flew lead, but on this occasion to facilitate the intercept I handled all the lead duties. This included the verification of the order to fire. This was the only time in my 20 year career that I ever used the matrix for verification and that by itself was unique. I was not too far from my date of return to the U.S. and we only stood alert a few times. We had some new pilots in the squadron and I am sure it was one of them. I have been talking to a UFOLOGIST (British) by the name of Harry Harris of Manchester (a solicitor) and he is aware that I have been looking for a hypnotist to see if we can come up with the unknown pilot. I think I have located one that I can use and I will try to schedule an appointment with him. Of the event, there are some clear recollections and some not so clear. BUT of this I am sure ---it happened pretty much as I described. I have instituted a search for a picture of me from the same period and have a few more places to look. I will not hold up this letter for it and I will send it off as well as e-mail it to you ASAP

Kelvedon Hatch UFO sighting

The enclosed report is self explanatory. It includes an illustration showing 'triangular UFO' activity on the 14th and 17th of November 1978 over the Kelvedon Hatch area.

ESSEX UFO STUDY GROUP

Unidentified Flying Object Sighting Report Form

Please give an account of your sighting:-

THERE WERE FOUR OF US IN OUR CAR TRAVELLING SOUTH FROM COLCHESTER TOWARDS LONDON ON THE A.12 AT ABOUT KELVEDON I SPOTTED A BRIGHT LIGHT BUT DIDN'T TAKE ALOT OF NOTICE UNTIL NEAR THE SILVER END TURN OFF WHEN I MENTIONED IT TO MY HUSBAND HE SAID HE HAD BEEN WATCHING IT ALSO, BY NOW WE COULD SEE IT WAS THREE LIGHT WE BOTH THOUGHT THAT A LARGE AERIAL OF SOMEKIND HAD BEEN PUT UP AND THIS WAS A WARNING LIGHT, BUT AS WE GOT NEARER TO WITHAM AND ON TO THE SLIP ROAD, YOU COULD SEE THERE WASN'T ANYTHING UNDER IT WE WENT THROUGH THE INDUSTRIAL SITE WHERE A VAN WAS PARKED ON THE MAIN ROAD INTO WITHAM ALSO WATCHING IT, NOW IT HAD STARTED TO MOVE WE PULLED UP IN THE MAIN ROAD OUTSIDE THE POLICE STATION AS WE WERE ABOUT TO GO INTO THE STATION TO SHOW SOMEONE, WHEN MY HUSBAND LOWERED HIS WINDOW TO LOOK CLOSER AT IT, I HAD TO LEAN FORWARD TO LOOK TOWARDS OUR RIGHT AS IT WAS NEARLY ABOVE US, WHEN THE CENTRE LIGHT WENT OFF THE THE TWO OUTSIDE LIGHTS WENT OFF IT LOOKED LIKE A FAINT BLUE HAZE THEN NOTHING IT JUST VANISHED WE SAT AND LISTENED BUT I DIDN'T HEAR ANYTHING.

Please answer the following questions as fully as possible:-
*Delete as appropriate

Date of sighting: Mon 30th JAN 78

Time of day: EVENING 8.30 APPOX B.S.T.(Daylight saving)/G.M.T.*

How many objects did you see? THREE LIGHTS (ONE OBJECT)

Where were you when you saw the object(s)?Exact location A.12 FROM KELVEDON TO WITHAM ESSEX

How long was the object(s) in sight for? TIME I SAW IT WAS ABOUT 10MINS
Certain/Fairly certain/Not very sure/Guess*

Was the object(s) in sight continuously? Yes/No* YES

Did the object(s) while under observation:
Move in front of anything / Move behind anything / Remain visible in the sky all the time*

Any other comments on this? STAYED IN ONE POSITION FOR SEVERAL MINUTES BEFORE MOVING. FROM SILVER END TURN OFF TO NEAR WITHAM POLICE STATION.

(3)

Draw a picture of the object(s) that you saw and indicate the direction of travel
with an arrow:-

WHITE HAZE
FROM BRIGHT LIGHT   STAR SIZE COMPARISON (ROUGH GUESS)
                         ONLY ROUGH GUESS

O O O *

THEY HOVERED
SEVERAL MINUTES

O °O   ← ← *

MOVED   APROX 50FT
BEFORE LIGHTS WENT OUT

How far from you do you think the object(s) was when closest?
Certain / Fairly certain / Not very sure / Guess*...IT LOOKED..THE HIGHT..OF..A LARGE
                                           AERIAL OR AS HIGH A CRYSTAL PALACE TOWER OR EVEN HIGHER.

At what height do you think the object(s) was when nearest to the ground?
Certain / Fairly certain / Not very sure / Guess*..AS HIGH..AS..AN..AIRCRAFT...
                                            IT LOOKED OR HIGHER

What size do you estimate the object(s) to have really been?..COULDN'T..BEGIN.TO.
Certain / Fairly certain / Not very sure / Guess*   GUESS.

If you held one of the following items at arm's length, which one would occupy the
same size as the object(s), when the object(s) was closest?   A pea / ½p coin /
Ping-pong ball / tennis ball / football / other item (please state)*
.SLIGHTLY...SMALLER..THAN.A.PING.PONG.BALL..FOR...EACH..LIGHT..(GUESS) *HAZE.
  BUT AT LEAST A FOOTBALL TO COVER ALL THREE LIGHTS COMPLETELY.
Could you estimate the object(s) speed?....WHEN.MOVING..NOT..VERY.FAST...
Did the object disappear while you were observing it?   YES.
If so, how? .FIRST.CENTRE.LIGHT.WENT.OFF..THEN..TWO.OUT.SIDE.LIGHTS
       THEN A BLUE HAZE WAS THERE, IN SECONDS NOTHING.
Weather conditions (circle as appropriate)
Clouds: (a) Clear sky CERTAIN   (c) Scattered clouds
               (b) Hazy   (d) Thick or heavy clouds

Weather: (a) Dry   (e) No wind

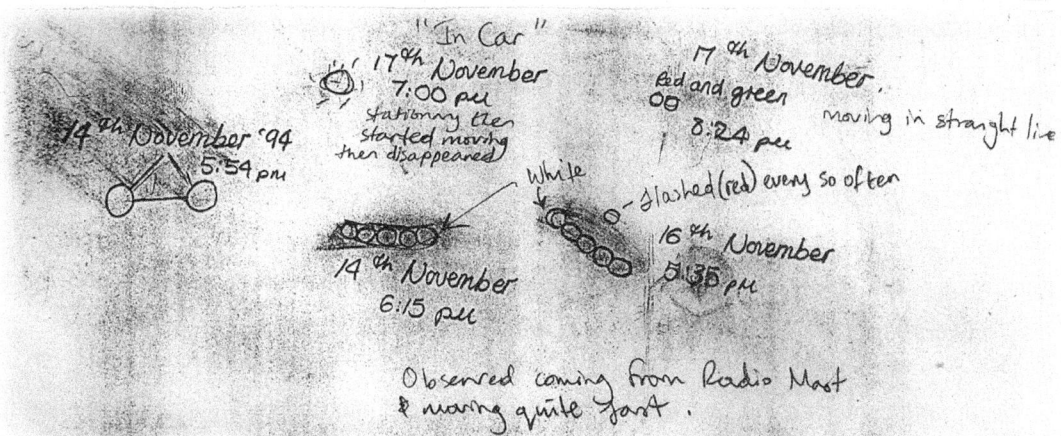

"In Car"
17th November
7:00 pu
stationary then
started moving
then disappeared

14th November '94
5:54 pm

17th November.
Red and green
OO
                 moving in straight line
8:24 pu

White
14th November
6:15 pu

- flashed (red) every so often
16th November
5:35 pm

Observed coming from Radio Mast
& moving quite fast.

1958-1962

UFO ACTIVITY OVER EAST ANGLIA

1958 – 19th April – RAF Jets from Lakenheath scrambled

On this day aircraft from RAF Lakenheath were scrambled to intercept UFOs plotted on the station's radar, ten miles away from the airbase – later explained away as being due to freak weather conditions.

One witness was Eric Apter (66) from Newmarket, Suffolk, with over forty years experience working with horses outside. He remembers, vividly, what he saw while exercising a horse along the main track at Newmarket racecourse, along with 20 other riders:

"…a silver UFO darting in and out of small clouds in the sky above us – almost as if playing a bizarre game of 'tag'; we watched it for about 20 minutes, until it left. The strangest thing is that none of us seemed to think it was out of the ordinary".

15th July – UFO sighted over Ipswich

Mrs Betty Wightman of 24, Freehold Avenue, Ipswich, was looking out her window towards the north-west, at 9.30pm, when she saw:

"…a long, square ended, orange tube-like object, completely motionless in the sky and silent. I rushed around and told my neighbour, who confirmed he could see it as well. About 15 minutes later my husband, John, came home, who is an aircraft modeller. He also saw it. It then looked like dumpy or rod-like in appearance, when seen at a distance. After a while it moved away, at great speed."

A spokesman at RAF Bentwaters and Woodbridge was contacted. He said there was no aircraft flying, at the time, and that nothing had been picked up on radar. Mrs Wightman went to the *Evening Star* newspaper office and looked at various pictures of aircraft, but was unable to identify what she had seen. After pursing the matter she came across an identical object, shown in the *Unidentified Flying Object Annual* for 1956, to that seen by her and the others over Ipswich.

(**Source:** *Evening Star*, 16.6.1958 – 'Mystery objects seen in sky')

January 1960 – Local newspaper has large file on UFOs

At 3.20pm, one afternoon in January 1960, Mr Tipping from Cransford, Suffolk, was asked by his poultry man to look at something strange in the sky, which he thought might have been a parachute.

"Through binoculars I saw a circular, apparently spinning object, flashing at great height (50,000ft) with a bright centre portion. After about 20 minutes it disappeared behind clouds."

Mr Tipping contacted the *East Anglia Daily Times*, who told him they had a large file relating to such reports!

Mr William Nailard was one of a group of men, working on the electrification of the Colchester railways line in the summer.

"I was looking at the sky, when I saw a 'star' moving fast across the sky. It then stopped directly overhead and turned immediately right. It carried on for a short distance then turned right again and disappeared from sight."

1961 – June 9th – UFO over RAF Woodbridge

Gordon Kinsey, in his excellent book – *Birth of a Beam* – tells of an incident that happened near RAF Woodbridge, Suffolk, on the 9th June 1961, when it was alleged an aircraft was seen to come down by one of the airmen at the Base. A full scale search by military personnel from RAF Bentwaters, and civilian emergency services, failed to find any trace of the 'aircraft' seen descending.

(Source: Personal conversations)

1961 – US Government denies existence of 'flying saucers'

Following disclosure made by US Government since 1947 that they have investigated 7,369 UFO sightings, they state that they are not spaceships from another planet, but more likely birds, balloons, hoaxes, or unusual lights in the sky!

Staffordshire UFO researcher – Wilfred Daniels

"The UFOs may not yet be proved to be spaceships from another world, but neither are they to be accounted for by any terrestrial yardstick, and therefore as true 'unknowns' are just as likely to be Venusian spaceships as anything else. While the 'flying saucer' has not been acceptably proved to be a spaceship, emphatically it has been proved to exist – to be a 'something', and not to be categorised with balloons, birds, lights, weather-effects, hoaxes, etc. Some there are, it seems, who 'scream the loudest' just before they are hurt. One might be inclined to wonder how – just after 15 years – the UFO would hurt the USA, for there is no Government that screams louder than that of the US on the subject of 'flying saucers.'"

(Sources: *Saucer Forum*, Vol. 2, 3, No. 4, November 1960/1961/*Saucer Forum*, Vol. 2, No. 2, May 1960/Orbit, Nov. 1960)

February 1962 – USAF scrambled to intercept gigantic UFO

Major George Filer said:

"I was stationed at the 420th RAF Air Refuelling Squadron Base, at RAF Scunthorpe, Lincolnshire, in February 1962. I was in orbit over the North Sea in a six engine K5-50 Tanker Aircraft, when we received a call over the radio from London Control, who excitedly asked us to have a look at an unidentified flying object, which had been picked up on radar, hovering between Oxford and Stonehenge.

After being given the intercept heading, the aircraft headed in towards the target, with further transmissions from London Control, informing us that all commercial aircraft had been cleared from our path, in order that we could intercept safely. We realised we were exceeding our maximum speed and had great trouble slowing the aircraft down.

At about 30 miles, my APS-23 radar seemed to pick up on the hovering, directly ahead of us. It was an exceptionally large radar return, reminding me of a huge bridge, or a ship, such as a destroyer – bigger than anything I had seen on radar in the air before.

The return was sharp and solid, as compared to the fuzziness of a rain cloud. My impression was that this UFO must have been made of something substantive, like metal or steel.

As we approached to now ten miles from the target, at a speed of around 425 miles per hour, it apparently sensed us, because we could now see a series of dim lights directly ahead of us, on what was a dark night. At five miles from intercept, the UFO seemed to come alive. The lights brightened and the object accelerated in a launch similar to the Space Shuttle, at night. Within a few seconds, it moved vertically upwards and was gone from sight.

We asked London Air Traffic Control if they had any rocket launches in the area. They replied in the negative and told us we were now clear to return to our mission. The incident was recorded in my navigator's log and mentioned the next day, on Operations, but no intelligence briefings ever took place."

(Source: Personal interviews)

George Filer

4ᵗʰ December – Three bright *'rods of light'* seen on UFO over Lowestoft

At 6.15am on 4th December 1962, Mrs Agnes Blanchflower (64), from 37, Marine Parade Lowestoft, Norfolk, happened to glance through the window overlooking the North Sea in a south-east direction, when she saw what she took to be the head of a whale floating above the sea, about two miles away.

"At first I thought it was a bright star, then the head of a whale. When I looked closer I was shocked to see it resembled a pillbox, showing a band of generated light at the rear, with three bright 'rods of light'. Every few minutes, it pulsated. When this happened, more 'rods of light' appeared, followed by a bright beam – like a searchlight. On two occasions, I saw an extra piece at the top, as if seeing it at a different angle."

(Source: *Evening Star*, 5.12.1962 – 'Saw strange object in sky – Lowestoft woman astounded')

1963

UFO ACTIVITY OVER EAST ANGLIA

1963 – Ghostly figure apprehended at East Gate, Woodbridge

At RAF Woodbridge -17 miles from Ipswich, Suffolk – Eddie McVee, a retired security officer, who served at the airbase, spoke about a number of intrusions, during 1963, by someone whom the Security Officers on the base nicknamed, 'East End Charlie', following fruitless attempts to apprehend him after he was seen loitering near the East Gate security entrance.

"He was often seen fading into the thick fog that occasionally rolls in from the nearby Rendlesham Forest and invariably the subject of much conversation, attracting speculation. The offender was either a ghost of a pilot, who had lost his life during a crash landing, or a figment of overactive imagination. For several months, there were a number of trailers parked north of the 78th TFS Alert Aircraft area, at Woodbridge, a few hundred yards west of East Gate, leading through the forest to RAF Bentwaters. These trailers were parked about 50 yards from the alert area and about the same distance from the base perimeter fence. On several occasions, we saw movement around these trailers, late at night, seeing a cigarette butt flicked out of the window.

When this happened, mobile patrols and K9 teams would be asked to check out the locality. Following their arrival the intruder, who became dubbed, 'East End Charlie', would run to the perimeter fence, scale it, and escape on a motorcycle.

After several failed attempts to catch this man, we contacted Suffolk Police, who set up observations around the airbase and caught him, one night, when we discovered he was a local youth and a member of an aircraft spotter group, who wore spiked shoes, motorcycle gloves,

reference:- AiR 2/17527

COPYRIGHT – NOT TO BE REPRODUCED PHOTOGRAPHICALLY WITHOUT PERMISSION

N/X 59/64
Qit
219A

MINISTRY OF DEFENCE
Main Building, Whitehall, LONDON S.W.I
Telephone: WHItehall 7022, ext.

Our reference:
Your reference:

24 June 1965

Mr Langton has shown us your letter of the 15th June about Project Blue Book.

In the United Kingdom, the Air Force Department of the Ministry of Defence has the primary responsibility for investigating reports of UFOs., and the reasons for this allocation of responsibility are exactly the same as in your case.

We investigate every case reported to us, and we use every assistance, civilian as well as military, available to us to identify a particular object. For example, we have frequently used the resources of Kodak Ltd., to examine photographs, films and equipment submitted to us. We do not, however maintain a special scientific staff for this purpose. It is normally handled as part of the routine work of our Air Force Technical Intelligence department. Unlike you, however, we do investigate single-observer sightings. Our results over the years are in line with yours viz. in some 90% of cases investigated, we are able to make a positive, rational identification, in 10% we are unable to do so because of insufficient data, and in no case have we unearthed any evidence of extra-terrestrial origin.

Our policy is to play down the subject of UFOs and to avoid attaching undue attention or publicity to it. As a result, we have never had any serious political pressure to mount a large-scale investigation such as Project Blue Book. Indeed, the matter has been raised only once in Parliament in the last 5 or 6 years, and then only in a perfunctory way.

The specific answers to your questions are as follows:-

a. No

b. No

c. Yes, a considerable number

d. We investigate about 70 case a year but there are others which are not reported to us, although sometimes reported in the newspapers.

We should be delighted to discuss the matter with Dr Hynek when he comes to London and no doubt you will let us know in due course when he will be here.

Lieutenant Colonel John P. Spaulding,
Civil Branch,
Community Relations Division,
Office of Information,
Department of the Air Force,
Washington DC
U.S.A.

and trousers. We never had any problem after that, but every time someone saw something, or thought they saw something, it was explained away as the station ghost, 'East End Charlie' – a myth, I understand, still perpetuates to this present day."

1965-1966

UFO ACTIVITY OVER EAST ANGLIA

June 1965 – MOD 'play down' UFO reports

It is of value to examine a document, dated 24th June 1965 (now declassified by the MOD), (previous page), which reveals an astonishing attitude towards dealing with UFO reports received from the public. There is a certain irony here with the date, understanding that on the same day, in 1947, Kenneth Arnold sighted a number of UFOs moving across the sky.

Many people believe that the policy of 'playing down' reports of UFOs received by the Air Ministry/MOD was to prevent causing widespread alarm to the population. It is also likely that their concerns would have been how to deal with criticism about the lack of capabilities by the RAF to respond accordingly, following incursions into British airspace.

Nick Pope:

"The MOD document that contains the bombshell quote, 'Our policy is to 'play down' the subject of UFOs' gives people a rare insight into the mindset of the mandarins on this issue. It was written by an official who doubtless thought the memo would never be released in his lifetime – or at least until long after he retired. It's like playing poker with the MOD and catching a glimpse of their cards. It exposes the duplicity that was standard policy for so many years: that we told Parliament, the media and the public, that we were only peripherally interested in UFOs, while all the while, every single sighting was thoroughly investigated, and behind the scenes, detailed research was being carried out, often with the involvement of intelligence experts. I'm sorry to have to admit that I too had to follow this line when I worked for the MOD. I know this has made me unpopular with the UFO community, and I can well understand their frustration. If it's any consolation, I was frustrated too."

1965 – 20th September – Man attacked by an alien being!

We came across an extraordinary version of events, involving an encounter with a UFO and its occupants, at Felixstowe. It is still the subject of local gossip and speculation over 40 years later. We therefore decided to conduct our own investigation, rather than accept the many garish accounts written in a number of UFO publications, showing an orange glowing man, covered in flames, supposedly encountered by a local man – Geoffrey Maskey – on 20th September 1965.

Weird noises heard & orange glowing object takes off

We spoke to Mr Maskey about the incident:

Miss Mavis Forsyth

"I was with my girlfriend, Mavis Forsyth, driving along Walton Avenue, Felixstowe, at 10.30pm, with my friend – Michael Johnson. 'Mick' asked me to stop the car, because he needed to attend to a call of nature. After a few minutes had elapsed, I began to wonder what had happened to him, especially when we heard what sounded like a mixture of very weird noises and a high-pitched humming noise, followed by the appearance of an orange, glowing, object lighting up part of the road as it headed off eastwards, over Walton Avenue, towards the coast"

Geoff Maskey

Rendered unconscious with burn on the neck

"Now worried, I reversed the car down the road, with the window open, calling out his name.

About fifteen minutes later, 'Mick' staggered out of the hedge at the side of the road, clutching the back of his neck, and fell onto the ground – apparently unconscious. We managed to put

'Mick', who had a noticeable burn mark on the back of his neck, into the Vanguard car and rushed him to Felixstowe Hospital."

Taken to hospital – visitors banned

"After arriving at the hospital, and explaining to the casualty staff what had happened, he became the butt of much humour – being referred to as the 'Martian' by his friends. 'Mick', who seemed completely oblivious to what was going on, seemed to have some sort of fit and tried to take his clothes off, flaying his arms about. It required the strength of three or four members of staff to restrain him before he was taken away for treatment."

When Geoff telephoned the hospital, the next morning, enquiring about his friend's condition, he was told that 'Mick' was being treated for severe shock and that nobody was allowed to visit him. Following his discharge from hospital, five days later, Geoff spoke to 'Mick' and asked him what had happened.

'Mick's' account

"I remember seeing a glowing silver/orange object descending next to where I was stood, about twelve feet above me. Standing on the side of this 'craft' were two humanoid 'figures', wearing steel coloured suits, with arms outstretched at chest height, showing long pointed fingers. I saw them go back into the 'craft', and the next thing I remember was waking up in hospital."

Geoff discovered the burn mark had now disappeared from the back of 'Mick's' neck.

Although police found nothing at the scene, a number people in the Suffolk area reported sighting UFOs moving over the coast, during the later part of the same evening.

16th October – Cigar-shaped object seen flat at one end, pointed at the other

Mr and Mrs Harvey Bloom from Southwold, Suffolk, who were known in the locality as portrait painters, were in the back garden at 5.15pm, when they saw a very strange object, low in the sky, towards the west direction.

27th October – Sky blue object over Woodbridge town centre

Mrs Mildred Moore was in Woodbridge town centre, at 6.28pm, when she saw a sky blue object overhead, about half the size of the moon, resembling a child's balloon, heading westwards. She watched it for 10 seconds, until it disappeared from view.

The general consensus of opinion, logically, was that it had been a balloon, although the witness did not accept this explanation.

July 1966 – UFO sighted over Lowestoft

Lowestoft, North-East Suffolk, England 1988   © Copyright 2001 www.davidsankey.com

1967-1968

UFO ACTIVITY OVER EAST ANGLIA

3rd September 1967 – UFOs sighted over Ipswich

12th September – Yacht buzzed by UFO

George Thake – the skipper of the yacht *Jonelle* – was sailing to Walton-on-the-Naze, from Ostend, three miles offshore, at 12.58am, when he noticed an object in the sky beaming down a light for approximately 20 seconds, from an estimated height of 400 feet.

STAR SEPT. 7

Former pilot saw U.F.O. over Ipswich
1967

A BATTLE of Britain pilot, Mr. Julian Kowalski, of 6 Charlton Avenue, Ipswich, last night in his garden spotted an object which moved so fast across the sky that he was unable to describe it.

Mr. Kowalski, whose hobby is astronomy, said that at 8.40 p.m. last night the object travelling in a north-north east to south-south west direction at about 5,000 feet took one-and-a-half seconds to travel from horizon to horizon. He estimated the speed at 3,000 m.p.h. The object gave off a "metallic hum", he said.

A spokesman for the United States Air Force said that their last airplane was grounded at 8.35 p.m.—and it was a light propeller type. He said that between 7.30 p.m. and 7.45 p.m. there was some air to ground lightning and cloud to cloud lightning.

A spokesman for the Ministry of Defence could offer no explanation and said they had had no other reports of this object.

interviewed on ANGLIA TX

"I thought it was a parachute flare to begin with; it was like a searchlight. The sea was calm, although visibility was not good. After hovering for a while it accelerated away, at fantastic speed, towards land, zigzagging like a graph."

Another crew member – Mr M. Murphy of Southgate – also witnessed it. The Controller from (USAF) RAF Bentwaters, was contacted about the incident. He said:

"It certainly was not an aircraft, or helicopter, from the description given by the men. Our aircraft would not be flying at 400 feet."

(Source: The *Evening Star*, 13.9.1967 – 'Four on yacht spotted UFO')

16th October – Bakery workers sight UFO – It was Venus!

A 'wave' of UFO activity over the UK was recorded for October, involving sightings of what resembled gold coloured *'flying crosses',* and other objects – later explained away by the British Astronomical Society as the planets Venus and Jupiter, with Regulus underneath Jupiter.

26th/27th October – *'Flying Cross'* activity over East Anglia

If we were to include reports of UFOs seen over the Colchester, Essex, area in this book, we would have to split the book into four parts and would serve no purpose other than to convey to the reader the tremendous amount of UFO sightings from around the UK during this period.

It included sightings of what were to became labelled the *'Flying Cross'* – a short-lived phenomena which was especially heavy towards the end of October 1967.

The East Anglia area was to also experience sightings of this bejewelled object as it passed silently through the sky.

At 3.15am, Kathleen Harvey (72), of Lincoln Terrace, reported sighting:

"…a bright orange, oval-shaped object, like a rugby-ball full of light, moving slowly above trees near my home. It headed away from the direction of Bawdsey, towards Felixstowe Dock".

Mrs Margaret Ward of Christchurch Street, Ipswich, awoke suddenly, at 4.30am on the morning of 26th October, and on going to the window, after alerting her husband, who joined her, saw:

"…a bright 'star' in the sky, resembling a cross-shaped object with little things, like points of light, between the antennae. It kept bobbing up and down, before moving out of sight."

(Source: The *Evening Star*, 27.10.1967 – 'UFOs reported over East Anglia')

Other witnesses included Roger Smith – a mechanic from Witnesham, Ipswich, – who was outside with his parents and neighbour, Mr G. Kirby, when they saw a blue and red coloured object, moving across the sky in peculiar jerks of movement.

A spokesman at RAF Bawdsey was consulted. He was unable to offer any explanation, other than when asked if it could have been a weather balloon, replied to the effect that it was possible.

However, he conceded that none were launched from airfields in Suffolk. Ipswich Police said they had received reports of a UFO locally. If the Police possessed a central system where reports of UFO sighted were recorded, then the picture would have been very much different!

1968 – Boy photographs UFO

27th August 1971 – Cigar-shaped UFO over Sudbury

Henry Harrison (42), of Churchill Drive, was driving to work along the A120 road, towards Halstead, and had just reached the Blue Bridge Industrial Estate, when:

"…something caught my eye. I looked and saw a cigar-shaped object – black on the base, with a silver top – completely stationary in the sky. It then began to descend, but my view of it was obscured by the industrial buildings. I drove around the estate but couldn't find any trace of it."

12th December – UFO seen in the sea off Suffolk coast

Richard Haxell (18) of Fleet Dyke Drive, Lowestoft, was out at sea in a deep sea trawler off the coast, at 10.15am.

"We were packing up, ready to go home for Christmas. We had stowed away our nets and tackle and were just about to start the engines, when we

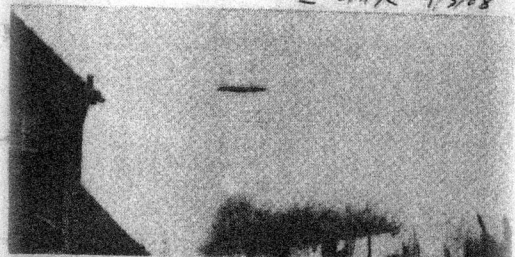

Pet dog first to spot Suffolk 'flying saucer'

E STAR 9/3/68

● One of the six photographs taken by Michael Albon of "the thing" which four people say flew over his home.

Schoolboy's claim

A 14-YEAR-OLD Sudbury boy claims to have taken six pictures of a flying saucer.

The photographs show an object which the boy, Michael Albon, of 36 Elm Road his father and two neighbours say they saw in the sky.

The story is: The boy was in his back garden taking a picture of his dog when the animal looked up and spotted the flying object. Michael called to his father to come outside and the "space ship" hovered in the sky for two to three minutes before moving off at a high speed.

Michael told the "Evening Star": "I would not have seen the thing had it not been for my dog Trudy. It looked like a big ashtray upside down and the bottom was black and the sides a silver colour.

"Although the bottom was probably smooth the sides of the object looked rough. It was silent and appeared to approach our house from the west and hovered around about 100 yards away and about the same distance up from the ground.

"The distance is really a guess and it could have been any size because of the uncertain distance. After hovering around it began to move away slowly and then went off

(TURN TO PAGE TEN)

● Michael Albon, with his dog Trudy, said to be the first to spot the flying object.

FROM PAGE ONE

quickly towards Great Cornard. It did not spin around but just floated."

Michael said his father, uncle and a next-door-neighbour saw the object but he had not told anyone about the incident and had waited until his film was developed.

He said he took the pictures on Kodak 35 mm black and white film on a Yashica Minister III on f.8 at 1/30 of a second. Local photographer, Mr. Richard Burn, who de-

veloped the film, said although he could not speak on how the pictures were taken there was no question of a hoax with the negatives as he had put them under a microscope and they were genuine.

Michael's father, Mr. Bob Albon, a machinist at a Cornard factory, said: "I have never seen anything like it before. I must say I did not believe in flying saucers before last week but I do not disbelieve in them now, although I have not really got the foggiest idea what it was. It was certainly several feet across —possibly several yards."

noticed this massive light green cloud just below the surface of the sea. It was at least 6,000 yards long and 100 yards wide, and was oval in shape. It wasn't picked up on our radar and was completely silent under the water. It moved underneath us and headed away towards Holland. We watched it for about 15 minutes before losing sight of it."

EAST ANGLIAN U.F.O. & PARANORMAL RESEARCH ASSOCIATION

SECTION A **SIGHTING ACCOUNT FORM**

Please write an account of your sighting, make a drawing of what you saw and then answer the questions in section B overleaf as fully as possible. Write in **BLOCK CAPITALS** using a ball point pen.

We were out in our deep sea trawler. This was on the 13th December 1971 we were packing up ready to get home for Christmas. We have stowed all our nets and tackle and were about to start the engine, when we noticed this massive light green object just below the surface of the sea. It was at least 600 yds long and wide I would say about 100 yds & seemed ovalish in shape. It made no effect on our radar nor could we hear anything. It moved beneath us and was lost going further out towards Holland. The time of our sighting was 10.15 AM and we watched the object for 15 minutes.

Please continue on a separate sheet if necessary.

DRAWING* *See blue green. Object Light Green.*

Your full name (Mr/Mrs/Miss/Ms)
RICHARD HAXELL   Age 18
Address.............................. DRIVE
LOWESTOFT SUFFOLK

Telephone No.................................(STD..................)

Occupation during last two years........................
Fisherman Deep Sea.

Any professional, technical or academic qualifications or special interests

....

....

Do you object to the publication of your name?
*Delete as applicable.

Today's Date.......6/1/92.....

Signature...........................

*If preferred, use a separate sheet of paper.

UFO ACTIVITY OVER EAST ANGLIA

16th March 1972 – UFO hovers over sub-electric station

Peter Mansfield (38) of Great Cornard, Suffolk – a draughtsman by trade – was outside, planting trees, at 2pm, near a recently-built sub power station, at Sudbury.

"I looked up and saw a silver-grey spherical object hovering silently, about 200 feet above some trees. I watched, fascinated, as I had never seen anything like this before in my life. About five minutes later it moved away, towards the north-east".

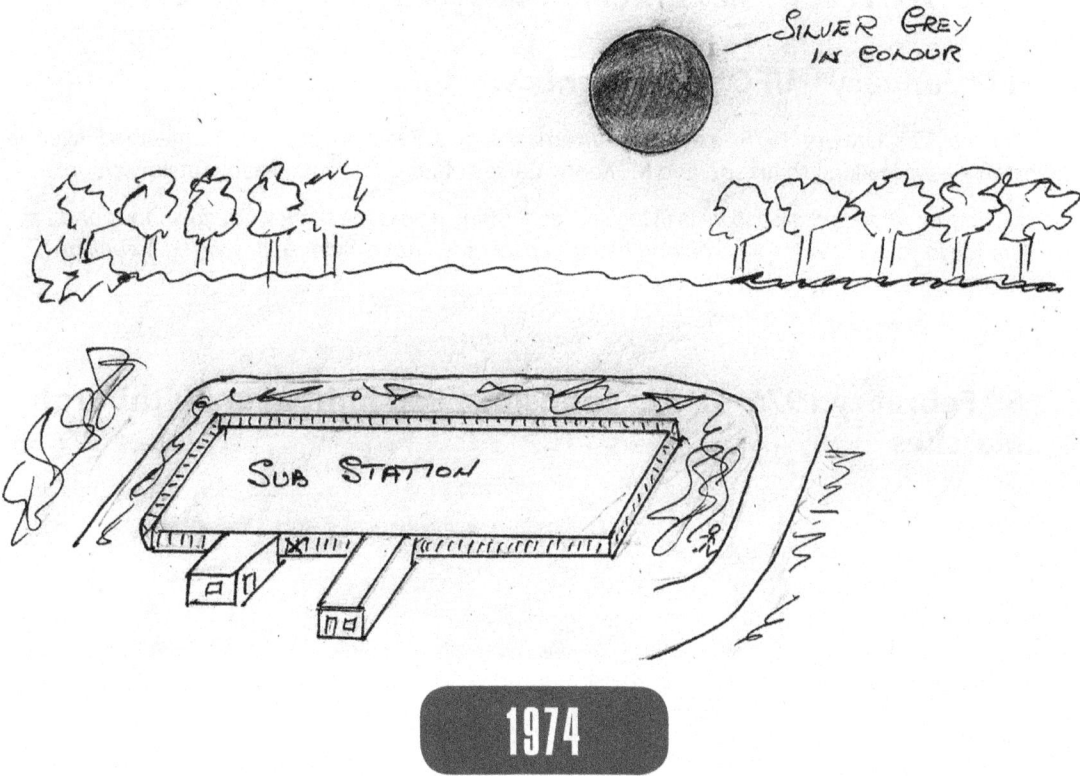

22nd August 1974 – UFO sighted over Bury St. Edmunds

A white cigar-shaped object was seen high in the sky over Bury St. Edmunds, during the afternoon. Several people fetched binoculars to try and obtain a clearer view of the glinting object, which floated high above Jets flying in and out of Mildenhall USAF Base. Despite a powerful telescope being set up on the pavement by local shopkeeper – Aubrey Davies – no further details could be made out. A spokesman at Honington Meteorological Office said that he did not believe it was a weather balloon.

> *"I have been in touch with Cardington, Bedforshire, where they are carrying out some experiments, but they denied having lost a balloon – it's a mystery."*

The Bury St. Edmunds area was to be the focus of many sightings during these years. Many of them took place over the British Sugar Corporation, just off the A14, also the scene of various reports.

1975

UFO ACTIVITY OVER EAST ANGLIA & NORWICH

17th January – UFO seen over Lowestoft

On the 17th January 1975, ex-RAF serviceman James Beachamp of 43, Homestead Avenue, Lowestoft – – was talking to his son and Mr Kenny Carsey of 26, Grosvenor Road, outside, when:

> *"…we saw what appeared to be a 'flying saucer' flashing across the sky. It was egg-shaped and orange in colour. It was very high and headed eastwards. I am convinced it wasn't a fireball or shooting star, or space debris."*

(Source: Ron West)

8th February 1975 – Peter Johnson – Red light over Blythburgh Marshes

Keith Payne was then living with his wife in a showman's caravan at Blythburgh, Suffolk. The caravan was situated on a promontory, which juts out into Bulcamp Marshes, which consist of low lying mudflats, through the centre of which runs a small river named the *Blyth*. This river is tidal and at high tide the marshes become flooded.

At about 3.30am Mr Payne was awoken by a deep humming noise, and went out to investigate. It was a dark night with slight mist over the marshes.

"I looked eastwards and saw a bright red light. The light was reflected in the water, but the outlines were indistinct, due to the misty conditions. It was about half a mile away and some 40 feet off the water. The humming noise was coming from the light. I could see its reflection in the water but no beam. I alerted my wife and we watched it for about an hour. We grew cold and went back to bed."

Peter Johnson.
U.F.O Investigator.
12th June 1975.

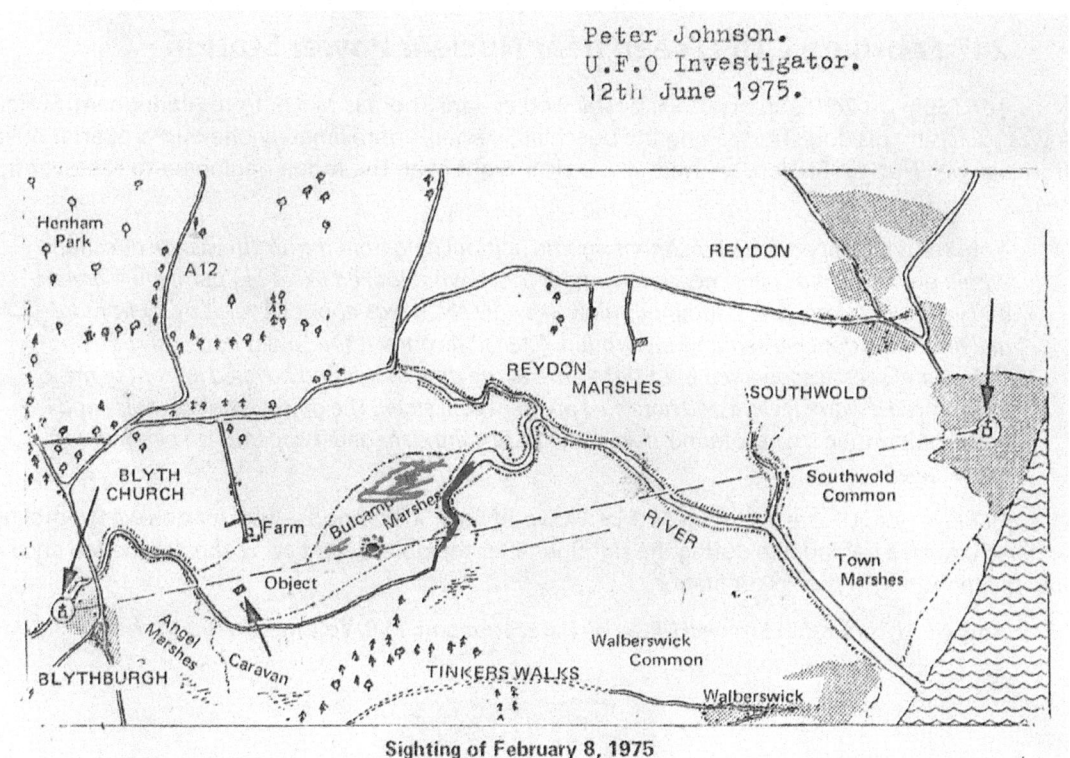

Sighting of February 8, 1975

Retired water engineer – Peter Johnson (63) of Sheringham, Norfolk, who had seen service with the RAF as a radar specialist – was then a regional Coordinator for BUFORA and an investigator for UFOIN. Peter described himself as being totally impartial and dispassionate about reports of UFO activity brought to his notice.

"I've always been interested in anything unusual or unexplainable, right from the early days when Kenneth Arnold saw his UFOs in 1947, and then reading the 1963 book, by George Adamski – 'Flying Saucers Have Landed'."

Peter spent a considerable amount of time interviewing people around the East Anglia area and placing their reports onto tape. Over the years, he built up a vast collection of reports and cuttings. It was his wish that when he passed away, somebody would house his collection in a museum and allow people the opportunity of seeing it for themselves. Sadly, fate was to decree that after his death all of his UFO effects were disposed of, and lost for ever.

Peter investigated a number of UFO incidents. They included Robin Peck from Docking, in 1969, whose car was immobilised by a saucer-shaped object, a UFO photographed hovering over trees close to Caistor Hall Country Club, in 1965, by Stanley Taylor, described as being the size of two busses, dull aluminum in colour, shaped like a rugby-ball, making a slight humming sound, and the sighting of a rugby ball-shaped object, with the base 'cut off', by a group of school children, which hovered 50 feet above the ground over Red Woods, near Taverham Hall Farm ,in May 1972, just outside Norwich. (He was assisted by Barry Marsh – a teacher at Taverham Hall School.)

24th February – UFO seen near Nuclear Power Station

At 6.55pm on 24th February 1975, postal worker – Mr Thomas Meyer from Aldringham, Suffolk – was exercising his dog, 'Titus', along the beech at Sizewell, approximately one-and-a-quarter miles from Sizewell Nuclear Station, on what was a clear night, with the moon beginning to rise over the sea.

"I noticed what appeared to be a 'shooting star' approaching from the north- eastern direction. Within seconds it was near me, close enough to see what looked like a big pumpkin – green and yellow in colour, with a luminous glow like a TV set. It was about 20 yards away from me and hovering about 6 feet above the ground. After 30 seconds, it sped away as quickly as it had arrived and soon disappeared from sight. During the time that it had hovered in front of me, I experienced a warm feeling and noticed a pungent acid smell. The object made no noise and I had an impression it was rotating. Its outlines were quite clear and it appeared to be some sort of machine."

Mr Meyer told UFO researcher – Mr M.K .Howe, of Bury St. Edmunds – that his dog was trembling and had cowered behind him during the sighting. After the object went away, the dog bolted and he found him waiting at the Power Station.

(**Source:** *Blythburgh & Sizewell UFOs*, by Peter Johnson, *FSR*, Volume 21, No. 5)

UFO ACTIVITY OVER EAST ANGLIA & NORWICH

1976 – UFO and brilliant flashes of light seen in adjacent County

Bread delivery man Roy Simpson, from Ipswich, was employed to deliver bread to Norwich, during 1976, working alternate shifts – either starting at 4.30am on the early shift, or 10pm on the late.

Roy:

"These past eight weeks, or more, I can say that there has hardly been a journey which passes without the sighting of brilliant flashes of light seen in the sky, outside Long Stratton, near Norwich. When I spoke to my colleagues at the bakery about this, they told me it's been going on for years!

On the 16th October 1976, at 4.40am, my mate – Bruce Carter – told me about an object moving across the sky, about a mile away. I went to the side door with another workman, called Herbert, and looked out and saw a star-shaped hazy 'disc', showing a red light and blue light, as if suspended in the sky over Ipswich. Bruce told me it had been there since 10am. It was still there when I finished, at 5.15am.

I felt, in some way, that I was being observed."

(Source: Letter to MAPIT)

1977

UFO ACTIVITY OVER EAST ANGLIA & NORWICH

March – Glowing yellow banana-shaped object seen over Felixstowe

Margaret Honoria Dye (72) of 4, Lancing Avenue, Ipswich, whom we never met personally but did visit her husband, George Bernard Dye, who was to sight a number of UFOs while returning home from a bombing mission to Germany in 1944, before he sadly passed away a few years ago.

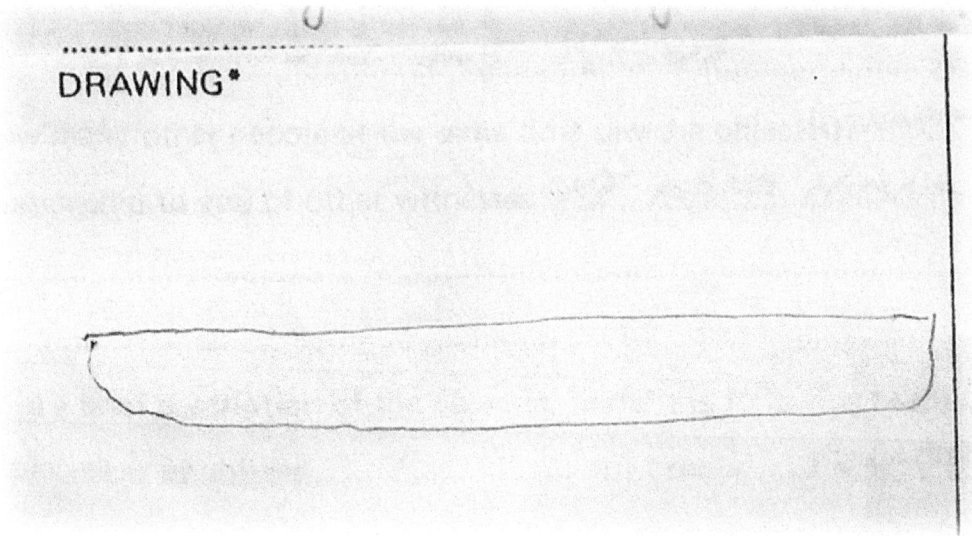

DRAWING*

SECTION A   SIGHTING ACCOUNT FORM

Please write an account of your sighting, make a drawing of what you saw and then answer the questions in section B overleaf as fully as possible. Write in **BLOCK CAPITALS** using a ball point pen.

MY WIFE & I WERE RETURNING, FROM VISITING FRIENDS OF OURS IN FELIXSTOWE (MR & MRS FRANK WISEMAN), WE WERE ABOUT FOUR MILES OUTSIDE FELIXSTOWE, WHEN WE NOTICED AND WATCHED A LARGE BRILLIANTLY LIT OBJECT FLOATING QUITE NEAR IN THE SKY., IT APPEARED TO BE PERHAPS THREE OR FOUR HUNDRED FEET LONG., I ESTIMATED A 1000 Ft HIGHT. THE ONLY PREVIOUS OBJECT TO RESEMBLE IN SIZE WAS THE GRAF ZEPPLIN & THE R101 WHICH I RECALL SEEING WHEN I WAS A YOUNG LAD, IN AMAZEMENT WE BOTH WATCHED, I HAD DECREASED MY SPEED FOR A BETTER OBSERVATION & DECIDED TO STOP AT THE NEXT LAY-BY, ALSO HOPING THAT OTHER DRIVERS WOULD STOP THEN WE COULD CONFER TOGETHER & DISCUSS WHAT WE WERE OBSERVING FOR SOME TWENTY MINUTES WE BOTH WATCHED THIS OBJECT. THE OBJECT MOVED AROUND THE SKY AT TIMES IT HOVERED ABOVE THE TREES & HOUSES, THEN IT WOULD ACCELERATE WITH GREAT SPEED TO SOME SEVERAL THOUSAND FEET, THESE MOVEMENTS OF FLIGHT WERE REPEATED MANY TIMES DURING THE TWENTY MINUTES THAT WE STOOD AT THE LAY-BY, AT TIMES IT WOULD BE

                                 P.T.O

Please continue on a separate sheet if necessary.

DRAWING*

*If preferred, use a separate sheet of paper.

Your full name (Mr/Mrs/Miss/Ms)
BERNARD GEORGE DYE.   Age 64

Address. 4 LANCING AVE.
IPSWICH SUFFOLK IP4 4DG

Telephone No. 728134 .....(STD........)

Occupation during last two years......
DISPLAY MANAGER

Any professional, technical or academic qualifications or special interests
WARRANT OFFICER AIR GUNNER.
AIR GUNNERS AND R.A.F.A. ASSOCIATIONS.

Do you object to the publication of your name?
*Yes/No. *Delete as applicable.

Today's Date....24. 8. 1988.

Signature....B. G. Dye.

– 2 –

HOVERING ABOVE OUR HEADS, THE FIRST THING I NOTICED WAS
THAT THERE WAS NO NOISE WHAT=SO-EVER COMING FROM THE
OBJECT, ALSO THER WAS NO OTHER AIRCRAFT IN THE SKY
I CHECKED THE SKY, FOR THE MOON, ALSO FOR CLOUDS, THINKING
PERHAPS, IF THERE WAS A MOON, REFLECTION OF THE MOON ONTO
DRIFTING CLOUDS MIGHT BE GIVING ME A FALSE IMPRESSION OF THE
OBJECT, THERE WAS NO MOON OR CLOUDS, THE SKY WAS
CLEAR & COVERED IN STARS.
THIS OBJECT APPEARED LOOKING LIKE A BANANA, (CIGAR) COLOUR
WAS BRILLIANT YELLOW & GAVE THE IMPRESSION OF TREMENDOUS HEAT
RADIATING FROM IT. WE DECIDED TO CONTINUE OUR WAY HOME TO
IPSWICH AND WE DROVE SLOWLY, OBSERVING THE OBJECT FOR
SOME EIGHT MILES, WHERE IT DISAPPEARED SLOWLY SOUTH
AT A VERY LOW HEIGHT INTO THE DISTANCE.
IT WAS A TRULY AMAZING EXPERIENCE. I AM PLEASED THAT
WE WITNESSED WHAT WE DID, EVEN IF OTHERS LAUGH AND
RIDICULE US, WE CAN ONLY DESCRIBE WHAT WE HAD SEEN,
DO I BELIVE IN U.F.O.S? THE ANSWER IS I DONOT KNOW,
I WOULD BE DELIGHTED IF SOMEONE COUND ENLIGHTEN US TO
WHAT WE HAD WITNESSED. HOW-EVER I DO FEEL THAT THERE IS
NOTHING ON OUR EARTH THAT MAN HAS INVENTED OR MADE
THAT COULD RESEMBLE WHAT WE HAD SEEN

B. F. Nye

During one evening in March 1977 my wife and I visited our friends (Mr & Mrs Frank Wiseman) who lived in Felixstowe. Before leaving our friends we enjoyed a cup of coffee, (no alcohol was consumed) we left and drove towards home in our van.

After about four miles my wife and I noticed and watched a large brilliantly lit object floating quite near in the sky.

It appeared to be perhaps three or four hundred feet long and I estimated a 1000 feet high. The only previous object to resemble in size was the Graf Zepplin and the R 101 which I recall seeing when I was a young lad.

In amazement we both watched, I had decreased my speed for better observation and decided to stop at the next lay-by, also hoping that other drivers would also stop. we could then chat together and discuss what we were observing.

For some twenty minutes we both watched this object, I was disapointed that no other vechicle stopped by.

I was thankful that my wife was with me to be a witness to what I was seeing.

The object moved around the sky, at times it hovered above the trees and houses, then it would accelarate with great speed to some several thousand feet. These movements of flight were repeated many times during the twemty minutes that we stood at the lay-by.

At times it would be hovereing above our heads, the first thing that I noticed that there was no noise what-so-ever coming from the object, also there was no other aircraft in the sky.

I checked the sky for the moon, also for clouds,
thinking perhaps if there was a moon, ..
reflection of the moon on drifting clouds might be
giving me a false impression of an object.

There was no moon, there was no clouds, the sky was
clear and covered in stars.

This object appeared looking like a Banana, colour was
a brilliant yellow and gave the impression of tremendous heat radiating from it.

We decided to continue our way home to Ipswich and
drove slowly observing for some eight miles where it
disappeared slowly south at a very low height into
the distance.

It was a truly amazing experience.

The next day I decided to write a letter to the Ipswich
Evening Star and tell them what we had both observed.
Hoping that others had seen this strange object and
would get in touch with me. The letter was not
published and received no reply from the E. Star.

I spoke to various members of the R.A.F.A. also to
members of the Ipswich Branch of air gunners of which
I am branch secretary, the response was laughter.

After one month my wife and I decided to tell our three
children what we had seen, their reaction was laughter.
they said "Why did you not tell us before", I replied
"You would only laugh at us as you are all doing so
now.

We have never forgotten that night, both my wife and
I served in the Royal Air Force during the war.
Many "Happenings" occured during my flying days, even
being chased for ten minutes by "Orange Balls of Fire",
which was never really explained to us what they
could have been.

I am pleased that we witnessed what we did, even if

others laugh and ridicule us.   We can only describe
what we had seen.

Do I believe in U.F.O.s ?   the answere is I do not
know,   I would be delighted if some-one could enlighten
to what I had witnessed.   How-ever I do feel that
there is nothing on our earth that man has invented
or made that could resemble what I had seen.

> Bernard Dye.
> 4 Lancing Avenue.
>   Ipswich. Suffolk.
>   IP4 4DG.
>
> Tel: 728134.

August – Triangular lights seen over Ipswich

Doreen Jones (16) has no problem remembering this incident, as it happened on her birthday.

"I was 16, at the time, and on my way home from school, at 3.30pm, with three friends. Susan said, 'what are those lights?' We looked up into the sky and saw three large, round white lights, forming a triangle; there was no beam just the lights. As I approached my home in Allenby Road, at 3.45pm, the lights just went out."

November – Glowing red *'ball of light'*

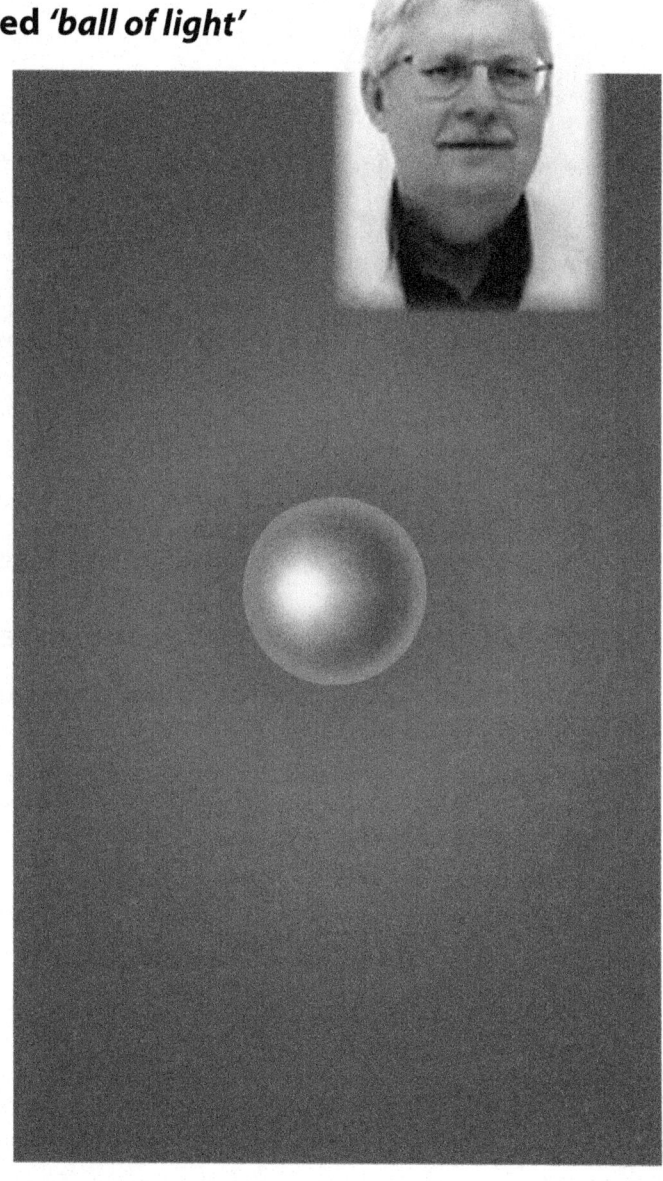

David and Ann Feakes from Needham Market, Suffolk, were travelling home to Ipswich, in torrential rain, at 7 pm on 5th November 1977. As they turned right onto the Ipswich Road, close to *The Barking Lion* Public House, they saw:

"…a great glowing red 'ball of light' moving along the hilltop to our left. It was flying just above ground level – far too slow to be an aircraft, and completely silent. As it reached the apex of the hill, it seemed to alter course and head off across the fields at a greatly increased speed, heading, eastwards. Suddenly, it veered south-east, towards Barham, or Claydon, before disappearing into the darkness beyond distant trees. There was no question of it being any firework; it was the strangest thing we had ever seen."

(Source: Personal interview)

UFO ACTIVITY OVER EAST ANGLIA & NORWICH

11th April 1978 – Red light in the sky

Mrs Brenda Pavelin from Hertford Road, Clare, a small town on the north bank of the *River Stour* in Suffolk, England, (14 miles from Bury St Edmunds and 9 miles from Sudbury), was walking an elderly relative home when she saw:

"…a red light in the sky. It came nearer; we didn't stop, because we were so scared."

The following night her son, Timothy (16), and his friend – David Peddar, came rushing into the house in a very agitated manner. Timothy told his mother that he had been followed by an orange light! The Police were notified and said they had not received any other reports. RAF Wattisham was just as mystified and could offer no explanation.

Other witnesses to strange events were Graham Lee and his wife, Elizabeth, who stopped the car to watch a bright orange 'light' hovering above the road, between Clare and Cavendish. Ten minutes later it shot away, leaving a small trail behind it.

On another occasion it was claimed the electrics of a vehicle cut out, after a UFO swooped low over it. Dr Simon Mitton – secretary of the Institute of Astronomy, at Cambridge University, was contacted. He had this to say:

"We have 4,000 highly professional astronomers throughout the world and there has never yet been anything reported that cannot be explained." [Authors: Incredible… words fail us!]

16th April 1978 – Fiery rocket seen over Lowestoft

At 1.10am, Angela Gooch (26) of Ontario Road, Lowestoft – a secretary by occupation – was with a Mr G. Newsome (20) of London Road, when they saw:

"…a round object that appeared in the sky, trailing smaller round objects behind it – similar to a rocket. It exploded in flight and a trail of smaller objects fell away from it. A small round object appeared in the sky, which then shot away out of sight."

(Source: Ron West)

April – RAF scrambles fighter aircraft over Suffolk

In April 1978, Staff Sergeant Thomas W. Wharton of the 91st Fighter Squadron (stationed at RAF Bentwaters, Suffolk, United Kingdom, between January 1977 and 1980) was to sight something inexplicable during April 1978. Whether there was any connection with the extraordinary event that took place a few years later, in December 1980, at RAF Woodbridge, is something we will never know.

Staff Sergeant Thomas W. Wharton (far right) in the Whitehouse with President Ronald Reagan

THE HALT PERSPECTIVE

Some time between midnight and 1am, during April 1978, Thomas was a front passenger in Staff Sgt. Mike Bugno's VW van, heading towards RAF Wethersfield, where he was living at the time with his wife, Helen. He had just passed through the small town of Finchingfield, off the main A12 road. As they approached the crest of a small hill, with the base lights of RAF Mildenhall clearly seen (although approximately 30 miles away), they noticed a bright 'light' in the sky, near Mildenhall, which illuminated the night sky. After a few seconds, it appeared to get bigger and brighter. Thomas said:

"I remember saying to Mike, 'Mike look at that light!' It was the brightest landing light (least I thought it was) I had ever seen. It lit up the entire sky near the base. I thought it was a C-5, or maybe a C-141, with new, bright landing lights (I had never seen anything so bright from so far away before). We both looked at it for a few moments longer. Since Mike was still driving and it was dark, he needed to watch the road, too, but I noticed it appeared to be headed our way. I said, 'Mike, look, it is headed this way!' He pulled over. He wanted to see what kind of aircraft this was. The lights got brighter and it was headed in our direction. We got out of the van. Just as we did that, within seconds (I mean this) it was right over our heads and there was no noise, none at all. The entire sky above us was so bright, we could not look up at the object…it was so weird, no noise, no shape could be seen of whatever this thing was.

We both looked at each other and said, 'What the hell is this?' We could not believe this. We kept trying to look up at it, but could not because it was so bright. We felt nothing – no humming, no noise, no movement of the grass around, nothing was happening. It was like we were in a void of some kind. It hovered over us for a few more seconds, then I heard a noise from behind me – it was a jet engine sound. I looked up, put my hands over my eyes to see better, and I saw two British F4s headed right towards our location.

They got so close; we could see the 'Union Jack' flag panel on their aircraft fuselage. They were deploying photo flash cartridges; we could hear and see what they were doing with them but nothing else above us. They were taking pictures of this thing (not that they needed more light – this thing was extremely bright as it was). Mike yelled out to me, 'What the hell is happening here'? I did not know either but a moment later, whatever this thing was, took off to the west towards London. It was like looking at a 'light sabre', or something like it, because it left a single line of bright light in the sky, as it headed away from us. It was like someone drew a white line in the sky. It was instantaneous. I could not believe it. One second it was above us, the next it was over London (you could see the lights of the city from our location).

The British F4s took off after it. They kicked their aircraft into 'burner', trying to catch or chase this thing. It was amazing to witness. They never caught it, but were headed towards London, too, when all of a sudden, this thing appeared over our heads again (no kidding, it was like in the wink of an eye…that fast). We tried to look up at it again, but it was useless to do so. I turned my head and saw the F4s headed back towards us again (I guess they were still taking pictures of this thing). We were right under it when it shot straight up; I mean it, straight up. All we saw was a white line in the sky until we could follow it no longer – still going straight up, without a sound, into space."

Mike and Thomas waited, but after nothing further was seen drove home to the base – which was just a few minutes away. As they approached the base main gate, it was clear from the excitement and behaviour of the American and British security guards stationed there, that they, too, had seen whatever this thing was. They told the security men what they had seen and were advised to report the matter to the MOD Police – which they subsequently did. When Thomas arrived home, he awoke his wife and told her what he had seen. She thought he had been drinking. Thomas had this to say:

"I decided to turn on the BBC radio. It was now two o'clock in the morning. The BBC radio stations were flooded with calls about a UFO sighting over London and fighters that were reported chasing it. It was an amazing night, to say the least. Of course I (we) also filed a report with the RAF Bentwaters OSI. They (OSI) took the report and that was that. We never heard another thing about it. During the rest of the tour, Mike and I talked about it often, but never really understood what happened that night. I (we) know it must have been a UFO, least that is what we think it was (so did all those folks in London) You know, I am sure many of you have had something strange or something happen that was so exciting or important happen to you, that you said to yourself, I will never forget this day or date in my life. The very day after the event, the very next morning, I and Staff Sgt Mike Bugno (Maintenance Operations, Weapons Controller) reported this event to the USAF, OSI at RAF Bentwaters, Suffolk, United Kingdom, and that was the last we ever heard about it."

Thomas is a credit to the USAF. He is man with an illustrious career, and we had the pleasure of talking to him recently, with regard to seeking permission to 'write-up' this incident. Thomas started his military career as an aircraft mechanic (basically) stationed at: Clark Air Base, Philippines (June 1970, F-4s) then DaNang Air Base, Republic of Vietnam (February 1971, flying F-4s). Between 1972 and 1975 he was posted to RAF Lakenheath, Suffolk, England. This was followed by a posting to Edwards AFB, California, (1975 & 1976, F-4 Tow Target Operator – In-flight) then he was sent back to RAF Bentwaters, Suffolk, England (1977 to 1980, flying F-4s, converted to A-10s). From 1980 to 1982 he served at Nellis AFB, Las Vegas, flying F-4s, then converted to F-16s. His other secondments included Hahn Air Base, Germany, (1982 to 1985, flying F-16s), Luke AFB, Phoenix, Arizona (1985 to 1988, flying F-16s and 12th AF F-16 Demo Team), Nellis AFB, Las Vegas, Nevada (1988 to 1991, F-16s – USAF Thunderbirds and two months with the Navy Blue Angels, F-18 Maintenance Exchange Program) RAF Lakenheath, Suffolk, England (1991 to 1996 F-15C/D/E).

Thomas retired in February 1996 – 26 years later and sixty (60) countries, either TDY/Deployed (countless deployments globally) or just vacationing with the family. As he says, *"What a ride the USAF was for me!"*

The 91st Tactical Fighter Squadron is an inactive United States Air Force unit. Its last assignment was with the 81st Tactical Fighter Wing, stationed at RAF Bentwaters, England. It was deactivated on 14th August 1992.

13th May 1978 – Dome-shaped UFO – *'figures'* seen

On 13th May, Tracey Segasby and Michaela Field – two teenagers, from Lowestoft – were stabling their horses in a paddock on the edge of Oulton Marshes, during the early evening, when they noticed a dome-shaped object hovering just above the ground, about a quarter-of-a-mile away.

Tracey:

"It had a silvery appearance with bright orange lights around it, which changed in colour, within a few minutes, to pink/red, then dazzling white, and began to slowly rise above the ground, stop, and slowly rested back on the ground again – the lights changing to bright orange, once

again. At this stage, we noticed four 'figures' moving towards us; two of them were large and stood side by side, the other two were smaller. They didn't continue their advance towards us. They moved in a 'jerky manner', in strides of 5 feet, or so. They then disappeared as the UFO gradually began to lift itself off the ground, once more, and faded away within ten seconds. Whatever it was really frightened the horses and dogs. They were going mad."

David Spoor

We had the pleasure of meeting David Spoor, who had tape-recorded the interview with the girls, some years later. Sadly, David (who was to himself obtain some outstanding film and photos of UFOs during the 1990s) is no longer with us, but his dedication to recording for posterity some of these accounts (often in the face of ridicule) is recognised, and will not be forgotten.

(Source: Ivan W. Bunn, the *'Lantern'* series/ Peter Johnson/David Spoor)

David Spoor

East Anglia Monthly magazine

Coincidentally, bearing in mind the huge number of UFO sightings that were to take place around Essex and its borders, involving reports of three unidentified flying objects, some ten years later, the front page of the *East Anglia Monthly* magazine, published in May 1978, also showed three UFOs – although they would not have known of this salient fact.

Project Blue Book

It appears that the surge of UFO interest was ironically brought about through films exported to the UK from the United States. One of them was *Project UFO* – a late 1970s NBC television series, which lasted two seasons (from 1978 to 1979). Based loosely on the real-life Project Blue Book, the show was created by *Dragnet* veteran Jack Webb, who pored through Air Force files looking for episode ideas.

The show features two US Air Force investigators with the Foreign Technology Division, at Wright-Patterson AFB, charged with investigating UFO sightings. The first season starred William Jordan as Major Jake Gatlin alongside Caskey Swaim as Staff Sgt. Harry Fitz. Jordan was a rather nondescript leading man, while Swaim, who had never had any significant acting experience before landing the role, added diversity as a Southerner with a pronounced accent. In season two, Jordan was replaced by Edward Winter as Capt. Ben Ryan. Aldine King ('Libby') was another regular. Dr. Joyce Brothers appeared in two episodes.

In the pilot episode, Gatlin informed the newly assigned Fitz that, since it is impossible to prove a negative, their job was to prove that each UFO sighting was real, by researching and disproving possible alternate explanations. Gatlin also told Fitz that he himself had once seen *"something I can't explain",* while flying as an Air Force pilot, which led to his interest in Blue Book.

Sadly, having spent many hours looking through the declassified Project Blue Book files, it became abundantly clear that an inaccurate picture had been presented through a card index system, which effectively wrote off many UFO accounts as insufficient information to classify etc. . . . The witnesses accounts told a different story!

13th May – 'Flying Triangle' seen over Polstead & Lawford

On the same evening (13th May) at Polstead – a small village and civil parish in the South of Suffolk, England, which lies 3 miles north-east of Nayland and 9 miles north of Colchester – was the venue for another strange report around the same time. It involved Colin Rayner (23) and Sally Bradshaw (17). They were sat in their car when they heard a loud screech, and saw something hovering in the sky in front of them.

"It was triangular-shaped and had a red light at the front, with two others shining down."

15th – UFO lit up the ground like daylight

Ian and Thelma Scrutton from Lawford, accompanied by her father Mr Gilbert Simms, were out in the garden. Gilbert was feeding chickens in the garden at the Limes Garden City, Lawford, when an object appeared low overhead. He shouted for his daughter, Thelma (24), and her husband Ian (26), to come and have a look at it.

They told of seeing an object with orange lights around the edges and two lights shining down from it that lit up the ground like daylight. It was last seen dropping down behind trees, before vanishing from sight. At the time, the family thought rationally that it might have been an aircraft. However, they changed their minds after reading what had taken place at Lowestoft two days earlier.

(Source: *Star*, 16.5.1978 – 'Close encounter of a strange kind')

Ian and Thelma Scrutton keep watch on the sky above their Lawford house where they claim they sighted a UFO

15th – 'Flying Cross' UFO over A45

Edward Birchall of Sunnydale Drive, Felixstowe, was driving home from Ipswich to Felixstowe late in the evening, when at a point near Levington he saw:

"...what I first thought was an aircraft or helicopter, moving towards the road from the Levington direction. It appeared to be stationary, and was covered in several red lights and lots of bright white ones. In addition I could see three or four spotlights shining towards the ground. It was too dark to see the shape of the object as it passed overhead, but the lights seemed to be arranged in the shape of a cross."

A spokesman at USAF Bentwaters and Woodbridge confirmed no helicopters were flying in that area at the time of the sighting, but suggested Edward had seen a night flying F-4 'Phantom', which was flying until 11.30pm and descending with its landing lights on. Unfortunately we do not know the exact time when Edward saw the object.

Miss Isobel Taylor and her boyfriend, Stephen Otto, were driving near Great Bentley, at 11.15pm the same evening, on what was described as foggy conditions, when they saw:

"...an object in the sky showing two orange-red lights, and two flashing white lights below"

Another witness to strange aerial activity was Ken Rice – a local journalist – who was also driving along the A45 (now the A14), heading towards Ipswich with his son, at about 9.50pm, when he saw:

"...a large object resembling a transport plane, hovering still in the sky. Two large 'cones of light' came off the objects and flooded the ground in an eerie glare."

(Source: *Star*, 17.5.1978 – 'UFO lights up Suffolk night'/*Star*, 19.5.1978 – 'Did reporter Ken have a close encounter?')

10th September 1978 – UFO display over Melton

A nurse from St. Audrey's Hospital, Melton, Suffolk, was on duty when she saw two *'globes of light'* in the sky, rotating around each other, before moving away. A spokesman at RAF Woodbridge, who was told about the sighting, confirmed that no aircraft were flying at the time.

(Source: *Daily Star*, 11.9.1978)

6th October – UFO over Lowestoft

At 9.40pm on 6th October 1978, Lowestoft couple – Mr and Mrs Bassett – were outside the house, saying goodbye to their neighbour, Mr Keeling, when they noticed a bright 'light' in the sky passing directly overhead. Looking up they saw, with great astonishment:

"...a large silver/grey tailed object, displaying red, green, and orange lights, resembling a skate fish, without a tail, showing a dome which had lead-like stripes on it. In front of the object were three large beams of light shining outwards into the air, for some 100 yards or more, with 'spiky-shaped things' visible underneath".

The huge *'craft'* was then seen to head off towards the south-west, making a low droning noise, before disappearing behind trees, creating an impression it was going to land.

(Source: Ivan W. Bunn)

19ᵗʰ November – UFO seen over Felixstowe

Mr Owen Bean of Brackley Close, Felixstowe, was returning home from work at 5pm on the 19ᵗʰ November, when he was astonished to see:

"…a silver coloured object, with a red tai, hovering in the sky over a nearby field. I watched it for ten minutes, until it suddenly moved away."

20ᵗʰ November – UFO seen over East Anglia

At 6.45am on 20ᵗʰ November 1978, Mr Victor Dennis – director of Dickerson Transport, Little Blakenham, in Suffolk – was on his way to work when he sighted a number of bright silvery, cigar-shaped, objects in the sky, over the Woodbridge area. He was not the only one. A number of other people also saw the phenomena, including two of his colleagues, at Great Blakenham.

At 7am, Gary Perkins of Fountains Road, Stoke Park, Ipswich, was on his way to work when he saw a bright silver, cigar-shaped object, over Woodbridge. A short time later, it moved away at high speed, before being lost from view. A spokesman from RAF Woodbridge Airbase – Captain David Schmidt – confirmed that flying did not start until 8am. He said:

"It could be the real thing this time. There could be other 'craft' in the area, of course, but there were certainly none of ours."

(Source: Brenda Butler/*Evening Star*, 20.11.1978 – 'UFOs over Suffolk?')

Mrs Eileen Holland of Church Lane, Westerfield, came out of her house at 7.10am, and saw

"…what looked like a squashed saucepan lid, red or orange, completely stationary in the sky, before it moved away a short time later. There was no vapour trail; it was not a plane. Although I couldn't estimate its distance, it looked quite big."

Police Spokesman

According to the police, they neither had nor received any other sightings.

Weatherman Ken Blowers suggested,

"…it was an aircraft, illuminated by the rising sun. The section of the 'contrail' was in the precise area of Red One airway (flight path off the East Anglian coast)".

(Source: Ron West/*The Star* Newspaper, 21.11.1978 – 'Trail in the sunrise key to UFO?)

December 1978 – UFO display at Harston

In December 1978, Michael Bradford – Licensee of the *Old English Gentleman* Public House, Harston, Cambridgeshire, situated on the A10 – was putting the cat out, at 1.30am, when:

"I noticed a 'star' to the south, which grew brighter, moved left, hovered for a brief time and then dropped down at a 45 degree angle, behind trees, 2-3 miles away, near the village of Newton. Intrigued, I jumped into my car and made my way towards the direction where I had seen the 'star' descend.

Just before Newton, I saw an orange glow in stubble field to my left. I stopped, got out, and made my way on foot, where I saw two pulsating orange lights, 25-30 feet off the ground, about 150 yards away, one constantly dimming as the other grew brighter. As I began to walk towards them, a bright light (about the size of a tennis ball) jumped almost from under my feet, reached a height of six feet, and then zigzagged towards the orange lights, disappearing between them. Over a period of several minutes, ten other similar 'white lights' appeared, from various parts of the field, and moved over to the 'orange lights', disappearing between them like their predecessors, forming a shape likened to that of the front of a mouth organ, i.e. an orange round rim, with downward divisions".

(**Source: Norman Oliver,** *BUFORA Journal*, **Volume 9, 1.3.1980**)

UFO ACTIVITY OVER EAST ANGLIA

UFO display – Harston Hill

The *Old English Gentleman* public house, at Harston, was again the scene of further reported UFO activity, during mid-January 1979, when amused regulars, including the Licensee – Michael Bradford – stood outside, watching a display of white and coloured 'lights' dance about in the sky above their heads. Amusement turned to consternation when something, resembling an airship, silently crossed over the sky, showing a white light at each end, with a yellow glow behind a line of 'windows' on the outside. One of the witnesses was David Flood, to whom we spoke, some years after the event:

"We saw this large 'ship' pass silently over the public house, looking like a huge fuselage, with illuminated windows down the side – like a square ended airship, or railway carriage."

May – Triangular-shaped UFO over Ipswich

Mrs Celia Stevens of Norwich Road, Ipswich, was just in the process of leaving the house, at 12.15am, when she noticed:

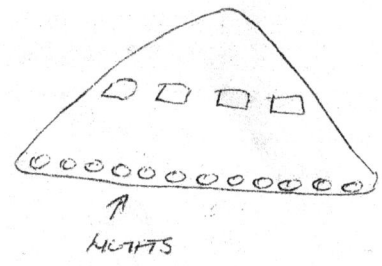

"...a bright orange domed object in the sky. It looked like a solid object – the size of an orange at arm's length. It had what appeared to be portholes, or windows, and displayed many lights at one edge. It was stationary in the sky for a short time, before suddenly moving away. As it did so, it changed shape and brightness. It flashed as the sun caught it during flight, before vanishing inexplicably from view."

Another witness was Mr Tony Reynolds of Old Hill, Martlesham, in Suffolk.

(**Source: Ron West**)

June – Three lights on UFO seen over Lowestoft

In June, Mrs Jennifer Hooks was making a telephone call from the BT box, situated at Victoria Road and Kirkley Run, Dell Estate, Lowestoft, at 7.00pm, when she happened to glance up into the sky and see:

"...a bright orange object, showing three large flashing lights on its side (as big as a double-decker bus in size) hovering in mid-air."

A few minutes later, it began to make a high-pitched whine and then took off, moving quickly towards the coast – the sound being heard for a few seconds after it had gone out of view.

Jennifer was not the only one to see it. An elderly man, waiting to use the telephone, dropped his pipe in amazement and walked off in a dazed state, before his details could be established.

(Source: Ivan W. Bunn/Dot Street, BUFORA)

6th July – RAF Honnington declines to comment

At 3.10pm on 6th July, an object – described as resembling an egg, with a black base – was seen low down in the sky over Bury St. Edmunds by-pass, by a motorist driving along the A45 (now the A14).When he contacted RAF Honnington to report the incident, he was advised that *'they were unable to comment'*.

(Source: Peter Johnson)

18th October – Spinning top UFO seen

At 7.45pm on 18th October 1979, Electricity Board employees – Norah Squires and Gail Dersley, from Wherstead, Ipswich, Suffolk – sighted a glowing object resembling a spinning top, flashing with red and green lights, moving over the town. Fifteen minutes later, an identical object was seen moving slowly through the air, a few hundred feet off the ground, by local resident – Ricky Double.

"We had just finished evening classes and were turning into Marlow Road, when we saw what looked like a child's spinning top – bright red in colour, showing green lights at the top and bottom. As we continued our journey home, people walking along the street stopped to point up at it. I don't know what it was but I can tell you it wasn't any aircraft, helicopter, or balloon."

(Source: Personal interview)

November – Alert at airbase

In November 1979, Brenda Butler and her then partner – Chris Pennington (an accomplished musician) – were socialising at the *Rod and Gun Club,* at RAF Woodbridge, in November, talking to their friend – USAF security guard *Steve Roberts* – when the general alarm went off all over the Base.

Brenda:

"Suddenly there were blue lights flashing all over the place; outriders and security guards came to the Club. Steve had to go; he came back about half an hour later dressed in his security guard

outfit, plus gun. He stood at the door and told everyone to sit down, as no one was allowed to leave for a while. I went over and asked him what was wrong. He said that he was not allowed to say, but it involved an aircraft and a lot of high ranking officers up on the flight line. We were kept there for about three hours, and then we were escorted off the Base. There were still blue flashing lights all around and the alert conditions still held. Two days later, word had got around that a UFO had landed on the runway at Bentwaters, and high ranking officers had gone out to it. This was the night we were at the Rod and Gun Club."

Chris Pennington

Charles Halt:

"This 'Alert' was a routine exercise, held at regular intervals on the airbase – not a UFO landing."

Triangular craft seen over Woodbridge area

Brenda Butler:

"Several people had reported seeing lights and black shapes during that year. I went to interview several of them in Woodbridge and Hollesley, who had seen weird lights. One gentleman had seen a black triangular shape, with white lights underneath, going towards Woodbridge Base. Another witness told me that he had spoken to some Americans, who told him that a strange

'craft' had landed on the Base, followed by a strange unknown plane. (Could this be the same night that we were kept in at the Rod and Gun Club?) In November 1979, I was called out to many places of UFO sightings. One of these was over the Base at Woodbridge; a 'craft' was seen hovering over the runway. Another 'craft', or maybe the same one, followed a young couple (Paul and Angela) along the Hollesley road.

They described it as a huge triangular shape, with lights underneath. It gave off a weird atmosphere as it passed over them. They were on a motorbike at the time. They stopped and watched it, before speeding off. When they arrived at Paul's home, they told his parents. His mother phoned me the next day. Although Paul and Angela were still in shock from this incident, they allowed me to interview them on tape. They said that the 'craft' went in the direction of Woodbridge Airbase. Another witness from the Hollesley area phoned to tell me that several residents had seen a 'craft' flying towards the base, around the end of November.

They had also seen the same thing a month earlier, in October – a large, *triangular-shaped 'craft', black in appearance, with lights underneath. Nearly all the sightings throughout October, November and December 1979, were triangular 'crafts'. Dot and I saw the exact same thing in 1983, while outside Colonel Halt's house. It came over the top of us; it was silent. If they were test flying the Stealth bomber around that time, I would say it was what we saw, as rumors were that it was being flown over Suffolk airbases."

Charles Halt:

"The triangular craft was probably an F-117 as they, as well as other classified aircraft, occasionally visited the base."

6th November – UFO seen over radio mast

In November of the same year Mr and Mrs Thacker were driving home along the A410, past the giant communications tower, at Mendlesham, at 10pm on the 6th November 1979.

"As we neared the Mendlesham mast, we saw a bright 'star' hovering over the top of it. I asked my husband whether he thought it was Venus, by which time it had changed colour to red. Perhaps it was Mars, I thought! Our curiously aroused, we decided to park at the side of the road and take a closer look at the object – now moving slowly southwards. Suddenly, it veered towards the mast again and split into two parts, before changing colour from white to orange, followed by the two halves merging into one and shooting across the sky – so fast we could hardly keep up with it, and gone out of sight."

Late 1970s – three holes found in the ground after strange 'figure' seen

Brenda Butler was living at Elm Tree Farm, Aldringham, just off the Al2, a short distance out of Leiston, during the late 1970s.

What she saw and experienced on that early morning in November 1979, forever remains in her memory.

"I was awoken by a bright 'flash of light' that flooded the room. On going to the window to look out, I saw a 'ball of brilliant light' hovering over the front meadow of the farm. As my eyes adjusted to the harsh light, I saw a 'figure' standing near the farm gate, clothed in a silvery garment, edged with gold, with some kind of lettering across the top of it. The next thing I knew was waking up, although I remembered, quite clearly, what I had experienced. Had it been a dream? When I arrived downstairs for breakfast, I started to chat to my Dad about everyday things, but was surprised when he asked me if I had seen a strange light outside the house earlier that morning. Straightaway, I realised it had been no dream. Later in the day, my father told me he had discovered three large holes in the ground, about 12 feet in diameter, with a large quantity of soil missing – as if someone, or something, had scooped it out. What intrigued him was that he couldn't find any sign of tyre marks, or footprints, but did notice the tops of some nearby trees had been burnt off completely … a real mystery."

November – 'Flying Saucer' captured on film

Chris Whitewick, from Leiston, Suffolk, was photographing cloud formations, just before sunset in November 1979, when he saw a saucer-shaped object (enhanced) crossing the sky.

"It was a million to one chance – being in the right place at the right time. I took a photo and sent the film to Mark Palmer, who runs a processing shop. I was so pleased to discover I had captured it on photo."

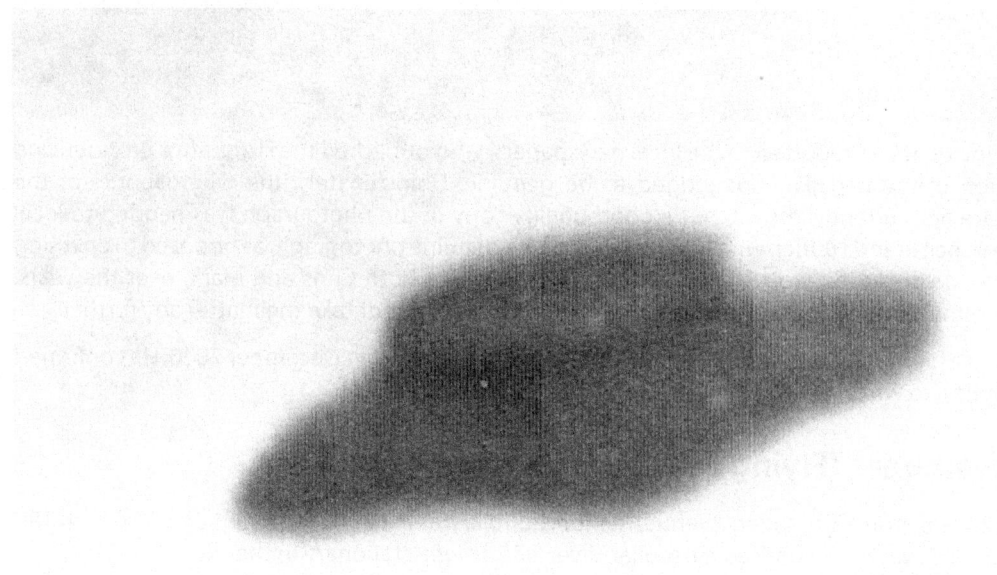

The incident was reported to the local newspapers, who published the story, after pronouncing examination of the negative was judged to be genuine. Unfortunately, the whereabouts of the negative are not currently known, but a good quality copy of the photograph was handed to local UFO Researcher, Brenda Butler, who believes this to be a genuine photograph, as opposed to anything fabricated – a conclusion we also reached, having spoken to both Chris and Mark, over the years. However, without the all too important negative, knew we could not take the matter any further.

Just as a footnote, this photograph was shown to Larry Warren, in December 2000. He confirmed it was identical to what he saw in December 1980!

November – 'Flying Saucer' seen over Melton

Mrs F. Ward, from Coronation Avenue, Melton, Suffolk, was in her back garden, at 5.00 pm on 18th November 1979, when she noticed a peculiar silver *'ball of light'* stationary in the sky.

"I continued to watch it, not knowing what to make of it, when in a flash, it changed to an orange saucer-shaped object, then made a slight buzzing noise and began to move away across the sky."

Her illustration was identical to the photo taken by Chris.

(Source: Brenda Butler)

WHAT THIS YEAR WAS ALL ABOUT

1980

ACCORDING to Wikipedia . . .

January – Workers at British Steel go on a nationwide strike over pay called by the Iron and Steel Trades Confederation, which has some 90,000 members among British Steel's 150,000 workforces, in a bid to get a 20% rise. It is the first steelworks strike since 1926.

The British record TV audience for a film is set when some 23,500,000 viewers tune in for the ITV showing of the James Bond film *Live and Let Die* (1973), starring Roger Moore who is at this time in the process of filming *For Your Eyes Only*.

Margaret Thatcher announces that state benefit to strikers will be halved. Winter Olympics in Lake Placid, New York, United States, one gold medal won by Robin Cousins for figure skating.

February – British Steel announces that more than 11,000 jobs will be axed at its plants in Wales by the end of next month. March –*Radio Caroline,* the pirate radio station, was forced to cease transmission when the ship on which it was based sank.

Vauxhall, the British division of General Motors, launches the Astra, a front-wheel drive hatchback which replaces the recently discontinued Viva and is based on the latest Opel Kadett.

April – The steelworkers' strike is called off.- Alton Towers Resort is opened by Madame Tussauds in Staffordshire. – The UK reaches agreement with Spain to re-open its border with Gibraltar. Zimbabwe becomes independent of the United Kingdom. Unemployment stands at a two-year high of more than 1.5million.30 April – The Iranian Embassy Siege begins. A six-man terrorist team calling itself the "Democratic Revolutionary Movement for the Liberation of Arabistan" (DRMLA) captures the Embassy of Iran in Prince's Gate, Knightsbridge, central London, taking 26 hostages.

May – The SAS storm the Iranian Embassy building, kill five out of the six terrorists and free all the hostages.

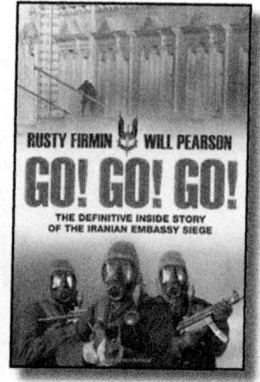

Inflation has risen to 21.8%.27 May – Inquest into the death of New Zealand born teacher Blair Peach (who was killed during a demonstration against the National Front last year) returns a verdict of misadventure, resulting in a public outcry. The UK economy slides into recession. June – Gail Kinchen (a pregnant 16-year-old) and her unborn baby are accidentally shot dead by a police marksman who entered the Birmingham flat where her boyfriend David Pagett is holding her hostage at gunpoint.

June – Secretary of State for Defence, Francis Pym reveals to the House of Commons that US nuclear cruise missiles would be located at RAF Greenham Common in Berkshire and the disused RAF Molesworth base in Cambridgeshire. June – Gunmen attack the British embassy in Iraq; three unknown attackers are shot dead by Iraqi security forces. – Unemployment is announced to have reached a post-war high of 1,600,000.30 June – The pre-decimal sixpence coin is withdrawn from circulation.

July – Miners threatening to strike demand a 37% pay increase, ignoring pleas from Margaret Thatcher to hold down wage claims, Alexandra Palace in London gutted by fire. September- The Marlborough diamond is stolen in London. September – Marlborough diamond thieves Joseph Scalise and Arthur Rachel are arrested in Chicago after getting off a British Airways flight in the city. However, the stolen diamond has not been found.

September – First CND rally at RAF Greenham Common

October – British Leyland launches the Austin Metro, a small hatchback which uses much of the Mini's mechanical design but an entirely different body which offers more space and practicality. Production of the 21-year-old Mini, however, is set to continue for the foreseeable future, although it is expected to be scaled back along with that of the larger Austin Allegro. – Margaret Thatcher makes her famous *"The lady's not for turning"* speech to the Conservative Party conference after party MP's warn that her economic policy was responsible for the current recession and rising unemployment.

James Callaghan, ousted as prime minister by the Conservative victory 17 months ago, resigns as Labour Party leader after four and a half years. October 28 – Margaret Thatcher declares that the government will not give in to seven jailed IRA terrorists who are on hunger strike in the Maze Prison in hope of winning prisoner of war status.

November – Michael Foot is elected Leader of the Labour Party. November – George Smith, a security guard, is shot dead when the van he is guarding is intercepted by armed robbers in Willenhall, West Midlands.

December – John Lennon is shot dead in New York. December – Thousands of music fans hold a 10-minute vigil in Liverpool for John Lennon.

A UFO is allegedly sighted near RAF Woodbridge. This and its subsequent sightings would be part of what was later known as the Rendlesham Forest incident, the most well known UFO incident to occur in Britain.

Brenda Butler and Dot Street – UFO researchers

According to Brenda Butler from Leiston, Suffolk – a veteran UFO researcher, whose investigations into the UFO/Paranormal subject spans over 25 years,

"1980 was a year of considerable activity. It started in March 1980, when a lady from Gorleston, near Yarmouth, Norfolk, telephoned me, reporting having seen a huge orange 'light' in the sky, heading towards the coast, which she believed came down somewhere near the sea. The woman told me she and her neighbours had gone outside, at 10.30 pm, after the house lights had begun to flash on and off."

Strange *'figure'* seen outside house, following UFO sighting!

"This was when they saw the UFO. I also remember interviewing another woman in Gorleston, living on the Yarmouth Road.

She saw this orange 'light' going across the sky. After having watched it, they went back inside the house. About an hour later, they were watching TV. A shadow went across the front room curtains. They opened the curtains and looked out and saw the figure of a man, wearing what looked like a helmet. Frightened, she sent her terrier dog outside but it ran back inside. Looking upwards, she was amazed to see the orange 'light' in the sky again. One of the young boys in the family told her he saw a man, dressed in a funny hat and black clothes, running out of the garden."

Brenda Butler and Dot Street

February 1980 – UFO seen over the forest by USAF officer

Rendlesham Forest was also the scene of another UFO sighting, during February 1980, this time involving now retired Captain Lori Rehfeldt – then a Law Enforcement Officer at RAF Bentwaters.

"I was on patrol with Airman Duffield, outside the Base near RAF Woodbridge, at 3am – a place that literally 'scared the hell out of me', when we saw a strange 'light' in the sky moving up and down, left and right – a bit like an 'Etch o' sketch board'. I contacted the Police Control room, at Bentwaters. They advised me to contact Woodbridge, which I did. They suggested we must have seen an aeroplane – an explanation I was not inclined to accept, but decided to drop the matter as some of the personnel had already begun to refer to Rehfeldt's UFO."

(Source: Richard Conway, BUFORA/Personal interview/www.facebook)

Our research into the mysterious events that had taken place in and around this forest, pleasant enough in the day but eerie at night and apparently devoid of animal life, revealed many others that had also witnessed the over-flight of mysterious objects in the skies over the air base.

We spoke to one woman and her boyfriend, who were living six or seven miles away from the air base. They described the frightening sight of a black triangular object, seen slowly heading across the sky, a few hundred feet above the ground toward the Bentwaters air base in the same period, during one sunny afternoon. They contacted the Air Traffic Control tower; the officer told them they must have mistaken an aircraft, although he confirmed nothing was showing on their radar. The couple rejected this as the explanation.

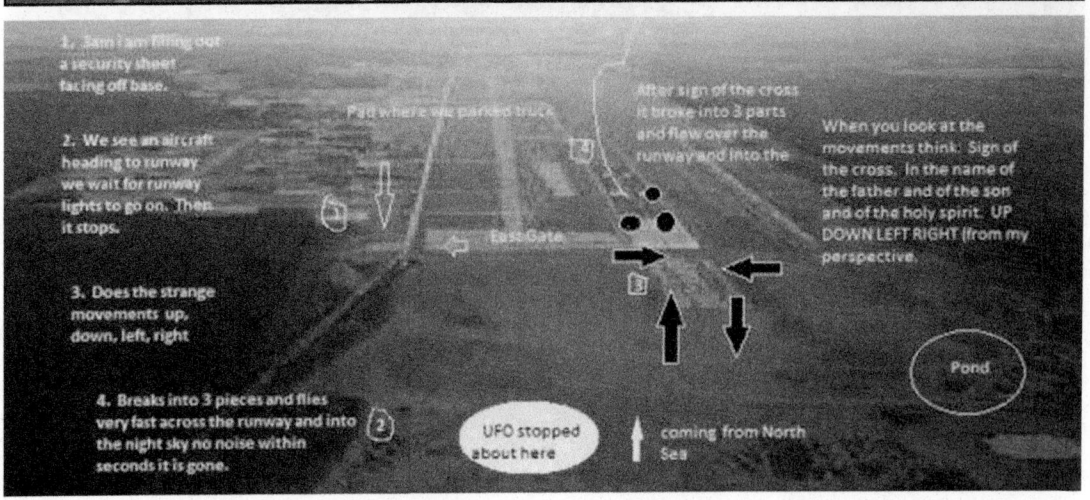

1. 3am I am filling out a security sheet facing off base.

2. We see an aircraft heading to runway we wait for runway lights to go on. Then it stops.

3. Does the strange movements up, down, left, right

4. Breaks into 3 pieces and flies very fast across the runway and into the night sky no noise within seconds it is gone.

Pad where we parked truck

East Gate

UFO stopped about here

coming from North Sea

Pond

After sign of the cross it broke into 3 parts and flew over the runway and into the

When you look at the movements think: Sign of the cross. In the name of the father and of the son and of the holy spirit. UP DOWN LEFT RIGHT (from my perspective.

Captain Lori Rehfeldt with younger brother in May 1978

RAF Bentwaters main gate in 1980

15th May 1980 – Cigar-shaped UFO seen over Orford Quay

At 6.30pm, Brian Murphy and his friend – Andrew Keen – were fishing off Orford Quay, Suffolk, when they saw a silver, cigar-shaped object, motionless in the sky.

"It moved away and then came back. It was as bright as the sun, and kept flickering and making a buzzing noise. It was a clear night. I would say it was about the size of a football in the sky. We watched it for about an hour, and then it just vanished in front of our eyes."

(Source: Ron West, EAPRA)

Recent photo of Lori Rehfeldt

Orford Quay

29ᵗʰ/30ᵗʰ May 1980 – Close encounter along the A14

The A14 – a busy dual-carriageway, linking the Midlands with the East Coast – was to become a familiar journey during our visits to Leiston, over the years. Although we had never seen anything unusual ourselves along this particular route, Dawn and I were to read about various encounters between motorists and mysterious 'globes of light' having taken place along this unlit stretch of road.

We contacted Marion Kennedy from Framlingham, in Suffolk, after listening to a tape-recorded interview conducted with her, by Brenda Butler and Dot Street, following an extraordinary incident, which took place along the A14.

Marion:

"We were driving to Baldock, in Hertfordshire, in the family Mini. There were three of us in the car; my eldest daughter – Sarah, driving, with my youngest daughter – Pamela, aged 11, in the back. We set off on the early evening. Right from the beginning we had problems with Pamela, who became quite emotional – for no apparent reason – followed by the sighting of dark red, flickering lightning – something we had never seen before."

Bright white 'light' seen in the sky

"As we approached Framlingham, we noticed a 'bright white light' in the sky, just above the horizon, that seemed to 'hang' in the sky rather peculiarly, as it was still daylight. We stopped the car and got out, in order to satisfy our curiosity whether this 'light' was actually moving, or not. It wasn't moving.

Now feeling a little uneasy, we recommenced our journey, agreeing that, if we saw a police car or Police Officer, we would bring the matter to his attention. When near to Bury St. Edmunds, a curious thing happened. The 'light', still prominent in the sky, seemed to 'hop over' to a bank of built-up black cloud, and disappear – much to our relief."

Journey appearing to take for ever

"After leaving Bury St. Edmunds, we continued along the A.14, when my eldest daughter, Sarah, drew my attention to the fact that the journey seemed a very queer one, as it appeared to be taking forever to complete and that the local countryside – a familiar route of ours – did not look right."

Patch of thick 'fog' encountered

"Suddenly, without any prior warning of unusual weather conditions, we entered what we took to be a patch of thick 'fog'. Actually, it was more like dense smoke, alternating between thick patches and swirling up from holes in the ground – the most remarkable thing I had ever seen in my life. By now, tensions inside the car were considerably heightened. Pamela (who had previously been asleep) was now wide awake. As we reduced speed, in order to cope with the hazardous driving conditions along this straight stretch of dual-carriageway – in complete contrast to what had been a clear, dry evening, illuminated by a full moon – we noticed what at

first we took to be the outlines of a number of heavy lorries, travelling towards the east, passing through this bank of 'fog'. In a way I find it difficult to explain – there seemed to be something horribly wrong about this part of the journey, although I cannot put my finger on what it was that created so much fear with the appearance of these strange Lorries. Pamela remarked that it was almost as if the Lorries were driving themselves and that they had evil faces. Naturally, I dismissed this as an overactive imagination."

Arriving at Baldock

"After arriving at the house in *Baldock, we settled down for the night – the three of us sharing the same bedroom, trying to forget about all the problems we had encountered – when my eldest daughter suddenly jumped out of bed, at 12.45am, shouting to me that she had just seen a 'red light' flash across the sky. We all rushed to the window, but there was nothing to be seen. It was a brilliant moonlit night – just like daylight. We stood at the window for a little while, and then I told the two girls that we were going into the garden."

Saucer-shaped object appears

"Later, thinking about my actions, I was curious why I decided to go into the garden on my own (as I am a nervous person), but felt impelled to go there. I stood in the garden, when I was amazed to see the appearance of an object travelling from the left, behind some barns in the near distance. It was enormous – the size of a house – totally silent, showing a number of curious red brick-shaped lights along its base and at the top. I couldn't distinguish the outline of the object, because of the dazzling white lights on its 'body'... then it dipped downwards, the

Saxmundham, Road, Framlingham

*Baldock – Paleolithic, Neolithic and Bronze Age settlements show the site of Baldock has been continuously occupied since prehistoric times. At the beginning of the Iron Age there was a hill fort at Arbury Banks, 5km to the north-east of Baldock that dominated the area. In the late Iron Age (c. 100BC) the local power base shifted from the hill fort to the vicinity of Baldock. The soil was easily farmed and transportation was more convenient. In the Roman and late Roman eras the community appears to have been both a market town and religious centre. The Roman settlement gradually disappeared. There is no entry for Baldock in the Domesday Book.

B P R S ~2266~ DATA SHEET

BRITISH PHENOMENA RESEARCH SOCIETY

2301

BRENDA BUTLER,
Elm Tree Farm,
Aldringham, Leiston,
Suffolk, IP16 4PU
LEISTON 830551.

P. Glover,
19, Myrtle Road,
Lancing, Sussex.
BN15 9HX

Lancing 64827

This questionnaire has been prepared so that you can give BPRS
as much information as possible concerning the unidentified
phenomenon that you have observed. Please try to answer as many
questions as you can. The information that you give will be used
for research purposes and will be regarded as confidential material
Your name will not be used in connection with any statements,
conclusions or publications without your permission. We request
personal information so that, if it is deemed necessary, we may
contact you for further details.

1. When did you see the object *30.* (day. *5* ...(mth). *80* (yr)

2. Time of day... *12.45 a.m*

3. Where were you when you saw the object *Standing in*
Garden., GOSMORE, HITCHIN

4. For how long did you see the object... *Difficult to say*
2-5 mins.

5. What was the condition of the sky, i.e. bright, dull. *Bright*
MOONLIGHT

6. If you saw the object during DAYLIGHT, TWILIGHT, or DAWN
where was the SUN located - please circle one of the following:

   (a) In front of you
   (b) Behind you   (d) To your left
   (c) To your right   (e) Overhead.

7. If you saw the object at NIGHT where was the MOON located -
please circle one of the following:-

   (a) In front of you ✓
   (b) Behind you   (d) To your left.
   (c) To your right   (e) Overhead.

8. Was the object brighter than the background of the sky.
YES/NO. ~Object~ *Object was not but*
lights were

9. Could you define the brightness of the object to any known
light sources. *Dazzling white lights*
.... *Bright red lights*

10. Did the object:-

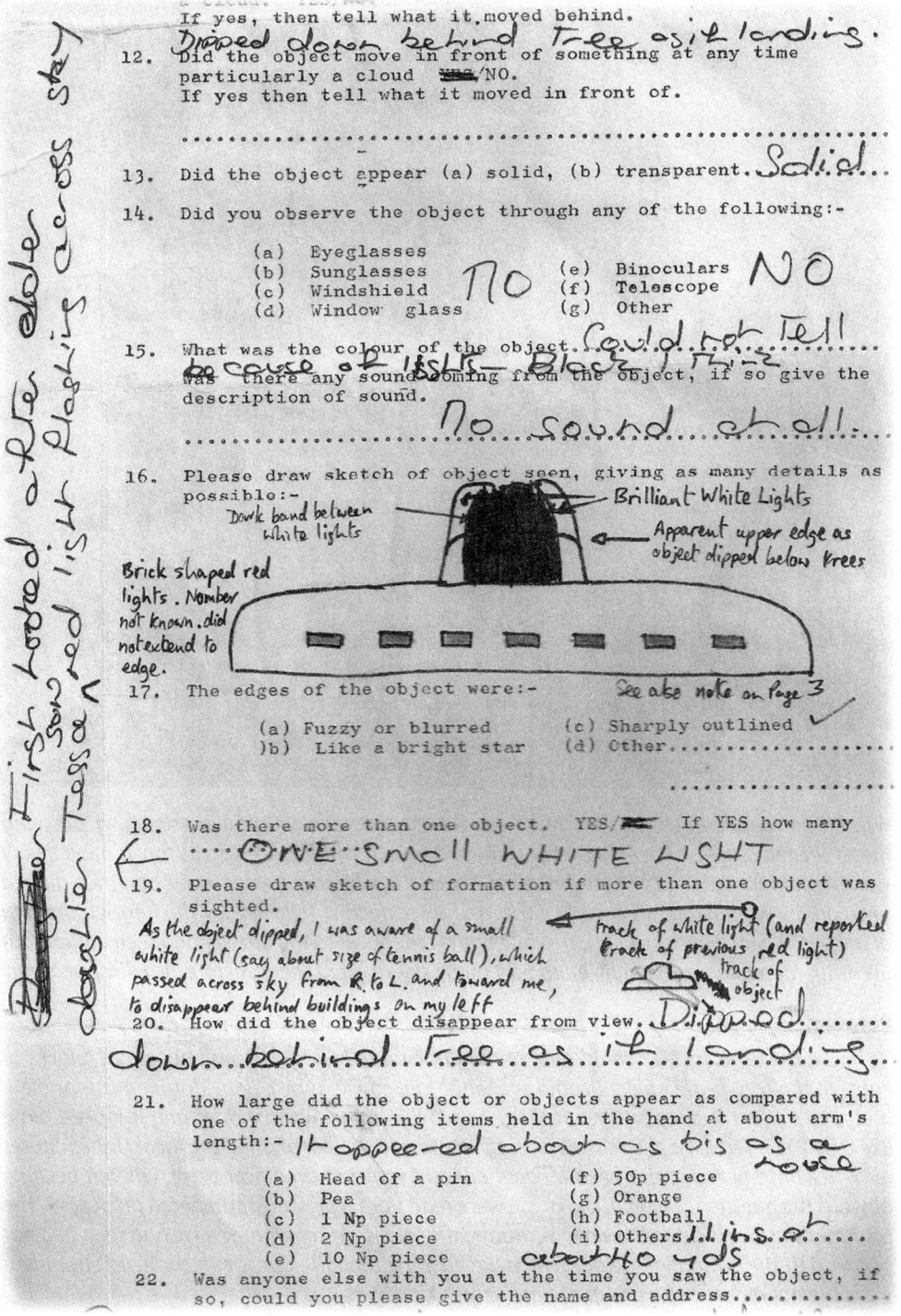

If yes, then tell what it moved behind.

Dipped down behind Tree as it landing.

12. Did the object move in front of something at any time particularly a cloud ~~YES~~/NO.
    If yes then tell what it moved in front of.

    ....

13. Did the object appear (a) solid, (b) transparent. *Solid*

14. Did you observe the object through any of the following:-

    (a) Eyeglasses
    (b) Sunglasses   (e) Binoculars   *NO*
    (c) Windshield *no*   (f) Telescope
    (d) Window glass   (g) Other

15. What was the colour of the object. *Could not Tell because of lights - Black Thing*
    Was there any sound coming from the object, if so give the description of sound.

    No sound at all.

16. Please draw sketch of object seen, giving as many details as possible:-

    Dark band between white lights

    Brilliant White Lights

    Apparent upper edge as object dipped below trees

    Brick shaped red lights. Number not known. did not extend to edge.

17. The edges of the object were:-   *See also note on page 3*

    (a) Fuzzy or blurred   (c) Sharply outlined ✓
)b) Like a bright star   (d) Other...................

    ....

18. Was there more than one object. YES/~~NO~~ If YES how many
    ONE small WHITE LIGHT

19. Please draw sketch of formation if more than one object was sighted.

    As the object dipped, I was aware of a small white light (say about size of tennis ball), which passed across sky from R. to L. and toward me, to disappear behind buildings on my left

    track of white light (and reported track of previous red light)

    track of object

20. How did the object disappear from view. *Dipped down behind Tree as it landing.*

21. How large did the object or objects appear as compared with one of the following items held in the hand at about arm's length:- *It appeared about as big as a house*

    (a) Head of a pin   (f) 50p piece
    (b) Pea   (g) Orange
    (c) 1 Np piece   (h) Football
    (d) 2 Np piece   (i) Others *I.I ins at*
    (e) 10 Np piece   *about 40 yds*

22. Was anyone else with you at the time you saw the object, if so, could you please give the name and address...............

First looked after older son and I saw red vessel shining across sky

white lights appearing to squash down – as if they had been withdrawn, somehow, allowing me to see the outline of a 'flying saucer' shaped object, with a dome on its top. It moved very slowly and went behind the bottom half of a tree, a few hundred yards away, and then dipped once again, went straight down to earth and disappeared, followed by the frenzied barking of dogs in the locality. Incredibly, a 'white light' – identical to the one we had seen earlier that evening – appeared in the right-hand part of the sky, at great speed, before also disappearing."

Pamela:

"It had a flat base. Inside I could see, running horizontally across, a number of red 'blocks of light'. In the top of the object I could see what looked like two 'pylons', forming a triangle – a bit like a heart in shape. When it tilted, this 'pylon thing' went shorter and it looked more like a saucer. I reported the matter to the police and then telephoned the local United States Air Force Base (it may have been Mildenhall) and spoke to an officer there, when it became obvious the questions being asked of me were read from a previously prepared pro forma. The next morning, we went to have a look around and realised that whatever we had seen had not occurred at the bottom of the garden, as we had first thought, but over a cornfield about two fields away, bordered by a group of electricity pylons."

Marion told us, following the UFO event, that the family was to experience unusual things occurring at the family home. They included household objects going missing, but reappearing a few days later, and problems with the electrical system on the Austin Mini. From our conversations held with this well-spoken, intelligent woman, we saw no reason not to believe her version of the events that had befallen the family.

(Source: Brenda Butler/Dot Street/Personal interview)

Was this another sighting of the same UFO?

Was there a connection with a UFO sighting which took place on the 23rd August 1994, at 8.00pm, involving a motorist who was travelling home to Codicote from Norfolk, on the A505 to Baldock, on what was described as a clear blue sky with dusk falling?

He was approaching the brow of the steep hill – level with dog kennels on his left – when in front of him appeared what he took to be a beautiful bright star. It suddenly moved in a straight line to his left, then on the same line to the right.

"I thought this was odd, then it moved to the right on the same line and came closer and did the same movement again, travelling silently to the left and right – so fast, unlike an aircraft or helicopter. It then came straight towards me and up over the car, clearly seen through the glass roof to be displaying orange/red lights in a vertical line in the middle of this silver orb. There must have been others on the road behind me that witnessed the same phenomena. It was fantastic and I am glad to have seen it."

(Source: *ufo-hunters.com*)

Summer 1980 – Mysterious *'beings'* seen in Rendlesham Forest

Brenda Butler told of being contacted by Mr Brian Jolly – then employed by the USAF personnel at the airbase, to keep the rabbit population down, during the summer of 1980. While driving through the forest, one afternoon, he noticed a *'ball of orange light'* through the vehicle's wing mirror, travelling a few feet off the ground behind. On another occasion, Mr Jolly was walking near the Weapons Storage Area, at Woodbridge Airbase (known locally as the 'bomb dump'), when he saw what he presumed to be three young children, moving about behind some trees in the forest.

Dressed in flowing brown cloaks

"Thinking they were from the airbase but curious as to their presence, he picked-up his telescopic gun sight and peered through it, recoiling in fright when he realised they were all dressed in brown cloaks, flowing to the forest floor."

Base police arrive and discover unusual traces on the ground

Shaken, he quietly made his way out of the forest and contacted the Base Police, at Woodbridge, who assembled an armed party of security officers to escort him back to the scene. When they arrived at the location, one of the airmen noticed a 'figure' disappearing into the forest, and shouted out – to no avail.

Mr Jolly:

"There was this strange luminous green sticky material covering the ground, but when picked-up it just dissolved. I was advised not to go anywhere near the 'bomb dump' again, on my own, unless escorted by an armed guard."

Another witness tells a similar story

In addition to this sighting was a similar report made by a civilian worker, employed on the construction of a road to the new helicopter landing pad, who saw what he took to be:

"…a number of small children gathered in the forest, wearing fancy dress, with brown coats and hats on their heads, near to where I was working, before realising that these were not children."

Stories, such as these, came of no surprise to us. Over the years, during a number of visits to Rendlesham Forest, we were to hear of all manner of strange things seen in and around the area, including strange creatures, UFOs, diminutive forest dwellers, dazzling 'orbs' (some of them seen with the naked eye), reports of tall spindly 'figures' with concealed faces, wandering about on the airbase, and in more recent times, curious falls of stones – a phenomenon experienced by ourselves, on many occasions.

15th June 1980 – Red *'globe'* seen over Rendlesham Forest Airbase

Something just as strange occurred close to Rendlesham Forest in the early morning of 15th June 1980, according to *Ken Kern – then a member of the Security Police, posted to 'B' Flight,

Ken Kern

> *"The exact words off my index card 'diary' were '15 June 80 – Interesting night – it's our 2nd mid and Wagner & Campbell have A-2. They sighted a UFO at five different occasions that night, described as a red globe 20ft in diameter. It hovered at times over aircraft pads/structures. Labrucherie also sighted the UFO; he had A-1. At one time they said the UFO glided over the trees to a meadow, where it suddenly disappeared into a white flash and then nothing; except two deer which they say were not there previously. I believe this story to be authentic.'"*

At first glance this seems too incredible to believe, but he was not the only one to claim bizarre sightings of what looked like small monk figures prowling the forest.

*Ken was instrumental in setting up a face book website *Lone Ranger,* which has attracted widespread interest over recent years with a continuing focus on the events that took place there – *"A meeting place for people who share a common interest in UFO sightings and phenomena at or near Rendlesham and the former RAF Bentwaters and RAF Woodbridge bases."* (Currently there are 1504 members (September 2015) He is a credit to the USAF and has also compiled a website of 81st SPS personnel which contains many interesting photographs contributed from who served during that period.

David Bryant – an ex Royal Navy pilot and a frequent speaker on the BBC with regard to his knowledge of astronomy and meteorites – was to sight what appeared to be similar *'figures'*, during a walk around the forest with his wife – Linda. Are they simulacra or an example of something so strange, beyond human comprehension?

18th June 1980 – UFO over Ipswich

Mr Andrews from Rainbow Close, Ipswich, was walking past Ipswich Hospital, at 10.30pm, when:

"I saw a long, narrow object, flying through the sky. It had five square windows on the side. One end was thicker than the other.

I watched it for several minutes, until it was lost in the distance."

(Source: Brenda Butler/Ron West)

20th August 1980 – Gigantic 'T'-shaped object seen

While the next sighting is a long way from Suffolk, it may have some association – bearing in mind what was seen just 45minutes later over Hopton, Norfolk, by members of the Frost family (which is not too many miles from Suffolk) but of course, strictly speaking, UFOs do not have boundaries!

It began at 9pm on the 20th August 1980, when schoolgirl Ruth Sutherland (then aged 14) was stood outside her house, at Poundsgate, Dartmoor, some four miles away from Newton Abbot, South Devon, talking to a friend. They noticed a small, spinning, egg-shaped object, gold in colour, heading across the sky towards them, which slowed down and changed direction.

"Two huge objects appeared in the sky, side by side, filling up the sky – so big we could barely see the sky at the side of them. They were three dimensional. We could see the nuts and bolts on the structure. One was saucer-shaped.

The other resembled a gigantic 'T' -shaped object. As they came nearer we could see lights underneath, flashing in sequences."

20th August 1980 – Triangular UFO seen by family, at Hopton

Just 45 minutes later, Mr Leslie Gary Frost – an Engineer by occupation, from Sidegate Road, Hopton, on the Norfolk coast – was helping his wife, Margaret, bring in the washing, as dusk fell, on a cloudless, moonlit, night, when he was staggered to see two jet- black massive structures, showing a pattern of red and white lights, moving towards him at approximately 150 feet above the ground.

"The top one was about two hundred feet off the ground. They appeared solid, rather than translucent. I stood there with my son, who had come out of the house, mesmerised by what we were seeing. The one reminded me of a huge manta ray, with three large red lights at its front and two brilliant lights at the rear. It halted in mid-air, throwing a shadow over us, and then there was a terrific flash of light and a small triangular object appeared, which began to circle the sky for ten minutes, over a nearby water tower."

Margaret:

"I went to fetch in the washing. Lots of lights came over very slowly, from the back field. They looked like a formation of planes coming in, displaying red and white lights. One of the red ones shone brighter than the others. They couldn't have been planes – they were moving too slowly and making a droning noise. My husband wanted to see more, so he and my son went to have a closer look. I went inside."

Anthony Mark Frost: (10)

"We went up the garden to get the washing in and Dad said, 'Look at that!' Me and mum looked and saw three red lights and two white lights. I, and dad, went to get a better view. There were two, because one broke off and it gave a flash and the big one went away, but the little one went around me and dad. We then went inside the house; then we went down to Hopton to phone the Police, and a Police lady came and she asked me some questions – then I went to bed."

Interviewed by a policewoman

Mr Frost confirmed that he was interviewed by a policewoman, who told him she would be sending a report to the MOD.

After nothing else was heard, Mr Frost contacted Brenda Butler and Dot Street, who interviewed him; otherwise, we would have been none the wiser.

Sensationalised by the newspaper

After details had been given to the Press, Mr Frost was dismayed to find that the published article failed to accurately reflect what had really happened, and he contacted the police at Lowestoft. He was then advised that his report had been passed to the MOD.

Mr Frost:

"I've often wondered if there was any connection with heavy interference to my television set, about a week before the UFO sighting took place. I knew it wasn't the TV, as a replacement set showed the same problem."

Received a visit by two men, who threatened him

"Some time after the incident I did receive a visit from two men, who told me they were from the University of Swindon, and very interested in looking at some scale models

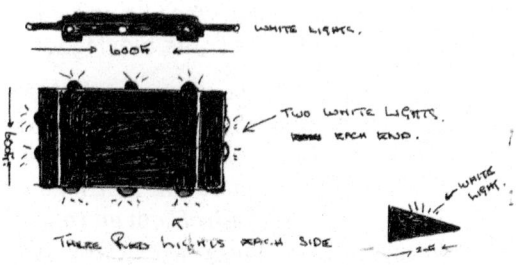

NAME. WAYNE SALT FROST
ADDRESS. 2-3 BRETT COTTAGES
SIDEGATE Rd. HOPTON
TELEPHONE NO. NIL
DATE. 24.8.80

.....F.Frost.....
(Signature)

Permission to use above statement for publication in News Letter or any other publication which may arise in connection with this sighting.

.....F.Frost.....
(Signature)

UFO SIGHTING ACCOUNT FORM

SECTION A

Please write an account of your sighting, make a drawing of what you saw and then answer the questions in section B overleaf as fully as possible. Write in **BLOCK CAPITALS** using a ball point pen.

WENT TO FETCH WASHING IN ABOUT 9-45 OR 9-30
LET OF LIGHTS COMING VERY SLOWLY OVER THE BACK
FIELD MY HUSBAND AND SON WANTED TO SEE MORE
CLEALY, SO WENT UP THE FIELD, I WENT IN THE HOUSE
LOOKED LIKE A FORMATION OF PLANES COMING
BUT TO SLOWLY. DROANING NOISE NOT QUITE LIKE A
PLANE. THEY WERE RED AND WHITE LIGHTS IT MUST HAVE
TURNED SLIGHTLY ONE OF THE RED LIGHT SHONE A LOT
BIGGER AND BRIGHTER I WAS ONLY OUT FOR ABOUT
3-4 MINUTES

DRAWING*

Your full name (Mr/**Mrs**/Miss/Ms)
.....MARGARET FROST. Age.....
Address.....2-3 BRETT COTTAGES.....
SIDE GATE Rd HOPTON.....
Telephone No......(STD.....)
Occupation during last two years.....House Wife.

UFO SIGHTING ACCOUNT FORM

SECTION A

Please write an account of your sighting, make a drawing of what you saw and then answer the questions in section B overleaf as fully as possible. Write in **BLOCK CAPITALS** using a ball point pen.

We went up the garden to get the washing in and Dad said Look at that and me and mum looked and I saw a 3 Red Light and 2 white light and me and dad went to have a better view there was two because one broke off and it give a flash and the big one went away but the litter went round me and dad for a and untill it went and me and dad went in and we went bawn Hopton te phone the polics and a police lady come and she ask some question and were she went I went to bed.

Please continue on a separate sheet if necessary.

DRAWING*   2 object

3 Red Light

2 white Light

2 white Light

3 Red Light

*If preferred, use a separate sheet of paper.

Your full name (Mr/Mrs/Miss/Ms)
Anthony mark Frost Age 10

Address 2-3 Brett cottages
Side Cots Rd Hopton on Ses

Telephone No. (STD)

Occupation during last two years

Any professional, technical or academic qualifications or special interests

Do you object to the publication of your name?
*Yes/No *Delete as applicable.

Today's Date 25.8.1980

Signature A Frost

I had built of the UFOs I had seen, after taking a number of photographs of those models. They told me, in a very threatening manner, 'Leave it alone', which is exactly what I did until you contacted me."

It appears that no such place existed, which should not come of any surprise. What gives these nameless, unidentified, persons the right to threaten people like Mr Frost? We presume that they are fearful of reports such as this being brought to the attention of the public.

(Source: Brenda Butler/Dot Street/Personal interview)

RAF Hopton tracks UFO on radar

Alan Brown – a former radar operator, who served at Royal Air Force Hopton in the 1950s, now a Devon resident – had this to say:

"I used to cycle to and from Gorleston, several evenings a week, to see my girlfriend (now my wife). I did not see any ghosts or unexplained apparitions, but always disliked riding along the section of the old main road before it was dual carriageway, which went down the dip then up again by Valley Farm, particularly on the side when coming to Hopton. I have no explanation for the feeling of unease and impending fear I experienced."

UFO shown on Radar

Alan recalls being on watch in the underground bunker in the cliffs near the Corton boundary when an image appeared on the radar scope resembling an aircraft way out over the sea, but stationary. After checking out the possibilities that it might have been a ship, odd weather condition, or weather balloon, he decided to stop the antenna on the cliff top pylon and use a hand control to position it, pointing it at that mystery response, simultaneously using another screen to expand the display to determine if there was more than one object there.

"However, as soon as we did this, the object vanished – almost as if it had detected that the radar beam was locked on to it".

The next day there, the unidentified object was tracked once again before disappearing off the scope.

Encounter with a ghostly horse

At 3am, in June 1970, a motorist was hurrying to Lowestoft from Gorleston, after a phone call from an elderly relative reporting that her husband had just died and she was alone with his body.

"As I drove into a patch of mist, my path was blocked by a black horse, only a few feet ahead. I slammed on the brakes and raised an arm to shelter my face, because it was impossible to avoid a head-on collision, but there was no impact and the car emerged from the mist on to a clear road. Tentatively I got out and walked back, but found nothing."

At least several other incidents have been reported along the A12, near Hopton, involving motorists who have sighted what appears to be the figure of a grey man in the road, wearing a long coat. It is claimed that these manifestations have occurred over the last 50 years!

13th November – Triangular UFO seen over Hollesley

Ernie Craine (78) of 3, Coronation Avenue, Hollesley, was outside with his wife, around 10pm, when they saw a strange object in the sky. The sighting is typical of what people were seeing around the East Anglia area during that time period.

CLOSED

EAST ANGLIAN U.F.O. & PARANORMAL RESEARCH ASSOCIATION

SECTION A **SIGHTING ACCOUNT FORM**

Please write an account of your sighting, make a drawing of what you saw and then answer the questions in section B overleaf as fully as possible. Write in **BLOCK CAPITALS** using a ball point pen.

MY WIFE AND I SAW THIS BIG BLACK TRIANGULER SHAPE CRAFT IN THE SKY, IT WAS LATE ONE EVENING, IT HAD THREE LIGHTS RED AND WHITE, IT MADE NO NOISE AS IT PASSED OVER OUR HOUSE - GOING TOWARDS THE BRENTWATERS AIR BASE
I THINK IT WAS AN USAF SPY PLANE GOING OVER.
WE GET A FEW OF THEM HERE.

DRAWING*

Your full name (Mr/Mrs/Miss/Ms)
ERNIE CRAINE .... Age 78
Address. 3 CORONATION AVE
HOLLERSLEY SUFFOLK
Telephone No......................(STD.........)
Occupation during last two years.....................
RETIRED

Any professional, technical or academic qualifications or special interests
....

Do you object to the publication of your name?
*Yes/No. *Delete as applicable.
Today's Date.... 8 - 9 - 88
Signature...... E. Craine

* If preferred, use a separate sheet of paper.

18th November 1980 – 'Flying Saucer' sighted

At 8pm on 18th November 1980, Mike Boyle from Saxmundham, Suffolk, sighted a grey and orange coloured saucer-shaped object, heading across the sky, over Butley, near to Rendlesham Forest. As it passed overhead, he heard a distinct *whooshing noise* before it passed out of sight, two minutes later.

(Source: Brenda Butler)

November 1980 – UFO chased by motorist!

Another witness to something strange in the Suffolk sky was now retired Hotelier, Barry Rey – then Manager of the Woodhall Country House Hotel, Shottisham (some six-and-a-half miles from Woodbridge, Suffolk) – a poplar venue for servicemen from RAF Bentwaters and Woodbridge.

"It was in November, 1980. Definitely not connected with the incidents that occurred at the end of December 1980, when something was alleged to have been seen in the forest. I remember the sun was beginning to set, when I noticed a strange 'light' hovering over the village. I knew, from its shape and appearance that it wasn't like any aircraft, or helicopter, I had seen before – so I jumped into my car and followed it, as it headed over fields towards the coast. It was disc-shaped, showing portholes of light projecting a powerful beam from its underneath. At one stage, it was only 50 feet away from me before it passed overhead, rose up slowly, and dropped down over some trees at the other side of the field and landed. I drove along the road, for a short distance, and then saw it hovering over a house belonging to Robin Pendle, before it finally moved away for good."

Barry wonders, as a result of what he saw, whether the date given for the now world-famous incident, involving Colonel Halt and others, is flawed – a supposition drawn rationally from his own experience. Unfortunately, Barry would not have realised, without the hindsight of many years research, that he was not the only one to sight UFOs over East Anglia – not forgetting other parts of the country, during this period.

(Source: Personal interview)

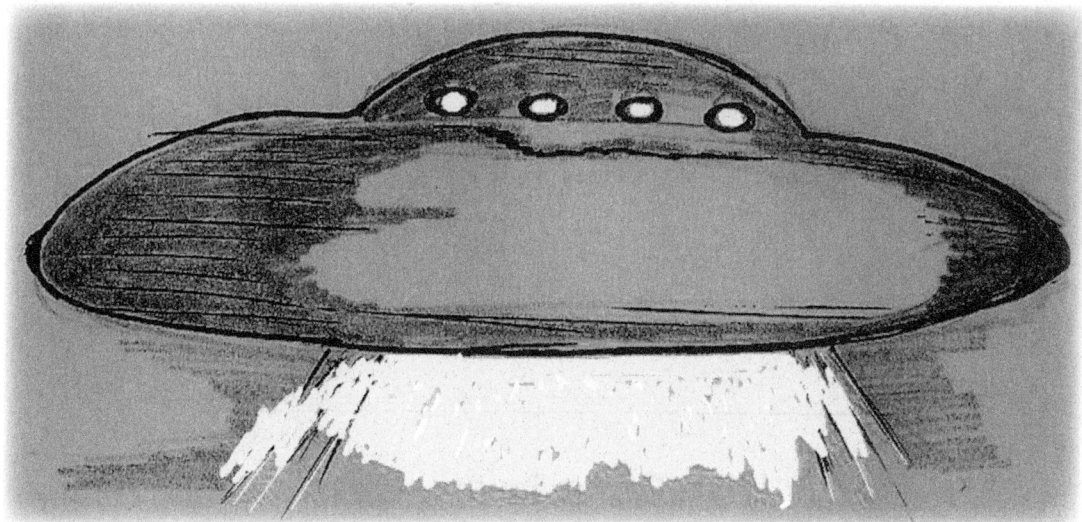

24th December 1980

The son of a Colonel known to Charles Halt, stationed at RAF Bentwaters Airbase, living in Marlsford, Woodbridge, was with two friends, at 11pm, when they sighted a strange glow above the forest. He later told Jenny Randles and Brenda Butler:

Old Fox Tower from Whiskey Tower.

Midnight 25th December 1980 – UFO flies over RAF Bentwaters

Carl Thompson Jr. – Former radio communications specialist at Bentwaters:

"At the time, I was a Senior Airman with the 2164 Communications Squadron. I was a radio relay repairman. On the first night – Christmas night, if I'm not mistaken – I was at the Weapons Storage Area, working on a piece of equipment in the security tower, trouble-shooting it. I think it was a motion-detection component, used for the security of the weapons. At midnight, the guy who was going to relieve me called and said that he would come out to the area.

So, I went back to the wide-band radio shop and finished up some paperwork."

UFO flies over security tower

"Now, I don't remember how much later it was, but he called me at the shop and said, 'We just saw a UFO!' He meant himself and the security guards. He was in the security tower cab at the time he called. You could plainly tell he was excited and maybe kind of anxious. He sounded matter-of-fact but also kind of half-scared. I asked, 'What did it look like?' He said, 'It was so bright that you couldn't look directly at it.' So I didn't get any details about its shape, how large it was any of that. It was just a really bright light.

He said it was hovering there for just a few seconds, then it went toward Woodbridge – so, maybe, that would be in a south-westerly direction. 'Did everybody see it?' He said that everyone had. Then he asked me, 'How am I going to report this?' I said, 'Is anyone else going to report it?' He said, 'No, they're not going to report it', so I said 'How are you going to look if the others, who were right there in the area, aren't going to report it? You're going to be on your own. If it were me, I would let it go.' I was the ranking person on that night, so I told him, 'I would advise against it, but it's up to you'. When I saw him later that night he had to order a part for the tower, so we crossed paths – he told me that he'd decided not to report the incident. At the time, we didn't know that the other base was involved. We had no idea that there had been some security police hunting it down, or whatever, in the woods."

27th December 1980 – Another UFO sighted

"I guess it was two nights later that the part for the equipment in the tower came in. We got notified about that just as my colleague was coming on shift, at midnight, so he said he would go out and install it. I stayed at the radio shop. A little while later (it had to be past 12.30am, since he had to pick up the part first), he called, really excited, and told me that he had just seen another UFO. It had followed the runway, which runs more or less east and, then it turned, and flew directly over the Weapons Storage Area. He said it came right at the tower and was so low that he and the guard hit the deck! He said it had hovered [nearby] for a few seconds. He couldn't say how long, and then it slowly moved off, over the trees. He said it was just above them, but then it dropped down into the trees. He didn't see it come back up, so that's when he called me on the landline. He said he heard a bunch of chatter on the radio in the tower – the guard there was talking to someone – and said [the Security Police] were going to have to report it this time, because it went down into the woods." **(Source: Robert Hastings)**

Official response following de-briefing

The next time Carl saw his colleague, he told him he had to file a report with the Security Police at their headquarters, approximately 30 yards away from the Weapons Storage Area.

Robert Hastings asks about the date of the incident

Robert Hastings asked Thompson:

"How do you know the first incident happened on Christmas night?"

Answer:

"Well, I'm not positive it did, but it was definitely during the holidays – the 25th, the 26th – because '......', and I, were working a longer shift on both of those nights. We were single and our sergeant asked us to volunteer for that, so the married guys could be with their families during Christmas. In return, we got some days off in January."

Robert then asked Thompson if '........' had described seeing one or more beams of light coming from the UFO, down into the Weapons Storage Area, on either night.

Answer: *"No, he didn't say anything about that."*

2.50am on 26ᵗʰ December 1980

According to the British Astronomical Association, a brilliant fireball was seen to burn up in the southern sky over England. Witnesses described it being comparable in brightness to that of the full moon

3am on 26ᵗʰ December 1980 – Lt. Fred Buran receives radio call

Lt. Fred 'Skip' Buran was on duty at Building 679 Central Security Control, when he received a call at 3am from John Burroughs.

He told him he had sighted some strange lights in the wooded area east of the runway, at Woodbridge.

John Burroughs sights weird lights in the forest

"We saw some weird red and blue flashing lights in the trees, east of the gate, and decided to go and have a look. We went down the East Gate road, turned right at the stop sign, and walked along the tarmac road, ten or twenty yards, before turning left along the forest road. At this point I saw a white light shining down onto the trees, accompanied by the red and blue flashing ones. At this point, we decided to return to East Gate and report the incident to the base."

John Burroughs   *Edward Cabansag*

Sgt. Penniston and Airman Edward Cabansag arrive

Following the arrival of Sgt. Penniston and his rider Airman Cabansag, Lt. Buran directed Staff Sgt. Coffey – the Duty Security Controller – to ask Jim Penniston whether they could have been marker lights. (***Continues on page 175***)

RADAR OPERATORS' VITAL NEW INFORMATION

Radar operator tells of 'UFO plotted on radar' – RAF Jets scrambled

Ex-RAF radar operator Malcolm Scurrah, who previously served at RAF Coltishall during the 1980s, was on a 5-12pm duty at RAF Neatishead, in November 1980, monitoring night-flying exercises 50 miles out to sea, over The Wash, involving two RAF 'Phantom' aircraft, using height finding radar apparatus. Just after 8pm a single 'target' appeared on the radar screen at a height of 5,000 feet and stationary. Checks made with Eastern Radar Air Traffic Control, to ascertain if this could have been a civil aircraft helicopter from one of the oil rigs, proved negative.

Suddenly the target accelerated upwards, from several thousand feet over the next 15 minutes, plotted in a series of 'jumps' to an altitude of 100,000 feet, unheard of before, being lost from the screen (presumably off the height indicator band). The only aircraft capable of reaching such high altitudes was the Lockheed SR-71 'Blackbird', but this was no steady climb – just a series of jumps, with nothing between them.

Malcolm:

"I learnt the unknown target had been tracked on the main radar screen, and performed impossible manoeuvres. The 'G' forces involved would have rendered a pilot unconscious or killed him. Following the appearance of the unidentified target, the night exercise was temporarily postponed. One of the RAF jets was guided towards the unidentified target. The pilot had described seeing a very bright light in front of him on his voice intercom, from a distance of some half a mile away from the object; suddenly it just flew off very fast."

Radar tapes seized – incident not mentioned again

The day after, it became common knowledge that two senior RAF Controllers at the main Section Operations Centre had been interviewed by high-ranking RAF Officers from London. From then onwards, they did not talk about it. **THEY TOOK THE RADAR TAPES WITH THEM.**

Malcolm:

"This was an unfamiliar occurrence. Tapes were normally removed in either a near miss or an accident. I do know that video images had been transmitted in 'real time' to the command centre at West Drayton."

Malcolm was a frequent guest at UFO meetings, held by Graham and Mark Birdsall, during the 1990s. Veteran UFO researcher/author and now *Flying Disk Press* publisher – Philip Mantle, met Malcolm several times, and spoke very highly of him, describing him as a friendly, down-to-earth man, who was completely genuine.

(Source: Graham Birdsall, *UFO Magazine*, May/June 1995) [See reports for November 1980 on page 165 and 166]

Radar operator tells of UFO plotted on radar over RAF Woodbridge

Nigel Kerr was stationed at RAF Watton. Some time near Christmas 1980, he received a telephone call from RAF Bentwaters, *"…enquiring if anything unusual had been plotted on radar, as strange 'lights' had been seen falling from the sky. I checked my radar screen and noticed a strange blip in the sky over the Woodbridge area, visible for three or four sweeps on the screen before disappearing. No report was logged of this matter."*

We know that Sgt. John Coffey contacted RAF Watton and confirmed they had tracked an object, which had disappeared into the forest area. Minutes after hearing this, Jim and John were out in the forest looking for the source of the strange *'lights'* they had seen earlier.

Radar operator tells of UFO plotted on radar – warned to keep quiet!

Ex-RAF Neatsihead serviceman Gary Baker (1979-1981), from Suffolk – an intelligent man with a professional background, having worked in nursing and the Territorial Army and now currently running his own business in the Ipswich area of Suffolk – had this to say:

"A UFO 'flap' occurred in late December 1980. I was in the briefing room when high-ranking officers and personnel in suits instructed the Squadron Ops staff that it didn't happen and not to talk about it. This is rubbish; there were two radars and both had cameras. If the cameras were switched off, what was the point of 'them' removing the operating room bridge logs and radar tapes? This was followed by the warning to both Squadrons not to discuss the matter.

I can tell you that the US Air Force personnel at Bentwaters, in the first instance, dealt with RAF Watton, their radar picture having been transmitted to them from RAF Neatishead. I refute the MOD stance on radar evidence to this incident. Intelligence and high-ranking officers' squadrons were told it didn't happen – we were warned not to talk about it. This refutes consistent claims that there were no radar tapes available, because the radar camera was switched off at Neatishead at 1627Z on that date. This was over three days and two radars, which both had cameras. The radar picture at Neatishead was also transmitted to West Drayton to Strike Command, to Eastern Radar and other radar stations, which came under the same umbrella of protection. I know for a fact that RAF Boulmer, in Newcastle, would have the coverage on their screens as well. Whether they would have picked up as much detail would depend on the curvature of the Earth that may have restricted the signal return, due to its geographical position. Neatishead, of course, was in excellent position being close to the source of the reported radar pictures and recordings, so they are lying about something. What exactly it is can only be anybody's guess."

(Sources: Russell Callaghan, *UFO Magazine* **(November/December, 2001 & February 2002)/ Personal interview, 2016) UFO sighting – 1983**

Gary told of an incident which had occurred in summer 1983, while out with his girlfriend in Attleborough.

"I never reported it at the time, because I feared, like others who had reported similar events, that I, too, would be the butt of ridicule. My girlfriend, and I, had been visiting a friend's house to play on one of the early computers. We left at about 3am on the way back to my parent's house, a short distance away. It was daybreak, just getting light, when we became aware of something large moving slowly in our peripheral vision. I looked up and saw a huge 'thing' – the size of several football pitches – about 200 feet above us, moving silently and slowly through the sky, accompanied by a sensation of electricity around us – as if the air was charged. We watched it move away – still very slow across Attleborough, where we lived – and head off over the Stanford Battle Area. The interesting thing is that neither of us talked about what we had seen for some years – never thought anything of it at the time – although something very odd took place. When we arrived home, minutes later, the sun was really quite high. It was much later than it should have been. Years later, I contacted my ex-girlfriend and discussed what we had seen. She confirmed what we had seen, without me telling her anything from my recollection – which matched it."

Gary also told me about a series of ***paranormal incidents*** which had plagued him and his (now) ex-wife, many years ago.

"To be fair, prior to what we experienced, I treated such reports with great scepticism – until it happened to us. I've had framed graduation photographs inexplicably moved from the wall and thrown across the room, light bulbs ejecting themselves from the sockets, and decorative plates moving seemingly of their own accord and keys going missing. It got to a disconcerting point where we had no choice but to move house. This brought home the realisation that such things happen but I can't say what it is evidence of, as I have never seen a ghost and hope I never will. All I can do is tell you what did take place."

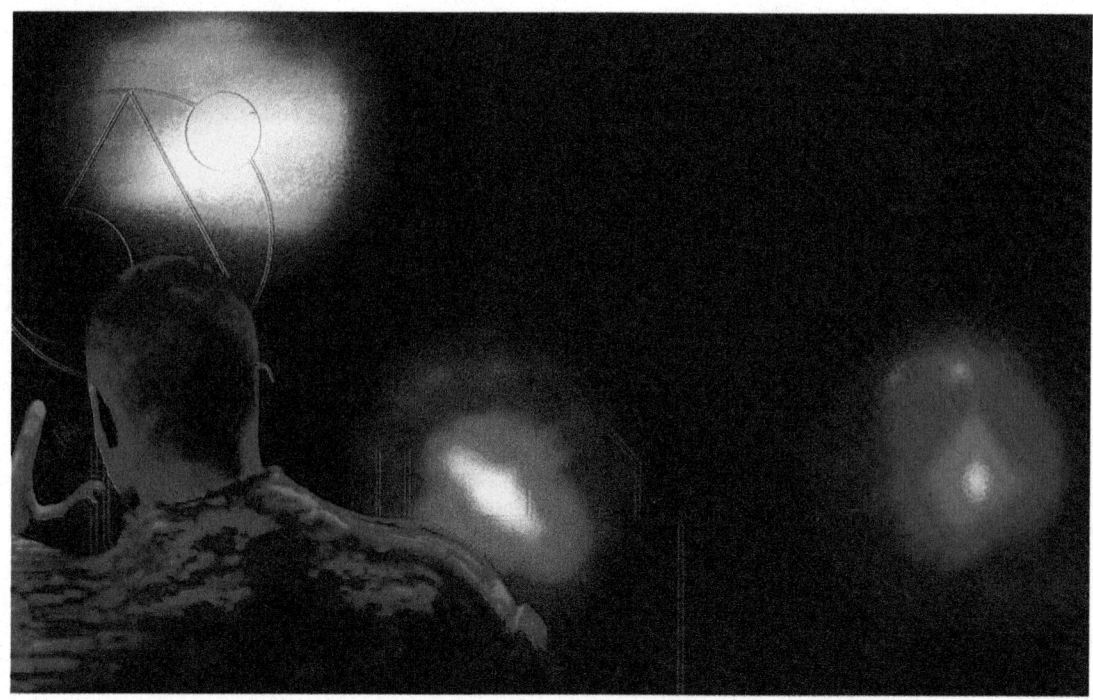

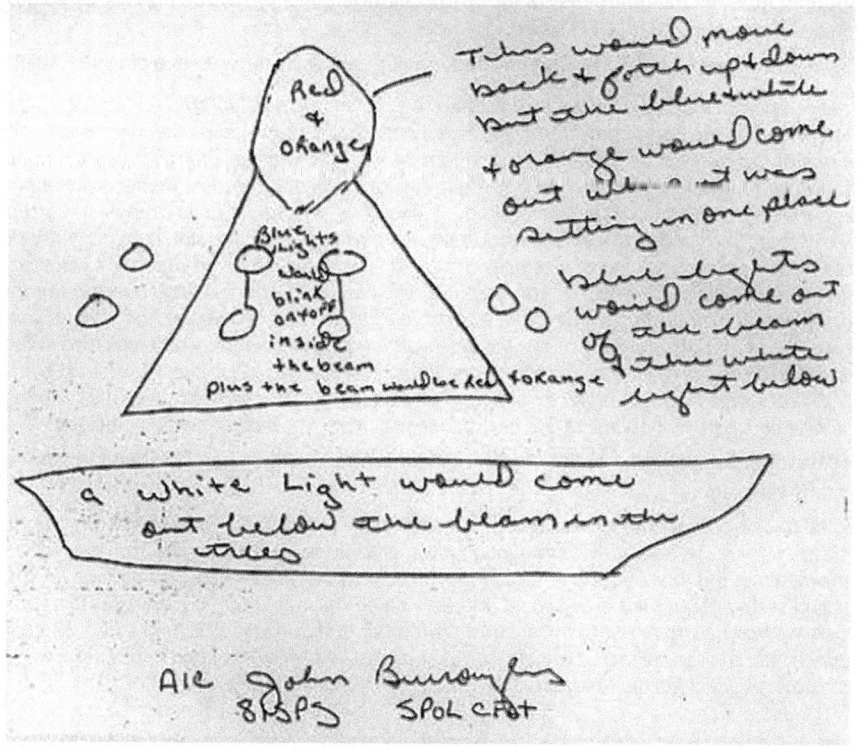

On 26 Dec 80, SSgt Penningston and I were on Security #6 at Woodbridge Base. I was the member. We were patroling Delta NAPA when we received a call over the radio. It stated that Police #4 had seen some strange lights out past the East Gate and we were to respond. SSgt Penningston and I left Delta NAPA, heading for the East Gate code two. When we got there SSgt Steffens and A1C Burroughs were on patrol. They told us they had seen some funny lights out in the woods. We notified CSC and we asked permission to investigate further. They gave us the go-ahead. We left our weapons with SSgt Steffens who remained at the gate,, Thus the three of us went out to investigate. We stopped the Security Police vehicle about 100 meters from the gate. Due to the terrain we had to on by foot. We kept in constant contact with CSC. While we walked, each one of us would see the lights. Blue, red, white, and yellow. The beckon light turned out to be the yellow light. We would see them periodically, but not in a specific pattern. As we approached, the lights would seem to be at the edge of the forrest. We were about 100 meters from the edge of the forrest when I saw a quick movement, it look visible for a moment . It look like it spun XIXHX left a quarter of a turn, then it was gone. I'd advised SSgt Penningston and A1C Borroughs. We advised CSC and proceeded in extreme caution. When we got about 75-50 meters, MSgt Chandler/Flight Chief, was on the scene. CSC was not reading our transmissions very well,, so we used MSgt Chandler as a go-between. He remained back at our vehicle. As we entered the forrest, the blue and red lights were not visible anymore. Only the beacon light, was still blinking. We figured the lights were coming from past the forrest, since nothing was visible when we past through the woody forrest. We would see a glowing near the beacon light, but as we got closer we found it to be a lit up farm house. After we had passed throught the forrest, we thought it had to be an aircr accident. So did CSC as well. But we ran and walked a good 2 miles past our vehicle, until we got to a vantage point where we could determine that what we were chasing was X only a beacon light off in the distance. Our route through the forrest and field was a direct one,■ straight towards the light. We informed CSC thàt the light beacon was farther than we thought,, so CSC terminated our investigation. A1C Burroughs and I took a road, while SSgt Penningston walked straight back from where we came. A1C Borroughs saw the light again, this time it was coming from the left of us , as we were walking back to our patrol vehicle. We got in contact with SSgt Penningston and we took a walk threw where we saw the lights. Nothing. Finally, we made it back to our vehicle, after making contact with the ₱C's and informing them of what we saw. After that we met MSgt Chandler and we went in service again after termination of the sighting.

EDWARD N. CABANSAG, A1C, USAF
81st Security Police Sq.

I'M CONVINCED THIS IS A "CLEANED UP" VERSION OF WHAT HAPPENED. I TALKED WITH AIIN CABANSAG + CAN SAY HE WAS SHOOK UP TO THE POINT HE DIDN'T WANT TO TALK. (personal comments removed)

Fred:

"Jim Penniston then asked permission to investigate and was joined by Security Flight Chief M.Sgt. Chandler. I monitored the progress of Penniston, Burroughs and Edward Cabansag, as they entered the wooded area, and appeared to get very close to the lights.

At one point, Staff Sgt. Penniston said it was a definite mechanical object. I warned them it might be a light aircraft that had crashed. Staff Sgt. Penniston then told me they had gone past it and were now looking at a marker beacon in the same general area of the 'lights'. He appeared somewhat agitated."

Chris Arnold – USAF Law Enforcement Officer, Bentwaters

"My flight chief, at Bentwaters, asked me if I wanted to head out to Woodbridge to meet up with Burroughs and see what was up.

I grabbed the back gate keys and took the back way to RAF Woodbridge. I met Burroughs at the East Gate of Woodbridge. We left our guns with the guy riding with Burroughs and drove to the end of the long access road. We left our vehicle and walked out there. There was absolutely nothing in the woods. We could see lights in the distance and it appeared unusual, as it was a sweeping light (we did not know about the lighthouse on the coast at the time). We also saw some strange coloured lights in the distance, but were unable to determine what they were. Contrary to what some people assert, at the time almost none of us knew there was a lighthouse at Orford Ness. Remember, the vast majority of folks involved were young people, 19, 20, 25 years old. Consequently it wasn't something most of the troops were cognizant of. That's one reason the lights appeared interesting, or out of the ordinary, to some people."

Sgt. James Penniston

"I have never seen lights like this before. They were red, blue, white, and orange lights, no further than 100 yards from the road east of the runway."

Jim later said:

"It was a 'craft'- the size of a tank – and triangular in shape, with a smooth surface, like glass. The fabric of the 'craft' was moulded like black glass, but opaque or misty. No landing gear was apparent, but it seemed like it was standing on fixed legs.

I walked around the 'craft' and finally walked right up to it and noticed it had an outer surface, consisting of what appeared to be smooth, opaque, black glass, with bluish lights fluctuating from black to grey, to blue. I was pretty much confused at this point. I kept trying to put this in some sort of perspective, hoping to find some logical explanation as to what it was and what was going on, against a background of silence – not even the noises of animals anymore. I felt like as if I was moving in slow motion. I had my notebook and camera with me, so began to make written notes of the object now in front of me, which was triangular in shape, with a top portion producing mainly white light, encompassing most of the upper section of the 'craft', with a small amount of white light spilling out of the bottom".

Statement continued

"After roughly 45 minutes the light from the 'craft' began to intensify. Burroughs and I then took a defensive position away from the 'craft' as it lifted off the ground, without any noise or air disturbance. It manoeuvred through the trees and shot off at an unbelievable rate of speed. It was gone in the blink of an eye. In my logbook (that I have right here) I wrote, Speed: IMPOSSIBLE. Over 80 Air Force Personnel, all trained observers assigned to the 81st Security

Sgt. James Penniston

Police Squadron, witnessed the take-off. The information acquired during the investigation was reported through military channels. The team and witnesses were told to treat the investigation as 'Top Secret' and no further discussion was allowed. **The photos we retrieved from the base lab (two rolls of 35 mm) were apparently over exposed.**

On its left side centre was a bluish light; the other side was red. The lights seem to be moulded into the exterior of the object, rather than any additional attachment, and were smooth, slowly fading into the rest of the outside of the structure of the 'craft'. I also made a point of memorizing as much detail as I could of the object in front of me, for what seemed like hours, but in fact was only minutes. Finally, I unleashed my camera case cover and brought the camera up to focus. I began snapping photo after photo, and took the full roll of 36 pictures."

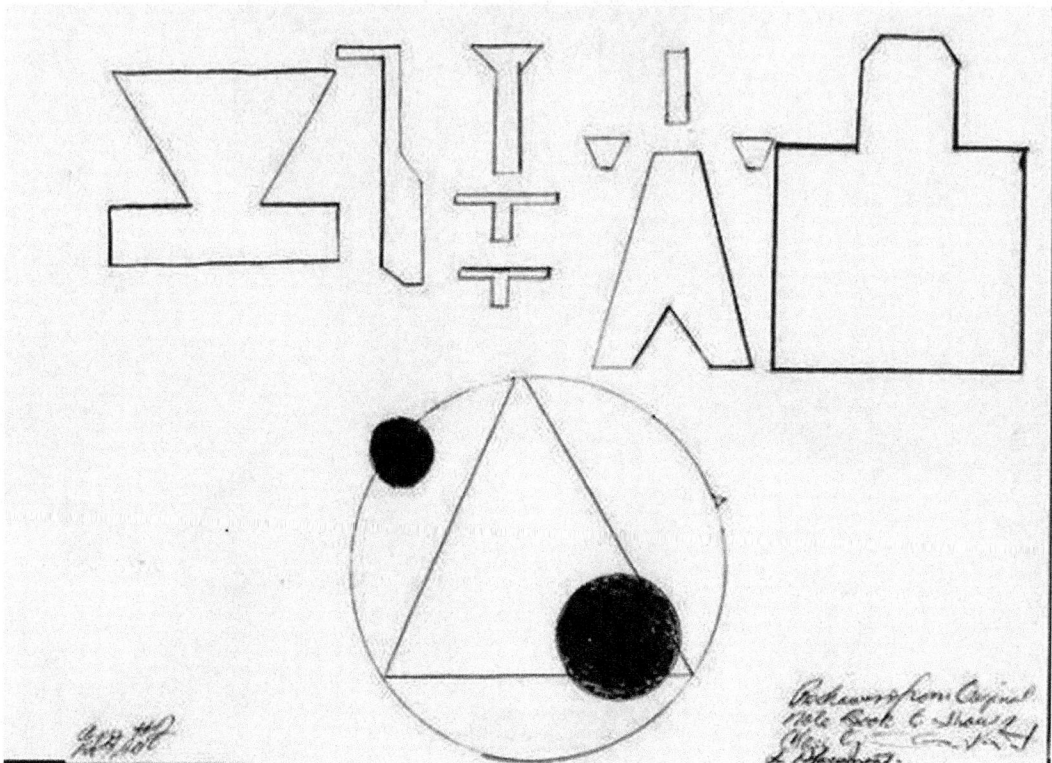

Symbols seen on the external surface

"On the 'craft's' smooth exterior shell there was writing of some kind, but I couldn't quite distinguish it, so I moved closer, seeing three-inch lettering, rather symbols, that stretched for the length of two feet – maybe a little more. I then proceeded to touch the object, but was only able to for a short time. I touched the symbols and I could feel the shapes, as if they were inscribed, or etched, or engraved like a diamond cut on glass. Suddenly, the white light on the object instantly grew brighter. John Burroughs and I jumped backwards in defence, and threw ourselves onto the floor for cover."

At the *National Press Club*, Washington D.C., in November 2007, as used in the documentary '*I know what I saw*', produced and directed by James Fox, Jim said:

> "*We completed a thorough on-site investigation, including a full physical examination of the 'craft'. This included photographs, notebook entries, and radio relays through airman Cabansag to the control centre, as required. On one side of the 'craft' were symbols that measured about three inches high and two and a half feet across. These symbols were pictorial in design; the largest symbol was a triangle, which was centred in the middle of the others. These symbols were etched into the surface of the 'craft', which was warm to the touch and felt like metal.*"

Ted Conrad refutes Jim's account – over 30 years later!

The *Daily Mail* (8.8.2011) published details of an interview, held between researcher Dr. David Clarke and Colonel Ted Conrad, with regard to Penniston and Burroughs' account, when they followed an unidentified light through the trees, which disappeared behind a low rise in the direction of a farmhouse.

Ted Conrad:

> "*There was no mention of an encounter, or a notebook. Penniston said he didn't get close enough for a detailed look.*"

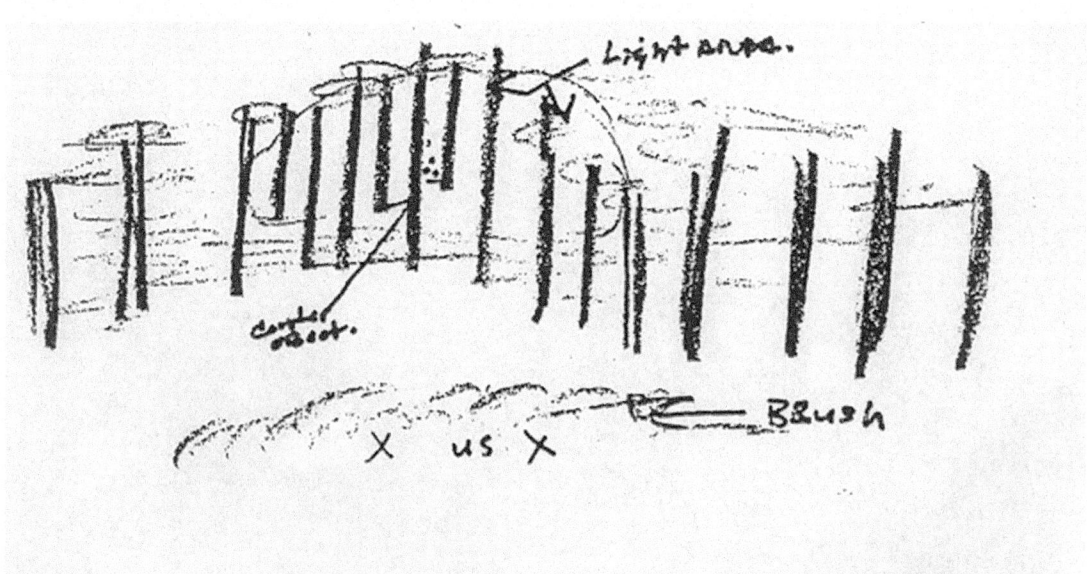

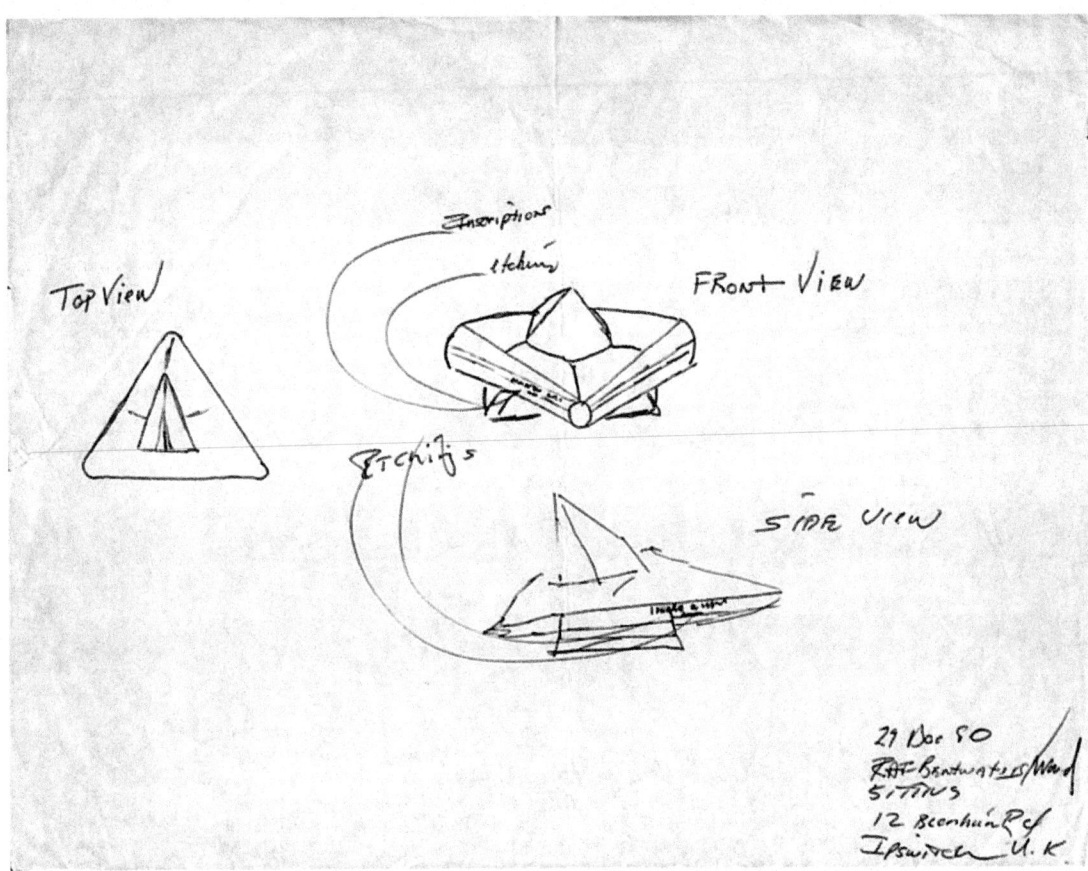

Binary code

Over 30 years later, Jim was to admit that during the encounter with the UFO, while running his hands over the exterior surface, he had experienced an extraordinary sensation when, while examining an etched or embedded circle with a large triangle running from top to bottom:

"...a stream of ones and zeroes ran relentlessly into my mind, obliterating my vision of the surroundings. I was scared, though I realised it was not harmful but required. I can't say how long this process occurred; the bright flashing light with the ones and zeroes, seconds or minutes, or even a brief moment. I found myself unable to pull my hand back, but finally it was released. As quickly as the release of my hand from the triangle so did the numbers stop. I checked my hand for damage – there was none.

The 'craft' then became bright again and began moving through the trees. It hovered at the top of the trees, before vanishing from sight."

These 16 pages were later the subject of examination by Professional Binary Code Expert Joe Luciano. This is what they revealed:

EXPLORATION OF HUMANITY – CONTINUOUS FOR PLANETARY ADVANCE – FOURTH CO-ORDINATE CONTINUOUS 'Time' is the fourth coordinate of (x, y, z, t).

Near the end of the message it says:

ORIGIN 52 0942532 N (north latitude) 1 3131269 W (west longitude) ORIGIN YEAR 8100.

These same "latitude, longitude, year" values were also given near the start of the message. Although two small parts of the message remain unclear, these three numbers seem to have been transmitted accurately, and can be relied upon to tell us where (or when) the UFO occupants come from.

In other words, the **Woodbridge UFO occupants seem to be time travellers from our distant future on Earth. They come from the year 8100 (possibly AD),** and from a latitude-longitude somewhere in **southern England**.

Next in the middle of the message we can see the word **'BEFORE',** along with six other sets of precisely defined latitudes or longitudes on Earth. No decimal points were encoded anywhere. Yet

1

01000101 01011000
01010000 01001100
01001111 01010010
01000001 01010101000
10010010 01001111000
1110 01001111 01000
111 01001000 010101
01010010 01010000 001
01001110 01010000 0104
01010100 01011001
00110011 00110011

00110011 00110000
00110001 00110000
00110000

all of those **'BEFORE'** co-ordinates show **six** digits past the decimal point in a self-consistent fashion. Two **'ORIGIN'** co-ordinates show **seven** digits past the decimal point, again in a self-consistent fashion. Another phrase is **'EYES OF YOUR EYES'**, which could be the assigned name for this scientific exploration effort. Perhaps a few time travellers have been sent back in time to see the past for 'themselves', while everyone else on Earth (6,000 years from now) will be watching their results?

Here is another example of strange writings following a claim of having been channeled by an aliens species according to Brenda Butler, a long term investigator of the UFO subject and prolific visitor to Rendlesham Forest Suffolk over the last 35 years!

1.13am on 11th August 2011 – Jim's response to Dr. David Clarke

"Thank you for indirectly posting something on this page. Good grief, I see that you have bitten off too much with this one . . . David some advice. Remember David, short dogs don't run through tall weeds. An old saying I have, and I think that it applies with you . . . The other piece of advice is: 'If you tell the truth, you don't have to remember anything.'

You must have forgotten about your emails where you said you did not have permission to publish Colonel Conrad's private letter. We are not upset with anyone. We are pretty used to the B.S. from the skeptics and naysayers . . . Let me remind you why we are a little disappointed about your lack of integrity.

I guess you have to stick with your story since you got caught telling something that was not true.

As for the Conrad letter that was written to you (original, unaltered) we are fine with it. We always have been . . . ever since its unauthorized publishing back in the fall of 2010.

Colonel Conrad was very supportive of us in the letter. He told as much as he could. I think everyone forgets the details of this incident are still classified and remain classified. So it restricts how much these officers can actually tell . . . He was somewhat hard with Halt though.

David we have many emails from you and others . . . I think the public would be shocked with the way you and others do business. We must think about making these public. That will be an eye opener for your paying public, I am sure.

As far as the extraordinary things, which have happened with us and Rendlesham, you will have to wait until we figure out a format for that release. Your first and biggest mistake is, **Rendlesham is not about UFOs (ET/Alien) and never was.**

David, let's bring these issues you claim on our page public . . . for everyone to hear and evaluate. How about an international radio or a national TV show. We will consist of John and I . . . and you can bring Colonel Conrad with you since you think you have some kind of relationship that transcends our military relationship with him, and what he has told us.

I think you would be very surprised what he would say if he actually went on the record. I personally would like Rob Simcox radio program to do it . . . Or we can go face-to-face in a television studio. The choice is yours. So let's arrange something, David. And as far as your childish comments of mob action and such, I think what you really mean is, I like to throw stones from the keyboard, but I can then retreat behind the keyboard at any time and hide, without being responsible for what I say . . . Keep in mind, we are only responding to disinformation which has been placed in British papers and the internet.

You don't have to remind us that this is the way you make your living . . . But, what we are saying, you're not going to publish rubbish and make money out of our situation by making things up and doctoring documents to meet your marketing needs . . . We will not allow it any more . . Jim."

Human beings from the future

Jim appears not to be suggesting that any military covert aircraft, satellite re-entries or downed Russian aircraft was what they encountered – but rather, visits by human beings from the future.

Georgina Bruni comments

Georgina made a reference to this matter on page 181 from her book – *You Can't Tell The People*.

"The most amazing part of the regression (1994) deals with an alien encounter at the scene of the incident. When asked about the possibility of being present, Penniston begins to talk about 'the visitors'. He describes them as being from our future – a dark and polluted world, with many difficulties. He explains that they are visiting in teams and each team is assigned a different task. Apparently, the teams know exactly which people they are to target when they arrive in our time. Penniston reveals that some of them are coming here to take sperm and eggs, which are necessary in order to help their species survive. It seems they have a serious problem with reproduction."

Could they be time travellers from the future?

Jim was asked about this in December 2010, bearing in mind his close proximity to the object and that he had undergone regression, and Jim reiterated:

"I believe the 'craft' is from the far off future and that it contained our distant descendants, returning as time travellers, to obtain genetic material to keep their ailing species alive."

Airman *Edward Cabansag

"On 26th December 1980, Staff Sgt. Penniston and I were on security duty at Woodbridge Base, when we received a call over the radio that Police 4 had seen some strange lights out past the East Gate and we were to respond. When we arrived at East Gate, Staff Sgt. Steffens and Airman Burroughs were on patrol. They told us they had seen some funny lights out in the woods. We notified Station Control and asked if we could investigate further; they gave us the go ahead.

We left our weapons with Staff Sgt. Steffens, who remained at the gate. We stopped the security police vehicle about 100 metres from the gate, and then set out on foot. We kept in constant contact with Control. While we walked, each of us would see the lights – blue, red, white and yellow. The beacon light turned out to be yellow light. We would see them periodically but not in a specific pattern.

As we approached the lights would seem to be at the edge of the forest. We were about 100 metres from the edge when I saw a quick movement; it looked visible for a moment. It looked like it spun left a quarter of a turn – then it was gone. I advised Staff Sgt. Penniston and Airman Burroughs.

---

*Edward Cabansag denies he typed the witness statement, which claims they were chasing a lighthouse beacon.

We advised Control and proceeded with extreme caution. When we got about 75/50 metres, Master Sgt. Chandler – Flight Chief – was on the scene. Control was not reading our transmission very well, so we used Master Sgt. Chandler as a go-between. He remained back at our vehicle. As we entered the forest the blue and red lights were not visible any more, only the beacon light was still blinking.

We figured the lights were coming from past the forest, since nothing was visible when we past through the woody forest. We could see a glowing near the beacon light, but as we got closer we found it to be a lit up farmhouse. After we had past through the forest, we thought it had to be an aircraft accident.

So did Control as well. But we ran and walked a good two miles past our vehicle, until we got to a vantage point where we could determine that what we were chasing was only a beacon light off in the distance. *Our route through the forest and field was a direct one straight towards the light. We informed Control that the light beacon was further than we thought, so they terminated our investigation. Airman Burroughs and I took the road, while Staff Sgt. Penniston walked straight back from where we had come from. Airman Burroughs saw the lights again; this time it was coming from the left of us. As we were walking back to our patrol vehicle, we got in contact with Staff Sgt. Penniston and we took a walk through where we saw the lights – nothing. Finally we made it back to the vehicle. We then met Master Sgt. Chandler and went into service again after termination of the sighting."*

3.45am on 26th December 1980 – Lt. Fred Buran terminates search

"At 3.45am, I terminated the search and ordered them back to the base. After talking with Staff Sgt. Penniston, face-to-face, I was convinced he saw something out of the realm of explanation. I found him to be a totally reliable and mature individual. Later that morning, I discovered there had been several others sightings."

After returning to the base, they were instructed to report to the shift Commander's office, and were told, according to John Burroughs:

"It is best you keep quiet about what you have just seen. You saw something. Heathrow tower confirms you saw something. You should go out and look for some physical proof of what happened."

Airman John Burroughs

"By the time we arrived, the lights were still in the sky above the woods. A security patrol turned up and we asked to go with them. After parking the truck we went on foot across an open field, when we heard what sounded like a woman screaming and many animal noises. The area was lit up with light. All three of us hit the ground when, whatever it was, started moving back towards the open fields. After a minute or two, we got up and moved into the trees and the lights moved out into the open field."

Now almost blinding the men with white light flooding out from the top, the object moved upwards off the ground, about 3 feet, and then silently started to move slowly, weaving back through the trees – maybe half a foot per second. Within a couple of minutes, it rose to a distance of about 200ft off the ground and, following a momentary pause, *'in the blink of an eye'*, was gone.

Object disappears from view

After the object had gone Burroughs and Penniston, dazed and confused from their encounter, became aware of everything returning to normal, seeing the lighthouse in the distance, and stars – almost as if time had slowed down while the experience had taken place.

Triangular marks discovered

As they walked back to the logging road, Burroughs noticed . . .

'. . . three triangular indentations in the forest floor, each about three metres apart, in the same place as the object was first sighted', and assumed 'it had been caused by the object sitting on the ground'.

After making a note of the three indentations, the two men continued on their way back to the base, where they met Cabansag and went back to the base. These marks were written off by the Police, later, as rabbit scratching.

"We found that just totally absurd. The ground was frozen and it was just impossible for that to happen."

4.11am on 26th December 1980 – Chris Arnold – 999 call to police made

At 4.11am on the 26th of December 1980 I telephoned the Suffolk Constabulary police reporting, some unusual lights in the sky. We have sent some unarmed troops to investigate. We are terming it as a UFO at present."

PC David King reports seeing strange lights

Police Constable David King and PC Martyn Brophy were posted to night duty and started at 10pm on the 25th December. If it was quiet, they would call in at RAF Bentwaters Law Enforcement Office Desk, normally between 2am and 5am.

"While we were there the security police telephoned through, reporting strange lights in the forest at East Gate, RAF Woodbridge. We were on the way there when we were redirected to Otley Post Office, after a report of a burglary in process. After arriving, we followed the security airmen in our police car into the forest, in an easterly direction, until the track stopped. We were then shown the direction in which other security personnel had gone on ahead of us, in search of the 'lights'.

We decided to make our way into the forest on foot, leaving the escorting airmen to return to base. We had no problems navigating our way through the forest, due to the lack of lower growth on the pine trees, which were close together. All we saw was a white flashing light in the distance, which I worked out was the Orford Lighthouse, and made our way back, where I noticed the airmen had all gone. I forgot about the incident until the next night, when I came on duty, at 10pm, and read through the logs for the day, when I came across a message, timed at 10am on 26th December 1980 (6 hours after our attendance) to the effect that the security police had returned to the forest and found marks in the ground, which could have been made by a UFO.

The 'message' indicated an officer from Woodbridge Police Station (PC Creswell) had attended and 'written-up' the log as, 'the indentations (marks) appeared to have been made by animals'.

I never gave the matter any further thought, until some years ago when I learnt about the book 'Sky Crash', and can only comment that I found it personally strange that the Deputy Commander was on base duty at the time, and that the security police went beyond their perimeter fence to investigate the matter before we arrived, taking into consideration the policy then in existence, being that they would always wait for us before venturing out into the forest, as this area was outside their jurisdiction. It was quite common for the English police officers to spend a lot of time on base. In fact, there was an office designated for their use on Bentwaters, specifically, as it was 'quite common' to call into the airbase at least once a night, to check if there were any matters that should be brought to their attention. I don't know what to make of the now well publicised incident. I never saw anything myself, although I did see some strange red lights, low on the horizon, near the village of Burstall. What it meant I don't know, but it was strange."

DAVID KING

TRIMLEY St MARY
FELIXSTOWE
SUFFOLK
IP11 :

TEL. 01394 .....

Dear JOHN.
A Reply to your letter to me about the UFO. sighting or sightings at Rendlesham Forest Near Woodbridge on 26th December 1980. and days to follow. I, like yourself Retired 3½ Years ago at 55 having served 26 years in the Suffolk Force. Most of the time in the Woodbridge area.

2

I will answer your questions first

'Yes' I did attend, with a young officer Martyn BROPHY He left the force a few years after the incident. (Nothing to do with the incident.) Martyn lived at Newmarket. I don't know what he is doing Now or where he is. I did Not sence any Mood of the USAF airmen, and we both felt we were on a "wild Goose chase." (I will explain later.) We never took any photographs because we never saw anything. and Never carried a camera anyway in those days. We were the only two officers on duty in the area at the time and "no one" else would have attended being Bank Holiday and as you know we were short of staff for 2 days.

THE INCIDENT.

(as far as I was concerned.)
Martyn and I were teamed up to cover the whole area of Woodbridge all very quiet, a clear and dry night. No wind.
Around 4am we were contacted by Headquarters to attend the "East Gate" entrance of RAF Woodbridge as strange lights were seen in the forest by security airmen.
We arrived and were escorted into the forest in a easterly

direction. We followed the security airmen in our vehicle until the track stopped.
We were then shown the direction in which other security airmen had gone off ahead of us in search of the strange lights.
We went on foot into the forest. The airmen who had taken us, must have gone back to base.
We walked for 15-20 minutes we could see quite clearly through the trees because fir trees close together do not have lower branches.
"All we saw was a white flashing light in the distance, which I worked out was "Orford Light House"

on the coast.
Being a Beach sea fisherman I have often seen and fished close to the Light House.
WE NEVER HEARD OR SAW ANYTHING ELSE. IT WAS QUIET AND CLEAR NIGHT. A STILL NIGHT
We made our way back to our vehicle. All other airmen had gone, there were no other vehicles to be seen. We went back to Woodbridge Police station, giving FHQ an update, who had in turn contacted Various airways and all said. No aircraft was or had been flying in the area.
I forgot about the incident.
Reporting back on duty at 10pm

that following evening. I checked through the logs for the day and found a message/log. timed at about 10.am 26/12/80 (6 hours after I attended) that the security Police on RAF Woodbridge had Returned to the forest and found Marks on the ground which could have been made by a UFO. Martin? Keller?
An officer from the Woodbridge Police station attend and Resulted the log. as, indentation's appeared to have been made by animals.
In the early hours of 27th December 1980. 2-3 am. Martyn and Myself called at. RAF Bentwaters Law enforcement Desk

as we normally did. (on night's) while there the security police of RAF Woodbridge contacted the law enforcement Desk stating strange Lights again in the forest. at East Gate RAF Woodbridge as we had Nothing better to do we decided to attend. Because Nothing was seen or heard 24 Hours previous I did not inform F.H.Q. that we were going. Before we arrived at RAF Woodbridge we received a call from our F.H.Q. of a 'Post office' being broken into (a burglary) at Otley which was in the opposite direction to RAF Woodbridge so we attended the burglary and

8.

finished our shift there. (6.am) The Next thing I knew about the incident was 4 or 5 years later when I was told about the book 'SKY CRASH' with contents about the UFO sighting in Rendlesham forest. In the book No one can make up their minds what Night is happened on. some say it happened on 2 or 3 nights.
I was interviewed by a Journalist 'HANK' (can not Remember his surname) from America about a year later and in 1995 I was interviewed by LWT (London Weekend T.V.) for their "Strange But True" programme I did not hear from either of them again. (I didn't say what they

9.

(wanted to hear I suppose.)

My comments about the incident. I found it strange that the Base Commander was on duty at the time and that security police from Base went beyond their perimeter fence to find out what it was, BEFORE we arrived. They never did before, they would always tell us and wait for us to arrive. even Col Halt's Report states 3 am on 27 December 1980. which it could have been because we were called on the second night at that time but were diverted as explained earlier.
I always found the americans

10.

quite a friendly lot but also found them stranger than the UFO. sightings. They even set up flood lights in the forest on the second night in case the UFO come back. so they could get a better look!! or so the book states. Perhaps I am strange.

I have enclosed a Paper cutting about the "Strange But True?" programme on T.V. 2 weeks ago. Did you see it?

Sorry I have gone on and on and my english is not perfect. or spelling. But I just write what I want to say.
                                    David King
anything else you want to Know? Ringo

The author's of *Haunted Skies* wrote to Dave King with further queries and he responded with answers shown in the letter shown below.

Suffolk Constabulary confirms knowledge of the incident

In November 1983, a letter sent to the Suffolk Constabulary, enquiring about their knowledge of the incident(s) was answered by the Chief Constable, Scott-Lee (who used to be John Hanson's shift Inspector at Acocks Green, Birmingham!)

"Police knowledge of this matter is limited to a telephone call of the alleged incident, timed at 4.11am on 26th December, and received from a person at RAF Bentwaters, together with the two subsequent visits to the location by police officers. The first visit followed immediately the reported incident and the two officers who attended made a search of the area, with a negative result. A note on the log indicates Air Traffic Control, at West Drayton, was contacted and that there was no known knowledge of aircraft in that area to coincide with the time of the sighting. Mention is also made on the log of reports received of aerial phenomena over southern England, during that night. The only lights visible to the officers visiting the incident were those from Orford Lighthouse."

Further visit to the forest – Plaster casts and photographs taken

Jim Penniston and John Burroughs went back into the forest to check for any evidence to support their story. Burroughs was hoping there would be nothing out there, but discovered what appeared to be scorch marks on the trees, along with branch damage and the three indentations which they had found earlier, so they decided to leave the area. Jim Penniston made his way to a friend's house, near Ipswich, and collected the necessary ingredients to make plaster casts, and made his way back to the forest, where he took plaster casts of the three indentations.

Site revisited – photographs taken

While he was doing this Major Drury, Mike Verrano and Ray Gulyas, accompanied by PC Brian Creswell, returned to the scene of the alleged 'landing site'. Ray took a number of photographs and handed the roll of film to Captain Verrano. Subsequently, Mike was later told that the photographs were fogged. Mike returned to the location, two days later, and took his own photos and plaster casts of the impressions (these were later written-off by the police officer as being rabbit scratching!)

According to Ray Gulyas, the width from each ground indentation was 12 feet centre to centre. The marks on the trees, as described by Monroe Nevel were found to be five feet off the ground.

Ray handed the film over to Richard Nunn, in early January 1981, who processed six photographs and gave them back to him.

In the spring of 1981, while returning to the US, the film negatives and plaster casts, mysteriously disappeared from Ray's personal possession. Georgina Bruni carried out some detective work and managed to obtain a contact strip of the six photographs from Richard's photographic files, in 1999; otherwise, there would be no photographs of the location.

One of those photographs shows a tall policeman (PC Brian Creswell) and Mike Veranno.

The landing site, according to Jim Penniston

A map drawn by James Penniston, endorsed 2am on 27th December 1980, identifies the route taken by vehicle from the security hut at East Gate, cutting across the Forestry Commission road, down track 12, where the vehicle stopped at the junction with track 10.

The occupants then made their way on foot along track 10 where, at a point midway between track 10 and 12, they headed away into the forest at an oblique angle for 150 yards, before coming across the UFO – a route confirmed by Colonel Halt.

5.30-5.45am on 26th December 1980 – Colonel Charles Halt visits Police Ops Centre

Charles Halt:

"Just before Christmas, in 1980, I was in the habit of going out and spending evenings riding around with the police, visiting the fire department, going to the dining hall, into the medics. Between 5.30am and 5.45am, on 26th December 1980, I happened to be visiting the Security Police Operations Centre, known as 'the Desk', pick up the 'blotters' for the previous 24-hour period – something I did if I happened to be out early and near the Police Station. The desk sergeant on that morning was Staff Sergeant 'Crash' McCabe. We called him 'Crash' for a very good reason – that's why he was on the 'Desk', instead of a patrol car. He said, 'Colonel, you're not going to believe this. Burroughs, Penniston, and Bustinza, were out in the woods last night, chasing a UFO'. I said, 'What?' We both had a chuckle. I said, 'Now, be more specific'. He replied, 'Well, the Lieutenant said (the Lieutenant being the Flight Commander for the evening, or that early morning shift) he didn't put it in the blotter'. I said, 'What happened? You got to put something in the blotter'. He said, 'I know they saw some lights, and something happened out there, and they think they saw something." I knew Jim Penniston was very credible . . . John Burroughs probably so. I didn't know Bustinza, so I said, 'Well, why don't you just put in the blotter that they saw some lights in the forest', and, uh, I got a chuckle out of it and didn't think too much about it. I picked up the blotters and went up to the office and read through them. Didn't see anything else too exciting in there, shared them with my boss, and we kind of had a chuckle – UFOs in the woods, oh great – and didn't think too much more about it."

10.13am on 26th December 1989 – Police called regarding 'landing marks' found

A further report was received at 10.13am on 26th December 1980, from a staff member at RAF Bentwaters, indicating that a place had been found where a 'craft' of some sort could have landed – two miles east of East Gate, at Bentwaters.

Fred Buran then awoke Major Edward Drury, who was deputy Squadron Commander to the more senior Major Malcolm Zickler and explained what had occurred.

Charles Halt debriefs the airmen

"I interviewed the three young airmen individually, who were involved in the incident, at the Base Commander's office, and obtained statements from them. Basically, what they said was that Airman John Burroughs was patrolling Woodbridge Base, as was one other patrol. We normally kept two patrols, Police 4 and Police 5, Law Enforcement type, on Woodbridge Base, and three on Bentwaters Base, due to it being a little larger base – more aircraft – and he had to do hourly, or semi-hourly, whatever it was, checks at the back gate and was going out to the East Gate, to check it for security, bearing in mind it was a combination lock, but sometimes the combination would be 'leaked', and people would take a short cut.

He went out and rattled the gate – it was locked – when he noticed something out in the woods. John Burroughs reported having seen some red, green, blue and white, lights in the woods, about 300 yards out, so I called back to Law Enforcement and said 'It looks like there's been a crash – looks like an airplane, probably a helicopter's gone down'. The Law Enforcement Desk Sergeant – Sergeant McCabe – immediately responded. He called our Woodbridge and Bentwaters control tower, but they were both down. Although there was manning there, they just weren't up and operational. They both said the same thing, 'There's nothing flying in the vicinity'.

Penniston can describe to this day the hieroglyphic-like symbols he saw on the side of the object that appeared to be raised – sort of like they were burned on with a welding rod, or something. The Master Sergeant is pretty smart. He says, 'Well, I'm not going out there. How about three, or four, of you guys go out there and see what happened? Check your weapons with me', so J.D. Chandler takes the weapons; bearing in mind you don't carry a gun in England. Penniston and Burroughs, and Bustinza, troop out into the woods. They go down the forest service road, turn on a kind of a trail, and go up in the pines and actually approach something, describing it as 'approximately nine feet in length on the side, triangular in appearance, with a tripod-like set of legs, showing various coloured lights.

Some five hours after the sighting, I informed my Commanding Officer about having seen 'red and white lights flying up into the trees, over the forest'. He then said, 'Let's go and see if we can find any physical proof of what is happening' and, following a visit into the forest, we found damage to the trees and three depressions in the ground, forming a triangle, measuring 3.4 metres between each depression."

Plaster casts taken on the impressions

"Jim Penniston made three plaster casts of the impressions found in the ground without telling anyone he had them, until someone stole one of them from his luggage while going through customs. I gave him another one, which he buried at the bottom of his garden in the States. They didn't get mine, though. I did have some tests carried out on them by Melissa Tittl, a producer and actress known for 'Hanger 1: The UFO Files' in 2010, but nothing untoward was found. The program turned out to be, despite promises, more entertainment that factual.

Soon after the incident, Jim Penniston asked me if he could be transferred to another base, as he was shaken after the event.

John Burroughs, who had been far more affected by the earlier UFO sighting, stayed out in the forest for days, waiting for the UFO to return. I sent out blankets and food to Burroughs, but he didn't accept them."

Major Edward Drury

Major Drury:

"I was in the shift commander's office, but not technically on duty at the time, when some of them were making statements; there was a pile of them, because I recall going through some of them. On reading the statements, I understood that it was a very big object – bigger than a Mini. There were marks in the trees quite high up, and someone said they had walked up to the object and it had left depressions. I went out the next day and saw the marks on the trees and the ground depressions, which weren't that deep, and I suggested we send someone to do some Geiger counter readings."

Charles Halt:

> *"None of the original statements given to me were classified. In fact, nothing I know of was classified. I do more than suspect there was a lot of 'behind the scenes' investigation that was classified, but I was never privy to that."*

STATEMENTS

J.D. Chandler's typed, signed statement, dated 2nd January 1981

In a signed typed statement dated the 2nd January 1981, J.D. Chandler had this to say:

"At approximately 3am on 26th December 1980, while conducting security checks on RAF Bentwaters, I monitored a radio transmission from Airman Burroughs, Law Enforcement patrol on RAF Woodbridge, stating he was observing strange lights, just beyond the access road leading from the East Gate at RAF Woodbridge. Staff Sgt. Security Advisor Penniston was contacted and directed to contact Burroughs at the East Gate. Upon arrival Staff Sgt. Penniston immediately notified CSC that he, too, was observing these lights and requested to make a closer observation. After several minutes, Penniston requested my presence.

*I departed RAF Bentwaters through Butley gate for RAF Woodbridge. When I arrived, Staff Sgt. Penniston, Airmen Burroughs and Cabansag, had entered the wooded area just beyond the clearing up the access road. We set up a radio relay between me, Staff Sgt. Penniston, and CSC. **On one occasion Penniston relayed that he was close enough to the object to determine that it was definitely a mechanical object**. He stated that he was within approximately 50 metres. He also stated that there were lots of loud noises in the area, which seemed to be animals running around. Each time Penniston gave me the indication that he was about to reach the area where the lights were, he would give an extended estimate location. He eventually arrived at a 'beacon light'. However, he stated that this was not the light or lights he had originally observed. He was instructed to return. While en route out of the area he reported seeing lights almost in direct pass where they had passed earlier. Shortly after this, they reported that the lights were no longer visible.*

Staff Sgt. Penniston returned to Woodbridge. After talking to the three of them, I was sure they had observed something unusual.

At no time did I observe anything from the time I arrived at RAF Woodbridge.

Signed, J.D. Chandler [Mr Chandler denies signing this document]

Georgina Bruni – regarding the statements taken

In 2002, Georgina Bruni had this to say about the authenticity of the statements taken from the airmen, some of which are not countersigned – others not signed by the witness

> *"According to the Deputy Base Commander of OSI for Bentwaters, such typewritten statements would not be regarded as official; only handwritten statements were deemed acceptable in order to avoid potential fraud."*

She cites Lieutenant Fred Buran's *'fact and fiction'* statement and points out that, although his signature appears real, he never read it but just signed it – which seems a strange thing to do, unless you are being coerced or threatened, and can only be speculation at this stage. Georgina also revealed to the audience (and to us, in conversation during her visits to the Forest with Brenda) that Jim Penniston told her that he had seen *"alien life forms, transparent and human looking"* and he was positive Lt. Colonel Halt had communicated with the aliens by using telepathy.

Fred Buran's statement

Fred was later interviewed in Building 679 at RAF Bentwaters, on 2nd January 1981, and had this to say in his typed-up statement:

> *"I do hereby and voluntarily and of my own free will make the following statement without having been subjected to any coercion, unlawful influence, or unlawful inducement."*
> [Very odd caption]

Original typed statement of James Penniston

*"My name is James Penniston, United States Air Force, retired. In 1980, I was assigned to the largest Tactical Fighter Wing in the Air Force, RAF Woodbridge in England. I was the senior security officer in charge of base security. At that time I held a top secret US and NATO security clearance and was responsible for the protection of war-making resources for that base. Shortly after midnight on 26th December 1980, Staff Sergeant Steffens briefed me that some lights were seen in Rendlesham Forest, just outside the base. He informed me that whatever it was didn't crash…it landed. I discounted what he said and reported to the control centre back at the base that we had a possible downed aircraft. I then ordered Airman Cabansag, AIC Burroughs to respond with me. When we arrived near the suspected crash site it quickly became apparent that we were not dealing with a plane crash or anything else we'd ever responded to. There was a bright light emanating from an object on the forest floor. As we approached it on foot, a silhouetted triangular craft, about 9 feet long by 6.5 feet high, came into view. The craft was fully intact sitting in a small clearing inside the woods. As the three of us got closer to the craft we started experiencing problems with our radios. I then asked Cabansag to relay radio transmissions back to the control centre. Burroughs and I proceeded towards the craft. When we came up on the triangular- shaped craft there were blue and yellow lights swirling around the exterior, as though part of the surface, and the air around us was electrically charged. We could feel it on our clothes, skin and hair. Nothing in my training prepared me for what we were witnessing. After ten minutes, without any apparent aggression, I determined the craft was non hostile to my team or to the base. Following security protocol; we completed a thorough on-site investigation, including a full physical examination of the craft. **This included photographs, notebook entries,** and radio relays through Airman Cabansag to the control centre as required. On one side of the craft were **symbols that measured about three inches high and two and a half feet across.** These symbols were pictorial in design; **the largest symbol was a triangle,** which was centered in the middle of the others. **These symbols were etched into the surface of the craft, which was warm to the touch and felt like metal. The feeling I had during this encounter was no type of aircraft that I've ever seen before."*

Authenticity of this statement in question

Jim Penniston was asked about the typed statement (as shown on previous page) which was believed to be part of the file of alleged witness statements officially submitted for Lieutenant Colonel Charles I. Halt, in January 1981.

"My statement was handwritten; if the one you have is typed, then it was not done by me. The statement seems original in content. However, the original was not typed. I think Charles Halt summarised the statement."

Some people have remarked on the difference between this apparent original version of events and the more up-to-date statement tended by him; an example being one which was submitted for the *National Press Club*, Washington D.C., in November 2007, as used in the documentary *I know what I saw*, produced and directed by James Fox.

Jim Penniston ordered to report to the AFOSI

In *New Alien Mysteries*, as shown on *Sky*, in 2013, Jim Penniston tells of receiving a telephone call after his UFO sighting, to report to OSI. During a subsequent interview he was then directed by them to write down a full account, leaving nothing out. After this was done, Jim handed over his statement which was then taken away. They returned some ten minutes later and handed Jim a typed copy, prepared from his written statement, which only contained about a quarter of the account put down on paper.

He asked them for the rest of it and, although he says he did not like the situation, signed it after stating that *"OSI operate outside the chain of normal command. Orders are orders – that's how it worked"*.

Underwent hypnosis

In 1994, Jim underwent hypnosis. From those sessions he learnt there was more to the UFO encounter than first thought, and that he was given sodium pentothal by the OSI officers during the interrogation. We are not saying that Jim or John is guilty of any fabrication – far from it; we have the greatest respect for them. However, we have some misgivings about the reliability of this evidence, gained through regression techniques rather than direct memory after the event.

There is no denying something highly unusual took place, involving what appears to be close encounters with unidentified flying objects, over some nights running – this is not in issue. However, accounts of binary code, along with stories of lost cities and visitors from the future, seem to have more in common with a Hollywood science fiction film than reality – or do they?

While it would be easy to dismiss Jim's claims as *confabulation, we should not do so until we can prove otherwise, especially bearing in mind that Brenda Butler has also claimed of having received messages and binary code, telepathically, during her visits to the forest since the early 1980s.

---

*Confabulation is a memory disturbance, defined as the production of fabricated, distorted or misinterpreted memories about oneself, or the world, without the conscious intention to deceive. Confabulation is distinguished from lying as there is no intent to deceive and the person is unaware the information is false. Although individuals can present blatantly false information, confabulation can also seem to be coherent, internally consistent, and relatively normal. Individuals who confabulate present incorrect memories, ranging from subtle alternations to bizarre fabrications, and are generally very confident about their recollections, despite contradictory evidence.

Charles Halt:

They contacted Wattisham Air Defence sector

"They contacted Wattisham Air Defence sector, and asked them if they had any knowledge of anything happening in the Bentwaters area, but were told nothing. Similarly, the same response was obtained from ATC London, Heathrow. In the meantime, Police 4 comes up and joins John Burroughs, and he sees it, so he calls back. About this time, the security patrol – the people that guard the airplanes – Jim Penniston, comes up. He and several other law enforcement people, including the Flight Chief Master said they had come very close to it."

Stories become confused

"At this point, their stories become somewhat muddled. They are not really sure whether they were onboard, whether they touched it, or exactly what happened. We do know they were out there for probably three to four hours – in fact, to the point where people were very, very, concerned on the base as to what happened to them. Burroughs thinks he may have been onboard, or so he has told me. They didn't tell me this initially, by the way, they were very secretive. They were concerned it was going to affect their military career, as we all were. They managed to find their way back onto the base, after claiming the 'craft' levitated and went off at a high speed. They made their way back onto the base, just prior to shift change, which would have been around four or five o'clock in the morning. Nobody knew quite what to do, so the Lieutenant, the Flight Lieutenant, decided nothing would happen – there would be no entries, although there was an entry made in the Law Enforcement Blotter at my insistence."

What happened to the Security blotter?

"I don't know what was entered in the Security blotter, because when I went back a year-and-a-half or two years later, to try and recover from the archives both the Security blotter (the record of what happened that night) and the Law Enforcement blotter, were gone. Somebody had picked them up – I suspect one of the individuals involved in the incident, probably, or a curiosity seeker, or somebody I don't know. I don't think it was an act on the part of any agency, or anything of that nature, because at that time it was pretty secretive. It didn't really get too far out, other than the base. Later that day, I started getting all sorts of reverberations from the Police Squadron or various agencies on the base about this UFO, and wondered if there was something to this. I still didn't think too much about it. It was just before Christmas and there was a lot of activity. Quite a few people were on vacation back to the States and off on the Continent."

John Burroughs

In an interview held in 1990, John described the object as:

"…a bank of lights; differently coloured lights that threw off an image of, 'like a craft'. (Other reports refer to an object showing a bank of blue lights on it). I never saw anything metallic, or anything hard. Everything seemed like it was different when we were in that clearing. The sky didn't seem the same … it was like a weird feeling, like everything seemed slower than you were actually doing, and all of a sudden, when the object was gone, everything was like normal again. To be honest, I was hoping when I got out there, after reporting it, that basically I would see nothing – there would be no tell-tale evidence of anything which would make it easier for me to accept, but when you get out there and you find damage to the trees and depressions in the ground, that makes it even more unexplainable."

John Burroughs – In an interview with UFO researcher Philip Mantle

During another interview with UFO researcher Philip Mantle, John Burroughs says the incident lasted between 3am and was finished by 5 or 6am, and that he only went into the forest twice.

"I did not hear any rumours or conversations the next day about the incident, as I lived off base. I was not officially told to keep quiet, threatened, interrogated, or that I could not talk about what had transpired. People have accused us of telling lies and then they tell us that it was this or that. We were hung out to dry."

In 2010, John Burroughs said:

"Now that I have had a chance to look at things, I have a funny feeling that what went on was to do with some sort of military testing."

Early evening of 26th December – UFO seen by motorists

During the early evening, Mr Gavin Harold was one of four witnesses who were in a car being driven between Thetford and Diss, when they saw a bright white *'light'* among the stars.

Gavin Harold

"It became evident that it was descending. It then changed from a constant bright white, to flashing lights of differing colours. It then hovered silently, approximately 100 feet above our now stationary car, for around 10 seconds, before departing vertically at high speed. This was the same night as the now famous events which were reported at Rendlesham, 20 miles south-east of our position."

(Source: WWW Internet/Personal Interview)

Evening of 26th December – USAF blocks road, orders civilians to leave!

In the evening of Boxing Day 1980, local resident – Graham Tilt – was having a drink at Woodhall – formerly an Elizabethan priory (now the Manor house Hotel).

"I was in the bar with Barry Rey, who owned the place. He went over to open the window (as it was getting hot) to let some air into the room, when we both saw a strange bright white 'light' fly silently across the sky. Barry said to me, 'How strange, there is no noise. I'm going to go and have a look'. He then drank up and went one way, while I went the other.

I made my way toward the direction of Felixstowe, and diverted off towards the Woodbridge Airbase. When about two miles along the Brawdy road, near to the communications centre, I was stopped from driving further by armed members of the USA Police, who told me, 'There has been an incident'. I then turned around and drove away. What amazed me was what on earth they could be doing outside the airbase. After all, they had no jurisdiction on English soil, and surely would not have been allowed off base."

(Source: Personal interview)

9-10pm on 26th December – UFO display witnessed over Ipswich by family

Wayne Burgess (12) and his family were in Bennett Road, near Ipswich, when they spotted half-a-dozen mysterious *'lights'* in the sky over Ipswich.

Wayne:

"I have never heard of another account from anyone else that resembles mine; however this is 100% accurate, as I was quite excited about it at the time. The one thing I am not certain about is the number of 'lights' that were there (5, 6 or 7) but I can say that they were individually moving, just slightly enough to know that they weren't part of the same object."

The family watched the *'lights'* – which showed an aura around them – for about 5-10 minutes and appeared to be individually moving across the sky, at a very slow speed. After a while, the family decided to move on, and left – the lights still slowly moving across the sky. It was later suggested that Wayne and his family could have seen meteors, or a satellite, re-entering the atmosphere.

Wayne rejects this as an explanation and said:

"I remember after the sighting, when the newspapers were released after Christmas, my father saying that he had read a report in the Press of a meteor shower. However the lights in the sky that I saw, although slightly moving, stayed in the same position in the sky whilst we stood and watched them. Although I understand it is always a temptation to connect it with something mysterious, I do not believe, in my humble opinion, that this is what I saw. These lights/objects did not have fiery tails, as a meteor or a burning-up satellite would do – only a slight haze around each 'globe of light'. Additionally, the meteors were only reported to have been visible on the <u>25th December, not the 26th in this case</u>. I did not realise until several years later, whilst reading an account of famous UFO sightings in the Sunday Times Magazine in the UK (during

the high profile Roswell case) that this was connected to the famous Rendlesham Forest sighting. I had, on several occasions, recounted my story to friends and was quite excited that, at last, my sighting coincided with an official UK mystery in print".

11pm on 26th December 1980 – Gerry Harris – Three strange lights over the airbase

Gerry Harris was then living in a house situated in the centre of Rendlesham Forest, overlooking the twin bases of RAF Bentwaters and RAF Woodbridge. At 11pm on 26th December, he happened to look out of the window and notice some unusual lights in the sky.

"The lights were going at a nice steady speed and were moving about in the sky. I walked out into the front yard and stood watching them. I couldn't hear any sounds at all. They were bobbing up and down, and moving from side to side; they continued to move about in this manner for three-quarters of an hour when, all of a sudden, they disappeared. However, just before they disappeared, there was a lot of activity on the base. I could hear vehicles driving about, and see flashing lights of vehicles moving about, and people shouting. I could hear their voices calling to each other, which at that time of night was unusual."

A few days later, he visited Rendlesham Forest and spoke to some of the Forestry Commission workers. They told him an area of trees had been felled and that there was an area contaminated with radiation, which he must stay away from.

Gerry Harris seen here with his wife in 1983.

In an interview conducted, he said:

"What I can't understand is that there were three objects in the sky. I must have looked away, because then there was only one. Whether they combined, I can't say – I got a bit fed up watching them. The bigger one in the middle descended down behind the trees. I thought to myself it's crashed. All of a sudden it came back up and rose into the sky until I lost sight of it. After hearing all the noise from the base I went down to have a look and found a military policeman there, standing next to a uniform civilian Police Constable. They wouldn't let me on to base. I had customers come to my garage afterwards, to pick up their cars; some of them were base personnel. I asked them what the hell had gone on at the base that night. One of them told me 'It's more than my life to talk about it.'"

A few days afterwards, Gerry noticed that a large area of trees in the nearby woods had disappeared almost overnight

Trees were radioactive!

When he asked a forester who called into the garage what had happened, he was shocked by the answer – *"The trees were radioactive; they had to go."*

11pm on 26th December – USAF blocks road and orders civilians away!

Another witness was the landlord of the *Ramshott Arms* Public House, Ramshott, near Woodbridge, who was driving on the outskirts of Woodbridge at 11pm on 26th December 1980, on his way home after collecting his wife and children from Butley.

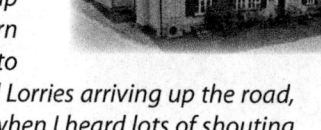

"As I came up the road, past the Butley Oyster Public House, I could see lights across the trees, over Rendlesham. Curious as to the cause, I turned up the forestry road and saw trucks and jeeps, with men getting out of them. I thought it was an Exercise and carried on up the road. A security guard then stopped me and ordered me to turn around and leave. I asked him what was going on. He refused to answer, and again ordered me to leave. I noticed more jeeps and Lorries arriving up the road, and drove away, but decided to park up at the side of the road, when I heard lots of shouting and saw bright lights over the forest. After about ten minutes, I decided to go home."

(Source: Brenda Butler)

11pm on 26th December – Strange lights seen

Travelling salesman Arthur Smekle, from Essex, was driving past Woodbridge Airbase when he noticed an object in the sky, heading low down towards the direction of Rendlesham Forest.

"I first thought it was an aircraft, but the lights were unlike anything I had ever seen before; they were both extensive and brilliant. I stopped my van to get a closer look but it went out of view, behind trees."

(Source: *Sky Crash*, page 87)

11.30pm on 26th December – Triangular-shaped UFO seen

At 11.30pm on 26th December 1980, Capel St. Andrew resident, Gary Collins – a builder working on upgrading the Bawdsey underground facility before being employed on building bunkers at RAF Bentwaters, where short-range nuclear weapons were kept, and who had also met Gladys Knight and Quincy Jones – was heading home, at 11.30pm, after drinking at the *Swan* in Alderton, when he saw 'lights' moving across the sky.

Gary stopped at Lions Corner, Capel Green, and parked up.

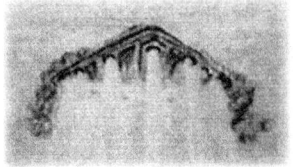

"It was intensely bright, like daylight, almost as if the area had been lit up with powerful floodlights. I heard a faint humming sound and looked up to see what appeared to be a 30 feet object, hovering about 60 feet above me. I can only describe its underside, which seemed to be triangular-shaped, black in colour but dripping liquid – like fluid dripping off it. That's the thing I remember – like melted ice.

Suddenly it went at an angle, slowly, then took off at tremendous speed and seemed to crash into the forest. I wish I had gone after it, but at the time I was so stunned. I went home and told my mother I had seen a UFO, but she thought I was drunk. I'm interested in planes – that's why I knew it was a UFO."

(Source: Georgina Bruni)

11.45pm on 26th December 1980 – Hull UFO sighting – RAF Woodbridge later notified!

During an interview with the secretary of Colonel Richard Spring – Chief of Base Operations & Training, at Woodbridge/Bentwaters – Georgina Bruni was told of a visit made by Hull police officers, with regard to a UFO incident under investigation by them, and that Colonel Richard Spring had himself gone to the railway station to pick up the officers.

Initially, we were puzzled why the Hull police should have contacted Colonel Richard Spring about any UFO incident which occurred hundreds of miles away from them. If it had been the end of December 1980, or early January 1981, one would be bound to query how the Hull police could have known what happened outside the airbase, as this was not readily known to the public until publication of the *News of the World* article, in 1983.

We now believe the visit by the Hull police officers was as a result of a UFO incident which took place at Ganstead, near Hull, during early January 1981. It involved members of the local CB Radio – the *'Hull Citizens Band'* – who, after hearing of the incident through eavesdropping on police transmissions, involving a landed UFO, made their way to the location concerned. Details of the incident were subsequently published in the *Hull Star*, on 16th January 1981.

In 2001, Humberside Police Officer P.C. Darren Parr, and Andy McCartney – members of the *Hull UFO Society* – decided to conduct their own investigations into the matter, following information received from local boxing coach, Michael Bromby.

Claim that police officers suffered trauma

We retraced their journey in 2013, and spoke to Mike Bromby (Senior), who told us of a conversation held with Peter – then a serving police officer – about two police officers known to him that had been directed to the UFO incident. As a result of what they had witnessed, it was alleged that the woman officer suffered some trauma. Both of them were warned never to discuss the matter again.

Mike Bromby:

"Peter told me of a cover-up involving the army, who had driven onto the Ganstead site and cleared the whole area. Two officers that were in attendance were warned to keep silent."

Andy told us that, following his original enquiries, he was able to determine that one of the CB enthusiasts was a Shaun Moxon. Obviously his information, like that of the two police officers, was vital. We knew that other accounts identified the location as being off the A165 at Skirlaugh, Hull. Unfortunately, we were unable to trace Shaun initially, but hoped, as time went on, that he would contact us,as we suspected, this was the reason for the Hull police officers' visit to Bentwaters Airbase sometime during the early 1980s. Ironically, this was not the only report made of UFO activity for the end of December 1980.

Mike Bromby

On 26th December 1980, Andrew McCartney (19) from Hull, East Yorkshire, was on his way home at about 11.30pm, after having visited the Wellington Club, which was a popular nightclub catering for people with an interest in punk rock music.

Andy:

"I'm the lad with the short black hair, dark black and blue stripy pants, shouting. Think I have a red and white scarf on, on the left, front. I had drunk a couple of bottles of beer and decided to take a short cut home. Approximately 15 minutes later, I saw what I thought initially was a large, bright white marquee, or dome tent, with what looked like a dry ice machine at its base, on the ground in Waterloo Street Park, next to a children's play area, close to a concrete tube. It was about 20ft across. I lit a cigarette near the tube, which was a drainage tube – probably put there for the kids to play in. My first impression was that someone had put it up for a party. It was very icy on the ground. I slipped over and fell on my back. I then realised that this was no tent or marquee; there was a strange eerie silence about. It was very white and bright inside – too bright to see anything, other than what I thought was a long table type thing."

Next recollection being at home

"That's all I remembered until the next morning when I woke up on the settee, hearing my mum shout my name 'Andrew'! My mum was standing in front of me. I was laid on her living room sofa, and she was pointing at my lack of attire! I still had my leather jacket on, though my T-shirt

was back to front. My brand new black, canvass Levi's were gone, as were my undergarments. How the hell had this happened? My calf length Para boots were still on, and laced right up. It would have been impossible to remove the skintight jeans without removing the boots first.

All I was concerned about was my missing Levi's; they had cost me a tenner! Also embarrassed at being found that way, I told my mum I had walked home like that for a bet (The alternatives were not an option for me). For years after that, at family gatherings, now and then, someone would utter 'Remember when you walked home naked for a bet?' I eventually forgot about that strange Christmas night, until a friend mentioned an event at an airbase in Suffolk."

Sean Tierney – Hull UFO Society

Sean Tierney

"I met up with Sean Tierney – now a good friend of mine, who runs HUFOS (Hull UFO Society) – who is neither a doubter nor a believer, but a very well-respected nice man. I read a lot about the incident at Rendlesham Forest and the more I read about it, I began to wonder why it seemed familiar. My dear mum said, quite matter of fact to me, 'Didn't you have something strange happen to you that Christmas week?'

The walking home naked bit surfaced again, and I said 'Mum, I didn't walk home like that' ... and it all came back to me in a flash – the tent, my hair standing on end, the fierce nosebleeds in 1981, the unexplained mark on my thigh that has never faded! Part of me thought there must be a rational answer to what I had experienced. Surely incidents like this only happened in science fiction comic books, not real life. Perplexed and unsure of how to deal with this and progress forward, I spoke to Larry Warren and felt that some of what he experienced felt very similar."

In early August 2013, we spoke to Sean Tierney – a highly respected UFO/paranormal researcher – about the incident, bearing in mind his experience within the field of UFO research and personal knowledge of Andrew (who was an old school friend). Sean agreed with us that there was no reason to dispute the authenticity of Andrew's encounter and that he had been a regular at their meetings.

Police Constable Darren Parr

Andy:

"After listening to my account, Sean introduced me to my good friend – Darren Parr – then a police constable, who agreed to assist me in conducting further research. We ascertained the archives containing Humberside police records for the year 1980 were stored at the 'Beverley' archive. We visited them and Darren produced his warrant card and requested the 'general notes files' for December 1980. The usher politely agreed and produced a dusty folder, adorned with a ribbon. He then asked, 'Are you wanting to look at these in a professional or private capacity?' Darren answered, 'Private'. The file was immediately withdrawn. He was told that if he wanted the file, he would need permission from above." (We emailed the Beverley Archive, in 2013, asking if they could confirm they were in possession of such a document. They told us that no such file existed.)

Colonel Richard Spring, of RAF Bentwaters, receives a visit from the Hull Police

Was this the UFO report that sparked off a visit by the Police to see Colonel Richard Spring, at RAF Bentwaters? If so, then it is clear that someone took the UFO sighting in the forest very seriously, to the extent of arranging a subsequent interview with him.

Was it possible that the Police took far more interest in what happened than they will ever tell?

Charles Halt:

> *"The last I knew of Dick Spring, he was back to flying as a Navigator with AWACS at Tinker AFB, in Oklahoma City.*
>
> *I think he retired there. I'll try and find out more."*

27th December 1980

12.10am (approx) on 27th December – three rotating lights seen over the forest

Lori Buoen was on 'D' Flight guard duty at the Woodbridge East Gate, and remembers Base Commander "Ted Conrad bringing Christmas dinner to her and other members of the night shift.

"While looking north over the Rendlesham Forest, from the small wooden East Gate guard shack in which I was standing, just after midnight on the 27th December 1980, I noticed a large, orange-red 'ball' of fiery light; it resembled three handfuls of coloured fire put together, as they flew through the sky – not blinking, but rotating – over towards RAF Woodbridge Control Tower, on my left, about a mile from the East Gate guard shack. It was heading in a straight north

direction across the dark flight line above Rendlesham Forest, before descending slowly into the forest. At the east end of the runway was a UK residence, called Folly House. About six miles straight east was the Orford Ness Lighthouse. This fiery sphere was in front of me on the north side of the runway, above the woods, where there is nothing but darkness from the trees, and, as I said before, the light just slowly disappeared (into the trees)."

(Source: Personal interview)

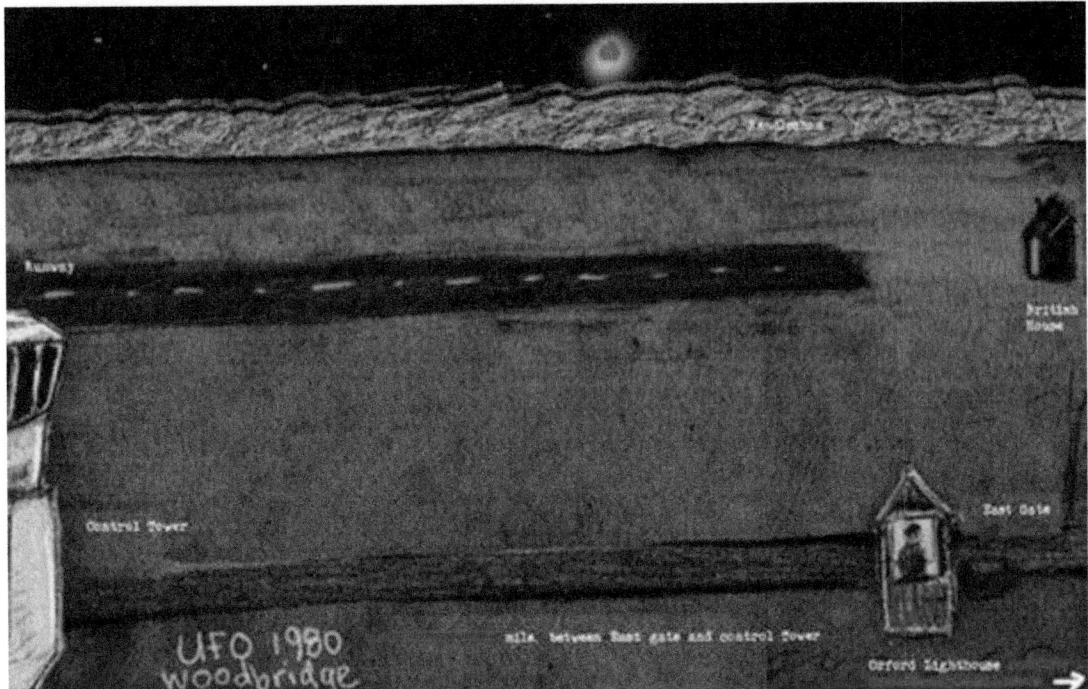

Police Lt. Bonnie Tamplin sights UFO in forest

This incident was brought to the attention of personnel from 'D' Flight, including desk Sergeant John Trementozzi, who made their way into the forest in time to see red, green, and white lights, which would appear at one location and then reappear at another point, indicating some sort of UFO display was taking place rather than anything orchestrated by human hands. However, this can only be speculation. In addition to this, Lori remembers a radio conversation held between security Police Lt. Bonnie Tamplin, Master Sergeant Bobby Ball, and others, talking on air, during the same shift.

"From the way in which radio protocol was broken, they were frightened and calling each other by first names, such as 'Bob Bob', where are you? I remember wishing I had brought a cassette tape, so I could have recorded it. I found out that Bonnie had gone out into the woods to see what the lights were and her vehicle quit running. Some kind of blue light flew through her vehicle. She totally lost her composure and was so upset they sent her home for the evening."

She was not the only one; apparently Bobby Ball was also to suffer some stress as a result of his experience – bad enough to seek medical assistance from a local hospital.

*"All I know about*Bonnie Tamplin is that she lives in Italy. If only I could find Joy Harper. She was my supervisor. I did contact Adrian Bustinza, two years ago; he didn't want to talk about it. He said he would share pictures with me, but we haven't talked much since."*

---

*Other accounts suggest Bonnie may have lost a loaded handgun, whilst out in the forest. Some people have speculated that the UFO story from the first night was used as a cover-up to give the USAF time to find a weapon. We discovered, from a reliable source, that she had lost an M-16 rifle. Presumably the weapon was recovered?

Lori Buoen and John Trementozzi on duty 1980

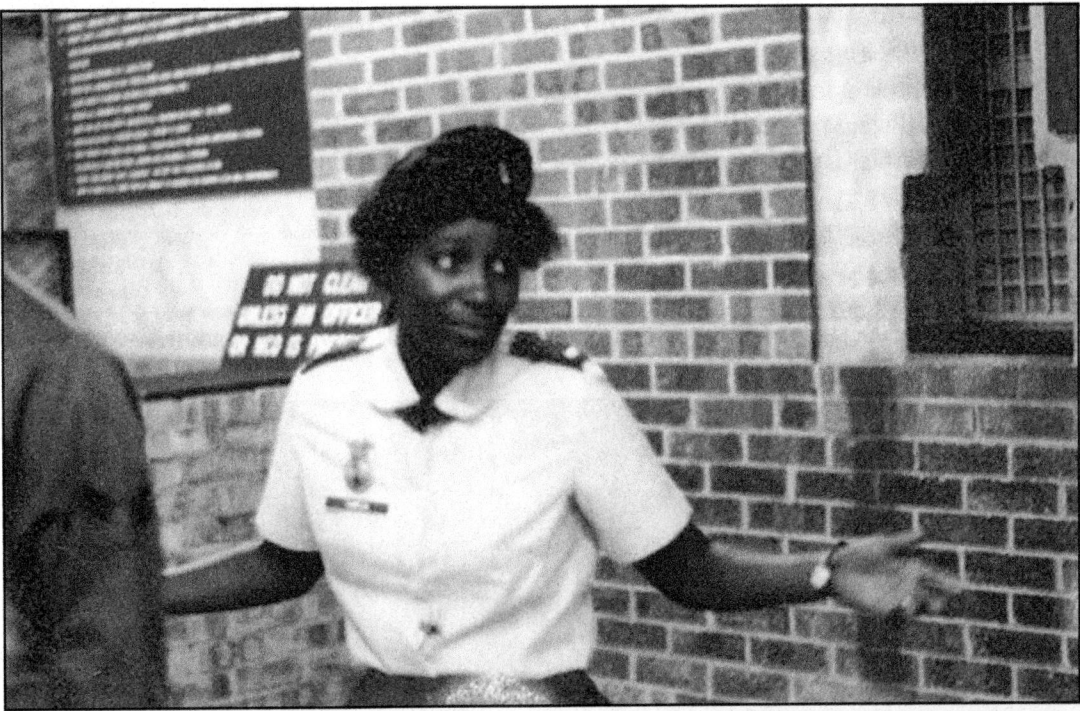

Police Lt. Bonnie Tamplin

Adrian Bustinza

Master Sergeant Bobby Ball

Charles Halt on Major Malcolm Zickler

> *"Something happened to Bonnie, and that gave them an excuse to get rid of her. The real answer would be to find Edward Drury. He knows a lot and will probably talk. Major Malcolm Zickler screwed him, as he was a bright academy graduate and Zickler couldn't stand that."*

Zickler later interviewed by Georgina Bruni

Malcolm Zickler was interviewed by Georgina Bruni on 11th June 1998, and asked about his involvement.

"No, I wasn't there on any night. I was advised on what they saw – an object. I went to the woods during the day and saw none of these things. When I knew Halt was out there I chose not to go, as I didn't see eye to eye with him. I was subordinate to him in rank, but I didn't work directly for him but for the base commander."

He was asked what he thought happened in the forest, and replied:

"I don't know. Halt seemed to think this was a major problem. I knew he did a report, but I was not privy to that and I've no idea of the response to that. The consensus of those that investigated it – the AFOSI – came to the conclusion that 'something happened', but there was insufficient evidence."

2.30am (approx.) on 27th December – UFO seen over Woodbridge

At about 2.30am, a Woodbridge resident – Mrs Webb – was driving her car on the outskirts of Rendlesham Forest, accompanied by her husband, Roy, who had their daughter, Hayley, on his knee. Hayley brought her parents attention to a 'star' that was following them.

Mrs Webb:

"I saw what looked like a bright 'star' following our car. All the time it stayed level with us. When we stopped in a lay-by, it remained with us. We sat there for a minute in the lay-by – then the light went up and vanished."

(Source: Brenda Butler)

6am on 27th December 1980 – John arrives back at the airbase

John Burroughs, in an interview conducted in 2009, told of hitching a lift back to the airbase, while off duty, at 6am (27th December 1980). He spoke to the desk sergeant – Sergeant O'Brien – who told him:

"Whatever you saw was back tonight! He then spoke about how again they'd seen lights out in the forest. They had sent the shift commander out. [Lori Buoen]. She went out into the woods to see what the lights were again and her vehicle stopped running – some kind of blue light flew through her vehicle. She totally lost her composure, as it had upset her a lot, and they sent her home for the evening. At that point I decided I was going to go back out that night and see what went on. I hung out with some guys at the dorm. At that time we had no idea there was going to be another incident."

Marks allegedly found in Rendlesham Forest

An unsigned letter from a woman staying with friends on the American Airbase describes an incident brought to her attention by a friend. She telephoned her, reporting that her husband had been on patrol when he heard, over his portable radio, of a UFO which had landed inside the airbase on the late night of 26th December/early hours of 27th December 1980. The man concerned told her that the other men had been frightened and moved away from the object. The woman, her curiosity aroused, made her way to the designated location but it had been cordoned off.

Three large marks in a triangle found

However, a short time later, she went back for another look and discovered three large marks, in a triangular position, where the alleged object had been seen. Unfortunately, as we do not know any further details, or the identity of the people concerned, we can only take this information on face value.

(Source: Brenda Butler)

Was this part of the Rendlesham UFO?

The mystery deepens with a claim made, over 35 years later, by a woman who told UFO enthusiast Ronny Dugdale that she was in possession of a piece of metal which had been recovered from the landing site. The woman gave the piece of metal to him and declined to identify herself, other than having an American accent. Most people's reactions would be to treat this with suspicion, but later analysis, conducted in the United States by scientist Nick Reiter, was to reveal some very interesting information about its content. More about this further into the book.

Evening of 27th December – 'Missile-like' object seen in Rendlesham Forest

Ron Gladstone – a resident of Woodbridge – was walking his dog in the forest in the evening, when he came across a crater in the ground, with what looked like a *silver missile* sticking out of it, with a parachute! Next to it were a number of men, wearing silver suits, in the process of covering the object with tarpaulin. Ron decided to leave and went home. The *News of the World* heard about his sighting and tried to interview him. Sadly, Roy's wife (who was only 26 years of age) died in mysterious circumstances, according to Brenda Butler.

(Source: Brenda Butler)

27th December – Highpoint Prison placed on alert

Mr George Wild from Ossett, in West Yorkshire, who had been employed as a senior prison officer at Armley Prison, Leeds – spoke to Graham Birdsall of *UFO Magazine,* in 1995, with regard to a conversation held with a fellow prison officer – then based at High Point Prison, Suffolk. The man told George that during the early evening, he and his fellow members of staff, received instructions warning them that they might have to evacuate the prison, due to an incident late that night. When staff questioned this, they were told it was a matter of National Security.

27th December – Sharply defined triangular UFO seen

Later the same evening, Mr Tony Sorrell – employed as food production manager, at Thetford – was on his way home after locking up the business premises, when he saw:

"…a sharply defined triangular-shaped object, like frosted glass, moving through the clear night sky. As it moved, the stars above dimmed. It was not moving very fast and was gone from view, 20 seconds later."

11pm on 27th December – 'Bright light' seen over Rendlesham Forest

At 11pm on the 27th December 1980, Mrs Sadler from Leiston was driving along the road, when she sighted a red 'ball of fire' over Tangham Forest, Rendlesham.

Brenda Butler:

"We spoke to another witness in a pub, at Wilford Bridge, who said he was travelling down to the airbase, between 11.30pm and 1am, on 27th or 28th December, when he saw a 'bright light' over the Rendlesham Forest area. He thought it was an aircraft, but couldn't understand why it remained motionless in the sky for 20 minutes. When he asked some of his friends on the base, they told him it was an Exercise alert. Importantly, he added that he had seen no sign of any activity, such as vehicles or soldiers."

(Source: Brenda Butler)

27th December – *Aliens, but not like aliens*

Airman Steve Wilkins telephoned Brenda Butler and told her he was working on the flight line on the 27th December 1980, when he noticed lots of lights and increased activity occurring in the forest, involving many Lorries and jeeps heading up the flight path.

He asked what was going on and was told it concerned *'Aliens, but not like aliens'.*

Brenda:

"Steve Wilkins phoned again on Saturday 8th October 1983, and told me the men who went to the area were briefed on what to say and it definitely was not a UFO. He said the men were told to say it was a UFO and to let people think it was something from outer space. To the men it was a UFO, because they didn't know what it was. He wouldn't say anymore. He was worried the phone was being monitored."

According to *Sky Crash*, Steve also mentioned that during the next afternoon, while talking to a colleague about the incident:

"I was told by one man that a small craft had come down in the forest; it had stood on legs. Four robot creatures were in control of it and that twenty four men, including senior officers, had been allowed to go near it".

27th December – Chuck Daldorf – No knowledge of UFO reports

Between December 1977 and 1981, Chuck was employed as an airman/aircraft field systems technician, at RAF Woodbridge, an E-5 Staff Sergeant, assigned to the 81st Tactical Fighter Wing. His duties included the repair of fuel tanks, in-flight fuelling and drop tanks from A10s, at Bentwaters and Woodbridge. He shared a very small tool shop building 307, with the 67th Aerospace Rescue and Recovery Squadron fuel repair crew. The 67th ARRS operated HC-130N/P fixed wing aircraft and heavy duty HH-53 Helicopters, used for combat search and rescue.

"Our building was located between the 67th ARRS helicopter hanger and the 81st EMS Hanger 202. During the time of the purported incident, both the 81st TFW and 67th ARRS were operating on a very limited duty, due to the holiday. Both operations generally had used their allocated flying hours, but kept a very small amount in case of an emergency. I was on duty on the 27th December, during the swing shift 4pm-1am, but on my own time, helping to organise and lead a hired coach through Big Ben Travel up to Scotland for the hogmanay celebrations. This trip would have been cancelled if there had been a military operation taking place, as I was part of the 67th personnel group, which included 28 people consisting of security police, mechanics, Para-rescue staff and admin clerks, supporting the 81st TFW Commanders.

The trip went off well, with no problems or delays, two days after the alleged incident. No one discussed the incident, or rumours of an incident which occurred at the Base. I never heard of the UFO story until almost May 1981. This happened when an enlisted woman, who shared my rented cottage at Tunstall – employed on the 31st Weather Squadron team, which worked 24 hours a day, seven days a week, with an unblocked 360° view of the airfield and surrounding area – told me what had taken place. I would swear, under oath, that no aircraft took off that evening. During that year, the HH-53s did engage in special ops and rescue simulations in the forest and on the coast. They carried out many low level hovers and dropped men into the forest and extracted them. British Special Forces also conducted operations in and around the area (they still do, despite the twin bases having been closed for some years).

The lighthouse at Orford is certainly one possibility of creating weird light effects, caused by drifting coastal fog and rain."

Secret compound at Orford Ness

"The British Department of Defence also ran a secret compound at Orford Ness. God knows what they did there. I believe it would have been impossible to have kept the UFO story quiet – there would have been rumours flying. I never heard anything till May, and it was said 'tongue in cheek'. It wasn't till the middle 1980s that I began to hear of the stories surrounding what was said to have happened."

(Source: Richard Conway)

27th December – Charles Halt – The UFO returns!

"We were having the Christmas dinner – a family dinner, a cover dish dinner for all the officers and combat support group – about 40 families – at the small Club at Woodbridge Base, known as the 'Twelve o'clock High' Club."

"While getting ready to start dessert and enjoy the evening's festivities – involving things like annual awards and the recognition for people who had done special things – the on-duty Flight Lieutenant for the Security Police Squadron came bursting in, with his MI6, and all red-faced and upset, and said to me, 'I've got to talk to you privately, right now', so I got hold of Ted Conrad, who was my Boss – the Base Commander, and we went into the cloakroom. It was the only private place to talk in the club, at that time.

He said, 'It's back'.

I said, 'What's back?

He said, 'The UFO's back'.

I said, 'How do you know that?'

He said, 'I've seen something'.

I said, 'Where?'

He said, 'Outside the East Gate, in the woods'.

I said, '...So what are you doing out in the woods in the East Gate?' ... (Bearing in mind England was a foreign country, as far as we're concerned.)"

Equipment fails

"We were guests there, and our mission was not to patrol the woods but to maintain the perimeter of the base.

He said, 'Some of the guys saw something, so we sent a patrol out there. We took some light-alls with us. (The NF2 light-alls were motor generators. They were nothing but a small, I think, a five horsepower 'Briggs and Stratton' engine with a couple of big mercury vapour lights on top, and a gas tank, and a lot of sheet metal.) The lights wouldn't work. The radios were acting up. When we looked in the woods with a starlight scope, we saw some strange things'.

I said, 'What did you see?'

He said, 'We saw a glow and some red lights'."

Chaos at the gas pumps

Tony Brisciano

Airman Tony Brisciano was on duty at the desk of the fuels management branch at Bentwaters on 27th December.

During the early hours of what he believed was the 28th December 1980, he received a call telling him that emergency vehicles at Woodbridge needed fuel. Tony decided to take the back gate, which was a quicker route, but bizarrely, after a few minutes drive, something in his head seemed to say, *'Do not go this way'* This message was so strong that he turned around and headed for the front gate.

"When I reached the gas pumps at Woodbridge, I never saw so many police vehicles and equipment waiting for fuel. It was especially unusual to see this as it was in the early hours of the morning. The vehicles were mostly pick-ups with light-alls attached, and there were a few police cars. I was having a difficult time with *Lieutenant Colonel Halt – the Deputy Base Commander. He was in a hell of a hurry and was bitching at me to snap it up and get the pumps going. After that I drove back to Bentwaters and didn't think any more about it, until rumours started to circulate about UFOs.

A few days later, an SP told me he had seen a UFO out in the forest; I was glad I followed my conscience and didn't take the back road to Woodbridge that night."

(Source: Georgina Bruni)

*Charles Halt denies any knowledge of this.

Charles Halt:

> *"Ted Conrad and I looked at each other, as he had to make all the presentations – or maybe that was his excuse.*
>
> *He said, 'Why don't you go out and see what this is all about?'*
>
> *Ok, I wasn't too excited, but I realised the cops had become preoccupied with this – both the Security Forces and the Law Enforcement – and they were more attuned to what was going on in the woods probably than what they should be doing; in other words, guarding the perimeter of the base and providing law enforcement. So I went to the Disaster Preparedness Officer and said, 'Would you have one of your key NCOs – whoever is on standby – go over to your office, pick up an ANP-27 Geiger counter and calibrate it?' and I knew who. She told me who was on duty. It was Sergeant Nevels. I knew he was a professional photographer, and had a degree in photography, so I said, 'Have him bring his camera along too', so she got on the phone and called him.*
>
> *I drove home."*

The route taken

"When I went out with the police, we went from Bentwaters to Woodbridge (as I remember) by way of the public road (through Eyke) onto Woodbridge, and then out the East Gate, down the road. We turned right onto the forest service road for a hundred or more feet – then left on the dirt road towards the sea. After several hundred yards, we turned left on a trail and continued for several hundred feet. From there we went right into the trees, towards the fence line. The 'landing site' was about 200-300ft from the fence, ahead, and to the left was the 'Boast' home."

Sergeant Nevels seen here with Charles Halt recently

July 3, 2002

Dear Brenda:

It was good to hear from you. I don't remember telling Georgina I did not want to be contacted. It sounds like you are really on to something. You are seeing and experiencing a lot more than we did. I seriously doubt the military has anything to do with it.

When I went out with the police we went from Bentwaters to Woodbridge (as I remember) by way of the public road (through Eyke) onto Woodbridge and then out the East Gate down the road. We turned right on the Forest service road for a hundred or more feet then left on the dirt road toward the sea. After several hundred yards we turned left on a trail and continued for several hundred feet. From there we went right into the trees toward the fence line. The "landing site" was about 200-300 feet from the fence. Ahead and to the left was the Boast home. Hope this helps.

The marks on the trees in the pictures are much larger than we noted on the infamous night. I also think you have mislocated the site in the picture of a map you sent. The map is not large enough and does not have enough clear references to say for sure. As far as posts. I did not see any and do not remember seeing any at later dates (1989 and when I did the filming).

Have you tried to catch some of the happenings on film? Infrared film?

Good luck- win the lottery and I'll join you for a party at the site.

Chuck

Met up with Master Sergeant Bobby Ball and Sergeant Monroe Nevels

"The police came by in a jeep and picked me up (Master Sergeant Bobby Ball) and I don't remember who else. We then went over and picked up Sergeant Nevels. I watched him calibrate two ANP, ANP-27's, and we picked what I thought was the better. Actually, they were both probably very good ... then we bundled into the jeep, and drove across the flight line. The two bases are about a mile and a half apart – a little closer if you drive right across the flight line and in the back gate. We unlocked the back gate and drove across, and to what, what's known as East Gate, at Woodbridge. Lo and behold, there's a crowd out there. Well, I was quite concerned, so I said to them, 'Let's keep all these people back. We don't need the publicity. We are kind of trespassing. This was the Queen's forest

– sort of like a National Forest. There's a lot of private property around here. We don't want to cause a lot of concern, or get people upset. They're going to wonder what we're doing stomping around out here in the woods', so he said, 'Ok'. At this time there were probably 30 or 40 people in total, with three or four light-alls which were acting up. They wouldn't run right, kept flickering off and on. I could hear comments: 'He didn't refuel them' and somebody else said, 'Yes, I did refuel them; I took them down to the motor pool before we brought them out'."

Dull glow sighted in the woods

"Bruce said, 'Let's look into the woods there', and he had a first generation starlight scope. We looked into the woods and, sure enough, in one area there was a dull glow. When you look through a starlight scope you don't see things as you normally would. It's a greenish-yellow tinge to them. It's a different spectrum, or different, uh, frequency and there was something I could see in there, but I wasn't really sure what it was. It didn't make a lot of sense to me ... and I'm not sure it's of great significance, but there was something."

Colonel Charles I Halt tape recording

"I had taken my small cassette recorder along with me, not specifically for this instance. It's just that any time I went around the Base, I would take this little recorder along, record things that need to be done, a fence that needed to be mended, or a road needing to be paved, or whatever I noticed, or something out of the ordinary ... and I'd bring it back and flip it to the secretary, and she'd type it up, then, at the next staff meeting, would mark who had the action on the items, and pass it them out for tasking ... so I'd taken it along that night, just because I thought I might need to take some notes and it was probably 35, 40 degrees, with a stiff wind blowing off the coast, and quite cold ... and I made a tape, which was later inadvertently released by a co-worker. I can't exactly repeat what's on there.

It's 1980, but I'll just go through what happened. I was afraid that wouldn't be too good, but the little pocket recorder I had has long since worn out. It gave up the ghost, and they've changed the format on tapes now so I put it on big tapes, while I could. Basically what happened, I took the pocket recorder along and just dropped it in my pocket, and I'd pick it up, and every few minutes I would say what was going on."

Three indentations found on the landing site forming a triangle

"When we approached the site, we found the three indentations. We measured them, and you can hear the distance on there. I think there were eight or nine, seven feet apart, very triangular, and the dosimeter was picking up definite readings which were above background radiation, seven to twenty times, dependant upon whom you talk to, and it was, the site was hottest, so to speak, in the centre formed by the triangle. Also the trees, the pine trees that were there, were approximately, I would say, anywhere from 8 to 15 inches diameter.

There were some marks on them. There were two, two sets of marks, or types of marks. There were blaze marks that were done with an axe, that were very clear. Someone had come through the forest not too long before, and marked trees – probably for cutting, but there were some big rub marks and, if you looked overhead, branches were broken as though something could have come up or come down, although I can't say that for a fact. It appeared that way. You could see the sky there and you couldn't see it anywhere else. We were walking around."

We sight a UFO!

We identified one of the indentations as point one and I'm measuring them and taking readings, so we have a record of all this, when suddenly, Bruce Englund, the Lieutenant who was with me, looks out and says a few words I won't repeat, and says, 'There's something out there – look at that', and it was a red thing. It's the only way I can describe it. It looked like an eye. It was oval and had a black centre, and it was winking. It just looked like an eye is what it looked like."

"It moved back and forth through the trees, horizontally, and not necessarily in a level plane.

It was moving through the trees. It was in the forest at that time. We watched it blink. Now some people have equated this to the Orford Ness lighthouse, which we were all very familiar with.

It moved through the forest, moved through the trees. We stood there in awe for quite a while, watching this thing … and, finally, I said 'Let's try and get closer', so we worked our way through the forest and, as we did, it receded. It moved out into the field. There was a large field on the other side of the forest. We came up to a barbed, an old barbed wire fence, and watched there for a few minutes. And it seemed to be centred almost in front of a farmer's house, and the farmer's house had a glow in all the windows, as though it were on fire inside. It's the only way I can describe it. It may have been a reflection off the glass in the windows. It probably was, but I didn't know for sure. I was quite concerned for whoever was in the farmhouse, if anybody was there, and it was an active farm. The animals were just going crazy on the farm. The horses, the cows, the pigs – everything was just making all kinds of noise. There was no activity that we could discern in the farmhouse at all. It was quiet."

"The object was there, probably for, I'm guessing, 30, 40 seconds – maybe a minute, and all of a sudden, it just silently exploded into five white objects and they disappeared – just gone like that! While we were watching it, it appeared to be dripping the equivalent of a molten metal. Something was, like, dripping off it, so when the object disappeared, I said, 'Let's go out in the field and see if we can find some burned evidence, or some spots on the ground where something has fallen – there has to be something' … and we went out, of course.

Lt. Bruce Englund (centre).

It was in the dark, and about all we did was step in cow pies, but we didn't find any evidence at all. We went around the farmer's house, went on out into a ploughed field, to get a better view, and all this time we could see the lighthouse. In fact, there was another lighthouse further down the coast we could see at that time, too. We're standing out in the ploughed field. We crossed it, and we all fell into a stream we didn't see and got good and wet.

We came out of that, into another ploughed field, and, I don't remember who, but somebody said, 'Look!', and we looked up to the North, and there were objects in the sky, to the North. In the meantime, we're having great problems with the radios. Uh, there were five of us there. We had all had radios, and each (three of us) were on different nets.

I was on the net with the command post. There was a cop on the security net with the Security Police, and one of the cops was on the Law Enforcement net, so we were talking to three different control centres, so to speak, all the time. Generally, we would have to relay, through one of the people that were back by the light-alls, because the radios would not carry that far and they were in the line of sight, yes, pretty much, but we were out in the open, in the clear, which was kind of puzzling because normally we should have gotten a good transmission right through."

UFO display

"It was a clear night, standing in the field, and somebody said, 'Look up there!', and here are these objects in the sky. The best way I can describe them – they look like a half, or a Cherokee moon, and they are well-illuminated, with multiple coloured lights, and they were moving about in sharp, angular, patterns – very fast, and as we watched them, they turned, from the equivalent of a Cherokee moon into a full circle. It was very amazing … and the way they were going, it appeared that they were doing some type of grid search, or doing some type of a pattern, or seemed to be some type of logic to their movement – really wasn't sure.

We probably watched them for twenty, thirty minutes, and suddenly, we noticed an object to the South. Contrary to what has been alleged I never told anybody any structure was penetrated by beams. I was several miles away. From my view, a beam or more came down near the Weapons Storage Area. I don't know for a fact that the beams landed there. I know they were in the area. I was too far away but relied on the radio chatter, which indicated the beams landed there."

Sgt. Monroe Ruby Nevels – Three Vessels or lights seen

As the men crossed a farmer's field, the object seemed to head straight for them – then disappeared. The sky above was a gray-white and three crafts were visible.

*"There were three objects or lights. The largest light was the leading or command vessel. The lights were three vessels that moved independently of each other. They were moving and were able to jump from Woodbridge and show up over Bentwaters in less than a second. While the craft was on the ground, pieces of flying debris were being shed, which appeared to be like molten steel in a boiler pot. It seemed to get hotter as the object was approached. I took *photos with a Nikon F3 and a 105mm f/2.8 lens, with TriX @ ASA 400. I processed them myself in my home photo lab. They were fogged, and after a few years I realized the reason: Radiation detected around the sight and on the trees. This is why none of the photographs could be viewed. By the way, I was and am a Professional Photographer. I was methodical with my work, and as a Disaster Preparedness Tech., I knew and did my job professionally. I KNOW WHAT I SAW!"*

Monroe also took numerous photographs of the lights and object; unfortunately these photographs, when developed by Monroe himself were found to be fogged. Colonel Conrad directed Monroe to scan the skies for several days after the incident.

In 2013 Monroe had this to say –

"Col. Halt and myself, along with the others on that night, saw, over to the left of the farmer's field, a yellowish object from a distance that looked as though it might be a very hot metal, or steel, burning at very high temperatures. It seemed to get brighter as we went over the fence, but suddenly was gone. As I looked up, I pointed out to Col. Halt they were in the sky. As I know how brightness can make the eye/brain think all sorts of things, I saw them moving, so to make sure

my statement was accurate I lay down on my back, closed my eyes and opened them again, several times. They were indeed moving. There were three of them. And, as sure as they were there, they were gone; they were also seen overhead by an excited group at RAF Bentwaters"

Colonel Halt – Arrival of secondary UFO – discharges beam of light

"This was a round object and it was approaching us at very high speed. It came in – and it's real clear on the tape. That's an interesting part of the tape, if you could hear it – it came in very, very close, I'm guessing within a quarter to a half mile, and stopped two, three, four thousand feet up, and sent down a beam. The best way I can describe the beam is a laser beam, because a light beam normally radiates out. This came down instead and it was six to eight, or maybe nine, inches in diameter and fell right at our feet. Well, that really had us upset because we weren't sure whether it was a warning, whether it was, you know, a shot at us, whether it was somebody trying to communicate, or what it was. We had no idea, and we just stood there and looked and nobody said anything and, all of a sudden, as fast as it came on, it was gone. The object receded."

In email, dated August 2015 – There were three objects!

"There were three objects to the North and two to the South. They looked like your attached picture only the ones to the North were higher and smaller and displayed multi coloured lights. While watching they turned into full round objects still displaying multi colored lights.

The whole time they were moving together at high speed and making sharp angular turns. It was like they were in formation and perhaps doing a search. The two objects to the South were seen as a light source. I could not discern a shape due to the brightness even when the one came directly overhead.

However, the Security Police in the WSA looking through 12 power glasses claim the objects to the South had a triangular shape. One of the patrolmen in the WSA claims to have seen a large object that could have been a mother ship. The "eye" was oval less than a meter in diameter.

It was glowing orange/red with a dark black oval like centre. The dark centre would disappear as though pulsing, like an eye winking. While in the field it appeared to be shedding or dripping glowing red/orange particles.

When it moved into the forest the blinking/shedding appeared to stop. After moving horizontally through the forest and at one point starting to approaching us it receded back into the field and silently exploded into five small white objects and disappeared. We searched the field for evidence of whatever was coming off the object but found nothing.

An important point is when the object was in the field the glow was reflecting off the farmhouse windows so brightly that the house appeared to be on fire."

Now over Bentwaters Airbase

"Now the one object to the south, when it receded, was back over Bentwaters Base and we could see beams of light coming down there, near the ˚weapons storage area, and we could hear the chatter on the radio.

The people over there could actually see the beams of light, too, so we stayed out there in the forest – I'm guessing, a total of about three and a half, maybe four hours. Now I can account for all our time, and you know, I, I've had every possible explanation, from an air inversion to ball lightning, to a meteor shower, to just about the lighthouse. Everything you can think of. And really, my original intent when I went out, was to put the whole thing to rest, so the 'cops' could get on with business, and here I was, kind of in a dilemma, and wishing 'Gee', I wish I hadn't got involved in this – this is the end of my Military career."

Somebody else who was there during the evening of December 27th into the early morning hours of December 28th 1980 was Adrian Bustinza, a Security Supervisor from RAF Woodbridge. He found himself witnessing a third night of UFO activity in Rendlesham Forest. (He retired from the USAF in 1982).

Spinning lights seen over the Forest!

Former security patrolman officer on 'D' Flight, Robert 'Charlie' Waters, who had been on duty at the Weapons Storage Area during the week of the UFO activity, was interviewed by Robert Hastings.

"There was some commotion in the Weapons Storage Area that night. Someone saw this object. I don't remember who, and called out to us. I think my ART partner was Rob Isbell, but I'm not certain, but we looked and saw this spinning light – multicoloured light. I can't really remember the colours – anyway, this craft was hovering and then slowly descended toward the forest. We ran up on one of the beams to get a better view of it. We then we reported it to Central Security Control. I remember I used a couple of expletives and was warned not to use profanity on the radio. I think I was talking to a guy named Alfred Coakley. Anyway, he's the one I remember talking to most of the time that night. The next morning, I talked to one of the operations

officers, who told me that a small group of security Police had gone out to the woods and had seen some burn marks on trees, about three feet off the ground. He said it looked like, whatever it was, had bounced from tree to tree coming down. The person who told me that wasn't our flight's shift commander. He was another officer, but I don't remember his name. I also think I saw something sticking out on the bottom, uh, like a rod, or something like that."

1-3am 28th December – Three *'lights'* seen over Airbase

Between 1am and 3am, twelve year-old Sarah Richardson, from Woodbridge, was up late and happened to look out of the window, when she saw:

"…three bands of red, blue and yellow, 'lights' appear over the woods at the side of the runway. They were star-like; one in the north direction, the other two in the south. I thought someone was having a party and they were fireworks. It was a cold and clear night; the lights were low in the sky. I opened the window and leaned out. The lights appeared solid and looked metallic. No moon was shining. The light kept changing colour. They were there till well after 3am or 4am, when they suddenly shot straight away and disappeared from sight."

(Source: Brenda Butler)

Members of 'D' Flight

The only female: Airman Lori Buoen with (front left, Sgt. Adrian Bustinza from D Flight Drill Team circa December 1980

Map drawn by Jim Penniston

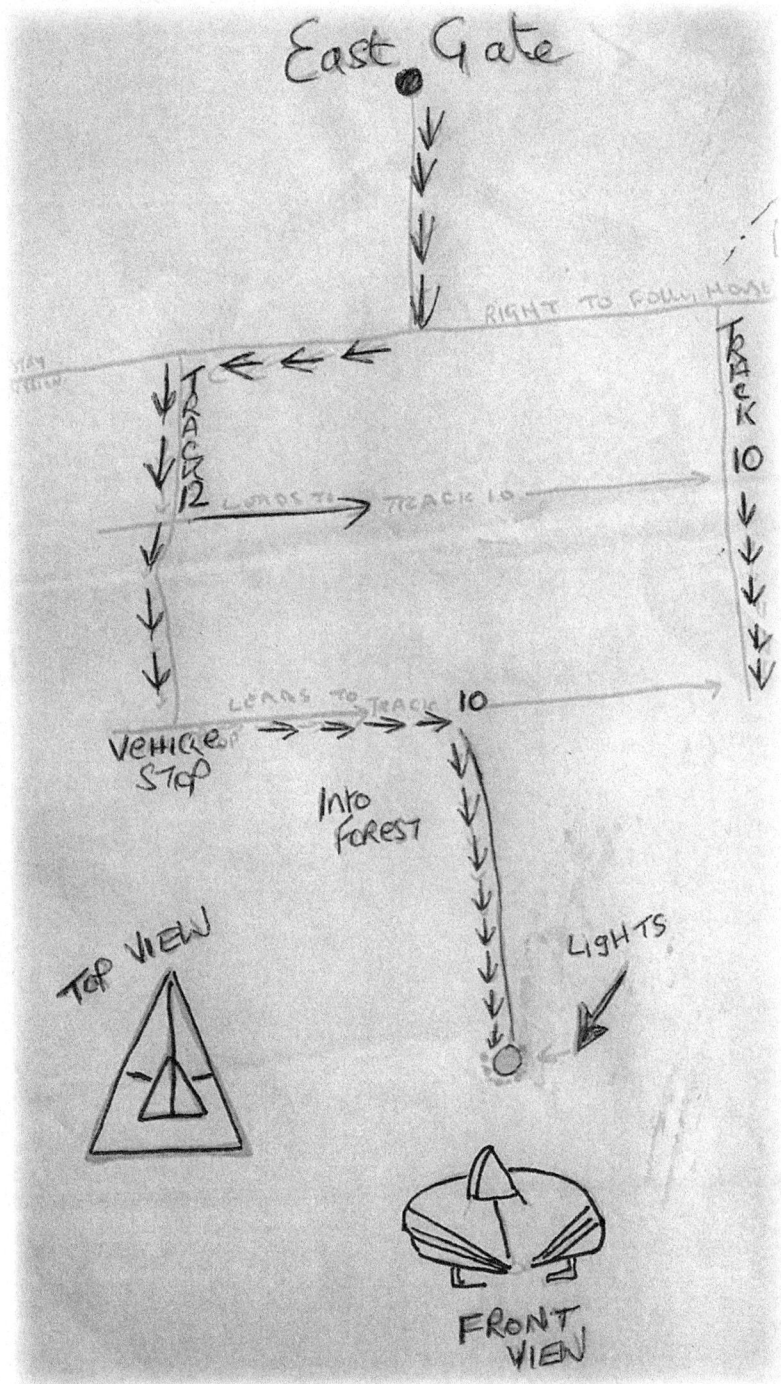

THE 'HALT TAPE RECORDING'

The following is a full transcript is of what was made by Lt. Colonel Halt, during his investigation into the Rendlesham Forest incident in December 1980. This was taken from the original copy, which is much clearer than the one in the public domain. It was sent by Colonel Sam Morgan, via General Gordon Williams.

There are background radio conversations throughout the recording; most feature radio transmissions between Sgt. Bustinza and Central Security Control. Due to these messages being in the background, however, more often than not they are overpowered by Colonel Halt's voice talking into his pocket recorder, so only those that are clear are translated here.

After leaving East Gate the men made their way into the forest

LT COLONEL HALT:

"150 feet or more from the initial, I should say suspected impact point. Having a little difficulty, we can't get the light-all to work. There seems to be some kind of mechanical problem. Let's send back and get another light-all. Meantime, we're gonna take some readings from the Geiger counter, and err, chase around the area a little bit waiting for another light-all to come out again."

SGT BUSTINZA: [on a radio in the background, obviously trying to organize more light-alls] ... to security control... that's mark ... 155 ... number...

LT COLONEL HALT: OK, we're now approaching an area within about 25-30 feet. What kind of readings are we getting, anything?

SGT Monroe Ruby NEVELS: (Geiger Operator) Just minor clicks

LT COLONEL HALT: Minor clicks.

LT COLONEL HALT: Where are the impressions?

SGT NEVELS: Just one, but...

VOICE OVER: [These voice overs are recorded over the initial recording and are not related to incident. It is the voice of Colonel Conrad, the Base Commander] Do you think it's going to be a nice day today?

VOICE OVER: Yeah, I think so.

LT COLONEL HALT: Is that all the bigger they are?

Sgt Monroe Ruby Nevels

SGT NEVELS: Well, there's one more well defined over here.

SGT BUSTINZA: [on a radio] ... Sergeant Bustinza to security control...

LT COLONEL HALT: We're still getting clicks

SGT BUSTINZA: ... Sergeant Bustinza. Well we're outta gas... we're at East Gate...East Gate, over.

LT COLONEL HALT: Can you read that on the scale?

SGT NEVELS: [examining the area with a Geiger counter] Yes Sir. We're now on a five tenths scale and we're reading about ... er ... third, fourth ...

LT COLONEL HALT: OK, we're still comfortably safe here?

SGT BUSTINZA: [on a radio] you don't have a light-all or [?] ... or anything ... duty security. Can you hear me? ... Sergeant... a light all, with gas please.

LT ENGLUND: [the on duty Flight Chief] we're still getting minor readings ... we're getting a good indentation.

SGT BUSTINZA: [on radio] ... security D to security.

SGT NEVELS: This one's dead.

LT ENGLUND: Let's go to the third one over here.

SGT NEVELS: Sort of, whatever it is.

SGT BUSTINZA: [on radio] ... Sergeant Bustinza ... security...

SGT NEVELS: Yes, now getting some residual.

LT COLONEL HALT: How can you read that? The meters definitely giving off pulse.

LT ENGLUND: About the center.

LT COLONEL HALT: Yes, I was gonna say, let's go to the center of the area next, see what kind of reading we get out there. Keep reading the clicks. I can't hear the clicks. Guess you all ... is that about center Bruce [asking Lt Bruce Englund].

LT ENGLUND: Yes

LT COLONEL HALT: OK let's go to the center.

SGT NEVELS: Yes I'm getting more ...

LT COLONEL HALT: That's about the best deflection of the needle I've seen yet. OK, can you do an estimation? We're on a point five scale, we're getting ... having trouble reading the scale.

[1.25am] LT ENGLUND: At err, approximately 0125 hours.

(Break in tape)

NOISE OVER: Deep cough

SGT NEVELS: We're getting rad at err a half a [sounds like millirem]

UNKNOWN VOICE: Chuck. [This is Colonel Halt's name, Charles, known as Chuck].

LT COLONEL HALT: ... best point, I haven't seen it go any higher.

LT ENGLUND: Well, it's still flying around.

LT COLONEL HALT: OK we'll go out toward the ...

LT ENGLUND: Now it's picking up ...

LT COLONEL HALT: This out toward the indentation were we first got the strongest reading. It's similar to what we got in the center.

SGT NEVELS: Right near the pod. It's right near the center.

LT ENGLUND: This looks like an area here across where there could be a blast. It's in the center.

LT ENGLUND: It jumped up towards seven ...

LT COLONEL HALT: What?

LT ENGLUND: It just jumped towards seven tenths there.

LT COLONEL HALT: Seven tenths, right there in the center?

LT ENGLUND: Ah, Ah.

LT COLONEL HALT: We found a small blast what looks like a blasted or scruffed up area here. We're getting very positive readings. Let's see, is that near the center?

LT ENGLUND: Yes it is.

SGT NEVELS: Well, we assume it is ...

LT ENGLUND: This is right in the center ... dead center ...

SGT NEVELS: Picking up more as you go along the whole area there now...

LT COLONEL HALT: Up to seven tenths ...

SGT BUSTINZA: [on radio, still struggling with the transmissions] ... 55, this is our last call...

LT COLONEL HALT: ... or seven units. It's going on the point five scale.

(Break in tape)

LT COLONEL HALT: OK why don't we do this, why don't we make a sweep now I've got my gloves on now. Let's make a sweep out around the whole area about ten foot out and make a perimeter run around it, starting right back at here at the corner, back at the same first corner where we came in. Let's go right back here ... now I'm gonna have to depend upon you counting the clicks.

LT ENGLUND: Right.

LT COLONEL HALT: OK, get the light-all on it.

LT ENGLUND: Lets sweep around it.

SGT NEVELS: It was flying.

(Break in tape)

LT COLONEL HALT: Put it on the ground every once in a while.

BACKGROUND: We have lights nearby...

LT ENGLUND: This looks like an abrasion on the tree...

LT COLONEL HALT: OK, we'll catch that on the way back, let's go around.

LT ENGLUND: We're getting interest right over here. It looks like it's an abrasion pointing into the center...

LT COLONEL HALT: It is.

LT ENGLUND: ... of the landing area.

LT COLONEL HALT: it may be old though. There's some sap marks or something like that. Let's go on back around.

(UNKNOWN VOICE)

(Break in tape)

SGT NEVELS: It also gives some extension on it.

LT COLONEL HALT: Hey, this is an awkward thing to use, isn't it?

SGT NEVELS: Normally you see I carry it on my... on my ears but this one broke.

LT COLONEL HALT: Are we getting any further? I'm gonna shut this recorder off until we find something.

SGT NEVELS: Picking up

LT COLONEL HALT: Pickin' up. What are we up to? We're up to two-three units deflection. You're getting in close to the pod?

SGT NEVELS: Picking up something... picking up.

LT COLONEL HALT: OK. It's still not going above three to four units.

SGT NEVELS: Picking up more though, more frequent.

LT COLONEL HALT: Yes, you're staying – you're staying steady up around two to three to four units now.

SGT BUSTINZA: [still struggling with the radio] 155

LT ENGLUND: Each one of these trees is facing at a blast, what we assume is a landing site, all have abrasion facing in the same direction towards the center. The same...

LT COLONEL HALT: Let's go around a circle here. Turn back down here.

MASTER SGT BALL: Try the other tree.

SGT NEVELS: Picking up something ... a ...

LT COLONEL HALT: Let me see that. You know I've got a funny ... you're worried about the abrasion. I've never seen a tree that's, err...

MASTER SERGEANT BALL: That's a small sap mark.

LT COLONEL HALT: I've never seen a pine tree that's been damaged, react that fast. [Interference, voices all talking together].

SGT NEVELS: You got a bottle to put that in?

LT COLONEL HALT: You got a sample bottle?

LT ENGLUND: Yes put out the... that's for the soil sample... [interference].

SGT NEVELS: Yes Sir.

VOICES: [excited]

LT COLONEL HALT: From now on let's [gap] let's...

LT ENGLUND: You'll notice they're all at the same...

LT COLONEL HALT: Let's, lets, lets identify that as point number one. That stake there. So you all know where it is if we have to sketch it. You got that Sergeant Nevels?

SGT NEVELS: Yes Sir. Closest to the Woodbridge...

LT COLONEL HALT: Closest to the Woodbridge base.

SGT NEVELS: Be point one?

LT COLONEL HALT: Be point one. Let's go clockwise from there.

SGT NEVELS: Point two?

LT ENGLUND: Go ahead...

LT COLONEL HALT: Point two. So this tree is between two and point three.

[Airman John Burroughs arrives with a patrol]

MASTER SGT BALL: Burroughs and two other personnel requesting ... riding on a jeep, that err, your location.

LT COLONEL HALT: Tell them negative at this time. We'll tell them when they can come out here. We don't want them out here right now.

Airman John Burroughs

(Break in tape)

LT COLONEL HALT: OK the sample, you gonna want this sample number one? Have them cut it off, include some of that sap and all... is between indentation two and three on a pine tree about err... about five feet away... about three and half feet off the ground.

SGT NEVELS: ...I'll just put it in there for now, I've got some more...

LT COLONEL HALT: There's a round abrasion on the tree about three and a half, four inches diameter. It looks like it might be old, but er, strange there's a crystalline...pine sap that's come that fast.

SGT FRAIL: [seems in the distance] ... Sergeant Frail...

LT COLONEL HALT: You say there are other trees that are damaged in a similar fashion?

LT ENGLUND: ...center of the landing site... [interference].

[First picture taken] LT COLONEL HALT: OK, why don't you take a picture of that and remember your picture. Hey, I hope you're writing this down. It's gonna be on the tape.

SGT NEVELS: You got a tape measure with you?

LT COLONEL HALT: This is your picture, the first picture will be at the first tree, the one between err... mark two and three. Meantime, I'm gonna look at a couple of those trees over here.

(Break in tape)

UNKNOWN VOICE: We are getting some

(Break in tape)

LT COLONEL HALT: We are getting readings on the tree. You're taking samples from on the side facing the suspected landing site?

Landing site

LT ENGLUND: Four clicks max.

LT COLONEL HALT: Up to four. Interesting…that's right were you're taking the sample now.

LT ENGLUND: Four.

LT COLONEL HALT: That's the strongest point on the tree?

SGT NEVELS: Yes sir … and if you come to the back, there's no clicks whatsoever.

LT COLONEL HALT: No clicks at all in the back.

SGT NEVELS: Maybe one or two.

LT COLONEL HALT: It's all on the side facing the… interesting.

LT COLONEL HALT: Looks like it f… twisted as it got… as it sat down on it, looks like something twisted it from side to side.

LT ENGLUND: Ah, Ah

LT COLONEL HALT: Very strange. We're at the same tree we took a sample of with this, what do you call it… the starscope.

LT ENGLUND: Ah ah, Stargazer

[Heat reflection] LT COLONEL HALT: Getting a definite heat reflection off the tree, about three to four feet off the ground?

LT ENGLUND: Yes... the same side in...

LT COLONEL HALT: The same place where the ...is

LT ENGLUND: ...we're getting heat directly behind us. I think we got the same thing off to your right.

[Three trees in the area]

LT COLONEL HALT: There are three trees in the area immediately adjacent to the site within ten feet of the suspected landing site; we're picking up heat reflection off the trees.

LT ENGLUND: Shine the light on that Bob [Sgt Bob Ball]

LT COLONEL HALT: What's that again?

LT ENGLUND: Well, shine the light on again Bob

LT COLONEL HALT: Why, you having trouble finding it... turn the light on.

LT ENGLUND: ... then when you want em you'll notice the white

[Suddenly there is a very strange humming sound and the men are silent]

LT COLONEL HALT: Hey... [long silent gap apart from humming noise]

LT COLONEL HALT: You're right, there's a white streak on the tree.

LT ENGLUND: Indicates er...

LT COLONEL HALT: Let's turn around and look at this tree over here now. Just a second. Watch, because you're right in front of the tree. I can see it. OK, give me a little side light so I can find the tree. OK, ahh...

SGT BUSTINZA: [still on the radio] Alpha 2 security...

LT COLONEL HALT: I've lost the tree.

LT COLONEL HALT: OK stop! Stop! Light off. Hey, this is eerie.

MASTER SGT BALL: Why don't you do the pods spots...

LT COLONEL HALT: This is strange! Hey, does anyone wanna look at the spots on the ground? Whoops! Watch you don't step...

BACKGROUND: Five beeps from a vehicle arriving on the scene.

LT COLONEL HALT: ... you're walking all over them. OK, let's step back and don't walk all over em. Come back here – somebody and put a beam on 'em. You're gonna have to be back about ten, fifteen feet. You see it ...

LT ENGLUND: OK fine...

LT COLONEL HALT: OK, lights off.

(Break in tape)

VOICE OVER: [Colonel Conrad] He took this long to document...

LT COLONEL HALT: What do you think about the spot?

[Radio interference in background]

LT COLONEL HALT: Yeah.

(Break in tape)

LT COLONEL HALT: ... ready at the first spot? OK, that's what we'll call spot number three. Let's go in the back corner and get spot number one. Spot number one, here's spot number one right there, spot number one right there. Do you need some light? There it is right here. ... you focused?

SGT NEVELS: Focused.

LT COLONEL HALT: OK... looking at spot number one through the starlight scope.

LT ENGLUND: Picking up a slight increase in light as I go over it.

LT COLONEL HALT: Slight increase in light in spot number one. Let's go look at spot number two. Spot number two's right over here. Right here, see it?

LT ENGLUND: ... Slight increase.

LT COLONEL HALT: OK, get focused on it. Tell me when, OK lights on. Let's see what we get on it.

LT ENGLUND: Slight increase.

LT COLONEL HALT: Just a slight increase?

LT ENGLUND: Try the center.

LT COLONEL HALT: The center spot, not really center, slightly off center. It's right there.

LT ENGLUND: Right here.

LT COLONEL HALT: OK, we're gonna get your reading on it right there.

LT ENGLUND: OK.

LT COLONEL HALT: Tell me when you're ready.

LT ENGLUND: Ready.

LT COLONEL HALT: OK lights on. It's the center spot we're looking at now; almost the center.

LT ENGLUND: Getting a slight increase.

LT COLONEL HALT: Slight increase there. This is slightly off center toward the err... one – two side. It's er... some type of abrasion or something in the ground where the pine needles are pushed back were we get a *high radiact... err high reading about a deflection of er, two to three, maybe four, depending on the point of it.

Note: [this abrasion corresponds with the exact same position – just off center in landing site photographs taken by Ray Gulyas]

[Ray Gulyas took photos]

LT ENGLUND: Someone wanna check it?

(Break in tape)

SGT NEVELS: Yes.

LT COLONEL HALT: Are you sure there's a positive after effect?

SGT NEVELS: Yes, there is, definitely. That's on the center spot, there is an after effect.

LT ENGLUND: What does that mean?

SGT NEVELS: It means that when the lights are turned off, once we all focused in, allowed time for the eyes to adjust, we are getting an indication of heat source coming out of that center spot... as err... which will show up on the ...

LT COLONEL HALT: Heat or some form of energy, it's hardly heat at this stage of the game.

SGT NEVELS: But it is still heat...

(Break in tape)

LT COLONEL HALT: Looking directly overhead, one can see an opening in the trees, plus some freshly broken pine branches on the ground underneath. Looks like some of them came off about fifteen to twenty feet up. Some small branches about inch or less in diameter.

(Break in tape)

[1.48am] LT COLONEL HALT: 01.48. We're hearing some strange sounds out of the farmers...

SGT NEVELS: Twenty eight... seven...

LT COLONEL HALT: ... barnyard animals. They're very active and making an awful lot of noise.

SGT NEVELS: ... definite pigmentation...

LT COLONEL HALT: You saw a light? Slow down. Where, where?

SGT NEVELS: Right on this position here. Straight ahead in between the trees... [Adrian Bustinza pointed out that someone saw a light going through the trees]

LT ENGLUND: There it is again... beginning of the gap... right there.

SGT NEVELS: It throws the hell off my flashlight there.

LT COLONEL HALT: Hey I see it too. What is it?

SGT NEVELS: We don't know sir.

[Strange small red light seen]

LT COLONEL HALT: OK, it's a strange small red light, looks to be out maybe a quarter – half mile, maybe further out. I'm gonna switch off for a...

(Break in tape)

LT COLONEL HALT: The light is gone now. It was approximately 120 degrees from the site.

SGT NEVELS: It's back again.

LT COLONEL HALT: Is it back again?

SGT NEVELS: Yes sir.

LT COLONEL HALT: Well douse flashlights then. Let's go back to the edge of the clearing then, so we can get a better look at it. See if you can get the starscope on it. The light's still there and all the barnyard animals have gotten quiet now. We're heading about 110 -120 degrees from the site, out through the clearing now... still getting a reading on the meter, about 2 clicks. Needles jumped 3-4 clicks getting stronger.

SGT NEVELS: Now it's stopped. Now it's coming up. Hold on, here we go. Now it's coming up about approximately 4 foot off the ground. The compass has 110 degrees.

(Break in tape)

LT COLONEL HALT: Right, I just turned the meter off. Better say that again, about 4 feet off the ground, about a 110 degrees, getting the reading of about 4 clicks.

SERGEANT NEVELS: Yes sir... [????] *Cough;* excuse me, now it's died.

LT COLONEL HALT: I ... I think it's something here on the ground. I think it's something... very large...

SGT NEVELS: ... a tree right over...

(Break in tape)

LT COLONEL HALT: We just bumped into the first light that we've seen. We're about a 150 to 200 yards from the site. Everything else is just deathly calm. There's no doubt about it, there's some kind of strange flashing red light ahead.

SGT NEVELS: Yeah, It's yellow.

LT COLONEL HALT: I saw a yellow tinge in it too. Weird... It appears to be making a little bit this way?

SGT NEVELS: Yes sir.

LT COLONEL HALT: It's brighter than it has been...It's coming this way. It's definitely coming this way.

MASTER SGT BALL: Pieces are shooting off.

LT COLONEL HALT: Pieces of it are shooting off.

MASTER SGT BALL: At about 11 o'clock... [referring to its position]

LT COLONEL HALT: There's no doubt about it; this is weird.

MASTER SGT BALL: Look to the left.

SGT NEVELS: There's two lights; one light to the right and one light to the left.

LT COLONEL HALT: Keep your flash light off. There's something very very strange. Check the headset out see if it gets any stronger. Give us...

SGT NEVELS: OK, I have an indication that this is a vague reading too.

LT COLONEL HALT: A vague reading?

SGT NEVELS: The cable has been removed

LT COLONEL HALT: OK... pieces are falling off it again.

MASTER SGT BALL: It just moved to the right... went off to the right.

LT COLONEL HALT: Yeah ... strange, Auh?

LT ENGLUND: Went off to the right.

LT COLONEL HALT: Strange. Ahhh. One again left. Let's approach the edge of the woods at that point. Can we do without lights? Let's do it carefully, come on… OK we're looking at the thing, we're probably about 2-3 hundred yards away.

[**Like an eye winking at you**]

It looks like an eye winking at you, it's still moving from side to side and when we put the starscope on it, it's sort of a hollow center right, a dark center, it's...

LT ENGLUND: It's like a pupil...

LT COLONEL HALT: It's like the pupil of an eye looking at you, winking . ... and the flash is so bright to the starscope, that err... it almost burns your eye.

(Break in tape)

[**Five lights seen**]

LT COLONEL HALT: We've passed the farmer's house and are crossing the next field and we now have multiple sightings of up to five lights with a similar shape and all, but they seem steady rather than pulsating – a glow with a red flash. We've just crossed the creek...

LT ENGLUND: Here we go...

LT COLONEL HALT: What kinda readings are we getting now? We're getting three good clicks on the meteor and we're seeing strange lights in the sky.

(Break in tape)

[2.44am] LT COLONEL HALT: 2.44: We're at the far side of the farmers, the second farmers field and made sighting again about 110 degrees. This looks clear out to the coast. It's right on the horizon... Moves about a bit and flashes from time to time... Still steady and red in colour. Also, after negative readings in the field, we're picking up slight readings 4-5 clicks now on the meter.

(Break in tape)

[3.05am-] – Two objects half moon shaped seen

LT COLONEL HALT: 3.05: We see strange err, strobe like flashes to the, err ... almost

sporadic, but there's definitely something there, some kind of phenomena. 3.05: At about err... 10 degrees horizon err directly north, we got two strange objects, err ...half moon shape, dancing about with colored lights on them. but err. it has to be about 5-10 miles out, maybe less. The half moons have now turned into full circles as though there was an eclipse or something there for a minute or two.

(Break in tape)

3.15am LT COLONEL HALT: 3.15: Now we've got an object about ten degrees directly south...

SGT NEVELS: There's one to the left.

LT COLONEL HALT: 10 degrees off the horizon and the ones to the north are moving; one's moving away from us.

SGT NEVELS: It's moving out fast.

LT COLONEL HALT: They're moving out fast.

MASTER SGT BALL: There's one on the right heading away too.

LT COLONEL HALT: Yeah, they're both heading north. Hey, here he comes from the south; he's coming in toward us now.

MASTER SGT BALL: Shit.

LT COLONEL HALT: Now were observing what appears to be a beam coming down to the ground.

[Excited shouting in the background]

MASTER SGT BALL: Look at the colors... shit

LT COLONEL HALT: This is unreal.

(Break in tape)

3.30am LT COLONEL HALT: 3.30: And the objects are still in the sky, although the one to the south looks like it's loosing a little bit of altitude. We're turning around and heading back toward the base. The object to the sou... the object to the south is still beaming down lights to the ground.

(Break in tape)

4am LT COLONEL HALT: 0:400 Hours one object still hovering over the Woodbridge base at about 5-10 degrees off the horizon. ...Still moving erratic and similar lights beaming down as earlier.

End of tape transcript

Nick Pope regarding the claims of radiation – Seven times normal

"Few aspects of the Rendlesham Forest incident have been as widely misunderstood or misrepresented as the radiation levels taken at the landing site. The primary source document is, of course, Charles Halt's 13th January 1981 memo to the MOD. This sets out the radiation levels recorded by Sgt. Nevels. This is, in effect, the raw data. A lesser-known but arguably more important document is a Defence Intelligence Staff memo dated 23rd February 1981. It's an assessment of the radiation levels. This document does two things.

Firstly, it states that the peak level recorded "seems significantly higher than the average background". Secondly, and better still, it quantifies this, by giving us the peak reading (0.1 milliroentgens) and the average background (around 0.015 milliroentgens). From this, we can calculate that the peak level was around seven time's normal – actually, for those who appreciate a little numerical spookiness, the number is 6.66! I rechecked the data on two separate occasions. The first time was in 1994, during a cold case review of the incident that I conducted at the MOD, with staff at the Defence Radiological Protection Service. The second time was in 2013, with Monroe Nevels, when I interviewed him as part of a Science Channel TV show that I was presenting."

Not thirty times normal!

"True believers have occasionally inflated the figure and claimed that the levels were thirty times normal. I have no idea who first came up with this figure and on what basis, but it's just plain wrong. Die-hard debunkers tried a different kind of dishonesty, suggesting that the radiation levels might not be as significant as the MOD suspected, by implying that the Geiger counter used was not appropriate for the task, and even speculating that the dial might have been misread. I'm wary when ufologists start trying to second guess the measurements taken by the military personnel who were actually there, or questioning the contemporaneous scientific assessment. There being no such thing as a UFO radiation detector, Nevels used the equipment available to him, and the Defence Intelligence Staff assessment was made on the basis of the readings reported to the MOD.

We can only use the data we have, not the data we'd like to have, or think we should have had. That's the way science works. In any case, such speculation misses the key point: the radiation readings peaked in the three indentations found where the craft was seen to have landed. It's like using a metal detector and hearing a signal; in a sense, it doesn't matter what make or model of metal detector you're using, or whether its dial reads 7 out of 10, or 8 out of 10; the key point is that you got a signal telling you that there's something noteworthy at the specific location.

Of course, the big unknown in all of this is the source of the radiation. There's even confusion over whether the radiation was beta or gamma. The instrument Nevels used has a beta shield that ensures only gamma radiation enters, and at one point on Halt's tape recording Nevels states that the shield has been removed, but it's not entirely clear when this was done. Additionally, because we don't know what radioactive element (isotope) was involved, we don't know the half-life. I've returned to the forest twice in the last few years, with a Geiger counter, while filming for two separate TV shows on the incident. In both cases I found some potentially interesting spikes in the vicinity of the landing site, but nothing that would currently pose a danger. "

Nick Pope – Project Condign

"The question of whether or not the radiation levels posed a health hazard at the time is a separate one. Many of the witnesses believe they've suffered health problems as a result of their encounter in Rendlesham Forest. John Burroughs, in particular, believes heart problems that nearly proved fatal were caused in this way. His attorney, Pat Frascogna, was getting nowhere with his struggle to get a settlement from the US Department of Veterans Affairs (VA), until he cited an obscure sentence from a declassified MoD intelligence study on UFOs, codenamed **Project Condign.** *The extract stated 'The well-reported Rendlesham Forest/Bentwaters event is an example where it might be postulated that several observers were probably exposed to UAP radiation for longer than normal UAP sighting periods'. Confronted with this quote, the VA settled in full with John Burroughs, in January 2015."*

If there was nothing there, then why did John get paid compensation?

"John Burroughs secured the settlement after years of trying to prove his ill-health was caused by the encounter in Rendlesham Forest. A former Ministry of Defence (MOD) official said the payout confirms what he saw was real and had caused him physical harm. Mr Burroughs put forward a declassified report as evidence he had been injured during the event on Boxing Day 1980.

He said disability coverage from the US Veteran's Association offered 'some closure', but that he now wanted unrestricted access to his full medical records." Every step along the way people have said it's not true. Some people will always say that.

We were denied access to records, mainly dating back to 1979, which we believe would have shown John had no health problems when he entered the air force, but that he developed heart problems and other ailments that arose from the incident.

Mr Frascogna said: 'Condign specifically mentions the incident and how radiation from unidentified aerial phenomena could cause injury. John was able to furnish that document, and another dating back to the incident, when a radiation reading found levels to be significantly higher than normal.'

Mr Burroughs, who suffers heart problems and has a pacemaker, said: 'I'm very happy we finally have some closure'.

Condign explained that there is a phenomenon that governments of this world are well aware of. The question is where it comes from."

Nick Pope

Nick Pope – author of *Encounter in Rendlesham Forest: The Inside Story of the World's Best-Documented UFO Incident* – who worked on the government's UFO desk in the early 1990, said:

"After years of denial, this is official confirmation that what they encountered was real and caused them physical harm. This welcome development doesn't give us a definitive explanation of the Rendlesham Forest incident, but it takes us ever closer to the truth."

Rick Bobo – Security patrolman hears airmen in woods_

"I think I was the first to report the sighting that night. I was on the tower at Bentwaters; you get a good view from up there.

There were several lights and there was this huge ship over the forest. I'd say it looked circular but, remember, I was over at Bentwaters and this was happening over at Woodbridge. I was instructed to watch it and can tell you that it was up there for about five hours, just hovering. I would say it was quite low in the sky. Someone came to the tower and watched it through a scope. I don't know who he was; he was from a different department. I wasn't told anything and I didn't get to look through the scope.

I heard some of the radio transmissions – not all of them, you understand, because there were different frequencies. I heard over the radio that London had spotted something on their radar. I heard some of the radio transmissions from some of the men who were out there. They were reporting a 'light' going through the woods, it had bumped into a tree and they were getting radioactive readings from the area. They were discussing three impressions and stuff moving through the woods, toward Woodbridge. They kept switching to different frequencies, so I couldn't hear everything. I know there was a colonel with them."

(Source: Interview conducted by Georgina Bruni)

Rick Bobo – Oblong-shaped UFO sighted

"As you probably know, the night I saw [the UFOs] I was in the tower at the Bentwaters Weapons Storage Area. **The main object hovered out there for a long, long time.** *It never really moved anywhere else. It was kind of hard to see,* **but it was slightly oblong**, *I guess, and I seem to recall it had bluish and reddish lights on it. Not really lights, like aircraft lights, just a tint. It wasn't a star or planet, and it wasn't a lighthouse, as some people claim.*

I would say it was, maybe, as large as a half-dollar coin, held out at arm's length, but I don't know how far away it was; it was so dark that night, I could just make out the forest. Anyway, at the same time, I was listening to all of the radio communications coming from our sister base – Woodbridge. There was lots of chatter on the radio. I think I heard that Heathrow [Airport] had it on radar. I'm surprised no one scrambled a fighter. And, of course, I talked to people too, at our CSC. It was my job to keep an eye on the UFO and to report it if anything happened. Tim [Egercic] had taken [CSC] over before all this started happening, so I was talking to him. And he let me hear some of the chatter from Halt's team in the woods. I couldn't switch my radio *frequency over to that, but when I called Tim, I could hear some of that on the phone. And I think I talked to Charlie Waters, but I'm not sure about that, but I did talk to our area supervisor. That was either Sgt. 'Willie' Williams or Sgt. 'Clarence' George that night. **He told me to keep a close watch on the object.** When the object first caught my eye, it was already stationary. I didn't see it move to where it was and I didn't see it leave. I never left the tower and I kept a close eye on the object most of the time, you know, trying to figure out what it was and what it might do next."*

Rick Bobo – Like little drones!

Rick was asked if he had observed anything resembling beams of light coming down from the object at any time. He paused a moment, then said:

"No, not beams of light, but after it was hanging there a long while, I saw things shooting off it, really, really fast, like little sparks or something, maybe four or five of them – little pieces of light, all leaving within a minute [of one another] like they were getting out of there. I hate to say it, but they looked like little ships, like drones maybe, but I don't know. They were shooting off in all directions, but up into the sky, not down to the ground. Right after that, the big object just disappeared. I was watching it, at least I thought I was, but it was just gone. I don't know what happened to it."

(Source: Interview conducted by Robert Hastings)

Eastern Radar – Nothing but the truth

Squadron Leader Derek Coumbe was on duty as RAF Commander of Eastern Radar on the same night when Colonel Charles Halt telephoned, requesting confirmation of his sightings.

"They were very jumpy and panicky on the phone, but I personally checked the radar picture and there was absolutely nothing to be seen. They kept coming back and implying there should be something, but we kept a watch on it through the whole period and nothing was seen."

Coumbe impounded the radar tapes. In January 1981 they were removed by a joint RAF/USAF team from the Military Air Traffic Operations centre (MATO) at Uxbridge. This was not unusual but quite a common procedure that followed incidents such as a near-miss involving aircraft.

Nick Pope:

"I was to discover years later, the UFO had been tracked, after all. I spoke to a former RAF radar operator called Nigel Kerr. He was stationed at RAF Watton in Christmas 1980 and received a call from somebody at RAF Bentwaters. They wanted to know if there was anything unusual on his radar screen. He looked and for three or four sweeps, something did show up, directly over the base. But it faded away and no official report was ever made. It was only years later that Kerr even heard of the Rendlesham Forest incident and realised he might have a missing piece of the puzzle."

Charles Halt:

"Another example of a blatant cover up regarding the events which took place over Suffolk. We had a situation where trained military personnel had seen something highly unusual and wanted confirmation, instead it was denied."

Colonel Charles Halt played the tape for Wing Commander

"I came back to the base and briefed my boss on it. I played the tape for the Wing Commander, Gordon Williams – he was then a Colonel, now he's a retired three star General – and he just raised his eyebrows. He said, 'Gosh, can I borrow the tape?' I told him, 'Of course you can borrow the tape, Boss'. I gave him the tape. He took it out and played it for the Third Air Force Commander, who was the Commander for US Forces, in England – General Bazley. He listened to it at a staff meeting and turned to his staff and said, 'Well, what do we do now?' There was silence."

General Robert W. Bazley

"He said, 'I guess this is a British affair. It happened on their turf. Give it back to them', so he brought the tape back and handed it to me, and says, 'Tell the 'Brits' about it'. It's exactly what he told me. Gosh. So I went over and the Liaison Officer – Don Moreland, who we called the British Base Commander (we had two British Officers stationed with us) was on vacation, so I told his assistant and he didn't want to touch it with a pole, so Don came back, a few days later, and I went over and said, 'Don, uh, why don't you make some calls and see what your Government want. I'm sure they'd want to investigate this'.

So I waited, and waited, and waited, and a week or so went by ... and I kept asking. He said, 'I haven't heard, I haven't heard'. Finally, he and I agreed I'd write a brief

Winfg Commander Gordon WIlliams

memo, so I wrote a brief, one-page, cleaned up, so to speak, version of what happened, to see how much interest there were, or was, and, what would happen. I gave it to him.

MoD

He sent it off the Ministry of Defence, in London, and it was never heard or seen again. A copy found its way to his boss, at Mildenhall, Third Air Force Headquarters. Somehow or other, that copy survived for several years and, two or three years later, a gentleman by the name of Larry Fawcett heard about it from a friend, and he contacted the USAF under the Freedom of Information Act for release of that document.

At that time, a friend of mine was Third Air Force Com-mander, Pete Bent. He called me up and said, 'I'm going to have to release this document'. I said, number one, 'How did you get it?' He said, 'Boy! It beats me, but it's in the file here'. I said, 'Well, it wasn't addressed to you. It was addressed to the Ministry of Defence'. He said, 'Well, we have it, and we're going to have to release it', and I said, 'Please, don't. Your life, and mine, will never be the same'. He said, 'I'm sorry, we're going to have to'. Well, I was right on. I can tell you that because, the day after it was released, I met BBC1, BBC2, ITV, Japanese TV, German TV, every local radio station, every reporter worth his salt. It was unbelievable what happened the next day. I had to go into hiding, almost, and I almost became a recluse after that, so that's how the story came out, and that's in essence what happened.

Now there's a lot more to it. I've told people through the years, probably the biggest story is what happened afterwards. There's been an awful lot of interesting things happen, and I don't want to go into too many details here, but I am firmly convinced that there're an awful, there's an awful lot of interest, at an awful lot of agencies in the Government, that compete for, how shall I say, information and access to certain data. And, uh, there's all, there's been an awful lot of intrigue. I do know one or, if not, two of the original participants were given injections and some, how shall I say, hypnosis, uh, right after the incident occurred. There was a lot of clandestine, uh, sleuthing around, by various agencies, both from this side of the pond and the other side of the pond.

I have never been officially approached, although people from Kirtland and various sundry agencies have invited me to lunch that had an interest in this subject and things, and I played games with them, like they did with me. I think the only thing that has kept me out of, out of the middle of it, so to speak, is that I have some very, very high contacts, including probably the most senior Senator in Washington, and, uh, my last position as the Director of Inspections, Director for the DOD IG, where I had total inspection oversight for the whole Department of Defence, and had some very good contacts there. It's probably protected me, but some of the other people have been bothered and meddled with and, unfortunately, it's caused a lot of personal problems for them."

Colonel Charles I. Halt – What really happened at Bentwaters?

"What really happened at Bentwaters? I honestly don't know. Something very strange happened. I've been back several times. I've gone back to the site. I've sat down with any and everybody I can think that, you know, could shed some light on it. I've batted this around with Jacques Vallee. I've met the foremost Astrophysicist, from Great Britain, and gone through things with him, and I have a lot of unanswered questions, and probably we'll never have them answered. I'd like to have them answered. But, it was a very interesting experience. I'm not sure, if I had the opportunity to go out again, whether I'd do it again or not."

The facts not speculation!

"I don't go on many radio talk shows. I have done some TV documentaries, but the agreement is in writing has been beforehand that it would be honest, factual, above-board, and that I'd get to review it before they publish, because there's some real interesting people out there, including one who, as far as I'm concerned, wasn't there and has been telling a distorted tale.

So that, in essence, is what I know of what happened at Bentwaters. Now, I say, there's a lot of other intrigue and so forth that happened after the fact. I was telling somebody at lunch that I've been accused of everything, from cohorting with the devil to having participated in the second coming of Christ, so you meet some very strange people sometimes! Awful lot of credible people, an awful lot of very interested people that have some of the same questions I have, so, where do we go from here? I really don't know. I was hoping, maybe, to learn a little more today. I have, through the years, prised some more information out of some of the other participants, because they, for very personal reasons, didn't come completely forward on everything; in other words, they were concerned for their career, for their health, for their family, et cetera, so its unfortunate things have to be that way, but I think most of you probably understand that." Further, I did not experience any sustained ill effects. I cannot speak for the other individuals involved, as I'm told that several feel they have sustained lasting health problems."

Robert Hastings interview with Colonel Charles Halt

In another interview conducted during recent years, Robert Hastings (Author of *UFOs and Nukes: Extraordinary Encounters at Nuclear Weapons Sites*) asked him to briefly summarise his experience.

He replied:

"We saw objects that were under intelligent control."

Robert asked:

"What was the source of the intelligence?"

He replied:

"I don't know. It had to be something beyond [human technology] because of the way the objects moved — the speeds, the angles they turned, and the things they did."

Could the objects have been remotely controlled?

"Certainly."

He asked Colonel Halt:

"So you're saying that it was a technology beyond anything any country on Earth would have?"

UFO danced about in the sky!

Colonel Halt replied:

"I never saw any little green men, but it's possible it was alien technology. I sure would like to have the answers, but don't think I'll ever get them."

(And so would the other thousands/millions of people who have, over the years, witnessed similar objects and have never obtained satisfactory answers from the World Wide authorities.)

"We could very clearly see the UFO. It sort of danced about in the sky and it sent down beams of light. I noticed other beams of light coming down from the same object, falling in different places on the base. My boss, Col. Ted Conrad, was standing in his front yard in Woodbridge and he could see the beams of light falling down, and the people in the [Bentwaters] Weapons Storage Area and several other places on the base also reported the lights."

Colonel Charles I. Halt – It was not the lighthouse!

To those who maintain, in the face of adversity, that the lighthouse was responsible (flying or not), we should take into consideration what Colonel Halt said:

"At this time we could see the lighthouse; it was off to the side of this object by about 30°. This object was no lighthouse; it was dancing about in the forest, woods and all. The lighthouse has three different beams. It has a white rotating beam that does go around about every five seconds; it has a red light, and a green light. The white light revolves. The red light and green light are fixed at sea. They cannot be turned, even manually, toward the land ... and I've gone back and talked to the lighthouse keeper personally to verify this, thinking, you know, there's got to be an explanation of the red light. The lighthouse could not have been what we saw."

Three objects seen

"The objects appeared elliptical and then they turned full round, which I thought was quite interesting <u>all three doing that</u>. They were stationary for awhile and then they started to move at high speed in sharp angular patterns as though they were doing a grid search. About that same time, somebody noticed a similar object [in the southern sky]. It was round—did not change shape—and at one point it appeared to come toward us at a very high speed. It stopped overhead and sent down a small pencil-like beam, sort of like a laser beam. It was an interesting beam in that it stayed—it was the same size all the way down the beam. It illuminated the ground about ten feet from us and we just stood there in awe wondering whether it was a signal, a warning, or what it was. We really didn't know. It clicked-off as though someone threw a switch, and the object receded, back up into the sky. Then it moved back toward Bentwaters, and continued to send down beams of light, at one point near the weapons storage facility. I wondered if it was searching for something."

Tape-recording Colonel Charles I. Halt:

"Another interesting thing is that the Command Post, the Senior Command Post not the Police Command Post, the one that my radio tied into (which only talked to the Commanders and the other agencies outside of the base) had a 12 hour 12 inch commercial tape recorder. This recorded everything said last night and everything said in the Command Post. Every shift that came on duty looked at that tape and turned it over if there was nothing of any great significance. I know for a fact that somebody kept that tape. They copied that transmission or wiped that portion of the tape because a friend of mine heard it from somebody else in intelligence."

Increase in radio traffic – Richard Kirk

Richard Kirk was an NCO on loan from Martlesham Heath and in charge of the Bentwaters Telephone Communication Facility (located next to the Base Commander's hut) a few days after Christmas 1980.

"All I can say is that radio traffic became really heavy. I had problems finding a spare channel to carry out daily testing of the appliances. There was also an increased volume of personal traffic between the Telecommunications Facility and the Base Commander's hut, suggesting that an 'Alert' was in progress, although I am unable to say what the cause of the build-up was."

(Source: Richard Conway)

Unscheduled Galaxy C5 landing at Airbase

An alleged conversation took place between Graham Birdsall and Colonel Halt in 1995.

"During the height of the UFO activity off Base, an unmarked aircraft made an un-scheduled landing at RAF Woodbridge. I was puzzled when the aircraft came to a stop at the end of the runway, rather than into the parking slot. I set off in a jeep and drove towards the aircraft. As I approached, I saw numerous figures in white overalls emerging from the aircraft and making their way towards the adjoining forest. Armed guards were positioned close to the Galaxy. These wore no insignia to identify unit or rank. I spoke with one of the guards, who told me as I did not have proper clearance I would have to leave the scene – which I did. Following that plane's arrival, unmarked helicopters were also seen over the landing site during the following days.

I would deny this conversation – You have to keep in mind this was a foreign country to us. We had no authority here whatsoever, but I can assure you if it were in the US, we'd have had the place cordoned off with Military Police... I believe there is a conspiracy covering UFOs up and agents also attend various conferences too. I believe there are agencies within my Government and at least one in your government who are actively working towards that. Its simple, if you do talk you could disappear – it's that serious."

FILMS & PHOTOGRAPHS

What happened to the films taken of the UFO landing site?

A roll of 35mm film was taken on the same night by Sgt. James Penniston. When developed, it was found to be fogged. Ray Boeche, an investigator based in the States who had interviewed some of the airmen involved told us that he had heard from a highly placed USAF official, at the Pentagon, that photos were indeed taken, *but not all of them* came out fogged.

John Burroughs – Photographs and written statement

It was alleged that John Burroughs took some photographs of the object when it landed, but had his film and camera taken away by Sergeant Combs and Trainee Sergeant Ingrams of the Air Force Office of Special Investigations (OSI).

We emailed John Burroughs, in July 2013, and asked him whether he was prepared to confirm the originality of his written statement and any photographs taken, bearing in mind the content of his written (but unsigned statement) which does not mention any lighthouse and confirms his closest approach to the object was 50 metres, and that he and John were 15-20 metres apart.

He told us:

"Nice try John, and you will have to wait for the book to come out just like everybody else. Oh and then you can add what we have to say to your book you're working on. The problem is you will have to start from scratch after we release everything we know!"

Following this exchange of information, in late July 2013, our email account was blitzed by emails from John saying:

'Goodbye tin soldier,' which we interpreted as rather childish, but do not bear him any ill. We had enjoyed talking to him at the previous conferences we had attended and wish him well.

Gary Tomoyasu, the Base Photographer

"I worked at the photo laboratory during the UFO incident. We did process film that was brought in by someone from SF or OSI – can't remember exactly. I do remember that an alert photographer was called out, but don't remember which day and if it was at night during the sojourn through the woods. I do remember someone from the shop went out during the day with SF, or one of the investigators, and I remember seeing photos of round indentions that were in a roughly triangular pattern. We gave the negatives and the proof sheets to the requestor, as was standard operating procedure. We kept some negatives from the Information Office (now Public Affairs) and some other types of jobs. I've always wondered about the UFO sightings, though we did kind of make light of the incident. I do remember a CNN three-part report the year after I got back to the States – 1983 – each part was only about three to five minutes long. We never really thought about printing copies for ourselves; after all, it was just pictures in the forest and dimples in the ground. Sorry this isn't much help. I do remember staying at Woodhall, in 1984, when on Temporary Duty Assignment from the States. The barman told us that Lt. Colonel Halt was back in England because of the UFO incident."

Georgina Bruni – Lighthouse was not the culprit!

"I would hope there is now enough of a reason to dispel the theory that the lighthouse was the culprit. Having been presented with more facts, both Vince Thurkettle and former policeman – Dave King, have reconsidered their original theory and have now admitted they are no longer certain that it was the lighthouse the witnesses saw. Let us also consider the testimonies of the witnesses themselves. Adrian Bustinza was forced into agreeing it was the lighthouse when interrogated by special agents.

Charles Halt, Jim Penniston, John Burroughs, and others are in no doubt that the lighthouse was not what they saw. Therefore, it looks as if the sceptics will have to turn to the AFOSI for support on this matter."

Christmas 1980 – UFO seen over Woodbridge

Other witnesses to something strange seen happening during the 1980 Christmas period included Anne Hopton-Scott, who was driving back from Woodbridge, one evening, when she saw a bright object moving through the sky, which appeared to follow the curve of the road

Anne Hopton-Scott

"Suddenly, it came up and went straight over my car, making a terrific whooshing noise."

Suffolk: December 1980 – 'Spinning top' UFO hovers over house

Mr Charles Prentice from Bury St Edmunds, Suffolk:

"During the end of December 1980, my wife and I were awoken by a light outside the window. We looked out to see the amazing sight of a craft, hovering at one point three feet away from our bedroom window; I could have opened the window and touched it. It was about the length of a large car; and the shape of a child's spinning top.

It had a brilliant white light on the top of it, with a bright pulsating light just below that. It was there for about three-quarters of an hour before it left." [See full report on page 338]

Fire service turned away from Airbase – warned to keep quiet!

Bearing in mind the possibility that an aircraft may have crashed, taking into consideration the airmen's early concerns, one presumes that in addition to the police being called out, then why didn't anybody ring the Ambulance and fire service?

Brenda Butler:

"I interviewed a retired fireman, some years ago, who told me that fire tenders were sent to RAF Woodbridge and RAF Bentwaters, following the UFO incidents reported in December 1980. Both appliances from Ipswich were refused entry and the firemen were warned that if they talked about their involvement, they would lose their pensions. Another thing that has crossed my mind, so many times, is to wonder why (if those marks found on the forest floor were rabbit marks) did they seal off the area and place posts in the ground, in the presence of a local police officer and USAF official?"

Major Cossa and interview by OSI Agents

Carl Thompson – the former radio communications specialist at Bentwaters – was to tell of another conversation with his (unnamed) colleague, following the UFO sighting.

"About a week or so later, the man was called by his Squadron Commander – Major Cossa – and told to report for a briefing.

He was gone most of an afternoon, but when he came back he was really agitated.

I asked him what's up. He replied 'we are not to speak about the UFO. I know what I saw!' "

He told Carl that, during the briefing, someone – he assumed it was OSI (Office of Special Investigations) – told everyone there that night they hadn't seen anything.

Carl Thompson:

"I think that upset my colleague more than anything. According to him, they called all the police liars.

My colleague said 'They told us that we did not see it, and were never to speak of it'. He was really upset. He said (the OSI agents), 'had talked to them as a group and then talked to them individually'... You know, went over their statements with them. He said they told him he was a liar, that he would never have a career, and all that. You know, threatening him, but he told me that he couldn't get into the details. We never talked about it again."

A while later Carl tried to ask some of the Security Police about the incident, when he saw them at the Weapons Storage Area, but they were fairly tight-lipped about it. They just told him that when they went into the forest on the night of December 27/28th, they took light-alls with them.

"All of a sudden, the lights quit working; the vehicle engines quit, and the radios had a lot of static on them. Then, after a few minutes, everything just started up again.

"I didn't know much more than that, until I saw all of the reports from Colonel Halt and the others on TV. That's about all I can think to tell you."

Security Patrolman Officer Bill Ferris hears talk of 'aliens'

He was living off Base at the time, and carrying out a patrol with another serviceman, when he learnt, from a colleague, of an incident involving strange *'lights'* seen by other Security Police in Rendlesham Forest, and that they had gone out to investigate.

"When they got there, they radioed the Base Commander to tell him that a craft had landed, as a result of which the officer had met up with the 'beings' from the craft. The next night there was another UFO incident. When the man first told me I thought it was incredible, but nobody else said anything to me, so I blew it off. I figured if it was that amazing, the Base would be buzzing and it wasn't."

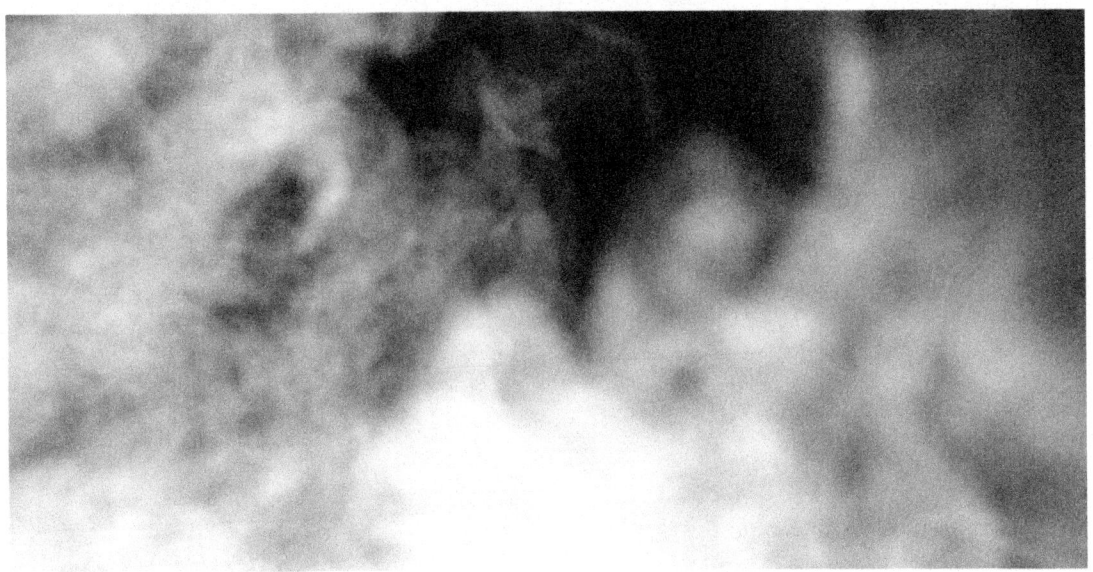

11pm on 28th December – Strange *'figure'* seen on the A12 road

Anne Clarke was the back seat passenger in a car travelling south, along the A12, at 11pm on 28th December 1980.

"Just past the South Wold turn, I saw a 'figure' sitting on a fence, well back from the right-hand side. I watched, as it got off the fence and walked to the edge of the road, in very small steps – as if weak, or suffering from illness – followed by another similarly dressed 'person', wearing a long and voluminous cloak, or habit, heavy cowled, preventing me from seeing their faces. Their hands, held high in front of them, were holding white cards, or something similar. I first thought to myself what a stupid place to hitch-hike, or were they in fancy dress? Such thoughts were dispelled almost immediately when, in that split second, I looked back and they had disappeared. When I told the others in the car what I had just seen, they all expressed surprise – having seen nothing at all."

(Source: Ivan W. Bunn/Personal interview)

Still the subject of media attention!

Here are some images depicting those pivotal moments that took place now over 35 years ago, which continue to attract the attention of people worldwide, who travel to that location eager to see for themselves what, when, and where, it happened. Inevitably, this even includes numerous cartoons showing those events some of which are malicious others in a more light hearted vein as created by UFO enthusiast Peter Parish who has spent a number of years recording the various phenomena which has manifested in the forest right up to the present day.

FINDINGS BY PETER GEORGE PARISH

TREE,S AROUND
WOODBRIDGE AND
BENTWATERS STILL
STANDING AFTER
THE STORM 1987.
SOME HAVE BEEN
MARKED WITH SCRAPES
AND BANGS WITH
A HEAVY SHARP OBJECT.
FROM GROUND TO
THE TOPS, SIGNS
OF TREE,S BEEN
HEATED AS WELL
SAP HAS BURST OUT OF THE
BARK IN MANY PLACES.

MARKS
HIT INTO CLEAN WOOD
30FT OR MORE

SAP BUBBELED OUT

I HAVE HAD, LOTS OF
REMARKS. NAME A FEW
1. LIGHTNING. SOME ARE LIKE,
2. (DEER) WITH LONG LEGS
3. STORM, YES A FEW MIGHT
   BE
4. FORSTERY MARKS
5. PLANE CRASH
6. OR ————

TREE SAP DRIPPING
OFF
COULD BE WHAT
HALT SAW

OLD MARK

POINT 2
POINT 3

P.G.P.

We cannot help but wonder if there is any connection with some very odd images captured on 35mm and digital cameras over the years. Are they paranormal in origin? Would such objects have been the basis of conversation in those days if caught on camera and then discarded, the effects attributed to camera defects? We shall never know.

Dawn Holloway (left) with Brenda Butler and Peter Parish.

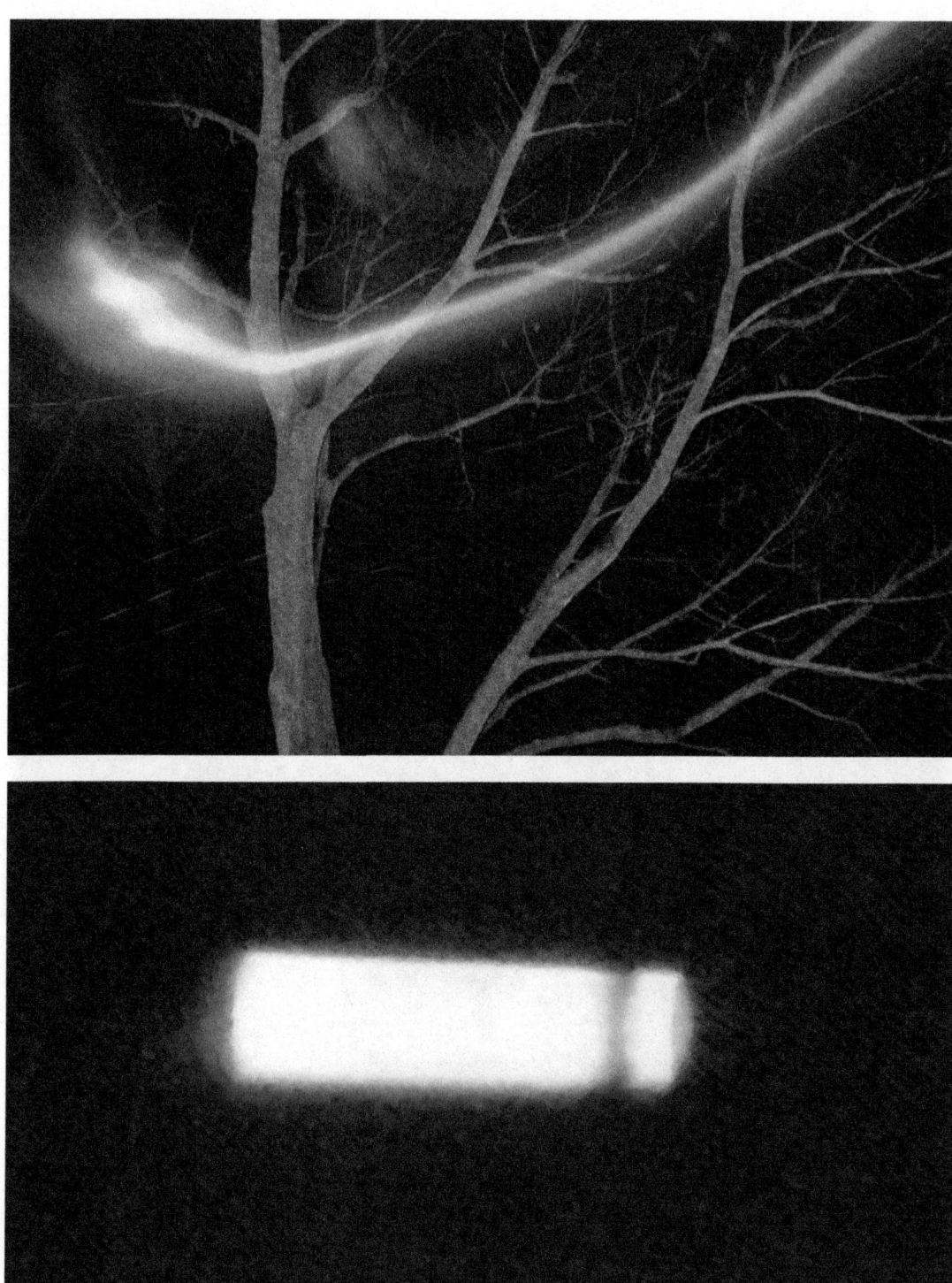

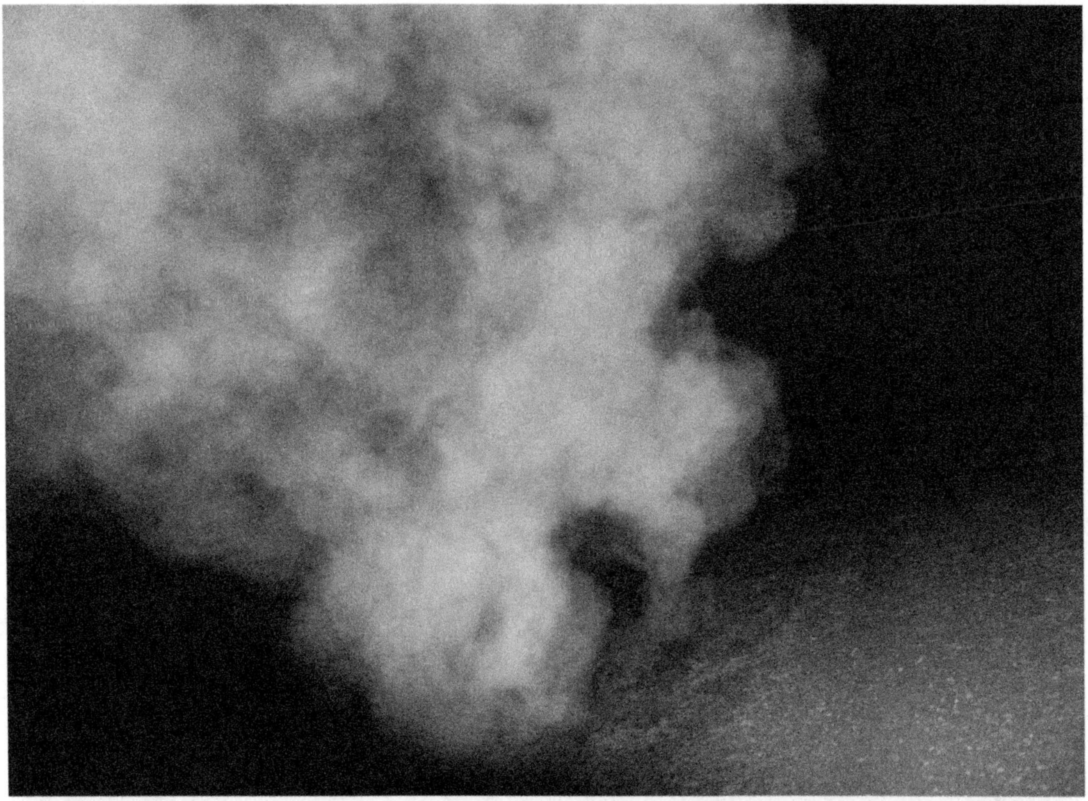

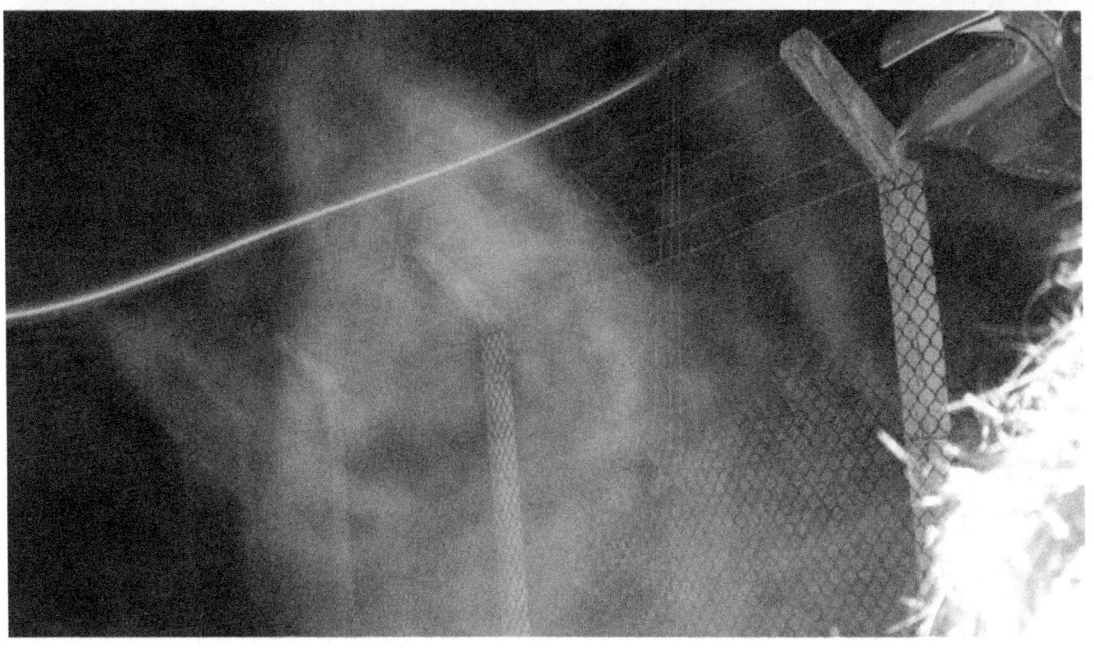

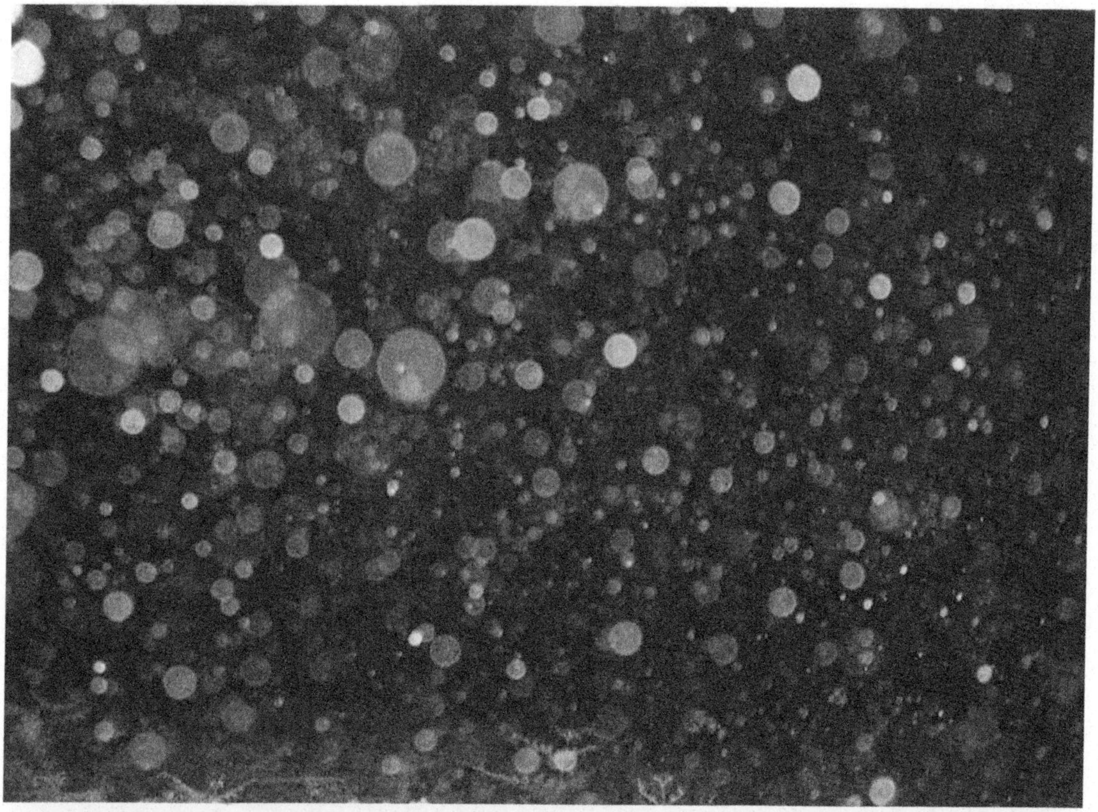

During our first visit to Suffolk in 1995 Dawn captured something odd in the sky over Bentwaters air base, this was not the first or the last occasion she would pick up anomalies on her 35mm camera.

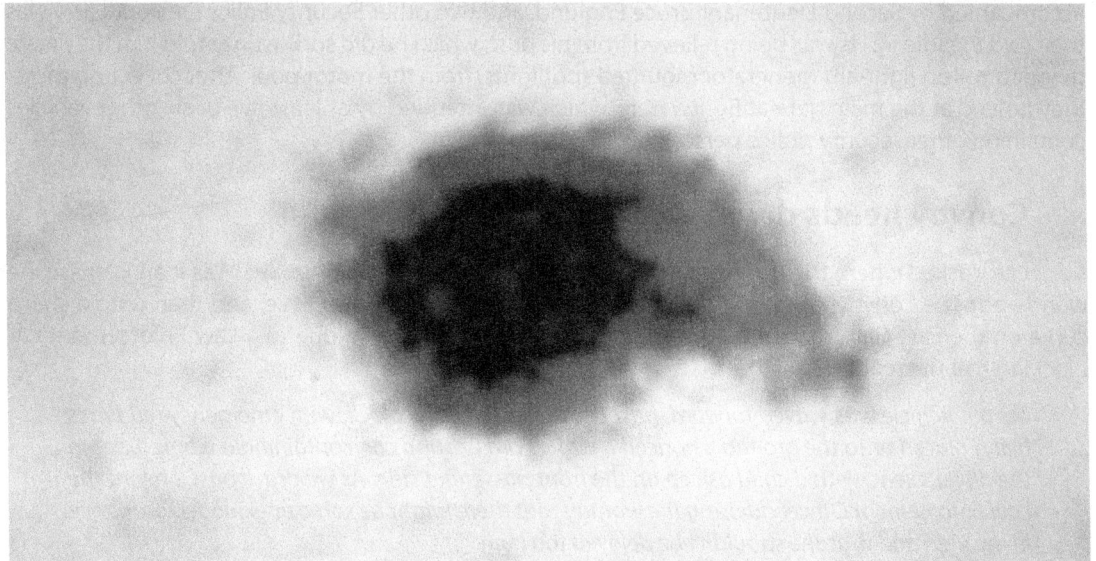

11.45pm on 28th December – Airman Larry Warren's account

At 11.45pm (approximately) on 28th December 1980, USAF Security Officer Airmen Lawrence 'Larry' Warren – then 19 years of age – was standing guard at Bentwaters perimeter post 18, when he overheard some radio transmissions being broadcast between the Bentwaters Weapons Storage Area and Woodbridge control tower.

Larry Warren

> *"…about some funny lights having been seen, bobbing up and down over the forest, near Woodbridge Airbase, some five miles away. (I had no knowledge of the incidents that had occurred over the previous nights). Suddenly, out of the darkness came five deer, clearly panicked by something. Two of them actually jumped the fence and were out of sight in seconds."*

Adrian Bustinza arrives

A few minutes later a Security Police truck arrived, driven by Sergeant Adrian Bustinza, accompanied by Second Lieutenant Bruce Englund, and two other Security Police Officers. Larry was then told to radio in. He was being relieved from his post, which he did so. Bustinza told him they were going to collect light-alls (generator mounted spotlights) from the motor pool. After collecting these, they arrived at the main gate at Bentwaters, which was attended by at least five or six other vehicles containing other security police personnel.

Convoy heads down along East Gate road

Larry asked where they were all going and was told Woodbridge Airbase. Was it an Exercise, he wondered? The 'convoy' sped on through the Suffolk countryside, past Eyke, and then onto a sharp curve on the East Gate road, where they were forced to slow down, due to a Law Enforcement car blocking half the road.

> *"As our vehicle was waved forward, past the makeshift road block, with emergency red flares being placed onto the ground, I noticed a white Ford Cortina car, containing a woman, sat in the driver's seat, with a child asleep on the front passenger side. As we drove past, I heard the Law Enforcement Officer advising the woman that there might be some unexploded ordnance in the area and that she shouldn't be delayed too long."*

The vehicles moved along a road with a pine forest on the left (Rendlesham). Somebody in the vehicle ahead shouted out, *"Where are we supposed to go?"* The reply was *"turn left at East Gate".*

12.30am on 29th December

Following a drive of approximately half-a-mile, the trucks entered a large clearing. Larry alighted, where he stood awaiting orders. After handing over their weapons, Larry checked his watch. It read 12.30am (29th December 1980). A Flight Commander with the rank of Captain approached and joined the group – now consisting of Larry Warren, Adrian Bustinza, and two other airmen – and instructed them that radio silence was to be maintained. They were then ordered to follow the Captain down the footpath and into the woods. Approximately a few hundred yards along the path, the group turned right and deeper into the forest.

Larry Warren:

"I heard a radio transmission, 'You people have to avoid those hot spots. Remember they're marked October Number One, over'.

I knew the code they were referring to – the First Officer at the scene. I thought, perhaps, we were going to be fighting a forest fire, but why is it not fire personnel? I started to feel uneasy. Things seemed almost surreal. The forest was, by now, deathly calm, although radio traffic was increasing. We continued on our journey into the forest, until we came up to field separated from the forest by a broken wire fence, about a hundred feet in front of us."

Beyond that could be seen military personnel apparently walking around something on the ground, which grew bright and then dimmed. As they approached the location, Adrian Bustinza whispered to Larry, *"That's what happened to me in Alaska"*.

Larry wondered what on earth was happening, after noticing an airmen clearly distressed, with his head in his hands, crying, being comforted by a Master Sergeant.

Encounters ground fog

"We moved even closer, enabling me to see what looked like a localized yellow/green, almost transparent coloured ground fog, about a foot in height, with something glowing very brightly inside. Close by were two disaster awareness officers, carrying yellow Geiger counters. Another man was taking photographs of the object, while others were filming; this was the sight that greeted me and about forty other service personnel."

Red light appears!

"I heard what sounded like a pilot's communication, followed by, 'here it comes, here it comes'. Over the far end of the field, towards the direction of the North Sea, a red light appeared in the sky at this time. I felt as if my physical movements had, in some way, slowed down. The light cleared the pine trees bordering the field and descended in an arc, until approximately twenty feet above the object, when it exploded in a blinding flash, shards and particles of light raining down onto the object on the ground."

Pyramidal object now appears

"In its place, occupying where the fog had been, appeared what looked like a machine – almost the shape of a pyramid – showing an off-red glow on the top, with a pearl white body, creating a rainbow effect, and a base of bright blue cobalt lights, and what looked like boxes, pipes, and strange extensions, covering its surface – its image constantly distorting, best seen on the edge of peripheral vision. My impression was it looked old, but advanced. I never saw any insignia, flags, windows, or identifying marks on it. From the main body of the object were three delta-like appendages protruding, giving it an almost threatening appearance."

An officer approached Adrain Bustinza and Larry Warren, ordering them to walk with him close to the object. When about ten to fifteen feet away, Larry's eyes began to water – at which point he and the others were ordered back to their original positions."

Colonel Gordon Williams arrives at the scene

According to Larry a staff car arrived, containing Colonel Gordon Williams and other officers – some dressed in civvies – who liaised with other officers already there.

"A glowing ball of bluish gold light moved slowly, with apparent purpose, from behind the right 'delta' of the object and came to a halt about ten feet away from the 'machine', enabling me to see, in the glow, what looked like kids."

Entities seen

"It then split into three separate glowing cylinders, each containing what appeared to be a living creature that I would describe as small, 3-4 feet high, ghost-like in appearance, showing large heads, with black eyes, wearing bright silvery clothing. Oddly, I never felt frightened while watching the drama unfurl in front of me. Colonel Williams approached them slowly and stood looking down at them. They cocked their heads at him and I felt the impression they were communicating with him in some way; suddenly, behind us, a loud noise was heard – as if something heavy, like a tree, had fallen. Immediately, the 'entities' moved their arms up to the front of their chests and floated backwards to almost under the craft, before slowly returning back towards Williams, who turned towards another officer and handed him something I was unable to make out."

At this point, Larry and his comrades were instructed to return to the trucks and wait. As he did so he looked back, seeing the object and entities were still there, with Colonel Williams still in conversation with other officers.

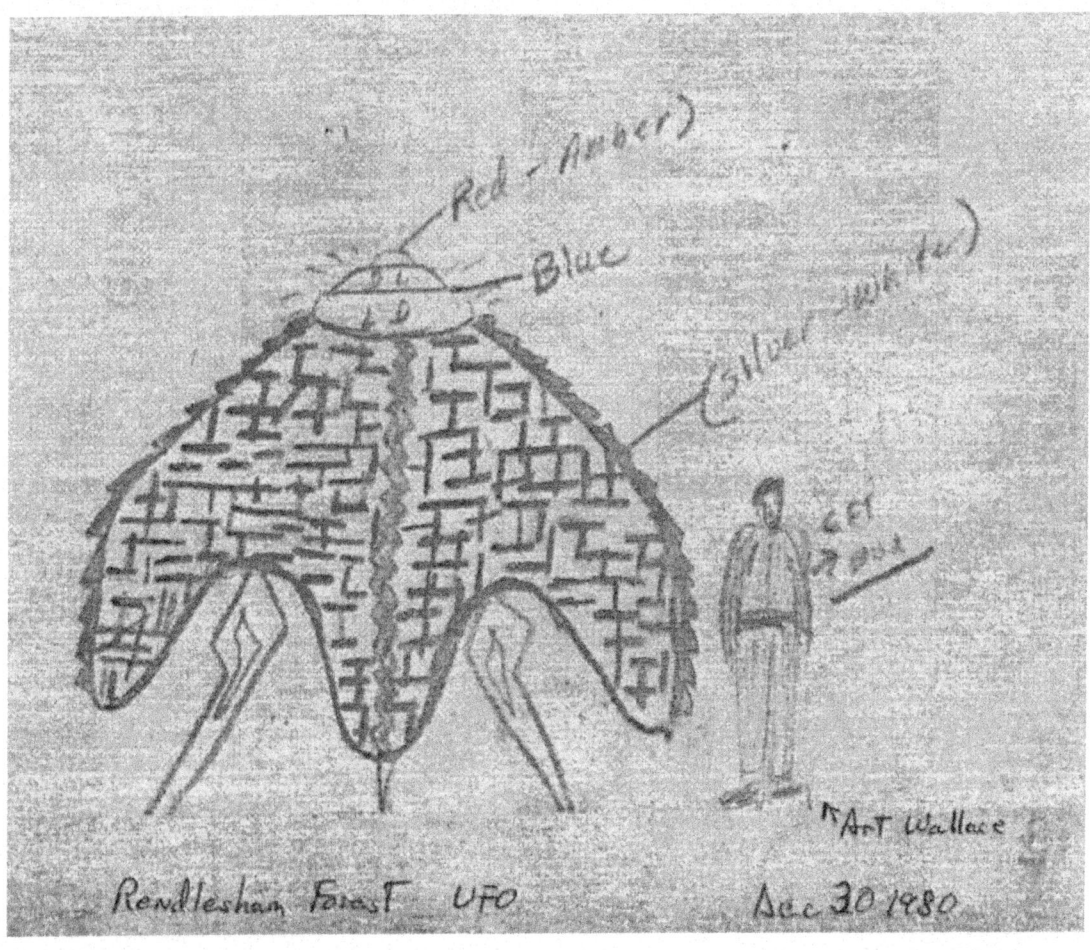

Sketches by "Art Wallace" of UFO entity, Rendlesham Forest Dec 30, 1980

Early morning of 29th December – Tim Egercic

On the early morning of 29th December 1980, someone from the Weapons Storage Area was asked to go to the tower and see if they could see the *'lights'*, now reported for the third night running. Training Sgt. Clarence George asked Tim if he wanted to go over and have a look – but he declined, not wanting to miss out on radio transmissions.

"I was posted all night in the alarm monitor building, so Sgt. Bob Sliwowski made his way over to the Alarm Monitor building. After returning from three days off, on 1st January 1981, someone (not me) on 'D' Flight asked M.Sgt. Ball during guard mount what happened, at which point he said he wasn't allowed to say what he saw. Charlie Waters, who was posted in the Weapons Storage Area, only stated he saw the object hovering before he saw it descend into the forest. At no point since the December 1980 UFO sightings have I come across anyone who claims a UFO hovered."

11pm – Late December 1980 – Domed UFO over Ipswich

Another witness to UFO activity during this period was Ron Bowers – a grounds man from Ipswich.

Ron Bowers and Peter Parish

"I can't be sure of the exact date. It would have been late December 1980, about 11pm, when my daughter – Kim, came rushing in to tell me she had seen something strange in the night sky. I looked out of the bedroom window and saw a domed object, hovering just above the horizon, over the Sutton Hoo direction (an ancient burial ground). I could see a number of smaller red and white lights moving in opposite directions around it. I thought it might have been some sort of top secret aircraft from the nearby Bentwaters/Woodbridge Airbase. It was only when I came across a copy of Sky Crash *that I wondered if there was any connection."*

(Source: Personal interview)

31st December – Chris Pennington

Actually, the first person who was told about a UFO having landed in the forest, at Tangham Forest, Rendlesham, near Woodbridge Airbase, between Christmas 1980 and the New Year was not Brenda Butler but her partner at the time – Chris Pennington – during a party held at the family farmhouse, at Aldringham, on New Year's Eve, 1980.

Chris Pennington was approached by an airman, referred to as 'Steve Roberts' who asked Chris whether he should tell Brenda. Chris told him to go ahead.

Downed UFO – fact or fiction!

Bizarre claims made that the authorities had been responsible for repairing a UFO which crashed in Rendlesham Forest seems an incredible scenario, stretching the bounds of imagination to say the least. In addition to what Larry Warren alleged, Brenda Butler was also given similar information by her 'informant' – John David Ingalls (Steve Roberts) – about parts being manufactured to repair a 'craft' which had landed in the forest, a few days after all of this was alleged to have taken place.

John Hanson – Claim of *'Spaceship'* stored at Woodbridge Airbase!

In 2009, USA UFO researcher – Mary Margaret Zimmer, contacted Philip Mantle, following a telephone call made to her from a John Traylor – formerly a resident of Greytriers Road, Woodbridge, Suffolk, now living in the United States.

Mary Margaret Zimmer

"Hello! This is Mary-Margaret Zimmer from MUFON in Miami, Florida, USA. This e-mail is in regard to the Bentwaters-Woodbridge incident in 1980.

I have spoken on the phone with a man named John Traylor, age 40, who lives in Boynton Beach Florida. He allowed me to tape the interview. He did not remember the date, but said that the weather was cold; he thought it was near the American Thanksgiving.

John's father was a serviceman and worked in munitions at the Rendlesham base, but the family lived in nearby Woodbridge. When John was 11 or 12 years of age he and his sister were playing "dodge the headlights". The area became very quiet and they looked up and saw a shimmering black triangle with a flat front and a white light underneath which flew over slowly. John said it was low enough to have been lifted on a crane. It landed in back of the school he attended, Kingston Middle School. The object then rose straight up high into the air, then went down and disappeared.

Mr Cannel the P.E. teacher went to see what had landed in the playing field behind the school. (The headmaster of the school was Mr Spicer.) The area was cordoned off. The children were told that a helicopter had landed. When the men in white suits came into the area the children were told that they were filming an episode of "Dr. Who." Several months' later the brand-new school was torn down and a retirement home was built in its place, supposedly because of radiation. John said that the "whole town" saw the object and some of them took pictures of it. John's mother took a picture which she still has in her possession.

This part is hearsay. John did not see these things himself, but heard them from a friend of his mother who was an SP on the base, from a brother-inlaw, and from others in Woodbridge.. After the triangular object left the school grounds it landed "behind the gate" in back of the base. It was pulled into the base and taken into a hanger. A colonel was present. The SP said that two tall slim, muscular blond blue-eyed people, got out of the craft. He said that they "spoke every language". They touched another SP and "knocked him out". According to the SP who spoke with John's mother, there was something wrong with the craft and instructions were given to repair it. The metal fabrication company in Ipswich, Ransom and Rapier, did the repairs and returned the part to the craft, which left. The company of Ransom and Rapier closed soon after that, supposedly after being given money to do so.

Townspeople were told not to talk about the object. They accepted this order calmly, but occasionally spoke about it "over a beer". John said he would contact his mother to try to obtain either a copy of the picture or the negative. The picture was taken in the dark, so it is not as clear as he would like. He would also contact his sister Stephanie who saw the object and was about 14 at the time. Stephanie was once married to David Pratt of Ipswich Engineering (or Ipswich Fabrication). David's father worked at Ransom and Rapier, the company that is alleged to have made the part to repair the craft."

John Hanson contacts John Traylor

He claimed that the object seen by the airmen in Rendlesham Forest was an alien craft, and that repairs were made. Philip then asked me to look into the allegations made by John Traylor. I spoke to John, and this is what he had to say:

"Following the sighting of a triangular UFO over the nearby Porter's Wood, towards the end of December 1980, my brother-in-law's father, Ken Pratt, who had connections with the Ipswich-based Company – Ransome & Rapier – owned a factory in Ipswich, which made the skeletons for Tesco Stores and supplied the steel for the bridge over the River Orwell. He was approached by someone who asked him to manufacture a piece of machinery for a 'spaceship, stored at RAF Woodbridge, in December 1980, and was shown a piece of metal he had never seen before. Unfortunately, Ken later committed suicide."

Talk of a UFO stored at the Airbase

"I spoke to John's mother, Yvonne – now living in the Berkshire area (who asked me not to reveal her full name) – on a number of occasions about this matter, over the telephone.

'They closed the airbase down at the back of Rendlesham Forest. Reports had it that the 'spaceship' was actually in one of the hangers. All of the airmen who saw it were shipped off back to the States. My husband was sworn to secrecy. Everybody was talking about it. I made the kids come indoors. It was real strange.'

The sighting of the UFO, as seen by her son and friends, was something Yvonne found easy to talk about. However, there appeared to be some, perhaps, understandable reluctance to discuss, in any depth, the extraordinary claims made by her son, regarding Ken's role in repairing a 'landed craft' at the airbase. Yvonne could only tell us that 'the spacemen wanted a piece made of strange metal' and seemed unwilling to discuss his involvement further.

Whether her attitude was due to a subsequent break-up in the marriage and, later, divorce of her (unnamed) daughter to Ken's son, some years ago, or her husband's current employment with the US Government is anybody's guess. Perhaps they feared attracting the attention of the media once this story was published.

It was in wintertime. The nights were drawing in. About 4pm, my youngest son at the time – John (now over 40) – arrived home.

I asked him where he had been. He told me he had been out playing with some other boys in Porter's Wood, one of whom was Johnny Cracknell (who died some years later, aged 20).

Johnny told him about a 'spaceship' in Porter's Wood. As dusk fell my children came in and asked whether they could go to Porter's Wood and have a look, because some other friends of theirs had told them the Dr. Who series was being filmed about a 'spaceship' in a clearing and two people 'like us' got out." I told my son it was getting dark and I wasn't going to let him go and have a look in the woods but said he could play outside in the street, where I could keep my eye on him, and that when the tea was ready they would have to come in. They were playing 'spotlight', or something (shining torches at cars).

When I went outside to get them in, they came running up the street and told me about a spaceship hovering overhead. It didn't make a sound. The kids kept shouting, 'Mum what is it?', so I fetched John out, my husband, and he picked up a camera – then this 'thing' just shot up in the sky, towards Rendlesham Forest.

It was about four stories high above the houses in height, covered in bright lights, triangular in shape, and lit up the road as it hovered overhead. The 'craft' went toward the direction of Rendlesham Forest. By the time my husband clicked the shutter, it had gone. When we developed the picture, all it showed was a bright star in the sky. The problem is that if you told people it was a spaceship they wouldn't believe you, as it looked like a star in the sky – it went so fast."

Report of UFO landing in Rendlesham Forest

"The next day, John went into work. When he came home, the news of the spaceship landing in Rendlesham Forest was all in the news. All the trees were down where it had landed. The animals had left the forest. There were lots of things going on at that base.

The airmen that were there (one of my friend's husband's) got sent back to the States. They weren't allowed to speak to anybody and tell them why they were going home. Lots of civilian people saw that spaceship, as well as my kids. (Do you remember Johnny Kemp?) He was a children's presenter. He used to make films for children's television – some of them at Woodbridge. One of the presenters from Blue Peter used to live there. I thought they must be making a film."

Yvonne believes the *'spaceship'* and *'men'* were real and that the children thought it was a movie set, although they didn't see any equipment lowering the spaceship. She told us that trees were broken in the forest, but was unable to remember who the other children were, but that *"many people who lived in Woodbridge, at the time, saw the craft"*.

She recommended the local newspaper archives and suggested we speak to David Jenkins – one of the 'boy' witnesses, who still lives in Woodbridge.

John Traylor also claims that a spare part was made for the UFO

I (John Hanson) telephoned John Traylor, in the States, and spoke to him about the allegations during mid-2009. He corroborated the sighting of the triangular UFO over Porter's Wood, and confirmed the information given regarding Ken Pratt, claiming he had connections with the company Ransome & Rapier in Ipswich, Suffolk. He was adamant this was the company that made the part for the UFO, held at RAF Woodbridge.

John Traylor

John:

"As for Kingston Middle School (where the UFO landed and then took-off again) if you have the opportunity to visit the location of the School for yourself, you may want to take a Geiger counter with you. I believe Mr Spicer was the Headmaster of the School. He may now be residing in Kesgrave. Finally, as for Ransome & Rapier, I was under the impression that the Company was shut down after the part was made (though some accounts state the Company simply changed its name) yet all senior bosses left very quickly."

Yvonne and her son, John, appeared to be genuine people, as opposed to any orchestrated deception, although I was concerned that they declined me the opportunity to interview them personally at their home address.

John Traylor also suggested I (John Hanson) contact David Jenkins – a lifelong friend of his, living in Woodbridge – who was a witness to the sighting of the UFO. Unfortunately, I discovered that Mr Jenkins had passed away, a few years ago, although he was well-known in the locality and a regular at the local Public House – *The Red Lion* – and left a daughter, as far as we know.

Despite appeals made in the local Newspaper, the *Evening Star*, asking for any information on the whereabouts of Ken and his son – apparently still employed as a metal fabricator in the Ipswich area, who was alleged to be connected with Ransome & Rapier (without any mention of the UFO connection) – I never received any reply. A letter, sent by recorded delivery to a business address in Ipswich, asking Ken to contact me with regard to this matter, was also not answered. Was his refusal to enter into correspondence with me due to the acrimonious domestic situation that had existed between him and Yvonne's daughter, following a divorce, or was there another reason?

Could we even be sure that this was the same man I wanted to interview? His evidence and knowledge is vital to this enquiry. The last thing I wanted was to cause any embarrassment to somebody who had the misfortune to have the same name as the person I sought to interview.

Without some corroboration, I effectively had nothing to support the claims made regarding Ken and John's part in this incident, given by John Traylor and his mother, but felt I had done as much as I possibly could under the circumstances.

However, we did receive a large number of letters and telephone calls from former employees of Ransome & Rapier, all of whom denied any knowledge of Ken Pratt and his son – which may not come of any surprise, understanding that it was never suggested they were employed directly by Ransome and Rapier but were connected through another company, which may well have independently supplied material to that firm. We discovered that Orwell Bridge – which carries the A14 road (then

A45) over the River Orwell, south of Ipswich, Suffolk – was constructed under contract to Stevin Construction B.V. – a Dutch company in October 1979, and was opened to road traffic in 1982.

Claimed the UFO originally landed in Woodbridge.

Enquiries made with them, to establish if they had sub-contracted to any Ipswich-based manufacturers (including Mr Ken Pratt and his son, David) to supply any steel or work on the bridge, proved unsuccessful. Yvonne told us that she had no knowledge of the 'spaceship' having landed at the nearby Kingston Primary School (Now Grove Court) as alleged by her son, but claimed the school – which was of recent construction – had to be demolished afterwards, following conversation with her son, John, who told her this course of action was orchestrated following the landing of the UFO, in the school grounds.

He believed that this was the same UFO which then took off and later crash-landed in the forest. We asked her if we could examine the photographic slide of the UFO and were told that she did not know where it was. Yvonne asked us not to reveal her surname, because of possible repercussions to her husband, John (an ex-USAF Tech Sergeant) who, in a separate conversation to us, admitted he knew Colonel Halt and had served under him at the airbase in 1980. John declined to discuss any information regarding Ransome & Rapier, but confirmed having sighted and photographed a triangular UFO.

Visit to the alleged scene

We visited Porter's Wood and the site where Kingston Middle School had stood, off Cherry Tree Lane, Woodbridge, in 2009, in company with Brenda Butler and Peter Parish. We took some photos of the 'school playing field' – now a grassed area of land belonging to the nearby Care Home for the elderly, which lies adjacent to the nearby railway line, but saw nothing of any note either on the grass or in the surrounding locality.

While it would be easy to believe the information corroborated with what Brenda had been told initially by her contact 'Steve Roberts', about parts being manufactured to repair a 'craft' which had landed in the forest, and of other sources which may or may not back up this version of events, we should be careful about jumping to the wrong conclusions. It is not that we necessarily disbelieve what Yvonne had told us – far from it, but we weren't prepared to accept such a sensational claim without being able to interview them personally, especially bearing in mind their general reticence to allow this course of action to take place.

School reorganization

Enquires made revealed that the old Kingston Middle School building which was opened in 1980 was initially used as a lower school (years seven and eight) for Farlingaye High School. This was seen by parents as a distinct advantage as it kept children in an environment similar to what they experienced in the middle schools. However, it was difficult for school organization and involved staff moving between the two sites. A small additional budget was provided to the school to compensate for non-productive travelling time. The Kingston building closed on 31st August 1988.

Inside information – spare part manufactured for UFO

Could this suggestion have been given some credibility, following information received by Brenda Butler and Del Newman, in November 1987, from 'Karin' – the wife of an airman, based at RAF Woodbridge (formerly Sutton Heath), who alleged that *"...an aircraft was sent to Germany, to bring back some spare parts for a Russian aircraft that had landed"* ? While Brenda and Derek Newman believe the woman was sincere, are we really expected to believe that the military authorities had intercepted a Russian aircraft, with a satellite on-board – then constructed an elaborate version of events, involving airmen on the base, to release a story about a UFO to cover-up an action, which, if discovered, would have precipitated some hostile action by a foreign power?

None of 'Karin's' claims have ever been corroborated by any other USA service personnel stationed at RAF Woodbridge or Bentwaters. This seems odd, understanding the nature of an alleged incident – the magnitude of which would have surely, in time, instigated other people to come forward, wishing to reveal what they knew behind what is still regarded, by many, as the most important UFO mystery of the 20th Century. If the Russian authorities had lost an aircraft off the Suffolk coast towards the end of December 1980, through ditching, having sustained engine/mechanical failure, or even landing at the base following defection, what a fantastic coup that would have made for the British/American authorities. Others claim it was a satellite film return capsule, ejected from a KH-9B Hexagon 'Big Bird' satellite, which was picked up off the coast.

Deliberate cover-up and deception

'Karin' maintained there was a deliberate cover up and deception, orchestrated by someone to camouflage the 'real truth' behind the leaked UFO story, following the release of the Halt memorandum. However, what if 'Karin' was deliberately or unknowingly manipulated by someone to disseminate information, knowing that this 'evidence' could have caused some embarrassment –not forgetting serious defense implications of such an allegation, unfounded or not, against the USA Government?

If we accept that what 'Karin' alleges is true, why should an American citizen want to betray her country in the first place?

She mentioned she had been suspected of an arson allegation on the base – involving damage – so presumably her name and criminal actions were known to security police on the base.

She handed over some documents and photographs to Brenda Butler and her colleague Derek Newman which may or may not have be connected with the incidents that took place eight years previously. The reader must make their own mind up on the content, of the documents which appear genuine.

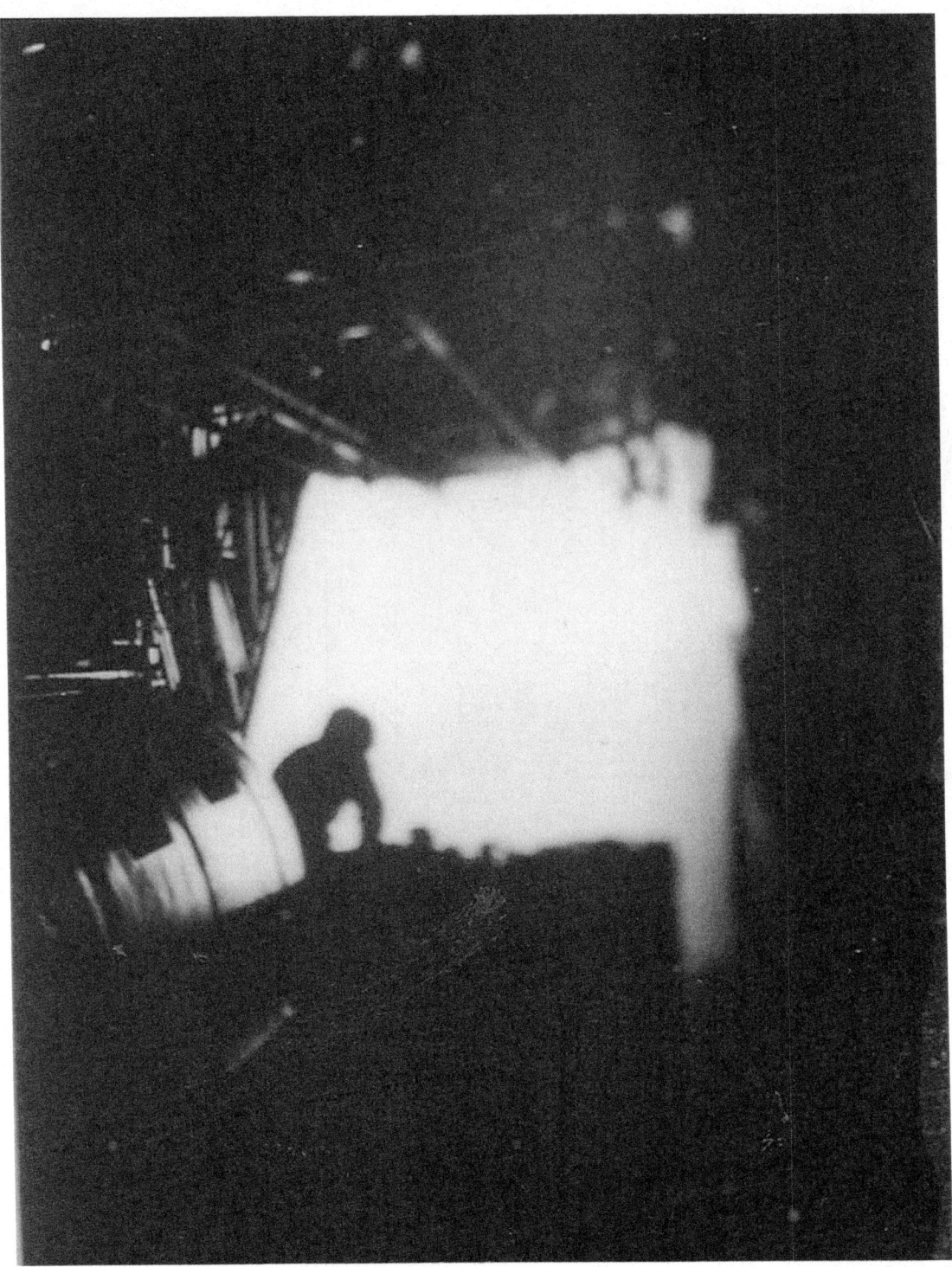

(THIS FORM IS SUBJECT TO THE PRIVACY ACT OF 1974 — SEE REVERSE)

TRAVEL VOUCHER OR SUBVOUCHER	(Complete by typewriter, ink, or ball point pen (PRESS HARD) do not use pencil)	10. FOR DO USE ONLY

READ PRIVACY ACT STATEMENT ON REVERSE PRIOR TO COMPLETING THIS FORM

DO VOUCHER NO. 08723

LAST NAME · FIRST NAME · MIDDLE INITIAL ~~(classified)~~ GRADE/RANK SSN

SUBVOUCHER NO.

CHECK MAILING ADDRESS (Include ZIP Code) DUTY PHONE NO

PAID BY

ORGANIZATION AND STATION
Classified

TRAVEL ORDERS (Paragraph, S.O. No., Issuing Hq., Date) (Include amending orders)
Top Secret

PRIOR TRAVEL PAYMENTS OR ADVANCES UNDER THESE ORDERS (Amount, DO Voucher No., Date received, Place paid, or DO Station No. If none, so state)

1. ITINERARY (See Item 25 for Symbols)

DATE 19__	LOCAL TIME (24 Hour Clock)	PLACE (Home, Office, Base, Activity, City and State, City and Country, etc)	MODE OF TRAVEL	REASON FOR STOP	2. COST OF LODGING	3. NUMBER OF MEALS GOV'T DED*	OPEN MESS	4. POC MILES
27	DEP 0200	Sembach AB GE						
	ARR 0600	RAF Woodbridge UK						
28	DEP 0500	RAF Woodbridge UK						
29	ARR 0200	Sembach AB GE						
	DEP 0200	Sembach AB GE						
03-28	ARR 0600	Kirtland AFB USA						
03-28	DEP 0600							
03-29	ARR 1200	Sembach AB GE						
	DEP							
	ARR							
	DEP							
	ARR							
	DEP							
	ARR							

5. REIMBURSABLE EXPENSES/CHARGE FOR DEDUCTIBLE MEALS* (See Item 24)

DATE	NATURE AND EXPLANATION	AMT CLAIMED	ALLOWED

6. Long distance telephone calls are certified as necessary in the interest of the Government.

APPROVING OFFICER (31 USC 680a)

7. TR'S/MTA'S/MT'S (If none, so state)

NUMBER	FROM	TO
24H-0011	Sembach AB GE	Kirtland
496-1110	Woodbridge	Semlach

8. LEAVE STATEMENT: _____ days _____ hours taken between _____ and _____

9. POC TRAVEL ☐ OWNER/OPERATOR (See Item 22d) ☐ PASSENGER

SUMMARY OF PAYMENT

Per Diem	
Actual Expense	
Mileage or Transp Allowances	
Reimbursable Expenses	
Total Entitlement	
Less Previous Payments	
Less Voucher Deductions	
Amt Charged to Acctg Class	

11. PAYMENT DESIRED ☐ CHECK ☐ CASH

12. ☐ PER DIEM REQUESTED

13. BAS RATE

PENALTY: The penalty for willfully making a false claim is: A MAXIMUM FINE OF $10,000 OR MAXIMUM IMPRISONMENT OF 5 YEARS, OR BOTH (U.S. Code, Title 18, Section 287)

I hereby claim any amount due me. The statements on face, reverse, and attached are true and complete. Payment or credit has not been received.

14. ~~(signature)~~ DATE 03-29

15. ACCOUNTING CLASSIFICATION
67 ARRS TOP SECRET $1335

16. COLLECTION DATA

17. COMPUTED BY Lt Col	18. AUDITED BY Nov	19. TVL RCRD POSTED BY	20. REC	21. AMOUNT PAID $1335

DD FORM 1 JUN 78 1351-2   PREVIOUS EDITION IS OBSOLETE.

Exception to SF 1012 and 1012a approved by NARS, GSA April 1978.

Was this the reason why she failed to disclose the information' until some years later, knowing that disclosure then would have 'blown her cover', following the December events being made public knowledge within the airbase – never mind the embarrassment caused to her and her husband, whom she claimed was a pilot on the base – or was this a case of 'sour grapes'?

We shall never know. If the UFO story was a ploy to cover up some covert activity, what does this mean for the integrity of the airmen concerned, who still maintain to this present date that UFO activity was sighted over separate nights in December 1980?

We personally found it hard to believe that any Alien vehicle which possessed the technology to cross the vastness of space would then crash-land into some trees a few feet off the ground. It seems too ridiculous to even consider. 'Karin' also claimed that Colonel Halt was an OSI Agent.

Colonel Charles Halt:

"John, there are bits of truth in some things she says. We did, from time to time, have classified planes land but almost always at Bentwaters, not Woodbridge.

We did have classified convoys but not UFOs, or Russian planes/satellites – just routine weapons movements. This was common and they were treated with great care. Photography was not allowed and large areas secured.

I liked the part of my replacement firing his secretary, because she was too tall. My replacement was quite tall, so I can just imagine how tall she must have been . . . Me, an OSI Agent? Her story isn't worth much comment."

The Lord Hill-Norton

The Lord Hill-Norton, former Chief of the British Defence Staff, wrote a number of letters to us one of which contained the following information.

"Dear Mr Hanson,

I have no doubt that something landed at this US Air Force Base and I have no doubt that it has got the people concerned into a considerable state. The Ministry of Defence has doggedly stuck to its normal line, that nothing of defence interest took place. Either large numbers of people, including the Commanding General, at Bentwaters, were hallucinating – and for an American Air Force Nuclear Base, this is extremely dangerous – or what they say did happen."

29th December 1980 – UFO sighted over Orford, Suffolk

Another extremely interesting sighting took place on the 29th of December involving Mr Gordon Levett. He was later interviewed by Manchester solicitor, Harry Harris.

Admiral of the Fleet The Lord Hill-Norton G.C.B.

Fordingbridge (01425)

HYDE,
FORDINGBRIDGE,
HAMPSHIRE.

Mr J Hanson
P O Box 6371
Birmingham
B48 7RW

26th November, 1999

Dear Mr Hanson

Thank you for your letter of 22 November, and the enclosures (which I have not read).

I remember hearing from you once before, but I have not kept your letter nor my reply. I have a vague memory that I said something like "....... I am not sure what you want me to do ....". That it my reaction to your latest letter.

I know some of the people you mention, particularly Gordon Creighton who is a reliable, sensible, well-informed UFO-man. Most of the other names mean nothing to me. In particular I do not think there is anything new to be said about Rendlesham, and it is highly unlikely, after about a dozen books, that Ms Butler has been favoured with the "real truth" about the affair. I think it is already well-known.

I can do nothing for you about Cosford, I no longer have any influence in the MOD, and I do not think you will get anything useful out of them.

I am sure you are sincere in your efforts but I do not think I can be of any use to you. I shall send your paper to Mr Timothy Good who is the best UFO-researcher in the business.

Yours sincerely,

Hill-Norton

STATUATORY DECLARATION

I, GORDON LEVETT, of ▇ Munday Lane, Orford, in the county
of Suffolk, Department Manager, DO SOLEMNLY AND SINCERELY
DECLARE as follows:-

1. I make this declaration realising that it is a document on
oath and in the knowledge that it may be shown to the general
public.

2. On or about the night of 28 or 29 December 1980 at
approximately 7 pm to 8pm, whilst residing at White Lodge,
Sudbourne, in the county of Suffolk, I was in the garden
putting my dog into its ~~kennel~~ *shed*. When my attention was
aroused by some unknown means I looked towards the coast
and observed a light which moved on a steady path towards
me. My dog also reacted and its attention became focused
on the object. The phenomenon glowed with a phosphorescence
and was unlike any conventional object with which I am
familiar. It descended and hovered for a few seconds
immediately above us at a height of no more than twice the
rooftop of the house and its size, wäre the object to be
placed on the ground, would be similar in size to the
rooftop. The object then moved away and disappeared over
the woods in the direction of Butley,Rendlesham Forest and
RAF Woodbridge. ~~My dog was frightened by the experience.~~

3. The following day there were still evident signs of distress
in my dog. It cowered within its kennel and was not keen to
come out. Having told my wife,June,immediately following
the experience I subsequently discussed it with several
friends, including Ron Macro ,a baker from Kesgrave in the
county of Suffolk.

4. I exhibit here, marked "A", a drawing of the object which
I saw.

AND I MAKE this solemn declaration conscientiously believing
the same to be true and by virtue of the provisions of the
STATUTORY DECLARATIONS ACT, 1835.

DECLARED at Orford, in
the county of Suffolk
this 17th day of July
1984.

Before me,

A solicitor

Manchester solicitor, Harry Harris

Gordon Levett

Were there any medical problems after the event?

Charles Halt was asked bearing in mind the ill effect sustained by the other airmen involved in the encounters whether he personally had experienced any ill effects, after the event.

Charles Halt

"Over the years I have been asked all manner of questions, including whether I experienced missing time, did I see any aliens, was I subjected to a vigorous interview by the Air Force Office of Special Investigations, was the whole thing an alert or elaborate exercise, designed to test the response of the security personnel on the base? The list goes on. All I can say is I did not sustain any ill effects. I cannot speak for the other individuals involved, as I'm told that several feel they have sustained lasting health problems. I talked with John Burroughs and Jim Penniston; they are now convinced that military experiments caused us to experience what we did, but I'm not convinced. The guys that hypnotized and drugged them are probably gloating over their success with all this disinformation. I did meet with Mike and Harry about 1982, and we all agreed not to reveal the meeting. General Williams was never involved.

Bustinza is a puzzle, as he was with me the whole time. We rode out in the jeep together and he stayed with our small group that went forward until we returned to the service road (where the other cops and the light alls were). He stuck to me like glue, as he was frightened. When we got back to the light alls, I ordered the cops back to the base. Some had already departed. Burroughs was still there. He again asked to go forward. As I remember, he and Bustinza were allowed to go to the 'landing site' while we waited."

> "All the other cops, except one or two, had departed. Then we all got in the jeep and remaining truck and returned to the base. If Warren was out, which I doubt, he would have long since departed."

Meeting with Intelligence operative in New Mexico

> "There were certain government agencies playing games with us. I'm firmly convinced of that, but I can't prove it – they're very discreet. Over the years I've also been approached by certain intelligence people, one from a certain installation in New Mexico. We had lunch. He asked me questions about what I had witnessed. I asked him what he wanted to do with it. He said 'it's classified'."

Barry Greenwood – who was the Intelligence Operative?

During the preparation of this book while in contact with Barry Greenwood, this meeting was brought to his attention. He asked Charles Halt who the 'intelligence operative' was.

Barry Greenwood

Charles Halt – on Colonel John Alexander

> "The intelligence person from New Mexico was *John Alexander. He claimed he was working on his own. He and I became friends but have differences on his connections. I did proof his book and assisted with the chapter on Bentwaters."

John Alexander UFOs – No Government Conspiracy

John Alexander, who is well-respected, has helped us with information previously published in the *Haunted Skies* books, regarding his knowledge of what might be classed as more esoteric rather than UFO. John does not believe there is any Government cover up or suppression of the UFO subject. We tend to disagree simply because many sightings that are covered in the *Haunted Skies* books, involving what one may allude to as close encounters, have never been released by the MOD, despite promises to do so. In many cases brought to our attention involving strange aerial objects hovering

---

*Alexander was born in New York in 1937. He enlisted in the Army as a private in 1956, and retired as a Colonel in 1988.

He graduated from the University of Nebraska (BGS, Sociology) in 1971; from Pepperdine University (MA, Education) in 1975; and from Walden University (PhD, Education) in 1980. Commander, Army Special Forces Teams, US Army, Thailand, Vietnam, 1966-69, Chief of human resources division, US Army, Ft. McPherson, GA, 1977-79. Inspector general, Department of Army, Washington, 1980-82. Chief of human technology, Army Intelligence Command, US Army, Arlington, VA 1982-83. Manager of Tech. integration, Army Materiel Command, US Army, Alexandria, VA, 1983-85. Director, advanced concepts US Army Lab. Command, Aldelphi, MD, 1985-88.

Alexander describes his assignment in 1971 as an infantry officer at Schofield Barracks, Hawaii, during which time he went diving in the Bimini Islands in search of the lost continent of Atlantis. During his career in the army he showed exceptional interest in esoteric techniques explored by Lt. Col. Jim Channon in his First Earth Battalion manual. An example is neuro-linguistic programming, with which he hoped to create "Jedi warriors" (according to his own account in his 1990 book ***The Warrior's Edge***). He has published another book, ***UFOs: Myths, Conspiracies, and Realities*** (ISBN 978-0-312-64834-3) (Source: Wikipedia)

above the ground, often seen a few feet away by people, the MOD have explained these away as aircraft or some other mundane cause, much to the consternation of the witnesses. It is clear that there is some form of suppression whether intentional or not. Many people believe that the MoD is part of some conspiracy to prevent the real truths about the UFO presence from being made public as it would cause concern.

Colonel John Alexander

Nick Pope agrees with John Alexander

"I agree with John Alexander's views on the cover-up/conspiracy issue, and indeed when we've sat down and discussed things, it's clear that there are many similarities between the work that we did for our respective governments. It's certainly true that for many years the MOD downplayed the true extent of its interest and involvement in UFO research to the point that a misleading impression was given to Parliament, the media and the public.

MOD officials were overly-defensive about the subject and, for example, freely admitted to 'examining UFO reports to see if they contained anything of any defence significance', while desperately avoiding use of the word 'investigate'. This was a kind of 'doublethink', because self-evidently one can't make a meaningful assessment of a sighting's defence significance issue without investigating it!

The MOD's overly-defensive attitude sometimes manifested itself in unwarranted support for sceptical explanations, and if officials heard of a sceptical theory they would sometimes repeat it to the media and the public if an opportunity arose. While stopping short of actual endorsement, this was sometimes implied, with phrases such as 'We are aware, however, that there was a meteor shower on the night in question'. The problem here was that officials lazily trotted out such explanations not just for high-altitude lights-in-the-sky sightings, but for incidents where the sceptical 'explanations' were clearly wide of the mark.

Trying to shoehorn an almost certainly bogus 'explanation' to fit the facts of a particular UFO sighting was a form of intellectual dishonesty that ultimately rebounded on the MOD. The intention was to maintain the appearance of being neutral about UFOs, while subtly boosting the sceptical position. But the result was that people formed the impression that the MOD was hiding something. Of course, in a sense we were far more interested and involved in UFO research and investigation than we let on. But the suspicion, inevitably, was that there was a bigger deception, and that we were actively covering up evidence of an extraterrestrial presence.

In a very real sense, therefore, we were authors of our own misfortune."

Update on Steve Wagner UFO sighting, June 1980

Following on from the account given to us by Ken Kern, relating to a mysterious event that took place in the forest, involving Airman Steven Wagner and Charles Campbell, Charles Halt contacted Steven Wagner, who had this to tell us:

"I can't tell you if this ever made the blotter. I think CSC and everyone else was laughing too hard to take it seriously. Typically weekend mid shifts were a boring affair; if you were lucky enough to be assigned post with someone you were friends with then you could pass the night enjoyably. Saturdays were tolerable due to some limited flight line activity, but Sundays were miserable. This particular Sunday was pretty eventful. Shift started with guard mount. Guard mount is a pre-shift formation where the flight chief and flight commander gauge each Security Patrolman's fitness for duty that day, share any pertinent security updates, and to give out post assignments.

This night, myself and Charles M. Campbell, both A1C at the time, were assigned to Alpha2 ART (area response team). Alpha 2 is a roving vehicle patrol within the Alpha 2 alert parking area for A10 Warthog aircraft. Airman Michael LaBrucherie was assigned Alpha1, which is the gate post. Although not close friends with Mike, all of us had little cliques we ran with; he was a nice enough guy. Chas and I made sure to look out for him, as gate duty on the weekends was brutal. Mitch Petersen delivered our meals at around 0145 and Chas, Mike and I, ate on the tailgate of the pick-up and chatted away generally.

The specific time frame of the occurrence I can't pinpoint for you (it's been 35 years!) sorry. I can tell you it started sometime around 0230-0300. I stepped out of the patrol vehicle and went to the side of the maintenance buildings to have a pee (there was a *berm that ran behind the buildings and the entire length of them."

Steven Wagner (left) with 'Bobby B'

*A berm is a mound of earth with sloping sides that is located between areas of approximately the same elevation.

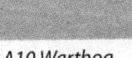
A10 Warthog

Steven Wagner

Saw lights appear in the trees

"I noticed 'lights' in the trees behind the berm and went to investigate. (I called in to report this; Chas got the transmission and came running.) For some reason I can't explain, the SRT (security response team) took forever to get there and by the time they did it was over."

[Sightings of curious objects like this are still being made. Here is an image taken a few years ago in the same forest]

Mysterious 'orb' hovers over aircraft

"A large 'orb' – reddish/orange in colour, and roughly the size of a large beach ball – rose from the sparse trees behind the berm and moved into the Alpha Area (at which time I almost crapped myself). LaBrucherie now was able to see it and babbled over the radio about the area being penetrated. The 'orb' hovered briefly over each of the A10's (the damn thing was within arm's reach of the planes)."

Splits into three separate lights

"When Chas and I finally got close enough to it, it moved outside the fence line with unbelievable speed – then rose to about 30 or 40 feet off the ground, split into three separate orbs, and with a blinding flash disappeared.

All that was seen now once again from the top of the berm were two very startled deer. The SRT finally got there and, of course, Chas, Mike and I, all looked like fools. Because I was deemed the one who initiated this, I caught hell. After we were relieved at the end of shift, I cornered M.Sgt. Ron Faile to plead my case (I was concerned about a PRP review and decertification). The RFI fixed all that."

Chris Pennington – convinced it was a satellite that landed!

"The 67th came to Woodbridge Airbase in about December 1969, with a complement of 250 personnel and their equipment, HC130 Hercules and HH53 Jolly Green Giants (helicopters) with in-flight refueling capabilities, and were responsible for aerospace rescue operations over almost a million square miles. It was the biggest Search & Rescue Squadron in the World. These units were set up primarily to pick up astronauts, wherever they may come down around the world, as back-up to US Space Operations, NASA.

Maybe it was just an excuse for the 67th to practice their arts. They never seemed to advertise their connection with the Space Race. They must have had equipment to practice with – if not the real thing, simulated models – which brings me to a conclusion that a Re-entry Module looks remarkably like some of the UFOs that were reported. If it were only a practice, why did John Warbiton tell us that Colonel Halt's boss, Colonel Ted Conrad, said, 'not allowed to say what happened, as it would embarrass Governments'?

As one may or may not know, for some reason or another, many things that Brenda Butler and 'Dot' Street wrote in the original Sky Crash were not included – just to mention two examples. (1) It was reported an aircraft was sent to Germany, In order to pick up spare parts for the craft. (2) Should the truth ever be revealed then Governments would topple.

I believe that we secretly let a Russian Aircraft land in the UK. There were reports on the National News that a Russian aircraft carrier had passed through the English Channel and Russian spy planes were seen flying deep into the funnel of the North Sea. (Were they looking for a lost satellite, maybe?) One must remember that courtesy exchanges between Russian and French Air Forces were being made at around that time, and one possible route was North Sea, English Channel. So long as they remained in International Airspace, one could do nothing.

How can you ignore the evidence of Ron – who visited the Rendlesham area at about midnight on the 27th December 1980 – after being told by a mate, who lived near Woodbridge, of unidentified lights sighted over the area? Ron told Brenda he was walking along the forestry trail, somewhere near the eastern perimeter of RAF Woodbridge, when he saw a lighted area in the woods. The next thing that happened was that he was escorted away from the area by two armed security guards and the film from his camera confiscated. He was then taken to Woodbridge Police Station, but later released without charge. They (SCUFORI) sent people down to the forest, who met up with Brenda and 'Dot', but following their investigation into the alleged incident, they concluded there was nothing to it and dismissed it as being of no *importance, which I felt was a personal slight on Brenda and 'Dot', who might have been only 'a couple of housewives' but knew something of importance had occurred.*

What you have to realise is that I was involved in all of this. 'Dot', by this time, was in touch with an American Group. They wrote to her and said, 'Hey, some of your stuff has been released under the USA FOI Act'. They sent 'Dot' a copy of the information, which included Colonel Halt's letter. We then went to High Wycombe, when the UFO Congress was on. It was obvious they were going to make fools of us, bearing in mind the visit by SCUFORI. In fact, I believe that's why they were invited. Harry Harris saw the document and came over to us and offered to be spokesman, on our behalf, at the meeting – as he was a member of BUFORA, which we weren't. They started 'booing' Brenda and 'Dot', saying they didn't know what they were talking about – things like they didn't have the experience, etc., but when the document was brought to the attention of the audience by Harry, they changed their tune."

Mark Birdsall with Harry Harris (centre) and Jenny Randles

Brenda Butler – Blackout on radio station broadcast

*"I heard of a Russian Tupolev military aircraft seen off our coast, and also on the TV News broadcast (in December 1980). When we contacted the TV Station, **they said it was a mistake and it should not have been broadcast.** In 2010, during the preparation of a documentary on the incident, Colonel Halt came to see us. In conversation with Chris Pennington, who showed him his research work relating to his theory that it was a satellite, Charles said to him, 'You are on the right track. I told Brenda to be more scientific, in 1983'. He then took the pamphlet and later left."*

1981

Claims that UFO crash-landed and needed repairing

ON the 2nd January 1981, 'Steve Roberts' came to see Chris Pennington and Brenda Butler at their house and told them about something having come down in Tangham Woods, involving a UFO, which crash-landed just outside the perimeter of Woodbridge. Bizarrely he said:

"They had to send to Germany for spares; two days later it was repaired and then took-off."

According to 'Steve', a local farmer – Mr Higgins – heard a noise over his farm and went out to have a look at the cattle, which were very agitated, one of which escaped and was hit by a passing taxi.

John 'Davey' Ingalls (aka Steve Roberts)

In Nick Pope's latest book *'Encounter in Rendlesham Forest',* he disclosed the real identity of Steve Roberts as Mr J. D. Ingalls, to whom we had previously written and had emailed him on a number of occasions, wishing to learn more about how this information had come to his notice in the first place, bearing in mind, as far as we know, 'JD' did not witness anything himself personally.

Charles Halt:

> *"I believe that he overheard Jim Penniston and probably others telling what they had seen in the forest."*

We gave him the opportunity of telling his side of the story now over 35 years later but unfortunately, he 'Davey' failed to reply to either of us even though we suggested we were willing to keep his name out of it.

Cattle scattered after craft flew overhead

Brenda Butler:

"Another farmer – Mr Flemming – was telephoned. He came and rendered assistance. Mr Higgins contacted the police and told them a plane, showing lots of lights, had gone over the cattle, frightening them, before heading off in the direction of the airbase and forest. The Base police sent some service personnel out to the perimeter fence, who reported seeing lights over the forest, as a result of which security officers from the airbase went out into the forest, accompanied by the Base Commander and some high ranking officers. When they approached closer to the lights, they saw what looked like a 'craft' of some sort, in trouble, accompanied by three 'entities', suspended in shafts of light. Shortly afterwards the 'craft' took off and hovered over the treetops for a while, before heading at great speed across the sky. An A10 was sent up to check for radiation and heat source. There were supposed to have been films and cine film taken, but these have been currently misplaced. Newspaper reporters were also supposedly to have been there, but were warned not to publish anything. The security guard said there was communication between the commanding officer and the entities."

11ᵗʰ January 1981 – Three-light UFO seen over Essex

Draw a picture of the object(s) that you saw and indicate the direction of travel with an arrow:-

EAST

GLARE

NORTH   GREEN LIGHT   BRIGHT LIGHT   BRIGHT LIGHT   SOUTH

WEST

How far from you do you think the object(s) was when closest?
Certain / Fairly certain / Not very sure / Guess*...... NOT VERY SURE

At what height do you think the object(s) was when nearest to the ground?
~~Certain~~ / ~~Fairly certain~~ / ~~Not very sure~~ / Guess*... VERY HIGH

What size do you estimate the object(s) to have really been?......
Certain / Fairly certain / Not very sure / Guess*

If you held one of the following items at arm's length, which one would occupy the same size as the object(s), when the object(s) was closest? ~~A pea~~ / ~~1p coin~~ / ~~Ping-pong ball~~ / ~~tennis ball~~ / football / other item (please state)*
... RESEMBLED ... FRONT ... OF LIT UP LORRY AT NGHT.

Could you estimate the object(s) speed?..... VERY SLOW
Did the object disappear while you were observing it? YES.
~~If so how?~~

Case No. 1981-1-1
1981-1-1

ESSEX UFO STUDY GROUP

Unidentified Flying Object Sighting Report Form

Please give an account of your sighting:-

I was traveling to work to "Tilbury Power Station" on Sunday morning on the 11-1-81, at about 6-30 AM when I saw this object in the sky, at first I thought it was an aircraft looking again I realized it was too bright a light for a plane, and there were no flashing lights and no sound. It resembled two bright lights, and a green light surrounded a glare, it was traveling from "North" to "South" approaching the "Kent coast." The Green light was facing the North end, I stopped my moped at the side of the Road for about a couple of minutes to watch, then suddenly it vanished I did'nt see it any more.

Please answer the following questions as fully as possible:-
*Delete as appropriate

Date of sighting: 11-1-81

Time of day: MORNING.... B.S.T.(Daylight saving)/G.M.T.*

How many objects did you see?.....ONE

Where were you when you saw the object(s)?Exact location.MARSH.FOOT,.DOCK
ROAD,.APPROACHING....TILBURY,.ESSEX.

How long was the object(s) in sight for?....TWENTY...TO..TWENTY.FIVE.FEET
Certain/Fairly certain/Not very sure/Guess*

Was the object(s) in sight continuously? Yes/No*.....YES

Did the object(s) while under observation:
Move in front of anything / Move behind anything / Remain visible in the sky all
the time*

Any other comments on this?.THEN..SUDDENLY..DISAPPEARED

12th January 1981 – Brenda Butler and 'Dot' Street visit the landing site

"'Dot' and I decided to go down into the forest and re-examine the landing site. First, we went to the East Gate barrier and chatted to 'Tom' – the armed guard on the gate, who thought the incident was just a story, fabricated by bored personnel. We then set off into the forest, ignoring a sign that read 'No Entry – Only By Permission Of Base Commander', and made our way to the Forestry Office where, during a conversation with them, they divulged that the farmer had reported the UFO to the Base police because one of his cows had been injured, and that the 'craft' had made a loud humming noise, had lots of lights on it, and was supposed to have landed for four hours, whist being repaired, on Tuesday 30th December, 1980."

MoD's X-Files shed light on

By TOM POTTER
tom.potter@eveningstar.co.uk

House of Lords group raised disturbing issues about Britain's Roswell incident

IT'S regarded by those with a penchant for the paranormal to be one of the most significant UFO sightings of modern times.

The Rendlesham Forest incident, or Britain's Roswell as it has come to be known, has kept people guessing about the existence of little green men for nearly 30 years.

For the second time this year, the Ministry of Defence has disclosed previously classified files on sightings in the UK reported between 1981 and 1996.

In March we heard about boomerang-shaped objects seen from airport control towers and a woman's encounter with a Scandinavian-sounding "alien" in Norfolk.

Now, a new set of files may shed light on Britain's Roswell, as well as some other bizarre encounters.

The release is part of a three-year project between the MoD and The National Archives, aimed at opening up records to a worldwide audience.

The Rendlesham file reveals previously unseen letters between the MoD and members of the public and includes a memo from Lt Col Charles Halt (USAF deputy base commander), who was present during one of the sightings in December 1980.

File DEFE 24/1948 ...

Fastfacts
More MoD revelations

■ Two men returning home from an evening out in Staffordshire were confronted by a lemon-headed alien who appeared from under a hovering UFO;

■ More than 30 sightings of bright lights were reported over central England in the space of just six hours in March 1993 – it was later discovered that most of the sightings were caused by a Russian rocket re-entering the earth's atmosphere;

■ The Belgian Air Force scrambled F-16 fighters to intercept UFOs reported by police officers and members of the public in March 1990 – the jets obtained "lock-ons" with their radars, but could not explain what caused the phenomena;

■ A young man returning home near Widnes ran off after seeing a UFO over a cemetery in July, 1996. He reported beams of light projecting on to the ground, a wailing noise and smoke rising from the ground. Investigators discovered four smouldering railway sleepers at the scene – one with a hole burnt through it and still smouldering.

■ Dozens of sightings of a brightly illuminated oval object were reported over London in 1993 – the lights were actually caused by a Virgin airship;

STRANGE DAYS INDEED: Brenda Butler and Dot Street at the alleged site of the Rendlesham UFO sighting.

These images were allegedly endorsed by Major Everett a pseudonym given to a pilot whose witness testimony was accepted as being authentic.

He claims of having been present in a meeting that took place with Wing Commander Gordon Williams when he and others were told of a UFO landing which had taken place on the 25/26th and 29th/30th of December 1980.

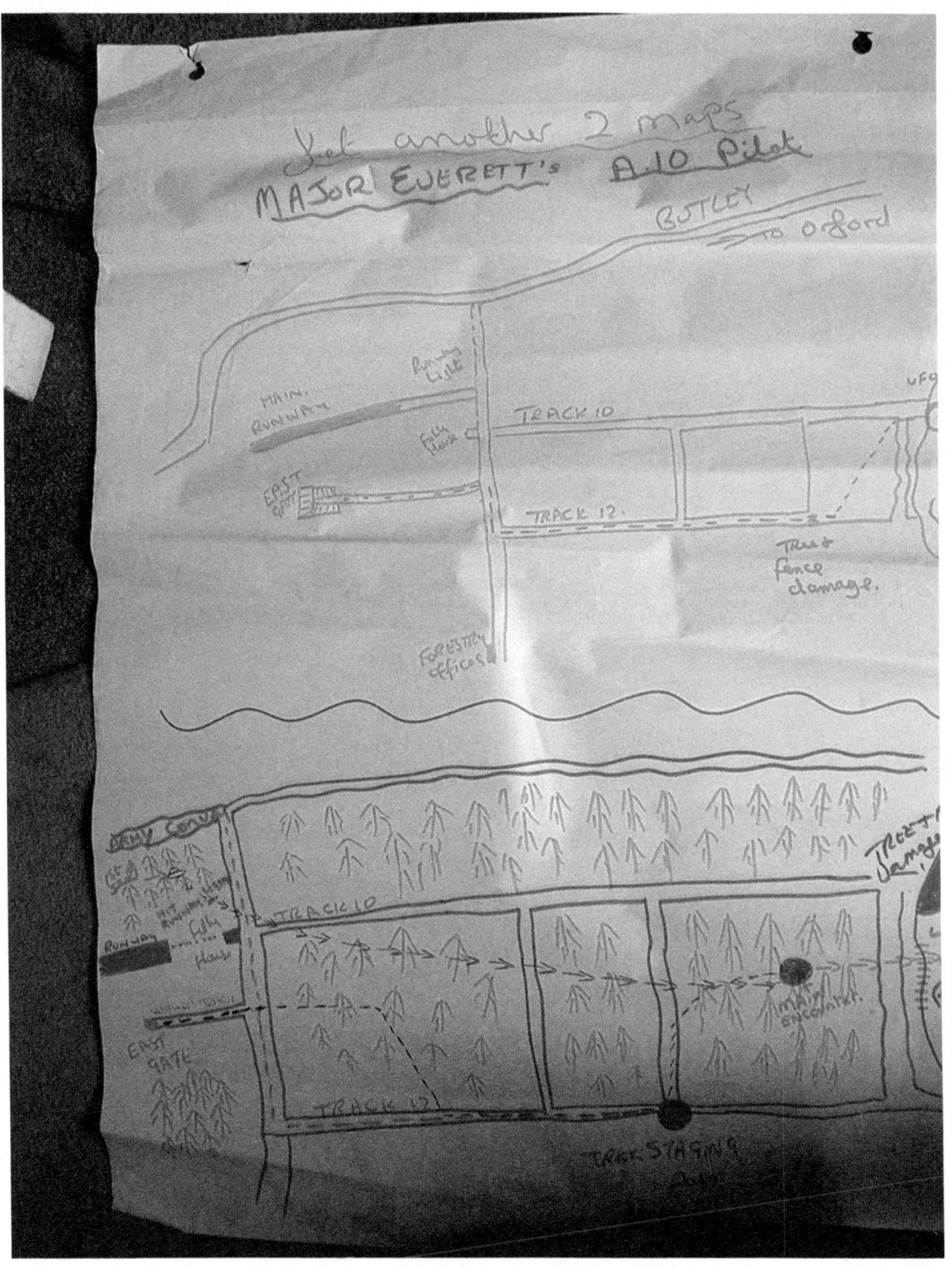

1981 – January – Cigar-shaped UFO seen over East Gate

USAF Serviceman – Steve La Plume, was on duty at the East Gate, at RAF Woodbridge, with Wendell Palmer, one evening in January 1981.

Steve La Plume

"We saw an object darting across the sky, continually changing course and altitude, in a series of up and down movements – almost too fast for the eye to catch, and contacted Security Control by radio, explaining what we were seeing. A short time later, Colonel Halt and General Williams arrived but, by then, there was nothing to be seen. After about 30 minutes, the UFO returned – now much closer, allowing us to see it was cigar-shaped, showing green, red and blue, lights on its underside. As it passed overhead, it illuminated the forest floor underneath it. What really annoyed me was that I couldn't remember what happened next. I have no memory of the object moving out of sight, or disappearing. We decided not to report the second sighting, fearing ridicule."

(Source: Personal interview)

Charles Halt:

"That is basically correct. I do remember the incident but by the time we reached their position whatever they reported having seen had gone. Steve has now joined forces with Larry, so who knows what he'll now say. What I can say is that having read through Steve's emails sent to me, of which you have copies; Steve declared vigorously that he believed Larry was lying about his version of the events which took place."

13th January 1981 – Questions in the House re UFO sightings

Sir Patrick Wall asked the Secretary of State for Defence (1) If he has seen the United States Air Force memo dated 13th January 1981, concerning unexplained lights near RAF Woodbridge (2) Whether, in view of the fact that the United States Air Force memo of 13th January 1981 on the incident at RAF Woodbridge has been released under the Freedom of Information Act, he will now release reports and documents concerning similar unexplained incidents in the United Kingdom (3) How many unexplained sightings or radar intercepts have taken place since 1980.

Reply to the question – 1,400 unexplained sightings

"Mr Stanley, I have seen the memorandum of 13th January 1981, to which my Honourable friend refers. Since 1980 the Department has received 1,400 reports of sightings of flying objects which the observers have been unable to identify. There were no corresponding unexplained radar contacts. Subject to normal security constraints, I am ready to give information about any such reported sightings that are found to be a matter of concern from a Defence standpoint, but there have been none to date."

Captain Jane McCollom – Press Officer at airbase

No doubt in subsequence of even more newspaper publicity aroused by the incident, the Press Officer – Captain McCollom – received a huge number of telephone calls by the Media during October. They included Guy Smith of *Radio Orwell*, who wanted to visit the office at Bentwaters, David Jack of the *Sunday People*, Ian Ridpath of *BBC Breakfast Time TV*, who asked what the weather was for the 26th/27th (1am-2am 5/8ths cloud, 3am 3/8th cloud, 4am 4/8ths cloud, 4.49am snow, 5am 7/8th cloud, 5.6am snow).

Further callers were *Southend Evening Echo*, who confirmed *"reports of lights also see around the town at the same time".*

They also mentioned *BBC TV Norwich*, Carolyn Grant of the *East Anglian Daily Times*, the *Anglia Press Agency*, Bob Graham of the *Sunday Express*, *Newcastle-on-Tyne* Newspaper *"We saw strange lights up there during the same time",* Linda Pullen *Press Association*, London, *News of the World*, and Chris Bell of *Anglia TV*, to name just a few that contacted the airbase.

Memo sent to RAF Mildenhall

On the 15th January 1981, Squadron Leader Donald Moreland, (who had returned to the airbase on or about the 7th of January 1981) in response to an enquiry sent to him, forwarded a copy of the report 'written-up' by Charles Halt to RAF Mildenhall.

1981 – 18th February – A visit to see Squadron Leader Donald Moreland

Brenda revisited the base with 'Dot' Street, after having telephoned Squadron Leader Donald Moreland, who agreed to see them on the 18th February 1981. When they arrived at the base, they were shown into the office. After introductions, Squadron Leader Moreland and his secretary erroneously presumed the two women were from the MOD and that their visit was with regard to an incident on the 31st December 1980. Brenda said, *"No ... the 27th December".* The secretary replied: *"The report was for the 31st".*

They looked like angels!

Brenda and 'Dot' asked Squadron Leader Moreland some questions. He replied: *"There were some lights out there – just a few, and some shiny 'beings' that looked just like angels".* When he discovered that Brenda and 'Dot' were not from the MOD, he slammed shut the UFO file, which his secretary had brought in, and told them to get in touch with the MOD in London.

1981 – February – The object was tracked on radar

In February 1981, Jenny Randles received information from Paul Begg – the author of *Into Thin Air* – who was in his local Norwich public house, one evening, when he entered into a conversation

Squadron Leader Donald Moreland with Lt Colonel Halt

with a man known to him – then employed as a radar operator at RAF Watton, in Norfolk. This man had not been on duty himself, but told Paul about a conversation which was told to him by one of the other radar operators. This man alleged having tracked an unusual object on the radar screen, during 27th December 1980. It was claimed that RAF Watton lost the target about 50 miles south, to the east of Ipswich and in the vicinity of Rendlesham Forest.

On the 29th December 1980, the same operator received a visit from USAF Intelligence Officers (which one may think suspicious, as this was a British tracking station) and asked for the log books and film of the radar recordings, covering a period of several days.

UFO had crashed in the woods

The men told him that a UFO had crashed in woodland near RAF Bentwaters, and that Watton may have tracked it on radar.

This seems very suspicious and smacks more of disinformation rather than the opposite.

Allegation of *'craft'* being repaired

In the book *Sky Crash* (published in 1983) on page 35, quote:

"The radar men were told that it was possible that what they had tracked was an object that had crash-landed into a forest near Ipswich. This had been a metallic UFO, a structured device of unknown origin. Men who had gone out to confront it from a nearby base had found the engine and lights of their jeep failing.

They then had to continue on foot. The object was on the ground for several hours before repairs could be undertaken by the aliens who had crewed it; during this period, high ranking officers from the base went into the forest and the base commander himself had conversed alone with the occupants."

According to the authors of *Sky Crash*, the informant alleged that RAF Bentwaters had contacted Watton during the time the visual sighting was taking place.

Jenny Randles

Jenny Randles, in original notes made, following a conversation with the radar operator, reported that the man told her:

"The Intelligence Officers had informed the Base Commander, and several officers had been called out into the forest from a party on base, which they were attending. This was in response to the original discovery of a landed UFO.

They took with them a battery operated portable tape-recorder and made a transcript."

During a visit to the forest on the 24th February 1981, 'Dot' had this to say in a letter sent to Ivan Bunn of the Lantern series:

A CLOSE ENCOUNTER OF THE THIRD KIND NEAR WOODBRIDGE, SUFFOLK? by Dot Street

(An account of this case initially appeared in "Lantern", Summer 1981, pp.17-18).

Early in February this year (1981) I heard from my friend and associate, Brenda Butler, about an alleged UFO landing near Woodbridge in Suffolk. We arranged to meet and visit the area, and our initial visit took place on Wednesday, February 18, 1981.

Brenda told me of what she knew at that time, namely that she had heard from several people who claimed to have witnessed a UFO landing in Rendlesham Forest sometime around the beginning of January this year. She had very little information regarding the sighting at this time, save that an object with three legs together with 'entities' who appeared to be doing something to the craft had been seen and that she had also heard that communication had been made between these 'entities' and personnel from the nearby USAF base at RAF Bentwaters.

On February 18th, Brenda and I went to the air-base and made an appointment to see the Base Commander. Whilst we were talking to his secretary and arranging to see the Commander, we mentioned that the sighting took place in January, to which his secretary replied (without prompting), "The beginning of January?" When we confirmed that this was so, she seemed more determined for us to see the Commander whom later that day we did see.

The Commander asked us for some form of identification. I showed him my BUFORA membership card, but he obviously did not accept it and said that without proper identification he could not say anything. As we told him what we knew of the sighting he told us, smiling all the time, that he didn't know anything about it. He then asked us if we were going to continue our investigation. I replied, "Yes." What would we do with our information, he asked. I said we would do the same as them - file it!

Although the Base Commander would not say anything concerning the report, we left his office with the distinct impression he knew far more than he had been saying.

We then went to the part of the forest where the landing had allegedly taken place, but we saw nothing out of the ordinary.

Several days later, Brenda heard from a man. He refused to give her his name, but said that the report was true and gave her directions as to how to get to the site where the object had landed. At a later date, this witness said that he had been told to speak to no-one about the sighting, and later still he denied all knowledge of it!

On February 24th, Brenda and I decided to pay another visit to Rendlesham Forest in an attempt to locate the landing site using the directions given to us by the anonymous caller. Unfortunately, owing to the fact that the directions were somewhat vague, we could not locate the place. Finally we went to the Forestry Commission's office where we had an interesting conversation with the man on duty. He told us that he had been working in the office on January 1st, when a man walked in and said that he had just been talking to a farmer who, on December 29th, 1980, had heard a very loud noise which had frightened his animals. The farmer also said that at the same time the area around his farm had been illuminated by a very bright, white light. He (the farmer) then telephoned RAF Woodbridge who sent men out to investigate. The whole episode, he said, lasted about four hours.

Unfortunately, no one seems to know who this farmer is, and we have heard that he has been told (presumably by the security people at the air-base) not to say anything about what happened. We have also been unable to trace the man who told this story to the Forestry Commission employee.

While we were in the office, another forestry worker came in and told us that his wife's friend's husband had also seen a UFO that same night, and that his account tied in with that of the other witnesses. He then showed us on a map exactly where the whole incident was supposed to have happened; he also said that his men had been right through that part of the forest but had not seen anything untoward, although it is worth noting that since the incident tree-felling has taken place in that part of the forest.

After leaving the Forestry Commission's office, we went to talk to people living in the immediate area. At one farm-house we were told that the residents had been visited by two men on January 1st, who had asked the same questions as us. One of these two unidentified visitors also mentioned that they had interviewed Forestry Commission workers. The people at this farm also told us that they had heard that something had happened that night, on the air-base bomb disposal site which is nowhere near the site pointed out to us by the Forestry Commission man. At all the other houses we visited everyone else said that they knew nothing of the report.

UFOs - A LOAD OF BALONEY? by Lionel Beer

When I took part in a 'phone-in' programme on LBC (London Broadcasting Company) on 19th May, 1981, one caller dogmatically informed us that UFOs were a "load of baloney" and couldn't possibly be visitors from outer space. He implied that anyone who 'believed' in them needed their head examined. Well I am not in the believing business, but I do regard UFOs as a subject worthy of serious scientific study. Millions of people the world over have reported strange objects or lights that they were unable to identify, and ufologists are interested in determining the cause of all these reports. Perhaps our LBC caller would maintain that life-peer Lord Kings Norton, an engineer and scientist with a long association with terrestrial flying machines and a distinguished public service career, needs his head examined? Kings Norton, although adopting a sceptical approach to UFOs is nonetheless President of the British UFO Research Association (BUFORA). He is a prominent member of the 'House of Lords All-Party UFO Study Group', which is open to MPs (Patrick Wall MP is a regular attender). The 'Lords Group' was formed following a three-hour debate on UFOs in the Chamber on 18th January 1979, initiated by the Earl of Clancarty. Clancarty, BUFORA Vice-President and founder of an international UFO group called 'Contact', has written five popular UFO books under his other name of Brinsley Le Poer Trench. Even Woolworths sell them! The 'Lords Group' has held frequent meetings with speakers from the USA, Canada, Denmark, Spain and Italy. In May 1981, Fred Hoyle, distinguished astronomer and author of sci-fi stories like 'A for Andromeda', addressed their Lordships. The Duke of Edinburgh is known to have had a passing interest in UFOs for many years and recently expressed interest in attending a meeting at the House of Lords. Lord Clancarty commented: "It has given the subject a marvellous Fillip!"

Both their Lordships along with several hundred ufologists attended the 2nd London International UFO Congress at the Mount Royal Hotel, Marble Arch over the Spring 1981 Bank Holiday, a premier event in the UFO buffs' diary. Delegates came from Reykjavik, Toronto, Washington, etc., and a Soviet Air Attache was also said to have been present! Dr. Bruce Maccabee, an optical physicist from the USA whose work for the US Navy is classified, outlined new information gleaned from the American intelligence agencies (FBI, CIA etc). There have been some startling attempts by the US Air Force in years past to track and detain UFOs, not to mention landing cases. What information there is has been prised out of the authorities using the full weight of the Freedom of Information Act. Pressure groups argue that we badly need a FOI Act in the U.K. but both Tory and Labour governments have been patronisingly obstructive.

There are rumours that a UFO and its small dead 'humanoid' occupants crashed near the Roswell Air Force Base in New Mexico in 1947. After being held at other bases, it is suggested that the 'remains' are now housed at the McDill A.F.B. in Florida, or at the CIA compound at Langley Field, Virginia.

March/April – UFO seen over Woodbridge, Suffolk

We contacted retired Police Constable Martyn Brophy, who was then partner of PC David King. He remembered the incident clearly and expressed surprise that a Colonel should have been on duty over the Christmas period. Unfortunately, he had nothing else to add with regard to what Dave King had told us. However, he was to describe something highly unusual that took place a few months later.

"I was driving a police car through Woodbridge, accompanied by another officer, during March/ April 1981. I happened to look upwards and see the amazing sight of a massive bank of lights, forming a rectangular shape, moving slowly across the sky. I felt the hairs on the back of my neck rising. I knew this was no aircraft and watched, in silence, unable to comprehend the sheer size of the 'craft'. From the look on my colleague's face, I knew he had also seen it."

The officers made their way back to the police station and sat down, trying to retain their composure. All of a sudden there was a frenzied knock at the front door, followed by the entrance of a man, wearing a crash helmet, who was shaking with fright. He told the officers:

"You'll never believe what I've just seen. I was riding towards Woodbridge, when this huge UFO swooped down over the top of me.

I thought it was going to strike me – then it disappeared."

The missing motorcyclist!

In July 2015 we were contacted by Kim Tester, who expressed a wish to purchase some tickets for the Charles Halt conference. During conversation, we learnt that he was the motorcyclist involved. Kim was invited to address the audience about the incident – which he did. This is what he had to say:

"I was driving along the Woodbridge road, with my girlfriend, when I saw these two huge 'lights' in the sky. They were completely stationary, side by side in the air, resembling car headlights. I can't give you any idea of the size of them. They didn't project any beams of light. I stopped my bike and took my crash helmet off. I wondered at first, being a structural engineer, whether they were some sort of construction. All of a sudden they started to move away silently, as if linked together in tandem. I was scared. I don't mind admitting that, because

Motorcyclist, Kim Tester

it made the hairs on the back of my head stand up. The objects then disappeared from sight. We got back on my bike and drove to Woodridge Police Station at a crazy speed. I hammered on the door until a Police Officer came out and asked me what I wanted. I told him what I had seen, at which point another officer appeared and told me he had been parked up when he had seen some strange coloured lights moving through the sky over the town, so in some way I felt relieved that I hadn't been the only one. I also remember that one of the officers telephoned RAF Woodbridge, to enquire if they had any low flying aircraft in the vicinity. The duty officer told him they had nothing up at that time."*

John Hanson

"In June 1996 I was accompanied by my son, when we saw an identical pair of huge objects cross the celestial arc of the sky over Alvechurch, Worcestershire, and disappear within seconds southwards. They appeared to be bolted together and were side by side.

I have no explanation and didn't even bother contacting the newspaper… what was the point?"

1981 – 23rd September – Diamond-shaped UFO over Lowestoft, Suffolk

On the 23rd September 1981, Anna Sidali and her children were on holiday at Lowestoft, in Suffolk, taking a breath of fresh air, before night fell.

"I noticed a beautiful silver, diamond-shaped object, appear in the sky. I wondered if it had anything to do with the nearby USAF Airbase when, all of sudden, it was overhead. Frightened, I took the children and ran inside. The oddest thing is that I felt as if we were being watched. It's difficult to explain, but the sighting took place against a backcloth of oppressive atmosphere."

(Source: Ivan W. Bunn)

29th October 1981 – UFO sighted over Orford

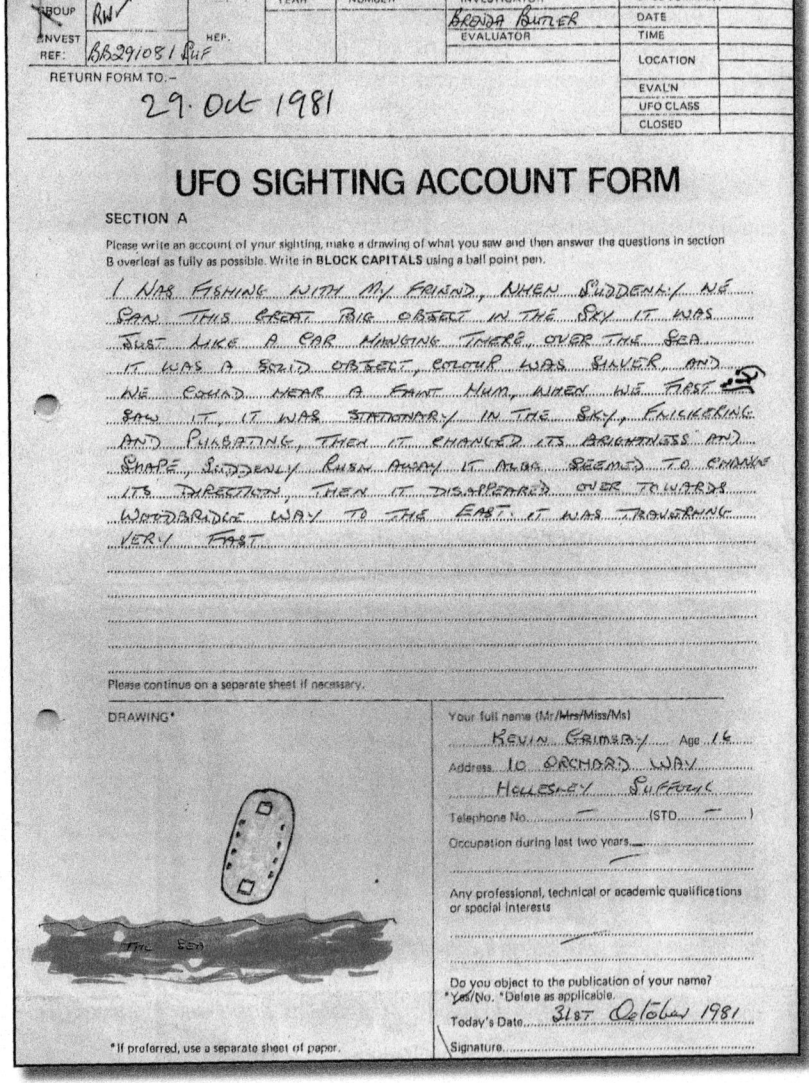

1981 – Early November – UFO over RAF Woodbridge

In early November 1981, security personnel at the USAF Base, at RAF Woodbridge, reported to their Base Commander of having seen *'a huge cigar-shaped object, estimated to be 100 yards long and 50 feet in diameter, move over from the coast, float silently over the Base, and complete a 'figure of eight' movement over the control tower, before heading back out to sea'*

Dear John and Dawn

I found your letter quite interesting. I was not aware that the former 67th ARRS building had been a mortuary during the Second World War.

Many of our Security Police had seen unexplained things at RAF Woodbridge. Several personally told of seeing "East End Charlie" (as they called him). He appeared to be a World War Two Aviator that wandered near the back gate. One particular event occurred on Guy Fawkes Night in 1981. A large cigar shaped craft silently floated over the airfield and circled the Air Traffic Tower before drifting off.

To the best of my knowledge I did not experience any unusual incidents immediately after the incident. Further, I did not experience any sustained ill effects. I can not speak for the other individuals involved as I'm told that several feel they have sustained lasting health problems.

Hope this helps. Say hello to Brenda for me.

Sincerely,

Charles I. Halt

22nd December – Four UFOs sighted

Yoxford, Suffolk, resident – Linda Jarvis – was walking to Saxmundham, at 4pm, when she noticed:

"Four, silver, round objects (the size of a new ten-pence piece) in the sky, travelling in a horizontal line in a North to South direction, stopping and starting in flight, as well as changing shape as they did so. Within five minutes, they had dropped in the sky behind houses, and that was the last I saw of them."

(Source: Ron West)

Robert Hastings interviews air traffic controllers

We spoke to Robert Hastings, considered a leading researcher on nuclear weapons-related UFO activity. Robert has interviewed over 150 witnesses to date, including former and retired US military

7ᵗʰ November 1981 – UFO sighted

Please give an account of your sighting:-

FURTHER NOTE ATTACHED

It was Saturday eve. & myself with 3 adults were standing around the bonfire at Devonshire Rd. I saw an object in the sky & pointed it out. It moved horizon to horizon & was a long-cylinder shape with orange-yellow light at the trailing end; it was totaly silent. No-one could identify it, though not an aircraft. Shape at front unknown – could be blunt or bullet-shaped, i.e.

🔲 or 🔲

Please answer the following questions as fully as possible:-
*Delete as appropriate

Date of sighting: 7 – 11 – 81

Draw a picture of the object(s) that you saw and indicate the direction of travel with an arrow:-

⬭⊃ ——— FLAME or light

How far from you do you think the object(s) was when closest? 5000 ft
~~Certain~~ / ~~Fairly certain~~ / Not very sure / ~~Guess~~*

At what height do you think the object(s) was when nearest to the ground?
Certain / Fairly certain / Not very sure / Guess* A.S. ABOVE

What size do you estimate the object(s) to have really been?
~~Certain~~ / ~~Fairly certain~~ / Not very sure / ~~Guess~~*

If you held one of the following items at arm's length, which one would occupy the same size as the object(s), when the object(s) was closest?   A pea / ½p coin / Ping-pong ball / tennis ball / football / other item (please state)*   A PEA

Could you estimate the object(s) speed? APPROX 600 M.P.H.
Did the object disappear while you were observing it?   NO
If so, how?

personnel, and has lectured on the UFO-Nuclear connection at over 500 colleges and universities in the United States.

His authoritative book, *UFOs and Nukes: Extraordinary Encounters at Nuclear Weapons Sites* was published in July 2008.

He has appeared on CNN's Larry King Live on 18th July 2008, together with three former US Air Force officers, who spoke about their involvement in classified UFO-related incidents.

What was tracked on radar?

In 2007, Robert Hastings interviewed the two now-retired USAF air traffic controllers, who had been on duty in the week of the UFO events at Bentwaters – James H. Carey and Ivan 'Ike' R. Barker. During a taped telephone call, Carey told him:

"At the time, I was a tech. sergeant – an air traffic controller with the 2164th Communications Squadron. The other controller was named 'Ike' Barker. A major named -------- was also there. What I remember seeing was a very fast object on the radar we had in the tower. The scope was variable – it had a zoom as far as its [displayed] range, between 5 and 60 miles radius, but I think it was set at 60 miles when the object appeared. It came in from the east, went straight west across the scope, and disappeared off the left side.

It took maybe four sweeps – each sweep was two or three seconds – to cross it entirely."

James H Carey – "UFO covers 120 miles in 8-12 seconds"

"So it covered 120 miles in [approximately eight to twelve] seconds. In the 15 years I was an air traffic controller, I'd never seen anything travel across the scope that fast. A few seconds later it came back on the scope, retracing its course, west to east, at the same speed. Then – I think it was maybe half or three-quarters of the way across – it did an immediate right-angle turn and headed south, off the bottom of the screen. I mean, it turned just like that, instantly. We couldn't believe it! I told Ike, 'Okay, that was not one of ours!'

So, that's all I remember, except for the chatter on the radio. I think it was on the Major's hand-held radio, which was tuned to the Command Post Net. That's who he always talked to [on other occasions]. I wasn't really listening to it, so I don't remember any of the details, but I do know that [the radio] was pretty quiet all night – then, all of a sudden, they're just yakking back and forth. They were kind of excited but that's all I recall. Besides, if they were going to discuss UFOs or security problems, or that kind of stuff, they would have gone to a restricted channel, which they scrambled. But the chatter did start up a little while after we tracked the object. Anyway, I only saw the unidentified object on radar, but 'Ike' told us that he saw something out the window."

'Ike' R. Barker – "Basketball-shaped, with orange glow"

This is what he had to say:

"There was a visual on [the UFO we were tracking]. When it hovered, I saw it out of the window. It was basketball-shaped, and had a sort of an orange glow – not bright orange, uh, sort of dim, maybe like the full moon would look behind a thin layer of clouds. There seemed to be

something across the centre of it, lighter-coloured shapes, like – don't laugh – portholes or windows, or even lights, in a row left to right, across its centre – maybe six or eight of them. They were stationary, not moving across the object, but it seemed spherical – not flat like a 'flying saucer'. I couldn't hear any noise. It wasn't huge, but I think it was bigger than an airplane. I would say it was maybe twice the size of an F-111."

Object seen over water tower

"Now, there's a water tower at Bentwaters. If you were in the air traffic tower, facing the runway, the tower is almost behind you. [From my vantage point] the object was directly over the top of the water tower, or just past it. The object [appeared] larger, maybe twice as large, as the tank on the water tower. It stopped in mid-air for a few seconds, probably 500ft, uh, maybe a 1,000ft above the tower, and then it left. I didn't see it turn, uh, rotate or anything like that before leaving, but what impressed me most was the speed this thing had. I have never seen anything so fast in my life! It was zoom . . . gone!"

When Robert Hastings told Barker that Carey had said he did not remember seeing the UFO out of the window, Barker replied emphatically:

"Oh, he saw it! They both saw it! But we weren't going to admit that. Just after I saw the object out the window, I turned to Jim and said, 'I didn't see that, did you?' One of them responded, 'No, I didn't see it either.' I don't remember who answered me, but they both saw it. But we made no log entries on anything, including the fast-moving target. We didn't really have a discussion about not telling anyone, because that was already understood."

Incident unrecorded in the Log

Barker then mentioned an earlier UFO incident, at a USAF base in Japan, during which he had been grilled by Air Force investigators.

"The controllers were harassed to the point that they said the object they saw was only aircraft lights. That taught me a lesson: Never go on the record. Never open your mouth. So, at Bentwaters, I think we were all scared to discuss it. I know I was. As I said before, we didn't even record it in the Log. After the object left, uh, maybe an hour later, we could see lights, actually a glow, in the direction of Woodbridge, but the trees blocked our view so we couldn't see what was causing it. Now that I think about it, I'm not sure if --- was still up [in the tower] at that time, but I know Jim was. The glow seemed like it was coming out of the forest; it wasn't like lights in the air. It could have even been vehicles on the ground, but I know one damn thing – it wasn't a lighthouse!"

Robert Hastings

"Importantly, a British radar unit apparently tracked the same object. Barker told me that he, or Carey, had called a British radar unit, known as Eastern Radar, to ask whether they were tracking anything anomalous. The importance of the radar tracking revelations can not be overstated. Two independent military units tracked an anomalous aerial object during the

peak week of UFO reports at the twin bases. Moreover, one of those units – the USAF controllers at RAF Bentwaters – had a visual on a hovering, spherical object, which correlated with that tracking. I finally asked 'Ike' Barker for his opinion about the object he tracked.

He replied: 'I can tell you that this was no manmade technology. I was very familiar with all types of aircraft, obviously, and I can tell you that what I saw was not from any country on Earth. I will never forget it!' "

Colonel Charles I. Halt:

"SSgt. John Coffey, from Bentwaters Air Traffic Control, contacted Heathrow Airport, in London, and Eastern Radar, who'd both seemingly tracked the manifestation on radar, first picking it up roughly 15 miles out over the east coast, but as it dropped beneath radar contact they couldn't identify it. In addition, RAF Watton reported a strange object on their scope as well. The two air traffic controllers on duty that night I was out, actually saw the glowing object, tracked it on their radar, and saw it descend into the forest where we were. They didn't tell anyone until they both retired, for fear of being decertified."

Nick Redfern writes to Eastern Radar at Watton

In October 1988, Nick Redfern wrote to the Royal Air Force Eastern Radar command at Watton, Thetford, enquiring about information concerning the whereabouts of radio and radar recording from the site. He was told by Squadron Leader E.E. Webster that they had been disposed of, but that *"Our log book for the period does indeed say that a UFO was reported to us by RAF Bentwaters at 0325 on the 28th December 1980".*

A further letter was sent to RAF Eastern Radar in January 1989, by Nick, asking for further information and any copies of log books.

Once again, he was advised that they had been disposed of. The only information available was *"Bentwaters Command Post contacted Eastern Radar and requested information of aircraft in the area – UA37 traffic southbound F3170 – UFO sightings at Bentwaters – they are taking reporting action."* (UA37 means the Upper Air Route Upper Amber 37, which runs approximately North-South, some 40 miles from Bentwaters, and is used by civilian airliners. F1370 means 37,000 feet in altitude."

Strange lights and mysterious *'beings'* seen outside RAF Watton

In Georgina Bruni's book *You Can't Tell The People,* she describes an incident involving two RAF Police dog handlers, who were instructed to investigate strange lights that were seen near RAF Watton. (This appears to have taken place after the Station's radar picked up a large moving target during the night of the 27th/28th December 1980)

During a search of the locality, it is said that the two officers came across several *'figures',* described as *'silvery and bulky',* that appeared to *'suck in the light from the men's torches'.* The following day, a high ranking British Police Officer questioned both men and advised them to forget what they had seen. The notebooks were confiscated and also the log book regarding the events recorded that night. Following this bizarre incident it is further claimed that four scientists from Porton Down drove into Rendlesham Forest, where they inspected the area after changing into bio-hazard suits.

While we have no reason to disbelieve the version of events as given by Georgina we would like to have seen more substantive evidence backing up what is to all intent and degree a forgotten but amazing incident if true!

'Dot' interviews Major Malcolm Zickler

'Dot' Street travelled to the United States with Jenny Randles. While there she telephoned Malcolm Zickler (now a retired Lt. Colonel, living in Florida) to interview him, regarding an allegation made that he had cleared the landing site by removing all traces.

He was not in, but his wife Linda was. When they told her of the nature of their enquiry, she replied, *"Oh, you mean the UFO landing!"* During a discussion that lasted about 90 minutes, Mrs Zickler confirmed that she and some of the officers' wives had seen the damage to the tree, although, according to her, the big event was on the first night when some photos had been taken.

Colonel Sawyer

The couple then telephoned Colonel Sawyer who was also unavailable, but his wife spoke to them. She confirmed having seen the damaged tree and of having taken her children into the forest to look for the UFO.

Mrs Sawyer takes film of a 'strange light' in the forest

In early January 1981, Mrs Sawyer claimed she had taken some cine film of a light in the forest. When they asked her to send the film to them, Mrs Sawyer appeared to change her mind and suggested it might have been the moon! She promised to send the film to Larry Fawcett, but this never happened. She also mentioned that on New Year's Eve, there was a party in the forest. Around 15 people were looking for UFOs and that an airman was arrested for taking *drugs and sent home.

Colonel Halt:

> *"I am aware of this information. Mrs Sawyer came on to the scene a few days later. In my judgement the claims made by her that she had taken photos and seen things was unsubstantiated; you should take anything she says with some suspicion, unless proved otherwise. Zickler knew a lot more than he was ever willing to say. He was very much a guy that worked in the background at the base and I believed he would have liaised with the AFOSI and other British and American agents to provide a cover story to explain what had taken place. He had to know that John, Larry, Jim, and Adrian, were messed with during the investigation held after the events."*

*Brenda and 'Dot' were told by local farmer – Mr Boast, and his wife – that the Police told them they had been investigating a drugs party in the forest, when a deer had been shot. Mr Boast also told a local newspaper that *"contrary to speculation, no animals had been scattered by the appearance of any UFO, as this was a forest and not farmers fields."*

Major Malcolm Zickler

According to Brenda Butler, she was told by 'Steve Roberts' that Malcolm Zickler – then head of the Police – was sent back to the United States, after he failed to complete a clear-up operation of the landing site.

Georgina Bruni:

"Lt. Colonel Zickler retired from the USAF in 1989, and lives with his wife, Linda, in Florida. He runs a business called Woodbridge Engineering. The fear imposed upon those individuals connected with the incident is still embedded deep in their minds".

It was also suggested that Major Malcolm Zickler ordered Sgt. James Penniston to report to the Air Force Office of Special Investigations (AFOSI) for a meeting, to tell his story to an AFOSI Special Agent and a US Air Force Major. Although officially AFOSI were not involved, others claim that he led the investigation into The Rendlesham Forest Incident – which one imagines would have been correct, if head of Police Security at the time.

Georgina Bruni herself describes the AFOSI agents as having a lot of power, with the ability to detain virtually anyone in the Air Force, including very senior officers. It is widely claimed that their interviews with airmen were conducted vigorously and included injections of Sodium Pentothal, given after permission rather than force.

Internet – 2015 informs us that . . .

Malcolm Zickler has been the President of Woodbridge Security Engineering Florida, since it's co-founding in February 1993.

He has been heavily involved in TASS (Tactical Automated Sensor System) from its inception, including developing training plans and deployment doctrine, as well as troubleshooting some initial failure paths. He blazed new ground while on active duty in the Air Force by **taking over an unused weapons storage area and conducting expected scenario training for his security personnel that included power and communications outages**. His focus has always been to make security personnel more effective.

He has supplied commercial and government interests with high quality security insight and consulting, based on years of practical experience in the USAF security forces. He established new procedures for installation and training, initiated and trained the contract trainers, then later supervised the contract trainers while they were training the initial military operators of the TASS in South-west Asia.

Strategic Defense Initiative Program

Before co-founding Woodbridge, Malcolm was Head of System Security Engineering and Chief of Operations Security at GE Aerospace, as well as Head of System Security Engineering for the Strategic Defense Initiative Program Office at GE Aerospace.

One of his key tasks during this period was heading the OPSEC Planning (Camouflage, Concealment and Deception) effort for the USAF Special Forces Mission Rehearsal Facility during

Desert Shield/Desert Storm. His work significantly altered the traffic flows for Special Forces attending training, providing military planners with additional, valuable time.

The Strategic Defense Initiative (SDI), also known as Star Wars, was a program first initiated on March 23, 1983 under President Ronald Reagan. The intent of this program was to develop a sophisticated anti-ballistic missile system in order to prevent missile attacks from other countries, specifically the Soviet Union. With the tension of the Cold War looming overhead, the Strategic Defense Initiative was the United States' response to possible nuclear attacks from afar. Although the program seemed to have no negative consequences, there were concerns brought up about the program "contravening" the anti-ballistic missile (ABM) of the Strategic Arms Limitation Talks years before. For this reason, in conjunction with budgetary constraints, the Strategic Defense Initiative was ultimately set aside.

Eglin Air Force Base

First F-35 Lightning arrives at Eglin AFB, Florida

Before joining GE, Malcolm Zickler was Chief, Active Defense Branch (ground defense, intelligence, counterintelligence, ground based air defenses) at Eglin AFB. Three notable projects that he headed during his tenure were developing the original Concept of Operations for what ultimately became TASS, developing the Mobile Weapon system for ground to ground and ground to air protection for air bases and developing the war fighting concept to evaluate security forces against the projected enemy. The result of his work was the first demonstration/exercise that used actual air and ground attackers to attempt to render a European Air Base unusable.

He went to *extensive lengths* to create a realistic scenario by cratering runways with explosives and cutting communications trunk lines. The exercise was a huge success and highlighted the need for ongoing realistic training and integrated base sensor systems.

17th October 1973 – UFO paces C130 aircraft

An unidentified object was tracked by a Duke Field radar unit during the same time period, and within the same area, that 10 to 15 people observed four strange objects flying in formation between Milton, Florida, and Crestview, along Interstate 10, according to Eglin officials. Reports from the base indicated that a bright glowing ball of light could be seen travelling parallel with an Air Force C-130 aircraft but at a much higher altitude.

1978-1982 – 81st SPS, RAF Bentwaters

From 1978 to 1982, Malcolm was back in Europe in command of the 81st SPS at RAF Bentwaters, the largest security police squadron in the USAF. Under his leadership, the 81st SPS passed all of their operational inspections, earning excellent on two, and a seminal event that had not occurred for over 35 years.

He also completed a course of study at the Air Command and Staff School. Between 1976 an 1978, he was in charge of security police inspections for USAFE, which included among other things, overseeing requirements and definitions for security systems for all types of Air Force installations, both conventional and nuclear.

Bearing in mind Major Zickler's association with carefully planned scenarios to test the effectiveness of ground troops is it no wonder then that some people have claimed the events that took place outside Woodbridge air base formed part of another carefully planned and ultimately orchestrated analysis and evaluation exercise to test the reactions of the security police in response to an alleged UFO landing. There is no proof of that but it provides food for thought!

In 2015 we emailed Malcolm and Linda Zickler hoping they might have time to comment on questions put to them – but never received any answer.

Charles Halt – No Exercises took place

"Lt. Colonel Malcolm S. Zickler was in charge of security for both bases. Both bases operated together within the same chain of command. We are simply talking about a report of unexplained lights; this in itself would not be reason enough to call out a Disaster Preparedness Team. Indeed, no such team was sent to the area. Captain McCollom was the Public Affairs Officer at the time.

Yes, we regularly had base exercises at least once a month. We did not have any the week between Christmas and New Year."

Further historical reports received over East Anglia

Even as this book was being compiled, further sightings continued to be brought to our attention from residents of the East Anglia area, following appeals in the press thanks to reporter Tom Potter who works for the *East Anglian Daily Times* newspaper.

Tom Potter

Whether any of these incidents can be associated with what took place in Rendlesham Forest during the end of December 1980, can only be speculation but one must surely take these into consideration.

22nd September 1965 – UFO seen over Felixstowe

Alan Tyrell (18) from Queens Road, Felixstowe, had unfortunately locked himself out of the family home and decided to sleep out in a nearby shelter. He had only been asleep for about ten minutes when he was awoken by an uncanny noise and flashing lights. Looking out of the window, he saw:

"Three lights heading out to sea, accompanied by a whooshing noise."

Was there a connection with what happened to Mr Geoffrey Maskey, who was out with his companions – Mavis Forsyth and Michael Johnson – the latter having been discharged from hospital, the previous evening, after having reported seeing an *'apparition'* close to one of the propane depots? (Details of this incident can be found in the earlier part of this book.)

Michael:

"People will think we are nuts, but it really happened. I do not believe what we saw came from the propane plant at Felixstowe."

However, a spokesman for the Suffolk Police said that on checking with the propane depot, it was found that the compressors were blown on the Monday night between 10.30pm and 11pm – the time at which the object was said to have appeared. Apparently, the compressors would have caused a huge propane flame and some noise from the flare stack.

(Source: *Evening Star*, 22.9.1965 – 'Object seen by man in shelter')

Mid 1960's – Weird noise over Suffolk

Elizabeth Bushby, now aged 86 (in November 2015) from Framlingham, spoke about a mysterious event that she and her husband – Rankin Bushby – experienced in the mid 1960s, while near the gate of the barn at the family farm at Monks Soham, one evening.

"We heard this slow 'err -err' buzzing noise coming from the sky above us, unlike anything we had ever heard before.

We stopped the car and got out to see this light moving across the sky, making this weird noise, which slowly moved away.

In the newspaper, the next day, we learned others had seen a UFO over the Ipswich area. It's something I have never forgotten to this present day."

We found Elizabeth to be an intelligent well-spoken lady, who, like so many others, just wanted to know what these things were and where they came from. She believes there is a cover-up and that the truths behind reported UFO activity are suppressed.

During conversation with her she remembered an occasion, when aged nine, whilst recovering from measles, of seeing a black and white object fly past the window. She mentioned the sighting to her parents but had, to a great degree, forgotten the incident – until now.

Rankin, who passed away six years ago, was a fine baritone during the mid 1950s. He sang the part of The Novices Friend in Britten's revised *Billy Bud* presentation, of 13th November 1960. In 1962, he appeared in the *BBC* recording of *Fennimore and Gerda*, which was released on vinyl. His second night of the proms performance followed in 1963, when he performed Brahm's *Liebeslieder* there with his 1958 IVC co-winner, Elisabeth Simon. He is also well-known for several radio broadcasts in his performance as Pompeo in the *BBC* 1963 broadcast of Berlioz's *Benvenuto Cellini*.

26th October 1967 – Sighting of dome shaped UFO seen over Ipswich

Young girls report UFO over Ipswich

TWO pupils from Nacton Road Girls' Secondary School, Ipswich, have reported seeing an unidentified flying object, with about 30 coloured lights around it, hovering in the night sky at Ipswich.

Elaine Godber, aged 12, of Clapgate Lane, Ipswich, and Marion Roberts, aged 11, of Nightingale Road, were returning home from a Girls' Brigade meeting in Morland Road with friends when they first saw the object.

Marion told a reporter. "There were a lot of coloured lights, but most seemed to be red".

She said that it was very near to the ground and it stopped above a house. "Elaine and I were frightened and hid behind a hedge", she said.

It moved towards the River Orwell and disappeared from sight.

Elaine said that the object looked like a flying saucer. "As it moved away it appeared as though there was a dark dome above the lights", she said.

Both girls said that there was no noise and the mystery object was too near the ground to be an aeroplane or helicopter.

When they arrived home they told their parents of the sighting.

"Mine did not believe me," Marion said. *STAR 27/10/67*

A DRAWING OF WHAT THEY SAY THEY SAW.

This newspaper account tells of a UFO sighting for the 26th October 1967 and relates to a dome-shaped object seen by two local girls.

We traced the one girl now married and left a telephone message with her, but she failed to contact us back.

Whilst we appreciate we have already outlined reports of UFO activity for that day earlier in the book as shown on page 106, we decided to let the reader see for themselves just how prolific that day was in the calendar of UFO history now nearly 50 years ago.

Microcosm of just one day's UFO activity!

Bearing in mind the obvious correlations between other sightings for this date we decided to show the readers how prolific activity was for one singe day! Therein lies the problem as the late Allen Hynek said: *"We are too rich in imagery"*.

They included many sightings of what people described as objects resembling a *'Flying Cross'* or *'Church Cross'*, which, on one occasion, was chased by Police Officers from Devon, during late October 1967. Despite the attempts of the media and MOD to explain away these incidents rationally as being examples of misidentification, it is clear this was not the case.

Police Constables Roger Willey and Clifford Waycott chased one of these objects through rural Devon and were later ridiculed for having the courage to simply tell what they saw. We met Roger – a likeable, friendly man, who was skipper of a narrow boat on a number of occasions, and were impressed by what he had to say. Sadly Roger passed away some years ago.

Roger would have been delighted to see this picture of his son Mark, partner and grandson, during a visit by us to see them to see him with regard to his life-long interest in what his father witnessed all those years ago.

With this amount of sightings for just one single day, thirteen years before the objects encountered by Colonel Charles Halt and his companions, does it not beggar belief that we should have any doubts that what the airman saw could be explained away rationally?

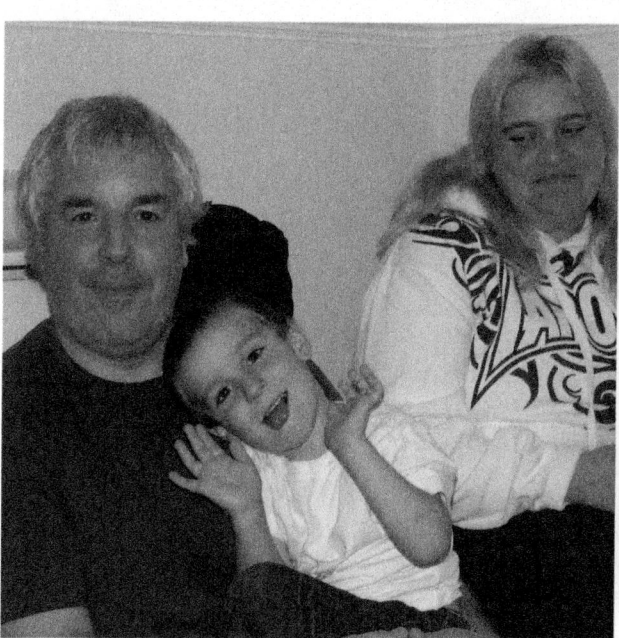

UFO Diary 26th October 1967 (extract)

At 2.05am, a light was seen in the sky over Basset's Cross, Hatherleigh Devon.

At 4.30am, a saucer-shaped UFO was seen over the A32 at Hook in Hampshire. It caused the electrics to fail on the vehicle.

At 5.5am, a mysterious 'light' was seen by a Police Officer over Anvil Corner, Devon.

At 5.25am, Mr J.D. Thatcher from Hillside, Sunderland, sighted a *'blue-white diamond-shaped object'* (estimated to be ten times the size of any star), apparently stationary in the sky towards the south-east, at 60 degrees elevation, fading and brightening in luminosity at ten second intervals. It was not Venus, as the planet could be seen low in the sky towards the south.

This was followed by the appearance of *'six to eight smaller objects',* forming a vertical oval-shaped formation, which took five minutes to pass from sight. (**Source: UFOLOG/TUFOS**)

At 6am, a Meriden, Warwickshire, resident – Mr F. Woodcock – was awoken by a bright light. Rushing to the window he looked out and saw what looked like a *"shining cross-shaped object, with its upright arms twice as long as its crosspiece. It was stationary for a couple of minutes, before accelerating away into the sky".*

At 6.20am, two men were feeding the pigs on a farm at Southwick, near Trowbridge, when they sighted *"a diamond white coloured 'Flying Cross', accompanied by three other objects, heading across the sky at fast speed, towards the direction of Bristol, at an angle of 45 degrees off the horizon".*

Between 6.30 and 7am, the *'Flying Cross UFO'* was next seen moving across the sky over the Daventry area, by several people. This was accompanied by a report of an unidentified flying object seen moving in irregular jerks across the sky over Warrington, at 6.30am, by teenager Ray Spencer.

At 6.45am, Margaret Fenwick from Sleaford, Lincoln, sighted *"a thing, shaped like the planet Saturn"* heading south. *"I wouldn't go as far as to say it was cigar-shaped. It was difficult to tell. I got the impression it was flashing and its behaviour was certainly erratic".* (**Source: *Sleaford Standard*, 3.11.1967** – **'Saucer shock for housewife'/South Lincolnshire UFO Study Group**)

At 7am on 26th October 1967, a woman living in Buckinghamshire sighted a glowing *'ball of light'* in the sky.

"It was sort of silvery in the centre, surrounded by a white halo of light – then it seemed as though it started to spin and dipped lower, moving in a circle, as though inspecting something on the ground, before moving across the sky northwards."

At around 7am, Susan Page (13) from Stratford-upon-Avon happened to be looking out of her bedroom window, when she noticed two bright silver objects, moving north-east to south-west, above the scurrying clouds.

"I called my mother and father, who stood with me watching them go over. To our surprise, three more identical objects appeared, not quite round – more like the baubles you get on a Christmas tree. What staggered us was that they were only going slow – not as fast as an airplane. They took 10-15 minutes to pass over. After the first five came two more identical

objects, making seven in total, all travelling sideways. Strangely, we also saw two much smaller lights heading the group. Unfortunately, we lost sight of the last two, as the sun was now rising."

In conversation with Susan, over 25 years later, she still considered the sighting the strangest thing she and her family had ever seen – never to be forgotten.

Enquiries made with the police, at Leek Wootton, Warwickshire, revealed:

"We have received a number of UFO sightings from several parts of the country, but not the Warwickshire area."

Details of the other reports were not disclosed. **(Source: personal interview/John D. Llewellyn)**

At 7.10am, six fluorescent green UFOs were seen crossing the face of the moon, by three miners, on their way to work at Springwell, near Gateshead.

"Four of them disappeared from sight; the other two remained stationary in the sky for five minutes, before vanishing into cloud."

(Source: UFOLOG/TUFOS)

At 11.25am, over Moigne Downs, halfway between Weymouth and Lulworth Cove, Dorset, a former (BOAC) Flight Administration Officer – Mr Angus Brooks – was out with his dog when he saw:

"A 'craft', prior to its levelling out to a hover position, comprised of a central circular chamber, with a leading fuselage in the front and **three separate fuselages** together at the rear. On slowing to a 'hover' position, the two outer fuselages at the rear moved to position at the side of the 'craft' to form four fuselages at equidistance around centre chamber. There were no visible power units and no noise of applied power for reverse thrust, movement of fuselages, or for hovering.

The 'craft' remained in this position for the next 22 minutes and 1 remained rather apprehensive in my position. As seen from my horizontal position, the craft's construction was of translucent material. The colour of the 'craft' took on the colour of the sky above it and changed with clouds passing over. It could have been a clear material at the top of the fuselage and centre clambers. There were dark centre shadows along the base of the fuselages and centre chambers. No movement was observed at any time of the operators and no portholes or crew viewing windscreens in the nose of fuselages.

The nose cones of the fuselage were the reverse to our conventional types and the groove fins along the base of the fuselage did not open or close. The possibility of power passing through the construction material could not be considered. The hover position was equidistant between Winfrith Power Station and the Portland Underwater Defence Station, about a mile inland from the USAF Communication Centre Unit, at Ringstead Bay. At 11.47am, two of the fuselages moved round to line up with a centre third fuselage.

The 'craft' then climbed with increasing speed east-north-east over Winfrith. The lead fuselage on 'departure' was a different one to the 'arrival' lead. Dimensions – approximately centre chamber diameter, height 12-25 feet, length of fuselage 75 feet, height 7 feet, width 8 feet."

As a result of his letter being sent to local newspapers and the MOD, Mr Brooks received a visit from Dr. John Dickison, of the Royal Aircraft Establishment at Farnborough, accompanied by Mr

Leslie Akhurst, of S4 (Air) MOD, and Alec Cassie – a RAF psychologist – who interviewed him about the incident and later sent him a letter, dated 5th April 1968, the gist of which suggested he saw *"a vitreous floater – a piece of loose matter – a dead cell, floating in the fluid of the eyeball"*.

At 3.25pm, a huge sparkling blue-white anchor-shaped object, pulsating every ten seconds, was seen over Sunderland, at 60 degrees elevation in the south-east, separate from Venus, prominent in the night sky, followed by the appearance of 6-8 smaller objects seen moving across the sky in an oval-shaped formation. (**Source: Tyneside UFO Society)**

At 5.30pm, a silver, oval object was seen in the sky over Maidenhead, apparently following the M4 Motorway, before splitting into six separate fragments of light. (**Source:** *Slough Observer*, **3.11.1967)**

At 7.15pm, Andrew Hindle (15), was at his home address in Goats Lane, Enfield, when he heard his parents, upstairs, shouting out in alarm.

> *"I rushed upstairs, wondering what was happening. They directed my attention towards what looked like the Nativity Star, motionless in the sky, about two miles away. It then began to decrease in size and disappeared from view, leaving a small black 'disc', with three lights at the end and a line across the centre. This then shot off westwards and was gone out of view."*

Andrew later said:

"I still don't know to this present day what it was we saw, but I do know that it wasn't Venus, a B52 Bomber refuelling, or mass hysteria, as suggested to us in the months afterwards."

At the same time a circular revolving globe of light, which gradually changed colour from yellow to red to silvery-white in the sky, was sighted moving south-east over the Hill View Estate, Sunderland, at 7.15pm on 26th October 1967, by three people.

(Source: *Evening Standard*, 27.10.1967 – 'The 'thing' drops into Enfield')

At 7.30pm, three schoolboys – S. Birkby, C. Taylor and M. Robinson, from Alderman Leach School, Darlington – sighted *'four bright flashing lights in a square formation'* flying through the sky, west to east, and out-of-sight in five minutes. Later that evening, other strange objects were seen in the night sky over the same locality, described as *'looking like squashed triangles'*, orange in colour.

(Source: *Surrey Advertiser*, 28th October 1967/UFOLOG)

At 8pm, *'a cigar-shaped object, showing a dozen red flashing lights',* was seen heading across the sky over the University of Kent, Canterbury – later explained away by the authorities as being an American aircraft, refuelling.

Many hundreds of miles away, a doctor and his wife contacted the police after having sighted *'a number of circular red and white flashing objects in the sky, towards the north, over the Spadeadam Rocket Establishment, near Carlisle* (opened in the late 1950s, as a test area for the British Intermediate Range Ballistic Missiles).

At 8.30pm, two unidentified lights were seen moving at great speed over Letchworth, North Hertfordshire, followed by the ejection of a third object, which made off in the opposite direction, trailing flames like a rocket engine.

A short time later, an object – six or seven times the size of a rugby ball – was seen over Hawick, Scotland, showing a brilliant light in its centre, heading towards the direction of Carlisle.

(Source: *Kent Messenger*, 3.11.1967/*Hertfordshire Express*, Hitchin, 2.11.1967)

At 8.50pm, Mr William Puffitt from Victoria Road, Cirencester, was staying with his relatives – Mr and Mrs Joan Muller – who contacted the police after sighting a *'triangular object in the sky, showing a white light at the front, with two red lights at the rear, passing over nearby rooftops'* – later suggested by Jodrell Bank to be Venus, at low elevation. **(Source: Personal interview)**

An illuminated 'saucer', projecting beams of light, was seen moving across the sky over Colchester United football ground, following an aircraft. It was then seen to stop in mid-air when reaching the aircraft and head away at great speed, before disappearing from sight. Other reports told of a star, or cross-shaped objects seen over Alnwick, Northumberland, and a bright glowing green cigar, trailing sparks, over Brighton. **(Source: *Edinburgh Evening News*, 26.10.1967/*Nuneaton Evening News*, 27.10.1967/*Bournemouth Evening Echo*, 27.10.1967)**

26th April 1968 – Two UFOs seen over Ipswich

At 8pm, Mr F. Kendall of Crowland Close, Ipswich, sighted a *"sparkling mass, heading over Belstead, low down over trees."*

Mr Fenton of Nacton Road, Ipswich, was in his back garden at 9.20pm. He said:

"I saw a bright blob, heading across the sky in a north-easterly direction; it was zigzagging. It then disappeared behind houses. Then a second one appeared, heading northwards, and crossed the path of the first one."

Ten minutes later, Mr McFadyen of Dukes Drive, Halesworth, sighted two UFOs moving through the sky:

"I estimated their height at about 65,000 feet. The first one showed the white light was zigzagging as it moved. The second had a smaller light. This came down from the sky at quite a speed and suddenly soared up again."

(Source: *Evening Star*, 27.4.1968 – 'More UFO sightings over Suffolk')

6th March 1969 – Three UFOs sighted over *River Orwell*

Former RAF officer – M. R.J. Hubbard of 5, Fonnereau Road, Ipswich – was sailing up the *River Orwell* in his motor boat, at 6.45pm.

"I was looking northwards when I saw three circular objects in the clear blue sky. They wheeled and showed full circle, before disappearing into a cloud bank. They were not aircraft."

(Source: Ron West, *Evening Star*, March 1969 – 'Ex RAF man sees objects in the sky')

7th September 1971 – 'Thing' seen in the sky over Suffolk

A mysterious object was seen heading through the sky over Ipswich and East Anglia, by many residents, before being later seen over the Devon area. Police Forces over the UK were swamped with telephone calls from the public reporting sightings of a 'blob' shaped object, which was later explained away as being a fluorescent chemical cloud ejected by a meteorological research balloon, launched from South Uist. However, a spokesman for the East Anglian Astronomical Society claimed that it was probably a *"False Moon – an image caused by ice particles high in the atmosphere."*

(Source: *Evening Star*, 8.9.1971 – 'Thing from the Hebrides')

10th November 1971 – Cigar-shaped UFO seen

Capel St. Mary, commonly known as Capel, is a village in Suffolk, England, about 6 miles south-west of Ipswich and 2 miles from Dedham Vale – a designated area of outstanding natural beauty. This was the scene of a UFO sighting at 4.45am, by Mr William McCann (37) of 12 Chapel Close, who described what he saw:

"It was cylindrical at the front, with a reddish glowing short sort of a tail. I would have ignored it but for the fact that a small black rounds speck shot up and away at tremendous speed."

Jonathon Pearce (12) of 19 Chapel Close was another witness.

This was the fourth time in a few weeks that Mr McCann and his family had seen a strange object in the sky over their home.

Suffolk Police were contacted at the time. They said no other reports had been received by them but that a weather balloon was launched in the sky at 5.15pm, which ruled out this as being an explanation for what was seen.

(**Source: Ron West**/*Evening Star*, 11.11.1971 – 'Mystery object in sky')

7th December 1971 – Freak sunset over Ipswich, Suffolk

A purple sky was seen by Ispwich, Suffolk, residents. The phenomena were reported to the USAF Bentwaters Weather Station, who suggested *"it had been caused by the angle at which the sun's rays had struck the foggy conditions and then refracted through it."*

16th February 1974 – Cigar-shaped UFO sighted and missing time

Mr Rick Chapman (52), of Park View, Alphamstone, Burres, Essex, close to the Suffolk border was bringing in the washing at 9.45pm, when he felt a sensation as if he was being watched. He looked around – there was nothing to be seen.

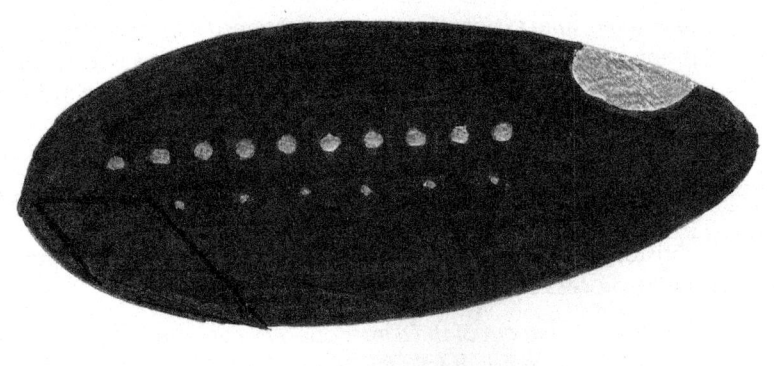

As he took the washing into the house he passed his wife, Maggie, and said to her *"Where are you going?"* She didn't reply, and headed off into the garden.

Curious he went back outside, noticing that the kitchen wall clock showed 9.50pm, and saw her at the bottom of the garden, looking up into the sky.

"I looked up and saw this cigar-shaped object in the sky, with yellow lights along its side, before it took off at tremendous speed. Excited, we went back into the house and made ourselves a cup of tea. I looked at the wall clock in the kitchen and was shocked to see that it was 1.20am.

I can only presume that there was something wrong with the clock, because we had only been outside for about ten minutes."

Ron West interviewed the couple concerned and found them to be very genuine. He was perturbed to find out that after the event Maggie found some unusual rashes on her arms, legs and stomach. She was examined by doctors who were unable to identify the cause of this condition.

27th November 1979 – Glowing red *'ball of light'* over Ipswich

Mrs Gillian Adams (37) of Fitzwilliam Close, Ipswich, was on the way to the local shops, at 3.30pm, when she was astonished to see:

"…a huge round 'ball' of red light in the sky. I wondered if it could have been the sun or the moon, a short distance away.

I stopped a woman and showed her the object; she pointed out the moon and the sun, which were in another part of the sky. A few minutes later it disappeared from sight."

Boxing Day – Mysterious light seen over Woodbridge, Suffolk

Joyce Reeves (78), from Martlesham, Suffolk, came forward in 2015 wanting to tell what she witnessed.

"I ought to have said something before this time, but as I am 78 feel that I should do now. It was late afternoon on a Boxing Day – probably late 70s, early 80s. I was living in Old Barrack Road, Woodbridge, at the time. I was taking our dog for a walk along Old Barrack Road, towards Warren Hill Road. When I approached an area just passed what is now the Co-op, I happened to look up to the sky on my left. At that time there was an open space, so I had an unobstructed view of the sky; the plot has since been developed.

I saw a 'light' moving steadily from right to left, i.e. from the Ipswich direction. It made no noise whatsoever – it just kept moving silently to the left. I was so certain that I had witnessed something quite extraordinary that I mentioned it to my family on my return. When we read in the press about a possible UFO, my husband urged me to pass on this information. However, I found the possibility of being questioned and interviewed rather daunting. I will always be convinced that what I witnessed was something very unusual."

22nd January 1980 – Mysterious light beams seen at Saxmundham

Christopher Peck (25) living in Benhall, Saxmundham – an agricultural mechanic by occupation – was in the process of locking the shed door, when:

"I saw something out of the corner of my eye and turned to see 'two parallel lines', about four inches apart and about four feet long, moving at an angle of 45 degrees down the garden; seconds later they were out of sight. They reminded me of fluorescent tubes, pink and purple light moving about four feet off the ground in a 'walking motion' The objects didn't make sense; I had never seen anything like that before. I did learn, the next day, that some electrical wire was found wrapped around trees in an adjoining field. Whether there was a connection I cannot say."

Mrs Janet Peck

Mrs Janet Peck (48) was, in fact, the witness who came across the wire. She told of letting the horse out into the paddock, at 8am, when she found a quantity of electric fence wire stretched around the trees and bushes, at a height of some 5 feet 6 inches.

As I turned to lock the shed door something caught my eye coming over the roof of the shed. I looked back down the garden a saw two parallel lines about four inches apart & about four foot long at an alternating angle of 45° & travelling down the garden.

As it was in January it was pitch black and these lines showed up as a pink/purple colour and lasted no more than a couple of seconds.

Best way of describing these was as two dimly lit flourescent tubes. Their centres being about 4 ft off the ground.

Please continue on a separate sheet if necessary.

DRAWING* 1st vision   2nd   3rd

4th

* If preferred, use a separate sheet of paper.

Your full name (Mr/Mrs/Miss/Ms)
CHRISTOPHER PECK   Age 25
Address. THE
BETHALL, SAXMUNDIAN. SUFFOLK
Telephone No. (STD 0728)
Occupation during last two years. AGRICULTURAL
MECHANIC.

Any professional, technical or academic qualifications
or special interests

Do you object to the publication of your name?
*Delete as applicable.
Today's Date. SEPTEMBER 27th 1988
Signature. Chris Peck

She believes there may be a connection, bearing in mind the line of direction with what her son witnessed and the wiring. Unfortunately, we are left with many questions but no answers. One presumes that it was not an aircraft, kite, or balloon. Could it have been a hoax – an elaborate contraption, constructed by someone to fly just off the ground? Hardly likely, we would have thought.

On the 30th October 2015, we visited Janet Peck – a woman with a love for horses and dogs – who showed us around the family home, which contained some lovely artwork drawn by her late mother. Following discussion with her, she had this to say:

"I saw Ken, the local baker, who was out delivering the next morning. He told me that the telephone wires were down and draped over the road. I told people at the village shop; they laughed at me."

She showed us the area concerned at the back of her house and remains perplexed as to how the telephones wires had been stretched *"…like spaghetti, hanging down from the poles. I have no idea what it was. I'm not saying my son saw a UFO – just what he told he had seen. It is inexplicable what happened."*

20th June 1980 – Bright orange *'light'* seen by many people

During the late evening, Mr Graham Lee and his wife, Elizabeth, were driving between Clare and Cavendish – villages situated in the West of Suffolk when , they saw a bright orange *'light'* hovering just above the road and stopped the car to have a closer look.

About ten minutes later the *'light '*shot away, leaving a small trail behind it. Within hours, other people were to contact the authorities reporting having seen a strange orange-red or bright yellow *'light'*, low down in the sky. Some of the witnesses told of seeing it move slowly; others reported it flashing away across the sky. It is claimed that on another occasion, the 'light' knocked out the engine of a car for a few seconds. Officialdom, who was consulted about the sightings, suggested people had seen Venus or aircraft activity.

UFO – like an 'upturned plate'

Other witnesses included Christine Day (13) of Cordell Place, Long Melford – a large village and civil parish in the County of Suffolk, England, situated on Suffolk's border with Essex, marked by the *River Stour*, approximately 16 miles from Colchester and 14 miles from Bury St. Edmunds.

"My friends and I were sitting on the swings in Cordell Place, at about 8.30pm, when suddenly we were aware of a strange object, which was like an upturned plate, for about five minutes. It then gradually moved upwards and disappeared, leaving a trail."

Doris Good, from Chelmsford, also saw a strange 'light' in the sky. Maurice Rufus of Newton Green was another witness. He saw it heading towards the direction of Clare.

Keith King of Brantocks Road, Great Waldingfield (two miles north-east of Sudbury) observed it,

"…moving in a big arc over Sudbury and leaving a trail; it was far too big to be a star and moved very quickly".

Caroline Waldron (18) of Uplands Road, Sudbury, saw an unusual small 'star' hovering over Springlands Estate.

"I watched it for about five minutes and I became a little bit frightened. It moved towards this bigger 'light', which then flew off leaving a trail behind it, heading onwards in the direction of Woodhall Close and Newton Green."

(Source: Ron West)

Sudbury resident Mrs Angie Christie, who was to witness a number of strange aerial phenomena around the nearby transmitter mast during the early 1990s (which will be found further into the book), told us of an incident involving a local youth named Ian (16), whose father was a local architect.

"He saw a strange 'light' over the transmitter in broad daylight, which then moved overhead, showing what he described as a triangular object. Ian was so unnerved that he fired his airgun at it, with no effect."

Unfortunately we have no further information on this incident, which took place in 1984 and are unable trace him without knowing his full name.

November 1980 – Blinding light illuminates Rendlesham Forest

A man contacted us about what he witnessed while poaching in Rendlesham Forest, during one early morning:

"Suddenly the whole of the forest lit up with a blinding light. You could see for miles. I was stunned as to what could be causing it. This illumination went on for about five minutes and then faded away."

Could this have been space debris, or a fireball, which in our opinion would normally last just a few seconds rather than minutes?

We asked David Bryant what he thought of this incident. He said:

"Neither of these could possibly take five minutes to transit the sky: meteorites enter the atmosphere travelling at 11 km/sec (25,000 mph), to 72 km/sec (160,000 mph): the recent whopper over Argentina took less than a minute to travel from horizon to horizon. Also, neither would really light up the sky with a constant illumination lasting that long. Of course, the witness could well be exaggerating: I'm no longer surprised by how 'imaginative' people can be when describing unfamiliar occurrences."

Early December 1980 – Mysterious object seen over Woodbridge

Mr Reginald Brown of Mill Lane, Waldringfield, Woodbridge, Suffolk – the owner of a boat yard – was awoken at 2.30am in early December 1980, by an extremely bright light, shining into the bedroom. On going to the window to see the source of the illumination, he saw:

"…an object – the size of a football – hovering in the sky. I watched it for about ten minutes until it shot silently away over the sea, before being lost from view."

(Source: Ron West)

December 1980 – 'Spinning top' UFO over Semer, Suffolk

Charles Prentice (69), now living in Bury St. Edmunds, Suffolk, contacted us in October 2015, after reading about our forthcoming book featuring Charles Halt, and the events that occurred towards the end of December 1980, wishing to bring our attention to something he had witnessed in December 1980, although he was unable to identify the exact day. Annoyingly to us, not to him, he had written down the date on a calendar at the time, but this had been lost as the years advanced.

Dawn Holloway and I went down to see him and his wife at their home on the 30th October 2015. We found him and his wife, Mary, a delightful couple. After some initial hesitance, borne from how we would receive his sighting – an attitude common to people who do not realise that they are not on their own with reports of this nature – he told us what happened, just before Christmas, when he and his wife were living in a rented cottage in an unmarked road at *Semer, near Hadleigh, Suffolk.

"I came round and thought I had overslept. I looked at the clock by the side of the bed; it was 1.45am. I thought where was the light was coming from. It was a beautiful night, with the stars showing. I looked out and saw this object about the length of a large car and the shape of a child's spinning top. It had a brilliant white light on the top of it, with a bright pulsating light just below it. At one point it was only three feet away from our bedroom window. I could have opened the window and touched it.

I had a loaded shotgun in the bedroom, which I kept in case any foxes tried to get at the chickens. I contemplated firing at it, but then decided not to. The object continued to hover for about three- quarters of an hour before it left."

Charles described how he attempted to wake up his wife, who struggled to do so as she had been feeding their small child and was very tired.

---

*Semer is a small village and civil parish in Suffolk, England. It is located adjacent to a bridge over the *River Brett* on the B1115, between Hadleigh and Stowmarket. The parish also contains the hamlets of Ash Street and Drakestone Green. Semer Wood, a designated wildlife site, is classified as ancient woodland. The parish was recorded in the 2011 census as having a population of 130; down from 158 in the previous census.

Charles:

"There appeared to be two square-shaped panels on the outer body of the object, although I cannot say these were doors or openings."

The object then shot upwards into the sky at phenomenal speed – soon only seen as a tiny point of light before disappearing from view.

The next morning, his employer – Mrs Arthey (known to him only as 'Madam' from the Priory) – came around to see him and said: *"I heard you had visitors last night."* Charles told her what he had seen and was stunned when she confirmed she had seen it as well.

We emailed her son – a local councillor, who still lives at the Priory about this matter. He replied, confirming he knew Charles, but had no knowledge of any UFO sighting. His mother, 'Madam', sadly passed away in 2013.

An unusual find

Charles told us about what he found in the ground, while digging post holes in the back garden of the house overlooking where he had seen the UFO, and showed us a beautiful intricately designed bronze dish, which is believed to have been made around the 13th/14th Century.

1990 – Green beam of light and missing time!

We spoke further with Charles – a quietly spoken man – and his pleasant wife until, after some prompting, Charles hesitatingly told us about a second encounter with something very odd, this happened approximately ten years later, at the nearby Hyde Wood, close to where he lives now. He was with his friend David Ashton and his son Ian (now 36), when they became engulfed in a mysterious green beam of light.

Charles:

"We had made arrangements to meet another gentleman up there, at about 3-4pm; the man was coming from Lakenheath.

We were in the wood when a strange beam of light came down over us. I don't know what happened after that. Eventually the light went out and they told me I was the first one to speak. It was dark by then.

On the way back we met up with the man from Lakenheath, who was very annoyed at us because we hadn't turned up. He wanted to know where on earth we had been. He said he had seen a strange green beam of light coming down from the sky over the wood and wanted to know what happened."

David Ashton

We telephoned David Ashton, who confirmed the version of events as given by Charles. He had this to say:

"We went to the wood to try and discover what was killing pheasants that were found with their heads ripped off. On one night alone, between two to three hundred birds were found dead in this manner. We presumed it was foxes or owls. We decided to stake out the woods and hopefully deal with the source of this attack on the pheasants and took shelter in some

conifers waiting for something to happen. The trees were so thick that we couldn't even see the sky – which is important, bearing in mind what was going to happen to us. We had also arranged to see Glen Sutton, who was going to talk to me about digging a pond out. Charles and I continued our vigilance armed with shotguns.

As twilight fell, a brilliant blue-green light bathed the whole area in light. We stood there as if frozen. Approximately 30 minutes later, the light went out. Charles was the first to speak. He said 'Are any of you going to say what just happened to us?' It was as if we were frozen in time – that's the only way I can describe it.

We made our way back to meet Mr Glen Sutton, who asked us where we had been and what was the strange green light he had seen over the woods."

In late November 2015 we spoke to Glen. He told us he was unable to remember any details concerning the incident although he had no reason to dispute what Charles and David claimed.

Mysterious 'sphere of light' seen in the sky

Mr Ashton also told us about an incident involving a mysterious *'sphere of light'* that was seen by himself and Charles, who was driving with his young daughter, when the object appeared in the sky. Charles went back to fetch a pair of binoculars. As he drove back with his daughter, he felt as if he was in 'limbo' and never used the binoculars.

Ghostly horseman seen at Barrow

David also told of sighting a white horse, with what looked like a cavalry officer on it, while motorcycling near Barrow, near Bury St. Edmunds, during the late 1960s, and a UFO in the upper atmosphere, performing a diamond-shaped formation across the sky.

23rd December 1980 – Impressions found earlier in the forest

In early November 2015, after having contacted former Security Policeman Steven Wagner about his UFO sighting in June 1980, we were surprised to later learn that Steven had, like his counterparts, also discovered some strange marks in the forest – the difference being that these were alleged to have been found a few days before the incidents involving the other airmen.

Out in the forest the same night as Charles Halt

Steven claimed, following conversation with Robert Hastings, in September 2015, that he had been out in the forest the same night as Charles Halt, and overheard discussions about him and a team being at a different location – possibly under the command of Lt Englund or 'Bobby' Ball, but he cannot remember who. He was told that there were some 30 security policemen in the forest that night, in small groups, at different locations.

23rd December 1980 – Flashing lights seen in the forest

In an interview conducted by Robert Hastings with Steven Wagner, made available on the internet on the 23rd November 2015, we learn the following:

Steven:

*"My involvement in the RFI was limited in scope, but I believe I was the first to report activity on RAF Woodbridge that week. I would like to say that this occurred on **Tuesday, December 23rd**, but I'm not positive. Senior Airman Robert 'Bobby Bo' Beauchamp and I were assigned as the SRT for Woodbridge that night. The gate guard – his name escapes me but he was from Arkansas and we nicknamed him Elmer, because he resembled Elmer Fudd – was posted to the last parking area nearest East Gate. I do not recall who the ART was that night. Elmer called us to his post, saying he saw something come down in the forest outside East Gate. The approximate position would have been roughly ENE of the gate post, maybe. I believe it was TSGTJames Middlebrooks, who was in charge of Woodbridge Security Police that night. He, Bob Beauchamp, and I ventured outside East Gate to do a cursory investigation regarding 'flashing lights' in the forest."*

Three depressions found 12 feet apart in clearing, forming a triangle

"We reported seeing nothing of note and returned to post. We did, however, come across a curious thing. In a clearing that was roughly 30 feet in diameter, there were a slew of tree branches scattered on the ground which appeared to have been sheared clean-off the surrounding trees, and in the centre of all this were three depressions that were spaced about 12 feet apart and formed a triangle.

Now keep in mind, it wasn't until the [1991] Unsolved Mysteries program about RFI that I realized what we'd discovered that night. I know it was the exact same spot. Jim Penniston and John Burroughs will swear that we were not on alert status during this period, but that's not true. I was in those woods the first night of RFI as a part of a recall, due to the activities that week."

Robert:

"You say you think the depressions in the ground that you found were the same ones that Penniston and Burroughs found later on. Could they have been another landing site? How do you know it was the 'exact same spot'?"

Wagner:

"It could have been another site; however, based on the conversation I had with Colonel Halt recently, I have some doubt about that. He described the area, mentioned landmarks that I was familiar with, and placed himself in the same area with relation to East Gate that I was in on the 23rd December. The only thing that would make me doubt is the claim of burn marks on the trees; I do not recall the trees being scorched."

Robert:

"Did you and the others report what you found?"

Wagner:

"I said nothing to anyone in regards to this; an irresponsible response on my part, largely due to the 'stick' I took after reporting my June 1980 sighting. As far as I know, Temporary Sgt Middlebrooks didn't either. No discussion about this ever took place between us."

Robert:

"Regarding the date, on what do you base your belief that it occurred on the 23rd? The Penniston/Burroughs UFO encounter occurred at approximately 3am on the 26th. At some point thereafter, Penniston found the three depressions and later took plaster casts of them. The widely-held assumption has always been that the landing pad marks were created that night, as the triangular craft set down on the ground. If your discovery did indeed take place on the 23rd, then there had to have been a landing in that area some three days prior to Penniston's discovery. Of course, there is no reason why this couldn't have happened, but I am just trying to imagine a plausible scenario and time-line that would account for everyone's observations."

Wagner:

"If memory serves me, the 23rd was our last mid-shift on B Flight; this would make the 26th our last day of break and would also explain our recall."

Robert:

"If he's correct, then the events in Rendlesham Forest in late December 1980 began even earlier than previously thought. In the context of the reported UFO activity occurring much earlier that year, as well as those following the now well-known events, such a revelation should not be too surprising".

Jim Penniston:

"We were on normal security status. The only time around that preiod. We were on base exercise in November '80 and in mid January '81. All local practice alerts."

26ᵗʰ December 1980 – Prison officer sights UFO

A former Prison officer at HMP Hollesley Bay Prison, Suffolk – Jeff Ralph – contacted us about what he saw, while out with friends, during the early morning of the 26ᵗʰ December 1980.

"I had been working Christmas day 1980. When I arrived home after what had been a stressful day, I decided to 'let off some steam' and go out with my wife, Christine, and our next door neighbour (who was a Prison officer) and his wife, over farmland at Hollesley Bay to shoot ducks. We had permission from the landowners. After picking up the shotguns we made out way to Shingle Street, waiting for the ducks to come up. We lay down in the dyke, looking out to sea. It was twilight at the time, with darkness beginning to descend. Suddenly this 'thing' appeared in the sky, as if from outer space travelling in a shallow arc, at about 15 degree the size of a small car and moving at fantastic speed heading towards the direction of Bentwaters. We all made a pact never to tell anybody about this, fearing ridicule, until now."

This puts the time around 4pm; could it have been a fireball? There are none reported for that time by the British Astronomical Association.

We spoke to Jeff again about the matter. He could only describe it as a light of some size, moving at terrific speed across the sky.

He was unable to discern any shape to it, but felt it was very low, about 60 feet above them, and had originated from outer space.

Christmas 1980 – Moth box in forest sparks off red alert!

Over the years, the reader has heard all manner of strange explanations for what took place in the forest during that fateful weekend of 1980 – ranging from the bizarre, lorry load of fertilizer, flashing beacon on police car – to the ridiculous, beams from the lighthouse.

In November 2015, Ipswich resident Ivan Potter (91) a former RAF air gunner on Wellington bombers during World War 2, and a member of Churchill's secret army 1940-1943 told of incident which took place at the camping site in Rendlesham Forest during December 1980.

Ivan Potter with wife, Sara

Ivan:

"I owned a caravan, which was kept on the camping site in Rendlesham Forest, close to Wood-bridge airbase. My wife Sara and I often used to stay there; sometimes, if I was working nights as a railway man, my wife and the two Yorkie dogs would use the van.

One evening, towards the end of December 1980, the base was on what was known locally as 'yellow alert'. All lights around the base were dimmed. Two men turned up at the campsite in a caravan. I chatted to them, as you do, and asked them what brought them down to the site at Christmas time. They explained they were from Oxford; one was in his late 60s, the other in his 40s. One of them also told me he was a professor. I was intrigued to find out that they were there to observe the migration of moths, which entailed setting up a number of moth traps. These were cardboard boxes about 18 inches square and a foot deep. In the middle was a hole, allowing a eight hour night light underneath located on top of a small piece of aluminum metal to attract moths, which then entered the box. The men asked me where the best places were to put the boxes so I showed them around some of the tracks, suggesting places to put them. One of them was about 50-70 yards away from the perimeter fence. They showed me these very long torches that projected a thin pencil of light up into the sky to attract the moths."

The next morning

The next morning the two men spoke to Ivan with a veritable tail of woe. Apparently, after having set the traps, they went into the forest during the night and accidently knocked over one of the moth traps, which set nearby bushes on fire. They ran about, flashing their torches, trying to extinguish the fire, and Ivan believes there was an association with this and the visit the next morning, to the campsite by an American jeep, with two men on, who went into the forest.

Ivan cannot be exactly sure of the date. He is an honorable man, who has served his country. He has nothing to gain by any fabrication. Whether this has anything to do with what happened outside the air base we cannot say, but found the report of interest.

Tony Prichard

In 2015 we contacted Tony Prichard from the Suffolk area, who is a specialist on moths, hoping to glean further information.

He told us, after being sent a copy of the report from Ivan:

"The description of moth traps is recognisable as being of the Skinner type moth trap. They used to be made in metal but cheaper wooden ones are now in vogue. The bulbs commonly in use at the time were either 1) mercury vapour – you can see one of these MV bulbs in the trap shown in the photo [See below photo]. They have changed a little since then, but are basically the same 2) blended bulb – which is a mixture of tungsten and MV. Probably the key feature here is that they tend to run quite hot.

Both of these bulbs run on mains electricity. The MV bulbs produce quite a bluish glow and both are quite bright for their wattage. Some of the home-made traps can be powered by all sorts of battery power and different bulbs can be used, so I can't be absolutely sure what electrics would have been in use.

The only thing which is a bit unexpected from my viewpoint is that they managed to set fire to the bushes with the bulbs. The bulbs do run hot, particularly the blended bulbs, but I'm not sure that the MV bulbs would get hot enough to set fire to any dry vegetation.

I don't have much experience with the blended bulbs, as they have fallen out of favour (they run very hot and have a tendency to shatter more easily than the MV) so can't comment. The top of the traps are clear plastic and cardboard egg trays are normally put inside to help hold the moths inside the trap. The crossbar holding the lamp is a bit unstable and may have toppled over to rest on the plastic sheet, but hard to imagine that it would set it alight.

It is usual practice to go and see what has turned up at the traps during the night, so I'm not surprised the mothers were wandering around in the dark.

Moth traps could have been run at any place within the forest. They would have needed a portable power source - generator or batteries – to run the traps, but serious mothers would have portable kit. How many traps are used is a completely individual choice but it is common practice to run more than one trap. They would try to spread these out over an area. If they had more than one generator, then there could be quite a distance between them."

Bearing in mind that it would be damp and cold, and not forgetting our own many visits to the area, we wondered why would the brush catch fire?

Tony:

"It seems rather implausible to me that the brush should catch fire but he gave quite a good description of how we would set up moth traps and run them. The forest is on quite sandy soil, so free-draining. It's a healthy site and the brush mentioned may well have been gorse, which does collect a lot of dead material in its branches and also as litter beneath it. This does burn quite nicely once it's going, even in winter. They've fallen out of use now, but paraffin Tilley lamps were popular with mothers at one stage and these could be another possible source of flame but does not seem to fit with the story. When we check these traps at night, we do tend to kneel around them"

We emailed Mr Robin Ford of Watkins & Doncaster, UK, who supply a range of moth boxes to the public, asking him about what kind of trap may have been in use.

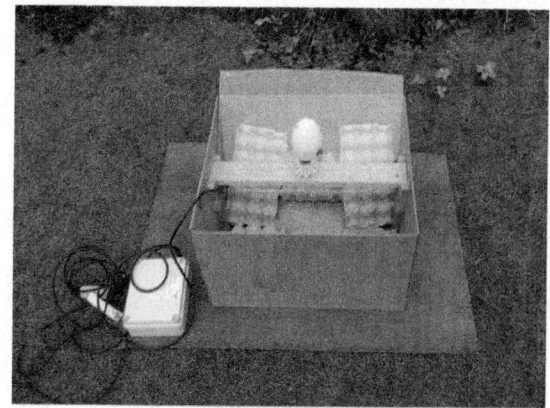

"This particular trap you describe is a Skinner Trap, designed by Bernard Skinner. The idea was to make a mercury vapour trap that was portable but using the same electrics as the original Robinson Trap. The Robinson was the first moth trap made to run off 240 volts in the 1950s and was a rigid round drum of 24 inches in diameter and 12 inches deep, so would not fold. This had a clear plastic collar that sat on the drum and a finned cone held the electrics where the moths entered the trap.

The Skinner trap had four aluminium sheets hinged together so that they folded flat. There was no base and the electrics were mounted on an aluminium bar across the centre, which also held the 4 sides together. Two sloping Perspex sheets on either side of the bar created a letterbox effect which allowed the moths to enter the trap. Usually a white sheet was placed under the trap. Various inferior wooden copies still exist as it is quite expensive to make an aluminium version, but with entomologists driving around in cars, a folding trap of this size is not so important. However, smaller folding traps are still in use originally designed by Heath. These are based around approximately a 12 inch cube and using a 12 volt tube to supply the light source, which makes them very portable. I would guess that the bug hunters used a cardboard box as a cheap moth trap base and if they were using a mains operated lamp these do get hot. We have known the

odd case where traps have caught fire, usually caused by an animal like a cat or fox jumping at the moths flying round the lamp and collapsing the light unit into the base. A trap made from a cardboard box would more than likely catch fire if the flame fell in; with the inside lined with egg trays there would be plenty of combustible material."

Neither Colonel Halt, who denies he was 'chasing moths', or myself, are claiming that any of the airmen misidentified a moth box with any UFO or what happened in the forest. All we are saying is that stories like this, however anecdotal, in light of the seriousness of what was encountered should not be omitted from history. There is no reason to disbelieve this incident didn't happen.

As **Charles Halt** has said on many occasions to me:

"It's about the facts, not about wild speculation or crazy allegations of encounters with alien beings in the forest that carried out conversations with the Base Commander".

Nick Pope – Moth boxes and J.D. Ingalls

"I have no reason to doubt that moth boxes were placed – as Ivan Potter states – but I see no evidence of any connection with the Rendlesham Forest incident. With such sceptical theories there's a tendency to believe that if one can point to evidence of any unusual lights in the forest, one has instantly solved the Rendlesham mystery. The problem, of course, is that not only does one have to account for the lights, but also the radar data, the anomalous radiation levels, and much, much more. Potter's views, while clearly well-intentioned, are just another red herring."

Occam's razor

"The Steve Roberts/J.D. Ingalls story is typical of much of the confusion that surrounds the Rendlesham Forest incident. It's tempting to ascribe the various twists and turns to a conspiracy: the deliberate hand of OSI, perhaps: 'I was helping spread the cover story' certainly sounds

better than 'I was shooting my mouth off in the local pubs'. But in all of this, Occam's razor (the philosophical principle most usually interpreted as stating that the simplest explanation is usually the correct one) suggests a very different interpretation, with no need to bring in cover-ups, conspiracies and disinformation. The most likely explanation here is that J.D. simply picked up bits and pieces of the story from seeing some of the police blotters and listening to some of the initial witness accounts. Larry Warren then picked up the story from J.D., and at every step more removed from the actual witnesses, the story changed – either through embellishment, or simply through the mechanism of 'Chinese whispers'."

RAF Bentwaters – The red phone rings!

Even though the incident is now 35 years old, it still continues to attract the attention of people who want to tell us what they know from their personal perspective. Many of those accounts include reports of mysterious objects seen in the sky; others perhaps judged more mundane, but still worthy of committing to history. One such example involved Elsie Baker, who lived in Bawdsey and worked as a nanny on the Bentwaters Airbase for some of the senior officers, for a number of years, according to her granddaughter – Claire Tolliday:

"I remember her telling me that she knew something odd was going on that day or night (and for some reason I have the sense that it was in the evening, but I might be wrong) as she was looking after the 'Colonel's' children. I think that he was the base commander at the time. She says that as well as the normal telephone in the house, there was also a 'red' phone. She says that the red phone rang that day – the only time that she ever had witnessed this in all of her years of working there. Granny was always very discreet about anything that she witnessed when on the base, and I again have a recollection that it was not until a few years later, when there was some publicity about the alleged incident, that she mentioned this." [Elsie sadly passed away a few years ago]

Charles Halt

"I don't remember an Elsie Baker. I didn't know all the housekeepers or nannies. Five or six of us had red phones, which were direct lines to the Command Post and would allow a direct call to just about anywhere. That's the phone I used when Dot and company would not leave my house, and using it caused all the excitement for the police."

John Hanson on Monroe Ruby Nevels

"I remained puzzled by the conversation with Monroe Ruby Nevels about his admission of already having been into the forest and found the 'landing site' before he was even asked by Lt. Colonel Halt to accompany him into the forest, and asked Charles Halt what he knew about this matter."

Charles Halt

"If Monroe had been to the landing site prior to our visit, he never mentioned it when we went out. In fact, he wasn't sure where the site was. His reaction when we found it was surprise. It certainly didn't happen the night we went out. Conrad did not have time during Englund's shift to go and Monroe was home baby sitting, as his wife spent the evening at a chapel program. Englund had to go and fetch him so he could participate. A day or two later I took Conrad and his family out and Conrad had no idea where the site was and never mentioned being there prior. Something doesn't sound right. Several years ago, I challenged Monroe about his comment of having been there prior and he did not give me an acceptable answer. That all being said, Conrad may have been read in on the 'cover-up', but they would have never have trusted Monroe. If you talk to Monroe, ask him specifically when he claims to have been out. It's certainly possible Conrad was out there earlier, but that puts him in the middle of the cover-up. Conrad is not being honest. His wife and son have told John Burroughs there's more to the story. Maybe one of them will talk more?"

Colonel Alan Brown

"Also as you are visiting Alan Brown, retired Colonel from the base, please ask him how he got a control radio and, secondly, who sent him to the ATC Tower when I was out there in the forest. Three individuals have confirmed he was in the Tower. I believe it was either Gordy Williams, or the director of Operations – Colonel Bowden."

Meeting up with Colonel Brown

On the 30th October 2015, Dawn and I finally met up with Sally Brown who had been a friend of the late Georgina Bruni. She and her husband Alan Brown (78), who made us very welcome at their impressive family home, situated at Bromeswell, Suffolk. Alan expressed his concern about having lost touch with Gordon Williams, as they had been friends for many years and played golf regularly. We promised to try and find out more, and sat listening to him while he told us about his early days as a pilot.

BROWN ALAN R. MAJOR
004-36-3974, 10 APRIL 72

> *"I literally fell into it. I didn't know whether I would like flying, but took to it like a duck to water. I joined the National Guard in 1956. I then moved to New Mexico. They were desperate for fighter pilots and that's how I got involved, until I retired in 1984. I still fly light aircraft as a co-pilot when I go over to the United States."*

Alan was very pleasant, quite jovial and very much at ease with their two delightful Labrador dogs – Boycie and Misha.

We asked him about whether he had been there on duty at the airbase when the UFO incident took place. He strongly denied having been there and said that he was off duty and at the local golf club. He did not learn of the incident until a few days later.

"I was actually playing golf with Gordy on the 28th December 1980, which was a Sunday. I had heard the rumours and asked him what he knew about the matter. He said 'You have to be kidding. I know nothing. No one told me anything'.

Alan:

"Some guys – a bunch of young people – were in the woods when they became frightened, after something scared the hell out of them. That's all I know, but I can tell you that something happened. The guys higher than me asked, as they didn't know. I heard that an air traffic controller saw some weird lights and one of the officers was out there, close to RAF Woodbridge. I asked Don Moreland, but he didn't know anything either."

Sally described the occasion when Georgina Bruni and her bodyguard – *Jacqueline Davis – visited them while researching the background to her (Georgina's) book. At midnight the three of them went for a walk around Rendlesham Forest, curious to see for themselves the effect of the lighthouse on the landscape. As a result of this, Georgina rejected any suspicion that the beam from the lighthouse had played any part in what had taken place.

Pilot sights UFO over Albuquerque, New Mexico

We asked Alan about his views on the UFO subject.

"I've never seen anything personally myself, but I was flying a F100 over Albuquerque in the early 1960s and a guy in front of me said he was being chased by a strange 'light'. He was scared – you could tell that in his voice. I told him to hang on and I would have a look. I came up and looked around; there was nothing to be seen. Of course it could have been anything, maybe a reflection or something, but strange nevertheless."

Georgina Bruni   Jacqueline Davis

Nick Pope:

"Monroe Nevels told me a while ago that he'd been out in the forest before he went out with Halt. I believe it may even be covered in my interview with him in the episode of The Unexplained Files, *titled 'Are Aliens Attacking our Nuclear Arsenal?' "*

John Hanson:

I viewed this film and found there was a re-ference by the programme host to Monroe having gone back out again to the landing site with Colonel Halt, but this was curiously all. I thought Monroe would have been invited to expand on that, but he wasn't asked.

In October 2015, I contacted Monroe Nevels with regard to sorting out this ambiguity. He told me that too many lies had been said about his role, and that *"I did go out to the site with Lt. Bruce Englund on the third night, after being directed to do so by Colonel Conrad, and reported my findings to him, before Colonel Halt asked me to go out with him."*

---

*In 2003 ex Police officer now bodyguard Jacqueline Davis who was then employed by author JK Rowling wrote a book entitled *"The Circuit'* about her career and exploits as a female celebrity bodyguard. The book is a fascinating account of one woman's amazing experiences involving the dangerous job of rescuing children and adults around the world to the more glittering world of guarding well-known celebrities such as Diana Ross, Liza Minnelli, J.K Rowling, Nicole Kidman, Princesses Beatrice and Eugenie, teenage heart-throb Justin Bieber and the Beckhams, to name but a few. In 2011 she was hired by tabloid celebrity Katie Price – AKA Jordan – following intelligence from police that a violent gang targeting premiership soccer stars also had its sights on her. The gang had been going to the homes of footballers and other rich individuals – holding people hostage as they demanded the combinations to safes. Jacquie comments that she never looks after anyone unless there is a real and genuine threat.

Nick Pope – further clarification on this issue

"The confusion over the earlier visit that Monroe Nevels made to the landing site is interesting, but it would be a shame if he and Charles Halt fell out over this, as it doesn't detract from the importance of the visit they made to the landing site together, as recorded on Halt's audio tape. I believe I asked Monroe about his earlier visit when I interviewed him for the episode of The Unexplained Files, entitled 'Are Aliens attacking our Nuclear Arsenal?', but if I did, it clearly didn't make the final edit. That's not surprising, as it is standard practice in the TV industry to film much more material than is required. I do clearly recall discussing this with Monroe informally, off camera, and if he says he was out in the forest earlier that day on the instructions of Colonel Conrad, then I accept that assurance absolutely. If anything, the revelation serves only to reinforce how seriously all the senior command personnel took the incident."

November – Triangular UFO seen

An airmen (who asked that his name be kept confidential) contacted us and had this to say:

"While at RAF Bentwaters and working the East gate at RAF Woodbridge, I observed a black triangle-shaped aircraft fly over the gate after dark. I observed three dim round lights on the underside of the craft. As it went over, there was no sound whatsoever. I was scared by this and was hesitant to call it in to the Law Enforcement desk. Just a moment later, Security in the WSA observed it and called it in over the WSA. At the end of shift I was questioned repeatedly about this. I had no idea something like this was ever seen in the past. I was on temporary duty to Bentwaters. I lived in the visiting airman's quarters. I did not know anyone at Bentwaters, other than the two others TDY, from Vance AFB, that I was with. It seemed to make a lot of people mad that I had also seen this aircraft. This was in late October or early November in 1981."

1982

September 1982 – A visit to Rendlesham Forest

IN late September 1982, Martin Shipp and Charles Affleck – members of the Swindon based UFO group 'Probe', run by Ian Mrzyglod – decided to visit Rendlesham Forest, Suffolk, and speak personally to Dot Street and Brenda Butler, in order to find out for themselves what lay behind the various stories circulating in the media, which alleged a UFO had landed in the forest. They pondered whether this was a story fabricated to conceal something else – such as a 'live' nuclear bomb having fallen from one of the aircraft, en route to the airbase, or was there another more rational explanation – perhaps a hoax? Their objective was not to actually investigate the story but to determine the sequence of events alleged to have taken place during December 1980 and identify the exact location of the landing site concerned. Unfortunately, they were unable to interview one single witness who had actually seen the object.

Charles Affleck – OS map reference Sheet 169: 362: 488

"Prior to my visit to the forest I had spoken to Dot, who told me following a recent visit to the

landing site, that it was still devoid of any plant growth over two years later. After parking the car, we accompanied Dot to the 'landing site' (as shown on the OS map reference Sheet 169 362 488, where we were amazed to see a huge area devoid of any plant growth. The ground was very dry and covered in pieces of branch and leaves; its location was directly in line with the end of the runway at RAF Woodbridge."

Using a Geiger counter, the ground was tested for radiation but did not detect anything untoward. The ground was closely examined and found several

From left to right: Dot Street, Annette Affleck, and former wife of Steven Shipp – Sandra.

examples of plant life sprouting through the dead leaves. The question that stunned the researchers was what could have caused such a huge area to be devoid of life?

A further examination of the locality revealed similar cleared areas of trees, from which it was surmised from the stacked up piles of timber nearby, that they had been felled by the Forestry Commission – as opposed to damage caused by an object crash-landing.

The investigators then examined other matters pertaining to the case. They included a complaint made by Brenda of an out-of- character vibration to her Ford Cortina Estate vehicle, while driving along the forest track to visit witnesses with Dot, which was suggested to be attributed to the proximity of overhead power cables or water running down the track. A drive along the same track by Martin and Charles failed to recreate the same conditions, but it was of significance to see the height of the forest wall as it was then (before the great storm of 1987).

Not even in our wildest dreams

Ironically, no one could have guessed in their wildest dreams of the huge wave of media interest which was to swamp the Suffolk area following the disclosures later made by Colonel Halt, Larry Warren, and others, although of course, none of this was known at the time by 'Probe', who concluded from their investigation into the matter, quote:

'As previously stated, it was not SCUFORI's intention to investigate the sighting – only to attempt to determine if the case was worthy of a detailed follow-up. The findings over the three days left a feeling of confusion, as previous readings in the other publications, Flying Saucer Review, BUFORA Bulletin, etc., all gave the impression that these events actually occurred as described. Naturally, due to the fact that key witnesses were not interviewed, any assessment of the whole case was made worse.'

Brenda Butler's reply

"I am one of the investigators on the Rendlesham case and half of what you have printed is untrue, and I would like to put it right. The landing sight – the UFO did not land where these four investigators went. I cannot understand why Dot Street took them there, as Dot knows where it landed (supposedly). The witness showed us where the landing sight was and it was certainly not at the place in the photographs. Dot says the forestry men told her where the site was on the map. The map I saw was covered in little green trees, and you could not tell one place from another."

The Group also brought to Brenda Butler's attention their misgivings that she was the only person told of the events by a person whose identity had been concealed.

Brenda:

"My witness asked me to keep quiet about the UFO on behalf of him. This I did for five weeks, but I had permission to use this information if I also got it from someone else. After I was told the same story by a forestry worker, whom I knew, I released the story – so I did not betray my confidence to the witness."

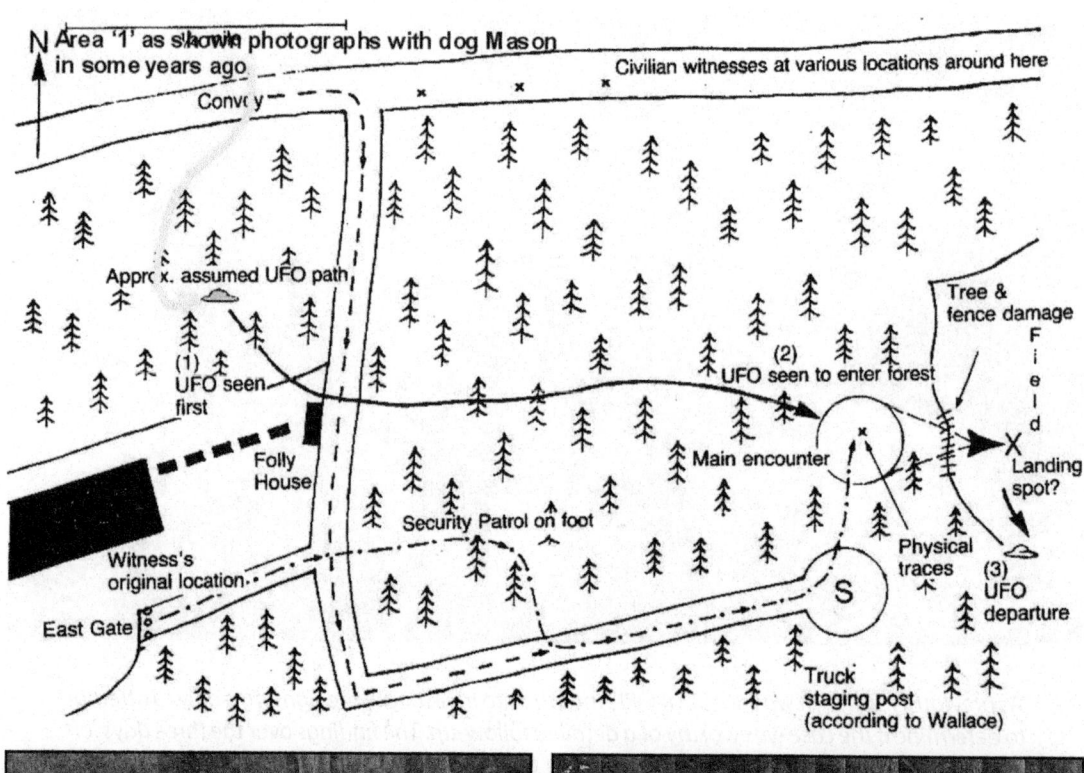

N

Area '1' as shown photographs with dog Mason in some years ago

Convoy

Civilian witnesses at various locations around here

Approx. assumed UFO path

(1) UFO seen first

Folly House

Witness's original location

East Gate

Security Patrol on foot

(2) UFO seen to enter forest

Main encounter

Truck staging post (according to Wallace)

S

Physical traces

Tree & fence damage

Field

X Landing spot?

(3) UFO departure

As it was questionable in the group's opinion whether something unusual had occurred at RAF Woodbridge in late December 1980, owing to what they saw as discrepancies raised which cast doubts on the alleged incidents they decided it did not warrant further investigation.

Hindsight

In hindsight it is all too easy to criticize SCUFORI – an organization which was run very professionally under the guidance of Ian Mrzyglod – for failing to accept something extraordinary had *apparently* taken place in this remote part of the forest, but how could they have possibly known the extent of information still hidden from British view, including the report submitted by Colonel Halt in January 1981? Acceptably mistakes and discrepancies occurred, but none of this should detract from the professionalism of all of the parties concerned, whose integrities have never been in question.

(Source: Martin Shipp/Charles Affleck/Ian Mrzyglod/Jenny Randles (Northern UFO Network)/*BUFORA Bulletin* 004, Page 20-21/Dot Street/*Flying Saucer Review*, Volume 27, No. 6, by Jenny Randles, *The Unexplained*, Volume 9, Jenny Randles, p.2101-2105A)

Colonel Brian Currie – *You Can't Tell The People*

At this point it is of relevance to mention a photograph shown to Gordon Williams by Author Georgina Bruni, during her investigation into the matter (see page 113 – *You Can't Tell The People*) Quote:

"When I showed Gordon Williams the photograph of the person that Larry Warren believed was him, he explained that it was his Vice Wing Commander – Brian Currie. Did Warren mistake the rather tall Colonel Currie for Williams?"

Nick Pope:

"It's clear that on a number of occasions Larry Warren has confused senior officers such as Williams, Halt and Currie. Taken in isolation such confusion doesn't necessarily invalidate his various claims, but again, it reflects the fact that his entire USAF service lasted only a few months. It's little wonder that he was unfamiliar with these individuals, and in his extremely short time in the service he would probably have had very little direct contact with these senior officers."

Romantic Liaison

Georgina then incredibly informs the reader that Currie was arrested by the Security Police after having been caught in an intimate liaison with a female Lieutenant on the front lawn of his Bentwaters house. He appeared before Gordon Williams, who disciplined him and confined him to quarters before sending him back to the United States.

On the surface this sounds very bizarre and almost unbelievable taking into account the rank and military service of this officer, who surely wouldn't have been so stupid to have sacrificed his career for a liaison of this nature.

Nick Pope:

"I've heard the allegation about Currie before, from Georgina Bruni and others, but I've seen no paperwork to support the assertions, and even if true, the story appears to have little or

no bearing on the Rendlesham Forest incident. But in case anyone thinks the story must be bogus because sexual relations between consenting adults isn't an offence, I should point out that in the military there are rules about sexual relations that don't apply in the civilian world. This applies, for example, to relations between superiors and subordinates in the same chain of command, on the basis of the perception of favouritism or misuse of position.

Colonel Currie for Williams? Nobody has ever considered that the Vice Wing Commander might have played a role in the incident and yet it would make perfect sense that Williams' subordinate would be more likely to have been involved, if only to check out the situation for his boss."

Charles Halt:

"The Lieutenant was a misfit. Who knows how she got in the Air Force? She worked in from Disaster Preparedness. Her first name was Tammy (Monroe can probably remember her last name). It was a real mess. A few days before this, he picked up the punch bowl at a formal dining occasion and spilled it all down his front. When he was caught on the lawn he fled in his car down the flight line.

I heard him call Zickler on the radio and say 'call off your dogs' as the cops were in pursuit. – A real disaster. Yes, he was confined and sent home! Zickler didn't arrest him but the base police did."

East Anglian Star Newspaper – Aliens carried out repairs on the craft!

The *East Anglian Star* published an article during this year, entitled: 'Duo still on trail of mysterious UFO landing in Forest'.

A photograph of Dot and Brenda is shown, accompanied by a quote from them relating to the evidence given to them by their 'key witness', who alleged three entities, about three feet tall, were seen dressed in silver suits and levitating in shafts of brilliant light.

An unarmed party of base personnel watched as 'the visitors' carried out repairs to their 'craft', which took off later.

USAF spokesman

A USAF spokesman, said:

"Every time I hear about this, it becomes more elaborated. All we know is that some people on duty that night saw some lights in the sky, which I understand were seen in other parts of the country."

In addition, the newspaper also included a drawing showing the UFO standing on three legs, which is the one supplied by the informant 'Steve Roberts'.

We have to say that this seems, at first glance, to be too preposterous to accept. The fact that other parties have also told a similar story is of concern, understanding that in normal circumstances, information obtained by separate parties should tend to corroborate accounts. It is the opposite, in our opinion!

Georgina Bruni was able to interview J.D. Ingalls in her book – the gist of which he told her he was present, but that no aliens had been involved, although he had seen the object at close range in the sky. He then said there had been five to six witnesses out in the forest with Charles Halt, but that he wasn't one of them.

In 1987, 'Steve Roberts' – returned to the UK. During a meeting with his old friends Brenda and Chris he told her that the incident initially brought to her attention had been a hoax! Brenda was devastated. 'Roberts' admitted that he had been ordered by his superiors to spread the story about the UFO landing, in order to cover-up what had really taken place, and that one day he would tell her the truth.

Even more worrying was that he told Brenda Butler he had been sent on a special course for three weeks after the incident. It involved being taken to an underground facility where he was shown films of balloons and airships, in what he perceived to be part of a brainwashing technique. He was then asked about the UFO drawing he gave to Brenda Butler in March 1981 and why it was saucer-shaped if he had only seen it in the sky! He declined to comment.

Georgina speaks to 'Steve Roberts'

Georgina Bruni tracked down 'Roberts' In an interview with him he says that –

1. *"There were five or six people out in the forest with Halt, and that he ('Roberts') wasn't one of them, but was unable to recall the names of those people."*

2. *"Bobby Ball's account was pretty accurate; he was with Halt. He was really caught up with it."*

3. *"Bruce Englund was out there as well."*

4. *"He denies seeing any aliens or landed craft."*

5. Roberts made no comment about the drawing he gave to Brenda Butler, in January 1981 (which shows what appears to be landed craft) However He did say: *"I am making no comment on that; it was the same as the one described in Halt's record."*

6. Georgina alludes to the 'Triangular craft' in Colonel Halt's record of the event, and asks him why this is a saucer-shaped one (as shown in the drawing) He replies: *"No comment"*.

7. He is asked about AFOSI and says: *"No I wasn't with AFOSI. I had something to do with them – but, no, I wasn't working with them; there were openings at the time but I never wanted to join them."*

He admits he was debriefed by AFOSI after the events and that this included being questioned, although he denies any *interrogation, and states, to his knowledge, that no others were interrogated.

Interrogation by the use of Sodium Pentothal

The reference to interrogation refers to a rigorous interview, involving the use of Sodium thiopental – also known as Sodium Pentothal, a rapid-onset short-acting barbiturate general anaesthetic, still used in some places as a truth serum to weaken the resolve of the subject and make them more compliant to pressure. The barbiturates as a class decrease higher cortical brain functioning. Some psychiatrists hypothesize that because lying is more complex than telling the truth, suppression of the higher cortical functions may lead to the uncovering of the truth. The drug tends to make subjects loquacious and cooperative with interrogators; however, the reliability of confessions made under thiopental is questionable. Sodium thiopental features as a truth serum in several Hollywood films, in comics and other literature, and even in popular music. Psychiatrists have used thiopental to desensitize patients with phobias, and to **facilitate the recall of painful repressed memories.**

Supreme Court rules such methods unconstitutional

In 1963, the USA Supreme Court ruled that a confession produced under the influence of truth serum was unconstitutionally coerced, and therefore inadmissible. We presume this would also cover witness testimonial evidence obtained by these means as well.

J.D. Ingalls (a.k.a. 'Steve Roberts')

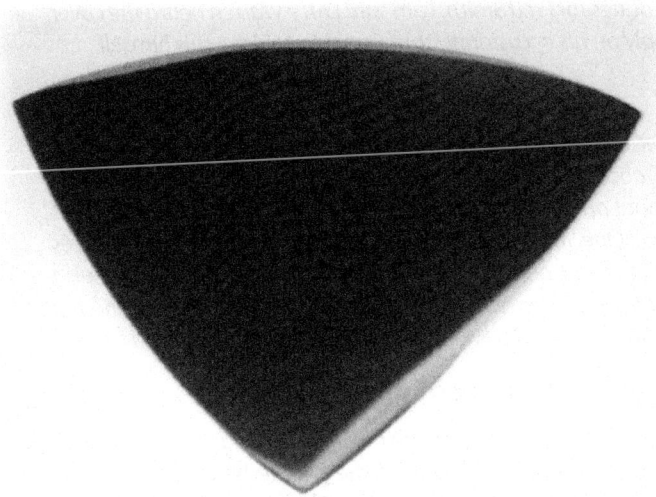
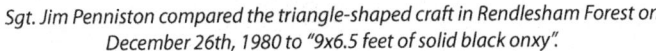

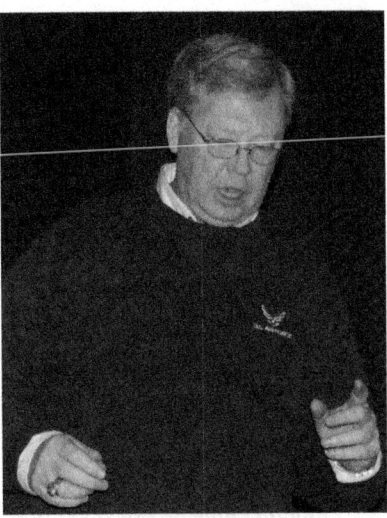

Sgt. Jim Penniston compared the triangle-shaped craft in Rendlesham Forest on December 26th, 1980 to "9x6.5 feet of solid black onxy".

Sgt. Jim Penniston

It was a hoax!

With all due respects, how on earth are we expected to approve the validity of anything this man has claimed? Simply because it won't stand up to any scrutiny, especially when the same man told Brenda in 1987 that the whole matter was a hoax. It just doesn't make sense. What is strange is that some people are prepared to still accept this information as being genuine, simply because it fits into their perceived cultural understanding of the UFO subject.

Charles Halt on J.D. Ingalls:

"I agree he was assigned to Police Investigations and may have seen any OSI reports. I doubt they would have shared anything that sensitive unless he was in on a disinformation scheme. I agree, he leaked what he heard and embellished it. He got in over his head and didn't know how to get out, or was told to spin the story. Hence, he doesn't want to talk today. I don't believe he was in the forest. He worked days and was probably at home."

Jim Penniston on J.D. Ingalls

"I knew him for a couple of years. I was the NCOIC of Security Police Plans and Programs, starting in February 1981. J.D. was the junior guy in Security Police Reports and Analysis. His office was about 50 yards down the street from mine. I was located adjacent to Security Police Supply. Both of our offices are on what is now called Thompson Drive. Ingalls visited me numerous times to shoot the breeze at Plans and Programs. He would then go over to SP Supply and shoot the breeze with M/Sgt. (Fred) Smith.

What is interesting is Warren was relieved of duty (SNAP) because he had his small arms access taken away and his Personal Reliability Program (PRP) was suspended. He was working in

Security Police Supply doing gopher duties for Fred Smith. I am sure Larry Warren heard the cover story from J.D. at Security Police Supply on his occasional stopovers. J.D. told me this himself."

Major Zickler

"J.D. worked close with Major Zickler and he was also bothering me a lot down in Plans and Programs, always asking questions about the incident. Of course I said to J.D., the matter of treating like Top Secret J.D., and I cannot and won't comment on it. It is fully understandable that Zickler took Ingalls into his confidence. One, Ingalls had a Top Secret clearance. Two, he also sees the initial reports such as the 1569s (Incident and Complaint Reports) Security and L.E. He also had access to both the Security and Law Enforcement Blotters as well, from all nights during the three nights in December 1980. He said (Zickler said) 'Make it like another UFO story', and he did."

Major Zickler – J.D. Ingalls and spreading of disinformation!

"However, J.D. told me that he was spreading rumours, in the local public houses under orders from Zickler, of aliens and spaceships being repaired. One of the people he told this to was Brenda Butler on one of his pub visits (the factious story, of course). The story he was spreading around the pubs is that this was pretty much another UFO story, and the base helped to repair it. It is very strange, that years later this cover story, which was directed by/or through Major Zickler for Ingalls to release in the pubs, is the same story that Warren told for a number of years. Warren's exact accounting changed after Halt and I went public; in 1991 for Halt and 1994 for me. What I always found odd is that the cover story is exactly what Warren said happened for about ten years after the incident. I think this speaks for itself."

This was deeply disappointing for Brenda Butler and her ex-partner, who still hold 'Steve'/J.D. in high esteem.

Charles Halt:

"I concur. I think Jim's got it right! "

John Hanson:

One should point out that the couple had known 'Steve'/J.D. for a number of years before his disclosure to them about the UFO landing.

Chris Pennington tells of meeting a 'giant of a man' way back in 1976, at the *Weybread Crown* Public House, where he was performing as a four-man band. According to Chris, a 'party trick' of Max (the piano player) was to play something appropriate when someone walked through the door. For example, if Max suspected he was Dutch he would play *Tulips from Amsterdam*; if he was American it would be *Yankee Doodle Dandy*, and so on. Following the entrance of 'Steve' into the pub, and the appropriate music, the 'new arrival', 'Steve' strolled over and struck up a conversation. He was to become a personal friend of Chris and Brenda's from that time on, and has remained in contact sporadically, despite having left the UK some years ago.

Elaborate Game played out?

Looking back on it now, was this just part of an elaborate game played out behind the scenes by people with their own special agenda to discredit the UFO subject and catapult this into the most controversial UK UFO sighting of the 20th Century, never mind the physical and mental damage caused to the unwilling participants involved? Would Major Zickler have had full authority to set this up – if so, for what reason? Ironically, bizarre reports of aliens seen in the forest, 'spaceships' being repaired and covert operations taking place under the base, have in fact made this an enduring enigma, rather like the many other thousands, if not millions, of UFO sightings/encounters worldwide, which have, to all intent and degree, been now completely forgotten.

John Hanson on Jenny Randles – her assessment on the incident published in 1997

Jenny Randles

Someone else who felt extremely concerned about the validity of the account given by 'Steve Roberts' was Jenny Randles, one of the original investigators of the incidents. Jenny wrote the foreword for the second Volume of *Haunted Skies* (now defunct), some years ago, and we are delighted to include her assessment of the overall situation, based on common sense and investigative skills, rather than believing automatically, without question, testimonials made by the witnesses – some of which do not stand up to scrutiny.

In 2016, we contacted Jenny and sent her a copy of the script – taken from John Rimmer's *Magonia* website (Jenny on *Magonia,* November 1997 Article – Getting It Right at East Gate-www.internet) which contained an overview of how she saw the case during the early 1980s.

Jenny – on Larry Warren

In this on-line article available on the Internet 2016, written by Jenny, reflecting her views about this matter (originally produced in 1997), and discussed with her, she reminded us, during a number of emails, that:

> *"As far as I know, what I reported in there was correct, but as years have passed since it was written **my views on the case have evolved.** Please make this point clear. At the time I was answering serious questions posed about Brenda, Dot and I, inside the book – Left At East Gate – and not an attempt to assess Larry Warren's story in context or his role in this case."*

Having listened to audio tape recordings made at BUFORA conferences in 1983 and 1984, by Ron West – an Essex-based UFO researcher – there were, perhaps understandably, concerns expressed by Jenny, Dot and Brenda, about the validity of Larry Warren's testimony – with regard to what took place after the UFO sighting in the Forest. This is not to suggest that all cases involving reports of 'entities' being seen near UFOs should be discarded – far from it. Each and every reported incident involving claims of aliens seen should be judged on their individual merits.

Colonel Charles Halt accepts he cannot categorically prove or disprove Warren and Bustinza's version of events which took place after the claimed UFO sighting, and can only refer to what he and his colleagues witnessed –

> **"Claims of Gordon Williams being present and meeting 'aliens' are flights of a vivid imagination!"**

THE HALT PERSPECTIVE

According to Brenda Butler and Chris, 'Steve Roberts' and his wife (who had been friends with them since 1975) through their mutual love of music and UFO interests in late 1980, claimed **he was a member of a security patrol that had gone out into the forest** in response to a UFO that had *'crashed'* there. He tells of seeing a landed *'craft'*, with strange little childlike beings suspended in beams of light. The overall wing commander – Brigadier General Gordon Williams – was out there in the woods and communicated with these beings using sign language, as the USAF guarded the damaged *'craft'* – eventually repaired by the aliens and took off again. **He told Georgina Bruni he hadn't been there!** With all due respect, how can anybody accept this version of events as being based on genuine testimony? The foundations of what he claimed appear to be 'shifting sands' rather than anything of substance.

'Steve' in an email sent during 1997, agreed the incident was based on fact; Charles Halt had been there and was telling the truth, but that **he had no knowledge of Larry Warren ever being there** – *"Wasn't in the cops when I was there".*

Why would he claim this, knowing that Larry had been there –was it to cause confusion?

Jenny herself remarked on the similarities in described events claimed by the witness 'Steve Roberts', involving *a landed craft with strange little childlike beings suspended in beams of light, and communication with the occupants by Brigadier General Gordon Williams*, who, it was alleged, used sign language as the USAF guarded the damaged *'craft'* and what she was told by Radar operatives at RAF Watton.

> "They were given a similar story by USAF officers – Frankly absurd as this story sounds; it struck a chord with me. When Brenda told me Roberts' version of events, she could not have known it matched precisely the story told to the staff at RAF Watton, on Monday 29th December 1980. This was when USAF intelligence officers had visited them. That visit was to take away for study the film of all their radar tracking's for the preceding weekend. I still have my notes penned from my first conversation, in late January 1981, with that operator at Watton."

Jenny on Left At East Gate

> "Left At East Gate is a strange book. I can understand why people unfamiliar with the case will be awed by it, because Warren and Robbins tell a fantastic tale that is just what people want to hear. It is exactly what you would expect to be turned into a movie. But will this benefit ufology? The big question is why the three initial sources of information – 'Steve Roberts', Watton radar and Larry Warren – all provide the more fantastic version of events.

> My guess has always been that 'Roberts' fed his line to a paranormal enthusiast, hoping that a wild version of the truth would kill off any immediate serious attention from people who mattered.

> The staff at Watton would – in my estimation – never have been told about aliens communicating with a wing com-mander whilst repairing their craft if this had really happened. They had absolutely no need to know and the radar film could have been taken from them on any pretext. To be told this was, to me, a dead giveaway that this story was disinformation."

Jenny – Larry Warren

"Of course, when Warren came forward the only military versions of the case on record, thanks to me, were those from 'Roberts' and Watton. Warren says he had not read them, but Barry Greenwood had. That's how he recognised Warren's story and why he wrote to me. You could, I guess, suggest that Warren saw the tales from 'Roberts' and Watton and decided that his version would have to match them to be believed. He utterly refutes that and we must accept his word. But his account matched 'Steve Roberts' account – an account that I now consider discredited. All the other versions I have heard since follow a different – less 'extraterrestrial' – path. This leaves me with a real problem evaluating Warren's story today."

Jenny discussed matter with Charles Halt and John Burroughs

"I have talked to Charles Halt and John Burroughs to get their take on Larry's story and set out my own thoughts on the problem of his evidence, along with three scenarios that might explain the confusion and contradiction. This would better express my present thoughts on Larry's story. May I suggest that you read my later book – 'Friend or Foe? 'UFO Crash Landing', (published 8.1.1998 in the UK), which includes attempts to put Larry's story into proper context."

We examined the relevant pages nominated by Jenny and would like to remind the reader what she wrote, to at least offer a balanced version of how she now sees things, rather than something written many years before.

"The case became public knowledge in the UK soon after Warren surfaced, thanks to the Halt memo which we took to the Press.

Larry behaved unlike the other military personnel who chose to remain silent, even with the backing of Halt's report. Warren was out of the Service and had his own reasons not to feel kindly disposed to the USAF. He appeared in the Press and on TV using the pseudonym (suitably masked with his voice electronically altered) stating that if he didn't hide his identity he might face danger (although by the end of the year he was lecturing at UFO Conferences)."

Jenny Randles

"Larry was always forthcoming in those early days and I met him several times in the States and in the UK, when he came over to research his story for a book Left At East Gate. I must say that I have always found Larry to be a friendly, likeable, and helpful man; if he stood alone in this case I would probably accept his testimony. However, not everyone seemed to share that view; several witnesses told me that they believed he wasn't there. Colonel Halt himself went on record to claim the same thing in June 1997, I spoke to Charles Halt about Left At East Gate, who then admitted he may have been out there on the third night, although he wasn't with his group, and that he was not out there officially."

Larry's role

Jenny: (over claims that General Gordon Williams was out there):

"Resolving the problem of Larry Warren's role in this case is perhaps its greatest single difficulty and will be exacerbated by the publication of this book – being the first of the military witnesses to go into print, he is sure to gain notoriety. Despite the fact that I personally like Larry Warren and greatly respect his cooperation in the past, I have no way of knowing if he was really present. I must take his word for that and yet also make my readers aware that others seem to dispute some (although by no means all) of what he has to say. The truth of this case lies somewhere beneath these two versions and we can only try to pick our way through the details of evidence and try to make reasoned judgement."

Three Options

"One that Warren may be telling the truth and that the witnesses who dispute that never came across him on that night. There was chaos in the forest that night so this possibility cannot be dismissed. As to his testimony a good deal of it matches what the other witnesses say and the stranger parts cannot be utterly rejected. It is worth recalling that other witnesses do hint at reality distortion and a period of missing time during close encounters. They infer that the object was under intelligent control – even if its controllers were never seen by them ... so Warren's story cannot be regarded as inconceivable."

Second option

"A second option was that Warren was peripherally involved on the Saturday night but has exaggerated some of his aspects of his story. Moreover, he is clearly aware of the case in detail and his testimony includes features that were not known to the investigators back in 1983, which have been subsequently verified in 1983. Therefore, Warren must at least be reporting as heard from someone really involved, or of course describing his personal association with the landing – however great that was. Warren also suggests he was subjected to intelligence agency interrogation techniques that involved mind altering substances – something he is partially supported in by at least one other witness.

One or two USAF witnesses that I spoke to have suggested that maybe this young man's distorted perception about what took place are the result of these methods, rather than a clear recall of what actually took place."

Third option

"That he is making it up for personal reasons – seems less likely to fit the facts. Warren appears to me to have been genuinely associated with the case in some way. Yet his evidence is sufficiently different that, clearly, it has to be viewed with a degree of circumspection."

Charles Halt:

"Although several others endorse Warren's story in his book Left At East Gate, some military personnel, closely involved, have gone on record saying that they refuse to believe his account. One shouldn't forget what this is all really about."

Interview with Colonel Halt

In August 1996 Colonel Halt and Brenda had lunch together in Manchester, during which time she asked him a number of prepared questions:

Brenda: *"Why was only one sighting picked up on radar when, according to the witnesses, there were three sightings?"*

Colonel Halt: *"The radar had closed down, as it was over the Christmas holidays."*

Brenda: *"Why, when we phoned up Watton Radar Station, did they tell us that they had not picked up anything on radar over those days in December 1980?"*

Colonel Halt: *"They were told to say that."*

Brenda: *"What fell off an aircraft that was so sensitive that it had to be covered up?"*

Colonel Halt: *"No comment."*

Brenda: *"Why, on your first tape, are there no forest noises, birds, or the sound of men walking? We have gone through the forest at night with a Walkman and we got noises on our tape. We could hear rabbits and deer running about, birds flying out of the trees, and our own footsteps quite clearly."*

Colonel Halt: *"I had them cut out of the tape."*

Brenda: *"I think that the tape was made in a building, as there is an echo-like sound rebounding off a wall."*

Colonel Halt: *"Maybe. I don't know."*

Brenda: *"Why is the Department of the Air Force withholding seven documents, which consists of inter-agency memoranda?"*

Colonel Halt: *"I don't know anything about these documents."*

Brenda: *"Why did you tell your son?"*

Colonel Halt: *"Is that what he told you? Wait till I see him!"*

Brenda: *"By 'it' being referred to as a UFO, does that mean that it was of unknown origin to you but not a space vehicle?"*

Colonel Halt: *"I do not know what it was."*

Brenda: *"Was it a cosmic incident, or were they practicing with a lunar command module or landing probe?"*

Colonel Halt: *"They do have a module they keep in practice with, the Aerospace Rescue and Recovery Squadron."*

Brenda: *"Were the Aerospace Rescue and Recovery Squadron involved in any activities on the 26th and 27th December?"*

Colonel Halt: *"They were all off base, as it was a holiday."*

Brenda: *"Is it true that you and Conrad shifted the dates for a cover-up to misdirect people?"*

Colonel Halt: *"No!"*

Brenda: *"A witness said that it was a silver object in a crater in the ground, with five men covering it up with a tarpaulin. The object looked like a missile."*

Colonel Halt: *"That's not what I saw."*

Brenda: *"The MOD said that it was of no threat to our security."*

Colonel Halt: *"It wasn't."*

Brenda: *"How do you know it wasn't a threat to our National Security if you didn't know what it was?"*

Colonel Halt: *"No comment."*

Brenda: *"Why were the Army, Navy and Air Force, all involved and why was HMS Norfolk off the coast?"*

Colonel Halt: *"I don't know. It's news to me."*

Brenda: *"Why were the men allowed to touch the craft they didn't know about the added danger of radiation?"*

Colonel Halt: *"It was up to them; no senior officer was present to stop them."*

Brenda: *"Why was the Russian Tupolev 'Bear' aircraft off the coast over international waters?"*

Colonel Halt: *"The 'Bear' is always going up and down the coast. I think there's more to be heard. Something very strange happened that night that I think a lot of people don't want out. An awful lot of people tend to overlook our testimony, but others want to know what's going on, not only with this but with other occurrences."*

Brenda: *"Is it true that American and Russian scientists are working together in diverse 'fields' of biology, medicines and space biology?"*

Colonel Halt: *"We do work alongside them,"*

Brenda: *"Why were the British MOD not involved in the incident; yet it took place on British soil?"*

Colonel Halt: *"We phoned the MOD; they were not interested and told us to handle it. We did call the British Police and they attended."*

Brenda: *"Why was there a Russian submarine off the coast over Christmas?"*

Colonel Halt: *"I don't know."*

Brenda: *"I phoned Mildenhall and spoke to their PR officer. He told me that you would not be allowed to talk about an incident; if you did it would mean a heavy fine, imprisonment, loss of pension, or a discharge from the service. This applies to all servicemen."*

Colonel Halt: *"You certainly have done your homework, haven't you?"*

Brenda: *"Was it a nuclear powered UFO, American, or Russian?"*

Colonel Halt: *"No."*

Brenda: *"I was told that the 141 Starlifter Transporter Aircraft had secret intelligence men onboard. What did they want?"*

Colonel Halt: *"I didn't know about this until a later date."*

Jenny Randles comments on Left At East Gate, *page 102*

"There is also a series of claims about how Barry Greenwood sent me the Halt memo secured by CAUS in the USA. This was obtained wholly thanks to Warren, he says. Yet Brenda Dot and I don't feature in this one"

Larry:
'In November we found out that Brenda Butler and Dot Street sold the Halt document to the News of the World for £2,000 – nearly five grand here…After that we broke off all contact with them.'

Jenny – The facts:

"Barry Greenwood sent me the Halt memo and I sent him my letter from the MOD, received a few weeks earlier dated 13 April 1983. This was some weeks before the USAF admitted there was a case and it was used by CAUS to help in their quest for documents. The MOD document admitted for the first time anywhere that there was an incident in Rendlesham Forest and that 'no explanation' had been found for it. Far from one way traffic we exchanged data. I have maintained a correspondence with Barry ever since and we had dinner together when I was in Boston, a year or two ago. Brenda, Dot and I were given permission to use the document as we saw fit to press for the truth and I also was happy for them to use my MOD letter in whatever way they wished. What we did was to take it to the MOD, in London, and confront them directly with a file they had been denying to me (despite at least three written requests). I also set up a seminar at the next BUFORA conference to present the evidence to the UFO community (including Allen Hynek and many others). This basically let Brenda and Dot have their day, after two years of ridicule from the UFO community chasing 'the case that never was'."

John Hanson – In the book *Halt in Woodbridge* 2015 by Peter Robbins, he publishes an email from Barry Greenwood, heavily criticizing the character of Harry Harris, details of which will not be included here as they are defamatory. Barry points out that Harry sold the story to the *News of the World*, which is not quite correct. There were three persons involved in this transaction **Jenny, Mike Sacks and Harry.** [Documentary evidence is published in the *HALT* book confirming this.] Barry also claimed in his email that Jenny, Brenda and Dot were paid $2,000 or £2,000 pounds each, with *"Harris pocketing the rest".*

Jenny:

"After the media discovered the existence of the memo and decided to go public, Harry Harris, a well-known figure in UFO circles, persuaded Brenda and Dot that the best option was to negotiate a deal with the paper keeping control of the story, as otherwise they would print a garbled version of the truth picked up from the UFO community rumour mill.

I agreed to go with Harry to the News of the World and brief them on the case. That is how the story on the front page of the News of the World, in October 1983, came about. Nor was this story sold for £2,000. It was a lot more than that. But this money went to many people who were paid for their information on many subjects given to the paper. To my knowledge the document itself was not sold, since it was not anyone's to sell. I do know that the money Brenda and Dot received (a fraction of the overall sum the paper paid) was used by them to fund further research into this case. Over the years they – and I – have spent far more than any of us have ever got back. In this instance I see nothing wrong in what we did. It was the only way to keep control of the story."

John Hanson – Mike Sacks

In an interview during May 2016 *Mike Sacks – a likable man, ex BUFORA Investigator (who had two close encounters with landed UFOs in 1979) – had this to say about the sale of the memo to the *News of the World*.

---

*Mike was a member of a group who had a number 1 hit in Turkey in 1966, 'Don't walk away' with the group 'The Idols'. Available on You Tunes.

"I telephoned the Editor, George Mackintosh, and told him we had a story to make his toes curl! We knew full well what the headline was going to be – UFO lands in Suffolk. I did it on purpose to go national, not a little story in a UFO magazine.

I wanted the bloody world to know about this story; contacting the news paper was totally my idea."

For those that would like to learn more about Mike's UFO close encounters, they can be found in Volume 7 of *Haunted Skies* [involving an object seen to descend into a quarry with a superstructure beneath it consisting of three dull red bands or rings, with blood-red lights on it, pulsing and rotating slowly in the air].

I spoke to Harry's wife, Susan, and was saddened to learn that she had endured a number of family bereavements in her life, including her son who died from a brain tumor at the age of 22.

"Harry went into a home, in February 2016, suffering from Alzheimer's. He has forgotten everything, although last time you spoke to him he had recall of the early days. Harry never made any more money out of the UFO case. He felt he took the right course of action with Mike and Jenny. I strongly condemn anybody who impugns his integrity.

In 1997, Charles Halt spoke at a conference, in Manchester, and Harry invited him to dinner. We found him charming and enjoyed the time he spent with us.

Harry could never understand why so many people turned on him. I am sorry that Harry is now unable to defend himself."

Barry Greenwood:

"The intent of sending the Halt memo was to use it for government inquiries, or to encourage witnesses to open up about their roles. The intent was not to contact a tabloid newspaper and sell it for a considerable amount of money, undermining the legitimate attempt to assist an honest investigation behind the scenes between investigators working to find out what had happened. This deal was kept in the dark so as not to let Larry Fawcett and I know how they were going to capitalize on our work."

Clearly there is little more to say on the subject. It is not for us to judge the ethics of what happened, although it is always sad when people like Barry Greenwood and Mike Sacks – who are both well respected in the UFO Community – fall out. However, it is important to record what took place, as it now forms part of our social history. We wish the best of luck to the parties concerned and thank them for their honesty and assistance in what is, after all, a sensitive matter.

'Cloud Busting' on the base

Jenny:

"There is also a curious attempt in the Left At East Gate book to suggest that parts of Rendlesham Forest were flattened in 1987 as a result of not a hurricane (as most of us recall) but some sort of Orgone energy experiment. This seems to be building on Andy Collins' fantastic scenario as to the true origin of that fabled storm, which he perceived as being due to a black magician (although, curiously, Collins followed that book with an attempt to link Orgone energy to UFOs and crop circles).

All I will note is that to my recall the hurricane devastated large parts of southern England – not just Rendlesham Forest."

John Hanson and Dawn Holloway asked Peter Robbins about this specific point, in 1995, during their visit to Cheltenham on the release of their book. He told them it was *"journalistic license and not true".*

John:

"At that time we had been in touch with Trevor James Constable and learnt a little about cloud busting from him and the work of Wilhelm Reich. We have never published this, as we had no intention of ever doing so – not wishing to cause any embarrassment to Peter Robbins, whom we considered a good friend until recent events meant metaphorically that 'the gloves were now off'!

On page 226 in *Left At East Gate,* Larry says he had seen what he believes to have been a 'Reich Cloud Buster' device, involving long pipes, painted black, and mounted on concrete bases with a multitude of large cables running from them into the concrete framed wells dispersed around the base.

Charles Halt:

"Not so; they were dummy missiles erected at base! This is bullshit. I explained this in my Woodbridge talk. Listen to the recording. Colonel Karl Berroth – my next door neighbour at Bentwaters and the Deputy Commander for Maintenance – made several dummy missiles to keep the Russian Photo Ops guys busy. We joked about it at the times we knew their over-flights were occurring. He would move them and even repainted them, from time to time, all for a chance to stir some concern. Most were 55 gallon barrels, welded together to look like weapons. Some were mounted on old trailers. All that nonsense about us modifying the weather and even causing the great storm that destroyed the forest is all garbage."

Jenny: Oxford Lighthouse and RAF Bodzy!

Jenny:

"There are also several worrying errors in the text. Some of these (Major Dury, several times instead of Drury) might be typographical. Others seem not – e.g. Oxford lighthouse (not Orford) – or even more hilariously – RAF Bodzy (when it is, in fact, RAF Bawdsey – as a glance at any map of the area would show). These, to me, represent both sloppiness and the real failing of this book. If the lighthouse explanation for this case was discussed (it is merely dismissed in passing) errors such as this would be unlikely. If the strange goings-on at Orford Ness and at RAF Bawdsey were debated (as they ought to be, since they are relevant to the case) the background to these places would presumably have been researched.

After almost 500 pages, I am not certain whether Larry Warren's story is either truth or fiction or – possibly – something in between the two. He even speculates himself about his memory being altered by secret service interrogations."

Nuclear Weapons on the base

"Firstly, we had been told by numerous sources by 1983 that there were nuclear weapons on the Base. This was emphatically denied by the USAF. That denial was a lie.

This had indeed been one of the biggest nuclear stores in the UK. This amply demonstrates my feeling at the time that – with the huge public outcry over bringing Cruise missiles into Europe – it might have seemed appropriate to cover-up an accident by creating a diversionary story so ludicrous nobody would believe it."

1956 near disaster

"There had, in fact, been a near disaster in 1956 at a USAF base nearby, when a store of weapons caught fire after a plane crash. The fact that nuclear weapons were at risk was denied for decades, but finally admitted years later on retirement of one of the key players in the cover-up Moreover, forestry workers told me that they had heard about a 'plane crash' from staff on the base and local man – Ron Gladwell – had told us about finding a crater in the forest, indicating that something had fallen from the sky and hit the ground with a thump. People from the airbase were seen evidently filling this in.

In Left At East Gate (p.216) Warren and Robbins use the fact that nobody supposedly saw a crater in the forest to denounce our 'silly' theory of a plane dropping a bomb. Evidently they missed Gladwell's story, even though it is in both Sky Crash and Out Of The Blue.

I submit that – right or wrong – this idea about a nuclear accident was a wholly legitimate speculation to make in 1983 based on these incidents (plus the various signs of mild radiation being present in the forest). It is not a theory that I adhere to today, having now had the chance to hear the detailed stories of witnesses like John Burroughs and Jim Penniston. They got within a few feet of the UFO on the first night and it was no discarded bomb. But it was wholly appropriate to bring this idea into the debate at the time to show the problems with the evidence fed out to the UFO community.

When I developed this theory there were no public revelations from any of the military eyewitnesses – just the dubious saga fed out to Watton and Brenda Butler that smelled to me exactly like disinformation. But if UFOs were disinformation then what was this story trying to hide?

The sad thing is that Left At East Gate does not really help us to make an easy decision as to which is the most likely of these possibilities. Each option is also fraught with serious ramifications for the rest of the case.

I remain convinced there is a significant close encounter at the heart of the Rendlesham Forest case. **But I am far from convinced that any aliens were floating in light beams beneath a starship.** The real key to this story lies on Orford Ness but not in the lighthouse. I was mostly saddened by this book because it promised much and delivered little. I ended up more confused than when I read the first page. If I only ever had the chance to read this book on the incident, I would probably agree with most people that this case is a load of nonsense. I can see why people would jump to that conclusion. Unfortunately, they would be very wrong to do so."

Nick Pope – Larry's Story

"Few of the alleged Rendlesham Forest witnesses are more controversial than Larry Warren. Larry was, unquestionably, one of the first Rendlesham whistle-blowers, and played a major role in getting the story out to the public. But his story – a boy's own tale of aliens, underground bases and Nazi-style interrogations by sinister Men-in-Black – has been roundly dismissed by the key players in the case, none of whom recall seeing Larry at any time during the various UFO encounters.

Their suspicion is that he picked up the story from the gossip doing the rounds at the twin bases shortly afterwards, and wrote himself into it.

I take no definitive position on any of this, but it may be telling that Larry's book on the case is the only UFO book I know of that has a nickname, being known in sections of the UFO community as 'Theft At East Gate', in view of the widely-held belief that Larry took other people's stories and made them his own."

Larry can be good company

"Larry is certainly a colourful character and can be good company. He's a strong personality and, as such, has what I can only describe as a small but vociferous 'fan club', who automatically defend him against any criticisms, and write gushing praise on Face-book every time he's interviewed on even the most obscure internet-only radio show. Chief among the cheerleaders, of course, is Peter Robbins. In fact, the relationship between Peter and Larry might best be described as ufology's most touching 'bromance.'"

Book – Encounter In Rendlesham Forest

"When John Burroughs, Jim Penniston and I wrote the bestselling book Encounter In Rendlesham Forest, *Peter wrote an entire book about our book, because it failed (in his opinion) to say much about Larry Warren, and asked some searching questions about his story. The central premise of Peter's 'book about our book' was that* Encounter In Rendlesham Forest *was part of a sinister government plot to discredit Larry.*

When Charles Halt gave a presentation in Woodbridge, in July 2015, he briefly mentioned Larry Warren. Whatever one thinks about Larry and his story, Halt's view (that he's a fraud and a 'wannabe' who wasn't there) is sincerely held.

Peter didn't attend Halt's talk but was soon at it again, writing an entire book about Halt's presentation! As with the accusations about Encounter In Rendlesham Forest, *the central idea of the book (actually, its only idea) was that Col. Charles Halt was engaged in a thirty-five year campaign to discredit Larry Warren.*

Quite why a retired Colonel with 28 years of service in the USAF would spend so much effort trying to discredit somebody who was discharged from the service a few months later after the UFO incident was never explained.

It would be easy to dismiss Peter's behaviour as riding on other people's coat-tails, or as an attempt to stay relevant when it comes to a case on which he's worked hard to portray himself as an expert. But clearly it goes deeper than that. The fact is that Peter has so much invested (emotionally as well as intellectually) in Larry's story that he's effectively staked his entire professional relationship on it. Thus, he knows that if Larry goes down, he goes down too – the reputational damage would probably be fatal to his standing in the UFO community. So he steadfastly defends Larry against not just criticisms, but even difficult questions. It is commendable loyalty, but it certainly doesn't help when it comes to an honest and even-handed evaluation of Larry's story."

1982 – Close encounter over Sudbury, Suffolk

In late September 1982, 'Ros' Reynolds-Parnham from Little Clacton, Essex, and her boyfriend at the time – Philip, decided to visit her relatives in Corby, Northamptonshire. They were travelling along the A1902, at Sudbury, in Suffolk, near the village of Stoke by Clare.

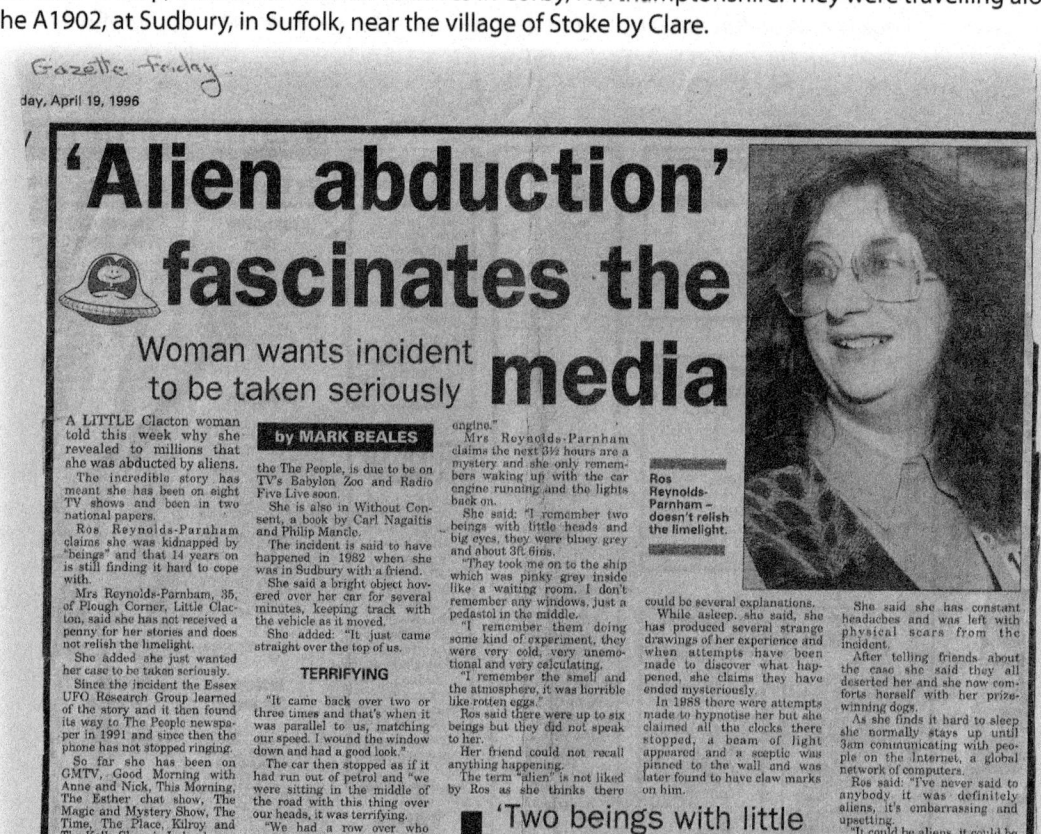

Gazette Friday.

day, April 19, 1996

'Alien abduction' fascinates the media

Woman wants incident to be taken seriously

by MARK BEALES

A LITTLE Clacton woman told this week why she revealed to millions that she was abducted by aliens.

The incredible story has meant she has been on eight TV shows and been in two national papers.

Ros Reynolds-Parnham claims she was kidnapped by "beings" and that 14 years on is still finding it hard to cope with.

Mrs Reynolds-Parnham, 35, of Plough Corner, Little Clacton, said she has not received a penny for her stories and does not relish the limelight.

She added she just wanted her case to be taken seriously.

Since the incident the Essex UFO Research Group learned of the story and it then found its way to The People newspaper in 1991 and since then the phone has not stopped ringing.

So far she has been on GMTV, Good Morning with Anne and Nick, This Morning, The Esther chat show, The Magic and Mystery Show, The Time, The Place, Kilroy and The Kelly Show in Ireland.

She has also been in Saturday's Daily Mirror and

the The People, is due to be on TV's Babylon Zoo and Radio Five Live soon.

She is also in Without Consent, a book by Carl Nagaitis and Philip Mantle.

The incident is said to have happened in 1982 when she was in Sudbury with a friend.

She said a bright object hovered over her car for several minutes, keeping track with the vehicle as it moved.

She added: "It just came straight over the top of us.

TERRIFYING

"It came back over two or three times and that's when it was parallel to us, matching our speed. I wound the window down and had a good look."

The car then stopped as if it had run out of petrol and "we were sitting in the middle of the road with this thing over our heads, it was terrifying.

"We had a row over who would get out of the car and the last thing I remember was Philip bending over the

engine."

Mrs Reynolds-Parnham claims the next 3½ hours are a mystery and she only remembers waking up with the car engine running and the lights back on.

She said: "I remember two beings with little heads and big eyes, they were bluey grey and about 3ft 6ins.

"They took me on to the ship which was pinky grey inside like a waiting room. I don't remember any windows, just a pedastol in the middle.

"I remember them doing some kind of experiment, they were very cold, very unemotional and very calculating.

"I remember the smell and the atmosphere, it was horrible like rotten eggs."

Ros said there were up to six beings but they did not speak to her.

Her friend could not recall anything happening.

The term "alien" is not liked by Ros as she thinks there

could be several explanations.

While asleep, she said, she has produced several strange drawings of her experience and when attempts have been made to discover what happened, she claims they have ended mysteriously.

In 1988 there were attempts made to hypnotise her but she claimed all the clocks there stopped, a beam of light appeared and a sceptic was pinned to the wall and was later found to have claw marks on him.

Ros Reynolds-Parnham – doesn't relish the limelight.

She said she has constant headaches and was left with physical scars from the incident.

After telling friends about the case she said they all deserted her and she now comforts herself with her prize-winning dogs.

As she finds it hard to sleep she normally stays up until 3am communicating with people on the internet, a global network of computers.

Ros said: "I've never said to anybody it was definitely aliens, it's embarrassing and upsetting.

"It could be aliens, it could be something else. I'm very, very open-minded about it. It's not in my head."

■ 'Two beings with little heads and big eyes'

"At 8pm, a horseshoe-shaped group of lights flew very low over the car, as we passed under some power cables. I remember the lights, the silence, and the blue tendrils bouncing off the cables. My first thought was it may have been a 'helicopter', but everything was wrong – its movement, speed, silence, etc.

I was abducted by aliens on the A1092 in Suffolk

CLOSEST ENCOUNTER: Ros with an impression of one of the aliens. Right, the spot where she was abducted

By AMANDA WARD

NIGHT had closed in as Ros Reynolds-Parnham and her boyfriend Philip drove along a quiet country road to a relative's house. Then a light caught her eye.

Suddenly, a blazing shape was hovering above them. Terrified, Philip put his foot down — and everything went blank.

Four hours later, Ros came round to find herself back in the car, her head spinning, a gash on her neck throbbing.

Then she remembered. It was an experience too terrifying to believe.

Ros had been abducted and "raped" by aliens.

The ghastly encounter on the A1092 in Sudbury, Suffolk, has taken a terrible toll on Ros — and denied her the chance of motherhood. She says she has not had a period since the incident 14 years ago.

"I'm not a weirdo," says the 35-year-old show dog breeder who still shudders when she looks at the sky. "I'm telling the truth. I'm just so scared that they will come back."

Ros is not alone in her fears — she is one of Britain's 100 "abductees".

Now strange encounters and weird happenings are the basis of the new six-part BBC2 series *Secrets Of The Paranormal.*

Ros, of Essex, says: "After the abduction, I can remember being on a perspex pedestal in this pinky-grey oval room. I can't remember any doors. There was a bright light above

it. I just felt terror. I couldn't move, scream or faint. It was as if I was an onlooker. There were grey figures all around me.

"They had very large heads and big black eyes. They didn't have a nose, had a slit for a mouth, no ears and they were about 3ft 6ins. They smelled like rotten eggs. They had long, spidery hands with four fingers.

"These aliens were very cold, calculating and they did some experiments. I know they did something because of the scars at the top of my legs. I felt raped, abused, dirty. They were saying something about 'juice'."

Ros and experts believe her abductors were interested in finding out about the human reproductive system.

She says: "I don't know what they did to me but I haven't had a period since."

Ros's hand reaches up to touch the small white scar on her neck — the result, she says, of the four-hour examination. The incident occurred in

September 1992. Ros says: "Philip and I were driving to see his relatives when this horse-shoe shaped object, about the size of a helicopter, swooped down.

"It had multicoloured lights blazing underneath. At first I thought it might have been reflection of my glasses. It was really bright but there was no sound.

"We were terrified and Philip accelerated. Then the car died. I thought Philip was joking. I was in a blind panic and neither of us wanted to get out. I remember saying that I would count to three and we'd get out together."

THE next thing Ros knew was that she was back in the car, with the engine running.

"I felt a bit dopey but I just wanted to get out of there. We didn't say a word as we drove to our destination.

"When the couple arrived it was 2am. They should have been there at 10pm. Ros says: "I woke up with a mark on my back and like a burn mark on

my neck. It kept itching." But there was something far more unsettling to come. "I began to 'sleep-write'. I'd get up in the night and draw things in dots. I looked at the first one and it was a pair of large eyes. Then I'd write strange formulas or type odd letters. I couldn't remember doing it."

Her symptoms got worse: "I got terrible headaches, as if someone was sticking a red-hot needle into my head. I'd also hear a noise at the same time, like a fax going off. I was backwards and forward to the doctor's but he only he gave me pills. I didn't take them. I didn't want to be drugged up."

The strain became too much and Ros and Philip split. She spiralled into despair.

She says: "Even now, I don't go to bed before 3am. I'm scared I'll start writing."

Last year the Ministry of Defence recorded 373 sightings of "aerial activity not immediately identifiable to the observer". That's compared to the 1994 figure of 250.

Philip Mantle of the British UFO Research Association (BUFORA) says: "Some abductees report seeing hieroglyphic type writing, or grey figures who smell like rotten eggs.

"More females are reporting this type of incident. Others report removal of sperm or ovum — perhaps for interbreeding. There are still many questions but this is one of the most convincing cases I've heard."

Ros shivers and says: "I ask myself why me? I know one thing — I won't go back to that road again."

● FOR more information, call BUFORA on 01924 444049.

Brits' close encounters

IF YOU find Ros's account difficult to believe, think again. There have been 100 recorded abductees in Britain in the past 50 years, says Philip Mantle of UFO researchers BUFORA.

"Calls are coming into the 1,000-member association at a rate of one month.

"Mr Mantle, who has also talked to countless abductees for his book *Without Consent*, believes alien kidnapping does happen.

He says: "It can happen to anyone, regardless of sex or where they live. We don't know why it happens, or why the people are chosen.

"But some of their accounts would really make your hair stand on end."

The article that appeared about the encounter in the Daily Mirror, on Saturday, April 13th, 1996

As we drove out through the town, through Long Melford, and headed along the Clare to Haverhill Road, it came back and zipped over the car, two or three times, scaring the pair of us. The 'thing' matched our speed and ran parallel with us, for some time, along the road. From the side it was a big, bright, egg-shaped light, with a faint set of smaller coloured lights rotating around inside. I guess it was between 50 and 100 feet away and the whole thing was at least the size of the length of our car, as it negotiated the hedges and telegraph wires. Philip was so scared he just looked straight ahead."

Engine of the car cuts out – UFO seen hovering over nearby field

"The car suddenly acted as if it had run out of petrol and died, along with the lights. We both had an argument as to who would look under the bonnet, and then got out together – me to keep my eyes on this thing, as it hovered silently over the field. The next thing I knew was that we were both back in the car – the engine now running and lights on, with the 'thing' still hovering. We basically felt very quiet and subdued, for want of a better explanation, and just drove off as fast as possible. We never spoke the rest of the way, or I do not think we did. We arrived at Corby – not at 10pm as expected, but at 1.30-1.45am!"

'Ros' and Philip made their excuses without even mentioning what had taken place, and returned home.

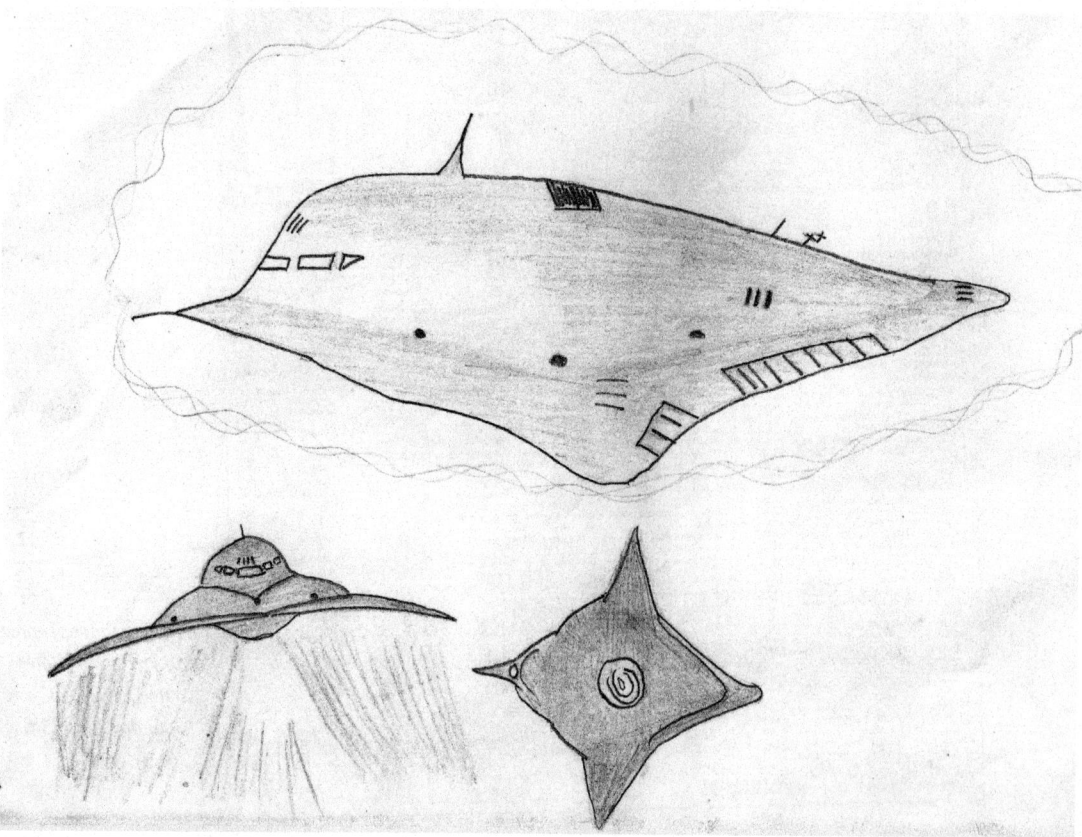

Medical ailments and out-of-character behaviour follows

Philip (for some reason only known to him) decided to hand paint the Ford Cortina a different colour, on the same day.

The following day, 'Ros' (completely out of character) suffered a severe nosebleed (she never had one before, or since), a very bad burn mark on her chest, which has scarred, and a 'V'-shaped incision on her back. Her lifestyle, eating habits and personality, was to completely change dramatically, including an avid interest in drawings, writing, and typing, although generally feeling quite ill but fine before the UFO encounter. She said:

> "I gave up drinking and smoking and developed a craving for sweets. Even stranger, I began to write complex notes on how the universe was formed, and wrote up the engine plans of the 'spacecraft'. This was so unlike me. Eventually, we split up. For three years I was afraid to go outside. I split with Philip on very violent terms; he was never a violent person before."

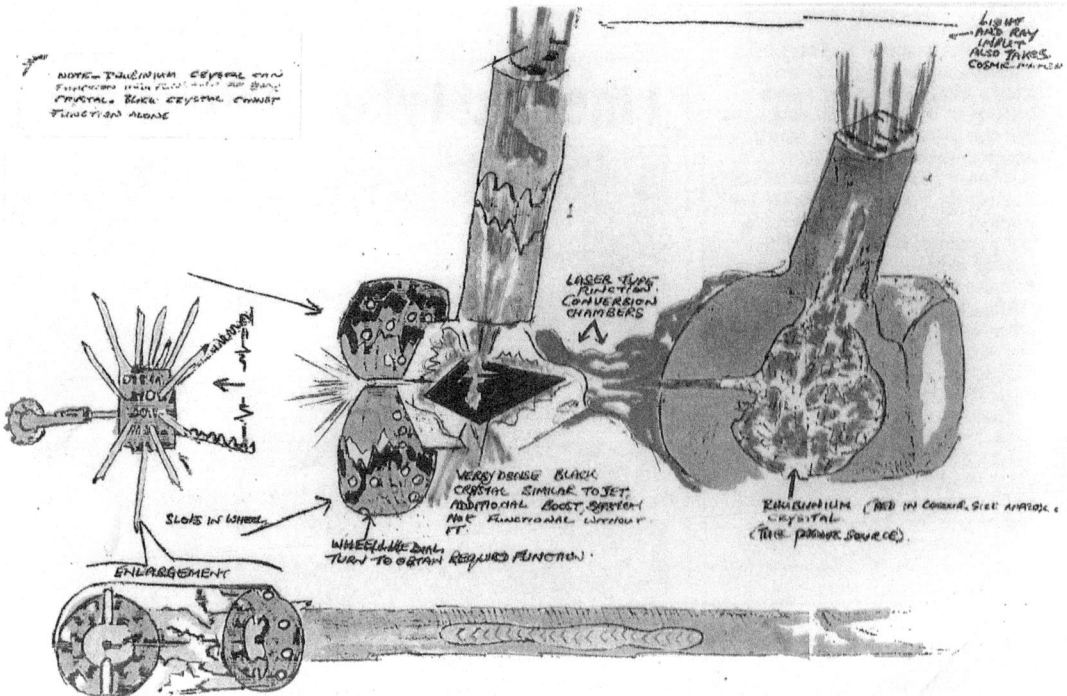

Hypnotic Regression

> "I sought medical help over some of the problems but never mentioned my fears of it being possibly UFO, partly as I didn't admit it to myself, and partly as I was embarrassed and felt I would be laughed at as a fool."

As a result of contacting a UFO organisation, who came to see her, it was suggested she be hypnotised, to extract further information regarding her encounter.

Aliens removed my uterus – then put it back

ROS REYNOLDS, 40, lives in Essex with her partner Danny and their son Nathaniel. In 1982, she was travelling with her then-boyfriend Philip to visit family when they were chased for miles by a UFO. The subsequent encounter changed her life forever.

I still get flashbacks of their little fingers. I remember struggling, but it was all internal. The outside was as still as could be, as if I was sedated.

We'd got as far as Sudbury in Suffolk when we were buzzed by what we initially thought was a helicopter. It flew over the top of us and was so low it actually went under a power cable.

It chased us for about six miles, flashing its lights, and then the car stopped. We both got out and the last memory I have is of Philip leaning over the bonnet, tinkering with the engine.

The next thing I was aware of, we were both back inside, the car had started and the lights were on. We had lost four hours. That was the end of my life as I knew it.

From then on I had a stream of medical problems, there was a noise like a fax machine going off in my head, Philip went ga-ga, and our friends deserted us. I had nightmares and was writing and drawing in my sleep. I can barely add up, but I would wake up to find that I had scrawled what experts

craft. I couldn't swear that it was a spaceship, but the air was weird, with a strange sense of gravity, and the whole feel of the place was clinical.

I have vague memories of four or five figures – the classic greys with the eyes. And a tall, crazy-looking fellow with blondy-white hair.

About four years ago I went for an ultrasound and the woman asked me when my uterus had been removed. I had no idea, but my periods had stopped from the time of the encounter.

That was the scariest moment of all, but I know it has been put back

because I had this experience in Rendlesham Forest in 2001. I lost about an hour and a half, I heard angels and buzzing and there was a ship going over. The bottom of the hull was scraping on trees.

By the end of the year I was pregnant, and I had Nathaniel in April.

● *Taken is on BBC2, Saturdays at 9pm. Without Consent, by Carl Nagaitis and Philip Mantle (Beyond Publications, £9.99), features more ordinary people's stories of extra-terrestrial contact and alien abductions in the UK.*

I thought I was seeing things

According to 'Ros':

"As the hypnotist started to put me under, a 'beam of light' appeared in the room."

Equipment malfunctions

"The video and audio equipment malfunctioned and spun around. The sceptic who came to observe was pinned to the chair with such force as to leave claw marks on his arms and all the clocks in the house stopped. I never got hypnotised, but they did bring in a psychic investigator. I was in a room with a large Perspex type pedestal table in the centre. I remember being led to it. I didn't struggle (don't know why not) and was laid down on the thing. I remember sensing the whole procedure was clinical – like the tagging, weighing and measuring, of a wild animal.

The 'Greys' never spoke out loud, just telepathically, and there was a taller blond haired person – that's all I remember. I get very emotional if I try and remember more."

We have to say that we were astonished at the depth of detail shown in the 'engine plans of the craft', powered by a source unknown to our science, although curiously, Rubidium, discovered in 1861 (being a soft silvery-white element of the alkali group, which ignites spontaneously in the air) was considered for use in Ion engines for space flight.

(Source: Personal interview)

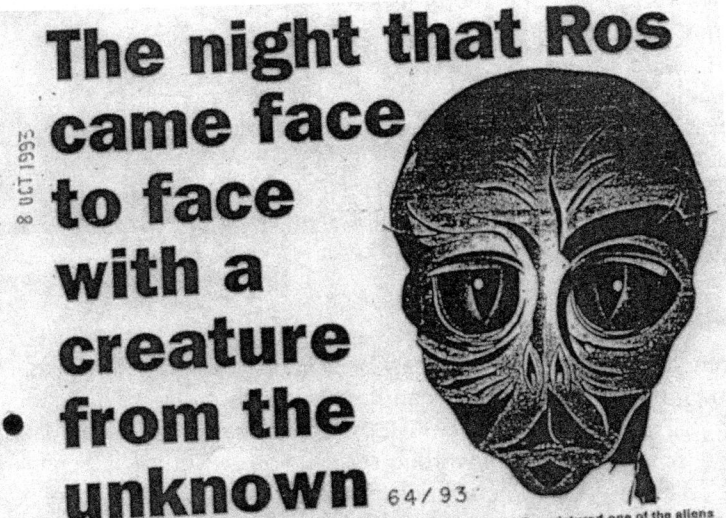

The night that Ros came face to face with a creature from the unknown

East Anglian Daily Times, Ipswich — 8 OCT 1993

64/93

■ Eerie : How Ros pictured one of the aliens

BY SHARON ASPLIN

ROS IS a normal woman – certainly not the sort to indulge in fantasies about little men from Mars or flying saucers.

But one evening she claims she was taken by force into an unidentified flying object and subjected to a terrifying examination by alien beings.

It was a difficult decision for Ros Reynolds-Parnham, 32, of Little Clacton, to speak publicly about her experiences. But she wants to reassure others who have undergone a similar ordeal and not leave them to go through the months of fear and doubt alone as she did.

Ros has now opened up to millions after appearing on the GMTV breakfast show and is eager for people to realise the seriousness behind her message.

Ten years ago Ros and her boyfriend of the time were travelling to see relatives. As they approached Sudbury Ros said she spotted a horse-shoe of bright lights in the sky, which noiselessly lowered over the car.

When they came to open countryside the lights returned two or three times and "locked" on to their vehicle. The car then went dead.

"We went out to discover what was wrong," she said. "As we had stopped so had the big light. It was very bright but it did not hurt your eyes – it is very difficult to describe."

Ros, who discovered only years later that she went inside the UFO, could not remember anything else. "All I know is we got on with our journey and when we got there we were three hours later than we should have been."

She had always been sceptical about UFOs but this started her thinking. She is now convinced things she had previously

ABDUCTED BY A UFO AN ESSEX WOMAN NEVER THOUGHT SHE WOULD HAVE THE CONFIDENCE OR COURAGE TO SPEAK ABOUT HER EXTRA-TERRESTRIAL ENCOUNTER ... UNTIL NOW

seen and passed off as aeroplanes in the sky were probably alien craft. Three weeks later she had an urge to type and draw. In her sleep she drew maps of the engine rooms and diagrams of how the earth was formed, and made notes about disasters and the truth behind great world mysteries, the future and how the earth was formed – all things she knew nothing about.

Ros says she has scars and other physical signs of her ordeal. She cannot have children because since that autumn night she has never had a monthly cycle.

"I got through being worried, I could not talk to anybody about it because I thought they would think I was a freak," she said. "I just bottled it up, I became a recluse for a while worrying about what had happened."

Eventually she managed to pull her life together again and then a few years ago saw an article in a local newspaper about an East Anglian UFO investigation team.

They arranged a hypnosis session at her Plough Corner home. It was a failure. "The video recording was wiped out, everything went wrong," she explained. "A bright beam of light came into the room and all the clocks stopped."

Through a mutual friend, she then got in touch with Mark Reynolds-Parnham. Mark claims he was born psychic and he uses his abilities to investigate cases like Ros. It was during the investigation the two fell in love and married.

Details of her experiences were pieced together in a second hypnosis session. Mark said his wife described four or five small aliens, around 3ft 6in to 4ft tall, who approached her and forced her to the craft.

Under hypnosis Mark realised Ros had been taken to an examination room and had become very agitated as the aliens undressed her and laid her on a table as they tried to study her.

What had happened, continued Mark, was a typical UFO abduction scenario, which had taken place with many people on this planet for many, many years.

Ros admits she is still frightened by what happened, and is obviously embarrassed by what she revealed, as she had to leave the room while her husband talked about it.

Most people have been quite open-minded and compassionate about their claims, the couple said, and so far no-one has denounced them as crazy. "Some are very interested because they believe it and some are interested because they want to be convinced," said Mark.

"But we have never had anyone come up to us and say we are lying."

■ Anyone who wants help or perhaps something unusual explained should contact the Bufora office, a professional investigation and counselling service, on (0582) 763218.

Colonel Dale C. Tabor takes command of Base

The Colonel (promoted to Major General in July 1988) was transferred to the 81st Tactical Fighter Wing, Royal Air Force Station, Bentwaters, England, in April 1982, and became wing commander in August 1982. In March 1984 he was assigned to Headquarters U.S. Air Forces in Europe, Ramstein Air Base, West Germany, and served as inspector general until June 1985, when he became assistant deputy chief of staff for operations. In May 1988 the general became commander of Technical Training Center, Lowry Air Force Base, in Colorado. He assumed his present command in March 1991. The general is a command pilot with more than 4,000 flying hours. His military awards and decorations include the Distinguished Service Medal, Legion of Merit, Distinguished Flying Cross, Bronze Star Medal, and Meritorious Service Medal with three oak leaf clusters, Air Medal with ten oak leaf clusters and Air Force Commendation Medal.

Flew 366 combat hours

The general completed Tactical Fighter Weapons School at Nellis Air Force Base, Nevada, while en route to the 35th Tactical Fighter Wing, Phan Rang Air Base, in South Vietnam. He flew 366.5 combat hours during 223 combat missions in F-100s in Southeast Asia. In February 1969, General Tabor began studying for a master's degree through the Air Force Institute of Technology program at UCLA. After graduating he served as an operations staff officer for the Directorate of Requirements, Headquarters Tactical Air Command, Langley Air Force Base, Va., from September 1970 to mid 1972, when he entered the Air Command and Staff College.

1983

UFO seen over Ipswich

IPSWICH resident – Mrs Angela Snook – contacted us in October 2015, wanting to bring to our attention what her daughter – Laura from Elmhurst Drive, Holy Wells Park – sighted in 1982/83. Unfortunately, the exact date is not known. This is not unusual; dates are often forgotten, but events are burnt into the memory!

During the school summer holidays or maybe a little later, perhaps autumn half-term, the family were at home around 2.30pm, when they heard a sudden violent noise and vibration.

Angela:

"I imagined a helicopter crashing into the house. The noise seemed to engulf myself and my eight or nine-year-old daughter downstairs, and two or three-year-old son resting in his cot upstairs.

Fearing the worst I placed my daughter against the staircase, believing as this was a pretty strong part of the house that she would be protected, and told her not to move while I dashed upstairs to get my small son.

Unknown to me my daughter, who has never taken instructions seriously, had run out of the backdoor! When I came downstairs I yelled for her, not realising she'd gone out.

At this stage the noise had began to recede as quickly. I ran outside and saw her. She pointed to where she believed the 'noise' was receding but I couldn't see anything. I went through our short drive and looked into the sky again, but saw nothing – not even a neighbour in sight! My daughter said it looked something like a hot water tank and had descended almost to between ourselves and our neighbour's house (there was only a single shared driveway to the rear garages between our semi-detached properties).

When my husband came home after work we told him, and his opinion was that no one would believe us and if nothing was said by anyone else then we best ignore it too. We had a board game at the time called 'Plumb Crazy', about winning plumbing pipes that

you joined onto an old patched-up boiler, and my daughter said the UFO looked something like that. I presumed that if it was a prank by some person on an airbase, then it still would be denied and told her there was nothing we could do about it."

In 2015, we discussed this matter with Laura Snook – now a successful internationally known journalist, currently the news editor of the *Phnom Penh Post,* Cambodia's leading daily newspaper.

Laura possesses BA (Dual Hons.) in English and Geography. She was a member of Keele University Ladies 1st XV Rugby Football club, and led an expedition to Zimbabwe – an impressive woman with impressive qualifications and a pleasure to talk to. She remains as perplexed now as she was then as to what it was that she had seen.

The description is not unfamiliar to us. Unidentified flying objects whose outer surface is apparently covered in square or rectangular striations have been reported from all over the world.

March – Ted Conrad talks about incident in *OMNI* Magazine

In an interview conducted with journalist Eric Mishara, published by *OMNI* magazine (Volume 5/6) in March 1983, Ted Conrad (who was alleged to have spoken with the aliens) recalled:

"At 10.30pm on that fateful night, four air policemen spotted lights from what they thought was a small plane descending into the forest. Two of the men tracked the object on foot and came upon a large tripod mounted 'craft'. It had no windows, but was studded with brilliant red and blue lights. Each time the men came within 50 yards of the 'ship', it levitated six feet in the air and backed away. They followed it for almost an hour through the woods and across a field, until it took off at phenomenal speed."

Acting on the reports made by his men, Colonel Conrad began a brief investigation regarding the incident in the morning. He went into the forest and located a triangular pattern, obviously made by the tripod legs. He claimed that he had never observed any aliens but did interview two of the eyewitnesses, and concluded: *"Those lads saw something, but I don't know what it was."*

Charles Halt:

"Conrad did not have time during Englund's shift to go and Monroe was home baby-sitting, as his wife spent the evening at a chapel program. Englund had to go and fetch him so he could participate. A day or two later, I took Conrad and his family out and Conrad had no idea where the site was and never mentioned being there prior. Something doesn't sound right."

Jim Penniston – Rendlesham is not about UFOs and never was!

Bob Tibbitts – A few questions:

Jim Penniston and John Burroughs

"Why would Sgt. Jim Penniston state that it was never about UFOs ('Rendlesham is not about UFOs and never was') but then state that he saw symbols on the side of a 'craft' and that he received certain binary codes directly into his mind and made drawings in his notepad of a craft? If he claims it isn't about UFOs, one can only assume that the 'craft' was identified. Bearing in mind comments made by Ted Conrad: 'Penniston said he didn't get close enough for a detailed look'.

If it was recognised as a craft of earthly origin (or from the future, as Jim believes) then perhaps there had been some reason for it to be in the airbase vicinity, and so stories of UFOs and their subsequent repair were encouraged by certain agencies to cover that fact."

Russian presence

"Was the Russian presence in the air an indication that they were very interested in the 'craft' and its origin and purpose near to a nuclear weapons-equipped airbase at a time of heightened cold war sensitivities? Or was this merely a routine, regular patrol near to our airspace, and just a coincidence? If the incident is still classified, then there must be a good reason for it to be so... and not necessarily because there may or may not have been UFO activity. Of course, it is quite possible that 'both' could have been the cause of all the activity; a prototype aircraft from an emerging alternative earth-based technology and also a craft from 'elsewhere'!

As in other cases where nuclear missiles are said to have been affected by the presence of 'unknown lights', are there any known documents that have been released, showing that the weapons stored at Woodbridge/Bentwaters were compromised in any way? If they had been, then that is a 'good reason' for the incident to remain classified.

There seems to be an ever-increasing deluge of questions about this incident. There is no definitive, clearly-stated, 'cause' that can be identified as the reason for the events at Rendlesham ... if there is one, then I guess that this remains 'classified' and probably with valid reasoning. Of course, if it is 'classified', then Nick Pope, James Penniston and John Burroughs, can only really fuel further speculation ... because they cannot break their security oaths."

Evidence was sent to Ramstein Airbase

According to Donald Moreland, the tape-recording made by Colonel Halt was handed over to General Gabriel, during a visit to the airbase. This would tie in with what Georgina Bruni suggested in her book – *You Can't Tell The People* – that this evidence was *"most likely to have been dispatched to Ramstein Airbase".* We believe, from other sources of available information, that she was right.

March – Larry Warren meets with Larry Fawcett

Another early 'whistle-blower' – this time on the United States side – was Larry Warren, who, after returning to America, was contacted by Larry Fawcett – a Police Lieutenant in the State of Connecticut, then working with Barry Greenwood, whom we had the pleasure of entering into email communication with regard to certain aspects of the forthcoming 'HALT book', in late 2015.

14th April – Colonel Henry Cochran replies

On 14th April 1983, the authors Larry Fawcett and Barry Greenwood filed a FOI request to 81st Combat Support Group at RAF Bentwaters, asking about unknown aircraft activity near RAF Bentwaters. On the 28th April, Colonel Henry J. Cochran replied:

> "There was allegedly some strange activity near RAF Bentwaters at the approximate time in question, but not on land under US Air Force jurisdiction, and therefore no official investigation was conducted by the 81st Tactical Fighter Wing. Thus the records you request do not exist."

Barry Greenwood:

> "I first took note of 'flying saucers' in 1964 with news about the Socorro New Mexico story. I was just dumbfounded that a cop would report such a thing. I had an engrained interest in science anyway, so this was an extension of that interest. It escalated after seeing more of this type of

thing in 1965 and thereon. Saw a few unusual objects at night but not particularly noteworthy, classic 'insufficient information' for me to evaluate. Re: the public postings of CAUS histories most ignore the 14 years I controlled its output. Gersten pretended that 1984-1998 didn't exist after he reclaimed the CAUS name, going off onto wild believer nonsense from 1998 for a short time, until he suspended operations. Originally, it was begun by Todd Zechel, Brad Sparks, and Gersten. Due to behind-the-scenes *chickanery, the active operator of CAUS, Zechel, suspended operations in 1980. Larry Bryant took it over for a few issues until 1982, when he suspended operations. Larry Fawcett and I revived it in 1984, after asking Gersten if it was OK.

News of the World fiasco & Larry Warren misrepresentation

> "The reasons CAUS bowed out of the story were due to the just described News of the World fiasco and Larry Warren misrepresenting his role in the report (using Bustinza's version as his own). As for the rest of the controversies, I'm not part of them and haven't been since the early stages of the story. If anyone asks me questions, whether it is you, Peter, or someone else, I will try to answer with what happened as far as my involvement went. You can circulate this and the last e-mails if you like. I like to do things above the table, not hidden underneath."

Following an interview, the famous *Halt Memorandum* was obtained after a FOI request by Larry Fawcett and Robert Todd, of *CAUS* (Citizens Against UFO Secrecy) on the 7th May 1983.

---

*Chickanery – the use of deception or subterfuge to achieve one's purpose. "Storylines packed with political chicanery, trickery, deception, deceit, deceitfulness, duplicity, dishonesty, unscrupulousness, underhandedness, subterfuge, fraud, fraudulence, sophistry, sharp practice, skulduggery, swindling, cheating, duping, hoodwinking. (**Source: Wikipedia**)

John Hanson:

A copy of this memo was then sent to Dot Street, who passed it on to Manchester solicitor – Harry Harris. He had been involved in the Alan Godfrey case and other UFO incidents, over the years. Harry then later sold it to the *News of the World* for £12,000 – this sum having been negotiated by Mike Sacks, who told us, in 2015, that the amount was then shared equally between the five persons involved.

15th March – Unexplained lights seen in sky over Upper Heyford

In answer to an enquiry made by the MOD, with regard to a report of a UFO tracked by radar at Upper Heyford on the 15th March 1983, a spokesman said:

> "The radar at Upper Heyford did not track an unidentified flying object on 15th March 1983, as alleged. The events were as follows: Just after dark, a local reporter for the Reading Evening Post telephoned the tower at Upper Heyford and asked if they could see the 'lights' at the opposite side of the airfield. The controllers assistant, after checking, told the reporter that the duty crew could indeed see the 'lights' and that they did not know what they were but they could have been some airfield lights traffic within the airfield or outside the airfield. The telephone conversation was then terminated. The US authorities at Upper Heyford reiterate that at no time did they track on the airfield radar any unidentified target. It is my belief that the reporter in question did not ask the right questions in the first place and has completely misinterpreted the answer he received."

Signed: J.R. Davies, Wing Commander Liaison Officer at RAF Mildenhall, Suffolk (15th April 1983).

Larry Fawcett of CAUS (Citizens Against UFO Secrecy)

May – Mystery of alleged UFO landing in forest

This was the headline from the *Woodbridge Reporter* newspaper, on the 6th May 1983. Once again there was a reference to the 'anonymous airmen', who told of seeing three entities 'three feet tall, dressed in silver suits, levitating in shafts of light' near their landed spacecraft in a remote part of Rendlesham Forest. A copy of the eye-witness' drawing of the UFO was included, followed by a denial of any contact with alien beings, according to the MOD.

Other contemporary newspaper sources included *Sunday Mirror* – 'Flying Saucer lands in Britain – I saw UFO land American Officer' and *News of the World* – 'We must be told'.

Although the incident(s) which occurred in Rendlesham Forest were now three years old, *"It continues to excite attention"*, according to Squadron Leader Donald Moreland, who wrote to Peter Lord Hill-Norton at the MOD to this effect on the 9th May 1983.

August – Secret meeting at the airbase

In *Sky Crash* (page 186) we were intrigued to hear of a secret meeting at the airbase, held between Colonel Halt, Mike Sacks and Harry Harris, sometime in August 1983. Although that meeting was kept secret from Jenny, Dot and Brenda, they learnt about it from another source. When confronted the two men explained that they had been sworn to secrecy by Colonel Halt and were not willing to discuss the matter further. For many years we remained curious as to the exact nature of what was discussed with Charles Halt. According to Mike Sacks, in an interview conducted in February 2013, he told us that . . .

Mike Sacks:

"Harry had telephoned General Gordon Williams, in the States, seeking permission to listen to a copy of that tape. Subsequently this was arranged and we were then allowed onto base, where we met up with Colonel Halt. After discussing UFOs generally, we sat around the table and he played the tape. We then signed a contract forbidding us from talking about what had been discussed that day, but chose to ignore the agreement made."

Colonel Halt:

"I did meet with Mike and Harry. It was about 1982 and we all agreed not to reveal the meeting, although I would refute any arrangement was made with General Gordon Williams. I was very disappointed when the gang – Brenda, Dot, Jenny, Harry and Mike – sold the story to the *News of the World. That wasn't supposed to happen and it took years before I trusted Harry and Mike again. If you're talking with them, say hello. I did forgive them, but it took a lot of time."

(*The story was sold to the *News of the World* and a contract provided to Mike, Harry, and Jenny)

NEWS of the WORLD

THE WORLD'S LARGEST SUNDAY SALE
NEWS GROUP NEWSPAPERS LTD.
A Subsidiary of News International PLC

Registered Office:
30 BOUVERIE STREET
FLEET ST., LONDON, EC4Y 8EX
Registered No. 679215 England
Telegraphic Address—
WORLDLY, LONDON, EC4
Telex No. 22897
Telephone 01-353 3030

15th December, 1983

Mrs Brenda Butler,
1 Masking Place,
Leiston,
Suffolk.

Dear Mrs Butler

NORTHERN OFFICE,
P.O. BOX 294,
1-23 WITHY GROVE,
MANCHESTER M60 4BP

Following our telephone conversation, I am
writing to confirm that only one contract was
entered into by the News of the World with
regard to the UFO incident at Woodbridge,
Suffolk.

The contract as you are aware, was between
this newspaper and Mr. H. Harris, Mr. M Sachs,
and Miss J. Randles.

I can assure you no other contract either
between yourself or anyone else, was agreed
with regard to this story.

I hope this makes the matter clear for you.

Yours sincerely,

Robert Warren
News Editor

12th August – Visit to see Colonel Halt

Brenda Butler and Dot Street went to see Colonel Halt, at 2pm on the 12th August. They were welcomed into his office and then asked if they had a tape-recorder with them, to which they replied in the negative.

Brenda:

"Colonel Halt told us he was annoyed about his 'memo' ever having been released, and that he had been promised by 'they' (whoever they are) that it would never be released. He remarked, 'The craft was triangular in shape, under some sort of control. There were no entities; I only know what the men have told me'.

When Dot showed him Larry Warren's statement, he said that 'It was rubbish; only bits and pieces made sense'. When we showed him Steve Roberts' statement, he said 'That's more like it, but no entities were seen'."

When the two women asked which bits were right, he replied *"That's for you two to figure out".* Laughing, he said: *"The truth is there somewhere!"* He took out a map and showed them the landing site, which was the same location as shown by 'Steve Roberts'.

16th August – Claim of embarrassment to World Governments

At 3pm on Tuesday, 16th August 1983, Brenda and Dot called to see John Warburton – the curator of the Anglo Saxon burial site and museum at Sutton Hoo, and a personal friend of the Base Commander, Ted Conrad.

Brenda:

"He told us he was a friend of Ted Conrad's and that Ted had told him we are not allowed to say anything about what happened, as it would cause embarrassment to World Governments; everyone was sworn to secrecy and the UFO story was put out as a cover-up. After a while, John told us 'something had fallen off an aircraft, which was very sensitive, and that the aircraft shouldn't have been in our airspace. John said he was having dinner with Conrad soon and would try to find out more, but he said it definitely was not a UFO as we know them."

Brenda later spoke to John again, when he told her that during a conversation with Conrad at a dinner party he attended, the officer mentioned about there being a machine – *a silver, long shape.* John did not know what it was, but guessed that someone did. He thought it was part of an aircraft but was not sure what.

1983 – Larry Warren regression

Charles Halt supplied a number of documents for perusal; one which was a sheaf of A4 typed up papers endorsed 'Larry Warren Regression', by Pat Gagliardo, who lives in Connecticut, USA.

Pat is a world renowned Police-Accredited Clairvoyant, medium and sensitive, and has endured two major surgeries and other serious medical conditions. She has impeccable credentials and is a very genuine lady.

A near-death experience led to the introduction of Guardian Angels (Spirit Guides) and communication with the spirit world and enlightenments, truth about life after death, reincarnation and the purpose of life. She has gained the respect of Law Enforcement, Federal and Government agencies and private persons nationwide, using her 'psychic' abilities in locating missing persons and assisting with various criminal cases as far away as Australia.

She first received national acclaim, in 1980, when she worked with the State's Attorney's Office, in

Pat Gagliardo

New London, CT. and led officials to a location which recovered the body of a missing Coast Guard warrant officer, Richard Eastman. The story received nationwide media coverage via AP newswire and the *National Enquirer*. Her involvement with the missing and murdered children of Atlanta, GA. (one of many) also received nationwide media coverage.

Connecticut experts rally to help in Atlanta murders

"I held the missing child's shirt and told them to stay in the area," said Pat Gagliardo. "The dogs picked up the scent and led them to a clearing. They started pawing the ground and when the men dug down in that spot, they found a bloody shirt and jacket."

"In our effort to see that we leave no stone unturned and tap all the available resources in the nation that may be of assistance to us," said Atlanta Public Safety Commissioner Lee. P. Brown, "we are bringing in this team of investigative consultants from police departments throughout the nation. To our knowledge this is the first time a police agency has tapped other police agencies for assistance."

In addition to tapping other police agencies and the F.B.I. which is investigating the possible violation of federal kidnapping laws, a little-publicized other form of investigation is being used: Part of the "no stone unturned."

A Connecticut psychic, 31-year-old Pat Gagliardo of Norwich, became part of the Atlanta investigation during a layover between planes in Atlanta a few weeks ago and continues her cooperation with the Atlanta police by phone from here.

"I was going to Dawson, Georgia to help on another missing person case on which I had been called by a woman named Nancy Ritter, whom I had helped before," Mrs. Gagliardo, a housewife, mother of two and part-time school bus driver, said, "I told her about the vision I had had about Atlanta on October 18th. I told her that I saw something about a Lincoln memorial statue and a cement

structure that appeared like a dam, but had no water; that there would be something in the area that would look like a shield and three other landmarks that I'm not at liberty to disclose.

"Mrs. Ritter called the sheriff of Peachtree County, which is 30 miles from Atlanta and he notified Atlanta Councilman Arthur Langford and they set up a task force to meet me in Atlanta."

The task force took her to Lincoln Park Cemetery, which fit the description she had given (though she had never been beyond Atlanta's airport before) and she did some psychometry on one of the missing children's shirts.

"Psychometry," she explained, "is 80 percent of my ability. By handling an object that belongs to someone, I begin to see a kaleidescope of colors and then I get a vision that is almost like a photograph. I held the missing child's shirt and told them to stay in the area. The dogs picked up the scent and led them to a clearing. They started pawing the ground and when the men dug down in that spot, they found a bloody shirt and jacket. The whole thing took about 30 minutes."

Since her return to Connecticut, she has had another vision and perceived another area which she has relayed to the Councilman. Because of the Please turn to Page 13.

Endorsement by Larry Fawcett

It is of interest to note the following endorsement from Lt. Lawrence Fawcett, Coventry Police Dept. CT, one of a number from Law Enforcement agencies that called on her aid.

"Our police department has used Ms. Gagliardo very successfully; through her psychic abilities we were able to close previously unresolved cases. I am satisfied with the fact that she is a true psychic. I can personally vouch for her integrity, honesty and moral character and would and have referred her to other police agencies in the country."

LYNDON STATE COLLEGE

Lyndonville, Vermont 05851
Telephone: (802) 626-6200
Fax: (802) 626-9770
TDD: (802) 626-6273

To whom it may concern;

Not often, although always asked, do I write a letter a letter of recommendation for an act. After seeing hundreds of entertainers throughout my 15 years in the field, they all are usually good but none usually blow me away. Except for the person this letter is in reference to, Patricia Gagliardo. I missed her show a year ago and heard students talking about how great she was and even though they said it was a small turnout, they were talking about her for months.

After walking into the theatre the night of the performance I was amazed at the packed house, not to mention a half-hour prior to showtime. Word spread like wild fire about Patricia and commuter and resident students alike filled our theatre. I was also impressed and surprised that usually if a performer takes a break, most of the students leave the event and never come back, but this wasn't the case with Patricia Gagliardo's performance. Not only did all the students come back; they ran to their residence halls to get more people to come to the event. Students and myself were blown away by her program, not only did she accurately read people she never has seen before she spent time walking the halls to see if the ghost from the previous year was still there.

I had so many students stop me after the show and say we need her back next year that I put a call into the agent to book her back that night. Patricia Gagliardo is a must see act. I can't imagine her not being a complete hit on any college campus. She is one of the few acts that I could honestly say spellbound the audience members and myself.

I highly recommend Patricia Gagliardo without reservation. If anyone would like any further information please feel free to call me direct at 802-626-6344.

Sincerely,

Frank A. Doldo
Director of Student Life

Contacting Patricia Gagliardo

Pat Gagliardo:

"Hi John, I apologize it has taken me this long to get back to you. I was involved with regressive hypnosis with someone from a very large base; however, it was a Japanese or Chinese organization that filmed my hypnotic session with the serviceman. Unfortunately, it was my friend – Lt. Lawrence Fawcett – that arranged that session so many years ago. Larry is now deceased. I believe the serviceman I hypnotized was from the Bentwaters, England, UFO sightings."

NTV Producer Junichi Yana

Transcript of regression

There are 24 and-a-half pages of unnumbered content, approximately a couple of hundred words on each sheet. (Mispronunciations of names will be kept faithful). We believe the file is in chronological order.

The first page outlines a visit to the chow hall for breakfast, followed by a visit to the Commander's officer, identified as Major Ziegler. The second page outlines being accompanied by John and Adrian and a reference to Sergeant Frieza and Major Ziegler.

Larry is called in and asked if he is working tonight by Major Jajury. *"We are not supposed to talk about what we saw."*

Pat: What aren't you supposed to talk about? **Larry:** "What we saw." **Pat:** What did you see? **Larry:** I don't know.

[30ᵀᴴ DECEMBER 1980 – Authors headline]

Larry is then 'taken back' to 30th December 1980, and asked by Pat to give a detailed description of the day's events. He explains that in the morning he was near the Corn Exchange in Ipswich, at 2.30pm, with Steve Clovis. After walking around, he caught the bus at 9.30pm.

Larry: Just had an alert. **Pat:** What kind of alert? **Larry:** Routine. Pat then asks him to go to the time when he was on duty.

Larry: Well we have to go on at 11.30 but we have guard mount though. **Pat:** Who is with you? **Larry**: Everyone. 'C 'Flight, we are on Bentwaters.

Larry then talks about Sergeant Follvey assigning posts, and that he is going to his post with Sergeant Smith, who dropped him off after this was done. Larry talks of being on his post and nothing unusual happening. He hears some kind of noise like a jet and talking about a light on the radio seen towards Woodbridge.

[SERGEANT BUSTINZA MENTIONED – Authors headline]

Larry: I can see it from the tower. **Pat:** Anything special about the light? **Larry:** Not to me. I can't see it. We are going to get relieved from my post, for **Sergeant Bustinza**. They are sending a truck and I am going with them.

Pat: Where are you going? **Larry:** I don't know. Further conversation then takes place.

Larry: saying, Lieutenant, we have to go to the motor pool and fill it up. They are not working.

[FRONT GATE AT WOODBRIDGE – Authors headline]

Larry: then talks of going to the front gate at Woodbridge with a 'black kid', Adrian and Lieutenant England, six cars or trucks, flares at the east end. **Larry:** The Commander's there. I fell in the mud, we just have to walk. **Pat:** Where are you walking to? **Larry:** The woods the trees. They stop. Adrian told me he was out here. **Pat:** What was? **Larry:** He was. Just like he had seen this before and what he was saying. Don't know why was doing that? **Pat:** Doing what? **Larry:** This walking and stopping and walking and stopping

Pat: How far do you believe you have walked already? **Larry:** A half a mile. There is a fence and it is broken. **Pat:** How many are there walking? **Larry:** Four of us here and thirty around some kind of light. **Pat:** What kind of light? **Larry:** It's not a light

Pat: Describe it. **Larry:** A house **Pat:** It is a house? What kind of house? **Larry:** I do not see it. **Pat:** This is a regular light? **Larry:** It may be a fire. **Pat:** How close to this light are you? **Larry:** A couple of yards. It is low. **Pat:** What colour is it? **Larry:** Whitish. It is the whole woods, light up. You can see everyone, the people the field it is a house. **Pat:** Why are you saying it is a house, can you describe it? **Larry:** A fog with a light. **Pat:** The fog is around the light. **Larry:** It is hard to tell what it is. Someone is sick.

Pat: Someone close to you? **Larry:** I passed him, a kid sitting down.

Pat tells Larry that she wants him to focus back on this house, the light; she is going to count from one to three. When she gets to three he will be able to open his eyes without affecting his trance. She asks him to draw the light, this object he is calling a house, even if he wants to use stick drawings.

Pat: Give me basic understanding of that this object is the house. 1-2-3-open your eyes without affecting your trance and draw me, this object, and where you are in reference to this object. Use stick type drawings, it is ok. Where are you?

[LIKE A PLASTIC ASPIRIN – Authors headline]

Pat: Now where is this object, just an outline? **Larry:** It is like a plastic aspirin, something. It is nothing. **Pat:** Where is it – on the ground? **Larry:** It is right here. **Pat:** Ok, can you give me a rough idea? **Larry:** Of what? **Pat:** Of the thing. **Larry:** It is round.

Pat: Like a plastic aspirin, you said? **Larry:** Yes, but it is on the ground. **Pat:** Ok, that is fine. Close your eyes now and take a nice deep breath. Now I want you to continue with what is happening next. What's happening now? Your images are very clear now. Your memory is very sharp. Nothing is hampering your memory. Go ahead. Continue, what is happening now? You have no reason to fear. Tell me exactly what is happening. **Larry:** Noise. **Pat:** What kind of noise? Where is it coming from? **Larry:** Something is wrong.

Pat: What is wrong? What is happening? Larry, I want you to tell me what is happening with the noise, the object and the people?

Do you still hear the noise? Answer. Do you still hear the noise? What is happening? Why aren't you speaking to me?

Larry: I couldn't hear **Pat:** You can't hear? Can you hear me now? **Larry:** There are some lights in the distance, like stars.

Pat: Are you looking at them? **Larry:** Yes. **Pat:** Are they stars?

[COWS ARE SEEN – Authors headline]

Larry: No, there are some cows out there … strange. **Larry:** They are standing next to each other? **Pat:** The cows? **Larry:** Yes.

Pat: Do you see them clearly? **Larry:** Yes. **Pat:** How far away from them are you? **Larry:** Twenty feet. **Pat:** What do they look like? **Larry:** Cows. **Pat:** Describe their colour. **Larry:** Brown, maybe? **Pat:** Did they just appear from nowhere? **Larry:** They may have been there. It is the base commander. It is officers, cameras and I don't understand this. **Pat:** What don't you understand? **Larry:** What this is. **Pat:** What, what is? Explain. **Larry:** I can't. **Pat:** Are the feeling of the other people the same? **Larry:** yes, that light. **Pat:** It is in the air. It is moving towards us. **Pat:** Can you see it clearly? **Larry:** Yes. It is small; it is moving towards us. **Pat:** What colour is the light? **Larry:** It is red or orange-red and it is stopped. **Pat:** It stopped where? Are you close to it? **Larry:** Yes it is right above. We are backing up. It is a red light. It is changing. **Pat:** Into what? **Larry:** It blew up. **Pat:** It blew up? What is happening with the other people watching this?

[SECURITY OPTION 3 – Authors headline]

Larry: They are just staring. **Pat:** They are just staring? **Larry:** They are into security option three. It is a possible nuclear explosion. What can you do? It is changed. **Pat:** Into what? You see it clearly? **Larry:** This thing. **Pat:** What thing? Describe it to me.

Larry: Maybe a ship? It is a red light. It is not a light, it is a haze. A blue light and I do not know. I am backing up. I don't know what it is. It is a Police that are there. I do not know what to do. **Pat:** What is everyone doing? **Larry**: Some ran. **Pat:** Why does it look like it is landing? **Larry:** It is there. It is on the ground. It is not that big. I don't know. (Points)

Pat: I am going to count to three. When you hear me say number three, you will be able to open your eyes without affecting your trance. You will draw for me this object as clearly as you can. Your memory is very sharp. Your images and visions are crystal clear. If you have to use stick type drawings it is ok. 1…2…3…now open your eyes. Is there anything significant about the colours or sounds while you are watching this time? **Larry:** There is a buzz. **Pat:** There is a buzzing sound? I want you to show me where you are. How close are you to it or how far? **Larry:** There is a thing here. It is a light-all along here. **Pat:** Multicoloured or one colour? **Larry:** Blue.

Pat: All blue? **Larry:** Yes. Red, there are things all over it that stick out. I don't know what. There is a light up here.

Pat: It that a blue light also? **Larry:** No. This kind of went to the point. It is a point here. It is concave. **Pat:** About how large would you say the object is? **Larry:** There is a tree here. **Pat:** Take a deep breath and close your eyes. I want you to continue with what is happening. Now the object has landed?

[THE OBJECT HAS LANDED – Authors headline]

Larry: They are checking it. **Pat:** Who is checking it? **Larry:** Some people. The Air Force, with a stick; I don't know what? They are on their knees, seeing what is under it. **Pat:** How many are about all there? **Larry:** A lot.

Pat: Give me an approximation. **Larry:** One hundred and fifty maybe? Base Commander and other people; they are talking, very nervous. **Pat:** Can you hear any conversation going on? What is happening? **Larry:** No, there is some kind of glow. **Pat:** Where is it coming from? **Larry:** The back of the thing. There is a …I can't believe it. **Pat:** What? What can't you believe?

[KIDS AND ADRIAN MENTIONED – Authors headline]

Larry: Some people are running, kids …**Pat:** Where are they coming from? **Larry:** I don't know. Just kids there. **Pat:** What is happening now? **Larry:** Three. **Pat:** Three what? **Larry:** I think they are kids. **Pat:** Where did they come from? **Larry:** Maybe the house. **Pat:** That house? **Larry:** Yes, maybe. **Pat:** What do the kids look like? **Larry:** Adrian is crying. He says they are not walking.

Pat: He says they are not walking? What does he say they are doing? **Larry:** They're not…..they can't be kids then. **Pat:** What does he think they are? **Larry:** he doesn't know. They are not kids. They are next to each other in this light. **Pat:** What do they look like? Are they big, short, tall or fat? **Larry:** They are small, couple of feet. **Pat:** Thin, fat? **Larry:** Very slight in built. **Pat:** What are they wearing? **Larry:** Some kind of material. I don't know… cloth. **Pat:** Shiny, flat? **Larry:** Can you see the colour? **Larry:** Yes, silver metal… brown. **Pat:** Without effecting your trance, when you hear the number three I want you to open your eyes and I want you to draw for me, even in some type of stick drawings, what these little creatures look like…1…2…3. Draw them as clearly as you can, just give me some kind of an idea. Go ahead, it is ok **Larry:** Like a shadow. **Pat:** A shadow around them? **Larry:** A light. **Pat:** What colour was the light? **Larry:** It is a yellow, a yellow. **Pat:** Are they walking, are they standing, are they sitting? What are they doing?

Larry: They are in the air. **Pat:** They are suspended? How high? **Larry:** A foot maybe. I don't know, that is all I can see.

Pat: How many did you say there were? **Larry:** Three. **Pat:** Are they standing together, or are they apart? **Larry:** They are next to each other. It is just like, I don't know. **Pat:** They have long arms down by their sides. They have arms? **Larry:** Yes. **Pat:** Take a nice deep breath. Now close your eyes. What are they doing now? **Larry:** Must be embarrassed, I think. **Pat:** You think they are embarrassed?

Larry: They don't want to be seen. **Pat:** Are they talking? **Larry:** No. **Pat:** These suits are they one piece or are they two-piece?

Larry: I can't tell. One, they must be one. **Pat:** Who is standing the closest to them? **Larry:** No one right now. **Pat:** Who was?

Larry: No one. They moved away.

[THE 'COMMANDER', WILLIAMS, AND BEINGS – Authors headline]

The commander is not too far away. I don't know why I am here? **Pat:** Why who is here?

Larry: Why I am here. **Pat:** What is happening? **Larry:** they are moving. Moving to Williams and . . . **Pat:** All of them together?

Larry: Yes and someone else, bald. I don't know, almost looking at each other. **Pat:** They are? **Larry:** Yes, at Williams.

Pat: Anything being said? **Larry:** I don't know. **Pat:** You can't hear? **Larry:** No, too far. There is a noise like a tree, maybe. They move back. They put their arms out. They have arms. **Pat:** You mean regular arms, not weapons? **Larry:** No. They are very close.

Pat: Are they shooting you? **Larry:** Just moving around. Someone ran away. **Pat:** Who? **Larry:** I don't know, someone. I do not know.

Pat: What is happening now? **Larry:** They go back in front of them. **Pat:** Who's going back? **Larry:** These things.

Pat: The three little things? People? **Larry:** Yes. **Pat:** Where are they going back to? **Larry:** They are not people. **Pat:** Ok.

Larry: The commander. **Pat:** They are going over to the commander? **Larry:** Yes. **Pat:** What is happening now? I want you to give me detailed description. **Larry:** They are just looking at each other. **Pat:** What is the commander doing? Look at the expression on his face. Does he look frightened? **Larry:** Serious. Yes. **Pat:** How close are these little beings to him? **Larry:** Right in front of him.

Pat: All together. **Larry:** Yes. **Pat:** Can you see them clearly now? **Larry:** Oh yes. **Pat:** What are their features like? **Larry:** Like a movie. **Pat:** Describe their features to me. **Larry:** They do not really have any. Their eyes stand out. **Pat:** Why? **Larry:** They are big.

Pat: They are big? **Larry:** Yes. **Pat:** Can you relate them to something – an animal, or something? **Larry:** Maybe a cat, but black eyes. **Pat:** How about their hands and feet? **Larry:** Hard to tell. **Pat:** You can't see their hands? **Larry:** No.

Pat: Do they look like hands? **Larry:** I don't know. There is nothing I have seen like that. **Pat:** Are their hands masked? You can't tell if there are any fingers? **Larry:** Maybe. It is that. There is something brought out. **Pat:** What? Who is bringing it out?

[A CRATE IS MENTIONED – Authors headline]

Larry: They brought it up an access road. It is a crate. A thing I do not know. **Pat:** What? **Larry:** I do not know? I saw it.

Pat: Back to the beings with the commander? **Larry:** Things. **Pat:** How are they moving? **Larry:** I don't see them.

Pat: What happened to them? They were standing by the ship, with the commander and what happened to them? **Larry:** I don't know. **Pat:** You don't know where they went to? **Larry:** No they are just gone. **Pat:** What were you doing that you didn't see them?

Larry: I think we are leaving? **Pat:** You are leaving? **Larry:** Yes. **Pat:** Who was taking you and where? **Larry:** Captain Verano.

We are going back [written above the word back *wasn't there*]. **Pat:** How were you leaving? **Larry:** Just walking. We can't talk.

Pat: Why? Were you instructed not to? **Larry:** Yes we can't talk the whole time. There is thunder or something. **Pat:** What kind of thunder?

Larry: I don't know. It is a thunder noise. **Pat:** You don't see it? You just hear it? **Larry:** Yes. We are just going back. He gives us our weapons back now. **Pat:** They took them from you? **Larry:** Yes. **Pat:** Who, the commander? **Larry:** The armory. They have a truck and we turned them in. **Pat:** What happens now?

[LEAVING THE LOCATION – Authors headline]

Larry: We are leaving. There are cars, civilian cars on the road. **Pat:** A lot. **Larry:** Three they stopped. There is a plane crash.

Pat: What plane crash, where? **Larry:** That is what they are saying, a plane crashed. Something's wrong. **Pat:** And you hear this? **Larry:** A woman I think, a kid. **Pat:** Who spoke to this woman? **Larry:** One of the cops. There are flares on the road at the east end. **Pat:** Where are you going now? **Larry:** Back to Bentwaters. **Pat:** What happens now?

Larry: We have coffee. **Pat:** Still not talking? **Larry:** No. **Pat:** What are you thinking? What is going through your mind?

Larry: I want to get out. **Pat:** Are you frightened? **Larry:** Oh yes! I just want to go home. Someone took pictures. It is a law enforcement guy. **Pat:** Do you know who he is? What is his name? **Larry:** Yes, Barrows. **Pat:** You saw him take photos?

Larry: No. He saw it first… had a camera. **Pat:** What is happening after you have coffee?

[BACK AT BASE – Authors headline]

Larry: We are sitting in a room. **Pat:** Where? **Larry:** In Security Control. **Pat:** Are there a lot of you there? **Larry:** Yes. They do not know what to do. It is just about time we are off duty. We check our weapons – that's all, and just go back to our room. **Pat:** Then what happens after that? **Larry:** Steve is leaving security control and everyone is saying what happened. What did you guys see what happened? **Pat:** What did you say? **Larry:** Nothing. **Pat:** You did not talk to anyone? **Larry:** No one said anything. Someone said you wouldn't believe it. **Pat:** Do you know who said it? **Larry:** No, I don't know who, blonde hair and glasses. **Pat:** What happens now? **Larry:** I went to bed.

[ASKED ABOUT THE GROUND FACILITY – Authors headline]

Pat: I want you to tell me about the ground facility you were taken to, underground. Can you describe it to me?

Larry: No. **Pat:** Why? **Larry:** There were other guys who went to that. **Pat:** Didn't you go too? **Larry:** No. **Pat:** You didn't go? **Larry:** No. **Pat:** How do you know they were taken and you weren't? Did anyone tell you? **Larry:** I don't know what happened.

Pat: Did anyone tell you about it? **Larry:** Yes. **Pat:** Will you tell me about it? I want to know about the underground facility. I want you to tell me. **Larry:** I don't know if I saw it. I don't think I saw it. **Pat:** Did someone else see it? **Larry:** Yes, Adrian. **Pat:** When was he taken there? **Larry:** Two days after. **Pat:** And you weren't? Are you sure? **Larry:** I don't know. No. **Pat:** Did he tell you about it? **Larry:** Yes. **Pat:** Then I want you to tell me about it. **Larry:** It was an elevator… got drugged, and the whole bit.

Pat: Where is this place? **Larry:** On Bentwaters. **Pat:** They drugged him? Meaning who? **Larry:** Yes, some people. **Pat:** From the Government? **Larry:** Yes. **Pat:** The Air Force? What did he see there? **Larry:** Intro rooms and this tunnel. **Pat:** Did he tell you where they went? **Larry:** Yes. **Pat:** What was there? **Larry:** This thing like we saw. **Pat:** Did he describe it to you? **Larry:** Just like we saw. **Pat:** The aspirin shape? **Larry:** No. **Pat:** Or the other one? Looked like a point? **Larry:** I think it is the same. **Pat:** What else was down there? **Larry:** There are people. **Pat:** What kind of people? Did he say anything else about those little beings? **Larry:** No.

Pat: Nothing? **Larry:** That is bad stuff. **Pat:** What is bad stuff? **Larry:** That under ground. **Pat:** Why? **Larry:** It is dangerous.

Pat: Is this Adrian told you? **Larry:** Yes. **Pat:** Why would he say it is dangerous? **Larry:** I don't want people to know. **Pat:** Who doesn't want people to know? **Larry:** The Government, the Air Force. **Pat:** Who is in control of it? **Larry:** Not us. **Pat:** Do you know who did? Adrian tell you? **Larry:** Yes. **Pat:** Tell me Larry: Those things maybe? **Larry:** I don't know.

Pat: How was it brought there? How was it taken there? **Larry:** In a car. **Pat:** Where? **Larry:** In a car. **Pat:** By whom? **Larry:** These people. **Pat:** What people? The people you described earlier? **Larry:** No. **Pat:** Regular people? **Larry:** Yes, not Air Force. **Pat:** What any branch of the service? **Larry:** No not that I know of. **Pat:** What are your feelings on what Adrian told you? I want you to tell me. **Larry:** Well it is hard to believe and sometimes it isn't. He says I was down there and I don't remember it. **Pat:** What was the day that Adrian was down there? You do know. **Larry:** 81. **Pat:** 1981? Do you know the month? **Larry:** January. **Pat:** What about the day? **Larry:** New Year's Day? **Larry:** I don't know. **Pat:** You were down there the same time? Did he tell you? **Larry:** Three days.

Pat: Three days, when? **Larry:** I don't know about that. **Pat:** Was it 1980 or 1981? **Larry:** 81. **Pat:** You don't know if it was the same time? **Larry:** No, same time. **Pat:** I want you to take another deep breath. Relax. Allow all these senses to fade away. Allow your memory to relax. I am going to count from 3 to 1 and when you hear the number one you will be going back into time.

December 29, 1980, 3…back 2… back 1. **Larry:** I have the day off. I went to see a football game. Not too much to do.

Pat: Did you see Adrian today? **Larry:** No, he's got a girlfriend I think he's with. He helps in changing the rooms.

Pat: When was the last time you talked to Adrian? **Larry:** Four days. **Pat:** What happened four days ago? **Larry:** Nothing. **Pat:** Ok, and nothing happening today? – Nothing specific? **Larry:** No. **Pat:** Take a nice deep breath and relax. I am now going to count to 3 to 1. The next time you hear the number one you will be backwards in time and it will be December 27, 1980. Your memory will be very sharp. Your visions will be very clear. 3 back, back 2… and 1. I want you to tell me where you are and what you are doing.

Larry: I'm back in the room with Barry. We have some records and Greg's there. **Pat:** Who else is there? **Larry:** I might go to London and Holland. **Pat:** Just for a vacation? **Larry:** A weekend. **Pat:** Who is going with you? **Larry:** Barry. **Pat:** Continue.

Larry: I see a movie on Base. **Pat:** Go ahead. Who else is there? **Larry:** Where? **Pat:** The Base. **Larry:** Just Greg and Barry and myself. That is it. **Pat:** OK, so what are you doing? Continue. **Larry:** We went to the club but we are going to see a movie at night. **Pat:** Did you go? **Larry:** Yes. **Pat:** Tell me about it. Then what? **Larry:** We went to a party. A place called The Loft. **Pat:** Where is it? **Larry:** near Wickham Market. **Pat:** Where is that? **Larry:** Five miles from the Base. **Pat:** Continue. What happens after the movie, after The Loft? **Larry:** That is it. **Pat:** You went back to the home. **Larry:** Yes. We drove. **Pat:** What happened?

Larry: Something happened to the car. **Pat:** What happened to it? **Larry:** It went off the road or something? **Pat:** Who was driving? **Larry:** Chris. **Pat:** Who else was with you? **Larry:** Steve, the new kid Dean. **Pat:** What happened when the car went off the road? **Larry:** It slid. **Pat:** Why on what? **Larry:** On black ice. **Pat:** On black ice? **Larry** Yes.

Pat: What happened then? **Larry:** I was stuck. **Pat:** Continue: **Larry:** We pushed on the road. **Pat:** OK. **Larry:** Went back to the Base. **Pat:** What time is all this happening? **Larry:** 2.30. **Pat:** What happened now? **Larry:** We went to bed. **Pat:** Take a deep breath and just relax. Larry, I just want you to relax now. I will be counting from one to five. When you hear the number 5 you will be wide awake and full of energy. With no aches or pains you will remember what your subconscious can relate to your conscious mind without giving any type of problems, any kind of detriment of any nature. You will remember exactly what you can handle.1… 2…3…4…5 **Larry:** That is weird. That is the strangest thing. There is no drug that does this stuff, I'll tell you guys. **Pat:** How long do you think you were under? Almost two hours. **Larry:** Really? I feel like I was really there.

Adrian Bustinza – interviewed by Georgina Bruni in 1998

Adrian Bustinza has recently (in 2015) come forward to tell of his experience at the airbase. Many people have suggested that this is the first time he has done this in over 35 years, in order to set the record straight. However, in 1998, he was interviewed by Georgina Bruni. In her excellent book, '**You can't tell the People**,' Adrian asked what had taken place during the interrogations and where they took place.

Adrian:

"I was debriefed in Major Zickler's office the first time, but later I remember being picked up in a car. I know this is going to sound like science fiction, but these men were your typical 'men in black' – black suits, white collar and tie, 'Rayban' type dark glasses. It was very scary and confusing, because I don't know where they were taking me."

He was asked where he was taken to.

Adrian:

"I was taken to the security area near where the metal bunkers are. I think it was the photo lab, but I can't remember leaving it. We went underground, down some stairs into a tunnel.

We walked through the tunnels and there were light bulbs hanging on the side of the walls. I was taken into a small room and ordered to sit on a wooden chair which was very uncomfortable. I was told to look directly ahead, neither left nor right, but straight ahead. It was difficult, because someone was shining a light bulb in front of my face and it was blinding me. I was really scared and confused and thought I had done something wrong; I remember thinking where is my staff sergeant, where is my lieutenant, why am I the only one here going through this.

Bentwaters Cold War museum

They asked me repetitive questions. They told me I would later be debriefed by my superiors. I was. They asked me the same questions over and over again. I wasn't allowed to ask any questions and they threatened me by mentioning some government code. I told them I worked for the government too. They told me I mustn't talk to no one about this. A tall man – I could only see his shadow – moved forward and said, 'Bullets are cheap, a dime a dozen'. It was very scary."

Adrian was asked what kind of questions was put to him

"They asked me what I saw. I told them. They asked me if anyone had filmed it, was anyone taking pictures of it. They asked me who I had talked to, who I had told. At about that time everything was fuzzy but I remember the two men who had picked me up, led me into the room, then left. There were two or three men in the room but I couldn't see their faces, because of the bright light shining at me. I could only see shadows, but the man asking the questions wore a black overall type uniform."

Bullets are cheap and a dime a dozen

"Forever, they just kept asking repetitive questions. They told me I had been chasing lights. I kept saying 'No we saw something else' but they kept repeating 'You don't get the picture do you? You saw a light and that light was the lighthouse beacon'. I said 'No, it wasn't a beacon and that's the moment the guy came over to tell us 'bullets are cheap and a dime a dozen'. At that stage I just wanted to get out of there, so I said 'Ok, it was a beacon'. They said 'Let's go over this again'. They wanted to make sure I knew it was a beacon."

Asked to describe the tunnels

"They were wide enough to get a truck through. There were tunnels all over the Base, but we weren't supposed to talk about them. They would take you from point A to point B; they were accessible through the security area. As far as I know they had been built in case of nuclear attack or for an emergency. They were escape routes. I know where they all led to."

After the interrogations

"I was upset after being treated so bad. I mean I was a sergeant with the Unites States Air Force. I considered going AWOL. The only comfort I got was when Major Zickler called us into his office and briefed us. He said that any information we gave would be confidential. I felt comfortable with him and my Lieutenant. Not one of us would talk about it afterwards. Sometimes we

would get ridiculed, guys going on about UFOs. We had to take it, we couldn't discuss it. There was a gag order on that incident and we were told that what we saw was a lighthouse beacon. There were many nightmares after that."

Nick Pope

"This is the infamous "The Air Force, with a stick" hypnosis session, where – assuming the transcript is accurate – we're led to believe that various USAF personnel are using a stick to examine a landed UFO. What can one say, politely, about any of this? There's no scientific consensus about the nature of hypnosis (is it an altered state of consciousness, as some believe, or simply a focused state of mind?) let alone any consensus that regression hypnosis can reliably recover suppressed memories. Indeed, many believe that through a process known as confabulation, regression hypnosis can distort genuine memories and create false memories. And can we even be sure that Larry Warren was hypnotized at all – might he simply have been playing along, giving the UFO researchers the story he thought they wanted to hear, cementing his position in the narrative?"

18th August – A visit to the MOD

On Thursday, 18th August 1983, Dot Street, Brenda Butler and Jenny Randles, met up with DS8 representative – Pam Titchmarsh, at the MOD, Whitehall, in London.

Brenda: We were asked to sign a document

"After a meeting with our publisher, at 2pm, we left there at 3.30pm and went to the MOD in Whitehall. We spoke to Pam Titchmarsh. Jenny did most of the talking, asking Pam questions about Radar and UFOs. Dot showed Pam some of the documents we had in our possession from The Deputy Base Commander, Charles Halt, to the MOD, which had been passed on to the USA Government. Pam said she didn't know how the USA Government had received these documents, as the MOD had not sent them.

The meeting went on for two hours. We were all talking about the Rendlesham Forest case. Pam said the MOD had checked it out, as far as they could, and found no case to proceed any further with their investigations, as they found that whatever it was, was no threat to our security. She said she didn't know much about the case, as she had only been there (at the MOD) for six months, so she probably only knew what she had been told. When Jenny cross-examined her, she kept repeating the same thing. She said basically, the MOD hadn't really investigated it, as they had been satisfied there was no reason to suspect that whatever happened was of no threat to any of our bases. She told us she had no knowledge of any radar tapes or radar traces. We were asked to sign a document.. Dot said, 'No'. Jenny and I said we would, if they could prove that what happened would harm our defence system. They couldn't, so we wouldn't sign anything."

September 1983 *Daily Star* reports (inaccurately) on the incident

'Spaceship Riddle Deepens' They claim that Colonel Halt saw bright lights and a space machine hovering on legs at Woodbridge Suffolk in December 1980 following the sighting of red ball of light in the sky.

1st October – Saucer-shaped object seen over Suffolk

A similar report was obtained from a qualified pilot and nurse – Melanie Hartley, of Bury St. Edmunds – who was driving home on 1st October 1983, at 11pm, near the village of Fornham All Saints, Suffolk, with her two daughters in the back – Emma (15) and Natasha (12) – when their curiosity became aroused after seeing a bright light reflecting off the bonnet. When they looked upwards, they saw a saucer-shaped object, *"the length of three double-decker buses hovering in the sky"*.

2nd October – *News of the World* account of incident.

'S OF THE WORLD

PLUS Sunday

STILL ONLY 25p
BEST VALUE FOR MONEY

BRITAIN'S BIGGEST SELLING SUNDAY NEWSPAPER   No. 7,291

- **Colonel's top secret report tells the facts**
- **Mystery craft in exploding wall of colour**
- **Animals flee from strange glowing object**

UFO LANDS IN SUFFOLK

And that's OFFICIAL

A UFO has landed in Britain— and that staggering fact has been officially confirmed.

Despite a massive cover-up, News of the World investigators have proof that the mysterious craft came to earth in a red ball of light at 3 a.m. on December 27, 1980.

It happened in a pine forest called Tangham Wood just half a mile from the United States Air Force base at RAF Woodbridge, in Suffolk.

An American airman who was there told us there were three beings in silver space suits aboard the craft.

Farm cattle and forest animals ran berserk as the spacecraft, a sloping silver dish about 20ft across its base, silently glided to land in a blinding explosion of lights.

About 200 military and civilian personnel, British

NEWS OF THE WORLD INVESTIGATES

By KEITH BEABEY

over the base by a number of airmen.

It sounds like aliens coming to earth in the film Close Encounters, but the PROOF that an Unidentified Flying Object landed

two-meter hitch. It illuminated the entire forest with a white light.

The object itself had a pulsing red light on top and a bank of blue lights underneath. The object was

appeared elliptical through an 8-12 power lens.

They then turned to full circles. The objects in the north remained in the sky for an hour or more. The object to the south was visible for two or three hours and beamed down a stream of lights from time to time.

Numerous people, including himself, witnessed these events, Colonel Halt concluded.

Last week he declined to say anything further

toward the department.

3. Later in the night a red sun-like light was seen through the trees. It moved about and pulsed. At one point it appeared to throw off glowing particles and then broke into five separate white objects and then disappeared. Immediately thereafter, three star-like objects were noticed in the sky, two objects to the north and one to the south, all of which were about 10° off the horizon. The objects moved rapidly in sharp angular movements and displayed red, green and blue lights. The objects to the north appeared to be elliptical through an 8-12 power lens. They then turned to full circles. The objects to the north remained in the sky for an hour or more. The object to the south was visible for two or three hours and beamed down a stream of light from time to time. Numerous people, including the undersigned, witnessed the activities in paragraphs 2 and 3.

CHARLES I. HALT, Lt Col, USAF
Deputy Base Commander

EVIDENCE DETAIL from Lt. Col. Charles Halt's confidential report about the sighting of "unexplained lights" and a strange glowing object that lit up the forest

NO HOAX SAYS THE

3rd October – *The Times* – 'UFO sighting in Suffolk is verified'

Forestry Commission worker Vincent Thurkettle was also interviewed by the *Times* about the incident. He is shown with Charles Halt during a visit to the Forest, in 2000. (Following page).

THE TIMES MONDAY OCTOBER 3 1983

Earthly beings: Mr Vincent Thurkettle and his dog at the forest site of the Christmas UFO "landing".

Down to earth approach to alien visitors

From Alan Hamilton, Woodbridge

The mission was to seek a close encounter, preferably of the third kind, but any kind would do.

The place was a vast clearing deep in the 10,000 acres of Aldewood Forest, Suffolk, where, according to yesterday's *News of the World*, an alien spacecraft landed at Christmas, 1980, flew among the trees, left imprints on the ground, and vanished only when the United States Air Force from Woodbridge base, half a mile away, came out to investigate.

Witnesses, according to the paper, have since greatly elaborated on the event, speaking of beings in silvery suits who practised levitation.

The first being encountered yesterday was clad in cordroy trousers and black wellingtons. He came, he said, not from outer space, but the Forestry Commission. His name was not the Mekon, but Vincent Thurkettle.

The second being closely resembled a collie dog, and was too busy chasing sticks to levitate.

"This is the site", said the first being, gesturing around a rough acreage of stumps and teigs. "When the UFO is supposed to have landed the whole area was covered by Corsican pines 75ft tall and only 10ft apart. It would have taken a fair feat of navigation to get among that lot."

He pointed to indentations in the ground that might have been made by the feet of a far-travelled craft. "Rabbits", he said. "They dig for roots."

But, surely, the searchers reported burn marks on the surrounding trees and radiation in the ground?

"The burns were the marks we put on the trees for felling. And as for radiation, a craft from outer space is going to use a far more sophisticated form of propulsion."

A third being, who said he was David Boast, and a gamekeeper, was quoted in the *News of the World* as saying how cattle panicked near his house on the night in question. "There are no cattle anywhere near here", he told me.

But surely, the US Air Force had taken the incident seriously. The base commander's report spoke of star-like objects in the sky, and a red light in the trees, and the report was now with the Pentagon?

"The Americans here will jump at anything," the first being said. "They come out regularly at night to investigate lights in the forest."

But why has it all surfaced now? "I think you will find", the first being said, "That a gullible earthling is just about to publish a book about it".

Suddenly, the second being levitated. But it was only to catch a stick.

Vincent Thurkettle, Charles Halt and Ian Ridpath

3rd October – Dot Street intends to travel to the United States

The *Evening Star* newspaper – *'US visit to probe sighting'* – informed its readers about the pending visit to the United States by Dot Street, who had been invited by the Citizens against Secrecy to attend the UFO Conference in Lincoln, Nebraska. They showed the 'turtle back UFO' illustration, along with a quote about *'little silver men'.*

5th October – *Stars and Stripes* – 'British Paper reports UFO landing near RAF base'

Stars and Stripes
October 11, 1983 Page 9

Bentwaters 'UFO' simply a lighthouse, paper says

LONDON (AP) — A newspaper's claim that a UFO landed in Britain in a ball of red light was dismissed by a rival publication Sunday, saying that the light was from a lighthouse.

The mass-circulation News of the World claimed a week ago that the UFO had three beings inside it in silver suits when it came down in a forest near RAF Bentwaters in Suffolk in eastern England, at the end of 1980.

The tabloid Sunday People sent a reporter to the site and quoted Vince Thurkettle, an officer for the state-run Forestry Commission, as saying: "The light from the Orford Ness lighthouse, on the coast, can be seen through the trees. From the hill where the site is, it appears to be practically at ground level and, of course, it flashes.

"As you walk toward it, because of the lie of the land, it disappears."

The News of the World said a report by USAF Lt. Col. Charles Halt on the UFO landing supported what some patrolmen had seen and that his report was suppressed in a coverup.

The Sunday People quoted a USAF spokesman as saying that Halt's report was based solely on what the patrolmen had reported they saw on Dec. 27, 1980, and it was never classified as secret.

The News of the World returned to the story in its latest issue Sunday and said that, since it published the first report, people from all over Britain have reported UFO sightings.

LANDING SITE— UFO hunters Brenda (left) and Dorothy at Tangham Wood, Suffolk, where the craft touched town

couldn't se any windows.

There were three groups of about four security men each circling the thing. I could see our shadows on the craft. As we walked, they moved. But when we stopped, the shadows seemed to take another pose. It was weird.

Suddenly, a green light came on at the top of the spaceship.

It moved down the sides of the craft until it reached our heads then bounced from one to the o'her along the side. Just like the ball bounces in a video game.

SHADOWS

Then I realised the spaceship was inhabited. There were beings aboard.

I didn't see them because I was on the wrong side of the craft. But others did.

They said there were three, and they were wearing silver suits. I had a strange feeling and seemed to black out.

The next thing I knew, it was about 5 a.m. and I was waking up, lying half across my bunk. I still had my uniform on and was up to my knees in mud.

To this day, I don't know how I got back to he barracks, or what happened to me after I watched the green light bounce off our shadows.

My room-mate said I'd been brought into the room by the people — he

didn't know who — and just dumped on thet bed.

Later that day, myself and several of the guys who had been at the field were given the once-over with a Geiger counter but we were never told why or what the results were. He assumed the Air Force must have thought the ship was radioactive.

We were all called to the base security office at Bentwaters and told what we'd seen had been classified top secret.

We were made to sign official USAF documents saying we understood that if we talked we could be punished.

Several civilians were doing all the talking. They said if we ever told the story, no one would believe us.

One guy added that if we did talk, then bullets were cheap.

I thought: this guy is actually threatening our lives. He obviously meant it.

Art Wallace — that isn't his real name — was honourably discharged from the USAF in June, 1981. He is now aged 22.

COPY

If named, he could receive a prison sentence for revealing what he saw.

Attempts to penetrate the wall of silence surrounding the mystery have been made by two Suffolk UFO spotters, Mrs Brenda Cutler, 38, of Leiston, and Mrs Dorothy Street, of Oulton Broad, near Lowestoft.

Brenda said: "We met a wall of secrecy."

But they linked up with American UFO expert

Harry Faucett, who questioned Art Wallace and obta ned a copy of the report on the incident by Lieutenant Colonel Halt USAF commander at RAF Woodbridge.

The colonel later spoke to Brenda and Dorothy. "He was up in his office" said Brenda.

He was upset because the report had leaked out, but then became more helpful.

"He even pointed out on our map the place he said the craft had landed.

"He said a security man tried climbing on to the craft but it moved away," added Brenda.

At the Defence Ministry in London, a spokesman refused to unravel the mystery. He told the News of the World:

"We are aware of the report, but this is a matter for the USAF, not us."

Yes, it is true

UFO expert, Larry Fawcett, a police lieutenant in Connecticut, says: "I am sure an alien flying craft did land in that forest.

"Despite intensive questioning by a number of people — ncluding myself, a professional policeman — Airman Wallace has never been caught out in

a lie or a change of story.

"We have also corroboration of his account."

Lieut. Fawcett, 44, a chief of the American organisation Citizens Against UFO Secrecy, added: "Both the British and American military know an awful lot more about this.

"You can't hide the truth for ever."

6th October – 'Suffolk UFO was no threat to security'

This was the headlines in the *Evening Star* on the 6th October 1983. Fuelled by a statement made in the Commons, the previous night, when Armed Forces Minister – Mr John Bradley, disclosed *"the incidents at the Suffolk airbase was just one of 1,400 unexplained incidents recorded in the last three years and that none of them posed any security threat and that none of them had been backed by radar contacts."* The paper also disclosed that Dot Street told them that according to a document in her possession claiming that over 200 military and civilian witnesses were present.

7th October – *Woodbridge Reporter* newspaper

They covered the story again and showed the 'turtle back' UFO illustration, accompanied by the quote: 'Little silver men in spaceship in Rendlesham Forest'.

10th October – Three strange lights seen over Shingle Street

Mr John. Button (40) of Coronation Avenue, Hollesley, contacted Brenda Butler and Ron West of the East Anglian Paranormal Association, wishing to tell them about three strange lights he and his wife Sandra had seen, along with their three children – Stephen (16) Sharon (13) and Darren (9) – at 7.45pm on 10th October 1983.

"While walking towards the grocery van, I noticed three large white and red lights (forming a triangular shape in the sky) over the treetops, in the Shingle Street direction; they seemed to be stationary, and were making this strange humming noise."

The driver of the van switched his engine off, so that they could hear any noise – there wasn't any.

Eventually the centre light dimmed, two or three times, and then the three lights rose up into the sky, passing overhead as they headed away towards the direction of the nearby USAF Base, 20 minutes later.

Another witness was a neighbour – Mary Potter, who said:

"As they did so, we could see small red and green lights and make out three triangular shapes. They made a weird humming noise as they went over us."

(Sources: Personal interview/*East Anglian Daily Times*, 12.10.1983 – 'Strange lights near Airbase')

Eerie lights forming a triangle seen

Another witness was local baker – Ron Macro, who was out on his rounds, when he saw:

"…three eerie lights, forming a triangle, rise up over nearby trees and stand still in the sky for several minutes, before moving away."

10th October – *BBC Breakfast Time* … It was the lighthouse!

On the 10th October, Ian Ridpath wrote to RAF Woodbridge and told them he had been to the forest with a *BBC TV* film crew on the 6th and videoed a pulsating light among the trees, which turned out to be the Orford Ness Lighthouse. The film and conclusions was subject of a broadcast by *BBC Breakfast Time* TV on the 7th October.

11th October – *Stars & Stripes* 'UFO simply a lighthouse'

11th October – *East Anglian Daily Times* 'Base visit for man in UFO mystery'

October – Three mysterious lights seen in the sky, car engine cuts out

Leiston resident – Deborah Foreman – was driving past Hollesley with her friend, Pauline Osborn, when the headlights on the car inexplicably dimmed and the engine cut out, following the appearance of mysterious lights in the sky.

According to Brenda Butler, at least eight people saw these lights; they included Mr William Wright from Alderton, a few miles away, who was preparing for a fishing trip, at 8.15pm, when he saw:

"…three large lights in the sky forming a triangle, moving towards me over the sea. As they passed overhead, I saw a red tail light behind each main light".

(Source: Personal interview)

Possible explanation by Bentwaters Airbase

Captain Kathy McCollom, of The Public Affairs Department at Bentwaters Airbase, suggested that they might have seen a C130 Hercules transport aircraft, due at that time, on Friday evening.

(Source: As above/Personal interviews/*News of the World*, 25.10.1983 – 'UFO Mystery continues'/*Ipswich Evening Star* – 'A flying triangle of fear')

6th November – Dot and Jenny travel to the United States

On the 6th November 1983, Jenny and Dot met at a London hotel. They spent the evening discussing various UFO related matters with a number of other investigators. The next morning, they caught a flight to Chicago. Rather charmingly, bearing in mind the way in which air flights have changed, Jenny, in her own meticulous manner, 'paints a picture' of Dot exercising her interviewing techniques on-board with the other passengers. Dot even brought the pilot back (we presumed she meant the co-pilot) and introduced him to Jenny, followed by a conversation about UFOs.

One cannot even visualise such a thing happening now. Jenny confessed she felt some trepidation, *"after realising that at 35,000ft, if something went wrong, how he would get back to the cockpit! I was not reassured to learn that a computer was flying the 747, especially after finding out that the in-flight movie was War Games, which was about how a nuclear holocaust was nearly caused by a computer."*

After a safe landing, the couple made their way to the home of Allen and Mimi Hynek at Evanston (headquarters for the Center for UFO Studies) – what a privilege that must have been!

Jenny Randles:

"I felt pleased to have discovered that even the vastly efficient Dr. Hynek and CUFOS have data retrieval problems; their case reports and materials tend to form lots of little piles on stairs, in boxes, and in any little nook and cranny they can find."

UFO conference at the University of Lincoln, Nebraska

At the conference, they met up with Larry Fawcett (he had obtained the Colonel Halt memo from the MOD, under the Freedom of Information Act) and Linda Moulton Howe. Lectures were given by Allen Hynek, Budd Hopkins and John Scheusler (Cash/ Landrum case, from Texas) who showed photographs of the gruesome effects of radiation sickness, caused by a UFO.

After the conference, Dot flew on to Connecticut with Larry Fawcett and Jenny headed for the University of Boulder – home of the Condon Report, where she spoke to some of the scientists involved – then back to Chicago, where she spent time with Jerome Clark, at the office of *FATE* magazine.

Jenny:

"I had travelled over 13,000 miles and over 4,000 by road and rail, but it was well worth it and I would do it again like a shot!"

(Source: *BUFORA Bulletin* of February 1984, The Freeway to American UFOLOGY)

Larry Fawcett

6 NOV 1983

News of the World, November 8, 19

A BUG-EYED ALIEN MEETS AIR CHIEF

From BOB SMITH in New York

AMAZING new facts about the night a UFO came to Britain have been revealed by the U.S. airman who saw the craft land.

The secrets were locked away in 22-year-old Art Wallace's mind. But following hypnosis, he has now given us:

● A full description of the aliens who manned the ship;

● Details of how a senior American officer actually communicated with one of the beings;

● Evidence that the U.S. Air Force may have helped repair the damaged craft.

The UFO landed near the American base at RAF Woodbridge, Suffolk, in December, 1980.

But the close encounter was kept secret—until last month when the massive cover-up was exposed by the News of the World.

Since Wallace – now a civilian back in the US – revealed to us what he saw that terrifying night, his life has been threatened.

Recently, he received a

UFO-FEVER STRIKES AGAIN

phone call at his home and an unidentified man told him: "If you don't shut your mouth then it will be shut for you."

This follows a frightening meeting he had with several men he believes were from the CIA, during which he was warned that bullets are cheap.

During his session with two top hypnotists, Wallace this is not his real name – recalled and only considered his original story, but made some astonishing new revelations.

SKIN

He now says he remembers seeing a face-to-face meeting between one of the aliens and the officer who was in charge of the U.S. base.

The alien was between three and four feet tall, with a very large head and huge saucer-like eyes that grew much larger every so often.

It appeared to have greyish skin and was wearing what looked like a dark jumpsuit and the outline of its figure glowed.

Wallace was unable to hear any voices as Wing Commander – now Brigadier General Gordon

ALIEN: Artist's impression

Williams and the being communicated with much hand waving and pointing at the strange triangular craft.

He said the four aliens appeared to be floating just above the surface of the ground and, at one point, became alarmed and formed themselves into a defensive line.

One of them floated over the UFO near to where Wallace was standing and he blacked out. The next thing he remembers, he was back in his barracks.

Wallace believes the craft needed repairs after hitting a tree.

CRAFT

He was told later by some of his pals on the base that a U.S. transport plane flew in from Germany just hours after the UFO landed and was immediately surrounded by armed military police.

A package from the plane was put in a jeep which then drove off towards the landing site at Tangham Wood. Later that day, the craft was gone.

The base's deputy commander Lt-Colonel Charles Halt, admits there is "one hell of a lot more" to come out.

Road to mystery

A NIGHT out at bingo ended in a chilling encounter with a UFO for three women and a schoolgirl last week.

As they drove home to Rippingale, Lincolnshire, they spotted a strange light in a field.

"We stopped and got out

of the car and stood there flabbergasted," said Mrs Jenny Clarke, 31.

"This object was literally dormant in the sky—it didn't move or anything.

"Then all of a sudden it started its engines and circled round us, before going away into the distance."

25th November

Donald Moreland – the RAF Liaison Officer at Woodbridge Air Force Base – wrote to Mrs Pamela Titchmarsh at Defence Secretariat Division 8a, at the MOD:

"Dear Pam,

Thank you for your letter and enclosure concerning the unexplained lights seen at Woodbridge during December 1980.

The incident is almost three years old and no one remembers it clearly. All we have is Lt. Colonel Halt's letter, dated 13th January 1981. A study of this letter shows that the first sighting was at 0300hrs on 27th December 1980, and that the second sighting was on the night of the 29th December 1980. I have no knowledge of any local constabulary involvement."

(Source: MOD declassified files)

10th December – BUFORA meeting in London

Also on the 10th December 1983, Jenny Randles chaired a BUFORA debate in London, during which Ian Ridpath gave his version of the events, as did Brenda Butler, Dot Street and Harry Harris.

Jenny:

"Needless to say, none of them were convinced that the Orford Ness Lighthouse (which has sat peacefully on the coast, five miles from Rendlesham Forest, for many a year) could suddenly have decided to take off on a little adventure and cavort around in the woods and bamboozle half the Air Force."

UPDATE on 'RAF scrambles fighter aircraft over Suffolk in 1978'

Staff Sergeant Thomas. Wharton of the 91st Fighter Squadron (stationed at RAF Bentwaters, Suffolk, United Kingdom, between January 1977 and 1980) was to still ponder on what it was that he and his companion saw in April 1978. Still shrouded in mystery, was there any connection with the extraordinary event that took place a few years later, in December 1980, at RAF Woodbridge, this is something we will probably never know!

Sgt. Tom Wharton
F-4D Phantom

Thomas:

"Strange, but that whole experience is still with me like it happened yesterday – strange, crazy stuff, to say the least. I just felt the need to share it. I know many folks won't believe it (thinking I am whacked), but at least Mike and I know it happened – that was one strange evening.

I was selected as one of the Twelve Outstanding Airmen of the United States Air Force in 1987. It was (is) still an honor I will never forget, I was based at Luke AFB. I and eleven other members of the USAF from around the globe were selected as the top managers and technicians in

Tom receives the Outstanding Airman Award in 1987

our fields. *We were all 'wined and dined' for a week at our Nations Capital, Washington, D.C where I was intro-duced to President Ronald Regan."*

Yet another witness to the sighting of a UFO, followed by what appeared to have been a response from the RAF over the British mainland, was Janet Bull, a young girl from Essex who told of seeing RAF jets apparently chasing an object across the sky in 1978.

She estimated the height as being 5000ft and the distance between her and the diamond shaped object and the two RAF jets as being half a mile away from her. In view of the importance of what Thomas had witnessed along with Mike Bugno we examined our UFO files and came across the following incidents of interest for that month.

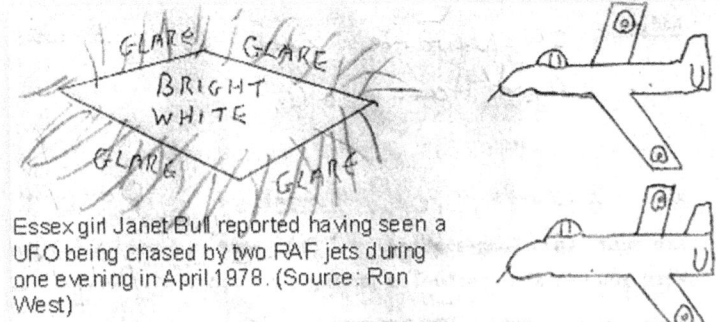

Essex girl Janet Bull reported having seen a UFO being chased by two RAF jets during one evening in April 1978. (Source: Ron West)

Cigar-shaped UFO seen

At 7.40pm on 5th April 1978, *"a gold coloured cigar-shaped ob-ject, showing red, green and blue, flashing lights on its side"*, with what looked like two windows in the side of the UFO, was seen hovering over a field, making a humming noise, by two boys from the Hawley Estate, Farnborough.

Bedminster Bristol UFO chased by a couple!

At 8.35pm, a yellow and red circular object – the size of a golf ball in the air from the ground – was seen almost stationary in the sky, over Bedminster, Bristol, moving slightly up and down, and from side-to-side, by a couple who gave chase in their car but lost sight of it.

When they returned home, they were shocked to see it back in its original position. About an hour later it moved away out of sight.

At 8.45pm, Maureen Slater – mother of the two boys – rushed back into the garden, with her sons, after the UFO was seen again – this time much higher in the sky. Using the football field floodlights as yardsticks of measurement, Maureen was able to estimate it was now a few hundred feet off the ground.

"It was spinning around showing flashing red, green, and blue lights, shooting off whitish sparks as it did so. I was scared, thinking the Russians may have sent it over here. I've been to Air Shows, at Farnborough, but never seen anything like that before.

Just after 9pm, it flew away towards the south-east and that was the last we ever saw of it."

Seven miles away

At 9.10pm, school caretaker Peter Inwood, who had seen service with The Royal Observer Corps, during the Second World War, was just about to pull the curtains together at his home, in Ash near Aldershot (some seven miles away from the previous sighting) when his attention was caught by a glittering object in the night sky, totally unlike any aircraft lights he normally saw passing over.

Like Mrs Slater, he ran outside and saw an object – *'electric blue in colour, which changed rapidly to red, white, green and gold, appearing to jump from side-to-side in the sky'* – and shouted for his wife and daughters – Jacqueline (18), and Christine (15) – to come outside and have a look, before dialling 999.

Police attend

Police Constable Alan Craggs, with previous service in the RAF, arrived (who was tragically killed in a car accident, some years later) and studied the object moving up and down, forming a *'cross'* in the sky for over 20 minutes, before telephoning the Police HQ, at Guildford, to explain what was happening. They advised him that the sighting would be passed to West Drayton.

At 10.05pm Mr Douglas Cooper, his wife, daughter, and son-in-law, sighted a stationary *'light'*, motionless in the sky for approximately five minutes, until it moved overhead, allowing them to see:

". . . a circular shape, with a dome on top, emitting a bright light through 'portholes'. In the centre were three coloured lights, forming a triangle, set into what appeared to be a very sooty underside. It flew silently away over a block of flats and disappeared from sight."

UFO over Staffordshire

Five minutes later, Mr J. Moss – a Surveyor and Town Planning consultant of Hartshill, Staffordshire – sighted a *'bright white light'* in the sky, approaching from the direction of Longton. As it came closer, the light increased in size and revealed a cluster of red lights above it, before passing over the Basford area and disappearing at an estimated speed of 500mph. and height of 8,000 feet.

(Source: Tony Pace, BUFORA)

Did this UFO land in Ashdown Forest?

At 10.30pm, a woman living in Clockhouse Lane, Nutley, on the edge of Ashdown Forest, East Grinstead, Sussex, contacted the authorities, after having seen, *'a ball of fire'* descending through the sky, over Kingstanding, then make a sharp turn and disappear into the forest, accompanied by flames and smoke. As the forest land caught fire, the Fire Service attended and found two *'seats of fire,'* which were extinguished; the first one, involving a spread of approximately one acre, the second being about three acres.

Received a visit by a USAF Colonel

At 11.30pm, Peter Inwood and his family, who had been watching the UFO for nearly two and-a-half hours, decided to go to bed.

Following considerable publicity given to the incident, Peter received a visit from two men in civilian clothes; one of whom showed him an ID card, identifying him as a Colonel in the Unites States Air Force; the other, a Government Official.

After tape-recording an interview with him, they left. Peter was to later express great regrets of having reported this matter in the first place, after being made the subject of ridicule.

A search conducted by a number of police officers with Geiger counters, including a dog handler, later that morning, in Ashdown Forest, revealed nothing untoward.

CLOSE ENCOUNTER
F THE REAL KIND

Calling all U.F.O. hunters...police cars in the forest

Police hunt

By JACK HILL and GILL MARTIN

Triangular lights seen in Staffordshire – 5th April 1978

Staffordshire motorist – Roy Twemlow – was driving to Leek Road, Weston Coyney, on the late evening of 5th April 1978, when he noticed a bright light ahead of him. Upon his arrival home, he picked up a pair of binoculars and, bringing them into focus, saw:

> "…three lights in the form of a triangle, although no connecting shape could be discerned. The lights began to move; an orange light appeared and began to flash, before swooping down to the right of the house, and disappeared in the direction of Ash Bank."

We wrote to the MOD, asking them if they had received any reports of UFOs sighted over the Hampshire/Sussex areas, during the early part of April 1978. They replied in the negative.

Appeal made in local newspaper

We then placed an appeal in the local newspaper, *The Aldershot News*, hoping that somebody who had information about this event would contact us. Two people did. One was Mr Roger Bradgate – a fireman at the time, but now Officer-in-Charge of Crowborough Fire Station, Sussex:

> "The fires were extinguished by the normal practice of beaters and hose reels, using Forestry fire fighting appliances. The suggestion that the fires had been started by a UFO caused much hilarity amongst the personnel attending this incident. To my knowledge, no radiation was picked-up on the Geiger counters used by the Police. I believe the fires were probably caused

by Army personnel, using flares and thunder flashes in the forest, as that particular area was regularly used by the Military on Exercise from Crowborough Army Camp, understanding this was not the first occasion that fires had been started in this manner."

Extensive coverage to the incident was given in the *Daily Express* (17.4.1978) – 'Close Encounter of the Real Kind' – which included a number of photographs of the police officers concerned, combing the area at first light.

The MOD suggested the fire may have been the result of accidental discharge of flares, used by soldiers on Exercise.

(Source: UFOSIS/Isle of Wight UFO Society)

Flying disc over Hampshire – 6th April 1978

At 12.30am on 6th April 1978, Barry Woodhouse – an employee of RAF Farnborough – was driving back from Bordon to Farnborough, along the Farnham by-pass, on a clear, still, night. As he headed for the 'Shepherd and Flock' roundabout, with a clear view of the well lit road, traffic being sparse, he noticed a flash of movement ahead, at lamp-post height, just behind two cars in front of him, some way ahead, which he took to be a bat, flying towards him, but was amazed to see:

"…a metallic 'disc' with two stubby wings – a classic 'flying saucer', heading towards me (about the size of a family car) travelling at a speed of 200mph. It was so low it almost touched the top of the lights. Within three or five seconds it had gone, passing across the road in front of me, followed by a rush of air."

(Source: Omar Fowler, SIGAP)

Egg shaped UFO over Bristol

At 8.30pm on 6th April 1978, an *'illuminated egg-shaped object'*, with bright colour changing lights on its onside, was seen hovering in the SSW of the sky over Downend, Bristol, by an ex-RAF Radar technician and other residents, and according to UFO researcher Peter Tate, was the subject of great excitement in the neighbourhood.

Later, the same day, Penny Sweetman (13), and her friend, Monica Mitchell (14), from *Churt – a small village, three miles south of Farnham – were out walking, close to the village, at 9pm, when their attention was attracted by a number of coloured lights, flashing fairly low down in the sky, which they thought might have been a helicopter, until they saw:

"…a huge oval glowing object – metallic in appearance, showing multi coloured lights. We watched it for four or five minutes, noticing two red lights on the top right-hand side, two white lights, (top left), with two green lights situated at the bottom centre of the craft, flashing much faster than the other two lights. The whole 'body' seemed to be shimmering silver in colour and hovered, quite stationary, in complete silence. Above the top rim of the UFO were what looked like a line of windows – not like portholes, but rather like insects eyes?"

*Churt is a village and civil parish in the borough of Waverley in Surrey, England. It is on the A287 road between Hindhead and Farnham. A clustered settlement set in areas acting as its green buffers, which include the Devil's Jumps. Churt is also home to a fantastic Sculpture Park which contains 600 interesting sculptures including this rather bizarre one "Homage to Matisse (The Dance)" by Wilfred Pritchard | by fotosforfun2

The girls decided 'enough was enough' and ran home, where they told Monica's grandparents – Mr & Mrs Mitchell – what they had seen, who thought, to begin with, that the girls were playing a practical joke, but then realised how serious they were and refused to go and have a look themselves. The girls summoned up the courage to return to the scene, a short time later, at 9.30pm, where they saw a pulsing object behind some trees and decided, once again, to leave as quick as they could, fearful for their safety.

Nine photos taken, whereabouts not known!

At 10.30pm, (6.4.78), *Echo* newspaper photographer – Gordon Jones, from Highcliffe (on the edge of the New Forest) – was walking back to his house, when he saw what looked like two pairs of piercing white lights in the sky, moving towards him at a tremendous speed. Reacting quickly, Gordon fetched his camera and took nine photos (using settings 135 mm. lenses at 1000th second F28) of the flashing lights, which appeared to be hovering overhead. Mr Jones called out his wife and a neighbour. The three of them watched the lights, as they began to move towards the sea. Gordon jumped into his car and attempted to 'give chase', but they disappeared in front of his eyes, according to Ernie Sears – a long standing veteran of the Southampton UFO Group. Enquiries made by him, with Gordon Jones, revealed the London *Daily Mirror* had sent the photos to NASA, for examination.

(Source: Omar Fowler, 'PRA'/Ernie Sears)

UFO over Dorset

We spoke to Terry Bishop, in 2002, after learning of what he saw and photographed during the early hours of the morning, in early April 1978, while getting ready for bed, after finishing his shift as a taxi driver, at Highcliffe, Dorset.

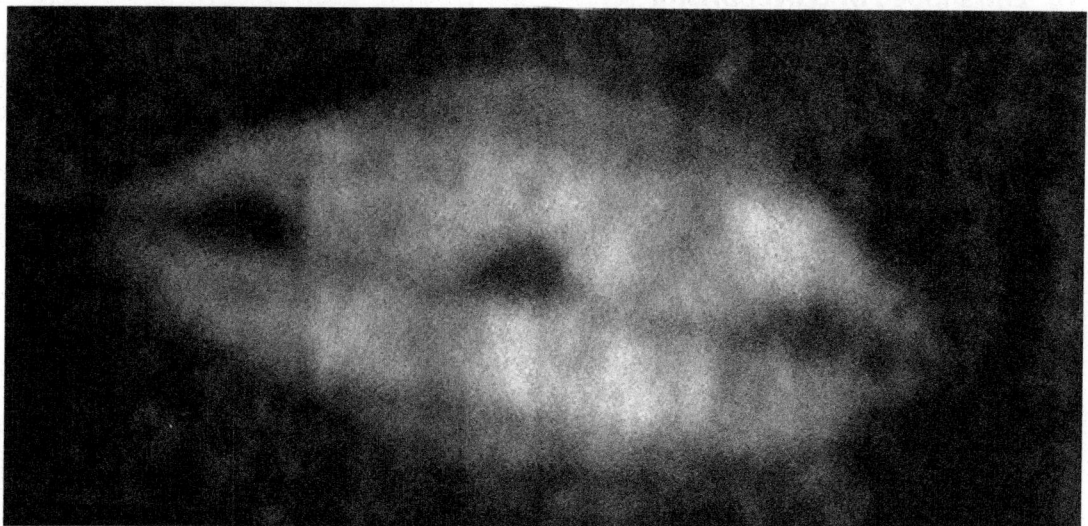

"It looked like two inverted saucers, placed on top of each other – the size of a double-decker bus – and tilted at an angle, hovering under a low cloud. I picked up my Polaroid camera and managed to take two photographs before the object went out of sight. I decided not to contact

TAXI DRIVER TERRY SNAPS THE TRIPPERS FROM SPACE'

By ALAN WHITTAKER

News of the World April 6th 1978

TAXI driver Terry Bishop was not at all frightened by his strange encounter. He simply put it on film.

On the night scores of people in southern England reported seeing an Unidentified Flying Object Terry dashed outside with his camera.

And now he says of the mystery flying object he photographed: "I'm convinced it is a spacecraft from another planet."

It happened at 2.45 a.m. when Terry, of Highcliffe, Dorset, had just finished work.

He was getting ready for bed when he saw a bright yellow light flash across the sky.

He grabbed his Polaroid camera, rushed into the garden, and fired off his last two shots of film.

SILENT

Said 29-year-old Terry, a married father of two: "The object was about the size of a double-decker bus and was tilted at an angle.

"It stayed motionless under a low cloud for perhaps eight or nine minutes. It looked like two inverted saucers placed together.

"The polar regions were red and the central part a yellow - orange colour. I reckon it was about half a mile away.

"Suddenly it zoomed away at an incredible speed into the clouds. It was uncannily silent."

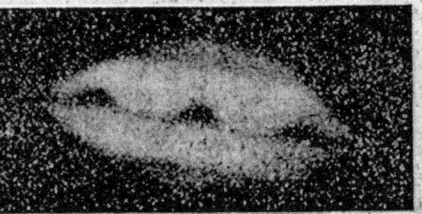

Terry Bishop's UFO photograph

Terry's first picture of the object was blurred, but the second one was clearer.

It showed three dark semi-circles in the centre, and dark blobs arranged in port-hole style.

Terry said: "Some people thought I'd faked the picture. They said it looked like a lampshade. But I took the picture in a hurry and it's genuine."

Professional photographer David Spokes has seen the original Polaroid print and says the photograph has definitely not been tampered with.

A spokesman for the magazine "Flying Saucer Review said: "There have been hundreds of photographs of UFOs during the last 20-odd years. This is a typical example."

Many other people confirmed that Terry was not alone in spotting a fiery object in the night sky.

The sightings were spread over a period of six hours on April 5-6.

AT 8 P.M. 11 - year - old Andrew Slater, of Hindle Close, Farnborough, Hants, was playing with a pal when they saw their UFO.

"There was a large cigar-shaped object hovering over the playing fields, said Andrew.

AT 9.50 PC Alan Craggs answered an emergency call at Ash, near Andover, Hants.

The call was made by school caretaker Peter Inwood, 50, a former member of the Royal Observer Corps, who had seen something odd in the sky.

FLAMES

Said PC Craggs: "My first impression when I arrived in the Panda car was that it was a very bright white star.

"But then I saw it was moving up and down and sideways and changing colours.

"I could see it wasn't passing aircraft. Vincent was it? Wasn't a plane."

AT 10.10 Mrs Mary Nutley looked out of her bedroom window at Yew Tree Farm, Clockhouse Lane, Nutley, on the edge of Ashdown Forest, Sussex, and saw what looked like a ball of fire hurtling silently through the sky.

She said: "It was certainly not a meteorological balloon because it made a very sharp turn and disappeared into the forest.

"I saw a sheet of flame and smoke and the forest land caught fire."

Police and firemen later found that bracken and gorse covering about three acres of the forest had been destroyed. But there was no trace of the UFO.

---

the newspaper, believing they would have poked fun at me and suggested it was a hoax. Unfortunately, I showed them to a mate at work, who telephoned them. The next thing I knew was that I was greeted by a reporter and photographer."

Terry's worst fears were realised when he saw the nature of the articles published by the popular Press. They included headlines like, 'A Close Encounter sends Terry the Taxi man snap happy!' and 'Day tripper from outer Space!'

"I was to become the target of ridicule and nasty suggestions of hoaxing – something I deny to this present day, not forgetting the photograph was examined by a professional photographer, David Spoke, who pronounced them authentic. I'm sorry but, due to house

THE HALT PERSPECTIVE

moves, I have mislaid the photo. All I can say is that I don't know if I saw and photographed any alien spaceship. I can only tell you what I saw. Arthur Shutlewood telephoned me and offered to make me a member of the Warminster 'Sky Watch' – but I declined, feeling overwhelmed by all the attention."

We tracked down a poor quality copy of the photo, showing a yellow cigar or oval shaped object, with three 'portholes' along its side, which we sharpened with 'Picture It' software, to give an idea of how it looked. Could this have been the same UFO seen by Thomas Wharton?

Unfortunately we don't know the exact date of either sighting, but one presumes logically there may well be a connection. The reader should bear in mind that we have a number of sightings for this month, which were published in Volume 7 of *Haunted Skies,* but space prevents us from covering them all. Was there a connection with what Janet Bull saw during the same month, being chased across the sky by jet fighters?

Update re 13/14th May 1978 – Dome-shaped UFO – *'figures'* seen

In December 2015 we were contacted by *Terry Hooper-Scharf who runs the Bristol based UFO group known as The *Anomalous Observational Phenomena Bureau.* Terry has been researching the UFO subject for many years and is widely regarded, and by ourselves, as being a leading authority on the chosen subject.

Terry pointed out that in our write-up of the event published in Volume 7 of *Haunted Skies,* and further back into this book, we hadn't mentioned the role of his group with regard to their investigation. It's never too late to put the record straight or, at the very least, ensure that not just some but all persons involved are credited.

Terry:

"The incident at Oulton Marshes Suffolk which involved a UFO and what were perceived to be its occupants were also investigated by Mr. R. T. Parsons (62), a retired teacher and a good artist. He drew the image of the object and entities. He contacted me about the newspaper item and I told him to go ahead and look into it. He couldn't get to the site until April, 1979 because of winter conditions – that made it even more obvious that what the girls saw could not have been people, it was very marshy. The only conclusion that can be drawn by 'UFO International' is that an event of 'High Strangeness' took place on the 14th May, 1978"

---

*Terry Hooper-Scharf. Between 1974 to the present date, Terry has acted as a wildlife consultant to UK Police Forces on exotic animals living in the UK, and is a noted naturalist. In the same year (1974) Terry set up the Bristol UFO Investigation Team (BUFOIT) and joined the British UFO Research Association (BUFORA), covering the West of England as an investigator and Regional Investigations Coordinator In 1976, Terry joined the oldest UK UFO group, the British Flying Saucer Bureau (formed 1952) and later became Head of Research & Investigation and also editor of the *UFO News Bulletin In* 1977, as an attempt to promote more scientific approach to UFO investigation, Terry set up UFO International, having established contact with Lord Clancarty and Air vice Marshal Sir Victor Goddard (a former head of RAF Intelligence and outspoken UFO believer, *pictured here to the right*).

Having discussed the incident further with Terry it was clear from personal information divulged that we were dealing with a very frightening incident the ramifications of which were incalculable. How on earth does one come to terms with having witnessed something like this? Can we gain any impression of what those girls saw by showing a photo taken at Cradle Hill during the same year.

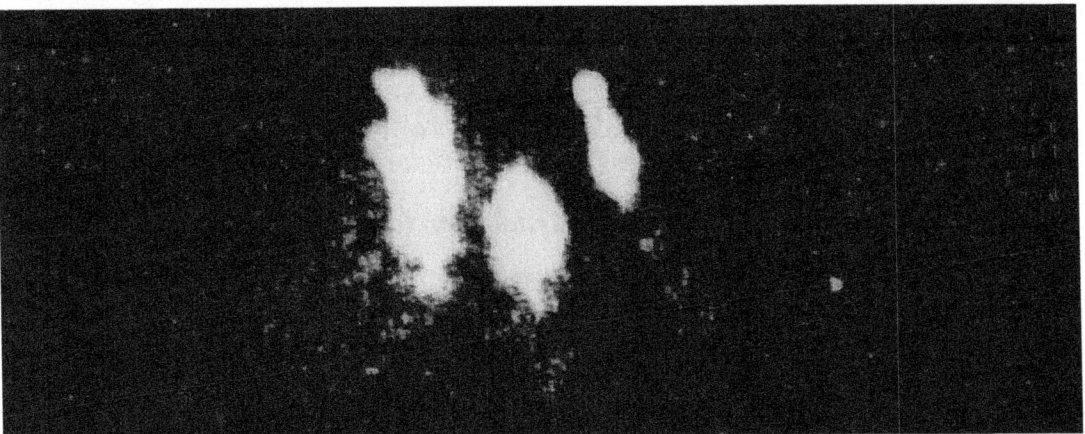

Photographed by Mr James Rose at Cradle Hill, Warminster during October 1978. They were described as 'three glowing figures'. We presume the UFOs were on the ground. We were unable to ascertain the exact date this took place, where or who else was involved. There have been many sightings of humanoid figures on the slopes of Cradle Hill over the years. The mystery endures to this present day!

Terry:

"Parsons used trick questions that were not obviously such and went over details several times. He simply could find no evidence of either girls lying or embellishing details, just the basic account. No follow-up 'we've seen them again' and I think the compulsion to go back meant the parents carefully watched them. I have no idea whether Parsons is still alive.

Had Parsons not decided to follow-up the Press report, which was local, this one would have been just a note somewhere. But his work meant we got as much detail as possible. Not much more I can add since all the case notes were apparently destroyed, but I kept what I had in my database just in case I ever heard from Parsons again."

Terry Hooper-Scharf – Men in black now identified

Terry Hooper was also able to finally supply the answers with regard to a visit made by two men, who spoke to Rendlesham Forestry Commission officer Mr James enquiring about the whereabouts of a local farmer Mr Boast.

Over the years, rumors have abounded that these two men were representative of the infamous 'men in black' whose reputation for threatening and intimidating UFO witnesses is well documented. It appears Terry and his colleague spoke to farmer David Boast, who told Brenda and Dot that he had received a visit by two men, although he then later denied this visit had taken place.

Contacted by Brenda and Dot – visit to Rendlesham Forest

Terry Hooper-Scharf

"I received a telephone call from two UFO International investigators – Dot Street and Brenda Butler (I think it was Brenda) about some USAF men, who reported seeing a UFO near Rendlesham Forest. I asked them to look into it further, which they did, but I remained puzzled why they involved Jenny Randles. As I was going to RAF Honington, I asked my driver if he could divert and have a look at the locality around the Orford Lighthouse and the Forest, where it was alleged that some form of UFO activity had occurred. We checked out the lighthouse and ascertained that it did not cast light overland. (I had lived a while on the Kent coast and know the trouble caused by lighthouses casting beams of light into people's homes!)

Nothing above normal background radiation found

"We checked the rough location of the 'landing' and the Geiger counter showed nothing above normal background radiation; a magnetometer did give a slightly high reading. No ground traces were found – or none were very obvious – although we discovered plenty of rabbit's traces and marks. We then talked to various people and said we were looking into a possible 'low level flight' incident (if you started saying 'we're looking at a UFO report', people either walked away, or you got every loony who had seen a satellite inundating you) as this was all part of being 'discreet'. We said that people might have seen a red or a blue or white light in the area – nothing. There was a farm, with some cattle in a field, but no-one there reported seeing anything (though they would have been in direct sight of the forest).

Saluted by the servicemen!

"We spoke to some USAF personnel who, on seeing our AOPB IDs (Anomalous Observational Phenomena Bureau) saluted us. We quickly pointed out that was not necessary! It seems that two black suited men with ID cards turning up and asking questions made it seem we were very official. I don't think any official report had been made at that time (even more 'suspicious'!). No mention of aliens, or even a constructed craft with lettering on, at that time.

Report sent to the MOD-not an alien craft!

We were pretty much convinced a natural phenomenon had been seen – even if impressive. We wrote a report and a copy went to the MOD. I am quite shocked at all the stuff added to the event since that time – including the fact that the two of us have now been called MIB and the things we were supposed to have done. Unofficially, the MOD let it be known the conclusion we reached was 'accepted' – we heard via Sir Victor Goddard, who had talked to 'one of the chaps'. I think natural phenomena were involved – I've seen these things myself – and a heck of a lot got made up since that time. But, yes, I and the driver (I've heard that he passed away recently) were the first real investigators there and neither of us believed an alien craft was involved!"

High Powered meeting in London

In the same year Terry, along with late colleague Franklyn A. Davin-Wilson, visited London for a meeting with Lord Clancarty, Goddard and others, having submitted a document calling for a National Aerospace Commission [NaComm]. Hooper was asked to mount an unofficial investigation into all aspects of the UFO phenomenon – a limited fund for travelling and living expenses was agreed upon. In January 1978, the Anomalous Observational Phenomena Bureau [AOPB] began its work building up a database on every aspect of UFOs – historical cases, trace, physiological and psychological, animal disturbance, EM cases and much more. Original members of the AOPB were Graham F.N. Knewstub [deceased], Dave Cowdy [deceased], Franklyn A. Davin-Wilson [deceased], and Terry Hooper. Between 1978-1984 there was much unofficial assistance given to the Bureau by professional astronomers [some publicly sceptical] and

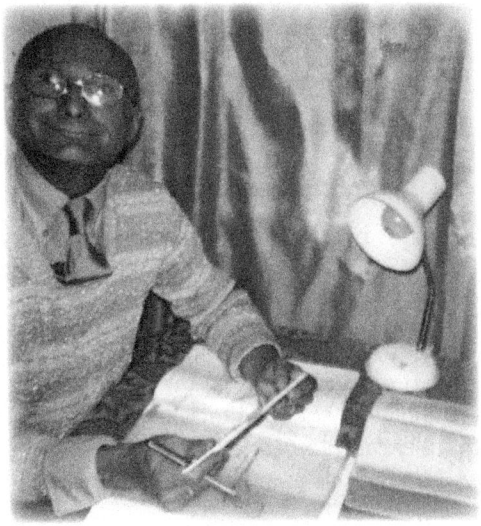

Franklyn A. Davin-Wilson

former members of the Armed Forces, Air Ministry, Ministry of Defence, as well as serving members of the Armed Forces and Police Forces.

A network of UFO investigation and research groups was set-up, including GUFOI & RG [Gloucestershire], Wessex UFO I & R Group [Somerset], Wiltshire UFO I & R Team, and so on. Much of this cooperation continued well past the closing of the Bureau in 1995, though Governmental changes in policy since then have restricted any cooperation. In 1984 a 2,000-page *British Report on Unidentified Flying Objects* [UFOs] was completed. This was later reduced to 1,500pp on editing.

THE HALT PERSPECTIVE

July 1979 – Diamond-shaped UFO sighted over RAF Coltishall

Recently retired Leicestershire Constabulary Police Constable 495 Brett Lynes (51) contacted us in January 2013, to tell us about a very strange encounter which took place in 1980, whilst serving with the RAF Police at RAF Coltishall.

This was to important not to include, firstly it isn't that far from Suffolk. Secondly it involved another RAF Station. Thirdly the object seen is identical to many others reported over the Suffolk and Essex localities during this period of time.

It is tempting to consider some association with what was sighted outside RAF Woodbridge later the next year, why not taking into consideration the amount of UFO activity now catalogued by myself and Dawn Holloway.

Brett:

"In July 1979 (aged 18) I joined the RAF Police and, after initial training, was posted to *RAF Coltishall, in Norfolk. This base is about 12 miles north of Norwich and at that time had three squadrons of Jaguars and the 202 Search and Rescue helicopter squadron. The RAF Police Flight was quite small and my shift consisted of a substantive Corporal and two acting Corporals (one being me). Our office was situated on the side of one of the aircraft hangers – away from the runway and near to a fuel storage depot.

The incident occurred during a night shift in either late August or early September 1980. We started work at 10pm and took over from the afternoon shift. The evening was fairly mild; so we had the single door to the office open while we had the usual cups of tea before thinking about starting our security patrols."

Loud booming noise heard

Just before midnight there was a very loud boom from somewhere close outside. The men's initial thoughts were that the fuel depot had exploded, and the three of them ran outside and across the road to investigate further. After ascertaining the fuel dump was obviously in order, they wondered if it could have been one of several others scattered around the base which had exploded.

They looked around the skyline to try and see if they could see any glow from a possible fire coming from those other sites, but saw nothing untoward, and wondered if it had been a loud thunderclap. Brett looked up at the sky and saw it was absent of clouds and the stars were visible. The weather was clear and mild and there had been no rainfall that day.

Brett:

"As we could not find any immediate cause for the sound of the explosion, we returned to the office and my shift commander – Corporal Dinning, rang the main guardroom, which was positioned at the entrance gate to the camp and staffed by a roster of airmen and one Sergeant taken from the other sections of the base. They would do one afternoon or nightshift every couple of months, and their duty was to go out and check certain fire point's once every hour or so. Cpl. Dinning asked if they had heard the 'explosion' and the duty Sergeant said no. Cpl. Dinning then asked that all fire patrols be sent out to check the base on foot, whilst we checked the airfield side in our police vehicles."

Cpl. Dinning and the other RAF police corporal went out together, and I went alone in my car to check various buildings and airfield installations. Nothing was found and, after about an hour, the fire pickets returned to the guardroom and we then settled back down to our normal routine of various security checks around the base."

Just before 5am in the morning, the shift was coming to an end and the men were winding down before being relieved. At 7am Brett volunteered to complete a task at the end of every night shift, involving the unlocking of the 'crash gates', situated on the far side of the runway used to allow emergency vehicles access, should they be required after an air crash on the base.

Loud booming noise – was the UFO returning?

"We had contractors working on the far side taxi way, repairing the concrete, and each morning they would come straight onto the airfield via one of those gates, which would be left unlocked for them. I said that I would drive over there and unlock the gate before they were due to arrive, around 6am. It was now light but a little overcast, with patchy clouds. This I did and I had just unlocked the padlock, when there was a terrifically loud 'boom' directly over my head. I instinctively flinched down and then looked up at the sky, where the noise had come from. There were now intermittent clouds, but moving between two of them was a very large diamond-shaped craft. It's hard to say how big it was, but I would easily equate it to the size of a large naval vessel, destroyer or similar. It was certainly several times bigger than any aircraft I had ever seen and its shape was like nothing I'd seen before."

Diamond-shaped craft appears in sky

"The whole underside of this craft was covered in equally spaced sets of diamond patterned lights. Several of the lights were of different colours, such as reds, oranges, purples, greens, yellows, but kept in groups of the same colour. There was no noise at all and the craft moved silently across the sky between two clouds.

Apart from being totally shocked, I managed to use my radio to call up the other two RAF policemen in our office. I asked Cpl. Dinning to run across the road outside the office and look up at the sky directly above my position at the crash gate, and tell me if he could see anything. I think the tone of my voice prevented them from delaying, as he called back after just a couple of seconds, saying he couldn't see anything apart from clouds.

After about 20 seconds, or so, the craft disappeared fully into, or was hidden by, the clouds from my view and I didn't hear or see anything else of it, although I waited a few minutes just in case it should reappear. I drove back to the office and explained to the others what had happened and even drew a plan of the craft with the position of its lights and their various colours. Unfortunately I did not retain it, even though Cpl. Dinning suggested I submit a recreation of massive diamond-shaped craft. Direction of flight was towards lower left horizon, going away from viewer.

I considered submitting an official UFO report but as I had only been in service for 14 months and did not think it would do my career any good if people started to think I was a fantasist, or worse, so I declined. I can say that the sound of the boom just before I looked up was pretty much the same sound we had all heard just before midnight, yet when I'd looked up at the sky then it seemed clear."

Similar sighting over Suffolk in 1979

"Many years later, sometime in 1997, or so, I recalled this sighting to another police officer friend and he told me about the Rendlesham incident, which I had never heard of. He lent me a book about that, but unfortunately I cannot remember the book's title, or author. In that book was a sighting prior to Rendlesham, by two men standing on the seafront at night, in Suffolk – about 20 miles or so from RAF Coltishall –

when they sighted what appears to have been the same diamond-shaped craft fly in over the coast from the sea and this, too, was silent. Their sighting was about 12 months after mine, in 1981. I spent six years in the RAF, at various operational flying stations, and I've never seen anything similar to that craft before or since. Its size and the unusual lights set it apart from anything made public, such as Stealth bombers, etc."

Britain's (now forgotten) Project Blue Book

Lord Clancarty, *Sir Victor Goddard, and others, including members of the House of Lords UFO Study Group, stated the report was *". . . the closest thing the UK will ever have to a Project Blue Book".* Although copies went to the Ministry of Defence and Sir Victor passed copies on to former subordinates and ex-heads of RAF Intelligence, private UFO groups condemned the Report without even having seen the summary offered. The report is currently being updated with more contemporary evidence being added.

Victor Goddard – His views on UFOs

On 3 May 1969, he gave a talk on UFOs at Caxton Hall in London, in which he said:

"That while it may be that some operators of UFO are normally the Para physical denizens of a planet other than Earth, there is no logical need for this to be so. For, if the materiality of UFO is Para physical (and consequently normally invisible), UFO could more plausibly be creations of an invisible world coincident with the space of our physical Earth planet than creations in the Para physical realms of any other physical planet in the solar system. . . . Given that real UFO are Para physical, capable of reflecting light like ghosts; and given also that (according to many observers) they remain visible as they change position at ultrahigh speeds from one point to another, it follows that those that remain visible in transition do not dematerialize for that swift transition, and therefore, their mass must be of a diaphanous (very diffuse) nature, and their substance relatively etheric . . . The observed validity of this supports the Para physical assertion and makes the likelihood of UFO being Earth-created greater than the likelihood of their creation on another planet . . . The astral world of illusion, which (on psychical evidence) is greatly inhabited by illusion-prone spirits, is well known for its multifarious imaginative activities and exhortations. Seemingly some of its denizens are eager to exemplify principalities and powers. Others pronounce upon morality, spirituality, Deity, etc . All of these astral exponents who invoke human consciousness may be sincere, but many of their theses may be framed to propagate some special phantasm, perhaps of an earlier incarnation, or to indulge an inveterate and continuing technological urge toward materialistic progress, or simply to astonish and disturb the gullible for the devil of it."

(Source: Wikipedia)

Transcript of interview with Sgt. Randy Smith

Randy D. Smith is an Honor Graduate from Air Training Command. A Security Specialist, Randy's Certificate of Appointment confirms he was assigned to RAF Bentwaters with the non-commissioned rank of Sergeant, on 1st September 1980.

"I was either a [Senior Airman] or Sgt. at the time. It was Christmas time, 1980. 'D' flight had been working the 3-11pm shift, while 'C' flight had been working the 11pm-7am shift. It was

---

*Air Marshal Sir Robert Victor Goddard KCB, CBE (6 February 1897 – 21 January 1987), known as Victor Goddard, was a senior commander in the Royal Air Force during the Second World War. Goddard is perhaps best known for his interest in paranormal phenomena; he claimed to have witnessed such as a 1946 incident on which the feature film *The Night My Number Came Up* (1955) was later based.

Now a full Colonel . . . this picture of Charles Halt at his desk

a quiet, clear night. I believe I was working 'Whiskey 5', which was the alarm response team in the weapons storage area on Bentwaters. I am unsure of my partner that night. I had free range of one half of the WSA and I was driving a pick-up truck. Clarence George was my area supervisor. Rick Bobo was the SPCDS [Small Permanent Communications Display Segment [a 'computerized alarm system'] tower operator in the WSA. The next thing I recall, not long after the shift began, perhaps midnight or so, I heard Bob Ball come over the radio and request that the aircraft control tower give him permission to cross the active runway; it saves 15 minutes driving time, as opposed to driving the perimeter road. At that point I knew SOMETHING was happening because no-one ever crossed the active runway unless there was an extreme emergency.

Bob, accompanied by Lt. Bruce Englund, crossed the runway on Bentwaters. They picked up Lt. Col. Halt, and some equipment, and returned by the same route. I would say that between 30 minutes to an hour had passed since Bob made his first request to cross. They then proceeded to re-cross the runway and went out the back gate, headed toward RAF Woodbridge. After that, the radio was quiet for a long time. It was a very quiet night – no planes, no helicopters flying."

Clarence George

"Clarence George came by to talk to me and he said that everyone in the WSA was in the SPCDS tower watching 'lights' and did I want to come check it out? So I did. Clarence thought they were

all crazy. It's a small tower and people were jammed in there, body to body, overloading the tower I'm sure. More people than I've ever seen in the tower at one time. I asked what everyone was looking at, and they pointed out three objects that appeared like stars to the naked eye"

Three objects seen triangular in shape

"Binoculars were being passed around and when I had my turn I saw VERY CLEAR images of three triangular-shaped craft that were hovering a few miles away, and above treetop level. They were triangular in shape, larger than a fighter jet, but smaller than a C5 – Definitely triangular, with lights that were arranged around the bottom that were perhaps different colors, but unable to distinguish at that distance.

I only stayed in the tower for an hour or so, and heard one of the guys with a turn on the binoculars, say: 'Wow, it just took off'. Two of the craft left at a high rate of speed. The one remaining craft was still in position when I left the tower. Regarding sound – very quiet, no motor sounds whatsoever. I also remember hearing the radio traffic regarding the light-alls [these were petrol powered, portable lights, which it's known were being used that night and proved problematic] and not working – replacing them didn't work, and then much later they all worked fine.

The following night, I went on duty. At Guard Mount, Bob Ball was very serious; he's almost never serious, a very jovial person. He said, 'I saw something last night, but I'm not at liberty to discuss it', and that was the 'end'. I later heard that the morning we got off our first midnight shift, an A-10 was scrambled and sent to Ramstein, Germany, by Lt. Col. Halt.

Randy described the object as effectively an upright pyramid, but was uncertain whether it may have been flat-surfaced or conical. However, he believed the objects were cone-shaped, as they "didn't look to be as flat as an actual pyramid. The lights underneath, which created somewhat of a backlit effect, enabling the shape of the crafts to be seen clearly was observed as 8-10 rectangular blocks, arranged in a circle".

Colonel Halt:

"Randy Smith was there and reliable. I'm not convinced he and a crowd were allowed in the WSA tower. He was part of the Immediate Response Team and should have remained on post. However, he could have gone up into the tower. I don't know of anyone else claiming to have gotten in the tower with Bobo. The remainder of his account sounds reasonably correct. A few years ago I heard from a former Security Cop that was on 'D' Flight. He was off the night of the event but told me Bobby Ball was so shaken by the event that the next day he went to the hospital for medication to calm down. This is the first I heard this.

Carl Thompson [see Page 169] was not an Air Traffic Controller – he was a Communications Specialist that told of him and a co-worker working on the tower sensors in the WSA the nights of both incidents. His co-worker told of seeing the UFO both nights and was frightened into silence. I have his name but not with me."

1983 – Lee Southgate, RAF Bentwaters

We spoke to Lee Southgate, who was employed as a civilian under the Official Secrets Act, at RAF Bentwaters, with top secret clearance about what he remembered from his time there. Lee explained he was not there in 1980, but recommenced employment in 1983.

"The event that happened in 1980 was still occasionally talked about in the Bentwaters Control Tower. People suggested all manner of explanations. I remember that on the shelf, in the middle of all the flight manuals and other technical books, was a copy of Sky Crash that stuck in my memory. Security was good at Bentwaters, but not quite the same at Woodbridge. I remember forgetting my pass, so I stuck an old farm pork sticker, green in colour, on the windscreen. The guy on the gate just waved me in."

Invariably, there was also tragedy. Lee told of Sergeant Carr – an ex-Vietnam Vet – who drove home one evening, in his Ford Cortina, the worse for wear.

"He hit a fence and was impaled on the railing, and died later. The next day I went to look at the car, which was hardly damaged. The railing had come through the front of the car, under the windscreen, and struck him – a chance in a million. Sorry about his passing; he was a really nice man and had plenty of tales to tell while serving in Vietnam."

Minister Ray Bouche

Ray Bouche

An interview with US Senator James Exon

USA UFO researchers Ray Bouche and his colleague, Scott H. Colborn, felt sufficiently concerned about the seriousness of what had taken place in the forest in rural Suffolk, UK, involving claims of Alien beings meeting with Air Force Officers, following the landing of a 'craft'. Eventually, after a number of calls made to an aide of Senator James Exon, a meeting was set up with him, as they felt that his position on the Armed Service Committee would be able to help them unravel this complex case.

On the 15th February 1985, they met up with the Senator at his Lincoln, Washington, address and were greeted cordially.

Senator James Exon

Following some discussion about the Woodbridge/Bentwaters incident, the Senator initially questioned if any of this had, in fact, taken place at all. The two men presented him with books – *Sky Crash* and *Clear Intent*.

The Senator told Ray and Scott that he would make some enquiries, but if it was under National Security Status he would be unable to comment. The men then left, after James asked them to contact him if further information came to light in due course.

Ray managed to track down Colonel Halt, who told him that he could vouch for photos and soil samples being taken and that he (Halt) had a sample on his desk.

No official cover-up

Armed with this new information they contacted an aide of James Exon, who told them that the Senator had called Charles Halt personally about the incident, as he wanted to deal with this himself rather than use aides. Accordingly, a letter was later sent to the two men by James Exon, who said, as far as he was concerned, there was no official cover-up, adding that he had spent more time on investigating this matter than with other issues since becoming a US Senator.

Ray:

"At one point, while I was attempting to clear-up some rather odd things that seemed to indicate some sort of surveillance of my personal communications, one of his aides in Washington stated, 'We have a file on you here that's just huge!' "

Adrian Bustinza

Ray, a credit to UFO research – now a Minister in Nebraska – was able to interview various people about the British UFO incident, one of whom was Adrian Bustinza.

"I was pleased to have found and spoken with Adrian Bustinza on, I believe — without digging out my files — two or possibly three occasions. One very brief conversation was taped by my colleague, Scott Colborn. The other conversation(s) were not taped, as those calls were made from my office at work, in an attempt to reach Adrian at a time convenient for him. I was also quite frustrated that Adrian would not share much, and even 30 years ago, stated exactly what he has told you; that this event traumatized him so badly that he just wanted to forget about it.

Adrian's mother really gave me a piece of her mind when I called once for Adrian and he wasn't home. She was quite upset that I was trying to convince Adrian to dredge up memories which he found quite unsettling, and had impacted his life in an extraordinarily negative fashion. My single conversation with Colonel Halt (which was not recorded, regardless of Harry Harris' insistence that I was keeping the tape a secret from him) certainly did include his assertion that 'film' (I don't recall whether he indicated if it was movie or still film) was taken and was flown directly to Ramstein Air Force Base, in Germany."

Gordon Williams collected film of the UFO to waiting aircraft

In Georgina Bruni's book she tells of the attempts made by Ray and Scott Colborn to attract the interest of Senator James Exon.

It is alleged, during conversation with Charles Halt, that Ray asked him about Gordon Williams' involvement.

Ray:

"I told him I was an independent researcher, but Halt thought I was representing Exon. I asked him if it was true that an officer drove Wing Commander Williams from the landing site to a waiting plane with a motion picture of the UFO. He said, 'Yes, I can verify that for the Senator.'"

Charles Halt:

"I also spoke extensively with Senator James Exon and told him the whole story. He was quite concerned about what I told him. After we talked he totally dropped the subject. Who got to him? I have the tape of Boeche's conversation with Bustinza and it doesn't make sense, as to an extent, he supports Larry. Remember Adrian was with me the whole time. If you want I'll send you the tape along with one of Larry's earlier talks. The more I learn the more I'm convinced there's a concerted behind-the-scene effort.

The question is who is pulling the strings as I think the 'spooks' are just tools?

The only film from either night was Penniston's and Nevels I never handled any film. A plane did go Germany soon after the event but it was supposedly to take some late promotion papers to a board. What I said was that I was told by others that Williams received something while in the cockpit of an A-10 bound for Germany. Mike Verano claimed it was film of the UFO. I think it was Mel Zicklers efficiency report that was late and they wanted it to get into his file before the promotion board. I remember talk of that happening. This was well after the event in the forest. I could be wrong but I don't think so. The only related film it possibly could have been is Neville's 35mm film. To have gotten it someone would have to have broken into his home and done a substitute. Not likely! Williams was never at the site. Ask him.

This wild tale is based on something Mike Verano remembered. We all know there was no video, only Monroe's 35mm film. If Williams told Mike that it was a cover for flying Zicklers late evaluation to the CINC for an endorsement so it could get into his promotion file. A video is wishful thinking"

1984

January 1984 – Jim Yaoi visits Rendlesham Forest

IN this month Japanese TV Film Producer Jimmy Yaoi visited Rendlesham Forest with his film crew during the making of their documentary on the *'Sky Crash'.* They were shown at the 'staging post' described by 'Art Wallace' where *"Trucks and jeeps were left there and the security officers approached the site on foot through the trees to the left of the picture"*

John Hanson – I wasn't aware that such a large track existed there, back in 1984. According to Brenda Butler this is what the majority of the forest tracks looked like in those days before.

23rd February 1984 – Intruders detained on Airbase

Although now three years had passed since the actual UFO incidents had taken place, followed by the release of the story in 1983, Dot Street and Brenda Butler continued to tenaciously badger Colonel Halt, hoping for even more morsels of information in their imitable style. Little did they even dream that over 35 years later, the incident and its aftermath (never mind the controversy which surrounds the case) still continues to be discussed by on-line magazines, who blatantly appear to ignore all of the other thousands of sightings which have provided the backcloth to what the UFO phenomena has been all about.

Colonel Halt:

"At about 6.40pm I received a telephone call from a Mrs Dorothy Street, who asked me to meet up with her in the bar at the Crown Hotel in Woodbridge. Knowing that it would be further attempts to interview me about the UFO incidents that had occurred at the end of December 1980, following various other attempts to speak to me at my home address, by both Dot and Brenda Butler, I declined saying I was to busy and warned them to keep away and to stop telephoning me. At 10.45pm I returned home to 620A

Bentwaters Housing and discovered Dot Street inside the front door. I discovered that she had previously awoken my son Charles, who had gone to answer the door, and then barged into the house. I asked her to leave. She replied, 'We have things to straighten out', and refused to leave. At 11pm I requested assistance by radio, asking them to inform the civilian police to attend, as I had trespassers in the house that wouldn't leave."

As a result of this call, dispatcher 1st Lt. Des Roches sent Ronald A. Burtle – a member of the 81st Security Police – to the scene.

He detained three persons, Dot Street, Brenda Butler – and Aldburgh man – David Taylor, who was in possession of an expired USAF Form 77, issued to Mr Taylor on the 18th August 1979 (expiry date – 12th October 1980). The three persons were then handed over to Police Constable 266 Marsh, and Police Constable 661 Stagg. After a short interview, they were warned about their conduct and later released.

Little did Charles Halt visualize in his wildest dreams that he would be standing on stage at Woodbridge Community Hall, Suffolk in 2015, talking about what happened – or sharing a friendly meeting with Dot Street and enjoying a pint of Speckled Hen at the *Bull Pub* Woodbridge, 12 months earlier!

John Hanson – Photo of UFO taken by Larry Warren?

While photographs of the 'landing area' and UFOs seen in and around Rendlesham Forest during the end of December 1980 are very rare, I wasn't sure what to make of an intriguing UFO photograph, claimed by Larry Warren to have been taken in the forest during that period of time. I questioned Larry about this a couple of years ago, after he was unable to provide me with details of the copyright holder. I then entered into an email dialogue with him about it, hoping to find out the circumstances in which it was taken and, more importantly, who had taken the image – understanding the importance of this purported unique photograph.

Charles Halt:

"This is absolute rubbish. I have never heard or seen it before and regard it as being the product of a fanciful imagination".

Larry Warren:

"It is from the negative . . . work has been done on it, the lights are part of a large triangular object that is dark in colour . . . also said object seems to be approximately 75 to 100 yards from photographer and on or above the ground . . . Further a mist of some sort can be seen just under the object . . . also Corsican pines are clearly visible in a clear copy as are ferns that are native

to Rendlesham Forest also small lights can be seen coming toward the photographer. Other photos in the set are fogged, beyond that, another of the fogged photos clearly shows the field ie Capel Green, to include the wire fence as it was in December 1980..."

Banned from using it!

Larry claimed that he was only the 'custodian' of the image – then, after further questioning, promptly banned me from using it! The photograph on the internet shows a group of lights apparently taken in a forest, judging by the pine trees that are just about discernible. Unfortunately the reproduced copy photograph is covered with swirls and marks consistent with wear and tear, but the lights are clearly visible against the alleged forest background.

I was surprised and disappointed in Larry's response. No doubt the reader will form their own conclusions about the evidential value of this image. I know I have.

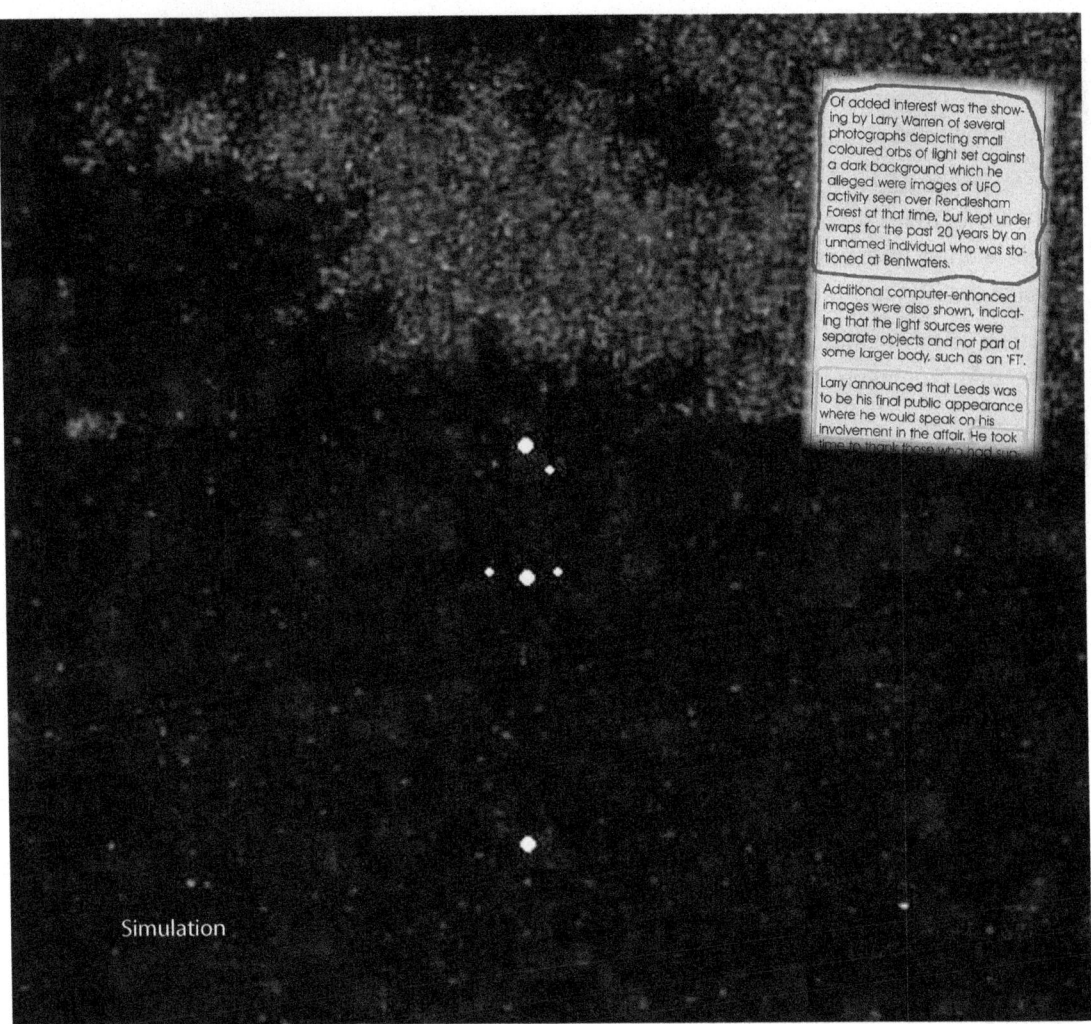

Of added interest was the showing by Larry Warren of several photographs depicting small coloured orbs of light set against a dark background which he alleged were images of UFO activity seen over Rendlesham Forest at that time, but kept under wraps for the past 20 years by an unnamed individual who was stationed at Bentwaters.

Additional computer-enhanced images were also shown, indicating that the light sources were separate objects and not part of some larger body, such as an 'FT'.

Larry announced that Leeds was to be his final public appearance where he would speak on his involvement in the affair. He took time to thank those who had sup-

Simulation

Photograph of the UFO taken in the forest – Fact or fiction?

Larry told Georgina Bruni in 1999 about the existence of actual photographs taken of the UFO, as encountered by Jim Penniston and John Burroughs, which he claimed to have been taken on the 25th/26th December 1980 by Mark – an accountant, living with his wife and family in the States. Apparently Mark had sent the negatives, a Bentwaters photographic folder, a map with directions to the landing site and a letter from the witness to Larry – care of his publisher – after having read *Left At East Gate*. Georgina understood that the witness had been one of two men from the Base, who had seen lights over the forest from their position at Eyke. They decided to investigate and, after collecting a camera from Bentwaters, made their way just past Folly Cottages (opposite what used to be track 10) – a well-known landmark to the 'sky watchers', who still sporadically meet up at the nearby car park there to this present date.

Mark approached the lights, now on his own (his friend was too scared), and was shocked to see two *'figures'* and a triangular UFO sitting in the clearing, at which point, when only five feet away, he took the photos. The UFO then lifted upwards and headed away into the forest, snaking its way through the trees.

Mark returned to the Base, replaced the film and took some photos of the ground, which he then handed over to his superiors, who later told him that the film was fogged! After having the 'original' film developed, he kept quiet about it for almost two years, until his tour was up when, following his arrival to the United States, he posted them to Larry Warren in 1998!

One of those photographs (the same as shown to me by Larry) was sent to Georgina – who judged that, if genuine, it was a good piece of evidence.

Different version of events

Sadly, after being promised a photocopy of the folder and a negative, Georgina was stunned when Larry admitted it was him that had taken the photograph! Larry told her a different version of events, involving driving to Ipswich railway station on Christmas Day with Mark (who was an airman with top secret clearance, worked for the NSA and was stationed at RAF Martlesham Heath), intending to make their way to London and then Germany to meet two German girls. They visited a music shop near the station. After some questioning from Georgina, who pointed out that the shop surely was closed on a Sunday, he changed his mind and claimed some men had been delivering goods to the shop and he had asked about prices.

On the way back to RAF Bentwaters

On their way back to Bentwaters airbase, they saw three strange lights in the sky, forming a triangle, making a droning noise. Mark drove to the Base, picked up a camera, and they headed towards the forest. At a point near Folly cottages, they saw a law enforcement vehicle parked on the road. Larry and Mark followed the noise of radios into the forest and eventually discovered a UFO, displaying three points of light and resembling a Christmas tree on the ground. As Larry took a photo with his Canon 35mm, the UFO moved up off the ground – at which stage the noise of the radios ceased.

'Figures' seen in the forest

Larry saw some *'figures'* that he did not recognize but claims he believes he may have been abducted, because as soon as the photos were taken the *'men'* disappeared. This, of course, is not the end of the story. Larry says that, as he was leaving the forest, he sighted John Burroughs stood next to a truck (although he didn't know him by name then). Mark expended the rest of the film (blank) and gave Larry the canisters to take back to his dormitory for safekeeping. Larry then says that he put the film canisters on the window sill, but his room-mate was uncomfortable with the situation [presumably his room-mate must have known their content] and urged Larry to report the matter.

Film of the UFO hidden

He took one blank film to Senior Master Sergeant Swain, who then asked him to speak to Major Drury, although Larry feels Drury was unaware of what was going on. Later that day he heard that someone called Burroughs had seen a UFO. Believing there might be a search of the building he wrapped the canister inside a sock and gave it to Steve La Plume, who refused to look after it. Larry then hid it under his mattress, and later smuggled it out of Bentwaters by placing it into the bottom of a Wedgewood beer mug which he had bought on a recent trip to Germany, and posted it to his mother – who knew nothing about the photos until he returned home, a few months later. The items were then placed into his sister's safe deposit box. It gets even more confusing when Larry later told Georgina that he had never been to Germany during the Christmas holidays, but had used the trip to cover the fact that he had been involved in the incident.

John Burroughs interview with Antonio Huneeus in 1990

In an interview conducted with John about this very matter, John Burroughs had this to say:

"Larry Warren has hurt this case quite a bit. The only thing I can say about Larry's testimony that aliens came out, his excuse was that CNN did a botched up job and he never described those little men like they were and stuff like that. There was something out there that was intelligent that (hurt the eyes especially) when there was the blue transparent type lights that were coming out and the different things that they were capable of doing. That is my stand on that. Now Larry Warren took it a step further and as far as I am concerned there was no contact between; he called him the base commander LT Colonel Williams at the time, and I do not see him out there. I know for a fact that Colonel Halt was out there and there is a small possibility, if I remember I did see for a brief moment possibly the new base commander, which could have been Colonel Conrad at the time. But there was nothing that I am aware of or through talking to other people that would describe what Larry Warren described to CNN, other than there were blue transparent lights that could be possibly – they did act intelligently, some of the stuff they did. There was something else that came off the main craft that was able to do different things and flew over the top of us and flew through a pick-up truck and did stuff like that."

[In March 2000 Larry attended a UFO conference in Nevada, where he spoke about the 'UFO photographs'. On this occasion he claimed they had come from another witness.]

Charles Halt:

"I was very skeptical. I found what allegedly had taken place hard to believe, and I was really going to debunk it quite frankly; and as events unfolded I became more and more concerned that there maybe something to this... I kept telling myself that there had to be some type of explanation for it, but I certainly couldn't find one and even to this day I can't explain what happened."

Jim Penniston – Comment

"Does this ever end with all this erroneous information from Larry Warren? No I haven't seen any photographs from Larry Warren and certainly no other persons were with me other than John and Eddie. No personal cameras would have been allowed; they would have had to have been US Air Force ones. He said he gave the film to master sergeant Swain; unfortunately, the guy's dead. The last person anybody would have handed over film of a classified incident or security incident would be to the first sergeant. Nothing even remotely is close to the truth with this. It shows Warren's lack of knowledge on the Air Force and procedures within the security police. I believe that Warren and Robbins are going to get caught out. Because of 30 years of disinformation. They're not on their own – there are many guys in this business for fame and glory, or hoping to make money."

Jim Penniston's new book

"If your book doesn't put everything out with the truth, I will guarantee this ... my new book on Rendlesham, when it is done, will be the definitive book on it. No one will get by unscathed. This includes everybody that was actually involved and people that thought they were involved or wish they were. Personally I don't care about the third night, it's not even relevant to me. And I suppose if you had been in my situation and experienced what I did on that first night of the investigation, you would certainly not care either about the third night."

Nick Pope

"The story of this photo epitomizes the wider problems with Larry Warren's testimony. In one version of the story, he took the photo himself, while in another version, somebody else took the photo but asked Larry to claim the image as his own work and get the story out on his behalf. As ever, Larry switches gears effortlessly. Perhaps the most telling moment came when investigative journalist Georgina Bruni picked Larry up on an apparently minor discrepancy: in part of one version of his story, Larry described a visit to a record store with some German girls. Then Georgina pointed out that at the time, most UK stores were closed on Sundays. Without missing a beat, Larry amended his story to sidestep the problem. As it happens, I've seen both a negative and a print of this photo. Bottom line: it's just dots of light against a dark background. It could be something, it could be nothing, but frankly, in evidential terms, it's worthless."

John Hanson

Yet another variation on an original theme can be seen in an interview conducted by veteran UFO researcher Omar Fowler, *FSR* Consultant, and one of the nicest men we have met. He is a credit to the UFO cause and a privilege to know him. Omar was able to interview Peter Robbins and Larry Warren, following their visit to the UK to see Tony James of the now defunct East Midlands UFO Association (I remember meeting Tony at Aston University, in 1995, after he gave a talk there on a number of subjects including Area 51.)

1994 – Omar Fowler writes to Gordon Creighton – Editor of *FSR*

"Dear Gordon,

Last Sunday I met two Americans involved in researching the famous Rendlesham Forest evening in Suffolk, in December 1980. One of them is Larry Warren, one of the USAF security guards who was there and was ordered with others to surround a glowing triangular UFO in Rendlesham Forest. He subsequently suffered radiation burns and damage to the retinas of his eyes. The other is Peter Robbins, who is a private UFO researcher now working closely with Budd Hopkins. When I mentioned that I was connected with *Flying Saucer Review*, he was delighted and said that in his opinion it was the leading UFO magazine.

Larry Warren, together with Peter Robbins and Tony James of the East Midlands UFO Association, recently visited the Rendlesham site for the first time since the UFO incident. A video was taken of their visit. I have seen this, and also listened to their account of the encounter. I queried one or two points and I have a pretty clear picture of what happened.

Peter Robbins asked if I would be writing a piece for *FSR* on their visit and I said that I would. I cannot recollect if *FSR* has published anything on the Rendlesham affair. No doubt it has, but I believe that I may have a number of new facts about what happened and subsequent events (one USAF witness blew his brains out a fortnight later).

Regards,

Omar Fowler, 31.3.1994."

Peter Robbins (left), Omar Fowler and Larry Warren (right). Far right, Gordon Creighton.

THE HALT PERSPECTIVE

Even at this stage there were claims that Larry Warren had not even been there at the time of the incidents according to Charles Halt, who spoke to an audience at the *Quest International* meeting on the 31st July 1994.

Omar:

"Larry was not stationed at RAF Woodbridge under Colonel Halt's command but at RAF Bentwaters, which lies four miles due north and on the opposite side of the forest."

Omar tells of a book being prepared by Larry and Peter, entitled *Left At Eastgate*. Larry supplied his account of what took place to Omar Fowler.

Larry's account

Larry outlines the fact that Bentwaters and Woodbridge had the biggest nuclear arms dump in all of NATO, and that just one nuclear bomb could have taken out East Anglia. Larry describes the events of the evening of the 28th December 1980, which is consistent with other accounts given by him, over the years. He speaks of seeing two English 'bobbies', senior personnel, and security police from 'D' flight, stood there in the field.

"I saw a disaster preparedness specialist move in. He had a Geiger counter and he started going around this thing on the ground."

Larry continues with his sighting report of the arrival of a *"red light, which exploded and showered down on the object"* – then, in the place of the mist, a more sold object was seen (Delta-shaped UFO, as later drawn by Betty Luca).

Larry Warren

"At this point Sgt. Bustinza, myself, a disaster preparedness man, and my shift commander, were ordered to move in on the object."

Larry then continues with his description of the shadows being cast from the object, followed by:

"...a light moved out from the side of the object and split into three. In each light you could make out what appeared to be individual beings of some kind. I saw clearly what looked like eyes, facial features, clothing and some other device, but I couldn't make out the legs of the lower extremities; it was almost as if the beings were translucent."

Gordon Williams

Larry then says he saw Wing Commander Lt. Colonel Williams approach the beings, at which point one of them adjusted his head to the officer's height, proving the 'things' were alive.

British 'Bobbies' taking photographs

The story continues with a reference to the British 'bobbies' who were still taking pictures, until their cameras were taken away from them.

Larry:

"I understand that they are no longer police officers at Woodbridge; one had a mental breakdown and the other was virtually ridiculed off the Police Force and now has an alcohol problem."

Strange lights seen

"...Then my shift commander told us to return to our vehicle. We went back over the rise and headed back to the trucks.

When we reached the parking area, we could see strange lights in the sky and these strange blue things moving around."

Boarded the vehicles and returned to Base

"We boarded our vehicles and headed back to Woodbridge with our group."

Larry – triangular object and 'being' seen to pass through windscreen

"According to other witnesses, a smaller triangular object appeared after I had gone. It was so small that one of the personnel grabbed the object by putting his arms around it. The object then moved about ten meters with him holding on to it. I know that the person concerned subsequently suffered severe health effects. Then another guy got into his pick-up truck and a being passed right through the windshield. It seemed they could go through metal and solid objects.

The driver could see its face quite clearly and he went 'bonkers' and kicked the windshield right out of the truck. Other witnesses at the scene have told me that a beam then shot down from the sky and this 'being' ran straight up into the beam into a dark shape hovering above. It wasn't possible to make out what it was."

The next morning

"The next morning I was back at Bentwaters, having coffee with a number of other guys who had been there at the incident.

I noticed that my eyes were watering profusely and I had a metallic taste in my mouth. My buddy looked at me across the table and said, 'What the hell happened to us?' I started to talk, but Sgt. Penniston told me to shut up."

Instructed to attend Security Office – asked to sign statement

At about 10am, Larry received a phone call from the Security Chief's office. When he arrived there he was met by people from the 'disaster preparedness team', who checked him and six or seven others for radiation. He was then asked to sign a security document, which consisted of a pre-typed statement which declared he had been off duty and had seen 'lights flipping through the trees'. The men were then ushered into an office and approached by members of the Armed Forces Security Service, who lectured about the 'problem'. (They didn't refer to UFOs or ET's.) The men were warned that if they communicated these events by mail, telephone, or in any shape or form, they would be court-martialed. A film was shown – "a debriefing tool", according to Larry, followed by them being warned again to "toe the line and that the Government would look after us."

Suicide on the airbase

Larry heard a humming sound to his right. He looked over and saw a man that he describes as being from the 'Bible belt', holding a small Bible, and reciting Hail Mary non-stop.

Larry:

"He went absent without leave two weeks later he was picked up by the FBI at Chicago airport, and returned to base.

I was on patrol the night he called in by telephone and said he was going to kill himself. We and another vehicle patrol responded but it was too late. He had put an M16 into his mouth; that was the first time I have ever seen violent death."

Burns to the eyes

After being fined $300 for telephoning his mother from the airbase, Larry made his way to the Optical Retina Clinic, at Lakenheath, as his eyes were causing him a problem on the 19th January 1981. He was told that he had burns to the retinas of both eyes.

[In 1984, according to Omar, Larry was told he was showing signs of radiation sickness.]

Receives an honorable discharge

In May 1981, he was given an honorable discharge on the grounds of 'breach of contract'. This is more or less the end of the interview, apart from the fact that Larry says, during an interview held with Charles Halt, in 1993, he admitted the actions of the UFOs had affected the nuclear weapons in the underground storage area. The UFO light beams had apparently penetrated the hardened nuclear storage bunkers and somehow affected the weapons stored within, making them useless.

(Source: Omar Fowler, *FSR*, Volume 40, Number 1, Spring 1995 – 'An Interview with eyewitness Larry Warren')

Nick Pope – My assessment of this

"This account of an early interview with Larry Warren perfectly illustrates the myriad of problems with Larry's story. It's a jumbled mish-mash of scenes, some of which appear completely made-up, but others of which have their roots in elements of other people's stories."

Mention of Disaster Preparedness Officer

"Take, for example, the reference to a disaster preparedness officer. The individual concerned is clearly Munroe Nevels, who was with Halt, Ball and Englund on the third night. He did indeed use his Geiger counter to check a location in the forest (not in a field, as Larry alleges) where a UFO was seen to land on the first night, but there was no UFO on the ground, and none of these individuals saw Larry at any time. The implication is clear: Larry picked up the story (or parts of it) from gossip going around the Twin Bases in the aftermath of these events, altered a few details, and then wrote himself into the story."

Mention of a 'being'

"The reference to a 'being' passing through a windshield sounds like an exaggerated version of the UFO sighting involving Bonnie Tamplin and Bobby Ball on the second night. The reference to a 'being' ascending a beam of light is interesting. Such accounts are commonplace in alien abduction stories, and Peter Robbins worked for many years as executive assistant to Budd

Hopkins, who specialised in abduction cases. So this sounds like a *meme that Larry picked up from Peter, knowing it would resonate with sections of the UFO community. The interrogation story similarly has its roots in reality, and indeed we have witness statements from Burroughs, Penniston, Cabansag, Buran and Chandler. There is, however, no witness statement from Larry – if he was a genuine witness and was interrogated, why wouldn't his statement be with the others?"

Death of a serviceman

"The claim about somebody being so traumatized by events that they committed suicide with an M16 is particularly distasteful. Key players who would have known about such a death (Williams, Halt, Penniston, etc.) say it never happened, and there are no MOD, DOD, USAF, or police records of any such suicide. Any death on a military establishment (whatever the circumstances) creates a paper trail, and with US bases in the UK, not only would the US military police be aware, but the UK civil police and the local coroner.

A question was asked in Parliament about this alleged suicide (Hansard, 28 October 1997) and it was determined that there were no records of any such death. While it's a dramatic and poignant story, it seems to have been completely fabricated."

Questions in Parliament – 28.10.1997 – Book *Left At East Gate*

Lord Hill-Norton asked Her Majesty's Government: Whether the allegations contained in the recently published book *Left At East Gate*, to the effect that nuclear weapons were stored at RAF Bentwaters and RAF Woodbridge, in violation of UK/US treaty obligations, are true.

Lord Gilbert: It has always been the policy of this and previous governments neither to confirm nor to deny where nuclear weapons are located either in the UK or elsewhere, in the past or at the present time. Such information would be withheld under exemption 1 of the Code of Practice on Access to Government Information.

Were nuclear weapons struck by light beams?

Lord Hill-Norton asked Her Majesty's Government: Whether they are aware of reports from the United States Air Force personnel that nuclear weapons stored in the Weapons Storage Area at RAF Woodbridge were struck by light beams fired from an unidentified craft seen over the base in the period 25-30 December 1980, and if so, what action was subsequently taken.

Lord Gilbert: There is no evidence to suggest that the Ministry of Defence received any such reports.

Suicide of Security Policeman from 81st Security Police Squadron

Lord Hill-Norton asked Her Majesty's Government: What information they have on the suicide of the United States security policeman from the 81st Security Police Squadron who took his life at RAF Bentwaters, in January 1981, and whether they will detail the involvement of the British police, Coroner's Office, and any other authorities concerned.

---

*A meme is an idea, behaviour, or style that spreads from person to person within a culture.

Lord Gilbert: MOD has no information concerning the alleged suicide. Investigations into such occurrences are carried out by the US Forces.

Lord Hill-Norton asked Her Majesty's Government: What information they have on the medical problems experienced by various United States Air Force personnel based at RAF Bentwaters and RAF Woodbridge, which stemmed from their involvement in the so-called Rendlesham Forest incident, in December 1980.

Lord Gilbert: Information on medical matters relating to US personnel is a matter for the US authorities.

Larry's description of the UFO in book *Left At East Gate*

In *Left At East Gate,* we are told (on page 107-108) that Bob Smith, from New York City, interviewed Larry on the telephone about his recollection of what had taken place. Interestingly Art Wallace (Larry) said:

"It appeared to have a triangular shape and was covered in pipes and valves and things. It was about 20 feet across the bottom, with sloping sides up to the top, 12ft high to 15ft high – certainly big enough to handle people."

One cannot help but compare this description with Ipswich women Laura and Angela Snook, seen during the early 1980s, and others that we had spoken to over the years.

Larry says:

"The 'ship' was inhabited. There were beings aboard. I didn't see them, because I was on the other side of the craft, but others did. They said there were three and they were wearing silver suits.

I had a strange feeling and seemed to black out. The next thing I knew it was about 5am and I was waking up, lying half across my bunk. I still had my uniform on and was up to my knees in mud. To this day I don't know how I got back to the barracks, or what happened after I saw the green light bounce off the shadows. My room-mate said I'd been brought into the room by some people – he didn't know who – and just dumped on the bed."

One wonders why Larry did not admit that it had been him that had seen the *'inhabitants'*, and why didn't he name the officer in charge who approached the *'beings'* on this occasion? Perhaps he felt some reluctance to involve himself, understanding the use of his pseudonym at that stage fearing possible retribution from the Security Services involved? Not forgetting that he was alleged to have been given drugs during the interviews that followed after the UFO sighting, which could explain away the inconsistencies between the accounts given over the years.

John Hanson on Larry Warren – Not on trial

I have been involved as a police officer in giving evidence at many 'Not guilty' Magistrate and Crown Court trials during my service – first as a uniform officer then as a detective. Common sense had always dictated that the quality of any evidence offered by the witness, particularly during cross examination, depends on it being consistent. Where there are inconsistencies there will always be concerns about the evidential value of a witness which will ultimately play a part in the final verdict.

Larry is not on trial. The facts of the matter are – this is what we are interested in. Over the years I have spoken personally to a number of witnesses who have seen what appear to be *'beings'*, stood next to a landed craft. Whether you and I would see them in the same way I cannot say, but I have no reason to disbelieve them or reject out of hand the likelihood that *'beings'* were actually aboard the craft seen in the forest that fateful weekend. Personally, I don't believe that these *'beings'* are representative of any alien/extraterrestrial incursions onto our world. I believe *'they'* are already here. What *'they'* are and where *'they'* come from I cannot say, because I do not know, but enough evidence has been offered, in my opinion, over the last 60 years, to support these hypotheses.

Charles Halt in 2014:

"What puzzles me is how much of what he says now is a result of downright lies and how much as my recently passed friend Budd Hopkins said to be induced memories. I know Larry was regressed by Patricia Gagliardo and then by Budd Hopkins. I am expecting Budd's tapes. Adrian Bustinza is another mystery. He gave me an initial statement and was then debriefed by AFOSI (Officers of Special Investigation). His version of events gets better after each session and is the basis of much of what Larry continues to say."

John Hanson

In July 2015 Charles Halt travelled to the UK (despite protestations, threats and defamatory emails sent to me over many months, by those people on face-book, who regarded the planned event at Woodbridge Community Centre, Suffolk, as something they did not want to happen).

On the day of the talk my fears were groundless, despite promise of disruption. I was pleased to see so many people from all walks of life, eager to shake Colonel Halt's hand and pose for a photograph. For me, David Bryant, and colleague Brenda Butler, the co-organiser, it was deemed a success.

Peter Robbins

This event and comments made by Charles Halt later attracted the attention of well respected Peter Robbins, co-author of *Left At East Gate*, who was known to me personally. Peter had kindly assisted us with information regarding his personal visit to the famous United Nations debate. Details of this were later published in one of the *Haunted Skies* books. He is a man that I had great respect for then. Sadly, Peter felt it appropriate to publish a book in September 2015, available on the Internet, as hard copy and E-Book – *Halt in Woodbridge: An Air Force Colonel's Thirty-Year Fight To Silence An Authentic UFO Whistle-Blower.*

The book launched an attack on the Colonel, David Bryant, and myself. Ironically Peter hadn't even been there but felt qualified to write what he did, even after I had emailed him to put the record straight following the visit of Colonel Halt. This is not the way that I conduct business – why couldn't he have emailed me or spoken to me on the telephone? More will be said on this at a later stage in the book.

The book also contained a number of questions from retired *Captain Robert Salas to Charles Halt. Once again, if Peter had emailed me, I would have asked Charles Halt to reply to those questions – then the questions could have been answered in Peter's book.

> **"The Air Force is lying about the national security implications of unidentified aerial objects at nuclear bases."**
>
> *Capt. Robert Salas (Ret.), ICBM Launch Officer, Malmstrom Air Force Base*
>
> **UFOs & Nukes: Serious Business**
> www.AfterDisclosure.com

Robert Salas

"Halt has stated that he went out in the field the third night (December 27 and 28) with four others (Zickler, Nevels, Englund, Bustinza) after Englund comes to him and says 'It's Back!', presumably because of the second night incident involving Bonnie Tamplin and Ball. Ball was there already or joined them. Halt said that Bustinza was at his side the entire time. Halt states that he was in radio contact with Colonel Williams (Wing Commander), who was back at the Command Post. (Reference: 'The Jimmy Church Show' – 2014) At some point in the evening/ early morning, some twenty or twenty-five others, airmen and civilian police came out to Capel Green, including Burroughs and Warren. Recently, Burroughs has confirmed that he saw Warren out there. Both he and Warren encountered a yellow coloured mist near ground level. He also confirmed that lights came from this mist and seemed to form some type of being, confirming a similar statement that Larry Warren has made. (Reference: KGRA radio show, 8/27/15)

WHY HAS HALT REPEATEDLY STATED THAT WARREN WAS NOT OUT THERE THAT NIGHT, WHEN OTHER WITNESSES HAVE VERIFIED IT?"

---

*Captain Robert L. Salas graduated from the U.S. Air Force Academy and spent seven years in active duty from 1964 to 1971. He also held positions at Martin Marietta and Rockwell and spent 21 years at the FAA. In the Air Force, he was an air traffic controller and a missile launch officer as well as an engineer on the Titan 3 missiles. Capt. Salas testified about a UFO incident in March of 1967, where he states that 16 nuclear missiles became non-operational at two different launch facilities immediately after guards saw UFOs hovering above. The guards could not identify these objects even though they were only about 30 feet away.

Charles Halt:

"There are two supposed witnesses, Greg Batrum and Adrian Bustinza. Greg has contradicted himself on at least two occasions and Adrian was with me the whole time I was out. John Burroughs did not even know Warren at that time. Adrian's voice even appears on my tape. After I sent the 15 or so cops back to the base, John Burroughs remained and I briefly talked with him. He asked if he and Adrian could go forward for a look. They briefly did, returned, and said nothing about any confrontation with any object or beings."

Robert Salas

"WHY HAS HALT FREQUENTLY MADE DERROGATORY STATEMENTS ABOUT WARREN'S TESTIMONY ABOUT THE EVENTS OF THAT NIGHT WHEN BUSTINZA, FOR ONE, HAS VALIDATED SOME OF HIS STATEMENTS?"

Charles Halt:

"Adrian was with me the whole time. Keep in mind he was subjected to a 'debriefing' soon after that could have influenced his memory."

Robert Salas

"Who ordered these other people to come out there and why? Halt was the senior officer in the field. He either gave the order, or Colonel Williams gave the order. Either way, Halt should have known about it. But what was the reason to have these other people out there? Halt had already reported strange lights all over the forest. There would have to be a specific purpose to have the others out there. And, since Halt would have known of their presence, he would have been involved in organizing their activities, since he would have been the senior officer. COL. HALT HAS NEVER OFFERED A DETAILED EXPLANATION AS TO WHY SO MANY PEOPLE WERE IN THE FIELD AND PREPARING FOR SOME INCIDENT. SINCE HE WAS THE SENIOR OFFICER IN THE FIELD, HOW DOES HE EXPLAIN THIS?"

Charles Halt:

"The 15 or so cops were already out there when I arrived. I was shocked and quite upset knowing the potential for an embarrassing public relations incident. Obviously, Bruce Englund took it upon himself to take the 'team' out."

Robert Salas

"In a recent radio interview, Adrian Bustinza admitted he was interrogated by US intelligence agents about the RFI. Halt has always claimed he was never interrogated by USAF intelligence agents or any other agency about the RFI.

SINCE EVERY OTHER WITNESS TO THE RFI WAS INTERROGATED (SOME BY EXTRAORDINARY TECHNIQUES), HOW DOES HALT EXPLAIN HIS CLAIM THAT HE WAS NOT INTERROGATED? HE

WAS ONE OF THE PRIMARY WITNESSES. IF GOVERNMENT AGENCIES WANTED TO OBTAIN AS MUCH TESTIMONY AS POSSIBLE TO EXPLAIN THE EVENTS, HIS TESTIMONY WOULD HAVE BEEN IMPORTANT. THIS RAISES THE QUESTION AS TO WHETHER OR NOT HALT COULD HAVE BEEN IN COLLUSION WITH THOSE AGENCIES."

Charles Halt:

"You obviously do not understand how the OSI and their counterparts operate. They do not report to anyone on the base and only notify the senior leadership when they feel it necessary. I personally confronted the OSI Commander, Chuck Matthews, and told him of the encounter. His reply was they were not interested – an obvious lie, as I later learned of the 'debriefings' and that they took place in his building. I am convinced I was left out, as they had already done a good job of using Warren and others with a planted story that would make the incident, if it ever got out, as unbelievably. Disinformation is an 'agency' speciality. Perhaps you didn't know that?"

Robert Salas

"Major Zickler was in charge of base security, but he worked for Halt and was with Halt on the third night. Halt claims he never knew about the interrogations, even though it was Zickler who ordered the men to report for the interrogations. Major Zickler was not with me. He stayed at the party, as did all the other police officers. Zickler did want to be involved publically. He certainly got involved later behind the scenes.

AS DEPUTY BASE COMMANDER, ONE OF HALT'S RESPONSIBILITIES WAS BASE SECURITY. WHY WAS HE NOT TOLD THAT THE MEN UNDER HIM WERE BEING INTERROGATED?"

Charles Halt:

"I already covered this earlier. When the OSI and their counterparts do things, they don't usually tell the base leaders."

Robert Salas

"In a recent statement, Adrian Bustinza said that Colonel Halt ordered him to confiscate all cameras and recorders in the field on the third night."

Charles Halt:

"I did not confiscate any cameras or recorders. The only recorder was my pocket cassette recorder and the only camera was the 35mm camera Nevels had."

Robert Salas

"WHY DID HE ORDER THAT ALL CAMERAS AND RECORDERS BE CONFISCATED? THIS WAS SUPPOSED TO BE AN INVESTIGATION. MORE PHOTOS WOULD HAVE HELPED IN SUCH AN INVESTIGATION."

Charles Halt:

"I did not order or have any equipment confiscated. There were no other cameras or recorders. Warren's claim of tripod mounted cameras and British Police is nonsense. I have statements from the Suffolk Police that deny any British participation while I was out. The Police Constables did make a daytime visit and wrote the incident off."

Robert Salas

"Halt has only released nineteen minutes of the tape recording he did that night.

HE WAS OUT THERE FOR ABOUT THREE HOURS. WHY HAS HE NOT RELEASED THE ENTIRE TAPE?"

Charles Halt:

"I only had one tape and no spare batteries, so I only recorded when I thought it important. I never expected to be out that long or to have such an experience."

Robert Salas

"He has told me (and others) that he is withholding some key information/evidence about the incident as a way to protect himself. WHY OR FROM WHOM DOES HE FEEL THE NEED TO PROTECT HIMSELF?"

Charles Halt:

"When it became public, I realized there was potential for an effort to silence me."

Robert Salas

"IF WHAT HE IS WITHOLDING WILL BRING SOME CLARITY TO THIS CASE, ISN'T HE DOING A DISSERVICE TO THE CAUSE OF TRUTH IN THIS MATTER?"

Charles Halt:

"What I have kept for safe keeping is a recording I later made that details what happened. It does not contain any new information. I did send a copy to Larry Facwett and Barry Greenwood as they were working with Warren at the time. They quickly discovered Warren to have lied to them and dropped the idea of a book. Warren even admitted to them he lied about his involvement. Read the new book when its available early next year as it's detailed."

Robert Salas

"Halt claims there was no underground facility at Bentwaters. He certainly should have known. He has claimed, as Deputy Base Commander, he knew everything about the base. It IS MY UNDERSTANDING THAT IT HAS RECENTLY BEEN DETERMINED THAT THERE WAS INDEED AN UNDERGROUND FACILITY. HOW DOES COL. HALT EXPLAIN THIS DISCREPANCY IN HIS TESTIMONY?"

Charles Halt:

"Who says there is an underground facility? Warren's book shows a picture of the command post and says that's where he entered an underground facility by way of an elevator. Go visit the command post, as it's a museum and open. This whole claim is so far out that I'm surprised it's in their book. Warren initially claimed he was kidnapped and taken underground. Later he say's it was Adrian. Warren's mother sums it up well when she says Larry was always a good liar."

18ᵗʰ April 1984 – Taped interview of Adrian Bustinza and Larry Warren

Adrian Bustinza identifies Colonel Halt as being there. Adrian's account-

"He pointed to the individuals he wanted to go with him, so we went back to Bentwaters, grabbed two lights-alls and had a patrol refuel them. When we got to point 'A' – the sighting of the UFO – the light-alls and the truck wouldn't run. We started to search.

One individual said he had spotted the object sitting on the ground. We proceeded to look and found triangular tripods burn into the ground at three different standpoints. They took radiation readings off the holes and they got a radiation reading, as I recall. Then I recall we were walking through the woods and we came upon the lights again, and that's when I first saw the object. We got, I think it was flight Chief Sergeant Ball and another individual officer. We kept searching the area, trying to follow the object moving through the trees. In the process we came across a yellow mist, about two or three feet off the ground; it was like dew, but nothing I've seen before. We ignored it . . . we were worried about the [other] object to see if we could locate it again, or catch up to it again. We did see the object again. It was hovering low, like moving up and down anywhere from 10-20ft, back up, back down. There was a red light on top and several blue lights on the bottom.

There was also like a prism [rainbow lights] on top and several other colours. It was a tremendous size. It even surprised me that it was able to fit into the clearing – a tremendous size, and I use the word carefully. It was round, circular shape. I hate to say like a plate, but it was thicker at the centre that at the edge. We were ordered to form a perimeter around the object at 15ft intervals. After about 30 minutes of observation, it suddenly took off, and was gone in a flash.

When it left we were hit by a blast of cold wind, which blew towards us for 5-10 seconds. It was a really scary feeling. I was just frozen in place, at first. My life actually passed in front of my eyes."

Claims that Gordon Williams was there

In this interview, Bustinza neither denied nor confirmed the presence of alien beings. But he said that the Base Commander – Gordon Williams – arrived at the site and that photograph and films were taken by both British and American personnel.

"There was two 'Bobbies' there. Colonel Halt approached myself and Larry Warren (was it Larry? I'm trying to remember) I'm not too sure of the other guy's name. Halt told us to approach

the individuals who were standing in the grass area; they had some sophisticated camera equipment, which wasn't unusual for the British. Halt told us to confiscate the material from them, which we did, and he (Colonel Halt) put it into a plastic bag, telling us it would be dealt with at the highest level of command. He didn't say exactly at what level or anything. I assume it went to the photography department on base; it could easily have been the intelligence department as well."

Charles Halt:

"According to Bustinza, he and Larry were out in the forest before I arrived, and then came back and went out with me; he never told me what he saw. He claims they saw a craft. Obviously, if this is true, it is of some importance with regard to the chronology of what happened down there. This may well have been the reason why Bruce Englund came out to get me on the evening. I must reiterate that apart from the report of yellow fog being seen by Larry Warren, there is no evidence to support the claims made that an alien craft landed and that Gordon Williams entered into some sort of a dialogue with the entities. This is completely untrue."

Alien meetings in the forest – disinformation!

On page 217 of the book *Clear Intent*, it is written: '*Wallace said that the version of the story leaked to the British media detailing alien meetings in the forest and landing marks on the ground were deliberately contrived by the military to mislead the public. The false evidence was intended to be discovered by UFO investigators so that a negative evaluation would be ascribed to the story, thus preserving secrecy.*'

Larry Fawcett and Barry Greenwood also remarked on the similarities with what 'Art' had to tell them and what Charles Halt had to say in his Memo.

Surprisingly in this account (which must have been fresh in the mind of the witness)

1. No evidence of any alien figures seen in the forest by the craft

2. There was no information about the threats made by the AFFS agents, i.e., 'Bullets are cheap'

3. The phone call to his mother.

4. The meeting with Captain Colman, who warned him about giving out sensitive information on the phone.

5. Being driven with Adrian Bustinza to a small cafeteria dining area, then subjected to some form of applied anaesthetic following which they were taken into a room accessed by an electronic seal (6 feet tall by 4 feet wide) and of being shown a large screen, behind which stood a small 'figure' – evidence of telepathic communication between the 'small figure' and Larry to the effect that they were *in a facility far below the airbase,* and that the installations contained many of its kind, along with human support personnel.

6. Told telepathically that the facility had been there since the 1940s and expanded in the late 1960s. The 'crafts' they travelled in entered and exited via an extensive tunnel system. One exit was a mile off Lowestoft, Suffolk, and the other near Orford Key. One might be inclined

to wonder why nobody who was employed at that facility has ever come forward during the last 35 years to confirm that this underground base existed.

Airman James David Hudnall – Three ghostly *'figures'* seen

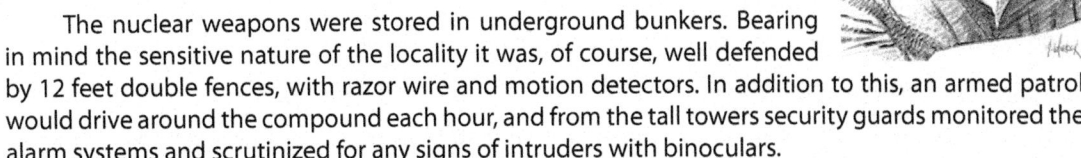

An example of yet another sighting which took place in the forest – this time involving three *'figures'* seen approaching the Tower from inside the compound – took place, according to ex serviceman *James David Hudnall, who served at RAF Bentwaters during the mid-1970s.

He remembers how eerie it was during night duty, while surrounded by thick forest. One winter foggy night, he and another airman (Andy) were on duty guarding the high security areas, which included the weapons storage area.

The nuclear weapons were stored in underground bunkers. Bearing in mind the sensitive nature of the locality it was, of course, well defended by 12 feet double fences, with razor wire and motion detectors. In addition to this, an armed patrol would drive around the compound each hour, and from the tall towers security guards monitored the alarm systems and scrutinized for any signs of intruders with binoculars.

Andy was the first to see the *'figures'*. Unfortunately he was unable to obtain any clear images, due to the conditions, but he knew they should not have been there and alerted the patrolling jeep by radio.

"As the headlights shone onto the 'figures', they disappeared from sight. A search was conducted, but no trace could be found of them."

Ghostly footsteps ascending the watchtower

The story doesn't end here. Later the same night, Andy heard footsteps moving up the metal steps of the tower, causing a vibration. Wondering who was there he opened the trapdoor and shone a torch down, but couldn't see anything.

"By this time they were getting louder, so I picked-up my firearm and stood waiting. The trapdoor swung wide open, but there was nothing to be seen."

Andy decided not to report this incident, fearing ridicule.

Ghostly tapping noises heard at the Quick Response area

Another incident, involving what appears to be a further example of ghostly manifestation, occurred at the Quick Response area at RAF Bentwaters. This was also a top secret installation where aircraft, carrying nuclear bombs, were fuelled up in a state of readiness, with a strip of runway between them, should they be called on to respond to a specific threat. For obvious reasons, this

*James D. Hudnall has been a professional writer of comics and articles since 1986. His comics' series *Harsh Realm*, with Andrew Paquette was made into a TV series on FOX. His latest project is *Blue Cat,* an online graphic novel published by Aces Weekly – an online anthology. Hudnall's first novel, *The Age of Heroes: Hell's Reward,* was released in October 2013. James is working on the final issue of *2 To the Chest*, which was published in 2014 as a completed graphic novel. A second series of novels, the Secret Team, is slated to debut in 2015.

was a well fortified place with high security presence, including an armed guard on each aircraft. The only way into this compound was via a gate shack manned by guards. One night, one of the men heard a tapping on the roof.

The grinning man appears

James David Hudnall

At first he thought it was starting to rain, but after not seeing any and with the tapping noise increasing in sound (now a thumping noise) he went out to have a look. He was amazed to see, on top of the gate shack, the figure of a man who appeared to be grinning as he stomped on the roof. The guard cocked his rifle and ordered him not to move, and called for back-up on the radio.

After hearing what he took to be the patrol car moving closer, he turned to have a look. When he looked back, the apparition had gone!

(Source: Personal interview & Georgina Bruni *'You Cant Tell The People'*)

The reader will hear of other accounts, involving strange 'figures' and allegations of ghostly manifestations, reported by the security personnel at RAF Woodbridge and RAF Bentwaters. Some of those people still find it emotive to talk about their experiences.

Airman Steve Wagner – Ghostly encounter

Steve Wagner himself witnessed what he described as the appearance of a *'Lady without a face'* which he says had also been seen by other servicemen.

> *"It wasn't anything that most would admit seeing. I do not recall the date, I was driving the van back from Woodbridge to Bentwaters after swing shift shift change and I came upon what I thought was a woman riding a bike. What got me to realize I was seeing "her" (I had heard previous stories about her) was the pace at which she was moving; because when I went to pass her she kept pace with the van (I was going about 45mph). I looked over and she turned what was a completely blank space (where her face should have been) to me. I punched it and took off. Only encounter I ever had with her."*

Lisa Landi

Lisa Landi joined an on-line website forum, wanting to tell them about her husband 'Mike's' experiences:

> *"I joined the group because my husband had two different experiences, while stationed at RAF/Bentwaters. I have been following Jim and John's story and there is so much more to go along with it that makes no sense. My husband was in 'C' flight as a security policeman. He has been suffering from terrible PTSD, due to the memories coming back. His one experience occurred before Jim and John's and was told to them and it freaked them out. He had another paranormal experience at Twin Oaks Farm House, where he was living with some buddies, which totally freaked out Jim and he ran away and it totally freaked out another guy to the point he became a bible thumper."*

Ghostly manifestations at other USAF Bases

To those that scoff at such reports, believing that they are the result of over excited imagination, we found other reports from locations, which included RAF Alconbury – involving an amazing encounter with a weird giant, hairy, humanoid creature, which jumped over the security fence and was then shot at by USAF Police officers guarding the perimeter. The same airbase was the scene of a number of chilling ghostly encounters, involving children being heard by the airmen on top of the security towers, according to California citizen – Wesley Uptergrove.

"On the third day of my duty at RAF Alconbury, in the early 1970s, I was instructed to take over the 8pm – 4am night shift for a member of the security patrol, who had gone sick. This involved keeping watch over the airbase from a 25 feet concrete tower, one of six that lined the inside of a corridor encircling the perimeter of the airbase. After being transported to the site, I climbed up the ladder and settled down for the night. As night descended I stood there, unable to even see the next tower, due to the darkness and foggy conditions.

I became aware of an area of clearing that stretched out from the fence, bordering a dense forest, which I found, for some strange reason, very unsettling, although I cannot identify why I felt like this. At about 6am, I was sat on the floor inside the tower, reading a book by flashlight, when suddenly I heard the unmistakable sound of happy children's voices, rising and falling – as if borne on the wind rather than a fixed source. Puzzled, I went out onto the catwalk and peered into the darkness, feeling perplexed rather than frightened. All of a sudden, the voices stopped. I was about to re-enter the tower when, in that split second, the voices were all around me – so close and so loud, as if I was in a school playground. With my heart racing, I made my way down the ladder to the ground; the voices were just as loud. I felt surrounded.... then they began to fade away, leaving me awe struck and amazed by what I regarded as a privileged experience."

Wesley described a visit to the local Library in an attempt to discover the folklore of the area, hoping to find a clue as to what had happened. He was surprised to learn that a number of children had been killed in a train derailment that had occurred close to the airbase, many years ago.

Wesley:

"I don't know if the two are connected. All I know is that however strange the story might seem, it actually happened and, apart from immediate members of my family, I have never told anybody about what I experienced and will never forget as long as I live."

Another frightening incident involved an airman who was on the runway, carrying out repairs on an aircraft, according to retired USAF serviceman Roger Barton, who worked there.

"He was carrying out some routine work to an F-5 Aircraft, parked on the runway – a job that should have been completed in an hour. When he failed to make the telephone call, requesting a lift back from the hangar, a search party went out to find him. They found him sitting in the aircraft, as white as a sheet, with the canopy closed. Although I asked him many times what it was that he had seen, he declined to tell me saying that it had frightened him so much, and refused to go anywhere near that location again."

Close encounter with creature close to nuclear bunker

Some time in the late 1960 RAF Alconbury security sergeants Randi Lee and Jackson were on patrol with their two dogs, when they saw some movement near the towers and called the Main Gate to check if any workmen were still on site. When told not, they asked for a truck response team to assist with searching the area. As they approached a tower, they came face-to-face with a hairy figure.

Randi:

"The dogs stopped in their tracks, absolutely terrified, frantically trying to get away. Jackson urged the dog to attack the intruder, but was bitten by his own animal – that's how frightened the dogs were. The truck arrived just in time to see the creature, whatever it was, climbing over the security fence, where it was last seen entering North Woods."

Security airman Wesley Uptergrove was another witness:

"I was the NCOIC of a group of three men and their dogs, charged with guarding bunkers, underneath which were stored, I believe, nuclear warheads within a large, fenced area. One foggy night, I received a radio call; there was an intruder within the perimeter and shots had been fired. I tore out in his truck and sped towards the location of the shooting. Seeing a figure in the fog, I pulled over, thinking it was one of he guards. I rolled down the window and was screamed at, full in the face, by what I can only be describe as a man-like, bipedal creature. I nearly wet myself in fear. In an instant the thing ran off at incredible speed; I drove after it."

Guards fired at the creature!

"Within moments it had sped past another of the guards, who also fired upon it. He missed, due to the fact he was practically dragged backwards by his guard dogs that were yelping and straining to flee in the opposite direction. The third guard and his dogs were running towards the scene when they turned the corner of a bunker, only to be intercepted by the creature running at full speed. As his dogs wailed, the thing hit the taut leashes and pulled them away from his grasp, lacerating a good deal of skin from the unfortunate man's forearm in the process. We saw this creature make fantastic, running bounds across the grounds before leaping over two tall, well-spaced barbed wire fences in a single bound. It disappeared into the surrounding woods. I only saw it briefly the whole situation was fast, confusing, and difficult to process. It was hairy, approximately 5ft 9ins. in height, and had intelligent, human-like eyes, a flat nose, and large ears. The teeth were large but not fanged. The lower face was rounded in a way that suggested the look of a walrus. The face was narrow around the eyes, but the head flared out again at the top. It had very muscular, frog-like thighs, with what appeared to be reversed articulated legs like a horse."

13th March 1984 – extract from *Hansard*

*Major Sir Patrick Wall asked the Secretary of State for Defence, Mr Lee (1) "how many alleged landings by Unidentified flying objects have been made in 1980, 1981 1983, and 1983 respectively; and how many have been investigated by his Department's personnel: (2) How many unexplained sightings there have been in 1980, 1981, 1982, and 1983, respectively; and which of these had been traced by radar and with what result?

Reply from Mr Lee (pursuant to his reply 9th March 1984 c 728j)

"For the years in question the MOD received the following numbers of reports of sightings of flying objects which the observer could not identify, 350, 600, 250 and 390; reports of alleged landings are not separately identified. The department was satisfied that <u>none of these reports</u> was of any Defence significance and in such cases, does not maintain records of the extent of its investigation."

19th April – UFO lands on runway!

Was there any connection with a report from three experienced air traffic controllers, who attempted to 'talk in' a UFO that landed on the runway before them, which occurred at an airbase in East Anglia. One can only wonder where this Airbase was and if there was any connection with Bentwaters or Woodbridge?

A senior air traffic controller (SATCO) was supervising his deputy and an assistant. According to the report, the deputy was in contact with a light aircraft preparing to land on runway 22, when the SATCO noticed lights approaching the other runway.

The unidentified object came in at speed, made a 'touch and go' on runway 27, then departed at terrific speed in a near vertical climb, according to the files. It was described as *"...a brilliant solid 'ball of light', bright silvery in colour"*. The file noted that 'witnesses do not wish to be identified in case their professional integrity is questioned'.

(Source: Declassified File, PRO)

10th May – Letter from the MOD re UFO sightings

Following consultation, the MOD decided, quote:

'Not to publish reports of alleged UFO sightings we receive. As you may know, we get several hundreds of these each year and to prepare them for publication would be a considerable editorial task for which we have neither the staff nor resources. This would also fall well outside our defence responsibilities. However for some time we have been prepared to release the details of particular reports to serious enquirers, provided the information was easily identifiable and readily to hand. That continues to be our policy.'

---

*Patrick Henry Bligh Wall, politician and Marine officer: born 19 October 1916; commissioned in the Royal Marines 1935, Acting Major 1943, Major 1949; MC 1945; MP (Conservative) for Haltemprice Division of Hull 1954- 55, for Haltemprice Division of East Yorkshire 1955-83, for Beverley 1983- 87; Chairman, Monday Club 1978-80; Kt 1981; married 1953 Sheila Putnam (died 1983; one daughter); died Chichester, West Sussex 15 May 1998.

June – Charles Halt promoted to full Colonel

In June 1984, Colonel Cochran left the Airbase. Charles I. Halt was then promoted to a full Colonel and Base Commander.

July – YUFOS (Civilian Aerial Phenomena Research Organization)

Mark Ian Birdsall of the Yorkshire UFO Society, who was very curious about the UFO incident, wrote to Captain Kathleen T. McCollum OIC, at Public Affairs Division, RAF Woodbridge, in late July 1984, asking her about whether the wooded area involved had been destroyed, and whether the object was, in fact, a remotely-controlled vehicle being jointly tested by the CIA and the MOD.

She replied:

"I am not in a position to verify or disprove anything printed about our supposed UFO sighting. There was no official investigation of any kind done, so I have no documents to refer to. Current policy is that we no longer investigate UFO sightings and we haven't done so for many years."

1984 – Book: *Clear Intent*

In this book (published in 1984 by Prentice-Hall Inc., Englewood Cliffs, New Jersey) Larry Warren's version of what happened to him, following interviews with Barry Greenwood and Larry Fawcett, is more or less identical in part to what was written in *Left At East Gate*. Larry (referred to as Art Wallace) describes the landing in the forest and of finding himself back in the barracks fully dressed and up to his knees in mud. He then tells of being summonsed to the Commander's office, along with other security policeman where civilians were gathered, who, according to Larry, gave an impression of being CIA agents. The policemen were warned politely not to discuss the matter and then led into another room, where civilians ordered them in a far more forceful manner not to discuss the matter with anyone else. They were also checked for radiation, debriefed for an hour, and shown films depicting aircraft and UFOs. Wallace was told that they were being shown this so they might understand the need for secrecy on the events of the 30th.

Charles Halt – Impossible scenario!

"In the book **Left At East Gate***, the authors misidentifies the Command Post as the photo lab as the entry point for the 'underground' facility. We all know that's impossible, as it sits on several feet of reinforced concrete and now is open as a museum.*

I would invite anyone to go look for themselves. This sounds more like science fiction than reality... what a load of rubbish. This is figments of imagination. I met up with Larry Warren and Peter Robbins in Washington, back in the early 1990s. Larry admitted then to me that he didn't trust his memory or the imagery that was in his mind, because of what happened to him. So with all due respects, how does he know what is real and what is not? Let's not forget I went out there to debunk the thing, after Lt. Bruce Englund told me that it's back. It's not as if I am a sceptic after what I saw. I appreciate that Larry and some of the other men were subjected to vigorous interview and that the use of drugs was used, which appears to have created some false memories. Obviously following on from their experiences in the forest, their accounts will always be open to question. I can only tell you what I know based on hard facts, rather than wild unsubstantiated claims involving aliens who met with Gordon Williams and conversations with non-human beings under the airbase."

Paranormal activity in Rendlesham Forest

As the reader is aware, over the years there has been all manner of strange things caught on camera and seen with the naked eye in and around Rendlesham Forest. Reports of small stones, mysteriously being levitated through the air and seen falling to the ground are not rare. Such events have been witnessed by many people, including ourselves.

Retired Disaster Preparedness administration clerk at RAF Bentwaters – 'Mitch' Fryman – was living at 105 Tangham, situated in the middle of Rendlesham Forest, Suffolk, during January 1984 to February 1986, close to RAF Woodbridge airbase.

Like so many others that we had spoken to over the years, he was initially very hesitant about telling us what he had experienced fearing possible ridicule.

What people fail to realise is that, over the years, Dawn Holloway and myself have heard so many extraordinary tales which, taken individually, would be only too easy to explain away with a myriad of natural explanations – anything rather than accepting the impossible! Collectively, these sightings and experiences teach us otherwise!

Mitchell Fryman

"My co-workers asked me what happened and I told them I thought a deer had hit me (knowing that was a lie). Seeing the damage, one co-worker commented that the impact alone should have broken the glass and didn't believe it to be a deer. I didn't think about the glass still being intact at the time of the accident, but it made sense. I took the car to a garage in Woodbridge for an estimate. I also told the repairman that I thought it was a deer, but he didn't think so either. He, too, was suspicious as to why the glass didn't break. He said 'I don't know what hit you mate, but you should have been eating glass.'

I was not injured. The door had to be replaced. I don't know what to conclude and it's still unexplainable. I realise deer will hit and run off objects and just because I didn't."

Mitchell:

"I lived across the alley from Vince Thurkettle (my front door faced the camp site) I did experience seeing a ball of fog once, while walking along a logging path not far from my house – the most traumatizing event that happened to me I will not discuss. It's too weird and I still have nightmares now and then."

September 1985 – Struck by an invisible force!

"One morning in late September 1985, I was my driving my 1984 Austin Mini to RAF Bentwaters for duty, after having left my house at 105 Tangham, at approximately 7am. The weather conditions were fair with just a slight fog. I was at the stop sign, intending to turn left onto the 'B' road to go to RAF Bentwaters."

Felt a thud on the car

"There were no cars, animals; nothing around at all. It was very quiet so I turned and drove along the road, changing from third gear to fourth, when I felt a thud around my driver's side rear wheel – like I had run over something, or hit a pothole.

Whatever it was applied enough force to spin me clockwise 180 degrees, and so now I was facing the other direction. Startled, I gathered myself and looked for an injured animal.

Realising I was mostly in the other lane, I u-turned and parked off the road. I got out and again looked for an injured animal. I didn't find one, so I then looked for a pothole – no pothole either – so I walked back to my car, only to have a shocking sight. My driver's door was completely smashed in. It was smashed from hinge to handle, from window to frame."

Damage appeared to have been sucked from the inside!

"The damage was self-contained to the door only and nothing to the quarter panels – as if the door had been the target. The damage was so weird, since the Austin Mini is such a small car. There was no blood, no saliva, no hair, no scratches anywhere, and oddly no impact point. It looked like it was sucked from the inside. There wasn't a noise either, like a bark or a yelp, etc.

Confused, I replayed the event over to understand what happened. Doing so raised some serious questions: (1) why did I spin in the first place? (2) How did I get in the other lane against the momentum of the spin? (3) Taking a direct side hit, why wasn't I pushed off the road? (4) How could that damage occur when I didn't feel an impact there?

I became very frightened and proceeded to Bentwaters. Why didn't I return home? – I don't know. It was difficult to drive because I was feeling faint and weepy, weaving about in the road. I was relieved to finally park at Disaster Preparedness.

Upon entering the building my supervisor noticed how shaken I was and commented that I looked like I'd seen a ghost."

Taken to local Garage for repair

Mitchell – Mysterious tapping noises in the attic:

"During the nearly two years living at 105 Tangham, it was fairly common to hear activity in the attic. In June 1984, I was changing out of my uniform when I first heard the tapping sound above my head, sounding like it was coming from the attic. I dismissed it as probably a squirrel or a bird that had got in there somehow.

A few days later I decided to check the attic for any evidence of an animal – but there was no nest or droppings, no scratch marks, no food scraps, no feathers or hair, etc., to verify that. It was never a sound of human footsteps or sounds of an animal either. It was a single tap in between the support beams along the front exterior wall going back and forth in my bedroom that would suddenly start and suddenly stop. I could hear an actual tap on the ceiling, but between the beams was fibreglass insulation so there shouldn't have been direct contact. It was never a scampering on the beam.

The taps would only occur when I was already in the room. It was always the same sound every few months or so. One time I actually followed along with it as it travelled back and forth. I never heard the sound anywhere else upstairs – always the same place, keeping the same course. One Sunday morning in November 1985, the taps were continuous to the point that it got annoying. Later, I got the stepladder and a flashlight and raised the attic hatch to again investigate what was making the sound, and again no evidence of anything unusual. While living there I was probably in the attic 5-6 times and never encountered anything whatsoever.

I suspect it's possible the house had an occasional entity because of the activity in the alley, but I never saw or felt a presence in the house. I don't know what caused the tap sounds, but I do know it wasn't an animal."

Strange images captured on camera at the Henry McPike Mansion

Mitchell told us about what he had photographed at Alton, Illinois – the location of a well-known haunted house – the Henry McPike Mansion.

"I have these two pictures of paranormal. Photo 1 – you will see, on the left, a close up of a girl's face, in the middle a human-shaped black shadow, a human face on its right 'arm', and on the right a girl standing (in a long white gown) where it should be brick.

Photo 2 – you will see four shadows on the staircase. These were taken just seconds apart. It is said that people report seeing a young girl in a white gown in the grounds sometimes. The owner of the house says the face is of Henry."

Photo 1

Photo 2

August – *Flying Saucer Review*

Jenny Randles wrote an article in *Flying Saucer Review*, relating to the ongoing investigation into the incident, which was published in August 1984. She praised Dot and Brenda for their *"phenomenal amount of hard work-over three years and still flat out".*

Jenny told the readers about 'Art Wallace' (Larry Warren) who had approached US Police Lieutenant Larry Fawcett, of CAUS, and Barry Greenwood – a regular US contributor to *FSR*.

"Art's story went a great deal further than anything we had yet heard, for he spoke of having been rendered unconscious and then waking up in an underground room where a secret liaison between the USAF and the aliens was explained! This was taking place underneath the Base."

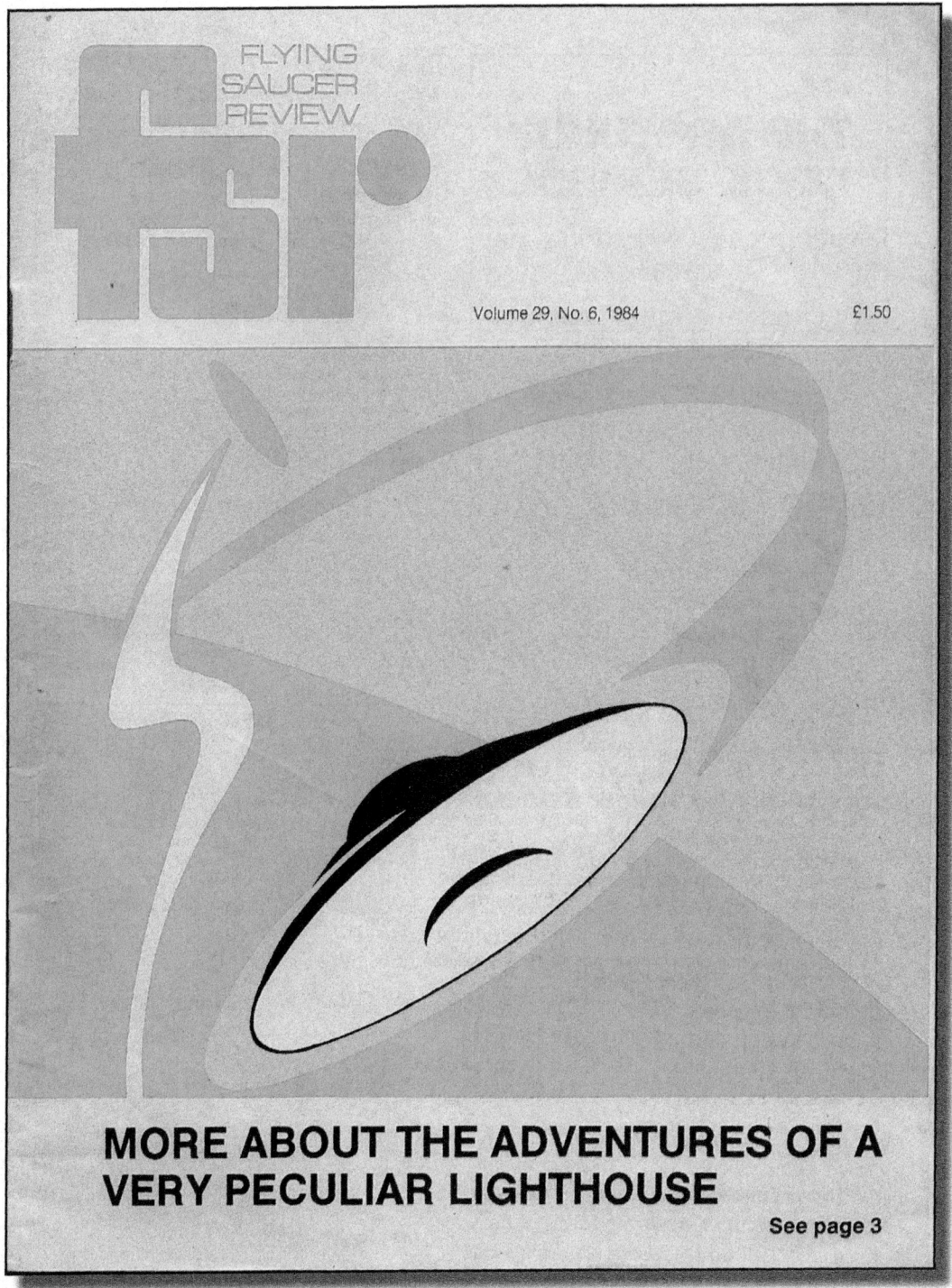

FLYING
SAUCER
REVIEW

fsr

Volume 29, No. 6, 1984 £1.50

MORE ABOUT THE ADVENTURES OF A VERY PECULIAR LIGHTHOUSE

See page 3

1984 – *Sky Crash* is published by Neville Spearman

(The name of the book was intended to be *'The Rendlesham Forest Mystery'*) Chris Pennington who was the partner of Brenda Butler showed us a sketch he had drawn depicting an idea of how the cover was going to be.

 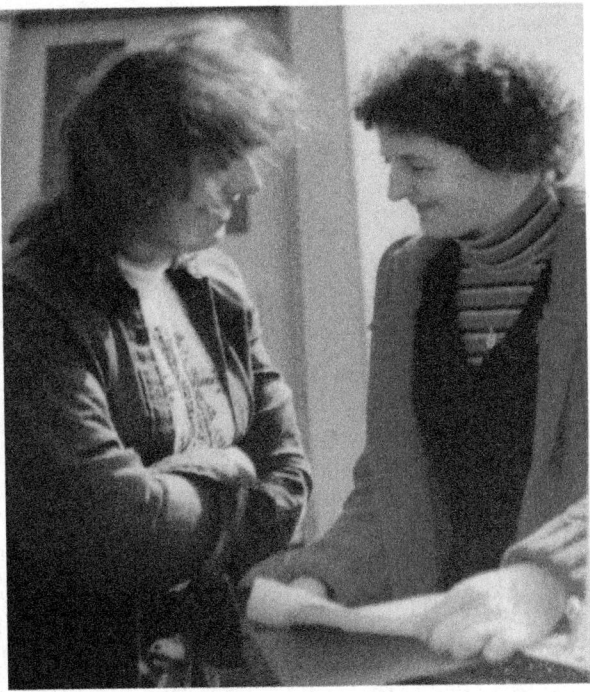

In a bid calculated to gain the reader's attention was the explosive announcement on the first page, quote:

'The figures were small; he estimated about three feet two inches in height. He saw three and they looked identical, wearing all over silver suits. They hovered close to the ground, suspended in a shaft of light that emerged from the underside of the craft. The Commander who had the contact – Wing Commander Williams – went forward, close up to the entities, and everybody else was ordered back. He then seemed to communicate with the aliens.'

Then prior to the prologue on page 1, is this statement:

"They don't know my real name. If they find out, they will ruin me.
They will blow my head off in the street, or something. If my name is used, I think I am a dead man."
– Art Wallace.

Sketch from a deep throat source

We asked Brenda about page 183 of *Sky Crash*, which showed an intriguing sketch endorsed *'based on the contents of the files of Colonel Halt'* from a *'deep throat source'* (deep throat is the

pseudonym given to secret informants), wondering where this had come from, as it referred to the 29th/30th December 1980. Brenda thought it may have been John Burroughs' sketch.

We contacted Colonel Halt, who denied ever having seen it. The only sketch he associated with John Burroughs was the one submitted by him, which has been previously shown in this book.

Jenny Randles

We emailed Jenny Randles about the identity of the sketch in late July 2013.

"Something at the back of my mind suggests it came from one of the face-to-face meetings that Halt had, in June 1983, with the small group of people who met him then. I was not one of them and did not know these meetings had occurred until Dot told me, a few weeks later. Allegedly, the Halt tape was played there also – a year before it was ever released to anyone – though the description of what was supposedly on it seems wrong. If I recall this was a sketch one of those attendees did, based upon the testimony they were shown during a visit to Halt from then unreleased evidence like the tape held on base. So not actually (a fake) a sketch directly by a witness but based on the account of a witness then not in the public domain (which in June 1983 was still pretty well everything). I think it is meant to portray the part on the tape where the lights 'explode' from the winking eye. It is certainly from the Saturday night – Halt reconnaissance site encounter – not the Burroughs/Penninston episode."

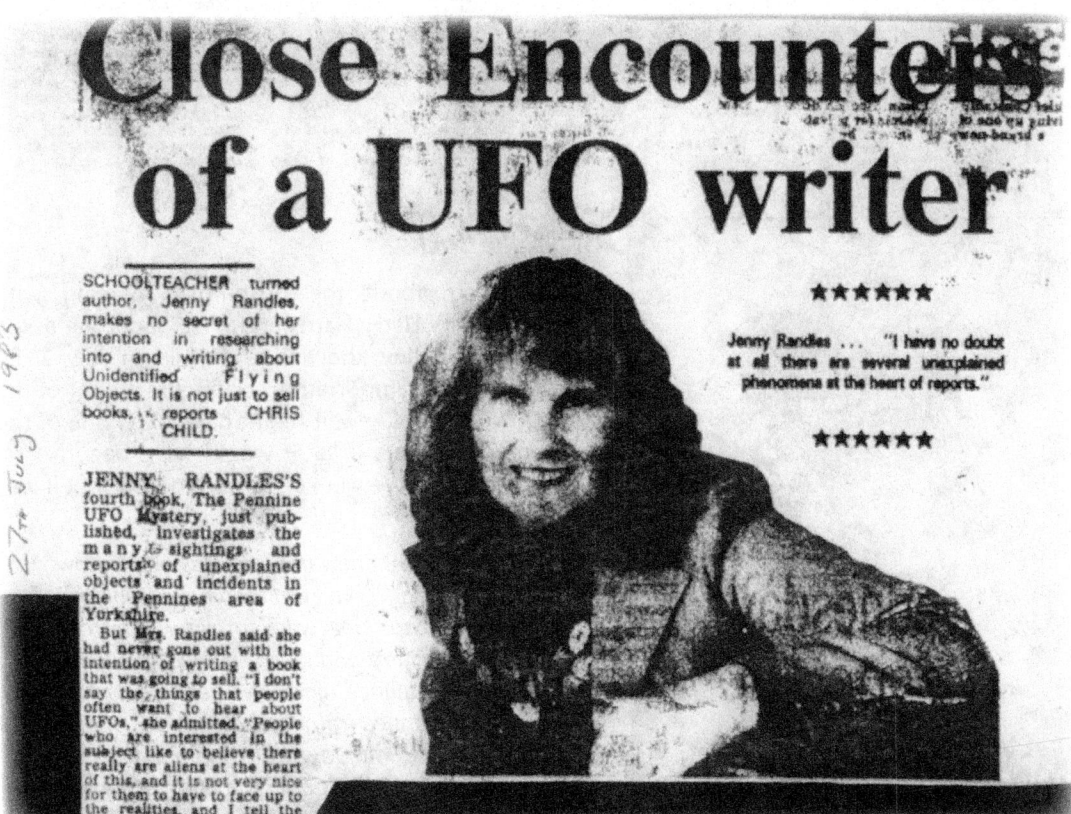

Close Encounters of a UFO writer

27th July 1983

SCHOOLTEACHER turned author, Jenny Randles, makes no secret of her intention in researching into and writing about Unidentified Flying Objects. It is not just to sell books, reports CHRIS CHILD.

JENNY RANDLES'S fourth book, The Pennine UFO Mystery, just published, investigates the many sightings and reports of unexplained objects and incidents in the Pennines area of Yorkshire.

But Mrs. Randles said she had never gone out with the intention of writing a book that was going to sell. "I don't say the things that people often want to hear about UFOs," she admitted. "People who are interested in the subject like to believe there really are aliens at the heart of this, and it is not very nice for them to have to face up to the realities, and I tell the realities."

★★★★★

Jenny Randles ... "I have no doubt at all there are several unexplained phenomena at the heart of reports."

★★★★★

Thirty-one-year-old Mrs. Randles, a former geology teacher in Cheshire, turned her attention full-time to UFOs five years ago. She first became intrigued with them on holiday in Blackpool 20 years ago. Now she is director of investigations for the British UFO Research Association, a job she carries out from her home at Wallasey, Merseyside.

Photographs

"We are learning pretty well to isolate the cases reported to us very quickly so that we now don't waste a lot of time with misidentification. We used to become very frustrated spending a lot of time on things that were completely worthless," she said.

Since the hit film Close Encounters of the Third Kind in 1978 there have been reports that sightings of UFOs had increased four-fold. But Mrs. Randles says that the opposite has happened — sightings have decreased considerably because people have become more aware of what there is in the sky.

In the past about 10 per cent of all sightings made were unexplainable. Now Mrs. Randles says that figure has risen to about 30 per cent.

The Pennines area is of particular interest to her because of the amount of UFO activity reported there during the past 10 years.

"There is no question that the Pennine area has definitely generated far more UFO sightings than anywhere in the U.K. over the past 10 years," she said.

But the hard work in researching the experience of people who have seen UFOs has turned up only about three photographs that have had anything about them, said Mrs. Randles.

"There is not a single movie film that shows a structured object. All the movie films show is nothing more than the best of what the ordinary photographs show."

Her scepticism about some of the photographs does not mean she has her doubts about strange happenings in the sky. "I have no doubt at all that there are several unexplained phenomena at the heart of the reports. I have seen too many cases over the years that can't be explained, but I don't think belief is a natural prerequisite to the research."

World

The fact that an object looks to be physically real is still not satisfactory proof, said Mrs. Randles.

"Only about half a dozen photographs in the whole world have any substance about them. I turned up three photos that had something about them, and two of those were over 30 years old."

Mrs. Randles is hoping that the change of attitude to UFOs by Governments from all over the world will help them to bridge the gap between the explained and the unexplained.

"About five or six years ago every Government would say: 'We have no evidence that there is anything going on here.' Then in the United States the Freedom of Information Act was passed and they had to release some of this information."

Activity

She said that since then other Governments had become far more open-minded about UFOs, including the Ministry of Defence, which she says are now likely to make some of their files freely available to her.

Mrs. Randles hopes this will provide more information for her next book — UFO Reality, a study of experiences and physical evidence throughout the world.

It may also include more references to the Pennines, which could become more noted for UFOs than Warminster did in the early days of sightings.

"There is far more activity along the Pennines than Warminster because it has been happening there without any stimulus," she said, referring to the great wave of publicity which followed the Warminster sightings of the 60s.

"Activity on the Pennines has continued to happen and has followed the same patterns, and is considerably above the average for Britain, without this kind of promotion."

Two of the investigators in the east Pennines area are Graham and Mark Birdsall, both from Leeds. They have had some 30 sightings reported to them from the area between Grassington and Carlton Moor, near Skipton, since the beginning of the year.

Mrs. Randles is aiming to keep in contact with the two researchers.

Mr. Birdsall has said that because of the lack of liaison between Mrs. Randles' organisation BUFORA and the research organisation Contact International of which the Yorkshire UFO Society belongs, that some of the sightings in the east Pennines had not been followed up by the author.

But she replies that the lack of communication had been on the part of the Birdsalls; and she was very keen to co-operate with them on their UFO sightings.

She said some of their research had not been included in the Pennine UFO Mystery because the details had had to go to print in January 1983.

Thus her next book sought to include more sightings from the Yorkshire side of the Pennines. Currently she receives about 12 sightings a week overall.

Mike Sacks

Mike Sacks

Knowing about the hush-hush meeting with Colonel Halt, by Harry Harris and Mike Sacks, we asked Mike if he had any knowledge of this, in July 2013, feeling that it was important to clarify the author of the sketch – for all we knew, it might have been one of the servicemen involved. If so, it would have been a vital piece of evidence. We were delighted to hear that it was indeed Mike's . . .

"Well I appreciate that time has passed; it's now over 30 years ago, but I feel that inexplicably, for whatever reason, we were totally written out of the loop. Harry and I went down there, after the initial enquiries made by Brenda and Dot (who were banned from the base, at one point). When Charles Halt played the audio tape to us, I remember another Commander was there; I think his name was `Jack. The tape was played

*and we had a chat in Colonel Halt's office afterwards. When I arrived home I drew the sketch from the description given on the tape. Tim Good also used the sketch in his book, Need To Know (page 331)." (*Jack being Colonel Jack Cochran) (The date is not included in this version).*

16th August – UFO photographed over Thetford Forest

This location was to be the source of a number of UFO sightings; on this occasion an object was photographed. Admittedly the picture is of poor quality, but it was from the collection of Ron West and believed genuine.

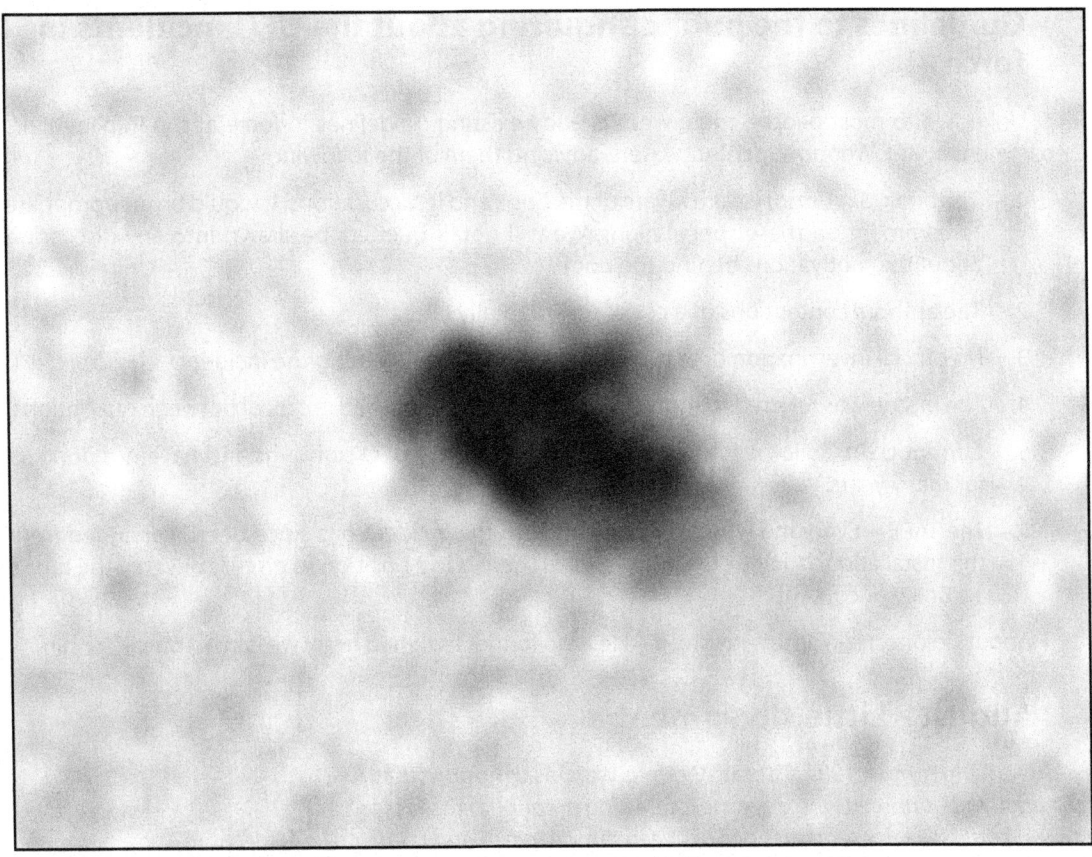

Enlargement of the UFO photographed over Thetford Forest in August 1984

22nd August – Mark Birdsall writes to the Air Base

In another letter sent this time to Captain Victor Warzinski, who replaced Kathleen McCullom at RAF Woodbridge, he was also asked about radiation returns found in the Forest and why so many people were reassigned so quickly after the event on the 1st August. He replied on the 22nd:

"To the best of my knowledge, this area has not been destroyed. You should know that our people serve established four lengths overseas – generally two years in duration, if you're unmarried or unaccompanied, or three years if you bring family. The only thing that ever brought the issue to light was a rather fanciful story, published two years after the event, by a couple of people who made a living selling this sort of copy. Please take another look at your 'massive evidence' and tell me if any official government source (or even credible witnesses) ever drew a conclusion in favour of an extraterrestrial visitation."

Mark persisted. In another letter written to the same representative, enquiring about any 'unknown vehicles stored underground at Bentwaters, in July 1985, he was advised:

"There are NO underground storage areas on either of the twin bases."

Guidelines to the public enquiring about the UFO incidents in force

Unknown to most people, there were already existing guidelines in force at the Public Affairs Department at RAF Woodbridge/Bentwaters, advising them of the following:

1. The book (*Sky Crash*) we are aware of the book and its accusations. It would be inappropriate to comment on these speculations. We will not, if queried, be drawn into any discussion about the motivations behind the book.

2. The authors' contentions of a cover-up are totally false.

3. No official investigation of any kind was ever done concerning the incident.

4. The matter was referred to the MOD according to established protocol between our Nations.

5. Current USAF Policy is that we no longer investigate UFO sightings and have not done so for many years.

6. The TAPE – Everyone who was involved with the incident has since been reassigned from this installation. No one currently assigned here is in a position to discuss or verify the tape's accuracy or content.

About Colonel Halt/others involved – He is no longer assigned here; we cannot speak for him.

August – Little silver men!

Oddly, in August 1984, Captain Victor L. Warzinski thought that *"the anonymous airmen who gave the interesting account to the Press of seeing little silver men, discussions between the silver men and USAF people, dancing 'balls of light' on people's foreheads, and blacking out to unexplainably awaken, caked with mud in his dorm room, to be later visited by black coated 'hush' men, etc."* was Sgt. John Burroughs!

Sgt. John Burroughs

22nd August – Like a fisherman's tale

The same spokesman wrote to Graham Birdsall.

"Regarding your question about who believes whom, I don't know that anyone has drawn any official conclusions. Colonel Halt informed the MOD of what he saw. The MOD chose not to investigate the matter. The USAF quit investigating UFOs years ago at the completion of Project Blue book study. There's a hint that the matter did not merit investigation. The only thing that ever brought the issue to light was a rather fanciful story, published two years after the event by a couple of people who make a living selling this sort of copy. Was the Woodbridge incident genuine? Was it a CIA hoax? Or was is simply an unexplained incident, blown completely out of proportion – like the fisherman's tale of the one that got away that keeps getting bigger and bigger with each retelling? Please take another look at your massive evidence and tell me if any official government source or even credible witness ever drew a conclusion in favour of an extraterrestrial visitation."

26th October – *The Evening Star* – American Officer's report sheds new light on UFO – Their comment on 'unidentified official secret'

Logically the probability of life on other planets is high. Why should we be alone in the vast ocean of galaxies? In practice, however, we ask rather more than the theory of probabilities or the speculation of scientists. We want a sign. The only sign in evidence throughout the saga of UFOs at the Woodbridge airbase has been 'Keep out. Ministry of Defence property' and that more than any concrete evidence has given us reason to consider the validity of the UFO claims. Why should the authorities have been so dogged in their determination to stamp out all the investigation into the phenomenon?

These days, of course, the authorities seem determined to communicate less and less with the public and no co-operation and official smokescreens are routine. We should congratulate the three authors of the book *Sky Crash – a cosmic conspiracy*, for their success in carving through the sullen official silence on the topic.

These ladies, it should be remembered, offer the spaceship theory as only one of a range of possibilities. The others, which include weapons testing and the recovery of part of a Russian satellite, sound much more plausible and would explain the official silence. They might even prefer us to believe the UFO theory!

26th October – *East Anglian Daily Times* – The real mystery

The newspaper pondered on the rather odd lack of interest by an unidentified spokesman from the Ministry of Defence, following questions put to him about the UFO, said to have been seen by US personnel near an important airbase. They concluded, irrespective of what he had to say, that:

"Plainly, if it were possible for anything to fly that close to a major Defence establishment without being tracked or traced, then it would be serious matter, whether military or civilian."

John Hanson

The simple undeniable truth is that the landscape and skies of our world, during the mid to later part of the 20th Century, has been the background to a colossal number of UFO sightings brought to man's attention, but he chooses to ignore them – probably because they shouldn't exist. Unfortunately, they do and their over-flights still remain the focus of much interest and curiosity to the present day.

5th November 1984 – UFO reports fanciful

Captain Victor L. Warzinski, of the Public Relations Division, wrote to Jenny Randles in response to a letter dated the 27th October 1984.

"I still regard various alarming scenarios, which span across witchcraft, drugs, space warfare, and a near nuclear holocaust, to quote the advance publicity flyer for Sky Crash as fanciful. I still regard Art Wallace's story, as reported in the News of the World, as fanciful. I still regard quite a bit more that has been written and said about the incident by a number of people beside you as fanciful. The word is used as defined: Imaginative not necessarily supported by facts. The first story metaphor supports this viewpoint. I will grant the Rendlesham Forest incident could leave some room for conjecture. However, I hope you will pardon my telling you that I'm still skeptic. Who needs to be convinced that anything more than an unexplained light sighting took place four years ago in the forest? However, I do not wish to establish an adversary relationship with you. I do wish to help you where I can, and am willing to attempt to answer any specific questions you may have on the subject.

Look forward to hearing from you."

In another letter to her dated 19th November 1984 (extract) he said,

"You ask at length for me to comment on the specific elements of your conclusions I'm afraid I'm not in a good position to do that. You see while I'm in the process of discounting little silver men teaching space psychology in our underground complex I'm also establishing myself as an authority who knows what did actually happen. And I will admit I don't know what actually happened."

1985

4th February – Domed object over Ipswich

PAT Hughes of the Walkway, Ipswich, was stood in her porch at 10.30pm, when she noticed:

"… A solid looking object in the sky; it was oval and had lights on its top and base. It was the size of a dinner plate and moved in a curious way – hovering and then speeding away quickly – before moving back to its original position; it changed its shape as it did so. It was also flickering or pulsating as it moved.

I watched it for ten minutes, until it was out of sight. I estimated it was at a height of about 2-3,000 feet."

25thApril – *Walter H. Andrus Jr. wrote to Philip J. Klass (extract)

"MUFON is also declining your generous offer to underwrite half the cost of a polygraph test for Larry Warren. Based upon our investigation in this case, Larry's version of events would probably fail any questions directly relating to his having personally observed the three occupants and their physical descriptions as depicted in the CNN film. We have other witnesses that confirm he was indeed present at the first sighting. However, one witness who now resides in Texas said he personally did not see the small humanoids that Larry described in the CNN film. Mr Warren apparently enjoys basking in the publicity because he tends to embellish his story each time it is told. We arranged to have a voice stress analysis test conducted by the leading authority on this device, using the CNN video tape audio as the medium for the test. Larry Warren failed the questions where he was describing the occupants.

Therefore, MUFON has no further need to conduct a polygraph test. We are relying upon the testimony of other witnesses present, including USAF Officers and enlisted security Police, since Larry Warren is not the principal witness – just one of many to the two incidents."

*Walter H. Andrus – his UFO sighting in 1948!

During daylights hours on August 15th 1948, Walt Andrus, his wife and son, sighted four objects flying in formation over downtown Phoenix, Arizona. This was to trigger off an interest in the UFO subject which was to last 67 years. Not unsurprisingly, 49 years later, lights in formation would once again be seen over Phoenix, Arizona.

Walter went on to be a founding member of the Mutual UFO Network (MUFON) in 1969, and the International Director of the MUFON from 1970 to July 16, 2000, when he was succeeded by John F. Schuessler. He also served on the staff of *Skylook*, as Editor in Chief of the *MUFON UFO Journal* and Editor or Co-editor of the annual *MUFON International UFO Symposium Proceedings*.

MUFON became the largest and best known organization in the world addressing the science of extraterrestrial-related phenomena and took up the mantle of NICAP as it was slowly dissembled by intelligence agency plants during the 1970s. Walter Andrus was born in Des Moines, Iowa, in 1920 and graduated from Roosevelt High School in 1938 and the Central Technical Institute in Kansas City, MO, in 1940. He is also a graduate of the US Navy Electronics Technician Program during World War II and taught in both technical schools. After the war he was employed by Mid-Continent Airlines as a station manager in Quincy, Illinois. Then from 1949 to 1975 he worked for Motorola, Inc. in successive capacities as Assistant Plant Manager, Manager of Quality Control and Operations Manager in their Quincy, Illinois facility.

In 1975, he transferred to the Seguin, Texas plant as a Production Manager. After 34 years with Motorola, Walt retired in 1982 and devoted full-time to the directorship of MUFON for the next 18 years. Walt was a member of the Board of Directors of the joint USA-CIS Aerial Anomaly Federation.

He was also on the Board of Directors for the influential UFO Research Coalition (URC), composed of Center for UFO Studies (CUFOS), Fund for UFO Research (FUFOR), and Mutual UFO Network (MUFON), organised in 1994. He has lectured all around the world and appeared on radio and television (including Oprah Winfrey and Larry King) too many times to list here. Walt has been an amateur radio aficionado since 1939 and a licensed pilot since 1947. He passed away on 16th September 2015.

Enquiries regarding existence of a UFO file

On 5th November 1985, Mr John Robert Kyniston of Portland, Oregon, wrote to Captain Victor Warzinski of the USAF Public Affairs Department at RAF Bentwaters, asking about the existence of this 'UFO file' and also if there was any information about the 'alleged' events between 27th–29th December 1980. John also commented on the actions of Mike Sacks, Harry Harris, Dot Street, David Taylor and Brenda Butler, with regard to the incident involving a visit to see Colonel Halt's son at his house on base, on the 23rd February 1984, which sparked off the arrival of security officers, who detained Dot, Brenda, and David.

In November 1985, John received a reply from the Department of the Air Force at New York. They told him, quote:

"I've checked with our current RAF Commander; his office has not been maintaining any special file on this incident. It is likely that one of the UFO enthusiasts probably saw Squadron Leader Donald Moreland 'dig' into a fairly thick file for a copy of Halt's original memo. What the enthusiast did not realise was that this file was also used to record complaints from the local population, concerning noisy or low flying aircraft. The RAF Commander receives numerous complaints over a given year and each complaint generates its own paperwork. Squadron Leader Moreland retired in February 1984."

No formal charges made against the UFO researchers

Captain Warzinski advised John to contact Colonel Halt himself, to find out his reactions to finding Brenda and Dot at his home address, who had been removed from the Base.

Bentwaters Base Newspaper

Captain Warzinski

"The Bentwater's Base paper never ran an article on the incident, with regard to your question concerning our no comment position with regard to Sky Crash. Generally speaking, the rationale behind this policy is that we have already released all that we know about this incident. All those associated with the incident are no longer at this base. We have not drawn any conclusions concerning the incident and consequently do not feel it would be appropriate to comment on the authors many conclusions. I suggested in a letter to one of the authors that she form a single solid conclusion, back it with sufficient evidence, and address it to a Member of Parliament."

May – Former head of MOD sights three UFOs over London

Ralph Noyes – former Head of DS8, the forerunner of Sec (AS) 2a (UFO Desk) at the MOD – who, in 1985, wrote a novel based on the Rendlesham Forest incident, entitled *A Secret Property,* also reported his own sighting of

"…three yellowish-white 'balls of light' flying in triangular formation, which stopped and hovered in the sky near Elstree Studios, one night in May 1985."

Ralph Noyes

Brenda Butler and Chris Pennington

Like The Lord Hill-Norton, Noyes was convinced that the MOD was hiding something, but discovered nothing further than the standard line that Halt's report had been examined and dismissed as 'of no Defence interest'.

Was David Daniels an alien?

Bizarrely Noyes had, in fact, been asked to go to that location by a man calling himself David Daniels, who claimed he was a Reptilian from the Pleiades and could arrange this to happen! Whatever you think of Daniels, who had met The Lord Hill-Norton at MOD Headquarters with Brenda Butler, and discussed his 'Alien' role, while it would be too easy to dismiss him as being in need of some psychiatric treatment, how on earth did he arrange the UFO sighting to take place or was it sheer coincidence? ... Chilling in its implications to say the least!

(Full details of this case involving Colonel Wendell Stevens are contained in Volume 9 of *Haunted Skies*)

Secrets of the Sky

In this year, Science writer – Ian Ridpath, wrote a 62-page book in colour, entitled: *Secrets of the Sky* (published by Hamlyn), in which he explains professionally and intelligently the science behind Rainbows, Mirages, Hurricanes, Stonehenge, Meteors, Aurora, Comets, Space junk, The Moon, Eclipses, Planets, Black Holes and the Milky Way. On the final page (62) Ian says:

"In 1980, American airmen at Woodbridge Airbase, in England, reported seeing a brilliant flashing UFO in a nearby forest. Investigators who visited the site found that the airmen had been looking at a lighthouse on the coastline."

A couple of paragraphs later, he states:

"Unfortunately, the disappointing truth is that there are no authenticated reports of visits by alien spaceships. Whether or not there are any spacecraft travelling around the Galaxy at present, there will be one day – the craft will be ours."

The reality of course, judging by the thousands if not millions of UFO reports worldwide tells a different story!

UFO activity over Suffolk – strange light

Mr Bruce Gowings (31) of Woodbridge, Suffolk – employed as a Fire Inspector for the USAF and an amateur astronomer – was driving towards Stradbroke, in Suffolk, on his way to work at 6.25am on 10th October, when he noticed a very bright light in the sky heading towards him.

"I stopped the car and got out, in order to obtain a better view of what I took to be an aircraft. I listened for noise but heard nothing. It crossed the road under which I was stood, and I was stunned to see a number of small twinkling lights at the rear of the object."

UFO activity over Suffolk – object making humming noise seen

"A 'ball of light', which passed overhead making a humming noise was seen", according to former teacher – Janet Richards, who was driving along the A12 at Blythburgh, with her daughter – Cathy. They were not the only ones; other people living in the Ufford and Ipswich areas also reported having observed the same object. The actual date is not known, only the year.

Colonel Halt lectures at Lancashire

In 1988, Colonel Halt travelled to England to attend a number of media engagements which had been arranged by Manchester based Solicitor – Harry Harris. Colonel Halt addressed a small gathering at Todmorden, Lancashire, before travelling to Centenary House, Leeds, where he spoke to 150 people about his role in the incident. (Tickets at £4.50pence).

Further Documents – Tape backs UFO incident

'Silver suit entities hung in light beam'

Tape backs book on UFO incident

SPELLBOUND American servicemen watched a spectacular display by an alleged alien space craft and an amazing array of accompanying lights in the night skies . . . according to their taped commentary during Suffolk's "Sky Crash" incident near Woodbridge airbase.

As they stood in bewilderment between 200 and 300 yards from what is alleged to be a space craft on its second visit to Rendlesham Forest in three days at the end of December, 1980, commentator Lt. Col. Charles Halt gasps, "It is like an eye winking at you."

The men watch the object with night-sight devices called starscopes and one says, "As you look at it through the starscope it appears to have a dark centre to it."

They refer to several lights in the sky and are heard to remark "There is no doubt about it, this is weird," and "This is unreal."

The object was hovering about four feet off the ground and the drama intensifies as, with a faltering voice, Halt says, "It is coming towards us . . . there appears to be a beam of light coming down to the ground."

Halt and his men decide to return to the airbase and the tape ends.

New evidence

The recording has emerged as a new and important part of the evidence in the investigations into the alleged double sighting which forms the basis of the book "Sky Crash — A Cosmic Conspiracy" which was published yesterday.

The tape has been said to be authentic by former Woodbridge airbase commander Col. Sam Morgan, who released it to UFO investigators

Dot Street, Brenda Butler and Jenny Randles.

It was played at a London Press conference yesterday, when a strong demand for a full public inquiry into the incidents was made by the book's authors.

The men in the forest at the time of the alleged second sighting had been taking radiation readings and measurements in the wake of the first claimed sighting . . . when contact was allegedly

John Grant

made with three silver-suited "entities" who hovered in a beam of light from their stricken craft as they repaired it.

The tape records the men's discovery of damage to trees and imprints on the ground where the craft is alleged to have landed.

Halt, who was acting base commander at the time and has since become a colonel and returned to America where he is said be be at a classified location and unavailable for comment, later made a report on both alleged sightings which was sent to the Ministry of Defence.

Major boost

When it was later leaked it gave the investigation a major boost.

Jenny Randles told the Press conference, "The MoD seriously ask us to believe

that following the receipt of the report from the acting U.S. commander, endorsed by the British base commander, involving all these trained witnesses and the alleged interception into British airspace of a craft, leaving damage and radiation right outside two NATO bases — they do absolutely nothing about it.

"There is sufficient evidence to give the lie to this," she claimed.

"Twelve days before the Halt report the only thing the MoD admit to having was even written, two officials interviewed civilians around the forest.

"Plaster casts were seen to be taken of the traces by Col. Halt on base, although he was not approached by the British people who took them, and radar tapes were taken from RAF Watton, Norfolk, by USAF intelligence officers which could only have happened, as the MoD admit, with MoD permission."

Strong case

The investigators had no vested interest in proving that an alien space craft was involved, but, Jenny said, they were concerned that authorities had lied, and deceived the British public.

"We are positive we have sufficient evidence here to

make a strong case that an incident happened, the events have been withheld and that the public has a right to know.

"Either the authorities should say they know what happened and they have it under control or they should say they do not know and let it all be openly investigated," she said.

"We cannot keep being fobbed off, the truth will come out because we know we are right," Jenny added.

U.S. charges mafia 'family'

Leaders of New York's Colombo "crime family" have been indicted in a federal court after a three-year undercover operation in which an FBI agent posed as a wealthy buyer of stolen goods while others spied on a pasta-import business.

"We have the mafia on the run," US Attorney-General William French Smith declared as he announced a 51-count indictment of 11 Colombo "family" members involving charges of racketeering, extortion, theft and bribery of federal officials.

The "family" named after Joseph Colombo, a reputed crime boss who died in 1978 of gunshot wounds received seven years earlier, has operated as one of the city's biggest crime groups for more than 50 years.

Thanks for Samaritan

AN elderly Colchester woman is trying to trace a mystery Good Samaritan.

While driving her car on the Hadleigh by-pass she fell ill but was aided by a

young lorry driver who looked after her until an ambulance arrived.

The man, aged about 25, refused to give her his name but the woman now wants

to get in touch and thank him personally.

As a widow she does not wish to give her name and address, but asks that the man get in touch with her through Hadleigh police.

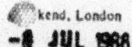

kend, London
-1 JUL 1988
WEEKEND MAGAZINE 1/7/86

PART ONE OF AN EARTH-SHATTERING SERIES

UFO QUEST WRECKED OUR LIVES

UFO investigator Brenda Butler admits now: "If I had known what this case would involve I would never have set things in motion."

Brenda, colleagues Dot Street and Jenny Randles, are all convinced they have proved their case of a Ministry of Defence cover-up over a UFO crash.

But they have paid a heavy price, both financially and personally, for investigating the mystery crash in Rendlesham Forest, Suffolk, over a period of five years.

It has led to:
● A marriage break-up
● A broken long-standing romance
● Threatening phone calls
● Bills of thousands of pounds
● Frustration that many vital facts still remain hidden behind the Official Secrets Act.

Widowed mother of two Brenda, of Leiston, Suffolk, who was the first of the trio to learn of the UFO crash, says: "I wish now that I had never acted upon what I was told by an American Air Force security officer.

"Pursuing this UFO case has cost friendships and the job of one American serviceman. Over a two-year period I had quarterly phone bills of up to £500, and weekly petrol bills of £25-£30.

Brenda, a home-nursing help, adds: "I had to take a lot of time off work which, with two children

then at school to clothe and feed, I could ill afford."

But her co-investigators, Dot Street and author Jenny Randles, say that their personal problems and financial hardships have been worth: "getting to the truth through a wall of official silence."

For Dot, who has a daughter 13 and a son, nine, penetrating that wall of silence has been traumatic. She says: "This case broke up

my marriage of seven years. My husband simply got fed up.

"But from the first moment I set foot in that forest I just knew something extraordinary had happened there—and that feeling wouldn't leave me alone."

She made several trips a week by moped from her home in Oulton Broad, Suffolk, to the USAF bases at Woodbridge and Bentwaters, which border Rendel-

sham Forest. And the bills for the 80-mile round trips mounted.

She says: "My quarterly phone bills were often £900."

One anonymous caller threatened her children.

Jenny Randles, director of investigations for the British UFO Research Association, says: "This case has been so costly I had to sell my house in Warrington; and I estimate it has cost me between £5,000 and £10,000 in expenses.

"It also came between me and the man I had lived with for two and a half years."

She was also warned she was "messing with something so serious you could end up at the bottom of the Thames."

"We don't know what it was ... but we do know that it has caused high-ranking people in a Government ministry to consistently evade, deny and lie," says Jenny.

A NEW book *Sky Crash* (Grafton, £2.95) by Brenda Butler, Dot Street and Jenny Randles poses intriguing questions: Did a UFO crash in Rendlesham Forest, Suffolk, near an American air base in 1980? And, if so, why have the authorities persisted in keeping it secret?

The authors embarked on a quest to uncover the truth amidst a welter of contradictions, hearsay, eyewitness reports and official denials. Now they tell *Weekend's* TONY WILMOT what their truth-seeking has cost them in financial and personal terms.

Jenny Randles: Sifting the UFO evidence

Sky Crash – The cost to the authors

Emphasising the pressure which fell onto the shoulders of the three women as they struggled to make sense of the various claims made by the witnesses involved can be seen in a newspaper article, which was published in July 1986.

Steve La Plume

In emails sent to us by Charles Halt, in 2015, was a number from American Security Policeman Steven Robert La Plume, which included further details relating to his sighting of a UFO in early 1981, at RAF Bentwaters (previously outlined earlier in this book). It shows an insight into what life was all about for this young man, who admits he had some issues while stationed at RAF Bentwaters.

Steve:

"I truly believe what happened to me did, in fact, happen and I also think the incident has been underplayed or even shadowed by the 'big show' that happened in late December of 1980. I accept I will never know what truly happened to me and what it was all about. It's taken me about twenty-nine years to accept this, but with this new found peace I can look at what happened to me objectively with no emotional attachment anymore. I honestly don't give a damn now about RAF Bentwaters."

Larry Warren and his UFO incident

"I was sitting in my dorm room, one day, when Larry Warren came into my room. I had just had a sighting, a few days prior, but kept my mouth shut after the incident. I did not want to talk about it to anyone other than those who I knew, and they wanted no part of it from what I saw. My Sergeant asked me what happened. I told him I missed the bus to the barracks and hitch-hiked in the rain back, after working all night. This was the morning after when I returned to Central Security Control. Larry comes in and asks if he can talk and then starts laying out this whole story about UFOs, walking back form Ipswich, when he saw it – triangular craft, lights splitting apart after all of them coming together, little green men, animals in the forest. You know his story and I don't need to go into detail about it, but I will say this. I never doubted when I was talking to him that what he said had happened had happened. He was deeply disturbed. I have a clear recollection of him talking about this incident. He never sat down, never moved, he just stood there and laid it all out in one foul swoop. Then he turned and left. I think he just needed to get it all out of his head."

Photography Building

"A good friend of mine met a girl; she was a photographer for the base and worked in the photography building, whatever that was. Larry mentioned there was an underground base under Bentwaters and that at some point he spoke either publicly or to me personally that he had come up through an elevator in the photography building. When he went outside, he realised what the building was. Mark Thompson has been overlooked as a key player in all of this as well. He was there in the incident on one of the nights, and told me he backed up Larry's story about the generated lights not working, the pump at the station not working correctly, going on and off when they were trying to fill the light-alls. After he went back to Santa Cruz, I never heard from him again."

Baroness Symons

Questions in the House regarding underground installations

Georgina Bruni commented about this in a reply published in *UFO Data 1*, January/February 2016, as a response to what the Minister of Defence – Baroness Symons, of Vernham Dean – said to The Lord Hill-Norton, in 2001. He asked the Baroness whether they will detail the underground facilities at the former RAF Bentwaters installation and, if so, the purpose of these facilities.

The Baroness told him: *"there are no underground facilities at the former RAF Bentwaters."*

Georgina:

"Actually there are underground facilities at Bentwaters, but they are sealed. The Security Chief at the installation, who gave me a guard and permission to investigate the buildings, told me the underground facilities were sealed when the MOD put the base up for sale. He had written several times to the MOD requesting details of these but, although they promised to look into the matter, received nothing. I also discovered a door in the main command post that was

clearly an entrance to an underground facility, because it could not lead to anywhere above ground. The guard had no keys for this important door, which was covered in warning signs. According to the Chief of Security, there are still several parts of the installation that are sealed. So the answer in essence is crafty, because as the facilities are now sealed one could surmise that there are none."

Nick Pope

"I think the answer to this one depends upon how one defines 'underground facilities'. If one means some sort of underground city – the sort of place inhabited by a villain in a James Bond movie – then no, that's fantasy. But if one means the sort of below-ground storage areas and bunkers that are commonly found at military facilities (for the obvious reason that putting something underground makes it harder to take out with bombs) then yes, absolutely."

German pilots and a Black Lincoln car

Steve:

"I was followed one night by two guys, claiming to be German pilots on TDY. I asked about them and no one knew them. I asked one for a cigarette. He gave me one and lit it. I told him I knew he was not a German pilot and that I was on to them. It went like this: 'Excuse me, do you have a light?' German pilot makes like he does not understand. 'Oh, you don't speak English?' I produce a cigarette that I got off the bartender (not being a smoker). 'You got a light?' I gesture a BIC lighter and he gets it and hands me a lighter. I hand it back and then I say in simple, slow English 'I know you're following me. Why are you following me?' German boy just looks at me and says nothing, but he screwed up because he did not gesture like he did not understand like he did before. We just made eye contact and started for a split second or so – then I walked away. When his partner came back (he had gone to get some food), from behind the lattice work I saw them talk and leave out the back door. 'That's odd', I thought, 'No one ever leaves out that back door'. There was nothing in the back but an alley. I went back and followed them. They got into a big dark Lincoln town car. I knew it was a Lincoln, because my uncle had one and I recognised it. I watched them through the barely cracked open door as they drove in the direction of the gate, and remember their tail light going on when the driver slowed for a moment. I saw enough and thought they may have seen me, so I closed the door and took off out of the front of the club. What in the hell were two German pilots on TDY (obviously they flew in to the base) doing in a Lincoln town car in Suffolk, England, in 1981? These were not a common car at all in that place and time."

Charles Halt comments

"I don't believe the claim about the German pilots. I do not remember any such visits at that time. All visits by foreign aircraft were discussed at the morning senior officer staff meeting. If they were pilots, they would have been commissioned officers and would not have been allowed in the enlisted club. Any big black limo would have caused a stir on the base and I would have known about it. Things like that would have had all of us talking."

Steve had many issues, which is why he was posted to work alongside Wendell Palmer (whom I found to be a well-respected, trusted individual) instead of being on post. The cigar-shaped craft fits with what others claimed on a later sighting, in November 1980. Perhaps he picked it up from there. I understand that the alleged underground facility has been retracted by Larry Warren. Wendell Palmer and Steve did report something, a few weeks later after the 'main events', and I responded after calling Colonel Williams. We found nothing and left. I have no knowledge of what happened after. If something did occur, they kept it quiet."

John Hanson – re the photo lab

Peter Robbins, in his book *Halt In Woodbridge,* published as a rebuttal to comments made by Charles Halt during the talk at Woodbridge Community Hall, Suffolk, on the 12th July 2015, tells the reader that following a comment by Charles that Larry claimed he was taken to the photo laboratory – this is wrong, quote:

Peter Robbins:

"Larry Warren never said or alleged or written that he was taken to the base photo lab. Not in Left At East Gate *or anywhere else. The reason being he wasn't."*

On page 62 of *Left At East Gate,* Larry says (after his ordeal in the underground base):

"I was back, but from where? I turned around with a vengeance and opened the door I'd just passed through. I had taken two steps forward when a female admin clerk behind the desk asked if she could help me. I stared at her looking for any hint of expression on her face that would tell me she knew – there was nothing. 'No thank you' I said, then turned and left the building, the Bentwaters photo processing lab."

Charles Halt:

"As I have remarked before, I have no knowledge of any such underground structure."

Steve La Plume's UFO sighting – further details

Whilst details have been previously covered with regard to what Steve saw, during January 1981 – a sighting which was brought to the attention of Colonel Halt – further information is now available about what Steve actually saw.

Checking East Gate

"At about 11pm, I and Wendell Palmer went back to the East Gate to check the lock. I was standing facing Palmer, who is facing me. We are looking over the Police cruiser, which I believe was facing away from the gate. I don't remember it turning around. Maybe we got in and then got out as we were a few metres away form the original position of the cruiser when I checked the gate. Maybe Palmer turned it around when I walked back. I just can't recall that detail.

We stood there, talking about what a brisk night it was – the sky clearing up a bit, maybe 15% cloud cover, clear for the most part. Stars were bright and it was generally a beautiful night, no fog.

It was Palmer who first mentioned about the lighthouse, UFO, and the forest to my left lying at the end of the long access road to the base. I could see the beacon of the lighthouse as it rotated, and I can't believe anyone could mistake this for a UFO overhead or in the trees".

Talk of UFOs and Little Green Men!

"We were talking about the UFOs and little green men and generally joking about it, when I saw something over Palmer's right shoulder. It was high up in the sky, about 45 degrees off the horizon.

What I saw looked at first like a satellite moving across the sky, maybe a bit brighter but not by much. I mentioned it to Palmer; he turned and looked. It was not travelling right to left on an even trajectory. It was dancing in the sky, up and down to a rhythm I can only liken to a heart monitor, but it was doing so really quickly. It was moving in an up and down direction while it went right to left, about 10 degrees either way in the southern sky, just real fast – up, down, up, down. It was a fast mover. I asked Palmer if he saw it too. He confirmed he did and we looked at it for a few moments.

Palmer jumped in the cruiser to go to the Control tower to check. By this time it had gone behind some cloud cover and was now in the south-east direction, some three or four minutes having already elapsed.

Palmer came back about 15 minutes later and reported the only thing up was a C-130 transport plane and a few Jolly Greens [helicopters] from the Para-Rescue Squadron.

Palmer said we had to call it in. He said that we were told if we saw anything odd to report it. So I said OK. He then got on the radio to CSC and said, 'La Plume just saw a UFO'. I yelled across the car to him. 'You saw it too!'"

Lt. Bruce Englund

"Within a few moments the phone in the guard shack at the East Gate rang. Palmer told me to answer it. I went over and answered the phone; it was Lt. Englund. He asked me what I saw, where was it, could I see it now, along with other questions. I told him we lost sight of it in some cloud cover over the forest."

Colonel Halt arrives – then General Gordon Williams

"He told us to stay there and observe; soon afterwards Colonel Halt showed up. I reported the post safe and secure and proceeded to tell him what happened. All the time Palmer stayed back and did not get too involved.

After the arrival of Colonel Halt, the stream of officers and higher ranking personnel kept coming. There was the Deputy Base commander, I believe of Woodbridge Base that brought his wife and teenaged son.

Eventually, the recently promoted General Williams, our Wing commander, turned up at the scene. I was instructed by Lt. Englund not to be nervous, but simply tell him what I saw. I did just that and then everyone, except Palmer and myself, jumped in an official Air Force station wagon and set out toward the forest. We had a starlight scope and were told to let them know if we saw anything else.

I was beside myself. Why did all these people show up? Why were the officer's wife and child here on official Air Force business? Why did she have a 35mm Nikon camera and make the comment. 'I hope we get to see one!'

I was completely clueless as to the events of the earlier UFO sightings in December 1980. I knew there was a sighting but at this point in time I knew no details, other than some security personnel claimed to have seen a UFO.

I did not understand why they insisted on going into the forest. The thing we saw was miles up in the sky and had gone behind some clouds – technically it was way over the forest, approximately 30,000 feet up, a rough guess. 'What the hell is going on here?' is about all I could think of. Palmer and I sat around with the scope and basically wasted time, until the officers all came back from the forest area. Nothing happened. We saw nothing and when they returned they seemed a bit let down.

After things calmed down Palmer took off to resume duty, but returned about an hour or so later. We talked a bit, but I can't remember what – I guess just that we went over the night's events. He mentioned the lighthouse and how they thought it might be that. Even then, people were trying to figure out about that damned lighthouse amongst ourselves and we all dismissed it as far as I know."

Its back!

"I was looking toward the forest, in particular the lighthouse. I mentioned that there was no way it could have been that. Maybe I thought it, but it was in my head at the time. Then I saw the lights of a plane coming in for a landing. I thought it was a plane. It was on about the right approach for the runway from what I saw. Then it got a bit closer. It was low, lower than I thought it should be. It was slow too. Was it an A-10? They can fly real slow and stay aloft.

It's over the forest now, nearing the road at the end of the East Gate access road. It's big. Those lights don't seem right and are about 1,000 feet off the deck. It's long – like a football field long, cigar-shaped form what I can tell, but there are a few clouds in the way.

Palmer and I exchanged a few words, basically confirming that we were both seeing it. After the craft got to the point it was coming up the access road toward the East Gate, I don't remember ever talking to Palmer again until the event was nearly all over."

UFO had square hatch on the base of the object, showing three lights

"I seem to recall a bluish light under it tracking the ground, but I cannot say for certain. I simply can't clearly remember, just partially. The craft was moving towards me. At the time I had an M-16 machine gun on my shoulder but never even thought to use it.

It was then nearly overhead. I was speechless and frozen to the spot. I stood just looking up at it. It's huge – the length of three American football fields, or so I perceive it to be. There is still a cloud around it, or fog, or something that is preventing me form seeing it clearly.

Now it's directly over my head. I saw what looked like a hatch – a square thing on the bottom. It's structural. There are some lights – a yellow one, a red one, and either a blue or green one. My only thought was 'wow, look at it, remember this moment, you'll never see anything like this again in your whole life. This is amazing'. It's moving to my right and towards the southern sky, much higher now and heading away at a slow pace while moving up at the same time.

I watched as it moved into the night sky and blended in with the stars – then lost from sight. I only see the night sky – clear, with no clouds and full of stars.

Palmer asks me 'do you want to call it in?' 'No', I reply quickly and with total certainty. He agrees and we agree to say nothing. Palmer and I never really talked about it after that. I went back to the CSC and talked to my Sergeant, who gave me about a one minute debrief asking me, 'La Plume what did you see?' I told him what I saw on the first sighting and nothing more. I played it down and knew if I mentioned anything I would be ridiculed, so I kept my big mouth shut, like I knew I should."

Larry and I kept in contact

"Larry and I kept in contact after we were civilians again. I met him a few times at his house in Connecticut on my way to a mission, or to do some training with Frank Camper in the Mercenary School. He mentioned the Omni magazine story and I think everyone knows what happened after that.

I was contacted by Larry Fawcett and gave him my story. I went to a meeting urged by Larry. I had no idea who they were or what they were about, but MUFON was their name. I had never heard of them. Larry and I told them what happened and they were thankful we stepped forward. I never spoke publically again after that. It was too uncomfortable.

I contacted Colonel Halt about the time Georgina Bruni was writing her book. I liked her and we met once in London. I stayed at her flat, along with my wife, one night, and her and I and Nick Pope and my wife finished off a few bottles of wine and talked about everything we could in the short time we had together. I counted Nick and Georgina as genuine friends. Nick and I still email each other every now and then. I was truly heartbroken to hear of Georgina's passing. I had not felt such heartache in a long, long time."

Larry Warren

"Larry Warren is a mess. I have no idea that what he says anymore is true or untrue… is it first-hand account or not? I have nothing bad to say about him, other than the fact that he was messed with. He was missing for a few days and returned with a story of underground UFO stations under the base. I know everyone involved has had issues some way or another. I never heard him say anything other than he was getting out, due to a problem with his wrist. I believe it was to do with an arthritic condition and at no time heard him state he was getting out due to the Air Force's breach of contract. So when he talks about breach of contact and suddenly finds out it was his wrist, he is making this up. I have nothing against the guy personally, but he is, in my opinion, distorting the fact very much towards his conspiracy theory."

Further update on 'Forgotten' UFO Sightings in the Suffolk area

1940 – UFO sighted over Woodbridge Airfield, Suffolk

During the morning of the 6th June, Mr William Green (aged 74 in 1995) living in Grays, Essex, was on night spotting duty, manning a gun site at Woodbridge Airfield, guarding dummy aircraft parked nearby. At about 2.30am, through binoculars, he sighted a grey-white, saucer-shaped object in the sky, between 10-15,000 feet and some 30 feet across.

"I went to the identification telescope on the gun platform and looked through it at the object, which appeared to be hovering over the dummy airfield. I immediately awoke the Sergeant Major and told him about it. He said, 'It's a weather balloon or meteor'. I then telephoned Headquarters and told them what I had been seeing. They confirmed that no searchlights were in use over our locality, or aircraft or weather balloons. They suggested I was seeing a gas cloud! The object started to move from left to right slowly, for a few minutes, before gathering speed and moving away. I logged it and was made the butt of humour by my colleagues."

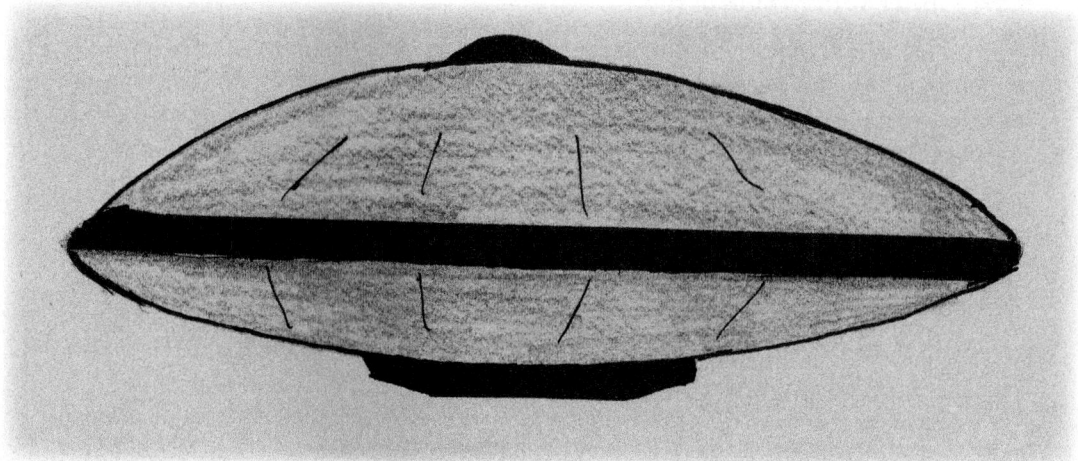

1980 – 25ᵗʰ December – Three lights sighted in the sky

George Henry White (now 69 in 2016) of Springfield Road, Kettering, in Northamptonshire – a welder by trade – was returning home at 9.10pm on the 25ᵗʰ December 1980, with his wife's parents in the car.

"We were approaching Findon on the A6, [a semi-rural clustered village, four miles north of Worthing], on what was a clear night with just one cloud in the sky. We saw what I took to be an aircraft on fire to my right, and I stopped the car. My father-in-law got out with me and we watched these three lights, which were egg-shaped, silver – like mercury, speeding across the sky."

Mr White switched-on his aircraft band radio and heard a pilot in the process of either landing or taking off from Luton Airport, calling Air Traffic Control, telling them he had just seen five UFOs in formation pass beneath him.

"We could only see three lights still in the sky. We stayed there for some minutes, but after not seeing anything else made our way to Rushden Police Station, where we reported the matter. In the paper, the next day, it was reported as a meteorite or space debris entering the Earth's atmosphere, which wasn't what we saw."

1980 – 25th December – 'Spinning top' UFO seen by farmer

"Neville Caley, who runs a farm in the Butley area of Suffolk with his father, spoke to us about what he sighted while on the way back home, at 2am on 27th December 1980. "I was on my way home in a local taxi, after a night out, when we saw this 'thing' coming in fast over the brow of a hill. It looked like a spinning top and was glowing red in colour. As it came over, a part of it fell off and landed in the nearby forest, close to Barrow Mound. Our curiosity aroused, we drove over to the location but were stopped by a Yankee copper, who was stood there. There were other guys about, some of them on the radios. I formed the impression they were waiting for something, but had to leave."

Red Alert at RAF Woodbridge

In March 2013, Matt Lyons – the previous Head of BUFORA – contacted us about some additional information received from East Anglia resident, David Morgan, following conversations held with David's father, who served in the USAF Armed Forces in the area of Shingle Street, during the Second World War.

The information (which was obtained by the son, during a recent visit to California, in the United States, after having tracked down his father) is split into two separate parts; the first relates to an abandoned village, situated close to Orford Ness:

Matt Lyons, previous Head of BUFORA

> *"If the public knew what lay beneath Shingle Street to this day, all hell would break loose because it's nothing like that's been said and unlike anything anyone could imagine."*

The second then alleges a connection between this and the event that took place on Woodbridge runway, on the 28th December 1980. This was obtained from a conversation with a friend – a retired USAF Sergeant – during a social drink, who was employed on the A10 aircraft at RAF Bentwaters. Following transfer to RAF Mildenhall, this man disclosed that he was a member of a team, stationed at RAF Mildenhall, whose job was to retrieve aircraft from crash sites.

In response to questions put to him by Matt Lyons, David Morgan outlined that on the night of the 28th December 1980, he and a team of men (seven) which included three low ranking officers, flew from RAF Midlenhall to RAF Woodbridge, in response to what they believed was a downed aircraft.

They were confined to the aircraft and not allowed off. A friend (unidentified) who was a member of the recovery crew, states that it was 10pm when they landed at RAF Woodbridge and that, upon their arrival, two jeeps and four to five personnel approached them. Three or four hours later, the men flew back to RAF Mildenhall. During a debriefing, they were informed that the base was on 'Red Alert' and that the standard rules of no discussions applied. It appears they were also warned not to say anything about what had happened that night. It was then alleged the airbases of Mildenhall, Bentwaters, and Woodbridge were placed on 'high alert'.

Charles Halt – no such thing as 'Red Alert'

> *"I have no knowledge of any special aircraft movements. However, I was told by one of the security officers (I believe it was Burroughs or Penniston), years later, that they were aware of a 'special' mission. Highly classified missions were fairly common due to weapons movements, the 67ARRS activities and Aerial Recon activity. The only time in the entire time I was at the base that I was in a jeep was the night I went out into the forest. I stand by my statement that I had no personal knowledge of any special aircraft movement related to the incident. It might have happened, but I have no first-hand knowledge of such. The use of 'Red Alert' was not used in the Air Force. I can tell you that, on occasion, we were asked to clear up situations that had taken place at Orford Ness, but I am not at liberty to explain the nature of our involvement there."*

John Hanson – Larry Warren regression tape-recorded interview

Toward the end of 2014, there was considerable discussion in the social media about a tape-recorded interview of the regression of Larry Warren by Budd Hopkins, (whose photo is shown on page 494, during a trip to England in 2006), which was sent to Colonel Halt by David Jacobs. As is usual with emotive subjects such as this, some people claimed vociferously that the acquisition of this tape had breached a code of professional etiquette by its release.

Having seen a number of emails from Charles Halt, relating to his correspondence with David Jacobs and vice versa, I emailed David hoping to use his opinions expressed in those emails to Charles Halt, with regard to the individuals concerned, but was instructed by David not to reveal the contents of them. Under the circumstances we can only wish him the best and thanked him for replying.

Carol Rainey – My views on line about the 'tape', 30th December 2014

On Tuesday, 30th December 2014, author *Carol Rainey, the ex-wife of Budd Hopkins, had this to say in an on-line blog with regard to the 'Security of Budd Hopkins Archive Called into Question, David Jacobs Shares Responsibility'

Carol Rainey

Jack Brewer website 'The UFO Trail'

Carol:

"Peter Robbins, who described himself on the Dec. 17th Jimmy Church 'Fade to Black' show as a former assistant and confidant to the late Budd Hopkins, told Church that David Jacobs recently provided retired Colonel Charles Halt with a copy of a tape-recorded regressive hypnosis session, conducted by Hopkins many years earlier on Larry Warren. Robbins framed the circumstances, about which Warren expressed outrage earlier this month, as a misunderstanding on the part of Jacobs.

This blog has previously explored issues central to the ethics of UFO research. They include how abduction researchers have dealt with in the past and continue to deal with witness confidentiality. The story of the leaking of Larry Warren's audio-taped session(s) to Charles Halt continues this exploration. Let's begin with a summary of some of the players and what was stated on recent podcasts."

---

*Carol Rainey is the former wife of the late Budd Hopkins. They co-authored *Sight Unseen: Science, UFO Invisibility, and Transgenic Beings*. Rainey has, in more recent years, asserted that substantial scrutiny is warranted concerning the research protocols and ethics of abduction researchers in general, and of Hopkins and his associates in particular instances.

December 10th – Martin Willis podcast

Carol:

Carol Rainey

"During a Dec. 10 podcast interview, conducted by Martin Willis, Colonel Halt made assertions with which Warren would later take serious issue. The Colonel's statements carried significant implications about the confidentiality and ethics surrounding the treatment of hypnosis subjects, as well as direct reference to Warren, who participated in hypnosis sessions with Budd Hopkins in the late 1980s and 1990s. Halt broached the subject of Hopkins by stating that the two became 'very good friends.'"

'He'd walk me through all the material he had, some really remarkable stuff that you guys would love to get your hands on', *Charles Halt said during the show with Willis, that he and Hopkins specifically discussed Larry Warren on occasion.*

'I've listened to some of Larry Warren's hypnosis tapes', *Halt added.* **'I have access to that.'"**

Larry Warren's response to Colonel Halt

Carol:

"Warren addressed Halt's allegations, summarising the circumstances and voicing concerns about confidentiality, among other issues. Apparently not yet aware that it was Jacobs who had provided Halt a copy of his (Larry's) taped hypnosis session, Warren stated, **'Somebody provided a man [Colonel Halt] – that is a longstanding, established adversary to me – private, confidential information that, frankly, only three people have ever heard: me, Peter Robbins and Budd.'**

Warren explained that since the death of Hopkins, in 2011, David Jacobs has been the guardian of most or all of the tape-recordings of Hopkins' regressive hypnosis sessions. That included some 600 hypnosis subjects, who believed their testimonies would be treated in confidence. **'David Jacobs has the archives – everything of Budd Hopkins',** *Warren continued.* **'I think Dave's an honourable man. I think Dave's an honest man and, you know, the confidentiality is so important. I wouldn't see any [betrayal] going on. It's kind of a career-ender, if that's a career'.**

Warren added that if he had been asked to grant Halt access to the tapes, he would probably have agreed, but that was beside the point. Peter Robbins would soon make public statements during yet another podcast that did not seem to fully fit with Warren's stance and those statements will be explored shortly.

Warren went on to emphasise that proper protection and care for possible abductees was essential, adding that he was concerned about personal tapes ... from these people being given **to absolute enemies** without permission."

Budd & the Intruders Foundation

Carol Rainey – Setting the record straight, 4th January 2015

Carol:

"Witness confidentiality and accompanying issues were recently explored on this blog in the post, 'Security of Budd Hopkins Archive Called into Question, David Jacobs Shares Responsibility'. Peter Robbins subsequently chose to voice some perspectives about the piece and make some related assertions. I would like to respond to Peter Robbins' categorical statement below, which was posted to Sacha Christie's Facebook page on January 1st.

For the record – Budd Hopkins **NEVER** allowed the release of any tape-recording or confidential file, except to the individual themselves. David Jacobs has always followed this policy as well – except in single case of the event in question [the release of Larry Warren's tape to Colonel Halt]."

A recent photograph of Carol Rainey

On Budd Hopkins

Carol:

"Budd Hopkins' supporters have shown a disturbing commitment to turn him into 'a Saint' by revising and sanitizing every act and event of his life. Budd was a human being – often warm and caring, but also often thoughtless and careless about other people's safety and needs. So are most of us divided between our good and our selfish impulses? So, please, folks, there is no need to attempt to present him as perfect and without flaw – in retrospect. That simply is not who he was. We were married for ten years, most of those happily, and long enough for me to know his character and his work.

Prior to his death, however, Budd did not make adequate provisions for the posthumous safety and protection of his subjects' records. In other fields, a researcher's archives are often given in trust to an academic institution or major library. The archives are transferred to these safe havens, along with strict legal contracts that specify who, why, and how other individuals with serious research projects may or may not use them. If I had been one of Budd's subjects, this would have been my strong preference for where my records would have ended up."

Peter is wrong – Budd did allow copies to be made

Carol:

"Peter is simply and utterly wrong when he asserts that Budd NEVER allowed the release of a tape or files to anyone but the individual themselves. What would Peter call the fact that Budd allowed David Jacobs, at some point in the late 1990s, to take hundreds of Budd's hypnosis tapes back to his home in order to make copies of those confidential 'patient records'?

We both know that Budd, in his studio or living room, often played excerpts of his subjects' regression sessions to visitors like Colonel Halt, Roger Leir, John Mack, and others. I saw him play these regression tapes for journalists, for television producers, and other abductees."

John Cortile videotaped interview shown

"He also played a videotaped interview with John Cortile, aged eight or nine when it was shot, in his studio for outsiders to see, although he'd promised John's mother that he would not.

It's public knowledge that in his first interaction with John Mack, Budd handed him a stack of his unopened, personal mail. These were letters, often up to eight pages long, that had been sent to him in confidence by people who spilled out their deepest fears that their anomalous experiences meant they might be abductees. The names and addresses of these confidential letters (often marked 'Confidential' on the envelopes) were fully in view. John has mentioned this in his writing and in conference presentations. Greg Sandow, too, has posted on the Web about Budd handing him, early on, a stack of unopened letters as a way of convincing him to take the phenomenon seriously."

Breach of promise

"In his last year of life, Budd (or his assignee) handed over to one of his supporter's videotape to be publicly posted on a website that defended the 'Witness' case. The unfortunate facts are that what Budd handed over to be made public was footage that belonged to me, footage that I'd shot with alleged abductees and witnesses for a documentary. I had obtained proper releases from each for inclusion in my film. But Budd had no release or contract whatsoever with the individuals on my film. Yet he was apparently untroubled by the ethical concerns of having handed over stolen material to be posted on a supporter's site in full violation of my copyright -- not to mention the rights of the subjects who were then publicly 'ousted'.

Although I have less knowledge of David Jacobs' policies and procedures, I am aware that Emma Woods has objected strongly, in the past, about his passing along the audiotapes of her own regressions to be listened to and transcribed by other alleged abductees."

In summary

*"In summary, I'd suggest to people concerned about such matters to familiarise themselves with the strict US Department of Health and Human Services HIPAA regulations. It is claimed that during the hypnosis regression session carried out in 1995, **four men were reportedly named by Larry Warren, indicating implications of covert psychological operations, although the men may, in reality, have no demonstrable involvement whatsoever in the hypnotically retrieved story."*** – Carole Rainey

John Hanson

Over the years I have, on occasions, received specific complaints from people who have suffered the trauma of an abduction experience, and then following hypnotic regression, were to discover many years later, that their private and confidential tapes had been used by the media in television documentaries. This then causes even more trauma, as the very people who one may have thought were there to protect them, failed in their duty.

Budd Hopkins wrote two popular books (*Missing Time*, 1981, and *Intruders*, 1987). He established the Intruders Foundation and has made innumerable appearances at conferences and in the media. Because of such strong endorsements and impressive affiliations, and of his untiring work on behalf of abductees, Hopkins became an influential figure in the UFO abduction field. We remember him complaining to us at that: *"I couldn't enjoy my lunch, as people wouldn't leave me alone; they kept pestering me for photographs."*

This is the price of fame. Perhaps we are better off without it! No disrespect to Budd – a likeable man, who was accompanied by some one else – he was a worldwide celebrity and people treated him as such. Of course, he is not the only one. We have met many others, over the years, whose knowledge does not match their fans' expectations! However, this does not stop them demanding to be treated like royalty!

Charles Halt – names kept confidential

*"Yes, Jacobs gave me a copy of Warren's tape. He had written authorisation to release it on demand. I have never revealed anything on the tape that wasn't already in the public domain and put there by Warren or Robbins. Perhaps Larry has forgotten that. I did not do anything underhanded. I've even kept the **three** names Larry mentions, confidential. I have not commented on anything in the recordings that were made.*

I met Carol Rainey during a visit as Budd's house guest. She was very curt and obviously not getting along with Budd. Budd never shared any tapes with me but did share comments, drawings, etc., but also never mentioned names. He did say to me that he was convinced Larry had induced or screen memories."

Philip Mantle on Budd Hopkins

"I am pleased to say that I got to know the late Budd Hopkins in the late 1980s and into the 1990s, and was still in contact with him before he passed away. For me his first book, Missing Time, *should be essential reading for anyone interested in this subject. I found Budd to be a warm and charming man, who was always willing to help; he had a great sense of humour and was just an all-round nice human being. I dare say he was no saint, but then who is?*

I remember he was one of the speakers at a conference I had organised in Sheffield in the early 1990s. Budd arrived in England a few days before the conference began and I had the pleasure of him staying with me at my home in West Yorkshire. The day before we were due to travel to Sheffield for the weekend conference a UFO researcher from Yugoslavia, by the name of Milos, turned up out of the blue. I had only one spare room at my house, so I asked Budd if he minded sharing one night with Milos as I couldn't turn him away. Budd had no problem with this, but luckily there were two single beds in the spare room.

The following morning Milos was the first to come down for breakfast. He was full of the joys of spring and I asked him if he had slept okay and he replied that he had and quickly sat down to a plate full of bacon and eggs. About 30 minutes later we were joined by Budd. I must admit he looked a little bit worse for ware. I asked him the same question I had asked Milos – 'Did you sleep okay?' For me his reply speaks volumes about Budd and his character. He replied with a wry smile on his face, 'Gee that guy can snore'.

What more can I say? I am pleased and proud to have known Budd Hopkins and had him as a guest in my home, even if he was kept awake all night by a snoring Yugoslavian UFO researcher."

Above:
Budd Hopkins
with Phillip Mantle
and below, with
Dawn Holloway.

John Hanson – Jasper Hamill of the *Daily Mirror* telephones

Just before Christmas 2015 Jasper Hamill from the *Daily Mirror* telephoned me, late one evening, in a gush of enthusiasm to inform me that the article relating to my interview held with him, following my visit to the *Daily Mirror* offices, in London, was going to be published. I was pleased that it would also offer an opportunity to let people know that I was working with Charles Halt on the *HALT Perspective* and naively thought something would be finally in print – nothing further was ever heard. It seems very odd that while many of my colleagues have, over the years, been the subject of newspaper publicity, our efforts to preserve UFO sightings as part of our social history continues to be ignored, despite now 20 years research into the subject never mind the enormous amount of personal money that Dawn and I have ploughed into this quest!

David Boardman

During a meeting with local UFO enthusiasts David Boardman – a retired teacher by profession – and his wife from Alvechurch, Worcestershire, who had travelled down to Woodbridge Community Hall to hear Charles Halt, in July 2015, we asked David if he was prepared to assist with carrying out searches on the internet, in order to track down former servicemen at RAF Woodbridge/ Bentwaters Airbases who may have information pertinent to this subject matter, which he agreed to.

One of those replies was from Lt. Colonel Dane E. Harrel, USAF (Retired), O'Fallon, Illinois.

Dane:

"I was a 25 year-old air traffic control officer at Bentwaters/Woodbridge, 88-89. I wish I had more to contribute but I remember talking with some of our controllers in the radar approach control (RAPCON) about primary targets (raw radar returns) that used to transit East Anglian airspace at what appeared to be incredible speeds."

Lt. Colonel Harrel – RAPCON picked up targets

"The RAPCON would watch the targets cross the radar display and would even get calls from RAF Wattisham controllers, asking if we saw the same targets that they were observing. In addition, some of the controllers who were assigned to the twin bases during the time of the Rendlesham Forest incident told me an F-4 was dispatched from Germany to Bentwaters immediately after the incident. The crew did a quick turn at Bentwaters and returned to Germany (probably Ramstein AB) with a roll of film, containing photos taken of the object witnessed on the ground."

Charles Halt:

"I will repeat what I said before about this. I learnt from others that Gordon Williams received something while in the cockpit of an

A-10 bound for Germany. Mike Verrano claimed it was film of the UFO. I think it was Mel Zickler's efficiency report that was late and they wanted it to get into his file before the promotion board. I remember talk of that happening. This was well after the event in the forest. I could be wrong but I don't think so. The only related film it possibly could have been is Neville's 35mm film. To have gotten it someone would have to have broken into his home and done a substitute. Not likely!"

Lt. Colonel Harrel

"I will add there appeared to be odd things happening in Rendlesham Forest well after the 1980 incident. It could have been people riding on ATVs, etc., but lights were observed outside the RAF Woodbridge fence on at least one occasion when I was in the air traffic control tower during a night shift. I can remember notifying security forces of unusual lights in the trees north of the airfield. When the security forces went out to investigate, the lights disappeared and then reappeared when the security forces personnel returned to the base. Like I said, it might have been people riding ATVs or something similar. I believe that Colonel Halt had a son who was an air traffic controller. If so, it adds credence to a story I was told by one of my controllers in Florida shortly after I returned from England. This controller told me he had worked with the son of Colonel Halt, and the son indicated his father – Colonel Halt, had told him 'there were things that took place in the forest nobody will ever know about'.

The son also told this individual the craft had communicated telepathically with Colonel Halt (maybe others, too) and conveyed a message to the effect, 'We are experiencing technical difficulties and mean you no harm. Please leave us alone'."

Charles Halt:

"I never told my son that I received any type of communication from a craft or object. I don't know where that came from."

Lt. Colonel Harrel

"I thoroughly enjoyed my UK assignment and consider my two years living in Woodbridge Town among the best experiences of my life. I'm living in my home town following retirement and this area, too, has had a significant UFO incident recently. Too many reputable people like Colonel Halt have witnessed these unusual events and our Government is/are stonewalling us.

. . . Best to you and Colonel Halt."

John Hanson – *X Files* now!

Towards the end of the year another Journalist from a National newspaper telephoned and asked me to put him in touch with Charles Halt, as he wanted a few words from him to go into an article celebrating the intended release of further declassified files by the MOD relating to the Rendlesham Forest Incident. In addition he mentioned any quotes would fit into advance publicity relating to some new episodes of the *X Files* being released after Christmas. He asked me a number of questions about UFOs and my opinion. He seemed impressed by the extent of our research and commitment to preserving what we pointed out was, after all, our social history. Suffice to say, none of this and our part was even remotely mentioned.

Christmas lights, 2015

Journalist Dan MacGuill of the Irish-based *Journal* contacted me in late October 2015, asking if I could put him in touch with Charles Halt, as he wanted to interview him about the incident.

I spoke to Dan at some length about the *Haunted Skies* books and reminded him about the heavy period of reported UFO activity around the Belgium area in the mid 1980s, which still spasmodically attracts considerable media interest after Air Force jets were scrambled to intercept reported 'triangular' UFOs seen in their airspace.

Parallels can be drawn

The irony of this is that strong parallels can be drawn between what happened over Belgium and literally hundreds of previously unpublished UFO sightings, many of which involved what appears to be structured craft over the Essex area and around the adjacent borders of Norfolk and Suffolk. Some of these bore similarities with what Colonel Halt had described seeing over the forest.

Dan's article – 'Christmas lights: The inside story of one of the world's most notorious UFO sightings'

Dan began with a quote from retired Colonel Halt, who was stationed in Okinawa, Japan, and worked at the Pentagon for four years. ***"In 1980, three jobs came up; they included US Commander in Iceland, and Deputy Base Commander at RAF Bentwaters in Suffolk. I chose Iceland, and got Suffolk."***

After outlining Charles Halt's version of the events during the visit into the forest, Dan continues by telling the reader the following:

"There are hundreds of UFO reports in Britain every year. In 2009 alone, the year the UK government got rid of its UFO hotline, there were 640 separate reports up to the end of November – 13 a week."

UFO flies into bag of crisps!

Dan then includes an all too familiar quip in coverage of UFO sightings by the media, which may not be intentional but relegates the matter to one of ridicule and humour when he includes:

"In one email, a teaching assistant from Dorset claims a fireball – the size of a football – flew through her kitchen window and landed in a plastic bag full of crisp packets.

Two others reporting flying objects in Kent and North Yorkshire began *'I am a bit embarrassed about reporting this',* and *'Can't believe I am writing this.'"*

Ian Ridpath

In a move calculated to offer a well-balanced overview of the chosen subject, Dan introduces the views of Ian Ridpath – an astronomy writer and BBC journalist, who has covered the Rendlesham Forest incident since the beginning.

"This case was materially different from others, because of the quality and number of the witnesses. Also, it was a highly unusual sighting since it described a flashing light low to the ground, whereas most are up in the sky. Hence, it was clear that a simple celestial solution was not possible for that part of the sighting."

Ian Ridpath:

"I recall thinking, when I started my investigation, that if this case failed to pan out then I could never, ever, take a UFO case seriously again. It didn't, and I haven't."

Release of the memo – Larry Warren and his claims

The memo, it turns out, had been released just a few months earlier, to a group called CAUS (Citizens Against UFO Secrecy), who filed a Freedom of Information request in the US.

The source of the rest of the story was later revealed to have been Larry Warren – a former Air Force police officer – who has himself become a controversial figure over the past 35 years.

Among many other claims, Warren says a Major General walked up to the spacecraft, touched it, and communicated with aliens in the woods.

Dan:

"Halt is adamant about that and other stories told in Left At East Gate *– the account of the incident written by Warren and Peter Robbins, in 1997, and advised* The Journal, *'It's garbage. It should be classified as fiction; it's so far off base.'"*

(Dan claims he asked Warren and Robbins to respond to this, but they didn't.)

Dan:

"What forced Chuck Halt to break his official silence after 11 years was what he calls the 'tremendous amount of disinformation' circulating about the events of Christmas night, 1980."

Charles Halt:

"I still didn't say much publicly until people started putting out all kinds of garbage and nonsense...

So much disinformation out there and people bugging me about what happened – I finally decided, it's time to tell the truth.

I believe the objects that I saw at close quarter were extraterrestrial in origin and that the security services of both the United States and the United Kingdom have attempted – both then and now – to subvert the significance of what occurred at Rendlesham Forest and RAF Bentwaters by the use of well-practised methods of disinformation.

I was a non-believer; I never really gave it a second thought before the incident. But I've got so much material from so many people, and talked to very credible people – people that do not want their names used – that are in very influential positions, including some that are as high in the government as you can get. I can tell you, we are not alone. I can guarantee you that."

Dan: Jim Penniston

Dan also brought the reader's attention to what he referred to as one of the most extraordinary claims surrounding the incident; that of Jim Penniston – one of the three men who went into the woods on Christmas night. Soon afterwards, he drew a set of sketches of the craft, on the request of Base Commander Ted Conrad.

Under hypnosis in 1994, he claimed to have touched the spacecraft, which was adorned with elaborate coded hieroglyphics, and telepathically downloaded a data set in binary code.

He also said he had encountered 'beings' who were not extraterrestrial, but rather human time travellers from the future.

Dan: Ian Ridpath consulted

"Ridpath points to a sci-fi channel movie called Official Denial, *which was released in November 1993. It features a landing on an Air Force base – abduction, and, just like Penniston's hypnosis, culminates in the revelation, 'They are us'. If he saw the film, Penniston's 'memory' could have been heavily influenced by it, but even if he didn't, a wide range of scientific studies have established that false memories can readily be created or even implanted during hypnosis.*

As for the lights seen on 27th December, when Halt brought his team out to the woods, Ridpath found a startlingly simple explanation for this almost as soon as he arrived in 1983, and talked to a local woodsman named Vincent Thurkettle.

Once Vince, the forester, had alerted me to the existence of the lighthouse in the same line of sight as the flashing UFO, I expected the case to die rapidly. Neither of us expected that it would grow into a celebrated classic.

The Orford Ness Lighthouse, on the Suffolk coast, shines in the direction of the farmhouse close to where Halt reported seeing a 'beam', and onto the purported landing site on the edge of Rendlesham Forest."

Charles Halt to Dan

"You did a great job and told the story well. I was taken back that Warren and Robbins declined to comment, especially after all the threats and profanity from Warren and derogatory comments from Robbins. I tried for years to put them on the right track, but finally gave up. Well done."

We sent Jim the link to the article, after putting Dan in touch with Charles Halt asking for any comment he might like to add.

Jim Penniston comments

"I would like to point out a couple of huge mistakes and there are many. First of all the drawing of the craft was accomplished on Monday morning of the 29th December 1980, I believe, at the AFOSI building, along with my four page handwritten statement. They (the people at the AFOSI) building actually returned the drawing to me there after showing little to no concern about the drawing, but they did photocopy it.

As far as Ian Ridpath's claim that the story from the TV show which was televised in 1993/1994 was an influencing factor with my hypnosis initiated by my Doctor – that is ludicrous. Cable Television did not provide the SyFy cable network channel here till the early two-thousands probably 2002 or 2003, I should know I have lived here since 1993.

Besides I was a VP for a Security Company here in Freeport, working twelve to fourteen hours a day in the early 1990s to mid- 1990s, I watched little to no TV . . . just did not have the time, so I would have to refute that.

Another point is something everyone glosses over and never addresses – is the physical evidence. There is only physical evidence from the night of contact that I participated in. No other physical evidence is available from any of the following nights. The Colonel debunking night was to go out there, because the Security Police were obsessed with looking at the sky and the Lt. said they had observed lights in the sky. They were looking at everything that moved. This is the reason Colonel Halt went out there, so he could put an end to their preoccupation away from their primary job. Lights in the sky and beams of light are not physical evidence. (I actually tell, in my new manuscript, how Warren obtained what he says is his account. It was done by multiple sources within the security police squadron – very interesting stuff)"

Jim – Now writing the definitive book on the incident

"We (my co-author and I) are writing the definitive book on RFI; it is the culmination of over three years of research and the results are at a minimum earth shaking and amazing. It is about

time to put guys like Warren, Robbins, Clarke and Ridpath to bed. The reality of the situation is that I am only concerned about contact night. Everything else on subsequent nights is not relevant to me.

I will guarantee this … my new book on Rendlesham, when it is done, will be the definitive book on it. No one will get by unscathed. This includes everybody that was actually involved and people that thought they were involved or wish they were. Personally I don't care about the third night; it's not even relevant to me. And I suppose if you had been in my situation and experienced what I did on that first night of the investigation, you would certainly not care either about the third night."

John Hanson

"I agree with what Jim says, despite not only his evidence but the evidence of literally millions of people worldwide who have experienced a variety of all manner of sightings, including close encounters with these objects. This is totally ignored in the scheme of things. We have seen a constant flow of documentaries devoted to the events that occurred at Rendlesham Forest, which depict what happened there (now over 35 years ago). However, the impact of what Jim and John Burroughs experienced (never mind the many others whose accounts are in this book) is nullified by Society's attitude towards a subject which should be taken seriously rather than the butt of humour, as can be seen so many times over, with the ridiculous allegations made by those sceptics who can't be bothered to get off their backsides and review the whole of the evidence. If they did, their opinions might change! At the end of the day it is about offering an explanation – no matter how ridiculous – which satisfies the majority of the population, who believe that people who report having sighted a UFO are the product of excess alcohol or vivid imagination. Surely, one day, the 'real truths' behind this will be known. Unless we are prepared to confront the reality instead of the scepticism surrounding the subject, we cannot move forward in understanding what lies behind this phenomena and its influence on our lives."

Ralph Noyes

Ralph Noyes, who was for four years the head of Defence Secretariat 8 (DS8), retiring in 1977 with the rank of Under-Secretary of State, wrote regarding this case:

"Our worried sceptical colleagues have already had to advance an extraordinary hotchpotch of explanations: space debris, a bright meteor, a police car, drink and drugs, a lighthouse, other lights on the coast, dear old Sirius.

Occam, you will remember, urged us to cut away unnecessary complications in our attempts to explain phenomena and to look for the simplest explanation. The simplest explanation of Halt's memorandum is that he was reporting – as precisely as wondrous events permit – what he and 'numerous individuals' encountered on December 29/30, together with such facts as he had been able to ascertain from his subordinates about the occurrences of December 26/27."

Ralph Noyes was another British government official, whose letters petitioning that the UFO matter be taken seriously, can be found in the UK UFO files. In 1969 he was head of Defence Secretariat 8 (DS8), and one of his responsibilities was to answer public questions about UFOs. He says he was not able to share his true opinions on the subject. In the files he stated:

THE HALT PERSPECTIVE

"It is only since I left the MOD (in 1977) that I have seriously tried to consider what may possibly lie behind the 'UFO phenomenon'. It was impossible to discuss it seriously within the Department; I would merely have 'rubbished' my working relationship with the RAF and scientific colleagues if I had disclosed the interest I felt in the better reports which reached us. What I retain from my MOD experience – greatly reinforced by much that I have since read – is that the 'phenomenon' is of importance."

1988

1988 – EAST ANGLIA UFO SIGHTINGS

6th March 1988 – UFO causes discomfort

PAULINE Godbold (then aged 14) was attending to her horse, 'Charlie', at the family home (the old station house) in Godmanchester:

"At 7.20pm I heard a faint noise, which I took to be an aircraft approaching. When I glanced casually upwards, I saw a blacker than black square object, making a terrible noise as it passed overhead, followed by the most disgusting smell. It looked about one and-a-half metres long and twenty millimetres thick. It was covered with perforations and had a small 'bump' set into the middle of the craft – like half a football, with something resembling antennas sticking out from each corner. I was very frightened and ran into the house, screaming. My mother and father, who hadn't seen the UFO, told me they had heard a loud vibrating noise, followed by the air being sucked out of the room, and then an awful smell."

Enquiries made with RAF Alconbury, Connington, Wyton and Little Storton, revealed that no aircraft or Exercises had been carried out over Godmanchester on that day.

Ron West interviews witness

Ron West – an Investigator for the East Anglian Paranormal Research Association, visited Pauline at her home address, in April 1988, and found that she was being treated for blurred eyesight – a condition described by her local doctor as 'enlarged pupils, somewhat sluggish'.

Headline 'Smelly spaceship'

For her courage in reporting the matter to the local newspaper (who featured the story alongside headlines such as 'Smelly Spaceship', together with an illustration of an 'alien', piloting a

Tea-hee . . . how the teabag UFO might look

Teabag UFO zaps Pauline

SCHOOLGIRL Pauline Emerson was stirred up yesterday—after a close encounter with a teabag-shaped UFO.

Pauline, 14, was feeding animals in her garden when the smelly spaceship—black with little perforations—zoomed within five yards of her.

Now she is off school and taking tranquillisers to get over the shock.

Yesterday she said: "It was like a teabag. It was so black it shone out. The smell was really disgusting.

"Charlie, my horse, was trembling and my radio went off."

Her mum Barbara was inside their home near Godmanchester, Cambs, at the time and remembers it shaking and the sensation of oxygen being sucked from it.

An education welfare officer who interviewed Pauline afterwards said: "She is a truthful kid, she wouldn't make this up."

Earlier this week a school dinner lady reported UFOs shaped like oranges flying over Beeston, Notts.

Pauline Emerson (Godbold)

teabag) Pauline was subjected to both verbal and physical abuse from the children at the school she attended.

Ridiculed for having the courage to report what she saw!

According to Mr West, the matter was discussed with the Education Welfare Officer, who told him that Pauline was highly regarded at the school and was considered truthful.

CASE NUMBER /88 611
SQUARE SHAPED U.F.O.
INVESTIGATORS NAME......R W WEST.
DATE....11/06/1988.
TYPE.CE1.

INVESTIGATORS SUMMARY:

On Wednesday 6th March 1988 at approxamatly 1930hrs Miss Pauline
Emerson,aged 14 years,residing at,22,Bridge Place,Godmanchester,
Cambridgeshire,was playing in her back garden when she heard a
faint noise,thinking it was an aircraft she ignored it at
first,as the noise persisted she looked up thus seeing a black
square object,approxamatly 1.5 metres long,20 millimetres
thick,the object was covered in perforations,with a small bump
in the middle like a half a football,it was travelling at a
great speed and creating a loud noise,on each corner pertruded
long antennas,during the encounter her portable radio(which was
playing beforehand)ceased playing.
The object first appeared over the top of the council
offices,which lie to the east,and dissapeared over the dual
carriageway bridge(A605)which in my assumption made the object
travel from east to north west,at a height of approx'tly 150
metres.
The length of the sighting was approx'tly one minute.
No lights were seen on the object.
Pauline stated that during the encounter there was a vile smell
somewhat linked to "bad eggs",the smell was also confirmed by
Mrs Barbara Emerson(mother)and by Mr F Godbold(father).
In a hysterical state,Pauline ran indoors to tell her parents of
what happened.
On going to collect Paulines pony from the field across the road
they found it leaning against a wall,trembling violently.
....
Upon invetigation of this case I contacted local police,they
stated no other reports had been filed for this date.
I contacted the duty officers at R.A.F Alconbury,R.A.F
Conington,R.A.F Wyton and R.A.F Little Staughton,they all stated
that they had no aircraft or exercises in operation at this time
and date.
I contacted Cambridge civil airport,the airport manager informed
me that they had no aircraft flying at that time.
I contacted the Cambridge Evening News(Mr Ian Millar,reporter)
who first covered the story,he was unable to throw further light
on Paulines case,he then agreed to run a further story asking
people to come forward with news of sightings for this date.
Due to the further story I was contacted by two people who had
seen similar sightings on different dates(please see reports
investigators ref:RW13488,and RW17488).
I contacted the meteoralogist centre at Bracknell asking for
weather conditions for that day,their report was;clear skies,
fresh breeze,16 knots.

On the 10th of May 1988,I again called to interview Pauline.I was informed by Mrs Emerson that;
Pauline had been under the doctor for the following symptoms, blurred eyesight,enlarged pupils,hysteria.
Pauline would not visit her bedroom unacompanied and would not venture out at night by herself,even to the extent of sleeping in the same bed as her mother,in fact her whole personality has changed since the sighting.
Pauline is also under suspension from school due to being unable to cope with the verbal and physical abuse she has been subject to since the news report.
I contacted Paulines doctor(Dr R Gupta)who confirmed Paulines condition,also stating that she had been to a specialist at the local hospital to try to find a reason for her enlarged pupils no reason has yet been found for the "sluggish behavior" of her pupils,(as in the terms of the doctor).
I contacted Mrs Sidebottom,Education Welfare Officer,who stated,"Pauline is a truthfull child and would not make this up,"I also confirmed with her school ref the suspension of which they replied they were trying to transfer her to another school.
In my opinion Pauline seems to be a truthfull and honest child and I would give her story full credability.
In my opinion I would give this sighting an S-P 8-7.
My reccommendation of this case would be to further the medical side,ref;eyes,hysteria,causes and possible solutions.
Copies,RW13488 and RW17488 are attached for your perusal, but are still under investigation currently by myself.
Case 88 conclusion UNKNOWN,still under investigation.

RON WEST.
P/INVESTIGATOR.BUFORA LTD............

Ron West. Investigator, Cambridgeshire.
Case: Square shape object.
Dated; 2nd March 1988.

10th May 1988.

Following up of my last visit of the 18th April 1988,
Called to get the R1 form completed.
Mrs Emerson informed me that Paulines condition had not improved, she was still under medical care, (Dr Guppa).
As stated in previous report her eyes were blurred, since when i have learned that Pauline has Anaemia and had enlarged pupils for a period of time after the sighting.
At present Pauline is suspended from school, because she is unable to cope with the verbal and physical abuse, she has been subjected to since the news report of her sighting.

Miss Sidebottom, Education welfare officer stated: " Pauline is a truthful child and would not make this up"

Mr Down. Headmaster of Paulines school.

XXXXXXXXXXXXXXXXXXXXXXXXXXXXXXXXXXXXXXXXXXXXXXXXXXXXXXXXXXXXXXXXXXXXXX

CASE STILL UNDER INVESTIGATION
OBJECT: UNKNOWN.

(Mother) Mrs Godbold

UFO SIGHTING ACCOUNT FORM

SECTION A

Please write an account of your sighting, make a drawing of what you saw and then answer the questions in section B overleaf as fully as possible. Write in **BLOCK CAPITALS** using a ball point pen.

On Wednesday the 2nd of March At 4 o clock I went out side to clean out My Animals At 7 o clock I was mucking out My Horses stable and he was out in the feid At 7.30 I was packing away my tools which I had been using and whent to pick up my radio which I had stood hear the wall. As I went to do this I heard a faint noise I didnt take any notice at first as I thought it would be an areoplane but then I looked again I could see a real black square in the sky blacker than black could ever be. It was making a terrible noise and there was a disgusting smell so horrible it is impossible for me to describe. It was about 1 and a ½ metres long and 20 mm

Please continue on a separate sheet if necessary.

DRAWING*

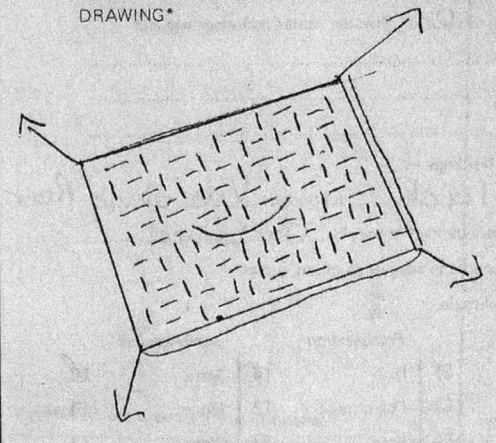

*If preferred, use a separate sheet of paper.

Your full name (Mr/Mrs/Miss/Ms)
PAULINE EMERSON   Age 14
Address 22 BRIDGE PLACE
GODMANCHESTER, CAMBRIDGESHIRE
Telephone No. 411838   (STD 0480)

Occupation during last two years
Schoolgirl

Any professional, technical or academic qualifications or special interests

Do you object to the publication of your name?
*Yes/No. *Delete as applicable.
Today's Date 9-5-88
Signature P. Emerson

FORA LTD
ITHWAY BURGESS HILL
X RH15 9ST

UFO SIGHTING ACCOUNT FORM

SECTION A

Please write an account of your sighting, make a drawing of what you saw and then answer the questions in section B overleaf as fully as possible. Write in **BLOCK CAPITALS** using a ball point pen.

thick. It had long points on each corner and a little bump in the middle of the square like half a foot ball. I had perforations all over it. It was very low as I thought it was going to hit our chimney. It came from the east and went north west. when I went in my mum had to come with me to get the horse in from his feid even he was trembling. As all this was happening my radio went off and came on again once the thing had passed. The smell from it didnt just fade away it was cut off like turning off a light. The thing had no lights on it.

Please continue on a separate sheet if necessary.

DRAWING*

Your full name (Mr/Mrs/Miss/Ms)
.... Age ....

Address..

Telephone No............................(STD...............)

Occupation during last two years........................

Any professional, technical or academic qualifications or special interests

Do you object to the publication of your name?
*Yes/No. *Delete as applicable.

Today's Date..............................

Signature..............................

*If preferred, use a separate sheet of paper.

Published by the British UFO Research Association (BUFORA LTD.) for the use of investigators throughout Great Britain. Further copies may be obtained from BUFORA Research Headquarters.; Newchapel Observatory; Newchapel; Stoke-on-Trent, Staffs:, England   Form R1

BUFORA LTD
16 COUTHWAY BURGESS HILL
SUSSEX RH15 8ST

Unfortunately, because of the unwarranted attention she was receiving, Pauline would have to be moved to another school. As a result of a newspaper appeal by Mr West, two other people came forward to report having seen a similar object but on different dates.

We spoke to Pauline, now married and living in the Lincoln area. She told us she still suffers from eyesight problems, despite many visits to various opticians, over the years, but that her vision appears to actually improve with age rather than deteriorate.

UFO SIGHTING ACCOUNT FORM

SECTION A

Please write an account of your sighting, make a drawing of what you saw and then answer the questions in section B overleaf as fully as possible. Write in BLOCK CAPITALS using a ball point pen.

I was sitting quietly with Mr Emerson indoors when all of a sudden there was a terrible noise, a fast rumbling noise, it seemed as if it was coming into the house, and Pauline came running into the house shouting and shaking her hands shaking madly, her legs were shaking madly for an hour, and it took us another hour to quieten her down.

Please continue on a separate sheet if necessary.

DRAWING*

N/A.

Your full name (Mr/Mrs/Miss/Ms) Mr S. GODBOLD   Age 84
Address 22 BRIDGE PLACE
GODMANCHESTER
HUNTS.
Telephone No. 411 838 (STD   )
Occupation during last two years RETIRED

Any professional, technical or academic qualifications or special interests

Do you object to the publication of your name?
*Yes/No. *Delete as applicable.
Today's Date 9/5/1988
* If preferred, use a separate sheet of paper.
Signature S. Godbold

Published by the British UFO Research Association (BUFORA LTD.) for the use of investigators throughout Great Britain. Further copies may be obtained from BUFORA Research Headquarters.; Newchapel Observatory; Newchapel, Stoke-on-Trent, Staffs., England   Form R1

BUFORA LTD.
16 SOUTHWAY BURGESS HILL
SUSSEX RH15 9ST

Dear John and Dawn,

Firstly I must apologise for replying to your letter after so long, but we have been busy with work and organising a dog show and so on....

In reply to your letter,

1- My eyesight problem - still after many years I am still suffering with my eyes and after using different opticians and doctors no one can find anything wrong with them that much as to cause the problems that I have, Although after my last 2-3 visits to the optician (which I have every 12-6months) my eyesight is getting better and they cannot understand this as as they say normally eyesight problems only get worse, but mine is improving all the time!

2 -Strange marks – no I have not had any of these but. I do seem to have dreams of the next day/future, I also seem to have a so called "groundhog" days, these happen quite frequent, I will do things such as open mail, perform a task or have a conversation about something in particular, but then a few days/weeks/months later I will do it all over again, and I know I've already done it and know what's going to happen but to everyone else, they will say they didn't have the conversation ect...

This must all seem a bit jumbled but I write as I speak so if this is relevant to you maybe we could speak more in person.

Lights in photos – Yes we did have some really strange but pretty looking lights appearing in photos and odd scenes we couldn't describe but unfortunately I think that due to them being odd and us thinking no more of it they have been thrown away, but if I find any I will certainly keep them for you to see if you like.

Cont...

Lastly the photo, - no it doesn't really look like what I saw but I have done a quick sketch of it for you.

I look forward to hearing from you in the future

From Pauline Godbold-Smith (nee Emerson)

Pauline Godbold-Smith

P.S it says that in the write up there was a elderly lady in the house with my mum, I think this is a misunderstanding as I only remember my mum being at home with my dad (although he was older than the average dad would be).

Thanks, Pauline.

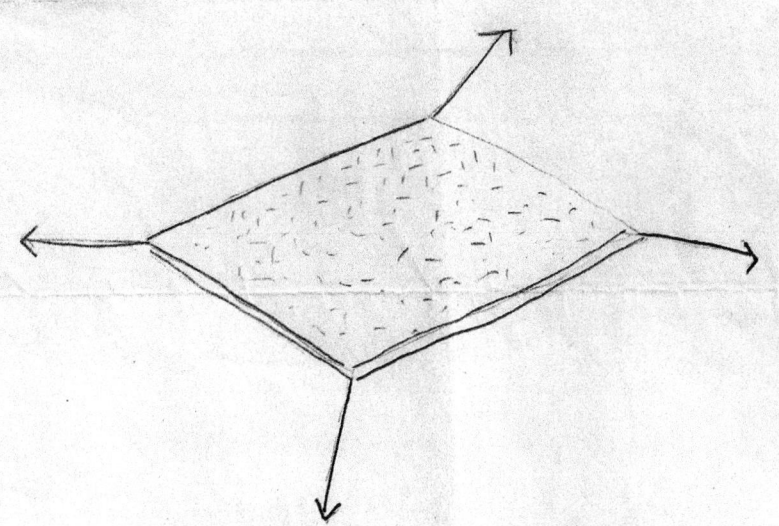

The underside had a bump like ⌣ in the middle.

7th May – Couple sight 'flying saucer'

At 10.15pm, Peter Fleming from Haverhill, Suffolk, was out exercising the family dog, 'Smudge', accompanied by his girlfriend – Julie Rondeau. As the couple strolled along Clarendon Road in the direction of Puddlebrook, picking out the constellations in the night sky, they noticed a bright pinprick of light towards the south-east horizon, and presumed it be the headlights of a car or the glow of a bonfire.

> "We kept our eye on it as we walked along, noticing that it was heading towards the direction of Ladygate Woods. To our surprise, it stopped in mid-air and hovered over the woods about a mile away from us. All of a sudden a 'beam of light' came on, illuminating the woods below it, allowing us to see that it was saucer-shaped with what appeared to be windows set into its side."

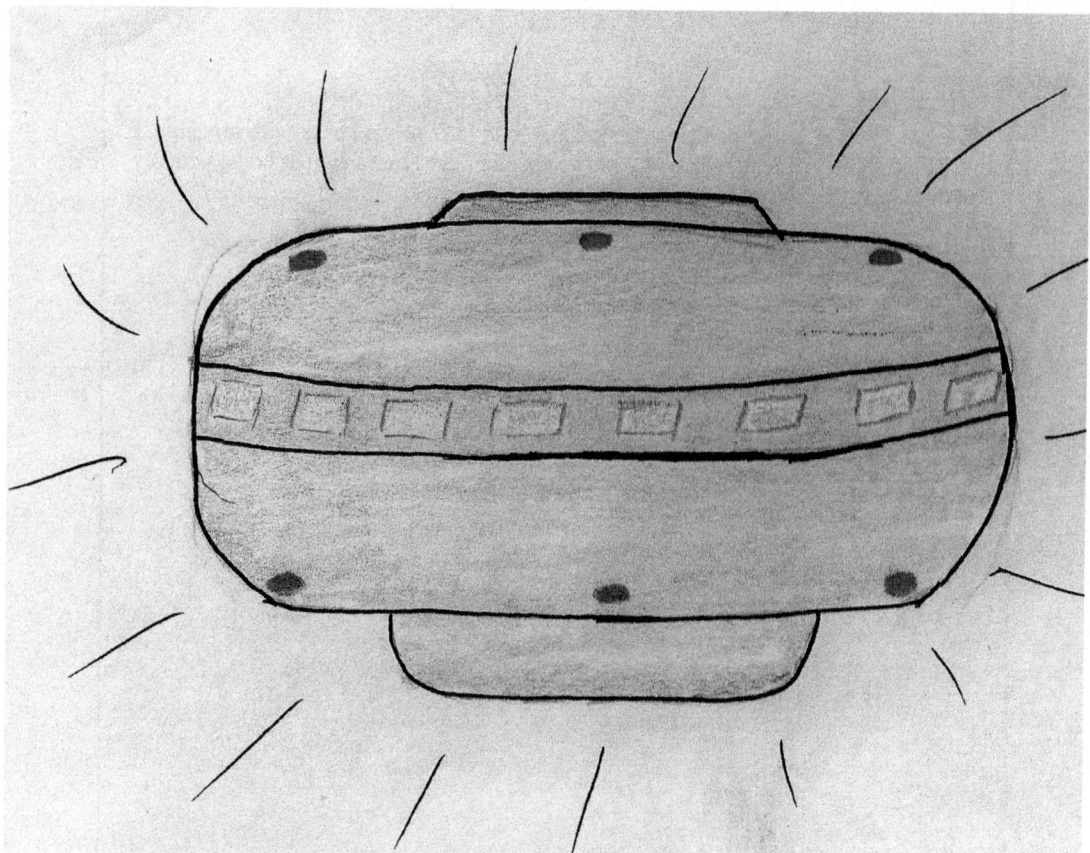

> "A short time later the beam was extinguished, and the 'saucer' began to move right to left in a zigzag manner across the sky, and then returned to its original position again, where the beam came on once more. We stood watching it for about twenty minutes, until it moved again. However, this time it headed towards where we were standing and passed overhead, enabling us to see what looked like a tennis ball, squashed in the middle with a sort of square

UFO SIGHTING ACCOUNT FORM

SECTION A

Please write an account of your sighting, make a drawing of what you saw and then answer the questions in section B overleaf as fully as possible. Write in **BLOCK CAPITALS** using a ball point pen.

The field is situated at the back of Greenacres way. to get to it we passed through a cross of hurdles just of the Clements estate. We didn't notice anything at first until pete pointed out something glowing to the right of ladygate woods, it could have been a fire or torch, but we realised it wasn't when it moved to left and up in the sky hovering just above the woods. and there was no sound at this point. sometimes it rose quickly and then very slowly or stayed still and seemed to light up the whole top of the trees. We both seemed transfixed on this object as we couldn't really believe what we were seeing. We stood there for about 25 minutes. The shape only appeared

Please continue on a separate sheet if necessary.

DRAWING*

Your full name (Mr/Mrs/Miss/Ms) Julie Rondeau Age 17
Address 9 Argyll Court Clements Estate. Haverhill
Telephone No. 704112 (STD 0440)
Occupation during last two years. Student/ Trainee secretary

Any professional, technical or academic qualifications or special interests
O Level, 5 CSE's. 2 city Grancids.

Do you object to the publication of your name? *Yes/No. *Delete as applicable.

Today's Date. 5/6/88
Signature Julie Rondeau

* If preferred, use a separate sheet of paper.

RAY BURGESS HILL
IRA LTD

Sheet 3

to be like star shape. For a moment we panicked as it seem to come towards us but it suddenly reared off to the right and an engine could be heard. It flew over the industrial estate turning on its side and out this point seemed to change shape. a sort of elipse ⬭ with red light going round and then disappeared back where we had first saw it. out of sight. The time was approx. 10-10.30. on 7th I haven't mentioned. we were out walking our dog at the time. 'Smudge' who wasn't distressed or anything. just seemed quiet which is unusual for him.

The colour at first was. like a star or light bulb. (white glowing light) we were about approx. 300 yards away from the woods. the shape appeared the size of an orange. but as it came towards our direction. (and I also add not very close) it got to be about 20-30 inches long. and as it went to the right the glow seemed to disappear and unsteril. tiny red lights could be seen about 3 or 4. and possible a green one. It moved very quickly.

Julie Rondeau
5/6/88

box underneath, displaying red and green lights. As it headed eastwards, I could just about make out its outline and what sounded like engines starting up. After arriving home we were astonished to discover that we had been out for some hours, rather than what appeared to be a much shorter time spell."

29th May – Unusual strange red light seen by motorist

Jane Freestone (28) of Willow Close, Park Road, Haverhill, Suffolk, was with a friend – Paula Patricia Everett (21) – travelling through the Parkway Estate, heading from the Queensway direction, at 11.30pm, when they saw:

"... a young man, who was walking down the hill opposite. He had a red light twirling around his back. Suddenly, the red light appeared on the car dashboard, moving around in small circles. About five seconds later, it vanished from view. There was no beam on it, just a red light. I have no idea what on earth it could have been."

(Source: Ron West)

26th July – Strange red light seen

Mrs Marion Moran (43) of Falklands Road, Haverhill – a hypnotherapist by profession – was outside her house, with her daughter Julie Horton (18), when they saw:

"...a pulsating red light rise up from behind nearby houses and hover for several minutes in the sky. After about ten minutes it moved to the left, still pulsing, and headed away – until lost from view."

11th September – UFOs and Crop Circle discovered near Bury St. Edmunds

At 9.30pm, schoolboy Peter Topham, aged 11, from Tutt Hill, Fornham All Saints, near Bury St. Edmunds, Suffolk (close to the junction with the B1106 and B1112) was getting ready for bed. He saw, through the open bedroom window, a bright object in the sky.

In a written interview, conducted by Derek Newman and Ron West, from the East Anglian Paranormal Research Association, on the 23rd September 1988, he told them:

"I went upstairs to get ready for bed, and looked out of the bedroom window, when I saw a bright light come out of the sky from nowhere – like a bullet. I went down to tell my sisters, who came upstairs. We could see other lights on it. I tried to stay awake all night, but I fell asleep.

The colours of the lights were four purple lights, with three different colours on it, and they changed colours – blue, changing to red. There was no noise or sparks going across the field."

Rebecca, his sister (15):

"After following my brother upstairs, I looked out of the window. The first thing I noticed was four purple lights. After a while, maybe ten minutes, a large rectangular light came on very brightly. While this was happening I saw small darting lights across the field (these were white). The

Peter Topham

	YEAR	NUMBER	INVESTIGATOR	CASE SUMMARY	
REF.	88	9/34	D NEWMAN / R. NES:	DATE	
			EVALUATOR	TIME	
Rw/DN11988				LOCATION	
N FORM TO:-				EVAL'N	
				UFO CLASS	CE1
				CLOSED	

T ANGLIAN U.F.O. & PARANORMAL RESEARCH ASSOCIATION

SECTION A   # SIGHTING ACCOUNT FORM

Please write an account of your sighting, make a drawing of what you saw and then answer the questions in section B overleaf as fully as possible. Write in **BLOCK CAPITALS** using a ball point pen.

went up stairs To get ready for bed then I looked out of my bedroom WINDOW then I sore a bright light came out of the ski from no were and came down like a bullet then I went down to tell my sissters then they come up and then we could see other lights on it then I tried to stay awake all night but I fell asleep we had head no noise and the colour of the lights was were four purple lights and three different lights on it and they changed colours. Blue changing red there was no noise sparks going across the feeled

Please continue on a separate sheet if necessary.

DRAWING*

Your full name (Mr/Mrs/Miss/Ms)
Peter Topham .... Age ... 11

Address .... C'est Ca Tut Hill
Farnham all st Bury

Telephone No... 6079 .... (STD. 0254 ...)

Occupation during last two years ....
Scnool Boy

Any professional, technical or academic qualifications or special interests
_____

Do you object to the publication of your name?
*Yes/No. *Delete as applicable.

Today's Date... 30th September

Signature... Peter Topham

*If preferred, use a separate sheet of paper.

		YEAR	NUMBER	INVESTIGATOR		CASE SUMMARY	
				Mick Newman Ron West		DATE	
RW/7N/1988	REF.	88	9/34	EVALUATOR		TIME	
						LOCATION	
URN FORM TO:–						EVAL'N	
						UFO CLASS	CE I
						CLOSED	

ST ANGLIAN U.F.O. & PARANORMAL RESEARCH ASSOCIATION

SIGHTING ACCOUNT FORM

SECTION A

Please write an account of your sighting, make a drawing of what you saw and then answer the questions in section B overleaf as fully as possible. Write in **BLOCK CAPITALS** using a ball point pen.

After following my brother up the stairs, I looked out of the window. The first thing I noticed was the four purple lights. After a while, maybe ten minutes a large rectangular shaped light came on, very brightly. While this was happening I saw small darting lights across the field (these were white). The following Monday we went up to the area where we had seen it land. There was a large round circle of flattened sugarbeet. On the Wednesday we took my dad to the area. He pointed out that the sugarbeet and soil in the circle was dry while the field was wet from rain. I didn't hear any noise.

Please continue on a separate sheet if necessary.

DRAWING*

dull purple
large white light

Your full name (Mr/Mrs/Miss/Ms)
Rebecca Topham   Age 15
Address "C'Est Ça", Tut Hill, Fornham
All Saints, Bury St Edmunds, Suffolk
Telephone No. 60074 (STD c 284)

Occupation during last two years
Paper girl / School girl

Any professional, technical or academic qualifications or special interests

Do you object to the publication of your name?
*Yes/No. *Delete as applicable.
Today's Date 30th September / 88
Signature R Topham

*If preferred, use a separate sheet of paper.

		YEAR	NUMBER	INVESTIGATOR	CASE SUMMARY	
RW/DN 11988	REF.	88	9/34	D. NEWMAN / R WEST	DATE	
				EVALUATOR	TIME	
..RN FORM TO:–					LOCATION	
					EVAL'N	
					UFO CLASS	CE1
					CLOSED	

..ST ANGLIAN U.F.O. & PARANORMAL RESEARCH ASSOCIATION

SECTION A   SIGHTING ACCOUNT FORM

Please write an account of your sighting, make a drawing of what you saw and then answer the questions in section B overleaf as fully as possible. Write in **BLOCK CAPITALS** using a ball point pen.

9.30 p/c came fishing to tell us to come up
so we went up and saw a Big light
in the middle and other lights either side and then
they started Flashing different colours then
a few minuets later the light in the middle
went even Brighter then I decided to go to
Bed
      Big light in the middle was a bright
      lights on left changed to green red
      Blue orange where on the other
      side

Please continue on a separate sheet if necessary.

DRAWING*

Your full name (Mr/Mrs/Miss/Ms)
Josephine Topham Age 10
Address C'est ca tut hill
farnham all Saints B.S.E
Telephone No. 62279 (STD 0284)

Occupation during last two years
SCHOOLGIRL

Any professional, technical or academic qualifications or special interests

Do you object to the publication of your name?
*Yes/No. *Delete as applicable.

Today's Date 30.9.88

Signature Josephine Topham

*If preferred, use a separate sheet of paper.

following Monday, we went up to the area where we had seen it land; there was a large round circle of flattened sugar beet. On the Wednesday, we took my Dad to the area. He pointed out that the sugar beet and soil in the circle was dry, while the field was wet from rain. I didn't hear any noise."

His other sister, Josephine (10) added:

"At 9.30pm Peter came rushing down to tell us to come up, so we went up and saw a big light in the middle and other lights either side, and then they started flashing different colours – a few minutes later, the light in the middle went even brighter (big light in the middle was white, lights on left changed to green, red, blue, orange, were on the other side). I then decided to go to bed."

Examination made of the scene

Derek and Ron made their way to the scene of the incident, where they examined the circle of flattened beet.

Derek:

"The ground was bone dry; the remainder of the field was moist. The sugar beet within this circle was flattened, compared to the rest of the field. The beet inside the circle was showing signs of decay, with yellowing leaves, in contrast to the outside which was still thriving with dark green leaves. We found no indentations within the circle or outside. We measured the flattened area and found it to be 30 metres, but it was not a perfect circle."

As a result of some considerable newspaper publicity given to the incident, along with an appeal from 'Del' and Ron seeking any other witnesses, a Mrs Susan Slinger of the White House, Bury Road, Fornham All Saints, claimed that she and her husband, Cecil, had seen:

"…a cigar-shaped object hovering in the night sky, at around the same period".

Other witnesses to something strange observed in the sky over Bury St. Edmunds, during this month, were Reuben Eaves and his sister – Esther. They were cycling home, close to Prigg Walk, Bury St. Edmunds, at 4pm, when they saw:

"…a long shape, to begin with, then it formed the shape of an umbrella and seemed to be moving like it was opening and closing. It was a frightening experience."

(Source: *Bury Free Press*, 28.10.1988 – 'Yes we also saw UFO'/ Ron West)

SIR: — I feel that I must ask you to publish my letter regarding your news item involving young Peter Topham and his sighting of a UFO in Fornham All Saints (BFP, 30/9/88).

The other evening, my husband — Cecil — was locking up for the night and putting the cat out when he came rushing up the stairs and lead me to the window which faces south. My gaze fell upon an extremely bright light which was cigar shaped, hovering in the night sky. It then seemed to fall very gracefully to the ground and was lost from sight. It was quite a long way away, but I should think it was between 200 and 300 feet long.

Confident

For the next few days I carefully followed local news on TV and Radio Saxon but no mention of the incident was made so you can imagine my pleasure when I read your article. Up until now I haven't dared to mention the sighting to anyone. But now I feel confident that I did see what I saw — a UFO!

Please publish my letter so that others who have seen local occurances which they can't understand can contact me. I am thinking of setting up a society. This was originally the idea of my father who until the day of his death swore that he saw the Grey Lady that haunts the West Stow Hall. And nobody believed him either. If my letter is too long please just publish my address. Sorry that I'm not on the telephone.

SUSAN SLINGER (Mrs)
Bury Road,
Fornham All Saints.

SIGHTING IN BRIEF. U.F.O.LANDING FORNHAM ALL SAINTS SUFFOLK.
——

On the 11th September 1988. Peter Topham was in his bedroom getting ready
for bed,the time was 9.30p.m. He looked out of his bedroom window, which
faces open farm land. (Sugar beet fields) when he noticed this bright light
in the sky, he called out to his family to come and see it! His sisters
Rebecca and Josephine came in and watched this bright light. Suddenly it
came down like a bullet, We could see other lights stated Peter! first
there was four purple lights, one large white light and then three blue
lights changing to red lights. Small darting lights were seen darting
about all over the field of sugar beet. No noise was heard by any of the
witnesses. Peter now felt very tired and went to bed and fell asleep.
(also his sisters)
The following day Monday 12th September 1988. Peter and his sisters went
over the sugar beet field to where they saw the lights,.and found a large
round circle of flattened sugar beet.
On Wednesday 14th September 1988. They took their father up to see this
circle. Mr Topham, pointed out,   the circle of flattened sugar beet, the
ground was dry,where as it had been raining overnight (Tuesday 13th) and
the rest of the field was wet!.

=============

INVESTIGATORS REMARKS.
————————————————————

On Friday 23rd September 1988, Del Newman and myself, interviewed Peter and
his Sisters, took signed statements. We investigated the field, where we
found a circle of flattened sugar beet, (See photographs). The ground was
bone dry, the remander of the field was moist. The sugar beet within this
circle was flattened compaired to the rest of the field. also the beet inside
the circle was showing signs of decay and yellowing leaves, whilst the outside
of the circle, the beet was still thriving and the leaves were of a deep
green. We found no indentations within the circle, or outside. In fact apart
from the circle we found no traces of a landing. On investigating the circle
we found it measured 30 meters, but it was not a perfect circle. (see drawing)
Both Del and myself believe what Peter and his Sisters saw on the 11th Sept,
and their stories about what happened are the truth. We believe them, and
can find no reason for them to lie.

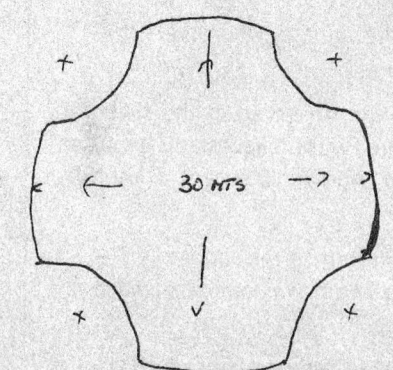

X DEEP GREEN LEAVES AND
HEALTHY GROWING SUGAR BEET.

————

INSIDE CIRCLE FLATTENED
AND YELLOWING LEAVES.

DRAWING OF
CIRCLE AT
LANDING SITE.

30 MTS

VEST REF:	RN2988	REF.	88	9/80	EVALUATOR		TIME	
RETURN FORM TO:–					LOCATION			
					EVAL'N			
					UFO CLASS		LIT 2	
					CLOSED			

EAST ANGLIAN U.F.O. & PARANORMAL RESEARCH ASSOCIATION

SECTION A   SIGHTING ACCOUNT FORM

Please write an account of your sighting, make a drawing of what you saw and then answer the questions in section B overleaf as fully as possible. Write in **BLOCK CAPITALS** using a ball point pen.

I WAS LAYING IN BED AND I COULD NOT SLEEP. THE SKY SUDDENLY LIT UP WITH LIGHTS, SO I SAT UP IN BED AND LOOKED OUT MY BACK DOOR AND SAW BRIGHT WHITE LIGHTS WITH SMALL GREEN LIGHTS ROUGHLY EVERY TWO BETWEEN. THE OBJECT LOOKED LONG AND OVAL SHAPED AS THIS WAS THE LIGHTS WHICH MADE IT THIS SHAPE. I SAT AND WATCHED IT FOR ABOUT 2-3 MINUTES, THEN LAYED BACK DOWN AND THOUGHT ABOUT IT FOR ABOUT 3 MINUTES, THEN SAT BACK UP AND WATCHED IT AGAIN BECAUSE I WAS TRYING TO WORK OUT HOW A FLYING OBJECT COULD MAKE NO NOISE AND JUST MOVED AT THE SAME HEIGHT AND ALSO BE ABLE TO COME DOWN SO LOW NEXT TO PEOPLES HOMES WITH NO DISTURBANCE. I COULD NOT COME UP WITH AN ANSWER SO I HAD WATCHED IT AGAIN FOR ABOUT ANOTHER 3-4 MINUTES THE SECOND TIME SO I LAYED BACK DOWN AND HID UNDER MY QUILT BECAUSE I FRIGHTENED MYSELF WITH SCIENCE FICTION THOUGHTS GOING

Please continue on a separate sheet if necessary. THROUGH MY HEAD. THE OBJECT WAS STILL IN THE SAME PLACE AT THIS TIME AND I DID NOT LOOK AROUND.

DRAWING

GREEN
WHITES

SEEMED TO BE END TO SIDE OF BACK VIEW. SORRY I'M A USELESS DRAWER.

*If preferred, use a separate sheet of paper.

Your full name (Mr/Mrs/Miss/Ms)

JACQUELINE .... Age 26

Address ... OF ARNEMOUTH PARK ROAD

SOUTHEND-ON-SEA, ESSEX

Telephone No. .... (STD 0702) X

Occupation during last two years.......................

MOTHER

Any professional, technical or academic qualifications or special interests

.... NO

Do you object to the publication of your name?
*Yes/No *Delete as applicable.

Today's Date... 6th October 88

Signature...................

12th September 1988 – UFO display over Thorpeness

Between 1am and 3am, six people walking along the beach at Thorpeness were stunned to see a proliferation of six or seven yellow lights, 'dancing about erratically across the sky', before disappearing from view. Was there a connection with what occurred at Bury St. Edmunds?

(Source: Call made to the Essex UFO Hotline, run by Ron West)

19th September – Half-moon shaped UFO seen

Dawn (46) from Grimwade Street, Ipswich – a teacher by employment – awoke at 6.45am and went to the window to look out.

"I was stunned to see a half-moon shaped object, hanging down in the morning sky. It was covered in red, blue, gold, and orange lights. After watching it for a while, I went back to bed."

(Source: Ron West)

22nd September – UFO over Stowmarket

Eric Bailey (46) of Hillside, Stowmarket, was driving along the Bury St. Edmunds to Brandon Road (a few miles from Brandon) at 8pm, when he noticed:

"…a large cluster of lights – wide in the middle, narrow at the front and end – moving slowly through the sky, just above tree cover. I braked and it slid slowly to my left, now over both sides of the road. I listened, but couldn't hear anything."

(Source: 'Second sighting of a UFO' The *Leader* 11.10.1988)

25th September – UFO seen over Lowestoft

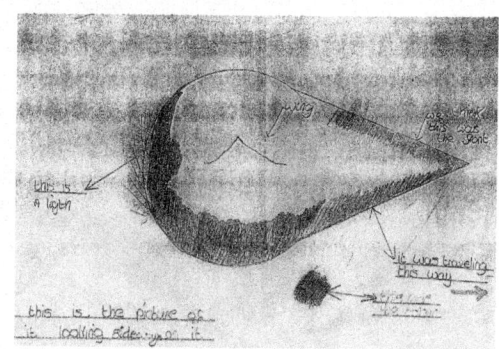

Heidi Brooks and Emma Scrivens (12), from Lowestoft, had just left their local youth club and were crossing a field, at 8.15pm, when they became aware of a buzzing noise. In a tape-recorded interview, later conducted by UFO enthusiast – David Spoor, Heidi had this to say:

"Emma and me carried on, until we got to the middle of the field, then I noticed this 'circle of light' going around us, at knee height – like a lighthouse – but it never touched the ground. We looked up and saw it gradually getting closer. Emma was so scared that she froze with fear. I grabbed hold of her and made her run away. When we got to the top of the field, we looked back and saw the UFO starting to come towards us again, so we ran home."

(Source: David Spoor/Personal interview)

8th October – Black circle seen in the sky over Stowmarket

At 7.20pm, Carol Elizabeth Howe (34) of Brettenham Road, Buxhall, was in her garden when she saw what looked like:

"…a big black circle slowly moving silently through the sky, before it disappeared into clouds 30 seconds later."

Another witness was Frank Wells (69) who was out clearing a hedge at the bottom of the playing field in Buxhall, at 7.25pm, when he noticed a bright light 'the size of a car headlight', shining in the sky in a northerly direction. He watched it for about 30 seconds, before it vanished from view.

25th October – Diamond-shaped UFO over Lowestoft

A diamond-shaped object was seen passing over Mutford, near Lowestoft, at 8.40pm, by Lowestoft Chemist – James Edington, who said:

"I have never seen anything like it before. I was standing with an elderly neighbour of mine. We both saw it, and noticed a flashing light at each point of the diamond. It was silent; all we could hear was the swishing of air as it passed over."

Enquiries with the nearby Ellough Airfield revealed that the only aircraft up at the time was a Sikorsky helicopter, which landed at 8.50pm.

(Source: *Lowestoft Journal & Mercury,* Suffolk, 28.10.88 – 'Mystery of the silent UFO'/ East Anglian Paranormal Group)

27th October – Blue flash of light seen over Ipswich

At 3.45am, Mr Geoffrey Abbott (65) of Carlford Court, Ipswich, arose early. He went into the kitchen to put the light on and make a cup of tea, when the room lit up – as if illuminated by a sheet of lightning. He looked out and saw:

"…a big white circle, like the moon but much bigger. I watched it for a few seconds, before it was out of sight."

Vivienne Humphrey (49) of Warrington Road was awake, at 3.50am, when she saw a bright blue flash of light, which lit up the bedroom, and wondered if it had been fork lightning. She went to the window and looked out; it was a clear night sky. Was it space debris or a fireball? We shall never know.

Enquiries made by Ron West, of the Essex UFO Group, revealed that others had seen the curious 'blue flash'. They included Bernard Barrell (69) of Tuddenham Road, who saw it head in a south-east direction, Brian Williams (44) of Brookfield Road, and Cecil Bailey (62) of Haverhill, Suffolk.

1st December – Bright blue 'ball' explodes in sky over Ipswich

Mr David Barrett was walking the family dog, at 2am, when he saw:

"…a blue light in the sky. It was very bright and reminded me of the novelty globes that you put on a Christmas tree – a bit bigger than a star. Suddenly it exploded into smaller pieces – say, 10 or 12 of them – which all shot off in the same direction. If it had been a shooting star surely it wouldn't have done this, in my opinion." Ron West, who interviewed the witness, believed it was likely to have been space debris.

23rd December – Military helicopter on exercise, not a UFO sighting

Mr Norman Trent, a keen 'sky watcher' from Eye – a small market town 17.5 miles north of Ipswich and 23 miles south-west of Norwich) was outside his house, at about 11pm, when:

"I saw, a long way away from Denham, near Eye, in an easterly direction, a beam of vertical light – like a car headlight – moving backwards and forwards, silently in the sky. I watched it for five minutes – then it went out. Twenty minutes later, I heard the noise of an aircraft. The light came back on, still vertical, moving backwards and forwards once again, as if searching for something.

Through binoculars I was able to establish that the light came from a large military helicopter – presumably engaged on Exercise."

Mr Trent, who was a very religious man and known for his interest in UFOs and crop circles, reminds us, *"Energy from prayers or emotional events sticks to the walls of churches and old buildings, eventually coating them with invisible but potent layers of energy particles. These emotionally charged energy particles create psychic atmosphere in ancient structures."*

An interesting letter is now published from Mr Trent, who was keenly interested in psychic research

AN ACCOUNT OF HEALING.

The PSI Group, which met every Thursday in a West London Hotel, had learned about a method of distant healing. Members were very keen to try it out. At a meeting held on a Thursday in June 1965 1975 a member introduced us to a lady who he had brought to the meeting. She was a professional singer of some distinction who sang on the stage, in cabaret and on cruise liners. She told us about a brain tumour she had developed which surgeons had pronouced incurable. She had just returned from a singing tour on a cruise ship together with her husband and her son; this was to be their last happy time together for she had only a few months to live.

At the next group meeting we decided to do something about it. We spent the whole evening giving her distant healing until some kind of energy flowed about the room giving everyone a tingling warm feeling.

A week later we heard that she felt much better. Two weeks later she went for a check up and a scan and was told that the tumour had gone. The doctors were astonished and said that there had been a "remission"   Feeling perfectly healthy she resumed her career.

A year later there occured an interesting sequel. Singing in a seaside variety show she strolled daily along the sea front when not on duty to get some fresh air. One morning she saw a small child in difficulties in the surf and ran down a slipway to the rescue. She never reached the child because she tripped up on a projecting paving stone and woke up in hospital. She was suffering from concussion, but did not understand why she was surrounded by four doctors, two of whom were specialists from Liverpool. It appeared that she had received a head scan from a piece of new equipment which had shown that a tumour had been removed from her brain at some time in the past. What puzzled the experts was the fact that they could not find any trace of a wound in the skull which would allow the tumour to be cut off and taken out. She did not tell them why.

Issue 4

N.E..TRENT

11ᵗʰ January – At 6.20pm

A large, glowing orange 'ball of light' was seen zigzagging across the sky over Diss, by five people.

5ᵗʰ January – At 8.25pm

A 'disc'-shaped object was seen over MOD land at Thetford, by two people.

20ᵗʰ January – At 11.10pm

A 'disc'-shaped object was seen over Anglia TV Centre, Norwich, by five people.

29ᵗʰ January – Triangular lights seen over A45 (A14)

Mr and Mrs Neal (54) of Northgate Avenue, Bury St. Edmunds, were out walking at 9pm, when they noticed three white lights forming a triangle in the sky.

"They were stationary and appeared to be over the A45 dual carriageway. They were the size of cricket balls. We kept our eyes on them all the way down Northgate Avenue. They were still in the same position five minutes by the time we arrived home. Later I went into the back garden; twenty minutes later they were gone."

(Source: Ron West)

Subsequently, triangle of lights seen over Suffolk

Another witness was John Miller (24) from Angel Hill. He was driving into Bury St. Edmunds with his girlfriend, at 9pm, from the direction of Fornham All Saints.

"I noticed, straight ahead of me in the sky, three strange lights making a triangle. They appeared to be over the British Sugar Corporation building. We stopped but didn't hear any noise. My girlfriend became frightened, so we left. At 9.15pm, they were still there."

At 9.15pm, over Bury St. Edmunds, Suffolk, three white lights were seen by farmer's wife – Anne Goddard (43), of Emswell, Suffolk, who was checking the buildings with her husband when they sighted three white lights, stationary in the sky over Bury St. Edmunds. Fifteen minutes later they had gone.

At 9.30pm Albert Mills (43), of Hardwick Park Gardens, was looking out of his front window when he saw three round lights, hovering in the sky above the town. He watched them for fifteen minutes and noted that they

"... appeared to be over the British Sugar Corporation works, by the Moreton Industrial Estate. I telephoned the Police; they said they would investigate but I never heard any more from them. I watched them for another thirty minutes, by which time they began to fade in luminosity before disappearing from sight."

Ron Fuller, Stuart Nunn (17) and Ian Campbell also confirmed having sighted them.

30th January – Triangular UFO seen over Bury St. Edmunds

At 9pm a triangular object, showing three white lights and a red light (presumably in the centre) was sighted in the sky just above the British Sugar Factory, by eight people.

1st February – Three yellow lights seen over Bury St. Edmunds, at 10.20pm.

2nd February – At 9.45pm

Four people sighted three amber lights, forming a triangle, moving slowly through the sky over Diss in erratic movements.

5th February – Three lights seen

At 9.35pm two residents of Bury St. Edmunds reported having seen three white lights and a red one, moving very slowly, before halting in mid-air for ten minutes and then heading off again.

At 9.50pm a triangular UFO, showing three white lights and a red one, was sighted by two people over Ashill. This appears to have been the same object seen by three people from Swaffham, more or less at the same time.

8th February – A large orange 'light' seen heading eastwards, at 12.35am

20th February – At 9pm

Over Bury St. Edmunds, two people reported having seen three white lights hovering in the sky over the Moreton Hall Industrial Estate (close to the Sugar factory).

18th March 1989 – Triangular UFO seen

Sightings of this object were reported over coasts of Yarmouth and Lowestoft areas, at 7pm and 7.10pm, showing us the slow speed of a UFO, which was often described as moving over the landscape in an almost majestic manner, *apparently* oblivious of human activity taking place below it. Once again, it was described as displaying three amber lights and a red one.

In the same month it is claimed the crew aboard the Shuttle also sighted a UFO!

20th April – Triangular UFOs sighted

Michael Bergdahi (28) of Crown Street, Bury St. Edmunds, was on his way home, at 11pm, when he noticed:

"…three white lights, forming a triangular shape in the sky. They were moving slowly towards the Ipswich direction. Suddenly they stopped in mid-air. Three other lights then moved silently overhead, some 3-4,000 feet high. The second set drew level with the first group, following which both sets of lights headed eastwards before disappearing into the distance, approximately 40 minuets later."

(Source: Ron West)

Other witnesses

Other witnesses were Peter Fox (52) of Eastgate Street, and his wife – Joyce. At 11.15pm they saw three lights, hovering in the sky over the Moreton Industrial Estate.

"We were shocked to see the arrival of another group of three lights, which took up a position next to the first group. A short time later, they moved slowly through the air, apparently following the course of the A45 [now A14] heading towards the Ipswich direction."

21st April – UFO hovers over power lines

Alan Blackburn of Risbygate Street, Bury St. Edmunds, was outside, at 9.15pm, when he saw a large white 'ball of light' moving across the sky, heading in an east to west direction.

"It then slowed down and descended to about 500 feet, before coming to a stop about half-a-mile away from where I was stood. I began to walk towards it and saw that it was oval shaped, hovering silently over power lines; it was about 30 feet across. Suddenly, it shot straight up into the sky and was gone about 15 minutes later."

29th April – UFO casting beams of light

At 11.45pm, Mrs Margaret Rose Harvey (49) of Broad Green, Steeple Bumpstead, Haverhill, Suffolk, was on her way home with her husband, in Fell Lane, Birdbrook.

"I saw this object in the sky, showing a white beam shining in all directions. There was a red light to one side. I had it in view for ten minutes, before it disappeared. It had been completely silent and found the experience frightening, leaving me shaking."

In an interview conducted by Peter Fleming and Julie Rondeau, Mr Fleming expressed concern that their sighting would be treated with mockery.

6th May – UFO seen over Thetford Forest

At 11.55pm, Lewis 'M' (21) – a member of the Armed Forces – was on leave and parked up with his girlfriend, Brenda Monks, in the picnic area in Thetford Forest, Suffolk.

"We saw a large white 'ball of light', which seemed to descend into the forest. After about 30 minutes, it shot straight up into the sky – no noise and about the size of a dustbin lid."

Another couple saw the UFO. Unfortunately, they also wished their identities be kept secret.

Leonard 'F':

"I was parked in Thetford Forest on the Spring Bank Holiday, with my girlfriend, listening to the car radio. We noticed a very large 'ball of light' come down and seem to land in the forest, completely silently. Thinking it was an aircraft descending we got out of the car, but could only see a faint light."

Vehicle clock stopped at 11.52pm

"As we never heard any explosion, we decided to get back into the car and, after waiting five minutes, left. When we reached the main road, the radio suddenly came back on again. I checked the car clock; it had stopped at 11.52pm. I looked at my wristwatch; it read 12.10pm."

Mr Digby also reported having sighted this object on the same day.
(Source: Ron West)

22nd May – Green lights and blue glow over Suffolk

At 9.30pm, six people saw a green light hovering over the sea at Southend, and Mrs Connie Yeowell of North Crescent, Southend, and her husband, sighted a bright light in the sky with pieces falling from it.

At 10pm, two teenage girls were walking along Hullbridge Road at South Woodham Ferrers, when they were confronted by a red 'ball of light', which stopped in front of them. The girls ran away, with the object apparently chasing behind, until they reached the safety of their home.

At 10.20pm, Joan Bealings of Arrendene Road, Haverhill, in Suffolk, went into the garden to fetch the washing, when she saw a blue glow shining onto her garden. Looking up, she saw an object flashing across the sky.

(Source: Unknown Suffolk newspaper, 25.5.1989 – 'Strange light in the sky')

6th June – Large orange 'ball of light' seen heading across the sky, at 8.25pm

16th June – Huge triangular object showing three lights, seen over Diss at 10.45pm

6th July – UFO seen over Denham, Suffolk

Mr Norman Trent (79) was at his home address in Denham, Suffolk, when he saw something unusual in the sky – as a result of which he later contacted Ron West, who asked him to complete a sighting report.

19th July – Did RAF jets chase UFO?

At 11.10pm a triangular object was reported, showing an all too familiar display of three amber lights as it headed away in an erratic manner of flight. The same UFO was seen over Hevingham, also at 11.10pm. Five minutes later it was sighted over Hoveton, by five people.

As a result of telephone calls to the Police (who presumably contacted the RAF) two RAF Jets appeared and were last seen chasing the object showing three white lights and a red one, as it headed out seawards.

3rd August – Triangular UFO over Thetford Forest

At 10.15pm Ernest Oswald (39) a heavy goods vehicle driver by occupation – was on his way home from a long drive with his wife, Helen, and decided to pull up in the forest for a break.

"We saw three white lights in the sky, forming a triangular pattern, hovering over the forest. I would say that they were at a height of about 1,500 feet. At this stage my wife began to get very edgy, so we left."

14th August – Triangular UFO sighted over airbase

Susan Forest (13) of High Street, Mildenhall, Suffolk, was sat in her bedroom (which overlooks Mildenhall Airfield) at 7.45pm, when she saw:

"...three white lights, stationary above the runway; they were the size of tennis balls. I stood watching them until they just suddenly disappeared, at 8.15pm."

15th August – Triangular UFO sighted over Bury St. Edmunds

George Baxter (56) of Abbeygate Street, Bury St. Edmunds – employed at Barclays Bank – was out walking the family dog, at 10.15pm, when:

"As I turned the corner into Eastgate Street, I saw people looking up at the sky [John Hunt (19) and Steve Bush (20)]. I looked up and saw three white lights forming a triangle. Suddenly, the silent lights flickered and then shot away at a fast speed five minutes later."

16th September – Large 'ball of white light' seen

Mrs Winifred Haines (80) of 2, King Street, Bury St. Edmunds, was in her kitchen at 10.15pm.

"I looked out of the window and saw 'a large ball of glowing light', moving straight across the sky. It was lost from view, a few seconds later."

22nd September – Triangular object reported over Norwich Airport

At 8.30pm, a large triangular UFO was seen hovering over Norwich Airport by at least four people, who contacted Ron West to report the sighting. He contacted the airport about the incident; they denied any reports of strange lights or anything being tracked on radar.

23rd September – Four UFOs in formation

Lance Pennington (28) – a plumber by occupation – from Valley Lane, Great Finborough, Stowmarket, was at his home address when there was a knock at the door. He opened it and spoke to two complete strangers, who asked him to come outside and have a look in the sky.

"I went out and saw four 'circles' or 'globes' in the sky. We watched them for about 45 minutes, illuminated in the bright light that shone over us. Suddenly they disappeared from view, leaving a wonderful cloud formation – something I had never seen before in my life."

(Source: Ron West)

5th October – Three white lights seen over RAF Lakenheath

At 10.45pm, housewife Karen Smith (31) was looking out of her bedroom window in the High Street, Lakenheath, Suffolk (which overlooks RAF Lakenheath) when she noticed three large white lights, stationary in the sky over the airbase.

"They formed a triangular shape, with a faint orange halo around them, and were about 2,000 feet up – the size of tennis balls from the ground. Suddenly, all the lights on the airbase went out and I could see a lot of vehicles moving about. I saw two aircraft take off; as they did so, the lights faded away. The only noise was the aircraft taking off."

On the 9th October, Ron West contacted the Duty Officer at RAF Lakenheath. He explained the reason for the call and was told:

"No comment. I wasn't on duty on that date."

On the 12th, Ron contacted the base again and was told:

"Nothing unusual happened on the night of the 5th October 1989".

1st January – Two cigar-shaped objects sighted over Woodbridge

At 1.20am on 2nd January 1990, Peter John Maddox (21) of Woodbridge, Suffolk – a RAF service-man – was walking home near Woodbridge, when:

"I noticed two cigar-shaped objects in the sky, heading in a north-south direction towards Essex. They were below cloud bank and completely silent. A cigarette, at arm's length, would have covered them. Ten seconds later, they were gone from sight."

At 1.30am, Anthony Weldon (49) was driving home with his wife, daughter and her boyfriend, along the A12 between Chelmsford and Ingatestone, after having celebrated New Year's Eve, when they saw two objects, side by side, heading across the sky towards the direction of Brentwood, some 1,500 feet up in the air. Five seconds later, they were lost from view.

Others that saw something highly unusual on this date were George T. Brown (26) of Sir Francis Way, Brentwood, Essex. He was standing outside his girlfriend's house in Park Road with his girlfriend – Susan Watson (20), at 1.30am, when they noticed:

"…two very large silver-grey in colour oval-shaped objects, moving at speed across the sky. They were at a height of about 2,000 feet, moving at 2,000 miles per hour. The ends of the objects were pointed and the fronts rounded. I last saw them heading towards the coast. Susan was so petrified, she ran indoors."

Mrs Edna Curtiss (56) of Station Road, Thetford, was drawing the curtains, at 10.30pm, when she saw:

"…two small silver white lights, moving fast across the sky. They suddenly stopped and silently hovered for two minutes, before heading across the sky again."

At 11pm this evening, a fireball was seen crossing the sky over Scotland.

4th January – Mysterious 'light' over Thetford Forest

At 7.30pm, Mrs B. Bellamy (65) of Thetford, Norfolk, was driving home after picking up the children from their grandparents, at Wootton, near Thetford Forest. This is what she had to say:

"I noticed that part of it was lit up with a brilliant white 'light', at ground level, which was emanating from inside the forest. There was no beam – just an intense white glow that lit up an area of about 100 yards. I slowed down, but then became frightened and drove as fast as I could past the 'light' and arrived home at 7.45pm."

According to Ron West, who interviewed Mrs Bellamy, she was still very frightened about what she had witnessed, when seen a couple of months later.

5th January – Triangular UFOs over Stowmarket

Roy Jackson (45) of the *Queens Head*, Station Road, Stowmarket, was talking to a customer – Peter Hulme (64) – at 9.30pm.

"I noticed three white 'globes of light', hovering in the sky at equal distance from each other. I couldn't see any beams coming from them. I watched them for about ten minutes and then had to go back into the pub. When I came back out, at 11pm, they were gone."

Mrs S.T. Vines (54) was in her back bedroom at Lime Tree Place, Stowmarket, at 9.15pm.

"I saw three white lights in the shape of a triangle, motionless in the sky. They reminded me of car headlights but with no beams. I watched them for 20 minutes and then went down to watch TV."

8th January – Two Triangular UFOs sighted over Ipswich

Doreen Jones (29) of Allenby Road, Ipswich, and her husband, were just leaving the house at 8.30pm, to go out, when they noticed:

"…these round lights in the sky, forming two triangular shapes, moving slowly from the east. They passed over the church tower silently and disappeared behind some flats, five minutes later."

Somebody else who saw them was Peter Rowland (16). He was walking home with his friend – John, at 8.30pm, when they saw three lights in the sky over Ipswich. A number of others also reported seeing the lights. Space prevents us from including them all.

9th January – Square-shaped UFO

Mr Harold Williams (49) of Vine Cottage, Walsham-le-Willows, was out exercising his dog, at 8.30pm, when he was astonished to see:

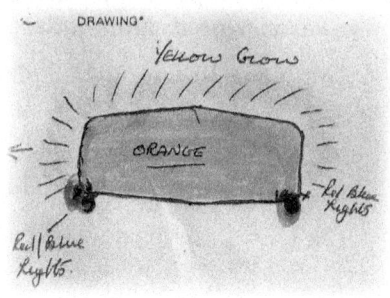

"…an orange square-shaped object, just sat in the sky. It was about the size of a rugby-ball in comparison, and had a yellow glow around it. I could also see red and blue lights on it. I watched it for an hour, before it shot off at high speed."

Another witness was Betty Clarke (32) of the same village.

"My daughter and I went into the back garden to collect our washing, at 8.35pm. As we were in the process of carrying out this task, I looked up into the sky and saw an orange glowing object. I thought it was the moon, at first, but then realised it wasn't the case, as the moon was visible in another part of the sky. The object was completely stationary in the air and silent. It then moved and stopped. My two daughters became frightened, so we rushed into the house, leaving the rest of the washing behind. I looked at it through the kitchen window and saw that it had moved its position. Suddenly, in a flash, it disappeared."

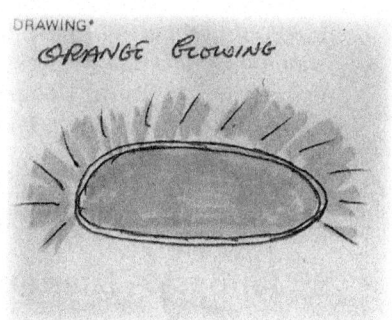

16th January – Triangular UFO over Woodbridge

Brian Webster (66) and his wife, from Grove Road, were in the back garden looking for 'Toby' (their cat), at 8.30pm, when they noticed three white lights over RAF Woodbridge.

"We thought it was a military aircraft, but it stayed in the same place for quite a long time. The lights formed a triangle; they were about the size of tennis balls in the air. By 8.50pm, we had found the cat and went back inside; the lights were still there."

Brenda 'M' (44) of Thetford, Norfolk, was driving home through Thetford Forest, at 9.50pm.

"My husband pointed out a silver-grey object, stationary in the sky, and slowed down the car. We looked and saw something like two saucers, one on top of each other. Seconds later, it began to fade away and then disappeared from sight."

Travelling in our Car home on Tuesday 16th January 90 the time was 9.50pm. My husband pointed out to me this object, Stationary in the sky. We were passing through Thetford forest at the time. My husband Slowed the car down to a crawl, and we looked at this object, It was saucer shaped, (two saucers one on top of the other) as big as a dustbin lid, no lights were showing we could hear no noise. We kept watching it, not knowing what it was or what to expect, then it suddenly started to fad out until it had completely disappeared. We saw no markings or indentations on it. It was a silver grey colour.

....

....

Please continue on a separate sheet if necessary.

DRAWING*	
	Your full name (Mr/Mrs/~~Miss/Ms~~)
	BRENDA .... Age .44
	Address........ QUEENSWAY/
	THETFORD, NORFOLK
	Telephone No....- ....(STD................)
	Occupation during last two years.............
	Housewife

At 10.40pm, Thetford woman Betty Rhodes (31) was putting the milk bottles out when she saw:

"...a rugby ball-shaped object, moving silently and quickly across the sky. Five seconds later, it was gone from view".

(Source: Ron West)

20th January – Thetford, Norfolk

At 10.30pm, a white 'light' was seen moving across the sky over Station Road, Thetford, by Mr E. Curtiss. The object stopped in mid-flight, for about two minutes, before heading away on its journey.

22nd January – Three lights over Woodbridge, Suffolk

Mr John Peterson (61) was out walking with his wife, at 9.15pm, when the couple saw three large white lights in the sky,

"…about the size of tennis balls forming a triangular shape. We watched them for about 30 minutes, until we arrived home at 9.45pm."

David Hillman (14) of Northgate Avenue, Bury St. Edmunds, was looking out of his bedroom window at 11.30pm, unable to sleep, when he saw:

"…three white lights, stationary in the sky over the British Sugar Corporation, on the A45. I looked at them through binoculars, but couldn't see any shape. About 25 minutes later they started to move away, towards the Ipswich direction, and were soon lost from view."

Another witness was Mrs Betty Brown (64) of the same street. She saw them in the sky at 11.40pm,

". . . hovering over the British Sugar Corporation works – until they faded away from view, 20 minutes later."

24th January – UFO seen over Thetford Forest

At 8pm, Peter Allcock (50) of Station Road, Thetford – an engineer by profession – was in his back bedroom, looking out of the window with his wife, when he saw:

"…three round white lights, motionless in the sky. They were hovering over a nearby industrial estate and were about the size of tennis balls. I watched them until 9.15pm, when they suddenly shot straight up into the sky, keeping in a triangular formation as they did so."

Jeanne Dorothy Holmes (48) was another witness to this phenomenon. She was at her home in Hale End Road, Waltham Forest, at 9pm, when her two sons came into the house and told her they had seen a UFO. She said:

"We ran into the back garden but our view was obstructed by the houses, so we went into Cobham Road. Suddenly, a circle of lights – five or six of them – appeared just in front of us, heading to our left and disappeared into clouds. A few seconds later, this was repeated. I asked my son to try and capture it on video. By the time he fetched his video camera, the lights had gone. It appeared to me that the lights were on the bottom of a large craft, circling as it moved through the sky. The formation was very similar to the markings left in the cornfields of Hampshire each year."

At 10.50pm, Julia Viking (18) of St. Mary's Court, Thetford, and her boyfriend – Bernard Jones, were in the car park in Thetford Forest, Norfolk.

"We were listening to the radio when, all of a sudden, a white 'light' appeared in the sky, about the size of our car, and slowly descended. As it did so, the car radio stopped playing. Bernard tried the switches – nothing, no signal at all, only static. The now white 'ball of light' was about 250 feet above the forest and about 600 feet away from us. The 'light' then changed to a glare, which extended outwards. At this stage we became frightened and were startled when the radio came on of its own accord. We started the car and drove away, very unnerved by what we had seen."

Other witnesses included Robert and his girlfriend Penny.

		YEAR	NUMBER	INVESTIGATOR *Ron West*	CASE SUMMARY
16 / 90	REF.	1990	E/90/75	EVALUATOR	DATE
					TIME
					LOCATION
N FORM TO:—					EVAL'N
					UFO CLASS
					CLOSED

T ANGLIAN U.F.O. & PARANORMAL RESEARCH ASSOCIATION

SECTION A   SIGHTING ACCOUNT FORM

Please write an account of your sighting, make a drawing of what you saw and then answer the questions in section B overleaf as fully as possible. Write in BLOCK CAPITALS using a ball point pen.

I was parked on the Santon Renick area, with my girlfriend, Penny   , that in Thetford forest area the time was 8·30 pm, we were talking when suddenly these three white lights appeared above the trees. They were in a triangular shape, but round, I would say they were a good 2,3000 feet up, the size of dinner plates, we heard no noise, we had the car radio on at the time, but there was not interference they were I would say about ½ to 1 mile away from us, at an angle of 45°. We watched these three lights for well over 1½ hours, then suddenly they all seemed to merge into one light and slowly it dimmed and went out. there was a type of halo left behind, which also faded out after a while

Please continue on a separate sheet if necessary.

DRAWING*

WHITE LIGHTS

Your full name (Mr/~~Mrs/Miss/Ms~~)
ROBERT   Age 24
Address.......... FIR CLOSE
MUNDFORD NORFOLK
Telephone No........................(STD..........)
Occupation during last two years........................
CARPENTER

Any professional, technical or academic qualifications or special interests
City & Guilds

Do you object to the publication of your name?
*Yes/~~No~~. *Delete as applicable.
Today's Date ..-2-90
Signature.......

*If preferred, use a separate sheet of paper.

26th January – Saucer-shaped object over Woodbridge

Nurse Barbara Jones (23) of Bilney Road was driving home along the A12 and had just come off the Orwell Bridge on the Felixstowe side, at 1.15am, when she saw:

"...straight ahead of me, about 2-3,000 feet up in the sky, a large saucer-shaped object. It had windows around it, with red, blue, yellow, and green lights, spinning around it in an anticlockwise direction. I estimated that it was about 3,000 feet across and a few hundred feet off the A12. As I approached closer it shot away, towards the direction of Felixstowe. I've never seen anything like that before in my life and was quite frightened."

5th February – Triangular lights over Stowmarket

Mrs Sylvia Vines (54) of Lime Tree Place, Stowmarket, Suffolk, described as highly intelligent, whose husband was a doctor, was looking out of her bedroom window, at 9.15pm, when she saw three white lights in the sky in the shape of a triangle.

"They were like car headlights, but without the beams. I watched them for 20 minutes and then went downstairs to watch TV."

8th February – Triangular group of lights over Ipswich

At 8.30pm, Peter Rowland (16) of Robin Drive was walking home with his friend – John, when they saw a 'group of lights' moving in the sky. As they approached closer, the two boys saw that they consisted of two separate sets of three lights, forming a triangle.

"One of the 'triangles' stopped in mid-air, for about a minute – then it began to follow the course taken by the first one, before we lost sight of them."

Another witness was John Costa (59). He was looking out of his lounge window in Hadleigh Road, Ipswich, at 8.30pm, when he saw:

"...two sets of three round lights, moving in an east to north direction, at about 5,000 feet – then out of sight, a few minutes later."

27th February – Three lights seen over RAF Mildenhall again

Typist Miss Joanne Spinks (20) of St. Andrew's Street, Mildenhall, looked out of the window, at 7pm, to see:

"...three lights showing an ornate tail, hovering in the sky above the airfield, about a quarter-of-a-mile away. Ten minutes later, they just disappeared from view".

Was there a connection with what appears to be the same phenomena reported on the 5th October, over the airbase?

2nd March – Three yellow lights over Suffolk

Linda Shotbolt of Bury Road, Cockfield, was preparing the family tea, when she was fetched outside by her husband, John (who had been summoned by their son) who told them he could see something strange in the sky.

"We stood and watched these three yellow 'lights', hovering above ground level over Cockfield Green. One was bigger than the rest; it looked like a triangle. The left one moved to the left, so did the right-hand one. The third one then took off across the sky, at speed."

(Source: Personal interview)

7th June – As seen over Essex and Norfolk

19th June – UFOs over Suffolk

In the early hours of this morning, residents of Newmarket reported having sighted strange luminous objects in the sky. One of them was Steven Milne of Tunbridge Close. He was out at 1.30am, when he saw:

"…strange green lights in the sky; there was a block of three going around in circles across the sky".

At 2am, Clive Humphries and his sister – Camilla, saw the same phenomena in the sky over Fresh-fields, Newmarket.

Enquiries were made with Mildenhall Airbase. However, they denied any knowledge.

One explanation for what was seen was laser lights being used to celebrate a 'May Ball', some-where!

(Source: Ron West/*Newmarket Journal*, Suffolk, 19.6.1990 – 'Lights in sky spark UFO mystery')

27th October – Diamond-shaped UFOs seen

22nd November – Three lights over the sugar factory

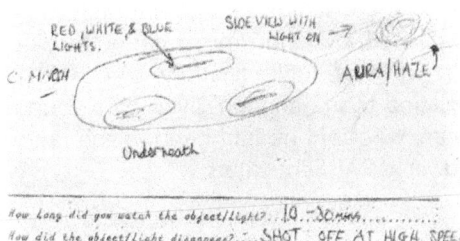

Mr Peter Jackson and his wife, from Avenue Approach, were looking out of the bedroom window, at 11.45pm, when they saw:

"…three white lights, hovering in the sky over the A45 road (now the A14) near the British Sugar Corporation Ltd. We kept them under observation for around 15 minutes, until they moved away".

1991

13th March 1991 – UFO photographed over Clacton, Essex.

We presume this was associated with reports of UFOs around the Suffolk area – proof is, of course, another matter!

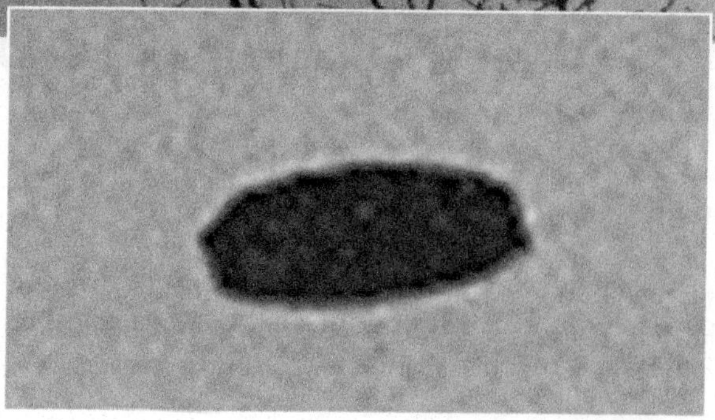

In the same year was an interesting letter sent by John Timmerman – the Vice President of Public relations of CUFOS – relating to information given by a young man, who said he had been in the radio tower at RAF Bentwaters.

In the same year, The *Independent on Sunday* newspaper – 'Space invader shocks

HAVERHILL ECHO, Thursday, June 22, 1989 5

Couple see the light after UFO sighting

STRANGE objects and lights in the sky are of special interest to a Haverhill couple who have become investigators after seeing a cigar-shaped UFO over Ladygate Woods.

Peter Fleming (20) and girlfriend Julie Rondeau (18) are currently looking into Haverhill's latest phenomenon – a blue glow which shone around Haverhill on the night of May 22 reported by several people who contacted the Echo.

The couple, who live at Argyll Court, joined EAUFOPRA – the East Anglian UFO Paranormal Research Association – after an incident just about a year ago while they were walking at night with their dog in the vicinity of Puddlebrook.

Peter, a forklift truck driver with Davis Engineering, said they were convinced what they saw was extra-terrestrial because of its behaviour.

'It came up as a distant

Peter and Julie ... no longer sceptical about UFO sightings.

glow and settled over Ladygate Woods,' he said. 'It gave off a strong beam of light that shone up the area. Then it zig-zagged around and moved up and down.

'After several minutes the light moved round in an arc and we could see it was a cigar-shaped object, very large, with portholes, showing green, yellow and red lights. There was no noise. When it moved away towards the south east we heard a sonic boom.'

Peter said for most of the time they were mesmerised, a little scared. Their labrador-cross dog, Smudle, was also unsettled by it.

Their sighting was reported to EAUFOPRA,

who checked everything out and found there was nothing from local air bases or airports that particular night that could account for their story.

The experience prompted them to join the UFO group and they have been issued with ID cards to investigate strange sky sightings in the Haverhill area.

Julie, a secretary at the Welding Institute at Abington, is just as enthusiastic as Peter after what they saw.

Peter said up to that night they were sceptical about UFO stories. Now they really do believe UFOs exist. Where they came from was anybody's guess but it was only by monitoring and investigating the phenomenon that they were ever likely to find out.

The couple can be contacted through the UFO hotline at Clacton, telephone 0255 431391.

UFO talk' (18.8.1991) – covered the 6th International UFO Congress held at Sheffield Central Library.

It is presented in the now imitable style of 'tongue in cheek' well-practiced journalism, calculated to have the reader chortling with laughter, including references to 'nutcases', cuddly ET dolls, and 'flying saucer' kits up for sale.

Even worse, the Journalist – Alex Renton, makes a very snide and distasteful comment about what one presumes may have been a hairpiece worn by Sir Patrick Wall – former Conservative MP and responsible for raising questions about the UFO subject in Parliament – sad journalism based on ridicule rather than any real investigation – but that's how it works and will always work!

CC. BARRY GREENWOOD

J. Allen Hynek
CENTER FOR UFO STUDIES
Not-For-Profit Illinois Corporation

Residence FAX:	(513) 843-2100
Office Phone:	(419) 228-3361
Office FAX:	(419) 228-7623
Time Zone:	Eastern USA

John P. Timmerman
Vice President, Public Relations
Manager, UFO Photo Exhibit Proj.
P. O. Box 1621
Lima, OH 45802, U.S.A.
(513) 843-3834 Residence

November 7, 1991

Raymond Fowler
13 Friendly Court
Wenham, MA 01984

Dear Ray,

While in Phoenix with the UFO Photo Exhibit Project on display at the Park Central Mall on October 18, 1991, a young man paused at the publications table and mentioned that he had been on duty as a radar technician in the radar tower at Bentwaters on the night of the widely publicized event.

He says he saw an object in the shape of a large orange sphere with distinct edges moving directly toward the tower and pass right over the top of the tower. He says he heard nothing at the time and it was not detected on radar.

He refused to be identified and would not permit me to record his remarks, for fear of penalties for revealing what he had been told not to reveal. My impression of the man and the conversation leads me to believe he was being truthful.

Best regards,

John Timmerman

1992

6th January – UFO over Sizewell Nuclear Power Station, Suffolk

At 11.50pm, orange and yellow 'lights' were seen hovering for ten minutes above the complex.

19th January – Do UFOs exist?

Solicitor Harry Harris, who was involved in the investigation into the reported UFO activity in Rendlesham Forest, Suffolk, addressed the 'Reach out for Outreach' crowd at Parkers Hotel, in Manchester.

(**Source:** *Jewish Gazette*, 17.2.1992)

In the same year was a newspaper report on the Rendlesham Incident, which claimed that the lights seen by the airman was the Lighthouse or the *Shipwash* lightship. Also appearing in the article was Kevin Conde.

Harry Harris

TV probe pledging to solve UFO puzzle

Documentary-makers claim mystery unravelled

By Alison Withers

A DOCUMENTARY will claim tonight the mysterious UFO spotted in Rendlesham Forest was, in fact, the lights from a lighthouse and a lightship.

The specially extended edition of the BBC series *Inside Out* says it will finally explain the mystery of the UFO sighting at the forest near Woodbridge more than 12 years ago.

It has been put together with the help of consultant James Easton, from Galashiels, near Glasgow, and contains new evidence and interviews never before revealed.

The mystery of the Rendlesham Forest UFOs began on December 26, 1980, when three members of the U.S. 81st Security Police Squadron, serving at RAF Bentwaters and Woodbridge, noticed some unfamiliar lights in the forest at about 3am.

It was claimed the trio – Staff Sgt Jim Penniston, Airman First Class John Burroughs and Airman Ed Cabansag – encountered a small, triangular-shaped craft which moved backwards through the forest before silently taking off.

The alleged sighting prompted a great deal of interest on the base and on the night of December 27, during an officers' Christmas party, Lieutenant-Colonel Charles Halt received a report of another alleged UFO in Rendlesham Forest.

He decided to put the whole thing to rest and assembled a team of five officers, taking a microcassette recorder with him to make notes.

The team spotted a light which Lt-Col Halt described on tape: "It looks like an eye winking at you. Still moving from side to side and when you put a starscope on it, it sorta has a hollow centre, a dark centre. It's like the pupil of an eye

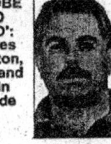

PROBE INTO 'UFO': James Easton, left, and Kevin Conde

looking at you, winking."

Looking back towards the base and its East gate he also spotted some beams of light, seemingly being directed downwards to the nuclear bunker from an unidentified source in the air.

Reports went to the Ministry of Defence in a memo from Lt-Col Halt and when science writer Ian Ridpath suggested the explanation for at least one of the two sightings was the Orford Ness Lighthouse and Shipwash lightship, he rejected that.

But Mr Easton has now discovered unpublished witness statements from the three airmen, which revealed that on their search on December 26 they discovered the so-called UFO were the lights from the lighthouse and lightship.

Mr Easton has confirmed this version of events in an interview with Mr Burroughs – and has an explanation for the light beams supposedly coming into the base's nuclear bunker.

He was contacted by former Command Sergeant Kevin Conde after he had come across Mr Easton's website and was told: "The only UFO incidents that occurred during my tour were hoaxes I participated in and the only alien that landed was Mrs Conde's little boy, Kevin."

Full details of the hoax will be revealed on tonight's programme, which will be broadcast at 7.30pm on BBC1.

alison.withers@eadt.co.uk

1993

1993 – MOD accused of cover-up

YOU UNIDENTIFIED LYING OBJECTS

UFO landing cover-up

DEFENCE chiefs are accused of lying over a News of the World report of the UK's first official UFO landing.

By KEITH BEABEY

Our exclusive story has been backed by Ralph Noyes, then the top civil servant dealing with UFO sightings.

We reported that a 20ft sloping silver craft had come down in woods 10 years ago near a U.S. Air Force base three years earlier. The UFO was briefly picked up on radar screens before mysteriously disappearing. Around 200 people reported seeing it.

One airman told us he saw three beings in silver suits on board.

The craft came down in a ball of blinding red light. Scorch marks found later on the ground were checked for radiation by airmen.

We obtained an official copy of a confidential report on the landing by Lieutenant Colonel Charles Halt, deputy commander of the base at Bentwaters, Suffolk.

It referred to "unexplained lights" and a strange glowing object that lit up the forest surrounding the base.

Halt's superior Wing Commander Gordon Williams backed the colonel, saying he would not try to trick either the Ministry of Defence or the U.S. air force department.

MAD

But MoD chiefs denied the landing in Tangham Wood at 3am on December 27, 1980 took place. Now Mr Noyes has revealed the story was true and the MoD were covering it up.

He says: "When they were asked if anything was seen on the radar or did anything come down, they said no, nothing. In effect, they lied."

In a Sky News special, to be screened tomorrow at 7.30pm and 10.30pm, Mr Noyes says: "If nothing happened, then were those men mad? If they were mad, why weren't they posted home?

"I think probably the MOD clammed up and actually got to the point of lying in order to avoid embarrassment."

The Government claimed the light seen by witnesses came from the nearby Orford Ness lighthouse.

But the airmen knew that was not the case because they often used the lighthouse as a guide.

Colonel Halt was quickly shipped back to the States and some of his men were transferred to other bases. All were ordered to keep quiet about what they saw.

UFO LANDS IN SUFFOLK

And that's OFFICIAL

FLASHBACK: Our UFO story

East Anglian Daily Times - Ipswich

15 MAR 1993

MoD accused of 'UFO cover-up'

DEFENCE chiefs will today be accused of a cover-up over reported sightings of a UFO near a Suffolk airbase.

A former top civil servant at the Ministry of Defence claims officials have concealed information about a spacecraft landing at RAF Bentwaters near Woodbridge.

About 200 people reported seeing some kind of craft landing near the base in 1980. A confidential report on the landing was made by Lieutenant Colonel Charles Halt, then deputy commander of the base, according to a national newspaper.

Lt Col Halt's report referred to "unexplained lights" and a strange glowing object that lit up the forest that surrounded the base, the paper said. The landing is supposed to have happened on December 27, 1980.

Ralph Noyes, a former top civil servant said to have responsibility for UFO sightings, is to tell a TV station that the MoD imposed a news black-out about the landing. Mr Noyes will claim the MoD said nothing about the alleged landing because it wanted to save any embarrassment.

But a spokesman for the MoD reacted coolly to the suggestions. "I would treat all this with some caution," he said. "As far as I am aware we don't have people who are responsible for UFO sightings. We do take an interest in what might be a threat to national security."

NEWS OF THE WORLD 14 MARCH 1993

18th November – Police Inspector sights UFO over Suffolk

We received a letter from Mike Topliss – a Police Inspector with the Suffolk Constabulary, in charge of Leiston, Saxmundham and Aldeburgh communities – regarding what he saw, while driving home on the 18th November 1993 and in 2015 went to see him when he had this to say:

"I was travelling home from Leiston Police Station, at approximately 10.15pm, driving along the B.1119 road, towards Saxmundham, in a gold colour Rover Montego Saloon. It was a clear night, with a bright moon that illuminated the countryside well enough to have driven without headlights. I was driving at approximately 45-50 miles per hour and slowed down to negotiate two 'S' bends between Leiston and Saxmundham, when, about a kilometre from the outskirts of Saxmundham, I came up behind a slower moving vehicle – a Morris Marina Saloon, containing four occupants, travelling at about 40 miles per hour."

Headlights seen behind vehicle

"Knowing the road well I checked my rear view mirror, intending to overtake, when I noticed what I presumed to be a set of headlights in the distance behind me, apparently gaining on me very quickly. I had hardly rounded a left-hand curve when the 'headlights' rushed aggressively up behind me, slowing suddenly to match my speed, about a car length away. The two 'lights' were consistent with the height, spacing, colour, and brightness of normal headlights on dipped beam. They were circular in shape, with no sign of any vehicle to which they were presumably attached. There was a noise consistent with the hiss of tyres on the road surface, but nothing unusual. My impression was of an impatient driver, waiting for the first opportunity to overtake me."

Now seen a few feet away from the car

"About a hundred metres after the left-hand curve, the 'lights' suddenly moved out to my offside, disappearing from the rear view mirror and appearing in my offside wing mirror. I glanced over my right shoulder and briefly caught a glimpse of them, about a metre away. The tyre on the road hissing noise emanating from them was still consistent with an overtaking vehicle, but I heard no engine noise or saw any actual vehicle. Suddenly both the 'lights' and road noise disappeared – as if someone had flicked a switch off."

Emergency stop carried out

"I instinctively performed an emergency stop, thinking that the 'overtaking vehicle' had lost control and crashed. The Marina driver in front of me also braked hard and came to a halt, some forty metres away – hard enough for both of us to leave skid marks on the road, clearly visible in the moonlight (still there the following day).

I looked at my watch. It was 10.25pm. I immediately got out of the car and looked all around me. There were no hedges. The fields were flat and bare. I could see for several hundreds of metres in all directions.

There was no sign of any tyre tracks, or marks, which would have been left from a vehicle leaving the road. The middle-aged Marina driver came over to me and asked me what happened to that car. I asked him, 'what exactly did you see?' He replied, 'there was a car overtaking you. It suddenly disappeared. I thought it had gone into a ditch.' After he had left the scene, I felt there was something about this whole incident which I found strangely embarrassing and this appeared to compromise my judgement. In retrospect I believe this was caused by the frustration of not being able to understand what had occurred and, at the same time, not wishing to be seen as some sort of weirdo.

I wondered if, perhaps, the incident could have been the result of a ghostly manifestation of a previous serious accident, although my enquiries, made later, revealed that no serious accidents had occurred at that location, (Map Reference TM394632, Landranger Series Sheet 156), precisely where the 30M contour line crosses the B.1119 The offside verge is marked by a leaning concrete post. The following day, in daylight, I returned to the scene. There was nothing further to be seen, other than the skid marks."

Mike Topliss   *The scene of the incident*

Prior to retirement

Ironically, Mike had been involved in writing to numerous interested parties that had contacted the Suffolk Police, during the 1980s, with regard to the role played by the police who had attended in the forest on that fateful morning. There is little doubt, without his own UFO sighting, he would have been even more sceptical of what had been claimed – not now!

30th May – UFO display over Essex and Suffolk

The *East Anglian Times* (30.5.1994) – 'Mystery light prompts call to the Police' – told of hundreds of people contacting the Police after sighting red, silver, and blue lights in the sky. The phenomena were attributed to meteorites, or space debris, entering the atmosphere. It was also said that people living in the Harlow area contacted the Police after seeing what a laser light display was. A police spokesman said, *"Many thought Planet Earth was being invaded; it was quite frightening for them."*

15th October – Triangular UFO over Suffolk

Andrew Crowe (22) of Anderson Walk, Bury St Edmunds – a chef by occupation – was driving home, at 8.30pm, from Hengrave to Bury, accompanied by his girlfriend, Lisa Mansfield, when he noticed a strange 'light' in the sky, hovering above a cold store on the Mildenhall Road Industrial Estate, about 300 feet away and a hundred feet high. He said:

> *"We pulled off the road and got out of the car. We watched as it stayed in the sky for about 20 seconds, before it banked and moved away at tremendous speed."* [Is this similar to the UFO as described by Pauline Godbold in 1988?]

6th November – UFO display over Suffolk

Angela Christie from Little Cornard, near Sudbury, Suffolk, close to the flight path for aircraft en route in and out of Stansted Airport, was exercising the family dog outside. In the garden,at 5.25pm

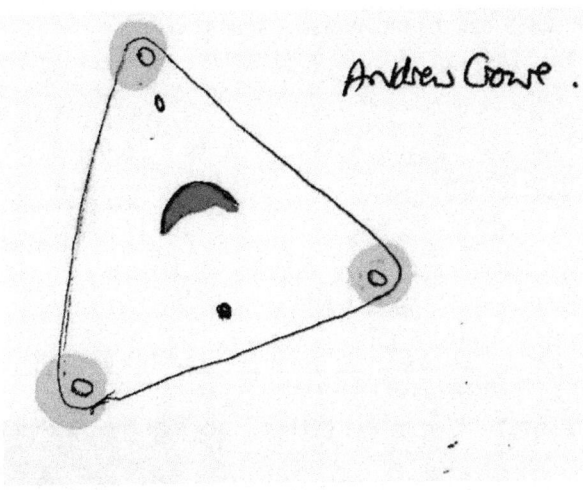

Andrew Crowe.

"I noticed a bright object quite big going west and on the same flight path going east a smaller object, both had flashing lights' watched them for ten minutes then called my husband Wally out. Suddenly the sky wherever you looked contained a flashing object .We watched this phenomena for 20 minutes then I contacted an amateur astronomer who lived nearby to come out to take a look. After about an hour I rang Wattisham, Stansted Airport and USAF Midlenhall they told me nothing was showing on their radar. The display went on for about 5hours by 10pm the sky was clear of them. This was followed by the arrival of a delta shaped object.

Although later newspaper accounts claimed we saw aircraft moving over there were no flights over the area on that evening!

We have transmitter pylons, hills and water around but they seemed to favour the transmitter moving over sweeping backwards and forwards east to west at an estimated height of 5-8000 feet. My husband saw smoke or vapour emitting from some of the craft."

Visited by many people

"Since the 9th of November we have been visited by different people from the TV and Radio, members of the Quest International UFO group, a British pilot, and Norfolk artist David Dane who was standing outside when we heard a powerful noise like a jet above the trees. Suddenly above us appeared a triangular object covered with flashing lights.

On another night I was on the A12 between Clacton and Colchester with my friends when we saw a large triangular object in the sky flashing with lights moving through the sky apex first. This wasn't the end of the sightings a short time later we saw two small craft stationary in the sky over the Clacton Colchester Transmitter. When we arrived home my husband told me he had seen flying triangles in the sky. We went outside and saw yet another flying triangle which started to flash a large white strobe light as it moved over us."

I wrote to the MOD and had a reply from Mr R.B Horsley Secretariat of Air Desk 2A dated 15.11.1994 telling us we had seen metroeties fire balls balloons etc in other words a cover up!"

(Source: Personal interviews/Ron West files)

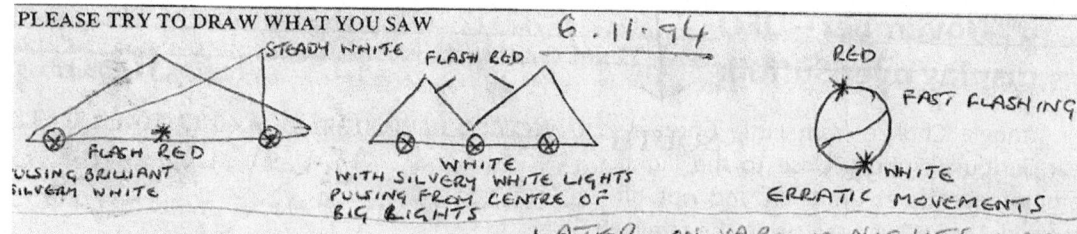

PLEASE TRY TO DRAW WHAT YOU SAW 6.11.94

STEADY WHITE   FLASH RED   RED

FLASH RED   FAST FLASHING
PULSING BRILLIANT   WHITE   WHITE
SILVERY WHITE   WITH SILVERY WHITE LIGHTS   ERRATIC MOVEMENTS
                      PULSING FROM CENTRE OF
                      BIG LIGHTS

LATER ON VARIOUS NIGHTS LARGE
STROBE WHITE LIGHTED OBJECT VERY BIG. WHITE FLASHING
SAW BEAM OF LIGHT DESCEND DOWN WITH WHITE OR CONSTANT
BALLED OBJECT ON END. THIS TURNED WEST AND FLEW OFF.
LARGE OBJECT THEN DISAPPEARED VERY SLOWLY. SAW THE BEAM

reports seeing strange 'orbs'

UFO FEVER has hit Suffolk with a vengeance after a group of people saw what they claim to be about a hundred alien craft hovering over their homes.

And their story is corroborated by a similar, albeit smaller-scale sighting, on the far side of Suffolk at Felixstowe pier.

While thousands across the county enjoyed firework displays over the weekend, residents of the Willowmere caravan park in Bures Road, Little Cornard, claim they were treated to a celestial spectacular with a difference.

By Rachel Jenkins
East Anglian Daily Times

"It was absolutely awesome," said Angie Christie. "I didn't know what I was looking at. I was very frightened to begin with and I certainly never expected in all my life to see anything like it."

Mrs Christie had taken her dog out for a walk at about 5.25 on Sunday evening when she saw what she describes as a pulsating object flying from west to east.

"I thought it was a funny-looking aircraft and I thought it strange that there should be no sound coming from such a big craft. Then I saw a second, smaller one coming towards it, flashing red and white.

"Then we saw another sort with blue and green lights and glowing steadily over. They were everywhere."

Anxious to prove she was not hallucinating, Mrs Christie went to fetch her husband, Wallace, a former RAF chief technical adviser with 23 years' service behind him.

"We stood out there for two and a half hours. We called our neighbour down — he's an amateur astronomer and he told us he'd never seen anything like it in his life."

The Christies also called their daughter and son-in-law, Adele and Adam Hanks, of Mallard Way, Great Cornard, who came over with friends to witness the phenomenon.

"I would say there were about 100 of them off and on. Some would stop in mid air, some zig-zagged, and we saw one go on top of another, all at a height of between 5-8,000 feet.

"They seemed to be doing a sweep of the area. I came to the conclusion that they were looking for something. They certainly didn't seem to care whether we saw them or not."

Neighbour Tom Wilkinson, who has been an amateur astronomer for more than 30 years, said what they had seen could not have been of this planet.

"They weren't going all that fast — they were mainly travelling west to east and when they got towards the horizon they bore round to the north.

Fishing

Meanwhile David Goddard of Levington Lane, Buckleshaw, was fishing off Felixstowe pier at about 6.20 pm when he saw three dully-glowing pinky-orange orbs coming from the Woodbridge direction at about 200mph.

All three stopped dead, then one headed off, followed closely by the other two and the trio zoomed out to sea in formation. The whole sighting lasted about 30 seconds.

● Angie Christie of Little Cornard with the drawings of the UFO sightings made by her husband Wallace.

4th November – UFO displays of star and 'disc'-shaped objects

Another witness to UFO activity in the same area was Mrs Petts of Turkentine Close, Great Cornard. She contacted the Essex UFO research group on the 16th November, and told them of having sighted UFO activity over the last few nights.

"We have seen star and 'disc'-shaped objects in the sky. They have varied in colour from white to green, red and white, sometimes accompanied by a high-pitched 'bleeping' noise as they flew in an east to west direction across the sky. On occasion I have seen them travelling towards each other at speed, then zigzag to avoid hitting each other."

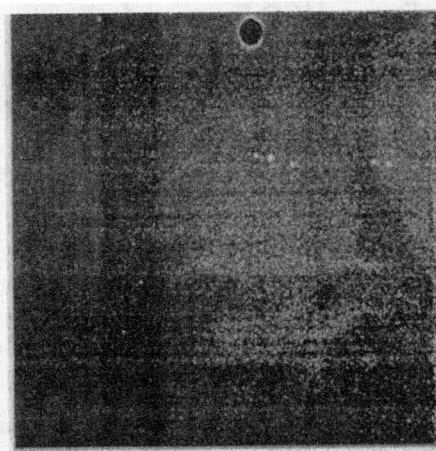

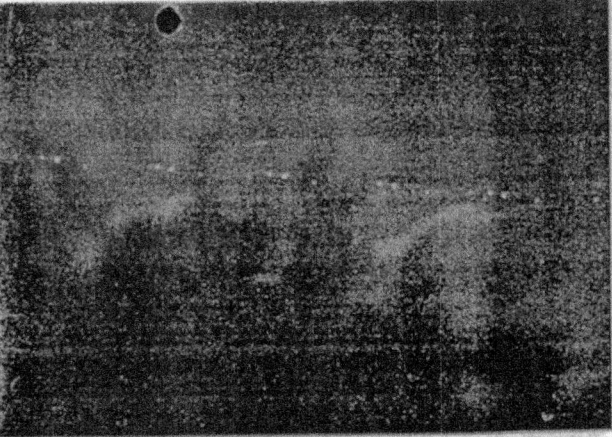

UFO fever has gripped the Suffolk/Essex border after people claim to have seen about 100 alien craft hovering over their homes.

Their story is corroborated by a similar sighting near Felixstowe pier.

However, EADT photographer Keith Mindham, who kept watch during a second night of celestial phenomena – *his picture appears above* – says he is convinced the "aliens" were nothing other than ordinary aircraft.

The sightings began at the Willowmere Caravan Park, Bures Road, Little Cornard,

Two separate incidents recorded

over Guy Fawkes weekend and were repeated over the next two or three evenings.

"It was absolutely awesome," said Angie Christie. "I didn't know what I was looking at. I was very frightened to begin with and I certainly never expected in all my life to see anything like it."

Mrs Christie had taken her dog out for an early evening walk when she saw what she describes as a pulsating object flying from west to east.

"I thought it was a funny-looking aircraft and I thought it strange that there should be no sound coming from such a big craft. Then I saw a second, smaller one coming towards it, flashing red and white.

"Then we saw another sort with blue and green lights and glowing steadily over. They were everywhere."

Anxious to prove she was not hallucinating, Mrs Christie went to fetch her husband, Wallace, a former RAF chief technical adviser with 23 years' service behind him.

"We stood out there for two-and-a-half hours. We called our neighbour down – he's an amateur astronomer and he told us he'd never seen anything like it in his life."

Zig-zagged

The Christies also called their daughter and son-in-law, Adele and Adam Hanks, of Mallard Way, Great Cornard, who came over with friends to witness the phenomenon.

"I would say there were about 100 of them off and on. Some would stop in mid air, some zig-zagged, and we saw one go on top of another, all at a height of between 5,000-8,000 feet.

"They seemed to be doing a sweep of the area. I came to the conclusion that they were looking for something. They certainly didn't seem to care whether we saw them or not."

said what they had seen could not have been of this planet.

"They weren't going all that fast – they were mainly travelling west to east and when they got towards the horizon they bore round to the north."

However, EADT photographer Keith Mindham, who was so intrigued by their story that he went to the Willowmere caravan park the following evening, is convinced there is a perfectly ordinary explanation.

"When I first arrived I thought it was quite interesting. There were various lights, maybe three or four at a time, which seemed to be travelling in different directions.

"I decided I had better investigate further so I took Mr Christie to a high point at Lamarsh where it became clear they were all travelling along a particular flight path.

"I wanted to believe they were UFO's but I have to say they were so similar to aircraft I can't believe they were anything else."

Meanwhile, over in Felixstowe, David Goddard of Levington Lane, Bucklesham, was fishing off the pier when he saw three dully-glowing, pinky-orange orbs coming from the Woodbridge direction at about 200mph.

All three stopped dead, then one headed off, followed closely by the other two and the trio zoomed out to sea in formation. The whole sighting lasted about 30 seconds.

■ Did you see anything? What do you think it was? Write to: The News Editor, East Anglian

4 DEC 1994

UFO landing was kept secret, says ex-defence chief

By DAVID JACK

A SERIES of chilling encounters with alien spacecraft have been covered up, claims Britain's former military top gun.

Lord Hill-Norton is convinced that the Defence Ministry is hiding the fact that a UFO landed in Britain.

The former Chief of the Defence Staff said: "The Ministry has doggedly denied that anything untoward happened and I simply don't believe them.

"Someone is sitting on information that should be in the public domain."

His claims centre on bizarre incidents at RAF Woodbridge in Suffolk, where American airmen claim to have seen UFOs.

The People has seen a top-secret report by American Lt Colonel Charles Halt which confirms sightings of UFOs "involving an

intelligence which didn't originate on earth".

And former US military intelligence officer Clifford Stone claims that the USA, NATO and Russia have long exchanged details of similar incidents under the code name Operation Moondust.

His evidence is due to be screened on LWT's Strange But True programme this Friday.

It centres on the mysterious events of December 27, 1980, when radar operators at RAF Watton, near Norwich, picked up an unusual blip.

As RAF Phantom jets closed on the object, pilots reported seeing intense, bright lights in the sky.

Former radar operator Mal Scurrah said: "As the Phantoms got close the hovering object shot upwards at phenomenal speed – monitored at

more than 1,000mph."

At RAF Woodbridge, airman John Burroughs and sergeant Jim Penniston investigated a dazzling fire in nearby Rendlesham Forest.

"The air was filled with electricity and we saw an object about the size of a tank," said Penniston.

"It was triangular, moulded of black glass and had symbols on it. Suddenly it shot off faster than any aircraft I have ever observed."

Next night the object returned and base deputy commander Lt Col Halt went to investigate.

He said: "I couldn't believe what I was seeing. It looked like the rising sun with a black pulsating centre. It appeared to be dripping molten metal."

Halt's tape recordings and photographs were confiscated by visiting US defence officials and there was an information black-out.

14th November-Crescent shaped UFO seen

Mr John Theobold (27) – a research student at the University of East Anglia – was driving on the A140 near Braiseworth, Suffolk, during the late evening, when he saw a crescent-shaped object moving through the sky, about 1,500 feet above him. He stopped the car and got out. He said:

"It was moving very slowly and had three or four lights – totally silent."

22nd November – Report prepared by Essex UFO Research Group

Following investigations carried out by Sheridan Lane, Paul David, and Richard Raynor, which included tape-reordered interviews with the witnesses, Yolanda Petts, husband Malcolm, Anna (12), James (14), and Andrew Barlow (neighbour), it was ascertained that the activity had first been seen on the 18th November. Prior to this date it was revealed that reporters from the *East Anglian Daily Times* had visited the area – presumably as a result of Angela Christie's sighting.

The area in which the sightings took place (all between 5-10pm) was in and around Great Cornard, situated just to the south of Sudbury, over Lamarsh Hilltop (known locally as Sackers Green), and Abbas Hall – a wooded copse, east of the Petts' family home, and Wilowmere Caravan Park near where Angela and 'Wally' live. The locations given are under or close to dedicated RAF flight paths and were seen 20-30 degrees above the horizon.

Anna claimed the lights first appeared in the direction of the nearby radio mast – then head towards Abbas Hall. This was confirmed by other family members.

Andrew Barlow told of seeing an object (thought initially to be a helicopter) showing white lights on the front and a red one to the rear, with lights on the outside. On the 14th November Andrew saw a single red light, heading across the sky at fast speed.

The group concluded that there was ample evidence to show close encounters of the first kind had been present during those few days.

January – Triangular object sighted over RAF Bentwaters

Paul Pittock was driving from Woodbridge to Melton, Suffolk, one evening in January 1995, when he saw a 'bright light' hovering in the sky above the now closed RAF Woodbridge/Bentwaters Airbase. Curious, he stopped the car and was surprised to see that the 'light' had now begun to move from side to side in the sky. Rushing home he picked up his telescopic sight and, accompanied by neighbour Richard Warnock, drove back to the airbase just in time to see whatever it was drop down towards the flight line and disappear.

"As we stood by the entrance gate to the base, wondering what was going on, over thirty military vehicles drove up; they included a military ambulance and a larger white vehicle, covered in aerials. After unlocking the gate, the convoy drove onto the Bentwaters Airbase (closed some 16 months ago). With tyres screaming and lights flashing, the vehicles drove around the airbase pointing searchlights into the sky, as if looking for something; there were even helicopters hovering overhead. We saw an orange-red glow emanating from the flight line – then a glowing triangular shape appeared. It had a distinct outline and could be seen clearing the slope. It stayed for a while and then left."

(Source: Personal interview)

19th February – *News of the World* article, 'The Real X Files'

'Roswell, Rendlesham – UFO lands in Suffolk' – was the offerings by this newspaper, which included interviews with Nick Pope, Charles Halt, and a quote from The Lord Hill-Norton. There was also a quote from BUFORA, who claimed (according to the newspaper) that they had logged 226 of 'flying saucers' and alien life forms in 1994. Another mention was given to the UFOs sighted over Little Cornard, which lasted for two hours, according to the frightened residents, and a UFO resembling a loaf of bread seen hovering in the sky, over Laverstock Down, near Salisbury, Wiltshire.

23rd March – Unusual object seen in night sky

Mr Wallace Christie – ex-RAF serviceman and husband of Angela, – was walking towards the *Brook Inn* on the Bures Road, at 10.20pm, when he noticed a bright, golden object, stationary in the sky on his left-hand side.

"I stopped to watch it for several minutes. It was south-east of Sudbury, over farmland, towards Bures. Other people also saw it. My impression was that it looked like part of a control room, being a part of a much larger object. Inside was what looked like forms or objects moving. I estimated it was 80 feet off the ground and 5,000 feet away from me."

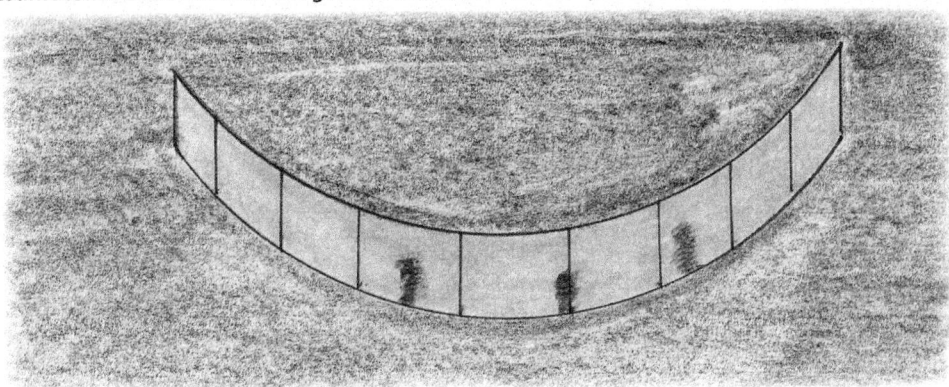

3rd July – UFO sighted over Sudbury, Suffolk

30th July – Oval object seen

Mr Shroff (49) of Sheepgate Lane, Clare, Suffolk, was in bed at 1.15am, when he awoke and looked through the window to see:

"...an oval, black object, with a white glowing base, moving at a speed I estimated to be 80-100 miles per hour through the sky, about half-a-mile away, heading in a west to east direction. As it did so, it occasionally stopped in flight before continuing on its journey."

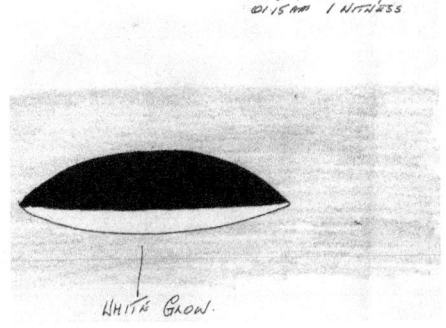

CLARE, SUFFOLK.
SUNDAY 3RD JULY 1995
01.15AM 1 WITNESS

WHITE GLOW.

11ᵗʰ August – UFOs sighted over Sudbury, Suffolk

At 10.25pm, Angela Christie was to find herself in the position of witnessing further examples of UFO activity over the same locality, as a result of which she contacted Ron West from the Essex UFO Research Group.

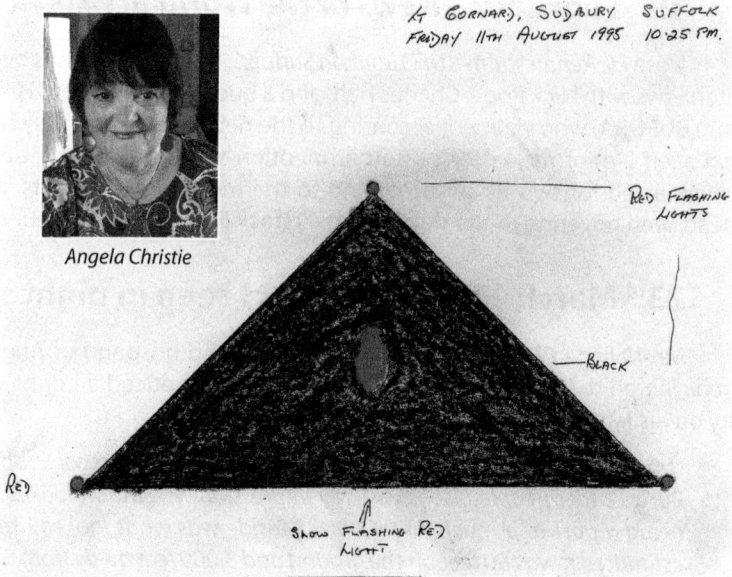

Angela Christie

Gt Gornard, Sudbury Suffolk
Friday 11th August 1995 10.25 pm.

Red Flashing Lights

Black

Red

Show Flashing Red Light

I was watering my garden by torchlight when a shooting star very bright made me look up. There coming in the direction S. to N. & right where the 'shooting star' had fallen was an object/craft. It floated by flashing all red lights apex first. On each corner was a red light but in the middle was a very large red light. When the lights flashed a distinct triangle craft was shown to us. It was identical in shape to all the others we have seen. Its speed was slow & it emitted a strange sound. 10 minutes later an aircraft used the same route but looked like & flashed like a normal large plane. The triangle's lights were entirely different. Luckily my husband arrived home at 10.25 & I called him. He also admitted it was strange & remarked on the red lights. They were extremely bright. I ran a tape of the 'Belgian Triangles' & one they mentioned had the same lighting system. We also admitted that the sound was strange but we had heard this sound before when the triangles were over here. The height is only an approximate estimation. It is very difficult to judge heights. All I can be sure of is that it was using the air route from our transmitter & following the same route as conventional aircraft.

The emission of the 'shooting star' definitely had something to do with the triangular object. It was as if it was ejecting something.

In earlier reports I also told of seeing 'shooting star' activity when the triangles visited us last year & on 6.11.94 I saw 2 such phenomenon.

17th August – Light bulb-shaped UFO seen

At 10.25pm on this date, housewife Angela Christie observed an object, described as resembling *"a huge light bulb in the sky"*, which was seen heading through the air in an east to west direction, before being lost from view, a few minutes later.

21st August – Three UFOs sighted over Sudbury, Suffolk

Housewife Jacqueline Wills – then aged 54, of Oak Road, Great Cornard – was out walking, at 8pm, watching the blue sky with an aura of darkness descending, when she saw:

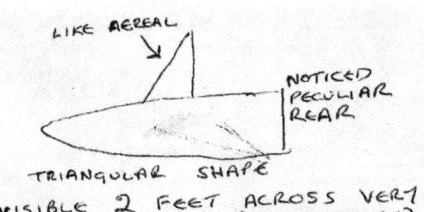

PLEASE TRY TO DRAW WHAT YOU SAW

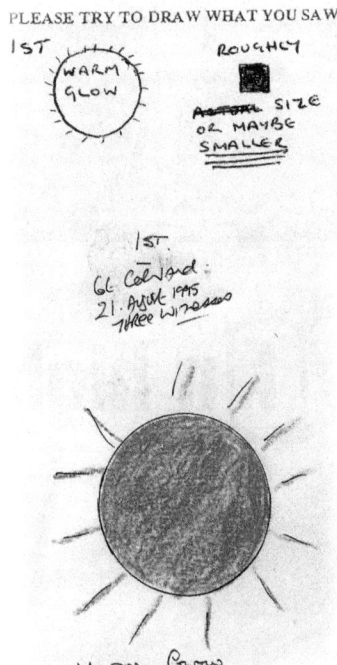

"…an orange 'ball of light' in the sky, moving towards my position from the western direction. It had what looked like a flame on its side. In the distance was a tiny black 'square', moving in the same direction. Behind this was a silver rectangular shaped object, with what looked like aerials on it, also travelling in the same direction. I tried to take a photo, but they were moving too quickly across the sky. By the time we walked down the bottom of Wells Head Road, they were all of sight."

18th October – Stanton Friedman lectures on Rendlesham Forest

As the reader can see from the following press cutting, it is ambiguous, to say the least, taking into consideration that it gives an erroneous (no doubt unintentional impression) of reported UFO activity, covering a British period of 42 years…..The frightening truth is, of course, completely different. In addition to the colossal number of UFO reports contained in Volume 1 to 11 of *Haunted Skies*, it appears that looking at the amount of files available for Volume 12 onwards – (1991) – that we may be talking about one book (Volume 13) covering the period 1995, sobering in its implications! Here is an example of just a few UFO sightings recorded around the Suffolk Essex borders-frightening in its implications. Certainly never covered by the Press!

Eastern Daily Press - Norwich

18 OCT 1995

Flying visit of UFO expert

One of the world's leading UFO experts will be in Norwich this weekend.

Stanton T Friedman, a nuclear physicist, was the original investigator of the 1947 Roswell Incident — the alleged US military cover-up of a crashed flying saucer complete with aliens.

Mr Friedman will be giving an illustrated lecture at the University of East Anglia on Sunday at 8pm.

Mr Friedman is convinced that Earth has been visited by alien craft, and he backs campaigners who want all documents released relating to UFO sightings in Britain — especially relating to the famous "landing" at Rendlesham in Suffolk.

Mr Friedman has spent years tirelessly harassing US Government departments to release documents about UFOs under the Freedom of Information Act.

At first there was a complete denial that any information existed. But eventually, he was given heavily-edited documents where 97 per cent of the text was blacked out.

Mr Friedman said: "Other documents have recently emerged proving that the US and other governments have been covering up this cosmic Watergate.

Tickets for the lecture cost £4 and doors open at 7.30pm. For more information, call Norwich 505401.

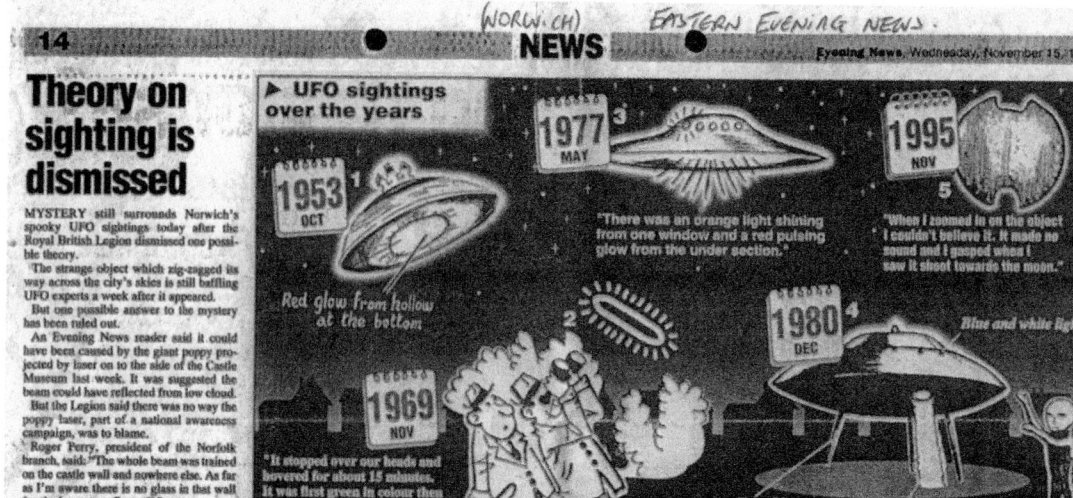

14 NEWS

Evening News, Wednesday, November 15, 199

Theory on sighting is dismissed

MYSTERY still surrounds Norwich's spooky UFO sightings today after the Royal British Legion dismissed one possible theory.

The strange object which zig-zagged its way across the city's skies is still baffling UFO experts a week after it appeared.

But one possible answer to the mystery has been ruled out.

An Evening News reader said it could have been caused by the giant poppy projected by laser on to the side of the Castle Museum last week. It was suggested the beam could have reflected from low cloud.

But the Legion said there was no way the poppy laser, part of a national awareness campaign, was to blame.

Roger Perry, president of the Norfolk branch, said: "The whole beam was trained on the castle wall and nowhere else. As far as I'm aware there is no glass in that wall for the beam to reflect off."

Meanwhile, more people have reported strange goings-on in the skies above Norfolk after a week of reports in the Evening News. The county's UFO society, which was already being flooded with dozens of new members, is getting even more calls now.

▶ UFO sightings over the years

1953 OCT

1977 MAY

1995 NOV

"There was an orange light shining from one window and a red pulsing glow from the under section."

"When I zoomed in on the object I couldn't believe it. It made no sound and I gasped when I saw it shoot towards the moon."

Red glow from hollow at the bottom

1980 DEC

Blue and white light

1969 NOV

"It stopped over our heads and hovered for about 15 minutes. It was first green in colour then it changed to violet."

Graphic by Claire Bretton

Tripod legs

Shaft of light in which entities hovered

Is there anybody out there ....

Unexpected Friends On high

4th November – UFO sighted over Suffolk

In 2015, we went to see Angela and 'Wally' Christie at their home address and thank them enough for allowing us the opportunuity to speak to them personally about their sightings. We wish them well.

Angela and 'Wally' Christie

1996

Experts shed light on some UFO mystery

Wolverhampton Express & Star
12 JUN 1997 (Circ: [combined] 189,316)

Face to face with black-eyed aliens

By SALLY-ANNE SWIFT

"AS MY mind tried to register what I was looking at, the ball of light exploded in a blinding flash. I couldn't move; I tried to cover my eyes, but was too late. Now, right in front of me was a machine occupying the spot where the fog had been."

No, this isn't an excerpt from some science-fiction novel. They're the words of Larry Warren, former United States Air Force security guard and self-proclaimed UFO eye-witness, in his new book Left at East Gate.

At a West Midland theatre tonight, he will be describing his experiences.

Warren claims to have seen first-hand the arrival of a UFO in a field, not in some obscure New Mexico town, but in the heart of rural Suffolk.

He also claims to have seen his alien occupants: "They were small, about three to four feet tall, and somewhat ghostlike in appearance. They had large heads with cat-like black eyes."

Warren, together with ufologist Peter Robbins, has spent the past ten years documenting his experiences and the result is the hefty 490-page

volume. In it they claim to have more evidence to support their story than was ever found at Roswell, New Mexico, where the remains of a crashed UFO were said to have been found exactly 50 years ago.

And they claim the whole thing was the subject of a massive cover-up operation on behalf of the British and American governments. Warren was stationed at RAF Bentwaters, one of Suffolk's largest Nato bases, in December 1980. One night he says he was ordered to drive to the east gate and turn left (hence the title of the book) to join other security personnel.

His story, in brief, is that he saw an alien craft land and strange beings emerge from it. Afterwards, he says,

he and his colleagues were debriefed and told to forget everything they saw.

Warren went public about his experience after he received an honourable discharge from the Air Force. Seventeen years later it has been set down in black and white for all to see.

ROBBINS says: "We have not written this book for UFO buffs. We have written it for everyone. It's a very human story."

Sceptics have put the alleged sighting down to a distant lighthouse, the planets Jupiter and Saturn, stars, a fireball or satellite re-entry. But Warren says he is unperturbed by the fact that some people will dismiss his book as nonsense.

"When they get a sense of the amount of evidence we have got they should know that this one can't be challenged," he says.

And he denies he is after a place on the best-sellers list.

"We do not care about best-sellers, that's not the issue. We have spent most of the money we had on this and I have experienced repercussions because of my public position. There has been a price to pay but it's worth it to change people's attitudes."

• Left At East Gate is published by Michael O'Mara Books (£16.99). Larry Warren and Peter Robbins are touring the UK talking about the book and will be at the Red Rose Theatre in Taylors Lane, Rugeley, at 7.30pm tonight.

X FILES COVER-UP AT AIR BASE

By ROBERT KELLAWAY

A FORMER US Air Force corporal has lifted the lid on the biggest UFO cover-up ever to take place on British soil.

Hundreds of servicemen at an RAF base leased to the Americans were silenced following a terrifying alien encounter which lasted three days.

Scores of recordings on video and audio tape were destroyed or confiscated by US security services following the incidents, it is claimed.

Now the security police corporal, Larry Warren, who witnessed the encounter, has written a full account.

But in the latest twist to the cover-up he and co-author Peter Robbins have been prevented from discussing it on ITV's Strange But True Live on Friday by a former USAF colonel who refused to appear on the show if they did as well.

Larry, 35, recalled exclusively for The People the night in December 1980 when an alien force descended on RAF Bentwaters, in Suffolk, a

OUT OF THIS WORLD: Sketch of the Rendlesham Forest incident drawn by an airman who witnessed it

Shadow of craft

major NATO installation. The incident began when lights were seen dropping out of the sky into Rendlesham Forest alongside the base on Boxing Day in 1980.

Larry, then 19, said: "Hundreds of Air Force personnel were involved in this incident. A search party was

ordered out. They encountered a triangular object which darted between trees and appeared instantaneously in front of them.

"When the group was finally found by a second search party four hours later, they believed they had only been missing for 60 minutes. I

Blue & white lights

Tripod legs

Shaft of light in which another boosed

became involved on the third night. We were driven out in a truck to a field where we saw a perfect circle of mist 50ft across and 1ft high.

"At that moment, movement became slow, and I saw one airman sink to his knees, clasp his hands to his forehead and burst into tears.

Video and movie footage of this phenomenon were being taken by USAF men throughout the incident.

"We saw a red light in the sky. Then, in a flash, the mist disappeared and in its place stood a pyramid-type object 20ft high and 30ft across.

"It was a kind of mother-of-pearl colour and if you looked straight at it the image dissolved. We became aware of three non-human beings floating about 1ft off the ground.

"They were 4ft tall, with ghost-like faces, were dressed and had arms but had no legs."

Larry was taken back to RAF Bentwaters. "We were taken into underground areas, brainwashed and treated with drugs for 24 hours.

"We were told, 'Keep your mouth shut. You have witnessed something that is classified. You can be silenced with bullets if necessary, they are very cheap'.

"They tried to make us so confused and scared in a 24-hour debriefing session that we would sound like lunatics if we ever tried to tell the truth."

THE People 22.6.97.

March 1996 – Felixstowe man tells of UFO sighting in April 1967

Brian Field of Grange Road, Felixstowe, was driving his nearly new Ford Anglia car between Orford and Tunstall, one late evening, when he was flagged down by a young man, who said he had been watching a UFO.

"I got out of the car and heard this humming noise. I then saw pink, green, yellow, and white lights in the sky. I saw a saucer-shaped

Brian Field

East Anglian Daily Times - Ipswich
(Circ: 49,029)

21 AUG 1997

ANGLIAN
Briefing

Interest in UFO book is growing

INTEREST in the world famous UFO sighting at Rendlesham Forest, near Woodbridge, has been rekindled by a new book by one of the eyewitnesses. Woodbridge Books has sold nearly 200 copies of Larry Warren's first-hand account entitled Left At East Gate since it went on sale during the summer.

The shop in the Thoroughfare sold 100 copies in 90 minutes when Mr Warren and his co-author Peter Robbins attended a book-signing session.

Now the shop has organised a second signing session on August 23 from 11am until 12.30pm to satisfy demand from the public to meet the authors and discuss the dramatic events in 1980 close to RAF Woodbridge.

In June up to 100,000 national television viewers said they believed aliens had visited Earth after watching evidence on the UFO. Eyewitnesses claim they saw a space ship on three legs and small beings alight in the forest near the east gate of the air base.

Speculation is expected to mount further in January when UFO investigator Jenny Randles publishes new evidence in a book about the sightings.

Authors: Larry Warren (left) and Peter Robbins

object, hovering about 250 feet up in the sky. The lights were coming from what appeared to be windows in the middle of it. Suddenly it shot up vertically, at incredible speed, and out of sight."

In September of the same year, Brian witnessed another sighting of a mysterious 'light' in the sky, while driving along the same route. He claimed that he arrived home an hour and-a-half later and believes there is a gap of 'missing time'.

He was to also experience nightmares, which involved some form of examination by 'strange beings' described as

". . . three and-a-half feet tall, with large heads and huge eyes, and long arms with webbed fingers."

557

Authors invited to UFO summit

A NEW book is cruising in like a Stealth bomber and threatening to blow the lid off the most famous UFO case ever – the riddle of Rendlesham Forest.

The launch of the book comes as the hit series the X-Files crashes onto our screens again with Agent Mulder ever closer to the truth about alien landings on earth.

The man behind the book is eye witness Larry Warren who was a security police officer at RAF Bentwaters when an alleged Unidentified Flying Object crashed into the forest and people saw strange lights in the sky.

Confident

Now The Evening Star is helping to link people for a proposed UFO conference in Ipswich next February, soon after the book is published. The conference is being organised by Gordon Goodger of Baylham.

We are confident we can attract Larry Warren here, together with his co-author Peter Robbins, a New York-based UFO researcher.

The conference may also pull in retired USAF colonel Charles Halt, who has always stuck by his original story about investigating a possible

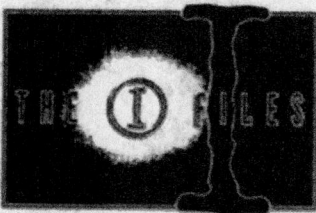

UFO landing site and watching weird lights moving through the forest. Today he lives in Virginia in the US and runs his own real estate company.

Leiston-based UFO researcher Brenda Butler, who co-wrote the book Sky Crash about the Rendlesham incident, has scorned Larry Warren's book even before she sees its contents.

Brenda, of Mafeking Place, has recently helped Meridian Television of the US which is producing a film on UFO sightings. After years of interviewing witnesses Brenda now believes the UFO story was a cover-up, and the "UFO" was a piece of experimental military hardware, possibly of US or Soviet origin.

Brenda is keen to attend the conference which should be a real sizzler.

■ The Star is holding the I Files open. If you see any strange lights or objects in the sky, contact Gavin Hodge on 01473 282310.

East Anglian Daily Times

13 NOV 1996

Comet-like object seen by woman

A SUFFOLK woman has spoken for the first time about a UFO – similar to the 1980 Rendlesham object – seen travelling towards an air base.

The woman had returned to her home in Woodbridge after walking her dog during a clear winter's evening when she saw a wedge-shaped glowing object shoot through the sky.

It appeared to come from the direction of Snape and was going towards RAF Woodbridge.

The woman, who declines to be named, says: "This was not a plane. It was the brightest, sharpest thing I have ever seen in my life. It was bright red, purple and gold with a gold line behind it."

The health worker originally thought it was a comet but changed her mind after watching a TV programme a few days later called Strange But True.

This included an account of Christmas 1980 incident when Americans stationed at RAF Woodbridge saw what they described as a UFO crash into the forest.

The woman said there were similarities between the object she saw on December 4 or 5, 1994, and the UFO 14 years earlier.

Her husband telephoned RAF Woodbridge to report the object and were disappointed that the air base, failed to report the results of its investigations.

East Anglian Daily Times - Ipswich

05 OCT 1996

Experts shed some light on UFO mystery

by RICHARD SMITH

EVIDENCE is mounting that a world famous UFO sighting near Woodbridge was nothing more sinister than lights from a lighthouse – or, was it?

There are still numerous explanations for the events of Christmas 1980 when American servicemen claim they saw a "strange glowing object" touching down in Rendlesham Forest, close to RAF Woodbridge.

A top-level campaign of disinformation shielding the truth, Russians up to mysterious activities on the Suffolk coast, a fireball in space, the after-effects of a boozy Christmas party or Orford Ness lighthouse all rank among today's possibilities for the 16-year-old mystery.

The riddle is taking on a new twist with the publication of a book by former MoD employee Nick Pope. He gives the Rendlesham incident the same billing as the American Roswell mystery when Americans claim they found a crashed saucer and aliens after the Second World War. No saucers or aliens were discovered near Woodbridge but there were enough clues to make people think the Americans had seen something suspicious on several occasions.

A discussion about the UFO at Rendlesham Forest was organised by Forest Enterprise and attracted many men, women and children still intrigued by the sightings.

Also present were Brenda Butler, of Leiston, who wrote a book about the UFO; astronomer Ian Ridpath and forester Vince Thirkettle who lived in the forest in 1980.

The group was taken to an area where the Americans saw unusual lights and discovered an object which "illuminated the entire forest with a white light".

A report written by deputy base commander at RAF Woodbridge, Lt Col Charles Halt, says: "The object was hovering on legs. As patrolmen approached it, it manoeuvred through the trees and disappeared. At this time the animals on a nearby farm went into a frenzy. The next day

UFO mix-up: Orford Ness lighthouse

three depressions one and half inches deep and seven inches in diameter were found where the object had been sited."

The area is in a direct line with the lighthouse whose lights can bounce off the clouds and trees to cast strange sights at night.

Mr Ridpath said: "We are being asked to believe something was coming back night after night. Normally, if you see a UFO you only see it once. When police came here on the first night they said all they could see was the lighthouse. At 3am a bright fireball was seen over Britain. Something like this can give the appearance of something coming down quite nearby."

Mr Thirkettle scotched rumours about strange marks after the sightings. He said a forester's axe cutting at trees makes a burn mark; rabbits are responsible for making a depression and trees that died were suffering from Dutch Elm disease.

However a woman, who declined to be named, told how she saw strange lights when she was a pregnant teenager while at a courting couples' spot in Tunstall Forest.

Her boyfriend said it was "the Yanks playing around" but the woman remains convinced they were UFO lights in an area from where you cannot see the lighthouse.

1997

19th August – Cylindrical UFO over Lowestoft, Suffolk

David Spoor from Oulton Broad, Lowestoft, Suffolk, was outside his home address when he noticed a white cylindrical object, moving across the sky.

"I ran into the house and picked up a friend's camcorder (Canon Hi 8) on loan to me, and managed to take a short piece of film as it passed overhead. After about 30 seconds it moved slowly downwards, and then accelerated upwards into the sky – faster than any jet aircraft I had ever seen. When I checked the film, later, I noticed what looked like two strobe lights flashing on its side. I was so intrigued with what I had captured that I telephoned the local newspaper and told them all about it, as a result of which I was contacted by 'Look East' television station for the East Anglia/Norfolk region, and then the BBC."

THESE are the most astonishing UFO pictures ever taken in Britain.

The stills come from an incredible 35-minute video filmed in Suffolk and passed exclusively to the News of the World, showing:

● THREE flying saucers shooting past in a blaze of lights in three separate incidents.

● A CIGAR-SHAPED craft accelerating at incredible speed, and

● HUGE triangular objects engaged in a mock dogfight.

We showed the full 35-minute video to acknowledged UFO experts—and they were stunned.

Graham Birdsall, editor of UFO Magazine, said after analysing it: "It is absolutely amazing, the most striking UK footage I have seen."

Nicholas Redfern, author of acclaimed UFO study A Covert Agenda, agreed and added: "It's on a par with anything filmed anywhere in the world. I firmly believe this is extra-terrestrial."

Convinced

The video was compiled over five months last year by UFO spotter David Spoor, 54, who said: "I still can't believe what I filmed.

"Now I am convinced there is another life out there. I'm SURE they are from another planet."

His wife, Labour district councillor Jean, 49, said: "I know of no earthly craft that could have behaved in this manner."

David said he filmed the first UFO last August from his three-bedroom bungalow in the village of Oulton Broad, near Lowestoft, Suffolk. He explained:

❝ I was just closing my garage door about 7.45pm when I looked up and saw a bright cigar-shaped object flying slowly through the sky.

I was so excited I grabbed my video camera from the house and started filming it.

I propped the camera on the fence and filmed it as it went towards the coast.

After about 30 seconds it suddenly accelerated at incredible speed—far faster than a jet plane ever

WORLD PREMIERE: David and camera

EXCLUSIVE
By PHIL TAYLOR and TIM LUCKETT

could—and just vanished. I couldn't believe what I had seen.

And when I popped it in my video to analyse it, I saw these little strobe lights flashing on either side.

The most amazing thing was they weren't attached to the craft.

Since then I have had the film analysed by experts from UFO Magazine and they say it is an extraordinary sight. They

cannot explain it.

Now I've found other people who also saw the UFO that night and were equally amazed.

I am just thrilled I caught it on video because I fear people would not have believed me otherwise. ❞

But that was just the opening shot of the extraordinary X-File film.

A month later his camera caught the first flying saucer. Recalls David: "It was just after 6pm when I looked out of the window and saw a very bright object in the sky. I grabbed the camera and rushed into the garden.

"I filmed this amazing saucer-shaped craft slowly moving from the East. It was very bright and had a shimmering appearance.

"I called Jean and she stood there open-mouthed in wonder alongside me.

"There was no sound and as it slowly moved towards me I saw a light on one side.

"We shouted out to our neighbours to witness it but they were too busy watching TV!"

Jean said: "It didn't spook me. It excited me. And it was exactly how I imagined a flying saucer would look."

On October 7 last year, David rushed for his camera again.

He revealed: "This one was almost identical to the last craft.

"I was in the garden and saw those amazing flashing lights towards the sea.

"I was so intrigued I jumped on my bicycle and rode towards the coast.

"There I saw this saucer-shaped object hovering over the sea and I filmed it for several minutes. Then it just vanished as though a light had been switched off."

In December came the third saucer. Said David: "This one arrived just before 6pm.

"When I started filming the saucer—which was emitting loads of light—it looked like it was still.

"Then it slowly moved behind a tree to the west.

"I went towards the front of the house to try and pick it up on camera again and it went behind my house. Then I lost it."

Jean said: "I loved watching it. I could even see what appeared like little portholes. There is no way it was a plane."

In November David also filmed what he described as "large black triangles" flying over a decommissioned MoD site on the coast at

Lowestoft.

He said: "They were doing aerobatic manoeuvres at high speed. I have no idea what they were.

"Everything I have caught on video completely baffles me."

Last month it was reported the RAF tracked a triangular-shaped UFO "as big as a battleship" off the South-east coast.

Two Dutch air force jets scrambled to intercept the object but could not keep up, it was reported.

RAF officials were themselves baffled by the bizarre sighting.

One source said: "It was definitely under control, judging by the manoeuvres it executed." But some UFO watchers believe the military deliberately releases such stories as a smokescreen to explain sightings of top-secret experimental craft.

Yesterday, as UFO experts from throughout Britain congregated in Southend, Essex, to discuss the latest findings, Graham Birdsall said: "The fact that we are having these kind of strange phenomena filmed over our shores is quite amazing."

Aware

Nicholas Redfern said: "In my opinion, David's video is the most important UFO footage ever filmed in Britain.

"It is important that people get to see it as they should know what is going on over their heads in our airspace."

The 32-year-old West Midlands author added: "I am not aware of anything the military has anything flying which even remotely resembles the objects in David's footage. And I would question the wisdom of any military agency which would risk flying classified experimental aircraft over built-up areas.

"I firmly believe that what has been filmed by David is extra-terrestrial," he added.

To research his disturbing book, Mr Redfern was granted unprecedented access to thousands of previously classified Ministry of Defence files on UFOs.

In A Covert Agenda, he claims: "Rationally-controlled machines from beyond Earth are routinely penetrating UK airspace.

"The military infrastructure has little or no control over the violation.

"Despite this, evidence is now being uncovered which shows that there has been an official shift in policy.

"There is now a desire to disseminate to the public hitherto top-secret UFO data collected over the past 50 years."

21st October – Triangular UFO sighted over Mildenhall

Derek was travelling back from a visit to Centre Parcs, on the late evening, along the A11 near Lakenheath Airbase, Mildenhall, with his family, when they noticed what looked like a 'flying Christmas tree' approaching their position, low down in the sky.

"The first thing we noticed about the unidentified flying object – which was triangular in shape, with many lights around its outer edges and a cluster of four larger lights in its centre – was how incredibly thin it looked. I thought, from its altitude and descent that it was actually coming in to land. As it moved closer, we heard three distinct noises – a top note, like the soft whine of a jet landing, a middle note, like a bag of nails in a washing machine, and a heavy 'thud, thud, thud', like rotor blades chopping through the air. Within seconds it had gone out of sight. I have to admit what I saw frightened me. I believe it was more likely to be an example of top secret technology than any 'Alien' spaceship – one of the reasons why I would prefer to remain anonymous, for fear of reprisal."

23rd October – Proceeding in Parliament, House of Lords

THE RENDLESHAM POWDER-KEG! By Gordon Creighton.

[A]   PROCEEDINGS IN PARLIAMENT, HOUSE OF LORDS.
HANSARD, WRITTEN ANSWERS.

Thursday, 23rd October, 1997.

Highpoint Prison.

Lord Hill-Norton asked Her Majesty's Government:

Whether staff at Highpoint Prison in Suffolk received instructions to prepare for a possible evacuation of the prison at some time between 25 and 30 December 1980, and if so, why these instructions were issued.

Lord Williams of Mostyn:

I regret to advise the noble Lord that I am unable to answer his question, as records for Highpoint Prison relating to the period concerned are no longer available. The governor's journal is the record in which a written note is made of significant events concerning the establishment on a daily basis. It has not proved possible to locate that journal.

Thursday, 28th October, 1997.

RAF Bentwaters and Woodbridge:
Nuclear Weapons Allegations.

Lord Hill-Norton asked Her Majesty's Government:

Whether the allegations contained in the recently published book *Left at East Gate*, to the effect that nuclear weapons were stored at RAF Bentwaters and RAF Woodbridge, in violation of UK/US treaty obligations, are true.

Lord Gilbert:

It has always been the policy of this and previous governments neither to confirm nor to deny where nuclear weapons are located, either in the UK or elsewhere, in the past or at present time. Such information would be withheld under exemption 1 of the Code of Practice on Access to Government Information.

Lord Hill-Norton asked Her Majesty's Government:

Whether they are aware of reports from the United States Air Force Personnel that nuclear weapons stored in the Weapons Storage Area at RAF Woodbridge were struck by light beams fired from an unidentified craft seen over the base in the period 25-30 December 1980, and if so, what action was subsequently taken.

Lord Gilbert:

There is no evidence to suggest that the Ministry of Defence received any such reports.

Lord Hill-Norton asked Her Majesty's Government:

What information they have on the suicide of the United States security policeman from the 81st Security Police Squadron who took his life at RAF Bentwaters in January 1981, and whether they will detail the involvement of the British police, Coroner's Office, and any other authorities involved.

Lord Gilbert:

MoD has no information concerning the alleged suicide. Investigations into such occurrences are carried out by the US Forces.

Lord Hill-Norton asked Her Majesty's Government:

What information they have on the medical problems experienced by various United States Air Force Personnel based at RAF Bentwaters and RAF Woodbridge, which stemmed from their involvement in the so-called Rendlesham Forest incident in December 1980.

Lord Gilbert:

Information on medical matters relating to US personnel is a matter for the US authorities.

[B]   PRESS-REPORT IN *THE PEOPLE*.
One solitary report in a British national newspaper, *The People*, of November 2, 1997.
(If there were other British press-reports, we at FSR have not seen them.)
Contributed by *D. Strudwick* in letter dated 4/11/97.

UFO ATTACKED OUR NUKES.

Britain's former military supremo is asking the Government to investigate whether aliens fired LASER BEAMS at our nuclear arsenal.

Admiral of the Fleet Hill-Norton, retired chief of the defence staff, wants the probe to be launched into the sighting of a UFO hovering over RAF Woodbridge in Suffolk. He has now tabled questions to the Ministry of Defence asking whether nuclear weapons stored at Woodbridge were struck by light beams fired from an unidentified craft.

He claims that US air force personnel who saw the "attack" filed reports which are being covered up by the MoD.

He said: "The Ministry has doggedly denied that anything untoward happened, and I simply don't believe them." Defence minister Lord Gilbert refused to confirm or deny whether the base was equipped with nuclear missiles.

He added: "There is no evidence to suggest that the Ministry of Defence received any such reports."

The mysterious sighting happened in December 1980 and was picked up on RAF radar. Phantom jets were scrambled and pilots reported intense, bright lights in the sky. ■

From 'Flying Saucer Review' Volume 43/1 Spring

David Spoor

7ᵗʰ December – Saucer-shaped object sighted

David Spoor from Oulton Broad, near Lowestoft, was at his home address when he and his wife, Jean, saw a saucer-shaped object in the sky.

"I rushed in and picked up my camcorder, hardly daring to believe that it was happening again to me. I trained the lens onto the image, which was lit up with light radiating from it, and took some film. As it headed away, now behind a tree on the horizon, I lost sight of it. When I dashed to the front garden, hoping to see it again, it had disappeared."

We appreciate that there are those who will regard David Spoor with some suspicion, feeling that the chances of capturing so many objects on film during that relatively short period, is highly improbable, but of course how many know Mr David Spoor? If they did, they would realise that that they were dealing with a very genuine, albeit naive man who, like so many others we were to come across over the years, ended up feeling disillusioned with the response of those who would not and could not accept the possibility that such things did exist.

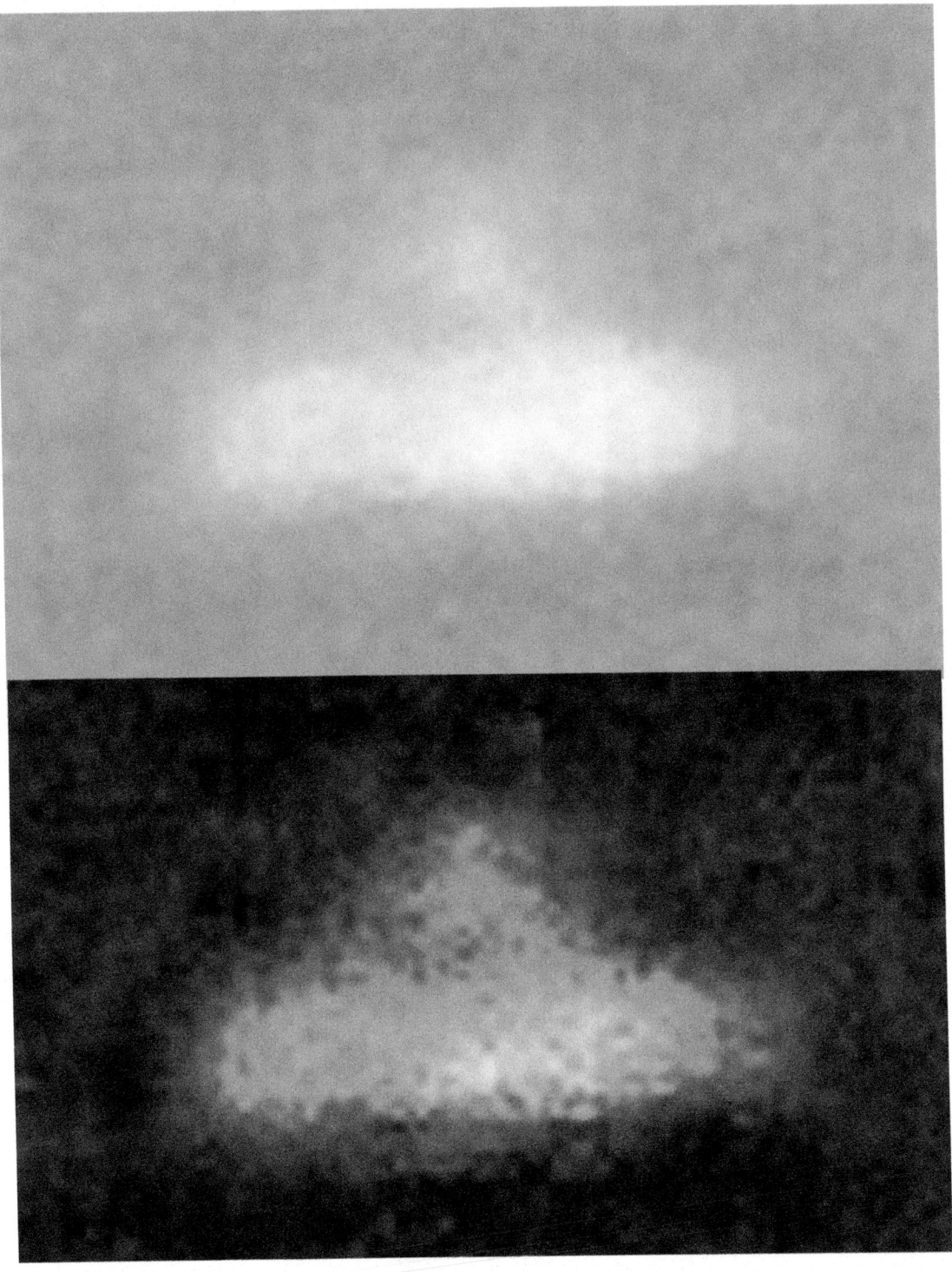

THE HALT PERSPECTIVE

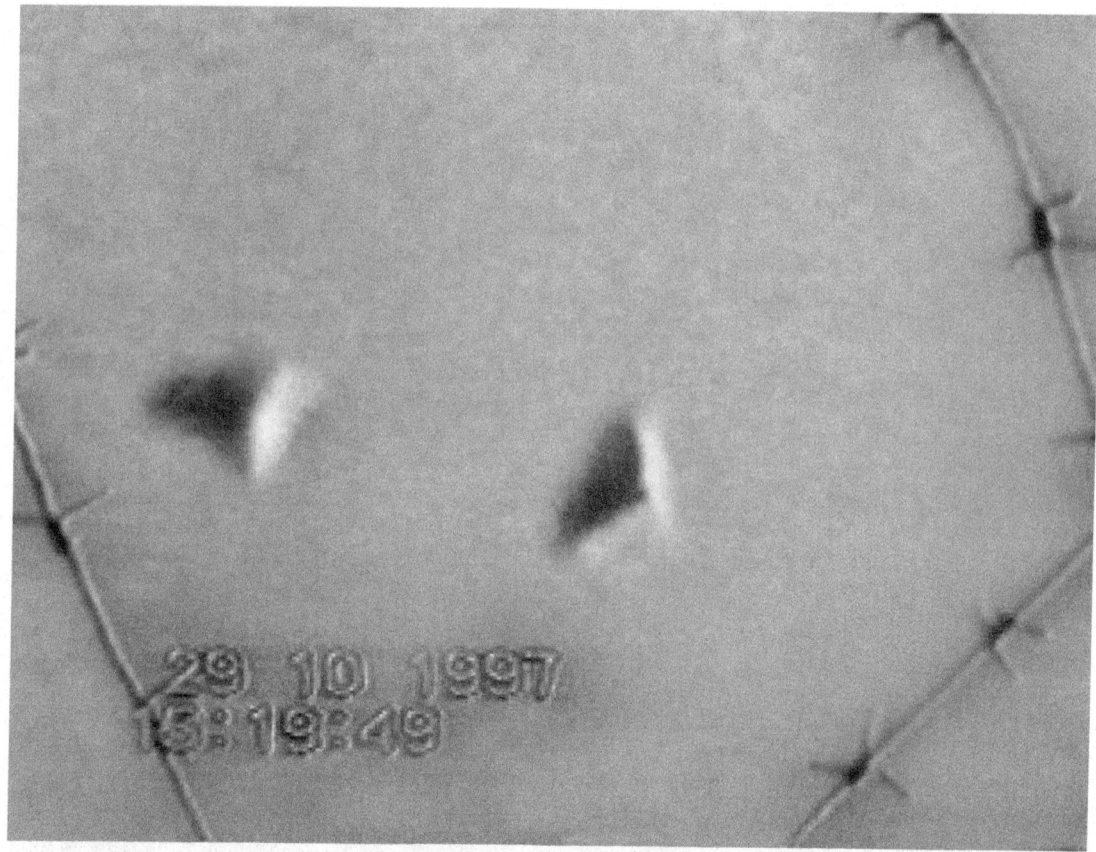

David:

"Yes, I was naïve at the time. I thought my UFO films were worth a lot on money – after all, it's not everyday that you have the opportunity to capture something so unusual going across the sky.

About 12 months after the sightings, I was contacted by John Purdie – a film producer. He seemed very interested in making a documentary about UFOs and asked me if I would be willing to assist him with a forthcoming film, entitled Riddle of the skies, (15.2.1999).

Sadly I was disappointed to discover, when the film went out, there were suggestions made that I had hoaxed the films – a matter that I strongly refute, and that the object I had filmed on the 7th December 1997, was either a cloud or a star! What seemed odd was that I did, in fact, take some film of Venus and send it to them to show the difference, but they never introduced this material into the programme."

What a shame that the coverage given to extraordinary film footage like that taken by David Spoor, and UFO accounts given by the public, should be whipped up in frenzy of sensationalism by those tabloid newspapers, which, while openly declaring that

UFOs no longer exist, still continue to publish garish accounts of bizarre UFO reports but refuse to acknowledge the evidence collected by so many organisations, over the years.

West Yorkshire Police Sergeant Tony Dodd

Retired West Yorkshire Police Sergeant Tony Dodd, the then Director of Quest International – an organisation of UFO investigators covering the UK – told of having received several UFO reports, in 1997, from people travelling along the A11 dual-carriageway, between Mildenhall, in Suffolk, and Cambridge. The witnesses included an off-duty RAF Pilot, a Company Director, and a family returning to their home in Norfolk, who stopped after sighting a UFO twenty-five feet away from their vehicle. According to Mr Dodd, the family told of sighting an object which had descended very close to the roadside, consisting of a rotating cloud of vapour, with a series of lights inside the 'cloud', estimated to be 300 feet in diameter, accompanied by a loud 'swishing' noise.

1997 – 21st August – Mother and son chased by UFO (*Ipswich Evening Star*)

THE TV KEPT GOING BLANK – THEN THEY SAW IT ...

Mum and son chase UFO in car

AN Ipswich teenager believes he saw a UFO as he and his mother drove home late at night through the Suffolk countryside.

Richard Tatterton, 16, and his mum Myrtle were on their way home to Spring Road when they saw a strange object in the sky over Bromeswell, near Woodbridge.

The pair had first noticed something was amiss as they watched television at the home of family friend David Caley in Eyke earlier on Tuesday night.

"It was about 10.30pm. There was some interference and the TV kept going blank and turning from a picture into a black screen," said Richard, a pupil of Farlingaye High School, Woodbridge.

Two minutes later, Richard and Myrtle left to begin the drive home to Ipswich.

Gliding

"At about 10.38pm, we were driving through Bromeswell and I saw a grey saucer-shape object in the sky. At first I thought it was a piece of dirt on the windscreen," he said.

"Then I saw it again and it was gliding fairly fast towards the Woodbridge air-base."

Housewife Myrtle, 54, stopped the car at a T-junction in Bromeswell and she and Richard watched the object hover in a field before it moved off towards the air base.

Richard confessed to being "anxious" as he watched the saucer, but fearless Myrtle drove after it in the direction of Hollesley, even getting out of the car to get a better look.

The object then changed into a triangle of lights with the bottom-left corner flashing and glittering, said Richard.

The pair stopped again at Wilford Bridge and watched the object, and saw it again near the Red Lion pub in Martlesham before finally losing sight of it near Suffolk police headquarters.

"I have been interested in UFOs for

BELIEVER: Richard, 16, has always wanted to see a UFO. Picture: JAMIE NIBLOCK

about three years, and I have always wanted to see one," said Richard.

"It definitely wasn't a figment of my imagination. If the bases at Woodbridge and Bentwaters were still open I would have said it could have been an aircraft but it was definitely a UFO.

"If I saw it again I wouldn't be scared I will be keeping my eyes open and watching the skies."

■ Did you see the strange object? If you did, call our newsdesk on 01473 282257.

7th October 1997 – Crop circles found

David Spoor who is now no longer with us who we had the pleasure of meeting some years ago came across five burnt or scorched circles 12ft in diameter on the beach in front of the old MOD radar Station, between Hopton and Corton. Poignantly David hoped to write a book about his sightings some of which were captured on film, but face decreed this was not to be.

1998

NEWS OF THE WORLD

Solihull UFO conference '98

UFO LANDS

By JAMES MILLBANK

TODAY the News of the World lifts the shroud of secrecy that surrounds Britain's most sensational UFO sighting.

A silver-shaped craft landed in the night at Tangham Wood just half a mile from the USAF base at RAF Woodbridge in Suffolk.

It appears to have been much like the one on the left, sensationally pictured over Los Angeles in 1989.

Lt Colonel Charles Halt, who witnessed the Suffolk close encounter, reported: "A sun-like light" that "moved and pulsed" in the forest.

That was almost 18 years ago. Since then an official blanket of silence has been thrown over the incident.

Now, as respected experts gather for the Solihull UFO conference '98, we reproduce in full our original News of the World exclusive on the next page so that investigators can again focus attention on one of the great mysteries of the paranormal.

CLOSE ENCOUNTER: A flying saucer skims the rooftops as the sun glints on its smooth, metallic surface

IN BRITAIN

OFFICIAL COLLECTORS' SOUVENIR FRONT PAGE INSIDE

15th January 1998 – MOD and 'the little green men'!

At 10.30pm, an object – described as being *"a long, dark object, with two bright lights at either end and several red ones in the middle"* – was sighted in the sky, between Badingham and Laxfield, in Suffolk. The matter was brought to the attention of the Station Staff Officer Lt. Col. (sec 40) at Wattisham Airfield, as a complaint of a low flying aircraft, who wrote to the couple about the incident, in which he advised them:

> *"None of the helicopters from the base were out that night, but as the sighting was made outside their airspace for which they had any responsibility, we would not have been aware of any aircraft flying between Laxfield and Badingham".*

Another document, endorsed *'Flying complaints progress report'*, submitted to the MOD in respect of enquiries carried out into the allegation, contains the following written note:

> *"To the best of our knowledge, this is not any aircraft from Wattisham – possibly a Lakenheath M3, or maybe a Puma from Odiham; other than this, 'the little green men have it.'"*

(Source: MOD declassified documents, February 2010 defe-24-1990)

Late 1990s – *'Project Flying Triangle'*

This was founded during the early 1990s by Omar Fowler, Victor Kean, and Ron West. The purpose of this project was to extract reports of the 'Flying Triangle' phenomenon from the more general UFO reports, many of which occurred over Suffolk, Essex and Kent, along the East Coast. It involved UFO researcher Tony Spurrier, and his colleague – Susan Addison, who undertook a number of visits to Sizewell B nuclear power station, in Suffolk.

Sizewell B

THE HALT PERSPECTIVE

Omar Fowler

Omar Fowler – Consultant to *Flying Saucer Review* and Director of the PRA (Phenomena Research Association), Derby – had himself written to Air Traffic Controllers, at Manchester Airport, warning of the likelihood of a pilot encountering what had become known as a 'Flying Triangle' (although he never received any reply).

Omar:

"Predominately, they always appear in darkness, and travel from east to west, returning in the opposite direction up to two hours later, usually travelling at around 30 miles per hour and approximately 800 feet in height. At times they produce a low humming noise. When travelling over open countryside, they may shoot a beam of light (like a searchlight). Their appearance and departure is

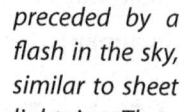

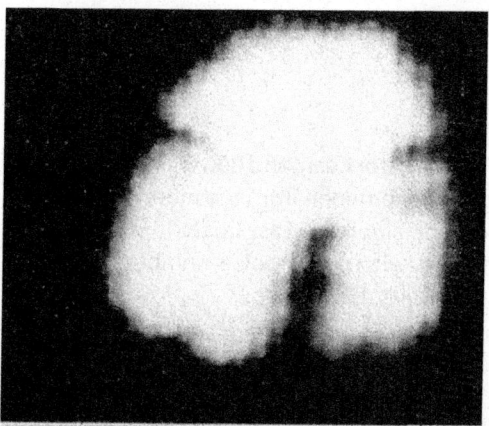

preceded by a flash in the sky, similar to sheet lightning. There were 52 'Flying Triangle' (FT) reports brought to my notice in and around the city of Derby, between December 1994 and May 1995, which included hovering illuminated craft, and in one instance a huge triangular craft was observed hovering over one of the main traffic islands (Spider Bridge) on the A5111 circular road. Many witnesses were able to sketch and describe the FT craft in detailed reports, which included FT craft hovering and shining down white beams of light onto the countryside at night; some people even managed to film them. These lights have been reported on numerous occasions but appear highly unlikely to be searchlights as such, taking into consideration that some witnesses have described the FTs white beam of light as sometimes ending in mid-air, like a fluorescent tube."

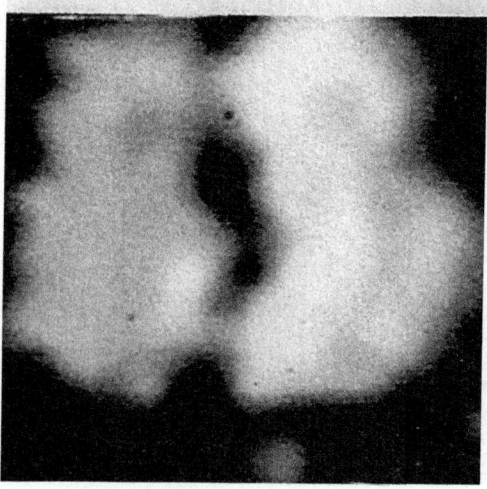

An example of the type of craft catalogued by Omar, during the mid 1990s, is shown, along with a photograph of a UFO seen in the Derbyshire area during this time period.

Chilling statistics – Appear to be moving in from the East Coast

"As the number of FT reports increased, pattern of behaviour began to emerge. They appeared to be moving in from over the East Coast of England and flying slowly across the countryside to various destinations, including other nuclear power stations, before returning back out to sea a few hours later."

Statistics from the Project FT database, compiled by Victor J. Kean, have shown the following statistics:

1995 Total FT reports – 1,797, of which 476 were observed over nuclear power stations.

1996 Total FT reports – 1,437, of which 988 were observed over nuclear power stations.

1997 Total FT reports – 1,339, of which 1,242 were observed over nuclear power stations.

Tony Spurrier – How it began

"During the mid to late 90s and the popularity of the internet, I joined Compuserve's UFO Forum. I had only a partial interest in UFOs, but joined the group and got involved in the discussions just to get an understanding of the subject. Before long I was asked to moderate the 'sightings section', which I was glad to do. Michael Hesemann and Victor Kean were both members of the forum and as moderator for the sightings section I ran a weekly live discussion on Tuesdays, at

7-9pm. Victor used to post his monthly sightings figures each month and would come along to some of the live sessions. We began talking on a personal note, as Victor was originally from North London and we both supported Arsenal."

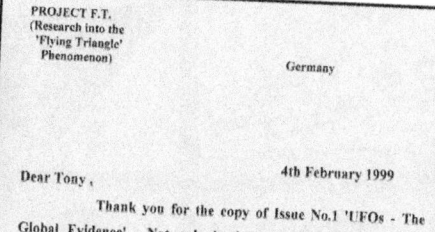

PROJECT F.T.
(Research into the
'Flying Triangle'
Phenomenon)
               Germany

Dear Tony,   4th February 1999

    Thank you for the copy of Issue No.1 'UFOs - The Global Evidence'. Not only is the newsletter excellent in its presentation, but you have 'hit' just the style which I personally prefer to see. Not full of sensational items, but with a tone of serious, reflective discourse about 'our subject'.

    The proposed visit to Wiltshire looks tempting, but alas the Berlin - Heathrow airfare is somewhat prohibitive for such a venture. I see that Nick Redfern is to be the 'Host' for the day. Nick and I have been in correspondence for some years now and one or two of my minor contributions were acknowledged in his latest work, 'A Covert Agenda'. My UFO database came up with a significant UFO report from Denmark during 'Operation Mainbrace' (Sept.20th 1952) which added to Nick's research. (You might mention in a future 'newsletter' that the database is freely accessed for UFO researchers.)

Sue Addison and Tony Spurrier

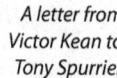

A letter from Victor Kean to Tony Spurrier

Victor J. Kean

*German journalist and author, *Michael Hesemann*

---

*Michael Hesemann (born March 22, 1964 in Düsseldorf) is a German journalist and author. In the late 1980s he became known in Germany as an author of several books on UFOs and extraterrestrial visitors on Earth. Later in his career he turned to topics related to catholicism. From 1984 to 1990 Hesemann published the German magazine *Magazin 2000,* dealing with paranormal phenomena and religious topics. In 1990, he sold the magazine and served for the next decade as its editor-in-chief. In 1995, together with his co-editor at *Magazin 2000,* Hesemann hosted a global UFO congress in Düsseldorf, Germany, where he presented alleged video evidence for the alien autopsy. In 1999, he was accredited to the Holy See Press Office. In 2010, the *Wall Street Journal* described him as "a religious historian, who helps the Vatican date relics". He is German representative of the Pave the Way Foundation (PTWF) for which he did research at the Vatican archives in 2010. He co-founded *Deutschland pro Papa,* a conservative catholic initiative which claims to represent the "silent majority of Rome-loyal Catholics". In 2013, he compiled an exhibition on the Turin Shroud for the Knights of Malta, touring through Germany and Austria as of 2015. **(Source: Wikipedia)**

Author, Philip Mantle

Tony – Sizewell Nuclear Power Station

"During one of our talks, Victor asked me if I could do him a favour. The favour was to visit Sizewell and see if I could corroborate the sighting reports he was receiving from the contributors in the area via Ron West.

Using the database of sightings we identified a commonality with UFO activity from 9pm onwards, bearing in mind Sizewell was getting 100-120 sightings per month and they were increasing in volume."

Tony Spurrier and Sue Addison, together with others, were asked to assist with field research and attempt to gain first-hand experience of the phenomenon, using the database of sightings –

which contained literally thousands of times and locations examined, in order to identify locations of high levels of UFO activity. Prior to this research, Tony – like ourselves – had preconceived ideas (misconceptions, some might say) that 'Flying Triangles' were probably aircraft flown covertly, rather than examples of 'alien' craft. Another characteristic of behaviour, endorsing the movement of these objects, is the fact that many of them had been sighted travelling slowly over the East Coast, around 100 feet off the ground.

Victor noted that the 'Flying Triangle' sightings began one hour after sunset, and the last sighting approximately one hour before sunset. He labelled this as being 'the work' period. At the beginning of 'the work' period, over 60 per cent of the sightings occurred in Essex, while at the end of this period 60 per cent of the sightings occurred in the Suffolk area. Minimal first and last sightings during that 'work' period were witnessed over Kent.

Tony:

"One particular aspect of the 'Flying Triangles' 'work' period habit was the alarming high number of over-flights, or visits, to Nuclear Power Stations along the East Coast. During the late 1990s, Kent was averaging one visit per night, Essex – between one and two sightings per night, and Suffolk – three sightings per night"

Tony pondered, additionally, as to why the 'Flying Triangles' were never seen arriving or leaving the area.

Victor pointed out that these objects were logged hovering above the nuclear reactor, from 30 seconds to 30 minutes during each sighting.

14th February 1998

Tony:

"On the 14th February 1998, I visited Sizewell and witnessed something very odd – something that couldn't be explained and something that resembled a 'Flying Triangle'. Despite this it was completely different to what I expected and I also encountered a different phenomenon, one which Victor explained was commonly associated with the 'Flying Triangle' phenomenon. And that's where this journey started . . .

My initial interest in UFOs was purely curiosity. I didn't have a belief either way; I suppose I enjoyed the idea of there being alien life but my involvement came from trying to corroborate the sightings Victor was receiving from Ron, which came from independent sources.

My work background is in Hotels, predominantly accountancy, but I ran a fraud investigation department. Therefore, I wasn't interested in just information – I wanted to separate facts from gossip, and the facts segregated into important facts and non-important facts. When I began conversing with Victor, and of the three nuclear power stations Sizewell was encountering the highest number of sightings per month, this seemed to be the obvious place to start."

Visiting the site – 100 UFO sightings reported per month!

"I went there to see for myself the level of reported activity, taking into consideration that Victor was reporting the power station sightings on a monthly basis, through the internet based

'Filer's Files', run by George Filer. Sizewell, by the end of the 90s, was receiving 100+ sightings per month. We placed ourselves 'objectively' where the highest number of sightings was being reported and were able to corroborate UFO activity occurring – witnessed by ourselves – as a result of access to the credible data obtained. These were not chance sightings."

Sizewell is the UFO capital!

"I find it quite humorous when I see Bonnybridge as the UFO capital of the UK (that may even have changed now). Sizewell is the capital of UFO sightings in the UK, due to the sheer number of sightings and even the limited footage we have (by design not chance).

Given its short distance from Rendlesham and the similarity in background behaviour and description, my opinion is that it may well be the same type of craft. [Authors agree]

I have no evidence to suggest that what is being seen is from other planets or star systems. They could be present on Earth, either within it, in a different dimension, or even some other answer we are yet to understand. Just to clarify, we have never promoted a theory; we have been looking for answers to questions. My own personal thoughts are you can't jump to any conclusions – just continue to look for answers to what is happening. UFOs are real but they are well beyond what we comprehend."

March 1998 – Observations carried out

They set-up observation one mile west of the power station complex, which is just over half-a-mile long and comprises Sizewell A –the decommissioned reactor, and Sizewell B – the domed active reactor.

Tony:

"Shortly after midnight I became aware of some moving amber lights to the north of the complex. These lights appeared in a triangular formation and were marginally above the street lighting within the complex 'Visitors car park'. The formation had a leading light, followed by two lights close together at the rear. I had trouble in identifying these lights due to the height, in comparison to the street lighting. It was evident that these lights had to be 'off ground' due to this and that there was no access from the north of the station. But I also couldn't readily identify the lights as a 'Flying Triangle' either, the reason being it didn't conform to the pictures which were available on the internet, which was my only guide to their apparent appearance.

Again, this brings us back to cognitive psychology. In order to identify something, our mind looks to its 'pictures' and compares these with what the eye sees. If we see something new the mind will either find its closest match or enter into a state known as 'reversed gestalt moment' or 'pattern interrupt' – a moment of temporary confusion. This was the state that I had entered, which was then quickly followed by another event that, coupled with this confusion, confirmed I was looking at something very unusual."

Lights moved instantaneously

"Whilst continuing to track these slow moving lights, they appeared to move instantaneously from a horizontal position to a vertical one. I was now looking at two lights at the same height as before, but now a single light above these in a central position, making a near perfect triangle formation of lights (figure 2 opp.). This event happened without any apparent movement and the lights continued their slow move south, towards the station. Literally a few seconds later, the formation of lights returned to their original formation; again this happened without any apparent movement, and continued towards the station until they were obscured by trees.

It was only after these lights were no longer visible that I could begin to think again about what I had witnessed. I realised that I must have witnessed a 'Flying Triangle' and understood why it was referred to as a phenomenon. It looked 'unreal' and references to this being a military stealth craft were ludicrous. But this was only the beginning of the night's events. Ten minutes later, I was aware of a sudden surge of lights around the centre of the complex. These lights appeared to be just 'turned-on' and again were just hovering above street light level.

These lights were very different from the first I had seen moving slowly. I was looking at a triangle formation of pinprick type amber lights around the triangle's perimeter. However, the top corner of the triangle was not lit (figure 3 opp.). These lights began to increase their brightness steadily until they were noticeably brighter than any of the lights visible in the complex. I was again hit with a 'reversed gestalt moment'. I could not make out what the lights were or how they had appeared there and this time not even in a triangle formation, although at the same time it was evident a triangle was present. The lights reached an extremely intense brightness when the lights at the top began to extinguish. They switched off in sequence down each side of the triangle, but at a much faster rate along the right-hand side (figure 4 opp.). It got to the point where only the bottom left-hand corner was illuminated (figure 5 opp.), and as these lights began to switch off, they moved to the right and I was aware of a dark structure behind the lights. Again, 'phenomenon' was the correct way to describe this, not necessarily 'craft.'"

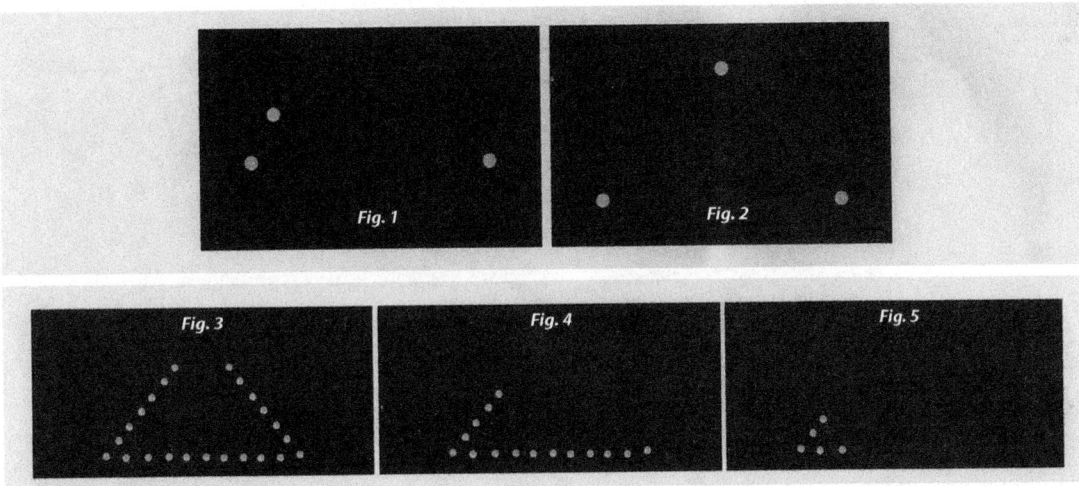

A return visit to Sizewell

Tony:

"About a month after the first visit, Sue and I returned to the location. (Due to dense fog on the previous visit, we were unable to scout the area completely.) We saw what we took to be two car headlights, behind trees, 100 feet to the south of our position. The lights then descended to about five feet above ground level and stayed the same distance apart. We first thought it was security patrol and assumed there was a road beyond our observation point, and that a vehicle had descended down the incline creating this. Then the white lights started to move apart. We took them to be torches being used by the security men aboard that car or vehicle. Another light then appeared – this one amber. We presumed this was maintenance work being carried out; the two white lights then moved back to their original position, while the amber light remained stationary. We had been discussing how lucky we were not to have got caught so close to the power station, when we then saw two red lights moving away in the same manner as the 'headlights' we had seen minutes earlier. Obviously, these were the rear lights of a vehicle driving back up the hill. Around midnight, the amber light went out and we left for home.

We arranged a visit, the following month, accompanied by German UFO researcher*Woolfgang Stelzig. The first thing we did was to show him the observation point we had used, on the previous occasion, overlooking the 'road' where the vehicles had been seen. After making our way along a path leading on to the end of a nature trail, to what we believed was the road concerned, we were stunned to discover no such road existed at all! The area was marshy, surrounded by trees."

---

*Wolfgang Stelzig is an engineer with Bosch, who has designed and built a stereoscopic photographic device to capture images of potential UFOs, if they appear in the environment of a location where this observation and recording unit is installed. A working prototype is under development now and ready to be tested. A 360° fish eye, automated camera covers the surrounding space during the 24 hours (it works at 1 frame/second). When a moving target appears, the camera sensors instruct a pan-tilt mechanism to place two digital cameras in the right position to take photographs of the target at the rate of 2-3 frames per second. It provides a stereoscopic view that also allows determining some objective magnitudes like the distance to the moving target. Recorded data are stored in a state-of-the-art computer.

Woolfgang Stelzig with his stereoscopic photographic device

1999

26th July 1998 – Conference – UFOs: The global evidence

Tony and Susan were responsible for arranging a 'Universal Promotions' conference, held in London on this date. The speakers were Dr Steven Greer, Michael Hesemann and Nick Redfern – Tickets £15 on the day, with concessions for OAPs.

13th November 1999 – 'Flying Triangle' captured on video

Sue and Tony showed us the next clip of film taken by them, following another visit to the location. She pointed out three lights, just above the horizon, which appeared around midnight (while she was in the car park) over the direction of Sizewell B, just above the street lights. We checked this piece of film, frame by frame, and found what appears to be an excellent still, showing three objects – on this occasion higher in the sky rather than just above the street light.

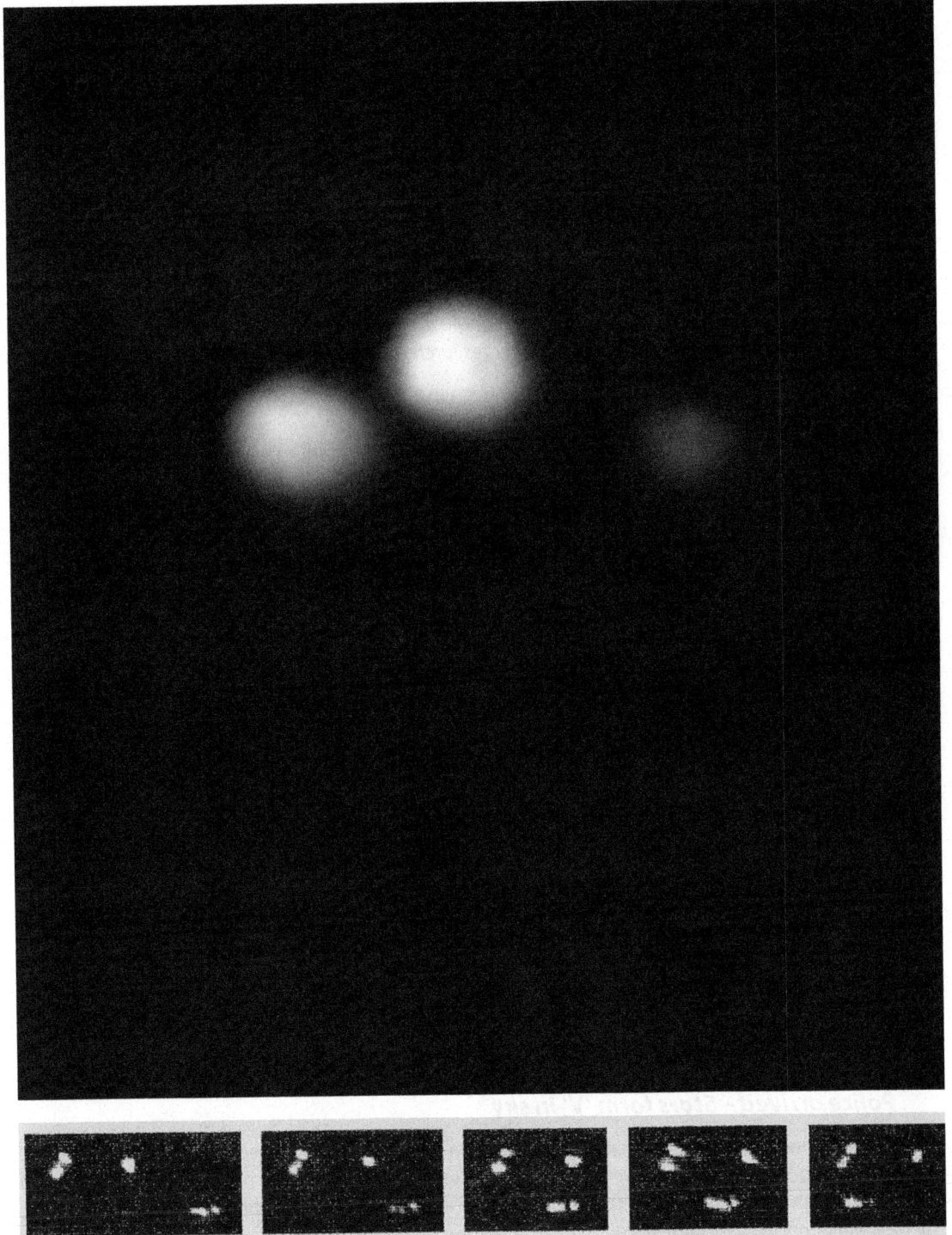

December 1999 – Tony contacts science writer David Hambling

Tony:

"Science writer -David Hambling, reported in the Guardian newspaper, that he believed these incursions could be attributed to the 'Solaris' – a large, experimental hybrid aircraft that would fly at high altitude during the day, and then descent during darkness using nuclear weapon seeking equipment. David theorized this craft was used along the East Coast to test its nuclear seeking equipment on emissions from the Nuclear Power Stations.

In December 1999, I discussed this matter with David Hambling. David admitted he was prejudiced against any Alien interpretation, but admitted 'Solaris' did not fit into the 'Flying Triangle' statistics, as recorded by this project. In fact, David could only match the TR-3 Black Manta aircraft with the size of the 'Flying Triangle', but accepted this aircraft could not hover silently. David went away to conduct further research into this matter and I never heard from him again."

2000

30th January 2000 – UFOs caught on film over Nuclear Power Station

On the 30th January 2000, Tony Spurrier travelled to Sizewell Power Station, Suffolk, accompanied by Susan Addison and colleagues, to conduct a 'sky watch'. Tony and four colleagues, set-up a observation point behind the main bank of the power station, while Sue and a colleague made

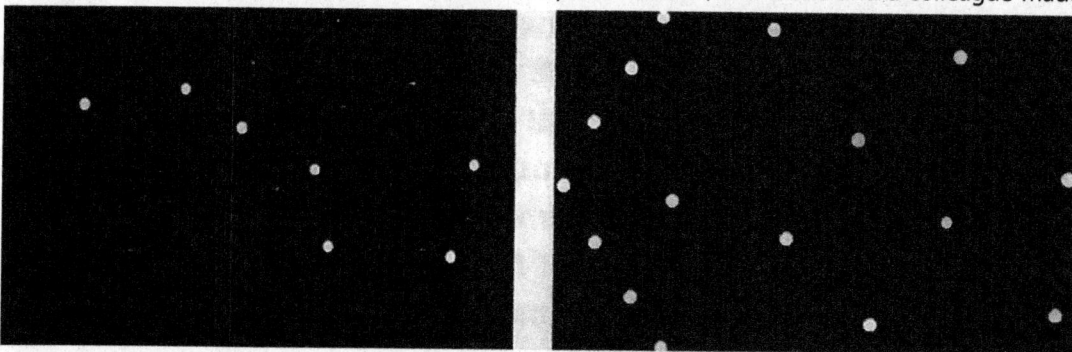

their way to the main site. At 12.50am, Tony received a message from Sue that a 'Flying Triangle' was approaching from the north, but was unable to see what Sue was watching, because of their restricted view.

Police arrived – Stars form 'V' in sky

The situation was made worse by the arrival of the police, who stopped Sue and her colleague, and after asking them what they were doing, instructed them to leave the area. At this point a huge formation of lights forming a 'V' in the sky were seen moving overhead – large enough to block out the Ursa Major constellation of stars.

The group decided to continue their observation from a southern position, away from the power station (which was now no longer visible) and were lucky enough, during the early hours, to see 'Flying Triangles' and other shaped craft, moving above an approach road, towards the power station. Tony told us that the footage we took was identical to what he filmed.

John Hanson and Dawn Holloway

This incident had always excited our curiosity, bearing in mind the film taken by us (12 months later) on the anniversary of the now famous but still controversial events that had taken place in Rendlesham Forest – now 36 years ago.

'Flying Saucer Review'

Although Tony and Sue had submitted an article to *Flying Saucer Review*, which was published in Volume 49, Number 2 (spring 2004), we had never had the opportunity of speaking to them personally about what must be regarded as a piece of unique film.

Hundreds of sightings logged every month

Obviously this was important – so in late February 2016 we went to see the couple, hoping to learn more about a phenomenon which was to plague Belgium in the late 1980s, not forgetting the massive amount of previously unpublished sightings around the Essex area (ignored by the local newspapers, despite us contacting them in 2015). We were also aware, from correspondence in our files from the late Ron West via Victor J. Kean, of a huge number of UFO sightings that occurred over Sizewell B Power Station, Suffolk, running into hundreds of sightings over each month. The problem is that we still hadn't reached this period of UFO activity in the Haunted Skies books, despite over 20 years research! The next book in the series would be Volume 12 (1991-1994).

Over fifty 'sky watches'!

We were staggered to learn that during the mid 1990s, the couple had carried out 'sky watches' at this site on at least 40 separate occasions… when film had been obtained of what one would refer to as examples of 'triangular UFOs' seen in the sky over the location.

Tony Spurrier – Criticism from within!

"The UFO public want answers – they are impatient, often lacking in intelligence, often include people that have something missing in life and look to UFOs for an answer or an escape. Therefore, they want something that may not be there. Differ from that and you become the enemy! That is why we kept ourselves to ourselves, but the motivation to continue left also. Originally I had many reasons to pursue the Sizewell sightings. There was the forum, the believers and the sceptics; there was UFO Updates with a long list of all the prominent UFO researchers and our own curiosity. We wanted to make a difference back then. Charlie was born and the priorities in our life changed. Situations changed and Sue's ex-husband no longer looked after his kids every two weeks. My kids, who were living with their mum, suddenly were living with us.

The research stopped, yet now with Charlie being 15 this year (you saw him on the video, he was just born), we could go back and see whether this is still happening. It may well have stopped, but that in itself is more intriguing than the sightings increasing through the late 90s. Only going there will answer the question!"

THE HALT PERSPECTIVE

Another still taken from the film by Tony and Susan shows an apparent faint, triangular, structure behind the light, with what appears to be a 'figure' standing in front.

"We contemplated that we may have inadvertently captured footage of a stationary but hovering 'Triangle', along with something from the triangle."

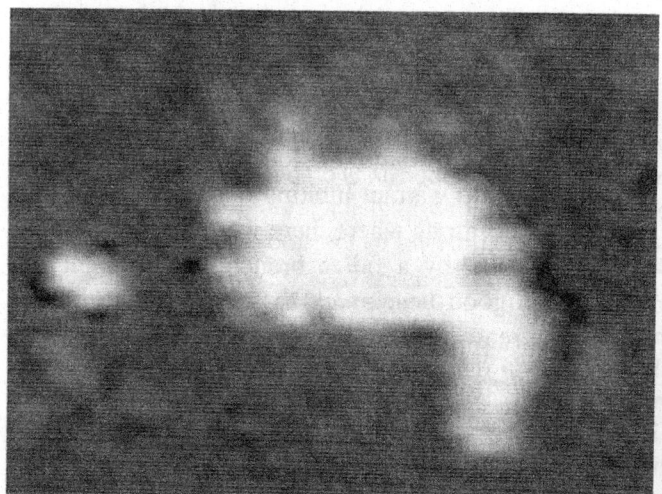
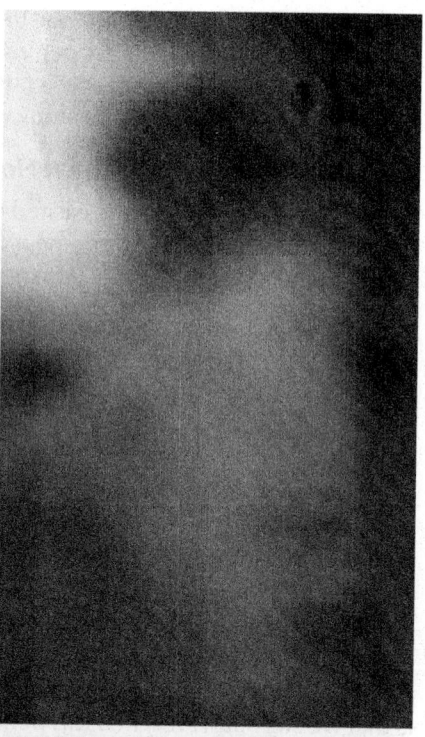

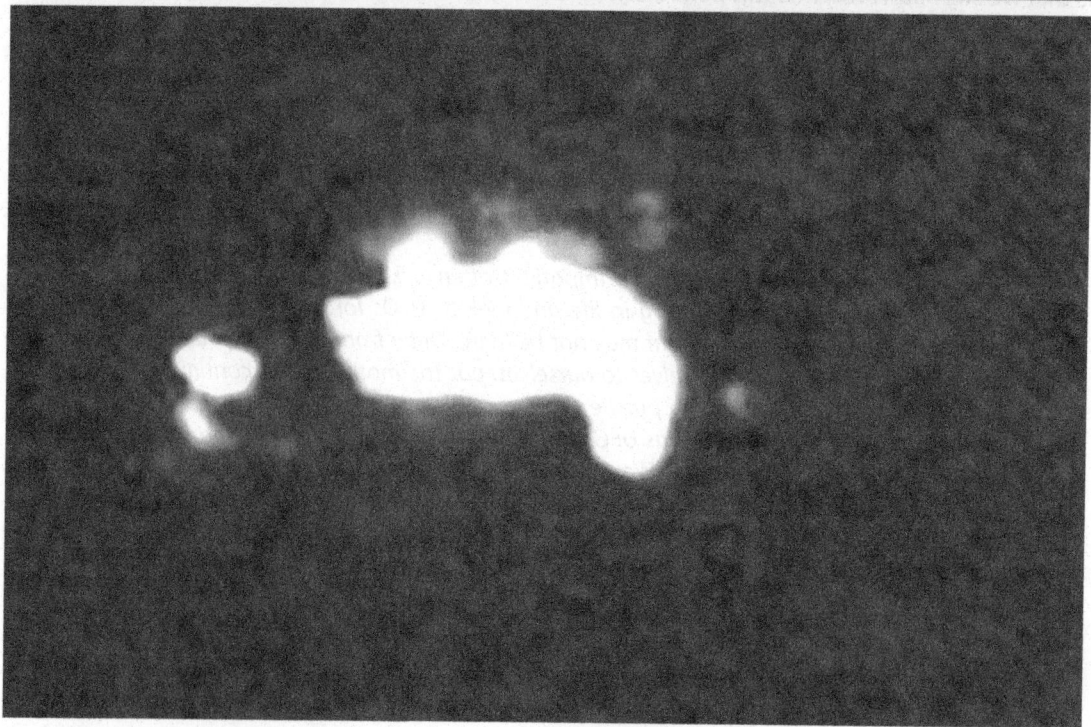

The 'Flying Triangle' phenomenon

Tony Spurrier:

"Our research created more questions than answers with regard to identifying the possibility that the 'Flying Triangles' were using the power stations as a source of energy. During our observations the lights on the objects increased in illumination, indicating they may have been recharging. It is evident that we were dealing with something beyond modern technological capabilities. Victor had his thoughts on 'humans visiting us from the future', yet I felt that we had witnessed something more paranormal in nature. During the time we committed ourselves to researching these phenomena, it is clear that we shouldn't be thinking of a 'Black Triangle' and all of its connotations. Don't think of a military aircraft, but accept we are talking about a 'Flying Triangle' Phenomena.

On another occasion during a visit to the location we earmarked our observation point, which was near a fallen branch, knowing that if we saw anything, we could revisit in daylight. Directly in front of us was a slope with bushes and beyond, a steep decline into an adjoining field. To the left were two cottages, about half a mile away. The gully was covered in a low-level mist, separated by the boundary hedge of each field. As we looked down into the gully, we saw something emerging from the bushes to the left of us. It was a grey misty 'thing', moving really slowly."

Sue:

"We first took it to be a security man, walking up the field. What we thought was a tall man at the other end of the field was actually about three feet high. You could hear 'it' walking in the grass, getting closer now, about 30 feet away from us. It looked like a 'Cluedo' figure."

Tony:

"As it came into closer view, now in the left-hand field, we speculated whether it could have been an elusive grey 'Triangle'. We saw what can only be described as a hooded entity, moving

through the mist – clearly visible with the naked eye. Through binoculars, a dark mass could be seen where the face was. We began moving towards it (this was done in turn, so that there was always one person keeping an eye on it.) Due to the slope we had to stop, as we would have lost sight of the entity 300 metres to the entry of the field. I was watching it through binoculars when it just vanished – moving one second, the next gone; it didn't face away. The whole incident seemed more in keeping with a ghostly manifestation than anything UFO."

Graham Birdsall – Victor Kean, 1931-2003

"Victor's contribution to the UFO community as a whole will be greatly missed following this sad news.

Following Victor's analysis of the FT sightings during December1999, I contacted Victor for more information. Unfortunately my attempts to contact Victor failed, until he saw a message I posted on the UFO Forum on Compuserve. What followed was a new dimension of research into the 'Flying Triangle' that comprised of the data collated by Victor and all the FT contributors throughout the UK.

As early as March 1998, from a research point of view, Victor's work was complimented with an independent sighting of unusual sightings in the vicinity of one of the 'hot spots' in the UK.

Following on from this, Victor was able to identify certain timelines which have greatly assisted in future investigations into these sightings.

Many things have been eliminated from this enquiry, most certainly lighthouses, airports, tractors, boats, cars, etc. One particular area comprises only marshes, which greatly eliminates anything other than a silent craft which houses red/white/amber lights, can hover for 30 minutes, appearing to change shape, only 100 feet from observers, and merely 30 feet above ground.

During the past five years we have been able to utilize the local residents association to eradicate local landmarks and also encourage free speech within the area of question. The locals are now very helpful and come along to see some very strange sights.

We took one local to a secluded field by the marshes. She saw, as we all did, a sudden appearance of a white 'glowing' pyramid-shaped object; two red lights on the bottom edge of the pyramid, on top a pulsating green light. This just appeared, materialized if you like. After a few minutes, this object blinked out like a light – it was gone.

This type of sighting is not unusual in the area Victor specified. His research was second to none, because he had identified areas of high activity. From conversations, over the years, Victor knew he had identified something of importance Even to the day he passed away, I doubt he realised how significant his research was.

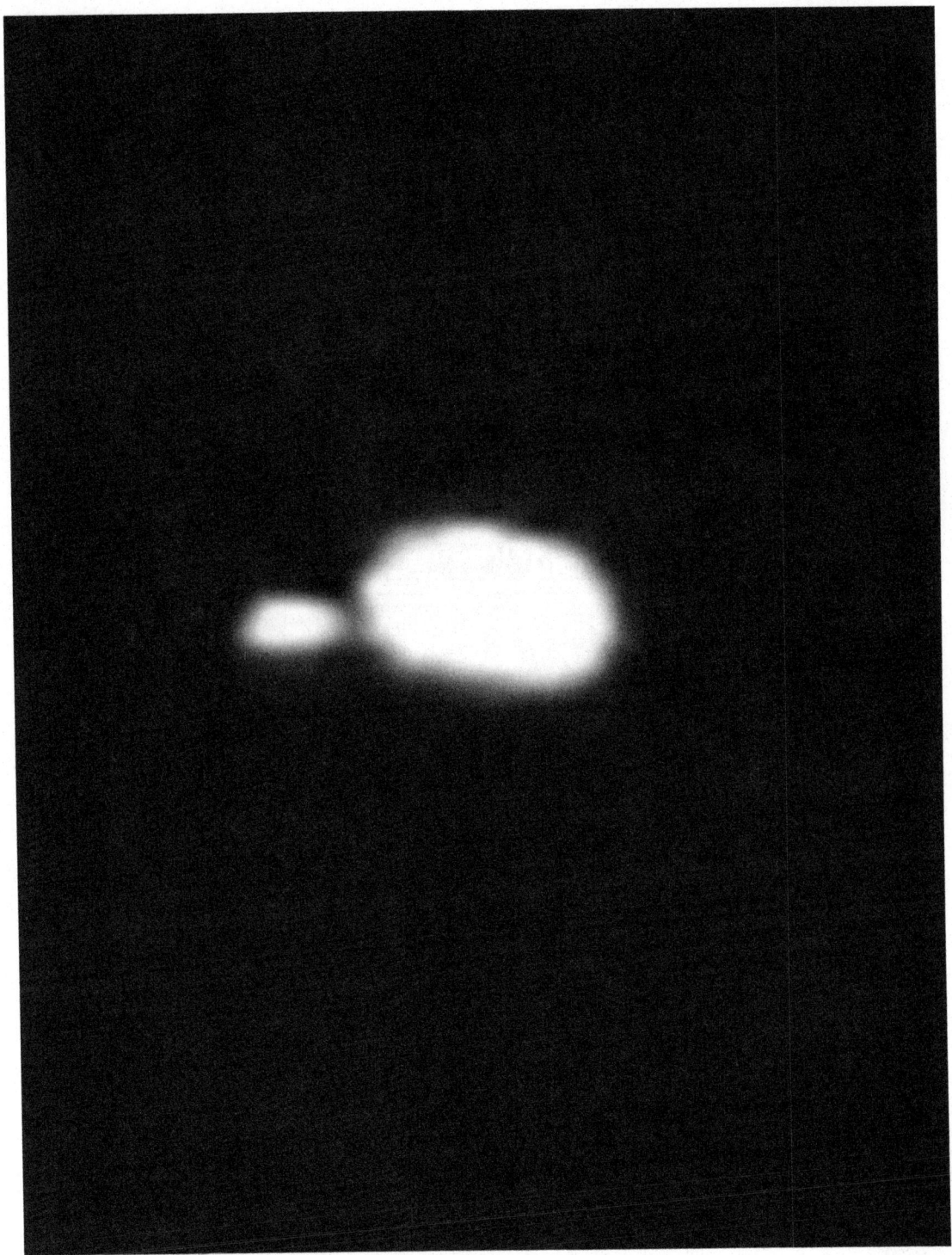

This field research will continue, as it has done from 1999. There has been some significant footage obtained, which, to my knowledge, has yet to be conventionally identified. There is one-piece of footage which absolutely fascinates us, but until it is independently verified as being anomalous and concurs with our own blown up images, it will remain a mystery.

So I would like to posthumously commend Victor on his research into reported UFO activity and for all the information he divulged which led to the ongoing investigation."

Graham Bridsall

14th March – New twist in UFO Mystery

EVENING STAR, Tuesday, March 14, 2000

www.eveningstar.co.uk/friends/index.htm *WANT TO GET IN TOUCH WITH A FRIEND FROM THE PAST? EVENING STAR FINDING FRIENDS*

GET A JOB
THERE ARE HUNDREDS ON OFFER IN TOMORROW'S EVENING STAR

New twist in UFO mystery

CONSPIRACY: Did top-level military officials use the UFO sightings near local air bases to hide the extent of their work at Orford Ness? Pictures: LIBRARY

BRIEF

Tribute paid to crash trio

A TEACHER has paid tribute to three former pupils and lifelong friends who were killed in a tragic car crash. Teenagers, Daryl Cutts, 17, Giles Cottam, 18, Alex Pantling, 17, who died in Friday's accident, were all former pupils at Samuel Ward Upper School, in Haverhill.
Deputy headteacher Howard Lay described the boys as positive, caring and friendly pupils with bright futures. Robert Beer, 17, who survived the crash, also went to the school. All the boys came from Clare, except Alex Pantling, who lived in near-by Stansfield, and their strong friendship was evident throughout their days at the school, teachers said.

Blazes in rubbish bins

FIREFIGHTERS went to Duke Street, Ipswich, after fires began in two rubbish containers shortly after 6.35 pm yesterday. A crew from Princes Street fire station extinguished the flames.

Young Sooty's gone astray

TEARFUL brothers are appealing for help to find their missing tom-cat Sooty which disappeared from Castle Hill, Ipswich, on Friday. The year-old black cat has white paws, white under his chin and blue eyes.
Sooty is described as very friendly but has never strayed from home for more than a night before and his young owners are missing him very much.
If you think you

25th September – Colonel Charles Halt emails Brenda Butler

"Your wild experiences really sound like something is heating up at East Gate. It's hard enough to believe what happened to us back in 1980, let alone what's going on now. I would suggest you try hard to establish a dialogue with whatever you have come in contact with. I would be most interested in hearing the results. If you do establish a dialogue and I can help, I am willing.

When I warned you to be careful, I was not talking about something beyond us. My concern was that an agency with secretive powers might do something. You be the judge of that. I do know that several of the airmen were hypnotized, drugged, and then threatened.

I have to assume now that you realise, when I gave up on your original Sky Crash trio, I have been telling the truth.

Keep in touch and be careful."

Brenda Butler

October – *News Of The World* publish an article on the incident

NEWS OF THE WORLD, October 29, 2000   33

SECRET US AIR FORCE

BY LEWIS PANTHER & GLORIA STEWART

STARTLING new evidence that a UFO landed in the British countryside can be unveiled today.

The findings finally confirm a famous News of the World report in October 1983 when we told how US airmen stationed in Suffolk encountered a strange craft in woods at the edge of their base.

We had clinched our Page One exclusive only when we obtained an official US military report on the sighting. This was after THREE YEARS of denials by the Ministry of Defence.

Even then the MoD, the police and the American government tried to play down the incident.

But a new book by eminent author Georgina Bruni contains a crucial 20-minute transcript of tape recordings made by Lieutenant Colonel Charles Halt at the moment he witnessed the close encounter.

The base was under the overall command of General Gordon Williams, but it was Halt who led the search party after strange lights were spotted. He is the key witness to the ET landing on December 27, 1980.

I can see a bright light coming this way. There's something

Deathly

On that tape Halt is heard speaking into a recorder as he moves through the undergrowth, providing almost a running commentary.

There are also snatches of conversation with three other airmen, Lieutenant Bruce Englund, Sergeant Munroe Nevilles and Master Sergeant Robert Ball.

Halt: We just bumped into the first light that we've seen. We're about 150 to 200 yards from the site. Everything else is just deathly calm. There's no doubt about it, there's some kind of flashing red light ahead.

Nevilles: Yeah, it's yellow.

Halt: I saw a yellow tinge in it too. Weird. It appears to be making a little bit this way. It's brighter than it's been. It's coming this way ... it's definitely coming this way.

Ball: Pieces are shooting off.

Halt: Pieces are shooting off.

Ball (indicating the direction): at about 11 o'clock.

Halt: This is weird.

Ball: Look to the left!

Nevilles: There's two lights. One light to the right and one light to the left.

Halt: Keep your flashlight off. There's something very, very strange. Check the headset out, see if it gets any stronger... (he is referring to the Geiger counter Neville is carrying to check for radiation.)

Nevilles: OK, I have an indication, a vague reading.

Halt: OK...pieces are falling off to the right.

Ball: It just 'moved' to the right... went off to the right.

Halt: Strange. Ahhh. One again left. Let's approach the edge of the woods at that point. Can we do without lights? Let's do it carefully, come on.

(He continues speaking directly into the tape recorder.)

OK, we're looking at the thing, we're probably about two to three hundred yards away. It looks like an eye winking at you, it's still moving from side to side and when we put the star-scope (night vision lens) on it, it's sorta a hollow centre, right, a dark centre, it's...

FOREST PATH: Leading to landing site

CONTROL TOWER: Manned by USAF

NEWS OF THE WORLD INVESTIGATES

Englund: Like a pupil.

Halt: It's like the pupil of an eye looking at you, winking...and the flash is so bright to the star-scope, that, er, it almost burns your eye.

After a break in the tape Halt goes on to talk about spotting "up to five lights with a similar shape." There is a further pause then the recording resumes as the group see further unidentified objects in the night sky.

Halt: 3.05. We see strange, er, strobe-like flashes to the, er...almost sporadic, but there's definitely something there, some kind of

phenomena. 3.05: at about, er, 10 degrees horizon, er, directly north, we got two strange objects, er, half-moon shape dancing about with coloured lights.

Eclipse

But, er, it has to be about five to 10 miles out, maybe less. The half-moons have now turned into full circles as though there was an eclipse or something there for a minute or two.

After yet another break in the tape Halt and his team talk about the objects moving away

from them. Author Georgina Bruni tracked down more than 100 people for her book on the Rendlesham Forest UFO mystery which she has called "You Can't Tell The People."

The title is a remark made by Margaret Thatcher when Georgina met her at a social function and managed to ask her about UFOs and the landings in Suffolk.

If left Georgina in no doubt that Thatcher knew what she was talking about but that she didn't feel the public should be allowed to know.

"If she thought the conversation was verging on the wacky, she wouldn't have stayed interested as long as she did," says Georgina.

"She'd have terminated the conversation with something like 'You've been watching too many

X files episodes, my dear'.The author told the News of the World: "When I spoke to Colonel Halt he admitted he saw lights, but denied the landing. But I spoke to a former sergeant, Adrian Bustinza, who was in his patrol and swears on his life that there was a landed UFO.

"Halt at first said Bustinza wasn't with 'us' but I later came across a tape with Bustinza's voice on it."

Mr Bustinza has since retired from the Air Force and is now a supervisor with the US State Department supervising criminal investigations.

During interviews with Georgina, he told her: "When I arrived it was going in and out through the trees and at one stage it was hovering. Then it went over to a clearing at

the edge of the forest. By the time we got to the clearing it had already landed.

"When this thing landed Halt was already there. I didn't see it land. I saw it take off. It kind of hovered at first and then took off.

"At that time I thought we were dealing with an extra-terrestrial visitation. I can't say I saw beings, but I saw outlines of something."

Landing

As well as Halt's audio tapes, Georgina's research has unearthed new pictures taken the morning after the incident.

"They were taken by a US airman, Ray Guylas, when he went out to investigate the landing, to take measurements and radiation readings." she said. "There were three landing

TAPE PROVES UFO LANDED IN B

FLATTENED EARTH: Area where the ___ UFO was seen is marked out in forest

Image of the craft drawn at the time by an airman. Below: our famous Page 1

WILLIAMS: Chief

SEARCH: Halt

UFO LANDS IN SUFFOLK
And that's OFFICIAL

AUTHOR: Georgina   COVER: Her book

marks."Georgina also discovered the covering letter that a Squadron Leader called Donald Moreland attached to a memo of Lt Col Halt's detailing the 'lights'.

"The interesting thing about it is that it's titled UFO," she said. "Now why did he call it that if it was anything else?"

■You Can't Tell The People by Georgina Bruni is published by Macmillan on November 10 at £17.99. Readers can order copies at the special price of £15 with free p&p in the UK by calling 01624 836000 and quoting ref YCTTP1 or visiting www.book post.co.uk.

■DO you have startling photo evidence of a close encounter? Call us any day between 10am and 6pm on 020 7782 4444.

26th October 2000 – UFO sighted over Claremont Pier, Lowestoft

Between 2pm and 2.15pm, Mr Derek Addison (the father of Susan Addison) was about 100 yards away from Claremont Pier, in Lowestoft, looking eastwards, when he was surprised to see a matt black object in the sea, at low tide. Within seconds it had disappeared from view.

27th December 2000 – Film taken of UFO over Rendlesham Forest

John Hanson: At 8.29pm on 27th December 2000, a group of us – including Brenda Butler, Jack Solomon (then head of the Norwich UFO Group), and members of the Essex UFO Branch (not forgetting the dog, Mason) – were stood talking on an elevated section of the forest, near to the end of track 10, opposite to the field nominated by Larry Warren (who was himself in the forest that night) as being the one where he saw the UFO land, 20 years ago.

A yellow 'light' was seen just above the horizon, towards the direction of Orford Ness Lighthouse. This was followed by a number of others which appeared in the sky, forming a horizontal line, approximately four to five miles away, apparently over the coast or out at sea. We do not maintain that this was any 'alien craft' – all we can say is that we have never seen any strange 'light' like this over the forest before, at this particular location. Fortunately, we managed to video the effect by using a Sony Handycam video camera, with night light 72x digital zoom.

27 12 2000
21:30:38

27 12 2000
21:32:15

27 12 2000
21:32:19

27 12 2000
21:32:22

The location in Rendlesham Forest from where the video footage was taken

17th November – UFO expert returns to Forest

Interviewed by local TV Station

John Hanson: The following day we were inter-viewed by the local TV Station, Look East, and Suffolk Advertiser, but it was not until many months later, that we discovered we were not the only ones to have witnessed something unusual occurring in the forest, at that time, during that evening – one of whom was Mark Doulton and members of the Southend UFO Group.

UFO expert to return after new sightings

By RICHARD CORNWELL

richard.cornwell@ecng.co.uk

THE first investigator to research the Rendlesham UFO sighting will return to the site of the alleged landing this month to look for other strange objects.

Ufologist Brenda Butler claims there has been a marked increase in unidentified flying objects in recent months, which are centred upon Rendlesham Forest, close to the former American air base at Woodbridge.

She will be among a group of UFO spotters from throughout East Anglia who will converge on the forest to spend time monitoring the skies to gain evidence to back up their claims.

Mrs Butler, who is writing a book about her UFO experiences, said: "Reports of orange balls, white balls, little people, discs, roaring noises, weird animal noises and footprints all go to show something is still not right in Rendlesham Forest."

Mrs Butler, supervisor in a home for people with learning difficulties, said: "Since 1980 there have been lots of sightings but in the last two years there has been an enormous number by members of Skywatch and people living in the area.

"There is very definitely something going on, if you take into account all these sightings, and I think they are coming in through a door in time. To me they look like holograms."

Mrs Butler takes part in Skywatch groups which meet monthly and she has compiled a dossier of evidence to illustrate that many unexplained events are occurring in the skies above the forest.

She was the first person to investigate the 1980 incidents close to the east gate of Woodbridge

Airfield after an American told a friend of Mrs Butler's what he had seen.

But it was not until 1983 the story became world famous with the publication of an official memo written by deputy base commander Lt Col Charles Halt.

He wrote about "unexplained lights" and the experience of three patrolmen who saw a glowing object.

"The object was described as being metallic in appearance and triangular in shape, approximately two to three metres across the base and about two metres high. It illuminated the entire forest with a white light.

"The object itself had a pulsing red light on top and a bank of blue lights underneath. The object was hovering or on legs. As the patrolmen approached the object, it manoeuvred through the trees and disappeared. At this time the animals on a nearby farm went into a frenzy," he said.

FRIDAY. (THE ~~EVENING STAR~~) 17-11-2000.

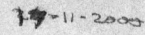

Mark Doulton:

"We arrived in the forest at about 8pm, and were immediately struck by the intense cold (some 15 degrees below freezing). We walked down track 12 but, finding nobody about, decided to look down track 10. Following consultation with Chris Martin, who was in our group and had been successful in capturing UFOs previously on film, we decided to meditate as part of an experiment.

Much to our surprise, some 20 minutes later, we were rewarded by the sight of a strange flashing in the sky above our heads. This 'flashing', whatever it was, had certainly not been visible before – apart from this, the sky was relatively clear.

We watched this strange 'flashing' for some minutes, before deciding to move to track 12, in order to meet up with other groups. We noticed the 'flashing' seemed to be concentrated in one area of the sky only. Not being experts on weather phenomena, we cannot say what this was, but having been to many countries and experienced severe storms I have to say this was nothing like what we saw that night."

Other witnesses

Following the publicity, people reported having seen strange lights over Woo Way, Orford, at about 8pm, along with a report of an orange 'ball of light' seen hovering over the sea, at 10.45pm, accompanied by the arrival of a helicopter – which appeared to be looking for something.

Whether it was a UFO could only be speculation. However, one should bear in mind that strange 'lights' seen over the coast would attract the attention of the Coastguard.

2001 ONWARDS

2001 – Newspaper interest in the incident 'Secret report on UFO opened'

Calls grow for inquiry into Rendlesham UFO sightings

EVENING STAR, Ipswich, England - Sept. 8, 2001

PRESSURE is growing on the Ministry of Defence to hold a fresh inquiry into the UFO sightings in East Anglia more than 20 years ago.

It follows the opening of secret files relating to the sightings by American servicemen of objects near the east gate of Woodbridge airfield in 1980.

The documents tell how the Ministry of Defence and the Royal Air Force dealt with the accounts of the sightings after they were made.

Until now public requests for information concerning the Government's role in the subject have been met with a response the incident was not considered to be of defence significance.

Author Georgina Bruni, who wrote a book entitled You Can't Tell the People on the subject, said the documents revealed defence intelligence staff had got involved in an investigation. She added the most important documents were the internal exchanges of correspondence between MoD departments.

Nick Pope, who headed the MoD's UFO department in the early 90s, told Ms Bruni: "I'm pleased, though surprised, that the MoD has released these papers, particularly as they include ones from specialist intelligence staff.

"The papers concerning the radioactivity at the landing site are hugely significant and show how the MoD's experts acknowledged that this UFO incident was corroborated by hard scientific evidence.

"You've now got the proof that this incident raised serious defence and national security issues. These revelations are sensational and I'm sure there will be pressure for an inquiry into both the incident itself and the subsequent actions of both the MoD and the United States Air Force. There are certainly some important – and as yet unanswered – questions about this whole affair."

A memo from Lt Col Charles Halt, deputy base commander at Woodbridge and Bentwaters, referred to radiation readings discovered after a triangular object landed in Rendlesham Forest. The object was hovering or was on legs and it vanished when patrolmen approached it, but later reappeared.

Defence staff were keen to discover if the radioactivity readings in these depressions made by the object were unusual. Staff later considered the readings were significantly higher than average background readings and an internal report said staff "cannot offer any explanation for the phenomena".

www.eadt.co.uk

Probe urged over MoD memos on UFO mystery

5/9/2001

by RICHARD SMITH

PRESSURE is growing on the Ministry of Defence to hold a fresh inquiry into UFO sightings more than 20 years ago.

It follows the opening of secret files on mysterious objects seen near the east gate of Woodbridge airfield in 1980 by American servicemen. The documents tell how the Ministry of Defence (MoD) and the Royal Air Force dealt with the puzzle.

Until now the official response was that the incident had no defence significance. Now author Georgina Bruni, who wrote a book *You Can't Tell the People* on UFOs said latest documents reveal defence intelligence staff held an investigation. She added the most impor-tant documents related to internal MoD correspondence.

Nick Pope, who headed the MoD's UFO department in the early 90s, told Ms Bruni: "The papers concerning the radioactivity at the landing site are hugely significant and show how the MoD's own experts acknowledged that this UFO incident was corroborated by hard scientific evidence.

"You've now got the proof that this incident raised serious defence and national security issues. These revelations are sensational and I'm sure there will be pressure for an inquiry into both the incident itself and the subsequent actions of both the MoD and the United States Air Force. There are certainly some important, and as yet unanswered, questions."

A memo from Lt Col Charles Halt, deputy base commander at Woodbridge and Bentwaters, two weeks after the sightings, referred to radiation readings after a triangular object landed in Rendlesham Forest. It was hovering or on legs and vanished through trees when patrolmen approached, but later reappeared.

The MoD information showed radiation readings were significantly higher than average background figures, and an internal report said staff "cannot offer any explanation for the phenomena".

richardsmith@ecng.co.uk

594

SECRET REPORT ON UFO OPENED

MoD files reveal US military inquiry into East Anglia sighting

A top-level investigation was ordered by British and US military experts into East Anglia's most famous UFO sighting, documents released by the Government reveal.

Contrary to the official line that the sighting in Rendlesham Forest 21 years ago was "not taken seriously", the United States Air Force and the Ministry of Defence both began full inquiries into the incident.

But some taped evidence gathered by the Americans was passed direct to senior personnel and not shared with British officials, the newly-released documents show.

Problems were also recorded on equipment at RAF Watton in Norfolk, more than 40 miles away from the alleged incident.

The MoD this week bowed to sustained pressure and finally opened the official file on the sighting – prompted by claims from American servicemen that they saw a UFO near Woodbridge air base in 1980.

The file has been made public nine years earlier than planned

and was unveiled after the Admiral of the Fleet Lord Hill-Norton asked 16 questions in the House of Lords since January.

Lord Hill-Norton demanded answers to issues raised by author Georgina Bruni in her book You Can't Tell The People, billed as the definitive account of the unidentified flying object mystery.

Lord Hill-Norton has been campaigning for several years to persuade the Ministry of Defence to give more details on the object, allegedly seen by Americans near the east gate of Woodbridge air base just after Christmas 1980.

Colonel Charles Halt was deputy commander at Bentwaters air base and his memo detailed the sighting of "unusual lights".

Two patrolmen who investigated saw a metallic triangular object hovering or on legs with a pulsing red light on top and a bank of blue lights underneath.

It then reportedly disappeared through the forest and animals on a nearby farm went into a frenzy.

The next day, three depressions 1.5in deep and 7in in diameter were found where the object had allegedly been sighted on the ground.

Since the sighting, there has

been worldwide interest in the incident, and scores of attempts to explain what the servicemen claimed to have seen.

Sceptics claim the main object was probably a brilliant meteor, the radiation readings were caused by natural sources and that the other lights were stars.

In 1997, Lord Hill-Norton wrote to the then defence minister Lord Gilbert saying: "My position, both privately and publicly expressed over the last dozen years or more, is that there are only two possibilities.

"Either an intrusion into our air space and a landing by unidentified craft took place at Rendlesham, as described.

"Or the deputy commander of an operational, nuclear-armed US Air Force base in England and a large number of his enlisted men were either hallucinating or lying."

After the government file was opened, Ms Bruni said: "The official view has always been that the US Air Force and MoD did not take the UFOs seriously and that

■ TURN TO PAGE 10

WEATHER 2, BUSINESS 23-25, LETTERS 26-27, COFFEE BREAK 32, ANNOUNCEMENTS 34-35

2001 – Rods captured in the Forest!

Peter Parish, from Woodbridge – whose vivid paintings of the forest and its UFOs record his many visits to the area, over the years – contacted the newspaper, after filming what he claimed to be rods moving over the track ways.

NEWS

www.eveningstar.co.uk

Evening Star, Friday, September 20, 2002 Page 13

Mystery of UFO rods spotted over forest

By MARK BULSTRODE

mark.bulstrode@eveningstar.co.uk

UFO fanatic Peter Parish claims that strange rod-like beings have been spotted in Rendlesham Forest, adding to the list of peculiar events said to have taken place there.

The latest unexplained phenomenon, which Mr Parish thinks is from another dimension, has been labelled the Rendlesham Rods.

Mr Parish, 44, of Thellusson Road, Rendlesham, first saw them on the evening of August 31 and has since caught them on camera.

There have already been reports of similar rods being seen in America, Scotland and throughout Europe.

Mr Parish and friend, Brenda Butler, 58, are fascinated by this phenomenon and he said: "They are either coming from another dimension or they are unknown creatures that can travel at a tremendous speed."

He claims they are invisible to the naked eye but can be picked up on camera. He believes the aliens can communicate with people and drop stones from the sky.

Mr Parish, who works as a groundsman, said: "They are quite intelligent. They seem to communicate with people. Stones have been dropping out of the sky but whether they are to do with the rods I don't know.

"I asked the rods if they were from another dimension. I told them to drop one stone if they were and two stones if they were not and they dropped one stone."

WEB LINK
www.roswellrods.com

EVIDENCE? Peter Parish, inset, and the image from his video which he claims is a UFO.

Pictures: PETER PARISH and DAVE KINDRED

Flower show hopes to make church tower bloom

A FLOWER festival is being staged at Bramford Church this weekend to help raise cash to repair the church tower.

The festival is the first major event being organised by the Friends of Bramford Church, which hopes to raise £107,000 to meet the cost of repairing the tower in Church Green.

Villagers are making flower arrangements for the festival, which runs tomorrow from 10am until 6pm and Sunday from 11am until 6pm.

Some of the flower arrangements will be sold off on Sunday evening to help raise additional funds for the appeal, which has now been running for 12 months.

Reverend Canon Roger Dedman said: "The appeal has started slowly so we are looking at improving on this. We have problems with the tower and need to replace the lead and woodwork spire.

"This is our first major fundraising event since we started the appeal and we hope it will prove to be a success."

He added that the church was in the process of applying to English Heritage in the hope of receiving a grant to help with the cost of repairs.

Refreshments, a raffle and a bric-a-brac stall will all be on offer at the event, with a local art display from children being held in the parish rooms.

Admission to the festival is free, although donations will be gratefully received.

8ᵗʰ September 2001 – *UFO Magazine* features incident

23rd September 2001 – Georgina Bruni appears at Leeds Conference

26th December 2001 – 'UFO lights seen over Ipswich'

EVENING STAR, Ipswich, England - Dec. 29, 2001

Couple saw night-time UFO lights over town

By NICK RICHARDS

nick.richards@ecng.co.uk

AN Ipswich couple were treated to an extra special sight on Christmas Day when they saw what appeared to be an unidentified flying object.

The family, who asked not to be named, saw the strange flashing object from their house in Valley Road, just 24 hours after Santa would have been in the middle of his Christmas deliveries.

The mother of the family said: "At about midnight my husband noticed a very bright light. He called me to look at it and I saw what seemed to be a large star. The strange thing was that our room was illuminated by the very strong light, which it emitted.

"I would normally have likened it to moonlight, but there was no moon to be seen. My husband continued to watch it as I fell asleep. He called me a few minutes later to tell me that it was flashing and emitting a blue hue around its base. He also saw two diagonal protrusions from either side towards the bottom."

The object, which was oval in shape, was smaller in the sky than the moon but bigger than a star and was viewed from Valley Road towards the Portman Road area.

The family said they knew it was not an aeroplane, a helicopter or even Christmas lights.

They said if it was a star it would have been there the following night but it left the Ipswich skyline after performing its ten-minute light show.

■ Did you witness the strange phenomenon over Ipswich at around midnight on Christmas Day/Boxing Day? Perhaps you photographed it?

If anybody knows what the peculiar sight was, contact the Evening Star newsdesk on 01473 282257 or e-mail nick.richards@ecng.co.uk

16

29th November 2002 – *Daily Mail* -'UFO scare they didn't want you to know about'

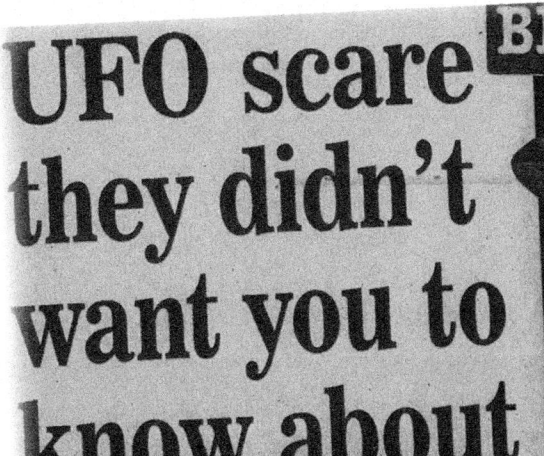

UFO scare they didn't want you to know about

BRITAIN'S X-FILES

A UFO model: The Suffolk sighting sent animals 'into a frenzy'

THE strange glowing object hovered over the forest, bathing it in brilliant light.

Watching from the ground were a group of bewildered and probably terrified servicemen.

As they drew nearer, the metallic craft vanished into the trees, only to be spotted again an hour later before disappearing altogether.

It could have been a scene from the X-Files. In fact, the UFO sighting is recorded in a secret Ministry of Defence file.

Yesterday, more than 20 years after the incident outside an American air base in Suffolk, the file was made public. It describes the sighting of the triangular object over Rendlesham Forest in the small hours of December 27, 1980.

It says a number of U.S. Air Force men witnessed the object appear to hover and illuminate the forest, sending farm animals into a 'frenzy'.

The next morning the Americans found radioactive circular impressions in the ground nearby.

In the report, entitled Unexplained Lights, USAF Lieutenant Colonel Charles I Halt told how he saw an object emitting a 'red sun-like light' moving through the trees.

Three USAF patrolmen were sent to investigate. They reported seeing a glowing object in the forest. The

Daily Mail Reporter

object was described as being metallic in appearance and triangular in shape, approximately two to three metres across the base and approximately two metres high.

'It illuminated the entire forest with a white light. The object itself had a pulsing red light on top and a bank of blue lights underneath. The object was hovering or on legs,' said Mr Halt.

'As the patrolmen approached the object, it manoeuvred through the trees and disappeared. At this time the animals on a nearby farm went into a frenzy.'

The UFO was spotted an hour later near the back gate to the base.

Mr Halt said: 'At one point it appeared to throw off glowing particles and then broke into five separate white objects and then disappeared.

'Immediately thereafter, three star-like objects were noticed in the sky, two objects to the north and one to the south, all of which were about ten degrees off the horizon.

'The objects moved rapidly in sharp angular movements and displayed red, green and blue lights. The objects to the north appeared to be elliptical through an 8-12 power lens. They then turned to full circles.'

Next morning Mr Halt and his men discovered three circular depres-

sions in the ground, seven inches across. In them they recorded radiation at a level ten times higher than normal, according to the file.

Although the servicemen had tried to capture the sightings on camera, a further docu-

Halt: 'White light'

ment disclosed that their film was faulty.

Nothing had shown up on the RAF's radar.

A memo from the MoD in the file shows some scepticism about the sightings, although it said it remained 'open-minded'.

'No evidence was found of any threat to the defence of the United Kingdom, and no further investigations were carried out,' it said.

The MoD said one theory about the sighting was that it could have been 'fireball activity', or the beam of the Orford Ness lighthouse, distorted by the trees.

The file was released under the Freedom of Information Act.

3rd December 2002 – MOD criticized for withholding records

INDEPENDENT, London, England - Dec. 3, 2002

MoD attacked for denying access to UFO details

THE MINISTRY of Defence was criticised yesterday for repeatedly withholding information, including documents concerning one of Britain's celebrated UFO sightings.

Ann Abraham, the parliamentary ombudsman, found the MoD broke rules on access to information three times in four months. Complaints about

DEFENCE

BY BEN RUSSELL

the MoD's refusal to list countries given priority for arms sales or reveal details of an armed services survey were also upheld.

Details of the infamous UFO scare in Rendlesham Forest,

Norfolk, more than 20 years ago have been released. Until last week the document had only been seen by about 20 people, who had requested access to it through the US Freedom of Information Act.

It describes the sighting of a triangular "strange glowing object" near RAF Woodbridge in the early hours of 27 De-

cember 1980. A number of US Air Force men witnessed the object hover in the darkness, transmitting blue pulsating lights and sending nearby farm animals into a "frenzy".

The ombudsman's quarterly report said: "Given their age and the fact that these documents contained no information not already in the

public domain, the Ombudsman saw no reason why they could not be disclosed."

Peter Kilfoyle, a former Labour defence minister, said: "The MoD is bedevilled by a culture of secrecy ... It is one of those departments that are not very attuned to what is required in a modern, open and accountable government."

6th December 2002 – *Daily Mail* 'The day aliens landed in Suffolk'

Daily Mail, Friday, December 6, 2002

Revealed: the UFO sighting the Government kept quiet for 20 years

The day the aliens landed... in Suffolk

by **Nick Craven**

THE YOUNG airmen ran through the crisp stillness of the forest towards the strange glow in the trees, fearing it might be a crashed aircraft.

Suddenly, the whole area was covered in a brilliant white light from above, where an unearthly triangular craft seemed to float silently above the trees.

Frozen in terror, the servicemen watched as the object hovered for a while, appearing to observe them, then shot off faster than any aircraft they had ever seen.

This was not Hollywood's latest venture into science fiction, but the genuine account of U.S. airmen at a Suffolk RAF base more than 20 years ago.

In December 1980, Rendlesham Forest near RAF Woodbridge was, according to alien watchers, the site of Britain's most celebrated UFO sighting, which the Government has tried to keep quiet ever since.

This week, the Ministry of Defence was criticised by the Parliamentary Ombudsman for repeatedly refusing to reveal the contents of the secret 'Rendlesham File', despite much of its contents being released in America under the U.S. Freedom of Information Act.

Now, the Ministry of Defence has finally — and reluctantly — released the Rendlesham files to public view under the British version of the Act, so we can — officially — learn exactly what a group of military witnesses saw in the forest on that chilly night 22 years ago. It makes for astonishing reading.

Between Christmas 1980 and New Year, two incidents occurred on successive nights near the U.S. Air Force nuclear base at RAF Woodbridge.

They were reported in a remarkable memo by the

LT COL HALT wrote: 'They reported seeing a strange glowing object in the forest... described as being metallic in appearance and triangular in shape, approximately two to three metres across the base and 2m high. It illuminated the entire forest with a white light.

'The object itself had a pulsing red light on top and a bank of blue lights underneath.

'The object was hovering or on legs. As the patrolmen approached, it manoeuvred through the trees and disappeared. At this time the animals on a nearby farm went into a frenzy.'

The next day, Lt Col Halt joined a patrol which found three depressions on the forest floor where the object had been sighted. Radiation readings of ten times the normal level were found around the site.

Not all Lt Col Halt's account has the hallmark of military efficiency. He got the date of the incident wrong, recording the initial sighting as December 27 when it was the 26th.

While checking the area, the officer recorded what he found on a Dictaphone, but the tape was to record something far more dramatic when the strange lights returned after nightfall.

The breathless officer can be heard saying: 'There's no doubt about it, there's a strange flashing red light

them... Yeah, they're both heading north. He's coming in towards us now... Now we're observing what appears to be a beam coming down to the ground.'

In the background there are excited shouts from members of the four-man patrol and another officer exclaims: 'Look at the colours... s***t!'

'This is unreal,' gasps Lt Col Halt.

Over the years, as the memo leaked out, other former officers went public, backing up the story. Most notable was another USAF security patrolman, Larry Warren. According to his account, there were not just lights, but something far more incredible.

He said the triangular object appeared right in front of him and he felt nauseous as the hairs on the back of his neck stood on end.

He claims to have seen three 'aeronaut entities' communicating telepathically with a senior officer. The aliens were 3ft tall and resembled 'kids in snowsuits'. He said they floated in bluish/gold balls of light out of their craft.

According to Warren, the next morning, he and the other airmen were checked over with a Geiger counter and instructed to sign statements which merely mentioned seeing 'unusual lights'. They were told by senior officers not to discuss the incidents.

Other parts of his story emerged during subsequent

told him they used the tunnels to get to the North Sea.

Warren's account, published in a book in 1997, merely allowed sceptics to rubbish the Rendlesham incident as fantasy, obscuring the facts that something inexplicable does seem to have happened that night, and that the witnesses, far from being anorak star-gazers, were seasoned Air Force personnel.

Ian Ridpath, editor of the Oxford Dictionary Of Astronomy, is not convinced. He believes the men were merely seeing the revolving beam of the Orford Ness lighthouse five miles away.

The depressions in the earth were merely rabbit diggings, he said, and the radiation was of naturally occurring levels.

ADDITIONALLY, he discovered that a very bright meteor had been visible in southern England that night.

'UFO hunters will continue to believe that an alien spaceship landed in Rendlesham Forest,' concludes Ridpath, dismissing it as 'a marvellous product of human imagination'.

Brenda Butler, one of a regular band of 'sky-watchers' who spend their nights in Rendlesham Forest, doesn't mind being accused of using her imagination or of being called downright 'nutty' when she tells people how she has been abducted by aliens three times.

The chirpy 58-year-old grandmother from Leiston, near Woodbridge, spends three nights a week in the woods with other devotees, and says she has seen spacecraft on no fewer than five occasions.

'People say I'm mad, but I just tell them they should keep an open mind until they've seen it for themselves,' she said. 'There's a portal between

who interviewed more than 100 witnesses for her book, You Can't Tell The People.

'I started out as a sceptic,' said Miss Bruni, 51, who became interested in the case five years ago.

'But after speaking to the people who saw it, I am sure this was an event of biblical proportions and it was not of this world.

'I'm less convinced by accounts of abduction by aliens and whatever, but something very strange happened here and the Government, by trying to deny it and put the lid on it, have given the conspiracy theorists a field-day.'

So what really happened at Rendlesham — was it just a case of over-excited Americans indulging in group hallucination? Did trained military personnel *really* mistake a lighthouse for a moving spaceship? None of the solutions seems to hold much water and we are forced to file the incident under 'unexplained'.

Rendlesham has been described as 'Britain's Roswell' — the alleged incident in which an alien spacecraft was recovered near the town in New Mexico in 1947 after crashing.

The U.S. government says it was a weather balloon, but that only fuelled the fascination of Hollywood producers and UFO-logists still further.

Initially, the MoD denied that anything out of the ordinary had been reported at Rendlesham. Years later, Georgina Bruni says she tackled Lady Thatcher about UFOs at a charity event and was told: 'You must have the facts and you can't tell the people.'

'That seems to have been the official line on UFOs for years, and it has helped maintain the sinister X-Files aura about the whole area.

After all, no good mystery is complete without attendant

March 2003 – *Loaded Magazine* -Rendlesham – 'The X Fools'

A Review

In an article, presented by the *Loaded Magazine* as light-hearted 'full of banter' edition of *'The X Fools'* (March 2003), we read of a visit to Rendlesham Forest, in Suffolk, by a journalist, to meet Brenda Butler and her companions,. The writer of the article first interviews Georgina Bruni *'sipping tea out of his X-Files mug'* in her London flat, and outlines the events of what happened in December 1980.

Two nights later the journalist and photographer are suitably enclosed in the room of Brenda Butler's house, along with her much loved dog – Mason, and companion – Peter Parish, after having hired a rented campervan to make the journey to Suffolk.

After driving down to the forest we are treated to a running dialogue of many quips, which include references to

THE X FOOLS

loaded investigates the 'British Roswell' and finds cover-ups, UFOs, Yetis and little brown monks

aliens

"Did this come from Uranus?"

"It's a UFO! shaped jumb[...]"

COMPUTER ENHANCEMENT

Despite the sheer number of eyewitnesses, the case remains extraordinarily complex, littered with conflicting accounts and alternative theories.

"Yes," says Georgina Bruni, a world expert on the mystery, "it is very, very complex."

The author, who spent five years researching a book on the incident – *You Can't Tell The People* – and interviewed over 100 people connected to it, has her legs curled underneath her in an armchair and is smoking a long cigarette. Her plush flat, just around the corner from Harrods, is testament to a life lived in the caviar lane. There are photos on display of herself with establishment icons like William Hague, Michael Portillo and Peter Stringfellow.

Sipping my tea, that's been served up in an *X-Files* mug, and eyeing a plate of expensive biscuits, I ask her what happened in late December 1980.

"On the first night, there was a landing," she smiles involuntarily and shakes her head, "I know, I didn't believe this myself. But a triangular-shaped craft landed in Rendlesham Forest on the perimeter of RAF Woodbridge."

THE UFO
In which our man first hears the unusual tale of the air force professionals and their extraordinary experiences in Rendlesham Forest.

During the long, paranoid years of the Cold War, RAF Woodbridge was leased to the American airforce. Late on Christmas night 1980, Airman First Class John Burroughs was patrolling the east gate of the installation when he saw strange lights over the dark forest canopy. Thinking that an aircraft must be in trouble, he contacted his supervisor, Staff Sergeant Bud Steffens, and they went out to investigate. They raced down an old logging road, known as Track 10, and saw a bright white light shining through the trees. To their horror, the light started to chase them. They tore back to the base, looking behind them to see the light stopping at the forest edge and two coloured lights hovering low in the sky. Back at the

base, they reported what had happened and we ordered to wait for another patrol. When they an they ventured down Track 10 again, leaving a panicking Steffens behind.

"Steffens refused an order," Bruni says, "I terrified. So Burroughs, Penniston and Caba went out and they saw this craft. It was a sma triangular thing. You know when we went to ! moon? We had that landing capsule? It remin of one of those."

A few nights later, word reached the base's c commander Lieutenant Colonel Charles Halt tha was back". Keen to scotch the talk of alien visitor had spread through the base, he rounded up a gr of senior personnel and organised a recce to go i the woods. Halt made a microcassette recording that trip and tantalising excerpts from this, as wel the report he wrote for the Ministry of Defence, ha kept the Rendlesham story alive for over two deca The memo begins by detailing the initial sighting Burroughs made on 25 December. It describes a "metallic, triangular object, approximately two to metres across" that "illuminated the entire forest object "manoeuvred through the trees", whereup "the animals on a nearby farm went into a frenzy". continues with the recce that Halt and his team ma into the forest. It describes a "red, sun-like light" t "moved about and pulsed" and "appeared to thro glowing particles and then broke into five separati white objects and disappeared". Immediatel after, the memo records, three objects wei seen in the sky that travelled "rapidly in sharp, angular movements". One of the objects "remained in the sky for an hour more" and "beamed down a stream of lig from time to time". Halt, who was later promoted to a full Colonel, finishes his report by noting that "numerous individuals, including the undersigned, witnessed the events.

The microcassette recording is similarly remarkable. It begins wit the airmen taking radiatl readings of the suppose landing area and ends wi Halt and other gobsmack personnel detailing the →

Author and Rendlesham expert Georgina Bruni (left)

"A triangular craft landed in Suffolk"

inane comments about Mars bars being only 2 pence in 1948, speculation about UFOs being camera crews from the future, filming historical documentaries, or bandits 'on the take' for future antiques.

A stake-out in the camper van follows with even more quips about a visit by a policewoman, discussion about ETs ,Yetis, Brown monks and a ghost hunter, followed by a tongue lashing from Brenda, who tells him and others off for walking too fast and talking loudly. Mix all this up with a photo of a Star Trek spaceship, Man with alien mask, profanity, and thinly veiled sarcasms, no wonder the Public think we are crackpots- entertaining but how embarrassing for those involved.

2nd July 2003– Kevin Conde … BBC – just a practical joke

The *Daily Mail* published details relating to yet another possible explanation for what took place in Rendlesham Forest, as reported by the airmen concerned. According to an entry found on the internet, dated the 30th June 2003, The *BBC Inside Out,* Rendlesham Forest Incident case revealed the following:

It was a hoax!

'Not only can we tell you that most of it was a hoax, but also how it was done. They included that a puzzled Halt referred on the tape-recording to: *"The red, white, and blue lights of the UFO are still hovering over Woodbridge".* However, former USAF Security Policemen – Kevin Conde, has exclusively revealed that these lights were the result of a practical joke he played on the gullible airman.

"I drove my patrol car out of sight from the gatehouse, turned on the red and blue emergency lights, and pointed white flashlights through the mist into the air. The bottom line is that, that was not a UFO – it was a 1979 Plymouth Volare!", explains a bemused Conde.'

John Hanson

The explanation was, of course, eagerly seized on by the media, including the *Daily Mail* and the *BBC,* who no doubt gleefully ensured that there was much coverage on this – anything rather than admitting the existence of a phenomena which continues to make itself known right up to the current day. Even if one accepted that Kevin Conde had carried out a prank, common sense dictates this wasn't the answer for what was seen by the airmen concerned. To those that believe it was him, then who was responsible for the massive number of UFO sightings which occurred in the Suffolk area and around the adjacent Essex borders, during the 1980-1990s, which appear to have been deliberately ignored by the media? We treat Conde's explanation as having no substance whatsoever.

Even as this book was being compiled, I received an email from a former airman on the base in December 1980, who claimed he had fired up rockets over the forest as he was bored! Needless to say he didn't give his name … yet another 'red herring'!

Georgina Bruni was to write a rebuttal on this explanation, based on a thorough investigation into all the points raised (typical of this lady, who had a very keen nose for the truth). This we had intended to include, but space being at a premium we decided against it.

DAILY MAIL, London, England - July 2, 2003

UFO-OLED!

By **Michael Hanlon**

For 23 years Britain's 'Roswell incident' has been cited as proof that UFOs landed. Today, a retired U.S. airman claims he was behind the hoax ... using a battered old police car and sticky tape

THOSE who find it difficult to believe that little green men from outer space visit the Earth on a regular basis have always found it pretty easy to demolish the claims of those who do.

All those photos of flying saucers, portholes around the edge? Painted dustbin lids thrown into the sky.

Stories of alien abductions aboard extra-terrestrial starships? Ramblings.

But, just occasionally, an incident takes place that leaves even the most cynical observers perplexed.

One such event occurred in the depths of Rendlesham Forest in Suffolk, in the early hours of December 27, 1980 – an incident that, in UFO circles, has become known as 'Britain's Roswell' (alluding to the famous incident in New Mexico in which many people still claim a flying saucer crash-landed in the desert).

That foggy night, a number of airmen at the U.S. Air Force base near Rendlesham saw something that was totally unexplained. Totally unexplained, that is, until today.

Now, the true nature of the mystery has been revealed – and it is an explanation which will amuse many and probably anger many more.

But first, it is necessary to recap what exactly it was claimed happened on that dark, cold night, 23 years ago.

Bored and tired, two military policemen, John Burroughs and Bud Steffans, guarding the back gates to the base saw a group of strange, flashing lights in the sky – eerie blues and greens, piercing through the fog.

Accompanying the lights was a terrifying noise, an electronic wailing that cut through the fog.

They radioed the base and soon a group of their colleagues ran out into the woods, thinking that perhaps a plane or a helicopter had come down or was in trouble.

WHAT they saw, it has been claimed, was the best evidence yet that the Earth had indeed been visited by beings from outer space.

The policemen trampled through the woods trying to locate the source of the lights. Eventually, they reported, they stumbled into a clearing and saw something quite amazing.

According to official reports from the base deputy commander, Lieutenant Colonel Charles Halt, the airbase had been visited by some sort of spacecraft.

Under the innocuous title 'Unexplained Lights', Lieutenant Colonel Halt wrote down what his men had seen.

'They reported seeing a strange glowing object in the forest . . . described as being metallic in appearance and triangular in shape, approximately two to three metres across the base and two metres high. It illuminated the entire forest with a white light.

'The object itself had a pulsating red light on top and a bank of blue lights underneath...it was hovering or on legs. As the patrolmen approached, it manoeuvred through the trees and disappeared.'

Amazing enough. But over the following days, more witness reports from the night in question emerged which, if true, would mean that a lonely corner of East Anglia was the site of one of the most extraordinary events in the history of Man.

One witness, another U.S. airman called Jim Penniston, together with John Burroughs and Ed Cabanasag, claimed to have seen a 'metallic craft', complete with 'hieroglyphic markings', descend into the woods.

Today, Mr Penniston, now a human resources manager, maintains that he even managed to touch the craft. 'This was a craft of unknown origin,' he says. 'It was triangular and my assessment was that it was not occupied.'

The night after the first sighting, Lieutenant Colonel Halt saw the UFO for himself. During an evening function, someone burst into the mess room on the base and screamed, 'Sir, it's back!' He rushed into the woods with some men, and a Geiger counter.

At the site of the alleged landing, they found radiation readings significantly above the background level, together with three mysterious depressions in the ground.

ALL this was written down in a series of official memos, and there was a British Ministry of Defence investigation, which contained all the reports from the U.S. airmen and concluded that whatever it was did not pose any direct threat to the defence of the realm.

The MoD report acknowledged that an unusual event had happened but drew no conclusions as to the nature of the UFO.

Word soon leaked out about the strange goings-on. Rendlesham became a hive of UFO activity.

Some have concluded that the area was no less than a portal to a parallel dimension, or perhaps the Earthbound terminus of an intergalactic 'sturgate'.

Over the years, hundreds claimed to have seen the object that had spooked the U.S. airmen, and there were reports of 'energy disturbances' and 'psychic fields'.

What few could have concluded was that the UFO was not an intergalactic spacecraft capable of travelling across the galaxy at three times the speed of light (2billion mph), but instead a rather more prosaic vehicle; to be precise, a battered 1979 Plymouth Volare – a standard issue American police car, capable of about 90mph.

The 'alien visitor' was the driver of this car, one Kevin Conde, another military policeman at the base. As bored as his colleagues manning the sentry post at the back gate, he decided to have a bit of fun.

'There was this one guy at the back gate, and he was known as a bit of a problem – he was always seeing things.

'He had seen lights before and reported them. It always turned out that it was a star or something. So I decided to play a practical joke.

'I had no idea what I had started by doing this.'

Mr Conde, now an IT consultant and part-time policeman in his native Sacramento, California, recalls how he turned his police car into a UFO with some stuck-on lenses.

'I drove down the taxiway in my car. I stuck the spotlight on, after sticking red and green lenses on it. I then drove round in circles, in the fog, with the PA loudspeaker going, flashing my lights.

'It was just a practical joke, we were always playing practical jokes. Then I turned my lights off and drove away.'

Mr Conde, who returned to the U.S. shortly after the incident, says he was unaware of the 'Rendlesham mystery' until recently, when he looked up his old base on a U.S. military website. He was flabbergasted by what he read.

'I was amazed. I had no idea about all this nonsense.

'Now, logic says that if life has evolved on Earth, it must have evolved elsewhere. But logic also says that if it has, it does not go around in flying saucers and land outside a quiet military base in the English countryside.

'I hate to be cynical, but when I see people making money out of this I have to ask myself if they are not nuts, what are they?'

The descriptions of 'metallic spacecraft' and 'depressions' are the result of embellishment over the years, Mr Conde said. There was a large helicopter which landed there the previous night – a helicopter with three landing skids.'

As to the radiation, Mr Conde said that as far as he was aware they found nothing above background levels. 'A lot of these stories have been exaggerated over the years.'

OF course, the true believers will not be convinced. Nick Pope, Britain's own Fox Mulder, who investigated UFO sightings for the MoD in the 1990s, said the Rendlesham incident remains a mystery.

'Frankly, there are a lot of people retrospectively trying to write themselves into this story,' he said.

Georgina Bruni, who has written a book, You Can't Tell The People, about the mystery, dismissed Mr Conde's story.

'I am amazed. The evidence is all there. All the files have been released by the MoD. Do you really think a colonel from the USAF is going to send a memo to the MoD about this?

'I even talked to Margaret Thatcher about this, and she said, "You have to have the facts, and you can't tell the people".

'I also spoke to former Defence Secretary Michael Portillo, who said it was very interesting, and that he knows a lot but can say very little. All these people are not morons.'

Confession: Kevin Conde

Charles Halt

"I knew Conde well. I wouldn't have put it past him to claim what he did. He was nowhere to be seen the night I was out. One possible explanation is that several nights later he may have opened the back gate, while on patrol at Woodbridge, and driven down the paved road and displayed his lights to mock the earlier incidents. John Burroughs told me that Conde was not on duty so could not have been involved."

26th October 2004 – UFO display over Suffolk

John Hanson

Dawn Holloway and I learnt of a UFO, captured on film at 2am on 26th October 2004, by Mr Peter Saxon – the Licensee of The Swan Inn, at Alderton, near Woodbridge – and decided to visit him in 2006, when he told us what happened.

Peter Saxon

"I was awoken by shouting, coming from outside, and after getting dressed, went into the back car park, where I saw what I initially thought was a helicopter, hovering in the sky over the houses opposite to the Swan. I soon realised that this could not be the case, as the 'light' began to move erratically in the sky, at which point I could see it had a jet black dome, with a long rectangular bar underneath, and a group of lights at each end. I could see it 'shaking', from side to side, and moving up and down.

Peter Saxon

I rushed into the pub and picked up my Sony camcorder hi 8 video camera and rushed out, expecting to see it; there was nothing there, but looking upwards into the sky, I spotted it once again – now much higher, surrounded by a luminous blue field. I then took a short clip of film, lasting a few minutes, before loosing sight of it."

Peter contacted the *Evening Star*, who published an article on 26th November 2004 – *'Were Bright Lights Over Village A UFO? X File Is Opened By Residents'*.

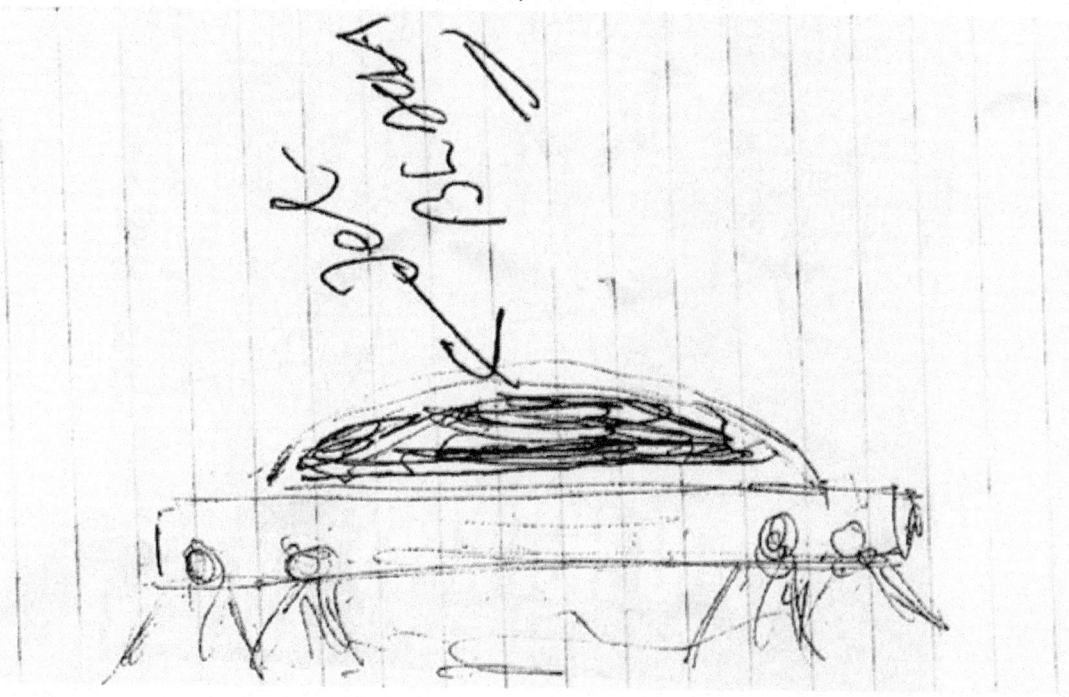

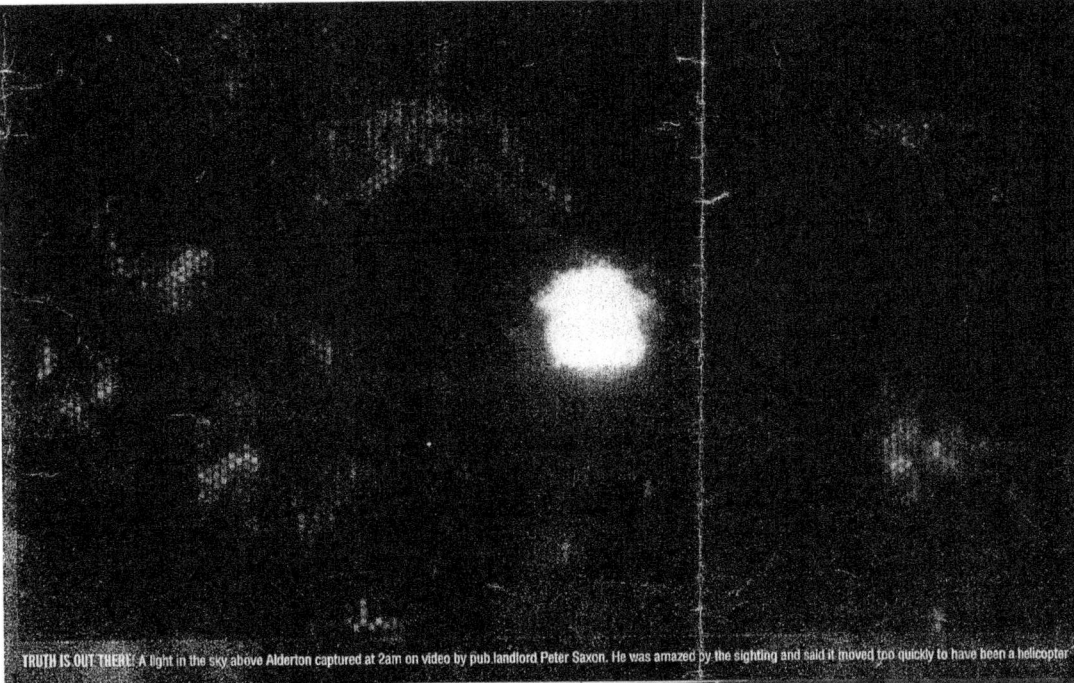

TRUTH IS OUT THERE: A light in the sky above Alderton captured at 2am on video by pub landlord Peter Saxon. He was amazed by the sighting and said it moved too quickly to have been a helicopter

Were bright lights over village a UFO?

By GRANT SHERLOCK
grant.sherlock@eveningstar.co.uk

X-file is opened by residents

SIGHTINGS of unexplained lights in the night sky above Alderton have got the village buzzing with talk of strange crafts and UFOs.

Residents have been left puzzled by stories of brightly lit flying objects illuminating the sky.

At least two residents say they spotted what they have described as an object capable of travelling at speeds faster than any craft they have ever seen.

Landlord Pete Saxon was so amazed at what he saw after being woken by shouting outside his pub, the Swan Inn in The Street, at 2am, that he ran to get his video camera and caught the object on tape.

"I walked out the back and came up at the back end of the car park. There was what I

WONDERING: Landlord Pete Saxon outside the Swan Inn in Alderton.

thought was a helicopter," Mr Saxon said.

"I watched it because it stood

out as it was quite bright. What happened next is unbelievable. It shot to the left at an alarming rate.

"It was really erratic movement. I couldn't understand anybody actually being inside it. It was some sort of structure but the movement wasn't what a helicopter would do."

The incident will evoke memories of an alleged sighting of a UFO in nearby Rendlesham forest in 1980.

On that occasion, an American airman spotted bright lights at 4am on December 26, sparking a heated debate which still carries on today between the cynics and those who believe alien spacecraft could exist.

In the latest incident at Alderton, Rick Thompson, 27, had been woken by his six-month-old baby when he looked out of a window in his Mill Hoo

home and saw a bright light. Mr Thompson said: "It was too bright to be a helicopter and too big a light and it was quiet.

"I didn't hear any noise. I suppose it was stationary for a couple of minutes, then it started doing things it shouldn't do.

"It was up then down, forward then back, left then right. It was frightening really."

Mr Saxon, 52, said the video images he captured have become the most talked-about subject in his pub.

"It was really, really unusual," he said.

"Along the bottom of it was a long strip with a bright light on the end.

"It was as big as a low jumbo. What made it a bit weird was that there was no noise. You could see the dome top and you could see the bottom was flat. It was luminous blue around the outside."

Swan Inn regular Brian Foster, a former coastguard from Bawdsey with experience of spotting lights at night, has seen the video and said: "The speed is so extraordinary that it's got to be something. We haven't got the technology to move at that pace.

"The movement was totally erratic, so it couldn't be one of the sea marks."

Rick Thompson – another witness

We spoke to another witness – Rick Thompson. This is what he had to say:

"I was awoken by my six month old baby; I looked out of the window and saw a bright light, stationary in the sky. It was too bright to be a helicopter, and too big, and was completely silent – then it began to move erratically in the sky, making these peculiar up and down, backwards and forwards, motions. I found it quite frightening."

MR R THOMPSON
17 MILL HOO
ALDERTON
WOODBRIDGE
SUFFOLK
IP123DA
01394 410020
07725557377
Richard.thompson1@homecall.co.uk

Dear Mr John Hanson,

Thank you for your letter regarding the ufo sighting over the swan public house on the 6th November 2004, here is a brief account of what I saw.
On the night in question I was up in the early hours seeing to my young daughter, the living room curtains were open and I noticed a bright light in the sky, not unusual around here but this one was different and my eyes seemed drawn to it due to the brightness, I watched the light for a short time and it began to move in a very erratic manor. I was aware that the way in which the light was moving made impossible to be a helicopter, but at the same time it was not possible for it to be an aeroplane. I watched the light for a while and it seemed to be dotting around and moving away and then coming back to the same area again, after a while the light just moved away at great speed and disappeared. I hope this helps you along a little, please let me know if you are coming to the swan and when and I will meet with you to discuss it further.

On a separate note with regards to your comment about strange globes of light following motorists along rural roads I know of an incident that happened to a friend of mine a few years ago that sounds like it might be exactly what you were talking about. Let me know if you are coming down and I will try to get my friend down to the pub to talk to you aswell.

Yours MR RICKY THOMPSON.

No virus found in this incoming message.
Checked by AVG Free Edition.

03/07/2006

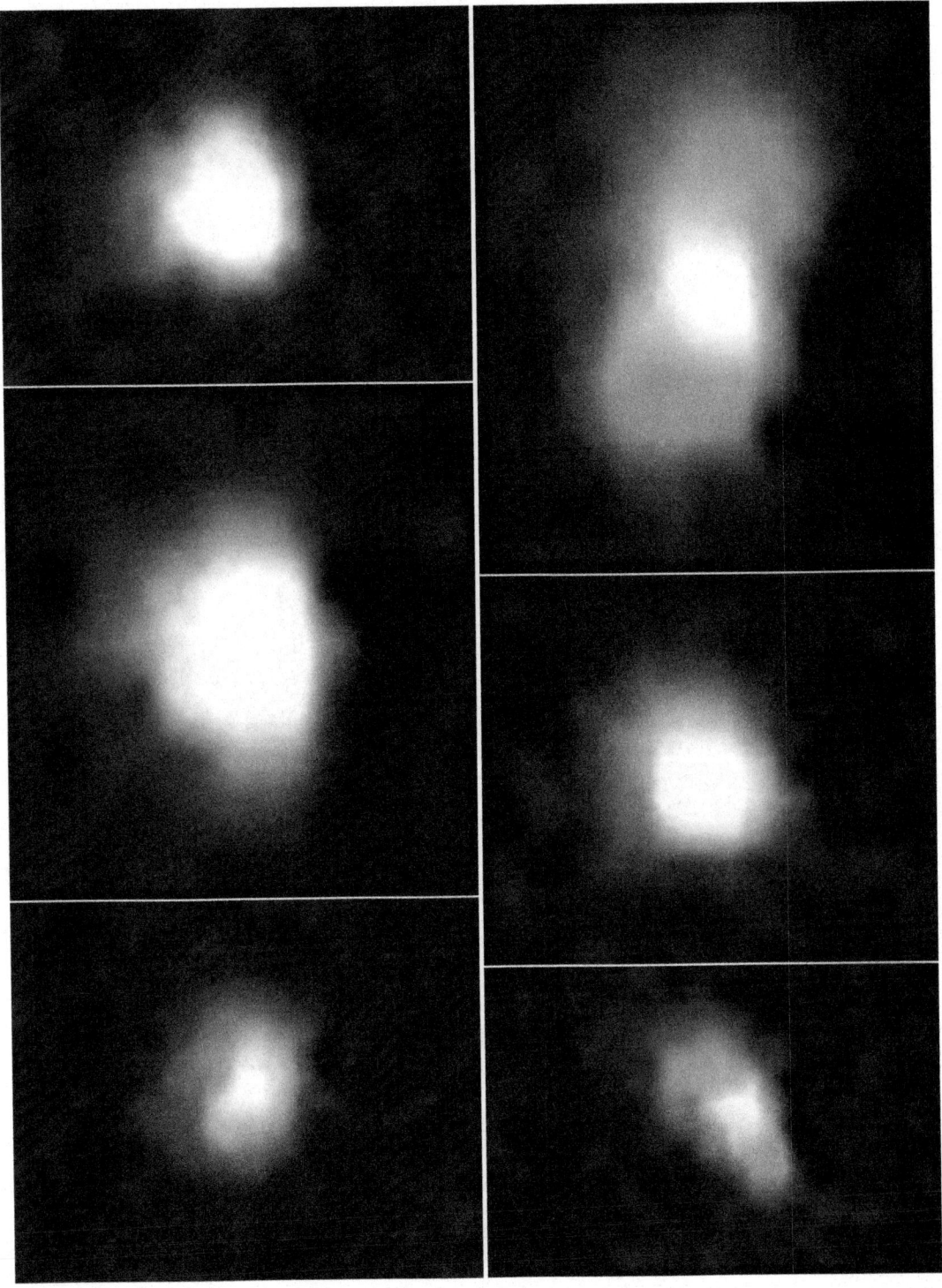

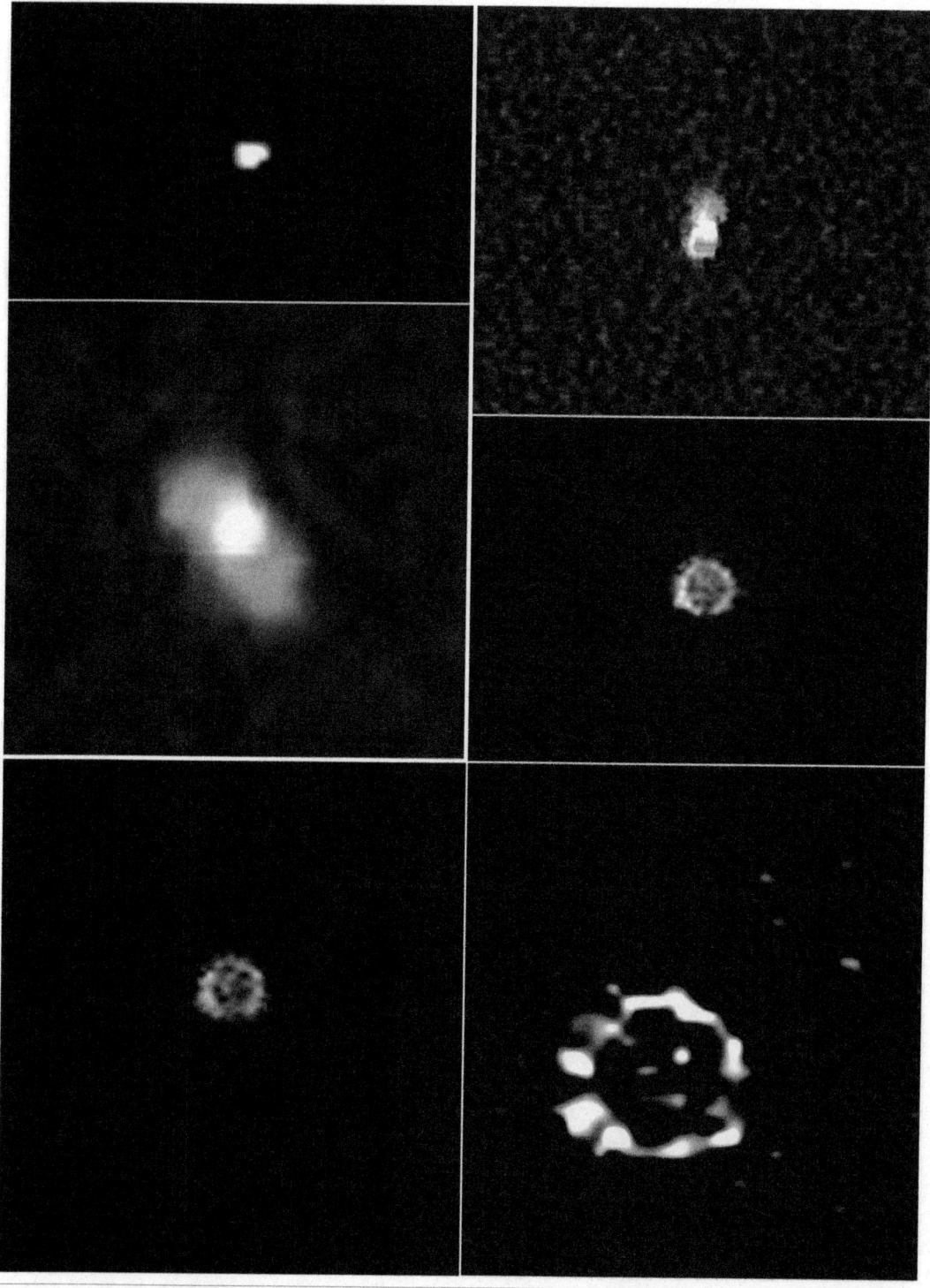

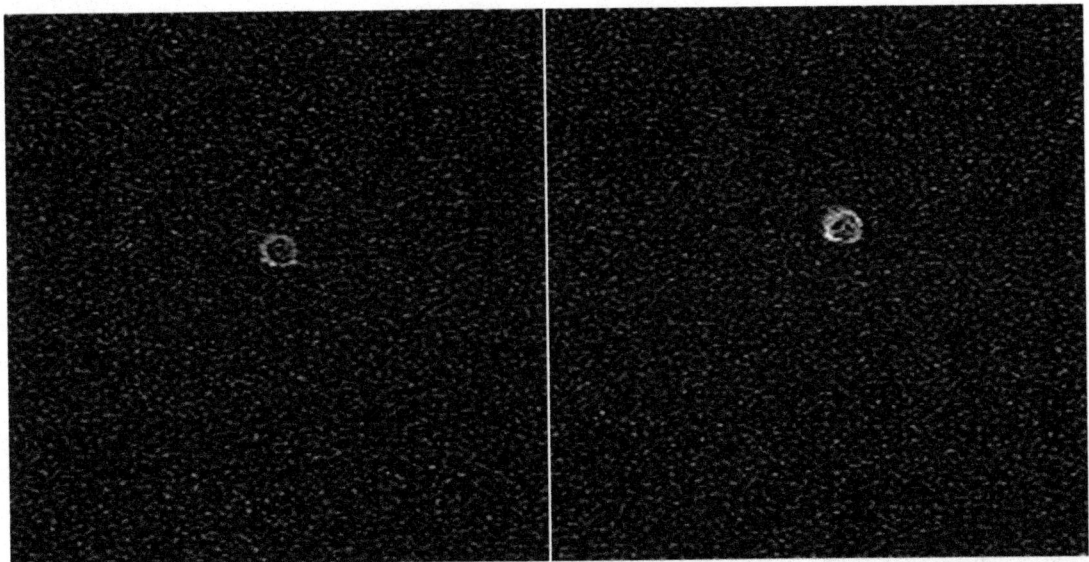

By the time we were in a position to examine the film taken by Peter, two years later, time had taken its toll. A good portion of the film (some nine minutes, towards the end of the clip) had been inadvertently erased, leaving us with a total footage of approximately 65 seconds.

We travelled down to see Licensee Peter Saxon accompanied by Sacha Christie, a UFO enthusiast from Leeds, who asked us to introduce her to Brenda Butler. We then asked Sacha to let Graham Birdsall have the UFO film in order that further examination could be made with a view to extracting some of the images on it. This was subsequently done. We can't say what the images represent but they are worth reproducing .

Of those 65 seconds, the first five seconds showed a brightly-lit object darting about in the sky. This was large enough, without the application of a zoom lens, to show something fairly substantial, viewed at an angle of approximately 90 degrees off the horizon (possibly 5-10 miles away) and likely to have been over the sea – conceding the difficulties faced with trying to establish distances and sizes without any other frames of references, bearing in mind that this clip of film was taken after the object rose upwards in the sky.

Our examination of the film showed us an object that had the propensity to extinguish its outer illumination but was still visible (under extreme scrutiny) in the sky. One again, we are left with the feeling that while we may not be dealing with any alien spaceships, we are dealing with an unidentified phenomenon. What it is and where 'it' or 'they' come from, we just don't know. However, what we do know is that 'they' continue to behave in the same manner, irrespective of how much time passes us. Generations may flourish and die, but UFOs appear timeless.

Forestry Commission obtains Lottery proceeds to create 'UFO Trail'

In 2005, the Forestry Commission used Lottery proceeds to create a trail in Rendlesham Forest, because of public interest, and nicknamed it the *UFO Trail*. In 2014, the Forestry Service commissioned an artist to create a work which has been installed at the end of the trail. The artist states the piece is modelled after sketches that purportedly represent some versions of the UFO claimed to have been seen at Rendlesham.

David Bryant with UFO sculpture in Rendlesham Forest

4th September 2005 – England: Diamond-shaped UFO caught on film

Elaine Wildman, from Portsmouth, contacted us some years ago, wishing to bring our attention to what we considered to be a remarkable piece of film, taken at 9pm on that evening. showing what looks like four lights clustered together .We appreciate that it has nothing to do with what took place in Suffolk, but common sense dictates that it is of importance to show it, especially bearing in mind the background of literally hundreds of 'Triangular' sightings reported along the adjacent borders of Essex and Norfolk – far too many to include in this book.

Elaine:

"We experienced three awful thunderstorms around the Portsmouth area over the last few weeks, which seemed so out of character for the area. Just before 9pm, my husband and I went down to the sea to watch the storm taking place. I took my Digital-camcorder with me, as I wanted to record it. When I downloaded the video onto the PC, I was astonished to see what I had captured, as neither of us had seen it with the naked eye. I have no idea what it was. The video was pointing out to sea, at the time, and was taken just before a ferry sailed by. The noise it makes as it takes-off sounds like an engine. I don't know what it is, but is certainly strange and unlike anything I have ever seen before on a video."

Whatever the object is, in one frame it releases a burst of as it hovers in the sky at what appears to be only a few hundred feet off the surface.

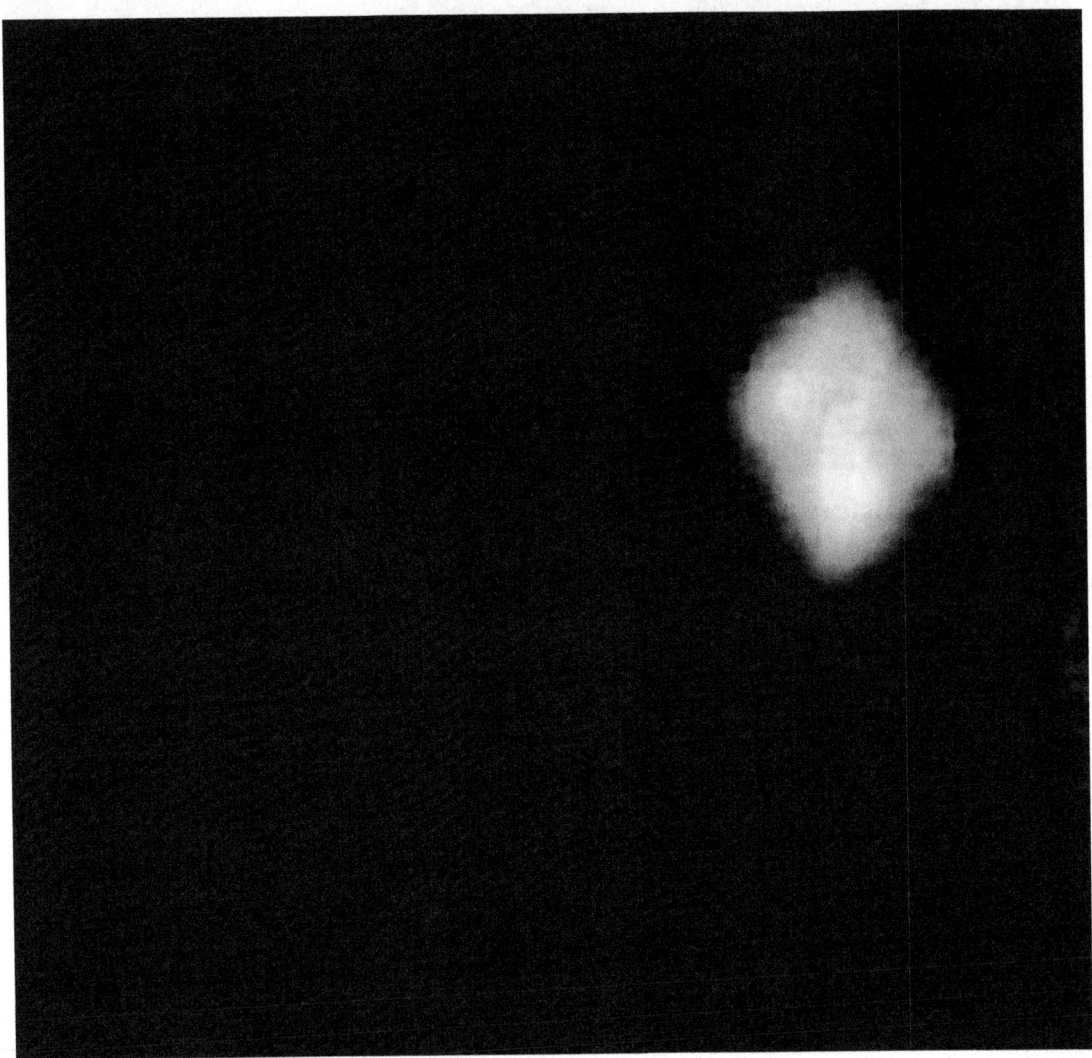

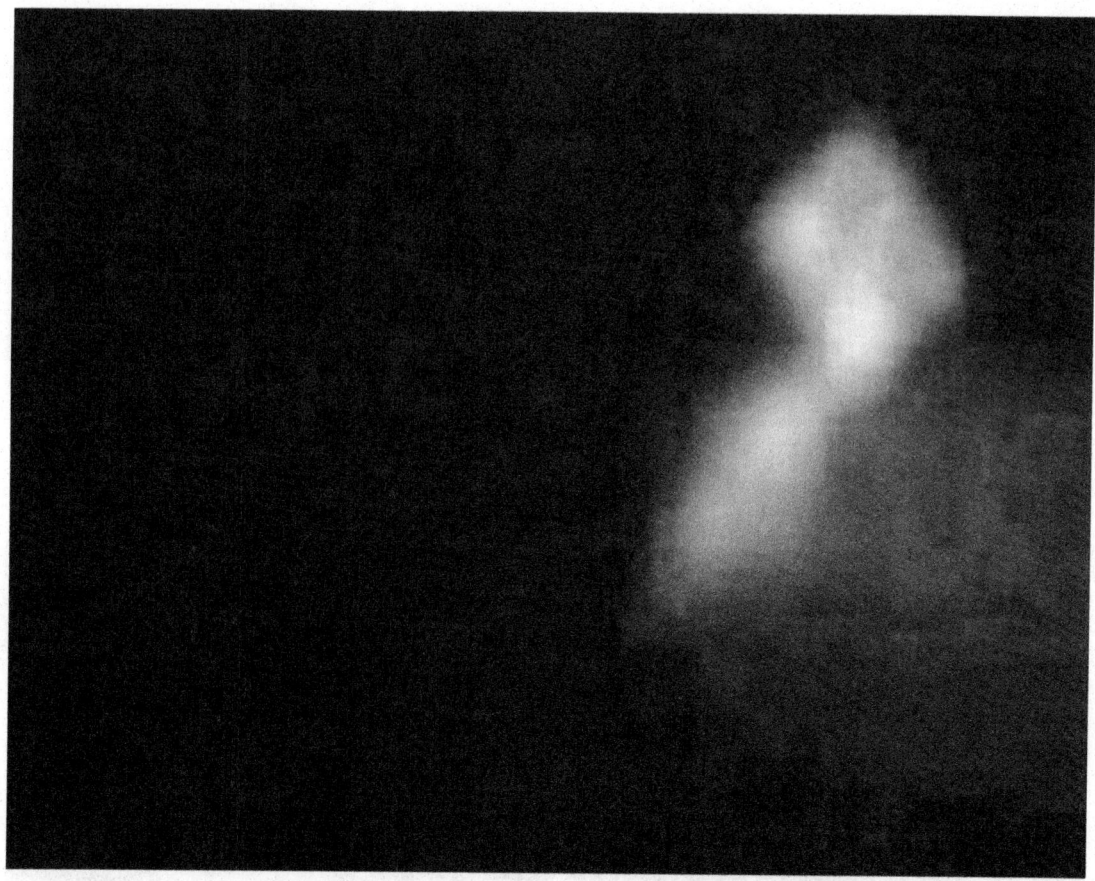

2008 – Apports recovered from Rendlesham Forest, Suffolk

One late Saturday evening, in 2008, Don Ramkin from Bexley Heath, Kent – a UFO/paranormal investigator – and his companion, Terry, made their way to Suffolk to meet up with Brenda Butler and walk around Rendlesham Forest, hoping to obtain further examples of photographic anomalies some of which have been previously shown in this book.

"The sky was a combination of clear patches with cloud, which was slowly moving away. Earlier that evening rain had fallen, so the forest was damp. After walking along some of the tracks, we ended up at the spot named locally as the 'alien tree' (on which an ET looking face naturally formed on the bark). We stood next to the base of the 'alien tree' and carried out some meditation (quiet contemplation) listening for sounds, waiting to see if anything was heard out of the ordinary. As a paranormal investigator, I have no qualms in saying that often it would be one of the strange shadows, which resemble figures – a phenomenon that has been witnessed by us, many times previously, around the forest on our weekend visits. It may sound incredible, but we weren't the only ones to have sighted what became known locally as the 'shadow people'. What they are and where they come from I can't say, but they have been seen many times, over the years.

614

We started to take a few random photographs, hoping to capture some anomalies, but only picked up moisture droplets in the air. We then heard a crackle through the branches of the surrounding trees, followed by a thud on the ground – quite close to where we were stood. We knew from our past visits to the forest, over many years, that this probably meant that an apport had just occurred.

We searched the surrounding area with torchlight and discovered, lying on top of the wet leaves, a fairly large white 'cheese cutter type stone', very warm to the touch – as if it had been near heat.

Over the space of maybe 20 minutes, a further two stones came down in our vicinity. I can clearly recall saying out loud, perhaps a bit sarcastically, 'Ok, we know you can throw stones but is that all you can do?' Within the space of maybe three minutes of my asking, behind us but to the right of the tree, we heard something that sounded like an object had dropped onto the forest floor, although not as loud or pronounced as a stone would have made.

We began scouring the ground with our torches in the area we thought it came from. Just in front of me, I saw a small grey object.

I walked forward. Bending down, I picked it up and was amazed to see a plastic toy elephant – not only that, but it was very warm to touch. You can imagine my excitement when I showed it to Brenda and Terry. I guess the spirits (if, indeed, it was a spirit) had answered my question."

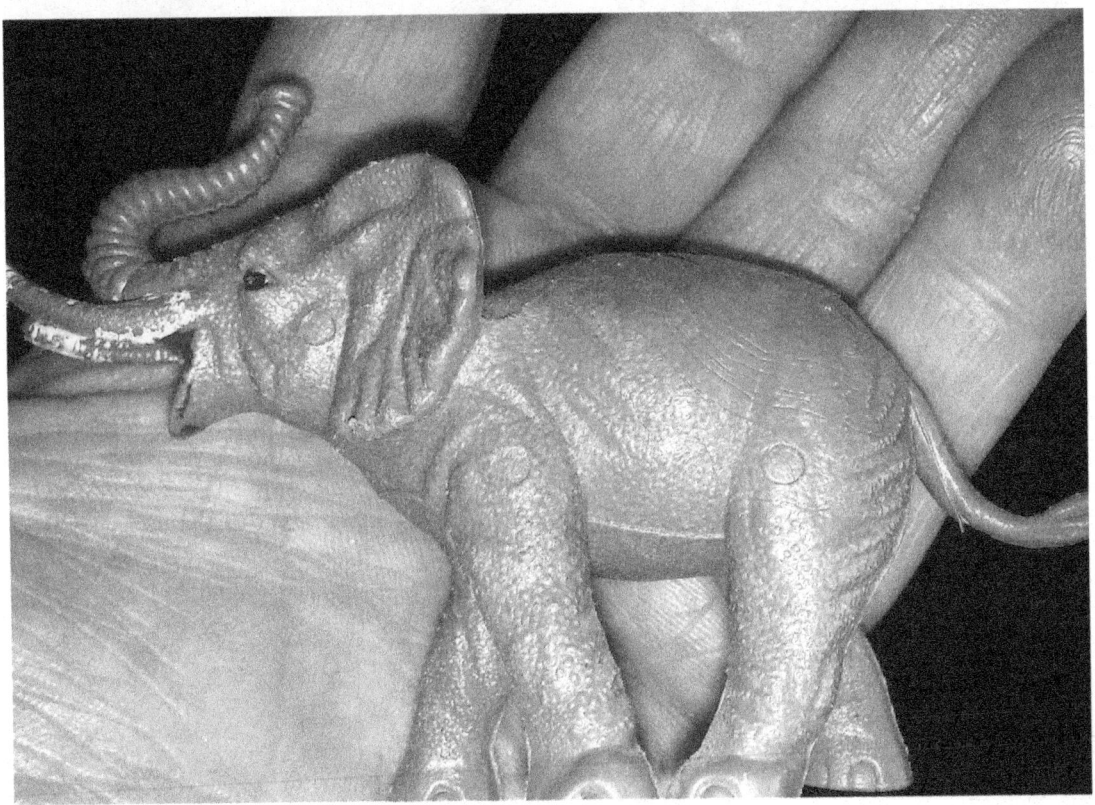

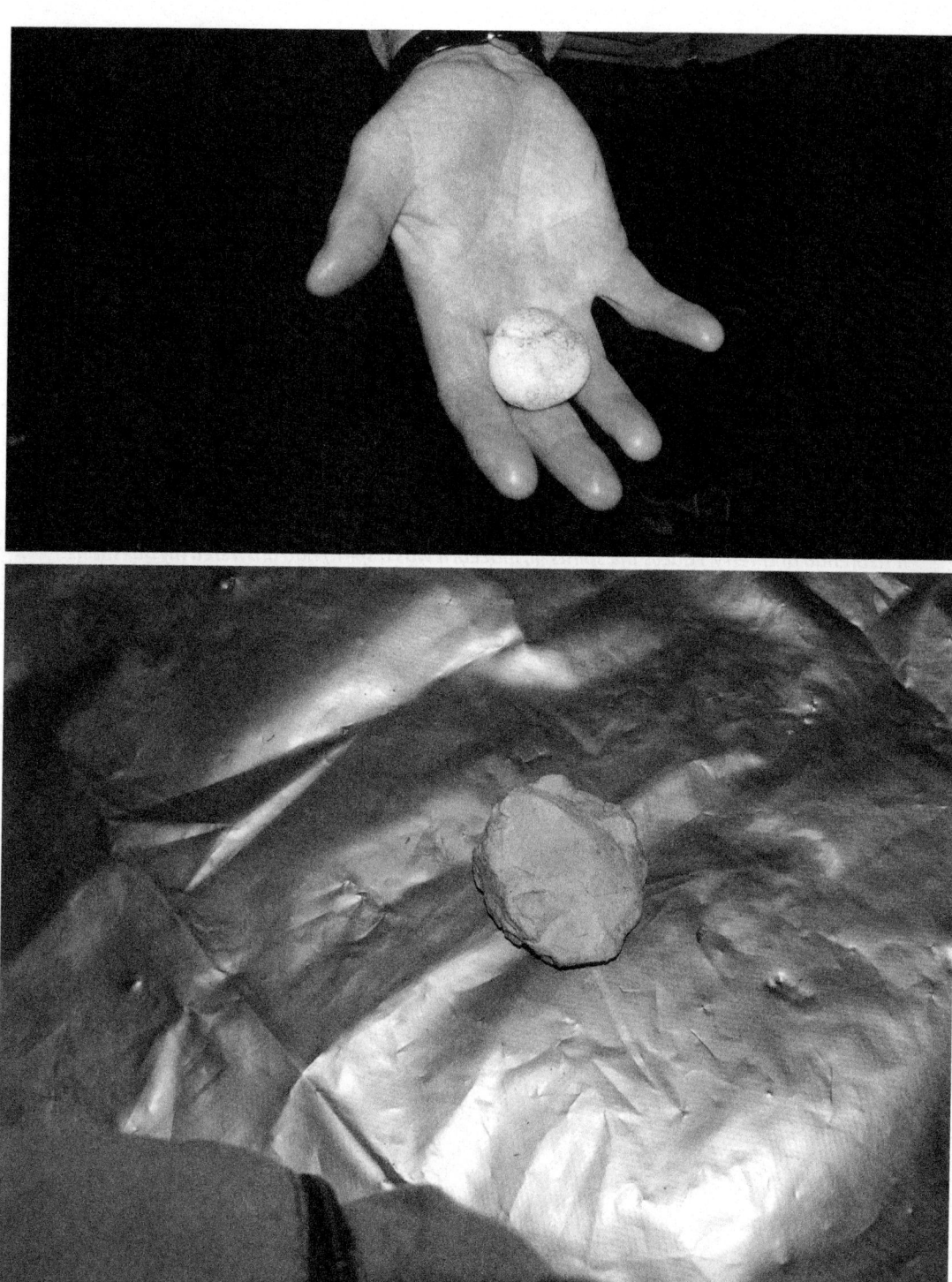

UFO/Paranormal investigator, Don Ramkin, studies one of the apports that appear in Rendlesham Forest

Having experienced on at least three occasions similar phenomena while in the forest, we asked a scientist to examine the apport (and a control stone, found in the same location) under the electron microscope. We were surprised to see that the 'control stone' showed a rough surface with cracks and fissures commensurate with its age, while the 'apport stone' was clean and smooth. However, to the eye they looked more or less the same in composition.

We should not draw any conclusions from this, but felt it was important to introduce this as a point of some discussion. Is this phenomenon indigenous to Rendlesham Forest, or would one find similar 'manifestations' at other wooded locations? Do the stones fall when nobody is in the forest? Are human beings, in some way, orchestrating their levitation off the ground? Whatever the answer, one thing is assured – the stones will continue to fall!

John Hanson – Simulacra

One of the greatest problems we face is of course visual interpretation of what the brain actually sees. Two examples are shown – the first is what Dawn and I discovered on a beach in Devon the other a fungus in Rendlesham Forest. Some people can see faces? What does the reader see?

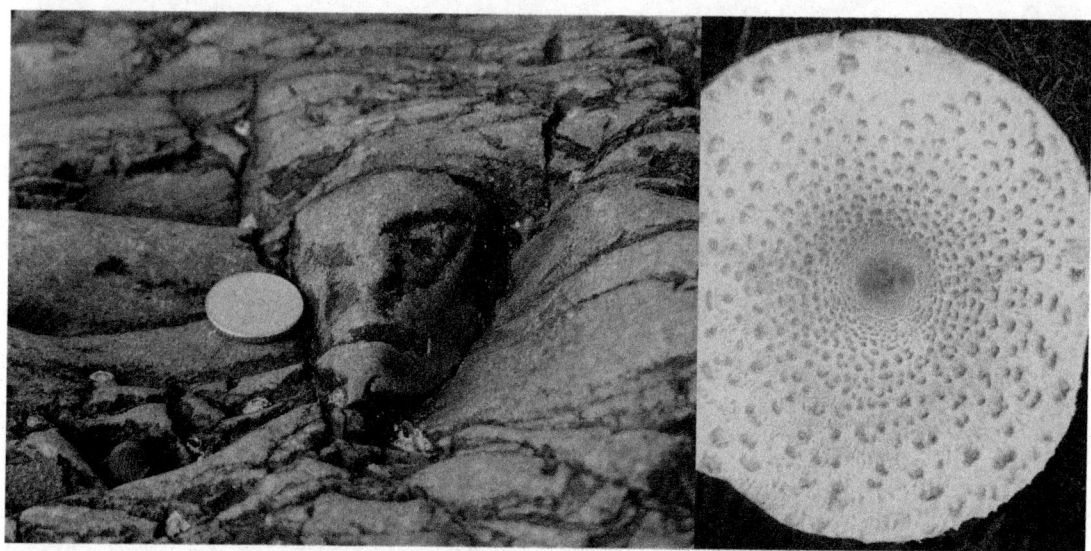

2009 – Charles Halt asked about date of first incident

In 2009, Charles Halt was asked about the date of the first UFO incident (involving Penniston and Burroughs) by Robert Hastings, and confirmed the morning of 26th December as now being correct.

"As I said to you before, there is no evidence to support the claims made that an alien craft landed and that Gordon Williams entered into some sort of a dialogue with the entities. This is completely untrue. Major Zickler was not present as he stayed at the party with Conrad, as he didn't want his name in it. Verano, Palmer, Combs and Thompson were not there and John Burroughs was held back and ordered to stay back on the service road. Now he talks about all kinds of things that I know didn't happen."

Bustinza's account

"The account from Bustinza is one of fabrication. I never ordered anyone to surround an object! There were no 'Bobbies' there. No-one, to my knowledge, was taking pictures (other than Nevels) and no film was confiscated. It appears from this version of events that Larry may not have been present. John, you have no idea how skilled these people are in fabricating disinformation. My advice is to be very cautious with regard to claims of this nature made, as they are untruthful.

Carl Thompson was one of the communications squadron guys on duty that night (he and his partner saw the object both on the screen and visually). There's no way Bustinza could have known his name, as he didn't come forward until recently and their duty roster is not known but to a few – just further evidence that someone messed with Adrian. The plot thickens! I can only recommend that you proceed with caution."

Airmen were given induced memories

"Warren, Penniston, and Burroughs have been given confusing and distracting memories. Even Larry has admitted this possibility to me. Perhaps you have read the recent news about NSA. What the paper has said only scratches the surface. I did an inspection of them 22 years ago, and I was shocked with the little bit I found. It is clear from the information I have gathered that Jim and John were messed with either in the forest, or in a debriefing which took place afterwards, or some such combination – and that as a result of this they have reality and fantasy confused. It's too bad, as they are unintentionally spreading disinformation.

For example, the 'cop' that sat next to Jim on the crew bus the morning of their encounter, while riding back from Guard Mount at CSC, has been found. He talked with Jim and John, took out a notebook and drew what he saw. He didn't see any other drawings or any code or inscriptions in the book. Jim and I did numerous programs together and the notebook was never mentioned until at the National Press Club, three years ago.

Several years ago, when Jim and I were doing a program on site, he took us to the wrong site and insisted it was correct. We know that to be wrong, as he and John had taken me to the original site, plus we know where the plaster casts were made. There are other inconsistencies."

17ᵗʰ June 2010

Colonel Halt made an affidavit relating to the incident, which was countersigned by Katherine Shaw, of the Commonwealth of Virginia.

In 2010, Jenny Randles – one of the co-authors of the 1984 book *Sky Crash: A Cosmic Conspiracy* – eventually voiced her doubts that the incident had ever had anything to do with extraterrestrial visitors:

"Whilst some puzzles remain, we can probably say that no unearthly craft were seen in Rendlesham Forest. We can also argue with confidence that the main focus of the events was a series of misperceptions of everyday things encountered in less than everyday circumstances."

Georgina passes away...

I am very sorry to have to report that Georgina Bruni died on the 19th January, following a long illness which she fought with great courage and dignity.

She led an extraordinary life and tried her hand at a wide variety of jobs, working variously as a dancer, fashion designer and nightclub manager. She travelled extensively and at various times lived in Jersey, Italy, Hong Kong and America, before settling in London in 1992.

She wrote poetry, designed a positive thinking course and founded Hot Gossip, an online magazine. She was a former director of the Yacht Club, where she was involved in hosting social events for MPs, diplomats and M.o.D officials. Later on she became a PR consultant and ran a social club, Le Club 2000.

Georgina is best known for her research into the Rendlesham Forest incident. She consulted on and contributed to various TV documentaries on the subject and her book on the case, You Can't Tell The People, won her praise not just from the UFO community but from former Chief of the Defence Staff Lord Hill-Norton and from Gordon Williams, who had been Commanding Officer of the twin bases of Bentwaters and Woodbridge when the incident occurred.

Nick Pope
25 January 2008

Our lovely GEORGINA, Editor in Chief of HotGossip has passed away and I and all her other hundreds of friends, business colleagues, HotGossip Editors and staff and members of her social club, CLUB 2000 are devastated. She suffered from cancer for almost a year but, being a fantastically brave and dignified lady, did not want anyone to know and feel sorry for her. She swore me to secrecy and I always hoped - and strongly believed - that she would beat it because she had such an indomitable spirit. But, alas, it was not to be. My condolences go to her devoted family.

Sally Neville
HotGossip February Issue, 2008

Angel fire

John Hanson:

In March 2016, I spoke again to Mike Topliss, a retired Suffolk Constabulary Police Inspector – a down-to-earth, very pleasant man – about the UFO incidents at Sizewell B Power Station, in the mid 1990s, taking into consideration his role in answering enquiries about police involvement and knowledge of the UFO incidents alleged to have taken place during the 1980s.

Ironically and perhaps understandably (given his previous position within the Force), despite having witnessed a UFO himself, he was still sceptical of the events that had taken place at Rendlesham.

I mentioned about rumours of incidents of high strangeness occurring at Sizewell Nuclear Power Station, during its construction.

Mike said:

"I've not heard any of this. I was privy as police representative to attend the meetings there, and if strange things had taken place I would have heard of it; maybe not from the Company Power Officials, but the local community representatives would have said something I'm sure. One thing we did have was a lot of smuggling activity. The smugglers were running these fast inflatable craft onto the beach; this was well-known to the Police. As far as 'lights in the sky' were concerned, I remember when the Americans were holding an exercise; they were using 'Angel fire' – which was an anti-missile system, firing off flares in all directions. To the untrained eye it did look like an angel, with spread wings, in the sky. The beach opposite Sizewell was littered with old flares, washed up."

Disinformation

Mike also suspects that the information given of 'aliens' and UFO landings, in late December 1980 (as mentioned in *Sky Crash*), may have been deliberately orchestrated as disinformation to cover-up something else, but admits that he has no idea what this was.

We suspect, from the nature of other evidence relating to triangular UFO activity, that this 'story' was implemented to cover-up an example of what may well have been a landing of such an object. Again this is only an opinion.

April 2009 – Ipswich man sights 'orange globe'

Searches made to identify the person concerned, and obtain a copy of the film, were unsuccessful, although we did come across a report in the *Advertiser* relating to a UFO sighting made by Ipswich man – Leonard Gibney, who spoke about seeing:

"...a number of 'reddish-pinkish lights' swarming across the sky over Belstead Brook and Spring Wood, situated close to the A14, during the summer of 1989."

On another occasion: *"I saw a luminous orb, descending from the clouds, which hovered 50 yards away from me, before vanishing ten seconds later."*

(Source: *Advertiser*, 16.4.2009 – 'My Close encounter – take it as RED, Leonard saw UFO in wood)

This was taken some years ago, overlooking the field in Rendlesham Forest nominated by the airmen as where the UFO was seen.

Media still fascinated by UFO incident

Interest in the events that took place in Rendlesham Forest, in 1980, continues to attract the attention of the media, despite them appearing to deliberately ignore the evidence of staggering numbers of UFO sightings reported along its adjacent borders, many of which have similarities of description to what Colonel Halt and his colleagues saw.

26th September 2009 – UFOs filmed over Rendlesham, offered for sale on e-Bay, July 2011

An unidentified person, who said he lived six miles away from Woodbridge Airbase, advertised a clip of film for sale on e-Bay, in July 2011, claiming to show four 'orange lights', taken at 10.30pm, above trees over the Rendlesham play area – a short distance from East Gate. This was accompanied by a report of two 'orange globes' in the sky, seen by a bus driver, over the *Ufford Park Hotel*, near

Woodbridge, which may have been presented to somehow authenticate the footage taken by Mr X. (We could not find any trace of this sighting.)

We were told, from another source, that this film was available for £2 million pounds but without speaking to the person, who only left a mobile number, remain unconvinced about any of this – especially the authenticity of the film. Did someone buy the film and, if so, for how much?

1st November 2010 – *BBC* began to publicize forthcoming event

BBC Suffolk started to air promotions for their big radio special on Rendlesham, scheduled for 17th December 2010. The Station created 26 promotions for the show that were aired almost every day. On the allocated date the long awaited special *Rendlesham Revealed* went out on air. Mark Murphy proposed a theory that on the first night of the incident, a dummy *Apollo* capsule was allegedly dropped in the forest by a helicopter from 67th Aerospace Rescue and Recovery Squadron, based at RAF Woodbridge. The 'third night' was explained away as being the helicopters return, because soldiers decided to recover the capsule'

20th November 2010 – Open air UFO conference in the forest

This occasion also celebrated the UFO incident which took place 30 years ago, with a party in the Forest. This was celebrated by many people, including Mark Murphy of the local *BBC Radio* station, who had expressed an interest in the subject.

This was well attended by many young people, who didn't know what to expect – but it was a rare opportunity to relax and enjoy the evening, despite being enveloped in thick smoke. There was even a burger van provided!

WHAT HAPPENED?

DEC 1980 Near ROF-USAF BENTWATERS & Woodbridge Air Base.

An open air event
Saturday 20th November 2010

7.30pm - 8.00pm: Mediumship with Philip Kinsella
8.00pm - 9.00pm: Talk on UFO's - Interactive discussion with Brenda Butler
9.00pm til late: Sky watch walk

Tickets: £10.00 - Tel: 01728 830757
email: nigel.turner@forestry.gsi.gov.uk
web: www.philipkinsella.com

Something so strange that the world Media took an interest in inustigation into the mysterious PHENOMENON that occurred at RENDELSHAM FOREST.

28th December 2010 – UFO meeting at Woodbridge Community Hall

This reunion took place at 6pm on the 28th December 2010, with appearances by Jim Penniston, John Burroughs, Linda Moulton Howe, Nick Pope, and Peter Robbins.

BBC Radio Suffolk presenter

BBC presenter – Mark Murphy – visited the hall where he interviewed John Burroughs, and prepared a new interview for his radio show on the 29th December. Mark asked him about the *Apollo* capsule theory and John Burroughs gave this reply:

JOHN BURROUGHS
LINDA MOULTON HOWE
JIM PENNISTON
NICK POPE
PETER ROBBINS

Admit One   £6.00   Ticket #

1 6 1

The Rendlesham Forest Incident-30th Anniversary
Conference
Woodbridge Community Hall,IP12 4AU,Tues.,Dec.28 at 6pm

"The fact that the airfield was shut down, the fact that you would hear helicopter lift off, we would know for helicopter lift off. I can honestly tell you, straight up, there was no helicopter activity. Now, on the third night with Colonel Halt, because I came out after it already started, I can't tell what was going on at the airfield, but I did not hear any helicopters at any time."

Mark Murphy:

"So you know they are keen, 30 years on, to say 'Look, I am sorry but this is what happened'. So the truth may still be out there – maybe we'll find it, maybe we won't. Jim Penniston claims that he touched the 'craft', and who am I to argue? I wasn't there. We'll have to do Rendlesham Revealed Revisited – part 2, at some point."

THE RENDLESHAM FOREST INCIDENTS
30th ANNIVERSARY CONFERENCE

TO BE HELD AT:

WOODBRIDGE COMMUNITY HALL

STATION ROAD, WOODBRIDGE, SUFFOLK IP12 4AU

ON

TUESDAY 28th DECEMBER, 2010

COMMENCING AT 6PM

JOHN BURROUGHS & JIM PENNISTON
Talk for the first time in Suffolk,
Joined by special guests NICK POPE,
PETER ROBBINS and LINDA MOULTON HOWE.

MAIN SPEAKER and prime Witness, John Burroughs

MAIN SPEAKER and prime Witness, Jim Penniston

NICK POPE- author, Journalist, and formerly in Charge of UFO files at M.O.D.

PETER ROBBINS- American researcher, Lecturer, activist & author

EMMY-NOMINATED American investigative Journalist and documentary Maker, Linda Moulton Howe

In late December 1980, over a three day period, unusual lights & aerial phenomena were observed by U.S. Air Force personnel, at the perimeter of RAF Woodbridge air base. Thirty years on, these extraordinary events remain unexplained, and on the 28th December 2010, two key witnesses return to Suffolk to recount their stories.

Airman First Class John Burroughs & Staff Sergeant Jim Penniston, of the 81st Tactical Fighter Wing, were patrolling the east gate at RAF Woodbridge, when they saw a moving light in the forest. This was the beginning of what has become one of the greatest UFO mysteries of our time.

Upon conclusion of the talk, the speakers will proceed to Rendlesham forest to re-visit the site of the incidents- all attendees of the conference will be welcome to join them.

At the request of the speakers, any profits from the event will be donated to the East Anglia Childrens Hospice Treehouse Appeal.

TICKETS @ £6.00

For more information, including ticket sales, please call: 01473 423143 or 07811021238 or email: info@spaceportuk.com

Poster advertising the event.

6th August 2011 – *The Daily Telegraph* …Colonel Conrad speaks out

On 6th August 2011, The Daily Telegraph published Jasper Copping's article Rendlesham Incident: US Commander speaks for the first time about The Suffolk UFO. The article is centred on Colonel Ted Conrad – ex-Base Commander of the twin airfields of Woodbridge and Bentwaters – and his views on the Rendlesham Incident. Copping writes in his article:

"Just after Christmas (1980), mysterious lights were seen in the sky above nearby Rendlesham Forest, and after a second night of reports from his men, Colonel Conrad investigated himself."

Colonel Conrad:

"The search for an explanation could go many places, including the perpetration of a clever hoax, natural phenomenon; such as, the very clear cold air having a theoretical ability to guide and reflect light across great distances, or even the presence of an alien spacecraft. If someone had the time, money, and technical resources to determine the exact cause of the reported Rendlesham Forest lights, I think it could be done. I also think the odds are way high against there being an ET spacecraft involved and almost equally high against it being an intrusion of hostile earthly craft."

8th August 2011 – *Daily Mail*: 'UFO sighting could have been a hoax'

On the 8th August 2011, the *Daily Mail* published an article – *'Suffolk UFO sighting could have been a hoax: US commander talks about Rendlesham Forest Incident for first time in 30 years'* – 'US Air Force Colonel Ted Conrad was base commander of the airfields at Woodbridge and Bentwaters, near Ipswich. At the time the base is believed to have stored nuclear weapons. After spotting some strange lights in the sky, two nights in a row, Colonel Conrad went to investigate and, after clearing some bushes, found some strange markings on trees which he believed could have indicated a spacecraft landing. He then picked a group of his own men and sent them into the forest that evening. Armed with night vision goggles and a camera, they searched the area and, after seeing nothing suspicious, some of the men returned to base.

However, Colonel Conrad's deputy – Lieutenant Colonel Halt – stayed behind and kept in touch with his superior via radio. Lt. Colonel Halt then reported he saw more lights on the ground and in the sky. Other senior officers on the base went outside to see if they could see the lights but nobody was able to, despite it being a perfectly clear evening. Speaking to Dr David Clarke – UFO adviser to the National Archives – Conrad said:

"He should be ashamed and embarrassed by his allegation that his country and England both conspired to deceive their citizens over this issue. He knows better."

The former Commander has also dismissed Sergeant Jim Penniston's claims that he had gone into the woods on the first night of the sightings and touched an alien aircraft. Colonel Conrad said he interviewed Penniston, who did not say that he had touched the aircraft but did say he saw lights in the distance, and that. . .

"we saw nothing that resembled Lt. Colonel Halt's descriptions either in the sky, or on the ground".

(The reporter is not identified in this article.)

Misleading

The same newspaper had apparently used the illustration from *Sky Crash* and labelled underneath it: *'Sighting: 'Lieutenant Colonel Halt's sketch of the alien spacecraft he claims to have seen in Rendlesham Forest'* – **which is completely false and misleading.**

The illustration is endorsed with the copyright © Corbis. The article also includes a photograph of Lt. Colonel Halt (on the left) and Kevin Conde.

Under the photograph of Charles Halt is the banner: 'Lt. Colonel Halt (on the left) filed a report to the MOD and said he believed the lights were extraterrestrial, while Kevin Conde (right) admitted to the BBC that he had played a prank on a colleague, while he was working at the base'. Once again, further inaccuracies!

We were intrigued about the copyright and searched the Corbis website for this image, but found no trace of it – so we emailed Corbis Images at 111, Salisbury Road, London NW6 6RG, United Kingdom, asking them if they had any images pertaining to the Rendlesham Forest UFO incident of 1980.

Orbis reply

On the 14th February 2013, Yuliya Stuart from Orbis replied:

"Unfortunately we do not have any images matching that description."

In another email, she responded:

"I tried to find an image of a UFO in Rendlesham Forest, but there wasn't any on our website."

We then sent her the original image and asked if they could explain why their corporate copyright was affixed to the image. Yuliya Stuart stated:

"Not sure about the image, as I couldn't find it. Perhaps it is on our site but has a different keyword."

One might think that they would know where this image was on their website, understanding its importance. The firm quoted us approximately £70 for copyright fee to use any of their UFO images. Had they purchased the image? If so from whom, and why weren't they more forthcoming with the details of the person acknowledged as original copyright holder? One presumes that they charged the *Daily Mail* a fee? Will they charge us a fee? Time will tell.

It seems that science and objectivity are being completely replaced by anecdotes and sensationalism. The media will always prefer sensationalism to a healthy scepticism.

Charles Halt responds to 'The Daily Telegraph'

In an email sent to journalist Jasper Copping, of *The Daily Telegraph*, in August 2011, Colonel Halt had this to say:

From: Halt@xxx.com To: jasper.copping@telegraph.co.uk

Subject: Re: Press query, *Sunday Telegraph*, London. Date: Tue, 9 Aug 2011 09:40:52 -0400 (EDT)

Jasper: I will have to assume you're looking to print the truth, not 'sell' a sensational story. Ted Conrad is having memory problems, has his head in the sand or continuing the cover-up. Even his son has admitted to family talk substantiating the incident. Let's start with his investigation. I interviewed the witnesses, collected their statements (I still have them) and then took the witnesses to Conrad to tell their account. I took Conrad and his family to the site in the forest and showed him the depressions. When I talked with Gordon Williams, neither he nor Conrad wanted their name mentioned with the incident. Thus, I was directed to get with Don Moreland (RAF) and see what he wanted as it was to become a British affair. I did so and he asked for a memo. I wrote it and it was typed by Conrad's secretary. Conrad read it, showed it to Williams and both approved. It was never meant for public dissemination. Conrad has his chronology mixed up but that's understandable. Through the years Conrad has made conflicting statements about the events. First he stated he never went out to look in the sky. Then stated he never saw anything. Apparently he doesn't remember talking to me on his radio [about seeing a UFO sending down beams of light onto the base]. He and you need to read Robert Hastings book *UFOs and Nukes: Extraordinary Encounters at Nuclear Weapons Sites*. Hastings has gotten confirmation from the Air Traffic Controllers on duty that saw the object flash by and go into the forest and even observed it on their scope; he's gotten statements from SP's as well as a Communications man working in the WSA stating their sightings. He's even dug up the RAF Controller that picked up something on his scope. Remind Conrad of his article in the *OMNI* Magazine, dated March 1983. It's on page 115 and titled UFO Update. In the article he describes the first incident in detail and concludes, *'those lads saw something, but I don't know what it was'*. Now he's smearing those involved. It's pretty clear there was a very intense confrontation with something in the forest. Does Conrad want to talk about how the airmen were then subjected to mind control efforts using drugs and hypnosis by British and American authorities?

Yes, Burroughs and Penniston have issues that relate to the events. There are a lot more details substantiating the event but I'm not going to bore you. I suppose having to look for details or the truth is less important than the 'story'. It's sad but I've come to understand how the mainstream press works.

Dr. David Clarke – Subject is dead!

In the same year, Dr. David Clarke – a Sheffield Hallam University academic and the UFO adviser to the National Archives – said:

"The subject is dead in that no one is seeing anything evidential. Look at all the people who now have personal cameras. If there was something flying around that was a structured object from somewhere else, you would have thought that someone would have come up with some convincing footage by now – but they haven't. The reason why nothing is going on is because of the internet. If something happens now, the internet is there to help people get to the bottom of it and find an explanation. Before then, you had to send letters to people who wouldn't respond, and you got this element of mystery and secrecy that means things were not explained. The classic cases like Roswell and Rendlesham are only classic cases, because they were not investigated properly at the time."

Charles Halt – Further on the memo and tape recording

"Another good reason to take anything you read in the media with a grain of salt. Remember their goal is to sell their publication – the truth be dammed. The only investigating Conrad did was to listen to the participants when I took them to him after interviewing them and taking statements. His only trip to the site was when I took him and his family out to look. Apparently he's not aware, or ignoring, all the witnesses such as the Air Traffic Controllers, cops and civilians. You might want to talk to Tony Cossa, the then Communications Group Commander, who ordered his two repairmen that also witnessed the event to keep quiet. Apparently the spooks took it seriously when they used hypnosis and drugs on the airmen to get the whole story and apparently 'plant' false memories. Conrad's such a coward – he didn't want his name involved; hence I was told to do the memo, which he read and approved. I was then 'hung out to dry' when it hit the Press. Everybody above me hid when it hit the Press. Disappointing! What you're seeing is some very skilful disinformation. You have no idea the ends some agencies will go to discredit this."

Wing Commander Gordon Williams

"Following my return from the forest, I was asked by Wing Commander Gordon Williams for my tape, to play it for the 3rd Air Force staff at their weekly staff meeting. I had no choice but to comply and was concerned about the reaction. It turned out that although they accepted the events that had been recorded they just wanted to distance themselves from the incident.

The Commander commented 'It happened off the base, so it's a British affair'. I was relieved and instructed by Colonel Williams to speak to the RAF Liaison Officer and let him handle it. Squadron Leader Donald Moreland was in Wales, at his home, so I had to wait 10-12 days before I could talk to him. He suggested a short memo, which I wrote out. He then forwarded it to the MOD, with a copy to his superior at 3AF."

Ted Conrad

"In the meantime, Colonel Ted Conrad, my boss and the Base Commander, asked me to make him a copy of the tape. I did this by taking my recorder and his into the conference room and laying them side by side and making him a copy. I now suspect he wanted it to share with superiors but can't confirm that. Early in 1981, the then Vice Wing Commander got himself into trouble with drinking problems, and when he was caught by the police on his front lawn in a compromising situation with a young female lieutenant from the Disaster Preparedness Office, he was relieved of his position and shipped stateside.

Needing a replacement, Colonel Conrad was selected to move up to become the Vice Wing Commander. This meant that we also required a replacement Base Commander.

Colonel Williams nominated an old friend, Colonel Sam Morgan, up to become the Base Commander. They had served together and were well acquainted.

This caused me some personal concern. Colonel Morgan was a 'gung ho' officer who went around boasting he was the world's greatest fighter pilot. He even passed out wine bottles with his own label stating he was the world's greatest fighter pilot. You may think this is a personal grievance or maybe a clash of personalities – not at all, but it may be important to bear certain facts in mind when looking at the overall big picture here with regard to the way in which this matter was originally handled, not forgetting the quote from Ted Conrad directed at me 'He should be ashamed and embarrassed by his allegation that his country and England both conspired to deceive their citizens over this issue. He knows better.'"

Criminal Damage

"There were other issues, involving allegations of criminal damage on quite a large scale, when over a hundred windows were shot at with an air rifle, which necessitated a Police investigation – especially when the target was also the Chief of Police's house on the base. This of course meant a number of people were subsequently interviewed, following an allegation that the son of Colonel Morgan and another youth were to blame. The matter was referred to the Chief of Police who asked me for advice, bearing in mind how delicate the matter was. Given Colonel Conrad's position at the airbase, the situation was embarrassing to say the least.

I told the Chief he had to do his job. He then went to Morgan's home to interview Morgan and his son. According to the Investigator, Morgan went off the deep end. He later complained to Colonel Williams, and anybody who would listen, that I had sent an armed police officer with a badge to his house.

Needless to say, the investigation didn't go anywhere: were they responsible? I can't say. Following this, Colonel Morgan was most unkind; blaming what had taken place on me personally. Soon after that, Williams was promoted and moved to a new assignment in Germany. Colonel (later General) Pascoe replaced him.

Morgan was then selected to replace Conrad as the Base Commander. Morgan let it be known that the first thing he was going to do as Base Commander was to fire me. Knowing this was likely to happen, I started looking for a new job. I contacted many friends and found one in Germany that needed a replacement with my skills. He passed my name and credentials up the chain to the 17th AF Commander.

He contacted Colonel Pascoe and asked for me by name. Pascoe told him no and called me into his office, confronting me as to why I wanted to leave. I told him about Morgan's comments and he became upset."

The Tape

> "He told me it wouldn't happen and to relax and do my job. We had a somewhat difficult relationship after that. Morgan found the copy of the tape from Dec 1980 that Conrad had left in the desk and asked about it. I explained what happened.
>
> Later I discovered he was playing the tape for friends, including some British UFO investigators. Somehow Harry Harris – a UFO Investigator from Manchester – talked Morgan into giving him a copy of the tape. Harry then sold the tape to a Japanese TV Producer for a significant sum of money. I was shocked and disappointed. Subsequently, things were of course very difficult between us: on occasion threats were made to me which I ignored."

Military decoration

> "After Colonel Morgan left the base, he asked for a high-ranking military decoration for his service time at Bentwaters. I was asked if I would write it. I flatly refused as, in my opinion, he was undeserving.
>
> Several years later, while I was serving as Director of Inspections for the Directorate I was in Hawaii, planning to brief the Pacific Commander on a pending inspection, when I ran into Morgan. I was in my dress uniform, walking to the Officers' Club for lunch, prior to my briefing, when a bus pulled up to the club entrance. Who should be the first off the bus but Colonel Morgan; I looked him in the eye and said 'Sam Morgan, I should punch you in the nose'. I looked directly behind him and who should I see but the four-star General he worked for. I made eye contact with the General and saw the puzzled look on his face. I immediately turned and went into the club. They went to a private dining room and I never saw them again. My briefing went well and I returned home and never heard any more.
>
> Morgan has long since retired and, according to several friends, has become very radical with his writing."

10th September 2011 – UFO Conference, Woodbridge

Admit One   £10 091

UFO Free Speech for All
Brenda Butler, Larry Warren, John Hanson,
David Bryant, Matt Lyons
Woodbridge Community Hall, Woodbridge, IP12 4AU
Saturday Sept 10, 2011 at 6.00pm

FOREST EYE PRODUCTIONS
PRESENTS

AN EVENING OF PRESENTATIONS & DISCUSSION PROMOTING
British UFO Free speech for All

What Col. Halt & co. witnessed in Rendlesham Forest in December 1980 was unarguably something extraordinary, and has rightly been the subject of exhaustive investigation and discussion, but behind the blaze of publicity that constantly attends the U.S. Airmens' experience lies a catalogue of un-disclosed incidents of high strangeness that have occurred in & around the forest over the last 30 years, and which are ongoing. Inexplicable phenomena have appeared to local people in various forms in the years since 1980, which, when examined collectively, give a strong indication that the forest is an active "window" area.
On September 10th, in addition to the scheduled speakers, local people will come forward to talk-some for the first time ever-about what they have seen. Some exclusive video footage will accompany the talks.

Confirmed speakers: BRENDA BUTLER; PETER PARISH – local paranormal researchers who have comprehensive knowledge and experience of the Rendlesham Forest area; DAVID BRYANT – A Norfolk-based lecturer on astronomical subjects who has met & interviewed a number of U.S. astronauts. David is also a paranormal researcher who has a keen interest in the Rendlesham site.

September 10th, 2011
At
WOODBRIDGE COMMUNITY HALL   Ticket Price - £10   profits from
this event will be donated to the Martlesham RSPCA Rescue Centre.
6pm – 11pm

TICKET SALES:
Please send stamped, self-addressed envelope to:
Mr G. GOODGER
108 Spring Road, Ipswich. IP4 2RR
Cheques payable to G. Goodger.   Paypal orders accepted via: paypal@spaceportuk.com. Please include a contact phone number & address to send tickets. For further info: call 01473 423143 or 07811021230.   email: info@spaceportuk.com

Also guest speaker John Hanson – Author of "Haunted Skies" & UFO lecturer –

2011 September – UFO captured on camera – was it a drone?

Matt Lyons – now former head of BUFORA – was invited to speak at the recent UFO conference at Woodbridge Hall, Suffolk, England, in September 2011, and took time out to visit the area, during daylight.

Matt, who was accompanied by his mother, proceeded along the marked pathway that leads towards East Gate, on what was an overcast day but with good illumination from a slowly clearing sky to the south, with a slight occasional drizzle of rain.

After some camera shots were taken of East Gate and the 'landing site', they made their way to the small clearing, which opened out into the large field, identified as where the main UFO sighting had taken place.

Matt Lyons

"On looking directly towards the lone farmhouse, central as a marking in the field in the mid-distance, we noted no birds or typically identifiable flying craft of any description. My mother noted the quiet stillness, with no whirr of microlights, helicopter, or any type of aircraft noise. We were interested to observe the soon to be decommissioned Orford Ness Lighthouse, but it was slightly misty in respect of longer distance vision towards the horizon line. After two minutes of observance and looking across the opening, we noticed a small blip in the distance to the airfield direction of the field, at a left bearing. By pure good fortune, it happened to be just when my mother happened to be taking some pictures with camera already poised across the wide rural field panorama. I recommended her to focus on this area and she took one photograph.

We had to wait until the following day to get a closer look at the object captured on this afternoon's encounter, as my mother's camera did not have a substantial LED review window-pane on this particular camera design she owned.

On attendance and speaking at the conference at Woodbridge, I decided to refrain from mentioning this at the time, as I was certain we had both seen something which would later be explained as a typical object. The following day, the camera card was downloaded and we were both surprised to see that the object retained a high degree of strangeness. The object can be seen to be of a rounded 'disc' shape, with some light distortions on the outer edges. This can be seen clearly before the pixels go to the extreme. There are hints of faint lines on the upper top centre of this daylight 'disc', but they are so slight as to not give any further clues. With the scope for all sorts of new drone technology and perhaps even advanced light reactive fuselages, this could offer a possible explanation for the object."

The object captured by Matt Lyons' mother in the Rendlesham Forest area

5th June 2012 – Anomalies captured on film at Rendlesham Forest

Former helicopter pilot – David Bryant, and his wife – Linda, are the UK's only full-time professional dealers of meteorites, and have been involved in their sale for now over 15 years.

They hold Degrees in Astronomy and Biology and are more than capable of being able to discuss their inventory with experience, enthusiasm and knowledge; they supply most of the UK's wholesalers, museums and educational institutions, and are members of the IMCA, and offer a lifetime guarantee of the authenticity of purchases to their clients. David and Linda were also instrumental in introducing me (John Hanson) personally to many Astronauts, during their visits to the UK, such as Dr. Edgar Mitchell, Buzz Aldrin, and retired General Charles Duke.

David is an accomplished lecturer and musician. He is frequently invited to talk by the media and professional institutions about his knowledge of meteorites and astronautics. During those talks he often recommends purchasing Haunted Skies, because he passionately believes, as we do, that reported UFO activity forms part of British social history and should be preserved. His expressed opinions about the existence of UFOs invariably will, and does, attract ridicule by those from academic and scientific institutions, who strongly feel there is no evidence to support such views.

We know personally, from conversations with David, that his UFO beliefs have occasionally influenced decisions by certain sections within the media, who have chosen not to engage his services fearing possible embarrassment should he inadvertently make references to the UFO subject.

Heathland Books

We are delighted that David Bryant now publishes his own books under the *Heathland* imprint title (2016) and we wish him and his wife Linda the best for the future.

David Bryant

"The 'balls' were on a photo I took on June 5th, 2012, to the south of RAF Woodbridge: we'd parked along Heath Road and walked north along a wide forestry track towards the perimeter fence. As I always do, I took lots of random photos, including an AWACS aircraft and escort, which flew over the base shortly afterwards! The 'balls' were on a panorama of the track and a group of lights at each end. I could see it 'shaking', from side to side, and moving up and down.

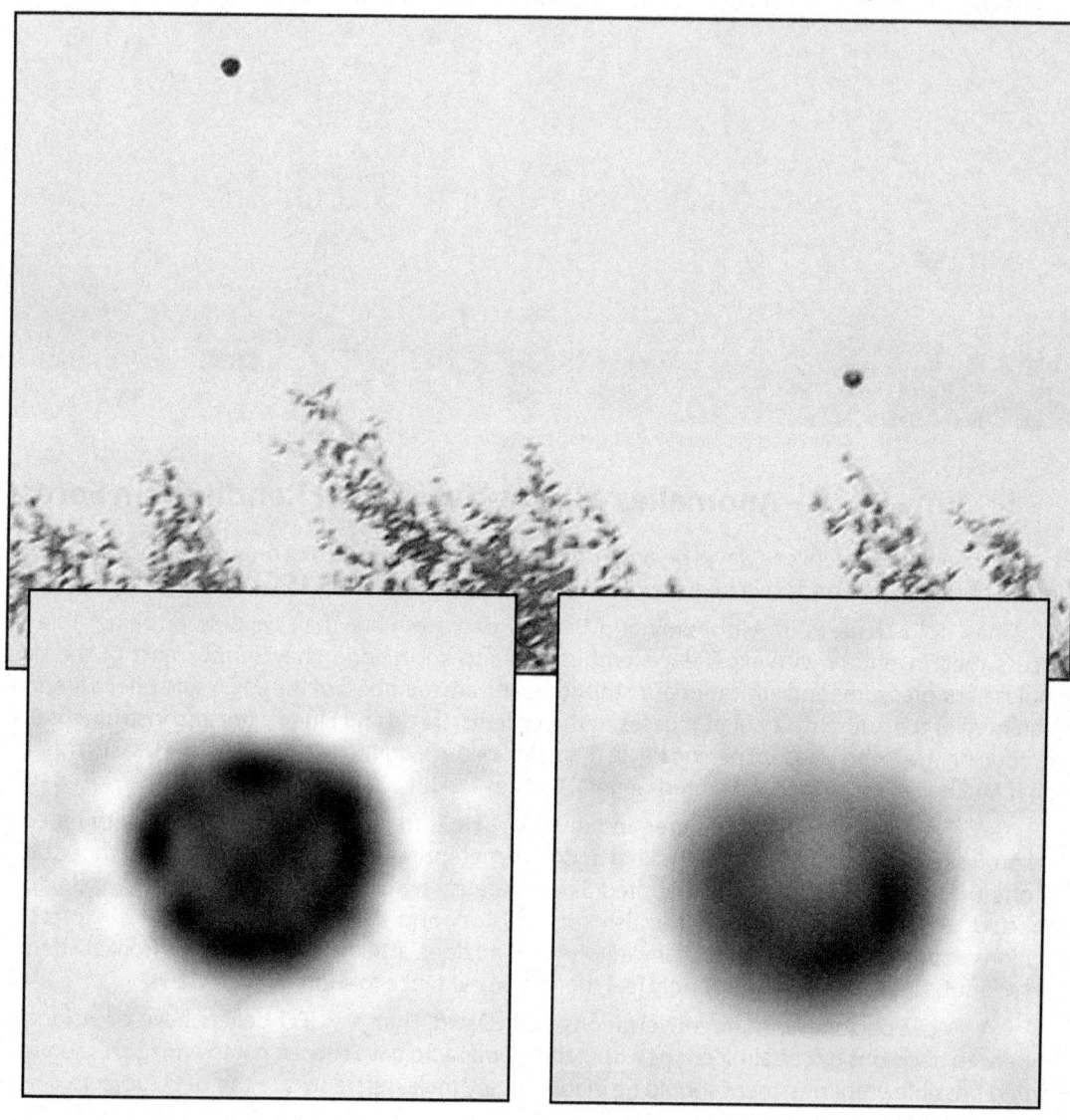

Charles Halt with David Bryant during a visit to Rendlesham Forest

16th/17th June 2012 – Conference at Woodbridge – Charles Halt did not attend on this occasion.

"They invited me, I told them I wouldn't attend if Larry was going."

SITUATION: GREEN
UFOs IN THE FOREST

TURKEY SPRINGS, ARIZONA, 1975

JOHN BURROUGHS
JIM PENNISTON
CHARLES HALT
MONROE NEVELS
TRAVIS WALTON
LARRY WARREN
PETER ROBBINS

RENDLESHAM FOREST, 1980

0 3 0

TWO DAY EVENT: 16th & 17th JUNE, 2012
AT
WOODBRIDGE COMMUNITY HALL & RENDLESHAM FOREST

ADMIT ONE   £40.00

Rendlesham Forest 2012 Conference

**Travis Walton, Charles Halt, John Burroughs, Jim Penniston, Monroe Nevels,
Larry Warren, Peter Robbins.**

Saturday June 16 and Sunday June 17.

Travis Walton, Col. Charles Halt USAF/retired, John Burroughs USAF/Retired, Jim Penniston USAF/retired, Larry Warren, Peter Robbins, Monroe Nevels USAF/retired.

Following on the success of the sold out 30th anniversary of the Rendlesham Forest UFO Incident Conference, we are proud to announce that the 2012 Rendlesham UFO Conference will take place this coming June 16 and 17.

We are pleased to announce Col. Charles Halt USAF/retired will be participating in this event. History will be made on June 16.

Charles Halt, John Burroughs & Jim Penniston: Saturday June 16. In December 1980 strange lights were seen by US Air Force personnel posted to the twin bases of RAF Bentwaters & Woodbridge. Their Command chain left them high and dry. Those who witnessed these events demand an explanation from the US government as to what they were exposed to. They demand the USAF release their classified files on the incident.
Following the 30th anniversary Conference, John and Jim are currently undertaking a review and investigation consisting of seven distinct stages. They hope to have this finished no later than late spring 2012. They will be back in Woodbridge to present a world exclusive on the findings of this investigation. A PowerPoint presentation will reveal new evidence followed by a Q&A session and open forum. For more information visit their Justice for the 81st Security Police Facebook page.

Col. Charles Halt:. Col. Charles Halt: For the first time Col. Charles Halt, Deputy Base Commander of RAF Bentwaters & RAF Woodbridge will be in Woodbridge, Suffolk to deliver a talk on the events of December 1980 and for the first time ever together since those actual events will appear with Sgt. Monroe Nevels. This will be nothing short of truly historic.

Monroe Nevels: Sgt. Nevels was with Lt.Col. Halt, and represented the RAF Bentwaters Disaster Preparedness Office, using the Radiac meter (Guiger counter), amd photographer. Sgt Nevels was with Halt in Rendlesham Forest when he made that infamous recording known as the "Halt" tape.

John and Jim released a joint statement on November 6 entitled: Timetable For Results. This statement can be found on the above mentioned Facebook page or by clicking here: www.spaceportuk.com/events_timetable.html.

Travis Walton: Fire in the Sky: Sunday June 17. The best documented case of alien abduction ever recorded. Travis talks for the first time in the UK at the Woodbridge Community Hall Sunday June 17 at 12 midday.

On the evening of November 5, 1975, 22-year-old Travis Walton was among a group of loggers in the Apache-Sitgreaves National Forest in Arizona that observed a strange, unusually bright light hovering over the forest. Overcome by curiosity, Walton left the safety of the loggers' truck and walked toward the source of the light. He was suddenly blasted by an energy bolt of unknown composition. When his companions observed this, they fled in fear, leaving Walton behind in the forest. After the departed loggers reported the incident to local law enforcement, a massive search was conducted for Walton, but he was not found until five days later, huddled inside a phone booth, disoriented and confused. He later revealed that, after being struck by the strange light beam, he had awakened inside a kind of hospital, where he was surrounded by unusual creatures that were clearly not human. After spending time in this bizarre environment, Walton was rendered unconscious by his captors and returned to Arizona.

Walton's encounter is one of the world's most studied and best known UFO abduction cases. He travels all over the world telling his story at UFO conferences and events. For more information please visit www.travis-walton.com.

Travis Walton, will tell the amazing story of being abducted by extraterrestrials and held captive for five days, at the Rendlesham Forest Conference 2012 on Sunday June 17. Commencing at 12 midday with a showing of the 1993 hit movie Fire in the Sky, inspired by Walton's experience.
His appearance in Woodbridge is an extremely rare opportunity for UK residents to hear first-hand the inside details of one of the most thrilling and well-researched UFO abduction cases in history. Following the screening of Fire in the Sky and Travis' presentation there will be an opportunity to buy a copy the movie on DVD and buy a copy of the rare book Fire in the Sky. There will also be a book signing. Travis has not appeared in the UK since a Paramount publicity event London 1993.

Peter Robbins: US based Investigative Writer - co-author of "Left At East Gate: A First Hand Account of the Rendlesham Forest UFO Incident, Its Cover-Up and Investigation.

Larry Warren: Formerly of the USAF 81st Security Police, eyewitness to the events on one night December 1980, co-author of "Left At East Gate" Larry is recognised as the Rendlesham Forest UFO incident whistle blower and the one who first got this story out.

All SEVEN will be in Suffolk on Saturday June 16 and Sunday June 17 at:

4th November 2012 – *Daily Telegraph* on the existence of UFOs

'Dozens of groups interested in unidentified flying objects have closed due to lack of interest'

'UFO Enthusiasts Admit The Truth May Not Be Out There After All – Declining numbers of "flying saucer" sightings and failure to establish proof of alien existence has led UFO enthusiasts to admit they might not exist after all'.

Jasper Copping, of *The Daily Telegraph* newspaper (4.11.2012), published another story on the UFO subject:

"But having failed to establish any evidence for the existence of extraterrestrial life, Britain's UFO watchers are reaching the conclusion that the truth might not be out there after all. Enthusiasts admit that a continued failure to provide proof and a decline in the number of "flying saucer" sightings suggests that aliens do not exist after all and could mean the end of "Ufology" – the study of UFOs – within the next decade. Dozens of groups interested in the 'flying saucers' and other unidentified craft have already closed, because of lack of interest, and next week one of the country's foremost organisations involved in UFO research is holding a conference to discuss whether the subject has any future. David Wood, chairman of the Association for the Scientific Study of Anomalous Phenomena (ASSAP), said the meeting had been called to address the crisis in the subject and see if UFOs were a thing of the past".

David Wood:

"It is certainly a possibility that in ten years' time, it will be a dead subject.

We look at these things on the balance of probabilities and this area of study has been ongoing for many decades. The lack of compelling evidence beyond the pure anecdotal suggests on the balance of probabilities that nothing is out there. I think that any UFO researcher would tell you that 98 per cent of sightings that happen are very easily explainable. One of the conclusions to draw from that is that perhaps there isn't anything there. The days of compelling eyewitness sightings seem to be over."

David commented that far from leading to an increase in UFO sightings and research, the advent of the internet had coincided with a decline. ASSAP's UFO cases have dropped by 96 per cent since 1988, while the number of other groups involved in UFO research has fallen from well over 100 in the 1990s to around 30 now. Among those to have closed are the *British Flying Saucer Bureau, the Northern UFO Network, and the Northern Anomalies Research Organisation. As well as a fall in sightings and lack of proof, Mr Wood said the lack of new developments meant that the main focus for the dwindling numbers of enthusiasts was supposed UFO encounters that took place several decades ago and conspiracy theories that surround them. In particular, he cited the Roswell incident, in 1947,

---

*The British Flying Saucer Bureau came to an end due to the ill health of Denis Plunkett, one of the nicest men I had the pleasure of ever talking to. I cannot recall specifically that anyone claimed a spaceship had landed at Rendlesham Forest. Hundreds, if not thousands, of sightings reports await our attention for the next book in the series of Haunted Skies 12. This will cover the period from 1991-1994, with Volume 13 (1995) expected to be on sale later this year. One senses that there is something flawed with comments made by people like David Wood, and others (no disrespect intended), who claim the subject will fizzle out and that UFO sightings can be attributed to a myriad of sensible, logical, rational explanations. Even if this was the case and that no further reports were made, well then one has to ask how on earth you can explain away the millions of UFO sightings that have been recorded over the last 65 years! Or should I say millions of years – long before there was any communication structure, or a way of recording fully the passage of those objects as they moved across the skies.

when an alien spaceship is said to have crashed in New Mexico, and the Rendlesham incident, in 1980 – often described as the British equivalent, when airmen from a US airbase in Suffolk reported a spaceship landing.

David Wood:

"When you go to UFO conferences it is mainly people going over these old cases, rather than bringing new ones to the fore. There is a trend where a large proportion of UFO studies are tending towards conspiracy theories, which I don't think is particularly helpful. The issue is to be debated at a summit at the University of Worcester on *November 17th and the conclusions reported in the next edition of the association's journal, Anomaly."

The organisation, which describes itself as an education and research charity, was established in 1981.

John Hanson – An unlikely scenario!

September 2012 – Colonel Halt addresses audience in Las Vegas

In September 2012, at the Smithsonian-affiliated National Atomic Testing Museum, Las Vegas, Charles Halt accused the government of a UFO cover-up that involves a secret agency to deal with what might be extraterrestrial visitations.

"Folks, there is an agency, a very close-held, compartmentalized agency that's been investigating this for years, and there's a very active role played by many of our intelligence agencies that probably don't even know the details of what happens once they collect the data and forward it. It's kind of scary, isn't it? In the last couple of years, the British have released a ton of information, but has anybody ever seen what their conclusions were, or heard anything about Bentwaters officially?

When the documents were released, the time frame when I was involved in the incident is missing – it's gone missing. Nothing else is missing. I have never been harassed over the reports I made about the Bentwaters UFO incidents, probably for a couple of good reasons – number one, my rank and some of the jobs I've held, but also very early on, I sat down and made a very detailed tape and made several copies of everything I know about it and they're secluded away. Maybe I'm paranoid. I don't know, but I think it was time well spent when I made the tapes."

November 2012– Simon Sharman writes to the *Daily Telegraph*

Simon Sharman – a professional, with background media experience, and member of the on-line Manchester UFO Truth Group – A Political Campaign (whom we met at the Colonel Halt talk, in July 2015) wrote the following email to Mr Tony Gallagher – Editor of the *Daily Telegraph*:

Simon Sharman (centre)

Mr Gallagher (Editor of *The Daily Telegraph*),

I want to bring to your attention Jasper Copping's piece on the end of ufology, dated 4.11.12. Having covered my main issues with his shoddy journalism in my on-line response found here, I must inform you of my concerns. It would appear that his entire article was based upon a statement made by Dave Wood, Chairman of something called the Association for the Scientific Study of Anomalous Phenomena (ASSAP). Considering this organisation, if it can even be called that, was the centre of Copping's argument one would assume that we were hearing from 'experts' in the field. Unfortunately for your night editor this couldn't be further from the truth. Here's why: 1) the group hold their meetings in pubs 2) they publish reports on anything from vampires to fairies 3) they have NO coverage of UFOs to be found in their on-line literature barring the most mundane of generic pieces, the most recent dated 2010. To publish statements on matters of the state of UFOlogy from a group such as this can only be described as 'Page 1 Google Journalism'. It simply isn't good enough for someone who's job description is night news editor, as I see no editorial skill on display. On top of that, Copping also wrongly cites a previous incorrect *Telegraph* 'report' concerning the date that the government UFO hotline was shut down (and clearly more page 1 Google investigation). A two minute effort would have ascertained that this occurred in 2009. The reality is that ufology is far from dead and there needed to be more balanced input from active and more qualified experts in the field. Dr. David Clarke does not come under this category as, although he may be qualified, he is well- known for his sceptical and debunking views. All in all to put out such badly researched and incorrect content, to a global audience, is nowhere near the mark. Having been a broadcaster myself for many years I would never get away with such lackluster efforts in my films or programs, and the printed word is often much more powerful (and therefore damaging) being far less transient. I hope you take this criticism in the tone that it is intended, which is that I would like to believe some form of internal follow action will be taken. I look forward to your reply,

Sincerely, Simon Sharman, of the Manchester UFO Truth Group

Simon writes to the Editor

Simon Sharman also felt it was necessary to write to Tony Gallagher – editor of the *Daily Telegraph*, on the 15th November 2012.

A reply came from Assistant Editor – Hugh Dougherty, a few hours later, in which he thanked him for the email but defended what Jasper had written as a fair and balanced piece of journalism.

15th November 2012 – Email from Simon to Hugh Dougherty

Dear Hugh,

Firstly I would like to thank you for taking the time to respond to my concerns so promptly, and for considering my issues with what appears to be some degree of thought.

Unfortunately, I believe that when one considers the title of the article was "UFO enthusiasts admit the truth may not be out there after all" and the sub-heading being, "Declining numbers of 'flying saucer' sightings and failure to establish proof of alien existence has led UFO enthusiasts to admit they might not exist after all", I think it's safe to assume that the general premise of Copping's piece is quite clear. The story is quite literally based upon the words of Mr Wood as I have previously said. If there was another basis for the piece which I somehow missed I would very much like to know what it was.

Although I thank you for pointing out the full name attributed to ASSAP, I am completely aware of what it stands for and, in fact, it is their wide area of interest that concerns me the most. To suggest the state of ufology is dead, based on comments made by an organisation that discusses the nature of fantasy figures such as vampires and fairies, is utterly incongruous if one knows anything about the nature of *some* UFO incidents, which are not mere 'fairy tales'. I'm not talking about the 90% of explainable cases that are misidentifications, natural phenomena or hoaxes. I'm referring to very serious incidents such as the RAF Woodbridge case of 1980, which was definitively a real event that even the late Hill-Norton, Admiral of the Fleet, became involved with. So concerned was he about the reality of the incident and its significance to our national security that he repeatedly made a fuss in parliament in search of answers. Of course there are many more real incidents I could make reference to, where corroborative evidence exists, such as radar confirmation etc., which definitely takes the subject well out of the 'ghosts and paranormal' arena.

With reference to your question of relevance regarding their meeting spot being a public house, and your comparison to literary greats such as Tolkien and CS Lewis, I feel it necessary to point out just one thing. Those creative geniuses were famous for precisely that – creating incredible works of fiction and fantasy, a process which is undoubtedly assisted by varying degrees of intoxication of some sorts or another. I, for one, am very grateful for their time spent in the pub if it helped them write those amazing books. On the contrary, any organisation which makes use of the words 'Scientific Study' in its very title cannot be expected to be taken seriously or 'scientifically' by conducting meetings in houses of intoxication. Also, as I pointed out previously, there appears to be no evidence of any scientific thought, work, or papers on UFOs, published anywhere on their website that I could find (there are a total of 3 very old pages on UFOs on their entire website, none of which have any real substance). This does not constitute a body that can legitimately call itself a scientific UFO body, and therefore could never be cited as a credible voice for ufologists across the UK.

Sincerely,

Simon Sharman

June 2013 – Was this metal fragment a UFO that landed in Suffolk?

Ronnie Dugdale – a laboratory technician and nurseryman, from Great Yarmouth, who has a long-standing personal interest in the UFO events reported to have taken place, in 1980, at Rendlesham Forest, and a friend of Brenda Butler, was serving on his plant stall at Campsea Ashe market, in Suffolk, when he was approached by a customer with an American accent.

"I asked her if she was from one of the airbases and she told me she was once married to an American airman and now living at Wickham Market, but she had previously lived, for many years, near Rendlesham Forest. I asked her if she had seen any UFOs, to which she smiled and told me she hadn't but knew that others had. I then told her of my interest in the event that had taken place in the forest at the end of December 1980, and after exchanging pleasantries she left. On the same morning she returned and handed over to me a bright metal object, which looked aluminum in composition and appeared extremely light for its size; I asked her what it was, to which she replied, 'It's from your UFO; it came from the field.'"

Ronnie handed it back, but she told him to keep it. She said she had some '81st' ephemera that Ronnie might find interesting and then left. Ronnie cannot say whether she is a regular to the market or not, as he has only been trading at that market for a few weeks.

He describes her as:

". . . smartly dressed, blond hair, well-spoken, and in her early sixties. She was wearing a distinctive red, white, and blue neckerchief, similar to what an air hostess would wear, so it may well have been a uniform. She paid for her plant and then left."

Even if we could prove the piece of metal was recovered on that date, and in that manner, it does not provide proof of anything, as the areas around RAF Woodbridge and Bentwaters must still be littered with parts of aircraft debris, understanding the role in which the runways played during the Second World War.

What is of interest is why this woman should wait 33 years before picking up the object from her house, and then handing it over.

If the sample had been a lump of insignificant, irregular-shaped steel or iron, which could have come from anywhere, we would not have shown as much interest. However, the photographs of the piece of metal, sent to us by Ronnie, appear to have superficial similarities with other incidents involving alleged pieces of metal recovered after UFO sightings.

Ronnie is open-minded about the artifact and makes no claims as to its authenticity, but he believes that the charming and friendly woman was genuine and disagrees with our suggestion that her actions were deliberately orchestrated to disseminate false disinformation about the incident, and points out that it was he who entered her into conversation regarding Rendlesham, rather than the other way around.

Margaret Westwood – Retired police officer

In *Haunted Skies*, Volume 5, we reported about the recovery of a piece of metal from Wentworth Drive, Harborne, Birmingham, by police officers Margaret and Geoffrey Westwood – then head of the Birmingham UFO Group, UFOSIS, in 1974. This took place after a number of UFO 'displays' had taken place over the suburb, which were brought to the attention of the MOD.

Sadly, Margaret passed away some years ago now. She was a credit to UFO research and was able to supply us with some interesting information about several investigations that she had been involved in, during the 1970s.

Aluminum, large traces of silicon and smaller amounts of iron

"I was told by the babysitter that she had seen a vivid lime-green coloured 'light' shoot over the house. The following morning, I discovered the top of a young eucalyptus (transplanted 12 months previously) was blackened – as if burnt. At the base of the tree, I found a fragment of material, about two inches in size, that I hadn't seen there before. When later analysed, it was found to be rich in aluminum, with large traces of silicon and smaller amounts of iron. I don't know whether it was connected, but the leaves on the tree grew very elongated. The tree itself grew to a height of 16 feet over 12 months – an abnormal growth rate."

Unfortunately, Margaret had mislaid the sample, and its present whereabouts are not known.

Incidents classified

We discovered MOD officials had written to several people living in the Harborne area, confirming that their reports were *"being examined, to see if there are any Defence implications"*.

Needless to say we have never seen any of these declassified documents, despite this having happened now 39 years ago!

Introducing Scientist Nick Reiter

Nick Reiter

We were intrigued with the composition of the metals found at the scene, and contacted Nick Reiter – a scientist at a solar research facility in Toledo, Ohio – who has also spent over 20 years researching UFOs and anti-gravity concepts. A copy of the incomplete graph, supplied by Margaret, was sent to Nick, who has worked on numerous cases involving the alleged recovery of UFO debris, in 2012.

"I did some comparative study of the old Harborne plot versus known sample plots of my own. Attached is the annotated version.

It looks like that metal was magnesium primarily, with aluminum and sodium being the other two main missing peaks. I would call it a magnesium alloy, with Al, Fe, Cu, and Ge added. It makes for a strange blend, I'll give you."

Nick has had the opportunity to work with many well-known investigators and authors, including Bud Hopkins, David M. Jacobs, PhD, and Linda Moulton Howe, and was one of the 'behind-the-scenes', formerly anonymous analysers, asked by Linda Moulton Howe, to examine the alleged Roswell UFO metal fragment that appeared on the Coast to Coast radio show, in the mid-1990s.

Nick's many original technical developments, and instruments, are currently being tested in the field for their effectiveness in providing solid, quantum physics-based solutions to anomalous experiences. You will find Nick's innovative techniques mentioned in the *Fortean Times, New Energy News, Journal of Borderland Research, UFO Forum, The Bulletin of Anomalous Experiences*, and *Nexus* magazines. He has also been featured in *Glimpses of Other Realties* (Volume II) by Linda Moulton Howe, and *Electric UFOs: Fireballs, Electromagnetic and Abnormal States*, by Albert Budden.

Ohio – Mr Bruce Reiter recovers metal fragment

In March 2003, Nick received a phone call from his father – Bruce Reiter – concerning an interesting piece of news from his old rural neighbourhood, north of Tiffin, Ohio. His father told Nick that his nearest neighbour – 'Ed' – had found a mysterious piece of metal in his side yard, while raking up the last fall's leaves and twigs. The object had been obscured over the winter by two heavy snowfalls and numerous lesser ones. 'Ed' had no explanation for the irregular metal blob, which was roughly six inches by two and a half inches, with a maximum thickness of one half-inch, or so.

The 'blob' had very apparently been molten at some point, and had solidified against a fairly flat or solid surface. While the piece had been found in the yard on the earth, the bottom side of the 'blob', when found, was generally smooth with some white oxides present. By reviewing the weather, over the course of the winter that year, he concluded that the 'blob' of metal – if it had not been placed by artifice at a later post-snow date – had apparently fallen onto a hard-packed, ice-crusted, snowdrift that had remained there since January of the year, up until the thaw in March.

Nick interviewed 'Ed' carefully and borrowed his 'blob' of mystery metal, after being granted permission to cut it open as desired.

Analysis of sample – Aluminum, carbon and silicon

Nick ended up sawing a roughly 2-inch portion from the main 'blob'. The interior of the metal appeared homogeneous. A small shaving was taken from both the interior and the surface and analysed, by Nick, with a Jeol 840 scanning electron microscope fitted with EDS. The sample was originally analysed using EDS (Energy Dispersive Spectroscopy) by Nick, which determined that the metal was primarily aluminum, with traces of carbon and silicon. A crude Archimedean test of density indicated that the aluminum was within a couple percent of appropriate mass weight, thus meaning it was likely not to be an unusual isotope. It was not noticeably radioactive when surveyed with a Baird Atomic rate meter (Geiger counter).

Metallic debris falls from UFO, Ohio

In late 2006, an uncannily similar account came to Nick's attention, by way of the Ohio UFO investigative community. The witness to this event was ex Vietnam veteran, named Benny Foggin, living in rural central Ohio, south-east of Newark. He told of sighting:

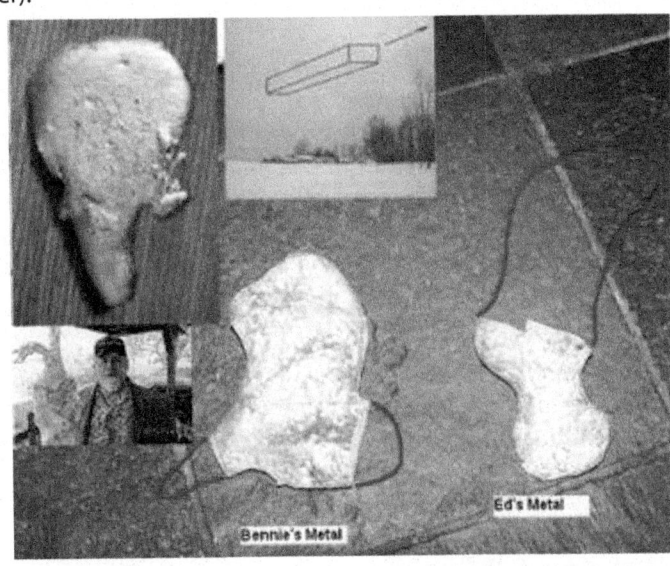

Ed's Metal

Bennie's Metal

> "...a large, dark, box-like UFO – the length of a commercial airliner – which glided silently over my home, at an estimated altitude of 100 to 200 feet. I say silent, but I did hear a rhythmic sound near one end that reminded me of the drum of a washing machine, scraping on bad bushings. As this noisy end of the 'craft' passed over, I heard a dull 'thud' from somewhere nearby, but was transfixed by the dramatic object above."

Benny Foggin

It was only after the 'craft' had vanished to the west, over the tree-line, that Benny thought to look for the source of the 'thud' sound he had heard, a few minutes before, and discovered what appeared to be a 'blob' of solidified and still hot aluminum lying in his gravel and dirt driveway. The material was recovered and placed into in a box, intending to show it to some of the Ohio UFO research community. However, domestic and personal issues at the time prompted him to delay, and within a few months the box had been misplaced and Benny and his wife had, by that time, moved to a new home in the area.

Phyllis Budinger, of Frontier Analytical Services, Cleveland

In 2006, the piece was rediscovered by the owner Benny who sent it to Ohio researcher – Joe Stets, in Columbus. Joe apparently had an unnamed party at his own work establishment take an informal analytical look at the material. However, another piece of the aluminum 'blob' was also sawed off and sent to Phyllis Budinger, of Frontier Analytical Services, Cleveland, who has done high quality analysis on 'unusual event' residues and artifacts, for some years. Phyllis used Infrared Spectroscopy on the sample then performed, in turn, by a colleague of Phyllis' – Dr. Sampath Ayengar. Dr. Ayengar is also well-known as analytical expert on matters of unusual or anomalous artifacts and materials.

2013 – Nick Reiter

"As you mentioned before, that certainly is similar in form to not just Benny Foggin's metal, but the 'Ed' metal, as well as two others I have now seen photos of. If ever there is a chance to get a small sample of the UK fragment sent to me I will cover the cost to get it analyzed or re-analyzed as the case may be. You might be interested to know that a couple of months ago, I had some isotopic ratio analysis performed on Ben's sample. Two values – Nickel 62 and Strontium 84 were interestingly out of bounds from textbook numbers. Odd that."

Nick Reiter – Nathan's Metal

"Nathan contacted me in early 2011. He and his young son found this cooled 'blob' in a meadow, close to a park, near the city of Youngstown, Ohio. There was no UFO story associated with it. Unfortunately, before I could get a sample for comparative testing, Nathan fell out of touch,

due to divorce and childcare issues in his life. He never replied back to later emails sent to him from me.

Oddly, here is the other Ohio artefact (discounting Bennie's metal, or 'Ed's' metal) which I found in 2008, when out walking through a field in extreme south-eastern Ohio, with some friends, exploring old house ruins in a region torn up for coal mining in the 1920s.

It was simply lying on the grassy, weedy ground, away from anything else. I thought it looked like Ben's metal in form (although smaller) and picked it up. I have done no testing on it yet, other than some simple chemical tests to say it is mostly aluminum (like all the others)."

Steve Roberts' specimen from the UFO landing site in 1980

In August 2013, Brenda Butler handed over to us the piece of metal given to her by Ronnie Dugdale. We photographed this, and the lightweight material given to her, 30 years ago, by 'Steve Roberts', who claimed it had been recovered from the UFO landing site in Rendlesham Forest.

October 2013

Tests were later carried out on this piece by a colleague of Nick's – Phyllis Budinger, who had this to say: *"The Rendlesham sample is polystyrene. Not surprised, especially when you said it was soluble in MEK. (Methyl Ethyl Keton) I don't detect any other components".*

Jim Penniston – Was it long underwear?

Jim Penniston was sent the photos of the material.

"As far as polystyrene, the only use that I know of at the time of Rendlesham is it was widely used in throw-away coffee cups! LOL. It is also used in long underwear in the military."

Nick Reiter – Regarding fragment handed to Ronnie Dugdale

"Potentially important – I was able to do some crude chemical and flame analysis on the metal bit. It is NOT a magnesium alloy; it indeed appears to be aluminum of some alloy or blend – so therefore, it does not match that old plot you had shared last year, from back in the 1980s (the one that showed magnesium from Margaret Westwood). Maybe it will match Ben's alloy. The material here, in this picture, looks like a granular sintered metal, or glassy substance – is this the same material seen in the earlier pictures from a couple of weeks ago (that looked like a melted and solidified metal blob)? Well, we have an interesting match it seems."

Similarities: US – Ohio sample and UK – Rendlesham Forest claim

In an update, a few days later, Nick had this to say:

"The 'rough' analysis by my colleague's SEM and EDS came back in. I've attached his report. You may use this – it looks like he 'sanitized' it by removing the company name, as is best. The upshot – the metal appears to indeed be similar (in

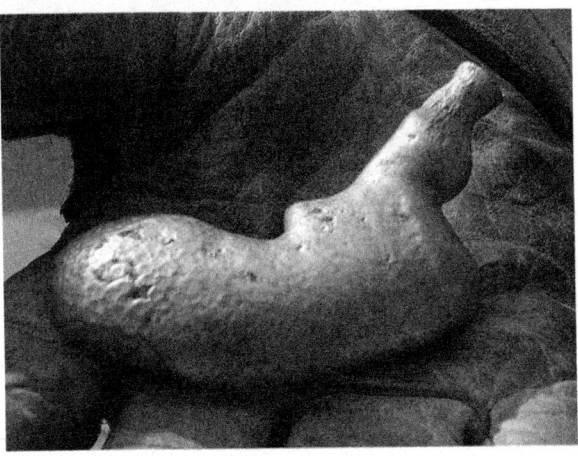

rough terms) to Ben Foggin's metal alloy – aluminum, with the main minor component being silicon. Also seen was some magnesium, in about the same ratio as Ben's. The next step will be to do ICPMS Inductively Coupled Plasma Mass Spectrometry on this, which would be the fine analysis. Ben Foggin, and I, both agreed that if this sample came back resembling his, we would pay for the ICP – Interesting findings!"

Death of Nick Reiter – Obituary – Rest in peace

GIBSONBURG: Gibsonburg resident, Nicholas Alan Reiter, 51 died Tuesday, November 19, 2013 at the St. Charles Mercy Medical Hospital in Oregon. Born on August 7, 1962, he was the son of Bruce and Rebecca (Buskirk) Reiter. He graduated from Old Fort High School and earned a degree in Electro Mechanical Robotics at Terra Community College. As a scientist, Nicholas worked for the Calyxo Company in Perrysburg. On June 29, 1984, he married Debora "Deb" Wheatley at the Trinity United Methodist Church in Lindsey. She survives; also surviving are his mother, Rebecca of Tiffin; sons, Trevor, Peter and Ian all of Gibsonburg; granddaughter,

Nick Reiter shown here with his family

Margot Reiter; and sister, Natalie (Dennis) Eberly of Tiffin. Nicholas was known to be a published author and has been broadcasted on TV and radio as a Paranormal Investigator. He enjoyed riding his Harley Davidson, travelling, cooking and spending time with his family and animals. He also attended the Trinity United Methodist Church in Gibsonburg. A time of gathering in remembrance will be offered on Tuesday, November 26, 2013, 2-8 p.m. at the Herman-Kinn-Veh Funeral Home & Cremation Services in Gibsonburg where an additional hour of gathering followed by a Memorial Service will be held on Wednesday, 11 a.m. Rev. Max Ulderich will officiate. Burial will follow at West Union Cemetery, Gibsonburg.

June 2013 – MOD declassify their UFO files

Declassified files, released by the National Archives in late June 2013, reveal that the MOD closed its UFO desk in 2009, claiming that any investigation into sightings *"would be an inappropriate use of defence resources".* The 25 files included 4,400 pages and cover the work carried out in the final two years of the MOD UFO desk – from late 2007 until November 2009. Officials decided to close the 'UFO hotline', as it was deemed to have *"no defence benefit",* and resources devoted to it were taking staff away from *"more valuable defence-related activities".* They include accounts of alleged abductions and contact with aliens, as well as UFO sightings near UK landmarks, including the Houses of Parliament.

In a briefing to then Defence Secretary – Bob Ainsworth – in November 2009, Carl Mantell, of the RAF Air Command, suggested the MOD *"should reduce the UFO desk, which is consuming increasing resources, but produces no valuable defence output".* He said that, in more than 50 years, *"No UFO sighting reported to (MOD) has ever revealed anything to suggest an extraterrestrial presence or military threat to the UK".*

An official MOD statement declared: *"The Ministry of Defence has no opinion on the existence, or otherwise, of extraterrestrial life. However, in over 50 years, no UFO report has revealed any evidence of a potential threat to the United Kingdom."*

John Hanson: Chris Clark – another witness to the events of 1980

In 2015, during the organisation of an opportunity for members of the public to hear Charles Halt speak about his experiences at Woodbridge Community Centre, I was contacted by Christopher Clark, who described himself as a surveyor, currently living in Woodbridge. Mr Clark told me that he knew Charles Halt very well and that he had dined with him and his family during his time as Deputy Base Commander.

Christopher, well-spoken and articulate, was insistent that he meet up with Charles Halt for dinner, but I had to tell him that this was not possible, owing to the Colonel's commitments. Chris told me that a few days after the UFO event he had asked Charles, during a visit to the Officers' mess on the base, in December 1980, if he could take him to where it had happened. Charles took him to the location – which was, according to Chris:

> *"…a cleared area, where some Americans were busy cleaning up. I checked the ground with my Geiger counter and found some radiation. I then helped Charles to obtain a plaster cast of one of the impressions in the ground, and asked him if he would allow me to interview the three men who had reported the incident. He declined, saying that this wasn't possible. I then took a roll of film, which I still have in my possession, which has never been processed".*

On the 11th July 2015, Chris and his daughter were introduced to Charles Halt. Charles still cannot specifically remember them, saying:

> *"I met so many people around that time frame, I'm sorry but I don't recall meeting them."*

Chris was asked if he had any recollection of where this piece of unique film was, but was unable to locate its current whereabouts – which may seem a little odd, bearing in mind its importance. If the film is ever found we shall, of course, update the reader.

22nd October 2014 – *ITV News*: Rendlesham film shown at Colchester

In addition to the never-ending story of US documentaries released into the British public domain by companies who offer all manner of explanations for what the airmen saw, ranging from bizarre to ridiculous, was a film produced by a Colchester man, during this year.

The film, based on the events of three days in December 1980, was premiered in a blaze of media publicity at the Colchester Film Festival and was written and directed by Daniel Simpson (Spiderhole, H) it tells the story of three UFO investigators plunging deep into Rendlesham Forest over three days.

Daniel spent nearly four years filming on hand-held cameras and created the special effects himself. He says the experience of talking to eyewitnesses from the events of 1980 has made him change his opinion.

"I've looked into it endlessly and I've looked into the faces and eyes of people telling the story and I just have to believe them – that's what you have to go on. I believe something happened that we will never know what it was, but I believe people do know."

February 2015 – Film released

The film, entitled *Rendlesham UFO Incident*, was made available on general release in the UK.

It was also released in America and Japan under the title 'Hangar 10'

A clip of film on You Tube 'Attitude Films' introduces three witnesses, who set off into the forest with their metal detectors, accompanied straightaway, by a shot of dead horses lying in a field. A jet screams over the top of them, followed by an elliptical object moving into cloud cover. Blue light charges through the trees … screams are heard.

'The Telegraph'

On the 16th February 2015, Rupert Hawksley of *The Telegraph* newspaper, published details of the film with the heading: 'Did an extraterrestrial craft land in a Suffolk forest, during the winter of 1980? The maker of a new film, *The Rendlesham UFO Incident*, believes so.

The film, available to purchase on Amazon, is described as: 'Documentary style sci-fi horror. When a couple (Robert Curtis and Abbie Salt) decide to go hunting for ancient Saxon gold in Rendlesham Forest, Suffolk, they are joined by their extraterrestrial-obsessed friend Jake (Danny Shayler), who wants to search the rumoured site of alien sightings and capture the entire experience on film. While exploring the surrounding forest, they begin to witness unusual activity in the skies directly above, and all their equipment starts to malfunction. Then, as they venture deeper into the wooded area, the group stumble upon an old abandoned army base that they hope will unlock the secrets behind the mysterious events'.

This is entertainment and akin to the *Blair Witch* productions of yesteryear.

Wikipedia – Rendlesham Forest Incident

Examples from the Wikipedia entry include a reference to Kevin Conde and his explanation.

It also includes 39 references as source material – sixteen from Ian Ridpath, five from Dr. David Clarke, Jenny Randles and others – accompanied by a singular reference [was this deliberately selected?] from Jasper Copping (6th August 2011) re the "Rendlesham Incident: US commander speaks for the first time about the 'Suffolk UFO'".

The Daily Telegraph quotes Colonel Conrad, who was scathing about his former deputy:

"We saw nothing that resembled Lt. Colonel Halt's descriptions either in the sky or on the ground.

He should be ashamed and embarrassed by his allegation that his country and England both conspired to deceive their citizens over this issue. He knows better."

This appears rather biased, in our opinion; others will disagree.

11th July 2015 – Talk by Colonel Charles Irwin Halt, at Woodbridge Community Hall, Suffolk

As the initiator and organiser of the event, I would like to thank my co-organiser Brenda Butler. For months we patiently discussed every logistical aspect in order to try to ensure that the meeting would be a success. We were soon made aware that there were a few people who (for their own reasons) did not want the Colonel to come over here at all – (Very strange, taking into consideration that at no stage had we ever criticised them, or any other speakers who had had the opportunity to give their accounts of the 'Rendlesham Forest Incident', at various events held at the same Hall over the past few years!)

Opposition

From the start of announcing the forthcoming conference 'opera' period of many months, I received a large proportion of quite aggressive hate mail, advising me not to go ahead. They included emails from Larry Warren, telling me to *"watch my back"* and *"tread lightly"* – rather childish, taking into consideration that I have never criticized Larry personally. In fact, I met up with him shortly before the conference (contrived by another party) in Rendlesham Forest. He is a charming, likeable man, but history must be shown to be impartial and reflect an accurate account of what took place. This is what we will do.

Many people expressed a wish to take Charles Halt out for dinner, during his visit to the UK; others wanted to accompany him into the forest to hear first-hand his account of the 'Rendlesham Forest Incident'. While we were overwhelmed by the excitement caused, we had to take a firm hand with some who felt they should be given special dispensation: there just wasn't the time and the Colonel and his son, Clifford, had expressed a wish that the numbers accompanying them be kept at a manageable level. Our visitors were only here for a few days, and we had to keep in mind the need for him to recover from the rigours of the flight from the USA to Heathrow.

655

David Bryant – Moderator and Master of Ceremonies

Brenda and I would like to thank everyone who was involved in organising the recent talks given by retired Colonel Charles Irwin Halt, especially our friend – David Bryant.

David was *not* a co-organiser of the event (as was stated in a recent, somewhat inaccurate book about Colonel Halt's visit, by Peter Robbins) but had been invited to give a talk about astronauts and the UFO phenomenon. Since he is a professional lecturer (with a loud voice!) we asked him to act as moderator of the 'Questions and Answers' session, and as our Master of Ceremonies for the evening.

Media interest – Thanks

Special thanks should go to Tom Potter and the Editor of the *East Anglian Daily Times,* for their support and subsequent newspaper publicity, advertising the scheduled visit by Colonel Charles Halt to Woodbridge.

James Hazel

We would also like to thank James Hazel, of *BBC Radio Suffolk* (who attended and interviewed Charles Halt), and the same TV Station for an interview conducted with Brenda Butler.

Nick Rigby

I would also like to thank Nick Rigby, of *BBC Radio Norfolk,* for his interview conducted in the hall, in the later part of that evening.

Jon Austin's online article – 'Daily Express'

On the afternoon of the 14th July, I was contacted by Mr Austin, who asked me for any information pertaining to the radar tapes. I suggested he look at what I had written in Volume 8 of *Haunted Skies* and sent him a PDF, along with requested photos and other information. I also spoke to him at length about my part in all of this and the *Haunted Skies* books. My only mention in the *Express* article was: *". . . organised by ex-cop UFO researcher John Hanson, who said Mr Halt was 'a reliable witness' and backed the 'cover up' claims".*

The Suffolk UFO enthusiasts

In addition, of course, we should also like to acknowledge the assistance of Beverley Plumridge, Derek Savory and his ex-wife (for providing refreshments), and his two sons (for ensuring there was no problem at the door), Journalist Gillian Madison (for interviews conducted with Charles Halt), Joe Laming (for his technical support with the PA/micro-phone system).

Ben Emlyn Jones

Thanks also to Steve Wills, David Feast, Bernie Hunt, Nicholas Scott Packer, wife, Brenda, Sarah and Steve Franklin, and web blogger Ben Emlyn Jones for filming the 'private' walk and evening one. We were surprised by the speed which this film was then posted onto YouTube 24 hours later – preventing us, the organizers, from asserting any editorial control.

This meant we were unable to pass on the video of Colonel Halt's morning walk in Rendlesham Forest to the Forestry Commission, for them to sell copies to provide income towards the upkeep of the forest. This had been a factor in Colonel Halt's agreeing to participate in the event, and ours in organizing it. We were also surprised to see photographs of myself and Dawn later uploaded onto the internet with facial featured blotted out accompanied by allegations that persons who had assisted us had not been paid. This is malicious – they were paid £50 each (Ben £60) – without them it wouldn't have been a successful Conference.

THE HALT PERSPECTIVE

Some moments captured as images of Colonel Charles Halt's visit to Woodbridge

COLONEL HALT WOODBRIDGE BRIEFING

Haunted Skies

(John Hanson & Dawn Holloway, with Brenda Butler)

Invite you to attend a talk given by

CHARLES HALT Colonel USAF Retired

(Former Deputy Base Commander and later Base Commander at RAF Woodbridge, 1980)

Plus a talk by Meteoricist

Mr David Bryant
(Master of Ceremonies)
What The Astronauts Have To Say About UFOs!

Saturday 11th July 2015
~ at ~

Woodbridge Community Hall
Doors open 7pm
Station Road, Woodbridge
Suffolk IP12 4AU

Entrance Fee
£20

HAUNTED SKIES PUBLISHING

Followed by a **WALK THROUGH RENDLESHAM FOREST**
With **BRENDA BUTLER**
At midnight, following the event

Tickets can be purchased from John Hanson Tel: 0121 445 0340
email: johndawn1@sky.com *or* Brenda Butler Tel: 01728 830757

Illustration: Sebastian Woszczyk at www.yoszko.com • Design: Bob Tibbitts iSET

Haunted Skies Publications presents

Col. Charles Halt

5.00 pm	Hall opens: meet & greet & book sales
7.00 pm	David Bryant: opening remarks
7.05 pm	Lionel Beer: Hon. Pres. Of BUFORA
7.15 pm	Short break
7.20 pm	David Bryant: 'Astronauts and UFOs'
8.00 pm	Short break
8.10 pm	Brenda Butler: 'The local witnesses'
8.30 pm	Long break: celebration cake cutting
9.00 pm	Col. Charles Halt: The RFI: Part 1
10.00 pm	Break
10.10 pm	Col. Charles Halt: Part 2
11.10 pm	Short break
11.20 pm	Moderated questions

Saturday, July 11th, 2015

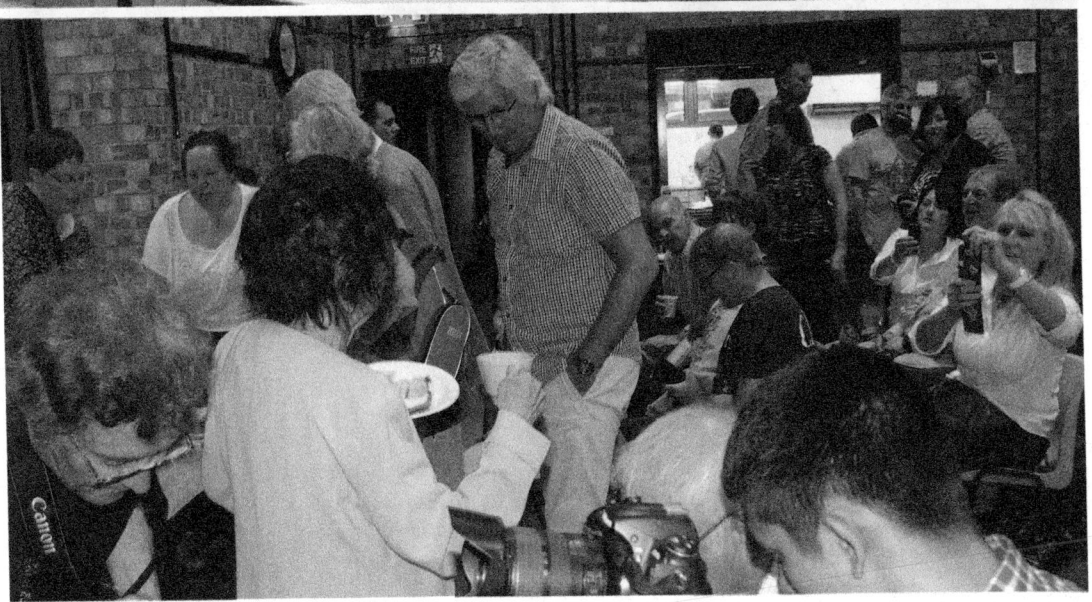

2016 – Jim Penniston – *'Rendlesham Code'* book coming soon

In March 2016 we learned that there had been further developments of the book being written by Jim Penniston and Gary Osborn about the binary code. They claim Jim will concentrate on the events which took place 72 hours after the UFO incident and of the way that a cover story was executed, this will include naming names and hopefully tell us why such a containment was initiated and more importantly for what reason.

John Hanson & Dawn Holloway – Media's fascination for the incident

In addition to this, of course, is the media's 'singular' fascination with the UFO events which took place in Rendlesham Forest during 1980. Charles Halt and his companions told of seeing three objects in the sky – and also half-moon shaped objects. Other airmen described seeing a black triangular object on the ground. Whilst many people offer ridiculous explanations for what was seen including the lighthouse, they never include any comments about the huge mass of sightings that was to plague not only the UK but East Anglia, whose parallels with the Belgium UFO 'wave,' cannot be ignored.

Colchester, Essex – The Harmonic Grid

What can we make of that? A look at a map places the UK adjacent to a country which once formed part of the same land mass.

There is little doubt that the majority of the sightings (which also encompasses reports of manifestations) occur along ley lines – matters that were known about by our ancient cultures. Bearing in mind the huge increase in reported UFO activity taking place around Colchester in the later part of the 20th Century 1990's – (an ancient town, which served as the first capital of Roman Britain) it is obvious that there is something very significant – not so much about the town itself – but its location on the surface of the planet. For some time now we have felt (judging from examination of the enormous amount of reports contained in our archives) that UFO sightings occur along specific corridors, rather than randomly.

Captain Bruce Leonard Cathie

We heartily endorse the theories put forward by Captain Bruce Leonard Cathie (11th February 1930 – 2nd June 2013) who was a New Zealand airline pilot who wrote seven books related to 'Flying Saucers' and a 'World energy grid'.

His central thesis was that he could use mathematics to describe a grid-like pattern on Earth (i.e. the Electro-dynamic field on Earth)

Bruce L. Cathie
Author/Researcher

that powers 'Flying Saucers' and controls the dates and places where nuclear bombs can function; in his book *The Harmonic Conquest of Space*.

He did claim to have successfully predicted and documented the detonation time of an early French nuclear test using his harmonic 'mathematics', which is based around trigonometry and geophysical latitude/longitude coordinates. His theories also resemble *Buckminster Fuller's Synergetics in that in reality everything is energy-vectors; which is reflected in his 'castling' of Einstein's relativity equations, i.e. based on those presumptions mass can be removed from E=mc^2.

Using complicated mathematical calculations, Captain Cathie formed a theory dubbed the World Energy Grid System.

Diagram 1, showing the relationship of a grid polar square to the geographic pole. Eac grid has a similar pattern. The pole of each grid is set at a different latitude and longitud

A = Geographic pole
B = Grid pole

C
D
E   = Corner aerial positions of grid polar square
F

B - C
B - D
B - E   = 2545.584412 minutes of arc
B - F

The displacement (A-B) has a different value for each Grid

(A - B)	Grid "A" = 1054.255313	minutes of arc
(A - B)	Grid "B" = 694.8832574	minutes of arc
(A - B)	Grid "C" = 867.6871800	minutes of arc

It is based on the idea that a grid-like energy pattern covers the Earth and which has the power to control or cause nuclear-based events, such as a nuclear explosion or bomb.

According to him, this same energy grid is also the power source for UFOs that regularly appear and are seen by people all around the world.

Nexus Magazine

In 1994, Captain Cathie described his calculations – the main one dubbed the 'harmonic equation' – to *Nexus Magazine*.

"I came to the conclusion that the speed of light, mass and gravity acceleration values must have some connection with the grid structure in order to explain the extraordinary manoeuvres carried out by the strange craft."

---

*Synergetics, according to E.J. Applewhite, was Fuller's name for the geometry he advanced based on the patterns of energy that he saw in nature. For Fuller, geometry was a laboratory science with the touch and feel of physical models – not rules out of a textbook. It gains its validity not from classic abstractions but from the results of individual physical experience.

In later years, Captain Cathie said he came to find that his energy grid system was a concept that was already widely understood by various scientists and international researchers. He told the magazine:

"It became obvious that the system had many military applications and that political advantage could be gained by those with secret knowledge of this nature."

John Hanson: *"I started research way back in 1995 – time flies"*

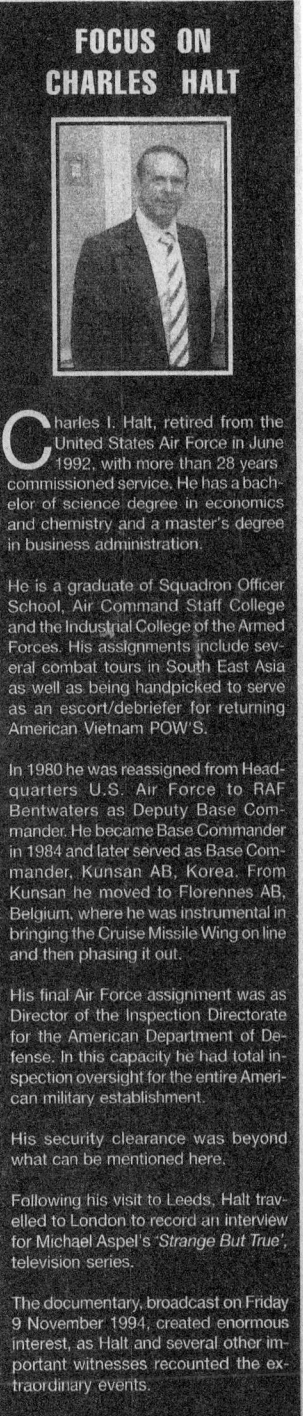

FOCUS ON CHARLES HALT

Charles I. Halt, retired from the United States Air Force in June 1992, with more than 28 years commissioned service. He has a bachelor of science degree in economics and chemistry and a master's degree in business administration.

He is a graduate of Squadron Officer School, Air Command Staff College and the Industrial College of the Armed Forces. His assignments include several combat tours in South East Asia as well as being handpicked to serve as an escort/debriefer for returning American Vietnam POW'S.

In 1980 he was reassigned from Headquarters U.S. Air Force to RAF Bentwaters as Deputy Base Commander. He became Base Commander in 1984 and later served as Base Commander, Kunsan AB, Korea. From Kunsan he moved to Florennes AB, Belgium, where he was instrumental in bringing the Cruise Missile Wing on line and then phasing it out.

His final Air Force assignment was as Director of the Inspection Directorate for the American Department of Defense. In this capacity he had total inspection oversight for the entire American military establishment.

His security clearance was beyond what can be mentioned here.

Following his visit to Leeds, Halt travelled to London to record an interview for Michael Aspel's *'Strange But True'*, television series.

The documentary, broadcast on Friday 9 November 1994, created enormous interest, as Halt and several other important witnesses recounted the extraordinary events.

A young woman in her 20s was driving home from work to Netherton shortly before midnight early in July.

Helen Smith had made the journey dozens of times before and knew the route so well she could almost have driven it blindfold.

Along the dual carriageway to Bromsgrove, then north-west towards Hagley, Stourbridge and the glittering Black Country skyline.

But the details of this particular journey are indelibly etched on her memory. During it, she witnessed something she had never seen before in her life - and has never seen since.

John Hanson: keeping an eye on time travellers dropping in on the Midlands.

Diamond shaped object spinning round and round

Helen was approaching Clent when blue lights flashing above the hills drew her eye. To her astonishment, she saw a strange, black diamond-shaped object spinning round and round in the sky.

Never letting it out of sight she sped back to Netherton where she climbed with her father up a nearby church tower to get a better look.

with red pulsing lights was seen in the sky above Stirchley. It vanished and reappeared in Cumbria only minutes afterwards.

And on another night in May this year a woman reported seeing a pulsating scallop-shaped craft in the sky above Longbridge.

Visible for about ten minutes, it was seen by someone else at Crabbs Cross, Redditch.

preoccupation with time travel is eternal.

Understandably, given the derision with which many such claims have been greeted in the past, those who see UFO's tend to be reticent about going public.

But modern technological advances have made "flying saucers" seem less of a fantasy, more a genuine possibility.

Retired West Midlands Police officer John Hanson treats all reports of sightings seriously. He keeps an open mind about UFO's, neither believing nor disbelieving in them.

In his role as Worcestershire agent for Quest International, he is setting out to build a comprehensive record of UFO sightings. It will help establish whether there really is life on other planets.

Quest International is an independent organisation which

John's son Keith, graphically illustrates each reported sighting in the Worcestershire area. As you can see from this illustration and the one opposite, shapes vary quite considerably.

Retired police officer 'on another planet' with UFO's!

At first he was incredulous but his scepticism swiftly evaporated when he, too, spotted the craft hovering overhead.

Even after studying it he was unable to identify the object before it disappeared into the darkness as suddenly as it had appeared.

Following stories in local newspapers three other witnesses confirmed they had also seen the object. No logical explantion for it has ever been found.

In January, a disc-shaped object

Until recently, these and many other similar unexplained incidents might have been put down to overactive imagination or a few too many pints at the local.

People have always been fascinated by outer space. The idea of little green men visiting Earth in spaceships is nothing new.

From H G Wells' War of the Worlds to Dr Who, 1001: A space Odyssey, Star Trek, E.T. and more ???ent sci-fi box office hits such as ???e, evidence shows
???er 1998

gathers and collates information about unexplained phenomena.

Father-of-three John, aged 49, is the point of contact for anyone who sees or wants to discuss a sighting which cannot be explained logically.

By collecting all the details at his Alvechurch home, studying and comparing them with other reported sightings, he aims to compile a vast library of information.

He also links up with other

Quest agents in Worcester and Shrewsbury to create a wider picture of possible alien activity.

"I am not a science fiction fan, I have both feet on the ground. But I finally believe there is a need for investigation of UFO sightings," says John.

"Too often, people have no chance to discuss what they have seen for fear of ridicule.

"They cannot talk about it, yet some stay traumatised for years. It has an impact on their lives.

"You've got to look at things scientifically. About 50 per cent of sightings can be explained.

"But there are others which don't resemble terrestrial craft. No one ever comes forward to say this is one of their new research aircraft, or that is one of their advertising balloons.

"Such craft conform to certain patterns. They never make any noise.

All move at a colossal speed

"All move at colossal speed and change their shape. Witnesses agree about this and there's no reason to dispute what they say.

"One man was with about 15 others on a pub car park in Yardley when he saw a disc-shaped craft. It happened in the 1970s and he still has nightmares about it today."

John's curiosity about UFO's was awakened by two police colleagues who personally experienced unexplained sightings. He says he has never seen anything himself.

Thorough investigation of circumstances

"I read about Quest International in a science journal. It was founded by an ex-policeman 15 years ago. Its headquarters are in Yorkshire.

"The idea is to communicate information via a nationwide network. We carry out a thorough investigation of circumstances surrounding a sighting and the object."John showed me a short clip from an amateur video of the UFO filmed near Longbridge. It showed a bright flashing light which darted around the screen, apparently following no direct flight path.

Definitive Catalogue of East Anglia UFO activity 1951-1996

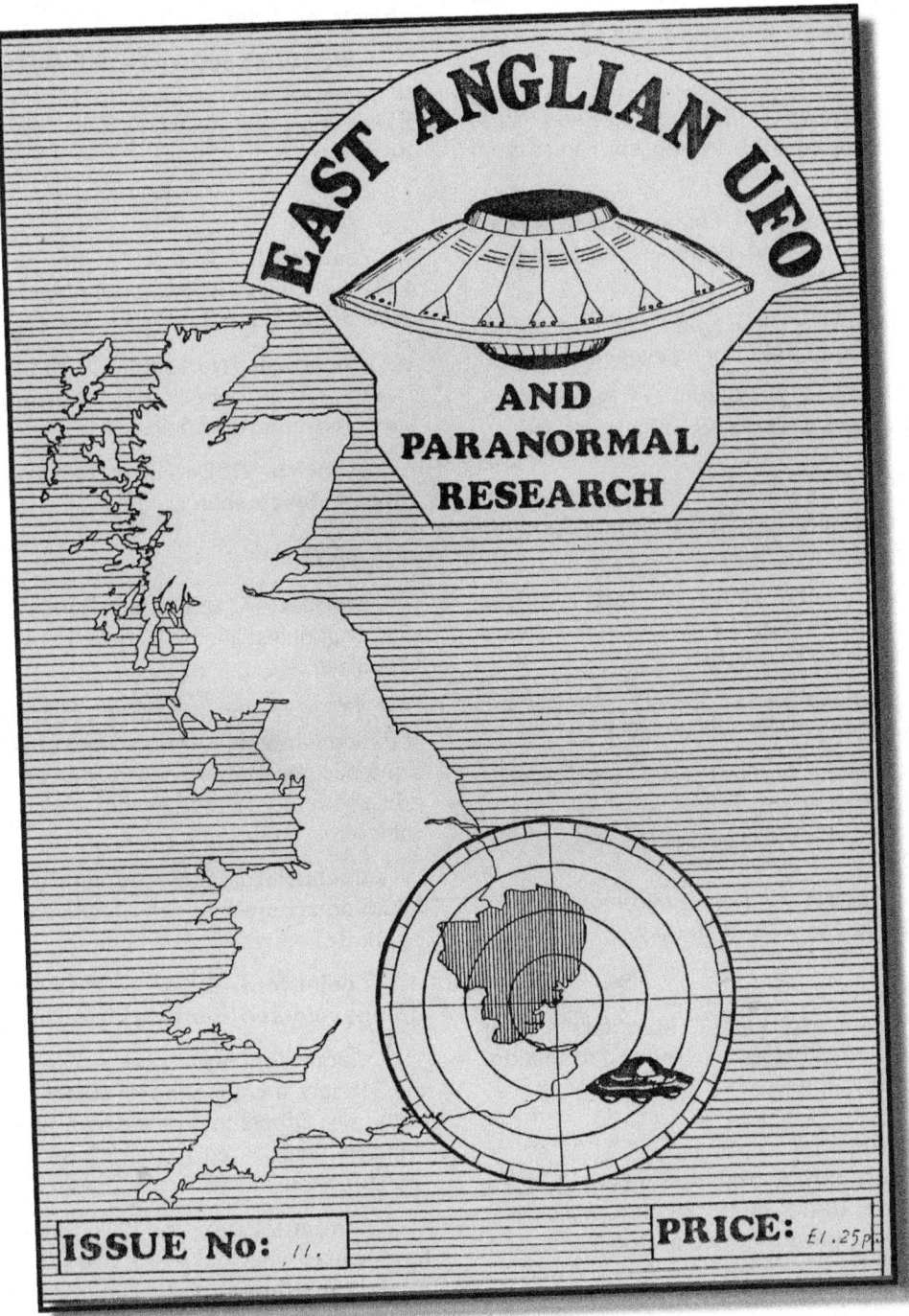

EAST ANGLIAN UFO

AND PARANORMAL RESEARCH

ISSUE No: 11.

PRICE: £1.25p

1951

Norwich – Three 'discs' seen following RAF Jets

1953

Felixstowe – RAF Serviceman sight **wedge-shaped UFO,** trailing **six** flames from rear.

Essex – August – Rotating **'flying saucer',** showing dome and portholes, seen moving through the sky.

Norwich – 6th October – **Domed object,** pulsating lights, seen during evening.

Dereham, Norfolk – 3rd November – **Silver object, with platform,** seen in sky.

1954

Lowestoft -1st March, 7.30pm – **'Spinning top' UFO** sighted.

Weybread Norfolk – 1st October – **Silver, cigar-shaped** object with prominent bulge, seen in sky by two men fishing.

Southend-on-Sea, Essex – 14th October – **Three 'flying discs'** seen by RAF Pilot

Southend-on-Sea Essex – 16th October – UFO reported having landed.

1955

Lowestoft – 7th July – Mid-morning glistening silver UFO seen in the sky

1956

13th August, 9.30pm – **Three 'dots'** plotted on radar, moving from **Holland** direction. Further 'dots' appeared – RAF scrambled.

1960

Cransford, Suffolk – January, 3.20pm – **Spinning UFO** seen in sky. *East Anglia Daily Times* told witness they had a large file relating to such reports!

Thetford – 1st September – UFO seen

and tracked on radar by RAF Mildenhall; Air Traffic Control picked up the presence of **three objects, on radar.**

Westcliff, Southend – 7th June, 11.20pm – UFO seen moving quickly across the sky, making a whistling sound, leaving a trail of yellow light behind it.

1962

Lowestoft, Suffolk – 4th December, 6.15am – Object, showing with **three bright 'rods of pulsating light',** seen over the sea.

Hempnall, Norfolk – 21st December, 7.15am – Bar-shaped UFO, **showing three lights,** hovering over field.

Norwich – 27th December, 9.45pm – **Saucer-shaped objects seen**

1963

Norfolk – At 5pm, a long dark object was seen motionless in the sky, near the disused Ellough airfield.

14th April, 7pm – A string of between five and nine **flame-coloured orange objects** was sighted, completely stationary, one behind the other, forming a curve in the sky. Later, they vanished from sight.

Chelmsford, Essex – 9th June, 11.10pm – A **luminous object** was observed in the sky for a period of between 10-15 minutes.

Chelmsford, Essex – 29th July, 9pm – **Orange coloured 'short stick'** seen in the sky.

Clacton-on-Sea, Essex – On or about the 31st July, a **cigar-shaped object** was seen in the sky. Others told of seeing a **'V'-shaped 'triangle',** with a red glowing base, that was seen to change into a circular shape.

Romford, Essex – In 1963, three schoolboys sighted what looked like **two soup plates, joined together,** orange-white in colour, with silvery ends, moving through the sky.

1965

Colchester, Essex – 14th September, 1am – Motorcyclist heard humming noise. The machine came to a halt, and a **spinning object** was seen in the sky.

Felixstowe – 20th September – Allegation of an encounter with a **landed UFO** and its occupant; witness taken to hospital – sustained **burns to the neck.**

Southwold, Suffolk -10th October, at 5.15pm – **Cylindrical object, with a pointed end** seen in the sky, which then split into five different vertical compartments, showing different coloured lights.

1966

Sawtry – 28th April – A lorry driver and his companion sight UFOs, while parked for the night. *"Suddenly the 'star' halted in the sky, conjoined by another one, the two of them changing places with each other and beginning to move in a series of semicircular patterns, rotating in an anticlockwise movement, across the sky."*

Outside Stiffkey, Norfolk – October, 9pm – Police officer sights UFO.

1967

Harold Hill, Essex – 6th June – **A bright domed object** was seen hovering in sky.

Cromer, Norfolk – 5th July – A fiery object, showing red and violet light bursting from its sides, was seen hovering in the sky. **Grays Thurrock, Essex** – August – **UFO seen, with occupant** (described as a white woman, with long shoulder length hair flicked up at the end) looking out of one of the windows. When she turned her head to the right, the hair bounced gracefully to the opposite side, and then bounced back into position again. She had large but normal looking eyes, slanted like a Chinese person, with a thin pointed nose, without any sign of nostrils. The UFO then tilted and gradually moved away over Dock Road, and

rose upwards – until a tiny 'dot of light' in the sky.

Chingford, Essex – Barry Gates was driving near Chingford Plain with his wife, at 11.45pm, during one weekend in August. They noticed a bright light, with a number of red lights, hovering in the air about six feet off the ground, above a nearby bridle path, about 75 yards away from them. They first thought they were fireworks and stopped the car. Mr Gates got out and was shocked to see what **looked like two 'miniature men', solid in appearance, next to the light source.**

750 sightings logged for 1967

Note: There were a total of <u>over 750</u> separate sightings of UFOs logged for 1967, with over 300 reports of UFOs recorded for the month of October. Only sixty-four of these reports related to the appearances of what became labelled as the 'Flying Cross'.

Ipswich, Suffolk -16th October, 1am – A star-shaped object, with a red and blue light on either side, was seen in the sky.

Caister-on-Sea, Norfolk – A cross-shaped object, with bright lights, was reported heading out to sea over the coast.

Colchester, Essex – 26th October – During a 'wave' of UFO activity that struck the UK for this day, an illuminated '**flying saucer**', projecting beams of light, was seen moving across the sky over Colchester United football ground, <u>following an aircraft</u>. It was then seen to stop in mid-air when reaching the aircraft, and head away at great speed, before disappearing from sight.

28th October – **A huge object, with flashing lights**, hovering over trees at Southend, was seen by a taxi driver. Five minutes later, it dipped down and rose up again, showing a single red light, before moving up into the sky – where it became lost in cloud.

Lowestoft, Suffolk – November – A huge '**flying saucer**' was seen about 20 yards away, hovering over an apple tree orchard, described as dark in colour, with a bulge at the top showing a number of slits of light running around it and the base, illuminating nearby trees. The vibration changed to a high-pitched screeching noise, before taking off.

Walton, near Clacton-on-Sea, Essex – 7th November, 4.30am – An object, resembling a dustbin lid, was sighted hovering over Walton Pier, moving backwards and forwards, shining a light downwards. Suddenly it shot off at terrific speed, towards Harwich, now looking like a 'cigar', but returned and again hovered over the Pier before shooting off northwards.

1968

Garboldisham, Norfolk, January 1968 – A married couple were driving along the road, between 10pm and 11pm at night, when they saw a silver, cigar-shaped object, showing portholes, in the sky. They later contacted the police at Enfield, and telephoned *Anglia TV,* at Norwich, who mentioned it as a newsflash.

1976

Basildon, Essex – Between 7.30pm and 10.30pm on 29th January, **a bowl-shaped object** was seen in the sky with various lights flashing on the bottom, and an orange band around the rim, showing a green light above – shiny metallic in appearance – moving silently, backwards and forwards across the sky.

Chelmsford – 24th September, 5.05pm – An object was seen, resembling **three 'balls', joined by a rod,** light grey in colour and not self-luminous. It drifted towards the south-east direction, before disappearing behind some houses.

Essex – 6th December, 5.45pm – **A white 'disc'-shaped object, with a large red glowing dome in the centre of its underside,** was seen in the sky. On each side of the rim were **two red lights,** and around the object itself was a shimmering effect. The 'disc' was spinning on its

axis, and what looked like short and long lines underneath it, apparently engraved into the surface, could be seen.

Vange, Essex – 12th December – A triangular object, sighted perfectly still in the sky, **showing three large red lights,** spaced quite far apart. On the right-hand side could be seen a large blue light. On the back were counted three lights, set close together, which were flashing on and off.

1977

Dagenham, Essex – 2nd March, 7.15pm – A white light, accompanied by a smaller red flashing light, was seen in the sky. The two lights were soon joined by another two, each red light being close to the white light at an angle of 75 degrees. Four such 'formations' were seen over the next half an hour. The lights then broke formation. One of the red lights flew slowly over the top of the witness, allowing him to view the underside, which consisted of eight circular holes that glowed red to black.

Chigwell, Essex- 3rd May – Following a 999 call made to the Police, at 3.55am, reporting a UFO hovering over a lake in Hainault Recreation Ground, Police Officers attended and came across an object, which was red in colour, **shaped like a bell tent** – the size of a thumbnail, at arm's length – which continuously pulsated from dull to bright red. Suddenly, it vanished from view.

Chelmsford, Essex -17th July – A Chelmsford police dog handler was on duty at 2.50am, when he saw: "*a cigar-shaped object, hanging vertically in the sky, about 30 degrees off the horizon, over the village of Arkesden, near Saffron Waldon, Essex".*

Gorleston, near Great Yarmouth – At 11pm, a roughly **cylindrical, or cigar-shaped object,** was seen moving slowly eastwards, at low altitude, above the shore of a nearby lake. The object had a ring of predominately fixed red and white lights towards it rear, rather than something flashing. It was watched for about 30 seconds, until the noise (like a low frequency rumble) stopped. The object then disappeared completely from view.

Cambridgeshire – 1st October, 11.30pm – A small 'red light' was seen in the sky, moving slowly eastwards. When it arrived in the north-east part of the sky it was joined by two similar objects, which had approached from different directions. **The three lights** then **formed an upside-down triangle.** After a few seconds two of them shot away, leaving the third one to carry on its course.

Chelmsford, Essex – 31st January, 6.45a.m – A bright light was seen high in the sky. An object was then seen to slowly appear from behind the rooftop of the English Electric Valve Company adjacent to the Marconi Radar Works on the other side of the road – first a wing tip, followed by two large bright yellow lights, then the other wing tip **making three lights**, before disappearing from view.

1978

Norwich – July – A massive silvery-white 'arrowhead', or triangular-shaped, object was seen moving very slowly through the air covered in lights like windows of a skyscraper lit up, but in triangular form.

Lowestoft, Suffolk – 13th May – Schoolgirls sight a **silver, dome-shaped, object** with bright orange lights around it, hovering just above the ground, about a quarter of a mile away. **Four 'figures'** were seen to move towards them in a 'jerky manner', in strides of 5 feet, or so. They then disappeared as the UFO gradually began to lift itself off the ground, once more, and faded away within ten seconds.

Weeley, Clacton-on-Sea, Essex – Late May – A huge dark-grey **saucer shaped object,** about 25 feet high and 90 feet in length, was seen lying on the ground, making a droning noise, close to the power lines. The witness walked over to it, noting that it had three

sections, with a dome on top and a tube shaped centre, slightly wider at the base than the top. In its middle were what looked like window slits. *"I could see a door, with a walled ramp, leading to the ground and two bright lights on either side of the centre section, resembling a German World War Two helmet; when I shone my torch into the darkened interior, it took-off and headed across the sky at a fantastic speed – gone in seconds."*

Essex – A formation of glowing objects was seen changing shapes in mid-air, under the main flight path heading into Heathrow Airport, followed by a **huge 'ball' of red light** in the sky, through which Concorde passed, at 9pm.

Clacton, Essex -12th September, 10.25am – An aircraft (possibly a Boeing 707) light blue in colour – military, rather than civilian – passed overhead, followed by a **'dark-brown, or metallic, circular object'**, approximately 400 yards behind it. The object closed-up rapidly with the aircraft – as if on a collision course – then the aircraft banked sharply, 80 degrees to starboard, leaving the UFO to turn at 90 degrees, which actually brought it crossing in front of the path of the jet before it headed out to sea, where it was lost from sight 30 seconds later.

Kirby-le-Soken, Clacton-on-Sea, Essex – Two 'bright lights' were seen in the sky, at 8pm, by a family working in the orchard. After passing overhead, the 'lights' circled the sky, before returning to their original position. One of the family members flashed his torch at the object, which **changed into a red triangular object**, showing a red pulsing light, accompanied by a humming noise. All of a sudden it shot off across the sky, heading south-west, at fantastic speed.

Ilford, Essex – 5th October, 7pm – Coloured lights were seen in the sky, 'dancing around', followed by the arrival of a very peculiar object, accompanied by **twelve coloured 'globes'**, which were constantly moving around the larger object. After remaining stationary in the sky for a brief period of time, it headed off towards the direction of London. Shortly afterwards, another object appeared – this time **cigar-shaped**, accompanied by numerous coloured 'globes of light' around it, making a humming noise. A woman, living in Haydon Road, had also seen the first object passing overhead, but reported that it was only accompanied by **three 'globes'**.

At 9.40pm on 6th October, a large silver/grey tailed object was seen, displaying red, green, and orange lights, resembling a skate fish, without a tail, showing a dome, which had stripes on it. In front of the object were **three large beams** of light shining outwards into the air, for some 100 yards or more, with 'spiky shaped things' visible underneath. The huge 'craft' was then seen to head off towards the south-west, making a low droning noise, before disappearing behind trees, creating an impression that it was going to land.

Dagenham, Essex – A **half-moon** shaped object was sighted over Green Lane, at 3pm on 7th October 1978.

Southend, Essex – 13th November – A coastguard on duty, at Southend Coastguard Station, sighted two very bright lights in the sky appearing to be above the pier head, although they could have been further down the river, towards London. They were horizontally apart and looked like a pair of headlights as they hovered in the sky, for a few minutes, before turning laterally, dimming slightly, and gradually rose upwards, towards the direction of Southend.

Saxlingham, Norfolk – 3rd December, 9.30pm – A bright 'light', was seen bout 500 yards ahead of a motorist and about the same distance off the ground. Curious, he stopped his van and got out, but after realising it was stationary in the sky, drove towards the triangular object. *"It then shot away into the sky, at high speed, before coming to a halt and began to head back towards me.*

I parked under a tree and switched-off the lights. When it was about 400 yards away, a concentrated wind enveloped the locality, lasting a few seconds, as the **black triangular object** moved slowly overhead, allowing me to see, quite clearly, a bright light at the front, with a small flickering red light at the rear and underside – like frosted windows – before disappearing southwards."

1979

Essex – 1st June, 10.30pm – A motorist was driving along Southend Road, Ilford, Essex, accompanied by his wife and young son, when they saw what appeared to be the headlight of an aircraft, descending through the sky. As they approached Beal High School, at Woodford Bridge Road, they saw flashing lights – now only a few hundred feet away – and realised this was no aircraft.

Mr Elkinson: *"I decided to stop the car and have a closer look. By now, I was becoming alarmed. I got out and stood underneath this 'thing' as it passed overhead, allowing me to see, quite clearly, a dull grey underside – completely devoid of any rivets, or bolts, one would have expected to see if it had been the outer skin of an aircraft.* **I was shocked to see a flat, rather than bulbous 'craft',** *with a pointed end. Suddenly, it rushed off across the sky, at terrific speed, and was gone out of sight in seconds."*

Lowestoft, Suffolk – June, 7pm – A bright orange object, showing **three large flashing lights** on its side (as big as a double-decker bus in size) was seen hovering in mid-air. A few minutes later, it began to make a high-pitched whine and then took off, moving quickly towards the coast – the sound being heard for a few seconds after it had gone out of view.

Witham Essex – 1st July – A **grey object, estimated to be 30-40 feet long**, was sighted motionless in the sky, hovering about 200 feet in the air. It then began to move up and down in flight. The Police were telephoned.

Bury St. Edmunds, Suffolk – 6th July, 3.10pm – An object, described as **resembling**

an egg, with a black base, was seen low down in the sky over Bury St. Edmunds by-pass, by a motorist driving along the A45 (now the A14). When he contacted RAF Honnington to report the incident, he was advised that *"they were unable to comment".*

Norfolk – 13th November, 7.20pm – An object, estimated to be 60 feet in width, showing a white flashing light on one side and coloured lights on the other, was sighted moving through the sky over Fleggburgh, Norfolk, at a height of about 200 feet, before heading southwards, in an arc, and disappearing.

1980

Cambridgeshire – 23rd January – A **giant, red glowing, semicircular object** was seen hovering over Marshalls Airport, making a low whirring noise. The same object seems to have been seen by a couple driving home, along the A45 from Newmarket towards Histon.

Gt. Waltham, Essex – 25th January, 10.40pm – A UFO was sighted in the sky for three minutes.

Chelmsford, Essex – 26th January – **A saucer-shaped object** was seen over North Avenue, for ten minutes.

An **oval-shaped** UFO was seen over the A130, at Rettendon, in Essex, at 10.30pm, and a **saucer-shaped object** was reported over Park Way, Chelmsford, at 10.35pm on 26th January, for a few minutes' duration. It was also seen from Readers Corner.

Cambridge – 27th January, 5.45pm – A **glowing orange half-moon shaped object** was seen in the sky, hovering over Hale Street, Cambridge, flashing a green light. Five minutes later, another one was seen to rise from behind houses, towards the direction of the airport.

Suffolk – 5th May, 6.30pm – Boys, fishing off Orford Quay, Suffolk, on a clear night, saw a **silver, cigar-shaped object**, motionless in the sky. It moved away and then came back as bright as the sun. It kept flickering and making a buzzing noise. About an hour later, it just vanished in front of their eyes.

Norfolk – During the end of August, Kim Sergeant was driving his girlfriend home towards Blofield, on the A47 (not too many miles away from the scene of a previous UFO incident, at Hopton) when they noticed a **glowing red 'ball of light',** hovering just above the skyline, which suddenly appeared to 'latch on' to their car. Much to the couple's consternation, the UFO continued to follow them.

"It reached the end of the road, just in front of us, and began to slowly descend. I stopped the car. To our further fright, it stopped motionless in the air and started to float towards us. I started up the car and raced away. To my relief, as we neared my girlfriend's house, it vanished behind some trees."

Dovercourt, Essex – 1pm on 15th September – A bright, round, silvery object – the shape of a children's swimming ring, was seen gliding through the sky, about 200 feet up. According to the witnesses, **it had a small dome on top** and, as it flew, it wobbled slightly, allowing view of a black underside, before it disappeared behind some trees**.** The incident was reported to the Harwich Police.

The MOD later confirmed they had received details of the incident and *"that it would be investigated, especially if it appeared to have defence implications. There was apparently a great deal of meteorite activity occurring from what was known as the Perseid shower and this was most likely to increase next year".* [Certainly not the case here]

1981

Lowestoft Suffolk – 23rd September – Anna Sidali and her children were on holiday. As night fell, they saw a **silver, diamond-shaped object** appear overhead in the sky. She wondered if it had anything to do with the nearby USAF Airbase. Frightened, she took the children and ran inside. The oddest thing is that she felt as if they were being watched.

Saxmundham, Suffolk, 4pm on 22nd December – **Four silver objects** were seen in the sky, travelling in a horizontal line in a North to South direction, stopping and starting in flight, as well as changing shape as they did so. Within five minutes, they had dropped in the sky behind houses and were lost from sight.

1983

Chelmsford Essex – At 7.15pm on 10th October – At Hatfield Peverel, several lights were seen towards the south-east, bearing 130 degrees. As they approached closer, a red light appeared followed by several others – yellow, white, and blue in colour, before they merged into one mass of light, containing what appeared to be six separate lights made up of multicoloured smaller lights. A group of four then split away, heading northwards; one of them shot off southwards to meet up with others. A **dome or half-moon shaped object,** with merging lights on is base, slowly descended through the sky. An investigation later held into the incident revealed the house clock to have lost 15 minutes of time, and heavy interference was seen on the television set during the incident taking place.

1986

Eastwood, Southend – At 5.30pm on 17th February – **A silver, long, pencil thin object, with a pointed tail at the base**, more like a missile than a jet aircraft, was seen slowly crossing the clear sky, approximately 20 miles away. After it dropped out of sight, leaving a vapour trail behind it, a 'military' helicopter appeared and flew over where the object had gone.

Wisbech, Cambridgeshire – James Aish, from Tydd St. Giles, was looking out of his bedroom window, one summer's day, when he saw *"a 'flying saucer',* as clear as day, with some sort of control tower just off the centre. It shook my belief in life in general.

There was something written on it, like a marking, but it was too far away to make out; it could have been a cockpit or something. When I told people, they laughed at me."

Felixstowe, Suffolk – On 27th October 1986, two British Rail employees were working in the shunting yards, at 3.45am, when the ground in front of them was flooded with bright blue light. Looking upwards, they saw *"a bright blue 'globe of light', with silver flames streaking from it, crossing the sky".*

Other sightings of what appears to have been the same UFO came from Ufford and Ipswich, which also included a sighting of *"a white 'ball of light' that passed overhead, making a humming noise",* according to former teacher – Janet Richards, who was driving along the A12 at Blythburgh, with her daughter, Cathy. A similar report was obtained from qualified Pilot and Nurse – Melanie Hartley, of Bury St. Edmunds, who was driving home at 11pm, near the village of Fornham All Saints, Suffolk, with her two daughters in the back, when their curiosity became aroused after seeing a bright light reflecting off the bonnet. When they looked upwards, they saw *"a saucer-shaped object, the length of three double-decker buses, hovering in the sky".*

1988

First reports of Triangular objects made over Essex

Leigh-on-Sea, Essex – 13th April, at 8pm – **Three lights, forming triangle** – two white, one red – were seen flying across sky.

Southend Pier, Essex – 14th April, at 8.20pm – Over thirty-one people sighted a **pink-mauve light** travelling inland, before disappearing from view behind trees on the top of the cliffs. They included a slightly elongated **glowing orange and red** object in the sky, **a mushroom-shaped object,** consisting of what looked like numerous globules of orange-red lights, apparently following the coastline, a **fairly large spherical**

object **rotating** with very bright lights seen heading south, a very bright orange and **red 'ball of light'** seen hovering between two bungalows. All of a sudden a smaller piece was seen to fall away from it, straight down, then the larger 'ball' went straight and disappeared from view. Other witnesses described seeing two **orange-red 'balls of light'** in the sky, which gradually fell downwards over the tree line at 8.15pm. In due course a letter was sent to the British Astronomical Association, asking them whether it could have been a fireball. This was very unlikely, as fireballs do not generally swerve or turn in mid-air!

Canvey Isalnd, Essex – At 2.30am, three lights were seen forming a triangle – two red, one white – 200 feet in air.

Southend, Essex – At 2.30am on 2nd September, the night sky was flooded with a brilliant light, followed by a number of bright long, oval lights, split by smaller green lights, **forming a semicircle in the sky**, hovering silently over the tops of nearby houses.

Pitsea, Basildon, Essex – At 10.30pm on 9th September, a number of **black rectangular shapes,** showing blue and white lights, were seen in the sky for a few minutes, before fading away, accompanied by a humming noise.

Rayleigh, Essex – At 8.30pm on 23rd September, strange 'flying lights' were seen all over the sky – two of them hovering over Southend Airport. The police were called and attended. As the 'lights' passed overhead, they **formed a triangle of lights,** showing a vapour trail in the shape of a 'V'.

Basildon – Over 32 separate UFO reports from this area alone were received. Interestingly it was said that a number of jet aircraft were seen flying overhead at the time of the incidents, which involved sightings of **three stationary lights** over Southend, later joined by a red glow. The cluster then moved away out to sea, turned back inland and disappeared behind trees.

Bury St. Edmunds – At 8pm on 24th September, a motorist was driving along Brandon Road, when he noticed a cluster of small red, green, and pale yellow lights, set into a much larger object heading across the sky, before losing sight of it.

Pitsea, Essex – On 29th October 1988, a gigantic silver/bronze rectangular object, with square windows inset, was reported.

Canvey Island, Essex – At 8pm **three lights** were seen forming a triangle in sky – two white and one red – which flew away eastwards.

Rayleigh, Essex – At 5.30pm on 3rd November, a triangular UFO was seen over Derwent Avenue.

November 1989 – Belgium 'wave' begins

The Belgian UFO 'wave' began in November 1989. The events of 29th November would be documented by no less than thirty different groups of witnesses, and three separate groups of police officers.

All of the reports related to a large object, flying at low altitude. The 'craft' was of a flat, triangular shape, with lights underneath. This giant 'craft' did not make a sound as it slowly moved across the landscape of Belgium. There was free sharing of information as the Belgian populace tracked this 'craft' as it moved from the town of Liege to the border of the Netherlands and Germany.

The Belgian UFO 'wave' peaked with the events of the night of 30–31st March 1990. On that night, unknown objects were tracked on radar, chased by two Belgian Air Force F-16s, and sighted by an estimated 13,500 people on the ground – 2,600 of whom filed written statements describing in detail what they had seen. Following the incident, the Belgian Air Force released a report detailing the events of that night.

691

1990

Wickford, Essex – On 1st September 1990, a mysterious pink cigar-shaped **'mass of light'** was seen hovering over a house.

Essex – At 2am on 4h September, a woman resident was awoken by a soft humming noise. She went to the bathroom and drew the curtains, and was astonished to see *"a large fiery, saucer-shaped object, motionless in the sky"*.

Essex – 13th September – A UFO, showing three red blue and green lights, was seen over Basildon by a fire officer.

Cambridge – 19th September 1990 – **Strange lights** were seen over Wandlebury Hill – an Iron Age hill fort at 7.25pm

Clacton, Essex – 21st September 1990 – At 10pm, a **'Flying Saucer'** was seen by Shirley Teresa Haynes (36) of Wellesley Road, Clacton, and her son – Stuart (13) – who observed *"a dark object high in the sky, between houses opposite, covered with flashing lights, like diamonds, creating an impression of moving anticlockwise in flight, heading towards Jaywick"*.

Near Ipswich, Suffolk – 25th September – Deborah Jones (37) was driving to Ipswich from Kirby Cross, with her husband and two sons. **Deborah:** *"As we continued on our journey, the road opened up and we all saw the object, which resembled a squashed silver diamond, with the top half revolving, as it headed along the side of a field. It then flew over a tractor and we saw the driver look up to see it. It then flew parallel to us for about 10 miles, at a speed of 60-70 miles per hour. As we began to see the chimneys of Ipswich Docks, it suddenly accelerated at tremendous speed, veered to the right, and shot out of sight."*

Colchester, Essex – 3rd October – Helen Robinson (30) was letting the dogs out into the back garden, at 11.15pm, when she saw

"…three 'blobs of light' in the sky, forming a triangle". Several photos were taken, but their whereabouts are not known.

Great Clacton, Essex – At 2.30am on 14th October, housewife Natalie Lawlor (23) of Elm Grove, Great Clacton, in Essex, was sat downstairs, when she heard what sounded like something moving about outside. She went upstairs to the front bedroom and looked out. Following her interview with members of Ron West's UFO Group, she wrote this account of what she and her father – Keith – saw, hovering over Holland Road. Keith described is as being a **yellow pear-shaped object** rather than triangular, and attempted to chase it, but lost sight of it near the seafront.

A12, Essex – 28th October – Mrs P. Bailey (57), a housewife from Wickford, was driving her white Mazda van along the A12, at 6.30pm, accompanied by her young son, after having been to see her mother in Rainham. The route back involved Hornchurch, Harold Hill Hospital, and then on to the A12. She said: *"As we neared Mountnessing roundabout, along the old Roman road, we noticed a bright 'light' in the sky and wondered what it could have been. When we reached the traffic island, we were shocked to see what I first took to be a big black Harrier Jet aircraft, hovering low in the sky, showing a powerful spotlight. I then realised I had never seen anything like this before in my life. I stopped for a better look but couldn't see anything, due to my vision being blocked by trees, so I turned around again – at which point it appeared to be circling in front of us and at one stage stopped in mid-air over the roof of a nearby house. Moments later it moved away and out of sight."*

Colchester, Essex – 5th November – At 10.30pm, Crystal Levesley of Wivenhoe, Colchester, was returning from an evening walk with her daughter, exercising the family dog, when they saw a large white 'light' high in the sky. Crystal rushed in to fetch a pair of binoculars and, looking through them, saw **three white lights forming a triangle.** She said: *"It then moved away; as it did so I saw a long hazy outline with a small green light at the rear."*

Clacton, Essex – 22nd November – A 'boomerang-shaped object, showing nine lights and a larger white light at the front edges', was seen by security guards at St. Osyth, heading eastwards over Clacton. At 2.30am, a triangular object was sighted passing through the sky, close to Clacton Pier, at an estimated height of just 50 feet, by two women, walking along the Clacton seafront.

"We could see yellow, blue, and green lights, around the centre of the craft, with a mass of red lights at the rear; it was moving slowly. We thought it was going to crash into the sea; we heard no noise. We estimated the size of the object to be 4-500 feet long. I saw what appeared to be an opening near the centre of the object; it wasn't an opening, it might have been a bulge."

1991

Basildon, Essex – 7.15pm on 12th April – A motorist travelling along the A13 road sighted a triangular UFO at a height of a few hundred feet above him, heading towards Thames Haven.

1993

Braintree, Essex – At 7.40pm on 29th March, a **matt black 'saucer' or triangular-shaped object** with multicoloured lights, showing an oblong port like a vacuum at the back, was sighted hovering over Notley School, by two boys, later, who later complained of having problems with their ears and strange dreams involving a dentist chair and some form of examination.

1994

Chingford, Essex – January, at 8pm – John Walter, a Conservative Councillor for the Larkswood area of Chingford, Essex, was walking along Larkswood Road. He said: "I looked up and saw a strange grey pattern in the air, resembling the wings of a helicopter, but no helicopter was there; whatever it was stayed there for some time, hovering over the ward".

Colchester, Essex – 12th September – Janet and Eric Clarke from Colchester, Essex, were just settling down to sleep, at 11pm, when they noticed a bright light shining through the bedroom window.

Janet: "I pulled back the curtains and was astonished to see a bright red light, projecting a yellow beam onto the ground – strong enough to illuminate local fields and buildings. I shouted for Eric to come and have a look. We stood watching, as it travelled backwards and forwards across the sky, occasionally circling, before heading off towards the direction of Broomfield. The next morning I telephoned Chelmsford Police HQ about the matter. They sent two officers to interview us later that morning."

Colchester, Essex – 13th September – Danny, a property developer, was awoken at 5am by a terrifying noise. He ran to the window and looked out, and saw "...an object hovering in the sky, estimated to be 100 metres across, brick-shaped, with a domed semicircular piece missing from either end, covered with little lights showing a yellow glow underneath".

During the period between the 28th November 1994 and the following few days, approximately **a hundred people** from places such as Clacton Wivenhoe and Witham, contacted the Essex UFO Research Association, reporting having seen a **brightly-lit object** hovering in the sky over the town, at 6pm. The witnesses included Mrs Patricia Arthey, from Copford, who saw what she described as something looking like "a giant stingray, moving slowly over the roof of my house, making the sound of a very smooth running car. I couldn't see any lights when it was approaching, but as it passed overhead I saw four big bright lights (like the headlights of a car) – like two lights on each side of the wing of an aircraft". Another witness was Peter Hogg, who was in the garden of his home with his five year-old daughter, at 5.30pm, when he saw what looked like two car headlights coming towards him in the sky. He said: "I joked to my daughter that it must have been Father Christmas, but as it got closer I could see more and more lights. It really was an unusual shape – like a stingray, without a tail, and completely silent". Initially the MOD suggested it may have been a helicopter, but a spokesman for RAF Wattisham disagreed, pointing out that aircraft flying at below 500 feet were required to book in with them and none had.

1995

Swaffham, Norfolk – 12th January – **Three sets of red lights** were seen crossing the sky, at tremendous speed, over Swaffham, Norfolk, between 7.30pm and 9.30pm, by local teenagers Nathan Hewitt, Nicholas Cade, and an unnamed third youth, who were driving towards North Pickenham just after 9.30pm. "each had a red flashing light fading from bright to dim, with a constant red light at the back. There was no shape – that was the weird part. One of them even flew level with us as we drove along the road. We tried to follow them and stopped when we saw one of the 'objects' hovering over a patch of woodland, before it dropped out of sight, followed by the second set."

Basildon, Essex – 1.47am on 23rd June – Following a bad dream, a housewife from Basildon, Essex, went to the bedroom window for air and saw "a bright white circular object, showing red, blue and green lights, in the night sky". After rousing her husband and daughter, the woman then telephoned the police. Two police officers arrived at 2.46am, but were unable to offer any rational explanation. They then contacted the Police Force Control room and two further officers arrived at the house. Through binoculars they described seeing "an object with a domed top and some sort of mesh pattern with green and red lights around the base, spinning clockwise in the sky in the direction of north-east, before being lost from view just after 4am."

One of the officers had this to say: "Through binoculars it was as big as a Jumbo Jet, 'disc'-shaped, with a dome on top and silvery in colour. It had a large number of lights around it and a large beam light around its centre. it appeared to have some sort of mesh around the centre.

Southend-on-Sea, Essex – 5th August, at midnight – Following a 999 call, six police officers sighted a UFO in the sky. After about 30 minutes the object began to move again, closer. Through binoculars, an object **resembling a 'crown' or 'cone'** was seen, with blue sparks falling away from it. It then began to move erratically, from left to right, up and down, with its lights pulsing. The police helicopter arrived and circled the sky looking for it. The pilot said that he couldn't see anything. At about 1am, the UFO was now a pinprick of light in the sky.

1996

Chelmsford, Essex – 8th February – "**A revolving golf ball-shaped object**, with a distinctive pattern of lights", was seen hovering over West Way, Chelmsford, Essex, by Mrs Hart of Braintree, who called the police reporting she "...thought a Spaceship had landed in her garden", after finding strange marks in the snow at her home address. Police Constable Lantzos attended the scene, and confirmed the presence of a number of strange squiggly lines in the snow – then spoke to a neighbour, who told the officer he had heard what sounded like an aircraft engine on the evening of 9th February 1996, and on looking outside he saw "a strange orange 'light' take-off and fly towards the direction of Chepstow."

The list above represents one tenth of overall reports for East Anglia!

We believe we have proved beyond all reasonable doubt that the airspace over the East Anglia area has been dominated, over the years, by all manner of strange aerial craft. Lack of space in the book now prevents us from including many hundreds of other sightings, which includes carefully drawn illustrations by the witnesses, later submitted to the Essex UFO Research Group, covering the late 1990s.

These will be covered in far more depth in Volume 12 of *Haunted Skies* – not forgetting these sightings only formed a tiny part of the overall mass of UFO observations that were reported over the UK leading up to the end of the 20th Century. Having examined the vast collection of UFO reports in our archives, it would be fair to say that the above list only represents **one tenth** of the overall reports – chilling in its implications.

Examples of East Anglia UFOs from the archives of Essex UFO Research Group

These images were drawn up by Ron West following his interviews with hundreds of people from the original illustrations; many of them have been signed by the witness as being a faithful reproduction of what they submitted themselves.

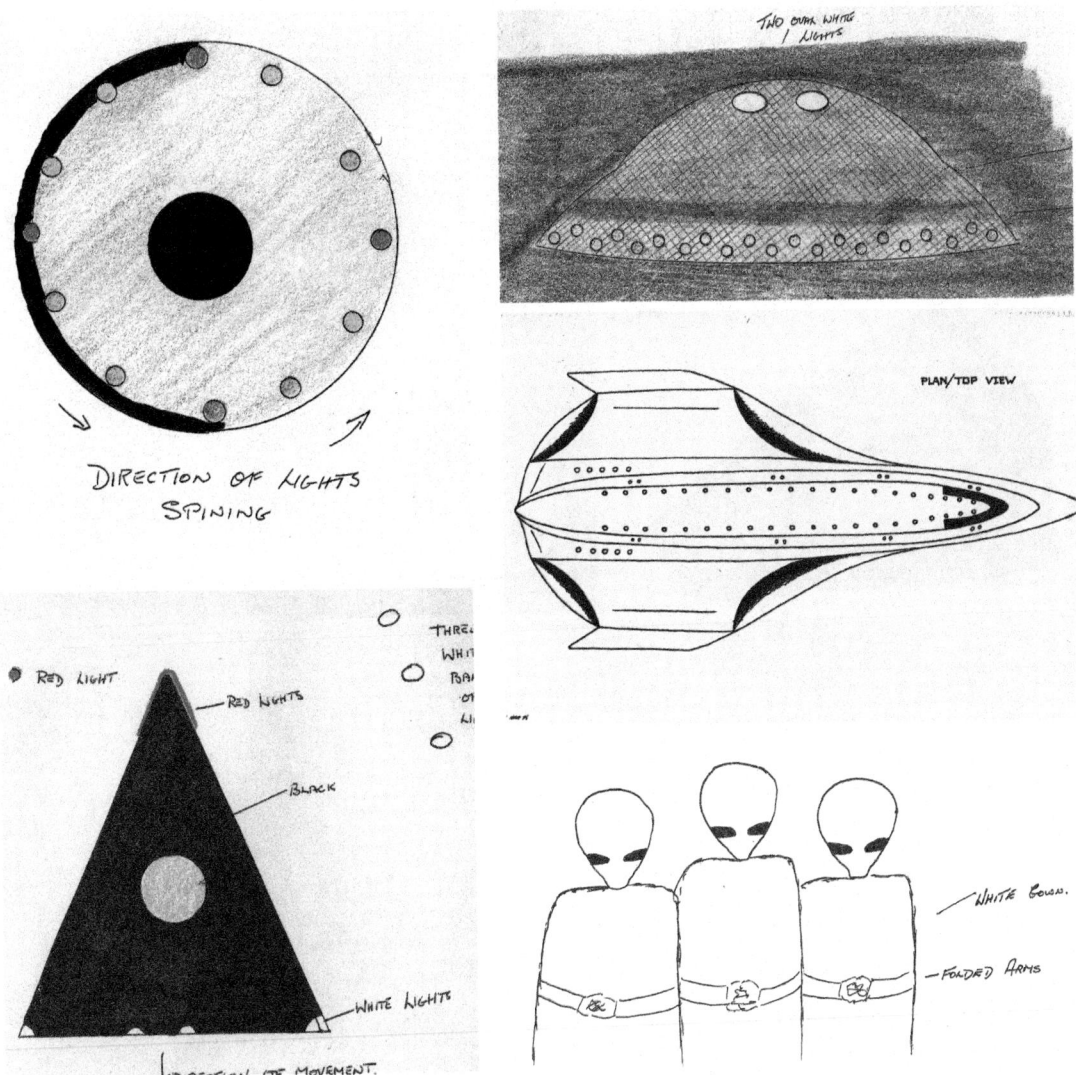

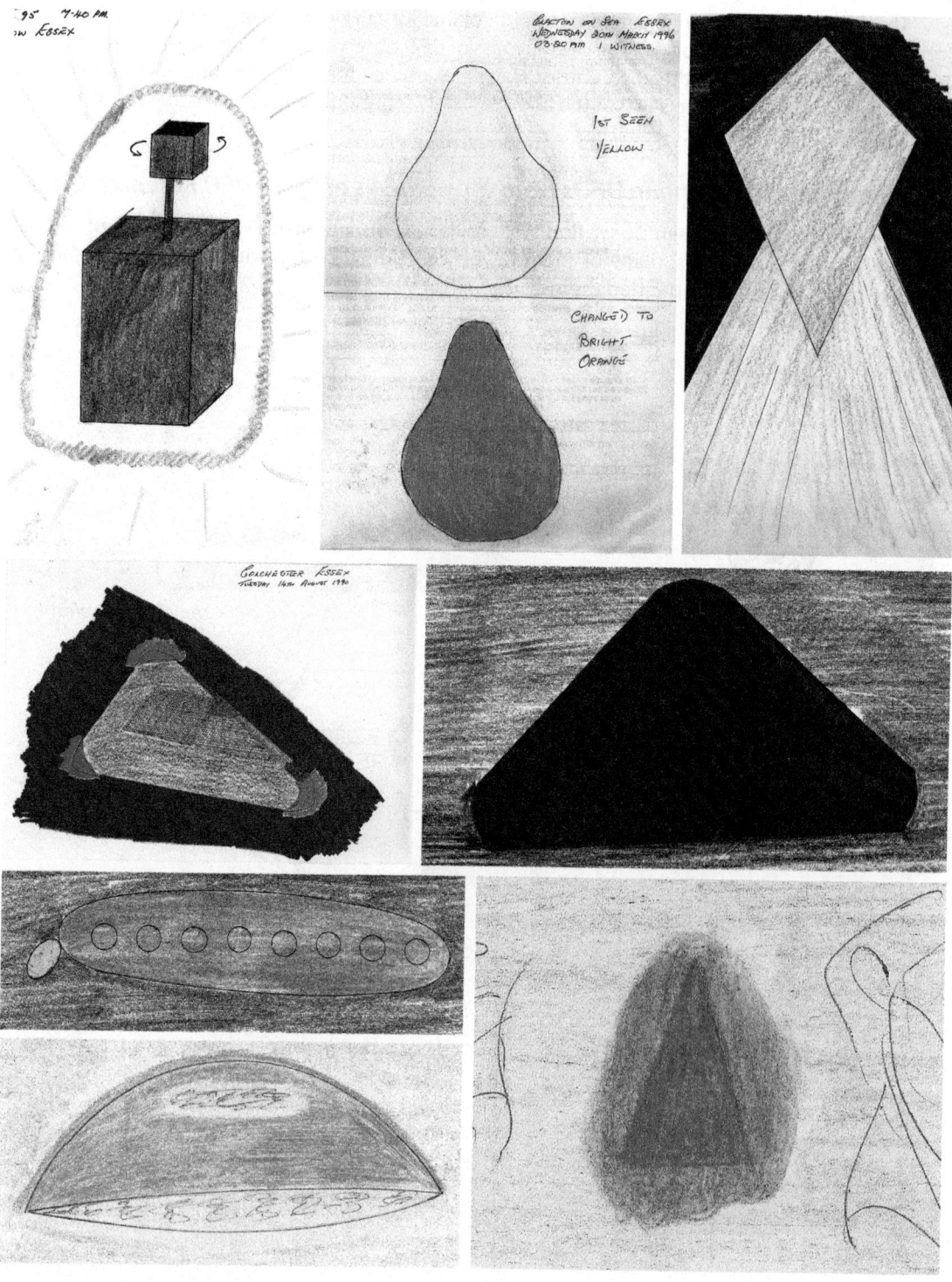

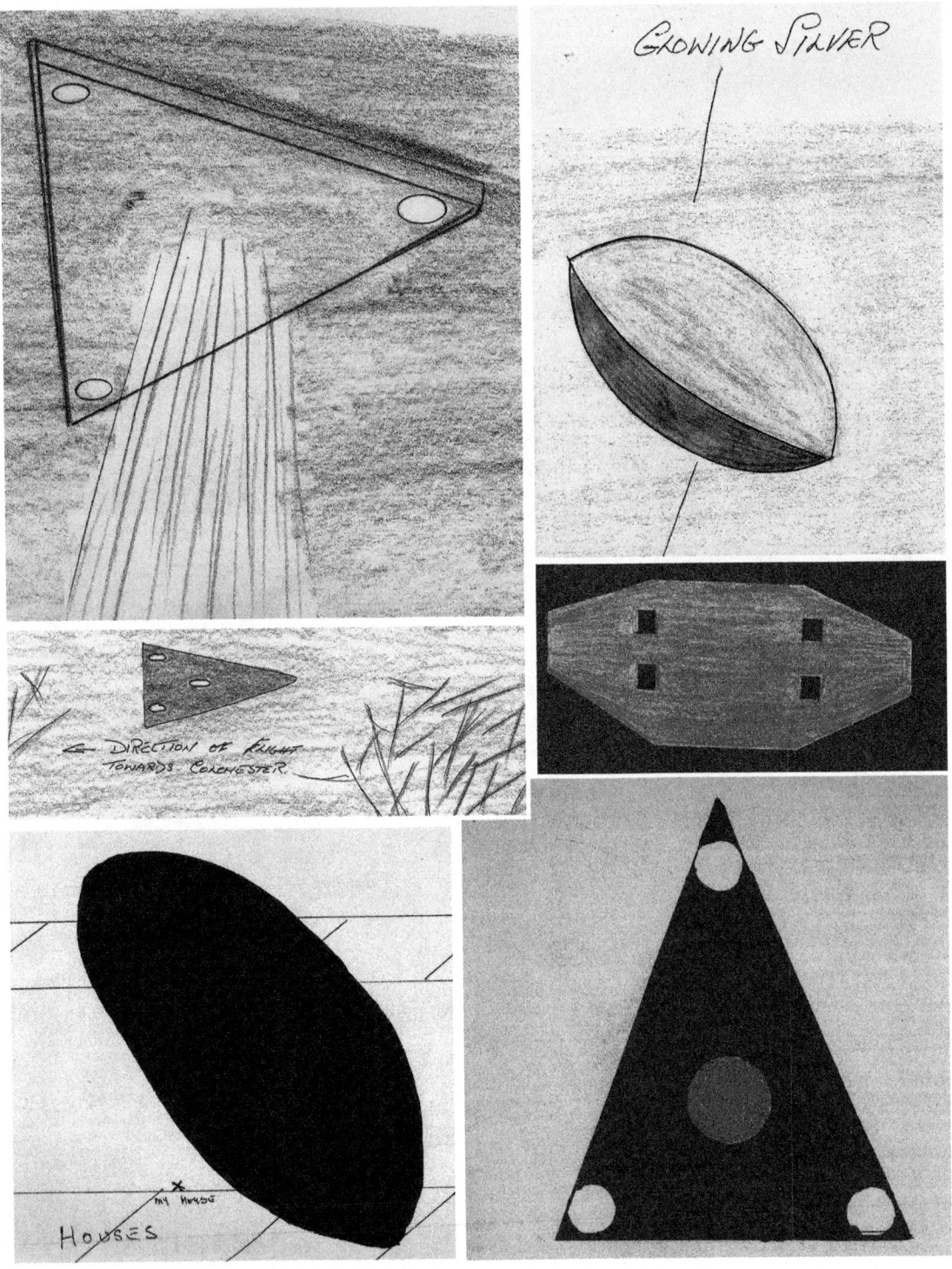

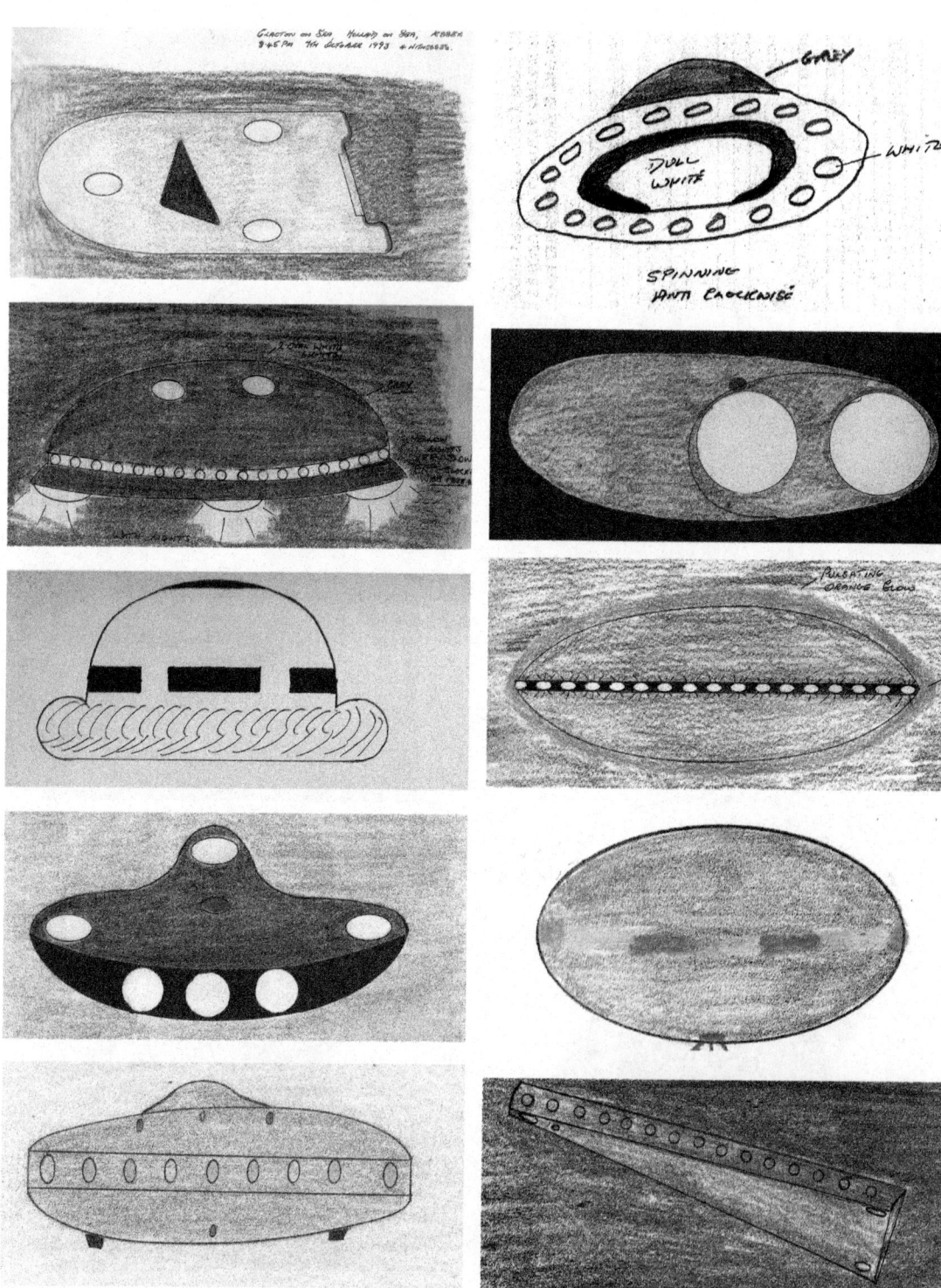

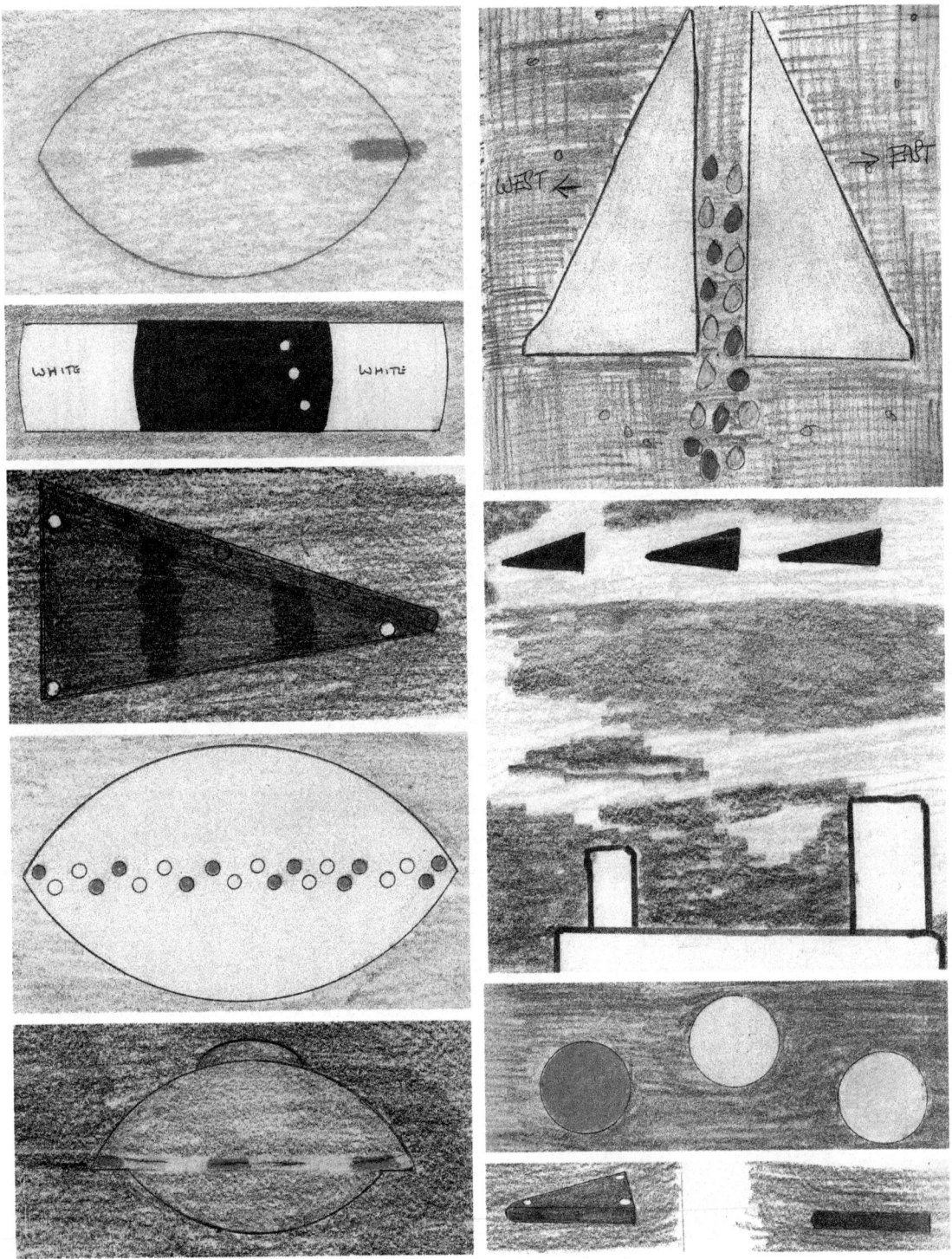

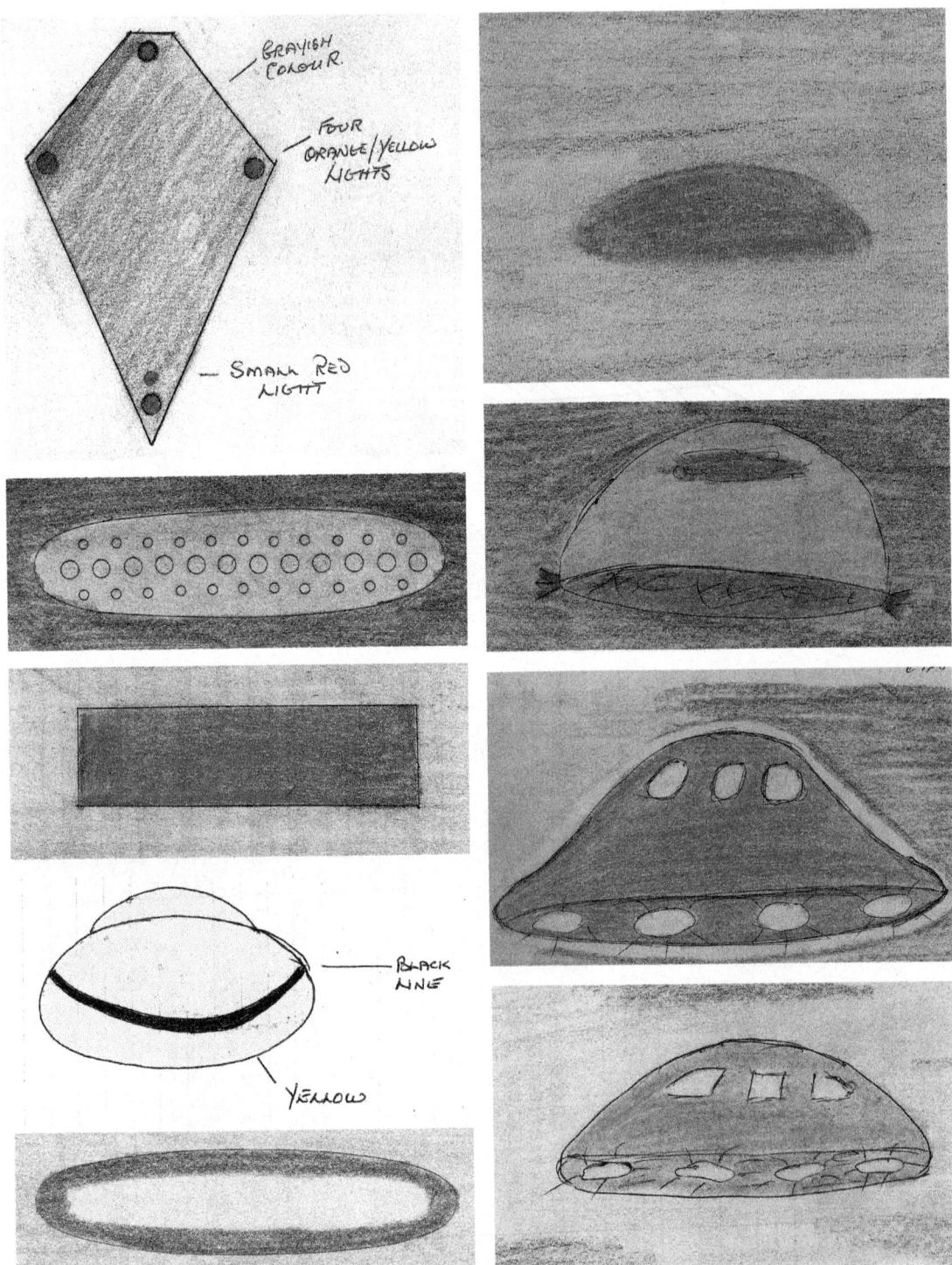

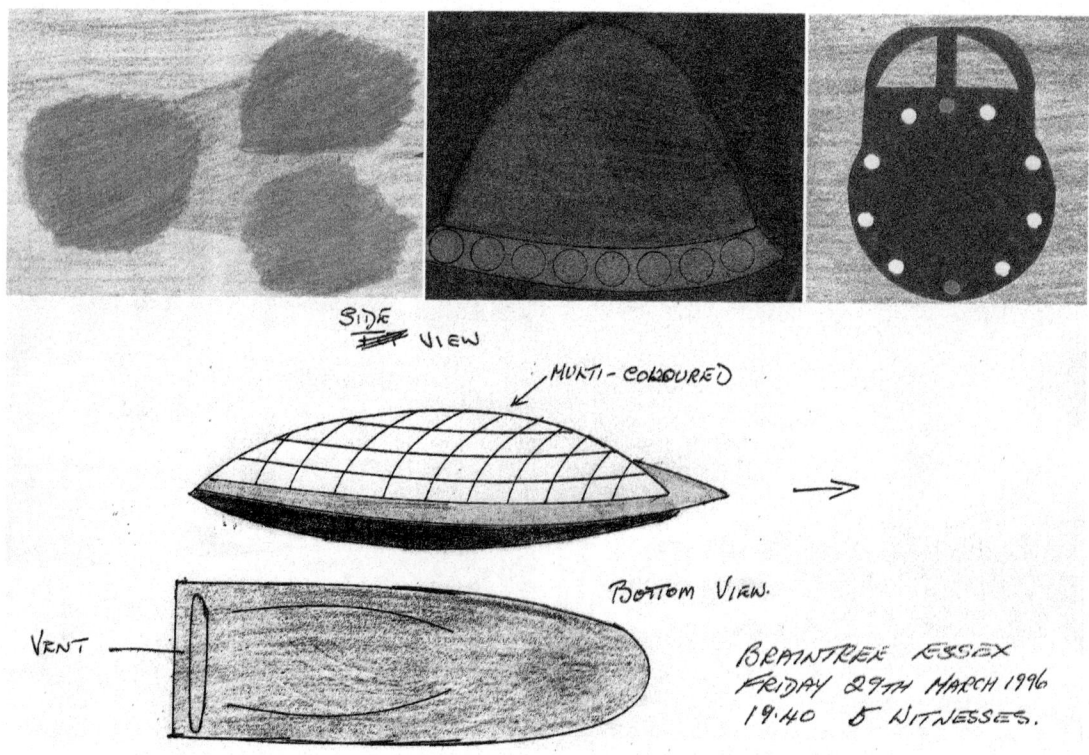

This peculiar shaped object was seen – following a flurry of UFO activity over Barking, Essex, in 1978.

UFO lands at pet farm

Although we have mentioned a claim which appears to be genuine of the landing of a UFO two years prior to the Rendlesham incident previously, it is of value to include further details of the incident which involved Mr Peter Duncan as it is relatively unknown to most of the readers. One should consider a possible association between the sighting and what was seen by the airmen, two years later.

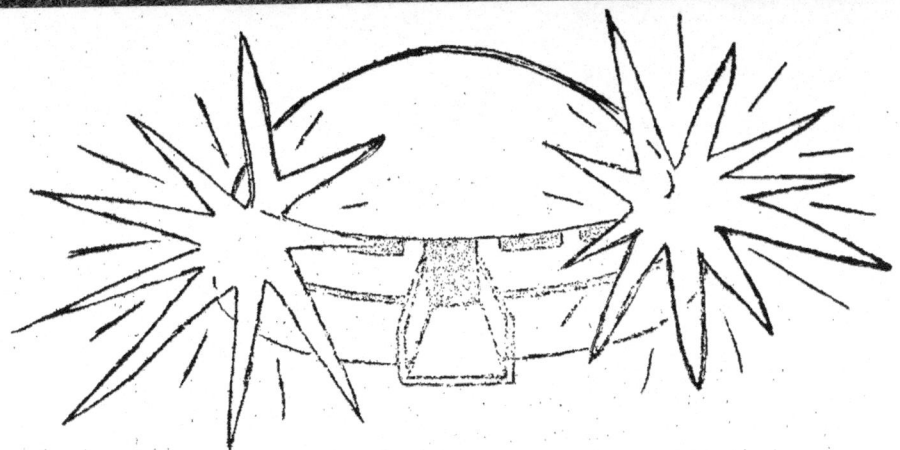

The UFO seen by Mr. Duncan in the horse field (Drawing by Mrs. Duncan according to her husband's description).

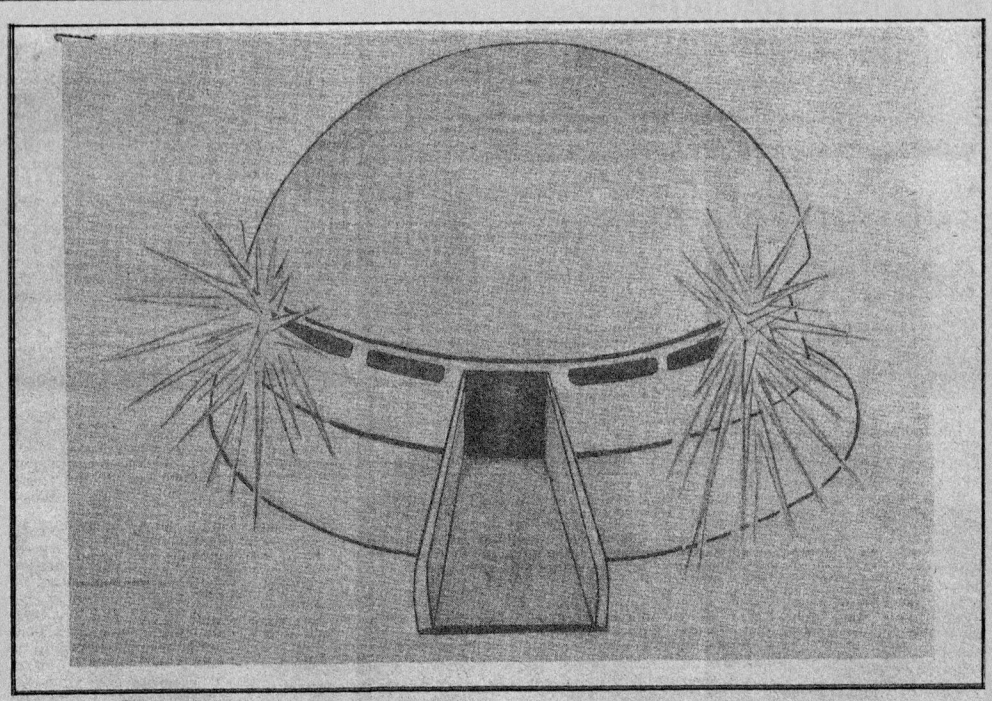

Mr Duncan's impression of the craft he says he saw at Weeley.

UFO experts probe spaceship report

BRITAIN'S leading UFO experts are investigating a report that a spaceship landed in Weeley.

Peter Duncan — part owner of Weeley Pet Farm — described his real-life close encounter on BBC radio on Tuesday. And he also revealed that he had kept the sighting secret for eight months because he was afraid of being ridiculed.

Mr Duncan claims that at one point he was only 20 yards from the space-ship.

By LEN ROBERTS

The sighting was late at night in May when Mr Duncan was making a final check on the dogs at his boarding kennels.

"As I came out of the food store there was a blinding light in our field. At first I thought a helicopter had landed but when I entered the field I could clearly see that it wasn't a helicopter — or anything else from this world," said Mr Duncan.

He said the craft had a dome-shaped top which covered — like and umbrella — a darker interior. There was a ramp or opening and a number of slit-shaped port holes, he said.

Mr Duncan continued: "The base was absolutely colossal — about 80 or 90ft —

and the craft was making a constant drone — similar to the sound of a buzz-bomb."

Mr Duncan said he was terrified but slowly edged closer to the craft and decided to try and get a better look at the darkened interior by shining his torch.

"As I did so, the craft lifted and sped off."

Mr Duncan — who before this incident had been sceptical of UFO sightings — only reported his alien visit after seeing a television film on the work of the UFO Research Centre in Oxford.

The centre is run by Contact UK which was set-up 14 years ago by the Earl of Clancarty who has instigated a debate in the House of Lords next week on UFOs. The TV film was part of the pre-publicity given to the debate.

● Continued on page 3

WEELEY UFO PROBE

● Continued from page one

Derek Mansell, a research officer at the centre's data processing division in Oxford, felt it was very likely that the craft was "manned" and that the landing was connected with the animals at the farm.

He explained there were now strong links between animal mutilation and UFO sightings. In America, he said, animals had been found with radiation poisoning in areas where UFOs had been spotted.

"There is a very good chance that there was someone in that craft and that they were going to examine the animals at the farm. Or, indeed, they may have already examined the animals before Mr Duncan disturbed them," he added.

Mr Mansell said he would be sending one of the centre's specially trained investigators to visit Mr Duncan and compile a report.

Bill Eden — an investigator for the Essex UFO Study Group — also plans to contact Mr Duncan.

Mr Eden pointed out that Essex recorded the second highest number of UFO sightings in Britain and that he was currently investigating several reports in the Chelmsford area.

ACTIVITY

And the general UFO activity has certainly been reflected locally with five sightings in the last fortnight. And in each case the report was filed before Mr Duncan's radio broadcast.

The first came from a 17-year-old Brightlingsea apprentice engineer who saw an oval-shaped object flash across the sky while he was exercising his dog on December 29.

Andrew Fairminer, of Lower Park Road, said he was walking on the recreation ground when his dog started to act strangely. It was then that he looked up and saw the craft pass overhead.

Thursday was a particularly busy day for UFO spotting with three separate reports. The first came from Hilda Denson of St Alban's Road, Clacton, who said she saw a space-craft hanging silently below cloud level at 6.15 am.

She said: "The vehicle consisted of two large, perfectly round circles of bright yellow light, not diffused in any way. Just below centre of these two lights was a much smaller orange coloured orb. There three lights appeared to be joined by a thin band of metal.

"It remained still in the strong gale wind for 15 minutes and then, without any manoeuvre, it quickly disappeared."

Twelve hours later there were two further sightings, the first by a couple at Weeley who reported a diamond-shaped object in the sky. Four lights — two very bright and two much smaller — were clearly visible and there was also a red glow from the centre. The craft hovered above the Tendring Council offices for some time before disappearing at speed.

And at about the same time there was a similar report from a St Osyth family who saw two very bright lights high in the sky over Frating.

The family — who were driving towards Tenpenny Hill, Thorington, later saw that there were four lights giving the impression of a star.

A sighting on New Year's Day has left John Culham with a legacy of car-failure.

Mr Culham, who works at QB Printers in Colchester, spotted two bright lights in the sky near the Weeley roundabout.

"The car immediately slowed down. Yet when I took my foot off the accelerator the speed increased to about 40-45 mph," said Mr Culham who lives in Abberton.

'Ring Angels' were they birds or UFOs?

At the beginning of the book we mentioned about 'Z' or 'U' shaped objects, tracked by RAF radar installations during the late 1940s and early 1950s, over the coast of East Anglia and the adjacent localities.

On the 20th March 1941, up to five separate stations plotted massive formations of 'blips' moving slowly across the Channel, heading towards land for two hours, before changing to single echoes –then fading away. RAF planes were scram-bled, but by the time they vectored on the locations there was nothing to be seen.

Their presence has never been explained, despite early suggestions that they were flocks of birds or temperature inversions.

We now know that secret investigations were conducted as to the cause by RAF Fighter Command in the intervening years when the phenomenon was ongoing. In 1959, Marconi's 'L' band radar at Chelmsford reported 'ring angels' on the scopes. They began at dawn as a point echo, and then expanded to form a perfect 'ring', followed by further concentric 'rings' – like the ripples on a pond – visible to a height of 2,000 feet. Once again, a visit to the location revealed nothing untoward. Fortunately, the problem was explained away as being birds moving from one tree to the other!

An early map shows the location of the plotted East Coast 'ring angel' locations. Is it merely coincidence that the same localities were to record heavy UFO activity in later years, the majority of which were most definitely not birds?! (**Source: Dr David Clarke**)

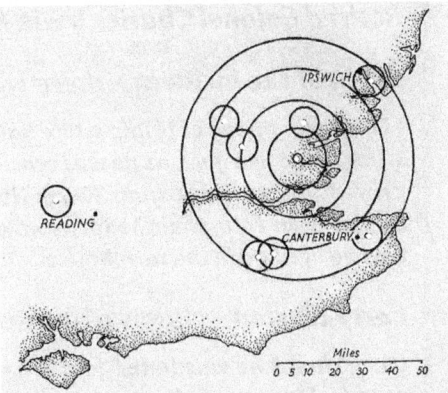

Fig. 1. Location of ring-angel centres in South-East England.

John Hanson – Other books published on the incident

As we enter the final stages of this book, people should know that in addition to *Sky Crash*, published in 1984 by Neville Spearman, was a slightly updated edition published by Grafton Books, in 1986. In addition to this, two other books are worth mentioning with regard to this case. The first one is *Out of the Blue*, by Jenny Randles, published for the USA audience in 1993, Berkley Books, New York, rather than British; the second *Sky Crash Throughout Time*, by Brenda Butler and Philip Kinsella, 2013 (Capall Bann Publishers).

Epilogue – putting the record straight!

Retired Colonel Charles Irwin Halt –

Night of the incident – there was no fog or bright white light

"There was no fog or bright white light. Adrian Bustinza was with me the whole time and stuck to me like glue, as he was scared but was not crying. There were never 150 people present – never more than 20-25. No British Police were present at night. As supported by the letter from their head, no cows were present as they were in the barn and there was no light on in the farmhouse.

Larry Warren – claims of a suicide – no such thing happened!

Larry claims he was in the forest and the next thing he knew he woke in his room all muddy. Strange, as it was very dry and we didn't see any mud. On another occasion he told of handing in his gun and went to the dining hall. There was no suicide. We did

AFFIDAVIT OF CHARLES I. HALT

(1) My name is Charles I. Halt

(2) I was born on

(3) My address is

(4) I served in the U.S. Air Force for 28 years, retiring in 1991 with the rank of Colonel. In December 1980, I was the Deputy Base Commander at the Anglo-American base, RAF Bentwaters, in Suffolk, England.

(5) Late in the evening on December 27th, and continuing into the pre-dawn hours of December 28th, in response to reports of unusual lights in nearby Rendlesham Forest, I led a team of USAF Security Policemen into the woods to investigate. This was the second such incident in as many days and rumors of UFO activity were rife on base. By going into the forest, my intention was find a logical explanation for the mysterious lights.

(6) While in Rendlesham Forest, our security team observed a light that looked like a large eye, red in color, moving through the trees. After a few minutes this object began dripping something that looked like molten metal. A short while later it broke into several smaller, white-colored objects which flew away in all directions. Claims by skeptics that this was merely a sweeping beam from a distant lighthouse are unfounded; we could see the unknown light and the lighthouse simultaneously. The latter was 35 to 40-degrees off where all of this was happening.

(7) Upon leaving the forest, our team crossed a farmer's field. As we did so, someone pointed out three objects in the northern sky. They were white and had multiple-colored lights on them. At first, the objects appeared elliptical but, as they maneuvered, turned full round. They were stationary for awhile and then they started to move at high speed in sharp angular patterns as though they were doing a grid search.

(8) About that same time, someone noticed a similar object in the southern sky. It was round and, at one point, it came toward us at a very high speed. It stopped overhead and sent down a small pencil-like beam, sort of like a laser beam. That illuminated the ground about ten feet from us and we just stood there in awe, wondering whether it was a signal, a warning, or what it was. It clicked-off as though someone threw a switch, and then the object receded back up into the sky.

(9) This object then moved back toward Bentwaters, and continued to send down beams of light, at one point near the Weapons Storage Area. We knew that because we could hear the chatter on the two-way radio. Several airmen present later told me that they saw the beams. I don't remember any names at this point. From my position in the forest, it appeared that one or more beams came down near the WSA. At the time, the object was just to the north of the facility. I had great concern about the purpose of the beams.

(10) In keeping with official U.S. Air Force policy, I can neither confirm nor deny that the Weapons Storage Area held nuclear weapons. However, I am aware that other former or retired USAF Security Police who worked there at the time of the incident are now on-the-record confirming the presence of tactical nuclear bombs at the WSA.

(11) I believe the objects that I saw at close quarter were extraterrestrial in origin and that the security services of both the United States and the United Kingdom have attempted—both then and now—to subvert the significance of what occurred at Rendlesham Forest and RAF Bentwaters by the use of well-practiced methods of disinformation.

(12) I have not been paid nor given anything of value to make this statement and it is the truth to the best of my recollection.

Signed: _____

Date: 6/17/10

Signature witnessed by: Katherine C. Snow

Notary: _____ My commission expires April 30, 2011

have an airman go AWOL and fly to Chicago at that time, but the desk Sergeant tracked him down and had the Chicago Airport Police put him back on a plane and returned, so he avoided the AWOL charge. His leaving had nothing to do with the event. He was frustrated, as his security clearance had not come through and he was doing menial tasks. He ended up with an administrative discharge.

Larry Warren did get an honorable discharge under provisions of either unsuitable or undesirable. There was no breach of contract, as he enlisted to be a Security Policeman and that's what he was assigned as. The incident and his talking about it may have figured into it all. I do know he was 'snapped' (lost his authorization to have a weapon or access to classified material). His associates told me he had a substance abuse problem."

I've been criticized over the years, many times, for what people regard as criticisms made by me on Larry Warren (and vice versa), but with all due respects, there is more than sufficient foundation for my misgivings about the role played by him in this matter.

Serious questions are raised

"Let me give you an example. Even the Sky Crash folk (Grafton Books 1986) admit on page 354, quote:

'Warrens story has been seriously questioned by us in this book, not least because of his mysterious 'sites photographs' which, wherever they were taken, certainly do not show the alleged landing site, or anywhere in the vicinity of it that we have been unable to discover. Warren's account of the events has also continued to vary. By August 1985, in an interview given with Dr. J. Allen Hynek, he attacked our book implying we had manufactured things we claimed he said. Yet all of our reporting on Larry Warren's testimony stems from recorded interviews. Now, Warren further insists that the underground 'complex' of his adventure did not happen to him. He was instead retelling something which in truth happened to Adrian Bustinza – his close colleague. However, Bustinza has come forward in the USA and, while he supports the UFO story all the way, he flatly denies being taken into any underground room or shown the alleged film which Warren incidentally still says he saw elsewhere on base. This suggests that at best Larry Warren has grafted bizarre elements on to his story, with the result that while some or most of it might be still true, we cannot be justified in treating it seriously.' *end of quote.*

The News of the World

"May I remind you that when Larry was interviewed by the News of the World on the 2nd October 1983, he said nothing about any aliens, but a month later was telling another story! I understand that he took part in a hypnosis regression with a Fred Max, who is described as a behavioral psychologist – none of this was mentioned in their book: Left At East Gate, although I see in Georgina Bruni's book You Can't Tell The People (available to read on the Internet), she brought this to the notice of Peter Robbins, who told her that Larry didn't want it in and that, 'Larry had not been put under hypnosis but had gone through the motions!' What is going on here? What have they to hide?

Even the authors of Sky Crash mentioned the role of Fred Max, who they claimed had conducted experiments with Betty Luca for Larry Fawcett and Ray Fowler."

The Command Post

"*Left At East Gate shows a picture of the Command Post and identifies it as the Base Photo Lab where the entrance to the 'underground facility' was accessed. Actually, the Command Post had a small concealed emergency escape hatch, which I was told was later sealed. We never used it, even in exercises, and few knew about it. It came up just outside the surrounding blast wall.*

In 2010, I was invited to talk. I've done a program for them in the past (2010). The Producer was Melissa Tittl – Director of Content at Gaia TV, Greater Los Angeles area; she actually had my soil sample analyzed … the results – nothing of great note. The program turned out, despite promises, to be more entertainment than factual."

The audio tape recording – putting the record straight

"*Over the years it has been alleged that there is a missing piece of conversation taken out of the alleged two-hour tape made by me, fueling further speculation that it has been removed deliberately because it's something that should not be made available to the public. Georgina Bruni herself claimed in September 2001, in a popular British UFO magazine, that the 18 minutes' recording was an edited version of an event that lasted approximately four hours. Let's put the record straight once and for all.*

There is no missing or withheld section of tape; I wasn't sure how good the batteries were or how much tape I'd use, so I only turned the tape on when I wanted to record something. As far as the horrendous belief to ever let people know what I saw is a bit of an excess. At the time Brenda and her gang were pestering me no end. I did tell Georgina there was another tape. It was made much later and done for Larry Facwett and Barry Greenwood. Barry probably still has it. I made it to assist them with a possible book, a follow on to Clear Intent. However, they discovered Larry Warren had lied to them and they gave up on the book.

I've also been asked about the odd interruptions that appeared in the first few minutes of the tape. There is nothing suspicious about this. All I can say is that one of those is just a bar of music I managed to record accidently pressing the play and record button together, whilst my daughter was playing the piano one day. The other voice I've no idea – perhaps it's been added by an investigator or somebody along the way."

Colonel Halt tape given to Colonel Williams

"*I would like to reiterate again about this tape. I gave it to Colonel Williams who played it for the General and his staff. Conrad asked me to make him a copy which I did. When he moved on he left the copy in the desk drawer and Morgan found it. He was playing it, without my knowledge, at social events and gave it or a copy to Harry Harris. Harry proceeded to sell it to the Japanese. Suddenly it was every where. I was shocked. To my knowledge the MOD was never given a copy of my tape. When I asked if they wanted a complete report of the events, personnel and measures taken, I was surprised to learn that this was not necessary. The summary was taken down by Squadron Leader Donald Moreland and then sent to the MOD. The tape was circulated around the United States and later released to Robert Todd of the Citizens Against UFO Secrecy (CAUS). It then fell into the hands of Sam Morgan, Ted Cochran, and Harry Harris. Ironically, the tape was played at some cocktail parties and treated with merriment before being returned to me, copies having been made –without my knowledge"* [According to Donald Moreland, the tape recording made by Colonel Halt was handed over to General Gabriel, during a visit to the airbase.]

Another visit to my house!

"On one occasion, I had to have them forcibly removed from my home by the police. I may have misled them out of frustration. Brenda Butler and Dot Street should remember how they hounded me. People ask me what the hell that was all about. It happened in 1982, when I returned briefly to the United States to clear up an issue and left my son Charles in the care of the then Base Commander. Unknown to me he made contact with the authors of Sky Crash and they began to ply him for information. I later learnt that he and several friends were enjoying the attention and free drinks provided at a local pub. When I arrived home I went jogging. I had no sooner returned to the house when the Sky Crash crowd came to the front door, demanding to come in for a meeting with my son. I was tired, sweaty, and still wearing my jogging clothes. They kept trying to push their way in. I finally went to the 'red' hotline phone and called the police and asked that they be removed. Somehow the police thought I was under duress and sent a force to be reckoned with. The next thing I knew there were armed cops everywhere. I heard the bullhorn announcement – 'Come out with your hands up'. I ran out, trying to explain there was no threat and I just wanted them to leave. The British Police arrived and removed them."

Dot Street

"Chuck Junior invited me and Brenda to the house. We went there because we already knew Chuck Junior personally through previous meetings with him. This included the time when we played a joke on solicitor Harry Harris by getting Chuck to take part in a video, pretending to be an anonymous witness at the airbase, and setting up Harry who was totally unaware of his identity. Harry still has the video as far as I know. As far as any claim of drinking alcohol was concerned Chuck Junior was never given alcohol. When he came up to my house he had a glass of milk. When we set off for the appointment we had something to eat in a pub, but we didn't have any alcoholic drink – Chuck was only 16 I recall at the time. On another occasion Brenda and I were going to the main airbase; I believe she was going to meet John Burroughs. Colonel Halt's phone number was in the phone book. I phoned and expected to speak to Colonel Halt but his son, Chuck Junior, answered. We told him what we were doing and he said I will meet you there. He then showed us the way back to his Dad's house. We met up with him on a number of occasions after that. When I heard Chuck Junior was going to the United States, Brenda didn't

want to go but I thought we should go and say goodbye to him, as he was like a son to us. When I arrived at the house, I left Brenda in the car and I spoke to Chuck Junior – that's when his Dad called the Police … the rest you know."

Airman John Burroughs writes an open letter

Jim and John signing a tee-shirt showing floating Orford Ness lighthouse! 28-12-2010

2009 – AN OPEN LETTER to General Gordon Williams – Wing Commander Col. Theodore J Conrad – Vice Wing Commander Col. Sam P. Morgan – Base Commander Col. Charles I. Halt – Deputy Base Commander Lt. Col. Malcolm Zickler – Security Police Commander

"As you may or may not know, I am currently in the process of putting together a reunion, next year, to commemorate the 30th anniversary of the unexplained incidents that took place in and around the twin bases of Bentwaters and Woodbridge in December 1980. The purpose of this reunion is to get as many witnesses together as possible with the eventual aim of finding some kind of explanation for these strange events. There are a number of organizations working to make this happen. Some of us now involved are having serious health issues related to the incident. I am very concerned about what we may have been exposed to out there, especially as I was exposed to something on two occasions."

Colonel Charles Halt

"Col. Halt you have offered to write a letter for Jim Penniston and I to give to the VA (Veterans

Health Administration), stating we were exposed to high doses of radiation and the interrogation techniques of the AFOSI, which included using drugs on some of the witnesses. Jim Penniston and I to this day have yet to receive this letter. We are left with an empty feeling that all of us who were out there have been deserted by our chain of command and the military who we so proudly served. We are now forced to worry what we have been exposed to and what will happen to our health in the future.

Over the years I have been told you have tried to keep me out of different shows about Bentwaters, for example the . . .

ABC, Sci-Fi and History Channel productions

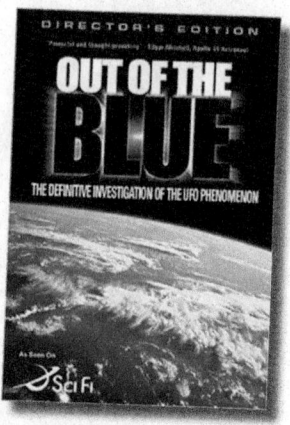

I was told by the producers you had no idea how to get hold of me, yet you were working with Jim Penniston, who had all my contact details and he passed them on to you. With regard to the movie *Out Of The Blue, produced and directed by Mr James Fox, you told him I was not out with you on the third night. Col. Halt when I first went public with my experience stating I was involved in the first and third night, you said I was never involved at all in the third night. Well your tape proved that I was. You then said I never came forward and met up with you. However, I have a taped interview where you state that I did indeed come forward and met up with your group. I have been told that your reasoning was that I was loose cannon and would talk too much to the press about the incident. You have now gone on the record and said we were exposed to what was something extraterrestrial in nature. What could I have ever said that would have caused more of a stir than that? I for one have no idea for sure what we were exposed to. How do you know for sure that the events were extraterrestrial? Col. Halt's memo and tape clearly shows something happened to all of us. The USAF stated to CNN that they stood by Col. Halt's memo. I can't help but feel the government is waiting for the health of all of us to fade without reaching out to help any of us. I have been told by more than one person who was involved in the command structure that there was no investigation done afterwards, which I do not believe."

Colonel Conrad

"You were the Base Commander at the time and you moved to the Vice Wing Commander afterwards. You stated you never saw anything from your house like Colonel Halt claims. After being asked certain questions years later, by Ben Jameson, you said you needed to talk to Lt. Colonel Zickler about the questions before you could answer them. Over the years I have reached out to all of you for help. Colonel Halt – you offered a letter, but we never received it."

---

*Out of the Blue a film – Advertised as 'The definitive investigation of the UFO phenomena' narrated by Peter Coyote, it is, according to the producers, widely considered the best documentary ever made about unidentified objects. The producers travelled around the world to investigate some of the most famous UFO events on record. Through exclusive interviews with high-ranking military and government personnel, this award winning film supports the theory that some of the UFOs are extra terrestrial in origin.

Not to be confused with the book *From Out Of The Blue, written by Jenny Randles and published in 1991, by *Berkley Books,* in the United States.

General Williams

"All you would do for us is say we were good men doing good work."

Colonel Morgan

"All you care about is what organization is sponsoring the reunion. Colonel Conrad – all you can do is contact Lt. Colonel Zickler before you could answer our questions … and then you never get back to us. Here we have the top four people involved in the incident and yet not one of you can agree on anything, including Colonel Halt's memo having the wrong dates and times of the incident. Everybody agrees Colonel Halt would have never made that kind of mistake; he even had the witness statements in front of him when he wrote the memo. I have also learned that there were statements written by all of the people involved in the third night and collected after the incident."

Lt. Colonel Zickler

"Lt. Colonel Zickler, I understand after you departed Bentwaters, you moved to Eglin Air Force Base, Florida, where there was then reported numerous UFO events. You then moved on to become head of System Security Engineering and Chief of Operation Security at GE Aerospace, to include going to extensive lengths to test and create realistic scenarios on an airbase. Everybody wonders how a Squadron Commander, in charge of Security Police and Law Enforcement, can ascend to working with the US Special Forces Counter Intelligence Deception Unit. This seems suspicious. Why have you never gone on record about the incident at Bentwaters/Woodbridge? When I contacted you this week, all you could offer was 'Cheer up, things will get better soon!' "

OSI involvement

"Colonel Halt stated that you ran a major investigation afterwards, involving OSI, yet I can find no one who will support those claims. On the questions of the paper trail of reports 1,569 and blotters, Colonel Halt stated they were stolen. Well everybody who worked back in the area stated they were not. They were available and maintained in the proper way and kept in storage the required amount of time. Everybody agrees that if they came up missing there would have been a major investigation done, because they were controlled items. The fact that nobody in my chain of command can agree is very interesting. That a Squadron Commander seems to run the show is even more interesting. These are just a few things I have uncovered and I would welcome your response. I would truly like for all of us to be able to get together next year and would welcome your involvement and support in the reunion. I have been in contact with Gary Heseltine on the movie screenplay he and Colonel Halt are putting together, and truly hope the project will happen.

I understand Mr Heseltine would be very happy to help with the reunion. – I'm asking now, General Williams, Colonel Conrad, Colonel Morgan, Colonel Halt, Lt. Colonel Zickler, would you like to be involved?

Yours Sincerely,

T/Sgt. John Burroughs"

Charles Halt – My involvement with obtaining medical help for Jim and John

"Going through my files I found copies of the letters Gordon Williams and I wrote to the authorities on behalf of John and Jim, attempting to get the medical help from the VA. I also found the letter from their attorney requesting our help. Additionally, I found the email I sent to Williams, explaining the background. Despite what the attorney claims, our letters are proved instrumental in obtaining the medical help."

June 12, 2012

VA Health Administration Center
CHAMPVA
Post Office Box 469064
Denver, Colorado 80246-9064

Department of Veterans Affairs
Attn: Timothy Graham
810 Vermont Avenue NW
10P2C1 VACO
Washington, D.C. 20420

Re: The Rendlesham Forest Incident at RAF Bentwaters, England, December, 1980

Dear Sirs:

In December of 1980 I was assigned by the U.S. Air Force to RAF Bentwaters, England as the Deputy Base Commander. Subsequently, I would become Base Commander for the same.

In December of 1980 I was called upon to investigate something for which I had never been trained.   Early in the morning of December 26, 1980 I went to the police station to collect the police blotters. I entered the station about 0630 hours to a Desk Sergeant who began laughing. I asked the Sergeant what was so funny. He then began to tell me that three policemen were out in the adjacent forest, called Rendlesham Forest, earlier that evening chasing an unidentified flying object (UFO), and he had been instructed by his Flight Lieutenant not to put it into the police blotter. I asked the Sergeant for more specifics and was told that an object was spotted just outside the base in Rendlesham Forest which initially was thought to be a downed aircraft with multi-colored lights. Three policemen, John Buroughs, Jim Penniston, and Ed Cabansac, were sent into the forest to investigate. Radio contact was lost with these gentlemen for an hour or more. After being told all of this by the Desk Sergeant I advised him to put what he had related to me into the police blotter. At the time, I was convinced there was a rational explanation for whatever the three policemen had encountered in Rendlesham Forest.   The rumor of contact with a UFO spread like wildfire through the base. Unknown to me at that time was the fact that numerous police officers went into the forest and found what they described as clearly a landing site.

Two nights later I was at our year-end recognition party when the On Duty Police Lieutenant came and told the Base Commander and I that "the UFO was back". Neither of us believed that but were forced to investigate to hopefully put the issue to rest. I was tasked to go out and determine exactly what was going on in the forest. I took a party of five and went into Rendlesham Forest. I was shown a landing site with three, equidistant,

VA Health Administration Center
Department of Veterans Affairs
Page Two of Three
June 12, 2012

equidistant, deep, and identical indentations in the forest floor. <u>We recorded radiation readings that were approximately ten (10) times normal</u> with the highest readings being in the center of the triangle formed by the three indentations in the forest floor. Rub marks were noted on the pine trees facing the landing site and, directly overhead of the site, there was a clearing in the forest canopy. While reviewing the site we noticed a strange glowing object just beyond the forest in an adjacent field. We observed this object move into the forest and horizontally through the trees. At one point, the object began to approach us before retreating back into the adjacent field. The object appeared to be shedding what I can only best describe as molten metal. The glow from the object reflected off the windows of a nearby farmhouse so intensely that it made the house appear to be ablaze. Suddenly, we observed the object silently explode into multiple white objects and disappear from view. We then moved out into the field to look for any evidence of what was "dripping" from the object. We found nothing but then noticed several objects above in the sky. These objects were multi-colored and moved at very high rates of speed and, despite their speed, were making very sharp turns in the process. The objects appeared to us to change shape from round to elliptical. One of the objects in the sky moved overhead and sent down a laser-like beam at our feet. Other objects in the sky sent down similar beams into the Bentwaters Base in or near the weapons storage area. We watched these objects for some time before eventually returning to base.

I called the Command Post and asked for a check air defense and local air traffic controllers to determine what we were observing could possibly be. I was advised that nothing was showing on radar. I subsequently learned that both the Bentwaters and air defense radars had <u>indeed</u> picked up something that evening. Years later after retiring from the Air Force the Bentwaters Tower Air Traffic Controllers admitted they had picked up the object moving at high speed and, moreover, had witnessed a glowing object descend into Rendlesham Forest. It was because of fear and ridicule that these men had not come forth earlier.

In the days following the incident I personally interviewed and took statements from the participants from the first night when a possible downed aircraft was investigated. John Borroughs and Jim Penniston <u>clearly</u> had some type of contact with a craft which has never been explained and whose origin remains a mystery. Ed Cabansac, who was one of the three policemen to enter the forest for the initial investigation, says that he witnessed John Burroughs "enter" the craft. Thankfully, the passage of time has allowed all who were involved in the Rendlesham Incident to discuss more fully, and freely, and with each other what they experienced. However, exactly what happened cannot be fully brought out even with regression hypnosis. Years after the incident I was told that the three policemen who initially entered the forest during the incident were shortly afterward interrogated by government, possibly military, personnel. These interrogations

VA Health Administration Center
Department of Veterans Affairs
Page Three of Three
June 12, 2012

took the form of what one would expect when trying to extract information from an enemy captive.

Senior Air Force Officers, at least on the surface, wanted nothing to do with the incident and told me to get with the RAF Liaison Officer since the events we were a part of had happened off the base. I was instructed to compose a memorandum, which I did and is now in the public domain that provided the details of what we encountered in Rendlesham forest. In my memorandum I described the first incident as occurring in the early hours of December 26, 1980 and the night I went to investigate as the night of December 27, 1980 and following morning of December 28, 1980. There was some confusion in the past regarding these dates due to a typographic error in my memorandum that went unnoticed for years.

To this day I have no answers for what happened in 1980 in England. I do know what I witnessed was a craft which was under intelligent control. I had known John Burroughs and Jim Penniston quite well prior to the incident in the forest. I can confidently state that they have never been the same since. Both John and Jim were undeniably adversely affected by whatever happened to them in Rendlesham Forest in 1980.

Sincerely,

Charles I. Halt
Col. USAF (Ret)

Subj: **Bentwaters**
Date: 3/10/2011 3:08:19 P.M. Eastern Standard Time
From: Haltc@aol.com
To: gowill57@comcast.net

General Williams:

I feel that I owe you an explanation for many things that have made the press for the last few years. First I would like to thank you for the example you set and the leadership displayed as the 81st Commander. It made a lasting impression.

After you left Bentwaters Sam Morgan began playing a copy of the tape I made in DEC 1980 at cocktail parties and for various British groups unbeknownst to me. He gave out copies of the tape and even mentioned my memo concerning the event. I was shocked as I was content to let the event die. An American writer named Larry Fawcett came in under the Freedom of Information Act for the memo. We didn't have an official copy so he went to 3rd AF. Pete Bent (acting 3rd AF CC) called me and told me he was going to release the memo. I pleaded with him to destroy it. My words were "if you release it your life and mine will never be the same". He released it and you know what happened after that. I was hounded to death. Finally, since there was so much disinformation and my name was out there I started telling the truth.

One result is many people came forward that knew part of what happened. Were you aware 4-5 or more of our airmen were drugged and hypnotized? One or more were given false memories. Not long after the incident General Gabriel came to visit. Recently released British files state he was given a copy of my tape. Nearby British residents as well as the Forest Service Staff all claim the were visited by strange men in trench coats asking questions about the nights in question. Everyone I asked, including the OSI, told me at the time they had no interest and we were not going to investigate. Last week the British Government released the remaining files. Strange but the files of our incident have gone missing. Just like both Sgt. Penniston and Sgt Nevilles 35mm film's. Even two of the plaster casts Penniston took of the indentations of the craft landing pads disappeared.To say nothing of the British radar tapes. Captain Verano has gone on record saying he delivered a package to you plane side which you stated was the UFO pictures bound for Germany. I know you must know something as Al Brown was in the B/W Control tower the night I was out. We weren't flying so his presence there is strange. The B/W Controllers have now come forward and confirm they all saw a glowing object, saw it streak at high speed across their scope and go into the forest at W/B. The WSA Tower Operator and a Comm man working there also saw something. A friend chased down the British Air Traffic Controller and he too says he saw something despite the tape disappearing.

When I retired I was debriefed. I asked if I could talk about the incident and was told yes. I would be interested in your comments. If you are not at liberty to talk could you at least admit there was an investigation. It really doesn't matter much to me but it may enable several of the involved airmen to finally put the issue to rest. What happened has really ruined their lives.

Chuck Halt

February 15, 2013

General Mark A. Welsh, III, Chief of Staff

UNITED STATES AIR FORCE

1000 Air Force Pentagon

Washington, D.C. 20330-1000

Re: John Frederick Burroughs & James William Penniston

General Welsh:

I am writing to you in hopes that you may offer assistance for two men who were under my command in 1980, Airman First Class John Frederick Burroughs, and Staff Sergeant James William Penniston.

In 1979 I was transferred to the 81st Tactical Fighter Wing, Royal Air Force Station Bentwaters, England, as vice commander. The following year in late December of 1980 and while in the line of duty at RAF Bentwaters, Airman Burroughs and Staff Sergeant Penniston responded to unexplained lights in the adjacent Rendlesham Forest. Within days following their encounter in the forest, both men began experiencing negative physiological effects. The adverse effect on the health of these men continues to this very day and has, just recently, nearly cost Airman Burroughs his life. Repeatedly, his physicians over the years have advised him that if they knew what he was exposed to in 1980 it would be of great value in treating him today. These men have tried in earnest to get whatever information they could from the government, including the enlistment of an attorney to help them with FOIA requests, however, their efforts have consistently been thwarted; none of their FOIA responses have offered anything but denial of the existence of any records. This is absurd given the fact that a formerly "UK Restricted" stamped document included herewith specifically cites the Rendlesham incident and potential negative health effects there from.

In closing, I request that the health of Airman John Burroughs and Staff Sergeant Jim Penniston be considered with a bit more concern and respect than that which has been previously shown. Any assistance you may be able to provide to these men would be very much appreciated.

Sincerely,

_____

Maj. Gen. Gordon E. Williams, USAF (Ret.)

GEW/

Subj: **Re: Shoot Details for October 5th**
Date: 10/7/2010 8:56:10 A.M. Eastern Daylight Time
From: Haltc@aol.com
To: melissa.tittl@prometheuspix.com

Melissa:
After a diligent search I found the soil sample. There's not as much as I remembered but I haven't opened the container since 1980. My undergraduate degree was in chemistry and I worked in a laboratory doing analytical work for a while so I have some background. If you can find a lab that will not only analyze the sample but look for any alteration that could have been a result of exposure to heat, radiation or other influence it would be helpful. No promise you'll find anything but it's certainly worth a try. You probably need to be honest with the lab even though the may think you strange. If there are detectable changes they'll most likely show up in the sand in the sample. Let me know.

I misplaced the lunch receipt so don't worry about it.

Chuck

Subj: **Fwd: Rendlesham soil sample - microscopy**
Date: 10/14/2010 3:33:04 P.M. Eastern Daylight Time
From: melissa.tittl@prometheuspix.com
To: Haltc@aol.com

---------- Forwarded message ----------
From: **Peter Febbroriello** <peterfebbroriello@sbcglobal.net>
Date: Thu, Oct 14, 2010 at 12:17 PM
Subject: Rendlesham soil sample - microscopy
To: Melissa Tittl <melissa.tittl@prometheuspix.com>

Hi Melissa,
The sand gains are typical glacial and riverbank sand, with the appearance of smoothly worn edges, and no recent fracturing. Some smaller fractures that are younger than the glacial particles are also worn, and no longer have the fine razor edges of immediate breakage. In the sample I used for the microscope slide, I see few broken pieces of the glacial material, which have hemispherical appearance. Apparently, the object that rested on the area was not very heavy, or the soil was too forgiving, and was too soft to allow the grains to be fractured. Some opaque particles with flat edges could be seen.
There are remnants of small wood fragments that could easily be pine needles. I will try to get measurements and determine if they have been charred or not. But I did find a hair that fits the description of deer hair and it did not appear to have any heat damage.
There are no obvious signs of mold or fungus spores, or insect skeletons of any kind, but I have only looked at a very small quantity of material.
I might try a petri dish culture to see if anything will grow.

--Peter

--
Melissa Tittl
Associate Producer, Ancient Aliens
Prometheus Entertainment
6430 Sunset Blvd, Suite 1450
Los Angeles, CA 90028
323-769-4023
melissa.tittl@prometheuspix.com

Charles Halt:

"I understand that Larry is telling people he passed a voice stress analyis concerning his version of events that he claims took place. I believe its only fair to include the letter from the Mutual UFO Network which shows a different picture."

April 25, 1985

Mr. Philip J. Klass
404 "N" Street Southwest
Washington, DC 20024

Dear Phil:

I am in receipt of your April 3, 1985 letter concerning a statement made in the MUFON Newsletter, February, 1985 issue which you say "is riddled with malicious errors and falsehoods." The word contact seems to be the only discrepancy. That is -- who contacted who? You incriminate yourself when you admit that Chuck de Caro called you on December 11, 1984 and you suggested a polygraph test for Larry Warren. Chuck de Caro then proceeded to negotiate this test with Larry Fawcett and Larry Warren.

Since our information came directly from Larry Fawcett, a copy of your letter was made available to him so as to evaluate your claims. When Larry Fawcett called Chuck de Caro to verify the contents of your April 3rd letter, Mr. de Caro confirmed that you had proposed that Larry Warren should undergo a polygraph test, which prompted him to contact Mr. Fawcett. However, when Larry Fawcett challenged some of your statements, Chuck de Caro having also received your letter, started to rescind by saying "maybe the polygraph test proposal that Phil Klass made was given in confidence." Without a doubt, you have intimidated Chuck de Caro as you have endeavored to do with so many others with your tactics.

We will not publish a retraction, since the facts speak for themselves. You have admitted in your letter and Chuck de Caro has confirmed your proposal to have Larry Warren take a polygraph test. We have the word of Chuck de Caro and Larry Fawcett that there is no validity to your claims, therefore your case is closed as far as we are concerned.

MUFON is also declining your generous offer to underwrite half the cost of a polygraph test for Larry Warren. Based upon our investigation in this case, Larry would probably fail any questions directly related to his having personally observed the three occupants and their physical descriptions as depicted in the CNN film. We have other witnesses that confirm that Larry was indeed present at the first sighting, however one witness, who now resides in Texas, said he personally did not see the small humanoids that Larry described in the CNN film. Mr. Warren apparently enjoys basking in this publicity because he tends to embellish his story each time that it is told.

We arranged to have a voice stress analysis test conducted by the leading authority on this device, using the CNN video tape-audio as the medium for the test. Larry Warren failed the questions where he was describing the occupants, therefore MUFON has no further need to conduct a polygraph test. We are relying upon the testimony of other witnesses present, including U.S.A.F. officers and enlisted security police, since Larry Warren is not the principal witness -- just one of many to the two incidents.

Sincerely,

Walt

Walter H. Andrus Jr.

cc: Chuck de Caro
    Larry Fawcett
  √ Marge Christensen

WHA:vc

Marge:

Thanks for your help and that of Larry and Barry by telephone on this letter. I feel this is an adequate response that should "hold Phil for a while". It is closed, however a response was in order.

Walt

Colonel Halt – Life on the Base – Detained at gunpoint!

"Bentwaters was really like a small American city with a total base population of nearly 14,000. Although there was little crime, there was always something going on. Most problem issues revolved around young airmen with drug or drink issues. Ted Conrad and I had only been on the job a week or so when we accidentally drove across a red line in front of alert aircraft and into a restricted area. We were taken at gunpoint as the guard, not knowing us, refused to accept we were the Base and Deputy Commanders. We had to call the command post on the radio to get the Chief of Police to get us released. It was our fault as we were new and were not aware of the restricted area."

Barber shop verses Beautician

"Some things I distinctly remember included the time the contract barber shop was found to be skimming off money and was closed while the contract was being re-advertised. That meant the men had a choice of driving into Ipswich (10 miles away) or going to the beauty shop. Due to being busy I went to the latter. What an experience! The gossip was beyond belief and I was constantly peppered with very personal questions that I would never consider asking a person. That was the first and last time I did that!"

Base High School

"One of my duties was to oversee the Base High School. Every time there was a discipline problem of note it ended up in my office. Everything from runaways to a hardened former member of a major stateside gang, who proudly showed off his bullet and knife wound scars, came before me. He had been involved in a fight that took five police officers to subdue him. When placed in the police car in handcuffs and leg restraints, he kicked the rear door off the car. Needless to say, he was heavily escorted to the airport and put on a plane to the United States. I remarked to the school principal that within six months he would be dead or in prison. We heard that a few months later he was on trial for murder."

Attempt to breach the front gate!

"On another occasion an outlawed motorcycle gang attempted to breach the base gate. I just happened to be in the area and found a lone policeman facing them. I quickly told him 'do not touch your gun'. We managed to convince them there was nothing on the base worth a confrontation."

Drugs bust on base

"One night, when out on patrol with the police, they decided to conduct a suspected drugs bust. After entering the barracks with a drug dog and breaching the suspect's door, found him in the act of him tossing the drugs out of the window. He was caught red-handed, as the police had someone outside expecting him to try and escape.

The look on his face was priceless as the policeman outside caught his drugs. I ran into his father, several years later, and found out he straightened up and was now a State cop in North Carolina. To this day I'm careful driving in the State, as I'm sure he'll remember me. Some things there hit close to home."

Family crisis!

"One Saturday morning my teenage son came running into the house, screaming 'where's the fire extinguisher?'. Apparently, when he went to start the lawn mower it caught fire while sitting next to the car. I quickly ran out, using a towel to beat out the flames. Needless to say, he had to borrow the neighbour's mower.

On another occasion I went looking for the gas can, only to be told it was at school. I inquired 'how did it get there'? Oh, I took it to school on the school bus. He said the driver never noticed. He said 'don't worry, I told all the kids not to smoke'. I later found out he had built a go-cart in the school metal shop. This I discovered when he was apprehended for driving it on the base roads."

Practical joke played on a colleague

"One evening I was having dinner in the Officer's Club when I noticed my college room-mate, who was heading up a visiting inspection team, sitting at a table across the room. He was always playing pranks on me while in school, so I decided to pay him back.

I quietly called the on-duty police flight chief and explained who he was, and asked him to help me. I had him call then Major Gunenon, and told him to arrest my ex-college room-mate and take him to our holding cell. I finished dinner and went to the police station and found him quite upset and demanding an attorney. Needless to say, he calmed down and he forgave me. We then had a good visit and reminisced about old times."

Princess Anne

"However, there were many very enjoyable moments like the opportunity I had to have a delightful luncheon with Princess Anne. She was visiting a Woodbridge Orphanage that the base had assisted. She wanted to thank me for the support.

Many good times were spent with the Territorial Army (the equivalent of our National Guard) celebrating their Remembrance Day and numerous other social events. I especially remember all the great friendships, good times and fond memories of the times spent with the Anglo-American Friendship Council.

All and all, Bentwaters was a fantastic tour."

Other Royal connections

1975 – Royal visit to Suffolk

Colonel Charles Halt wasn't the only one to enjoy meeting members of British Royalty. Prior to this, Queen Elizabeth II flew in to RAF Bentwaters to open a local Post Office on the 21st November 1975. This was no local Post Office. BT opened its global research and development headquarters in Adastral Park, Martlesham, formerly known as the Post Office Research Station, Martlesham Heath. It replaced the wartime Dollis Hill research station in North London. Antony Maddox was able to obtain a photograph of her.

> *"It was an honour to have had the opportunity to get that close to the Queen. She walked like an angel … Awesome lady."*

(Source: Antony Maddox)

1975 – Tea with Prince Charles!

Someone else who lived on Woodbridge Air Force Base, during the late 1970s, was Chad Teed (then aged between 7 and 10) who has wonderful memories of life there. His father was Commander of the 67 ARRS – Colonel Charles M. Teed.

Chad:

"He even had tea with Prince Charles. My father is now retired and lives with my mother (Mary Belle Teed) in Roseville, California. The British were wonderful people. Many of my friends lived off base, giving me ample time to play in the countryside."

1984 – Dancing with Prince Charles

My ex-father in law, Edward 'Ted' West, was an ex-Royal Navy Chief Petty Officer from Birmingham, UK – a proud man that ruled with a 'rod of iron' and a 'heart of gold'. He also had a propensity for drinking home-made beer and *'Pussers'* rum! He served under 'Captain' Lord Louis Mountbatten, aboard *HMS Kelly*, and shot down a German Stuka dive-bomber while the ship was

beginning to sink off Crete, on the 21st May 1941. Following the death of Lord Louis, Prince Charles hosted the reunion dinner, held aboard a stone frigate in London. Ted's daughter, Christine Smith (nee West) – my sister-in-law, now living for many years in Los Angeles – was invited, along with her husband, Harvey, to one of those dinners.

"It was a totally private function – no Press – so Charles could just be himself and enjoy. After the dinner and speeches were over, it was dance time. I had a nice chat with Charles, as it was Olympic year 1984 in LA. We talked about Princess Anne, who was staying very close to where I lived. I then had a dance with him when the music changed to the chicken dance. He actually did it with everyone cheering him on."

The Queen – Happy 90th Birthday your Majesty

APPENDICES AND SNIPPETS OF INFORMATION

More on 'Cloud busting'

Page 371 of this book relates to allegations of 'cloud busting' taking place around the forest. Further evidence supporting the view of the authors that no such practice took place emanates from Paul and Kathy Topolosky.

Paul:

"While I was at Bentwaters and Woodbridge, I purchased a book about the UFO incident and it described some missile launching vehicles seen moving around the base and showed photographs of the vehicles. The vehicles were actually broken down 1965 model fuel trucks with the 5,000 gallon tanks removed, and old 55 gallon drums welded together with a cone and fins attached to be used as decoys. I worked in the fuels section at Woodbridge and we would laugh

ROSWELL DAILY RECORD'S
Roswell
INCIDENT
roswellincident.com

Join us for the Roswell Daily Record's "Roswell Incident." Meet with some of the top UFO authors, directors, researchers, screen writers and ex-government officals. Don't forget the Special VIP event held Saturday, July 2nd 2016. Visit roswellincident.com for more details.

NICK POPE used to run the British Government's UFO project and, while he left the UK's Ministry of Defense in 2006, many people in the UFO and conspiracy theory community believe that he's still secretly working for the government.

KEITH AREM has recently directed his first feature film, The Phoenix Incident, and is developing several additional feature film and television projects, many of which are based on his highly successful graphic novels, including "Ascend," "Index" and "Dead Speed."

LEE SPEIGEL, a journalist, and UFO eyewitness, Speigel explores numerous dramatic interactions between military officers and unexplained aerial phenomena. Beginning with the 1947 events surrounding the now legendary reported Roswell, New Mexico, UFO crash.

COLONEL HALT was assigned from the Pentagon to RAF Bentwaters in 1980 as the Deputy Base Commander and later promoted and became the Base Commander. He will describe the remarkable events that occurred over a three-day period, the impact, agency involvement and further developments.

DR. JOHN ALEXANDER a retired senior Army officer who has explored various phenomena on all seven continents, he also retired from Los Alamos National Laboratory, served with the Army Science Board, on National Research Council studies, and was a senior fellow at a Defense University.

FRIDAY & SATURDAY | JULY 1ST - 2ND, 2016
9AM - 6PM · GINSBERG BUILDING · 201 N MAIN ST, ROSWELL, NM 88201 · CORNER OF MAIN AND 2ND ST.

RED CARPET VIP EVENT STARTS AT SATURDAY 5:30PM JULY 2ND
RED CARPET MEET & GREET @ GALAXY 8 · PHOENIX INCIDENT SCREENING
9 PM DINNER PARTY · VISIT ROSWELLINCIDENT.COM FOR VIP PASS INFORMATION

about that often when we went out to take spare parts off the decoy trucks to keep ours operating. The decoys didn't even have engines in them and would have to be towed to different locations every so often, to make it look like they were real."

Charles Halt:

"As I said before, earlier, the dummy missile launch trucks were put together by Colonel Karl G Berroth, to tease the Russian photo interpreters. They fooled Peter Robbins and Warren into thinking they were for weather modification."

Fuel tank falls to earth

Occasionally, of course, no doubt accidents did happen. According to Captain Paul Aranha one such incident involved the recovery of a fuel tank from a T-33 based at RAF Bentwaters that came crashing to earth in the forest.

"It just missed the classroom in which I was being educated. It sounded like the Iron Curtain had fallen down. I think I charged 1/- each for prints. I know I made a lot of extra cash that day. I am very impressed, and also delighted, with how much good stuff there is about Woodbridge on the Web – and how much is put there by *you."

(Crediting *Linn Barringer for his excellent source of information)

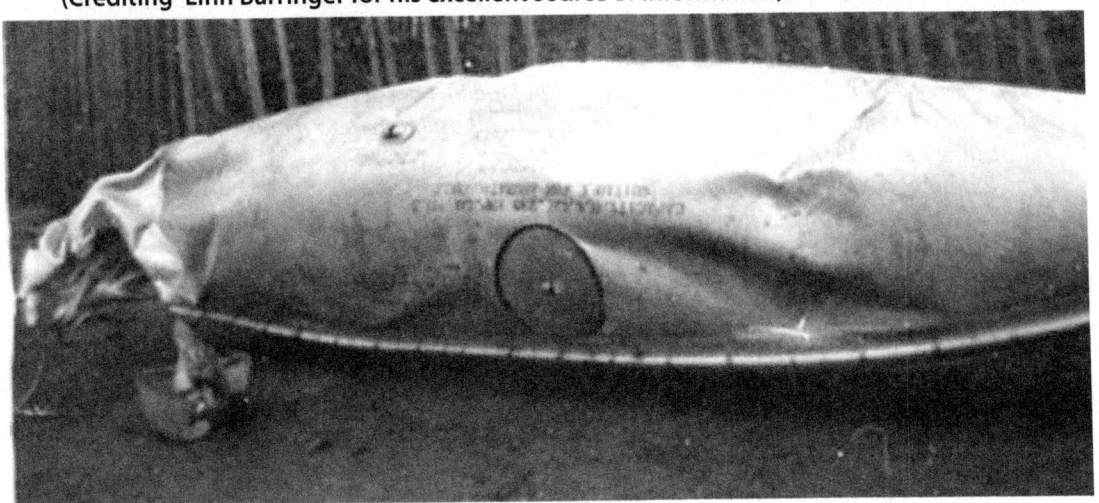

Paranormal activity on base

In this book various 'ghostly' images have been shown which are of course open to individual interpretation, along with other accounts of high strangeness. It is of interest to learn what retired Captain Larry Hammer had to say about such reports, who served at RAF Woodbridge from February 1971 to December 1974.

"I worked many a night on the flightline at Woodbridge Base. For over four years at Woodbridge, I never saw any UFOs. However, something far more problematic to the American Service

personnel was the ghosts which inhabited the base. We had many people who refused under the threat of Court Martial or Article 15 punishments to work alone, or at night, due to the various ghostly paranormal activities on the base. I know a lot of attention has, over the years, been aimed at the UFO incident. However, the ghosts were there a long time before and will be there a long time after the UFO incident."

From *Left At East Gate* – Larry Warren (page 102)

"In November 1983, we found out that Brenda Butler and Dot Street had sold the Halt document to the News of the World for two thousand pounds – nearly five grand here. CAUS, solely responsible for obtaining the document with the formation I had provided, had sent them the copy gratis solely to assist in their own research. After that, we broke off all contact."

Mike Sacks – May 2016

"One thing I wanted to tell you was that another reason why I contacted the News of the World with the story [for which he later received £12,000 pounds] was that we heard the National Enquirer was going to run the Halt Memo and the story. This also takes into consideration a previous attempt by Jenny and Dot to publish the story with another newspaper that offered them £600 – we turned it down. That was when they then contacted Harry Harris. Some people might say that was good money, but there were a number of out-of-pocket expenses to take into consideration – travel and accommodation, plus lost earnings, as my tailor's shop was closed for some time while I was involved in the investigation. People have mentioned about some repairs being carried out to the 'craft' that landed. I am sorry but I don't believe any of that – it's like giving a Stone Age man a spanner and asking him to repair a Jumbo Jet! The

last time I saw Charles Halt was at Todmorden, when he brought one of the plaster casts over here. I still remember being down there on base with Harry and Colonel Halt when he played the tape for us. Not one of us spoke a word while we listened to it, including Halt himself; it was as if he was reliving it all over again. It made such an impression on him. I have no reason to doubt his honesty or sincerity at all."

Harry Harris

A photograph has just been obtained showing Susan and Harry Harris around 1992, at the wedding of her mother.

Larry Warren

In May of this year (2016) Larry expressed his feelings (again), after telling me he was going to take the house off us!

"Read Halt In Woodbridge – a nice companion to the Hanson Halt Book. .i hope lessons were learned ..and a must for anyone that wasted 20 quid last july. .or dont.. And Dear David im reading lots of falsehoods being stated as fact on this page lol lots has changed since i took a break from it Cheers Lori Rehfeldt girl,i shall keep an eye on this...........ruin a few folks days i bet also the FULL story about THIS letter (a historic record) is on You TUBE for ALL to via......via Gary Hesiltine and his work on it .further simply ASK ME? is that so hard i guess so? This Letter is the ONLY orig Record of ANY of the events and one week before the Halt memo............ya dont get how important that is i guess? Some of you wouldn't anyway............THe hows and whys.......... just ask dont spin as i will correct whomever choses to do so! cheers"

Another message

"John as i told you to your face you and those that support you arecowards.....................you and your focus owes me a BIG SORRY........but your a coward,,,(i think my son scared you more ?) but i do hope to see it in chucks Book,,,,,,,,,,,,,i would truly love to know about his life !......i know more than you and your pals ever will ! FACT ! Should you choose to slander, down play or other dirty tricks..on me again !...........................Mate i will own your house ! trust it Me mate ! i wont go after you as you dont make a penny ! lol Folks Read HALT IN WOODBRIDGE BY Peter Robbins its on amazone and all you fans need to know !......nick if you remove this ,,,,,,,,,,well............................. ..lol ps if ya want my phone number JH just ask mate,,,,,,,,,,,,,i got yours !and the folks working with you should hang heads..i truly would love to read about my old boss,,,,,,,,,,,,on base he sure was good to me and i consider him as much a victim as any of us under him.........................but folks ? dont be dazzled by the eaglel wings..in the usaf we called it Razzle dazzle!,,,,,,,,,,,,,if im disrespected as i was in woodbridge,,,,,,lawyers will go after its author...........Mr Hanson.......as i live in the uk aswell ....trust it johnny ! this was never a game.. ....and again Perter Robbins clearly showed the game afoot in his Book...its a hit on Amazone............decide for your selves !   its askin alot i know lol"

The never ending story – 18th May 2016

Over the last few months there have been concerted attacks on the character of Larry Warren by his ex-Liverpool based friend, Sacha Christie, who advertises herself on the Internet as UK Director of ICAR and representative for Exopolitics for Leeds-UK Director, Beeston, Leeds, United Kingdom International Centre for Abduction Research Abductee network and support. This 'falling out' seems to have manifested after Larry left her family home, following a dispute.

This book is not about Larry Warren and his personal attacks on us or others parties, against him, although it will show the reader something about Larry's volatile character – make of it what they will – as it may have some bearing on what took place all those years ago or, of course, it may not!

Fact or fiction – Let the reader decide

However, while we have no intention in reproducing some very undignified profane comments, which are now freely available for all and sundry in the 'Court of *Face-book* law' to see, it is perhaps something to take into consideration, bearing in mind one of the now long-running allegations made by Sacha Christie, quote:

"Larry Warren told Linda Moulton Howe, in 1984, during a taped interview, that he had incorporated Adrian Bustinza's story because he wanted it out and he (Adrian) was never going to talk about it. Well even though this is the truth it is still a lie. Adrian didn't give Larry permission to do so. When Larry told me this himself, he said that he had spoken to Adrian about what he had done and that Adrian 'was ok about it – we're ok now'. I guess you could say I was/am lying still/again but I said he had told me he had stolen Adrian's account, Adrian says in his interview he was alone during the visit to the building on Woodbridge where the photography shop was, where he alone was told bullets are cheap, and now here it is from Linda Moulton Howe and her transcript. So, am I lying? Of course I'm not. I'm not an attention seeking narcissist, I am an agenda bender!! He took me for a ride and showed me the truth along the way. I am about the truth not the accolade. If I wanted to capitalise on this or anything else I have done, you'd have all been spammed to death and I would be prolific. I find that behaviour incredibly needy and ugly and basically I don't care what you believe about me. I care about the truth. I hate lies and greed and I hate the toxic waste this man leaves wherever he turns up. This is a screen shot of part of one of the emails Linda MH sent me when she transcribed the conversation between herself and Larry Warren."

We do not intend to show the screen shot, as we do not know how authentic such allegations are. However, we did email Linda Moulton Howe today, (18.5.2016) and asked her if she was willing to comment.

A no-win situation

Neither I nor Colonel Halt have ever answered any of these rants and have no intention of doing so in the near future, because it is a pointless waste of energy and undignified. It illustrates the ever-shifting sands of intrigue which now dominates this incident for now over 36 years. The continual falling-out of people – friends one minute, enemies the next – is nothing new and has been occurring since the early 1980s. Whilst we have our own opinions on what has been alleged against Larry, which many find entertaining, judging by the comments on *Face-book* over the last couple of months, where is the evidence in support of these allegations? It seems sad that people can make such slanderous remarks against each other on the Internet social websites.

Friends fall out

Previously the two protagonists – Christie and Warren – were friends and allies and have supported each other in various podcasts, taking an antagonistic attitude towards Colonel Halt. Peter Robbins and Larry Warren are talking at the SPI (Scottish UFO & Paranormal Conference Glasgow, on the 25th of June, 2016. It appears that Sacha may or may not attend – It is claimed serious physical threats have been made against her by Larry Warren, should she attend. No doubt this will lead to a surge in ticket sales. Clearly, it is time to move on. We have neither the inclination nor space left in this book to continue to bring such matters to the attention of the readers as this saga promises to self perpetuate over time.

Sky Crash

The inside cover of *Sky Crash* is self-explanatory in its dramatic statement of a meeting between alien beings and General Gordon Williams, although it is worth remembering that a number of names were suggested for the book originally. They included, *The Mysterious Landing-Visitor From Beyond,*

The figures were small, he estimated about 3 feet 2 inches in height. He saw three and they looked identical, wearing all-over silver suits. They hovered close to the ground, suspended in the shaft of light that emerged from the underside of the craft. The commander who had the contact, Wing Commander Williams, went forward, close up to the entities, and everybody else was ordered back. He then seemed to communicate with the aliens . . .

Good Luck
Happy Hunting
Brenda Butler x
10th Sept 2011

Best Wishes
Dot Street

Landing At Midnight, The Thing From The Sky, The Suffolk Forest UFO Landing, Nocturnal Manoeuvres, UFO Crash In A Suffolk Forest and, The Rendlesham Forest Mystery. The book was reviewed by Allen Hynek in the United States. He said:

> *"It is destined to become a classic work in the UFO literature, a gripping mystery story about what will rank as one of the most significant UFO events of all time."*

The third is a copy of the local newspaper, published in 1997 – now nearly 20 years ago – in which Brenda Butler was interviewed about her UFO knowledge.

The front cover of Jenny's book – *UFO Crash Landing?* (Seen right)

An illustration drawn by Mick Sacks, showing the *'craft'* he saw landing a year before the Rendlesham Forest Incident.

CLOSE ENCOUNTER: Brenda Butler and her book

First to tell of strange sighting

SUFFOLK "ghostbuster" Brenda Butler and her friend Dot Street wrote one of the first accounts of the Rendlesham "UFO."

Their book *Skycrash*, which appeared in 1983, soon after the story broke, alleged that the base commander at the time confirmed contact with aliens had been made – and that was why he was transferred from the base to a top secret installation in Colorado soon afterwards!

Details of the Rendlesham incident were certainly hushed up by the powers that be, until the *News of the World* broke the story in 1983.

Brenda, from Leiston, did not believe it was an isolated event.

"The areas between Woodbridge, Rendlesham and Orford are particularly active and we are getting dozens of sightings every month," she said, in March, 1988.

"For some strange reason, we get a dramatic increase in UFO sightings every seven years.

"From last November until the end of January, we had a whole range of new sightings, which does seem to fit into the seven-year pattern."

Brenda admitted it was difficult to verify UFO reports because few people were willing to be interviewed, afraid they would be ridiculed.

But she is convinced that there was another alien landing in the Heritage Coast area in the seventies, at Elm Tree Farm, Aldringham.

During the night, an alien spacecraft landed in a field, gouging out two large holes, she said.

She had a blurred photograph apparently showing one of the holes.

"There were no tyre marks or footprints, just these two holes. Also the tops of the trees around the field were burnt off."

The story was supported by a number of sightings of a UFO hovering around Aldeburgh and Sizewell, reported in the EADT at the time.

UFO
CRASH LANDING?
BEHIND OR POST
JENNY RANDLES

Top dome did not rotate.

light rays from aperture

Hull shown up by the top dome light rays.

Dark grey hull against intense black sky

Very prominent band much lighter in colour.

Red glow from hollow at the bottom

(Left) The illustration provided by Mr Potter, whose UFO sighting is outlined in page 57 of this book.

(Below) A rare photo of Chuck, Nick, Brenda and Chris Pennington, taken during filming between 4th November and 7th November 2010 following a visit to the UK. This was a film that was produced by the US-based company O2C Global Content Services and formed the subject of an hour long documentary.

Charles Halt:

"I kept pressing as to what was going on and never got a good answer. Some of the interviews were good – especially with Vince Thurkettle, when he admitted we couldn't have mistaken the object for the lighthouse."

Retired Head of the Mod discusses Rendlesham UFO incident with *News of the World* Editor

Ralph Norton Noyes was born in the tropics and spent most of his childhood in the West Indies. He served in the RAF from 1940 to 1946 and was commissioned as aircrew, engaging in active service in North Africa and the Far East. He entered the civil service in 1949 and served in the Air Ministry and subsequently the unified Ministry of Defence. In 1969 Ralph Norton Noyes was head of Defence Secretariat 8 (DS8), and one of his responsibilities was to answer public questions about UFOs. He says he was not able to share his true opinions on the subject.

> "It is only since I left the MOD (in 1977) that I have seriously tried to consider what may possibly lie behind the 'UFO phenomenon'. It was impossible to discuss it seriously within the department. I would merely have 'rubbished' my working relationship with the RAF and scientific colleagues if I had disclosed the interest I felt in the better reports which reached us. What I retain from my MOD experience – greatly reinforced by much that I have since read – is that the phenomenon is veridical and important, and that the expert methodology developed over the past century by scholarly people in the field of the so-called 'paranormal' may possibly be relevant. All I can be sure of is that we in Ufology are dealing with transient and somewhat insubstantial events of a bizarre character, and that we are not alone in doing so. I think they matter. I also think that we and the 'parapsychologists' might have some useful exchanges."

*Girlie magazines

Ralph published a number of light-hearted science fiction articles in the late 1970s. Oddly, some were published in *Penthouse*, *Playboy* and *Mayfair* magazines, which are known more for their presentation of heavenly female bodies rather than concepts of futuristic science and technology!

Following the release of the Colonel Halt memo, Ralph contacted the ex-editor of the *News of the World* – Derek Jameson [who was fired in 1984 by Rupert Murdoch, after claiming the Australian Prime Minister Harold Holt, who had gone missing on a beach in Australia, had been a communist spy] and asked to meet for lunch.

Ralph:

> "We spoke about the UFO incident; the only point which emerged from our conversations was that he was totally sceptical of the lighthouse explanation which Ian Ridpath was then beginning to put around. Jameson's view was that it could have been an experimental American aircraft or space capsule, which had come down in Tangham Wood, and that the resulting story was an attempt to camouflage this fact."

Not little green men!

Ralph:

> "My view of the Woodbridge case, and quite a number of cases around the world, is that we are not dealing with 'little green men'. The ETH just doesn't hold water, for all the excellent reasons explored in many books. There are too many varieties of 'vehicles'. The logistical problems would be absurdly difficult. Why the hell should 'they' bother? – If they <u>are</u> bothering, why coyness, for decade after decade, if not century after century. Why so many joky elements? – It isn't American experiments or Russian ones with new hardware, well not in the Woodbridge case anyway (in a pine wood?) and without causing more damage to vegetation etc. – I simply can't believe it. It's not devils out of hell! Though I must say, sometimes it looks very like it."

---

*On occasion people such as Johnny Carson and Dr Allen Hynek have submitted articles to this genre of magazines. Incredibly one such magazine published an article after conducting an excellent investigation into reported UFO incidents, which put to shame any tabloid assessment of a subject normally presented as tongue-in-cheek articles – or even any investigation carried out by the authorities!

THE HALT PERSPECTIVE

So what is it?

Ralph:

"I'm exploring a particular line of argument in a novel I am writing postulating a very important earthbound phenomenon, drawing to some extent on the ingenious guesses of Paul Devereux but going somewhat beyond them. I will be assuming that it has potentially tremendous implications for defence, which the American, French and Russian Ministries of Defence are now pursuing in deadly earnest and frightening competition (well I said it was a bit of fiction!).

Apart from my fictional endeavours, two questions linger in my mind; why was Halt's statement so readily made public?

We know that the Americans can still keep something under wraps when they want to, e.g. the 137 documents recently barred from disclosure by the Supreme Court. So they want us to believe the Halt story? The other question is what did Harry Harris see at Woodbridge which caused him – voluntarily – to give solicitor's undertaking not to make it public? I've written to him at some length about this and I'm awaiting his answer with impatient curiosity. Perhaps a third question is why did the MOD take four months to send me the bland brush off?"

Ralph then wrote to the MOD, asking for further information about the incident. It took four and a half months, two reminders and a phone call to obtain an answer – you've guessed it ... the standard response to letters from the public, asking about UFOs!

Oakley Street, London

Is there a Blue Plaque at number 9?

In 1984, Ralph was living at 9, Oakley Street, London SW3 5NN, which was a six bedroom freehold terraced house – a street that seems to have acquired some famous personalities, over the years. They included Captain Scott, Antarctic explorer, who lived at No. 56, which carries a blue plaque. Lady Wilde, mother of Oscar Wilde, lived at No. 87; this has a blue plaque. Dame Sybil Thorndike, the actress, and her husband Lewis Casson, lived at No. 74. George Best, footballer, lived at No. 87.

OBTAINED RECENTLY – FURTHER UFO REPORTS FOR DECEMBER 1980

20th December 1980 – Pyramidal UFO showing three lights seen

Mr John Perkins of Easterley Road, Leeds, was outside his house at 10.10pm.

"I was astonished to see an object about sixty yards away from me and fifty feet off the ground. I estimated it to be four to five yards across and about four yards high. The shape of it was difficult to define, but this became clearer later. It seemed to be revolving on its axis. It was bright, bluish-white in colour and gave off a glow, reminding me of an electric arc welder. Suddenly, within a few seconds, it accelerated vertically into the night, and then stopped at a height of between five hundred to one thousand feet. Its shape was that of a pyramid and it had three lights on it. It stayed in this position, unmoving for at least twenty minutes – until it then began to rotate on its axis again, the shape changed, and it disappeared totally from view. In October 1983, the News of the World *newspaper published reports of UFOs – so I contacted Graham Birdsall, and told him what I had seen. I believe there is a connection with what was seen in Rendlesham Forest and that there was other sightings from around the Leeds area, the week after mine."*

(Source: *Awareness*, Volume 24, No. 2)

25th December 1980 – Three red lights over direction of RAF Manston

Between 11pm and midnight, Mr A. Munday (15 at the time) from Margate, Kent, was in his bedroom, playing records, when his mother came rushing into the house, telling her young son and husband that she had seen three red lights, 'with a touch of gold', darting about in the sky towards the general direction of RAF Manston. They went outside, but nothing was seen.

"My mother telephoned RAF Manston and asked them if anyone had reported seeing strange lights, or whether an exercise was taking place. My recollection is that they weren't rude but less than forthcoming, although they admitted having received other calls. She felt a little stupid after reporting the occurrence, after being met with a cool response. My mum, who later passed away at 47, two and a half years later, was an incredibly realistic, rational, smart woman – not easily swayed or excited by most things. She was so emphatic and convinced of what she had seen, late Christmas night, that there was never any doubt in her, or mine or my father's mind, that she had experienced something quite uncommon and extraterrestrial. I'd like Colonel Charles Halt of the USAF, and all the other servicemen involved, to know that they were not

alone in what they witnessed. I'm convinced both sightings are related, due to their similar and graphic descriptions."

(Source: Letter to (USA) *UFO Magazine*, March 2006)

26th December 1980 – Golden torpedo-shaped object seen

According to the British Astronomical Association, a brilliant fireball was seen to burn up in the southern sky over England, at 2.50am.

Witnesses described it being comparable in brightness to that of the full moon; it appears that this was the explanation for what the following two witnesses saw, as the description may be used to contrast with what was seen by the airman *Professor Brian Griffin.

"In the very early hours of December 26th, I was driving my wife and brother-in-law back from my wife's parents in Chorleywood. As we drove along the feeder route, east to west from Beaconsfield to the M40, a few very bright lights in the sky were approaching the car. Frightened, I immediately thought it was a Jumbo Jet that had missed Heathrow, for some reason, and was going to use this strip of road to crash-land.

My first hurried reaction was to pull the car into a lay-by to my left, where Lorries normally park for the night. All three of us jumped out of the car and noticed, looking south, 'a golden torpedo' showering sparks as it made its way from west to east over London. The whole experience revolved around shapes of light and at no time did we see a physical structure.

In the mid 90s I was shocked, when reading a 'write-up' of that evening's sightings in the Nick Pope book, and have visited the forest many times since, as well as reading many books regarding the affair."

(Source: Email, July 2016)

26th December 1980 – Rocket-shaped UFO sighted

At 2.30am on 26th December 1980, Dennis Porley from Harwich, Essex, (a mate on a tug boat) was driving along the A137, and had just passed the turn-off for Alton Water, on his left.

"I saw what I took to be a marine distress flare, or rocket, going up over Mistley Quay, but then realised that this could not be the case as it did not explode in flight. I continued on my journey – now descending a steep hill – at which point I lost sight of whatever it was. As I ascended the hill on the other side, close to a nearby railway line, I saw the object again in the sky. It looked like a rocket, or plane on fire, about the size of a full moon but more red in colour. I lost sight of it, once again, due to the contours of the countryside, but then saw it again – this time behind me. I decided to pull-up halfway between Brantham and Stutton, to obtain a closer look, as it slowly moved over Stutton Point, before descending over Hollesley Bay, where I lost sight of it.

---

*Professor Brian Griffin was born in Birmingham in 1948. He is a freelance photographer of international repute and has been the recipient of various honors including being made granted freedom of the City of Arles in France in 1987 for his one man show at the National Portrait Gallery. In 1989 *The Guardian* proclaimed that he was the best photographer of the decade. Other accolades include being awarded the best photography book in the world at Barcelona in 1991. From 1991- 2002 he worked as a film director making TC Commercials, music videos and short films. In 2003 he worked on Birmingham's bid to be the European Capital City of Culture.

When I returned to work after the Christmas period, I happened to mention what I had seen to a colleague. He suggested it might have been a large meteorite, which I don't believe was the case. Neither could it have been the *Cosmos 749 Russian Satellite, as this had splashed down one day previously."

Enquiries made revealed a bright fireball meteor was seen to cross the early morning sky, over East Anglia, according to records kept by the British Astronomical Association. The BAA report notes that this fireball was seen at 02.50 UT (± 5 minutes) on Boxing Day 1980, by four witnesses, locations not given but seemingly in southern England, all of whom estimated its brightness as comparable to the gibbous (i.e. three-quarter) moon and of 3 to 4 seconds duration.

27th December 1980 – Four red lights seen near RAF Base

At 3am on the 27th December 1980, David John Storer of Warwick Road, Banbury, Oxfordshire, was out with his wife driving near RAF Greatworth Airbase, Oxon., when they saw an unusual object for twenty minutes in the eastern part of the sky – described as 'various shapes, showing red square lights' – a solid object with a glowing trail, on a cold but dry, windy night.

"On Boxing night 1980, my wife and I had been to a party at a friend's house in Greatworth, North Oxon. I had had more than my share of drink, so my wife was driving home. We were just driving past RAF Greatworth when the brake of the car failed. We managed to stop the car. I got out and checked the brake fluid reservoir, finding it empty. As I walked to the back of the car to get some brake fluid, I glanced at the south-eastern sky on what was a cold and frosty, bright moonlit night. On the horizon, I noticed four red lights with a glow behind them. I then went to the front of the car and started to fill the reservoir, noticing that the red lights were now a quarter of the way across the sky heading in a north direction.

I could see them clearly; they were about the size of a ten pence piece, held at arm's length away. It was rectangular with a red light in each corner. Stretching out behind, at least three times the length of the object, was a glowing trail. It looked very high and was moving very fast.

On seeing this I panicked, felt very frightened, and spilt half the brake fluid over the engine of the car. I felt that I was very prone and that whatever it was, was out to get me."

(Source: *Contact UK International)

*Contact UK – *UFO Register*, 1980 … over 300 UFO reports!

In one of the Contact International UK *UFO Register* magazines, published from Oxford, in England, by the 'evergreen' team of Geoff Ambler (Vice President), Mike Soper (Press and Media spokesman/ Lecturer), Bill Foley (Investigator Control, Archivist, Librarian), and Frances Copeland (Secretarial membership, case files), Volume 15, 1994, there were a number of brief catalogued sightings that took place in 1980; (320 worldwide reports).

They included a bright glowing globe, sighted on the 3rd December 1980, at 10pm, over Myrtle Street, Hillsborough, New Hampshire, USA, a triangular object, showing a row of lights, seen at 7pm over Wilcox Avenue, Arizona, followed by a report on the 17th December 1980 from Clifton, Arizona, of a red delta winged object seen passing through the night sky.

At 8pm on the 24th December 1980, the local *Wyoming Tribune* newspaper told of a sighting involving eight objects, seen moving overhead, making a humming noise, projecting beams of light downwards.

CONTACT INTERNATIONAL UFO RESEARCH

AWARENESS

JULY 2015   VOLUME 34 No 3
+ Pluto – The Final Frontier
+ Rendlesham – New Facts

The whole truth & nothing but the truth

May 2016 – Larry Warren and his allegations

John Hanson: Initially, Colonel Charles Halt and I had no intention to get involved any further with the ongoing Internet dispute between Sacha Christie and Larry Warren. He had lodged with her for a period of some six weeks on and off, between December/January/February, and until the start of June 2015. Previously Sacha and Larry – then friends – accompanied by Peter Robbins, had spoken in various podcasts and conferences, one of which is shown here.

UFO Paranormal Radio Network
The Rendlesham Forest Incident

Alyson Dunlop – ADX 24 podcast – 'Enemies Within'
(Some extracts from the broadcast)

However we decided, after discussion, that we should include additional information showing the character of Larry Warren, following a number of defamatory comments made by him in an ADX 24 podcast, posted on the Internet hosted by Alyson Dunlop, in May 2016. [Not forgetting the previous podcast (10) made by this woman with Peter Robbins on the 17th August 2015 'Peter Robbins responds to Halt's slanderous allegations'.

11th October 2015 – Show repeated

The Podcast (24) entitled appropriately 'Enemies Within' was set up to advertise the forthcoming SPI conference on the 25th of June, in which a number of people would be talking about a range of subjects. This included interviews with the forthcoming speakers which included Larry Warren and Peter Robbins.

Podcast timed at 06:16:400 – Larry Warren:

"You know it I'm looking forward to the conference in Scotland you know, you know because I'm not a researcher. I don't wannabe. I'm a whistleblower that – that the ugliest – well there's a lot of things that go on in the world and people say but I would really bet good money that there is nothing that has drawn in some of the finest people and some of the sickest mental cases. Disingenuous-type folks I've ever seen. I've said this for years but it just escalates. These are people with a real strong need for a life you know er, so anything you wanna ask about?"

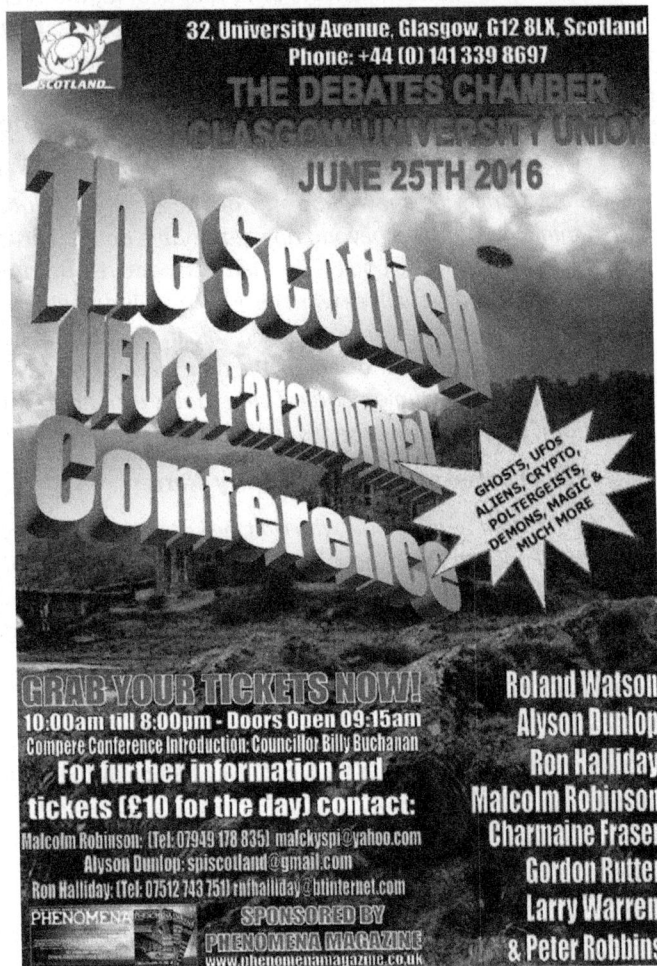

Podcast timed at 07:09:175 – Peter Robbins

The interview promised seven subjects of discussion with a promise of UFOs being 'last not least' at the end of the agenda. Instead the first 20 minutes were taken up initially with a short comment made by Peter Robbins, who reminded the listeners that Charles Halt had had it in for Larry since 1983 and that . . .

". . . he had been taking pot-shots at Larry slagging him off, and that it came to a head last year following the talk arranged at Woodbridge by John Hanson, but as anyone familiar with the ongoing operatic saga that we call Rendlesham Forest knows he devoted the last forty minutes or so of the talk to the most extraordinary deception packed character attack on Larry, on the book by implication on myself and after listening to it – its posted . . . anybody can listen to it – obviously it needed responding to, but it was not something I could do on a radio show like yours or even a lot of radio shows or in some Facebook post or you know Conference talk and my response with the air of a small corp. of colleagues – no one gave more assistance than you, Alyson, and I will always be in your debt for that. I ended up refuting point by point all of his specious nonsense. If he made thirty-five points, thirty-three were completely inaccurate, bogus, mistaken, wrong, which is beyond outrageous."

Peter Robbins – Threats of action against the authors!

"I also knew I had to do it in a very professional manner and my standard was not my feelings or my fairly wide knowledge on – on the incidents – but on slander under English law, which I think I established beyond any reasonable doubt. This case will explode again this autumn when Charles Halt's book – The Halt Perspective – becomes available in the United States and in the UK, and we will see what he has to say and whether or not his co-author is foolish enough to put some of the things that Halt said in his talk that have now – that would now – then be addressed in print for a year by the time his book comes out in print in his book, because that becomes libel, [Dunlop agrees], and that is actionable and as Mister' T' used to say 'I pity the fool' if that comes to pass. It's just the way it is. Nothing personal, but…"

Podcat timed at 09:39:635 – Larry Warren:

"Right, right … you know with Halt, he just spoke in Los Angeles with Nick (Pope) and you know basically did the same thing without you know, a little less riffing, so I am not certain on what the ego on people like him – or Nick – that they actually ever even read that book."

Hanson, trolls and trailer trash!

This was then followed by Larry Warren's 'rant' against the *Haunted Skies* books, Charles Halt, Sacha Christie, Ronnie Dugdale and others.

Larry Warren:

"Hanson, you call him a writer, but the reality – he's a guy, if you've ever seen his books – they're just clippings from other people's writing that make up a book, and that's a fact."

Larry Warren

Later rebuttal now included.

John Hanson:

"I would refute that statement. People like Malcolm Robinson, the Lord Nicholas Hill-Norton, Edgar Mitchell, Paul Hellyer, Jenny Randles, Nick Pope, Nick Redfern, Reg Presley, Colin Andrews, Ray Dorsey, Moira McGee, Busty Taylor, Matt Lyons, Robert Hastings, Philip Mantle, Bill Chalker, Robert Salas, Kevin Moore, Mary Rodwell, Timothy Good, Richard D. Hall and Trevor James Constable, are just a few people that have given support over the years. The UK Prime Minister even wrote to us, after having read some of the books. I would like to say that at no stage have I ever been invited by Alyson to talk about the publication of now eleven Volumes of Haunted Skies *or at the very least allow me the opportunity of defending myself. Suffice to say I will not now become involved with these people and their biased radio shows."*

2013 – Malcolm Robinson foreword, Volume 7 of Haunted Skies

"I have followed John Hanson and Dawn Holloway's UFOlogical career over the years and for me, their work in bringing together a UFOlogical Encyclopaedia of British UFO cases covering different years, is to be congratulated. It's a mammoth task and one which has taken them a considerable amount of time, if not, patience and endeavor. So I was very pleased to have been invited to write the foreword for this one. The UFO cases presented in this book will not only astonish you but will make you realize that the subject of UFOs is quite clearly worthy of serious study and the volume of cases assembled here make it quite clear to me that we are dealing with something highly unusual. So sit back and buckle up, you're about to take a UFOlogical ride that you won't forget."

Malcolm Robinson (Founder, Strange Phenomena Investigations)

Trolls

In another conversation Warren said:

"Well you have a troll like Christie, who puts herself forth as some sort of expert on anything or a researcher or this. All I direct people to look at – when I gave her first speaking opportunity, as far as I know in Woodbridge – she got up and by the end of of it, no one knew what the 'F' she was talking about. She was staggering around the place. In fact all the shit she wrote about me is on computer. I gave her one as a gift – lovely isn't it?"

Later rebuttal now included – Email from Captain Robert Salas, 14.6.2016:

"Hello John, what I can verify is that, on the day of my talk at Woodbridge, on June 17, 2012, I had lunch with Sacha Christie and Dave Kelly. I think Sacha also spoke on that day. I sat next to Sacha during that lunch and can attest to the fact that she was not drunk, or inebriated, or incapacitated in any way. There is a photo showing us together at that time. My wife was also present."

[Other matters of some considerable concern were also raised but we have decided not to include these at this time]

Alyson Dunlop podcast continued . . . 'Brands' and 'Waves'

Podcast timed: 16:51:970 – Dunlop:

"So what are you guys going to be talking about? Are you going to be talking about all this at the conference?"

Warren:

*"No, what I think we're going to do I think that the people that are causing – Peter can look into this and he probably gets disappointed with people. Me, I always have vibes like something's not right but you know, you find out the hard way at times, but what they're doing is trying to rewrite. I will address certain things but I think we are probably best – we haven't worked together in years and years – we're best when we get up and we'll – you know – we'll entertain. **We'll tell the facts and things but I'm not going to go through the Rendlesham Forest Incident. I can cut right through the little things. You know I stopped doing that so long ago."***

Robbins:

"Well I would definitely like to take some time and lay out what is the absolute best evidence. Certainly in Rendlesham all surrounds Larry, and I mean physical, legal, every kind of evidence imaginable. Now you understand I did a radio show with the much kind of wondered-about Adrian Bustinza who was with me and Adrian came out – and this is when they all went crazy – uh, and said because he had written it.

But you know then he said it and he said this happened to Larry and actually these things – entity, whatever they – and John goes 'were they around me?' and Adrian goes 'no, they were all around Larry' which I don't recall – don't want to remember. We all have about fourteen hours missing time."

Sacha – Her comments on a whistleblower!

Sacha:

"Warren tells Dunlop that he will not be talking about his part in the Rendlesham Forest Incident, because he stopped doing that a long time ago!! That's what he is known for. That is his 'thing'. He is the self-proclaimed whistleblower of the event, yet he thinks that people want to hire him not to talk about the only thing he is known for. Also on the back of my claims wouldn't you think that it would be the perfect time to 'set the record straight' and explain his involvement, rather than refusing to talk about it? This is the man that calls me a fake because he got vibes... We have known each other nine years and he was happy for me to carry him into the public after Colonel Halt revealed he was a substance abuser. I have to beg the question was he lying then when he said he believed me and gave me a conference spot, or is he lying now? When one person tells two narratives of the same timeline, one of them is a lie. Nine years of using me or just now, abusing me? All you have to do is to listen to him over the past nine years speak of me. MUFON 2010 he mentioned me. Listen to the radio shows between December 2014 and June 2015, the ones I staged for him. Was he lying then? Or is he lying now? More importantly, why won't he talk about what he says happened to him on that third night of events? Because he is

above that now, is it beneath him? I thought he was the whistleblower? Not whistling anymore is he? No, he is avoiding, now why would he do that? At least they said they would answer ANY questions asked, so I hope someone has the courage to ask him about what Adrian [Bustinza] says in comparison to what he says."

Podcast timed: 11:28:486 – Warren attacks the character of Ronnie Dugdale

"Where I have a problem – I mean Halt and I are always going to have that dynamic and I got some secondary apology – wished he hadn't said all that stuff. He didn't say it to me but I heard it from someone that interviewed him and I said 'Well that's nice you know. Good on him.' But

Ronnie Dugdale

the real problem I have now is when you extend – after battling with another witness – and you extend yourself to this person and finally – you know – we met numerous times way many years ago and 80s, 90s and you seem to be making headway – I'm talking about John Burroughs – and NOW where he is allowing slander to be posted unchecked, unchallenged – secondary slander by the way – second-hand – as posted by our dear friend Ronnie Dugdale, who was never a friend, by the way.

Well he's an unknown to anyone really listening to this but he's a guy from Norfolk and – you know – I've only heard of him since I went online – you know, again, I've been here from day one so I knew who was involved in any form of note with Rendlesham from day one – you know. I knew Malcolm many years ago was – you know – enquiring – you know – I was a name long before I met him this side. (Brenda) Butler and (Dot) Street, I knew about, but not this guy. Another internet creation like Miss Christie is full of it out there but what Ronnie has done is that he's – you know you've got to understand that the early researchers and I've not wanted to do this, and I didn't do it in our book because we had a lot to cover while we were writing it and I didn't want to really go after women like Brenda and Dot."

Warren criticizes Brenda Butler, Dot Street and Ronnie Dugdale

"Jenny (Randles) you know we got, I got the Halt memo out with C.A.U.S and it came out because I'm seeing on the Lone Ranger that never happened, by the way, Peter, today, and it was Brenda and Dot that did it. But what I am – all the money I cost them by calling me and everything – well in reality is like I posted today on this Rendlesham Lone Ranger, I posted it you know on reality. I am very happy to get into all the havoc that those particular local researchers put me and my family through in those early days – the 'phone calls at the weirdest of hours and all kinds and you know. I don't want to pick on Dot but Brenda opened her trap and said I don't want to get involved and I said, 'Honey, you got yourself involved thirty-five years ago'. You

know, a lot of people want their toast buttered one way or another but Mr Dugdale has, I mean, gone to the level of saying when my father died at least he went in the ground proud of his son. I mean this is our buddy, Peter, you know. And just pure filth and what he's done is he has infiltrated Dot and Brenda and they've gone back into the early tapes and there was 'Sky Crash' and a lot of bullshit in that – like Georgina Bruni wrote, like it quotes like I said I saw aeronautic entities in a huge spaceship. I don't speak that way. Peter's known me thirty-five years."

Podcast timed: 15:08:115 – Warren attacks Sacha Christie

"You have The Troll out there – you know who – S.C. – and just absolute action – I should be meeting my lawyer – but you can't get blood from trailer trash. You can't do it. And there's nothing you can do to people that have mental health visitors every day and they're protected you know they're allowed to do all these things, pose as researchers and have people almost commit suicide in their house – people who have never had a UFO experience by the way. I'm a veteran of many Budd Hopkins groups. I've had the experience of my life since I was a child – whatever it is – and you know when someone is."

Death threat made to Sacha Christie

In an email sent to her previously, Larry Warren had this to say:

"This is the outlaw way and I'm sorry I have to post. I will have family and very close friends at the venue! If you (whomever) makes a move on me or those I love – understand this, I will jump off stage and put your windpipe thru your spine. You are a threat at that point and your life will end! REALLY and faster than venue security could deal with! I am telling you all this as public service message ....heed it for your own good! But what fantastic PR for the great Glasgow gig! I don't need protection But if I Really did Id bring in my Detroit brother James Moorhead whom dealt with a similar deal with me and Peter Robbins years ago. Be smart stay home on your chickenshit internet baby!"

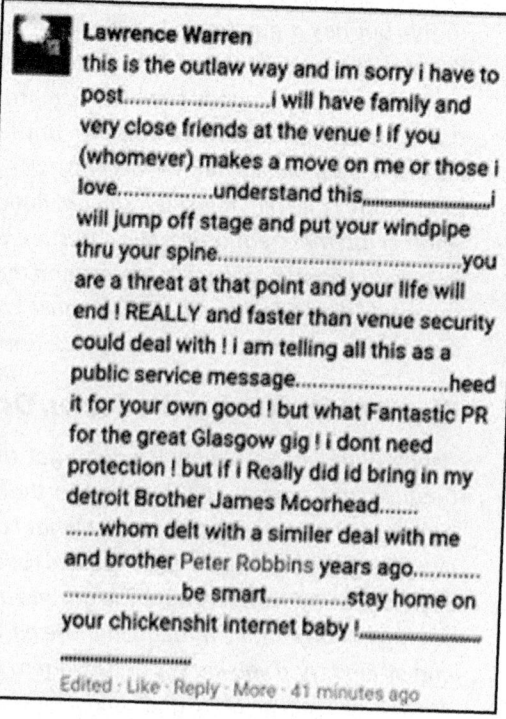

Podcast Timed: 19:47:617

Warren:

"Well listen. I mean you know I mean there are people who've known me for thirty, forty – they think Peter is just an idiot probably – and the things that have been written just staggering. I won't go into it here. It'll be dealt with, believe me. Things happen to people like that, they just do and it's the way the world – karma – everything works".

Podcast timed: 22:02:505 – Larry Warren – about Brenda Butler, Ronnie Dugdale and the binary code

"In the end of the day here is that you've got to pick a person – like Dugdale that infiltrated – what his angle is now. He's gone back with poor Dot, you know. I have some time for Dot. Brenda I've never believed any utterance of the woman. You know, Jim says there's the Binary crap and then suddenly Brenda's been doing it since 1979. I mean, this is just games and bullshit and these are people that probably not much goes on in the village, you know, and this is the best thing that ever happened to some of them, you know."

Podcast timed: 24:31:757 – Larry Warren (other extracts also contained in the podcast)

*"We're not coasting on someone else's wave. **I was the wave.** And they don't like that either. And then Peter came along and he put more time than anyone. The rest, Nick Pope, the rest, they're opportunists. They know that and I'm not in the belief business at all. Don't care if you've read our book and I can tell in about a sentence or a word from someone if they've read our book."*

Warren:

***But don't you dare assault my family. Don't you dare, because sooner or later – England is not a big place.** At the end of the day, anyone makes a threat on me, my friends, my family; I will protect me, mine and my name. **It's a brand!** – And my lawyers will be meeting some of them. That's probably the legal way to go isn't it? **I'll tell you, it's over. It's over. You move – you – you attack my son, anything – I'll tell you Peter, anything – I'll go after them one way or another."*

[The reader can listen to the full version of the ADX 24 podcast on the Internet if they chose to do so.]

Later rebuttal Sacha Christie – 'putting the record straight'

"Having known Larry for some nine years I allowed him to stay with us after he told us he was homeless. During many conversations held with him over the months, about his role in the Rendlesham Forest Incident I was perturbed to discover his sighting of the 'Craft' in December 1980 wasn't at Capel Green at the nominated place chosen by him but on the other side of the field. I also firmly believe that Larry stole Adrian Bustinza's story. According to Adrian Bustinza, (who said that they turned right at East Gate,) after seizing cameras from the people, Adrian and Larry parted ways. Adrian and John Burroughs then left the scene together.

Sacha Christie

What ensues is the very same story but it doesn't involve Larry and Adrian; it involves John and Adrian. Adrian has stated that the first person he bumped into the next day was Larry Warren. Adrian was taken along to Woodbridge and into the building where the photography shop was situated. He was taken along into that room with three men and was asked, over and over again, what he had seen. The officer told Adrian he was mistaken and that he had seen the lighthouse. Adrian argued with him and finally asked what the consequences would be if he did not say it was the lighthouse; the reply was 'Bullets are a dime a dozen, bullets are cheap'. The next thing he did was to leave a note under Larry Warren's door and then tell him absolutely everything. Adrian then called his mother.

As a result of his unruly behavior my partner, Dave, threw him out of the house.

I also have an email from Linda Moulton Howe, admitting that Larry admitted to her in 1984 that he had taken over Busnitza's story; this isn't speculation but fact. You don't have to take my word for it, if you read Left At East Gate, then everything you read you will recognise as being the testimony of Larry Warren. You will realise that what you have read in that book is a combination of Larry's bit part, and the rest is about Adrian Bustinza and John Burroughs. John was asked to walk towards the UFO by Colonel Charles Halt while Adrian was with him not Larry."

Authors: [Despite a number of emails sent to Linda Moulton Howe at her private e-mail address and on Facebook, in June 2016, I (John) was unsuccessful in receiving any reply. This seems odd, especially as I had met Linda at one of the UFO conferences at Woodbridge Community Hall, some years ago. Sacha Christie has apologised to Colonel Halt, saying he was right about Larry being a substance abuser, admitting . . .

Linda Moulton Howe

> "I took cocaine with Larry at the Weird Weekend in 2007; he had taken some drugs with him. I gave up taking drugs a number of years ago, because I wanted to face my experiences instead of running from them. I no longer wanted to escape my life, I wanted to live it"

Colonel Halt:

> "Sacha has it right. When the five of us returned to the vehicles, John Burroughs was still there. He asked me if he and Bustinza (who had been with me the whole time) could go forward a bit (to the original site) and I agreed. They soon returned and we all went back to the base. They never mentioned seeing anything. In fact, we had them in sight the whole time. The only filming was by Nevels and John did not walk to a craft that night. John did claim he saw a blue object and it flew through the open vehicle windows. There were others present, but John is the only one claiming to have seen a blue object."

John Hanson:

"Having already experienced some personal threats made against me by Larry personally, which I took 'with a pinch of salt' being an ex-CID Officer, who had served for nearly 30 years in the Force, I was still shocked at the level of unprecedented hatred directed on Facebook to Sacha Christie and her family. I spoke at some length to her partner, David Kelly, who has relatives in the Police, and expressed my concern about this 'wave' of hatred, along with my support to the family. I will not sit back and by doing so condone internet threats and bullying irrespective of who it is."

Malcolm Robinson comments on the ADX 24 podcast

"As Larry says, it's a great shame that we have all these 'wannabees' who want to make a name for themselves off the back of Larry and Peter, because there's no denying that the Rendlesham Forest case stands head and shoulders above any case we have here in the British Isles. It's a marvellous case; lots of factual evidence out there. But we have certain people – I won't personally name them – but we have certain people out there who just want to stir the pot, stir it up and make a noise and try and gain some attention – and that for me, personally, is the sad side of UFOlogy, where we have these people who want to do this."

John Hanson:

"It is sad that while there is so much talk about UFO disclosures, which one hopes, ultimately, may be achieved through public debate and UFO conferences, we have now created a platform which has provided the facility for individuals to attack others in the same community, egged on by the host. Over the years, I have been to many UK conferences with lectures given by Peter and Larry, and at no time have I ever expressed any opinions about them, their book or what they have spoken on. I naively thought this podcast was produced to promote disclosure of the UFO subject and enlighten the listeners with details of the forthcoming SPI conference. The event will be forever tarnished for me personally. I would have liked to have attended the conference and listen to the speakers, but felt it was likely that I (and Charles Halt) would be the subject of further attacks on our characters by Peter and Larry. Under the circumstances I decided it was wise not to go – disappointing, as anything that Malcolm Robinson puts together is always worth attending. Malcolm is well-respected in the field of UFO research, and has been one of the bastions of what this is all about … very much 'a champion of the UFO cause.'"

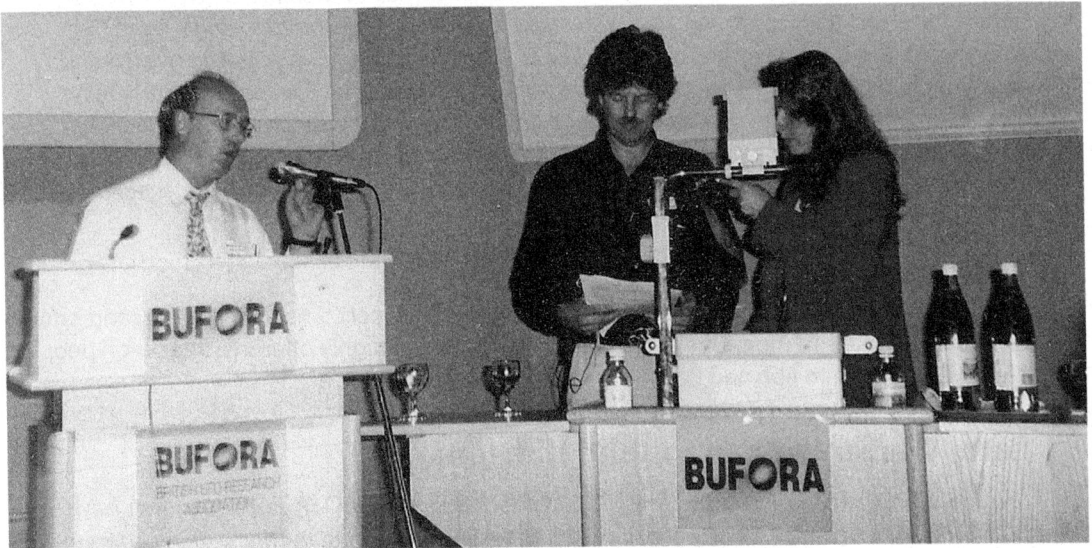

Malcolm Robinson (centre) in the mid-1990's at a BUFORA Conference

Malcolm Robinson – Facebook, June 2016 – *"Roar like a lion"*

"Questions can be asked and questions will be given no matter what. We will never hold back from giving you an answer contrary to what you might have heard. The truth will out, not just at this conference but afterwards where our tsunami of truth will be presented to all, the other side of the coin will be upon British UFOlogy!!! All will be revealed in due course. The quietness of SPI will soon roar like a lion. Please note that anyone can ask any questions at our Conference in Glasgow. There will be no gags on any questions. After the conference we at SPI will address the lies and accusations spread by an individual which are totally false. Don't you worry you'll soon see what's been really going on. The conference is still on and we are all looking forward to showing that no matter how hard you try, you'll never stop the conference or the truth getting out. We remain quiet at the moment but boy when the conference is over tie your house down; the other side of the story which you haven't properly heard due to insane rambling lies will be told."

Alyson – "Larry was upset – might have been more than coffee involved"

On the 6th June 2016, Alyson posted up a message on Facebook:

"It all became very silly to be honest. What people don't know is that things had been said about Larry … bad things. He was upset; it was in the middle of the night and there might have been more than coffee involved. We've all been there. Those in glass houses shouldn't throw stones. What Larry said was on my group. It was not aimed at anyone – just an angry response to what was said to him. After speaking to him at 2am he was less upset almost immediately. I deleted the comment but someone took a screen shot and sent it on without context. So yes it looks awful. And no one involved condones violence as has been implied. Screen shots of some banter and larking around were also taken, the meaning distorted to imply more than they meant. But it has been a lesson for all of us that even in jest, things will be twisted and made out to be something they are not for the agenda of people who want to use something against you. I wholeheartedly apologise for anything that caused upset to anyone. I hope that we can perhaps move forward and onto more important things. Everyone involved has my good wishes and I can only hope that we can try to have a little compassion and understanding for one another in the future."

John Hanson:

Personally, while having the greatest respect for Malcolm, I feel comments like this (and others) can only aggravate the situation. One thing is assured – personal highly offensive attacks on people's characters will continue to ebb and flow – will there ever be an end to it?"

Larry Warren's email to John Hanson:

"No threats bubba.........you best read HALT IN WoodBridge By PETER Robbins.....then have YOUR brief do a legal REVIEW of your 'Book' … then think hard about my name going on your Mail Box …!"

26th May 2016 – Phenomenon Radio – Adrian Bustinza

In a previous email sent to Sacha and available on Facebook, Adrian Bustinza said:

"I appreciate your interest, support and research. You've definitely been listening with an open mind and surely have a lot of questions. However, the very reason I have stayed a distance is because it hasn't gone away! And it probably never will! I still get phone calls from unlisted numbers and private numbers who I can't identify – because I don't know who they are, but I know that sometime soon I, with John [Burroughs], after I'm able to sit down face-to-face with John again, will come forward and face the critics who have no earthly idea of what rigorous interrogations took place and what they tried to do to us. Some people want the limelight … and then there are those of us who just want to know why?

I'm USAF veterans, who served wholeheartedly and still believe in what our nation stands for! Ronnie [Dugdale] has been very understanding, along with John, and supportive of my keeping my distance. Reason being is because some of us out there want glory and they don't experience what John and I have for the past 35 years, which has been denial, nightmares, health issues, critics and most of all lies and deception from our own brothers, only to have the truth surface through others like yourself that have taken the time to listen! Our own Brothers, who are bent on taking ownership and credit for something that others experience but can't give details, is just outright disgusting! I don't say much, but I can assure you of one thing and that's that I have nothing to say except the truth, and that's how it will always be. So many witnesses that won't come forth … do you blame them?"

Colonel Halt:

"Adrian must be talking about Larry Warren and some of his supporters. Another blatant lie is that he claimed 'Alaska' (nickname) committed suicide. He was a young cop awaiting a security clearance that got frustrated. He went to London and took a flight to Chicago. Law Enforcement 'C' Flight found out and called the Airport Police in Chicago and had him returned. They didn't want him charged as a deserter. He was later discharged and did not commit suicide. At one point Larry even wrongly claimed 'Alaska' was his room-mate."

John Hanson – Larry was posted to RAF Alconbury

Larry Warren also claimed that it was common knowledge, during his service at the base, that pilots hanged themselves, and people committed suicide by shooting themselves – not forgetting the suicide of his colleague. He also said that while initially he had been posted to RAF Alconbury, in December 1980, he had managed to exchange his posting with a colleague, who told him that his girlfriend lived near Alconbury airbase. I made a FOI request, with regard to obtaining information about any suicides of serviceman who had served on the base between the time Larry was there, but found nothing relevant to those dates.

Squadron Leader Donald Moreland

"I have no such knowledge of any airmen having committed suicide while I was there. I know of Larry Warren and his involvement in the alleged matters, but reiterate I have no knowledge personally of any deaths by suicide involving the use of firearms at that base where I was the RAF Liaison Officer."

Malcolm Robinson praises *Haunted Skies* books

On the 22nd June 2016, Malcolm Robinson posted the following comments on Facebook:

"Just finished reading Haunted Skies, *Volume 8, the Rendlesham Forest Special – wow brilliant – John and Dawn have done a cracking job, excellent."*

Larry Warren

On the 25th June 2016, SPI held its conference at the new venue – Queen Margaret, University Gardens, Glasgow.

Larry Warren failed to appear personally on stage following alleged claims of disruption. Instead, Larry was introduced by Gary Heseltine (by way of a short video clip of film, previously recorded) in which nothing contentious was said. Peter Robbins then, on behalf of Larry, outlined Larry Warren's involvement in the 1980 UFO incident, which included a report of police constables being escorted away from the scene of the incident and their cameras were seized. Then the arrival of the base Commander Gordon Williams at the location in his evening dress, following which he approached the three entities who at some stage all in unison cocked their heads back before disappearing – the craft on its tripod legs then took off, making a humming sound and was quickly gone from view. Peter then tells what happened next, after Larry wakes up in his room with no conscious memory of how he got there, the telephone call to his mother, the meeting with three officials and threats made that *'bullets are cheap.'* A photo produced by Larry, showing a UFO above an A10 photographed in the sky over the base, the next day, purported to have similarities with the UFO shown in *Left At East Gate* book, as described by Larry is shown.

Beams from the UFO <u>had</u> affected the ordnance briefly

A comment made by Peter, in which he confirmed he and Larry were told by Charles Halt that the *'beams from the UFO had affected the ordnance briefly'* –

Charles Halt:

"I have never made an issue about any weapons, especially any being damaged or degraded. Even if I wanted to make a statement I was in no position to know. It's interesting that now Peter says Larry woke up in his bed not knowing how he got there. That means all his earlier talk about turning in his weapon and having breakfast with other cops, including Pennistion, is now a different story. I can tell you if he didn't turn in his weapon, the base would have been turned upside-down. About that time another cop tried to steal an automatic weapon and the reaction was something to behold. We found the weapon and he went to jail. More BS! Will it ever stop?"

Ronnie Dugdale

At 8pm EST on the 30th of June (USA) (1st July 2016, UK) UK UFO enthusiast and frequent podcast speaker – Ronnie Dugdale – spoke about the Rendlesham Forest Incident on *Phenomenon* Radio, hosted by John Burroughs and Linda Moulton Howe.

Owing to problems with our server, we weren't able to listen to the broadcast. Fortunately, some of the conversations brought to the attention of the listeners were made available on Ronnie's Facebook site on the 2nd July 2016.

Ronnie:

"Over the many years Larry Warren has repeatedly denied that he talked to the News of the World, *but recently admitted he had, in fact, spoken to a reporter from* The News of the World *for five minutes, claiming he would not give them a full interview until others came forward. This is incorrect. I have listened to a tape in my possession, which belongs to Dot Street, who tape-recorded an hour long telephone conversation between* News of the World *reporter Keith Beabey and an unidentified airman (Larry Warren), which nullifies Warren's claim the article in the* News of the World *was distorted beyond belief."*

[Dot Street confirms (2.7.2016) that the *'unidentified airman'* in that tape-recording was Larry Warren.]

Steve Roberts aka John David Ingalls

"Larry tells Dot and then Keith that he had already given a detailed account to another reporter from a National UK newspaper journalist – Bob Smith. Bob was the US representative for the News of The World *and had been sent to talk to Warren by the* News of the World *editor. Recently on Phenomenon Radio, Larry Warren told the listeners that the quotes attributed to him were not his but those of Brenda Butler's informant – Steve Roberts!"*

Larry is asked about the actual date of the UFO incident

Due to space in this book being at a premium, there is no point in including the whole of this recorded one-hour-long transcript into the book; we shall, however, refer to the following extracts:

Keith Beabey: *"What date was that, can you remember? Was it the twent.........?"*

Larry: *"You know I have trouble remembering that. I do know it was before New Year's Day."*

Keith Beabey: *"Yes, right, that's it, yes – 27th, 28th, 29th – right? Was it on the occasion of the first sighting or the second?"*

Larry Warren: *"I think it was the second."*

Keith Beabey: *"That would make it the *29th in fact."*

Larry Warren: *"It's clearer for other people than it is for me."*

Keith Beabey: *"It's only clear for me because I have it written down here … December the 29th, about 10 o'clock in the evening."*

**Left At East Gate gives the 28th December 1980.*

Major Zickler was there at the scene

Larry speaks of being relieved from his sentry position and taken to a clearing in the woods where, after dropping off their weapons, he tells of seeing motion cameras set up, with rescue helicopters flying overhead.

Following the arrival of the object, he said:

*"I went with our Lieutenant. We were ordered by a commander, **Major Zickler,** chief of the security police. We broke up into three, four-man groups and had to circle it; we were only maybe a foot away from it, we were very close."*

Larry:

"I woke up in my room, the next morning, oh about 5.30-6, as my room-mate was leaving. I was still in uniform with mud up to my ankles and he said I was brought in by some people about an hour or so before, maybe an hour and a half."

Keith Beabey: *"So you were brought in about 4 o'clock in the morning?"*

Larry Warren: *"In that area, yes."*

About 'Triple A' security clearance

Larry Warren:

"Yes, highly classified and they immediately upgraded our security clearance to 'Triple A'. I believe the clearance was as high as you can get in the military."

Keith Beabey:

"Alright. Was there any question of any aliens or thing that might have been on board that thing? You would have mentioned it, I presume?"

Larry Warren:

*"Ok. Yes, there was, and I heard that from almost everyone that was involved. They were on the ground and they were on the outside of the craft. **They said there were three but I myself don't remember seeing them.** I remember feeling a presence to this day that they were there and I think that I couldn't comprehend seeing them and blocked it out of my mind."*

Charles Halt:

"There is no such clearance and no one on the Base can upgrade a clearance. To upgrade a clearance takes an expanded background check and takes many months ... just another wild story that sounds good but not true."

In *Left At East Gate* – Page 107, Keith Beabey reports:

The Colonel's report confirms the strange events in the forest that night, but lacks the eyewitness detail given to us by Art Wallace, a USAF Security Policeman, and now back in America as a civilian. He was sent to the site in a convoy of military vehicles from nearby Bentwaters and describes what he saw . . .

"We looked up in the sky and saw a red ball of light coming towards us from the trees. There was no noise, no sound at all; we were all mesmerized. All of a sudden, the red light exploded. The place was filled with an explosion of colours, all kinds of colours. We were momentarily blinded and when the colours died down, there was a machine."

Art said there were beings in the craft, but he could not see them as he was on the wrong side.

"But others did; they said there were three, wearing silver suits."

Keith:

"Art Wallace – we have changed his name for security reasons – tells his story on page 3 today."

Further Updates & general comments

Sacha Christie – Larry's honourable discharge

"There were several rumours about Larry being thrown out of the Air Force for being a drug user. I asked him outright if this was the case, but he absolutely denied it. However, Edward Cabansag remembers seeing Larry in the supply hut and was told by a fellow airman that <u>Warren was waiting for his release as a result of his involvement with drugs</u>. Larry reminded me that he had an honourable discharge from the Air Force (I have a copy of this document) and was never associated with drugs. He believes these rumours were started to discredit him as a witness, because the Air Force knew he was talking about the incident. If Larry had been busted for drugs he would probably have received the same treatment and may even have been discharged. I have in my possession a copy of a document with the stamp of Wing Commander Gordon E. Williams' signature, which proves that Larry himself requested separation from the Air Force and not the other way around."

[Larry alleges that in March/April 1981, following a tip-off by Steve La Plume, OSI wanted to 'set him up'. He was subjected to an interview by two OSI agents, who produced a file which claimed he had committed a number of drug offenses on Bentwaters, between August and November 1980. Clearly this could not have been the case, as he hadn't started employment at the base until the 1st December].

Colin Persky, Base lawyer?

Larry says he spoke with Colin Persky – a Base lawyer – about his 'predicament' and was told he could use a breach of contract on the Air Force's part, i.e. he wasn't doing the job he had been trained to do and signed the 'Request for Separation form'.

On the 18th May 1981, he received his approval for discharge and speaks of meeting up with Bustinza after 10pm that night, and after conversation (which included photographs taken of the UFO, by John Burroughs), Larry said:

"We shared our thoughts on the underground base and, although I was unsure about what was real and what was imagined, he (Adrian) assured me the place existed and was an alien installation."

One may wonder why Larry had then taken it upon himself previously, to conduct enquiries about the existence of this *underground base. Larry admits he was caught searching through confidential files by Major Drury, during February 1981, who Larry claims was highly sceptical of his explanation for being there. (**Source:** *Left At East Gate*)

[*Surely, underground facilities (rather than any underground base) would have existed in order to ensure the safety of a variety of military hardware used in the running of this airbase, such as munitions – bearing in mind the vulnerability of enemy attack by storing these on the ground?]

Charles Halt:

"Lt. Colonel Arnold †Persky was Judge Advocate (head of the Base legal department). He would have never advised Warren that he could get out because of a breach of contract. Even when Warren was snapped (PRP decertified) he was put in police supply which was in the contracted career field. His claim about finding classified files about an underground facility in an insecure file cabinet is more nonsense. Larry was thrown out under the provisions of AFR 39-10 or 39-12 unsuitability or undesirable. Yes, they gave him an Honorable Discharge; it was an easy way to get rid of him without a lot of noise. You don't just get released on your own request.

He had been 'snapped', lost his (PRP) and put in supply, where he could be watched and was not allowed around sensitive things or to have a weapon. The loss of PRP was probably from drugs and they kept him for a while due to his running his mouth about the incident. Cabansag had it right! All my time in the Air Force, I never saw anyone released because they wanted out. Even Steve La Plume had to fake suicide and more to get out."

Footnote:

†In 1983, Colonel Arnold Persky, of Maxwell Air Force Base, is mentioned by the *Daily Item*, Sumter, S.C. as the Presiding Judge during the trial of a Major charged with a variety of sexual offences. On the 7th June 2016, Aaron Persky – the judge responsible for convicted rapist Brock Turner's disputed six-month sentence – faced some media criticism for his light sentence. Is there a connection with Arnold Persky? In June 2016, Judge Michael Aaron Persky was elected without opposition for another six-year term on the bench.

John Hanson:

We are now approaching the end of what has been a tumultuous book covering an incredible amount of space and time, with a gigantic number of images/sketches included into the framework of this well over 760 page book. If we have made any mistakes we will rectify them and add anything of interest in a special edition of updates in the next Volume of *Haunted Skies*.

We apologise for having to introduce what some will feel to be further attacks on Larry Warren's character, especially in view of the more recent developments surrounding the SPI Conference in Scotland, during late June 2016, when he was prohibited from talking. But history must record all of the facts, however painful they are, particularly bearing in mind the continuing verbal assaults and criticism made on the character of Charles Halt over the years and me, by not only Larry Warren, but also Peter Robbins.

Charles Halt:

*"I have repeatedly, over the years, attempted to help Larry personally in setting the record straight, but Peter has always intervened. I really feel sorry for Larry. I think he's been used. If one accepts that he was given drugs etc., during the debriefing process following an extraordinary, highly unusual event, which I have no reason to disbelieve took place, then logically this indicates the possibility this may have affected him psychologically – which may well be one of the reasons why he appears incapable of separating fact from fiction in his constantly ever-changing version of events. While I was aware, at the time, that he and his colleagues had been interviewed following the sightings and under normal protocol, I was shocked to learn, years later, of the involvement of the OSI and their harsh interrogations, which included the use of, I believe, to have been Sodium Amytal, or *something similar, which may well have had a damaging effect on their characters. It is time for the reader to judge for themselves the authenticity of what happened in the forest all those years ago. One thing is abundantly clear, what we saw was not an isolated incident, bearing in mind the nature of other reported UFO sightings by the public, presented here in this book. What they are and where they come from I have no idea, but the evidence is overwhelming in my opinion."*

*All of these truth serums work in the same manner: They depress the central nervous system and interfere with judgment and higher cognitive function. Specifically, tests carried out on patients under the influence of Amytal, another popular truth serum, showed that they were capable of telling lies and that many supposed 'truths' were likely a combination of fact and fiction. A person is also highly 'susceptible to outside suggestion' under the influence of the drug, meaning that they might agree to something that the interviewer says, even if it isn't true. Subjects also sometimes randomly make things up for no apparent reason. Thus, any information given under the influence of a truth serum needs to be corroborated by other evidence in order to weigh whether it is actually true.

The famous American author wrote in Mark Twain's Notebook (published posthumous in 1935): *"If you tell the truth, you don't have to remember anything."*

In 1963 the Supreme Court ruled that a confession produced under the influence of truth serum was unconstitutionally coerced, and therefore inadmissible. After that, the use of such drugs fell rapidly from popularity in the USA but truth serums may not be gone for good, as the Supreme Court asserted shortly after 9/11 that terrorism may require *"heightened deference to the judgments of the political branches with respect to matters of national security."*

(Source: Wikipedia, 2016)

Dedicated to Georgina Bruni, died on the 19th January 2008

Nick Pope about Georgina

"Investigative journalist, events organiser and socialite Georgina Bruni was one of the most meticulous researchers to turn her attention to the Rendlesham Forest incident. Such was her persistence that even the normally unflappable Charles Halt described being quizzed by her as being an experience on par with an OSI interrogation! She was well-connected politically, and

had various friends at Westminster and Whitehall. Indeed, the launch party for her excellent book on the case – You Can't Tell The People – was held in the Henry VIII Wine Cellar in MOD Main Building, starting various conspiracy theories about her working for the government!

Her contributions to the public's understanding of the Rendlesham Forest incident fall into three main categories. Firstly, she tracked down more witnesses and peripheral 'players' than any ufologist ever managed, and placed their accounts in her book. Secondly, working alongside former Chief of the Defence Staff Lord Hill-Norton, she drafted Parliamentary Questions about Rendlesham that led to the government having to reply officially in the House of Lords. While most of the answers were of the standard deny/downplay variety, they are important statements in and of themselves. Thirdly, and again in conjunction with Lord Hill-Norton, she used the Code of Practice on Access to Government Information to obtain the MOD's case file on the incident – having correctly deduced that despite the official denials, there must be more in the file than just Charles Halt's 13th January 1981 memo.

Bruni was a tough character that stood up to what she saw as a largely misogynistic group of ufologists and witnesses who had tried to position themselves as experts on the case. She had no qualms about calling out Sheffield-based ufologist David Clarke for plagiarism when he tried to take credit for discovering some MOD documents she believed she found first. She was similarly unfazed by Larry Warren's attempts to disparage her research when she concluded he'd made up most – if not all – of his story. When Warren furiously demanded to know where she'd got the libellous claim that he'd attempted suicide, Bruni hilariously referred him to page *279 of his own book, where a botched suicide attempt was indeed described. Warren clearly hadn't read the book that Peter Robbins had ghost-written for him, or had told so many falsehoods over the years that he was having difficulty remembering them all. Grudges are obviously still held to this day, which, sadly, is par for the course with this case and with ufology more generally. Clarke continues to snipe at Georgina occasionally, on his 'Pooterish' blog, even though he knows she died of cancer back in 2008 – classy guy! And Warren lapses into an occasional anti-Georgina monologue on Facebook – all block capitals and poor grammar.

Georgina was a bon vivant, one moment sipping cocktails with Baroness Margaret Thatcher at a charity fundraiser, the next dancing with a foreign ambassador at an embassy ball. One of my fondest memories of her is a meal that she, General Gordon Williams and I had at trendy Knightsbridge eatery Signor Sassi. This is a world totally alien (pun intended) to the likes of Clarke and Warren, and one suspects that inverted snobbery lies at the heart of such people's dislike of her.

Georgina was a 'work hard play hard' person, whose love of parties and the good things in life hid a razor-sharp intellect. The world is a less interesting place with her no longer in it. I'm proud to say that she was my friend, and I hope I was a good friend to her too."

*This was one of over 400 errors brought to her attention by Larry Warren, some years ago:

Quote: Ms Bruni, In your book you state that I more than once contemplated suicide based on what source do you conclude this? First it is bull****, second, it is legally actionable, and third, – Did you read East

Gate? Had you done so, why did you not report accurately what happened to me 14 years ago and why? Why was it necessary to write this inaccurate and slanderous statement at all? Please don't tell me that I told you that! Because I will then ask you to produce the audio tape of me doing so, OK! So please answer why you tried to create such an inaccurate and unstable picture of Larry Warren? In fact, you put more effort into slandering me then resolving the case, why?"

Answer: There is no need to produce further evidence because I did read your book, but did you? Turn to page 490 (index) in *Left At East Gate* and read: Warren, suicide attempt, 279. A paragraph on your attempted suicide in 1988 concludes with, *"I couldn't even kill myself properly."* Then turn to page 82, referring to the year 1981: *"Drinking was a constant in my life and some moments I thought about ending it all."* Now turn to page 289, where your co-author Peter Robbins is discussing your problems in 1988 and had learnt that . . . *"he [Larry] had come pretty close to killing himself the month before."*

Valerie Austin "My friend Georgina"

Another good friend of Georgina's – who can't speak highly enough of her – is Mrs Valerie Austin, a trained hypnotherapist, lecturer, author and journalist, whose business premises has included a successful practice in London's Harley Street, London where she worked as a consultant to psychiatrists, plastic surgeons and The Priory Hospital, Roehampton.

In conversation with Valerie, she spoke of that memorable occasion when she took the now famous photograph (one of three taken of Margaret Thatcher), following the conversation between the Honourable Lady and Georgina.

In August 2006, Georgina – Editor in Chief in *Hot Gossip*, in August 2006 – had this to say about the circumstances that led to the photo being taken:

"Hello readers and welcome to our sunny August issue of HOT GOSSIP, UK. Ten years on–line and still going strong! This month we have a bumper issue of great summer reading. Catch up on the latest product news right here (see below) on SPOTLIGHT, and don't forget to check out all the other pages. Valerie [Austin] has some important news about food and healthy living and Joan introduces readers to the HOUSE OF LORDS. PHOTOS OF THE MONTH: Not a great image of me – but it was a sweltering hot day! It was nice to meet (again) the charismatic former Prime Minister, Margaret Thatcher, on the terrace at the House of Commons."

Valerie has written five international best-selling self-hypnosis books and audio products, which are published internationally in English, Spanish, Japanese, Hebrew and Polish. They are *Self Hypnosis*, (Thorsons, 1992), *Slim While You Sleep*, (Blake Publishing, 1995), *Hypnosex* (Thorsons, 1996), *Free Yourself from Fear* (Thorsons, 1998), *Stop Smoking in One Hour* (Blake Publishing, 2000).

Valerie kindly supplied us with the following photographs taken of Georgina and friends.

Titles with two pictures....One of the people in the picture was Valentina, really very good Psychic. He had a room in these offices then and got me in there. I was still at Harley Street but it was my surplus office where I trained hypnotherapists and allowed them to rent the rooms I had leased. I had one large, one medium and one small with toilets and showers. James Pool my husband took these as I had just had a workshop in my office and Georgina had joined me and we were about to go for cocktails. It was at my lovely office in Green Park overlooking the park the next block to Hard Rock. Lovely times.

Valerie spoke about conversations held with Georgina about her visit to an airbase in America, during the 1980s, and that a lot of personal knowledge gained through investigations into UFO events, both in the USA and at RAF Bentwaters/Woodbridge, had not been released to the public.

[John Hanson: Georgina told me of having experienced some UFO encounters going back to childhood, but never expanded on the nature of what exactly took place.]

Valerie: *"I was involved myself in researching remote viewing. My partner at that time was David Moorhouse. We did get some weird people admittedly, but this wasn't anything flamboyant; behind it was a very secure research centre. I have experienced some of this myself in the late 1990s."*

GEORGINA BRUNI

Georgina's original name was Linda Naylor born in 1947 Rotherham, Yorkshire, England, UK
Below from top left: With Gordon Williams ©Nick Pope, Chris and Brenda, Lady Thatcher, Valerie Austin and Valentina

The latest insights on bullying and drug use on Base

In July 2016, Larry Warren appeared on a podcast hosted by Ben Emlyn Jones, where he was given free rein to once again deliver a personal attack on the character of an 'unnamed female individual', although it was apparent to most people who that was.

Presumably breaching his code of self-imposed etiquette with regard to not naming people on this occasion, Larry was quite happy to direct further threats against me (John) warning me not to publish anything in the forthcoming 'Halt' book about himself, or his recent non-appearance at the Glasgow SPI Conference.

At a very late stage in the completion of this book I was contacted by Sacha Christie, who has been in touch with Colonel Halt, wishing to bring our attention to a recent development relating to her current discussion with an ex-security member of the 81st Tactical Fighter Wing, who was employed at RAF Bentwaters during the time in question.

This person, whose identity is known to us, confided to Sacha that they, too, had been the subject of a vigorous 'debriefing' interview by members of the Air Force Police (OSI). This involved being administered with drugs, followed by a threat that 'bullets were cheap' [in an effort to presumably dissuade the witness from speaking about what they had seen]. This person also spoke of bullying and drug taking which took place on the base. It is hoped that this person (who is known to many) will find the courage to come forward and tell more about what happened but fears being the target of expected harassment.

In an email sent in August 2016, Charles Halt had this to say:

"I finally listened to Peter Robbins on the 'Where Did The Road Go?' You Tube posting, from 5th December 2015. He clearly states Larry Warren's discharge was under the provisions of Air Force Code AFR 35-10, which is for unsuitability or undesirable behaviour, and for the convenience of the United States Air Force. I always suspected this was the case, but 'they' would never show the actual discharge documents. Additionally, Peter stated that Larry had been employed on a special work party picking up rocks from the roadside. This was Major Malcolm Zickler's road gang for drug abuse offenders, waiting to be discharged from the Air Force. The only way to get into that scheme was to have been caught taking drugs. As you know, drug raids were carried out on the airbases and severely enforced by the authorities, as part of a zero tolerance towards drug abuse. Both the base Judge Advocate, and I, felt this was demeaning work for treatment of offenders and not in accordance with laid down policy, so we finally convinced Major Zickler to abandon it. This information supplied by Peter Robbins indicates to me that Larry Warren was in line for a drug discharge. I suspect the 'spooks' (OSI) had him seconded into police jurisdiction until they could arrange for him to be discreetly discharged. His 'honourable discharge' was endorsed with a code that meant he would be unable, at a later date, to rejoin the military or obtain a security clearance, taking into consideration his unreliability in the post that he was selected to serve."

*Above: Ike Barker being interviewed by Robert Hastings in his 2016 film, UFOs and Nukes: The Secret Link Revealed.
Below: Jim Carey. Both U.S. Air Force air traffic controllers tracked a bona fide UFO on radar the night Colonel Halt
and his team were in Rendlesham Forest.*

AFTERWORD

BY ROBERT HASTINGS

SO why have I been chosen to write a few words for this book? Col. Charles Halt has been accused by skeptics of misinterpreting what he saw in the sky, while other detractors have accused him of misrepresenting certain subsequent events. The information below is designed to refute those claims and charges, although some people will undoubtedly continue to promote failed theories and false "facts".

While I cannot be considered a leading investigator of the UFO incidents at the twin bases and nearby Rendlesham Forest, in December 1980, I have nevertheless interviewed key individuals who provide us with an informed perspective regarding the events that occurred there during the week between Christmas and New Year's.

In 2007, I identified and located the two U.S. Air Force air traffic controllers who were on duty at the RAF Bentwaters ATC tower that week, Ike Barker and Jim Carey, both of whom unequivocally state that they tracked a bona fide UFO on radar the night Col. Halt and his team were in the woods – an object which travelled 120 miles in approximately 8-12 seconds, performing an instantaneous right-angle turn as it left the vicinity!

Further, Barker saw the object out of the tower's windows, as it briefly hovered over a nearby water tower, describing it as an luminous orange sphere with a series of apparent portholes around its equator, through which light from the craft's interior glowed.

Both controllers' taped testimony appears in my 2008 book, *UFOs and Nukes: Extraordinary Encounters at Nuclear Weapons Sites*, and my 2016 film, *UFOs and Nukes: The Secret Link Revealed*. The importance of these revelations cannot be overstated, given the continued insistence by debunkers – none of whom were present for the events of that week – that Colonel Halt and his team had misidentified the beam from the Orford Ness lighthouse, shining through the forest, as a UFO.

Actually, this unfounded claim was discredited as long ago as 1997, when Halt gave a taped interview to journalist A.J.S. Rayl, in which he said that the members of his team had all seen the flashing lighthouse beam and the mysterious moving light *simultaneously*, with the former being horizontally separated from the latter by some 30-to-40 degrees of arc.

THE HALT PERSPECTIVE

Predictably, the naysayers ignored this on-the-record remark and continued to chant their "It was a lighthouse" mantra. Inconvenient facts that challenged their worldview were not to be acknowledged under any circumstances. That Halt and the others saw an actual aerial object which defied prosaic explanation could not possibly be true.

Now, however, credible, detailed testimony from two professional air traffic controllers makes clear that an anomalous, unbelievably advanced craft was indeed in the vicinity that night. Considering the specifics of the tracking, as recounted by both controllers, it seems unlikely that the UFO was one of those operating in close proximity to Halt's team, given that it raced toward RAF Bentwaters from more than 60 miles out – the extent of the radar's range – briefly hovered north of the base's runway, then left the area without stopping, disappearing off the scope, again at a distance of 60 miles.

Moreover, because multiple, unknown aerial objects were reported by Halt and his team, including those subsequently observed from a farmer's field, it's unclear as to why only one UFO was tracked – although the various objects' altitudes may have been a factor. (Retired ATC controller Ike Barker told me that no aircraft could have been tracked below 500 feet in altitude.) Or, perhaps, some of those anomalous craft had stealth capability. Obviously, this is speculation on my part and a number of questions about that night's events remain unanswered.

In any case, the two controllers have at last provided a detailed, authoritative account of what was present in the sky at the time Halt's team was visually reporting unidentified aerial objects performing astounding feats. While it would be a mistake to *directly* associate that tracked object with those manoeuvring through the trees or, later on, above Halt's head, it is reasonable to assume that the reported craft were of the same basic nature as the one captured on radar, given their spherical/oval shapes and hovering/maneuvering capabilities – as opposed to being a wandering lighthouse or a group of wildly cavorting stars, as the skeptics would have us believe.

Of course, the debunkers will disagree. After all, what else can they do? Admit that they were wrong? Not likely. We can all expect some number of them to offer, in the days ahead, their oh-so-astute explanations as to why the controllers didn't actually track an actual UFO and why one of those men could not possibly have seen an orange-colored sphere hovering nearby.

Regardless, not only did Col. Halt accurately report multiple, intelligently-controlled aerial craft hovering and maneuvering in the vicinity that night – something partially confirmed by the air traffic controllers – he subsequently and somewhat reluctantly confessed to hearing on the radio that one of those craft was sending down beams of light into or near the RAF Bentwaters Weapons Storage Area (WSA).

At the time, he almost certainly could not have known that very similar incidents had already occurred at the WSAs on Loring, Wurtsmith and Kirtland Air Force Bases during the preceding five years, according to now-declassified documents released via the American Freedom of Information Act.

In other words, what Halt reported – listening to excited and probably frightened chatter from several guards posted at the Bentwaters facility, as laser-like beams from a glowing aerial object fell near them – fit into a pattern of existing UFO activity at other nuclear weapons sites.

While some sceptics continue to cling to the fiction that we still don't really know that nukes were stored at Bentwaters – in part due to the Air Force's official policy of neither confirming nor denying the locations of nuclear weapons – abundant evidence long available confirms this was so. Indeed, the specificity of the information provided to me by veterans who were directly or indirectly involved with those weapons, including one retired colonel who worked for the NATO nuclear weapons security apparatus, leave no doubt as to what the Bentwaters bunkers held.

That gentleman, whom I must not identify, told me that two tactical nuclear bombs had been removed from one bunker shortly after the UFO incident and flown, via a C-5A aircraft, to the Air Force's Weapons Laboratory at Kirtland AFB, New Mexico, for inspection. While he had been privy to the details contained in the shipping manifest, he was not in the loop for the lab's findings. Nevertheless, those two bombs – as opposed to others in the bunker – had presumably been selected for a *reason*. Had they been somehow damaged by the beams? If so, you and I will never learn the facts.

But, once again, Col. Halt's statements about one of the aerial objects manoeuvring near the Bentwaters WSA – based on what he heard on his radio while standing in a farmer's field, miles away – are consistent with what investigators know about UFOs' longstanding interest in nukes. Indeed, my own four-decade research project confirms that virtually every nuclear weapons laboratory, test range, storage depot and deployment site in the U.S. has been visited at one time or another. Therefore, another of Halt's reports, about hearing chatter regarding beams from the UFO falling into or near the Bentwaters WSA, is credible.

In fact, I have interviewed one of the former Security Policemen posted at the weapons depot, Robert "Charlie" Waters, who told me that he and others had witnessed a brightly glowing sphere in the sky near the WSA, which quickly lost altitude and disappeared into the woods. It was so close, or perhaps so big, that it appeared "as large as a cantaloupe" held at arm's length. Waters only saw the craft after another guard screamed at him to turn and look at it.

While he did not see any beams emanating from the UFO, Waters did discern what appeared to be a rod protruding from the bottom of it. I have speculated it was that appendage from which the beams had emerged moments earlier, before Waters turned around. But we will probably never know with certainty.

Finally, let me say a few words regarding Col. Halt's long-term consistency. I first interviewed him on audio tape in 2006. Over the past 11 years, he and I have exchanged more than 500 emails. In short, I possess recorded and written statements from him which one can review. Not once has he contradicted himself, as regards his recounting of what he saw and later did relating to the UFO incidents.

While others (they know who they are) have changed their stories or even made up tales out of thin air – which have now been convincingly discredited – Chuck Halt has remained a reliable source for straightforward, unembellished, chronologically-organized information. In this, he has few peers.

REVELATIONS FROM SERVICEWOMAN 'COOKIE'

'COOKIE' – LARRY WASN'T THERE!

IN September 2016, after much deliberation, US servicewoman 'Cookie' – who worked in the supply depot at RAF Bentwaters, during the period in question, and then girlfriend of Larry Warren for a while – finally plucked up the courage to confide in Sacha Christie, wishing to tell her side of the story during December 1980. I (John) learnt about this some time ago, but 'Cookie', declined to allow us to publish her comments in *The Halt Perspective* book. Fortunately, 'Cookie' changed her mind but insisted her full identity should not be revealed publicly.

It is a damning indictment on Larry Warren's character and one can only salute the courage it took for her to finally put something at rest, which had been worrying her for so long.

Does this add extra weight to what Colonel Charles Halt has always maintained that, in all probability, Larry wasn't there!

According to Georgina Bruni, during an exchange of conversation with Larry, some years before her death, Larry said to her: *"You also state that I was talking to 'everyone about the UFO' – again, not true! 'Cookie' was my girlfriend at that time, as you know, from speaking to her yourself!* **I never told her about it!** *You have your facts ass backwards again! And you seem to be hell-bent to create an untrue picture of me. Please explain your research methods of this issue?"*

Georgina: *"'Cookie' was surprised that you __had not__ mentioned the incident to her, but explained that it was something of a fleeting romance. If I recall correctly, she was not your girlfriend at the time of the actual incident, but soon after."*

FIRST NIGHT

'Cookie': *"Larry Warren claimed to be personally involved in the first documented night's events, which took place in Rendlesham Forest, Suffolk, but I know he wasn't working. He was actually at the bar, listening to a few people talk about the incident and, the next day, wrote himself into it. He said he was there the first night it started; he __was NOT on duty that weekend__, and he even named his book inaccurately. It should not have been Left At East Gate but 'Right At East Gate'! Following my experiences which began in the forest on the first night, along with a few other people, involving sightings of several silent craft which were seen to separate into three to five others, (I reported these sightings to my superior but was ridiculed and told I was an over active female!) We were in the Dormitory bar discussing what had occurred. Larry*

was there he was very jealous that he had not been involved. **The next day, his friends told me he had gone around telling people about __his__ involvement in the UFO sighting and thereby wrote himself into history. He says he was in Germany, but he wasn't."*

SECOND NIGHT – WITNESSED UFO ACTIVITY

'Cookie': *"On the second night I was out driving but decided to park up and go into the forest, attempting to investigate reports of strange 'lights' seen, never thinking they could have been UFOs – just puzzled from which country they were from? After all, this was an airbase where many different 'birds' (aircraft) were stationed from other countries. That was my first thought, to begin with, but then became aware of the absence of noise from animals, birds, dogs, or from the 'craft', making you wonder what it was, what in the world is going on?"*

OVER THE NEXT FEW NIGHTS

"Over the next few nights I was too busy to pay Larry any attention. He was **NOT** *at either place along the back road between the two bases. I picked up some of the security cops and took them to the motor pool; I know for sure 'Busty' (Bustinza) was one, and I believe the others included 'Smitty' and 'Ed', but I can't be 100% sure, as so many years have elapsed. It was four guys the first time, and five the next. They were all dazed. We were all in something like a sub reality – thoughts of going crazy – and we all felt a prickly sunburn sensation on our hands, arms, faces and necks."*

John Hanson: In *Left At East Gate*, Larry tells of making a journey to Germany, after being invited to do so by two German girls they had met about a week before Christmas.

"We had a great time, despite a severe language barrier. However, I think the girls lost interest in Mark and me on the second night. We just sat around and stared at their parents and them at us, while the girls went out with their German boyfriends. On or about **27th December,** *we flew back to RAF Mildenhall to begin our shift the next night (28th)."*

NICK POPE: TRIP TO GERMANY – 'RED HERRING'

"Without access to official paperwork detailing Larry Warren's periods of duty and leave, it's impossible to be certain where he was at the time of the various UFO incidents. As for the trip to Germany, he's told so many different versions of his story over the years, that not only can't we be sure of the dates, we cannot even be certain the trip took place at all. Did he make up the story to add a little 'colour', but then panic and change the details when the correct

dates of the UFO sightings came out, realising he'd just taken himself out of the very story he'd been so desperate to write himself into? In the final analysis, the Germany trip is a 'red herring' – that's because any reasonable assessment of the evidence can only lead to the conclusion that irrespective of whether Larry Warren was in Germany or the UK, he wasn't a witness to any of the UFO encounters. Sadly, it seems the nearest he got to any of the action was hearing snatches of the story in a bar."

STEALING FROM THE BASE

In a review, by Michael Miley, of their book *Left At East Gate*, published in the (USA), *UFO Magazine*, number 48, Volume 12, No. 5, 1997, Michael quotes: *"Included are facsimiles of Warren's military records, which he managed to <u>steal from the base</u> after the incident, because he anticipated having troubles as a result of calling his mother the next day, from a pay phone, to tell her of the UFO – a call which was cut off by eavesdroppers at the base."*

If, in fact, this was not the case, then we apologise for impugning the integrity of Mr Warren!

Nick Pope: *"I've heard the story before, but can't recall when, or from whom. As ever with Larry, it's all but impossible to nail down the truth. Stealing papers would certainly be consistent with his nature. However, for all I know, these were documents he was given on his discharge, with the story about them being stolen having been made up – perhaps to make it look like he 'put one over' on the USAF. That's certainly consistent with the bad boy/rebel/maverick image he and Peter have cultivated for him, and with his status as a whistleblower.* (**Sources: Georgina Bruni – *You Can't Tell the People* / Nick Pope – *Encounter in Rendlesham Forest: The Inside Story of the World's Best-Documented UFO Incident*, available on Kindle and hardback, Amazon Macmillan. Publisher / Interviews with 'Cookie' September 2016 – Sacha Christie)**

It appears that 'Cookie's' confidence gained new levels after a surprise development when she appeared on *KGRA* radio, on the 22nd September 2016 – hosted by Linda Moulton Howe and John Burroughs, following announcements made of a new witness, who had approached them.

To be fair to 'Cookie', the subject of discussion held with her before had been about the role played by Larry Warren, but we could not understand why important additional details concerning conversations (albeit briefly) with Charles Halt, John Burroughs, Adrian Bustinza, Jim Penniston and others, over the three nights concerned, had never been brought to anybody's attention previously. 'Cookie' is on *Facebook* and is a fairly regular user. She has posted up comments to

people like John Burroughs (who is on her friends list), and many of her former Air Force colleagues, and yet, at no stage has she sought to tell them about what she witnessed – remembered with startling clarity now many years on. Is it possible that these memories were subconscious ones and have only just come to the surface, or is there another explanation? The reader should contrast her statement of events (shown on page 767) – relating to observations conducted in the middle of the night in an unlit area, when visibility was poor, with not even a flashlight to illuminate nearby surroundings, a short distance away from what was to become the topic of so much media interest (now 36 years later) – with the amount of personal information she divulged during that radio broadcast, a couple of days later, with Linda and John Burroughs, which now included seeing an object hovering in the sky, to then later being close enough to see Jim running his hands over the craft itself and background information to what took place over three nights running! I am sure the reader will understand why Charles Halt, Nick Pope, Jim Penniston and I, remain puzzled by this rapid turn of events! This was the first time we had any inkling of any meetings between 'Cookie' and the other airmen, whose testimonials have been previously outlined. Nobody had mentioned her role before. I also contacted Monroe Nevels, asking him if he remembered seeing 'Cookie', but from previous conversation held with him about his role and what he saw and who he saw, I do not believe this will be the case either.

KGRA Podcast – 'Cookie' speaks of what she witnessed on the 2nd night – *<u>a few minutes past midnight</u>* on the 26th December 1980. 'Cookie' identifies the location where the lights were seen by her as being along the service road to the *right* of East Gate, about 30 feet into the forest. It is of value to note that this appears to be the same position from where John Burroughs sighted the mystery 'lights', although his report of this phenomenon, radioed through to Lt. Buran, was made at <u>3am.</u> Sergeant Penniston and Edward Cabansag were asked to attend the scene. It is undoubtedly, according to 'Cookie', the same occurrence **<u>but took place some hours before,</u>** which may indicate that the 'lights' phenomenon was ongoing for at least three hours over the same locality – not unusual for UFO activity, or the fact that 'Cookie' also describes seeing US personnel, shouting and yelling, approximately 100 feet into the forest – again not a problem but problematical, because she now identifies Jim and John as being there (at that time), which will lead to all manner of speculative theories as to how this could have happened, including, no doubt, a theory of missing time.

It is important to scrutinise the questions put to 'Cookie' by Linda and John, in order to learn exactly the answers given by 'Cookie' with regard to who she says she saw, just off the perimeter road, close to the East Gate entrance. Conjecture and speculation is one thing, but hard facts are another. No doubt the reader will decide for themselves!

John Burroughs: *"I want you to describe to me what you were seeing and how many personnel you think were there – then we will go into the other details when you saw other people coming from a different direction."*

'Cookie' describes the reason for her being there at that time – (to pick up four security personal, and take them back to Woodbridge) – but says she only saw three, followed by: *"You guys kind of made up a perimeter around the 'lights' and I was looking at who I think was Jim and when I went back, you* [John Burroughs, presumably] *were just gone. There was more shouting and a few minutes later – not really great with time, but I think it was eight to ten minutes later – you were just there again."* **John Burroughs** asks 'Cookie' to confirm the location again, labouring the point that it wasn't out in the forest – to which she agrees. **Linda** asks 'Cookie': *"if you are seeing John Burroughs, and others, in a perimeter around a craft, and you were surprised that you said it was smaller than you expected."* **'Cookie':** *"We had all been to a party, **a few months earlier,** and this 'thing' was huge over the field where the farmhouse was and then someone said it went up into several craft, although I didn't personally see that, but what I saw then, at the edge of the woods, was something so small."* **Linda:** *"Was John Burroughs, and how many other men, in a circle around a round, smaller craft they are circling?"* **'Cookie':** *"I can only see two others; I never saw a fourth person at that time."* **Linda:** *"This could have been John Burroughs and Edward Cabansag and Jim Penniston?"'* **'Cookie':** *"Right."* Linda then asked John to confirm that this was the same place where, during the filming of *Ancient Aliens*, Jim was pointing up into the sky – to which he agrees.

John Burroughs: *"The crazy thing about is that it doesn't match our statements what I can remember. Anything and he [JP] had gone back over there [UK]. I guess when they did the sci-fi piece, took Colonel Halt and Vince Thurkettle to that area, it was kind of like one of those moments when I looked at him and what – there is no way that we heard what was going on. It was further down across the road and into the main forest and when she told me that when we got there, it was one of those low moments because Jim was adamant that's where we were."* **Linda** asks 'Cookie' if she will confirm the time and date as being, *"after midnight on the 26th December"* … to which, once

again, **'Cookie'** agrees, saying *"Yes M'aam – it was just about 5-8 minutes past midnight."* **Linda:** *"What I'm wondering, you may be one the keys to explain what has been so puzzling. Jim Penniston, John Burroughs and Edward Caban-sag went out into Rendlesham, but when we were there with 'Ancient Aliens', we were surprised at the distance that was one of the first [sites]? Then we ended up all the way over to Capel Green, in another part of the forest where Penniston thought that the whole encounter with the 'light' and the symbols took place and there is a huge distance between the two. Do you think that it is possible that you were seeing them at this location and that you literally saw John Burroughs 'pop in' and 'pop out.'"* **'Cookie':** *"He definitely disappeared and it wasn't a shimmer – a fade out – he was just there and he was gone."* **John** mentions another 'key point': *"Penniston was on the record earlier on and some other people where it happened, right after midnight. I always said it was around 3am – that's what I remembered when the statements released showed 0300. 'Cookie' remembers being out there just after midnight, and that's what Jim had said earlier, too; he was in the dining hall when he got called out to the gate. So both of those things support what Penniston says and goes against our statements."* **Linda:** *"'Cookie', we know that we are dealing with frequencies that can be emitted from these technologies that can manipulate minds, and you may be one of the only objective observers. Do you think it is possible (from what you remember) that this, a few minutes after midnight, was the beginning of something that went on all the way to sunrise?"'* **Cookie':** *"Yes I actually had the guys back, dropping them off at the motor pool by 3am; when they got checked out they were released by dawn. It was never a long drawn-out process – just a few hours."*

Linda: *"What do you supposed happened between those few minutes after midnight and 3am with John, Jim and Ed Cabansag?"* **'Cookie':** (sigh) *"It seems like it went a lot faster than it did, but I thought John was only gone for only two to fifteen minutes – was it longer and they stayed? – The lights were there. I never saw it. The question in my mind – it didn't look like it landed on the ground; it looked more like it was hovering. There were lights underneath and, as dark as it was, my flashlight would never work during these times. It wasn't dark, dark. It was only two hours before I took them back to the motor pool. It seems like it was so much longer; other times shorter."* **Linda:** *"Did you see them throughout the two hours?"'* **Cookie':** *"Yes."* **Linda:** *"I mean you can understand the discrepancy if all of this started near the East Gate, and yet Jim Penniston and John think that they ended up near Capel Green – we will call it the complex where Jim remembers the 'light' and dragging his fingers over the symbols. Could they have moved in those two* hours and you did not know, or are we talking about mental manipulation of you and them?" **'Cookie'**: **"Penniston kept putting his hand toward it and talking.** Of course I wasn't close enough. I couldn't hear what they were saying." **Linda**: "What kind of craft shape did you see? What was the shape and the colour and the size?" **'Cookie'**: "Kind of a triangular, footballer's type of thing – never like people keep saying about a dome. I never saw a dome; to me it had sharp angles – triangular to the point. How can I describe it? … Like when you're looking at the lacing on a football, that shape of it." **Linda**: "The colour?" **'Cookie'**: "Coppery, dark metallic colour." **Linda**: "Did you see lights?" **'Cookie'**: "Underneath and around." **Linda**: "Did they move?" **'Cookie'**: "One underneath seemed to rotate." **Linda**: "Penniston told me long ago, in 2009, in a vivid description on recording, that he was mesmerized by watching red, blue, and I believe white circular lights, moving underneath the skin of what he thought was dark, glassy material, but that these lights were moving underneath the surface." **'Cookie'**: "To me it was more metallic and I thought it was more like yellow, not white, but he was closer obviously." **Linda**: "What do you think right now – possibly explain two very different locations this far apart right outside the East Gate, and the other one right into the forest at Capel Green? How could both have been involved with these three guys, the 26th December 1980, between a little after midnight, and 3am?" **'Cookie'**: "Well, we already know there was more than one craft – so – and Jim was probably out there more than just the first night." **Linda**: "Well, John, you can see the discrepancy here. What do you think, because you and Jim went on behalf of 'C' Flight and it was 'D' Flight that came on at 11pm, on the 26th/27th?"

John: "Right, there is more to add to this. I think what I want to do is move forward from this point and then go into what happened afterwards and the next night and the third night and maybe we can get back if we have time. So Lindy, ('Cookie') you ended up, you were supposed to pick us up; you said, at one point, that you saw some others with red on us, on your bodies – as if the skin was burnt." **'Cookie'**: "When I tried to get close to your guys, I noticed I just felt prickly and a painful prickle up the backs of my hands, and my arms were red in the glow. When you guys started to finally wander out towards me, one of you was rubbing (arm?) the others were looking at your hand, cheeks, forehead – everything had like a sunburn look." **John**: "So then you took us back and why don't you describe what happened, because this happened the second night and the third night also." **'Cookie'**: "You didn't even try and get into the vehicle that was out there by mine. I greeted everybody but nobody was right at me; they were dazed and confused – everybody was just really weirded out. Nobody said anything but sat there; I dropped you off. One person came out of another truck.

He was wearing a white coat, looked at everybody, and looked at the communal sunburn areas – Jim's shoulders. Every time I picked up people and dropped them off that would happen." **John**: "That was your transfers back to Bentwaters to the motor pool, right?" **'Cookie'**: "Yes, I didn't take you guys to Woodbridge." **Linda**: "John, there is a discrepancy here. I'm trying to understand, even in your hypnosis, in 1988, you and Jim described being in a pick-up truck called the 'three pack', and driving out of the East Gate and taking a logging road, and you were in a truck and pulled up in some part of the forest that we were trying to find, when we were there in 'Ancient Aliens' production, so 'Cookie' wasn't involved in that scenario. How do you reconcile all of this?"

John: "Well, I think she was there – I actually think about in a weird sort of way that it could, because first of all do you remember Jim being in a jeep, and I always thought it was a truck?... now she remembers a jeep being out there, and the other thing is that Jim looked at that area and not to the area where we ended up, so I can't reconcile all of this yet, but what I can say is that a lot of what she described to me is what Jim remembered and the time even, and none of this has never been made public – not been talked about – so, yes, there is no doubt that there is a discrepancy, Linda, but at the same time what she did say was that this took over a two hour period. Did we end up going out further? I don't know, but the interesting thing was is that she supports a lot of what Penniston says."

Linda: "'Cookie' – this is so important, because do you think that you have a linear memory from beginning to end what happened – could your mind have been manipulated by John's, Jim's, or Edward Cabanasag?" **'Cookie'**: "I didn't ever want to think that, but when John and I were talking, said a couple of key phrases to him to begin his reaction, he did react and now, unfortunately, something has been done." **Linda**: "You all have been affected?" **'Cookie'**: "Correct."

THE SECOND NIGHT

John Burroughs: "You took people over the second night, right? You came out when Lt. Bonnie Tamplin and Sergeant Ball were out there, correct?" **'Cookie'**: "Right." **John Burroughs**: "Briefly, as we don't have a lot of time left, describe the scenario. What happened when you got out there and took them to the same place?" **'Cookie'**: "That night it was, I didn't even know I was going to be called. I was on a routine drop to 'Woody' and then I was told that something had come up and a couple of people needed my help. I believe I knew Bob Ball, but I don't know if I knew Lt. Bonnie Tamplin before that. He seemed fine. They were already at the side of the road. She [**Lt. Tamplin**] was horrible; it was really bad for her. She seemed like she was in shock. Her body was shaking – she was shivering, she was sweaty, her voice had gone from screaming so much – something had terrified her." **Linda:** *"Did she say anything about someone pulling a gun on her?"* **'Cookie':** *"I don't think I heard anything like that – she was just saying mainly, 'No, No, please stop – they're over there."* **Linda:** *"Did you interpret the 'they' to be extraterrestrials?"* **'Cookie':** I did, but I didn't know. Maybe they saw something (stuff?) from our own people to quieten them down and take care of the situation. I didn't know." **Linda:** *"…and Ball wasn't reacting at all?"* **Cookie':** *"Not like her. He was like everybody else – dazed, confused."* **Linda:** *"Where were you exactly when you picked them up?"'* **Cookie':** *"I was way much closer to Woodbridge."* **Linda:** *"Do you remember where?"'* **Cookie':** *"No, like I told John, people have tried to pinpoint me down to exact road names. I used to have journals with everything written down, but they got taken away long ago."*

THIRD NIGHT – COLONEL HALT

John asked 'Cookie' about the third night: *"You went back out there – that was the night **Colonel Halt** was out there and basically you met them again, including Colonel Halt. Were they transported also?"'* **Cookie':** *"Right. He seemed fine, you know, nobody else would ever really talk. He talked, telling everybody it was going to be fine – everything was going to be straightened out, bla bla bla. When I dropped him off, he seemed kind of surprised that they treated him like everybody and made him get in the truck, whatever."* **John:** *"Do you remember how many people were there? I think you said that I was out there as well, correct?"* **'Cookie':** *"Right."* **John:** *"Did you see anything else going on that night in the woods, or anything like that the second night?"* **'Cookie':** *"The first night was. I can see everything. The second – that's what surprised me – I didn't even feel anything was going on. The third night was more activity."*

John: *"Did you see anything the third night? What were you seeing?"* **'Cookie':** *"That night I never saw it close up or anything, but I could see the 'lights' moving around."*

John: *"Alright, but are you sure 100% that, all three nights, everybody involved were checked out? Was it medically? What did it look like was taking place?"* **'Cookie':** *"It looked like I said. There were other people in the truck, but the man in a white coat would step out and seemed really concerned – talking, comfortingly tapping people on the shoulders; it looked like they were going to take a medical."*

John: *"Any more questions? Unfortunately we are running out of time."* **Linda:** *"What I would really like to do, 'Cookie', is to – when we close out this show – I can talk to you on the phone. Will you stay on?"*

'Cookie': *"Sure."* **John:** *"'Cookie', right before we close the show tonight, I understand that Colonel Halt is coming out with a new book and from what I have been told you may be included in the book?"* **'Cookie':** *"That's what somebody said."* **John:** *"So you actually did do an interview with Colonel Halt and some of that ended up in his book?"* **'Cookie':** *"If that's what Old King Cole wants."* [Much laughter ensues.] **John:** *"I just want to tell you thanks for coming forward, like I told you earlier – like I told 'Doc Lore and Rick – where a bunch of us can get together in the summer, you really helped me understand a couple of things. Like I said, the craziest thing of all is most people were looking at Penniston like something was wrong, but what you remember and saw supports a lot of what he was saying so…* **End of interview** ['believed to be Dock Rhodes, Lori Ann Buoen (not Lori Rehfeldt) and Rick Bobo.]

CHARLES HALT – A RESPONSE

In an answer to a question posed by Tim Egercic about what happened after the event –

"I have no knowledge of meeting any young female airwoman in the forest during the night that I was out there, or knowledge of any female officer having been out there at any time over the three nights running, apart from the role which was played by Lt. Bonnie Tamplin. 'Cookie' worked in supply, delivering parts/material. We were not working, especially at night, due to the holidays, so she should not even have had access to a vehicle.

When I returned from the forest I went home and took a shower, had a small breakfast, couldn't sleep so I went to the office. It was Sunday morning. I ran into Gordon Williams at the entry way. Our offices were in the same building. We talked (he heard me on the radio in the forest, talking to the command post) and I played the tape and at his request gave him the tape. We were the only ones in the office. I did finally go home and rested, as it had been a trying night.

'Cookie' – my appraisal

Under the circumstances I now have to regard 'Cookie' with some suspicion as a potential OSI informant, and possibly working for the security services. I'm sorry but when someone makes allegations of this nature and involves conversation held with me on the night in question, this can only be construed as impugning my integrity. When 'they' found out she had a relationship with Warren they used her. Let's not forget she has admitted being subjected to drugs and hypnosis. They don't do that to informants unless they want something else. She has been silent for 35 years. But it appears she has now been directed to 'muddy the waters' by coming forward.

They thought they had this contained. I guess the Security personnel are worried about the book. 'Cookie' was definitely not out in the forest. The cops never used anyone other than cops to transport their members. Major Zickler, the Commander, wouldn't let anybody else get involved, even to go to the Colchester Firing Range when cops drove. When we had a panic recall, the cops drove the bus. She says she picked up cops and dropped them at the Bentwaters motor pool. Nobody went there. They all went back to the gate and picked up their weapons and on to the armoury. They knew that if they didn't turn in their weapons all hell would break loose. Can you believe a young female supply enlistee was allowed to wander into the woods at night, on three occasions? She can't even give me the name of the authorising officers that gave her permission. This is absurd! Nobody can corroborate her being there.I saw enough of our National Security Agency to know there is nothing they wouldn't stoop to do. They all thought they were James Bond."

Tim Egercic: *"I contacted Busty – Adrian Bustinza – about this matter; he got back to me and said <u>he remembered 'Crash' aka 'Cookie' but doesn't remember her out there</u>. He also included he doesn't remember how he got back to Bentwaters."*

[Adrian Bustinza was not mentioned in the podcast but referred to in the statement on page 767]

Nick Pope: *"So far as I'm aware, 'Cookie' was 81st Supply. Thus, it's difficult to argue with Chuck's observation that she wouldn't have been driving any of the cops around. Even if she had been, her statements imply she was pretty close to the action, and that's difficult to reconcile with the testimony of the other key witnesses, who don't mention her. Simply put, if she was close enough to see the things she describes, it's hard to understand how these witnesses wouldn't have seen her and mentioned her presence in their testimony – which they don't. This is particularly true of the USAF as it was in 1980, where females were hugely outnumbered by males. The presence of a female would, therefore, have been especially memorable."*

Jim Penniston, September 2016

"I deny any knowledge of any meeting in the forest either before or after with 'Cookie', or aware of her being there during what I witnessed. When my definitive book comes out it will tell things that were never known before and negates a whole lot of stuff you're referring to. The recent podcast (that I was sent a transcript of) by Linda Howe and John Burroughs is, in my opinion, pure entertainment and completely unreliable and misleading. I know what I saw and experienced - that's the facts. How can anyone just take on board information like this and disseminate without at least conducting some research into the claims made that aren't corroborated by anyone as far as I know is unbelievable journalism. John Burroughs remembers nothing about the incident. He is desperate for information and hoping someone can tell him something about what took place, now 36 years ago. This is why he eagerly snatches any opportunity to take on board information supplied to him, which can be seen under scrutiny to be a sham at best. I can believe nothing Burroughs says, especially in the last three years, since him being apparently bought and paid for.

Linda Howe, in my opinion, is a UFO entertainer and knows little about UFO research let alone what took place in Rendlesham Forest, Suffolk. If you are addressing issues over Warren, his girlfriend, or other non-witnesses, sorry but you are doing the Rendlesham Forest Incident no favor. It is perpetuating the misinformation and the containment story. John and Linda claim we were all messed with. This is simply not true in any sense. Secured evidence shows the opposite of this. Of course they did want to know what we knew and that is the extent of it. Zickler was a used source in containment, probably not known to him at the time – just like Colonel Halt was kept out of the loop on a couple things. As far as I know, by my observations following a meeting in 2009 with John, it is my strong opinion that something happened to him after leaving Bentwaters to 2009. He had a series of dubious hypnosis sessions done by UFO inspired people. It is also very apparent, after further research carried out, that John was 'messed with' through the years after from my research, somewhere in 1994-1995. I suspect by being involved in various indirect government sponsored hypnosis. An example of my postulation was Emenegger and Ward and their federal project and others sponsored by Bob Bigelow - owner of Bigelow Industries/Aerospace."

John mentioned Dr. Christopher Kit Green, who was involved with Bob Bigelow. In the 1970s, Dr Green was assigned to the CIA's effort to develop psychic spies to match alleged Soviet mental superpowers. He was the key forensic expert at the CIA during an investigation into covert assassination using a poison pellet shot from an umbrella. The story of Dr. Green's role in solving the 'umbrella assassination plot' was told in an episode of the PBS TV series 'Secrets of the Dead'.

UPDATE – SEPTEMBER 2016

IN addition to the highly offensive ADX podcast, there have been many others during recent years, in which the character of Charles Halt has been much impugned with all manner of derogatory, slanderous, comments made about his career and allegations forming part of a campaign of ongoing personal attacks by Larry Warren and Peter Robbins.

In another EDX 10 (East Dunbartonshire radio broadcast, aired on the 16.8.2015), Alyson Dunlop accuses the Colonel of misleading the audience at the conference in July 2015, during her support of the guest speaker – Peter Robbins, who also comments on what he perceives to be slanderous allegations made by Colonel Halt against his colleague – Larry Warren – at the same venue, with a tirade of very personal disproportionate comments made against the Colonel.

IN THE COLD LIGHT OF DAY!

Things took an unexpected twist when, very un-expectedly, Alyson – a stalwart of Larry and bastion of Scottish comfort for the support of Peter Robbins – made a statement of apology on the 18th August 2016, after the SPI Conference, which was made available on the internet. It shows, once again, the never-ending story about how loyalties can chop and change in a business which, indeed, seems more suited to some comic soap opera than based on any sense of fairness. Surely, if people are going to be 'attacked in the Court of social media', then they should be, at the very least, given the opportunity to defend themselves. Worse, this statement contains allegations of criminal activities against Larry Warren, which we are not prepared to include for obvious reasons. Innocent until proved guilty!

It is sad to have to include this further outburst, but history must record all of the pertinent facts. If Colonel Halt had berated himself on the internet and apologised profusely for his conduct, the media would have gleefully seized upon the opportunity. It is not about exposing Larry Warren, it is about showing the character of a man whose claims of what happened, so many years ago, are very much in question now.

ALYSON DUNLOP'S EDITED APOLOGY ON THE CONDUCT OF LARRY WARREN

"The reason Larry Warren was barred from attending the SPI conference was because he made an appalling comment which, although it did not directly threaten anyone in particular, was clearly still a threat of violence. It was certainly disgusting and completely unacceptable. I deleted the comment, and phoned Larry at home. I spoke with him for an hour at 2am. In my opinion, he seemed to be under the influence of something, and was raving for the most part about various things. I assessed the situation and decided that a conversation about his conduct would be pointless. Due to having the knowledge of the public fall out between Sacha Christie and Larry Warren, I panicked at the thought our conference would be disrupted by Ms Christie. Whatever question she had in mind, I felt it would be a bad idea for her to turn up. One comment led to another, and things did get heated. Everyone said things in the heat of the moment. At the time, I had no idea of the impact it would eventually have.

The intention was to diffuse the situation, although I can clearly see it did not read that way, and for that I would like to apologise. I have no personal grudge against Sacha Christie. In fact, I respect her intellect and exhaustive research. My focus throughout was the success of the conference. Following several phone calls with Mr Warren, I began to feel very differently about the decision to have him as a speaker at all. However, with only a few weeks to go, we had little choice but to keep moving forward. Furious though I was at Larry Warren's behaviour, I knew people wanted to hear him. As a conference organiser, my personal feelings and growing apprehension had to be put to one side.

Fuel was added to the fire when Larry Warren spoke out on my radio show, ADX-Files. This time, he actually named Sacha Christie as his antagonist. His conduct on the show was embarrassing, as he threw caution to the wind with harsh and boorish remarks. I asked the other organisers if they felt I should edit his comments out, but it was decided that no, it should be left as it was. He was entitled to his opinion. We did feel one particular statement should be edited out. Much has been made of Malcolm Robinson saying we talked for longer. We did. There was an issue with Skype – which listeners can briefly hear discussed. It meant that Larry Warren's very interesting account of his Bigfoot sighting was unusable. Every second word was omitted, making it completely distorted. This resulted in the recording of that section being unintelligible. It would have been incredibly annoying for the listener, who would not have been able to understand what was being said in any case.

The conference radio show, however, was disastrous. Glasgow University Union was informed of the comments made on SPI Scotland's Facebook page by Larry Warren. Several complaints were raised with them, and they immediately banned Mr Warren from being on their premises. This, I knew, was a major blow to our conference. However, I did secure the other union at the University of Glasgow, the Queen Margaret Union. Two days before the conference, Thursday 23rd June, we were informed that they too had decided to ban Larry Warren from attending the conference. Larry was immediately informed. There was absolutely nothing more we could do to ensure that he was a speaker. The QMU and the university were, in my opinion, well within their rights to ban him as it affected their reputation as much as it did ours. At that point; the only focus had to be that the conference went ahead. We had invested not just time, but an enormous amount of money. Speakers' travel expenses were about £1000 alone, hotel bills of approximately £550 and the venue hire of £300. On top of these expenses, the QMU insisted, due to the violent nature of the threats made by Larry Warren on social media, that we pay a further £450 for university security.

Strangely, Larry Warren decided that even although he was banned from attending the conference, he would still travel up to Glasgow on the Friday night and partake of our hospitality. As we were not responsible for him being banned, and we could not cancel the first night's accommodation in any case, we agreed. We had hoped that, although disappointed, he might speak with conference attendees afterwards in a more informal setting. His response to this suggestion was "Fuck that!" and he abruptly ended our telephone conversation. On arriving in Glasgow, Larry and his friends proceeded to give us the cold shoulder. He made an excuse to leave my company twice when I approached him. I did not attempt a third time. On the morning of the conference, I was surprised again to see Mr Warren in the car that came to pick me up (along with 100 of his books which had been lying in my flat for several weeks). He seemed more amiable, and helped to take books up to the front step of the QMU, loudly voicing how disgusted he felt at the way he had been treated. Leaving his co-author with only six copies of Left at East Gate, he returned with his friends to his hotel room and filmed something which could be presented to the audience before Peter Robbins' talk, who was our final speaker of the day.

The conference was a great success. Larry Warren refused to join myself or the other organisers, nor did he invite us to join his company, although he did invite some people to join him for drinks. Having been in his corner for so long, we were extremely hurt that he seemed to have turned on us. We were also bemused that we were being treated this way, especially when we were footing the bill for his bed and breakfast for three nights. He left on the Sunday morning, having barely spoken to myself, Malcolm, or Ron. We had to therefore also pay the hotel bill for a night that was not used.

On the Monday, I was even more astonished to be added to a private Facebook conversation along with Larry Warren, Peter Robbins, and the other organisers. For some reason Tino Megaro had included Sue McAllister, Ben Emlyn-Jones and Gary Heseltine in the conversation. I have no idea what any of the events actually had to do with those three people, or in fact with Mr Megaro. Again, I was bemused. The gist of the thread was how we could "Move forward" as a united front against Sacha Christie's attacks. Ms McAllister pointedly commented that she believed the conference organisers had "allowed" Larry to be banned, and had not tried hard enough to ensure that he got to speak. At this point, I had heard quite enough. I stated, as I will state now, that I wanted nothing more to do with any of them. My words were not so polite, I must admit.

I have since seen Larry using the same terminology that the organisers "allowed" him to be banned and did not try hard enough. I have read his derogatory comments about the University of Glasgow, and even that he was proud to have been banned by them. He should not be proud. He should be ashamed. Not once has he, or his "team" ever addressed the real issue: that Mr Warren threatened Sacha Christie by stating in writing that he would "put your windpipe through your spine" and "your life will end", both expressions being extremely disgusting and frightening terminology to use. However, it is my understanding that it is not the first time that Mr Warren has used such threats. On another occasion, he told Ms Christie that she was "so fucked" and that she "best move". I truly wish there had been some way of removing myself from the whole sorry saga before it escalated as it did. I have said to my closest confidantes that I completely understand Ms Christie's anger. I do. Absolutely. I had to make

a decision with no time to spare. My priority had nothing to do with my own personal views. My priority was purely with the success of the conference. There was far too much as stake, not just financially, but for those who had booked flights and hotels in Glasgow. I was aware that many people were coming from all over the UK and Europe. I apologise sincerely that Ms Christie was treated the way she was. I also apologise if she felt bullied by the organisers. The comments that were made in the heat of the moment were unprofessional, regardless of the circumstances.

Many people have become increasingly baffled by what Larry Warren does and says. I have not been in contact with him since the conference, although I have been in contact with Peter Robbins who remains a friend. In my personal opinion, Mr Warren's behaviour and conduct has become increasingly absurd and openly arrogant when he finds it acceptable to pretend to inexplicably forget the name of SPI Scotland, as he apparently did on Ben Emlyn-Jones' HPANWO radio show: Larry Warren Speaks. It was reminiscent of Colonel Halt who pretended to forget the name of Left at East Gate last year during a walk in Rendlesham Forest. In the last few days, Mr Warren has taken the decision to unfriend me on Face book, along with several people who are friends of mine, for what reason we do not know. I am not particularly bothered by this, as I am indifferent to what Mr Warren does and does not do. His conduct before, during, and after the conference showed what kind of man he actually is. I do feel sorry for those he has also recently unfriended who considered themselves to be his friends, fans, or just interested researchers. However, I am not sure if I would want to be associated with someone who makes, seemingly, uncontrolled and unfiltered threats on social media. After reading this, I know there will be tears. You **no doubt invested a lot of energy and most importantly your trust in this one symbol of truth**. To find out that he is far from that ideal is shattering. **To learn that your hero is actually nothing more than what I would describe as a con-man,** I know, is devastating. What else can we conclude, given the evidence? I will always respect the 18 year-old who witnessed the Rendlesham UFO, as Adrian Bustinza confirms. I will always respect the 21 year-old who told the world about it. Sadly, I have lost all respect for the man he became."

ALYSON DUNLOP – Glasgow – 18th August 2016

MAIN INDEX

USA SERVICEMEN ACCOUNTS AND OTHER SOURCES

THE HALT PERSPECTIVE

SECONDARY INDEX

CIVILIAN ACCOUNTS

CREDITS

Page 174 – UFO sketch
  ©John Burroughs
Page 174 – UFO illustration ©Wayne
  Mason
Page 175 – report ©Edward Cabansag
Page 177,183 – photo/sketches
  ©Jim Penniston
Page 179 – UFO illustration
  ©Wayne Mason
Page 184 – sketch ©Brenda Butler
Page 189, 192 – letter ©David King
Page 193 – photo ©Georgina Bruni
Page 195, 196 – photo ©Charles Halt
Page 201 – photo ©Gavin Harold
Page 203 – photo ©Gerry Harris
Page 206 – photo ©Mike Bromley
Page 207 – photo ©Sean Tierney
Page 208, 211 – photos & UFO
  Illustration ©Lori Bouen
Page 212 –photo Major Malcolm Zickler
  ©Not established
Page 214 – photo ©John Hanson
Page 218 – photo ©Tony Brisciano
Page 219 – photo of Halt and Nevels
  ©Source unidentified
Page 220 –E-mail ©Charles Halt
Page 223 – photo ©Source not
  established
Page 225 – UFO sketch ©Artist 'Modo'
Page 227 – photo ©John Hanson
Page 228 – www.Internet
  ©Not established
Page 229 – UFO sketch ©Jim Penniston
Page 230 – sketch ©Artist 'Modo'
Page 231, 232, 238 – photos
  ©John Hanson
Page 243, 244 – UFO sketches
  ©Steve Franklin
Page 250, 251 – ©www.Internet
Page 254 – UFO illustration
  ©Wayne Mason
Page 257 – photo ©John Hanson
Page 257 – photo ©Anne Hopton-Scott
Page 259 – photo ©John Hanson
Page 261, 262 – UFO art ©Peter Parish
Page 263 – photo ©John Hanson
Page 265, 268 – photos ©John Hanson &
  Brenda Butler
Page 269 – photo ©Dawn Holloway
Page 270, 271 – photos ©John Hanson
Page 273 – UFO artwork ©David Sankey
Page 274, 275 – www. Internet
  ©Art Wallace/Larry Warren

Page 276 – photo ©John Hanson
Page 277 – photo ©Mary Zimmerman
Page 279 – photo ©John Hanson
Page 280 – photo ©John Traylor
Page 281 – photos ©John Hanson
Page 283 – photo ©www. Internet
Page 284, 286 – ©Brenda Butler
Page 288 – letter ©John Hanson
Page 289, 291 – UFO report /photos
  ©Brenda Butler/Harry Harris
Page 292 – photo ©Barry Greenwood
Page 293 – photo ©John Alexander
Page 294, 295 – photos ©Steve Wagner
Page 295 – photo ©John Hanson
Page 296 – photo ©Brenda Butler
Page 297 – photo ©John Hanson
Page 298 – photo ©confidential source
Page 299 – photo ©Philip Mantle
Page 301 – photo ©Brenda Butler
Page 302, 303 – UFO report ©Ron West
Page 305, 306 – sketch ©Major Everett
  (pseudonym)
Page 307 – photo ©Steve La Plume
Page 309 – photo ©Donald Moreland
Page 311, 312 – letter ©Dorothy Street
Page 313 – photo ©John Hanson
Page 314 – UFO report ©Ron West
Page 311 – E-mail ©John Hanson
Page 316 – UFO report ©Ron West
Page 322 – ©www.Internet
Page 324 – photo ©Tom Potter
Page 325 – ©Star 27th October 1967
Page 325 – photo ©Elizabeth Bushby
Page 326 – photos ©John Hanson
Page 327 – UFO illustration
  ©Steven Franklin
Page 330 – UFO illustration
  ©David Sankey
Page 333 – UFO sketch ©Ron West
Page 334, 336 – photos ©John Hanson
Page 335 – UFO report ©Ron West
Page 339, 340 – photos ©John Hanson
Page 338 – UFO illustration
  ©Steven Franklin
Page 344 – photos ©Ivan Potter
Page 346, 347 – ©www.Internet
Page 348 – photo ©Claire Tolliday
Page 349,350,351 – photos
  ©John Hanson
Page 351 – ©www.Internet
353, 355 – photos ©Martin Ship
  (SCUFORI)

Page 356 – photos ©Dawn Holloway
Page 356 – UFO sketch ©not known
Page 360 – photo ©Brenda Butler
Page 361 – photo ©Jim Penniston
Page 363, 365 – photos ©www.Internet
Page 376, 377 – sketches
  ©Ros Reynolds-Parnham
Page 382 – photo ©Angela Snook
Page 383 – photo ©www.Internet
Page 385 –photo ©www. Internet
Page 387 – letter ©Brenda Butler
Page 389, 390 – photo ©www.Internet
Page 399 – photo ©David Feast
Page 401 – ©News of the World
Page 402 – ©The Times
Page 403 – photo ©Ian Ridpath
Page 407 – photo ©UFO Magazine (US)
Page 408, 409 – photos
  ©Thomas W. Wharton
Page 411 – photo ©www.Internet
Page 414 – photo ©Terry Bishop
Page 416, 417, 419 – photos
  ©Terry Hooper-Scharf
Page 417 – UFO photo ©James Rose
Page 422 – UFO Illustration
  ©Steven Franklin
Page 422 – photos ©Brett Lynes
Page 424 – photo ©Charles Halt
Page 426 – photo ©Ray Bouche
Page 427 – ©www.Internet
Page 429 – ©not known
Page 430 – photo ©Brenda Butler
Page 431, 432 – photos ©John Hanson
Page 433 – photo simulation
  ©John Hanson
Page 437 – photo ©Gordon Creighton
Page 437 – photo ©Omar Fowler
Page 444, 445 – photos ©Robert Salas
Page 451, 452 photos ©James Hudnall
Page 455 – photo ©John Hanson
Page 455 – artwork ©Wayne Mason
Page 458, 461 –photos ©Mitch Fryman
Page 462 – front cover of FSR
  ©Gordon Creighton
Page 463 – photo (left) ©John Hanson
Page 463 – photo (right) ©Brenda Butler
Page 464 – front cover sketch
  ©Chris Pennington
Page 466, 467 – photo & sketch
  ©Mike Sacks
Page 468, 469 ©Ron West
Page 470 – photo ©not known

THE HALT PERSPECTIVE

The original volumes 1 to 6 of *Haunted Skies* are unavailable. However, these books are being revised and updated – the first new volume of this updated series is now available.

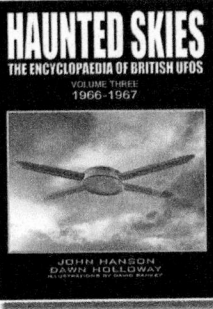

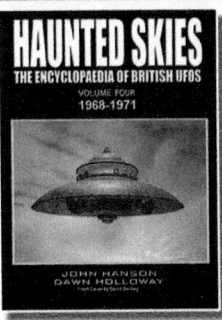

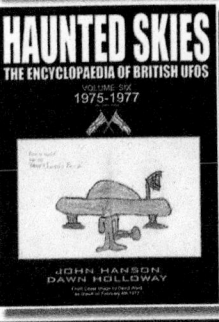

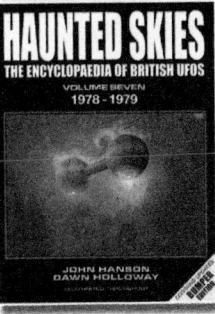

DISCLAIMER

Should we have inadvertently missed anybody, we unreservedly apologize and will credit the copyright in *Haunted Skies*; Volume 12. Special thanks go to Robert Townshend, Steven Franklin, David Sankey, Wayne Mason, Bob Tibbitts, and to Dawn Holloway for proof reading the book. Also thanks to many others that have contributed over the years. All statements made by the people involved are opinions expressed by them and should be treated as such. The publisher and the co-author Colonel Charles Halt do not accept liability or responsibly for statements made by the participants involved. All rights are reserved; this book or parts thereof may not be reproduced in any form, stored in any retrieval system or transmitted in any form by any means-electronic, mechanical, photocopy or otherwise, without permission from the publisher or Colonel Charles Halt.

These books have cost us a great deal of money to produce, but we strongly believe that this information forms part of our social history and rightful heritage. It should therefore be preserved, despite the ridicule still aimed at the subject by the media. *All previous titles – pictured above – are currently available.*

If anyone is willing to assist us with the preparation of any illustrations, it would be much appreciated. We can be contacted by letter at **31, Red Lion St, Alvechurch, Worcestershire B48 7LG**, by telephone **0121 445 0340**, or email: **johndawn1@sky.com**

CPSIA information can be obtained
www.ICGtesting.com
ted in the USA
W07s2334221116
597BV00011B/4/P

...*to reality*

If the Nautilus™ is a dream, here is the reality. B&W's Nautilus™801, flagship of a stunning new range, fuses the innovative Nautilus™ tube technology with a series of industry firsts: Fixed Suspension Transducer™, Kevlar® drive units, Matrix® cabinet bracing and Flowport™ technology. The result is an unprecedented purity of sound. The reason EMI's Abbey Road studios, along with the biggest and best in the recording industry, are now upgrading to the Nautilus™801. Listen and you'll see – at your nearest authorised Nautilus™ 800 Series dealer. For more information please contact B&W: 01903 750 750 or visit our website http://www.bwspeakers.com

LISTEN AND YOU'LL SEE

Alan Parsons is highly regarded in the recording industry. Principal engineer on Pink Floyd's 'Dark Side of the Moon', and producer of Al Stewart's 'Year of the Cat', Alan has worked with Paul McCartney, and has ten Grammy award nominations to his name. Himself a dedicated musician (The Alan Parsons Project), the former chief recording engineer at EMI's Abbey Road Studios says of the new loudspeakers: "The Nautilus™800 Series will undoubtedly make a major impact on the professional recording world, and influence loudspeaker technology well into the next millennium."

B&W

LISTEN AND YOU'LL SEE

Sir John Eliot Gardiner, Composer

B&W Nautilus™ 802

Luz Vargas is a noted
Colombian architect who
now lives in London's
Notting Hill. Music is
as much a part of
her background as her
chosen profession; and
Luz understands the
importance of combining
design aesthetics with
musical performance.
Her choice is the
Nautilus™805 – the
perfect mix of
sculptural elegance
and audio power.

B&W

LISTEN AND YOU'LL SEE

Luz Vargas, Architect

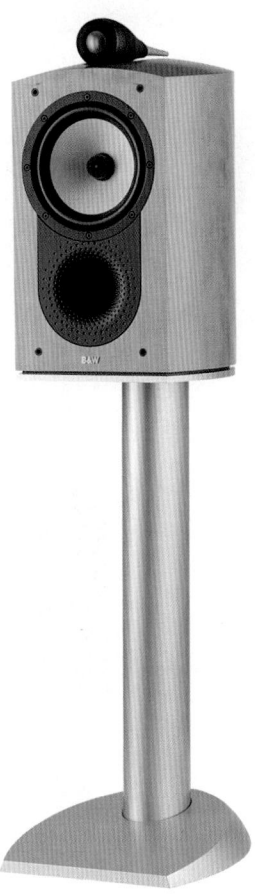

B&W Nautilus™805

Nautilus™ 800 Series

Nautilus™ 801

A new benchmark in loudspeaker design, the Nautilus™801 features B&W's radical Nautilus technology for tweeter and mid-range drivers. This professional studio monitor unleashes a titanic power, whilst retaining all the subtle dynamics so vital to the world's best recordings.

Nautilus™ 802

The Nautilus™802 offers all the virtues of B&W's flagship Nautilus™801 in a slimmer, curved cabinet. Performance is beyond question, delivering audio response that is as pure as it is powerful.

Nautilus™ 803

A floorstander that will grace any home with its purposeful beauty. Featuring Nautilus tweeter technology, the Nautilus™803 produces a class leading purity of sound which makes it ideal for any audiophile set-up or high-end surround sound.

Nautilus™ 805

Beautifully crafted and engineered to the same audiophile standards as the rest of the range, the Nautilus™805 is a compact monitor that will enhance any hi-fi or surround sound system. It can easily be used on a bookshelf or on the optional stand featured.

For more information contact
B&W Loudspeakers (UK) Ltd on: 01903 750 750
or visit our website http://www.bwspeakers.com

B&W

LISTEN AND YOU'LL SEE

Gramophone
Classical
GOOD CD GUIDE
1999

Gramophone magazine, founded by the novelist and writer Compton Mackenzie and the broadcaster Christopher Stone, has been published monthly since 1923. As one of the first magazines devoted to the discussion of recorded music, *Gramophone* has maintained its position as the most informed and influential publication of its kind. Calling on the wealth of talent of a panel of the world's leading writers on music, *Gramophone* is the record collector's bible and it is from these writers and in the tradition of *Gramophone* that this book is published. Each month the magazine carries over 200 reviews of music across a wide spectrum and talks to the leading performers of the day. We are once again delighted to be publishing the **Good CD Guide** in association with a fellow British company, B&W Loudspeakers, whose dedication to producing fine loudspeakers closely matches the ideals of *Gramophone* itself: expertise drawing on experience, consistency and an awareness of the requirements of the consumer.

Published by

**Gramophone Publications Limited,
135 Greenford Road,
Sudbury Hill, Harrow,
Middlesex HA1 3YD,
Great Britain.**

© **Gramophone Publications Limited 1998**

UK ISBN 1-902274-02-4

US ISBN 1-902274-03-2

Recording companies reserve the right to withdraw any Compact Disc without giving prior notice, and although every effort is made to obtain the latest information for inclusion in this book, no guarantee can be given that all the discs listed are immediately available. Any difficulties should be referred to the issuing company concerned. When ordering, purchasers are advised to quote all the relevant information in addition to the disc numbers. The publishers cannot accept responsibility for the consequences of any error.

Sales and distribution

North America	**Music Sales Corporation**
	257 Park Avenue South,
	New York, NY 10010, USA
	Telephone (212) 254 2100
	Fax (212) 254 2013
Record Trade (excluding North America)	**Gramophone Publications Limited**
	135 Greenford Road,
	Sudbury Hill, Harrow,
	Middlesex HA1 3YD, Great Britain
	Telephone +44 (0)181-422 4562
	Fax +44 (0)181-869 8404
UK and Rest of World Book Trade	**Music Sales**
	8/9 Frith Street,
	London W1V 5TZ, Great Britain
	Telephone +44 (0)171-434 0066
	Fax +44 (0)171-734 2246

Editorial Director	**Christopher Pollard**
Editor	**Máire Taylor**
Editorial Assistants	**Alex Newby** **Mark Walker**
Production	**Dermot Jones**

Contributors

Andrew Achenbach • **Nicholas Anderson**
Mary Berry • **Alan Blyth** • **Joan Chissell**
Robert Cowan • **Peter Dickinson**
John Duarte • **Adrian Edwards**
Richard Fairman • **David Fallows**
David Fanning • **Iain Fenlon**
Hilary Finch • **Fabrice Fitch**
Jonathan Freeman-Attwood
Edward Greenfield • **David Gutman**
Stephen Johnson • **Lindsay Kemp**
Tess Knighton • **Andrew Lamb**
Robert Layton • **Ivan March** • **Ivan Moody**
Bryce Morrison • **David Nice**
Patrick O'Connor • **Michael Oliver**
Richard Osborne • **Stephen Plaistow**
Nicholas Rast • **Guy Rickards**
Marc Rochester • **Julie-Anne Sadie**
Stanley Sadie • **Lionel Salter**
Alan Sanders • **Edward Seckerson**
Robert Seeley • **John Steane**
Michael Stewart • **Jonathan Swain**
John Warrack • **Arnold Whittall**
Richard Wigmore

Cover illustration Richard Jenkins
Printed in England by William Clowes Limited,
Beccles, Suffolk, NR34 9QE

Contents

Suggested Basic Library

Albéniz
Iberia
Allegri
Miserere
Bach
Brandenburg Concertos
Cantatas Nos. 78, 82, 140, 147
Goldberg Variations
Mass in B minor
St Matthew Passion
Toccata and Fugue in D minor (organ)
Violin Concertos
Barber
Adagio for Strings
Bartók
Concerto for Orchestra
Piano Concertos Nos. 1-3
Violin Concertos Nos. 1 and 2
Beethoven
Fidelio
Missa solemnis
Piano Concertos Nos. 1-5
Piano Sonatas Nos. 8, "Pathétique",
  14, "Moonlight", 21, "Waldstein"
  and 23, "Appassionata"
Piano Trio No. 7, "Archduke"
Symphonies Nos. 1-9
33 Variations on a Waltz by Diabelli
Violin Concerto
Violin Sonatas Nos. 5 and 9
Berg
Three Orchestral Pieces
Violin Concerto
Berlioz
Grand messe des morts
Symphonie fantastique
Les nuits d'été
Bernstein
West Side Story
Bizet
L'Arlésienne – Concert Suites Nos. 1 and 2
Carmen
Symphony in C major
Borodin
Prince Igor – Polovtsian Dances
Brahms
Clarinet Quintet
Ein deutsches Requiem
Hungarian Dances
Piano Concertos Nos. 1 and 2
Piano Quintet
Symphonies Nos. 1-4
Variations on a Theme by Haydn,
  "St Antoni Chorale"
28 Variations on a Theme by Paganini
Violin Concerto
Britten
Les illuminations
Peter Grimes – Four Sea Interludes
Serenade for Tenor, Horn and Strings
War Requiem
The Young Person's Guide to the Orchestra
Bruch
Violin Concerto No. 1

Bruckner
Symphonies Nos. 3, 4, 5, 8 and 9

Byrd
Mass for four voices
Mass for five voices
Canteloube
Chants d'Auvergne
Chabrier
España
Chopin
Piano Concertos Nos. 1 and 2
Piano Sonatas Nos. 2 and 3
Various Solo Piano Works
Copland
Appalachian Spring
Rodeo – Four Dance Episodes
Debussy
Images
La mer
Nocturnes
Piano Préludes
Prélude à l'après-midi d'un faune
String Quartet
Delibes
Coppélia
Delius
Brigg Fair
In a summer garden
On hearing the first cuckoo in Spring
Sea Drift
A Village Romeo and Juliet – Walk to the
  Paradise Garden
Dohnányi
Variations on a Nursery Theme
Donizetti
L'elisir d'amore
Lucia di Lammermoor
Dowland
Various Solo Lute Works
Dukas
Sorcerer's Apprentice
Dvořák
Cello Concerto
Piano Quintet
Piano Trio No. 4, "Dumky"
Serenade for Strings
Slavonic Dances
String Quartet No. 12, "American"
Symphonies Nos. 7, 8 and 9, "From
  the New World"
Elgar
Cello Concerto
The Dream of Gerontius
Introduction and Allegro for Strings
Pomp and Circumstance Marches
Symphonies Nos. 1 and 2
Variations on an Original Theme, "Enigma"
Violin Concerto
Falla
Noches en los jardines de España
El sombrero de tres picos
Fauré
Requiem
Franck
Symphonic Variations
Symphony in D minor
Gershwin
An American in Paris
Piano Concerto

Porgy and Bess
Rhapsody in Blue
Glazunov
Violin Concerto
Glinka
Ruslan and Ludmilla – Overture
Górecki
Symphony No. 3
Gounod
Faust
Grieg
Holberg Suite
Peer Gynt
Piano Concerto
Handel
Concerti grossi, Opp. 3 and 6
Messiah
Music for the Royal Fireworks
Organ Concertos, Opp. 4 and 7
Water Music
Haydn
Cello Concerto in C major
Die Schöpfung
String Quartets, Opp. 20, 33 and 76
Symphonies Nos. 94, "Surprise", 100,
   "Military", 101, "Clock", 103, "Drumroll"
   and 104, "London"
Holst
The Planets
Janáček
The Cunning Little Vixen
Glagolitic Mass
Sinfonietta
Kodály
Háry János – suite
Lalo
Symphonie espagnole
Lehár
Die Lustige Witwe
Leoncavallo
Pagliacci
Liszt
Piano Concertos Nos. 1 and 2
Piano Sonata in B minor
Les Préludes
Various Solo Piano Works
Mahler
Kindertotenlieder
Das Lied von der Erde
Symphonies Nos. 1, 4, 5, 8, "Symphony
   of a Thousand" and 9
Mascagni
Cavalleria Rusticana
Massenet
Werther
Mendelssohn
A Midsummer Night's Dream – incidental
   music
Octet
Symphonies Nos. 3, "Scottish", 4, "Italian"
   and 5, "Reformation"
Violin Concerto in E minor
Monteverdi
Vespers of 1610
Mozart
Clarinet Concerto
Clarinet Quintet
Così fan tutte
Don Giovanni
Eine kleine Nachtmusik
Horn Concertos Nos. 1-4
Le nozze di Figaro
Piano Concertos, Nos. 14, 20, 21,

"Elvira Madigan", 22, 24, 25 and 27
Requiem
Serenade No. 10, "Gran Partita"
Sinfonia concertante for violin and viola
Symphonies Nos. 29, 35, "Haffner",
   36, "Linz", 38, "Prague", 39, 40
   and 41, "Jupiter"
Violin Concertos Nos. 1-5
Die Zauberflöte
Mussorgsky
A Night on the Bare Mountain
Pictures at an Exhibition
Orff
Carmina burana
Pachelbel
Canon and Gigue
Paganini
Violin Concerto No. 1
Prokofiev
Lieutenant Kijé – suite
Peter and the Wolf
Piano Concerto No. 3
Romeo and Juliet
Symphonies Nos. 1, "Classical" and 5
Violin Concertos Nos. 1 and 2
Puccini
La bohème
Madama Butterfly
Tosca
Turandot
Purcell
Dido and Aeneas
Rachmaninov
Piano Concertos Nos. 2 and 3
Rhapsody on a theme of Paganini
Symphony No. 2
Ravel
Boléro
Daphnis et Chloé
Gaspard de la nuit
Piano Concerto in G major
Shéhérazade
La valse
Respighi
Fountains of Rome
Pines of Rome
Roman Festivals
Rimsky-Korsakov
Scheherezade
Rodrigo
Concierto de Aranjuez
Rossini
Il barbiere di Siviglia
La Cenerentola
Overtures
Stabat mater
Saint-Saëns
Carnaval des animaux
Piano Concerto No. 2
Symphony No. 3, "Organ"
Satie
Gymnopédies
Schoenberg
Chamber Symphonies Nos. 1 and 2
Verklärte Nacht
Schubert
Impromptus
Octet
Piano Quintet, "Trout"
Piano Sonata No. 21
Die schöne Mullerin
String Quartet No. 14, "Death and the
   Maiden"

String Quintet
Symphonies Nos. 3, 5, 8, "Unfinished"
  and 9, "Great"
Wanderer Fantasy
Winterreise
Schumann
Cello Concerto
Dichterliebe
Frauenliebe und -leben
Kinderszenen
Piano Concerto
Piano Fantasie in C major
Symphonies Nos. 1-4
Shostakovich
Piano Concerto No. 2
Symphonies Nos. 5 and 10
Sibelius
Finlandia
Karelia Suite
Swan of Tuonela
Symphonies Nos. 1, 2 and 5
Valse triste
Violin Concerto
Smetana
Má vlast
J. Strauss II
Die Fledermaus
Various Waltzes, Polkas and Overtures
R. Strauss
Also sprach Zarathustra
Don Juan
Four Last Songs
Ein Heldenleben
Metamorphosen
Der Rosenkavalier
Till Eulenspiegels lustige Streiche
Stravinsky
The Firebird
Petrushka
The Rite of Spring
Symphony of Psalms
Tchaikovsky
1812 Overture

Capriccio italien
The Nutcracker
Piano Concerto No. 1
Romeo and Juliet – fantasy overture
Serenade in C major
Sleeping Beauty – ballet suite
Swan Lake
Symphonies Nos. 4, 5 and 6, "Pathétique"
Violin Concerto
Tippett
A Child of our Time
Piano Concerto
Symphony No. 2
Vaughan Williams
The Lark Ascending
Serenade to Music
Symphonies Nos. 2, "A London Symphony",
  4 and 6
The Wasps – Overture
Verdi
Aida
Falstaff
Otello
Requiem
Rigoletto
La traviata
Il trovatore
Vivaldi
Concerti grossi, "L'estro armonico"
Gloria
Violin Concertos, "The Four Seasons"
Wagner
Parsifal
The Ring – Die Walküre
Siegfried Idyll
Tristan und Isolde
Walton
Belshazzar's Feast
Façade – Suites
Viola Concerto

Using the Guide

The presentation and design of this Guide is similar to that of its parent publication, *Gramophone*. Reviews of works generally appear in the following sequence: Orchestral, Chamber, Instrumental, Choral and Operatic (for ease of use, operas appear in alphabetical, as opposed to chronological, order). The rating system – one, two or three ⊕s – is applied to releases which the reviewers consider to be recordings of particular distinction, having attained or deserving to attain classic status. As with previous editions, works which merit attention but not, perhaps, a full review, are provided under "Suggested listening" and "Further listening" (both of which categories appear in the sequence outlined above). The original *Gramophone* review date is provided for readers who might wish to investigate further. Generally, where more than three composers are represented on a single disc, if it receives a full review this appears in the Collections section which starts on page 1087 and the reader is referred to the Index. The Index to Artists applies only to those represented by full reviews.

Although every effort is made to obtain the latest information for inclusion in this book, no guarantee can be given that all the discs listed are immediately available. We have experienced particular difficulty this year in obtaining deletions lists from record companies. Any queries concerning availability should be referred to the issuing company concerned. When ordering, purchasers are advised to quote all the relevant information in addition to the disc numbers.

The title for each review contains the following information: Composer(s), work(s), artist(s), record company or label, price range and disc number. The text within the brackets indicates the number of discs (if there is more than one), timing, mode of recording and the original review date in *Gramophone*. Period-instrument performances are highlighted by the use of a symbol. If the issue under review is a reissue, details are given of its provenance. Recording dates are also provided, when available.

Key to symbols

Ⓕ   Full price £10 and over
Ⓑ   Bargain price £5 – £6·99

Ⓜ   Medium price £7 – £9·99
Ⓢ   Super bargain price £4·99 and below

AAD/ADD/DDD denote analogue or digital stages in the recording/editing or mixing/mastering or transcription processes in CD manufacture.

🖋   Recordings where period instruments are used.

*   Where this appears after a disc number, it is an indication that the recording quality may not be up to the highest standards. This generally applies to pre-1960 recordings.

Some titles also highlight the following information:

Gramophone *Classical 100* – a selection of the 100 greatest classical recordings of all time which have become corner-stones of the catalogue. This features some of the leading names in classical music this century, including Furtwängler, Karajan, Solti, Beecham, Heifetz and Callas.

Gramophone *Award winner* – Award winners from 1977 to 1997.

Gramophone *Editor's choice* – in every issue of *Gramophone* ten outstanding discs are selected from the month's reviews.

Selected by Soundings/Sounds in retrospect – *Gramophone*'s listening panel appraises recordings from the technical standpoint and singles out those which are notable for their particularly excellent sound quality (from January 1996 this panel selection became known as *Soundings*).

Abbreviations

aas	all available separately	**mez**	mezzo-soprano
alto	countertenor/male alto	**mndl**	mandolin
anon.	anonymous	**narr**	narrator
arr	arranged	**oas**	only available separately
attrib.	attributed	**ob**	oboe
b	born	**Op.**	opus
bar	baritone	**orig.**	original
bass-bar	bass-baritone	**org**	organ
bn	bassoon	**perc**	percussion
c	circa (about)	**pf**	piano
cl	clarinet	**picc**	piccolo
clav	clavichord	**pub.**	publisher/published
cont	continuo	**rec**	recorder
contr	contralto	**rev.**	revised
cor ang	cor anglais	**sax**	saxophone
cpsr	composer	**sngr**	singer
cpte(d)	complete(d)	**sop**	soprano
d	died	**spkr**	speaker
db	double bass	**stg**	string
dig pf	digital piano	**synth**	synthesizer
dir	director	**tbn**	trombone
ed.	edited (by)/edition	**ten**	tenor
exc	excerpt	**timp**	timpani
fl	flute	**tpt**	trumpet
fl	flourished	**trad.**	traditional
fp	fortepiano	**trans.**	transcribed
gtr	guitar	**treb**	treble
harm	harmonium	**va**	viola
hn	horn	**va da gamba**	viola da gamba
hp	harp	**vars.**	variations
hpd	harpsichord	**vc**	cello
keybd	keyboard	**vib**	vibraphone
lte	lute	**vn**	violin

The Reviews

Alan Abbott
British 1926

Suggested listening ...
...*Alla caccia. Coupled with works by various composers.* **David Pyatt** (hn); **Martin Jones** (pf).
Erato 3984-21632-2 (4/98). *See review in the Collections section; refer to the Index.*

Carl Friedrich Abel
German/British 1723-1787

Suggested listening ...
...String Quartet in A major, Op. 8 No. 5. *Coupled with works by various composers.*
Salomon Quartet. Hyperion CDA66780 (3/96). *See review in the Collections section; refer to the Index.*

Lora Aborn
American 1907

Suggested listening ...
...'Tis Winter now. Shall I compare thee to a Summer's day? Make me an instrument of Thy peace.
Coupled with works by various composers. **Jennifer Larmore** (mez); **Antoine Palloc** (pf).
Teldec 0630-16069-2 (12/97). *See review in the Collections section; refer to the Index.*

Robert Abramson
American 1928

Suggested listening ...
...*Soldier, Soldier. Coupled with works by various composers.* **Jennifer Larmore** (mez);
Antoine Palloc (pf). Teldec 0630-16069-2 (12/97). *See review in the Collections section; refer to the Index.*

Adolphe Adam
French 1803-1856

Adam Giselle. **Slovak Radio Symphony Orchestra / Andrew Mogrelia.**
Naxos ⑤ 8 550755/6 (two discs: 114 minutes: DDD: 4/95). Recorded 1994.
Naxos offer this complete version of Adam's classic ballet score which comes complete with traditional interpolations attributed to Burgmüller and Minkus. It is on any count highly enjoyable, with some especially rewarding passages such as the Act 1 "Pas seul". Many readers, of course, may well prefer a single-CD abridged version and nobody should imagine that he or she will be losing anything of major value. For them any of the admirable alternatives might suit, though they will not come cheaper than this super-budget set. Light of step and light on the pocket, it is also commendably economical on shelf-space in its sensible single-CD-width case.
Additional recommendations ...
...**Vienna Philharmonic Orchestra / Herbert von Karajan.**
Decca Ovation Ⓜ 417 738-2DM (60 minutes: ADD).
...**London Symphony Orchestra / Michael Tilson Thomas.**
Sony Classical Ⓕ CD42450 (77 minutes: DDD: 3/92).
...**Royal Opera House Orchestra, Covent Garden / Mark Ermler.**
Royal Opera House Records Ⓕ ROH007 (74 minutes: DDD: 4/94).   Ⓖ

Adam Le toréador. **Michel Trempont** (bar) Don Belflor; **Sumi Jo** (sop) Coraline; **John Aler** (ten)
Tracolin; **Welsh National Opera Orchestra / Richard Bonynge.** Decca Ⓕ 455 664-2DHO
(77 minutes: DDD: 4/98). Notes, text and translation included. Recorded 1996.   ⒼⒼ
Richard Bonynge's ability to persuade Decca to record out-of-the-way nineteenth-century French stage works has been to our repeated benefit over the past 40 years. Yet few of the results have been more welcome than this delightful operatic soufflé. Despite the title, there is little specifically Spanish about the piece beyond the Barcelona setting and the cuckolded elderly husband who just happens to have been a toreador. The love interest is between the former opera-singer wife and her flautist admirer, and it is the important contribution of the flute (almost a fourth character, and admirably played by Jonathan Burgess) that accounts for much of the aforementioned incidental music. The admirer identifies himself by means of assorted operatic airs and grades the seriousness of the husband's infidelities by whether he plays a fandango or a cachucha. The score's most familiar number is a set of variations on *Ah, vous dirai-je, maman* (*Twinkle, twinkle, little star*, if you like); but there is much else that brings out Sumi Jo's crystal-clear, effortless coloratura to marvellous effect, as well as showing off John Aler's ardent, elegant tenor and Michel Trempont's well-practised comic baritone. This is a delightful recording.
Further listening ...
...Le corsaire. **English Chamber Orchestra / Richard Bonynge.** Decca 430 286-2DH2 (10/92).

Adam de la Halle

French c1240-c1286

Suggested listening ...

...Je muir d'amourete. *Coupled with works by various composers.* **Anne Azéma** (sop/spkr); **vocal and instrumental ensemble.** Erato 0630-17072-2 (12/97). ☛ *See review in the Collections section; refer to the Index.*

John Adams

American 1947

J. Adams Shaker Loops[a]. Phrygian Gates[b]. Chamber Symphony[a]. [b]**Hermann Kretzschmar** (pf); [a]**Ensemble Modern / Sîan Edwards.** RCA Victor Red Seal Ⓕ 09026 68674-2 (73 minutes: DDD: 1/98). Recorded 1996-97.
Shaker Loops is a minimalist quartet that became a septet, then a piece for full string band. "There are the partisans who favour the clarity and individualism of the solo septet version", wrote Adams in the course of his Nonesuch booklet-note, "and there are those who prefer the orchestral version for its added density and power." Here, Sîan Edwards and Ensemble Modern combine clarity and individualism with density and power. Comparing this with Adams's 1988 recording finds Edwards and her band raging wild, hotting virtually to boiling-point two or so minutes into the first movement. Turning back to Adams is like comparing urbanity with revolution, though some might prefer the relative refinement of the composer's own rendition. Edwards's reading tops Adams both for its rapturous lyricism and high-octane energy. The recording, too, is spectacularly good. The *Chamber Symphony* took its cue from a combination of hyperactive cartoons and Schoenberg's Op. 9. It suggests a sort of friendly panic, acrobatic, unpredictable and mischievous, though the head-on confrontation between rock-style rhythms and atonal chatter is irresistible, and the recording captures every maverick strand of the score. *Phrygian Gates* is a more difficult listen. "Minimalism's first solo work suitable for solo performance," says annotator Frank J. Oteri. It is a sort of *Mikrokosmos* turned 'Makrokosmos' (Bartókian exercises run riot), though its restless shifting of colour and pulse – not to mention its frequently dense chordal writing – reminds one more of broken sleep patterns on an uncomfortable mattress. *Phrygian Gates* sounds choppy and ungrateful to play, though Kretzschmar drives fairly hard and the recording captures him with admirable clarity.
Additional recommendations ...
...Violin Concerto[a]. Shaker Loops[b]. [a]**Gidon Kremer** (vn); [a]**London Symphony Orchestra / Kent Nagano;** [b]**Orchestra of St Luke's / John Adams.**
Nonesuch Ⓕ 7559-79360-2 (59 minutes: DDD: 6/96).   ⓠ
...Grand Pianola Music. Chamber Symphony. **London Sinfonietta / John Adams.**
Elektra Nonesuch Ⓕ 7559-79219-2 (53 minutes: DDD: 3/95).   ⓠ

J. Adams Harmonielehre. The Chairman Dances. Two Fanfares – Tromba lontana; Short Ride in a Fast Machine. **City of Birmingham Symphony Orchestra / Sir Simon Rattle.** EMI Ⓕ CDC5 55051-2 (62 minutes: DDD: 6/94). Recorded 1993.
Harmonielehre was inspired by a dream vision of a massive tanker that suddenly took flight, displaying a "beautiful brownish-orange oxide on the bottom part of its hull"; the 'setting' was just off San Francisco Bay Bridge. "Those pounding E minor chords are like a grinding of gears," says John Adams of its violent, gunshot opening. Scored for a huge orchestra and structured in three contrasted sections, *Harmonielehre* is probably the nearest thing on offer to a minimalist symphony, and for that reason alone it could well appeal beyond the élite coterie of minimalist-fanciers. Rattle's recording has great heft and dynamic range, an informative balance and a vivid sense of aural perspective. The brass components of those opening chords have enormous weight and presence, and the ringing marimbas thereafter, a bright complexion. Adams's frequent requests for subtle tempo transitions are subtly honoured by the conductor. There are three fill-ups: the Copland-inspired *Short Ride in a Fast Machine* and *Two Fanfares*, and *The Chairman Dances*, a 'foxtrot for orchestra' that utilizes material from Adams's opera, *Nixon in China*. Rattle's view of Adams is recommended particularly to mainstream collectors who aren't yet sold on minimalism.
Additional recommendations ...
...The Chairman Dances. *Coupled with works by various composers.* **Baltimore Symphony Orchestra / David Zinman.** Argo Ⓕ 444 454-2ZH (71 minutes: DDD: 7/95).
...Short Ride in a Fast Machine (arr. L.T. Odorn)[a]. Grand Pianola Music[b]. **D. Lang** Are you experienced?[c] Under Orpheus[d]. [c]**David Lang** (narr); [b]**Lindsay Wagstaff**, [b]**Kym Amps**, [b]**Ruth Holton** (sops); [bd]**Ellen Corver**, [bd]**Sepp Grotenhuis** (pfs); **Netherlands Wind Ensemble / Stephen Mosko.** Chandos New Direction Ⓕ CHAN9363 (76 minutes: DDD: 10/95).
Further listening ...
...El Dorado. *Coupled with works by* **Busoni** *and* **Liszt** Hallé Orchestra / Kent Nagano.
Nonesuch 7559-79359-2 (4/97). *Gramophone Editor's choice.*   ⓠ
...Hoodoo Zephyr. Coast. Disappointment Lake. Tourist Song. Tundra. Bump. Cerulean.
John Adams (bar/synth). Elektra Nonesuch 7559-79311-2 (4/94).
...The Death of Klinghoffer. **Soloists; London Opera Chorus; Lyon Opera Orchestra / Kent Nagano.**
Elektra Nonesuch 7559-79281-2 (3/93).

Stephen Adams

British 1844-1913

Suggested listening ...
...The Holy City. *Coupled with works by various composers.* **Lesley Garrett** (sop); **Britten Sinfonia /**
Ivor Bolton. Conifer Classics 75605 51329-2 (12/97). *See review in the Collections section; refer to*
the Index.

Richard Addinsell

British 1904-1977

Suggested listening ...
...Warsaw Concerto. *Coupled with works by various composers.* **Cristina Ortiz** (pf);
Royal Philharmonic Orchestra / Moshe Atzmon. Decca 414 348-2DH (9/86). *See review*
in the Collections section; refer to the Index. **G**

Thomas Adès

British 1971

Adès Arcadiana, Op. 12[a]. The Origin of the Harp, Op. 13[b]. Sonata da caccia, Op. 11[c]. Living Toys,
Op. 9[d]. Gefriolsae me, Op. 3b[e]. [c]**Michael Neisemann** (ob); [c]**Andrew Clark** (hn); [c]**Thomas Adès**
(hpd); [a]**Endellion Quartet** (Andrew Watkinson, Ralph de Souza, vns; Garfield Jackson, va; David
Waterman, vc); [e]**King's College Choir, Cambridge / Stephen Cleobury;** [b]**instrumental ensemble /**
Thomas Adès; [d]**London Sinfonietta / Markus Stenz.** EMI Debut ® CDZ5 72271-2 (64 minutes:
DDD: 5/98). Text and translation included. **GGG**
This collection fully lives up to the excited expectations aroused by the first disc of Adès's music but
does not suggest that he is yet at all ready to settle down into a predictable style. The five pieces here
suggest a composer as delightedly surprised by his prodigal inventiveness as we are. *Arcadiana*, for
example, is a seven-movement string quartet whose central and longest (four minute) movement
contains an extraordinary range of precisely imagined, highly original textures and yet in its
penultimate section can settle to a serene and wonderfully beautiful *adagio* whose sound and mood
can only be conveyed by the adjective 'Beethovenian'. Far more overtly, the engaging *Sonata da caccia*
uses elements that are very directly derived from Couperin, but the sensibility is entirely modern, even
when you strongly suspect that this or that phrase is a note-for-note quotation. However, as with
Adès's first collection, his is an imagination that you can trust. *Living Toys* has a quite Birtwistle-like
sense of ritual to it, though more lyrical, quite frequently with a tangible jazz element. *The Origin of*
the Harp is a dark, dramatic chamber tone-poem. *Gefriolsae me*, for male voices and organ, is a brief
but impressive motet to Middle English words. All five pieces are finely performed, all are further
evidence of a rich, still developing but clearly exceptional talent. *Arcadiana*, with its exquisite textures
and sheer melodic richness, is perhaps Adès's finest achievement so far, a work constantly aware of
the musical past (including the string quartet's past) but renewing that past with astonishing freshness.
Further listening ...
...Catch, Op. 4[a]. Darknesse visible[b]. Still sorrowing, Op. 7[c]. Under Hamelin Hill, Op. 6[d]. Five Eliot
Landscapes, Op. 1[e]. Traced overhead, Op. 15[f]. Life story, Op. 8b[g]. [e]**Valdine Anderson,** [g]**Mary**
Carewe (sops); [a]**Lynsey Marsh** (cl); [a]**Anthony Marwood** (vn); [a]**Louise Hopkins** (vc); **Thomas Adès**
(pf/[d]org); [d]**David Goode,** [d]**Stephen Farr** (orgs). EMI Debut CDZ5 69699-2 (6/97). *Gramophone*
Editor's choice. **G**

Alexander Agricola

Franco-Dutch ?1446-1506

Suggested listening ...
...De tous biens plaine (two versions). Fortuna desparata. *Coupled with works by various*
composers. **Early Music Consort of London / David Munrow.** Virgin Classics Veritas
VED5 61334-2 (11/97). ✐ *See review in the Collections section; refer to the Index.*

Kalevi Aho

Finnish 1949

Aho Rejoicing of the Deep Waters. Symphony No. 10. **Lahti Symphony Orchestra / Osmo Vänskä.**
BIS Ⓕ CD856 (59 minutes: DDD: 10/97). Recorded 1996-97. **G**
This is music with big personality, full of intellectual and imaginative power. It is also virtually
impossible to label. Here is a broadly traditional four-movement symphony, which ranges from lilting,
almost tonal tunefulness to ferocious, harshly glittering dissonance in the space of a few bars. The
range of mood and character is breathtaking: serenity alternates with violence, innocence meets grim
experience head on. There's a persuasive symphonic thinking here too: a purposeful narrative of long-
term tension and resolution, of seeking and finding. So after all, the humanist symphony still lives.
Admittedly you may not be convinced by everything on first hearing. Invoking Bruckner at the
beginning of a long slow movement is dangerous – does Aho's *Adagio* live up to that monumental

exemplar? But this is music that invites the ear back to try again, and it reveals more the deeper you probe. So, too, does the elemental orchestral fantasy, *Rejoicing of the Deep Waters*. The playing of the Lahti Symphony Orchestra is excellent – both as an ensemble and as a team of soloists – and Osmo Vänskä shows what a fine conductor he is: inspiring, galvanizing and firmly controlled. The recordings are first-class.

Further listening ...
...Symphony No. 8[a]. Pergamon[b]. [b]Lilli Paasikivi, [b]Eeva-Liisa Saarinen, [b]Tom Nyman,
   [b]Matti Lehtinen (narrs); [a]Hans-Ola Ericsson, [b]Pauli Pietiläinen (orgs); **Lahti Symphony
   Orchestra / Osmo Vänskä.** BIS CD646 (3/95).
...Symphony No. 9[a]. Cello Concerto[b]. [a]Christian Lindberg (tbn); [b]Gary Hoffman (vc);
   Lahti Symphony Orchestra / Osmo Vänskä. BIS CD706 (2/96).

Jehan Alain   French 1911-1940

Alain Suite. Climat. Prélude et Fugue. Choral dorien. Choral phrygien. Aria. Variations sur "Lucis créator". Berceuse sur deux notes qui cornent. Deux préludes profanes. Monodie. Ballade en mode phrygien. Choral cistercien pour une élévation. Variations sur un thème de Clément Janequin. Le jardin suspendu. Litanies. Fantasmagorie. Trois danses. Quatre pièces. Grave. Petite pièce. Intermezzo. Lamento. Première fantaisie. Deuxième fantaisie. Deux dances à Agni Yavishta. Cinque pièces faciles – Complainte à la mode ancienne; Fugue en mode de Fa; Verset-Choral; Berceuse. Postlude pour l'office de Complies. Page 21 du huitième cahier de notes de Jehan Alain. **Kevin Bowyer** (org). Nimbus Ⓕ NI5551/2 (two discs: 146 minutes: DDD: 7/98). Played on the Marcussen Organ, Chapel of St Augustine, Tonbridge School, Kent. Recorded 1997. *Gramophone Editor's choice.*

This is the most comprehensive and by far and away the most impressive recording yet of Alain's organ music. Bowyer offers nine pieces (among them four of the five *Pièces faciles*, a set previously only represented in part on discs of Alain's piano music) not included on Eric Lebrun's two-disc survey, although as this adds only 16 minutes to the overall playing time it's clear these are not among Alain's most substantial creations. Even so, putting aside any desire for completeness, Alain enthusiasts would not like to be without any of these, least of all the intensely moving page from one of Alain's notebooks setting out his musical reactions to the death, in a mountaineering accident, of his sister, Marie-Odile.

Bowyer's performances are thought-provoking, stimulating and often inspired. His tempos are not especially quick – certainly never approaching the manic velocity of Lebrun's hectic account of *Litanies* – although he does turn out the fastest performance ever recorded of the *Intermezzo*. Yet even here the choice of speed is symptomatic of Bowyer's whole approach; nobody could deny that when played so rapidly the work takes on an altogether new dimension. Apart from the superbudget price-tag the main attraction of the Naxos sets (listed below) is the choice of the rich and atmospheric Cavaillé-Coll organ in Paris's Saint-Antoine des Quinze-Vingts. Unfortunately the recording quality wipes out this advantage by obscuring much of the detail. For their part Nimbus achieve a near-perfect balance between clarity and atmosphere on the brand new Marcussen in Tonbridge School's recently rebuilt Chapel. When the disarming dialogue between a single reed and the flutes of the charming *Petite pièce* can be revealed in such detail nobody could realistically ask for a better setting for this magical music. Bowyer proves to be an unusually perceptive and persuasive advocate of Alain's music, and not only do these discs conclusively outstrip all present-day competition but one suspects it will be a long time before a serious contender to this outstanding release comes along.

Additional recommendations ...
...Deux danses à Agni Yavishta. Intermezzo. Litanies. Aria. *Coupled with works by various
   composers.* **Marie-Claire Alain** (org).
   Erato Ⓜ 0630-15343-2 (five discs: 351 minutes: ADD/DDD: 1/97).
...Litanies. *Coupled with works by various composers.* **Christopher Herrick** (org). Hyperion
   Ⓕ CDA66676 (75 minutes: DDD: 8/94). *See review in the Collections section; refer to the Index.*
...Deuxième fantaisie. Le jardin suspendu. *Coupled with works by various composers.* **Piet Kee** (org).
   Chandos Ⓕ CHAN9188 (72 minutes: DDD: 10/93). *See review in the Collections section;
   refer to the Index.*
...Litanies. Petite pièce. Le jardin suspendu. Deuxième fantaisie. Variations sur un thème de
   Clément Janequin. Deux danses à Agni Yavishta. Deux préludes profanes. Choral cistercian pour
   un élévation. Climat. Monodie. Ballade en mode phrygien. Choral phrygien. Suite.
   Eric Lebrun (org). Naxos Ⓢ 8 553632 (64 minutes: DDD: 9/97).
...Trois danses. Intermezzo. Variations sur "Lucis creator". Berceuse. Grave. Lamento. Première
   fantaisie. Prélude et Fugue. Choral dorien. Aria. Postlude pour l'office de Complies.
   Eric Lebrun (org). Naxos Ⓢ 8 553633 (66 minutes: DDD: 9/97).

Further listening ...
...Prière pour nous autres charnels (orch. Dutilleux). *Coupled with works by* **Dutilleux**
   Martyn Hill (ten); **Neal Davies** (bar); **Olivier Charlier** (vn); **BBC Philharmonic Orchestra /
   Yan Pascal Tortelier.** Chandos CHAN9504 (11/96).

Alonso Perez de Alba
Spanish d after 1519

Suggested listening ...
...Stabat mater. *Coupled with works by various composers.* **The Hilliard Ensemble.** Virgin Classics
Veritas VED5 61394-2 (11/97). *See review in the Collections section; refer to the Index.*

Isaac Albéniz
Spanish 1860-1909

Albéniz (orch. Halffter). Rapsodia española, Op. 70.
Falla Noches en los jardines de España.
Turina Rapsodia sinfónica, Op. 66. **Alicia de Larrocha** (pf); **London Philharmonic Orchestra /
Rafael Frühbeck de Burgos.** Decca Ⓕ 410 289-2DH (52 minutes: DDD: 10/84).
From 410 289-1DH (6/84).   Ⓖ
The three magically beautiful nocturnes which make up Falla's *Nights in the gardens of Spain* express
the feelings and emotions evoked by contrasted surroundings, whilst Albéniz's enjoyably colourful
Rapsodia española is a loosely assembled sequence of Spanish dances such as the *jota* and the
malagueña. Like Falla's *Nights* the work was conceived as a piano solo, but this disc contains a version
with orchestra arranged by Cristobal Halffter. The disc is completed by Turina's short, two-part work
for piano and strings. All three pieces are excellently performed, but it is the Falla work which brings
out the quality of Larrocha's artistry; her ability to evoke the colour of the Spanish atmosphere is
remarkable. Frühbeck de Burgos supports her magnificently and persuades the LPO to produce some
very Latin-sounding playing. The recording is suitably atmospheric.

Albéniz Iberia[a] (arr. Gray) – El Albaicín; Triana; Rondeña.
Granados Valses poéticos (trans. Williams).
Rodrigo Invocación y Danza. En los trigales.
Anonymous (arr. Llobet). Ten Catalan Folk-songs. **John Williams** (gtr); [a]**London Symphony
Orchestra / Paul Daniels.** Sony Classical Ⓕ SK48480 (71 minutes: DDD: 7/92).
Recorded 1989-91.   Ⓖ
The amalgam of technical guitaristic perfection in the face of daunting demands, fluid musicality and
exemplary tone-production, caught in this exceptionally lifelike recording, represents a landmark in
the instrument's march towards true parity with other instruments. Granados's *Valses* are unabridged,
Rodrigo's moody *Invocación y Danza* comes in its original and more effective form, and two of the
charming settings of Catalan folk-songs arranged by Llobet have no other recording. Nothing in
Albéniz's virtuosic *Iberia* is accessible to the solo guitar, but with the aid of the London Symphony
Orchestra and Gray's enchantingly evocative arrangements, Williams shows three of its movements in
a new and colourful light. To anyone with the slightest interest in the guitar or Spanish romantic
music this disc is a required purchase.

Additional recommendations ...
...Iberia. Navarra (compl. de Séverac). Suite española, Op. 47. **Alicia de Larrocha** (pf).
Decca Ⓕ 417 887-2DH2 (two discs: 126 minutes: DDD: 6/88).   ⓊⓊ
...Iberia (orch. Arbós). **Falla** El sombrero de tres picos – ballet[a]. [a]**Jill Gomez** (sop); **Philharmonia
Orchestra / Yan Pascal Tortelier.** Chandos Ⓕ CHAN8904 (72 minutes: DDD: 4/91).
...Iberia. Cantos de España, Op. 232. **Rafael Orozco** (pf).
Auvidis Valois Ⓕ V4663 (two discs: 112 minutes: DDD: 11/92).

Albéniz Iberia[a]. Navarra[a].
Granados Goyescas[b]. **Alicia de Larrocha** (pf). Double Decca Ⓜ 448 191-2DF2 (two discs:
141 minutes: ADD: 4/96). Items marked [a] from SXL6586/7 (10/73), [b]SXL6587 (12/77).
Recorded 1972-76.   Ⓖ
Alicia de Larrocha has been playing these works, the greatest in the Spanish repertoire of piano
music, all her life; and immersed as she was from her earliest childhood in the authentic tradition (her
mother, her aunt and she herself were all trained at Granados's own school, of which she later became
director), she has several times been asked to re-record them. She once said, rather wistfully, that she
didn't consider herself a specialist but that Spanish music was what the public constantly demanded
of her. Larrocha is not unique in mastering the terrors of these extremely demanding works; but
though there have been other distinguished interpreters, her readings have consistently remained a
touchstone. She employs plenty of subtle rubato (for example in Albéniz's "Almería" and Granados's
"Los requiebros") but possesses the ability to make it sound as natural as breathing; yet she can also
preserve a stimulating tautness of rhythm, as in "El puerto". In the true sense of that much-misused
word, this is *classical* playing, free from any superimposed striving for effect but responding fully to
the music's sense of colour; and even in the densest of textures (as in "Eritaña") she is able to control
conflicting tonal levels. *Goyescas*, which can tempt the unwary into exaggerated 'expressiveness',
brings forth a wealth of poetic nuance, without losing shape. The recorded quality throughout always
was good and here emerges as fresh as ever. Anyone who does not already possess these recordings in
one of their previous issues should not hesitate to acquire them now – all the more so since the two
discs together cost the same as one full-price one.

Additional recommendations ...
...Navarra. *Coupled with works by various composers.* **Artur Rubinstein** (pf).
RCA Victor Gold Seal Ⓜ 09026 61445-2 (64 minutes: ADD: 10/93). *See review in the Collections section; refer to the Index.*   ⒼⒼⒼ
...Navarra (arr. Marshall). *Coupled with works by various composers.* **Sequeira Costa, Artur Pizarro** (pfs). Collins Classics Ⓕ 1466-2 (62 minutes: DDD: 10/96). *See review in the Collections section; refer to the Index.*   Ⓖ

Albéniz Mallorca, Op. 202. Suite española, Op. 47. Cantos de España, Op. 232 – Córdoba.
Granados Cuentos de la juventud – Dedicatoria. 15 Tonadillas – El majo Olvidado. 12 Danzas españolas, Op. 37 – Villanesca; Andaluza (Playera). 7 Valses poéticos.
Rodrigo Tres Piezas españolas. **Julian Bream** (gtr). RCA Navigator Ⓢ 74321 17903-2 (77 minutes: DDD: 3/95). Recorded 1982-83.   Ⓖ
In 1982 Julian Bream recorded a solo recital of music by Albéniz and Granados in his favourite recording venue, Wardour Chapel in Wiltshire. It offers playing of extraordinary magnetism and an almost total illusion of the great guitarist seated in the room making music just beyond one's loudspeakers; this effect is particularly striking in Albéniz's *Cordoba* and the *pianissimo* reprise of the central section of the Granados *Danza española* No. 5, which is quite magical. The other works included are all played with comparable spontaneity. RCA here reissue this disc at super-bargain price on their enterprising Navigator label; moreover, they have added another 15 minutes of music in the form of Rodrigo's *Tres Piezas españolas*, recorded a year later. The second of these, a seven-minute "Passacaglia", is quite masterly, while the final "Zapateado" brings characteristically chimerical virtuosity from the soloist. It is difficult to identify another recital of Spanish guitar music that surpasses this, and it is now one of the great bargains in the Navigator catalogue.
Additional recommendation ...
...Suite española – Sevilla; Cádiz; Aragón; Castilla. Pavana capricho, Op. 12. Iberia – Triana.
Navarra. *Coupled with works by various composers.* **Katia** and **Marielle Labèque** (pfs).
Philips Ⓕ 438 938-2PH (59 minutes: DDD: 9/94). *See review in the Collections Section; refer to the Index.*
Further listening ...
...Piano Sonatas – No. 3, Op. 68; No. 4, Op. 72; No. 5, Op. 82. L'automne, Op. 170. **Albert Guiovart** (pf). Harmonia Mundi Iberica HMI98 7007 (12/94).

Eugen d'Albert   Scottish/German 1864-1932

---

d'Albert Piano Sonata in F sharp minor, Op. 10. Piano Pieces, Op. 16 – No. 2, Scherzo; No. 3, Intermezzo. Eight Piano Pieces, Op. 5. Serenata. Capriolen, Op. 32. **Piers Lane** (pf). Hyperion Ⓕ CDA66945 (79 minutes: DDD: 1/98). Recorded 1996.   ⒼⒼ
Here is a superb recital, provoking astonishment that music of such quality could have lain neglected for so long. Variety is, indeed, the spice of d'Albert, the legendary, six-times-married pianist so greatly admired by Liszt. Tending to leave his wives as soon as they bore him children (one for the Freudians), his occasional sense of confusion hardly detracted from a dazzling career and a series of compositions of a special richness. Brahms's influence, particularly that of his Op. 76 Pieces, may dominate d'Albert's Op. 5 yet in the tempest-tossed pages of No. 1, for example, his texture and syncopation are boldly individual. Again, the play of octaves and thirds in No. 5 may evoke Brahms's D minor Piano Concerto yet the writing is sufficiently personal to form a tribute rather than an act of plagiarism. By way of diversion the storm clouds of No. 6 remind us of Rachmaninov's inchoate whirl in his Op. 32 F minor Prelude but in No. 8 we return to Brahms's early heroics as well as to a glowing and exultant lyricism. The enchanting *Serenata*, on the other hand, inhabits another world, one of piquant 'guitar' strokes and if the end is half-whimsical, half-Lisztian, the overall effect is like an extended Kreisler lollipop. But it is, perhaps, when you compare the very ambitious Sonata, with its triple fugue finale, and the Op. 32 miniatures that you fully realize the extent of d'Albert's gifts. In Op. 32 the Sonata's swashbuckling and, again, Brahmsian bravura give way to a pinpoint wit and delicacy, to the sad fate of an overly ambitious butterfly, a very French *faux-naïf* waltz, more mischievous than 'cosy', a passing glance at America in "Missie-Missa" with its startling appearance of "In Dixieland I take my stand ..." and finally a visit to a circus full of braying fanfares, jugglers and the spirit of adventure. The Op. 16 "Scherzo" may be more familiar but the "Intermezzo", with its sly, side-stepping harmonies, provides another delightful surprise. No praise could be high enough for Piers Lane whose playing throughout is of a superb musical intelligence, sensitivity and scintillating brilliance. The recordings are of an ideal warmth and range.

Tomaso Albinoni   Italian 1671-1751

Albinoni Concertos, Opp. 7 and 9. **Anthony Robson, Catherine Latham** (obs); **Collegium Musicum 90 / Simon Standage** (vn). Chandos Chaconne Ⓕ CHAN0579/0602/0610 (three discs, oas: 72, 63 and 65 minutes: DDD: 5/95, 4/97, 2/98). ✒ Recorded 1993 and 1996.   ⒼⒼ

CHAN0579: Op. 7 – No. 3 in B flat major; No. 6 in D major; No. 9 in F major; No. 12 in
C major. Op. 9 – No. 2 in D minor; No. 5 in C major; No. 8 in G minor; No. 11 in B flat major.
CHAN0602: Op. 7 – No. 1 in D major; No. 2 in C major; No. 4 in G major; No. 5 in C major.
Op. 9 – No. 1 in B flat major; No. 3 in F major; No. 4 in A major; No. 6 in G major. Sinfonia in
G minor. *CHAN0610:* Op. 7 – No. 7 in A major; No. 8 in D major; No. 10 in B flat major;
No. 11 in C major; Op. 9 – No. 7 in D major; No. 9 in C major; No. 10 in F major; No. 12 in
D major.

Albinoni's Op. 7 and Op. 9 consist of four concertos *with* (rather than *for*, as the composer insisted)
one oboe, four with two oboes and four for strings only. Overall, the last show a strong family
resemblance, with vivacious outer movements and suave slow movements that tend to be more
chromatic; there is a general reliance on sequential treatment; but the Op. 9 Concertos here include a
solo violin part, at times very elaborate. The first volume contains the works for solo oboe and strings.
Albinoni treats the oboe like a voice (another wind instrument), whereas Vivaldi (whose oboe works
were written at about the same time) has the agile violin more in mind. There isn't one 'filler' in either
set, which means that there isn't one in the programme either, and the slow movements have tunes that
stay in the mind. The second volume contains the string and double-oboe concertos. All are three-
movement *da chiesa* works, with cheerful outer movements and slow ones that often remind you that
Albinoni wrote a good deal of vocal music. The two oboes 'sing' together for the most part, either in
thirds or in unison, but in two of the concertos of Op. 9 (collectively more adventurous and highly
developed than those of Op. 7) they are used to evoke horns (No. 3) and fifes (No. 6). The concertos
on Vol. 3 for two oboes display rather more individuality – the joyous finale of Op. 7 No. 11
intriguingly sharpens the fourth of the scale, Op. 9 No. 9 allows the oboes more independence of each
other, especially in its unusually expressive *Adagio* and breezy finale, while in the outer movements of
Op. 9 No. 12 the oboes put up a good pretence at being trumpets. Anthony Robson and Catherine
Latham contribute deftly to the spirit of enjoyment that emanates from the whole of this disc.
Collegium Musicum 90 are one of the very best baroque bands around and here they are in their
element. The recorded balance is just right, keeping soloists and strings in equal perspective. In every
positive sense these recordings bid strongly for a place on every shelf.

Additional recommendations ...

...Op. 9 Nos. 2, 6 and 9. Concerto in C major. **Vivaldi** Concertos – C major, RV560;
F major, RV457; C major, RV559. **Paul Goodwin** (ob); **King's Consort / Robert King.**
Hyperion Ⓕ CDA66383 (70 minutes: DDD: 6/91). 🗡

...Op. 7 Nos. 1-12. Sinfonie e concerti a cinque, Op. 2 – No. 5 in D major;
No. 6 in G minor. **Heinz Holliger, Maurice Bourgue** (obs); **I Musici.**
Philips Ⓕ 432 115-2PH2 (two discs: 94 minutes: DDD: 1/93).

...Op. 9 Nos. 2, 3ᵃ, 5, 8, 9ᵃ and 11. **Anthony Camden,** ᵃ**Julia Girdwood** (obs);
London Virtuosi / John Georgiadis. Naxos Ⓢ 8 550739 (64 minutes: DDD: 3/94).

...Op. 7 No. 3 (transcribed for trumpet). *Coupled with works by various composers.*
Håkan Hardenberger (tpt); **I Musici.** Philips Ⓕ 442 131-2PH (54 minutes: DDD: 5/95).
See review in the Collections section; refer to the Index.   Ⓖ

...Sinfonia in G major (arr. Camden). Op. 7 Nos. 1, 2, 3, 8 and 9. Op. 9 – No. 6 in G major.
Anthony Camden, Alison Alty (obs); **The London Virtuosi / John Georgiadis.**
Naxos Ⓢ 8 553002 (58 minutes: DDD: 9/96).

...Op. 7 Nos. 4, 5, 6, 11 and 12. Op. 9 No. 12. **Anthony Camden, Alison Alty** (obs); **The London
Virtuosi / John Georgiadis.** Naxos Ⓢ 8 553035 (52 minutes: DDD: 9/96).

Further listening ...

...Adagio in G minor. *Coupled with works by various composers.* **New College Choir, Oxford;**
Capricorn / Edward Higginbottom. Erato 3984-21659-2 (6/98). *Gramophone Editor's choice.*
See review in the Collections section; refer to the Index.

...Concerti a cinque, Op. 10. **Piero Toso, Giorgio Carmigola** (vns); **I Solisti Veneti / Claudio Scimone.**
Erato 0630-11222-2 (2/96).

...Six Sonate da chiesa, Op. 4. 12 Trattenimenti armonici per camera, Op. 6. **Locatelli Trio.**
Hyperion CDA66831/2 (4/95). 🗡   Ⓖ

...Il nascimento dell'Aurora. **Soloists; I Solisti Veneti / Claudio Scimone.**
Erato 4509-96374-2 (7/95).   Ⓖ

Hugo Alfvén
Swedish 1872-1960

Alfvén Swedish Rhapsodies – No. 1, Op. 19, "Midsummer Vigil"; No. 2, Op. 24, "Upsala-rapsodi";
No. 3, "Dalarapsodi". A Legend of the Skerries, Op. 20. Gustav Adolf II, Op. 49 – Elegy.
Iceland Symphony Orchestra / Petri Sakari. Chandos Ⓕ CHAN9313 (70 minutes: DDD: 3/95).
Recorded 1993.

Petri Sakari gives us the most natural, unaffected and satisfying *Midsummer Vigil* to be heard on disc.
He is light in touch, responsive to each passing mood and every dynamic nuance, self-effacing and
completely at the service of the composer. Moreover in the *Upsala-rapsodi* and its later companion,
he is fresher and more persuasive than any of his rivals on record. Even the Wagnerian-Straussian
echoes from the skerries sound convincing. The only reservation concerns the *Elegy* from the

incidental music to Ludwig Nordström's play about Gustav Adolf II, which might have benefited from greater reticence. Unusually for Sakari, he does not tell the tale simply or let the music speak for itself. The recorded sound is refreshingly free from analytical point-making; everything is there in the right perspective, though listeners whose first response is to find the recording recessed will find that a higher level of playback than usual will produce impressively natural results on high-grade equipment.

Additional recommendations ...
...A Legend of the Skerries. Symphony No. 4, Op. 39, "From the Outermost Skerries"[a].
[a]**Soloists; Stockholm Philharmonic Orchestra / Neeme Järvi.**
BIS Ⓕ CD505 (64 minutes: DDD: 8/92).
...Swedish Rhapsody No. 1. **Montreal Symphony Orchestra / Charles Dutoit.** Decca Ⓕ 452 482-2DH (70 minutes: DDD: 5/97). *See review in the Collections section; refer to the Index.*

Alfvén Symphony No. 5 in A minor, Op. 54. The Mountain King – Suite. Gustav II Adolf, Op. 49 – Elegy. **Royal Stockholm Philharmonic Orchestra / Neeme Järvi.** BIS Ⓕ CD585 (68 minutes: DDD: 1/94). Recorded 1992.
The first movement of the Fifth Symphony (1942-52) is a long one lasting over 17 minutes, with echoes of Wagner and Sibelius – and in the second group a reminder of Bax. Given the fervent advocacy it receives here from Neeme Järvi and the Royal Stockholm Philharmonic, it makes a strong impression. So, too, do the dreamy musings of the slow movement. Järvi is also at his most persuasive and gets marvellously responsive and committed playing from the Stockholm orchestra especially in the first two movements and *The Mountain King* – and the touching "Elegy" from *Gustav II Adolf*, perhaps Alfvén's most affecting and deeply felt piece. The BIS team have come up with a state-of-the-art recording, natural and lifelike. The perspective could hardly be improved upon and each orchestral strand has presence and is effortlessly truthful in timbre.

Further listening ...
...Symphony No. 2 in D major, R28. Midsummer Vigil – Swedish Rhapsody No. 1, R45.
Stockholm Philharmonic Orchestra / Neeme Järvi. BIS CD385 (7/88).
...Songs, Op. 28 – No. 3, I kiss your hand; No. 6, The forest sleeps. *Coupled with works by various composers.* **Anne Sofie von Otter** (mez); **Bengt Forsberg** (pf). DG 449 189-2GH (5/96). *See review in the Collections section; refer to the Index.*   ⒼⒼ

Richard Alison

British fl 1592-1606

Suggested listening ...
...Our Father which in Heaven art (two versions). *Coupled with works by various composers.*
Mhairi Lawson (sop); **Circa 1500.** ASV Gaudeamus CDGAU163 (12/97). ✒ *See review in the Collections section; refer to the Index.*

Charles-Valentin Alkan

French 1813-1888

Alkan 25 Préludes dans les tons majeurs et mineur, Op. 31.
Shostakovich 24 Preludes, Op. 34. **Olli Mustonen** (pf). Decca Ⓕ 433 055-2DH (76 minutes: DDD: 10/91). Recorded 1990. *Gramophone Award Winner 1992.*   ⒼⒼ
It was brave of Decca to launch the career of their then newly-signed pianist with a disc of miniatures few people actually know, since the *oeuvre* of Charles-Valentin Alkan is usually confined to specialist labels and second-rate executants. The 25 Préludes are a reasonably benign introduction to Alkan's idiosyncratic world – elusive and quirky to be sure but less ruthlessly barnstorming than much of his output. They are by no means easy pieces to bring off, but you wouldn't know it from Mustonen's exceptionally assured, brilliantly poised readings. Where rival versions are content to offer the 25 Préludes without coupling, Mustonen adds deft and sparkling performances of Shostakovich's not exactly insubstantial Op. 34 Preludes. Exceptional pianism, excellent, bright recording and helpful notes.

Alkan Transcription de Concert (Beethoven's Piano Concerto No. 3 in C minor, Op. 37 – first movement). Three Etudes, Op. 76.
Busoni Sonatina No. 6 super Carmen (Kammerfantasie).
Chopin/Alkan Piano Concerto No. 1 in E minor, Op. 11 – Romanza.
Medtner Danza festiva, Op. 38 No. 3. **Marc-André Hamelin** (pf). Hyperion Ⓕ CDA66765 (72 minutes: DDD: 3/95). Recorded live in 1994.   ⒼⒼ
The solo transcriptions on the first half of this disc are not intended as substitutes for the real thing, at least not in the context of this disc, but are presented here as supreme examples of the art of piano transcription in the late nineteenth century. In addition, they are superb display pieces, revealing not only the subtleties of the transcriber's art and, in this case, the pianist's ability to render them audible, but also Hamelin's extraordinary ability to make the pieces sound like originals rather than transcriptions. Indeed, in the Alkan transcription of the first movement of Beethoven's Third Piano

Concerto, the absence of the orchestra never becomes a concern. The principal glory of the disc, however, is Hamelin's account of Alkan's *Etudes*, Op. 76, for the hands separately and reunited an exceptionally formidable opus (one that Ronald Smith claims "alone establish[es] Alkan as the rival, if not indeed the peer, of Liszt as the joint architect of transcendental piano technique") which here receives an equally formidable and awe-inspiring performance. We also have the added *frisson* of knowing that what we hear is a single take before a live audience; listen to the hair-raising final study, a blistering, unbroken five-minute salvo of *prestissimo* semiquavers. The remaining items on the disc, a scintillating account of Busoni's *Sonatina* No. 6 and Medtner's ebullient *Danza festiva* from Op. 38, provide further evidence that Hamelin is a considerable presence in the pianistic world. The recorded sound varies a little from piece to piece (they were recorded over three evenings in the Wigmore Hall in London) but all are excellent in quality and have a natural, intimate ambience.

Alkan 12 Etudes dans les tons mineurs, Op. 39. Trois petites fantaisies, Op. 41. Allegro barbaro, Op. 35 No. 5. La chanson de la folle au bord de la mer, Op. 31 No. 8. **Ronald Smith** (pf).
APR Ⓜ APR7031 (two discs: 150 minutes: ADD: 8/97). From HMV SLS5100 (2/78). Recorded 1977.
Veteran enthusiasts of Alkan will need no introduction to Ronald Smith's superlative 1977 recording of the complete *Etudes*, Op. 39, and other pieces. These reissues from APR are superbly transferred and annotated. The *Etudes* are most notable for the inclusion of two of Alkan's most famous solo piano pieces – the Symphony for solo piano (comprising *Etudes* Nos. 4-7) and the Concerto for solo piano (*Etudes* Nos. 8-10). Both works have had their champions over the years but few would deny that it is Ronald Smith to whom we perhaps owe the greatest debt of gratitude for rescuing these particular pieces from musical oblivion. Other studies in the set include the curiously titled and innovative "Le festin d'Esope" and the finger-blistering "Comme le vent". As fill-ups we also get the breathtaking *Allegro barbaro* from the Op. 35 *Etudes* (which is said to have influenced Bartók's similarly titled study), the atmospherically titled and even more bizarre sounding *La chanson de la folle au bord de la mer*, and the *Trois petites fantaisies*. Smith is one of the supreme exponents of Alkan's music who had lived with and performed these pieces for many years prior to these recordings. For those approaching Alkan's music for the first time this set would be an ideal starting place.

Additional recommendations ...
...Etudes dans les tons mineurs, Op. 39 Nos. 8-10. Concerto pour piano seul. **Marc-André Hamelin** (pf). Music and Arts Ⓕ CD724 (50 minutes: DDD: 8/93).
...Etudes dans les tons mineurs, Op. 39 Nos. 3 and 12. 12 Etudes dans les tons majeurs, Op. 35. **Bernard Ringeissen** (pf). Marco Polo Ⓕ 8 223351 (78 minutes: DDD: 11/93).
...Etudes dans les tons mineurs, Op. 39. Préludes, Op. 31 – La chanson de la folle au bord de la mer; No. 12, Le temps qui n'est plus; No. 13, J'étais endormie, mais mon coeur veillait. Nocturne, Op. 22. Etude in F major, Op. 35 No. 5. Assez vivement, Op. 38 No. 1. Esquisses, Op. 63 – No. 2, La staccatissimo; No. 4, Les cloches; No. 11, Les soupirs; No. 61, En songe. Gros temps, Op. 74, First Suite No. 2. Barcarolle, Op. 65 No. 6. **Jack Gibbons** (pf).
ASV Ⓕ CDDCS227 (two discs: 155 minutes: DDD: 11/95). ⒼⒼ

Further listening ...
...Concerti da Camera, Op. 10 – No. 1 in A minor; No. 2 in C sharp minor. *Coupled with* **Henselt** Piano Concerto in F minor, Op. 16. Concert variations on "Quand je quittai la Normandie" from Meyerbeer's "Robert le Diable", Op. 11. **Marc-André Hamelin** (pf); **BBC Scottish Symphony Orchestra / Martyn Brabbins**. Hyperion CDA66717 (8/94).
Gramophone Editor's choice. See review under Henselt; refer to the Index. ⒼⒼ
...Grand duo concertante in F sharp minor, Op. 21. Sonate de concert in E major, Op. 47. Trio in G minor, Op. 30. **Trio Alkan**. Marco Polo 8 223383 (8/93). Ⓖ
...Esquisses, Op. 63. **Laurent Martin** (pf). Marco Polo 8 223352 (4/95).
...Grande sonate, Op. 33, "Les quatre âges". **Ronald Smith** (pf). EMI CDM7 64280-2 (5/92).
...Grande sonate, Op. 33, "Les quatre âges". Sonatine, Op. 61. Barcarolle, Op. 65 No. 6. Etudes dans les tons mineurs, Op. 39 – No. 12, "Le festin d'Esope". **Marc-André Hamelin** (pf). Hyperion CDA66794 (12/95). Ⓖ
...Quatre impromptus, Op. 32 (1). Deuxième recueil d'impromptus, Op. 32 (2). Salut, cendre du pauvre!, Op. 45. Alleluia, Op. 25. Rondeau chromatique, Op. 12. Variations on a theme from Steibelt's Orage Concerto, Op. 1. Super flumina Babylonis, Op. 52. **Laurent Martin** (pf). Marco Polo 8 223657 (4/95).

Gregorio Allegri
Italian *c*1582-1652

Allegri Miserere mei (two versions). Missa Vidi turbam magnam. De ore prudentis[a]. Repleti sunt omnes[a]. Cantate domino[a]. **A Sei Voci / Bernard Fabre-Garrus** with [a]**Dominique Ferran** (org). Auvidis Astrée Ⓕ E8524 (62 minutes: DDD: 9/95). Texts and translations included. Recorded 1994.
Gregori Allegri's fame rests upon a single piece, a simple enough setting of the psalm *Miserere mei* into which extravagantly ornamented passages for a second choir of soloists are interpolated. In practice it was these passages, which for centuries remained a jealously guarded secret of the papal choir who alone had access to the music and performed it once a year (during Holy Week), that

ensured Allegri's reputation. This record presents two versions of the piece. The first is sung with ornamentation added by the French musicologist, Jean Lionnet following seventeenth-century models, while the second presents the Burney-Alfieri version familiar from the classic 1963 recording made by King's College Choir directed by David Willcocks. The curiously named group A Sei Voci (in fact there are ten of them) produce a rather varied sound, at times somewhat flat and white but at its best with an appropriate Italianate edge. For the most part the embellishments are negotiated with style and verve; just occasionally (in the first *Miserere*) they are fuzzy or insecure. *Miserere mei* apart, hardly any of Allegri's music is heard either liturgically or in the concert-hall. By training a pupil of Nanino, a distinguished follower of Palestrina, his best music is confidently written in the High Renaissance contrapuntal manner. The six-voice *Missa Vidi turbam magnam*, composed on one of his own motets, is a fine work, and shows that the *stile antico*, far from being a mere academic exercise, could still be vividly sonorous and dramatic, qualities which are successfully brought out in this reading. The record is nicely rounded out with a selection of short continuo motets in the popular new manner, well established in Northern Italy, which was then becoming fashionable in Rome.

Additional recommendations ...

...Miserere mei. **Palestrina** Stabat mater a 8. Hodie beata virgo. Senex puerum portabat. Magnificat a 8. Litaniae de Beata Vergine Mariae I a 8. **Roy Goodman** (treb); **King's College Choir, Cambridge / Sir David Willcocks.** Decca Ovation Ⓜ 421 147-2DM (56 minutes: ADD: 5/89).   Ⓖ

...Miserere mei. *Coupled with works by* **Lotti** *and* **Palestrina** The Sixteen / Harry Christophers. Collins Classics Ⓕ 5009-2 (56 minutes: DDD: 10/90).   Ⓖ

...Miserere mei *Coupled with works by various composers.* **Jeremy Budd** (treb); **St Paul's Cathedral Choir / John Scott** with **Andrew Lucas** (org). Hyperion Ⓕ CDA66439 (76 minutes: DDD: 10/91). *See review in the Collections section; refer to the Index.*

...Miserere mei. *Coupled with works by various composers.* **Trinity College Choir, Cambridge / Richard Marlow.** Conifer Ⓕ CDCF219 (79 minutes: DDD: 2/94). *See review in the Collections section; refer to the Index.*

...Miserere mei. *Coupled with works by various composers.* **Soloists; Westminster Cathedral Choir / James O'Donnell.** Hyperion Ⓕ CDA66850 (72 minutes: DDD: 5/96). *See review in the Collections section; refer to the Index.*

...Miserere mei. *Coupled with works by various composers.* **Westminster Abbey Choir; Abbey Consort / Martin Neary.** Sony Classical Arc of Light Ⓕ SK66615 (77 minutes: DDD: 7/96).

Antônio Carlos Nóbrega de Almeida   Brazilian 1952

Suggested listening ...

...Rasga do Nordeste. *Coupled with works by various composers.* **Quinteto da Paraíba.** Nimbus NI5483 (10/96). *See review in the Collections section; refer to the Index.*

Laurindo Almeida   Brazilian 1917-1995

Suggested listening ...

...Historia do Luar. *Coupled with works by various composers.* **Sharon Isbin** (gtr) with **Gaudencio Thiago de Mello** (perc). Teldec 0630-19899-2 (7/98). *Gramophone Editor's choice. See review in the Collections section; refer to the Index.*   ⒼⒼ

Francisco Alonso   Spanish *fl* 1500

Suggested listening ...

...La tricotea. *Coupled with works by various composers.* **The Hilliard Ensemble.** Virgin Classics Veritas VED5 61394-2 (11/97). *See review in the Collections section; refer to the Index.*

William Alwyn   British 1905-1985

Alwyn (arr. Palmer) Odd Man Out – Suite. The History of Mr Polly – Suite. The Fallen Idol – Suite. The Rake's Progress – Calypso Music. **London Symphony Orchestra / Richard Hickox.** Chandos Ⓕ CHAN9243 (72 minutes: DDD: 3/94). Recorded 1993.   Ⓖ

William Alwyn, like Malcolm Arnold, made his name as a composer of film music in the great days of British cinema. In the immediate post-war years he wrote the scores on the present disc. British films in those days had 'symphonic' scores and were awash with orchestral sound. *Odd Man Out* inspired the most powerful and lyrically poignant music here, while *The History of Mr Polly* (a much-liked movie, with John Mills memorable in the title-role) is charmingly lightweight, especially in the "Punting scene", and is really rather touching in the "Utopian sunset" of the finale. *The Fallen Idol* (an outstanding movie, written by Graham Greene) is about a small boy who witnesses a death and is in danger of implicating his friend, the Butler (Ralph Richardson). The music subtly underlines the action and feelings of the characters. The original scores were unwittingly destroyed at Pinewood Studios but Christopher Palmer lovingly restored each one for this disc. Hickox conducts all this music with total commitment and it is beautifully played and recorded.

Further listening ...

...Concerto for Flute and Eight Wind Instruments[a]. Suite for Oboe and Harp[b]. Music for Three Players[d]. Trio for Flute, Cello and Piano[e]. [ace]**Kate Hill** (fl); [d]**Joy Farrall** (cl); [d]**Leland Chen** (vn); [e]**Caroline Dearnley** (vc); [c]**Ieuan Jones** (hp); [bde]**Julius Drake** (pf); [a]**London Haffner Wind Ensemble / Nicholas Daniel** ([b]ob). Chandos CHAN9152 (10/93).

...Lyra Angelica[a]. Autumn Legend[b]. Pastoral fantasia[c]. Tragic Interlude. [a]**Rachel Masters** (hp); [b]**Nicholas Daniel** (cor ang); [c]**Stephen Tees** (va); **City of London Sinfonia / Richard Hickox.** Chandos CHAN9065 (10/92).⊕

...Violin Concerto[a]. Symphony No. 3. [a]**Lydia Mordkovitch** (vn). **London Symphony Orchestra / Richard Hickox.** Chandos CHAN9187 (1/94).

...Symphonies – No. 1 in D major; No. 4. **London Philharmonic Orchestra / William Alwyn.** Lyrita SRCD227 (7/92).⊕

...Symphony No. 1 in D major. Piano Concerto No. 1[a]. [a]**Howard Shelley** (pf); **London Symphony Orchestra / Richard Hickox.** Chandos CHAN9155 (5/93).

...Symphonies – No. 2; No. 3; No. 5, "Hydriotaphia". **London Philharmonic Orchestra / William Alwyn.** Lyrita SRCD228 (10/92).⊕

...Clarinet Sonata[a]. Flute Sonata[b]. Oboe Sonata[c]. Divertimento[d]. Crépuscule[e]. Sonata impromptu[f]. [bd]**Kate Hill** (fl); [c]**Nicholas Daniel** (ob); [a]**Joy Farrall** (cl); [e]**Ieuan Jones** (hp); [f]**Leland Chen** (vn); [f]**Clare McFarlane** (va); [abc]**Julius Drake** (pf). Chandos CHAN9197 (11/94).

...String Quartets – No. 1 in D minor; No. 2, "Spring Waters". **London Quartet.** Chandos CHAN9219 (5/94).

...Invocations[a]. A Leave-taking[b]. [a]**Jill Gomez** (sop); [b]**Anthony Rolfe Johnson** (ten); [a]**John Constable**, [b]**Graham Johnson** (pfs). Chandos CHAN9220 (6/94).

...Miss Julie. **Soloists; Philharmonia Orchestra / Vilem Tausky.** Lyrita SRCD2218 (3/93). *Gramophone Editor's choice.*⊕

Joseph-Marie Amiot

French 1718-1793

Amiot Divertissements chinois.
Pedrini Sonate a Violono Solo col Basso del Nepridi, Op. 3 – No. 1 in A major; No. 4 in G minor; No. 5 in G major; No. 7 in B flat major; No. 10 in C minor. **XVIII-21, Musique des Lumières** (Jean-Christophe Frisch, fl; Patrick Bismuth, vn; Hager Hanana, vc; Claire Antonini, theorbo; Martine Chappuis, hpd). Auvidis Astrée Ⓕ E8609 (67 minutes: DDD: 10/97). Recorded 1996.

Teodorico Pedrini was an Italian organist sent by the Pope to Peking in 1701, in answer to a request from the Emperor of China for a European musician to join his service. Western music had been an increasingly strong presence at the Imperial court ever since the first Italian musician, a Jesuit missionary, had arrived in Peking about 100 years earlier. Pedrini actually took ten years to reach China but once there he stayed until his death in 1746. The five sonatas for solo instrument and continuo served up here from his only surviving publication are Italian – more specifically Corellian – to the core. What makes this release special is that each sonata is prefaced by a *Divertissement chinois* from a set compiled in the 1770s by the French Jesuit priest, Joseph-Marie Amiot. Apparently European musicians in China performed the local music as well, and Amiot's pieces seem to be a collection of Chinese unaccompanied tunes put into Western notation for practical purposes. XVIII-21, Musique des Lumières, perform this exotic fare with some flair and plenty of imagination; although Pedrini's sonatas were advertised as being for violin, two of the five divertissement-sonata pairs are played on the flute and one on cello, with each player demonstrating a strongly expressive approach both to the Italian music and to the Chinese. Patrick Bismuth is a violinist noted for his bold interpretations, while Jean-Christophe Frisch's flute-playing is hauntingly convincing in the Amiot, if less so in the Pedrini. Overall, this is a fascinating, compelling and very probably unique recording.

Firket Amirov

USSR 1922-1984

Suggested listening ...

...Six Pieces. *Coupled with works by various composers.* **Leslie Newman** (fl); **Amanda Hurton** (pf). Cala CACD88026 (6/96). *See review in the Collections section; refer to the Index.*

Louis Andriessen

Dutch 1939

Suggested listening ...

...Hout. Hoketus. *Coupled with works by various composers.* **Bang on a Can All-Stars.** Sony Classical SK66483 (2/96). *See review in the Collections section; refer to the Index. Selected by Soundings.*

Anonymous

Anonymous Missa Caput (ed. Curtis). The story of the Salve regina. Salve regina. Jesu for thy
mercy[a]. Clangat tuba. Alma redemptoris mater. Old Hall Manuscript – Agnus Dei.
Smert Jesu fili Dei[a].
Traditional Make we merry[a]. Nowell, nowell, nowell. [a]**Shirley Rumsey,** [a]**Christopher Wilson** (ltes);
  Gothic Voices / Christopher Page ([a]lte). Hyperion Ⓕ CDA66857 (66 minutes: DDD: 2/97).
  Texts and translations included. Recorded 1996. *Gramophone Editor's choice.*   Ⓖ
This recording (going by the title "The Spirits of England and France, Volume 4") breaks new ground
for Gothic Voices in terms of repertory. For the first time, the group tackles a large-scale, multi-
movement work. One could hardly imagine a more appropriate Mass for their début in the genre than
the anonymous English *Caput* cycle. Composed *c*1440 and long thought to be by Dufay, it lays fair
claim to being the single most influential work of the fifteenth century. Its most innovative technical
features were widely copied by continental composers, but on this recording we can at last begin to
appreciate what all the fuss was about: few on the continent at the time were capable of writing music
of such breathtaking confidence. One can feel the impact, the delighted surprise of contemporary
listeners on hearing that very first burst of four-note writing in the *Kyrie*. In that respect, it is sobering
to think that the identity of this supremely influential composer may forever remain a mystery.
That phrase 'breathtaking confidence' aptly describes Gothic Voices, who are on the top of their
form. Initially one could hardly fail to be surprised by the briskness of this performance, but there is
little sign of hurry even in the most demandingly athletic places. Although the declamation of the
text is kept fairly low-key, the sense of phrase and line, of the notes taking their place amid a
kaleidoscope of changing sounds, is all beautifully judged. And with intonation and ensemble of this
consistency, it is possible to revel in sheer sonority. What else? The accompanying items, consisting
mostly of carols, make for lighter listening and a nicely balanced programme. This, then, is
a disc that grows in stature with each hearing. Anyone who might be put off by the 'anonymous'
listing can rest assured that this is music of the very highest order. The recording is unobtrusively
impressive.

Anonymous Missa, "Veterem hominem". Jesu, fili virginis. Doleo super te. Gaude Maria virgo.
  Deus creator omnium. Jesu salvator. A solis ortus. Salvator mundi. Christe, qui lux es. To many a
  well. Sancta Maria virgo. Mater ora filium. Ave maris stella. Pange lingua.
Dunstable Beata mater. **Gothic Voices** (Catherine King, contr; Steven Harrold, Julian Podger,
  Leigh Nixon, tens; Stephen Charlesworth, Donald Greig, bars) **/ Christopher Page.**
  Hyperion Ⓕ CDA66919 (65 minutes: DDD: 10/97). Texts and translations included.
  Recorded 1996.
As in their previous recordings, Gothic Voices' peculiar brand of extrovert dynamism puts a new spin
on the performance of fifteenth-century Mass music; more than just a Mass, what we have here is a
glimpse (one might say) into the very mind of a medieval composer. Music as contemplation,
certainly, but active, not passive; music in which each single voice conveys weight, number,
proportion. Thus, the recurring head-motif at the beginning of each movement of the *Veterem
hominem* Mass cycle is experienced not so much as a structural device as a manifestation of divine
immutability. In a similar spirit, the same tempos are retained in all the movements; this has not been
attempted very often, but far from being unrelenting, the result suits both pieces very well. If Page
and friends let rip in the Mass and in the carols (delivered with exhilarating brashness), they
deliberately adopt a more placid, even 'mainstream' approach for some of the smaller Marian pieces.
As to the chants that intersperse the polyphony, they certainly provide contrast; but can it be that the
fifteenth-century singers who polished off their polyphony with such gusto, took their 'daily bread'
of plainsong with so little salt?

Anonymous Old Hall Manuscript. **The Hilliard Ensemble** (David James, Ashley Stafford, altos;
  Rogers Covey-Crump, John Potter, Mark Padmore, tens; Gordon Jones, bar; Paul Hillier, bass).
  Virgin Classics Veritas Ⓜ VER5 61393-2 (65 minutes: DDD: 10/97). Texts and translations
  included. From EMI CDC7 54111-2 (1/92). Recorded 1990.
The Old Hall Manuscript is the principal source for the school of composers from which Leonel
Power and John Dunstable sprang (though many of the composers in this quintessentially English
source have French-sounding names). The Hilliards' Old Hall recital is very even-handed in its
representation both of composers and styles (though Power, as far and away the best-represented
composer in the source, gets more than most). As the only disc of its kind it warrants a strong
recommendation, even though the performances occasionally lack the dynamic quality so abundantly
present on other Hilliard recordings. The acoustic may have something to do with it: here it is so
reverberant that details are all too often drowned out, and in a few places there are displeasing flashes
of 'countertenor glare' (e.g. the *Credo* by Pennard). In the more demanding selections one has the
inexplicable impression that the ensemble has somehow failed to click, and there is occasionally a hint
of strain (as in *Gloria* by Pycard). Yet, there are moments of great beauty: the three-voice, descant-
based *Pia mater* comes to mind, or the two pieces by Forest, perhaps one of the younger composers
in the manuscript. As an album to be dipped into, rather than taken at one sitting, this disc is
eminently recommendable.

Anonymous Vigil in Kiev. **Russian Patriarchate Choir / Anatoly Grindenko.** Opus 111
Ⓕ OPS30-223 (78 minutes: DDD: 5/98). Texts and translations included. Recorded 1997.
Here is a revelatory exploration of unknown Russian riches, here monastic polyphony. This is a
repertory that contains more or less familiar versions of harmonized chants and often some
spectacularly startling variants: notable are the Deacon's *Priidite* (invitatory, monophonic), the
elaborate fourfold response "Tebe Gospodi" in the insistent litany, and the astonishing chromatic
'slips' in the *Canticle of Simeon*, the *Megalynarion* and in the *Trisagion* at the end of the *Great
Doxology*. Another item worthy of note is the Vespers prayer in which the bass is given the lion's
share, especially at cadences, while the upper voices move smoothly from chord to chord. Full texts
are provided, though there are one or two oddities in the English translation. The singing is sublime.
There can be few choirs in the world who are able to combine such richness of sound with such
prayerful attention to text, always perfectly declaimed.

Anthonello de Caserta   Italian *fl* 14th/15th century

Suggested listening ...
...Beauté parfaite. *Coupled with works by various composers.* **Alla Francesca.** Opus 111 OPS30-173.
See review in the Collections section; refer to the Index.   ⒼⒼⒼ

Jean-Baptiste Arban   French 1825-1889

Suggested listening ...
...Variations on a theme from Bellini's "Norma". Variations on a Tyrolean Theme. *Coupled with
works by various composers.* **Sergei Nakariakov** (tpt); **Alexander Markovich** (pf).
Teldec 4509-94554-2 (6/95). *See review in the Collections section; refer to the Index.*   ⒼⒼ

Jacques Arcadelt   ?Flanders ?1505-1568

Suggested listening ...
...En ce mois délicieux. Margot, labourez leg vignes. De temps que j'estois amoureux. Sa grand
beauté. *Coupled with works by various composers.* **The Scholars of London.**
Naxos 8 550880 (2/95). ☞ *See review in the Collections section; refer to the Index.*

Anton Arensky   Russian 1861-1906

Arensky Piano Concerto in F minor, Op. 2. Fantasia on Russian Folksongs, Op. 48.
Bortkiewicz Piano Concerto No. 1 in B flat major, Op. 16. **Stephen Coombs** (pf); **BBC Scottish
Symphony Orchestra / Jerzy Maksymiuk.** Hyperion Ⓕ CDA66624 (71 minutes: DDD: 3/93).
Recorded 1992.   Ⓖ
It is suggested in the insert-note which accompanies this recording that "there must always be a place
for those like Arensky and Bortkiewicz who reflect so elegantly and expertly on what has gone before,
rather than shake us by the ears and grab us (sometimes screaming) into the future". This observation
is most pertinent to the works here. All three are reminders of the pleasures of easy-listening music
from an age before the whole concept was hijacked by commercialism. If this is the sort of thing you
like, you'll surely like this sort of thing, as they say. Both concertos fall pleasantly on the ear. Arensky's
early Op. 2 (1881) is an engaging cocktail with overtones of Liszt, Chopin and Grieg. Bortkiewicz's
Op. 16 is a true product of Russia's Silver Age, the scent of the Nicholas and Alexandra era evoked by
a blend of Rachmaninov and Wagner. Stephen Coombs and the BBC Scottish SO present the music
with wholehearted advocacy. Hyperion's engineering has the piano rather backward, not allowing it to
sparkle quite as it should; otherwise this is a model issue from this ever-enterprising source.

Arensky Piano Trios – No. 1 in D minor, Op. 32; No. 2 in F minor, Op. 73. **Beaux Arts Trio**
(Ida Kavafian, vn; Peter Wiley, vc; Menahem Pressler, pf). Philips Ⓕ 442 127-2PH (63 minutes:
DDD: 6/95). Recorded 1994.   Ⓖ
The presence of Tchaikovsky hovers benignly over Arensky in many pieces, not least in the First Trio:
though Arensky does not have Tchaikovsky's felicity of invention, he can actually solve the problems
of writing for piano and strings more steadily, and the work would surely have a more secure place in
the repertory were it attached to a more famous name. While it has become something of a popular
item, his Second languishes, with only two recorded versions available. Both are fine works, and the
Beaux Arts Trio on Philips give beautiful, perceptive performances. Again, comparisons with
Tchaikovsky's Piano Trio are inevitable, and by no means odious. Arensky may not have
Tchaikovsky's distinctive musical personality, but he can write at least as effectively for the difficult
medium, sometimes more originally, and he never lapses into the mighty chordal piano textures with

which Tchaikovsky can make problems for his players. Moreover, he has a melodic charm that is much in the manner of Tchaikovsky, who, with some reservations, was appreciative. The *Elegy* of the First Trio and the *Romanza* of the Second are beautiful inventions, and both *Scherzos* speed along delicately and wittily. Another influence for the good was Mendelssohn. It is important not to overplay the resemblances in performance, and indeed not to overplay at all: less makes more in this music, and does so in these admirable interpretations. Balance is very well managed throughout by both players and the producer.

Additional recommendation ...

...No. 1. **Tchaikovsky** Piano Trio in A minor, Op. 50. **Cho-Liang Lin** (vn); **Gary Hoffman** (vc); **Yefim Bronfman** (pf). Sony Classical Ⓕ SK53269 (76 minutes: DDD: 9/94). *See review under Tchaikovsky; refer to the Index.* **Gramophone** *Editor's choice.*

Further listening ...

...Silhouettes (Suite No. 2), Op. 23. *Coupled with* **Scriabin** No. 3 in C minor, Op. 43, "Le divin poème". **Danish National Radio Symphony Orchestra / Neeme Järvi.** Chandos CHAN8898 (10/91).

...String Quartet No. 2 in A minor, Op. 35. *Coupled with* **Tchaikovsky** Souvenir de Florence, Op. 70. **Raphael Ensemble.** Hyperion CDA66648 (2/94).

...Suites for Two Pianos – No. 1 in F major, Op. 15; No. 2, Op. 23, "Silhouettes"; No. 3, Op. 33, "Variations"; No. 4, Op. 62. **Stephen Coombs, Ian Munro** (pfs). Hyperion CDA66755.

...Intermezzo in F minor, Op. 36 No. 12. Le ruisseau dans la forêt. Romance, Op. 53 No. 5. *Coupled with works by various composers.* **Margaret Fingerhut** (pf). Chandos CHAN9218 (4/94).

Dominik Argento
American 1927

Suggested listening ...

...Six Elizabethan Songs. *Coupled with works by various composers.* **Barbara Bonney** (sop); **André Previn** (pf). Decca 455 511-2DH (2/98). *See review in the Collections section; refer to the Index. Selected by Soundings.*   ⒼⒼ

Attilio Ariosti
Italian 1666-c1729

Suggested listening ...

...La rosa. *Coupled with works by various composers.* **Ann Monoyios** (sop); **Berlin Barock Compagney.** Capriccio 10 459 (10/95). ☞ *See review in the Collections section; refer to the Index.*   Ⓖ

Thomas Arne
British 1710-1778

Arne Favourite Concertos – No. 1 in C major (solo hpd version)[a]. Keyboard Sonatas – No. 1 in F major[a]. Trio Sonatas – No. 2 in G major; No. 5; No. 6 in B minor; No. 7 in E minor. **Le Nouveau Quatuor** (Utako Ikeda, fl; Catherine Weiss, vn; Mark Caudle, vc; [a]Paul Nicholson, hpd). Amon Ra Ⓕ CD-SAR42 (58 minutes: DDD: 5/90). ☞ Recorded 1989.

If the music history books offer little more than a passing reference to the slim repertoire of enchanting chamber music by Thomas Arne, the ordinary man in the street, who can at least whistle *Rule Britannia*, is unlikely even to have heard that any exists. This disc comes therefore as something of a revelation and as a valuable contribution to the composer's discography. The members of the Nouveau Quatuor perform on instruments dating from the composer's lifetime, tuned down a semitone. The trio sonatas, originally published for two violins and continuo, are played here by a mixed quartet of flute, violin, cello and harpsichord, which is believed to have been what the composer really intended. The introduction of the flute adds colour, brightness and definition to these charming pieces and gives the listener a chance to savour the admirable tone and phrasing of the flautist, Utako Ikeda. Paul Nicholson's harpsichord solos are distinguished as much by their elegance as by their extraordinary power and brilliance. A word, finally, in praise of Peter Holman's excellent insert-notes: they are both scholarly and extremely readable.

Further listening ...

...Artaxerxes. **Soloists; The Parley of Instruments / Roy Goodman.** Hyperion CDA67051/2 (6/96). ☞

Richard Arnell
British 1917

Arnell Punch and the Child – ballet[a].
Berners The Triumph of Neptune – ballet suite[b].
Delius Paris: The Song of a Great City[c]. [b]**Robert Grooters** (bar); [ac]**Royal Philharmonic Orchestra;** [b]**Philadelphia Orchestra / Sir Thomas Beecham.** Sony Classical Essential Classics Ⓑ SBK62748* (68 minutes: ADD: 12/96). Item marked [a] from Columbia LX1391/3 (5/51). Recorded 1950), [b]CBS 61431 (7/74. 1952), [c]Philips ABL3089 (2/56. 1955).   Ⓖ

Delians everywhere will rejoice at the reappearance of Beecham's 1955 recording of *Paris*. Comparison with this conductor's marvellous 1934 version shows his earlier offering to be the better co-ordinated of the two (both orchestrally and structurally), yet there are moments to treasure in this RPO performance and Beecham's poetic instincts do not desert him – witness his surpassingly lovely treatment of Delius's secondary lyrical material when it reappears at 15'21". Richard Arnell's ballet, *Punch and the Child*, dates from 1948, a commission for the American company, Ballet Caravan (later known as the New York City Ballet). Beecham conducted the English concert-hall première in 1949 and recorded it the following year with the RPO in Kingsway Hall. It's an attractively rumbustious creation, reminiscent at times of Bliss in ballet mode, and delivered here with much gusto. Beecham twice recorded music from Lord Berners's 1926 ballet, *The Triumph of Neptune*. The present 1952 account of the Suite with the Philadelphia restores those two substantial numbers ("Cloudland" and "The Frozen Forest") not found on Beecham's earlier 1937 LPO set. Again, good transfers, though in *Paris* the sound has not the extraordinary richness and depth that distinguishes Anthony Griffith's superb restoration of that earlier Columbia production.

Additional recommendation ...
...Paris. Eventyr. Fennimore and Gerda – Intermezzo. Over the Hills and Far Away. Irmelin Prelude. **London Philharmonic Orchestra / Sir Thomas Beecham.** Sir Thomas Beecham Trust mono Ⓜ BEECHAM2* (61 minutes: ADD: 6/89).

Sir Malcolm Arnold British 1921

Arnold Clarinet Concertos – No. 1, Op. 20; No. 2, Op. 115. You know what sailors are – Scherzetto (arr. Palmer).
Britten (orch. Matthews). Movement for Clarinet and Orchestra.
Maconchy Concertinos Nos. 1 and 2. **Thea King** (cl); **English Chamber Orchestra / Barry Wordsworth.** Hyperion Ⓟ CDA66634 (65 minutes: DDD: 12/93). Recorded 1992.   Ⓖ

Designed in part as a tribute to Frederick Thurston, who died 40 years ago, this collection of short *concertante* works for clarinet makes an exceptionally attractive disc, beautifully recorded and superbly performed, with Thurston's widow and star-pupil, Thea King, as soloist. With her ever-seductive tone, at once sensuously beautiful yet clear, never letting you forget that this is a reed instrument, King perpetuates the qualities Thurston sought to instil, not least in the works on the disc written for him. These include the first of Arnold's concertos and the first of Maconchy's concertinos, while the *Scherzetto*, a delightfully jaunty piece adapted by Christopher Palmer from Arnold's music for the film, *You know what sailors are*, also seems to have been inspired directly by Thurston's playing. The other direct influence here is Benny Goodman. He turned in 1942 to the young Benjamin Britten, then in the United States, to write a concerto for him. It is a highly attractive short piece, alternately energetic and poetic, with material adroitly interchanged, and with percussion used most imaginatively. The second of the Arnold concertos was written for Goodman too and it shows Arnold at his most endearing, with sharp ideas leading to broad, memorable melodies that echo popular music, without ever cheapening the result. Both King and the ECO under Barry Wordsworth bring out the warmth as well as the rhythmic drive of all this music.

Additional recommendations ...
...Clarinet Concerto No. 1[b]. Double Violin Concerto, Op. 77[d]. Flute Concerto No. 1, Op. 45[a]. Horn Concerto No. 2, Op. 58[c].[a]**Karen Jones** (fl); [b]**Michael Collins** (cl); [c]**Richard Watkins** (hn); [d]**Kenneth Sillito,** [d]**Lyn Fletcher** (vns); **London Musici / Mark Stephenson.** Conifer Classics Ⓟ CDCF172 (56 minutes: DDD: 8/89).
...Flute Concerto No. 2, Op. 111[a]. Clarinet Concerto No. 2[b]. Horn Concerto No. 1, Op. 11[c]. Piano Duet and Strings, Op. 32[d]. [a]**Karen Jones** (fl); [b]**Michael Collins** (cl); [c]**Richard Watkins** (hn); [d]**David Nettle,** [d]**Richard Markham** (pfs); **London Musici / Mark Stephenson.** Conifer Classics Ⓟ CDCF228 (72 minutes: DDD: 12/93).
...Clarinet Concertos Nos. 1 and 2[a]. Three Shanties, Op. 4[b]. Sonatina, Op. 29[c]. Fantasia, Op. 87. Divertimento, Op. 37[d]. **Emma Johnson** (cl); [bd]**Jaime Martin** (fl); [bd]**Jonathan Kelly** (ob); [b]**Claire Briggs** (hn); [b]**Susanna Cohen** (bn); [c]**Malcolm Martineau** (pf); [a]**English Chamber Orchestra / Ivor Bolton.** ASV Ⓟ CDDCA922 (61 minutes: DDD: 7/95).

Arnold Flute Concertos[a] – No. 1, Op. 45; No. 2, Op. 111. Three Shanties, Op. 4[b]. Sonatina for Flute and Piano, Op. 19[c]. Fantasia, Op. 89[e]. Divertimento, Op. 37[f]. Flute Sonata, Op. 121[g].
James Galway (fl); [b]**James Galway Wind Quintet** ([bf]Gareth Hulse, ob; [bf]Antony Pay, cl; [b]Rachel Gough, bn; [b]Philip Eastop, hn); [cg]**Philip Moll** (pf); [a]**Academy of St Martin in the Fields / Sir Neville Marriner.** RCA Victor Red Seal Ⓟ Ⓘ 09026 68860-2 (69 minutes: DDD: 4/98). Recorded 1995. *Gramophone Editor's choice.*

In this expert, sweet-toned and resourceful music-making, these fine artists audibly enjoy themselves hugely, responding to Arnold's idiomatic and resourceful writing as to the manner born. Galway and friends are particularly enjoyable in the sparkling early *Three Shanties* for wind quintet and the delicious *Divertimento* for flute, oboe and clarinet Cast in six pithy movements (and masterfully played here), the latter piece contains invention of great freshness and charm, with definite echoes of the *English Dances* from the same period. In the wistful central *Andante* of the First Flute Concerto,

Sir Neville Marriner and his beautifully prepared Academy strings provide a poignant backdrop to Galway's ravishing playing, and this music's kinship with the great slow movement of Arnold's Second Symphony is most perceptively brought out. In fact, the performances of both concertos are probably the best we've ever had. Galway himself was, of course, the lucky recipient of the Flute Sonata (whose première he gave at the 1977 Cardiff Festival), and he and Philip Moll do full justice to this work's entrancing mix of lyricism (the lilting *Andantino* centrepiece boasts a particularly indelible main idea) and exhilarating virtuosity. Recording quality is nicely integrated, too, with Galway never overprominently balanced, though Moll's piano can sound just a touch rough in its lowest reaches. A delightful anthology all the same.

Arnold Four Scottish Dances, Op. 59 (arr. Farr). Four English Dances, Op. 27 (arr. Farr). Four Engiish Dances, Op. 33 (arr. Farr). Four Cornish Dances, Op. 91. Little Suites – No. 1, Op. 80; No. 2, Op. 93. Fantasy, Op. 114. The Padstow Lifeboat, Op. 94[a]. **Grimethorpe Colliery Band / Elgar Howarth;** [a]**Sir Malcolm Arnold.** Conifer Classics Ⓕ CDCF222 (66 minutes: DDD: 12/93). Recorded 1993.   Ⓖ

The composer was present throughout these recordings and he conducted the final item, the *Padstow Lifeboat* march with its insistent off-key foghorn. The sheer ebullience of the playing is immediately breathtaking in the first of the *Scottish Dances*, and in the second the 'drunken' solo bass trombone is in the best tradition of the British brass experience. The eight *English Dances* are played with equal sophistication and brilliance. The *Mesto* (Op. 27 No. 3) is quite haunting and the players get round the colour problem in the first dance in Op. 33 by whistling the air themselves! The more melancholy atmosphere of the *Cornish Dances* is touchingly caught. The two *Little Suites* demonstrate how well the composer – once a trumpeter himself in the LPO – understands the medium. The finest of the original band works is the *Fantasy,* a highly imaginative series of joined vignettes. The recording is natural, and beautifully balanced, making the most of the hall's ambience without any loss of detail.

Additional recommendations ...

...Cornish Dances. English Dances – Op. 27; Op. 33. Irish Dances, Op. 126. Scottish Dances. Solitaire – Sarabande; Polka. **London Philharmonic Orchestra / Malcolm Arnold.** Lyrita Ⓕ SRCD201 (61 minutes: ADD/DDD: 12/90).   ⒼⒼ

...*As Lyrita.* **Philharmonia Orchestra / Bryden Thomson.** Chandos Ⓕ CHAN8867 (48 minutes: DDD: 10/90).

...Four Scottish Dances[c]. **Vaughan Williams** Job[a]. The Wasps – Overture[b]. **London Philharmonic Orchestra /** [ab]**Sir Adrian Boult,** [c]**Sir Malcolm Arnold.** Everest Ⓕ EVC9006 (57 minutes: ADD: 5/95).

...English Dances – Op. 27; Op. 33. Scottish Dances. Cornish Dances. Four Irish Dances, Op. 126. Four Welsh Dances, Op. 138. **Queensland Symphony Orchestra / Andrew Penny.** Naxos Ⓢ 8 553526 (55 minutes: DDD: 10/96).

...English Dances – Op. 27; Op. 33. *Coupled with works by* **Elgar** and **Walton** **London Philharmonic Orchestra / Sir Adrian Boult.** Belart mono Ⓑ 461 359-2* (67 minutes: ADD: 9/97).

Arnold Symphonies – No. 1, Op. 22; No. 2, Op. 40. **London Symphony Orchestra / Richard Hickox.** Chandos Ⓕ CHAN9335 (61 minutes: DDD: 3/95). Recorded 1994.

Here is an entirely appropriate coupling of the first two symphonies, superbly played by the LSO and given demonstration sound in what is surely an ideal acoustic for this music, with striking depth and amplitude and a wholly natural brilliance. The dynamic range is wide but the moments of spectacle, and there are quite a few, bring no discomfort. Richard Hickox shows himself thoroughly at home in both symphonies and the readings have a natural flow and urgency, with the two slow movements bringing haunting, atmospheric feeling. The First Symphony opens with thrusting confidence on strings and horns and at its climax, where the strings soar against angry brass ostinatos, the playing generates great intensity; then at the start of the slow movement the purity of the flute solo brings a calm serenity which returns at the close. There are only three movements and the plangent lyrical melancholia of the expansive march theme of the finale is filled out by some superb horn playing which is enormously compelling. The first movement of Symphony No. 2 brings a most winning clarinet solo (Arnold's fund of melodic ideas seems inexhaustible), there is an energetic, bustling scherzo to follow, but again it is the slow movement which one remembers for its elegiac opening, its arresting climax and lovely epilogue-like close. Above all these are real performances without any of the inhibitions of 'studio' recording.

Additional recommendations ...

...No. 2. A Grand Grand Overture, Op. 57. Concerto for Two Pianos (three hands), Op. 104[a]. Carnival of Animals, Op. 72. [a]**David Nettle,** [a]**Richard Markham** (pfs); **Royal Philharmonic Orchestra / Vernon Handley.** Conifer Classics Ⓕ CDCF240 (59 minutes: DDD: 12/94). *Gramophone Editor's choice.*

...Nos. 1 and 2. **National Symphony Orchestra of Ireland / Andrew Penny.** Naxos Ⓢ 8 553406 (56 minutes: DDD: 5/96).

...Nos. 1 and 5. **Royal Philharmonic Orchestra / Vernon Handley.** Conifer Classics Ⓕ 75605 51257-2 (58 minutes: DDD: 10/96).

Arnold Symphonies – No. 3, Op. 63; No. 4, Op. 71. **London Symphony Orchestra / Richard Hickox.**
Chandos Ⓕ CHAN9290 (74 minutes: DDD: 9/94). Recorded 1993.
These two Arnold symphonies share comparatively little of the amiable optimism which distinguishes so many of his shorter works. Instead they reflect his experience of life over a broader span, with disillusion and even tragedy as part of their symphonic ethos. As it happens the Third Symphony does have an exuberant, upbeat finale, but even here there is a last-minute change of mood in the coda, with a sudden Holst-like, plangent rhythmic warning; nevertheless the final few bars are distinctly positive. The work, commissioned by the Royal Liverpool Philharmonic Society and first performed in 1957, produces a long, striking and expressively bleak string melody in the opening movement, while the despairing isolation of its *Lento* slow movement is similarly harrowing. The first movement of the Fourth Symphony is dominated by one of those entirely winning Arnoldian lyrical tunes even though there is jagged dissonance in the central episode, and it has been suggested that this ambivalence was prompted by the contemporary Notting Hill race-riots, which also may have brought the Caribbean percussion instruments into the orchestra. Richard Hickox has the full measure of both symphonies and the Chandos recording is superb, full of colour and atmosphere.
Additional recommendations ...
...No. 4. **London Philharmonic Orchestra / Sir Malcolm Arnold.**
Lyrita Ⓕ SRCD 200 (54 minutes: DDD: 11/90).
...No. 3[a]. **Vaughan Williams** Symphony No. 9 in E minor[b]. **London Philharmonic Orchestra /** [a]**Sir Malcolm Arnold,** [b]**Sir Adrian Boult.** Everest Ⓕ EVC9001 (70 minutes: ADD: 4/95).
...Nos. 3 and 4. **Royal Liverpool Philharmonic Orchestra / Vernon Handley.**
Conifer Classics Ⓕ 75605 51258-2 (69 minutes: DDD: 12/96).

Arnold Symphonies – No. 5, Op. 74; No. 6, Op. 95. **London Symphony Orchestra / Richard Hickox.**
Chandos Ⓕ CHAN9385 (58 minutes: DDD: 12/95). Recorded 1995. Ⓖ
Arnold's Fifth Symphony is one of his most accessible and rewarding works. The inspiration for the symphony was the early deaths of several of the composer's friends and colleagues: Dennis Brain, Frederick Thurston, David Paltenghi and Gerard Hoffnung. They are all remembered in the first movement and Hoffnung's spirit clearly pops up in the third and fourth. The Chandos recording is richly resonant and reinforces the impression that in Hickox's hands the *Andante* has an added degree of acceptance in its elegaic close, while the last two movements are colourfully expansive. The Sixth Symphony is nothing like as comfortable as the Fifth, with a bleak unease in the unrelenting energy of the first movement, which becomes even more discomfiting in the desolate start to the *Lento*. This leads to a forlorn suggestion of a funeral march, which then ironically quickens in pace but is suddenly cut down; the drum strokes become menacingly powerful and the despairing mood of the movement's opening returns. Hickox handles this quite superbly and grips the listener in the music's pessimism, which then lifts completely with the energetic syncopated trumpet theme of the rondo finale. Although later there are moments of ambiguity, and dissonant reminders of the earlier music, these are eclipsed by the thrilling life-asserting coda. In both symphonies the splendidly expansive Chandos recording increases the weight and power of utterance and though Handley's earlier version of the Sixth is riveting, Hickox is even more compelling.
Additional recommendation ...
...No. 6, Op. 95. Fantasy on a theme of John Field, Op. 116[a]. Sweeney Todd, Op. 68*a*. Tam O'Shanter, Op. 51. [a]**John Lill** (pf); **Royal Philharmonic Orchestra / Vernon Handley.**
Conifer Classics Ⓕ CDCF224 (78 minutes: DDD: 2/94). *Gramophone Editor's choice. Selected by Sounds in Retrospect.*

Arnold Symphony No. 9, Op. 128. **National Symphony Orchestra of Ireland / Andrew Penny.**
Naxos Ⓢ 8 553540 (57 minutes: DDD: 5/96). Includes an interview between the composer and the conductor. Recorded 1995. *Gramophone Editor's choice.* Ⓖ
This culmination to Arnold's symphonic series is both characteristic and distinctive. As the late Hugo Cole put it in his survey of Arnold's music (Faber: 1989), "Arnold composes with his ear. His music speaks to us first of all through its sounds." If at the start and elsewhere one is reminded of Shostakovich, the instrumentation is quite distinctive. The ear is regularly tweaked by the terracing of sounds, at extremes of register as well as of dynamic, culminating in the long slow finale, almost as long as the other three movements combined. With two poignant themes, the mood of tragedy and disillusion is clear. The parallel with the final *Adagio* of Mahler's Ninth Symphony comes obviously to mind. Yet unlike Mahler the music conveys no hint of neurosis or self-pity. The other three movements are just as direct, bald in their arguments but ever pointful, not facile, built on instantly memorable material. Andrew Penny draws not just a concentrated, consistently committed performance from the Irish players, but a warmly resonant one, with the strings sounding glorious and the woodwind and brass consistently brilliant. The recording is rich and full.
Additional recommendation ...
...No. 9[a]. Oboe Concertino, Op. 28*a* (orch. Steptoe)[b]. Fantasia, Op. 90[c].
[bc]**Nicholas Daniel** (ob); [ab]**Bournemouth Symphony Orchestra / Vernon Handley.**
Conifer Classics Ⓕ 75605 51273-2 (62 minutes: DDD: 4/97).

Further listening ...
...The Fair Field Overture. A Sussex Overture, Op. 31. Beckus the Dandipratt, Op. 5. The Smoke, Op. 21. Commonwealth Christmas Overture, Op. 64. **London Philharmonic Orchestra / Sir Malcolm Arnold.** Reference Recordings RRCD48 (6/92).

...Guitar Concerto, Op. 67. *Coupled with works by* **Rodrigo** and **Takemitsu** Julian Bream (gtr); **City of Birmingham Symphony Orchestra / Sir Simon Rattle.** EMI CDC7 54661-2 (7/93). ⓖ

...Film Suites (arr. Palmer) – The Bridge on the River Kwai; The Inn of the Sixth Happiness; Hobson's Choice; Whistle down the Wind. The Sound Barrier, Op. 38. **London Symphony Orchestra / Richard Hickox.** Chandos CHAN9100 (2/93).

...Sinfoniettas – No. 1, Op. 48; No. 2, Op. 65; No. 3, Op. 81. Flute Concerto No. 1, Op. 45[a]. Oboe Concerto, Op. 39[b]. [a]**Edward Beckett** (fl); [b]**Malcolm Messiter** (ob); **London Festival Orchestra / Ross Pople.** Hyperion CDA66332 (3/90).

...Symphonies – No. 7, Op. 113; No. 8, Op. 124. **Royal Philharmonic Orchestra / Vernon Handley.** Conifer Classics CDCF177 (3/91). ⓖ

...Hobson's Choice (arr. Hogan) – Overture and Shoe Ballet; Willie and Maggie; Wedding Night; Finale. Five Pieces, Op. 84. Fantasy, Op. 130. Homage to the Queen, Op. 42 – Suite. Piano Trio, Op. 54. **St Clair Trio.** Koch International Classics 37266-2 (11/96).

...String Quartets – No. 1, Op. 23; No. 2, Op. 118. **McCapra Quartet.** Chandos CHAN9112 (10/92).

...Allegro in E minor. Three Piano Pieces. Serenade in G major. Day dreams. Two Piano Pieces. Piano Sonata. Three Piano Pieces. Prelude. Variations on a Ukrainian folk-song, Op. 9. Children's Suite, Op. 16. Two Bagatelles, Op. 18. Eight Children's Pieces, Op. 36. Three Fantasies, Op. 129. **Benjamin Frith** (pf). Koch International Classics 37162-2 (2/95).

Juan Crisóstomo Arriaga
Spanish 1806-1826

Arriaga String Quartets – No. 1 in D minor; No. 2 in A major; No. 3 in E flat major. **Sine Nomine Quartet** (Patrick Genet, François Gottraux, vns; Nicolas Pache, va; Marc Jaermann, vc). Claves Ⓕ CD509501 (75 minutes: DDD: 9/95). Recorded 1994. *Gramophone Editor's choice.* ⓖ

Arriaga had written an octet (among other things) by the age of 11, had had an opera performed when he was 13, and three months after entering the Paris Conservatoire (aged 15) was declared to have "completely mastered harmony": two years later the highly critical Cherubini called an eight-part choral piece of his a masterpiece. By that time, however, Arriaga had already composed much, including, in a genre then greatly in vogue in Paris, the present three quartets. (An extraordinary slip in the translation states that Arriaga had hoped to have them performed at the court of King Edward VII – who had yet to be born! The king in question was in fact Fernando VII of Spain.) These quartets are written with a sureness and maturity of technique and a felicitous flow of invention that almost justify Arriaga having been called "the Spanish Mozart" (apart from his having been born 50 years to the day after his great predecessor): indeed, there is a Mozartian shadow over the dramatic opening movement of the D minor work. Other influences have been adduced but particularly in the E flat Quartet, notably in the remarkable second and third movements, a distinctive personality is unmistakable. Even more than those other teenage phenomena, Rossini's string sonatas and Mendelssohn's string symphonies, these quartets have a right to be judged by the highest criteria. The young Swiss ensemble Sine Nomine offer unquestionably the best performances of these now available: at times pushing speeds but their playing shows real commitment as well as considerable polish and nuance.

Additional recommendation ...
...Nos. 1-3. **Guarneri Quartet.** Philips Ⓕ 446 092-2PH (75 minutes: DDD: 7/96).

Emanuele d'Astorga
Italian 1680-?1757

Suggested listening ...
...Stabat mater. *Coupled with works by* **Durante** and **Pergolesi** Ann Monoyios (sop); **Balthasar Neumann Choir; Freiburg Baroque Orchestra / Thomas Hengelbrock.** Deutsche Harmonia Mundi 05472 77369-2 (10/97). ✐ *See review under Durante; refer to the Index.*

Kurt Atterberg
Swedish 1887-1974

Atterberg Cello Concerto, Op. 21[a]. Cello Sonata in B minor, Op. 27[b]. **Werner Thomas-Mifune** (vc); [b]**Carmen Piazzini** (pf); [a]**Berlin Radio Symphony Orchestra / Karl Anton Rickenbacher.** Koch Schwann Ⓕ 315852 (63 minutes: DDD: 2/98). Recorded 1994.

Atterberg's B minor Sonata (1925) was designed to be played by a single stringed instrument – violin, viola or cello – and in 1955 the composer himself made a very effective transcription for horn. Each solo instrument subtly alters the expressive character of the piece and listening to the various versions there is something of the four ages of man, or the seasons perhaps, about them: the youthful (spring-like) ardour of the violin, the slightly blowzier summer-vigour of the horn, the cello and viola increasingly mellow – autumn and winter, perhaps. (Atterberg's preferred version was for his own instrument, the cello.) What is noticeable about this account is the treatment of the central *Adagio molto*, Thomas-Mifune taking (at 10'43") around four minutes longer than the Marco Polo performances, for horn and for violin (see below), which seem much close to *Andante*. Thomas-Mifune is clearly closer to the truth (maybe a shade *too* slow). Oddly, this gentle movement's expressive character changes little with the variation of instrument. The Cello Concerto (1917-22) does not exist in an alternative version, although the composer later created a nominal 'Second' from his Horn Concerto, Op. 28. Atterberg's style tends to be identifiable by what it is not as much as by its own characteristics; in the Cello Concerto there are a variety of resonances of the sound worlds of others, especially the Sibelius of the Violin Concerto, while in the finale some of the orchestral writing points (briefly but remarkably) towards Villa-Lobos! It is a rather lovely piece, and receives a most sympathetic interpretation from Thomas-Mifune and Rickenbacher. The sound quality is nicely judged.

Additional recommendations ...
...Piano Quintet, Op. 31[a]. Suite No. 1, "Orientale"[b]. Horn Sonata in B minor, Op. 27[c]. [c]**Imre Magyari** (hn); [b]**György Kertész** (vc); [ab]**Ilona Prunyi** (pf); [a]**New Budapest Quartet.**
Marco Polo Ⓕ 8 223405 (62 minutes: DDD: 9/93).
...Violin Sonata in B minor, Op. 27[c]. Autumn Ballads, Op. 15[a]. Rondeau rétrospectif, Op. 26[b]. Trio concertante in G minor/C major, Op. 57[d]. Valse monotone in C major[e]. [c]**Eszter Pérényi**, [d]**András Kiss** (vns); [d]**György Kertész** (vc); [d]**Deborah Sipkay** (hp); [abce]**Ilona Prunyi**, [b]**Sándor Falvay** (pf).
Marco Polo Ⓕ 8 223404 (65 minutes: DDD: 9/94).

Daniel-François-Esprit Auber
French 1782-1871

Auber Le domino noir. **Sumi Jo** (sop) Angèle d'Olivarès; **Isabelle Vernet** (sop) Brigitte de San Lucar; **Bruce Ford** (ten) Horace de Massarena; **Patrick Power** (ten) Count Juliano; **Martine Olmeda** (mez) Jacinthe; **Jules Bastin** (bass) Gil Perez; **Doris Lamprecht** (mez) Ursule; **Jocelyne Taillon** (mez) La tourière; **Gilles Cachemaille** (bar) Lord Elfort; **London Voices.**
Auber Gustav III, ou Le bal masqué – Overture; Ballet Music. **English Chamber Orchestra / Richard Bonynge.** Decca Ⓕ 440 646-2DHO2 (two discs: 144 minutes: DDD: 1/96). Notes, text and translation included. Recorded 1993-95. *Gramophone Editor's choice.* ⒼⒼ
Auber's operas were tremendously successful in the nineteenth century, but have hardly been performed in the twentieth at all. *Le domino noir* clocked up 1,200 performances in Paris alone, after its 1837 première, and was soon seen in London and in New Orleans. This spiffing recording – the only previous one was a much-abridged affair from French radio – is the surest blow yet to be struck for a revival of Auber's popularity in our time. The music is tuneful, danceable, constantly surprising in its form, and full of interesting orchestration. The story is a variation on the usual masked-ball romantic comedy. The heroine, Angèle, is sung by Sumi Jo who sounds even more confident than she did in the recital of French arias ("Carnival!", reviewed in the Collections section; refer to the Index) which she and Bonynge recorded at the same time as this. As the young man in pursuit of the beautiful masked stranger, Bruce Ford sings with a good deal of elegance, taking the high notes in full voice, rather than the head tone which was probably customary in the 1830s. Both he and Sumi Jo deal pretty well with the French language – most of the rest of the cast consists of distinguished French singers: Isabelle Vernet as Angèle's confidante, Martine Olmeda splendid as the housekeeper, Jacinthe, and the veteran Jules Bastin as Gil Perez, porter at the convent.

One of Auber's most successful tragic operas was another masked ball – *Gustav III*, the libretto of which, also by Scribe, later served for Verdi's *Un ballo in maschera*. As a fill-up on the second disc we get the ball scene from that opera, which is a ballet in itself. Bonynge conducts with his usual flair, keeping everything going at a sparkling pace and encouraging some really imaginative singing. Gilles Cachemaille has a cameo as one of those satirical English milords who were so much a part of nineteenth-century Parisian comedy. Auber and Scribe produced 50 operas together. No wonder the streets on either side of the Paris Opéra are named after them.

Further listening ...
...Overtures – Le Cheval de bronze. Fra Diavolo. La Muette de Portici. *Coupled with* **Suppé** Overtures – Die schöne Galathee. Pique Dame. Leichte Kavallerie. Dichter und Bauer. Ein Morgen, ein Mittag, ein Abend in Wien. Boccaccio. **Detroit Symphony Orchestra / Paul Paray.** Mercury 434 309-2MM.
...Fra Diavolo. **Soloists; Jean Laforge Chorale Ensemble; Monte Carlo Philharmonic Orchestra / Marc Soustrot.** EMI CDS7 54810-2 (1/94).

Georges Auric
French 1899-1983

Suggested listening ...
...Adieu New York. *Coupled with works by various composers.* **Marcelo Bratke** (pf).
Olympia Explorer OCD487 (12/96). *See review in the Collections section; refer to the Index.*

Carl Philipp Emanuel Bach   German 1714-1788

C.P.E. Bach Cello Concertos – A minor, H432; B flat major, H436; A major, H439.
  Bach Collegium Japan / Hidemi Suzuki (vc). BIS Ⓕ CD807 (68 minutes: DDD: 2/98).
  Recorded 1996. *Gramophone Editor's choice.*

Writing in the booklet for this release, Hidemi Suzuki wonders why it is that cellists who bemoan their lack of concerto repertory continue to neglect C.P.E. Bach's three essays in the genre. One can only agree with him that it is indeed a mystery, for these are excellent pieces, full of infectious nervous energy in their outer movements and tender lyricism in central ones. The Bach concertos are not unknown to the recording catalogues, however, not least because they also exist in alternative versions which the composer made for flute and harpsichord respectively. It is not known in what order the three instrumentations of these concertos originally came, but as Suzuki points out there are times when the low-lying cello has difficulty making itself heard properly against the orchestra, having said which, he proceeds to make light of the matter in performances whose agility, lightness and textural clarity make those of Bylsma and the larger-sounding OAE sound heavy-handed by comparison. But while Suzuki – thanks to a generally thinner sound – is the more successful in the way he transmits the surface excitement and energy of the quick movements, he cannot match Bylsma's vocal inspiration in the eloquent, sometimes brooding *Empfindsamkeit* poetry of the slow movement – in such music, the Dutchman is always worth listening to. Suzuki's, nevertheless, are refreshing and enlivening performances of attractive and substantial music.

Additional recommendations ...
  ...**Anner Bylsma** (vc); **Orchestra of the Age of Enlightenment / Gustav Leonhardt.**
    Virgin Classics Veritas Ⓕ VC7 59541-2 (70 minutes: DDD: 2/90). ✍
  ...**Miklós Perényi** (vc); **Liszt Chamber Orchestra / János Rolla.**
    Harmonia Mundi Musique d'abord Ⓑ HMA190 3026 (70 minutes: DDD: 8/94).
  ...**Timothy Hugh** (vc); **Bournemouth Sinfonietta / Richard Studt.**
    Naxos Ⓢ 8 553298 (71 minutes: DDD: 8/96).

C.P.E. Bach Harpsichord Concertos – G minor, H409; A major, H411; D A major, H421.
  Miklós Spányi (hpd); **Concerto Armonico / Péter Szüts.** BIS Ⓕ CD767 (68 minutes: DDD: 2/97).
  Recorded 1995.

Whilst these particular concertos are not always consistently engaging, they nevertheless demonstrate the emerging inventiveness of C.P.E.'s musical personality within a growing trend towards public concerts in the mid-eighteenth century. In fits and starts there are those sparsely etched landscapes, complete with an unsettled weather front, which at their best can captivate us. If decorum sometimes gets overworked, Bach's originality is even more remarkable given that the ritornello structure inherited from his father's generation, with its alternating solo and string sections, is less easy to sustain in a relatively uncontrapuntal style. Contrast is therefore a key element and Bach needs a soloist who can discern how the relationship between the harpsichord and the orchestra can be manipulated to good effect. Miklós Spányi and Concerto Armonico, led by Péter Szüts, give wonderfully lucid, flexible and clearly articulated readings. Moreover, Spányi's cultivated asides are matched by a string ensemble which graciously responds to the soloist's discretion. The shading in the finale of the G minor and middle movement of the D major Concertos is also energized by a naturally discursive balance, a deft textural palette for which artist and engineer can take equal credit. With such eloquent and fresh playing, this volume of world première recordings will give the listener more than just an opportunity to refine his perspective on Bach's achievements. Much of this music gets under the skin in its own right, and more so on repeated listening. It deserves a welcoming audience.

C.P.E. Bach Keyboard Concertos – D major, H414; E major, H417; A major, H422.
  Concerto Armonico / Miklós Spányi (fp). BIS Ⓕ CD785 (74 minutes: DDD: 12/97). ✍
  Recorded 1996.

With his fifth volume of C.P.E. Bach's complete keyboard concertos Miklós Spányi comes to three works composed in the mid-1740s, which he plays on a copy of a Silbermann fortepiano of that period – not only because such instruments existed at Frederick the Great's court, where Carl Philipp was employed, but because the keyboard layout is more suited to the fortepiano than the harpsichord, and because the A major work here – a first recording, like that of the D major – includes the marking *pianissimo* (impossible on the harpsichord). The present instrument is light and silvery in tone, which makes for some difficulties of proportion in the D major, which is performed with additional manuscript parts found in Brussels for trumpets and drums. The more embellished version of the A major Concerto is adopted here. The first movement displays some particularly athletic passagework for the piano. The second movement is striking in starting with a long unison melodic line over a rudimentary bass, with no internal harmonic filling: the attractive finale is characterized by a happy freshness. In the E major Concerto the instrumentation is augmented by horn parts found in a Berlin manuscript. Musically it is the most inventive and unusual, harmonically certainly the most adventurous, of the present three works – a splendid concerto that deserves to be better known. The recording has occasional problems with balance but the performances by Spányi and Concerto Armonico are praiseworthy.

C.P.E. Bach Keyboard Concertos – E minor, H418; B flat major, H429; G minor, H442. **Miklós Spányi (fp); Concerto Armonico / Péter Szüts (vn).** BIS Ⓕ CD786 (73 minutes: DDD: 5/98). ☞ Recorded 1996.
On this recording Miklós Spányi has exchanged his previous harpsichord or fortepiano for a tangent piano: this was like a fortepiano but had the strings struck vertically by tangents (as in the clavichord) rather than at an angle by hammers; its tone could also be modified by raising the dampers completely or only in the treble, employing only one of each note's two strings (*una corda*), inserting a leather strip ('moderator') between tangents and strings, or creating a harp-like effect by damping the strings with small pieces of cloth. The boldness and unusual style of Emanuel's concertos took his contemporaries aback even though compelling their admiration, and even now they can surprise. The extrovert E minor work, for example, begins with dramatic energy but is interrupted by extraordinary, tentative-sounding broken phrases at the soloist's first entry before being allowed to continue on its way: the *Adagio*, which includes striking chromatic progressions, has imitative interplay between the solo instrument and the violins. The finale of the otherwise more 'normal' *galant* G minor Concerto (in whose central movement two flutes join the strings) generates very vehement chordal attacks – or are these being overdone in this performance? Spányi's playing throughout has vitality and neatness, although his lifting of the dampers in running passages inevitably causes them to become blurred.

C.P.E. Bach Sinfonias, H663-6 – No. 1 in D major; No. 2 in E flat major; No. 3 in F major; No. 4 in G major.
W.F. Bach Sinfonia in F major. **Salzburg Chamber Philharmonic Orchestra / Yoon K. Lee.**
Naxos ⑨ 8 553289 (52 minutes: DDD: 4/96). Recorded 1994. *Gramophone Editor's choice.* Ⓖ
The exhilarating C.P.E. Bach symphonies presented here are not the more frequently recorded, surprise-filled string symphonies of 1773 (H657-62), but the set of four for strings, flutes, oboes, bassoons and horns which Bach wrote a couple of years later. They are no less astonishing. Bewildering changes of direction, disorientating rhythmic games and unexpected solos all turn up in this nervous, excitable music, which for originality and sheer life-force could surely only have been matched in its day by that of Haydn. The Salzburg Chamber Philharmonic, under their founder Yoon K. Lee, turn in crisp, spirited and (the odd moment of slack tuning apart) disciplined performances which do the music full justice. They are not timid about making the most of Bach's strong contrasts, although they produce them more by the release of some thunderous *forte* passages than by the pursuit of too many unearthly *pianissimos*. The overall effect is wholly convincing, and only in the symphony by Emanuel's older brother Wilhelm Friedemann – more old-fashioned and less successful as a piece, though in its way just as determinedly unorthodox – does the use of modern instruments begin to get in the way of the spirit of music. This is an undeniably good buy.

C.P.E. Bach Viola da gamba Sonatas – C major, Wq136; D major, Wq137; G minor, Wq88[ab]. Keyboard Sonatas – E major, H26[b]; A minor, H30[b]. **London Baroque** ([a]Charles Medlam, William Hunt, vas da gamba; [b]Richard Egarr, hpd). Harmonia Mundi Ⓕ HMC90 1410 (68 minutes: DDD: 1/93). ☞ Recorded 1991. Ⓖ
C.P.E. Bach's three sonatas for viola da gamba must be among the very last solo pieces outside France for an instrument which had gradually been supplanted by the cello. Two of the sonatas (Wq136/137) are of the continuo-accompaniment type and date from the mid-1740s. The third (Wq88), written in 1759, is, by contrast, more up-to-date in style with a fully written out harpsichord part on an equal footing with the gamba. From the gambist's viewpoint all three works are virtuoso pieces. The partnership of Charles Medlam and Richard Egarr, with William Hunt in the two continuo sonatas, is an effective one. Medlam's tone is well focused, he articulates clearly and has a lively rapport with the north German *Empfindsamer Stil*, present to a greater or lesser extent in almost all C.P.E. Bach's music after 1740 or so. Medlam responds to the music with a happy blend of head and heart, realizing at the same time one of Bach's own tenets for a good performance, "the ability through singing or playing to make the ear conscious of the true content and effect of a composition". Two keyboard sonatas complete this entertaining programme, one from the *Prussian* set, the other from the *Württemberg*. Richard Egarr plays them stylishly with a lively response to ornaments.
Additional recommendations ...
...Sonatas – Wq88; Wq136; Wq137. Fantasia in C major, Wq59 No. 6. **Siegfried Pank** (va da gamba); **Christiane Jaccottet** (clav/fp). Capriccio Ⓕ 10 102 (56 minutes: DDD: 10/88). ☞
...Sonata, Wq88 – Larghetto. Quartet for Keyboard, Flute, Viola and Continuo in D major, H538. Trio Sonatas – Two Violins and Continuo in C minor, H579; Flute, Violin and Continuo in C major, H571[d]. Solo Flute Sonata in A minor, H562. **Florilegium.**
Channel Classics Ⓕ CCS11197 (59 minutes: DDD: 1/98). Ⓖ
...Sonata, Wq88. *Coupled with works by* **J.S. Bach** *and* **W.F. Bach** Nobuko Imai (va); **Roland Pöntinen** (hpd). Philips Ⓕ 454 449-2PH (71 minutes: DDD: 6/98).

C.P.E. Bach Flute Sonatas – C major, H504; D major, H505; E major, H506; G major, H508; G major, H509; C major, H515; G minor, H542 No. 5 (BWV1020); B flat major, H543; E flat major, H545 (BWV1031); B flat major, H578. **Barthold Kuijken** (fl); **Bob van Asperen** (hpd). Sony Classical Vivarte Ⓕ S2K53964 (two discs: 140 minutes: DDD: 5/94). ☞ Recorded 1993. Ⓖ

This album contains C.P.E. Bach's five sonatas for flute with obbligato harpsichord. The playing is lively in spirit. Kuijken's tone is warmly coloured, softly spoken and pleasingly rounded and he clearly has much affection for Bach's expressive idiom. The balance between flute and harpsichord is effective, too, with Bob van Asperen proving himself an ideal partner both on account of his playing, which is particular in and attentive to detail, and his sympathy with the music. A first-rate recital, stylishly played with outstanding virtuosity and sympathetically recorded.

C.P.E. Bach Keyboard Sonatas – "Prussian", H24-29[a]; "Württemberg", H30-35[b]. Harpsichord Concerto in C major, H190[c]. **Bob van Asperen** (hpd). Teldec Das Alte Werk Ⓜ 9031-77623-2 (three discs: 175 minutes: ADD: 7/93). ✔ Items marked [ac] recorded 1977-79, new to UK, [b]EK6 35378 (6/79).   Ⓖ
C.P.E. Bach Keyboard Sonatas – B minor, H35; E major, H39; F minor, H40; C major, H41; B flat major, H51. **Colin Booth** (hpd). Olympia Ⓕ OCD433 (78 minutes: DDD). ✔
From Soundboard Records SBCD921 (8/93). Recorded 1992.
C.P.E. Bach's sets of *Prussian* and *Württemberg* Sonatas played by Bob van Asperen typify why back catalogues are as important as ever; not only have these veracious performances of the earlier *Prussian* Sonatas never reached these shores before, but neither of these sets are currently available complete. In the *Württemburg* Sonatas van Asperen's playing is of the utmost brilliance and he rarely misses a trick in communicating Bach's variegated style with exuberance and refinement. Such qualities abound too in the dazzling *Concerto per il Cembalo solo*. The recorded sound is suitably clear and fresh throughout. One interesting feature of these keyboard sonatas is the stylistic variety that is contained within individual movements. Recitative-like passages jostle with orchestrally conceived ideas, lyricism with more robust, challenging gestures, counterpoint with homophonic texture and baroque disciplines with *galant* phraseology. Rhythmic and harmonic uncertainties abound and all this is placed at the service of expression. Colin Booth plays with technical fluency and a ready awareness of all the little quirks and pitfalls in Bach's style which can be the undoing of players with a more prosaic outlook. He plays his own copy of a two-manual Mietke harpsichord – he was the maker who supplied an instrument to the Cöthen court during J.S. Bach's time there. This is a worthy single disc alternative and a recital well worth becoming acquainted with, above all for the music but also for the sympathetic playing and the distinctive sound of the harpsichord.

C.P.E. Bach Organ Sonatas – F major, H84; A minor, H85; D major, H86; G minor, H87;
A major, H133; B flat major, H134. **Marie-Claire Alain** (org). Erato Ⓕ 0630-14777-2 (70 minutes: DDD: 3/97). ✔ Recorded on the organ of the Karlhorst-Kirche, Berlin.
Bach's sonatas for organ were originally written for Princess Anna Amalia; "a princess who could not play the pedal or cope with difficulties, even though she had built for herself a beautiful organ with 2 manuals and pedal and liked to play on it". It is on that very organ that these sonatas have here been recorded (the connecting thread could be further spun by pointing out that they are played by a veritable princess of the organ, Marie-Claire Alain). The organ was built in 1755 by two German builders, Peter Migendt and Ernst Marx and had a chequered career before finally settling into its present home, but it makes a simply magical sound, beautifully captured in Erato's intimate, crystal-clear recording. The music may avoid the kind of technical demands with which Princess Anna could not cope and certainly does not require the kind of vast registration resource on which Alain seems to thrive – although she has taken the trouble to guide us through her registration – as usual, we can only marvel at the unending variety of sounds she has been able to conjure up from just 22 speaking stops. But these are endearing performances of undeniably charming music. Little hints of Mozart, maybe even of Bach *père* appear momentarily. For the most part, though, it is Bach's distinctive individual voice which comes through with an approach to the organ which owes nothing to his father other than the skill in writing music which suits the instrument to perfection.

Further listening ...
...Concerto for Harpsichord, Two Flutes and Strings in F major, H454. Harpsichord Concerto in B minor, H440. Concerto for Harpsichord, Two Horns and Strings in C minor, H448.
Les Amis de Philippe / Ludger Rémy (hpd). CPO CPO999 350-2 (2/96). ✔
...Double Concerto for Harpsichord and Fortepiano in E flat major, H479[a]. Double Harpsichord Sonatina in D major, H453[b]. Double Harpsichord Concerto in F major, H408[c].
[ab]**Eric Lynn Kelley** (hpd); [a]**Jos van Immerseel** (fp); [b]**Jos van Immerseel** (hpd); [c]**Alan Curtis** (hpd); [c]**Gustav Leonhardt** (hpd); **Collegium Aureum**.
Deutsche Harmonia Mundi Baroque Esprit 05472 77410-2 (6/96). ✔
...Flute Concerto in G major, H445. *Coupled with works by various composers.* **Patrick Gallois** (fl); **CPE Bach Chamber Orchestra / Peter Schreier**. DG 439 895-2GH (2/95). *See review in the Collections section; refer to the Index.*
...Harpsichord Concertos – G major, H406; A major, H410; F major, H415. **Miklós Spányi** (hpd); **Concerto Armonico / Péter Szüts**. BIS CD708 (7/96). ✔
...Harpsichord Concertos – G major, H412[a]; D major, H416[b]; D minor, H420[a]. **Miklós Spányi** ([a]hpd/[b]fp); **Concerto Armonico / Péter Szüts** (vn). BIS CD768 (11/97). ✔
...Organ Concertos[a] – G major, H444; E flat major, H446. Prelude in D major, H107. Fantasia and Fugue a 4 in C minor, H103. **Roland Munch** (org); [a]**CPE Bach Orchestra / Hartmut Haenchen**. Capriccio 10 135 (10/88).

...Sinfonias – E flat major, H654; F major, H656; C major, H649; F major, H650; E minor, H653.
CPE Bach Orchestra / Hartmut Haenchen. Capriccio 10 103 (9/87).
...Symphonies, Wq183 – No. 1 in D major; No. 2 in E flat major; No. 3 in F major; No. 4 in
G major. **CPE Bach Orchestra / Hartmut Haenchen.** Capriccio 10 175 (10/88).
...Flute Sonatas[bc] – E minor, H551; D major, H556. Sonatas for Harpsichord and Flute[c] – G major,
H509; C major, H515. Flute Sonata in A minor, H562. 12 Two- and Three-part Pieces, H628[ac].
Nancy Hadden, [a]**Elizabeth Walker** (fls); [b]**Erin Headley** (va da gamba); [c]**Lucy Carolan** (hpd/clav).
ASV Gaudeamus CDGAU161 (6/97). 🎵
...Trio Sonatas – A minor, H582; F major, H576; E minor, H577; B flat major, H584; D minor,
H590. **London Baroque.** Harmonia Mundi HMC90 1511 (9/95). 🎵   ⓠ
...Trio Sonata in C major, H573. *Coupled with works by various composers.* **Musica ad Rhenum.**
Vanguard Classics Ⓕ 99130 (57 minutes: DDD: 11/96). *See review in the Collections section;*
refer to the Index.
...Four Duets, H610-13. *Coupled with works by various composers.* **Christopher Hogwood, Christophe**
Rousset (hpds/clavs/fps). L'Oiseau-Lyre 440 649-2OH (8/96). 🎵 *See review in the Collections*
section; refer to the Index.
...Fantasia and Fugue a 4 in C minor, H103. Organ Prelude in D major, H107. Organ Sonatas –
F major, H84; A minor, H85; D major, H86; G minor, H87. **Jacques van Oortmerssen** (org).
BIS CD569 (5/93).
...Fantasia e fuga a 4 in C minor, H103. Adagio per il organo a 2 claviere e pedal in D minor, H352.
Prelude in D major, H107. Fuga in D minor, H372. Fuga a 4 in E flat major, H102. Fuga sopra il
nome de Bach, H373. *Coupled with works by various members of the Bach Family.* **Marie-Claire**
Alain (org). Erato 0630-17073-2 (A/97). *See review in the Collections section; refer to the Index.*
...Pièces caractéristiques – La Borchward, H79; La Pott, H80; La Gleim, H89; La Bergius, H90;
La Stahl, H94; La Boehmer, H81; La Louise, H114. *Coupled with works by various composers.*
Christine Schornsheim (hpd/fp). Capriccio 10 424 (4/95). 🎵
...Magnificat in D minor, H772 – Quia respexit. *Coupled with works by various composers.*
Elly Ameling (sop); **Various soloists.** Deutsche Harmonia Mundi 74321 26617-2 (12/95).
See review in the Collections section; refer to the Index.
...Die Auferstehung und Himmelfahrt Jesu, H777. **Hillevi Martinpelto** (sop); **Christoph Prégardien**
(ten); **Peter Harvey** (bass); **Ghent Collegium Vocale Choir; Orchestra of the Age of Enlightenment /**
Philippe Herreweghe. Virgin Classics Veritas VC7 59069-2 (9/92). 🎵

Georg Christoph Bach   German 1642-1697

Suggested listening ...
...Siehe, wie fein und lieblich (Geburtstagkantate). *Coupled with works by various composers.*
Julian Podger, Robert Evans (tens); **Michael McCarthy** (bass); **Florilegium.**
Channel Classics CCS9096 (7/96). *See review in the Collections section; refer to the Index.*

Johann Christian Bach   German 1735-1782

J.C. Bach Harpsichord Concertos – D minor; B flat major; F minor. **Hanover Band / Anthony**
Halstead (hpd). CPO Ⓕ CPO999 393-2 (57 minutes: DDD: 11/97). 🎵 Recorded 1995.
The works of J.C. Bach's Berlin years are almost indistinguishable from those of his brother, C.P.E.,
and anyone putting on this disc could be excused for thinking the first movement of the D minor
Concerto – with its purposeful, energetic scales, its stark textures, its heavily used motifs, its rushing
harpsichord writing, its sombre minor key and its total lack of lyricism – to be wholly C.P.E.'s work.
It is in fact a very accomplished piece for a composer less than 20 years old and there are glimmerings
of J.C.'s own voice in the *Adagio affettuoso* that follows; it still sounds like North German music,
untouched by Italian softness and sunshine, but the harpsichord cantilena certainly has a more
personal expressive character and so does some of the string writing in the ritornellos and
accompaniment. The slow movements throughout seem the most individual and appealing in a sense
that C.P.E.'s are not. The quick movements, especially in the B flat Concerto, contain gestures of the
abrupt and musically violent kind that C.P.E. so often used. The finale of the D minor has a curious
element of fantasy and an imaginative use of pizzicato behind the first solo entry. Halstead uses a
small orchestra, strings only, 3.3.1.1.1, which is quite sufficient and very alert. The solo playing is
extremely fluent and indeed brilliant; Halstead plays with ample energy and rhythmic precision and
he realizes the elaborate melodic lines effectively. One may not be entirely convinced by some of his
cadenzas, which seem to go harmonically too far afield too quickly; but this is a small blemish in an
admirable disc which brings two virtually unknown works into the catalogue.

J.C. Bach Six Harpsichord Concertos, Op. 1 – No. 1 in B flat major; No. 2 in A major; No. 3 in
F major; No. 4 in G major; No. 5 in C major; No. 6 in D major. **Graham Cracknell, Adrian**
Butterfield (vns); **Angela East** (vc); **Anthony Halstead** (hpd). CPO Ⓕ CPO999 299-2
(66 minutes: DDD: 7/96). Recorded 1994.

The Op. 1 Keyboard Concertos were published in 1763: they are chamber works, played here, as they should be, with just two solo violins and a cello. They are slight pieces, neatly and gracefully formed but for the most part slender in musical content and often harmonically rather static. Nos. 1, 2, 3 and 5 are in the *galant* two-movement form, the second usually an extended minuet showing J.C. Bach's characteristic warmth of invention. The first movements, which vary in tempo from *Andante* to *Allegro*, are embryonic versions of the concerto form familiar to us from Mozart. Nos. 4 and 6, which Bach called "Concerto o Sinfonia", are quite different: each is in three movements, fast-slow-fast, the first of them not in concerto form at all but with the material shared equally between strings and keyboard, and fully integrated, more like a true keyboard quartet. The opening *Allegro* of No. 4 is a particularly good piece, with a vitality and momentum to the music that is otherwise in short supply. And the slow movements of both these two have an expressive keyboard cantilena that is very appealing. The finale of No. 6 is a charming set of variations on *God save the King*. Anthony Halstead gives plain and direct performances, with many delicate touches of timing and articulation. There is some quite brilliant playing in the first movement of No. 4. Here and there one might wish for a shade more flexibility in rhythm; it's always worth thinking, in music of this kind, in terms of a vocal line. However, all of this music is very finely represented.

J.C. Bach Six Symphonies, Op. 6 – No. 1 in G major; No. 2 in D major; No. 3 in E flat major; No. 4 in B flat major; No. 5 in E flat major; No. 6 in G minor. **Hanover Band / Anthony Halstead.** CPO Ⓕ CPO999 298-2 (56 minutes: DDD: 3/96). ✔ Recorded 1994.
In the Op. 6 Symphonies, the frothy Italianate music of the composer's Italian and early London years was behind him; these pieces, dating from the late 1760s, though still of course Italian-influenced in their formal clarity and their melodic style, are sturdier music, more carefully composed, more symphonic in feeling. Both the E flat works in this set have something of the solidity and warmth associated with that key, and each has a C minor *Andante*; the G major's first movement has the confident ring and thematic contrasts of his mature music, and the D major contains Mannheim crescendos and some delightful textures, with flutes and divided violas, in its charming and slightly playful middle movement. The set ends with Bach's single minor-key symphony in G minor, very similar in spirit to Mozart's No. 25; this piece, often recorded before, shows an unfamiliar side to his musical personality. Anthony Halstead and his players convey the strength and the spirit of the music convincingly. The lively finales all go with a swing, and the opening movements have plenty of energy. The slow movements are not always quite so persuasive: the third C minor slow movement of the G minor Symphony is a little overdeliberate and becomes detached and modest in expressive impact. But generally these are strong and appealing performances of some attractive and unfamiliar music, clearly, slightly drily recorded, and admirers of the London Bach and his music need not hesitate.
Additional recommendation ...
...Symphonies – C major, Venier No. 46 (two versions); No. 1 in G major; F major. Simphonies pérodiques, Op. 8 – No. 2 in G major; No. 3 in D major; No. 4 in F major. **Hanover Band / Anthony Halstead.** CPO Ⓕ CPO999 383-2 (64 minutes: DDD: 9/97).

J.C. Bach Adriano in Siria – Overture. Six Grand Overtures, Op. 18 – No. 1 in E flat major; No. 4 in D major. Symphony in D minor, Op. 6 No. 6. Sinfonia concertante in C major, T289 No. 4 (ed. Maunder). **Academy of Ancient Music / Simon Standage** (vn). Chandos Chaconne Ⓕ CHAN0540 (65 minutes: DDD: 12/93). ✔ Recorded 1993.
The G minor Symphony is a magnificently fiery piece, similar in manner to Haydn's No. 39 and Mozart's No. 25; it is done here with plenty of *Sturm und Drang*, notably in the very forceful finale, and the fine, noble ideas of the slow movement are well caught too. The opening item is a three-movement D major Symphony, in effect, with a well-worked first movement and an *Andante* with rich wind writing. No other composer, besides of course Mozart, seems to have had as keen a feeling as J.C. Bach for the sensuous beauty of wind textures. The *Sinfonia concertante* isn't quite as successful a piece, being rather repetitive, but it is never less than charming and enjoyable music, again with some beautiful windy textures in the *Larghetto* and a delightful "Two lovely black eyes" theme in the rondo. The solo playing is admirable. Recommended to anyone sympathetic to J.C. Bach's music.

J.C. Bach Overtures – Gioas, re di Giuda; Adriano in Siria; Zanaida; Orione. La clemenza di Scipione – Overture; No. 5, March in G major; No. 22, March in E flat major. Carattaco – Overture; No. 20, March in B flat major; No. 26, March in G major. Symphony in D major, Schmitt Op. 18 No. 1. **Hanover Band / Anthony Halstead.** CPO Ⓕ CPO999 488-2 (58 minutes: DDD: 12/97). ✔ Recorded 1996.
Small-scale but elegantly fashioned, melodious and pleasurable music: it is no wonder that the London public in the 1760s and 1770s took Johann Christian to their hearts – though in their fickle way they then barely noticed his (in straitened circumstances) death in the following decade. Here we have the overtures to six works of his that were performed at the King's Theatre in the Haymarket – from his first opera there, *Orione* in 1763, to his last, *La clemenza di Scipione* in 1778, and the 1770 oratorio, *Gioas*, plus a symphony which is a *pasticcio* of the *Clemenza* overture with additional trumpets and drums and a revised version of the *Andante* from the overture to his only completed French opera, the 1779 *Amadis de Gaule*. With the exception of this last and of *Adriano in Siria*, all

are either first recordings or the first in their original versions. The most striking feature about all these works, apart from their vigorous openings, is the freedom in the use of wind instruments: *Zanaida* has *soli* clarinets, and the trio of *Orione*'s minuet is for wind band only, as are passages in *Adriano*, the E flat March in *Clemenza* and the brilliant final *Presto* of *Carattaco*. The Hanover Band's playing is vital and fresh, rhythmically crisp and tonally clean-cut; and the recording is first-rate.

Further listening ...
...Concerto for Flute, Two Horns and Strings in D major, T286/7[a]. Concerto for Oboe, Two Horns and Strings in F major, T290/7[b]. Bassoon Concerto in E flat major, T288/4[c]. [a]**Rachel Brown** (fl); [b]**Anthony Robson** (ob); [c]**Jeremy Ward** (bn); **Hanover Band / Anthony Halstead.** CPO CPO999 346-2 (1/97). 🖉
...Keyboard Concertos – Op. 1; Op. 7. **Ingrid Haebler** (fp); **Vienna Capella Academica / Eduard Melkus.** Philips 438 712-2PM2 (2/94). 🖉
...Keyboard Concerto in B flat major, Op. 13 No. 4. *Coupled with works by various composers.* **Marinus Flipse** (pf); **Concertgebouw Orchestra / Willem Mengelberg.** Archive Documents Mengelberg Edition mono ADCD112* (5/95).
...Sinfonie concertanti – E flat major, T288 No. 4[a]; G major, T284 No. 1[b]; E flat major, T286 No. 8[c]. **Graham Cracknell, Anna McDonald** (vns); [a]**Anthony Robson** (ob); [bc]**Angela East** (vc); **Hanover Band / Anthony Halstead.** CPO CPO999 348-2 (10/97).
...Sinfonia concertante in E flat major, T284/6. *Coupled with works by* **C.P.E. Bach** and **W.F. Bach** **Jürg Schaeftlein** (ob); **Anner Bylsma** (vc); **Anneke Uittenbosch, Alan Curtis** (hpds); **Jean Antonietti** (fp); **Leonhardt Consort, Vienna Concentus Musicus / Gustav Leonhardt.** Teldec Das Alte Werk 0630-12326-2 (9/96). 🖉
...Fugue on B-A-C-H, T348/4. *Coupled with works by various members of the Bach Family.* **Marie-Claire Alain** (org). Erato 0630-17073-2 (A/97). *See review in the Collections section; refer to the Index.*
...Keyboard Sonatas – Op. 5 Nos. 5 and 6; Op. 17 Nos. 2, 3 and 5. **Virginia Black** (hpd). CRD CRD3453 (2/90). 🖉
...Sonata for Keyboard, Violin and Cello in G major, T313/1 (Op. 2 No. 2). *Coupled with works by various composers.* **Florilegium.** Channel Classics CCS9096 (7/96). *See review in the Collections section; refer to the Index.*
...Salve regina in E flat major. *Coupled with works by* **Mozart** and **Pergolesi** Ruth Ziesak (sop); **La Stagione / Michael Schneider.** Deutsche Harmonia Mundi 05472 77335-2 (11/96).
...Amadis des Gaules (sung in German). **Soloists; Stuttgart Gächinger Kantorei; Stuttgart Bach Collegium / Helmuth Rilling.** Hänssler Classic 98 963 (9/93).

Johann Christoph Bach
German 1642-1703

Suggested listening ...
...Ich lasse dich nicht[ab]. Der Mensch, vom Weibe geboren[bc]. Lieber Herr Gott, wecke uns auf[bc]. *Coupled with works by various members of the Bach Family.* **Trinity College Choir, Cambridge;** [a]**Rickman Godlee** (vc); [b]**Martin Peck** (db); [c]**Andrew Lamb** (org) **/ Richard Marlow.** Conifer Classics 75605 51306-2 (11/97). *See review in the Collections section; refer to the Index.*

Johann Christoph Friedrich Bach
German 1732-1795

Suggested listening ...
...Trio Sonatas, HWVII/1-7 – No. 2 in A major; No. 3 in F major; No. 5 in G major; No. 6 in A major. Sonata in G major, HWX/2. **London Baroque.** Harmonia Mundi HMC90 1587 (4/97). 🖉
...Fughetta on the name H-C-F-B-B-A-C-H, HWXII/14. *Coupled with works by various members of the Bach Family.* **Marie-Claire Alain** (org). Erato 0630-17073-2 (A/97). *See review in the Collections section; refer to the Index.*
...Wachet auf, ruft uns die Stimme, HWXV/1. *Coupled with works by various members of the Bach Family.* **Trinity College Choir, Cambridge; Rickman Godlee** (vc); **Christopher Allsop** (org) **/ Richard Marlow.** Conifer Classics 75605 51306-2 (11/97). *See review in the Collections section; refer to the Index.*

Johann Ernst Bach
German 1722-1777

Suggested listening ...
...Violin Sonata in F minor. Sammlung auserlesener Fabeln I – Die ungleichen Freunde; Die Unzufriedenheit; Der Affe und die Schäferin; Der Hund. *Coupled with works by various composers.* **Catherine Bott** (sop); **Florilegium.** Channel Classics CCS9096 (7/96). *See review in the Collections section; refer to the Index.*

Johann Hans Bach

Suggested listening ...

...Sei nun wieder zufrieden, meine Seele[abc]. Unser Leben ist ein Schatten[bcd]. *Coupled with works by various members of the Bach Family.* **Trinity College Choir, Cambridge;** [a]**Rickman Godlee** (vc); [b]**Martin Peck** (db); [c]**Christopher Allsop,** [d]**Andrew Lamb** (orgs) / **Richard Marlow.** Conifer Classics 75605 51306-2 (11/97). *See review in the Collections section; refer to the Index.*

Johann Ludwig Bach

Suggested listening ...

...Das ist meine Freude[ac]. Unsere Trübsal[abc]. Es danken Dir, Gott[abc]. *Coupled with works by various members of the Bach Family.* **Trinity College Choir, Cambridge;** [a]**Rickman Godlee** (vc); [b]**Martin Peck** (db); [c]**Christopher Allsop** (org) / **Richard Marlow.** Conifer Classics 75605 51306-2 (11/97). *See review in the Collections section; refer to the Index.*

Johann Michael Bach

Suggested listening ...

...Nun hab'ich überwunden[ac]. Halt, was du hast[bc]. Fürchtet euch nicht[abc]. Sei, lieber Tag, willkommen[abc]. *Coupled with works by various members of the Bach Family.* **Trinity College Choir, Cambridge;** [a]**Rickman Godlee** (vc); [b]**Martin Peck** (db); [c]**Andrew Lamb** (org) / **Richard Marlow.** Conifer Classics 75605 51306-2 (11/97). *See review in the Collections section; refer to the Index.*

Johann Sebastian Bach

Bach Harpsichord Concertos – D minor, BWV1052[a]; D major, BWV1054[a]. Concerto for Flute, Violin, Harpsichord and Strings in A minor, BWV1044[a]. Das wohltemperierte Klavier, BWV846-93 – Preludes and Fugues: F major, BWV880; B major, BWV892. [a]**Le Concert Français / Pierre Hantaï** (hpd). Auvidis Astrée Ⓔ E8523 (70 minutes: DDD: 1/95). ✏ Recorded 1993. *Gramophone Editor's record of the month.* ⓖⓖ

The concertos come over well. Ensemble is tautly controlled and the string playing effectively articulated, though on occasion the first violin is a little too favoured in the recorded balance. However, the string playing is so unanimous in sound and purpose that there is little to worry about in this department. Hantaï himself is impressive for his wonderfully rhythmic playing, the clarity with which he interprets both his own keyboard textures and those which support and punctuate it, and not least for his supple, muscular concept of the music. These are extraordinarily invigorating performances, which draw the listener deep into the harmonic and contrapuntal complexities and conceits of Bach's art. Take for instance the elusive *Adagio* of BWV1052, where careful punctuation and sensitive interaction between solo and tutti make for a rewarding coherence. In the A minor Triple Concerto, Hantaï is joined by his flautist brother, Marc, and François Fernandez (violin), the leader of the ensemble. The work is a Leipzig arrangement of movements from earlier pieces not in concerto form, whose extent sources were almost certainly copied after Bach's death. The opening *Allegro* is a little too heavy, but the essentially three-part texture of the middle movement is realized with affection. Altogether a stimulating disc.

Additional recommendations ...

...BWV1052; BWV1053; BWV1054; **Hae-won Chang** (pf); **Camerata Cassovia / Robert Stankovsky.** Naxos Ⓢ 8 550422 (62 minutes: DDD).

...BWV1052, E major, BWV1053; BWV1054; **The English Concert / Trevor Pinnock** (hpd). Archiv Produktion Ⓔ 415 991-2AH (58 minutes: DDD: 9/87). ✏

...BWV1044[a]. Oboe Concerto in D minor, BWV1059[b]. Oboe d'amore Concerto in D major, BWV1053a[e]. Cantatas – No. 21, Ich hatte viel Bekümmernis – Sinfonia[c]; No. 12, Weinen, Klagen, Sorgen, Zagen – Sinfonia[d]. [a]**Lisa Beznosiuk** (fl); [a]**Paul Nicholson** (hpd); **Anthony Robson** ([b]ob/[e]ob d'amore); [a]**Age of Enlightenment Choir;** [bcde]**Orchestra of the Age of Enlightenment / Elizabeth Wallfisch** ([a]vn). Virgin Classics Veritas Ⓔ VC5 45190-2 (64 minutes: DDD: 7/97). ✏

...BWV1052; BWV1054; F major, BWV1057; BWV1044[a]. [a]**Claudio Rufa** (fl); [a]**Francesca Vicari** (vn); **Concerto Italiano / Rinaldo Alessandrini** (hpd). Opus 111 Ⓔ OPS30-153 (72 minutes: DDD: 8/97). ✏

Bach Violin Concertos – No. 1 in A minor, BWV1041; No. 2 in E major, BWV1042. Double Violin Concertos[a] – D minor, BWV1043; D minor, BWV1060. [a]**Rachel Podger** (vn); **Academy of Ancient Music / Andrew Manze** (vn). Harmonia Mundi Ⓔ HMU90 7155 (57 minutes: DDD: 4/97). ✏

This recording of violin concertos by Bach contains not only the three well-known pieces, but also another D minor work (BWV1060), which is almost invariably heard, nowadays, in its putative version, sometimes in C minor, for violin and oboe. Here, it is treated as a double concerto for two violins. Manze's playing, and that of his partner in the double concertos, Rachel Podger, is engaging on a number of different levels. Welcome indeed, is the absence of intrusive mannerism, the offspring of too rigid an adherence to dogma. Instead these artists allow the poetry of Bach's music to unfold in a comfortably measured, lucidly punctuated and eloquently inflected way. Manze himself projects a highly developed sense of fantasy in his interpretations and, for the most part, it proves immensely effective here. The opening of the A minor Concerto is a particularly telling instance, but there are countless others to be found in the *ripieno* sections of each work. The two double concertos come over lyrically and with splendid rhythmic energy. The relationship between the two violins is not as close as that which exists in the other, great D minor work (BWV1043) but, as Manze remarks in his note, the poetic *Adagio* does come off uncommonly well on what one might be permitted to describe in these pages as a "matched pair". Here is a disc which is likely to have wide appeal. Everything is done with thought and affection for Bach's music as well as with a recognition of its expressive potential.

Additional recommendations ...
...Nos. 1ª and 2ª. Double Violin Concerto, BWV1043ᵇ. Triple Violin Concerto in D major, BWV1064ᶜ. ᵇAlison Bury, ᶜPavlo Beznosiuk, ᶜCatherine Mackintosh (vns); **Orchestra of the Age of Enlightenment / Elizabeth Wallfisch** (ᵃᵇᶜvn).
Virgin Classics Veritas Ⓕ VC7 59319-2 (63 minutes: DDD). 🎵
...Nos. 1 and 2. Double Violin Concerto, BWV1043. Violin and Oboe Concerto. **Anne-Sophie Mutter** (vn); **English Chamber Orchestra / Salvatore Accardo** (vn).
EMI Ⓕ CDC7 47005-2 (53 minutes: DDD: 2/84).
...Nos. 1 and 2. Double Violin Concerto, BWV1043. Violin and Oboe Concerto. **Arthur Grumiaux, Herman Krebbers** (vns); **Heinz Holliger** (ob); **Les Soloists Romands / Arpad Gerecz.**
Philips Ⓜ 420 700-2PSL (61 minutes: DDD: 5/88).   Ⓖ
...No. 1. Harpsichord Concertos – E major, BWV1053; A major, BWV1055; G minor, BWV1058. **Christophe Rousset** (hpd); **Jaap Schröder** (vn); **Academy of Ancient Music / Christopher Hogwood.**
L'Oiseau-Lyre Ⓕ 443 326-2OH (57 minutes: DDD: 10/95). 🎵

Bach Double Concertos – D minor for Two Violins, BWV1043ª; C minor for Violin and Oboe, BWV1060ᵇ; C minor for Two Harpsichords, BWV1060ᶜ; C minor for Two Harpsichords, BWV1062ᶜ. ªJaap Schröder, ªChristopher Hirons, ᵇCatherine Mackintosh (vns); ᵇStephen Hammer (ob); ᶜChristophe Rousset (hpd); **Academy of Ancient Music / Christopher Hogwood** (ᶜhpd).
L'Oiseau-Lyre Florilegium Ⓕ 421 500-2OH (58 minutes: DDD: 9/89). 🎵 Item marked ª from DSDL702 (8/82), ᵇ and ᶜ new to UK.
The concept of a concerto with two or more soloists grew naturally out of the *concerto grosso*, and Bach was among those baroque composers who explored its possibilities. The Concerto in D minor, BWV1043, for two violins is perhaps the best known of his works in the *genre*, which Bach himself reworked as a Concerto for Two Harpsichords, BWV1062, in the key of C minor. No alternative version has survived in the case of the two-harpsichord Concerto BWV1060, also in C minor, but musicological evidence suggests that it was originally intended for two single-line instruments – two violins or one violin and an oboe. The work has thus been notionally reconstructed in the latter form. Baroque music never sounds better than when it is played on period instruments, in proper style, and by performers of the quality of those in this recording, not least the well-matched soloists. The famous slow movement of BWV1043 is taken a little faster than usual, convincingly stripped of the specious sentimentality with which it is often invested. The recording is of suitably high quality.

Bach Oboe Concertos – F major, BWV1053; A major, BWV1055; D minor, BWV1059. **Chamber Orchestra of Europe / Douglas Boyd** (ob, ob d'amore). DG Ⓕ 429 225-2GH (46 minutes: DDD: 4/90). Recorded 1989.
Although Bach is not known to have written any concertos for the oboe he did entrust it with some beautiful *obbligato* parts, so he clearly did not underrate its expressive capacities. He did, however, rearrange many of his works for different instrumental media and there is musicological evidence that original oboe concertos were the (lost) sources from which other works were derived. The Harpsichord Concerto in A major, BWV1055, is believed originally to have been written for the oboe d'amore, whilst the other two Oboe Concertos have been reassembled from movements found in various cantatas. Whatever the validity of the academic reasoning, the results sound very convincing. Douglas Boyd is a superb oboist, with a clear sound that is free from stridency, and a fluency that belies the instrument's technical difficulty. He plays the faster, outer movements with winsome lightness of tongue and spirit, and with alertness to dynamic nuance; the slow ones, the hearts of these works, are given with sensitivity but without sentimentality – which can easily invade that of BWV1059, taken from Cantata No. 156, *Ich steh mit einem Fuss im Grabe*. The Chamber Orchestra of Europe partners him to perfection in this crisp recording.

Bach Brandenburg Concertos, BWV1046-51 – No. 1 in F major; No. 2 in F major; No. 3 in G major; No. 4 in G major; No. 5 in D major; No. 6 in B flat major. **Tafelmusik / Jeanne Lamon** (vn). Sony Classical Vivarte Ⓕ S2K66289 (two discs: 93 minutes: DDD: 4/95). 🎵
Recorded 1993-94.   Ⓖ

Bach Brandenburg Concertos, BWV1046-51. **Boston Baroque / Martin Pearlman** (hpd).
Telarc Ⓕ CD80354/68 (two discs, oas: 52 and 41 minutes: DDD: 2/96). ✔   Ⓖ
CD80368 – No. 1 in F major; No. 2 in F major; No. 3 in G major. *CD80354* – No. 4 in
G major; No. 5 in D major; No. 6 in B flat major.

Tafelmusik's *Brandenburgs* come straight from the heart and as such they are performances which
invite repeated listening and are furthermore both easy and enjoyable to live with. There are no
startling novelties here and nothing which attempts to impede the natural course of musical flow.
Tempos are sensibly chosen and, once chosen, consistently adhered to. That is not to say that there is
an absence of affective gesture or a lack of rhetorical awareness. Everything in fact is punctuated in
a way that allows the listener to follow the subtly shaded nuances of Bach's dialogue. Some readers
may feel that these interpretations lack the stamp of a strong personality at the helm but any such
fears of interpretative neutrality are largely dispelled by the sensibility of the players and their
hitherto proven skill at reaching the heart of the music without the assistance either of pretension or
muddled intellectual clutter. Reservations chiefly concern minutiae of tuning and to a much lesser
extent, ensemble. Neither these weaknesses, nor the occasional blip or thwack, hindering the
production of clean notes from oboe, horns or trumpet, spoil enjoyment of Tafelmusik's Nos. 1 and
2. It is a pity that the first movement of No. 3 is marred by indifferent tuning in the lower strands of
the texture and, more disturbingly, by a marked acceleration in speed beginning at bar 84 (3'26"); but
the second *Allegro* of the work is so well done that you are inclined to forgive them. Tafelmusik's
account of this brilliant binary movement is not to be missed.

Boston Baroque are a close-knit group of highly accomplished and stylish instrumentalists. On their
discs their enthusiasm is clear in the bustling outer movements; it's a wise leader who knows his team,
in this case Martin Pearlman, who no doubt set the tempos. In the slow movements there is the
breathing-space which is often found lacking. The soloists are first-class (though Friedemann Immer's
trumpet trills in Concerto No. 2 sound a mite uncomfortable) and the multi-talented Daniel Stepner
(violone piccolo in No. 2, violin soloist in Nos. 4 and 5, and viola soloist in No. 6) and Pearlman
himself (harpsichord) are especially impressive. It is, however, the ensemble, supported by a finely
balanced recording, that makes these accounts so outstanding, and those who are allergic to thin or
nasal string sounds will find nothing to cringe from in the warmth of tone that characterizes these
performances. The annotation states (but without explanation) that Concerto No. 6 "must remain a
chamber piece with one player to a part": whether it must or not, the recording shows it to be wholly
effective played in that way. We are also told that "it includes the transparent sounds of gambas" and
so it does, but we are left to guess who their players might be. No matter how many horses enter a
race the winner is usually clear, but it is not so with oft-recorded works such as the *Brandenburgs* (as
is evidenced by the list which follows). There can be no clear 'best', but the Telarc set is likely to
remain amongst those which will prove to be enduring.

Additional recommendations ...
...Nos. 1-3. **Academy of St Martin in the Fields / Sir Neville Marriner.**
Philips Ⓕ 400 076-2PH (45 minutes: ADD: 3/83)
...Nos. 1-6[a]. Orchestral Suites, BWV1066-9[b]. **The English Concert / Trevor Pinnock.**
Archiv Produktion Ⓜ 423 492-2AX3 (three discs: 173 minutes: DDD/ADD: 10/88). ✔   Ⓖ
...Nos. 1-6. Orchestral Suites. **Adolf Busch Chamber Players / A. Busch.**
EMI Références mono Ⓜ CHS7 64047-2* (three discs: 195 minutes: ADD: 12/91).
...Nos. 1, 2 and 4. Orchestral Suite No. 2. **Vienna Concentus Musicus / Nikolaus Harnoncourt.**
Teldec Digital Experience Ⓜ 9031-75858-2 (73 minutes: DDD: 9/92). ✔   Ⓖ
...Nos. 3, 5 and 6. Orchestral Suite No. 3. **Vienna Concentus Musicus / Nikolaus Harnoncourt.**
Teldec Digital Experience Ⓜ 9031-75859-2 (75 minutes: DDD: 9/92). ✔
...Nos. 1-6. **New London Consort / Philip Pickett.**
L'Oiseau-Lyre Ⓕ 440 675-2OH2 (two discs: 95 minutes: DDD: 1/95). ✔
...Nos. 1-6. Orchestral Suites – No. 2 in B minor, BWV1066; No. 3 in D major, BWV1067.
Vienna Concentus Musicus / Nikolaus Harnoncourt.
Teldec Ⓜ 4509-95980-2 (two discs: 148 minutes: DDD: 5/95). ✔
...Nos. 1-6. **La Petite Bande / Sigiswald Kuijken.**
Deutsche Harmonia Mundi Ⓕ 05472 77308-2 (two discs: 97 minutes: DDD: 6/95).
...Nos. 1-6. Concertos for Flute, Violin, Harpsichord and Strings – A minor, BWV1044; D major,
BWV1050[a]. **La Stravaganza / Siegbert Rampe** (hpd).
Virgin Classics Ⓕ VCD5 45255-2 (two discs: 126 minutes: DDD: 6/97). ✔
...No. 2. Violin Concerto in D minor, BWV1052 (arr. Linder-Dewan)[a]. **Zelenka** Sinfonia a 8 in
A minor, ZWV189. [a]**Kerstin Linder-Dewan** (vn); **Fiori Musicali / Penelope Rapson.**
Metronome Ⓕ METCD1019 (54 minutes: DDD: 3/98).

Bach Orchestral Suites, BWV1066-69 – No. 1 in C major; No. 2 in B minor[a]; No. 3 in D major;
No. 4 in D major. [a]**Wilbert Hazelzet** (fl); **Amsterdam Baroque Orchestra / Ton Koopman.**
Deutsche Harmonia Mundi Ⓕ RD77864 (two discs: 79 minutes: DDD: 1/90). ✔
Recorded 1988. *Gramophone Award Winner 1990.*   ⒼⒼⒼ
Bach's Orchestral Suites are deservedly well represented in the catalogue, with versions in plenty by
orchestras of period and modern instruments alike. Koopman captures the contrasting colours and
textures of these works with a sure feeling for orchestral sonority, but over and above that he is most

persuasive in his gestures, graceful at times, ceremoniously pompous at others. Thus the Sarabande of the B minor Suite is one of the high-water marks of the entire set, exquisitely poised and lovingly articulated by the flautist, Wilbert Hazelzet, an artist of rare sensibility. Other dances in this suite fare equally well, with a Menuet redolent of courtly gesture and a Polonaise with an easy, carefree gait. As a general rule, Koopman favours rather slower tempos than many of his rival colleagues and he is to be applauded for doing so. The Rondeau of the B minor Suite is, comparatively speaking, slow yet avoiding monotony; the Forlane of the C major Suite is delightfully airy, as are the two Bourrées and the pleasingly leisurely Passepieds. Loveliest of all, perhaps, in this performance of the C major Suite, are the relaxed and affectingly articulated Courantes and the refined Menuets, whose kinetic energy is subtly realized under Koopman's direction. Koopman draws the strongest contrast between lighter textured dances and galanteries such as these, and the grandiose music contained in the two D major Suites. The Overtures in both instances are magnificent with commendably vibrant timpani and snarling trumpets which set the blood coursing through the veins. This is robust Bach playing but without a hint of vulgarity and in no sense lacking in appropriate restraint. This is a considerable achievement and if some listeners are mildly irked by Koopman's own brilliant but perhaps overbusy keyboard continuo realizations, they are unlikely to be able to resist the subtle inflexions and ravishing inner-part understanding of Suite No. 2; and, it should be added, the sheer exuberant spirit of occasion which shines through the performances of the other three suites. Splendid recorded sound.

Additional recommendations ...
...Nos. 1-4. **Cologne Musica Antiqua / Reinhard Goebel.**
   Archiv Produktion Ⓕ 415 671-2AH2 (two discs: 111 minutes: DDD: 10/86). ✔   ⒼⒼ
...Nos. 1-4. **Academy of St Martin in the Fields / Sir Neville Marriner.**
   Decca Serenata Ⓜ 430 378-2DM (78 minutes: DDD: 7/91).
...Nos. 1-4. Cantata No. 110, Unser Mund sei voll Lachens – Unser Mund sei voll Lachens[a].
   Cantata No. 174, Ich liebe den Höchsten von ganzem Gemüte – Sinfonia Concerto. Easter
   Oratorio, BWV249 – Sinfonia. Cantata No. 42, Am Abend aber desselbigen Sabbats – Sinfonia.
   Cantata No. 52, Falsche Welt, dir trau ich nicht – Sinfonia. [a]**The English Concert Choir;**
   The English Concert / Trevor Pinnock. ✔ Archiv Produktion Ⓕ 439 780-2AH2
   (two discs: 121 minutes: DDD: 12/95).
...Nos. 1-4. **Academy for Ancient Music, Berlin / René Jacobs.**
   Harmonia Mundi Ⓕ HMC90 1578/9 (two discs: 98 minutes: DDD: 8/96). ✔
...Nos. 1-4. Cantatas: No. 29, Wir danken dir, Gott, wir danken dir – Sinfonia; No. 42, Am Abend
   aber desselbigen Sabbats – Sinfonia; No. 209, Non sa che sia dolore – Sinfonia. Sinfonia in
   D major, BWV1045. **The Brandenburg Consort / Roy Goodman** (vn).
   Hyperion Dyad Ⓑ CDD22002 (two discs: 113 minutes: DDD: 11/96).
...Nos. 1-4. **Orchestra of the Age of Enlightenment / Frans Brüggen.**
   Philips Ⓕ 442 151-2PH2 (two discs: 81 minutes: DDD: 9/97). ✔   Ⓖ

Bach Orchestral Suite No. 4 in D major, BWV1069. Concerto for Three Violins and Strings in
   D major, BWV1064. Cantata No. 42, Am Abend aber desselbigen Sabbats – Sinfonia.
Vivaldi Concertos – Strings in A major, RV158; Four Violins and Strings in B minor, Op. 3 No. 10.
   L'Olimpiade – Overture. **Freiburg Baroque Orchestra / Thomas Hengelbrock.** Deutsche Harmonia
   Mundi Ⓕ 05472 77289-2 (64 minutes: DDD: 4/94). ✔ Recorded 1991-92.   Ⓖ
The Freiburg Baroque Orchestra score ten out of ten for vitality in their pleasingly varied programme. Bach's Orchestral Suite No. 4 is heard in what is probably a pre-Leipzig version, which excludes trumpets and drums. That may not sound too promising for readers who like their 'fix' of brass and timpani, yet the immensely rewarding sonorities created by strings, three oboes and bassoon together with invigorating rhythmic patterns, provides wonderful mental and aural refreshment. However, the two Menuets in the Leipzig version are also missing. Of the two Vivaldi concertos, the A major piece for ripieno strings foreshadows the style of the early Mannheim symphonists, with its tremolos, breaks and short runs punctuated by trills in the outer movements, and the B minor, the tenth of the 12 which Vivaldi published under the title *L'estro armonico*, among the most inventive of the set. This enjoyable release is well recorded and helpfully documented.

Bach The Art of Fugue, BWV1080[a]. A Musical Offering, BWV1079[b]. Canons, BWV1072-78;
   1086-87[a]. **Cologne Musica Antiqua / Reinhard Goebel.** Archiv Produktion Ⓕ 413 642-2AH3
   (three discs: 140 minutes: ADD: 4/85). ✔ Items marked [a] from 413 728-1AH2 (4/85);
   [b]2533 422 (11/79).   ⒼⒼ
The great compilation of fugues, canons and a trio sonata which Bach dedicated to King Frederick the Great is one of the monuments of baroque instrumental music. Every contrapuntal device of canon at various intervals, augmentation, inversion, retrograde motion and so on is displayed here, and the performances are splendidly alive and authentic-sounding. It goes without saying that period instruments or modern replicas are used. The intellectually staggering *Art of Fugue* is a kind of testament to Bach's art and for this recording the instrumentation, unspecified by the composer, has been well chosen. The 14 miniature Canons which close this issue are for the most part a recent discovery and were written on a page of Bach's own copy of the *Goldberg Variations*; of curiosity value certainly but not much more than that. Excellent recording for these performances which have great authority.

Additional recommendations ...
...The Art of Fugue. **Hespèrion XX / Jordi Savall.**
  Auvidis Astrée Ⓕ E2001 (two discs: 92 minutes: ADD: 11/88). ✐
...The Art of Fugue. **Amsterdam Bach Soloists.** Ottavo Ⓕ OTRC48503 (72 minutes: DDD: 8/89). ✐
...A Musical Offering (orch. Webern) – Ricercar a 6. **Bruckner** Symphony No. 9 in D minor.
  Royal Concertgebouw Orchestra / Riccardo Chailly.
  Decca Ⓕ 455 506-2DH (71 minutes: DDD: 10/97).

Bach Flute Sonatas – No. 1 in B minor, BWV1030; No. 2 in E flat major, BWV1031; No. 4 in
C major, BWV1033; No. 5 in E minor, BWV1034; No. 6 in E major, BWV1035. Violin Sonata in
G minor, BWV1020 (arr. fl). **James Galway** (fl); **Sarah Cunningham** (va da gamba); **Philip Moll**
(hpd). RCA Victor Red Seal Ⓕ 09026 62555-2 (75 minutes: DDD: 6/95). Recorded 1993.
Gramophone Editor's choice.   Ⓖ
The basic six flute sonatas, BWV1030-35, can be accommodated on a single disc, but Galway plays
safe by keeping to what Bach (or someone else) actually wrote, omitting the unfinished A major
Sonata, BWV1032, which other players have chosen to present in variously completed forms. There
is, from the purist's point of view, still a 'risk' since it remains unproven that Bach was the composer
of BWV1031, 1033 and 1020 – with the last of which Galway replaces BWV1032; however, their
quality justifies their inclusion – if Bach didn't write them one doubts that he would have disowned
them. The booklet-notes do not mention the doubts concerning BWV1031 and 1033. Galway is at his
warm, velvet-toned best, phrasing immaculately, caressing the slow movements and fleet of tongue in
the quicker ones. His tempos are well chosen and he never allows virtuosity to get the better of his
judgement. The 'supporting cast' are no less beyond reproach, but whilst the flute and viola da gamba
are well balanced the harpsichord might profitably have been allowed a rather more equal say in
BWV1030 and BWV1031, in which it has an obbligato role. This will serve well as an introduction to
this repertory, but you may prefer to have a complete account of this *oeuvre*, such as that by Janet See
(baroque flute) and Davitt Moroney, albeit at the expense of a second disc.
Additional recommendations ...
...BWV1030-35. Partita in A minor, BWV1013. **Stephen Preston** (fl); **Trevor Pinnock** (hpd); **Jordi
  Savall** (va da gamba). CRD Ⓕ CRD3314/5 (two discs: 98 minutes: ADD: 1/90). ✐
...BWV1030-35. G minor, BWV1020. **Janet See** (fl); **Davitt Moroney** (hpd); **Mary Springfels**
  (va da gamba). Harmonia Mundi Ⓕ HMU90 7024/5 (two discs: 114 minutes: DDD: 11/91). ✐
...BWV1030-35. **William Bennett** (fl); **George Malcolm** (hpd); **Michael Evans** (vc).
  ASV Quicksilva Ⓢ CDQS6108 (77 minutes: ADD: 3/94).   Ⓖ

Bach Trio Sonatas, BWV525-30 (arr. Palladian Ensemble) – No. 1 in E flat major; No. 3 in
D minor; No. 5 in C major; No. 6 in G major. Four Duets, BWV802-05. 14 Verschiedene
Canones, BWV1087. **Palladian Ensemble** (Pamela Thorby, recs; Rachel Podger, vn; Susanna
Heinrich, va da gamba; William Carter, gtr/archlte/theorbo). Linn Records Ⓕ CKD036
(75 minutes: DDD: 8/95). ✐ Recorded 1994.
The Palladian Ensemble consists of young early-music players whose fluent techniques have been
directly developed on period instruments and who are well informed and imaginative – "We've read
all the books on performance practice and style, but we're not overawed by them. This is how we *feel*
the music, and we're very well equipped to do it *our* way." The Trio Sonatas are 'properly' transposed
to keys more suited to the chosen instruments, and the Four Duets are given to the violin and viola
da gamba: the annotator describes them as "too rarely performed" – he should look on the
Gramophone Database! How do you bring a perpetual canon to an end? One way is by means of a
fade-out, as happens with the fourteenth of the *Goldberg* canons, the colourful presentation of which
as a whole drives a horse and cart through any notion that canons are just dry, academic exercises.
Hairpin dynamics sometimes come close to sounding mannered and Rachel Podger does not always
wash the tonal acid from her etched lines, but these are very tiny flies in the ointment of performances
that are refreshingly committed and which stray from old paths in stimulating and revealing ways.
Enjoy them, and feel compassion for anyone who is unable to do so.
Additional recommendations ...
...BWV525-30. **The King's Consort / Robert King** (org/hpd).
  Hyperion Ⓕ CDA66843 (71 minutes: DDD: 8/96). ✐
...BWV525-30 (arr. Linsenberg). **Musica Pacifica.**
  Virgin Classics Veritas Ⓕ VC5 45192-2 (70 minutes: DDD: 12/96).
...No. 5 – Largo (arr. Feinberg). *Coupled with works by various composers.* **Arcadi Volodos** (pf).
  Sony Classical Ⓕ SK62691 (61 minutes: DDD: 10/97). *Gramophone Editor's choice.*
  Selected by Soundings. See review in the Collections section; refer to the Index.   ⒼⒼ

Bach Violin Sonatas, BWV1014-19 – No. 1 in B minor; No. 2 in A major; No. 3 in E major; No. 4
in C minor; No. 5 in F major; No. 6 in G major. **Fabio Biondi** (vn); **Rinaldo Alessandrini** (hpd).
Opus 111 Ⓕ OPS30-127/8 (two discs: 90 minutes: DDD: 7/96). ✐ Recorded 1995.
Bach Violin Sonatas, BWV1014-19 – No. 1 in B minor; No. 2 in A major; No. 3 in E major; No. 4
in C minor; No. 5 in F major; No. 6 in G major. **Dimitry Sitkovetsky** (vn); **Robert Hill** (hpd).
Hänssler Classic Ⓕ CD98 154 (76 minutes: DDD: A/97). Recorded 1996.   Ⓖ

Biondi and Alessandrini are probably the two most fêted members of Italy's growing early music community, but interest in them so far has depended a lot on the fact that they have been performing Italian music, in which, it is felt, caprice and a little bit of red-blooded passion have an important part to play. Such qualities are not so easy to apply to Bach, even if you wanted to; better here to play intelligently, in tune and with good articulation, and let Bach's robust notationally more complete music speak for itself. This is just what Biondi and Alessandrini do, though at the same time bringing a moving lyricism to slow movements, and above all a bold and biting energy to faster ones such as the last movement of BWV1014, the second movement of BWV1015 with its upward arpeggios, or the finale of the same sonata. Alessandrini, better known internationally as the Director of Concerto Italiano, is a crisp harpsichordist and shows considerable dexterity in the last movement of BWV1016, among others. The recording is fairly close for both instruments, which it needs to be for the harpsichord if it is to contribute much to the music's dialogue; but perhaps the violin could have been given a little more space, so that we do not have to hear Biondi breathing or the friction of his bow on the string. A very small complaint which does not detract from a warm recommendation.

There is still much to be said for having these wonderful works played on a (relatively) modern violin – especially by someone of Dimitry Sitkovetsky's stature. The tone is bright, intonation spot on, vibrato intelligently graded, the top line sweet but never saccharine and the phrasing subtly influenced by the 'period performance' school. Listeners averse to the astringent tones of a period violin will naturally gravitate to this recording. Robert Hill's harpsichord playing is pert and supple, often more prominent than the violin line (the harpsichord part in any case holds much of the musical interest) and very well recorded. Sitkovetsky presents the Sixth Sonata in its final version, which includes the delightful solo-harpsichord third movement *Allegro* and ends with a reprise of the heady *Presto* that opens the work. The closing *Allegro* quotes music from Bach's *Wedding* Cantata. Arthur Grumiaux's tonally distinctive and warmly phrased 1978 Philips recordings with Christiane Jaccottet come closest to Sitkovetsky's in terms of overall style, though Sitkovetsky's approach is more 'modern-authentic' than Grumiaux's, and Hill's harpsichord playing more imaginative than Jaccottet's. Sitkovetsky and Hill are definitely among the front runners in the digital field.

Additional recommendations ...

...BWV1014-19. Sonatas for Violin and Continuo, BWV1020-25ª – Nos. 2 and 4. **Catherine Mackintosh** (vn); ª**Jennifer Ward Clarke** (vc); **Maggie Cole** (hpd). Chandos Chaconne Ⓕ CHAN0603 (two discs: 123 minutes: DDD). 🎵

...BWV1014-19. **Susanne Lautenbacher** (vn); **Leonore Klinckerfuss** (hpd). Bayer Ⓕ BR100086/7 (two discs: 98 minutes: DDD: 10/90). 🎵

...BWV1014-19. **Sigiswald Kuijken** (vn); **Gustav Leonhardt** (hpd). Deutsche Harmonia Mundi Editio Classica Ⓜ GD77170 (two discs: 94 minutes: ADD: 10/90). 🎵

...BWV1014-19. Sonatas for Violin and Continuo, BWV1020-25 – No. 1 in G minor, BWV1020; No. 2 in G major, BWV1021; No. 3 in F major, BWV1022; No. 4 in E minor, BWV1023. **Arthur Grumiaux** (vn); **Christiane Jaccottet** (hpd). Philips Duo Ⓜ 454 011-2PM2 (two discs: 138 minutes: ADD: 7/96).

Bach Six Keyboard Partitas, BWV825-30. Italian Concerto in F major, BWV971. Overture in the French style in B minor, BWV831. **Andreas Staier** (hpd). Deutsche Harmonia Mundi Ⓕ 05472 77306-2 (three discs: 184 minutes: DDD: 2/95). 🎵 Recorded 1993. ⓖⓖ

On which level these wonderfully rich pieces speak to us is, of course, largely in the hands of the performer: now we have persuasive accounts from, amongst others, Christophe Rousset and Andreas Staier. The latter is a performer with a keen understanding of decorum though it is the darkly imbued suites where he is especially penetrating. He takes a stark and disturbing view of the C minor Partita. The opening is remarkably powerful and rhetorical but the way he juxtaposes this with an almost ironically free-flowing *andante* before setting into an exacting and exhilarating *fugato* is musicianship of real conviction and flair. Staier's impeccable digital facility and steadiness is often at the root of the colourful devices which he imparts to the A minor Partita and before that a rounded and genial Sarabande, and finally a dreamy Gigue – a rare thing indeed! Rousset is exceptional in the First Partita, and of course in others too, though he does not deliver the emotional range which these pieces afford in the hands of some others. Let's make no mistake: Staier's performances are still in the very top bracket, always thought-provoking and clearly argued, with moments of matchlessly vital and exquisite playing (the Gigue of the G major Partita, for instance). Staier's set also includes Part Two of the *Clavier-übung*, an extra disc with the *Italian Concerto* and the B minor *Overture in the French style*, both beautifully played. Here, as elsewhere, his Keith Hill harpsichord after German examples gives a clearly defined attack and a focus which will have you on the edge of your seat.

Additional recommendations ...

...Italian Concerto. French Overture. Four Duets, BWV802-05. **Kenneth Gilbert** (hpd). Harmonia Mundi Musique d'abord Ⓑ HMA190 1278 (56 minutes: DDD: 2/90). 🎵

...Four Duets. Italian Concerto. French Overture. Chromatic Fantasia and Fugue in D minor, BWV903. **Christophe Rousset**. L'Oiseau-Lyre Ⓕ 433 054-2OH (68 minutes: DDD: 5/92). 🎵 *Selected by Sounds in Retrospect.*

...Keyboard Partitas. **Christophe Rousset** (hpd). L'Oiseau-Lyre Ⓕ 440 217-2OH2 (two discs: 154 minutes: DDD: 9/93). 🎵

...Keyboard Partitas. Preludes, BWV924-29, BWV930. Six Little Preludes, BWV933-38. Preludes and Fughettas – D minor, BWV899; E minor, BWV900; G major, BWV902. Preludes and Fugues – A minor, BWV895; G major, BWV902*a*. Two Fugues in C major, BWV952 and BWV953. Fughetta in C minor, BWV961. **Glenn Gould** (pf). Sony Classical Glenn Gould Edition Ⓜ SM2K52597* (two discs: 148 minutes: ADD: 11/94).

...Keyboard Partita in B flat major, BWV825. *Coupled with works by various composers.* **Dinu Lipatti** (pf). EMI Références mono Ⓜ CDH5 65166-2* (73 minutes: ADD: 12/94). *See review in the Collections section; refer to the Index.*   ⒼⒼⒼ

...Four Duets. Chromatic Fantasia and Fugue. Six English Suites, BWV806-11. Six French Suites, BWV812-17. Italian Concerto. French Overture. Keyboard Partitas, BWV825-30. Das wohltemperierte Klavier, BWV846-93. Goldberg Variations, BWV988. 15 Two-Part Inventions, BWV772-86. 15 Three-Part Inventions, BWV787-801. **András Schiff** (pf). Decca Ⓜ 452 279-2DM12 (12 discs: 791 minutes: DDD: 3/97).

...Italian Concerto[ac]. Aria variata in A minor, BWV989[b] (both arr. Lawrence-King). *Coupled with works by various composers.* [a]**Harp Consort / Andrew Lawrence-King** ([b]hp/[c]hpd). Deutsche Harmonia Mundi Ⓕ 05472 77366-2 (70 minutes: DDD: 4/98). *See review in the Collections section; refer to the Index.*

Bach Six Partitas, BWV825-30. **Angela Hewitt** (pf). Hyperion Ⓕ CDA67191/2 (two discs: 143 minutes: DDD: 6/97). Recorded 1996-97. *Gramophone Editor's choice.*   ⒼⒼ

After ages without any recordings of the Partitas on the piano, along comes Angela Hewitt and saves the situation, effortlessly eclipsing all competitors. If Bach is to be played on the piano, this is the kind of way to do it. Inherent in all her playing is a rhythmic vitality, always under control, that sweeps one along with its momentum, subtly varied articulation, dynamics that follow the natural rise or fall of phrases without exaggerations, an appreciation of Bach's harmonic tensions, an ability to differentiate between the strength of contrapuntal lines, and an unfailing clarity of texture. This is a sane and sensible interpretation, deeply musicianly and devoid of eccentricity. Her attitude, rather like Toscanini's, is to accept the text *com' è scritto* and then to make legitimate adjustments, so we get double-dotting and assimilation of rhythms. Technically she is immaculate, with the cleanest possible ornaments. In the great E minor Sarabande Hewitt is justifiably emotional, without becoming soggy: only in the first half of the A minor Allemande is there a hint of coyness. No, the whole disc gives unalloyed pleasure.

Bach Partita No. 1 in B flat major, BWV825. Five Preludes, BWV939-43. Prelude in C minor, BWV999. Fugue in C major, BWV953. Three Minuets, BWV841-3. French Suite No. 5 in G major, BWV816. Fughetta in C minor, BWV961. Clavier-Büchlein for W.F. Bach – Preludes: C major, BWV924; D major, BWV925; D minor, BWV926; F major, BWV927; F major, BWV928; G minor, BWV930. Concerto in F major, BWV971, "Italian Concerto". Anna Magdalena Notenbuch – Minuets: G major, BWVAnh114; G minor, BWVAnh115. **Richard Egarr** (hpd). EMI Debut Ⓑ CDZ5 69700-2 (78 minutes: DDD: 5/97). 🎵 *Gramophone Editor's choice.*   Ⓖ

Richard Egarr's programme is an attractive one in which three major solo harpsichord works – the Partita (BWV825), the *French Suite* (BWV816), and the *Italian Concerto* (BWV971) – are interspersed with Preludes, Minuets and two Fugues from the Kellner Collection, the *Clavier-Büchlein* for Wilhelm Friedemann Bach, "the son I love, the one who fills me with joy", and the *Notenbuch* for Bach's second wife, Anna Magdalena. The character of Egarr's instrument, a copy by Joel Katzman of a 1638 Ruckers, has been effectively recorded, capturing its warm timbre in an intimate, domestic-sounding ambience. Egarr's B flat Partita is an unhurried affair, reflective in its Prelude and Allemande and rhythmically supple. Some readers may not at once respond to the extent to which he leans on notes, thereby breaking up that strict regularity of pulse that used to be the order of the day. His articulation and rhythmic flexibility are both illuminating and communicative. The music breathes, and with each breath comes a natural pause in the declamation allowing for rhetorical gesture and a feeling for scansion. Just occasionally in the Sarabande phrases are a little too clipped and skimped over, but such instances, both here and in the *French Suite*, are few and far between and certainly insufficiently intrusive to spoil your listening enjoyment. How refreshing, too, to hear minuets delivered in poised and eloquent terms. Each of the little Preludes and Minuets is lovingly shaped and played with affection for, and understanding of, the music's poetry. In short this is an outstanding disc, both for Egarr's technically accomplished playing and for his delicacy of feeling.

Additional recommendation ...

...(all arr. J. Williams): Prelude in C minor, BWV999; Suite in G minor, BWV995; Suite in E minor, BWV996; Partita in C minor, BWV997; Fugue in G minor, BWV1000. **John Williams** (gtr). Sony Classical Essential Classics Ⓜ SBK62972 (64 minutes: ADD: 7/97).

Bach The Art of Fugue, BWV1080. **Davitt Moroney** (hpd). Harmonia Mundi Ⓕ HMC90 1169/70 (two discs: 99 minutes: DDD: 5/86). 🎵 *Gramophone Award Winner 1986.*   ⒼⒼ

Bach died before the process of engraving his last great work had been completed, thus leaving a number of issues concerning performance in some doubt. However, Davitt Moroney is a performer-scholar who has a mature understanding of the complexity of Bach's work; in a lucid essay in the booklet, he discusses the problems of presenting *The Art of Fugue* whilst at the same time explaining his approach to performing it. Certain aspects of this version will be of particular importance to prospective buyers: Moroney himself has completed Contrapunctus 14 but he also plays the same Contrapunctus in its unfinished state as a fugue on three subjects. He omits Bach's own reworkings for two harpsichords of Contrapunctus 13 on the grounds that they do not play a part in the composer's logically constructed fugue cycle; and he omits the Chorale Prelude in G major (BWV668*a*) which certainly had nothing to do with Bach's scheme but was added in the edition of 1751 so that the work should not end in an incomplete state. Moroney's performing technique is of a high order, placing emphasis on the beauty of the music which he reveals with passionate conviction. Exemplary presentation and an appropriate recorded sound enhance this fine achievement.

Additional recommendations ...
...The Art of Fugue (earlier version). **Kenneth Gilbert** (hpd).
   Archiv Produktion Ⓕ 427 673-2AH (59 minutes: DDD: 4/90). ✇
...The Art of Fugue. Overture in the French style in B minor, BWV831. Italian Concerto in
   F major, BWV971. Prelude, Fugue and Allegro in E flat major, BWV998. **Gustav Leonhardt,**
   Bob van Asperen (Art of Fugue) (hpds). Deutsche Harmonia Mundi Editio Classica
   Ⓜ GD77013 (two discs: 132 minutes: ADD: 12/90). ✇
...The Art of Fugue – Contrapunctus 1-12, 14, 15. **Wolfgang Rübsam** (org).
   Naxos Ⓢ 8 550703 (72 minutes: DDD: 1/94).
...The Art of Fugue – Contrapunctus 13 and 17-19. Passacaglia and Fugue in C minor, BWV582.
   Sei gegrüsset, Jesu gütig, BWV768.**Wolfgang Rübsam** (org).
   Naxos Ⓢ 8 550704 (78 minutes: DDD: 1/94).
...The Art of Fugue. **Nancarrow** Three Canons for Ursula. Studies for Player Piano Nos. 3*c*,
   6 and 11. **Joanna MacGregor** (pf). Collins Classics Ⓕ 7043-2
   (two discs: 108 minutes: DDD: 10/96). *See review under Nancarrow; refer to the Index.*
...The Art of Fugue – Contrapunctus 13. Concerto for Two Harpsichords in C major, BWV1061*a*.
   Coupled with works by various composers. **Christopher Hogwood, Christophe Rousset**
   (hpds/clavs/fps). L'Oiseau-Lyre Ⓕ 440 649-2OH (65 minutes: DDD: 8/96). ✇
   See review in the Collections section; refer to the Index.

Bach Sonatas and Partitas for Solo Violin, BWV1001-06: Sonatas – No. 1 in G minor; No. 2 in
A minor; No. 3 in C major. Partitas – No. 1 in B minor; No. 2 in D minor; No. 3 in E major.
Arthur Grumiaux (vn). Philips Duo Ⓜ 438 736-2PM2 (two discs: 113 minutes: ADD: 2/94).
From A02205/7L (3/62). Recorded 1960-61. *Gramophone Editor's choice.*   ⒼⒼ Ⓖ
Bach Sonatas and Partitas for Solo Violin, BWV1001-06: Sonatas – No. 1 in G minor; No. 2 in
A minor; No. 3 in C major. Partitas – No. 1 in B minor; No. 2 in D minor; No. 3 in E major.
Monica Huggett (vn). Virgin Classics Veritas Ⓕ VCD5 45205-2 (two discs: 152 minutes: DDD:
1/98). ✇ Recorded 1995.

The totally innocent ear, deprived of any comparison, could be forgiven for judging Grumiaux's to be definitive performances of Bach's Partitas and Sonatas. There is little of the sweetness of a Heifetz, the passing whimsy of a Shumsky here. And yet they define, indeed, as few other performances do, the structural frame and rhythmic working-out of each movement with extraordinary determination and authority. The purity of intonation is absolute; the energy locked into the sheer sound of the instrument startling. *And* two discs, as they say, for the price of one! Those who know and love the artistry of Grumiaux will be thrilled to rediscover these Berlin recordings of the early 1960s, sharply remastered and sounding out in a roomy acoustic. The platinum gleam glancing off every moment of double-stopping, and the flinty brightness struck where contrapuntal voices meet ring out as never before. The arpeggios of the *Presto* of the G minor Sonata flash like light from a prism; and the same mesmeric steadiness of *moto perpetuo* makes for a heady finish to the C major Sonata. What dominates, though, is the rhythmic rigour of Grumiaux's playing. His perfectionism, fused with a real sense of struggle, brings sheer might to the fugues of the Sonatas: it is rather like watching a climber scaling a vast rock face, securing himself with a pick and leaping across the next crevasse.

   With her impressive performances (on her beautiful-toned Amati) Monica Huggett sweeps most other baroque interpretations off the board. Her aim, she says, in her introductory note, is a characteristically bright and sweet seventeenth-century timbre, and she declares herself less interested in the virtuoso aspect of the music, more in the "interior spirituality of the sonatas and the gracious elegance of the partitas". That certainly does not imply any absence of virtuosity: there have been few recordings of these pillars of the repertoire so impeccable in intonation and so free from any tonal roughness. Her rhythmic flexibility may upset some traditionalists, but it gives her readings a thoughtfully spontaneous air, and is always applied to clarify the phrasing. The B minor Corrente and D minor Allemande, for example, become more expressive through this subtle phrasing, and her G minor *Presto* and E major Prelude are not merely mechanically fluent. She is adept at balancing the interplay of internal parts and at preserving continuity of line (as in the D minor Sarabande) and rhythmic flow despite the irruption of chords: only in places in the gigantic C major Fugue does this feel under strain and at the start of the B minor Bourrée lost. There is a lively bounce in her D minor Courante and E major Gigue, and she is splendidly neat in the *double* of the B minor Courante and in the C major's finale. For the most part she is very sparing with embellishments, but then suddenly becomes lavish in the repeats of the A minor *Allegro*. Her musicianly readings are most rewarding.

Additional recommendations ...
...**Sigiswald Kuijken** (vn). Deutsche Harmonia Mundi Editio Classica Ⓜ GD77043
(two discs: 128 minutes: ADD: 4/89). ✔   ⒼⒼⒼ
...**Oscar Shumsky** (vn). ASV Ⓕ CDDCD454 (two discs: 147 minutes: ADD: 9/87).   ⒼⒼ
...**Nathan Milstein** (vn). EMI mono Ⓜ ZDMB7 64793-2*
(two discs: 114 minutes: ADD: 5/94).   ⒼⒼⒼ
...**Partitas Nos. 1-3. Viktoria Mullova** (vn). Philips Ⓕ 434 075-2PH (77 minutes: DDD: 6/94).   ⒼⒼ
...(trans. North) **Nigel North** (lte). Linn Records Ⓕ CKD013, CKD029
(two discs, oas: 70 and 68 minutes: DDD: 4/95). *Gramophone Editor's choice.*
...**Gérard Poulet** (vn). Arion Ⓕ ARN268296 (two discs: 131 minutes: DDD: 8/96).
...**Henryk Szeryng** (vn). DG Ⓜ 453 004-2GTA2 (two discs: 129 minutes: ADD: 11/96).
...**Ida Haendel** (vn). Testament Ⓕ SBT2090 (two discs: 159 minutes: AAD: 1/97).
...**Partita No. 1.** *Coupled with works by various composers.* **Michelle Makarski** (vn).
ECM New Series Ⓕ 449 957-2 (74 minutes: DDD: 7/97). *See review in the Collections section;
refer to the Index.*
...(orch. Stokowski) Sonatas and Partitas for Solo Violin – Partita No. 1 in B minor: Sarabande.
Partita No. 3 in E major: Preludio. Passacaglia and Fugue in C minor, BWV582. Musicalisches
Gesang-Buch G. C. Schemelli, BWV439-488 – Komm, süsser Tod, BWV478 (melody by Bach);
Mein Jesu! was für Seelenweh, BWV487. English Suites, BWV806-11 – No. 2 in A minor:
Bourrée No. 1. Cantata No. 80, BWV80, "Ein' feste Burg ist unser Gott" – Ein' feste Burg ist
unser Gott. Christmas Oratorio, BWV248 – Sinfonia. Fugue in G minor, BWV578. Orchestral
Suites, BWV1066-9 – No. 3: Air, "Air on a G String". Toccata and Fugue in D minor, BWV565.
symphony orchestra / Leopold Stokowski.
EMI Angel Ⓜ CDM5 66385-2* (71 minutes: ADD: 8/97).
...**Nathan Milstein** (vn). DG The Originals Ⓜ 457 701-2GOR2* (two discs: 127 minutes: ADD: 6/98).

Bach Solo Cello Suite Suites, BWV1007-12 – No. 1 in G major[a]; No. 2 in D minor[b]; No. 3 in
C major[c]; No. 4 in E flat major[d]; No. 5 in C minor[e]; No. 6 in D major[f]. **Pablo Casals** (vc).
EMI Références mono Ⓜ CHS7 61027-2* (two discs: 130 minutes: ADD: 3/89). Item marked [a]
from HMV DB3671/3 (2/39), [b]DB3399/401 (6/38); [c]DB3402/04 (6/38); [d]DB6538/40 (8/48);
[e]DB6541/4S (8/48); [f]DB3674/7 (2/39). Recorded 1936-39. *Gramophone classical 100.*   ⒼⒼⒼ
Bach Solo Cello Suites, BWV1007-12 – No. 1 in G major; No. 2 in D minor; No. 3 in C major;
No. 4 in E flat major; No. 5 in C minor; No. 6 in D major. **Anner Bylsma** (vc).
Sony Classical Vivarte Ⓕ S2K48047 (two discs: 115 minutes: DDD: 1/93). ✔ Recorded 1992.
Young music-lovers today may find it difficult to believe that, 60 years ago, major works by Bach were
considered to be of such specialized appeal that recordings could be obtained only in a limited
"Society" edition. The cello suites – nowadays available in dozens of versions – had never been
recorded until Fred Gaisberg, after protracted efforts, finally persuaded Casals to play them for
HMV: Nos. 2 and 3 in London in November 1936, the rest in Paris in July 1938 and July 1939. Casals
had hesitated for 35 years before committing to disc these works – long regarded as unplayable, and
never performed in their entirety – which he had discovered at the age of 13 and worked on for 12
years before playing them to an astonished public. To do so he had to evolve new techniques and,
intellectually, to delve deeply into the character and inner structure of the music. He stressed the
dance basis of the movements; and his vitality, rhythmic flexibility (to clarify the shape of phrases)
and tonal nuance, and the vigour and variety of his bowing, still leap from the discs to impress the
listener. EMI's term "Références" could not be more apt, since these performances remain the classic
yardstick by which all later ones must still be judged. The transfers from the original 78s, yielding an
astonishingly clean ambience to the cello, represent a technical triumph for Keith Hardwick.
    Anner Bylsma's set is his second complete version of the Cello Suites. In a period of some 13 years
between the first and second recordings, Bylsma's concept of these works has not undergone any
fundamental changes. The difference between them is rather one of degree for, as Bylsma himself says,
"one keeps finding new relationships between the notes and every motif can be played in so many
different ways – and always with meaning, too". In this version Bylsma intensifies the musical
gestures which characterized the earlier one. He is, if anything, more spontaneous in his playing here
and he takes greater risks. What we have, in fact, are 'performances' as opposed to studio-correct
readings; and so listeners concerned with niceties of intonation, for instance, may sometimes be
mildly disconcerted by what they hear. But from a purely interpretative standpoint the newer set is
bolder, more relaxed and more broadly expressive. Indeed, were it not for his impeccable 'early music'
credentials Bylsma might be targeted by critics for excessive romanticism. Pierre Fournier was thus
condemned for his Bach playing, yet his performances of the *Preludes* of these Suites, made in
1962-63, were in many respects far stricter than those of Bylsma. All this and much else make it clear
that convenient generalizations and tidy compartments are less acceptable than ever. Bylsma is an
artist who is not afraid to express himself individually, intensely and even, at times audaciously. Open-
minded readers will find much to admire and much that is satisfying in these passionate, warmly
expressive performances.
Additional recommendations ...
...**Heinrich Schiff** (vc). EMI Ⓕ CDS7 47471-8 (two discs: ADD).
...**Yo-Yo Ma** (vc). Sony Classical Ⓜ S2K37867 (two discs: 125 minutes: DDD).

...**Anner Bylsma** (vc). RCA Ⓕ RD70950 (two discs: 126 minutes: DDD). ✔
...**Pierre Fournier** (vc).
   DG The Originals Ⓜ 449 711-2GOR2 (two discs: 139 minutes: ADD: 3/89).   ❹❹
...**Mstislav Rostropovich** (vc). EMI Ⓕ CDS5 55363-2 (two discs: 147 minutes: DDD: 6/95).
...**János Starker** (vc). RCA Victor Red Seal Ⓕ 09026 61436-2 (two discs: 144 minutes: DDD: 9/97).
...**Jaap ter Linden** (vc). Harmonia Mundi Ⓕ HMU90 7216/7 (two discs: 146 minutes: DDD: 10/97).
...**Yo-Yo Ma** (vc). Sony Classical Ⓕ S2K63203 (two discs: 143 minutes: DDD: 2/98).
...**Julius Berger** (vc). Wergo Ⓕ WER4041-2 (two discs: 133 minutes: DDD: 6/98).

Bach Das wohltemperierte Klavier, "The Well-tempered Clavier", Books 1 and 2 – 48 Preludes and
Fugues, BWV846-893. **Kenneth Gilbert** (hpd). Archiv Produktion Ⓕ 413 439-2AH4 (four discs:
256 minutes: DDD: 2/87). ✔ From 413 439-1AH5 (9/84). Recorded 1983.   ❹❹
In Book 1 there are virtually no markings and so the performer carries heavy responsibility for
phrasing and articulation. Gilbert's blend of scholarship and technique with artistic sensibility makes
for notably convincing, often poetic playing. The D minor Prelude is one of many instances where his
interpretation haunts the memory. Gilbert's vital rhythmic sense and love of refinement are qualities
in his artistry which can be strongly felt throughout this vast project. Some readers may feel that he
is comparatively unadventurous in his registration – others, for example, make a35 greater point of
differentiation through instrumental colour – but it is one of the features of Gilbert's performance
that is particularly praiseworthy, since he clearly and effectively achieves his contrasts through
interpretation, renouncing the facility to emphasize them by more artificial means. In textural clarity
he yields nothing to his competitors in this repertoire and, in short, arrives at a solution which is
refined, lyrical and sometimes dazzlingly virtuosic, as in the Prelude in B flat, BWV866. The acoustic
of the Musée de Chartres, where the *48* were recorded, is pleasantly resonant. Gilbert plays a
seventeenth-century Flemish harpsichord enlarged first by Blanchet and then by Taskin in the
following century. A satisfying achievement and an important issue.
Additional recommendations ...
...Books 1 and 2. **Edwin Fischer** (pf).
   EMI Références mono Ⓜ CHS7 63188-2* (three discs: 237 minutes: ADD: 3/90).   ❹
...Books 1 and 2. **Colin Tilney** (clav/hpd). Hyperion Ⓕ CDA66351/4
   (four discs: 304 minutes: DDD: 10/90). ✔ *Selected by Sounds in Retrospect.*
...Das wohltemperierte Klavier – Preludes and Fugues: C major, BWV846; C sharp minor,
   BWV849; D major, BWV850; D minor, BWV851; E flat minor/D sharp minor, BWV853.
   Coupled with works by various composers. **Sviatoslav Richter** (pf).
   DG Double Ⓜ 447 355-2GDB2 (two discs: 150 minutes: ADD: 12/95).
...Books 1 and 2. **Davitt Moroney** (hpd). Harmonia Mundi Musique d'abord Ⓑ HMA190 1285/8
   (four discs: 272 minutes: DDD: 10/96). ✔

Bach Das wohltemperierte Klavier, Book 1, BWV846-869. **Masaaki Suzuki** (hpd). BIS Ⓕ CD813/4
(two discs: 119 minutes: DDD: 6/97). ✔ Recorded 1996.
It argues a considerable act of faith to entrust a recording of what is announced as Bach's "complete
keyboard works" to a newcomer, but BIS's Robert von Bahr has a sure instinct, which is confirmed
on the evidence of this first issue in the series. Masaaki Suzuki, a former pupil of Ton Koopman and
now professor of harpsichord and organ at Tokyo National University, has hitherto swum into our
ken only as conductor of the Bach Collegium Japan; but here he proves himself a Bach player of
distinction. He has great vitality, and constantly conveys a strongly rhythmic sense of momentum and
forward impulse, though not mechanically; his phrasing is subtly flexible, his part-playing (on a fine
Ruckers copy) is transparent, and he displays the far from universal virtue of consistency of
articulation between contrapuntal voices. His enjoyment of Bach in vivacious mood is evident. Here
and there he discreetly adds extra ornaments, in accordance with what is reported as having been
Bach's own practice. The only place in which his ornamentation is misguided is in the D major Fugue,
where it confuses the shape of the subject. On the whole this is a thoroughly rewarding set, presented
with an exceptionally comprehensive and informative booklet-note.

Bach Das wohltemperierte Klavier – Book 1, BWV846-69. **Jenö Jandó** (pf). Naxos Ⓢ 8 553796/7
(two discs: 111 minutes: DDD: 2/98). Recorded 1995. *Gramophone Editor's choice.*
Jandó is an eminently sane, no-nonsense artist in total control throughout, who phrases perceptively
and gives each movement real character. He is devoid of mannerisms and eccentricities, with a feeling
for period style; his playing is tonally sensitive without overdoing gradations of dynamics, firmly
rhythmical without either stiffness or anachronistic rubatos, convincingly pianistic (no misconceived
imitations of the harpsichord) but not indulging in latter-day approaches or inappropriate kinds of
articulation. He adopts intelligent tempos (occasionally exhilaratingly fast, as in the G major Prelude)
and gets his ornaments right; and his part-playing is illuminating, though avoiding 'hunt the slipper'
accentuation of fugal entries. He appears to be using one of the 1989 editions of the works based on
Bach's autograph fair copy in the Deutsche Staatsbloithek, Berlin – either Dürr's *Neue Bach
Ausgabe* or Richard Jones's admirable edition for the Associated Board. One of the notorious pitfalls
for piano interpretations of Book 1 is the E flat minor Prelude. Jandó takes it with due gravity, slower
than would be effective on the harpsichord but without becoming maudlin (though at times faintly

humming to himself, as he also does elsewhere): the relevant fugue is an outstanding example of his finely judged control. His rhythmic propulsion and sense of continuity are perhaps best exemplified in the colossal B minor and A minor Fugues; but he also shows splendid vitality in the D minor and E major Preludes and the E minor Fugue, and great vigour in his F sharp minor and A minor Preludes and G minor Fugue. This set at its low price is indeed a super-bargain.

Bach Six English Suites, BWV806-811. **Glenn Gould** (pf). Sony Classical Glenn Gould Edition
    Ⓜ SM2K52606 (two discs: 112 minutes: ADD: 4/96). From CBS 79208 (3/78). Recorded 1971-73.
No more original genius of the keyboard has existed than Glenn Gould, but this can lead to drawbacks as well as thrilling advantages. You may, for instance, sense how Gould can sacrifice depth of feeling for a relentless and quixotic sense of adventure. Yet love it or deride it, every bar of these lovingly remastered discs (the hiatus is explained in some riveting accompanying notes) tingles with *joie de vivre* and an unequalled force and vitality. Try the opening of the First Suite. Is such freedom glorious or maddening, or is the way the odd note is nonchalantly flicked in the following sustained argument a naughty alternative to Bach's intention? The pizzicato bass in the second Double from the same Suite is perhaps another instance of an idiosyncrasy bordering on whimsy, an enlivenment or rejuvenation that at least remains open to question. But listen to him in virtually any of the sarabandes from the Suites and you will find a tranquillity and equilibrium that can silence such criticism and even at his most piquant and outrageous his playing remains, mysteriously, all of a piece. The Gigue from the Second Suite is taken at a spanking *Presto* and the Prelude from the Third Suite is a gloriously true *vivace*, never rigid or merely metronomic. The fiercely chromatic, labyrinthine argument concluding the Fifth Suite is thrown off with a unique brio, one of those moments when you realize how Gould can lift Bach out of all possible time-warps and make him one of music's truest modernists. Sony's presentation is superb.
Additional recommendations ...
...English Suites Nos. 1-6. **Andras Schiff** (pf).
    Decca Ⓕ 421 640-2DH2 (two discs: 129 minutes: DDD: 12/88).
...English Suites Nos. 3, 4 and 6. French Suites Nos. 2, 4 and 6. Toccatas – D minor, BWV913;
    G major, BWV916. Fantasia in C minor, BWV906. Clavier-übung – Italian Concerto in F major,
    BWV971; Overture in the French style in B minor, BWV831. Four Duets, BWV802-5.
    Sviatoslav Richter (pf). Philips Ⓕ 438 613-2PH3 (three discs: 214 minutes: DDD: 8/94).   Ⓖ

Bach Six French Suites, BWV812-817. **Andrei Gavrilov** (pf). DG Ⓕ 445 840-2GH2 (two discs: 93
    minutes: DDD: 7/95). Recorded 1993.
Bach compiled his *French Suites*, so-called – the composer himself did not give them this title – towards the end of his Cöthen period and at the beginning of his final appointment at Leipzig. Like others before him, Andrei Gavrilov acknowledges his debt to Glenn Gould, sensing a fellow spirit throwing down the gauntlet and challenging convention at every turn with his fearless mix of directness and idiosyncrasy. Yet as his performances so eloquently convey, there are depths and subtleties in these ever-fascinating cosmopolitan Suites which are often erased by Gould's manic determination to redefine the parameters of Bach interpretation. Gavrilov has a way, for instance, of casting light on even the simplest, least polyphonic of the composer's arguments. He may retain some of his former headstrong pugnacity yet in the Sarabandes, which like pools of reflection form the nodal and expressive centre of each Suite, he finds an often glorious ease, repose and gently luminous sense of texture. Even those for whom such open-hearted espousal of the modern piano's resources ("the piano wins hands down" exclaims Gavrilov of arguments concerning harpsichord versus piano) is anachronistic will surely be touched and convinced. Predictably there are moments when Gould has the razor's edge over Gavrilov and, indeed, every other pianist, when it comes to clarity and dexterity. Yet even in the volleys of notes in, say, the Courante from the Sixth Suite, his dayglo, acidic brilliance is more arresting than poetically engaging. Touchingly and endearingly and by his own admission, Gavrilov sees Bach as "the key to comprehending the universe". The DG sound quality is exemplary.
Additional recommendations ...
...French Suites. **Gustav Leonhardt** (hpd). RCA Victor Seon Ⓜ GD71963
    (two discs: 78 minutes: ADD: 5/90). 🎵
...French Suites. Overture (Partita) in the French style in B minor, BWV831. **Glenn Gould** (pf).
    Sony Classical Glenn Gould Edition Ⓜ SM2K52609 (two discs: 85 minutes: ADD: 7/95).
...French Suites[a]. English Suite No. 3 in G minor, BWV808[b]. Concerto in the Italian style,
    BWV971, "Italian Concerto"[b]. [a]**Andrei Gavrilov**, [b]**Stanislav Bunin** (pfs).
    EMI Forte Ⓜ CZS5 69479-2 (two discs: 126 minutes: DDD: 3/97).

Bach Six French Suites, BWV812-817. Sonata in D minor, BWV964. Five Preludes, BWV924-28.
    Prelude in G minor, BWV930. Six Preludes, BWV933-8. Five Preludes, BWV939-43. Prelude in
    C minor, BWV999. Prelude and Fugue in A minor, BWV894. **Angela Hewitt** (pf).
    Hyperion Ⓕ CDA67121/2 (two discs: 151 minutes: DDD: 2/96). Recorded 1995.
    Gramophone Editor's choice.   Ⓖ
Even the most out-and-out purists who blench at the thought of Bach on so alien an instrument as the piano (as if Bach himself ever showed any reluctance at transferring his work from one instrument to another!) will find it hard not to be won over by Angela Hewitt's artistry. This Canadian pianist,

eschewing all hieratic pretentiousness on the one hand and self-regarding eccentricities on the other, gives us Bach performances that are not only admirable in style but marked by poise and what used to be called a 'quiet hand': 'chaste' might not be too fanciful a term, so long as that does not suggest any lack of vitality. There is intelligence in her carefully thought-out phrasing and subtle variety of articulation: gradations of sound are always alive without their becoming precious. The bulk of this recording is devoted to the *French Suites* (in which Hewitt includes a second Minuet in No. 2 and, more controversially, a Prelude and a vivacious second Gavotte in No. 4). Particularly enjoyable is the lightness of her treatment of the Airs of Nos. 2 and 4, the vigour of No. 5's Bourrée and the freshness of No. 6's Allemande; the extra decorations she adds in repeats everywhere sound properly spontaneous and are in the best of taste; ornaments are always cleanly played (though her mordants sometimes fall before, rather than on, the beat) and matched up in imitative voices.

Additional recommendation ...
...Sonata in D minor, BWV964. Suite in E minor, BWV996. Toccatas – D minor, BWV913; E minor, BWV914; G minor, BWV915. Fantasia in G minor, BWV917. Praeludium in D major. **Pierre Hantaï** (hpd). Virgin Classics Veritas Ⓕ VC5 45284-2 (72 minutes: DDD: 2/98).

Bach Goldberg Variations, BWV988. **Glenn Gould** (pf). Sony Classical Glenn Gould Edition Ⓜ SMK52619 (51 minutes: DDD: 8/93). From CBS 37779 (1/83). Recorded 1981. *Gramophone classical 100.*									ⒺⒼⒺ
Bach Goldberg Variations, BWV988. **Pierre Hantaï** (hpd). Opus 111 Ⓕ OPS30-84 (77 minutes: DDD: 4/94). 🎵 Recorded 1992. *Gramophone Award Winner 1994.* *Gramophone Editor's choice.*									ⒺⒼ

This truly astonishing performance was recorded 26 years after Gould's legendary 1955 disc. Gould was not in the habit of re-recording but a growing unease with that earlier performance made him turn once again to a timeless masterpiece and try, via a radically altered outlook, for a more definitive account. By his own admission he had, during those intervening years, discovered 'slowness' or a meditative quality far removed from flashing fingers and pianistic glory. And it is this 'autumnal repose' that adds such a deeply imaginative dimension to Gould's unimpeded clarity and pin-point definition. The Aria is now mesmerically slow. The tremulous confidences of Variation 13 in the 1955 performance give way to something more forthright, more trenchantly and determinedly voiced, while Var. 19's previously light and dancing measures are humorously slow and precise. Var. 21 is painted in the boldest of oils, so to speak, and most importantly of all, Landowska's 'black pearl' (Var. 25) is far less romantically susceptible than before, has an almost confrontational assurance. The Aria's return, too, is overwhelming in its profound sense of solace and resolution. Although Gould devotees probably wouldn't want to be without any of Gould's recordings, it has to be said that this is surely the finest. The recording is superb.

Pierre Hantaï's approach to the *Goldberg Variations* is tremendously spirited and energetic but also disciplined. What is most appealing about this playing, though, is that Hantaï clearly finds the music great fun to perform; some players have been too inclined to make heavy weather over this music. He makes each and every one of the canons a piece of entertainment while in no sense glossing over Bach's consummate formal mastery. Other movements, such as Var. 7 (gigue) and Var. 11, effervesce with energy and good humour and he is careful to avoid anything in the nature of superficiality. Not for a moment is the listener given the impression that his view of the music is merely skin deep. Indeed, there is a marked concentration of thought in canons such as that at the fourth interval (Var. 12). Elsewhere his feeling for the fantasy and poetry of Bach's music is effective and well placed (such as in Var. 13). The character of Bruce Kennedy's copy of an early eighteenth-century instrument by the Berlin craftsman, Michael Mietke is admirably captured by the effectively resonant recorded sound.

Additional recommendations ...
...Goldberg Variations. **Trevor Pinnock** (hpd). Archiv Produktion Ⓕ 415 130-2AH (61 minutes: ADD: 8/85). 🎵						Ⓔ
...Goldberg Variations. **András Schiff** (pf). Decca Ⓕ 417 116-2DH (73 minutes: DDD: 12/86).
...Goldberg Variations. **Glenn Gould** (pf). Sony Classical Glenn Gould Edition mono Ⓜ SMK52594* (46 minutes: ADD: 4/93).									ⒺⒼⒺ
...Goldberg Variations. 14 Three-Part Inventions, BWV788-801. **Glenn Gould** (pf). Sony Classical Glenn Gould Edition Ⓜ SMK52685* (61 minutes: ADD: 11/94).
...(arr. Sitkovetsky) Goldberg Variations. **New European Strings Chamber Orchestra / Dmitry Sitkovetsky** (vn). Nonesuch Ⓕ 7559-79341-2 (60 minutes: DDD: 9/95).
...Goldberg Variations. **Christophe Rousset** (hpd). L'Oiseau-Lyre Ⓕ 444 866-2OH (77 minutes: DDD: 11/95). 🎵						Ⓔ
...Goldberg Variations. Das wohltemperierte Klavier – Preludes and Fugues: E flat major, BWV876; E major, BWV878; F sharp minor, BWV883; B flat minor, BWV891. **Glenn Gould** (pf). CBC Records Perspective Series mono Ⓕ PSCD2007* (66 minutes: ADD: 1/96).
...Goldberg Variations. **Kenneth Gilbert** (hpd). Harmonia Mundi Suite Ⓜ HMT790 1240 (67 minutes: DDD: 12/96). 🎵
...(arr. Busoni) Goldberg Variations. **Busoni** Fantasia nach J. S. Bach. **David Buechner** (pf). Connoisseur Society Ⓕ CD4212 (66 minutes: DDD: 1/98).
...Goldberg Variations. **Masaaki Suzuki** (hpd). BIS Ⓕ CD819 (73 minutes: DDD: 3/98).

Bach Goldberg Variations, BWV988.
Mozart Keyboard Sonata in C major, K330/K300*h*.
Schoenberg Suite, Op. 25.
Sweelinck Fantasia. **Glenn Gould** (pf). Sony Classical mono Ⓜ SMK53474*
(76 minutes: ADD: 9/95). Recorded live in 1959.

Glenn Gould's recordings of Bach's *Goldberg Variations* are scattered like gold-dust throughout the catalogue. Such is Gould's nature and pianism that each and every reading casts its own spell; creates its own ambience and fascination. Here, his performance forms the major part of his legendary 1959 Salzburg recital, given when he was 27 and already near the end of his brief but dazzling public career. Elfin and teasing, Gould has rarely worn his astonishing expertise more lightly or engagingly, or illuminated every facet of Bach's timeless masterpiece with a more nonchalant sense of its glory. His 'black pearl' is lightened with a silvery clarity that he would later darken with greater speculation and time and again Bach's polyphony is playfully but never irresponsibly pointed and coloured. His virtuosity in Vars. 5 and 6 is ethereal rather than pressured and, throughout, the constant play of light and shade suggests only the most transcendental pianism and musicianship. As a bonus you can hear Sweelinck's solemnities offered with rare significance, Schoenberg's Op. 25 spun off with hallucinatory magic, and Mozart's K330 Sonata played with a truly extraordinary cunning, elegance and artifice. Here, indeed, is an assuaging alternative to later utterances which sometimes crystallized into pedantry and affectation. This is a disc beyond price; a crowning touch to Gould's endlessly fascinating discography.

Bach Fantasia in C minor, BWV906. 15 Two-Part Inventions, BWV772-786. 15 Three-Part
Inventions, BWV787-801. Chromatic Fantasia and Fugue in D minor, BWV903. **Angela Hewitt**
(pf). Hyperion Ⓕ CDA66746 (63 minutes: DDD: 11/94). Recorded 1994. *Gramophone Editor's*
choice.   Ⓖ

Angela Hewitt's approach may be gleaned from her refreshingly lucid annotation, or simply by listening to what she does. "A skilful player can [bring out the different voices] with different colours" and "To be capable of producing a true legato without using the pedal will serve a pianist well in any repertoire": Hewitt puts her fingers where her thoughts are, to signal effect. She never upsets the balance of the lines that it is in the nature of the harpsichord (Bach's chosen instrument) to yield, and her economy with the sustaining pedal helps to preserve their clarity. The two- and three-part *Inventions* are treated as music in their own right, not simply as the invaluable exercises they are; each is given its distinctive character, with a wonderful variety of sensitive touch and shapely rubato that never once threatens to become anachronistic. Her readings of the C minor *Fantasia* and the *Chromatic Fantasia and Fugue* are as eloquent and stimulating as any yet recorded by a harpsichordist.

Additional recommendations ...
...BWV772-786. BWV787-801. **Glenn Gould** (pf).
Sony Classical Glenn Gould Edition Ⓜ SMK52596 (50 minutes: ADD: 6/93).
...BWV772-786. BWV787-801. Anna Magdalena Notenbüch – Minuets: G major, BWVAnh114,
F major, BWVAnh115, G major, BWVAnh116, F major, BWVAnh132; Polonaises: G minor,
BWVAnh119, G minor, BWVAnh125; March in D major, BWVAnh122; Musette in D major,
BWVAnh126. **János Sebestyén** (pf). Naxos Ⓢ 8 550679 (58 minutes: DDD: 6/94).
See the end of the J.S. Bach section for details of availability of Complete Organ Works.

Bach Fantasias and Fugues – C minor, BWV537; G minor, BWV542; C minor, BWV562;
G major, BWV572. Preludes and Fugues – D major, BWV532; F minor, BWV534; A major,
BWV536; G major, BWV541; A minor, BWV543; B minor, BWV544; C major, BWV545;
C minor, BWV546; C major, BWV547; E minor, BWV548, "Wedge"; E flat major, BWV552,
"St Anne". **Christopher Herrick** (org). Hyperion Ⓕ CDA66791/2. (two discs: 150 minutes: DDD:
4/94). Played on the organ of the Jesuitenkirche, Lucerne, Switzerland. Recorded 1993.   ⒼⒼ

These 15 works constitute some of the finest and most important music ever written for the organ. They are such mainstays of the repertory that no serious lover of organ music could consider a world without them. Herrick's performances are authoritative, scholarly and perceptive, but if that were all it would merely be putting Bach on a pedestal, making him accessible only to those who already possess the key to the door. Herrick's genius is in bringing the music vividly to life, injecting it with a sense of fun and a directness of appeal without for a moment compromising artistic integrity. Few could fail to be captivated by the wonderfully vibrant and smiling countenance of the great E flat Prelude while those of us who have laboured long and hard just to get our feet round that most ankle-twisting of all fugue subjects must surely surrender in the face of Herrick's effortless fluency in BWV542. The glorious Swiss instrument has been brilliantly recorded, portraying not just the instrument itself but its sumptuous aural setting.

Additional recommendations ...
...Fantasia and Fugue, BWV542. Fugue in G minor, BWV578. Canzona in D minor, BWV588.
Preludes and Fugues – C major, BWV531; A minor, BWV543; BWV544. Fantasias and Fugues –
BWV562; G major, BWV570; BWV572. Passacaglia and Fugue in C minor, BWV582.
Ton Koopman (org). Teldec Das Alte Werk Ⓕ 4509-94458-2 (74 minutes: DDD). ✍

...Prelude and Fugue, BWV532. Clavier-übung III, BWV669-89 – Christe, aller Welt Trost, BWV670. *Coupled with works by various composers.* **Roger Sayer** (org). Priory Ⓕ PRCD495 (76 minutes: DDD: 4/96). *See review in the Collections section; refer to the Index.*

...Preludes and Fugues – BWV532; BWV534; F major, BWV540; BWV548. Fantasia super "Valet will ich dir geben", BWV735. Herzlich tut mich verlangen, BWV727. Nun komm, der Heiden Heiland, BWV659. Vor deinen Thron tret'ich, BWV668. **Michael Murray** (org). Telarc Ⓕ CD80385 (73 minutes: DDD: 5/97).

...Fantasia and Fugue, BWV537 (orch. Elgar). **Elgar** Falstaff, Op. 68. Nursery Suite. Dream children, Op. 43. Pomp and Circumstance March No. 3. **London Philharmonic Orchestra / Sir Adrian Boult.** Testament mono Ⓕ SBT1106* (77 minutes: ADD: 8/97).

...(all orch. Schoenberg) Prelude and Fugue, "St Anne". Schmücke dich, o liebe Seele, BWV654. Komm, Gott Schöpfer, BWV631. **Brahms** Piano Quartet No. 1 in G minor, Op. 25. **Houston Symphony Orchestra / Christoph Eschenbach.** RCA Victor Red Seal Ⓕ 09026 68658-2 (70 minutes: DDD: 10/97). *See review under Brahms; refer to the Index.*

Bach Preludes and Fugues – C major, BWV545; E flat major, BWV552, "St Anne". Trio Sonata in E minor, BWV528. Largo in A minor, BWV529. Fantasia in C minor, BWV562. Schübler Chorales, BWV645-50. **Piet Kee** (org). Chandos Chaconne Ⓕ CHAN0590 (66 minutes: DDD: 8/96). Played on the Schnitger organ of the Martini Church, Groningen, The Netherlands. Recorded 1995.

This is playing of heart-warming humanity and spiritual equilibrium, combining deep thought with complete spontaneity. Kee's control of the long, singing line goes hand in hand with a poetic command of baroque instrumental articulation. Dip anywhere into the Schübler Chorales (unusually, the prelude normally heard last, *Kommst du nun, Jesu* is given first, for unexplained reasons) or to either of the Trio Sonata slow movements (that of Sonata No. 5 is heard here, as in one early manuscript, framed by the Prelude and Fugue in C, BWV545) and you can hear the separate melodic lines not only given individual character, shape and direction but combined with ease and gentle authority. Tempos in extrovert movements are unusually moderate, Bach's markings of *Vivace* and *Allegro* being taken by Kee as indications of mood rather than velocity, and yet the musical discourse is always involving and full of wit, helped by registrations (listed in detail in the booklet) that are both simple and wise. The disc is crowned by a magnificent performance of the Prelude and Fugue in E flat, one that fully exploits the vivid contrasts of theme and texture and yet binds the work into a structural unity without a hint of haste or stiffness. Rightly, the recording presents this refined, robust organ as heard within its natural acoustic habitat and Kee has subtly absorbed the church's acoustic into his interpretations.

Bach Prelude and Fugue in E flat major, BWV552. Clavier-übung III, BWV669-89. Four Duets, BWV802-05. Canonic variations on "Vom Himmel hoch", BWV769*a*. **Ton Koopman** (org). Teldec Ⓕ 4509-98464-2 (two discs: 125 minutes: DDD: 10/97). Played on the Silbermann organ of Freiburg Cathedral, Germany. Recorded 1996.

Three great joys await listeners to this pair of discs. First there is the sublime collection of chorale preludes, framed by one of the most majestic of all Bach's Preludes and Fugues, which forms the *Clavier-übung III*. Then there is the glorious instrument, its unspeakably beautiful flutes, its delicate and subtle reeds, its invigorating full organ all captured magnificently in this vivid Teldec recording. And third there is the playing of Ton Koopman, who brings to his Bach a wealth of authority and perception flavoured with unflagging enthusiasm. He soothes those jagged double-dotted rhythms of the Prelude without losing one iota of the work's great stature. He imbues the 21 chorale preludes with an almost prayerful atmosphere, and to the four Duets he brings a lighter, more openly joyful nature, as if gently to relax the mood before the final, supremely celebratory Fugue. The overall effect is to re-create in purely musical terms the celebration of the Mass itself. He compares rather than contrasts the preludes with pedals with those for manuals alone, and thus achieves an unusually coherent sense of progress through the work, resulting in a refreshingly and convincingly unified performance. Throughout, ornamentation is not so much discreet as downright rare. His unusual reticence in this respect extends to a magnificent account of the *Canonic variations* where the clarity of the canonic lines is remarkably vivid. An immensely worthwhile issue.

Bach Orgelbüchlein, BWV599-644. **Simon Preston** (org). DG Ⓕ 431 816-2GH (76 minutes: DDD: 3/92). Played on the Lorentz organ of Sorø Abbey, Denmark. Recorded 1989.

Bach Orgelbüchlein, BWV599-644. **Christopher Herrick** (org). Hyperion Ⓕ CDA66756 (72 minutes: DDD: 9/95). Played on the Metzler organ in the Stadtkirche, Rheinfelden, Switzerland.   Ⓖ

Bach's *Orgelbüchlein* ("Little Organ Book") contains 46 short preludes based on the chorale melodies used in the Lutheran church. It is arranged to follow the course of the church's year, beginning in Advent, passing through Christmas, Lent, Easter, Ascension, Pentecost and Trinity and ending with those miscellaneous areas classified in most hymn-books as "General". But Bach was not merely providing the church organist with something useful (although its enduring usefulness is still evident today – walk into almost any church and at some point you are likely to find the organist delving into a copy of Bach's *Orgelbüchlein*), he also intended these as teaching pieces. The title page describes them as offering "instruction in the various ways of working out a chorale, and also practice in the use of the pedals". What wonderful teaching pieces these are for any organ student – training exercises of this calibre would surely be enough to tempt anyone into learning how to play the organ! On the DG disc with that accomplished organist, Simon Preston, playing a ravishing Danish instrument sumptuously recorded, the full genius of Bach is revealed.

The fifth volume in Hyperion's ongoing Bach series finds another wonderful Swiss organ. With just two manuals and 32 speaking stops it's relatively small but still offers sufficient scope for Herrick to find a different registration for each of these 45 Preludes. The softer sounds used for *Herr Jesu Christ, dich zu uns wend* are preferable to the rather coarse *pleno* (*In dir ist Freude*) but it makes an undeniably ravishing sound. The *Orgelbüchlein's* 46 Chorale Preludes (here the almost identical pair on *Liebster Jesu* are merged, accounting for the disc's 45 tracks) are so brief that listening to them all in one sitting is the musical equivalent of eating salted peanuts one at a time in quick succession. In an attempt to make it all more palatable Herrick tries two tricks. First, he plays remarkably fast – which some people may not find particularly rewarding – *Der Tag, der ist so freudenreich* has as much of a relaxed air as an athletics track. Secondly, he revises the playing order, interspersing those Preludes based on 'general' themes between those for particular times in the church's year, and even mixing up the ones within each group. However, the booklet thoughtfully provides the tracking order to programme into your player if you wish to hear the pieces in the original sequence. On the subject of the booklet, suffice it to say it deserves paeans of praise. Robin Langley's notes are the perfect match for Herrick's playing: scholarly, erudite, infinitely rewarding and so easily communicative one is barely aware one is absorbing some of the most complex and intellectually demanding ideas. If the *Gramophone* Awards were to include a category for CD booklets this would be a strong contender.

Bach Organ works, Volume 1 – Fantasia and Fugue in G minor, BWV542. Trio Sonata No. 1 in E flat major, BWV525. Toccata and Fugue in D minor, BWV565. Pastorale in F major, BWV590. Organ Concerto No. 1 in G major, BWV592. Chorale Prelude – Erbarm' dich mein, O Herre Gott, BWV721. Organ Chorale – Aus tiefer Not schrei ich zu dir, BWV1099. **Kevin Bowyer** (org). Nimbus Ⓕ NI5280 (67 minutes: DDD: 10/92). Played on the Marcussen organ of St Hans Kirke, Odense, Denmark. Recorded 1991.

Organist Kevin Bowyer and record company Nimbus have set out to record every note Bach wrote for the organ, is believed to have written or is now known not to but in the past was thought to have written. It is a mammoth project planned to take several years. The first disc, perhaps inevitably, includes the best-known of all Bach's organ pieces – although some would dispute that it is an organ piece or even that Bach wrote it; Bowyer's account of the *Toccata and Fugue* in D minor is invigorating, exciting and very fast. It sets the scene for a CD of virtuoso performances and sound musicianship. The whole is a well-chosen, self-contained programme which also includes an indisputably 'great' organ work, a Trio Sonata, a transcription Bach made of an effervescent concerto by Ernst, a youthful chorale prelude as well as one from a collection only discovered in 1985 and one real oddity. Much thought has gone into the choice of organ and this instrument serves its purpose admirably; roaring magnificently in the *Fantasia* and emulating the tranquil sounds so characteristic of the *Pastorale*. If the remaining discs are going to be this good then it's a series well worth collecting.

Additional recommendations ...

...Toccata and Fugue, BWV565. Fantasia and Fugue, BWV542. Preludes and Fugues – A major, BWV536; E minor, BWV548. Passacaglia and Fugue in C minor, BWV582. Fantasia in G major, BWV572. **Anton Heiller** (org). Vanguard Classics Ⓕ 08.2005.71 (65 minutes: ADD).

...Toccatas and Fugues – BWV565; F major, BWV540; D minor, BWV538, "Dorian". Toccata, Adagio and Fugue in C major, BWV564. Passacaglia and Fugue in C minor, BWV582. **Christopher Herrick** (org). Hyperion Ⓕ CDA66434 (64 minutes: DDD: 4/91).

...Organ works, Volume 3. Preludes and Fugues – F minor, BWV534; A minor, BWV543. Trio Sonata No. 2 in C minor, BWV526. Organ Concerto No. 5 in D minor, BWV596. Sei gegrüsset, Jesu gütig, BWV768. **Kevin Bowyer** (org). Nimbus Ⓕ NI5290 (64 minutes: DDD: 6/93).

...Organ works, Volume 8. Fugue in C minor on a theme by Legrenzi, BWV574. Concerto in F major (after Vivaldi), BWV978. Chorale Preludes – An Wasserflüssen Babylon, BWV653b; Herr Jesu Christ, dich zu uns wend, BWV709; Herr Jesu Christ, dich zu uns wend, BWV726; Liebster Jesu, wir sind hier, BWV731; Wir glauben all'an einen Gott, BWV765. Preludes and Fugues – C major, BWV531; B minor, BWV544; C major, BWV547; A minor, BWV895. Schübler Chorales, BWV546-50. Toccata and Fugue in D minor, BWV538, "Dorian". Trio Sonata in G major, BWV1039/1027a. Chorale Preludes from the Neumeister Collection – Wir glauben all'an einen Gott, BWV1098; Gott ist mein Heil, mein Hilf und Trost, BWV1106; Herzlich lieb hab ich dich, o Herr, BWV1115; Was Gott tut, das ist wohlgetan, BWV1116. **Kevin Bowyer** (org). Nimbus Ⓕ NI5500/1 (two discs: 114 minutes: DDD: 5/97).

...Pastorale in F major, BWV590. *Coupled with works by various composers.* **Peter King** (org). Priory Ⓕ PRCD618 (78 minutes: DDD). *See review in the Collections section; refer to the Index.*

Bach Organ works, Volume 4: Toccatas – G minor, BWV915; G major, BWV916. Fugues on themes of Albinoni – A major, BWV950; B minor, BWV951. Fugue in C minor, BWV575. Preludes and Fugues – C major, BWV553; D minor, BWV554; E minor, BWV555; F major,

BWV556; G major, BWV557; G minor, BWV558; A minor, BWV559; B flat major, BWV560.
Fantasia con imitazione in B minor, BWV563. **Kevin Bowyer** (org). Nimbus Ⓕ NI5377
(74 minutes: DDD: 2/94). Played on the Marcussen organ of St Hans Kirke, Odense,
Denmark. Recorded 1992.
While critical opinion and academic argument may deter others, Bowyer is content to let the music
speak for itself, whether it is "by J.S. Bach, J.L. Krebs or A.N. Other". On this disc the music speaks
with absolute conviction. One thinks of the gloriously dramatic rhetoric Bowyer brings to the two
Toccatas (BWV915 and 916). Harpsichordists may claim these as their own but who could deny this
lovely Odense organ the opportunity to glitter with such flamboyant music? The eight 'short' Preludes
and Fugues have a muscular, clean-shaven feel to them underlined by plain and simple registrations.
While other recordings of such indefinable pieces seem like scraps from the cutting-room floor,
Bowyer sets them firmly in the mainstream of high baroque organ music.
Additional recommendation ...
...Toccatas – F sharp minor, BWV910; C minor, BWV911; D major, BWV912; D minor, BWV913;
E minor, BWV914; G minor, BWV915; G major, BWV916. **Glenn Gould** (pf).
Sony Classical Glenn Gould Edition Ⓜ SM2K52612 (two discs: 81 minutes: ADD: 9/94).

Bach Organ works, Volume 1 – Toccata and Fugue in D minor, BWV565. Herzlich tut mich
verlangen, BWV727. Fugue in G major, BWV577. Erbarm' dich mein, O Herre Gott, BWV721.
Fugue on a theme by Corelli in B minor, BWV579. Prelude and Fugue in G major, BWV541.
Pastorale in F major, BWV590. Clavier-übung III, BWV669-89 – Wir glauben all'an einen Gott,
BWV680. Orgel-Büchlein, BWV599-644 – O Mensch, bewein' dein Sünde gross, BWV622.
Passacaglia and Fugue in C minor, BWV582. **Peter Hurford** (org). EMI Eminence
Ⓜ CD-EMX2218 (63 minutes: DDD: 3/94). Played on the organ of Martinikerk,
Groningen, Holland. Recorded 1993.   Ⓖ
"Peter Hurford playing organs of Bach's Time". For his earlier recordings on Argo, Hurford played
mainly modern, neo-baroque instruments and while Bach on 'authentic' instruments is no novelty, we
certainly don't hear enough of the wondrous Ahrend organ which begins this series in such style.
Ahrend? Builders of Bach's time? Well we're obviously going to have to take the title with a hefty
pinch of salt. Although it dates back over 500 years, in its present form the organ dates back only as
far as 1984. Bach never played it, and even if he had he certainly wouldn't recognize it now, but it
sounds wonderful; Henry Mitton and Mark Nations have recorded it magnificently, closely focusing
the sound within an aura of spaciousness. Splendid playing by Hurford too, of course. He begins (as
everyone does) with the ubiquitous Toccata and Fugue in D minor. But what a performance!
Everything else is given warmly communicative, unpretentious and immensely appealing
performances. Hurford knows and loves his Bach, something which shines out of every note he plays.

Bach Organ works, Volume 2 – Concerto in D minor after Vivaldi's Op. 3 No. 11, BWV596. Vater
unser im Himmelreich, BWV737. Aria in F major, BWV587. Der Tag, der ist so freudenreich,
BWV719. Trio Sonata No. 5 in C major, BWV529. Nun danket alle Gott, BWV657. Liebster
Jesu, wir sind hier, BWV731. Fantasia super Valet will ich dir geben, BWV735. Nun freut euch,
lieben Christen gmein, BWV734. Toccata, Adagio and Fugue in C major, BWV564. ✔
Peter Hurford (org). EMI Eminence Ⓜ CD-EMX2226 (66 minutes: DDD: 12/94). ✔
Played on the Schnitger organ in the Ludgerikirche, Norden, Germany. Recorded 1993.   ⒼⒼ
Hurford continues his tour of Bach's organ works on an organ that dates from Bach's own time. There
may be stylistic quibbles: for instance, given the virtues of the marvellous Schnitger organ at Norden
(a clear, 'oakey' brilliance, imposing but not austere) it is perhaps a mite surprising that Hurford still
occasionally shows a liking for frothy, high-pitched registrations which may be too neo-baroque for
some tastes. But set against that, and far more important, is his increased ability to convey energy
without haste. Indeed, his relaxed control (without any diminution of authority or personality) in
quick movements, especially the outer movements of Sonata No. 5 and the Toccata, Adagio and
Fugue, results in performances that are, without exception, more mellow, humane and witty than his
earlier ones. And in terms of textual clarity they are exemplary. The close marriage of music and
instrument is most fruitful in the chorale settings (BWV737, 719, 657 and 735), all of them displaying
rather formulaic imitative techniques. But, of course, Hurford knows exactly what he is about: with
registrations carved from the meat of the instrument – solid choruses and reeds – these works are
revealed as quintessential meditations for the Lutheran liturgy, dogma in music, patient, strong and
assured. *Nun danket alle Gott*, in particular, is given an outstandingly trenchant performance. The
engineering is first-rate, the slightly recessed pedal balance reflecting (but not distractingly so) the
unusual layout of the instrument, which is fully explained in the insert-notes.
Additional recommendation ...
...Concerto after Vivaldi, BWV596. Fuga sopra il Magnificat BWV733. Vom Himmel hoch
Variations, BWV769. Prelude and Fugue in C major, BWV547. Toccata and Fugue in D minor,
BWV565. Trio Sonata, BWV529. Fugue in G minor, BWV578. Trio – Adagio after BWV1027;
Allegro in G major, BWV1027a. 14 Verschiedene Canones, BWV1087. Musikalisches Opfer,
BWV1079 – Canons. Cantata No. 35, Geist und Seele wird verwirret – Sinfonia No. 2ª. *Coupled
with works by various composers.* **Marie-Claire Alain** (org); ª**chamber orchestra / Jean-François
Paillard.** Erato Ⓜ 0630-15343-2 (five discs: 351 minutes: ADD/DDD: 1/97).

...(arr. Busoni) Nun freut euch, lieben Christen gmein. *Coupled with works by various composers.*
Vladimir Horowitz (pf). APR mono Ⓜ APR5517* (71 minutes: ADD: 5/98). *See review in the
Collections section; refer to the Index.*

Bach (arr. Liszt) Fantasie and Fugue in G minor, BWV542. Six Preludes and Fugues – A minor,
BWV543; B minor, BWV544; C major, BWV545; C minor, BWV546; C major, BWV547;
E minor, BWV548. **Artur Pizarro** (pf). Collins Classics Ⓕ 1498-2 (73 minutes: DDD: 9/97).
Recorded 1996.

Whether paraphrasing operas, appropriating songs, or proselytizing great symphonic works, Liszt
responded with imagination and resourceful variety to his chosen material for transcription. These are
among Liszt's most straightforward and literal arrangements: his reverence for Bach, his devotion and
fidelity to the spirit of his source, tempers the natural exuberance of his pianistic idiom. The G minor
Fantasie has considerable grandeur and chromatic intensity, and Liszt accords it a suitably grand
setting, creating the required mass of sound by fleshing out some of the textures. The *Six Preludes
and Fugues*, on the other hand, are almost entirely literal re-castings, with Liszt using the piano's
sustaining pedal to overcome the lack of the organ's pedal board. When one considers that these are
early transcriptions (dating from the 1840s yet seemingly incongruous with Liszt's period of virtuosic
glamour) one realizes how seriously he took his homage to Bach. Artur Pizarro approaches these
works with a rigorous intensity, with refined sensitivity and impeccable judgement. In his hands the
original Bach shines through every bar, and this is of course exactly how these transcriptions should
sound – that they do is a tribute both to Pizarro and to Liszt. Tempos are well paced, ensuring a
natural sense of flow and momentum. Everything is almost ideally shaped, and the sustaining pedal
(absolutely essential in these transcriptions) is most sensitively deployed. Try the Preludes from
BWV544 and 547 for an idea of Pizarro's beautifully crafted performances; with playing like this any
questions of 'authenticity', of the validity of transcriptions, should become unimportant. The
recording is excellent, even if occasionally one might like the sound to ring more resonantly.

Additional recommendations ...

...Preludes and Fugues – BWV544; BWV547. An Wasserflüssen Babylon, BWV653. Von Gott will
ich nicht lassen, BWV658. Wer nur den lieben Gott lässt walten, BWV690 and BWV691. Vom
Himmel hoch, da komm ich her, BWV700 and BWV701. Jesus, meine Zuversicht, BWV728.
Liebster Jesu, wir sind hier, BWV730 and BWV731. Meine Seele erhebt den Herren, BWV733.
Fantasia and Fugue in C minor, BWV537. Fugue in G minor, BWV578. Trio in D minor,
BWV583. **Nicholas Danby** (org).
Sony Classical Digital Club Ⓜ SMK64239 (69 minutes: DDD: 5/95).

...Preludes and Fugues – E minor, BWV533; G minor, BWV535; C minor, BWV537; BWV546;
C minor, BWV549; G major, BWV550. Fugue in C minor, BWV575. Preludes – G major,
BWV568; A minor, BWV569. Allabreve in D major, BWV589. **Ton Koopman** (org).
Teldec Das Alte Werk Ⓕ 0630-13155-2 (62 minutes: DDD: A/97).

Bach Six Trio Sonatas, BWV525-30 – No. 1 in E flat major. No. 2 in C minor. No. 3 in D minor.
No. 4 in E minor. No. 5 in C major. No. 6 in G major. **Christopher Herrick** (org). Hyperion
Ⓕ CDA66390 (72 minutes: DDD: 11/90). Played on the Metzler organ of the Parish Church of
St Nikolaus, Bremgarten, Switzerland. Recorded 1989.　　　　　　　　　　　　　ⓆⓆⓆ

The common assumption is that Bach wrote his six Trio Sonatas as training studies for his son
Wilhelm Friedmann, and certainly to this day young organists regard the ability to play these pieces
as a prerequisite in establishing proper organ technique. But if ever the notion that this is music "first
to practise and secondly to admire" was shown to be false, this stunning disc presents an unanswerable
argument. Christopher Herrick's performances are immense fun, brimming over with real affection
for the music. He allows himself occasional displays of enthusiasm (adding a few exuberant *glissandos*
in the last movement of the E flat major Sonata, for example) and he chooses his stops both to
enhance the vitality of the quick movements and to underline the sheer beauty of the slower ones.
Never has this music sounded less like a training study! The Hyperion recording of the sumptuous
Swiss instrument makes this disc a worthwhile buy if only for its glorious sound; the organ speaks
into a rich, opulent acoustic which treats each note as a priceless jewel, to be enhanced by its setting
but not in any way to be obscured. A disc of rare beauty and a real gem in any collection.

Additional recommendation ...

...Nos. 1-6. **Ton Koopman** (org). Teldec Das Alte Werk Ⓕ 4509-94460-2 (75 minutes: DDD: 7/96).

Bach Allabreve in D major, BWV589. Aria in F major, BWV587. Canzona in D minor, BWV588.
Four Duets, BWV802-5. Fantasias – A minor, BWV561; C major, BWV570. Fantasia con
imitazione in B minor, BWV563. Fugues – C minor, BWV575; G major, BWV576; G major,
BWV577, "Jig Fugue"; G minor, BWV578. Pastorale in F major, BWV590. Preludes – A minor,
BWV551; G major, BWV568; A minor, BWV569. Preludes and Fugues – E minor, BWV533;
G minor, BWV535; D minor, BWV539; D minor, BWV549*a*; G major, BWV550. Toccata and
Fugue in E major, BWV566. Trios – C minor, BWV583; C minor, BWV585; G major, BWV586.
Trio Sonata in G major, BWV1027*a* (arr. cpsr). Musikalisches Opfer, BWV1079 – Ricercar a 3;
Ricercar a 6. **Christopher Herrick** (org). Hyperion Ⓕ CDA67211/2 (two discs: 156 minutes: DDD:
9/97). Played on the organ of the Stadtkirche, Rheinfelden, Switzerland. Recorded 1996.

Some might be tempted to describe what we have here as the 'scrapings from the barrel', for when you've taken out the chorale-based works, the trio sonatas, the concertos and the big preludes, fantasias, toccatas, passacaglias and fugues this is what's left. One could, however, be tempted almost to prefer these crumbs from the table of great genius to those stupendous musical feasts which are everybody's idea of the real J.S. Bach. And when you have those crumbs seasoned with such loving care, such elegance and such finesse as Christopher Herrick gives to, say, the G minor fugue (BWV578) or the enchanting Trio Sonata (BWV1027a), you realize that here is music every bit as worthy of close attention as anything Bach wrote for the organ. In matters of registration, tempo, articulation and phrasing, Herrick displays immaculate taste. This is playing of the very highest order. The modest two-manual Metzler, built in 1992, makes an enchanting sound, and the recording fully supports the superlative artistry of the playing.

Additional recommendation ...
...Musikalisches Opfer, BWV1079 – Trio Sonata in C minor. *Coupled with works by various composers.* **Musica ad Rhenum.** Vanguard Classics Ⓕ 99130 (57 minutes: DDD: 11/96). *See review in the Collections section; refer to the Index.*

Bach Schübler Chorales, BWV645-50[a]. Chorales, BWV651-68[b]. Chorales[a] from Cantatas Nos. 36, 59, 62 and 180. Wenn wir in höchsten Nöten sein, BWV431[b]. Du heiliger Brunst, süsser Trost, BWV226 No. 2[b]. An Wasserflüssen Babylon, BWV267[b]. Herr Jesus Christ, dich zu uns wend', BWV332[b]. O Lamm Gottes, unschuldig, BWV401[b]. Nun danket alle Gott, BWV386[b]. Von Gott will ich nicht lassen, BWV418[b]. Allein Gott in der Höh' sei Ehr', BWV260[b]. Jesus Christus, unser Heiland, BWV363[b]. Komm, Gott Schöpfer, heiliger Geist, BWV370[b]. [a]**Amsterdam Baroque Choir / Ton Koopman** ([b]org). Teldec Das Alte Werk Ⓕ 4509-94459-2 (two discs: 142 minutes: DDD: 6/96). Organ works played on the organ of the Grote Kerk, Leeuwarden. Texts and translations included. Recorded 1994.

Koopman's performances have a glorious sense of spontaneity born of the understanding that, with a cantata and a fistful of chorale preludes to compose and perform every week, Bach was hardly involved here in deep, painstaking creativity. Koopman seems totally attuned to the essential practicality of this music. As a result he can indulge in outrageously ebullient ornamentation, which from any other organist might seem merely bad taste, and maintain his light, dispassionate approach even through those Preludes usually afforded particular emotional significance, yet make it all sound stylistically convincing. A link between organ and cantata cycles is forged here by pairing each prelude with its chorale, sung by the choir with whom Koopman is currently working his way through the complete cantatas for Erato. The complete unity of approach between organist and singers is ingeniously underpinned by the use of organ accompaniment where unaccompanied singing might create a sense of dissociation. There is occasional variation but throughout, the singing of the Amsterdam Baroque Choir is an unalloyed joy. Koopman isn't going to be everybody's cup of tea every time, but with this beautifully recorded pair of discs any reservations are completely outweighed by the sheer musical integrity of what are truly wonderful performances.

Bach Schübler Chorales, BWV645-50. Leipzig Chorales, BWV651-88. Kirnberger Chorales, BWV690-91 and BWV694-713. **Christopher Herrick** (org). Hyperion Ⓕ CDA67071/2 (two discs: 147 minutes: DDD: 8/96). Played on the Metzler organ of the Jesuitenkirche, Lucerne, Switzerland. Recorded 1995.

The Schübler Chorales are mostly drawn from cantata movements, the Leipzig, sometimes known as the '18' and sometimes as the 'great' due to their large stature (including in BWV652 the longest chorale prelude Bach wrote), and some miscellaneous chorale preludes which have absolutely nothing in common beyond the fact that Johann Philipp Kirnberger, a pupil and admirer of Bach, bundled them all together. Keenly aware of the artificiality of the situation – obviously no organist in Bach's day would have dreamt of playing 44 chorale preludes in one go – Herrick has approached the task with businesslike vigour. *Wachet auf* fizzes like champagne at a wedding – no wonder the sleepers seem so eager to waken with such a riotous wedding feast clearly already in full swing. But such unrelenting bubbliness can also seem misplaced: Schumann's description of *Schmücke dich, o liebe Seele* (BWV654) as "priceless, deep and full of soul" hardly fits this dancing performance. Perhaps, then, not a recording from which to extract single preludes, but certainly one which can withstand repeated bouts of continuous listening. As ever, not only has Herrick found a simply ravishing Swiss organ which he uses with impeccable good taste (and his invariably sensitive registrations are all detailed in the booklet) but the Hyperion team have come up with a top-notch recording.

Bach Cantatas – No. 4, Christ lag in Todesbanden[c]; No. 131, Aus der Tiefen rufe ich, Herr, zu dir[b]; No. 182, Himmelskönig, sei willkommen[a]. [b]**Julianne Baird**, [a]**Christine Brandes**, [c]**Judith Nelson** (sops); [a]**Judith Malafronte** (mez); [b]**Drew Minter**, [c]**Daniel Taylor** (altos); [c]**Benjamin Butterfield** (ten); [c]**Kurt-Owen Richards**, [ab]**James Weaver** (basses); **American Bach Soloists / Jeffrey Thomas** ([a]ten). Koch International Classics Ⓕ 37235-2 (67 minutes: DDD: 3/96). ✍
Texts and translations included. Recorded 1994.

This programme contains three early works from Mühlhausen and Weimar. These are the cantatas that benefit most from scaled-down forces since they are, in most cases, more closely related to the Lutheran sacred concerto and motet of the late seventeenth century. Thomas, following in Joshua

Rifkin's steps, adheres strictly to the one-to-a-part principle. Judith Malafronte's beautifully coloured voice has a timbre, clarity and understanding of Bach's melodic demands that make you long to hear her in many more of Bach's cantatas. Sadly, she sings in only one work on the disc, Bach's Annunciation/Palm Sunday Cantata, *Himmelskönig, sei willkommen*. The equivalent vocal range in the remaining two cantatas is served by countertenor Drew Minter who also makes a fine contribution though a less satisfying one than Malafronte. There is in fact much good singing throughout, James Weaver and Julianne Baird being but two whose expressive warmth enhances the music. Thomas and his team apply a wealth of effective stylistic ideas. There is, for instance, a wonderfully lyrical approach by the recorder player in the alto aria of No. 182; the shaping of phrases is carefully thought out, he leans slightly on all the notes that call for it and punctuates the music with all the skill of a seasoned rhetorician. Thomas himself, in the extended declamatory tenor aria from the same work, has similarly persuasive ideas though occasionally lacks the assured vocal technique to see him through. In summary, there is plenty of food for thought here and much that is both stylistically apposite and emotionally satisfying. Some readers will want a stronger vocal presence in the choral movements but overall the performances are recommended. Good recorded sound.

Additional recommendations ...

...(Nos. 1-199, excluding Nos. 15, 53, 118, 141, 142, 189, 190, 191 and 193.) **Soloists; Tölz Boys' Choir; Vienna Boys' Choir; Hanover Boys' Choir; Choir of King's College, Cambridge; Ghent Collegium Vocale; Chorus Viennensis; Leonhardt Consort / Gustav Leonhardt; Vienna Concentus Musicus / Nikolaus Harnoncourt.** Teldec Das Alte Werk ⑧ 4509-91765-2 (60 discs: ADD/DDD: 2/95). ☞ Texts and translations included. Also available as ten six-disc mid-price sets, as follows: *4509-91755-2* (387 minutes): Nos. 1-14 and 16-19. *4509-91756-2* (385 minutes): Nos. 20-36. *4509-91757-2* (416 minutes): Nos. 37-52 and 54-60. *4509-91758-2* (389 minutes): Nos. 61-78. *4509-91759-2* (385 minutes): Nos. 79-99. *4509-91760-2* (369 minutes): Nos. 100-117. *4509-91761-2* (371 minutes): Nos. 119-137. *4509-91762-2* (403 minutes): Nos. 138-140, 143-159, 161 and 162. *4509-91763-2* (366 minutes): Nos. 163-182. *4509-91764-2* (299 minutes): Nos. 183-188, 192 and 194-199.

...(Nos. 1-200, excluding Nos. 15, 53, 118, 141, 142 and 189.) Christmas Oratorio, BWV248. Easter Oratorio, BWV249. **Soloists; Frankfurt Kantorei; Indiana University Chamber Singers; Stuttgart Gächinger Kantorei; Stuttgart Gedächtniskirche Choir; Stuttgart Bach Collegium, Württemberg Chamber Orchestra / Helmuth Rilling.** Hänssler Classic Ⓜ 98 841 (69 discs: AAD/DDD: 2/95).

...Volume 5 – No. 5, Wo soll ich fliehen hin; No. 26, Ach wie flüchtig, ach wie nichtig; No. 38, Aus tiefer Not schrei ich zu dir; No. 55, Ich armer Mensch, ich Sündenknecht; No. 56, Ich will den Kreuzstab gerne tragen; No. 60, O Ewigkeit, du Donnerwort; No. 70, Wachet! betet! seid bereit allezeit; No. 80, Ein' feste Burg ist unser Gott; No. 96, Herr Christ, der einge Gottessohn; No. 106, Gottes Zeit ist die allerbeste Zeit; No. 115, Mache dich, mein Geist bereit; No. 116, Du Friedefürst, Herr Jesu Christ; No. 130, Herr Gott, dich loben alle wir; No. 139, Wohl dem, der sich auf seinen Gott; No. 140, Wachet auf, ruft uns die Stimme; No. 180, Schmücke dich, o liebe Seele. **Soloists; Munich Bach Choir and Orchestra / Karl Richter.** Archiv Produktion Ⓕ 439 394-2AX5 (five discs: 342 minutes: ADD: 1/95).

...No. 7, Christ unser Herr zum Jordan kam[a]; No. 11[b]; No. 30, Freue dich, erlöste Schar[c]; No. 68, Also hat Gott die Welt geliebt[d]; No. 104, Du Hirte Israel, höre[b]. [b]**Hedy Graf,** [c]**Emiko Iiyama,** [d]**Agnes Giebel** (sops); [abc]**Barbara Scherler,** [d]**Claudia Hellmann** (mezzos); [a]**Georg Jelden,** [bd]**Kurt Huber,** [c]**Theo Altmeyer** (tens); [abd]**Jakob Stämpfli,** [c]**Bruce Abel,** [d]**Erik Wenk** (basses); **Heinrich Schütz Choir, Heilbronn; Pforzheim Chamber Orchestra / Fritz Werner.** Erato Ⓜ 0630-12978-2 (two discs: 140 minutes: ADD). 🅖🅖

...Volume 4 – No. 8, Liebster Gott, wann werd' ich sterben; No. 9, Es ist das Heil uns kommen her; No. 17, Wer Dank opfert, der preiset mich; No. 27, Wer weiss, wie nahe mir mein Ende!; No. 33, Allein zu dir, Herr Jesu Christ; No. 45, Es ist dir gesagt, Mensch, was gut ist; No. 51, Jauchzet Gott in allen Landen!; No. 78, Jesu, der du meine Seele; No. 100, Was Gott tut, das ist wohlgetan; No. 102, Herr, deine Augen sehen nach dem Glauben; No. 105, Herr, gehe nicht ins Gericht mit deinem Knecht; No. 137, Lobe den Herren, den mächtigen König der Ehren; No. 148, Bringet dem Herrn Ehre seines Namens; No. 178, Wo Gott der Herr nicht bei uns hält; No. 179, Siehe zu, dass deine Gottesfurcht; No. 187, Es wartet alles auf dich; No. 199, Mein Herze schwimmt im Blut. **Soloists; Munich Bach Choir and Orchestra; Ansbach Bach Week Soloists Ensemble / Karl Richter.** Archiv Produktion Ⓕ 439 387-2AX6 (six discs: 358 minutes: ADD: 1/95).

...Volume 1 – No. 13, Meine Seufzer, meine Tränen[adfhj]; No. 28, Gottlob! nun geht das Jahr zu Ende[aefhj]; No. 58, Ach Gott, wie manches Herzelied[bh]; No. 61, Nun komm, der Heiden Heiland[afhj]; No. 63, Christen, ätzet diesen Tag[adfhj]; No. 64, Sehet, welch eine Liebe[adhj]; No. 65, Sie werden aus Saba alle kommen[gij]; No. 81, Jesus schläft, was soll ich hoffen?[dfhj]; No. 82, Ich habe genug[h]; No. 111, Was mein Gott will, das g'scheh allzeit[adfij]; No. 121, Christum wir sollen loben schon[adfhj]; No. 124, Meinen Jesum lass ich nicht[cegij]; No. 132, Bereitet die Wege, bereitet die Bahn[adfij]; No. 171, Gott, wie dein Name, so ist auch dein Ruhm[aefhj]. [a]**Edith Mathis,** [b]**Sheila Armstrong,** [c]**Lotte Schädle** (sops); [d]**Anna Reynolds,** [e]**Hertha Töpper** (mezzos); [f]**Peter Schreier,** [g]**Ernst Haefliger** (tens); [h]**Dietrich Fischer-Dieskau** (bar); [i]**Theo Adam** (bass-bar); **Munich Bach** [j]**Choir and Orchestra / Karl Richter.** Archiv Produktion ⑧ 439 369-2AX4 (four discs: 278 minutes: ADD: 3/94). 🅖

...No. 36, Schwingt freudig euch empor[a]; No. 61, Nun komm, der Heiden Heiland; No. 62, Nun komm, der Heiden Heiland[a]. **Nancy Argenta** (sop); [a]**Petra Lang** (mez); **Anthony Rolfe Johnson** (ten); **Olaf Bär** (bar); **Monteverdi Choir; English Baroque Soloists / Sir John Eliot Gardiner.** Archiv Produktion Ⓕ 437 327-2AH (61 minutes: DDD: 2/93). ⓢ
...No. 54, Widerstehe doch der Sünde[a]; No. 170, Vergnügte Ruh', beliebte Seelenlust[a]. Mass in B minor, BWV232 – Agnus Dei[a]. **Handel** Orlando – Ah Stigie larve![b]. Jephtha, HWV70 – 'Tis Heaven's all-ruling pow'r[b]. Theodora, HWV68 – Kind Heav'n, if Virtue be thy care; Sweet Rose, and Lilly, flow'ry Form[b]. **Alfred Deller** (alto); [a]**Leonhardt Baroque Ensemble / Gustav Leonhardt** (org); [b]**Handel Festival Orchestra / Sir Anthony Lewis.** Vanguard Classics Alfred Deller Edition Ⓜ 08.5069.71* (59 minutes: ADD: 1/95). ⓢ　Ⓖ Ⓖ
...Nos. 56, 82 and 158. **Peter Kooy** (bass); **La Chapelle Royale Choir and Orchestra / Philippe Herreweghe.** Harmonia Mundi Ⓕ HMC90 1365 (52 minutes: DDD: 10/92). ⓢ
...Nos. 56, 82 and 158. **Olaf Bär** (bar); **Scottish Chamber Orchestra / Peter Schreier.** EMI Ⓕ CDC7 54453-2 (48 minutes: DDD: 6/93).
...No. 82[a]. **Brahms** Lieder[b]. **Hans Hotter** (bass-bar); [b]**Gerald Moore** (pf); [a]**Philharmonia Orchestra / Anthony Bernard.** EMI Références mono Ⓜ CDH7 63198-2* (69 minutes: ADD: 4/90). 　Ⓖ
...No. 198, Lass, Fürstin, lass noch einen Strahl (Trauer Ode)[a]; No. 158, Der Friede sei mit dir[b]; No. 27, Wer weiss, wie nahe mir mein Ende![c]. [ac]**Rotraud Hansmann** (sop); [ac]**Helen Watts** (contr); [a]**Kurt Equiluz** (ten); **Max van Egmond** (bass); **Monteverdi Choir; Concerto Amsterdam / Jürgen Jürgens.** Teldec Das Alte Werk Ⓜ 4509-93687-2 (67 minutes: ADD: 10/94). ⓢ　Ⓖ Ⓖ
...No. 213, Hercules auf dem Scheidewege; No. 201, Geschwinde, ihr wirbeln die Winde (Phoebus und Pan); No. 205, Der zufriedengestellte Aolus; **Soloists; Berlin RIAS Chamber Choir; Academy of Ancient Music, Berlin / René Jacobs.** Harmonia Mundi Ⓕ HMC90 1544/5 (two discs: 134 minutes; DDD: 8/96). ⓢ

Bach Cantatas – No. 5, Wo soll ich fliehen hin – Ergeisse dich reichlich; No. 13, Meine Seufzer, meine Tränen – Meine Seufzer, meine Tränen; No. 26, Ach wie flüchtig, ach wie nichtig – So schnell ein rauschend Wasser schiesst; No. 55, Ich armer Mensch, ich Sündenknecht[a]; No. 102, Herr, deine Augen sehen nach dem Glauben – Erschrecke doch.
Hoffmann (attrib.) Meine Seele rühmt und preist.
Telemann Ich weiss, dass mein Erlöser lebt. [a]**RIAS Chamber Choir, Berlin; C.P.E. Bach Chamber Orchestra / Peter Schreier** (ten). Philips Ⓕ 442 786-2PH (59 minutes: DDD: 5/98). Texts and translations included.
It was a good idea of Peter Schreier to include the two cantatas for solo tenor, once upon a time thought to have been by Bach, but now known to be the product of other talents. *Ich weiss, dass mein Erlöser lebt* is by Telemann and used to take its place in the Bach canon as BWV160. The authorship of *Meine Seele rühmt und preist* has not been firmly established, but is currently attributed to Georg Melchior Hoffmann, a Dresden contemporary of Bach and Telemann. The position of the piece in the Bach numbering system used to stand at BWV189. Its removal leaves only one cantata for solo tenor as a genuine product of Bach's pen: *Ich armer Mensch, ich Sündenknecht* (No. 55). This is a notoriously difficult work to bring off successfully. The elaborate and often high-lying vocal writing makes huge demands upon the soloist. Schreier offers a very fine account of the piece, revealing nuances in Bach's music which are left undiscovered by many a rival. But it is the other two cantatas which make the disc particularly interesting. The Telemann piece is seldom performed, while the other has enjoyed a far less high profile than it deserves, since its erstwhile seemingly impeccable pedigree was exposed a long time ago as fraudulent. Its opening aria, one of three, is particularly alluring; but why substitute a transverse flute for the intended recorder, especially when two recorders are available and used to effect in the aria from Cantata No. 13? Otherwise, the performance of this lovely piece comes over well, as do the isolated arias from Bach's cantatas. Schreier is on top form, bringing out the poetry in the music. The C.P.E. Bach Chamber Orchestra give sympathetic support to the voice and yield up some fine obbligatos, above all from the flute in No. 55.

Bach Cantatas – No. 6, Bleib' bei uns, denn es will Abend werden; No. 41, Jesu, nun sei gepreiset; No. 68, Also hat Gott die Welt geliebt. **Barbara Schlick** (sop); **Andreas Scholl** (alto); **Christoph Prégardien** (ten); **Gotthold Schwarz** (bass); **Accentus Chamber Choir; Limoges Baroque Ensemble / Christophe Coin** (vc). Auvidis Astrée Ⓕ E8555 (63 minutes: DDD: 5/96). ⓢ
Texts and translations included. Recorded 1995.
These three cantatas are Leipzig compositions dating from 1725. No. 41 is a New Year piece, No. 6 an Easter one, while No. 68 was written for Whitsun. Though belonging to the same year, these cantatas are varied in structure, only No. 41 adhering to that unifying thematic pattern which was such a distinctive feature of the chorale-based works of the 1724-75 annual cycle. The many illuminating features of Coin's lively direction elsewhere ensure a high level of enjoyment; and his own violoncello piccolo solos convey the poetry of the music with wonderfully intuitive expression and grateful gesture. Happily, the four vocal soloists are outstanding and the small choir sound well, on the whole, though they do not always make their presence sufficiently felt. The opening chorus of No. 6, Schweitzer's "masterpiece of poetry in music", is handled with extraordinary sensibility by Coin, who brings out details in Bach's scoring, such as the throbbing quavers of the upper and middle string parts, with loving tenderness. This gentleness of approach, together with a close identity and

warm rapport with Bach's kaleidoscopic tonal palette, are virtues common to all three discs and sterling qualities that will survive the fickleness of changing fashion. And what is so refreshing about these recordings is the absence of intrusive mannerism. There are no empty gestures here, just total absorption in the music, and a disarming humility. A release of great distinction.

Bach Cantatas – No. 8, Liebster Gott, wann werd' ich sterben[a]; No. 26, Ach wie flüchtig, ach wie nichtig[b]; No. 43, Gott fähret auf mit Jauchzen[c]; No. 61, Nun komm, der Heiden Heiland[d]; No. 85, Ich bin ein guter Hirt[e]; No. 130, Herr Gott, dich loben alle wir[b]; No. 182, Himmelskönig, sei willkommen[f]. [abcdf]**Frederike Sailer,** [e]**Ingeborg Reichelt** (sops); [abcdf]**Claudia Hellmann,** [e]**Hertha Töpper** (mezzos); **Helmut Krebs** (ten); [abf]**Erik Wenk,** [cd]**Jakob Stämpfli,** [e]**Franz Kelch** (basses); **Heinrich Schütz Choir, Heilbronn;** [a]**South-West German Chamber Orchestra,** [bcdef]**Pforzheim Chamber Orchestra / Fritz Werner.** Erato Ⓜ 4509-97407-2* (two discs: 147 minutes: ADD: 5/95). Item marked [a] from STU70086 (recorded 1961), [bd]STU70085 (1961), [cf]STU70087 (1961), [e]STU70042 (1959).　　　　　　　　　　　　　　　　　　　　　　　Ⓖ

Fritz Werner, conductor and composer, died in 1980 and were it not for enterprising releases such as this, we would have little cause to remember a man who championed Bach's cantatas in the 1960s and early 1970s with rare integrity and unaffected eloquence. The disc comprises reissues of seven cantatas, chosen from over 50 he recorded from 1958-74, and is skilfully conceived to cover all the important seasons of the church calendar. The Advent cantata is the magnificent *Nun komm, der Heiden Heiland,* which is touchingly natural in its expression. The soloists here feature the sensitive singing of tenor, Helmut Krebs, who may not have an effortless vocal technique but his open-throated and committed performances are full of personality and his recitatives nobly delivered. Jakob Stämpfli, too, is a fine and highly consistent Bachian. The Heinrich Schütz Choir are also well suited to Werner's spontaneous and smooth transitions and classical pacing. How thrilling are the trumpets and drums in the bass aria of No. 130, no holds barred, crackling articulation and an inimitable moment when in the excitement of it all they get slightly out. And the free-flowing flute obbligato in the same cantata (again, with Krebs on top form) has a recognizable personality gently coaxed by a sympathetic, untyrannical director. Other than Nos. 61 and 130, No. 8, *Liebster Gott,* is another outstanding all-round performance. The opening chorus is instilled with compassion and radiant phrasing. The substantial *Himmelskönig, sei willkommen* for Palm Sunday (No. 182) is less consistent overall. This is a sobering release of near 'historical' (in its true sense) Bach cantatas, conceived by musicians whose innate perception of what they were doing relied principally on good artistry. Recorded sound transfers are good. Documentation is not up to scratch for such an important release.

Additional recommendations ...

...No. 4, Christ lag in Todesbanden (with appendix); No. 21, Ich hatte viel Bekümmernis (with appendix); No. 31; No. 71, Gott ist mein König; No. 106, Gottes Zeit ist die allerbeste Zeit, "Actus tragicus"; No. 131, Aus der Tiefe rufe ich, Herr, zu dir; No. 151, Nach dir, Herr, verlanget mich; No. 185, Barmherziges Herze der ewigen Liebe; No. 196, Der Herr denket an uns. **Barbara Schlick** (sop); **Kai Wessel** (alto); **Guy de Mey** (ten); **Klaus Mertens** (bass); **Amsterdam Baroque Choir and Orchestra / Ton Koopman.** Erato Ⓕ 4509-98536-2 (three discs: 198 minutes: DDD: 9/95).

...No. 5, Wo soll ich fliehen hin; No. 6; No. 7, Christ unser Herr zum Jordan kam; No. 8. **Paul Esswood** (alto); **Kurt Equiluz** (ten); **Max van Egmond** (bass); **Vienna Boys' Choir; Chorus Viennensis; Vienna Concentus Musicus / Nikolaus Harnoncourt; Regensburger Domspatzen; King's College Choir, Cambridge; Leonhardt Consort / Gustav Leonhardt.** Teldec Ⓜ 2292-42498-2 (two discs: 87 minutes: ADD: 9/85). 🎙　　　　　Ⓖ

...No. 8[a]; No. 156, Ich steh mit einem Fuss im Grabe[b]; No. 198, Lass, Fürstin, lass noch einen Strahl, "Trauer-Ode". [a]**Julianne Baird,** [c]**Judith Nelson** (sops); [c]**Judith Malafronte** (mez); [ab]**Steven Rickards** (alto); [c]**William Sharp** (bar); [ab]**James Weaver** (bass); **American Bach Soloists / Jeffrey Thomas** (ten). Koch International Classics Ⓕ 37163-2 (68 minutes: DDD: 4/93).

...No. 12, Weinen, Klagen, Sorgen, Zagen; No. 18, Gleich wie der Regen und Schnee; No. 61; No. 132, Bereitet die Wege, bereitet die Bahn; No. 152, Tritt auf die Glaubensbahn; No. 172, Erschallet, ihr Lieder; No. 182, Himmelskönig, sei willkommen; No. 199, Mein Herze schwimmt im Blut; No. 203, Amore traditore. Quodlibet, BWV524. **Soloists; Amsterdam Baroque Choir and Orchestra / Ton Koopman.** Erato Ⓕ 0630-12598-2 (three discs: 183 minutes: DDD: 5/96). 🎙 *Selected by Soundings.*

...No. 12[a]; No. 54, Widerstehe doch der Sünde; No. 162, Ach! ich sehe, jetzt, da ich zur Hochzeit gehe[a]; No. 182, Himmelskönig, sei willkommen[a]. [a]**Soloists; Bach Collegium Japan / Masaaki Suzuki.** BIS Ⓕ CD791 (79 minutes: DDD: 11/96).

Bach Cantatas – No. 11, Lobet Gott in seinen Reichen; No. 43, Gott fähret auf mit Jauchzen; No. 44, Sie werden euch in den Bann tun. **Barbara Schlick** (sop); **Catherine Patriasz** (contr); **Christoph Prégardien** (ten); **Peter Kooy** (bass); **Collegium Vocale / Philippe Herreweghe.** Harmonia Mundi Ⓕ HMC90 1479 (67 minutes: DDD: 3/94). 🎙 Texts and translations included. Recorded 1993.

Gott fähret auf mit Jauchzen is resonant in its joyful celebration of Christ's Ascension to Heaven and the right hand of God the Father. The orchestra includes three trumpets, drums and two oboes, as well as the basic string band, and these all play a part in the majestic opening chorus. By comparison,

Sie werden euch in den Bann tun is a modestly conceived piece. The Ascension 'Oratorio' (No. 11), though listed among Bach's cantatas, is an oratorio in more than just name, making use of a narrator who relates the events surrounding Christ's Ascension. Like Bach's two other oratorios, this one makes extensive use of music which had previously been written for other contexts. It also contains the music which eventually was to become the *Agnus Dei* of the B minor Mass. Herreweghe paces all three works with assurance and fluency and is supported by the excellence of his singers and instrumentalists. Fine recorded sound and an informative booklet complete an accomplished issue.

Additional recommendation ...
...No. 11. Easter Oratorio, BWV249. **Monika Frimmer** (sop); **Ralf Popken** (alto); **Christoph Prégardien** (ten); **David Wilson-Johnson** (bar); **Choir and Orchestra of the Age of Enlightenment / Gustav Leonhardt.** Philips Ⓕ 442 119-2PH (73 minutes: DDD: 10/94). 🎵 Ⓖ

Bach Cantatas – No. 18, Gleich wie der Regen und Schnee[a]; No. 143, Lobe den Herrn, meine Seele[b]; No. 152, Tritt auf die Glaubensbahn[c]; No. 155, Mein Gott, wie lang, ach lange[d]; No. 161, Komm, du süsse Todesstunde[e]. [acd]**Midori Suzuki**, [b]**Ingrid Schmithüsen** (sops); [de]**Yoshikazu Mera** (alto); [abde]**Makoto Sakurada** (ten); [abcd]**Peter Kooy** (bass); **Bach Collegium Japan / Masaaki Suzuki** ([bce]org). BIS Ⓕ CD841 (78 minutes: DDD: 1/98). Texts and translations included. Recorded 1997. *Gramophone Editor's choice. Selected by Soundings.* Ⓖ

The fifth volume of Bach's sacred cantatas performed by the Bach Collegium Japan continues their Weimar survey with five pieces written between *c*1713 and 1716. It begins with No. 18, performed in its Weimar version – Bach later revived it for Leipzig, adding two treble recorders to the purely string texture of the upper parts of the earlier composition. The scoring of No. 152 is more diverse, featuring in its opening Sinfonia a viola d'amore, viola da gamba, oboe and recorder. A conspicuous feature of No. 155 is its melancholy duet for alto and tenor with bassoon obbligato. While the vocal writing sustains something of the character of a lament the wonderfully athletic, arpeggiated bassoon solo provides a magical third voice. The accompanying essay is confused here, emphasizing the importance of a solo oboe which in fact has no place at all in this work. No. 161 is a piece of sustained beauty, scored for a pair of treble recorders, obbligato organ, strings and continuo. Bach's authorship of No. 143 has sometimes been questioned. Much of it is indeed un-Bach-like, yet at times it is hard to envisage another composer's hand. The performances are of unmatched excellence. Masaaki Suzuki's direction never falters and his solo vocalists go from strength to strength as the series progresses. Suzuki makes a richly rewarding contribution with beautifully poised singing, a crystal-clear voice and an upper range that only very occasionally sounds at all threatened. Mera and Sakurada sustain a delicately balanced partnership in the elegiac duet of No. 155, the limpid bassoon-playing completing this trio of outstanding beauty. Kooy is a tower of strength, a sympathetic partner to Suzuki in the dance-like duet between Jesus and the Soul (No. 152), and resonantly affirmative in his aria from the same cantata. But the highest praise should go to Mera and Sakurada for their affecting performance in No. 161. All the elements of this superb cantata are thoroughly understood and deeply felt by all concerned. The disc is admirably recorded and, apart from the aforementioned confusion, painstakingly and informatively documented.

Bach Cantatas – No. 35, Geist und Seele wird verwirret; No. 54, Widerstehe doch der Sünde; No. 170, Vergnügte Ruh', beliebte Seelenlust. **Andreas Scholl** (alto); **Collegium Vocale Orchestra / Philippe Herreweghe.** Harmonia Mundi Ⓕ HMC90 1644 (59 minutes: DDD: 5/98). Texts and translations included. Recorded 1997. *Gramophone Editor's choice.* ⒼⒼ

Some 12 years separates the composition of the Weimar cantata, *Widerstehe doch der Sünde*, from the Leipzig cantatas *Vergnügte Ruh'* and *Geist und Seele wird verwirret* (1726). All three are scored for a solo alto voice with strings and, in the case of the Leipzig pieces, various members of the oboe family and obbligato organ. Andreas Scholl is on top form in *Widerstehe doch der Sünde*, paying close attention to the relationship between text and music. *Vergnügte Ruh'* has long been a favourite piece with singers and audiences alike. Scholl sets an effectively contemplative tempo in the tender introductory aria but, while unquestionably expressive, he just fails to convey the same degree of ardour achieved by Alfred Deller in his extraordinary recording of the early 1950s with Gustav Leonhardt directing and Nikolaus Harnoncourt playing. Scholl's version is very beautiful, all the same, and he sounds comfortable with Bach's broadly spun melody. The remaining work, in two parts, is conceived on an ambitious scale, opening with an extended concerto movement for organ obbligato, oboe d'amore and strings, and containing another, similarly scored piece which serves as an introduction to Part Two. Organist Markus Märkl, with lively support from the orchestral players of the Collegium Vocale, gives a pleasingly jaunty, animated performance of these movements which together with the first aria may have belonged to a lost concerto. Scholl sings his music with warmth and technical fluency, generating a high level of interest for heart and mind alike.

Bach Cantatas – No. 39, Brich dem Hungrigen dein Brot; No. 93, Wer nur den lieben Gott lässt walten; No. 107, Was willst du dich betrüben. **Agnès Mellon** (sop); **Charles Brett** (alto); **Howard Crook** (ten); **Peter Kooy** (bass); **Collegium Vocale Chorus and Orchestra / Philippe Herreweghe.** Virgin Classics Veritas Ⓕ VC7 59320-2 (61 minutes: DDD: 3/94). 🎵 Texts and translations included. Recorded 1991. Ⓖ

The three pieces included here are mature examples of Bach's cantata writing; two of them, Nos. 93 and 107, were written in 1724 for the Fifth and Seventh Sundays after Trinity respectively, and thus belong to Bach's great second cycle in which he concentrated on a chorale-based scheme. The remaining cantata, No. 39, is a masterly work, above all in the concerto-like construction of the opening chorus, scored for voices with treble recorders, oboes and strings. Agnès Mellon is beguiling both in her three arias – one per cantata – and in her duo with Charles Brett. Both Crook and Kooy are on characteristically fine form. Enjoyable, too, are the contributions from the chorus and orchestra, and, as usual, the oboe playing of Marcel Ponseele is a constant pleasure, above all for his poetic phrasing and communicative articulation. Excellent recorded sound.

Bach Cantatas – No. 49, Ich gehe und suche mit Verlangen; No. 115, Mache dich, mein Geist bereit; No. 180, Schmücke dich, o liebe Seele. **Barbara Schlick** (sop); **Andreas Scholl** (alto); **Christoph Prégardien** (ten); **Gotthold Schwarz** (bass); **Concerto Vocale; Limoges Baroque Ensemble / Christophe Coin** (vc). Auvidis Astrée Ⓕ E8530 (71 minutes: DDD: 2/95). ✍ Texts and translations included. Recorded 1993.   ⒼⒼ

Three of Bach's Leipzig church cantatas form a characteristically well-thought-out programme from the French gamba player, cellist and director, Christophe Coin. *Schmücke dich, o liebe Seele* (No. 180) and *Mache dich, mein Geist, bereit* (No. 115) are among the most overlooked of the cantatas, outside 'complete editions'; but they are towering masterpieces which deserve to be as popular as, for instance, *Wachet auf!* (No. 140) or any of the others which find their way, albeit infrequently, into concert programming. There is a more particular reason, however, beyond that of sheer musical excellence, why Coin has chosen to perform these works: it is that in each of them Bach has included a movement calling for the obbligato presence of a small, five-stringed cello, the violoncello piccolo. Nine of Bach's cantatas contain a part for this distinctive-sounding instrument, in each of which the composer employs it with telling effect. No. 180 is a delicately scored piece for two recorders, oboe, oboe da caccia and strings, with an affecting undercurrent of elegy. Coin's direction, his overall grasp of the musical idiom and his evident care over textual detail lead to the heart of the piece. Not everything is refined – there are, for example, some rough moments in the instrumental tuttis – but the spirit of the performance carries everything along with it. This much is true for the remaining cantatas, too. No. 115 contains music of quite extraordinary inventive richness and nowhere more so than in its two *da capo* arias for alto and soprano, respectively: the second, in B minor, seems to lead us into almost uncharted emotional territory in its contemplative profundity. This heart-rending trio for soprano, flute, violoncello piccolo and continuo is one of the most astounding achievements in the entire canon; and it is beautifully sung by Barbara Schlick. The Leipzig Concerto Vocale (a mixed choir of men's and women's voices), and the Limoges Baroque Ensemble have gathered under Coin's direction in performances which probe far beyond musical superficialities.

Additional recommendation ...

...No. 49. No. 58, Ach Gott, wie manches Herzelied. No. 82, Ich habe genug. **Nancy Argenta** (sop); **Klaus Mertens** (bass); **La Petite Bande / Sigiswald Kuijken** (vn). Accent Ⓕ ACC9395 (63 minutes: DDD: 3/94). ✍   Ⓖ

Bach Cantatas – No. 50, Nun ist das Heil und die Kraft; No. 50, Nun ist das Heil und die Kraft (recons. Kleinbussink); No. 59, Wer mich liebet, der wird mein Wort halten[ad]; No. 69, Lobe den Herrn, meine Seele[abcd]; No. 69a, Lobe den Herrn, meine Seele[abcd]; No. 75, Die Elenden sollen essen[abcd]; No. 76, Die Himmel erzählen die Ehre Gottes[abcd]; No. 104, Du Hirte Israel, höre[cd]; No. 179, Siehe zu, dass deine Gottesfurcht[acd]; No. 186, Argre dich, o Seele, nicht[abcd]; No. 190, Singet dem Herrn ein neues Lied![bcd]. [a]**Ruth Ziesak** (sop); [b]**Elisabeth von Magnus** (contr); [c]**Paul Agnew** (ten); [d]**Klaus Mertens** (bass); **Amsterdam Baroque Choir and Orchestra / Ton Koopman** (org). Erato Ⓕ 3984-21629-2 (three discs: 195 minutes: DDD: 4/98). Texts and translations included. ✍ Recorded 1997.   Ⓖ

This is the sixth volume in Ton Koopman's exhaustive series of Bach's complete cantatas. Koopman is here engaged in the great Leipzig period from 1723. Bach's inaugural offering was a pair of substantial bipartite cantatas, Nos. 75 and 76. Koopman gives us the second one initially, *Die Himmel erzählen die Ehre Gottes*, in a muscular and assertive performance. The fine opening chorus, with its swaggering trumpet obbligato, is zestfully negotiated and appropriately full-blooded. The same commitment and character are plentiful in the formidably worked-out contrapuntal edifice of No. 75 – a movement passionately declaiming the rewards of seeking God – and the wonderfully evocative imagery in No. 104, *Du Hirte Israel, höre*. Memorable for different reasons is *Singet dem Herrn*, No. 190, a cantata whose opening two movements require major reconstruction. Koopman has completed the task with a dynamic scoring around the existing vocal parts. If a somewhat over-elaborate setting, it is nevertheless thrilling, and employs the sort of fervent Reformation-like unisons and belting brass which cannot fail to stir. Koopman has found in Ruth Ziesak a soprano who can get round the notes, sing consistently in tune (despite one under-par aria in No. 186) and express the meaning of the music with rhetorical personality. She dances around the lithe "Ich nehme mein Leiden" from No. 75. This latter cantata abounds in arresting arias, none more so than the delicious "Mein Jesus soll", a creation of such ingenious and agreeable melodic inflexion that Paul Agnew can but relish it devotedly. Both Agnew's and Klaus Mertens's singing throughout is a joy, a happy blend of technical security, musicianly shaping and tonal elegance. Elisabeth von Magnus is, in truth, the weak link. Her contribution to the stirring Part 2 of No. 76 is not especially undistinguished but her languid sound is repeatedly enervating, and too often the pitch dips unacceptably. In all other respects this is quite a turn-up for the books after the hits and misses of previous volumes. Bach was clearly intent on impressing his new employers with the most accomplished work he could produce; one only has to hear the richness of these scores (a bonanza here for those who like trumpets, and brilliantly played too) to suppose that Koopman has found similar inspiration at exactly the right time.

Bach Cantatas – No. 67, Halt im Gedächtnis Jesum Christ[a]; No. 108, Es ist euch gut, dass ich hingehe[a]; No. 127, Herr Jesu Christ, wahr' Mensch und Gott[b]. [b]**Antonia Fahberg** (sop); [a]**Lilian Benningsen** (contr); **Sir Peter Pears** (ten); **Kieth Engen** (bass); **Munich Bach Choir; Munich State Opera Orchestra / Karl Richter.** Teldec Das Alte Werk Ⓜ 9031-77614-2* (61 minutes: ADD: 5/93). Texts and translations included. Recorded 1958. New to UK. ⒼⒼⒼ

Collectors of Bach's choral music have strong views on Richter's performances, especially the church cantatas which represented the majority of his recorded output for Archiv. Most would agree that Richter's special affinity with Bach's music found its mark most persuasively in the 1960s before his mysterious adoption of the cloudy neo-romantic sound which did little to project his profound understanding of Bach's inner strength. Here we have a rarity from the late 1950s (a 'one-off' from Teldec not available in this country before) which forces us to revise our opinions about Richter's rigidity. These three cantatas were caught before the Munich Bach Orchestra had been formed though you would not know that they were not Bachians to the core; this is a state opera orchestra inspired by invigorating musical expression, blessed with an ignorance of self-conscious fashion. Certainly there are a few distracting mannerisms and a voice, notably Lilian Benningsen, which in hindsight seem somewhat out of place but they never detract from the prevailing conviction of the performances. In Cantata No. 67 the spirit of the text is directly and lucidly communicated by a spruce and well-balanced choral group, supported by the inimitable Peter Pears (a treasure or two here for his fans). The bass Keith Engen is also a Bach singer out of the top drawer; the opening aria of Cantata No. 108 is lovingly sung and the legendary Edgar Shann delivers an obbligato oboe line which is worth the cost of the disc alone, even without the other priceless revelations here.

Bach Cantatas – No. 73, Herr wie du willt, so schicks mit mir; No. 105, Herr, gehe nicht ins Gericht mit deinem Knecht; No. 131, Aus der Tiefen rufe ich, Herr, zu dir. **Barbara Schlick** (sop); **Gérard Lesne** (alto); **Howard Crook** (ten); **Peter Kooy** (bass); **Ghent Collegium Vocale Chorus and Orchestra / Philippe Herreweghe.** Virgin Classics Veritas Ⓔ VC7 59237-2 (58 minutes: DDD: 5/93). 🖉 Texts and translations included. Recorded 1990.

Philippe Herreweghe's choir consists of some 16 voices to which he has added four excellent soloists, all of whom are experienced artists in this repertory. *Aus der Tiefen rufe ich* is one of Bach's earliest cantatas dating back to 1707 or 1708. The text is a setting of Psalm 130, *De profundis* with additional verses from a Lenten hymn. Herreweghe conveys the sombre intensity of the piece and is especially well served by his soloists, choir and solo oboist, with a particularly lyrical contribution from Howard Crook. Harmonically, No. 73 is a work of considerable strength. The Gospel-based text underlines the contrasting states of human frailty on the one hand and God's omnipotence on the other. Counterpart and subtle instrumentation play a part in the work's dark climax, a bass recitative and aria in which Bach's extraordinary gifts at evoking musical-textual imagery are on display. Peter Kooy is resonant, declamatory and affecting and is well supported on the whole by the strings, though the violins are thin at times. The beautiful *Herr, gehe nicht ins Gericht* is masterly from start to finish. The text focuses on two themes, the parable of the unjust steward and St Paul's warning to the Corinthians against idolatry and pride. Barbara Schlick is on top form, making this perhaps the interpretative high point of the entire recording; Bach's musical concept, furthermore, is breathtakingly original. She is affectingly partnered by Marc Ponseele whose delicately shaded oboe playing is all that one could wish for. Kooy declaims with firm control and a feeling for the poetry, and Crook is effective in his aria dispelling the emotional intensity of the earlier sections. Herreweghe manages all with tenderness and emotional restraint, achieving a sustained often deeply affecting performance. Three wonderful works, affectionately realized with solo contributions of distinction.

Additional recommendation ...
...No. 71, Gott ist mein König[a]; 106, Gottes Zeit ist die allerbeste Zeit[b]; 131[a]. [a]**Midori Suzuki,** [b]**Aki Yanagisawa** (sops); **Yoshikazu Mera** (alto); [b]**Gerd Türk** (ten); **Peter Kooy** (bass); **Bach Collegium Japan / Masaaki Suzuki.** BIS Ⓕ CD781 (63 minutes: DDD: 9/96). ⒼⒼ

Bach Cantatas – No. 84, Ich bin vergnügt mit meinem Glücke; No. 202, Weichet nur, betrübte Schatten; No. 209, Non sa che sia dolore. **Nancy Argenta** (sop); **Ensemble Sonnerie / Monica Huggett.** Virgin Classics Veritas Ⓕ VC5 45059-2 (54 minutes: DDD: 6/95). 🖉 Texts and translations included. Recorded 1993. Ⓖ

Of the three works on this disc, No. 84 is the only sacred cantata. Unlike the better-known *Ich habe genug* (No. 82), its two alternating recitatives and arias are followed by a four-part chorale set to a melody which occupies an important place in Bach's work, *Wer nur den lieben Gott lässt walten*. Nos. 202 and 209 are, respectively, a wedding cantata – though not one which is linked in any way to the marriage service – and a piece commemorating the departure on a journey of an unidentified friend, presumably of the composer, whoever he may been, since Bach's authorship is also sometimes questioned. Bach or not, it is a very engaging work with an extended concerto movement for flute and strings in B minor in which Bach unquestionably must have had at least a hand. The performances are very good indeed. Both Nos. 84 and 202 are dominated by oboe writing rich in fantasy and this aspect is well understood by oboist Paul Goodwin, above all in the wonderfully expressive opening arias of each work. Argenta's youthful voice is well suited to all this music yet it is, perhaps, especially alluring in the Italian cantata, No. 209, in whose more galant idiom she sounds completely at home. This is a captivating performance in which Argenta is sensitively partnered by the limpid flute playing of Lisa Beznosiuk.

Additional recommendation ...

...No. 198, Lass, Fürstin, lass noch einen Strahl[a]; No. 201, Geschwinde, ihr wirbeln den Winde (Phoebus and Pan)[g]; No. 204, Ich bin in mir vergnügt[f]; No. 209[e]; No. 211, Schweigt stille, plaudert nicht[c]; No. 214, Tönet, ihr Pauken! Erschallet, Trompeten[d]; No. 215, Preise dein Glücke, gesegnetes Sachsen[b]. [aef]**Lisa Larsson,** [bd]**Els Bongers,** [c]**Anne Grimm,** [g]**Caroline Stam** (sops); [ad]**Elisabeth von Magnus** (contr); [g]**Peter de Groot** (alto); [abcdg]**Paul Agnew,** [g]**Jeremy Ovenden** (tens); [abcdg]**Klaus Mertens,** [g]**Donald Bentvelsen** (basses); **Amsterdam Baroque** [abcdg]**Choir and Orchestra / Ton Koopman.** Erato Ⓕ 0630-15562-2 (three discs: 219 minutes: DDD: 7/97). ✍

Bach Cantatas. [a]**Allan Bergius,** [b]**Christoph Wegmann,** [a]**Helmut Wittek,** [d]**Stefan Gienger** (trebs); [e]**Kurt Equiluz** (ten); **Thomas Hampson** (bar); **Vienna Concentus Musicus / Nikolaus Harnoncourt.** Teldec Ⓕ 9031-74798-2 (55 minutes: DDD: 4/92). ✍ Recorded 1983-87.
No. 140, Wachet auf! ruft uns die Stimme – Wann kommst du, mein Heil?[a]; Mein Freund ist mein![a]. No. 146, Wir müssen durch viel Trübsal in das Reich Gottes eingehen – Wie will ich mich freuen[e] (all from 6 35653, 1/85). No. 147, Herz und Mund und Tat und Leben – Ich will von Jesu Wundern singen (6 35654, 7/85). No. 152, Tritt auf die Glaubensahn – Tritt auf die Glaubensbahn; Wie soll ich dich, Liebster der Seelen[b]. No. 153, Schau, lieber Gott, wie meine Feind – Fürchte dich nicht, ich bin bei dir. No. 154, Mein liebster Jesus ist verloren – Wisset ihr nicht (6 35656, 4/86). No. 185, Barmherziges Herze der ewigen Liebes – Das ist der Christen Kunst (2292-44179-2, 9/89). No. 192, Nun danket alle Gott – Der ewig reiche Gott[c]. No. 194, Höchsterwünschtes Freudenfest – Was des Höchsten Glanz erfüllt; O wie wohl ist uns geschehn[d] (2292-44193-2, 5/90). No. 196, Der Herr denket an uns – Der Herr segne euch[e] (2292-44194-2, 5/90).
This disc is both an alluring shop window for Teldec's complete series of Bach cantatas – though in no sense a substitute – and an attractive programme in its own right. Bach's sacred cantatas are richly endowed with vocal duets and the present issue offers only a selection from them. The common factor is the baritone, Thomas Hampson, who is partnered by some of the talented boy trebles who made such a distinctive contribution to the complete edition, and by the tenor, Kurt Equiluz. Hampson joined the team when the series was already two-thirds of the way through, so the earliest cantata to feature here is No. 140, *Wachet auf! ruft uns die Stimme.* That work, however, provides an auspicious starting-point since it contains two especially fine duets which are also among the most popular with audiences. Much else, though, will be comparatively unfamiliar to all but well-seasoned Bach cantata enthusiasts. In short, a very attractive compilation which, if it draws unsuspecting listeners into Bach's sacred dramatic wonderland will have more than fulfilled its purpose. Texts are not included, alas, but an accompanying note provides useful signposts to travellers in a strange land.

Additional recommendations ...

...No. 19, Es erhub sich ein Streit; No. 40, Dazu ist erschienen der Sohn Gottes; No. 70, Wachet, betet, seid bereit allezeit; No. 140; No. 149, Man singet mit Freuden vom Sieg; No. 180, Schmücke dich, o liebe Seele. **Soloists; Heinrich Schütz Choir, Heilbronn; Pforzheim Chamber Orchestra / Fritz Werner.** Erato Ⓜ 0630-11223-2 (two discs: 146 minutes: ADD: 2/96). Ⓖ
...No. 4, Christ lag in Todesbanden; No. 150, Nach dir, Herr, verlanget mich; No. 196. **Soloists; Bach Collegium Japan / Masaaki Suzuki.** ✍ BIS Ⓕ CD751 (45 minutes: DDD: 6/96).

Bach Cantatas – No. 163, Nur jedem das Seine[a]; No. 165, O heilges Geist-und Wasserbad[b]; No. 185, Barmherziges Herze der ewigen Liebe[c]; No. 199, Mein Herze schwimmt im Blut[d]. [cd]**Midori Suzuki,** [ab]**Aki Yanagisawa** (sops); [ab]**Akira Tachikawa** (alto); [abc]**Makoto Sakurada** (ten); [abc]**Stephan Schreckenberger** (bass); **Bach Collegium Japan / Masaaki Suzuki.** BIS Ⓕ CD801 (66 minutes: DDD: 6/97). Texts and translations included. Recorded in 1996.
The level of vocal and instrumental artistry of the Bach Collegium Japan is consistently and fairly uniformly high, and the many editorial decisions that have to be made in a project such as this have been taken practically and sensibly. No. 199 is a generously proportioned work for solo soprano, obbligato oboe, viola and strings with continuo. Midori Suzuki's light, tonally pure and somewhat boyish timbre suits the music well, though some readers may find her at times expressively bland. Suzuki does not perhaps possess the mature accomplishments of her rival Barbara Schlick who sings the same piece for Ton Koopman's recording yet her vocal production is less strained than Schlick. Bach made provision, at different times and for different performances, for a variety of instruments to accompany the tenderly expressive choral movement preceding the concluding aria. Here a viola is preferred to the bass viol, violoncello piccolo or even perhaps standard cello which featured in subsequent performances. It works well and always strikes the ear as the happiest solution. The three remaining cantatas are all smaller in dimension than No. 199. For the most part they come over well

though neither Yanagisawa nor Tachikawa perhaps quite match Suzuki in tonal allure. Sakurada and Schreckenberger both make strong contributions. It would be remiss to conclude without commending the excellence of oboist, Alfredo Bernardini, one of only two Europeans taking part in the enterprise, the fine continuo playing and the beautifully balanced one-to-a-part vocal ensemble comprising the soloists, which provides the chorale element. Deeply felt, sincerely expressed performances such as these deserve to win many friends.

Additional recommendation ...

...No. 51, Jauchzet Gott in allen Landen!. No. 82, Ich habe genug. No. 199. **Nancy Argenta** (sop); **Ensemble Sonnerie / Monica Huggett** (vn).
Virgin Classics Veritas Ⓕ VC5 45038-2 (62 minutes: DDD: 12/94). ✍

...No. 22, Jesus nahm zu sich die Zwölfe[fhi]; No. 23, Du wahrer Gott und Davids Sohn[g]; No. 54, Widerstehe doch der Sünde[g]; No. 63, Christen, ätzet diesen Tag (with appendix)[cfhi]; No. 155, Mein Gott, wie lang, ache lange[bfhi]; No. 161, Komm, du süsse Todesstunde[fh]; No. 162, Ach! ich sehe, jetzt, da ich zur Hochzeit gehe (with Appendix)[afhi]; No. 163[dfhi]; No. 165[bfhi]; No. 208, Was mir behagt, ist nur die muntre Jagd[aehij]. [a]**Barbara Schlick,** [b]**Caroline Stam,** [c]**Ruth Holton,** [d]**Els Bongers** (sops); **Elisabeth von Magnus** ([e]sop/[f]contr); [g]**Andreas Scholl** (alto); [h]**Paul Agnew** (ten); [i]**Klaus Mertens** (bass); **Amsterdam Baroque Choir and Orchestra / Ton Koopman** ([j]hpd/org).
Erato Ⓕ 0630-14336-2 (three discs: 195 minutes: DDD: 11/96). ✍

Bach Cantatas – No. 211, Schweigt stille, plaudert nicht, "Coffee"; No. 212, Mer hahn en neue Oberkeet, "Peasant". **Emma Kirkby** (sop); **Rogers Covey-Crump** (ten); **David Thomas** (bass); **Academy of Ancient Music / Christopher Hogwood.** L'Oiseau-Lyre Ⓕ 417 621-2OH (52 minutes: DDD: 10/89). ✍ Texts and translations included. **Ⓖ**

These two most delightful of Bach's secular cantatas here receive sparkling performances fully alive to the humour and invention of the music. The *Coffee* Cantata illustrates a family altercation over a current enthusiasm, the drinking of coffee. A narrator tells the story whilst the soprano and bass soloists confront each other in a series of delightful arias. Thomas brings out the crabby dyspeptic side of Schlendrian's character imaginatively and Kirkby makes a charming minx-like Lieschen. Covey-Crump's sweet light tenor acts as a good foil. The *Peasant* Cantata also takes the form of a dialogue, here between a somewhat dull and simple young man and his sweetheart Mieke, a girl who intends to better herself. Through the 24 short movements Bach conjures up a wonderfully rustic picture with some vivid dance numbers and rumbustious ritornellos. The soloists' nicely rounded characterizations emerge with great humour and Hogwood directs with vitality and sprightly rhythmic control. The recording is excellent.

Additional recommendations ...

...No. 202, Weichet nur, betrübte Schatten, "Wedding Cantata"[a]. No. 209, Non sa che sia dolore[a]. Nos. 211 and 212[abc]. [a]**Elly Ameling** (sop); [b]**Gerald English** (ten); [c]**Siegmund Nimsgern** (bass); **Collegium Aureum.** Deutsche Harmonia Mundi Editio Classica Ⓜ GD77151 (two discs: 106 minutes: ADD: 10/90). ✍

...No. 211. No. 213, Hercules auf dem Scheidewege. **Barbara Bonney** (sop); **Ralf Popken** (alto); **Christoph Prégardien** (ten); **David Wilson-Johnson** (bar); **Orchestra and Choir of the Age of Enlightenment / Gustav Leonhardt.** Philips Ⓕ 442 779-2PH (74 minutes: DDD: 7/95). ✍

...No. 82, Ich habe genung – Ich habe genug!; Schlummert ein; No. 202, Weichet nur, betrübte Schatten; No. 209, Non sa che sia dolore; Nos. 211 and 212 – excerpts. Anna Magdalena Notenbuch – Bist du bei mir. *Coupled with works by various composers.* **Elly Ameling** (sop); **Various soloists;** Deutsche Harmonia Mundi Ⓕ 74321 26617-2 (four discs: 239 minutes: ADD: 12/95). *See review in the Collections section; refer to the Index.*

Bach Motets – Singet dem Herren, BWV225; Der Geist hilft unsrer Schwachheit auf, BWV226; Jesu meine Freude, BWV227; Fürchte dich nicht, BWV228; Komm, Jesu, komm, BWV229; Lobet den Herren, BWV230. **Greta de Reyghere, Katelijne van Laetham** (sops); **Martin van der Zeijst, Sytse Buwalda** (altos); **Hans Hermann Jansen** (ten); **Johannes-Christoph Happel** (bar); **La Petite Bande Choir; La Petite Bande / Sigiswald Kuijken.** Accent Ⓕ ACC9287 (65 minutes: DDD: 5/93). ✍ Texts and translations included. Recorded 1992.

Bach Motets – Singet dem Herren, BWV225; Der Geist hilft unsrer Schwachheit auf, BWV226; Jesu meine Freude, BWV227; Fürchte dich nicht, BWV228; Komm, Jesu, komm, BWV229; Lobet den Herren, BWV230. **Netherlands Chamber Choir / Ton Koopman.** Philips Ⓕ 434 165-2PH (63 minutes: DDD: 5/93). ✍ Texts and translations included. Recorded 1986-87.

These two approaches to Bach's Motets differ strongly from one another. Sigiswald Kuijken directs performances with *colla parte* instrumental support, that is to say with instruments doubling each of the vocal strands. Ton Koopman, on the other hand, prefers the vocal strands *a cappella* with instruments providing only the basso continuo. The choir in each version is made up of women sopranos and countertenors with the men's voices. Choosing between the versions is difficult and, to a large extent must be a matter of which approach you prefer. Kuijken's performances are more relaxed than those of Koopman. He avoids anything in the nature of overdirection and, while neither singing nor playing is always quite as tidy as it might be, there is a lively spontaneity, especially rewarding in the radiant performance of *Singet dem Herren.* Koopman draws more sharply articulated singing than Kuijken from the Netherlands Chamber Choir though sometimes at the expense of natural declamation and spontaneity. But there is greater linear clarity here than in the other and it pays off handsomely in *Komm, Jesu, komm*. It is a pity that Koopman does not avail himself of the surviving instrumental parts for *Der Geist hilft* but, in other respects, the strengths and weaknesses of the two performances are fairly evenly distributed and both are highly recommended.

Additional recommendations ...

...*As above*. O Jesu Christ, meins Lebens Licht, BWV118. **Agnès Mellon, Greta de Reyghere** (sops); **Vincent Darras** (alto); **Howard Crook** (ten); **Peter Kooy** (bass); **Collegium Vocale; La Chapelle Royale Chorus and Orchestra / Philippe Herreweghe.** Harmonia Mundi Ⓕ HMC90 1231 (67 minutes: DDD: 12/86). ✍

...*As above*. **Trinity College Choir, Cambridge / Richard Marlow** with **Graham Jackson and Richard Pearce** (orgs). Conifer Classics Ⓕ CDCF158 (66 minutes: DDD: 12/88).

...*As above*. **Stockholm Bach Choir; Vienna Concentus Musicus / Nikolaus Harnoncourt.** Teldec Ⓜ 0630 17430-2 (63 minutes: DDD: 7/97).

...*As above*. **The Scholars Baroque Ensemble.** Naxos Ⓢ 8 553823 (63 minutes: DDD: 10/97).

Bach Magnificat in D major, BWV243[a].

Vivaldi Ostro picta, RV642[b]. Gloria in D major, RV589[c]. [abc]**Emma Kirkby,** [ac]**Tessa Bonner** (sops); [ac]**Michael Chance** (alto); [a]**John Mark Ainsley** (ten); [a]**Stephen Varcoe** (bar); **Collegium Musicum 90 Chorus and Orchestra / Richard Hickox.** Chandos Chaconne Ⓕ CHAN0518 (64 minutes: DDD: 7/91). ✍ Texts and translations included. Recorded 1990. Ⓖ

This issue was the first CD release featuring the then newly founded Collegium Musicum 90 under its directors Richard Hickox and Simon Standage. The Collegium embraces both choir and orchestra who are joined in this programme of Bach and Vivaldi by a comparably fine team of soloists. Hickox sets effective tempos in Bach's *Magnificat* and points up the many striking contrasts in colour and texture with which the piece abounds. From among the many successful features of the recording Stephen Varcoe's "Quia fecit mihi magna" and the "Et misericordia" sung by Michael Chance and John Mark Ainsley stand out. Vivaldi's *Gloria*, RV589 is the better known of two settings by the composer in D major. In this programme it is prefaced by an introductory motet *Ostro picta*, which may well in fact belong to the *Gloria* and is here sung with warmth and radiance by Emma Kirkby. Hickox's performance of this evergreen vocal masterpiece comes over with conviction. It is gracefully phrased, sensitively sung and affectingly paced with an admirable rapport between vocalists and instrumentalists. The recorded sound is first-rate.

Additional recommendations ...

...Magnificat. Cantata No. 51, Jauchzet Gott in allen Landen!. **Soloists; English Baroque Soloists / Sir John Eliot Gardiner.** Philips Ⓕ 411 458-2PH (41 minutes: DDD: 9/85). ✍

...Magnificat. **Vivaldi** Gloria. **Soloists; Academy of St Martin in the Fields Chorus and Orchestra / Sir Neville Marriner.** EMI Ⓕ CDC7 54283-2 (56 minutes: DDD: 3/92).

...Magnificat. Cantata No. 63, "Christen, ätzet diesen Tag". Sanctus in D major, BWV238. **Soloists; New London Consort / Philip Pickett.** L'Oiseau-Lyre Ⓕ 452 920-2OH (64 minutes: DDD: 12/97).

Bach Mass in B minor, BWV232. **Nancy Argenta** (sop); **Catherine Denley** (mez); **Mark Tucker** (ten); **Stephen Varcoe** (bar); **Collegium Musicum 90 Chorus and Orchestra / Richard Hickox.** Chandos Chaconne Ⓕ CHAN0533/4 (two discs: 108 minutes: DDD: 1/93). ✍ Texts and translations included. Recorded 1992. ⒼⒼ

Richard Hickox, his soloists and the Collegium Musicum 90 Chorus and Orchestra deliver a performance of this Mass which is satisfying on many levels. Hickox has a proven track-record with choirs and here he comes across as an effective disciplinarian in his firm control both of voices and instruments. Yet he avoids imposing that autocratic will on his forces which sometimes lessens the spontaneity of rival performances. Perhaps his strength lies more in the handling of the extrovert and most joyful sections of the Mass than in the contemplative ones. Thus the *Et in terra pax*, for instance, comes over especially well with articulate and transparently textured choral singing supported by robust but none the less sympathetic orchestral playing. The solo vocalists make a strong, even team and the use of a mezzo-soprano offers a welcome alternative in the *Agnus Dei* which, in most period instrument performances, has unjustly become the sole preserve of countertenors. It may be that some other versions intermittently achieve greater heights of intensity but, taken as a whole, this lively, spontaneous and consistently accomplished version is a fine achievement.

Additional recommendations ...

...**Soloists; Monteverdi Choir; English Baroque Soloists / Sir John Eliot Gardiner.** Archiv Produktion Ⓕ 415 514-2AH2 (two discs: 105 minutes: DDD: 2/86). ✍ Ⓖ

...**Soloists; Netherlands Bach Society Collegium Musicum; La Petite Bande / Gustav Leonhardt.** Deutsche Harmonia Mundi Editio Classica Ⓜ GD77040 (two discs: 111 minutes: ADD: 6/90). ✍ Ⓖ

...**Soloists; The Sixteen Choir and Orchestra / Harry Christophers.** Collins Classics Ⓕ 7032-2 (two discs: 106 minutes: DDD: 11/94). ✍

...**Soloists; Vienna Singakademie Chorus; Stuttgart Chamber Orchestra / Karl Münchinger.** Decca Double Ⓜ 440 609-2DF2 (two discs: 119 minutes: ADD: 12/94).

...**Soloists; Vienna Boys' Choir; Viennensis Chorus; Vienna Concentus Musicus / Nikolaus Harnoncourt.** Teldec Das Alte Werk Ⓜ 4509-95517-2 (two discs: 107 minutes: ADD: 4/95). ✍

...**Soloists; Bavarian Radio Chorus; Baverian Radio Symphony Orchestra / Eugen Jochum.**
EMI Forte Ⓜ CZS5 68640-2 (two discs: 122 minutes: ADD: 5/96).
...**Soloists; Tölz Boys' Choir; The King's Consort Choir; The King's Consort / Robert King.**
Hyperion Ⓕ CDA67201/2 (two discs: 110 minutes: DDD: 3/97).

Bach Masses – A major, BWV234; G minor, BWV235. Sanctus in D major, BWV238. **Agnès Mellon** (sop); **Gérard Lesne** (alto); **Christoph Prégardien** (ten); **Peter Kooy** (bass); **Ghent Collegium Vocale Chorus and Orchestra / Philippe Herreweghe.** Virgin Classics Veritas Ⓕ VC7 59587-2 (64 minutes: DDD: 1/91). 🎵 Texts and translations included. Recorded 1989.

That Bach's four short Masses have excited so little interest is doubtless a result of the bad press they have attracted over the years: "more barbaric parodies cannot be imagined" was Albert Schweitzer's opinion, and his evaluation – if rather blunt – is typical of the disdain felt for these works by Bach scholars who could not forgive the composer for recycling a few of his cantatas and thereby treading on their romantic notions of the original creative artist. But unless the B minor Mass itself – just as much a patchwork of secondhand material – is also to be classed as 'barbaric', few listeners today will be able to find much to object to in these charming pieces, in which Bach's personality shines through just as strongly as in any of his more reputable creations. And how many people *know* Cantata No. 187? Philippe Herreweghe's recordings of the Masses in G minor and A major – along with the sprightly (and original) D major Sanctus, BWV238 – should not, then, be of interest only to Bach enthusiasts. Both Masses share the same formal outline, the main contrast between them arising instead from their instrumental colouring, as Bach supplements the strings with oboes in BWV235, and flutes in BWV234. Herreweghe maximizes this gentle distinction by fixing his efforts on achieving a smooth blend and a rich, reverberant sound, in which he is undoubtedly helped by the echoing church acoustic of the Abbaye aux Dames in Saintes. If the sheer nobility and tenderness of Bach's church music appeals to you then you will have no problems with this disc.

Additional recommendations...
...BWV235[a]; G major, BWV236[b]. **Soloists; Stuttgart Gächinger Kantorei;** [a]**Stuttgart Bach Collegium;** [b]**Stuttgart Chamber Orchestra / Helmuth Rilling.**
Hänssler Classic Ⓕ 98 962 (52 minutes: DDD: 10/93).
...F major, BWV233; BWV234; BWV235; G major, BWV236. Sanctus in C major, BWV237. Sanctus, BWV238. Sanctus in D minor, BWV239. Sanctus in G major, BWV240. Sanctus in D major, BWV241. Christe eleison in G minor, BWV242. **Lausanne Vocal Ensemble and Chamber Orchestra / Michel Corboz.** Erato Ⓕ 4509-97236-2.
...BWV233[a]; BWV234[b]. **Soloists; Stuttgart Gächinger Kantorei;** [a]**Franz Liszt Chamber Orchestra;** [b]**Stuttgart Bach Collegium / Helmuth Rilling.** Hänssler Classic Ⓕ 98 924 (55 minutes: DDD: 2/96).

Bach St John Passion, BWV245 (sung in English). **Sir Peter Pears** (ten) Evangelist; **Gwynne Howell** (bass) Jesus; **Heather Harper, Jenny Hill** (sops); **Alfreda Hodgson** (contr); **Robert Tear, Russell Burgess, John Tobin, Adrian Thompson** (tens); **John Shirley-Quirk** (bar); **Wandsworth School Boys' Choir; English Chamber Orchestra / Benjamin Britten.** Double Decca Ⓜ 443 859-2DF2 (two discs: 130 minutes: ADD: 7/95). Recorded 1971.

Britten's recording of the *St John Passion* is very special indeed. He apparently preferred to perform this Bach choral work because of its natural potential for drama. With Sir Peter Pears a superb Evangelist (and you can hear every word!) this account takes over the listener completely. The soloists are all splendid, though one must single out the glorious contribution of Heather Harper, and the choral response is inspirational in its moments of sheer fervour. Britten's direction is both urgent and volatile, the Wandsworth School Boys' Choir sing out full-throatedly and the English Chamber Orchestra underpin the whole performance with gloriously rich string textures. (Listening to this unique recording one is tempted to conclude that the 'authentic' string sound, for all its clarity and bite, is less desirable than modern instruments in an expansive work of this kind.) Then there is the analogue recording itself which offers a demonstration of ambient fullness, vividness of detail and natural balance. In fact, one gets the impression that a live performance at The Maltings, Snape has been transported to the area just beyond one's speakers! As a bonus it is available at mid price.

Additional recommendations ...
...**Soloists; Monteverdi Choir; English Baroque Soloists / Sir John Eliot Gardiner.**
Archiv Produktion Ⓕ 419 324-2AH2 (two discs: 107 minutes: DDD: 2/87). 🎵   Ⓖ
...**Soloists; Ghent Collegium Vocale; La Chapelle Royale Orchestra / Philippe Herreweghe.**
Harmonia Mundi Ⓕ HMC90 1264/5 (two discs: 115 minutes: DDD: 5/88). 🎵
...**Soloists; La Petite Bande Choir and Orchestra / Sigiswald Kuijken.** Deutsche Harmonia Mundi Editio Classica Ⓜ GD77041 (two discs: 122 minutes: ADD: 6/90). 🎵
...St John Passion – Ruht wohl. *Coupled with works by various composers.* **New College Choir, Oxford / Edward Higginbottom.** Erato Ⓕ 3984-21659-2 (66 minutes: DDD: 6/98).
Gramophone Editor's choice. See review in the Collections section; refer to the Index.

Bach (attrib.) St Luke Passion, BWV246. **Mona Spägele** (sop); **Christiane Iven** (contr); **Rufus Müller, Harry van Berne** (tens); **Stephan Schreckenberger, Marcus Sandmann** (basses); **Alsfeld Vocal Ensemble; Bremen Baroque Orchestra / Wolfgang Helbich.** CPO Ⓕ CPO999 293-2 (two discs: 106 minutes: DDD: 9/97). 🎵 Text and translation included. Recorded 1996.

Those who love Bach will want to investigate the *St Luke Passion*; we know that Bach performed it at Leipzig at least twice, and evidently admired it for what it is: a succinct and highly competent blend of Lutheran *Kapellmeister* craft and a few fashionable *galant* nuances. In terms of scale, rhetorical intensity, structural and stylistic sophistication, musical invention and artistic ambition generally, this work finds no common ground with Bach's two extant passions. That said, Bach, whose hand appears at the start of the only existing source, judged that a simple, if austere, juxtaposition of chorus-(chorale)-recitative-chorus, with the occasional aria, could hold its own in the traditional deliberations of Leipzig's Holy Week. The modern listener will find much that is intimate and touching about this Passion setting. The meditative element comes less from contemplative arias than from a continuous and freshly fashioned narrative, although the arias, with their favoured wind obbligato parts, are often skilled and affecting. Wolfgang Helbich and his Bremen forces pitch the dramatic climate just about right all the way through. Smoothly articulated, unmannered and technically accomplished, the chorales and *turba* scenes are especially well judged. The Evangelist, Rufus Müller, conveys the Gospel with soft-grained clarity and understated dignity and the other soloists do more than justice to the six arias. Indeed, for all the many qualities of the performance, especially the affectionate contribution of the Alsfeld Vocal Ensemble, this enterprising recording ever sharpens the distinction of Bach and his relatively functional role as Kantor with the parallel workings of his compositional mind. Whether this is Wolfgang Helbich's tacit intention, Bach's genius glows ever brighter.

Bach St Matthew Passion, BWV244. **Anthony Rolfe Johnson** (ten) Evangelist; **Andreas Schmidt** (bar) Jesus; **Barbara Bonney, Ann Monoyios** (sops); **Anne Sofie von Otter** (mez); **Michael Chance** (alto); **Howard Crook** (ten); **Olaf Bär** (bar); **Cornelius Hauptmann** (bass); **London Oratory Junior Choir; Monteverdi Choir; English Baroque Soloists / Sir John Eliot Gardiner.** Archiv Produktion Ⓕ 427 648-2AH3 (three discs: 167 minutes: DDD: 10/89). ✒ Text and translation included.
Gramophone Award Winner 1990. ❸❸❸
What makes John Eliot Gardiner's *St Matthew Passion* stand out in the face of stiff competition is perhaps more than anything his vivid sense of theatre. Bach's score is, after all, a sacred drama and Gardiner interprets this aspect of the work with lively and colourful conviction. That in itself, of course, is not sufficient to ensure a fine performance but here we have a first-rate group of solo voices, immediately responsive choral groups in the Monteverdi Choir and the London Oratory Junior Choir – a distinctive element this – and refined obbligato and orchestral playing from the English Baroque Soloists. Anthony Rolfe Johnson declaims the Evangelist's role with clarity, authority and the subtle inflexion of an accomplished story-teller. Ann Monoyios, Howard Crook and Olaf Bär also make strong contributions but it is Michael Chance's "Erbarme dich", tenderly accompanied by the violin obbligato, which sets the seal of distinction on the performance. Singing and playing of this calibre deserve to win many friends and Gardiner's deeply-felt account of Bach's great Passion does the music considerable justice. Clear recorded sound.
Additional recommendations ...
...**Soloists; Ghent Collegium Vocale; La Chapelle Royale Chorus and Orchestra / Philippe Herreweghe.** Harmonia Mundi Ⓕ HMC90 1155/7 (three discs: 171 minutes: DDD: 11/85). ✒ ❸
...**Soloists; Tölz Boys' Choir; La Petite Bande Men's Chorus and Orchestra / Gustav Leonhardt.** Deutsche Harmonia Mundi Ⓕ RD77848 (three discs: 172 minutes: DDD: 5/90). ✒
...**Soloists; Munich Boys' Choir; Munich Bach Choir; Munich Bach Orchestra / Karl Richter.** Archiv Produktion Ⓜ 439 338-2AX3 (three discs: 197 minutes: ADD: 6/94).
...**Soloists; Hungarian Festival Chorus; Hungarian Radio Children's Choir; Hungarian State Philharmonic Orchestra / Géza Oberfrank.** Naxos Ⓢ 8 550832/4 (three discs: 163 minutes: DDD: 8/94).
...**Soloists; Rheinische Kantorei; Das Kleine Konzert / Hermann Max.** Capriccio Ⓕ 60 046-2 (two discs: 153 minutes: DDD: 7/96). ✒

Bach Christmas Oratorio, BWV248. **Theo Altmeyer** (ten) Evangelist and arias; **Hans Buchhierl** (treb); **Andreas Stein** (boy alto); **Barry McDaniel** (bar); **Tölz Boys' Choir; Collegium Aureum / Gerhard Schmidt-Gaden.** Deutsche Harmonia Mundi Editio Classica Ⓜ GD77046 (three discs: 163 minutes: ADD: 4/88). Notes, text and translation included. From EMI CDS7 49119-8 (4/88). Recorded 1973. ❸
This performance of Bach's *Christmas Oratorio* possesses radiance and spontaneity. It is not without its weaknesses, mainly in passages of insecure instrumental playing; but these are outweighed by its merits chief among which, perhaps, are the contributions, both solo and choral, of the Tölz Boys' Choir. All the soprano and alto solos are sung by boys and in the choruses it is boys rather than countertenors who sing the alto line. Gerhard Schmidt-Gaden effectively relaxes tempos which may at first sound too leisurely to ears accustomed to the frenetic pace chosen by some rival versions. Occasionally, he is a little too slow as, for instance, in the opening chorus of Part Four but for the most part he directs a performance free from intrusive mannerisms which bedevil too many performances of baroque music today. The treble, Hans Buchhierl and the alto, Andreas Stein, are outstanding, and the tenor Theo Altmeyer and the baritone, Barry McDaniel, are hardly less impressive. With its spirit of innocent joy and in its simple but sensitive response to the music this performance comes closer than most to the contemplative heart of Bach's Christmas masterpiece.

Additional recommendations ...

...Soloists; Vienna Boys' Choir; Chorus Viennensis; Vienna Concentus Musicus /
Nikolaus Harnoncourt. Teldec Ⓕ 9031-77610-2 (two discs: 155 minutes: DDD: 12/86). 🎵
...Soloists; Monteverdi Choir; English Baroque Soloists / Sir John Eliot Gardiner.
Archiv Produktion Ⓕ 423 232-2AH2 (two discs: 140 minutes: DDD: 12/87). 🎵
...Soloists; Munich Bach Choir and Orchestra / Karl Richter.
Archiv Produktion Ⓜ 427 236-2AX3 (three discs: 168 minutes: ADD: 3/89).
...Soloists; Ghent Collegium Vocale Chorus and Orchestra / Philippe Herreweghe.
Virgin Classics Veritas Ⓕ VCD7 59530-2 (two discs: 150 minutes: DDD: 12/89). 🎵   Ⓖ
...Soloists; Amsterdam Baroque Choir and Orchestra / Ton Koopman (org).
Erato Ⓕ 0630-14635-2 (two discs: 143 minutes: DDD: 3/97). 🎵

Further listening ...

...Harpsichord Concertos – A major, BWV1055; F minor, BWV1056; F major, BWV1057.
Hae-won Chang (pf); Camerata Cassovia / Robert Stankovsky. Naxos 8 550423.
...Trio Sonatas – D minor, BWV1036; C major, BWV1037; G major, BWV1038; G major,
BWV1039. London Baroque. Harmonia Mundi HMC90 1173 (6/86). 🎵
...Viola da gamba Sonatas – No. 1 in G major, BWV1027; No. 2 in D major, BWV1028; No. 3 in
G minor, BWV1029. Kim Kashkashian (va); Keith Jarrett (hpd).
ECM New Series 445 230-2 (1/95).
...Viola da gamba Sonatas – No. 1 in G major, BWV1027; No. 2 in D major, BWV1028; No. 3 in
G minor, BWV1029. *Coupled with works by* C.P.E. Bach *and* W.F. Bach Nobuko Imai (va);
Roland Pöntinen (hpd). Philips 454 449-2PH (4/98).
...Jauchzet dem Herrn, alle Welt, BWV Anh160. *Coupled with works by various members of the
Bach Family.* Trinity College Choir, Cambridge; Rickman Godlee (vc); Christopher Allsop (org) /
Richard Marlow. Conifer Classics 75605 51306-2 (11/97). *See review in the Collections section;
refer to the Index.*
...Easter Oratorio, BWV249. Cantata No. 66, Erfreut euch, ihr Herzen. Barbara Schlick
(sop); Kai Wessel (alto); James Taylor (ten); Peter Kooy (bass); Collegium Vocale /
Philippe Herreweghe. Harmonia Mundi HMC90 1513 (5/95). 🎵   Ⓖ
...St Mark Passion, BWV247 (ed. Heighes). Soloists; Ring Ensemble of Finland;
European Union Baroque Orchestra / Roy Goodman. Musica Oscura 070970 (2/97). 🎵
Complete Organ Works:
...Kevin Boyer (org) – *Volume 1*, Nimbus NI5377 (2/94). *Volume 2*, Nimbus NI5289 (3/93).
...Michel Chapuis (org) – Auvidis Valois V4425-2 (1-4). *Also available separately.*
...Hans Fagius (org) – *Volume 1*, BIS CD235/6 (11/86). *Volume 2*, BIS CD308/9. *Volume 3*, BIS
CD329/30. *Volume 4*, BIS CD343/4 (10/91). *Volume 5*, BIS CD379/80. *Volume 6*, BIS CD397/8.
Volume 7, BIS CD439/40 (10/91). *Volume 8*, BIS CD443/4. *Volume 9*, BIS CD445 (10/91).
...André Isoir (org) – Calliope CAL9703/17 (*Volumes 1-5*, 2/93). *Volume 6*, CAL9708. *Volume 7*,
CAL9709. *Volume 8*, CAL9710 (8/89). *Volume 9*, CAL9711 (4/88). *Volume 10*, CAL9712.
Volume 12, CAL9714. *Volume 13*, CAL9715. *Volume 14*, CAL9716. *Volume 15*, CAL9717.

Wilhelm Friedemann Bach

German 1710-1784

W.F. Bach Sinfonias – D major, F64; D minor, F65; F major, F67, "Dissonance". Suite in
G minor, BWV1070 (attrib.). Harpsichord Concerto in D major, F41ª. ªCharlotte Nediger (hpd);
Tafelmusik / Jeanne Lamon (vn). Sony Classical Vivarte Ⓕ SK62720 (72 minutes: DDD: 2/98).
🎵 Recorded 1996.   Ⓖ
The well-known painting of W.F. Bach reproduced on the cover of this CD must be one of the most
immediately attractive composer portraits ever made. The wide-brimmed hat, the fur-lined coat, the
wisp of steely hair and, above all, the reddened but unmistakable genial face (displaying what looks
like his father's nose) suggest a man one would want to accompany straight away to the nearest coffee-
house. But Friedemann was actually a little more complex than that, both as a person who could be
lazy and argumentative and as a talented musician torn between the styles of the late baroque and
early classical periods, so it is perhaps no surprise to find that there is considerable variety in the music
on this disc. The opening Sinfonia in D major is one of those sunnily optimistic works that revel in
the splendid new sound of the classical orchestra, but the D minor Sinfonia which follows is a highly
serious piece for church use, containing a solemnly drooping fugue. There is also an Ouverture-Suite
once attributed (pretty implausibly) to Johann Sebastian which, though undeniably attractive and
individual, is now thought unlikely to be by Friedemann either; a quirkily expressive but perhaps
rather rambling harpsichord concerto; and a by-now familiarly protean and surprise-filled Sinfonia in
F major. Tafelmusik are the perfect ensemble to perform this music. Like much of it, they delight
in sheer orchestral sound, enjoying the advantage themselves of being able to turn it out in
particularly pleasing and well-finished form. Recommended to any lover of eighteenth-century
orchestral music.

Additional recommendation ...

...Harpsichord Concertos – F41; F minor, F44; A minor, F45. London Baroque.
Harmonia Mundi Ⓕ HMC90 1558 (54 minutes: DDD: 5/96). 🎵

Further listening ...
...Adagio and Fugue in D minor, F65. Duetto for Two Flutes in E minor, F54. *Coupled with works by various composers.* **Florilegium.** Channel Classics CCS9096 (7/96). *See review in the Collections section; refer to the Index.*
...Double Harpsichord Concerto in E flat major, F46. *Coupled with works by* **J.C. Bach** and **C.P.E. Bach Anneke Uittenbosch, Alan Curtis** (hpds); **Leonhardt Consort, Vienna Concentus Musicus / Gustav Leonhardt.** Teldec Das Alte Werk 0630-12326-2 (9/96). ✏
...Double Keyboard Concerto in F major, F10. *Coupled with works by various composers.* **Christopher Hogwood, Christophe Rousset** (hpds/clavs/fps). L'Oiseau-Lyre 440 649-2OH (8/96). ✏ *See review in the Collections section; refer to the Index.*
...Sinfonia in F major. *Coupled with* **C.P.E. Bach** Sinfonias, H663-6 – No. 1 in D major; No. 2 in E flat major; No. 3 in F major; No. 4 in G major. **Salzburg Chamber Philharmonic Orchestra / Yoon K. Lee.** Naxos 8 553289 (4/96). *Gramophone Editor's choice. See review under C.P.E. Bach; refer to the Index.* ⓖ
...Viola Sonata in C minor (arr. Pessl). *Coupled with works by* **C.P.E. Bach** and **J.S. Bach** **Nobuko Imai** (va); **Roland Pöntinen** (hpd). Philips 454 449-2PH (6/98).
...Eight Fugues, F31. Chorales – Nun komm der Heiden Heiland; Christe, der du bist Tag und Licht; Jesu, meine Freude; Wir, Christenleut. *Coupled with works by various members of the Bach Family.* **Marie-Claire Alain** (org). Erato 0630-17073-2 (A/97). *See review in the Collections section; refer to the Index.*
...Cantatas, Volume 1 – Lasset uns ablegen die Werke der Finsternis, F80; Es ist eine Stimme eines Predigers in der Wüste, F89. **Barbara Schlick** (sop); **Claudia Schubert** (contr); **Wilfried Jochens** (ten); **Stephan Schreckenberger** (bass); **Rheinische Kantorei; Das Kleine Konzert / Hermann Max.** Capriccio 10 425 (11/94). ✏ ⓖⓖ
...Cantatas, Volume 2 – Sinfonia in D major, F64; Dies ist der Tag, F85[a]; Erzittert und fallet, F83[a]. [a]**Barbara Schlick** (sop); [a]**Claudia Schubert** (contr); [a]**Wilfried Jochens** (ten); [a]**Stephan Schreckenberger** (bass); [a]**Rheinische Kantorei; Das Kleine Konzert / Hermann Max.** Capriccio 10 426 (11/94). ✏ ⓖⓖ
...Keyboard Sonatas – G major, F7; No. 2 in A major, F8; No. 7 in C major, F2. Eight Fugues, F31. March, F30. Prelude, F29. Suite in G minor, F24. **Christophe Rousset** (hpd). Harmonia Mundi Musique d'abord ⓑ HMA190 1305 (65 minutes: DDD: 8/94). ✏

Daniel Bacheler
British ?c1574-after 1610

Suggested listening ...
...The Earl of Essex Galliard, P89 (arr.). *Coupled with works by various composers.* **Paul O'Dette** (lte). Harmonia Mundi HMU90 7164 (7/97). *See review under Dowland; refer to the Index.*

Ernst Bacon
American 1898-1923

Suggested listening ...
...One thought ever at the fire. *Coupled with works by various composers.* **Thomas Hampson** (bar); **Craig Rutenberg** (pf). EMI CDM5 55028-2 (10/97). *See review in the Collections section; refer to the Index.* ⓖⓖⓖ

Simon Bainbridge
British 1952

Suggested listening ...
...Henry's Mobile. *Coupled with works by various composers.* **Fretwork.** Virgin Classics VC5 45217-2 (12/97). *See review in the Collections section; refer to the Index.*

William Baines
British 1899-1922

Baines The chimes. Paradise gardens. Seven Preludes. Coloured Leaves. Silverpoints. Idyll. Tides. The naiad. Twilight Pieces. Pool-Lights. Etude in F sharp minor. **Eric Parkin** (pf). Priory ⑤ PRCD550 (73 minutes: DDD: 9/97). Recorded 1995.
The name William Baines may be unfamiliar to many readers but he should certainly be placed among the major figures in English piano music in the early part of this century. The output he produced during his tragically short life is truly phenomenal. Not only did he compose a remarkable amount of very fine and highly original piano music, but he also produced a Symphony, a *concertante* work for piano and orchestra, a tone-poem entitled *The Island of the Fay* after an Edgar Allan Poe poem, as well as a dozen or so songs. This is only the second commercial recording ever made of his music (Eric Parkin also recorded a volume of piano music for Lyrita back in the 1970s) so Priory are to be greatly applauded for their vision and enterprise in releasing this long overdue tribute. Baines

fell under the spell of of Scriabin and Cyril Scott early on in his musical development but one need only sample, say, the evocative seascape "Goodnight to Flambro" from *Tides* or the shimmering *Pool-Lights* to realize just how fast Baines assimilated these influences into his own personal voice. All of the pieces presented on this disc are delightful, but you could single out the beautiful *Paradise gardens*, *Tides*, *Twilight Pieces* and the *Seven Preludes* of 1919 as representing Baines at his most inspired. Parkin, who of course is no stranger to this music, plays beautifully and with conviction, and the recorded sound is good, if a little hard-edged in some of the more forceful passages. If you have the slightest interest in English music you are urged to explore this very rewarding disc.

Sir Edward Bairstow
British 1874-1946

Suggested listening ...
...The Lamentation. Psalm 114, When Israel came out of Egypt. *Coupled with works by various composers.* **St Paul's Cathedral Choir / John Scott** with **Andrew Lucas** (org).
Hyperion CDA66916 (A/97). *See review in the Collections section; refer to the Index.*

Mily Balakirev
Russian 1837-1910

Balakirev Piano Concertos – No. 1 in F sharp major, Op. 1; No. 2 in E flat major, Op. posth.
Rimsky-Korsakov Piano Concerto in C sharp minor, Op. 30. **Malcolm Binns** (pf); **English Northern Philharmonia / David Lloyd-Jones.** Hyperion Ⓔ CDA66640 (61 minutes: DDD: 7/93). Recorded 1992.   Ⓖ
'Op. 1' and 'Op. posth.' say a lot about Balakirev's two piano concertos. The First is a single movement only, composed at the age of 18 and massively indebted to the Chopin concertos. The Second was begun not long after, in 1861, but abandoned after the first movement; he was only persuaded to write the other movements down near the end of his life. At his death in 1910 the finale had to be completed by Lyapunov, which may be partly why it sounds so splendidly rambunctious, so close in places, to Gershwin. The concerto was certainly worth the efforts of all concerned; the first movement's fugal episodes and the slow movement's tinges of Russian Orthodox gloom stay in the mind, compensating for Balakirev's occasional recourse to inflating and overdecorating short sub-phrases. The First Concerto, too, has little flashes of individuality which keep you listening despite the obvious naïvety and derivative quality of the material. The Rimsky-Korsakov has come and gone from the catalogue over the years. It is in effect more of a folk-song fantasia than a concerto, but there is much post-Liszt-and-Griegian charm, as well as a striking foretaste of Rachmaninov's *Paganini* Rhapsody (Paganini's famous opening motif coincidentally also begins the second strain of Rimsky's chosen theme). These three works make an excellent programme, then. And Malcolm Binns, though not the most sparkling of soloists, plays with commendable solidity. The quality of the orchestra's contribution is high, and all in all this is an admirably conceived and executed disc.

Balakirev Symphonies – No. 1 in C major[a]; No. 2 in D minor[b]. [a]**USSR State Symphony Orchestra / Evgeni Svetlanov;** [b]**USSR State Radio and TV Grand Symphony Orchestra / Gennadi Rozhdestvensky.** Revelation Ⓜ RV10038 (74 minutes: ADD: 10/97). Item marked [a] recorded live in 1974, [b]1973.
These recordings were made by Soviet Radio. Svetlanov was subsequently to re-record both symphonies in richer, more spacious sound for Hyperion, and there is no doubt that, both in terms of orchestral finesse and recorded sound, these later versions score higher marks. But when it comes to vitality and excitement the Soviet performances win hands down. Rhythms are crisp and well lifted and the readings have the urgency one expects of Russian music-making. The trumpets and trombones are blatant, but even that adds to the bite. At the gentle opening of the C major Symphony the violins shape their cantilena with allure, and when one comes to the *Andante* the listener is immediately transported to the exotically sinuous world of Rimsky-Korsakov. The effect is ravishing, with richly coloured wind solos following one another glowingly, and the strings hardly less enticing. The performance is unforgettable, both for its orchestral palette and heavy romanticism; the exotic woodwind return in the dancing finale, the oriental flavour becoming more and more insistent. The Second Symphony has been described as a paler copy of the First. Here the opening movement under Rozhdestvensky's baton generates much Slavic energy; tuttis are more noticeably brash, but they are certainly not dull. Both symphonies have a second movement scherzo; that in the Second is marked *alla cosacca* and Rozhdestvensky makes the most of its rumbustious character, whereas in the First, Svetlanov has sought out the movement's charm. In the repetitive *Polacca* finale the brazen Russian brass become a little wearing, although the performance retains a genial, spirited character. In short, both readings are strongly characterized and enjoyably full of life; the stereo is warm and vivid, if lacking something in amplitude; but one feels the composer himself would have been well pleased with the results.
Additional recommendations ...
...No. 1. Russia – symphonic poem. **Philharmonia Orchestra / Evgeni Svetlanov.**
Hyperion Ⓔ CDA66493 (60 minutes: DDD: 12/91).

...No. 2. Tamara – symphonic poem. Overture on the themes of three Russian songs.
  Philharmonia Orchestra / Evgeni Svetlanov. Hyperion Ⓕ CDA66586 (68 minutes: DDD: 9/92).
...No. 2. Russia – symphonic poem. **Russian State Symphony Orchestra / Igor Golovschin.**
  Naxos Ⓢ 8 550793 (54 minutes: DDD: 9/94).
Further listening ...
...Fantasy on themes from Glinka's "A Life for the Tsar". *Coupled with works by* **Paderewski**
  and **Scharwenka** Earl Wild (pf); **London Symphony Orchestra / Arthur Fiedler.**
  Elan CD82266 (7/96).   Ⓖ
...La Fileuse. Scherzo No. 2 in B flat minor. Mazurkas – No. 6 in A flat major; No. 7 in E flat
  minor. Spanish Melody. Polka in F sharp minor. Nocturne No. 2 in B minor. Tarantella in
  B major. Waltz No. 4 in B flat major. Valse mélancholique. Fantasy on themes from Glinka's
  "A Life for the Tsar". **Nicholas Walker** (pf). ASV CDDCA940 (11/96).
...Islamey. *Coupled with works by various composers.* **Boris Berezovsky** (pf).
  Teldec 4509-96516-2 (7/96). *See reviews in the Collections section; refer to the Index.*
...20 Songs – The bright moon; My heart is torn; Song of Selim; When I hear thy voice. Three
  Forgotten Songs – Thou art so captivating; Spanish song. 10 Songs – Over the lake; I loved him.
  Coupled with works by various composers. **Olga Borodina** (mez); **Larissa Gergieva** (pf).
  Philips 442 780-2PH (8/95).
...Thou art so captivating. Barcarolle. Look, my friend. *Coupled with works by various composers.*
  Sergei Larin (ten); **Eleonora Bekova** (pf). Chandos CHAN9547 (6/97).

Pietro Baldassare   Italian c1690-c1768

Suggested listening ...
...Sonata for Cornett, Strings and Continuo in F major (transcribed for trumpet). *Coupled with
  works by various composers.* **Håkan Hardenberger** (tpt); **I Musici.** Philips 442 131-2PH (5/95).
  See review in the Collections section; refer to the Index.   Ⓖ

Adriano Banchieri   Italian 1568-1634

Banchieri Il zabaione musicale. Festino nella sera del giovedì grasso avanti cena, Op. 18. **Lugano
  Radio Svizzera Choir; Sonatori de la Gioiosa Marca, Treviso / Diego Fasolis.** Naxos Ⓢ 8 553785
  (62 minutes: DDD: 4/98). Texts and translations included. Recorded in 1995.
How far a sixteenth-century *zabaione* resembled the dessert we know and enjoy today is unsure. But
it's an appetizing title for a light, jolly, pastoral entertainment which must have accommodated some
sort of staging. This kind of event seems to have been a speciality of Banchieri's (whose *Barca di
Venetia per Padova* exists today in several fine recordings). The accompanying *Festino* is a longer work
in a similar vein, and includes both a solo for Jews' harp and a chorus of cat, dog, owl and cuckoo
improvising over a *cantus firmus*. This is the sort of jollification that took place at the ducal court of
Munich in 1568, at which Lassus dressed up as one of the characters from the *commedia dell'arte*.
Incidentally, those familiar with Lassus's *villanelle* will recognize the same musical idiom in much of
Banchieri's score: it is undemanding but varied, well made and very amusing. The same might be said
of these performances, which successfully convey the impression of a staged element (though it's
uncertain whether the titles of successive sections are intended to be declaimed alongside the linking
texts between them, which clearly are). The ensemble consists of a dozen singers at most, with a small
group of strings and continuo. There is no more information to hand, since Naxos's fairly detailed
notes give the musicians no individual credit. At barely more than the cost of the edible variety in the
average restaurant, this *zabaione* is well worth sampling.

Sir Granville Bantock   British 1868-1946

Bantock Violin Sonata No. 3 in C major.
Dunhill Violin Sonata in F major, Op. 50.
Stanford Violin Sonata in D major, Op. 11. **Susanne Stanzeleit** (vn); **Gusztáv Fenyö** (pf).
  Cala United Ⓕ CACD88031 (76 minutes: DDD: 7/96). Recorded 1994.
All Anglophiles should investigate this disc. The last of Sir Granville Bantock's three violin sonatas
(completed in 1940) is a lyrically serene, touchingly unaffected outpouring, whose spare-textured,
intimate manner and clean-limbed concision will surprise those who know Bantock only through his
vast, bewitchingly colourful orchestral canvases. The disc opens with the fluent and engaging Second
Sonata of Thomas F. Dunhill (1877-1946). As befits the work of a composition pupil of Stanford at
the Royal College of Music, it is an impeccably crafted, highly mellifluous affair, featuring a central
Adagio lamentoso of no mean depth and grave nobility (the piece was written during the First World
War). Stanford's own First Sonata (an early effort dating from around 1880) also makes very
agreeable listening. Again, the writing is always skilful and melodious and, again, it's the passionate
Allegretto moderato slow movement which stands out. Performances and recordings are persuasive.

Bantock Sappho[a]. Sapphic Poem[b]. [a]**Susan Bickley** (mez); [b]**Julian Lloyd Webber** (vc); **Royal Philharmonic Orchestra / Vernon Handley.** Hyperion Ⓔ CDA66899 (75 minutes: DDD: 11/97). Text included. Recorded 1997. *Gramophone Editor's choice.*

Sappho was the fourth in a series of exotic song-cycles with piano accompaniment Bantock composed from 1898 to 1905. The orchestral version (subtitled "Prelude and Nine Fragments") lasts around an hour and Bantock would appear to have scored individual songs as and when they were first heard in the concert-hall. *Sappho* derives its text from the tiny, but enormously influential output of the eponymous Greek poetess – or rather, from a free refashioning of the fragments by the composer's wife, Helen, into a dramatically effective sequence of nine poems. Prefaced by a magnificently imposing orchestral introduction, it is a hugely ambitious, yet curiously compelling outpouring, by turns yearningly passionate, ecstatic, sensuous and darkly jealous to mirror the capricious emotions of the lovesick Sappho herself. Elsewhere, it's difficult not to be hugely impressed by the positively Wagnerian intensity and profound emotional scope of Bantock's writing in the fifth song, "The moon has set". Note, too, the psychological insight in the last stanza of the second song, "I loved thee once, Atthis, long ago", where Bantock's colouring of the phrase "Thou art nought to me" acutely conveys the resignatory self-deception of the poetess's true feelings. Certainly, *Sappho* can be viewed as an intoxicating celebration of love in all its guises. Some may find Bantock's inspiration too relentlessly wan and lacking in truly memorable thematic invention; others will revel in its endearing decadence. No praise can be too high for Susan Bickley's remarkable assumption of what sounds like an exceedingly tricky vocal part (with its demandingly wide tessitura); Handley and the RPO, too, cover themselves in glory. The 15-minute *Sapphic Poem* for cello and orchestra acts as a wholly charming pendant to the main work. Delicately scored (with some lovely touches for the woodwind in particular) and beautifully conceived for the medium, it is a richly melodious, sweetly expressive outpouring, raptly performed here by Julian Lloyd Webber, who in turn receives exemplary support from Handley and the RPO.

Further listening ...
...Atalanta in Calydon. Vanity of vanities. **BBC Singers / Simon Joly.** Albany TROY180 (9/96).
...Celtic Symphony. The Witch of Atlas. The Sea Reivers. Hebridean Symphony.
  Royal Philharmonic Orchestra / Vernon Handley. Hyperion CDA66450 (5/91).
...Pagan Symphony. Fifine at the Fair. Two Heroic Ballads. **Royal Philharmonic Orchestra /**
  Vernon Handley. Hyperion CDA66630 (3/93).   Ⓖ

Seymour Barab   American 1921

Suggested listening ...
...One Perfect Rose. *Coupled with works by various composers.* **Dame Felicity Lott** (sop);
  Graham Johnson (pf). Hyperion CDA66937 (10/97). *See review in the Collections section;*
  refer to the Index.

Bartolomeo Barbarino   Italian before 1593-*c*1617

Suggested listening ...
...Audi, dulcis amica mea. Ardens est cor meum. *Coupled with works by* **G. Gabrieli**
  Gabrieli Consort and Players / Paul McCreesh. Archiv Produktion 449 180-2AH (1/97).
  Gramophone Editor's choice. See review under G. Gabrieli; refer to the Index.   Ⓖ

Samuel Barber   American 1910-1981

Barber Cello Concerto, Op. 22[a]. Violin Concerto, Op. 14[b]. Capricorn Concerto, Op. 21[c]. [a]**Steven**
  Isserlis (vc); [b]**Kyoko Takezawa** (vn); [c]**Jacob Berg** (fl); [c]**Peter Bowman** (ob); [c]**Susan Slaughter** (tpt);
  St Louis Symphony Orchestra / Leonard Slatkin. RCA Victor Red Seal Ⓔ 09026 68283-2
  (65 minutes: DDD: 5/96). Recorded 1994-5.   Ⓖ

The Cello Concerto is a restless work touched through and through by the shock, uncertainty and fragile optimism of a world just coming out of war. Steven Isserlis is in many respects just the player for the piece. His agility is a boon in ensuring that it never becomes overly strenuous, that its capriciousness, its touches of irony (all those quizzical pizzicato *glissandos* and harmonics) are not lost in the shadows. The slow movement's cantilena really does warm to his personal touch, his long, canonic duet with oboe for once not a mismatch. Isserlis's cello is the lightest of Lieder baritones with the flexibility and imagination to fine-spin phrases as very few can and do. Listen to his withdrawal into the heart of the slow movement. Isserlis reflecting, Isserlis lost in thought, is always special. Kyoko Takezawa is not a player to keep much to herself. The casual opening page of the Violin Concerto, starting as it does mid sentence through a shared confidence, is soon impatient to go public. Her sound – intense and focused – seems to reach way beyond the length of each phrase. She is mindful, too, of the fiercer contrasts, seeking always to maximize them. It's a very 'operatic' performance, the lyric and dramatic elements grippingly interacted. The big 'aria' – in which the first oboe gets to be the envy of all the surrounding players – comes, of course, with that ravishing principal subject of the slow movement, and when Takezawa does finally come to embrace it, the feeling of release, of fulfilment, is worth the wait. Slatkin responds with a full-throated tutti in the strings. All of which is wickedly offset by that mad highland fling of a finale, twirling woodwinds and fractured trumpet fanfares as belligerent as you could wish. Between the two main courses comes the sorbet. Barber's *Capricorn Concerto* (for flute, oboe, trumpet and strings) is a playful *concerto grosso* for the New World, a sharp take on baroque procedures, a streetwise *Brandenburg* No. 2.

Additional recommendation ...
...Cello Concerto. **Shostakovich** Cello Concerto No. 1 in E flat major, Op. 107. **Raphael Wallfisch** (vc); **English Chamber Orchestra / Geoffrey Simon.** Chandos Ⓕ CHAN8322 (DDD: 2/85).

Barber Violin Concerto, Op. 14.
Bloch Baal Shem.
Walton Violin Concerto in B minor. **Joshua Bell** (vn); **Baltimore Symphony Orchestra /**
David Zinman. Decca Ⓕ 452 851-2DH (68 minutes: DDD: 7/97). Recorded 1996.
Gramophone Editor's choice.   ⒼⒼⒼ
Joshua Bell's coupling of the Barber Violin Concerto with Walton and Bloch brings together three highly romantic *concertante* works. In the Barber, Bell is placed less forward than in the rich-sounding recordings of Gil Shaham and Itzhak Perlman, but if anything the results are even more intense. In the central slow movement the opening oboe solo leads to a magically hushed first entry for the violin, and the balance of the soloist also allows a quicksilver lightness for the rushing triplets in the *moto perpetuo* finale. Shaham may find more humour in that brief movement, but Bell's view is equally valid. From an American perspective, Walton can well be seen as Barber's British counterpart. The playing of this American orchestra is warmly idiomatic, defying the idea that non-British orchestras find Walton difficult. Bell gives a commanding account of the solo part – his expansive treatment of the central cadenza of the first movement, making it more deeply reflective – is most appealing. Not just there but in many gentle moments the rapt intensity of his playing is magnetic. Bell's is among the finest versions ever, with Bloch's own 1939 orchestration of *Baal Shem* offering a fine, unusual makeweight.

Additional recommendations ...
...Violin Concerto[a]. **Korngold** Violin Concerto, Op. 35[a]. Much ado about nothing, Op. 11[b] – The maiden in the bridal chamber; Dogberry and Verges; Intermezzo; Hornpipe. **Gil Shaham** (vn);
[a]**London Symphony Orchestra / André Previn** ([b]pf).
DG Ⓕ 439 886-2GH (71 minutes: DDD: 9/94). *Gramophone Editor's choice.*   Ⓖ
...Violin Concerto. *Coupled with works by* **Bernstein** *and* **Foss** Itzhak Perlman (vn); **Boston Symphony Orchestra / Seiji Ozawa.** EMI Ⓕ CDC5 55360-2 (67 minutes: DDD: 6/95).   Ⓖ

Barber Violin Concerto, Op. 14[a]. Piano Concerto, Op. 38[b]. Adagio for Strings, Op. 11[c]. Essay for Orchestra No. 2, Op. 17[d]. The School for Scandal Overture, Op. 5[d]. [a]**Isaac Stern** (vn); [b]**John Browning** (pf); [ad]**New York Philharmonic Orchestra /** [a]**Leonard Bernstein,** [d]**Thomas Schippers;** [b]**Cleveland Orchestra / George Szell;** [c]**Philadelphia Orchestra / Eugene Ormandy.** Sony Classical Theta Ⓜ SMK60004 (74 minutes: ADD: 2/98). Item marked [a] from CBS SBRG72345 (9/65), [b]Columbia SAX2575 (7/65), [c]Philips ABL3200 (3/58), [d]CBS 61898. Recorded 1964-5.   Ⓖ
Isaac Stern's 1964 recording of the Barber Violin Concerto with Bernstein and the New York Philharmonic was the recording which belatedly gave this warmly expressive masterpiece the international currency it plainly deserved. It was written at very much the same period, just as the Second World War was beginning, as two British works with which it has clear links, the violin concertos of both Walton and Britten, both also dating from 1939. The superb performance from Stern and Bernstein can stand comparison with any version since, easily fluent in the two lyrical movements, demonically intense in the *moto perpetuo* finale. That movement, initially disappointing as a resolution to the first two, may not match the finales of the Walton and Britten in weight, but it certainly makes a powerful conclusion here. The only reservation is that with close-up CBS sound for the soloist you rarely get a true *pianissimo*. Even more welcome, when it has long been unavailable, is John Browning's première recording of the Piano Concerto. This is an interpretation of the highest voltage, the more daring and bitingly intense for having been recorded after a long series of performances on tour, full of bravura, with recorded sound rather fuller and more clean than that of the Violin Concerto. Ormandy's resonant recording of the *Adagio*, taken at a flowing speed, and Schippers's dazzling, tautly controlled accounts of the *Essay* No. 2 and the Overture, also well transferred, make this an ideal disc for anyone wanting to investigate Barber at his finest.

Additional recommendations ...
...Essays for Orchestra – No. 1, Op. 12; No. 2; No. 3, Op. 47. **Ives** Symphony No. 1.
Detroit Symphony Orchestra / Neeme Järvi. Chandos Ⓕ CHAN9053 (70 minutes: DDD: 3/92).
...Essay for Orchestra No. 2. Adagio for Strings. A Hand of Bridge. Music for a Scene from Shelley, Op. 7. A Stopwatch and an Ordnance map, Op. 15. Serenade for String Orchestra, Op. 1. Let Down the Bars, O Death, Op. 82 No. 2. **Soloists; Robert De Cormier Chorale; Washington DC Cathedral Choir; Zagreb Soloists / Antonio Janigro; Symphony of the Air, New York / Vladimir Golschmann.** Vanguard Classics Ⓜ 08.4016.71 (52 minutes: ADD: 8/92).

...Adagio for Strings. Medea's Meditation and Dance of Vengeance, Op. 23. *Coupled with works by various composers.* **Boston Symphony Orchestra / Charles Munch.**
RCA Victor Gold Seal Ⓜ 09026 61424-2 (61 minutes: ADD: 9/93).
...Adagio for Strings. Symphony No. 2, Op. 19. *Coupled with* **Bristow** Symphony No. 2 in F sharp minor, Op. 26. **Detroit Symphony Orchestra / Neeme Järvi.**
Chandos Ⓕ CHAN9169 (73 minutes: DDD: 10/93).

Barber Symphony No. 1, Op. 9. The School for Scandal Overture, Op. 5.
Beach Symphony in E minor, Op. 32, "Gaelic". **Detroit Symphony Orchestra / Neeme Järvi.**
Chandos Ⓕ CHAN8958 (72 minutes: DDD: 10/91). Recorded 1991. Ⓖ
Amy Beach (or Mrs H.H.A. Beach, as she was known professionally in her lifetime) was born in Henniker, New Hampshire in 1867. By all accounts she was a prodigiously talented youngster – she could sing 40 tunes by the age of two, and at four she was composing small pieces for the piano. She made her 'official' début as a pianist at the age of 16 playing Chopin's Rondo in E flat major and Moscheles's G minor Piano Concerto, but after her marriage to a noted Boston surgeon in 1885 she abandoned her concert career and devoted her time exclusively to composition. The *Gaelic* Symphony (her only work in the genre) dates from 1896. Like Dvořák's *New World* Symphony, which had received its American première just a few years earlier, it draws its inspiration from folk material; though Beach's sources are drawn not from native America but rather from her Gaelic forebears. The writing reveals a remarkable degree of craftsmanship and maturity, and although the music contains perhaps more imitation than originality (Brahms, Tchaikovsky and Parry spring to mind) there is nevertheless plenty of enjoyment to be had from this fresh and engaging work. Barber's First Symphony made a welcome return after a protracted absence from the catalogue. Slatkin's account might in some ways be more satisfactory as his orchestra seems more comfortable, and the American conductor clearly has an innate grasp of the music's style. This one-movement, highly compact work deserves to be much better known as it contains some of Barber's most invigorating and memorable material. Stylistically it finds allegiance with the post-romanticism of symphonies such as Walton's First and Howard Hanson's Second (*Romantic*). The disc also includes Barber's equally engaging Overture to *The School for Scandal*. Committed performances.
Additional recommendations ...
...No. 1[a]. Piano Concerto, Op. 38[b]. Souvenirs, Op. 28[c]. [bc]**John Browning** (pf);
[ab]**St Louis Symphony Orchestra / Leonard Slatkin** ([c]pf).
RCA Victor Red Seal Ⓕ RD60732 (70 minutes: DDD: 11/91). Ⓖ
...No. 1. Adagio for Strings. Essays for Orchestra Nos. 1 and 2. Music for a Scene from Shelley, Op. 7. School for Scandal Overture. **Baltimore Symphony Orchestra / David Zinman.**
Argo Ⓕ 436 288-2ZH (64 minutes: DDD: 1/93).

Barber String Quartet, Op. 11.
Britten String Quartet No. 2 in C major, Op. 36.
Takemitsu A Way A Lone. **Tokyo Quartet** (Peter Oundjian, Kikuei Ikeda, vns; Kazuhide Isomura, va; Sadao Harada, vc). RCA Victor Red Seal Ⓕ 09026 61387-2 (61 minutes: DDD: 2/94).
Recorded 1992. ⒼⒼ
Three very different minds grappling with the intricacies of four-way musical dialogue. Takemitsu, a habitual aesthete wandering in the thick of sensual Bergian textures; Barber, a compelling New World romantic revelling among memories of Dvořák and, perhaps, Nielsen; and then Britten, a bold, incandescent voice in prime condition, proclaiming during the year (1945) that also witnessed *Peter Grimes* and *The Holy Sonnets of John Donne*. All are summoned among the sonorous ranks of the Tokyo Quartet for performances that combine rigour, warmth and textual acuity. It's a compelling mix, the standard of playing is uniformly high, the recording pleasingly full-bodied and the programme itself well chosen, offering "the responses of three composers to the challenge of tradition".
Additional recommendations ...
...String Quartet. *Coupled with works by various composers.* **Lindsay Quartet.** ASV Ⓕ CDDCA825 (77 minutes: ADD: 1/93). *See review in the Collections section; refer to the Index.*
...String Quartet – Adagio. *Coupled with works by various composers.* **Dumisani Maraire** (ngoma/hosho); **Astor Piazzolla** (bandoneon); **Patty Manning, John Taylor, Larry Caballero** (vocs); **Djivan Gasparian** (duduk); **Kronos Quartet.** Nonesuch Ⓕ 7559-79394-2 (two discs: 101 minutes: DDD: 2/96). *See review in the Collections section; refer to the Index.*

Barber Ballade, Op. 46. Excursions, Op. 20. Nocturne, Op. 33. Piano Sonata, Op. 26. Souvenirs, Op. 28. **Eric Parkin** (pf). Chandos Ⓕ CHAN9177 (63 minutes: DDD: 10/93). Recorded 1992.
This is not quite the Complete Works for Solo Piano, as claimed in the title, nor is it "the entire output for solo piano, save for a single childhood essay" as stated in the booklet. This is the complete published piano music, apart from *Three Sketches*, and there are quite a lot of unpublished pieces. None of this matters when the playing is as polished and sympathetic as Parkin's. He responds wonderfully to the nostalgic melancholia of Barber. The ballet score, *Souvenirs*, is available in the orchestral and piano-duet versions, but this solo piano treatment is just as engaging. Parkin knows exactly how to present this side of Barber and his treatment of the *Four Excursions* based on different

popular idioms is equally convincing. A performer as well versed as Parkin in British post-romantics such as Ireland and Bax finds home ground again in Barber's *Nocturne* and the late *Ballade*. In Barber's classic, the Sonata, Parkin is in competition with several other recordings including Horowitz's. Parkin treats the work lyrically and never forces us to regard the finale, especially, as a hard-hitting block-buster in the way that so many young pianists do. He is transparent in the scherzo; sings in the *Adagio*; and the final fugue subject has exactly the catchy, swinging quality that many players miss. At times there is a lack of brilliance, which the rather dull recording emphasizes, but this is a winning anthology of this major American romantic.

Additional recommendation ...
...Piano Sonata. *Coupled with works by various composers.* **Vladimir Horowitz** (pf).
RCA Victor Gold Seal mono/stereo Ⓜ GD60377* (65 minutes: ADD: 7/94).   ⊖⊖⊖

Barber Twelfth Night, Op. 42 No. 1. To be sung on the water, Op. 42 No. 2. Reincarnations, Op. 16. Agnus Dei, Op. 11. Heaven-Haven. Sure on this shining night[a]. The monk and his cat[a]. The Virgin Martyrs, Op. 8 No. 1. Let down the bars, O Death, Op. 8 No. 2. God's Grandeur.
Schuman Perceptions. Mail Order Madrigals. [a]**Anthony Saunders** (pf); **The Joyful Company of Singers / Peter Broadbent.** ASV Ⓕ CDDCA939 (66 minutes: DDD: 11/96). Texts included. Recorded 1995.

Newcomers should make haste to track 6 for a pleasant surprise. Here they will encounter Samuel Barber's indestructible *Adagio* in its alternative and mellifluous 1967 vocal guise, set to the text of the *Agnus Dei*. Peter Broadbent's Joyful Company of Singers acquit themselves extremely well. Elsewhere, one particularly relishes the exquisite Op. 42 pairing of *Twelfth Night* and *To be sung on the water*, the carefree lilt of *The monk and his cat* and, above all, the majestic, strikingly ambitious 1938 setting of Gerald Manley Hopkins's sonnet, *God's Grandeur* (perhaps the single most impressive achievement on the disc). Further delights are provided by Barber's countryman and contemporary, William Schuman. The concise, beautifully sculpted *Perceptions* (1982) are settings of choice aphorisms from the pen of Walt Whitman, while the *Mail Order Madrigals* (1972) wittily utilize the flowery prose drawn from advertisements contained within a Sears and Roebuck catalogue of 1897. A most attractive issue, in short, excellently produced and engineered.

Additional recommendation ...
...Agnus Dei, Op. 11. *Coupled with works by* **Bernstein** and **Copland** Corydon Singers / **Matthew Best.** Hyperion Ⓕ CDA66219 (54 minutes: DDD: 9/87).

Barber A Slumber Song of the Madonna[ac]. There's Nae Lark[bc]. Love at the door[bc]. Serenades[bc]. Love's Caution[ac]. Night Wanderers[bc]. Oh that so sweet imprisonment[ac]. Strings in the Earth and Air[bc]. The Beggar's song[bc]. In the dark pinewood[bc]. Three Songs, Op. 2[bc]. Three Songs, Op. 10[abc]. Four Songs, Op. 13[ac]. Dover Beach, Op. 3[bd]. Two Songs, Op. 18[ac]. Nuvoletta, Op. 25[ac]. Mélodies passagères, Op. 27[bc]. Hermit Songs, Op. 29[ac]. Despite and Still, Op. 41[bc]. Three Songs, Op. 45[bc]. [a]**Cheryl Studer** (sop); [b]**Thomas Hampson** (bar); [c]**John Browning** (pf); [d]**Emerson Quartet** (Eugene Drucker; Philip Setzer, vns; Lawrence Dutton, va; David Finckel, vc). DG Ⓕ 435 867-2GH2 (two discs: 110 minutes: DDD: 5/94). Notes and texts included. Recorded 1991-2.
Gramophone Award Winner 1994. Gramophone Editor's choice.   ⊖⊖

Sung in chronological order these songs are almost an autobiography and the set provides a compelling argument for regarding Barber's songs as his art at its most complete. There's hardly a weak song in the collection. Hampson brings to this music a remarkable range of expression and colour, a subtle use of words and a conviction that not a few of these songs are masterpieces. Studer has a slightly cooler approach, but often provides the vocal glamour, the ability to sketch long curves and floated high notes, that Barber (singer himself and connoisseur of singing) so often demanded. And John Browning, to whose virtuosity Barber tailored his Piano Concerto, sounds not only like a man who has yearned to accompany these singers in these songs for a long while, but like a considerable accompanist indeed, matching Hampson's dynamic range and expressive flexibility and Studer's seamless line with resourceful sympathy. The recorded sound is flawless.

Additional recommendations ...
...Knoxville: Summer of 1915. Dover Beach. Hermit Songs. Andromache's Farewell, Op. 39.
Soloists; Juilliard Quartet; Dumbarton Oaks Orchestra / William Strickland;
New York Philharmonic Orchestra / Thomas Schippers.
CBS Masterworks Portrait Ⓜ MPK46727* (51 minutes: AAD: 10/91).   ⊖
...Nocturne, Op. 13 No. 4. Hermit Songs[a]. Sleep now, Op. 10 No. 2[a]. The daisies, Op. 2 No. 1[a]. Nuvoletta[a]. Knoxville[b]. Antony and Cleopatra[b] – Give me some music; Give me my robe.
Leontyne Price (sop); [a]**Samuel Barber** (pf); [b]**New Philharmonia Orchestra / Thomas Schippers.**
RCA Victor Gold Seal Ⓜ 09026 61983-2* (63 minutes: ADD: 8/94).   ⊖
...Dover Beach[ac]. Serenade, Op. 1[c]. Three Songs, Op. 2[ab]. Three Songs, Op. 10[ab]. Four Songs, Op. 13[ab]: Sure on this shining night; Nocturne. Despite and Still: Solitary Hotel[ab]. Three Songs, Op. 45[ab]. String Quartet, Op. 11[c]. [a]**Thomas Allen** (bar); [b]**Roger Vignoles** (pf); [c]**Endellion Quartet.**
Virgin Classics Ⓕ VC5 45033-2 (64 minutes: DDD: 10/94).   ⊖
...With rue my heart is laden, Op. 2 No. 2. *Coupled with works by various composers.*
Anthony Rolfe Johnson (ten); **Graham Johnson** (pf). Hyperion Ⓕ CDA66471/2
(two discs: 124 minutes: DDD: 8/95). *See review in the Collections section; refer to the Index.*

...Hermit Song – No. 6, Sea-snatch. I hear an army, Op. 10 No. 3. Sure on this shining night,
Op. 13 No. 3. Bessie Bobtail, Op. 2 No. 3. *Coupled with works by various composers.*
Samuel Ramey (bar); **Warren Jones** (pf). Sony Classical Ⓕ SK68339 (71 minutes: DDD: 2/97).
See review in the Collections section; refer to the Index.
...Bessie Bobtail, Op. 2 No. 3. Three Songs, Op. 10. Sure on this shining night, Op. 13 No. 3.
Coupled with works by various composers. **Jennifer Larmore** (mez); **Antoine Palloc** (pf).
Teldec Ⓕ 0630-16069-2 (75 minutes: DDD: 12/97). *See review in the Collections section;*
refer to the Index.
...Hermit Songs. *Coupled with works by various composers.* **Barbara Bonney** (sop); **André Previn** (pf).
Decca Ⓕ 455 511-2DH (76 minutes: DDD: 2/98). *See review in the Collections section; refer to the*
Index. Selected by Soundings.
Further listening ...
...Cello Sonata, Op. 6. *Coupled with works by* **Bernstein** and **Foote**. Andrés Díaz (vc);
Samuel Sanders (pf). Dorian DOR90241 (2/98).
...Knoxville: Summer of 1915, Op. 24. *Coupled with works by* **Gershwin** and **Previn**
Kathleen Battle (sop); **Orchestra of St Luke's** / **André Previn**. DG 437 787-2GH (1/96).   Ⓖ
...Vanessa. **Soloists; New York Metropolitan Opera Chorus and Orchestra / Dimitri Mitropoulos.**
RCA Victor Gold Seal GD87899 (7/90).

Jacques Barbireau   Dutch c1420-1491

Suggested listening ...
...Een wrolick wesen. *Coupled with works by various composers.* **Early Music Consort of London /**
David Munrow. Virgin Classics Veritas VED5 61334-2 (11/97). 🖊 *See review in the Collections*
section; refer to the Index.

Woldemar Bargiel   German 1828-1897

Suggested listening ...
...Adagio in G major, Op. 38. *Coupled with works by* **Schumann** Steven Isserlis (vc); **Deutsche**
Kammerphilharmonie / Christoph Eschenbach. RCA Victor Red Seal 09026 68800-2 (12/97). 🖊
Gramophone Editor's choice. See review under Schumann; refer to the Index.

Augustin Barié   French 1884-1915

Suggested listening ...
...Trois Pièces. *Coupled with works by various composers.* **Marie-Bernadette Dufourcet** (org).
Priory PRCD422 (6/95). *See review in the Collections section; refer to the Index.*

Vytautas Barkauskas   Lithuanian 1931

Suggested listening ...
...Partita. *Coupled with works by various composers.* **Gidon Kremer** (vn). Teldec 0630-14654-2
(11/97). *Gramophone Editor's choice. See review in the Collections section; refer to the Index.*

Agustín Barrios   Paraguayan 1885-1944

Suggested listening ...
...Valses, Op. 8 – Nos. 3 and 4. Julia Florida – Barcarola. *Coupled with works by various composers.*
Jason Vieaux (gtr). Naxos 8 553449 (11/97). *See review in the Collections section; refer to the*
Index.
...Waltz, Op. 8 No. 4. Julia Florida. **Sharon Isbin** (gtr). Teldec 0630-19899-2 (7/98).
Gramophone Editor's choice. See review in the Collections section; refer to the Index.   ⒼⒼ

Béla Bartók   Hungarian 1881-1945

Bartók Piano Concertos – No. 1, Sz83; No. 2, Sz95; No. 3, Sz119. **Peter Donohoe** (pf); **City of**
Birmingham Symphony Orchestra / Sir Simon Rattle. EMI Ⓕ CDC7 54871-2 (77 minutes: DDD:
11/93). Recorded 1990-92. *Gramophone Editor's choice.*   ⒼⒼⒼ
Bartók Piano Concertos – No. 1, Sz83; No. 2, Sz95; No. 3, Sz119. **András Schiff** (pf);
Budapest Festival Orchestra / Iván Fischer. Teldec Ⓕ 0630-13158-2 (76 minutes: DDD: 3/97).
Recorded 1996.   ⒼⒼ

Making Bartók's First Piano Concerto sound fun must have taken some doing, but Donohoe and Rattle have certainly managed it. The recording blends the instrument in among the orchestra, so that Rattle's sensitivity to nuance, Donohoe's lightness of touch and the accommodating acoustic of Birmingham's Symphony Hall transform what we frequently hear as an angular confrontation into something genuinely palatable. The Second Concerto, in this impressively urgent account, could hold its own in any company, even though there are one or two passages where articulation momentarily falters. The rest is either pungent or evocative: the second movement's 'night music' *Adagio* sections are beautifully sustained and the finale has terrific *élan*. Taken overall, this is a marvellous trio of performances and serves as a fresh reminder of just how great these works are.

Although Schiff's free-flowing renditions are never too far from the written page, they rarely stick rigidly to the letter. The first solo statement in the Second Concerto, for example, is lilting and capricious, quite unlike the earnest pronouncements of Anda, Donohoe or Kocsis. True, his *Presto* isn't quite as nimble as Anda's but most readers will rejoice in the many subtle shifts in pace and dynamics that colour Schiff's performances. Fischer's Budapest Festival Orchestra are on great form; woodwind solos are characterful, brass choirs have immense force and the juggernaut big drums thrash thunder into the last movement of the Second Concerto. The First Concerto suggests a sense of play that rivals Donohoe and Rattle, especially in the first movement – although never letting you forget Donohoe's mesmerizing account of the *Andante*. The Third Concerto suits Schiff best of all: his tone is nicely rounded, his chords perfectly weighted and there's some nifty fingerwork. He virtually sings these concertos, which makes for a near-ideal Third but, in the case of the Second, prompts something of an uneven confrontation. Schiff's contribution to the Second is consistently bright, nimble, even a little coquettish, while Fischer's response is brazen and athletic. The same might be said of the First Concerto, except that there the sound is so astonishingly lifelike that it virtually amounts to an aural drama on its own terms.

Additional recommendations ...
...Nos. 1 and 2. **Maurizio Pollini** (pf); **Chicago Symphony Orchestra / Claudio Abbado.**
DG Ⓕ 415 371-2GH (52 minutes: ADD: 9/86).   ⓖⓔ
...Nos. 1-3. **Jenö Jandó** (pf); **Budapest Symphony Orchestra / Andras Ligeti.**
Naxos Ⓢ 8 550771 (77 minutes: DDD: 2/95).
...Nos. 1-3. **Géza Anda** (pf); **Berlin RIAS Symphony Orchestra / Ferenc Fricsay.**
DG The Originals Ⓜ 447 399-2GOR* (78 minutes: ADD: 5/95).   ⓖⓔ
...Nos. 1-3. **Zoltán Kocsis** (pf); **Budapest Festival Orchestra / Iván Fischer.**
Philips Ⓕ 446 366-2PH (74 minutes: DDD: 12/95).   ⓖⓔⓖ

Bartók Piano Concerto No. 3, Sz119[a].
Schumann Symphony No. 4 in D minor, Op. 120. [a]**Géza Anda** (pf); **Staatskapelle Dresden /**
Herbert von Karajan. DG Ⓜ 447 666-2GDO (55 minutes: ADD: 10/95). Recorded live in 1972. ⓖ
Gramophone Editor's choice.
Trying to imagine the broader profile of Herbert von Karajan's approach to this sunniest of Bartók concertos isn't at all difficult and, sure enough, its constituent virtues include the expected executive refinement, lustrous string tone, cosseting legato and heavily weighted tutti. So far as tempo is concerned, things are more or less comparable with Anda's legendary recording under Fricsay, and although the live performance is marginally slower, there's plenty of arresting detail. For example, start at 4'48" into the *Adagio religioso* and witness how Anda softens his tone and how Karajan builds towards a seething *tremolando* on the strings. Then there is the sheer beauty of it all, be it Anda's supremely cultured pianism or Karajan's stylishly shaped accompaniment. The finale, in particular, is far darker than usual, more beefy, while the sheer force of Anda's playing reminds us of Bartók's Lisztian pedigree. In the Schumann there is much sensitive phrase shaping, most especially from the strings, while the transition from *Scherzo* to finale has a Furtwänglerian aura, replete with vivid premonitions of Bruckner and beyond. The finale itself (without repeat) is remarkably pliant: a broadly paced, ruminative affair, infinitely flexible, yet tensing its limbs for an exultant coda. As in the Bartók, there are a few executive mishaps, but all are significantly outweighed by the players' commitment. The recording is decent save for underprojected horns. This CD is a refreshing, even heartening experience, and light years removed from so many chromium-framed Karajan studio sessions that hail from the same period.

Bartók Viola Concerto, Sz120[a]. Music for Strings, Percussion and Celesta, Sz106[b].
[a]**Wolfram Christ** (va); **Berlin Philharmonic Orchestra / Seiji Ozawa.** DG Ⓕ 437 993-2GH.
(52 minutes: DDD: 4/94). Item marked [a] recorded in 1989, [b]recorded live in 1992. ⓖⓔ
The performing edition of this affecting but uncompleted Viola Concerto takes obvious heed of Bartók's other 'late' works: yet Tibor Serly's 'completion' relates a strongly individual brand of musical poetry, not least via the lonely *più dolce* passage for viola and bassoons (4'02") and the sinister *Lento parlando* (12'25") that precedes the slow movement. The *Adagio religioso* visits an unruffled calm parallel to that in the Third Piano Concerto's similarly named centre-piece, while the finale achieves a lilting, 'folksy' sense of release. Wolfram Christ and Seiji Ozawa take a fairly gentle view though they offer us manifold interpretative insights and Christ's instrument has the textural warmth of seasoned mahogany. Neither the performance nor the (clean but close) recording can be found wanting: both do justice to the music's subtle but pensive sense of tonal fantasy. This recording of the

Music for Strings, Percussion and Celesta has pin-point definition, a rich bass and a startlingly realistic piano sound. It is a compelling performance and a worthy coupling for the most wholly recommendable version of the Viola Concerto currently available.

Additional recommendations ...

...Viola Concerto. **Hindemith** Der Schwanendreher. **Tabea Zimmermann** (va); **Bavarian Radio Symphony Orchestra / David Shallon.** EMI Ⓕ CDC7 54101-2 (48 minutes: DDD: 3/93).

...Viola Concerto. *Coupled with works by* **S. Albert** and **Bloch** Yo-Yo Ma (alto vn); **Baltimore Symphony Orchestra / David Zinman.** Sony Classical Ⓕ SK57961 (78 minutes: DDD: 3/95). Ⓖ

...Music for Strings, Percussion and Celesta. *Coupled with works by* **Janáček** and **Martinů** Joela Jones (pf); **Cleveland Orchestra / Christoph von Dohnányi.** Decca Ⓕ 443 173-2DH (70 minutes: DDD: 4/95).

...Music for Strings, Percussion and Celesta[b]. Dance Suite, Sz77[a]. The Wooden Prince, Sz60[a]. **Scriabin** Le poème de l'extase, Op. 54[a]. [a]**New York Philharmonic Orchestra,** [b]**BBC Symphony Orchestra / Pierre Boulez.** Sony Classical Boulez Edition Ⓜ SM2K64100 (two discs: 123 minutes: ADD: 9/95).

Bartók Violin Concerto No. 2, Sz112. Rhapsodies – No. 1, Sz87; No. 2, Sz90. **Kyung-Wha Chung** (vn); **City of Birmingham Symphony Orchestra / Sir Simon Rattle.** EMI Ⓕ CDC7 54211-2 (59 minutes: DDD: 6/94). Recorded 1990-92. *Gramophone Award Winner 1994.* ⒻⒼⒼ
Bartók Violin Concerto No. 2, Sz112.
Stravinsky Violin Concerto in D major. **Viktoria Mullova** (vn); **Los Angeles Philharmonic Orchestra / Esa-Pekka Salonen.** Philips Ⓕ 456 542-2PH (57 minutes: DDD: 5/98). Recorded 1997. ⒼⒼ

It is rare indeed to encounter a concerto recording where the critical honours can be evenly distributed, but the EMI recording really does suggest a strong team spirit. Heard purely for its own sake, Chung's playing is sinewy, agile and occasionally a mite brittle. Yet one soon realizes that every passage has been carefully thought through – the opening sequence, for example, which Chung traces as a continuous line of monologue. However, it is when soloist and conductor grapple in dialogue that the sparks really start to fly. Rattle and his players make the very most of Bartók's orchestral commentary: instrumental interplay is always alert, rhythms are keenly focused and his way of cushioning Chung, palpably convincing. The well-matched *Rhapsody* recordings are, again, revealing. The solo line is nicely attenuated, and the overall approach one of fine-tuned improvisation. Detail is legion (note how the solo violins and woodwinds intertwine at the beginning of the Second *Rhapsody*'s second movement), with Rattle compounding the rhapsodic idea by shaping his phrases with imaginatively applied rubato. Chung is certainly a more probing Bartókian than she was in her recording under Solti; her poignantly expressed intelligence will doubtless prove a durable virtue.

The Philips recording is as strong a contender as any for top digital rating in these concerto masterpieces, forthright and confident, with energetic support from Salonen and his orchestra. The engineering sounds like a digital upgrade of Mercury's Living Presence technique: instrumental imaging is startlingly immediate, the sound stage is very well defined and the bottom end of the spectrum has enormous power, the bass drum especially. Mullova's playing is committed and intense, with a ripe tone and some filigree passagework in the second-movement variations, where Salonen is careful to clarify every bejewelled strand in Bartók's scoring. The first movement is well thought through, though the timing exceeds Bartók's own (as printed in the score) by some three minutes. Still, most rivals are similarly expansive, and the second movement is actually a few seconds faster than prescribed, which is perhaps one of the reasons why it works so well. The finale is again clearly focused, but the big surprise comes with the inclusion – or, rather, substitution – of Bartók's rarely heard original ending, where the soloist retires and the orchestra alone shoulder the whole of the coda. The Stravinsky concerto is another winner, with pert outer movements and a ravishing account of the second "Aria". Tempos are well chosen, the sound is again first-rate. This performance of the Stravinsky ranks higher than any digital rival. As to the Bartók, Mullova is on a par with the best.

Additional recommendations ...

...No. 1[a]; No. 2[b]. **Kyung-Wha Chung** (vn); [a]**Chicago Symphony Orchestra;** [b]**London Philharmonic Orchestra / Sir Georg Solti.** Decca Ovation Ⓜ 425 015-2DM (59 minutes: ADD/DDD: 2/91). Ⓖ

...No. 2. **Moret** En rêve. **Anne-Sophie Mutter** (vn); **Boston Symphony Orchestra / Seiji Ozawa.** DG Ⓕ 431 626-2GH (58 minutes: DDD: 11/91). Ⓖ

...Nos. 1 and 2. **Gerhard Hertzel** (vn); **Hungarian State Symphony Orchestra / Iván Fischer.** Nimbus Ⓕ NI5333 (63 minutes: DDD: 7/93). ⒼⒼ

...No. 2[c]. Piano Concertos Nos. 1-3[ab]. Concerto for Orchestra[d]. [c]**Henryk Szeryng** (vn); [ab]**Stephen Kovacevich** (pf); [a]**London Symphony Orchestra;** [b]**BBC Symphony Orchestra / Sir Colin Davis;** [cd]**Concertgebouw Orchestra / Bernard Haitink.** Philips Duo Ⓜ 438 812-2PM2 (two discs: 151 minutes: ADD: 2/94). ⒼⒼⒼ

...Rhapsody No. 1. Contrasts, Sz111. *Coupled with works by various composers.* **Joseph Szigeti** (vn); **Béla Bartók** (pfs). Biddulph mono Ⓜ LAB070/71* (two discs: 129 minutes: ADD: 7/94). *See review in the Collections section; refer to the Index.* ⒼⒼ

...No. 2. **Dohnányi** Violin Concerto No. 2 in C minor, Op. 43. **Mark Kaplan** (vn); **Barcelona Symphony Orchestra / Lawrence Foster.** Koch International Classics Ⓕ 37387-2 (70 minutes: DDD: 9/97). *See review under Dohnányi; refer to the Index.*

Bartók The Miraculous Mandarin[a]. Hungarian Peasant Songs, Sz100. Hungarian Sketches, Sz97. Romanian Folkdances, Sz68. Transylvanian Dances, Sz96. Romanian Dance, Sz47a. [a]**Hungarian Radio Chorus; Budapest Festival Orchestra / Iván Fischer.** Philips Ⓕ 454 430-2PH (67 minutes: DDD: 8/97). Recorded 1996. *Gramophone Editor's record of the month.* ⒼⒼⒼ
As *Mandarins* go, they don't come more miraculous than this – a vivid, no-holds-barred performance. Everything tells – the flavour is right, the pacing too and the sound has a toughened, raw-edged quality that is an essential constituent of Bartók's tonal language. Although lurid – even seedy – in narrative detail, *The Miraculous Mandarin* is ultimately a tale of compassion, and Fischer never forgets that fact. Observable detail – all of it musically significant – occurs virtually by the minute. Delicacy trails bullish aggression, forcefulness alternates with an almost graphic suggestiveness – and it's all there in the full score. Fischer never vulgarizes, brutalizes or overstates the case and, what is most important, he underlines the quickly flickering, folkish elements in Bartók's musical language that other, less intuitive conductors barely acknowledge. The strongly individual character of the Budapest Festival Orchestra is delightful; they sound as if they have sprung from native soil rather than from some amorphous pool where all orchestras are alike; never mind about the odd minor imprecision. The strings have a biting edge, the woodwinds a gipsy-style reediness, while brass and percussion are forceful and incisive but never raucous. All these qualities also come into their own in the five folk-music-inspired works. This is Hungarian-grown Bartók that actually *sounds* Hungarian; it makes one wish that other European orchestras would reclaim parallel levels of individuality.

Additional recommendations ...
...The Miraculous Mandarin[a]. **L. Weiner** Suite on Hungarian Folk-tunes, Op. 18. [a]**London Voices; Philharmonia Orchestra / Neeme Järvi.** Chandos Ⓕ CHAN9029 (62 minutes: DDD: 3/92). Ⓖ
...The Miraculous Mandarin[a]. Two Portraits, Sz37[b]. **Janáček** Sinfonietta[c]. [b]**Shlomo Mintz** (vn); [a]**Ambrosian Singers;** [ab]**London Symphony Orchestra,** [c]**Berlin Philharmonic Orchestra / Claudio Abbado.** DG Masters Ⓜ 445 501-2GMA (66 minutes: DDD: 12/94). Ⓖ
...The Miraculous Mandarin. Concerto for Orchestra, Sz116.
City of Birmingham Symphony [b]**Chorus and Orchestra / Sir Simon Rattle.**
EMI Ⓕ CDC5 55094-2 (70 minutes: DDD: 1/95). *Selected by Sounds in Retrospect.* ⒼⒼ

Bartók Concerto for Orchestra, Sz116[a]. Music for Strings, Percussion and Celesta, Sz106[b]. Hungarian Sketches, Sz97[b]. **Chicago Symphony Orchestra / Fritz Reiner.**
RCA Victor Living Stereo Ⓜ 09026 61504-2 (76 minutes: ADD: 3/94). Items marked [a] from VICS1110 (12/65), [b]VICS1160 (1/66). Recorded 1955. *Gramophone classical 100.* ⒼⒼⒼ
Bartók Concerto for Orchestra, Sz116. Kossuth (1903). **San Francisco Symphony Orchestra / Herbert Blomstedt.** Decca Ⓕ 443 773-2DH (59 minutes: DDD: 7/95). Recorded 1993.
Reiner's recordings were made in Chicago's Orchestra Hall in October 1955 (not that sampling reveals their age – quite the contrary). RCA's sound reportage of the *Concerto for Orchestra's* quieter moments has uncanny realism and if the climaxes are occasionally reined in, the sheer fervour of Reiner's direction more than compensates. The "Pair Play" is a very brisk 6'26", the finale taut and agile: compare the movement's opening with, say, Boulez's version, and Reiner's greater precision and control is immediately apparent. His couplings are excellent: a *Music for Strings, Percussion and Celesta* that goes all out for smooth transitions and fleet execution, and a stylishly turned set of *Hungarian Sketches* – with a substantially augmented percussion line in "Bear Dance". These too sound better than ever, the *Music for Strings, Percussion and Celesta* having lost a confusing layer of distortion that hampered some earlier LP editions. Reiner's *Concerto* and *Music for Strings, Percussion and Celesta* is basic library fare, but if you need digital sound, Blomstedt and any of the other sets listed in this section remain among the best available.
Blomstedt's cogently argued *Concerto for Orchestra* which, although less overtly characterful than Rattle's and less virtuosic than Reiner's, boasts a clarity, intelligence and calm sense of purpose that lend the work an almost symphonic logic. The engineering, too, is usefully revealing. Don't expect a high-octane, tough-fisted *tour de force* (although the closing pages have plenty of impact), but readers in search of a lively, keen-eyed and, particularly, a superbly recorded overview are unlikely to be disappointed. *Kossuth* was Bartók's first completed orchestral work To be quite honest, it's a pretty weak piece, full of obvious derivations (Strauss, Wagner, Liszt and so on) although you do occasionally hear intimations of Bartók's own First Suite, and even *Bluebeard's Castle*. Lajos Kossuth was, to quote Decca's notes, "the soul and motor for the campaign for Hungarian independence one and a half centuries ago". The campaign failed but Kossuth remained a hero, especially for the youthful nationalist Bartók, who commemorated him in a programmatic mini-epic, the synopsis for which reads like a sequence of silent film subtitles. *Tristan und Isolde* looms large in Section 6, while the approaching Austrian troops mutter among the bassoons and enter into a very clumsily wrought musical battle. 'Good fun' might seem a rather half-hearted, even patronizing form of commendation, but the performance serves as a sobering reminder of a great composer's unpromising immaturity. A valuable, artistically accomplished coupling.

Additional recommendations ...
...Concerto for Orchestra. Music for Strings, Percussion and Celesta. **Oslo Philharmonic Orchestra / Mariss Jansons.** EMI Ⓕ CDC7 54070-2 (68 minutes: DDD: 1/91).

...Concerto for Orchestra[a]. Dance Suite, Sz77. Two Portraits, Sz37. Mikrokosmos – From the diary of a fly. [a]**London Symphony Orchestra; Philharmonia Hungarica / Antál Dorati.**
Mercury Ⓜ 432 017-2MM* (72 minutes: ADD: 11/91).　ⒼⒼⒼ
...Concerto for Orchestra. The Miraculous Mandarin. Four Pieces, Sz51. **Philadelphia Orchestra /**
Eugene Ormandy.
Sony Classical Essential Classics Ⓑ SBK48263* (74 minutes: ADD/DDD: 5/93).
...Concerto for Orchestra. Four Pieces, Sz51. **Chicago Symphony Orchestra / Pierre Boulez.**
DG Ⓕ 437 826-2GH (60 minutes: DDD: 3/94).　　　　　　　　　　　Ⓖ
...Concerto for Orchestra. The Miraculous Mandarin. Two Pictures, Sz46. **Philharmonia Orchestra /**
Hugh Wolff. Teldec Ⓕ 9031-76350-2 (76 minutes: DDD: 9/94).
...Concerto for Orchestra[a]. Music for Strings, Percussion and Celesta[b]. [a]**Berlin Radio Symphony**
Orchestra, [b]**Berlin RIAS Orchestra / Ferenc Fricsay.**
DG mono The Originals Ⓜ 447 443-2GOR* (65 minutes: ADD: 5/96).
...Concerto for Orchestra. Divertimento, Sz113. **Royal Philharmonic Orchestra / Daniele Gatti.**
Conifer Classics Ⓕ 75605 51324-2 (68 minutes: DDD: 1/98).

Bartók The Wooden Prince, Sz60. Cantata profana, Sz94[a]. [a]**John Aler** (ten); [a]**John Tomlinson**
(bass); **Chicago Symphony** [a]**Chorus and Orchestra / Pierre Boulez.** DG Ⓕ 435 863-2GH
(73 minutes: DDD: 3/93). Recorded 1991.　ⒼⒼⒼ
Bartók's parable of fathers, sons and fleeing the nest, his 1930 *Cantata profana* is a mesmerizing, symmetrically designed masterpiece, where words and music are forged into an action-packed 18 minutes. Boulez provides what is by far the best studio recording the work has ever had (also the first to be digitally recorded), and truly state-of-the-art in terms of sound. Boulez is able to command a shimmering, hushed *pp* yet the battle-hardy *Allegro molto* with its hectoring syncopations and warlike percussion is full of grit and muscle. John Aler is wonderfully adroit with Bartók's high-flying solo tenor line, John Tomlinson sounds like an authentic Magyar, and the Chicago Symphony Chorus egg the proceedings on with tireless zeal. Turn then to *The Wooden Prince* and you confront the final flowering of Bartók's post-romantic phase; it's an effulgent, exotic piece, full of wistful, melancholy wind solos (clarinet and saxophone figure prominently) and billowing, heavily-scored climaxes. How astonishing to reflect that it was written *after* the composer's trail-blazing opera, *Bluebeard's Castle*. Again, the soft music is wonderfully atmospheric: the *ppp* muted violins in the Prelude have a ghostly pallor that is so typical of this orchestra's quiet string playing, yet when all are engaged at full throttle, the effect is shattering. Detail is legion throughout: the basses, brass and drums have immense presence. Järvi and the Philharmonia Orchestra are also very good, if rather more reverberantly recorded.
Additional recommendation ...
...The Wooden Prince. Hungarian Sketches, Sz97. **Philharmonia Orchestra / Neeme Järvi.**
Chandos Ⓕ CHAN8895 (66 minutes: DDD: 10/91).

Bartók String Quartets – No. 1, Sz40; No. 2, Sz67; No. 3, Sz85; No. 4, Sz91; No. 5, Sz102; No. 6,
Sz114. **Takács Quartet** (Edward Dusinberre, Károly Schranz, vns; Roger Tapping, va; András
Fejér, vc). Decca Ⓕ 455 297-2DH2 (two discs: 152 minutes: DDD: 4/98). Recorded 1996.　ⒼⒼⒼ
Gramophone Editor's choice. Selected by Soundings.
These performances are up there among the best, with more impressive sampling points than one could hope to enumerate in a single review. The First Quartet's oscillating tempo-shifts work wonderfully well, all with total naturalness. Characterization is equally strong elsewhere, not least the first movement of the Second Quartet where Debussian arpeggios engage the senses, and the second movement where Fejér races back into the rustic opening subject. The nightmare climax in the last movement has rarely sounded more prophetic of the great *Divertimento*'s central movement. The middle quartets work very well, with prominent inner voices in the Third and plenty of swagger in the Fourth. The high spots of No. 4 are Fejér's improvisational cello solo in the third movement and a finale where the violent opening is a hefty legato to compare with the sharper, more Stravinskian attack of, say, the Tokyo Quartet. Likewise, the sudden dance-like episode in the first movement of the Fifth Quartet, savage music played from the pit of the stomach, while the third movement's bleary-eyed viola melody over teeming violin triplets suggests peasants in caricature. The Takács are especially responsive to Bartók's sardonic humour – the 'barrel-organ' episode at the end of the Fifth Quartet, and the corny "Burletta" in the third movement of the Sixth. The Sixth itself features some of the saddest, wildest and wisest music written in the last 100 years: the opening viola solo recalls Mahler's Tenth and the close fades to a mysterious question. Throughout the cycle, Bartók's metronome markings are treated more as guidelines than as literal commands. Relative strengths shared between rival versions make choosing a secure 'front runner' very difficult, and personal taste will inevitably prove a deciding factor. Those favouring dry sound and precision-tooled execution are well served by DG with either the Tokyo or the Emerson Quartets, or the Végh's Astrée set, a classic recording that relates a campfire-style rightness of idiom, albeit with the occasional technical blemish. This latest set proudly stands its ground, even in such exalted company. It communicates Bartók's all-embracing humanity, and if the greatest string quartets after Beethoven are still unknown to you, then this Takács set may well prove the musical journey of a lifetime. The recording here has ambient, full-bodied sound that is more reminiscent of the concert-hall than of the studio.

Additional recommendations ...
...No. 1. **Franck** String Quartet in D major. **Pro Arte Quartet.**
Biddulph mono Ⓜ LAB106* (79 minutes: ADD). Ⓖ
...Nos. 1-6. **Janáček** String Quartets – No. 1, "Kreutzer Sonata"; No. 2, "Intimate Letters".
Tokyo Quartet. RCA Victor Red Seal Ⓕ 09026 68286-2 (three discs: 199 minutes: DDD).
...Nos. 1-6. **Végh Quartet.** Auvidis Astrée Ⓕ. Nos. 1 and 2: E7717 (57 minutes: DDD: 3/87). Nos. 3
and 4: E7718 (38 minutes: DDD: 3/87). Nos. 5 and 6: E7719 (60 minutes: DDD: 3/87). ⒼⒼ
...Nos. 1-6. **Emerson Quartet.** DG Ⓕ 423 657-2GH2 (two discs: 149 minutes: DDD: 12/88).
Gramophone Award Winner 1989. ⒼⒼ
...Nos. 1-6. **Lindsay Quartet.** ASV Ⓕ CDDCS301 (three discs: 163 minutes: DDD: 3/89). ⒼⒼ
...Nos. 1-6. **Tokyo Quartet.** DG 20th Century Classics Ⓜ 445 241-2GC3 (three discs: 159 minutes:
ADD: 10/94). *Gramophone Award Winner 1981.* ⒼⒼ
...Nos. 1-6. **Novák Quartet.** Philips Duo Ⓜ 442 284-2PM2 (two discs: 158 minutes: ADD: 10/94).

Bartók Violin Sonata No. 1, Sz75[a]. Solo Violin Sonata, Sz117. **Isabelle Faust** (vn); [a]**Ewa Kupiec**
(pf). Harmonia Mundi Les Nouveaux Interprètes Ⓑ HMN91 1623 (69 minutes: DDD: 3/97).
Gramophone Editor's choice. Gramophone Award Winner 1997. Ⓖ
Bartók's First Violin Sonata is notoriously reluctant to yield its secrets: many have braved its pages
and although most available recordings convey the scale of the movement, none is more
comprehensively perceptive than this recording by the young violinist Isabelle Faust. Harmonia
Mundi count Faust among the "cream of the new generation of musicians" and, on the evidence
presented here, no one could rightly counter that claim. Ewa Kupiec provides Faust with motivated
support. Faust favours a sensual approach that draws active – and unexpected – parallels with the
music of Berg. She ventures deep among the first movement's more mysterious episodes. This is truly
empathetic playing, candid, full of temperament and always focused securely on the note's centre. The
crescendoing processional that sits at the heart of the second movement is charged with suspense and
the steely finale suggests an almost savage resolve. Faust and Kupiec visit corners and perspectives in
this score that others merely gloss over, and the recording supports them all the way. The Solo Sonata
is virtually as impressive. Here Faust approaches the music from a Bachian axis: her tone is pure, her
double-stopping immaculate and her sense of timing acute. Faust is a persuasive narrator; she and her
piano partner break down barriers in the First Sonata that, for some readers, will mean the difference
between approachability and continuing bafflement. Do give them a try.
Additional recommendations ...
...No. 1. *Coupled with works by* **Janáček** and **Messiaen** Gidon Kremer (vn);
Martha Argerich (pf). DG Ⓕ 427 351-2GH (57 minutes: DDD: 1/91). Ⓖ
...No. 1[a]; No. 2, Sz76. For Children, Sz42 (trans. Szigeti)[c] – No. 28, Parlando; No. 18, Andante non
molto; No. 42, Allegro vivace; No. 33, Andante sostenuto; No. 38. [ac]**David Oistrakh,**
[bc]**Gidon Kremer** (vns); [ac]**Frida Bauer,** [b]**Oleg Maisenberg** (pfs).
Praga Ⓕ PR250038 (60 minutes: ADD: 10/93).
...No. 1. Rhapsody No. 2, Sz89. 15 Hungarian Peasant Songs, Sz71 (trans. cpsr and Országh).
Piano Sonatine, Sz55 (trans. Gertler). Hungarian Folktunes, Sz66 (trans. Szigeti).
Susanne Stanzeleit (vn); **Gusztáv Fenyö** (pf). ASV Ⓕ CDDCA883 (69 minutes: DDD: 6/94). ⒼⒼ
...Nos. 1 and 2. Contrasts, Sz111[a]. **György Pauk** (vn); [a]**Kálmán Berkes** (cl); **Jenö Jandó** (pf).
Naxos Ⓢ 8 550749 (75 minutes: DDD: 9/94). *Gramophone Editor's choice.* Ⓖ

Bartók Violin Sonata in E minor, Op. posth. Andante. Slovak Folk Songs (arr. Móži). Burlesques,
Sz47 – A Bit Tipsy (arr. Urai). For Children, Sz42 – Ten Pieces (arr. Zathureczky). Contrasts,
Sz111[a]. **Susanne Stanzeleit** (vn); [a]**Michael Collins** (cl); **Gusztáv Fenyö** (pf). ASV Ⓕ CDDCA982
(65 minutes: DDD: 3/97).
An interesting case of 'before and after', with the early E minor Sonata representing Bartók in
'czardas' mode and the late *Contrasts* echoing the earthy tang of genuine Hungarian folk music.
Susanne Stanzeleit brings a wide range of gipsy-style inflexions to the various short pieces and the
tipsy *Burlesque* finds her wisely avoiding a sober straight line. A touch of ruggedness suits the
Contrasts, though there the real star of the show is clarinettist Michael Collins. True, Fenyö and
Stanzeleit set the scene, but Collins's witty, lightly inflected solo has immense colour and personality.
The little *Andante* for violin and piano (it lasts for just 3'18" in this performance) was written for Adila
Arányi as a 'thank you' for a house party, but wasn't actually premièred until 1955. It's a pleasant but
fairly uncharacteristic piece, whereas the half-hour Sonata of 1903 that precedes it contains many
auguries of the mature Bartók. Strauss is an audible influence and so is Wagner: the very opening
rises out of post-romantic mists, gently brushed by arpeggiated pizzicatos. Although not a
masterpiece to compare with the two mature violin sonatas, the E minor Sonata is attractive,
memorable and well worth bringing into the repertoire. ASV's recordings are very nicely balanced.

Bartók Sonata for Two Pianos and Percussion, Sz110.
Ravel (arr. Sadlo) Ma mère l'oye – Pavane de la Belle au bois dormant; Les entretiens de la Belle
et la Bête; Petit Poucet; Laideronette, Impératrice des Pagodes; Le jardin féerique. Rapsodie
espagnole. **Martha Argerich, Nelson Freire** (pfs); **Peter Sadlo, Edgar Guggeis** (perc). DG
Ⓕ 439 867-2GH (56 minutes: DDD: 10/94). Recorded 1993. *Gramophone Editor's choice.* ⒼⒼⒼ

The Bartók is an extremely impetuous affair, with excitable tempos, alarmingly wide dynamics and the odd smudged detail. However, it is also one of the most compelling performances ever recorded, with the emphasis placed firmly on continuous argument and a level of intensity that extends as much to the quieter moments as, for example, to the fraught climax of the first movement's fugue. What is particularly wonderful here is the degree of subtle rubato that Argerich and Freire allow themselves, treating the music as music, and not as some modernist manifesto. As to the Ravel, the arrangements are remarkably respectful of Ravel's originals, *Ma mère l'oye* resembling Gaston Choisnel's two-piano version of 1911, the *Rapsodie* also reducing well to this particular instrumental formula (the "Habanera" was in any case originally composed for the two-piano medium). Sadlo's pitched-percussion garnishings are based largely on those that Ravel himself concocted for his orchestrations, but even those that aren't work wonderfully well. Aside from the expected tam-tam and xylophone in "Empress of the pagodas", there is the most exquisite high percussion in "The fairy garden", so beautifully handled that the absence of strings is hardly noticed. This CD should be considered an inspired 'one-off', where four top-ranking players teamed-up purely for the fun of making wonderful music together. Considered as such, it's a disc in a million.

Additional recommendation ...

...Sonata for Two Pianos and Percussion[a]. Suite for Two Pianos, Sz115a. **Jean-François Heisser, Georges Pludermacher** (pfs); [a]**Guy-Joel Cipriani**, [a]**Gérard Perotin** (perc). Erato Ⓕ 2292-45861-2 (58 minutes: DDD: 4/93).   ⒼⒼ

Bartók Contrasts, Sz111[ab]. Rhapsodies – No. 1, Sz86; No. 2, Sz89[b]. Six Romanian Folk Dances, Sz56 (arr. Székely)[b]. Solo Violin Sonata, Sz117. [a]**Michael Collins** (cl); **Krysia Osostowicz** (vn); [b]**Susan Tomes** (pf). Hyperion Ⓕ CDA66415 (72 minutes: DDD: 4/91). Recorded 1990.   Ⓖ
Unusually for a composer who wrote so much fine chamber music Bartók was not himself a string player. But he did enjoy close artistic understanding with a succession of prominent violin virtuosos, including the Hungarians Jelly d'Arányi, Joseph Szigeti and Zoltán Székely and, towards the end of his life, Yehudi Menuhin. It was Menuhin who commissioned the Sonata for solo violin, but Bartók died before he could hear him play it – Menuhin was unhappy with the occasional passages in quarter-tones and the composer had reserved judgement on his proposal to omit them. It was Menuhin's edition which was later printed and which has been most often played and recorded; but Krysia Osostowicz returns to the original and, more importantly, plays the whole work with intelligence, imaginative flair and consummate skill. The Sonata is the most substantial work on this disc, but the rest of the programme is no less thoughtfully prepared or idiomatically delivered. There is the additional attraction of an extremely well balanced and natural-sounding recording. As a complement to the string quartets, which are at the very heart of Bartók's output, this is a most recommendable disc.

Additional recommendations ...

...Solo Violin Sonata. Rhapsody No. 1. Violin Sonata No. 2, Sz76. Romanian Folk Dances, Sz56. **Susanne Stanzeleit** (vn); **Gustáv Fenyö** (pf). ASV Ⓕ CDDCA852 (64 minutes: DDD: 6/93).
...Rhapsodies Nos. 1 and 2[a]. Solo Violin Sonata. Six Romanian Folkdances (arr. Székely)[a]. For Children, Sz42 – Seven Hungarian Folktunes (arr. Szigeti)[a]. **Mark Kaplan** (vn); [a]**Bruno Canino** (pf). Arabesque Ⓕ Z6649 (62 minutes: DDD: 12/94).
...Solo Violin Sonata (arr. viola). *Coupled with works by* **Shostakovich** *and* **Stravinsky** **Raphael Hillyer** (va). Koch Schwann Ⓕ 311612 (74 minutes: DDD: 5/95).

Bartók Solo Piano Works. **György Sándor** (pf). Sony Classical Ⓜ SX4K68275 (four discs: 287 minutes: DDD: 11/95). Recorded 1993-5.
For Children, Sz42. The First Term at the Piano, Sz53. 15 Hungarian Peasant Songs, Sz71. Three Hungarian Folksongs from the Csík District, Sz35a. Hungarian Folktunes, Sz66. Eight Improvisa-tions on Hungarian Peasant Songs, Sz74. Three Rondos on (Slovak) Folktunes, Sz84. Romanian Christmas Carols, Sz57. Six Romanian Folkdances, Sz56. Two Romanian Dances, Sz43. Suite, Sz62, with original Andante. Piano Sonata, Sz80. Sonatina, Sz55. 14 Bagatelles, Sz38. Four Dirges, Sz45. Petite Suite, Sz105. Violin Duos, Sz98 (arr. Sándor) – No. 1, Teasing Song; No. 17, Marching Song; No. 35, Ruthenian kolomejka; No. 42, Arabian Song; No. 44, Transylvanian Dance. 10 Easy Pieces, Sz39. Allegro barbaro, Sz49. Out of doors, Sz81. Seven Sketches, Sz44. Two Elegies, Sz41. Three Burlesques, Sz47. Nine Little Pieces, Sz82. Three Studies, Sz72.
There can't be many pianists on the current circuit whose fund of experience extends to working with a major twentieth-century master; but of those still recording, György Sándor must surely take pride of place. Sándor prepared Bartók's first two piano concertos under the composer's guidance and gave the world premières of the Third Concerto and the piano version of the *Dance Suite*. The present collection is Sándor's second survey of Bartók's piano music and he programmes all the major works apart from *Mikrokosmos*. Many of these performances are exceptionally fine, even though the passage of time has witnessed something of a reduction in Sándor's pianistic powers, mostly where maximum stamina and high velocity fingerwork are required (as in the first *Burlesque*). However, you may be astonished at the heft, energy and puckish humour of Sándor's 1994 recording of the Piano Sonata, a more characterful rendition than its predecessor, with a particularly brilliant account of the folkish *Allegro molto* finale. The *Allegro barbaro* is similarly 'on the beam', while Sándor brings a cordial

warmth to the various collections of ethnic pieces, the *Romanian Christmas Carols* especially. His phrasing, rubato, expressive nuancing, attention to counterpoint and command of tone (sample the *15 Hungarian Peasant Songs*) suggest the touch of a master, while his imagination relishes the exploratory nature of the *Improvisations*, *Bagatelles* and *Miraculous Mandarin*-style *Studies*.

Viewed overall, Kocsis offers the more painstakingly precise reportage of Bartók's notation and a rather more sharply focused presentation of the music's multi-faceted rhythmic personality. He is also the more adroit technician, whereas his acute musical intuition guarantees a high level of interpretative individuality. Like Sándor, he approaches the texts (either written or recorded) as guidelines, and it is fair to say that in this respect at least, the differences between the two pianists are more a matter of degree than principle. Both give their all wherever Hungarian folk music predominates: sample Kocsis in the first of the *Csík* Folksongs, Sz35a or Sándor in "Evening with the Széklers" from *Ten Easy Pieces* and you'd be hard pressed to choose between them. Which leaves scant space to promote the music's abundant qualities, be they harmonic or rhythmic innovation, powerful emotion telescoped into a minute time-span (*For Children* and the various sequences of short pieces), humour (*Burlesques*), introspection (*Dirges*), autobiography (the various manifestations of Steffi Geyer's theme), ethnic variety or the sheer scope and complexity of Bartók's piano writing in general. Sándor connects with it all. His principal rivals are, for the moment at least, severely compromised by being 'incomplete'. In sum, intuitive interpreters, especially those who knew and understand the composers they perform, are becoming an increasingly rare breed. In that respect alone, György Sándor's Bartók deserves an honoured place in every serious CD collection of twentieth-century piano music.

Additional recommendations ...

...Duos. **Sándor Végh, Albert Lysy** (vns). Auvidis Astrée Ⓕ E7720 (50 minutes: ADD: 3/88). ⒼⒼ

...For Children. Mikrokosmos, Sz107 – progressive pieces for piano in six volumes (complete, Books 1-6). **Dezsö Ránki** (pf). Teldec Ⓜ 9031-76139-2 (three discs: 200 minutes: ADD: 10/92). Ⓖ

...Two Romanian Dances. Three Hungarian Folksongs from the Csík District. Allegro barbaro. Four Dirges. Suite. Romanian Christmas Carols. Three Studies. Three Rondos on Folktunes. The First Term at the Piano. **Zoltán Kocsis** (pf). Philips Ⓕ 442 016-2PH (71 minutes: DDD: 11/94). *Gramophone Editor's choice.* Ⓖ

...Duos. **Fuchs** 20 Duos, Op. 55. **Eugene Drucker, Philip Setzer** (vns). Biddulph Ⓜ LAW007 (74 minutes: DDD: 3/95). ⒼⒼ

...Vol. 3. For Children. **Zoltán Kocsis** (pf). Philips Ⓕ 442 146-2PH (75 minutes: DDD: 6/95). ⒼⒼ

...For Children. **Géza Anda** (pf). *Coupled with works by various composers.* Testament mono Ⓕ SBT1065* (79 minutes: ADD: 10/95). *See review in the Collections section; refer to the Index.* Ⓖ

Bartók Piano works, Volume 1 – 14 Bagatelles, Sz38. Two Elegies, Sz41. Sonatine, Sz55. Six Romanian Folk Dances, Sz56. Three Hungarian Folktunes, Sz66. **Zoltán Kocsis** (pf). Philips Ⓕ 434 104-2PH (54 minutes: DDD: 1/94). Recorded 1991. ⒼⒼⒼ

Bartók himself admitted that his *Bagatelles* (1908) were largely experimental, and indeed at least half-a-dozen of them could easily have fallen from a jazz-pianist's copybook (Nos. 7, 11 and 12, particularly), their sensual harmonies and capricious rhythmic computations prophetic of so much that was to happen in that world. Debussy, too, is much in evidence (No. 3), as is Bartók's love of folk-song (Nos. 4 and 5). The *Elegies* would sit nicely among the shorter works of Busoni. These virtuosic effusions recall the moon-flecked world of late Liszt, albeit flushed with a Hungarian rather than a gipsy complexion. Folk-song proper informs Kocsis's last three selections: the familiar *Six Romanian Folk Dances*, the cheerful and ingenious *Sonatine* and the relatively dense *Hungarian Folktunes*, Sz66 – the last bringing us to the far edge of the Great War. It's a cliffhanger of a finale, and has us eager for more. Kocsis's readings are absolutely on target. A peach of a disc.

Bartók Piano Works, Volume 4 – Piano Sonata, Sz80. Out of doors, Sz81. Nine Little Pieces, Sz82. Petite Suite, Sz105. **Zoltán Kocsis** (pf). Philips Ⓕ 446 369-2PH (49 minutes: DDD: 7/97). Recorded 1996. *Selected by Soundings.* ⒼⒼⒼ

Kocsis's mastery of tone, rhythm and articulation, allied to his painstaking attention to important source material, make for a level of pianistic distinction that is fairly unique in this repertory. To say that with Kocsis 'less is more' is to suggest executive reticence, which is certainly not the case. The first movements of the Sonata and *Out of doors* (both works dating from 1926) hit hard without hammering, the former displaying a multitude of tiny inflexional gestures and pulse changes, the latter, a quick-boiling final chase of great intensity. Playing of this calibre takes us back to the days of 78s – playing where so much rhythmic flexibility is achieved within such a disciplined interpretative framework. In *Out of doors*, Kocsis's ability to command differing colours simultaneously heightens the musical effect, especially in the "Barcarolla" and what is surely the most exquisitely tooled performance of "The Night's Music" ever recorded. "The Chase" is pin-sharp, its every gear-change expertly negotiated, while Kocsis makes maximum capital out of the rich harmonic world in "Musettes". The *Nine Little Pieces* transcend their brevity, "Menuetto" recalling the second movement of the First Piano Concerto (another product of 1926), the closing "Preludio – All'Ungherese" providing a little mini-suite all on its own. The disc closes with the *Petite Suite*, a tuneful half-dozen ingeniously refashioned from the *44 Duos* for two violins. This production is of superb quality and although 49 minutes is short measure for a full-price, solo piano CD, this is unquestionably one of the great piano records of the post-war period.

...Out of doors. Suite, Sz62. Eight Improvisations on Hungarian Peasant Songs, Sz74. *Coupled with works by various composers.* **Murray Perahia** (pf). Sony Classical Ⓜ SX4K63380 (four discs: 270 minutes: DDD/ADD: 4/98). *See review in the Collections section; refer to the Index.*

Bartók Piano works. **Béla Bartók** (pf). Pearl mono Ⓜ GEMMCD9166* (69 minutes: ADD: 6/96). From HMV, Patria, Columbia and Continental originals; recorded 1929-42.

László Somfai observed how Bartók's manner of playing was "fortified with his rich experiences of Classical interpretation and adopted very carefully the truly personal 'accentuations' of his own music". In most instances, Bartók didn't so much transcend his own rules as allow himself maximum freedom within them: time and again one notices minute adjustments in matters of rhythm, dynamics or inflexion, none of which disrupts the flow or distorts the character of the music. This compilation, the most comprehensive available on a single disc, offers full-bodied transfers of some fascinating commercial recordings, not least of Liszt's "Sursum corda" (*Années de pèlerinage – Troisième année*) which, in contrast with, say, Alfred Brendel's beautifully delineated account on Philips (2/96), sounds like a spontaneous transcription of an orchestral piece – such is its rugged grandeur. The next track (17) finds Bartók unsteady at the start of *Mikrokosmos's* "Staccato", but how thrilling are the hungry, almost Schnabelian 'snatched' phrases of the succeeding "Ostinato" and the wicked caprices of that underrated masterpiece, *Improvisations on Hungarian Peasant Songs* (which Bartók recorded only in excerpt). There are 38 tracks in all on this disc, with the Suite, Op. 14, and the First *Romanian Dance* taking pride of place as Bartók's finest solo recordings. The *Allegro barbaro* is also good, though nowhere near as barbaric as some – a significant fact given a plethora of fierce-fisted Bartókians, all of whom should make an effort to hear this invaluable CD.

Bartók Duke Bluebeard's Castle. **John Tomlinson** (bass) Bluebeard; **Anne Sofie von Otter** (mez) Judith; **Sandor Elès** (spkr); **Berlin Philharmonic Orchestra / Bernard Haitink.** EMI Ⓕ CDC5 56162-2 (63 minutes: DDD: 9/96). Notes, text and translation included. Recorded 1995. *Gramophone Editor's choice.*   ⓖⓖ

Bartók Duke Bluebeard's castle. **Walter Berry** (bass-bar) Bluebeard; **Christa Ludwig** (mez) Judith; **London Symphony Orchestra / István Kertész.** Decca The Classic Sound Ⓜ 443 571-2DCS (59 minutes: ADD: 4/95). Notes, text and translation included. From SET311 (5/66). Recorded 1965.   ⓖⓖ

Bernard Haitink's poetic axis is vividly anticipated in the rarely recorded spoken prologue where Sandor Elès bids us search beneath the story's surface. Elès's timing and his sensitivity to word-colouring and the rhythmic inflexions of his native language greet the Gothic imagery of Bartók's solemn opening bars. The main protagonists soon establish very definite personalities, Bluebeard/Tomlinson as commanding, inscrutable and just a little arrogant, von Otter/Judith as profoundly frightened but filled with curiosity. Haitink and the Berlin Philharmonic paint a rich aural backdrop that is neither too slow nor overly lugubrious and that shows due appreciation of Bartók's seamless scoring, especially in terms of the woodwind. The disembodied sighs that greet Judith's violent hammering on the first door mark a momentary retreat from the Philharmonie's ambient acoustic (or so it seems) and in so doing suggest – quite appropriately – a chilling 'world beyond'. Judith's shock as she recoils in horror is conveyed in clipped, halting tones by von Otter (note too how seductively she manipulates Bluebeard into opening the first door).

Beyond the expansive introduction come the doors themselves, and here too Haitink balances the 'outer' and 'inner' aspects of Bartók's score to perfection – whether in the torture chamber, the glowing textures of "The Secret Garden"or the Brucknerian expanses of the fifth door, "Bluebeard's Kingdom" (the opera's structural apex), launched here on a series of epic crescendos. Von Otter's stunned responses suggest lonely disorientation within a vast space, whereas the sullenness of the "Lake of Tears" prompts an exquisite blending of instrumental timbres, most particularly between brass and woodwind. Haitink draws an aching curve to the string writing, but when Judith rushes panic-stricken towards the seventh door, fearful of Bluebeard's secret murders, he effects a gradual but cumulatively thrilling *accelerando*. The internment itself is devastating, while Bluebeard's helpless retreat marks a slow journey back to the questioning void. Recording live can have its pitfalls, but here the atmosphere is electric, the grasp of Bartók's sombre tone-painting – whether sung or played – absolute. EMI's engineering favours a full sound-stage rather than picking out specific instrumental details, but the overall effect remains comprehensively satisfying.

As to rivals, Haitink is now a definite first digital choice, while among older alternatives, readers in search of sharp-edged instrumental accents or the texture and tang of native Hungarian singers should search out Dorati's 1962 version for Mercury. Kertész, on the other hand, favours a far richer sound-stage, with softer contours (his armoury suggests more weight than glinting steel, his torture chamber, anxiety rather than cruelty) and a passionate swell to the string writing. When it comes to the husband-and-wife team of Walter Berry and Christa Ludwig, one senses more a woman discovering sinister aspects of the man she loves than an inquisitive shrew intent on plundering Bluebeard's every secret. Here, Judith seems perpetually poised to take Bluebeard's arm and linger lovingly about him, while Berry's assumption of the title-role – which is beautifully, if not terribly idiomatically, sung – suggests neither *Angst* nor impatience. Ludwig, too, was in wonderful voice at the time of this recording, and instances of her eloquence are far too numerous to list individually.

Placing this classic recording in the context of its finest rivals is fairly easy, in that Kertész represents the opera's compassionate core, whereas Boulez opts for maximum drama, Dórati, mobility and native inflexion. If you don't already know the piece and are happiest when listening to mainstream romantic opera, then try either this splendid-sounding reissue or the (sonically inferior) Boulez. The Kertész transfer is superb, with a thunderous organ beyond the fifth door and merely the odd rogue edit or spot of tape hiss to betray the passing years.

Additional recommendations ...

...Soloists; **Bavarian State Orchestra / Wolfgang Sawallisch.**
DG 20th Century Classics Ⓜ 423 236-2GC (58 minutes: ADD: 9/88).   ⒼⒼ

...Duke Bluebeard's Castle[a]. [a]**Olga Szönyi** (sop) Judith; [a]**Mihály Székely** (bass) Bluebeard.
Berg Wozzeck – excerpts[b]. [b]**Helga Pilarczyk** (sop); **London Symphony Orchestra / Antál Dorati.**
Mercury Living Presence Ⓜ 434 325-2MM (73 minutes: ADD: 7/93).   ⒼⒼ

...Soloists; **BBC Symphony Orchestra / Pierre Boulez.**
Sony Classical Boulez Edition Ⓜ SMK64110 (61 minutes: ADD: 3/95).   ⒼⒼⒼ

Further listening ...

...Dance Suite, Sz77. *Coupled with works by various composers.* **Philharmonia Orchestra /**
Igor Markevitch. Testament mono SBT1060* (2/96).

...Dance Suite, Sz77. Two Pictures, Sz46. Hungarian Sketches, Sz97. Divertimento, Sz113.
Chicago Symphony Orchestra / Pierre Boulez. DG 445 825-2GH (9/95).

...Divertimento for Strings, Sz113. *Coupled with works by* **Schoenberg** and **Hindemith**
English Chamber Orchestra / Daniel Barenboim. EMI Matrix CDM5 65079-2 (12/94).   Ⓖ

...Two Pictures, Sz46. *Coupled with* **Stravinsky** Le baiser de la fée.
La Scala Philharmonic Orchestra, Milan / Riccardo Muti. Sony Classical SK58949 (9/95).

...Rhapsody, Sz27. Scherzo, Sz28. *Coupled with* **Dohnányi** Variations on a Nursery Theme, Op. 25.
Zoltán Kocsis (pf); **Budapest Festival Orchestra / Iván Fischer.**
Philips 446 472-2PH (4/96).

...Sonatina, Sz55. *Coupled with works by* **Liszt** and **Delibes/Dohnányi**
Géza Anda (pf); **Philharmonia Orchestra / Alceo Galliera.**
Testament mono SBT1067* (10/95). *See review in the Collections section; refer to the Index.*   Ⓖ

...Violin Sonata No. 2, Sz76. *Coupled with works by various composers.* **Gidon Kremer** (vn);
Oleg Maisenberg (pf). Teldec 0630-13597-2 (7/97). *Gramophone Editor's choice.*

...Violin Sonata No. 2. *Coupled with* **Penderecki** Violin Concerto No. 2, "Metamorphosen".
Anne-Sophie Mutter (vn); **Lambert Orkis** (pf);
London Symphony Orchestra / Krzysztof Penderecki.
DG 453 507-2GH (4/98).

...Three Studies, Sz72. *Coupled with works by various composers.* **Erika Haase** (pf). Tacet Tacet53 (2/98).

...Cantata profana, Sz94. *Coupled with works by* **Kodály** and **Weiner** Tamás Daróczy (ten);
Alexander Agache (bar); **Hungarian Radio and Television Chorus; Budapest Festival Orchestra /**
Sir Georg Solti. Decca 458 929-2DH (6/98). *Gramophone Editor's choice. See review under*
Weiner; refer to the Index.

...Five Songs, Sz61[a]. Five Songs, Sz63[a]. Hungarian Folksongs, Sz64 – Black is the earth;
My God, my God; Wives, let me be one of your company; So much sorrow; If I climb
the rocky mountains. Five Songs, Sz61 (orch. Kodály)[b]. Five Hungarian Folksongs, Sz101[b].
Júlia Hamari (contr); [a]**Ilona Prunyi** (pf); [b]**Hungarian State Orchestra / János Kovacs.**
Hungaroton HCD31535 (7/93).   ⒼⒼⒼ

Giovanni Bassano   Italian c1558-1617

Suggested listening ...

...Vestiva i colli. *Coupled with works by various composers.* **His Majestys Sagbutts and Cornetts.**
Hyperion CDA66847 (11/96). *See review in the Collections section; refer to the Index.*

Antoine-Edouard Batiste   French 1820-1876

Suggested listening ...

...Offertoire in D minor. *Coupled with works by various composers.* **Christopher Herrick** (org).
Hyperion CDA66457 (9/91). *See review in the Collections section; refer to the Index.*   ⒼⒼⒼ

Sir Arnold Bax   British 1883-1953

Bax Symphonies – No. 1 in E flat major[a]; No. 7[b]. **London Philharmonic Orchestra /**
[a]**Myer Fredman,** [b]**Raymond Leppard.** Lyrita Ⓕ SRCD232 (78 minutes: ADD: 12/92).
Item marked [a] from SRCS53 (8/71), [b]SRCS83 (11/75).   Ⓖ

Few English composers have expressed such intense and fiercely passionate emotions as Bax has in the first two movements of his First Symphony. Such rage and grief as can be found there seem to suggest a psycho-drama being played out, and when we learn that at the time of its composition (1921) Bax may still have been coming to terms with the aftermath of the Great War, the loss of friends in the Easter Rising in Ireland and the irretrievable breakdown of his marriage, it is tempting to imagine that the symphony is indeed exercising some kind of personal exorcism on these events. Bax himself, however, was always reluctant to admit the existence of such a 'programme' behind the symphony, and in many ways he was probably right to do so. Whatever personal experiences Bax had poured into it, the end result is unquestionably a powerful, cogent symphony of universal appeal. The Seventh and last of Bax's symphonies makes an intelligent and well-contrasted coupling. The first movement, though not without tension and some storm-tossed passages (very much a Baxian seascape this), has a prevailing mood of hope and expectation – as though embarking on some adventurous seaward journey to new lands, whilst the second movement finds Bax in wistful 'legendary' mood so evocative of the early tone-poems. The last movement begins by echoing the optimism of the first movement, but finally gives way, in the long and beautiful epilogue, to a mood of autumnal nostalgia and sad farewell. These are classic Lyrita recordings, with exceptionally fine performances from Fredman and Leppard and superb digital transfers.

Additional recommendation ...
...Nos. 1-7. **London Philharmonic Orchestra; Ulster Orchestra / Bryden Thomson.**
Chandos Ⓕ CHAN8906/10 (five discs: 300 minutes: DDD).

Bax Symphony No. 1 in E flat major. In the Faery Hills. The Garden of Fand. **Royal Scottish National Orchestra / David Lloyd-Jones.** Naxos Ⓢ 8 553525 (64 minutes: DDD: 4/98). Recorded 1996.

The performance of the First Symphony is a commendable achievement all round. David Lloyd-Jones directs with intelligence, a pleasing sense of purpose and obvious commitment. Moreover, he draws playing of genuine fire and discipline from the RSNO, whose strings sound both richer and more refined than usual. Like Myer Fredman before him, Lloyd-Jones steers a thrusting, confident course through the opening *Allegro moderato e feroce* and shapes the remarkable central *Lento solenne* with notable authority. There's plenty to admire here: the unbridled verocity of the introduction; those "wailing" violins at 2'41" as Bax prepares us for the meltingly lovely secondary idea (tenderly given both times round); the fine rhythmic snap of the somewhat Holstian development. That shattering, gong-topped climax at 6'10" (where Bax seems to be peering into some monstrous abyss) is impressively prepared and the movement never threatens to hang fire the way it occasionally does under Bryden Thomson (who is over two minutes slower than either of his rivals). Perhaps it's Fredman who distils the greater sense of tragedy in this elemental invocation, whereas conversely Lloyd-Jones brings marginally more grip to the finale with its unsettling mix of the playful, grotesque and ultimately brutal. Although not necessarily rating Lloyd-Jones above Fredman, still sounding pretty stunning, anyone coming to this defiant score for the first time will be left in no doubt as to the astonishing emotional breadth and often seismic power of Bax's driven inspiration. As for the couplings, both *In the Faery Hills* and *The Garden of Fand* are thoroughly accomplished and expertly held together but perhaps lack a little in tingling atmosphere and sheer enchantment. The latter, affectionately shaped though it is, doesn't erase memories of Boult's magical recording. For the symphony alone, then, this Naxos release is definitely worth its modest asking-price.

Additional recommendation ...
...Northern Ballad No. 1. Mediterranean. The Garden of Fand. Tintagel[a].
November Woods. **London Philharmonic Orchestra / Sir Adrian Boult.**
Lyrita Ⓕ SRCD231 (62 minutes: ADD: 9/92). Ⓖ

Bax Symphony No. 3 in C major. Four Orchestral Sketches – Dance of Wild Irravel. Paean. **London Philharmonic Orchestra / Bryden Thomson.** Chandos Ⓕ CHAN8454 (59 minutes: DDD: 12/86). Recorded 1986. Ⓖ

Bax's Third Symphony has a long and gravely beautiful epilogue, one of the most magical things he ever wrote: a noble processional with a disturbing, motionless glitter at its centre and, just before the very end, a sudden bitter chill. It is pure Bax, and will haunt you for days. We may associate some of the Symphony with the lonely sands and the shining sea of Morar in Invernessshire (where the work was written), the impassioned string music that rises from that sea in the centre of the slow movement with deep emotion, the war-like dance of the finale with conflict or war and the frequent violent intercuttings of lyricism and darkness with what we know about Bax's temperament. But it is harder to explain in programmatic terms why lyric can become dark or vigour become brooding within startlingly few bars, why that epilogue seems so inevitable, why the Symphony for all its wild juxtapositions does not sound like a random sequence of vivid memories and passionate exclamations. That it is a real symphony after all, powered by purely musical imperatives, is suggested by this finely paced and tautly controlled performance, one of the finest in Thomson's Bax cycle. The enjoyable racket of *Paean* and the glittering colour of *Irravel* respond no less gratefully to the sumptuousness of the recording.

Additional recommendation ...
...Festival Overture[a]. Christmas Eve on the Mountains[b]. Dance of Wild Irravel[c]. Paean[c]. Nympholept[d]. Tintagel[e]. [abcd]**London Philharmonic Orchestra, [e]Ulster Orchestra / Bryden Thomson.** Chandos Ⓕ CHAN9168 (76 minutes: DDD: 2/94). *Selected by Sounds in Retrospect.* Ⓖ

Bax Octet[a]. String Quintet. Concerto. Threnody and Scherzo. In Memoriam. [a]**Margaret Fingerhut** (pf); **Academy of St Martin in the Fields Chamber Ensemble.** Chandos Ⓕ CHAN9602 (72 minutes: DDD: 5/98). Recorded 1997. *Gramophone Editor's choice.*   ⒼⒼ
This is a beautiful and enterprising collection of works by Bax. *In Memoriam* for cor anglais, harp and string quartet probably dates from 1917. Subtitled "An Irish Elegy", and like the *Elegiac Trio* from the same period, its poignant mood reflects Bax's despair at the tragic events of the Easter Rising. In the single-movement String Quintet (completed in January 1933) Bax draws some luscious, almost orchestral sonorities from his chosen forces. Scored for horn, piano and string sextet, the 1934 Octet (labelled "Serenade" on the short score) is a two-movement work of strong appeal and engaging charm: the magically evocative opening brings with it echoes of those unforgettable horn solos in the Third Symphony's central *Lento*, while the icy glitter of the piano part from 1'53" in the second-movement scherzo momentarily conjures up the far-Northern landscape of *Winter Legends*. The *Threnody and Scherzo* for bassoon, harp and string sextet of 1936 is perhaps less immediately striking. The writing is as fluent and accomplished as ever but the melodic material isn't quite as fresh as one might have wished. By contrast, the Concerto for flute, oboe, harp and string quartet now stands revealed as one of Bax's most likeable chamber offerings. This is a captivating transcription for septet of a Sonata for flute and harp from 1928 and proves to be an exquisite gem, its deft and joyous outer movements framing a lovely central "Cavatina". The dedicated, sensitive performances have been accorded warm, transparent sound.

Bax Nonet[a]. Oboe Quintet[b]. Elegiac Trio[c]. Clarinet Sonata[d]. Harp Quintet[e]. **Nash Ensemble** ([ac]Philippa Davies, fl; [ab]Gareth Hulse, ob; [ad]Michael Collins, cl; [abe]Marcia Crayford, [be]Iris Juda, [a]Elizabeth Wexler, vns; [abce]Roger Chase, va; [abce]Christopher van Kampen, vc; [a]Duncan McTier, db; [ce]Skaila Kanga, hp; [ad]Ian Brown, pf). Hyperion Ⓕ CDA66807 (73 minutes: DDD: 5/96). Recorded 1995. *Gramophone Editor's choice.*   ⒼⒼ
A truly first-rate modern recording of Bax's Nonet. What a bewitching creation it is, overflowing with beguiling invention and breathtakingly imaginative in its instrumental resource (the sounds created are often almost orchestral). Bax worked on the Nonet at the same time (1929-30) as he was composing his Third Symphony and there are striking similarities between the two works. The Nash Ensemble (under the direction of Ian Brown) give a masterly, infinitely subtle reading – a worthy successor to the classic 1937 recording with the Griller Quartet and distinguished colleagues (now beautifully refurbished by Dutton Laboratories). The remainder of the disc brings comparable pleasure. The delightful Oboe Quintet (written for Leon Goossens in 1922) receives immensely characterful treatment, especially the jaunty, Irish-jig finale (such sparkling, richly communicative playing). The same is true of the lovely Harp Quintet, which is essayed here with a rapt intensity and delicious poise. In the hands of these stylish artists, the *Elegiac Trio* possesses a delicacy and gentle poignancy that are really quite captivating. That just leaves the engaging Clarinet Sonata, a work that has fared well in the recording studio over the last few years. Suffice to report, Michael Collins and Ian Brown are compelling advocates, and theirs is a performance to set beside (if not supersede) those of Emma Johnson and Malcolm Martineau and Janet Hilton and Keith Swallow. Beautiful sound and expert balance throughout.

Additional recommendations ...
...Clarinet Sonata. *Coupled with works by various composers.* **Pamela Woods** (ob); **Audubon Quartet.** Telarc Ⓕ CD80205 (55 minutes: DDD: 10/89).
...Clarinet Sonata. *Coupled with works by various composers.* **Emma Johnson** (cl); **Malcolm Martineau** (pf). ASV Ⓕ CDDCA891 (74 minutes: DDD: 7/94).
...Nonet. *Coupled with works by various composers.* **Joseph Slater** (fl); **Leon Goossens** (ob); **Frederick Thurston** (cl); **Anthony Pini** (vc); **Victor Watson** (db); **Maria Korchinska** (hp); **Griller Quartet.** Dutton Laboratories mono Ⓜ CDAX8014* (72 minutes: ADD: 12/95).
...Oboe Quintet. *Coupled with works by* **Bliss** *and* **Britten** **Gordon Hunt** (ob); **Tale Quartet.** BIS Ⓕ CD763 (51 minutes: DDD: 10/97).

Bax Piano Trio in B flat major.
Holst Short Piano Trio in E major.
Stanford Piano Trio No. 2 in G minor, Op. 73. **Pirasti Trio** (Nicholas Miller, vn; Alison Wells, vc; Jeffrey Sharkey, pf). ASV Ⓕ CDDCA925 (72 minutes: DDD: 9/95). Recorded 1994.
A valuable, uncommonly rewarding collection. Especially impressive here is the Stanford Second Piano Trio of 1899 (there are two others, dating from 1889 and 1918). This is immensely civilized music, solidly constructed, inventive, eloquent (especially in the *Andante* slow movement) and always distinguished by impeccable craft. Holst completed his Trio in E in 1894, a year into his studies at the Royal College of Music. Stanford was his composition tutor from 1893 to 1898, and the present work (one of his "early horrors", as he later labelled his student efforts) is melodious, neat and unpretentious – only at the rapt close of the central *Adagio* do we catch just the merest whiff of the composer's mature style. Bax's Trio, on the other hand, dates from towards the end of his career (the score was finished in January 1946). It is a most attractive, engagingly tuneful creation, its comparatively relaxed demeanour characteristic of Bax's later manner. These are fervent, beautifully accomplished performances and the sound is admirably natural.

Bax Cello Sonata in E flat major. Folk Tale. Cello Sonatina in D major. Legend-Sonata in F sharp
minor. **Bernard Gregor-Smith** (vc); **Yolande Wrigley** (pf). ASV Ⓔ CDDCA896 (76 minutes: DDD:
8/94). Recorded 1993.
There are three beautiful slow movements here, and all three of them are wistful backward glances;
quotes from *Spring Fire*, *The Garden of Fand*, and, in the *Sonatina*, Delius's *Brigg Fair*. Poignant
regret for the vanished past is one of the things one expects from Bax; another is that unstable
alternation of mood out of which he paradoxically wove some of his most powerful symphonic
structures. That is here too, most overtly in the first movement of the E flat Sonata. Old Bax hands
will know his way of reducing a melody to its basic rhythm and then allowing that to sprout new
melodic ideas. That happens here; so does that other Bax ploy of touching an apparently new vein,
but only in order to spark a coda. The outer movements of the *Sonatina* are problem- and shadow-
free Bax; the *Folk Tale* is no such thing, but another haunted recollection, grave, poignant and angry
by turns. The Irish dream? Lost love? Vanished youth? The essence of Bax would perhaps vanish if
we were able to put a precise label on his nostalgias, sorrows and regrets. All four pieces are given
strong and eloquent performances, and are cleanly recorded; Gregor-Smith's tone is sinewy rather
than plummily rich, which serves the composer well.

Bax Whirligig. What the Minstrel told us. Legend. Dream in exile. A mountain mood.
Mediterranean. Serpent Dance. Ceremonial Dance. The slave girl. In the Night. Toccata. Paean.
Salzburg Sonata in B flat major – Lento espressivo[a]. **Eric Parkin** (pf). Chandos Ⓕ CHAN9561
(77 minutes: DDD: 6/98). Recorded 1996 and [a]1991.
This is a welcome addition to Eric Parkin's previous Bax anthologies for Chandos. The playful
Whirligig (written in 1920) launches proceedings in delectable style. Published that same year (though
probably conceived in 1913), the dashing *Toccata* bears an inscription to Hamilton Harty. Harriet
Cohen (who described the *Toccata* as a "knockabout, virtuoso piece") was the recipient of the 1915
'melody and variations' entitled *A mountain mood* and the magnificent *What the Minstrel told us*. This
haunting ballad was composed in 1919, the year of Bax's first visit to his beloved Ireland since the
1916 Easter Rising (an event which shook the composer to his core), and the very essence of that
island seems to course through its enchanted veins. A similar bardic sweep informs the wintry *Legend*
from 1935. No less entrancing is *Dream in exile*: not only does it boast a yearningly poignant
secondary idea, but the writing is exquisite in its pellucid assurance. Elsewhere, that winsome picture-
postcard, *Mediterranean*, and the confidently striding *Paean* will already be familiar from their
subsequent orchestral versions, while both the *Serpent Dance* and *Ceremonial Dance* derive from
Bax's incidental music to *The Truth about the Russian Dancers*, which featured the legendary Ballets
Russes ballerina, Tamara Karsavina, and dates from 1920. That same year, Karsavina was also the
dedicatee of *The slave girl*, an exotic and sinuous confection. The brooding 1914 passacaglia, *In the
Night* had to wait until 1986 for its first professional airing (in a BBC broadcast given by Martin
Roscoe). The pretty, Mozartian pastiche of the *Lento espressivo* from the so-called *Salzburg Sonata*
of 1937 was recorded as long ago as June 1991; the remaining items date from August 1996. Parkin
is an unfailingly perceptive exponent of this ravishing repertoire and he has been well served by the
Chandos technicians. A self-recommending issue for all Baxians.

Bax Epithalamium[a]. I sing of a maiden. Lord, thou hast told us. [a]Magnificat. Mater ora filium.
This worldës joie.
Villette Attende Domine. Hymne à la Vierge. O magnum mysterium. O sacrum convivium. Salve
regina. **Rodolfus Choir / Ralph Allwood** with [a]**Christopher Hughes** (org). Herald Ⓕ HAVPCD176
(60 minutes: DDD: 9/95). Recorded 1993.
This is rather special. The Rodolfus Choir's members, aged between 16 and 25, are graduates of Ralph
Allwood's popular Eton Choral Courses for young singers. Allwood has the gift of exploiting the
vocal colour of young voices to thrilling effect (only the tenors are very occasionally betrayed by their
youth), but he also manages to harness the sense of zeal that characterizes the best endeavours of
young people together with a remarkable corporate musical intelligence and sensitivity. The sound is
lovely within a wide dynamic and tonal spectrum but there is real understanding also, not just of text
and mood, but of musical processes as well. That is just as well since this programme is a sumptuous
pudding of rich choral textures and harmonic elaboration. Pierre Villette (b.1926) was Director of the
Besançon and Aix-en-Provence Conservatoires, and his Latin motets written between 1944 and 1983
mine a harmonic vein somewhat akin to Poulenc at his most consistently gorgeous. In other hands it
might all seem just too self-indulgent, but here the added-note harmonies are balanced with
painstaking delicacy and the phrasing is controlled eloquently and without exaggeration. The meat of
the programme is in the Bax works. The unaccompanied works are masterpieces, in particular *This
worldës joie* and above all *Mater ora filium*, which makes technical demands almost equal to those of
the big Richard Strauss motets while possessing greater emotional truth and urgency. Fine though the
performances by Paul Spicer's Finzi Singers are, Allwood's direction has even more poetry and the
Rodolfus Choir rise above the technical challenges to convey a sense of radiance and elation. There
is a perceptive accompanying note by David Goode and, despite the varied size of the choir in
different pieces, the recording (made in Eton College Chapel) of the *a cappella* works is perfectly
judged in perspective, acoustic and clarity. A marvellous disc.

Additional recommendations ...

...I sing of a maiden. This worldës joie. Mater ora filium. Five Greek Folk-Songs. *Coupled with works by* **Howells** Finzi Singers **/** Paul Spicer. Chandos Ⓕ CHAN9139 (63 minutes: DDD: 6/93).

...Mater ora filium. I sing of a maiden. This worldës joie. *Coupled with works by* **Vaughan Williams** and **Finzi** Soloists; King's College Choir, Cambridge **/** Stephen Cleobury. EMI British Composers Ⓜ CDM5 65595-2 (73 minutes: [a]ADD/DDD: 1/97).

Further listening ...

...Cello Concerto[a]. Northern Ballad No. 3 – Prelude for a Solemn Occasion. Cortège. Mediterranean. Overture to a Picaresque Comedy. [a]**Raphael Wallfisch** (vc); **London Philharmonic Orchestra / Bryden Thomson.** Chandos CHAN8494 (11/87).

...Violin Concerto. Legend. Romantic Overture. Golden Eagle – incidental music. [a]**Lydia Mordkovitch** (vn); **London Philharmonic Orchestra / Bryden Thomson.** Chandos CHAN9003 (4/92).   Ⓖ

...Symphonic Variations in E major. Morning Song, "Maytime in Sussex". **Margaret Fingerhut** (pf); **London Philharmonic Orchestra / Bryden Thomson.** Chandos CHAN8516 (2/88).

...Spring Fire. Symphonic Scherzo. Northern Ballad No. 2. **Royal Philharmonic Orchestra / Vernon Handley.** Chandos CHAN8464 (9/86).   ⒼⒼ

...Winter Legends. Saga Fragment. **Margaret Fingerhut** (pf); **London Philharmonic Orchestra / Bryden Thomson.** Chandos CHAN8484 (2/87).   Ⓖ

...Tintagel[a]. *Coupled with* **Vaughan Williams** Symphony No. 5 in D major[b]. [a]**London Symphony Orchestra**; [b]**Philharmonia Orchestra / Sir John Barbirolli.** EMI British Composers CDM5 65110-2 (3/95).

...Tintagel. *Coupled with works by various composers.* **London Philharmonic Orchestra / Sir Adrian Boult.** Belart mono 461 354-2* (9/97).   Ⓖ

...Piano Quintet[a]. String Quartet No. 2 in E minor. [a]**David Owen Norris** (pf); **Mistry String Quartet.** Chandos CHAN8795 (4/91).

...Violin Sonatas – No. 1 in E major; No. 2 in D major. **Erich Gruenberg** (vn); **John McCabe** (pf). Chandos CHAN8845 (9/90).

...Legend for Viola and Piano. *Coupled with works by various composers.* **Paul Coletti** (va); **Leslie Howard** (pf). Hyperion CDA66687 (10/94). *See review in the Collections section; refer to the Index.*   Ⓖ

...Piano Sonatas – No. 1 in F sharp minor; No. 2 in G major. Lullaby. Country Tune. Winter Waters. **Eric Parkin** (pf). Chandos CHAN8496 (12/87).

...Two Russian Tone Pictures – Nocturne, "May Night in the Ukraine"; Gopak, "National Dance". The Maiden with the Daffodil – Idyll. The Princess's Rose Garden – Nocturne. Apple Blossom Time. On a May Evening. O Dame get up and bake your pies – Variations on a North Country Christmas carol. Nereid. Sleepy Head. A romance. Burlesque. **Eric Parkin** (pf). Chandos CHAN8732 (7/90).

...The Boar's Head. *Coupled with works by various composers.* **London Madrigal Singers / Christopher Bishop; Baccholian Singers of London; Philip Jones Brass Ensemble; English Chamber Orchestra / Ian Humphris.** EMI British Composers CMS5 65123-2 (2/96). *See review in the Collections section; refer to the Index.*

...Enchanted Summer[a]. Walsinghame[b]. Fatherland[c]. [a]**Anne Williams-King**, [ab]**Lynore McWhirter** (sops); [bc]**Martyn Hill** (ten); **Brighton Festival Chorus; Royal Philharmonic Orchestra / Vernon Handley.** Chandos CHAN8625 (10/89).   Ⓖ

Frederic Bayco   British 1913-1970

Suggested listening ...

...Elizabethan masque. *Coupled with works by various composers.* **Pro Arte Orchestra / George Weldon.** EMI British Composers CDM5 66537-2 (1/98). *See review in the Collections section; refer to the Index.*

Francis Bayer   French 1938

Suggested listening ...

...Die Puppenfee – Suite. *Coupled with works by various composers.* **Vienna Philharmonic Orchestra / Rudolf Kempe.** Testament SBT1127 (3/98). *See review in the Collections section; refer to the Index.*

Antonio Bazzini   Italian 1818-1897

Suggested listening ...

...La Ronde des lutins, Op. 25. *Coupled with works by various composers.* **Maxim Vengerov** (vn); **Itamar Golan** (pf). Teldec 9031-77351-2 (4/94). *See review in the Collections section; refer to the Index.*

Amy Beach   American 1867-1944

Suggested listening ...
...Symphony in E minor, Op. 32, "Gaelic". *Coupled with works by* **Barber**
Detroit Symphony Orchestra / Neeme Järvi. Chandos CHAN8958 (10/91). *See review under*
Barber; refer to the Index.   Ⓖ

Sally Beamish   British 1956

Suggested listening ...
...*in dreaming. Coupled with works by various composers.* **Paul Agnew** (ten); **Fretwork.**
Virgin Classics VC5 45217-2 (12/97). *See review in the Collections section; refer to the Index.*

David Bedford   British 1937

Bedford Recorder Concerto. **Piers Adams** (recs); **BBC Symphony Orchestra / Martyn Brabbins.**
NMC (special price) NMCD045S (19 minutes: DDD: 12/97). Recorded 1997.
What could be more experimental on the ultra-pluralistic contemporary scene than a composer
unconcerned with individuality? For much of the time, David Bedford's Recorder Concerto offers the
kind of discreetly accompanied scales and arpeggios that have been standard issue from Vivaldi to
Malcolm Arnold. But surely the post-modern aim is to create a false sense of security, to proceed from
quotation to deconstruction? Well – not really. There are occasional features which can be explained
in terms of Bedford's robust musical past – rhythmic patterns deriving from pop music, even the odd
noise-like instrumental effect. But this concerto has made its peace with history. It tells you to forget
about progress, and to accept that, after a century of exceptional storm and stress, this is the only kind
of music that comes naturally. Piers Adams and the strings of the BBC SO, the ever-adaptable
Martyn Brabbins at the helm, make sure that the Concerto's natural sparkle and sense of fun come
across. The recording places the soloist well to the fore, his progress across the five movements from
bass to sopranino plain for all to hear. In the end, ironically, it is the total lack of radical edge that is
so personal. Bedford's Recorder Concerto may be disconcertingly genteel, but it is definitely not
anonymous.
Further listening ...
...*Fridiof Kennings. Coupled with works by various composers.* **Apollo Saxophone Quartet; Mike**
Hamnett (perc). Argo 443 903-2ZH (8/95). *See review in the Collections section; refer to the Index.*
...*The Golden Wine is Drunk. Coupled with works by various composers.* **Netherlands Chamber**
Choir / John Alldis. Globe GLO5170 (2/98). *See review in the Collections section; refer to the*
Index.

Ludwig van Beethoven   German 1770-1827

Beethoven Piano Concertos – No. 1 in C major, Op. 15; No. 2 in B flat major, Op. 19; No. 3 in
C minor, Op. 37; No. 4 in G major, Op. 58; No. 5 in E flat major, "Emperor", Op. 73.
Maurizio Pollini (pf); **Berlin Philharmonic Orchestra / Claudio Abbado.** DG Ⓟ 439 770-2GH3
(three discs: 174 minutes: DDD: 6/94). Recorded live in 1992-93.   ⒼⒼⒼ
Whilst Gilels and Kempff were alive, Pollini was one of the heirs apparent; now they are gone he is
king – in Beethoven, at least. There may be more individual and idiosyncratic interpreters of the
music but there is none whose command, at best, is sovereign. The Fourth Concerto has a keenly felt
sense of the evolving drama, and a slow movement where the dialogue between piano and orchestra
is spellbinding in its intensity. Maybe Pollini is not yet entirely reconciled to Beethoven's prankish first
concerto, the Concerto No. 2 in B flat. In the outer movements, he can seem brusque: ill-at-ease with
Beethoven in his rumbustious, amorous, Hooray Henry mood. By contrast, the performance of the
Third is a joy from start to finish. Abbado and Pollini are hand-in-glove, which gives this cycle a
cohesiveness which Pollini's previous set (1/89) with Böhm and Jochum rather obviously lacked,
though the Berliners don't play the first movement of the *Emperor* Concerto as commandingly as
Böhm and the Vienna Philharmonic on the earlier recording. But the slow movement goes well, and
the finale is more jovial than before. Musically, though, there are evident gains – in these live
recordings – moments where the tension is palpable in a way that it rarely is in the recording
studio. The sound is full-bodied and immediate, with applauses, a few squeaks, bumps and ill-timed
coughs.
Additional recommendations ...
...Nos. 1-5[a]. Triple Concerto in C major, Op. 56[b]. [a]**Leon Fleisher,** [b]**Eugene Istomin** (pfs);
[b]**Isaac Stern** (vn); [b]**Leonard Rose** (vc); **Philadelphia Orchestra / Eugene Ormandy.**
Sony Classical Ⓑ SB3K48397 (three discs: 205 minutes: ADD).
...Nos. 1-5. **Claudio Arrau** (pf); **Dresden Staatskapelle / Sir Colin Davis.**
Philips Ⓟ 422 149-2PH3 (three discs: 189 minutes: DDD: 1/89).   ⒼⒼ

...Nos. 1-5. Choral Fantasia[a]. **Daniel Barenboim** (pf); [a]**John Alldis Choir; New Philharmonia Orchestra / Otto Klemperer.** EMI Ⓜ CMS7 63360-2 (three discs: 211 minutes: ADD: 3/90).   Ⓖ
...Nos. 1-5. 25 Bagatelles. Presto in C minor, Wo052. Allegretto in C major, Wo056. **John Lill** (pf); **City of Birmingham Symphony Orchestra / Walter Weller.**
Chandos Ⓕ CHAN9084/6 (three discs: 235 minutes: DDD: 1/93).
...Nos. 1-4. Romances. **Stephen Kovacevich** (pf); **Arthur Grumiaux** (vn); **BBC Symphony Orchestra / Sir Colin Davis; Concertgebouw Orchestra / Bernard Haitink.**
Philips Duo Ⓜ 442 577-2PM2 (two discs: 152 minutes: ADD: 8/95).
...Nos. 1-5[a]. Two Rondos, Op. 51. Piano Sonatas – No. 8 in C minor, Op. 13, "Pathetique". No. 14 in C sharp minor, Op. 27 No. 2, "Moonlight". **Radu Lupu** (pf); [a]**Israel Philharmonic Orchestra / Zubin Mehta.** Decca Ⓜ 448 000-2DM3 (three discs: 225 minutes: ADD/DDD: 3/96).

Beethoven Piano Concertos – No. 1 in C major, Op. 15[a]; No. 2 in B flat major, Op. 19[b]; No. 3 in C minor, Op 37[c]; No. 4 in G major, Op. 58[d]; No. 5 in E flat major, Op 73, "Emperor"[e]. Rondos, Op. 51[f]. **Wilhelm Kempff** (pf); **Berlin Philharmonic Orchestra / Paul van Kempen.** DG Dokumente mono Ⓜ 435 744-2GDO3* (three discs: 189 minutes: ADD: 4/93). Item marked [a] from DGM18129 (6/56), [b]DG16071 (9/56), [c]DGM18130 (12/55), [d]DG16072 (9/55), [e]DGM18131 (7/55), [f]EPL30121 (3/57). Recorded 1953. *Gramophone classical 100.*   ⒼⒼⒼ
Wilhelm Kempff's Berlin cycle with Paul van Kempen has long been a collectors' item, often preferred to Kempff's famous 1960s Leitner set, also on DG. Apart from Kempff's whimsical though not ineffective line in home-grown cadenzas, these are exemplary performances in matters of style and execution. Yet they are something more. The 1953 cycle gives an extraordinary sense of the imaginative dimension of the first four concertos. As the eighteenth century turned into the nineteenth so the mists of romanticism began to drift across the landscape. It was what Gombrich, writing of the painter Claude, called the concreteness and calm of a dream world. Kempff's cycle catches that mood in a very special way. The 1960s stereo set has an equally fine First Concerto and a better recorded *Emperor*. There is generally more glitter and dash. But the Second, Third and Fourth Concerto Concertos are all more revealingly realized in 1953. The mono recordings have been strikingly refocused. What on LP sounded recessed here takes on a startlingly physical immediacy. Whether this is an advance is debatable. At first it seems to be all gain: the slightly dim sounding ritornellos given a new weight and presence. On the other hand, the recordings are now rather more wearing on the ear. In the *Emperor* Concerto, for example, the mono recording sounds – and makes the piano sound – much coarser than one had remembered. However, with suitable doctoring of filters you will be able to come up with a tolerable mix of new-found immediacy and old-fashioned clarity and warmth. A marvellous set, none the less.

Beethoven Piano Concertos – No. 1 in C major, Op. 15[a]; No. 2 in B flat major, Op. 19[b]. **Wilhelm Kempff** (pf); **Berlin Philharmonic Orchestra / Ferdinand Leitner.** DG Galleria Ⓜ 419 856-2GGA (65 minutes: ADD: 9/88). Item marked [a] from SLPM138774 (6/62), [b]SLPM138775 (9/62). Recorded 1960s.   ⒼⒼ
The Second Piano Concerto was in fact written before the First, and recent research suggests that an initial version of the so-called Second Concerto dates back to Beethoven's teenage years. If the Second Concerto inevitably reflects eighteenth-century classical style, it has Beethoven's familiar drive and energy and a radical use of form and technique. The First Concerto pre-dates the revolutionary *Eroica* Symphony by some eight years and still shows classical influences, but it is on a larger scale than the Second Concerto, and has greater powers of invention. Kempff's recording of these two works dates from the early 1960s, but the sound quality is pleasingly open and full-bodied, so that the soloist's pearly, immaculate tone quality is heard to good effect. Kempff and Leitner enjoy what is obviously a close rapport and their aristocratic, Olympian but poetic music-making suits both works admirably.
Additional recommendations ...
...No. 1[a]. *Coupled with works by* **Mozart** **Walter Gieseking** (pf); **Berlin State Opera Orchestra / Hans Rosbaud.** APR mono Ⓜ APR5511* (75 minutes: ADD).
...Nos. 1 and 2. **Murray Perahia** (pf); **Concertgebouw Orchestra / Bernard Haitink.**
CBS Ⓕ SK42177 (70 minutes: DDD: 4/87).
...Nos. 2 and 3. **Till Fellner** (pf); **Academy of St Martin in the Fields / Sir Neville Marriner.**
Erato Ⓕ 4509-98539-2 (66 minutes: DDD: 9/95).
...Nos. 2 and 3. **Michael Roll** (pf); **Royal Philharmonic Orchestra / Howard Shelley.**
Tring International Royal Philharmonic Collection Ⓢ TRP076 (65 minutes: DDD: 1/97).

Beethoven Piano Concertos – No. 1 in C major, Op. 15 (with composer's cadenzas); No. 2 in B flat major, Op. 19. **Lars Vogt** (pf); **City of Birmingham Symphony Orchestra / Sir Simon Rattle.** EMI Ⓕ CDC5 56266-2 (66 minutes: DDD: 3/97). Includes a bonus disc of Piano Concerto No. 1 with Glenn Gould's cadenzas. Recorded 1995. *Gramophone Editor's record of the month.*   ⒼⒼ
This is a remarkable record, as fine a recorded account of these two concertos as we have had for many a long year. Alongside these performances, most rivals sound unduly one-dimensional. Vogt's playing in the two slow movements is wonderfully pellucid, but deep too. One thinks of Kempff, here and in the exquisite shaping of the lyric meditation midway through the Second Concerto's first

movement. The CBSO's playing is also a miracle of finely wrought colours and despite the fact that these performances have evidently been worked out with great care, they remain spontaneously alive in a way that is rare on record. In the B flat Concerto, the dialogue between soloist and orchestra in the first movement has a Haydnesque alertness. The slow movement is exquisitely done; the finale is an almost perfect re-enactment of Beethoven's impish game of musical hide-and-seek. Vogt is a great admirer of Glenn Gould. So much so that we have here a rather strange 'bonus'. The performance of the First Concerto is reprinted on a separate CD not with Beethoven's cadenzas (Vogt uses the big third cadenza in the first movement of the main performance) but with Gould's. Although it would probably not sway you one way or another in deciding whether or not to buy this disc, who needs further persuasion when faced with performances of this order of delight?

Additional recommendations ...

...No. 1[a]; No. 2[b]; No. 3[c]; No. 4[d]; No. 5[d]. **Glenn Gould** (pf); [abc]**Columbia Symphony Orchestra;** [d]**New York Philharmonic Orchestra;** [e]**American Symphony Orchestra / [a]Vladimir Golschmann;** [bcd]**Leonard Bernstein;** [e]**Leopold Stokowski.**
Sony Glenn Gould Edition Ⓜ SM3K52632 (three discs: 180 minutes: DDD: 4/93).

...Nos. 1 and 2. **Mitsuko Uchida** (pf); **Bavarian Radio Symphony Orchestra / Kurt Sanderling.**
Philips Ⓕ 454 468-2PH (70 minutes: DDD: 4/98).

Beethoven Piano Concertos – No. 1 in C major, Op. 15; No. 2 in B flat major, Op. 19. Rondo in B flat major, WoO6. **Robert Levin** (fps); **Orchestre Révolutionnaire et Romantique / Sir John Eliot Gardiner.** Archiv Produktion Ⓕ 453 438-2AH (75 minutes: DDD: A/97). ✍ Recorded 1996.
What is striking about Levin's Beethoven concertos is not so much the distinctive sound world of his chosen instruments and orchestral accompaniment, as the subtlety of imaginative insight, vigour of intellect and sheer delight expressed in his music-making. This reaches boiling-point in his thrillingly improvised lead-ins and cadenzas where instinct so vibrantly recharges understanding. The period instruments of the ORR and the carefully chosen fortepianos are simply the highly efficient tools with which the musicians' vision is shaped. And the tension of newly assured, propulsive energy coiled within the first movement of the Concerto No. 1 in C surely re-creates about as convincingly as possible Beethoven's sheer excitement and struggle in working with both a developing language and fast-evolving instruments. But first things first. The dancing dotted rhythms of the opening of the Concerto No. 2 point to where this music came from as much as where it is going to. As Levin writes in his penetrating booklet-notes, in matters of rhetoric and thematic development Beethoven looked to Haydn; but his rhythmic and harmonic vocabulary was Mozart's. Levin's deep study of both enriches his voyage into Beethoven. The silvery treble of this fortepiano makes this movement far from earthbound; and the more luminous voice of the instrument chosen for the C major Concerto guides the articulation and breathing of its second movement in such a way that its pulse seems to find new, steady health. This disc also generously offers a revealing reconstruction of Beethoven's discarded and as yet unpublished *Rondo* in B flat.

Beethoven Piano Concertos – No. 1 in C major, Op. 15; No. 5 in E flat major, Op. 73, "Emperor". **Michael Roll** (pf); **Royal Philharmonic Orchestra / Howard Shelley.** Tring International Royal Philharmonic Collection Ⓢ TRP075 (70 minutes: DDD: 4/98). Recorded 1995.　　Ⓖ
This is a fresh, festive and properly assertive account of the *Emperor* Concerto, coupled with a performance of the C major Concerto (an unusual pairing but a shrewd one) in which the earlier work reveals its own imperial ambitions. Such faults as there are, are usually faults in the right direction. The finale of the C major Concerto is here very fast and fierce: quicker than Beethoven's *Rondo-Allegro*, and not especially *scherzando*. What comes out is the aggressive, iconoclastic side of Beethoven's personality. It is also a big-boned performance, deploying a substantial orchestra in a lively acoustic. This suits the *Emperor* but could be thought to give the earlier work a slightly bloated feel. If, in the final analysis, it does not, it is because the performance itself has an all-redeeming urgency and spontaneity about it. In the end, what marks these performances out from their more run-of-the-mill rivals is the musicianly accord that exists between Michael Roll and his pianist-conductor, Howard Shelley. The performance of the *Emperor* is strong and grammatical but it is no mere hammer-and-tongs affair; the visionary side of the work is caught in a host of fine shadings and quiet accommodations of rhythm and sound between piano and orchestra. There is one such accommodation in the slow movement of the *Emperor*. It is fleeting and barely audible and we shall not say where it is since you must find it for yourself. What was it the poet Blake said about seeing a "World in a grain of sand"?

Beethoven Piano Concertos – No. 2 in B flat major, Op. 19; No. 5 in E flat major, Op. 73, "Emperor". **Evgeni Kissin** (pf); **Philharmonia Orchestra / James Levine.** Sony Classical Ⓕ SK62926 (69 minutes: DDD: 9/97). Recorded 1996. *Gramophone Editor's choice.*　　Ⓖ
From his very first entry, in the B flat Concerto, Kissin is revealed as a Beethoven player of great articulacy, brilliance and sensitivity after the manner of such pianists as Kempff, Solomon, and Gilels. The playing is vital and fluent, the technique awesome, not least in the way Kissin is able to refine his tone and taper dynamics in the high-lying coloratura passages where Beethoven's writing is at its most inspired and rarefied. The recitative at the end of the slow movement is predictably beautiful: intense and otherworldly. Kissin's is, of course, a technique put exclusively to the service of the music. Only in the first movement cadenza does he trade in disciplined artistry for a gaudy display

of tricks of the pianist's trade, just as Beethoven intended. Kissin also takes Beethoven at his word in the finale of the B flat Concerto: *Molto allegro* it says and *Molto allegro* it is. Levine draws from the Philharmonia playing that is both spirited and engaged. The recorded sound is admirable, too: strong and clean yet appropriately intimate. The performance of the *Emperor* Concerto is also very fine. If you take the view that this is essentially a symphony with piano obbligato, you may hanker after a grander kind of musical theatre than that provided by Levine. He directs with decision and accompanies superbly. Kissin, too, plays with great flair and technical security. If there is a problem here it is with the articulation of the simple-seeming lyric statements where a degree of self-consciousness occasionally creeps in: where the flow is arrested and music suddenly seems to be walking on stilts. There is an element of this in the slow movement, though Kissin's playing of the bleak, trailing 24-bar-long *diminuendo* close is masterly. Kissin takes a rather dashing view of the finale. This is very much a young man's view of the music, but weighty too, such is the power of his technique.

Beethoven Piano Concertos – No. 3 in C minor, Op. 37; No. 4 in G major, Op. 58ᵃ.
   Mitsuko Uchida (pf); **Royal Concertgebouw Orchestra / Kurt Sanderling.** Philips Ⓕ 446 082-2PH
   (72 minutes: DDD: 5/96). Recorded 1994, item marked ᵃ recorded live.   Ⓖ
The playing on this formidable pairing of works is at once brilliant and sensitive, rigorous and free-spirited. Of the two performances, that of the Fourth Concerto is perhaps the more memorable. Uchida re-creates the solo part with flair and imagination, and dazzling technique. And what a wonderful voyage of discovery the slow movement is here. If the performance seems a touch mellower and more confiding than that of the C minor Concerto, it is perhaps because it was being played live to an audience in the Concertgebouw, a hall whose famous acoustic can be a shade severe when empty. What we have here in the Fourth Concerto is a first-rate concert-hall perspective (with the applause edited out). Some might argue that the C minor Concerto is a severe piece. Certainly, this generally appears to be Sanderling's and Uchida's view of the first movement. The performance is wonderfully alive, which is more than can be said for 75 per cent of extant recordings of this music, but there are pianists – Kempff for example – who has made the music of the first movement move a shade more gracefully and songfully than Uchida does here. The slow movement, by contrast, emerges as a wonderfully rapt soliloquy for the solo pianist, the orchestra doing little more than make simple acts of obeisance before the soloist. (Rather stiff acts of obeisance: throughout the C minor Concerto Sanderling is inclined to make the orchestra sit rather heavily on down-beats and *sforzandos*.) The recording of the C minor Concerto is best heard at a safe distance. Played too loud or heard too close it can seem unduly fierce and odd blemishes show up.
Additional recommendations ...
...Nos. 3 and 4. **Wilhelm Kempff** (pf); **Berlin Philharmonic Orchestra / Ferdinand Leitner.**
   DG Galleria Ⓜ 419 467-2GGA (67 minutes: ADD: 9/87).
...Nos. 3 and 4. **Alfred Brendel** (pf); **London Philharmonic Orchestra / Bernard Haitink.**
   Philips Silver Line Classics Ⓜ 420 861-2PSL (69 minutes: ADD: 5/88).
...No. 3. Andante favori in F major. 25 Bagatelles. **Vladimir Ashkenazy** (pf); **Vienna Philharmonic
   Orchestra / Zubin Mehta.** Decca Ⓜ 436 471-2DM (68 minutes: DDD: 7/93).
...No. 3ᵃ. Piano Trio in B flat major, Op. 97, "Archduke"ᵇ. ᵇ**Henry Holst** (vn); ᵇ**Anthony Pini** (vc);
   Solomon (pf); ᵃ**BBC Symphony Orchestra / Sir Adrian Boult.**
   Dutton Laboratories mono Ⓑ CDLX7015* (71 minutes: ADD: 11/95).

Beethoven Piano Concertos – No. 4 in G major, Op. 58ᵃ; No. 5 in E flat major, Op. 73,
   "Emperor"ᵇ. **Wilhelm Kempff** (pf); **Berlin Philharmonic Orchestra / Ferdinand Leitner.**
   DG The Originals Ⓜ 447 402-2GOR* (71 minutes: ADD: 5/95). Item marked ᵃ from
   SLPM138775 (9/62), ᵇSLPM138777 (5/62). Recorded 1961.   ⒼⒼ
Kempff was never a heavyweight among Beethoven pianists. What he had was intellect and imagination in perfect balance, a fabulous touch, great rhythmic *élan*, and a kind of improvisatory zeal that – translated into other terms – can best be described as a true and abiding sense of wonder. In the Fourth Piano Concerto you may be less than happy with his decision to use his own cadenzas, for all that they are an earnest of Kempff's own improvisatory instinct. But the performance as a whole is such a joy, so light-filled, that even that qualification tends to fade into insignificance. And how beautifully Leitner and the Berlin Philharmonic accompany Kempff. This was the new young Berlin Philharmonic of the early 1960s, poet-musicians to a man, trained to listen and respond and then, in performance, take wing into precisely those areas of mind and imagination that were Kempff's own natural habitat. The 1961 Fourth sounds especially radiant in these transfers. Despite a touch of gruffness in some of the orchestral tuttis in the *Emperor* it, too, generally comes up with glistening clarity, the balances between solo and orchestral voicings flawlessly judged by the balance engineer and the musicians themselves. A record like this is a joy to return to.
Additional recommendations ...
...No. 5ᵃ. **Schumann** Piano Concerto in A minor, Op. 54ᵇ. **Walter Gieseking** (pf);
   ᵃ**Berlin Radio Orchestra / Artur Rother;** ᵇ**Berlin Philharmonic Orchestra / Wilhelm Furtwängler.**
   Music and Arts ᵃstereo/ᵇmono Ⓕ CD815* (67 minutes: ADD).
...No. 5. **Murray Perahia** (pf); **Royal Concertgebouw Orchestra / Bernard Haitink.**
   Sony Classical Masterworks Ⓕ SK42330 (DDD: 11/87).

...No. 5. **Arturo Benedetti Michelangeli** (pf); **Vienna Symphony Orchestra / Carlo Maria Giulini.** DG Ⓕ 419 249-2GH (42 minutes: ADD: 2/88). ⒼⒼ
...No. 5. Choral Fantasia in C minor, Op. 80[a]. **Melvyn Tan** (fp); [a]**Schütz Choir of London; London Classical Players / Roger Norrington.** EMI Reflexe Ⓔ CDC7 49965-2 (52 minutes: DDD: 4/90). ✍
...No. 5. Triple Concerto in C major, Op. 56[a]. **Leon Fleisher** (pf); **Cleveland Orchestra / George Szell; Eugene Istomin** (pf); [a]**Isaac Stern** (vn); [a]**Leonard Rose** (vc); [a]**Philadelphia Orchestra / Eugene Ormandy.** Sony Classical Essential Classics Ⓜ SBK46549 (74 minutes: ADD: 8/91). ⒼⒼⒼ
...No. 5. Grosse Fuge in B flat major, Op. 133 (arr. string orch.). **Australian Chamber Orchestra / Stephen Kovacevich** (pf). EMI Eminence Ⓜ CD-EMX2184 (53 minutes: DDD: 3/92). ⒼⒼ
...No. 5. Choral Fantasia[a]. **Alfred Brendel** (pf); **London Philharmonic** [a]**Choir and Orchestra / Bernard Haitink.** Philips Insignia Ⓜ 434 148-2PM (61 minutes: ADD: 7/92).
...Nos. 4[a] and 5[b]. **Bach** Keyboard Partita in B flat major, BWV825 – Menuets I and II; Gigue. **Walter Gieseking** (pf); [a]**Saxon State Orchestra / Karl Böhm;** [b]**Vienna Philharmonic Orchestra / Bruno Walter.** APR mono Ⓜ APR5512* (68 minutes: ADD: 3/96).
...No. 5. Fantasy for Piano, Chorus and Orchestra in C minor, Op. 80[a]. **Robert Levin** (fp); [a]**Monteverdi Choir; Orchestre Révolutionnaire et Romantique / Sir John Eliot Gardiner.** Archiv Produktion Ⓕ 447 771-2AH (60 minutes: DDD: 12/96). ✍

Beethoven Piano Concertos – No. 4 in G major, Op. 58[a]; No. 5 in E flat major, Op. 73, "Emperor"[b]. **Emil Gilels** (pf); **Philharmonia Orchestra / Leopold Ludwig.** Testament Ⓕ SBT1095* (73 minutes: ADD: 4/97). Item marked [a] from Columbia SBO2752 (3/59), [b]Columbia SAX2252 (8/58). Recorded 1957. ⒼⒼⒼ
Gilels's 1957 EMI recording of Beethoven's Fourth Concerto with Leopold Ludwig and the Philharmonia Orchestra is one of the – perhaps *the* most – perfect accounts of the Fourth Concerto ever recorded. Here poetry and virtuosity are held in perfect poise, with Ludwig and the Philharmonia providing a near-ideal accompaniment. The recording is also very fine, though be sure to gauge the levels correctly by first sampling one of the tuttis. If the volume is set too high at the start, you will miss the stealing magic of Gilels's and the orchestra's initial entries and you will be further discomfited by tape hiss that, with the disc played at a properly judged level, is more or less inaudible. The recording of the *Emperor* Concerto is also pretty good, not quite on a par with that of the Fourth Concerto. Ludwig and the orchestra tend to follow Gilels rather than integrate with him in the way that Menges and the Philharmonia do on Solomon's classic 1955 recording. There are times, too, especially in the slow movement, when Gilels's playing borders on the self-indulgent. This is not, however, sufficient reason for overlooking this fine and important Testament reissue.
Additional recommendation ...
...Nos. 2[a], 3[b], 4 [c] and 5[d]. Piano Sonata No. 14 in C sharp minor, Op. 27 No. 2, "Moonlight". **Solomon** (pf); **Philharmonia Orchestra /** [ac]**André Cluytens,** [d]**Herbert Menges;** [b]**BBC Symphony Orchestra / Sir Adrian Boult.** EMI Références mono Ⓜ CHS5 65503-2* (two discs: 150 minutes: ADD: 11/95).

Beethoven Piano Concerto No. 4 in G major, Op. 58. Triple Concerto in C major, Op. 56[a]. [a]**Jean-Jacques Kantorow** (vn); [a]**Raphael Wallfisch** (vc); **Michael Roll** (pf); **Royal Philharmonic Orchestra / Howard Shelley.** Tring International Royal Philharmonic Collection Ⓢ TRP077 (66 minutes: DDD: 6/97). *Gramophone Editor's choice.* Ⓖ
This is another excellent disc in the Tring/RPO Beethoven series. It is beautifully conducted throughout and Michael Roll is an extremely alert and sensitive soloist in the Fourth Piano Concerto. Equally, a team of soloists has been assembled for the Triple Concerto that really is a team, musically distinguished but modest too, no mere aggregation of stars. The playing is fresh, alert, sensitive and full of joy. And the recording? That too is superb. So, are there no drawbacks? Perhaps one could point to an occasional roughness of intonation in Kantorow's playing in the Triple Concerto and the occasional moment of stiffness in Roll's detailing of some of the stellar passagework of the first movement of the Fourth Concerto, but that would be to set up a Council of Perfection into which other things in both performances (including much of Wallfisch's contribution) would be openly admitted. This is a super bargain in every way, a disc you will want to return to for the high finish of its musicianship and its irresistible freshness.

Beethoven Violin Concerto in D major, Op. 61. Two Romances – No. 1 in G major, Op. 40; No. 2 in F major, Op. 50. **Gidon Kremer** (vn); **Chamber Orchestra of Europe / Nikolaus Harnoncourt.** Teldec Ⓕ 9031-74881-2 (57 minutes: DDD: 12/93). Recorded live in 1992. ⒼⒼⒼ
Gidon Kremer offers one of his most commanding performances, both polished and full of flair, magnetically spontaneous from first to last. Rarely do you hear such consistently pure tone in this work and the orchestral writing too is superbly realized, with magical sounds in the slow movement in particular. It has become customary to treat the long first movement as expansively as possible – Chung and Perlman provide outstanding examples – but Kremer takes a much more urgent view and after his thoughtful and dedicated, slightly understated reading of the slow movement, he and Harnoncourt round the performance off magically with a finale that skips along the more infectiously thanks to light, clean articulation and textures. Traditional performances seem heavyweight by comparison. The controversial point for some will be the cadenza in the first movement where he uses

a transcription of the big cadenza which Beethoven wrote for his piano arrangement of the work. However, this is altogether one of the most refreshing versions of the concerto ever committed to record, backed up by crisp, unsentimental readings of the two *Romances*.

Additional recommendations ...

...Violin Concerto[a]. **Mozart** Violin Concerto in A major, K219, "Turkish".
Berlin Philharmonic Orchestra / Wolfgang Schneiderhan (vn), [a]**Eugen Jochum.**
DG The Originals Ⓜ 447 403-2GOR* (75 minutes: ADD).
...Violin Concerto. **Itzhak Perlman** (vn); **Philharmonia Orchestra / Carlo Maria Giulini.**
EMI Ⓕ CDC7 47002-2 (44 minutes: DDD: 2/84).
...Violin Concerto[a]. **Mendelssohn** Violin Concerto in E minor, Op. 64[b]. **Yehudi Menuhin** (vn);
[a]**Philharmonia Orchestra;** [b]**Berlin Philharmonic Orchestra / Wilhelm Furtwängler.**
EMI Références Ⓜ CDH7 69799-2* (71 minutes: ADD: 10/89).   ⒼⒼ
...Violin Concerto. Two Romances. **Itzhak Perlman** (vn); **Berlin Philharmonic Orchestra /**
Daniel Barenboim. EMI Ⓕ CDC7 49567-2 (61 minutes: DDD: 11/89).
...Piano Concerto in D major, Op. 61 (transcribed by the composer from the Violin Concerto)[a].
Two Romances[b]. [a]**Daniel Barenboim** (pf); [b]**Pinchas Zukerman** (vn);
[a]**English Chamber Orchestra,** [b]**London Philharmonic Orchestra / Daniel Barenboim.**
DG Galleria Ⓜ 429 179-2GGA (61 minutes: ADD: 4/90).
...Violin Concerto. *Coupled with works by various composers.* **Fritz Kreisler** (vn); **Berlin State Opera**
Orchestra / Leo Blech. Biddulph mono Ⓜ LAB049/50* (two discs: 155 minutes: ADD: 9/92).
...Violin Concerto. Romance No. 2. **Oscar Shumsky** (vn); **Philharmonia Orchestra / Andrew Davis.**
ASV Quicksilva Ⓑ CDQS6080 (54 minutes: ADD: 12/92).   ⒼⒼ
...Violin Concerto. **Mendelssohn** Violin Concerto in E minor, Op. 64.
Kyung-Wha Chung (vn); **Vienna Philharmonic Orchestra / Kyrill Kondrashin.**
Decca Ⓜ 430 752-2DM (71 minutes: DDD: 2/93).
...Violin Concerto. **Sibelius** Violin Concerto in D minor, Op. 47. **David Oistrakh** (vn); **Stockholm**
Festival Orchestra / Sixten Ehrling. Testament mono Ⓕ SBT1032* (75 minutes: ADD: 7/94).
...Violin Concerto (with first movement cadenzas by Auer, Beethoven, Busoni, David, two by
Joachim, Kreisler, Laub, Milstein, Saint-Saëns, Schnittke, Vieuxtemps, Wieniawski and Ysaÿe).
Ruggiero Ricci (vn); **Chianti Orchestra / Piero Bellugi.**
Biddulph Ⓜ LAW017 (78 minutes: DDD: 6/96).
...Violin Concerto. **Bruch** Violin Concerto No. 1 in G minor, Op. 26.
Ida Haendel (vn); **Philharmonic Orchestra / Rafael Kubelík.**
Testament mono Ⓕ SBT1083* (68 minutes: ADD: 10/96).
...Violin Concerto. **Lalo** Symphonie espagnole, Op. 21. **Bronislaw Huberman** (vn);
Vienna Philharmonic Orchestra / Georg Szell.
APR Signature Series mono Ⓜ APR5506* (64 minutes: ADD: 10/96).
...Romances Nos. 1 and 2. *Coupled with works by various composers.* **Gil Shaham** (vn);
Orpheus Chamber Orchestra. DG Ⓕ 449 923-2GH (58 minutes: DDD: 3/97).
...Violin Concerto[a]. Two Romances[b]. **Sir Yehudi Menuhin** (vn);
[a]**Lucerne Festival Orchestra;** [b]**Philharmonia Orchestra / Wilhelm Furtwängler.**
Testament mono Ⓕ SBT1109* (63 minutes: ADD: 11/97).

Beethoven Triple Concerto in C major, Op. 56[a]. Choral Fantasia in C minor, Op. 80[b]. **Beaux Arts**
Trio ([a]**Ida Kavafian,** vn; [a]**Peter Wiley,** vc; Menahem Pressler, pf); [b]**Mid-German Radio Chorus;**
Leipzig Gewandhaus Orchestra / Kurt Masur. Philips Ⓕ 438 005-2PH (52 minutes: DDD: 6/94).
Recorded 1992-93.   ⒼⒼⒼ
Beethoven Triple Concerto in C major, Op. 56[a]. Choral Fantasia in C minor, Op. 80[b].
[a]**Itzhak Perlman** (vn); [a]**Yo-Yo Ma** (vc); [b]**Chorus of the Deutsche Oper, Berlin; Berlin Philharmonic**
Orchestra / Daniel Barenboim (pf). EMI Ⓕ CDC5 55516-2 (55 minutes: DDD: 12/95).
Text and translation included. Recorded live in 1995.   Ⓖ

Kurt Masur has rarely conducted more electrifying Beethoven performances on disc. The opening tutti of the concerto establishes a speed markedly faster than usual, and if the three soloists modify it slightly, the characteristic which marks this performance is its urgency. But there is no feeling of breathlessness, simply exhilaration. The evenness and clarity of Pressler's articulation in scales and passagework is a delight. As for the brief central meditation, led – like most main themes in this work – by the cello, it flows very warmly and naturally, with Peter Wiley just as rich and positive an artist as Pressler. This now stands as one of the very finest versions of a work which at last looks like being appreciated, not as a rarity, but as a pillar of the Beethoven canon. The *Choral Fantasia* is hardly likely to establish itself in a comparable niche, but this performance is most persuasive. The variations on the corny main theme are regularly pointed with engaging wit, not just by Pressler but by the wind soloists, and the brass sound is glorious. It is rather like having the choral finale of the Ninth anticipated with tongue-in-cheek. Balances are always difficult, not just in this work but notoriously in the Triple Concerto. The soloists are well focused and the orchestral sound is warm and full.

Though EMI's Berlin sound for Barenboim is warm with plenty of presence, and the soloists are justly balanced not too far in front, the textures grow opaque in tuttis. There is also an edge on the solo violin and cello tone, particularly the former, which is occasionally distracting. Even so, anyone responding to the zestful, infectiously sprung Berlin performance is unlikely to be overcritical of the sound, and the brass is very well caught. In this concerto the cellist is the leader, and Yo-Yo Ma's cello tone here is not as ample as, for example, Rostropovich's in an earlier EMI recording from Berlin, along with David Oistrakh and Sviatoslav Richter and with Karajan conducting. Yet Ma's sound brings positive advantage in the tender, hushed intensity of his big opening solo in the slow movement. Choice between this and the Philips disc is hard to assess, and might well be left to a preference between crisp co-ordination and the inspiration of the moment. Unlike many so-called 'live performances' put on disc, these Berlin readings keep a few seconds of applause at the end of each work. If that for the *Fantasia* is markedly more enthusiastic than for the Concerto, the larger forces with chorus may partly account for that, as well as Barenboim's Furtwängler-like whipping up of speed in the final coda, an endearing touch.

Additional recommendations ...

...Triple Concerto[a]. Choral Fantasia[b]. [a]**Christian Funke** (vn); [a]**Jürnjakob Timm** (vc); [a]**Peter Rösel,** [b]**Jörg-Peter Weigle** (pfs); [b]**Leipzig Radio Chorus; Dresden Philharmonic Orchestra / Herbert Kegel.** Capriccio Ⓕ 10 150 (54 minutes: DDD: 9/87).   ⒼⒼ

...Triple Concerto[a]. **Brahms** Double Concerto in A minor, Op. 102[b]. [ab]**David Oistrakh** (vn), [ab]**Mstislav Rostropovich** (vc); [b]**Sviatoslav Richter** (pf); [a]**Berlin Philharmonic Orchestra /** **Herbert von Karajan;** [b]**Cleveland Orchestra / George Szell.** EMI Studio Plus Ⓜ CDM7 64744-2 (70 minutes: ADD: 7/93).   ⒼⒼ

Beethoven Overtures – Coriolan, Op. 62; Die Geschöpfe des Prometheus, Op. 43[a]; Die Ruinen von Athen, Op. 113[b]; Fidelio, Op. 72[c]; Leonore – No. 1, Op. 138[b]; No. 2, Op. 72a[b]; No. 3, Op. 72a[d]; Egmont, Op. 84[c]. **Chamber Orchestra of Europe / Nikolaus Harnoncourt.** Teldec Ⓜ 0630-13140-2 (76 minutes: DDD: 2/97). Item marked [a] recorded live in 1993, [b]1996, [c]1994, [d]1993. *Gramophone Editor's choice.*   ⒼⒼ

Harnoncourt's Beethoven overtures are highly eventful affairs that will have your critical faculties working overtime. Surprises emerge virtually by the bar. For example, the orchestral sonority is 'heated' not by the strings, but by the woodwind section. Here, the COE's string tone is sinewy and chaste, with lightly brushed bowing and agile phrasing, while the woodwinds sound far mellower than on most rival discs. Harnoncourt's preference for limpid, baleful woodwind phrasing is familiar from his recordings of baroque music and the option works well in this context. *Coriolan* features a mobile though never overprominent cello line, the coda more suggesting recollected tragedy than the torture of Coriolan's plight. *Prometheus* opens to thunderclap chords, then busies along excitedly with much animated banter between woodwinds. *Die Ruinen von Athen* is neon-lit and keenly attenuated and the *Fidelio* 'foursome' – the opera's overture plus the three *Leonores* – is delivered with a dramatic impetus that occasionally borders on abruptness. *Fidelio* itself features a majestic introduction and a leisurely, open-plan *Allegro* where individual voices take the lead and where the opening motive gallops back with tremendous vigour. *Leonore* No. 1 goes with a swing, the introduction to *Leonore* No. 2 suggests intimations of Berlioz and the way Harnoncourt tiers the accumulating woodwind lines is very impressive. A natural ebb and flow is common to both of these 'bigger' *Leonore* overtures; both feature a first-rate off-stage trumpet, and both have fiery codas (*Leonore* No. 3's 'last blast' climaxes with colossal power). The disc ends with a fairly forceful *Egmont* overture. All the recordings except *Coriolan* are live and convey a luminous, dynamic and realistically three-dimensional sound-stage. Purchase will be mandatory for those without preconceptions.

Additional recommendation ...

...Die Geschöpfe des Prometheus, Op. 43. **Scottish Chamber Orchestra / Sir Charles Mackerras.** Hyperion Ⓕ CDA66748 (63 minutes: DDD:11/94).

...Die Geschöpfe des Prometheus, Op. 43. **Orchestra of the Eighteenth Century / Frans Brüggen.** Philips Ⓕ 446 702-2PH (62 minutes: DDD: 12/96). 🎯

Beethoven Symphonies – No. 1 in C major, Op. 21. No. 2 in D major, Op. 36. No. 3 in E flat major, Op. 55, "Eroica". No. 4 in B flat major, Op. 60. No. 5 in C minor, Op. 67. No. 6 in F major, Op. 68, "Pastoral". No. 7 in A major, Op. 92. No. 8 in F major, Op. 93. No. 9 in D minor, Op. 125, "Choral"[a]. [a]**Charlotte Margiono** (sop); [a]**Birgit Remmert** (mez); [a]**Rudolf Schasching** (ten); [a]**Robert Holl** (bass); [a]**Arnold Schoenberg Choir; Chamber Orchestra of Europe / Nikolaus Harnoncourt.** Teldec Ⓕ 2292-46452-2 (five discs: 358 minutes: DDD: 11/91). Recorded live in 1990-91. *Gramophone Award Winner 1992.*   ⒼⒼⒼ

Beethoven Symphonies. [a]**Lucia Popp** (sop); [a]**Carolyn Watkinson** (contr); [a]**Peter Schreier** (ten); [a]**Robert Holl** (bass); [a]**Netherlands Radio Chorus; Concertgebouw Orchestra / Bernard Haitink.** Philips Bernard Haitink Symphony Edition Ⓑ 442 073-2PB5 (five discs: 725 minutes: DDD: 9/94). Recorded 1987.

No. 1 in C major, Op. 21. No. 2 in D major, Op. 36. No. 3 in E flat major, Op. 55, "Eroica". No. 4 in B flat major, Op. 60 (all from 416 822-2PH6, 6/88). No. 5 in C minor, Op. 67 (420 540-1PH, 10/87). No. 6 in F major, Op. 68, "Pastoral" (416 822-2PH6). No. 7 in A major, Op. 92 (420 540-1PH). No. 8 in F major, Op. 93. No. 9 in D minor, Op. 125, "Choral"[a]. Egmont, Op. 84 – Overture (all from 416 822-2PH6).   ⒼⒼ

Brimful of intrepid character and interpretative incident, Nikolaus Harnoncourt and the splendid Chamber Orchestra of Europe give us what is surely one of the most stimulating Beethoven symphony cycles of recent times. As Harnoncourt himself states in a lively interview for the accompanying booklet to this set: "It has always been my conviction that music is not there to soothe people's nerves ... but rather to open their eyes, to give them a good shaking, even to frighten them." So it transpires that there's a re-creative daring about his conducting – in essence an embracement of recent scholarly developments and Harnoncourt's own pungent sense of characterization – which is consistently illuminating, thus leaving the listener with the uncanny sensation that he or she is in fact encountering this great music for the very first time. In all of this Harnoncourt is backed to the hilt by some superbly responsive, miraculously assured playing from the COE: their personable, unforced assimilation of Harnoncourt's specific demands (complete with period-style lean-textured strings and bracingly cutting brass and timpani), allied to this conductor's intimate knowledge of the inner workings of these scores, make for wonderfully fresh, punchy results. In this respect Symphonies Nos. 6-8 in particular prove immensely rewarding, but the *Eroica* and (especially) the Fourth, too, are little short of superb. In sum, it's a cycle which excitingly reaffirms the life-enhancing mastery of Beethoven's vision for the 1990s and into the next century beyond.

Haitink's second Beethoven cycle was greeted warmly when it first appeared; his virtues of textural rhythmic clarity well in evidence. He is often at his most impressive in the allegedly 'lighter' symphonies; Nos. 1, 8 and especially No. 4 are very enjoyable – vital, flexible, elegantly shaped and balanced, and thoroughly civilized. Perhaps the problem with the *Eroica*, Fifth, Seventh and *Choral* Symphonies is that they are a degree *too* civilized. This is no vision of a Beethoven – as one critic put it – "storming heaven with his boots on". Still, there is more than one way of approaching any great work, and for most of the set the phrase "intensely agreeable" seems a good, bite-sized summary. Tempos almost always seem well chosen – except perhaps the slowish *Scherzos* of Nos. 2 and 4 – and it's good to find Haitink taking a less extreme view of scherzo-trio contrasts in No. 7 (and observing all the repeats in the *Scherzo*). The recordings have lost none of their virtues – breadth, depth, clarity, warmth of tone – in the transfers.

Additional recommendations ...
...Nos. 1-9. **Cleveland Orchestra / George Szell.** Sony Essential Classics SB5K48396.
...Nos. 1-9. **Berlin Philharmonic Orchestra / Herbert von Karajan.**
 DG Ⓜ 429 036-2GX5 (five discs: 332 minutes: ADD: 1/90).
...Nos. 1-9. Overture – Leonore No. 3, Op. 62*a.* **NBC Symphony Orchesta / Arturo Toscanini.**
 RCA Gold Seal mono Ⓜ GD60324* (337 minutes: ADD: 5/90).   ⒼⒼⒼ
...Nos. 1-9. **Orchestre Révolutionnaire et Romantique / Sir John Eliot Gardiner.** Archiv Produktion
 Ⓕ 439 900-2AH5 (five discs: 328 minutes: DDD: 11/94). 🎵 *Gramophone Editor's choice.*   Ⓖ
...Nos. 1-9. Overtures – Egmont; Leonore No. 3, Op. 72*a.* **Soloists; Dresden State Opera Chorus;**
 Staatskapelle Dresden / Sir Colin Davis.
 Philips Ⓜ 446 067-2PH6 (six discs: 403 minutes: DDD: 12/95). *Gramophone Editor's choice.* ⒼⒼ
...Nos. 1-9. Coriolan, Op. 62 – Overture. **Soloists; Kaunas State Choir; Sinfonia Varsovia /**
 Sir Yehudi Menuhin. IMP Classics Ⓢ 30368 00025 (five discs: 359 minutes: DDD: 4/96).

Beethoven Symphonies – No. 1 in C major, Op. 21; No. 3 in E flat major, Op. 55, "Eroica".
 Royal Concertgebouw Orchestra / Wolfgang Sawallisch. EMI Ⓕ CDC7 54501-2
 (77 minutes: DDD: 6/95). Recorded 1993.

Collectors who swear by their fine old 1950s mono LPs of the Beethoven symphonies made in the Concertgebouw under conductors like Erich Kleiber, Eugen Jochum, Eduard van Beinum or Pierre Monteux will find Sawallisch's Concertgebouw recording of the First Symphony to be a great delight. True, the slow movement is rather comatose – *Andante cantabile* but barely *con moto* – but all three quicker movements are played with a clarity and zest that you will not find, for instance, in Harnoncourt's performance, where the first movement is played in a way that is oddly tired-sounding: mannered and circumspect. The EMI recording for Sawallisch is of a piece with the playing, electrically alive. In the *Eroica*, Sawallisch does one or two old-fashioned things. There is no exposition repeat and there are some expressive slowings in the course of the exposition. What follows is, though, of a piece with this: a reading that has an irresistible and continuing sense of forward motion but not one that is bought at all cost, as Sawallisch's direction of the long and musically profound lead-back to the recapitulation makes abundantly clear.

Additional recommendations ...
...Nos. 1 and 4. Egmont Overture. **Berlin Philharmonic Orchestra / Herbert von Karajan.**
 DG Galleria Ⓜ 419 048-2GGA (64 minutes: ADD: 4/88).   ⒼⒼ
...Nos. 1 and 6. **London Classical Players / Roger Norrington.**
 EMI Reflexe Ⓕ CDC7 49746-2 (66 minutes: DDD: 9/88). 🎵   ⒼⒼ
...Nos. 1 and 2. **Cleveland Orchestra / Christoph von Dohnányi.**
 Telarc Ⓕ CD80187 (59 minutes: DDD: 6/89).   Ⓖ
...Nos. 1 and 7. **Royal Philharmonic Orchestra / Barry Wordsworth.**
 Tring International Royal Philharmonic Collection Ⓢ TRP033 (64 minutes: DDD: 8/95).
...Nos. 1-3. Coriolan, Op. 62. **London Symphony Orchestra / Wyn Morris.**
 Carlton Classics LSO Doubles Ⓜ 30368 01157 (two discs: 122 minutes: DDD: 1/98).

Beethoven Symphonies – No. 2 in D major, Op. 36; No. 4 in B flat major, Op. 60. **North German**
 Radio Symphony Orchestra / Günter Wand. RCA Victor Red Seal Ⓕ RD60058 (68 minutes:
 DDD: 9/89). Recorded 1988.   ⒼⒼ

Seldom has Beethoven's Second Symphony sounded as fresh, dynamic or persuasive as this. The work occupies a transitional place in the symphonic line as begun by Mozart and Haydn; on the one hand it forms the climax of that line, on the other it looks forward to new beginnings. Günter Wand's stance clearly leans towards those new beginnings, with a reading that is more 'Beethovenian' in approach than most, highlighting the fingerprints of the composer's future symphonic style. The Fourth Symphony has always tended to be eclipsed by the towering edifices of the Third and Fifth Symphonies, but the Fourth takes stock, and with the maturity gained in the writing of the Third, looks back once more in an act of homage to the triumphs of the past. Wand's performances are inspired; he is a conductor who never imposes his own ego and never does anything for the sake of effect, resulting in performances that are honest, direct and unpretentious. His tempos are superbly judged; brisk, but not hurried, allowing the pristine articulation of the strings to come shining through (this needs to be heard to be believed; orchestral playing such as this is rare indeed). The orchestral balance is ideal, with woodwind textures nicely integrated into the orchestral sound, and this is supported by the excellent recorded sound which approaches demonstration quality. A very fine issue indeed.

Additional recommendations ...
...Nos. 2 and 4. **Philharmonia Orchestra / Otto Klemperer.**
  EMI Studio Ⓜ CDM7 63355-2* (73 minutes: ADD: 8/90).   ⒼⒼ
...Nos. 2 and 8. **Royal Philharmonic Orchestra / James Lockhart.**
  Tring International Royal Philharmonic Collection Ⓢ TRP039 (62 minutes: DDD: 11/95).

Beethoven Symphony No. 3 in E flat major, Op. 55, "Eroica"[a]. Overtures[b] – Leonore No. 2;
  Leonore No. 3. **Philharmonia Orchestra / Otto Klemperer.** EMI mono Ⓜ CDM7 63855-2*
  (76 minutes: ADD: 4/92). Item marked [a] from Columbia 33CX1346 (7/56), [b]33CX1270 (9/55).
  Item marked [a] recorded 1955, [b]1954. *Gramophone classical 100.*   ⒼⒼⒼ
Beethoven Symphony No. 3 in E flat major, Op. 55, "Eroica"[a]. Overture – Leonore No. 3,
  Op. 72a[b]. **North German Radio Symphony Orchestra / Günter Wand.** RCA Victor Ⓕ RD60755
  (65 minutes: DDD: 10/91). Recorded live in [a] 1989, [b]1990.   ⒼⒼ
"This is a great performance" was Trevor Harvey's unvarnished opening to his *Gramophone* review of Klemperer's account of the *Eroica* in July 1956. In 1955 the Philharmonia Orchestra itself was at the peak of its powers. And what cogency there is sustaining and feeding the drama. Where other orchestras and conductors whip themselves into a terrible lather at the start of the finale, Klemperer and the Philharmonia sail majestically on. This is a great performance, steady yet purposeful, with textures that seem hewn out of granite. (Once or twice they cause a slight buzz of distortion for which EMI apologise in their booklet.) There is no exposition repeat, and the trumpets blaze out illicitly in the first movement coda, but this is still one of the great *Eroicas* on record. As Karajan announced to Klemperer after flying in to a concert performance around this time: "I have come only to thank you, and say that I hope I shall live to conduct the Funeral March as well as you have done". The *Eroica* seems to come at us out of a bigger, livelier acoustic than Klemperer's recordings of the Fifth or Seventh symphonies, despite an identical venue (London's Kingsway Hall) and identical recording dates. In the *Leonore* Overtures, recorded in 1954, the playing is a bit more rough-edged.

Günter Wand's live performance of the *Eroica* represents a worthy alternative to Klemperer's landmark recording. In many ways Wand stands as a legitimate successor to Klemperer as one of the holders of the great Teutonic tradition of interpreting Beethoven in terms of struggle and triumph. Certainly he launches into the symphony with tremendous vigour and power and he sustains these characteristics throughout. Following an opening movement in which the tension never relaxes at all, Wand leads a reading of the Funeral March which is deeply felt but without self-indulgence. The scherzo and trio provide well-pointed relief prior to an epic reading of the triumphant final movement, which carries all before it. The fill-up, an equally powerful reading of the *Leonore* Overture No. 3, precedes the performance of the *Eroica* and acts as an excellent curtain-raiser and introduction to Wand's interpretative style: genuine and powerful and wholly without self-indulgence. The North German Radio recording is excellent, capturing the involved atmosphere of a live performance without any of the distractions normally to be expected from such venues.

Additional recommendations ...
...No. 3. Leonore Overture No. 1. **Berlin Philharmonic Orchestral / Rafael Kubelík.**
  Belart Ⓑ 450 037-2 (66 minutes: ADD).
...No. 3. Grosse Fuge in B flat major. **Philharmonia Orchestra / Otto Klemperer.**
  EMI mono Ⓜ CDM7 63356-2* (70 minutes: ADD: 8/90).   ⒼⒼⒼ
...No. 3. **Mozart** Symphony No. 40 in G minor, K550. **NBC Symphony Orchestra /**
  Arturo Toscanini. RCA Victor Gold Seal Ⓜ GD60271* (69 minutes: ADD: 10/92).
...Nos. 3, 5 and 6. **Schubert** Symphony No. 9 in C major, D944, "Great". **Berlin Philharmonic**
  Orchestra / Wilhelm Furtwängler. Tahra mono Ⓜ FURT1008/11* (four discs: 243 minutes:
  ADD: 3/95). Also includes previously unpublished recordings of works by Brahms, Dvořák,
  Mendelssohn, Schubert, Schumann and R. Strauss; recorded 1930-54.
...Nos. 3, 7 and 8. The Consecration of the House, Op. 124. **Berlin Philharmonic Orchestra /**
  Paul van Kempen. Philips Ⓜ 438 533-2PM2* (two discs: 124 minutes: ADD: 3/94).   ⒼⒼ
...No. 3. **Mussorgsky** A Night on the Bare Mountain. **London Philharmonic Orchestra /**
  Klaus Tennstedt. EMI Ⓕ CDC5 55186-2 (63 minutes: DDD: 11/94).

...No. 3. *Coupled with works by various composers.* **Concertgebouw Orchestra / Pierre Monteux.**
Philips The Early Years Ⓜ 442 544-2PM5 (five discs: 311 minutes: ADD: 12/94).
See review in the Collections section; refer to the Index. ⒼⒼⒼ
...No. 3; No. 9ᵃ. Overtures – Egmont; Coriolan; Die Geschöpfe des Prometheus.
ᵃ**Dame Gwyneth Jones** (sop); ᵃ**Tatiana Troyanos** (mez); ᵃ**Jess Thomas** (ten); ᵃ**Karl Ridderbusch**
(bass); ᵃ**Vienna State Opera Chorus; Vienna Philharmonic Orchestra / Karl Böhm.**
DG Double Ⓜ 437 368-2GX2 (two discs: 146 minutes: ADD: 4/95).
...No. 3. Coriolan Overture, Op. 62. **Le Concert des Nations / Jordi Savall.**
Auvidis Fontalis Ⓕ ES8557 (52 minutes: DDD: 7/97). ⌁

Beethoven Symphonies – No. 4 in B flat major, Op. 60; No. 5 in C minor, Op. 67.
La Scala Philharmonic Orchestra / Carlo Maria Giulini. Sony Classical Ⓕ SK58921
(73 minutes: DDD: 11/95). Recorded 1993.
Giulini's Fifth, which ends with a piccolo singing high in the stratosphere as C major sounds
majestically beneath, is not a performance in the histrionic (or historic) sense of the word. Rather, it
is a meditation on the work's informing vision, what Goethe called "the Fall upwards", the transition
from dark to light, the seeds of spiritual regeneration planted in the very ground of despair. And that
is not an elaborately periphrastic way of saying that the performance is a bit dull, that the old boy is
not quite what he was. Giulini's desire is to give the music time to breathe and be heard. And he is
absolutely the master of how best to bring that about. You hear this in the time he allots to the
opening fermatas (and in the fineness of their sound, rich and unforced); you hear it in the slight 'lift'
he imparts to the rhythm, the time they are given to dance; and you hear it in the steady, unflustered
pulse of the whole. The final two movements are treated as a seamless robe. Logically – since there is
no repeat of the *Scherzo*'s first half – Giulini omits the finale's exposition repeat. The music is thus
allowed to move forward with a simple momentum of its own. Climaxes are finely judged, and rarely
has the *Scherzo*'s unexpected return within the finale seemed so fine an invention as it does here. The
symphony's slow movement, incidentally, is played as though it is first cousin to Schubert's *Unfinished*
Symphony. Giulini has never previously recorded the Fourth Symphony and coming to it late has its
risks. The slow introduction, the slow movement and the still points of the *Allegro vivace*'s turning
world are wonderfully well reimagined and realized. The word *vivace*, though, implies a slightly more
spirited gait than Giulini allows. But if parts of the first movement seem a touch lumpy, the finale is a
miracle of unforced motion, the La Scala playing relaxed, the mood gamesome as it invariably is
when the conductor takes note of Beethoven's written instruction: *Allegro ma non troppo.* (Klemperer
was always very persuasive in this movement.) Sony's Milan recordings place the orchestra a shade
distantly, giving a slightly veiled quality to the string tone, but since this is consonant with the sound
Giulini draws from the orchestra it is hardly a matter of great concern.
Additional recommendations ...
...Nos. 4 and 6. **NBC Symphony Orchestra / Arturo Toscanini.**
RCA Gold Seal Ⓜ GD60254* (69 minutes: ADD). ⒼⒼⒼ
...Nos. 4 and 7. König Stefan – Overture. **Cleveland Orchestra / George Szell.**
Sony Classical Essential Classics Ⓑ SBK48158 (74 minutes: ADD).
...Nos. 4 and 6. **Royal Liverpool Philharmonic Orchestra / Sir Charles Mackerras.**
EMI Eminence Ⓜ CD-EMX2245 (71 minutes: DDD: 11/96).
...Nos. 4 and 7. **South-West German Radio Symphony Orchestra / Michael Gielen.**
EMI Ⓜ CDM5 60092-2 (DDD: 10/96).

Beethoven Symphonies – No. 5 in C minor, Op. 67; No. 6 in F major, Op. 68, "Pastoral".
Zurich Tonhalle Orchestra / David Zinman. Arte Nova Classics Ⓢ 74321 49695-2
(74 minutes: DDD: 12/97). Recorded 1997. *Gramophone Editor's choice.*
This production claims to be the "world première recording according to the new Bärenreiter
Edition" and parades a good number of textual novelties. Both scores are visited by all manner of
dynamic *crescendos, diminuendos* and other emphases (mostly applied to short phrases) and the sum
effect is notably refreshing. Readers who know the Tonhalle Orchestra only from likeable old records
by Josef Krips, Otto Ackermann and Franz Lehár will be astonished at the brilliance and polish of
these performances. David Zinman assumed the orchestra's Music Directorship for the 1995-6 season
and his skill as an orchestral trainer has consolidated a dramatic improvement in playing standards.
Tempos are very fast, phrasing trimly tailored (sometimes even a trifle abrupt) and rubato kept well
in check. In the Fifth Symphony, Zinman plays all three repeats (first movement, *Scherzo* and finale)
and his handling of the *Scherzo*'s double-bass Trio deserves a round of applause. The *Pastoral*'s proto-
minimalist first-movement development section flies off at a fair lick and the slimline peasants make
merry with energy to spare. This disc is particularly recommended to readers who know their
Klemperers, Toscaninis and Furtwänglers backwards and who fancy investigating some scholarly
emendations but who dislike period-instrument sonorities. Zinman's performances offer a peach of a
bargain, although Arte Nova offer no comment on the Edition used. The sound quality is truly
state-of-the-art.
Additional recommendation ...
...Nos. 5ᵃ and 6ᵇ·ᵃ**London Philharmonic Orchestra / Felix Weingartner;** ᵇ**Vienna Philharmonic**
Orchestra / Bruno Walter. Avid Master Series mono Ⓑ AMSC583* (71 minutes: ADD: 7/97). Ⓖ

Beethoven Symphonies – No. 5 in C minor, Op. 67[a]; No. 7 in A major, Op. 92[b]. **Vienna Philharmonic Orchestra / Carlos Kleiber.** DG The Originals Ⓜ 447 400-2GOR (72 minutes: ADD: 5/95). Item marked [a] from 2530 516 (6/75), [b]2530 706 (9/76). *Gramophone classical 100.* ⒼⒼⒼ
The recording of the Fifth, always very fine, comes up superbly in this transfer. What, though, of the Seventh Symphony, an equally distinguished performance though always perceptibly greyer-sounding on LP, and on CD? Well, it too is superb. What the Original-Image Bit-Processing has done to it, heaven only knows, but the result is a performance of genius that now speaks to us freely and openly for the first time. In some ways this is a more important document than the famous Fifth. Great recordings of the Seventh, greatly played and greatly conducted, but with first and second violins divided left and right, are as rare as gold-dust. Freshly refurbished, this Kleiber Seventh would go right to the top of any short list of recommendable Sevenths. It is wonderful to have these two legendary performances so expertly restored and placed together on one disc for the first time.
Additional recommendations ...
...Nos. 5 and 7. **Vienna Philharmonic Orchestra / Rafael Kubelík.**
Belart Ⓑ 450 038-2 (75 minutes: ADD).
...Nos. 5 and 7. *Coupled with works by various composers.* **Philharmonic Symphony Orchestra of New York / Arturo Toscanini.** Pearl mono Ⓜ GEMMCDS9373* (three discs: 230 minutes: ADD: 3/90). *Gramophone classical 100. See review in the Collections section; refer to the Index.* ⒼⒼⒼ
...Nos. 5 and 7. **Royal Liverpool Philharmonic Orchestra / Sir Charles Mackerras.**
EMI Eminence Ⓜ CD-EMX2212 (68 minutes: DDD: 12/93).
...Nos. 5 and 6. **Berlin Philharmonic Orchestra / Herbert von Karajan.**
DG Ⓑ 439 403-2GCL (67 minutes: ADD: 1/94).
...Nos. 5 and 6. **South-West German Radio Symphony Orchestra / Michael Gielen.**
EMI Ⓜ CDM5 60093-2 (DDD: 10/96).
...No. 6. Egmont Overture. Leonore Overture No. 3. **Philharmonia Orchestra / Vladimir Ashkenazy.**
Decca Eclipse Ⓜ 448 986-2DEC (71 minutes: DDD: 2/97).

Beethoven Symphonies – No. 5 in C minor, Op. 67; No. 6 in F major, Op. 68, "Pastoral". **North German Radio Symphony Orchestra / Günter Wand.** RCA Victor Red Seal Ⓕ 09026 61930-2 (79 minutes: DDD: 5/94). Recorded live in 1992. ⒼⒼ
Beethoven Symphony No. 6 in F major, Op. 68, "Pastoral". Overtures – Coriolan, Op. 62; Egmont, Op. 84. **La Scala Philharmonic Orchestra, Milan / Carlo Maria Giulini.** Sony Classical Ⓕ SK53974 (65 minutes: DDD: 5/94). Recorded 1993. *Gramophone Editor's choice.* ⒼⒼ
To judge from this live performance of the Fifth Symphony, Wand has the trick of keeping something back for the performance itself; a remarkable skill in repertory as familiar as this after so much detailed preparation. In matters of rhythm and phrasing and the balancing of lines, Wand is difficult to fault. Indeed, you will hear things in these performances – from the basses and bassoons and, in the Fifth Symphony, from the trombones – which are all too often glossed over. Apart from a curiously measured *Scherzo*, the Fifth Symphony goes exceptionally well. The first movement is not overdriven, yet the finale has real *élan*, the reading, for want of a better word, suddenly and surprisingly rather Furtwänglerish. In the *Pastoral* Symphony it is Wand's exemplary account of the Scene by the Brook that most obviously stands out. Here he has the knack of marrying the music's necessary forward movement with the murmurous beauty of its inner detailing. Wand's *Pastoral* gives profound pleasure, as, in its very different way, does Giulini's, his third recording of the Symphony and, by some distance, his finest. Superbly sustained and expressively moulded, this is a performance in which every sentence is gloriously phrased and where individual string lines are always richly distinct; not a note is extraneous to Beethoven's purpose. The whole performance is wonderfully at odds with the hell-for-leather spirit of an agnostic age. It is, in the end, a deeply *spiritual* performance of a work which was conceived by Beethoven, first and last, as an essentially spiritual experience. The disc begins with a profoundly satisfying *Coriolan* Overture and the dramatic opening of the *Egmont* Overture is played with a near-ideal blend of trenchancy and *espressivo* intensity. As for the coda, the so-called 'Victory Symphony', few have brought out as vividly as Giulini its musical and moral sure-footedness.
Additional recommendations ...
...No. 6. Overtures – Die Geschöpfe des Prometheus, Op. 43; Coriolan, Op. 62.
Northern Sinfonia / Richard Hickox. ASV Quicksilva Ⓢ CDQS6053 (59 minutes: DDD).
...Nos. 6 and 8. **Vienna Philharmonic Orchestra / Hans Schmidt-Isserstedt.**
Decca Ⓜ 433 622-2DSP (55 minutes: ADD: 3/90). Ⓖ

Beethoven Symphony No. 6 in F major, Op. 68, "Pastoral"[a].
Schubert Symphony No. 5 in B flat major, D485[b]. **Vienna Philharmonic Orchestra / Karl Böhm.**
DG The Originals Ⓜ 447 433-2GOR (74 minutes: ADD: 1/96). Item marked [a] from 2530 142 (2/72, recorded 1971), [b]2531 279 (11/80, recorded 1979). *Gramophone classical 100.* ⒼⒼⒼ
Karl Böhm's Beethoven is a compound of earth and fire. His VPO recording of Beethoven's Sixth of 1971 dominated the LP catalogue for over a decade, and has done pretty well on CD on its various appearances. His reading is generally glorious and it remains one of the finest accounts of the work ever recorded. It still sounds well (perhaps the bass is a bit lighter than on LP) and the performance

(with the first movement exposition repeat included) has an unfolding naturalness and a balance between form and lyrical impulse that is totally satisfying. The brook flows untroubled and the finale is quite lovely, with a wonderfully expansive climax. This latest coupling (the Schubert Fifth) is as unexpected as it is successful and dates from the end of Böhm's recording career. It is a superb version of this lovely symphony, another work that suited Böhm especially well. The reading is weighty but graceful, with a most beautifully phrased *Andante* (worthy of a Furtwängler), a bold Minuet and a thrilling finale. The recording is splendid. If you admire Böhm this is a worthy way to remember his special gifts.

Additional recommendation ...

...Nos. 6-8[a]; Overtures[b] – Fidelio; Leonore No. 3. [a]**Vienna Philharmonic Orchestra;** [b]**Dresden Staatskapelle / Karl Böhm.** DG Double Ⓜ 437 928-2GX2 (two discs: 130 minutes: ADD: 4/95). *No. 6 is the same recording as the one reviewed above.*   ⊖⊖⊖

Beethoven Symphony No. 6 in F major, Op. 68, "Pastoral"[a]. Egmont, Op. 84 – Overture[b]; Die Trommel gerühret[b]; Freudvoll und leidvoll[c]; Klärchens Tod bezeichnend[b]. Die Geschöpfe des Prometheus, Op. 43 – Overture[d]. [c]**Birgit Nilsson** (sop); [abc]**Philharmonia Orchestra;** [d]**New Philharmonia Orchestra / Otto Klemperer.** EMI Studio Ⓜ CDM7 63358-2* (69 minutes: ADD: 8/90). Items marked [a] from SAX2260 (10/58), [bc]33CX1575 (11/58), [d]HMV SXDW3032 (6/77). Recorded 1957.   ⊖⊖⊖

Klemperer's most revered Beethoven recordings date from the middle and late 1950s. In its day, his account of the *Pastoral* was notorious for the slow *Scherzo* – "it's a Ländler" – he is said to have retorted grumpily – but once again the performance as a whole offers a wonderful example of Klemperer's ability to sustain dramatic interest within generously conceived spaces. The result is an overwhelming sense of vital but unhurrying reflection. The *Egmont* numbers on this disc are also very fine. Birgit Nilsson is wonderfully fresh in the two arias, and the rarely recorded "Klärchens Tod bezeichnend" is very affecting. As for the famous overture, Klemperer's account is steadily paced, and as cogent and gauntly explicit a reading of this symphonic music-drama as any on disc. It is a reading of great power and nobility in which nothing is overdone; the coda is a particular success.

Additional recommendation ...

...Nos. 6 and 8. **Berlin Philharmonic Orchestra / Herbert von Karajan.** DG Privilege Ⓑ 431 159-2GR (ADD).

Beethoven Symphony No. 9 in D minor, Op. 125, "Choral". **Anna Tomowa-Sintow** (sop); **Agnes Baltsa** (mez); **Peter Schreier** (ten); **José van Dam** (bass-bar); **Vienna Singverein; Berlin Philharmonic Orchestra / Herbert von Karajan.** DG Galleria Ⓜ 415 832-2GGA (67 minutes: ADD: 4/87). Text and translation included. From 2740 172 (10/77). Recorded 1976.
Beethoven Symphony No. 9 in D minor, Op. 125, "Choral". **Alessandra Marc** (sop); **Iris Vermillion** (mez); **Siegfried Jerusalem** (ten); **Falk Struckmann** (bar); **Berlin State Opera Chorus; Berlin Staatskapelle / Daniel Barenboim.** Erato Ⓕ 4509-94353-2 (74 minutes: DDD: 7/94). Text and translation included.

All collections need Beethoven's *Choral* Symphony as one of the works at the very core of the nineteenth-century romantic movement. Within its remarkable span, Beethoven celebrates both the breadth and power of man's conception of his position in relation to the Universe; his sense of spirituality – especially in the great slow movement – and in the finale the essential life-enhancing optimism emerges, which makes human existence philosophically possible against all odds. Karajan lived alongside the Beethoven symphonies throughout his long and very distinguished recording career, and he recorded the Ninth three times in stereo. Sadly the most recent digital version, in spite of glorious playing in the *Adagio*, is flawed, but both analogue versions are very impressive indeed. His 1976 version is the best of the three. The slow movement has great intensity, and the finale brings a surge of incandescent energy and exuberance which is hard to resist. All four soloists are excellent individually and they also make a good team. The reading as a whole has the inevitability of greatness and the recording is vivid, full and clear. At mid price this is very recommendable indeed.

Barenboim's is an important recording in that it re-establishes – in its own way and with a telling eloquence that is specially its own – that the Ninth is a work of the new romanticism, a prophetic work that cannot be adequately dealt with by so-called 'authenticists' desirous of tethering it either to the letter of the written text or to performance practice in Beethoven's own lifetime. The literalists and authenticists have had some powerful advocates on record – Toscanini, for example, not easily gainsaid. Barenboim's Ninth starts deep in the *Urwald*, far away, wreathed in the mists of time. Yet it is a measure of his mastery that the reading never appears to meander or hold fire. On the contrary, the development and recapitulation blaze quietly, from within. 'Quietly' because the Erato recording, made in Berlin's Jesus-Christus Kirche, is rather soft-grained. Important solo voicings, human or instrumental, are neither obscured nor specifically 'lit'. In the finale, words sound clearly enough whilst at the same time being part of the performance's general euphony. The extreme inwardness of Barenboim's reading at key points – the symphony's opening bars, most of the slow movement, the very slow *molto pianissimo* start of the first instrumental statement of the "Joy" theme – is complemented by considerable ebullience in the *Scherzo* and in the later stages of the finale. The soloists are generally reliable, the choir first-rate, the orchestra more than adequate to the considerable task in hand.

Additional recommendations ...
...No. 9. **Soloists; Philharmonia Chorus and Orchestra / Otto Klemperer.**
EMI Studio Ⓜ CDM7 63359-2* (72 minutes: ADD: 8/90).   Ⓖ
...No. 9. **Soloists; Royal Liverpool Philharmonic Choir and Orchestra / Sir Charles Mackerras.**
EMI Eminence Ⓜ CD-EMX2186 (61 minutes: DDD: 12/91). *Selected by Sounds in Retrospect.* Ⓖ
...No. 9. **Soloists; Bruno Kittel Choir; Berlin Philharmonic Orchestra / Wilhelm Furtwängler.**
Music and Arts mono Ⓕ CD653* (74 minutes: ADD: 5/94).
...No. 9. **Soloists; Lucerne Festival Chorus; Philharmonia Orchestra / Wilhelm Furtwängler.**
Tahra mono Ⓕ FURT1003* (78 minutes: ADD: 3/95). *Gramophone Award Winner 1995.*   Ⓖ
...No. 9. **Soloists; Amsterdam Toonkunst Choir; Concertgebouw Orchestra / Willem Mengelberg.**
Archive Documents Mengelberg Edition mono Ⓕ ADCD113* (72 minutes: AAD: 5/95).
...No. 9. **Soloists; Ambrosian Singers; Royal Philharmonic Orchestra / Raymond Leppard.**
Tring Royal Philharmonic Collection Ⓢ TRP051 (70 minutes: DDD: 11/96).
...No. 9. **Soloists; Vienna State Opera Chorus; Vienna Philharmonic Orchestra / Felix Weingartner.**
Avid Master Series mono Ⓑ AMSC591* (63 minutes: ADD: 7/97).   Ⓖ

Beethoven Symphony No. 9 in D minor, Op. 125, "Choral". **Elisabeth Schwarzkopf** (sop);
Elisabeth Höngen (mez); **Hans Hopf** (ten); **Otto Edelmann** (bass); **Bayreuth Festival Chorus and
Orchestra / Wilhelm Furtwängler.** EMI mono Ⓜ CDH7 69801-2* (75 minutes: ADD: 2/91).
From ALP1286/7 (11/55). Recorded at a performance in the Festspielhaus, Bayreuth
on July 29th, 1951). *Gramophone classical 100.*   ⒼⒼⒼ
This performance has become a legendary one, as much for the occasion of its happening as for the
music-making itself. The reopening of Wagner's Festival Theatre in Bayreuth in 1951 after the
catastrophe of war was nothing if not symbolic. If anything could lay the ghost of Bayreuth's
immediate past, the years from 1930 to 1944 when the theatre was run by the English-born, Nazi-
worshipping Winifred Wagner, it might be a performance of the Ninth Symphony under the most
celebrated of the German conductors who had lived through Nazi rule without being, in any real
sense, morally or artistically party to it. Certainly, it is not difficult to think of the slow movement's
second subject, unfolded here in a way that has never been bettered, as an atonement and a
benediction. However, not everyone will respond to this vision of the Ninth: as an interpretation it is
broadly based, with some slow tempos and some quirky adjustments of pace; though beneath
everything – beneath the gear changes and failures in ensemble – a great current massively flows. The
solo vocal and choral work in the finale is electric after the fugato but is breezily, bumpily Teutonic
before that; Hans Hopf is his usual restless, hectic self. The CD transfer provides some added clarity
of image for the generally excellent mono recording; and it also provides an all-important continuity.
Instrumental bass frequencies are rather wooden but the recording reproduces higher frequency
string, wind, and vocal sound more smoothly than was often the case at this time. Many collectors
will be looking to a stereo, digital recording of the Ninth as a CD library acquisition; yet we would
be prepared to argue that this performance has a prior, if not ultimate and absolute, claim on
collectors' attention.

Beethoven Piano Quintet in E flat major, Op. 16[a].
Spohr Septet in A minor, Op. 147[b]. [b]**Chantal Juillet** (vn); [b]**Christopher van Kampen** (vc);
Pascal Rogé (pf); **London Winds** ([b]Philippa Davies, fl; [a]Gareth Hulse, ob; Michael Collins, cl;
Robin O'Neill, bn; Richard Watkins, hn). Decca Ⓕ 443 892-2DH (64 minutes: DDD: 4/96).
Recorded 1994.   Ⓖ
Beethoven modelled his Quintet on Mozart's Quintet, K452; however, the Decca coupling with
Spohr's A minor Septet suggests comparisons with romantic models rather than classical ones.
Perahia and the ECO on Sony (listed below) eloquently express the music's genial mood, presenting
its civilized discourse with abounding charm and classical elegance. All the instruments are excellently
balanced, and the ensemble is beautifully recorded in Sony's superb, naturally lit production,
highlighting the piano's brilliance on the Decca disc. In the present instance, Pascal Rogé and London
Winds produce a fuller, more robust sound, with the piano tone given a softer edge that emphasizes
the music's romantic tendencies. Effusive phrasing and bold projection throughout imbue the first
movement with greater dramatic potency, give the second movement increased warmth and expressive
intensity and bring the work to a more exuberant close in the finale. Spohr's Septet was his last
chamber work with piano, and its unusual instrumental forces inspired the composer to write music
of astonishing freshness and vitality, which is conveyed in this performance with infectious
enthusiasm and charm. The opening *Allegro* has a persuasive romantic sweep; the lush autumnal
atmosphere of the "Pastorale" is vividly evoked; the *Scherzo*'s 'orchestral' richness is effectively
captured, with the finale culminating in concerto-like brilliance.

Additional recommendations ...
...Quintet. **Mozart** Quintet for Piano and Wind in E flat major, K452. **Murray Perahia** (pf);
members of the **English Chamber Orchestra.**
Sony Classical Ⓕ SK42099 (53 minutes: DDD: 12/86).
...Quintet[a]. **Mozart** Quintet[a]. Adagio and Rondo in C minor, K617[b]. [b]**Imre Kovács** (fl);
József Kiss (ob); [a]**Béla Kovács** (cl); [a]**Jenö Kevéházi** (hn); [a]**Jozsef Vajda** (bn); [b]**György Konrád** (va);
[b]**Tamás Koó** (vc); **Jenö Jandó** ([a]pf/[b]celesta). Naxos Ⓢ 8 550511 (59 minutes: DDD: 4/93).

...Quintet. *Coupled with works by various composers.* **Murray Perahia** (pf); **Neil Black** (ob); **Thea King** (cl); **Graham Sheen** (bn); **Anthony Halstead** (hn). Sony Classical Ⓜ SX4K63380 (four discs: 270 minutes: DDD/ADD: 4/98). *See review in the Collections section; refer to the Index.*

Beethoven Piano Quintet in E flat major, Op. 16[a].
Mozart Piano Quintet in E flat major, K452[a]. Sinfonia concertante in E flat major, K297*b*[b].
[a]**Walter Gieseking** (pf); **Philharmonia Wind Quartet** (Sidney Sutcliffe, ob; Bernard Walton, cl; Dennis Brain, hn; Cecil James, bn); [b]**Philharmonia Orchestra / Herbert von Karajan.**
Testament mono Ⓕ SBT1091* (80 minutes: ADD: 3/97). Items marked [a] from Columbia 33CX1322 (1/56), [b]33CX1178 (11/54). ⒼⒼⒼ
There have never been any doubts about these performances. In their original reviews Denis Stevens called the horn playing in the *Sinfonia concertante* "unsurpassable" and in the quintets Roger Fiske thought Gieseking's "lightness and clarity and sense of style ... beyond praise". He found his tempos on the slow side in the first movement of the Mozart and the finale of the Beethoven but added that "somehow with [Gieseking], slow tempi have a way of seeming just about right". Richard Osborne's excellent notes quote a letter from Sidney Sutcliffe of touching modesty. Speaking of their run-through of the Mozart, he says, "On reaching the *Allegro moderato*, the great man played two bars at an absolutely perfect tempo and then stopped and asked in the most gentle and hesitant manner, 'Will that be all right for you?' So it was a most happy occasion although I found it a grave responsibility matching the artistry of my colleagues when Bernard [Walton], Cecil [James] and Dennis [Brain] were producing sounds of breath-taking beauty". Breathtaking is just the right word for all concerned on what is, after all, one of the great chamber music records of the LP era. Great pains have been taken with the transfers, which sound fresher and more full-bodied than on any earlier LP transfers.

Beethoven Septet in E flat major, Op. 20[a]. Piano Trio in B flat major, Op. 11[b]. **Walter Boeykens Ensemble** (Walter Boeykens, cl; [a]Brian Pollard, bn; [a]Jacob Slagter, hn; [a]Marjeta Korosec, vn; [a]Therese-Marie Gilissen, va; Roel Dieltiens, vc; [a]Etienne Siebens, db; [b]Robert Groslot, pf).
Harmonia Mundi Ⓕ HMC90 1518 (65 minutes: DDD: 12/95). Recorded 1995.
Beethoven's Septet is a charming work whose importance lies not only in its consolidation of its composer's style before its composition in 1799/1800 but also in its anticipation of his further development as a composer. Moreover, its scoring for clarinet, bassoon, horn and strings and its divertimento structure offer music which is exquisite both in form and textural diversity. The Walter Boeykens Ensemble reveal the work's exquisitely proportioned balance between its six movements. They play with stronger determination and brilliance than the Gaudier Ensemble on Hyperion. In the first movement, for example, the Boeykens' focused ensemble sounds lively and spontaneous, enhanced by a pronounced contrast of tempo between the *adagio* slow introduction and the following *allegro*. The Gaudier's relaxed, civilized approach is clear and well balanced, but it lacks the panache of the Boeykens version. For the Trio, clarinettist Walter Boeykens is joined by Roel Dieltiens on cello and Robert Groslot on piano in a performance of engaging verve and energy.
Additional recommendations ...
...Septet. **Mendelssohn** Octet in E flat major, Op. 20. Members of the **Vienna Octet.**
Decca Ⓜ 421 093-2DM* (74 minutes: ADD: 5/88). Ⓖ
...Septet. Sextet. **Gaudier Ensemble.** Hyperion Ⓕ CDA66513 (57 minutes: DDD: 7/92).
...Septet. String Quintet in C major, Op. 29. **Hausmusik.**
EMI Reflexe Ⓕ CDC7 54656-2 (72 minutes: DDD: 6/93).
...Complete Quartets. **Emerson Quartet.**
DG Ⓕ 447 075-2GH7 (seven discs: 491 minutes: DDD: 7/97).

Beethoven Sextet in E flat major, Op. 71. March in B flat major, WoO29. Octet in E flat major, Op. 103. Rondino in E flat major, WoO25. Duets, WoO27 – No. 1 in C major. **Charles Neidich** (cl); **Mozzafiato** (Gerard Reuter, Marc Schachman, obs; Charles Neidich, Ayako Oshima, cls; Dennis Godburn, Michael O'Donovan, bns; William Purvis, Stewart Rose, hns).
Sony Classical Vivarte Ⓕ SK53367 (65 minutes: DDD: 8/94). 🎤 Recorded 1992-3.
Beethoven composed the Octet, Op. 103, and *Rondino*, WoO25,, some time around 1792 and, although it was published separately, there is evidence to suggest that the *Rondino* was originally intended as the fourth movement of a five-movement work. Mozzafiato play the *Rondino* after the Octet, suggesting that the *Presto* finale was written to replace the *Rondino*. Their full-bodied tone-quality creates a warm, broadly conceived result: the oboe and bassoon solos which open the *Andante* second movement sound heavenly; the Minuet and Trio is cheerfully witty; a more flexible approach to the *Presto* finale produces a heightened dramatic effect and, in the *Rondino*, they deliciously reveal the music's textural diversity. In the Sextet, Op. 71, Neidich's clarinet playing is stupendous and his mellifluous virtuosity, especially in the faster outer movements, is well matched by the other performers to demonstrate this group's fine soloistic skills as well as their strong corporate identity. Enchanting performances of the March, WoO29, and the Duo for clarinet and bassoon, WoO27 No. 1, complete a delightful and immensely enjoyable concert.
Additional recommendation ...
...Octet, Op. 103[a]. Rondino, WoO25[b]. Trio in C major, Op. 87[c]. Variations in C major on "Là ci darem la mano" from Mozart's "Don Giovanni", WoO28[c]. Sextet, Op. 71[a]. Three Equali,

WoO30[d]. Marches[e] – F major, WoO18, "für die böhmische Landwehr"; F major, WoO19;
D major, WoO24; WoO29. March with Trio in C major, WoO20[e]. Ecossaise in D major, WoO22[e].
Polonaise in D major, WoO21[e]. [c]**Heinz Holliger**, [c]**Hans Elhorst** (obs); [c]**Maurice Bourgue** (cor ang);
[b]**Netherlands Wind Ensemble**; [d]**Philip Jones Brass Ensemble**; [ae]**Berlin Philharmonic Wind Ensemble**
/ [e]**Hans Priem-Bergrath**.
DG Complete Beethoven Edition Ⓜ 453 779-2GCB2 (two discs: 108 minutes: ADD: A/97).

Beethoven Piano Quartet in E flat major, Op. 16.
Schumann Piano Quartet in E flat major, Op. 47. **Isaac Stern** (vn); **Jaime Laredo** (va); **Yo-Yo Ma**
(vc); **Emanuel Ax** (pf). Sony Classical Ⓕ SK53339 (65 minutes: DDD: 10/94). Recorded 1992.
ⒼⒼ
There are numerous recordings of Beethoven's Op. 16 in its original Mozart-inspired quintet version
for piano and wind against only a few for the piano quartet arrangement in which it rapidly re-
emerged – that's the current *Gramophone* Database listing. But this 1992 performance of the quartet
from Isaac Stern and his eminent younger colleagues makes it hard to believe that it was conceived
for any other combination than theirs – and what higher praise than that? The *Andante cantabile*, with
its delicately embellished melodic strands, surely gains in expressive eloquence from the more personal
inflexions of caressing strings. And with their bold dynamic contrasts and piquant accentuation, what
drama all four players draw from the opening movement. As a brilliant young pianist himself,
Beethoven entrusted the pianist with a load of responsibility, at once arrestingly and effortlessly
discharged here by Emanuel Ax. As for Schumann's Piano Quartet, no longer is it dwarfed in
popularity by its immediate predecessor in the same key, the Piano Quintet. This recording will surely
win it a host of new friends – and not only for the mercurial lightness and grace of the
Mendelssohnian sprites in the *Scherzo* and the glowing but essentially unsentimentalized intimacy of
the *Andante cantabile* (as dedicated a love-song as Schumann ever wrote). The performers' impulse in
the two flanking movements is unflagging and the overall impression is of spontaneous enjoyment –
a group of friends making music together for their own delight rather than as just another
professional engagement. The recording is as vibrant as the playing.

Beethoven Piano Quartets – E flat major, WoO36 No. 1; D major, WoO36 No. 2; C major,
WoO36 No. 3; E flat major, Op. 16. **Raphael Oleg** (vn); **Miguel da Silva** (va); **Marc Coppey** (vc);
Philippe Cassard (pf). Auvidis Valois Ⓕ V4715 (two discs: 88 minutes: DDD: 5/95).
Recorded 1994.
This issue of the three piano quartets Beethoven completed at the age of 15 but subsequently
suppressed, in double harness with the 26-year-old composer's piano quartet arrangement of his
Op. 16 Quintet for piano and wind, is more than welcome – despite its shortish playing time. Indebted
to the still youthful Mozart the teenage Beethoven may well (and should) have been, as also tempted
to entrust too much to the piano. But the unpredictability of even immature genius is striking. Never
can you for a second foretell what surprise, whether of key, harmony, rhythm or scoring, lies just
around the corner. His fluent, confident craftsmanship makes you marvel no less. Even when
borrowing the three-movement sequence of Mozart's G major Violin Sonata (K397) for his own
E flat major work, Beethoven gives his chromatically intensified opening *Adagio assai*, his stormy
minor-key *Allegro* and even the beguiling variations, an unmistakable stamp of his own. The playing
itself of course contributes to the pleasure, with first praise to Philippe Cassard for never allowing the
keyboard to dominate. But all four Paris Conservatoire-trained colleagues are artists of taste and
finesse. Their characterization is most sensitively attuned to the music's own true scale. Never does
point-making sound self-consciously inflated. In the more familiar Op. 16 work they are just as
persuasive as Isaac Stern and his colleagues who opt for sharper accentuation and more urgency in
the faster flanking movements. The Auvidis Valois recording itself has a pleasingly soft-grained
intimacy.

Beethoven String Quartets – No. 3 in D major, Op. 18 No. 3; No. 7 in F major, Op. 59 No. 1,
"Rasumovsky". **Orpheus Quartet** (Charles-André Linale, Emilian Piediciuta, vns; Emile Cantor,
va; Laurentiu Sbarcea, vc). Channel Classics Ⓕ CCS6094 (68 minutes: DDD: 12/94).
Recorded 1993.
Ⓖ
The Orpheus do not use this music as a vehicle for their virtuosity or prowess; and they do not draw
attention to their spot-on ensemble, immaculate intonation and tonal finesse, though they possess all
these qualities in no small measure. Take the *Presto* finale of the D major: we are not presented with
the headlong rush favoured by many ensembles. The sense of pace is in harmony with the horse-drawn
rather than the jet-driven; every note speaks, every phrase tells and the overall effect is all the more
exhilarating. Generally speaking, the Orpheus find the *tempo giusto* throughout. They remain attuned
to the sensibility of the period and relate their pace to a dance movement in a manner that their rivals
have lost. There is something very natural about the players' music-making. They are inside these
scores and convey their involvement; no auto pilot, no *ersatz* feeling, no exaggerated or mechanized
sforzatos. What a relief! All the same, they are not preferable in the slow movement of the F major
Rasumovsky to the Végh or the Talich (on a seven-disc set), or in the first movement to the Tokyo,
who have a symphonic breadth which conveys just how revolutionary this movement is. The recording
is bright and clean, and enhances the claims of this impressive issue.

Additional recommendations ...

...Complete Quartets: Op. 18 Nos. 1-6. No. 7 in F major, Op. 59 No. 1, "Rasumovsky". No. 8 in
E minor, Op. 59 No. 2, "Rasumovsky". No. 9 in C major, Op. 59 No. 3, "Rasumovsky". No. 10
in E flat major, Op. 74, "Harp". No. 11 in F minor, Op. 95, "Serioso". No. 12 in E flat major,
Op. 127. No. 13 in B flat major, Op. 130. No. 14 in C sharp minor, Op. 131. No. 15 in A minor,
Op. 132. No. 16 in F major, Op. 135. **Talich Quartet.**
Calliope Ⓕ CAL9633/9 (seven discs: 502 minutes: AAD: 1/89).   ⒢⒢
...Complete Quartets. Grosse Fuge in B flat major, Op. 133. **Hungarian Quartet.**
EMI Ⓜ CZS7 67236-2* (seven discs: 476 minutes: ADD).
...Complete Quartets. Grosse Fugue in B flat major, Op. 133. **Quartetto Italiano.**
Philips Ⓜ 454 062-2PB10 (ten discs: 544 minutes: ADD: 2/90).   ⒢⒢
...Nos. 1-6. **Quartetto Italiano.** Philips Ⓜ 426 046-2PM3 (three discs: 163 minutes: ADD: 2/90).
...Nos. 1, 3, 4, 10, 12, 13 and 14. **Alban Berg Quartet.**
EMI Ⓕ CDS7 54587-2 (four discs: 242 minutes: DDD: 10/93).
...Nos. 2, 5, 6, 8, 9, 11, 15 and 16. Grosse Fuge. **Alban Berg Quartet.**
EMI Ⓕ CDS7 54592-2 (four discs: 259 minutes: DDD: 10/93).
...Nos. 1-6. String Quartet in F major, H34 (transcribed from Piano Sonata in F major, Op. 14,
No. 1). String Quintet in C major, Op. 29. **Tokyo Quartet** with **Pinchas Zukerman** (va).
RCA Victor Red Seal Ⓕ 09026 61284-2 (three discs: 204 minutes: DDD: 9/93).   ⒢
...Nos. 4-6. **Brandis Quartet.** Nimbus Ⓕ NI5353 (75 minutes: DDD: 9/94).
...Nos. 1, 9 and 11-16. Violin Sonata in E flat major, Op. 12 No. 3ᵃ. *Coupled with works by*
Schubert and **Mendelssohn** ᵃ**Rudolf Serkin** (pf); **Busch Quartet.**
EMI mono Ⓜ CHS5 65308-2* (four discs: 270 minutes: ADD: 1/95).
...Nos. 1 and 14. **Petersen Quartet.**
Capriccio Ⓕ 10 510 (66 minutes: DDD: 3/95). *Gramophone Editor's choice.*
...No. 13. Grosse Fuge, Op. 133. **Brandis Quartet.** Nimbus Ⓕ NI5465 (61 minutes: DDD: 4/96).
...Nos. 1, 4, 6, 9 and 11. String Quintet in C major, Op. 29ᵃ. **Budapest Quartet;** ᵃ**Milton Katims** (va).
Sony Classical Masterworks Heritage mono Ⓜ MH2K62870*
(two discs: 150 minutes: ADD: 5/98).

Beethoven String Quartets – No. 4 in C minor, Op. 18 No. 4; No. 15 in A minor, Op. 132.
Petersen Quartet (Conrad Muck, Gernot Süssmuth, vns; Friedemann Weigle, va;
Hans-Jakob Eschenburg, vc). Capriccio Ⓕ 10 722 (63 minutes: DDD: 4/96). Recorded 1995. ⒢⒢
The Petersen Quartet possess impeccable technical address, immaculate ensemble, flawless intonation
and tonal finesse. Tempos are judged with real musicianship, and dynamic markings are observed
without being exaggerated. The C minor Quartet, Op. 18 No. 4, has dramatic tension without loss of
lyrical fervour and the *Scherzo* has wit. When we move to the first movement of the A minor Quartet
the sound-world changes as if youth has given way to wisdom and experience. They hardly put a foot
wrong here and their *Heiliger Dankgesang* is rapt and inward-looking. They press ahead fractionally
in one or two places – on the reprise of the main section in the second movement and when the main
theme returns in the finale. But one or two minor reservations apart, theirs is quite simply the most
satisfying late Beethoven to have appeared in recent years. Above all the Petersen do not invite you to
admire their prowess. They appear to be untouched by the three 'g's (Gloss, Glamour and Glitz) and
their concern is with truth rather than beauty.

Beethoven String Quartets, Op. 18 – No. 5 in A major; No. 6 in B flat major. **Quatuor Mosaïques**
(Erich Höbarth, Andrea Bischof, vns; Anita Mitterer, va; Christophe Coin, vc). Auvidis Astrée
Ⓕ E8541 (58 minutes: DDD: 7/95). 🎙 Recorded 1994. *Gramophone Editor's choice.*
Of the Op. 18 works the A major probably has most to gain from a responsive performance on period
instruments. Its light textures and air of amiable elegance are particularly resistant to the brilliance of
certain modern-instrument ensembles; and the Mosaïques, most imaginative and penetrating of
'original' quartets, give an almost ideal reading. The imitative interplay of the finale gains particularly
from the textural clarity easier to achieve on period instruments played with sparing vibrato. The
tempo, characteristically, is on the broad side here. But few ensembles have brought such wit and
grace, such a subtle variety of colour and bowing, to the quicksilver instrumental dialogues. Yet the
Mosaïques' delicacy and intimacy do not preclude an authentic Beethovenian trenchancy in the
development, bows biting deeply into gut strings in those vehement *fortissimo* exchanges. The *Andante*
variations can often outstay their welcome; but these players bring an unusual grave eloquence to the
theme itself. In the B flat Quartet they are hardly less persuasive. The epigrammatic opening *Allegro*
is as spring-heeled and quick-witted as you could wish, yet avoids the clipped, relentlessly sportive
approach heard in many performances. In the *Adagio ma non troppo* Erich Höbarth brings a rare
sense of fantasy to the conventional-looking violin *fioriture*; and the protracted ending is, for once,
witty rather than tedious. For musical insight the Mosaïques' beautifully recorded readings of these
quartets hold their own with any of the modern-instrument versions in the catalogue.

Additional recommendations ...

...Nos. 5 and 6. **Kodály Quartet.** Naxos Ⓢ 8 550560 (56 minutes: DDD: 9/96).
...No. 5 – Minuet; Nos. 12, 14, 15 and 16. **Budapest Quartet.** Sony Classical Masterworks Heritage
mono Ⓜ MH2K62873* (two discs: 139 minutes: ADD: 5/98).

Beethoven String Quartets – No. 7 in F major, Op. 59 No. 1, "Rasumovsky"; No. 8 in E minor, Op. 59 No. 2, "Rasumovsky"; No. 9 in C major, Op. 59 No. 3, "Rasumovsky". **Lindsay Quartet** (Peter Cropper, Ronald Birks, vns; Roger Bigley, va; Bernard Gregor-Smith, vc). ASV Ⓜ CDDCS207 (two discs: 115 minutes: DDD: 4/95). From CDDCA554 (1/89). Ⓖ
In the few years that separate the Op. 18 from the Op. 59 quartets, Beethoven's world was shattered by the oncoming approach of deafness and the threat of growing isolation. The Op. 59 consequently inhabit a totally different plane, one in which the boundaries of sensibility had been extended in much the same way as the map of Europe was being redrawn. Each of the three quartets alludes to a Russian theme by way of compliment to Count Rasumovsky, who had commissioned the set. The immediate impression the F major Quartet conveys is of great space, breadth and vision; this is to the quartet what the *Eroica* is to the symphony. The neglect of Beethoven's C major Quintet is unaccountable for it is a rewarding and remarkable score, written only a year before the First Symphony. At one time the presto finale earned it the nickname "Der Sturm", doubtless on account of the similarity, or rather anticipation of the storm in the *Pastoral* Symphony. Although the Lindsays may be rivalled (and even surpassed) in some of their insights by the Végh and the Talich, taken by and large, they are second to none and superior to most. In each movement of the E minor they find the *tempo giusto* and all that they do as a result has the ring of complete conviction. The development and reprise of the first movement are repeated as well as the exposition and how imaginatively they play it too! The C major is not quite in the same class though the opening has real mystery and awe and some listeners might legitimately feel that the whole movement could do with a little more momentum. On the other hand, they move the second movement on rather too smartly. Yet how splendidly they convey the pent-up torrent of energy unleashed in this fugal onrush. Even if it does not command quite the same elevation of feeling or quality of inspiration that distinguishes their F major and E minor quartets, it is still pretty impressive.
Additional recommendations ...
...Nos. 8 and 9. **Végh Quartet.** Auvidis Valois Ⓕ V4404 (71 minutes: ADD: 4/88). ⒼⒼⒼ
...Nos. 7 and 8. **Budapest Quartet.**
Sony Classical Essential Classics Ⓑ SBK46545* (70 minutes: ADD: 8/91).
...Nos. 7-11. **Quartetto Italiano.** Philips Ⓜ 420 797-2PM3 (three discs: 165 minutes: ADD: 2/90). ⒼⒼ
...Nos. 7-9 and 11. **Tokyo Quartet.**
RCA Victor Red Seal Ⓕ RD60462 (three discs: 170 minutes: DDD: 3/92).
...Nos. 7-9. **Brandis Quartet.** Nimbus Ⓕ NI5382 (72 minutes: DDD: 6/94).
...Nos. 7-11. **Emerson Quartet.**
DG Complete Beethoven Edition Ⓜ 453 764-2GCB2 (two discs: 140 minutes: DDD: A/97).

Beethoven String Quartets – No. 8 in E minor, Op. 59 No. 2, "Rasumovsky"[b]; No. 13 in B flat major, Op. 130[a]. **Talich Quartet** (Petr Messiereur, Jan Kvapil, vns; Jan Talich, va; Evzen Rattai, vc). Calliope Ⓕ CAL9637 (73 minutes: ADD: 3/87). Item marked [a] from CAL1637/40, [b]CAL1634/6. ⒼⒼ
The Beethoven quartets are one of the greatest musical expressions of the human spirit and they must be represented in any collection. The advantage of this Talich recording is that it couples a masterpiece from Beethoven's middle period, the great E minor Quartet, with one of the greatest of his last years. The B flat was the third of the late quartets to be composed and at its first performance in 1826 its last movement, the *Grosse Fuge*, baffled his contemporaries. Later that same year, he substituted the present finale, publishing the *Grosse Fuge* separately. The Talich Quartet have a no less impressive technical command than other ensembles but theirs are essentially private performances, which one is privileged to overhear rather than the overprojected 'public' accounts we so often hear on record nowadays. At 73 minutes this is marvellous value too.

Beethoven String Quartets – No. 11 in F minor, Op. 95, "Serioso"[a]; No. 15 in A minor, Op. 132[b]. **Végh Quartet** (Sándor Végh, Sándor Zöldy, vns; Georges Janzer, va; Paul Szabó, vc). Auvidis Valois Ⓕ V4406 (68 minutes: ADD: 4/88). Item marked [a] from Telefunken EX6 35041 (8/76); [b]EX6 35040 (10/74). ⒼⒼⒼ
Beethoven String Quartets – No. 15 in A minor, Op. 132[a]; No. 16 in F major, Op. 135[b]. **Talich Quartet** (Petr Messiereur, Jan Kvapil, vns; Jan Talich, va; Evzen Rattai, vc). Calliope Ⓕ CAL9639 (68 minutes: ADD: 12/86). Item marked [a] from CAL1639, (6/80), [b]CAL1640 (6/80). ⒼⒼ
After the expansive canvas of the Op. 59 Quartets and the *Eroica*, Beethoven's F minor Quartet, Op. 95, displays musical thinking of the utmost compression. The first movement is a highly concentrated sonata design, which encompasses in its four minutes almost as much drama as a full-scale opera. With it comes one of the greatest masterpieces of his last years, the A minor, Op. 132. The isolation wrought first by his deafness and secondly, by the change in fashion of which he complained in the early 1820s, forced Beethoven in on himself. Opus 132 with its other-worldly *Heiliger Dankgesang*, written on his recovery from an illness, is music neither of the 1820s nor of Vienna, it belongs to that art which transcends time and place. Though other performances may be technically more perfect, these are interpretations that come closer to the spirit of this great music than any other on CD. Collectors need have no doubts as to the depth and intelligence of the Talich

Quartet's readings for they bring a total dedication to this music: their performances are innocent of artifice and completely selfless. There is no attempt to impress the listener with their own virtuosity or to draw attention to themselves in any way. The recordings are eminently faithful and natural, not 'hi-fi' or overbright but the overall effect is thoroughly pleasing.

Additional recommendation ...

...No. 11 (arr. Mahler). **Mahler** Symphony No. 2 in C minor, "Resurrection"[a]. [a]**Tina Kilberg** (sop); [a]**Kirsten Dolberg** (mez); [a]**Danish National Radio Choir; Danish National Symphony Orchestra / Leif Segerstam**. Chandos Ⓕ CHAN9266/7 (two discs: 116 minutes: 10/95).

Beethoven String Quartets. **Végh Quartet** (Sándor Végh, Sándor Zöldy, vns; Georges Janzer, va; Paul Szabó, vc). Auvidis Valois Ⓕ V4405, V4408 (two discs, oas: 71 and 66 minutes: ADD: 6/87). Items marked [a] from Telefunken EX6 35041 (8/76), [b]Telefunken SKA25113T/1-4 (10/74).
V4405 – No. 10 in E flat major, Op. 74, "Harp"[a]; No. 12 in E flat major, Op. 127[b]. *V4408* – No. 14 in C sharp minor, Op. 131[b]; No. 16 in F major, Op. 135[b].   ⒼⒼⒼ
Beethoven stepped both outside and beyond his period nowhere more so than in the late quartets and the last five piano sonatas. The Op. 127 has been called Beethoven's "crowning monument to lyricism", whilst the Op. 131 is more inward-looking. Every ensemble brings a different set of insights to this great music so that it is not possible to hail any single quartet as offering the whole truth – yet these are as near to the whole truth as we are ever likely to come. The Végh give us music-making that has a profundity and spirituality that completely outweigh any tiny blemishes of intonation or ensemble. One does not get the feeling of four professional quartet players performing publicly for an audience but four thoughtful musicians sharing their thoughts about this music in the privacy of their own home. They bring us closer to this music than do any of their high-powered rivals.

Additional recommendations ...

...(orch. Mitropoulos/Bernstein) Nos. 14 and 16. **Vienna Philharmonic Orchestra / Leonard Bernstein**. DG Ⓕ 435 779-2GH (77 minutes: ADD/DDD: 11/92).   ⒼⒼ
...No. 12. **Mozart** String Quartet No. 19 in C major, K465, "Dissonance". **Amadeus Quartet**. Orfeo mono Ⓕ C358941B* (63 minutes: ADD: 10/95).
...Nos. 14 and 15. **Capet Quartet**. Biddulph mono Ⓜ LAB099* (78 minutes: ADD: 12/95).
...Nos. 12-16. Grosse Fuge in B flat major, Op. 133. **Hollywood Quartet**. Testament mono Ⓕ SBT3082* (three discs: 193 minutes: ADD: 1/97).
...Nos. 12, 13 and 16. Grosse Fuge in B flat major, Op. 133.**Quartetto Italiano**. Philips Duo Ⓜ 454 711-2PM2 (two discs: 126 minutes: ADD: 4/97).
...Nos. 12-16. Grosse Fuge in B flat major, Op. 133. **Budapest Quartet**. Bridge Ⓜ BCD9072* (three discs: 188 minutes: ADD: 6/97).
...Nos. 14 and 15. **Quartetto Italiano**. Philips Duo Ⓜ 454 712-2PM2 (two discs: 90 minutes: ADD: 4/97).
...Nos. 12 and 14. **Cleveland Quartet**. Telarc Ⓕ CD80425 (78 minutes: DDD: 10/97).

Beethoven String Quartets – No. 12 in E flat major, Op. 127[a]; No. 13 in B flat major, Op. 130[b]; No. 14 in C sharp minor, Op. 131[c]; No. 15 in A minor, Op. 132[d]; No. 16 in F major, Op. 135[a]. Grosse fuge in B flat, Op. 133[b]. **Quartetto Italiano** (Paolo Boriciani, Elsa Pegreffi, vns; Piero Farulli, va; Franco Rossi, vc). Philips Ⓜ 426 050-2PM4 (four discs: 216 minutes: ADD: 2/90). Items marked [a] from SAL3703 (4/70), [b]SAL3780 (4/70), [c]SAL3790 (4/70), [d]SAL3638 (9/68). Recorded 1967-9. *Gramophone classical 100*.   ⒼⒼⒼ
As recordings, these Philips issues made between 1967 and 1969 can hold their own against more recent rivals and their musical merits well withstand the test of time. The Quartetto Italiano recordings have appeared in a variety of reincarnations since they first came out as individual issues (first, as a boxed set of the four LPs, then as part of a complete ten-LP set, then as double-packs at mid price and so on) and their merits are so well known that there is no need for a long review. Not all of them received universal acclaim at the time of their first release. But then no one ensemble ever penetrates all the depths of this sublime music and these performances still strike a finely judged balance between beauty and truth, and are ultimately more satisfying and searching than their rivals. Take care of the sense and the sound takes care of itself: the sonority that the Quartetto Italiano produce is better-blended and has a greater variety of tone-colour than the Végh and the Talich Quartets, although these latter have special claims and give searching and deeply-felt accounts, even if in the case of the Végh, they are not always immaculate technically. However, the Quartetto Italiano can be confidently recommended.

Beethoven String Quartets – No. 13 in B flat major, Op. 130; No. 16 in F major, Op. 135. Grosse Fuge in B flat major, Op. 133. **Juilliard Quartet** (Robert Mann, Joel Smirnoff, vns; Samuel Rhodes, va; Joel Krosnick, vc). Sony Classical Ⓕ SK62792 (76 minutes: DDD: 2/98). Recorded 1996.
The Juilliard take Op. 130's long first-movement repeat then play the *Grosse Fuge* as its rightful finale, relegating the lighter-hearted 'rewrite' to encore status at the very end of the piece. Hearing the fugue as a structural summation rather than a disembodied torso makes good musical sense (its replacement turns most of Op. 130 into a sort of elevated divertimento), and the Juilliard's concentration more than justifies their decision. The performance itself is full of subtle beauties, not least in the first

movement, at the point near the onset of the development (around 8'29") where *Allegro* fragments prompt *espressivo Adagio* responses and where the players gauge the music's oscillating moods with characteristic perception. Similarly, there is a sense of infinite sadness at 5'16" into the *Andante con moto* third movement, whereas the *Presto* and *Alla danza tedesca* are, by turns, fleeting and elegant; the *Grosse Fuge* struts, sings and swings, and the 'second' finale dances to a pointed staccato. This is profound, deeply pondered music-making, the sort that would be impossible to achieve in less than half a lifetime. Op. 135 is similarly persuasive, with a playfully disruptive *Vivace*, a heart-rending *Lento assai* and, most significantly, an account of the finale that includes the important – though rarely played – second repeat. Sony's recordings achieve a warm blend of voices.

Beethoven String Quartets – No. 15 in A minor, Op. 132; No. 16 in F major, Op. 135.
  Cleveland Quartet (William Preucil, Peter Salaff, vns; James Dunham, va; Paul Katz, vc).
  Telarc Ⓕ CD80427 (69 minutes: DDD: A/97). Recorded 1995.
Comparing this with the Emerson Quartet's Beethoven, it is striking how different these two highly accomplished American groups are. The Emersons are always searching for something out of the ordinary, pushing tempos and dynamics to extremes, and trying to give the fullest expression to the music's individuality. By contrast, the Cleveland Quartet offer fewer surprises; they're upholders of tradition, rather than seekers after new truths. One of this ensemble's most notable characteristics is their rich, warm tone, well captured here. The first movement of the A minor Quartet has a level of emotional commitment that's quite compelling – all the details of this complex music fall into place and contribute to the overall effect. If the rest of the quartet isn't quite so outstanding it's still very good, with a lovely swinging rhythm to the second movement, and delightfully sprightly accounts of the *Andante* episodes in the slow movement – absolutely "feeling new strength", as Beethoven's caption puts it. Their Op. 135 is also very impressive. The *Scherzo* doesn't quite match the breakneck intensity of the Emerson, but the *Lento* is more deeply felt, their rich sound really coming into its own. And the finale must be one of the best versions on record – spirited, touching, playful, as the music's mood demands.

Beethoven Piano Trios – E flat major, Op. 1 No. 1; G major, Op. 1 No. 2; C minor, Op. 1 No. 3;
  B flat major, Op. 11; D major, Op. 70 No. 1, "Ghost"; E flat major, Op. 70 No. 2; B flat major,
  Op. 97, "Archduke"; B flat major, WoO39; E flat major, WoO38; E flat major, Op. 44; G major,
  Op. 121*a*. **Beaux Arts Trio** (Daniel Guilet, vn; Bernard Greenhouse, vc; Menahem Pressler, pf).
  Philips The Early Years Ⓜ 438 948-2PM3 (three discs: 235 minutes: ADD: 11/94).
  From SAL3527/30 (1/66). Recorded 1965.   ⒼⒼ
Beethoven Piano Trios – C minor, Op. 1 No. 3; B flat major, Op. 11ᵃ. Allegretto in B flat major,
  WoO39. ᵃ**Wolfgang Meyer** (cl); **Erich Höbarth** (vn); **Christophe Coin** (vc); **Patrick Cohen** (pf).
  Harmonia Mundi Ⓕ HMC90 1475 (60 minutes: DDD: 1/95). 🎧 Recorded 1993.
Beethoven Piano Trios – B flat major, Op. 11; B flat major, Op. 97, "Archduke". **Chung Trio**
  (Kyung-Wha Chung, vn; Myung-Wha Chung, vc; Myung-Whun Chung, pf).
  EMI Ⓕ CDC5 55187-2 (61 minutes: DDD: 1/95). Recorded 1992.
It's the immediacy and freshness, the wholehearted commitment of the playing by the Beaux Arts Trio that holds you spellbound in almost every context. To begin with, in the *joie de vivre* of the E flat and G major Op. 1 Trios, it's so good to be reminded that a colossus like Beethoven was once so young at heart – in the persuasive lyricism of slower tempos no less than the teasing, devil-may-care sparkle and wit of their finales (taken at a breathless pace without for a moment sounding gabbled). The crowning performance is nevertheless the *Archduke*. The players' expansive yet warmly human nobility in the opening *Allegro moderato*, their urgent, mercurial response to the undertones of the *Scherzo*, their raptness in the visionary serenity of the slow movement and their pungency in the finale convince you that no greater piano trio has ever been written. Here, too, you're given the fullest chance to enjoy the silken beauty of Guilet's violin and the velvet richness of Greenhouse's now legendary 1707 Stradivari cello; also the wonderful blend of tone achieved by all three in contexts like the pizzicato/staccato of the first movement's development, or the eerie chromatic start to the trio of the *Scherzo*. Hailed in the booklet as "the soul of the entire ensemble", Pressler himself achieves many miracles of delicacy and fleetness.

Harmonia Mundi give us a welcome recording of Beethoven's original version of the Trio, Op. 11. Although Beethoven later adapted the work for the more frequently chosen violin, nothing can capture the opening movement's hiding and seeking quite like the clarinet. Meyer marks, teases and imitates with glee just as he phrases and articulates with high mischief in the first variation of Beethoven's nine on Joseph Weigl's aria, *Pria ch'io l'impegna*. Cohen's fortepiano here is, as the note cryptically puts it, "Clarke d'après Walter, 1986". This was the Viennese Anton Walter, whose early pianos, with their hammer-heads resting directly on the keys, Mozart grew to favour. In the Op. 1 No. 3 Trio, its sweet, short metallic resonance brings a sting to the accents and raging scale passages in an uncompromising opening movement of a work Haydn much admired, but warned Beethoven not to publish. Its dangers and disturbances, as well as the delicate patterning of its slow movement, shine out anew in this entirely engaging performance. Six-and-a-half minutes' worth of the single *Allegretto* movement of Beethoven's B flat Trio make up an hour's listening on this irresistible disc.

The playing of Kyung-Wha Chung on the EMI disc – sweet, sentient and sharply defined – almost persuades you again of the violin's adapted and adopted role in the Op. 11 Trio. And what the modern piano loses in the immediacy of its own voice and its empathy with the others is generously compensated by Myung-Whun's nimble, light-filled playing. This piano's warmer resonance comes into its own in the long distances of the rolling crescendos and decrescendos which form the heart of the *Adagio*, and lift it into the major. The real wonder of this disc, though, is the Chungs' performance of the Op. 97 Trio in B flat. Beethoven dedicated it "in deep reverence" to Austria's Archduke – and Myung-Whun never forgets it, whether in his awed, reverential opening, or in the simplicity of the wonderfully hushed frame of his slow movement theme. Violin and cello merely brush, rather than gush, against it, and lead it into a dream sequence of variations. The Chungs' gentle unfolding and nourishing of this opening movement – everything is done within a veiled undertone – leave plenty of fuel unburned for the *scherzo*, which starts on tiptoe, and whose dark chromatic shadows in the trio are never overbriskly dissipated by what can often be an overassertive waltz. This is chamber-music-making at its most perceptive and rewarding.

Additional recommendations ...

...Complete Piano Trios. Variations Op. 121*a*. Variations, Op. 44. Allegretto in E flat major.
  Borodin Trio. Chandos Ⓕ CHAN8352/5 (four discs: 271 minutes: DDD: 7/87).
...Op. 1 Nos. 1 and 2. **London Fortepiano Trio.**
  Hyperion Ⓕ CDA66197 (58 minutes: DDD: 11/87) 🎵
...Op. 1 Nos. 1-3. "Ghost". "Archduke". Variations, Op. 121*a*. 14 Variations, Op. 44. Allegretto in
  E flat major. **Pinchas Zukerman** (vn); **Jacqueline du Pré** (vc); **Daniel Barenboim** (pf).
  EMI Studio Ⓜ CMS7 63124-2 (three discs: 230 minutes: ADD: 8/89).
..."Archduke". "Ghost". **Henryk Szeryng** (vn); **Pierre Fournier** (vc); **Wilhelm Kempff** (pf).
  DG Ⓜ 429 712-2GGA (71 minutes: ADD: 9/90).
..."Archduke"[b]. Op. 1 No. 3[a]. "Ghost"[c]. Cello Sonatas – F major, Op. 5 No. 1[d]; G minor, Op. 5
  No. 2[e]; F major, Op. 17[g]; C major, Op. 102 No. 1[f]. [abc]**Sándor Vegh.** (vn); **Pablo Casals** (vc);
  [c]**Karl Engel,** [abefg]**Mieczysław Horszowski,** [d]**Wilhelm Kempf** (pfs).
  Philips Ⓜ 438 520-2PM3 (three discs: 200 minutes: ADD: 3/94).
..."Archduke". B flat major, Op. 11. **Alexander Schneider** (vn); **Pablo Casals** (vc); **Eugene Istomin**
  (pf). Sony Classical Casals Edition mono Ⓜ SMK58990* (65 minutes: ADD: 5/94).
...E flat major, Op. 1 No. 1. G major, Op. 1 No. 2. **Stuttgart Piano Trio.**
  Naxos Ⓢ 8 550946 (63 minutes: DDD: 7/94).
...C minor, Op. 1 No. 3. E flat major, WoO38. E flat major, Op. 44. Trio movement in E flat major,
  Hess No. 48. **Stuttgart Piano Trio.** Naxos Ⓢ 8 550947 (60 minutes: DDD: 7/94).
..."Ghost". Op. 70 No. 2. **Stuttgart Piano Trio.** Naxos Ⓢ 8 550948 (57 minutes: DDD: 12/94).
..."Archduke". **Brahms** Piano Trio No. 1 in B major, Op. 8. **Viktoria Mullova** (vn);
  Heinrich Schiff (vc); **André Previn** (pf). Philips Ⓕ 442 123-2PH (75 minutes: DDD: 8/95).
...B flat major, Op. 11. *Coupled with works by* **Brahms** and **Mozart** Richard Stoltzman (cl);
  Yo-Yo Ma (vc); **Emanuel Ax** (pf). Sony Classical Ⓕ SK57499 (70 minutes: DDD: 1/96).
...Op. 1 Nos. 1 and 2. **Erich Hobarth** (vn) **Christophe Coin** (vc); **Patrick Cohen** (fp).
  Harmonia Mundi HMC90 1361 (70 minutes: DDD: 2/96). 🎵
..."Ghost"; "Archduke"; Op. 70 No. 2; G major, Op. 121*a* . **Solomon Trio.**
  IMP Masters Ⓜ 30366 0010-7 (two discs: 132 minutes: DDD: 8/96).
...E flat major, Op. 1 No. 1. B flat major, Op. 11 No. 4. B flat major, WoO39. **Vienna Piano Trio.**
  Nimbus Ⓕ NI5508 (58 minutes: DDD: 7/97).

Beethoven String Trios – E flat major, Op. 3; Op. 9 – No. 1 in G major; No. 2 in D major; No. 3
in C minor. Serenade in D major, Op. 8. **Itzhak Perlman** (vn); **Pinchas Zukerman** (va); **Lynn Harrell**
(vc). EMI Ⓕ CDS7 54198-2 (two discs: 143 minutes: DDD: 2/93). Recorded live 1989-90.   Ⓖ
Beethoven String Trios, Op. 9 – No. 1 in G major; No. 2 in D major; No. 3 in C minor.
L'Archibudelli (Vera Beths, vn; Jürgen Kussmaul, va; Anner Bylsma, vc).
Sony Classical Vivarte Ⓕ SK48190 (68 minutes: DDD: 9/92). 🎵 Recorded 1991.   Ⓖ

Whereas the last of Beethoven's six Piano Trios, the *Archduke*, was not written until he was 41, all five of his String Trios date from his twenties, with the six-movement E flat Trio, Op. 3, appearing in 1792, to be followed by the *Serenade* in D, Op. 8, some five years later. But after banishing all such eighteenth-century entertainment connotations in his three next classically designed, four-movement String Trios (Op. 9) of 1798, he thereafter preferred to write not for three but rather, four strings in what grew into a legendary, life-long cycle of string quartets. The double-stopping in the noble slow movement of the high-powered C minor String Trio already portends pursuit of richer textures. So it is essentially the artist as a young man that we meet on the EMI set, and what a revelation of youthful genius they offer in imaginative range. Recorded live in New York, the playing is eloquent testimony to that little extra piquancy and boldness of characterization that an audience can draw from artists even as studio-friendly as Perlman, Zukerman and Harrell – perhaps all the more fresh in their approach because not in daily harness as an ensemble. Tone is splendidly vibrant. And incidentally they score over their also excellent, but less succulently reproduced DG rivals, by including the arresting extra trio Beethoven subsequently provided for the *Scherzo* of the G major Trio.

A group with "a special love for historical stringed instruments" is how L'Archibudelli is described, as might be gleaned from their name (an Italian compilation of bows and strings), plus the fact that Anner Bylsma plays a 1835 Gianfrancesco Pressenda cello, Vera Bath a 1727 Stradivari violin and Jürgen Kussmaul a 1785 William Forster viola. But though striving for a special period quality of sound they are anything but antiquarian in their approach to these works, all of them striking enough to have placed Beethoven among the immortals even if he had written nothing else. With their brisk tempo, strong dynamic contrast and piquant accentuation, they leave no doubt of the urgency inherent in the key of C minor for this composer. The other two Trios in major keys are equally imaginatively characterized and contrasted. Some listeners might even feel they are overvolatile in their response to every detailed innuendo, at the expense of firmly drawn, classical line. But their relish of the music wins the day. Once or twice busy figuration in the lower strings emerge a bit bottom-heavy. The recording is true to life.

Additional recommendations ...

...*As EMI.* **Anne-Sophie Mutter** (vn); **Bruno Giuranna** (va); **Mstislav Rostropovich** (vc). DG Ⓕ 427 687-2GH2 (two discs: 139 minutes: DDD: 7/89).

...E flat major. Serenade, Op. 8. **L'Archibudelli.** Sony Classical Vivarte Ⓕ SK53961 (71 minutes: DDD: 5/94). ✏

...Op. 9 Nos. 1-3. **Cummings Trio.** Unicorn-Kanchana Ⓜ UKCD2081 (73 minutes: DDD: 4/97).

Beethoven Cello Sonatas – No. 1 in F major, Op. 5 No. 1[a]; No. 2 in G minor, Op. 5 No. 2[b]; No. 3 in A major, Op. 69[c]; No. 4 in C major, Op. 102 No. 1[d]; No. 5 in D major, Op. 105 No. 2[e]. Menuet in G major, WoO10 No. 2 (arr. vc/pf)[f].
Brahms Cello Sonata No. 2 in F major, Op. 99[g]. **Pablo Casals** (vc); [abdeg]**Mieczyslaw Horszowski,** [cf]**Otto Schulhof** (pfs). EMI Références mono Ⓜ CHS5 65185-2* (two discs: 136 minutes: ADD: 10/94). Item marked [a] from HMV DB3908/10, [b]DB3911/13 (both recorded 1939), [c]DB1417/19 (10/31), [d]DB3065/6 (7/37), [e]DB3914/16 (4/41), [f]DB1419, [g]DB3059/62 (8/40). ⒼⒼⒼ

Beethoven Cello Sonatas – No. 1 in F major, Op. 5 No. 1; No. 2 in G minor, Op. 5 No. 2; No. 3 in A major, Op. 69; No. 4 in C major, Op. 102 No. 1; No. 5 in D major, Op. 102 No. 2. 12 Variations on Mozart's "Ein Mädchen oder Weibchen", Op. 66. 12 Variations on Handel's "See the conqu'ring hero comes", WoO45. Seven Variations on Mozart's "Bei Männern, welche Liebe fühlen", WoO46. **Raphael Wallfisch** (vc); **John York** (pf). EMI Eminence Ⓜ CD-EMXD2506 (two discs: 143 minutes: DDD: 2/97). *Gramophone Editor's choice.* ⒼⒼ

Sensitive phrasing was the very hub of Pablo Casals's art, and these CDs are more revealing than many of how this most communicative of cellists could mould and energize a musical line, reducing his tone to a soulful tenor then thrusting a powerful *sforzando* for maximum dynamic contrast. The Beethoven sonatas are endlessly rewarding in this respect, but even they must bow to the marginal supremacy of Casals's 1936 account of the Brahms F major Sonata, one of the truly great cello recordings. No one since has projected the work's heroic opening with as much confidence (the repeat is observed, by the way), nor brought greater suppleness or tonal variety to the *Adagio affetuoso.* Note, too, how both Casals and Horszowski explore the winding musical thickets of the *Allegro passionato* and make play with the closing *Allegro molto.* The Beethoven sonatas are equally indelible, the Op. 5 works sounding very much their innovatory selves, and those of Op. 102 more probing and explosive than most. Both players invest Op. 102 No. 2's searching *Adagio con molto sentimento d'affetto* with an intriguing sense of the numinous, then dig deep into the succeeding *Allegro fugato* – a gritty debate on the preceding mystery. Casals recorded the Op. 69 Sonata some nine years before Opp. 5 and 102, not with Horszowski, but with the stylish and facilitating Otto Schulhof. It differs from its companions in being more songful than soulful and with a *bel canto* solo line that extends to the charming Menuet makeweight. Recordings of this unique quality deserve painstaking restoration, and Andrew Walters's transfers are excellent. Surface levels are low, the solo cello sounds clean and immediate, and the piano is more recognizably itself than on some 78s from the 1930s.

The modern piano, with its far greater bass strength and sonority, can very easily obscure details of the cello part and it's rare to hear such a well-balanced account of Beethoven's music for cello and piano. Wallfisch and York are, for a start, admirably recorded. The acoustic is intimate but in no way constricted, and it's remarkable, too, how York, whilst never seeming to underplay, succeeds by careful control of pedal and dynamics in leaving room for the cello to flourish. And Raphael Wallfisch's wide range of tone-colour, by turn gutsy, opulent and bright, is responsive to all the expressive nuances. You do wonder whether these performances are perhaps a little 'ordinary', by comparison with the playing of such musical personalities as Argerich. However, York and Wallfisch present the music's character at each turn of phrase, from the inside, as it were, and without affectation. The result is far from boring. For repeated listening at home of a modern version, Wallfisch and York are now among the most recommendable versions.

Additional recommendations ...

...Nos. 1 and 2. 12 Variations in F major on "Ein Mädchen oder Weibchen" from "Die Zauberflöte", Op. 66. Seven Variations in E flat major on Mozart's "Bei Männern, welche Liebe fühlen" from "Die Zauberflöte", WoO46. **Mischa Maisky** (vc); **Martha Argerich** (pf). DG Ⓕ 431 801-2GH (66 minutes: DDD: 2/92). ⒼⒼ

...Nos. 1-5. Variations, WoO46. Variations, Op. 66. **Pablo Casals** (vc); **Rudolf Serkin** (pf). Sony Classical Casals Edition mono Ⓜ SM2K58985* (two discs: 158 minutes: ADD: 5/94).

...Nos. 1-5. Variations, Op. 66. Variations, WoO46. Variations, WoO45. **Mischa Maisky** (vc); **Martha Argerich** (pf). DG Ⓕ 439 934-2GH2 (two discs: 139 minutes: DDD: 2/95).

...No. 1; E flat major, Op. 64. 12 Variations on Handel's "See the conqu'ring hero comes", WoO45. **Anssi Karttunen** (vc); **Tuija Hakkila** (fp). Finlandia Ⓕ 4509-95584-2 (71 minutes: DDD: 11/95). ✏

Beethoven Cello Sonatas – No. 2 in G minor, Op. 5 No. 2; No. 3 in A major, Op. 69; No. 5 in
D major, Op. 102 No. 2. **David Watkin** (vc); **Howard Moody** (fp).
Chandos Chaconne Ⓕ CHAN0561 (70 minutes: DDD: 10/96). ✒ Recorded 1994.
If you're not sure about the advantages of original-instrument performance of classical chamber
music, try this disc! Watkin and Moody demonstrate that 'authentic' Beethoven need not in any way
diminish the grandeur and emotional depth of his music. David Watkin, very correctly, uses vibrato
discreetly and selectively, and is most imaginative in finding just the right bow-stroke for each musical
nuance – his urgent phrasing of the G minor Sonata's first *Allegro*, and the way he breathes the
phrases at the start of the D major's slow movement are two examples of many memorable details.
Howard Moody plays two original period instruments – a Rosenberger fortepiano of *c*1800 for the
G minor Sonata, and an 1826 Graf for the two later works – and seems always able to find reserves
of sonority to encompass Beethoven's most dramatic moments. The climactic codas of the A major
Sonata's outer movements are especially exciting. The 'big' feeling of these performances is partly due
to the lively, intimate recording – the sound is not diluted in any large spaces and we can also hear
quite a bit of mechanical noise from the piano, and sniffs from the players.

Beethoven Violin Sonatas – No. 1 in D major, Op. 12 No. 1 (from SXL6790, 7/77); No. 2 in
A major, Op. 12 No. 2 (SXL6632, 2/75); No. 3 in E flat major, Op. 12 No. 3 (SXL6789, 12/76);
No. 4 in A minor, Op. 23; No. 5 in F major, Op. 24, "Spring" (both from SXL6736, 7/76); No. 6
in A major, Op. 30 No. 1; No. 7 in C minor, Op. 30 No. 2 (both from SXL6791, 12/77); No. 8 in
G major, Op. 30 No. 3 (SXL6789); No. 9 in A major, Op. 47, "Kreutzer" (SXL6632); No. 10 in
G major, Op. 96 (SXL6790). **Itzhak Perlman** (vn); **Vladimir Ashkenazy** (pf).
Decca Ovation Ⓜ 421 453-2DM4 (four discs: 239 minutes: ADD: 1/89). Recorded 1973-5.   Ⓖ
Although Beethoven designated these works as "for piano and violin", following Mozart's example,
it is unlikely that he thought of the piano as leading the proceedings, or the violin either, for that
matter: both instruments are equal partners and in that sense this is true chamber music. Perlman and
Ashkenazy are artists of the first rank and there is much pleasure to be derived from their set. Such
an imaginative musician as Ashkenazy brings great subtlety to these works composed by a supreme
pianist-composer. And the better the pianist is in this music, the better does the violinist play.
Discernment is matched by spontaneity and the whole series is remarkably fine, while their celebrated
performance of the *Kreutzer* Sonata has quite superb eloquence and vitality. The recording boasts
unusually truthful violin sound capturing all the colour of Perlman's playing – and that is saying
something. Ashkenazy's vivid attack is always faithful to the Beethoven idiom.

Additional recommendations ...
...Nos. 1-10. **Sir Yehudi Menuhin** (vn); **Wilhelm Kempff** (pf).
 DG Ⓜ 415 874-2GCM4 (four discs: 272 minutes: ADD: 6/87).
...Nos. 8-10. **Jascha Heifetz** (vn); **Emmanuel Bay** (pf).
 RCA Victor Gold Seal mono Ⓜ GD87706* (72 minutes: ADD: 11/88).   ⒼⒼ
...Nos. 5 and 9. **Takako Nishizaki** (vn); **Jenö Jandó** (pf).
 Naxos Ⓢ 8 550283 (56 minutes: DDD: 3/91).
...Nos. 5, 9 and 10. **Zino Francescatti** (vn); **Robert Casadesus** (pf).
 Sony Classical Essential Classics Ⓑ SBK46342* (76 minutes: ADD: 3/91).
...Nos. 5 and 9. **Thomas Zehetmair** (vn); **Malcolm Frager** (fp).
 Teldec Digital Experience Ⓜ 9031-75856-2 (59 minutes: DDD: 6/92). ✒
...Nos. 5, 8 and 9. **Pinchas Zukerman** (vn); **Daniel Barenboim** (pf).
 EMI Studio Plus Ⓜ CDM7 64631-2 (78 minutes: ADD: 3/93).
...Nos. 1-10. **Mozart** Violin Sonatas Nos.18, 21, 24, 26, 32 and 35. **Arthur Grumiaux** (vn);
 Clara Haskil (pf). Philips Ⓜ 442 625-2PM5 (five discs: 310 minutes: ADD: 11/95).
...Nos. 1-10. **Gidon Kremer** (vn); **Martha Argerich** (pf).
 DG Ⓕ 447 058-2GH3 (three discs: 226 minutes: DDD: 1/96).   Ⓖ
...Nos. 1-1 **Petr Messiereur** (vn); **Stanislav Bogunia** (pf).
 Calliope Ⓕ CAL9251/3 (three discs: 217 minutes: DDD: 3/96).
...Nos. 3, 5 and 7. **Adolf Busch** (vn); **Rudolf Serkin** (pf).
 APR mono Ⓜ APR5541* (60 minutes: ADD: 5/96).
...Nos. 7, 8 and 9. **Olivier Charlier** (vn); **Brigitte Engerer** (pf).
 Harmonia Mundi Ⓕ HMC90 1580 (79 minutes: DDD: 6/96).

Beethoven Violin Sonatas – No. 6 in A major, Op. 30 No. 1; No. 7 in C minor, Op. 30 No. 2;
 No. 8 in G major, Op. 30 No. 3. **Gidon Kremer** (vn); **Martha Argerich** (pf). DG Ⓕ 445 652-2GH
 (64 minutes: DDD: 1/95). Recorded 1993. *Gramophone Editor's choice.*   ⒼⒼ
Beethoven's Op. 30 Violin Sonatas are three irresistibly lively and individual spirits in the hands and
imaginations of Martha Argerich and Gidon Kremer. The first, in A major, has that particular
quality of blithe and elusive joy reminiscent of the *Spring* Sonata, and created here by the lightest and
truest touch on string and key, fused with bright rhythmic clarity. The slow movement is a tremulous
song of long-forgotten, far-off things, in which violin and piano find an intimate balance of tone. The
second sonata of the group is here less an heroically clenched C minor fist, more the unfolding of a
gripping and tense *Märchen*: a dark children's fairy-tale told through the rapid tapering of a phrase-

ending on the violin, the gutsy ebb and flow of a piano crescendo, the sudden *pianissimo* picking up after the loud chords of a second theme. At the start of the development, Argerich even seems to be asking if her listeners are sitting comfortably – and rather hoping they are not. The G major Sonata's centrepiece is its Minuet and Trio, which Argerich and Kremer cunningly tease and charm into revealing its archaic qualities: a dance glimpsed through a lace veil. It is framed by two fast movements that would identify their performers anywhere, with their high-voltage velocity and wittily imaginative anticipation of each other's every move.
Additional recommendations ...
...Nos. 6-8. **Pamela Frank** (vn); **Claude Frank** (pf).
MusicMasters Ⓕ 67106-2 (66 minutes: DDD: 3/97).

Beethoven 12 Variations on Handel's "See the conqu'ring hero comes", WoO45. 12 Variations on Mozart's "Ein Mädchen oder Weibchen", Op. 66. Seven Variations on Mozart's "Bei Männern, welche Liebe fühlen", WoO46. Horn Sonata, Op. 17 (arr. vc). **Pieter Wispelwey** (vc);
Lois Shapiro (fp). Channel Classics Ⓕ CCS6494 (45 minutes: DDD: 4/95). 🎵 Recorded 1994.
There may be only 45 minutes of it, but this recital of Beethoven variations teems with fresh insights in the irresistible serendipity of its playing. Lois Shapiro partners Pieter Wispelwey's 1701 cello on a 1780 Viennese fortepiano whose wiry energies she unleashes without more ado in an attention-grabbing opening theme for Handel's *See the conqu'ring hero comes*. Her bright-eyed first variation glints as phrases dart from dynamic shadow to light and back again. Then the cello's lean, slightly astringent voice makes itself felt in no uncertain terms before the keyboard gets its own back in mercurial scale passages. The players' delight in teasing, sparring and debating with each other comes into its own in the variations on *Ein Mädchen oder Weibchen*. The theme itself struts forward cheekily, only to peck its way through the first variation, before the cello makes the most of the wry harmonic subtext of the second. In the seventh, one half of a shared phrase caresses and preens the other; the tenth casts the shadow of Papageno's noose. Each player's imagination and technique is tested to the full in an absorbing account of the more abstracted *Bei Männern* variations. The world of *Singspiel* is not far away, either, in this performance of the Sonata in F major, Op. 17: Wispelwey and Shapiro summon up the nascent world of Marzelline and Jacquino in their quick, ardent responses to the music and to each other's playing.
Additional recommendation ...
...Horn Sonata in F major, Op. 17. *Coupled with works by various composers.* **David Pyatt** (hn); **Martin Jones** (pf). Erato Ⓕ 3984-21632-2 (66 minutes: DDD: 4/98). *See review in the Collections section; refer to the Index.*

Beethoven Bagatelles – Op. 33; Op. 119; Op. 126; A minor, WoO59, "Für Elise"[a]; B flat major, WoO60. Rondo in C major, Op. 51 No. 1. Allegretto in C minor, WoO53. **Alfred Brendel** (pf).
Philips Ⓕ 456 031-2PH (77 minutes: DDD: 1/98). Item marked [a] from 412 227-2PH (8/85, recorded 1984). Recorded 1996.
Listening to Beethoven's *Bagatelles* can be like looking over the composer's shoulder as he works. A scrap of a theme, a repeated chord, a formulaic accompanying figure – suddenly blossoms into something rich and strange; the one-dimensional turns magically into the three-dimensional. An unassuming little *Andante con moto* tune dissolves into a cadenza, then emerges transfigured in ecstatic counterpoint (Op. 126 No. 1); an innocent, almost plain folk-melody reappears floating on high, a voice from another world (Op. 119 No. 11). And so often in the *Bagatelles* humour is at the core. If there's such a thing as profound levity, this is it. Brendel, who has written so effectively about humour in Beethoven, plainly revels in this aspect of the *Bagatelles*. The quirkiness, the delight in pulling the rug from under the listener's feet – he seems to have made it all his own. One could argue with the approach here or there – Op. 119 No. 5 strikes one as more laboured than *Risoluto*; the strange half-pedal at the end of Op. 119 No. 3 produces a momentarily metallic aura around the notes – but much more often, character and texture are calculated to a nicety. And could any merely human pianist be expected to please in all of these hugely contrasted miniatures? He also conveys a sense of Op. 126 as – in Beethoven's own words – a "cycle of *Bagatelles*", the extraordinary No. 11 (a gorgeous *Andante amabile* framed by music-hall fanfares) making a very thought-provoking finale.
Additional recommendations ...
...Op. 33. Op. 119. Fantasia in G minor, Op. 77. Seven Variations in C major on "God save the King", WoO78. Five Variations in D major on "Rule Britannia", WoO79. **Melvyn Tan** (fp).
EMI Ⓕ CDC7 54526-2 (71 minutes: DDD: 12/92). 🎵   Ⓖ
...Op. 33. Op. 119. Op. 126. Allegretto in C major, WoO56. Presto in C minor, WoO52.
John O'Conor (pf). Telarc Ⓕ CD80423 (60 minutes: DDD: 11/96).

Beethoven Six Variations in F major on an Original Theme, Op. 34[a]. Six Variations in D major, Op. 76. 15 Variations and a Fugue on an Original Theme in E flat major, Op. 35, "Eroica"[a].
Chopin Four Scherzos[b] – No. 1 in B minor, Op. 20; No. 2 in B flat minor, Op. 31; No. 3 in C sharp minor, Op. 39; No. 4 in E major, Op. 54.
Schumann Etudes symphoniques, Opp. 13 and posth[a]. Bunte Blätter, Op. 99[b]. **Sviatoslav Richter** (pf). Olympia Ⓕ OCD339[a] and OCD338[b] (two discs, oas: 77 and 75 minutes: ADD: 4/94).
Recorded by Eurodisc 1970-77.   Ⓖ Ⓖ

Remarkably well recorded considering the source, one performance after another here is so memorable as to rank among the best versions around of the piece in question. There is such richness in the Beethoven Variations that it seems pointless and unfair to highlight any one in particular. Nevertheless, the *Eroica* Variations end with Richter playing most pianists under the table. He is not usually thought of as a very credible Chopin player, and yet he strides through the four *Scherzos* with an abundance of technique and deftly coloured textures that make this version a definite front-runner. His Schumann, on the other hand, has always been dazzling, because he has a temperament that convincingly responds to the extreme swings in mood. The reading of the *Etudes symphoniques* is an overwhelming experience. The fourth of the supplementary variations emerges as an exotic lament of ravishing beauty and the pianist's very large hands enable him to attack the chords of the finale with ferocious confidence.Well-chosen and excellent in sound, these performances should not be missed.

Additional recommendations ...
...Variations, Op. 34. 15 Variations, Op. 35, "Eroica". Rondos, Op. 51 – No. 1 in C major; No. 2 in
  G major. Bagatelle in A minor, WoO59, "Fur Elise". **Louis Lortie** (pf).
  Chandos Ⓕ CHAN8616 (58 minutes: DDD: 10/90).
...Variations, Op. 34. Six Variations, WoO70. 15 Variations and a Fugue. 32 Variations on an
  Original Theme in C minor, WoO80. **Jenö Jandó** (pf). Naxos Ⓢ 8 550676 (54 minutes: DDD: 9/93).

Beethoven 33 Variations in C major on a Waltz by Diabelli, Op. 120. **Alfredo Perl** (pf).
  Arte Nova Classics Ⓢ 74321 27761-2 (58 minutes: DDD: 7/97). Recorded 1993.
If you can find room for only one recording of the *Diabelli* Variations, or if you are new to the work, then you can hardly go wrong with Alfredo Perl's outstanding performance. It complements his survey of the complete Beethoven sonatas, and many of the qualities found in those discs are evident here. From the outset Perl's sense of rhythmic propulsion and dynamic incident gives his performance a rare vitality and character. The rigour and urgency of Variations. 7 and 23, for example, and the excitement of the demanding Var. 10, are typical of Perl's dramatic approach. He also manages to convey the elements of comedy, such as the Leporello quotation from Mozart's *Don Giovanni* (Var. 22) and the pointed silences of Var. 13. One can find greater spiritual depth from Brendel (his live recording from 1976), but for its lucid clarity and directness, yet searching thoughtfulness, Perl's account is reminiscent of Stephen Kovacevich's classic 1968 recording and makes a safe overall recommendation.

Additional recommendations ...
...Diabelli Variations. **Artur Schnabel** (pf). Pearl Ⓕ GEMMCD9378* (ADD). ⒼⒼ
...Diabelli Variations. **Stephen Kovacevich** (pf).
  Philips Concert Classics Ⓑ 422 969-2PCC (54 minutes: ADD: 8/90).
...Diabelli Variations. Piano Sonata No. 31 in A flat major, Op. 110.
  Coupled with works by various composers. **Mieczyslaw Horszowski** (pf).
  Pearl Ⓕ GEMMCDS9979 (two discs: 155 minutes: ADD: 12/93).
...Diabelli Variations. **Daniel Barenboim** (pf). Erato Ⓕ 4509-94810-2 (58 minutes: DDD: 8/94).
...Diabelli Variations. Piano Sonata No. 28 in A major, Op. 101. **Peter Donohoe** (pf).
  EMI Ⓕ CDC7 54792-2 (64 minutes: DDD: 8/94).
...Diabelli Variations. 15 Variations and Fugue on an Original Theme in E flat major, Op. 35,
  "Eroica". **Tatyana Nikolaieva** (pf). Olympia Ⓜ OCD570 (65 minutes: ADD: 6/95).
...Diabelli Variations. **William Kinderman** (pf). Hyperion Ⓕ CDA66763 (55 minutes: DDD: 8/95).

Beethoven 33 Variations in C major on a Waltz by Diabelli, Op. 120. 32 Variations on an
  Original Theme in C minor, WoO80. **Benjamin Frith** (pf). ASV Quicksilva Ⓢ CDQS6155
  (62 minutes: DDD: 2/96). Recorded 1990.   Ⓖ
This bargain on ASV's super-budget Quicksilva label offers a currently almost unbeatable coupling of the *Diabelli* Variations and the *32 Variations on an Original Theme*. Benjamin Frith is one of those artists whose musical perceptions are not to be doubted, and whose playing is almost never troubled by technical blemishes, and certainly not here. In short, both performances are masterly, the interpretations clearly thought through, concentrated in tension and feeling. With excellent recording this disc is unsurpassed, even by Brendel who, of course, has his own insights to offer in the *Diabelli*. But then so has Frith, and very impressive they are too.

Additional recommendation ...
...Diabelli Variations. **Alfred Brendel** (pf). Philips Ⓕ 426 232-2PH (53 minutes: DDD: 8/90). ⒼⒼ

Beethoven Complete Piano Sonata. **Artur Schnabel** (pf). EMI Références mono
  Ⓜ CHS7 63765-2* (eight discs: 605 minutes: ADD: 7/91). *Gramophone classical 100*.   ⒼⒼⒼ
  No. 1 in F minor, Op. 2 No. 1 (from HMV DB2463/4. Recorded 1934); No. 2 in A major, Op. 2
  No. 2 (DB2086/9. 1933); No. 3 in C major, Op. 2 No. 3 (DB2646/8, 4/36); No. 4 in E flat major,
  Op. 7 (DB3151/4, 9/37); No. 5 in C minor, Op. 10 No. 1 (DB3343/4, 3/38); No. 6 in F major,
  Op. 10 No. 2 (DB2354/5. 1933); No. 7 in D major, Op. 10 No. 3 (DB3345/7, 3/38); No. 8 in
  C minor, Op. 13, "Pathétique" (DB2356/8. 1934); No. 9 in E major, Op. 14 No. 1 (DB1818/19,
  3/33); No. 10 in G major, Op. 14 No. 2 (DB2465/6. 1934); No. 11 in B flat major, Op. 22
  (DB2211/13, 8/34); No. 12 in A flat major, Op. 26 (DB2850/52, 10/36); No. 13 in E flat major,
  Op. 27 No. 1, "quasi una fantasia" (DB1820/21, 3/33); No. 14 in C sharp minor, Op. 27 No. 2,

"Moonlight" (DB2089/90. 1934); No. 15 in D major, Op. 28, "Pastoral" (DB1953/5,8/33); No. 16 in G major, Op. 31 No. 1 (DB3154/7, 9/37); No. 17 in D minor, Op. 31 No. 2 "Tempest" (DB2619/51, 4/36); No. 18 in E flat major, Op. 31 No. 3 (DB2358/60. 1932); No. 19 in G minor, Op. 49 No. 1 (DB1956, 8/33); No. 20 in G major, Op. 49 No. 2 (DB2214, 8/34); No. 21 in C minor, Op. 53, "Waldstein" (DB2853/5, 10/36); No. 22 in F major, Op. 54 (DB2651/2, 4/36); No. 23 in F minor, Op. 57 "Appassionata" (DB2215/17 8/34); No. 24 in F sharp major, Op. 78 (DB1659/60. 1932); No. 25 in G major, Op. 79 (DB3348, 3/38); No. 26 in E flat major, Op. 81a, "Les adieux" (DB2091/2. 1933); No. 27 in E minor, Op 90 (DB1654/5. 1932); No. 28 in A major, Op. 101 (DB2467/9. 1934); No. 29 in B flat major, Op. 106, "Hammerklavier" (DB2955/60 11/36); No. 30 in E major, Op. 109 (DB1822/4, 3/33); No. 31 in A flat major, Op. 110 (DB1957/9, 8/33); No. 32 in C minor, Op. 111 (DB1656/9. 1932).

In Alfred Brendel's collection of essays, *Music Sounded Out* (Robson: 1991), there is an absorbing conversation entitled "On Schnabel and Interpretation" between Brendel and the late Konrad Wolff, author of *The Teaching of Artur Schnabel* (London: 1972). Brendel neither knew Schnabel nor heard him play in the concert-hall. Like most people nowadays, he came to Schnabel's playing through gramophone recordings, an experience that seems to have left him a passionate but critical admirer, and no acolyte. Wolff himself argues that the best reproduction of Schnabel's actual sound comes, not in studio recordings, but in 'unofficial' ones. (Unfortunately, he doesn't state which; some, it has to be said, are an embarrassment, particularly those made in the United States in the mid-1940s.) At the same time, both Wolff and Brendel seem to be of the opinion that many of Schnabel's studio recordings are hyperactive, with Wolff once more tossing into the embers that old chestnut about artists rushing to fit the music on to short 78rpm sides. In fact, as Brendel concedes, Schnabel was almost ideologically committed to extreme tempos; something you might say Beethoven's music thrives on, always provided the interpreter can bring it off.

By and large Schnabel did. There are some famous gabbles in this sonata cycle, notably at the start of the *Hammerklavier*, with him going for broke. In fact, Schnabel also held that "It is a mistake to imagine that all notes should be played with equal intensity or even be clearly audible. In order to clarify the music it is often necessary to make certain notes obscure." As Brendel wrily observes, this admirable insight is one which it is virtually impossible to get past the average record producer nowadays. If it is true, as some contemporary witnesses aver, that Schnabel was a flawless wizard in the period pre-1930, there is still plenty of wizardry left in these post-1930 Beethoven recordings. They are virtuoso readings that demonstrate a blazing intensity of interpretative vision as well as breathtaking manner of execution. Even when a dazzlingly articulate reading like that of the *Waldstein* is home and dry, the abiding impression in its aftermath is one of Schnabel's (and Beethoven's) astonishing physical and imaginative daring. And if this suggests recklessness, well, in many other instances the facts are quite other, for Schnabel has a great sense of decorum. He can, in many of the smaller sonatas and some of the late ones, be impeccably mannered, stylish and urbane. Equally he can (within the parameters of the finished work of art) be devilish or coarse.

At the other extreme, Schnabel is indubitably the master of the genuinely slow movement. Listen to the way that from the earliest sonatas to the final movement of Op. 111, Schnabel is able to reconcile a calm and concentrated slowness with a breathing pulse and stirring inner life that is beyond the wit of most latter-day imitators. No one now distils these imaginative essences quite as Schnabel did. And though it is dangerous to suggest such a thing in the present climate of 'authentic performance', such playing doesn't date. Recorded sound does date though, but in this respect, CD is a godsend. There is nothing that can be done about the occasional patch of wow or discoloration but, in general, the old recordings come up very freshly indeed. Collectors in search of a complete sonata cycle in more modern sound should also consider the budget-price, nine-disc DG cycle by Schnabel's nominated heir, Wilhelm Kempff.

Additional recommendation ...

...Nos. 14-18. Variations on an Original Theme in F major, Op. 34. Seven Bagatelles, Op. 33. **Artur Schnabel** (pf). Pearl mono Ⓜ GEMMCDS9123* (two discs: 141 minutes: AAD: 11/94). ⒼⒼⒼ

Beethoven Complete Piano Sonatas. **Richard Goode** (pf). Elektra Nonesuch Ⓕ 7559-79328-2 (ten discs: 608 minutes: DDD: 3/94). Items marked [a] from 7559-79213-2 (4/92), [b]979 212-2 (9/90), [c]979 211-2 (9/89). Remainder new to UK.

No. 1 in F minor, Op. 2 No. 1; No. 2 in A major, Op. 2 No. 2; No. 3 in C major, Op. 2 No. 3; No. 4 in E flat major, Op. 7; No. 5 in C minor, Op. 10 No. 1[a]; No. 6 in F major, Op. 10 No. 2[a]; No. 7 in D major, Op. 10 No. 3[a]; No. 8 in C minor, Op. 13, "Pathétique"; No. 9 in E major, Op. 14 No. 1; No. 10 in G major, Op. 14 No. 2; No. 11 in B flat major, Op. 22; No. 12 in A flat major, Op. 26; No. 13 in E flat major, Op. 27 No. 1, "quasi una fantasia"; No. 14 in C sharp minor, Op. 27 No. 2, "Moonlight"; No. 15 in D major, Op. 28, "Pastoral"; No. 16 in G major, Op. 31 No. 1[b]; No. 17 in D minor, Op. 31 No. 2, "Tempest"[b]; No. 18 in E flat major, Op. 31 No. 3[b]; No. 19 in G minor, Op. 49 No. 1; No. 20 in G major, Op. 49 No. 2; No. 21 in C minor, Op. 53, "Waldstein"; No. 22 in F major, Op. 54; No. 23 in F minor, Op. 57, "Appassionata"; No. 24 in F sharp major, Op. 78; No. 25 in G major, Op. 79; No. 26 in E flat major, Op. 81a, "Les adieux"; No. 27 in E minor, Op. 90; No. 28 in A major, Op. 101[c]; No. 29 in B flat major, Op. 106, "Hammerklavier"[c]; No. 30 in E major, Op. 109[c]; No. 31 in A flat major, Op. 110[c]; No. 32 in C minor, Op. 111[c]. ⒼⒼⒼ

Until the last few years Richard Goode was active principally as an ensemble player, in chamber music, a field in which he excels. Whoever commissioned the long essay for the booklet from Michael Steinberg did the set a fine service. The production and engineering are credited to Max Wilcox and his expertise and care leave one with little to quibble with. The sound and balance rate from good to very good and they're pretty consistent over the ten CDs. The lower end of the dynamic range is very well defined, perhaps better than the other. In the first movement of the *Hammerklavier* Sonata and the *Scherzo* of the A flat Sonata, Op. 110, Wilcox hasn't been completely successful in dissuading Goode from stamping on the pedal, but this habit is not obtrusive elsewhere. There is some unevenness of achievement in Goode's playing but the level, in general, is wonderfully high, with no lapses from grace. Everything demands assessment in the company of the best there is. The interpretation of the A major Sonata, Op. 101, is one of the finest ever put on record. Reservations? You may have a doubt as to whether all the playing represents everything Goode is capable of: sometimes he disappoints, slightly, by appearing to hold back from the listener the boldness and fullness of communication the greatest players achieve. One might say that, for all their insight and illumination, some of the performances lack the final leap and a degree of transcendence. In the first movement of the A flat major, Op. 110, Goode sounds as if he's trying too hard. Yet he is marvellous later in the sonata, taking the listener through the 'heartbeat' chords at the close of the *Arioso*'s reprise into the inversion of the Fugue and by way of the difficult transition to the serenity and triumph of the final pages with a sureness and quality of imagination that are exceptional. Any small regrets are probably attributable to the business of record-making.

Consideration of that enormous span of slow music in the *Hammerklavier* brings to mind the great 'set-piece' slow movements of the early sonatas as well: in Op. 2 Nos. 2 and 3, Op. 7, Op. 10 Nos. 1 and 3. Those processional, inward, even monumental and ineluctable qualities which they share demand intense concentration on both sides of the microphone and Goode makes them eloquent, even though they could smile a little more. In Op. 14 No. 2 in G he is delicious – perfect. There is abundant wit, as he plays it, in the first movement of Op. 10 No. 2 in F too. A quality often to be observed in Goode is allure. Maybe that is why his playing is so very likeable: the finish of his playing, technical and musical, is immaculate but on top of that he is exciting. His sound always makes you listen. His feeling for it and for fine gradations of sound from one end of his wide dynamic range to the other are those of a virtuoso and inform everything he does. And when he's more obviously on virtuoso territory, as in the *Waldstein* and *Appassionata*, he responds to their demands for brilliance and thrilling projection as to the manner born. He is constantly inside the music, not on the outside looking in, and what a lively, cultivated, lucid and stimulating guide he is. There is nothing diffident or half-hearted about the way he makes this cycle of Beethoven resound wonderfully, the earlier sonatas appearing as no less masterly or characteristic of their composer than the later.

Additional recommendations ...

...Nos. 1-32. **Alfred Brendel** (pf). Philips Ⓕ 412 575-2PH11 (11 discs: 659 minutes: ADD: 1/85). ⒼⒼ

...Nos. 1-32. **Daniel Barenboim** (pf). EMI Ⓑ CZS7 62863-2 (ten discs: 687 minutes: ADD: 10/90). ⒼⒼ

...Nos. 1-32. **Wilhelm Kempff** (pf). DG Ⓑ 429 306-2GX9 (nine discs: 594 minutes: ADD: 3/91). ⒼⒼ

...Nos. 1-32. Piano Variations. **Claudio Arrau** (pf).
Philips Ⓜ 432 301-2PM11 (11 discs: 739 minutes: ADD: 1/92). Ⓖ

...Nos. 1-10. **Jean-Bernard Pommier** (pf).
Erato Ⓕ 2292-45598-2 (three discs: 215 minutes: DDD: 9/93).

...No. 5. *Coupled with works by* **Mozart Till Fellner** (pf); ªLausanne Chamber Orchestra / Uri Segal.
Claves Ⓕ CD50-9328 (62 minutes: DDD: 9/94).

...Nos. 5-7. **Louis Lortie** (pf). Chandos Ⓕ CHAN9101 (56 minutes: DDD: 3/93).

...Nos. 7, 9, 30 and 31. **Awadagin Pratt** (pf). EMI Ⓕ CDC5 55290-2 (74 minutes: DDD: 5/96).

...Nos. 11-14. **Tatyana Nikolaieva** (pf). Olympia Ⓕ OCD564 (76 minutes: ADD: 1/95).

...Nos. 11-20. **Jean-Bernard Pommier** (pf).
Erato Ⓕ 2292-45812-2 (three discs: 191 minutes: DDD: 9/93).

...Nos. 8, 14, 15 and 24. **Wilhelm Kempff** (pf).
DG Galleria Ⓜ 415 834-2GGA (60 minutes: ADD: 8/87).

...Nos. 8, 14, 23 and 26. **Arthur Rubinstein** (pf).
RCA Victor Gold Seal Ⓜ 09026 61443-2 (76 minutes: ADD: 10/93).

...Nos. 14, 21 and 23. **Vladimir Ashkenazy** (pf).
Decca Ovation Ⓜ 417 732-2DM (66 minutes: ADD: 12/87).

...Nos. 15-17. **Tatyana Nikolaieva** (pf). Olympia Ⓜ OCD565 (69 minutes: ADD: 6/95).

...Nos. 18-22. **Tatyana Nikolaieva** (pf). Olympia Ⓜ OCD566 (78 minutes: ADD: 6/95).

...Nos. 28 and 29. **Tatyana Nikolaieva** (pf). Olympia Ⓜ OCD568 (67 minutes: ADD: 6/95).

...Nos. 30-32. 32 Variations on an Original Theme in C minor, WoO80. **Tatyana Nikolaieva** (pf).
Olympia Ⓜ OCD569 (76 minutes: ADD: 6/95).

...Nos. 1-32; E flat major, WoO47 No. 1; F minor, WoO47 No. 2; D major, WoO47 No. 3.
Andante favori in F major, WoO57. **Malcolm Bilson, Tom Beghin, David Breitman, Bart van Oort, Ursula Dütschler, Zvi Meniker, Andrew Willis** (fps).
Claves Ⓑ CD50-9707/10 (ten discs: 689 minutes: DDD: 3/98). 🏆

...32 Variations on an Original Theme in C minor, WoO80. *Coupled with works by various composers.* **Vladimir Horowitz** (pf). APR mono Ⓜ APR5517* (71 minutes: ADD: 5/98).
See review in the Collections section; refer to the Index.

Jenö Jandó's reliable complete super bargain set of the sonatas is available on Naxos on two sets comprising five CDs each (8 505002 and 8 505003). They are also available on ten separate CDs, the details of which follow (the volume numbers do not indicate the numerical order of the sonatas).
...(Vol. 3) Nos. 1-3. Naxos Ⓢ 8 550150 (67 minutes: DDD: 12/90).
...(Vol. 5) Nos. 5, 6, 7 and 25. Naxos Ⓢ 8 550161 (63 minutes: DDD: 12/90).
...(Vol. 8) Nos. 4, 13, 19, 20 and 22. Naxos Ⓢ 8 550167 (68 minutes: DDD: 12/90).
...(Vol. 6) Nos. 9, 10, 24, 27 and 28. Naxos Ⓢ 8 550162 (72 minutes: DDD: 12/90).
...(Vol. 1) Nos. 8, 14 and 23. Naxos Ⓢ 8 550045 (56 minutes: DDD: 2/91).
...(Vol. 10) Nos. 15 and 33-38. Naxos Ⓢ 8 550255 (69 minutes: DDD: 2/91).
...(Vol. 2) Nos. 17, 21 and 26. Naxos Ⓢ 8 550054 (63 minutes: DDD: 2/91).
...(Vol. 7) Nos. 12, 16 and 18. Naxos Ⓢ 8 550166 (64 minutes: DDD: 6/91).
...(Vol. 9) Nos. 11 and 29. Naxos Ⓢ 8 550234 (64 minutes: DDD: 6/91).
...(Vol. 4) Nos. 30, 31 and 32. Naxos Ⓢ 8 550151 (64 minutes: DDD: 6/91).

Beethoven Complete Piano Sonatas. **Wilhelm Kempff** (pf). DG Dokumente mono
Ⓜ 447 966-2GDO8* (eight discs: 511 minutes: ADD: 4/96). From DG originals reviewed between 4/56 and 12/59, and previously unpublished (Sonata No.11; recorded 1956). Includes bonus disc, "Wilhelm Kempff – An All-Round Musician". Recorded 1951-56.   ⒼⒺ
Wilhelm Kempff was the most inspirational of Beethoven pianists. Those who have cherished his earlier stereo cycle for its magical spontaneity will find Kempff's qualities even more intensely conveyed in this mono set, recorded between 1951 and 1956. Amazingly the sound has more body and warmth than the stereo, with Kempff's unmatched transparency and clarity of articulation even more vividly caught, both in sparkling *Allegros* and in deeply dedicated slow movements. If in places he is even more personal, some might say wilful, regularly surprising you with a new revelation, the magnetism is even more intense, as in the great *Adagio* of the *Hammerklavier* or the final variations of Op. 111, at once more rapt and more impulsive, flowing more freely. The bonus disc, entitled "An All-Round Musician", celebrates Kempff's achievement in words and music, on the organ in Bach, on the piano in Brahms and Chopin as well as in a Bachian improvisation, all sounding exceptionally transparent and lyrical. Fascinatingly, his pre-war recordings of the Beethoven sonatas on 78s are represented too. Here we have his 1936 recording of the *Pathétique*, with the central *Adagio* markedly broader and more heavily pointed than in the mono LP version of 20 years later.

Beethoven Piano Sonatas, Volumes 1-4. **Alfredo Perl** (pf). Arte Nova Classics Ⓢ 74321-27762-2/ 30459-2/ 30460-2/27764-2 (four discs, oas: 73, 73, 72 and 74 minutes: DDD: 3/97).
74321-27762-2: No. 1 in F minor, Op. 2 No. 1; No. 2 in A major, Op. 2 No. 2; No. 3 in C major, Op. 2 No. 3. *74321-30459-2:* No. 4 in E flat major, Op. 7; No. 13 in E flat major, Op. 27 No. 1, "quasi una fantasia"; No. 14 in C sharp minor, Op. 27 No. 2, "Moonlight"; No. 24 in F sharp major, Op. 78. *74321-30460-2:* No. 5 in C minor, Op. 10 No. 1; No. 6 in F major, Op. 10 No. 2; No. 7 in D major, Op. 10 No. 3; No. 26 in E flat major, Op. 81*a*, "Les adieux". *74321-27764-2:* No. 8 in C minor, Op. 13, "Pathétique"; No. 12 in A flat major, Op. 26; No. 27 in E minor, Op. 90; No. 28 in A major, Op. 101.
Alfredo Perl does not follow the sonatas strictly in sequence: this may irritate some collectors, but it does allow each disc to stand as an independent 'recital' while also forming just one part of the complete journey. There is an enormous amount to celebrate in these performances. The rhythmic power of these works is communicated with a genuine sense of enjoyment, and one of the most striking features of Perl's playing, particularly in the outer movements, is that he never shies away from the *sforzandos* or the *subito pianos* which are so important to Beethoven's style. Indeed, he attacks these dynamic accents and contrasts with such dramatic rigour that certain movements – the finale to the *Moonlight*, for example – are animated with a rare vitality. It is in the more highly charged movements where Perl is most compelling (the outer movements of the *Pathétique*, the opening movement of Op. 10 No. 1, and the finales of Op. 2 No. 1 and Op. 10 No. 2). The A major Sonata, Op. 101, receives a tremendous performance, both musically and technically, and the second movement in particular is a marvel of understated virtuosity. In the movements of more lyrical simplicity Perl can be less convincing. In the second movement of Op. 90, for example, he does not make the piano sing, and his tone can occasionally sound a little bland. His *fortes*, too, can be rather hard-edged, although the bright recording does not help him here. Perl's tempos have been the cause of some debate: he favours extremes, juxtaposing especially rapid fast movements with protracted slow movements. In Op. 101, for example, he follows the march-like second movement, taken dangerously fast, with a particularly drawn-out *Adagio*. If you wish to sample just one disc from this series to get a flavour of Perl's playing, then try Vol. 4 (ranging from the *Pathétique* to Op. 101). Perl has entered a hugely competitive field, but once his cycle is complete it could be one of the finest versions by a young pianist to have emerged in recent years.

Beethoven Piano Sonatas, Op. 2 – No. 1 in F minor; No. 2 in A major; No. 3 in C major.
Alfred Brendel (pf). Philips Ⓕ 442 124-2PH (70 minutes: DDD: 7/95).
Brendel reminds us here that, in their different ways, these works of Beethoven's first maturity are as finished and as characteristic as the later ones, and it's a measure of his artistry that he makes us aware

of the Op. 2 trilogy as three "highly profiled individuals" – the description in the notes – and not just as generalized 'early' Beethoven. You need to play this disc at a reasonably high level to savour the full range of Brendel's dynamics and colouring. Perhaps not everything is communicated here as vividly as Brendel habitually achieves in the concert-hall. The playing conveys a total vision and is musically alive as few can rival, but one is inclined to regret that no place had been found for a passing breeze of impetuosity. The spellbinding inner worlds of the great slow movements in the A major and C major Sonatas of Op. 2 are as demanding for the player as any. The piano has to be transcended. Brendel treats the *Largo appassionato* of the A major as a processional, and keeps it nicely on the move; even finer is his control of nuance and movement in the E major *Adagio* of Op. 2 No. 3 – the end is marvellous. His simpler, sculpted eloquence in the slow movement of the F minor Sonata is also touching, and in general, he allows himself plenty of time for reflectiveness and quasi-improvisatory exploration. The first movement of the A major Sonata is a particularly interesting journey: *Allegro vivace* certainly, two in a bar, but never a rush, so one can be all the more aware of the teeming incident on the way. The radiant finale of this Sonata is another high spot, clearly hugely enjoyed by him in this affectionate account of it. This is fresh, youthful Beethoven in which there is room for caprice and laughter and good humour as well as profundity and the shocks of the new.

Additional recommendations ...
...Nos. 1-3. **John O'Conor** (pf). Telarc Ⓕ CD80214 (67 minutes: DDD: 9/90).
...Nos. 1-3. **Tatyana Nikolaieva** (pf). Olympia Ⓕ OCD561 (71 minutes: ADD: 1/95).
...Nos. 3, 11, 18, 23, 24, 29 and 30. Bagatelle in A minor, WoO59, "Für Elise". Six Ecossaises, WoO83. Variations – F major, Op. 34; D major on "Rule Britannia", WoO79; G major, WoO70 on "Nel cor più non mi sento"; 33 in C major on a Waltz by Anton Diabelli, Op. 120; 15 Variations, Op. 35, "Eroica". Andante favori, WoO57. Bagatelles, Op. 126. Piano Concertos – No. 4 in G major, Op. 58; No. 5 in E flat major, Op. 73, "Emperor". **Alfred Brendel** (pf); **Chicago Symphony Orchestra / James Levine.** Philips Ⓜ 446 922-2PM5 (five discs: 373 minutes: ADD/DDD: 2/96).

Beethoven Piano Sonatas – No. 4 in E flat major, Op. 7; No. 15 in D major, Op. 28, "Pastoral"; No. 20 in G major, Op. 49 No. 2. **Alfred Brendel** (pf). Philips Ⓕ 446 624-2PH (65 minutes: DDD: 2/96). Recorded 1994. *Gramophone Editor's record of the month.*   Ⓖ
Brendel's interpretation of the *Pastoral* has changed – and its status has stratospherically soared – in two interrelated respects. In the first place, the two outer movements are both slower than on either the 1960s Turnabout recording or the 1970s Philips version. What we have here is not some amiable musical ramble; rather, it is a multi-layered music-drama in which the pianist's relish in debating the issues the music is already asking itself makes for the most exhilarating kind of listening. And what a debate it is, substantial and charged with feeling. The lead back to the recapitulation – the lurch into B major, the sudden silence, the restatement in B minor, a further silence, the unresolved question on the home dominant – is realized with quite heart-stopping intensity. But, then, intensity is very much the order of the day in this latest cycle of recordings, a throwing open of the gates, with a far greater use of declamatory effects and rhetorical tropes than was the case in either of his two earlier cycles. Not that Brendel has thrown overboard any of his wryness, wit or natural sense of balance. He plays the two inner movements of the *Pastoral* Sonata every bit as elegantly as before. And yet here again one notices sudden deepenings and new-found beauties. The performance of the E flat Sonata, Op. 7 is similarly grand, open and free-spirited. And here a word needs to be said about the recordings, which are thrillingly loyal to the music-making. The sound, like the playing, can be both grand and awesomely quiet. Above all, it offers a persistently clear view of the rich ensemble of inner voices that is so vital to Brendel's purpose. The engagingly brief G major Sonata makes a delightful postlude. and again Brendel has changed tack, playing the second of the two movements, the *Tempo di Menuetto* much more swiftly than previously.

Additional recommendations ...
...Nos. 4, 11 and 13. **John O'Conor** (pf). Telarc Ⓕ CD80363 (70 minutes: DDD: 8/94).
...Nos. 4-6. **Tatyana Nikolaieva** (pf). Olympia Ⓕ OCD562 (63 minutes: ADD: 1/95).
...No. 4; No. 8 – Adagio cantabile; No. 32 . Andante favori in F major, WoO57. Six Variations on "Nel cor più non mi sento", WoO70. Heiligenstadt Testament[a]. **Elly Ney** (pf/[a]spkr). Biddulph mono Ⓜ LHW033* (80 minutes: ADD: 3/96).

Beethoven Piano Sonatas, Op. 10 – No. 5 in C minor[a]; No. 6 in F major[a]; No. 7 in D major. **Alfred Brendel** (pf). Philips Ⓕ 446 664-2PH (59 minutes: DDD: 11/96). Recorded 1995. Items marked [a] recorded live. *Gramophone Editor's choice.*   ⒼⒼ
The two shorter sonatas, each in its own right a miracle of concentrated wit and musical daring, thrive not only on the wit and acumen of Brendel's playing but on the clear sense there is here of the music being played *for* someone. (After which, in No. 7, one rather misses – or, rather, one senses Brendel may be missing – the generally unobtrusive Frankfurt audience.) The one movement in the two shorter sonatas which Brendel would appear to have thought and rethought down the years is the F major Sonata's central minor-key *Allegretto* and its awed D flat major Trio, the music's strangeness and hushed inward mood wonderfully gathered in only to be, as it were, played out again. It is the art of the public expression of private emotion brought to its highest level of sophistication. The much grander D major Sonata has its share of wit, and here Brendel's treatment of the first movement has

never been quite as orderly or sure-footed as that of pianists like Kempff and Arrau; on the other hand, there is a world of difference between what Brendel aims at and achieves here and the rather more erratically delivered insights of Richard Goode on his rival Nonesuch recording of the Op. 10 Sonatas. As to the D major Sonata's great slow movement, D minor *Largo e mesto*, here Brendel has always treated the opening eight-bar threnody slowly and rather formally, allowing the note of tragic dejection to sound only at the appearance of the lovely *cantabile* transition theme. Others have seen the music differently. Schnabel, slowest of all but never for a moment merely static, brought to the music a strikingly 'drained' quality. With Arrau it was high tragedy from the outset. And no one has articulated better than Kempff the sense of a kind of speaking sadness, the *mesto* quality immediately present. Brendel's playing of the concluding eight bars, by contrast, is as telling as anyone's. To adapt Malcolm's tribute to the Thane of Cawdor, nothing in the movement becomes Brendel like the leaving it. Jenö Jandó's Naxos disc is an admirable bargain, a neat way of collecting the three Op. 10 Sonatas in perfectly nice performances. The Brendel, though, stands apart in a class of its own.

Beethoven Piano Sonatas – No. 7 in D major, Op. 10 No. 3; No. 25 in G major, Op. 79; No. 26 in E flat major, Op. 81*a*, "Les adieux"; No. 27 in E minor, Op. 90. **Emil Gilels** (pf). Revelation Ⓜ RV10029 (63 minutes: ADD: 10/96). Recorded live in 1980.

These live Beethoven performances by Emil Gilels are distinguished by his customary profound artistic penetration. Nikolaieva's Beethoven sonata cycle (recorded in the same venue in the 1980s) is robust and dynamic, and her perceptive interpretations, though not always note-accurate, frequently reveal startling insights of voice-leading and large-scale structure. However, enhanced by closer, softer-edged recording, Gilels's firmer technical security here helps to create accounts of even greater stature. Listen to the compelling forward motion he generates in the first movement of the D major Sonata, or the beguiling relationship he achieves between pulse and expressive timing in the slow movement. He also gives a sleeker account of the G major Sonata, with impressively smooth lines in the first movement, a winning blend of atmosphere and lyrical spontaneity in the *Andante* and stylish panache in the witty finale. Nikolaieva gives a striking portrayal of the programmatic character of *Les adieux* – most notably in her violently explosive reading of the finale – yet even here Gilels conveys a broader artistic vision with nimbler fingerwork and a startling moment of reflection on the last page of the finale. A superb account of Sonata No. 27 Op. 90 completes this wonderful Gilels programme.

Additional recommendations ...

...Nos. 7-10. **Tatyana Nikolaieva** (pf). Olympia Ⓔ OCD563 (74 minutes: ADD: 1/95).
...Nos. 23-27. **Tatyana Nikolaieva** (pf). Olympia Ⓔ OCD567 (76 minutes: ADD: 6/95).

Beethoven Piano Sonatas – No. 8 in C minor, Op. 13, "Pathétique"[a]; No. 23 in F minor, Op. 57, "Appassionata"[b]; No. 31 in A flat major, Op. 110[c].
Handel Keyboard Suite in D minor, HWV428[d] – Prelude; Air and Variations; Presto. Chaconne and Variations in G major, HWV435[e]. **Edwin Fischer** (pf). APR Signature mono Ⓜ APR5502* (72 minutes: AAD: 12/94). Item marked [a] from HMV DB3666/7 (12/38), [b]DB2517/19 (10/35), [c]DB3707/08 (recorded 1938), [d]DB2378 (9/35), [e]HMV DA4401 (12/32). Ⓖ

On this invaluable APR disc, expertly grouped and presented, are some of Fischer's finest and most legendary performances. His very first published recording (1931) of the Handel Chaconne, for example, was made at a time when his matchless *leggiero* and radiant tone were unimpeded by obvious blemishes or erratic pianism. Both this performance and that of the pieces from the Suite No. 3 have an improvisatory magic, a strength and grace and supreme assurance. Fischer commences the *Pathétique* with a scrupulous adherence to Beethoven's *fp* marking, a sudden shift of sound that is fascinatingly modernist or prophetic. The *Allegro di molto e con brio* is exactly that, dancing with an irrepressible lightness and urgency; and if one listens to the slow octave descent just before the final outburst one will hear a rapt 'all-passion-spent' quality, something Fischer could achieve with supreme naturalness, without even a hint of artifice or calculated effect. All past vicissitudes are finally resolved in Op. 110 in a blaze of heroic glory, and time and again he makes you pause to consider key points and details that somehow elude others. There is here a richness and humanity, a sheer quality that was uniquely Fischer's.

Beethoven Piano Sonatas – No. 8 in C minor, Op. 13, "Pathétique". No. 14 in C sharp minor, Op. 27 No. 2, "Moonlight". No. 15 in D major, Op. 28, "Pastoral". No. 17 in D minor, Op. 31 No. 2, "Tempest". No. 21 in C major, Op. 53, "Waldstein". No. 23 in F minor, Op. 57, "Appassionata". No. 26 in E flat major, Op. 81*a*, "Les Adieux". **Alfred Brendel** (pf). Philips Duo Ⓜ 438 730-2PM2 (152 minutes: ADD: 4/94). Recorded 1970-77. ⒼⒼ

Beethoven Piano Sonatas – No. 8 in C minor, Op. 13, "Pathétique"[a]; No. 23 in F minor, Op. 57, "Appassionata"[b]. Fantasia in C minor, Op. 80[c]. Bagatelles[a] – Op. 33 Nos. 3 and 5; Op. 119 Nos. 2, 7 and 9; Op. 126 Nos. 1, 4 and 6. **Sviatoslav Richter** (pf); [c]**Russian State Academic Choir;** [c]**Moscow Radio Symphony Orchestra / Kurt Sanderling.** Melodiya mono Ⓜ 74321 29462-2* (80 minutes: ADD: 6/96). Items marked [a] recorded 1959, [b]1960, [c]1952.

The Philips reissue, containing seven of Beethoven's most popular named sonatas admirably played by Alfred Brendel, is in every way an outstanding bargain, well worth obtaining, even if duplication is involved. All the performances are authoritative and offer consistently distinguished playing, while the recording is very realistic indeed. The *Tempest* resonates in the memory and the central movements of the *Pastoral* are most beautifully shaped. The *Pathétique, Moonlight* and *Appassionata* all bring deeply satisfying readings that are compellingly conceived and freshly executed. This set can be recommended without any reservations whatsoever. The booklet-notes with the Melodiya reissue claim that Richter's live 1960 Moscow *Appassionata* is his favourite among his recorded performances of the work, and from the elemental power it unleashes one can well believe it. The *Pathétique* is magnificently implacable, while the *Choral Fantasia* is a remarkable curiosity – cavernous acoustic, fierce recording, the text in Russian, sung with intimidating gusto. The mono sound is acceptable.

Additional recommendations ...
...Nos. 8, 14, 21 and 23. **Wilhelm Kempff** (pf).
  DG The Originals Ⓜ 447 404-2GOR (79 minutes: ADD: 9/95).
...Nos. 8, 14 and 17. **Cristina Ortiz** (pf). Tring International Ⓢ TRP027 (57 minutes: DDD: 10/95).
...Nos. 12, 21, 24 and 26. **Dénes Várjon** (pf). Capriccio Ⓕ 10 714 (71 minutes: DDD: 3/96).
...Nos. 21, 23 and 26. **Emil Gilels** (pf). DG Ⓕ 419 162-2GH (ADD: 8/86).   ⓆⒼ
...Nos. 21 and 31. **Stephen Kovacevich** (pf). EMI Ⓕ CDC7 54896-2 (53 minutes: DDD: 2/94).
  Gramophone Editor's choice.
...Nos. 30, 31 and 32. **Vladimir Feltsman** (pf). MusicMasters Ⓕ 67098-2 (66 minutes: DDD: 6/94).
...Nos. 14, 21 and 23. **Vladimir Horowitz** (pf).
  RCA Victor Gold Seal Ⓜ GD60375 (65 minutes: ADD: 7/94).
...Nos. 23, 24, 25 and 27. **Alfred Brendel** (pf). Philips Ⓕ 442 787-2PH (59 minutes: DDD: 11/95).

Beethoven Piano Sonatas – No. 9 in E major, Op. 14 No. 1[a]; No. 11 in B flat major, Op. 22[b]; No. 12 in A flat major, Op. 26[c]; No. 27 in E minor, Op. 90[c].
Haydn Keyboard Sonatas[c] – No. 39 in D major, HobXVI/24; No. 62 in E flat major, HobXVI/52.
Weber Piano Sonata No. 3 in D minor, J206[c]. **Sviatoslav Richter** (pf). Philips Ⓕ 438 617-2PH2 (two discs: 131 minutes: ADD/DDD: 8/94). Item marked [a] from SAL3457 (9/64), [b]SAL3456 (9/64), remainder new to UK. Items marked [ab] recorded 1963, [c]1994.   ⓆⒼ
Richter's greatness is due partly to his limitless artistic and technical ability and partly to his extraordinarily wide range of repertoire. His unique capacity to surprise derives from a profound understanding of musical processes, and his concerts are events in a continuous sequence of musical discovery. In Haydn's E flat Piano Sonata, Richter's extreme sensitivity to detail produces a captivating performance of great delicacy and charm. Haydn's D major Sonata provides further evidence of Richter's wholly unselfconscious approach: the opening movement is expressed with transparent clarity; the *cantabile Adagio* is beautifully judged, and the finale has an engaging ethnic gait. He recorded the Beethoven sonatas in 1963 and, though there is a noticeably drier quality to the sound, the performances have retained a remarkable freshness of resonance. The dramatic intensity of the E major work, for example, is heightened by Richter's tendency to controversial extremes of tempo in both directions. Specifically, Richter rejects the *Allegretto* marking for the second movement in favour of a speed that is closer to *Adagio* to which the finale provides a scintillating conclusion. His wide dynamic and expressive range in both of these sonatas creates effects that are quite simply miraculous. The versions of the Sonatas, Op. 26 and Op. 90 are digital recordings, but there are no signs that Richter has lost any of his interpretative power or originality. His command of broad structural relationships is as assured as ever, as is his scrupulous attention to the music's harmonic and motivic detail. His comprehensive exploitation of the music's intrinsic possibilities generates great energy and pace as a means of intensifying its natural warmth and expressiveness. The set concludes with a startling performance of Weber's Third Piano Sonata. The first movement, marked *Allegro feroce*, contrasts a powerfully driven opening with music of simple melodic charm which, after a richly diverse variation slow movement, culminates in a bravura finale of breathtaking virtuosity. As is so often the case with Richter's performances, then, these are landmarks in piano playing.

Additional recommendations ...
...No. 9. *Coupled with works by* **Liszt** and **Brahms** Gina Bachauer (pf).
  Mercury Living Presence Ⓜ 434 340-2MM (77 minutes: ADD: 9/95).
...Nos. 27, 28 and 32. **Stephen Kovacevich** (pf). EMI Ⓕ CDC7 54599-2 (60 minutes: DDD: 10/92).

Beethoven Piano Sonata No. 14 in C sharp minor, Op. 27 No. 2, "Moonlight".
Brahms Variations on a Theme by Paganini, Op. 35.
Franck Prélude, choral et fugue. **Evgeni Kissin** (pf). RCA Victor Red Seal Ⓕ 09026 68910-2 (57 minutes: DDD: 6/98). *Gramophone Editor's choice.*   ⓆⒼⒼ
Strange how many top-flight pianists find it difficult to achieve a natural delivery in the opening movement of the *Moonlight*. With some it's a case of exaggerated hesitation on the upbeats; with Kissin it's a tendency to place the melody fractionally before the left-hand octaves, the reverse of the old left-before-right mannerism. This is vaguely unsettling at first, then positively distracting once you realize the cause. The young Russian does little to temper his strongly projected sound for the intimacy of the recording studio; occasionally climaxes have more metal in the tone than some may like, even in a relatively undemonstrative piece such as the second movement of the Beethoven. Nor does he make concessions as regards sustained intensity of phrasing or ostentatiously grand rubato, especially in the Franck. Yet how much richness of experience you'd be missing if you resist Kissin's manner. And who would want to resist it anyway, when the sense of intellectual, emotional and

pianistic identity with the music is so strong? Listen to the lonely arching-up of the lines in Beethoven's first movement as they win temporary freedom from the opening broken chords; or their long-term destination in the defiant arpeggios in the finale, here wonderfully articulate and full of tensile strength; or the sensitivity to each cross-current in Franck's chromatic maelstrom; or the solidity and authority of every one of the Brahms *Variations*; or the staggering dexterity of the notorious seventh and eleventh variations from Book Two. Listen to these and then say that this is anything other than a wonderful disc. If you do, it can only be that you are allergic to the forcefully projected piano tone. To which one can only say that there are others just as forceful, but very few who have comparable musical insights to project. This is modern piano playing at its finest. The recording quality is of the finest too, combining clarity and impact with perspective and bloom.

Beethoven Piano Sonatas – No. 16 in G major, Op. 31 No. 1; No. 17 in D minor, Op. 31 No. 2, "Tempest"; No. 18 in E flat major, Op. 31 No. 3. **Stephen Kovacevich** (pf). EMI Ⓕ CDC5 55226-2 (64 minutes: DDD: 11/95). Recorded 1994. *Gramophone Editor's choice.* ⒼⒼ

The Op. 31 Sonatas offer a wonderful way into the Beethoven sonatas, not least because they have done unusually well on record. And what to buy? Well, this offering from Stephen Kovacevich from his emergent Beethoven sonata cycle is very brilliant, an exceptional record in every way. There is stiff competition from Brendel and Richard Goode, to name just two. With Goode, the D minor Sonata, the *Tempest*, is wonderfully well done, finely painted on the keyboard. There is much in the festive E flat Sonata that is gloriously right – the *Scherzo* is played to perfection – but after that *tour de force* Goode gives an inexplicably laboured account of the *Menuetto*. Brendel is measured here, too. Kovacevich finds a middle way in this *Menuetto* that seems effortlessly right. His tempo is more or less exactly what one imagines a *moderato e grazioso* should be, and it serves Minuet and Trio equally well. The preceding *Scherzo* is a touch fiercer than Goode's or Brendel's, the finale a show-stopping *Presto, con fuoco* which Goode attempts and which Brendel rather capriciously avoids. Brendel's performances of the G major and E flat Sonatas offer a fine mixture of caprice and intellectual rigour. There are more fluctuations of pulse than with Kovacevich and a much greater use of diversionary tactics. There are more zig-zags of emotion, too, in the *Tempest*, which Brendel plays in a fit of high passion that borders on outright anger. Kovacevich's playing can be just as angry but it is always terrifically focused. EMI have been obliged to take on board some pretty ferocious playing. The recording occasionally threatens to fray at the edges but never quite does. War-weary and battle-hardened it bears these marvellous performances triumphantly home.

Additional recommendations ...

...Nos. 17, 18 and 26. **Murray Perahia** (pf).
CBS Masterworks Ⓜ MK42319 (61 minutes: DDD: 2/88).
...Nos. 16-18. **Alfred Brendel** (pf). Philips Ⓕ 438 134-2PH (72 minutes: DDD: 7/93).
...Nos. 16 and 32. Six Bagatelles, Op. 126. **Mia Chung** (pf).
Channel Classics Ⓕ CCS7195 (72 minutes: DDD: 6/95).

Beethoven Piano Sonatas – No. 19 in G minor, Op. 49 No. 1; No. 20 in G major, Op. 49 No. 2; No. 22 in F major, Op. 54; No. 23 in F minor, Op. 57, "Appassionata"; No. 30 in E major, Op. 109; No. 31 in A flat major, Op. 110; No. 32 in C minor, Op. 111. **Sviatoslav Richter** (pf). Philips Ⓕ 438 486-2PH2 (two discs: 122 minutes: DDD: 8/94). Recorded 1992. Ⓖ

Beethoven Piano Sonatas – No. 18 in E flat major, Op. 31 No. 3; No. 28 in A major, Op. 101. Two Rondos, Op. 51. Piano Trio in B flat major, Op. 97, "Archduke"[a]. Quintet for Piano and Wind in E flat major, Op. 16[b]. **Sviatoslav Richter** (pf); [a]members of the **Borodin Quartet;** [b]members of the **Moraguès Quintet.** Philips Ⓕ 438 624-2PH2 (two discs: 131 minutes: DDD: 8/94). Recorded 1986-92. Ⓖ

There are times in a reviewer's working life when he or she folds away the notebook, discards the score, and just listens – the performance demands it. This was one such event. Those whose chief pleasure as critics is to pounce on minute blemishes (preferably blemishes no one else has noticed) would no doubt have a joyous time here – Richter is no chromium-plated perfectionist. But to go glitch-hunting in the face of playing of this quality would surely require a heroic degree of insensitivity. Granted, Richter would hardly be Richter if there wasn't something bizarre to pick out, and there is one detail that does call for comment. In the Quintet for piano and wind, Op. 16, Richter and the four members of the Moraguès Quintet repeat not only the first movement exposition, but the exposition plus the slow introduction. For those who listen for structural signposts it is disorientating; and yet it is all so wonderfully played – the colour, the vitality, the sense of creative give-and-take between the players are all you could wish for in this sunny, in every sense young piece. Throughout these two sets the sheer aliveness of the playing can be breathtaking – no exaggeration. It doesn't matter whether the territory is the most searching late Beethoven or an early, 'easy' sonata (Beethoven's own description) such as the G minor, Op. 49 No. 1. One could make endless lists of favourite details – little touches that show how thorough Richter's understanding is, but what finally distinguishes Richter's Beethoven is a quality ... the word is 'improvisatory': it is as though you were hearing the music not merely played, but composed. This is what holds the attention even when Richter's conscious decisions go against what you expect of the music – the slow tempos in the scherzo and fugue of Op. 110, for instance. These four discs form another valuable counterweight to the modern nostalgists' claim that great playing – and especially great Beethoven playing – is a thing of the remote past. The transfers serve Richter excellently: intrusive audience noise is minimal, in fact in Op. 111 you might only realize that there is an audience at all when the clapping and cheering thunders in at the end. The engineering is good.

Beethoven Piano Sonatas – No. 21 in C major, Op. 53, "Waldstein"; No. 24 in F sharp major, Op. 78; No. 31 in A flat major, Op. 110. **Stephen Kovacevich** (pf). EMI Ⓕ CDC7 54896-2 (53 minutes: DDD: 2/94). Recorded 1992.   Ⓠ

Few pianists today – not Brendel, not Ashkenazy, not Serkin – can free themselves of self-awareness enough to find the tender simplicity of the opening *Moderato cantabile* of Beethoven's Op. 110. Kovacevich can, and he goes on to fill each moment of figuration and trilling with light. His finale has a mesmeric inwardness generated by the seemingly infinite nuances he can find in a single repeated note. A steadiness of purpose in the *Arioso* leads naturally into the quiet self-assurance of the effortless building of the Fuga. The coupling – with the little Op. 78 and the *Waldstein* – makes for a sensitively built recital in its own right. Again, Kovacevich's skill at drawing the listener in marks the Op. 78 Sonata, with its effervescent figurework and spontaneous major-minor changes. The same nimble fingerwork, over a thrumming bass, makes the *Waldstein* positively tingle with life: Kovacevich's joy in the physical excitement and momentum of the writing is equalled by his strength in delineating the song at its heart.

Additional recommendation ...
...Nos. 21, 23 and 26. **Melvyn Tan** (fp).
Virgin Classics Ⓜ VER5 61160-2 (63 minutes: DDD: 5/88). ✒

Beethoven Piano Sonatas – No. 26 in E flat major, Op. 81*a*, "Les adieux"[a]; No. 29 in B flat major, Op. 106, "Hammerklavier"[b]. **Alfred Brendel** (pf). Philips Ⓕ 446 093-2PH (62 minutes: DDD: 8/96). Item marked [a] recorded 1994, [b]live in 1995.   ⒼⒼ

Brendel, aged 65 in 1997, has said that this is the last recording of the *Hammerklavier* Sonata we shall have from him. He felt that this one, given in Vienna in the Musikverein, was good enough to be "a decent way of leaving the piece". Surely there can't be any doubt about that for Brendel is at his very best. At the start, applause fades and off he goes, at ease with his timing and the scale and rhetoric and, it would seem, completely confident of how the work is to be seen through to the finish. As listeners, the reassurance is excellent to have: we know straight away that he is going to be not just a reliable guide but an inspiring one. Having embarked on the huge journey – likened in the excellent booklet essay to a "progression of heroic struggle and suffering leading to a rebirth of creative possibilities" – we sense the musical experience is to prove supremely satisfying, even if discomfiting in the course of it. (But one doesn't turn to the *Hammerklavier* Sonata for solace.) Brendel has played this mighty work for more than 40 years and commands it. The fusion of sound and sense is thrilling. The *Hammerklavier* Sonata realized only in the interpreter's head is not much good and the pianism here is marvellous, an object-lesson in how technique, at this level, is above all a matter of knowing what you're doing and of fortune favouring the brave. Hats off! The recording is credited to the Austrian Radio. It's a good one: we are in the Musikverein but also of course at home, and the distance from the sound is just right, with a wide dynamic range defined at all levels just as one would have experienced it there. The production is impeccable too, with applause fore and aft but no extraneous noise to irritate in between; and (most important) the pauses between movements have been correctly judged as part of the performance. Brendel in the E flat Sonata – less agitated, warmer and more relaxed than many players – is very enjoyable, but this is a disc you buy for his *Hammerklavier*.

Beethoven Piano Sonatas – No. 27 in E minor, Op. 90[a]; No. 28 in A major, Op. 101[b]; No. 29 in B flat major, "Hammerklavier", Op. 106[c]; No. 30 in E major, Op. 109[d]; No. 31 in A flat major, Op. 110[e]; No. 32 in C minor, Op. 111[f]. **Solomon** (pf). EMI Références mono/stereo Ⓜ CHS7 64708-2* (two discs: 141 minutes: ADD: 7/93). Item marked [a] from HMV ASD294 (12/59), recorded 1956; [b]HMV ALP1272 (11/55), recorded 1956; [c]ALP1141 (9/56), recorded 1956; [d]ALP1062 (3/54), recorded 1951; [e]ALP1900 (8/62), recorded 1956; [f]ALP1160 (4/56), recorded 1951.
Gramophone classical 100. *Gramophone* Editor's choice.   ⒼⒼⒼ

Solomon's 1952 recording of the *Hammerklavier* Sonata is one of the great recordings of the century. Truth to tell, few performances that have been recorded since have either matched it or significantly improved upon it. At the heart of Solomon's performance there is as calm and searching an account of the slow movement as you are likely to hear this side of the Great Divide. And the outer movements are also wonderfully well done. Music that is so easy to muddle and arrest is here fierily played; Solomon at his lucid, quick-witted best. The CD transfer is astonishing. It is as though previously we have merely been eavesdropping on the performance; now, decades later, we are finally in the presence of the thing itself. It is all profoundly moving. What's more, by an agreeable piece of planning, EMI have retained the juxtaposition of the 1969 LP reissue: Solomon's glorious account of the A major Sonata, Op. 101 as the *Hammerklavier*'s proud harbinger. We must be grateful that Solomon had completed his recording of these six late sonatas before his career was abruptly ended by a stroke in the latter part of 1956. The Sonatas, Op. 90 and Op. 110 were recorded in August 1956. The warning signs were, in retrospect, already there as Bryan Crimp's note interestingly reveals. The sessions were a nightmare for the pianist, whose hitherto infallible touch was being all too obviously undermined. One lapse in the finale of Op. 110 was never completely tidied, hence the delay in issuing the recording. (It finally appeared in 1962 on the occasion of his 60th birthday.) Now, how bitter the irony seems; Solomon on the verge of a catastrophic illness recording a sonata Beethoven himself had written as a song of thanksgiving for the resolution of tribulations past. Yet, listening to these edited tapes one would hardly know anything was amiss. There is the odd fumble in the Scherzo of Op. 110; but, if anything, the playing has even greater resolve, both in Op. 110 and in a songful (but never sentimental) account of Op. 90. The recordings of Opp. 109 and 111 date from 1951. Sonata, Op. 109 is very fine; Op. 111 is – by Solomon's standards – a shade wooden in places, both as a performance and as a recording. Still, this is a wonderful set, very much a collectors' item.

Beethoven Piano Sonatas – No. 27 in E minor, Op. 90[a]; No. 28 in A major, Op. 101[b]; No. 29 in B flat major, Op. 106, "Hammerklavier"[c]. **Sviatoslav Richter** (pf). Praga Ⓑ CMX354003 (75 minutes: ADD: 6/96). Item marked [a] recorded 1965, [b]1986, [c]1975.
These entirely unedited performances feel not only live but somehow extraordinarily real. Not that Richter ever gives the impression of playing for the microphone, and his vision of musical structures remains constant whether he is in the studio or the concert-hall. Nevertheless the atmosphere within which that vision is realized differs from venue to venue, and in Prague it seems to have been extraordinarily conducive. This is outstanding Beethoven playing, though frustratingly the 1965 *Hammerklavier* has a little memory black-out at 8'20" in the first movement, without which it might have grown into something even more extraordinary.

Beethoven Piano Sonata No. 29 in B flat major, Op. 106, "Hammerklavier". **Emil Gilels** (pf). DG Ⓕ 410 527-2GH (49 minutes: DDD: 2/84). From 410 527-1GH (12/83).
Gramophone Award Winner 1984. ⒼⒼ
The great Soviet pianist Emil Gilels died in 1986, not many months before his seventieth birthday, and left behind him a major legacy of recorded performances. This account of the *Hammerklavier* is a fine memorial. The work is very long and exceedingly taxing technically and the pianist must plumb its often turbulent emotional depth, not least in the enormous 20-minute slow movement which requires deep concentration from player and listener alike. After the recording was made in 1983, the pianist told his producer: "I feel that the weight has been lifted, but I feel very empty". Gilels manages to give it more tonal beauty and warmth than most pianists, without any loss of strength or momentum. His is measured and beautiful playing, and finely recorded too.
Additional recommendations ...
...Nos. 27-29. **John O'Conor** (pf). Telarc Ⓕ CD80335 (73 minutes: DDD: 8/93).
...Nos. 28 and 29. **Vladimir Ashkenazy** (pf). Decca Ⓕ 436 735-2DH (66 minutes: DDD: 4/94).
...Nos. 28 and 29. **Louis Lortie** (pf). Chandos Ⓕ CHAN9435 (64 minutes: DDD: 8/96).

Beethoven Piano Sonatas. **Maurizio Pollini** (pf). DG Ⓜ 429 569/70-2GH (two discs, oas: 63 and 62 minutes: AAD: 7/90). From 419 199-2GH2 (12/86). Recorded 1975-77. ⒼⒼ
429 569-2GH – No. 28 in A major, Op. 101; No. 29 in B flat major, Op. 106, "Hammerklavier".
429 570-2GH – No. 30 in E major, Op. 109; No. 31 in A flat major, Op. 110; No. 32 in C minor, Op. 111.
If Beethoven's 32 piano sonatas may be likened to a range of foothills and mountains, then these five sonatas are the last lofty pinnacles, difficult of access but offering great rewards to both pianist and listener. No library is complete without them. Pollini's playing must be praised for its interpretative mastery as well as its exemplary keyboard skill. These are prize-winning issues which have been widely admired, not least for the magnificent last sonata, Op. 111, and the recordings hardly show their age.
Additional recommendations ...
...Nos. 30-32. **John O'Conor** (pf). Telarc Ⓕ CD80261 (65 minutes: DDD: 11/92).
...Nos. 27-32. **Alfred Brendel** (pf).
Philips Duo Ⓜ 438 374-2PM2 (two discs: 148 minutes: ADD: 8/93).
...Nos. 27-32. **Charles Rosen** (pf).
Sony Classical Essential Classics Ⓑ SB2K53531 (two discs: 150 minutes: ADD: 11/94).
...Nos. 30-32. **Inger Södergren** (pf). Calliope Approche Ⓑ CAL6648 (68 minutes: ADD: 11/95).
...Nos. 27-32. **Wilhelm Kempff** (pf). DG Ⓜ 453 010-2GTA2 (two discs: 131 minutes: DDD: 11/96).
...Nos 30-32. **Sviatoslav Richter** (pf). Revelation Ⓜ RV10096 (62 minutes: ADD: 4/98).

Beethoven Piano Sonatas – No. 30 in E major, Op. 109; No. 31 in A flat major, Op. 110; No. 32 in C minor, Op. 111. **Alfred Brendel** (pf). Philips Ⓕ 446 701-2PH (66 minutes: DDD: 12/96). Recorded 1995. Ⓖ
Since it is the critic's job to pontificate, what does one do about a performance so satisfying that, after it, even a single well-honed sentence seems an irrelevance? Retire, possibly, and devote oneself to a more useful and benign trade such as growing vegetables. So much, then for Brendel's performance of the E major Sonata, Op. 109. Op. 111 is a brute of a thing interpretatively. Mismanaged, it can sound more like an imposition than a work of art. Fortunately, Brendel has always been one of its most lucid exponents, neither stalling the introduction, which he plays with a well-nigh ideal blend of grandeur and impetus, nor mismanaging the shifting pulses of the subsequent *Allegro con brio ed appassionato*.

Nowadays, he delivers the theme of the second movement less as an *Arietta*, more as an aria, more *Adagio*, less *semplice*. In the opening of Op. 110 there is a noble, grieving air that openly anticipates the journey to come: the "Passion music" (Brendel's phrase) of the great complex of movements – recitative, arioso and fugue – that makes up the sonata's latter half. Brendel plays the whole sonata superbly. Again, it is a 'big' sound but the sounding of recitative and arioso is masterly and the fugue is finely paced and elucidated both on its initial appearance and on the return. Brendel's playing here is lucidity itself, the music "little by little getting back to life again" in a way that seems at once natural, moving, and true to the letter of Beethoven's text.

Beethoven Egmont – incidental music, Op. 84. **Pilar Lorengar** (sop); **Klaus-Jürgen Wussow** (spkr); **Vienna Philharmonic Orchestra / George Szell.** Decca The Classic Sound Ⓜ 448 593-2DCS (48 minutes: ADD: 9/96). Text and translation included. From SXL6465 (10/70). Recorded 1969.   Ⓖ

As a simple demonstration of what it is to conduct a great orchestra properly, Szell and the Vienna Philharmonic in the *Egmont* music will do very nicely. It is, indeed, a classic set that is likely even now to remain unsurpassed for many years to come. Masur's live New York performance is good, too, but not quite in this class. Some may object to short measure on the Decca disc but it will appeal to the tidy-minded library builder. In any case, why should a great recording have to rub shoulders with some distracting fill-up? Why should it not assert its singularity? The original 1969 recording was indeed in 'classic sound' – sound, that is, which comes from a great orchestra directed and balanced *at source* by a great conductor (not by the engineers) in a hall that is entirely sympathetic to the matter in hand. (If people ask in years to come about the disappearance of proper conductors it will largely be because meddlesome technology has rendered them about as useful as a spavined horse.) In the circumstances, there is little Decca's engineers can usefully do to 'improve' the sound, apart, that is, from reassert and redefine once and for all the peerless quality of the original. This they have done. The timpani sound is 0·002 per cent cleaner; Szell's groans in the overture's coda 0·003 per cent less ghostly. The result: perfection. And all this lavished on words and music which – the overture apart – might not be given the time of day were the name of Beethoven not associated with it. Here, though, it makes compelling listening from first to last.

Additional recommendation ...

...Egmont – incidental music. Symphony No. 5 in C minor, Op. 67. **Sylvia McNair** (sop); **Will Quadflieg** (narr); **New York Philharmonic Orchestra / Kurt Masur.** Teldec Ⓕ 9031-77313-2 (75 minutes: DDD: 1/94).   Ⓖ

Beethoven Folksong Arrangements: 25 Scottish Songs, Op. 108[a]. 25 Irish Songs, WoO152[b]. Two Irish Songs, WoO153[c]. 12 Irish Songs, WoO154[d]. 26 Welsh Songs, WoO155[e]. 12 Scottish Songs, WoO156[f]. 12 Songs of various nationality, WoO157[g]. 23 Songs of various nationality, WoO158*a*[h]. Seven British Songs, WoO158*b*[i]. Six Songs of various nationality, WoO158*c*[j].
[abcdfg]**Dame Felicity Lott,** [adgh]**Janice Watson,** [aej]**Catrin Wyn-Davies,** [acdefghj]**Ruby Philogene** (sops); [adij]**Sarah Walker,** [bdg]**Ann Murray** (mezzos); [abdefgj]**John Mark Ainsley,** [abghi]**Timothy Robinson,** [achj]**Toby Spence** (tens); [abfghj]**Thomas Allen,** [abceh]**Christopher Maltman** (bars); [abcdfgj]**Elizabeth Layton,** [adghij]**Krysia Osostowicz,** [bcdefg]**Marieke Blankestijn** (vns); **Ursula Smith** (vc); **Malcolm Martineau** (pf). DG Complete Beethoven Edition Ⓜ 453 786-2GCB7 (seven discs: 476 minutes: DDD: A/97). Texts and translations included. Recorded 1996-97.

If up to now the reader has enjoyed Beethoven's folk-song arrangements in small doses but rather fancies that seven CDs might be too many, then this set could well change your mind. This is Beethoven at his most genial, most engaging, informal and collaborative. Of all the melodies that come his way, not one fails to set him off on a course that is, miraculously, both his own and the song's. All sorts of off-beat ideas come into his head, melodic or rhythmic figures that nobody else could have thought of, yet which at the same time arise out of the given tune. Or it will be that the melody suggests a mood, and the instrumental parts are written in accordance, perhaps with deep sonorities and an affectionately straight support for the voice, or perhaps with staccato emphasis or a rhythmic lift provided by a deftly placed pizzicato. Partly of course it is the great musician's tribute to folk-song itself, melody which has proved its strength and which seems incapable of bad taste. The lyrics may be another matter: many are not 'folk' poetry at all, some need footnotes, a few have a verse or two too many. Most are heartfelt, or witty, or both. Beethoven himself seems to have had little or nothing to do with the texts, so that a great deal in these verse-songs depends on the performers. Not only the singers but the players need to know, understand and respond, and it is one of the great merits of this edition that they consistently do so. All the singers do good work. One example of each: Dame Felicity Lott lovely in the cadenzas of "Awake my lyre", Janice Watson charmingly fresh of voice and manner in "O who, my dear Dermot", Catrin Wyn-Davies spry and vivid in "The Cottage Maid", Ann Murray sympathetic when singing gently in "His boat comes on the sunny tide", Ruth Philogene rich and spirited in "Come, Darby dear", John Mark Ainsley forthright and stylish in "Sir Johnnie Cope", Timothy Robinson drawing a clean-cut line in "Red gleams the sun", Christopher Maltman resonantly good-humoured in "Let brain-spinning swains". Most enjoyable were the contributions of Toby Spence and Sarah Walker (one of them young, the other getting on a bit but both on fine form with character in their voices), and, most especially, of Thomas Allen, ever-welcome and, for beauty of tone and evenness of production, in a class of his own. The hero of the set is Malcolm Martineau. Essentially, it is through the piano-part that Beethoven speaks, and the pianist must understand his language. In all these seven discs – 168 tracks – Martineau uses not only his well-trained fingers but a finely tuned intelligence to catch Beethoven's delight and hand it on. The notes are excellent.

Additional recommendation ...

...Scottish Songs, Op. 108 – No. 2, Sunset; No. 3, Oh! sweet were the hours; No. 5, The sweetest lad was Jamie; No. 13, Come fill, fill, my good fellow; No. 20, Faithfu' Johnie; No. 24, Again, my lyre. Irish Songs, WoO152 – No. 1, The Return to Ulster; No. 5, The Massacre of Glencoe; No. 10, The Deserter; No. 21, Morning a cruel turmoiler is. Irish Songs, WoO153 – No. 9, The kiss, dear maid, thy lip has left; No. 11, When far from the home. Irish Songs, WoO154 – No. 1, The Elfin Fairies; No. 4, The Pulse of an Irishman; No. 5, Oh! who, my dear Dermot. Welsh Songs, WoO155 – No. 12, Waken lords and ladies gay; No. 15, When mortals all to rest retire; No. 21, Cupid's Kindness; No. 25, The Parting Kiss; No. 26, Good Night. **Wolfgang Holzmair** (bar); **Fontenay Trio.** Philips Ⓕ 442 784-2PH (61 minutes: DDD: 4/98).

Beethoven An die ferne Geliebte. Op 98[a]. Adelaide, Op. 46[a]. Zärtliche Liebe, WoO123[a]. L'amante impaziente, Op. 82 Nos. 3 and 4[a]. In questa tomba oscura, WoO133[a]. Maigesang, Op. 52 No. 4[a]. Es war einmal ein König, Op. 75 No. 3[a].
Brahms Vier ernste Gesänge, Op. 121[b]. O wüsst' ich doch den Weg zurück, Op. 63 No. 8[c]. Auf dem Kirchhofe, Op. 105 No. 4[c]. Alte Liebe, Op. 72 No. 1[c]. Verzagen, Op. 72 No. 4[c]. Nachklang, Op. 59 No. 4[c]. Feldeinsamkeit, Op. 86 No. 2[c]. **Dietrich Fischer-Dieskau** (bar); **Jörg Demus** (pf). DG Ⓕ 415 189-2GH* (71 minutes: ADD: 9/85). Text and translations included. Items marked [a] from SLPM139216/18 (2/67), [b]SLPM138644 (10/61), [c]SLPM138011 (5/59).   ⒼⒼⒼ

Beethoven's small *oeuvre* of songs is rich and varied. The six songs of *An die ferne Geliebte* follow the unrequited lover's reflections on his beloved, with the piano weaving its way between the individual songs setting the mood and gently assisting the narrative; indeed, it even has the last word. Fischer-Dieskau's intelligent and intense delivery are assisted by his warm tone and easy legato. He adds Beethoven's great song *Adelaide* and, among others, three Italian settings, lightening the tone and raising the spirits for the second half of the programme. Brahms's *Vier ernste Gesänge*, drawn from the image-laden texts of the Old Testament, reflect on man's fate in the great order of life and more particularly on death. The songs have a solemn character and settle in the lower register of the baritone's vocal range. The remainder of the recital draws on similarly severe songs, making for a well-devised programme with a consistent theme. Jörg Demus accompanies sensitively and the elderly recordings sound well.

Additional recommendations ...

...Lieder, Op. 52 – Das Liedchen von der Ruhe; Maigesang (Mailied); Die Liebe; Marmotte. Lieder, Op. 75 – Neue Liebe, neues Leben; Aus Goethes Faust; Der Zufriedene. Drei Lieder, Op. 83. Sechs Lieder, Op. 48. Adelaide, Op. 46. Andenken, WoO136. Lied aus der Ferne, WoO137. Sehnsucht, WoO146. Der Wachtelschlag, WoO129. An die Hoffnung, Op. 94. Der Kuss, Op. 128. Abendlied unterm gestirnten Himmel, WoO150. Resignation, WoO149. Zärtliche Liebe (Ich liebe dich), WoO123. In questa tomba oscura, WoO133. **Dietrich Fischer-Dieskau** (bar); **Hertha Klust** (pf). Testament mono Ⓕ SBT1057* (77 minutes: ADD: 10/95).

...Lieder, Op. 75 – No. 2, Neue Liebe, neues Leben; No. 3, Es war einmal ein König. Mailied, Op. 52 No. 4. *Coupled with works by various composers.* **Dietrich Fischer-Dieskau** (bar); **Karl Engel** (pf). Orfeo D'Or mono Ⓕ C389951B* (72 minutes: ADD: 2/96).

Beethoven An die ferne Geliebte, Op. 98. Maigesang: Mailied, Op. 52 No. 4. Adelaide, Op. 46. Andeken, WoO136. Drei Lieder, Op. 83. Der Liebende, WoO139. Resignation, WoO149. Der Kuss, Op. 128. Lieder, Op. 75 – No. 2, Neue Liebe, neues Leben; No. 3, Aus Goethes Faust: Es war einmal ein König. Zartliche Liebe, WoO123, "Ich liebe dich". Lied aus der Ferne, WoO137. An die Hoffnung, Op. 94. Der Wachtelschlag, WoO129. Zwei Lieder, WoO118. Abendlied unterm gestirnten Himmel, WoO150. **Peter Schreier** (ten); **András Schiff** (pf). Decca Ⓕ 444 817-2DH (74 minutes: DDD: 8/96). Texts and translations included.

Beethoven, even now underrated as a composer in this genre, emerges as quite as great an innovator as Schubert, not least because Schiff instils the piano parts with such individuality of utterance, such pellucid tone in support of Schreier's acknowledged mastery of Beethoven song. Take the final lines of the fifth song of *An die ferne Geliebte*: the pair fill words and notes with such meaning that you can feel the falling of the tears being mentioned in the text. Then, in the next and final song of the cycle, time seems to stand still in the couplet beginning "Und sein letzter Strahl verglühet...". The long and searching second version of the Tiedge setting, *An die Hoffnung*, becomes the great expression of sorrow it should be, looking as far ahead as Wolf in its daring harmonies and word setting. But the pair are no less satisfying in the lighter pieces, bringing a delightful verve to *Mailied* right at the start and to *Der Wachtelschlag* near the end. At all times pacing seems apt, Schiff giving a unifying shape to every song. If we are occasionally aware that Schreier's tone is no longer that of a young tenor we are consoled by his increased understanding of every facet of his contributions, and in Beethoven's last song, *Abendlied unterm gestirnten Himmel*, written when he was working on the *Missa solemnis*, that tone is absolutely right for its valedictory feelings. The perfect recording in Vienna's Brahmssaal completes wholehearted pleasure in this issue.

Beethoven Cantata on the death of the Emperor Joseph II, WoO87[a]. Cantata on the accession of the Emperor Leopold II, WoO88[b]. Opferlied, Op. 121*b*[c]. Meeresstille und glückliche Fahrt, Op. 112. [a]**Janice Watson,** [b]**Judith Howarth** (sops); [abc]**Jean Rigby** (mez); [ab]**John Mark Ainsley** (ten); [ab]**José van Dam** (bass-bar); **Corydon Singers and Orchestra / Matthew Best.**
Hyperion Ⓕ CDA66880 (80 minutes: DDD: 4/97). Texts and translations included.
Recorded 1996. *Gramophone Editor's choice.*　　　　　　　　　　　　　　Ⓖ

Beethoven was only 19 when in Bonn he was commissioned to write this 40-minute cantata on the Emperor's death. It was never performed, the musicians claiming it was too difficult, and remained buried for almost a century. Arguably Beethoven's first major masterpiece, it was one of his few early unpublished works of which the master approved. When he came to write *Fidelio*, he used the soaring theme from the first of the soprano arias here, "Da stiegen die Menschen an's Licht", for Leonore's sublime moment in the finale, "O Gott! Welch' ein Augenblick". The tragic C minor power of the choruses framing the work is equally memorable. Dramatic tension is then kept taut through all seven sections, with recitatives clearly indicating the young composer's thirst to write opera. Matthew Best conducts a superb performance, at once fresh, incisive and deeply moving, with excellent soloists as well as a fine chorus. In this first cantata the solo quartet simply contribute to the opening and closing choruses. The second cantata, only a little more than half the length of the first, was written soon after, when Leopold II had succeeded as Emperor. It is apt to have the two works presented successively, when one seems to develop out of the other. This second work is less ambitious, expressing less deep emotions, yet it brings fascinating anticipation of later masterpieces. Much more specific is the way that the finale of the cantata, "Heil! Stürzet nieder, Millionen", clearly anticipates the choral finale of the Ninth Symphony (even with the word "Millionen"), a point reinforced by the key of D major. The two shorter pieces, both dating from Beethoven's difficult interim period between middle and late, with Jean Rigby as soloist in the *Opferlied*, make a generous fill-up, performed with equal dedication. With plenty of air round the chorus, the recording has ample weight yet is transparent enough to clarify even the heaviest textures. A revelatory issue.

Additional recommendation ...
...Cantata on the death of the Emperor Joseph II. Cantata on the accession of the Emperor Leopold II. **Bodil Arnesen** (sop); **Markus Schäfer** (ten); **Alan Titus** (bass); **Berlin Radio Symphony Chorus and Orchestra / Karl Anton Rickenbacher.** Koch Schwann Ⓕ 314352 (67 minutes: DDD: 10/95).

Beethoven Mass in C major, Op. 86[a]. Ah! perfido, Op. 65[b]. Meeresstille und glückliche Fahrt, Op. 112[c]. [ab]**Charlotte Margiono** (sop); [a]**Catherine Robbin** (mez); [a]**William Kendall** (ten); [a]**Alistair Miles** (bar); [ac]**Monteverdi Choir; Orchestre Révolutionnaire et Romantique / Sir John Eliot Gardiner.**
Archiv Produktion Ⓕ ① 435 391-2AH (62 minutes: DDD: 11/92). ✐ Recorded [ac]1989, [b]1991.
Gardiner's genius – for that is what his capacity for renewal amounts to – is plentifully in evidence here. Of course it is true that the opening movement, the *Kyrie eleison*, is a plea for mercy. But its opening bars speak of comfort: there is almost the simple good faith of a quiet, very Germanic carol about them. Gardiner sets a mood of deliberate seriousness, with lowered period, pitch and a tempo rather slower than that suggested by Beethoven's direction: *Andante con moto, assai vivace, quasi allegretto ma non troppo.* He also appears to have encouraged the soloists, especially the soprano, to shape and shade the phrases, so intensifying the feeling of seriousness and deliberation. Happily, this policy prevails for only a short time, and to some extent the music itself goes out to meet it. As the second *Kyrie* (following the *Christe*) moves towards its climax, the *fortissimo* brings suspensions where the alto part grinds against the soprano, and then come sudden *fortissimos* with intense modulations and momentary discords, all of which are particularly vivid in this performance. Chailly's highly likeable Decca recording already grows dim by comparison. What follows has the same exhilarating quality as that which was so applauded in Gardiner's *Gramophone* Award-winning *Missa solemnis* (which was also the Record of the Year in 1991) and, just as he did there, Gardiner is constantly illuminating detail while maintaining an apparently easy natural rightness throughout. As in the *Missa solemnis*, an outstanding contribution is made by the Monteverdi Choir. Splendidly athletic, for instance, are the leaps of a seventh in the fugal "Hosanna". The tone-painting of *Meeresstille* finds them marvellously alert and vivid in articulation. *Ah! perfido* brings a similar sense of renewal: there is not even a momentary suspicion of concert routine, but rather as though it is part of an exceptionally intense performance of *Fidelio*. Charlotte Margiono sings the angry passages with the concentration of a Schwarzkopf, and brings to those that are gentler-toned a special beauty of her own. The other soloists in the Mass sing well if without distinction. Distinction is certainly a word to use of the disc as a whole.

Additional recommendation ...
...Mass[a]. Missa solemnis[b]. Soloists; [a]**Senff Chamber Chorus;** [a]**Berlin RIAS Chamber Chorus;** [a]**Berlin Radio Symphony Orchestra / Riccardo Chailly;** [b]**Chicago Symphony Chorus and Orchestra / Sir Georg Solti.** Double Decca Ⓜ 455 014-2DF2 (two discs: 126 minutes: DDD).

Beethoven Mass in D major, Op. 123, "Missa solemnis". **Charlotte Margiono** (sop); **Catherine Robbin** (mez); **William Kendall** (ten); **Alastair Miles** (bass); **Monteverdi Choir; English Baroque Soloists / Sir John Eliot Gardiner.** Archiv Produktion Ⓕ 429 779-2AH (72 minutes: DDD: 3/91).
✐ Text and translation included. Recorded 1989. *Gramophone Award Winner 1991.*　　Ⓖ Ⓖ

The *Missa solemnis* is generally agreed to be one of the supreme masterpieces of the nineteenth century, but attempts to record a genuinely great performance have over many years run into difficulties. Usually the greatness itself is flawed, perhaps in the quality of the solo singers or in some particular passages where the conductor's approach is too idiosyncratic or momentarily not up to the challenge of Beethoven's inspiration (an example is Klemperer's heavy-handedness in the fugues). The strain upon the choir, especially its sopranos, is notorious; similarly the technical problems of balance by producer and engineers. In the last several years many recordings have appeared, all of which rank with the best as performances. The version under John Eliot Gardiner remains a very probable first choice. It combines discipline and spontaneous creativity, the rhythms are magically alive and the intricate texture of sound is made wonderfully clear. The great fugues of the *Gloria* and *Credo* achieve at the right points their proper Dionysiac sense of exalted liberation. Gardiner uses a choir of 36 and an orchestra of 60 playing on period instruments, aiming at a "leaner and fitter" sound. With Gardiner, the exceptional clarity of his smaller body of singers and players, their meticulous responsiveness to direction and concentrated attention to detail is as impressive as ever; yet one is very aware of it *as* a performance. Sometimes, as in the first sounding of drums and trumpets signifying war, Gardiner's extra intensity brings a real gain.

Additional recommendations ...

...Missa solemnis[a]. Choral Fantasia in C minor, Op. 80[b]. Soloists; [a]New Philharmonia Chorus; [b]John Alldis Choir; New Philharmonia Orchestra / Otto Klemperer.
EMI Ⓜ CMS7 69538-2 (two discs: 100 minutes: ADD: 12/88). ⒼⒼ

...Missa solemnis. Soloists; Leipzig Radio Chorus; Swedish Radio Chorus; Eric Ericson Chamber Choir; Vienna Philharmonic Orchestra / James Levine. DG Ⓕ 435 770-2GH2 (two discs: 83 minutes: DDD: 11/92). *Selected by Sounds in Retrospect.* Ⓖ

...Missa solemnis. Soloists; Arnold Schöenberg Choir; Chamber Orchestra of Europe / Nikolaus Harnoncourt. Teldec Ultima Ⓜ 0630-18945-2 (two discs: 81 minutes: DDD: 4/93). 🎗 ⒼⒼ

...Missa solemnis. Soloists; Berlin Radio Chorus; Berlin Philharmonic Orchestra / Sir Georg Solti. Decca Ⓕ 444 337-2DH (77 minutes: DDD: 6/95). Ⓖ

...Missa solemnis. Soloists; Chapelle Royale Chorus; Collegium Vocale; Orchestra of the Champs-Elysées Théâtre, Paris / Philippe Herreweghe. Harmonia Mundi Ⓕ HMC90 1557 (77 minutes: DDD: 12/95). 🎗 Ⓖ

...Missa Solemnis. **Mozart** Mass in C major, K317, "Coronation". Soloists; Vienna Singverein; Berlin Philharmonic Orchestra / Herbert von Karajan. DG Double Ⓜ 453 016-2GTA2 (two discs: 111 minutes: ADD: 7/97).

...Missa solemnis[a]. **Mozart** Symphony No. 38 in D major, K504, "Prague"[b]. [a]Dame Elisabeth Schwarzkopf (sop); [a]Christa Ludwig (mez); [a]Nicolai Gedda (ten); [a]Nicola Zaccaria (bass); [a]Vienna Singverein; Philharmonia Orchestra / Herbert von Karajan. Testament Ⓕ SBT2126* (two discs: 157 minutes: ADD: 6/98).

Beethoven Fidelio. Christa Ludwig (mez) Leonore; Jon Vickers (ten) Florestan; Walter Berry (bass) Don Pizarro; Gottlob Frick (bass) Rocco; Ingeborg Hallstein (sop) Marzelline; Gerhard Unger (ten) Jacquino; Franz Crass (bass) Don Fernando; Kurt Wehofschitz (ten) First Prisoner; Raymond Wolansky (bar) Second Prisoner; Philharmonia Chorus and Orchestra / Otto Klemperer. EMI Ⓕ CDS5 56211-2 (two discs: 128 minutes: ADD: 1/90). Notes, text and translation included. From Columbia SAX2451/3 (6/62). Recorded 1962. *Gramophone classical 100.* ⒼⒼⒼ

Fidelio teems with emotional overtones and from the arresting nature of the Overture, through the eloquence of the quartet, through the mounting tension of the prison scene to the moment of release when the wrongly imprisoned Florestan is freed, Beethoven unerringly finds the right music for his subject. Klemperer's set has been a classic since it first appeared way back in 1962. The performance draws its strength from his conducting: he shapes the whole work with a granite-like strength and a sense of forward movement that is unerring, while paying very deliberate attention to instrumental detail, particularly as regards the contribution of the woodwind. With the authoritative help of producer Walter Legge, the balance between voices and orchestra is faultlessly managed. The cumulative effect of the whole reading is something to wonder at and shows great dedication on all sides. Most remarkable among the singers is the humanity and intensity of Christa Ludwig's Leonore. In her dialogue as much as in her singing she conveys the single-minded conviction in her mission of rescuing her beleaguered and much-loved husband. As her Florestan, Jon Vickers convincingly conveys the anguish of his predicament. One or two moments of exaggeration apart this is another memorable assumption. Walter Berry, as Pizarro, suggests a small man given too much power. Gottlob Frick is a warm, touching Rocco, Ingeborg Hallstein a fresh, eager Marzelline, Gerhard Unger a youthful Jacquino and Franz Crass a noble Don Fernando. This is a set that should be in any worthwhile opera collection.

Additional recommendations ...

...Fidelio. Soloists; Vienna State Opera Chorus; Vienna Philharmonic Orchestra / Leonard Bernstein. DG Ⓕ 419 436-2GH2 (two discs: 135 minutes: ADD: 6/87).

...Fidelio. Soloists; Dresden State Opera Chorus; Dresden Staatskapelle / Bernard Haitink. Philips Ⓕ 426 308-2PH2 (two discs: 133 minutes: DDD: 1/91). *Selected by Sounds in Retrospect.*

...Fidelio. Soloists; Chorus; NBC Symphony Orchestra / Arturo Toscanini. RCA Victor Gold Seal mono Ⓜ GD60273* (two discs: 112 minutes: ADD: 10/92).

...Fidelio. Leonore Overture No. 3, Op. 72[a]. **Soloists; Bavarian State Opera Chorus; Bavarian State Orchestra;** [a]**Berlin Philharmonic Orchestra / Ferenc Fricsay.** DG Dokumente Ⓜ 437 345-2GDO2* (two discs: 128 minutes: ADD: 5/93).
...Fidelio. **Soloists; Vienna State Opera Chorus; Vienna Philharmonic Orchestra / Wilhelm Furtwängler.** EMI Références mono Ⓜ CHS7 64901-2* (two discs: 150 minutes: ADD: 5/93).
...Fidelio[a]. **Weber** Oberon – Ozean du Ungheuer![b]. **Soloists;** [b]**Hilde Konetzni** (sop); [a]**Vienna State Opera Chorus and Orchestra / Karl Böhm;** [b]**Vienna Symphony Orchestra / Leopold Ludwig.** Preiser mono Ⓕ 90195* (two discs: 146 minutes: AAD: 8/94).
...Fidelio. **Soloists; Arnold Schoenberg Choir; Chamber Orchestra of Europe / Nikolaus Harnoncourt.** Teldec Ⓕ 4509-94560-2 (two discs: 119 minutes: DDD: 10/95).   ⒼⒼ
...Fidelio. **Soloists; Vienna State Opera Concert Choir; Vienna Philharmonic Orchestra / Lorin Maazel.** Double Decca Ⓜ 448 104-2DF2 (two discs: 119 minutes: ADD: 11/96).

Beethoven Leonore. **Hillevi Martinpelto** (sop) Leonore; **Kim Begley** (ten) Florestan; **Matthew Best** (bass) Pizarro; **Franz Hawlata** (bass) Rocco; **Christiane Oelze** (sop) Marzelline; **Michael Schade** (ten) Jaquino; **Alastair Miles** (bass) Don Fernando; **Robert Burt** (ten) First Prisoner; **Colin Campbell** (bar) Second Prisoner; **Monteverdi Choir; Orchestre Révolutionnaire et Romantique / Sir John Eliot Gardiner.** Archiv Produktion Ⓕ 453 461-2AH2 (two discs: 138 minutes: DDD: 11/97). 🖉 Notes, text and translation included. Recorded 1996.   ⒼⒼⒼ
Romain Rolland, writing specifically of Beethoven's *Leonore*, described the work as "a monument of the anguish of the period, of the oppressed soul and its appeal to liberty". John Eliot Gardiner, in the first complete recording of *Fidelio*'s predecessor for more than two decades, reveals both musically and verbally how the early, more radical opera has worked its spell on him, too. This, he says, is Beethoven struggling to recover the revolutionary fervour of his Bonn years; this is the score where the direct expression of spontaneous emotion, rather than the nobility of philosophical abstraction, is really to be found. This recording brings in its wake both a reappraisal of all the available source material, and insights aplenty gathered from the touring production which preceded it. The slower musical pace of *Leonore* is counterbalanced by a stronger narrative thrust and the actor, Christoph Bantzer, contributes a sprightly narration which interleaves, deftly and movingly, brief asides from the likes of Wordsworth, Goethe and Hölderlin.
And then, of course, there is the music. The *Leonore* No. 2 Overture is distinguished by the telling contrasts Gardiner draws between brooding strata of strings and the pearly light of the woodwind; and a reversal of the first two numbers gives Christiane Oelze a head start as a radiant Marzelline. The trio (Rocco, Marzelline and Jaquino) which prepares the Quartet, "Mir ist so wunderbar", does tend to impede the momentum but it has a telling effect on the beat of the work's human heart, and Gardiner's sensitivity to its pulse throughout makes good any shortfall in dramatic impetus. The D major March which introduces Act 2 is here restored to its original place for the first time since the première. With brass and timpani making menacing circumstance out of what can be mere pomp, it makes the entry of Don Pizarro darker still. Matthew Best is, in articulation if not in range, one of the most blood-curdling Pizarros on disc, just as Alastair Miles is one of the noblest Don Fernandos. "Komm, Hoffnung" reveals the resilience and steady, gleaming core of Hillevi Martinpelto's Leonore. There are times when one craves a fiercer edge of passion; but, with the equally sharply focused tenor of Kim Begley, it is a joy to hear "O namenlose Freude" perfectly paced, and really *sung*. This Florestan sings his great aria without *Fidelio*'s vision of an "Engel Leonore": Begley, no Heldentenor after all, is particularly well suited to the constant, dark minor key of this "Lebens Frühlingstagen", which presages Gardiner's triumphant – and often surprising – finale.
Additional recommendation ...
...Leonore[a] (*this is the same recording as the one reviewed above*). Fidelio[b]. Leonore Overture No. 1, Op. 138[c]. **Soloists;** [a]**Monteverdi Choir;** [a]**Orchestre Révolutionnaire et Romantique / Sir John Eliot Gardiner;** [b]**Vienna State Opera Chorus; Vienna Philharmonic Orchestra /** [b]**Leonard Bernstein,** [c]**Claudio Abbado.** DG Complete Beethoven Edition Ⓜ 453 719-2GCB4 (four discs: 282 minutes: ADD/DDD: A/97).

Vincenzo Bellini   Italian 1801-1835

Bellini I Capuleti ed i Montecchi. **Edita Gruberová** (sop) Giulietta; **Agnes Baltsa** (mez) Romeo; **Dano Raffanti** (ten) Tebaldo; **Gwynne Howell** (bass) Capellio; **John Tomlinson** (bass) Lorenzo; **Royal Opera House Chorus and Orchestra, Covent Garden / Riccardo Muti.** EMI Ⓜ CMS7 64846-2 (two discs: 130 minutes: DDD: 2/95). Text and translation included. Recorded live in 1984. From EX270192-3 (12/85).
When Covent Garden revived this work in April 1984, for the first time since 1848, praise for the opera, Muti's conducting and the singing was almost universal. That same enthusiasm can now be extended to this reissue. Muti and his two principals, caught at white heat on the stage of Covent Garden, offer a rendition of Bellini's supple, eloquent score that gave the work a new definition and standing in the Bellini canon. Away from the limbo of studio recording, the music lives at a heightened level of emotion and the sound reflects a true opera-house balance. Muti persuades his singers and the Royal Opera House players to noble utterance. Baltsa's Romeo has a Callas-like

conviction of phrase and diction: here is a Romeo who will go to his death for the love of his Juliet. Who wouldn't do that when that role is sung so delicately and affectingly as by Gruberová, then at the absolute height of her powers, as indeed was Baltsa? Raffanti's open-throated Italian tenor is just right for Tebaldo's bold incursions. Gwynne Howell and John Tomlinson both contribute effectively to what is a wholly engrossing performance.

Additional recommendations ...

...I Capuleti ed I Montecchi – Eccomi in lieta vesta ... Oh! quante volte. La sonnambula[a] – Oh! se una volta sola ... Ah! non credea mirarti ... Ah! non giunge. *Coupled with works by various composers.* **Kathleen Battle** (sop); [a]**Randi Stene** (contr); [a]**Richard Croft** (ten); [a]**Mark S. Doss** (bass); **London Philharmonic Orchestra / Bruno Campanella.** DG Ⓕ 435 866-2GH (56 minutes: DDD: 12/93).

... I Capuleti ed i Montecchi – Se Romeo t'uccise un figlio ... La tremenda ultrice spada. *Coupled with works by various composers.* **Vesselina Kasarova** (mez); **Soloists; Bavarian Radio Chorus; Munich Radio Orchestra / Friedrich Haider.** RCA Victor Red Seal Ⓕ 09026 68522-2 (64 minutes: DDD: 2/97). *Gramophone Editor's record of the month. See review in the Collections section; refer to the Index.* ❷❷

Bellini Norma. **Maria Callas** (sop) Norma; **Ebe Stignani** (mez) Adalgisa; **Mario Filippeschi** (ten) Pollione; **Nicola Rossi-Lemeni** (bass) Orovesco; **Paolo Caroli** (ten) Flavio; **Rina Cavallari** (sop) Clotilde; **Chorus and Orchestra of La Scala, Milan / Tullio Serafin.** EMI Callas Edition mono Ⓕ CDS5 56271-2* (three discs: 160 minutes: ADD). Notes, text and translation included. From Columbia mono 33CX1179/80 (11/54). Recorded 1954.

Norma may be considered the most potent of Bellini's operas, both in terms of its subject – the secret love of a Druid priestess for a Roman general – and its musical content. It has some of the most eloquent music ever written for the soprano voice and two duets that show Bellini's gift for liquid melody. The title-role has always been coveted by dramatic sopranos, but there have been few in the history of the opera who have completely fulfilled its considerable vocal and histrionic demands: in recent times the leading exponent has been Maria Callas. The mono recording comes up sounding remarkably forward and immediate on CD, and it captures Callas's commanding and moving assumption of the title part, the vocal line etched with deep feeling, the treatment of the recitative enlivening the text. Stignani is a worthy partner whilst Filippeschi is rough but quite effective. Serafin knew better than anyone since how to mould a Bellinian line to best effect.

Additional recommendations ...

...**Soloists; London Symphony Chorus and Orchestra / Richard Bonynge.** Decca Ⓜ 425 488-2DM3 (three discs: 171 minutes: ADD).

...**Soloists; Chorus and Orchestra of La Scala, Milan / Tullio Serafin.** EMI Ⓜ CMS5 66428-2* (three discs: 161 minutes: ADD: 7/89). Highlights from the above recording are also available separately. Details are as follows: Casta diva; Va, crudele; O rimembranza; O non tremare; Introduction, Act 2; Mira, o Norma; Guerra, guerra; In mia man' alfin tu sei; Taci, ne ascolta appena. EMI Ⓜ CDM7 63091-2* (64 minutes: ADD: 7/89).

Bellini La sonnambula. **Maria Callas** (sop) Amina; **Nicola Monti** (ten) Elvino; **Nicola Zaccaria** (bass) Count Rodolfo; **Fiorenza Cossotto** (Mez) Teresa; **Eugenia Ratti** (sop) Lisa; **Giuseppe Morresi** (bass) Alessio; **Franco Ricciardi** (ten) Notary. **Chorus and Orchestra of La Scala, Milan / Antonino Votto.** EMI Callas Edition mono Ⓕ CDS5 56278-2* (two discs: 121 minutes: ADD). Notes text and translation included. From Columbia 33CX51469, 33CX1470/1 (10/57). Recorded 1957.

Bellini La sonnambula. **Dame Joan Sutherland** (sop) Amina; **Nicola Monti** (ten) Elvino; **Fernando Corena** (bass) Count Rodolfo; **Margreta Elkins** (mez) Teresa; **Sylvia Stahlman** (sop) Lisa; **Giovanni Foiani** (bass) Alessio; **Angelo Mercuriali** (ten) Notary; **Chorus and Orchestra of the Maggio Musicale Fiorentino / Richard Bonynge.** Decca Grand Opera Ⓜ 448 966-2DMO2 (two discs: 136 minutes: ADD: 5/97). Notes, text and translation included. From SET239/41 (2/63).

Dramatically this opera is a tepid mix which might be subtitled *The mistakes of a night* if that did not suggest something more amusing than what actually takes place. Musically, the promise of a brilliant finale keeps most people in their seats until the end, and there are half-a-dozen charming, sometimes exquisite items on the way. But it is all a little insubstantial, and much depends upon the performance, especially that of the soprano. The name of Maria Callas is sufficient to guarantee that there will be a particular interest in the work of the heroine. As usual, her individuality is apparent from the moment of her arrival. Immediately a character is established, not an insipid little miss but a woman with a potential for tragedy. This is the pattern throughout and much has exceptional beauty of voice and spirit. Nicola Monti has all the sweetness of the traditional lyric tenor. Nicola Zaccaria sings the bass aria gracefully, and carrying off her small role with distinction is Fiorenza Cossotto, at the start of her career. The orchestral playing is neat, the conducting sensible and the recording clear.

La sonnambula was Bonynge's and Sutherland's first Bellini recording, although their second version, which has Luciano Pavarotti as Elvino, is in better sound. Sutherland's Amina in the early 1960s was sung with such extraordinary freedom and exuberance that this is probably the set to have, arguably emerging as the best *Sonnambula* on disc. It's no good comparing Sutherland with Callas at this late stage – but it is inevitable where this is concerned, especially as the Elvino, Nicola Monti, sings the role on both sets. No Sutherland admirer is going to convert to Callas in this opera, but it is fascinating to find one's remembered reactions sometimes wrong. (Callas does superb things in the coloratura of "Sovra il sen", Sutherland is full of dramatic fire in the scene in the inn.)

Additional recommendations ...
...**Soloists; London Opera Chorus; National Philharmonic Orchestra / Richard Bonynge.**
Decca Ⓕ 417 424-2DH2 (two discs: 141 minutes: DDD: 4/87).
...**Soloists; Netherlands Radio Choir and Chamber Orchestra / Alberto Zedda.**
Naxos Ⓢ 8 660042/3 (two discs: 135 minutes: DDD: 1/98).

Further listening ...
...Oboe Concerto in E flat major. *Coupled with works by various composers.* **Roger Lord** (ob);
Academy of St Martin in the Fields / Sir Neville Marriner.
Double Decca 443 838-2DF2 (7/95). *See review under Rossini; refer to the Index.*
...Vaga luna che inargenti. L'abbandono. Malinconia, ninfa gentile. Il fervido desiderio. Torna,
vezzosa Fillide. Vanne, o rosa fortunata. Dolente imagine di figlia mia. La farfalleta. Per pietà,
bell'idol mio. *Coupled with works by* **Rossini** and **Donizetti** **Cecilia Bartoli** (mez); **James Levine**
(pf). Decca 455 513-2DH (11/97). *Gramophone Editor's choice. See review in the Collections
section; refer to the Index.*
...Beatrice di Tenda. Opera Arias. **Soloists; Ambrosian Opera Chorus; Maggio Fiorentino Chorus
and Orchestra / Richard Bonynge.** Decca 433 706-2DMO3 (2/93).
...Il pirata. **Soloists; Rome RAI Chorus and Orchestra / Gianandrea Gavazzeni.**
EMI CMS7 64169-2 (2/93).
...I Puritani. **Soloists; Chorus and Orchestra of La Scala, Milan / Tullio Serafin.**
EMI Callas Edition mono CDS5 56275-2*.
...I Puritani. **Soloists; Chorus of the Royal Opera House, Covent Garden;
London Symphony Orchestra / Richard Bonynge.** Decca 417 588-2DH3 (4/95).
...Zaira. **Soloists; Chorus and Orchestra of the Teatro Massimo Bellini, Catania / Paolo Olmo.**
Nuova Era 698283 (7/91).

Georg Benda
Bohemian 1722-1795

Suggested listening...
...Flute Concerto in E minor. *Coupled with works by various composers.* **Patrick Gallois** (fl);
CPE Bach Chamber Orchestra / Peter Schreier. DG 439 895-2GH (2/95). *See review in the
Collections section; refer to the Index.*

Cesare Bendinelli
Italian c1686-1757

Suggested listening ...
...Sonata CCC-XXXIII. Sarasinetta. *Coupled with works by various composers.* **Gabrieli Players /
Paul McCreesh.** Virgin Classics Veritas VC7 59006-2 (5/90). 🏆 **Gramophone** *Award Winner
1990. See review in the Collections section; refer to the Index.* ⒼⒼ

Richard Rodney Bennett
British 1936

Bennett Guitar Concerto[a].
Arnold Guitar Concerto, Op. 67[b].
Rodrigo Concierto de Aranjuez[c]. **Julian Bream** (gtr); **Melos Ensemble /** [c]**Sir Colin Davis.**
RCA Julian Bream Edition Ⓕ 09026 61598-2 (62 minutes: ADD: 6/94). Item marked [a] recorded
in 1972, [b]1959, [c]1963.
Sir Malcolm Arnold's Concerto was written for Julian Bream in 1957. Bream made his record in
partnership with the composer – directing the Melos Ensemble – two years later and the results are in
every way definitive. The recording was made for RCA by Decca engineers and is beautifully balanced
and strikingly warm and atmospheric. The couplings include Bream's first stereo recording of the
Rodrigo *Concierto de Aranjuez* with Sir Colin Davis in charge of the accompaniment and Richard
Rodney Bennett's Guitar Concerto, written in 1970 and also dedicated to Bream. Its imaginative
variety of texture, lustrous and transparent, consistently titillates the ear. The performance, like that
of the Arnold, is definitive and the 1972 recording is excellent.

Further listening ...
...Diversions. Violin Concerto[a]. Symphony No. 3. [a]**Vadim Gluzman** (vn); **Monte Carlo Philharmonic
Orchestra / James DePreist.** Koch International Classics 37341-2 (6/97).
...Concerto for Stan Getz. *Coupled with works by* **Myers** and **Torke** **John Harle** (sax);
BBC Concert Orchestra / Barry Wordsworth. Argo 443 529-2ZH (7/95).
...Four Piece Suite. *Coupled with works by* **Martinů** and **Poulenc.** **Jennifer Micallef, Glen Inanga** (pfs).
Royal Over-Seas League Ⓕ CD2000 (60 minutes: DDD: 2/98).

...A Garland for Marjory Fleming. *Coupled with works by various composers.* **Tracey Chadwell** (sop); **Pamela Lidiard** (pf). British Music Society BMS420/1CD (3/98). *See review in the Collections section; refer to the Index.*

...Sermons and Devotions. *Coupled with works by various composers.* **The King's Singers**. RCA Victor Red Seal 09026 68255-2 (8/96). *See review in the Collections section; refer to the Index.*

Alban Berg

Austrian 1885-1935

Berg Violin Concerto.
Rihm Gesungene Zeit. **Anne-Sophie Mutter** (vn); **Chicago Symphony Orchestra / James Levine.**
DG Ⓕ 437 093-2GH (52 minutes: DDD: 1/93). Recorded 1992. *Selected by Sounds in Retrospect.* ⒼⒼ

Berg Violin Concerto[a].
Stravinsky Violin Concerto in D major[a].
Ravel Tzigane[b]. **Itzhak Perlman** (vn); [a]**Boston Symphony Orchestra / Seiji Ozawa;** [b]**New York Philharmonic Orchestra / Zubin Mehta.** DG The Originals Ⓜ 447 445-2GOR (57 minutes: [a]ADD/[b]DDD: 7/96). Items marked [a] from 2531 110 (3/80), [b]423 063-2GH (12/87). ⒼⒼ

One of the very few 12-note pieces to have retained a place in the repertory, Berg's Violin Concerto is in fact a work on many levels. Behind the complex intellectual facade of the construction is a poignant sense of loss, ostensibly for Alma Mahler's daughter, Manon Gropius, but also for Berg's own youth; and behind that is a thoroughly disconcerting mixture of styles which resists interpretation as straightforward Romantic consolation. Not that performers need to go out of their way to project these layers; given a soloist as comprehensively equipped as Anne-Sophie Mutter and orchestral support as vivid as the Chicago Symphony's they simply cannot fail to register. Their recording, then, makes a fine demonstration-quality recording alternative to the even more idiomatically insightful historic version of Krasner and Webern. Perlman's account of the Berg Violin Concerto with the Boston orchestra under Ozawa has long occupied a respected place in the catalogue. The original reviewer in *Gramophone* in March 1980 was completely convinced by Perlman's "commanding purposefulness". As to the recording, he wrote that "though Perlman's violin – beautifully caught – is closer than some will like, there is no question of crude spotlighting". Eighteen years later and in a different competitive climate, his verdict ("These are both performances to put with the very finest") still holds good. Perlman is also a little too close in the *Tzigane*, the recording of which sets him very firmly front-stage again. All the same, this is playing of stature and still among the best available versions. There are, however, more desirable recordings now available of the Stravinsky Concerto.

Additional recommendations ...
...Violin Concerto[a]. Lyric Suite (original version)[b]. [a]**Louis Krasner** (vn); [b]**Galimir Quartet;** [a]**BBC Symphony Orchestra / Anton Webern.** Testament Ⓕ SBT1004* (57 minutes: ADD: 6/91). *Gramophone Award Winner 1991.* ⒼⒼ
...Violin Concerto. *Coupled with works by* **Janáček** *and* **Hartmann** Thomas Zehetmair (vn); **Philharmonia Orchestra / Heinz Holliger.** Teldec Ⓜ 4509-97449-2 (60 minutes: DDD: 6/95).

Berg String Quartet, Op. 3. Lyric Suite (original version). **Alban Berg Quartet** (Günther Pichler, Gerhard Schulz, vns; Thomas Kakuska, va; Valentin Erben, vc). EMI Ⓕ CDC5 55190-2 (46 minutes: DDD: 11/94). Recorded 1991-92.

This disc brings into focus Berg's two masterpieces for the medium. EMI offer a broad perspective, the four players very forward and distinct. Details may at times seem too intrusive for the good of an integrated interpretation, and the concern to make every emotional nuance tell risks spilling the music over into melodrama. The Berg Quartet probe the extremes of the music determinedly, and their unfailingly bright sound can sometimes seem larger than life. However, there's no doubting the emotional power of the recording.

Additional recommendation ...
...String Quartet. *Coupled with works by* **Schoenberg** *and* **Webern** Brindisi Quartet.
Metronome Ⓕ METCD1007 (70 minutes: DDD: 6/95).

Berg Piano Sonata, Op. 1.
Liszt Piano Sonata in B minor, S178. Nuages gris, S199. R.W. – Venezia, S201. Schlaflos, Frage und Antwort, S203. Elegie No. 2, S197.
Webern Variations, Op. 27. **Barry Douglas** (pf). RCA Victor Red Seal Ⓕ 09026 61221-2 (61 minutes: DDD: 12/92). Recorded 1991.

Liszt's Piano Sonata leads something of a double life in the musical world. First of all it is a calling card for virtually every young virtuoso seeking to make a big impression; secondly it is recognized as one of the great path-breaking achievements in terms of compositional innovation, since its four-movements-in-one structure is a source of inspiration for the early works of Schoenberg. Even more strikingly, the near-atonal intensity of the late piano works prepares for the harmonic explorations of Schoenberg, Berg and Webern. So Barry Douglas has been extremely astute in planning this recital. Berg's single-movement Sonata shares its home tonality with the Liszt Sonata and its main motif with that of *Nuages gris*, while the Webern *Variations* show the distant consequences of essentially the same line of thought. The outstanding performance is of the Berg, where Douglas is more responsive to the expressive ebb and flow than any current rival. His Liszt Sonata does not approach the heights of a Zimerman or a Brendel, but it is still an impressive achievement and the other works give much satisfaction too. The warm acoustic of Watford Town Hall lends a welcome glow to the recorded sound.

Additional recommendations ...

...Piano Sonata. *Coupled with works by* **Krenek** and **Webern** Marcelo Bratke (pf).
Olympia Ⓕ OCD431 (57 minutes: DDD: 4/94).

...Piano Sonata. *Coupled with works by* **Schoenberg** and **Webern** Glenn Gould (pf).
CBC Records Perspective Series mono Ⓕ PSCD2008* (65 minutes: ADD: 1/96).

...Piano Sonata. *Coupled with works by various composers.* **Shura Cherkassky** (pf).
Decca Ⓕ 433 657-2DH (79 minutes: ADD: 2/96).   Ⓖ

...Piano Sonata. *Coupled with works by* **Schoenberg** and **Webern**
Houston Symphony Chamber Players / Christoph Eschenbach (pf).
Koch International Classics Ⓕ 37337-2 (74 minutes: DDD: 12/96).

...Piano Sonata (orch. Verbey). **Mahler** Symphony No. 1 in D major. **Royal Concertgebouw**
Orchestra / Riccardo Chailly. Decca Ⓕ 448 813-2DH (70 minutes: DDD: 1/97).
Gramophone Editor's choice. See review under Mahler; refer to the Index.   Ⓖ

...Piano Sonata. *Coupled with works by various composers.* **Murray Perahia** (pf).
Sony Classical Ⓜ SX4K63380 (four discs: 270 minutes: DDD/ADD: 4/98). *See review in the Collections section; refer to the Index.*

Berg Three Orchestral Pieces, Op. 6. Seven Early Songs[a]. Der Wein[a]. [a]**Anne Sofie von Otter** (mez);
Vienna Philharmonic Orchestra / Claudio Abbado. DG Ⓕ 445 846-2GH (49 minutes: DDD: 7/96).
Texts and translations included. Recorded 1992-93.   ⒼⒼ

Anne Sofie von Otter included the *Seven Early Songs* on a recital disc, a programme glowing in the sunset of German romanticism. Making comparisons between that and this recording of the orchestral version has been a test of self-discipline. There is so much to delight in the earlier performance that it is difficult to tear oneself away, whatever the different pleasures to be encountered here. Singing with orchestra, von Otter naturally works on a larger scale. The words are more firmly bound into the vocal line; there is not the detailed give-and-take that was possible with a pianist. But the outline of her interpretation remains that of a true Lieder singer, always lighting upon unexpected subtleties of colour and emphasis to inflect the poetry. In all this Abbado is an equal partner. Von Otter needs careful accompaniment in the concert-hall if she is to dominate an orchestra and Abbado, in co-operation with DG's technical team, has produced a balance that never drowns her, but still sounds fairly natural. The other leading collaboration on record is Pierre Boulez and Jessye Norman. In *Der Wein*, Berg's late concert aria, von Otter and Abbado catch the lilt of the jazz rhythms. In the *Seven Early Songs* are von Otter and Abbado a touch too cool? Perhaps, but in the final song, "Sommertage", they throw caution to the winds and end the cycle on a passionate high. Abbado has recorded the *Three Orchestral Pieces* before and his main rival is his younger self. His 1970s recording has long been one of the standard versions of this work and the opportunity to see how his thoughts have developed since then brings more surprises than one might have expected. In short, his outlook is progressing from the Italianate to the Germanic. No doubt the influence of the Vienna Philharmonic Orchestra has much to do with this and that marvellously eloquent playing is one of the prime attractions of the disc. In their company Abbado finds more depth and complexity in the music than before, although that does mean that the March loses the Bartókian attack and driving rhythms that made his first version so exciting. The earlier performance, now available at mid-price, is coupled with Margaret Price in ravishing readings of the *Altenberg Lieder* and *Lulu* Suite. On this disc von Otter makes an equally enticing vocal attraction, though prospective purchasers should note that the playing time is under 50 minutes.

Additional recommendations ...

...Three Orchestral Pieces. Lulu – Symphonie[a]. Funf Orchesterlieder nach Ansichtkartentexten von
Peter Altenberg, Op. 4[a]. [a]**Dame Margaret Price** (sop); **London Symphony Orchestra /**
Claudio Abbado. DG 20th Century Classics Ⓜ 423 238-2GC (67 minutes: ADD: 8/88).   Ⓖ

...Seven Early Songs[a]. Funf Orchesterlieder nach Ansichtkartentexten von Peter Altenberg[a]. Wo
der Goldregen steht[b]. Lied des Schiffermädels[b]. Sehnsucht II[b]. Geliebte Schöne[b]. Vielgeliebte,
schöne Frau[b]. Ferne Lieder[b]. Schattenleben[b]. Vorüber![b]. Liebe[b]. Mignon[b]. Grabschrift[b]. Schliesse
mir die augen beide Nos. 1 and 2[b]. Er klagt, dass der Frühling so kortz blüht[b].
Jessye Norman (sop); [b]**Ann Schein** (pf); [a]**London Symphony Orchestra / Pierre Boulez.**
Sony Classical Ⓕ SK66826 (48 minutes: DDD: 3/95).

Berg Funf Orchesterlieder nach Ansichtskartentexten von Peter Altenberg, Op. 4[a]. Lyric Suite
(arr. cpsr; originally for string quartet). Lulu – Symphonie[a]. [a]**Juliane Banse** (sop);
Vienna Philharmonic Orchestra / Claudio Abbado. DG Ⓕ 447 749-2GH (54 minutes: DDD:
10/96). Texts and translations included. Recorded 1994.
It is obviously high time that Claudio Abbado recorded *Lulu*. His account of the suite is ravishingly beautiful, with a warmly poetic ardour to Alwa's music that so few real-life singers can give it (the

"Hymne", too, is genuinely hymn-like). The concluding scene has a dark, passionate vehemence and pity that are deeply moving. Any suspicion that he might be overbeautifying the music (and there are hints of him doing just that in the opening movement of the *Lyric Suite*) is erased by the hectic, almost garish drama of the second movement ostinato and the sober gravity that both he and Juliane Banse bring to the "Lied der Lulu". Banse is admirable in the *Altenberg* Lieder, too: expressive, unhampered by the range of the vocal line, and bringing to the last song a wide-spanning lyricism that seems almost a foretaste of Geschwitz's death-song in *Lulu*. Aside from a slightly blunted edge, even a slight loss of wit, in its opening movement, the *Lyric Suite* has the same admirable combination of richness and orchestral detail as the *Altenberg* Lieder – in the central movement Abbado demonstrates that clarity and a marking of *misterioso* are not incompatible – and the third movement, as it should be, is the Suite's emotional nub: the Vienna Philharmonic's strings respond with glowing passion. One can say no better of the recording than it sounds as though Abbado did his own balancing.

Additional recommendations ...

...Lyric Suite (arr. cpsr). Three Pieces for Orchestra, Op. 6. *Coupled with works by* **Schoenberg** and **Webern Berlin Philharmonic Orchestra / Herbert von Karajan.**
DG Ⓜ 427 424-2GC3 (three discs: 181 minutes: ADD: 9/89). ⒼⒼ

...Lulu – Symphonie. *Coupled with works by* **Schoenberg** and **Webern** Arleen Auger (sop); **City of Birmingham Symphony Orchestra / Sir Simon Rattle.**
EMI Ⓕ CDC7 49857-2 (66 minutes: DDD: 11/89).

...Lulu – Symphonie. **Weill** Die sieben Todsünden[a]. **Angelina Réaux** (sop); [a]**Hudson Shad; New York Philharmonic Orchestra / Kurt Masur.**
Teldec Ⓕ 4509-95029-2 (68 minutes: DDD: 12/94). *See review under Weill; refer to the Index.*

...Lyric Suite (arr. cpsr). Fünf Orchesterlieder nach Ansichtskartentexten von Peter Altenberg[a].
Zemlinsky Ein lyrische Symphonie, Op. 18[b]. [ab]**Vlatka Orsanic** (sop); [b]**James Johnson** (bar); **South West German Radio Symphony Orchestra / Michael Gielen.**
Arte Nova Classics Ⓢ 74321 27768-2 (67 minutes: DDD: 10/97).

Berg Seven Early Songs.
Korngold Liebesbriefchen, Op. 9 No. 4; Sterbelied, Op. 14 No. 1; Gefasster Abschied, Op. 14 No. 4; Drei Lieder, Op. 18; Glückwunsch, Op. 38 No. 1; Alt-spanisch, Op. 38 No. 3; Sonett für Wien, Op. 41.
R. Strauss Wie sollten wir geheim sie halten, Op. 19 No. 4; Ich trage meine Minne, Op. 32 No. 1; Der Rosenband, Op. 36 No. 1; Hat gesagt – bleibt's nicht dabei, Op. 36 No. 3; Meinem Kinde, Op. 37 No. 3; Befreit, Op. 39 No. 4; Die sieben Siegel, Op. 46 No. 3. **Anne Sofie von Otter** (mez); **Bengt Forsberg** (pf). DG Ⓕ 437 515-2GH (64 minutes: DDD: 6/94). Texts and translations included. Recorded 1991-93. *Gramophone Editor's choice.*

The chosen Strauss songs here are characteristically gentle and affectionate, a mood in which von Otter is often at her best. Not that, having captured a mood, she is content to let it lie dully over as much as a verse or a line. In *Der Rosenband* she is always sensitive to the modulations; in *Ich trage meine Minne* the voice darkens with the change of tonality in verse two; in *Wie sollten wir geheim sie halten* she captures the subdued excitement of the opening as she does the frank exultation of the close. For lightness of touch, the Op. 38 songs endear themselves among the Korngold group: *Glückwunsch* has an unaffected, comfortable way with it (a little adaptation could turn it neatly into Roger Quilter or even Jerome Kern), and *Alt-spanisch* (with its reminiscence of "On yonder hill there stands a maiden") is a charmer. At the centre of the recital are the *Seven Early Songs* of Alban Berg. The first, "Nacht", which is also the longest and most readily memorable, is taken rather more slowly than usual, but gaining in its subtler evocations of the mists and then the silvered mountain paths. Von Otter's draining the voice of all vibrato also helps create the sense of watchful stillness, just as in the sixth song, "Liebesode", it makes for an almost other-worldly dreaminess, deepening to a full-bodied passion as the rose scent is borne to the love-bed. Always the mezzo-soprano voice is resourcefully used, able to colour deeply at such points, to float a pure head-tone in "Traumgekrönt" or launch a radiant high A in "Die Nachtigall".

Berg Lulu (orchestration of Act 3 completed by Friedrich Cerha). **Teresa Stratas** (sop) Lulu; **Franz Mazura** (bar) Dr Schön, Jack; **Kenneth Riegel** (ten) Alwa; **Yvonne Minton** (mez) Countess Geschwitz; **Robert Tear** (ten) The Painter, A Negro; **Toni Blankenheim** (bar) Schigolch, Professor of Medicine, The Police Officer; **Gerd Nienstedt** (bass) An Animal-tamer, Rodrigo; **Helmut Pampuch** (ten) The Prince, The Manservant, The Marquis; **Jules Bastin** (bass) The Theatre Manager, The Banker; **Hanna Schwarz** (mez) A Dresser in the theatre, High School Boy, A Groom; **Jane Manning** (sop) A 15-year-old girl; **Ursula Boese** (mez) Her Mother; **Anna Ringart** (mez) A Lady Artist; **Claude Meloni** (bar) A Journalist; **Pierre-Yves Le Maigat** (bass) A Manservant; **Paris Opéra Orchestra / Pierre Boulez.** DG Ⓕ 415 489-2GH3 (three discs: 172 minutes: ADD: 11/86). Notes, text and translation included. From 2740 213 (10/79).
Gramophone Award Winner 1986. Recorded 1979. ⒼⒼ

Now here's a masterpiece that fulfils all the requirements needed for a commercial smash hit – it's sexy, violent, cunning, sophisticated, hopelessly complicated and leaves you emotionally drained. *Lulu* was Berg's second opera and easily matches his first – *Wozzeck* – for pathos and dramatic impact. The meaningful but gloriously over-the-top story-line, after two tragedies by Frank Wedekind, deserves acknowledgement. Lulu, mistress of Dr Schön, is married to a medical professor. An artist also has the hots for her, but just as his passion gets interestingly out of hand, her husband walks in, catches them approaching the act and dies of shock. She marries the artist, who learns about Dr Schön and kills himself; then she marries the jealous Dr Schön, and eventually kills *him*. Smuggled out of prison by an adoring lesbian, she sets up home in Paris with Schön's son, gets blackmailed and ends up in London as one of Jack the Ripper's victims! And that's not the half of it – but we'll spare you the rest. What matters is that Berg's music is magnificent, romantic enough to engage the passions of listeners normally repelled by 12-tone music, and cerebral enough to keep eggheads fully employed. It's opulent yet subtle (saxophone and piano lend the score a hint of jazz-tinted decadence), with countless telling thematic inter-relations and much vivid tonal character-painting. Berg left it incomplete (only 390 of the Third Act's 1,326 bars were orchestrated by him), but Friedrich Cerha's painstaking reconstruction is a major achievement, especially considering the complicated web of Berg's musical tapestry. This particular recording first opened our ears to the 'real' Lulu in 1979, and has transferred extremely well to CD. The booklet contains a superb essay by Boulez which in itself is enough to stimulate the interest of a potential listener. Performance-wise, it is highly distinguished. Teresa Stratas is an insinuating yet vulnerable Lulu, Yvonne Minton a sensuous Gräfin Geschwitz and Robert Tear an ardent artist. Dr Schön is tellingly portrayed by Franz Mazura (who also turns up as Jack the Ripper), Kenneth Riegel is highly creditable as Schön's son and that Boulez himself is both watchful of detail and responsive to the drama, hardly needs saying. It's not an easy listen, but it'll certainly keep you on your toes for a stimulating, even exasperating evening.

Additional recommendations ...

...**Soloists; French National Orchestra / Jeffrey Tate.**
EMI Ⓕ CDS7 54622-2 (three discs: 172 minutes: DDD: 1/93).

...**Soloists; Danish National Radio Symphony Orchestra / Ulf Schirmer.**
Chandos Ⓕ CHAN9540 (three discs: 171 minutes: DDD: 9/97).

Berg Wozzeck. **Franz Grundheber** (bar) Wozzeck; **Hildegard Behrens** (sop) Marie; **Heinz Zednik** (ten) Captain; **Aage Haugland** (bass) Doctor; **Philip Langridge** (ten) Andres; **Walter Raffeiner** (ten) Drum-Major; **Anna Gonda** (mez) Margret; **Alfred Sramek** (bass) First Apprentice; **Alexander Maly** (bar) Second Apprentice; **Peter Jelosits** (ten) Idiot; **Vienna Boys' Choir; Vienna State Opera Chorus; Vienna Philharmonic Orchestra / Claudio Abbado.** DG Ⓕ 423 587-2GH2 (two discs: 89 minutes: DDD: 2/89). Notes, text and translation included. Recorded live in 1987.   ⒼⒼⒼ

A live recording, in every sense of the word. The cast is uniformly excellent, with Grundheber, good both at the wretched pathos of Wozzeck's predicament and his helpless bitterness, and Behrens as an outstandingly intelligent and involving Marie, even the occasional touch of strain in her voice heightening her characterization. The Vienna Philharmonic respond superbly to Abbado's ferociously close-to-the-edge direction. It is a live recording with a bit of a difference, mark you: the perspectives are those of a theatre, not a recording studio. The orchestra is laid out as it would be in an opera house pit and the movement of singers on stage means that voices are occasionally overwhelmed. The result is effective: the crowded inn-scenes, the arrival and departure of the military band, the sense of characters actually reacting to each other, not to a microphone, makes for a grippingly theatrical experience. Audiences no longer think of *Wozzeck* as a 'difficult' work, but recordings have sometimes treated it as one, with a clinical precision either to the performance or the recorded perspective. This version has a raw urgency, a sense of bitter protest and angry pity that are quite compelling and uncomfortably eloquent.

Additional recommendations ...

...**Wozzeck. Lulu (two-act version). Soloists; Chorus and Orchestra of the Deutsche Oper, Berlin / Karl Böhm.** DG Ⓜ 435 705-2GX3 (three discs: 217 minutes: ADD: 1/93).   ⒼⒼ

...**Wozzeck. Soloists; Vienna State Opera Chorus. Schoenberg** Erwartung, Op. 17. **Anja Silja** (sop); **Vienna Philharmonic Orchestra / Christoph von Dohnányi.**
Decca Ⓕ 417 348-2DH2 (two discs: 123 minutes: DDD: 2/89).   ⒼⒼⒼ

...**Wozzeck. Soloists; Berlin State Opera Chorus; Staatskapelle Berlin / Daniel Barenboim.**
Teldec Ⓕ 0630-14108-2 (two discs: 94 minutes: DDD: 3/97).

...**Wozzeck.** *Coupled with works by* **Krenek** *and* **Schoenberg** . **Soloists; High School of Music and Art Chorus; New York Schola Cantorum / Dimitri Mitropoulos.** Sony Classical Masterworks Heritage mono Ⓜ MH2K62759* (two discs: 134 minutes: ADD: 2/98).

Further listening ...

...Chamber Concerto for Piano, Violin and 13 Wind Instruments[a]. Four Pieces for Clarinet and Piano, Op. 5[b]. Piano Sonata, Op. 1. **Daniel Barenboim** (pf); [a]**Pinchas Zukerman** (vn); [b]**Anthony Pay** (cl); [a]**Ensemble InterContemporain / Pierre Boulez.**
DG The Originals 447 405-2GOR (7/95).

...(trans. Schnittke) Four-part Canon. *Coupled with works by* **Schnittke Gidon Kremer** (vn); **Yuri Bashmet** (va); **Mstislav Rostropovich** (vc); **Moscow Soloists.** EMI CDC5 55627-2 (5/96).

...Four Pieces, Op. 5. Chamber Concerto – Adagio (arr. cpsr). *Coupled with works by various composers.* **Sabine Meyer** (cl); **Gidon Kremer** (vn); **Oleg Maisenberg** (pf).
DG 447 112-2GH (4/96). *See review in the Collections section; refer to the Index.*

Luciano Berio
Italian 1925

Berio Complete Works for Solo Piano – Cinque Variazioni; Wasserklavier; Sequenza IV; Rounds; Erdenklavier; Luftklavier; Feuerklavier; Brin; Leaf; Petite Suite. **David Arden** (pf).
New Albion Ⓕ NA089CD (49 minutes: DDD: 10/97). Recorded 1996.
Given that line is as important to Berio as to Bellini, it's not surprising that he has written relatively little solo piano music. Even including a rather bland student effort, the *Petite Suite*, this disc can muster less than 50 minutes of material. Despite the short measure, however, the music is characteristically probing in the way it seeks out new approaches to keyboard sonority. The attractions of the disc are also enhanced by the well-controlled, never over-incisive playing of David Arden, recorded in dryish but decently realistic sound. After the early *Variations*, which demonstrate Berio's personal brand of expressionism with a turbulence that never strays into congestion, tempered as it is by moments of Dallapiccola-like lyricism, Berio waited a full decade before composing what remains his most extended solo piano piece, *Sequenza IV* (1965-66). The texture, woven from a tissue of clusters and brief linear flourishes, may derive from the fixed explosions of Stockhausen's seminal *Piano Piece X*, but there is a more relaxed volatility to Berio's coherent disconnections, and to the way he articulates a form through varied degrees of action and repose. All the other pieces are much shorter, but they contain such gems as *Wasserklavier*, an early example of Berio's liking for wry allusions to tonal music (here Schubert and Brahms) and the two memorial pieces from 1990, *Brin* ("Wisp") and *Leaf*, which offer potent distillations of procedures and ideas explored more fully in other works. A pity about the price-tag, then, but this is an essential addition to the Berio discography.

Berio Recital I for Cathy[a]. 11 Folk Songs[b].
Weill (arr. Berio. Sung in English) Der Dreigroschenoper – Ballade von der sexuellen Hörigkeit[c]. Marie Galante – Le grand Lustucru[c]. Happy End – Surabaya-Johnny[c]. **Cathy Berberian** (mez); [a]**London Sinfonietta;** [b]**Juilliard Ensemble / Luciano Berio.** RCA Victor Gold Seal Ⓜ 09026 62540-2 (65 minutes: ADD: 7/95). Texts included. Items marked [a] from SER5665 (4/73), [b]SB6850 (3/72), [c]new to UK. Recorded 1972.   ⒼⒼ
These are classic recordings that no contemporary music enthusiast or Berberian/Berio admirer will want to be without. This disc could be regarded as a fitting tribute to Cathy Berberian and her inimitable vocal genius. As an artist she was unique. As a champion of contemporary music (particularly music by her one-time husband Luciano Berio) she was second to none – not only for her interpretative prowess but also the inspirational quality of her highly individual style; many composers (including Stravinsky) wrote music specifically with her voice in mind. The recordings gathered together here were all composed, or arranged for her, by Luciano Berio. The two principal items are perhaps among the most famous of the Berberian/Berio collaborations. *Recital I for Cathy* makes use of Berberian's dramatic training in a composition in which the vocalist, frustrated by the non-appearance of her pianist, struggles through the programme whilst simultaneously sharing a Beckett-like stream-of-consciousness monologue with her audience. Berberian's performance here is a monumental *tour de force*. Another example of the extraordinary qualities of Berberian's voice can be found in the celebrated *Folk Songs* of 1964. The three songs by Kurt Weill reveal Berberian as a natural Weill interpreter (perhaps the best since Lotte Lenya). They are something of a find, this being their first ever release on disc. All in all, this is a wonderful tribute to a phenomenal talent.

Additional recommendation ...
...11 Folk Songs[a]. Formazioni. Sinfonia[b]. [a]**Jard van Nes** (mez); [b]**Electric Phoenix; Royal Concertgebouw Orchestra / Riccardo Chailly.** Decca Ⓕ 425 832-2DH (70 minutes: DDD: 8/90). Ⓖ

Further listening ...
...Continuo. *Coupled with works by* **Carter** *and* **Takemitsu** Chicago Symphony Orchestra / **Daniel Barenboim.** Teldec 4509-99596-2 (8/95).
...Sinfonia[a]. Eindrücke. [a]**Regis Pasquier** (vn); [a]**New Swingle Singers; French National Orchestra / Pierre Boulez.** Erato 2292-45228-2 (7/88).   Ⓖ
...Sequenza X. *Coupled with works by various composers.* **Håkan Hardenberger** (tpt); **Peter Solomon** (pf). Philips 446 065-2PH (11/96).
...Les mots sont allés. *Coupled with works by various composers.* **Matt Haimovitz** (vc). DG 445 834-2GH (12/95).
...Coro for Voices and Instruments. **Cologne Radio Chorus and Symphony Orchestra / Luciano Berio.** DG 20th Century Classics 423 902-2GC (10/88).   Ⓖ
...Laborintus II. **Soloists; Chorale Expérimentale; Ensemble Musique Vivante / Luciano Berio.** Harmonia Mundi Musique d'abord HMA190 764 (12/87).
...Notturno. *Coupled with works by* **Haydn** Alban Berg Quartet. EMI CDC5 55191-2 (10/95).

Sir Lennox Berkeley
British 1903-1989

Berkeley Piano Sonata, Op. 20. Six Preludes, Op. 23. Five Short Pieces, Op. 4. Palm Court Waltz, Op. 81 No. 2[a]. Sonatina for Piano Duet, Op. 39[a]. Theme and Variations, Op. 73[a]. **Raphael Terroni,** [a]**Norman Beedie** (pfs). British Music Society Ⓕ BMS416CD (58 minutes: DDD: 3/94). Recorded 1993.

This is some of the finest British piano music of the century. If you find Bax turgid, Ireland too sweet, Tippett gawky or repetitive, Britten and Walton virtually non-existent in the solo repertoire, then Sir Lennox Berkeley's consistently melodic piano writing should be a real discovery. Both Terroni and Headington really understand the Berkeley style: the latter pianist was Berkeley's first pupil at the Academy. The outer movements of the Sonata demand a special feeling for flow to give quite diverse material continuity. Both Terroni and Headington achieve this. Terroni's finale is excellent, and the overwhelming impression confirms Malcolm Williamson's description: "a flawless masterpiece". There are real delights, too, in the rest of Terroni's offering. His *Six Preludes* are just right, musically dedicated and unidiosyncratic. The *Five Short Pieces* are a microcosm of Berkeley's style in the 1930s, as are the *Preludes* for the 1940s. Terroni gauges them beautifully – the balance of melody and accompaniment in No. 4 is sheer perfection. And his duo with Norman Beedie is everything one could ask for in the *Sonatina* and *Theme and Variations*, exquisite piano duets in the great tradition of Schubert, Fauré or Satie.

Additional recommendation ...
...Piano Sonata. Six Preludes. Five Short Pieces. Three Pieces, Op. 2. Polka, Op. 5*a*.
Three Mazurkas, Op. 32 No. 1. Paysage (1944). Improvisation on a Theme of Falla,
Op. 55 No. 2. Mazurka, Op. 101 No. 2. **Christopher Headington** (pf).
Kingdom Ⓕ KCLCD2012 (61 minutes: DDD: 6/89).

Berkeley Five Poems, Op. 53[b]. Night covers up the rigid land, Op. 14 No. 2[b]. Lay your sleeping head, my love, Op. 14 No. 2*b*[b].
Britten On this Island, Op. 11[b]. Fish in the unruffled lakes[b]. Night covers up the rigid land[b]. To lie flat on the back[b]. The sun shines down[b]. What's on your mind?[b]. Underneath the abject willow (two versions [ab] and [b]). When you're feeling like expressing your affection[a]. Four Cabaret Songs[a].
[a]**Della Jones** (mez); [b]**Philip Langridge** (ten); **Steuart Bedford** (pf). Collins Classics Ⓕ 1490-2 (61 minutes: DDD: 4/98). Texts included. Recorded 1995 and 1997.
The treasure-trove of previously undiscovered Britten songs is still growing. Langridge and Bedford give us three enjoyable additions to the canon: the somewhat cynical *The sun shines down*, the flighty *What's on your mind?* and the love-song *Underneath the abject willow*. They are among the highlights of this cornucopia of Britten's, and Berkeley's, settings of the poet, of which the centrepiece is the well-known, early cycle, *On this Island*, which the partnership sing with their flair for going to the heart of the matter. We are consoled for the fact that Langridge's tone now judders uncomfortably when it comes under pressure by the imagination he brings to his word-painting. He also offers three settings, *Fish in the unruffled lakes*, *Night covers up the rigid land* and *To lie flat on the back*: the readings are admirable. The second of these, *Night covers up the rigid land*, was also set by Berkeley, at the time friend of the poet and his fellow composer, and the two pieces offer a nice contrast in style, Britten's the more economical, Berkeley's the more haunting and direct. Langridge sings them both with a fine line and inner understanding. Britten was intending to set the erotic *Lay your sleeping head, my love*, but in the event Berkeley musicked it, a song of seductive beauty. His later Op. 53 set of *Five Poems* doesn't have quite such an individual quality but it's well worth hearing. Della Jones gives the *Cabaret Songs* everything she's got. It's strong stuff, but only faint hearts will wilt at her wholly involving style. Even so, many will prefer Jill Gomez's subtler, more intimately recorded version. Then Jones and Langridge come together for the earlier setting of *Underneath the abject willow*, meltingly sung by Langridge. Bedford's playing is an asset throughout. The recordings of all bar the too-resonant *Cabaret Songs* are excellent.

Further listening ...
...Symphony No. 3, Op. 74[b]. Serenade, Op. 12[a]. Divertimento in B flat major, Op. 18[a]. Partita,
Op. 66[a]. Sinfonia concertante, Op. 84 – Canzonetta[a] (with Roger Winfield, ob). *Coupled with*
Berkeley/Britten Mont Juic, Op. 9[c]. **London Philharmonic Orchestra / Sir Lennox Berkeley.**
Lyrita SRCD226 (3/93).
...Because I liked you better. He would not stay for me. *Coupled with works by various composers.*
Anthony Rolfe Johnson (ten); **Graham Johnson** (pf). Hyperion CDA66471/2 (8/95). Includes
various poems from Housman's "A Shrophire Lad" read by Alan Bates. *See review in the
Collections section; refer to the Index.*
...Baa Baa Black Sheep. **Soloists; Chorus of Opera North; English Northern Philharmonia /
Paul Daniel.** Collins Classics 7036-2 (4/95).

Hector Berlioz

French 1803-1869

Berlioz Harold in Italy, Op. 16[a]. Tristia, Op. 18[b]. Les troyens à Carthage – Act 2, Prelude[c].
[a]**Nobuko Imai** (va); [b]**John Alldis Choir; London Symphony Orchestra / Sir Colin Davis.**
Philips Ⓕ 416 431-2PH (70 minutes: ADD: 12/86). Texts and translations included.
Item marked [a] from 9500 026 (3/76), [b]9500 944 (6/83), [c]SAL3788 (3/70). ⒼⒼ
Berlioz Harold in Italy, Op. 16[a]. Tristia, Op. 18[b]. [a]**Gérard Caussé** (va); [b]**Monteverdi Choir;
Orchestre Révolutionnaire et Romantique / Sir John Eliot Gardiner.** Philips Ⓕ 446 676-2PH
(60 minutes: DDD: 8/96). ✍ Text and translation included. *Gramophone Editor's choice.*
Selected by Soundings. ⒼⒼ

Berlioz was much influenced by the British romantic poet, Byron, and his travels in Italy – where he went in 1831 as the winner of the Prix de Rome – led him to conceive a big orchestral work based on one of Byron's most popular works, *Childe Harold's Pilgrimage*. Like Berlioz's earlier *Symphonie fantastique*, *Harold in Italy* was not only a programme work but brilliantly unconventional and imaginative in its structure and argument. A commission from the great virtuoso, Paganini, led him to conceive a big viola concerto, but the idea of a Byronic symphony got in the way of that. Though there is an important viola solo in the symphony as we know it – richly and warmly played on Davis's recording by Nobuko Imai – it is far from being the vehicle for solo display that Paganini was wanting. Sir Colin Davis's 1975 performance, beautifully transferred to CD, emphasizes the symphonic strength of the writing without losing the bite of the story-telling. The shorter works are also all valuable in illustrating Berlioz's extraordinary imagination. Excellent sound on all the different vintage recordings.

It is to Gardiner's credit that, like Davis, he conveys that element of wildness without ever slackening control. With Gardiner dynamic contrasts are extreme, far more strikingly so than in most period-instrument performances, and some of the *pianissimos* from the ORR strings are ravishing. The central *Canto religioso* of the second movement of the Pilgrims' hymn provides a remarkable instance, with the arpeggios *sul ponticello* of the solo viola far more eerie than usual. Gardiner's soloist, Gérard Caussé, uses vibrato sparingly. Yet for the smooth phrases of Harold's theme, the work's motto, Caussé consciously produces warm tone. It is a fine solo performance, but not so dominant that one feels the lack of a soloist in the last three-quarters of the finale. It is there that Gardiner's reading, intense from the start, reaches white heat, and it is worth noting that there, as in the rest of the performance, his speeds are never excessively fast. Altogether a thrilling performance, highly recommendable to those who would not normally consider a version with period instruments. In the three movements of *Tristia* Gardiner, using his own Monteverdi Choir, gives equally refreshing performances, and here even more strikingly the dynamic contrasts are more extreme than in Davis's analogue recording. So the epilogue to the "Hamlet Funeral March", the third of the three movements, is the more chilling and broken in mood for the extreme hush of the *pianissimo*. Gardiner's disc has cleanly focused sound against a warm acoustic.

Additional recommendations ...

...Harold in Italy. Rêverie et caprice, Op. 8. **Yehudi Menuhin** (vn/va); **Philharmonia Orchestra /
Sir Colin Davis.** EMI Studio Ⓕ CDM7 63530-2 (53 minutes: ADD: 11/90). Ⓖ

...Harold in Italy (arr. Liszt). *Coupled with works by* **Liszt** Leslie Howard (pf); **Paul Coletti** (va).
Hyperion Ⓕ CDA66683 (73 minutes: DDD: 11/93).

...Harold in Italy[a]. La Damnation de Faust, Op. 24[b] – Hungarian March; Ballet des Sylphes;
Menuet des Follets. Les Troyens – Trojan March[c]; Royal Hunt and Storm[d].
[a]**Joseph de Pasquale** (va); **Philadelphia Orchestra /** [ac]**Eugene Ormandy,** [b]**Charles Munch;**
[d]**Orchestre de Paris / Daniel Barenboim.**
Sony Classical Essential Classics Ⓑ SBK53255 (74 minutes: ADD: 8/94).

...Harold in Italy. *Coupled with works by* **Bach** *and* **Respighi** Donald McInnes (va);
French National Orchestra / Leonard Bernstein. EMI Ⓜ CDM5 65921-2 (73 minutes: ADD: 9/96).

...Harold in Italy[a]. Overtures – Le corsaire, Op. 21; Le carnaval romain, Op. 9; Benvenuto Cellini.
[a]**Laurent Verney** (va); **Orchestra of the Opéra-Bastille, Paris / Myung-Whun Chung.**
DG Ⓕ 447 102-2GH (69 minutes: DDD: 3/97).

...Tristia – La mort d'Ophélie. Zaïde, Op. 19 No. 1. *Coupled with works by various composers.*
Cecilia Bartoli (mez); **Myung-Whun Chung** (pf). Decca Ⓕ 452 667-2DH (68 minutes: DDD:
12/96). *Gramophone Editor's record of the month. See review in the Collections section;
refer to the Index.* ⒼⒼⒼ

Berlioz Le carnaval romain, Op. 9[a]. Béatrice et Bénédict – Overture[a]. Le corsaire, Op. 21[a].
Les troyens – Royal Hunt and Storm[a]. Benvenuto Cellini – Overture[a]. Roméo et Juliette, Op. 17 –
Queen Mab scherzo[b].
Saint-Saëns Le rouet d'Omphale in A major, Op. 31[c]. **Boston Symphony Orchestra /
Charles Munch.** RCA Victor Gold Seal Ⓜ 09026-61400-2* (61 minutes: ADD: 11/93).
Items marked [a] from SB2125 (10/61), [b]LDS6098 (10/62), [c]SB2041 (9/59). Recorded 1957-61.

This particular Berlioz concert has long enjoyed classic status. Munch secures an electrifying response from his great Boston orchestra, whose playing is virtuosic and tender by turns. Highlights include truly exhilarating renderings of *Le corsaire* and *Benvenuto Cellini* as well as a quite riveting Royal Hunt and Storm, which attains a breathtaking poetry in the horn-led moments of repose. The bonus item, Saint-Saëns's colourful tone-poem, *Le rouet d'Omphale*, is also superbly managed here: its central climax has surely never sounded more gripping. Recordings are a bit thin in the treble, but not enough to take the shine off what is an irresistible mid-price anthology.

Additional recommendations ...

...Le carnaval romain. *Coupled with works by various composers.* **London Philharmonic Orchestra /
Sir Thomas Beecham.** Dutton Laboratories mono Ⓑ CDLX7009* (75 minutes: ADD: 10/94).
See review in the Collections section; refer to the Index.

...Le carnaval romain. Le corsaire, Op. 21. *Coupled with works by various composers.*
Paris Conservatoire Orchestra / Jean Martinon.
Decca Classic Sound Ⓜ 448 571-2DCS (64 minutes: ADD: 2/96).

Berlioz Symphonie fantastique, Op. 14[a]. Le carnaval romain, Op. 9[b]. Le corsaire, Op. 21[b].
Harold in Italy, Op. 16[c]. Symphonie funèbre et triomphale, Op. 15[d]. [c]**Nobuko Imai** (va);
[d]**John Alldis Choir; London Symphony Orchestra / Sir Colin Davis.** Philips Duo Ⓜ 442 290-2PM2
(two discs: 150 minutes: ADD: 10/94). Item marked [a] from SAL3441 (5/64), [b]SAL3573 (10/66),
[c]9500 026 (3/76), [d]SAL3788 (3/70). Recorded 1963-75.   Ⓖ

Davis's performances of Berlioz remain among the finest of our time, and in the days when there was
still a cause to be won they played a crucial part in establishing a central place in the repertory for that
wayward romantic genius. The recordings offered to us here have long been favourites with collectors
and it is splendid, and splendid value, to have them here assembled in Philips's convenient two-disc
Duo format. The oldest, the *Symphonie fantastique*, has been more sumptuously recorded since, but
not conducted more perceptively or more excitingly, not least since Davis never goes for mere
excitement: his charge of energy comes from a deeper involvement with the music, so that the
liveliness of "Un bal" can emerge from a tinge of the sinister in the opening figures and the "Marche
au supplice" thuds with menace beneath the crack of the rhythms. Nobuko Imai's performance of
Harold is confident, warm and smooth and it is a fine performance, as is that of the *Symphonie
funèbre et triomphale*. The two overtures make up a full pair of discs in a highly recommendable
package.

Additional recommendations ...

...Symphonie fantastique. **London Classical Players / Roger Norrington.**
Virgin Classics Veritas Ⓜ VC5 61379-2 (53 minutes: DDD: 4/89). ✒   Ⓖ
...Symphonie fantastique. **Vienna Philharmonic Orchestra / Sir Colin Davis.**
Philips Ⓕ 432 151-2PH (56 minutes: DDD: 5/92).   ⒼⒼ
...Symphonie fantastique. **Orchestre Révolutionnaire et Romantique / Sir John Eliot Gardiner.**
Philips Ⓕ 434 402-2PH (53 minutes: DDD: 6/93). ✒
...Symphonie fantastique. Overtures – Le carnaval romain; Le corsaire. La Damnation de Faust –
Hungarian March. Les Troyens – Trojan March. **Detroit Symphony Orchestra / Paul Paray.**
Mercury Ⓜ 434 328-2MM (73 minutes: ADD: 9/93).
...Symphonie fantastique[a]. Lélio, Op. 14b[b]. Béatrice et Bénédict[c] – Overture; Entr'acte.
Les Troyens – Royal Hunt and Storm[c]. Benvenuto Cellini – Overture[c]. Le carnaval romain[c].
Les nuits d'été, Op. 7[d]. La mort de Cléopatre[e]. [b]**Jean-Louis Barrault** (narr);
[de]**Yvonne Minton** (mez); [d]**Stuart Burrows**, [b]**John Mitchinson** (tens); [b]**John Shirley-Quirk** (bar);
London Symphony [b]**Chorus and** [ab]**Orchestra;** [c]**New York Philharmonic Orchestra;**
[de]**BBC Symphony Orchestra / Pierre Boulez.**
Sony Classical Boulez Edition Ⓜ SM3K64103 (three discs: 199 minutes: ADD: 3/95).
...Symphonie fantastique. **Dutilleux** Métaboles. **Orchestra of the Opéra-Bastille, Paris /
Myung-Whun Chung.** DG Ⓕ 445 878-2GH (67 minutes: DDD: 4/96).   Ⓖ
...Symphonie fantastique[a]. Roméo et Juliette[b] – Love scene; Queen Mab scherzo.
[a]**Concertgebouw Orchestra,** [b]**London Symphony Orchestra / Sir Colin Davis.**
Philips Solo Ⓜ 446 202-2PM (80 minutes: ADD: 6/96).
...Symphonie fantastique. **Gran Canaria Philharmonic Orchestra / Adrian Leaper.**
Arte Nova Ⓢ 74321 46492-2 (57 minutes: DDD: 10/97).

Berlioz Les nuits d'été, Op. 7. Benvenuto Cellini – Tra la la ... Mais qu'ai-je donc?. Les Troyens –
Je vais mourir ... Adieu, fière cité. Béatrice et Bénédict – Dieu! Que vien-je d'entendre? ... Il m'en
souvient. La damnation de Faust ... D'amour l'ardente flamme. **Susan Graham** (mez);
Royal Opera House Orchestra, Covent Garden / John Nelson. Sony Classical Ⓕ SK62730
(61 minutes: DDD: 10/97). Texts and translations included. Recorded 1996-97.
Gramophone Editor's choice.

It would be hard to imagine a more inspiriting and rewarding display of Berlioz singing than this from
a singer who has the composer's style in her voice and heart. Running the gamut of Berlioz's writing
for the female voice Graham manages to explore and deliver the soul of each of her chosen pieces,
her voice – firm yet vibrant, clear yet warm – responding interpretatively and technically to the
appreciable demands placed on it by this programme. In *Les nuits d'été*, she faces the greatest
challenge from revered favourites and meets it head on, catching in almost every respect the varied
moods of each song. Her French pronunciation is excellent and she uses the language to evoke the
atmosphere of each song without a hint of exaggeration. In comparison with the most famous
readings she comes somewhere between the extreme sensuousness of Crespin and the deep intensity
of Baker. Marguérite's nobly impassioned solo from *Damnation* is confidently voiced, managing in
the studio to conjure up all the heroine's longing, quite arrestingly so at "Je suis à ma fenêtre".
Throughout the piece Graham maintains a wonderfully secure tone and a long line. The noble dignity
of her account of Dido's farewell, in particular at the recollection of the love duet, is deeply moving,
and Béatrice's equivocal thoughts about her lover are another triumph, the touch of the martial at
"Les Mores triomphaient" nicely contrasted with the sensual tone of the repeated "Il m'en souvient".
The fleeter, lighter side of Graham's art is caught in the rapturous cabaletta to Béatrice's aria and in
Ascanio's excitable aria from *Benvenuto Cellini*, both dispatched securely. Nelson and the LSO
provide idiomatic support, and the recording catches the full colour of the singer's performances.
Here is a disc as thoughtfully planned as it is executed.

Additional recommendations ...

...Les nuits d'été. *Coupled with works by various composers.* **Régine Crespin** (sop);
Suisse Romande Orchestra / Ernest Ansermet. Decca Ⓕ 417 813-2DH (68 minutes: ADD: 11/88).
See review in the Collections section; refer to the Index.

...Herminie[a]. Les nuits d'été[b]. [a]**Mireille Delunsch** (sop); [b]**Brigitte Balleys** (mez);
Orchestre des Champs-Elysées, Paris / Philippe Herreweghe.
Harmonia Mundi Ⓕ HMC90 1522 (54 minutes: DDD: 10/95).   Ⓖ

Berlioz Herminie[a]. La mort de Cléopâtre[b]. La mort de Sardanapale[c]. La mort d'Orphée[c].
[a]**Michèle Lagrange** (sop); [b]**Béatrice Uria-Monzon** (mez); [c]**Daniel Galvez Vallejo** (ten);
[c]**Choeur Régional Nord, Pas de Calais; Lille National Orchestra / Jean-Claude Casadesus.**
Harmonia Mundi Ⓕ HMC90 1542 (61 minutes: DDD: 9/96). Notes, texts and translations
included. Recorded 1994-95.

Musical competition juries have frequently been accused of bias, skulduggery or incompetence; but
those involved in Berlioz's four attempts at the Prix de Rome were prize specimens. They disqualified
his first, *La mort d'Orphée*; his second, *Herminie*, was awarded second prize, Berlioz afterwards
learning that he had upset some of the jury by writing a prayer instead of a final *agitato*, as expected;
by tradition, second prize winners were assured of first prize on their next entry, but *La mort de
Cléopâtre* so frightened the jury by its boldness that no prize was awarded; and only when Berlioz
cynically put in his most "commonplace" cantata (as he called it), *La mort de Sardanapale*, was he
declared the winner. It is an irony that only a fragment of this latter now survives: now that we have
a chance to hear it, it proves – despite Berlioz's deprecation of the work – to contain very
characteristic orchestral sections; but here it is lent distinction by the singing of Daniel Galvez
Vallejo, a splendid tenor with a heroic ring in his voice and a fine unforced top register. He is also
heard to advantage in *Orphée*, the most impressive parts of which are the pastoral opening and the
postlude (which Berlioz felt "had its point"). Of *Herminie* the composer said that if it contained
anything good, it was the prayer (the one that caused the dissension) which precedes the extremely
original ending. Michèle Lagrange enters fully into the emotions of the piece and, with admirable
backing from Casadesus and brilliant orchestral support, produces the most rewarding performance
of the cantata now available. The whole disc is warmly recommended to all Berlioz lovers.

Berlioz L'enfance du Christ, Op. 25. **Jean Rigby** (mez); **John Aler, Peter Evans** (tens);
Gerald Finley, Robert Poulton (bars); **Alastair Miles, Gwynne Howell** (basses); **St Paul's Cathedral
Choir; Corydon Singers and Orchestra / Matthew Best.** Hyperion Ⓕ CDA66991/2 (two discs:
101 minutes: DDD: 12/95). Text and translation included. Recorded 1994. *Selected by Soundings.*

Berlioz L'enfance du Christ, Op. 25. **Véronique Gens** (sop); **Paul Agnew** (ten); **Olivier Lallouette**
(bar); **Laurent Naouri, Frédéric Caton** (basses); **La Chapelle Royale; Collegium Vocale;
Orchestre des Champs-Elysées / Philippe Herreweghe.** Harmonia Mundi Ⓕ HMC90 1632/3
(two discs: 95 minutes: DDD: 12/97). Text and translation included. Recorded live in 1997.
Gramophone Editor's choice.

Gardiner, while acknowledging the drama of *The infant Christ*, classified it as "theatre of the mind";
Best, however, is anxious to get away from "the rather pious oratorio approach in favour of something
more human and dramatic". He therefore treats the work as overtly operatic, not so much by cast
movements or varied microphone placings as by his pacing of the action and by encouraging his
artists to throw themselves wholeheartedly into the emotions of the story. He gets off to a tremendous
start with a superb reading by a black-voiced Alastair Miles as a Herod haunted by his dream and
startled into belligerent wakefulness by the arrival of Polydorus. Later, there is desperate urgency in
the appeals for shelter by Joseph (an otherwise gently lyrical Gerald Finley), harshly rebuffed by the
chorus. And, throughout, there are spatial perspectives – the soldiers' patrol advancing (from
practically inaudible pizzicatos) to centre stage and going off again; a beautifully hushed and
atmospheric faraway "Amen" at the end. The angels' warning to the Holy Family in Part 1, however,
is miscalculated by the voices being too distantly placed for their words to be audible. Balance in
general is excellent, a notable passage being the duet in the tender scene at the manger. The clear
enunciation (in very good French) of nearly everyone is a plus point: only Jean Rigby, sweet-toned
and radiating innocence as Mary, might have given her words greater precision. The chorus's response
to the mood and meaning of words is always alert and sensitive, matched by the nuanced orchestral
playing. The scurrying of the Ishmaelite family to help, played really *pianissimo*, is vividly graphic;
and their home entertainment on two flutes and a harp, which sometimes marks a drop in the interest,
here has great charm. But overall it is Best's pacing which makes this recording distinctive. This
recording of Berlioz's appealing work well stands comparison with its much-praised predecessors.

Herreweghe paces his performance perceptively, without any of the misjudgements of tempo that
cause a few reservations about Gardiner's vividly dramatic performance. And if it cannot quite match
the impact that Colin Davis's 1960 recording made at the time, it makes a strong claim to figure
among the most recommendable present-day interpretations. Though recorded at public
performances, the sound is extraordinarily clean and fresh, and the balance deserves much praise for
the technicians as well as the artists. Care is taken over dynamics; the distance of the angels' warning
to the Holy Family has been well judged, the result being better in focus than for Best; the orchestra's
soft scurrying for the bustle in the Ishmaelite house is atmospheric; and the forward sound for the

flutes-and-harp trio lends illumination to the spirited central episode. The chorus are admirable – flexible and alert, their words not merely clear but sensitively coloured. All the singers on this recording use their mother tongue and it does make a difference. Of the soloists, chief honours go to Paul Agnew as the narrator and to Véronique Gens in her touchingly tender portrayal of Mary. Frédéric Caton exudes kindly sympathy as the benevolent Ishmaelite father; Olivier Lallouette makes more of an impression as Polydorus than in voicing Joseph's increasing despair in Saïs, though his duet with Mary at the crib is treated with sensitivity. On the whole this latest recording can be cordially welcomed.

Additional recommendations ...

...L'enfance du Christ. **Soloists; Monteverdi Choir; Lyon Opéra Orchestra / Sir John Eliot Gardiner.** Erato Ⓕ 2292-45275-2 (two discs: 96 minutes: DDD: 1/88). ⚐

...L'enfance du Christ[a]. Tristia, Op. 18 – Méditation religieuse; La mort d'Ophélie[b]. Sara la baigneuse, Op. 11[c]. La mort de Cléopâtre[d]. **Soloists;** [abc]**St Anthony Singers;** [a]**Goldsbrough Orchestra;** [bcd]**English Chamber Orchestra / Sir Colin Davis.** Double Decca Ⓜ 443 461-2DF2 (two discs: 142 minutes: ADD: 12/94).

Berlioz Roméo et Juliette. **Olga Borodina** (mez); **Thomas Moser** (ten); **Alastair Miles** (bass); **Bavarian Radio Chorus; Vienna Philharmonic Orchestra / Sir Colin Davis.** Philips Ⓕ 442 134-2PH2 (two discs: 96 minutes: DDD: 10/96). Text and translation included. Recorded 1993. ⓖⓖ

Berlioz Roméo et Juliette. **Catherine Robbin** (mez); **Jean-Paul Fouchécourt** (ten); **Gilles Cachemaille** (bar); **Monteverdi Choir; Orchestre Révolutionnaire et Romantique / Sir John Eliot Gardiner.** Philips Ⓕ 454 454-2PH2 (two discs: 136 minutes: DDD: 3/98). Text and translation included. Includes earlier variants. Recorded 1995. *Gramophone Editor's choice.* ⓖⓖ

Davis's return to Berlioz's highly demanding dramatic symphony is more than welcome. He has not substantially rethought what was by some way the finest recorded performance, but he has lived through the music again and been allowed by the recording to clarify what was before in places obscure. But the gains are also musically more positive. Thomas Moser sings the vocal version of "Queen Mab" with a verve and wit that make it all sound easy, which it is not. Olga Borodina is excellent in the "Strophes", phrasing with a long but internally detailed line which is essentially Berliozian, and adding just the right throb of vibrato when he lovingly asks for it at the sacred word "Shakespeare". Alastair Miles has more difficulty with the problematic role of Friar Laurence, and his French is less secure than that of the others, but this cantata finale, never the strongest part of the work, stands up well and he leads it firmly, supported by the excellent chorus. Davis himself makes of this as good a case as possible for a reconciliatory conclusion to a whole symphonic experience, one whose variety as well as quasi-symphonic cohesion he understands better than any other conductor.

If not exactly a 'variorum' edition, Gardiner's is one that adds to the standard version much of the discarded music that has been rescued (often from under *collettes*, glued-on pieces of paper). Track programming will allow listeners to chart their preferred course through the work, 'standard' or so-called 'original' or Gardiner's own mixture of the two. Briefly, the main differences are as follows. Berlioz expanded the original Prologue so as to bring in more glimpses of music later to be heard and the revised "Queen Mab" Scherzo has a more strongly composed ending. This Second Prologue seems not to have been orchestrated, and it is, here, by Oliver Knussen with a quick Berliozian ear. The finale had the most alterations; they are mostly to do with shortening Friar Laurence's sermon which is the better for it. This often maligned finale is more than justified in Gardiner's performance. Gilles Cachemaille's voice is a little light for Père Laurence but he has an intelligent perception of the part, and sings with an affecting ruefulness as well as firmness. The "Strophes" are attractively sung by Catherine Robbin, a light contralto such as Berlioz would have known. Jean-Paul Fouchécourt throws off the difficult Queen Mab *Scherzetto* with the panache he might bring to a comic opera aria. Robbin is probably using more vibrato than singers of the day would have done. The question of how much vibrato would have been used by a Paris orchestra of the time is arguable; Gardiner is almost certainly right to discourage it. Yet he also appears to discourage portamento, which was coming in as an expressive device. It may partly account for him pressing the music rather hard in consequence, where Davis can allow the great rapturous phrases to unfold more naturally. Gardiner also presses the "Queen Mab" Scherzo hard, where Davis floats the phrases on the light, speeding tempo. But he gives "Romeo in the Tomb of the Capulets" a brilliantly eloquent account and his reading of the Ball is vigorous and exuberant, even if it lacks the whiff of foreboding which Davis scents in it. No one with a care for Berlioz will want to be without Gardiner's remarkable set. Sir Colin's recordings are more devoted to the inward emotions, and touch more eloquently on the tragedy of young love destined never to flourish, but never to fade. There is room for both views of a wonderful work.

Additional recommendations ...

...Roméo et Juliette[a]. Symphonie funèbre et triomphale, Op. 15[b]. [a]**Soloists;** [b]**Jeffrey Budin** (tbn); [a]**Montreal Tudor Singers;** [ab]**Montreal Symphony Chorus; Montreal Symphony Orchestra / Charles Dutoit.** Decca Ⓕ 417 302-2DH2 (two discs: 131 minutes: DDD: 12/86).

...Roméo et Juliette. **Soloists; London Symphony Chorus and Orchestra / Sir Colin Davis.** Philips Ⓕ 416 962-2PH2 (two discs: 97 minutes: ADD: 6/88).

...Roméo et Juliette[a]. Les nuits d'été[b]. [b]**Victoria de los Angeles** (sop); [a]**Soloists;** [a]**Harvard Glee Club;** [a]**Radcliffe Choral Society; Boston Symphony Orchestra / Charles Munch.** RCA Victor Gold Seal mono Ⓜ GD60681* (two discs: 122 minutes: ADD: 4/93).

Berlioz Grande messe des morts[a]. Symphonie funèbre et triomphale[b]. [a]**Ronald Dowd** (ten); [b]**Dennis Wick** (tb); [a]**Wandsworth School Boys' Choir;** [b]**John Alldis Choir; London Symphony Chorus**[a] **and Orchestra / Sir Colin Davis.** Philips Ⓕ 416 283-2PH2 (two discs: 127 minutes: ADD: 4/86). Notes, texts and translations included. Item marked [a] from 6700 019 (9/70), [b]SAL3788 (3/70). Ⓖ

Berlioz's Requiem is not a liturgical work, any more than the *Symphonie funèbre* is really for the concert hall; but both are pieces of high originality, composed as ceremonials for the fallen, and standing as two of the noblest musical monuments to the French ideal of a *gloire*. The Requiem is most famous for its apocalyptic moment when, after screwing the key up stage by stage, Berlioz's four brass bands blaze forth "at the round earth's imagin'd corners"; this has challenged the engineers of various companies, but the Philips recording for Sir Colin Davis remains as fine as any, not least since Davis directs the bands with such a strong sense of character. He also gives the troubled rhythms of the *Lacrymosa* a stronger, more disturbing emphasis than any other conductor, and time and again finds out the expressive counterpoint, the emphatic rhythm, the telling few notes within the texture, that reveal so much about Berlioz's intentions. The notorious flute and trombone chords of the *Hostias* work admirably. Ronald Dowd is a little strained in the *Sanctus*, but the whole performance continues to stand the test of time and of other competing versions. The same is true of the *Symphonie funèbre et triomphale*, which moves at a magisterial tread and is given a recording that does well by its difficult textures. A fine coupling of two remarkable works.

Additional recommendations ...

...Grande messe[a]. Symphonie fantastique[b]. [a]**Léopold Simoneau** (ten); [a]**New England Conservatory Chorus; Boston Symphony Orchestra / Charles Munch.**
RCA Victor Red Seal Ⓕ RD86210 (two discs: 130 minutes: [a]stereo/[b]mono: ADD: 2/88).

...Grande messe. Le carnaval romain, Op. 9. La damnation de Faust, Op. 24 – Invocation.
Plácido Domingo (ten); **Paris Orchestra and Chorus / Daniel Barenboim.**
DG Ⓜ 437 638-2GGA2 (two discs: 108 minutes: ADD: 7/93).

...Grande messe[a]. Symphonie fantastique, Op. 14[b]. [a]**Robert Tear** (ten); [a]**London Philharmonic Choir;** [a]**London Philharmonic Orchestra;** [b]**London Symphony Orchestra / André Previn.**
EMI Forte Ⓜ CZS5 69512-2 (two discs: 148 minutes: ADD/[a]DDD: 12/96).

Berlioz Béatrice et Bénédict. **Susan Graham** (sop) Béatrice; **Jean-Luc Viala** (ten) Bénédict; **Sylvia McNair** (sop) Héro; **Catherine Robbin** (mez) Ursule; **Gilles Cachemaille** (bar) Claudio; **Gabriel Bacquier** (bar) Somarone; **Vincent Le Texier** (bass) Don Pedro; **Philippe Magnant** (spkr) Léonato; **Lyon Opera Chorus and Orchestra / John Nelson.** Erato MusiFrance Ⓕ 2292-45773-2 (two discs: 111 minutes: DDD: 6/92). Notes, text and translation included. Recorded 1991.

We have to note that the title is not a French version of *Much Ado about Nothing*, but that it takes the two principal characters of Shakespeare's play and constructs an opera around them. The comedy centres on the trick which is played upon the protagonists by their friends, producing love out of apparent antipathy. Much of the charm lies in the more incidental matters of choruses, dances, the magical "Nocturne" duet for Béatrice and Héro, and the curious addition of the character Somarone, a music-master who rehearses the choir in one of his own compositions. There is also a good deal of spoken dialogue, the present recording having more of it than did its closest rival, a version made in 1977 with Sir Colin Davis conducting and Dame Janet Baker and Robert Tear in the title-roles (see below). Perhaps surprisingly, the extra dialogue is a point in favour of the more recent set, for it is done very effectively by good French actors and it makes for a more cohesive, Shakespearian entertainment. John Nelson secures a well-pointed performance of the score, comparing well with Davis's, and with excellent playing by the Lyon Orchestra. Susan Graham and Jean-Luc Viala are attractively vivid and nimble in style, and Sylvia McNair makes a lovely impression in Héro's big solo. The veteran Gabriel Bacquier plays the music-master with genuine panache and without overmuch clownage. There is good work by the supporting cast and the chorus and the recording is finely produced and well recorded.

Additional recommendation ...

...**Soloists; John Alldis Choir; London Symphony Orchestra / Sir Colin Davis.**
Philips Ⓕ 416 952-2PH2 (two discs: 98 minutes: DDD: 9/87).

...**Soloists; Chorus of the Orchestre de Paris; Orchestre de Paris / Daniel Barenboim.**
DG Ⓜ 449 577-2GX2 (two discs: 103 minutes: ADD: 9/96).

...Béatrice et Bénédict[a]. Irlande, Op. 2[b]. Le trébuchet[b]. Tristia, Op. 18 – No. 2, La mort d'Ophélie[b]. La damnation de Faust, Op. 24 – Chant de la fête de Pâques[b]. [b]**Soloists;** [a]**St Anthony Singers;** [a]**London Symphony Orchestra / Sir Colin Davis;** [b]**Monteverdi Choir / Sir John Eliot Gardiner.**
Double Decca Ⓜ 448 113-2DF2 (two discs: 143 minutes: ADD: 9/96).

Berlioz La damnation de Faust, Op. 24. **Susan Graham** (sop); **Thomas Moser** (ten); **José van Dam** (bass-bar); **Frédéric Caton** (bass); **Chorus and Orchestra of Opéra de Lyon / Kent Nagano.**
Erato Ⓕ 0630-10692-2 (two discs: 122 minutes: DDD: 11/95). Text and translation included. Recorded 1994. Ⓖ

New versions of *Faust* have been appearing more or less annually in recent years, but it is rare to encounter one as good as Kent Nagano's. At its centre is a perception of Berlioz's extraordinary vision, in all its colour and variety and humour and pessimism, and the ability to realize this in a broad downward sweep while setting every detail sharply in place. *La damnation* is a work about the steady failure of consolations in a romantic world rejecting God, until all Faust's sensations are numbed and Mephistopheles has him trapped in the hell of no feeling. Every stage of the progress is mercilessly depicted here. The chorus are brilliant in all their roles, offering in turn the lively charms of peasant life, raptures of faith in the Easter Hymn, beery roistering in Auerbach's Cellar that grows as foul as a drunken party, cheerful student Latin bawls (those were the days); later they sing with delicacy as Mephistopheles's spirits of temptation and finally become a vicious pack of demons. Nagano takes the Hungarian March at a pace that grows hectic as the dream of military glory turns hollow. These are sharp perceptions, brilliantly realized. There is the same care for orchestral detail. Nagano seems to be conducting from the New Berlioz Edition score, and he uses his imagination with it. He has an unerring sense of tempo, balancing weight of tone against speed, and he can light upon the telling contrapuntal line, or point a detail of instrumental colour (like the viola tremolo that 'betrays' the will-o'-the-wisps as the devil's creatures) or even a single note (like the snarl in the Ride to the Abyss), elements that give Berlioz's marvellous orchestration its expressive quality. José van Dam is an outstanding Mephistopheles, curling his voice round phrases with hideous elegance, relishing the mock-jollity of the Serenade and the Song of the Flea, taunting Faust with lulling sweetness on the banks of the Elbe, yet also disclosing the sadness of the fallen spirit. Thomas Moser sings gravely and reflectively as he is first discovered on the plains of Hungary, and rises nobly to the challenge of the Invocation to Nature (*très large et très sombre*, as Berlioz wanted), but is almost at his finest in the many recitative passages as he twists and turns in Mephistopheles's tightening grasp. Susan Graham does not match these two superb performances, but she sings her two arias simply and well. This is, all round, the best version since that of Sir Colin Davis made in 1973, and sets Nagano among the outstanding Berlioz conductors of the day.

Additional recommendations ...

...Soloists; **Wandsworth School Boys' Choir; Ambrosian Singers; London Symphony Chorus and Orchestra / Sir Colin Davis.** Philips Ⓕ 416 395-2PH2 (two discs: 131 minutes: ADD: 1/87).

...Soloists; **Edinburgh Festival Chorus; Lyon Opera Orchestra / Sir John Eliot Gardiner.** Philips Ⓕ 426 199-2PH2 (two discs: 124 minutes: DDD: 3/90).

Berlioz Les Troyens. **Josephine Veasey** (mez); Dido; **Jon Vickers** (ten) Aeneas; **Berit Lindholm** (sop) Cassandra; **Peter Glossop** (bar) Corebus, Corebus's ghost; **Heather Begg** (sop) Anna; **Roger Soyer** (bar) Narbal, Spirit of Hector; **Anthony Raffell** (bass) Panthus; **Anne Howells** (mez) Ascanius; **Ian Partridge** (ten) Iopas; **Pierre Thau** (bass) Priam, Mercury, Trojan Soldier; **Elizabeth Bainbridge** (mez) Hecuba, Cassandra's ghost; **Ryland Davies** (ten) Hylas; **Raimund Herincx** (bar) Priam's ghost, First Sentry; **Dennis Wicks** (bar) Hector's ghost, Second Sentry; **David Lennox** (ten) Helenus; **Wandsworth School Boys' Choir; Chorus and Orchestra of the Royal Opera House, Covent Garden / Sir Colin Davis.** Philips Ⓕ 416 432-2PH4 (four discs: 241 minutes: ADD: 12/86). Notes, text and translation included. Recorded 1969. *Gramophone classical 100.* Ⓖ Ⓖ Ⓖ

Les Troyens is a masterpiece, but one that demands understanding and dedication of a peculiar intensity if it is to assume its true stature. The old accusations against it were based partly on ignorance, partly on inadequate playing (the Covent Garden orchestra are at their superlative best here) and insensitive conducting. Davis has lived with the score for many years, and clearly believes in every note. This is basically the original Covent Garden cast and players. But all that was troublesome on that edgy first night has been set true, and Colin Davis here asserts his eminence as the greatest Berlioz conductor of his day. His command of the score has never seemed more complete. He understands with total instinct how the whole work presents one great imaginative act, from the disaster at Troy through all the Trojans' adventures to the dying Dido's final vision of Rome: this was Berlioz's theme, and to it all the incident falls second. And so the climactic moments are not the diversions nor even the intense lyricism of the Carthage love scenes – which assume an extra poignancy by their sense of transience – but the scenes in which the score is possessed by a sense of urgency as the call to Rome is felt. A splendid rhythmic impetus lies at the heart of Davis's interpretation, matching the nervous intensity of the metres and the constant sense of unrest. Davis builds his large structures upon a closely observed rhythmic detail, down to the crisp beat of the *constructeurs* and the witty trudge of the two soldiers and up to the hectic, despairing thrust of Cassandra's "Non, je ne verrai pas" and the inexorable tread of the *Marche et Hymne* (No. 4). For once, the prophetic vision of Rome really does seem to crown the work.

Dido and Aeneas, as at Covent Garden, are Josephine Veasey and Jon Vickers. Veasey's Dido does not attempt the queenly dignity and tragic passion of Janet Baker's great performance; but if smaller, it is womanly, touching, decided and sung with great musical intelligence. Vickers is at his finest in the heroic scenes: his first irruption into Troy is thrilling, and he never loses his grip on Aeneas's sense of mission. Only in the duet does he slip into the habit of allowing phrases to distort under tonal pressure: but his aria "Ah! quand viendra l'instant" is affectingly done. He pairs Veasey intelligently, though there are times when the balance seems to favour him. Cassandra is new: Berit Lindholm. Not even she, with admirably strong, ardent support from Peter Glossop's Corebus, can make much of their duet; but she characterizes the unhappy priestess superbly, conveying a sense of constant, unremitting tragedy without ever allowing her voice to slip into the lachrymose, and carrying an extraordinary weight of suffering in her bitter phrase, "mon inutile vie". She leads her doomed Trojan women into a fine spirit and a glistening top B. The smaller parts are no less carefully cast. Heather Begg supports Veasey almost too discreetly, though Anna is not an easy role to distinguish without self-assertion; Ian

Partridge sings Iopas beautifully, with a ravishing soft A flat and C at the end of his song, where most tenors cannot resist ruining the piece for the sake of their own effect; Roger Soyer descends unruffled to a low F in his noble, sombre performance of Narbal; Anne Howells is a touching Ascanius. The chorus, though not always getting top marks in French Oral, sing magnificently. The recording itself is worthy of the whole enterprise, the 1969 sound superbly focused, giving a vivid sense of presence.

It is a tribute to the quality of Sir Colin Davis's set that it remained unchallenged by any rival on record for a quarter of a century. Then in 1993 came Charles Dutoit and the Montreal Symphony Orchestra, who have established themselves as second to none in the French repertory. Add to that a largely French-speaking cast, on balance even more sensitive and tonally more beautiful than Davis's, plus two minor but valuable textual additions, and the challenge is clear. Throughout the opera Dutoit's degree of rhythmic freedom intensifies the controlled frenzy behind much of the most dramatic writing, and although Françoise Pollet's Dido may not have the dark colourings of a Baker or a Veasey, her dramatic power is just as intense. There is barely a weak link in the rest of the huge cast. Though on balance the Covent Garden Chorus for Davis sing with even crisper ensemble, the passionate commitment of the Montreal chorus matches the fire of Dutoit's whole reading. It is a thrilling set which has one marvelling afresh at the electric vitality of Berlioz's inspiration.

Additional recommendations ...

...**Soloists; Montreal Symphony Chorus and Orchestra / Charles Dutoit.**
Decca Ⓕ 443 693-2DH4 (four discs: 238 minutes: DDD: 12/94). *Gramophone Editor's record of the month. Selected by Sounds in Retrospect.* Ⓖ

...Act 5, scenes 2 and 3[c]. Les nuits d'été, Op. 7[a]. La mort de Cléopâtre[b]. **Dame Janet Baker** (mez); [c]**Bernadette Greevy** (contr); [c]**Keith Erwen** (ten); [c]**Gwynne Howell** (bass); [c]**Ambrosian Opera Chorus;** [a]**New Philharmonia Orchestra / Sir John Barbirolli;** [bc]**London Symphony Orchestra / Sir Alexander Gibson.** EMI Studio Ⓜ CDM7 69544-2 (78 minutes: ADD: 11/88).

Further listening ...

...Rêverie et caprice, Op. 8[a]. *Coupled with* **Lalo** Symphonie espagnole, Op. 21[a]. **Saint-Saëns** Violin Concerto No. 3 in B minor, Op. 61[b]. **Itzhak Perlman** (vn); **Orchestre de Paris / Daniel Barenboim.** DG Digital Masters 445 549-2GMA (7/95).

...Messe Solennelle. **Soloists; Monteverdi Choir; Orchestre Révolutionnaire et Romantique / Sir John Eliot Gardiner.** Philips 442 137-2PH (4/94). 🖉 *Gramophone Editor's choice.* ⒼⒼ

...Benvenuto Cellini. **Soloists; Royal Opera House Chorus, Covent Garden; BBC Symphony Orchestra / Sir Colin Davis.** Philips 416 955-2PH3 (1/89).

Lord Gerald Berners

British 1883-1950

Berners Lieder Album[a]. Le poisson d'or. Dispute entre le papillon et le crapaud. Trois chansons[a]. Trois petites marches funèbres. Three English Songs[a]. Fragments psychologiques. Three Songs[b]. Portsmouth Point. Dialogue between Tom Filuter and his man by Ned the Dog Stealer[b]. Polka. Valse. Red Roses and Red Noses[a]. The Expulsion from Paradise. March. Come on Algernon[a].
Bach (arr. Berners) In dulci jubilo, BWV729. [a]**Dame Felicity Lott** (sop); [b]**Roderick Kennedy** (bass); **Peter Lawson** (pf). Albany Ⓕ TROY290 (59 minutes: DDD: 7/98). Texts and translations included. Recorded 1994-96. *Gramophone Editor's choice.*

This is a superlative release consisting of virtually all Lord Berners's most original and characteristic music – the core of his output. The performances are everything the composer could have wished. He could hardly have dreamt that one of the finest singers of an entire international generation would lend her authority to such ideal interpretations of his songs. Her pianist also shows an unerring command of the idiom. The sets of songs give Berners's perspective on German, French and English idioms, beautifully delivered by Lott – witness the rapturous *Lullaby* and its controlled ending, although the piano is not quite angry enough in Robert Graves's caricature of a lady do-gooder which follows. When it comes to two final comic songs, Lott again gets it absolutely right. She has already recorded *Red Roses and Red Noses* for Hyperion – it must be one of the finest comic songs in the language – and her touch of crude cockney for the *double-entendre*-infested *Come on Algernon* is simply hilarious. The use of a bass, and a fine one, in the *Three Songs*, the sea shanties written for high voice, was a surprise. The first one is too slow but the others work and then the epigrammatic *Dialogue* is perfectly characterized. Lawson's style for the avant-garde solo pieces Berners wrote in Rome during the First World War is correctly dry and ironic. The funeral marches and the *Fragments* are classics of British piano music: Lawson catches perfectly the funereal pseudo pomp for the statesman, the excruciating poignancy for the canary and the wicked glee over the rich aunt. The *Fragments* are brilliant expressionist studies as close to the frontiers as Schoenberg's *Pierrot lunaire*. In quite a different style, Lawson delivers a subtle *Polka* and a waywardly Chopinesque *Valse*. Well recorded and with informative notes, this is an essential CD for anyone interested in the solo song, British piano music, humour in music – all from a composer who contributed with unique individuality to all three.

Additional recommendation ...

...Red Roses and Red Noses. *Coupled with works by various composers.* **Dame Felicity Lott** (sop); **Graham Johnson** (pf). Hyperion Ⓕ CDA66937 (65 minutes: DDD: 10/97). *See review in the Collections section; refer to the Index.*

Further listening ...
...Caprice péruvien. Cupid and Psyche. Les sirènes[a]. [a]**Miriam Blennerhassett** (contr);
  RTE Sinfonietta / David Lloyd-Jones. Marco Polo 8 223780 (4/96).
...The Triumph of Neptune. *Coupled with works by* **Arnell** *and* **Delius** Robert Grooters (bar);
  Royal Philharmonic Orchestra / Sir Thomas Beecham. Sony Classical Essential Classics mono
  SBK62748* (12/96). *See review under Arnell; refer to the Index.*

Leonard Bernstein   American 1918-1990

Bernstein Candide – Overture[a]. West Side Story – Symphonic Dances[b]. On the Waterfront –
Symphonic Suite[b]. Fancy Free[a]. **New York Philharmonic Orchestra / Leonard Bernstein.**
Sony Classical Bernstein Century ⓜ SMK63085 (69 minutes: ADD). Items marked [a] from
CBS SBRG72406 (5/66), [b]Philips SBBL562 (2/62). Recorded 1960-63.
When Bernstein died, there was a widespread feeling that he had tried to do too much, and yet, in
these days of crossover and musical pluralism, his reckless eclecticism might best be seen as prophetic:
his film- and show-derived concert music is more popular than ever and these performances have long
been considered definitive. All but *Fancy Free* were taped in New York's Manhattan Center in the
early 1960s, a problematic venue in which the original sound engineers sought to reconcile the close-
miking of individual sections and sometimes individual players with a substantial reverberation
period. The results have a synthetic, larger-than-life quality which suits most of the music here. The
exception is the Overture to *Candide*, a more driven sort of reading, the brashness of Broadway
insufficiently tempered by the rapid figurations of Rossini, the academicism of Brahms, the *joie de
vivre* of Offenbach: subtler details tend to disappear into a fog of resonance. In the Symphonic
Dances from *West Side Story*, the players eschew the customary shouts in the "Mambo" but it is
doubtful whether there will ever be a more idiomatic reading of what was then essentially 'new music'.
The score, by no means a straightforward 'greatest hits' selection, had only recently been unveiled,
with Lukas Foss conducting, at a gala concert intended to raise funds for the New York Philharmonic
pension fund. Here certainly was the "aura of show business" which so irked Harold Schonberg, the
influential music critic of the *New York Times*: Bernstein's own recording from March 6th has the
quality of an unanswerable rejoinder. *On the Waterfront* is if anything even more intense, its lyrical
core dispatched with an overwhelming ardour. Last up is what is almost the best of all possible *Fancy
Free*s. It was originally sung in inimitable style by Billie Holiday. That recording is now out of
copyright but it has not been reinstated here as is now common practice.
Additional recommendations ...
...Candide – Overture. On the Town. Trouble in Tahiti. On the Town – Three Dance Episodes.
  Fancy Free. West Side Story – Symphonic Dances. On the Waterfront – Symphonic Suite.
  Facsimile choreographic essay.
  Soloists; Columbia Wind Ensemble; New York Philharmonic Orchestra / Leonard Bernstein.
  Sony Classical Portrait ⓜ SM3K47154 (three discs: 203 minutes: ADD: 5/92).   ⓖⓖ
...Candide – Overture. West Side Story – Symphonic Dances. **Gershwin** An American in Paris.
  Rhapsody in Blue[a]. **New York Philharmonic Orchestra / Leonard Bernstein** ([a]pf).
  Sony Classical ⓜ SMK47529 (60 minutes: ADD: 11/92).

Bernstein Songfest[a]. Chichester Psalms[b]. [a]**Clamma Dale** (sop); [a]**Rosalind Elias,** [a]**Nancy Williams**
(mezzos); [a]**Neil Rosenshein** (ten); [a]**John Reardon** (bar); [a]**Donald Gramm** (bass); [b]soloists from the
Vienna Boys' Choir; [b]**Vienna Jeunesse Choir;** [a]**National Symphony Orchestra of Washington,**
[b]**Israel Philharmonic Orchestra / Leonard Bernstein.** DG ⓕ 415 965-2GH (62 minutes: ADD:
5/86). Texts and, where appropriate, translations included. Item marked [a] from 2531 044 (11/78),
[b]2709 077 (9/78). Recorded 1977.
"I, too, am America", is the message of Leonard Bernstein's orchestral song-cycle *Songfest*. The
subject of the work is the American artist's emotional, spiritual and intellectual response to life in an
essentially Puritan society, and, more specifically, to the eclecticism of American society and its many
problems of social integration (blacks, women, homosexuals and expatriates). As expected from a
composer/conductor equally at home on Broadway or in Vienna's Musikverein, the styles range
widely. The scoring is colourful, occasionally pungent, always tuneful. Bernstein's soloists are well
chosen and sing with feeling. This vivid live recording of the *Chichester Psalms* offers the full
orchestral version and the performers all give their utmost.
Additional recommendations ...
...Chichester Psalms. *Coupled with works by* **Barber** *and* **Copland** Dominic Martelli (treb);
  Rachel Masters (hp); **Gary Kettel** (perc); **Corydon Singers / Matthew Best.**
  Hyperion ⓕ CDA66219 (54 minutes: DDD: 9/87).
...Symphonies – No. 1, "Jeremiah"[af]; No. 2, "The Age of Anxiety"[bf]; No. 3, "Kaddish"[acf].
  Chichester Psalms[cdf]. Serenade after Plato's Symposium[ef]. Prelude, Fugue and Riffs[g].
  [a]**Jennie Tourel** (mez); [d]**John Bogart** (alto); [c]**Felicia Montealegre** (spkr); [e]**Zino Francescatti** (vn);
  [g]**Benny Goodman** (cl); [b]**Philippe Entrement** (pf); [c]**Camerata Singers;** [c]**Columbus Boy Choir;** [f]**New
  York Philharmonic Orchestra;** [f]**New York Philharmonic Orchestra;** [g]**Columbia Jazz Combo /
  Leonard Bernstein.** Sony Classical ⓜ SM3K47162 (three discs: 162 minutes: ADD: 3/92).

...Songfest – To what you said. *Coupled with works by various composers.* **Thomas Hampson** (bar); **Craig Rutenberg** (pf). EMI ⓜ CDM5 55028-2 (67 minutes: DDD: 10/97). *See review in the Collections section; refer to the Index.* ⒼⒼⒼ

Bernstein Candide (1988 final version). **Jerry Hadley** (ten) Candide; **June Anderson** (sop) Cunegonde; **Adolph Green** (ten) Dr Pangloss, Martin; **Christa Ludwig** (mez) Old lady; **Nicolai Gedda** (ten) Governor, Vanderdendur, Ragotski; **Della Jones** (mez) Paquette; **Kurt Ollmann** (bar) Maximilian, Captain, Jesuit father; **Neil Jenkins** (ten) Merchant, Inquisitor, Prince Charles Edward; **Richard Suart** (bass) Junkman, Inquisitor, King Hermann Augustus; **John Treleaven** (ten) Alchemist, Inquisitor, Sultan Achmet, Crook; **Lindsay Benson** (bar) Doctor, Inquisitor, King Stanislaus; **Clive Bayley** (bar) Bear-Keeper, Inquisitor, Tsar Ivan; **London Symphony Chorus and Orchestra / Leonard Bernstein.** DG Ⓕ 429 734-2GH2 (two discs: 112 minutes: DDD: 8/91). Notes and text included. Recorded 1989. *Gramophone Award Winner 1992.* Ⓖ

Here it is – all of it – musical comedy, grand opera, operetta, satire, melodrama, all rolled into one. We can thank John Mauceri for much of the restoration work: his 1988 Scottish Opera production was the spur for this recording and prompted exhaustive reappraisal. Numbers like "We Are Women", "Martin's Laughing Song" and "Nothing More Than This" have rarely been heard, if at all. The last mentioned, Candide's 'aria of disillusionment', is one of the enduring glories of the score, reinstated where Bernstein always wanted it (but where no producer would have it), near the very end of the show. Bernstein called it his "Puccini aria", and that it is – bittersweet, long-breathed, supported, enriched and ennobled by its inspiring string counterpoint. And this is but one of many forgotten gems. It was an inspiration on someone's part (probably Bernstein's) to persuade the great and versatile Christa Ludwig and Nicolai Gedda (in his sixties and still hurling out the top Bs) to fill the principal character roles. To say they do so ripely is to do them scant justice. Bernstein's old sparring partner Adolph Green braves the tongue-twisting and many-hatted Dr Pangloss with his own highly individual form of *sprechstimme*, Jerry Hadley sings the title role most beautifully, *con amore*, and June Anderson has all the notes, and more, for the faithless, air-headed Cunegonde. It is just a pity that someone didn't tell her that discretion is the better part of comedy. "Glitter and Be Gay" is much funnier for being played straighter, odd as it may sound. Otherwise, the supporting roles are all well taken and the London Symphony Chorus have a field-day in each of their collective guises. Having waited so long to commit every last note (or thereabouts) of his cherished score to disc, there are moments here where Bernstein seems almost reluctant to move on. His tempos are measured, to say the least, the score fleshier now in every respect: even that raciest of Overtures has now acquired a more deliberate gait, a more opulent tone. But Bernstein would be Bernstein, and there are moments where one is more than grateful for his indulgence: the grandiose chorales, the panoramic orchestra-scapes (sumptuously recorded), and of course, that thrilling finale – the best of all possible Bernstein anthems at the slowest of all possible speeds – and why not (prepare to hold your breath at the choral *a cappella*).

Bernstein On the Town. **Frederica von Stade** (mez) Claire; **Tyne Daly** (sngr) Hildy; **Marie McLaughlin** (sop) Ivy; **Thomas Hampson** (bass) Gabey; **Kurt Ollmann** (bar) Chip; **David Garrison** (sngr) Ozzie; **Samuel Ramey** (bass) Pitkin; **Evelyn Lear** (sop) Madame Dilly; **Cleo Laine** (sngr) Nightclub singer; **London Voices; London Symphony Orchestra / Michael Tilson Thomas.** DG Ⓕ 437 516-2GH (75 minutes: DDD: 10/93). Notes and text included. Recorded 1992. *Gramophone Award Winner 1994.* ⒼⒼ

On the Town is a peach of a show, a show which positively hums along on the heat of its inspiration, a show rejoicing in the race of time, but regretful of its passing, a show which lovingly encapsulates those transitory moments seized and then lost amidst the impatient, pulsating heart and soul of the lonely city – the Big Apple. On two amazing nights Michael Tilson Thomas and this starry cast brought New York City to the Barbican in London. Recording this semi-staged performance live must have been a living nightmare for DG's engineers, but one wonders if they might not have pulled off a more up-front balance for the voices. Only Cleo Laine gets to be really intimate with her bluesy nightclub song "Ain't got no tears left". You'll hang on every breath Laine takes. Many of the notes are threadbare, but who needs the notes when you've got instincts like hers. As to the major roles there are happily no grave misjudgements in casting such as marred the composer's own rendition of his by now infamous *West Side Story* on this label. Mind you, you know you're in big-league production when you get Samuel Ramey delivering (gloriously) the Brooklyn Navy Yard Workers' ode to morning "I feel like I'm not out of bed yet". And Ramey was an inspired choice for Clare's monumentally boring boyfriend, Pitkin. His "Song", a masterpiece of arch formality, is very funny indeed. In performance, Tyne Daly's cab-driving Hildy knocked 'em in the aisles with her huggable personality, and the three sailors, Gabey, Chip, Ozzie – Thomas Hampson, Kurt Ollmann, David Garrison – are just perfect. Not only are they well matched vocally, but you could put them on any stage and never look back. Hampson's two big numbers – "Lonely Town" and "Lucky to be Me" – are handsomely sung with careful avoidance of that peculiarly 'operatic' articulation. The real heroes of this dizzy enterprise are Tilson Thomas and the London Symphony Orchestra, every last player a character, an individual. John Harle's soaring, throaty sax and rhythms are so hot, tight and idiomatic that you'd never credit this wasn't an American band. The playing here is stunning; there's no other word for it.

Bernstein West Side Story. **Tinuke Olafimihan** Maria; **Paul Manuel** Tony; **Caroline O'Connor**
Anita; **Sally Burgess** Off-stage voice; **Nicholas Warnford** Riff; **Julie Paton** Rosalia;
Elinor Stephenson Consuela; **Nicole Carty** Francisca; **Kieran Daniels** Action; **Mark Michaels**
Diesel; **Adrian Sarple** Baby John; **Adrian Edmeads** A-rab; **Garry Stevens** Snowboy;
Nick Ferranti Bernardo; **chorus and National Symphony Orchestra / John Owen Edwards.**
TER Ⓕ CDTER2 1197 (two discs: 101 minutes: DDD: 2/94). Recorded 1993.   Ⓖ
To cap the composer's own recording of *West Side Story*, even given his controversial casting of opera
stars, is something of an achievement. The set starts with the major advantage of being inspired by a
production at the Haymarket, Leicester, so that many of the cast are really inside their roles. They
have youth on their side, too. Paul Manuel from that company may not have a large voice, but his
sympathetic portrayal of Tony, both in his solos and duets with Maria, makes one feel that he
identifies totally with the part. Moreover, the way in which he can float a high note, as at the end of
the alternative film version of "Something's coming" puts him on a par with Carreras (for Bernstein).
His Maria, Tinuke Olafimihan, is a gem. Her ability to interact with him and to express the laughter
and the tragedy of the heroine is very real. At the heart of the "Somewhere" ballet, Sally Burgess
voices the lovers' plea for peace with a magnificent rendition of its famous soaring tune. Nicholas
Warnford as leader of the Jets gives no less than his rival in the tricky "Cool" sequence and Jet song.
John Owen Edwards directs Bernstein's score as if he believes in every note of it. Moreover, he has
imparted to his players the very pulse that sets this music ticking.
Additional recommendation ...
...**Dame Kiri Te Kanawa** (sop); **José Carreras** (ten); **Tatiana Troyanos** (mez); **Kurt Ollmann** (bar);
    composite chorus and orchestra from 'on and off' Broadway / **Leonard Bernstein** with
    Marilyn Horne (mez). DG Ⓕ 415 253-2GH2 (two discs: 98 minutes: DDD: 4/85).
Further listening ...
...Halil. *Coupled with works by various composers.* **Michael Faust** (fl); **Cologne Radio Symphony**
    Orchestra / Alun Francis.
    Capriccio 10 495 (12/94). *See review in the Collections section; refer to the Index.*
...Serenade. *Coupled with works by* **Barber** *and* **Foss** *Itzhak* **Perlman** (vn); **Boston Symphony**
    Orchestra / Seiji Ozawa. EMI CDC5 55360-2 (6/95). *Gramophone Editor's choice.*   Ⓖ
...Symphony No. 1, "Jeremiah"[a]. Songfest[b]. Anniversaries – In Memoriam: Nathalie Koussevitzky[c].
    [b]**Linda Hohenfeld** (sop); [a]**Nan Merriman**, [b]**Wendy White**, [b]**Patricia Spence** (mezzos); [b]**Walter Planté**
    (ten); [b]**Vernon Hartman** (bar); [b]**John Cheek** (bass); [ab]**St Louis Symphony Orchestra** / [a]**Leonard**
    Bernstein, [b]**Leonard Slatkin** ([c]pf). RCA Victor Red Seal [a]mono/[b]stereo 09026 61581-2* (6/94).
...Clarinet Sonata. *Coupled with works by various composers.* **Yo-Yo Ma** (vc); **Jeffrey Kahane** (pf).
    Sony Classical SK53126 (4/94). *See review in the Collections section; refer to the Index.*   Ⓖ
...Mass – Three Meditations. *Coupled with works by* **Barber** *and* **Foote** *Andrés* **Díaz** (vc);
    Samuel Sanders (pf). Dorian DOR90241 (2/98).
...West Side Story – I feel pretty. Candide – Glitter and be gay. The Madwoman of Central Park
    West – My new friends. *Coupled with works by various composers.* **Dawn Upshaw** (sop);
    orchestra / Eric Stern. Elektra Nonesuch 7559-79345-2 (12/94). *Gramophone Award Winner 1995.*
    See review in the Collections section; refer to the Index.   ⒼⒼ

Franz Adolf Berwald   Swedish 1796-1868

Berwald Symphonies – No. 1 in G minor, "Sinfonie sérieuse"; No. 2 in D major, "Sinfonie
capricieuse"; No. 3 in C major, "Sinfonie singulière"; No. 4 in E flat major. Konzertstück for
Bassoon and Orchestra[a]. [a]**Christian Davidsson** (bn) **Malmö Symphony Orchestra / Sixten Ehrling.**
BIS Ⓕ CD795/6 (two discs: 131 minutes: DDD: 4/97). Recorded 1996.
As one would expect, given Sixten Ehrling's excellent account of the *Singulière* and the E flat
Symphonies with the LSO for Decca way back in the late 1960s and his no less impressive 1970
Swedish Radio version of the *Sérieuse*, the performances are *echt*-Berwald. The *Singulière* is
greatly preferable to Järvi's all too brisk account. Ehrling gives us plenty of space without ever
lingering too lovingly. Even apart from the *tempo giusto*, one feels rather more comfortable with
Ehrling's handling of phrasing and balance. He is very attentive to dynamic markings and
sometimes, as at the beginning of the *Sinfonie singulière*, *pianissimo* becomes *pianopiano-
pianissimo*! The recording reproduces these dynamic extremes flawlessly. Needless to say the
Gothenburg set has a great deal to recommend it and it also has the advantage of the wonderfully
warm and alive acoustic of the Gothenburg Concert Hall. However, the Malmö Concert Hall where
this set was made has a good acoustic too. Generally speaking the recordings are excellent, though
there seems to be more back-to-front perspective and air around the players in the *Singulière* and
E flat Symphonies than in the *Sérieuse*. Generally speaking, the recording is truthful and vivid, and
the soloist in the *Konzertstück* is excellently balanced. One has to conclude that Ehrling and his fine
players bring us closer to the spirit of this music than do any of the current rivals.
Additional recommendations ...
...Nos. 1 and 4. **San Francisco Symphony Orchestra / Herbert Blomstedt.**
    Decca Ⓕ 436 597-2DH (63 minutes: DDD: 1/94).

...Nos. 1-4. Estrella de Soria – Overture. The Queen of Golconda – Overture. Symphony in
A major (cptd. Druce). **Swedish Radio Symphony Orchestra / Roy Goodman.**
Hyperion Ⓕ CDA67081/2 (two discs: 145 minutes: DDD: 6/96).   Ⓖ
...Nos. 1 and 2. Estrella de Soria – Overture. **Helsingborg Symphony Orchestra / Okko Kamu.**
Naxos Ⓢ 8 553051 (71 minutes: DDD: 6/96).
...Nos. 3 and 4. Piano Concerto in D major[a]. [a]**Niklas Sivelöv** (pf); **Helsingborg Symphony
Orchestra / Okko Kamu.** Naxos Ⓢ 8 553052 (78 minutes: DDD: 6/96).
...Nos. 1-4. **Gothenburg Symphony Orchestra / Neeme Järvi.**
DG Masters Ⓜ 445 581-2GMA2 (two discs: 112 minutes: DDD: 6/96).

Berwald Piano Quintet No. 1 in C minor[a]. Piano Trio No. 4 in C major[b]. Duo for Violin and Piano
in D major. **Susan Tomes** (pf); **Gaudier Ensemble** (Marieke Blankestijn, [a]Fiona McCapra, vns;
[a]Iris Juda, va; [ab]Christoph Marks, vc). Hyperion Ⓕ CDA66835 (59 minutes: DDD: 6/97).
Recorded 1996.
Although Berwald's chamber music has only a peripheral hold on the repertory outside Sweden, it is
worth getting to know. Berwald keeps the piano busy pretty well all the time throughout the C minor
Piano Quintet and Susan Tomes copes with the demands of the part with great flair and delicacy of
feeling. I can't imagine her playing will be surpassed in its sense of style and finesse. Much the same
must be said of the Gaudier Ensemble who are little short of superb. The Piano Trio No. 4 comes
from 1853 and had to wait until 1896 before a Copenhagen publisher brought it out. It is a refreshing
and delightful piece, to which Marieke Blankestijn, Christoph Marks and Tomes bring an abundant
artistry. The *Duo* in D major is a relatively uninteresting if not downright feeble piece but the
partnership of Blankestijn and Tomes will almost (but maybe not quite) persuade you to the contrary.
At times in both the Trio and Quintet, Blankestijn favours too great a reticence which the microphone
balance enhances. The recording is otherwise very natural in timbre.
Additional recommendation ...
...Piano Quintet. Piano Trios – No. 1 in E flat major; No. 3 in D minor. **Stefan Lindgren** (pf);
Berwald Quartet. Musica Sveciae Ⓕ MSCD521 (68 minutes: DDD: 10/93).

Berwald String Quartets – No. 1 in G minor; No. 2 in A minor; No. 3 in E flat major.
Yggdrasil Quartet (Fredrik Paulsson, Per Oman, vns; Robert Westlund, va; Per Nyström, vc).
BIS Ⓕ CD759 (77 minutes: DDD: 2/97). *Gramophone Editor's choice.*   Ⓖ
Berwald's G minor quartet is highly inventive and assured, full of bold and imaginative modulations.
The trio section of the minuet is almost Schubertian though it is impossible that Berwald could have
known any Schubert. But then so many of the harmonic sleights of hand we find in Schubert or in
the young Arriaga were 'in the air' during the period. The E flat major is one of Berwald's most
original structural inventions: not only is the scherzo sandwiched in the middle of the slow movement
(as was the case with the *Sinfonie singulière*) but that in turn is enfolded into the body of the first
movement. The A minor, too, is a highly inventive and forward-looking piece. The opening theme of
the finale almost looks forward to Nielsen. The Yggdrasil Quartet were formed in 1990 and what a
good quartet they are, absolutely first-rate in every respect, and the most accomplished of the young
Scandinavian quartets to have emerged for a long time. Their readings are thoughtful, with well-
judged tempos; they are musically phrased, full of rhythmic life, and distinguished by a refined tonal
blend. BIS provide good, well-balanced recorded sound.
Additional recommendation ...
...No. 1. **Wikmanson** String Quartet No. 2 in E minor, Op. 1 No. 2. **Chilingirian Quartet.**
CRD Ⓕ CRD3361 (53 minutes: ADD: 3/95).

Berwald Piano Trio No. 2 in F minor[a]. Quartet for Piano and Wind in E flat major[b].
Grand Septet in B flat major[c]. **Gaudier Ensemble** ([bc]Richard Hosford, cl; [bc]Robin O'Neill, bn;
[bc]Jonathan Williams, hn; [ac]Marieke Blankestijn, vn; [c]Iris Juda, va; [ac]Christoph Marks, vc;
[c]Stephen Williams, db; [ab]Susan Tomes, pf). Hyperion Ⓕ CDA66834 (67 minutes: DDD: 8/96).
Recorded 1995. *Gramophone Editor's choice.*   Ⓖ
The Septet is innovative and anticipates the *Sinfonie singulière*, in enfolding the scherzo into the body
of the slow movement, and its invention is delightfully fresh. The Gaudier Ensemble bring elegance
and finesse not only to the Septet but also to its companions. The early E flat Quartet for piano and
wind of 1819 is more conventional in its formal layout and is musically less interesting, but at the same
time there are touches of that intelligence and wit that illumine all Berwald's music and the piece
shines in the Gaudier's hands. The much later F minor Piano Trio of 1851 is more substantial and an
unqualified delight. The writing is full of original touches and rhythmic vitality. Its placid surface is
disturbed by all sorts of characteristic flourishes: in the theme of the slow movement there is one of
those sudden and unexpected modulations for which Berwald's contemporaries were always berating
him. Susan Tomes handles the demanding piano part with exemplary skill and taste. It is all hugely
enjoyable and well recorded too, with very present and finely detailed sound.
Additional recommendations ...
...Grand Septet[a]. Serenade in F major[b]. Quartet for Piano and Wind[c]. [b]**Thomas Annmo** (ten);
[ab]**Mikael Björk** (db); [bc]**Joakim Kallhed** (pf); [ac]members of the **Arion Wind Quintet;**
[ab]members of the **Schein Quartet.** Naxos Ⓢ 8 553714 (61 minutes: DDD: 12/97).

...Grand Septet. **Hummel** Septet in D minor, Op. 74. **Nash Ensemble.**
    CRD Ⓕ CRD3344 (55 minutes: ADD: 6/89).   Ⓖ
...Grand Septet. *Coupled with works by* **Spohr** and **Weber** Melos Ensemble.
    EMI Matrix Ⓜ CDM5 65995-2 (69 minutes: ADD: 12/96).
Further listening ...
...The Queen of Golconda – Overture. Piano Concerto in D major[b]. The Festival of the Bayadères.
    Violin Concerto in C sharp minor, Op. 2[a]. Serious and joyful fancies. [a]**Arve Tellefsen** (vn);
    [b]**Marian Migdal** (pf); **Royal Philharmonic Orchestra / Ulf Björlin.**
    EMI Matrix CDM5 65073-2 (6/94).

Heinrich Biber
Bohemian 1644-1704

Biber Sonatae tam aris quam aulis servientes. **Purcell Quartet** (Catherine Mackintosh,
    Catherine Weiss, vns; Richard Boothby, violone; Robert Woolley, hpd/org);
    Katherine McGillivray, Jane Rogers, Tim Cronin (vas); **Mark Bennett, Michael Laird** (tpts).
    Chandos Chaconne Ⓕ CHAN0591 (67 minutes: DDD: 6/96). Recorded 1995. ✔
    Gramophone Editor's choice.   Ⓖ
The Purcell Quartet are experienced interpreters of Biber, having recorded the composer's complete
Harmonia artificiosa sonatas to deserved plaudits. *Sonatae tam aris* is perhaps a less arcane collection
overall: the violins are tuned normally and the emphasis is on a more pithy ensemble sonata, rather
than a projection of subtle and sophisticated solo effects. Five of the works employ either one or two
trumpets, working typical motifs into an imaginative web of violins and violas, each with lines of true
polyphonic integrity. The Purcell Quartet give these wonderfully striking and noble textures a sense
of space and composure. If the all-string works, like Sonata No. 6, are less deliberately calculated and
theatrical than with the Freiburg consort, then the Purcells certainly communicate a soft warmth
which says much about the simple freshness of these delightful works; the group also provide the
dance-like sections with enough of an uplift to allude to the odd rustic root without, as the
Freiburgers do – very convincingly, revelling in rustic and gipsyish antics. The Purcells take more 'as
read' than the free-spirited Germans. Whilst the virtuosity of the Freiburg group has the listener on
the edge of the seat in the Fourth Soanta, one is drawn to the sheer beauty and intimacy of the
ensemble playing here, enhanced by the impeccable trumpet playing of Mark Bennett and Michael
Laird. If not as cultivated or polished as the Germans, the English group have special things
to say about this music and they display a pure, unadulterated pleasure in Biber's delicious
creations.
Additional recommendations ...
...Sonatae tam aris, quam aulis servientes – No. 1 in C major; No. 4 in C major; No. 6 in
    F major; No. 7 in C major; No. 8 in G major; No. 10 in G minor; No. 12 in C major.
    Coupled with works by **Schmelzer** **Freiburg Baroque Orchestra Consort.**
    Deutsche Harmonia Mundi Ⓕ 05472 77348-2 (74 minutes: DDD: 7/96). ✔
...Sonatae tam aris quam aulis servientes – Nos. 1, 8, 9 and 12. Ballettae a 4 violettae. Battalia a 10
    in D major. Sonata a 7 in D major. Sonata a 6 in B, "Die Pauern Kirchfahrt genannt".
    Vienna Concentus Musicus / Nikolaus Harnoncourt.
    Teldec Das Alte Werk Ⓜ 4509-97914-2 (50 minutes: ADD: 9/96). ✔
...Sonatae tam aris quam aulis servientes – No. 9 (ed. Janetzky). *Coupled with works by various*
    composers. **Timofei Dokshitzer** (tpt); **Moscow Chamber Orchestra / Rudolf Barshai.**
    Melodiya Ⓜ 74321 32045-2 (70 minutes: ADD: 2/97).

Biber Harmonia artificioso – ariosa. **The Rare Fruits Council** (Manfredo Kraemer, vn/va d'amore;
    Pablo Valetti, vn/va/va d'amore; Balázs Máté, vc; Lorenz Duftschmid, violone/va da gamba;
    Mara Galassi, hp; Rolf Lislevand, theorbo/gtr; Alessandro de Marchi, org/hpd).
    Auvidis Astrée Ⓕ E8572 (79 minutes: DDD: 9/96). ✔ Recorded 1995.
The Purcell Quartet were the first to record the pieces and whilst they convey much of Biber's subtle
rhetorical power, they pursue classical decorum and good taste *a priori*, exquisite in the Third Suite
but, in retrospect, a touch delimiting and unadventurous elsewhere. Biber certainly encourages
reflective and poetically shaped playing, but he is also transparently rough-hewn and unpredictable,
delighting in the science of piecemeal contrast and improvisatory freedom of speech – of which he is
undeniably a master. Indeed, at best, Biber mesmerizes his listeners by making his virtuosity count for
more than mere exhibitionism, eliciting his players to construct a cohesive dramatic framework for an
all-action plot. This is where The Rare Fruits Council make an outstanding contribution to the Biber
discography and they are unquestionably in a league of their own, as Partita No. 6 demonstrates,
during movements where *tour de force* kaleidoscopic violin playing becomes the order of the day. But
above all, it is the rich, grainy ensemble and bright-eyed conviction which imposingly cuts swathes
through the Variations of that work, for the most part leaving the competition in the shade.
Tafelmusik become rather less diverting by the minute, but the Purcell Quartet remain a cultivated
force for good when Kraemer and Veletti (the violin/viola d'amore players) force the issue with the
occasional hard-driven movement. All three recordings make for rich pickings but Rare Fruits win by
a short stalk.

Additional recommendations ...
...Harmonia artificiosa – ariosa: diversi modi accordata. **Purcell Quartet / Elizabeth Wallfisch.**
Chandos Chaconne Ⓜ CHAN0575/6 (two discs: 90 minutes: DDD: 11/94). 🎯
...Harmonia artificiosa – ariosa. **Tafelmusik / Jeanne Lamon.**
Sony Classical Vivarte Ⓕ SK58920 (78 minutes: DDD: 5/95). 🎯

Biber 12 Sonatas, "Fidicinium sacro-profanum"[a]. Nisi Dominus[b]. Battalia a 10[c]. Laetatus sum[d].
Balletti lamentabili[e]. Serenada, "Der Nachtwächter"[f]. Passacaglia for Violin[g]. [df]**Peter Harvey,**
[bd]**Richard Wistreich** (basses); **Anna McDonald** ([c]vn/[de]va); [acdef]**Katherine McGillivray,** [ac]**Annette**
Isserlis, [cdf]**Rachel Byrt,** [c]**Pamela Cresswell** (vas); [c]**William Hunt** (violone); [acf]**Purcell Quartet**
([bdg]Catherine Mackintosh, [e]Catherine Weiss, vns; [de]Richard Boothby, violone; [bde]Robert
Woolley, hpd). Chandos Chaconne Ⓕ CHAN0605 (two discs: 119 minutes: DDD: A/97). 🎯
Texts and translations included. Recorded 1996-97.
During the resurgence of interest in Biber's instrumental music, of the five published collections,
Fidicinium sacro-profanum has been rather overlooked. If the virtuosity, for which Biber was justly
acclaimed, plays second fiddle in *Fidicinium* to a *prima inter pares* ensemble ethos, then this is
certainly no reason to dismiss it as humdrum. The arrival at Salzburg of Georg Muffat may well have
enabled Biber to assimilate the effects of a new refinement in part-writing which Muffat demonstrates
so gloriously in his *Armonico Tributo*, also published in the early-1680s, but these 12 sonatas have
their own distinctive rhetorical character, many values of which are prescient of eighteenth-century
chamber music. In the best of the music we can experience the mid-baroque aesthetic of contrast at
its most intensely riveting and well proportioned. The Purcell Quartet do nothing but enhance
Fidicinium's reputation with playing that is delicately nuanced and sensitively voiced; the latter virtue
is especially apposite in Biber's long *chiesa*-like lines which are heard to good effect in the opening
sonata and, even more poignantly handled, in the *Balletti lamentabili*. There is much to be said for
their bright and breezy accounts, especially when guided by Catherine Mackintosh's sweet-toned and
eloquent lead. If some of the imitative passages between violins are not as evenly matched in their
dialogue as one would wish – and this mainly means articulation and intonation – the overriding
impression is of musicians intent on communicating Biber's fresh and buoyant language. Their
accompaniment to the bass voices of Peter Harvey and Richard Wistreich results in a vibrant mixed
ensemble, packed with colour and virtuosity. Harvey is especially impressive in the *Serenada*,
more so than is the comparatively soft-centred singing of Wistreich in *Nisi Dominus*. Also included
in this set is a boldly conceived *Battalia* and the magnificent Passacaglia for solo violin
which concludes Biber's *Mystery Sonatas*, adding to the constantly refreshing eclecticism of this
release.

Biber Eight Sonatas for Violin and Continuo (1681). Sonata violino solo representativa in
A major. Sonata, "La Pastorella". Passacaglia for Solo Lute[a]. Mystery Sonatas – Passacaglia in
G minor[b]. **Romanesca** ([b]Andrew Manze, vn; [a]Nigel North, lte/theorbo; John Toll, hpd/org).
Harmonia Mundi Ⓕ HMU90 7134/5 (two discs: 127 minutes: DDD: 2/95). 🎯 Recorded
1993-94. **Gramophone** *Award Winner 1995.* **Gramophone** *Editor's choice. Selected by Sounds in*
Retrospect.   ❸❸
Whilst the more famous *Mystery Sonatas* have quickly found friends with their touching cameo-
representations of the 15 Mysteries, the 1681 set is still largely unknown amongst players and listeners
alike. Yet what is immediately noticeable from this première recording of the sonatas is that Biber is
not only a legendary virtuoso, probably never bettered in the seventeenth or eighteenth centuries, but
one of the most inventive composers of his age: bold and exciting, certainly but also elusive, mercurial
and mysterious. The majority of the works comprise preludes, arias and variations of an unregulated
nature: improvisatory preludes over naked pedals and lucid arias juxtaposing effortlessly with
eccentric rhetorical conceits are mixed up in an unpredictable phantasm of contrast, and yet at its best
it all adds up to a unified structure of considerable potency. Whatever the philosophical key to Biber's
intangible and unstable world may be, Andrew Manze is the protagonist *par excellence* for music
which requires a notable degree of considered response to complement the adventurous spirit of the
virtuoso. In short, this is masterful playing in which Manze has enough confidence in his subject not
to overcharacterize Biber's volatile temperament. Hence the preludes are often sweet and restrained
and yet often there is also a held-back, almost smouldering quality, which is skilfully pitched against
the free-wheeling energy of the fast music.
Additional recommendations ...
...Sonata violino solo representativa[a]. Mensa sonara. **Cologne Musica Antiqua / Reinhard Goebel**
([a]vn). Archiv Produktion Ⓕ 423 701-2AH (62 minutes: DDD: 11/89). 🎯
...Sonata for Violin and Continuo, "Victori der Christen" (arr. A. Schmelzer). *Coupled with works*
by **Schmelzer** Romanesca. Harmonia Mundi Ⓕ HMU90 7143 (67 minutes: DDD: 10/96). 🎯
See review under Schmelzer, refer to the Index.

Biber Mystery Sonatas. **John Holloway** (vn); **Davitt Moroney** (org/hpd); **Tragicomedia**
(Stephen Stubbs, lte/chitarrone; Erin Headley, va da gamba/lirone; Andrew Lawrence-King,
hp/regal). Virgin Classics Veritas Ⓕ VCD7 59551-2 (two discs: 131 minutes: DDD: 5/91). 🎯
Recorded 1989. **Gramophone** *Award Winner 1991.*   ❸❸

Biber was among the most talented musicians of the late seventeenth century. He was a renowned violinist and his compositions, above all for the violin, are technically advanced and strikingly individual. The 15 *Mystery Sonatas* with their additional *Passacaglia* for unaccompanied violin were written in about 1678 and dedicated to Biber's employer, the Archbishop of Salzburg. Each Sonata is inspired by a section of the Rosary devotion of the Catholic Church which offered a system of meditation on 15 Mysteries from the lives of Jesus and His mother. The music is not, strictly speaking, programmatic though often vividly illustrative of events which took place in the life of Christ. All but two of the 16 pieces require *scordatura* or retuning of the violin strings; in this way Biber not only facilitated some of the fingerings but also achieved sounds otherwise unavailable to him. The Sonatas are disposed into three groups of five: Joyful, Sorrowful and Glorious Mysteries whose contrasting states are affectingly evoked in music ranging from a spirit reflecting South German baroque exuberance to one of profound contemplation. John Holloway plays with imaginative sensibility and he is supported by a first-rate continuo group whose instruments include baroque lute, chitarrone, viola da gamba, a 15-string lirone, double harp and regal.

Additional recommendations ...
...Cologne Musica Antiqua / Reinhard Goebel (vn).
    Archiv Produktion Ⓕ 431 656-2AH2 (two discs: 114 minutes: DDD: 10/91). ✏
...Gabriela Demeterová (vn); Jaroslav Tůma (org). Supraphon Ⓕ SU3155-2 (60 minutes: DDD: 5/97).
...Passacaglia in G minor. *Coupled with works by various composers.* Michelle Makarski (vn).
    ECM New Series Ⓕ 449 957-2 (74 minutes: DDD: 7/97). *See review in the Collections section; refer to the Index.*

Further listening ...
...Missa alleluja. *Coupled with works by various composers.* Vienna Hofburgkapella Schola;
    Concerto Palatino / Konrad Junghänel. Deutsche Harmonia Mundi 05472 77326-2 (7/95). ✏
...Requiem a 15 in A major. Vesperae a 32ᵃ. Els Bongers, Anne Grimm (sops); Kai Wessel, ᵃPeter de
    Groot (altos), ᵃMarcel Reyans, Simon Davies (tens); René Steur (bass); Kees-Jan de Koning (bass);
    Amsterdam Baroque Choir and Orchestra / Ton Koopman. Erato 4509-91725-2 (9/94). ✏   Ⓖ
...Arminio. Soloists; Salzburg Hofmusik / Wolfgang Brunner. CPO CPO999 258-2 (6/95). ✏   Ⓖ

Gilles Binchois

French c1400-1460

Binchois Triste plaisir et douleureuse joie. Amours merchi de restout mon pooir. Je me recommande humblement. En regardant vostre tres doulx maintiens. Se la belle n'a le voloir. Je vous salue. Adieu mes tres belles amours. De plus en plus. Lune tres belles. Les tres doulx yeux. Amoureux suy et me vient toute joye. Adieu, adieu, mon joieulx souvenir. Jamais tant. Adieu, m'amour et ma maistresse. Dueil angoisseus. Pour prison ne pour maladie. Filles à marier.
Ensemble Gilles Binchois / Dominique Vellard (ten). Virgin Classics Veritas Ⓕ VC5 45285-2 (60 minutes: DDD: 6/98). Texts and translations included. Recorded 1996-97.
Binchois's songs have rarely appeared in any quantity on CD, yet the booklet-notes to this timely offering set out an objective case for considering Binchois a more significant song composer than his more famous contemporary, Dufay. If one turns to the music, the reasons for Dufay's greater popularity are equally obvious: Binchois's songs yield their secrets more slowly, and operate within a more limited expressive ambit. They demand repeated listening, whereas Dufay's songs tend to make their impact at first hearing. True, Binchois's surface charm is most beguiling, broken as it is by the occasional disconcerting dissonance or quirk of line; but so too is the sense of extreme stylization. Some characteristic turns of phrase recur between pieces. It is all the more important for recordings of his music to bear repeated listening as well. This one certainly fulfils that requirement, and there is sufficient variety of scoring to sustain interest from song to song. Perhaps the crux of interpreting Binchois is whether to match his fabled restraint in performance, or to coax the songs' expressivity to the surface. Dominique Vellard seems to prefer the former approach, which relies for its effectiveness on the innate vocal qualities of his singers. For the most part, they respond admirably. The special artistry of Lena Susanne Norin, whose increasing involvement in this repertory (as here, in *Adieu, adieu* and especially *Je vous salue*) is a cause for celebration; Anne-Marie Lablaude's contributions (such as *Pour prison*) are lighter in tone, but graceful and supple, yet you do wonder whether a more impassioned delivery of the text might not be appropriate – particularly in *Dueil angoisseus*, surely one of the finest poems set to music in the fifteenth century. And it continues to be puzzling that certain stanzas are shorn of their text to allow for instrumental participation (especially with texts of this quality). For this piece, Gothic Voices' hieratic, supra-personal interpretation is preferable. The Binchois discography makes up in quality for what it lacks in quantity, and notwithstanding these reservations, this disc sits comfortably in a distinguished niche of the repertory.

Additional recommendations ...
...Qui veut mesdire si mesdie. Amoureux suy et me vient toute joye. Adieu mon amoureuse joye.
    Ay douloureux disant helas. Magnificat secundi toni. Se la belle n'a le voloir. *Coupled with works by various composers.* Gothic Voices / Christopher Page. Hyperion Ⓕ CDA66783
    (67 minutes: DDD: 1/96). *See review in the Collections section; refer to the Index.*
...De plus en plus. *Coupled with works by various composers.* The Clerks' Group / Edward Wickham.
    ASV Gaudeamus Ⓕ CDGAU153 (72 minutes: DDD: 1/97).

...Adieu, jusques je vous revoye. Ay douloureux disant helas. *Coupled with works by various composers.* **Alla Francesca.** Opus 111 ℗ OPS30-173 (68 minutes: DDD). *See review in the Collections section; refer to the Index.*

Ronald Binge
British 1910-1979

Suggested listening ...
...Miss Melanie[a]. The Watermill[b]. Elizabethan Serenade[c]. *Coupled with works by various composers.* [a]**Pro Arte Orchestra / George Weldon;** [b]**Light Music Society Orchestra / Sir Vivian Dunn;** [c]**Studio Two Concert Orchestra / Reginald Kilbey.** EMI British Composers CDM5 66537-2 (1/98). *See review in the Collections section; refer to the Index.*

Sir Harrison Birtwistle
British 1934

Birtwistle The Triumph of Time. Gawain's Journey. **Philharmonia Orchestra / Elgar Howarth.** Collins Classics ℗ 1387-2 (55 minutes: DDD: 7/93). Recorded 1993.
Gawain's Journey offers a substantial set of extracts from Birtwistle's opera *Gawain* (vocal lines allotted to instruments) which forms a convincing whole and reinforces the impression that this is one of the weightiest dramatic scores of this or any other age. It has the immediate, unmeditated forcefulness so typical of Birtwistle. It may verge on the unremitting, but there's no mistaking the visceral theatrical power. In no sense is *The Triumph of Time* operatic, but its structure and material (which Birtwistle linked to the Bruegel engraving) is vividly dramatic, the sure-footed skill and economy of its gradual accumulation of tension and density still unsurpassed in Birtwistle's output – this triumphant return to the catalogue of a 1970s masterwork is cause for jubilation.

Birtwistle Pulse Sampler[a].
Holt Banshee[a].
Maxwell Elegy[b]. **Melinda Maxwell** (ob); [b]**Jan Gruithuyzen** (pf); [a]**Richard Benjafield** (perc). NMC (special price) NMCD042S (33 minutes: DDD: 10/97). Recorded 1996.
Music for solo oboe seems naturally to gravitate towards images of snake-charming and witches' sabbaths, something that Simon Holt wittily and scarily acknowledges in *Banshee*. The atmosphere is all the more effective for being conjured up with such fine feeling for the unpredictable and the shapely, and the combination of oboe and percussion (the latter very much an accompaniment, but with not a single note wasted) is explored with unfailing skill and imagination. Birtwistle's *Pulse Sampler* may not have such a strong pictorial dimension, but its accumulating patterns are highly dramatic, as the oboe's rivetingly flexible melody interacts with the stark, unresonant clackings of the claves, at once impersonal and hypnotic. Both these performances are excellent, Melinda Maxwell displaying that phenomenal range of colour and superfine technical control which inspired these composers to write for her. Her own *Elegy* for oboe and piano is less virtuosic, and indeed its principal virtue is an economy which, combined with a clear sense of line and direction, establishes a mood that is all the more effective for its restraint. This well-conceived and excellently recorded programme is an attractive introduction to much that is most appealing in contemporary British music.

Birtwistle The Mask of Orpheus. **Jon Garrison** (ten) Orpheus: Man; **Peter Bronder** (ten) Orpheus: Myth, Hades; **Jean Rigby** (mez) Euridice: Woman; **Anne-Marie Owens** (mez) Euridice: Myth, Persephone; **Alan Opie** (bar) Aristaeus: Man; **Omar Ebrahim** (bar) Aristaeus: Myth, Charon; **Marie Angel** (sop) Aristeus: Oracle of the Dead, Hecate; **Arwel Huw Morgan** (bar) Caller; **Stephen Allen** (ten) Priest, First Judge; **Nicholas Folwell** (bar) Priest, Second Judge; **Stephen Richardson** (bass) Priest, Third Judge; **Juliet Booth** (sop) Woman, First Fury; **Philippa Dames-Longworth** (sop) Woman, Second Fury; **Elizabeth McCormack** (mez) Woman, Third Fury; **Ian Dearden** (sound diffusion); **BBC Singers; BBC Symphony Orchestra / Andrew Davis, Martyn Brabbins.** NMC Ⓜ NMCD050 (three discs: 162 minutes: DDD: 12/97). Notes and text included. Recorded 1996.
Birtwistle's opera is about the Orpheus myth, but the familiar story has been fragmented, several different versions of its main events being presented, sometimes simultaneously, often non-chronologically. Each of the principal characters is represented by two singers and a (silent) dancer, and much of what happens is not directly described in the libretto. Without following the libretto you will not be able to follow all of what is being sung; at times very little (the text is sometimes broken up; some passages, including much of Act 3, are sung in an invented language). Rituals are often at their most powerful when they appeal to the imagination rather than to reason, and here the sense of ritual is awesomely powerful: solemn and often gravely beautiful in Act 1, much tougher and more complex but at the same time hugely exciting in Act 2 and with a formidable, gathering sense of culmination in Act 3. It is an extraordinarily patterned opera, with many varied repetitions, all meticulously labelled ("First Structure of Decision", "Second Time Shift" and so on) in the score. The ritual repetitions, the elaborate patternings and allegorical structures make their own effect. In the boldest of these, the 17 'arches' over which Orpheus passes in his quest for Euridice in Act 2,

Birtwistle aids comprehension by quite extensive use of speech. But the music says far more than the sometimes enigmatic words, and the ceremonial retelling of the whole story in Act 3, would perhaps have less impact if the words of the song verses were comprehensible. Birtwistle communicates his refracted but gripping myth with, above all, orchestral colour: an orchestra of wind, percussion and plucked instruments (plus tape, sampler and a small chorus) used with vivid mastery. The sheer sound of this opera is quite haunting and, not least at the end when the myth dissolves, moving. *The Mask of Orpheus* is a masterpiece, and this performance is fully worthy of it. There are no weak links at all in the extremely fine cast. Although it is unfair to single out any singer for special mention, Jon Garrison's portrayal of Orpheus the Man is outstanding. The recording, direct and pungent but by no means lacking in atmosphere (the electronic tape is pervasive in the right sense: it is the voice of Apollo), leaves nothing to be desired.

Further listening ...

...Antiphonies[a]. Nomos[b]. An Imaginary Landscape[b]. [a]**Joanna MacGregor** (pf); [a]**Netherlands Radio Philharmonic Orchestra / Michael Gielen;** [b]**BBC Symphony Orchestra / Paul Daniel.**
Collins Classics 1414-2 (12/94).

...Earth Dances. **BBC Symphony Orchestra / Peter Eötvös.**
Collins Classics 2001-2 (3/92). *See review in the Collections section; refer to the Index.*   ⓖⓖ

...Melencolia I[a]. Ritual Fragment. Meridian[b]. [b]**Mary King** (mez); [a]**Antony Pay** (cl);
[b]**Michael Thompson** (hn); [b]**Christopher van Kampen** (vc); [a]**Helen Tunstall** (hp);
[b]**London Sinfonietta Voices; London Sinfonietta / Oliver Knussen.** NMC NMCD009 (8/93).

...Secret Theatre. Nenia: the Death of Orpheus[a]. Ritual Fragment. [a]**Rosemary Hardy** (sop);
Musikfabrik NRW / Johannes Kalitzke. CPO CPO999 360-2 (5/96).

...Tragoedia. Five Distances. Three Settings of Celan[a]. Secret Theatre. [a]**Christine Whittlesey** (sop);
Ensemble InterContemporain / Pierre Boulez. DG 439 910-2GH (9/95).

...Gawain. **Soloists; Chorus and Orchestra of the Royal Opera House, Covent Garden /**
Elgar Howarth. Collins Classics 7041-2 (5/96). *Gramophone Editor's choice.*
Selected by Soundings. Gramophone Award Winner 1996.   ⓖ

...Punch and Judy. **Soloists; London Sinfonietta / David Atherton.** Etcetera KTC2014 (12/89).
Gramophone Record Award Winner 1980.

Georges Bizet   French 1838-1875

Bizet Symphony in C major. Overture in A major (ed. d'Almeida). Patrie, Op. 19. La jolie fille de
Perth – Suite. **Montreal Symphony Orchestra / Charles Dutoit.** Decca ⓕ 452 102-2DH
(72 minutes: DDD: 1/97). Recorded 1995.

The early Overture in A minor/major is a rarity of which no other recording currently exists; it is an oddly proportioned work in four sections, the second a sudden brief theatrical storm, the substantial third an expressive Italian *Andante* (which Dutoit shapes most lovingly): it ends in an energetic but more conventional finale. The work was never heard in Bizet's lifetime. The same fate befell his Symphony, written in the same year: in fact, it was not performed until 80 years later. It is hard to resist the delicately exotic *Adagio*, the fresh, vigorous scherzo, or the compelling vivacity of the finale, with its Schubertian key-shifts. One of its themes was to reappear in the sparkling opera buffa *Don Procopio* composed five years later: that in turn furnished the *Serenade* borrowed for *La jolie fille de Perth*, the orchestral suite from which was put together by Bizet's publishers after the composer's death. The title of *Scènes bohémiennes* springs from the fourth movement, which anticipates the gipsy dance in *Carmen*. Splendidly vivid playing throughout, and recording too (at times even too bright).

Additional recommendations ...

...Symphony. Jeux d'enfants – petite suite. **Debussy** Danse sacrée et danse profane.
Vera Badings (hp); **Concertgebouw Orchestra / Bernard Haitink.**
Philips ⓕ 416 437-2PH (50 minutes: ADD: 10/86).

...Symphony[a]. L'Arlésienne – Suite No. 1[b]; Suite No. 2 (arr. Guiraud)[b]. [a]**French Radio National**
Symphony Orchestra, [b]**Royal Philharmonic Orchestra / Sir Thomas Beecham.**
EMI ⓕ CDC7 47794-2* (65 minutes: ADD: 11/87).   ⓖ

...Symphony. *Coupled with works by* **Britten** *and* **Prokofiev** Orpheus Chamber Orchestra.
DG ⓕ 423 624-2GH (64 minutes: DDD: 1/89).

...Symphony. Roma. Patrie, Op. 19. **Toulouse Capitole Orchestra / Michel Plasson.**
EMI ⓕ CDC5 55057-2 (73 minutes: DDD: 5/95).

...L'Arlésienne – Suite No. 1. Carmen – Suite. *Coupled with works by* **Saint-Saëns** Philadelphia
Orchestra / Leopold Stokowski. Biddulph mono Ⓜ WHL012* (72 minutes: ADD: 8/95).

Bizet Carmen. **Julia Migenes** (mez) Carmen; **Plácido Domingo** (ten) Don José; **Faith Esham** (sop)
Micaëla; **Ruggero Raimondi** (bass) Escamillo; **Lilian Watson** (sop) Frasquita; **Susan Daniel** (mez)
Mercédès; **Jean-Philippe Lafont** (bar) Dancairo; **Gérard Garino** (ten) Remendado;
François Le Roux (bar) Moralès; **John Paul Bogart** (bass) Zuniga; **French Radio Chorus;**
French Radio Children's Chorus; French National Orchestra / Lorin Maazel.
Erato ⓕ 2292-45207-2 (three discs: 151 minutes: DDD: 9/85). Notes, text and translation
included. From NUM75113 (3/84).   ⓖⓖⓖ

Bizet Carmen. **Béatrice Uria-Monzon** (mez) Carmen; **Christian Papis** (ten) Don José;
Leontina Vaduva (sop) Micaëla; **Vincent le Texier** (bass-bar) Escamillo; **Maryse Castets** (sop)
Frasquita; **Martine Olmeda** (mez) Mercédès; **Franck Leguérinel** (bar) Dancaïre; **Thierry Trégan**
(ten) Remendado; **Olivier Lallouette** (bass) Moralès; **Lionel Sarrazin** (bass) Zuniga; **Paul Renard**
(spkr) Lillas Pastia; **Bordeaux CNR Children's Choir; Bordeaux Theatre Chorus;**
Bordeaux Aquitaine Orchestra / Alain Lombard. Auvidis Valois Ⓕ V4734
(two discs: 142 minutes: DDD: 10/95). Notes, text and translation included. Recorded 1994.

With some justification, *Carmen* is reckoned to be the world's most popular opera. Its score is
irresistible, its dramatic realism riveting, its sense of *milieu* unerring, though it has to be remembered
that the work was not an immediate triumph. Too many recordings have blown up the work to
proportions beyond its author's intentions but here Maazel adopts a brisk, lightweight approach that
seems to come close to what Bizet wanted. Similarly Julia Migenes approaches the title part in an
immediate, vivid way, exuding the gipsy's allure in a performance that suggests Carmen's fierce temper
and smouldering eroticism, and she develops the character intelligently into the fatalistic person of
the card scene and finale. Her singing isn't conventionally smooth but it is compelling from start to
finish. Plácido Domingo has made the part of Don José very much his own, and here he sings with
unstinting involvement and a good deal of finesse. Ruggero Raimondi is a macho Toreador though
Faith Esham is a somewhat pallid Micaëla.

Any performance has to be considered on its own merits, but since competition on disc is so intense
with a work like *Carmen*, there has to be something special to make it appear high on a list of
recommendations. Having a French singer in the title-role is one of the advantages of the Auvidis set.
Béatrice Uria-Monzon is a full-bodied Mediterranean mezzo: her Carmen is bold and earthy, with
thrilling contralto-like tone for such important moments as the "Tra-la-la" replies to her interrogators
in Act 1. She handles the dialogue with Don José very well, before the Séguidille, in which she
pretends that, like him, she is from Navarre (this is usually cut). This weight of voice rather tells
against her where charm is concerned, with the "Chanson bohème" sounding haughty rather than
festive. The version of *Carmen* used here reverts to spoken dialogue rather than the spurious
recitatives. Leontina Vaduva is a good Micaëla but Christian Papis's Don José isn't really a match for
either of his leading ladies. In "Parle-moi de ma mère" he exhibits an unfortunate beat in the voice
that makes it all sound too tragic – after all he should really just seem nostalgic and quite happy to
be talking to his young visitor, although he can produce effective, soft notes, as at the end of "Là bas,
là bas". One has nothing but sympathy for Carmen's preference for Vincent le Texier's Escamillo
whose performance is the best among the other principals. For a quick summing-up, this is a
well-recorded, authentically French *Carmen*, conducted with flair by Alain Lombard.

Additional recommendations ...

...**Soloists; Les Petits Chanteurs de Versailles; French National Radio Chorus and Orchestra /**
Sir Thomas Beecham. EMI Ⓕ CDS5 56214-2* (three discs: 161 minutes: ADD: 6/88).

...**Soloists; Ambrosian Singers; London Symphony Orchestra / Claudio Abbado.**
DG Ⓜ 427 885-2GX3 (three discs: 157 minutes: ADD: 2/88).   Ⓖ

...**Soloists; Vienna Boys' Choir; Vienna State Opera Chorus; Vienna Philharmonic Orchestra /**
Herbert von Karajan. RCA Ⓜ 74321 39495-2 (three discs: 160 minutes: ADD: 10/88).

...**Soloists; Manhattan Opera Chorus; Metropolitan Opera Children's Chorus and Orchestra /**
Leonard Bernstein. DG Ⓑ 427 440-2GX3 (three discs: 160 minutes: ADD: 9/91).

...**Soloists; René Duclos Choir; Jean Pesneaud Children's Choir; Paris Opera Orchestra /**
Georges Prêtre. EMI Ⓕ CDS5 56281-2 (two discs: 146 minutes: ADD: 5/92).   Ⓖ

...**Soloists; Geneva Grand Theatre Chorus; Suisse Romande Orchestra / Thomas Schippers.**
Decca Double Ⓜ 443 871-2DF2 (two discs: 142 minutes: ADD: 7/95).

...**Soloists; Paris Opéra-Comique Chorus; Paris Opéra-Comique Orchestra / André Cluytens.**
EMI mono Ⓜ CMS5 65318-2* (two discs: 130 minutes: ADD: 9/95).

Bizet Les pêcheurs de perles. **Barbara Hendricks** (sop) Leïla; **John Aler** (ten) Nadir; **Gino Quilico**
(bar) Zurga; **Jean-Philippe Courtis** (bass) Nourabad; **Toulouse Capitole Chorus and Orchestra /**
Michel Plasson. EMI Ⓕ CDS7 49837-2 (two discs: 127 minutes: DDD: 1/90). Notes, text and
translation included. Recorded 1989.

Let a tenor and a baritone signify that they are willing to oblige with a duet, and the cry will go up
for *The Pearl Fishers*. It's highly unlikely that many of the company present will know what the duet
is about – it recalls the past, proclaims eternal friendship and nearly ends up in a quarrel – but the
melody and the sound of two fine voices blending in its harmonies will be quite sufficient. In fact
there is much more to the opera than the duet, or even than the three or four solos which are
sometimes sung in isolation; and the EMI recording goes further than previous versions in giving a
complete account of a score remarkable for its unity as well as for the attractiveness of individual
numbers. It is a lyrical opera, and the voices need to be young and graceful. Barbara Hendricks and
John Aler certainly fulfil those requirements, she with a light, silvery timbre, he with a high tenor
admirably suited to the tessitura of his solos. The third main character, the baritone whose role is
central to the drama, assumes his rightful place here: Gino Quilico brings genuine distinction to the
part, and his aria in Act 3 is one of the highlights. Though Plasson's direction at first is rather square,
the performance grows in responsiveness act by act. It is a pity that the accompanying notes are not
stronger in textual detail, for the full score given here stimulates interest in its history. One of the

changes made in the original score of 1863 concerns the celebrated duet itself, the first version of which is given in an appendix. It ends in a style that one would swear owed much to the 'friendship' duet in Verdi's *Don Carlos* – except that Bizet came first.

Additional recommendations ...

...**Soloists; Paris Opéra Chorus and Orchestra / Georges Prêtre.**
Classics for Pleasure ⑧ CD-CFPD4721 (two discs: 104 minutes: ADD: 10/91).
...**Soloists; Chorus and Orchestra of the Opéra-Comique, Paris / André Cluytens.**
EMI mono Ⓜ CMS5 65266-2* (two discs: 107 minutes: ADD: 9/95).

Further listening ...

...Jeux d'enfants. *Coupled with works by* **Prokofiev** and **Saint-Saëns** **Royal Philharmonic Orchestra / Andrea Licata.** Tring International Royal Philharmonic Collection TRP046 (11/95).
...Jeux d'enfants. *Coupled with works by various composers.* **Paris Conservatoire Orchestra / Jean Martinon.** Decca The Classic Sound Ⓜ 448 571-2DCS (2/96).
...Agnus Dei. *Coupled with works by various composers.* **New College Choir, Oxford / Edward Higginbottom.** Erato 3984-21659-2 (6/98). *Gramophone Editor's choice.*
See review in the Collections section; refer to the Index.
...Chant d'amour. Ouvre ton coeur. Adieux de l'hôtesse arabe. Tarantelle. La Coccinelle. Les filles de Cadix. *Coupled with works by various composers.* **Cecilia Bartoli** (mez); **Myung-Whun Chung** (pf). Decca 452 667-2DH (12/96). *Gramophone Editor's record of the month. See review in the Collections section; refer to the Index.*   ⓖⓖⓖ
...La Coccinelle. Adieux de l'hôtesse arabe. Pastel. Vous ne priez pas. *Coupled with works by various composers.* **Sylvia McNair** (sop); **Roger Vignoles** (pf). Philips 446 656-2PH (5/97).
...Djamileh. **Soloists; Bavarian Radio Chorus; Munich Radio Orchestra / Lamberto Gardelli.**
Orfeo C174881A (4/89).

Boris Blacher

German 1903-1975

Blacher Concertante Musik, Op. 10. Fürstin Tarakanowa – suite, Op. 19a. Two Inventions, Op. 46. Music for Cleveland, Op. 53. Clarinet Concerto[a]. [a]**Dmitri Ashkenazy** (cl); **Deutsches Symphony Orchestra, Berlin / Vladimir Ashkenazy.** Ondine Ⓕ ODE912-2 (55 minutes: DDD: 7/98). Recorded 1997. *Gramophone Editor's choice.*

The chances are that if you had telephoned Boris Blacher, whistled a couple of notes and asked him to make a satisfying piece of music from permutations of them he would have done it. The second (and final) movement of his Clarinet Concerto is a set of variations on a not particularly complex chord. Like much of Blacher's music it is fast, rhythmically alert and light on its feet. His very restricted material leads not to monotony but to fertile fantasy until the music reaches a slower middle section, lyrical and quiet, the soloist almost unaccompanied, in which there is a real sense that every note has meaning, purpose and a reason for being there. This absorbingly planned disc demonstrates how he arrived at that point of masterly economy (the Concerto, written in 1971, counts as a fairly late work). The *Concertante Musik*, from 1937, was his first success, and was once widely played. No wonder: redolent both of neo-classicism and of jazz, it has strong, syncopated rhythm and clean textures; it is catchy and is scored with exuberant brilliance. The Suite from the opera, *Princess Tarakanowa* (premièred, amazingly, in Germany in 1941, when Blacher was a known anti-Nazi and an acknowledged admirer of such 'degenerates' as Stravinsky, Bartók and Berg) adds a rather Shostakovich-like astringency (a strutting, menacing march) and touches of melodic grace and of an appealing expressiveness that was not obvious in the *Concertante Musik*. With the post-war works Blacher's preoccupation with extreme economy, making endlessly resourceful use of brief motifs, is obvious in the rather bony *Two Inventions*, more impressive and more entertaining still in the *Music for Cleveland*, in which a great variety of texture, including a lot of vividly brilliant brass-writing, is drawn from and palindromically retreats to a deliberately un-theme-like 12-note cell. His music is open, even bare in texture, but it is anything but arid. The Clarinet Concerto, in particular, is an entrancingly inventive work by a composer who clearly hated using ten notes when one perfectly placed one would be at least as effective. Both Ashkenazys, father and son, have clearly fallen for this lean, clean and invigorating music: those adjectives would do very well for these performances, which have been no less cleanly recorded.

Further listening ...

...Variations on a theme of Niccolà Paganini, Op. 26. *Coupled with works by* **Elgar** and **Kodály**
Vienna Philharmonic Orchestra / Sir Georg Solti. Decca 452 853-2DH (3/97).

Sir Arthur Bliss

British 1891-1975

Bliss A Colour Symphony. Adam Zero. **English Northern Philharmonia / David Lloyd-Jones.**
Naxos Ⓢ 8 553460 (74 minutes: DDD: 10/96). Recorded 1995. *Gramophone Editor's record of the month. Selected by Soundings.*   ⓖⓖ

David Lloyd-Jones's exciting and idiomatic account of *A Colour Symphony* proves easily more than a match for all current competition, including the composer's own 1955 recording so spectacularly transferred by Dutton Laboratories. Speeds are judged to perfection – nicely flowing for the first and third movements, not too hectic for the flashing scherzo – and countless details in Bliss's stunning orchestral canvas are most deftly attended to. Phrasing is sensitive and ideally affectionate, solo work is consistently excellent (the slow movement's delicate woodwind arabesques are exquisitely voiced), and tuttis open out superbly in what is technically the finest recording to date from Naxos (magnificently keen-voiced horns throughout). Whereas *A Colour Symphony* was inspired by the heraldic associations of four different colours (one for each movement), the theme of *Adam Zero* is the inexorable life-cycle of humankind. In its entirety, this 1946 ballet score does admittedly have its occasional *longueurs*, but for the most part Bliss's invention is of commendably high quality. Certainly, the vivid exuberance and theatrical swagger of numbers like "Dance of Spring" and "Dance of Summer" have strong appeal. Equally, the limpid beauty of both the "Love Dance" and the hieratic "Bridal Ceremony" which immediately ensues is not easily banished, while the darkly insistent "Dance with Death" distils a gentle poignancy which is most haunting.

Additional recommendations ...
...A Colour Symphony. Checkmate – Suite. **Ulster Orchestra / Vernon Handley.**
Chandos Ⓕ CHAN8503 (56 minutes: DDD: 4/87).
...A Colour Symphony[a]. Introduction and Allegro[a]. Things to come – Suite[b]; excerpts[c]. Men of
Two Worlds – Baraza[d]. [d]**Eileen Joyce** (pf); [abc]**London Symphony Orchestra / Sir Arthur Bliss;**
[d]**National Symphony Orchestra / Muir Mathieson.**
Dutton Laboratories [acd]mono/[b]stereo Ⓑ CDLXT2501* (77 minutes: ADD: 8/95).

Bliss Clarinet Quintet, T50.
Rawsthorne Clarinet Quartet[a].
Routh Clarinet Quintet. **Nicholas Cox** (cl); **Nicholas Ward,** [ac]**Peter Pople** (vns);
Ivo-Jan van der Werff (va); **Paul Marleyn** (vc). Redcliffe Recordings Ⓕ RR010
(63 minutes: DDD: 11/96). Recorded 1995.
In this release two clarinet works – a quartet by Rawsthorne and a quintet by Routh – receive first recordings, whilst the Clarinet Quintet by Arthur Bliss joins just one other version in the catalogue. Quite why the Bliss Quintet should have received only two recordings in recent years is a mystery, as the quality of this lovely, rhapsodic work is extremely high indeed. The intricately spun melodies of the first movement are here beautifully rendered by Nicholas Cox and his colleagues, and the elegiac slow movement is most movingly delivered too. Alan Rawsthorne's astringent Clarinet Quartet of 1946 is very fine, and a worthwhile discovery also. Although it displays a clear debt to Viennese serialism its lyrical qualities are exceptionally strong and it is by no means an unapproachable piece. Francis Routh's five-movement Clarinet Quintet was composed in 1994, but in a stylistic sense could easily be contemporary with, or even earlier than, the Rawsthorne. Nevertheless, it is a pleasant and finely crafted work which here receives a spirited reading from its dedicatee, Nicholas Cox. The recorded sound is very natural indeed.

Further listening ...
...Cello Concerto[a]. The Enchantress[b]. Hymn to Apollo. [b]**Linda Finnie** (mez); [a]**Raphael Wallfisch**
(vc); **Ulster Orchestra / Vernon Handley.** Chandos CHAN8818 (7/91).
...Music for Strings. Pastoral: Lie Strewn the White Flocks[a]. [a]**Della Jones** (mez);
[a]**Sinfonia Chorus; Northern Sinfonia / Richard Hickox.** Chandos CHAN8886 (7/91).
...Music for Strings. Cello Concerto, T120[a]. Two Studies, T16. [a]**Tim Hugh** (vc);
English Northern Philharmonia / David Lloyd-Jones. Naxos 8 553383 (1/97).
Gramophone Editor's choice.   Ⓖ
...Music for Strings. *Coupled with works by* **Vaughan Williams** and **Smyth**
BBC Symphony Orchestra / Sir Adrian Boult. Dutton Laboratories mono CDAX8016* (1/97).
...Piano Concerto, Op. 58[a]. March, Op. 99, "Homage to a Great Man".
[a]**Philip Fowke** (pf); **Royal Liverpool Philharmonic Orchestra / David Atherton.**
Unicorn-Kanchana Souvenir UKCD2029 (8/90).
...Oboe Quintet, T44. *Coupled with works by* **Bax** and **Britten Gordon Hunt** (ob); **Tale Quartet.**
BIS CD763 (10/97).
...String Quartets – No. 1 in B flat major; No. 2. **Delmé Quartet.** Hyperion CDA66178 (11/89).
...Checkmate – Suite. *Coupled with works by* **Lambert** and **Walton English Northern Philharmonia**
/ David Lloyd-Jones. Hyperion CDA66436 (3/91). *Selected by Sounds in Retrospect.*   ⒼⒼ
...Morning Heroes[a]. Investiture Antiphonal Fanfares[b]. Prayer of St Francis of Assisi[c].
[a]**Brian Blessed** (narr); [ac]**East London Chorus;** [a]**Harlow Chorus;** [a]**East Hertfordshire Chorus;**
[ab]**London Philharmonic Orchestra / Michael Kibblewhite.** Cala CACD1010 (2/93).

Marc Blitzstein   American 1905-1964

Suggested listening ...
...Juno – I wish it so. No for an Answer – In the clear. Reuben, Reuben – Never get lost.
Coupled with works by various composers. **Dawn Upshaw** (sop); **orchestra / Eric Stern.**
Elektra Nonesuch 7559-79345-2 (12/94). *Gramophone Award Winner 1995. See review
in the Collections section; refer to the Index.*   ⒼⒼ

Ernest Bloch
Swiss/American 1880-1959

Bloch America[a]. Concerto grosso No. 1[b]. **Patricia Michaelian** (pf); [a]**Seattle Symphony Chorale and Orchestra / Gerard Schwarz.** Delos Ⓕ DE3135 (61 minutes: DDD: 8/94). Text included. Recorded 1993.   Ⓖ

Ernest Bloch's "Epic Rhapsody for Orchestra", *America,* is a warming musical flight across the history of the United States, and uses the anthem of the same name as a leitmotif that helps bind English, American Indian and Jewish-style themes into a homogeneous and hugely accessible whole. There are three variegated movements, each a dramatic tone-poem reflecting such universal ideas as "Struggle and Hardships" or "Hours of Joy – Hours of Sorrow" (the second movement's subtitle), with the third visiting the world of jazz and culminating in a full-throated choral celebration of the anthem itself. However, Bloch's 'programme' is fairly specific. *America* might be best described as a great film score that never was, a highly emotive thanksgiving from a man who had himself only recently arrived in his new home, with tender references to such perennial favourites as *John Brown's Body* and *Dixie*. There are also veiled references to other of Bloch's works, including *Schelomo* and the delightful *Concerto grosso* that Gerard Schwarz programmes as *America*'s coupling. Demonstration standard sound.

Additional recommendations ...

...Concerto grosso. *Coupled with works by various composers.* **Irit Rob** (pf); **Israel Chamber Orchestra / Yoav Talmi.** Chandos Ⓕ CHAN8593 (62 minutes: DDD: 8/88).

...Concerti grossi Nos. 1 and 2. **Q. Porter** Ukrainian Suite. **San Diego Chamber Orchestra / Donald Barra.** Koch International Classics Ⓕ 37196-2 (52 minutes: DDD: 12/94).

Bloch Symphony in C sharp minor. Schelomo[a]. [a]**Torleif Thedéen** (vc); **Malmö Symphony Orchestra / Lev Markiz.** BIS Ⓕ CD576 (78 minutes: DDD: 5/93). Recorded 1990-92. *Gramophone Editor's choice.*

Bloch's early symphony is an endearing and at times impressive showcase for a young composer (he was 23) endowed by nature and nurture with all the gifts save individuality (though there are hints in the later movements that that too is on the way). He can write impressively strong, expansive melodies, develop them with real ingenuity and build them into monumental climaxes. Climax-building, indeed, is what young Bloch seems most interested in at this stage of his career, that and a love for all the rich contrasts of colour and texture that a big orchestra, imaginatively used, can provide. He is so very good at his craft, so adept at pulling out still more stops when you thought there could hardly be any left, so sheerly and likeably clever that one is scarcely ever made impatient by the occasional feeling that this or that movement could have ended two or three minutes earlier. It's a pleasure, too, to listen for fulfilled echoes of that youthful exuberance in the mature 'biblical rhapsody' *Schelomo*. Just as Lev Markiz adroitly avoids any impression of overpadded grossness in the symphony, so he and his fine soloist find more than richly embroidered oriental voluptuousness in this portrait of King Solomon; there is gravity and even poignancy to the music as well, and Thedéen's subtle variety of tone colour gives the work shadow and delicacy as well as richness. The recording is excellent.

Additional recommendations ...

...Schelomo. **Georges Miquelle** (vc); **Eastman Rochester Orchestra / Howard Hanson.** Mercury Ⓜ 432 718-2MM (63 minutes: ADD: 11/91).

...Schelomo[a]. **R. Strauss** Don Quixote, Op. 35[b]. **Emanuel Feuermann** (vc); **Philadelphia Orchestra / ** [a]**Leonard Stokowski,** [b]**Eugene Ormandy.** Biddulph mono Ⓜ LAB042* (58 minutes: ADD: 12/91).

...Schelomo. *Coupled with works by* **S. Albert** and **Bartók** Yo-Yo Ma (vc/); **Baltimore Symphony Orchestra / David Zinman.** Sony Classical Ⓕ SK57961 (78 minutes: DDD: 3/95).   Ⓖ

Further listening ...

...Three Jewish Poems. Two Last Poems ... (Maybe ...)[a]. Evocations. [a]**Alexa Still** (fl); **New Zealand Symphony Orchestra / James Sedares.** Koch International Classics 37232-2 (9/94).

...Symphony in E flat. Three Jewish Poems. In Memoriam. Macbeth – Interludes, Acts 1 and 3. **Royal Philharmonic Orchestra / Dalia Atlas Sternberg.** ASV CDDCA1019 (3/98).

...Violin Concerto. Baal Shem. *Coupled with* **Serebrier** Momento psicológico. Poema elegíaca. **Michael Guttman** (vn); **Royal Philharmonic Orchestra / José Serebrier.** ASV CDDCA785 (5/92).

...Piano Quintets Nos. 1 and 2. **American Chamber Players.** Koch International Classics 37041-2.

...Baal Shem. *Coupled with works by various composers.* **Joseph Szigeti** (vn); **Andor Foldes** (pf). Biddulph mono LAB070/71* (7/94). *See review in the Collections section; refer to the Index.*   ⒼⒼ

...Baal Shem. *Coupled with works by* **Barber** and **Walton** Joshua Bell (vn); **Baltimore Symphony Orchestra / David Zinman.** Decca 452 851-2DH (7/97). *Gramophone Editor's choice. See review under Barber, refer to the Index.*

John Blow
British 1649-1708

Blow God spake sometime in visions. How doth the city sit solitary. The Lord is my shepherd. God is our hope and strength. I beheld and lo! a great multitude. Turn thee unto me, O Lord. Blessed is the man. Lift up your heads. O Lord I have sinned. O give thanks unto the Lord. O Lord, thou hast searched me out. Cry aloud and spare not. Lord, who shall dwell in thy tabernacle. I said in the cutting off of my days. **Robin Blaze** (alto); **Joseph Cornwell, William Kendall** (tens);

Stephen Varcoe, Stephen Alder (bars); **Winchester Cathedral Choir / David Hill;**
The Parley of Instruments / Peter Holman. Hyperion Ⓟ CDA67031/2 (two discs: 116 minutes:
DDD: 3/96). ✐ Texts included. Recorded 1995.

In choosing a range of Blow's best and most representative anthems, Peter Holman and David Hill
have had quite a task on their hands: Blow was even more prolific than Purcell in this domain. They
have sensibly cast their critical eyes over those works written in the 'golden' age of Charles II, several
of whose reputations go before them. The dignity and sobriety of the fine coronation anthem *God
spake sometime in visions* is a joy to behold and it is given a grand and spacious reading here. David
Hill, ever the choral director to sustain and shape a line, is peerless in the opening paragraph. Here,
as in other distinguished works like *I beheld and lo!*, the success of these performances is determined
by deft recognition of the structural strengths and solecisms of Blow's music. As with a number of
Purcell's symphony anthems, Blow cannot always find the exit and needs a helping hand to get back
on track. Hill has a breezy approach in such circumstances which serves him well, as in the overlong,
if imaginative *O give thanks unto the Lord*. He is helped too by a pleasing integration between soloists,
choir and instruments – caused as much by the sensitivity of soloists as adept recording – which
ensures that occasional formal disparity does not find an ally in the textural isolation of 'groups' from
one another.

Blow's particular attraction is the disarming tunefulness of *The Lord is my shepherd* in the tradition
of airiness which Pelham Humfrey had introduced to the chapel following his French sojourn, and
touchingly performed by excellent soloists (even if the work does rather tail off towards the end). So,
too, the idiomatic simplicity of expression of *Turn thee unto me*, where the fine treble soloist is
complemented by a cathedral choir whose feel for the work's gentle and intimate contours has a
resigned elegance. In a similar vein is the tormented *O Lord I have sinned*, a work which has a
distinctive Purcellian flavour with its chromatic inflexions and unpredictable contrapuntal movement.
Yet it fails to plumb the depths as in the similar type of piece which became something of a Purcell
speciality. Indeed, for all Blow's quality there are several works here that just miss the mark despite
their distinctive place in English Restoration musical life. Whether or not such a state of affairs
warrants two discs is arguable, but there is no doubt that this is an important addition to Hyperion's
English Orpheus series.

Blow Venus and Adonis. **Catherine Bott** (sop) Venus; **Michael George** (bass) Adonis;
Libby Crabtree (sop) Cupid; **Julia Gooding** (sop) Shepherdess, First Grace; **Andrew King** (ten)
First Shepherd; **Simon Grant** (bass) Second Shepherd, Third Huntsman, Third Grace;
Christopher Robson (alto) Third Shepherd, First Huntsman, Second Grace; **Paul Agnew** (ten)
Second Huntsman; **Westminster Abbey School Choristers; New London Consort / Philip Pickett.**
L'Oiseau-Lyre Ⓟ 440 220-2OH (57 minutes: DDD: 7/94). ✐ Notes and text included.
Recorded 1992. *Gramophone Editor's choice.* Ⓖ

This recording reveals Blow's opera (and lamentably one of only two real 'all-sung' dramas to emerge
from England in the Restoration period), to be a work of rare quality and pathos with Philip Pickett
at his most luminous. Whilst Charles Medlam and London Baroque take a robust and homespun view
of the Overture, Pickett has his listener mentally prepared from the outset for the opera's solemn
denouement. The noble and eloquent opening (with some minor ensemble infelicities) sets the scene
in more ways than one since Pickett is not content to see the Prologue's traditional machinations
undermine the cultivated expression he believes this work merits. Consequently, the introduction of
Venus and Adonis emerges sumptuously from Blow's skilful preparations, notably in the beautifully
sung chorus refrain "In these sweet groves" and an ethereal Act Tune of three recorders which delivers
the doomed lovers to their first intimate exchanges. Catherine Bott is the most telling and sensual
Venus imaginable, her singing always captivating in its tonal variety and emotional nuance. Her
relationship with Adonis is never mannered but tense and simmering, and in its chilling realism allows
the listener to experience the brutal psychology of an anonymous adaptation. (Story line: Venus
insists that Adonis goes hunting and the former suffers incessant grief when he meets his match with
an Aedalian boar.) Michael George, as Adonis, plays his part thoughtfully in the striking immediacy
of the tragedy, elegantly shaping his lines with a prescient tinge of melancholy before he is led in
wounded at the start of Act 3.

Additional recommendation ...
...**Soloists; Chorus; London Baroque / Charles Medlam.**
Harmonia Mundi Musique d'abord Ⓑ HMA190 1276 (50 minutes: DDD: 9/88). ✐

Further listening ...
...Awake, my lyre. Salvator mundi. Stay, gentle Echo. Poor Celadon, he sighs in vain. St Cecilia's
Day Ode, "Begin the song" – Music's the cordial of a troubled heart. Go, perjur'd man. Help,
Father Abraham. Chloe found Amintas. Whilst on Septimnius's panting breast. Gloria patri, qui
creavit nos. Paratum cor meum. Sing ye Muses. Sonata in A[a]. Ground in G minor[a]. **Red Byrd;**
[a]**The Parley of Instruments.** Hyperion CDA66658 (1/94). ✐
...No more the dear, lovely nymph's no more. The Self-banished. Lovely Selina, innocent and free.
O turn not those fine eyes away. Fairest work of happy nature. Flavia grown old. O that mine
eyes would melt into a flood. O mighty God, who sit'st on high. Sabina has a thousand charms.
O all the torments, all the cares. The Queen's Epicedium, "No, Lesbia, no, you ask in vain".
A Choice Collection of Lessons[a]: Suite No. 1 in D minor; Suite No. 3 in A minor. Prelude in

G major[a]. Morlake Ground[a]. Grounds: G minor[a]; C major[b]. Voluntary in G minor[c].
John Mark Ainsley (ten); **Paula Chateauneuf** (theorbo/gtr); **Timothy Roberts** ([a]spinet/[b]hpd/[c]org).
Hyperion CDA66646 (10/93). *Gramophone Editor's choice.*

Luigi Boccherini
Italian 1743-1805

Boccherini Cello Concertos[a] – No. 3 in D major, G476; No. 7 in G major, G480; No. 9 in B flat
major, G482. Concert aria – Se d'un amor tiranno, G557[b]. [b]**Marta Almajano** (sop); **Limoges
Baroque Ensemble / Christophe Coin** (vc). Auvidis Astrée Ⓔ E8517 (62 minutes: DDD: 4/94). *
Recorded 1993.

Christophe Coin throws off in the deftest fashion the typical Boccherinian filigree figuration, the little
ornamental flourishes perfectly placed and timed, the numerous stratospheric excursions above the
treble stave sweet-toned and delicate. And with it he shows a command of Boccherini's style,
affectionately graceful, sometimes with a faintly quizzical air. The tone of Coin's instrument is light
and translucent, and with this small orchestra the sound in the solos, which are anyway lightly
accompanied, is particularly sweet: in the first movement of G482 (the concerto known from the
Grützmacher version) the unassuming handling of the virtuoso writing has a special kind of charm
and the rather grander manner called for in the D major work G476 is also very happily caught, not
without a hint of the romantic at times, for Coin is no austere stylist. The aria that completes his disc
is a large-scale duet for cello, in its full concerto manner, and soprano; the lines are full of eloquent
appoggiaturas and there is some beguiling duetting for the voice and the instrument. Marta Almajano
has a big, clear top register and plenty of drama to her singing.

Additional recommendations ...
...Nos. 4 and 6-8. **Anner Bylsma** (vc); **Concerto Amsterdam / Jaap Schröder.**
Teldec Das Alte Werk Ⓜ 9031-77624-2 (61 minutes: ADD: 7/93). *
...No. 9. *Coupled with works by various composers.* **János Starker** (vc); **Philharmonia Orchestra /
Carlo Maria Giulini, Walter Susskind.** EMI mono/stereo Ⓜ CZS5 68485-2*
(six discs: 398 minutes: ADD: 12/95). *See review in the Collections section; refer to the Index.*
...No. 9 (arr. Grützmacher). *Coupled with works by various composers.* **Pablo Casals** (vc); **London
Symphony Orchestra / Sir Landon Ronald.** Biddulph mono Ⓜ LAB144 (79 minutes: ADD: 1/98).
See review under Elgar; refer to the Index.

Boccherini Symphonies, Op. 37 – No. 1 in C major, G515; No. 3 in D minor, G517; No. 4 in
A major, G518. **Academia Montis Regalis / Luigi Mangiocavallo.** Opus 111 Ⓕ OPS30-168
(55 minutes: DDD: 9/97). * Recorded 1996. *Gramophone Editor's choice.*   Ⓖ
"Sinfonie a grande orchestra", says Boccherini's own catalogue, in description of his Op. 37, a set of
four symphonies written in 1786-7 (only the three recorded here survive). Here they are played by a
rather *piccola* orchestra yet the performance is brilliant and effective, with its very light and
translucent textures conveying the detail with remarkable clarity. All the music sparkles with life –
specially effective movements are the finale of the C major, with its curiously fragmented textures, and
the *Andante* of the A major, one of Boccherini's loveliest orchestral slow movements, with the gentle
and graceful melancholy of its oboe theme. There are attractive minuets here too – listen to the
exquisitely played bassoon solo in the Trio of the D minor work or the oddly ambiguous rhythms in
the C major. The conductor paces the music well and brings plenty of spirit and vivacity to the quick
movements. In general this is an outstanding disc.

Additional recommendation ...
...Nos. 1, 3 and 4. Symphony in D major, G520 (Op. 42). **London Festival Orchestra / Ross Pople.**
Hyperion Ⓕ CDA66904 (72 minutes: DDD: 4/97).

Boccherini Symphonies – No. 4 in D minor, G506 (Op. 12), "La casa del diavolo"; No. 4 in
F major, G512 (Op. 12); C minor, G519 (Op. 41). **Academy of Ancient Music / Christopher
Hogwood.** L'Oiseau-Lyre Ⓕ 436 993-2OH (58 minutes: DDD: 2/95). * Recorded 1992.
In this issue the incisive edge of the orchestra's period instruments offers a vivid expression of the
music's dramatic content. In *La casa del diavolo*, for example, the AAM match the radiance of the
German Academy in the opening *Allegro* and gentle pathos in the second movement, but crisper,
clearer textures in the finale create a more chilling representation of the music's diabolical character.
The AAM's stylish response to Boccherini's imaginative rhythms and inventively varied textures is
delightfully apparent in the F major Symphony, where the finale's sudden diversion into a minuet is
deftly handled. The four-movement C minor Symphony is the most expansive and truly 'symphonic'
of the three works recorded here. The AAM's taut control of the opening movement's dialogue
between various instrumental groupings, the engagingly pastoral tone in the *Lentarello*, the suitably
rustic minuet and trio and astonishing brilliance in the tarantella-like finale, produce a genuinely
compelling result. These fresh, vigorous accounts are attractively presented in resonant recorded
sound.

Additional recommendation ...
...Symphonies, Volumes 3-6. **German Chamber Academy, Neuss / Johannes Goritzki.**
CPO Ⓕ CPO999 173/6-2 (four discs, oas: 55, 61, 49 and 52 minutes: DDD: 1/94).

CPO999 173-2 – Op. 12: No. 4 in D minor, G506; No. 5 in B flat major, G507; No. 6 in A major, G508. *CPO999 174-2* – Op. 21: No. 1 in B flat major, G493; No. 2 in E flat major, G494; No. 3 in C major, G495; No. 4 in D major, G496; No. 5 in B flat major, G497. *CPO999 175-2* – Op. 21: No. 6 in A major, G498. Op. 35: No. 1 in D major, G509; No. 2 in E flat major, G510; No. 3 in A major, G511. *CPO999 176-2* – Op. 35: No. 4 in F major, G512; No. 5 in E flat major, G513; No. 6 in B flat major, G514. Op. 37: No. 1 in C major, G515.

Boccherini String Quintets, Op. 11 – No. 4 in F minor, G274; No. 5 in E major, G275; No. 6 in D major, G276. **Smithsonian Chamber Players** (Marilyn MacDonald, Jorie Garrigue, vns; Anthony Martin, va; Anner Bylsma, Kenneth Slowik, vcs). Deutsche Harmonia Mundi
Ⓕ RD77159 (67 minutes: DDD: 4/92). ✔ Recorded 1988.   Ⓖ
Boccherini was a virtuoso cellist and often played together with a family string quartet in Madrid and the experience was obviously a very pleasant one, for he wrote 100 quintets for two violins, viola and two cellos. He was never at a loss for ideas: the quintets are richly varied in form and texture, the latter enhanced by Boccherini's intimate knowledge of the techniques and sound-qualities of the bowed-string instruments. Many of us know the famous Minuet – but how many are familiar with the work from which it comes? The Quintet in E, the fifth of the six Quintets of his Op. 11 (1775), of which it is the third movement, is one of those in this recording. The bucolic Quintet in D, *dello l'ucceleria*, ("The aviary") is a cyclic work with bird-song, shepherd's pipes and hunting sounds. If Boccherini was, as Giuseppe Pupo described him, "the wife of Haydn", his music has the charm, grace and poise of the best wives, and there is nothing wrong with that! The Smithsonian Players play like good Italians, which none of them is, and are superbly recorded in this irresistibly attractive album. They all use Stradivarius instruments, producing clear sounds and textures such as may have been heard in Boccherini's time.
Additional recommendation ...
...No. 5. **Schubert** String Quintet in C major, D956.
Isaac Stern, Cho-Liang Lin (vns); **Jaime Laredo** (va); **Yo-Yo Ma, Sharon Robinson** (vcs).
Sony Classical Ⓕ SK53983 (76 minutes: DDD: A/97).

Boccherini Cello Sonatas – No. 2 in C minor, G2*b*[b]; No. 4 in A major, G4[a]; No. 10 in E flat major, G10[a]; No. 17 in C major, G17[a]; No. 23 in B flat major, G565[b]. **Richard Lester** (vc); [a]**David Watkin** (vc continuo); [b]**Chi-Chi Nwanoku** (db). Hyperion Ⓕ CDA66719 (67 minutes: DDD: 1/96). Richard Lester's slightly impetuous playing of these sonatas seems to capture very happily their character: their somewhat wayward invention, their sense of being formalized versions of a cellist's improvisations. The momentary hesitancies hint at the player-composer who is deciding as he goes which of the ideas in his mind to try out next. Yet beneath it is a strong rhythm and a very sure compositional technique. The music is very high lying: the cellist has prolonged spells in high thumb positions with quite rapid passagework, and these Lester executes with great brilliance and crispness – there is just one passage, in the finale of the C major work, where accuracy of intonation momentarily eludes him, but otherwise one cannot imagine playing of greater exactitude. The opening movement of that sonata is a particularly fine piece, with its pensive moments and its sudden flights of fancy; there is an eloquent central *Largo* and a dashing, witty finale. The E flat work has jaunty syncopations, the A major a first movement of particular brilliance and again there is an intensely expressive slow movement. The final sonata here is the B flat work that was evidently the model for the outer movements of the famous Boccherini-Grützmacher Concerto – it sounds vastly better without the late-romantic harmonizations of the concerto version and with the curious array of tempo changes in the finale that Grützmacher ironed out. Lester's bowing is vigorous, his tone warm and sharply defined with very little vibrato. Usually these sonatas are accompanied by a keyboard but here the practice, undoubtedly very common in Boccherini's day, of using another string instrument is preferred. In two sonatas a double-bass is used: the effect is a bit gruff, with something of a chasm between top and bottom when the cello is in its upper reaches. The two cellos are much more persuasive, especially when the second is as supportively played as it is here.
Additional recommendation ...
...No. 2[a]; No. 8 in B flat major, G8[b]; No. 9 in F major, G9[c]; No. 9 in G major, G15[e]; No. 10[d].
Six Fugues, G73 – No. 2 in F major; No. 3 in B flat major; No. 5 in A major[f].
Anner Bylsma, [abdef]**Kenneth Slowik** (vcs); [bce]**Bob van Asperen** (fp).
Sony Classical Vivarte Ⓕ SK53362 (77 minutes: DDD: 3/94). ✔
Further listening ...
...Boccherini Edition, Volumes 1-5. **Soloists; Petersen Quartet; New Berlin Chamber Orchestra / Michael Erxleben** (vn). Capriccio (5/93) available as follows: *Volume 1 – 10 450:* String Sextets, Op. 23 – No. 1 in E flat major, G454; No. 3 in E major, G456; No. 4 in F minor, G457; No. 6 in F major, G459. *Volume 2 – 10 456:* Sextets (Divertimentos), Op. 16 – No. 1 in D major, G461; No. 4 in E flat major, G464; No. 5 in A major, G465; No. 6 in C major, G466. *Volume 3 – 10 457:* Symphonies, Op. 37 – No. 1 in C major, G515; No. 3 in D minor, G517; No. 4 in A major, G518. *Volume 4 – 10 458:* Symphonies – C minor, Op. 41, G519; D major, Op. 42, G520; D major, Op. 43, G521; D minor, Op. 45, G522. *Volume 5 – 10 451:* String Quartets – D major, Op. 15 No. 1, G177; G minor, Op. 24 No. 6, G194; A major, Op. 39, G213; F major, Op. 64 No. 1, G248.

...Oboe Quintets – No. 1 in G major. No. 2 in F major. No. 3 in D major. No. 4 in A major. No. 5
in E flat major. No. 6 in D minor. **Lajos Lencsés** (ob); **Parisii Quarte.** Capriccio 10 454 (4/94).
...Piano Quintets, Op. 56 – No. 1 in E minor, G407; No. 2 in F major, G408; No. 5 in D major,
G411. **Patrick Cohen** (fp); **Quatuor Mosaïques.** Auvidis Astrée E8518 (4/94). ✐   ⓖ
...Piano Quintets, Op. 56 – No. 4 in E flat major, G410; No. 6 in A minor, G412; Op. 57 – No. 3 in
E minor, G415; No. 6 in C major, G418. **Les Adieux.**
Deutsche Harmonia Mundi Baroque Esprit 05472 77448-2 (4/97). ✐
...Piano Quintets, Op. 57 – No. 2 in B flat major, G414; No. 3 in E minor, G415; No. 6 in C major,
G418. **Patrick Cohen** (fp); **Quatuor Mosaïques.** Auvidis Astrée E8721 (12/92). ✐
...String Quartets, G201-6 (Op. 32) – No. 1 in E flat major; No. 2 in E minor; No. 3 in D major;
No. 4 in C major; No. 5 in G minor; No. 6 in A major. **Esterházy Quartet.**
Teldec Das Alte Werk 4509-95988-2 (10/95). *Gramophone Editor's choice.*
...String Quintets, G337-339. String Quartet No. 4 in G major, Op. 44, "La Tiranna".
Ensemble 415. Harmonia Mundi Suite HMT790 1334 (12/96). ✐
...String Sextets, Op. 23 – No. 1 in E flat major, G454; No. 2 in B flat major, G455; No. 5 in
D major, G458. **Ensemble 415.** Harmonia Mundi HMC90 1478 (6/94). ✐
...Stabat mater, G532 (1781 version)[a]. String Quintet in C minor, G328 (Op. 31 No. 4).
[a]**Agnès Mellon** (sop); **Ensemble 415.** Harmonia Mundi HMC90 1378 (9/92). ✐

Jack Body   New Zealand 1944

Suggested listening ...
...Long-Ge. *Coupled with works by various composers.* **Kronos Quartet.** Nonesuch 7559-79457-2
(12/97). *Gramophone Editor's choice. See review in the Collections section; refer to the Index.*

Léon Boëllmann   French 1862-1897

Suggested listening ...
...Suite gothique, Op. 25. *Coupled with works by various composers.* **Simon Lindley** (org).
Naxos 8 550581 (3/93). *See review in the Collections section; refer to the Index.*

Georg Böhm   German 1661-1733

Suggested listening ...
...Vater unser im Himmelreich, WK ii 138. *Coupled with works by various composers.* **Peter King**
(org). Priory PRCD618. *See review in the Collections section; refer to the Index.*

Joseph Bodin de Boismortier   French 1689-1755

Boismortier Six Concertos, Op. 15 – No. 1 in G major; No. 2 in A minor; No. 3 in D major;
No. 4 in B minor; No. 5 in A major; No. 6 in E minor. **Soloists of Le Concert Spirituel**
(Jocelyn Daubigney, Anne Savignat, Jan de Winne, Vincent Touzet, Jacques-Antoine Bresch, fls).
Naxos Ⓢ 8 553639 (50 minutes: DDD: 10/97). ✐ Recorded 1995.
Five solo flutes is not a sound you hear every day, and when those flutes are mellow-toned baroque-
style instruments, all copies of a single Flemish model dating from the 1720s, then you really do have
something to make you sit up and take notice. Boismortier may have written over 100 opus numbers,
but only one of them was devoted to this unusual instrumental combination, and we may speculate
that whatever it was that inspired him to such innovation also enough to prevent him from falling
victim to the facility for which he was, and still is, so often criticized. And in any case in Op. 15,
published in 1727, he was a man with a mission. These were the first works by a Frenchman to carry
the Italian appellation 'concerto', and indeed their style, though French in its surface details, clearly
derives from the Vivaldian style of ritornello concerto. The soloists of Le Concert Spirituel are fine
interpreters of this music, with a polished sense of style and, for the most part, a commendable
uniformity of intonation and ensemble (the unison passages are particularly remarkable in this
respect). As usual with recordings of complete opus numbers, you probably would not want to listen
to this one from beginning to end; but this is pleasantly melodious music, and linked as it is to a
strange and beautiful sound, it certainly deserves repeated listening.
Further listening ...
...Sonata in G minor, Op. 34 No. 1. *Coupled with works by* **Leclair** *and* **Corrette**
Florilegium Ensemble; Scott Pauley (theorbo). Channel Classics CCS7595 (12/95). ✐
See review under Leclair; refer to the Index.
...Suites de Pièces, Op. 35 – No. 3 in G major; No. 5 in B minor; No. 6 in A major[a].
Four Suites de Pièces de clavecin, Op. 59. [a]**Luc Urbain** (fl); **Mireille Lagacé** (hpd).
Calliope Approche CAL6865 (8/96). ✐

...Les quatre saisons. **Isabelle Desrochers** (sop); **Hervé Lamy** (ten); **Max van Egmond** (bar); **L'Ensemble Arion.** CBC Records MVCD1098 (1/98).
...Don Quichotte chez la Duchesse. **Soloists; Le Concert Spirituel / Hervé Niquet.** Naxos 8 553647 (6/97).

Arrigo Boito
Italian 1842-1918

Boito Mefistofele. **Cesare Siepi** (bass) Mefistofele; **Mario del Monaco** (ten) Faust; **Renata Tebaldi** (sop) Margherita; **Floriana Cavalli** (sop) Elena; **Lucia Danieli** (mez) Marta, Pantalis; **Piero De Palma** (ten) Wagner, Nereo; **Chorus and Orchestra of the Santa Cecilia Academy / Tullio Serafin.** Decca Grand Opera Ⓜ 440 054-2DMO2* (two discs: 141 minutes: ADD: 4/94). Notes, text and translation included. From SXL2094/6 (6/59). Recorded 1958.

This recording has in Siepi a real Italian bass with a fine sense of line and a genuine enjoyment of Boito's words. Phrases that are often merely snarled are here truly sung, and Siepi's is the only devil to suggest in the quartet that he is trying to seduce Martha, and that he will very probably succeed. There is incisiveness and grain there, too, to add menace to his suavity. Tebaldi gives one of the best accounts of "L'altra notte" on record, strongly sung and very touching in its suggestion of grieving guilt. Del Monaco sings "Dai campi, dai prati" without the slightest acknowledgement of its poetry, but the splendour of the sound and his instinctive feeling for legato have their own allure, and they give nobility to his finely phrased "Giunto sul passo estremo". The recording doesn't allow Serafin to make a sonic spectacular of the outer scenes, but his care for Boito's often rather old-fashioned *cantabile,* his quirky rhythms and orchestral colours is scrupulous throughout.

Additional recommendation ...
...**Soloists; Trinity Boys' Choir; London Opera Chorus; National Philharmonic Orchestra / Oliviero de Fabritiis.** Decca Ⓕ 410 175-2DH3 (three discs: 147 minutes: DDD: 12/85).

Further listening ...
...*See also the* **Great Singers at the Maryinsky Theatre** *review in the Collections section; refer to the Index.* Nimbus NI7865 (3/95).

William Bolcom
American 1938

Suggested listening ...
...Cello Sonata. *Coupled with works by various composers.* **Richard Slavich** (vc); **Alice Rybak** (pf). Crystal Records CD639 (5/98). *See review in the Collections section; refer to the Index.*

Joseph Bonnal
French 1880-1944

Suggested listening ...
...Paysages Euskariens. *Coupled with works by various composers.* **Roger Sayer** (org). Priory PRCD495 (4/96). *See review in the Collections section; refer to the Index.*

Guillaume Boni
French d c1594

Suggested listening ...
...Rossignol mon mignon. Las! sans espoir. Quand je dors. Ha, bel accueil. Comment au départir. *Coupled with works by various composers.* **Clément Janequin Ensemble / Dominique Visse** (alto). Harmonia Mundi HMC90 1491 (2/95). *See review in the Collections section; refer to the Index.*

Joseph Bonnet
French 1884-1944

Suggested listening ...
...Romance sans paroles. *Coupled with works by various composers.* **Simon Lindley** (org). Naxos 8 550581 (3/93). *See review in the Collections section; refer to the Index.*
...In Memoriam – Titanic, Op. 10 No. 1. *Coupled with works by various composers.* **Christopher Herrick** (org). Hyperion CDA66917 (8/97). *See review in the Collections section; refer to the Index.*

Giovanni Bononcini
Italian 1670-1747

Suggested listening ...
...Polifemo – Respira, alma, respira ... Dove sei, dove t'ascondi; Non soffrirà, mai Circe ... Pensiero di vendetta[a]. Cefalo e Procride – Cintia, il tuo nome invoco ... Sacro dardo, in te confido; Numi

del ciel pietosi ... Bella auretta[a]. *Coupled with works by various composers.* [a]**Ann Monoyios** (sop);
Berlin Barock Compagney. Capriccio 10 459 (10/95). ☞ *See review in the Collections section;*
refer to the Index.   Ⓖ

Alexander Borodin   Russian 1833-1887

Borodin Symphonies – No. 1 in E flat major; No. 2 in B minor; No. 3 in A minor. Prince Igor –
Overture; Dance of the Polovtsian Maidens; Polovtsian Dances[ab]. String Quartet No. 2 in
D major – Notturno (orch. N. Tcherepnin). In the Steppes of Central Asia[b]. Petite Suite (orch.
Glazunov). [a]**Torgny Sporsén** (bass); **Gothenburg Symphony** [a]**Chorus and Orchestra / Neeme Järvi.**
DG Ⓕ 435 757-2GH2 (two discs: 148 minutes: DDD: 9/92). Items marked [b] from 429 984-2GH
(3/91), others new to UK. Recorded 1989-91.   Ⓖ
While it is possible to imagine performances of even greater power and finesse in this strangely
unfashionable repertoire, Järvi's Borodin set is arguably the best to have appeared in recent years. The
extravagant layout means we get not just the symphonies but a rich supplement of orchestral works,
including even the *Petite Suite* as arranged by Glazunov. Another rarity, Nikolay Tcherepnin's
orchestration of the famous *Notturno* will astonish those familiar with the chaste original: Tcherepnin
transforms it into an exotic Scriabin-like tableau, almost as remote from Borodin as its kitschy *Kismet*
mutation. The more recognizable *Steppes* are negotiated with ample eloquence and the *Prince Igor*
excerpts include a brief contribution from the great Khan himself, reminding us of the music's
original operatic context. The main works are equally persuasive. Järvi plays the the First Symphony
for all its worth, with DG's big, resonant sound boosting the work's symphonic credentials. The
unfinished Third is also tougher and more dramatic than usual, no mere pastoral reverie in Järvi's
interventionist view. The Second Symphony is rather different, suitably epic and yet unusually long-
drawn and thoughtful. Thus, the *Scherzo* is bubbling but sensibly articulate, while the *Andante* is
daringly broad with a superbly sensitive horn solo.
Additional recommendations ...
...No. 2. In the Steppes of Central Asia. Prince Igor – Overture; March; Dance of the Polovtsian
  Maidens; Polovtsian Dances. **John Alldis Choir; National Philharmonic Orchestra /**
  Loris Tjeknavorian. RCA Victor Silver Seal Ⓑ VD60535(64 minutes: ADD: 8/77).
...Nos. 1-3. **CSR Symphony Orchestra, Bratislava / Stephen Gunzenhauser.**
  Naxos Ⓢ 8 550238 (76 minutes: DDD: 8/91).
...Nos. 1 and 2. In the Steppes of Central Asia. **Royal Philharmonic Orchestra /**
  Vladimir Ashkenazy. Decca Ⓕ 436 651-2DH (71 minutes: DDD: 8/94).
...Prince Igor – Overture[a]. Symphony No. 2[b]. *Coupled with works by various composers.*
  Hallé Orchestra / [a]**Leslie Heward,** [b]**Constant Lambert.**
  Dutton Laboratories mono Ⓜ CDAX8010* (67 minutes: ADD: 2/95).
...No. 2[a]. **Tchaikovsky** Manfred Symphony, Op. 58[b]. **Philharmonia Orchestra / Paul Kletzki.**
  Testament mono Ⓕ SBT1048* (78 minutes: ADD: 3/95).
...In the Steppes of Central Asia. *Coupled with works by various composers.* **Louis Zimmerman,**
  Ferdinand Hellmann (vns); **Concertgebouw Orchestra / Willem Mengelberg.**
  Pearl mono Ⓜ GEMMCD9154* (76 minutes: ADD: 3/96).

Borodin Symphony No. 2 in B minor. In the Steppes of Central Asia. Prince Igor – Overture;
Polovtsian Dances; Polovtsian March. **Royal Philharmonic Orchestra / Ole Schmidt.**
Tring International Ⓢ TRP104 (65 minutes: DDD: 10/97). Recorded 1996. *Gramophone Editor's*
choice.
This is an excellent version of the Second Symphony, beautifully played and recorded, and with an
ideal coupling, at super-budget price, making it an outstanding bargain. In the first movement of the
Symphony Schmidt avoids the pitfall of adopting too slow a speed, avoiding any ponderousness, while
giving the music an idiomatically earthy tang. So, the flurries at the opening have a fiercely Slavonic
bite, heightened by the way that Schmidt slightly exaggerates the pauses between them, and from then
on rhythms are delectably strong. After that brisk first movement Schmidt takes a relatively relaxed
view of the *Scherzo*. At a nicely flowing tempo the great horn solo of the slow movement is gloriously
played by the RPO's long-time principal, Jeffrey Bryant. In the finale Schmidt springs rhythms so
infectiously that the music is given panache rather than fierceness or urgency, with the second subject
melody emerging with extra warmth. The rich, open orchestral sound is just as impressive in the
fill-ups. The *Prince Igor* Overture brings more glorious horn-playing, while the Polovtsian Dances and
March show off the brilliance of the RPO wind soloists. Percussion is superbly caught too, as it is in
the Symphony, and at a broad, flowing speed *In the Steppes of Central Asia* could hardly be more
evocative, highlighting its thematic links to *Prince Igor*.

Borodin Song of the dark forest. The sleeping princess. The pretty girl no longer loves me[a].
  The fishermaiden[a]. Listen to my song, little friend[a]. For the shores of thy far native land. Pride.
  Arabian melody. The magic garden. Those folk. The sea princess.
Dargomïzhsky Elegy (Deep down). I am in love, my maiden, my beauty. The worm. It is both
  tedious and sad. The night zephyr stirs the air. I am sad. The Miller. Lullaby. The Titular

Councillor. It's all the same to me. Eastern romance. The Old Corporal. **Sergei Leiferkus** (bar); [a]**Leonid Gorokhov** (vc); **Semion Skigin** (pf). Conifer Classics Ⓕ 75605 51275-2 (63 minutes: DDD: 12/96). Texts and translations included. Recorded 1996.

Borodin's songs have become better known in the West of late, and this recital should draw further attention to some beautiful and original music. Leiferkus includes about two-thirds of Borodin's total output, and makes out a good case for their range by skilfully modifying tone and manner to each of their various needs. Perhaps he is rather overemphatic with *Song of the dark forest*, but it does help to set in contrast his charmingly tender handling of *The sleeping princess* and the warmth he brings to *For the shores of thy far native land*, skilfully invoking the richness of Schumann. *The pretty girl no longer loves me* is ruefully not tragically sung, with a sly tinge of irony. Dargomïzhsky, more of a Slavophile than Borodin, had the realism and the sharp wit to turn various poems into little dramatic sketches that depend more on sharp observation than on forms. *The Titular Councillor* who gets rejected paces away from the girl with an awkward dignity exactly caught in Semion Skigin's stiff rhythms and Leiferkus's mock dignity. Pushkin's miller, drunkenly muddling his boots with a pair of buckets, lurches with a good deal less security. *The worm* who allows the Count's attentions to his wife attracts a brilliant sarcasm. And nothing in this whole recital is more affecting than the handling of what is perhaps Dargomïzhsky's masterpiece among his songs, the scena in which the old corporal who has insulted a young popinjay of an officer stiffens up his comrades' resolve and sets the pace as they march to where he must be shot. A last puff at his pipe, an angry rejection of a blindfold, and he wishes them a safe journey home. Leiferkus's refusal of sentimentality, and Skigin's quiet delivery of the very short postlude, say all that need be said.

Additional recommendation ...

...The pretty girl no longer loves me[a]. For the shores of thy far native land. *Coupled with works by various composers.* **Sergei Larin** (ten); [a]**Alfia Bekova** (vc); **Eleonora Bekova** (pf). Chandos Ⓕ CHAN9547 (67 minutes: DDD: 6/97). *See review in the Collections section; refer to the Index.*

Borodin Prince Igor. **Mikhail Kit** (bar) Igor; **Galina Gorchakova** (sop) Yaroslavna; **Gegam Grigorian** (ten) Vladimir; **Vladimir Ognovenko** (bass) Prince Galitzky; **Bulat Minjelkiev** (bass) Khan Kontchak; **Olga Borodina** (mez) Kontchakovna; **Nikolai Gassiev** (ten) Ovlour; **Georgy Selezniev** (bass) Skula; **Konstantin Pluzhnikov** (ten) Eroshka; **Evgenia Perlasova** (mez) Nurse; **Tatyana Novikova** (sop) Polovtsian Maiden; **Kirov Opera Chorus and Orchestra /
Valery Gergiev**. Philips Ⓕ 442 537-2PH3 (three discs: 209 minutes: DDD: 4/95). Notes, text and translation included. Recorded 1993. *Selected by Sounds in Retrospect.*   Ⓖ

Prince Igor, even after 18 years of work, remained unfinished at Borodin's death in 1887, and it was finally completed by Rimsky-Korsakov and Glazunov. Borodin's main problem with *Prince Igor* was the daunting task of turning what was principally an undramatic subject into a convincing stage work. In many ways he never really succeeded in this and the end result comes over more as a series of epic scenes rather than a musical drama. Despite this, however, one is nevertheless left with an impression of a rounded whole, and it contains some of Borodin's most poignant and moving music, rich in oriental imagery and full of vitality. Curious things happen long before the official surprises of this vitally fresh *Prince Igor*, not least in the Overture, where Gergiev takes the horn's beautiful melody at a very slow pace. Gergiev is anxious to prepare us for the weighty events which follow and his particular point with the theme is to relate it to its place in the opera as the heart of Igor's great aria. There, in league with the bass-baritone timbre of Gergiev's prince, Mikhail Kit, it solemnly underlines the fact that this is an aria of potency frustrated, sung by a hero who spends most of the opera in captivity; and that is further emphasized by a second aria which no listener will ever have heard before. It is the most significant of the passages discovered among Borodin's papers, rejected by Rimsky-Korsakov in his otherwise sensitive tribute to Borodin's memory but specially orchestrated for this recording by Yuri Faliek.

The other problem with the *Prince Igor* we already know is the way that Act 3 rather weakly follows its much more imposing Polovtsian predecessor. Gergiev obviates both that, and the problem of too much time initially spent in Igor's home town of Putivl, by referring to a structural outline of Borodin's dating from 1883 which proposes alternating the Russian and Polovtsian acts. In the theatre, we might still want the famous Polovtsian *divertissement* as a centrepiece; but on the recording the new order works splendidly, not least because Gergiev is at his fluent best in the scenes of Galitzky's dissipation and Yaroslavna's despair, now making up the opera's Second Act. While Borodina executes Kontchakovna's seductive chromaticisms with astonishing breath control and focus of tone, Bulat Minjelkiev's Kontchak is a little too free and easy, at least in comparison with Ognovenko's perfectly gauged Galitzky, a rogue who needs the extra rebellion music of the more recent version to show more threatening colours. There's just the right degree of relaxation, too, about his drunken supporters Skula and Eroshka. It takes two Russian character-singers to make sense of this pair – "with our wine and our cunning we will never die in Russia", they tell us truthfully – and their comical capitulation on Igor's return wins respect for Borodin's daring happy-end transition here. It's beautifully paced by Pluzhnikov, Selezniev and their conductor, and crowned by a choral cry of joy which brings a marvellous rush of tearful adrenalin. That leaves us with Gorchakova, so touching in Yaroslavna's first aria but not always projecting the text very vividly and clearly not at her best in the big scena of the last act. Still, in terms of long-term vision, orchestral detail and strength of ensemble, Gergiev is ahead of the competition.

Additional recommendations ...
...Soloists; Sofia National Opera Chorus; Sofia Festival Orchestra / Emil Tchakarov.
Sony Classical Ⓕ S3K44878 (three discs: 210 minutes: DDD: 6/90).   Ⓖ
...Prince Igor (Act 3 omitted). Songs – Those people; Song of the dark forest; From my tears; The
queen of the sea; The beauty no loves me; The magic garden; Arabian melody; The Fisher-
maiden; Listen to my song, little friend; The sleeping princess; Arrogance; The sea; Why art thou
so early, dawn? There is poison in my songs; The false note; For the shores of thy far native land.
Boris Christoff (bass); **Soloists; Chorus and Orchestra of the National Opera Theatre, Sofia /**
Jerzy Semkov; ᵇ**Lamoureux Concerts Orchestra / Georges Tzipine.**
EMI Studio Ⓜ CMS7 63386-2 (three discs: 203 minutes: ADD: 6/90).
...**Soloists; Chorus and Orchestra of the Bolshoi Theatre, Moscow / Mark Ermler.**
Melodiya Ⓜ 74321 29346-2 (three discs: 196 minutes: DDD: 10/96).
...Prince Igor – Daylight is fading. *Coupled with works by various composers.* **Sergei Larin** (ten);
Philharmonia Orchestra / Gennadi Rozhdestvensky. Chandos Ⓕ CHAN9603
(75 minutes: DDD: 5/98). *See review in the Collections section; refer to the Index.*
Further listening ...
...String Quartet No. 2 in D major. *Coupled with works by* **Shostakovich** and **Tchaikovsky**
Borodin Quartet. Decca 425 541-2DM (5/90).
...String Quartet No. 2 in D major. *Coupled with works by* **Glazunov** and **Tchaikovsky**
Hollywood Quartet. Testament mono SBT1061* (8/95).
...String Quartet No. 2 in A major. String Quintet in F minorᵃ. Serenata alla spagnola.
ᵃ**Alexander Gotthelf** (vc); **Moscow String Quartet.** CdM Russian Season RUS288 142 (4/98).
...The false note. The sea princess. *Coupled with works by various composers.* **Olga Borodina** (mez);
Larissa Gergieva (pf). Philips 442 780-2PH (8/95).

Sergei Bortkiewicz   Austrian/USSR 1877-1952

Suggested listening ...
...Piano Concerto No. 1 in B flat major, Op. 16. *Coupled with works by* **Arensky**
Stephen Coombs (pf); **BBC Scottish Symphony Orchestra / Jerzy Maksymiuk.**
Hyperion CDA66624 (3/93). *See review under Arensky; refer to the Index.*
...Lamentations and Consolations, Op. 17. Aus Andersens Märchen, Op. 30. Ten Preludes, Op. 33.
Stephen Coombs (pf). Hyperion CDA66933 (10/97).

Marco Enrico Bossi   Italian 1861-1925

Suggested listening ...
...Pièce héroïque in D minor, Op. 128. Scherzo in D minor, Op. 49 No. 2. *Coupled with works by*
various composers. **Christopher Herrick** (org). Hyperion CDA66457 (9/91). *See review in the*
Collections section; refer to the Index.   ⒼⒼⒼ

Rutland Boughton   British 1878-1960

Suggested listening ...
...String Quartets – F major, "From the Welsh Hills"; A major, "On Greek Folk Songs".
Oboe Quartet No. 1ᵃ. Three Songs without Wordsᵃ. ᵃ**Sarah Francis** (ob); **Rasumovsky Quartet.**
Hyperion CDA66936 (8/97).
...The Immortal Hour. **Soloists; George Mitchell Choir; English Chamber Orchestra /**
Alan G. Melville. Hyperion CDA66101/2 (8/87).   ⒼⒼ

Pierre Boulez   French 1925

Boulez Rituel (1974-75). Messagesquisse (1976). Notations I-IV (1945-78). **Orchestre de Paris /**
Daniel Barenboim. Erato Ⓕ 2292-45493-2 (41 minutes: DDD: 10/90). Recorded 1988-89.
Barenboim clearly has his own approach to Boulez's music, and the technical skill to realize it
convincingly with a first-class French orchestra. Boulez himself now tends to underline the public
ceremonial of *Rituel* (a tribute to the Italian composer and conductor Bruno Maderna), whereas
Barenboim, restraining the cumulative clangour of the music's dialogues between the implacable
reiterations of gongs and tamtams and the seven other instrumental groups, preserves more of the
intimacy of personal regret and loss. *Rituel* is unusual for Boulez in the clear-cut logic of its gradually
evolving form, and Barenboim does well to convey that logic without making the whole design seem
too predictable for its own good. He is equally attentive to the need to balance striking details with a
feeling for overall shape in the shorter but no less personal structures of *Notations* and
Messagesquisse. The recording is outstanding in its spaciousness and tonal range.

Boulez Piano Sonatas Nos. 1-3. **Idil Biret** (pf). Naxos Ⓢ 8 553353 (64 minutes: DDD: 11/95). Recorded 1995.

It sometimes seems as if Boulez has spent a lifetime paying the penalty for having found composition so easy as a young man. The first two piano sonatas, works of his early twenties, are formidably assured in technique and tremendously rich in ideas. Those sections of the Third Sonata released for performance sound cold and tentative by comparison. Or is it that the Third Sonata's much more extreme rejection of tradition is itself a triumph, an authentic modernity that stands out the more prominently for its individualism? Such thoughts are inspired by Idil Biret's absorbing disc. In the first movement of the First Sonata the broader picture proves to be well fleshed-out, the argument kept on the move, the young composer's impatience and arrogance palpable in Biret's steely touch and the rather dry but never merely harsh recorded sound. The Second Sonata is no less confidently played. This is a strong alternative to Pollini's magisterial account, not least in those passages in the second and fourth movements where a strange kind of atonal Debussian reflectiveness can be heard. Is it in the Second Sonata's diverse finale that premonitions of the Third Sonata's rejections of continuity begin to appear? Quite possibly – and yet the power of the Second Sonata as a whole suggests why such experiments as No. 3 represents could never be a last word for Boulez. This disc is not the first to bring us the three sonatas together, and Claude Helffer's recording has many virtues. But Biret's musical persuasiveness, and the up-to-date sound, earn this Naxos issue a strong recommendation.

Additional recommendations ...

...Nos. 1-3. **Claude Helffer** (pf). Auvidis Astrée Ⓕ E7716 (55 minutes: ADD: 8/88).

...No. 2. *Coupled with works by various composers.* **Maurizio Pollini** (pf).
  DG The Originals Ⓜ 447 431-2GOR (68 minutes: ADD: 6/95). *Gramophone Classical 100.*
  See review in the Collections section; refer to the Index.   ⒼⒼⒼ

...No. 1[b]. Le marteau sans maître[a]. [a]**Linda Hirst** (sop); [b]**Marc Ponthus** (pf); [a]**Lontano /
  Odaline de la Martinez.** Lorelt Ⓕ LNT108 (47 minutes: DDD: 3/96).

Boulez Pli selon pli. **Phyllis Bryn-Julson** (sop); **BBC Symphony Orchestra / Pierre Boulez.**
  Erato Ⓕ 2292-45376-2 (68 minutes: DDD: 3/89). From NUM75050 (5/83). Recorded 1981.   ⒼⒼ
  Gramophone Award Winner 1983.

Pli selon pli, composed between 1957-62, is one of the great pillars of post-war musical modernism. If that proclamation merely makes it sound forbidding, then it could scarcely be less appropriate. 'Pillar' it may be, but as exciting in its moment-to-moment shifts of colour and contour, and as compelling in its command of large-scale dramatic design as anything composed since the great years of Schoenberg and Stravinsky. Easy, no: enthralling and rewarding – yes. This is no grand, single-minded work in the great Germanic symphonic tradition, but a sequence of distinct yet balanced responses to aspects of the great symbolist poet Mallarmé. On his second recording of the piece, Boulez is prepared to let the music expand and resonate, the two large orchestral tapestries enclosing three "Improvisations", smaller-scale vocal movements in which the authority and expressiveness of Phyllis Bryn-Julson is heard to great advantage. The sound is brilliantly wide-ranging and well balanced, and while the contrast between delicacy and almost delirious density embodied in *Pli selon pli* does take some getting used to, to miss it is to miss one of modern music's most original masterworks. His first version has a special historical status as embodying the composer's view of the work near the time of its actual completion, when forcefulness, and even ferocity, seemed to count for more as foils to the music's moments of relative restraint than the sustained densities so strongly emphasized in the Erato recording.

Additional recommendations ...

...Pli selon pli[a]. Livre pour cordes[b]. [a]**Halina Lukomska** (sop); [a]**BBC Symphony Orchestra,**
  [b]**New Philharmonia Orchestra / Pierre Boulez.**
  Sony Classical Boulez Edition Ⓜ SMK68335 (71 minutes: ADD: 7/96).

Further listening ...

...12 Notations[a]. Structures pour deux pianos, Livre 2[b]. ... explosante-fixe ...[c]. [c]**Sophie Cherrier,**
  [c]**Emmanuelle Ophèle,** [c]**Pierre-André Valade** (fls); [ab]**Pierre-Laurent Aimard,** [b]**Florent Boffard** (pfs);
  Ensemble InterContemporain, Paris / Pierre Boulez. DG 445 833-2GH (12/95).

...Rituel in memoriam Bruno Maderna[a]. Eclat/Multiples[b]. [a]**BBC Symphony Orchestra** and
  [b]**Ensemble InterContemporain / Pierre Boulez.** Sony Classical SMK45839 (8/90).

...Structures pour deux pianos. **Alfons Kontarsky, Aloys Kontarsky** (pfs). Wergo WER6011-2 (6/93).

...Le visage nuptial[a]. Le soleil des eaux[b]. Figures, Doubles, Prismes. [ab]**Phyllis Bryn-Julson** (sop);
  [a]**Elizabeth Laurence** (mez); [ab]**BBC Singers; BBC Symphony Orchestra / Pierre Boulez.**
  Erato 2292-45494-2 (12/90).

Paul Bowles   American 1910

Suggested listening ...

...They cannot stop death. Blue Mountain Ballads. *Coupled with works by various composers.*
  Samuel Ramey (bar); **Warren Jones** (pf). Sony Classical SK68339 (2/97). *See review in the
  Collections section; refer to the Index.*

William Boyce

Boyce Eight Symphonies, Op. 2. **Academy of Ancient Music / Christopher Hogwood.**
L'Oiseau-Lyre Ⓕ 436 761-2OH (61 minutes: DDD: 4/94). ✒ Recorded 1992.

The Boyce *Eight Symphonys* (as he himself spelt the title) are one of the treasures of English eighteenth-century music, cheerful, unassuming and confident, full of good tunes, and typically English in style – their quirky lines, their refusal to follow the regular procedures, their mixture of baroque and classical features, with their fugues declining to remain fugal, their very un-French French overtures: all this is part of their particular charm. Hogwood catches the eccentric character of the music well and gives a great deal of attention to the textural depth of the music and its inner detail. All the fugal movements go well, done with vitality and a feeling for their logic.

Boyce Peleus and Thetis[a]. Corydon and Miranda[b]. Incidental music – Florizel and Perdita[c]; Romeo and Juliet[d]. **Julia Gooding,** [bcd]**Philippa Hyde** (sops); [a]**Robin Blaze** (alto); **Joseph Cornwell** (ten); [ad]**Andrew Dale-Forbes** (bass); [c]**Jilly Bond,** [c]**Jack Edwards** (spkrs); **Opera Restor'd / Peter Holman** (hpd). Hyperion Ⓕ CDA66935 (68 minutes: DDD: 9/97). ✒ Texts included. Recorded 1996.

Boyce was in his time one of the leading theatre composers. *Peleus and Thetis* is a short masque, based on a simple story reminiscent of *Acis and Galatea*, except that here the jealous Jupiter resigns his amorous claims on Thetis on learning that her son would outshine his father (he was of course Achilles). Among the best moments are Peleus's spirited song of defiance, Jupiter's fine, richly contrapuntal one of renunciation and the lovers' duet at the end. Boyce's music has a flavour all its own, and at its best a very appealing one; Peter Holman conducts the piece in lively fashion, and uses singers with a good command of the style. Two of the other items are incidental music to Shakespeare productions. The little amorous competition of Mopsa and Dorcas for *The Winter's Tale* (in *Florizel and Perdita*) will remind the listener of Purcell. It is sung here in something of a brogue, which would probably be more persuasive on stage than on a recording. Then there is a dirge for Romeo and Juliet, a touching, richly harmonized setting of words as Juliet's body is carried across the stage. The "Pastoral interlude", *Corydon and Miranda*, in which a shepherd chooses between rival claimants for his love, consists of four airs, mostly in a simple, melodious style, but a final fiery one for the girl who loses, linked by recitative, and a final chorus. It isn't great music, but it is tuneful, in a characteristically English way, and it shows sensitivity to the words and their sense. A very agreeable disc.

Further listening ...

...Overtures Nos. 1-9. **Cantilena / Adrian Shepherd.** Chandos CHAN6531 (10/91).

...Overtures Nos. 10-12. Concerti grossi – B minor; B flat major; E flat major. **Cantilena / Adrian Shepherd.** Chandos CHAN6541 (6/92).

...Trio Sonatas Nos. 1-15. **The Parley of Instruments; The Parley of Instruments Baroque Orchestra / Peter Holman** (hpd). Hyperion CDA67151/2 (4/97). ✒

...Trio Sonatas Nos. 1-15. **The English Concert / Trevor Pinnock** (hpd). Archiv Produktion 419 631-2AH (9/87). ✒

...Anthems – O where shall wisdom be found?; Wherewithal shall a young man; I have surely built thee an house; O praise the Lord; Turn thee unto me; O give thanks; By the waters of Babylon; The Lord is King be the people never so impatient. Voluntaries[a] – Nos. 1, 4 and 7. **New College Choir, Oxford / Edward Higginbottom** with [a]**Gary Cooper** (org). CRD CRD3483 (10/92). ✒

...Solomon – serenata. **Bronwen Mills** (sop); **Howard Crook** (ten); **The Parley of Instruments / Roy Goodman.** Hyperion CDA66378 (11/90). ✒

May Brahe

Suggested listening ...

...Bless this house. *Coupled with works by various composers.* **Lesley Garrett** (sop); **Britten Sinfonia / Ivor Bolton.** Conifer Classics 75605 51329-2 (12/97). *See review in the Collections section; refer to the Index.*

Johannes Brahms

Brahms Violin Concerto in D major, Op. 77.
Sibelius Violin Concerto in D minor, Op. 47. **Tasmin Little** (vn); **Royal Liverpool Philharmonic Orchestra / Vernon Handley.** EMI Eminence Ⓜ CD-EMX2203 (72 minutes: DDD: 2/93). Recorded 1991.   Ⓖ

Brahms Violin Concerto in D major, Op. 77.
Schumann Violin Concerto in D minor, Op. posth. **Joshua Bell** (vn); **Cleveland Orchestra / Christoph von Dohnányi.** Decca Ⓕ 444 811-2DH (68 minutes: DDD: 5/96). Recorded 1994.

Tasmin Little admits that she prefers not to commit her interpretations to disc until she has "something to say and the means with which to say it". That is certainly the case with the Brahms

Concerto, a clear, considered reading (much aided in the slow movement by Jonathan Small's excellent oboe solo), quite without mannerism and beautifully accompanied by Vernon Handley and the Royal Liverpool Philharmonic. The Sibelius has even more character, and here Little adds to an impressive roster of the work's many great female interpreters (Neveu, Wicks, Bustabo, Ignatius, etc). Handley is an impressive Sibelian whose feel for the idiom is apparent in every bar, and both recordings are excellent. As a coupling the two performances are irresistible.

Bell's first entry in the Brahms instantly demonstrates the soloist's love of bravura display, his gift for turning a phrase individually in a way that catches the ear, always sounding spontaneous, never self-conscious. Regularly one registers moments of new magic, not least when, in the most delicate half-tones, *pianissimos* seem to convey an inner communion, after which the impact of bravura *fortissimos* is all the more dramatic. He rounds off the movement with his own big cadenza and a magically hushed link into the coda, rapt and intense. The slow movement, sweet and songful, gains too from Bell's love of playing really softly, not least in stratospheric registers. In the finale the vein of fantasy is less apparent. Next to others this can seem a little plain. Dohnányi and the Cleveland Orchestra provide weighty and sympathetic support and the generous Schumann coupling in another commanding performance adds to the attractions of the disc. There too Dohnányi and the Cleveland Orchestra add to the weight and dramatic impact of a performance that defies the old idea of this as an impossibly flawed piece, with Bell bringing out charm as well as power. The central slow movement has a rapt intensity rarely matched, and the dance-rhythms of the finale have fantasy as well as jauntiness and jollity, with Bell again revelling in the bravura writing. The recording is full-bodied and well balanced.

Additional recommendations ...

...Violin Concerto. *Coupled with works by various composers.* **Gidon Kremer** (vn); **Berlin Philharmonic Orchestra / Herbert von Karajan.** EMI Forte Ⓜ CZS5 69334-2 (two discs: 151 minutes: ADD). *See review in the Collections section; refer to the Index.* Ⓖ

...Violin Concerto. **Itzhak Perlman** (vn); **Chicago Symphony Orchestra / Carlo Maria Giulini.** EMI Ⓕ CDC7 47166-2 (43 minutes: ADD: 1/87).

...Violin Concerto[a]. **Sibelius** Violin Concerto in D minor, Op. 47[b]. **Ginette Neveu** (vn); **Philharmonia Orchestra / [a]Issay Dobroven, [b]Walter Susskind.** EMI mono Ⓜ CDH7 61011-2* (70 minutes: ADD: 3/88).

...Violin Concerto[b]. **Mendelssohn** Violin Concerto in E minor, Op. 64. **Xue-Wei** (vn); **London Philharmonic Orchestra / Ivor Bolton.** ASV Ⓕ CDDCA748 (67 minutes: DDD: 4/91).

...Violin Concerto. **Itzhak Perlman** (vn); **Berlin Philharmonic Orchestra / Daniel Barenboim.** EMI Ⓕ CDC7 54580-2 (40 minutes: DDD: 2/93).

...Violin Concerto. **Tchaikovsky** Violin Concerto in D major, Op. 35. **Jascha Heifetz** (vn); **Chicago Symphony Orchestra / Fritz Reiner.** RCA Victor Living Stereo Ⓜ 09026 61495-2* (64 minutes: ADD: 4/93). ⒼⒼⒼ

...Violin Concerto[b]. Violin Sonata No. 1 in G major, Op. 78[a]. [a]**Isaac Stern, Pincas Zukerman** (vns); [b]**Orchestra de Paris / Daniel Barenboim** ([a]pf). DG Classikon Ⓑ 439 405-2GCL (70 minutes: ADD: 1/94).

...Violin Concerto. **Mendelssohn** Violin Concerto in E minor, Op. 64. **Johanna Martzy** (vn); **Philharmonia Orchestra / Paul Kletzki.** Testament mono Ⓕ SBT1037* (68 minutes: ADD: 9/94).

...Violin Concerto[a]. **Tchaikovsky** Violin Concerto in D major, Op. 35[b]. **Ida Haendel** (vn); [a]**London Symphony Orchestra / Sergiu Celibidache;** [b]**Royal Philharmonic Orchestra / Sir Eugene Goossens.** Testament mono Ⓕ SBT1038* (76 minutes: ADD: 10/94).

...Violin Concerto. **Viktoria Mullova** (vn); **Berlin Philharmonic Orchestra / Claudio Abbado.** Philips Ⓕ 438 998-2PH (40 minutes: DDD: 11/94).

...Violin Concerto. **Mendelssohn** Violin Concerto in E minor, Op. 64. **Anne-Sophie Mutter** (vn); **Berlin Philharmonic Orchestra / Herbert von Karajan.** DG Masters Series Ⓜ 445 515-2GMA (71 minutes: DDD: 12/94).

...Violin Concerto. *Coupled with works by various composers.* **David Oistrakh** (vn); **Dresden Staatskapelle / Franz Konwitschny.** DG The Originals stereo/mono Ⓜ 447 427-2GOR2 (two discs: 142 minutes: ADD: 6/95).

...Violin Concerto. **Mozart** Violin Concerto No. 3 in G major, K216. **Frank Peter Zimmermann** (vn); **Berlin Philharmonic Orchestra / Wolfgang Sawallisch.** EMI Ⓕ CDC5 55426-2 (60 minutes: DDD: 5/96). *See review under Mozart; refer to the Index.*

...Violin Concerto. **Schumann** Fantasie in C major, Op. 131. **Anne-Sophie Mutter** (vn); **New York Philharmonic Orchestra / Kurt Masur.** DG Ⓕ 457 075-2GH (54 minutes: DDD: 12/97).

...Violin Concerto[a]. Violin Sonata No. 3 in D minor, Op. 108[b]. Variations on a Theme by Paganini, Op. 35[c]. [ab]**Joseph Szigeti** (vn); [bc]**Egon Petri** (pf); [a]**Hallé Orchestra / Sir Hamilton Harty.** EMI Références mono Ⓕ CDH5 66421-2* (79 minutes: ADD: 1/98).

...Violin Concerto[a]. Symphony No. 2 in D major, Op. 73[b]. [a]**Erica Morini** (vn); [a]**Royal Philharmonic Orchestra;** [b]**Pittsburgh Symphony Orchestra / [a]Artur Rodzinski, [b]William Steinberg.** Millennium Classics Composers Collection Ⓜ UMD80394 (76 minutes: ADD: 4/98).

Brahms Violin Concerto in D major, Op. 77[a]. Double Concerto in A minor, Op. 102[b]. **Gidon Kremer** (vn); [b]**Clemens Hagen** (vc); **Royal Concertgebouw Orchestra / Nikolaus Harnoncourt.** Teldec Ⓕ 0630-13137-2 (69 minutes: DDD: 11/97). Item marked [a] recorded live in 1996, [b]1997.

A radical rethink of two great concertos and as good a justification as any for repertoire duplication. These captivating performances illustrate Harnoncourt's habitual fondness for tapered phrase-shaping and pin-sharp articulation. Kremer's first entry in the Violin Concerto is bold and forceful, and yet listen to his sensitive handling of the triplets at 4'43" or his knowing interpretation of Brahms's prescribed *piano lusingando* at 14'50" and the degree of his perception soon registers. He plays a startlingly original 1903 cadenza by Enescu and takes a swift view of the *Andante*, albeit one that is both lissom and flexible. The finale, on the other hand, suggests the impulsive gaiety of a Hungarian dance (the charming 'hiccup' that characterizes the opening theme is fairly typical), with fast speeds and rugged textures. Generally speaking, it is a more daring, less overtly 'virtuoso' Violin Concerto than other versions. In the Double Concerto Clemens Hagen employs a subtle, variegated tonal palette and Harnoncourt underlines the concerto's symphonic dimensions (especially in the first movement). The *Andante* second movement moves on, lasting 6'06", and the effect suggests parallels with the piano *Intermezzos* or even the middle movements of the Third Symphony. Intimate interludes abound but time and again one senses, above all, great strength of purpose, particularly in the return of the first theme. Harnoncourt, Kremer, Hagen and the orchestra invest both concertos with a wealth of insights, leaving nothing to chance but within a highly spontaneous interpretative framework. Like Harnoncourt's Brahms symphonies, they will usefully supplement – if not always challenge – other fine (perhaps sweeter-toned) recordings. The sound is pleasingly ambient, with precious few coughs or extraneous noises and no applause.

Brahms Piano Concertos[a] – No. 1 in D minor, Op. 15; No. 2 in B flat major, Op. 83. Seven Piano Pieces, Op. 116[b]. **Emil Gilels** (pf); [a]**Berlin Philharmonic Orchestra / Eugen Jochum.**
DG The Originals Ⓜ 447 446-2GOR2 (two discs: 125 minutes: ADD: 6/96). Items marked
[a] from 2707 064 (12/72), [b]2530 655 (7/76). Recorded 1972-75. *Gramophone classical 100.* ⒼⒼⒼ
The booklet-notes make reference to the original *Gramophone* review, in which Gilels and Jochum were praised for "a rapt songfulness that in no way detracts from Brahms's heroism, and so comes closer to that unique and complex combination of attitudes that for me is Brahms more than any other performances of these concertos I have ever heard, on records or otherwise". One might add that Jochum and the Berlin Philharmonic make plain sailing where others struggle with choppy cross-currents (admittedly sometimes to Brahms's advantage) and that the recordings don't sound their age. Abbado and Brendel have perhaps probed a little deeper here and there, Kovacevich and Sawallisch won a *Gramophone* Award for their recording of No. 1 and sundry reissues have reminded us of such contrasted partnerships as Rubinstein with Reiner in the First Concerto and, in the Second, Serkin with Szell. Neither concerto rests content with a single interpretation, the Second especially. As for the Seven Piano Pieces, Gilels viewed the opus as a single piece, a musical novella in several chapters.
Additional recommendations ...
...Nos. 1 and 2. Scherzo in E flat minor, Op. 4. Four Ballades, Op. 10. Eight Pieces, Op. 76.
    Stephen Kovacevich (pf); **London Symphony Orchestra / Sir Colin Davis.**
    Philips Ⓜ 442 109-2PM2 (two discs: 141 minutes: ADD/DDD).   Ⓖ
...Nos. 1 and 2. Two Rhapsodies, Op. 79. Piano Pieces. **Wilhelm Backhaus** (pf);
    Vienna Philharmonic Orchestra / Karl Böhm. Decca Ⓜ 433 895-2DM2 (ADD).
...No. 1. **Alfred Brendel** (pf); **Berlin Philharmonic Orchestra / Claudio Abbado.**
    Philips Ⓕ 420 071-2PH (49 minutes: DDD: 11/87).
...No. 2. **Alfred Brendel** (pf); **Berlin Philharmonic Orchestra / Claudio Abbado.**
    Philips Ⓕ 432 975-2PH (49 minutes: DDD: 6/92).
...No. 2. Fantasias. **Emil Gilels** (pf); **Berlin Philharmonic Orchestra / Eugen Jochum.** DG Galleria
    Ⓜ 435 588-2GGA (*coupled with No. 1 and reviewed above*) (74 minutes: ADD: 9/92).   ⒼⒼⒼ
...No. 1[a]. Zwei Gesänge, Op. 91[b]. **Stephen Kovacevich** (pf); [b]**Ann Murray** (mez); [b]**Nobuko Imai** (va);
    [a]**London Philharmonic Orchestra / Wolfgang Sawallisch.** EMI Ⓕ CDC7 54578-2 (59 minutes:
    DDD: 10/92). *Gramophone* Award Winner 1993. *Selected by Sounds in Retrospect.*   Ⓖ
...No. 1. Rhapsody in B minor, Op. 79 No. 1. Capriccio in B minor, Op. 76 No. 2. Intermezzo in
    E flat minor, Op. 118 No. 6. **Artur Rubinstein** (pf); **Chicago Symphony Orchestra / Fritz Reiner.**
    RCA Victor Gold Seal Ⓜ 09026 61263-2 (65 minutes: ADD: 2/93).
...No. 2. **Tchaikovsky** Piano Concerto No. 1 in B flat minor, Op. 23. **Vladimir Horowitz** (pf);
    NBC Symphony Orchestra / Arturo Toscanini.
    RCA Victor Gold Seal Ⓜ GD60319* (74 minutes: ADD: 9/93).
...No. 2. **Strauss** Burleske. **Rudolf Serkin** (pf); **Cleveland Orchestra / George Szell.**
    Sony Classical Ⓜ SBK53262 (67 minutes: ADD: 3/94).
...No. 1[a]. Scherzo in E flat minor, Op. 4. Four Ballades, Op. 10 – No. 1 in D minor; No. 2 in
    D major. Waltzes, Op. 39 – No. 1 in B major; No. 2 in E major; No. 15 in A flat major.
    Hungarian Dances – No. 6 in D flat major; No. 7 in A major. **Wilhelm Backhaus** (pf); [a]**BBC**
    Symphony Orchestra / Sir Adrian Boult. Biddulph mono Ⓜ LHW017* (67 minutes: ADD: 9/94).
...No. 2[a]. Variations on an original theme in D major, Op. 21 No. 1. Variations on a Theme by
    Paganini, Op. 35. **Wilhelm Backhaus** (pf); [a]**Saxon State Orchestra / Karl Böhm.**
    Biddulph mono Ⓜ LHW018* (71 minutes: ADD: 9/94).
...No. 1. Variations and Fugue on a Theme by Handel, Op. 24. **Solomon** (pf); **Philharmonia**
    Orchestra / Rafael Kubelík. Testament mono Ⓕ SBT1041* (73 minutes: ADD: 10/94).   Ⓖ

...No. 2ᵃ. Lieder, Op. 105ᵇ. **Stephen Kovacevich** (pf); ᵇ**Ann Murray** (mez);
ᵃ**London Philharmonic Orchestra / Wolfgang Sawallisch.**
EMI Ⓕ CDC5 55218-2 (62 minutes: DDD: 10/94). *Selected by Sounds in Retrospect.*
...No. 2. Intermezzos – B flat minor, Op. 117 No. 2; C major, Op. 119 No. 3. Rhapsody in G minor,
Op. 79 No. 2. **Solomon** (pf); **Philharmonia Orchestra / Issay Dobrowen.**
Testament mono Ⓕ SBT1042* (58 minutes: ADD: 10/94).　　　　　　　　Ⓠ
...No. 1. **Dohnányi** Variations on a Nursery Theme, Op. 25. **Mark Anderson** (pf);
Hungarian State Symphony Orchestra / Adám Fischer.
Nimbus Ⓕ NI5349 (75 minutes: DDD: 3/95). *See review under Dohnányi; refer to the Index.*
...No. 2. Variations on a Theme by Paganini, Op. 35 – Book 2. *Coupled with works by* **Beethoven**
and **Liszt** Gina Bachauer (pf); **London Symphony Orchestra / Stanislaw Skrowaczewski.**
Mercury Living Presence Ⓜ 434 340-2MM (77 minutes: ADD: 9/95).
...Nos. 1 and 2. Theme and Variations (from String Sextet No. 1, Op. 18). Four Ballades, Op. 10.
Coupled with works by **Schumann** Alfred Brendel (pf); **Heinz Holliger** (ob);
Berlin Philharmonic Orchestra, London Symphony Orchestra / Claudio Abbado.
Philips Ⓜ 446 925-2PM5 (five discs: 334 minutes: ADD/DDD: 2/96).
...Seven Piano Pieces, Op. 116ᶜ. **Saint-Saëns** Piano Concerto No. 2 in G minor, Op. 22ᵃ.
Le carnaval des animauxᵇ. **Emil Gilels,** ᵇ**Yakov Zak** (pfs); ᵃᵇ**USSR State Symphony Orchestra /**
ᵃ**Kyrill Kondrashin,** ᵇ**Karl Eliasberg.**
Revelation ᵃᵇmono/ᶜstereo Ⓜ RV10014* (69 minutes: ADD: 10/96).
...Nos. 1ᵃ and 2ᵇ. Two Rhapsodies, Op. 79. Pieces, Op. 116 – No. 1, Capriccio in D minor; No. 2,
Intermezzo in A minor; No. 4, Intermezzo in E major. Pieces, Op. 119 – No. 1, Intermezzo in
B minor; No. 2, Intermezzo in E minor; No. 3, Intermezzo in C major. Hungarian Dances – No. 6
in D flat major; No. 7 in A major. Pieces, Op. 76 – No. 2, Capriccio in B minor; No. 7, Intermezzo in
A minor; No. 8, Capriccio in C major. Pieces, Op. 117 – No. 1, Intermezzo in E flat major; No. 2,
Intermezzo in B flat minor. Six Pieces, Op. 118. **Wilhelm Backhaus** (pf);
ᵃ**BBC Symphony Orchestra / Sir Adrian Boult;** ᵇ**Saxon State Orchestra / Karl Böhm.**
EMI Références mono Ⓕ CHS5 66418-2* (two discs: 157 minutes: ADD: 1/98).

Brahms Piano Concertos – No. 1 in D minor, Op. 15ᵃ; No. 2 in B flat major, Op. 83ᵇ.
25 Variations and Fugue on a Theme by G. F. Handel, Op. 24ᶜ. 16 Waltzes, Op. 39ᶜ.
Leon Fleisher (pf); ᵃᵇ**Cleveland Orchestra / George Szell.** Sony Classical Masterworks Heritage
ᶜmono/stereo Ⓜ Ⓞ MH2K63225* (two discs: 138 minutes: ADD: 4/98). Item marked ᵃ from
Columbia SAX2526 (5/64), ᵇSAX2534 (8/64), ᶜColumbia 33CX1839 (6/63).
Leon Fleisher and George Szell were two extraordinary and mutually responsive artists, Fleisher once
being described by Pierre Monteux as "the pianistic find of the century". In the First Concerto's
opening tutti Szell generates a flame-like peak and momentum that are matched to perfection by
Fleisher's youthful, tightly coiled pianism. You may find Szell's opening to the central *Adagio* plain-
speaking to a fault but Fleisher's reply, his "still small voice of calm", provides a haunting
compensation, and their combined forces in the finale are like a river in full spate: fierce and virtuosic
indeed. However, despite such white-hot intensity nothing is omitted, and there are constant
reminders of Artur Schnabel, Fleisher's "sainted" teacher (his own words), of a robust eloquence that
is, however, underlined by a formidably controlled and focused technique. Again, in the Second
Concerto Fleisher and Szell share their belief in the inexorable impetus and logic of great music and
yet there is no lack of lyrical speculation in, say, the opening or in a moment at 0'46" in the *Allegro
appassionato* of an almost Schumannesque ardour and gentleness. The *Andante's* dreaming *più lento*
is ideally poised and inward and in the finale the taut muscularity of Fleisher's and Szell's
musicianship suggests an underlying volcanic force that forbids all possible dalliance or superficiality.
The substantial encores or solo items, too, show Fleisher as one of those special artists who can
achieve the most concentrated musicianship without a hint of exaggeration or sentimentality. He can
take a severe hand to Brahms's *grazioso* in Var. 18 from Op. 24 but in the musical-box chimes of
Var. 20 his light pedal haze provides an imaginative recompense for a certain glassiness or severity
elsewhere. In the Op. 39 *Waltzes* he is as affectionate as he is vivacious and, overall, the resolution,
athleticism and authority of all these performances frequently silence criticism. The recordings may
show their age but they have been excellently remastered.

Brahms Piano Concerto No. 1 in D minor, Op. 15ᵃ.
Franck Symphonic Variationsᵇ.
Litolff Concerto symphonique No. 4 in D minor, Op. 102 – Scherzoᵇ. **Sir Clifford Curzon** (pf);
ᵃ**London Symphony Orchestra / George Szell;** ᵇ**London Philharmonic Orchestra / Sir Adrian Boult.**
Decca The Classic Sound Ⓜ 425 082-2DCS (74 minutes: ADD: 4/95). Item marked ᵃ from
SXL6023 (12/62), ᵇSXL2173 (2/60). *Gramophone classical 100.*　　　　ⒼⒼⒼ
It is debatable as to whether there is any other recording of the D minor Concerto that so instantly
takes fire and which burns thereafter with so pure and steady a flame. To all outward appearances,
Curzon and Szell were an oddly contrasted couple; yet they worked wonderfully well together, in
Mozart and here in Brahms. The 1962 recording still comes up phenomenally well, despite some
occasional muzzling of the orchestra's bass texturing. A merciful muzzling, you might think, given the
frequency with which Szell detects and detonates the small arsenal of explosive devices Brahms has

hidden in the undergrowth. We obviously don't lack great recordings of this concerto but this 1962 Decca version remains as collectable as any. The fill-ups to this repackaged CD are also welcome. The Franck is beginning to sound its age technically but the performance is charming. As for the Litolff, it is irresistible, a gem of a performance, well recorded.

Brahms Piano Concerto No. 1 in D minor, Op. 15. **Hélène Grimaud** (pf); **Staatskapelle Berlin / Kurt Sanderling.** Erato Ⓕ 3984-21633-2 (50 minutes: DDD: 7/98). Recorded live in 1997.
Gramophone Editor's choice.   Ⓖ

None of the classic recordings are live (though they sound it, the two Szell-conducted recordings in particular). This one is. Indeed, the fact of being able to play the concerto live with Kurt Sanderling, grandest and most charismatic of living Brahms conductors, is something the soloist, Hélène Grimaud, makes much of in a lengthy interview in the CD booklet, Sanderling's greatest Brahms monument being his 1971 Dresden symphony cycle. What is remarkable about the present performance is the way it so richly meets, matches and enriches the vision of the work that Sanderling sets before us. Grimaud is not Arrau nor is she Serkin, but the weight of sound and clarity of detail she brings to the work has elements of both their styles. Her critics will say that there are times when she plays in a way that is distressingly old-fashioned, with spread chords and elasticated rhythms. So rhapsodic a style goes against the grain of an age whose opinion-formers would confiscate Brahms entirely from the romantic tendency if left to their own devices. Indeed, such a style would go against the grain of Brahms's concerto itself were its riper manifestations not confined to the big solo meditations. In the end, Grimaud cannot take too many liberties because Sanderling – for all his imaginative generosity – is a stickler over dynamics and a benign despot where rhythm and pulse are concerned. In the slow movement, Grimaud's playing is both grand and simple, which is not so much a matter of technique or private inclination as a case of her being symbiotically at one with a conception of the work that treats the two opening movements as different sides of the same coin. The recording is very fine. How the performance will wear is difficult to predict. You are, however, urged to try it and find yourself marvelling afresh at the work – which is usually a good sign.

Brahms Piano Concerto No. 2 in B flat major, Op. 83. **Maurizio Pollini** (pf); **Berlin Philharmonic Orchestra / Claudio Abbado.** DG Ⓕ 453 505-2GH (49 minutes: DDD: 4/98). Recorded live in 1995.   ⒼⒼⒼ

Pollini's and Abbado's Second is among the most formidably single-minded on record. This does not mean a chilling exclusivity, one that, humanly speaking, omits too much in its quest for a crystalline perfection. On the contrary, the sense is of a granitic reading stripped of all surplus gesture, preening mannerism or overt display, intent only on the unveiling of a musical or moral truth. Again, this is hardly the sort of performance which allows you to savour this or that pianistic luxury, to delight in spectacular octaves here or a ravishing *dolce* there, and there will be listeners who, more in love with pianism than with great music-making, will turn away awed but unmoved, ultimately feeling short-changed. Their opening at once suggests a promise of the epic journey to come and in that moment when, as Tovey once put it, "the air seems full of whispering and the beating of mighty wings" their performance achieves a rare sense of transcendence, of an inspiration above and beyond the printed page. Again, in the *Scherzo* or *Allegro appassionato* Brahms's octave and double-note play at 5'00" is less an opportunity for technical wizardry than a scarifying musical commentary. It is also doubtful whether many artists have achieved such sublimity in the *Andante* (not forgetting the Berlin Philharmonic's most eloquent but unsung cellist) where they combine, most notably in the *più Adagio*, to create an astonishing sense of "the still centre of the turning world". Their way, too, with Brahms's "great and child-like finale" (Tovey again) has a tensile strength that forbids all dalliance. This recording is a memento of a grand and almost palpable occasion that clearly stunned its audience – there is never a sneeze or sniffle – into submission. Here, surely, is a performance above the vagaries of changing taste and fashion; one which could achieve a timeless validity.

Brahms Double Concerto in A minor, Op. 102ª. Piano Quartet No. 3 in C minor, Op. 60ᵇ.
Isaac Stern (vn); ᵇ**Jaime Laredo** (va); **Yo-Yo Ma** (vc); ᵇ**Emanuel Ax** (pf); ª**Chicago Symphony Orchestra / Claudio Abbado.** CBS Masterworks Ⓕ MK42387 (68 minutes: DDD: 6/88).
Brahms Double Concerto in A minor, Op. 102ª.
Schumann Cello Concerto in A minor, Op. 129. ª**Ilya Kaler** (vn); **Maria Kliegel** (vc);
National Symphony Orchestra of Ireland / Andrew Constantine. Naxos Ⓢ 8 550938
(59 minutes: DDD: 10/95). *Gramophone Editor's choice.*

The grave, declamatory utterances at the beginning of the Double Concerto tell us much about the nature of what will follow. They can also reveal a great deal about the two soloists who enter in turn with solo cadenzas separated by thematic orchestral material. On the CBS disc, perhaps surprisingly, it is the much younger man, Yo-Yo Ma, who brings out most strongly the noble gravity of the composer's inspiration, while the relatively veteran Isaac Stern is more melodious and spontaneous-sounding. The music's steady but unhurried paragraphs are very well handled by Claudio Abbado and the excellent Chicago Symphony Orchestra is responsive and pretty faithfully balanced with the soloists. This is a performance to satisfy rather than to thrill, perhaps, but satisfy it does. The recording is rich and rather reverberant, notably in orchestral tuttis. The powerful C minor Piano

Quartet is also well played and provides a substantial partner to the concerto. Apparently Brahms once said that it had the mood of a man thinking of suicide, but one hastens to say that it is nothing like as gloomy as that would suggest.

The Brahms and Schumann concertos make an excellent and apt coupling, here on Naxos given warmly spontaneous-sounding performances, very well recorded. The violinist, Ilya Kaler, is as clean in attack and intonation as Maria Kliegel. Kliegel in her opening cadenza allows herself full freedom, but any feeling that this is to be an easygoing, small-scale reading is dispelled in the main *Allegro*, which is clean and fresh, sharp in attack, helped by full-bodied sound. Kaler and Kliegel make the second subject tenderly expressive without having to use exaggerated rubato. Similarly there is no self-indulgence in the soaring main melody of the central *Andante*, but no lack of warmth or tenderness either. The finale is then unhurried but has dance-rhythms so beautifully sprung and such delicate pointing of phrases that any lack of animal excitement is amply replaced by wit and a sense of fun. In the Schumann Kliegel takes a spacious, lyrical view of the first movement, using a soft-grained tone at the start with wide vibrato. She then builds up the power of the performance, and with Constantine providing sympathetic accompaniment, the spontaneous expression is most compelling. So, too, is the simple, dedicated playing in the central *Langsam*, and, as in the Brahms, Kliegel brings witty pointing to the finale, not least in the second subject. The balance of the soloist is good.

Additional recommendations ...

...Double Concerto[b]. **Beethoven** Triple Concerto in C major, Op. 56[a]. [a]**Rudolf Serkin** (pf); [a]**Jaime Laredo**, [b]**Isaac Stern** (vns); [a]**Leslie Parnas**, [b]**Leonard Rose** (vcs); [a]**Marlboro Festival Orchestra / Alexander Schneider;** [b]**Philadelphia Orchestra / Eugene Ormandy.** CBS Masterworks Portrait Ⓜ MPK44842* (71 minutes: ADD: 11/89). Ⓖ Ⓖ Ⓖ

...Double Concerto[a]. **Strauss** Don Quixote, Op. 35[b]. [a]**Nathan Milstein** (vn); [b]**Joseph de Pasquale** (va); **Gregor Piatigorsky** (vc); [a]**Philadelphia Robin Hood Dell Orchestra / Fritz Reiner;** [b]**Boston Symphony Orchestra / Charles Munch.** RCA Ⓜ 09026 61485-2* (71 minutes: ADD: 10/93).

...Double Concerto[a]. **Mendelssohn** Violin Concerto in E minor, Op. 64. **Itzhak Perlman** (vn); [a]**Yo-Yo Ma** (vc); **Chicago Symphony Orchestra / Daniel Barenboim.** Teldec Ⓔ 0630-15870-2 (59 minutes: DDD: 7/97).

Brahms 21 Hungarian Dances. **Stuttgart Radio Symphony Orchestra / Georges Prêtre.** Forlane Ⓕ UCD16770 (57 minutes: DDD: 3/98). Recorded 1997.

Georges Prêtre has been honorary guest conductor of the Stuttgart Radio Symphony Orchestra since 1995 and he brings a touch of Gallic flamboyance to these delightful, variously orchestrated dances. The playing is mostly spirited and responsive, and the recording pleasantly blended save that the brass are sometimes a mite recessed. The First *Hungarian Dance* is bouncy and keenly accented; the Fourth features a novel 'question-and-answer' effect between the two halves of the principal melody; the Fifth is more elegant than rustic; the Tenth pleasingly vivacious; the Fourteenth broad and bold (almost like a majestic fragment from one of Brahms's larger orchestral works); the Sixteenth warmly impassioned (with some of the best string-playing on the disc) and the Twentieth employs some telling rubato. There is also a 'CD-ROM/extra multimedia' rehearsal and concert track – six minutes' worth – for use with your PC. This is an enjoyable disc and a fine sampling of a highly competent radio orchestra on good form.

Brahms Serenades – No. 1 in D major, Op. 11; No. 2 in A major, Op. 16. **West German Sinfonia / Dirk Joeres.** IMP Classics Ⓜ PCD2046 (79 minutes: DDD: 5/93). Recorded 1992.

If the term serenade suggests something which is open-hearted and uncomplicated then Brahms's two compositions in this form follow classical conventions up to a point. Each work has an appealing geniality and mellow warmth, but Brahms had a perpetually serious side to his nature, and there's always a nearby cloud threatening to move over the sun. Such mixed characteristics are particularly evident in the Second Serenade, which is scored without violins, and lacks the brightness which upper strings bring to orchestral textures. It is no easy task for a conductor to balance the opposing elements in either work, but Dirk Joeres manages this very successfully. He has at his disposal a very fine body of players, who are given clear, high-quality recordings. In the faster, more outgoing sections of each score he points the rhythms very skilfully, and he shapes the slower, more inward movements in a highly sympathetic, attentive fashion. Even the First Serenade's long *Adagio no troppo* movement, which so easily loses direction, is kept on course through Joeres's subtle use of phrase and pulse.

Additional recommendation ...

...No. 1. **Elgar** In the South, Op. 50. **La Scala Philharmonic Orchestra, Milan / Riccardo Muti.** Sony Classical Ⓕ SK57973 (71 minutes: DDD: 1/95).

...Nos. 1 and 2. **London Symphony Orchestra / Michael Tilson Thomas.** Sony Classical Theta Ⓜ SMK60134 (78 minutes: DDD: 2/98).

Brahms Orchestral Works. **Concertgebouw Orchestra / Bernard Haitink.** Philips Bernard Haitink Symphony Edition Ⓑ 442 068-2PB4 (four discs: 291 minutes: ADD: 9/94). Recorded 1970-80. Symphonies – No. 1 in C minor, Op. 68 (from 6500 519, 11/73); No. 2 in D major, Op. 73 (6500 375, 7/75); No. 3 in F major, Op. 90 (6500 155, 3/71); No. 4 in E minor, Op. 98 (6500 389, 10/73). Variations on a Theme by Haydn, Op. 56*a*, "St Antoni" (6500 375). Tragic Overture, Op. 81 (6500

155). Academic Festival Overture, Op. 80 (412 002-1PS, 8/84). Hungarian Dances – No. 1 in
G minor; No. 3 in F major; No. 10 in F major (all new to UK. Recorded 1980). Serenades –
No. 1 in D major, Op. 11 (9500 322, 2/78); No. 2 in A major, Op. 16 (412 002-1PS).   Ⓖ
Concertgebouw standards at the time of Haitink's survey (1970-80) left little to be desired. Perhaps
the clarinets don't always overcome reservations about their tone and intonation with the sensitivity
of their phrasing; but the horns invariably do, and more often than not Brahms's favourite instrument
is a source of joy in these recordings, blazing gloriously at appropriate moments (especially in the
Fourth Symphony), or opening up and sustaining huge vistas in the 'dawn' of the First's finale. As to
the strings, Haitink's insistence on firmly defined (though never over-emphatic) rhythms from the
bass-lines up is altogether exceptional; there are countless examples, but most memorable of all is the
cellos' and basses' ostinato that sees the Second Symphony's finale in the home strait. What an
articulate, integrated Brahms sound this is, too; a case of conductor and engineers easily achieving
their aims working in a familiar acoustic. Nor is that acoustic to be taken for granted; how
unappealing is the equally informative but stark sound of Klemperer's Philharmonia and Toscanini's
NBC tapings in comparison. There is a degree of tape hiss, most noticeable in the Third Symphony
where there is also a trace of hardness, and a chill to the string tone in parts of the Second Symphony,
but none of this is serious. The only movement you may initially find overly sober is the first of the
Third Symphony, taken very broadly, though it is determined and imposing, and the launching of the
coda is stupendously powerful. All in all, there is no better way of getting to know the Brahms
orchestral works on a budget.

Additional recommendations ...
...Nos. 1-4. Variations on a Theme by Haydn. Academic Festival Overture. Hungarian Dances
Nos. 17-21. Tragic Overture. **Cleveland Orchestra / George Szell.**
Sony Classical Ⓑ SB3K48398 (three discs: 214 minutes: ADD).
...Hungarian Dances Nos. 1-21. **Budapest Symphony Orchestra / István Bogár.**
Naxos Ⓢ 8 550110 (49 minutes: DDD).
...Variations on a Theme by Haydn. *Coupled with works by various composers.* **Philharmonic**
Symphony Orchestra of New York / Arturo Toscanini. Pearl mono Ⓕ GEMMCDS9373*
(three discs: 230 minutes: ADD: 3/90). *Gramophone classical 100. See review in the Collections*
section; refer to the Index.   ⒼⒼⒼ
...Nos. 1-4. Academic Festival Overture. Tragic Overture, Op. 81.
Chicago Symphony Orchestra / Sir Georg Solti.
Decca Symphony Editions Ⓑ 430 799-2DC4 (four discs: 199 minutes: ADD/DDD: 4/92).
...Nos. 1-4. Variations on a theme by Haydn. Tragic Overture. Academic Festival Overture.
Chicago Symphony Orchestra / Daniel Barenboim.
Erato Ⓕ 4509-94817-2 (four discs: 212 minutes: DDD: 11/94).
...Nos. 1[a]; No. 2[b]; No. 3[c]; No. 4[d]. Tragic Overture[c]. Variations on a Theme by Haydn[e].
Berlin Philharmonic Orchestra / Rudolf Kempe.
Testament [bde]mono/[ac]stereo Ⓕ SBT3054* (three discs: 190 minutes: ADD: 4/95).
...Nos. 1-4. **North German Radio Symphony Orchestra / Günter Wand.**
RCA Ⓑ 74321 20283-2 (two discs: 158 minutes: DDD: 5/95).   Ⓖ
...Variations and Fugue on a Theme by Haydn. *Coupled with works by various composers.*
The Solti Orchestral Project, Carnegie Hall / Sir Georg Solti. Decca Ⓕ 444 458-2DH (77 minutes:
DDD: 12/95). *See review in the Collections section; refer to the Index.*   Ⓖ
...Nos. 1-4. Variations on a Theme by Haydn[a]. Hungarian Dances[a] – No. 1 in G minor; No. 3 in
F major; No. 10 in F major. **Beethoven** Overtures – Coriolan, Op. 62[a]; Leonore No. 2, Op. 72[b].
[a]**Vienna Philharmonic Orchestra;** [b]**Berlin Philharmonic Orchestra / Wilhelm Furtwängler.**
EMI Références mono Ⓜ CHS5 65513-2* (three discs: ADD: 2/96).   ⒼⒼ
...Nos. 1-4. Variations on a Theme by Haydn. **Staatskapelle Dresden / Kurt Sanderling.**
RCA Victor Classical Navigator Ⓑ 74321 30367-2 (three discs: 197 minutes: ADD: 1/97).
...Nos. 1-4. Variations on a Theme by Haydn. Academic Festival Overture. **Scottish Chamber**
Orchestra / Sir Charles Mackerras. Telarc Ⓕ CD80450 (three discs: 199 minutes: DDD: 10/97).
Includes original version of the second movement of Symphony No. 1.

Brahms Symphonies – No. 1 in C minor, Op. 68; No. 2 in D major, Op. 73; No. 3 in F major,
Op. 90; No. 4 in E minor, Op. 98. Variations on a Theme by Haydn, Op. 56a, "St Antoni
Chorale". Academic Festival Overture, Op. 80. Tragic Overture, Op. 81. **Berlin Philharmonic**
Orchestra / Nikolaus Harnoncourt. Teldec Ⓕ 0630-13136-2 (three discs: 214 minutes: DDD:
11/97). Recorded live 1996-7. *Gramophone Editor's record of the month.*
Any fears that Nikolaus Harnoncourt's Brahms will be quirky, provocative or abrasive can be
dispelled. There are interpretative novelties (freshly considered articulation and clarified
counterpoint) and the Berlin strings project a smooth, curvaceous profile that is quite unlike, say,
Abbado's leanness, Furtwängler's lunging sonorities or the solid mass of tone habitually favoured by
Karajan. Harnoncourt makes a beeline for the brass, and the horns in particular. The live recordings
have remarkable presence and are mostly cough-free. The *Haydn* Variations serves as a useful sampler
for Harnoncourt's Brahms style as a whole, with an unforced vitality and many salient details subtly
underlined. The First Symphony's opening *Un poco sostenuto* seems a trifle soft-grained but the
pounding basses from bar 25 are beautifully caught and the first-movement *Allegro* is both powerful

and broadly paced. The *Andante sostenuto* slow movement is both limpid and conversational, with trance-like dialogue between oboe and clarinet and sparing use of vibrato among the strings. Harnoncourt makes real chamber music of the third movement, though he drives the trio section to a fierce climax, and the finale's first accelerating pizzicatos are truly *stringendo poco a poco* – the excitement certainly mounts, but only gradually. The main body of the movement generates considerable tension and moments are overwhelmingly exciting.

The Second Symphony's first movement is relatively restrained. Harnoncourt's strategy is to deliver a sombre exposition and a toughened development. Again, the slow movement is fluid and intimate, with some tender string playing. The third movement's rustling trio is disarmingly delicate and the finale, tightly held, keenly inflected and heavily accented: the coda threatens to break free and the effect is thrilling. First impressions of Harnoncourt's Third suggest a marginal drop in intensity, yet the first movement's peroration is so powerful, so insistent, that one retrospectively suspects that everything prior to it was mere preparation. The middle movements work well but it is the rough-hewn, flexibly-phrased finale that really 'makes' the performance. Like the Third, the Fourth opens with less import than some of its older rivals, yet the development intensifies perceptibly, the recapitulation's hushed *piano dolce* opening bars are held on the edge of a breath and the coda is recklessly headstrong. The slow movement has some heartfelt moments, the top-gear *Scherzo* is quite exhilarating and the finale, forged with the noble inevitability of a baroque passacaglia. Ultimately, Harnoncourt delivers a fine and tragic Fourth. The two overtures are hardly less absorbing. Harnoncourt's Brahms is the perfect antidote to routine, predictability and interpretative complacency.

Brahms Orchestral and Vocal Works. **NBC Symphony Orchestra / Arturo Toscanini.**
RCA Victor Gold Seal mono Ⓜ GD60325* (four discs: 267 minutes: ADD: 5/90).
Texts and translations included. Recorded 1948-53.
Symphonies – No. 1 in C minor, Op. 68 (from HMV ALP1012, 11/52); No. 2 in D major, Op. 73 (ALP1013, 11/52); No. 3 in F major, Op. 90 (ALP1166, 10/54); No. 4 in E minor, Op. 98 (ALP1029, 6/53). Double Concerto in A minor, Op. 102 (with Mischa Mischakoff, vn; Frank Miller, vc. RB16066, 7/58). Variations on a Theme by Haydn, Op. 56*a* (ALP1204, 12/54). Tragic Overture, Op. 81 (VCM3, 4/67). Academic Festival Overture, Op. 80 (VCM3, 4/67). Hungarian Dances – No. 1 in G minor; No. 17 in F sharp minor; No. 20 in E minor; No. 21 in E minor (ALP1235, 5/55). Gesang der Parzen, Op. 89 (Robert Shaw Chorale. AT125, 4/74). Liebeslieder-Walzer, Op. 52 (Chorus; Artur Balsam, Joseph Kahn, pfs. Recorded 1948. New to UK). ⒼⒼⒼ
Despite many reissues, technical tinkerings, and critical re-evaluations, the recordings of the great Italian maestro Arturo Toscanini still stand head and shoulders above those which have the unenviable task of rivalling his genius as conductor and interpreter. This generous Brahms set is an excellent example of why Toscanini's recordings are still essential. The readings of the four symphonies must stand as benchmarks against which others are compared, and generally are found wanting. Toscanini's command of this music is total: his sense of architecture is unfailing, his control of tempos and rubato are masterly, and his ability to persuade the NBC Symphony Orchestra to play with extraordinary dynamic variety and tonal beauty is proof of his genius. In addition to the symphonies the set contains a fiery performance of the Double Concerto with the orchestra's principals as eloquent, if occasionally overshadowed, soloists and excellent readings of the essential shorter works of Brahms: the *Haydn Variations, Academic* and *Tragic* Overtures and *Hungarian Dances*. And to round off the set there are good, if not perfect, performances of two choral works, the rarely performed *Song of the Fates* and the *Liebeslieder Waltzes, Op. 52*. The transfer to CD of the original tapes has been handled particularly well: the worst tonal excesses have been successfully tamed, and there is a fine sense of balance throughout. With such a giant as Toscanini recommendation really becomes superfluous. Suffice it to say that these recordings are testimony to the genius of one of the greatest conductors this century has ever known.
Additional recommendation …
…Hungarian Dances. **Dvořák** Symphonic Variations, B70. Czech Suite, B93. **North German Radio Symphony Orchestra / Sir John Eliot Gardiner.** DG Ⓕ 437 506-2GH (62 minutes: DDD: 6/93).

Brahms Symphony No. 1 in C minor, Op. 68. Gesang der Parzen, Op. 89[a].
[a]**Berlin Radio Chorus; Berlin Philharmonic Orchestra / Claudio Abbado.**
DG Ⓕ 431 790-2GH (58 minutes: DDD: 10/91). Recorded 1990. Ⓖ
Brahms Symphony No. 1 in C minor, Op. 68[a].
Wagner Siegfried Idyll[bc]. Siegfried – Siegfried's horn-call[c]. [c]**Dennis Brain** (hn);
[ab]**Philharmonia Orchestra / Guido Cantelli.** Testament mono Ⓕ SBT1012*
(62 minutes: ADD: 2/93). Item marked [a] from HMV ALP1152 (7/54),
[b]HMV DB9746/7 (4/52), [c]HMV C3622 (11/47). Recorded 1947-53. Ⓖ
Abbado's tempos are generally broad: his first movement (without its repeat) is as boldly emphatic as Klemperer's but he never stints on affection, and few would find fault with his warm, lyrical handling of the beautiful *Andante*, 'sostenuto', indeed! Abbado ventures between the score's little nooks and crannies, highlighting small details without impeding the music's flow or weakening the performance's overall structure. When the finale breaks from *Più Andante* to *Allegro non troppo, ma con brio* (not *too* fast, but with plenty of spirit), Abbado really goes for the burn, very much as Furtwängler did before

him. It's a truly inspired reading, grand but never grandiose; appreciative of Brahms's thick-set orchestration, but never stodgy. The fill-up is of enormous import, and opens with one of the composer's most inspired musical gestures: a bold, burgeoning *Maestoso*, anticipating the words "The gods should be feared/by the human race ...". *Gesang der Parzen*, or "Song of the Fates" is a setting of a particularly unsettling poem by Goethe, one that warns how the uplifted have particular reason to fear the gods, those who "turn their beneficent eyes away from whole races." Abbado surely sensed the terrible truth of that prophesy, and his reading of Op. 89 breathes a deeply disquieting air.

Cantelli conducts an interpretation of the Symphony which is free of any idiosyncrasy. Yet there is an extraordinary electricity in his conducting, a sense of concentration and conviction which lifts the performance into one of the greatest ever set down on record. The fiery young Italian makes the vintage Philharmonia play in an inspired fashion, and the 1953 mono recording is very acceptable. A slightly edgy string sound betrays the 1951 origin of the *Siegfried Idyll* recording, but the performance has a tenderness, warmth and eloquence which has never been surpassed. Dennis Brain's exuberant horn-call completes a very desirable Testament disc.

Additional recommendations ...
...No. 1. Tragic Overture. Academic Festival Overture. **Philharmonia Orchestra / Otto Klemperer.**
    EMI Studio Ⓜ CDM7 69651-2 (67 minutes: ADD: 1/90).
...No. 1. Variations on a Theme by Haydn. **London Classical Players / Roger Norrington.**
    EMI Ⓔ CDC7 54286-2 (61 minutes: DDD: 10/91). 🗲
...No. 1. **Royal Liverpool Philharmonic Orchestra / Marek Janowski.**
    ASV Quicksilva Ⓢ CDQS6101 (46 minutes: DDD: 9/93).
...No. 1. Variations on a Theme by Haydn. **North German Radio Symphony Orchestra /**
    Wilhelm Furtwängler. Tahra mono Ⓕ FURT1001* (69 minutes: ADD: 3/95).
...No. 1. **Schumann** Symphony No. 1 in B flat major, Op. 38, "Spring". **Berlin Philharmonic**
    Orchestra / Herbert von Karajan. DG The Originals Ⓜ 447 408-2GOR (76 minutes: ADD: 7/95).
...No. 1. Tragic Overture, Op. 81. **Staatskapelle Dresden / Kurt Sanderling.**
    RCA Victor Classical Navigator Ⓑ 74321 21285-2 (ADD: 1/97).
...No. 1. Nänie, Op. 82ᵃ. ᵃ**Tanglewood Festival Chorus; Boston Symphony Orchestra /**
    Bernard Haitink. Philips Ⓕ 442 799-2PH (60 minutes: DDD: 6/97).

Brahms Symphony No. 2 in D major, Op. 73. Tragic Overture, Op. 81. **Boston Symphony**
    Orchestra / Bernard Haitink. Philips Ⓕ 432 094-2PH (62 minutes: DDD: 10/92). Recorded 1990.
Brahms Symphony No. 2 in D major, Op. 73. Academic Festival Overture, Op. 80. **New York**
    Philharmonic Orchestra / Kurt Masur. Teldec Ⓕ 9031-77291-2 (50 minutes: DDD: 5/93).
    Recorded 1992.   Ⓖ
Brahms's Second Symphony is the warmest, most lyrical of the four, and Haitink's performance brings out those qualities to the full. His reading is very straightforward and unselfconscious: he allows the first movement to blossom attractively, but ensures that this process is achieved within a strong framework – one is always aware that detail has its secure place within the musical argument. The second movement's basic pulse is on the slow side, but Haitink's affectionate, watchful conducting ensures that the music flows naturally. The third movement is brought to life quite gently too, but accents are light and rhythms are sharp enough to ensure that the mood is still outgoing. In the finale Haitink sets a fast initial tempo, but he allows the music to breathe through the use of subtle inflexions and changes of pulse. There's plenty of excitement, but nothing is too hectic. In the Overture his basic tempo is quite measured, but again accents are sharp, and the score's dramatic element is well brought out. The playing of the Boston Symphony Orchestra is superlative, and the recording is excellent, apart from an occasional moment of slightly acid string tone.

Masur also brings warmth and affection to the symphony. In the first movement he maintains a strong sense of line, and paces the music more objectively than Haitink. The structure is clearer, but there's also a natural, unforced lyricism. The *Adagio* has a natural ebb and flow, and once again Masur makes the listener aware of the music's shape and argument very clearly. After a neatly pointed *Allegretto* the finale is given a beautifully balanced, strongly argued reading which eschews superficial excitement, but satisfies through the feeling of a symphonic argument brought to a logical conclusion. To sum up, Haitink caresses the music with more subjective warmth than Masur, whose reading by no means lacks affection, but is more architectural and objective. The New York Philharmonic respond to Masur with highly sensitive, very accomplished playing, and Teldec's attractively warm but clearly recorded disc is completed by a genial, uplifting *Academic Festival Overture*.

Additional recommendations ...
...Nos. 2 and 3. **Columbia Symphony Orchestra / Bruno Walter.**
    Sony Classical Bruno Walter Edition Ⓜ SMK64471 (75 minutes: ADD).
...No. 2. Alto Rhapsody, Op. 53ᵃ. ᵃ**Christa Ludwig** (mez); ᵃ**Philharmonia Chorus; Philharmonia**
    Orchestra / Otto Klemperer. EMI Studio Ⓜ CDM7 69650-2 (51 minutes: ADD: 1/90).   ⒼⒼ
...No. 2. Alto Rhapsodyᵃ. ᵃ**Marjana Lipovšek** (contr); ᵃ**Ernst Senff Choir; Berlin Philharmonic**
    Orchestra / Claudio Abbado. DG Ⓕ 427 643-2GH (60 minutes: DDD: 2/90).   Ⓖ
...No. 2. **Schumann** Symphony No. 2 in C major, Op. 61. **Berlin Philharmonic Orchestra /**
    Herbert von Karajan. DG Ⓜ 435 067-2GGA (75 minutes: ADD: 11/91).
...No. 2. **Royal Liverpool Philharmonic Orchestra / Marek Janowski.**
    ASV Quicksilva Ⓢ CDQS6102 (58 minutes: DDD: 11/93).

...No. 2. Tragic Overture. **London Classical Players / Roger Norrington.**
 EMI Reflexe Ⓕ CDC7 54875-2 (55 minutes: DDD: 12/93). ✔
...Tragic Overture. *Coupled with works by various composers.* **London Philharmonic Orchestra /**
 Sir Thomas Beecham. Dutton Laboratories mono Ⓑ CDLX7009* (75 minutes: ADD: 10/94).
 See review in the Collections section; refer to the Index.
...No. 2. Academic Festival Overture. Tragic Overture. *Coupled with works by various composers.*
 London Symphony Orchestra / Pierre Monteux. Philips The Early Years Ⓜ 442 544-2PM5* (five
 discs: 311 minutes: ADD: 12/94). *See review in the Collections section; refer to the Index.* ⒼⒼⒼ
...Nos. 2 and 3. **Cleveland Orchestra / George Szell.**
 Sony Classical Essential Classics Ⓑ SBK47652 (74 minutes: AAD/ADD: 6/96).
...Nos. 2 and 3. **Staatskapelle Dresden / Kurt Sanderling.**
 RCA Victor Classical Navigator Ⓑ 74321 17894-2 (ADD: 1/97).
...No. 2. *Coupled with works by* **Mozart** *and* **R. Strauss** Vienna Philharmonic Orchestra /
 Herbert von Karajan. EMI Karajan Edition mono Ⓜ CDM5 66390-2* (72 minutes: ADD: 9/97).

Brahms Symphony No. 3 in F major, Op. 90. Tragic Overture, Op. 81. Schicksalslied, Op. 54[a].
 [a]**Ernst-Senff Choir; Berlin Philharmonic Orchestra / Claudio Abbado.** DG Ⓕ 429 765-2GH
 (68 minutes: DDD: 1/91). Ⓖ
Brahms Symphony No. 3 in F major, Op. 90.
Schoenberg Chamber Symphony No. 1, Op. 9. **Royal Concertgebouw Orchestra /**
 Riccardo Chailly. Decca Ⓕ 436 466-2DH (58 minutes: DDD: 9/93). Recorded 1991-2.
Abbado's disc is gloriously programmed for straight-through listening. He gets off to a cracking start
with an urgently impassioned *Tragic Overture* in which the credentials of the Berlin Philharmonic to
make a richly idiomatic, Brahmsian sound – already well accepted – are substantially reaffirmed. A
wide-eyed, breathtaking account of the *Schicksalslied* ("Song of Destiny") follows to provide sound
contrast before the wonders of the Third Symphony are freshly explored. This is a reading of the
Symphony to be savoured; it is underpinned throughout by a rhythmic vitality which binds the four
movements together with a forward thrust, making the end inevitable right from the opening bars.
Even in the moments of repose and, especially, the warmly-felt *Andante*, Abbado never lets the music
forget its ultimate goal. Despite this, there are many moments of wonderful solo and orchestral
playing along the way in which there is time to delight, and Abbado seems to bring out that affable,
Bohemian-woods, Dvořák-like element in Brahms's music to a peculiar degree in this performance.
The Symphony is recorded with a particular richness and some may find the heady waltz of the third
movement done too lushly, emphasized by Abbado's lingering tempo. Nevertheless, this is splendid
stuff, and not to be missed.
   Chailly's No. 3 is a very likeable, impressive reading which just seems to lose confidence in itself
from time to time. The recording is outstanding, as is the playing of the full orchestra. Chailly's
account of the first movement is well conceived, although lacking a certain natural flow. The basic
tempo is ideal, there is plenty of spirit and expression, but the music seems slightly ill at ease with
itself. Matters improve greatly in the second movement, which moves forward calmly and easily, with
plenty of natural warmth. Only an occasional awkwardness in the phrasing disturbs an otherwise
almost ideal account of the third movement, and the finale is very impressively managed throughout.
Although Abbado remains the top recommendation, this disc is very desirable, perhaps mainly for the
coupling. Schoenberg's *Chamber Symphony* dates from an early stage in his development, and shows
tonality under severe pressure and in fact cracking apart under the composer's assault. This feeling of
pressure, of music somehow fighting to get out, is something which needs to be brought out strongly
in performance, and Chailly succeeds brilliantly in conveying the score's wild intensity. He drives the
music very hard, chooses fast, almost hectic tempos, and gets superbly committed playing from his 15
orchestral soloists. The influence of the older composer is apparent not only in the work's few quieter
passages, which are shaped very beautifully by Chailly, but in certain rhythmic characteristics, which
sound rather like Brahms caught up in a nightmare. The recording is faultless.
Additional recommendations ...
...No. 3 . Variations on a Theme by Haydn. **Royal Liverpool Philharmonic Orchestra /**
 Marek Janowski. ASV Quicksilva Ⓢ CDQS6103 (53 minutes: DDD).
...No. 3. Variations on a Theme by Haydn. **Hallé Orchestra / Stanislaw Skrowaczewski.**
 IMP Classics Ⓜ PCD2039 (60 minutes: ADD: 4/89).
...Nos. 3 and 4. **Philharmonia Orchestra / Otto Klemperer.**
 EMI mono Ⓜ CDM7 69649-2* (76 minutes: ADD: 1/90).
...No. 3. Serenade No. 1 in D major, Op. 11. **Belgian Radio and Television Philharmonic Orchestra,**
 Brussels / Alexander Rahbari. Naxos Ⓢ 8 550280 (77 minutes: DDD: 1/92).
...Nos. 3 and 4. **London Classical Players / Roger Norrington.**
 EMI Ⓕ CDC5 56118-2 (73 minutes: DDD: 8/96). ✔

Brahms Symphony No. 3 in F major, Op. 90[a].
Schubert Symphony No. 5 in B flat major, D485[b].
Mendelssohn The Hebrides, Op. 26[c]. **Chicago Symphony Orchestra / Fritz Reiner.**
 RCA Victor Gold Seal Ⓜ 09026 61793-2 (69 minutes: ADD: 9/95). Items marked [a] from SB2007
 (12/58), [b]SB2134 (1/62), [c]SB2059 (2/60). Ⓖ

Perhaps the very opening of the Brahms is unexceptional; it's not very passionate; maybe there is a little too much of what Reiner called his "self-controlled control". However, slowly but surely, the benefits of that control make themselves felt. The first movement is tautly drawn; no undue roaming in the pre-recapitulation gloaming. Speaking of control and pivotal points, as we turn into this movement's coda, the reins are loosened and the ride is fabulously exciting. The slow movement's mellow (here, very autumnal) pastoral takes its time, and is wonderfully phrased and shaded. The concentration is so intense you can almost sense the falcon eye surveying the scene. And this is how to record Brahms: forget the over-ripe textures and fudged balances of many a modern Brahms symphony recording; here one-and-all is for all to hear (with, admittedly, a moderate amount of tape hiss). No small thanks to Reiner, this is a lean, athletic, supremely articulate, eloquent and well-tempered Brahms sound. With slimmed-down strings, the Schubert is as light on its feet, as perfectly balanced, as poised and as stylishly pointed as any period-instrument or chamber orchestra performance, and very few of them are as immaculately precise. As in the Brahms, there are no repeats, except in the Minuet and Trio, where the repeats are subtly varied and the *ritardandos* consummately handled. The whole is suave and sleek, but shaped, savoured and illumined by the hand of an epicure. As to *The Hebrides*, the way Reiner holds on to the long notes in those wind calls about a third of the way in is very striking indeed, as is the timpani playing, superbly forthright (and very clear) but always musical. Drawbacks? Well, it's as Reiner commented on receipt of the news that he and his orchestra had become box office: "One must take the good with the good".

Brahms Symphony No. 4 in E minor, Op. 98. **Vienna Philharmonic Orchestra / Carlos Kleiber.**
   DG Ⓕ 400 037-2GH (39 minutes: DDD: 9/85). From 2532 003 (4/81). Recorded 1980.
   Gramophone classical 100.   ⒼⒼⒼ
Brahms Symphony No. 4 in E minor, Op. 98. Variations on a Theme by Haydn, Op. 56*a*,
   "St Antoni". **Boston Symphony Orchestra / Bernard Haitink.** Philips Ⓕ 434 991-2PH (62 minutes:
   DDD: 9/94). Recorded 1992.
Carlos Kleiber's reading of Brahms's Fourth Symphony is highly individual and thought-provoking but those listeners who know Kleiber from his thrilling recordings of Beethoven's Fifth and Seventh Symphonies and are expecting similarly uncompromising, high-tension performances with enormous muscular energy are in for a surprise!. His reading certainly has plenty of muscle, but he shows considerable patience and generosity in his handling of Brahms's long, constantly developing melodic lines. Sound is generally good, though the bass may need assistance on some equipment. There is a little more separation of timbre in the sound of Haitink's Boston Brahms Fourth and *Haydn* Variations than in his previous 1972-73 Amsterdam recordings; perhaps marginally less ambient warmth in tuttis, though certainly more than in Kleiber's. However, the 20 years that separate Haitink's accounts have brought some much more marked musical changes, not only in his overall view – he adds a minute to each of the symphony's first two movements – but in a more acute moment-by-moment control (comparable, at times to Kleiber's), pliant pacing and communicative phrasing. The first movement is now not so much an older man's Brahms as an older Brahms, more poignantly reflective, more given to mysterious depths, less heroic and purposeful in overall cast though still able to bestir himself mightily, and when the coda arrives, to declaim with the terrifying rage of age. The second movement (smoother clarinet tone in Boston), now serene and very slow indeed has a timeless Brucknerian tread. The *Scherzo* is quite as fearsomely jocular as before, though with more interesting shadings. This is Brahms playing, conducting and recording of real stature, not as intensely dramatic in the symphony as the exacting Kleiber, but worthy to stand alongside him.
Additional recommendations ...
... No. 4. Variations on a Theme by Haydn. **Boston Symphony Orchestra / Bernard Haitink.**
   Philips Ⓕ 434 991-2PH (62 minutes: DDD: 9/94).
...No. 4. Academic Festival Overture. **Chicago Symphony Orchestra / Daniel Barenboim.**
   Erato Ⓜ 4509-95194-2 (51 minutes: DDD: 11/94).
...No. 4. Variations on a Theme by Haydn. **Staatskapelle Dresden / Kurt Sanderling.**
   RCA Victor Classical Navigator Ⓑ 74321 24206-2 (ADD: 1/97).

Brahms (orch. Schoenberg) Piano Quartet No. 1 in G minor, Op. 25.
Bach (orch. Schoenberg) Prelude and Fugue in E flat major, BWV552, "St Anne". Schmücke dich,
   o liebe Seele, BWV654. Komm, Gott Schöpfer, BWV631. **Houston Symphony Orchestra /**
   Christoph Eschenbach. RCA Victor Red Seal Ⓕ 09026 68658-2 (70 minutes: DDD: 10/97).
   Recorded 1995.
In terms of style, the Schoenberg Piano Quartet orchestration is rather like a private conversation re-scripted for the theatre. Only the most sensitive Brahms conductors can make it work and this is an excellent performance from Eschenbach and the Houston orchestra. Tempos are generally quite broad although the "Intermezzo" second movement is both keenly accented and properly pensive. Eschenbach grants considerable weight to the brass lines, while in the *Andante con moto*, burbling woodwinds are extraordinarily clear. Only the *Rondo alla zingarese* third movement seems to be marginally underpowered, although it, too, is crystal clear. Certainly Schoenberg's desire "once to hear everything in the piece" is vividly realized and the recording captures the whole dazzling spectacle, from glittering high percussion, through tactile *col legno* strings to sonorous low brass. The couplings are both highly appropriate and superbly performed. Best is *Schmücke dich* which, although

heavily modified contrapuntally, has a mellow grandeur that is inherent in the original. *Komm, Gott*, with its bony textures and filled out harmonies, is both rugged and celebratory and the *St Anne* Prelude and Fugue's principal glory is its variously orchestrated triple fugue. Still, Eschenbach and his players do all four transcriptions proud and, viewed as a whole, this excellent CD can be recommended virtually without reservation.

Brahms String Sextets – No. 1 in B flat major, Op. 18; No. 2 in G major, Op. 36. **Raphael Ensemble** (James Clark, Elizabeth Wexler, vns; Sally Beamish, Roger Tapping, vas; Andrea Hess, Rhydian Shaxson, vcs). Hyperion Ⓕ CDA66276 (74 minutes: DDD: 1/89). Recorded 1988. **Ⓖ**
Completed after the First Piano Concerto, but still comparatively early works, the Sextets are typified by lush textures, ardent emotion, and wonderfully memorable melodic lines. The first is the warmer, more heart-on-the-sleeve piece, balancing with complete naturalness a splendidly lyrical first movement, an urgent, dark set of intricate variations, a lively rustic dance of a *Scherzo*, and a placidly flowing finale. The Second Sextet inhabits at first a more mysterious world of half-shadows, occasionally rent by glorious moments of sunlight. The finale, however, casts off doubt and ends with affirmation. Both works are very susceptible to differing modes of interpretation, and the Raphael Ensemble has established very distinctive views of each, allowing the richness of the texture its head without obscuring the lines, and selecting characteristically distinct tone qualities to typify the two works. The recording is clear and analytic without robbing the sound of its warmth and depth. Altogether an impressive recording début for this ensemble.
Additional recommendations ...
...Nos. 1 and 2. **Academy of St Martin in the Fields Chamber Ensemble.**
   Chandos Ⓕ CHAN9151 (78 minutes: DDD: 8/93).
...No. 1ᵃ. Piano Trio No. 1 in B major, Op. 8ᵇ. **Isaac Stern,** ᵃ**Alexander Schneider** (vns); ᵃ**Milton Katims,** ᵃ**Milton Thomas** (vas); **Pablo Casals,** ᵃ**Madeline Foley** (vcs); ᵇ**Dame Myra Hess** (pf).
   Sony Classical Casals Edition mono Ⓜ SMK58994* (77 minutes: ADD: 5/94). **ⒼⒼ**
...Nos. 1 and 2. **L'Archibudelli.** Sony Classical Vivarte Ⓕ SK68252 (70 minutes: DDD: 12/96). 🖝

Brahms Clarinet Quintet in B minor, Op. 115ᵃ. String Quartet No. 2 in A minor, Op. 51 No. 2.
ᵃ**Karl Leister** (cl); **Leipzig Quartet** (Andreas Seidel, Tilman Büning, vns; Ivo Bauer, va; Matthias Moosdorf, vc). Dabringhaus und Grimm Ⓕ MDG307 0719-2 (71 minutes: DDD: 5/97).
One of the most attractive qualities of this version of a well-loved quintet is the skill with which the artists, abetted by the record producer, have integrated the clarinet into the string textures. Having listened more creatively than any other composer to Mozart's example, Brahms allows the clarinet to become part of the tone colour in the string ensemble; and he has also followed the implications, as not all his interpreters seem to understand. Here, the little falling third theme, one of his lifelong obsessions, moves in and out of the musical texture with wonderful subtlety, so that the return of the opening figure at the very end needs no special emphasis but is a natural conclusion. Leister is an artist of long skill and experience, and also of great musical intelligence; the qualities tell. They also mean that there is no need to confer upon the performance anything approaching the sentimentality which can afflict it, in the name of 'nostalgia' as the old composer looks affectionately back upon his life's work. This is quite a robust performance, clearly appreciated by the enthusiastic young string quartet, who give a suitably matching account of the Op. 51 work which was one of the first quartets Brahms allowed into the light of day. There are, of course, any number of performances of the quintet (a familiar coupling is, naturally, Mozart's quintet), but this is a unique one.
Additional recommendations ...
...Clarinet Quintet. Clarinet Trio in A minor, Op. 114. **Thea King** (cl); **Gabrieli Quartet;**
   Karina Georgian (vc); **Clifford Benson** (pf). Hyperion Ⓕ CDA66107 (65 minutes: DDD: 2/87).
...Clarinet Quintetᵃ. **Mozart** Clarinet Quintet in A major, K581ᵇ. **Gervase de Peyer** (cl);
   Members of the **Melos Ensemble.** EMI Ⓜ CDM7 63116-2 (65 minutes: ADD: 11/89) **Ⓖ**
...Clarinet Quintetᵃ. Clarinet Trioᵃᵇ. **József Balogh** (cl); ᵃ**Csaba Onczay** (vc); ᵇ**Danubius Quartet;**
   ᵃ**Jenö Jandó** (pf). Naxos Ⓢ 8 550391 (59 minutes: DDD: 9/93).
...Clarinet Quintet. **Mozart** Clarinet Quintet in A major, K581. **Harold Wright** (cl);
   Boston Symphony Chamber Players. Philips Ⓕ 442 149-2PH (72 minutes: DDD: 9/94).
...Clarinet Quintet. **Mozart** Clarinet Quintet in A major, K581. **David Campbell** (cl);
   Bingham Quartet. Olympia Ⓕ OCD637 (70 minutes: DDD: 6/98).

Brahms Piano Quintet in F minor, Op. 34ᵃ. String Quartet No. 2 in A minor, Op. 51. **Borodin Quartet** (Mikhail Kopelman, Andrei Abramenkov, vns; Dimitri Shebalin, va; Valentin Berlinsky, vc); ᵃ**Elizo Virzaladze** (pf). Teldec Ⓕ 4509-97461-2 (77 minutes: DDD: 5/95). Recorded 1990. **ⒼⒼ**
These were recorded at The Maltings, Snape which provides warm, reverberant reproduction very much in keeping with these players' vision of the well-nourished composer in middle age, a Brahms aglow yet at the same time more traditionally Germanic than the acutely susceptible, highly charged Viennese Brahms from the translucently textured Alban Berg Quartet. Always the Borodins prefer the longer line (as in the opening of the slow movement), the broader view, to the Bergs' spontaneous response to detail. Choice is very much a matter of taste since it goes without saying that in all matters of intonation, balance and interplay, both world-renowned teams are exemplary. With the incisive Elizo Virzaladze at the keyboard, the Piano Quintet emerges with magisterial strength and breadth.

Not even an earthquake could disrupt the rhythmic stability underpinning each movement (and not least the *Scherzo*), or shake the absolute certainty of each player's conviction. If the Brahms as guardian of classical tradition looms larger than the romanticist, there are still memorable reminders of the vulnerable heart behind it all – as notably in the stabbing intensity they bring to the finale's *poco sostenuto* introduction and temperamental coda.

Additional recommendations ...

...Piano Quintet. **Maurizio Pollini** (pf); **Quartetto Italiano.**
　DG Ⓕ 419 673-2GH (43 minutes: AAD: 6/87). *Gramophone Award Winner 1980.*　　　ⒼⒼⒼ
...Piano Quintet. **Schumann** Piano Quintet in E flat major, Op. 44. **Jenö Jandó** (pf);
　Kodály Quartet. Naxos Ⓢ 8 550406 (67 minutes: DDD: 2/91).
...Piano Quintet. **Schumann** Piano Quintet in E flat major, Op. 44. **Rudolf Serkin** (pf);
　Busch Quartet. Pearl mono Ⓜ GEMMCD9275* (65 minutes: ADD: 8/97).

Brahms String Quintets – No. 1 in F major, Op. 88; No. 2 in G major, Op. 111. **Walter Trampler** (va); **Juilliard Quartet** (Robert Mann, Joel Smirnoff, vns; Samuel Rhodes, va; Joel Krosnick, vc). Sony Classical Ⓕ SK68476 (59 minutes: DDD: 12/96). Recorded 1995.

Brahms String Quintets – No. 1 in F major, Op. 88; No. 2 in G major, Op. 111. **Gérard Caussé** (va); **Hagen Quartet** (Lukas Hagen, Rainer Schmidt, vns; Veronika Hagen, va; Clemens Hagen, vc). DG Ⓕ 453 420-2GH (59 minutes: DDD: 5/97). Recorded 1996.

What playing! Listen to how the Juilliard Quartet tackle the Second Quintet's opening: the pulse is vibrant, articulation is clean but never exaggerated, chords are properly weighted and when we reach the development's shimmering first bars at 5'54" – absolute rapture – there's simply no other word for it. The *Adagio's* sombre outer sections are both expressive and transparent and one has to cite the opening bars of the *Un poco Allegretto* third movement as among the most perfect examples of instrumental voicing ever heard on a chamber music record: *everything* tells, and yet the phrasing remains mobile and expressive. The First Quintet is virtually as good, with a warmly cosseted account of the first movement's waltz-like second set and an impressive build-up of tension from, say, 6'41" – one of the most Dvořákian passages in all of Brahms. Readers who only know the Juilliard Quartet from their lean, intense and tonally fragile RCA/CBS recordings of the late 1950s and early 1960s will find these performances far warmer and more 'European' in tone – although a binding intelligence is common to virtually all of the group's recordings (even through various changes of personnel).

The affirmative *Allegro* that launches the Second String Quintet on its course is exhilarating and the recording by the augmented Hagen Quartet greets the air like an unexpected sunbeam. This particular recording combines clarity and substance; nothing is left to chance and the end result is notably colourful, both in tone and in feeling. The First Quintet is crisply pointed, with crystalline textures, a pleasantly laid-back account of the first movement's lovely second set and a finely tensed development section. Furthermore, the heavily contrapuntal finale is played with great precision and rhythmic *élan*. Both performances include first-movement exposition repeats and both represent the Hagens' 'stylistic grid' at its most convincing, in other words, with vividly attenuated dynamics, occasional volatility, a consistent sense of line, impressive internal clarity, equal distribution of voices and a remarkable degree of concentration. Very well recorded and expertly annotated.

Additional recommendation ...

...No. 1[a]. Clarinet Quintet in B minor, Op. 115[b]. [b]**Karl Leister** (cl); [a]**Brett Dean** (va);
　Brandis Quartet. Nimbus Ⓕ NI5515 (67 minutes: DDD: 8/97).

Brahms Piano Quartets – No. 1 in G minor, Op. 25; No. 2 in A major, Op. 26; No. 3 in C minor, Op. 60. **Isaac Stern** (vn); **Jaime Laredo** (va); **Yo-Yo Ma** (vc); **Emanuel Ax** (pf). Sony Classical Ⓕ S2K45846 (two discs: 128 minutes: DDD: 3/91). Recorded 1986-89.

Gramophone Award Winner 1991. Selected by Sounds in Retrospect.　　　　　　　　Ⓖ

These three piano quartets belong to the middle of Brahms's life. They have all the power and lyricism that we associate with his music, as well as the fine craftsmanship that he acquired when young and, with the high standards he set himself, demonstrated in every work thereafter. The mood of the music is again Brahmsian in that alongside a wealth of melodic and harmonic invention there are some shadows: all we know of Brahms's life suggests that he was never a happy man. But if this is reflected in the music, and especially the C minor Quartet, we can recognize the strength of intellect and will that keeps all in proportion so that there is no overt soul-bearing. These quartets are big pieces which often employ a grand manner, though less so in No. 2 than the others. For this reason, the present performances with their exuberant sweep are particularly telling, and although no detail is missed the players offer an overall strength. Top soloists in their own right, they combine their individual gifts with the ability to play as a well integrated team. The recording is close but not overwhelmingly so. Only the booklet, with notes in four languages, mars at least some copies of this issue, for it has some blank pages and details of the movements are missing, as are parts of the English and Italian notes.

Additional recommendations ...

...No. 1. Variations and Fugue on a Theme by Handel, Op. 24 (orch. Rubbra). **London Symphony Orchestra / Neeme Järvi.** Chandos Ⓕ CHAN8825 (71 minutes: DDD: 2/91).
...Nos. 1-3. String Quartet No. 2 in A minor, Op. 51 No. 2. Piano Quintet in F minor, Op. 34.
　Schumann Piano Quintet in E flat major, Op. 44. **Victor Aller** (pf); **Hollywood Quartet.**
　Testament mono Ⓕ SBT3063* (three discs: 220 minutes: ADD: 1/95).

...Nos. 1 and 3. **Peter Csaba** (vn); **Matti Hirvikangas** (va); **Frans Helmerson** (vc); **Ralf Gothoni** (pf). Ondine Ⓕ ODE843-2 (77 minutes: DDD: 10/96).

Brahms Piano Quartet No. 1 in G minor, Op. 25[a]. Four Ballades, Op. 10[b]. **Emil Gilels** (pf); members of the **Amadeus Quartet** (Norbert Brainin, vn; Peter Schidlof, va; Martin Lovett, vc). DG The Originals Ⓜ 447 407-2GOR (65 minutes: ADD: 6/95). Item marked [a] from 2530 133 (11/71), [b]2530 655 (7/76).

We have to thank members of the Amadeus Quartet for two outstanding performances of Brahms's G minor Piano Quartet – a comparatively recent one with Murray Perahia (see below), unforgettable for its spontaneity and uninhibited romantic warmth and verve, and this much earlier (1971) version with Gilels, here reissued at medium price in DG's Originals series. The booklet reminds us that the recording made history at that date since "a contract between an artist from the Soviet Union and a Western label was a sensational event in cultural diplomacy". Reproduced with respect for the sound quality of its time, the playing has a glowing strength and intensity throughout. Only in the first movement's opulent textures does the keyboard occasionally dominate. From Gilels we're also given a maturely unhurried, essentially 'inward' recording (made some five years later) of Brahms's four youthful *Ballades*, with their strange, almost supernatural undertones. A bargain.

Additional recommendations ...

...No. 1. **Murray Perahia** (pf); members of the **Amadeus Quartet.**
CBS Ⓕ SK42361 (40 minutes: DDD: 12/87).

...No. 1. *Coupled with works by various composers.* **Murray Perahia** (pf); **Norbert Brainin** (vn); **Peter Schidlof** (va); **Martin Lovett** (vc). Sony Classical Ⓜ SX4K63380 (four discs: 270 minutes: DDD/ADD: 4/98). *See review in the Collections section; refer to the Index.*

Brahms String Quartets – No. 1 in C minor, Op. 51 No. 1; No. 3 in B flat major, Op. 67.
Borodin Quartet (Mikhail Kopelman, Andrei Abramenkov, vns; Dimitri Shebalin, va; Valentin Berlinsky, vc). Teldec Ⓕ 4509-90889-2 (69 minutes: DDD: 11/94). Recorded 1993. ⊙⊙
Brahms String Quartets, Op. 51 – No. 1 in C minor; No. 2 in A minor. **Cleveland Quartet** (William Preucil, Peter Salaff, vns; James Dunham, va; Paul Katz, vc). Telarc Ⓕ CD80346 (68 minutes: DDD: 2/95). Recorded 1993.

It's essentially the mature, middle-aged composer that the Borodin Quartet evoke in their full-bodied, spacious and firmly-contoured performance of the C minor Quartet. Comparing it with the Alban Berg Quartet, the first and most obvious difference is the Borodin's more deliberate tempo for the powerful flanking movements in the home key. They prefer breadth to their rivals' urgency. In the *Romanze*, richly romantic from both teams, the Borodin favour a riper sound-world, warmly fortified by their viola and cello, as against the Berg's more translucent sonority, with its ethereal *pianissimo* often evoking the rapt magic of moonlight. Differences in the B flat Quartet are less marked: both readings are vividly characterful. But again – and perhaps most of all in the finale – the overriding impression is of more traditionally Germanic romanticism from the Russians, whereas from the Viennese team we meet a more minutely impressionable as well as a more highly-strung composer. The Teldec recording, made in this company's Berlin studio, is as full, warm and open as the playing. Whichever group you choose, you will not be disappointed.

Though the Cleveland Quartet have changed both their leader and viola player in recent years, all their old tonal opulence is still very much there. So is all the old fire, and equally, their determination to wring the last drop of expression from even the most intimate confession. In short, you would be unlikely to meet a more overtly romantic composer than the Brahms you meet here. In the C minor Quartet's *Romanze* some listeners might in fact prefer the very mellow but more emotionally reticent Borodin Quartet, or the Alban Berg with their ethereally withdrawn *pianissimo*. In the bolder flanking movements they are as compulsive as the highly-strung, impressionable Alban Berg while often finding a broader, suaver, melodic sweep. The venue was their favoured Mechanics Hall at Worcester, Massachusetts, a warmly reverberant building – as the sheer fullness of the sound makes plain.

Additional recommendations ...

...Nos. 1 and 2. **Gabrieli Quartet.** Chandos Ⓕ CHAN8562 (61 minutes: DDD: 4/88).

...Nos. 2 and 3. **Orlando Quartet.** Ottavo Ⓕ OTRC68819 (75 minutes: DDD: 6/90).

...Nos. 1 and 2. **New Budapest Quartet.** Hyperion Ⓕ CDA66651 (67 minutes: DDD: 4/93).

...Nos. 1-3. **Alban Berg Quartet.** EMI Ⓕ CDS7 54829-2 (two discs: 102 minutes: DDD: 2/94). ⊙

...Nos. 1-3. **Dvořák** String Quartet No. 13 in G major, B192[b]. **Alban Berg Quartet.** Teldec Ⓜ 4509-95503-2 (two discs: 134 minutes: ADD: 2/95).

...Nos. 2 and 3. String Quintets – No. 1 in F major, Op. 88; No. 2 in G, Op. 111. String Sextet No. 2 in G major, Op. 36. **Alfred Hobday, Hans Mahlke** (vas); **Anthony Pini** (vc); **Budapest Quartet.** Biddulph mono Ⓜ LAB120/1* (two discs: 144 minutes: ADD: 12/96).

...Nos. 1-3. Clarinet Quintet in B minor, Op. 115[a]. [a]**Charles Draper** (cl); **Léner Quartet.** EMI Références mono Ⓕ CHS5 66422-2* (two discs: 133 minutes: ADD: 1/98).

Brahms Piano Trios[a] – No. 1 in B major, Op. 8; No. 2 in C major, Op. 87; No. 3 in C minor, Op. 101. Horn Trio in E flat major, Op. 40[b]. Clarinet Trio in A minor, Op. 114[c]. [c]**Richard Hosford** (cl); [b]**Stephen Stirling** (hn); [a]**Florestan Trio** ([b]Anthony Marwood, vn; [c]Richard Lester, vc; [bc]Susan Tomes, pf). Hyperion Ⓕ CDA67251/2 (two discs: 137 minutes: DDD: 6/98). Recorded 1997. ⊙

Aided by an especially clear, vivid, yet spacious recording, the Florestan Trio and their two colleagues allow us to hear far more of this music than usual – the elaborate decoration of Op. 114's *Adagio*, or the sinister detail of the more delicate passages in Op. 8's *Scherzo*. Much of the credit for this goes to Susan Tomes; her playing is an object-lesson in sensitivity and in matching the other voices. Balance and blend are a special feature of these performances. Anthony Marwood and Richard Lester match their sounds perfectly for the lovely duet passages in the slow movements of Op. 8 and Op. 101. What is less expected, and less usual, is the matching of violin and horn, cello and clarinet. But perhaps the single outstanding feature of all the performances is the way the music is shaped. It's not only that the phrases are projected clearly and expressively – the approach moves outwards to encompass the music's larger paragraphs and, indeed, whole movements. These are very desirable recordings, then. But what of the competition? The Beaux Arts are a similarly finely integrated group, with a very strong emotional commitment to the music. There's less tonal variety in their versions, though, and the sound quality can't compare with the Florestan recording. Pires, Dumay and Wang offer big-toned performances on the grand scale of Opp. 8 and 87, splendidly recorded. It's not easy to choose between them and the wholehearted, but more intimate approach of the Florestan. It is also difficult to forget the 1933 HMV recording of the Horn Trio with vintage Serkin and Busch and the poetical strains of Aubrey Brain's narrow-bore horn. Tomes, Marwood and Stirling, however, do manage to match many of the qualities of this classic version, and if their *Adagio* doesn't quite achieve the deep sadness of Busch and his colleagues, it has its own, highly persuasive atmosphere of mystery.

Additional recommendations ...

...Horn Trio[a]. Clarinet Quintet in B minor, Op. 115[b]. [a]**Reginald Kell** (cl); [b]**Aubrey Brain** (hn); [b]**Rudolf Serkin** (pf); [a]**Busch Quartet.** Testament Ⓕ SBT1001 (65 minutes: AAD: 6/91).   ⒼⒼ

...No. 1; No. 2 in C major, Op. 8; No. 3 in C minor, Op. 101; A major, Op. posth. (attrib. Brahms). **Beaux Arts Trio.** Philips Duo Ⓜ 438 365-2PM2 (two discs: 119 minutes: DDD: 1/88).

...Nos. 1-3; A major, Op. posth; Horn Trio E flat major, Op. 40[c]; Clarinet Trio in A minor, Op. 114[c]. **Odeon Trio;** [c]**Rainer Moog** (va).
Capriccio Ⓕ 10 633 (three discs: 175 minutes: DDD: 7/93).

...Nos. 1-3[a]; A major, Op. posth. Horn Trio in E flat major, Op. 40[b]. Clarinet Trio in A minor, Op. 114[c]. [ad]**Beaux Arts Trio;** [c]**George Pieterson** (cl); [b]**Francis Orval** (hn); [b]**Arthur Grumiaux** (vn); [b]**Gyorgy Sebok** (pf). Philips Duo Ⓜ 438 365-2PM2 (two discs: 130 minutes: ADD: 8/93).

...No. 1[a]. String Sextet No. 1 in B major, Op. 18[b]. **Isaac Stern,** [b]**Alexander Schneider** (vns); [b]**Milton Katims,** [b]**Milton Thomas** (vas); **Pablo Casals,** [b]**Madeline Foley** (vcs); [a]**Dame Myra Hess** (pf). Sony Classical Casals Edition mono Ⓜ SMK58994* (77 minutes: ADD: 5/94).

...No. 1. **Beethoven** Piano Trio No. 7 in B flat major, Op. 97, "Archduke". **Viktoria Mullova** (vn); **Heinrich Schiff** (vc); **André Previn** (pf). Philips Ⓕ 442 123-2PH (75 minutes: DDD: 8/95).

...No. 1. **Mendelssohn** Piano Trio No. 1 in D minor, Op. 49. **Chung Trio.**
Decca Ⓕ 421 425-2DH (65 minutes: DDD: 4/95).   Ⓖ

...Nos. 1 and 2. **Grieg Trio.** Virgin Classics Ⓕ VC5 45184-2 (64 minutes: DDD: 4/96).

...Nos. 1-3. **Augustin Dumay** (vn); **Jian Wang** (vc); **Maria-João Pires** (pf).
DG Ⓕ 447 055-2GH (67 minutes: DDD: 5/96).   Ⓖ

Brahms Horn Trio in E flat major, Op. 40. Piano Quintet in F minor, Op. 34. **Nash Ensemble** (Marcia Crayford, Elizabeth Layton, vns; Roger Chase, va; Christopher van Kampen, vc; Frank Lloyd, hn; Ian Brown, pf). CRD Ⓕ CRD3489 (73 minutes: DDD: 9/94). Recorded 1991.

It would be hard to imagine more amiable performances of these two strongly characterized Brahms works. The Nash Ensemble's comfortable approach is intense as well as warm, plainly derived from long experience performing this music in concert. The speeds in both works are markedly slower than on other versions, and the ensemble is a degree less polished, but in their expressive warmth they are just as magnetic, with a sense of continuity that the higher-powered readings do not always convey. The romanticism of the Nash approach comes out particularly strongly in the opening *Andante* of the Horn Trio, with the horn soloist, Frank Lloyd, producing an exceptionally rich, braying tone, reminiscent of Dennis Brain. After relaxed accounts of the first three movements the galloping finale is then given with great panache. Thanks partly to the CRD recording, the Nash performances are made to sound satisfyingly beefy, almost orchestral, though some may find the full-bodied sound a degree too reverberant, with the piano rather in front of the strings. The disc can be strongly recommended, particularly as this is the only available coupling of these two works.

Additional recommendations ...

...Horn Trio. *Coupled with works by* **Beethoven** and **Krufft** Lowell Greer (hn); Stephanie Chase (vn); **Steven Lubin** (fp). Harmonia Mundi Ⓕ HMU90 7037 (65 minutes: DDD: 9/92). 🎀

...Horn Trio[a]. **Franck** Violin Sonata in A major. [a]**Barry Tuckwell** (hn); **Itzhak Perlman** (vn); **Vladimir Ashkenazy** (pf). Decca The Classic Sound Ⓜ 452 887-2DCS (56 minutes: ADD).

Brahms Cello Sonatas – No. 1 in E minor, Op. 38; No. 2 in F major, Op. 99. **Heinrich Schiff** (vc); **Gerhard Oppitz** (pf). Philips Ⓕ 456 402-2PH (55 minutes: DDD: 3/98). Recorded 1996.

Brahms's cello sonatas make for an ideal coupling, not merely because there are only two of them. The differences between them are significant, both in terms of tone and character – the First being fairly mellow and soft-spoken, the Second full of bold contrasts. Oppitz is already well known for some excellent Brahms recordings, primarily the solo works, and his subtlety follows through in this recording. Schiff and Oppitz enjoy a warm, intimate acoustic (at Reinstadl, Neumarkt in Germany) that suits the fastidiously articulated profile of their performances. True, they are rather less passionate in the Second Sonata's *Allegro vivace* first movement than Harrell and Kovacevich, but their handling of the eerie F sharp minor development is particularly fine and Schiff's vibrant pizzicatos near the start of the *Adagio affettuoso* create precisely the sort of sound world that Brahms must have envisaged. They are also enjoyable in the First Sonata's elegant *Allegretto quasi Menuetto* (Harrell and Kovacevich make it sound more like a waltz), and the way they slowly edge into the third movement of the Second Sonata. This is a delicate partnership, sensitive to nuance and attentive to phrasal minutiae. Schiff's refined performance readily connects with the music's song-like, musing qualities. This coupling is a delight, comely music-making much enhanced by a fine balance of head and heart.

Additional recommendations ...

...Nos. 1ª and 2ª. Intermezzos – C sharp minor; Op. 117 No. 3; A major, Op. 118 No. 2; E flat minor, Op. 118 No. 6; E minor, Op. 119 No. 2; C major, Op. 119 No. 3. ªGregor Piatgorsky (vc); **Artur Rubinstein** (pf). RCA Victor Gold Seal Ⓜ 09026 62592-2* (74 minutes: ADD/mono)

...Nos. 1 and 2. **Mstislav Rostropovich** (vc); **Rudolf Serkin** (pf).
DG Ⓕ 410 510-2GH (58 minutes: DDD: 9/83). Ⓖ

...Nos. 1 and 2. **Steven Isserlis** (vc); **Peter Evans** (pf).
Hyperion Ⓕ CDA66159 (50 minutes: DDD: 4/86).

...Nos. 1 and 2. Violin Sonata No. 3 in D minor, Op. 108 (trans. cello). Yo-Yo Ma (vc); **Emanuel Ax** (pf). Sony Classical Ⓕ SK48191 (75 minutes: DDD: 11/92).

...Nos. 1 and 2. **Pieter Wispelwey** (vc); **Paul Komen** (pf).
Channel Classics Ⓕ CCS5493 (53 minutes: DDD: 1/94). 🎵 Ⓖ

...Nos. 1 and 2. Violin Sonata No. 1 in G major, Op. 78 (arr. Klengel). **Karina Georgian** (vc); **Pavel Gililov** (pf). Biddulph Ⓜ LAW014 (two discs: 88 minutes: DDD: 9/94).

...No. 2. Coupled with works by **Beethoven** Pablo Casals (vc); **Mieczyslaw Horszowski** (pf). EMI Références mono Ⓜ CHS5 65185-2* (two discs: 136 minutes: ADD: 10/94).
See review under Beethoven; refer to the Index. ⒼⒼⒼ

...Nos. 1 and 2. **Peter Bruns** (vc); **Olga Tverskaya** (fp).
Opus 111 Ⓕ OPS30-144 (52 minutes: DDD: 4/97). 🎵

...Nos. 1 and 2ª. 25 Variations and Fugue on a Theme by G. F. Handel, Op. 24. ªLynn Harrell (vc); **Stephen Kovacevich** (pf). EMI Ⓕ CDC5 56440-2 (78 minutes: DDD: 3/98).

Brahms Clarinet Sonatas, Op. 120 – No. 1 in F minor; No. 2 in E flat major. Clarinet Trio in A minor, Op. 114ª. **Michel Portal** (cl); ªBoris Pergamenschikow (vc); **Mikhail Rudy** (pf). EMI Ⓕ CDC7 54466-2 (70 minutes: DDD: 5/93).

To be given the Clarinet Trio as well as the two sonatas is generous measure in itself. So how good to be able to say that this disc is an even greater bargain in terms of quality. The insert-notes remind us of the inspirational source of all three works, specifying the "polish and almost feminine sensitivity" as the qualities in the playing of Richard Mühlfeld (principal clarinettist of the Meiningen Court Orchestra) that Brahms so much admired. One feels that he would feel just the same about Michel Portal. His tone is as liquid as his playing is super-sensitive. Mikhail Rudy and Boris Pergamenschikow are ideally attuned partners for him: all three respond with a loving intimacy to the music's glowing and nostalgic lyricism. Yet there is no lack of strength when required. These very finely balanced performances banish all misconceptions of the composer as a brusque and burly academic. Instead, we're reminded of his acutely vulnerable heart – such as in the magically ethereal coda of the Trio's first movement. The recording is excellent.

Additional recommendations ...

...Clarinet Sonatas. **Thea King** (cl); **Clifford Benson** (pf).
Hyperion Ⓕ CDA66202 (43 minutes: DDD: 10/87).

...Clarinet Sonatas. **Gervase de Peyer** (cl); **Gwenneth Pryor** (pf).
Chandos Ⓕ CHAN8563 (43 minutes: DDD: 3/88).

...Clarinet Sonatas. Scherzo in C minor, WoO2, "FAE Sonata". Zwei Lieder, Op. 91 (both arr. Berkes). **Kálmán Berkes** (cl); **Jenö Jandó** (pf). Naxos Ⓢ 8 553121 (63 minutes: DDD: 7/97).

Brahms Violin Sonatas – No. 1 in G major, Op. 78; No. 2 in A major, Op. 100; No. 3 in D minor, Op. 108. **Viktoria Mullova** (vn); **Piotr Anderszewski** (pf). Philips Ⓕ 446 709-2PH (64 minutes: DDD: 5/97). Recorded 1995.

Mullova and Anderszewski give a wonderful impression of having thought through every detail of their interpretations. They deliver the melodies of Op. 78's opening movement with passionate ardour; those of the same sonata's finale are played in a contrastingly gentle and wistful manner. The two scherzo sections (in Opp. 100 and 108) are given with quicksilver delicacy, whilst the *Adagio* of Op. 108, so often dark and turgid, emerges here as a touchingly melancholic lyrical movement, with occasional outbursts of intensity. These are performances of exceptionally wide expressive range, then, and part of the secret of the achievement lies in the clarity of performance and recording. Piotr Anderszewski only produces a dry sound when Brahms asks for it, but with his carefully balanced chords and restrained use of the pedal he makes the most complex Brahmsian textures sound rich, not thick.

Additional recommendations ...
...Nos. 1-3. **Arthur Grumiaux** (vn); **György Sebök** (pf).
Philips Solo Ⓜ 446 570-2PM (66 minutes: ADD).
...Nos. 1-3. **Itzhak Perlman** (vn); **Vladimir Ashkenazy** (pf).
EMI Ⓕ CDC7 47403-2 (70 minutes: DDD: 2/87). Ⓖ
...Nos. 1-3. **Krysia Osostowicz** (vn); **Susan Tomes** (pf).
Hyperion Ⓕ CDA66465 (68 minutes: DDD: 11/91).
...Nos. 1-3. **Augustin Dumay** (vn); **Maria-João Pires** (pf).
DG Ⓕ 435 800-2GH (72 minutes: DDD: 3/93).
...Nos. 1 and 2[a]; No. 3[b]. **Gioconda De Vito** (vn); [a]**Edwin Fischer**, [b]**Tito Aprea** (pfs).
Testament mono Ⓕ SBT1024* (71 minutes: ADD: 12/93).
...Nos. 1-3. **Nicolas Chumachenco** (vn); **Daniel Levy** (pf).
Edelweiss Ⓕ ED1036 (72 minutes: DDD: 4/96).

Brahms Variations on a Theme by Paganini, Op. 35.
Schumann Arabeske in C major, Op. 18. Etudes symphoniques, Opp. 13 and posth.
 Jean-Yves Thibaudet (pf). Decca Ⓕ 444 338-2DH (65 minutes: DDD: 10/95).
This is a refreshingly individual, though never quirky, display of imaginative vitality in the two most virtuosic works for solo piano that Schumann and Brahms ever wrote. Predictably the technical challenges of Brahms's notorious *Paganini* Variations hold few fears for Thibaudet. Even Horowitz once admitted that in Liszt's *Faust* Waltz he'd heard Thibaudet's fingers do things that his own couldn't in dexterity, clarity of articulation and general command. But virtuosity is never an end in itself. What surprises and pleases most is Thibaudet's readiness to relax and revel in the romance, the mystery, the lyrical charm and the sheer tonal seductiveness of the less demonstrative, the more personally expressive, variations. Some listeners may of course find his whole approach too fancifully Gallic, insufficiently Germanic for interpretations of works by these composers. But more than one road leads to Rome, and arguably even Brahms himself would succumb to the spring-like allure of this one. Schumann's *Arabeske*, delectably liquid (despite its overhasty second A minor episode) brings brief respite before the *Etudes symphoniques*, which, like nearly everyone today, Thibaudet plays in the posthumously published 1861 edition (reinstating the two numbers excluded by Schumann in his own 1852 revision though retaining its tautened finale). His leisurely unfolding of the theme, followed by an uncommonly brisk first variation (marked only *un poco più vivo*) typifies his immediacy of response to every changing mood, which once more, as in the Brahms, results in a reading perhaps more memorable for variety than continuity. But again his fingers sing as finely as they sparkle. He wisely plays the five posthumously published, rejected early variations as a separate group at the end of the work, rightly reserving his most intimately poetic revelations for the last two, both beautifully done. Sound reproduction throughout is at once natural and never too forward for comfort in your own room.
Additional recommendations ...
...Variations on a Theme by Paganini. *Coupled with works by* **Beethoven** and **Franck**
 Evgeni Kissin (pf). RCA Victor Red Seal Ⓕ 09026 68910-2 (57 minutes: DDD: 4/98).
 Gramophone Editor's choice. See review under Beethoven; refer to the Index. ⒼⒼⒼ

Brahms Piano works. **Julius Katchen** (pf). Decca Ⓜ 430 053-2DM6
(six discs: 388 minutes: ADD: 2/91). Recorded 1962-66.
Variations on a Theme by Paganini, Op. 35. Variations and Fugue on a Theme by Handel, Op. 24 (both from SXL6218, 4/66). Four Ballades, Op. 10 (SXL6160, 5/56). Variations on a Theme by Schumann, Op. 9. Variations on an Original Theme, Op. 21 No. 1. Variations on a Hungarian Song, Op. 21 No. 2 (all from SXL6219, 3/66). Waltzes, Op. 39. Two Rhapsodies, Op. 79 (both from SXL6160, 5/65). Piano Sonatas – No. 1 in C major, Op. 1; No. 2 in F sharp minor, Op. 2 (both from SXL6129, 12/64); No. 3 in F minor, Op. 5. Scherzo in E flat minor, Op. 4 (both from SXL6228, 6/66). Piano Pieces – Op. 76. Fantasias, Op. 116 (both from SXL6118, 9/64); Op. 118; Op. 119. Three Intermezzos, Op. 117 (all from SXL6105, 5/64). Hungarian Dances (with Jean-Pierre Marty, pf. SXL6217, 12/65).
The American pianist Julius Katchen made his name in the early 1950s and died in 1969, but although one thinks of him as a distinguished figure from the last generation, it is salutary to realize that he would probably be performing today if his career had not ended when he was only 42. Even so, his legacy of recordings reminds us of his gifts and the breadth of his repertory, and the present Brahms cycle has distinction. It begins with an account of the *Paganini* Variations that gives ample proof of his splendidly assured technique: the playing tells us at once that the challenging variations in sixths (Nos. 1 and 2 in Book 1) held no terrors for him, and the athleticism here is matched by a fluency in the *leggiero* writing of the variation that follows. In general, though, he makes one more aware of a keyboard virtuoso in this work, rather than a poet; there are other performances which balance these two qualities more finely. Tempos tend to rapidity, too, and the piano sound tends to have a hardish brilliance. However, he does bring a gentler quality to the three other sets of variations here, not least in his freer use of rubato and tonal nuance, as witness (say) the serene Variations Nos. 11-12 in the big *Handel* set, where the recording from three years earlier is easier on the ear too. Here, as elsewhere, there is a little tape hiss, but it is not enough to distract.

If praise over the *Paganini* Variations seems a touch grudging, it should be said at once that poetry is to be found in good measure in Katchen's playing of the Four Ballades, Op. 10. These pieces belie the composer's youth in their deep introspection, though the pianist takes a brisk view of the *Andante con moto* tempo in No. 4. The 16 Waltzes of Op. 39 are attractive too in their crispness and charm, and the early *Scherzo* in E flat minor has the right dour vigour. The three sonatas are also impressive in their strong, energetic interpretative grasp, though one could wish that the first-movement repeat of No. 1 had been observed. Also, slow movements could have a still more inward quality to convey that brooding self-communion which is so characteristic of this composer (though that of Sonata No. 3 in F minor is pretty near it). But the great F minor Sonata is spacious and thoughtful as well as leonine, and this is a noble performance, well recorded in 1966. The shorter pieces are finely done also. Katchen is in his element in the Two Rhapsodies of Op. 79, balancing their stormy and lyrical qualities to perfection. The *Fantasias*, Op. 116, are not so well recorded (the sound is a bit muffled, as if the engineers wished to tame the pianist's attack). However, the playing is masterly and Katchen's sympathy for the idiom is evident, with tenderness, tragedy, twilight mystery and storm and stress fully playing their part and giving a golden glow to such pieces as the lovely E major Intermezzo which is No. 6 of the set and the A major Intermezzo, Op. 118, No. 2. Possibly more sensuous gipsy charm could be found in, say, the B minor Capriccio of Op. 76, but it is very attractive playing and the playful C major Intermezzo in Op. 119 is delightful, as is the tender lullaby that begins Op. 117. Only the first 10 of the 21 Hungarian Dances exist in the composer's own (extremely difficult) version for piano solo, and in the others, written for piano duet, Katchen is joined by Jean-Pierre Marty; there's plenty of fire here and much to enjoy. Altogether, this Brahms set is a fine memorial to Katchen and a worthy issue; purchasers will not be disappointed.

Additional recommendations ...

...Four Ballades. **Schubert** Piano Sonata in A minor, D537. **Arturo Benedetti Michelangeli** (pf).
DG Ⓕ 400 043-2GH (48 minutes: ADD: 3/83).

...Four Ballades. Four Scherzos. **Vladimir Ashkenazy** (pf).
Decca Ⓕ 417 474-2DH (74 minutes: ADD: 2/87).

...Variations and Fugue on a Theme by Handel. Rhapsodies. Six Piano Pieces, Op. 118.
Emanuel Ax (pf). Sony Classical Ⓕ SK48046 (68 minutes: DDD: 10/92).

...Variations on an Original Theme. Variations on a Hungarian Song. Five Piano Studies.
Idil Biret (pf). Naxos Ⓢ 8 550509 (56 minutes: DDD: 8/94).

...Piano Sonatas – No. 1; No. 2 in F sharp minor, Op. 2. Variations on a Theme by Paganini.
Capriccio in C major, Op. 76 No. 8. Intermezzo in E minor, Op. 116 No. 5. Ballade in G minor,
Op. 118 No. 3. Rhapsody in E flat major, Op. 119 No. 4. *Coupled with works by* **Schumann**
Sviatoslav Richter (pf). Philips Ⓕ 438 477-2PH3 (three discs: 184 minutes: DDD: 8/94).
See review under Schumann; refer to the Index. ⒼⒼ

...Variations and Fugue on a Theme by Handel. Two Rhapsodies, Op. 79. Variations on a
Theme by Paganini. **Gerhard Oppitz** (pf).
RCA Victor Red Seal Ⓕ 09026 61811-2 (69 minutes: DDD: 9/94).

...Two Rhapsodies, Op. 79. *Coupled with works by various composers.* **Martha Argerich** (pf).
DG The Originals Ⓜ 447 430-2GOR (71 minutes: ADD: 6/95). *Gramophone Classical 100.*
See review in the Collections section; refer to the Index. ⒼⒼⒼ

...Variations on a Theme by R. Schumann. Variations and Fugue on a Theme by Handel,.
Variations on a Hungarian song. Theme and Variations in D minor. **Mikhail Rudy** (pf).
EMI Ⓕ CDC5 55167-2 (64 minutes: DDD: 7/95).

...Variations on a Theme by Paganini – Book 2. *Coupled with works by various composers.*
Shura Cherkassky (pf). Decca Ⓕ 433 657-2DH (68 minutes: ADD: 2/96).

...Piano Pieces, Op. 76 – No. 2, Capriccio in B minor; No. 3, Intermezzo in A flat major. Capriccio
in D minor, Op. 116 No. 7. Intermezzo in E flat major, Op. 117 No. 1. Intermezzo in C major,
Op. 119 No. 3. *Coupled with works by various composers.* **Dame Myra Hess** (pf). Biddulph mono
Ⓜ LHW025* (76 minutes: ADD: 3/96). *See review in the Collections section; refer to the Index.* Ⓖ

...Variations on a Theme by R. Schumann. Variations and Fugue on a Theme by Handel.
Four Ballades, Op. 10. **Jorge Federico Osorio** (pf).
ASV Quicksilva Ⓢ CDQS6161 (68 minutes: DDD: 5/96).

...Seven Piano Pieces, Op. 116. Three Piano Pieces, Op. 117. Six Piano Pieces, Op. 118. Four Piano
Pieces, Op. 119. **Hélène Grimaud** (pf). Erato Ⓕ 0630-14350-2 (75 minutes: DDD: 12/96).

...Variations on a Hungarian Song. Variations on an original theme in D major, Op. 21 No. 1.
Six Piano Pieces, Op. 118. Four Piano Pieces, Op. 119. **Mark Anderson** (pf).
Nimbus Ⓕ NI5521 (62 minutes: DDD: 8/97).

Brahms Piano Sonata No. 3 in F minor, Op. 5[a]. Intermezzos[b] – E flat major, Op. 117 No. 1;
C major, Op. 119 No. 3.
Schubert Piano Sonata No. 21 in B flat major, D960[b]. **Sir Clifford Curzon** (pf).
Decca The Classic Sound Ⓜ 448 578-2DCS (77 minutes: ADD: 7/96). Item marked [a] from
SXL6041 (5/63), [b]SXL6580 (12/73).

It took wild horses to drag Curzon into the studio, at least in his last years, and he was a record company's nightmare when it came to agreeing what might be issued. One could say that Curzon was not a natural pianist, yet he developed a technique which admirably served the force of his will: and when the two were in harness and in good shape the transcendental aspects of his playing could produce an indelible musical experience. These recordings have lost none of their freshness. The little holes and imperfections are quite unimportant because at every moment Curzon is conveying an exactitude of character and sense. His sound 'speaks' and persuades you to listen to something precise. Nothing is generalized. Yet the overview is there as well as the detail, particularly in the Schubert. As with every great pianist, the quality of his sound is distinctive: tightly focused, crystalline, refulgent. With his sovereign control of line and timing, the pianism seems at all times to be perfectly weighted and to have everything within its sights. You could say that about other great interpreters, no doubt, but there is a special attractiveness about Curzon's ability to delight the senses while penetrating to the heart of the matter. When he was on form he could talk of the most serious things while singing at you like a nightingale. How crude most performances of the Brahms F minor Sonata seem when compared with his. All the climaxes well up from within (and how they glow), yet its scale and range are thrillingly made manifest. This is terrific value at mid price. The sound is fair to good in both the big pieces – and only slightly inferior in the earlier recording. The two Brahms *Intermezzos* are in a very dry acoustic as if Curzon had recorded them at home (perhaps he did?); but so they were on the original LP.

Additional recommendations ...
...Piano Sonata No. 3. Four Ballades, Op. 10. **Idil Biret** (pf).
  Naxos Ⓢ 8 550352 (63 minutes: DDD: 12/92).
...Piano Sonata No. 3. Intermezzo. Romance in F major, Op. 118. No. 5.
  Four Ballades, Op. 10. **Artur Rubinstein** (pf).
  RCA Victor Gold Seal mono/stereo Ⓜ 09026 61862-2* (63 minutes: ADD: 9/94).
...Piano Sonata No. 3. Four Ballades, Op. 10. **Grigory Sokolov** (pf).
  Opus 111 Ⓕ OPS30-103 (67 minutes: DDD: 3/95).
...Piano Sonata No. 3[a]. Theme and Variations in D minor[a]. **Schubert** Piano Sonata No. 5
  in A flat major, D557[b]. Two Scherzos, D593[b]. **Radu Lupu** (pf).
  Decca Ovation Ⓜ 448 129-2DM (74 minutes: [a]DDD/[b]ADD: 9/96).

Brahms Piano Sonata No. 3 in F minor, Op. 5[a].
Liszt La leggierezza, S144 No. 2[b]. Années de pèlerinage, Première Année, S160, "Suisse" – Au bord d'une source[b]. Hungarian Rhapsody No. 15 in A minor, S244[c].
Schumann Carnaval, Op. 9[d]. **Solomon** (pf). Testament mono Ⓕ SBT1084* (79 minutes: ADD: 7/97). Item marked [a] from HMV ALP1358 (7/56), recorded 1952, [b]Columbia LX57 (10/30), recorded 1930, [c]Columbia DX441 (3/33), recorded 1932, [d]HMV HQM1077 (4/67, recorded 1952).
Solomon's 1952 recordings of Schumann's *Carnaval* and the Brahms Sonata in F minor are essential for the desert island, so this well-produced Testament compilation, generously filled out with Liszt, recommends itself. If you've heard tell of Solomon's reputation but don't know his work, or perhaps know only his Beethoven, snap it up. The sound has come up astonishingly well, also in the Liszt pieces which were made in 1930 and 1932. Solomon's performance of "Au bord d'une source" is a match for Liszt's poetic inspiration, as few recordings of it are. Technical address and refinement on this level constitute a small miracle.

Brahms Piano Sonata No. 3 in F minor, Op. 5.
Liszt Années de pèlerinage, deuxième année, Italie, S161 – Après une lecture du Dante (fantasia quasi sonata).
Schumann Toccata in C major, Op. 7. **Mark Anderson** (pf). Nimbus Ⓕ NI5422 (67 minutes: DDD: 7/95). Recorded 1993. *Gramophone Editor's choice.*
Mark Anderson's Brahms is aglow with warmth and sincerity, a far cry from the glib, impersonal expertise of many other winners of glittering prizes. The opening is magnificently forthright and imperious and, whether in ardent rhetoric or cloudy introspection, Anderson is stylish and assured. Some momentary failures of concentration (at 8'39", for example) and an occasional lack of impetus (the perennial problem, particularly in the vast spans of this work, of reconciling 'line' and detail) are marginal concerns given such strength of purpose, such essential *gravitas*. Liszt's Dante Sonata is, if anything, an even greater success. The absence of all obvious display and the concentration on purely musical values are deeply impressive. From Anderson, Liszt's fulminating response to Dante emerges in all its first glory and the performance is quite without the fustian and bombast that so often seem inseparable from this piece. The Schumann *Toccata* is, again, notable for sensitive as well as athletic virtues, its bustling and headlong flight poetically and brilliantly realized. Even in a market place crowded with celebrities, Anderson's Brahms has a special validity and authority, while his Liszt and Schumann are among the finest available. The recordings, made in Nimbus's splendid concert-hall, are a far cry from some of their earlier efforts.

Brahms 16 Waltzes, Op. 39. Ten Hungarian Dances. **Idil Biret** (pf).
  Naxos Ⓢ 8 550355 (52 minutes: DDD: 10/94). Recorded 1992.
Both the *Waltzes* and the *Hungarian Dances* are extremely demanding in their two-hand form, and in the latter collection one could often believe that the 20 fingers of two duettists must be involved, so many notes are being played in all registers (for an example, try No. 8 in A minor). However, the

technical problems evidently hold no terrors for this pianist and her performances are both convincing and attractive. What more need be said about this playing of music in which Brahms portrayed, in turn, sophisticated Vienna and untamed Hungary? Well, not a great deal. The quicker *Waltzes* have plenty of vivacity, and the slower ones are lyrical in an aptly Viennese manner. Tempos, textures, phrasing, rubato and pedalling are well managed and the playing has a very convincing blend of subtlety and simplicity. She treats these 16 pieces as a sequence, as Brahms's key structure allows, and leaves relatively little gap between them. The *Hungarian Dances* have a darkly surging Magyar energy and sound that are very pleasing: indeed, Biret seems totally at home in this music. The recording is a bit larger than life, but perfectly acceptable.

Additional recommendations ...

...16 Waltzes. 21 Hungarian Dances. **Yaara Tal, Andreas Groethuysen** (pf duet). Sony Classical Ⓕ SK53285 (68 minutes: DDD: 4/94).

...16 Waltzes. Pieces, Op. 76 – No. 2, Capriccio in B minor; No. 7, Intermezzo in A minor; No. 8, Capriccio in C major. Two Rhapsodies, Op. 79. Pieces, Op. 116 – No. 1, Capriccio in D minor; No. 2, Intermezzo in A minor; No. 4, Intermezzo in E major. Pieces, Op. 117 – No. 1, Intermezzo in E flat major; No. 2, Intermezzo in B flat minor. Six Pieces, Op. 118. Pieces, Op. 119 – No. 1, Intermezzo in B minor; No. 2, Intermezzo in E minor; No. 3, Intermezzo in C major. **Wilhelm Backhaus** (pf). Biddulph mono Ⓜ LHW019* (77 minutes: ADD: 9/94).

...16 Waltzes. Variations on a Theme by Haydn, Op. 56*b*, "St Antoni Chorale". Sonata in F minor, Op. 34*b*. **Martha Argerich, Alexandre Rabinovitch** (pfs). Teldec Ⓕ 4509-92257-2 (64 minutes: DDD: 1/95).

...21 Hungarian Dances (arr. Piatti). **Schmidt** Drei Phantasiestücke nach ungarischen Nationalmelodien. **Nancy Green** (vc); **Frederick Moyer** (pf). Biddulph Ⓕ LAW010 (66 minutes: DDD: 5/95).

...21 Hungarian Dances (arr. Joachim). **Joachim** Andantino in A minor. Romance in B flat major. **Marat Bisengaliev** (vn); **John Lenehan** (pf). Naxos Ⓢ 8 553026 (67 minutes: DDD: 2/96).

Brahms Two Rhapsodies, Op. 79 – No. 1 in B minor; No. 2 in G minor. 16 Waltzes, Op. 39. Six Piano Pieces, Op. 118. **Stephen Kovacevich** (pf). Philips Ⓕ 420 750-2PH (53 minutes: DDD: 4/88). From 6514 229 (4/83). Ⓖ

Brahms 16 Waltzes, Op. 39. Eight Piano Pieces, Op. 76. Two Rhapsodies, Op. 79 – No. 1 in B minor; No. 2 in G minor. **Mikhail Rudy** (pf). EMI Ⓕ CDC7 54233-2 (59 minutes: DDD: 5/93). Recorded 1991-92.

The Op. 79 *Rhapsodies* have been described as the "most temperamental" of all Brahms's later keyboard works. It would certainly be hard to imagine more vehement performances than those given by Kovacevich, thanks to his robust tone, trenchant attack and urgent tempos – perhaps even a shade too fast for the *Molto passionato, ma non troppo allegro* of the Second. But the pleading second subject of No. 1 in B minor brings all the requisite lyrical contrast. The Waltzes, too, have their tenderer moments of *Ländler*-like sentiment and charm. However, they emerge faster and more excitable than usual, as if Kovacevich were trying to remind us of Brahms's old love of Hungary no less than his new love of Vienna. "It is wonderful how he combines passion and tenderness in the smallest of spaces" was Clara Schumann's comment on the miniatures and the phrase fits Kovacevich's warmly responsive account of the Op. 118 set just as well. The piano is faithfully and fearlessly reproduced in what sounds like a ripely reverberant venue.

Mikhail Rudy's account of the Two *Rhapsodies* and the 16 Waltzes makes a pleasing alternative to Stephen Kovacevich's disc. For a start, the younger pianist has been exceptionally well recorded in the Salle Wagram in Paris, and he also plays a fine instrument that is in perfect condition. Of course that is not all: Rudy brings great character to the Eight Pieces, Op 76, with each one fully (but not exaggeratedly) characterized, not least in matters of texture, dynamics and pedalling. Similarly, this pianist effortlessly encompasses the blend of passion and gentler poetry that we find in the *Rhapsodies*. As for the Waltzes, this golden chain of Viennese melody and lilting charm comes across with affection and panache, as well as idiomatic rubato, not least in the famous A flat major Waltz which is the penultimate number. Repeats, too, are never mechanical, but often reveal something subtly new about the music which we could not have with a single playing. Finally, the frequent difficulty of Brahms's idiosyncratic piano writing, both here and in the other pieces, presents no more than a pleasing challenge to this intelligent and sensitive artist and all proceeds fluently, though never in a routine way.

Additional recommendation ...

...Two Rhapsodies. Three Intermezzos, Op. 117. Six Piano Pieces. Four Piano Pieces, Op. 119. **Radu Lupu** (pf). Decca Ⓕ 417 599-2DH (71 minutes: ADD: 8/87). Ⓖ Ⓖ

Brahms Two Motets, Op. 74. Fest- und Gedenk-sprüche, Op. 109. Three Motets, Op. 110. Missa Canonica. Two Motets, Op. 29. **RIAS Chamber Choir, Berlin / Marcus Creed.** Harmonia Mundi Ⓕ HMC90 1591 (61 minutes: DDD: 5/96). Texts and translations included. Recorded 1994-95.

These wonderful pieces, which, hearing, you would suppose to be all heart, looking at, you think must be all brain, and in fact are compounded of both, the one feeding upon and stimulating the other. In no other department of his work is Brahms quite so conscious of his heritage. Writing in the midday of romanticism, he finds the great formal, contrapuntal tradition not a weight upon him but a refreshment. He draws upon Schütz as upon Bach, and from the Italian polyphonists and masters of the double choir as well as from his own German background. The innocent ear would never suspect the mathematical intricacies, the sheer musical logic, and yet it tells, even without conscious recognition: one senses the workmanship, and the emotion which would in any case go out to greet such strong, vivid word-setting is immeasurably enhanced. A striking example is provided by the three movements, all that survive, from the *Missa Canonica*, undertaken in 1856. The *Sanctus* is set in deeply reverential mood and, like the flowing triple-time *Benedictus*, betrays nothing of its origin as an academic exercise. The *Agnus Dei* is overtly polyphonic yet that too gives way to a gently lyrical mode, in the "Dona nobis pacem". They were published in 1984 and this is their first recording. The motets, of course, have been recorded many times and very well too, yet, on balance, no more satisfyingly than they are here. The RIAS Chamber Choir produce a fine quality of homogeneous tone and, under Marcus Creed, show themselves fully responsive to both words and music. In the exciting "Wenn ein starker Gewappneter" movement of Op. 109 the Trinity College forces are preferable, in terms of clarity and immediacy, but the RIAS disc remains a strong recommendation, especially for its inclusion of the surviving *Missa Canonica* fragments.

Additional recommendation ...
...Two Motets, Op. 74. Two Motets, Op. 29. Three Motets, Op. 110. Three Motets, Op. 37.
Psalm 13, Op. 27. Ave Maria, Op. 12. Fest- und Gedenkspruche. Geistliches Lied, Op. 30.
Trinity College Choir, Cambridge / Richard Marlow.
Conifer Classics Ⓕ CDCF178 (65 minutes: DDD: 2/90).

Brahms 15 Romanzen aus "Die schöne Magelone", Op. 33. **Brigitte Fassbaender** (mez/narr); **Elisabeth Leonskaja** (pf). Teldec Ⓕ 4509-90854-2 (78 minutes: DDD: 10/94). Texts and translations included. Recorded 1993. *Gramophone Editor's choice.*   Ⓖ
Fassbaender has conceived the rewarding idea of marrying Brahms's cycle with the tale, by Ludwig Tieck, that inspired it. Thus, she prefaces every song with the appropriate section of the story, so that we are involved in the adventures of Peter and his beautiful love Magelone. We see before us the lovely girl, the handsome knight who entrances her and Magelone's go-between nurse; then follow their courtship, so rudely interrupted by natural forces (an interfering raven, always a symbol of evil in this imaginary world), Peter's adventures in a Moorish country, his escape and eventual and improbable reunion with his beloved for the happy end. Each of Brahms's songs captures the mood – happy, histrionic and sad – of the moment it illustrates in the text. It makes for a fascinating essay in narrative and music, and nobody is better equipped than Fassbaender to play the dual role of speaker and singer. She reads the high romantic text with as much emotional and intellectual control as she sings Brahms's pieces, which are greatly improved by being heard in context. She is partnered by the like-minded Leonskaja, something of a Brahms specialist, who plays the piano parts with welcome authority. She is nicely balanced with the singer in an exemplary recording. The whole project is a success and certainly the best way to encounter this music. Accept no substitutes.

Brahms Gesänge – Op. 17[a]; Op. 42; Op. 104. Sieben Lieder, Op. 62. Deutsches Volkslieder, WoO33 – In stiller Nacht. [a]**Stefan Jezierski**, [a]**Manfred Klier** (hns); [a]**Marie-Pierre Langlamet** (hp); **RIAS Chamber Choir, Berlin / Marcus Creed.** Harmonia Mundi Ⓕ HMC90 1592 (62 minutes: DDD: 1/97). Texts and translations included. Recorded 1995-96.
The RIAS Chamber Choir's blend of voices is impeccable and the tone-quality perfectly lovely. They are sensitive to word and phrase, responding all as one to their conductor's shading and shaping. Without comparisons, their performances give pleasure enough for one to ask nothing further. But Gardiner and company on Philips do present themselves as a rival choice. The Monteverdi Choir offer the *Liebeslieder*, Op. 52 as their major item, but also find room for Opp. 17, 42, 92 and 104. With them, the Gardiner touch is likely at any moment to bring a revelation; indeed in the *Gesänge*, Op. 104 he has the effect of an expert cleaner of old paintings, so that suddenly the lines and colours are clarified and the whole thing enjoys a more vivid life. Yet on the whole, one finds oneself returning to the RIAS performances enlightened somewhat by the other but grateful for the sheer beauty of sound in this newer recording, which preserves the gentler, more romantic qualities of the music more faithfully; and there is never any question of dullness, for text and music are both lovingly tendered. The pieces themselves always have more to them than one at first thinks, and the sureness of Brahms's feeling for choral sound impresses immediately. All are unaccompanied save Op. 17, where the harp and horns bring a delightful enrichment. This is quiet late-night listening, of the kind that helps to ease the day into retrospective contentment.

Additional recommendation ...
...Liebeslieder, Op. 52[a]. Gesänge – Op. 17[b]; Op. 42; Op. 104. Vier Quartette, Op. 92[c]. [a]**Teresa Shaw** (mez); [a]**Philip Salmon** (ten); [b]**Delyth Wynne** (hp); [b]**Anthony Halstead** (hn); [b]**Christian Rutherford** (hn); [ac]**Robert Levin**, [a]**John Perry** (pfs); **Monteverdi Choir / Sir John Eliot Gardiner.**
Philips Ⓕ 432 152-2PH (68 minutes: DDD: 8/92).

Brahms Liebeslieder, Op. 52. Neue Liebeslieder, Op. 65. Three Quartets, Op. 64. **Edith Mathis** (sop); **Brigitte Fassbaender** (mez); **Peter Schreier** (ten); **Dietrich Fischer-Dieskau** (bar); **Karl Engel, Wolfgang Sawallisch** (pf duet). DG Ⓕ 423 133-2GH (55 minutes: DDD: 12/88). Texts and translations included. From 2740 280 (6/83).   ⒼⒼ

These delightful works will be eagerly snapped up by lovers of these seemingly simple but, in fact, quite complex settings for one, two or four voices. The performances are thoroughly idiomatic, both as regards the singers and pianists, with full value given to the words and their meaning. It is not merely a question of fine singing, which with this quartet one may more or less take for granted: the subtlety and charm of the interpretations makes what can all too often be a dreary sequence of three-four numbers into a poetic response to the nature of the waltz. There is an intelligent give-and-take between the soloists, so that voices move in and out of the limelight, as the skilful recording allows, and an extra dimension of the music is disclosed here that is too often obscured. The immediate sound is here a great advantage. This is a very worthwhile and welcome reissue of a most attractive individual record.

Additional recommendations ...

...Liebeslieder. Neue Liebeslieder. **Schumann** Spanische Liebeslieder, Op. 138. **Barbara Bonney** (sop); **Anne Sofie von Otter** (mez); **Kurt Streit** (ten); **Olaf Bär** (bar); **Bengt Forsberg, Helmut Deutsch** (pf duet). EMI ℗ CDC5 55430-2 (64 minutes: DDD: 10/95).

...Liebeslieder[b]. Liebeslieder[d]. Waltzes, Op. 39[a]. Waltzes, Op. 39[c] – Nos. 2, 6 and 15. Waltzes, Op. 39[e] – Nos. 1, 2, 5, 6, 10, 14 and 15. [b]**Irmgard Seefried**, [d]**Marie-Blanche de Polignac** (sops); [b]**Elisabeth Höngen**, [d]**Irène Kedroff** (contrs); [b]**Hugo Meyer-Welfing**, [d]**Hugues Cuénod** (tens); [b]**Hans Hotter** (bass-bar); [d]**Doda Conrad** (bass); [a]**Wilhelm Backhaus**, [bc]**Friedrich Wührer**, [bc]**Hermann von Nordberg**, [de]**Dinu Lipatti**, [de]**Nadia Boulanger** (pfs). EMI Références mono ℗ CDH5 66425-2* (70 minutes: ADD: 7/97).

...Liebeslieder[a]. Sieben Gesänge, Op. 62 – No. 1, Rosmarin; No. 3, Waldesnacht. Darthulas Grabesgesang, Op. 42 No. 3. Fünf Gesänge, Op. 104 – No. 4, Verlorene Jugend; No. 5, Im Herbst. Ruf zu Maria, Op. 22 No. 5. Ave Maria, Op. 12[b]. Regina coeli laetare, Op. 37 No. 3. Geistliches Lied, Op. 30[b]. Drei Motetten, Op. 110. [a]**Francis Pott** (pf); **Jeremy Filsell** ([a]pf/[b]org); **Serenata Voices / David Beavan.** Guild ℗ GMCD7134 (68 minutes: DDD: 10/97).

Brahms Lieder. **Dame Margaret Price** (sop); **Graham Johnson** (pf). RCA Victor Red Seal ℗ 09026 60901-2 (61 minutes: DDD: 5/94). Notes, texts and translations included. Recorded 1992.

Op. 96 – No. 1, Der Tod, das ist die kühle Nacht; No. 3, Es schauen die Blumen; No. 4, Meerfahrt. Op. 85 – No. 1, Sommerabend; No. 2, Mondenschein. Es liebt sich so lieblich im Lenze!, Op. 71 No. 1. Op. 14 – No. 1, Vor dem Fenster; No. 2, Vom vernundeten Knaben; No. 7, Ständchen; No. 8, Sehnsucht. Mädchenfluch. Op. 69 No. 9. Klage, Op. 105 No. 3. Op. 148 – No. 4, Gold überwiegt die Liebe; No. 6, Vergangen ist mir Glück und Heil. Op. 84 – No. 4, Vergebliches Ständchen; No. 5, Spannung. Deutsche Volkslieder, WoO33 – No. 6, Da unten in Tale; No. 15, Schwesterlein, Schwesterlein; No. 37, Du mein einzig Licht. Op. 97 – Dort in den Weiden, No. 4. Zigeunerlieder, Op. 103 – No. 1, He, Zigeuner, greife; No. 2, Hochgetürmte Rimaflut; No. 3, Wisst ihr, wann mein Kindchen; No. 4, Leiber Gott, du weisst; No. 5, Brauner Bursche führt zum Tanze; No. 6, Röslein dreie in der Reihe; No. 7, Kommt dir manchmal; No. 11, Rote Abendwoken ziehn.

With Graham Johnson to devise intelligent, logical programmes, Dame Margaret Price and himself to interpret them, a remarkable unanimity of thought and confidence of manner is being achieved, the delights there for the taking. Here we begin with six contrasted settings of Heine, all reasonably familiar songs, each given with a nice balance between breadth of phrasing and warmth of feeling. The account of *Mondenschein* fully realizes its autumnal melancholy in phrases that seem to linger endlessly in the air. The judicious choice of *Volkslieder* settings once more indicates Brahms's deep understanding of the originals and just how to clothe them in appropriate harmonies, as in the antique Dorian mode of *Sehnsucht* and *Vergangen ist mir Glück und Heil*, both sung and played here with an exquisite sense of longing. Finally, the partnership lavish a winningly uninhibited *élan* on the *Zigeunerlieder*. If we are occasionally aware of a momentary strain on Price's present resources, we are consoled by the passionate spontaneity of the results. The intimate recording is ideally balanced.

Additional recommendations ...

...Alto Rhapsody, Op. 53[a]. Lieder, Op. 63[b] – No. 5, Junge Lieder I; No. 8, Heimweh II. Lieder, Op. 47[c] – No. 1, Botschaft; No. 3, Sonntag; No. 4, O liebliche Wangen. Lieder, Op. 43[d] – No. 1, Von ewiger Liebe; No. 2, Die Mainacht. Regenlied, Op. 59 No. 3[e]. Am Sonntag Morgen, Op. 49 No. 1[f]. Minnelied, Op. 71 No. 5[g]. Uber die Heide, Op. 86 No. 4[h]. Deutsche Volkslieder, WoO33 – No. 5, Die Sonne scheint nicht mehr[il]; No. 6, Da unten in Tale[il]; No. 8, Ach, englische Schäferin[ikl]; No. 14, Maria ging aus wandern[i]; No. 15, Schwesterlein[ikl]; No. 16, Wach' auf mein' Herzensschöne[kl]; No. 25, Mein Mädel hat einen Rosenmund[kl]; No. 30, All' mein' Gedanken[kl]; No. 31, Dort in den Weiden steht ein Haus[il]; No. 36, Es wohnet ein Fiedler[il]; No. 42, In stiller Nacht, zur ersten Wacht[ik]; No. 46, Es war einmal ein Zimmergesell[ij]; No. 49, Verstohlen geht der Mond auf[ij]. [i]**Edith Mathis** (sop); [a]**Christa Ludwig** (mez); [k]**Peter Schreier** (ten); [bcdefgh]**Dietrich Fischer-Dieskau** (bar); [bcdefgh]**Daniel Barenboim**, [l]**Karl Engel**, [j]**Gernot Kahl** (pfs); [j]**North German Radio Chorus**; [a]**Vienna Singverein**; [a]**Vienna Philharmonic Orchestra** / [b-j]**Günther Jena**, [a]**Karl Böhm.** DG Classikon Ⓜ 439 441-2GCL (74 minutes: ADD/DDD).

...Lieder, Op. 57 – No. 2, Wenn du nur zuweilen lächelst; No. 3, Es träumte mir; No. 4, Ach, wende diesen Blick; No. 8, Unbewegte laue Luft. Deutsche Volkslieder, WoO33 – No. 12, Feinsliebchen, du sollst mir nicht barfuss geh'n; No. 15, Schwesterlein, Schwesterlein; No. 33, Och Moder, ich well en Ding han!; No. 41, Es steht ein' Lind'; No. 42, In stiller Nacht, zur ersten Wacht. Lieder, Op. 107 – No. 3, Das Mädchen spricht; No. 5, Mädchenlied. Vergebliches Ständchen, Op. 84 No. 4. Ständchen, Op. 106 No. 1. Am Sonntag Morgen, Op. 49 No. 1. Trennung, Op. 97 No. 6. Während des Regens, Op. 58 No. 2. O kühler Wald, Op. 72 No. 3. Von ewiger Liebe, Op. 43 No. 1. *Coupled with works by various composers.* **Elly Ameling** (sop); **Various soloists.** Deutsche Harmonia Mundi Ⓕ 74321 26617-2 (four discs: 239 minutes: ADD: 12/95). *See review in the Collections section; refer to the Index.*

...Deutsche Volkslieder, WoO33 – No. 6; No. 12, Feinsliebchen; No. 42, In stiller Nacht. Die Trauernde, Op. 7 No. 5. *Coupled with works by* **Schumann** Irmgard Seefried (sop); **Erik Werba** (pf). Orfeo D'Or Salzburg Festspieldokumente mono Ⓕ C398951B* (77 minutes: ADD: 3/96).

...Wie Melodien zieht es mir, Op. 105 No. 1. Feldeinsamkeit, Op. 86 No. 2. Von ewiger Liebe, Op. 43 No. 1. Meine Liebe ist grün, Op. 63. *Coupled with works by various composers.* **Lisa della Casa** (sop); **Arpad Sándor** (pf). EMI Salzburg Festival Edition mono Ⓜ CDH5 66571-2* (64 minutes: ADD: 2/98). *See review in the Collections section; refer to the Index.*

...Neun Lieder, Op. 63. Fünf Lieder, Op. 71. Fünf Lieder, Op. 72. Fünf Lieder, Op. 94. Vier ernste Gesänge, Op. 121. **Olaf Bär** (bar); **Helmut Deutsch** (pf). EMI Ⓕ CDC5 56366-2 (71 minutes: DDD: 4/98).

...Geistliches Lied, Op. 30 (arr. Higginbottom). *Coupled with works by various composers.* **New College Choir, Oxford; Capricorn / Edward Higginbottom.** Erato 3984-21659-2 (6/98). *Gramophone Editor's choice. See review in the Collections section; refer to the Index.*

Brahms Lieder – Vier ernste Gesänge, Op. 121. Vergebliches Ständchen, Op. 84 No. 4. Vorschneller Schwur, Op. 95 No. 5. Das Mädchen spricht, Op. 107 No. 3. Alte Liebe, Op. 72 No. 1. Meine Liebe ist grün, Op. 63 No. 5. Dein blaues Auge, Op. 59 No. 8. Sapphische Ode, Op. 94 No. 4. Nachtigall, Op. 97 No. 1. Komm bald, Op. 97 No. 7. Herbstgefühl, Op. 48 No. 7. **Schumann** Liederkreis, Op. 39. **Brigitte Fassbaender** (mez); **Elisabeth Leonskaja** (pf). Teldec Ⓕ 9031-74872-2 (69 minutes: DDD: 10/94). Texts and translations included. Recorded 1992. Ⓖ

Because Fassbaender is such an idiosyncratic singer, no one who loves her art will want to be without this fresh manifestation of her impulsive, spontaneous skills. Likewise those unlucky ones who abhor her voice and style will remain unconvinced. The very first song of the Schumann cycle shows many of Fassbaender's singular ways – her use of portamento and vibrato, her underlining of specific words are there for all to hear. In the second song, "Intermezzo", the emphasis she gives to "Mein Herz" at the start of the second verse and the repetition of the opening "Dein Bildnis" go to the heart of the matter. Leonskaja proves an ideal partner for this singer. Her big, strong playing in "Waldesgespräch" matches Fassbaender's operatic approach to this romantic outpouring but she can be just as effective in more delicate matters, as "Schöne Fremde" reveals. So, all in all this is, as one would expect, an absorbing, thought-provoking interpretation, yet one that is always held within the bounds of sensible speeds and forward-moving rhythms. The scale of the pair's reading of Brahms's *Vier ernste Gesänge* is announced in the first song, again operatic in its breadth and strength of expression (the extreme pessimism of the second song is achieved partly through harsh tone and forceful vibrato). Urgency in *Vergebliches Ständchen*, with a subtle rubato at the close; a wonderful joy in voice and piano in *Das Mädchen spricht*; a rich melancholy about love gone by forever in *Alte Liebe*; a dark richness in *Sapphische Ode* are typical of the insights on display, typical too of the full, ideally balanced recording of voice and instrument.

Additional recommendation ...

...Vier ernste Gesänge, Op. 121[c]. Alto Rhapsody, Op. 53[a]. Nänie, Op. 54[b]. Lieder, Op. 94[c]. [a]**Helen Watts** (contr); [c]**John Shirley-Quirk** (bar); [c]**Martin Isepp** (pf); [ab]**Suisse Romande Radio Choir,** [ab]**Lausanne Pro Arte Choir;** [ab]**Suisse Romande Orchestra / Ernest Ansermet.** Belart Ⓑ 461 245-2* (56 minutes: ADD: 11/96).

Brahms Die Trauernde, Op. 7 No. 5. Sehnsucht, Op. 14 No. 8. Mädchenfluch, Op. 69 No. 3. Mädchenlied, Op. 85 No. 3. Lieder, Op. 95 – No. 5, Vorschneller Schwur; No. 6, Mädchenlied. Lieder, Op. 107 – No. 3, Das Mädchen spricht; No. 5, Mädchenlied. Deutsche Volkslieder, WoO33 – No. 34, Wie komm'ich denn zur Tür herein?; No. 41, Es steht ein Lind; No. 42, In stiller Nacht, zur ersten Wacht. Regenlied. **Mahler** Lieder und Gesänge – No. 1, Frühlingsmorgen; No. 2, Erinnerung; No. 3, Hans und Gretche; No. 6, Um schlimme Kinder artig zu machen; No. 7, Ich ging mit Lust durch einen grünen Wald; No. 9, Starke Einbildungskraft; No. 11, Ablösung im Sommer; No. 12, Scheiden und Meiden; No. 13, Nicht wiedersehen!. **Lucia Popp** (sop); **Geoffrey Parsons** (pf). Arts Music Ⓢ 47367-2 (47 minutes: DDD: A/97). Texts included. Recorded 1983.

Here is treasure indeed to add to our precious storehouse of Popp recordings. Recorded in Munich in 1983, this recital catches the well-remembered soprano in fine voice and at the top of her interpretative form in an intelligent programme devoted to folk-settings or quasi folk-songs by Brahms and Mahler. To these pieces the singer and that other late, lamented performer, Geoffrey Parsons, bring just the right balance between the artless and the sophisticated: in other words they bring all their considered artistry to bear on basically unassuming pieces without ever overloading them with too much conscious interpretation. Though she is predictably charming in the lighter, teasing songs, Popp is particularly affecting in the sad songs of loss and/or yearning as regards the loved one, where her peculiarly plaintive timbre comes very much into its own. In the Brahms settings such as "Sehnsucht" or "Es steht ein Lind" you sense the inner feelings of the bereft protagonist, and in two of Mahler's most affecting early songs, "Nicht wiedersehen!" and "Erinnerung", Popp emphasizes key phrases with an added tranche of intensity, in the final couplet of the first, and at "Die Liebe immer wieder!" in the second. The recording is full and clear. The quality and the super-budget price console you for the short measure.

Brahms Lieder. **Anne Sofie von Otter** (mez); **Bengt Forsberg** (pf). DG Ⓕ 429 727-2GH (61 minutes: DDD: 4/91). Texts and translations included. Recorded 1989.
Zigeunerlieder, Op. 103 – No. 1-7 and 11. Dort in den Weiden, Op. 97 No. 4. Vergebliches Ständchen, Op. 84 No. 4. Die Mainacht, Op. 43 No. 2. Ach, wende diesen Blick, Op. 57 No. 4. O kühler Wald, Op. 72 No. 3. Von ewiger Liebe, Op. 43 No. 1. Junge Lieder I, Op. 63 No. 5. Wie rafft' ich mich auf in der Nacht, Op. 32 No. 1. Unbewegte laue Luft, Op. 57 No. 8. Heimweh II, Op. 63 No. 8. Mädchenlied, Op. 107 No. 5. Ständchen, Op. 106 No. 1. Sonntag, Op. 47 No. 3. Wiegenlied, Op. 49 No. 4. Zwei Gesänge, Op. 91 (with Nils-Erik Sparf, va).

Many of the Lieder here are but meagerly represented in current catalogues, so that this recital is all the more welcome, particularly in view of the perceptive musicality of both singer and pianist. They show a fine free (but unanimous!) flexibility in the *Zigeunerlieder*, with a dashing "Brauner Bursche" and "Röslein dreie" and a passionate "Rote Abendwolken"; but there is also lightness, happy in "Wisst ihr, wann mein Kindchen", troubled in "Lieber Gott, du weisst"; and Otter's coolly tender tone in "Kommt dir manchmal in den Sinn" touches the heart. Also deeply moving are the profound yearning and the loving but anxious lullaby in the two songs with viola obbligato (most sensitively played). Elsewhere, connoisseurs of vocal technique will admire Otter's command of colour and legato line in the gravity of *O kühler Wald*, the stillness of *Die Mainacht* and the intensity of *Von ewiger Liebe*, and her lovely *mezza voce* in the *Wiegenlied* and the partly repressed fervour of *Unbewegte laue Luft*; but to any listener her remarkable control, her responsiveness to words and, not least, the sheer beauty of her voice make this a most rewarding disc, aided as she is by Forsberg's characterful playing.

Additional recommendation ...
...Die Mainacht, Op. 43 No. 2. Sonntag, Op. 47 No. 3. Ständchen, Op. 106 No. 1.
Coupled with works by various composers. **Aksel Schiøtz** (ten) with various artists.
Danacord mono Ⓕ DACOCD453* (69 minutes: ADD: 4/97). *See review in the Collections section; refer to the Index.*

Brahms Ein deutsches Requiem, Op. 45. **Elisabeth Schwarzkopf** (sop); **Dietrich Fischer-Dieskau** (bar); **Philharmonia Chorus and Orchestra / Otto Klemperer.** EMI Ⓕ CDC5 56218-2 (69 minutes: ADD: 6/87). Notes, text and translation included.
From Columbia SAX2430/1 (2/62). Recorded 1961. *Gramophone classical 100.* ⒼⒼⒼ
Brahms Ein deutsches Requiem, Op. 45. **Margaret Price** (sop); **Samuel Ramey** (bar); **Royal Philharmonic Orchestra; Ambrosian Singers / André Previn.** Teldec Digital Experience Ⓜ 9031-75862-2 (75 minutes: DDD: 6/87). Notes, text and translation included. Recorded 1986.

Brahm's *German Requiem*, a work of great concentration and spiritual intensity, is rather surprisingly, the creation of a man barely 30 years old. Klemperer's reading of this mighty work has long been famous: rugged, at times surprisingly fleet and with a juggernaut power. The superb Philharmonia are joined by their excellent chorus and two magnificent soloists – Schwarzkopf offering comfort in an endless stream of pure tone and the superb solo contribution from Fischer-Dieskau, still unequalled, taking us closer to the work's emotional, theological and musical sources than any other. Digital remastering has not entirely eliminated tape noise on the Klemperer set, but the engineers appear to have encountered few problems with the original tapes (some tight editing apart). It remains a uniquely revealing account of the work.

Those seeking a more up-to-date recording would be well advised to investigate the Previn. He may not be so electrifying at nodal points as Klemperer but his performance comes from the heart, with love and understanding. It is cast from strength (Price and Ramey are perhaps the finest soloists since Schwarzkopf and Fischer-Dieskau for Klemperer), with a first-rate choir (the Ambrosian Singers vying, again, with Klemperer's Philharmonia Chorus), and eloquent orchestral playing from the RPO. It is evident from his pacing and phrasing of the music that Previn knows the score from within and knows the pitfalls it presents. Nowhere is the music overdriven or overindulged. Previn's careful handling of the orchestral writing brings instrumental parallels to mind time and time again. The Teldec recoring was made in All Saint's, Tooting in an acoustic that sheds a mellow light over string and wind detailing whilst giving a pleasing depth, not inconsistent with inner clarity, to the choir's distinguished contribution. Price, singing with heavenly assurance in "Ihr habt nun Traurigkeit", has a slight edge about her tone but the recording is generally free of unattractive sibilance.

Additional recommendations ...
...Ein deutsches Requiem. **Charlotte Margiono** (sop); **Rodney Gilfry** (bar); **Monteverdi Choir; Orchestre Révolutionnaire et Romantique / Sir John Eliot Gardiner.** Philips Ⓕ 432 140-2PH (66 minutes: DDD: 4/91). ✐ Ⓖ
...Ein deutsches Requiem. **Felicity Lott** (sop); **David Wilson-Johnson** (bar); **London Symphony Chorus and Orchestra / Richard Hickox.** Chandos Ⓕ CHAN8942 (74 minutes: DDD: 1/92).

...Ein deutsches Requiem[a]. Begräbnisgesang, Op. 13. [a]**Lynne Dawson** (sop); [a]**Olaf Bär** (bar); **Schütz Choir of London; London Classical Players / Roger Norrington.** EMI Reflexe Ⓕ CDC7 54658-2 (68 minutes: DDD: 4/93). ✔

...Ein deutsches Requiem. **Sylvia McNair** (sop); **Håkan Hagegård** (bar); **Westminster Symphonic Choir; New York Philharmonic Orchestra / Kurt Masur.** Teldec Ⓕ 4509-98413-2 (60 minutes: DDD: 2/96).

...Ein deutsches Requiem. **Christiane Oelze** (sop); **Gerald Finley** (bar); **Collegium Vocale; La Chapelle Royale Chorus; Orchestra of the Champs-Elysées, Paris / Philippe Herreweghe.** Harmonia Mundi Ⓕ HMC90 1608 (66 minutes: DDD: 11/96).

...Ein deutsches Requiem – Wie lieblich sind deine Wohnungen (sung in English). *Coupled with works by various composers.* **Choir of St Mary's Cathedral, Edinburgh / Timothy Byram-Wigfield** with **Peter Backhouse** (org). Priory Ⓕ PRCD557 (64 minutes: DDD: 10/97). *See review in the Collections section; refer to the Index.*

Further listening ...

...Variations on a theme by Schumann, Op. 23. 16 Waltzes, Op. 39. Souvenir de la Russie. 15 Neue Liebeslieder Waltzes, Op. 65a. **Silke-Thora Matthies, Christian Köhn** (pf duet). Naxos 8 553139 (10/97). *Selected by Soundings.*

...Viola Sonata No. 1 in F minor. *Coupled with works by* **Dvořák** *and* **Hindemith** **Wilfried Strehle** (va); **Karina Wisniewska** (pf). Nimbus NI5473 (9/96).

...Zwei Lieder, Op. 91. *Coupled with works by various composers.* **Mitsuko Shirai** (mez); **Tabea Zimmermann** (va); **Hartmut Höll** (pf). Capriccio 10 462 (9/95). *See review in the Collections section; refer to the Index.* Ⓖ

Tiberiu Brediceanu
Romanian 1877-1968

Suggested listening ...

...Mult mă'ntreabă inima. *Coupled with works by various composers.* **Angela Gheorghiu** (sop); **Malcolm Martineau** (pf). Decca 458 360-2DH (5/98). *See review in the Collections section; refer to the Index.*

Havergal Brian
British 1876-1972

Brian Fantastic Variations on an Old Rhyme. Symphonies – No. 20 in C sharp minor; No. 25 in A minor. **National Symphony Orchestra of Ukraine / Andrew Penny.** Marco Polo Ⓕ 8 223731 (63 minutes: DDD: 6/96). Recorded 1994.

The *Fantastic Variations* (the 'Old Rhyme' on which they are based is *Three Blind Mice*) are early Brian, exuberant music written when he had only just turned 30, but although Symphony No. 20 dates from over 55 years later it is not so much a late work as one from his 'middle period', when he was still experimenting and developing. Only Symphony No. 25, completed just before his ninetieth birthday in 1966, really counts as 'late' Brian. The *Variations* are hugely resourceful, already fantastic before the theme has even been properly stated. Of course Brian is showing off his orchestral mastery, and the range of grotesque, bizarre and troubling ideas that he can draw from such an unpromising theme, but only once or twice do you get the feeling that the contrast between material and treatment is getting a little extreme. The two symphonies are descendants of the *Variations* in their ingenuity of thematic development. Both are intensely dramatic, but their drama is never mere gesture; both are impressive in their long-term strategy, the way that themes are recalled by subtle allusion instead of mere recurrence. Symphony No. 25 is a fine example of this, sowing a new and beautiful melody in the midst of the first movement's development, but only revealing that melody in its full form at the end, where it becomes an obvious, satisfying and moving conclusion. Once or twice the Ukrainian players sound a bit baffled by the idiom, but they clearly believe in the Symphony No. 25, the finest work here, and give it an absorbing, vivid reading. There is a touch of rawness to the sound at times, but Andrew Penny is always alert to the often striking, often surprising colours of Brian's orchestra.

Further listening ...

...The Jolly Miller. Violin Concerto in C major[a]. Symphony No. 18. [a]**Marat Bisengaliev** (vn); **BBC Scottish Symphony Orchestra / Lionel Friend.** Marco Polo 8 223479 (8/94).

...Symphony No. 1, "Gothic". **Soloists; Slovak Philharmonic Choir; Slovak National Theatre Opera Chorus; Slovak Folk Ensemble Chorus; Lucnica Chorus; Bratislava Chamber Choir; Bratislava Children's Choir; Youth Echo Choir; Czechoslovak Radio Symphony Orchestra, Bratislava; Slovak Philharmonic Orchestra / Ondrej Lenárd.** Marco Polo 8 223280/1 (7/90).

...Symphonies Nos. 7 and 31. Comedy Overture – The Tinker's Wedding. **Royal Liverpool Philharmonic Orchestra / Sir Charles Mackerras.** EMI British Composers CDM7 64717-2 (9/93).

...Complete Piano Music: Prelude, "John Dowland's Fancy". Four Miniatures. Three Illuminations[b]. Preludes and Fugues – C minor; D minor/major. Double Fugue in E flat major. Songs[a] – The Land of Dreams; The Birds; The Defiled Sanctuary. **Raymond Clarke** (pf) with [a]**Esther King** (mez); [b]**Tessa Spong** (spkr). Athene ATHCD12 (4/98).

Frank Bridge

Bridge String Sextet in E flat major, H107[a].
Goossens Concertino, Op. 47. Phantasy Sextet, Op. 37[b]. **Academy of St Martin in the Fields Chamber Ensemble** ([ab]Kenneth Sillito, [ab]Malcolm Latchem, [b]Rita Manning, Robert Heard, vns; [ab]Robert Smissen, [a]Stephen Tees, vas; [ab]Stephen Orton, [ab]Roger Smith, vcs).
Chandos Ⓕ CHAN9472 (59 minutes: DDD: 8/97). Recorded 1995.

This admirable programme presents three fine chamber offerings, excellently realized. Goossens's high-quality invention and effortless craft are strikingly evident in the *Concertino*, here performed in its original 1928 guise for string octet and also the elegantly structured *Phantasy Sextet* of 1923. Scored for three violins, one viola and two cellos, this impressive composition is consistently fertile, tightly knit and confidently conceived for the medium. Bridge's Sextet is laid out for the more traditional line-up comprising pairs of each instrument, and is at once the most ambitious and sumptuous of the composer's early chamber offerings. Perhaps the most striking music can be found in the central *Andante con moto*, a wistfully lilting threnody which itself frames a brief scherzo of nervy propulsion. As usual with Bridge, the elegant formal design, captivating lyrical flow and satisfying cogency yield enormous pleasure. The playing is splendid and the sound and balance are impeccable.

Bridge String Quartets – No. 2 in G minor, H115; No. 3, H175. **Bridge Quartet**
(Catherine Schofield, Kaye Barker, vns; Michael Schofield, va; Lucy Wilding, vc).
Meridian Ⓕ CDE84311 (58 minutes: DDD: 8/97). Recorded 1996.

The string quartets of Frank Bridge are some of the most rewarding in the repertoire and here the composer is, on the whole, eminently well served by this eponymous group. In the glorious Second Quartet of 1915, the Bridge Quartet acquit themselves well. Theirs is a thoughtful rendering which, in its comparatively restrained manner, will undoubtedly give pleasure. By the time we reach the superb Third Quartet of 1926, Bridge's command of the medium is total. This score is one of his most searching, deeply felt utterances. The musicians impress it with the honest and hard-working integrity of their playing; however, you may feel that they fight rather too shy of the darker emotional undertow of Bridge's expressionist vision – the intellectual sinew and questing harmonic scope of this marvellous creation are perhaps not as comprehensively conveyed here as one would wish. A most pleasing coupling, however, boasting very good recorded sound.

Additional recommendation ...
...No. 2. Cherry ripe, H119[b]. An Irish melody, H86, "Londonderry air". Sally in our alley, H119[a].
Sir Roger de Coverley, H155. **Delmé Quartet.** Chandos Ⓕ CHAN8426 (45 minutes: DDD: 9/87).

Bridge Cello Sonata in D minor, H125. Four Short Pieces, H104 – Spring Song. Melodie, H99.
Scherzo, H19[a].
Britten Cello Sonata, Op. 65. **Steven Doane** (vc); **Barry Snyder** (pf).
Bridge Ⓕ BCD9056 (52 minutes: DDD: 4/96). Recorded 1994.

A good pairing, of course. Bridge's increasingly progressive European outlook after the First World War seems to have held back his career. However, the two-movement Cello Sonata of 1917 is very English in its rich eloquence, although there is an affinity with Fauré, a composer with whom Bridge shared qualities of quietly glowing passion and unerring craftsmanship. The sonata's deeply emotional second movement is masterly. Collectors already possessing the outstandingly played and recorded 1968 performance by Rostropovich and Britten (see review under Britten) will already know the worth of this music, but this performance by the American duo of Steven Doane and Barry Snyder is warmly sympathetic and thoroughly enjoyable. The Bridge miniatures that accompany it are equally effective. Britten's Sonata, written for Rostropovich, is equally unconventional in having five movements of which Nos. 2, 4 and 5 each last less than three minutes but are none the less characterful and telling. This duo also respond keenly to the younger man's crisper invention and here is another strong yet sensitive performance. Again, of course, collectors may already have Rostropovich and the composer, playing with an authority impossible to surpass. But if you want these two sonatas together this attractive disc provides a safe recommendation and Steven Doane is clearly a cellist to watch. The recording favours the cello, but is otherwise faithful and pleasing.

Additional recommendations ...
...Cello Sonata. Four Short Pieces – Meditation; Spring song. *Coupled with works by*
Debussy and **Dohnányi** Bernard Gregor-Smith (vc); Yolande Wrigley (pf).
ASV Ⓕ CDDCA796 (68 minutes: DDD: 9/92).
...Cello Sonata. **Schubert** Sonata for Arpeggione and Piano in A minor, D821.
Mstislav Rostropovich (vc); **Benjamin Britten** (pf).
Decca The Classic Sound Ⓜ 443 575-2DCS (52 minutes: ADD: 4/95). Ⓖ Ⓖ

Bridge Songs. [a]**Janice Watson** (sop); [b]**Louise Winter** (mez); [c]**Jamie MacDougall** (ten); [d]**Gerald Finley** (bar); [e]**Roger Chase** (va); **Roger Vignoles** (pf). Hyperion Ⓕ CDA67181/2 (two discs: 119 minutes: DDD: 1/98). Texts included. Recorded 1996-97.
When most I wink, H5[a]. If I could choose, H12[d]. The Primrose, H13[c]. A Dirge, H21[b]. The

Devon Maid, H25[c]. Dawn and Evening, H26[d]. Two Heine Songs, H27[c]. Blow, blow, thou winter wind, H33[d]. Go not, happy day, H34[c]. Night lies on the silent highways, H36[d]. A Dead Violet, H38[d]. Cradle Song, H46[a]. Lean close thy cheek, H50[c]. Fair Daffodils, H51[a]. Adoration, H57[b]. So perverse, H61[d]. Tears, idle tears, H62[d]. The Violets Blue, H70[c]. Come to me in my dreams, H71[a]. My pent-up tears oppress my brain, H72[d]. Three Songs, H76[be]. All things that we clasp, H77[a]. Love is a rose, H81[a]. Dear, when I look into thine eyes, H85[d]. Isobel, H102[d]. O that it were so!, H105[b]. Strew no more red roses, H109[c]. Where she lies asleep, H113[b]. Love went a-riding, H114[a]. Thy hand in mine, H124[b]. So early in the morning, O, H130[a]. Mantle of Blue, H131[b]. The Last Invocation, H136[b]. When you are old and gray, H142[d]. Into her keeping, H143[c]. What shall I your true love tell?, H145[b]. 'Tis but a week, H146[d]. Three Tagore Songs, H164[ac]. Goldenhair, H165[a]. Journey's End, H167[c].

Bridge's two most popular songs, *Go not, happy day* and *Love went a-riding*, are so immediately memorable that one always fancies that others of their kind, less striking perhaps but still readily attractive, must exist to be discovered among his complete and quite considerable song output. His characteristic idiom, however, was from first to last less 'catchy', less exuberant, more thoughtful and inward-looking. His development accelerated sharply in his last years as a song-writer, so that the three Tagore settings of 1924 and 1925, with *Journey's End*, the last song of all, have a fluidity of movement that removes them entirely from the category of Edwardian or Georgian 'ballad'. Yet he was hardly a writer of that kind even in his earliest days, the vocal line fastidiously avoiding obviousness and sentimentality, while the piano part develops interests of its own and often calls for some fairly advanced technical skill in the player. After listening to these discs, starting with a student composition from 1901 and ending with the work of a mature composer in his mid forties, one rests with a sense of respect and of a not entirely reticent pleasure, yet not with tunes to hum or depths having been disturbed. Janice Watson's fresh soprano ideally suits the attractive setting of *Fair Daffodils*, and one of the loveliest of the songs, *Come to me in my dreams*. Louise Winter is at her best in the quietly moving *Mantle of Blue* and *What shall I your true love tell?*. Jamie MacDougall finds just the right coloration for "Dweller in my deathless dreams" (from the *Three Tagore Songs*) and Gerald Finley responds well to both the delicacy and the passion of the Yeats setting, *When you are old and gray*. All benefit from Roger Vignoles's scrupulous and sensitive playing. These discs, finely recorded and thoughtfully presented, are a valuable addition to the catalogue.

Additional recommendations ...

...The last invocation. *Coupled with works by various composers.* **Thomas Hampson** (bar); **Craig Rutenberg** (pf). EMI Ⓜ CDM5 55028-2 (67 minutes: DDD: 10/97). *See review in the Collections section; refer to the Index.* ⒼⒼⒼ

...'Tis but a week. Goldenhair. When you are old and gray. So perverse. Journey's End. *Coupled with works by various composers.* **Sir Peter Pears** (ten); **Benjamin Britten** (pf). Belart Ⓑ 461 550-2 (69 minutes: ADD: 12/97). *See review in the Collections section; refer to the Index.*

Further listening ...

...Oration – Concerto elegiaco, H180. *Coupled with* **Britten** Cello Symphony, Op. 68. **Steven Isserlis** (vc); **City of London Sinfonia / Richard Hickox**. EMI CDM7 63909-2 (2/92). Ⓖ

...Phantasm. *Coupled with works by* **Ireland** and **Walton** Kathryn Stott (pf); **Royal Philharmonic Orchestra / Vernon Handley**. Conifer Classics CDCF175 (1/90). Ⓖ

...Sir Roger de Coverley, H155. *Coupled with works by various composers.* **English Chamber Orchestra / Benjamin Britten**. Decca The Classic Sound 448 569-2DCS (2/96).

...Elegy, H47. Scherzetto, H19. *Coupled with works by* **Ireland** and **Stanford** **Julian Lloyd-Webber** (vc); **John McCabe** (pf). ASV CDDCA807 (2/93).

...Three Idylls, H67. *Coupled with works by* **Elgar** and **Walton** Coull Quartet. Hyperion CDA66718 (10/94).

...Pensiero, H53a. Allegro appassionato, H82. *Coupled with works by various composers.* **Paul Coletti** (va); **Leslie Howard** (pf). Hyperion CDA66687 (10/94). *See review in the Collections section; refer to the Index.* Ⓖ

...Three Pieces, H56. Three Pieces, H63. Three Pieces, H106. Three Pieces (1939). Lento. *Coupled with works by* **Vaughan Williams** Christopher Nickol (org). Priory PRCD537 (12/96).

...A Sea Idyll, H54a. Capriccios – No. 1 in A minor, H52; No. 2 in F sharp minor, H54b. Three poems – Ecstasy, H112b. The Hour Glass, H148. Piano Sonata, H160. Vignettes de Marseille, H166. **Kathryn Stott** (pf). Conifer Classics CDCF186 (9/91).

Benjamin Britten (Lord Britten of Aldeburgh) British 1913-1976

Britten Piano Concerto in D major, Op. 13[a]. Violin Concerto, Op. 15[b]. [b]**Mark Lubotsky** (vn); [a]**Sviatoslav Richter** (pf); **English Chamber Orchestra / Benjamin Britten**. Decca London Ⓜ 417 308-2LM (67 minutes: ADD: 10/89). From SXL6512 (8/71). Recorded 1970. Ⓖ

Just after Britten's performances were released on LP in 1971, the composer admitted with some pride that Sviatoslav Richter had learned his Piano Concerto "entirely off his own bat", and had revealed a Russianness that was in the score. Britten was attracted to Shostakovich during the late 1930s, when it was written, and the bravado, brittleness and flashy virtuosity of the writing, in the march-like finale most of all, at first caused many people (including Lennox Berkeley, to whom it is dedicated) to be wary of it, even to think it somehow outside the composer's style. Now we know his music better, it is easier to accept, particularly in this sparkling yet sensitive performance. The Violin Concerto dates from the following year, 1939, when Britten was in Canada, and it, too, has its self-conscious virtuosity, but it is its rich nostalgic lyricism which strikes to the heart and the quiet elegiac ending is unforgettable. Compared to Richter in the other work, Mark Lubotsky is not always the master of its hair-raising difficulties, notably in the scherzo, which has passages of double artificial harmonics that even Heifetz wanted simplified before he would play it (Britten refused), but this is still a lovely account. Fine recordings, made at The Maltings at Snape.

Additional recommendations ...

...Piano Concerto[a]. Violin Concerto[b]. [a]**Joanna MacGregor** (pf); [b]**Lorraine McAslan** (vn); **English Chamber Orchestra / Steuart Bedford.** Collins Classics Ⓕ 1301-2 (66 minutes: DDD: 9/92).

...Violin Concerto[a]. Canadian Carnival, Op. 19. **Britten/Berkeley** Mont Juic, Op. 12. [a]**Lorraine McAslan** (vn); **English Chamber Orchestra / Steuart Bedford.** Collins Classics Ⓕ 1123-2 (58 minutes: DDD: 12/90).

...Piano Concerto. **Copland** Piano Concerto. **Gillian Lin** (pf); **Melbourne Symphony Orchestra / John Hopkins.** Chandos Collect Ⓜ CHAN6580 (51 minutes: ADD: 3/93).

...Piano Concerto[a]. Soirées musicales, Op. 9. Matinées musicales, Op. 24. [a]**Ralf Gothóni** (pf); **Helsingborg Symphony Orchestra / Okko Kamu.** Ondine Ⓕ ODE825-2 (71 minutes: DDD: 1/95). *Gramophone Editor's choice.*   **ⓖ**

...Violin Concerto, Op. 15 (orig. version). *Coupled with works by* **Heming** and **Rubbra** **Theo Olof** (vn); **Hallé Orchestra / Sir John Barbirolli.** EMI British Composers mono Ⓜ CDM5 66053-2* (71 minutes: ADD: 5/97).

...Piano Concerto[a]. Lachrymae, Op. 48[b]. Cello Sonata, Op. 65[c]. [b]**Yuri Bashmet** (va); [c]**Natalia Gutman** (vc); **Sviatoslav Richter** (pf); [a]**USSR State Symphony Orchestra / Evgeni Svetlanov.** Revelation Ⓜ RV10060 (69 minutes: ADD: A/97).

Britten Gloriana, Op. 53[a]. Four Sea Interludes, Op. 33[a]. The Prince of the Pagodas, Op. 57[a] – Pas de Six. **Royal Liverpool Philharmonic Orchestra / Takuo Yuasa.** EMI Eminence Ⓜ CD-EMX2231 (53 minutes: DDD: 3/95). Recorded 1993.

Takuo Yuasa's *Grimes* Interludes are a match for the finest available: with the RLPO on powerfully responsive form, his sensitive reading steers a satisfying middle course between Slatkin's cool objectivity and Hickox's more warmly expressive manner. Certainly, "Sunday Morning" attains a marvellous, bustling climax, notable for some sparkling work from superbly assertive Liverpool trumpets, whilst both "Dawn" and "Moonlight" are at once pleasingly atmospheric yet immensely refined of texture. Yuasa's "Storm" undoubtedly generates great physical excitement. The six numbers which comprise the "Pas de Six" from Act 3 of *The Prince of the Pagodas* contain some of that ambitious ballet's most engaging invention. Yuasa and his colleagues positively relish all the music's drama, glitter and poise, and prove themselves no less dashingly committed exponents of the *Gloriana* concert suite. Here the opening fanfares and popular sequence of "Courtly Dances" are delivered with genuine panache, whilst RLPO principal oboist Jonathan Small creates a ravishing impression in the second movement "Lute Song" (which utilizes Essex's hauntingly wistful aria "Happy were he"). Indeed, the whole performance possesses memorable vibrancy, polish and swagger. The only complaint about this disc is its duration: just 53 minutes of music is a touch on the stingy side.

Additional recommendation ...

...Four Sea Interludes. Johnson over Jordan. The Young Person's Guide to the Orchestra. Suite on English Folk Tunes (A time there was ...), Op. 90. **Bournemouth Symphony Orchestra / Richard Hickox.** Chandos Ⓕ CHAN9221 (67 minutes: DDD: 3/94).

Britten Prelude and Fugue, Op. 29[a]. Lachrymae – Reflections on a Song of Dowland, Op. 48a[b]. Elegy[c]. Simple Symphony, Op. 4[a]. Variations on a theme of Frank Bridge, Op. 10[d]. [bc]**Lars Anders Tomter** (va); [abd]**Norwegian Chamber Orchestra / Iona Brown.** Virgin Classics Ⓕ VC5 45121-2 (78 minutes: DDD: 10/95). Item marked [d] from Simax PSC1035 (1/89). *Gramophone Editor's choice.* Recorded 1988-91.   **ⓖ**

The *Frank Bridge* Variations are finely disciplined, strongly characterized and benefit from sumptuous engineering. The hushed intensity achieved in such variations as the "Adagio" and "Chant" recalls Britten's own remarkable interpretation – and there can be no higher praise than that! In the *Simple Symphony* the infectious "Playful Pizzicato" could perhaps have been given with a greater sense of fun; elsewhere, though, there can be no complaints about the outer movements (both wonderfully crisp and vital), whilst the lovely "Sentimental Sarabande" has surely seldom enjoyed such tenderly expressive advocacy. The *Prelude and Fugue* is brought off with exhilarating poise and panache, and it is difficult to imagine a more eloquent contribution than that of violist Lars Anders Tomter in the early solo *Elegy* and haunting, Dowland-inspired *Lachrymae*. Consistently superior sound, Michael Oliver's admirable booklet-notes and an uncommonly generous playing time add to the considerable attractions of this Virgin Classics release.

Additional recommendations ...

...The Young Person's Guide to the Orchestra. Variations on a Theme of Frank Bridge. Peter Grimes – Four Sea Interludes, Op. 33a; Passacaglia. **BBC Symphony Orchestra / Andrew Davis.** Teldec British Line Ⓕ 9031-73126-2 (68 minutes: DDD: 8/91). *Selected by Sounds in Retrospect.*

...Simple Symphony. Variations on a theme of Frank Bridge. Prelude and Fugue for String Orchestra, Op. 29. **Bournemouth Sinfonietta / Ronald Thomas.**
Chandos Collect Ⓜ CHAN6592 (51 minutes: ADD: 11/93).
...Simple Symphony. Prelude and Fugue, Op. 29. *Coupled with works by various composers.*
English Chamber Orchestra / Benjamin Britten.
Decca The Classic Sound Ⓜ 448 569-2DCS (58 minutes: ADD: 2/96).

Britten Temporal Variations[a]. Six Metamorphoses after Ovid, Op. 49. Two Insect Pieces[b].
Phantasy, Op. 2[c].
Poulenc Oboe Sonata[d]. Trio for Oboe, Bassoon and Piano[e]. **François Leleux** (ob);
[e]**Jean-François Duquesnoy** (bn); [c]**Guillaume Sutre** (vn); [c]**Miguel da Silva** (va); [c]**Marc Coppey** (vc);
[abde]**Emmanuel Strosser** (pf). Harmonia Mundi Les Nouveaux Interprètes Ⓑ HMN91 1556
(76 minutes: DDD: 2/96). Recorded 1995.   Ⓖ
The pairing of these composers is apt, for they were friends and their musical high spirits – frequent in the Parisian, less so in the uneasy East Anglian – often have a darker side. The oboist here, French and very young (he was born in 1971), possesses an excellent technique and is a deeply sensitive artist. Both qualities quickly become evident in the flowing, quietly poignant opening melody of Poulenc's Sonata, where Leleux's tone is not only beautiful but also admirably responsive to the subtle dynamic shading and rhythmic flexibility. Yet this is far from the whole story, and the *grotesquerie* of the passage starting at 2'16" shows that there is more to his playing than gentleness – as does the mercurial *Scherzo*, delivered with delightful point and relish. The final *Déploration* of this sonata, as played here, is infinitely moving and nothing less than superb. Fortunately Leleux and his pianist partner, who is equally attuned to Poulenc's world, have been extremely well recorded. This performance and that of the bouncy Trio both give keen pleasure. So do the Britten pieces, three of them early (the characterful *Six Metamorphoses* being the exception) and edgy. Performed as vividly as this, they are undoubtedly worth having. The booklet gives no information on the music beyond titles and timings. Otherwise there is only praise for a fine, generously filled disc, recommended even if you already possess some of the music.
Additional recommendations ...
...Phantasy[ac]. Holiday Diary, Op. 5[b]. Six Metamorphoses after Ovid[a]. Temporal Variations[ab]. Five Waltzes[b]. Two Insect Pieces[ab]. Night Piece (Notturno)[b]. [a]**Sarah Francis** (ob); [b]**Michael Dussek** (pf); [c]members of the **Delmé Quartet.** Hyperion Ⓕ CDA66776 (75 minutes: DDD: 2/96).
...Temporal Variations[a]. Two Insect Pieces[a]. Phantasy in F minor[c]. Alla marcia[d]. Three Divertimentos[d]. Phantasy, Op. 2[e]. [ae]**Derek Wickens** (ob); [a]**John Constable** (pf); [cd]**Gabrieli Quartet.**
Unicorn-Kanchana Souvenir Ⓜ UKCD2060 (58 minutes: DDD: 6/93).
...Phantasy. *Coupled with works by* **Bax** *and* **Bliss** **Gordon Hunt** (ob); **Tale Quartet.**
BIS Ⓕ CD763 (51 minutes: DDD: 10/97).

Britten The Young Person's Guide to the Orchestra, Op. 34[a]. Simple Symphony, Op. 4[b]. A Spring Symphony, Op. 44 – Spring, the sweet spring[c]. Noyes Fludde[d] – Noye, Noye, take thou thy company ... Sir! heare are lions. Serenade for Tenor, Horn and Strings, Op. 31 – Nocturne[e]. Folk Songs[c] – The Plough Boy; Early One Morning. Billy Budd – Interlude and Sea Shanties[f].
A Ceremony of Carols, Op. 28 – Adam lay i-bounden[g]. A Hymn to the Virgin[g]. War Requiem – Lacrimosa[f]. Peter Grimes – Interlude (Dawn)[h]. [ce]**Sir Peter Pears** (ten); [e]**Barry Tuckwell** (hn); [cdfgh]**various soloists; choirs, choruses and orchestras,** [aef]**London Symphony Orchestra,** [bd]**English Chamber Orchestra / Benjamin Britten** (pf); [d]**Norman Del Mar.** Decca Ⓜ 436 990-2DWO
(74 minutes: ADD: 6/93). Item marked [a] from SXL6110 (9/64), [b]SXL6405 (6/69).   ⒼⒼ
Although when dealing with the music of a single composer Decca's "World of ..." series tends to offer a series of single movements rather than complete works, this reissue, "The World of Britten", is very welcome as it includes the composer's own 1963 recording of *The Young Person's Guide to the Orchestra* with the LSO and his complete 1968 ECO version of the *Simple Symphony*. The latter is delightfully fresh and is unforgettable for the joyful bounce of the "Playful Pizzicato", helped by the resonant acoustic of The Maltings, Snape. *The Young Person's Guide*, adapted from a theme by Purcell, came about through a film which would demonstrate to children the instruments of the orchestra. Here, Britten wisely omits the now rather dated text. He adopts quick tempos that must have been demanding even for the LSO players, with more spacious ones for the more introspective sections. This is beautiful playing, possessing wit and brilliance, with all kinds of memorable touches. If this transfer is a little dry in sonority this disc is invaluable for these two performances alone. As a bonus we also get ten short excerpts from other major Britten works, including *Billy Budd*, the *War Requiem*, *Peter Grimes* and the haunting, echoing "Nocturne" from the *Serenade* (sung by Peter Pears with Barry Tuckwell playing the horn obbligato). We also get Pears's singing of Britten's arrangements of *Early One Morning* and *The Plough Boy* (with the boisterous whistling refrain heard in the upper register of the piano accompaniment). The only curious inclusion here is the exuberant excerpt from Norman Del Mar's *Noyes Fludde*.
Additional recommendations ...
...The Young Person's Guide to the Orchestra. Cello Symphony[a]. Peter Grimes – Four Sea Interludes, Op. 33a. **Pärt** Cantus in memory of Benjamin Britten. [a]**Truls Mørk** (vc);
Bergen Philharmonic Orchestra / Neeme Järvi. BIS Ⓕ CD420 (75 minutes: DDD: 6/89).

...Noye's Fludde[a]. The Golden Vanity, Op. 78[b]. [ab]Soloists; [b]Benjamin Britten (pf); [a]English Opera
Group Orchestra; An East Suffolk Children's Orchestra / Norman Del Mar; [b]Wandsworth School
Boys' Choir / Russell Burgess. Decca London Ⓜ 436 397-2LM (66 minutes: ADD: 11/93).   Ⓖ
...The young Person's Guide to the Orchestra, Op. 34. *Coupled with works by* **Holst** and **Purcell**
Minnesota Orchestra / Sir Neville Marriner.
EMI British Composers Ⓜ CDM7 64300-2 (68 minutes: DDD: 7/94).
... The Young Person's Guide to the Orchestra. *Coupled with works by various composers.*
Hugh Downs (narr); Boston Pops Orchestra / Arthur Fiedler.
RCA Victor Living Stereo Ⓜ 09026 68131-2 (76 minutes: ADD: 12/95).
...A Ceremony of Carols[d]. Around the Village Green – Irish Reel[a]. Soirées musicales[a]. Way to the
Sea[b]. Introduction and Rondo alla burlesca, Op. 23 No. 1[c]. Mazurka elegiaca, Op. 23 No. 2[c].
[c]Sir Clifford Curzon (pf); [d]Maria Korchinska (hp); [b]Geoffrey Tandy (narr); [d]Morriston Boys' Choir
/ Ivor Sims; [a]Charles Brill Orchestra / Charles Brill; chamber ensemble / Benjamin Britten ([c]pf).
Beulah mono Ⓜ 1PD14* (63 minutes: ADD: 11/96).

Britten Solo Cello Suites[a] – No. 1, Op. 72; No. 2, Op. 80. Cello Sonata, Op. 65[b].
Mstislav Rostropovich (vc); [b]Benjamin Britten (pf). Decca London Ⓜ 421 859-2LM
(68 minutes: ADD: 10/89). Items marked [a] from SXL6393 (6/70), [b]SXL2298 (1/62).   ⒼⒼ
This is a classic recording of the Cello Sonata, with Rostropovich and the composer playing with an
authority impossible to surpass, and is here coupled with the unaccompanied First and Second Cello
Suites. The Sonata is unconventional in having five movements of which Nos. 2, 4 and 5 each last less
than three minutes but are none the less characterful and telling. The suggestive, often biting humour,
masks darker feelings. However, Britten manages, just, to keep his devil under control. Rostropovich's
and Britten's characterization in the opening *Dialogo* is stunning and their subdued humour in the
Scherzo-pizzicato also works well. In the *Elegia* and the final *Moto perpetuo*, again, no one quite
approaches the passion and energy of Rostropovich. This work, like the two Suites, was written for
him and he still remains the real heavyweight in all three pieces. Their transfer to CD is remarkably
successful; it is difficult to believe that the recording of the Sonata is over 35 years old and that of the
Suites 27 years.
Additional recommendations ...
...Nos. 1-3. **Peter Wispelwey** (vc). Globe Ⓕ GLO5074X (79 minutes: DDD: 8/92).
...Suite, Op. 6[a]. Elegy[b]. Cello Sonata[c]. Six Metamorphoses after Ovid, Op. 49[d]. [d]Roy Carter (ob);
[a]Alexander Barantschik (vn); [b]Paul Silverthorne (va); [c]Moray Welsh (vc);
[a]John Alley, [c]John Lenehan (pfs).
EMI Anglo-American Chamber Music Series Ⓕ CDC5 55398-2 (59 minutes: DDD: 7/95).
...Cello Sonata. *Coupled with works by* **Mayer** and **Rubbra** Timothy Gill (vc); Fali Pavri (pf).
Guild Ⓕ GMCD7114 (79 minutes: DDD: 4/96).
...Cello Sonata. *Coupled with works by* **Bridge** Steven Doane (vc); Barry Snyder (pf).
Bridge Ⓕ BCD9056 (52 minutes: DDD: 4/96). *See review under Bridge; refer to the Index.*
...Nos. 1-3. **Robert Cohen** (vc). Decca London Ⓕ 444 181-2LH (69 minutes: DDD: 6/96).

Britten Cello Symphony, Op. 68[a]. Sinfonia da Requiem, Op. 20[b]. Cantata misericordium, Op. 69[c].
[a]Mstislav Rostropovich (vc); [c]Sir Peter Pears (ten); [c]Dietrich Fischer-Dieskau (bar); [c]London
Symphony Chorus and Orchestra, [a]English Chamber Orchestra, [b]New Philharmonia Orchestra /
Benjamin Britten. Decca London Ⓜ 425 100-2LM (75 minutes: ADD: 9/89). Text and translation
included. Item marked [a] from SXL6138 (12/64), [bc]SXL6175 (9/65). Recorded 1964.   ⒼⒼⒼ
This disc offers two of Britten's finest works, the *Cello Symphony* and the *Sinfonia da Requiem*. The
latter was written in 1940 and is one of the composer's most powerful orchestral works, harnessing
opposing forces in a frighteningly intense way. From the opening drumbeat the *Sinfonia* employs a
sonata form with dramatic power, though the tone is never fierce or savage; it has an implacable tread
and momentum. The central movement, "Dies irae", however, has a real sense of fury, satirical in its
biting comment – the flutter-tongued wind writing rattling its defiance. The closing "Requiem
aeternam" is a movement of restrained beauty. On this recording from 1964 the New Philharmonia
play superbly. The Cello Symphony, written in 1963 as part of a series for the great Russian cellist
Mstislav Rostropovich, was the first major sonata-form work written since the *Sinfonia*. The idea of
a struggle between soloist and orchestra, implicit in the traditional concerto, has no part here; it is a
conversation between the two. Rostropovich plays with a depth of feeling that has never quite been
equalled in other recordings and the playing of the ECO has great bite. The recording too is
extraordinarily fine for its years. The *Cantata misericordium*, one of Britten's lesser known works, was
written in 1962 as a commission from the Red Cross. It takes the story of the Good Samaritan and is
scored for tenor and baritone soloists, chorus, string quartet and orchestra. It is a universal plea for
charity and here receives a powerful reading. This is a must for any collector of Britten's music.
Additional recommendations ...
...Sinfonia da Requiem. The Young Person's Guide to the Orchestra, Op. 34. Peter Grimes –
Four Sea Interludes; Passacaglia. **Royal Liverpool Philharmonic Orchestra / Libor Pešek.**
Virgin Classics Ⓜ CUV5 61195-2 (63 minutes: DDD: 4/90).
...Cello Symphony. **Bridge** Oration – Concerto elegiaco, H180. **Steven Isserlis** (vc);
City of London Sinfonia / Richard Hickox. EMI Ⓜ CDM7 63909-2 (68 minutes: DDD: 2/92).   Ⓖ

…Cantata misericordium, Op. 69. Deus in adjutorium meum. Chorale on an old French carol.
Coupled with works by **Finzi** and **Holst** John Mark Ainsley (ten); Stephen Varcoe (bar);
Britten Singers; City of London Sinfonia / Richard Hickox.
Chandos Ⓕ CHAN8997 (67 minutes: DDD: 3/92).
…Cello Symphony. **Walton** Cello Concerto. Julian Lloyd Webber (vc); **Academy of St Martin
in the Fields / Sir Neville Marriner.** Philips Ⓕ 454 442-2PH (71 minutes: DDD: 8/97).
Gramophone Editor's choice.

Britten Four Cabaret Songs[a]. When you're feeling like expressing your affection[a]. On this Island –
As it is, plenty[a]. Blues (arr. Runswick)[b] – The Spider and the Fly; Blues; The clock on the wall;
Boogie-Woogie.
Porter Paris – Let's do it[a]. Gay Divorce – Night and Day[a]. Leave it to Me – My heart belongs to
daddy[a]. Miss Otis Regrets[a]. Nymph Errant – The Physician[a]. [a]**Jill Gomez** (sop); [a]**Martin Jones**
(pf); [b]**instrumental ensemble** (David Roach, cl/sax; Graham Ashton, tpt; Beverley Davison, vn;
Chris Lawrence, db; John Constable, pf; Gregory Knowles, perc).
Unicorn-Kanchana Ⓕ DKPCD9138 (52 minutes: DDD: 9/93). Texts included. Recorded 1992.
Gramophone Editor's choice.   Ⓖ
Britten's cabaret songs were written for the singing actress Hedli Anderson; there were more than four,
but these are the only ones to have seen publication so far. The texts by Auden are full of the spirit
that William Coldstream described, writing about one of Anderson's performances, "teaching of
carefree lucidity and the non-avoidance of banality". *When you're feeling like expressing your affection*
which is published and performed here for the first time is one of the results of Auden and Britten's
work for the GPO in the 1930s. Apart from the references to "any telephone kiosk" and "Press button
A" it would still serve well as an encouragement to make use of the telephone. "As it is, plenty", the
last song from *On this Island*, being also in the ironic popular-music style, rounds off the group nicely.
Jill Gomez's performances are perfect in every nuance, her beautiful tone, clear diction and just
hinted-at irony, never overdoing it, give the songs the exact weight they need. The Cole Porter encores
and Daryl Runswick's arrangements of four *Blues* by Britten complete a quite delicious record.
Additional recommendation ...
…Four Cabaret Songs. When you're feeling like expressing your affection. On this Island, Op. 11.
Fish in the unruffled lakes. Night covers up the rigid land. To lie flat on the back. The sun shines
down. What's on your mind?. Underneath the abject willow (two versions). *Coupled with works by*
Berkeley Della Jones (mez); **Philip Langridge** (ten); Steuart Bedford (pf).
Collins Classics Ⓕ 1490-2 (61 minutes: DDD: 4/98). *See review under Berkeley; refer to the Index.*

Britten A Spring Symphony, Op. 44[a]. Cantata Academica, Op. 62[b]. Hymn to St Cecilia, Op. 27[c].
[ab]**Jennifer Vyvyan** (sop); [a]**Norma Procter**, [b]**Helen Watts** (contrs); [ab]**Sir Peter Pears** (ten); [b]**Owen
Brannigan** (bass); [a]**Emanuel School Boys' Choir;** [a]**Chorus and Orchestra of the Royal Opera House,
Covent Garden / Benjamin Britten; London Symphony** [bc]**Chorus / Orchestra / George Malcolm.**
Decca London Ⓜ 436 396-2LM (74 minutes: ADD: 9/93). Texts and translation included.
Item marked [a] from SXL2264 (5/61), [bc] L'Oiseau-Lyre SOL60037 (10/61). Recorded 1960-61.ⒼⒼ
Britten's performance of the *Spring Symphony* fairly leaps out of one's loudspeakers, and the 1960
sound is as crisp and alive as the performance and the work itself. In the last two pieces George
Malcolm's direction is as vivid as Britten's elsewhere. The *Cantata Academica* (1959) is one of Britten's
happiest pieces, bubbling over with warmth, jollity and good fellowship. Indeed the Latin title is only
one of mock-solemnity. Try "Tema seriale con fuga" to hear how this composer could make living
music out of the most perniciously academic device of our troubled century. Further high points are
Owen Brannigan's marvellously pompous bass aria and the boisterous "Canone ed ostinato". The
performance of the *Hymn to St Cecilia* is skilful, idiomatic and touching.
Additional recommendation ...
…A Spring Symphony[a]. Four Sea Interludes, Op. 33[ab]. The Young Person's Guide to the Orchestra,
Op. 34[b]. [a]Jo Vincent (sop); [a]Kathleen Ferrier (contr); [a]Sir Peter Pears (ten); [a]St Willibrord's Boys'
Choir; [a]Netherlands Radio Chorus; Concertgebouw Orchestra, Amsterdam / Eduard van Beinum.
Decca Historic Series mono Ⓜ 440 063-2DM* (75 minutes: ADD: 9/94).

Britten A Spring Symphony, Op. 44[a]. Hymn to St Cecilia, Op. 27. Five Flower Songs, Op. 47.
[a]**Alison Hagley** (sop); [a]**Catherine Robbin** (mez); [a]**John Mark Ainsley** (ten); [a]**Choristers of Salisbury
Cathedral; Monteverdi Choir;** [a]**Philharmonia Orchestra / Sir John Eliot Gardiner.**
DG Ⓕ 453 433-2GH (62 minutes: DDD: 6/97). Texts included. *Selected by Soundings.*
John Eliot Gardiner directs a memorable and thoroughly invigorating account of Britten's vernal
paean. Right from the start, one registers the exceptional refinement and transparency of his
approach, to say nothing of the exciting realism of DG's sound. No praise can be too high for the
marvellously nimble and extremely well-focused contribution of the Monteverdi Choir or the
Philharmonia's superbly disciplined response throughout. The Choristers of Salisbury Cathedral also
emerge with great credit. High-spots abound: the smiling, easy sway of "Spring, the sweet Spring"
(whose bird-call cadenzas are delightfully attended to); an exceptionally perceptive "Waters above",
whose truly *pppp diminuendo* conclusion leads magically into "Out on the lawn I lie in bed"; the
terrific bounce and clean-limbed swagger of the triptych comprising Part 3 (both "Fair and fair" and

"Sound the flute" come close to perfection); and, of course, the joyous, bank holiday clangour of the finale (splendidly dapper and affirmative on this occasion), with its heart-stopping appearance of "Sumer is icumen in" – a moment which never fails to send shivers down the spine (though the four horns might perhaps have cut through the orchestral fabric just a touch more than they do here?). Gardiner's soloists are very good, if perhaps not quite a match for the finest. Ainsley stands out for his honeyed tone, and the intelligence of his word-pointing always catches the attention, as does the warmth and projection of Alison Hagley's soprano. Overall, then, while not displacing the composer's classic recording, Gardiner's version can hold its own against all-comers and should give much pleasure to seasoned Brittenites. Both *a cappella* fill-ups are also a treat: an exquisitely poised and supremely touching *Hymn to St Cecilia*, followed by the delicious *Five Flower Songs*.

Additional recommendation ...
...Five Flower Songs. *Coupled with works by various composers.* **Netherlands Chamber Choir / John Alldis.** Globe Ⓕ GLO5170 (59 minutes: DDD: 2/98). *See review in the Collections section; refer to the Index.*

Britten Hymn to St Cecilia, Op. 27. A Ceremony of Carols, Op. 28[a]. Rejoice in the Lamb, Op. 30[b]. Missa brevis in D major, Op. 63[b]. Sacred and Profane, Op. 91. A hymn to the Virgin. [a]**Frances Kelly** (hp); [b]**Christopher Allsop** (org); **Trinity College Choir, Cambridge / Richard Marlow.** Conifer Classics Ⓕ 75605 51287-2 (79 minutes: DDD: 12/97). Texts included. Recorded 1996.

Britten's genius as a writer of choral music in his early years is laid before us in this attractive, vividly performed programme: the extraordinary variety of these settings shows unerringly his response to the needs of the text in hand and/or for the specific occasion for which the music was written. Marlow and his famed Trinity College Choir have assembled a logical programme and sing with confidence, *élan* and, above all, awareness of Britten's needs. Their accounts, for instance, of *A Ceremony of Carols* and *Rejoice in the Lamb* are well disciplined and responsive to the texts. Marlow seems aware of the fact that Britten eschewed cathedral tradition. While his choir's readings don't altogether replace the composer's classic versions (the more distanced recording means diction is often occluded), they have a life and vigour of their own that is most exhilarating. Marlow includes a subtle performance of the early *Hymn to St Cecilia* as well as the wondrous *Missa brevis*, with its many touches of Brittenesque inspiration and its pre-echoes, particularly in the "Benedictus", of the *War Requiem*. He ends with the late *Sacred and Profane*, where the composer's settings of medieval texts shows that he had lost none of his skills in the last years of his life.

Additional recommendation ...
...Antiphon, Op. 56*b*[b]. Te Deum in C major[b]. A Wedding Anthem, Op. 46[b]. Rejoice in the Lamb, Op. 30[b]. The Sycamore tree. The Ballad of Little Musgrave and Lady Barnard[a]. Advance Democracy. Sacred and Profane, Op. 91. **The Sixteen / Harry Christophers** with [a]**Stephen Westrop** (pf); [b]**Margaret Phillips** (org). Collins Classics Ⓕ 1343-2 (70 minutes: DDD: 6/93). *Gramophone* Editor's choice.

Britten Folk-song Arrangements[a]. Folk-song Arrangements – orchestral versions[b]. King Herod and the Cock[c]. The Twelve Apostles[d]. The Holly and the Ivy[e]. [a]**Felicity Lott** (sop); [abcd]**Philip Langridge** (ten); [ab]**Thomas Allen** (bar); [a]**Carlos Bonell** (gtr); [a]**Osian Ellis** (hp); [a]**Christopher Van Kampen** (vc); [a]**Graham Johnson**, [cd]**David Owen Norris** (pfs); [cd]**Wenhaston Boys' Choir / Christopher Barnett**; [e]**BBC Singers / Simon Joly**; [b]**Northern Sinfonia / Steuart Bedford.** Collins Classics Ⓕ 7039-2 (three discs: 199 minutes: DDD: 11/95). Texts included.

Those who bought the attractive Hyperion set of Britten's 'complete' folk-song arrangements probably thought that they had at least one area in their collection which was complete and need not be reconsidered. Now comes another set, on three CDs rather than two. So the questions run: "What is the extra material?", "How good is it?" and "How do the performances compare?" Eight unpublished settings for solo or duet, one for choir and tenor and one unidentified folk-song setting plus 14 of the published songs rearranged for voice and orchestra: that is the tally. Additions to the voice-and-piano repertoire include *Greensleeves* and *The Crocodile* (the song of a sailor who spins a yarn for landsmen gullible enough to swallow the 500-mile length of croc with attendant wonders). *I wonder as I wander*, a favourite encore in Sir Peter Pears's concerts, is here on record for the first time. These and two light-hearted duets all give pleasure, though perhaps not so acute as to make the purchase imperative. More unexpected, perhaps, is the setting which goes under the title of *The Stream in the Valley* and which turns out to be *Da unten im Tale*, best known today in the arrangement by Brahms. In this Britten introduces to very lovely effect a part for cello. Interest, then, begins to add up. The orchestrations may not add much more, though it is striking to find that the remoteness of tonality in *Fileuse* and to some extent *Eho* (Vol. 2) seems increased.

The choral settings are fun (perhaps more than that), and the great discovery among them is the unfinished, comparatively large-scale arrangement of *The Bitter Withy*, a fascinating piece and apparently going so well that it is astonishing to find Britten putting it aside and never returning to it. Certainly for first-time buyers this is the set to have. As to the performances, much in a Britten collection of this kind depends on the tenor, and Philip Langridge quickly establishes himself as a worthy successor to Pears, a singer of intelligence and bold, distinctive character. In most of the volumes he shares with Felicity Lott, who is comparably sensitive to modulations and underlying feeling. Thomas Allen makes only a brief appearance, but it is good to hear his warm tone and fine legato in the version of *The Sally Gardens* with strings. Fine playing by Osian Ellis and the guitarist Carlos Bonell and a strong contribution from the Wenhaston Boys' Choir are further attractions. Graham Johnson's playing is uniformly excellent. The set is well recorded, the Collins engineers skilfully aligning the acoustics of their five different locations.

Additional recommendations ...

...The Rape of Lucretia (abridged)[a]. Folk-song Arrangements[b] – Voici le printemps; Fileuse; Quand j'étais chez mon père; Le roi s'en va-t'en chasse; La belle est au jardin d'amour; The Salley Gardens; Little Sir William; Oliver Cromwell; The Bonny Earl o' Moray; The ash grove; Quand j'étais chez mon père; There's none to soothe; Sweet Polly Oliver; Le roi s'en va-t'en chasse; The plough boy; The foggy foggy dew; Come you not from Newcastle?; O waly waly. **Soloists;** [b]**BBC Theatre Chorus;** [a]**English Opera Group Chamber Orchestra,** [b]**Orchestra of the Royal Opera House, Covent Garden / Sir Reginald Goodall.** EMI British Composers mono Ⓜ CMS7 64727-2* (two discs: 156 minutes: ADD: 2/94). *Gramophone Editor's choice.*   Ⓖ

...Folk Song Arrangements. **Lorna Anderson, Regina Nathan** (sops); **Jamie MacDougall** (ten); **Bryn Lewis** (hp); **Craig Ogden** (gtr); **Malcolm Martineau** (pf). Hyperion Ⓕ CDA66941/2 (two discs: 125 minutes: DDD: 2/95).

...Folk Song Arrangements[b] – The Salley Gardens; Little Sir William; The ash grove; Oliver Cromwell. Seven Sonnets of Michelangelo, Op. 22[a]. Introduction and Rondo alla burlesca, Op. 23 No. 1[c]. Mazurka elegiaca, Op. 23 No. 2[c]. Serenade for Tenor, Horn and Strings[d]. **McPhee** Balinese Ceremonial Music[e]. [abd]**Sir Peter Pears** (ten); [d]**Dennis Brain** (hn); [e]**Colin McPhee,** [c]**Sir Clifford Curzon** (pfs); [d]**Boyd Neel String Orchestra / Benjamin Britten** ([abce]pf). Pearl mono Ⓜ GEMMCD9177* (78 minutes: ADD: 10/95).

Britten Harmonia Sacra – Lord! I have sinned; Hymn to God the Father; A Hymn on Divine Musick. This way to the Tomb – Evening; Morning; Night. Night covers up the rigid land. Fish in the unruffled lakes. To lie flat on the back with the knees flexed. A poison tree. When you're feeling like expressing your affection. Not even summer yet. The red cockatoo. Wild with passion. If thou wilt ease thine heart. Cradle song for Eleanor. Birthday song for Erwin. Um Mitternacht. The Holy Sonnets of John Donne, Op. 35. **Ian Bostridge** (ten); **Graham Johnson** (pf). Hyperion Ⓕ CDA66823 (65 minutes: DDD: 1/96). Texts included. Recorded 1995. *Gramophone Editor's record of the month.*   ⒼⒼ

Bostridge is in the royal line of Britten's tenor interpreters. Indeed his imaginative response to words and music may come closer than any to Pears himself. He is heard here in a veritable cornucopia of by and large unfamiliar and even unknown songs (the Donne cycle apart), mostly from the earliest period of Britten's song-writing career when his inspiration was perhaps at its most free and spontaneous. The three settings from Ronald Duncan's *This way to the Tomb* nicely match that poet's florid, vocabulary-rich style as Britten was to do again two years later in *Lucretia*, with "Night", based on a B minor ground bass, a particularly arresting piece. The Auden settings, roughly contemporaneous with *On this Island*, all reflect Britten's empathy with the poet at that time. The third, *To lie flat on the back*, evinces Britten's gift for writing in racy mode, as does *When you're feeling like expressing your affection*, very much in the style of *Cabaret Songs*. Much deeper emotions are stirred by the two superb Beddoes settings (*Wild with passion* and *If thou wilt ease thine heart*), written when the composer and Pears were on a ship returning home in 1942. *The red cockatoo* itself is an early setting of Waley to whom Britten returned in *Songs from the Chinese*. All these revelatory songs are performed with full understanding and innate beauty by Bostridge and Johnson, who obviously have a close artistic rapport. They form a lengthy and rewarding prelude to their shattering account of the Donne Sonnets. They are as demanding on singer and pianist as anything Britten wrote, hence their previously small representation in the catalogue. Both artists pierce to the core of these electrifying songs, written after, and affected by, Britten's visit to Belsen with Menuhin in 1945 shortly after the war's end. Fully documented notes, and the skills of the recording team in catching the immediacy of these riveting performances complete one's pleasure in this richly satisfying issue.

Additional recommendation ...

...The Holy Sonnets of John Donne. Seven Sonnets of Michelangelo. Winter Words. If it's ever spring again. The children and Sir Nameless. **Philip Langridge** (ten); **Steuart Bedford** (pf). Collins Ⓕ Classics 1468-2 (67 minutes: DDD: 8/96).

Britten Seven Sonnets of Michelangelo, Op. 22. The Holy Sonnets of John Donne, Op. 35. Winter Words, Op. 52. **Justin Lavender** (ten); **Julian Milford** (pf). Carlton Classics Ⓜ 30366 0056-2 (66 minutes: DDD: 9/97). Texts and translations included. Recorded 1996.

The highlight of this recording is the *Donne* Sonnets, where Lavender has the advantage, over other Britten tenor interpreters to date, of an Italianate metal in his tone, just what these dramatic, even heroic settings call for. He also has the range and technique to make them sound less intractable, vocally speaking, than they often seem, which is not to imply that he is unable to fine away his tone to a silvery line as required by that great Schubert-like song, "Since she whom I lov'd". Together with Milford's eager response to the stringent challenge to his technical resources, this is a convincing reading. That Italianate sound also serves Lavender well in the more extrovert *Michelangelo* Sonnets. These are sung with a fine feeling for line and verbal colouring. In *Winter Words*, intelligently as he enters into the quirky, intense world of this wonderful cycle, he doesn't quite match Philip Langridge on Collins in tonal management or verbal acuity, but the difference is slight and, with Milford again a resourceful and vital partner, this is an interpretation to cherish. The recording ambience sometimes lends a slight edge to the singer's tone, but as a whole this issue is recommendable on every count.

Britten Phaedra, Op. 93[a]. Lachrymae, Op. 48a[b]. Sinfonietta, Op. 1. The Sword in the Stone, Movement for Wind Sextet. Night Mail – End sequence[c]. [a]**Jean Rigby** (mez); [c]**Nigel Hawthorne** (narr); [b]**Roger Chase** (va); **Nash Ensemble / Lionel Friend.** Hyperion Ⓕ CDA66845 (65 minutes: DDD: 9/96). Text included. Recorded 1995.

A chronologically wide-ranging Britten programme performed with unerring sensitivity and much quiet insight. The *Movement* for wind sextet (here receiving its première recording) dates from 1930. Britten composed it during his last term at Gresham's School and annotator Philip Reed suggests that a hearing of Janáček's identically scored *Mládí* may have acted as a possible spur. The *Sinfonietta*, which Britten completed two years later while still a student at the Royal College of Music, represents a remarkable achievement for one so young. Amazingly inventive and concise, it bears a dedication to his mentor, Frank Bridge, whose tangily pastoral idiom can be discerned in the rapt central *Andante.* The Nash Ensemble's account could hardly be bettered: in this same movement, for example, how perceptively Friend and his colleagues gauge (and sustain) the mood of gentle rapture, and how effortlessly they handle the almost Sibelian transition into the "Tarantella" finale. Britten's and Auden's unforgettable collaboration for the end sequence from the documentary *Night Mail* dates from 1936 when both artists were briefly employed by the GPO Film Unit. Remarkably, this is its first commercial recording – and a marvellous one it is, too, with Nigel Hawthorne the exemplary reciter. Three years later, Britten was approached by the BBC to write the incidental music for an adaptation of T. H. White's *The Sword in the Stone.* Scored for a small ensemble the suite abounds in witty motivic borrowings from *The Ring.* Compared with Iona Brown's version of *Lachrymae* with the Norwegian CO on Virgin Classics, not only is this Hyperion version swifter, it perhaps better conveys the unremitting concentration of Britten's questing inspiration, not to mention the wonderful luminosity of the string writing (this 1976 arrangement of the 1950 viola and piano original was Britten's last completed work). The disc opens with a persuasive rendering of *Phaedra* from Jean Rigby. Eloquently though she responds (and the final climax certainly rises to a memorable pitch of intensity), her contribution overall is perhaps not quite as characterful or involving as that of, say, Dame Janet Baker (the work's dedicatee) or Felicity Palmer. With first-rate sound and balance throughout this is an excellent anthology.

Additional recommendations ...
...Sinfonietta[a]. String Quartets[b] – No. 2 in C major, Op. 36; No. 3, Op. 94. [a]**Vienna Octet;** [b]**Amadeus Quartet.** Decca London Ⓜ 425 715-2LM (68 minutes: ADD: 9/90).
...Les illuminations, Op. 18[a]. Phaedra[b]. Folk Song Arrangements – Fileuse; La belle est au jardin d'amour; Eho! Eho!; Quand j'étais chez mon père; Le roi s'en va-t'en chasse[b]. [a]**Jill Gomez** (sop); [b]**Felicity Palmer** (mez); **Endymion Ensemble / John Whitfield.**
EMI British Composers Ⓜ CDM5 65114-2 (50 minutes: DDD: 7/95).

Britten An American Overture, Op. 27. King Arthur – Suite (arr. Hindmarsh). The World of the Spirit (arr. Hindmarsh)[a]. [a]**Susan Chilcott** (sop); [a]**Pamela Helen Stephen** (mez); [a]**Martyn Hill** (ten); [a]**Stephen Varcoe** (bar); [a]**Hannah Gordon,** [a]**Cormac Rigby** (spkrs); [a]**Britten Singers; BBC Philharmonic Orchestra / Richard Hickox.** Chandos Ⓕ CHAN9487 (79 minutes: DDD: 6/97). Text included. *Gramophone Editor's choice.*   ⊙⊙

The performance of the Coplandesque *An American Overture* by Hickox and the excellent BBC Philharmonic has exemplary polish, commitment and dash. The remaining items owe their revival to the considerable efforts of Paul Hindmarsh. Britten wrote his incidental music for a BBC radio dramatization of the King Arthur legend in 1937. It was the first of his 28 radio commissions and contains much high-quality invention. Hindmarsh has fashioned the 23-year-old composer's inventive inspiration into a terrific four-movement orchestral suite lasting some 25 minutes, which Hickox and the BBC PO duly devour with audible relish. The 'radio cantata' *The World of the Spirit* dates from May 1938. Commissioned by the BBC as a successor to *The Company of Heaven* (1937), it intersperses sung and spoken texts chosen by R. Ellis Roberts. Once again, Britten's fertile compositional powers are very much in evidence. Indeed, the work contains a whole string of memorable numbers, from the lilting barcarolle-like treatment of Emily Brontë's "With wide-embracing love", via the joyful strut and swagger of Part 2's concluding "The Spirit of the Lord" with its unmistakable echoes of Walton's *Belshazzar's Feast*, to a strikingly imaginative setting of Gerard Manley Hopkins's *God's Grandeur*, a poem which also features in Britten's unaccompanied choral suite of a year later entitled *A.M.D.G.* Framing the whole 42-minute edifice are two radiant settings of the Whitsuntide plainsong, *Veni Creator Spiritus* – an idea possibly inspired by a recent encounter with Mahler's Eighth Symphony at the Queen's Hall in a performance under Sir Henry Wood. Superbly wide-ranging, realistic recording.

Britten A Ceremony of Carols, Op. 28[a]. Missa brevis in D major, Op. 63[b]. A Hymn to the Virgin. A Hymn of St Columba, "Regis regum rectissimi"[b]. Jubilate Deo in E flat major[b]. Deus in adjutorum meum. [a]**Sioned Williams** (hp); **Westminster Cathedral Choir / David Hill** with [b]**James O'Donnell** (org). Hyperion Ⓕ CDA66220 (49 minutes: DDD: 2/88). From A66220 (12/86). Texts included.

A Ceremony of Carols sets nine medieval and sixteenth-century poems between the "Hodie" of the plainsong Vespers. The sole accompanying instrument is a harp, but given the right acoustic, sensitive attention to the words and fine rhythmic control the piece has a remarkable richness and depth. The Westminster Cathedral Choir perform this work beautifully; diction is immaculate and the acoustic halo surrounding the voices gives a festive glow to the performance. A fascinating *Jubilate* and *A Hymn to the Virgin*, whilst lacking the invention and subtlety of *A Ceremony*, intrigue with some particularly felicitous use of harmony and rhythm. *Deus in adjutorum meum* employs the choir without accompaniment and has an initial purity that gradually builds up in texture as the psalm (No. 70) gathers momentum. The *Missa brevis* was written for this very choir and George Malcolm's nurturing of a tonal brightness in the choir allowed Britten to use the voices in a more flexible and instrumental manner than usual. The effect is glorious. St Columba founded the monastery on the Scottish island of Iona and Britten's hymn sets his simple and forthright prayer with deceptive simplicity and directness. The choir sing this music beautifully and the recording is first rate.

Additional recommendations ...

...A Ceremony of Carols. A Boy is Born, Op. 3. Friday Afternoons, Op. 7. Psalm 150, Op. 67.
Various choirs and soloists / Benjamin Britten.
Decca London Ⓜ 436 394-2LM* (74 minutes: ADD: 9/93).
...A Hymn to the Virgin. A Boy is Born, Op. 3[a]. Christ's Nativity[b]. A Shepherd's Carol. Jubilate Deo[c]. Te Deum in C major[c]. [b]**Susan Gritton** (sop); [b]**Catherine Wyn-Rogers** (contr); **Holst Singers;** [a]**St Paul's Cathedral Choristers / Stephen Layton** with [c]**David Goode** (org).
Hyperion Ⓕ CDA66825 (67 minutes: DDD: 3/96).
...A Hymn of St Columba. *Coupled with works by various composers.* **St Paul's Cathedral Choir / John Scott** with **Andrew Lucas** (org). Hyperion Ⓕ CDA66994 (71 minutes: DDD: 12/97).
See review in the Collections section; refer to the Index.
...Noye's Fludde[a]. A Ceremony of Carols[b]. [a]**Soloists;** [a]**BBC Concert Orchestra;** [b]**Jeffrey Dyball** (hp); [b]**Finchley Children's Music Group / Nicholas Wilks.**
Somm Recordings Ⓕ SOMMCD212 (73 minutes: DDD: 5/98).

Britten Hymn to St Peter, Op. 56a[a]. A Hymn of St Columba, "Regis regum rectissimi"[a]. A Hymn to the Virgin. Hymn to St Cecilia, Op. 27. Rejoice in the Lamb, Op. 30[a]. Choral Dances from "Gloriana". A.M.D.G. **Finzi Singers / Paul Spicer** with [a]**Andrew Lumsden** (org).
Chandos Ⓕ CHAN9511 (67 minutes: DDD: 4/97). Texts included.

The four hymns which open this recital cause one to marvel afresh at this creativity which made everything new and individual yet totally of the composer's unmistakable substance. Each is a small masterpiece, not least the *Hymn of St Columba* (1962), less than three minutes long, and the *Hymn to the Virgin* (1930) written with unfaltering taste and clarity of purpose at the age of 16. Of the other works included here, *Rejoice in the Lamb* (1943) must be the most often recorded, and *A.M.D.G.* the least. A set of seven poems by Gerard Manley Hopkins, it dates from 1939 when the outbreak of war prevented the scheduled première. Shortly afterwards Britten withdrew it, still unpublished, and it remained unheard till 1984, eight years after his death. It commands attention and gains an admiration that one can't quite see growing into affection. By contrast, the remaining work here, the *Choral Dances from "Gloriana"*, inspired love on first meeting and have continued to move and delight ever since. This is the first volume of a projected series, a Britten Choral Edition, with the Finzi Singers taking part throughout. Its obvious rival at present is The Sixteen. With two such expert choirs, both of them so successfully directed, the listener is unlikely to experience any great loss whichever is chosen, but, so far, comparisons encourage a marginal preference for the newer recording. On the merits of performance, then, there is no clear-cut decision. Balance differs somewhat in the two recordings, The Sixteen having a fuller, more sonorous presence, the Finzis giving more prominence to the organ in accompanied items. Andrew Lumsden's contribution may indeed help to tip the balance further in the Finzis' favour for he is constantly bringing out something in colour or rhythm that adds flavour and distinction.

Additional recommendation ...

...Missa Brevis[c]. Festival Te Deum in C major, Op. 32[c]. Jubilate Deo in C major. Hymn to St Peter[ac]. A Hymn to the Virgin. A Hymn of St Columba[c]. Sweet was the Song the Virgin sang. A New Year Carol[b]. A Shepherd's Carol. A Ceremony of Carols[b]. **The Sixteen / Harry Christophers** with [a]**Sioned Williams** (hp); [b]**Stephen Westrop** (pf); [c]**Margaret Phillips** (org).
Collins Classics Ⓕ 1370-2 (61 minutes: DDD: 7/93).

Britten The Rescue of Penelope. Phaedra, Op. 93[a]. [a]**Lorraine Hunt** (mez); **Alison Hagley** (sop) Athene; **Catherine Wyn-Rogers** (mez) Artemis; **John Mark Ainsley** (ten) Hermes; **William Dazeley** (bass) Apollo; **Dame Janet Baker** (narr); **Hallé Orchestra / Kent Nagano.**
Erato Ⓕ 0630 12713-2 (52 minutes: DDD: 7/96). Notes and text included.   Ⓖ

Soon after his return from America, at the height of the war in 1943, Britten wrote the incidental music for a radio play by Edward Sackville-West on the Homeric subject of Odysseus's return to Penelope. Drawn from the complete score with barely any amendment of the original, and compressed into a 36-minute cantata, with Chris de Souza tailoring the text and Colin Matthews, Britten's last amanuensis, most tactfully editing the music, the result is extraordinarily powerful. The most important role is that of the narrator, here masterfully taken by Dame Janet Baker who brings the story vividly to life despite the stylized classical language (e.g. "Odysseus, Lord of sea-girt Ithaca" or "His fair wife, white-armed Penelope"). Rather confusingly Athene also appears as a soprano, with the radiant Alison Hagley sounding totally unlike Dame Janet. She is one of a godly quartet of singers who contribute Greek-style commentaries – vocal passages which regularly add to the atmospheric beauty of the piece. The surprise is that the idiom is not for the most part very Britten-like, except in the vitality of the writing. Here with a bigger orchestra than was usual for him, he allows himself far richer sounds, with the strings in particular often sounding like Walton. The result is hugely enjoyable, and for all the unexpected echoes – not just of Walton's film music but also of Elgar and Wagner – the more one listens, the more one identifies Britten. Who else but Britten would have thought of giving the theme of the heroine, Penelope, most poignantly, to an alto saxophone? This is music which is not just illustrative but strong and purposeful in heightening the drama, in bringing home emotions. It is welcomes addition to the Britten *oeuvre*. It is apt that another encapsulated classical drama should provide the coupling, particularly one inspired by the singing of Dame Janet Baker. *Phaedra* was Britten's last vocal work, and after the richness of the early work the spareness of the writing hits one the more sharply. Lorraine Hunt's performance may not quite match that of Dame Janet in conveying the heroine's agony, but there is comparable intensity, with vocal colouring of similarly grave beauty and variety; with Hunt this is above all the portrait of a deranged woman, chillingly powerful. In both works Kent Nagano draws strongly committed playing from the Hallé, with some fine solo work, instrumental as well as vocal. Though, reasonably enough, Dame Janet's narration is rather close in the bigger work, the sound is full and well balanced.

Additional recommendation ...
...The Rape of Lucretia[a]. Phaedra[b]. **Soloists; English Chamber Orchestra /** [a]**Benjamin Britten,** [b]**Steuart Bedford.** Decca London Ⓕ 425 666-2LH2 (two discs: 124 minutes: ADD: 5/90).

Britten Serenade for Tenor, Horn and Strings, Op. 31[a]. Les illuminations, Op. 18[b]. Nocturne, Op. 60[c]. [abc]**Sir Peter Pears** (ten); [c]**Alexander Murray** (fl); [c]**Roger Lord** (cor ang); [c]**Gervase de Peyer** (cl); [c]**William Waterhouse** (bn); [ac]**Barry Tuckwell** (hn); [c]**Dennis Blyth** (timp); [c]**Osian Ellis** (hp); [ac]**strings of the London Symphony Orchestra;** [b]**English Chamber Orchestra /** [abc]**Benjamin Britten.** Decca London Ⓜ 436 395-2LM* (73 minutes: ADD: 9/93). Texts included. Item marked [a] from SXL6110 (9/64), [b]SXL6316 (11/67), [c]SXL2186 (5/60). Recorded 1959-66. ⒼⒼ

No other instrument was more important to Britten than the human voice and, inspired by the musicianship and superb vocal craftsmanship of his closest friend, Peter Pears, he produced an unbroken stream of vocal works of a quality akin to those of Purcell. Three of his most haunting vocal pieces are featured on this wonderful CD. The performances date from between 1959 and 1966 with Pears in penetratingly musical form, even if the voice itself was by now a little thin and occasionally unsteady. The ECO and LSO are superb in every way and of course Britten was his own ideal interpreter. The recordings are vintage Decca and excellent for their time. This welcome mid-price reissue is strongly recommended.

Additional recommendations ...
...Les illuminations[a]. Simple Symphony, Op. 4. Phaedra, Op. 93[a]. [a]**Christiane Eda-Pierre** (sop); **Jean-Walter Audoli Instrumental Ensemble / Jean-Walter Audoli.** Arion Ⓕ ARN68035 (56 minutes: DDD: 6/89).
...Les illuminations[af]. Serenade[def]. Nocturne[dg]. Quatre chansons françaises[af]. Our Hunting Fathers, Op. 8[bf]. Phaedra, Op. 93[cf]. [a]**Felicity Lott,** [b]**Phyllis Bryn-Julson** (sops); [c]**Ann Murray** (mez); [d]**Philip Langridge** (ten); [e]**Frank Lloyd** (hn); [f]**English Chamber Orchestra;** [g]**Northern Sinfonia / Steuart Bedford.** Collins Classics Ⓕ 7037-2 (two discs: 127 minutes: DDD: 12/94). ⒼⒼ
...Les illuminations[a]. Sinfonia da Requiem, Op. 20[b]. Seven Sonnets of Michelangelo, Op. 22[c]. [ac]**Sir Peter Pears** (ten); [a]**CBS Symphony Orchestra / Benjamin Britten** ([c]pf); [b]**New York Philharmonic Orchestra / Sir John Barbirolli.** NMC mono Ⓕ NMCD030* (61 minutes: ADD: 2/96).
...Les illuminations. Serenade[a]. Nocturne. **John Mark Ainsley** (ten); [a]**David Pyatt** (hn); **Britten Sinfonia / Nicholas Cleobury.** EMI Eminence Ⓜ CD-EMX2247 (73 minutes: DDD: 7/96).
Gramophone Editor's choice. Ⓖ
...Les illuminations. Serenade[a]. Nocturne. **Adrian Thompson** (ten); [a]**Michael Thompson** (hn); **Bournemouth Sinfonietta / David Lloyd-Jones.** Naxos Ⓢ 8 553834 (70 minutes: DDD: 6/98).

Britten Serenade for Tenor, Horn and Strings, Op. 31[a].
R. Strauss Horn Concertos – No. 1 in E flat major, Op. 11; No. 2 in E flat major, AV132. [a]**Ian Bostridge** (ten); **Marie Luise Neunecker** (hn); **Bamberg Symphony Orchestra / Ingo Metzmacher.** EMI Ⓕ CDC5 56183-2 (57 minutes: DDD: 8/97). Text included. Recorded 1996.

On each hearing, Britten's *Serenade* still has the power to astonish anew for its amazingly apt setting of the diligently chosen poems and for the deftly woven, dazzling horn part written for Dennis Brain. There is something inevitable and predestined about these pieces, as though they existed for all time, an impression enhanced by this performance. Bostridge sounds fresh and eager, his interpretation suggesting the work had just been conceived. One small reservation concerns a weakness in the lower register in the Keats Sonnet, "Oh soft embalmer of the still night". Neunecker is as lithe and full-toned as any that has gone before in the horn contribution. The conductor follows tradition in tempo matters and his players are alive to every nuance of the diaphanous scoring. As all other versions are attached to other Britten works, you will buy this one either because of, or in spite of, the coupling, so comparisons seem irrelevant. In the Strauss concertos Neunecker's technique is faultless and she enters into the alternating exuberance and romantic inwardness of Strauss's writing. In the famous flurry of notes at the close of the first piece, she can even stand comparison with Brain's legendary dexterity on yet another, much earlier EMI recording (listed under R. Strauss).

Britten War Requiem, Op. 66[a]. Sinfonia da Requiem, Op. 20. Ballad of Heroes, Op. 14[b].
[a]**Heather Harper** (sop); [a]**Philip Langridge,** [b]**Martyn Hill** (tens); [a]**John Shirley-Quirk** (bar);
[a]**St Paul's Cathedral Choir; London Symphony** [ab]**Chorus and Orchestra / Richard Hickox.**
Chandos Ⓕ CHAN8983/4 (two discs: 125 minutes: DDD: 11/91). Texts and translations
included. *Gramophone Award Winner 1992. Gramophone classical 100.*
Selected by Sounds in Retrospect.   ⒼⒼⒼ
Britten's *War Requiem* is the composer's most public statement of his pacifism. The work is cast in six movements and calls for massive forces: full chorus, soprano soloist and full orchestra evoke mourning, supplication and guilty apprehension; boys' voices with chamber organ, the passive calm of a liturgy which points beyond death; tenor and baritone soloists with chamber orchestra, the passionate outcry of the doomed victims of war. The most recent challenger to the composer's classic Decca version offers up-to-date recording, excellently managed to suggest the various perspectives of the vast work, and possibly the most convincing execution of the choral writing to date under the direction of a conductor, Richard Hickox, who is a past master at obtaining the best from a choir in terms of dynamic contrast and vocal emphasis. Add to that his empathy with all that the work has to say and you have a cogent reason for acquiring this version even before you come to the excellent work of the soloists. In her recording swan song, Harper at last commits to disc a part she created. It is right that her special accents and impeccable shaping of the soprano's contribution have been preserved for posterity. Shirley-Quirk, always closely associated with the piece, sings the three baritone solos and duets with rugged strength and dedicated intensity. He is matched by Langridge's compelling and insightful reading, with his notes and words more dramatic than Pears's approach. The inclusion of two additional pieces, neither of them short, gives this version an added advantage even if the *Ballad of Heroes* is one of Britten's slighter works.
Additional recommendations ...
...War Requiem. **Soloists; Christ Church Cathedral Choir, Oxford; City of Birmingham Symphony Chorus and Orchestra / Sir Simon Rattle.** EMI Ⓕ CDS7 47034-8 (two discs: DDD: 12/84).
Selected by Sounds in Retrospect.   Ⓖ
...War Requiem. **Soloists; Bach Choir; Highgate School Choir; London Symphony Chorus; Melos Ensemble; London Symphony Orchestra / Benjamin Britten.**
Decca Ⓕ 414 383-2DH2 (two discs: 81 minutes: ADD: 4/85).   ⒼⒼⒼ
...War Requiem. **Soloists; Atlanta Symphony Chorus and Orchestra / Robert Shaw.**
Telarc Ⓕ CD80157 (two discs: 83 minutes: DDD: 12/89).
...War Requiem. **Soloists; American Boychoir; Westminster Symphonic Choir; New York Philharmonic Orchestra / Kurt Masur.** Teldec Ⓕ 0630 17115-2 (two discs: 83 minutes: DDD: 4/98).

Britten Albert Herring. **Sir Peter Pears** (ten) Albert Herring; **Sylvia Fisher** (sop) Lady Billows;
Johanna Peters (contr) Florence Pike; **John Noble** (bar) Mr George; **Owen Brannigan** (bass)
Mr Budd; **Edgar Evans** (ten) Mr Upford; **April Cantelo** (sop) Mrs Wordsworth; **Sheila Rex** (mez)
Mrs Herring; **Joseph Ward** (ten) Sid; **Catherine Wilson** (mez) Nancy; **English Chamber Orchestra /
Benjamin Britten.** Decca London Ⓕ 421 849-2LH2 (two discs: 138 minutes: ADD: 4/97). Notes
and text included. From SET274/6 (10/64).
Britten Albert Herring. **Christopher Gillett** (ten) Albert Herring; **Dame Josephine Barstow** (sop)
Lady Billows; **Felicity Palmer** (mez) Florence Pike; **Peter Savidge** (bar) Mr George; **Robert Lloyd**
(bass) Mr Budd; **Stuart Kale** (ten) Mr Upford; **Susan Gritton** (sop) Mrs Wordsworth; **Della Jones**
(mez) Mrs Herring; **Gerald Finley** (bar) Sid; **Ann Taylor** (mez) Nancy; **Northern Sinfonia /
Steuart Bedford.** Collins Classics Ⓕ 7042-2 (two discs: 142 minutes: DDD: 4/97). Text included.
Recorded 1996. *Selected by Soundings.*
As in all his recordings, Britten is a hard act to follow. Yet when his version of *Albert Herring* appeared in 1964 (17 years after the première) there were plenty who found Sylvia Fisher's classic portrayal of Lady Billows not really up to their memories of Joan Cross, nor April Cantelo as deliciously funny a Miss Wordsworth as her creator, Margaret Ritchie, or her peerless successor Jennifer Vyvyan. Cantelo's is an enchanting portrayal, and those who have grown up with it may find Susan Gritton not *quite* her equal ... and so on: it is that sort of opera. Its superbly varied recitative and its pungent, thumbnail-sketch 'arias' provide resourceful singer-actors with the juiciest chances imaginable to become obstinately memorable. Gritton seizes those chances with both hands, sounding at times uncannily like Vyvyan. Felicity Palmer is a splendid Florence, relishing gossip, moral outrage and her authority as Lady Billows's ADC. Of course Christopher Gillett cannot erase memories of Pears in the title-role. But there is more sense of a worm turning in his performance, less of a feeling that no one so irredeemably daft and downtrodden could possibly escape from Mum's apron-strings, firmly tied though they are by Della Jones. Ann Taylor and Gerald Finley are admirable, believable both as lovers and as baker's girl and butcher's boy respectively. The village worthies are all sharply done, with Robert Lloyd especially good as an irascible Superintendent Budd. The one reservation

concerns Josephine Barstow's Lady Billows. She is formidably authoritative, at her best when she loses her notes in mid-speech but improvises with magnificent clichés ("Cleanliness is next to ... God for England and Saint ... Keep your powder dry and leave the rest to nature!"). But, at least as recorded here, her voice has a very sharp edge to it, all the more apparent since she almost never sings quietly. Of course the newer recording cannot supersede Britten's own, but when the next version arrives there will be many who ruefully decide that Miss X cannot measure up to Gritton nor Mr Y to Gillett. There will probably be some who sigh that no other Lady Billows has Barstow's vocal equivalent of an imperious basilisk glare. Bedford is worthy of the opera, in short, and as good as Britten at making clear that *Albert Herring* is as central to the Britten canon as any of his other operas.

Britten Billy Budd (four-act version). **Thomas Hampson** (bar) Billy Budd; **Anthony Rolfe Johnson** (ten) Captain Vere; **Eric Halfvarson** (bass-bar) John Claggart; **Russell Smythe** (bar) Mr Redburn; **Gidon Saks** (bass) Mr Flint; **Simon Wilding** (bass) Lt Ratcliffe; **Martyn Hill** (ten) Red Whiskers; **Christopher Maltman** (bar) Donald; **Richard Van Allan** (bass) Dansker; **Andrew Burden** (ten) Novice; **Christopher Gillett** (ten) Squeak; **Matthew Hargreaves** (bass) Bosun; **Ashley Holland** (bass) First Mate; **Simon Thorpe** (bar) Second Mate, Arthur Jones; **Robert Johnston** (ten) Maintop; **William Dazeley** (bar) Novice's Friend; **Manchester Boys' Choir; Northern Voices; Hallé Choir and Orchestra / Kent Nagano.** Erato Ⓕ 3984-21631-2 (two discs: 148 minutes: DDD: 3/98). Notes and text included. Recorded live in May 1997.

This recording is an exciting achievement; it restores to circulation the original, four-act version of the score. The crucial difference between this and Britten's two-act revision is a scene at the close of what is here Act 1, in which 'Starry' Vere addresses his crew and is hailed by them as the sailors' champion, thus establishing the relationship between captain and foretopman. It is thus an important scene though musically not particularly distinguished. One can quite see why Britten wanted a tauter two-act drama. Nagano gives us a wonderfully full-bodied, accurate and detailed account of the many-faceted score. There are electrifying moments, not least the battle scene, where the listener feels very much in the middle of things, and the end of Act 3 where those tremendous and ominous series of chords represent Vere telling Budd of the sentence of death. Britten, in his 1967 studio recording, prefers a leaner sound and a slightly tauter approach all-round – in his hands you feel the tension of the personal relationships even more sharply than with Nagano. Hampson is very good, singing with all his customary beauty of voice and intelligence of style, though he imparts a touch of self-consciousness that goes against the grain of the writing. Halfvarson, as Budd's antagonist, the evil Claggart, gives us a mighty presence, singing with power and bite, though not always a steady tone. Rolfe Johnson sings his heart out as he presents Vere's tormented soul. For the rest, Gidon Saks makes a dominant Mr Flint, the sailing-master, Richard Van Allan, is here, predictably, a characterful Dansker, and Andrew Burden stands out as a properly scared Novice, far preferable to Tear's placid reading on Decca. The sum here is greater than the parts, and this Erato set can be heartily recommended. In Manchester's Bridgewater Hall, where the recording was made (though, to judge by the absence of background noise, there must have been sessions without an audience), the orchestral contribution was, apparently, exceptionally clear. That has been carried over into the amazingly wide spectrum of sound on the recording: indeed sometimes the orchestra is simply too loud.

Additional recommendation ...
...Billy Budd. The Holy Sonnets of John Donne, Op. 35. Songs and Proverbs of William Blake, Op. 74. **Soloists; Ambrosian Opera Chorus; London Symphony Orchestra / Benjamin Britten.** Decca Ⓕ 417 428-2LH3 (three discs: 205 minutes: ADD: 6/89). ⒼⒼ

Britten Gloriana. **Josephine Barstow** (sop) Queen Elizabeth I; **Philip Langridge** (ten) Earl of Essex; **Della Jones** (mez) Lady Essex; **Jonathan Summers** (bar) Lord Mountjoy; **Alan Opie** (bar) Sir Robert Cecil; **Yvonne Kenny** (sop) Penelope; **Richard Van Allan** (bass) Sir Walter Raleigh; **Bryn Terfel** (bass-bar) Henry Cuffe; **Janice Watson** (sop) Lady-in-waiting; **Willard White** (bass) Blind ballad-singer; **John Shirley-Quirk** (bar) Recorder of Norwich; **John Mark Ainsley** (ten) Spirit of the Masque; **Peter Hoare** (ten) Master of Ceremonies; **Welsh National Opera Chorus and Orchestra / Sir Charles Mackerras.** Argo Ⓕ 440 213-2ZHO2 (two discs: 148 minutes: DDD: 7/93). Notes and text included. Recorded 1992. *Gramophone Award Winner 1994.* *Gramophone Editor's choice.* Ⓖ

Four decades on from the ill-fated première of Britten's Coronation opera where, instead of the staid pageant expected by the bejewelled and stiff audience assembled for a royal gala, they were given an intimate study of the ageing Queen's torment as she copes with the conflict of private emotions in the midst of public pomp, *Gloriana* has now at last been given a complete recording on CD. Sir Charles Mackerras presents it here with the utmost conviction, drawing together the motivic strands of the score into a coherent whole (not an altogether easy task), appreciating the contrast of the public and private scenes, exposing the sinews of the writing for the two principal characters, and drawing superb playing from his own WNO Orchestra. Josephine Barstow crowns her career with her performance as Queen Elizabeth, commanding the opera by her vocal presence, her imposing, vibrant tone, her vital treatment of the text, and her attention to detail. Philip Langridge projects all the vehement impetuosity of Essex but also, in the famous lute songs, the poetic ardour of the handsome if unruly Earl. There is much discerning interpretation elsewhere and the recording is worthy of the performance. Any small reservations are as nothing before the triumph of the achievement as a whole.

Britten A Midsummer Night's Dream. **Alfred Deller** (alto) Oberon; **Elizabeth Harwood** (sop) Tytania;
Sir Peter Pears (ten) Lysander; **Thomas Hemsley** (bar) Demetrius; **Josephine Veasey** (mez)
Hermia; **Heather Harper** (sop) Helena; **John Shirley-Quirk** (bar) Theseus; **Helen Watts** (contr)
Hippolyta; **Owen Brannigan** (bass) Bottom; **Norman Lumsden** (bass) Quince; **Kenneth Macdonald**
(ten) Flute; **David Kelly** (bass) Snug; **Robert Tear** (ten) Snout; **Keith Raggett** (ten) Starveling;
Richard Dakin (treb) Cobweb; **John Prior** (treb) Peaseblossom; **Ian Wodehouse** (treb) Mustardseed;
Gordon Clark (treb) Moth; **Stephen Terry** (spkr) Puck; **Choirs of Downside and Emanuel Schools;
London Symphony Orchestra / Benjamin Britten.** Decca London 425 663-2LH2 (two discs: 144
minutes: ADD: 5/90). Notes and text included. From SET338/40 (5/67). Recorded 1966.   ⓖⓖⓖ
Britten A Midsummer Night's Dream. **Brian Asawa** (alto) Oberon; **Sylvia McNair** (sop) Tytania;
John Mark Ainsley (ten) Lysander; **Paul Whelan** (bar) Demetrius; **Ruby Philogene** (mez) Hermia;
Janice Watson (sop) Helena; **Brian Bannatyne-Scott** (bass) Theseus; **Hilary Summers** (contr)
Hippolyta; **Robert Lloyd** (bass) Bottom; **Gwynne Howell** (bass) Quince; **Ian Bostridge** (ten) Flute;
Stephen Richardson (bar) Snug; **Mark Tucker** (ten) Snout; **Neal Davies** (bar) Starveling;
David Newman (treb) Cobweb; **Claudia Conway** (sop) Peaseblossom; **Sara Rey** (sop) Mustardseed;
Matthew Long (treb) Moth; **Carl Ferguson** (spkr) Puck; **New London Children's Choir;
London Symphony Orchestra / Sir Colin Davis.** Philips Ⓕ 454 122-2PH2 (two discs:
148 minutes: DDD: 12/96). Notes and text included. Recorded 1995. *Selected by Soundings.*   ⓖ
The Philips set is in almost every respect immediate and present, almost to a fault, yet there are few
if any attempts at suggesting the perspectives you hear on the 30-year-old Decca set for the composer.
For instance, on Decca, Puck seems to be everywhere, on the newer version you are in the front stalls
listening to an enjoyable concert with little attempt to simulate a stage. That may have influenced the
often leisurely pacing of Davis's reading. Everything is heard with great clarity, the sensuousness of
Britten's ravishing score, with all its mysterious harmonies and sonorities, is fully realized, action and
reaction among the singers are keenly heard, yet something of the midsummer magic of Britten's
direction eludes Davis and his team. On Decca we hear this music fresh-minted, unadorned; in Davis's
hands the work is viewed through a tougher, more modern prism, something that those who know the
original set will need to become accustomed to. One wonders if any members of the LSO today were
in the orchestra under the composer back in 1966: they are certainly as acute if not more so in their
playing than their predecessors. As for pacing, if you try either Oberon's "I know a bank" or Tytania's
solo "Come, now a roundel and a fairy song" you will immediately hear how much tauter is Britten's
approach, Davis allowing his singers more licence. In the case of McNair this gives her space to
develop what is a knowingly sophisticated approach to her role, even more evident in her sensual
account of the Act 2 solo "Hail, mortal, hail". Her singing is in itself lovely, but it is an earthly
reading where Elizabeth Harwood for Britten suggests a more other-worldly Queen of the Fairies.
    Similarly the luscious, vibrant voice of the American countertenor Brian Asawa is very different
from Deller's ethereal delicacies. Like McNair's singing, Asawa's, taken on its own terms, is most
seductive, certainly a new look at the familiar, but disconcerting at first hearing. Puck is also upfront,
not so much puckish as rough-hewn. With Bottom we meet another thought-provoking
interpretation. Lloyd makes the weaver sound more high-born than his predecessor. This is almost a
noble craftsman, with no hint of the rustic portrayed unforgettably by Owen Brannigan, the role's
creator, who savours the text so lovingly. Lloyd scores with his splendidly resonant account of "O
grin-look'd night" in the play. One thing is sure: there has never been a more amusing Flute than Ian
Bostridge (hilarious as Thisbe) or a better sung Quince than Gwynne Howell. Another plus for Davis
is the casting of the lovers with young singers in their early prime, a small advance on the Britten set.
In particular, Philogene's ripe mezzo as Hermia and Ainsley's ardent tenor as Lysander stand out as
ideal interpretations. Neither Hippolyta nor Theseus matches the regal authority of Helen Watts and
Shirley-Quirk on the composer's set. You will derive a great deal of pleasure from the newcomer with
its exemplary recording and careful preparation on all sides. It is now the prime recommendation for
a modern set. But the Decca, one of the most successful opera recordings of all time, remains as fresh
and inspired as the day it was made; Britten's taut, disciplined yet magical reading unsurpassed.

Britten Peter Grimes. **Sir Peter Pears** (ten) Peter Grimes; **Claire Watson** (sop) Ellen Orford; **James
Pease** (bass) Captain Balstrode; **Jean Watson** (contr) Auntie; **Raymond Nilsson** (ten) Bob Boles;
Owen Brannigan (bass) Swallow; **Lauris Elms** (mez) Mrs Sedley; **Sir Geraint Evans** (bar) Ned
Keene; **John Lanigan** (ten) Rector; **David Kelly** (bass) Hobson; **Marion Studholme** (sop) First
Niece; **Iris Kells** (sop) Second Niece; **Chorus and Orchestra of the Royal Opera House, Covent
Garden / Benjamin Britten.** Decca Ⓕ 414 577-2DH3* (two discs: 144 minutes: ADD: 4/86).
Notes and text included. From SXL2150/52 (10/59). Recorded 1958. *Gramophone Award Winner
1986. Gramophone classical 100. Selected by Sounds in Retrospect.*   ⓖⓖⓖ
Britten Peter Grimes. **Philip Langridge** (ten) Grimes; **Janice Watson** (sop) Ellen Orford; **Alan Opie**
(bar) Balstrode; **Ameral Gunson** (mez) Auntie; **John Graham-Hall** (ten) Bob Boles; **John Connell**
(bass) Swallow; **Anne Collins** (contr) Mrs Sedley; **Roderick Williams** (bar) Ned Keene;
John Fryatt (ten) Rector; **Matthew Best** (bass) Hobson; **Yvonne Barclay** (sop) First Niece;
Pamela Helen Stephen (mez) Second Niece; **London Symphony Chorus; City of London Sinfonia /
Richard Hickox.** Chandos Ⓕ CHAN9447/8 (two discs: 147 minutes: DDD: 5/96).
Notes and text included. Recorded 1995. *Gramophone Editor's choice. Selected by Soundings.*   ⓖ

The Decca set has long been regarded as the definitive recording which, in 1958, introduced this opera to many listeners and one which has never been superseded in its refinement or insight. Britten's conducting, lithe, lucid and as inexorable as "the tide that waits for no man", reveals his work as the complex, ambiguous drama that it is. Sir Peter Pears, in the title-role which was written for him, brings unsurpassed detail of nuance to Grimes's words while never losing sight of the essential plainness of the man's speech. The rest of the cast form a vivid portrait gallery of characters. The recording is as live and clear as if it had been made yesterday and takes the listener right on to the stage. The bustle of activity and sound effects realize nicely Britten's own masterly painting of dramatic foreground and background. For Hickox on Chandos there is Langridge's tense, sinewy, sensitive Grimes. Predictably he rises to the challenge of the Mad scene; this is a man hugely to be pitied, yet there is a touch of resignation, of finding some sort of peace at last, after all the agony of the soul. Earlier he doesn't quite match either Pears (Britten) or Rolfe Johnson (Haitink) in poetic tone for "What harbour" and the Pleiades solo, and he can't carry his voice over the ensemble later in that Inn scene as Vickers (Davis) easily does, but the compensations are appreciable. The portrayal is more tense and immediate than that of Rolfe Johnson, more accurate than, and just as anguished as, that of Vickers and a match for that of Pears in personal identification – listen to the eager touch at "We strained in the wind".

The next composite heroes are the members of the chorus. Electrifying as their rivals are, the LSO singers, trained by Stephen Westrop, seem just that much more arresting, not least in the hue-and-cry of Act 3, quite terrifying in its immediacy as recorded by Chandos. Hickox's whole interpretation has little to fear from the distinguished competition. Many details are placed with special care, particularly in the Interludes and the parodistic dances in Act 3, and whole episodes, such as the Grimes/Balstrode dispute in Act 1, have seldom sounded so dramatic. Once or twice one would have liked a firmer forward movement, as in the fifth Interlude (Britten's own direction of this Passacaglia is that bit more urgent), but the sense of total music-theatre is present throughout and it's excitingly laid before us by the City of London Sinfonia and the recording. Of the other soloists, the one comparative disappointment is Janice Watson's Ellen Orford. She sings the part with tone as lovely as any of her rivals on disc and with carefully wrought phrasing and is very much part of a convincing team but doesn't have the experience to stand out from the village regulars and sound important, as Ellen should. Britten's set remains *hors concours* (the composer's own taut conducting is unsurpassed), but that recording stretches over three CDs. Hickox is the finest of the modern recordings: as sound it is quite spectacular, vast in scale, with well-managed perspectives and just enough hints of stage action to be convincing.

Additional recommendations ...

...Soloists; Chorus and Orchestra of the Royal Opera House, Covent Garden / Sir Colin Davis.
Philips Ⓕ 432 578-2PM2 (two discs: 146 minutes: ADD: 11/91).
...Soloists; Chorus and Orchestra of the Royal Opera House, Covent Garden / Bernard Haitink.
EMI Ⓕ CDS7 54832-2 (two discs: 145 minutes: DDD: 7/93). *Gramophone Editor's choice.* Ⓖ

Britten The Turn of the Screw. **Philip Langridge** (ten) Prologue; **Robert Tear** (ten) Quint;
Helen Donath (sop) Governess; **Michael Ginn** (treb) Miles; **Lilian Watson** (sop) Flora; **Ava June**
(sop) Mrs Grose; **Heather Harper** (sop) Miss Jessel; **Orchestra of the Royal Opera House,**
Covent Garden / Sir Colin Davis. Philips Ⓕ 446 325-2PH2 (two discs: 108 minutes: ADD: 9/96).
Notes and text included. From 410 426-1PH2 (1/84). Recorded 1981.

Davis yields little if anything to the composer or to Steuart Bedford in realizing the taut, claustrophobic feeling of the score. The players of the ROH Orchestra are quite as alert as Britten's and Bedford's chamber ensembles to the minutiae of the fastidious instrumentation, bringing out the genius of Britten's variation form. Davis unerringly pinpoints the change from the lyrical euphony of some of the earlier scenes and the sinister, otherworldly suggestions of the later ones. The cast stands comparison with its rivals – though Tear, for all his competence, cannot quite match the peculiarly haunting quality of Pears's tone as Quint in a role specifically tailored to Britten's partner. Tear doesn't attempt to double with the Prologue, here sung with predictable intelligence and refined poetic expectancy by the young Langridge, who memorably doubles the roles on the Collins set. Donath very properly lets a note of nervous agitation enter into her tone and evinces full understanding of the Governess's predicament, "Lost in my labyrinth" rightly given as a whispered, interior monologue, though she doesn't build all the tensions as unerringly as Vyvyan (Britten) or Dame Felicity Lott (Bedford). Heather Harper, herself an erstwhile Governess, is a rightly hard-bitten Miss Jessel, preferable to either of her rivals. Ava June is even more articulate than her teacher Joan Cross (Britten) as Mrs Grose, though not superior to Bedford's excellent Phyllis Cannan. Lilian Watson makes a more vivid Flora than her counterparts on the other sets, but Michael Ginn, accomplished treble though he is, doesn't suggest the paradox of evil in innocence as David Hemmings so amazingly does on Decca. The years make one newly aware of the historic importance of Britten's own reading but each version is wholly worthy of this extraordinary score.

Additional recommendations ...

...Soloists; English Opera Group Orchestra / Benjamin Britten.
Decca London mono Ⓕ 425 672-2LH2* (two discs: 105 minutes: ADD: 5/90). Ⓖ
...Aldeburgh Festival Ensemble / Steuart Bedford. Collins Classics Ⓕ 7030-2 (two discs: 106 minutes:
DDD: 6/94). *Gramophone Editor's choice. Selected by Sounds in Retrospect.* Ⓖ

Further listening ...

...String Quartets – No. 1 in D major, Op. 25; No. 3, Op. 94. Three Divertimentos. Alla marcia.
Sorrel Quartet. Chandos CHAN9469 (9/96).

...String Quartets – No. 2 in C major, Op. 36; No. 3, Op. 94. **Britten Quartet.**
Collins Classics 1025-2 (12/90).

...String Quartet No. 3, Op. 94. *Coupled with* **Tippett** String Quartet No. 4. **Lindsay Quartet.**
ASV CDDCA608 (5/88).

...Solo Cello Suite No. 3, Op. 87. *Coupled with works by various composers.* **Matt Haimovitz** (vc).
DG 445 834-2GH (12/95).

...Solo Cello Suite No. 3, Op. 87. *Coupled with* **Tavener** The Protecting Veil[a]. Thrinos.
Steven Isserlis (vc); [a]**London Symphony Orchestra / Gennadi Rozhdestvensky.**
Virgin Classics VC7 59052-2 (3/92). *Gramophone Award Winner 1992.*   🅶🅶

...Holiday Diary, Op. 5. *Coupled with works by various composers.* **Shura Cherkassky** (pf).
Decca 433 657-2DH (2/96).

...Nocturnal after John Dowland, Op. 70. *Coupled with works by* **Schafer** *and* **Tippett**
Norbert Kraft (gtr). Chandos CHAN8784 (1/90).

...The Ballad of Little Musgrave and Lady Barnard. *Coupled with works by various composers.*
**London Madrigal Singers / Christopher Bishop; Baccholian Singers of London; Philip Jones Brass
Ensemble; English Chamber Orchestra / Ian Humphris.** EMI British Composers CMS5 65123-2
(2/96). *See review in the Collections section; refer to the Index.*

...Hölderlin Fragments, Op. 61 – No. 5, Hälfte des Lebens. *Coupled with works by various
composers.* **Mitsuko Shirai** (mez); **Hartmut Höll** (pf). Capriccio 10 534 (12/94). *See review in the
Collections section; refer to the Index.*

...Peter Grimes – Embroidery in childhood. *Coupled with works by various composers.*
Renée Fleming (sop); **Jonathan Summers** (bar); **London Symphony Orchestra / Sir Georg Solti.**
Decca 455 760-2DH (10/97). *Gramophone Editor's choice. See review in the Collections section;
refer to the Index.*

...Purcell Realizations. **Soloists; Graham Johnson** (pf). Hyperion CDA67061/2 (11/95).

...Saint Nicolas, Op. 42[a]. Christ's Nativity[b]. Psalm 150, Op. 67[c]. [a]**Nicholas Elstob** (treb);
[a]**Philip Langridge** (ten); [a]**David Owen Norris,** [a]**Rolfe Hind** (pfs); [a]**Joseph Cullen** (org); [a]**Tallis
Chamber Choir;** [b]**BBC Singers;** [a]**New London Children's Choir;** [a]**English Chamber Orchestra,**
[c]**London Schools Symphony Orchestra / Steuart Bedford.** Collins Classics 1483-2 (12/96).

...Te Deum in C major. *Coupled with works by various composers.* **St Paul's Cathedral Choir /
John Scott** with **Andrew Lucas** (org). Hyperion CDA66916 (A/97). *See review in the Collections
section; refer to the Index.*

...The Burning Fiery Furnace. **Soloists; English Opera Group / Benjamin Britten.**
Decca 414 663-2LM (10/90).   🅶

...Curlew River. **Soloists; English Opera Group / Benjamin Britten** and **Viola Tunnard.**
Decca London 421 858-2LM (9/89).

...Curlew River. **Soloists; Guildhall Chamber Choir and Ensemble.** Koch Schwann 313972 (5/96).

...Death in Venice. **Soloists; English Opera Group Chorus; English Chamber Orchestra /
Steuart Bedford.** Decca London 425 669-2LH2 (5/90).   🅶🅶

...Owen Wingrave[a]. Six Hölderlin fragments, Op. 61[b]. The Poet's Echo, Op. 76[c].
[a]**Soloists;** [a]**Wandsworth School Boys' Choir; English Chamber Orchestra / Benjamin Britten.**
[b]**Sir Peter Pears** (ten); [c]**Galina Vishnevskaya** (sop); [c]**Mstislav Rostropovich** ([b]pf).
Decca London 433 200-2LHO2 (11/93).   🅶

...Paul Bunyan. **Soloists; Plymouth Music Series Chorus and Orchestra / Philip Brunelle.**
Virgin Classics VCD7 59249-2 (8/88). *Gramophone Award Winner 1988. Selected by Sounds in
Retrospect.*

...The Prodigal Son. **Soloists; English Opera Group / Benjamin Britten.**
Decca 425 713-2LM (9/90).

...The Rape of Lucretia. Phaedra. **Soloists; English Chamber Orchestra / Steuart Bedford.**
Decca London 425 666-2LH2 (5/90).

Prepositus Brixiensis
Italian 15th century

Suggested listening ...

...O spirito gentil, tu m'ay percosso. *Coupled with works by various composers.* **Hilliard Ensemble.**
Isis CD030 (7/97). *See review in the Collections section; refer to the Index.*

Nicholas Brodszky
German/American 1905-1958

Suggested listening ...

...Be my love. *Coupled with works by various composers.* **Angela Gheorghiu** (sop);
Malcolm Martineau (pf). Decca 458 360-2DH (5/98). *See review in the Collections section;
refer to the Index.*

Bartolomeus Brollo
Italian *fl* c1430-1450

Suggested listening ...
...Nulx ne pourroit ymaginer. *Coupled with works by various composers.* **Hilliard Ensemble.**
Isis CD030 (7/97). *See review in the Collections section; refer to the Index.*

Sébastien de Brossard
French 1655-1730

Suggested listening ...
...In Convertendo Dominus. Miserere mei, Deus. Canticum eucharisticum pro pace.
Soloists; Accentus Chamber Choir; Limoges Baroque Ensemble / Christophe Coin.
Auvidis Astrée E8607 (A/97).

Leo Brouwer
Cuban 1939

Brouwer Guitar Concerto No. 4, "Concerto de Toronto"[a]. Elogio de la Danza. El decamerón
negro. Hika, "In memoriam Toru Takemitsu". **John Williams** (gtr); [a]**London Sinfonietta /
Steven Mercurio.** Sony Classical Ⓕ SK63173 (61 minutes: DDD: 1/98). Recorded 1997.
Gramophone Editor's choice.
Brouwer Danza característica. Estudios Sencillos. Preludio (1956). Fuga No. 1. Tres piezas sin
título. Dos aires populares cubanos. Tres apuntes (1959). Canción de cuna. Ojos brujos. Elogio
de la danza. **Ricardo Cobo** (gtr). Naxos Ⓢ 8 553630 (62 minutes: DDD: 1/98). Recorded 1995.
Brouwer is a seminal figure in the guitar's twentieth-century world and richly deserving of focused
tributes such as these. The Naxos disc is designated as Vol. 1, suggesting more to come. Brouwer's
work has passed through several phases, ranging from folkloric to aleatoric and atonal, so an integral
recording would call for a highly virtuosic performer who can convincingly run the whole gamut;
Ricardo Cobo seems on present evidence to be excellently qualified for the task. Incisive rhythm and
folk-musical influences, not least Afro-Cuban, are rarely absent from Brouwer's music and they
abound in the early works here; even the gritty *Fuga* No. 1 has a syncopated subject. The building of
technique has long centred on nineteenth-century studies, with little comparable material to follow
(the Studies of Villa-Lobos are not for the struggler); at least that was the situation before Brouwer
wrote his four books of colourful *Estudios Sencillos*, sharply brought to life by Cobo. The remaining
works are authoritatively dispatched with energy, sensitivity and an impeccable technique.
    Brouwer's skills as a composer, an erstwhile guitar virtuoso and a conductor who knows the
orchestra intimately, are strongly united in his guitar concertos. The *Concerto de Toronto*, his fourth,
was written for John Williams and a finer performance of it would be hard to envisage. It is a powerful
and prismatically orchestrated work in three movements of which the second consists of a theme and
four contrasting variations, and in which elements (rhythmic and melodic) that have appeared as
'fingerprints' in even the earliest of Brouwer's works are brought to their apotheosis. Though its
appeal is less 'popular' than that of Rodrigo's ubiquitous *Concierto de Aranjuez*, this is possibly the
finest guitar concerto to be written this century – and spectacular with it. Likewise, Williams's intense
performances of the oft-recorded *Elogio de la Danza* and *El decamerón negro* and the clearly
'fingerprinted' and previously unrecorded *Hika* are those of an artist at the height of his musical
maturity and technical power. Both discs are superbly recorded so that no serious guitar-lover would
choose to be without them.
Additional recommendation ...
...Canción de cuna (arr. Grenet). *Coupled with works by various composers.* **Sharon Isbin** (gtr);
Gaudencio Thiago de Mello (perc). Teldec Ⓕ 0630-19899-2 (55 minutes: DDD: 7/98).
Gramophone Editor's choice. See review in the Collections section; refer to the Index. ⒼⒼ
Further listening ...
...Guitar Sonata. *Coupled with works by various composers.* **Julian Bream** (gtr).
EMI CDC7 54901-2 (4/94). *See review in the Collections section; refer to the Index.*

Max Bruch
German 1838-1920

Bruch Violin Concerto No. 1 in G minor, Op. 26.
Mendelssohn Violin Concerto in E minor, Op. 64. **Maxim Vengerov** (vn); **Leipzig Gewandhaus
Orchestra / Kurt Masur.** Teldec Ⓕ 4509-90875-2 (51 minutes: DDD: 4/94). Recorded 1993.
Gramophone Editor's choice. Ⓖ
As one might expect with Mendelssohn's own orchestra, the Leipzig Gewandhaus, under Kurt Masur,
there is a freshness and clarity in the Mendelssohn which ideally matches the soloist's playing, at once
keenly felt and expressive but clean and direct, with articulation of diamond precision and fine tonal
shading. If anyone has ever thought this work at all sentimental, this shatters any such idea, and
characteristically Masur encourages a flowing speed in the central *Andante*, which brings out the
songfulness of the main theme. It is consistent with this approach that in his expressiveness Maxim

Vengerov is more inclined to press ahead than to hold back, so that with a dashingly fast speed for the finale one is left breathless at the end. The slow movement of the Bruch gains from being taken at a flowing speed and Vengerov finds a rare depth of expressiveness, which makes the movement a meditation rather than simply a lyrical interlude. With outstanding recorded sound, warm yet clear and detailed, there is now no more recommendable disc of this coupling.

Additional recommendations ...

...Violin Concerto. **Mendelssohn** Violin Concerto. **Nathan Milstein** (vn); **Philharmonia Orchestra / Leon Barzin.** Classics for Pleasure ⓑ CD-CFP4374 (48 minutes: ADD).   ⓖ

...Violin Concerto. **Mendelssohn** Violin Concerto. **Anne-Sophie Mutter** (vn); **Berlin Philharmonic Orchestra / Herbert von Karajan.** DG ⓕ 400 031-2GH (57 minutes: DDD: 3/83).

...Violin Concerto. Scottish Fantasy, Op. 46. **Cho-Liang Lin** (vn); **Chicago Symphony Orchestra / Leonard Slatkin.** CBS Masterworks ⓜ SK42315 (53 minutes: DDD: 7/87). *Selected by Sounds in Retrospect.*   ⓖⓖ

...Violin Concerto. Scottish Fantasy, Op. 46. **Vieuxtemps** Violin Concerto No. 5 in A minor, Op. 37. **Jascha Heifetz** (vn); **New Symphony Orchestra / Sir Malcolm Sargent.** RCA Victor ⓜ 09026 61778-2* (65 minutes: ADD: 3/88).

...Violin Concerto. **Mendelssohn** Violin Concerto. **Joshua Bell** (vn); **Academy of St Martin in the Fields / Sir Neville Marriner.** Decca ⓕ 421 145-2DH (54 minutes: DDD: 5/88).

...Violin Concerto. **Mendelssohn** Violin Concerto. **Schubert** Rondo in A major, D438. **Nigel Kennedy** (vn); **English Chamber Orchestra / Jeffrey Tate.** EMI ⓕ CDC7 49663-2 (71 minutes: DDD: 1/89).

...Violin Concerto. **Dvořák** Violin Concerto in A minor, Op. 53. **Tasmin Little** (vn); **Royal Liverpool Philharmonic Orchestra / Vernon Handley.** Classics for Pleasure ⓑ CD-CFP4566 (60 minutes: DDD: 7/90). *See review under Dvořák; refer to the Index.*

...Violin Concertos – No. 1; No. 2 in D minor, Op. 44; No. 3 in D minor, Op. 58. Adagio appassionato, Op. 57. Romance, Op. 42. Scottish Fantasy[a]. Konzertstück, Op. 84. Serenade, Op. 75. In Memoriam, Op. 65. **Salvatore Accardo** (vn); [a]**Elizabeth Unger** (hp); **Leipzig Gewandhaus Orchestra / Kurt Masur.** Philips Silver Line ⓜ 432 282-2PSL3 (three discs: 214 minutes: ADD: 7/91).

...Violin Concerto. **Beethoven** Violin Concerto in D major, Op. 61. **Ida Haendel** (vn); **Philharmonia Orchestra / Rafael Kubelík.** Testament mono ⓕ SBT1083* (68 minutes: ADD: 10/96).

...Violin Concerto. Scottish Fantasy, Op. 46. **Yuzuko Horigome** (vn); **Royal Philharmonic Orchestra / Yuri Simonov.** Tring International ⓢ TRP108 (56 minutes: DDD: 10/97).

Bruch Violin Concerto No. 2 in D minor, Op. 44.
Goldmark Violin Concerto No. 1 in A minor, Op. 28. **Nai-Yuan Hu** (vn); **Seattle Symphony Orchestra / Gerard Schwarz.** Delos ⓕ DE3156 (60 minutes: DDD: 12/95). Recorded 1993-4.

Hu is a virtuoso in the best sense of that word, with uncommon lyrical gifts, who can shape phrases with a sense of gentle rapture and coax his violin to produce the most lovely sounds. Both performances come into direct competition with those of Itzhak Perlman (differently coupled), and when compared Hu by no means comes out second best. Perlman may at times be more dazzling (and in the passagework he achieves a stronger profile), but his preference for a very forward spotlight is a distinct minus point in a pair of warm-hearted concertos where the intimacy of feeling shared between soloist and orchestra is better caught by a more natural balance. Even though the Bruch was specifically written for Sarasate, neither of these concertos impresses primarily by its brilliance. Here both gain from the understanding partnership attained by Hu with Schwarz and his excellent Seattle orchestra within a kindly acoustic. Having attended the première of Bruch's Second Concerto, Brahms wrote to Simrock: "Hopefully a law will not be necessary to prevent any more first movements being written as an *Adagio*. That is intolerable for normal people." Bruch's riposte was, "If I meet with Brahms in heaven, I shall have myself transferred to Hell". He could not understand why the popularity of the First Concerto precluded performance of the others, "which are just as good if not better". Certainly Hu's superb reading here bears out the composer's evaluation of the D minor Concerto. The ardently simple presentation of the glorious main theme of that maligned *Adagio* goes right to the heart.

Additional recommendation ...

...Violin Concerto. Scottish Fantasy, Op. 46. **Itzhak Perlman** (vn); **Israel Philharmonic Orchestra / Zubin Mehta.** EMI ⓕ CDC7 49071-2 (54 minutes: DDD: 6/88).

Bruch Scottish Fantasy, Op. 46.
Lalo Symphonie espagnole, Op. 21. **Tasmin Little** (vn); **Royal Scottish National Orchestra / Vernon Handley.** EMI Eminence ⓜ CD-EMX2277 (68 minutes: DDD: 6/97). Recorded 1996.

It is an excellent idea to couple Bruch's evocation of Scotland with Lalo's of Spain, both works in unconventional five-movement *concertante* form. Anne Akiko Meyers coupled them earlier in light, sensitive performances on RCA, but Tasmin Little takes a riper, more robust and passionate view of both works, projecting them more strongly, as she would in the concert-hall. Nor is she lacking in the poetry which Meyers so tenderly brings out. Generally, Tasmin Little's speeds are a degree broader than those of Meyers, which gives her more freedom to point rhythms infectiously, to play with an extra degree of individuality in her phrasing, daringly using portamentos or agogic hesitations in a way that adds to the character of the reading. Little has the gift of sounding totally spontaneous on disc, with no feeling of strict studio manners. In this she is here greatly helped by the splendid, keenly polished playing of the Scottish orchestra under Vernon Handley, a most sympathetic partner. Handley is also excellent in pointing the rhythms of the fast movements of the Lalo, matching his soloist, and the recording is superb, with brass in particular vividly caught. Fine though Meyers's performances are on RCA, thoughtful and refined, this issue takes priority, not just for the warmer performances, but for the fact that Meyers makes a substantial cut in the finale of the Bruch, where Little plays it complete. In addition, the Eminence disc comes at mid price – an issue to recommend warmly to anyone wanting either work.

Additional recommendation ...
...Scottish Fantasy. Violin Concerto No. 1 in G minor, Op. 26. **Lalo** Symphonie espagnole, Op. 21. **Anne Akiko Meyers** (vn); **Royal Philharmonic Orchestra / Jesús López-Cobos.** RCA Victor Red Seal Ⓕ RD60942 (60 minutes: DDD: 9/92).

Bruch Symphonies – No. 1 in E flat major, Op. 28; No. 2 in F minor, Op. 36; No. 3 in E major, Op. 51. **Cologne Gürzenich Orchestra / James Conlon.** EMI Ⓕ CDS5 55046-2 (two discs: 103 minutes: DDD: 4/94). Recorded 1992-93.

Bruch's three symphonies are works whose rather reticent melodic style, at times dense scoring and formal stiffness, need affectionate help if their genuine qualities are to emerge and outweigh their flaws. Carefully handled there is real romantic charm (and some agreeably brusque sturdiness) to the first movement of the Third Symphony; its *Adagio* has sonorous solemnity and an ardent climax, and its *Scherzo* some fire. The Second Symphony, its over-extended finale apart, is stronger still. Conlon and his Cologne players cannot always disguise passages of awkwardly coarse scoring, but their sound, though full, is lean and that is in itself an advantage. Conlon is also more likely than Masur to relax into Bruch's genial melodies, to linger and shape them with affectionate rubato. For some tastes Masur's urgency will compensate for his at times lumbering massiveness of sound. Although *longueurs* are obvious in both conductors' hands, Conlon seems the more concerned to persuade us not to mind them. For anyone wanting all the symphonies of this neglected but likeable composer his set is a pretty safe recommendation.

Additional recommendation:
...Nos. 1-3. Swedish Dances, Op. 63. **Leipzig Gewandhaus Orchestra / Kurt Masur.** Philips Ⓕ 420 932-2PH2 (two discs: 105 minutes: DDD: 3/89).

Further listening ...
...Concerto for Clarinet, Viola and Orchestra in E minor, Op. 88[a]. Romance, Op. 85[b]. Eight Pieces, Op. 83[c]. [ac]**Paul Meyer** (cl); **Gérard Caussé** (va); [c]**François-René Duchâble** (pf); [ab]**Orchestra of the Opéra National de Lyon / Kent Nagano.** Erato 2292-45483-2 (11/97).
...Double Piano Concerto, Op. 88a. *Coupled with* **Mendelssohn** Double Piano Concerto in E major. **Katia and Marielle Labèque** (pfs); **Philharmonia Orchestra / Semyon Bychkov.** Philips 432 095-2PH (7/93). Ⓖ
...Kol Nidrei, Op. 47. *Coupled with works by various composers.* **Pablo Casals** (vc); **London Symphony Orchestra / Sir Landon Ronald.** Biddulph mono LAB144* (1/98). *See review under Elgar; refer to the Index.*
...Acht Stücke, Op. 83. *Coupled with* **Mozart** Clarinet Trio, K498, "Kegelstatt". **Ludmila Peterková** (cl); **Josef Suk** (va); **Josef Hála** (pf). Supraphon SU3014-2 (2/97).
...String Quartets – No. 1 in C minor, Op. 9; No. 2 in E major, Op. 10. **Academica Quartet.** Dynamic CDS29 (5/94).

Anton Bruckner
Austrian 1824-1896

Bruckner Symphonies – No. 1 in C minor (Linz version); No. 2 in C minor (ed. Nowak. Both from 2740 264, 6/82); No. 3 in D minor (1889 version, ed. Nowak. 2532 007, 7/81); No. 4 in E flat major, "Romantic" (2530 674, 10/76); No. 5 in B flat major (2702 101, 10/78); No. 6 in A major (2531 295, 11/80); No. 7 in E major (2707 102, 4/78); No. 8 in C minor (ed. Haas. 2707 085, 5/76); No. 9 in D minor (2530 828, 6/77). **Berlin Philharmonic Orchestra / Herbert von Karajan.** DG Karajan Symphony Edition Ⓜ 429 648-2GSE9 (nine discs: 520 minutes: ADD/DDD: 3/91). Recorded 1975-81. ⒼⒼ
Bruckner Symphonies – No. 0 in D minor, "Die Nullte" (from SAL3602, 4/67); No. 1 in C minor (6500 439, 6/73); No. 2 in C minor (SAL3785, 5/70); No. 3 in D minor (SAL3506, 7/65); No. 4 in E flat major, "Romantic" (SAL3617, 2/68); No. 5 in B flat major (6700 055, 6/72); No. 6 in A major (6500 164, 11/71); No. 7 in E major (SAL3624/5, 9/67); No. 8 in C minor (6700 020, 10/70); No. 9 in D minor (SAL3575, 10/66). **Concertgebouw Orchestra / Bernard Haitink.** Philips Bernard Haitink Symphony Edition Ⓑ 442 040-2PB9 (nine discs: 592 minutes: ADD: 8/94). Recorded 1963-72. Ⓖ

It is often said that the essence of good Bruckner conducting is a firm grasp of structure. In fact that is only a half-truth. Of course one must understand how Bruckner's massive statements and counterstatements are fused together, but a performance that was nothing but architecture would be a pretty depressing experience. Karajan's understanding of the slow but powerful currents that flow beneath the surfaces of symphonies like the Fifth or Nos. 7-9 has never been bettered, but at the same time he shows how much more there is to be reckoned with: strong emotions, a deep poetic sensitivity (a Bruckner symphony can evoke landscapes as vividly as Mahler or Vaughan Williams) and a gift for singing melody that at times rivals even Schubert. It hardly needs saying that there's no such thing as a perfect record cycle, and Karajan's collection of the numbered Bruckner symphonies (unfortunately he never recorded "No. 0") has its weaknesses. The early First and Second Symphonies can be a little heavy-footed and, as with so many Bruckner sets, there's a suspicion that more time might have been spent getting to know the fine but elusive Sixth – and there's an irritating throwback to the days of corrupt Bruckner editions in the first big crescendo of the Fourth Symphony (high swooping violins – nasty!) – but none of these performances is without its major insights, and in the best of them – particularly Nos. 3, 5, 7, 8 and 9 – those who haven't stopped their ears to Karajan will find that whatever else he may have been, there was a side to him that could only be described as 'visionary'. As for the recordings: climaxes can sound a touch overblown in some of the earlier symphonies, but on the whole the image is well focused and atmospheric. A valuable set, and a landmark in the history of Bruckner recording.

Right from the start of Haitink's cycle, you sense here is a man who briefed his team, read the map and is raring to go. The cycle began in 1963 with Symphony No. 3. The playing is alert, rousing even, though inclined to edginess. This is partly to do with the sound of the post-war Concertgebouw (marginally more Francophone in those days), partly a matter of an as yet not-quite-symbiotic bond between Haitink and the players. The Fourth Symphony followed in 1965. This suggests some deepening and refining of the bond between conductor and orchestra and is a very fine performance. The *Scherzo* is particularly exciting. The Ninth Symphony (also 1965) came surprisingly early in the cycle. The performance explains why. Both conductor and orchestra play the symphony as if in the grip of a deep compulsion. The orchestral response alone has a terrific explicitness and immediacy. As for Haitink, he plays the work very dramatically, as a symphonic psycho-drama, "a vastation" as thinkers and theologians of Bruckner's time often termed breakdown and purgation of the spirit. When it comes to the great central tetralogy, Symphonies Nos. 5-8, there are some problems. Most problematic is the Eighth Symphony. The Seventh has a quick first movement; but it survives. Not so the Eighth. The first movement just about hangs together, thanks to some finely concentrated playing at critical junctions. But the *Scherzo* is absurdly quick, as is the finale. Haitink's account of the Sixth Symphony is less of a problem than it is with some rivals. The recording is exceptionally fine – everything thrillingly immediate, finely 'terraced'. It is a quicker performance than Klemperer's classic version for EMI. The *Adagio* always sounded well and so it remains, the keening Dutch oboe and bright trumpets the perfect foil for the Rembrandt-colourings of the strings and lower brass. Symphonies Nos. 1, 2, 5 and 6 were the last to be recorded. (Haitink actually ended with this rousing account of No. 1.) They are all very fine. This is one of the best Fifths ever made; dramatic where Karajan is epic but fascinatingly alive and well integrated. The Second Symphony also receives an exceptional performance (the text, as elsewhere in the cycle, is Haas). Philips's CD remastering realizes just how vivid and astonishingly natural these Concertgebouw-played, Concertgebouw-made recordings are. You will need a supplementary account of the Eighth; but is this too much to ask when the set as a whole is being offered, new-minted, at a knock-down price?

Additional recommendations ...
...Nos. 1-9. **Cologne Radio Symphony Orchestra / Günter Wand.** Deutsche Harmonia Mundi
    Editio Classica Ⓜ GD60075 (ten discs: 559 minutes: ADD/DDD: 2/90).
...Nos. 1, 4 and 7-9 – **Berlin Philharmonic Orchestra;** Nos. 2, 3, 5 and 6 – **Bavarian Radio Symphony
    Orchestra / Eugen Jochum.** DG Ⓜ 429 079-2GX9 (nine discs: 552 minutes: ADD: 2/90).   ⒼⒶ
...No. 0. **Chicago Symphony Orchestra / Sir Georg Solti.**
    Decca Ⓕ 452 160-2DH (38 minutes: DDD: 9/96).

Bruckner Symphony No. 1 in C minor (Linz version). **Chicago Symphony Orchestra /
Sir Georg Solti.** Decca Ⓕ 448 898-2DH (47 minutes: DDD: 4/96). Recorded 1995.
Gramophone Editor's choice.   ⒼⒼ
In its original 1866 Linz version, Bruckner's First Symphony is something of a cheeky chappy among the nine, a delightful romp of a symphony but also tender and affecting and rich in intimations of things to come. There have been times in the past when Solti has seemed a restless Brucknerian, inclined to harry the music or drive it too hard. Here there is a thrilling sense of forward propulsion, apt to a young man's work, yet nothing is forced or gratuitously aggressive. This is even true of the *Scherzo* which Solti takes extremely briskly. It is also a very sensitive performance and a very observant one. The slow movement's lovely counter-subject is most beautifully played, the phrasing levitated with all the care and grace one looks for at the equivalent moment of the Seventh Symphony's slow movement. Bruckner is, by and large, sparing of egregious gestures in this symphony as elsewhere, but where there is an unexpected harmonic or dynamic nuance to be registered, Solti and his players are as swift and sensitive in execution as they are musically observant. The Chicago players are on superb form. It is difficult to imagine the symphony being better played than it is here. The Barenboim performance on DG is fine enough, but the Solti's reading has a vibrancy and beauty about it, a quality of flawless yet unassuming virtuosity that is the mark of an élite orchestra at the very height of its powers. The many difficult, high-lying violin passages are

played not only with confidence, but with imagination. The playing of the violas and cellos is consummate in its eloquence. In the circumstances, it would be difficult for the engineers to go wrong. But the recording, too, is of a piece with the rest. As Bruckner recordings go, it is of demonstration quality, ripe yet clear, immediate yet rich in atmosphere.

Additional recommendations ...
...No. 1. (1866 version)[a]. Te Deum[b]. [a]**Jessye Norman** (sop); [b]**Yvonne Minton** (mez); [b]**David Rendall** (ten); [b]**Samuel Ramey** (bass); **Chicago Symphony** [b]**Chorus and Orchestra / Daniel Barenboim.** DG Galleria Ⓜ 435 068-2GGA (70 minutes: DDD: 12/91).
...No. 1. **Vienna Philharmonic Orchestra / Claudio Abbado.**
DG Ⓕ 453 415-2GH (48 minutes: DDD: 5/97).

Bruckner (ed. Haas) Symphony No. 2 in C minor. **Saarbrücken Radio Symphony Orchestra / Hiroshi Wakasugi.** Arte Nova Classics Ⓢ 74321 27770-2 (61 minutes: DDD: 4/97). Recorded 1992.
Budget-price Bruckner is something of a rarity in the record catalogues; super-budget Bruckner more or less unheard of. The reasons are not far to seek. Front-rank orchestras at full strength do not come cheap. As for reissues: here one is up against the fact that the grandees who record Bruckner best (and their heirs and benefactors) are often disinclined to do business with labels that promise to pile 'em high and sell 'em cheap. Arts Nova Classics, a BMG subsidiary, threaten to put an end to all that. Hiroshi Wakasugi's performance of the Second Symphony is a delight. He plays the complete text and plays it with fluency and affection. He has a keen eye for the letter of the score, a keen ear for its Schubertian sonorities, and an even keener instinct for the flow and continuity of its rhythms and the logic of the whole. This couldn't replace the Karajan but anyone happening upon this recording is likely to find a friend for life, in both the music and its performance.

Additional recommendations
...No. 2. **Berlin Philharmonic Orchestra / Herbert von Karajan.**
DG Ⓕ 415 988-2GH (61 minutes: DDD: 2/87).
...No. 2. **Royal Concertgebouw Orchestra / Riccardo Chailly.**
Decca Ⓕ 436 154-2DH (67 minutes: DDD: 3/94).
...No. 2. **Houston Symphony Orchestra / Christoph Eschenbach.**
Koch International Classics Ⓕ 37391-2 (71 minutes: DDD: 3/97).

Bruckner (ed. Nowak) Symphonies – No. 3 in D minor[a] (1889 version); No. 4 in E flat major, "Romantic"[b]. **Vienna Philharmonic Orchestra / Karl Böhm.** Double Decca Ⓜ 448 098-2DF2 (two discs: 125 minutes: ADD: 3/96). Item marked [a] from SXL6505 (10/71), [b]6BB171/2 (10/74).   ⒼⒼⒼ
The 1973 Böhm Bruckner Fourth is a classic, widely praised and much reissued, but the 1970 recording of the Third Symphony (the tidied-up 1889 edition) is every bit as fine. Some slightly dusty, quiet string tone apart, the recording verges on the spectacular, as does the playing, sophisticated and folksy by turns. The VPO respond splendidly throughout (Bruckner's rustic trio section is inimitably Viennese in its earthy gait). There is something mountainously grand in their response in full cry under Böhm. They also have it game, set and match over their competitors in the Austrian dance subjects of the *Scherzo* and finale. The exemplary focus and spectacular dynamic range of this Sofiensaal production really does take one's breath away. As for the Fourth Symphony, that has been more or less *hors concours* for a generation. This is its third or fourth appearance on CD. Buy now if you missed it earlier.

Additional recommendations ...
...(1877 version). **Vienna Philharmonic Orchestra / Bernard Haitink.**
Philips Ⓕ 422 411-2PH (62 minutes: DDD: 3/91).
...No. 3. **North German Radio Symphony Orchestra / Günter Wand.**
RCA Victor Red Seal Ⓕ 09026 61374-2 (54 minutes: DDD: 3/93).
...No. 4. **Vienna Philharmonic Orchestra / Karl Böhm.**
Decca Ovation Ⓜ 425 036-2DM (68 minutes: ADD: 3/93). *This is the same recording
as the one reviewed above with No. 3.*   ⒼⒼⒼ
...No. 3 (1873 version). **London Classical Players / Roger Norrington.**
EMI Ⓕ CDC5 56167-2 (57 minutes: DDD: 1/97). ✍
...No. 3 (1877, ed. Nowak). **Berlin Philharmonic Orchestra / Daniel Barenboim.**
Teldec Ⓕ 0630-13160-2 (60 minutes: DDD: 2/97).

Bruckner Symphony No. 4 in E flat major, "Romantic". **Philadelphia Orchestra / Wolfgang Sawallisch.** EMI Ⓕ CDC5 55119-2 (67 minutes: DDD: 9/94). Recorded 1993.   Ⓖ
The Philadelphians have always had their special sound, nurtured and lovingly preserved down the years by Stokowski, Ormandy and Muti; and to judge by this fine Bruckner Fourth it is something that Sawallisch will not willingly forego. Indeed, the genius of this particular reading lies in its Protean quality, the very way the sound is so interestingly adapted and applied. The Fourth is an odd work. Popular, certainly, but popular for certain specific moments: the mistily romantic opening, the fine hunting *Scherzo* and the finale's magnificent peroration. As for the larger structure – well, it is a work that undergoes something of a sea-change after the *Scherzo*. The finale does not so much round off

the work as propose the kind of grounds on which it might originally have been built. Which is where Sawallisch's reading, and the Philadelphians' realization of it, is so interesting. Apart from one passage midway through the slow movement, where the mood darkens and the music mysteriously broods, the first two movements can have an almost straightforwardly classical feel. This seems to be Sawallisch's view. The Philadelphia playing here is lucid and eloquent – the feel of "clean stonework", to borrow Robert Simpson's helpful phrase. How different is the finale! Here we are deep in the Wagnerian forest – the dramatic change of mood graphically registered. "First make your palette", Karajan used to say. To judge by this performance, the orchestra have several palettes ready-prepared which Sawallisch has used to brilliant effect in this reading. After the clean stonework of the first three movements, the finale is a Wagnerian revel, Stokowski-style. What sounded at first light like just another Bruckner Fourth has proved to be anything but. The recording is glorious.

Additional recommendations ...

...No. 4. **Philharmonia Orchestra / Otto Klemperer.**
  EMI Studio Ⓜ CDM7 69127-2 (61 minutes: ADD: 12/88).   ⒼⒼ
...No. 4. **Berlin Philharmonic Orchestra / Eugen Jochum.**
  DG Ⓑ 427 200-2GR (65 minutes: ADD: 9/89).
...**Vienna Philharmonic Orchestra / Claudio Abbado.**
  DG Ⓕ 431 719-2GH (69 minutes: DDD: 4/91).   Ⓖ
...(original version). **Frankfurt Radio Symphony Orchestra / Eliahu Inbal.**
  Teldec Digital Experience Ⓜ 9031-77597-2 (68 minutes: DDD: 12/92).
...No. 4. **Berlin Philharmonic Orchestra / Herbert von Karajan.**
  DG Galleria Ⓜ 439 522-2GGA (64 minutes: ADD: 1/94).
...No. 4. **Berlin Philharmonic Orchestra / Daniel Barenboim.**
  Teldec Ⓕ 9031-73272-2 (68 minutes: DDD: 3/94).   Ⓖ
...No. 4ᵃ. Overture in G minorᵇ. **Philharmonia Orchestra / Lovro von Matačić.**
  Testament ᵃmono/ᵇstereo Ⓕ SBT1050* (76 minutes: ADD: 2/95).
...No. 4. *Coupled with works by* **Smetana** and **Weber** NBC Symphony Orchestra **/ Bruno Walter.**
  Pearl mono Ⓜ GEMMCD9131* (74 minutes: AAD: 2/95).

Bruckner (ed. Haas) Symphony No. 4 in E flat major, "Romantic". **Berlin Philharmonic Orchestra / Herbert von Karajan.** EMI Karajan Edition Ⓜ CDM5 66094-2 (70 minutes: ADD: 4/97). From HMV SLS811 (1/72). Recorded 1970-71.
There was always something very special about the EMI recordings of the Fourth and Seventh Symphonies by Karajan and the Berlin Philharmonic. Both works had, of course, been in Karajan's repertory for many years. He had first conducted the Fourth Symphony (to magnificent effect, by all accounts) in Aachen in 1936 at the age of 28 and the Seventh had been a regular fixture in his concert programmes from 1941 onwards. Curiously, though, it was not until 1970 that he made these, his first recordings of either work. The recording of the Fourth Symphony is one of the finest ever made in Berlin's Jesus-Christus Kirche, the church's clear but spacious acoustic allowing the Berlin playing to be heard in all its multicoloured, multi-dimensional splendour. On LP, the grandeur of the sound and the reach of Karajan's reading meant that the symphony had to be accommodated on three sides at a time when all other recordings were fitted on to a single LP. Hence the coupling with the Seventh Symphony as part of a three-LP set; hence, too, the recording's slightly compromised status.

Bruckner (ed. Nowak) Symphony No. 5 in B flat major. **London Philharmonic Orchestra / Franz Welser-Möst.** EMI Ⓕ CDC5 55125-2 (70 minutes: DDD: 4/95). Recorded live in 1993.
Welser-Möst has looked, listened, and decided 'enough is enough'. Enough pussy-footing around the Fifth as though it were some sacred monolith, enough of circumspection. This is a performance, sensual and exciting, that could have been filmed by Ken Russell or apostrophized by Dylan Thomas. Not everyone will approve, of course. You can already hear the drone of lobbyists urging the Home Secretary to outlaw the making of love to a Bruckner symphony in public. Certainly, this is not a CD for those of a nervous disposition or those who genuinely seek the longer view such as Karajan provides. Welser-Möst's reading is more in the Jochum style where analysis doesn't drive out passion, where what is contemplated in the study doesn't entirely predetermine what is experienced in performance. Welser-Möst takes risks with the finale, where the fugue is driven fiercely on, and in the *Adagio* where his observation of the *alla breve* marking gives a generous pendulum-swing to the crotchet-triplet accompaniment. This can make for a reading that is unconsidered and overquick, but not here. The play of two against three is beautifully realized as the basis for one of the most richly expressive of all recorded accounts of this movement. In general, Welser-Möst favours an almost Beethoven-like drive and directness. Yet there is plenty of space around the lyric subjects and chorales. In the first movement the gearing of the transitions whereby this is achieved is especially elaborate. He is most obviously himself, the boy from Linz, in the *Scherzo* and Trio. It begins fiercely, as Bruckner requires, but then opens out in a wonderfully broad lolloping Upper Austrian dance. The London Philharmonic play gloriously throughout and the engineers get superb results from the Vienna Konzerthaus auditorium.

Additional recommendations ...

...No. 5. **Concertgebouw Orchestra / Eugen Jochum.**
  Tahra Ⓜ TAH247* (two discs: 83 minutes: ADD).

...No. 5. **Berlin Philharmonic Orchestra / Daniel Barenboim.**
　Teldec Ⓕ 9031-73271-2 (72 minutes: DDD: 3/93).
...No. 5. **Cleveland Orchestra / Christoph von Dohnányi.**
　Decca Ⓕ 433 318-2DH (74 minutes: DDD: 8/93). *Gramophone Editor's choice.*　　　　Ⓖ
...No. 5. **Royal Concertgebouw Orchestra / Riccardo Chailly.**
　Decca Ⓕ 433 819-2DH (75 minutes: DDD: 11/93).
...No. 5. **Vienna Philharmonic Orchestra / Wilhelm Furtwängler.**
　EMI Salzburg Festival Edition mono Ⓜ CDH5 65750-2* (70 minutes: ADD: 1/95).
...No. 5. **Royal Scottish National Orchestra / Georg Tintner.**
　Naxos Ⓢ 8 553452 (77 minutes: DDD: 10/97).

Bruckner (ed. Haas). Symphony No. 6 in A major. **New Philharmonia Orchestra / Otto Klemperer.**
EMI Studio Ⓜ CDM7 63351-2 (55 minutes: ADD: 3/90). From Columbia SAX2582 (9/65).
Recorded 1964.　　　　　　　　　　　　　　　　　　　　　　　　　　　　　ⒼⒼ
Bruckner Symphony No. 6 in A major.
Bach (orch. Webern) Musikalisches Opfer, BWV1079 – Fuga ricercarta a 6. **Cleveland Orchestra /**
　Christoph von Dohnányi. Decca Ⓕ 436 153-2DH (63 minutes: DDD: 10/94). Recorded 1991-93. Ⓖ
No Brucknerian will want to be without Klemperer's legendary performance, indeed it has long been
regarded as perhaps the finest recorded interpretation of this symphony. Part of Klemperer's success
lies in his unerring ability to project the symphony's architectural and organic content through
Bruckner's ever changing terrain. His vigorous and resolute approach is apparent from the outset,
where the opening ostinato string figure, crisp and rhythmically assured, tell us that this is no routine
performance. His handling of Bruckner's frequent *fortissimo* 'blaze ups' is always dramatic,
exhilarating and sonorous, whilst never destroying the beautifully clear and lucid textures he achieves
throughout the symphony. The adagio is one of Bruckner's most sublime creations. Klemperer's
choice of tempo may seem fast here, but is entirely justified by the resulting sense of momentum and
forward drive: and you will be hard pressed to find a better rendering of the tender and expansive
second theme as it burgeons out of the sombre introduction. The Scherzo, with its incessant bass and
cello ostinato tread is given a subtle and evocative reading, building the tension superbly before
resolving into the haunting and mysterious trio section with its Tristanesque horn calls. The
recording, made in the Kingsway Hall in 1964, is excellent.
Dohnányi's is an extraordinarily bold and vivid account and the Severance Hall sound is as
analytical as ever; yet on this occasion it also provides the kind of multifaceted perspectives that help
give a Bruckner symphony its special character. Listening to this recording, one is left in little doubt
that this is Bruckner's most strikingly scored symphony to date, its "tumultuous surface sparkling like
the Homeric seas" as Sir Donald Tovey put it many years ago. Recording after recording of the Sixth
has come apart at the seams as a result of the conductor's inability to gauge the pulse of the two outer
movements. Bruckner's tempo indications and his bowing marks both imply a certain breadth of
utterance that has to be reconciled none the less with pulsing rhythms and demystified textures. No
one sorts this out better than Klemperer; he has hawk-like patience and a hawk-like keenness of
vision. Dohnányi sets a very good basic tempo in the first movement, which he then proceeds to
modify in ways that don't always accord with Bruckner's carefully documented wishes; and quite a
good tempo in the finale. The flux is not always Bruckner's. However, as Eugen Jochum often proved,
a living response to Bruckner can be mightily effective. Dohnányi's reading of the two inner
movements deserves nothing but praise. He allows the *Adagio* the space it needs. (Klemperer is
quicker, though, from the keening start onwards, always wonderfully articulate emotionally.) The
quality of the Cleveland sound in the grieving C minor funeral lament at fig. D (5'01") is such as to
make one want to rank this slow movement alongside those of the better-known Seventh and Eighth
Symphonies. And how beautifully the slow movement's coda is handled and characterized. This is
pure *Meistersinger*, Bruckner dressed in Sachs's garb. The slowish, minor-key *Scherzo* is also perfectly
judged. Rarely can the trio's sweet academic debate between horns, woodwinds and strings have
sounded more irresistible or affecting than it does here. After so fabulously played a Bruckner Sixth,
the finale all complexity and clamour, the sudden dip into the cooler waters of Webern's
hallucinatorily beautiful orchestration of the Ricercar from Bach's *Musical Offering* is as welcome as
a solitary stroll at eventide.
Additional recommendations ...
...No. 6. **Bavarian State Orchestra / Wolfgang Sawallisch.**
　Orfeo Ⓕ C024821A (55 minutes: ADD: 6/84).
...No. 6. **North German Radio Symphony Orchestra / Günter Wand.**
　RCA Victor Red Seal Ⓕ RD60061 (55 minutes: DDD: 2/91).
...No. 6. **Berlin Philharmonic Orchestra / Daniel Barenboim.**
　Teldec Ⓕ 4509-94556-2 (55 minutes: DDD: 9/95).
...No. 6. **Berlin Philharmonic Orchestra / Herbert von Karajan.**
　DG Galleria Ⓜ 447 525-2GGA (58 minutes: ADD: 3/96).

Bruckner (ed. Haas) Symphony No. 7 in E major. **Berlin Philharmonic Orchestra /**
　Herbert von Karajan. EMI Karajan Edition Ⓜ CDM5 66095-2 (68 minutes: ADD: 4/97).
　From HMV SLS811 (1/72). Recorded 1970-71.　　　　　　　　　　　　　　　ⒼⒼ

'Glowing' is an apt word with which to describe this account of the Seventh. Very much *sui generis*, this is arguably the most purely beautiful account of the symphony there has ever been on record. Other readings may surge and carol more than this but none captures so intense a sense of spiritual longing within the context of a calm yet unerringly sure articulation of the symphonic structure. Oddly, the recording has moments of slightly wispy string sound which sound wispier here than they did on EMI's earlier less spacious, less full-bodied – digital remastering. That, though, is not enough to undermine the recommendation as such.

Bruckner (ed. Haas) Symphony No. 7 in E major. **Vienna Philharmonic Orchestra /
Herbert von Karajan.** DG Karajan Gold Ⓕ 439 037-2GHS (66 minutes: DDD: 3/96).
From 429 226-2GH (5/90). Recorded 1989.   ⓖⓖ
The Vienna Philharmonic feature on what was Karajan's last recording, an idiomatic account of the Seventh Symphony, lighter and more classical in feel than either of his two Berlin recordings yet loftier, too. As for the Original-image bit-processing you need go no further than the first fluttered violin *tremolando* and the cellos' rapt entry in the third bar to realize how ravishingly 'present' the performance is in this reprocessing. Or go to the end of the symphony and hear how the great E major peroration is even more transparent than before, the octave drop of bass trombone and bass tuba 13 bars from home the kind of delightfully euphoric detail that in 1989 only the more assiduous score-reader would have been conscious of hearing. This remastered Bruckner Seventh is definitely pure gold.
Additional recommendations ...
...No. 7. **Vienna Philharmonic Orchestra / Claudio Abbado.**
DG Ⓕ 437 518-2GH (64 minutes: DDD: 5/94).
...No. 7. **Vienna Philharmonic Orchestra / Hans Knappertsbusch.**
Music & Arts mono Ⓕ CD209* (62 minutes: AAD: 12/95).
...No. 7. **Concertgebouw Orchestra / Bernard Haitink.**
Philips Solo Ⓜ 446 580-2PM (65 minutes: ADD: 6/96).
...No. 7[a]. **Mahler** Lieder aus "Des Knaben Wunderhorn"[b] – excerpts [b]**Brigitte Fassbaender** (mez);
[a]**Berlin Radio Symphony Orchestra,** [b]**Deutsches Symphony Orchestra, Berlin / Riccardo Chailly.**
Decca Eclipse Ⓑ 448 710-2DEC (76 minutes: DDD: 8/96).   ⓖ
...No. 7. **Saarbrücken Radio Symphony Orchestra / Stanislaw Skrowaczewski.**
Arte Nova Classics Ⓢ 74321 27771-2 (69 minutes: DDD: 4/97).

Bruckner (ed. Haas) Symphony No. 8 in C minor. **Vienna Philharmonic Orchestra /
Herbert von Karajan.** DG Ⓕ 427 611-2GH2 (two discs: 83 minutes: DDD: 10/89). Recorded 1988.
Selected by Sounds in Retrospect. **Gramophone** classical 100.   ⓖⓖⓖ
Bruckner (ed. Nowak) Symphony No. 8 in C minor. **Vienna Philharmonic Orchestra /
Carlo Maria Giulini.** DG Masters Ⓜ 445 529-2GMA2 (two discs: 88 minutes: DDD: 2/95).
From 415 124-2GH2 (7/85). Recorded 1984.   ⓖⓖⓖ
As if by some strange act of providence, great conductors have often been remembered by the immediate posthumous release of some fine and representative recording. With Karajan it is the Eighth Symphony of Bruckner, perhaps the symphony he loved and revered above all others. It is the sense of the music being in the hearts and minds and collective unconscious of Karajan and every one of the one hundred and more players of the Vienna Philharmonic that gives this performances its particular charisma and appeal. It is a wonderful reading, every bit as authoritative as its many predecessors and every bit as well played but somehow more profound, more humane, more lovable if that is a permissible attribute of an interpretation of this Everest among symphonies. The end of the work, always astonishing and uplifting, is especially fine here and very moving. Fortunately, it has been recorded with plenty of weight and space and warmth and clarity, with the additional benefit of the added vibrancy of the Viennese playing. The sessions were obviously sufficiently happy for there to shine through moments of spontaneous eloquence that were commonplace in the concert-hall in Karajan's later years, but which recordings can't always be relied upon to catch.

Ten years on from its making in Vienna in 1984, Giulini's performance can confidently be claimed as one of the great Bruckner recordings of the age. It is an immensely long-breathed performance yet it is of a piece with itself and the music it serves. It is a reading that is suffused from start to finish with its own immutable logic, cast and voiced, you might say, like a great tenor bell. The playing of the Vienna Philharmonic is similarly whole: luminous as though lit from within, immensely strong, yet flawless in every aspect of tone and touch. You might argue that Giulini's case is helped by his use of the tidied Nowak text; that Karajan, in his last and greatest recording, goes one stage further by conjuring from the fuller Haas edition a performance of even greater grandeur and sweep. But the two are not in contention. Both is a miracle sufficient unto itself; the Karajan a shade earthier, perhaps, a shade rougher-hewn than the Giulini which glows, in this magnificent transfer, like Carrara marble lit by the evening sun.
Additional recommendations ...
...No. 8. **Vienna Philharmonic Orchestra / Wilhelm Furtwängler.**
Music & Arts mono Ⓕ CD764* (77 minutes: ADD).
...No. 8. **Bavarian Radio Symphony Orchestra / Rafael Kubelík.**
Orfeo Ⓕ C203891A* (71 minutes: ADD: 8/90).

...No. 8. **Concertgebouw Orchestra / Eduard van Beinum.**
 Philips The Early Years mono Ⓜ 442 730-2PM* (72 minutes: ADD: 3/96).
...No. 8. *Coupled with works by* **Wagner Berlin Philharmonic Orchestra / Herbert von Karajan.**
 EMI Seraphim Ⓜ CES5 69092-2 (two discs: 122 minutes: ADD: 5/96).
...No. 8. **R. Strauss** Metamorphosen, AV142. **Staatskapelle Dresden / Giuseppe Sinopoli.**
 DG Ⓕ 447 744-2GH2 (two discs: 105 minutes: DDD: 11/96).
...No. 8[a]. String Quintet in F major – Adagio[b]. [a]**Saarbrücken Radio Symphony Orchestra /**
 Stanisław Skrowaczewski; [b]**Collegium Mozarteum, Salzburg / Jürgen Geise.**
 Arte Nova Classics Ⓢ 74321 34016-2 (two discs: 100 minutes: DDD: 4/97).

Bruckner Symphony No. 9 in D minor. **Vienna Philharmonic Orchestra / Carlo Maria Giulini.**
 DG Ⓕ 427 345-2GH (68 minutes: DDD: 8/89). Recorded 1988.   ⒼⒼⒼ
Bruckner Symphony No. 9 in D minor. **Berlin Philharmonic Orchestra / Herbert von Karajan.**
 DG Ⓕ 429 904-2GGA (62 minutes: ADD: 3/91). From 2530 828 (6/77). Recorded 1976.   ⒼⒼ
Giulini's Ninth is an idiosyncratic reading – nearly seven minutes longer than Karajan's – but it has
about it a kind of immutable breadth and boldness of utterance that is not to be gainsaid. Despite the
slowness, there is very much the sense of his being the master of his own brief. As a concept it is quite
different from the musically dynamic readings of others. In the first movement's main *Gesangsperiode*
it can seem dangerously broad with the Vienna strings rather tensely following the contours of
Giulini's protracted beat. Here the wary score-watcher may notice some unevenness in ensemble
though, that said, this is a reading which should be patiently heard rather than proof-read. The
Scherzo is very effective, with drive and dynamism. After that, the orchestra are at their finest in the
concluding *Adagio*, not only the Viennese horns, but the entire ensemble in the difficult broad
transitions and in the literally terrific C sharp minor climax. The recording is magnificent. Karajan's
1976 recording has long been something of a classic, capturing the conductor and the Berlin
Philharmonic on top form. From the opening of the titanic first movement to the final grinding
dissonance of the lofty *Adagio* Karajan's control of phrase lengths, tempo and rhythmic swing are
gloriously apparent. Karajan's beautifully recorded performance seems refreshingly urgent, cohesive
and properly threatening. Exceptionally vivid, it was sometimes difficult to tame on LP, but the CD
version gives unalloyed pleasure.
Additional recommendations ...
...No. 9. **Berlin Philharmonic Orchestra / Daniel Barenboim.**
 Teldec Ⓕ 9031-72140-2 (63 minutes: DDD: 10/91).   ⒼⒼⒼ
...Nos. 7 and 9. **Berlin Philharmonic Orchestra / Wilhelm Furtwängler.**
 DG Double mono Ⓜ 445 418-2GX2* (two discs: 121 minutes: ADD: 1/96).
...No. 9. **Concertgebouw Orchestra / Eduard van Beinum.**
 Philips The Early Years mono Ⓜ 442 731-2PM* (59 minutes: ADD: 3/96).
...No. 9. **Bach** (orch. Webern) A Musical Offering, BWV1079 – Ricercar a 6. **Royal Concertgebouw**
 Orchestra / Riccardo Chailly. Decca Ⓕ 455 506-2DH (71 minutes: DDD: 10/97).

Bruckner String Quintet in F major[a]. Intermezzo in D minor[a]. Rondo in C minor.
 String Quartet in C minor. **L'Archibudelli** (Vera Beths, Lis Rautenberg, vns; Jürgen Kussmaul,
 [a]**Guus Jeukendrup, vas; Anner Bylsma, vc). Sony Classical Vivarte Ⓕ SK66251**
 (76 minutes: DDD: 3/95). ✍ Recorded 1994.
"Bruckner is long, he takes time", remarked Anner Bylsma in a *Gramophone* interview in March
1995; not exactly controversial, but it is important in understanding his, and his ensemble's approach
to the Quintet. The first movement in particular is more spacious than any other version. But there is
more to it than tempo. What matters here is the subtlety of phrasing and fineness of the shading,
giving vitality and inner intensity to patterns that can easily sound repetitive, especially at this speed.
Much of the Quintet is marked *p*, *pp* or *ppp*; L'Archibudelli show how magically suggestive so many
of the quiet passages can be and how important it is to respect those dynamic gradings. They also
make the work as a whole sound as unified and sublimely purposeful as the best of the symphonies.
As for coupling: the 22-minute student Quartet, with its hints of Mendelssohn and rather more
obvious debt to Haydn, is beautifully played, and there is more than one pre-echo of greater things
to come. The spaciousness of the Sony sound suits the Quintet especially well, the more obviously
'chamber' textures of the Quartet perhaps less so.
Additional recommendations ...
...String Quintet. Intermezzo. **Alberni Quartet** with **Garfield Jackson** (va).
 CRD Ⓕ CRD3456 (47 minutes: DDD: 6/91).
...String Quintet. **Brahms** String Quintet No. 2 in G major, Op. 111. **Brett Dean** (va);
 Brandis Quartet. Nimbus Ⓕ NI5488 (75 minutes: DDD: 12/96).

Bruckner Masses – No. 1 in D minor[a]; No. 2 in E minor[b]; No. 3 in F minor[c]. [a]**Edith Mathis,**
 [c]**Maria Stader** (sops); [a]**Marga Schiml,** [c]**Claudia Hellmann** (mezzos); [a]**Wiesław Ochman,** [c]**Ernst**
 Haefliger (tens); [a]**Karl Ridderbusch,** [c]**Kim Borg** (basses); **Bavarian Radio Chorus and Symphony**
 Orchestra / Eugen Jochum. DG The Originals Ⓜ 447 409-2GOR2 (two discs: 148 minutes:
 ADD: 5/95). Item marked [a] from 2530 314 (7/73), [b]2720 054 (3/73), [c]SLPM138829 (3/63).
 Text and translation included. *Gramophone Classical 100.*   ⒼⒼⒼ

Like Bruckner, Eugen Jochum came from a devout Catholic family and began his musical life as a church organist. He would have known the Mass texts more or less inside out, which explains why his readings focus not on the sung parts – which, for the most part, present the text in a relatively foursquare fashion – but on the orchestral writing which, given the gloriously full-bodied playing of the Bavarian orchestra, so lusciously illuminates familiar words. He approaches the Masses with many of the same ideas he so eloquently propounds in his recordings of the symphonies and the music unfolds with a measured, almost relaxed pace which creates a sense of vast spaciousness. This can have its drawbacks: one is so entranced by the beautfully moulded orchestral introduction to the *Benedictus* from the D minor Mass that the entry of a rather full-throated Marga Schiml comes as a rude interruption. DG's digital transfers are extraordinarily good – they really seem to have produced a sound which combines the warmth of the original LP with the clarity of detail we expect from CD.

Bruckner Mass No. 1 in D minor. Te Deum in C major. **Joan Rodgers** (sop); **Catherine Wyn-Rogers** (contr); **Keith Lewis** (ten); **Alastair Miles** (bass); **Corydon Singers and Orchestra / Matthew Best** with **James O'Donnell** (org). Hyperion Ⓕ CDA66650 (67 minutes: DDD: 11/93). Texts and translations included. Recorded 1993. *Gramophone Editor's choice.*   Ⓖ Ⓖ
Earth-shaking is the only way to describe Bruckner's great *Te Deum* – literally as well as metaphorically with, on this disc, the thundering Westminster Cathedral organ (sensitively superimposed). The considerably enlarged Corydon Singers sing with consummate skill, rooting out all the subtleties and nuances of Bruckner's magnificent score yet always faithful to Matthew Best's thrusting, athletic direction. It is followed with a performance of the D minor Mass of extraordinary power and strength. From the dazzling orchestral colour and the electrically charged climaxes piling in one on top of the other, to the opulent writing for voices encompassing a vast array of human emotions, Bruckner's debt to Wagner is everywhere apparent. This is very much Bruckner the symphonist – the orchestra certainly dominate the work – and this orchestra produce playing of the very highest calibre.

Additional recommendation ...
...Te Deum[a]. **Mozart** Mass in D minor, K626, "Requiem"[b]. [a]**Agnes Giebel**, [b]**Elisabeth Grümmer** (sops); **Marga Höffgen** (contr); [a]**Josef Traxel,** [b]**Helmut Krebs** (tens); **Gottlob Frick** (bass); **St Hedwig's Cathedral Choir, Berlin; Berlin Philharmonic Orchestra /** [a]**Karl Forster,** [b]**Rudolf Kempe.** EMI Références mono Ⓜ CDH5 65202-2* (80 minutes: ADD: 10/94).

Bruckner Mass No. 2 in E minor[bcd]. Afferentur regi[bcd]. Ave Maria in F major (1861)[bd]. Ave Maria (1882, with Peter King, org)[a]. Ecce sacerdos magnus[bcd]. Locus iste[bd]. Aequali for Three Trombones, Nos. 1 and 2[c]. [a]**Anne-Marie Owens** (mez); [b]**City of Birmingham Symphony Chorus;** [c]**Birmingham Symphony Orchestra Wind Ensemble /** [d]**Simon Halsey.** Conifer Classics Ⓕ CDCF192 (64 minutes: DDD: 1/91). Texts and translations included. Recorded 1990.   Ⓖ
Bruckner's religious works require for their full realization an elusive combination of classical restraint and romantic fervour. In this excellent recording this style is captured perfectly. Under conductor Simon Halsey the chorus's finely tuned singing and rich tone are ideally suited both to the E minor Mass of 1866 and the four brief but intense motets which provide an excellent makeweight. The CBSO Wind Ensemble's accompaniment in the Mass, and solo playing in the two *Aequali* for three trombones, is well balanced and sonorous, qualities which are also shared by Conifer's atmospheric recorded sound. These choral works display a more personal side to Bruckner's character than the mighty symphonies, and so help to round out in a unique way the musical portrait of this great composer. Thus this finely prepared CD, completed by the first-ever recording of the *Ave Maria*, is an essential complement to the more well known, and more public, works.

Additional recommendations ...
...Mass No. 2. Libera me in F minor (Colin Sheen, Roger Brenner, Philip Brown, tbns). Aequali for three trombones, Nos. 1 and 2 (Sheen, Brenner, Brown). **Corydon Singers; English Chamber Orchestra Wind Ensemble / Matthew Best.** Hyperion Ⓕ CDA66177 (53 minutes: DDD: 9/86).
...Afferentur regi. Ave Maria (1861). Christus factus est. Ecce sacerdos magnus[b]. In St Angelum custodem, "Iam lucis orto sidere". Inveni David. Libera me[b]. Locus iste. Os justi. Pange lingua. Salvum fac populum. Tantum ergo[b]. Tota pulchra es[a]. Vexilla regis. Virga Jesse floruit. [a]**Daniel Norman** (ten); **St Bride's Church Choir, Fleet Street / Robert Jones** with [b]**Matthew Morley** (org). Naxos Ⓢ 8 550956 (62 minutes: DDD: 7/95).

Bruckner Mass No. 3 in F minor. Psalm 150 in C major. **Juliet Booth** (sop); **Jean Rigby** (mez); **John Mark Ainsley** (ten); **Gwynne Howell** (bass); **Corydon Singers and Orchestra / Matthew Best.** Hyperion Ⓕ CDA66599 (68 minutes: DDD: 3/93). Texts and translations included. Recorded 1992.   Ⓖ Ⓖ
Bruckner Mass No. 3 in F minor (ed. Nowak). Te Deum in C major. **Jane Eaglen** (sop); **Birgit Remmert** (contr); **Deon van der Walt** (ten); **Alfred Muff** (bass); **Linz Mozart Choir; London Philharmonic Orchestra / Franz Welser-Möst.** EMI Ⓕ CDC5 56168-2 (79 minutes: DDD: 11/96). Texts and translations included. Recorded 1995. *Gramophone Editor's choice.*   Ⓖ
Bruckner, the devout Catholic who poured his very soul into his devotional, liturgical choral pieces often seems a very different being from Bruckner, the composer of gargantuan, almost self-indulgent symphonies rich in luscious orchestral colour and sensuous harmony. Where the two combine the

result can be something almost other-worldly. The F minor Mass can certainly be regarded as being among the finest music he ever created. The intensity of religious feeling is heightened rather than diminished by the sumptuous orchestral support, and the soaring melodies and opulent harmonies are somehow purified and enriched by the devotional character of these familiar texts. Matthew Best's performance, by understating the music's abundant richness, gives tremendous point to the inner conviction of Bruckner's faith. His orchestra, brought together for this recording but sounding as if they have been playing this music all their days, play with commendable discretion, balancing admirably with a relatively small choral body. As with everything the Corydon Singers and Best turn their hands to, it is an impeccable performance, infused with real artistry and sensitive musicianship. Enhanced by the glorious solo voices from a high-powered team this is a CD of rare depth and conviction.

Welser-Möst's quartet of soloists, for all their manifest strengths, give the impression of trying a little too hard for their own good yet Best, in focusing his interpretation on the spiritual side of Bruckner's sublime creation, misses out on the sheer, almost operatic, spectacle of Welser-Möst's riveting performance. Raw excitement on an almost primeval level sets the scene for the exhilarating *Te Deum*. Here again Welser-Möst goes at it with all guns blazing. Joakim Svenhedren treats us to a ravishing solo violin obbligato in the "Aeterna fac" but this is only the briefest of respites in a performance which sweeps all before it in a consuming whirlwind of energy. Again there is very strong competition from Best and the Corydons who find a greater depth to this music than Welser-Möst and his team. But if it's sheer, unbridled excitement you want nothing beats the outstanding EMI disc.

Further listening ...

...Overture in G minor. *Coupled with works by various composers.* **Queen's Hall Orchestra /**
  Sir Henry Wood. Dutton Laboratories mono 2CDAX2002* (9/94).
...Christus factus est. *Coupled with works by various composers.* **St Paul's Cathedral Choir /**
  John Scott with **Andrew Lucas** (org). Hyperion CDA66916 (A/97). *See review in the Collections*
  section; refer to the Index.
...Christus factus est. *Coupled with works by various composers.* **New College Choir, Oxford;**
  Capricorn / Edward Higginbottom. Erato 3984-21659-2 (6/98). *Gramophone Editor's choice.*
  See review in the Collections section; refer to the Index.
...Requiem in D minor. Psalms – 112 in B flat major; 114 in G major. **Soloists; Corydon Singers;**
  English Chamber Orchestra / Matthew Best. Hyperion CDA66245 (1/88).
...Virga Jesse floruit. *Coupled with works by various composers.* **St Paul's Cathedral Choir /**
  John Scott. Hyperion CDA66994 (12/97). *See review in the Collections section; refer to the Index.*

Joan Brudieu   French/Catalonian c1520-1591

Suggested listening ...

...En los mon pus sou dotada del set goigs. *Coupled with works by various composers.*
  Ensemble Clément Janequin / Dominique Visse (alto). Harmonia Mundi HMC90 1627 (4/98).
  Gramophone Editor's choice. See review in the Collections section; refer to the Index.   ⒼⒼ

Antoine Brumel   French c1460-c1515

Suggested listening ...

...Du tout plongiet/Fors seulement. *Coupled with works by* **Ockeghem** and **La Rue**
  The Clerks' Group / Edward Wickham. ASV Gaudeamus CDGAU168 (5/97).
  Gramophone Editor's choice. Gramophone Award Winner 1997. See review under Ockeghem;
  refer to the Index.   Ⓖ
...Du tout plongiet/Fors seulement. Missa "Et ecce terrae motus". *Coupled with works by various*
  composers. **Early Music Consort of London / David Munrow.**
  Virgin Classics Veritas VED5 61334-2 (11/97). 🖅 *See review in the Collections section; refer to*
  the Index.

Gavin Bryars   British 1943

Bryars Cello Concerto, "Farewell to Philosophy"[a]. One Last Bar, Then Joe Can Sing[b]. By the Vaar[c].
  [a]**Julian Lloyd Webber** (vc); [c]**Charlie Haden** (db); [b]**Nexus** (Bob Becker, Bill Cahn, Robin Engelman,
  Russell Hartenberger, John Wyre, perc); [ac]**English Chamber Orchestra / James Judd.**
  Point Music Ⓟ 454 126-2PTH (75 minutes: DDD: 11/96). Recorded 1995.
  Gramophone Editor's choice.   Ⓖ
Rather like Sibelius's *Swan of Tuonela*, Gavin Bryars's 1995 Cello Concerto (or *Farewell to Philosophy*, to quote its Haydn-inspired subtitle) emerges from among shadows, its solo line climbing sadly and patiently until the long first section takes its leave among *Parsifal*-style string figurations. Section two is more animated, at least initially (timpani set the scene), until the mood darkens again; the fifth recalls

the orchestration of Haydn's *Philosopher* Symphony ("pairs of English and French horns playing alternating legato phrases, muted violins and unmuted lower strings accompanying with staccato quavers") and the sixth, blurring dissonances and a softly chiming bell. The *Farewell* connection, again after Haydn, greets the tender final section with its progressive reduction of forces, a haunting twentieth-century parallel to the various *fin de siècle* swansongs of Franz Liszt. Lloyd Webber's tone seems perfectly suited to the job, being full-bodied and expressive but relaxed enough to blend with the components of a predominantly dark accompaniment. *One Last Bar, Then Joe Can Sing* (1994) was an Arts Council commission for the percussion quintet Nexus and, to quote Bryars himself, "is a reflexion on aspects of percussion history, both personal and musical". The work's opening takes as its starting-point the last bar at the end of the first part of Bryars's opera *Medea*, then calls on varieties of tuned percussion (the glow of marimbas in contrast to the glitter of high bells), prompts some haunting modulations and fades to a tranquil coda. *By the Vaar* (a river in Flanders and the scene of another Bryars opera) was written for – and is performed by – jazz bass-player Charlie Haden, whose specific sound (he uses gut strings) inspired a husky, mellow "extended *adagio*". Much of the solo work is played pizzicato which of course underlines the jazz element, while bass clarinet, percussion and strings set up a warming backdrop. It's a nice piece, but the Cello Concerto is rather more than that, and *One Last Bar, Then Joe Can Sing*, more still.

Further listening ...

...Incipit Vita Nova[a]. Glorious Hill[b]. Four Elements[c]. Sub Rosa[d]. [a]**Hilliard Ensemble;** [a]**Annemarie Dreyer** (vn); [a]**Ulrike Lachner** (va); [a]**Rebecca Firth** (vc); [c]**chamber ensemble;** [d]**Gavin Bryars Ensemble.** ECM New Series 445 351-2 (5/94).

...In nomine. *Coupled with works by various composers.* Virgin Classics VC5 45217-2 (12/97). *See review in the Collections section; refer to the Index.*

...A Man in a Room, Gambling[a]. Les fiançailles[b]. The North Shore[c]. The South Downs[d]. [a]**Juan Muñoz** (spkr); [c]**Bill Hawkes** (va); [d]**Sophie Harris** (vc); [d]**Gavin Bryars** (pf); [abc]**Gavin Bryars Ensemble / [c]Roger Heaton.** Point Music 456 514-2PTH (11/97).

...Prologue. String Quartet No. 1, "Between the National and the Bristol". First Viennese Dance. Epilogue. **Pascal Pongy** (hn); **Charles Fullbrook, Gavin Bryars** (perc); **Arditti Quartet.** ECM New Series 829 484-2 (3/87).

...String Quartets – No. 1, "Between the National and the Bristol"; No. 2. Die letzten Tage. **Balanescu Quartet.** Argo 448 175-2ZH (2/96).

...Jesus' Blood never failed me yet. **Tom Waits** (sngr); **Hampton Quartet; chorus; orchestra / Michael Riesman.** Point Music 438 823-2PTH (10/93). *Gramophone Editor's choice.*   Ⓖ

...The Sinking of the Titanic. **Westhaston Boys' Choir; Camilla Thornton** (va); **Ziella Bryars, Orlanda Bryars, Lucy Thornion** (vcs); **Gavin Bryars Ensemble.** Point Music 446 061-2PTH (2/95).

John Bull   British ?1562/3-1628

Bull In Nomines – IV; V; IX; XII. Pavan in the second tone. Galliard. Lord Lumley's galliard. The King's Hunt. Duke of Brunswick's alman. Germain's alman. English toy. Irish toy. Why ask you. Fantasias – X; XV. Dutch Dance. Fantastic Pavan and Galliard. Chromatic Pavan and Galliard. Melancholy Galliard. Dr Bull's goodnight. Salvator mundi Deus. **Pierre Hantaï** (hpd). Auvidis Astrée Ⓔ E8543 (74 minutes: DDD: 9/95). *◢* Recorded 1994.

In view of the fact that Bull was perhaps the greatest of Elizabethan keyboard virtuosos and writers, it is surprising that not more harpsichordists have leapt at the chance of recording his exceptionally diverse output. For sheer exuberant brilliance, outstanding here, apart from the variations of *Doctor Bull's goodnight*, are the galliards, especially No. 78 in the *Musica Britannica* volume (listed in the heading as *Galliard*). There are also virtuosic strings of thirds in *Lord Lumley's galliard* and the remarkable *In Nomine* that is No. 9 in the *MB* numbering, which is actually in 11/4 time. Of the other examples of this peculiarly English form rooted in polyphony, No. 4 is very fine and No. 5 notable for its rhythmic surprises. Observable in Bull's music too, however, is a strong vein of melancholy, even in such straightforward little pieces as the *English toy* or the *Dutch Dance*; and his famous bold harmonies and 'false relations' can be heard in the *Fantastic Pavan* and, above all, in the magnificent *Chromatic Pavan and Galliard* (thought to have been written in memory of Queen Elizabeth). Hantaï's enjoyment in the more extrovert pieces is evident, but he also enters fully into Bull's more contemplative moods. On a well-recorded Italian instrument of 1677, he is perhaps over-emphatic in *Why ask you*, and certainly very free in rhythm and pace in the *Chromatic Pavan*, but otherwise he compels nothing but wholehearted admiration: his diversity of articulation (legato, semi-staccato and staccato) in *The King's Hunt* is worth every harpsichordist's study.

Additional recommendations ...

...In Nomine. *Coupled with works by various composers.* **Sophie Yates** (virg). Chandos Chaconne Ⓔ CHAN0574 (71 minutes: DDD: 12/95). *◢*

...Chromatic Pavan and Galliard, "Queen Elizabeth's". Fantastic Pavan and Galliard. Melancholy Pavan. Pavan and Galliards, "St Thomas Wake". Trumpet Pavan. Italian Galliard. The Prince's Galliard. The Quadran Pavan and Galliard – No. 2; No. 3. Spanish Pavan. **Joseph Payne** (hpd). BIS Ⓔ CD729 (63 minutes: DDD: 3/96). *◢*

Giovanni Buonamente
Italian late 16th century-1642

Suggested listening ...
...Sonata a 6. Canzona a 6. *Coupled with works by various composers.* **His Majestys Sagbutts and Cornetts.** Hyperion CDA66847 (11/96). *See review in the Collections section; refer to the Index.*

Henry Burleigh
American 1866-1949

Suggested listening ...
...Ethiopia saluting the colours. *Coupled with works by various composers.* **Thomas Hampson** (bar); **Craig Rutenberg** (pf). EMI CDM5 55028-2 (10/97). *See review in the Collections section; refer to the Index.* ⒼⒼⒼ

Gerald Busby
American 1935

Suggested listening ...
...Behold this swarthy face. *Coupled with works by various composers.* **Thomas Hampson** (bar); **Craig Rutenberg** (pf). EMI CDM5 55028-2 (10/97). *See review in the Collections section; refer to the Index.* ⒼⒼⒼ

Adolph Busch
German 1891-1952

Suggested listening ...
...Nun die Schatten dunkeln. Wonne der Wehmut. Aus den Himmelsaugen. *Coupled with works by various composers.* **Mitsuko Shirai** (mez); **Tabea Zimmermann** (va); **Hartmut Höll** (pf). Capriccio 10 462 (9/95). *See review in the Collections section; refer to the Index.* Ⓖ

William Busch
British 1901-1945

Suggested listening ...
...The echoing Green. The shepherd. If thou wilt ease thine heart. Come, o come, my life's delight. *Coupled with works by various composers.* **Sir Peter Pears** (ten); **Viola Tunnard** (pf). Belart 461 550-2 (12/97). *See review in the Collections section; refer to the Index.*

Alan Bush
British 1900

Suggested listening ...
...Voices of the Prophets, Op. 41. *Coupled with works by various composers.* **Sir Peter Pears** (ten); **Alan Bush** (pf). Belart 461 550-2 (12/97). *See review in the Collections section; refer to the Index.*

Antoine Busnois
French c1430-1492

Suggested listening ...
...Victimae Paschali laudes. *Coupled with works by various composers.* **The Clerks' Group / Edward Wickham.** ASV Gaudeamus CDGAU139 (3/95). *See review under Ockeghem; refer to the Index.*
...Fortuna disperata. *Coupled with works by various composers.* **Early Music Consort of London / David Munrow.** Virgin Classics Veritas VED5 61334-2 (11/97). ✐ *See review in the Collections section; refer to the Index.*

Ferruccio Busoni
Italian/German 1866-1924

Busoni Piano Concerto, Op. 39. **Garrick Ohlsson** (pf); Men's voices of the **Cleveland Orchestra Chorus; Cleveland Orchestra / Christoph von Dohnányi.** Telarc Ⓟ CD80207 (72 minutes: DDD: 4/90). Recorded 1989. ⒼⒼ
Busoni's Concerto is a thundering vehicle for virtuosity and one doubts whether the concerto has ever been performed as outstandingly as this, by the conductor and his players as well as the soloist. The second scherzo is so infectiously exciting that one feels tempted to cheat and play it all over again before proceeding to the finale, and the enormous central movement has a formidable sense of scale and pacing, to which Ohlsson's sonorous pianism is a bonus as well as a contributing factor. The orchestral sound is outstandingly beautiful and transparent and the piano produces crags of grandiose tone without ever seeming to approach its limit or to have been helped by the engineers.

Busoni Turandot – Suite, Op. 41.
Casella Paganiniana, Op. 65.
Martucci Nocturne in G flat major, Op. 70 No. 1. Novelletta, Op. 82 No. 2. Giga, Op. 61 No. 3.
   La Scala Philharmonic Orchestra, Milan / Riccardo Muti. Sony Classical Ⓕ SK53280
   (59 minutes: DDD: 4/94). Recorded 1992.   ⒼⒼⒼ
Riccardo Muti takes time out here to present some of the lesser known, rarely heard orchestral scores
of his fellow countrymen, and a superbly played, enjoyable concert it is too. Proceedings commence
with a fine and spirited performance of Alfredo Casella's divertimento *Paganiniana* – not a great piece
by any means but a work possessing plenty of charm and humour nevertheless; the outer movements
are a bit of a romp (very *opera buffa*) and must have been as much fun to write as they clearly are for
the La Scala Philharmonic to play. The tone and temperature rise a few degrees in Martucci's
gorgeously lyrical *Nocturne*, Op. 70 No. 1 – a sort of Mahler-meets-Puccini-meets-Respighi love song
– and this is nicely contrasted with the affable if somewhat lightweight musings of his *Novelletta* and
Giga. The high point of the disc, though, must surely be Muti's account of Busoni's *Turandot* Suite,
Op. 41, the work that, after several tinkerings, finally ended up forming the basis of his 1917 opera.
The recording is exceptionally clear and well focused, if at times a little dry.
Additional recommendation ...
   ...Turandot – Suite. Nocturne symphonique, Op. 43. Rondo arlecchinesco, Op. 46. Divertimento for
   Flute and Orchestra, Op. 52[a]. Two Studies from "Doktor Faust", Op. 51. Clarinet Concertino,
   Op. 48[b]. Tanzwalzer, Op. 53. [a]**Jean-Claude Gérard** (fl); [b]**Ulf Rodenhäuser** (cl); **Berlin Radio**
   Symphony Orchestra / Gerd Albrecht. Capriccio Ⓕ 10 479 (76 minutes: DDD: 6/94).   Ⓖ

Busoni Violin Sonatas – No. 1 in E minor, Op. 29; No. 2 in E minor, Op. 36*a*. Four Bagatelles,
   Op. 28. **Per Enoksson** (vn); **Kathryn Stott** (pf). BIS Ⓕ CD784 (60 minutes: DDD). Recorded 1996.
Busoni's virtuosic understanding and command of the piano, allied to his deep knowledge of the
classical repertoire, is evident on every page of the Violin Sonatas – which strictly speaking should be
titled (as the Second Sonata originally was) sonatas for piano and violin. The importance of the piano
is very much emphasized in these recordings by the far greater artistic presence of the pianist,
Kathryn Stott, than that of her partner, Per Enoksson, who is efficient but rarely inspired. Busoni's
admiration for Brahms is very much in evidence in the First Sonata (especially in the finale), though
the first movement, with its striking conflict between bold romantic gesture and severe classicism, is
strikingly original in voice. The Second Sonata is by far the more interesting of the two, and it is here
that both artists come into their own. Several Busoni commentators have noted a close-spirited
relationship between this work and Beethoven's Piano Sonata, Op. 109, though this is more a
relationship of structure than of content – most obviously in the variation and fugue which make up
the finale. The sudden appearance here of Bach's *Wie wohl ist mir, O Freund der Seelen* is very moving
and has the same effect as the introduction of Dowland's original melody at the close of Britten's
Lachrimae. This disc can be highly recommended to all wishing to discover more of the music of this
most enigmatic of composers. The interesting filler is the group of *Four Bagatelles*, dedicated to the
pianist Egon Petri (who was only seven years old at the time but clearly already a remarkable talent).
Particularly intriguing is the title of the first *Bagatelle* – "From the Age of Pigtails".

Busoni Fantasia contrappuntistica[a]. Fantasia nach J. S. Bach[a]. Toccata[b]. **John Ogdon** (pf).
   Continuum Ⓕ CCD1006 (60 minutes: AAD: 7/89). Items marked [a] from Altarus AIR-2-9074
   (10/88), [b]new to UK.   ⒼⒼⒼ
Busoni's *Fantasia contrappuntistica* is of legendary difficulty, density and length and pianists are
understandably very reluctant to learn it. John Ogdon plays it with consummate virtuosity, clarity and
sustained concentration, and alongside the technical assurance there is in evidence a firm intellectual
grasp of Busoni's prodigious structure and a lofty eloquence in expressing his faith. It is a formidable
feat of musicianship as well as pianism. The two other pieces are more personal and many readers
may find them even more moving. The *Fantasia nach J.S. Bach* is freer in structure than the *Fantasia
contrappuntistica* and with its dedication to his father's memory it is as though Busoni has chosen
particularly beloved and appropriate pages for his tribute, adding his own meditations on them. The
very late *Toccata* is a resurgence of the Faustian vein that runs throughout Busoni's work, but now
dark and pessimistic. The three works add up to a sort of triple self-portrait and Ogdon characterizes
them finely. Busoni's piano-writing demands a huge range of sonority as well as endurance and sheer
dexterity; in these performances (and this superb recording) Busoni's piano is rendered full-size.

Busoni Sonatinas – No. 2; No. 6, super Carmen (Kammerfantasie). Elegien – No. 2, All'Italia!;
   No. 4, Turandots Frauengemach; No. 7, Berceuse élégiaque. An die Jugend – No. 3, Giga,
   Bolero e Variazione. Sechs Stücke, Op. 33*b* – No. 6, Exeunt omnes. Fantasia nach J. S. Bach.
   Indianisches Tagebuch, Book 1. Toccata.
Bach (arr. Busoni) Prelude and Fugue in D major, BWV532. **Geoffrey Tozer** (pf).
   Chandos Ⓕ CHAN9394 (77 minutes: DDD: 9/96). Recorded 1993-94.
This issue fills a conspicuous gap in the catalogue. Yes, there are other recordings of most of these
pieces to choose from but the fact that they are here brought together on one disc makes it particularly
valuable. Also, not only are we given a generous 77 minutes' worth of music but a well-balanced cross-

section of Busoni's piano music at that. Tozer opens with a finely crafted reading of the *Kammerfantasie super Carmen*, full of subtle nuance and sensitive phrasing. Not perhaps as bold and overtly virtuosic as Marc-André Hamelin on Hyperion but a valid and enjoyable reading none the less. After the slight and Schumannesque "Exeunt omnes" from Op. 33*b* come three pieces from the *Elegien*: a suitably dark and shadowy "All'Italia!" (which draws on material used in the massive Piano Concerto), a brightly lit and sparkling "Turandots Frauengemach" and a moving, if slightly fast, account of the beautiful "Berceuse". Elsewhere Tozer gives solid, musicianly readings of the rarely heard *Indianisches Tagebuch* of 1915, the brooding *Sonatina* No. 2 and the powerful *Toccata*, whilst Busoni's fascination with the music of Bach is represented by the *Fantasia nach J. S. Bach* and his transcription of the Prelude and Fugue in D major. In sum, a well-planned disc presenting several strands of Busoni's art that can be safely recommended to Busoni enthusiasts and newcomers alike. The recorded sound is good, if at times slightly overbright in the upper register.

Additional recommendations ...
...Suite Campestre, Op. 3. Fantasia in modo antico, Op. 33*b* No. 4. Elegien – No. 1, Nach der Wendung; No. 7. Macchietti medioevali. Sonatinas – No. 4 in dic Nativitas Christi MCMXVIII; No. 6. *Coupled with works by* **Bach** William Stephenson (pf).
Olympia Ⓕ OCD461 (60 minutes: DDD: 11/94).
...Sonatina No. 6. *Coupled with works by various composers.* **Marc-André Hamelin** (pf).
Hyperion Ⓕ CDA66765 (72 minutes: DDD: 3/95). *See review under Alkan; refer to the Index.* ⒼⒼ
...An die Jugend – Giga, bolero e variazione (study after Mozart). *Coupled with works by various composers.* **Anatol Ugorski** (pf). DG Ⓕ 447 105-2GH (62 minutes: DDD: 3/96). *See review in the Collections section; refer to the Index.*

Busoni Arlecchino. **Robert Wörle** (ten) Arlecchino (Peter Matié), Leandro; **Marcia Bellamy** (mez) Colombina (Katharina Koschny); **René Pape** (bass) Ser Matteo del Sarto; **Siegfried Lorenz** (bar) Abbate Cospicuo; **Peter Lika** (bass) Dottor Bombasto; **Berlin Radio Symphony Orchestra / Gerd Albrecht.** Capriccio Ⓕ 60 038 (67 minutes: DDD: 11/94). Notes and synopsis included. Recorded 1992. ⒼⒼ
Albrecht's *Arlecchino* is one of the finest readings of a Busoni opera yet committed to disc. Fine as Nagano's reading is, Albrecht projects a greater feeling of drama and dramatic pace (as well as the *commedia dell'arte* aspects of the opera) and seems to have absorbed the Busoni spirit far more successfully; the presence of Busoni's final masterpiece, *Doktor Faust*, is exceptionally strong. Marcia Bellamy is a shade more suited to the role of Colombina than Susanne Mentzer (Nagano), and there are some exceptionally good performances from René Pape, Siegfried Lorenz and Peter Lika in the roles of Matteo, Abbate Cospicuo and Dottor Bombasto. The master-stroke, however, is the casting of Robert Wörle in both the Arlecchino and Leandro roles, an inspired idea and one which is delivered with great aplomb and panache – his Leandro is more sharply characterized than Stephan Dahlberg's for Nagano. Albrecht draws superb orchestral playing from the Berlin Radio Symphony Orchestra (especially in the wind and brass departments) and the recording is well balanced and atmospheric.

Additional recommendation ...
...Arlecchino. Turandot. **Soloists; Chorus and Orchestra of the Opéra de Lyon / Kent Nagano.**
Virgin Classics Ⓕ VCD7 59313-2 (two discs: 137 minutes: DDD: 11/93). *Selected by Sounds in Retrospect.*

Further listening ...
...Violin Concerto in D major, Op. 35*a*[a]. Violin Sonata No. 2 in E minor, Op. 36*b*[b]. [ab]**Joseph Szigeti** (vn); [b]**Mieczyslaw Horszowski** (pf); [a]**Little Orchestra Society / Thomas Scherman.**
Sony Classical mono MPK52537* (5/93).
...Berceuse élégiaque, Op. 42. *Coupled with works by* **Schoenberg** and **Weill** New Philharmonia Orchestra / Frederik Prausnitz. EMI Matrix CDM5 65869-2 (4/96).
...Berceuse élégiaque (arr. Adams). *Coupled with works by* **J. Adams** and **Liszt** London Sinfonietta / John Adams. Nonesuch 7559-79359-2 (4/97). *Gramophone Editor's choice.* See review under J. Adams; refer to the Index. Ⓖ
...Tanzwalzer. *Coupled with works by various composers.* **Philharmonia Orchestra / Igor Markevitch.** Testament mono SBT1060* (2/96).
...String Quartets – No. 1 in C minor, Op. 19; No. 2 in D minor, Op. 26. **Pellegrini Quartet.** CPO CPO999 264-2 (1/96).
...Doktor Faust. **Soloists; Bavarian Radio Chorus and Symphony Orchestra / Ferdinand Leitner.** DG 20th Century Classics 427 413-2GC3 (8/89).
...Turandot. **Soloists; Berlin RIAS Chamber Choir; Berlin Radio Symphony Orchestra / Gerd Albrecht.** Capriccio 60 039 (11/93). Ⓖ

Fernando Bustamente
Argentinian

Suggested listening ...
...Misionera (arr. Morel). *Coupled with works by various composers.* **Jason Vieaux** (gtr).
Naxos 8 553449 (11/97). *See review in the Collections section; refer to the Index.*

George Butterworth
British 1885-1916

Butterworth Bredon Hill and other songs. A Shropshire Lad.
Finzi Let us garlands bring, Op. 18.
Ireland Sea Fever. The Vagabond. The Bells of San Marie.
Vaughan Williams Songs of Travel. **Bryn Terfel** (bass-bar); **Malcolm Martineau** (pf).
    DG Ⓕ 445 946-2GH (77 minutes: DDD: 8/95). Texts included. Recorded 1995.
    Gramophone Editor's record of the month.   ❸❸❸
As in all the best singing of songs, whatever the nationality, there is strong, vivid communication:
Terfel will sometimes sing so softly that if he had secured anything less than total involvement he
would lose us. There is breadth of phrase, variety of tone, alertness of rhythm, all the musical virtues
are there; and yet that seems to go only a little way towards accounting for what is special. In more
detail then. *Bredon Hill*: "a happy noise to hear" is the robust observation of a fulfilled and carefree
man, "and come to church in time" is exultant *hubris*, "I hear you" has anger in it, "I will come"
resentful submission. Finzi's "O mistress mine": "in delay there lies no plenty" is the free, open-
throated call of lovers to make time run (since we can't make it stand still), and "Youth's a stuff will
not endure" is a lightly intimated *memento mori*, half seriousness, half joke. "When I was one-and-
twenty" (*A Shropshire Lad*): the "wise man" who pedalled his tuppenny-ha'penny thought-for-the-day
is a pompous loud-mouth, "but oh 'tis true" has the groan of acknowledgement, and the repeated "'tis
true" comes from the private recesses of the soul, which *knows* it is! One after another, these songs are
brought to a full life. intelligence and the genuine flash of inspiration. Malcolm Martineau's playing
is also a delight: his touch, in its way, is as sure and illuminating as the singer's. From the recording
you might prefer less hall-reverberance around the voice. From the songs themselves you could not
possibly wish anything more: hearing them performed like this you probably won't swap them for half
the German song repertoire or the whole of the French.
Additional recommendations ...
...A Shropshire Lad. Two English Idylls. The banks of green willow. *Coupled with works by*
    Coleridge-Taylor and **MacCunn** **Royal Liverpool Philharmonic Orchestra / Grant Llewellyn.**
    Argo Ⓕ 436 401-2ZH (68 minutes: DDD: 6/93).
...Bredon Hill. When the lad for longing sighs. On the idle hill of summer. A Shropshire Lad.
    Coupled with works by various composers. **Anthony Rolfe Johnson** (ten); **Graham Johnson** (pf).
    Hyperion Ⓕ CDA66471/2 (two discs: 124 minutes: DDD: 8/95). Includes various poems from
    Housman's "A Shrophire Lad" read by Alan Bates. *See review in the Collections section; refer to
    the Index.*
...A Shropshire Lad. The banks of green willow. *Coupled with works by various composers.*
    London Philharmonic Orchestra / Sir Adrian Boult.
    Belart mono Ⓑ 461 354-2* (60 minutes: ADD: 9/97).   ❸
...A Shropshire Lad. Two English Idylls. The banks of green willow. *Coupled with works
    by various composers.* **Academy of St Martin in the Fields / Sir Neville Marriner.**
    Decca Double Ⓜ 452 707-2DF2 (two discs: ADD: 8/97).

Dietrich Buxtehude
German c1637-1707

Buxtehude Nimm von uns, Herr, BuxWV78. Jesu, meines Lebens Leben, BuxWV62. Mit Fried
    und Freud, ich fahr dahin, BuxWV76. Führwahr, er trug unsere Krankheit, BuxWV31. Herzlich
    lieb, hab ich dich o Herr, BuxWV41. Der Herr ist mit mir, BuxWV15. **Claron McFadden** (sop);
    Franciska Dukel (mez); **Jonathan Peter Kenny** (alto); **Marius van Altena** (ten); **Stephan MacLeod**
    (bass); **Collegium Vocale; The Royal Consort; Anima Eterna Orchestra / Jos van Immerseel.**
    Channel Classics Ⓕ CCS7895 (65 minutes: DDD: 7/95). Texts included. Recorded 1994.
    Gramophone Editor's choice.   ❸❸
This disc includes six of Buxtehude's vocal works, only two of which appear to have been previously
recorded. Jos van Immerseel, more familiar to readers as a fortepianist and harpsichordist, here
directs Philippe Herreweghe's Collegium Vocale together with his own instrumental ensemble, Anima
Eterna, and a gamba quartet, The Royal Consort. The solo vocalists come from further afield but
have been carefully chosen and are, in the main, effective. The North German middle ground between
chorale concertato and the early cantatas of Bach is an interesting one, especially in the hands of
composers of Buxtehude's stature. In these cantatas the disparate textual elements of bible passage,
hymn and devotional poetry, typical of the time, are complemented by the composer's skill in drawing
together the comparably disparate musical ones of sonata, concertato principles, aria and chorale.
That in itself might give these cantatas only an ephemeral charm, but Buxtehude was a musician who
was gifted in the art of word-painting and, above all, in the expression of deep, often grief-stricken
emotions. He could be brilliant, too, in his lyrical approach to texts, but it is an all-pervading
melancholy which seems to characterize most strongly much that is most profound in his sacred vocal
music. These six works demonstrate Buxtehude's formal versatility with two large-scale chorale
cantatas; a beautiful ostinato-based strophic aria, with an almost startling dissonance; the famous,
austere and highly contrapuntal *Canticum Simeonis ("Mit Fried und Freud")* which Buxtehude
performed at his father's funeral in 1674; and two *concertante* pieces, one consisting of a sinfonia and

multisectional aria, the other of a sinfonia, aria and alleluia. The performances respond to the highly charged emotional outpouring of these works but occasionally lack polish. However, the music is first-rate (the ostinato- and chaconne-based movements make particularly strong appeal) and Immerseel's direction is stylish and sensitive. The cantata texts are in German only but there is a translation of Immerseel's interesting introductory essay.

Further listening ...

...Trio Sonatas – C major, BuxWV266; G major, BuxWV271; B flat major, BuxWV273. *Coupled with works by* **Pachelbel Cologne Musica Antiqua / Reinhard Goebel.** Archiv Produktion Galleria 427 118-2AGA (6/89). 🔎

...Sonatas, Op. 1 – Nos. 1-7. **John Holloway** (vn); **Jaap ter Linden** (va da gamba); **Lars Ulrik Mortensen** (hpd). Da Capo 8 224003 (1/96). 🔎

...Sonatas, Op. 2 – Nos. 1-7. **John Holloway** (vn); **Jaap ter Linden** (va da gamba); **Lars Ulrik Mortensen** (hpd). Da Capo 8 224004 (1/96) 🔎

...Ach Gott und Herr, BuxWV177. Ach Herr mich armen Sünder, BuxWV178. Canzona in C major, BuxWV166. Canzonetta in C major, BuxWV167. Canzonetta in D minor, BuxWV168. Canzonetta in E minor, BuxWV168. Ciacona in C minor, BuxWV159. Jesus Christus, unser Heiland, BuxWV198. Komm, heiliiger Geist, Herre Gott, BuxWV199. Komm heiliger Geist, Herre Gott, BuxWV200. Prelude and Fugue in F major, BuxWV144. Prelude and Fugue in F major, BuxWV145. Prelude and Fugue in F sharp minor, BuxWV146. Prelude and Fugue in G minor, BuxWV150. Te Deum laudamus, Phrygian, BuxWV218. **Michel Chapuis** (org). Auvidis Valois V4431 (12/89).

...In dulci jubilo, BuxWV197. Der Tag, der ist so freudenreich, BuxWV182. Magnificat primi toni, BuxWV203. *Coupled with works by various composers.* **Marie-Claire Alain** (org). Erato 0630-15343-2 (1/97).

...Preludes and Fugues – D major, BuxWV139; D minor, BuxWV140; E minor, BuxWV142; F major, BuxWV145; F sharp minor, BuxWV146; G minor, BuxWV149; A minor, BuxWV153. Prelude, Fugue and Chaconne in C major, BuxWV137. Toccata and Fugue in D minor, BuxWV155. Passacaglia in D minor, BuxWV161. Toccata and Fugue in F major, BuxWV156. Fugue (Gigue) in C major, BuxWV174. Ciaconas – C minor, BuxWV159; E minor, BuxWV160. Canzonetta in G major, BuxWV171. Wie schön leuchtet der Morgenstern, BuxWV223. Ach Herr mich armen Sünder, BuxWV178. Magnificat primi toni, BuxWV203, "Dorian". Durch Adams Fall ist ganz verderbt, BuxWV183. Vater unser im Himmelreich, BuxWV207. In dulci jubilo, BuxWV197. Der Tag, der ist so freudenreich, BuxWV182. Te Deum laudamus, BuxWV218. Komm, heiliger Geist, Herre Gott, BuxWV199. Nun komm, der Heiden Heiland, BuxWV211. **Marie-Claire Alain** (org). Erato 0630-12979-2 (6/96).

...Prelude, Fugue and Chaconne in C major, BuxWV137. *Coupled with works by various composers.* **Peter King** (org). Priory PRCD618 (7/98). *See review in the Collections section; refer to the Index.*

...Toccata and Fugue in F major, BuxWV156. Herr Jesu Christ, ich weiss gar wohl, BuxWV193. Von Gott will ich nicht lassen, BuxWV220. Te Deum laudamus, BuxWV218. *Coupled with works by various composers.* **Kristian Olesen** (org). Priory PRCD444 (5/97).

...Aperite mihi portas justitiae, BuxWV7. *Coupled with works by various composers.* **Aksel Schiøtz** (ten) with various artists. Danacord mono DACOCD453* (4/97). *See review in the Collections section; refer to the Index.*

William Byrd

British 1543-1623

Byrd Gradualia – Volume 1i: Saturday Lady Masses in Advent[a]. Domine quis habitabit[a]. Omni tempore benedic Deum[a]. Christe redemptor omnium[a]. Sermone blando a 3[b]. Miserere[b]. Ne perdas cum implis[a]. Lamentations of Jeremiah[a]. Christe, qui lux es a 5[a]. Christe qui lux es a 4[b]. Sanctus[b]. Audivi vocem de caelo[a]. Vide Dominum quoniam tribulor[a]. Peccavi super numerum (all ed. Skinner)[a]. [a]**The Cardinall's Musick;** [b]**Frideswide Consort** (Caroline Kershaw, Jane Downer, Christine Garratt, Jean McCreery, recs) / **Andrew Carwood.** ASV Gaudeamus Ⓕ CDGAU170 (70 minutes: DDD: 11/97). Texts and translations included. Recorded 1996.

This is the first volume of ASV's project to record Byrd's complete output. The series has been planned with a view to making it as user-friendly as possible – not just a desirable aim, but a necessary one in an undertaking of this size. The discs devoted to Byrd's sacred music (like this volume) are interspersed with those containing secular vocal and instrumental music. Some of the shorter motets are entrusted to The Cardinall's' habitual instrumental accomplices, the Frideswide Consort. In line with The Cardinall's' general approach, a full list of sources are given for each piece, along with appropriate editorial commentary. Since Byrd set certain texts a number of times, such precision seems only sensible. Much of this music is new to the CD catalogue, and even in this selection of largely unpublished motets, there are impressive finds (the nine-voice *Domine quis habitabit*, for instance). This repertory is the mother's-milk of English choristers, and of the younger generation of English vocal ensembles The Cardinall's Musick remain perhaps the closest to that tradition outside of actual choral establishments. So they respond to Byrd with a suavity and confidence born of longstanding acquaintance. The expansive penitential pieces, such as the early *Lamentations*, are far removed from the small-scale forms of the *Gradualia*. The Cardinall's respond effectively to these different functions and moods, and their favourite recording venue (the Fitzalan Chapel of Arundel Castle) complements them admirably. The ultimate success of the enterprise will need to be viewed in the round, and that will take years; but this is a great start, and few groups could inspire greater confidence in their ability to bring it off.

Byrd Gradualia – Volume 2: Nativity of our Lord Jesus Christ – Puer natus est; Viderunt ... omnes fines terrae; Dies sanctificatus; Tui sunt coeli; Viderunt omnes fines terrae; Hodie Christus natus est; O admirabile commercium; O magnum mysterium. Ave regina caelorum. O salutaris hostia. Confitemini Domino. In exitu Israel (with Sheppard and Mundy). Laudate pueri Dominum. Decantabat populus. Deus in adjutorium. Ad Dominum cum tribularer (all ed. Skinner).
The Cardinall's Musick / Andrew Carwood. ASV Gaudeamus Ⓕ CDGAU178 (73 minutes: DDD: 7/98). Texts and translations included. *Gramophone Editor's choice.* Ⓖ
This second volume of The Cardinall's Musick's Byrd edition is, if anything, more impressive than the first. It may be a matter of programming, for the works recorded here seem to be of a higher overall calibre: even an obviously experimental piece such as *O salutaris hostia* could have been included on merit alone – yet this appears to be its first recording. Complete surveys sometimes turn up items of lesser interest, yet they also allow one to hear pieces that might have difficulty in finding a home elsewhere: witness the responsory, *In exitu Israel*, an intriguing collaborative effort by Byrd and his contemporaries, Mundy and Sheppard. Finally, one can judge for oneself the authenticity of works that modern scholarship has deemed doubtful (such as the opening *Ave regina caelorum*). Most of the pieces here involve male altos on the top line. The centrepiece is a collection of Propers from the *Gradualia* of 1607, this time for the Nativity. As on their first set, Skinner's and Carwood's decision to structure each volume around a set of Propers proves an astute piece of programming, integrating shorter items as it does (such as the various *Alleluia* settings) within a framework that allows them their own space. The singers are on very fine form indeed. It takes confidence to carry off *O salutaris hostia*, whose fierce false relations could so easily have sounded merely wilful. Only in the final, extended settings does the pace flag: the disc's last moments (roughly from 8'20" of *Ad Dominum cum tribularer*) are rather ponderous. That aside, this is a disc to delight Byrd-lovers everywhere.

Byrd Fantasia a 6. Pavan and Galliard – Kinbourough Good, MB32. The Queen's Alman, MB20, "Hugh Ashton's Ground". Pavan and Galliard a 6. Pavan and Galliard, MB14. Browning. Pavan a 5. The Carman's Whistle, MB36. The Irish March, MB94. My Lord of Oxenford's Maske. Pavan, MB17. A Fancie, MB25. Praeludium and Ground. Pavan and Galliard, MB60.
Anonymous Pavans – Mille regretz; Belle qui tiens ma vie. **Capriccio Stravagante / Skip Sempé** (hpd). Auvidis Astrée Ⓕ E8611 (73 minutes: DDD: 9/97). 🎵 Recorded 1997.
Gramophone Editor's choice.
This is technically superb and musically distinctive. Skip Sempé and his musicians grab hold of each piece and play it in a way that leaves no doubt why it was chosen; that is, they have something new and interesting to say musically about each work. The sound is also wonderful: Sempé plays on a Skowroneck harpsichord that he enthusiastically describes as "one of the first truly admirable harpsichords of the 20th century"; the viols and the recorder group are beautifully recorded, with every detail of the dense polyphony clear. So this is the kind of disc you could play to almost any music-lover as a way of explaining that Byrd is not just a great composer but one of the greatest. On the other hand, those who know the music may well feel a touch uncomfortable. While Sempé plays with often truly dazzling skill and virtuosity, many may wish that his pavans were a touch steadier. He also has a slightly mannered way of overdotting cadential bass figurations. The ensemble pieces are sometimes heavily orchestrated: the great six-part *Fantasia* that opens the disc, for example, has recorders and continuo instruments added to the viols as though to underline contrasts that some would think were already there in the music. These caveats are just a warning. This is an invigorating disc which gives you a new understanding of some of the finest masterpieces of English music.

Byrd All in a garden green[a]. La volta No. 1 in G major, "Lady Morley". O mistress mine I must[a]. Wolsey's Wild[a]. O Lord, how vain are all our delights[bc]. Psalmes, Sonets and Songs – Who likes to love; My mind to me a kingdom is[bc]; Farewell, false love[bc]. Triumph with pleasant melody[bc]. Truth at the First[bc]. Ad Dominum cum tribularer[b]. Cantiones sacrae – Attollite portas; Da mihi auxilium; Domine secundum actum meum; Miserere mihi, Domine[b]. [a]**Sophie Yates** (virg); [b]**I Fagiolini / Robert Hollingworth;** [c]**Fretwork.** Chandos Chaconne Ⓕ CHAN0578 (73 minutes: DDD: 8/95). 🎵 Texts and translations included. Recorded 1994.
This disc adopts an imaginative approach to programming Byrd's music by presenting works in different genres grouped together to demonstrate a single stage in his development. And how amazingly many-sided was the young Byrd, who burst like a star on the then somewhat enfeebled state of English music, not only being appointed organist of Lincoln Cathedral at the age of 20 and of the Chapel Royal ten years later but, with his teacher Tallis, embarking on an important publishing venture. This disc includes Latin motets, keyboard dances and variations on popular songs of the day, and sacred and secular songs (and a dialogue) with viols. There is so much here that wins our admiration: the dazzling contrapuntal elaboration of *Attollite portas*, the close-knit texture of *Da mihi auxilium* and the massive *Ad Dominum cum tribularer*; the exuberant variations on *O mistress mine* (neatly played by Sophie Yates) and Byrd's melodic gift in the strophic *O Lord, how vain*. The

singers' adoption of period pronunciation of English – so that, for example, "rejoice" emerges as "rejwace" – affects the tuning and the musical sound, it is claimed here, but without rather clearer enunciation the point remains not proven. Probably more upsetting to many will be the Anglicized pronunciation of Latin. The viol consort gives quiet, stylish support and is well balanced, the Fagiolini sopranos occasionally 'catch the mike' on high notes (e.g. in the passionate pleas of *Miserere mihi, Domine*), and the recorded level of the virginals might have been a little higher without falsifying its tone. But these are very minor criticisms of a most rewarding disc.

Byrd Harpsichord works.
Gibbons Harpsichord works. **Laurent Stewart** (hpd). Pierre Verany Ⓕ PV795051
(62 minutes: DDD: 3/96). 🎵 Recorded 1994.
Byrd My Lady Nevell's Ground, BK57. French Corantos, BK21 – No. 1; No. 3. Pavan and
Galliard in G minor, BK3, "Sir William Petre". Rowland, BK7. Volte in G major, BK91. Alman
in G major, BK11. Prelude in A minor, BK12. Fantasia in A minor, BK13. **Gibbons** Fantasias –
D minor, MBXX/5; G major, MBXX/6; D minor, MBBXX/8; A minor, MBXX/11; A minor,
MBXX/12; C major, MBXX/14. Preludes – A minor, MBXX/1; A minor, MBXX/4. Galliard,
MBXX/20, "Lady Hatton". Ground in A minor, MBXX/26. French Coranto, MBXX/38. Pavan
and Galliard in A minor, MBXX/18-19, "Lord Salisbury". The Italian ground, MBXX/27.
The Queen's command, MBXX/28.
Byrd and Gibbons form an ideal partnership for a two-composer programme of English virginals music. Byrd fanciers may regret that he occupies only about one-third of the playing time, but no one could suggest that Gibbons's more rarely recorded music is less worthy of an outing. In his short life Gibbons wrote far less than Byrd but, except in its inclusion of six of his ten splendid fantasias, the programme does not deal in quantities (quality is to be found in abundance) but rather in the presentation of both composers in a variety of genres. Byrd's many magnificent pavan-galliard pairings are central to his output, but Gibbons strangely wrote only one such – and it is not set against Byrd's genuflexion to the same dignitary. However, it is not the programme that is the most remarkable feature of this recording, rather it is the performance. Stewart might have celebrated the triumphant return of Lord Willoughby a little less soberly, but in every other respect his playing is of the highest order. His tempos are convincing, phrasing is lucid, rubato subtly absorbed within a firm pulse, choice of registration apt and economically varied, and real gravity or joy of spirit illuminates every item. He plays a copy of a Ruckers harpsichord of 1612 (a date within the life span of both composers), tuned with unequal temperament and, surprisingly, to A = 440; the sound is sumptuous but clear, with every contrapuntal line sharply etched. The recording is excellent.
Additional recommendation ...
...Prelude in A minor, BK12. Fantasia in A minor, BK13. Pavan, BK54. Galliard, BK55. Barley
Break, BK92. Pavan and Galliard in G minor, BK3, "Sir William Petre". The woods so wild,
BK85. Hugh Ashton's Ground, BK20. The Bells, BK98. *Coupled with works by various
composers.* **Sophie Yates** (virg). Chandos Chaconne Ⓕ CHAN0574 (71 minutes: DDD: 12/95).

Byrd Cantiones Sacrae (1575) – Tribue, Domine. Siderum rector. Domine secundum. Fantasias[a] –
C major; D major. Attollite portas. Miserere mihi. Aspice Domine. Peccantem me quotidie.
Salvator mundi II[a]. O lux, beata Trinitas. **New College Choir, Oxford / Edward Higginbottom** with
[a]**Timothy Morris** (org). CRD Ⓕ CRD3492 (64 minutes: DDD: 2/98). Texts and translations
included. Recorded 1994.
There is so much wonderful six-part writing in this attractive selection from the 1575 *Cantiones Sacrae* that such a medium appears in a new light, particularly when performed by the choir and in the acoustic of New College Chapel – where, as Edward Higginbottom reminds us, they "have been rehearsing for 500 years". The beauty and balance of the musical architecture is constantly conveyed to the listener, particularly in the six-part writing. It doesn't matter whether these compositions were intended for liturgical or domestic use, or as a noble offering to the Queen: from a purely musical point of view they are superb. To give a single example, the little Vespers hymn *O lux, beata Trinitas*, displays consummate craftsmanship through the ingenious use of the number three – three high, then three low voices, three diverse voices, a canon three-in-one, three strophes, triple time, and so on, building up to a tremendous final "Amen". The point made by this recording is that it all sounds natural, uncontrived, magnificent. The three organ pieces are a welcome addition: with their brilliant fingerwork and gentle registrations they present a charming and lively contrast to the vocal settings.

Byrd Masses – Three Voices; Four Voices; Five Voices. Motet – Ave verum corpus a 4.
The Tallis Scholars / Peter Phillips. Gimell Ⓕ 454 945-2PH (67 minutes: DDD: 3/86). 🎵
From BYRD345 (5/84).   ⓆⒶ
Byrd was a fervently committed Roman Catholic and he helped enormously to enrich the music of the English Church. His Mass settings were made for the many recusant Catholic worshippers who held services in private. They were published between 1593 and 1595 and are creations of great feeling. The contrapuntal writing has a much closer texture and fibre than the Masses of Palestrina and there is an austerity and rigour that is allowed to blossom and expand with the text. The beautifully restrained and mellow recording, made in Merton College Chapel, Oxford, fully captures the measure of the music and restores the awe and mystery of music that familiarity has sometimes dimmed.

Additional recommendations ...

...Mass for Five Voices. Mass Propers for the Feast of All Saints. Motets. **Christ Church Cathedral Choir, Oxford / Stephen Darlington.** Nimbus Ⓔ NI5237 (52 minutes: DDD: 12/90).

...Masses. **King's College Choir, Cambridge / Sir David Willcocks.** Decca Ⓜ 433 675-2DM (75 minutes: ADD: 10/92).

...Masses. Anglican Music – The Great Service. O Lord, make thy servant. O God, the proud are risen against me. Sing joyfully unto God our strength. **The Tallis Scholars / Peter Phillips.** Gimell Ⓔ CDGIM343/4 (two discs: 132 minutes: DDD: 7/93).

...Masses – Five Voices; Four Voices. Infelix ego. **Oxford Camerata / Jeremy Summerly.** Naxos Ⓢ 8 550574 (65 minutes: DDD: 7/93).

...Ave verum corpus. Civitas sancti tui. Haec dies. *Coupled with works by various composers.* **Soloists; Westminster Cathedral Choir / James O'Donnell.** Hyperion Ⓔ CDA66850 (72 minutes: DDD: 5/96). *See review in the Collections section; refer to the Index.*

...Lamentations of Jeremiah. Mass for Four Voices. **Tallis** Lamentations of Jeremiah. Audivi vocem de caelo. **Clerks of New College Choir, Oxford / Edward Higginbottom.** Collins Classics Ⓔ 1487-2 (66 minutes: DDD: 7/96).

...Ave verum corpus. *Coupled with works by various composers.* **New College Choir, Oxford / Edward Higginbottom.** Erato Ⓔ 3984-21659-2 (66 minutes: DDD: 6/98). *Gramophone Editor's choice. See review in the Collections section; refer to the Index.*

Byrd Mass for Five Voices (with Propers for the Feast of Corpus Christi). Gradualia ac cantiones sacrae: Part 2 – Corpus Christi. Gradualia seu cantionum sacrarum, liber secundus: Votive Mass for the Blessed Sacrament – Ab ortu solis; Alleluia: Cognoverunt discipuli. **Winchester Cathedral Choir / David Hill.** Hyperion Ⓔ CDA66837 (73 minutes: DDD: 12/96). Texts and translations included. Recorded 1995.

One cannot but marvel at the cool fearlessness of the ageing composer who took upon himself to publish his three Mass settings and the two volumes of his *Gradualia* in the face of constant danger for Catholic recusants. On this CD the five movements of Byrd's Mass for five voices are interspersed with the five pieces of the Proper for the Feast of Corpus Christi. We can therefore transport ourselves back in time to the end of the sixteenth and beginning of the seventeenth century, and imagine their being performed, in early summer, at a live celebration of Mass in one of the great houses of the Catholic nobility. Winchester Cathedral Choir have purposely sought out an enclosed space in the great cathedral to make this recording, so that the sound captures something of the immediacy of singers performing in a small hidden room. One is particularly struck by the quality of the trebles – the slight edge to the gentle tone of very young singers – and also by the the teamwork of the whole choir. The secret of this recording lies in its unity of theme and in its understanding of Byrd's triumphant statements of belief, expressed in music of great tenderness as well as strength.

Additional recommendation ...

...Masses –Three Voices; Four Voices; Five Voices. Great Service in F major – Magnificat; Nunc dimittis. Ave verum corpus. *Coupled with works by* **Taverner** **King's College Choir, Cambridge / Sir David Willcocks.** Double Decca Ⓜ 452 170-2DF2 (two discs: 147 minutes: ADD: 2/97).

Byrd Gradualia – The Marian Masses. **William Byrd Choir / Gavin Turner.** Hyperion Ⓔ CDA66451 (80 minutes: DDD: 11/91). Texts and translations included. Recorded 1990.
Mass Propers – Feasts of the Purification of the BVM, the Nativity of the BVM, the Annunciation of the BVM, the Assumption of the BVM; Votive Masses of the BVM: Advent, Christmas to the Purification, Purification to Easter, Easter to Pentecost and Pentecost to Advent.

This useful recording explores the cycle of motets Byrd composed for English Roman Catholics to sing in their clandestine services. He began the project soon after writing the three Masses (which date from the mid 1590s), and took ten years to bring it to completion. Like so much of Byrd's late music, the *Gradualia* motets are compact and economical in expression: miniature masterpieces that glow with the warmth of the composer's personal religious convictions, and miraculously balance exquisite musical design with the most intelligent word-setting. Their chamber-music scale is nicely captured in these performances by the William Byrd Choir, headed by a superb team of five solo voices. Everything on the disc belongs to feasts of the Blessed Virgin, many of which share texts with one another. Byrd economized by setting each text once only, and to play them in their correct liturgical order the various tracks of the CD have to be pre-selected. This is great fun to do; but the disc also makes perfectly satisfying listening when played straight through from start to finish.

Further listening ...

...Keyboard Works: Fantasias – No. 2 in C major; No. 2 in G major. Pavans and Galliards – No. 2 in F major, "Ph. Tregian"; No. 2 in G major; No. 3 in G minor. The Carman's Whistle; The Woods so Wild; Walsingham; All in a garden green. The Queen's Alman. The Bells. Ut re mi fa sol la. La volta – No. 1 in G major. **Ursula Duetschler** (hpd). Claves CD50-9001 (10/90).

...Keyboard Works: My Lady Nevell's Ground. O mistress mine I must. John come kiss me now. Passamezzo Pavan and Galliard. The Carman's Whistle. Walsingham. Hugh Ashton's Ground. Fortune my foe. Sellinger's Round. **Elaine Thornburgh** (hpd). Koch International Classics 37057-2 (4/92).

...Pavan and Galliard a 6 in C major, BE17/15^d. Fantasia a 6 in G minor No. 2, BE17/13^d. In Nomine a 4 No. 2, BE17/17^d. Fantasia a 4 in G minor, BE17/4^d. Fantasia a 6 No. 3^d. In Nomine a 5, BE17/18-22^d. John come kiss me now, BK81^c. Pavan in A minor No. 1, BK14^c. Qui passe (Chi passa) for my Lady Nevell, BK19^c. Susanna fair^{ad}. Fair Britain Isle^{ad}. Rejoice unto the Lord^{ad}. In angel's weed^{ad}. Have mercy upon me, O God^{bd}. Triumph with pleasant melody^{bd}. Christ rising again^{bd}. ^{a}**Tessa Bonner** (sop); ^{b}**Red Byrd;** ^{c}**Timothy Roberts** (hpd); ^{d}**Rose Consort of Viols.** Naxos 8 550604 (6/95). ✏

...Christe, qui lux es et dies. O Lord, make thy servant Elizabeth our Queen. *Coupled with works by various composers.* **Choir of St Mary's Cathedral, Edinburgh / Timothy Byram-Wigfield.** Priory PRCD557 (10/97). *See review in the Collections section; refer to the Index.*

...Laetentur coeli. *Coupled with works by various composers.* **St Paul's Cathedral Choir / John Scott.** Hyperion CDA66994 (12/97). *See review in the Collections section; refer to the Index.*

...Morning Service – Venite; Te Deum; Benedictus; Creed. Evening Service – Magnificat; Nunc dimittis. Anthems – O God, the proud are risen against me; O Lord make thy servants. Sing joyfully unto God our strength. **The Tallis Scholars / Peter Phillips.** Gimell 454 911-2PII (6/87).

...Motets: In resurrectione tua; Aspice Domine de sede; Vide Domine afflictionem; Domine tu iurasti; Vigilate; Domine secundum multitudinem; Tristitia et anxietas; Ne irascaris Domine; O quam gloriosum. **New College Choir, Oxford / Edward Higginbottom.** CRD CRD3420 (12/91).

...Fauxbordons Service. *Coupled with works by various composers.* **St Edmundsbury Cathedral Choir / Mervyn Cousins** with **Scott Farrell** (org). Priory PRCD554 (1/97).

David Byrne   American 1952

Suggested listening ...
...High Life. *Coupled with works by various composers.* **Balanescu Quartet.** Argo 436 565-2ZH (3/93). *See review in the Collections section; refer to the Index.*

Giulio Caccini   Italian c1545-1618

Suggested listening ...
...Ave Maria (arr. Ingham). *Coupled with works by various composers.* **Lesley Garrett** (sop); **Britten Sinfonia / Ivor Bolton.** Conifer Classics 75605 51329-2 (12/97). *See review in the Collections section; refer to the Index.*

John Cage   American 1912-1992

A Chance Operation The John Cage Tribute. **Various Artists.** Koch International Classics Ⓟ 37238-2 (two discs: 141 minutes: DDD: 8/94). Works performed by their composers unless indicated.
Cage 30 Pieces for String Quartet – excerpts (Kronos Quartet). Dance No. 1 for Two Prepared Pianos (Patrick Moraz, Charles Turner). Concert for Piano and Orchestra – Three Solos for Trumpet (Earle Brown). Living Room Music (David Van Tieghem). 4'33" (Frank Zappa). Aria (Meredith Monk). New York City – street noises outside Cage's apartment (Steven Smith). **Jackson Mac Low/Anne Tardos** First Four-Language Word Event in Memoriam John Cage. **Christian Wolff** Six Melodies Variation for Solo Violin (Roger Zahab). **Ken Nordine** A Cage Went In Search of a Bird. **Laurie Anderson** Cunningham Stories – At the Age of Twelve ... ; Merce Cunningham Phoned His Mother ... ; Every Morning ... ; The Cunningham Company ... . **Ryuichi Sakamoto** Haiku FM. **Larry Austin/Robert Black** art is self-alteration is Cage is ... (Robert Black, db). **David Tudor** Webwork – excerpts. **Yoko Ono** Georgia Stone. **Oregon** (group composition): Chance/Choice. **Takehisa Kosugi** 75 Letters and Improvisation. **James Tenney** Ergodos I. **Robert Ashley** Factory Preset. **John Cale** In Memoriam John Cage – Call Waiting.   ⊛⊛

"Music was the main way John Cage made himself into who he was" writes David Revill, one of the many contributors to "A Chance Operation". And the Cagean aesthetic is indeed one of constantly shifting contexts for everything that 'sounds', be it interrupted silence, teeming radio signals, standard instruments employed in tonal exploration (including Cage's own prepared pianos) or that ongoing, undifferentiated improvisation that we habitually call noise. Cage remains the pivotal force, and the fulcrum for all 22 composers gathered together on these two CDs: most selections are either by him (texts or music), inspired by him or dedicated to him. His spirit is felt everywhere, yet rather than stifling or inhibiting, it served to liberate a veritable flood of invention. Indeed, it is both touching and apposite that Cage's legendary 4'33" of inhabited silence be entrusted to the late Frank Zappa who, the odd shuffle notwithstanding, simply sits by and lets it all happen. Laurie Anderson's quietly hypnotic *Cunningham Stories* (to texts by Cage himself) arrive in four short instalments, while the first CD ends with Yoko Ono's lengthy but accessible *Georgia Stone*, a montage comprising culturally significant voices (John Lennon, Martin Luther King, unnamed victims of political oppression, etc.), rhetorical sound patterns and sundry musical impressions. Then there are Meredith Monk's outlandish vocalizations, Ryuichi Sakamoto's ear-stretching *Haiku FM*, David Tudor's punishing *Webwork*, the mournful double-bass drone of *art is self-alteration is Cage is ...* by Larry Austin and Robert Black, after one of Cage's own key concepts. Koch International's method harbours an xtra ace, one that you too can play. Each work is split into a number of tracks, which means that the first disc has 11 pieces divided by 98; the second a further 11 divided by 85. By using the 'random' button on your compact disc player, you can prompt a totally 'new' programme consisting of freshly juxtaposed extracts from any of the 22 works – a sort of DIY Cage kit, and immense fun to play with.

Cage Complete Piano Music, Volume 1. Bacchanale. Totem Ancestor. And the Earth Shall Bear
   Again. Primitive. In the Name of the Holocaust. Our Spring will come. A Room. Tossed as it is
   Untroubled. The Perilous Night. Root of an Unfocus. The Unavailable Memory Of. Spontaneous
   Earth. Triple Paced. A Valentine Out of Season. Prelude for Meditation. Mysterious Adventure.
   Daughters of the Lonesome Isle. Music for Marcel Duchamp. Two Pastorales. Sonatas and
   Interludes. **Steffen Schleiermacher** (prepared pf). Dabringhaus und Grimm Ⓕ MDG613 0781-2
   (three discs: 171 minutes: DDD: 3/98). Recorded 1996.   ⊖⊖
The German composer and pianist, Steffen Schleiermacher, is a truly outstanding musician and this series of Cage's piano music is certain to become a landmark, bringing the highest performance standards to this core repertory of mid-century keyboard music. One inevitably starts by assessing the most extended work, the *Sonatas and Interludes*, although the whole set has sensibly been arranged chronologically. Schleiermacher has swept previous interpretations away with a performance of total control and admirable clarity. What a wealth of ravishing textures the prepared piano provides in discriminating hands! Right at the start of the first CD we have the *Bacchanale*, which is followed by almost completely different sonic personalities for each later piece, mostly written for Cunningham's dances. *And the Earth Shall Bear Again* sports a near-jazz-rock riff; *Primitive* sounds like suspended glass bowls of the kind used by Partch; *A Room* sounds like disembodied guitars; *Tossed as it is Untroubled* is as dry as an amplified harpsichord lute stop; and so on. *The Perilous Night* is a suite of six movements with a wide range of prepared sounds.

   The assumption that most of what Cage had to offer through the prepared piano is contained in the *Sonatas and Interludes* is further refuted when one turns to the second CD of short pieces or sets, where there are discoveries every time. *Triple Paced*, in G major, has a lively neo-classical flavour and it even includes scales; *Mysterious Adventure* employs honking sounds not heard elsewhere; but *Music for Marcel Duchamp* works with a limited gamut, rather like the mesmeric unprepared piano pieces *Dream* and *In a Landscape* from the same period. The *Two Pastorales* are from 1952, that crisis year of *4'33"*. These are the only pieces here that were written after the *Sonatas and Interludes* and after the *Concerto for prepared piano and chamber orchestra*. The preparations are only partial and there are clusters, plucked strings and whistled pitches. Cage is moving on, less given to the charm of pretty sounds and closer to abdicating intention through using chance operations: he's now more Zen than Indian. The *Two Pastorales* conclude a truly fascinating collection of the prepared piano music, enabling us to consider it whole for the first time. Excellently recorded too.

Additional recommendations ...
...The Perilous Night (1944)[a]. Four Walls (1944)[b]. [b]**Joan La Barbara** (sop); **Margaret Leng Tan**
   ([a]prepared pf; [b]pf). New Albion Ⓕ NA037CD (71 minutes: DDD: 1/92).
...In a Landscape. Music for Marcel Duchamp. Souvenir. A Valentine Out of Season. Suite for Toy
   Piano. Bacchanale. Prelude for Meditation. Dream. **Stephen Drury** (keybds).
   Catalyst Ⓕ 09026-61980-2 (59 minutes: DDD: 7/95).
...Bacchanale for Prepared Piano. In a Landscape. Daughters of the Lonesame Isle. The Seasons.
   Suite for Toy Piano. Ophelia. In the Name of the Holocaust. Music for Piano No. 2.
   Margaret Leng Tan (pfs). New Albion Ⓕ NA070CD (70 minutes: DDD: 7/95).
...Sonatas and Interludes. **Philipp Vandré** (prepared pf).
   Mode Records Ⓕ Mode50 (64 minutes: DDD: 2/97).
...Sonatas and Interludes. **Yuji Takahashi** (prepared pf).
   Fylkingen Records Ⓕ FYCD1010 (59 minutes: DDD: 2/98).
Further listening ...
...Concert for Piano and Orchestra[a]. Atlas eclipticalis. [a]**Joe Kubera** (pf); **SEM Ensemble Orchestra /**
   Petr Kotik. Wergo John Cage Edition WER6216-2 (12/93).
...13 Harmonies. *Coupled with* **Zahab** Verging Lightfall. **Roger Zahab** (vn); **Eric Moe** (pf/hpd/org).
   Koch International Classics 37130-2 (11/95).
...Roaratorio: An Irish Circus on Finnegans Wake[a]. Laughtears[b]. Writing for the Second Time
   through Finnegans Wake[a]. **John Cage**, [b]**Klaus Schöning** (spkrs); [a]**Joe Heaney** (sngr);
   [a]**Matt Malloy** (fl); [a]**Seamus Ennis** (uilleann pipes); [a]**Paddy Glackin** (vn); [a]**Peadher Mercier,**
   [a]**Mel Mercier** (bodhrans). Mode Records Mode 28/9 (10/94).   ⊖
...String Quartet in four parts. Music for four. **Arditti Quartet.** Mode Records mode27 (12/93).
...Ten. Ryoanji. Fourteen. **Ives Ensemble.** Hat-Hut Hat Now Series ARTCD6159 (2/96).
...Totem Ancestor (arr. Salzman). Quodlibet. *Coupled with works by various composers.*
   Kronos Quartet. Nonesuch Ⓕ 7559-79457-2 (69 minutes: DDD: 12/97). *Gramophone Editor's*
   choice. See review in the Collections section; refer to the Index.

...Winter Music[a]. Atlas eclipticalis[b]. [b]Eberhard Blum (fls); [a]Mats Persson, [a]Steffen Schleiermacher, [a]Kristine Scholz, [a]Nils Vigeland (pfs). Hat Hut Now Series ARTCD6141 (10/94).

...Etudes Australes. Grete Sultan (pf). Wergo WER6152-2 (7/93).

...Souvenir. *Coupled with works by* **Pärt** *and* **Scelsi** Christoph Maria Moosmann (org). New Albion NA074CD (2/96).

...Music for Three[a]. Eight Whiskus[b]. Four[c]. Joan La Barbara (sngr); [c]John Cage (voc); [ac]Leonard Stein (pf/voc/perc); [ac]William Winant (perc). Music & Arts CD875 (8/96).

Jorge Calandrelli
Argentinian 20th century

Suggested listening ...

...Tango Remembrances. *Coupled with works by* **Piazzolla** Yo-Yo Ma (vc); **Astor Piazzolla** (bandoneón). Sony Classical SK63122 (2/98). *See review under Piazzolla; refer to the Index.*

Antonio Caldara
Italian c1670-1736

Caldara Maddalena ai piedi di Cristo. **Maria-Cristina Kiehr, Rosa Dominguez** (sops); **Bernarda Fink** (contr); **Andreas Scholl** (alto); **Gerd Türk** (ten); **Ulrich Messthaler** (bass); **Schola Cantorum Basiliensis / René Jacobs.** Harmonia Mundi Ⓔ HMC90 5221/2 (two discs: 126 minutes: DDD: 11/96). Notes, text and translation included. Recorded 1995. *Gramophone Editor's choice. Gramophone Award Winner 1997.* Ⓖ

Caldara was the most prolific and famous oratorio composer of his day and this one, written around 1700, is wonderfully rich in fresh and attractive invention. Practically devoid of external action, it is dramatically tense and concentrates on the continuous struggle between the forces of good and evil, the sinner Magdalen being urged towards penitence by her sister Martha; the roles of Christ and a Pharisee are considerably smaller. The work opens in immediately arresting fashion, with an agitated sinfonia followed by the hypnotic aria "Dormi, o cara": then come another 27 brief *da capo* arias with their associated recitatives. There is no lack of variety: some arias are accompanied only by a continuo instrument; others are furnished with different usages of the five-part strings. René Jacobs furthers the dramatic impact by his pacing, of the recitatives in particular; and his casting is flawless. He has the highly effective idea of differentiating the parts of Earthly and Celestial Love by allocating the former to a mezzo and the latter to a countertenor. Both are excellent, but so are all the participants in this performance. It seems almost invidious to single out highlights but one must cite the aria "Diletti" for Magdalen (Kiehr) and the succeeding ornate "Vattene" for Martha (Dominguez) and, even more, two florid arias from Scholl rejoicing in the eventual triumph of good and two, delivered passionately by Fink, of fury by evil at its overthrow. You are urged to acquire this disc.

Further listening ...

...Cantatas[a]: Medea in Corinto. Soffri, mio caro Alcino. D'improvviso. Vicino a un rivoletto. 12 Suonate da camera, Op. 2 – No. 3 in D major. 12 Suonate a 3, Op. 1 – No. 5 in E minor. **Il Seminario Musicale / Gérard Lesne** ([a]alto). Virgin Classics Veritas VC7 59058-2 (11/91). 🎵

...Madrigals – Fra pioggie, nevi e gelo. Dell'uom la vita. Fugge di Lot a moglie. Vedi co'l crine sciolto. Là su morbide. De piacari. Cantatas – Lungi dall'idol mio; Il Dario; La forriera del giorno; Stella ria; Il Gelsomino. **Wren Baroque Soloists / Martin Elliott.** Unicorn-Kanchana DKPCD9130 (2/93). 🎵 Ⓖ

Thomas Campion
British 1567-1620

Suggested listening ...

...How hath Flora robb'd her bower. Ayres – Come let us sound with melodie the praises; Turne backe you wanton flier. Author of light, revive my dying spright. Oft have I sigh'd for him that heares me not. *Coupled with works by* **Dowland** Brian Asawa (alto); **David Tayler** (lte). RCA Victor Red Seal 09026 68818-2 (12/97). *See review in the Collections section; refer to the Index.*

...I care not for these ladies. My love hath vow'd. My sweetest Lesbia. *Coupled with works by various composers.* **Andreas Scholl** (alto); **Andreas Martin** (lte). Harmonia Mundi HMC90 1603 (9/96). *Gramophone Editor's choice. See review in the Collections section; refer to the Index.* Ⓖ

José Cano
Spanish 20th century

Suggested listening ...

...Luna – Epilogo. *Coupled with works by various composers.* **Renée Fleming** (sop); **English Chamber Orchestra / Jeffrey Tate.** Decca 458 858-2DH (3/98). *See review in the Collections section; refer to the Index. Selected by Soundings.*

Benito Canonico
Brazilian 20th century

Suggested listening ...

...Aire de Joropo (arr. Lauro/Diaz). *Coupled with works by various composers.* **Sharon Isbin** (gtr);
Gaudencio Thiago de Mello (perc). Teldec 0630-19899-2 (7/98). *Gramophone Editor's choice.*
See review in the Collections section; refer to the Index.   ⓖⓠ

Joseph Canteloube
French 1879-1957

Canteloube Chants d'Auvergne – La pastoura als camps; Baïlèro; L'ïo de rotso; Ound' onorèn
gorda; Obal, din lou Limouzi; Pastourelle; L'Antouèno; La pastrouletta è lo chibaliè; La
delïssádo; N'aï pas iéu de mio; Lo calhé; Lo fiolaïré; Passo pel prat; Lou boussu; Brezairola;
Maluros qu'o uno fenno. Jou l'pount d'o Mirabel; Oï, ayaï; Pour l'enfant; Chut, chut; Pastorale;
Lou coucut; Postouro sé tu m'aymo; Quand z-éyro petituono; Té, l'co tèl; Uno jionto postouro;
Hél beyla-z-y-dau fél; Obal, din lo combuèlo; Là-haut, sur le rocher; Lou diziou bé.
Villa-Lobos Bachianas Brasileiras No. 5. **Dame Kiri Te Kanawa** (sop); **English Chamber Orchestra /
Jeffrey Tate**. Double Decca Ⓜ 444 995-2DF2 (two discs: 111 minutes: DDD: 1/96).
Notes, text and translation included. Recorded 1982-83.   ⓖ
Although Canteloube's collection of the *Chants d'Auvergne* is well represented in the current
catalogue, Dame Kiri Te Kanawa's richly sensuous approach to these delightful songs is undoubtedly
very seductive, especially when the accompaniments by Jeffrey Tate and the ECO are so warmly
supportive and the sound so opulent. Her account of the most famous number, "Baïlièro", must be
the most relaxed on record, yet she sustains its repetitions with a sensuous, gentle beauty of line,
supported by lovely wind playing from the orchestra which seems to float in the air. There is a
resonance given to the sound, which means that certain of the brighter, more obviously folksy
numbers, lose a little of their rustic sharpness. However, there is no question that the overall effect is
very appealing, particularly when Dame Kiri's voice (recorded in the early 1980s) is so young and
fresh and the sound so lustrously beautiful. As an encore we are offered another famous lollipop
which she makes her own in the same languorous, Scheherazade-like manner – the Villa-Lobos
Bachianas Brasileiras No. 5, an "Aria" for soprano and cellos. She sings this in Portuguese and the
result is ravishing, almost decadent at its softly intoned reprise. An enticing disc.
Additional recommendations ...

...Chants d'Auvergne, Volume 1 – excerpts. **Dawn Upshaw** (sop); **Orchestra of the Opéra de Lyon /
Kent Nagano**. Erato Ⓕ 4509-96559-2 (47 minutes: DDD: 2/95).
...Chants d'Auvergne – Baïlero. *Coupled with works by various composers.* **Renée Fleming** (sop);
English Chamber Orchestra / Jeffrey Tate. Decca Ⓕ 458 858-2DH (70 minutes: DDD: 3/98).
See review in the Collections section; refer to the Index. Selected by Soundings.

Canteloube Chants d'Auvergne, Volume 2 – La pastoura als camps; Baïlèro; L'ïo dè rotso; Ound'
onorèn gorda; Obal, din lou Limouzi; L'Antouèno; La pastrouletta è lo chibaliè; N'aï pas iéu de
mio; Lo calhé; Maluros qu'o uno fenno; Pour l'enfant; Quand z-éyro petituono; Hél
beyla-z-y-dau fél; Là-haut, sur le rocher; Lou diziou bé.
Emmanuel Chansons bourguignonnes du Pays de Beaune, Op. 15 – Quand j'ai sôti de mon
villaige; Il était une fille, une fille d'honneur; Le pommier d'Août; Noël; Complainte de Notre
Dame; Aidieu, bargeire!. **Dawn Upshaw** (sop); **Orchestra of the Opéra de Lyon / Kent Nagano**.
Erato Ⓕ 0630-17577-2 (63 minutes: DDD: 10/97). Texts and translations included. Recorded
1996.
Canteloube Chants d'Auvergne – Baïlèro[a]; L'ïo dè rotso[a]; Ound' onorèn gorda[a]; Obal, din lou
Limouzi[a]; L'Antouèno[a]; La delïssádo[a]; N'aï pas iéu de mio[a]; Lo calhé[a]; Lo fiolaïré[a]; Passo pel
prat[a]; Brezairola[a]; Oï, ayaï[a]; Pour l'enfant[a]; Chut, chut[a]; Lou coucut[a]; Tè, l'co, tè[a]; Uno jionto
postouro[a]; La pastoura als camps[b]; Pastourelle[b]; La pastrouletta è lo chibaliè[b]; Lou boussu[b];
Malurous qu'o uno fenno[b]; Jou l'pount d'o Mirabel[b]; Pastorale[b]. **Frederica von Stade** (mez);
Royal Philharmonic Orchestra / Antonio de Almeida. Sony Classical Essential Classics
Ⓑ SBK63063 (73 minutes: DDD: 10/97). Items marked [a] from CBS 37299 (2/83), recorded 1982,
[b]CBS IM37837 (7/86), recorded 1985.
Let us start with the unfamiliar. Having finished her tour of the Auvergne, Dawn Upshaw completes
this recital disc by foraging into less well-charted territory. A selection of songs from another area of
France, the Pays de Beaune, makes a neat idea for a filler, as Maurice Emmanuel's arrangements of
his local Burgundian folk-songs are obvious antecedents to what Canteloube was to do a decade or
two later. Although none of these songs seems destined to become a popular hit, the pithier style does
have its attractions. This is the second disc that Dawn Upshaw has devoted primarily to Canteloube's
Songs of the Auvergne. The favourites not included there, such as "Baïlèro", now turn up here, so this
second recital makes the natural first choice of the two. Before they started, Upshaw and Nagano
seem to have taken a conscious decision to re-establish a link with the music's folk texts and banish as
much sentimentality as they can. Their "Baïlèro" is keenly dramatized and positively refuses to
wallow. The simple "Pour l'enfant" is bright-eyed with detail; and "L'ïo dè rotso" is given a more
sarcastic edge than usual. In general, there is a grittiness to the performances here that sets them apart

from most other recordings, thanks to Upshaw's determination to put across the words and Nagano's restraint in the orchestra, encouraging cool strings to let the bright Lyon wind section pipe through clearly. Perhaps we do scent more of the smells of the countryside in this version.

The Sony selection with Frederica von Stade is an old friend. Two sets of recordings have been combined and all the best-known songs are here in more conventional performances than are found on the Erato disc. Von Stade varies her tone according to the sense of each song, but the overall mood is less sharp, more comfortable if you like, than with Upshaw. The Royal Philharmonic Orchestra sound a lot richer than their Lyon counterparts and, at generally slower speeds, Antonio de Almeida provides big-orchestra accompaniments, where Nagano prefers chamber-music detail. The record-buying public will probably find that the consoling romanticism of the *Songs of the Auvergne*, as they appear on this tried-and-trusted disc, is more what they had in mind.

Lourenço da Capiba
Brazilian 1904

Suggested listening ...
...*Toada e desafio. Coupled with works by various composers.* **Quinteto da Paraíba.** Nimbus NI5483 (10/96). *See review in the Collection section; refer to the Index.*

André Caplet
French 1878-1925

Caplet Suite Persane – Nihavend. Légende pour Orchestre. Marche triomphale et pompière. **Debussy** (orch. Caplet) Children's Corner. Pagodes. Suite bergamasque – Clair de lune.
Rheinland-Pfalz State Philharmonic Orchestra / Leif Segerstam. Marco Polo Ⓕ 8 223751 (56 minutes: DDD: 9/95). Recorded 1987.

The valuable services that André Caplet rendered his friend Debussy – besides the pieces orchestrated here he also completed *Gigues* and *Boîte à joujoux*, scored the *Martyre de Saint-Sébastien* and conducted its first performance – have overshadowed his own gifts as a composer. Colour plays a large part in Caplet's early (1901) *Nihavend*, despite its having originally been scored only for double wind quintet: it is a kind of Rimskian passacaglia or set of variations on a simple, and apparently authentic, Persian melody. The *Légende* of four years later is also an orchestral expansion, from a nonet: a solo saxophone has a prominent role in both versions. Highly charged emotionally and clearly structured, it is disquieting in mood: like the previous piece, it has nothing Debussian about it. The Debussy items are well done, especially *Pagodes*, which culminates in a shimmering web of exotic sound with its combination of celesta, string trills and *glissandos* in contrary motion from two harps. Although the violins are not always totally, in general the performances are very persuasive.

Caplet Conte fantastique[a]. Les prières[b]. Deux Divertissements[c]. Deux Sonnets[d]. Septet à cordes vocales et instrumentales[e]. Septet[e]. [be]**Sharon Coste,** [de]**Sandrine Piau** (sops); [e]**Sylvie Deguy** (mez); [acd]**Laurence Cabel** (hp); [abe]**Ensemble Musique Oblique.** Harmonia Mundi Musique d'abord Ⓑ HMA190 1417 (55 minutes: DDD: 7/97). Recorded 1992.

The music of André Caplet is particularly haunting, and surely few listeners will fail to respond to the evocative opening of the harp version of his *Conte fantastique* for harp and strings based on Poe's *Masque of the Red Death*. It is dramatic too, but far from lurid in its menace, with the harp itself chiming to represent Death. The other three major works on this disc are even more appealing and often quite ravishing: *Les prières*, for soprano and string quartet; *Deux Sonnets* for soprano and harp; plus the *Septet à cordes vocales et instrumentales* in which both sopranos, plus mezzo-soprano (Sylvie Deguy) are richly integrated into, and juxtaposed with, the string quartet. In short the composer makes a memorable success of this combination of voices and strings, helped by lovely singing, sensitive playing, and warmly atmospheric sound. Two solo *Divertissements* for harp make a central interlude. If you enjoy Ravel's chamber music, you are bound to respond to this captivating Caplet anthology.

Further listening ...
...*Rêverie. Coupled with works by various composers.* **Anna Noakes** (fl); **Gillian Tingay** (hp). ASV White Line CDWHL2101 (11/96). *See review in the Collections section; refer to the Index.*
...*Myrrha. Tout est lumière. Coupled with works by* **Debussy** *and* **Ravel** Soloists; **Chorus and Orchestra of the Sorbonne, Paris / Jacques Grimbert.** Marco Polo 8 223755 (10/95).

Manuel Cardoso
Portuguese 1566-1650

Cardoso Missa Miserere mihi Domine. Magnificat Secundi Toni. **Ensemble Vocal Européen / Philippe Herreweghe.** Harmonia Mundi Ⓕ HMC90 1543 (52 minutes: DDD: 5/97). Texts and translations included. Recorded 1994. *Gramophone Editor's choice.* Ⓖ

One wonders what the seventeenth-century Portuguese composer Manuel Cardoso, for most of his life a monk at a Carmelite monastery in Lisbon, would have made of the idea that his music would enjoy a revival in the 1990s? This recording of his *Missa Miserere mihi Domine* (a first) from the

Ensemble Vocal Européen is a further – and very welcome – contribution to our knowledge and appreciation of the flowering of sacred polyphony in Portugal in the first half of the seventeenth century, music that, seen in a wider European context, seems "out of phase with its time" (to quote the accompanying notes). With music as fine as this, however, any latter-day perception of an unbroken line of musical progress seems completely irrelevant. Cardoso's setting, highly reminiscent of Victoria with its never-ending sequence of suspensions, is up there with the best. Only the more straightforward, five-voice *Magnificat* lightens the tone of a disc that otherwise wallows in glorious misery. The choir sing superbly, responding sensitively to the words and creating a full and sonorous sound that well suits Cardoso's music. Full credit, too, to Herreweghe – and the Harmonia Mundi technicians – for achieving such an exceptionally satisfactory balance between the voice parts.

Additional recommendations ...

...Magnificat Secundi Toni. Requiem. Non mortui. Sitivit anima mea. Mulier quae erat. Nos autem gloriari. **The Tallis Scholars / Peter Phillips.** Gimell Ⓕ 454 921-2PH (70 minutes: DDD: 10/90).

...Magnificat secundi toni. Lamentatio. *Coupled with works by various composers.* **Ars Nova / Bo Holten.** Naxos Ⓢ 8 553310 (63 minutes: DDD: 3/96).

Further listening ...

...Magnificat Primi Toni. *Coupled with works by various composers.* **La Colombina.** Accent ACC9394D (8/94).

...Missa Regina caeli. Sitivit anima mea. Tulerunt lapides. Non mortui. *Coupled with works by* **D. Lôbo** The Sixteen / **Harry Christophers.** Collins Classics 1407-2 (8/94).

Richard de Bellengues Cardot   French 1380-1470

Suggested listening ...

...Pour une fois et pour toute *Coupled with works by various composers.* **Gothic Voices / Christopher Page.** Hyperion CDA66783 (1/96). *See review in the Collections section; refer to the Index.*

Jan Carlstedt   Swedish 1926

Suggested listening ...

...String Trio, Op. 5. Divertimento for Oboe and String Trio, Op. 17. Ballata, Op. 18. Metamorphoses. **Bengt Rosengren** (ob); **Tobias Carron** (fl); **Mats Zetterqvist** (vn); **Håkan Olsson** (va); **Torleif Thedéen, Ewa Rydström** (vcs). Phono Suecia PSCD101 (1/98).

Andrew Carter   British 20th century

Suggested listening ...

...Toccata on Veni Emmanuel. *Coupled with works by various composers.* **St Paul's Cathedral Choir / John Scott** (org). Hyperion CDA66994 (12/97). *See review in the Collections section; refer to the Index.*

Elliott Carter   American 1908

Carter Piano Concerto[a]. Concerto for Orchestra. Three Occasions. [a]**Ursula Oppens** (pf); **South West German Radio Symphony Orchestra / Michael Gielen.** Arte Nova Classics Ⓢ 74321 27773-2 (62 minutes: DDD).

Oppens and Gielen have collaborated in a recording of the Piano Concerto before, and their long familiarity with the work brings an air of confidence to an account which is admirable in its feeling for the essential character as well as the formal logic of a score whose shoals of notes will defeat all but the most dedicated of interpreters. Gielen's ability to bring a convincing sense of shape and a persuasive expressive profile to complex music is no less apparent in an admirable reading of the *Concerto for Orchestra.* Again and again, the solo lines marked in the score are brought out, although the recording isn't able to give ideal clarity to the highly detailed string writing (a compositional problem, perhaps). But Gielen's is as compelling a presentation of this turbulent yet strangely affirmative music as one could hope to hear. In *Three Occasions* Gielen (in what appears to be a public performance, though the booklet makes no mention of it) is weighty, perhaps to excess in the often delicate third piece. Nevertheless, the interpretation is full of character, and the orchestra confirm their excellence in this demanding repertory. Recommended, despite the inadequate insert-notes.

Additional recommendation ...

...Piano Concerto[a]. Variations for Orchestra. [a]**Ursula Oppens** (pf); **Cincinnati Symphony Orchestra / Michael Gielen.** New World Ⓕ NW347-2 (45 minutes: DDD: 4/87).

Further listening ...

...Partita. *Coupled with works by* **Berio** and **Takemitsu** Chicago Symphony Orchestra / **Daniel Barenboim.** Teldec 4509-99596-2 (8/95).

...Gra. Enchanted Preludes. Duo. Scrivo in Vento. Changes. Con Leggerezza Pensosa: Omaggio a Italo Calvino. Riconoscenza per Goffredo Petrassi. Cello Sonata. **The Group for Contemporary Music.** Bridge BCD9044 (12/94).
...Emblems. The harmony of morning. Heart not so heavy as mine. Musicians wrestle everywhere. *Coupled with works by various composers.* **John Oliver Chorale / John Oliver.** Koch International Classics 37178-2 (5/95).

Ferdinando Carulli Italian 1770-1841

Suggested listening ...
...Andante affetuoso, Op. 320. *Coupled with works by various composers.* **Marta Almajano** (sop); **José Miguel Moreno** (gtr). Glossa GCD920202 (2/96). *See review in the Collections section; refer to the Index.*

Robert Carver British c1490-1550

Carver Missa Dum sacrum mysterium. O bone Jesu. Magnificat (attrib.). **The Sixteen / Harry Christophers.** Collins Classics Ⓕ 1478-2 (68 minutes: DDD: 7/97). Texts and translations included. Recorded 1996.
The music enjoyed by the royal houses of Scotland reached a peak around the year 1513.The young Robert Carver most probably composed his Mass, *Dum sacrum mysterium*, for the coronation of the infant King James V, which took place on the Feast of St Michael, September 29th, 1513. Such an occasion was a gift for a young composer, and called for exuberance and rejoicing. The Sixteen give a magnificent performance, revelling in Carver's boldly architectural design, but also delightfully articulating the lighter passages with groups of solo voices of varying tessitura. The dovetailing and balance are well judged, and St Jude's Church, Hampstead offers a surprisingly clear acoustic: every detail is audible. The Mass is preceded by the *Magnificat* antiphon upon which it is based, and which would normally have been sung at First Vespers by the Canons. Carver's 19-voice votive antiphon, *O bone Jesu*, is sung with passion. It is a liturgical curiosity, almost too embarrassingly a personal devotion to be suitable for public worship. As for the anonymous *Magnificat*, this is of interest to the musical historian, as it is an example of the use of a faburden tenor as a cantus firmus. So much of interest, such fine singing in a clean and clear acoustic: what more could one desire?
Additional recommendation ...
...Missa Dum sacrum mysterium. O bone Jesu. Gaude flore virginali. **Cappella Nova / Alan Tavener.** ASV Gaudeamus Ⓕ CDGAU124 (62 minutes: DDD: 10/91).
Further listening ...
...Missa L'Homme armé. Mass for Six Voices. **Cappella Nova / Alan Tavener.** ASV Gaudeamus CDGAU126 (10/91).
...Missa Fera pessima. Missa Pater creator omnium. **Cappella Nova / Alan Tavener.** ASV Gaudeamus CDGAU127 (5/92).

Doreen Carwithen British 1922

Carwithen Overtures – ODTAA, "One damn thing after another"; Bishop Rock. Concerto for Piano and Strings[a]. Suffolk Suite. [a]**Howard Shelley** (pf); **London Symphony Orchestra / Richard Hickox.** Chandos Ⓕ CHAN9524 (58 minutes: DDD: 5/97). Recorded 1996.
Doreen Carwithen, vigorous in her music as well as warmly lyrical, hid her light for over 40 years, selflessly devoting herself instead to the music of her husband, William Alwyn. Her music relates more to that of Walton than of Alwyn. *ODTAA*, suggested by John Masefield's novel of that name, was her first full orchestral work to be performed, premièred in 1947, a flamboyant piece full of striking ideas, with Waltonian echoes spiced with one or two of Stravinsky and even of the pastoral Vaughan Williams. She learnt her trade practically over the following years as a film composer, producing some 30 scores. The wonder of the delightful, unpretentious little *Suffolk Suite* is that though this is music written for schoolchildren to play, you would hardly guess that from the richness of the scoring. The *Bishop Rock* Overture, premièred in 1952, opens as a craggy sea-picture, vividly evocative, lashed by vigorous syncopations. The main theme is later transformed to show the sea in gentle but menacing mood, with the cor anglais especially evocative. By far the longest work is the Concerto for piano and strings of 1948, which, despite a bald opening in bare octaves, belies any expectation of a limited work, with strong, virtuoso piano writing set against richly textured strings. Here, too, the argument is always inventive, with themes colourfully transformed, easily sustaining its length; the first movement alone lasts 12 minutes and the other two just over eight minutes each. The deeply melancholy slow movement is dominated by a solo violin, in parallel with the piano, accompanied by muted strings. But then the finale contrasts chattering, sharply rhythmic passages with warmly lyrical sections. Howard Shelley as soloist responds strongly to the purposefulness of the writing, as do Hickox and the LSO.

Further listening ...
...String Quartets[a] – No. 1; No. 2. Violin Sonata[b]. [b]**Lydia Mordkovitch** (vn); [b]**Julian Milford** (pf); [a]**Sorrel Quartet.** Chandos CHAN9596 (3/98).

Alfredo Casella
Italian 1883-1947

Suggested listening ...
...Paganiniana, Op. 65. *Coupled with works by* **Busoni** *and* **Martucci** La Scala Philharmonic Orchestra, Milan / Riccardo Muti. Sony Classical SK53280 (4/94). *See review under Busoni; refer to the Index.* ⓖⓖⓖ
...Harp Sonata, Op. 68. *Coupled with works by various composers.* **Naoko Yoshino** (hp). Philips 446 064-2PH (2/96). *See review in the Collections section; refer to the Index.*

John Casken
British 1949

Suggested listening ...
...Sharp Thorne. *Coupled with works by various composers.* **The Hilliard Ensemble.** ECM New Series 453 259-2 (1/97). *See review in the Collections section; refer to the Index.*

Gaspar Cassadó
Spanish 1896-1966

Suggested listening ...
...Requiebros (arr. Berkovitz). *Coupled with works by various composers.* **Sequeira Costa, Artur Pizarro** (pfs). Collins Classics 1466-2 (10/96). *See review in the Collections section; refer to the Index.* ⓖ

Dario Castello
Italian 1590-1644

Suggested listening ...
...Sonate concertate in still moderno – Sonata duodecima. *Coupled with works by various composers.* **His Majestys Sagbutts and Cornetts.** Hyperion CDA66847 (11/96). *See review in the Collections section; refer to the Index.*

Mario Castelnuovo-Tedesco
Italian/American 1895-1968

Castelnuovo-Tedesco Guitar Concerto No. 1 in D major, Op. 99.
Rodrigo Concierto de Aranjuez.
Villa-Lobos Guitar Concerto. **Norbert Kraft** (gtr); **Northern Chamber Orchestra / Nicholas Ward.** Naxos Ⓢ 8 550729 (60 minutes: DDD: 4/94). Recorded 1992.
The time has long passed when it was possible to point to any one recording of any of these concertos (the Rodrigo in particular) as 'The Best'; as with players, one can only discern a 'top bracket' within which choice depends finally on personal preference – or allegiance to one's favourite performer, or indeed with the other works on the disc. Norbert Kraft's accounts of these concertos takes its place therein. In this recording Kraft is placed forwardly enough for every detail to be heard, but not to create an impression of artificiality. The Northern Chamber Orchestra plays with freshness and are alert to every detail and the beautifully clear recording catches it faithfully. At super-budget price this disc is an exceptional bargain.
Further listening ...
...Violin Concerto No. 2, "I profeti". *Coupled with works by various composers.* **Jascha Heifetz** (vn); **Joseph de Pasquale** (va); **Gregor Piatigorsky** (vc); **Lilian Steuber** (pf); **Los Angeles Philharmonic Orchestra / Alfred Wallenstein.** RCA Victor Gold Seal GD87872 (9/90). ⓖⓖⓖ
...Sonata, Op. 77, "omaggio a Boccherini". *Coupled with works by* **José** *and* **Paganini** **Julian Bream** (gtr). EMI CDC5 55362-2 (11/96).
...Tonadilla, sur le nom de Andrés Segovia, Op. 170 No. 5. *Coupled with works by various composers.* **Elliot Fisk** (gtr). MusicMasters 67174-2 (4/97). *See review in the Collections section; refer to the Index.*

Cavadia

Suggested listening ...
...Umbra. *Coupled with works by various composers.* **Angela Gheorghiu** (sop); **Malcolm Martineau** (pf). Decca 458 360-2DH (5/98). *See review in the Collections section; refer to the Index.*

Emmanuel Chabrier

Chabrier España. Suite pastorale. Joyeuse marche. Bourrée fantasque. Le Roi malgré lui – Fête polonaise; Danse slave. Gwendoline – Overture.
Roussel Suite in F major, Op. 33. **Detroit Symphony Orchestra / Paul Paray.**
Mercury Ⓜ 434 303-2MM* (68 minutes: ADD). Recorded 1957-60.   ⒼⒼⒼ
Paray's classic Chabrier collection radiates a truly life-enhancing spontaneity, an all-too-rare commodity in this day and age. His *España* has to be one of the most twinklingly good-humoured ever committed to disc – an account overflowing with rhythmic panache and unbuttoned exuberance – whilst the adorable *Suite pastorale* has rarely sounded so fresh-faced and sheerly disarming, even though Paray's very swift "Sous bois" does admittedly take some getting use to. The excerpts from *Le Roi malgré lui* are dispatched with memorable theatrical charisma and huge gusto, qualities which extend to a blistering rendition of the remarkable, almost feverish overture to *Gwendoline*. But Paray reserves perhaps his finest achievement for the uproarious *Joyeuse marche* and *Bourrée fantasque* (an astonishingly quick-witted, vital conception). The orchestra respond with irrepressible spirit and characteristic Gallic poise, and the Mercury engineering astonishes in its intrepidly wide range of dynamic and full-blooded brilliance (just sample those wonderfully hefty bass-drum thwacks towards the end of *España*). All this and Roussel's bustling, neo-classical *Suite* too! An irresistible confection.

Additional recommendations ...
...Joyeuse marche. Suite pastorale. Bourrée fantasque. España. Gwendoline – Overture. Le roi malgré lui – Danse slave. **French National Orchestra / Armin Jordan.**
Erato Ⓜ 4509-96370-2 (54 minutes: DDD).
...España. Suite pastorale. **Dukas** L'apprenti sorcier. La péri. **Ulster Orchestra /**
Yan Pascal Tortelier. Chandos Ⓕ CHAN8852 (57 minutes: DDD: 2/91).
...Suite pastorale. Habanera. España. Larghetto[a]. Prélude pastoral. Joyeuse marche. Gwendoline – Overture. Le Roi malgré lui – Fête polonaise. [a]**Ronald Janezic (hn); Vienna Philharmonic Orchestra / Sir John Eliot Gardiner.** DG Ⓕ 447 751-2GH (66 minutes: DDD: 10/96).
Gramophone Editor's choice. Selected by Soundings.   Ⓖ

Chabrier Dix Pièces pittoresques. Pièces posthumes. Impromptu in C major. Trois valses romantiques (with Elizabeth Burley, pf). **Kathryn Stott** (pf). Unicorn-Kanchana Ⓕ DKPCD9158 (74 minutes: DDD: 5/95). Recorded 1994.   ⒼⒼ
Listening to these delectable performances of piano pieces by Chabrier it is easy to see why alert musical minds like Ravel and Poulenc held him in such admiration. Cortot declared that his style of piano writing was unique; this may have been partly due to Chabrier's brilliance in keyboard improvisation, a talent which he was delighted to show off, and whose sometimes unstructured nature is illustrated in No. 8 of the *Pièces pittoresques* and, more particularly, in his early *Impromptu* in C major (described by Poulenc as "ravishing") and also in the "Caprice" of the *Pièces posthumes*. Throughout the disc Kathryn Stott is at her most sparkling and subtle best, with ebullient gaiety in the "Scherzo-valse", fragile delicacy in the gentle "Sous bois", rhythmic gusto in the "Danse villageoise", quiet lyricism in "Idylle" (all from the *Pièces pittoresques*), and wistful charm in "Feuillet d'album" and enchanting lightness in "Ballabile" (from the *Pièces posthumes*): there is freshness and imaginative nuance in evidence everywhere. She is joined by Elizabeth Burley in neat, scintillatingly spirited performances of the two-piano *Trois valses romantiques* – only the third of which really lives up to its title (with playful filigree decoration): the Second is coquettishly lyrical, the First just sheer fun. Aided by first-class recording, this is an immensely enjoyable disc.

Additional recommendations ...
...Dix Pièces pittoresques. Pièces posthumes – Ballabile; Caprice; Feuillet d'album. Bourrée fantasque. Petite valse. Habanera. **Georges Rabol** (pf).
Naxos Ⓢ 8 553009 (56 minutes: DDD: 2/95).
...Trois valses romantiques. Cortège burlesque. *Coupled with works by various composers.*
Walter Klien, Rena Kyriakou (pfs).
Carlton Classics Turnabout Ⓑ 30371 0014-2 (78 minutes: ADD: 10/96).

Further listening ...
...Piano Works, Volume 2 – Marche des Cipayes. Julia, Op. 1. Impromptu in C major. Pièces posthumes – Aubade; Ronde Champêtre. Capriccio in C sharp minor. Souvenirs de Brunehaut.
Georges Rabol (pf). Naxos 8 553010 (2/95).
...Piano Works, Volume 3 – España. Trois Valses romantiques. Prélude. Marche française. Cortège burlesque[a]. Souvenirs de Munich: quadrille on themes from "Tristan und Isolde" (Wagner)[a].
Air de ballet[a]. Suite de valses[a]. **Georges Rabol, **[a]**Sylvie Dugas** (pfs). Naxos 8 553080 (2/95).
...L'étoile – O petite étoile; Je suis Lazuli!. *Coupled with works by various composers.* **Lesley Garrett** (sop); **Crouch End Festival Chorus; Royal Philharmonic Concert Orchestra / James Holmes.**
Silva Screen Classics SILKTVCD1 (2/96). *Gramophone Award Winner 1996. See review in the Collections section; refer to the Index.*
...Lied. Toutes les fleurs. *Coupled with works by various composers.* **Dame Felicity Lott** (sop);
Graham Johnson (pf). Hyperion CDA66937 (10/97). *See review in the Collections section; refer to the Index.*

...Briséïs. **Soloists; Scottish Opera Chorus; BBC Scottish Symphony Orchestra / Jean Yves Ossonce.**
Hyperion CDA66803 (8/95).
...Le Roi malgré lui. **Soloists; French Radio Chorus; French Radio New Philharmonic Orchestra /**
Charles Dutoit. Erato 2292-45792-2.

George Whitefield Chadwick

American 1854-1931

Chadwick Suite symphonique in E flat major. Aphrodite. Elegy: "in memoriam Horatio Parker".
Czech State Philharmonic Orchestra / José Serebrier. Reference Recordings Ⓕ RRCD74
(72 minutes: DDD: 6/97).
This is a landmark for Chadwick, since all three works are virtually unknown and these are first
recordings. The *Suite symphonique* (1909) sounds surprisingly like Elgar, especially in this key, since
both composers drew on similar continental sources. Chadwick commands his own dialect in this
mainstream European idiom and brings a distinctive sense of humour. He knew all about whole-tone
scales in Debussy but makes fun of them in the "Intermezzo and Humoreske". *Aphrodite* (1912) is a
full-blown, half-hour symphonic poem based on a classical Greek statue taken to Boston's Museum
of Fine Arts. The *Suite symphonique* is rooted in early Wagner, but *Aphrodite* draws with equal
conviction on *Tristan* or even Franck. Horatio Parker was Chadwick's pupil – he finally sent him to
Rheinberger – and Ives's teacher at Yale. The *Elegy* is dignified and restrained, a New Englander's
expression of grief. Chadwick was not an original composer. In many ways he exemplified the
Germanic subservience that Charles Ives hated and later generations of Americans went to Paris to
avoid. But what tips the balance in his favour here is the outstanding quality of these performances
under Serebrier, brilliantly recorded too.
Further listening ...
...Symphonic Sketches. Melpomene – overture. Tam O'Shanter. **Czech State Philharmonic**
Orchestra / José Serebrier. Reference Recordings RRCD-64 (2/96).
...Symphonic Sketches. Symphony No. 2 in B flat major. **Detroit Symphony Orchestra /**
Neeme Järvi. Chandos CHAN9334 (4/95).
...Symphony No. 2 in B flat major. *Coupled with* **H. Parker** A Northern Ballad, Op. 49.
Albany Symphony Orchestra / Julius Heygi. New World NW339-2 (9/87).
...Symphony No. 3 in F major. *Coupled with works by* **Barber** Detroit Symphony Orchestra /
Neeme Järvi. Chandos CHAN9253 (10/94).

Cécile Chaminade

French 1857-1944

Chaminade Piano Sonata in C minor, Op. 21. Rigaudon, Op. 55 No. 6. Les Sylvains, Op. 60.
Arabesque, Op. 61. Prelude in D minor, Op. 84 No. 3. Troisième Valse brillante, Op. 80.
Inquiétude, Op. 87 No. 3. Quatrième Valse, Op. 91. Valse-Ballet, Op. 112. Album des Enfants –
Book 1, Op. 123: No. 4, Rondeau; No. 5, Gavotte; No. 9, Orientale; No. 10, Tarantelle; Book 2,
Op. 126: No. 1, Idylle; No. 2, Aubade; No. 9, Patrouille; No. 10, Villanelle. Le passé, Op. 127
No. 3. Cortège (Fragment), Op. 143. Sérénade espagnole, Op. 150. **Peter Jacobs** (pf).
Hyperion Ⓕ CDA66846 (74 minutes: DDD: 11/96). Recorded 1995.
Cécile Chaminade's craftsmanship, talent for graceful melodic inventiveness, easy natural charm and
effective keyboard writing are indisputable even by those whose tastes are for more elaborate or more
solid fare. This volume from Peter Jacobs offers eight of her children's pieces of Opp. 123 and 126 –
small but far from the conventional pap so often palmed off on children, as is shown by the
scintillating *Tarantelle* (which is not all that easy!). There are more substantial concert works here too:
the emotional *Le passé*, the once very popular *Sérénade espagnole* which Kreisler took up, and the
immensely engaging *Troisième Valse brillante*. Since Chaminade is usually thought of as a miniaturist,
however, the big eye-opener here is a relatively early C minor Sonata which, if not a masterpiece,
reveals that as well as knowing her Chopin and Schumann she had a firm sense of form and an
enviable abundance of ideas; the lyrical *Andante* is unexpectedly thoughtful, and the spirited finale
goes well beyond Norman Demuth's rather patronizing remark that she was "nearly a genius who
knew what and how to write for pianists of moderate ability" – which perhaps is best exemplified here
in a brilliant D minor *Prelude* that sounds harder than it is. As before, Peter Jacobs shows himself to
be fluent, clean-fingered, elegantly delicate where required, and able to invest the music with fine
nuances of tone and pace – an ideal interpreter of Chaminade.
Additional recommendation ...
...Sérénade espagnole (arr. Kreisler). Piano Trios – No. 1 in G minor, Op. 11; No. 2 in A minor,
Op. 34. Ritournelle (arr. Marcus). Serenade, Op. 29 (arr. Cottin/Marcus). Pastorale enfantine,
Op. 12 (arr. Marcus). **Tzigane Piano Trio.** ASV Ⓕ CDDCA965 (57 minutes: DDD: 8/96).
Further listening ...
...Air à danser, Op. 164. Air de ballet, Op. 30. Contes bleus No. 2, Op. 122. Danse créole, Op. 94.
Six Etudes de concert, Op. 35 – No. 2, Automne. Feuillets d'album, Op. 98 – No. 4, Valse
arabesque. Guitare, Op. 32. La lisonjera, Op. 50. Lolita, Op. 54. Minuetto, Op. 23. Pas des
écharpes, Op. 37. Pas des sylphes: Intermezzo. Piéces humoristques, Op. 87 – No. 4, Autrefois.

Pierette, Op. 41. Romances sans paroles, Op. 76 – No. 1, Souvenance; No. 3 Idyll; No. 6, Méditation. Sérénade, Op. 29. Sous le masque, Op. 116. Toccata, Op. 39. **Eric Parkin** (pf). Chandos CHAN8888 (8/91).
...Arlequine, Op. 53. Poème romantique, Op. 7 No. 1. Chanson Brétonne. Divertisse-ment, Op. 105. Six Pièces humoristiques, Op. 87 – Sous bois; Consolation. Passacaille in E major, Op. 130. Nocturne, Op. 165. Scherzo-Valse, Op. 148. Etude symphonique, Op. 28. Feuillets d'Album, Op. 98 – Elégie. Gigue in D major, Op. 43. Au pays dévasté, Op. 155. Pastorale, Op. 114. Libellules, Op. 24. Valse tendre, Op. 119. Tristesse in C sharp minor, Op. 104. Six Etudes do concert, Op. 35 – Impromptu; Tarantella. **Peter Jacobs** (pf). Hyperion CDA66706 (11/94).

Brian Chapple
British 1945

Suggested listening ...
...Ecce lignum Crucis. *Coupled with works by various composers.* **St Paul's Cathedral Choir / John Scott** with **Andrew Lucas** (org). Hyperion CDA66916 (A/97). *See review in the Collections section; refer to the Index.*

Gustave Charpentier
French 1860-1956

G. Charpentier Louise. **Berthe Monmart** (sop) Louise; **André Laroze** (ten) Julien; **Louis Musy** (bar) Father; **Solange Michel** (mez) Mother; **Paris Opéra-Comique Chorus and Orchestra / Jean Fournet.** Philips mono Ⓜ 442 082-2PM3* (three discs: 163 minutes: ADD: 9/94). Notes, text and translation included. Recorded 1956. ⒼⒼ
This recording has the air of authority and authenticity throughout. All the principals were members of the company at the Opéra-Comique during the 1950s, when Jean Fournet was its Music Director. The appropriately-named Berthe Monmart who sings the title-role may not be the soprano of one's dreams, but her singing is full of charm, and she manages moments such as the leap to a soft high G at "des pétales de roses" in the opening love duet without apparent strain. Of course, every prima donna has recorded "Depuis le jour" (Melba, Callas, Price, Caballé, Sutherland, the list is endless) and it is useless to suggest that Monmart has such vocal allure, but she achieves complete conviction. All the singers have well-nigh perfect diction – essential in this supreme example of French *verismo*. What genius Charpentier mustered for this one work. When the Father makes his entrance in Act 1, to his 'tired' music and asks if the soup is ready, the psychological portrait is completed – mother/father/daughter, caught in this early picture of youth in rebellion. Musy's career had begun in the 1920s, and he had sung the entire baritone repertory at the Opéra-Comique before becoming its director of productions. André Laroze is the real thing – a French tenor. In the duet that follows "Depuis le jour" he and Monmart get up steam in fine ecstatic fashion. Fournet's pacing of the score achieves excitement at the climactic moments, the lovers' duets, Louise's almost hysterical apostrophe to Paris in the closing scene, while making the faintly mystical opening of Act 2 a miniature poem, with its street cries and little ripples of *chanson*. The mono sound is amazingly vivid – you are swept along by its fresh sense of theatricality and by the true *opéra-comique* style of all concerned.
Additional recommendations ...
...Soloists; **Ambrosian Opera Chorus; New Philharmonia Orchestra / Georges Prêtre.** Sony Classical Ⓕ S3K46429 (three discs: 172 minutes: ADD: 6/91).
...Louise – Depuis le jour. *Coupled with works by various composers.* **Renée Fleming** (sop); **English Chamber Orchestra / Jeffrey Tate.** Decca Ⓕ 458 858-2DH (70 minutes: DDD: 3/98). *See review in the Collections section; refer to the Index. Selected by Soundings.*

Marc-Antoine Charpentier
French 1643-1704

Charpentier Leçons de Ténèbres du Vendredi Saint. **Agnès Mellon** (sop); **Ian Honeyman** (ten); **Jacques Bona** (bar); **Il Seminario Musicale / Gérard Lesne** (alto). Virgin Classics Veritas Ⓕ VC7 59295-2 (71 minutes: DDD: 9/95). ✍ Texts and translations included. Recorded 1994.
Charpentier wrote many settings of the *Tenebrae*, or *Leçons de Ténèbres* as they were known in France, and they invariably inspired him to great heights of expressive intensity. Their texts come from the *Lamentations of Jeremiah the Prophet*, but are interspersed with affective, ornamental, melismatic phrases inspired by letters of the Hebrew alphabet. In addition to the *Leçons* the sequence includes Antiphons and Responses as well as plainchants with their faburdens for the Psalms, and occasional instrumental ritornellos. Not quite all of this music is by Charpentier. There are, for instance, pieces by Nivers, one of the greatest French organists of the time, included in the sequence; but though most of the assembled chants with their harmonizing faburdens were common property of the Catholic Church throughout Europe, one faburden at least is by Charpentier (H156). The French baroque *Leçons de Ténèbres* are deeply moving, with their distinctive blend of Italian monodic *lamentazioni* and French *air de cour*. The idiom allows for dramatically highly charged effects and, in the hands of composers like Charpentier and Couperin, such effects are often realized with thrilling suspensions,

dissonances and impassioned declamation. Indeed, with Charpentier one often senses the composer's love for, and experience in writing for, the stage in the many theatrical gestures and in his vividly depictive handling of the texts. Certainly this highly emotive blend of sacred and secular ingredients resulted in music of extraordinary intensity, none of which is lost on Gérard Lesne and his ensemble, Il Seminario Musicale. His style presents no problems for these artists; they are sensible to the myriad expressive nuances suggested by the texts and realized in music of reflective intensity.

Additional recommendations ...

...Leçons de Ténèbres du Mercredi Saint. **Catherine Greuillet, Caroline Pelon** (sops); **Christopher Purves** (bass); **Il Seminario Musicale / Gérard Lesne** (alto). Virgin Classics Veritas Ⓕ VC5 45107-2 (64 minutes: DDD: 9/95). ✍

...Leçons de Ténèbres du Jeudi Saint. **Sandrine Piau** (sop); **Gérard Lesne** (alto); **Ian Honeyman** (ten); **Peter Harvey** (bass); **Il Seminario Musicale / Gérard Lesne** (alto). Virgin Classics Veritas Ⓕ VC5 45075-2 (66 minutes: DDD: 9/95). ✍

Charpentier Te Deum, H147. Mass, H1. Precatio pro filio regis, H166. Panis quem ego dabo, H275. Canticum Zachariae, H345, "Benedictus Dominus Deus". **Le Concert Spirituel / Hervé Niquet.** Naxos Ⓢ 8 553175 (57 minutes: DDD: 8/97). Texts and translations included. Recorded 1996. *Gramophone Editor's choice.*

This early Mass is a beautiful piece, intimately scored for voices with two melody instruments and continuo. Charpentier's vocal requirements consist of pairs of sopranos, alto, tenor and bass soloists, with a four-part chorus that splits into two four-part entities for the "Pleni sunt coeli ... Hosanna" of the *Sanctus*. The Mass is harmonically richly inventive with passages of characteristically vivid word-painting. Taken as a whole the work is perhaps less immediately arresting than the larger-scale Masses that were to follow; yet it is generously endowed with subtle inflexions, a pervasive element of contemplation, and effectively varied rhythmic juxtapositions which enliven the text and hold our attention. Conductor Hervé Niquet has appropriately included an Offertory, *Precatio pro filio regis*, and an Elevation, *Panis quem ego dabo*, to conform with standard practice. The *Te Deum*, for four soloists, four-part choir and *colla parte* instruments, is not that one for which Charpentier is renowned but a smaller, later piece belonging to the last years of his life. Modest in scale it may be but musically it is impressive and emotionally satisfying. The choir and instrumentalists of Le Concert Spirituel are on their usual lively form. Some of the solo vocal contributions are more focused than others but the choir maintain a high standard of vocal blend and secure intonation almost throughout. The recorded sound is very good indeed and all is directed with stylistic assurance by Niquet.

Additional recommendations ...

...Te Deum. Litanies de la vierge, H83. Missa Assumpta est Maria. **Philidor, le Cadet** Marche de timbales[a]. **Les Arts Florissants Vocal and Instrumental Ensemble / William Christie** with [a]**Marie-Ange Petit** (perc). Harmonia Mundi Ⓕ HMC90 1298 (75 minutes: DDD: 9/89). ✍

...Te Deum – Prelude. *Coupled with works by various composers.* **Wynton Marsalis** (tpt); **English Chamber Orchestra / Anthony Newman.** Sony Classical Ⓕ SK66244 (58 minutes: DDD: 11/96).

...Te Deum, H146[a]. Missa Assumpta est Maria, H11[a]. Domine salvum fac regem, H303[a]. **Roberday** Fugues et Caprices – Fugue No. 9[b]. [b]**John Toll** (org); [a]**St James's Singers and Baroque Players / Ivor Bolton.** Teldec Das Alte Werk Ⓕ 0630-12465-2 (60 minutes: DDD: 9/96). ✍

Charpentier Vespres à la Vierge. **Le Concert Spirituel / Hervé Niquet.** Naxos Ⓢ 8 553174 (61 minutes: DDD: 3/96). Texts and translations included. Recorded 1995. Ⓖ

Charpentier Beatus vir, H221. Laudate pueri, H149. Laetatus sum, H216. Nisi Dominus, H150. Lauda Jerusalem, H210. Ave maris stella, H60. Magnificat, H72. Salve regina, H24.

Nivers Antiphonarium Monasticum, Antiennes I-VI.

This release offers a liturgical reconstruction of the Vespers office. The five Vesper psalms and *Magnificat* belong to different periods in Charpentier's life and the six antiphons are not by him at all but by his organist-composer contemporary, Nivers. The reconstruction works well though the documentation omits any catalogue identification either of the *Laetatus sum* (Psalm 122) or the *Nisi Dominus* (Psalm 127). The relevant numbers, without which the pieces are virtually impossible to identify, are given above. Le Concert Spirituel, under Hervé Niquet's direction, here demonstrate their rapport with Charpentier's music. The vocal sound is fresh and the wide range of musical *Affekt* shows off a greater diversity of tonal colour. Tenors and basses incline towards a roughness of timbre here and there yet, overall, the bright and full-blooded choral sound is pleasing and vital. Some readers may feel that the recording balance of the psalms and canticle is a fraction too close, creating the atmosphere of a drawing-room Vespers rather than one in more spacious, ecclesiastical surroundings. The antiphons fare much better in this respect, being given a deeper aural perspective. In summary, this is a richly rewarding programme of music which never disappoints. Some of the pieces are harmonically arresting and none, perhaps, more than the setting for three choral groups of the *Salve regina* with its passages of striking chromaticism. Warmly recommended.

Charpentier Incidental Music – Les fous divertissants. Le mariage forcé. **New Chamber Opera** (Rachel Elliott, sop; Christoph Wittman, alto; Nicholas Hurndall Smith, ten; John Bernays, bass); **The Band of Instruments / Gary Cooper** (hpd). ASV Gaudeamus Ⓕ CDGAU167 (63 minutes: DDD: 4/98). Texts and translations included. Recorded 1996.

The "Trio des rieurs" (*Les fous divertissants*) and the "Trio grotesque" (*Le mariage forcé*) must have been among the very first pieces representative of Charpentier's comic genius ever to have been recorded. That was in 1958 with an ensemble that included the French tenor, Jean Giraudeau, and in editions by Guy-Lambert. Both items feature in this delightful performance of Charpentier's music for Raymond Poisson's comedy, *Les fous divertissants*, and for the far better-known comedy by Molière, *Le mariage forcé*. Lully had originally provided the music for the latter, during the heyday of his partnership with Molière but, following the rift between the two, the playwright engaged Charpentier as his collaborator. His music for a revival of *Le mariage forcé* and the *Ouverture de la Comtesse d'Escarbagnas*, dating from 1672, were probably his first pieces for the stage. *Les fous divertissants* followed eight years later. Most of the incidental music for these plays is small scale and of brief duration. The New Chamber Opera and The Band of Instruments, under the direction of harpsichordist Gary Cooper, bring the music to life with imagination, humour and a lively, stylish awareness which may be felt especially in matters of rhythm and ornament. The four singers have settled comfortably into a musical idiom which has eluded many a bigger name in the past, and they bring both humour and pathos to Charpentier's expressively varied musical vocabulary. This ranges from the aforementioned 'Laughters' trio for three carefree, tipsy musicians, and the even more crazily inconsequential patter of the trio of grotesques, also musicians, to pieces inspired by the poignant sharpness and deadly accuracy of Cupid's arrows. One such instance is provided by the "Hélas, hélas, hélas ... nous sommes amoureux" (tracks 3 and 6) of *Les fous divertissants*, and another, even more affecting, by the duo "Que tout parle à l'envy" (track 19). This is from *Le mariage forcé* sung by the ardent lovers, Leander and Angelica, an *haute-contre* and soprano respectively. It is perhaps one of the loveliest pieces on the disc. In short, an entertaining and well thought out project whose zany, *commedia dell'arte*-style humour unquestionably reaches a climax in the antics of the three grotesques who have a very high opinion of their musical prowess.

Charpentier Médée. **Lorraine Hunt** (sop) Médée; **Bernard Deletré** (bass) Créon; **Monique Zanetti** (sop) Créuse; **Mark Padmore** (ten) Jason; **Jean-Marc Salzmann** (bar) Oronte; **Noémi Rime** (sop) Nérine; **Les Arts Florissants / William Christie**. Erato Ⓕ 4509-96558-2 (three discs: 195 minutes: DDD: 6/95). ☞ Texts and translations included. Recorded 1994.   ⒼⒼⒼ

William Christie himself answers the question that everyone is bound to ask: why has he chosen to make a new recording of this splendid (but still little-known) early opera – Charpentier's only *tragédie-lyrique* – only ten years after his previous version (Harmonia Mundi, 3/85 – recently deleted)? For a start, the new issue is of the complete work and the experience of staging the opera has changed Christie's view of its pacing and sharpened the response of the orchestra (an unusually large one for its period) and continuo. Here we have an entirely new cast. Lorraine Hunt's Medea is something of a *tour de force*. She invests every word with meaning and produces the widest range of colour to express all the emotional nuances in Medea's complex character – jealousy, indignation, tenderness, sorrow, fury, malignity and outright barbarism: she is especially outstanding in Act 3, one of the most superb acts in all baroque opera, in which she has no fewer than four great monologues, the first with affecting chromatic harmonies, the second accompanied by feverish rushing strings, the third the sombre "Noires filles du Styx" with its eerie modulations, the fourth with dark orchestral colours. Charpentier's orchestration and texture, indeed, are wonderfully effective: string writing varies between extreme delicacy (beautifully played here) and savage agitation; the cool sound of the recorders is refreshing and the many dances featuring recorders and oboes – for of course the work had to create substantial opportunities for ballet, as well as spectacular stage effects – are enchanting. As Jason Mark Padmore, a real *haute-contre*, sings with admirable ease and intelligence and the tragic Creusa, poisoned by the vengeful Medea is the light-voiced Monique Zanetti, the very embodiment of youthful innocence and charm: her death scene, still protesting her love for Jason, is most moving. A notable detail in all the principals, incidentally, is ftheir absorption of *agréments*, with Hunt showing special mastery in this regard. There is a large cast for the numerous minor roles, all well taken; and the chorus sing cleanly and with evident commitment. All told, a considerable achievement, and a triumph for Christie, whose decision to re-record the work is amply justified by the result.

Further listening ...
...Canticum in honorem Beatae Virginis Mariae inter homines et angelos, H400. Prélude a 3, H509. Pour la conception de la Vierge, H313. Nativité de la Vierge, H309. Prélude pour Salve regina a 3, H23a. Salve regina a 3, H23. Pour la fête de l'Epiphanie, H395. Prélude pour le Magnificat a 4, H533. Magnificat a 4, H80. Stabat mater pour des religieuses, H15. Litanies de la Vierge, H83. **Le Concert des Nations / Jordi Savall**. Auvidis Astrée E8713 (2/90). ☞   Ⓖ
...Messe des morts, H7. Litanies de la Vierge, H89. Psalms – Nisi Dominus, H160; Laudate pueri, H203; Confitebor tibi, H220. Elévation à 5 sans dessus de violon, "Transfige dulcissime Jesu", H251. **Le Concert Spirituel / Hervé Niquet**. Naxos 8 553173 (6/95). ☞
...Messe pour les trespassés. **Soloists; Lisbon Gulbenkian Foundation Choir and Orchestra / Michel Corboz**. Erato 4509-97238-2 (3/95).
...Office de ténèbres – Incipit oratio Jeremiae, H95. Leçons de ténèbres – Manum suam, H92; Ego vir videns, H93. Responsories – Eram quasi agnus, H116; O Juda, H119; O vos omnes, H134. Miserere, H157. **Le Parlement de Musique / Martin Gester** (org/hpd). Opus 111 OPS55-9119 (9/92). ☞

...Les plaisirs de Versailles, H480[a]. Airs sur les stances du Cid, H457-9[b]. Amor vince ogni cosa, H492[c]. [ac]**Sophie Daneman,** [c]**Patricia Petibon** (sops); [a]**Katalin Károlyi** (mez); [a]**Steve Dugardin** (alto); [ac]**François Piolino,** [bc]**Paul Agnew** (tens); [a]**Jean-François Gardeil,** [c]**Olivier Lallouette** (bars); **Les Arts Florissants / William Christie.** Erato Ⓕ 0630-14774-2 (53 minutes: DDD: 2/97). *✔*
...Quatuor anni tempestatis, H335-8. Psalms – Quemadmodum desiderat cervus, H174. Nisi Dominus, H231. Notus in Judea, H179. **Françoise Semellaz, Noémi Rime** (sops); **Bernard Delétré** (bass); **Le Parlement de Musique / Martin Gester.** Opus 111 OPS30-9005 (9/91). *✔*
...Le reniement de St Pierre. Méditations pour le Carême. **Les Arts Florissants Vocal and Instrumental Ensemble / William Christie.**
Harmonia Mundi Musique d'abord HMA190 5151 (7/86). *✔*   Ⓖ
...Veni creator pour un dessus seul au catechisme, H69[a]. Messe pour le Port Royal, H5[a]. O salutaris hostia, H261[a]. Domine salvum sine organo in C major, H290. Psalmus David, 116us sine organo, H182, "Laudate Dominum omnes". Ave maris stella, H63[a]. Pour Ste Thérèse, H342, "Flores o gallia"[a]. Magnificat, H81[a]. **Les Demoiselles de Saint-Cyr / Emmanuel Mandrin** with [a]**Michel Chapuis** (org). Auvidis Astrée E8598 (9/97).
...Actéon. **Soloists; Les Arts Florissants Vocal and Instrumental Ensemble / William Christie.** Harmonia Mundi Musique d'abord HMA190 1095 (5/83). *✔ Gramophone Award Winner 1982-3.*   ⒼⒼ
...La descente d'Orphée aux enfers. **Soloists; Les Arts Florissants / William Christie.** Erato 0630-11913-2 (5/96). *✔ Gramophone Editor's record of the month.*   Ⓖ
...Le malade imaginaire. **Soloists; Les Arts Florissants Chorus and Orchestra / William Christie.** Harmonia Mundi HMC90 1336 (4/91). *✔* Included with this CD is a complementary CD (41 minutes) containing Charpentier's "'O' Anthems for Advent", H36-43; "In nativatem Domini nostri Jesus Christi canticum", H414; "Noëls dur les instruments", H534.

Ernest Chausson   French 1855-1899

Chausson Concert for Violin, Piano and String Quartet in D major, Op. 21[a].
Franck Violin Sonata No. 1 in A major, Op. 13. **Pierre Amoyal** (vn); **Pascal Rogé** (pf); [a]**Ysaÿe Quartet** (Christophe Giovaninetti, Luc-Marie Aguera, vns; Miguel da Silva, va; Michel Poulet, vc). Decca Ⓕ 444 172-2DH (70 minutes: DDD: 2/96). Recorded 1994.   Ⓖ
In Franck's Violin Sonata one recognizes the totally idiomatic response of this all-French team to this high romantic music in its own free use of rubato, natural and unaffected. It is remarkable how Amoyal and Rogé allow themselves great freedom over rhythm and tempo without ever seeming undisciplined. So the opening *Allegretto* emerges as a dreamy meditation, a happy preparation for more serious arguments later. This is a reading full of fantasy, giving the impression of music emerging spontaneously on the spur of the moment. The full and immediate recording helps, and so it does in Chausson's *Concert* for violin, piano and string quartet, which receives just as warmly spontaneous-sounding a performance. It has unusual force and scope for chamber music and the composer draws our attention to this from the start. Although a 'Concert' is not quite the same as a concerto, the full title rightly suggests that, along with the piano, one violin is more important than the other two. The focus of the recording is sharp, the sense of presence keen, and that adds to one's involvement, with clear contrasts of dynamic and texture, of light and shade. The string quartet is given its full weight, instead of being a mere addendum, and that owes much also to the playing of the Ysaÿe Quartet, who give most persuasive performance of this late romantic masterpiece.

Chausson String Quartet, Op. 35 (cpted d'Indy).
Franck Piano Quintet in F minor[a]. [a]**Michaël Levinas** (pf); **Ludwig Quartet** (Jean-Philippe Audoli, Elenid Owen, vns; Padrig Faure, va; Anne Copery, vc). Naxos Ⓢ 8 553645 (68 minutes: DDD: 6/98). Recorded 1996.
Chausson had only completed two movements of his String Quartet at the time of his sudden death. Vincent d'Indy finished the third movement, adapting the composer's sketches to conclude in C major, the key of the whole work. The complete four-movement Quartet would surely have been one of Chausson's finest achievements; the torso is fascinating, even if not entirely satisfying. Curiously, the Pierre Verany recording also pairs it with the Franck Quintet; the performances, by both groups of both works, are fine ones. There is, however, a distinct contrast in playing and recording styles. Tacchino and the Athenaeum-Enesco Quartet adopt more spacious tempos, and are given a more spacious acoustic. In the big tutti sections of the Franck, this leads to a problem one often finds in live performances of this work, of the piano resonance swamping the string sound. But there's some impressive grand-style pianism, and many imaginative interpretative touches. The Naxos recording of the Franck is more favourable to the strings, and rather more intimate. The overall sound, even at the expense of losing some detail in the piano part, is preferable, and it suits the players' infectiously ardent, enthusiastic approach to the music. The Chausson shows similar differences. In the lovely, tranquil second movement, the Athenaeum-Enesco are preferable, with better balance and more sensuous tone, but the Ludwig Quartet's view of the third movement is far more compelling, with the different motifs of this strange, slowish *Scherzo* beautifully contrasted. Go for the newer disc; nothing about it suggests the bargain basement.

Additional recommendation ...
...String Quartet. **Franck** Piano Quintet[a]. [a]**Gabriel Tacchino** (pf); **Athenaeum-Enescu Quartet.**
Pierre Verany Ⓕ PV792032 (72 minutes: DDD: 12/92).

Further listening ...
...Symphony in B flat major, Op. 20[a]. Poème, Op. 25[b]. *Coupled with* **Saint-Saëns** Introduction
and Rondo capriccioso, Op. 28[b]. [b]**David Oistrakh** (vn); **Boston Symphony Orchestra /**
Charles Munch. RCA Victor Gold Seal GD60683. Ⓖ
...Piano Trio in G minor, Op. 3. *Coupled with* **Ravel** Piano Trio. **Beaux Arts Trio.**
Philips 411 141-2PH (4/85).
...Poème, Op. 25. *Coupled with works by various composers.* **George Enescu, S. Schlüssel** (pfs).
Symposium mono 1156* (1/97).
...Quelques danses, Op. 26. Paysage, Op. 38. *Coupled with works by* **Franck** and **Dukas**
Jean Hubeau (pf). Teldec 4509-96221-2 (4/96).
...Chanson perpétuelle. *Coupled with works by* **Delage** and **Jaubert Dame Felicity Lott** (sop);
Kammerensemble de Paris / Armin Jordan. Aria Music 592300 (5/97).
...Poème de l'amour et de la mer, Op. 19[a]. Poème, Op. 25[b]. *Coupled with works by* **Fauré**
[a]**Linda Finnie** (contr); **Ulster Orchestra / Yan Pascal Tortelier** ([b]vn). Chandos CHAN8952 (12/91).
...Le temps des lilas. *Coupled with works by various composers.* **Dame Felicity Lott** (sop);
Graham Johnson (pf). Hyperion CDA66937 (10/97). *See review in the Collections section; refer to*
the Index.
...La légende de Sainte Cécile. La tempête. **Soloists;** women's voices of the **French Radio Chorus;**
Paris Orchestral Ensemble / Jean-Jacques Kantorow. EMI CDC5 55323-2 (4/96).

Gang Chen
Chinese 1935

Chen/Ho Butterfly Lovers Concerto[a].
Vanessa-Mae Violin Fantasy on Puccini's "Turandot"[b]. Happy Valley – The 1997 Re-Unification
Overture, 1997[c]. **Vanessa-Mae** (vn); [c]**Chinese Ladies' Choir;** [a]**London Philharmonic Orchestra /**
Viktor Fedotov, [bc]**Royal Opera House Orchestra, Covent Garden /** [b]**Viktor Fedotov,** [c]**David Arch.**
EMI Ⓕ CDC5 56483-2 (45 minutes: DDD: 2/98). Recorded 1997.
This compilation very much reflects Vanessa-Mae's maternal ancestry (although her father is British). The idiom of the main piece is 'classically' Chinese, with a direct popular appeal, its narrative line having much in common with Chinese 'opera'. The *Butterfly Lovers Concerto* is certainly a vivid, often touching, and at times spectacular *concertante* work which illustrates an old Chinese legend about a pair of star-crossed lovers who can only achieve a "happy musical ending" when, after their earthly affair has been hopelessly thwarted, they are united "in after-death as butterflies". Their fluttering is represented by a delicate figure on the flute at the opening of the first and third sections of the score, and the piece is dominated by a striking Chinese theme, which is later transformed but is charmingly fragile when first presented, gently and seductively by the soloist, against piquant woodwind. A light-hearted, spring-like *scherzando* section follows, before the mood of optimism evaporates. The solo line, with its occasional touches of Eastern portamentos, is ravishing on Vanessa-Mae's bow, its delicate nuances wholly idiomatic, and though the work is loosely structured, its melodies are effectively used and beguiling. The *Fantasy on Puccini's "Turandot"* which follows on quite naturally shows how well Puccini created a musically idiomatic Eastern atmosphere for his opera. But the effect of Vanessa-Mae's arrangement with its sumptuous orchestration is to transform this luscious pot-pourri into a kind of film score, with an opulent "Nessun dorma" as its 'title' theme. *Happy Valley* turns out to be a somewhat ingenuous celebration of the return of Hong Kong to Chinese control, and after its exotic virtuoso opening display, the juxtaposition of violinistic fireworks with infectiously folksy choral singing is undoubtedly winning in its unashamedly populist style, based on a repeated, very catchy folk-song. Throughout, the recording is warmly atmospheric, and this whole collection makes agreeably easy listening.

Luigi Cherubini
Italian 1760-1842

Cherubini Overtures – Ali-Baba; Les Abencérages; Les deux journées; Lodoïska; Médée;
Anacréon; Faniska; L'hôtellerie portugaise. **City of Birmingham Symphony Orchestra /**
Lawrence Foster. Claves Ⓕ CD50-9513 (70 minutes: DDD: 10/96). Recorded 1995.
Cherubini was a musician whom Beethoven regarded as the greatest living composer (when asked to leave himself out of consideration), whom Berlioz vilified in his writings and passionately admired in his music and is not to be dismissed as a footnote to history. Revivals of *Médée* have demonstrated his mastery of the stage and of instrumental colour, among much else, and many more of his operas, represented here by their overtures, well merit revival. For the curious, this is a good introduction to Cherubini's style. There is the brilliant use of instruments, especially the capacity for individualizing them so that the actual sound bears dramatic expression: this is the true beginning of romantic orchestration, profoundly influential on Weber and thence on Berlioz. There is the rhythmic *élan*, the charge of energy that inspired Beethoven's admiration. There is the shrewd sense of structure, and of

using this to encapsulate the drama to come. There is gaiety and brightness. There is, not least, a passion in the invention that seems at odds with the crabbed countenance of the portraits and the tales of the dry contrapuntalist ferociously disciplining his Conservatoire students. Cherubini was a man of contradictions, a composer of, if something short of genius, certainly profound and exciting talent. The enthusiastic performances here are enjoyable in their own right, and suggest his variety and range; they also keep alive hopes that more of his operas may yet be recorded.

Additional recommendation ...

...Overtures – Eliza; Médée; L'hôtellerie portugaise; Les deux journées; Anacréon; Faniska; Les Abencérages. Concert Overture. **Academy of St Martin in the Fields / Sir Neville Marriner.** EMI Ⓕ CDC7 54438-2 (67 minutes: DDD: 9/92).

Cherubini Requiem Mass No. 1 in C minor[a]. Marche funèbre. [a]**Corydon Singers; Corydon Orchestra / Matthew Best.** Hyperion Ⓕ CDA66805 (54 minutes: DDD: 4/96). Text and translation included. Recorded 1995. Ⓖ

It would be an oversimplification to suggest that Matthew Best emphasizes the Beethoven rather than the Berlioz aspect of the main work here; but he does seem less interested in the fascinating use of colour as an element in the actual invention than in the rugged moral strength and the force of the statements. The recording reflects this emphasis, and is firm and clear without being especially subtle over orchestral detail. The choir deliver the *Dies irae* powerfully, and much dramatic vigour is recalled in the fugue traditionally reserved for "Quam olim Abrahae". Presumably this idea derives from the suggestion of generation upon generation of Abraham's children inheriting God's promise: whoever first thought of it, many composers have taken up the device. Berlioz, however, was satirical about Cherubini's fugues, and saved his admiration for the wonderful long *decrescendo* that ends the *Agnus Dei*. This is beautifully controlled here. Like Christoph Spering and the Cologne Chorus Musicus, who give a more colourful, 'Berliozian' performance, Best includes the tremendous *Marche funèbre*. There was inspiration here again for Berlioz (especially in his *Hamlet* funeral march). Best handles this superbly, opening with a merciless percussion crash and sustaining the pace and mood unrelentingly. In his hands, it sounds more original than ever, a funeral march that, rather than mourn or honour, rages against the dying of the light.

Additional recommendations ...

...Requiem Mass[a]. **Verdi** Messa da Requiem[b]. Soloists; [a]**Ambrosian Singers;** [b]**Ambrosian Chorus; Philharmonia Orchestra / Riccardo Muti.** EMI Forte Ⓜ CZS5 68613-2 (two discs: 135 minutes: [a]ADD/[b]DDD: 7/96).

...Requiem Mass[a]. In Paradisium[a]. Marche funèbre. [a]**Cologne Chorus Musicus; Das Neue Orchester / Christoph Spering.** Opus 111 Ⓕ OPS30-116 (56 minutes: DDD: 2/95). 🖉

Further listening ...

...Horn Sonata in F major. *Coupled with works by various composers.* **Barry Tuckwell** (hn); **Academy of St Martin in the Fields / Sir Neville Marriner.** Double Decca 443 838-2DF2 (7/95). *See review under Rossini; refer to the Index.*

...Horn Sonata in F major. *Coupled with works by various composers.* **Barry Tuckwell** (hn); **Academy of St Martin in the Fields / Sir Neville Marriner.** EMI Forte CZS5 69395-2 (2/97). *See review in the Collections section; refer to the Index.*

...Mass in D minor[a], "Messe solennelle". *Coupled with* **Haydn** Mass in C major, HobXXII/9[b,] "Missa in tempore belli". [ab]**Soloists; Stuttgart Gächinger Kantorei;** [a]**Stuttgart Bach Collegium;** [b]**Stuttgart Chamber Orchestra / Helmuth Rilling.** Hänssler Classic 98 981 (5/93).

Fryderyk Chopin
Polish 1810-1849

Chopin Piano Concertos[a] – No. 1 in E minor, Op. 11; No. 2 in F minor, Op. 21. Mazurkas – F minor, Op. 63 No. 2; F minor, Op. 68 No. 4. Waltz in E minor, Op. posth. **Evgeni Kissin** (pf); [a]**Moscow Philharmonic Orchestra / Dmitri Kitaienko.** RCA Victor Red Seal Ⓜ 09026 68378-2 (71 minutes: ADD: 2/96). From Olympia OCD149 (9/89). Recorded live in 1984. Ⓖ

Here is a living rather than fabricated example of just what is possible from a 12-year-old genius. It is no exaggeration to say that these performances, taken from a 1984 Moscow concert, are among the most phenomenally assured and meteoric of any on record. Every page blazes with youthful confidence and a stylistic know-how that would be astonishing from a pianist twice Kissin's age. Even at that age he possessed the peculiar attributes of Russian pianism at its greatest, with flawless, even strength and the most full-bodied *cantabile*. At 10'18" in the first movement of the E minor Concerto you will hear playing of great expressive fullness; already he has all the time in the world to make his points (usually the hallmark of older, more experienced players). His punishing attack on Chopin's double-note elaboration at 5'27" in the finale will leave you breathless and so, too, will the way his playing so effortlessly takes wing at 2'07". True, there are moments (the opening of the F minor Concerto's central *Larghetto*) where he sounds too relentlessly upfront, too aggressively thrusting, and doubtless, when he comes to re-record these concertos in his maturity he will find an even wider spectrum of colour and nuance; a greater subtlety. However, it is doubtful whether he will ever surpass the infallible and propulsive brilliance of these performances. RCA have trumped Olympia's original 1989 ace, not only with three superbly played encores but in greatly improved, immaculate sound.

Additional recommendations ...

...No. 1. **Liszt** Piano Concerto No. 1 in E flat major, S124. **Martha Argerich** (pf);
London Symphony Orchestra / Claudio Abbado. DG The Originals Ⓜ 449 719-2GOR
(56 minutes: ADD: 4/85). *See review under Liszt; refer to the Index.*   ⒼⒼ

...Nos. 1 and 2. **Murray Perahia** (pf); **Israel Philharmonic Orchestra / Zubin Mehta.**
Sony Classical Ⓕ SK44922 (76 minutes: DDD: 6/90).   ⒼⒼ

...No. 1[a]. No. 2[b]. **Tamás Vásáry** (pf). **Berlin Philharmonic Orchestra /** [a]**Jerszy Semkow,**
[b]**János Kulka.** DG Privilege Ⓑ 429 515-2GR (75 minutes: ADD: 6/90).

...Nos. 1 and 2. **Emil Gilels** (pf); **Philadelphia Orchestra / Eugene Ormandy.**
Sony Classical Essential Classics Ⓑ SBK46336 (72 minutes: ADD: 3/91).

...Nos. 1 and 2. **Nikolai Demidenko** (pf); **Philharmonia Orchestra / Heinrich Schiff.**
Hyperion Ⓕ CDA66647 (73 minutes: DDD: 11/93).

...Nos. 1 and 2. **Martino Tirimo** (pf); **Philharmonia Orchestra / Fedor Glushchenko.**
Conifer Classics Ⓜ 75605 51247-2 (76 minutes: DDD: 6/95).

...No. 1[a]. 12 Etudes, Op. 25. Ballade No. 1 in G minor, Op. 23. **Géza Anda** (pf);
[a]**Philharmonia Orchestra / Alceo Galliera.** Testament mono Ⓕ SBT1066*
(80 minutes: ADD: 10/95). *See review in the Collections section; refer to the Index.*   Ⓖ

Chopin Piano Concerto No. 1 in E minor, Op. 11[a]. Ballade in G minor, Op. 23[b]. Nocturnes, Op. 15
– No. 1 in F major[b]; No. 2 in F sharp minor[b]. Nocturnes, Op. 27 – No. 1 in C sharp minor; No. 2
in D flat major. Polonaise No. 6 in A flat major, Op. 53, "Heroic"[b]. **Maurizio Pollini** (pf);
[a]**Philharmonia Orchestra / Paul Kletzki.** EMI Studio Plus Ⓜ CDM5 66221-2 (73 minutes: ADD:
11/92). Item marked [a]from ASD370 (11/60), recorded 1960, [b]ASD2577 (8/70), 1968.
Gramophone classical 100.   ⒼⒼⒼ

This disc is a classic. The concerto was recorded shortly after the 18-year-old pianist's victory at the
Warsaw competition in 1959. Nowadays we might expect a wider dynamic range to allow greater
power in the first movement's tuttis, but in all other respects the recording completely belies its age,
with a near perfect balance between soloist and orchestra. This is, of course, very much Pollini's disc,
just as the First Concerto is very much the soloist's show, but effacing as the accompaniment is,
Pollini's keyboard miracles of poetry and refinement could not have been achieved without one of the
most characterful and responsive accounts of that accompaniment ever committed to tape. The
expressive range of the Philharmonia on top form under Kletzki is at once, and continuously,
exceptional, as is the accord between soloist and conductor in matters of phrasing and shading. The
solo items are a further reminder of Pollini's effortless bravura and aristocratic poise. His tonal
shading in the two accompanying Op. 27 *Nocturnes* is equally exquisite. Also on offer are the paired
Op. 15 *Nocturnes*, the G minor *Ballade* and the recital ends stirringly with the A flat *Polonaise.*

Additional recommendations ...

...Nos. 1 and 2. **Krystian Zimerman** (pf). **Los Angeles Philharmonic Orchestra / Carlo Maria Giulini.**
DG Ⓕ 415 970-2GH (72 minutes: ADD: 9/86).   Ⓖ

...No. 1. Fantasia on Polish Airs, Op. 13. Andante spianato and Grande polonaise brillante in
E flat major, Op. 22. **Idil Biret** (pf). **Czecho-Slovak State Philharmonic Orchestra, Košice /
Robert Stankovsky.** Naxos Ⓢ 8 550368 (74 minutes: DDD: 4/92).

...No. 1[a]. Piano Sonata No. 2 in B flat minor, Op. 35. Also includes 23 other short works by
Chopin. **Alexander Brailowsky** (pf); [a]**Berlin Philharmonic Orchestra / Julius Prüwer.**
Danacord mono Ⓕ DACOCD336/7* (two discs: 135 minutes: ADD: 11/95).

Chopin Piano Concerto No. 2 in F minor, Op. 21[a]. Preludes, Op. 28. **Maria-João Pires** (pf);
[a]**Royal Philharmonic Orchestra / André Previn.** DG Ⓕ 437 817-2GH (74 minutes: DDD: 10/94).
Recorded 1992.   Ⓖ

Here, beautifully and responsibly partnered by Previn and the Royal Philharmonic, and recorded with
the greatest warmth and clarity, Pires gets the treatment she deserves. What gloriously imposing
breadth as well as knife-edged clarity she brings to each phrase and note; absolutely nothing is taken
for granted. The intricacy and stylishness of her rubato remind us that the inspiration behind the F
minor Concerto was Constantia Gladkowska, a young singer and Chopin's first love. Listen to Pires's
fioritura in the heavenly *Larghetto* or her way of edging into the finale's scintillating coda and you will
gasp at such pianism and originality. Indeed, the opening of her finale may surprise you with its
dreaminess (*Allegro vivace?*) but as with all great pianists, even her most extreme ideas are carried
through with unshakeable conviction and authority. Pires's 24 Preludes, too, remind us that she is the
possessor of one of the most crystalline of all techniques. More importantly, her way with the more
interior numbers among Chopin's teeming and disparate moods is of exceptional drama and intensity.
Understatement plays little part in her conception and those who prefer the more classically biased
playing of artists such as Pollini are in for some surprises. In No. 4, for example, her reading is
intensely 'laden', the *stretto* climax super-charged, the entire performance virtually choked by its own
emotion. Yet how memorably she allows the central unease of No. 13 to dissolve into tranquillity,
and, returning to fire and fury, what rhetorical force she unleashes in No. 18. In short, you will rarely
hear Chopin playing of greater mastery or calibre. In her own scrupulously modern way she surely
embodies the spirit of the great pianists of the past; of Kempff, Edwin Fischer and, most of all,
Cortot. Ashkenazy, Biret and Richter – amongst her modern rivals – are also highly recommendable.

Additional recommendations ...

...No. 2[a]. **Tchaikovsky** Piano Concerto No. 1 in B flat minor, Op. 23[b]. **Vladimir Ashkenazy** (pf); **London Symphony Orchestra / [a]David Zinman, [b]Lorin Maazel.** Decca Ovation Ⓜ 417 750-2DM (66 minutes: ADD: 1/89).

...No. 2. Variations on "Là ci darem le mano", Op. 2. Concerto Rondo in F major, Op. 14, "Krakowiak". **Idil Biret** (pf). **Czecho-Slovak State Philharmonic Orchestra, Košice / Robert Stankovsky.** Naxos Ⓢ 8 550369 (67 minutes: DDD: 4/92).

...No. 2. Ballade No. 1 in G minor, Op. 23. *Coupled with works by various composers.* **Murray Perahia** (pf); **Israel Philharmonic Orchestra / Zubin Mehta.** Sony Classical Ⓜ SX4K63380 (four discs: 270 minutes: DDD/ADD: 4/98). *See review in the Collections section; refer to the Index.*

Chopin Piano Concertos (chamber versions) – No. 1 in E minor, Op. 11; No. 2 in F minor, Op. 21. **Fumiko Shiraga** (pf); **Jan-Inge Haukås** (db); **Yggdrasil Quartet** (Fredrik Paulsson, Per Oman, vns; Robert Westlund, va; Per Nyström, vc). BIS Ⓕ CD847 (72 minutes: DDD: 6/97). Recorded 1996.

This recording is not intended as another salvo in the ongoing debate about Chopin's abilities as an orchestral or chamber composer. Its ambition is more modest: to reproduce the sound of a hybrid reduction of Chopin's two piano concertos, a reduction for piano and string quintet that may have existed as a rehearsal vehicle, or a more marketable chamber score for those without access to full orchestra. The recording is offered simply "to recreate a historical performance practice, as well as to exploit the musical advantages implicit therein". But fools will rush in. This is, indeed, one of the most exciting Chopin recordings in recent years because it confronts and deepens the uneasiness that Chopin lovers have with his concertos. They are more comfortable as chamber works, the chamber works he never succeeded in writing when he confronted that form head on. If you find Chopin's ideas inflated when cast in orchestral form, this recording will remove the last traces of doubt. Pianist Fumiko Shiraga has reduced the scope of the music, and wisely so. The heroism and grandeur is of the sort one finds in Schumann's piano-chamber context, the dynamic and expressive extremes that Shiraga achieves are no less compelling than a pianist unleashed against a large orchestra. Shiraga doubles in some tutti passages – a surprise at first, but again a wise decision. She adds gravity and fullness to the Yggdrasil Quartet's excellent accompaniment while remaining hidden, diligently underscoring but never overbearing.

Chopin Piano Trio in G minor, Op. 8[a]. Cello Sonata in G minor, Op. 65[b]. Introduction and Polonaise brillant in C major, Op. 3 (versions for [d]pf, [c]vc and pf, arr. Feuermann). [a]**Pamela Frank** (vn); [abc]**Yo-Yo Ma** (vc); [abc]**Emanuel Ax,** [d]**Eva Osinska** (pfs). Sony Classical Ⓕ SK53112 (72 minutes: DDD: 6/95). Recorded 1989-92.

This most welcome reminder of the 'chamber music' Chopin of course starts with his G minor Piano Trio (1828-29) dedicated to his compatriot, the music-loving would-be composer-cum-cellist, Prince Radziwill. Rarely has it enjoyed what might be termed 'bigger-named' rescue on disc which is inexplicable. For even if Chopin's beloved piano gets the best of it, a performance as imaginatively characterized as this makes you salute the teenage work anew with those well-worn words (albeit in a different context) "Off with your hats, gentlemen – a genius". Despite the procrustean (for Chopin) demands of sonata-form, the minor-key challenges of the opening *Allegro con fuoco* are conveyed with appealing urgency before the amiable grace of the *Scherzo*, the smouldering romance of the *Adagio sostenuto* and the dance-like gaiety of the finale. Shortly after accepting the Trio's dedication, Prince Radziwill invited Chopin to stay at his country estate – hence the Op. 3 *Polonaise brillant* in C (the slow introduction came later) for the Prince to play with his bewitching 17-year-old pianist daughter. Here, Yo-Yo Ma chooses Emanuel Feuermann's reworking of the cello part – as Chopin himself might well have enhanced it with decorative *fioriture* had the Prince's fingers been as agile as his daughter's. More importantly, the disc offers what is thought to be the first recording of this work in a solo-piano version, recently discovered by the Polish pianist-musicologist, Jan Weber. It is played here with spirited affection by Weber's pupil, Eva Osinska. The mature Cello Sonata, written in 1845-46 for Chopin's good friend, August Franchomme, is no stranger to the catalogue. And it is good to say that this tactfully balanced, persuasively fluid performance from Yo-Yo Ma and Emanuel Ax ranks with the best of its rivals. The recording is vivid and true.

Additional recommendations ...

...Cello Sonata. *Coupled with works by various composers.* **Jacqueline du Pré** (vc); **Daniel Barenboim** (pf). EMI Ⓑ CZS5 68132-2 (six discs: 437 minutes: ADD: 8/94). *See review in the Collections section; refer to the Index.* ⒼⒼ

...Introduction and Polonaise brillant. *Coupled with works by various composers.* **Henri Demarquette** (vc); **François-Frédéric Guy** (pf). Pierre Verany Ⓕ PV795101 (75 minutes: DDD: 4/96).

...Cello Sonata. *Coupled with works by* **Fauré** and **Poulenc** Pieter Wispelwey (vc); **Paolo Giacometti** (pf). Channel Classics Ⓕ CCS10797 (67 minutes: DDD: 3/98).

Chopin Cello Sonata in G minor, Op. 65. Polonaise brillante in C major, Op. 3 (ed. Feuermann). Grande duo concertante in E major on themes from Meyerbeer's "Robert le Diable". Nocturne in C sharp minor, Op. posth. (arr. Piatigorsky). Etude in E minor, Op. 25 No. 7 (arr. Glazunov).

Waltz in A minor, Op. 34 No. 2 (arr. Ginzburg). Etude in D minor, Op. 10 No. 6 (arr. Glazunov).
Maria Kliegel (vc); **Bernd Glemser** (pf). Naxos Ⓢ 8 553159 (64 minutes: DDD: 11/96).
Recorded 1994.
Here are Chopin's complete works for cello and piano complemented by an intriguing garland of
encores. Performed with a relish inseparable from youth, impressively balanced and recorded, this is
a notable offering, particularly at Naxos's super-bargain price. Clearly, Kliegel and Glemser have few
reservations concerning the sonata's surprisingly Germanic overtones. Recognizably Chopin in
virtually every bar there remains an oddly Schumannesque bias, particularly in the finale's tortuous
argument – an irony when you consider that Chopin had so little time for his adoring colleague. Yet
this awkward and courageous reaching out towards a terser form of expression is resolved by both
artists with great vitality and, throughout, they create an infectious sense of a live rather than studio
performance. Kliegel and Glemser are no less uninhibited in Chopin's earlier show-pieces, written at
a time when the composer had a passing passion for grand opera and for what he himself dismissed
as "glittering trifles". Their additions (transcriptions by Glazunov, Piatigorsky and Ginzburg) remind
us how singers, violinists and cellists beg, borrow or steal Chopin from pianists at their peril. As
Chopin put it, "the piano is my solid ground; on that I stand the straightest", and his muse has proved
oddly and, indeed, magically resistant to change or transcription. Still, even though the selection
often suggests an alien opacity, the performances are, again, most warmly committed.

Chopin Fantasie in F minor, Op. 49. Waltzes – No. 2 in A flat major, Op. 34 No. 1; No. 3 in
A minor, Op. 34 No. 2; No. 5 in A flat major, Op. 42. Polonaise No. 5 in F sharp minor, Op. 44.
Nocturnes – No. 1 in C sharp minor, Op. 27 No. 1; No. 2 in D flat major, Op. 27 No. 2; No. 10 in
A flat major, Op. 32 No. 2. Scherzo No. 2 in B flat minor, Op. 31. **Evgeni Kissin** (pf);
RCA Victor Red Seal Ⓕ 09026 60445-2 (67 minutes: DDD: 5/94). Recorded live in 1993.
Gramophone Editor's choice.   ⒼⒼⒼ
Evgeni Kissin's playing at 21 (which he was when these performances were recorded) quite easily
outmatches that of the young Ashkenazy and Pollini – and most particularly in terms of the maturity
of his musicianship. The programme launches off with a reading of the great F minor *Fantasie*,
which, though a bit measured, is integrated to perfection. The power and determination of the
performance certainly make one sit up and listen, but at the same time it would be difficult not to be
moved by the heartfelt lyricism of the melodic passages. Although Kissin may be a little unsmiling in
the three waltzes, at least he has admirable sophistication in being able to add interest to the
interpretations. His control in the tricky A flat, Op. 42 is quite amazing. The *Nocturne* in C sharp
minor is a jewel. This reading is amongst the most darkly imaginative and pianistically refined on disc.
The release is rounded off by a powerfully glittering performance of the Second *Scherzo*.

Additional recommendations ...

...Introduction and Variations in E major on a German air ("Der Schweizerbub"). Four Scherzos –
No. 1 in B minor, Op. 20; No. 2; No. 3 in C sharp minor, Op. 39; No. 4 in E major, Op. 54.
Variations in B flat major on "Là ci darem la mano", Op. 2. **Nikolai Demidenko** (pf).
Hyperion Ⓕ CDA66514 (63 minutes: DDD: 1/92).
...Scherzos Nos. 1-4. **Howard Shelley** (pf). Chandos Ⓕ CHAN9018 (55 minutes: DDD: 7/92).
...Nocturnes Nos. 11-19. **Idil Biret** (pf). Naxos Ⓢ 8 550357 (55 minutes: DDD: 7/93).
...Fantasie. Marche funèbre in C minor, Op. 72 No. 2. Etudes, Op. posth. – No. 1 in F minor; No. 2
in A flat major; No. 3 in D flat major, Barcarolle in F sharp major, Op. 60. Berceuse in D flat
major, Op. 57. Polonaise-fantaisie in A flat major, Op. 61. Contredanse in G flat major.
Cantabile in B flat major. Feuille d'album. Fugue in A minor. Variations in A major,
"Souvenir de Paganini". **Fou Ts'ong** (pf).
Sony Classical Essential Classics Ⓑ SBK53515 (66 minutes: ADD/DDD: 12/94).
...Scherzos Nos. 1-4. *Coupled with works by* **Beethoven** *and* **Schumann** Sviatoslav Richter (pf).
Olympia Ⓕ OCD338 (75 minutes: ADD: 4/94). *See review under Beethoven; refer to the*
Index.   ⒼⒼ
...Waltzes – No. 1 and Nos. 3-14. *Coupled with works by various composers.* **Dinu Lipatti** (pf).
EMI Références mono Ⓜ CDH5 65166-2* (73 minutes: ADD: 12/94). *See review in the*
Collections section; refer to the Index.   ⒼⒼⒼ
...Fantasie. Ballade No. 1 in G minor, Op. 23. Waltz in E flat major, Op. posth. *Coupled with works*
by various composers. **Arturo Benedetti Michelangeli** (pf).
Testament mono Ⓕ SBT2088* (two discs: 130 minutes: ADD: 12/96). *See review in the Collections*
section; refer to the Index.

Chopin Preludes Nos. 1-24, Op. 28. Scherzo No. 2 in B flat minor, Op. 31. Mazurkas – No. 13 in
A minor, Op. 17 No. 4; No. 15 in C major, Op. 24 No. 2; No. 25 in B minor, Op. 33 No. 4.
Polonaise No. 5 in F sharp minor, Op. 44. **Seta Tanyel** (pf). Collins Classics Ⓕ 1330-2
(69 minutes: DDD: 4/94). Recorded 1992-93.
Chopin Preludes Nos. 1-24, Op. 28. Preludes – No. 25 in C sharp minor, Op. 45; No. 26 in A flat
major, Op. posth. (all from 2530 721, 2/78). Barcarolle in F sharp major, Op. 60 (SLPM138672,
1/68). Polonaise No. 6 in A flat major, Op. 53 (SLPM139317, 5/68). Scherzo No. 2 in
B flat minor, Op. 31 (2530 530, 6/75). **Martha Argerich** (pf). DG Galleria Ⓜ 415 836-2GGA
(62 minutes: ADD: 4/88).   ⒼⒼ

Avoiding all overtly self-conscious point-making in pursuit of expression, Seta Tanyel gets to the heart of the matter with a stylish simplicity. And how beautifully she makes the piano sing within a sound-world that is wholly Chopinesque in its translucency. That said, there is certainly no lack of strength, either of motivation or sheer tonal weight, as the more demonstratively disturbed of the 24 Preludes make very clear. However stormy the outburst or complex the figuration she nevertheless always manages to reveal a hidden melodic thread. Slower numbers carry their weight of sentiment without being allowed to drag. Nothing in the first half of the recital is more pleasing than the three *Mazurkas*. Each tells its own personal tale while – with a spring-like tonal delicacy and freshness – never allowing you to forget its origin in the dance. In the flanking B minor *Scherzo* and F sharp minor *Polonaise*, darker undertones of disquiet and defiance are conveyed with an urgent nervous energy far more telling than bombast. And what beguiling *cantabile* she draws from her instrument in the gracious mazurka-like trio of the Polonaise. The Abbey Road reproduction is pleasing enough.

Professor Zurawlew, the founder of the Chopin Competition in Warsaw was once asked which one of the prize-winners he would pick as having been his favourite. Looking back over the period 1927-75, the answer came back immediately: "Martha Argerich". Her disc reviewed here could explain why. There are very few recordings of the 24 Preludes that have such a perfect combination of temperamental virtuosity and compelling artistic insight. Argerich has the technical equipment to do whatever she wishes with the music. Whether it is in the haunting, dark melancholy of No. 2 in A minor or the lightning turmoil of No. 16 in B flat minor, she is profoundly impressive. It is these sharp changes of mood that make her performance scintillatingly unpredictable. In the *Barcarolle* there is no relaxed base on which the melodies of the right hand are constructed, as is conventional, but more the piece emerges as a stormy odyssey through life, with moments of visionary awareness. Argerich, it must be said, is on firmer ground in the *Polonaise*, where her power and technical security reign triumphant. The CD ends with a rippling and yet slightly aggressive reading of the second Scherzo. This is very much the playing of a pianist who lives in the 'fast lane' of life. The sound quality is a bit reverberant, an effect heightened by the fact that Argerich has a tendency to overpedal.

Additional recommendations ...
...Mazurkas Nos. 1-51. **Artur Rubinstein** (pf).
  RCA Victor Red Seal Ⓕ RD85171 (two discs: 140 minutes: ADD: 9/89).
...24 Preludes – No. 2 in A minor; No. 4 in E minor; No. 5 in D major; No. 6 in B minor;
  No. 7 in A major; No. 8 in F sharp minor; No. 9 in E major; No. 10 in C sharp minor; No. 11 in
  B major; No. 13 in F sharp major; No. 19 in E flat major; No. 21 in B flat major; No. 23 in
  F major. *Coupled with works by* **Schumann** Sviatoslav Richter (pf).
  Olympia Ⓕ OCD287 (63 minutes: DDD: 10/92).
...24 Preludes. Prelude in A flat. Piano Sonatas – No. 1 in C minor, Op. 4; No. 2 in B flat minor,
  Op. 35; No. 3 in B minor, Op. 58. Rondos – C minor, Op. 1; F major, "à la mazur", Op. 5.
  Four Ballades. Introduction and Rondo in C minor/E flat major, Op. 16. Rondo in C major,
  Op. 73. **Garrick Ohlsson** (pf).
  Arabesque Ⓕ Z6628/30 (three discs, oas: 78, 66 and 64 minutes: DDD: 10/93).
...Preludes: Nos. 1-24; No. 25 in C sharp minor, Op. 45; No. 26 in A flat major. Op. posth. Spring,
  Op. 74 No. 2. Allegretto and Mazur. Two Bourées. Ecossaise, Op. 72 No. 3. Three Ecossaises,
  WN27. Boléro in C major, Op. 19. Contredanse in G flat major. Galop marquis in A flat major.
  Allegretto in F sharp minor. Feuille d'album in E major. Cantabile in B flat major. Fugue in
  A minor. **Cyprien Katsaris** (pf). Sony Classical Ⓕ SK53355 (69 minutes: DDD: 10/93).
...24 Preludes – No. 6 in B minor; No. 7 in A major; No. 8 in F sharp minor; No. 9 in E major;
  No. 10 in C sharp minor; No. 11 in B major; No. 17 in A flat major; No. 19 in E flat major;
  No. 23 in F major; No. 24 in D minor. Barcarolle in F sharp major, Op. 60. Nocturne in F major,
  Op. 15 No. 1. Etudes – Op. 10: No. 1 in C major; No. 2 in A minor; No. 3 in E major; No. 4 in
  C sharp minor; No. 6 in E flat minor; No. 10 in A flat major; No. 11 in E flat major; No. 12 in
  C minor. Op. 25: No. 5 in E flat minor; No. 6 in G sharp minor; No. 7 in C sharp minor; No. 8 in
  D flat major; No. 11 in A minor; No. 12 in C minor. Polonaises – C sharp minor, Op. 26 No. 1;
  C minor, Op. 40 No. 2; A flat major, Op. 61. *Coupled with works by* **Liszt** Sviatoslav Richter (pf).
  Philips Ⓕ 438 620-2PH3 (three discs: 202 minutes: DDD: 8/94).
...Mazurkas – No. 20 in D flat major, Op. 30 No. 3; No. 25 in B minor, Op. 33 No. 4; No. 33 in
  B major, Op. 56 No. 1; No. 34 in C major, Op. 56 No. 2; No. 35 in C minor, Op. 56 No. 3;
  F minor, Op. 68 No. 4. Boléro, Op. 19. Ballade No. 2 in F major, Op. 38. Barcarolle in F sharp
  major, Op. 60. Scherzo No. 4 in E major, Op. 54. Nocturnes, Op. 62 – No. 1 in B major; No. 2 in
  E major. **Roland Pöntinen** (pf). BIS Ⓕ CD673 (78 minutes: DDD: 11/96).

Chopin Nocturnes Nos. 1-19. **Maria João Pires** (pf). DG Ⓕ 447 096-2GH2 (two discs:
  109 minutes: DDD: 10/96). *Gramophone Editor's choice*. Recorded 1996.   ⓖⓖ
Passion rather than insouciance is Pires's keynote. Here is no soft, moonlit option but an intensity and drama that scorn all complacent salon or drawing-room expectations. How she relishes Chopin's central storms, creating a vivid and spectacular yet unhistrionic contrast with all surrounding serenity or 'embalmed darkness'. The *con fuoco* of Op. 15 No. 1 erupts in a fine fury and in the first *Nocturne*, Op. 9 No. 1, Pires's sharp observance of Chopin's *appassionato* marking comes like a prophecy of the coda's sudden blaze. Such resolution and psychological awareness make you realize that Chopin, like D.H. Lawrence, may well have thought that "there must be a bit of fear, and a bit of horror in your

life". Chopin, Pires informs us in no uncertain terms, was no sentimentalist. More intimately, in Op. 15 No. 3 (where the music's wavering sense of irresolution led to the sobriquet 'the Hamlet Nocturne') Pires makes you hang on to every note in the coda's curious, echoing chimes, and in the *dolcissimo* conclusion to No. 8 (Op. 27 No. 2) there is an unforgettable sense of 'all passion spent', of gradually ebbing emotion. Pires with her burning clarity has reinforced our sense of Chopin's stature and created a new range of possibilities (showing us that there is life after Rubinstein). Naturally, Rubinstein's legendary cycles possess a graciousness, an ease and elegance reflecting, perhaps, a long-vanished *belle époque*. Yet moving ahead, as we all must, one has no hesitation in declaring Maria João Pires – a pianist without a trace of narcissism – among the most eloquent master-musicians of our time.

Additional recommendation ...
...Nocturnes Nos. 1-19. **Artur Rubinstein** (pf). RCA Victor Red Seal Ⓕ RD89563* (ADD).
...Nocturnes Nos. 1-19. Piano Concertos – No. 1 in E minor, Op. 11; No. 2 in F minor, Op. 21. Waltz in C sharp minor, Op. 64 No. 2. **Artur Rubinstein** (pf); **London Symphony Orchestra / Sir John Barbirolli.**
EMI Références mono Ⓜ CHS7 64491-2* (two discs: 161 minutes: ADD: 7/93). ⒼⒼ
...Nocturnes Nos. 1-19. **Fou Ts'ong** (pf).
Sony Classical Essential Classics Ⓑ SB2K53249 (two discs: 101 minutes: ADD: 11/93).
...Three Impromptus. Fantaisie-impromptu. Barcarolle in F sharp major, Op. 60. Piano Sonata No. 3 in B minor, Op. 58. **Howard Shelley** (pf).
Chandos Ⓕ CHAN9175 (57 minutes: DDD: 11/93).
...Nocturnes Nos. 1-19. Fantaisie-impromptu. Barcarolle in F sharp major, Op. 60. **Kathryn Stott** (pf). Unicorn-Kanchana Ⓕ DKPCD9147/8 (two discs: 124 minutes: DDD: 7/94). Ⓖ
...Fantaisie-impromptu. *Coupled with works by various composers.* **Anatol Ugorski** (pf).
DG Ⓕ 447 105-2GH (62 minutes: DDD: 3/96). *See review in the Collections section; refer to the Index.*
...Fantaisie-impromptu. *Coupled with works by various composers.* **Dame Moura Lympany** (pf).
Dutton Laboratories mono Ⓕ CDCLP4000* (77 minutes: ADD: 1/97). *See review in the Collections section; refer to the Index.*
...Fantaisie-impromptu. Polonaises – A major, Op. 40 No. 1; A flat major, Op. 53. Nocturnes – E flat major, Op. 9 No. 2; F sharp major, Op. 15 No. 2. Waltzes, Op. 64 – No. 1 in D flat; No. 2 in C sharp minor. Etudes, Op. 10 – No. 3 in E major; No. 12 in C minor. Preludes, Op. 28 – No. 7 in A major; No. 15 in D flat major. Mazurkas – B flat major, Op. 7 No. 1; D major, Op. 33 No. 2. Ballade No. 1 in G minor, Op. 23. **John Ogdon** (pf).
Altamira Ⓕ RJ2723 (54 minutes: ADD: 3/97).
...Nocturnes Nos. 1-19. **Elisabeth Leonskaja** (pf).
Teldec Ultima Ⓜ 0630-18949-2 (two discs: 127 minutes: DDD: 2/98).
...Nocturnes Nos. 1-19. **Peter Katin** (pf).
IMP Classics Ⓑ 30367 0235-7 (two discs: 111 minutes: ADD: 2/98).

Chopin Waltz No. 2 in A flat major, Op. 34 No. 1 (from HMV DB1168, 2/30). Mazurkas Nos. 1-51 (DB3802/8, 9/39 and DB3839/45, 2/42). Four Scherzos (DB1915/8, 11/33). Barcarolle in F sharp major, Op. 60 (DB1161, 8/28). Berceuse in D flat major, Op. 57 (DB2149, 7/34). Polonaises – No. 1 in C sharp minor, Op. 26; No. 2 in E flat minor, Op. 26; No. 3 in A major, Op. 40, "Military"; No. 4 in C minor, Op. 40 No. 2; No. 5 in F sharp minor, Op. 44; No. 6 in A flat major, Op. 53, "Heroic"; No. 7 in A flat major, Op. 61, "Polonaise-fantaisie"(DB2493/6, 7/36 and DB2497/9, 8/36). Andante spianato and Grand polonaise in E flat major, Op. 22 (DB2499/500, 8/36). **Artur Rubinstein** (pf). EMI Références mono Ⓜ CHS7 64697-2* (three discs: 233 minutes: ADD: 1/93). Recorded 1928-39. ⒼⒼ
Artur Rubinstein is popularly remembered as Chopin's genial, sparkling elder statesman; but, up until now, only seasoned collectors have been aware of his many pre-war recordings – where "aristocratic poise" (Rubinstein's best-known interpretative attribute) went hand-in-hand with impulsiveness, spontaneity and dazzling virtuosity. To compare these 1932-35 versions of the *Scherzos* and Polonaises with Rubinstein's wise, elegant post-war recordings for RCA is to pit "emotion recollected in tranquillity" against the hot-headed impact of immediate experience. There's less of a contrast with the Mazurkas, although – again – these first recordings (Rubinstein made two subsequent sets) have that extra degree of 'lift' and tension. Readers will of course ask themselves whether transfers from old 78s really can deliver as much musical pleasure as modern recordings. But in this case, so-called 'surface noise' is never intrusive and the quality of the playing is so exceptional that the mono sound and relative lack of dynamic range soon cease to pose a problem.

Additional recommendations ...
...Nos. 1-7. **Maurizio Pollini** (pf). DG Ⓕ 413 795-2GH (ADD: 3/85).
...Polonaises Nos. 1-7. **Artur Rubinstein** (pf).
RCA Victor Red Seal Ⓕ RD89814 (60 minutes: ADD: 12/86).
...Polonaises – No. 7; No. 12 in G flat major; No. 13 in G minor; No. 14 in B flat major; No. 15 in A flat major; No. 16 in G sharp minor. Bolero in A minor, Op. 19. Allegro de concert, Op. 46. Berceuse in D flat major, Op. 57. Tarantelle in A flat major, Op. 43. **Nikolai Demidenko** (pf). Hyperion Ⓕ CDA66597 (66 minutes: DDD: 11/92).

...Four Scherzos. Polonaise No. 7. **Claudio Arrau** (pf).
Philips Solo Ⓜ 442 407-2PM (55 minutes: DDD: 9/94).
...16 polonaises. Allegro de concert, Op. 46. Etudes, Opp. 10, 25 and posth – F minor, Op. posth;
A flat major, Op. posth; D flat major, Op. posth. Tarantelle in A flat major, Op. 43. Fugue in
A minor. Albumleaf in E major. Polish songs, Op. 74 – Spring. Galop marquis. Berceuse in
D flat major, Op. 57. Barcarolle, Op. 60. Two Bourrées. **Vladimir Ashkenazy** (pf).
Double Decca Ⓜ 452 167-2DF2 (two discs: 145 minutes: DDD/ADD: 2/97).
...Polonaise No. 7. Nocturne in E flat major, Op. 55 No. 2. Mazurkas – F minor, Op. 7 No. 3;
Op. 17: No. 1 in B flat major; No. 3 in A flat major; No. 4 in A minor; B major, Op. 41 No. 3.
Scherzo No. 4 in E major, Op. 54. Barcarolle in F sharp major, Op. 60. **Richard Goode** (pf).
Nonesuch Ⓕ 7559-79452-2 (48 minutes: DDD: 4/98).

Chopin Scherzo No. 1 in B minor, Op. 20. Polonaises – C sharp minor, Op. 26 No. 1; A flat major,
Op. 53. Waltzes, Op. 64 – No. 1 in D flat major; No. 2 in C sharp minor. Mazurka in A minor,
Op. 59 No. 1. Fantasie in F minor, Op. 49. Nocturnes, Op. 27 – No. 1 in C sharp minor; No. 2 in
D flat major. **Ronan O'Hora** (pf). Tring International Royal Philharmonic Collection Ⓢ TRP086
(62 minutes: DDD: 1/97). Recorded 1995.
Here is Chopin playing to ravish the senses while maintaining an unerring sense of perspective,
allowing the music's innate quality to surface without fuss or impediment. O'Hora tempers valour
with discretion and is never led into neurosis by the composer's fire and fury. You may have heard a
more trenchant, heart-stopping call to arms in the *Polonaise*. Yet, again, you will find yourself
compelled to return to playing of such unforced eloquence and inner strength. In the C sharp minor
Polonaise O'Hora's pensiveness reminds you, most unusually, that the seeds of the *Polonaise-fantaisie*
were already sown and his delicacy and translucency in the elegiac C sharp minor *Waltz* weave their
entirely unindulgent spell. All these performances are of an exquisite musical civility and the
recordings are a great advance on Tring's sometimes overly resonant earlier offerings. More Chopin
from this artist is imperative.

Chopin Four Ballades – No. 1 in G minor, Op. 23; No. 2 in F major, Op. 38; No. 3 in A flat major,
Op. 47; No. 4 in F minor, Op. 52. Mazurkas – No. 7 in F minor, Op. 7 No. 3; No. 13 in A minor,
Op. 17 No. 4; No. 23 in D major, Op. 33 No. 2. Waltzes – No. 1 in E flat major, Op. 18; No. 5 in
A flat major, Op. 42; No. 7 in C sharp minor, Op. 64 No. 2. Etudes, Op. 10 – No. 3 in E major;
No. 4 in C sharp minor. Nocturne No. 1 in F major, Op. 15. **Murray Perahia** (pf).
Sony Classical Ⓕ SK64399 (61 minutes: DDD: 12/94). Recorded 1994. *Gramophone Award*
Winner 1995. Gramophone Editor's choice. Selected by Sounds in Retrospect.   ⒼⒼⒼ
This is surely the greatest, certainly the richest, of Perahia's many exemplary recordings. Once again
his performances are graced with rare and classic attributes and now, to supreme clarity, tonal
elegance and musical perspective, he adds an even stronger poetic profile, a surer sense of the
inflammatory rhetoric underpinning Chopin's surface equilibrium. In other words the vividness and
immediacy are as remarkable as the finesse. And here, arguably, is the oblique but telling influence of
Horowitz whom Perahia befriended during the last months of the old wizard's life. Listen to the First
Ballade's second subject and you will hear rubato like the most subtle pulsing or musical breathing.
Try the opening of the Third and you will note an ideal poise and lucidity, something rarely achieved
in these outwardly insouciant pages. From Perahia the waltzes are marvels of liquid brilliance and
urbanity. Even Lipatti hardly achieved such an enchanting lilt or buoyancy , such a beguiling sense of
light and shade. In the mazurkas, too, Perahia's tiptoe delicacy and tonal irridescence (particularly in
Op. 7 No. 3 in F minor) make the music dance and spin as if caught in some magical hallucinatory
haze. Finally, two contrasting *Etudes*, and whether in ardent lyricism (Op. 10 No. 3) or shot-from-
guns virtuosity (Op. 10 No. 4) Perahia's playing is sheer perfection. The recording beautifully captures
his instantly recognizable, glistening sound world as well as the immense grandeur of his conceptions.
Additional recommendations ...
...Ballades. Barcarolle in F sharp major, Op. 60. Fantasie in F minor, Op. 49.
Krystian Zimerman (pf). DG Ⓕ 423 090-2GH (60 minutes: DDD: 10/88).   ⒼⒼⒼ
...Ballades. Piano Sonata No. 2 in B flat minor, Op. 35. **Andrei Gavrilov** (pf).
DG Ⓕ 435 622-2GH (57 minutes: DDD: 6/92).
...Ballades. Barcarolle. Berceuse. Fantasie. **Alexeï Lubimov** (fp).
Erato Ⓕ 2292-45990-2 (63 minutes: DDD: 7/93). ✍
...Ballade No. 1. Nocturne No. 1. 12 Etudes, Op. 10. Scherzo No. 2 in B flat minor, Op. 31.
Cécile Licad (pf). MusicMasters Ⓕ 67124-2 (60 minutes: DDD: 10/95).
...Ballades. Berceuse in D flat major, Op. 57. Impromptu No. 2 in F sharp major, Op. 36.
Etude in A flat major, Op. 25 No. 1. 24 Preludes, Op. 28. **Alfred Cortot** (pf).
Music & Arts mono Ⓕ CD871* (77 minutes: ADD: 6/96).   Ⓖ

Chopin Waltzes – No. 1 in E flat major, Op. 18. No. 2 in A flat major, Op. 34 No. 1. No. 3 in
A minor, Op. 34 No. 2. No. 4 in F major, Op. 34 No. 3. No. 5 in A flat major, Op. 42. No. 6 in
D flat major, Op. 64 No. 1. No. 7 in C sharp minor, Op. 64 No. 2. No. 8 in A flat major, Op. 64
No. 3. No. 9 in A flat major, Op. 69 No. 1. No. 10 in E minor, Op. 69 No. 2. No. 11 in G flat
major, Op. 70 No. 1. No. 12 in F minor, Op. 70 No. 2. No. 13 in D flat major, Op. 70 No. 3.

No. 14 in E minor, Op. posth. No. 15 in E major, Op. posth. No. 16 in A flat major, Op. posth. No. 17 in E flat major, Op. posth. No. 18 in E flat major, Op. posth. No. 19 in A minor, Op. posth. **Jean-Bernard Pommier** (pf). Erato Ⓕ 4509-92887-2 (57 minutes: DDD: 3/94). Recorded 1993.

This pianist has given long and careful thought as to what aspect of the composer he feels these waltzes should reveal: while recognizing them as "fashionable" Chopin, he never allows his fingers just to trip their way along. The result is never less than pleasing for judicious choice of tempo, for several stimulating textual variants taken from original manuscripts, and a general surefootedness. Perhaps the disc doesn't haunt the memory in quite the same way as several CD reissues of legendary waltzers of yore. Lipatti immediately springs to mind. Of these, the one with whom Pommier has least in common is the mercurial, light-fingered Lipatti, someone too loved by the gods to have time for second thoughts about some questionably breathless tempos or swiftness of internal vacillations of mood, but who so miraculously conveyed the "rapture and poignancy of first sensations". Maybe Pommier more often looked to Rubinstein's finely integrated last recording of these waltzes – though without wholly achieving the eloquent simplicity of phrasing and naturalness of rubato of that artist in later days – or indeed his life-long fingertip magic. But the trenchancy with which the French pianist makes his every point is undeniably impressive. Full, clear-toned recording.

Additional recommendations ...

...Nos. 1-14. **Artur Rubinstein** (pf). RCA Victor Red Seal Ⓕ RD89564* (ADD). ⒼⒼ

...Nos. 1-14. Mazurka No. 32 in C sharp minor, Op. 50 No. 3. Barcarolle in F sharp major, Op. 60. Nocturne No. 8 in D flat major, Op. 27 No. 2. **Dinu Lipatti** (pf). EMI Références mono Ⓜ CDH7 69802-2* (65 minutes: ADD: 7/89). ⒼⒼⒼ

...17 Waltzes. Polonaises – G minor, Op. posth; B flat major, Op. posth. **Allan Schiller** (pf). ASV Quicksilva Ⓢ CDQS6149 (60 minutes: DDD: 4/95).

Chopin Etudes, Opp. 10 and 25. **Maurizio Pollini** (pf). DG Ⓕ 413 794-2GH (56 minutes: ADD: 5/85). From 2530 291 (11/72). ⒼⒼⒼ

Chopin Etudes: Op. 10[a] – No. 4 in C sharp minor; No. 10 in A flat major; No. 11 in E flat major; Op. 25 – No. 5 in E minor; No. 8 in D flat major; No. 11 in A minor; No. 12 in C minor. Nocturnes[a] – E major, Op. 62 No. 2; E minor, Op. 72 No. 1. Polonaise in A flat major, Op. 61[a].

Scriabin Piano Sonatas[b] – No. 2 in G sharp minor, Op. 19; No. 5 in F sharp major, Op. 53. **Sviatoslav Richter** (pf). Praga Ⓑ CMX354007 (61 minutes: ADD: 6/96). Items marked [a] recorded live in 1988, [b]live in 1972.

The 24 *Etudes* of Chopin's Opp. 10 and 25, although dating from his twenties, remain among the most perfect specimens of the genre ever known, with all technical challenges – and they are formidable – dissolved into the purest poetry. With his own transcendental technique (and there are few living pianists who can rival it) Pollini makes you unaware that problems even exist – as for instance in Op. 10 No. 10 in A flat, where the listener is swept along in an effortless stream of melody. The first and last of the same set in C major and C minor have an imperious strength and drive, likewise the last three impassioned outpourings of Op. 25. Lifelong dislike of a heart worn on the sleeve makes him less than intimately confiding in more personal contexts such as No. 3 in E major and No. 6 in E flat minor from Op. 10, or the nostalgic middle section of No. 5 in E minor and the searing No. 7 in C sharp minor from Op. 25. Like the playing, so the recording itself could profitably be a little warmer at times, but it is a princely disc all the same. Chopin Studies were never Richter's ideal repertoire. But in 1988, when the magisterial technique was starting to fray in some repertoire, he turned in some glorious sustained performances, and his wonderful hall-filling sound is finely captured here. Of the Scriabin sonatas, No. 5 is unbelievably daring and No. 2 has you hanging on every note.

Additional recommendations ...

...Etudes. **Vladimir Ashkenazy** (pf). Decca Ⓕ 414 127-2DH (63 minutes: DDD: 1/85). Ⓖ

...Etudes. **Liszt** Mephisto Waltz No. 1, S154, "Der Tanz in der Dorfschenke". **Vladimir Ashkenazy** (pf). Melodiya mono Ⓜ 74321 33215-2* (72 minutes: ADD: 8/96).

...Etudes. **Louis Lortie** (pf). Chandos Ⓕ CHAN8482 (68 minutes: DDD: 1/87).

...Etudes. Impromptus Nos. 1-3. Piano Concerto No. 2 in F minor, Op. 21[a]. Waltzes Nos. 1-14. Preludes Nos 1-24. Piano Sonatas Nos. 2 and 3. Four Ballades. Berceuse in D flat major, Op. 57. Nocturnes Nos. 2, 4, 5, 7, 15 and 16. Polonaise No. 6 in A flat major, Op. 53, "Heroic". Fantasie in F minor, Op. 49. Tarantelle in A flat major, Op. 43. Barcarolle in F sharp major, Op. 60. Polish songs, Op. 74 – My darling. **Liszt** Chants polonais, S480 – Frühling; Das Ringlein. **Alfred Cortot** (pf); [a]orchestra / **Sir John Barbirolli.** EMI Ⓜ CZS7 67359-2* (six discs: 429 minutes: ADD/mono: 6/92). ⒼⒼ

...Etudes. **John Bingham** (pf). Meridian Ⓕ CDE84221 (67 minutes: DDD: 5/93).

...Etudes, Op. 10. Rondos – C minor, Op. 1; F major, Op. 5, "à la Mazur"; C major, Op. 73 (two versions, for one and two pianos). Introduction and Rondo in E flat major, Op. 16. **Frederic Chiu** (pf). Harmonia Mundi Ⓕ HMU90 7201 (77 minutes: DDD: 8/97).

...Etudes, Op. 10: Nos. 4, 5 and 8; Op. 25: No. 3 in F major. Mazurkas – F minor, Op. 7 No. 3; E minor, Op. 41 No. 2; C sharp minor, Op. 50 No. 3. Scherzo No. 4 in E major, Op. 54. Piano Sonata No. 2 in B flat minor, Op. 35, "Funeral March" – Grave ... doppio movimento. *Coupled with works by various composers.* **Vladimir Horowitz** (pf). APR mono Ⓜ APR5516* (69 minutes: ADD: 5/98). *See review in the Collections section; refer to the Index.*

Chopin Piano Sonata No. 2 in B flat minor, Op. 35. Nocturnes – F sharp major, Op. 15 No. 2;
C minor, Op. 48 No. 1; E major, Op. 62 No. 2; C sharp minor, Op. posth. Barcarolle in F sharp
major, Op. 60. Scherzo in B flat minor, Op. 31. **Mikhail Pletnev** (pf). Virgin Classics
Ⓕ VC5 45076-2 (68 minutes: DDD: 3/95). From VC7 90738-2 (4/90). Recorded 1988. *Selected by
Sounds in Retrospect.*
These are superb and audacious performances. Love them or hate them you will never – not for a
minute, not for a second – remain indifferent. Is his *Barcarolle* daringly free or scrupulously true to
both the music's outer and inner manifestation? Dare one mention a glaring rhythmic distortion in
the closing octaves, a vulgarization of Chopin's nobility in the second bar of the C minor *Nocturne*,
or question the *forte* rather than *pianissimo* start to the *doppio movimento* in the same *Nocturne*? Such
questions are asked in a spirit of awe rather than impertinence and are, in any case, invariably silenced
by Pletnev's technical and musical imperiousness. The Second Sonata will have experts (and
particularly Polish experts) locked in furious debate when not mesmerized by the spine-tingling drama
Pletnev achieves at the start of the first-movement development, the sinister underlying waltz rhythm
he finds in the *Scherzo*, the chillingly exact 'timpani' rolls in the Funeral March and, most of all, the
terrifying miasma emanating from the finale. Rarely, too, has the *Nocturnes*' erotic undertow surfaced
so tellingly through their civilized veneer. In short, not since Michelangeli's heyday has Chopin been
played with such compulsive brilliance, individuality and pianistic mastery. The recordings capture
Pletnev's sound-world to perfection and are of optimum range and clarity.
Additional recommendations ...
...Nos. 2 and 3. Scherzo No. 3 in C sharp minor, Op. 39. **Martha Argerich** (pf).
DG Ⓜ 419 055-2GGA (56 minutes: ADD).
...Piano Sonatas Nos. 1-3. **Idil Biret** (pf). Naxos Ⓢ 8 550363 (75 minutes: DDD).
...Piano Sonata No. 2. 12 Etudes, Op. 25^b. **Grigory Sokolov** (pf).
Opus 111 Ⓕ OPS30-83 (59 minutes: DDD: 1/94).
...Barcarolle in F sharp major. Scherzo No. 3 in C sharp minor, Op. 39. *Coupled with works by
various composers.* **Martha Argerich** (pf). DG The Originals Ⓜ 447 430-2GOR (71 minutes: ADD:
6/95). *Gramophone* Classical 100. *See review in the Collections section; refer to the Index.* ⒼⒼⒼ
...Piano Sonatas Nos. 1-3. **Vladimir Ashkenazy** (pf).
Decca Ovation Ⓜ 448 123-2DM (76 minutes: ADD: 2/97).
...Piano Sonata No. 2. *Coupled with works by* **Mozart** *and* **Shostakovich** Emil Gilels (pf).
Testament mono Ⓕ SBT1089* (64 minutes: ADD: 5/97).

Chopin Piano Sonata No. 2 in B flat minor, Op. 35. Polonaises – No. 5 in F sharp minor, Op. 44;
No. 6 in A flat major, Op. 53. Impromptu No. 3 in G flat major, Op. 51. Nocturne No. 2 in D flat
major, Op. 27. Barcarolle in F sharp major, Op. 60. Etudes – Op. 10: No. 4 in C sharp minor;
No. 5 in G flat major; Op. 25: No. 1 in A flat major; No. 5 in E minor. Waltzes – Op. 34: No. 1 in
A flat major; No. 2 in A minor. **Artur Rubinstein** (pf). Revelation Ⓜ RV10013 (78 minutes: ADD:
3/97). Recorded live in 1964.
After a prolonged absence Rubinstein returned to Russia in 1964, gave one of his greatest recitals, and
set musical Moscow by the ears. The intention is unmistakable in every blazing and heroic bar.
Dazzled and, possibly, chastened, the Russians listened in awe to the confirmation of a legend. Here
is the pianist who changed the parameters of Chopin for ever, freeing him of all neurosis
and salon sentimentality and sending his spirit soaring with an overwhelming force and fantasy.
Beckmessers will, of course, note how, in the heat of the moment (and the temperature is white-hot),
assorted *piano* and *pianissimo* markings turn into *fortissimos*, and eyebrows will also be raised over a
wrong turning that wreaks momentary havoc with the *Scherzo* from the Second Sonata. Then there is
the way the A flat *Polonaise*'s central equestrian gallop is launched with a blistering inaccuracy. Yet
such things are somehow part and parcel of the total experience and it is difficult to imagine this
recital without them. Even a hint of playing or recording for safety and the overwhelming intensity
would have been lost. As it is, the Second Sonata's opening *Grave* and *doppio movimento* become
virtually one and the same thing, and who but Rubinstein could declaim the climax of the first
movement's development with such rhetorical defiance? In the second movement, too, where Chopin
hurls blocks of sound in all directions simultaneously, Rubinstein creates a true Mephisto scherzo.
But it is in Chopin's more intimate and confiding pages in, say, the D flat *Nocturne* or A minor *Waltz*
that Rubinstein shows his most aristocratic and cardinal quality. Here, pulse and vocal 'line' never fail,
yet the fluctuations within that pulse are like some infinite and sophisticated poetic play. Such
charisma is, perhaps, more familiar to great singers than pianists and, again, in the *Barcarolle*,
Rubinstein's largesse, his supreme generosity of spirit, illuminates every bar. Rubinstein could play the
aristocrat to the hilt, but he was also a force of nature transcending all carefully prescribed notions
of neatness, musical taste or decorum. To a greater extent than any other pianist he set Chopin's
turbulent genius free to charm and intimidate, to sing and resonate across the universe.

Chopin Piano Sonatas – No. 2 in B flat minor, Op. 35; No. 3 in B minor, Op. 58.
Maurizio Pollini (pf). DG Ⓕ 415 346-2GH (52 minutes: DDD: 8/86).   ⒼⒼ
These two magnificent romantic sonatas are Chopin's longest works for solo piano. The passion of
the B flat minor Sonata is evident throughout, as is its compression (despite the overall length) – for

example, the urgent first subject of its first movement is omitted in the recapitulation. As for its mysterious finale, once likened to "a pursuit in utter darkness", it puzzled Chopin's contemporaries but now seems totally right. The B minor Sonata is more glowing and spacious, with a wonderful *Largo* third movement, but its finale is even more exhilarating than that of the B flat minor, and on a bigger scale. Pollini plays this music with overwhelming power and depth of feeling; the expressive intensity is rightly often disturbing. Magisterial technique is evident throughout and the recording is sharp-edged but thrilling.

Additional recommendations ...

...Nos. 2 and 3. Fantaisie in F minor, Op. 49. **Artur Rubinstein** (pf).
  RCA Victor Red Seal Ⓕ RD89812 (61 minutes: ADD: 2/87). ⓖⓖ
...Nos. 2 and 3. **Murray Perahia** (pf). CBS Ⓕ MK76242 (50 minutes: ADD: 3/89). ⓖⓖ
...No. 3ᵃ. Polonaisesᵇ – C sharp minor, Op. 26 No. 1; E flat minor, Op. 26 No. 2; A major, Op. 40 No. 1; C minor, Op. 40 No. 2; F sharp minor, Op. 44; A flat major, Op. 53. ᵃ**Emil Gilels,** ᵇ**Lazar Berman** (pfs). DG Galleria Ⓜ 449 090-2GGA (76 minutes: ADD: 8/96).

Chopin Piano Sonata No. 3 in B minor, Op. 58. Mazurkas – A minor, Op. 17 No. 4; B flat minor, Op. 24 No. 4; D flat major, Op. 30 No. 3; D major, Op. 33 No. 2; C sharp minor, Op. 50 No. 3; C major, Op. 56 No. 2; F sharp minor, Op. 59 No. 3; B major, Op. 63 No. 1; F minor, Op. 63 No. 2; C sharp minor, Op. 63 No. 3; F minor, Op. 68 No. 4. **Evgeni Kissin** (pf).
  RCA Victor Red Seal Ⓕ 09026 62542-2 (65 minutes: DDD: 11/94). Recorded live in 1993.
  Gramophone Editor's record of the month. ⓖⓖ

At 23 Kissin is unquestionably among the master-pianists of our time, and in their poise and maturity all these performances seem light-years away from colleagues twice his age. What magnificence and assertion he finds in the B minor Sonata's opening (for once truly *maestoso*), what menace in the following uprush of chromatic scales, his deliberate pedal haze capturing one of Chopin's most truly modernist moments. Kissin may relish left-hand counter-melody in the return of the second subject and elsewhere, yet such detail is always offered within the context of the whole, within the most bracing and invigorating sense of propulsion. A momentary failure of concentration at 1'04" in the *Scherzo*'s central section comes as reassuring evidence of human fallibility but elsewhere one can only marvel at a manner so trenchant, musicianly and resolutely unsentimental. The equestrian finale is among the most lucid on record and concludes in a controlled triumph that has the audience cheering to the heavens. The 12 *Mazurkas* are no less remarkable for their strength and discretion. Nothing is rushed, everything is unfolded with complete naturalness and authority. Kissin's rubato is beautifully idiomatic yet so stylishly applied that you are only aware of a musical 'breathing', of the finest fluctuations of pulse and emotion. Few other pianists have gone to the heart of the matter with such assurance (always excepting Artur Rubinstein). The recording captures Kissin's clear, unnarcissistic sonority admirably and audience noise is kept to a minimum.

Chopin Piano Sonata No. 3 in B minor, Op. 58. Polonaise-Fantaisie in A flat major, Op. 61. Nocturne in C minor, Op. 48 No. 1. Scherzo No. 4 in E major, Op. 54. Barcarolle in F sharp major, Op. 60. Ballade No. 4 in F minor, Op. 52. **Nelson Goerner** (pf).
  EMI Debut ⑧ CDZ5 69701-2 (77 minutes: DDD: 8/97). Recorded 1996.

EMI's Debut series recalls DG's long-defunct but similarly invaluable venture; a golden opening for young artists of exceptional talent. Nelson Goerner is Argentinian, a student of Maria Tipo, and devotes his most personal and inflammatory recital to Chopin's later masterpieces. How fearlessly he launches the B minor Sonata's imperious opening, never using Chopin's *maestoso* instruction as an excuse for undue rhetoric or inflation. Even the startling sense of hiatus contained in the first movement repeat (can this really be authentic?) makes sense given such voltage and intensity. His second movement *Scherzo* is as colourful as it is volatile and in the *Largo* the playing is, again, gloriously free-spirited and keenly felt. His transition out of the *Polonaise-Fantaisie*'s central *Più lento*, back to Chopin's principal idea, shows a compelling sense of the composer's depth and introspection, and if his choice of the Fourth *Scherzo* is surprising, given such seriousness, he is once more brilliantly attuned to one of Chopin's most elusive and mercurial major-key flights of fancy. The C minor *Nocturne* pulses with a profound sense of elegy, its central octaves fired off like so many ceremonial cannons, and Goerner makes something very special out of the Fourth *Ballade*'s coda, tempering Chopin's bravura with a fine sense of melodic intricacy. Finally, EMI have provided this most personal and distinctive artist with an impressively bold and spacious recording.

Further listening ...

...(trans. Franchomme) Grand duo concertante in E major on themes from Meyerbeer's "Robert le diable". *Coupled with works by* **Franchomme** Anner Bylsma (vc); **Lambert Orkis** (fp); **Smithsonian Chamber Players.** Sony Classical Vivarte SK53980 (4/95). 🎵
...Rondo in C minor, Op. 1. Rondo "à la Mazur" in F major, Op. 5. Introduction and Rondo in C minor/E flat major, Op. 16. Rondo in C major, Op. 73. Mazurkas, Op. posth. – G major; B flat major; C major; A flat major; D major. Introduction and Variations in E major on "Der Schweizerbub". Introduction and Variations in B flat major on a theme from Hérold's "Ludovic", Op. 12. Souvenir de Paganini (Variations in A major). Variations No. 6 in E major on a March from Bellini's "I Puritani". Introduction, Theme and Variations (with Martin Sauer, pf). **Idil Biret** (pf). Naxos 8 550508 (5/93).

Francesco Cilea

Cilea Adriana Lecouvreur. **Renata Scotto** (sop) Adriana Lecouvreur; **Plácido Domingo** (ten) Maurizio; **Sherrill Milnes** (bar) Michonnet; **Elena Obraztsova** (mez) Princesse de Bouillon; **Giancarlo Luccardi** (bass) Prince de Bouillon; **Florindo Andreolli** (ten) Abbe de Chazeuil; **Lillian Watson** (sop) Jouvenot; **Ann Murray** (mez) Dangeville; **Paul Crook** (ten) Poisson; Major-domo; **Paul Hudson** (bass) Quinault; **Ambrosian Opera Chorus; Philharmonia Orchestra / James Levine.** Sony Ⓕ M2K 79310 (two discs: 135 minutes: ADD: 3/90). Notes, text and translation included. From 79310 (6/78). Recorded 1977.

Adriana Lecouvreur is an archetypal prima donna vehicle. Look at the plot coldly, without reference to the music, and it is costumed hokum of an improbability that takes the breath away (of course there's jealousy, of course there's a death-scene, but what do you say to a bunch of poisoned violets as a murder weapon?). Even with the music, even allowing that Cilea was a much shrewder man of the theatre and a much more able musician than his detractors can bear to allow, it is still ... well, hokum with some damned good tunes. But Cilea wrote his opera in the full knowledge that an essential five per cent of its appeal would be added by the prima donna. Not with faultless vocalism, though that's a prerequisite too, but with the sort of allure of vocal personality that elsewhere would be called "star quality". With that extra five per cent, arguments about the artifice of the plot and the occasional thinness of the score fall away as the irrelevancies that they are. And you can tell very soon whether the soprano in question has that quality: after Cilea's brief but evocative scene-setting (telling us that we're back-stage at the Comédie Française in the eighteenth century, a world of glamour and intrigue), she enters, a prima donna portraying a prima donna, and tells us, to a sumptuous melody, that star though she is she's but the humble handmaid of her art. If you are not moved despite yourself, despite the obvious artifice (is it Adriana or the soprano herself speaking?) proceed no further; either this opera or this performance is not for you. Scotto has that magic quality, in abundance. That Domingo is an ardent hero, Milnes a touching elderly admirer, Obraztsova a baleful rival and Levine an enthusiastic exponent of the subtleties and ingenuities of a composer often despised for having written prima donna vehicles is all bonus, making this a performance that you can return to again and again. But the centre of its allure, its *raison d'être*, is Renata Scotto. Her entrance is electrifying, her death moving and everything between is more than life-size.

Additional recommendation ...

...**Soloists; Welsh National Opera Chorus; Welsh National Opera Orchestra / Richard Bonynge.** Decca Ⓕ 425 815-2DH2 (two discs: 134 minutes: ADD: 9/90).

Domenico Cimarosa

Cimarosa Il matrimonio segreto. **Arleen Auger** (sop) Carolina; **Julia Varady** (sop) Elisetta; **Dietrich Fischer-Dieskau** (bar) Geronimo; **Júlia Hamari** (contr) Fidalma; **Ryland Davies** (ten) Paolino; **Alberto Rinaldi** (bar) Count Robinson; **English Chamber Orchestra / Daniel Barenboim.** DG Ⓜ 437 696-2GX3 (three discs: 165 minutes: ADD: 8/93). Text and translation included. From 2709 069 (9/77). Recorded 1975. *Gramophone Editor's choice.* Ⓖ

The music may not have the more adventurous harmony or contrapuntal dexterity of Mozart (whose opening of the *Zauberflöte* Overture only four months earlier Cimarosa must almost certainly have cribbed), but it abounds in delightfully fresh melodic invention and rhythmic vitality – its bubbling patter-work too is worthy of Rossini at his best. Together with its construction, with as many ensembles as solo arias and with skilfully planned finales, and its scoring, primarily aimed at supporting the singers but giving the orchestra some independent interest, it marks not merely an expert craftsman but a composer of distinction whose wide popularity at the time is understandable. Barenboim makes the music dance along with the utmost sparkle, and he is fortunate in having a splendid cast, in whom it is almost invidious to praise Ryland Davies (with free tone-production, fine breath-control and native-sounding Italian) and the silver-voiced Arleen Auger as the young couple at the centre of the plot. But Alberto Rinaldi also brings a real sense of character to the blustering Count Robinson (was this personage intended as a dig at the British?), who sets his heart on the clandestinely married Caroline and ends up, most improbably, marrying her shrewish elder sister whom he had previously declared he would rather die than wed; and Julia Varady gives a stunning performance of that character's big florid aria in the last act. An issue not to be missed.

Additional recommendation ...

...**Soloists; Orchestra of Eastern Netherlands / Gabriele Bellini.** Arts Ⓢ 47117-2 (three discs: 192 minutes: DDD: 1/97).

Jeremiah Clarke

Suggested listening ...

...**Three Trumpet Ayres.** *Coupled with works by various composers.* **Crispian Steele-Perkins** (tpt); **Bournemouth Sinfonietta / Richard Studt** (vn). Carlton Classics 30366 0038-2 (4/97). *See review in the Collections section; refer to the Index.*

Rebecca Clarke

British 1886-1979

Suggested listening ...
...Viola Sonata. Lullaby. Morpheus. *Coupled with works by various composers.* **Paul Coletti** (va); **Leslie Howard** (pf). Hyperion CDA66687 (10/94). *See review in the Collections section; refer to the Index.*

Clemens non Papa

French/Flemish c1510-c1556

Suggested listening ...
...Prière devant le repas. Action des Graces. *Coupled with works by various composers.* **The Scholars of London.** Naxos 8 550880 (2/95). *See review in the Collections section; refer to the Index.*

Muzio Clementi

Italian/British 1752-1832

Clementi Piano Sonatas – B flat major, Op. 24 No. 2; F sharp minor, Op. 25 No. 5; B minor, Op. 40 No. 2; D major, Op. 40 No. 3. **Nikolai Demidenko** (pf). Hyperion Ⓟ CDA66808 (69 minutes: DDD: 10/95). Recorded 1994.
Several recent excellent releases – on period and modern instruments – have done much to counter Mozart's evaluation of Clementi as a "mere mechanicus". For those who remain unconvinced, Demidenko's issue of Clementi sonatas (on a modern piano) provides a comprehensive demonstration of the composer's skill and imagination that should ensure an enthusiastic following. The B flat Sonata, Op. 24 No. 2, which Clementi played at Joseph II's court in December 1781, is an exuberant exhibition piece. Demidenko's spontaneous keyboard virtuosity and delightful variety of touch underlines the music's surprising diversity. Indeed, the soft lighting of his performances in general heightens the emotional impact of his interpretations. Two of the Op. 40 Sonatas offer remarkable illustrations of Clementi's dramatic and expressive power. Demidenko's performance of the dazzling D major Sonata reveals its potent cocktail of Beethovenian boldness and Mozartian *dolce* in the first movement, and luxuriates in its poignant, improvisatory melody and rich harmony in the second. However, Demidenko's tonal range, technical polish and musical intelligence are even more impressive in the B minor Sonata. Here, his apt characterization of the first movement's turbulent mix of icy reserve and fiery bravura, and deft handling of the second movement's fusion of *adagio* and finale, compellingly evoke the music's spirit of fantasy.
Additional recommendations ...
...F minor; F sharp minor; G minor, Op. 7 No. 3; B flat major, Op. 24 No. 2; D major, Op. 25 No. 6. **Peter Katin** (fp). Athene Ⓟ ATHCD4 (75 minutes: DDD: 12/93). ⚡
...G minor, Op. 8 No. 1; F minor, Op. 13 No. 6; F sharp minor, Op. 25 No. 5; D major, Op. 40 No. 3. Batti, batti (after the aria from Mozart's *Don Giovanni*). **Maria Tipo** (pf). EMI Ⓟ CDC7 54766-2 (73 minutes: DDD: 2/94).
...Op. 24 No. 2; Op. 25: No. 2 in G major, No. 5 in F sharp minor; D major, Op. 37 No. 2. Six Keyboard Sonatinas, Op. 36. **Balázs Szokolay** (pf). Naxos Ⓢ 8 550452 (71 minutes: DDD: 9/95).
Further listening ...
...Symphonies, Op. 18 – No. 1 in B flat major; No. 2 in D major. Minuetto pastorale in D major. Piano Concerto in C major. **Pietro Spada** (pf). **Philharmonia Orchestra / Francesco D'Avalos.** ASV CDDCA802 (2/93).
...Symphonies – No. 1 in C major; No. 3 in G major, "Great National Symphony". Overture in C major. **Philharmonia Orchestra / Francesco D'Avalos.** ASV CDDCA803 (2/93).
...Symphonies – No. 2 in D major; No. 4 in D major. Overture in D major. **Philharmonia Orchestra / Francesco D'Avalos.** ASV CDDCA804 (2/93). These three recordings are also available as part of a three-disc mid-price set (ASV CDDCS322).

Eric Coates

British 1886-1957

Coates Orchestral works. [a]**Royal Liverpool Philharmonic Orchestra / Sir Charles Groves;** [b]**London Symphony Orchestra / Sir Charles Mackerras;** [c]**City of Birmingham Symphony Orchestra / Reginald Kilbey.** Classics for Pleasure Ⓑ CD-CFPD4456* (two discs: 129 minutes: ADD: 9/89). From CFPD414456-3 (11/86). Recorded 1956-71.
Saxo-Rhapsody. Wood Nymphs. Music Everywhere (Rediffusion March). From Meadow to Mayfair. The Dam Busters – march ([a] all from Columbia TWO226, 12/68); London. Cinderella – phantasy. London Again ([a] TWO321, 12/70). The Merrymakers – Miniature Overture. Summer Days – At the dance. By the Sleepy Lagoon. The Three Men – Man from the sea. The Three Bears – Phantasy ([b] CFP40279, 3/78). Calling all Workers – March. The Three Elizabeths ([c] TWO361, 12/71). ⊕⊕
Eric Coates reached a vast public through the use of his music as signature tunes for radio programmes such as "In Town Tonight" ("Knightsbridge" from the *London Suite*), "Music While You

Work" (*Calling all Workers*) and "Desert Island Discs" (*By the Sleepy Lagoon*). The cinema furthered the cause with the huge success of *The Dam Busters* march. There is much more to his music, though, than mere hit themes. Suites such as *London, London Again, From Meadow to Mayfair* and *The Three Elizabeths* offer a wealth of delights and are all the better for the juxtaposition of their contrasted movements. The two tone-poems for children, *Cinderella* and *The Three Bears* are splendidly apt pieces of programme music – simple to follow, ever charming, never trite. The miniature overture *The Merrymakers* and the elegant waltz "At the dance" (from the suite *Summer Days* are other superb pieces of light music, whilst the *Saxo-Rhapsody* shows Coates in somewhat more serious mood. Throughout there is a rich vein of melody, and an elegance and grace of orchestration that makes this music to listen to over and over again with ever increasing admiration. The three conductors and orchestras featured adopt a no-nonsense approach that modestly suggests that his music should not be lingered over, never taken too seriously. Considering that the Mackerras items were first issued in 1956 (the rest being from 1968-71), the sound is of astonishingly good and remarkably uniform quality. This is a veritable feast of delightful music and, at its low price, a remarkable bargain.

Additional recommendation ...
...Calling All Workers. *Coupled with works by various composers.* **New London Orchestra / Ronald Corp.** Hyperion Ⓔ CDA66868 (78 minutes: DDD: 7/96). *Gramophone Editor's record of the month.*   Ⓖ

Further listening ...
...Springtime[a] – Dance in the twilight: Valse. Impression of a Princess[b]. Wood nymphs[b]. The Dam Busters[b]. *Coupled with works by various composers.* [a]**Pro Arte Orchestra / George Weldon;** [b]**orchestra / Eric Coates.** EMI British Composers CDM5 66537-2 (1/98). *See review in the Collections section; refer to the Index.*

Coates Sweet Seventeen. Summer Afternoon. Impressions of a Princess[a]. Salute the Soldier. Two Light Syncopated Pieces. For Your Delight. The Unknown Singer[a]. I Sing to You. Coquette. Over to You. Idyll. Under the Stars. By the Tamarisk. Mirage. Last Love. The Green Land. [a]**Peter Hughes** (sax); **BBC Concert Orchestra / John Wilson.** ASV White Line Ⓜ CDWHL2107 (79 minutes: DDD: 8/97). Recorded 1996.

The title of these pieces won't ring much of a bell with any but the most avid Coates fans. But what delights there are! It goes without saying that Coates's craftsmanship is in evidence from start to finish. Yet so often, one wonders just *why* a particular piece never quite made it in the way his most popular works did. Isn't *Summer Afternoon* every bit as delightful as *By the Sleepy Lagoon*? And wouldn't *Salute the Soldier* have served just as well as other marches as a radio signature tune? Most simply, aren't *Under the Stars, For Your Delight* and others just simply such utter charmers? The BBC Concert Orchestra play beautifully, and the 24-year-old conductor, John Wilson, seems thoroughly imbued with the Coates style. The recorded sound is crisp and clean, too. A splendid collection.

Coates Songs[a] – Rise up and reach the stars; At vesper bell; The young lover; The grenadier; Four old English songs; Because I miss you so; Sigh no more, ladies; Tell me where is fancy bred; The fairy tales of Ireland; Music of the night; Betty and Johnny; The mill o' dreams; When I am dead; The little green balcony; Ship of dream; The outlaw's song; Your name; Beautiful lady moon; Princess of the dawn. First meeting[b]. [a]**Richard Edgar-Wilson** (ten); [b]**Michael Ponder** (va); **Eugene Asti** (pf). Marco Polo Ⓔ 8 223806 (69 minutes: DDD: 4/96). Texts included. Recorded 1994.

This is very much a sequel to the existing ASV collection of Coates songs performed by Brian Rayner Cook and Raphael Terroni. The performers and label may be different, but the recording location and producer are the same. Most particularly, there is no overlap of programmatic content. Uncommonly for a sequel, this collection is every bit the equal of its predecessor both in content and performance. Richard Edgar-Wilson has a delightfully natural, free-ranging and expressive tenor voice, his words coming through with complete clarity, while Eugene Asti clearly revels in Coates's luxurious accompaniments. Such, moreover, is the consistency of Coates's inspiration and musicianship that, though his best-known songs are all in the ASV collection, the selection here is equally enjoyable. At the most obviously popular end of the spectrum *The grenadier* has one of those rousing Fred Weatherly lyrics after the fashion of *Stonecracker John*, while at the more ambitious end are some delightfully fresh Shakespeare settings, as well as the short song-cycle *The mill o' dreams*. By way of variety the collection also includes a piece for viola and piano that Coates composed for his teacher Lionel Tertis. This gives producer Michael Ponder a chance to step into the limelight, which he richly deserves for this utterly diverting collection.

Further listening ...
...The Seven Dwarfs. The Jester at the Wedding. Four Centuries. **East of England Orchestra / Malcolm Nabarro.** ASV White Line CDWHL2075 (8/93).
...Knightsbridge: March. *Coupled with works by various composers.* **The New London Orchestra / Ronald Corp.** Hyperion CDA66968 (5/97). *Gramophone Editor's choice.* .   Ⓖ
...Reuben Ranzo. I heard you singing. Brown eyes I love. I pitch my lonely caravan at night. The dreams of London. A song remembered. The green hills o' Somerset. Bird songs at eventide. A dinder courtship. Always as I close my eyes. Little lady of the moon. Through all the ages. Stonecracker John. At sunset. I'm lonely. Homeward to you. Today is ours. A song of summer. **Brian Rayner Cook** (bar); **Raphael Terroni** (pf). ASV White Line CDWHL2081 (3/87).

Jean Cocteau French 1889-1963

Suggested listening ...
...Le bel indifférent[b]. *Coupled with* **Poulenc** La voix humaine[a]. [a]**Denise Duval** (sop); [b]**Edith Piaf** (spkr); [a]**Paris Opéra-Comique Orchestra / Georges Prêtre;** [b]**instrumental ensemble.** EMI L'Esprit Français CDM5 65156-2* (10/94). *See review under Poulenc; refer to the Index.*

Edward Collard British fl c1595-1599

Suggested listening ...
...A Ground. *Coupled with works by various composers.* **Mhairi Lawson** (sop); **Circa 1500.** ASV Gaudeamus CDGAU163 (12/97). ☞ *See review in the Collections section; refer to the Index.*

Anthony Collins British 1893-1963

Suggested listening ...
...Vanity fair. *Coupled with works by various composers.* **Pro Arte Orchestra / George Weldon.** EMI British Composers CDM5 66537-2 (1/98). *See review in the Collections section; refer to the Index.*

Edouard Commette French 1883-1967

Suggested listening ...
...Scherzo. *Coupled with works by various composers.* **Gerard Brooks** (org). Priory PRCD558 (4/98). *See review in the Collections section; refer to the Index.*

Loÿset Compère French c1445-1518

Suggested listening ...
...Crux triumphans. *Coupled with works by various composers.* **Orlando Consort.** Metronome METCD1015 (4/97). *See review in the Collections section; refer to the Index.*
...O bone Jesu. *Coupled with works by various composers.* **Early Music Consort of London / David Munrow.** Virgin Classics Veritas VED5 61334-2 (11/97). ☞ *See review in the Collections section; refer to the Index.*

Justin Connolly British 1933

Suggested listening ...
...Sonatina in Five Studies, Op. 1. *Coupled with works by various composers.* **Steven Neugarten** (pf). Metier MSVCD92008 (1/96). *See review in the Collections section; refer to the Index.*

Aaron Copland American 1900-1990

Copland Piano Concerto[a]. Orchestral Variations. Short Symphony. Symphonic Ode.
[a]**Garrick Ohlsson** (pf); **San Francisco Symphony Orchestra / Michael Tilson Thomas.** RCA Victor Red Seal Ⓟ 09026 68541-2 (66 minutes: DDD: 3/97). Recorded 1996.
Selected by Soundings.
According to Virgil Thompson, jazz was Aaron Copland's "one wild oat". Page after page of *Music for the Theatre* and its first cousin, the 1926 Piano Concerto, featured here, read like the blueprints for symphonic dance to come. Bernstein's *On the Town* began here. But Copland arrived first, and middle America was taken aback – temporarily. An erstwhile *succès de scandale* became 'the best roar from the roaring twenties'. A bold proclamation passed between trumpets and trombones, a 'fanfare for ...'; but before you can finish the sentence, a dramatic cut to the wide shot: a glorious lyric effusion, its sights set on yet another gleaming skyline. Brave new world or lonely town? The quizzical solo piano isn't entirely sure, but the yearning grows: rhapsody in blue. Garrick Ohlsson kicks into this rhythm-bending mood-swing with terrific aplomb, and the San Francisco Symphony stretch every sinew to get their long limbs co-ordinated. Tilson Thomas has them well blooded in the ways of this music: it's slick, it's tight, but it still retains that sense of wilful precariousness. Copland, 'the modernist', alludes to skylines a great deal here. It's hard to imagine that the *Orchestral Variations* were ever laid down in anything but orchestral terms, their sonority and harmony stretched from top to bottom of the score in spare, spacey chords. Copland's very particular brand of rhetoric. And then you remember that in its ground-breaking piano original it was as if the keyboard itself had been

surrealistically elongated. It has the look of a modern metropolis in sound, this music: lean, clean, oblique. *Symphonic Ode* – Copland's first big orchestral piece after the Piano Concerto – proceeds onwards and upwards in sky-scraping, octave-leaping tower blocks of sound. It's so very much a young man's America, alternately monolithic and toughly contrapuntal. A jazzy hint of misbegotten adolescence, a reflective heart and a tremendous conclusion as proud and implacable as the US Constitution itself. A couple of sensational modulations, and Tilson Thomas's San Francisco horns are quite literally reaching for the sky. Because there is no place to go but up. The performance *knows* just how good it is – and that's a fact. Deep-set, blockbusting recording. A winner.

Additional recommendations ...

...Piano Concerto. **Britten** Piano Concerto. **Gillian Lin** (pf); **Melbourne Symphony Orchestra / John Hopkins.** Chandos Collect Ⓜ CHAN6580 (51 minutes: ADD: 3/93).

...Appalachian Spring. Billy the Kid – suite. Rodeo. Fanfare for the Common Man. **New York Philharmonic Orchestra / Leonard Bernstein.** Sony Classical Bernstein Royal Edition Ⓜ SMK47543 (63 minutes: ADD: 5/93).   ⒺⒼⒺ

...Piano Concerto[a]. Appalachian Spring[b]. Symphonic Ode[c]. [a]**Lorin Hollander** (pf); **Seattle Symphony Orchestra / Gerard Schwarz.** Delos Ⓕ DE3154 (62 minutes: DDD: 4/96).

Copland Concert Suites – The Red Pony; Our Town; Music for Movies. The Heiress – Prelude; Finale. Prairie Journal (Music for Radio). **St Louis Symphony Orchestra / Leonard Slatkin.** RCA Victor Red Seal Ⓕ 09026 61699-2 (67 minutes: DDD: 11/94). Recorded 1991-92.   Ⓖ

Though the front cover bears the title "Music for Films", the earliest offering here was written in 1936 following a commission from the CBS radio network. *Music for Radio* (also known as *Saga of the Prairies* or *Prairie Journal*) was one of Copland's first conscious efforts to attain a greater simplicity of utterance and stronger melodic appeal, and its clean-cut, out-of-doors demeanour is relished to the full by these performers. Copland wrote eight film scores in all, the first three of which – *The City* (1939), *Of Mice and Men* (1939) and *Our Town* (1940) – formed the basis for his 1943 concert suite, *Music for Movies*. Slatkin gauges the differing moods of each of the five tableaux with unerring perception. Perhaps Copland's most enduring achievement in this particular field remains his 1948 score for *The Red Pony*. Again, the performance is all one could wish and there's real swagger in the joyous "Happy Ending" number. In addition, Slatkin also gives us the heart-warmingly evocative concert suite Copland compiled from his score for *Our Town*, as well as a first commercial recording for Arnold Freed's idiomatic 1990 reconstruction of Copland's Academy Award-winning 1948 score for *The Heiress*, which happily restores the "Prelude" that director William Wyler rejected for the final print. With excitingly full-bodied sound, this is an unmissable Copland collection.

Copland El salón México[a]. Dance Symphony[a]. Fanfare for the Common Man[a]. Rodeo – Four Dance Episodes[a]. Appalachian Spring – suite[b]. **Detroit Symphony Orchestra / Antál Dorati.** Decca Ovation Ⓜ 430 705-2DM (74 minutes: DDD: 8/91). Items marked [a] from SXDL7547 (10/82), [b]414 457-2DH (6/86). Recorded 1981-84.   ⒺⒼ

This glorious disc shows how well Antál Dorati assimilated the music of Aaron Copland. The big-boned swagger of "Buckaroo Holiday" from *Rodeo* with its vision of open spaces and clear blue skies is established straightaway in Dorati's performance with keen rhythmic drive and fine orchestral articulation. The "Hoe Down" is properly exciting while the other two dance episodes are wonderfully expressive. In the 1945 suite of *Appalachian Spring* Dorati secures marvellous phrasing and dynamics but tends to understate the poetic elements of the score. Decca's sound quality is exemplary and is of demonstration standard in *Fanfare for the Common Man*, as it is in the enjoyable curtain-raiser, the sturdy, big-hearted *El salón México*. Dorati's vast experience as an interpreter of Stravinsky and Bartók pays fine dividends in Copland's gruesome *Dance Symphony*, music inspired by the vampire film fantasy, *Nosferatu*. This survey of Copland's most popular orchestral works is a welcome addition to the mid-price catalogue.

Additional recommendations ...

...Fanfare for the Common Man. Rodeo – Four Dance Episodes. Appalachian Spring – suite. Quiet City. Billy the Kid – suite. **Cincinnati Pops Orchestra / Erich Kunzel.** Telarc Ⓕ CD80339 (77 minutes: DDD).

...Fanfare for the Common Man[a]. Rodeo – Three Dance Episodes[b]. An Outdoor Overture[b]. The Red Pony – suite[c]. Lincoln Portrait[d]. [d]**Adlai Stevenson** (narr); [ad]**Philadelphia Orchestra / Eugene Ormandy;** [b]**Cleveland Pops Orchestra / Louis Lane;** [c]**St Louis Symphony Orchestra / André Previn.** Sony Classical Essential Classics Ⓑ SBK62401 (64 minutes: ADD).

...El salón México[c]. Danzón cubano[e]. An Outdoor Overture[e]. Quiet City[e]. Our Town[e]. Las agachadas[c]. Fanfare for the Common Man[e]. Lincoln Portrait[be]. Appalachian Spring – suite[e]. Rodeo – Four Dance Episodes[e]. Billy the Kid – suite[e]. Music for Movies[d]. Letter from Home[e]. John Henry[e]. Symphony No. 3[d]. Clarinet Concerto[af]. [a]**Benny Goodman** (cl); [b]**Henry Fonda** (narr); [c]**New England Conservatory Chorus;** [d]**New Philharmonia Orchestra;** [e]**London Symphony Orchestra;** [f]**Columbia Symphony Orchestra / Aaron Copland.** Sony Classical Ⓜ SM3K46559 (three discs: 226 minutes: ADD: 7/91).   ⒼⒼ

...El salón México. Clarinet Concerto[a]. Connotations. Music for the Theatre. [a]**Stanley Drucker** (cl); **New York Philharmonic Orchestra / Leonard Bernstein.** DG Ⓕ 431 672-2GH (74 minutes: DDD: 8/91).   Ⓖ

...Appalachian Spring – suite[a]. Billy the Kid[b]. Danzón cubano[c]. El salón México[d].
[ab]**London Symphony Orchestra**; [cd]**Minneapolis Symphony Orchestra / Antál Dorati.**
Mercury Living Presence Ⓜ 434 301-2MM (76 minutes: ADD: 8/91).
...Fanfare for the Common Man. Billy the Kid – suite. El salón México. Rodeo – Hoe-Down.
Appalachian Spring – suite. **Royal Philharmonic Orchestra / Philip Ellis.**
Tring International Royal Philharmonic Collection Ⓢ TRP040 (65 minutes: DDD: 12/95).
...(arr. Bernstein) El salón México. *Coupled with works by various composers.* **Shura Cherkassky** (pf).
Decca Ⓕ 433 657-2DH (79 minutes: ADD: 2/96).　　　　　　　　　　　　Ⓖ
...Fanfare for the Common Man[a]. Appalachian Spring[b]. Lincoln Portrait[c]. Quiet City[d]. Music for
Movies[e]. Ceremonial Fanfare[f]. Old American Songs[g] – Long time ago; Simple gifts; I bought me
a cat; At the river; Ching-a-ring Chaw. El salón México[h]. Dance Symphony[h]. Rodeo – Four
Dance Episodes[h]. [g]**Marilyn Horne** (mez); [c]**Gregory Peck** (spkr); [abc]**Los Angeles Philharmonic
Orchestra / Zubin Mehta;** [d]**Academy of St Martin in the Fields / Sir Neville Marriner;**
[e]**London Sinfonietta / Elgar Howarth;** [f]**Philip Jones Brass Ensemble;** [g]**English Chamber Orchestra /
Carl Davis;** [h]**Detroit Symphony Orchestra / Antál Dorati.**
Double Decca Ⓜ 448 261-2DF2 (two discs: 132 minutes: ADD: 8/96).
...El salón México. *Coupled with works by various composers.* **Boston Symphony Orchestra /
Serge Koussevitzky.** Dutton Laboratories mono Ⓜ CDAX8015* (75 minutes: ADD: 1/97).

Copland Organ Symphony[a]. Short Symphony. Dance Symphony. Orchestral Variations.
[a]**Simon Preston** (org); **St Louis Symphony Orchestra / Leonard Slatkin.** RCA Victor Red Seal
Ⓕ 09026 68292-2 (67 minutes: DDD: 6/96). Recorded 1993-5.
Copland's *Organ Symphony* is an oddly eclectic mix born of oddly eclectic elements. Russian
immigrant parents, a French teacher, jazz – the new national identity: all have a hand in the
composition. But still the voice which emerges most strongly is American. Something stirs in the great
outdoors but, as yet, it's untamed and more than a little unpredictable. In the *Dance Symphony* young
Copland taps once more into his French connections, to indulge himself, to bring on the cornets and
two harps, to lend a Berlioz-like enchantment to the solo bassoon; the second movement's shadowy
waltz is the one that never made it into the *Symphonie fantastique*. The fact is that the real Copland
only fully emerges with the *Short Symphony* (No. 2) of 1932-3. The Stravinsky factor is strong, of
course (wiry, angular, busy neo-classical tone and a folkloric homespun quality), but the true grit is
entirely Copland's own. The rhythmic bounce and the sometimes belligerent syncopations are all his,
too. Slatkin and his band are as spry as can be in that respect. The most exciting item on the disc,
however, comes last in the chronology. Nearly three decades after Copland famously got tough with
his *Piano Variations* (1930), he laid them out for orchestra – they came up sounding like a brand-new
piece. This is Copland outreaching himself, theoretical ingenuity allied to vision. And rather like this
sharp, smart, punchy performance, the overriding impression is of evolution – onwards and upwards.

Copland Violin Sonata[a]. Duo for Flute and Piano[b]. Rodeo – suite (arr. cpsr). Piano Quartet[c].
[b]**Jeanne Baxtresser** (fl); [a]**Glenn Dicterow**, [c]**Charles Rex** (vns); [c]**Rebecca Young** (va);
Alan Stepansky (vc); [c]**Israela Margalit** (pf). EMI Anglo-American Chamber Music
Ⓕ CDC5 55405-2 (77 minutes: DDD: 10/96). Recorded 1995. *Gramophone Editor's choice.*　Ⓖ
Schub's account of Copland's eloquent Violin Sonata (1942-43) is very fine. Experienced NYPO
concert-master Glenn Dicterow invests Copland's memorably serene and sinewy melodic lines with
great imaginative intensity and flair, and his partnership with pianist Israela Margalit must be deemed
a great artistic success. Margalit then teams up with the NYPO's principal flautist, Jeanne Baxtresser,
for a stylish rendering of the *Duo* (1971), an ingratiating, witty offering based on thematic ideas from
Copland's sketch-books from the 1940s. Margalit also makes a decent showing in the 1962 *Rodeo*
excerpts for solo piano and the challenging Piano Quartet of 1950, a work of purpose and substance,
is here given a performance which does full justice to its striking integrity and admirable ambition.
Additional recommendation ...
...Violin Sonata. Nocturne. *Coupled with works by various composers.* **Anne Akiko Meyers** (vn);
André-Michel Schub (pf). RCA Victor Red Seal Ⓕ 09026 68114-2 (55 minutes: DDD: 8/96).
See review in the Collections section; refer to the Index.
Further listening ...
...Ballets – Grohg[a]; Hear ye! Hear ye![b]. Prelude[b]. [a]**Cleveland Orchestra;** [b]**London Sinfonietta /
Oliver Knussen.** Argo 443 203-2ZH (10/94). *Gramophone Editor's choice.*　　　　　　Ⓖ
...Clarinet Concerto. *Coupled with works by* **Nielsen** and **Lutosławski** Janet Hilton (cl);
Royal Scottish Orchestra / Mattias Bamert. Chandos CHAN8618 (10/88).
...Symphony No. 3. Quiet City. **New York Philharmonic Orchestra / Leonard Bernstein.**
DG 419 170-2GH (11/86).
...Billy the Kid – Waltz; Celebration. *Coupled with works by various composers.* **Richard Slavich** (vc);
Alice Rybak (pf). Crystal Records CD639 (5/98). *See review in the Collections section; refer to the
Index.*
...Duo. *Coupled with works by various composers.* **Gregory Fulkerson** (vn); **Robert Shannon** (pf).
New World 80313-2 (2/96).
...In the Beginning[a]. Four Motets. *Coupled with works by* **Barber** and **Bernstein**
[a]**Catherine Denley** (mez); **Corydon Singers / Matthew Best.** Hyperion CDA66219 (9/87).

...Old American Songs, Set 2 – The little horses; Zion's walls; At the river; Ching-a-ring. *Coupled with works by various composers.* **Jennifer Larmore** (mez); **Antoine Palloc** (pf). Teldec 0630-16069-2 (12/97). *See review in the Collections section; refer to the Index.*

...12 Poems of Emily Dickinson. *Coupled with works by various composers.* **Barbara Bonney** (sop); **André Previn** (pf). Decca 455 511-2DH (2/98). *See review in the Collections section; refer to the Index. Selected by Soundings.* 🅖🅖

Chick Corea
American 1941

Suggested listening ...
...Children's Songs Nos. 2-4, 6, 7, 11, 16 and 18. *Coupled with works by various composers.* **Apollo Saxophone Quartet; John Harle** (keybds); **Mike Hamnett** (perc). Argo 443 903-2ZH (8/95). *See review in the Collections section; refer to the Index.*

Arcangelo Corelli
Italian 1653-1713

Corelli 12 Concerti grossi, Op. 6 – No. 1 in D major; No. 2 in F major; No. 3 in C minor; No. 4 in D major; No. 5 in B flat major; No. 6 in F major; No. 7 in D major; No. 8 in G minor; No. 9 in F major; No. 10 in C major; No. 11 in B flat major; No. 12 in F major. **The English Concert / Trevor Pinnock.** Archiv Produktion Ⓕ 423 626-2AH2 (two discs: 130 minutes: DDD: 1/89). 🎵 *Gramophone Award Winner 1989.* 🅖

In his working life of about 40 years Corelli must have produced a great deal of orchestral music, yet the 12 *Concerti grossi*, Op. 6 form the bulk of what is known to have survived. Their original forms are mostly lost but we know that those in which they were published in Amsterdam by Estienne Roger had been carefully polished and revised by the composer – and that they were assembled from movements that had been written at various times. The first eight are in *da chiesa* form, the last four in *da camera* form – without and with named dance movements respectively, and the number of their movements varies from four to seven. Each features the interplay of a group of soloists, the *concertino* (two violins and a cello) and the orchestra, the *ripieno*, the size of which Corelli stated to be flexible. These are masterpieces of their genre, one that was later developed by, notably, Bach and Handel, and they are rich in variety. The scores leave scope for embellishment, not least in cadential and lining passages, and the players of The English Concert take full advantage of them.

Additional recommendations ...
...**Ensemble 415 / Chiara Banchini** (vn); **Jesper Christensen** (hpd). Harmonia Mundi Ⓕ HMC90 1406/7 (two discs: 147 minutes: DDD: 6/92). 🎵
...**Guildhall String Ensemble / Robert Salter** (vn). RCA Victor Red Seal Ⓕ RD60071 (two discs: 128 minutes: DDD: 9/91).
...Nos. 1, 3, 7, 8, 9 and 11. **Tafelmusik Baroque Orchestra / Jean Lamon** (vn). Deutsche Harmonia Mundi Ⓕ RD77908 (66 minutes: DDD: 12/89). 🎵
...No. 8. **A. Scarlatti** Abramo, il tuo sembiante[a]. [a]**Rossana Bertini**, [a]**Elena Cecchi Fedi** (sops); [a]**Claudio Cavina** (alto); [a]**Sandro Naglia** (ten); [a]**Sergio Foresti** (bass); **Concerto Italiano / Rinaldo Alessandrini.** Opus 111 Ⓕ OPS30-156 (71 minutes: DDD: 3/97). 🎵

Corelli Trio Sonatas, Op. 3[a] – F major; D major[c]; B flat major; B minor; D minor[c]; G major. Trio Sonatas, Op. 4[b] – C major; G minor; A major; D major; A minor; E major. [c]**Jakob Lindberg** (theorbo); **Purcell Quartet** (Catherine Mackintosh, [a]Elizabeth Wallfisch, [b]Catherine Weiss, vns; Richard Boothby, vc); **Robert Woolley** ([a]hpd/[b]org). Chandos Chaconne Ⓕ CHAN0526 (76 minutes: DDD: 12/92). 🎵 Recorded 1990 (Op. 3), 1992 (Op. 4).

Corelli's chamber music was reprinted 84 times during his lifetime and 31 more during the rest of the eighteenth century, a record that most composers would find enviable even today. The Sonatas of Op. 3 are *da chiesa*, those of Op. 4 are *da camera* (with dance-titled movements); the recording contains the first six of each set – the remaining ones are on another disc (Chandos CHAN0532), should you (as is probable) be tempted to add them to your collection. They are small gems: most have four movements and their durations range from five-and-a-half to seven-and-a-half minutes, within which they pack a wealth of invention, pure beauty and variety of pace and mood. Surviving evidence suggests that they were played at a much lower pitch than today's standard, the lower string tension adding warmth and opulence to the sound. Catherine Mackintosh takes full advantage of the works' opportunities for pliant phrasing and added embellishments; Elizabeth Wallfisch 'converses' with her in her own characteristic way, whilst Catherine Weiss follows her example more closely. The Purcell Quartet's oneness of thought and timing is a joy to hear and the recording is superb in all respects.

Additional recommendation ...
...Trio Sonatas – B flat major, Op. 3 No. 3; C major, Op. 4 No. 1. **A. Scarlatti** Humanità e Lucifero[a]. [a]**Rossana Bertini** (sop); [a]**Massimo Crispi** (ten); **Europa Galante / Fabio Biondi** (vn). Opus 111 Ⓕ OPS30-129 (61 minutes: DDD: 2/96). 🎵 *See review under A. Scarlatti; refer to the Index.*

Further listening ...
...(trans. Geminiani) Sonata in D minor, Op. 5 No. 12, "La follia". *Coupled with* **Geminiani** Six Concerti grossi, Op. 3. **Europa Galante / Fabio Biondi** (vn). Opus 111 OPS30-172 (1/98). ✎
...Sonata in G minor, WoO2. Trio Sonata in G major, Op. 2 No. 12. *Coupled with works by various composers.* **Ann Monoyios** (sop); **Berlin Barock Compagney.** Capriccio 10 459 (10/95). ✎
See review in the Collections section; refer to the Index. ⓖ
...Sonata for Trumpet and Strings in D major. *Coupled with works by various composers.* **Håkan Hardenberger** (tpt); **I Musici.** Philips 442 131-2PH (5/95). *See review in the Collections section; refer to the Index.* ⓖ

John Corigliano

American 1938

Corigliano Symphony No. 1[a]. Of Rage and Remembrance[b]. [b]**Michael Accinno** (treb); [b]**Michelle DeYoung** (mez); [b]**Washington Oratorio Society;** [b]**Washington Choral Arts Society; National Symphony Orchestra / Leonard Slatkin.** RCA Victor Red Seal Ⓕ 09026 68450-2 (53 minutes: DDD: 1/97). Text and translation included. Item marked [a] recorded live in 1995, [b]1995-9f6.
Corigliano's First Symphony is an elegy in memory of the composer's friends who have died of AIDS. The violent first movement expresses fury over this plague, leading to the first of three elegies for particular friends, with the Albéniz *Tango* in Godowsky's piano arrangement poignantly heard from off-stage. The "Tarantella" scherzo of the second movement then builds on a trivial piano piece that Corigliano had written for a pianist friend – anger expressed in distortions of triviality. As a culmination the long third movement, "Giulio's Song", is both a chaconne on a 12-note theme and an elegy for a cellist friend, whose improvisation Corigliano found on a tape after his death, and here uses in the most moving section of all, with solo cellos interweaving. In a brief epilogue the composer simply refers back to each of the previous movements in turn, and closes the work peacefully. What makes this disc even more recommendable is the inclusion as a prelude to the symphony of the related choral work, *Of Rage and Remembrance.* This is substantially a reworking of "Giulio's Song" with the words filled in. Corigliano built the later part of "Giulio's Song" on a poem by William M. Hoffman, librettist of his opera, *The Ghosts of Versailles,* with references by name to the friends commemorated. Corigliano then left out the words, using instruments alone. The choral work – with the central mezzo soprano part superbly sung by Michelle DeYoung – restores the words, leading to a section involving free spoken chant, with chorus members individually naming those they have lost.

Further listening ...
...Aria. *Coupled with works by various composers.* **Humbert Lucarelli** (ob); **Mark Wood** (perc); **Brooklyn Philharmonic Orchestra / Michael Barrett.** Koch International Classics 37187-2 (7/94)..
...Clarinet Concerto[a]. *Coupled with* **Barber** Third Essay for Orchestra, Op. 47. [a]**Stanley Drucker** (cl); **New York Philharmonic Orchestra / Zubin Mehta.** New World NW309-2 (5/88). ⓖⓖ
...Piano Concerto[a]. Tournaments Overture. Fantasia on an Ostinato. Elegy. [a]**Barry Douglas** (pf); **St Louis Symphony Orchestra / Leonard Slatkin.** RCA Victor Red Seal 09026 68100-2 (11/96).
...Piano Concerto[a]. *Coupled with* **Ticheli** Radiant Voices. Postcard. [a]**Alain Lefevre** (pf); **Pacific Symphony Orchestra / Carl St Clair.** Koch International Classics 37250-2 (11/96).
...To Music. Voyage[a]. Campane di Ravello. Elegy. Promenade Overture. Creations[b]. [b]**Sir Ian McKellen** (narr); [a]**Paul Edmund-Davies** (fl); **I Fiamminghi / Rudolf Werthen.** Telarc CD80421 (3/97).
...Troubadours. *Coupled with works by* **Foss** and **Schwantner** Sharon Isbin (gtr); **Saint Paul Chamber Orchestra / Hugh Wolff.** Virgin Classics CDC5 55083-2 (8/96). ⓖ
... Violin Sonata. *Coupled with* **Beach** Violin Sonata, Op. 34. **Curtis Macomber** (vn); **Diane Walsh** (pf). Koch International Classics 37223-2 (8/95).

William Cornysh

British 1468-1523

Cornysh Ave Maria, mater Dei. Magnificat. Gaude virgo, mater Christi. Salve regina.
Prentes Magnificat.
Turges Magnificat. **The Cardinall's Musick / Andrew Carwood.** ASV Gaudeamus Ⓕ CDGAU164 (73 minutes: DDD: 9/97). Texts and translations included. Recorded 1996.
The sacred music of William Cornysh is perhaps demanding technically but in this recording The Cardinall's Musick meet the challenge handsomely. The inevitable comparison must be with The Tallis Scholars' anthology, which ranks as one of their finest achievements. The Cardinall's Musick have the deeper sound, enhanced by a marginally warmer acoustic, and their approach to phrasing and tempo is somewhat more relaxed than The Tallis Scholars. The Cardinalls' account of the *Salve regina* is the more dramatic of the two, and in *Gaude virgo* their choice of a tenor on the top line (rather than a countertenor) seems the more effective. Enthusiasts of this period will welcome the addition to the catalogue of the *Magnificats* by Turges and Prentes. The Cardinall's Musick continue to go from strength to strength, and clearly thrive in their preferred recording venue, the Fitzalan chapel of Arundel Castle.

Additional recommendations ...

...Ave Maria, mater Dei. Magnificat. Gaude virgo, mater Christi. Salve regina. Ah, Robin. Adieu, adieu, my heartes lust. Adieu courage. Woefully arrayed. Stabat mater. **The Tallis Scholars / Peter Phillips.** Gimell Ⓕ 454 914-2PH (65 minutes: DDD: 4/89).   Ⓖ

...Ave Maria, mater Dei. *Coupled with works by various composers.* **The Sixteen / Harry Christophers.** Collins Classics Ⓕ 1342-2 (61 minutes: DDD: 7/93). *See review in the Collections section; refer to the Index.*   Ⓖ

Further listening ...

...Ah, Robin. *Coupled with works by various composers.* **I Fagiolini.** Metronome METCD1012 (3/97). *Gramophone Editor's choice.*   ⒼⒼ

...Blow thi horne hunter. Ah, Robin. *Coupled with works by various composers.* **Oxford Camerata / Jeremy Summerly.** Naxos 8 553088 (5/97).

Francisco Correa de Arauxo   Spanish c1583/4-1654

Suggested listening ...

...Tiento de segundo tono. *Coupled with works by various composers.* **His Majestys Sagbutts and Cornetts.** Hyperion CDA66847 (11/96). *See review in the Collections section; refer to the Index.*

Michel Corrette   French 1709-1795

Suggested listening ...

...Concerto comique No. 25, "Les Sauvages et la Furstemberg". *Coupled with works by* **Boismortier** and **Leclair Florilegium Ensemble; Jane Rogers** (va); **Scott Pauley** (theorbo). Channel Classics CCS7595 (12/95). 🎙 *See review under Leclair; refer to the Index.*

Elvis Costello   British 20th century

Suggested listening ...

...Put away forbidden playthings. *Coupled with works by various composers.* **Fretwork.** Virgin Classics VC5 45217-2 (12/97). *See review in the Collections section; refer to the Index.*

François Couperin   French 1668-1733

F. Couperin Livre de clavecin, Premier livre – Premier ordre. Concerts royaux – No. 1 in G major[a]; No. 2 in D major[b]. **Laurence Cummings** (hpd); **Reiko Ichise** ([a]viol/[b]viola da gamba). Naxos Ⓢ 8 550961 (71 minutes: DDD: 4/97). 🎙 Recorded 1994. *Gramophone Editor's choice.*   Ⓖ

The heading "Music for Harpsichord, Vol. 1" on this disc raises high hopes for the future of this Couperin series. Cummings presents the *Concerts royaux* in the harpsichord version authorized by the composer (here calling on the services of a viol for the extra part in the last number of each *Concert*), though many will prefer the richer scoring in which they were played before Louis XIV. But Cummings, besides being an exceptionally clean player, with intelligent phrasing, the neatest possible ornaments unobtrusively incorporated into the textural lines, splendidly rhythmic yet not at all inflexible, is a persuasive stylist: all his performances are marked by a vitality that is most appealing. In the *Premier ordre*, with its several references to the Duke and Duchess of Maine's circle, he captures the tender expressiveness of "Les Sentimens", the pomposity of "La Majesteuse" and the delicacy of "Les Abeilles"; and in the *Concerts royaux* his Allemandes are particularly exhilarating, while his treatment of "Les échos" is very effective. A very fine copy of a Taskin harpsichord is recorded with striking fidelity.

Additional recommendations ...

...*HMA190 351/3* (152 minutes) – Premier livre de clavecin. *HMA190 354/6* (191 minutes) – Deuxième livre de clavecin: Ordres 6-12. L'art de toucher le clavecin. *HMA190 357/8* (150 minutes) – Troisième livre de clavecin: Ordres 13-19. *HMA190 359/60* (152 minutes) – Quatrième livre de clavecin: Ordres 20-27. **Kenneth Gilbert.** Harmonia Mundi Musique d'abord Ⓑ HMA190 351/60 (two triple- and two double-disc sets: ADD: 10/89). 🎙

...Premier livre de clavecin. **Christophe Rousset** (hpd). Harmonia Mundi Ⓕ HMC90 1450/2 (three discs: 182 minutes: DDD: 7/95).

F. Couperin L'art de toucher le clavecin – Prelude No. 6 in B minor. Troisième livre de clavecin[a] – Treizième ordre; Quatorzième ordre; Quinzième ordre. **Robert Kohnen** (hpd); [a]**Barthold Kuijken** (fl). Accent Ⓕ ACC9399D (64 minutes: DDD: 4/96). 🎙 Recorded 1993.

Kohnen has chosen the first three *ordres* of Couperin's *Troisième livre de clavecin* which was published in 1722; and he has prefaced his recital with the sixth of eight preludes from Couperin's didactic *L'art de toucher le clavecin* which first appeared in 1716. His playing is rhythmically incisive, fastidious in detail – Couperin was hot on that – and full of character. If, on first acquaintance, his realization of Couperin's vignette "Les lis naissans" (*Ordre* No. 13) seems a shade spiky then his lyrical approach to the flowing 6/8 melody of the rondeau "Les rozeaux", which follows, reassures us that Kohnen does have the poetry of the music at heart, and intends that it should be so. Less appealing are Kohnen's somewhat intrusive vocal introductions to "Les folies françoises". This information is provided in the booklet so it hardly needs to be reiterated. In a concert recital such snatches of actuality can be effective; on a disc, after repeated listening, they become an unwelcome interruption. Occasional departures from the norm in the following two *ordres* are of an altogether more agreeable nature. In "Le rossignol-en-amour" (*Ordre* No. 14) Kohnen takes Couperin up on his suggestion to use a transverse flute, played here with a beautifully rounded tone by Barthold Kuijken. Likewise, in the jaunty rondeau, "La Julliet", the trio texture is realized by flute and harpsichord rather than the more usual two-harpsichord texture. This piece is beautifully done, as is the subtly bell-like "Carillon de Cithère" which follows it. In short, a stylish and entertaining release – apart from the aforementioned spoken prefaces – which is as likely as any to draw the cautious listener into Couperin's refined, allusory and metaphor-laden idiom.

F. Couperin Quatrième livre de clavecin. **Christophe Rousset** (hpd). Harmonia Mundi
Ⓕ HMC90 1445/6 (two discs: 152 minutes: DDD: 10/94). ✒ Recorded 1993. ⓖⓖ
Couperin's Fourth Book of harpsichord pieces, his last, published in Paris in 1730 though completed around three years earlier does not, perhaps, contain as many masterpieces as the First and Second Books, but a high proportion of them possess a character nevertheless poignant and sometimes enigmatic which both stimulates the imagination and haunts the memory. For example, pieces such as "L'Amphibie", a noble passacaille, "L'Arlequine" bringing to mind Watteau's clown, "L'Epineuse", a rondeau with an almost Schubertian melancholy (Couplet 3), and a rare excursion into the key of F sharp major (Couplet 4), and "La Pantomime", whose deliciously angular gestures were probably inspired by Scaramouche, the central figure in the Comédie Italienne popular in Paris in the early eighteenth century. All this and, as they say, much more make this anthology a deeply rewarding one. Rousset is fastidious in matters of ornament – for that he would have gained Couperin's wholehearted approval – and has a lively response to the many and varied musical gestures, some of them of enormous subtlety. He has, furthermore , the technique to implement Couperin's requirements with absolute fluency, and the sense to eschew exaggerated or misplaced mannerisms.

Additional recommendations ...
...Quatrième livre de clavecin. **Olivier Baumont** (hpd).
Erato MusiFrance Ⓕ 2292-45824-2 (two discs: 142 minutes: DDD: 8/93). ✒
...L'art de toucher le clavecin: Préludes – C major; D minor; G minor; B flat major; F minor; A major. Premier livre: Troisième ordre – Allemande La ténébreuse; Courantes I and II; Sarabande La lugubre; L'espagnolète; Chaconne La favorite. Cinquième ordre – Sarabande La dangereuse; Les ordes. Dixième livre: Sixième ordre – Les baricades mistérieuses. Huitième ordre – La Raphaéle; Allemande L'Ausoniène; Courantes I and II. Sarabande L'unique; Gavotte; Rondeau; Gigue; Passacaille. Troisième livre: Quinzième ordre – Le dodo ou L'amour au berçeau. Quatrième livre: Vingt-troisième ordre – L'arlequin. Vingtquatrième ordre – Les vieux seigneurs. **Skip Sempé** (hpd). Deutsche Harmonia Mundi Ⓕ RD77219 (72 minutes: DDD: 1/91). ✒
...Troisième livre de clavecin. **Olivier Baumont, Davitt Moroney** (hpds).
Erato MusiFrance Ⓕ 4509-92859-2 (two discs: 134 minutes: DDD: 2/94). ✒
...Deuxième livre de clavecin[a]. L'art de toucher le clavecin. **Olivier Baumont, [a]Davitt Moroney** (hpds). Erato Ⓕ 4509-96364-2 (three discs: 178 minutes: DDD: 3/95). ✒ *Selected by Soundings.*
...Deuxième livre de clavecin[a]. L'art de toucher le clavecin. **Christophe Rousset, [a]William Christie** (hpds). Harmonia Mundi Ⓕ HMC90 1447/9 (three discs: 182 minutes: DDD: 3/95). ✒
...Deuxième livre de clavecin: Les Baricades Mistérieuses; Passacaille; Troisième livre: Les Folies françoises, ou Les Dominos; Les Fauvétes Plaintives; Le Dodo, ou L'Amour en berceau; Le Tic-Toc-Choc, ou Les Maillotins; La Muse-Plantine; Quatrième livre de clavecin: L'Arlequine; Les Ombres Errantes. *Coupled with works by various composers.* **Marcelle Meyer** (pf). EMI mono Ⓜ CZS5 68092-2* (four discs: 275 minutes: ADD: 6/95). *See review in the Collections section; refer to the Index.* ⓖⓖⓖ
...Troisième Livre de clavecin: Quatorzième ordre – Le Rossignol-en-amour; Le Carillon de Cithere. *Coupled with works by various composers.* **George Malcolm** (hpd). Decca Ⓜ 444 390-2DWO (75 minutes: ADD: 11/95). ✒

F. Couperin Trois Leçons de Ténèbres. Quatre Versets du Motet. **Sophie Daneman, Patricia Petibon** (sops); **Les Arts Florissants** (Marc Hantaï, Charles Zebley, fls; Monica Huggett, Emilia Benjamin, vns; Anne-Marie Lasla, bass viol) / **William Christie** (hpd). Erato Ⓕ 0630-17067-2 (47 minutes: DDD: 7/97). ✒ Texts and translations included. Recorded 1996.
All three of Couperin's Lessons for the Wednesday of Holy Week – the first two for a single voice, the third for a pair – represent the composer at his most heart-rendingly intense, underlining the character of the text by chromaticisms, expressive appoggiaturas and ornaments (on the interpretation of which he set great store). Each verse of these Lamentations of Jeremiah is preceded by an elaborate melisma on a successive letter of the Hebrew alphabet, like an illuminated capital in a medieval manuscript.

On this disc the gamba continuo line is filled out only by harpsichord, whereas Boulay relies more on organ and lute. Both sets focus on two intelligent and stylish singers, well matched (as they need to be) in the singularly beautiful intertwining lines of the introductory letters. Christie's ladies are sweeter-voiced and gentler than Boulay's more trenchant duo, but if the former are more touching in the First Lesson's "plorans ploravit" and the Third's "desolatam", the latter bring more poignancy to the Second's "Recordare est" (on an eight-bar ground bass) and the Third's "si est dolor sicut dolor meus". Unusually, Daneman and Petibon adopt a Gallic pronunciation of the Latin, with French nasal vowels in words like "princeps" and "gentes". Erato may well have put you in a quandary by issuing these two recordings: but do hear them both if you can.

Additional recommendation ...

...Trois Leçons de Ténèbres. Motet – Victoria! Christo resurgenti. Magnificat. **Mieke van der Sluis** (sop); **Guillemette Laurens** (mez); **Pascal Monteilhet** (lute); **Marianne Muller** (va da gamba); **Laurence Boulay** (hpd, org). Erato Musifrance Ⓕ 2292-45012-2 (61 minutes: DDD: 8/90). ✍

F. Couperin Messe à l'usage ordinaire des paroisses (with plainchant). **Marie-Claire Alain** (org); **Les Chantres de la Chapelle de Versailles / Emmanuel Mandrin**. Erato Ⓕ 0630-17581-2 (66 minutes: DDD: 12/97). Text and translation included. Played on the Clicquot organ of Cathédrale St Pierre de Poitiers, France. Recorded 1996.

Couperin's two Organ Masses are his earliest known compositions. Marie-Claire Alain here plays the larger of the two, the parish Mass, which is spaciously laid out and was designed for the liturgy on the principal church feast days. Couperin supplied details of organ registration for both Organ Masses, though left matters concerning ornamentation and phrasing to the discretion of the performer. An effective feature of this recording is the placing of the music in an appropriate context. Thus the various sections of Couperin's Mass are integrated with an irregularly alternating pattern of Gregorian chant. This is sung by Les Chantres de la Chapelle de Versailles under the direction of Emmanuel Mandrin. He has chosen ornamented versions of the plainsong melodies based on those which were in use at the end of the seventeenth century. The contrasting colours of Couperin's Organ Masses, whether merely the product of his highly imaginative registration or of textual affinity, are among their most glorious features. Intimacy, exuberance, grandiose declamation and the quiet fervour of prayer all take their turn in a work of great nobility. The late-eighteenth-century Clicquot organ of Poitiers Cathedral is well known to organ music specialists and sounds splendid in the context of this music. In summary, this is a satisfying, sometimes thrilling recital.

Additional recommendation ...

...Messe à l'usage ordinaire des paroisses[a]. Messe pour les couvents de religieux et religieuses[b]. O misterium ineffabile[c]. Domine salvum fac regem[d]. Quid retribuam tibi domine[e]. [abcd]**Isabelle Poulenard** (sop); [abe]**Jacques des Longchamps** (alto); [abcd]**François Le Roux** (bar); [ab]**Val-de-Grâce Gregorian Choir; Jean-Patrice Brosse** (org). Virgin Classics Veritas Ⓜ VED5 61298-2 (113 minutes: DDD: 9/96).

Further listening ...

...Pièces de violes. Les goûts-réunis[a] – Douzième Concert in A major; Troisième Concert in G major. **Wieland Kuijken,** [a]**Kaori Uemura** (vas da gamba); **Robert Kohnen** (hpd). Accent ACC9288 (4/94). ✍   Ⓖ

Louis Couperin   French c1626-1661

L. Couperin Harpsichord Works – Suites: D major; A minor; C major; F major. Tombeau de Monsieur de Blancrocher. **Laurence Cummings** (hpd). Naxos Ⓢ 8 550922 (74 minutes: DDD: 3/95). Recorded 1993.

Cummings handles the ticklish problems of Couperin's free-rhythm Preludes with assurance, producing very convincing readings; and his brisk lift to the rhythm of the "changement de mouvement" in the F major and A minor Preludes (the latter "in imitation of M. Froberger") is invigorating. He applies *inégalités* and stylish embellishments and variants with an easy spontaneity, brings off the grandiose C major Passacaille with panache, and is neat at fitting in the intricate rhythms of the C major Courante (for crossed hands). He is particularly happy in the high spirits of "La Piémontaine" and the "Branle de Basque". But when his rhythm is so good, why does he disturb the flow of the D major Sarabande by lingering overlong at the end of the second and fourth bar? This apart, one can have little but praise for this disc; and at its low price it is a real bargain which should be eagerly snapped up.

Additional recommendations ...

...Harpsichord Suites – A minor; D minor; Prélude in C major; Pavanne in F sharp minor. *Coupled with works by various composers.* **Jane Chapman** (hpd). Collins Classics Ⓕ 1421-2 (71 minutes: DDD: 4/95). ✍ *See review in the Collections section; refer to the Index.*

...Harpsichord Suites – complete. Pavanne in F sharp minor. Prelude and Chaconne in G minor; Two Pieces in B flat major. Three Pieces in G minor. Four Pieces in G major. **Davitt Moroney** (hpd). Harmonia Mundi Musique d'abord Ⓑ HMA190 1124/7 (four discs: 315 minutes: ADD: 4/90). ✍

...Tombeau de Monsieur de Blancrocher. *Coupled with works by various composers.*
Pierre Trocellier (hpd/org). Auvidis Astrée Ⓔ E8592 (73 minutes: DDD: 12/96). ✒
Gramophone Editor's choice. See review under Lalande; refer to the Index. Ⓖ

Ruth Crawford
American 1901-1953

Crawford Music for Small Orchestra[d]. Three Chants[ac]. Study in Mixed Accents[b]. Three Songs[ad].
String Quartet[f]. Two Ricercare[ab]. Andante[d]. Rissolty Rossolty[d]. Suite[e].
Charles Seeger John Hardy[d]. [a]**Lucy Shelton** (sop); [b]**Reinbert de Leeuw** (pf); [c]**New London
Chamber Choir / James Wood;** [d]**Schönberg Ensemble** ([e]Govert Jurriaanse, fl; [e]Marieke Schut, ob;
[e]Pierre Woudenberg, cl; [e]Wilma van den Berge, bn; [e]Hans Dullaert, hn; [f]Marijke van Kooten,
[f]Heleen Hulst, vns; [f]Karin Dolman, va; [f]Hans Woudenberg, vc) **/ Oliver Knussen.**
DG Ⓕ 449 925-2GH (72 minutes: DDD: 12/97). Texts and translations included.
Recorded 1996. Ⓖ
This is an excellently conceived portrait of a remarkable American pioneer. Crawford wrote most of
her music in Chicago in the 1920s and in New York in the early-1930s. She studied with Charles
Seeger in New York and then was the first woman to obtain a Guggenheim Fellowship to study in
Europe, where she showed her work to leading figures such as Berg, Bartók, Honegger and Roussel.
When she returned to New York she married Seeger. It was his involvement with folk music, their
commitment to Communism and raising a young family in the Depression that gradually cut her off
from writing her own exploratory music. She died at only 52 in 1953, just when she might have been
finding her way back to composition with the Suite for wind quintet included here. She had her own
voice even when she was in Chicago, well before she met Seeger, although his ideas were a significant
influence from 1930. The earliest work here, the *Music for Small Orchestra* (1926), demonstrates this.
The first movement is based on ostinato and there are suggestions of Ives as chords build into clusters
but she could hardly have heard anything of his at that time. The second movement employs some
elements of neo-classicism in a distinctly personal, even bantering way. Crawford's best-known work
is her String Quartet of 1931. This radical piece has been acclaimed for its anticipations of Carter and
patches of clusters that would not sound out of place in Penderecki's early works. It is certainly a
courageous document and its *Andante* works well in her 1938 setting for string orchestra, although it
builds up such intensity that it seems slightly short. There are also novelties here, such as the *Three
Chants* – an ingenious reflection of monks singing in heterophony in an invented language. Crawford
knew and admired the poet, Carl Sandburg, and in her *Three Songs* to his verse she is absolutely at
one with his images, from the mechanical violence of the second song to the spooky moonscape of
the last. All the songs are splendidly delivered by Lucy Shelton. *Rissolty Rossolty* is an orchestral
setting of three folk-songs which date from 1939. This is altogether sparkling and delightful and is
followed by a Charles Seeger setting. Finally the late Suite for wind quintet harks back to Crawford's
earlier style, featuring her characteristic use of ostinato and octaves. It is neatly imagined and a
sad reminder of what might have been. Informative booklet-notes enhance this outstanding and
valuable disc.

Giovanni da Crema
Italian *fl* 1540-100

Crema Ricercar quinto. Ricercar sexto. Ricercar tredecimo. Ricercar duodecimo. Ricercar
decimoquarto. Ricercar decimoquinto. Saltarello ditto Bel fior. Saltarello ditto El Giorgio.
Saltarello ditto El Maton. Saltarello ala bolognesa. Con lacrime e sospiri. Lasciar il velo.
De vous servir. O felici occhi miei. Pass'e mezo ala bolognesa.
Dall'Aquila Ricercars – MBS15, 16, 18, 19, 22, 24, 28, 33, 70 and 101. Ricercar-Fantasias –
MBS26; GAC7 and 29. Saltarello, MBS38, "La traditora". Priambolo, MBS71. Amy souffrez,
MBS62. La cara cosa, MBS36*f*. **Christopher Wilson** (lte). Naxos Ⓢ 8 550778
(58 minutes: DDD: A/97). Recorded 1994.
In a publication of 1536 Francesco Marcolini described the triumvirate of Marco Dall'Aquila, Albert
de Rippe and Francesco da Milano as the worthy successors of the earlier, Petrucci generation of
lutenists, in developing the new contrapuntal style of ricercar. Dall'Aquila, the eldest, defined "the
parameters of the newer soloist polyphonic manner" (as the annotator puts it), one that was to
dominate the shape of lute fantasias for the next 100 years. Da Crema, who may also have been a
violist – very little is known of his life – was one of those who followed in the wake of Dall'Aquila
and da Milano. Some of his ricercars are adapted from works by Julia da Modena Segni and one is a
parody, but they are little less worthy in their own right. All these men shared a taste for settings of
popular songs and dances, of which there are numerous examples in this recording, and intabulations
of vocal works – here by Moulou, Verdelot, Arcadelt and Sermisy. This is music to which you must
come – it does not *demand* your attention – a world of small, cultured sounds and structures. Having
entered it you will find it described with great clarity, warmth of sound, and suppleness of delivery
by Christopher Wilson. Neither composer has been generously treated on disc, and the limited
amount of overlapping with the programmes of other recordings does nothing to reduce the value of
this disc.

Lyell Cresswell
New Zealand/Scottish 1944

Suggested listening ...
...Words for Music. *Coupled with works by various composers.* **Tracey Chadwell** (sop);
  Pamela Lidiard (pf). British Music Society BMS420/1CD (3/98). *See review in the Collections*
  section; refer to the Index.

Paul Creston
American 1906-1985

Suggested listening ...
...String Quartet, Op. 8. *Coupled with works by various composers.* **Arthur Gleghorn** (fl); **Mitchell**
  Lurie (cl); **Ann Mason Stockton** (hp); **Hollywood Quartet; Concert Arts Strings / Felix Slatkin.**
  Testament mono SBT1053* (3/95). *See review in the Collections section; refer to the Index.* ⒼⒼ

George Crumb
American 1929

Crumb Quest[a].
Ruders Psalmodies[c].
J.A. Lennon Zingari[b]. David Starobin (gtr); [ac]Speculum Musicae / [a]William Purvis, [c]Donald Palma;
[b]SMU Meadows Symphony Orchestra / David Milnes. Bridge Ⓕ BCD9071 (72 minutes: DDD:
6/97). Item marked [a]new to UK, [b]BCD9042, [c]BCD9037 (5/93).
It is important for the guitar's absorption into mainstream music-making, that the gap bewteen lone
recitalist and concerto soloist should be bridged; the two works by Crumb and Ruders, in which the
guitar plays a *concertante* role, make a valuable contribution to that end. Crumb's work is an eight-
movement sextet in which he uses a remarkable variety of instruments to produce haunting sounds.
His 'quest', prompted by quotations from Dante and Lorca, is "a long tortuous journey towards an
ecstatic and transfigured feeling of arrival", in which interjected phrases from *Amazing grace* have a
moving effect akin to that of the Bach chorales in Berg's Violin Concerto and Takemitsu's *Folios*. The
title of Ruders's 11-movement *Psalmodies* has "no specific religious content or aim"; he compares its
message with that of his First Symphony, *Of Joy and Grief; of Worship and Oblivion.* He uses more
conventional forces than Crumb but does so to equally arresting effect: "Solo for two", for guitar and
cello, left hands only, is one of many instrumental *tours de force.* Here, then, are two of the most
remarkable twentieth-century ensemble works ever written for the guitar, albeit not for the faint-
hearted. John Anthony Lennon pays tribute to gipsy culture and the spontaneity of its music. He
describes *Zingari* as "a suite of [five] concert arias rather than a concerto in the classic form". Here
the 'conventional' listener will find the most familiar ground. Only a guitarist of the highest technical
skill and musical insight could play and empathize with these works: Starobin is a model of the ilk,
teamed with other players of similar calibre. This is a remarkable and magnificently recorded disc,
nothing less than a milestone in the progress of the twentieth-century guitar.
Further listening ...
...Black Angels. *Coupled with works by various composers.* **Kronos Quartet.**
  Elektra Nonesuch 7559-79242-2 (4/91). *See review in the Collections section; refer to the Index.* ⒼⒼ
...Black Angels. *Coupled with* **Schubert** String Quartet in D minor, D810,
  "Death and the Maiden". **Brodsky Quartet.** Teldec 9031-76260-2 (9/93).
...Cello Sonata. *Coupled with works by* **Escher** and **Kodály** Pieter Wispelwey (vc).
  Globe GLO5089 (12/94).

Bernhard Crusell
Finnish 1775-1839

Crusell Clarinet Concerto No. 1 in E flat major, Op. 1.
L. Koželuch Clarinet Concerto in E flat major.
Krommer Clarinet Concerto in E flat major, Op. 36. **Emma Johnson** (cl); **Royal Philharmonic**
  Orchestra / Günther Herbig. ASV Ⓕ CDDCA763 (67 minutes: DDD: 9/91).
The idiom of Stockholm-based composer Bernhard Crusell embraced elements of Mozart, Spohr,
Weber, Rossini and even Beethoven. But in the hands of Emma Johnson, his music has a personality
all its own. Here she turns her attention to his First Clarinet Concerto which is full of engaging ideas.
The slow movement is beautifully done and in the finale the soloist is at her very best – full of
impulsive charm and swagger. Although the Koželuch concerto seems less distinctive, the slow
movement of the Krommer is undeniably affecting and its finale bounces along in fine style. Emma
Johnson plays throughout with a winning spontaneity and the RPO, arguably just a shade tubby of
timbre for such music, back her up with distinction. The generous acoustic is effectively caught.
Additional recommendation ...
...Clarinet Concertos – No. 1; No. 2 in F minor, Op. 5; No. 3 in B flat major, Op. 11.
  Orchestra of the Age of Enlightenment / Anthony Pay (cl).
  Virgin Classics Veritas Ⓕ VC7 59287-2 (72 minutes: DDD: 12/93). 🖋

Further listening ...
...Clarinet Concerto No. 2 in F minor, Op. 5. *Coupled with works by various composers.*
Emma Johnson (cl); **English Chamber Orchestra / Sir Charles Groves.**
ASV CDDCA559 (11/86).   ❷❷

Frederic Curzon   British 1899-1973

Suggested listening ...
...Punchinello[a]. The boulevardier[b]. *Coupled with works by various composers.* [a]**Pro Arte Orchestra /**
George Weldon; [b]**Light Music Society Orchestra / Sir Vivian Dunn.** EMI British Composers
CDM5 66537-2 (1/98). *See review in the Collections section; refer to the Index.*

Luigi Dallapiccola   Italian 1904-1975

Suggested listening ...
...Tre poemi[a]. Liriche Greche[b]. Quattro liriche di Antonio Machado[b]. Commiato[a].
[a]**Luisa Castellani,** [b]**Natalia Zagorinskaja** (sops); **Ensemble Contrechamps / Giorgio Bernasconi.**
Stradivarius STR33462 (5/98).

Marco Dall'Aquila   Italian c1480-after 1538

Suggested listening ...
...Ricercars – MBS15, 16, 18, 19, 22, 24, 28, 33, 70 and 101. Ricercar-Fantasias – MBS26;
GAC7 and 29. Saltarello, MBS38, "La traditora". Priambolo, MBS71. Amy souffrez, MBS62.
La cara cosa, MBS36*f. Coupled with works by* **Crema** Christopher Wilson (lte).
Naxos 8 550778 (A/97). *See review under Crema; refer to the Index.*

Henri Dallier   French 1849-1934

Suggested listening ...
...Cinq Invocations. *Coupled with works by various composers.* **Gerard Brooks** (org).
Priory PRCD558 (4/98). *See review in the Collections section; refer to the Index.*

Philip Dalmas   American ?-1928

Suggested listening ...
...As I watch'd the ploughman ploughing. *Coupled with works by various composers.*
Thomas Hampson (bar); **Craig Rutenberg** (pf). EMI CDM5 55028-2 (10/97). *See review in the*
Collections section; refer to the Index.   ❸❸❸

Jean-Michel Damase   French 1928

Suggested listening ...
...Pavane variée. Berceuse, Op. 19. *Coupled with works by various composers.* **David Pyatt** (hn);
Martin Jones (pf). Erato 3984-21632-2 (4/98). *See review in the Collections section; refer to*
the Index.
...Sicilienne variée. *Coupled with works by various composers.* **Naoko Yoshino** (hp).
Philips 446 064-2PH (2/96). *See review in the Collections section; refer to the Index.*

Jean-François Dandrieu   French c1682-1738

Dandrieu Premier livre d'orgue – Mass and Vespers for Easter Sunday[a].
Gregorian Chant Mass and Vespers for Easter Sunday[b]. [b]**Paris Gregorian Choir / Jaan-Eik Tulve**
with [a]**Jean-Patrice Brosse** (org). Pierre Verany Ⓔ PV794034 (59 minutes: DDD: 6/95).
Texts and translations included. Played on the organ of St Bertrand-de-Comminges, France.
Recorded 1993.
A peculiarly French recording, this. Jean-Patrice Brosse plays Dandrieu's organ music for Easter Day
Mass on the splendid instrument at St-Bertrand-de-Comminges (the town where Herod Antipas is
supposed to have spent his last years), and the chant is supplied by the Paris Gregorian Choir.
Dandrieu's music is – while naturally more restrained than his harpsichord works – colourful and
inventive, though not as memorable as Couperin's Organ Masses, and is extremely well played by

Brosse. Certainly the most impressive piece is the "Offertoire sur les grands jeux on 'O filii et filiae'". What makes the recording interesting is the liturgical context in which Dandrieu's music is placed. Bells are rung, the choir sound suitably monkish, and there is a sense of connection between the chant and the organ music which is of course essential (for example, in the *Kyrie* or the *Sanctus*), but in practice extremely difficult to achieve on a recording. The sound quality itself is excellent.

Richard Danielpour
American 1956

Danielpour Cello Concerto.
Kirchner Music for Cello and Orchestra.
Rouse Cello Concerto. **Yo-Yo Ma** (vc); **Philadelphia Orchestra / David Zinman.** Sony Classical
Ⓕ SK66299 (79 minutes: DDD: 3/97). *Gramophone Editor's choice. Selected by Soundings.*   Ⓖ
All these works were commissioned for Yo-Yo Ma which makes the performances definitive in at least one sense. Fortunately, David Zinman secures committed playing from the Philadelphia Orchestra and the sensitive recording team make a positive contribution. Whether you want the disc will depend on how you respond to the idiom of the three composers represented here. The most straightforward music is provided by the youngest of the three men, Richard Danielpour. His music and even his movement titles are derivative of Leonard Bernstein's but you may think that no bad thing. Danielpour is a shameless eclectic who wants his music to have "an immediate, visceral impact" and so it does. What one misses is memorable melodic invention. Leon Kirchner, Ma's sometime teacher at Harvard, places greater stress on internal logic and intellectual consistency even if he has moved away from the world of Arnold Schoenberg (his own teacher) to forge a personal style of "euphonious dissonance". There is here a rich, loving, almost Korngoldian lyricism, at first suppressed, at length permitted to flower.

Christopher Rouse is one of the more genuinely individual composers working in America today and his neglect over here is a puzzle. Having incorporated elements of rock music into his own before such things were fashionable (and introduced the first academically respectable course on the subject at the Eastman School of Music in Rochester, New York), his mode of address is both boldly communicative and formally coherent, rarely lapsing into the obvious paths of professorial post-expressionism and/or workmanlike nostalgia. If his Cello Concerto is less effective than some of his other pieces that may be because it does not quite measure up to its stated programme as "a meditation upon death". Rouse is good at the noisy accumulation of rhythmic energy, less original in the contemplative, static processional of his second movement. Concluding with a death rattle – one last reprise of the hissing and rattling percussion idea from the first movement – this *Adagiati* encompasses references to other people's death pieces – Monteverdi, Schumann and, seemingly, Pärt's *Cantus* in memory of Benjamin Britten, although that section might also be said to constitute an unravelling of the rather banal ascending idea that opens the concerto.
Further listening ...
...Concerto for Orchestra. Anima mundi. **Pittsburgh Symphony Orchestra / David Zinman.**
    Sony Classical SK62822 (9/97).

Franz Danzi
German 1763-1826

Suggested listening ...
...Horn Concerto in E major. *Coupled with works by* **Haydn** and **Rosetti** Hermann Baumann (hn);
    Concerto Amsterdam / Jaap Schröder. Teldec Das Alter Werk 0630-12324-2 (8/96).
    See review under Haydn; refer to the Index.

Louis-Claude Daquin
French 1694-1772

Daquin Nouveau livre de noëls, Op. 2. **Christopher Herrick** (org). Hyperion Ⓕ CDA66816
    (65 minutes: DDD: 12/95). Played on the organ of St Rémy, Dieppe. Recorded 1995.
    Gramophone Editor's choice.   Ⓖ
Le coucou is probably the only thing many people know of Daquin, Louis XV's prized court organist, hailed by contemporaries such as Marchand as a supreme virtuoso and recognized even by Rameau as the finest improviser of his day. His only organ compositions to have survived are the present 12 *Noëls* – treatments of traditional Christmas carols – a genre dating from Lebègue's collection about 60 years earlier. Daquin's *Noëls*, written around 1740, employ a technique of variations of ever-increasing brilliance: they extend from the swaggering boldness of No. 1, the bucolic No. 3 over a long drone bass and the briskly breezy No. 4 to the charmingly naïve No. 9 (on flutes), the aggressively cheerful No. 10 and the stunningly exultant No. 12. This is something all organ lovers will want to have. The splendid instrument, almost exactly contemporary with the work presented (much rebuilt but in 1992 restored on historical lines), allows Christopher Herrick to display both his own virtuosity and the organ's rich range of colours (the specification is provided) with vividness – he has fun with multiple echo effects in Nos. 6 and 10 – and the recording is wonderfully fresh in sound. Smashing!

...Le coucou. *Coupled with works by various composers.* **George Malcolm** (hpd).
  Decca 444 390-2DWO (11/95). ✐

Alexander Dargomïzhsky Russian 1813-1869

Suggested listening ...
...Elegy, "She is coming". *Coupled with works by various composers.* **Mitsuko Shirai** (mez);
  Tabea Zimmermann (va); **Hartmut Höll** (pf). Capriccio 10 462 (9/95). *See review in the*
  Collections section; refer to the Index.   Ⓖ
...Elegy (Deep down). I am in love, my maiden, my beauty. The worm. It is both tedious and sad.
  The night zephyr stirs the air. I am sad. The Miller. Lullaby. The Titular Councillor. It's all the
  same to me. Eastern romance. The Old Corporal. *Coupled with works by* **Borodin**
  Sergei Leiferkus (bar); **Leonid Gorokhov** (vc); **Semion Skigin** (pf).
  Conifer Classics 75605 51275-2 (12/96). *See review under Borodin; refer to the Index.*
...Rusalka – Some unknown power. *Coupled with works by various composers.* **Sergei Larin** (ten);
  Philharmonia Orchestra / Gennadi Rozhdestvensky.
  Chandos CHAN9603 (5/98). *See review in the Collections section; refer to the Index.*

Harold Darke British 1888-1976

Suggested listening ...
...Evening Service in A minor. *Coupled with works by various composers.* **Hereford Cathedral Choir /**
  Roy Massey. Priory PRCD535 (7/96). *See review in the Collections section; refer to the Index.*

Michael Daugherty American 1954

Suggested listening ...
...Sing Sing: J. Edgar Hoover. *Coupled with works by various composers.* **Kronos Quartet.**
  Nonesuch 7559-79372-2 (11/96). *See review in the Collections section; refer to the Index.*

Carl Davis American/British 1936

Suggested listening ...
...(arr. Longstaff) A Christmas Carol – ballet suite. *Coupled with works by* **Muldowney** and
  Feeney **Northern Ballet Theatre Orchestra / John Pryce-Jones.**
  Naxos 8 553495 (3/96). *See review under Feeney; refer to the Index.*

Richard Davy British c1465-c1507

Suggested listening ...
...Joan is sick and ill at ease. Ah mine heart, remember thee well. *Coupled with works by*
  Sheppard and **Mason** **The Magdalen Collection / Harry Christophers.**
  Collins Classics 1511-2 (7/97). *See review under Sheppard; refer to the Index.*
...Salve regina. In honore summae matris. *Coupled with works by various composers.*
  The Sixteen / Harry Christophers.
  Collins Classics 1462-2 (3/96). *See review in the Collections section; refer to the Index.*

Claude Debussy French 1862-1918

Debussy Images[a].
Ravel Boléro[b]. La valse[b]. Rapsodie espagnole[b]. **Boston Symphony Orchestra / Charles Munch.**
  RCA Victor Living Stereo Ⓜ 09026 61956-2 (74 minutes: ADD: 12/94). Item marked [a] from
  VICS1162 (3/66), [b]SB2019 (3/59). Recorded 1955-97.   Ⓖ
Munch, as one writer put it, "preferred 'taking-off' at concerts instead of nit-picking at rehearsals".
Though he didn't generally live as dangerously in his studio recordings, you are unlikely to hear a
more bracing "Rondes de Printemps". And his "Gigues" most certainly does 'take-off' as soon as the
opportunity arises, after perhaps the most atmospheric opening on disc (whose secret is in the barely
audible muted trumpet – what control! – and the flute vibrato). No matter what Munch does, he
seems to be able to rely on an orchestra who move with him, with grace, at the speed of light, and
with not a musical hair out of place. Brass playing in particular is truly 'legendary'; in other words,
faultless, but expressive, not merely ostentatious. And was there ever a more hauntingly distant horn

solo from 3'05" in the slow movement of "Ibéria", or a conductor and leader who drew more humour from the (here, delightfully tipsy) strolling fiddler in its last movement? There is marginally more fantasy, flair and fun in Munch's *Images* than any other. Boston's orchestra and its hall have rarely, if ever, had a more natural stereo showing on disc. Assuredly not from RCA themselves when, in the years following this recording, the microphone quota increased. Compared with other remakes, these older recordings have more detail, a more convincing balance, livelier timbres and more of the hall's acoustic. *Boléro* starts at Ravel's surprisingly fast marking, and gradually gets faster; and *La valse* finds Munch and the orchestra at their greatest (trumpets in a spin in the final bars – once heard never forgotten). There isn't today's dynamic range, of course (though the *Images* come very close).

Additional recommendations ...

...Images. Nocturnes[a]. [a]**Montreal Symphony Orchestra Chorus; Montreal Symphony Orchestra / Charles Dutoit.** Decca Ⓕ 425 502-2DH (60 minutes: DDD: 6/90).

...Images. Le martyre de St Sébastien – symphonic fragments. *Coupled with works by various composers.* **London Symphony Orchestra / Pierre Monteux.**
Philips The Early Years Ⓜ 442 544-2PM5* (five discs: 311 minutes: ADD: 12/94). *See review in the Collections section; refer to the Index.*   ⒼⒼⒼ

...Images. **Elgar** Variations on an Original Theme, Op. 36, "Enigma". **Berlin Philharmonic Orchestra / James Levine.** Sony Classical Ⓕ SK53284 (67 minutes: DDD: 2/95).

...Images. Le Martyre de Saint Sébastien. **London Symphony Orchestra / Pierre Monteux.**
Philips Pierre Monteux The Early Years Ⓜ 442 595-2PM (58 minutes: ADD: 10/96).

...Images. Prélude à l'après-midi d'un faune. La mer. **Los Angeles Philharmonic Orchestra / Esa-Pekka Salonen.** Sony Classical Ⓕ SK62599 (72 minutes: DDD: 6/97).

Debussy Berceuse héroïque[a]. Images[b]. Danse sacrée et danse profane (with Vera Badings, hp)[b].
Jeux[c]. Nocturnes[c]. Marche écossaise sur un thème populaire[d]. Prélude à l'après-midi d'un faune[d].
La mer[d]. Première rapsodie (George Pieterson, cl)[d]. **Concertgebouw Orchestra / [a]Eduard van Beinum, Bernard Haitink.** Philips Duo Ⓜ 438 742-2PM2
(two discs: 141 minutes: ADD: 3/94). Items marked [a] from SABL130 (2/60),
[b]9500 509 (5/79), [c]9500 674 (11/80), [d]9500 359 (4/78). *Gramophone classical 100.*   ⒼⒼⒼ

Philips have repackaged Haitink's late-1970s recordings on two CDs for the price of one. Space has also been found for Debussy's last orchestral work, the short *Berceuse héroïque* conducted by Eduard van Beinum (in excellent 1957 stereo). In every respect this package is a genuine bargain. In *La Mer*, like the 1964 Karajan on DG Galleria, there is a concern for refinement and fluidity of gesture, for a subtle illumination of texture; and both display a colourist's knowledge and use of an individually apt variety of orchestral tone and timbre. It is the wind playing that you remember in Haitink's *Images*: the melancholy and disconsolate oboe d'amore in "Gigues"; and from "Ibéria", the gorgeous oboe solo in "Les parfums de la nuit", and the carousing clarinets and raucous trumpets in the succeeding holiday festivities. And here, as elsewhere in the set, the Concertgebouw acoustic plays a vital role. Haitink's *Jeux* is slower and freer than average, and possessed of a near miraculous precision, definition and delicacy. The jewel in this set, for many, will be the *Nocturnes*, principally for the purity of the strings in "Nuages"; the dazzling richness and majesty of the central procession in "Fêtes"; and the cool beauty and composure of "Sirènes". It is in this last movement where interpretation and balance differ most widely, with Haitink opting for an ethereal distance. With him, there may be passages where you are unsure if they are singing or not, but the effect is quite as magical as the entry of the offstage choir in "Neptune" from *The Planets*.

Additional recommendations ...

...La mer. **Rimsky-Korsakov** Scheherazade, Op. 35. **Chicago Symphony Orchestra / Fritz Reiner.**
RCA Victor Gold Seal Ⓜ GD60875 (69 minutes: ADD).

...La mer. Prélude à l'après-midi d'un faune. Jeux. **London Philharmonic Orchestra / Serge Baudo.**
EMI Eminence Ⓜ CD-EMX9502 (52 minutes: DDD: 10/87).   Ⓖ

...La mer. Prélude à l'après-midi d'un faune. **Ravel** Daphnis et Chloé – Suite No. 2. Boléro.
Berlin Philharmonic Orchestra / Herbert von Karajan.
DG Galleria Ⓜ 427 250-2GGA (64 minutes: ADD: 7/89). *Gramophone classical 100.*   ⒼⒼⒼ

...La mer. Prélude à l'après-midi d'un faune. Jeux. Le martyre de Saint Sébastien.
Montreal Symphony Orchestra / Charles Dutoit. Decca Ⓕ 430 240-2DH (75 minutes: DDD: 2/91).

...La mer. Nocturnes. Prélude à l'après-midi d'un faune. Danse. **Philadelphia Orchestra / Eugene Ormandy.** Sony Classical Essential Classics Ⓑ SBK53256* (65 minutes: ADD: 3/94).

...La mer. Nocturnes[a]. Première rapsodie[b]. Jeux. [b]**Franklin Cohen** (cl); [a]**Cleveland Chorus and Orchestra / Pierre Boulez.** DG Ⓕ 439 896-2GH (71 minutes: DDD: 3/95). *Gramophone Editor's record of the month.*   ⒼⒼ

...Danse sacrée et danse profane. *Coupled with works by various composers.* **Arthur Gleghorn** (fl);
Mitchell Lurie (cl); **Ann Mason Stockton** (hp); **Hollywood Quartet; Concert Arts Strings / Felix Slatkin.** Testament mono Ⓕ SBT1053* (73 minutes: ADD: 3/95). *See review in the Collections section; refer to the Index.*   ⒼⒼ

...Nocturnes. Prélude à l'après-midi d'un faune. Danse sacrée et danse profane. Préludes, Book 1 –
No. 10, La cathédrale engloutie. Estampes – Soirée dans Grenade (both orch. Stokowski).
Ravel Rapsodie espagnole. **Philadelphia Orchestra / Leopold Stokowski.**
Biddulph mono Ⓜ WHL013* (77 minutes: ADD: 8/95).

...La mer. **Respighi** The Pines of Rome. The Fountains of Rome. **Chicago Symphony Orchestra /**
Fritz Reiner. RCA Victor Living Stereo Ⓜ 09026 68079-2 (62 minutes: ADD: 9/95).   Ⓖ
...La mer. Prélude à l'après-midi d'un faune. **Ravel** Pavane pour une infante défunte. Ma mère
l'oye. **Royal Concertgebouw Orchestra / Carlo Maria Giulini.**
Sony Classical Ⓕ SK66832 (64 minutes: DDD: 11/95).
...La mer. *Coupled with works by* **Mussorgsky** and **Ravel** Berlin Philharmonic Orchestra /
Herbert von Karajan. DG The Originals Ⓜ 447 426-2GOR (75 minutes: ADD: 12/95).
...La mer. Jeux. Nocturnes – Nuages; Fêtes. **Respighi** Fontane di Roma.
Orchestra of the Santa Cecilia Academy, Rome / Victor de Sabata.
Testament mono Ⓕ SBT1108* (70 minutes: ADD: 4/98).

Debussy Nocturnes[a] – Nuages; Fêtes. Prélude à après-midi d'un faune[b]. Le martyre de
Saint Sébastien[c] – symphonic fragments. La mer[c]. **Philharmonia Orchestra / Guido Cantelli.**
Testament mono Ⓕ SBT1011* (67 minutes: ADD: 10/92). Item marked [a] from HMV BLP1089
(2/57), [b]ALP1207 (9/55), [c]ALP1228 (3/55). Recorded 1954-55. *Gramophone classical 100.* ⒼⒼⒼ
The death of Guido Cantelli in an air crash at the age of 36 in 1956 was one of the most crucial losses
in post-war musical life. In a career lasting just 13 years he made his way right to the top of his
profession, although at the end of his life he was still developing and maturing, and would surely have
been one of the most important artists of our time. Fortunately he made a number of superlative
recordings over a period of seven years and this disc, which contains all his Debussy, shows clearly
why concert audiences in the 1950s were bowled over by him. It is a pity that he never conducted all
three *Nocturnes*, for "Nuages" flows beautifully and expressively and he chooses just the right tempo
for "Fêtes". He does not press this piece too hard as most conductors do, and its colour and piquant
personality thus flower freshly and easily. *L'après-midi* is also given plenty of room to breathe: the
playing cool, elegant, beautifully poised, yet very eloquent. In *La mer* Cantelli avoids the ham-fisted,
overdramatic approach of so many conductors, and instead we have a performance with clear,
gleaming textures. The first movement ebbs and flows in a movingly poetic fashion: every detail makes
its effect and everything is perfectly in scale. The middle movement is taken quite briskly, but phrasing
is hypersensitive and appropriately fluid. In the last movement there is plenty of drama and
excitement, although climaxes are kept within bounds in a way which paradoxically makes for a
greater effect than if they were given Brucknerian proportions, as they often are. During Cantelli's
lifetime *Le martyre de Saint Sébastien* was strangely regarded as a tired, feeble work, yet he conducted
the 'Symphonic fragments' quite frequently. His approach is very much of the concert-hall in that he
gives the four pieces a life of their own rather than relating them to the unfolding drama.
Nevertheless, he still captures the music's peculiarly fervent, religious-cum-exotic flavour very
effectively. The Philharmonia play with extraordinary subtlety throughout the programme, and the
recordings sound very well indeed.

Debussy Printemps. La boîte à joujoux. Children's Corner. La plus que lente. **Montreal Symphony**
Orchestra / Charles Dutoit. Decca Ⓕ 444 386-2DH (69 minutes: DDD: 8/95). Recorded 1992-94.
Children's Corner and the main work here – the ballet *La boîte à joujoux* – are variously linked. Both
were intended for Debussy's daughter ChouChou, whose toys were the inspiration for most of the
portraits of the former and also for the latter's "pantomime" (as Debussy originally called it) and both
were (very idiomatically) orchestrated by André Caplet. *La boîte à joujoux*, to quote David Cox, "has
not the sustained musical invention of *Children's Corner*, though with the interest focused on the stage
action it could undoubtedly be an attractive entertainment for children and adults alike". And indeed
it would be for the listener at home, if a full printed scenario and linked tracking (or indexing) points
were provided. Yet neither Decca's notes (otherwise excellent), nor those that accompany Tilson
Thomas's more artful and atmospheric account, give us much more than an outline of the story. Still,
even without moment-by-moment knowledge of the stage action, many will surely respond to the
gentle humour, whimsy, parody and the touching tenderness of the piece. Performance and recording
are generally up to Decca/Montreal standards – the very slow and dream-like "Jimbo's lullaby" from
Children's Corner is especially effective.
Additional recommendation ...
...Printemps. *Coupled with works by* **Caplet** and **Ravel** Brigitte Desnoues (sop);
Chorus and Orchestra of the Sorbonne, Paris / Jacques Grimbert.
Marco Polo Ⓕ 8 223755 (65 minutes: DDD: 10/95).

Debussy La boîte a joujoux. Prélude à l'après-midi d'un faune. Jeux.
London Symphony Orchestra / Michael Tilson Thomas. Sony Classical Ⓕ SK48231
(63 minutes: DDD: 11/92). Recorded 1991.   ⒼⒼ
"Something to amuse the children, nothing more" wrote Debussy about *La boîte à joujoux* (mostly
written in 1913, but completed after his death by Caplet). The children would have been a lot more
amused by the goings-on of the occupants of Tilson Thomas's toy box had Sony provided a decent
synopsis, but his characterization, storytelling and evocation of atmosphere are so vivid that
foreknowledge of events is almost unnecessary. Strictly adult entertainment is provided by this
languorous *Prélude*, with particularly lovely, long-breathed playing from the LSO's principal flute;
and the suspect shenanigans of *Jeux*, where Tilson Thomas eschews some of Haitink's miraculous

acuity of rhythm and texture, in favour of greater urgency and spontaneity. Recorded levels are higher for the *Prélude* than the rest of the programme, but this disc is superbly engineered: the sound has both a fine bloom and a tactile presence.

Additional recommendations ...

...La boîte à joujoux. **Prokofiev** Peter and the wolf, Op. 67[a]. [a]**Patrick Stewart** (narr);
Orchestra of Opéra de Lyon / Kent Nagano. Erato Ⓕ 4509-97418-2 (61 minutes: DDD: 8/95).
...Prélude à l'après-midi d'un faune. Nocturnes. La mer. **Paris Orchestra Chorus;**
Orchestre de Paris / Daniel Barenboim. DG 439 407-2GCL (61 minutes: DDD/ADD: 1/94).
...Prélude à l'après-midi d'un faune. *Coupled with works by* **Mozart** and **Brahms**
Dresden Philharmonic Orchestra / Carl Schuricht.
Berlin Classics mono Ⓜ 0090732BC* (50 minutes: ADD: 7/96).

Debussy Khamma.
Ravel Daphnis et Chloé[a]. [a]**Het Groot Omroepkoor; Royal Concertgebouw Orchestra /**
Riccardo Chailly. Decca Ⓕ 443 934-2DH (74 minutes: DDD: 10/95). Recorded 1994.
You would expect this *Daphnis* to sound superb, and, of course, it does. Rattle and EMI didn't have the advantage of the Concertgebouw acoustic: the full flood of choral tone at the climax of Chailly's "Daybreak" (the famous first scene of Part 3) has to be heard to be believed (Chailly's timing of this sunburst is masterly), and it hardly needs saying that this disc's ability to astonish with decibels at climaxes is greater than Decca's previous Dutoit or Monteux recordings of works by Ravel. Possibly the wind machine is cranked with excessive enthusiasm, and the strange lights scenes of *Daphnis* do not seem to be enjoyed or exploited for the strangeness that can result from even the ordinary (i.e. musical) instruments being asked to play or phrase in unusual ways. Chailly is faster, too, in the dance scenes where, if you are Sir Simon Rattle, lingering leads to marvels of characterization (Daphnis's "Dance gracieuse", Chloé's "Dance of Supplication" and the "Pantomime"), which is not to say that Chailly is bland. And blandness is emphatically the last word to use in describing Chailly's way with Debussy's *Khamma* (Rattle's coupling is *Boléro*). This immediately pre-*Jeux* (conceptually speaking) ballet is a sort of Egyptian *Salome*-cum-*Rite of Spring*, in as much as Khamma dances herself to death for the Sun God Amun-Ra that he might be persuaded to save the city from siege. The ominous opening pages here are immediately gripping: a Nibelheim-like family of lower woodwind slithering around, marvellously focused drum, and trumpet fanfares that genuinely do "give one the shivers" as Debussy once asserted. In general, Chailly, Decca and these superb musicians realize more of the score's "discoveries of harmonic chemistry" and sheer theatre than one dared imagine possible. But why no linked tracking with the synopsis? When the piece is unfamiliar, and the musicians and recording team have gone to this much trouble, it won't do for post-production to relegate it to the status of a filler.

Debussy Images – Ibéria.
Ravel Rapsodie espagnole. Pavane pour une infante défunte. Valses nobles et sentimentales.
Alborada del gracioso. **Chicago Symphony Orchestra / Fritz Reiner.** RCA Victor Gold Seal
Ⓜ GD60179 (68 minutes: ADD: 1/90). Recorded 1956-57.   ⒼⒼ
These performances are seldom less than mesmeric. The extremes of tempo and dynamics are exploited to the full in the Spanish night/day pieces: has any other conductor managed the gradual transition from *Ibéria*'s "perfumes of the night" to the gathering brilliance of the succeeding morning's holiday festivities, with such a delicate, yet precisely focused tracery of sounds? This is the very stuff of a waking dream. And the disc opens with what has to be the slowest, most languid account of the "Prélude" from the *Rapsodie espagnole* ever recorded; the resulting total concentration of the players on their conductor for control of rhythm and dynamics can be felt in every bar; it's not just a musical stunt, it creates a unique tension and atmosphere. Just listen to the finesse of the playing throughout, particularly the percussion, and marvel at how Reiner balances the textures in even the most riotous outbursts of the *Rapsodie*'s explosive "Feria". And the sound? Normally this *Guide* carries caveats for discs recorded in the mid 1950s, and audio boffins might nod their heads at a minuscule degree of tape saturation and hiss, but it is difficult to think of any modern recording that renders the spectacle, colour and refinement of these scores with more clarity and atmosphere.

Additional recommendation ...

...Images – Ibéria. *Coupled with works by* **Schubert** and **Tchaikovsky** New York Philharmonic
Symphony Orchestra / Sir John Barbirolli.
Dutton Laboratories Essential Archive mono Ⓑ CDEA5000* (69 minutes: ADD: 1/96).

Debussy String Quartet in G minor, Op. 10.
Ravel String Quartet in F major.
Webern String Quartet (1905). **Hagen Quartet** (Lukas Hagen, Rainer Schmidt, vns;
Veronika Hagen, va; Clemens Hagen, vc). DG Ⓕ 437 836-2GH (70 minutes: DDD: 6/94).
Recorded 1992-93.   ⒼⒼ
The first movement of the Debussy is taken fastish, but its passionate urgency convinces and it is not forced tonally or tempo-wise. Indeed, the playing is beautifully polished, and this fine ensemble also fully understand the emotional world of the music, the slow movement (again more flowing than usual) offering an acid test which they pass easily. The finale is thrilling. In the Ravel, the playing is

sensitive and skilful. Webern's one-movement Quartet was inspired by a painting entitled "Evolving, Being, Passing Away", and the music begins with a motif akin to Beethoven's "Muss es sein?" figure in his String Quartet, Op. 135. The scenario here is predictable: youthfully Germanic heart-searching and struggle, but with little that is memorable, and ultimately somewhat constipated. Still, this performance is persuasive, and the work deserves to be heard when played as well as this. The recording deserves praise: the sound is excellent, not least for viola and cello.

Additional recommendations ...

...String Quartet[a]. Cello Sonata in D minor[b]. Violin Sonata in G minor[c]. Sonata for Flute, Viola and Harp[d]. Syrinx[e]. [e]**Roger Bourdin** (fl); [c]**Arthur Grumiaux** (vn); [d]**Colette Lequien** (va); [b]**Maurice Gendron** (vc); [d]**Annie Challan** (hp); [b]**Jean Françaix**, [c]**István Hajdu** (pfs); **Quartetto Italiano**. Philips Solo Ⓜ 442 655-2PM (72 minutes: ADD).

...String Quartet. **Ravel** String Quartet. **Chilingirian Quartet**. Classics for Pleasure Ⓑ CD-CFP4652 (55 minutes: DDD).

...String Quartet. **Ravel** String Quartet. **Quartetto Italiano**. Philips Silver Line Ⓜ 420 894-2PSL (57 minutes: ADD: 10/88). Ⓖ

...String Quartet. *Coupled with works by* **Ravel** and **Dutilleux** Juilliard Quartet. Sony Classical Ⓕ SK52554 (74 minutes: DDD: 3/94).

...String Quartet. *Coupled with works by* **Ravel** and **Menu** Parisii Quartet. Auvidis Valois Ⓕ V4730 (68 minutes: DDD:10/95).

...String Quartet. *Coupled with works by* **Ravel** and **Stravinsky** Lindsay Quartet. ASV Ⓕ CDDCA930 (61 minutes: DDD: 12/95).

...String Quartet. *Coupled with works by* **Fauré** and **Ravel** Pro Arte Quartet. Biddulph mono Ⓜ LAB105* (78 minutes: ADD: 6/96). Ⓖ

Debussy Violin Sonata[a]. Sonata for Flute, Viola and Harp[b].
Franck Violin Sonata in A major[a].
Ravel Introduction and Allegro[b]. [a]**Kyung-Wha Chung** (vn); [b]**Osian Ellis** (hp); [a]**Radu Lupu** (pf); [b]**Melos Ensemble**. Decca Ⓜ 421 154-2DM (67 minutes: ADD: 1/89). Items marked [a] from SXL6944 (9/80), [b]SOL60048 (9/62). Items marked [a] recorded in 1977, [b]1962. Ⓖ

Debussy Violin Sonata.
Franck Violin Sonata in A major.
Ravel Berceuse sur le nom de Gabriel Fauré. Pièce en forme de habanera. Tzigane.
Augustin Dumay (vn); **Maria-João Pires** (pf). DG Ⓕ 445 880-2GH (56 minutes: DDD: 10/95). Recorded 1993. Ⓖ

Debussy Violin Sonata.
Poulenc Violin Sonata.
Ravel Violin Sonata. Tzigane[a]. **Tasmin Little** (vn); **Piers Lane** (pf). EMI Eminence Ⓜ CD-EMX2244 (61 minutes: DDD: 12/95). Item marked [a] from CD-EMX2196 (12/92). Recorded 1991-5.
Gramophone Editor's choice. ⒼⒼ

The Decca disc must be one of the best CD bargains around, with three masterpieces from the French tradition in excellent performances that have won the status of recording classics. Kyung Wha Chung and Radu Lupu are a fine duo who capture and convey the delicacy and poetry of the Franck Sonata as well as its rapturous grandeur, and never can the strict canonic treatment of the great tune in the finale have sounded more spontaneous and joyful. They are no less successful in the different world of the elusive Sonata which was Debussy's last work, with its smiles through tears and, in the finale, its echoes of a Neapolitan tarantella. The 1977 recording is beautifully balanced, with a natural sound given to both the violin and piano. The Melos Ensemble recorded the Ravel *Introduction and Allegro* 15 years before, but here too the recording is a fine one for which no allowances have to be made even by ears accustomed to good digital sound; as for the work itself, this has an ethereal beauty that is nothing short of magical and Osian Ellis and his colleagues give it the most skilful and loving performance. To talk about this disc as one for every collection savours of cliché, but anyone who does not have it may safely be urged to make its acquisition.

On the DG disc there is a spacious, eloquent view of Franck's Sonata, in which Dumay's essentially sweet tone also has the requisite strength; as for Pires, she accompanies where necessary and yet can offer a partner's contribution too, as well as being equal to the composer's considerable pianistic demands, not least in terms of large stretches. Although the recorded balance favours the violinist, the brilliant second movement is very effective, and so is the flowing canonic finale, in which the players rightly think in long phrases. Debussy's emotionally fragile world fares even better: this playing has the right flexibility of time and tone, and the rapidly shifting moods of this essentially sad music, so different from Franck's with its emotional assurance, are unerringly captured; and the sound is excellent here. Dumay and Pires are also at home in Ravel's music with its characteristic delicate tenderness and – in *Tzigane* at least – glittering virtuosity.

Even by today's high standards EMI Eminence's disc is outstanding, perfectly recorded by Andrew Keener and Mike Hatch. It begins with Ravel's Sonata, of which the first movement is played with a crisp coolness that may be off-putting to ears expecting cajolery but rightly emphasizes the titillating acidity of the world-weary 1920s idiom. Indeed the playing has great subtlety and there can be nothing but praise for Tasmin Little's acutely judged sonority as well as the actual beauty of her tone. Piers Lane is no less admirable: listen, for example, how he shapes and textures the elegantly edgy phrases of the (finally) flagellatory central Blues. The duo bring the same insight, unselfishness and sheer affection to the very different worlds of Poulenc and Debussy. Time and again one notes details that come up freshly minted, and you might decide to upwardly reassess Poulenc's Sonata on hearing this performance, which goes beyond consistent skill to offer enormous energy and feeling. Debussy's wonderful but fragile Sonata again comes alive in a quite extraordinary way. Nothing is routine, and yet nothing is out of place. Little and Lane have all the virtues of sensitivity and virtuosity of Dumay and Pires plus an extra flair and intensity which puts them in a class of their own.

Additional recommendations ...

...Violin Sonata. Sonata for Flute, Viola and Harp. Syrinx. Cello Sonata. Première Rapsodie. Petite pièce for Clarinet and Piano. **Athena Ensemble.**
Chandos Ⓕ CHAN8385 (55 minutes: ADD: 5/87).

...Violin Sonata. *Coupled with works by various composers.* **Arthur Grumiaux** (vn); **Riccardo Castagnone** (pf).
Philips The Early Years mono Ⓜ 438 516-2PM3* (three discs: 196 minutes: ADD: 11/93).   ⒼⒼ

...Violin Sonata. *Coupled with works by* **Ravel** *and* **Pierné** Gérard Poulet (vn); Noël Lee (pf).
Arion Ⓕ ARN68228 (65 minutes: DDD: 9/94). *Gramophone Editor's choice. See review under Ravel; refer to the Index.*   Ⓖ

...Sonata for Flute, Viola and Harp. *Coupled with works by various composers.* **Aurèle Nicolet** (fl); **Nobuko Imai** (va); **Naoko Yoshino** (hp). Philips Ⓕ 442 012-2PH (64 minutes: DDD: 12/94).

...Rapsodie for Saxophone and Piano. Syrinx. Première rapsodie. Sonata for Flute, Viola and Harp. Le petit nègre. Petite pièce. Rapsodie. *Coupled with works by* **Saint-Saëns** Various artists.
Cala Ⓜ CACD1017 (two discs: 129 minutes: 2/95).

...Violin Sonata. *Coupled with works by* **Fauré** *and* **Poulenc** Isabelle van Keulen (vn); **Ronald Brautigam** (pf). Koch Schwann Ⓕ 315272 (56 minutes: DDD: 10/95).

...Violin Sonata. *Coupled with works by* **Poulenc** *and* **Ravel** Cho-Liang Lin (vn); **Paul Crossley** (pf). Sony Classical Ⓕ SK66839 (77 minutes: DDD: 7/96).

Debussy Cello Sonata[a].
Schubert Sonata in A minor, D821, "Arpeggione"[b].
Schumann Fünf Stücke im Volkston, Op. 102[a]. **Mstislav Rostropovich** (vc); **Benjamin Britten** (pf). Decca Ⓕ 417 833-2DH (59 minutes: ADD: 9/87). Items marked [a] from SXL6426 (10/70), recorded 1968, [b]SXL2298 (1/62), recorded1961.   ⒼⒼⒼ

As if being one of the greatest composers this country has produced was not enough, Benjamin Britten was also supremely gifted as a conductor and pianist and here we hear him interpreting the music of others. The bewildering concentration of mood and imagery in Debussy's avowedly classical temperamental 15-minute Sonata presents special challenges to the players and its subtleties reveal themselves only after many hearings. It is a piece which is never easy to bring off, with its *commedia dell'arte* transparency and specialized effects. Britten and Rostropovich bring to it and the other works a depth of understanding which it would be hard to imagine bettered. The Schubert Sonata is an engaging work, whilst the five Schumann pieces have a rustic simplicity and strength which these performers turn entirely to Schumann's advantage. Certainly a collector's item, this CD ought to be part of every chamber music collection. The analogue recordings have transferred extremely well.

Additional recommendations ...

...Cello Sonata. *Coupled with works by* **Martin** *and* **Poulenc** William Conway (vc); **Peter Evans** (pf). Linn Records Ⓕ CKD002 (51 minutes: DDD: 11/91).

...Cello Sonata. *Coupled with works by* **Bridge** *and* **E. Dohnányi** Bernard Gregor-Smith (vc); **Yolande Wrigley** (pf). ASV Ⓕ CDDCA796 (68 minutes: DDD: 9/92).

...Cello Sonata. *Coupled with works by various composers.* **Paul Tortelier** (vc); **Gerald Moore** (pf). EMI Références mono Ⓜ CDH5 65502-2* (78 minutes: ADD: 12/95).

Debussy En blanc et noir[b]. Petite suite[a]. Nocturnes (arr. Ravel)[a] – Nuages; Fêtes. Six épigraphes antiques[a]. Lindaraja[b]. **Katia and Marielle Labèque** ([a]pf duet/[b]pfs). Philips Ⓕ 454 471-2PH (58 minutes: DDD: 6/98). Recorded 1996.

Katia and Marielle Labèque give us here a Debussy programme which is stylish and scintillating. Whatever sparkles and delights is here in superabundance. Playing with a fierce, recognizably French clarity and verve they make you doubly aware of the extraordinary force of nature that consumed Debussy during his final years. Faced with the outbreak of war, the possible destruction of his beloved France and his own terminal illness, he composed, among other masterpieces, his *En blanc et noir*, a wild dreamscape containing some of his most startling and original music. And if the Labèques play with an electrifying bravura, they are no less enviably refined, registering every detail of the score with scrupulous precision and sensitivity (and never more so than in the finale's flickering play of light and shade). They are no less dazzling in the more openly endearing *Petite suite* and if "Fêtes" (from the *Nocturnes*) explodes in an orgy of brilliance, such open display is poetically balanced in *Epigraphes antiques*, where the duo are hauntingly memorably. Time and again they show how the finest insights are only available to pianists liberated from all difficulty, who are free to concentrate on a purely musical discourse. The recordings are immaculate and combined with the Labèque sisters' verve and pianistic aplomb provide a special, crystalline experience.

Additional recommendations ...
...En blanc et noir[a]. Petite Suite[a]. Six épigraphes antiques[a]. Lindaraja[a]. Marche écossaise[a]. Ballade slave. Berceuse héroïque. Danse. Danse Bohémienne. Etudes – Books 1 and 2. D'un cahier d'esquisses. Hommage à Haydn. Masques. Nocturne. Le petit nègre. La plus que lente. Rêverie. Suite bergamasque. Valse romantique. **Werner Haas**, [a]**Noël Lee** (pfs).
Philips Duo Ⓜ 438 721-2PM2 (two discs: 155 minutes: ADD: 4/94).
...Petite Suite. *Coupled with works by* **Ravel** and **Satie**. **Cleveland Orchestra / Louis Lane.**
Sony Classical Essential Classics Ⓑ SBK63056 (68 minutes: ADD: 4/98).

Debussy Complete Piano Works. **Walter Gieseking** (pf); [a]**Hessian Radio Orchestra, Frankfurt / Kurt Schröder.** EMI mono Ⓜ CHS5 65855-2* (four discs: 276 minutes: ADD: 6/96). Recorded 1951-55. *Gramophone Award Winner 1996.* ❶❷❸
Préludes, Books 1 and 2 (from Columbia 33CX1098, 1/54 and 33CX1304, 11/55). Pour le piano. Estampes. Images, Sets 1 and 2 (all from 33CX1137, 3/54). Children's Corner (Columbia 33C1014, 6/53). 12 Etudes. D'un cahier d'esquisses (both from 33CX1261, 2/57). Rêverie. Valse romantique (Columbia LX1598, 1/54). Masques. L'îsle joyeuse. La plus que lente. Le petit nègre. Berceuse héroïque. Hommage à Haydn. Danse bohémienne. Mazurka. Deux Arabesques. Nocturne. Tarantelle styrienne. Ballade (33CX1149, 5/54). Suite bergamasque (HMV HQM1225, 11/70). Fantaisie[a] (previously unpublished. Recorded live in 1951).
Gieseking's insight and iridescence in Debussy are so compelling and hypnotic that they prompt either a book or a blank page – an unsatisfactory state where criticism or assessment is concerned! First and foremost, there is Gieseking's sonority, one of such delicacy and variety that it can complement Debussy's witty and ironic desire to write music "for an instrument without hammers", for a pantheistic art sufficiently suggestive to evoke and transcend the play of the elements themselves ("the wind, the sky, the sea ..."). Lack of meticulousness seems a small price to pay for such an elemental uproar in "Ce qu'a vu le vent d'Ouest", and Puck's elfin pulse and chatter (*pp aérian*) are caught with an uncanny deftness and precision. The final Debussian magic may not lie in a literal observance of the score, in the unfailing dotting and crossing of every objective and picturesque instruction, yet it is surely the start or foundation of a great performance. More domestically, no one (not even Cortot) has ever captured the sense in *Children's Corner* of a lost and enchanted land, of childhood re-experienced through adult tears and laughter. "Pour les tièrces", from the *Etudes*, may get off to a shaky start but, again, in Debussy's final masterpiece, where pragmatism is resolved into a fantasy undreamed of even by Chopin, Gieseking's artistry tugs at and haunts the imagination. Try "Pour les sonorités opposées", the nodal and expressive centre of the *Etudes*, and you may well wonder when you have heard playing more subtly gauged or articulated, or the sort of interaction with a composer's spirit that can make modern alternatives seem so parsimonious by comparison. So here is that peerless palette of colour and texture, of a light and shade used with a nonchalantly deployed but precise expertise to illuminate every facet of Debussy's teeming and insinuating imagination. An added bonus, a 1951 performance of the *Fantaisie* for piano and orchestra (an ecstatic and scintillating work, played here with a life-affirming chiaroscuro) completes an incomparable set of discs. The transfers are a triumph, with an immediacy much less obvious in the originals. These records should be in every musician's library, be they singer or conductor, violinist or pianist.

Additional recommendations ...
...La plus que lente. Images, Set 2 – Poissons d'or. Préludes – Book 1: La fille aux cheveux lin; Book 2: Général Lavine – eccentric; Feux d'artifice. Rêverie. **Smetana** Czech Polkas and Dances, T112. **Rudolf Firkušný** (pf).
EMI Firkušný Edition mono Ⓜ CDM5 66069-2* (69 minutes: ADD).
...(arr. Bozza) Le petit nègre. *Coupled with works by various composers.* **Reykjavik Wind Quintet.**
Chandos Ⓕ CHAN9362 (63 minutes: DDD: 10/95).
...Images – Reflets dans l'eau; Hommage à Rameau; Cloches à travers les feuilles; Et la lune descend sur le temple qui fût. *Coupled with works by various composers.*
Arturo Benedetti Michelangeli (pf).
Testament mono Ⓕ SBT2088* (two discs: 130 minutes: ADD: 12/96).
See review in the Collections section; refer to the Index.
...Pour le piano. Suite bergamasque – Clair de lune. *Coupled with works by* **Poulenc** and **Satie**
Kun Woo Paik (pf). Virgin Classics Ultraviolet Ⓜ CUV5 61327-2 (76 minutes: DDD: 2/97).
...Estampes – Pagodes (orch. Grainger). *Coupled with works by* **Grainger** and **Ravel**
City of Birmingham Symphony Orchestra / Sir Simon Rattle.
EMI Ⓕ CDC5 56412-2 (70 minutes: DDD: 8/97). *Gramophone Editor's choice.*
See review under Grainger; refer to the Index.

Debussy Préludes – Books 1 and 2. **Krystian Zimerman** (pf). DG Ⓜ 435 773-2GH2 (two discs: 84 minutes: DDD: 3/94). Recorded 1991. *Gramophone classical 100. Gramophone Award Winner 1994. Gramophone Editor's choice.* ❶❷❸
Two discs, retailing at a high mid price and playing for a total of 84 minutes? The playing and the recording had better be in the luxury class. Fortunately they are. Zimerman is the very model of a modern virtuoso. His overrriding aim is vivid projection of character. His quasi-orchestral range of dynamic and attack, based on close attention to textual detail (there are countless felicities in his

observation of phrase-markings) and maximum clarity of articulation, is the means to that end. As a result, he draws out the many connections in this music with the romantic tradition, especially in pianistic *tours de force* such as "Les collines d'Anacapri", "Ce qu'a vu le vent d'Ouest" and "Feux d'artifice", which are treated to a dazzling Lisztian *élan*. The instrument he has selected is itself something of a star and DG's recording combines opulence with razor-sharp clarity. At the other extreme Zimerman displays an exquisite refinement of touch that makes the quieter pieces both evocative and touching. Such sensitively conceived and wonderfully executed Debussy playing stands, at the very least, on a level with a classic recording such as Gieseking's.

Additional recommendations ...
...Préludes. Three Estampes. Images – Reflets dans l'eau. **Yuri Egorov** (pf).
Classics for Pleasure Silver Doubles Ⓢ CD-CFPSD4805 (two discs: 98 minutes: DDD).
...Préludes. **Walter Gieseking** (pf).
EMI Références mono Ⓜ CDH7 61004-2* (70 minutes: ADD: 4/88).   ⒼⒼⒼ
...Préludes. Images – Sets 1 and 2. Estampes. **Claudio Arrau** (pf).
Philips Ⓜ 432 304-2PM2 (two discs: 134 minutes: ADD: 2/92).
...Préludes. Deux Arabesques. Children's Corner. Estampes. Images – Sets 1 and 2.
Mazurka, L'îsle joyeuse. Pour le piano. **Werner Haas** (pf).
Philips Duo Ⓜ 438-718-2PM2 (two discs: 157 minutes: ADD: 4/94).

Debussy Préludes – Books 1[a] and 2[b]. Images[c]. Children's Corner[c]. **Arturo Benedetti Michelangeli** (pf). DG Ⓕ 449 438-2GH2 (two discs: 128 minutes: [ac]ADD/[b]DDD: 5/96). Item marked [a] from 2530 200 (11/78), [b]427 391-2GH (3/89), [c]2530 196 (12/71). Recorded 1971-88.   Ⓖ
Of Debussy playing his own music Alfredo Casella said "he made the impression of playing directly on the strings of the instrument with no intermediate mechanism – the effect was a miracle of poetry". This is not Michelangeli's way. He can certainly be poetic and produce miracles but his manner is not ingratiating. Generalized 'atmosphere' doesn't interest him. His superfine control is put at the service of line and movement, above all, and the projection of perspectives. He gives you a sense not just of foreground and background but of many planes in between. Try "Feux d'artifice", the last of the Second Book of *Préludes* (second disc, track 12), for instances of this: the murmuring ostinato at the beginning (*léger, égal et lointain*) is 'positioned' with absolute precision, and as you're drawn into the picture it's as if you can see exactly where everything is coming from. Michelangeli was capable of a transcendental virtuosity, not always noticed, that had nothing to do with playing fast and loud and everything to do with refinement, and it is very much in evidence here – in many other *Préludes* and especially in the first two *Images* of the Second Book; also, less expectedly, in "The snow is dancing" from *Children's Corner*. The clarity of texture and the laser-like delineation can sometimes be disconcerting if you're accustomed to a softer, more ethereal style, but they have a way of making Debussy's modernism apparent and thrilling. He sounds here as if he has had nothing to do with the nineteenth century. The *Images* and *Children's Corner* are among the finest versions ever recorded. But in some of the *Préludes*, particularly in Book 1, the sound is rather close and dry – maybe how Michelangeli wanted it. He uses as little pedal as he can get away with – Marguerite Long reported that Debussy, like Chopin, considered the art of the pedal as a "sort of breathing", but you don't get much sense of that here. In the Breton seascape "Ce qu'a vu le vent d'ouest" do you really *want* to hear every note? There are people who regard Gieseking as unparalleled in this music, but after a quarter of a century the best of Michelangeli, similarly, will run and run. Today's generation of Debussy pianists will be expected to work from a less corrupt text, quite rightly, but they will have far to go before they can rival the penetrating qualities of Michelangeli's Debussy at its best. He could take your breath away and he was illuminating in this repertoire in a rare way.

Additional recommendations ...
...Images – Hommage à Rameau; Poissons d'or. Préludes – La cathédrale engloutie; Ondine.
Coupled with works by various composers. **Artur Rubinstein** (pf).
RCA Victor Gold Seal Ⓜ 09026 61445-2 (64 minutes: ADD: 10/93).
...Children's Corner. *Coupled with works by* **Tchaikovsky** *and* **Schumann** Idil Biret (pf).
Naxos Ⓢ 8 550885 (66 minutes: DDD: 10/94).
...Préludes. Children's Corner. La plus que lente. Nocturne. Valse romantique. Ballade. Le petit nègre. Elégie. Morceau de concours. Mazurka. Tarantelle styrienne. **Zoltán Kocsis** (pf).
Philips Ⓕ 456 568-2PH2 (two discs: 123 minutes: DDD: 4/98).

Debussy Suite bergamasque. Images oubliées. Pour le piano. Estampes. **Zoltán Kocsis** (pf).
Philips Ⓕ 412 118-2PH (55 minutes: DDD: 4/85). *Selected by Sounds in Retrospect.*   ⒼⒼ
Debussy Images – Sets 1 and 2. D'un cahier d'esquisses. L'îsle joyeuse. Deux arabesques.
Hommage à Haydn. Rêverie. Page d'album. Berceuse héroïque. **Zoltán Kocsis** (pf).
Philips Ⓕ 422 404-2PH (62 minutes: DDD: 2/90). Recorded 1988. *Gramophone Award Winner 1990.*   ⒼⒼ
Zoltán Kocsis stands out as an especially idiomatic exponent of Debussy's piano style. On the first disc here, he plays four relatively early sets of pieces of which all but the *Suite bergamasque* are in the composer's favourite triptych form that he also used in *La mer*. The most 'classical' of them are the oddly titled *Pour le piano*, in which the Prelude echoes Bach's keyboard writing, and the *Suite bergamasque* with its eighteenth-century dances, but even in the latter work we find the composer's

popular "Clair de lune" memorably impressionistic in its evocation of moonlight. In the *Estampes*, the last pieces played, he displayed a still more fully developed impressionism in musical pictures of the Far East, Moorish Spain and lastly a mysteriously rainswept urban garden. The rarity here is the *Images oubliées*, pieces dating from 1894 that Debussy left unpublished, doubtless because he reworked material from them in the *Estampes* and very obviously in the Sarabande of *Pour le piano*, but they are fine in their own right and here we can compare the different treatments of the similar ideas. The second recital is also a revealing portrait of the composer, its items discerningly offsetting the familiar with the less-known. It also brings playing not only of exceptional finesse, but at times of exceptional brilliance and fire. The main work is of course *Images*, its two sets completed in 1905 and 1907 respectively, by which time the composer was already master of that impressionistic style of keyboard writing so different from anything known before. For superfine sensitivity to details of textural shading Kocsis is at his most spellbinding in the first two numbers of the second set, "Cloches à travers les feuilles" and "Et la lune descend sur le temple qui fût". He is equally successful in reminding us of Debussy's wish to "forget that the piano has hammers" in the atmospheric washes of sound that he conjures (through his pedalling no less than his fingers) in *D'un cahier d'esquisses*. The sharp, clear daylight world of *L'isle joyeuse* reveals a Kocsis exulting in his own virtuosity and strength as he also does in the last piece of each set of *Images*, and even in the second of the two familiar, early *Arabesques*, neither of them mere vapid drawing-room charmers here. The recording is first rate. Both discs are highly recommendable. Zoltán Kocsis brings refinement and brilliance to all this music and the piano sound is exceptionally rich and faithful.

Additional recommendations ...
...Suite bergamasque – Prélude. Le petit nègre. Deux Arabesques. Images – Poissons d'or.
   Children's Corner. La plus que lente. Préludes – Des pas sur la neige; Les terrasses des audiences; Ondine; Feux d'artifice. Etudes – Pour les cinq doigts; Pour les arpèges composés. L'isle joyeuse. **Dame Moura Lympany** (pf). Classics for Pleasure Ⓑ CD-CFP4653 (74 minutes: DDD: 10/94).
...Pour le piano. Estampes. **Ravel** Miroirs. Sonatine. Jeux d'eau. **Lilya Zilberstein** (pf).
   DG Ⓕ 439 927-2GH (74 minutes: DDD: 2/95).
...(orch. Caplet) Children's Corner. Estampes – Pagodes. Suite bergamasque – Clair de lune.
   Coupled with works by **Caplet Rheinland-Pfalz State Philharmonic Orchestra / Leif Segerstam.** Marco Polo Ⓕ 8 223751 (56 minutes: DDD: 9/95). *See review under Caplet; refer to the Index.*
...Estampes. Préludes, Book 1 – Voiles; Le vent dans la plaine; Les collines d'Anacapri.
   Coupled with works by various composers. **Sviatoslav Richter** (pf).
   DG Double Ⓜ 447 355-2GDB2 (two discs: 150 minutes: ADD: 12/95).
...Suite bergamasque. Nocturne. Danse bohémienne. Rêverie. Mazurka. Deux arabesques.
   Valse romantique. Ballade. Tarantelle styrienne. Pour le piano. **François-Joël Thiollier** (pf).
   Naxos Ⓢ 8 553290 (71 minutes: DDD: 1/96).

Debussy Deux Arabesques. Suite bergamasque – Clair de lune; Passepied. Rêverie. Children's Corner – The little shepherd; Golliwog's cakewalk. Prélude, Book 1 – Voiles; Les sons et les parfums; La fille aux cheveux de lin; La cathédrale engloutie; Minstrels. Images – Hommage à Rameau. L'isle joyeuse. **Ronan O'Hora** (pf). Tring International Ⓢ TRP068 (65 minutes: DDD: 4/97). Recorded 1995.
Even in a crowded market-place this recital takes its place among the most distinguished Debussy recordings. Nothing is taken for granted, everything is recreated with such care and affection that a largely popular selection at once seems fresh and unfamiliar. How many pianists can set the stage in "La cathédrale engloutie" with such understated skill, ideally capturing Debussy's direction, *profondément calme, dans une brume doucement sonore* or, later, make such a subtle differentiation between *forte, più forte* and *fortissimo*? The "Passepied" (from the *Suite bergamasque*) is kept briskly on the move yet there is ample time for the most judicious pointing and colouring, and "Hommage à Rameau" (from *Images*, Book 1) seems exemplary in its lucidity, its avoidance of the sort of brittleness or affectation common to pianists anxious to make their mark at any price. Finally, you may have heard or seen more joyous islands (*L'isle joyeuse*) yet O'Hora's performance beautifully captures the spirit of romance and there is no lack of animation in the exultant close. Everything is given time to register, to weave its spell, and although the resonant recordings cast a haze over the sound the ear quickly adjusts, particularly when the performances are so distinguished.

Debussy Etudes – Books 1 and 2. **Mitsuko Uchida** (pf). Philips Ⓕ 422 412-2PH (47 minutes: DDD: 7/90). Recorded 1989. ⒼⒼⒼ
Near the beginning of his career, Debussy's *Prélude à l'après-midi d'un faune* (1894) opened the door (so it is often said) for modern music. His late works, including three chamber sonatas and the set of 12 piano studies (1915), opened another door, through which perhaps only he could have stepped. But his death from cancer in 1918 at the age of 56 put paid to that prospect. The harmonic language and continuity of the *Studies* is elusive even by Debussy's standards, and it takes an artist of rare gifts to play them 'from within', at the same time as negotiating their finger-knotting intricacies. Mitsuko Uchida is such an artist. On first hearing perhaps rather hyperactive, her playing wins you over by its bravura and sheer relish, eventually disarming criticism altogether. This is not just the finest-ever recorded version of the *Studies*; it is also one of the finest examples of recorded piano playing in modern times, matched by sound quality of outstanding clarity and ambient warmth.

Additional recommendations ...
...Etudes – Books 1 and 2. Pour le piano. **Gordon Fergus-Thompson** (pf).
ASV Ⓕ CDDCA703 (62 minutes: DDD: 7/90).
...Etude No. 11 "Pour les arpèges composés". *Coupled with works by various composers.*
Vladimir Horowitz (pf). APR mono Ⓜ APR5517* (71 minutes: ADD: 5/98). *See review in the Collections section; refer to the Index.*

Debussy Le martyre de Saint-Sébastien. **Sylvia McNair** (sop); **Ann Murray** (mez);
Nathalie Stutzmann (contr); **Leslie Caron** (narr); **London Symphony Chorus and Orchestra /
Michael Tilson Thomas.** Sony Classical Ⓕ SK48240 (66 minutes: DDD: 3/93). Text and
translation included. Recorded 1991. *Gramophone Award Winner 1993. Selected by
Sounds in Retrospect.* ⒼⒼ
"Archers aim closely, I am the target; whoever wounds me the most deeply, loves me the most. From
the depths I call forth your terrible love ... again ... again! ...AGAIN!" cries the Saint in ecstasy. What
Oscar Wilde did to the story of Salome, so the Italian writer D'Annunzio did to the story of Saint
Sebastian (a young Roman officer ordered to be killed by his own archers because of his sympathy
for persecuted Christians). This was the first modern recording, not of the complete play (which
lasted five hours!), but of an intelligent and effective reduction of the written text using the Saint as
narrator, and incorporating all of an hour's worth of Debussy's incidental music. And it must be
deemed a triumph. Leslie Caron's Saint is quietly intense and a model of restraint; Sylvia McNair's
vox coelestis is just that, a gift from God; and the chorus and orchestra respond with total conviction
to what is evidently, from Tilson Thomas, direction with a mission. The sheer sorcery of Debussy's
music, as strongly imbued as his *Pélleas* with Wagner's *Parsifal*, benefits enormously from the acoustic
of, appropriately, All Saints' Church in Tooting, London.
Additional recommendation ...
...Le martyre de Saint-Sébastien. Images. Ibéria. **Boston Symphony Orchestra / Charles Munch.**
RCA Victor Gold Seal Ⓜ GD60684 (73 minutes: ADD). ⒼⒼ

Debussy La damoiselle élue[a]. Prélude à l'après-midi d'un faune. Images – Ibéria. [a]**Maria Ewing**
(sop) Damoiselle; [a]**Brigitte Balleys** (contr) Narrator; **London Symphony** [a]**Chorus and Orchestra /
Claudio Abbado.** DG Ⓕ 423 103-2GH (49 minutes: DDD: 3/88). Text and translation included.
Selected by Sounds in Retrospect. Ⓖ
La damoiselle élue, scored for soprano, women's chorus and orchestra, sets verses from Dante Gabriel
Rossetti's *The Blessed Damozel*. It is cast into four short movements and owes a clear debt to Wagner's
Parsifal. The *Prélude à l'après-midi d'un faune* was Debussy's first real masterpiece and this evocation
of Mallarmé's poem introduced a whole palette of new, supremely beautiful sounds, combining them
into a musical structure both concise and subtly complex. Once heard it can never be forgotten.
"Ibéria" is the central component of the orchestral set of *Images* and its three movements employ
Spanish rhythms and harmonies to conjure up a perfect picture of the Spanish/Mediterranean climate
in its various moods. A fine Debussian, Abbado penetrates to the heart of all these works and is given
fine orchestral support throughout. Maria Ewing is an impressive Damoiselle and the women of the
LSO chorus are in excellent voice. The recording is most successful, with good atmosphere and clarity.
Additional recommendationS ...
...La Damoiselle élue[a]. Nocturnes[b]. Le martyre de Saint Sébastien – La Cour de Lys;
Danse extatique; La Passion; Le Bon Pasteur. [a]**Dawn Upshaw** (sop); [a]**Paula Rasmussen** (mez);
[ab]**Los Angeles Master Chorale; Los Angeles Philharmonic Orchestra / Esa-Pekka Salonen.**
Sony Classical Ⓕ SK58952 (68 minutes: DDD: 12/94).
...La damoiselle élue. *Coupled with opera arias by various composers.* **Bidù Sayão** (sop) with various
artists. Sony Classical Masterworks Heritage mono Ⓜ MHK63221* (73 minutes: ADD: 4/98).
See review in the Collections section; refer to the Index.

Debussy Pelléas et Mélisande. **Claude Dormoy** (ten) Pelléas; **Michèle Command** (sop) Mélisande;
Gabriel Bacquier (bar) Golaud; **Roger Soyer** (bass) Arkel; **Jocelyne Taillon** (mez) Geneviève;
Monique Pouradier-Duteil (sop) Yniold; **Xavier Tamalet** (bass) Doctor, Shepherd; **Burgundian
Chorus; Orchestra of the Opéra de Lyon / Serge Baudo.** RCA Opera Ⓑ 74321 32225-2
(two discs: 147 minutes: ADD: 7/96). Synopsis and text included. From Eurodisc 452 266,
recorded 1978. ⒼⒼ
Maeterlinck's play was the inspiration for Debussy's sole masterpiece in the operatic genre. *Pelléas et
Mélisande* tells of a medieval princess who falls in love with her husband Golaud's younger half-
brother Pelléas, who is then killed by Golaud before Mélisande herself dies in childbirth. The story
has a Wagnerian parallel in *Tristan und Isolde*, but the music is very different, being more restrained
on the surface while suggesting no less powerful passions beneath. There have been many fine historic
recordings of *Pelléas et Mélisande*: reissues have included Desormière's of 1941 and Cluytens's of
1956 – and here another, from Baudo, a conductor with a great reputation as an interpreter of
French music and closely associated with this particular work. The excellence of this performance
leaves one wondering why it took the best part of 20 years to reappear. Baudo produces a warm sound
from the Lyon orchestra, knows how to shape Debussy's subtle phrases, and is notably good at
making use of silences. He is fortunate to have a cast without a single weak member. It is often the

case that the central figure of Golaud, tortured by blind jealousy, steals the show, but Gabriel Bacquier is superb, capturing every nuance from tenderness to abrupt anger (at the news of the loss of the ring) or agonized frustration beside Mélisande's deathbed. Michèle Command, here at an early stage of her career, and entirely free from the undue weightiness that has sometimes characterized her work since, makes a shy, fey Mélisande who remains an enigmatic figure; she invests the famous solo about her long hair with a sense of melancholy. The big surprise of this set is the Pelléas, a sensitive singer who seems, inexplicably, to have appeared in only one other recording (*The merry wives of Windsor*), made in the year before this – in a bass role! Listed here as a tenor, he is more a high baritone (which is appropriate for the part), just occasionally sounding a trifle stretched on a high note. The part of Arkel is given nobility by Roger Soyer; and the Yniold sounds convincingly childlike. Care has been taken in the production, as can be heard in the hollower acoustic of the scene in the vaults; only the perspective of the sailors on the unseen ship – always a problem in recordings – is a little uncertain. Make no mistake: this is a very rewarding version of this masterpiece, and as a two-disc bargain-price issue is a real snip. Even at bargain price, however, there is no excuse for RCA's rank carelessness in listing a principal character as "Goulad".

Debussy Pelléas et Mélisande. **Jacques Jansen** (bar) Pelléas; **Irène Joachim** (so) Mélisande;
 Henri Etcheverry (bar) Golaud; **Paul Cabanel** (bass) Arkel; **Germaine Cernay** (mez) Geneviève;
 Leila ben Sedira (sop) Yniold; **Emile Rousseau** (bass) Shepherd; **Armand Narçon** (bass) Doctor;
 Yvonne Gouverné Choir; symphony orchestra / Roger Desormière. EMI Références mono
 Ⓜ CHS7 61038-2* (three discs: 196 minutes: ADD: 8/88). Booklet with translation included.
 Recorded 1941. *Gramophone classical 100.*   ⒼⒼⒼ
The strength of the performance owed much to the fact that Irène Joachim, Jacques Jansen and Henri Etcheverry had already sung the work many times under Desormière at the Opéra-Comique. Irène Joachim had studied the role of Mélisande with its creator, Mary Garden; and both she and Jansen had been coached by Georges Viseur, who with Messager had been the *répétiteur* for the opera's first performance. Jansen with his free, youthful-toned production and Joachim with her silvery voice and intelligent response to every verbal nuance, set standards for the doomed lovers that, though nearly equalled, have never been surpassed; but even more impressive is Etcheverry's interpretation of Golaud, a role in which, arguably, he has yet to be rivalled. Leila ben Sedira gives one of the most convincing portrayals ever heard of the child Yniold; and Germaine Cernay and Paul Cabanel (who alone is just a trifle free with the text in places) fill the parts of the older characters with distinction. In this recording, the placing of the voices is such that every single word is crystal-clear. More important, every word is invested with meaning by a native French cast – in other versions allowances sometimes need to be made for non-French singers – which had immersed itself totally in the emotional nuances and overtones of the text. Every shade of expression is caught, but nevertheless the overall feeling is of subtle Gallic understatement – with Golaud's self-tormenting jealousy and Pelléas's final inability to resist declaring his love for his brother's mysterious, fey wife creating the great emotional climaxes. Keith Hardwick's alchemy in transforming these old recordings into sound of improved quality (and with only minimal vestiges of the 78rpm surfaces) is nothing short of amazing. He has not, of course, been able to correct the thin 1941 recording of the woodwind, but one soon comes to terms with the dated instrumental sound because of Desormière's inspired pacing and moulding of the score, the committed orchestral playing, and the well-nigh perfect casting.

Additional recommendations ...
...**Soloists; Montreal Symphony Chorus and Orchestra / Charles Dutoit.** Decca Ⓕ 430 502-2DH2 (two discs: 151 minutes: DDD: 3/91). *Selected by Sounds in Retrospect.*
...**Soloists; Vienna State Opera Chorus; Vienna Philharmonic Orchestra / Claudio Abbado.**
 DG Ⓕ 435 344-2GH2 (two discs: 148 minutes: DDD: 3/92).   Ⓖ
...**Soloists; Raymond St Paul Chorus; French Radio National Orchestra / André Cluytens.**
 Testament mono Ⓕ SBT3051* (three discs: 161 minutes: ADD: 6/95).
...**Soloists; Choeur Régional Nord, Pas de Calais; Lille National Orchestra / Jean-Claude Casadesus.**
 Naxos Ⓢ 8 660047/9 (three discs: 157 minutes: DDD: 7/97).

Debussy Rodrigue et Chimène (recons. Langham Smith and orch. Denisov). **Laurence Dale** (ten)
 Rodrigue; **Donna Brown** (sop) Chimène; **Hélène Jossoud** (mez) Iñez; **Gilles Ragon** (ten) Hernan;
 Jean-Paul Fouchécourt (ten) Bermudo; **José van Dam** (bass-bar) Don Diègue; **Jules Bastin** (bass)
 Don Gomez; **Vincent le Texier** (bass-bar) King; **Jean-Louis Meunier** (ten) Don Juan d'Arcos;
 Jean Delescluse (ten) Don Pèdre de Terruel; **Chorus and Orchestra of the Opéra de Lyon /**
 Kent Nagano. Erato Ⓕ 4509-98508-2 (two discs: 109 minutes: DDD: 10/95). Notes, text and
 translation included. Recorded 1993-94. *Gramophone Editor's choice.*   ⒼⒼ
It may come as a surprise to many who treasure the unique magic of *Pelléas et Mélisande* that Debussy toyed with some 30 other plans for operas, and two years before *Pelléas* had all but completed his first operatic venture. Debussy very soon realized that the libretto's blustering tone was alien to his ideals of half-hinted action in short scenes, and became increasingly restive, finally abandoning it and claiming that it had been accidentally destroyed. In reality it survived complete in a sketch in short score, though some pages have since been lost. Richard Langham Smith reconstructed the work from the manuscripts in the Piermont Morgan Library in New York, it was completed and orchestrated, with a remarkable insight into Debussian style, by Edison Denisov, and

in 1993 it was presented by the Opéra de Lyon to mark the opening of its new house. Inconsistencies of style reveal something of Debussy's uncertainties and doubts over a subject inappropriate for him. There is little in Act 3 that would lead anyone to identify him as the composer, and virtually the only sections of the work with a harmonic idiom that was later to become characteristic of him are Rodrigue's and Chimène's mutual declaration of love at the start of Act 1 (after a reflective modal prelude with a tinge of Russian influence), the orchestral prelude to Act 2 and the unexpected quiet interlude that precedes Rodrigue's mortal challenge to his beloved's father Don Gomez, who had shamed his own father. Debussy is less at home with the choral scene leading up to the angry conflict between the two initially friendly houses, the heroic and warlike atmosphere of much of Act 2, and the bombastic assembling of the royal court; but all these are tackled, if not with individuality, at least with vigour. Don Gomez's death scene is affecting, and the unaccompanied choral requiem for him makes an effective close to Act 2. Unlike *Pelléas*, there are a number of extended set pieces for the singers, including Rodrigue's dutiful dilemma, Don Diègue's hymn to the concept of honour, Chimène's lament for her father and her final anguish as she is torn between love and hate for Rodrigue. As a performance and recording, this is in the highest class. Nagano's orchestra play for him with finesse, and the work is cast from strength. Laurence Dale is a near-perfect Rodrigue – youthful, ardent, sensitive to changes of mood, and with a free vocal production that is a constant pleasure to hear; Donna Brown makes a passionate Chimène, though occasionally just too close to the microphone for sudden outbursts and José van Dam is his always reliable self, with nobility in his voice. Clarity of enunciation throughout (except, at times, from the chorus) is to be applauded.

Further listening ...

...Premier Trio in G major. *Coupled with works by* **Fauré** and **Saint-Saëns**
  Golub Kaplan Carr Trio. Arabesque Z6643 (7/95).
...Premier Trio in G major. *Coupled with works by* **Ravel** and **Schmitt** Joachim Trio.
  Naxos 8 550934 (8/95).
...Six ariettes oubliées. *Coupled with works by various composers.* **Sylvia McNair** (sop);
  Roger Vignoles (pf). Philips 446 656-2PH (5/97).
...Pantomime. En sourdine. Mandoline. Clair de lune. Fantôches. Coquetterie posthume. Silence
  ineffable. Musique. Paysage sentimental. Voici que le printemps. La romance d'Ariel. Regret.
  Six ariettes oubliées. Cinq poèmes de Charles Baudelaire. **Dawn Upshaw** (sop); **James Levine** (pf).
  Sony Classical SK67190 (7/97).

Juan Francés de Iribarren   Spanish 1698-1767

Suggested listening ...

...Quién nos dira de una flor. Viendo que Jil, hizo raya. *Coupled with works by various composers.*
  Al Ayre Español / Eduardo López Banzo. Deutsche Harmonia Mundi 05472 77325-2 (8/95).
  See review in the Collections section; refer to the Index.   Ⓖ

Leo Delibes   French 1836-1891

Delibes Coppélia. **Orchestra of the Opéra de Lyon / Kent Nagano**. Erato Ⓕ 4509-91730-2
  (two discs: 99 minutes: DDD: 5/94). Recorded 1993. *Gramophone Editor's choice.*   ⒼⒼ
Though the text played absolutely complete may be straightforward Delibes, the interpretation instantly announces itself as being anything but straightforward. Every phrase, every accent, every nuance seems to be newly considered, without losing the feel for the action that is taking place on the stage. The overriding impression here is of the rightness and naturalness of Nagano's whole reading. The rare quality of the performance is evident at once from the way the music lights up at the *cantando* section in the twelfth bar of the Prelude. Later, in Act 2, the Boléro has a rare dash and brio, while the opening March of Act 3 has a similarly compelling onward momentum. The sequence of speciality dances that makes up most of the final Act is delightfully turned, with a quite heavenly viola solo in "La Paix" and a thrilling final Galop. It is unfortunate that the recording is spread over two CDs, but anyone who loves this music should make a point of hearing Nagano's outstanding reading.

Additional recommendations ...

...**Orchestra of the Royal Opera House, Covent Garden / Mark Ermler**.
  Royal Opera House Ⓕ ROH006 (74 minutes: DDD: 7/93).
...Coppélia. La Source, ou Naïla – Suítes Nos. 2 and 3; Intermezzo.
  Slovak Radio Symphony Orchestra, Bratislava / Andrew Mogrelia.
  Naxos Ⓢ 8 553356/7 (two discs: 130 minutes: DDD: 6/96).

Delibes Sylvia.
Saint-Saëns Henry VIII – Ballet-divertissement. **Razumovsky Sinfonia / Andrew Mogrelia**.
  Naxos Ⓢ 8 553338/9 (two discs: 114 minutes: DDD: 6/96). Recorded 1995. *Gramophone
  Editor's choice.*
Of Delibes's two full-length ballets, *Coppélia* is the more obviously popular, the one with the bigger tunes and the greater number of recordings. However, *Sylvia* is also a superbly crafted score, full of

haunting melodies. Andrew Mogrelia's Naxos series is one to be collected and treasured: there is loving care applied to selection of tempos, shaping of phrases, orchestral balance and refinement of instrumental detail. Here you thrill to *Sylvia*'s Act 1 Fanfare, marvel at the control of tempo and refinement of instrumental detail in the "Valse lente" and "Entrée du sorcier", and revel in the sheer ebullience of Sylvia's return in Act 2. The inclusion of the ballet music from Saint-Saëns's *Henry VIII* was an admirably enterprising move, even though it doesn't amount to anything major apart from the "Danse de la gitane", being essentially a collection of mock 'Olde Britishe' dances. All the same, a quite remarkable bargain.

Additional recommendation ...

...Sylvia[a]. Coppélia[b]. [a]**London Symphony Orchestra / Anatole Fistoulari;**
[b]**Minneapolis Symphony Orchestra / Antál Dorati.**
Mercury Living Presence Ⓜ 434 313-2MM3 (three discs: 173 minutes: ADD: 3/93).   Ⓖ

Further listening ...

...Les filles de Cadix. *Coupled with works by various composers.* **Cecilia Bartoli** (mez);
Myung-Whun Chung (pf). Decca 452 667-2DH (12/96). *Gramophone Editor's record of the
month. See review in the Collections section; refer to the Index.*   ⒼⒼⒼ
...Les filles de Cadix. *Coupled with works by various composers.* **Angela Gheorghiu** (sop);
Malcolm Martineau (pf). Decca 458 360-2DH (5/98). *See review in the Collections section;
refer to the Index.*
...Lakmé. **Soloists; Monte-Carlo Opera Chorus; Monte-Carlo National Opera Orchestra /
Richard Bonynge.** Decca Grand Opera 425 485-2DM2 (12/89).

Frederick Delius   British 1862-1934

Delius Fantastic Dance[a]. A Dance Rhapsody No. 1[b]. A Dance Rhapsody No. 2[c]. A Song of the
High Hills[d]. Three Preludes[e]. Zum Carnival[e]. [d]**Maryetta Midgley** (sop); [d]**Vernon Midgley** (ten);
[e]**Eric Parkin** (pf); [d]**Ambrosian Singers;** [abcd]**Royal Philharmonic Orchestra /** [acd]**Eric Fenby,**
[b]**Norman Del Mar.** Unicorn-Kanchana Souvenir Ⓜ UKCD2071 (65 minutes: DDD: 8/95).
Item marked [a] from DKP9008/09 (10/81), [b]DKPCD9108 (3/92), [cd]DKPCD9063 (1/88),
[e]DKP9021 (7/83). Recorded 1981-90.
Delius Irmelin Prelude[a]. A Song of Summer[a]. A Late Lark[b]. Piano Concerto in C minor[c].
Violin Concerto[d]. [b]**Anthony Rolfe Johnson** (ten); [d]**Ralph Holmes** (vn); [c]**Philip Fowke** (pf);
Royal Philharmonic Orchestra / [ab]**Eric Fenby,** [d]**Vernon Handley,** [c]**Norman Del Mar.**
Unicorn-Kanchana Souvenir Ⓜ UKCD2072 (71 minutes: DDD: 8/95). Items marked
[ab] from DKP9008/09 (10/81), [c]DKPCD9108 (3/92), [d]DKP9040 (7/85). Recorded 1981-90.
Delius Koanga – La Calinda (arr. Fenby)[a]. Idyll: Once I passed through a populous city[b]. Songs of
Sunset[c]. A Village Romeo and Juliet – The Walk to the Paradise Garden[d]. [b]**Felicity Lott** (sop);
[c]**Sarah Walker** (mez); [bc]**Thomas Allen** (bar); [c]**Ambrosian Singers; Royal Philharmonic Orchestra /**
[abc]**Eric Fenby,** [d]**Norman Del Mar.** Unicorn-Kanchana Souvenir Ⓜ UKCD2073
(73 minutes: DDD: 8/95). Items marked [ab] from DKP9008/09 (10/81), [c]DKPCD9063 (1/88),
[d]new to UK. Recorded 1981-90.

The unique insight that the late Eric Fenby would bring as an interpreter of Delius was the reason for many of these Unicorn recordings, but we owe the idea and its realization to their producer, the late Christopher Palmer. As well as providing Delians with some of the most illuminating and inspiring text on the music (in books and sleeve-notes), Palmer, in the studio, and especially in a work like *A Song of the High Hills*, was able to put his understanding (and Fenby's, of course) into practice. You don't need the score of *A Song of the High Hills* to tell you that the passage from 9'54" represents "The wide far distance, the great solitude". That to which you are listening – totally spellbound – could be nothing else (and by nobody else). Ralph Holmes's recording of the Violin Concerto (with Vernon Handley) is a warm, leisurely reading. The Piano Concerto, as recorded here, is a grand showstopper in the best romantic piano concerto tradition, yet Fowke and Del Mar alert you to all the Delian reverie in the making (the dynamic range of Fowke's piano is colossal). But the outlay for Vol. 2 is justified by Anthony Rolfe Johnson alone, in the all too brief six minute-long *A Late Lark* ("one of Delius's works that is surely entirely without flaw, a most moving farewell", as Trevor Harvey put it in his original review).

In Vol. 3, Fenby's control in *Songs of Sunset* does not always match his insight (choral work is often sloppy and too distantly recorded); the recent Hickox, or the 1957 Beecham is to be preferred. But without Fenby in the recording studio (or at Grez!), we would never have had *Idyll*: Whitman texts combined with a late reworking of music from an earlyish opera, *Margot la Rouge*, to provide a reflective then rapturous love duet that looks back to Delius's Paris as well as to his *Paris* – this makes Vol. 3 indispensable, especially as sung and played here. And a very considerable bonus to be found in Vol. 3 is Del Mar's previously unissued *Walk to the Paradise Garden*. This is not the Beecham version for reduced orchestra, as stated in the otherwise excellent notes, though it incorporates many of Beecham's dynamics and tempo indications. It is, most assuredly, a *Walk* on the grandest (11'00" to Beecham's 8'38"), most passionate scale (there's not a bar-line in earshot, either), and turns out to be yet another of these three discs' memorials to inspired Delians who died in our, but before their, time.

Additional recommendations ...
...Summer Evening. Sleigh ride. Fennimore and Gerda Intermezzo. On Hearing the First Cuckoo in Spring. Summer Night on the River. A Song before Sunrise. Koanga – La Calinda. Irmelin Prelude (arr. Fenby). Hassan – Serenade; Hassan falls under the shadow of the fountain. Air and Dance. **Northern Sinfonia / Richard Hickox.**
EMI British Composers Ⓜ CDM5 65067-2 (56 minutes: DDD: 7/94).
...Violin Concerto. Suite. Légende. **Ralph Holmes** (vn); **Royal Philharmonic Orchestra / Vernon Handley.** Unicorn-Kanchana Ⓕ DKPCD9040 (53 minutes: DDD: 9/85).
...Paris. In a Summer Garden. Summer Night on the River. Brigg Fair. On Hearing the First Cuckoo in spring. A Song of Summer. **London Symphony Orchestra / Anthony Collins.**
Dutton Laboratories mono Ⓕ CDLXT2503* (76 minutes: ADD: 8/95).
...Dance Rhapsodies Nos. 1 and 2. North Country Sketches. In a Summer Garden. A Village Romeo and Juliet – The Walk to the Paradise Garden. **Bournemouth Symphony Orchestra / Richard Hickox.** Chandos Ⓕ CHAN9355 (77 minutes: DDD: 9/95).
...Piano Concerto in C minor. *Coupled with works by* **Finzi** *and* **Vaughan Williams**
Piers Lane (pf); **Royal Liverpool Philharmonic Orchestra / Vernon Handley.**
EMI Eminence Ⓜ CD-EMX2239 (61 minutes: DDD: 11/95). *See review under Finzi; refer to the Index.*
...A Village Romeo and Juliet – The Walk to the Paradise Garden. Irmelin Prelude[a]. On Hearing the First Cuckoo in Spring. Fennimore and Gerda – Intermezzo. Idyll: Once I passed through a populous city. A Song of Summer. Two Aquarelles. A Song Before Sunrise[a]. **Sylvia Fischer** (sop); **Jess Walters** (bar); **Hallé Orchestra,** [a]**New Symphony Orchestra / Sir John Barbirolli.**
Dutton Laboratories mono/stereo Ⓜ CDSJB1005* (68 minutes: ADD: 2/97).
...A Village Romeo and Juliet – The Walk to the Paradise Garden. Hassan – Interludes between Scenes 1 and 2; Serenade (violin solo). A Song before Sunrise. On Hearing the First Cuckoo in Spring. Summer Night on the River. Koanga – La Calinda. *Coupled with works by various composers.* **Academy of St Martin in the Fields / Sir Neville Marriner.**
Decca Double Ⓑ 452 707-2DF2 (two discs: 8/97).

Delius Over the Hills and Far Away[a]. North Country Sketches[b]. Eventyr[c]. Koanga – Closing scene[d]. [d]**BBC Chorus; Royal Philharmonic Orchestra / Sir Thomas Beecham.**
Sony Classical British Pageant mono Ⓑ SBK62747* (64 minutes: ADD: 11/94).
Item marked [a] from Columbia 33C1017 (12/53), [b]Columbia LX1399/1401 (7/51), [c]LX8931/2 (9/52), [d]LX1502 (1/52). Recorded 1950-59. ⒼⒼⒼ
No one, it seems, could quite 'magick' the music of Frederick Delius the way that Sir Thomas Beecham did. Listen, if you will, to "Autumn, the wind soughs in the trees", the first of the wonderfully atmospheric, seldom-heard *North Country Sketches*: one doubts whether the desolate beauty of the Yorkshire uplands has ever been more hauntingly evoked, whilst in the closing bars time really does seem to stand still. Indeed, all this music-making undoubtedly distils a very real sense of enchantment: *Eventyr* has never been given with more poetry and *Over the Hills and Far Away* is simply captivating, a performance which far outstrips Beecham's later stereo-remake in fantasy, joyful vigour and spontaneity. Transfers have been expertly managed, with one irritating exception – the very start of "The March of Spring" (the last of the *North Country Sketches*) has been fractionally clipped. In sum, a collection that should be in every self-respecting Delian's library, for none of this music has ever been surveyed with greater imagination and intuitive rapture than here.
Additional recommendations ...
...North Country Sketches. Florida – Suite. **Ulster Orchestra / Vernon Handley.**
Chandos Ⓕ CHAN8413 (67 minutes: DDD: 12/86).
...Paris: The Song of a Great City. Eventyr. Fennimore and Gerda – Intermezzo. Over the Hills and Far Away. Irmelin Prelude. **London Philharmonic Orchestra / Sir Thomas Beecham.**
Sir Thomas Beecham Trust mono Ⓜ BEECHAM 2* (61 minutes: ADD: 6/89).
...Appalachia[ce]. Koanga – Closing scene[de]. Hassan[e] – Intermezzo; Serenade; Closing scene[b].
On Hearing the First Cuckoo in Spring[f]. Summer Night on the River[f]. Cradle Song[a]. Twilight Fancies[a]. The Nightingale[a].[a]**Dora Labbette** (sop); [b]**Jan van der Gucht** (ten); [c]**BBC Chorus;** [d]**London Select Choir;** [b]**Chorus of the Royal Opera House, Covent Garden;** [e]**London Philharmonic Orchestra,** [f]**Royal Philharmonic Society Orchestra / Sir Thomas Beecham** ([a]pf).
Dutton Laboratories mono Ⓜ CDLX7011* (78 minutes: ADD: 10/94). ⒼⒼ
...Appalachia[a]. A Song of the High Hills[b]. Over the Hills and Far Away. [b]**Rebecca Evans** (sop); [b]**Peter Hoare** (ten); [a]**Daniel Washington** (bar); **Welsh National Opera** [ab]**Chorus and Orchestra / Sir Charles Mackerras.** Decca London Ⓕ 443 171-2LH (78 minutes: DDD: 1/96). *Gramophone Editor's choice.*
...Florida Suite. Over the Hills and Far Away. Idylle de printemps. La quadroône (Rapsodie floridienne). Scherzo. Koanga – Closing scene[a]. [a]**Soloists; English Northern Philharmonia / David Lloyd-Jones.** Naxos Ⓢ 8 553535 (79 minutes: DDD: 6/97).

Delius Paris: The Song of a Great City. Double Concerto[ab]. Cello Concerto[b]. [a]**Tasmin Little** (vn); [b]**Raphael Wallfisch** (vc); **Royal Liverpool Philharmonic Orchestra / Sir Charles Mackerras.**
EMI Eminence Ⓜ CD-EMX2185 (64 minutes: DDD: 3/92). Recorded 1991. Ⓖ

Paris is an extravagant nocturnal impression of the city where "Le grand anglais", as Delius was known to his friends (who included Gauguin and Eduard Munch) spent a decade of his life, during which he developed, as Eric Fenby put it, "a painter's sense of orchestral colour". Premièred in 1901, it shows Delius relishing the full palette of his Straussian-sized orchestra to conjure an intoxicating merry-go-round of the city's night-life. Mackerras's performance is very physical, propelling the dancing to wild, whirling climaxes, and his balance engineers place us firmly among the excitement. In the Cello Concerto, a personal favourite of Delius's, Raphael Wallfisch and Mackerras seek out the contrasts inherent in the score, and, for the first time on disc, its pervasive dreaminess is offset by faster decorative passages, and a genuine playfulness. In short, it dances as well as sings. They are joined by Tasmin Little for an account of the Double Concerto that has never before received teamwork of such confidence, security and unanimity of purpose. This Eminence disc is an essential acquisition for all Delians, especially at the modest asking price.

Additional recommendations ...
...Cello Concerto. *Coupled with works by* **Holst** and **Vaughan Williams** Philharmonia Orchestra / **Vernon Handley.** RCA Victor Red Seal Ⓕ RD70800 (48 minutes: DDD: 7/87).
...Cello Concerto. *Coupled with works by various composers.* **Jacqueline du Pré** (vc) with various artists and orchestras. EMI Ⓑ CZS5 68132-2 (six discs: 437 minutes: ADD: 8/94). *See review in the Collections section; refer to the Index.* ⒼⒼ
...Cello Concerto. *Coupled with works by various composers.* **Jacqueline du Pré** (vc); **Royal Philharmonic Orchestra / Sir Malcolm Sargent.** EMI Ⓕ CDC5 55529-2 (73 minutes: ADD: 11/95).
...Paris[a]. Suite[b]. Fennimore and Gerda Intermezzo[c]. Arabesque[d]. [d]**Thomas Allen** (bar); [b]**Ralph Holmes** (vn); [d]**Ambrosian Singers; Royal Philharmonic Orchestra /** [a]**Norman Del Mar,** [b]**Vernon Handley,** [cd]**Eric Fenby.** Unicorn Kanchana Souvenir Ⓜ UKCD2076 (67 minutes: DDD: 4/96).
...Paris. *Coupled with works by* **Arnell** and **Berners** Royal Philharmonic Orchestra; Philadelphia Orchestra / **Sir Thomas Beecham.** Sony Classical Essential Classics mono Ⓑ SBK62748* (68 minutes: ADD: 12/96). *See review under Arnell; refer to the Index.* Ⓖ

Delius Brigg Fair. In a Summer Garden. Paris: The Song of a Great City. On Hearing the First Cuckoo in Spring. Summer Night on the River. A Village Romeo and Juliet – The Walk to the Paradise Garden. **BBC Symphony Orchestra / Andrew Davis.** Teldec British Line Ⓕ 4509-90845-2 (77 minutes: DDD: 1/94). Recorded 1992. *Gramophone Editor's choice. Selected by Sounds in Retrospect.*

This *Brigg Fair* is unique. What a lovely surprise to hear real London sparrows sharing the air space of St Augustine's Church with Delius's translated Lincolnshire larks (flute and clarinet) in the opening minutes of the work, albeit much more distantly. Very effective too are those almost still pools of string sound (early morning mists?), given the extended boundaries of this acoustic, and the familiar warmth and depth of tone Davis draws from the orchestra's strings. In the final magnificently broad climax (pealing bells, for once, very clear), you cannot fail to be impressed by the depth, coherence and articulacy of the sound – hallmarks, indeed, of the entire disc. Davis's strings come into their own in the *Walk to the Paradise Garden.* For *In a Summer Garden,* Davis mutes his strings more often than Delius asks; but the reading's delicacy of texture and hazy, suffusing warmth are difficult to resist; it will please those who don't respond to the more animated freshening up of the score by other conductors.

Additional recommendation ...
...Brigg Fair. In a Summer Garden. Eventyr. A Song of Summer. **Hallé Orchestra / Vernon Handley.** Classics for Pleasure Ⓑ CD-CFP4568 (56 minutes: DDD: 8/90).

Delius Cello Sonata. Caprice and Elegy. Hassan – Serenade (arr. Fenby). Romance.
Grieg Cello Sonata in A minor, Op. 36. Intermezzo in A minor, CW118. **Julian Lloyd Webber** (vc); **Bengt Forsberg** (pf). Philips Ⓕ 454 458-2PH (66 minutes: DDD: 4/98). Recorded 1996.

The links, both musical and personal, between Grieg and Delius are many, which makes this a very apt and attractive coupling, bringing together all the works each composer wrote for this medium. This is Julian Lloyd Webber's second recording of the Delius Cello Sonata. His earlier version was made in 1981. The contrasts are fascinating. The overall duration this time is almost two minutes shorter, and the easier flow goes with a lighter manner and a less forward balance for the cello. The result in this freely lyrical single-movement structure is more persuasive, less effortful, with greater light and shade, and with just as much warmth in the playing. Lloyd Webber is splendidly matched by the playing of Bengt Forsberg, whose variety of expression and idiomatic feeling for rubato consistently match those of his partner. The *Caprice and Elegy* of 1930, originally dictated to Eric Fenby, much slighter pieces with obsessively repetitious phrases, inspire equally free and spontaneous performances, and it is particularly good to have the tuneful *Romance* of 1898, which inexplicably remained neglected for 80 years till Lloyd Webber revived it. The Grieg Sonata, too, among the most inspired and intense of his longer works, prompts magnetic playing, again with more light and shade than is common, helped by not having the cello spotlit, in a natural recording acoustic. The mystery of the very opening is intensified, and the *pianissimos* from both cellist and pianist are daringly extreme, especially so in the central slow movement with its haunting quotation from Grieg's *Sigurd Jorsalfar* "Homage March". The lyrical *Intermezzo* provides an attractive makeweight. Though a very high proportion of the music here is reflective, the meditative intensity of the playing sustains it well.

Delius Violin Sonatas Nos. 1-3[a]. Cello Sonata[b]. [a]**Ralph Holmes** (vn); [b]**Julian Lloyd Webber** (vc);
   Eric Fenby (pf). Unicorn-Kanchana Souvenir Ⓜ UKCD2074 (65 minutes: ADD/DDD: 8/95).
   Items marked [a] from RHS310 (5/73), [b]DKP9021 (7/83). Recorded 1972-81.   Ⓖ
Delius Violin Sonatas – B major; No. 1; No. 2; No. 3. **Tasmin Little** (vn); **Piers Lane** (pf).
   Conifer Classics Ⓕ 75605 51315-2 (77 minutes: DDD: 9/97). Recorded 1997.   ⒼⒼ
The Unicorn-Kanchana disc gives us selfless, utterly dedicated music-making, always spontaneous-
sounding yet never losing the organic thread of Delius's remarkable, free-flowing inspiration. In the
First Sonata there may never be a performance to match the extraordinarily fluid, re-creative rapture
of May Harrison's 1929 recording with Arnold Bax, but Holmes and Fenby come close. There is a
slight fragility to Holmes's distinctive, silvery tone that is extremely moving, and Fenby, though no
virtuoso practitioner, accompanies with intuitive sympathy. The recording of the piano (the
instrument used is the three-quarter Ibach grand left to Fenby by Delius himself) remains a touch
boxy and wanting in bloom, though the balance is otherwise natural and the overall effect nicely
intimate. In the Cello Sonata Lloyd Webber and Fenby adopt a mellow, notably ruminative approach.
Dedicatee Beatrice Harrison's 1926 recording (with Harold Craxton) should be sought out by all
discerning Delians, for through the surface crackle emerge a rapt wonder, generous flexibility and
instinctive sense of line that are something special. A small textual observation of note: Lloyd Webber
(like Harrison before him) eschews the cello's final D major chord.
   Tasmin Little's Delian instincts are formidable indeed, here amply confirmed by Conifer's rewarding
coupling. The wonderful First Sonata receives big-hearted, confident advocacy here. These
marvellously sensitive performers strike a near-ideal balance between flexibility and purposeful
concentration. Even by the standards of May Harrison recording (the same team also went on to
première the Third Sonata in November of the following year), and Holmes and Fenby who also
remain mandatory listening, Little and Lane are not out of place in such august company. Likewise,
the Second Sonata is given a commandingly articulate, thoughtful interpretation that never once
threatens to hang fire. In the Third Sonata Little's playing positively glows with fervour and
understanding. Moreover, she and Lane see to it that the fine Sonata in B major (1892) emerges in
infinitely convincing fashion. To both outer movements they bring fiery propulsion as well as a firm
sense of direction, while the haunting central processional of the lovely *Andante molto tranquillo*
(which so impressed Grieg) really captures the imagination. The recording is full-bodied, though the
piano focus could be sharper within a church acoustic that is surely too expansive for such intimate
repertoire. The sessions (as Little relates in her touching booklet-notes) were lent an extra poignancy
by the news of Eric Fenby's death on the first day of recording.
Additional recommendation ...
...Violin Sonata No. 1. Cello Sonata. Hassan – Serenade. **May Harrison** (vn/pf); **Beatrice Harrison**
   (vc); **Margaret Harrison, Sir Arnold Bax, Harold Craxton** (pfs).
   Symposium mono Ⓕ CD1140* (76 minutes: ADD: 3/93).

Delius Sea Drift[a]. Songs of Sunset[b]. Songs of Farewell. [b]**Sally Burgess** (mez); [ab]**Bryn Terfel**
   (bass-bar); **Waynflete Singers; Southern Voices; Bournemouth Symphony Chorus and Orchestra /**
   Richard Hickox. Chandos Ⓕ CHAN9214 (77 minutes: DDD: 11/93). Texts included.
   Recorded 1993. *Gramophone Award Winner 1994. Gramophone Editor's choice.*   ⒼⒼ
Sea Drift is a sublime conjunction of Whitman's poetry and Delius's music describing love, loss and
unhappy resignation, with the sea (as Christopher Palmer put it) as "symbol and agent of parting".
Written in 1903-04 (the same years as Debussy's *La mer*), it is surely Delius's masterpiece; right from
the swaying opening bars its spell is enduring and hypnotic. Hickox in his second recording of the
work now gives us the finest recorded post-Beecham *Sea Drift*. The shaping of the opening falling
woodwind figures at a slow tempo more than usually (and very beautifully) portends the sad turn of
events; and the climax is broad and superbly co-ordinated. Terfel's bar-by-bar characterization (and
glorious voice), conveys the full expressive range of the role from impassioned appeal to gentle call
without artifice; and the choral singing from Hampshire's finest is superb. The whole is recorded with
warmth, spaciousness, depth and clarity. If Hickox's Sally Burgess is taxed a little by the high notes
in the *Songs of Sunset*, Hickox is greatly to be preferred to Fenby (see below) in the *Songs of Farewell*,
where Fenby's chorus have difficulty with some of his broad tempos – there's a lot more life in
Hickox's last three songs, particularly the "Old Sailor" of the final song. A strongly recommended
recording.
Additional recommendations ...
...Songs of Sunset (with Maureen Forrester, contr; John Cameron, bar; Beecham Choral Society).
   Over the Hills and Far Away. Sleigh Ride. Irmelin Prelude. Dance Rhapsody No. 2. Summer
   Evening. Brigg Fair. On Hearing the First Cuckoo in Spring. Summer Night on the River.
   A Song before Sunrise. Marche Caprice. Florida – Suite. Fennimore and Gerda – Intermezzo.
   Royal Philharmonic Orchestra / Sir Thomas Beecham. EMI Ⓕ CDS7 47509-8* (ADD: 6/87).
   Gramophone classical 100.   ⒼⒼⒼ
...Songs of Farewell[a]. Cynara[b]. Caprice and Elegy[c]. Two Aquarelles[d]. Lebenstanz[e]. Légende[f].
   [b]**Thomas Allen** (bar); [f]**Ralph Holmes** (vn); [c]**Julian Lloyd Webber** (vc); [a]**Ambrosian Singers;**
   Royal Philharmonic Orchestra / [abcd]**Eric Fenby,** [e]**Norman Del Mar,** [f]**Vernon Handley.**
   Unicorn-Kanchana Souvenir Ⓜ UKCD2077 (67 minutes: DDD: 4/96).

Delius A Mass of Life[a]. Requiem[b]. [a]**Joan Rodgers,** [b]**Rebecca Evans** (sops); [a]**Jean Rigby** (mez);
[a]**Nigel Robson** (ten); **Peter Coleman-Wright** (bar); **Waynflete Singers; Bournemouth Symphony
Chorus and Orchestra / Richard Hickox.** Chandos Ⓔ CHAN9515 (two discs: 129 minutes: DDD:
5/97). Texts and translations included. Recorded 1996.

This is only the third commercial recording of *A Mass of Life*. The previous two recordings were the
1952 Beecham (no longer available) and the 1971 Groves. You might imagine modern recording would
best place this vast canvas between your loudspeakers. And yes, Hickox's dynamic peaks are
marginally higher, his perspectives marginally wider and deeper (echoing horns fade magically away).
Actually, some of this has as much to do with Hickox's own pacing and shading as the engineering.
In general, this 'idealized' light- and air-filled sound brings a sharper, bright presence for the chorus,
and such things as the piccolo trilling atop the final "Hymn to Joy". What it doesn't bring is the sense
of performers in a specific acoustic space, and the resonance which real walls impart to their tone.
Heard after the Groves, you might feel a lack of profile for the orchestra's lower voices. But the chorus
shine in the prominent role which the Chandos balance gives them, with ringing attack for all entries
where it is needed, and singing as confident as it is sensitive, even if one has to make the odd allowance
for not quite perfect pitching on high (Delius's demands are extreme, and the Groves chorus are no
better) and moments where they are too loud. The quartet of soloists is a fine one, if less distinguished
than that for Groves. Hickox's baritone, Peter Coleman-Wright, has a good line in stirring, virile
address, though little of Benjamin Luxon's nobility, inwardness and true legato.

What makes the Hickox *Mass* preferable to the Groves (but only just) is the conductor's inspired
handling of each part's central dance panels. Hickox makes you believe in them, with a judicious
drive, lift to the rhythms, and really incisive, eager singing and playing. After the climax of the first of
them, Zarathustra does (and has reason to) sound transported. Which leaves the couplings. Hickox
has only the second-ever commercial recording of the Requiem: more Nietzsche, but this time dogma
not poetry, all the more unpalatable/embarrassing (regardless of your faith) for being in English, but
containing much unique Delius. It's a professional job, but without any special pleading.

Additional recommendation ...
...A Mass of Life[a]. Songs of Sunset[b]. Arabesque[c]. [abc]**Soloists;** [a]**London Philharmonic Choir;**
[bc]**Liverpool Philharmonic Choir;** [a]**London Philharmonic Orchestra;**
[bc]**Royal Liverpool Philharmonic Orchestra / Sir Charles Groves.**
EMI British Composers Ⓜ CMS7 64218-2 (two discs: 66 minutes: ADD: 6/93).

Further listening ...
...Two Aquarelles. *Coupled with works by various composers.* **English Chamber Orchestra /
Benjamin Britten.** Decca The Classic Sound 448 569-2DCS (2/96).
...String Quartet. *Coupled with* **Elgar** String Quartet in E minor, Op. 83. **Brodsky Quartet.**
ASV CDDCA526 (7/89).
...String Quartet. *Coupled with works by* **Howells** Britten Quartet.
EMI British Composers CDC5 55349-2 (4/97). *See review under Howells; refer to the Index.*
...To Daffodils. *Coupled with works by various composers.* **Sir Peter Pears** (ten); **Viola Tunnard** (pf).
Belart 461 550-2 (12/97). *See review in the Collections section; refer to the Index.*
...Twilight Fancies[bd]. Wine Roses[bd]. The Bird's Story[ad]. Let Springtime come[ad]. Il pleure dans mon
coeur[cd]. Le ciel est par-dessus le toit[ad]. La lune blanche[cd]. To Daffodils[bd]. I-Brasil[cd]. Twilight
Fancies[be]. The Violet[ae]. Let Springtime come[be]. In the Seraglio Garden[ae]. Silken shoes[e]. Young
Venevil[ae]. Autumn[be]. Irmelin Rose[ae]. Il pleure dans mon coeur[e]. Le ciel est par-dessus le toit[e].
La lune blanche[ce]. Chanson d'automne[be]. Avant que tu ne t'en ailles[ae]. To Daffodils[be]. So white,
so soft, is she[ce]. I-Brasil[ce]. [a]**Felicity Lott** (sop); [b]**Sarah Walker** (mez);
[c]**Anthony Rolfe Johnson** (ten); [d]**Royal Philharmonic Orchestra / Eric Fenby** ([e]pf).
Unicorn Kanchana Souvenir UKCD2075 (4/96).
...Fennimore and Gerda. **Soloists; Chorus and Symphony Orchestra of Danish Radio /
Meredith Davies.** EMI British Composers CDM5 66314-2 (9/97).
...Fennimore and Gerda (sung in German). **Soloists; Danish National Radio Choir and
Symphony Orchestra / Richard Hickox.** Chandos CHAN9589 (12/97).

Harry Dexter
British 1910-1973

Suggested listening ...
...Siciliano. *Coupled with works by various composers.* **Pro Arte Orchestra / George Weldon.**
EMI British Composers CDM5 66537-2 (1/98). *See review in the Collections section; refer
to the Index.*

Nathaniel Dett
American 1882-1943

Suggested listening ...
...Listen to the lambs. *Coupled with works by* **W. James** London Adventist Chorale / Ken Burton.
EMI Debut CDZ5 69707-2 (9/97). *See review in the Collections section; refer to the Index.*

Alphons Diepenbrock
Dutch 1862-1921

Suggested listening ...
...Im grossen Schweigen[a]. *Coupled with* **Mahler** Symphony No. 7 in E minor. [a]**Håkan Hagegård**
(bar); **Royal Concertgebouw Orchestra / Riccardo Chailly.**
Decca 444 446-2DH2 (5/95). *See review under Mahler; refer to the Index.*   🅖🅖

Bernard van Dieren
Dutch/British 1887-1936

Suggested listening ...
...Dream pedlary. Take, o take those lips away. *Coupled with works by various composers.*
Sir Peter Pears (ten); **Viola Tunnard** (pf).
Belart 461 550-2 (12/97). *See review in the Collections section; refer to the Index.*

Robert Docker
British 1919-1992

Suggested listening ...
...Tabarinage. *Coupled with works by various composers.* **Light Music Society Orchestra /**
Sir Vivian Dunn.
EMI British Composers CDM5 66537-2 (1/98). *See review in the Collections section;*
refer to the Index.

Ernö Dohnányi
Hungarian 1877-1960

Dohnányi Piano Concertos – No. 1 in E minor, Op. 5; No. 2 in B minor, Op. 42.
Martin Roscoe (pf); **BBC Scottish Symphony Orchestra / Fedor Glushchenko.**
Hyperion Ⓕ CDA66684 (75 minutes: DDD: 5/94). Recorded 1993.   🅖
This coupling provides a salutary reminder of two of Dohnányi's most substantial if sadly neglected
works. Both concertos – separated by 50 years, but mildly rather than radically different in their
musical language – burgeon with heartfelt melody and high-flying pianistics. And if Dohnányi hardly
provides anything so important as a bridge between Liszt and Bartók, his alternation of dark and
scintillating ideas is accomplished with an easy and professional aplomb. The Second Concerto's
crisply accented finale in whirling and nationalistic duple time is notably attractive. Martin Roscoe's
superbly authoritative performances are majestic and glittering as required, and his survival of his
recessed placing in relation to the orchestra is doubly to his credit. Fedor Glushchenko's partnership
is excellent and, overall, the recordings are of high quality.

Dohnányi Violin Concerto No. 2 in C minor, Op. 43.
Bartók Violin Concerto No. 2, Sz112. **Mark Kaplan** (vn); **Barcelona Symphony Orchestra /**
Lawrence Foster. Koch International Classics Ⓕ 37387-2 (70 minutes: DDD: 9/97).
Recorded 1996.
Dohnányi's immensely likeable Second Violin Concerto nails its wide roster of colours to the mast
with "a declamatory sequence of chords" (as the annotator would have it), then launches into a wild
cadenza astride a timpani roll, sundry expressive leaps and a hauntingly lyrical second theme.
Throughout the concerto, the general idea is to keep the solo line as busy and as prominent as
possible, even to the extent of dispensing with orchestral violins. The first movement features a
furious fugato, Straussian tutti passages and Kreislerian solo writing (especially when double-
stopped). The scherzo recalls Reger at his most mischievous, and the slow movement has a warmth
reminiscent of Brahms. A spirited finale features a novel cadenza with solo horn and the overall effect
of the concerto is of spontaneous invention bursting at the seams. Mark Kaplan's idiomatically
luscious performance is given alert support from Lawrence Foster's Barcelona orchestra, and the
recording is more than acceptable. Kaplan's Bartók is equally forceful and the partnership with Foster
works particularly well when soloist and orchestra indulge in vigorous banter. This is a strong,
spontaneous and warmly felt reading, flexible in gesture and with the added interest of Bartók's
brassy original coda – a more powerful ending than the revision, albeit without any contribution from
the soloist. It provides an enjoyable coupling for the more-ish Dohnányi concerto.

Dohnányi Symphony No. 2, Op. 40. Symphonic Minutes, Op. 36. **BBC Philharmonic Orchestra /**
Matthias Bamert. Chandos Ⓕ CHAN9455 (65 minutes: DDD: 12/96). Recorded 1995.
Selected by Soundings.
Dohnányi's 50-minute Second Symphony is a most engaging piece redolent of Brahms, Bruckner and
especially Reger – the latter in terms of Bachian resonances, some richly expressive modulations and
the highly eventful six-minute fugue that crowns the finale. The symphony was conceived in the midst
of war, Dohnányi having been forced to disband the Budapest Philharmonic and flee abroad. It was
premièred in London in 1948, whereas the revised version was given its first performance some nine

years later by the Minneapolis Symphony Orchestra under Antál Dorati. Cast in four movements, it opens to a jagged, unison theme before a lyrical, somewhat Lisztian second set gives way to an agitated development and various failed attempts to regain its former serenity. The *Adagio* has a Brucknerian feeling of spaciousness and the raucous *Burla* scherzo features *glissando* trombones, meaningfully banal themes and a tonal profile that's not dissimilar to the more cynical statements of Bartók and Shostakovich. Anyone sold on Strauss, Korngold, Schmidt or Zemlinsky will likely take this work very much to heart. Dohnányi's far lighter *Symphonic Minutes* (1933) has been recorded before. The first is a brightly lit, Straussian "Capriccio", the second an aromatic "Rapsodia" reminiscent of early Bartók, the third an off-beat, keenly inflected *Scherzo* incorporating chorale-style themes, the fourth an atmospheric theme and variations and the last a sort of latter-day "Dance of the Comedians". The performances are excellent and the recording first-rate

---

Dohnányi Variations on a Nursery Theme, Op. 25.
Brahms Piano Concerto No. 1 in D minor, Op. 15. **Mark Anderson** (pf); **Hungarian State Symphony Orchestra / Adám Fischer.** Nimbus Ⓕ NI5349 (75 minutes: DDD: 3/95). Recorded 1994.
Brahms had the good grace to say of Ernö Dohnányi's C minor Piano Quintet, "I could not have written it better". It was no use. Years later, when he came to write his wonderfully skittish *Variations on a Nursery Theme*, Dohnányi sent the old boy up something rotten. Like many of the best parodies, it is done with a completely straight face; so much so that Dohnányi's Variation No. 3 could probably go directly into the finale of Brahms's B flat Concerto without anyone noticing a thing. On this Nimbus disc, it is the D minor Concerto that plays Wise to Dohnányi's Eric Morecambe, so the joke is slightly obscured. Mark Anderson gives a glittering performance of the Dohnányi, and a spontaneous one; he is superbly accompanied by Adám Fischer and the Hungarian State SO. Nimbus's recording is admirable in everything but the backward placing of the woodwind in general and the bassoons in particular. One thing the Dohnányi *Variations* share with the D minor Brahms Concerto is a passionate minor key opening. Again Fischer and his Hungarian orchestra are superb, the playing incisive and gloweringly vivid. It is a measure, too, of the accord that exists between conductor and soloist that the pianist enters the fray with the perfectly groomed musical manners of a soloist in a baroque concerto. And it is the logic of Anderson's playing, his sweet reasonableness, that holds the attention, even though Brahmsians who, like farmers at market, look for a solid well-hung beast, may find Anderson a shade light-toned in bravura passages. The Brahms obviously faces tough competition, but the Dohnányi is a very fine performance in its own right.

Additional recommendations ...
...Variations on a Nursery Theme. *Coupled with works by* **Bartók** Zoltán Kocsis (pf); **Budapest Festival Orchestra / Iván Fischer.** Philips Ⓕ 446 472-2PH (77 minutes: DDD: 4/96).
...Variations on a Nursery Theme. *Coupled with works by* **Rachmaninov** Julius Katchen (pf). Dutton Laboratories mono Ⓕ CDLXT2504* (79 minutes: ADD: 5/96).

Dohnányi Sextet in C major, Op. 37ᵃ.
Fibich Quintet in D major, Op. 42. **Endymion Ensemble** (Mark van de Wiel, cl; Stephen Stirling, hn; Krysia Osostowicz, vn; ᵃIris Juda, va; Jane Salmon, vc; Michael Dussek, pf). ASV Ⓕ CDDCA943 (66 minutes: DDD: 2/96). Recorded 1995. Ⓖ
Both composers employ their chosen resources with great expertise, Dohnányi in a richly harmonized Sextet that opens among the clouds and ends in a mood of dance-like exuberance, Fibich with a more conventional structure and a genial stream of melody. Each work owes something to Brahms although in the case of Fibich's Quintet, Schumann seems as much in evidence, not only through the score's specific melodic complexion, but in a *Scherzo* that features two contrasting trios. Smetana is another possible point of reference, especially at the start of the finale, although – as Jan Smaczny usefully points out in his excellent booklet-note – the younger Fibich "often anticipated the achievements of the elder composer". Dohnányi's Sextet is a far darker piece, opening as it does among rolling string arpeggios and toughening for a fairly tense development. The "Intermezzo" second movement suggests (at least initially) Brahms as siphoned through the imagination of Schoenberg, whereas the eventful third movement suddenly breaks into a rhythmically upbeat finale that sounds as much Afro-Caribbean as Hungarian, albeit with a luscious 'big' tune to offset the fun. The Endymion Ensemble do both Fibich and Dohnányi proud and the recordings are excellent.

Dohnányi String Quartets – No. 2 in D flat major, Op. 15; No. 3 in A minor, Op. 33.
Kodály Intermezzoᵃ. **Lyric Quartet** (ᵃPatricia Calnan, Harriet Davies, vns; ᵃNick Barr, va; ᵃDavid Daniels, vc). ASV Ⓕ CDDCA985 (60 minutes: DDD: 1/98). Recorded 1996.
Dohnányi's output is nothing if not rich in contrasts: both slow movements of these appealing quartets are visited by animated, mood-changing faster sections. The precise manner of these 'interruptions' varies according to musical context, stormy and passionate in the Second Quartet, skittish in the Third. The earlier quartet is the more wholesomely romantic of the two, with a *Presto acciacato* second movement that recalls the orchestral storm sequence at the beginning of Wagner's *Die Walküre*. The Second Quartet's heart is in its poignant slow movement finale, much as the heart of Bartók's Second Quartet is in *its* slow finale. Furthermore, Dohnányi's finale incorporates references to previous movements, another ploy that Bartók used, albeit towards the end of his career,

in his Sixth Quartet. In all other respects, however, Dohnányi's musical language is more akin to Strauss, Brahms and Mendelssohn, with the Third Quartet's cynically argumentative first movement providing the grittiest musical activity on the disc. The earliest work programmed is by Kodály, a pleasant but uncharacteristic *Intermezzo* from 1905 that the Lyric Quartet perform – like everything else – with gusto and warmth.

Additional recommendation ...
...String Quartet No. 2. Piano Quintet No. 1 in C minor, Op. 1. **Wolfgang Manz** (pf); **Gabrieli Quartet.** Chandos Ⓕ CHAN8718 (61 minutes: DDD: 5/89).

Further listening ...
...Konzertstück in D major, Op. 12. *Coupled with works by various composers.* **János Starker** (vc); **Gerald Moore** (pf); **Philharmonia Orchestra / Carlo Maria Giulini, Walter Susskind.** EMI mono/stereo CZS5 68485-2* (12/95). *See review in the Collections section; refer to the Index.*
...Konzertstück in D major, Op. 12. *Coupled with* **Dvořák** Cello Concerto in B minor, B191. **Raphael Wallfisch** (vc); **London Symphony Orchestra / Sir Charles Mackerras.** Chandos CHAN8662 (5/89).
...Violin Concerto, Op. 27[a]. American Rhapsody, Op. 47. [a]**Ulf Wallin** (vn); **Frankfurt Radio Symphony Orchestra / Alun Francis.** CPO CPO999 308-2 (4/97).
...Cello Sonata in B flat minor, Op. 8. *Coupled with works by* **Bridge** and **Debussy** **Bernard Gregor-Smith** (vc); **Yolande Wrigley** (pf). ASV CDDCA796 (9/92).
...Piano Quintets[a] – No. 1 in C minor, Op. 1; No. 2 in E flat minor, Op. 26. Suite in the Old Style, Op. 24. **Martin Roscoe** (pf); [a]**Vanbrugh Quartet.** ASV CDDCA915 (5/95).   Ⓖ
...Piano Quintets – No. 1 in C minor, Op. 1; No. 2 in E flat minor, Op. 26. Serenade in C major, Op. 10. **Schubert Ensemble of London.** Hyperion CDA66786 (11/96).
...Four Pieces, Op. 2. Passacaglia in E flat minor, Op. 6. Variations and Fugue on a Theme by E.G., Op. 4. **Annette Servadei** (pf). Continuum CCD1064 (5/95).

Gaetano Donizetti   Italian 1797-1848

Donizetti Sinfonia in G minor (recons. Päuler). Sonata in C minor (orch. Hoffmann). Oboe Sonata in F major (orch. Hoffmann). Concerto for Violin, Cello and Orchestra in D minor (recons. Wojciechowski). Cor Anglais Concerto in G major. Clarinet Concertino in B flat major (recons. Meylan). Sinfonia in D minor (recons. Andreae). **Budapest Camerata / László Kovács.** Marco Polo Ⓕ 8 223701 (64 minutes: DDD: 10/95). Recorded 1994.

This is an intriguing issue of instrumental concertos, recorded for the first time. As in his string quartets, Donizetti's dramatic flair and imaginative instrumentation provide the main points of interest, while the G major Concerto for cor anglais – a theme and variations – provides an opportunity to sample Donizetti's formal ingenuity and thematic invention. After a crisp performance of the buoyant G minor *Sinfonia*, the Budapest Camerata offer a group of solo concertos featuring a variety of instruments. The C minor flute *Concertino* and F major oboe *Concertino* – originally intended as instrumental sonatas – are presented in Wolfgang Hoffmann's sensitive orchestrations. Contrasts (textural, dramatic and dynamic) are well defined, with admirably clear recording. The infectiously exuberant *allegros* are not especially profound, but Donizetti's slow movements are often most effective. The D minor Concerto for violin, cello and orchestra is the longest and most impressive work here. The Budapest Camerata balance solo and ensemble forces with subtle refinement throughout this charming piece, whose brief *Andante* has genuine pathos, and smiling finale has engaging wit.

Donizetti Don Pasquale. **Renato Bruson** (bar) Don Pasquale; **Eva Mei** (sop) Norina; **Frank Lopardo** (ten) Ernesto; **Thomas Allen** (bar) Malatesta; **Alfredo Giacomotti** (bass) Notary; **Bavarian Radio Chorus; Munich Radio Orchestra / Roberto Abbado.** RCA Victor Red Seal Ⓕ 09026 61924-2 (two discs: 120 minutes: DDD: 12/94). Notes, text and translation included. Recorded 1993.   Ⓖ

Roberto Abbado balances equably the witty and more serious sides of this score, finding a gratifying lightness in the "A quel vecchio" section of the Act 1 finale and creating a delightful sense of expectancy as Pasquale preens himself while awaiting his intended bride. Abbado and the slightly po-faced Muti play the score complete and respect Donizetti's intentions. This set has many strengths and few weaknesses: indeed it would be hard to cast the piece more successfully today. Pasquale is usually assigned to a veteran singer. In the case of Bruscantini (Muti), allowances definitely have to be made for the singer's age: both men cleverly compensate with the vocal equivalent of guying for failing voices. With Bruson you hear a voice hardly touched by time and a technique still in perfect repair. Apart from weak low notes, he sings and acts the part with real face, and his vital diction, particularly in recitatives, is a pleasure to hear. He works well with Thomas Allen's nimble, wily Malatesta, an unexpected piece of casting that proves to be inspired. Like Bruson, Allen sings every note truly and relishes his words, evincing a sense of comedy as he prepares, cruel to be kind, to gull his friend. Eva Mei's Norina is an ebullient creature with a smile in her tone, much more pointed and pert than the admittedly warmer-voiced Freni (Muti). The edge to Mei's voice seems just right for Norina though others may find it tends towards the acerbic under pressure. Her skills in coloratura are as exemplary as you would expect from a reigning Queen of Night. Lopardo is that rare thing, a tenor who can sing in an exquisite half-voice, as in "Com' è gentil", yet has the metal in his tone to suggest something heroic in "E se fia", the cabaletta to "Cercherò lontana terra", which in turn is sung in a plangent, loving way, just right. As the recording here is exemplary as compared with the EMI (too reverberant), this version is now the outright recommendation.

Additional recommendations ...
...Soloists; **Ambrosian Opera Chorus; Philharmonia Orchestra / Riccardo Muti.**
EMI Ⓕ CDS7 47068-2 (two discs: 123 minutes: DDD: 8/88).
...Soloists; **Lyon Opera Chorus and Orchestra / Gabriele Ferro.**
Erato Ⓕ 2292-45487-2 (two discs: 120 minutes: DDD: 11/90).

Donizetti L'elisir d'amore. **Mariella Devia** (sop) Adina; **Roberto Alagna** (ten) Nemorino;
Pietro Spagnoli (bar) Belcore; **Bruno Praticò** (bar) Dulcamara; **Francesca Provvisionato** (mez)
Giannetta; **Tallis Chamber Choir; English Chamber Orchestra / Marcello Viotti.**
Erato Ⓜ 0630-17787-2 (two discs: 129 minutes: DDD: 6/93). Notes, text and translation included.
Recorded 1992. *Gramophone Editor's choice.*   Ⓖ
A modern and completely recommendable set of this delightful piece, country cousin to *Don Pasquale*, was badly needed – and here it is. It is a delight from start to finish, making one fall in love all over again with this delightful comedy of pastoral life. The plot is a variant of the much used theme of the fake love potion. Here the potion is supplied by the charlatan Doctor Dulcamara to the shy young Nemorino to help him win the love of Adina. Roberto Alagna, disciple of Pavarotti, sings Nemorino with all his mentor's charm and a rather lighter tone appropriate to the role. He also evinces just the right sense of vulnerability and false bravado that lies at the heart of Nemorino's predicament. Here is a tenor with a great future if only he stays with roles within his range. He is partnered by Mariella Devia who has every characteristic needed for the role of Adina. With a fine sense of buoyant rhythm, she sings fleetly and uses the coloratura to enhance her reading. She can spin a long, elegiac line where that is needed, and her pure yet full tone blends well with that of her colleagues. She also suggests all Adina's high spirits and flirtatious nature. The other principals, though not as amusing in their interpretations as some of their more experienced predecessors, enter into the ensemble feeling of the performance. All are helped by the lively but controlled conducting of Viotti and by the ideal recording.

Additional recommendations ...
...Soloists; **Ambrosian Opera Chorus; English Chamber Orchestra / Richard Bonynge.**
Decca Ⓕ 414 461-2DH2 (two discs: 141 minutes: ADD: 6/86).
...Soloists; **Turin Radio Symphony Chorus and Orchestra / Claudio Scimone.**
Philips Ⓕ 412 714-2PH2 (two discs: 127 minutes: DDD: 6/86).   ⒼⒼ
...Soloists; **Chorus and Orchestra of the Metropolitan Opera, New York / James Levine.**
DG Ⓕ 429 744-2GH2 (two discs: 119 minutes: DDD: 2/91).
...Soloists; **Chorus and Orchestra of La Scala, Milan / Tullio Serafin.**
Classics for Pleasure Ⓑ CD-CFPD4733 (two discs: 111 minutes: ADD: 5/94).
...Soloists; **Chorus and Orchestra of the Maggio Musicale Fiorentino / Francesco Molinari-Pradelli.**
Double Decca Ⓜ 443 542-2LF2* (two discs: 108 minutes: ADD: 7/95).

Donizetti L'elisir d'amore. **Angela Gheorghiu** (sop) Adina; **Roberto Alagna** (ten) Nemorino;
Roberto Scaltriti (bar) Belcore; **Simone Alaimo** (bar) Dulcamara; **Elena Dan** (sop) Giannetta;
Chorus and Orchestra of the Opéra National de Lyon / Evelino Pidò. Decca Ⓕ 455 691-2DHO2
(two discs: 123 minutes: DDD: A/97). Notes, text and translation included. Recorded 1996.   Ⓖ
This work, ideally combining the needs of comedy and sentiment, has always been a favourite of opera goers. This set catches these contrasting moods to perfection under Pidò's alert and affectionate conducting, not least because the recording is based on live performances at the Lyon Opera. The main interest is undoubtedly on how our most sought-after operatic pairing fare in the central roles. Gheorghiu presented her credentials as Adina at Covent Garden prior to this recording; some found her dramatically a shade shrewish in the part, but Adina is a feisty, temperamental girl, and a touch of steel doesn't seem inappropriate. It makes her capitulation when she realizes the true depth of Nemorino's feelings that much more moving. She provides plenty of flirtatious fire in the early scenes and turns Nemorino away with determination, making her intentions clear in pointed attack in the recitative, but her concern for him is never far below the surface and comes to the fore in her colloquy with Dulcamara. All this is conveyed in singing that matches warmth with pointed diction and fleet technique, something essential at Pidò's sometimes racy speeds. Alagna's Nemorino is almost on the same level. He obviously enjoys himself greatly as the lovelorn yokel, one with a vulnerable soul as he shows at his moment of greatest heartbreak, "Adina, credimi" in the Act 1 finale. His sense of fun is obvious in the bottle-shaking episode when he thinks he has found the elixir of the title. The two Italians in the lower roles are admirable. Scaltriti may not be as preening as some Belcores but he sings the part with a firmness that older singers miss and he is fully in character. Alaimo is a naturally witty Dulcamara and never indulges in unwanted *buffo* mugging though he lacks the ripe, rich timbre of Taddei on the Serafin version (listed above). The Erato set, at mid price, presents formidable opposition. Devia is a less wilful, less vivid Adina than Gheorghiu, but her style is, if possible, even more idiomatic. There's not much to

choose between the other roles, but as a whole the Decca sounds, not surprisingly, the more lifelike reading and thus becomes a clear and welcome choice, worth every penny of the asking price. Decca have provided an ideally balanced sound picture which has plenty of natural presence.

Donizetti Linda di Chamounix. **Mariella Devia** (sop) Linda; **Luca Canonici** (ten) Carlo; **Alfonso Antoniozzi** (bar) Marquis de Boisfleury; **Petteri Salomaa** (bass) Antonio; **Sonia Ganassi** (mez) Pierotto; **Donato di Stefano** (bar) Prefect; **Francesca Provvisionato** (mez) Maddalena; **Boguslaw Fiksinski** (ten) Intendant; **Koor van de Nationale Reisopera; Orchestra of Eastern Netherlands / Gabrielle Bellini.** Arts Music Ⓢ 47151-2 (three discs: 177 minutes: DDD: 2/97). Italian text included. Recorded 1992.

For a newcomer to *Linda di Chamounix*, it may be helpful to think of it as Donizetti's *Luisa Miller*. There are similarities in subject – a strong father-and-daughter relationship, a simple family and communal life threatened by the high-and-mighty. More than that, both operas evoke a strong sense of compassion. Donizetti's is lighter, with a comic element, a happy ending, and reassurance from the start in that the 'villain' is only the *buffo* bass-baritone whom operatic convention will not allow to win. Still, tragedy looms and the situations involve heartache of various kinds, of which the separation of soprano-and-tenor lovers is not the only one. Musically, it suffers at first hearing from having its best and most famous number (Linda's "O luce di quest'anima") at the start. There is also a homeliness about the melodies and their harmonies that makes it seem all rather tame. Yet the proof, or at any rate evidence, that this is far from the whole story lies in the way that this opera has of deepening its impression on each encounter over the years. The Nightingale version is in almost every way a delight, a concert performance in Stockholm, recorded live in 1993 with Edita Gruberová in the title-role. Readers who have that version would not find it worth their while to replace it with this newer one, but for those who have to choose this is certainly a viable alternative and in certain respects to be preferred. *Linda di Chamounix* is generally thought of as 'the soprano's opera', and obviously much depends upon her. Mariella Devia sings with purity of tone and brilliancy of range and technique; though Gruberová leaves a stronger impression of the character, Devia too presents a fully human Linda and no mere coloratura-singing doll. In the main supporting roles, the two recordings each have an advantage, the Haider performance gaining from the livelier Carlo of Don Bernardini, the newer one from the outstanding bass of Petteri Salomaa. The 'trousers' role of Pierotto is sung here by the rather fruitily vibrant Sonia Ganassi, and Monica Groop, though somewhat maternal, is perhaps preferable. Both versions offer a suitably authoritative Prefect and a discreetly *buffo*-ish Marquis. Both are fine in ensemble, chorus work and orchestral playing. Friedrich Haider moves it along at a livelier pace; Gabrielle Bellini is more contemplative. Haider's live recording has the singers further forward; the newer one brings more orchestral detail to notice. One advantage lies with its predecessor – it includes an English translation of the libretto – but it also costs about twice as much.

Additional recommendation ...

...**Soloists; Mikaeli Chamber Choir; Swedish Radio Symphony Orchestra / Friederich Haider.** Nightingale Classics Ⓕ NC070561-2 (three discs: 168 minutes: DDD: 9/94).

Donizetti Lucia di Lammermoor. **Cheryl Studer** (sop) Lucia; **Plácido Domingo** (ten) Edgardo; **Juan Pons** (bar) Enrico; **Samuel Ramey** (bass) Raimondo; **Jennifer Larmore** (mez) Alisa; **Fernando de la Mora** (ten) Arturo; **Anthony Laciura** (ten) Normanno; **Ambrosian Opera Chorus; London Symphony Orchestra / Ion Marin.** DG Ⓕ 435 309-2GH2 (two discs: 138 minutes: DDD: 4/93). Notes, text and translation included. Recorded 1990.

With 15 recordings currently available, *Lucia di Lammermoor*, once regarded as *passé*, appears to be in remarkably good health. Not so long ago it was dismissed as little more than a convenient vehicle for the latest coloratura soprano, who could enjoy a double success, first in the Fountain Scene where she would be applauded on entry and then able to warm up for the celebrated Mad Scene, which was the real culmination of the evening even to the extent (in Melba's day, for instance) of finishing the opera on Lucia's final high note and eliminating the tenor's big scene which is to follow. Nowadays, while the opera is still a *tour de force* for the soprano, the tenor shares the honours and the whole thing is much more of a company production. Its likely hero is Donizetti himself, whose music has strengths of many kinds, including expert and evocative orchestration. Recordings by Callas and Sutherland are generally respected as permanent classics of the gramophone, but recent versions deserve consideration, and this one, with Studer and Domingo in the leading roles, is certainly fit as a whole to stand alongside its eminent predecessors. The fine deep colours of the orchestra, the sturdy dramatic cohesion and well-wrought climaxes, are well brought out; passages traditionally omitted are in place (and deserve to be). The role of Lucia's confidante is sung with distinction by Jennifer Larmore, and though Juan Pons could do with more bite to his tone and Samuel Ramey with more expressiveness in his vocal acting these have their strengths too. Studer combines beautiful tone, technical accomplishment and touching pathos. Details include an extended cadenza in the Mad Scene, which ends on a not too exposed high E flat (D being the ceiling elsewhere). Domingo triumphantly overcomes the difficulties such a role must pose at this stage of his career: Edgardo di Ravenswood in this recording is as firmly at the centre of the opera as is its eponymous heroine.

Additional recommendations ...

...**Soloists; Royal Opera House Chorus and Orchestra, Covent Garden / Richard Bonynge.** Decca Ⓕ 410 193-2DH3 (three discs: 140 minutes: ADD: 11/85).

...Soloists; **Philharmonia Chorus**; **Philharmonia Orchestra / Tullio Serafin.**
EMI Callas Edition Ⓕ CDS5 56284-2 (two discs: 111 minutes: ADD: 1/87).
...Soloists; **Chorus of La Scala, Milan; Berlin RIAS Symphony Orchestra / Herbert von Karajan.**
EMI mono Ⓜ CMS5 63631-2* (two discs: 119 minutes: ADD: 2/91).
...Soloists; **Ambrosian Singers; London Symphony Orchestra / Richard Bonynge.**
Teldec Ⓕ 9031-72306-2 (two discs: 143 minutes: DDD: 11/92).
...Soloists; **Ambrosian Opera Chorus; New Philharmonia Orchestra / Jesús López-Cobos.**
Philips Ⓜ 446 551-2PM2 (two discs: 143 minutes: ADD: 3/96).
...Lucia di Lammermoor – Il dolce suono ... Ardon gli'incensi ... Alfin son tua ... Spargi d'amaro
pianto. *Coupled with works by various composers.* **Mariella Devia** (sop); **Svizzera Italiana
Orchestra / Marcello Rota.** Bongiovanni Ⓕ GB2513-2 (63 minutes: DDD: 10/94).

Donizetti Poliuto. **Franco Corelli** (ten) Poliuto; **Maria Callas** (sop) Paolina; **Ettore Bastianini** (bar)
Severo; **Nicola Zaccaria** (bass) Callistene; **Piero de Palma** (ten) Nearco; **Rinaldo Pelizzoni** (ten)
Felice; **Virgilio Carbonari, Giuseppe Morresi** (basses) Christians; **Chorus and Orchestra of
La Scala, Milan / Antonino Votto.** EMI mono Ⓜ CMS5 65448-2* (two discs: 111 minutes:
ADD: 11/97). Notes, text and translation included. Recorded live in 1960.
This is the first appearance of this recording in the official canon, by incorporation into EMI's Callas
Edition; and the quality is certainly an improvement on the previous 'unofficial' incarnation. The
sound is clear and faithful to the timbre of the voices, which are slightly favoured in the balance at the
expense of the orchestra. The theatre's acoustic tends to sound boxy on record, but that at least helps
definition and does nothing to disguise the raw edge that in some of her more strenuous passages was
likely by then to have become notable in Callas's voice. With it comes unforgettable testimony to what
was clearly a great night at La Scala. Its place in the Callas history owes less to the importance of this
new role in her repertory than to the triumph of her return to the house she had left in high dudgeon
in 1958. The part of Paolina in this Roman tragedy is restricted in opportunities and leaves the centre
of the stage to the tenor. In other ways it suits her remarkably well, the Second Act in particular
involving the heroine in grievous emotional stress with music that here runs deep enough to give it
validity. There is a big part for the chorus, who sing with fine Italian sonority. Nicola Zaccaria, La
Scala's leading *basso cantabile*, has not quite the sumptuous quality of his predecessors, Pasero and
Pinza, but is still in their tradition. Ettore Bastianini is rapturously received and, though wanting in
polish and variety of expression, uses his firm and resonant voice to exciting effect. The tenor
comprimario, Piero de Palma cuts a by no means inadequate vocal figure by the side of Corelli, who,
for the most part, is stupendous: it is not just the ring and range of voice that impress, but a genuinely
responsive art, his aria "Lasciando la terra" in Act 3 providing a fine example. It is for his part in the
opera, quite as much as for Callas's, that the recording will be valued.

Donizetti Rosmonda d'Inghilterra. **Renée Fleming** (sop) Rosmonda; **Bruce Ford** (ten) Enrico II;
Nelly Miricioiu (sop) Leonora di Guienna; **Alastair Miles** (bass) Gualtiero Clifford;
Diana Montague (mez) Arturo; **Geoffrey Mitchell Choir; Philharmonia Orchestra / David Parry.**
Opera Rara Ⓕ ORC13 (two discs: 150 minutes: DDD: 2/97). Notes, text and translation included.
By the criteria appropriate to its kind, *Rosmonda d'Inghilterra* is a very good opera, inferior to *Lucia
di Lammermoor* but not annihilatingly so. To say that score and libretto are highly workmanlike may
register as a kind of belittlement, though it should not do so, and it needs saying since we know that
Donizetti worked fast and turned out operas by the dozen and so are inclined to assume that he must
have been slipshod. In fact, this, his forty-first, shows the confident mastery of form that can make
useful, unselfconscious innovations, and there is scarcely more than a single item in which he seems
not to be writing with genuine creativity. The performance could hardly be improved. David Parry
conducts with what feels like a natural rightness. More than that, the playing of the Philharmonia is
of unvaryingly high quality – the Overture is one of Donizetti's best, and the orchestral score shares
interest on equable terms with the voice-parts. These include two virtuoso roles for sopranos, who in
the final scene confront each other in duet. As Rosmonda, the immured and misled mistress, Renée
Fleming shows once again that not only has she one of the most lovely voices to be heard in our time
but that she is also a highly accomplished technician and a sympathetic stylist. Nelly Miricioiu is the
older woman, the Queen whose music encompasses a wide range of emotions with an adaptable vocal
character to match. Whether by design or by the condition of her voice in the different recording
sessions, she fits the Second Act more happily than the First, where for much of the time the tone
appears to have lost its familiar incisive thrust. Bruce Ford is an excellent, incisive Enrico, and
Alastair Miles makes an authoritative father and councillor as Clifford. The *travesto* role of Arturo
is taken by the ever welcome Diana Montague, and it is good to find that a solo has been dutifully
included for 'him' in Act 2, even if it is a less than inspired piece of music. The only complaint with
the recording concerns balance, which sometimes accords prominence and recession in a somewhat
arbitrary way. The opera and performance, however, are strong enough to take that on board.
Further listening ...
...String Quartets – No. 7 in F minor; No. 8 in B flat major; No. 9 in D minor. **Revolutionary
Drawing Room.** CPO CPO999 170-2 (1/95)
...String Quartet No. 13 in E minor. *Coupled with works by* **Puccini** and **Verdi** Alberni Quartet
CRD3366 (5/89).

...String Quartet in D major (1828). *Coupled with works by various composers.*
Academy of St Martin in the Fields / Sir Neville Marriner.
Double Decca 443 838-2DF2 (7/95). *See review under Rossini; refer to the Index.*
...Ah, rammenta, o bella Irene. La ninna-nanna. *Coupled with works by various
composers.* **Rebecca Evans** (sop); **Michael Pollock** (pf). EMI Debut CDZ5 69706-2 (5/97).
...Anna Bolena – Piangete voi? ... Al dolce guidami. *Coupled with works by* **Verdi Carol Vaness**
(sop); **Melinda Paulsen** (mez); **Dennis O'Neill, Anton Rosner** (tens); **Ambrogio Riva** (bass);
Bavarian Radio Chorus; Munich Radio Orchestra / Roberto Abbado.
RCA Victor Red Seal 09026 61828-2 (1/97). *See review under Verdi; refer to the Index.*
...Anna Bolena – Sposa a Percy ... Per questa fiamma indomita ... Ah! pensate che rivolti (with
soloists). La favorita – Fia dunque vero ... O mio Fernando!. *Coupled with works by various
composers.* **Vesselina Kasarova** (mez); **Bavarian Radio Chorus; Munich Radio Orchestra /
Friedrich Haider.** RCA Victor Red Seal 09026 68522-2 (2/97). *Gramophone Editor's
record of the month. See review in the Collections section; refer to the Index.*   🅖🅖
...Il barcaiolo. Ah, rammenta, o bella Irene. Amore e morte. La conocchia. Me voglio fa'na casa.
Coupled with works by **Rossini** and **Bellini Cecilia Bartoli** (mez); **James Levine** (pf).
Decca 455 513-2DH (11/97). *Gramophone Editor's choice. See review in the Collections section;
refer to the Index.*
...Canto d'Ugolino; L'amor funesto; Il trovatore in caricatura; Spirito di Dio benefico; Viva il
matrimonio. French Songs – Le renégat; Noé, scène du Deluge; Le départ pour la chasse; Un
coeur pour abri; Le hart (chant diabolique). **Ian Caddy** (bass-bar); **Melvyn Tan** (fp).
Meridian CDE84183 (4/90). 🎵
...L'elisir d'amore – Chiedi all'aura lusinghiera[a]. Lucia di Lammermoor – Regnava nel silenzio ...
Quando rapito in estasi[b]; Soffriva nel pianto[c]. *Coupled with works by various composers.*
Inessa Galante (sop); [a]**Janis Sprogis** (ten); [c]**Samsons Izjumovs** (bar); [a]**Latvian National Symphony
Orchestra,** [bc]**Latvian National Opera Orchestra /** [a]**Paul Mägi,** [bc]**Alexander Vilumanis.**
Campion RRCD1344 (A/97). *See review in the Collections section; refer to the Index.*
...La favorita – Un ange, une femme inconnue; Je ne méritais pas ... Qui ta voix m'inspire;
La maîtresse du roi? ... Ange si pur. Messa da Requiem – Ingemisco. Gabriella di Vergy –
Si compia il sacrificio ... Io l'amai. *Coupled with works by* **Rossini Justin Lavender** (ten);
Bournemouth Symphony Orchestra / Howard Williams. IMP Classics 30367 0010-2 (3/96).
See review under Rossini; refer to the Index.
...La favorita – Ma de' malvagi invan ... Vien, Leonord, a' piedi tuoi ... De' nemici tuoi[b]; Ebben,
così si narra! ... Quando le soglie paterne ... In questo suol a lusingar[ab]; Fia dunque vero? ...
O mio Fernando[a]. *Coupled with opera arias and duets by various composers.* [a]**Olga Borodina**
(mez); [b]**Dmitri Hvorostovsky** (bar); **English Chamber Orchestra / Patrick Summers.**
Philips 454 439-2PH (6/98). *See review in the Collections section; refer to the Index.*
...Anna Bolena. **Soloists; Chorus and Orchestra of Hungarian Radio and Television /
Elio Boncompagni.** Nightingale Classics NC070565-2 (9/96).
...L'Assedio di Calais. **Soloists; Geoffrey Mitchell Choir; Philharmonia Orchestra / David Parry.**
Opera Rara ORC009 (7/91).
...Emilia di Liverpool. L'eremitaggio di Liwerpool. **Soloists; Geoffrey Mitchell Choir; Philharmonia
Orchestra / David Parry.** Opera Rara ORC008 (5/92).
...La fille du régiment. **Chorus; Chorus and Orchestra of the Royal Opera House, Covent Garden /
Richard Bonynge.** Decca 414 520-2DH2 (11/86).
...La fille du régiment. **Soloists; Bavarian Radio Chorus; Munich Radio Orchestra / Marcello Panni.**
Nightingale Classics NC070566-2 (9/96).
...Gabriella di Vergy. **Soloists; Geoffrey Mitchell Choir; Royal Philharmonic Orchestra /
Alun Francis.** Opera Rara ORC003 (9/94).
...Lucrezia Borgia. **Soloists; RCA Italiana Opera Chorus and Orchestra / Jonel Perlea.**
RCA Victor Gold Seal GD86642 (9/90).
...Maria Padilla. **Soloists; Geoffrey Mitchell Choir; London Symphony Orchestra / Alun Francis.**
Opera Rara ORC6 (2/93).
...Maria Stuarda. **Soloists; Bologna Teatro Communale Chorus and Orchestra / Richard Bonynge.**
Decca 425 410-2DM2 (9/90).
...Ugo, Conte di Parigi. **Soloists; Geoffrey Mitchell Choir; New Philharmonia Orchestra /
Alun Francis.** Opera Rara ORC001 (12/90).

John Dowland   British c1563-1626

Dowland Lachrimae, or Seaven Teares. **Christopher Wilson** (lte); **Fretwork** (Wendy Gillespie,
Richard Campbell, Julia Hodgson, William Hunt, Richard Boothby, viols).
Virgin Classics Veritas Ⓔ VC5 45005-2 (60 minutes: DDD: 7/94). 🎵 From VC7 90795-2 (11/89),
recorded 1987 and VC7 91117-2 (3/91), 1989.   🅖
Did Dowland ever expect this collection to be played in its entirety, at one sitting? If so, in what order?
Whatever your own 'answers' to these unanswerable questions may be, you can (if you feel strongly
about it) easily impose them on any of the various integral versions on CD. Fretwork's reissue

presents them as an entirety, with the dances in their original published order – the whole book 'as is'. The performances are laudable in their characterization (of the pavans in particular), discreet embellishment of the dances, clarity of detail (the product of pleasantly dry string sound and acoustic) and overall balance, in which the lute is neither backgrounded nor obtrusive. Christopher Wilson adds a firmly propulsive edge to the dances. This is the best available version of Dowland's monumental work, graced with Peter Holman's splendid notes and blessed with superbly engineered recording. The recording by The Parley of Instruments Renaissance Violin Consort is also recommended, being the only one to avail itself of Dowland's "or Violons" option; Holman directs the proceedings – you can't keep a good man down!

Additional recommendation ...
...Lachrimae[b]. Captain Digorie Piper his Pavan[b]. The King of Denmarke his Galliard, P40[a]. Moritz, Landgrave of Hessen-Kassel: Pavan[a]. [a]**Paul O'Dette** (lte); [b]**The Parley of Instruments Renaissance Violin Consort / Peter Holman.**
Hyperion Ⓕ CDA66637 (69 minutes: DDD: 8/93). ✦

Dowland The First Booke of Songes or Ayres – If my complaints could passions moue; Can she excuse my wrongs with vertues cloake; Deare if you change ile neuer chuse againe; Go Cristall teares; Sleepe wayward thoughts; All ye whom loue or fortune hath betraide; Come againe: sweet loue doth now enuite; Awake sweet loue thou art returnd. The Second Booke of Songs or Ayres – I saw my Lady weepe; Flow my teares fall from your springs; Sorrow sorrow stay, lend true repentant teares; Tymes eldest sonne, old age the heire of ease; Then sit thee down, and say thy "Nunc Dimitis"; When others sings "Venite exultemus"; If fluds of tears could clense my follies past; Fine knacks for Ladies, cheap, choise, braue and new; Come ye heavie states of night; Shall I sue, shall I seeke for grace. **Paul Agnew** (ten); **Christopher Wilson** (lte).
Metronome Ⓕ METCD1010 (59 minutes: DDD: 5/96). Texts included. Recorded 1995.
Lovesongs and Sonnets of John Donne and Sir Philip Sidney [a]**Paul Agnew** (ten); **Christopher Wilson** (lte). Metronome Ⓕ METCD1006 (62 minutes: DDD: 5/96). Texts included. Recorded 1994.
G. Tessier In a grove most rich of shade[a]. **Dowland** O sweet woods, the delight of solitarie-nesse[a]. Sweete stay a while, why will you?[a]. Preludium. **Morley** Who is it that this darke night[a]. **Coprario** Send home my long strayde eies to mee[a]. **A. Ferrabosco II** So breake off this last lamenting kisse[a]. **Corkine** The Fire to see my woes for anger burneth[a]. 'tis true, 'tis day, what though it be?[a]. **Hilton II** A Hymne to God the Father[a]. **Anonymous** Come live with me[a]. So breake off this last lamenting kisse[a]. Goe my flocke, goe get you hence[a]. Goe and catch a fallinge star[a]. O deere life when shall it be[a]. Sir Philip Sidney's Lamentacion. Dearest love I doe not goe[a].
In the Dowland Paul Agnew is light of step in the quicker songs, and he languishes longer than most over the variously sorrowful ones; it says much for his artistry, that in "Flow my teares" and "I saw my Lady weepe" he protesteth neither too much nor too long. Many of his choices now enjoy 'pop' status, but his inclusion of the beautiful trilogy of which "Tymes eldest sonne" is the first part, commonly neglected in mixed programmes such as this, is particularly welcome. He receives the most sensitive of support from Wilson, clearly articulated, warm in tone, and perfectly complementary in completing the contrapuntal textures – neither intrusively nor coyly balanced with the voice. Dowland's lute songs have generated many fine recordings, as they richly deserve, and here is one more, beautifully presented, with a booklet containing first-class annotation and all the texts.

Love is a familiar peg on which to hang a song recital, and if there is a further focus it is usually on the composer of the music; Agnew and Wilson turn the tables, for once, by spotlighting the writers of the texts, namely Sir Philip Sidney and John Donne. Their poems are set by Tessier, Dowland, Morley, Coprario, Alfonso Ferrabosco II, Corkine, John Hilton and the ever-present Anonymous, the last being recovered from a variety of sources. Of the songs, only those by Tessier and Dowland, and one by Anon have any other current recording. Sidney's sonnets *Astrophel and Stella*, written between 1581 and 1583, may have been addressed to the daughter of the Earl of Essex but she was unwillingly married to Lord Rich in 1581, so Sidney may have had in mind the daughter of Sir Francis Walsingham, whom he married in 1583. The emotional range of Donne's *Songs and Sonets* may also mirror the fluctuating fortunes of his own, basically happy marriage. In both cases the operative word is 'may'. To the good features of the recording of the Dowland songs are to be added notably clearer diction and some graceful embellishments (trippingly lithe in *Dearest love I doe not goe*) from Agnew, and two well-chosen lute solos by way of interludes from Wilson.

Additional recommendations ...
...The First Booke of Songes. **Consort of Musicke / Anthony Rooley.**
L'Oiseau-Lyre Ⓕ 421 653-2OH (76 minutes: DDD: 10/89). ✦   ⒼⒼ
...The First Booke of Songes. **Rufus Müller** (ten); **Christopher Wilson** (lte).
ASV Gaudeamus Ⓕ CDGAU135 (74 minutes: DDD: 10/93). ✦
...The First Booke of Songes – Can she excuse my wrongs with vertues cloake. I saw my Lady weepe. Sorrow sorrow stay, lend true repentant teares. Shall I strive with words to move?. *Coupled with works by various composers.* **Michael Chance** (alto); **Christopher Wilson** (lte).
Chandos Chaconne Ⓕ CHAN0538 (65 minutes: DDD: 10/94).   Ⓖ
...The First Booke of Songes or Ayres. **John Elwes** (ten); **Matthias Spaeter** (lte).
Pierre Verany Ⓕ PV794091 (79 minutes: DDD: 3/95).

...The First Booke of Songs or Ayres – Can she excuse my wrongs?[a]; All ye, whom love or fortune[a]. The Second Booke of Songs or Ayres – I saw my Lady weep[a]; Flow my teares fall from your springs[a]; Sorrow sorrow stay, lend true repentant tears[a]. The Third and Last Booke of Songs or Ayres – Behold a wonder here[a]; Me, me and none but me[a]; Say, love, if ever thou did'st find[a]. The Lady Russell's pavan. Go from my window. *Coupled with works by various composers.* [a]**Andreas Scholl** (alto); **Andreas Martin** (lte).
Harmonia Mundi Ⓕ HMC90 1603 (69 minutes: DDD: 9/96). *Gramophone Editor's choice.*
See review in the Collections section; refer to the Index.   Ⓖ

...M. John Langtons Pauan[bc]. Mistresse Nichols Almand[bc]. The Earle of Essex Galiard[bc]. A Shepherd in a shade[ab]. Lasso vita mia[bc]. Buctons Galiard[bc]. M. Henry Noell his Galiard[bc]. M. Thomas Collier his Galiard[bc]. Farwell (on the "In Nomine" theme)[b]. Semper Dowland Semper Dolens[bc]. Sweete stay a while[ab]. Can she excuse my wrongs[ab]. A Fancy[b]. M. Giles Hobies Galiard[bc]. Captaine Digorie Piper his Galiard[bc]. The King of Denmarks Galiard[bc]. Burst forth my teares[bc]. Resolucon (Dowland's adew for Master Oliuer Cromwell)[bc]. M. Nicholas Gryffith his Galiard[bc]. M. George Whitehead his Almand[bc]. Sir John Souch his Galiard[bc]. All ye whom loue or fortune[ab]. Sir Henry Umptons Funerall[bc]. [a]**Catherine King** (mez); [b]**Jacob Heringman** (lte); [c]**Rose Consort of Viols.** Naxos Ⓢ 8 553326 (70 minutes: DDD: 11/97). ✏

...The First Book of Songs or Ayres – Can she excuse my wrongs with vertues cloake; Now, O now I needs must part; Go Cristall teares; Come againe: sweet loue doth now enuite; His goulden locks time hath to siluer turnd; Awaie with these selfe louing lads. The Second Booke of Songs or Ayres – Flow my teares fall from your springs; Sorrow sorrow stay, lend true repentant teares; A Sheperd in a shade his plaining made. The Third and Last Book of Songs or Aires – Time stands still; It was a time when silly Bees could speake. *Coupled with works by* **Campion Brian Asawa** (alto); **David Tayler** (lte). RCA Victor Red Seal Ⓕ 09026 68818-2 (74 minutes: DDD: 12/97). *See review in the Collections section; refer to the Index.*

Dowland The Second Booke of Songes. **The Consort of Musicke / Anthony Rooley** (lte). L'Oiseau-Lyre Ⓕ 425 889-2OH (70 minutes: ADD: 8/91). ✏ Texts included.
From DSLO528/9 (9/77). Recorded 1976.   ⒼⒼ
This recording originally appeared in 1977 as part of Florilegium's complete Dowland cycle. The "Second Booke of Songes" dates from 1600 and contains two of Dowland's most famous compositions, *Flow my teares* and *I saw my Lady weepe*, though here these are presented unusually (and not entirely convincingly) as vocal duets. In fact there is a surprisingly wide variety of vocal and instrumental combinations throughout the disc, from consort song to four-part vocal to the more familiar sound of solo voice and lute, all of which were suggested as performance possibilities by Dowland himself. It is partly as a result of this that the recording retains its freshness in spite of its age, but it would be wrong to ignore the contribution made by the intelligent and sensitive singing of Emma Kirkby and Martyn Hill, both of whom sound completely in their element.

Dowland Preludium, P98. Fantasias – P6; P71. Pavans – Lachrimae, P15; The Lady Russell's Pavan, P17; Pavana Johan Douland, P94; La mia Barbara, P95. Galliards – Frog Galliard, P23; Galliard (upon a galliard by Dan Bachelar), P28; The Lord Viscount Lisle, his Galliard, P38; The Earl of Essex, his Galliard, P42a; Galliard to Lachrimae, P46; A Galliard, P82; Galliard on "Awake sweet love", P92. An Almand, P96. My Lord Willoughbie's Welcome Home, P66a. Loth to departe, P69. The Shoemakers Wife, a Toy, P58. Coranto, P100. Come away, P60.
Paul O'Dette (lte). Harmonia Mundi Ⓕ HMU90 7163 (64 minutes: DDD: 2/97). ✏
Cadential trills played on one string are a recurrent problem for performers; the less well equipped use a *rallentando* or slurr them, whilst guitarists tend to play them across two strings. No one is more adept at delivering them cleanly and in tempo than O'Dette, whose technical armoury shows no weak spot. It is in the suppleness of his phrasing, clarity of his contrapuntal lines and close attention to the functional purpose of every note, that O'Dette is pre-eminent – and has the edge over Lindberg. This disc has all the virtues of its predecessors, and though it is doubtful that the Earl of Essex would have been happy to dance his galliard at O'Dette's (and others') pace, you can share the sentiment of its last track – you will be loath to leave it. Lindberg's 'complete' Dowland occupies four discs and Paul O'Dette's, issued on separate discs, has reached the same total. Of the firmly ascribed pieces O'Dette has thus far omitted the *Complaint* (P63) and *Round battle galliard* (P39), but otherwise they differ only in their versions; at this point there are marked differences in their choice amongst those pieces to which, for various reasons, Diana Poulton did not allot numbers (*John Dowland*: London: 1972).

Dowland Complete Lute Works, Volume 5. **Paul O'Dette** (lte). Harmonia Mundi Ⓕ HMU90 7164 (73 minutes: DDD: 7/97). Recorded 1996.
A fancy, P73. Pavana Dowlandi Angli. Doulands rounde battell galyarde, P39. The Erle of Darbies galiard, P44. Mistris Norrishis delight, P77. A jig, P78. Galliard, P76. Une jeune fillette, P93. Gagliarda, P103. Squires galliard. A fancy, P72. Sir Henry Umptons funerall. Captayne Pipers galliard, P4. A fantasie, P1. **Bacheler** (arr.?) The Earl of Essex galliard, P89.
Moritz, Landgrave of Hessen (arr. Dowland?) Pavin. **Joachim Van Den Hove** Pavana Lachrimae. **Holborne** Hasellwoods galliard. **R. Dowland** Sir Thomas Monson, his Pavin and Galliard. Almande.

Given the odd transmission of John Dowland's lute music, any 'complete' recording of it is inevitably going to include a fair number of works that can have had little to do with him. Paul O'Dette has boldly put most of these together in his fifth and last volume, adding for good measure the three surviving works of the master's son, Robert Dowland. O'Dette is engagingly candid in expressing his views about the various works and their various degrees of authenticity. The only works he seems to think authentic are the *Sir Thomas Monson* pavan and galliard that survive only under the name of Robert Dowland. The collection is none the less fascinating for all that. They are nearly all thoroughly worthwhile pieces, some of them very good indeed (including the one now agreed to be by Holborne and the one O'Dette thinks likely to be by Daniel Bacheler); and he ends with what he considers a late adaptation of one of Dowland's most famous fantasies. O'Dette continues to show that in terms of sheer freedom of technique he is hard to challenge among today's lutenists: the often complicated counterpoint is always crystal clear; and he invariably conveys the strongest possible feeling for the formal design of the works. He plays with a thoughtfulness and control that are always invigorating. Anyone who is fascinated by the work of the prince of lutenists will want to have this disc.

Additional recommendations ...

...Complete Solo Lute Works. **Jakob Lindberg** (lte/orpharion).
BIS Ⓜ CD722/4 (four discs: 261 minutes: DDD: 11/95).
...Pavan (Mylius 1622). Almains – The Lady Laitones Almone, P48; Almain, P49; Mistris Whittes thinge, P50; Almain, P51. Ballads and Other Popular Tunes – Orlando Sleepeth, P61; Go from my Window, P64; My Lord Willoughby's Welcome Home, P66; What is a day, P79. Fantasies – Farwell, P3; Fantasie, P5. Galliards – Frog Galliard, P23 and P23a; Melancholy Galliard, P25; Galliard, P27; M. Gilles Hobies Galiard, P29; Galliard in G minor, P30; Galliard, P35; Mr Knights Galliard, P36; My Ladie Riches Galyerd, P43a; Galliard, P104. Jigs, Corantos, Toys – Mistris Winters Jumpe, P55; Mrs Whites Nothing, P56. Pavans – Dr Cases Pauen, P12; Pavan, P18; A Dream, P75. **Paul O'Dette** (lte/orpharion).
Harmonia Mundi Ⓕ HMU90 7160 (64 minutes: DDD: 11/95).
...Almains – Sir John Smith his Almain, P47; My Lady Hunsdons Allmande, P54. Pavans – Piper's Pavan, P8; Solus cum sola, P10; Mrs Brigide Fleetwoods paven alias Solus sine sol, P11; Lachrimae, P15; Pavan, P18. Ballad Settings – The George Aloe, P68; Robin, P70. Galliards – Captaine Digorie his Galliard, P19; Dowlands Galliard, P20; Capitain Candishe his Galliard, P21; Dowlands First Galliard, P22; Sir John Souch his Galliard, P26; Mrs Vaux Galliarde, P32; Mignarda, P34; Can she excuse, P42. Fantasies – A Fantasie, P1a; Farwell, P4. Mrs Vauxe's Gigge, P57. A Coye Toye, P80. Sir Henry Guilforde's Almaine. As I went to Walsingham,. Monsier's Almaine. Suzanna Galliard, P91. **Paul O'Dette** (lte).
Harmonia Mundi Ⓕ HMU90 7161 (67 minutes: DDD: 8/96).
...The King of Denmark, his Galliard, P40; Sir John Langton his Pavin, P14. Mr Langtons galliard, P33. A Fancy, P7. A Pavan, P16. Queene Elizabeth, her Galliard, P41. Mrs Cliftons Allmaine, P53. The Lady Cliftons Spirit, P45. Tarletones riserrectione, P59. Tarletons Willy, P81. Fortune, P62. The Queenes galliard, P97. Walsingham, P67. A Galliard (on Walsingham), P31. Dowlands adew for Master Oliver Cromwell, P13. The Earle of Darby, his Galliard, P44a. Lord Strangs March, P65. Mistresse Nichols Almand, P52. Forlorne Hope Fancye, P3. Mr Dowland's Midnight, P99. Semper Dowland semper dolens, P9. **Paul O'Dette** (lte). ✒
Harmonia Mundi Ⓕ HMU90 7162 (65 minutes: DDD: 12/96).

Dowland Almains – Sir John Smith his Almain, P47; My Lady Hunsdons Puffe, P54. Ballads and Other Popular Tunes – Fortune, P62; Go from my Window, P64; My Lord Willoughby's Welcome Home, P66a; Walsingham, P67; Robin, P70. Fantaisies – Fantasie, P1a; Forlorne Hope Fancye, P2. Galliards – Captaine Digorie his Galliard, P19; Frog Galliard, P23a; Melancholy Galliard, P25; Mignarde, P34; The King of Denmarke his Galliard, P40; The most sacred Queene Elizabeth, her Galliard, P41a; Can she excuse, P42; Galliard to Lachrimae, P46. Jigs, Corantos, Toys – Mistris Winters Jumpe, P55; Mrs Vauxe's Gigge, P57; The Shomakers Wife, P58. Pavans – Piper's Pavan, P8; Semper Dowland Semper Dolens, P9; Lachrimae, P15. Preludium, P98. **Nigel North** (lte). Arcana Ⓕ A36 (72 minutes: DDD: 3/97). ✒
Recorded 1995. Ⓖ

The disc contains 24 items, but of the 42 in Robert Dowland's anthology of 1610 Dowland contributed only seven, not all of which are included here. If this disappoints anyone who might expect a direct connection between the album's title, "Lute Lessons" and that of Robert Dowland's book, there is more than ample compensation in the marvellous quality of playing on this disc, and in the appearance of "Volume 1" on the cover, suggesting that it may herald yet another integral set of Dowland's lute works. If this should be the case we should have a clear market-leader in the field. The present disc is quite simply superb. Whilst North's fingers are always ready to dance to Dowland's more joyous tunes, they sometimes take a little longer to allow the more contemplative music plenty of breathing space, as in *Semper Dowland* and *Forlorne Hope Fancye*, delivered with the utmost eloquence. His readiness to embellish is unequalled in quantity, quality and the smoothness with which it blends into the lines. Nor does anyone put rubato to more telling use. In his *Musick's monument* (1674) Thomas Mace describes the "sting" – vibrato – as an ornament, and though there is no evidence that the resource was used in earlier times, North's application of it is so effective that it is hard to believe that it was not; added to his beautiful tone, it is a potent aid to expressiveness.

Further listening ...

...Frogg galliard, P90 (arr. van Eyck). *Coupled with works by various composers.*
Mhairi Lawson (sop); **Circa 1500.** ASV Gaudeamus CDGAU163 (12/97). ✍
See review in the Collections section; refer to the Index.

...(Arr. Kronos Quartet) Lachrimae Antiquae. *Coupled with works by various composers.* **Wu Man**
(dzhong ruan/da ruan); **Kronos Quartet.** Nonesuch 7559-79457-2 (12/97). *Gramophone Editor's*
choice. See review in the Collections section; refer to the Index.

Robert Dowland

British c1591-1641

Suggested listening ...

...Sir Thomas Monson his Pavin and Galliard. Almande. *Coupled with works by various composers.*
Paul O'Dette (lte). Harmonia Mundi HMU90 7164 (7/97). *See review under John Dowland;*
refer to the Index.

Eustache du Caurroy

French 1549-1609

Du Caurroy Missa pro defunctis. Veni sanctus spiritus. Benedicamus Domino. Ave Maria.
Ave virgo gloriosa. Salve regina. Christe, qui lux es. Victimae Paschali Laudes. **New College**
Choir, Oxford / Edward Higginbottom. Collins Classics Ⓕ 1497-2 (67 minutes: DDD: 10/97).
Texts and translations included. Recorded 1996. *Gramophone Editor's choice.*
Eustache Du Caurroy is one of the unsung heroes of the French renaissance. He served as master of
the French royal chapel under three successive kings, and while his European reputation may have
been eclipsed by that of his contemporary Lassus, in France he was held in the highest esteem long
after his death. Perhaps his best-known work, the Requiem was first performed following the
assassination of Henry IV in 1610 (by which time the composer too was dead). It resonates with the
echoes of many other Requiem settings of the previous century. By contrast, Du Caurroy's other
works show an awareness of more contemporary fashion (such as the affectingly simple *Salve regina,*
set entirely in the *musique mesurée* style popularized by Le Jeune and others); but above all, this is
music of very high quality, and on that count alone Edward Higginbottom's initiative in Du Caurroy's
favour is most welcome. Just as importantly, he leads the New College choristers in a correspondingly
fine performance. English choral enthusiasts will note the distinctively reedy, slightly plangent sound
of New College's trebles, very different from the silvery purity so often associated with choirboys.
There is considerable refinement, too, in the dynamic shaping of pieces, and the trebles contribute as
much to its expressive effect as anyone. To cap it all, the recital was recorded in the Abbey of Valloires
(Somme), with its magnificent acoustic: a distinctive recording indeed.

Théodore Dubois

French 1837-1924

Suggested listening ...

...Grand Choeur in B flat major. *Coupled with works by various composers.* **Christopher Herrick**
(org). Hyperion CDA66457 (9/91). *See review in the Collections section; refer to the Index.* Ⓖ Ⓖ

Guillaume Dufay

French c1400-1474

Dufay Complete secular music. **Timothy Penrose** (alto); **Rogers Covey-Crump, John Elwes, Paul**
Elliott (tens); **Paul Hillier, Michael George** (bars); **Medieval Ensemble of London / Peter Davies**
and **Timothy Davies.** L'Oiseau-Lyre Ⓑ 452 557-2OC5 (five discs: 321 minutes: ADD: 11/97).
Texts and translations included. From D237D6 (12/81).
The passage of time has not diminished the grandeur of the achievement of the Medieval Ensemble
of London. The opportunity of hearing the entire corpus of Dufay's songs from the same
interpretative perspective is irreplaceable – it is doubtful that any record company today would be
willing to undertake such an ambitious project. More than just the scope of Dufay's invention (that
is hardly surprising in a career that spanned nearly 60 years), it is its astonishing consistency that
strikes the listener – nearly every song has something to delight, to intrigue, to teach. The rough
chronology, traced from first to last, is a programme in itself, beginning with the jaunty, seemingly
effortless songs of his youth, catchy and dazzling by turns, to the increasingly involving works of
maturity, culminating in the sublime poise of his last years.. Although the ensemble doesn't always
match Dufay's phenomenal consistency, it's hard to argue with a line-up that includes Paul Elliott,
Rogers Covey-Crump and John Elwes, all of them in their prime. And yes, one can disagree with the
odd phrase here, spot a fluffed note among the instrumentalists (or, rather more rarely, the singers),
or wonder at some surprising glitches in the CD transfer but with the last song, the beautiful, canonic
Les doleurs lingering in the mind's ear, one accepts the series's limitations as its many virtues endure.
Every serious collector should have this.

Dufay Missa S Jacobi. Rite majorem Jacobum canamus. Balsamus et munda cera. Gloria "Resurrexit dominus" and Credo "Dic Maria". Apostolo glorioso. **The Binchois Consort** (Mark Chambers, David Gould, Fergus McLusky, Robin Tyson, altos; James Gilchrist, Chris Watson, Andrew Carwood, Edwin Simpson, tens) / **Andrew Kirkman.** Hyperion Ⓔ CDA66997 (67 minutes: DDD: 7/98). Texts and translations included. *Gramophone Editor's record of the month.*   ⒺⒼ

In what is only their second CD, The Binchois Consort show absolute mastery of Dufay's difficult early style, with immaculate balance, wonderfully free phrasing, and crystalline clarity. Moreover in the *Missa S Jacobi* Andrew Kirkman shows an uncanny ability to set the perfect tempo every time, so that the music emerges with its full force. The *Missa S Jacobi* is an odd but supremely important work. It is one of two early Dufay Mass cycles that have rarely been recorded, partly because they are less obviously part of the grand tradition than his later four-voice cantus firmus Masses. And this one is particularly difficult because its many different textures and styles present a severe challenge if it is not to seem fragmented and incoherent. Here it stands as a glorious masterpiece, its nine movements spanning over 40 minutes, with the various styles acting as necessary contrast and culminating in the famous Communion that Heinrich Besseler many years ago argued was the earliest example of *Fauxbourdon* writing. Strangely, two of the motets work less well: both the earlier *Rite majorem* and the later *Balsamus* seem to go too fast for the details to have their full effect, perhaps because they are so strikingly different in style from the other works performed here. And it seems a touch perverse to use the now fashionable 'old French' pronunciation of Latin, particularly in a motet composed for a papal ceremony (even if the original singers would have been Franco-Flemish): in all his early motets the text seems centrally important, and this kind of pronunciation loses too many of the consonants. But the Italian-texted *Apostolo glorioso* is again quite superb, as is the astonishing *Gloria* and *Credo* pair. Briefly, then, this is as close to a perfect Dufay CD as any available.

Dufay Missa Sancti Anthonii de Padua. Veni creator spiritus. **Pomerium / Alexander Blachly.** Archiv Produktion Ⓔ 447 772-2AH (69 minutes: DDD: 9/96). Text and translation included. Recorded 1995.
Dufay Missa Sancti Anthonii de Padua. O proles Hispaniae/O sidus Hispaniae. **The Binchois Consort** (Mark Chambers, Fergus McLusky, altos; Edwin Simpson, Matthew Vine, Andrew Carwood, Chris Watson, tens) / **Andrew Kirkman.** Hyperion Ⓔ CDA66854 (59 minutes: DDD: 9/96). Texts and translations included. Recorded 1996.

A major work of the fifteenth century, the Mass for St Anthony of Padua introduces a period of Dufay's career that has mostly gone unrepresented on CD. That is basically because very little sacred music appears to survive from the middle of Dufay's career (*c*1440-50). The work will fascinate those who are familiar with the Dufay of the late four-voice Masses (such as *Ecce ancilla*, *Ave regina*, *Se la face ay pale* and *L'homme armé*). An apt comparison might be with the middle and last periods of Haydn, the first full of quirks and more obviously experimental, the second Apollonian and more classically balanced. Since this is in fact a Plenary cycle (containing both the Ordinary of the Mass and the Propers of the Saint), there are noticeable stylistic differences between sections, commented on by both directors in their fine accompanying notes. The newly formed Binchois Consort employs countertenors on the top line, with two singers to each line. That corresponds pretty closely to the nine men with whom Dufay is thought to have sung the Mass in Padua in 1450. Andrew Kirkman's interpretation may come as a surprise to some listeners on account of the brisk tempos and very energetic approach to phrasing. The Binchois Consort's vigour leads to inevitable rough edges here and there, but the payoff in terms of energy is ample compensation: listen to the breathtaking rhythmic verve at the Verse in the Gradual, for instance. Blachly's approach is altogether more equable and placid, closer perhaps in spirit to the Dufay for the four-voice Masses. Kirkman and Pomerium use sopranos on the top line of most movements. Despite a slightly higher pitch-standard, the lie of the music is lower in the women's range than it is for Kirkman's countertenors, hence the smoother sound. Blachly also underlines the stylistic shift in the Offertory and the Communion (for which he doubts Dufay's authorship) by knocking the pitch downwards, and reassigning the top voice to men. It would be wrong to prefer one of these recordings over the other, since they are equally successful at projecting their own interpretation. No, the real winners here are the listener and Dufay himself, one of whose masterpieces is now restored for all to hear.

Dufay Nuper rosarum flores. Alma redemptoris mater II. Letabundus. Ecclesie militantis. Magnificat sexti toni. Benedicamus Domino II. Recollectio Festorum Beate Marie Virginis: Plainchant for Vespers I. **Pomerium / Alexander Blachly.** Archiv Produktion Ⓔ 447 773-2AH (60 minutes: DDD: 10/97). Texts and translations included. Recorded 1995-6.

Following up their success with the Mass for St Anthony of Padua, Pomerium here present the other new addition to our knowledge of Dufay's music. This is the set of plainchants he wrote for a new feast, the Recollection of the Feasts of the Virgin Mary, composed in 1458 and identified a few years ago by the American scholar, Barbara Haggh. The work is fascinating in many ways: as one of the very few cases of liturgical chant by a named composer, let alone the greatest composer of his age; as an example of Dufay's work in his full maturity (he was perhaps 60 years old at the time), and entirely different from what we know of his late polyphony; and as a case of unambiguously dated chant composition. Pomerium perform only the music for the First Vespers, a mere fragment of the whole feast. Perhaps there could have been more than four singers for these chants: elegant though the performance is, it hardly sounds like a cathedral *schola*. But the longer pieces are particularly persuasive: the hymn *Gaude redempta* and the Responsory *Surge propera*. For the rest, they add two of Dufay's most famous motets and a group of very rarely heard polyphonic liturgical works, particularly the glorious *Letabundus* setting and the *Magnificat* in the sixth tone, both of which are very welcome additions to the catalogue and are sung with superb lucidity. As before, Pomerium sing with men and women, showing an attractive vibrant energy, everything neatly controlled. The sound in the Grotto Church of Notre Dame, New York, is well captured.

Additional recommendation ...
...Ecclesie militantis. Balsamus et munda cera/Isti sunt agni novelli. Supremum est mortalibus
  bonum. *Coupled with works by various composers.* **Orlando Consort.**
  Metronome Ⓔ METCD1008 (71 minutes: DDD: 11/95).   Ⓖ

Further listening ...
...J'atendray tant qu'il vous. Quel fronte signorille. Ce moys de may. Je me complains pitieusement.
  Ma belle dame souveraine. Navré je suis d'un dart penetratif. Entre vous, gentils amoureux. Belle,
  veuilles moy retenir. Je veux chanter de cuer joyeux. Ce jour l'an. Par droit je puis bien
  complaindre. *Coupled with works by various composers.* **Hilliard Ensemble.**
  Isis CD030 (7/97). *See review in the Collections section; refer to the Index.*
...J'ay mis mon cuer. Je vous pri/Ma tres douce amie/Tant que mon argent. *Coupled with works by*
  various composers. **Alla Francesca.** Opus 111 OPS30-173 (7/98). *See review in the Collections*
  section; refer to the Index.   ⒼⒼⒼ
...Triste plaisir et douleureuse joye – Rondeaux, Ballades and Lamentations. *Coupled with*
  Binchois Rondeaux and Ballades. **Ensemble Gilles Binchois / Dominique Vellard.**
  Virgin Classics Veritas VC7 59043-2 (3/92).   Ⓖ
...Missa "Se la face ay pale". Gloria ad modum tubae. Chanson "Se la face ay pale".
  Early Music Consort of London / David Munrow. Virgin Veritas Edition VER5 61283-2 (9/96).
...Navre je sui d'un dart penetratif. Lamentio Sanctae Matris Ecclesiae Constantinopolitanae. Par
  droit je puis bien complaindre. Donnes l'assault. Helas mon dueil. Vergine bella. Ce moys de
  may. La belle se siet. *Coupled with works by various composers.* **Early Music Consort of London /**
  David Munrow. Virgin Veritas Edition VER5 61284-2 (9/96).
...Victimae paschali laudes. Vexilla regis prodeunt *Coupled with works by various composers.*
  Orlando Consort. Metronome METCD1015 (4/97). *See review in the Collections section;*
  refer to the Index.

Paul Dukas   French 1865-1935

Dukas L'apprenti sorcier.
Saint-Saëns Symphony No. 3 in C minor, Op. 78, "Organ"[a]. [a]**Simon Preston** (org);
  Berlin Philharmonic Orchestra / James Levine. DG Ⓕ 419 617-2GH (47 minutes: DDD: 8/87). Ⓖ
James Levine and the BPO, on cracking form, offer a performance of Saint-Saëns's Third Symphony which is still among the best available. The balance between the orchestra and organ, here played powerfully by Simon Preston, is well judged and the overall acoustic very convincing. Levine directs a grippingly individual reading, full of drama and with a consistently imaginative response to the score's detail. The organ entry in the finale is quite magnificent, the excitement of Preston thundering out the main theme physical in its impact. The music expands and blossoms magnificently, helped by the spectacular dynamic range of the recording. Levine's choice of coupling is a happy one, especially as his account of Dukas's masterpiece is still the best in the catalogue. It was Stokowski who made *The sorcerer's apprentice* famous (with the help of Walt Disney) and his Philadelphia version remains the yardstick. Levine chooses a faster basic tempo than Stokowski, but justifies his speed by the lightness of his touch and, of course, the clean articulation and rhythmic bounce of the Berlin Philharmonic playing help considerably. The climax is thrilling, but Levine reserves something for the moment when the sorcerer returns to quell the flood. Levine must have Disney's imagery in his mind in the closing pages of the story, for the picture of the crestfallen Mickey handing back the broom to his master springs readily to mind. A marvellous finish to an exhilarating listening experience.

Additional recommendations ...
...L'apprenti sorcier. *Coupled with works by various composers.* **Philadelphia Orchestra /**
  Leopold Stokowski. Biddulph mono Ⓜ WHL011* (70 minutes: ADD: 8/95).
...L'apprenti sorcier. *Coupled with works by various composers.* **Philharmonic Symphony Orchestra of**
  New York / Arturo Toscanini. Pearl mono Ⓔ GEMMCDS9373* (three discs: 230 minutes: ADD:
  3/90). *Gramophone classical 100. See review in the Collections section; refer to the Index.* ⒼⒼⒼ
...L'apprenti sorcier. *Coupled with works by* **Falla** National Symphony Orchestra / Enrique Jordá.
  Dutton Laboratories mono Ⓜ CDK1202* (77 minutes: ADD: 12/96).
...L'apprenti sorcier[a]. La Péri[a]. Polyeucte[a]. **d'Indy** Symphonie sur un chant montagnard français[b].
  [b]**Marie-Françoise Bucquet** (pf); [a]**Rotterdam Philharmonic Orchestra,** [b]**Monte Carlo National**
  Opera Orchestra / [a]**David Zinman,** [b]**Paul Capolongo.**
  Philips Solo Ⓜ 454 127-2PM (75 minutes: ADD: 4/97).

Dukas Symphony in C major. Polyeucte – overture. **BBC Philharmonic Orchestra /**
Yan Pascal Tortelier. Chandos Ⓕ CHAN9225 (56 minutes: DDD: 6/94). Recorded 1993.
Selected by Sounds in Retrospect.
Before *L'apprenti sorcier*, the tradition Dukas was following was that of Franck, and he was also
heavily influenced by the Wagnerianism then holding French composers in thrall. Both models can be
discerned in the overture *Polyeucte*: nevertheless, and despite extensive Wagnerian use of the brass,
there is a clarity (even delicacy in the third of its five sections) and an imaginative sense of colour
which are individual to him. The finely crafted Symphony composed four years later, in 1896 –
daringly in C major at a time when tonality was undergoing such general buffeting – shows Dukas as
essentially a classicist, although the middle section of the central movement reveals that Nature
romanticism had not passed him by. The eloquent performance here gives the vigorous first
movement a splendid *élan* while also luxuriating in the Franckian secondary subjects, there is lovely
warm, lyrical playing and sensitive nuance in the second movement, and the finale (even more
Franckian in its harmonic thinking) bubbles over with nervous energy. Exemplary recording quality.

Dukas L'apprenti sorcier (arr. Rabinovitch).
Ravel La valse (arr. cpsr).
R. Strauss Symphonia domestica, Op. 53 (arr. Singer). **Martha Argerich, Alexandre Rabinovitch**
(pfs). Teldec Ⓕ 4509-96435-2 (62 minutes: DDD: 7/96). *Gramophone Editor's choice.* ⒼⒼ
Here is a disc to set the music world on fire, ablaze with the sort of pianistic panache and poetic
empathy from which legends are made. However, those of a nervous disposition and with a bias
towards serenity, should be warned that such fire is of an aptly sinister and engulfing nature. After all,
Dukas's *L'apprenti sorcier* and Ravel's *La valse* both inhabit worlds of exuberant nightmare, and
although one can marvel at the concentrated wit and verve of Argerich and Rabinovitch, it is their
uncanny evocation of unsettled states where all equilibrium is lost and the "ceremony of innocence"
is well and truly drowned that forms the most lasting impression. Such vividness brings parts of *La
valse* to a near standstill before accelerating away and achieving an effect not unlike suddenly applied
centrifugal force. The opening quivers with unease, the commencement of a vision where even the
most opulent Viennese gaiety and extravagance is menacingly clouded and distorted. The Dukas, too,
develops from sinister hints to a situation diabolically out of control yet one sustained by both players
with an iron grip all the more remarkable when you consider the immense virtuoso resources involved.
Otto Singer's skilful version of Strauss's *Symphonia domestica* hardly transcends its orchestral origin
yet it is illuminated at every point – whether in rhetorical uproar or flickering, Lisztian half-lights –
by playing of an overwhelming brio and crystalline clarity. If anything Argerich's blow-torch
incandescence has increased rather than diminished over the years. The recordings are close but
unconfined, capturing with fine fidelity the dazzling impact of these performances.

Dukas Piano Sonata in E flat minor.
Dutilleux Piano Sonata.
Schmitt Deux mirages. **John Ogdon** (pf). EMI Matrix Ⓜ CDM5 65996-2 (79 minutes: ADD:
11/96). From HMV SLS868 (8/74). Recorded 1972.
The first of Schmitt's *Mirages*, written in 1920 and published in memory of Debussy, is a haunting,
elaborately textured elegy; the second, a ferocious rendering of the story of Mazeppa's tragic ride, was
dedicated to Cortot. One wonders whether he would ever have had the technique to play it: Ogdon,
however, revels in its enormous demands. His fluency and limpid clarity are to be admired, too, in the
Dutilleux Sonata, whose spiky first movement veers from fragile delicacy to pounding *fortissimo*
chords; its slow movement (headed "Lied") is deeply moving in its intensity; and rather more
diatonicism marks the final massive chorale, with its brilliant ensuing variations. The main work here,
however, is the big Dukas Sonata, written at the turn of the century, and advanced for its time. It has
always been hailed by French critics as a masterpiece, but despite that it is not often performed, at
least in this country. There have been more recent recordings, by Jean Hubeau, whose performance,
though he was a pupil of Dukas himself, is rather limp, and by the talented and musicianly Margaret
Fingerhut; but Ogdon brings greater power to the climactic passages and makes its drama more vivid.
The sonata's Franckian harmonic and melodic traits are combined with a pianistic exuberance which
suits his temperament admirably, as does the demonic *Scherzo*, but this is balanced by his air of
mystery in its trio section and by Ogdon's tonal purity in the quiet slow movement. This disc brings
home to us how outstanding a pianist we lost in John Ogdon.

Additional recommendations ...
...Piano Sonata. Variations, Interlude and Finale on a theme by Rameau. Prélude élégiaque.
La plainte, au loin, du faune. **Margaret Fingerhut** (pf).
Chandos Ⓕ CHAN8765 (76 minutes: DDD: 1/90).
...Piano Sonata. Variations, interlude et final sur un thème de Rameau. La plainte, au loin, du
faune. Prélude élégiaque. *Coupled with works by various composers.* **Jean Hubeau** (pf).
Teldec Ⓑ 4509-96221-2 (two discs: 134 minutes: DDD: 4/96).

Further listening ...
...Ariane et Barbe-Bleue. **Soloists; French Radio Chorus; French Radio New Philharmonic**
Orchestra / Armin Jordan. Erato Libretto 2292-45663-2 ((9/91).

John Duke
American 1899-1984

Suggested listening ...
...In the fields. Twentieth century. Heart! we will forget him!. *Coupled with works by various composers.* **Jennifer Larmore** (mez); **Antoine Palloc** (pf). Teldec 0630-16069-2 (12/97). *See review in the Collections section; refer to the Index.*

Guillaume Dumanoir
French 1615-1697

Dumanoir Suite in F major. Suite du Ballet de Stockholm.
La Voye-Mignot Suite in B flat major.
Mazuel Suite in G major.
Anonymous Fantaisie, "Les pleurs d'Orphée ayant perdu sa femme". **Le Concert des Nations / Jordi Savall.** Auvidis Fontalis Ⓕ ES9908 (60 minutes: DDD: 3/98). 🎵 Recorded 1995.
Of these mid-seventeenth-century names only Guillaume Dumanoir is at all familiar, even to specialists in the baroque period in France. He was the leader of Louis XIV's famous "Vingt-quatre violons du roi" and later promoted to "roi des violons", in charge of some 200 performers and composers; but four years later he was replaced with establishement of the Académie Royale de Danse under Lully. Courantes and sarabandes were much the most numerous of the dances by Dumanoir and others of his group, of whom Michel Mazuel was one: gigues are rare, and minuets even more so. But already there was a move away from a basic choreographic character towards stylization (particularly in the allemandes); and the sarabande by the theorist, La Voye-Mignot, and a remarkably fine, chromatically expressive anonymous lament display a welcome contrapuntal contrast to the prevailing homophony. Some Italian influence is present (as, for example, in fast-speed sarabandes); a pompous F major Overture by Dumanoir foreshadows the later French overture form; and in the *Ballet de Stockholm* a surprise is an exciting Hungaresca. Overall this is agreeably melodious music that can easily be imagined as effective in its original balletic context: away from it, the high spots are a fetching bourrée by Mazuel, the anonymous *Fantaisie* and the highly entertaining, diversely scored suite for Stockholm. Jordi Savall deserves our thanks for so persuasively presenting, with the accomplished players of the Concert des Nations, this all but unknown repertoire.

Henri Dumont
· French 1610-1684

Dumont Pavane. Two Preludes. Litanies de la Vierge. Allemande Gravis. Antienne de St Cecile. O Sponse mi. Symfonia. Domine salvum fac, Regem.
Anonymous Veni sponsa mea. Pater noster. Egredimini Filiae Sion. O veneranda Trinitas.
Ensemble Dumont / Peter Bennett (org). Linn Records Ⓕ CKD067 (65 minutes: DDD: 12/97). 🎵
Texts and translations included. Recorded 1997. *Gramophone Editor's choice.*   Ⓖ
For most people, the achievements of Henri Dumont have been obscured by the more famous figures of Lully and Lalande. For Peter Bennett, however, he "can justifiably be seen as the foundation on which French sacred music would stand for the next half-century", a composer who had a modernizing effect on a repertoire whose style in the 1650s lagged behind that of other countries in Europe. This beautifully recorded and enterprisingly programmed disc reconstructs a sacred concert as it might have been heard in the Parisian household of Louis's pious brother (and Dumont's employer), Philippe of Anjou, mixing some of the composer's sacred works for two to five voices and continuo with pieces for small viol consort. There are also four anonymous works which seem to be old-style unaccompanied vocal pieces to which continuo parts were added during the 1750s. This is music which is quietly rather urgently expressive but it is almost unremittingly beautiful, and Ensemble Dumont's singing and viol-playing have a grace and refined sound which serve the pieces rather well. Quite simply, this is a gorgeous disc that you will never regret buying.

Trevor Duncan
British 1924

Suggested listening ...
...Little Suite – March. *Coupled with works by various composers.* **Light Music Society Orchestra / Sir Vivian Dunn.** EMI British Composers CDM5 66537-2 (1/98). *See review in the Collections section; refer to the Index.*

Thomas Dunhill
British 1877-1946

Suggested listening ...
...Violin Sonata in F major, Op. 50. *Coupled with works by* **Stanford** and **Bantock**
Susanne Stanzeleit (vn); **Gusztáv Fenyö** (pf). Cala United CACD88031 (7/96).
See review under Bantock; refer to the Index.

John Dunstable
British c1390-1453

Dunstable Descendi in ortum meum. Ave maris stella. Gloria in canon. Speciosa facta es. Sub tuam protectionem. Veni, Sancte spiritus/Veni creator spiritus. Albanus roseo rutilat/Quoque ferundus eras/Albanus domini laudus. Specialis virgo. Preco preheminencie/Precursor premittitur/ textless/Inter natos mulierum. O crux gloriosa. Salve regina mater mire. Missa Rex seculorum. **Orlando Consort.** Metronome Ⓕ METCD1009 (74 minutes: DDD: 2/96). Texts and translations included. Recorded 1995. *Gramophone Editor's choice. Gramophone Award Winner 1996.* Ⓖ

Dunstable Veni Sancte Spiritus et emitte/Veni Sancte Spiritus et infunde/Veni Creator Spiritus mentes tuorum. Alma redemptoris I. Mass Cycle Da gaudiorum premia. Agnus Dei. Salve scema sanctitatis/Salve slus servulorum/Cantant celi agmina/textless. Gaude virgo salutaris/Gaude virgo singularis/Virgo mater comprobaris/Ave gemma. Quam pulchra es. Salve regina misericordiae. Preco preheminencie/Precursor premittitur/textless/Inter natos mulierum. **The Hilliard Ensemble** (David James, Ashley Stafford, altos; Paul Elliott, Leigh Nixon, Rogers Covey-Crump, tens; Paul Hillier, Michael George, basses). Virgin Classics Veritas Ⓜ VER5 61342-2 (54 minutes: ADD: 10/97). From HMV ASD146703-1 (4/85). Texts and translations included. Recorded 1984.

Metronome's disc contains three of Dunstable's well-known motets – *Preco preheminencie, Veni veni* and *Albanus* – but the rest are rarely performed. For some of the delicious antiphons, it is hard to see why: *Salve regina mater mire* is particularly striking – one of those pieces that sounds far more impressive than it looks on the page. There are also some total novelties. The canonic *Gloria* was discovered in Russia: it is a massively inventive work that adds a substantial new dimension to our knowledge of Dunstable. And *Descendi in ortum meum*, though discovered and published a quarter of a century ago, surely stands as the latest known work of its composer: a magnificent piece that builds an entirely new kind of edifice with the materials of his characteristic style. Most impressive of all, though, is the Mass, *Rex seculorum*, which ends the disc. This may or may not be by Dunstable – which is probably why it has never been recorded. Whoever the composer, though, it is a key work in the history of the polyphonic mass cycle, brimming with invention. The Orlando Consort have a wonderfully forward style that beautifully matches the music and helps the listener to understand why Dunstable achieved such an enormous reputation on the continental mainland. If they are occasionally a touch rough, these are classic performances that will be hard to challenge.

Virgin Veritas's Hilliard Edition marks a belated tribute to one of the most enduring names of the early music scene, and the long-awaited return to the catalogue of some of its finest work. English music often brings out the best in The Hilliard Ensemble. The disc's sheer sound quality is mesmeric, the four-voice motets in particular sounding almost preternaturally luminous. That's partly to do with the acoustic of the church of Boxgrove Priory, Chichester; but there is also the allocation of two singers on those long tenor parts, positioned at a slight distance from the other voices. That touch of genius creates a core of stillness against which the other voices move to magical effect. Magical, too, is just the word for the singing of David James. Dunstable is very much a melodist, and on this disc the top line gets the lion's share. James brings a restrained expressivity to every nuance and inflexion.

Further listening ...
...Beata Dei genitrix. *Coupled with works by various composers.* **Gothic Voices / Christopher Page.** Hyperion CDA66783 (1/96). *See review in the Collections section; refer to the Index.*

Marie Eugène Duparc
French 1848-1933

Duparc L'Invitation au voyage. Sérénade florentine. La Vague et la cloche. Extase. Phidylé. Le Manoir de Rosemonde. Lamento. Testament. Chanson triste. Elégie. Soupir. La Vie antérieure. Le Galop. Sérénade. Au pays où se fait la guerre[a]. Romance de Mignon[a]. La Fuite[a]. **José van Dam** (bass-bar); [a]**Florence Bonnafous** (sop); **Maciej Pikulski** (pf). Forlane Ⓕ UCD16692 (67 minutes: DDD: 1/94). Texts and translations included. Recorded 1993.

These songs may justly be held to represent the peak of development of the French *mélodie* in their sensitivity, intensity, scope of expression and unfaltering taste. Influences may be seen of his teacher César Franck in his emotionalism and chromatic texture, of Gounod in the rippling piano part of a song like *Chanson triste*, and particularly of Wagner in the harmonic colouring of *Soupir* and the almost Tristanesque *Extase*; but it has been well observed that the sinister drama of *Le Manoir de Rosemonde*, with its insistent rhythm, is worthy of Hugo Wolf, and that the bleak tints of *Lamento* foreshadow Ravel's *Le gibet*. Despite all this, however, Duparc is very much an individual genius; and the breadth of his stylistic range, from the passionate lyricism of *L'Invitation au voyage* or the haunting sensuousness of *Phidylé* to the simple heartbreak of *Au pays où se fait la guerre*, makes any *intégrale* of his songs riveting. Particularly so when sung with such insight, commitment and verbal intensity as by José van Dam here. He is expertly partnered by a responsively musical accompanist.

Additional recommendation ...
...L'invitation au voyage. Soupir. Testament. Sérénade florentine. La vague et la cloche. Lamento. La Vie antérieure. Phidylé. Extase. Elégie. Le Manoir de Rosemonde. Chanson triste. *Coupled with works by various composers.* **Camille Maurane** (bar); **Lily Bienvenu** (pf). Philips The Early Years mono Ⓜ 438 970-2PM2* (two discs: 157 minutes: ADD: 12/95).

Marcel Dupré
French 1886-1971

Suggested listening ...
...Cortège et Litanie, Op. 19 No. 2. *Coupled with works by various composers.* **Christopher Herrick**
(org). Hyperion CDA66457 (9/91). *See review in the Collections section; refer to the Index.* ❹❹❹
...Scherzo, Op. 16. *Coupled with works by various composers.* **Marie-Bernadette Dufourcet** (org).
Priory PRCD422 (6/95). *See review in the Collections section; refer to the Index.*
...Evocation, Op. 37 – Allegro deciso. *Coupled with works by various composers.* **Roger Sayer** (org).
Priory PRCD495 (4/96). *See review in the Collections section; refer to the Index.*

Francesco Durante
Italian 1684-1755

Durante Magnificat in B flat major.
Astorga Stabat mater[a].
Pergolesi Confitebor tibi Domine[a]. [a]**Ann Monoyios** (sop); **Balthasar Neumann Choir;**
Freiburg Baroque Orchestra / Thomas Hengelbrock. Deutsche Harmonia Mundi ℗ 05472 77369-2
(59 minutes: DDD: 10/97). ✍ Texts and translations included. Recorded 1995.
The common factor in this programme is the adherence of its three composers to what is generally
called the Neapolitan style. Durante was one of its most important representatives during the first
half of the eighteenth century, and Pergolesi his most celebrated pupil. Astorga was a Spaniard whose
family had settled in Italy, though he himself eventually returned to Spain and Portugal. The
Magnificat in B flat by Durante, is an immediately appealing, expressively vital piece, concise, tautly
constructed and tonally radiant. Both its opening and concluding sections are closely linked by the
quotation of its psalm tone, *cantus firmus*, similarly treated in each instance. Altogether, this is a
warmly satisfying setting of the canticle with sumptuous choral homophony colouring the short but
effective "Gloria patri". Astorga's *Stabat mater* in C minor is of a very different expressive hue. It's
an extended piece with a spacious opening chorus in which occasional unexpected modulations
colour the musical rhetoric. The remainder of the work is shared between solo voices, vocal ensembles
and choruses. Pergolesi's psalm setting, *Confitebor tibi Domine*, is close in spirit and in style to the
Magnificat of his teacher, Durante. Pergolesi introduces a larger solo element with only four choral
sections as opposed to Durante's six. Pergolesi was foremost an opera composer, Durante,
exceptionally among Neapolitan composers, was not, and it is in this respect that the two works reveal
the most interesting contrasts. The performances are very good indeed. The Balthasar Neumann
Choir consist of 14 voices from which various soloists in various groupings emerge as required. Over
and above these, however, are the valuable contributions from Ann Monoyios. Her "Sancta mater" in
the Astorga is beautifully sung, as are the remaining five solos apportioned to her in that work and
the Pergolesi psalm.
Further listening ...
...Concerto for Two Violins, Viola and Continuo in G minor. *Coupled with works by*
various composers. **Il Giardino Armonico / Giovanni Antonini** (rec).
Teldec Das Alte Werk 4509-93157-2 (11/94). ✍   ❹
...Lamentationes Jeremiae Prophetae. **Monika Frimmer, Mechthild Bach** (sops); **Margarete Joswig**
(contr); **Cologne Chamber Choir; Collegium Cartusianum / Peter Neumann.**
CPO CPO999 325-2 (4/96). ✍   ❹

Louis Durey
French 1888-1979

Suggested listening ...
...Trois Préludes à la mémoire de Juliette Méérowitch, Op. 26. *Coupled with works by various*
composers. **Marcelo Bratke** (pf). Olympia Explorer OCD487 (12/96). *See review in the Collections*
section; refer to the Index.

Sebastián Durón
Spanish 1660-1716

Durón Tono a la Pasión de Christo, "Quando muere el Sol". Lamentación segunda, del Viernes
Santo.
Navas Tono di Miserere, "Si mis hierros os tienen pendiente".
Torres Miserere. Lamentación segunda, del Jueves Santo. **Al Ayre Español / Eduardo López Banzo.**
Deutsche Harmonia Mundi ℗ 05472 77376-2 (66 minutes: DDD: 7/97). ✍
Texts and translations included. Recorded 1996. *Gramophone Editor's choice.*   ❹❹❹
This CD, part of Al Ayre Español's "Barroco Español" series, focuses on Latin-texted sacred music
from the Royal Chapel in Madrid in the years before and just after 1700. The music, all of a
penitential nature, is of a consistently high quality, and the performances from Al Ayre Español
represent their most polished yet. An excellent quartet of Spanish soloists is given superb support by
the more international team of instrumentalists, and Eduardo López Banzo, as usual, takes the music

by the scruff of the neck and shakes off the accumulated dust of centuries in interpretations of real fervour and vitality. The two settings of the Lamentations – one by José de Torres, the other by Sebastián Durón – are brilliantly conceived, the string accompaniments constantly shifting in texture and *Affekt*, providing the perfect foil to the vocal lines. This is particularly the case in the Durón Lamentations, where the writing for three violins is really quite remarkable, while the solo part is sung with consummate mastery and beauty of tone by the young countertenor, Carlos Mena – Spain's answer to Michael Chance? A minor reservation: the plucked strings (chitarrone and theorbo) are excellently and imaginatively played, but where is the harp, so characteristic of the continuo in Spanish sacred music of this period? Overall, however, these are outstanding performances which bring out the intensity and drama inherent in this music.

Further listening ...

...Veneno es de amor la envidia – Ondas riscos, pezes, mares. El impossible mayor en amor le venze Amor – Donde vas; Danae, cuya belleza; Oye, escucha, aguarda, espera. *Coupled with works by* **Literes** and **Martín y Coll** Al Ayre Español / Eduardo López Banzo.
Deutsche Harmonia Mundi 05472 77336-2 (1/96). ✔   Ⓖ

Maurice Duruflé
French 1902-1986

Duruflé Prélude et Fugue sur le nom d'Alain, Op. 7[c]. Requiem, Op. 9[c]. Quatre Motets sur des thèmes grégoriens, Op. 10[b].
Fauré Requiem, Op. 9[a]. Cantique de Jean Racine, Op. 11[a]. Messe basse[b].
Poulenc Mass in G major[d]. Salve Regina[d]. Exultate Deo[d]. Litanies à la vierge noire[d].
Jonathon Bond, Andrew Brunt, Robert King (trebs); **Benjamin Luxon** (bar); **Christopher Keyte** (bass); **St John's College Choir, Cambridge; Academy of St Martin in the Fields / George Guest** with **Stephen Cleobury** (org). Double Decca Ⓜ 436 486-2DF2 (two discs: 149 minutes: ADD: 7/94). Items marked [a] from Argo ZRG841 (4/76), [b]ZRG662 (2/71), [c]ZRG787 (5/75), [d]ZRG883 (6/78). Recorded 1969-76.   Ⓖ

Here is almost two-and-a-half hours of bliss. These are recordings to set aside for the time when, as the prayer says, "the busy world is hushed". Asked to characterize Fauré's and Duruflé's Requiems as compared with others, we might suggest words such as 'delicate', 'restrained', 'meditative', 'undramatic'; but that last would be a mistake. These performances certainly do not go out of their way to 'be' dramatic or anything else other than faithful to the music but one is struck by the power exercised by those rare moments that rise to a *forte* and above. In Fauré the orchestral crescendo introducing the baritone soloist has the effectiveness of a spotlight brought up gradually upon a motionless figure on stage; the entry of brass in the *Sanctus* has breadth and majesty incommensurate with its scoring and duration; the brief orchestral climax of the *Lux aeterna* looms imposingly like the front of a great cathedral. Duruflé too is dramatic, but in the way that (say) Westminster Cathedral is dramatic, with stillness and space, and the light of candles amid a brooding darkness. The choir is surely at its best, the trebles with their fine, clear-cut, distinctive tone, the tenors (so important in the Fauré) graceful and refined without being precious, the altos exceptionally good, and only the basses just occasionally and briefly plummy or obtrusive in some way. The Poulenc works further test a choir's virtuosity yet in the extremely difficult Mass, the choir seems secure, and in the *Salve Regina* they catch the necessary tenderness. Of the treble soloists, Andrew Brunt sings most beautifully in the *Messe basse*, while Jonathon Bond's high, well-floated tones have ethereal effect in the *Agnus Dei* of Poulenc's Mass in G. Christopher Keyte dramatizes almost too convincingly in Duruflé's "tremens factus", and Benjamin Luxon, his production less even, builds finely in Fauré's *Libera me*. Stephen Cleobury, the organist throughout, contributes an admirably played solo written by Duruflé as a tribute to the young organist Jehan Alain, killed early in the war. These recordings have a vividness, certainly in the choral sound, that modern recordings generally lack.

Additional recommendations ...

...Requiem[a]. Quatre Motets. [a]Ann Murray (mez); [a]Thomas Allen (bar); Corydon Singers; [a]English Chamber Orchestra / Matthew Best with [a]Thomas Trotter (org).
Hyperion Ⓕ CDA66191 (51 minutes: DDD: 4/87).

...Quatre Motets. Mass "Cum jubilo, Op. 11". *Coupled with works by* **Fauré** and **Messiaen**
Mark Griffiths (bar); Trinity College Choir, Cambridge with Richard Pearce (org).
Conifer Classics Ⓕ CDCF176 (73 minutes: DDD: 10/90).

...Prélude sur l'introit de l'Epiphanie. Prélude et Fugue sur le nom d'Alain. Suite, Op. 5. Scherzo, Op. 2. Prélude, Adagio et Choral Varié sur le "Veni Creator", Op. 4[a]. Fugue sur le carillon des heures de la Cathédrale de Soissons, Op. 12. [a]men's voices of St Paul's Cathedral Choir; John Scott (org). Hyperion Ⓕ CDA66368 (70 minutes: DDD: 1/91).

...Requiem[a]. Quatre Motets. Notre père. Mass "Cum jubilo"[b]. [a]Aaron Webber (treb); [ab]Simon Keenlyside (bar); [a]Natalie Clein (vc); Westminster Cathedral Choir / James O'Donnell with [ab]Iain Simcock (org). Hyperion Ⓕ CDA66757 (71 minutes: DDD: 6/95).

...Requiem[abcde]. Quatre Motets[d]. Scherzo, Op. 2[c]. Notre père, Op. 14[d]. Prélude et Fugue sur le nom d'Alain[c]. Béatrice Uria-Monzon (mez); [b]Didier Henry (bar); [c]Eric LeBrun (org); [d]Michel Piquemal Vocal Ensemble; [e]Orchestre de la Cité / Michel Piquemal.
Naxos Ⓢ 8 553196 (67 minutes: DDD: 11/95).

...Mass "Cum jubilo"[bcde]. Prélude, Adagio et Choral varié sur le "Veni Creator"[c]. Suite, Op. 5[c].
[b]Didier Henry (bar); [c]**Eric LeBrun** (org); [d]**Michel Piquemal Vocal Ensemble;** [e]**Orchestre de la Cité /
Michel Piquemal.** Naxos Ⓢ 8 553197 (62 minutes: DDD: 11/95).
...Quatre Motets sur des thèmes grégoriens. *Coupled with works by various composers.* **St Thomas
Church Choir / Gerre Hancock.** Koch International Classics Ⓕ 37228-2 (53 minutes: DDD: 9/96).

Duruflé Requiem, Op. 9[a].
Fauré Requiem, Op. 48[b]. [a]**Dame Kiri Te Kanawa,** [b]**Lucia Popp** (sops); **Siegmund Nimsgern**
(bass-bar); **Ambrosian Singers;** [a]**Desborough School Choir;** [a]**New Philharmonia Orchestra,**
[b]**Philharmonia Orchestra / Andrew Davis.** Sony Classical Essential Classics Ⓑ SBK67182
(79 minutes: ADD: A/97). Item marked [a] from CBS 76633 (10/77), [b]76734 (12/78).
Recorded 1997.
No musical coupling is more natural than that of these Requiems, and for the record-buyer it is most
convenient to have them on a single disc. The recordings under Andrew Davis, made within six
months of each other with substantially the same forces and in the same church, were issued
separately but obviously go together. Both had outstandingly good reviews in *Gramophone* and
although textural matters have arisen to enrich the choice and complicate the issue, if what were then
regarded as the standard versions (in full orchestral score) are required, then the recommendations
can remain. Davis's superiority over more recent versions is especially apparent in the Duruflé. His
way with the opening is typical: the flow, the gentle wave-like motion, is beautifully caught and in the
"Libera me" he discovers the full richness of Duruflé's colours. Dame Kiri Te Kanawa sings with
feeling and is incomparably lovely in sheer sound. There may be a few misgivings about the sound
produced in remastering, but it settles down (or one's ears do).

Henri Dutilleux
French 1916

Dutilleux Cello Concerto, "Tout un monde lointain"[a]. Métaboles. Mystère de l'instant.
[a]**Boris Pergamenschikov** (vc); **BBC Philharmonic Orchestra / Yan Pascal Tortelier.**
Chandos Ⓕ CHAN9565 (60 minutes: DDD: 2/98). Recorded 1997. *Selected by Soundings.* Ⓖ
This is the third issue in the Chandos Dutilleux series with the BBC Philharmonic and Yan Pascal
Tortelier. The virtues of those earlier issues remain evident here, with meticulously prepared, well-
played performances, and recordings carefully adapted to the coloristic subtlety and textural delicacy
of the music. *Métaboles* is particularly tricky to bring off, but this version is admirable in the way it
builds through some dangerously episodic writing to underline the power of the principal climaxes.,
although a more sharply delineated sound picture could have reinforced these contrasts even more
appropriately. Boris Pergamenschikov is an eloquent soloist in the Cello Concerto, without aspiring
to dominate in the way that both Rostropovich and Lynn Harrell tend to do. Tortelier's account of
Mystère de l'instant – using a full orchestral complement of strings – is excellently done. As with
Métaboles, the structure is shaped with great flexibility and feeling for its ebb and flow, and as a result
this emerges as a highly dramatic score, despite the inherent reticence of Dutilleux's style. Taken as a
whole, then, the Tortelier/Chandos Dutilleux series deserves a place in everyone's collection.
Additional recommendations ...
...Cello Concerto[a]. **Lutoslawski** Cello Concerto[b]. **Mstislav Rostropovich** (vc); **Orchestre de Paris /**
[a]**Serge Baudo,** [b]**Witold Lutoslawski.** EMI Ⓕ CDC7 49304-2 (53 minutes: ADD: 5/88).
...Mystère de l'instant[a]. Métaboles[b]. Timbres, Espace, mouvement[b]. [a]**Zurich Collegium Musicum /
Paul Sacher;** [b]**French National Orchestra / Mstislav Rostropovich.**
Erato MusiFrance Ⓕ 2292-45626-2 (46 minutes: ADD/DDD: 8/92).
...Métaboles. Timbres, espace, mouvement (rev. 1991). Symphony No. 2, "Le double".
Orchestre de Paris / Semyon Bychkov. Philips Ⓕ 438 008-2PH (63 minutes: DDD: 5/94). Ⓖ
...Métaboles. *Coupled with* **Berlioz** Symphonie fantastique, Op. 14. **Paris Opéra-Bastille
Orchestra / Myung-Whun Chung.** DG Ⓕ 445 878-2GH (67 minutes: DDD: 4/96). Ⓖ

Dutilleux Violin Concerto, "L'arbre des songes"[a]. Cello Concerto, "Tout un monde lointain"[b].
[a]**Pierre Amoyal** (vn); [b]**Lynn Harrell** (vc); **French National Orchestra / Charles Dutoit.**
Decca Ⓕ 444 398-2DH (51 minutes: DDD: 3/95). Recorded 1993. *Selected by Sounds in
Retrospect.* ⒼⒼ
It was high time that Dutilleux's two concertos were brought together on disc, and this fine recording
should help to win him new admirers. The Cello Concerto, first performed in 1970, was written for
Rostropovich and Lynn Harrell boldly confronts this formidable precedent; there is certainly no sense
of undue reticence or constraint in his playing. The many technical challenges present no problems:
more significantly, Harrell the interpreter has the full measure of the music's tricky blend of boldness
and delicacy. From the start of the "very free and flexible" first movement the undertones of mystery
and menace which reflect the music's source in Baudelaire's poetry are fully in evidence, and Harrell
has the advantage of first-class (1993) recorded sound. The cello is placed well forward, but the
orchestra are never recessed to compensate. The Violin Concerto (1985) builds on the sultry, surreal
Baudelairean spirit of the Cello Concerto – the 'tree' of the title seems tropical, the 'dreams' mainly
unquiet – and Pierre Amoyal, with admirable support from Dutoit and the FNO, succeeds brilliantly

in shaping the rhapsodic solo line with a mixture of intensity and fantasy, so that the piece works well as both structure and expression. Here, too, the production team have ensured that the concerto's rich textures can be heard without strain or artificiality. The whole enterprise can be warmly recommended.

Additional recommendation ...

...Violin Concerto[b]. Timbres, espace, mouvement. Deux Sonnets de Jean Cassou (orch. cpsr)[c].
J. Alain (orch. Dutilleux) Prière pour nous autres charnels[a]. [a]**Martyn Hill** (ten); [ac]**Neal Davies** (bar); [b]**Olivier Charlier** (vn); **BBC Philharmonic Orchestra / Yan Pascal Tortelier.** Chandos Ⓕ CHAN9504 (58 minutes: DDD: 11/96).

Dutilleux Symphonies – No. 1; No. 2, "Le double". **BBC Philharmonic Orchestra / Yan Pascal Tortelier.** Chandos Ⓕ CHAN9194 (60 minutes: DDD: 11/93).
Gramophone Award Winner 1994. Selected by Sounds in Retrospect.   Ⓖ
This pair of relatively early works by Henri Dutilleux, completed in 1951 and 1959 respectively, show him poised to inherit the Honegger/Martinů strand of the symphonic tradition. Yet, while an almost Simpsonian *élan* in the first movement of No. 2 promises a rich vein for further exploration, the Stravinskian strategies of the finale, ending with a virtual recomposition of the chorale that concludes the *Symphonies of Wind Instruments*, reveals a more modernist tendency, and leads away from the well-made, tonally-resolving symphony altogether. With their broad thematic vistas and persuasive adaptations of traditional forms, Dutilleux's symphonies offer considerable rewards to interpreters and listeners alike. Yan Pascal Tortelier and the BBC Philharmonic allow the music all the space it needs in strongly characterized, rhythmically well-sprung performances with uniformly excellent solo playing in No. 2, and the Chandos sound is rich and natural.

Additional recommendations ...

...Nos.[a] 1 and 2. Mystère de l'instant[b]. Métaboles[c]. Timbres, espace, mouvement[c]. Les citations[d]. Piano Sonata[e]. Deux figures de résonances[f]. Trois préludes[e]. Trois strophes sur le nom de Sacher[g]. Ainsi la nuit ...[h]. Deux sonnets de Jean Cassou[i]. [i]**Gilles Cachemaille** (bar); [d]**Maurice Bourge** (ob); [g]**David Geringas** (vc); [d]**Bernard Cazauran** (db); [d]**Huguette Dreyfus** (hpd); [d]**Bernard Balet** (perc); [ef]**Geneviève Joy**, [fi]**Henri Dutilleux** (pfs); [h]**Sine Nomine Quartet** (Patrick Genet, François Gottraux, vns; Nicolas Pach, va; Mars Jaermann, vc); [a]**Orchestre de Paris / Daniel Barenboim;** [b]**Collegium Musicum, Zurich / Paul Sacher;** [c]**French National Orchestra / Mstislav Rostropovich.** Erato Ⓜ 0630-14068-2 (three discs: 192 minutes: ADD/DDD: 12/96).
...No. 1. Timbres, espace, mouvement. **Lyon National Orchestra / Serge Baudo.** Harmonia Mundi Suite Ⓜ HMT790 5159 (48 minutes: DDD: 4/98).

Further listening ...

...Piano Sonata. *Coupled with works by* **Dukas** *and* **Schmitt John Ogdon** (pf). EMI Matrix CDM5 65996-2 (11/96). *See review under Dukas; refer to the Index.*
...Piano Sonata. Préludes. Tous les chemins ... mènent à Rome. Bergerie. Blackbird. Résonances. Figures de résonances (with Christian Ivaldi, pf). Au gré des ondes. **Anne Queffélec** (pf). Virgin Classics VC5 45222-2 (5/97).
...Sonatine. *Coupled with works by various composers.* **Emmanuel Pahud** (fl); **Eric Le Sage** (pf). EMI CDC5 56488-2 (3/98). *See review in the Collections section; refer to the Index. Selected by Soundings.*

Balys Dvarionas   Latvian 1904-1972

Suggested listening ...

...Elegie. *Coupled with works by various composers.* **Gidon Kremer** (vn); **Deutsche Kammerphilharmonie.** Teldec 0630-14654-2 (11/97). *Gramophone Editor's choice. See review in the Collections section; refer to the Index.*

Antonin Dvořák   Bohemian 1841-1904

Dvořák Cello Concerto in B minor, B191[a]. Silent woods, B173[b]. Rondo in G minor, B171[b]. Slavonic Dance in A flat major, B147 No. 8[b]. **Heinrich Schiff** (vc); [a]**Vienna Philharmonic Orchestra / André Previn** ([b]pf). Philips Ⓕ 434 914-2PH (54 minutes: DDD: 9/93).
Recorded 1992.   Ⓖ
Schiff's cello is recorded in a more natural balance than is common in this concerto, so that the solo instrument's first entry does not give the impression of a super-cello, as most recordings do, but the concentration and tension bear witness to the scale and power of the interpretation. When it comes to the great second subject melody Schiff's hushed *pianissimo* is ravishingly gentle, and unlike almost every rival he avoids drawing the tempo out, observing Dvořák's *In tempo* marking at a very marginally broader speed. The result has a touching simplicity and tenderness. André Previn is a fresh and understanding partner, pointing rhythms even more crisply, and the Vienna Philharmonic brings out the Slavonic tang in the score. The bright detailed recording helps, with the Vienna horns – so important in this work from the opening tutti on – sounding glorious. Schiff's flowing speed in the

slow movement again brings out the freshness of folk-based ideas. Only in the finale does the balance of the cello mean that the result is less biting. Few versions come near to matching this. The coupling is apt. These are not the usual orchestral arrangements but have Previn as a sparkling piano accompanist.

Additional recommendations ...

...Cello Concerto. **Schubert** Sonata in A major, D821, "Arpeggione". **Lynn Harrell** (vc); **London Symphony Orchestra / James Levine**. RCA Papillon Ⓜ GD86531 (67 minutes: ADD: 11/87).

...Cello Concerto. *Coupled with works by* **Bloch** and **Bruch** **Pierre Fournier** (vc); **Berlin Philharmonic Orchestra / George Szell**. DG Privilege Ⓑ 429 155-2GR (71 minutes: ADD: 5/90).

...Cello Concerto. *Coupled with works by* **Bruch** and **Elgar** **Pablo Casals** (vc); **Czech Philharmonic Orchestra / George Szell**. EMI Références mono Ⓜ CDH7 63498-2* (75 minutes: ADD: 8/90). ⒼⒼ

...Cello Concerto. **Elgar** Cello Concerto. **Maria Kliegel** (vc); **Royal Philharmonic Orchestra / Michael Halász**. Naxos Ⓢ 8 550503 (73 minutes: DDD: 9/92).

...Cello Concerto. *Coupled with works by various composers.* **Pierre Fournier** (vc); **Philharmonia Orchestra / Rafael Kubelík**. Testament mono Ⓕ SBT1016* (77 minutes: ADD: 7/93).

...Cello Concerto[a]. Piano Concerto in G minor, B63[b]. [a]**Mstislav Rostropovich** (vc); [b]**František Maxián** (pf); **Czech Philharmonic Orchestra / Václav Talich**. Supraphon Historical mono Ⓜ 11 1901-2* (77 minutes: ADD: 3/94).

...Cello Concerto. Silent woods, B182. *Coupled with works by various composers.* **Jacqueline du Pré** (vc) with various artists and orchestras. EMI Ⓑ CZS5 68132-2 (six discs: 437 minutes: ADD: 8/94). *See review in the Collections section; refer to the Index.* ⒼⒼ

...Romance, B39. Hussite, B132. Silent woods. *Coupled with works by various composers.* **Malcolm Stewart** (vn); **Timothy Walden** (vc); **Alan Pendlebury** (bn); **Royal Liverpool Philharmonic Orchestra / Libor Pešek**. Virgin Classics Ⓕ VC7 59285-2 (76 minutes: DDD: 11/94).

...Cello Concerto. **Schumann** Cello Concerto in A minor, Op. 129. **Arto Noras** (vc); **Finnish Radio Symphony Orchestra / Sakari Oramo**. Finlandia Ⓕ 4509-98886-2 (64 minutes: DDD: 10/95).

...Cello Concerto in B minor, B191[a]. **Elgar** Cello Concerto in E minor, Op. 85[b]. **Jacqueline du Pré** (vc); [a]**Chicago Symphony Orchestra / Daniel Barenboim**; [b]**London Symphony Orchestra / Sir John Barbirolli**. EMI Ⓕ CDC5 55527-2 (72 minutes: ADD: 11/95). *The Elgar Cello Concerto is the same recording as the one reviewed under Elgar; refer to the Index.* ⒼⒼⒼ

...Cello Concerto. *Coupled with works by various composers.* **János Starker** (vc); **Gerald Moore** (pf); **Philharmonia Orchestra / Carlo Maria Giulini, Walter Susskind**. EMI mono/stereo Ⓜ CZS5 68485-2* (six discs: 398 minutes: ADD: 12/95). *See review in the Collections section; refer to the Index.*

...Cello Concerto[a]. Symphony No. 9 in E minor, B178, "From the New World". [a]**Pablo Casals** (vc); **Czech Philharmonic Orchestra / George Szell**. Dutton Laboratories Essential Archive mono Ⓑ CDEA5002* (74 minutes: ADD: 1/96). Ⓖ

...Cello Concerto. **Herbert** Cello Concerto No. 2 in E minor, Op. 30. **Yo-Yo Ma** (vc); **New York Philharmonic Orchestra / Kurt Masur**. Sony Classical Ⓕ SK67173 (61 minutes: DDD: 4/96).

Dvořák Cello Concerto in B minor, B191.
Tchaikovsky Variations on a Rococo Theme, Op. 33. **Mstislav Rostropovich** (vc); **Berlin Philharmonic Orchestra / Herbert von Karajan**. DG The Originals Ⓜ 447 413-2GOR (60 minutes: ADD: 5/95). From 139044 (10/69). Recorded 1968. *Gramophone classical 100.* ⒼⒼⒼ

This splendid disc offers a coupling that has justifiably held its place in the catalogue at full price (both on LP and CD) for nearly 30 years. The upper surface of the CD itself is made to look like a miniature reproduction of the original yellow label LP – complete with light reflecting off the simulated black vinyl surface. As can be seen from the above, there have been a number of outstanding recordings of the Dvořák Concerto since this DG record was made, but none to match it for the warmth of lyrical feeling, the sheer strength of personality of the cello playing and the distinction of the partnership between Karajan and Rostropovich. Any moments of romantic licence from the latter, who is obviously deeply in love with the music, are set against Karajan's overall grip on the proceedings. The orchestral playing is superb. You have only to listen to the beautiful introduction of the secondary theme of the first movement by the Principal Horn to realize that the Berlin Philharmonic are going to match their illustrious soloist in eloquence, while Rostropovich's many moments of poetic introspection never for a moment interfere with the sense of a spontaneous forward flow. The recording from 1969 is as near perfect as any made by DG in that vintage analogue era. The CD transfer has freshened the original and gives the cello a highly realistic presence, and if the passionate *fortissimo* violins lose just a fraction in fullness, and there seems to be, comparably, just a slight loss of resonance in the bass, the sound picture has an impressively clear and vivid focus. In the coupled Tchaikovsky *Rococo* Variations, Rostropovich uses the published score rather than the original version. However, he plays with such a masterly combination of Russian fervour and elegance that any criticism is disarmed. The music itself continually demonstrates Tchaikovsky's astonishing lyrical fecundity, as one tune leads to another, all growing organically from the charming 'rococo' theme. The recording here is marvellously refined and the illusion of the artists sitting out beyond one's speakers is very real indeed. The description 'legendary' is not a whit too strong for a mid-price reissue of this calibre.

Dvořák Violin Concerto in A minor, Op. 53.
Bruch Violin Concerto No. 1 in G minor, Op. 26. **Tasmin Little** (vn); **Royal Liverpool Philharmonic Orchestra / Vernon Handley.** Classics for Pleasure ⑧ CD-CFP4566 (60 minutes: DDD: 7/90). Recorded 1989.

This rare coupling of Dvořák and Bruch from Tasmin Little, Vernon Handley and the Royal Liverpool Philharmonic delivers performances of a positive assurance to stand comparison with any. In quality of recording as well as artistry this is in every way a match for full-price rival recordings, with on balance the best sound of all. Little brings to Dvořák an open freshness and sweetness, very apt for this composer, that is equally winning. The firm richness of her sound, totally secure on intonation up to the topmost register, goes with an unflustered ease of manner, bringing little or no spotlighting of the soloist. She establishes her place firmly with sound that co-ordinates the soloist along with the orchestra. She is particularly successful in the finale and plays the syncopations of the dance-like main theme with a happy lilt. In the Bruch the movement where Little's individuality comes out most clearly is the central *Adagio*, raptly done, with a deceptive simplicity of phrasing; totally unselfconscious, matching the purity of her sound. Her speeds in the outer movements are broad and although the finale may not have quite the thrusting excitement of some of her rivals, the clarity and precision of her playing are fair compensation, along with the fuller, more faithful sound. At full price this would be highly recommended; at Classic for Pleasure's modest price it is a quite outstanding bargain.

Additional recommendations ...

...Violin Concerto[a]. **Sibelius** Violin Concerto in D minor, Op. 47[b]. **Salvatore Accardo** (vn); [a]**Concertgebouw Orchestra;** [b]**London Symphony Orchestra / Sir Colin Davis.** Philips Silver Line ⓜ 420 895-2PSL (68 minutes: ADD: 10/88).

...Violin Concerto. **Suk** Fantasy, Op. 24. **Josef Suk** (vn); **Czech Philharmonic Orchestra / Karel Ančerl.** Supraphon Crystal Collection ⑧ 11 0601-2 (56 minutes: ADD: 9/89).

...Violin Concerto. **Glazunov** Violin Concerto in A minor, Op. 83. **Frank Peter Zimmermann** (vn); **London Philharmonic Orchestra / Franz Welser-Möst.** EMI ⑥ CDC7 54872-2 (52 minutes: DDD: 3/94).

...Romance, B39[a]. Ten Legends, B122. Nocturne in B major, B47. [a]**Stephanie Gonley** (vn); **English Chamber Orchestra / Sir Charles Mackerras.** EMI Eminence ⓜ CD-EMX2232 (57 minutes: DDD: 3/95).

...Violin Concerto. Romance, B39. **Glazunov** Violin Concerto in A minor, Op. 82. **Ilya Kaler** (vn); **Polish National Radio Symphony Orchestra / Camilla Kolchinsky.** Naxos ⑨ 8 550758 (63 minutes: DDD: 4/95).

...Violin Concerto[a]. Symphony No. 9 in E minor, B178, "From the New World". **Smetana** The bartered bride – Overture. [a]**Josef Suk** (vn); **Czech Philharmonic Orchestra / Karel Ančerl.** Orfeo Festspiel Dokumente mono ⑥ C395951B* (78 minutes: ADD: 4/96).

...Romance B39. *Coupled with works by various composers.* **Gil Shaham** (vn); **Orpheus Chamber Orchestra.** DG ⑥ 449 923-2GH (58 minutes: DDD: 3/97).

Dvořák Czech Suite, B93. Festival March, B88. The Hero's Song, B199. Hussite, B132. **Polish National Radio Symphony Orchestra / Antoni Wit.** Naxos ⑨ 8 553005 (65 minutes: DDD: 8/95). Recorded 1993-94.

Wit's achievement, especially in the case of *The Hero's Song*, is considerable. This colourful, rather sprawling tone-poem was Dvořák's last orchestral work and is not an easy piece to bring off. Wit finds genuine nobility in it, while his gentle, mellow way with the lovely *Czech Suite* also gives much pleasure. The opening "Praeludium" is just a touch sleepy, but there is no want of lyrical affection or rhythmic bounce elsewhere and the whole performance radiates an idiomatic, old-world charm that really is most appealing. As for the *Hussite* overture, Wit's clear-headed reading impressively combines dignity and excitement. Given such finely disciplined orchestral playing, the results are once again both eloquent and characterful. All of which just leaves the rousing *Festival March* of 1879, splendidly done here, with the excellent Katowice brass sounding quite resplendent in their introductory call-to-arms. Recordings throughout possess a most agreeable bloom and transparency.

Dvořák Overtures and Symphonic Poems – My home, B125a[a]. Hussite, B132[b]. In nature's realm, B168[b]. Carnival, B169[b]. Othello, B174[b]. The water goblin, B195[c]. The noon witch, B196[c]. The golden spinning-wheel, B197[d]. The wild dove, B198[d]. Symphonic Variations, B70[c]. **Bavarian Radio Symphony Orchestra / Rafael Kubelík.** DG Galleria ⓜ 435 074-2GGA2 (two discs: 157 minutes: ADD: 11/91). Items marked [a] from 2530 593 (12/75), [b]2530 785 (2/78), [c]2530 712 (11/76), [d]2530 713 (11/76). Recorded 1973-76. ⓖⓖⓖ

Writing about Richard Strauss's *Don Juan*, Tovey remarked that "programme music ... either coheres as music or it does not". Perhaps Dvořák's symphonic poems have never attained the popularity of those by Richard Strauss because there are a few too many seams in his musical narrative. Equally, the gruesome local folk ballads on which they are based (and which Dvořák gleefully brings to life) afforded him less range for depth of human characterization. But there are lots of good reasons to value them. There's his inimitable stream of heart-easing melody, and alongside the obvious debt to Liszt and Wagner, their harmonic boldness and magical instrumental effects look forward to Suk,

Martinů and Janáček. Indeed, in the central section of *The golden spinning-wheel*, where the wheel and assorted paraphernalia are offered to the false queen in return for the various dismembered portions of the heroine's body, the repeated patterns on muted strings sound like pure Janáček. And the exquisite closing pages of *The wild dove* could be the best thing Martinů ever wrote. Also written when Dvořák was at the height of his power (in the 1890s), these two mid-priced discs offer the chance to hear his three concert overtures – *In nature's realm, Carnival* and *Othello* – as he originally conceived them: a thematically linked three movement 'symphonic' work on the theme of nature, life and love. The earlier and no less worthy *Symphonic Variations* and *My home* and *Hussite* overtures complete a set that would be fine value in terms of minutes for your money even if the performances were mediocre. As it is you won't find a finer account at any price. Knowing when to keep this music on the move is the secret of Kubelík's success, but the mobility is always marked by freshness of spirit rather than plain drive. The whole set is informed with his burning belief in the value of the music and his experience in drawing precisely what he wants from his own Bavarian players. DG's mid-1970s recordings project this with clarity and coherence and need fear nothing from more recent digital contenders.

Additional recommendations ...

...In Nature's Realm. Carnival. Othello. Scherzo capriccioso. **Ulster Orchestra / Vernon Handley.**
   Chandos Ⓕ CHAN8453 (53 minutes: DDD: 7/86).
...The water goblin. Piano Concerto in G minor, B63[a]. [a]**Jenö Jandó** (pf); **Polish National Radio
   Symphony Orchestra / Antoni Wit.** Naxos Ⓢ 8 550896 (62 minutes: DDD: 12/94).

Dvořák Slavonic Dances, B83 and B147. **Vienna Philharmonic Orchestra / André Previn.**
   Philips Ⓕ 442 125-2PH (71 minutes: DDD: 10/94). Recorded 1993.   Ⓐ
Dvořák Slavonic Dances, B83 and B147. **Russian National Orchestra / Mikhail Pletnev.**
   DG Ⓕ 447 056-2GH (72 minutes: DDD: 11/95). *Selected by Soundings.*
Previn, with his rhythmic flair, brings out the playfulness of the *Slavonic Dances* as few others do. One is regularly reminded of the proximity of Dvořák's Bohemia to Vienna, when in the warm Musikverein acoustic, these dances become first cousins to the waltzes and polkas of the Strauss family. Previn also brings out more than his rivals the many warm cello descants which normally go unnoticed, but which here surge up in rich, yet transparent, textures. The energetic dances, too, regularly bring a rush of adrenalin at the climaxes, such as one gets from this orchestra every New Year's Day. In their different ways Szell and Dohnányi, both with the Cleveland Orchestra on peak form) are fiercer than Previn in such *Furiant* dances as Nos. 1 and 8, with their respective recordings adding weight of sound. Yet helped by the acoustic, Previn has more light and shade, and sounds just as easily idiomatic, if anything more so than Dohnányi, for whom the Cleveland Orchestra respond almost too precisely. Though Dohnányi's *allegros* and *prestos* are generally a shade brisker than Previn's, it is the reverse with the slower tempos, where Previn keeps the music flowing more, so that the *Lento grazioso* of the final dance, No. 8 in A flat of the second group, keeps its dance overtones.
   Though Pletnev has Slavonic musicians, the results are not quite traditionally Czech, with refinement and crispness of ensemble the keynotes rather than earthier qualities. His is a distinctive and highly enjoyable version of Dvořák's colourful dances. These are, after all, works which for all their lack of pretension are open to all kinds of subtleties of interpretation, with different views totally valid. At times with such refined playing one might even dub Pletnev's approach as Mozartian, with elegance a regular element, and with even the wildest *furiants* kept under control. The crispness of ensemble and clarity of texture give a sharpness of focus that avoids any idea that these are performances lacking in bite, though after the Previn one might well feel they are on the cool side, with the extrovert joy of the music rather underplayed. So the Dumka lament of the second dance is lighter and cooler than with Previn, charming rather than warmly expressive. Dynamic contrasts are sharply defined through all the dances, and Pletnev and his Russian players consistently make one marvel at the beauty of the instrumentation. Like the Previn version, but in a totally different way, this is a disc to give a fresh view of well-loved music.

Additional recommendations ...

...Slavonic Dances, B78 and B145. **Artur Balsam, Gena Raps** (pf, four hands).
   Arabesque Ⓕ Z6559 (63 minutes: DDD: 3/87).
...Slavonic Dances, B83 and B147. **Rheineland-Pfalz State Philharmonic Orchestra / Leif Segerstam.**
   BIS Ⓕ CD425 (78 minutes: DDD: 7/89).
...Slavonic Dances, B83 and B147. **Cleveland Orchestra / Christoph von Dohnányi.**
   Decca Ⓕ 430 171-2DH (74 minutes: DDD: 12/90).
...Slavonic Dances, B83 and B147. Carnival – Overture, B169. **Czech Philharmonic Orchestra /
   Václav Talich.** Slavonic Dances. **Czech Philharmonic Orchestra / Václav Talich.**
   Music and Arts mono Ⓕ CD658* (75 minutes: AAD: 6/92).
...Slavonic Dance, B147 (arr. Clements). Serenade in D minor, B77. *Coupled with works by*
   Krommer and **Mysliveček** New York Harmonie Ensemble / Steven Richman.
   Music and Arts Ⓕ CD691 (59 minutes: DDD: 8/92).
...Slavonic Dances, B83 and B147. **Cleveland Orchestra / George Szell.**
   Sony Classical Essential Classics Ⓑ SBK48161 (74 minutes: ADD: 11/92).
...Slavonic Dances, B83 and B147. **Berlin Radio Symphony Orchestra / Karel Ančerl.**
   Tahra mono Ⓕ TAH118* (70 minutes: DDD: 11/95).

Dvořák Complete Symphonies and Orchestral Works. **London Symphony Orchestra /
István Kertész.** Decca Ⓑ 430 046-2DC6 (six discs: 431 minutes: ADD: 4/92). Recorded 1963-66.
Symphonies – No. 1 in C minor, B9, "The Bells of Zlonice" (from SXL6288, 10/67); No. 2 in
B flat major, B12 (SXL6289, 9/67); No. 3 in E flat major, B34 (SXL6290, 5/67); No. 4 in
D minor, B41 (SXL6257, 4/67); No. 5 in F major, B54 (SXL6273, 3/67); No. 6 in D major, B112
(SXL6253, 11/66); No. 7 in D minor, B141; No. 8 in G major, B163 (SXL6044, 7/63); No. 9 in
E minor, B178, "From the New World" (SXL6291, 11/67). Scherzo capriccioso, B131 (SXL6348,
7/63). Overtures – In nature's realm, B168 (SXL6290, 5/67); Carnival, B169 (SXL6253, 11/66);
My home, B125a (SXL6273, 3/67).   ⒼⒼ
István Kertész recorded the Dvořák symphonies during the mid-1960s and his integral cycle was
quick to achieve classic status, with his exhilarating and vital account of the Eighth Symphony (the
first to be recorded in February 1963) rapidly becoming a special landmark in the catalogue. The
original LPs, with their distinctive Breughel reproduction sleeves are now collectors' items in their
own right, but these magnificent interpretations became available again in 1992, in glitteringly refined
digitally remastered sound, and it is a tribute to the memory of this tragically short-lived conductor
that this cycle continues to set the standard by which all others are judged. Kertész was the first
conductor to attract serious collectors to the early Dvořák symphonies which, even today are not
performed as often as they should be; and his jubilant advocacy of the unfamiliar First Symphony,
composed in the composer's twenty-fourth year, has never been superseded. This work offers
surprising insights into the development of Dvořák's mature style, as does the Second Symphony.
Kertész shows that Symphonies Nos. 3 and 4 have much more earthy resilience than many
commentators might have us believe, insisting that Dvořák's preoccupation with the music of Wagner
and Liszt had reached its zenith during this period. The challenging rhetoric of the Fourth has never
found a more glorious resolution than here, with Kertész drawing playing of gripping intensity from
the London Symphony Orchestra. The Fifth Symphony, and to a still greater extent, its glorious
successor, Symphony No. 6, both reveal Dvořák's clear affinity with the music of Brahms. Kertész's
superb reading of the Sixth, however, shows just how individual and naturally expressive this
underrated work actually is, whilst the playing in the great climax of the opening movement and the
vigorous final peroration remains tremendously exciting, even almost 30 years after the recording first
appeared. In the great final trilogy, Kertész triumphs nobly with the craggy resilience of the Seventh
Symphony, and his buoyant ardour brings a dynamic thrust and momentum to the Eighth Symphony,
whereas his *New World* is by turns indomitable and searchingly lyrical. The six-disc set also offers
assertive and brilliant readings of the Overtures *Carnival*, *In nature's realm* and the rarely heard *My
home*, together with a lucid and heroic account of the *Scherzo capriccioso*. These definitive
performances have been skilfully reprocessed, the sound is astonishingly good, even by modern
standards, and the playing of the London Symphony Orchestra is often daringly brilliant under the
charismatic direction of one of this century's late-lamented masters of the podium.

Additional recommendations ...
…Nos. 1-9. **Royal Scottish Orchestra / Vernon Handley.**
  Chandos Ⓜ CHAN9008/13 (six discs: 378 minutes: DDD).
…No. 6. My home. Hussite. Carnival. **Czech Philharmonic Orchestra / Karel Ančerl.**
  Supraphon Ⓕ 11 1926-2 (75 minutes: ADD).   Ⓖ
…No. 3. Carnival. Symphonic Variations. **Scottish National Orchestra / Neeme Järvi.**
  Chandos Ⓕ CHAN8575 (63 minutes: DDD: 5/88).
…No. 2. Slavonic Rhapsody No. 3 in A flat major, B86. **Scottish National Orchestra / Neeme Järvi.**
  Chandos Ⓕ CHAN8589 (61 minutes: DDD: 7/88).
…Nos. 1-9[a]. Scherzo capriccioso[b]. Carnival[b]. The wild dove[b]. [a]**Berlin Philharmonic Orchestra;**
  [b]**Bavarian Radio Symphony Orchestra / Rafael Kubelík.**
  DG Ⓜ 423 120-2GX6 (six discs: 425 minutes: ADD: 10/88).   ⒼⒼ
…No. 4. Ten Biblical Songs, B185[a]. [a]**Brian Rayner Cook** (bar); **Scottish National Orchestra /
  Neeme Järvi.** Chandos Ⓕ CHAN8608 (68 minutes: DDD: 12/88).
…No. 1. The Hero's Song, B199. **Scottish National Orchestra / Neeme Järvi.**
  Chandos Ⓕ CHAN8597 (74 minutes: DDD: 4/89).
…No. 6. **Suk** Serenade in E flat major, Op. 6. **Czech Philharmonic Orchestra / Václav Talich.**
  Koch Legacy mono Ⓕ 37060-2* (72 minutes: AAD: 1/92).   Ⓖ
…No. 6. The wild dove. **Czech Philharmonic Orchestra / Jiří Bělohlávek.**
  Chandos Ⓕ CHAN9170 (63 minutes: DDD: 11/93).
…Nos. 1-3. **London Symphony Orchestra / Witold Rowicki.**
  Philips Duo Ⓜ 446 527-2PM2 (two discs: 140 minutes: ADD: 3/96).
…Nos. 1-3. **Staatskapelle Berlin / Otmar Suitner.**
  Berlin Classics Ⓜ 0092 822BC (two discs: 121 minutes: ADD: 5/97).

Dvořák Symphonies – No. 3 in E flat major, B34; No. 7 in D minor, B141. **Vienna Philharmonic
Orchestra / Myung-Whun Chung.** DG Ⓕ 449 207-2GH (71 minutes: DDD: 5/97). Recorded 1995.
Gramophone Editor's choice.   Ⓖ
An impressive coupling. Myung-Whun Chung takes an affectionately fleet-of-foot view of the Third
Symphony. With the Vienna Philharmonic on their toes throughout (and audibly enjoying

themselves), Chung's reading is notable for its newly minted freshness and intelligent sense of proportion. So we find that the opening *Allegro moderato* emerges in shapely, sensitive fashion, yet with no lack of cumulative intensity at its close. In the ideally flowing slow movement Chung locates both dignity and drama. Again, phrasing is always imaginative and thoughtful, while the stately central processional has never sounded more luminously refined. The performance of the Seventh is an interpretation of red-blooded fervour and rugged contrasts, whose dramatic impact is greatly heightened by the burnished glow of the VPO's contribution, to say nothing of DG's enormously ripe, close-knit sound. In Chung's pungently characterful, ever flexible hands, the first movement progresses with pleasing dignity and purpose, nowhere more striking than in the coda where his decision not to press ahead too soon pays handsome dividends. Equally, Chung sees to it that the sublime second subject really takes wing both times round, the Viennese warmth and charm much in evidence. The succeeding *Poco adagio* is distinctive, possessing an almost Brucknerian hush and concentration. Whatever Chung's *Scherzo* slightly lacks in home-grown, idiomatic lilt, the arresting vigour and clean-limbed transparency of the playing provide fair compensation. What's more, the anxious Trio is voiced with unusual clarity, its many subtle details set in bold relief. The storm-tossed finale is magnificent, a conception of irresistible rigour and muscular conviction. Dvořák releases don't come much more stimulating than this.

Dvořák Symphony No. 5 in F major, B54. Othello, B174. Scherzo capriccioso, B131.
   Oslo Philharmonic Orchestra / Mariss Jansons. EMI Ⓕ CDC7 49995-2 (64 minutes: DDD: 7/90). Recorded 1989.

Of all the romantic composers, it is probably Dvořák who best evokes a sunlit, unspoiled and relatively untroubled picture of nineteenth-century country life. Light and warmth radiate from his Fifth Symphony, composed in just six weeks when he was in his early thirties. It has been called his "Pastoral Symphony", and it is easy to see why, especially in a performance as fresh and sunny as this one. Mariss Jansons brings out all the expressiveness and heart of the music without exaggerating the good spirits and playful humour that are so characteristic of the composer, and one would single out for praise the fine wind playing of the Oslo Philharmonic Orchestra (and not least its golden-toned horns) were it not for the fact that the strings are no less satisfying. The lyrical *Andante con moto* brings out the fine interplay of the instrumental writing, the bouncy *Scherzo* is uninhibited without going over the top and the exciting finale has plenty of momentum. The other two pieces are nicely done, the *Scherzo capriccioso* having both lilt and vigour and the rarely played *Othello* overture (a late work) being a suitably dramatic response to Shakespeare's tragedy. The recording is warm and clear.

Additional recommendations ...
...No. 5. The water goblin. **Scottish National Orchestra / Neeme Järvi.**
   Chandos Ⓕ CHAN8552 (61 minutes: DDD: 12/87). *Selected by Sounds in Retrospect.*
...No. 5. The noon witch. Scherzo capriccioso. **Czech Philharmonic Orchestra / Jiří Bělohlávek.**
   Chandos Ⓕ CHAN9475 (69 minutes: DDD: 2/97).

Dvořák Symphonies – No. 7 in D minor, B141; No. 8 in G major, B163. **Oslo Philharmonic Orchestra / Mariss Jansons.** EMI Ⓕ CDC7 54663-2 (74 minutes: DDD: 6/93). Recorded 1992.
   Gramophone Editor's choice. Ⓖ
Dvořák Symphonies – No. 7 in D minor, B141; No. 9 in E minor, B178, "From the New World".
   London Philharmonic Orchestra / Sir Charles Mackerras. EMI Eminence Ⓜ CD-EMX2202 (79 minutes: DDD: 2/93). Recorded 1991.

Mariss Jansons's popular pairing makes most agreeable listening. With clean-cut playing from the fine Oslo orchestra and natural, unexaggerated sonics, these are engagingly alive, refreshingly energetic readings, if not quite as warm-hearted or openly affectionate as some Dvořákians might like. Jansons's sophisticated sense of texture impresses throughout, however, and the outer movements of No. 8 in particular emerge with genuinely vivid freshness. Jansons's clean-heeled direction brings with it a certain endearing spontaneity and rhythmic resilience that will undoubtedly give pleasure. Sir Charles Mackerras's long-standing authority in the Czech repertoire is of course well known by now, so his thoughts are not to be dismissed lightly, especially when, at nearly 80 minutes, Nos. 7 and 9 make a terrifically generous pairing. In the tragic Seventh, Mackerras concentrates largely on the more endearingly lyrical side of Dvořák's invention; in this respect both inner movements are particularly memorable in their open-hearted grace and charm. However, those who (rightly) crave a greater degree of intensity and symphonic rigour in the two great flanking outer movements such as one encounters with rival interpreters will perhaps come away not quite so satisfied. Similarly, this *New World* is an affectingly unfussy traversal. The slow movement glows ravishingly at an exceptionally broad tempo, and in the finale Mackerras draws Dvořák's structural threads together with undemonstrative cogency. Overall, this is undoubtedly a fine account, if not quite as winningly spontaneous an experience as Kubelík's famous BPO recording for DG. With all that, Mackerras's are still warmly affectionate readings, superbly played and resplendently recorded.

Additional recommendations ...
...Nos. 7 and 8. **Czech Philharmonic Orchestra / Václav Talich.**
   Koch International Classics Legacy mono Ⓕ 37007-2* (ADD).
...Nos. 7 and 8. **Cleveland Orchestra / Christoph von Dohnányi.**
   Decca Ovation Ⓜ 430 728-2DM (73 minutes: DDD: 12/91).

...No. 8. Scherzo capriccioso. Legends, Op. 59 Nos. 4, 6 and 7. **Hallé Orchestra / Sir John Barbirolli.**
EMI Phoenixa Ⓜ CDM7 64193-2* (61 minutes: ADD: 6/92).   ⒼⒼ
...Nos. 7-9. Symphonic Variations, B70[a]. **Concertgebouw Orchestra; [a]London Symphony Orchestra /**
Sir Colin Davis. Philips Duo Ⓜ 438 347-2PM2 (two discs: 139 minutes: ADD: 8/93)
...Nos. 7 and 9. **Royal Concertgebouw Orchestra / Carlo Maria Giulini.**
Sony Classical Ⓜ SX2K58946 (two discs: 91 minutes: DDD: 11/94).
...No. 7[c]. Piano Concerto in G minor, B63[a]. Cello Concerto in B minor, B191[b]. Slavonic Dances,
B83 and B147[b] – No. 9 in B major; No. 16 in A flat major. [a]**František Maxián** (pf); [b]**Mstislav**
Rostropovich (vc); [b]**Toronto Symphony Orchestra;** [ac]**Hessian Radio Orchestra, Frankfurt,** [d]**Czech**
Philharmonic Orchestra / Karel Ančerl. Tahra Ⓕ TAH136/7 (two discs: 153 minutes: ADD: 3/96).
...Nos. 7 and 8. **Philharmonia Orchestra / Rafael Kubelík.**
Testament mono Ⓕ SBT1079* (75 minutes: ADD: 10/96).
...Nos. 7-9. Scherzo capriccioso. **Cleveland Orchestra / Christoph von Dohnányi.**
Double Decca Ⓜ 452 182-2DF2 (two discs: 127 minutes: DDD: 2/97).

Dvořák Symphony No. 8 in G major, B163. Symphonic Variations, B70. **London Philharmonic**
Orchestra / Sir Charles Mackerras. EMI Eminence Ⓜ CD-EMX2216 (60 minutes: DDD: 4/94).
Recorded 1992.   Ⓖ
This is an unmissable account of the Eighth Symphony. Mackerras realizes all the score's indications
of shading, pointing and phrasing, or to put it another way, all its elegance and bittersweet ambiguity.
In this, amongst the listed comparisons above, he has no peers. He has a spirited and willing LPO in
the palm of his guiding, illuminating hand. Articulation and emphases are consistently light, and not
only in the energetic tuttis. In the flute solo some 40 seconds into the first movement the LPO
principal, without disturbing the tranquillity of the scene, animates the solo to suggest bird-song (all
the solo and ensemble flute work on the Mackerras disc is outstanding). It is this wide range of
pictorial suggestion and emotion, and an orchestra audibly fired up by the occasion, that mark
Mackerras's performance of the Symphony as an example of great Dvořák conducting. Has anybody,
one wonders, made as much of the contrast between the joyous pealing of bells and fanfares that end
the first appearance of the slow movement's second subject, and the abrupt hush for its chorale-like
conclusion, as if the traveller has suddenly entered the dark interior of a church and encountered a
solemn procession. And revelation follows revelation: you can't fail to notice the tension as the *ppp*
strings prepare for the anguished transformation of the movement's opening theme. Mackerras
relaxes in the *Symphonic Variations* but keeps the work flowing along and gives as fine a performance
of this work as you are likely to hear. The Eminence sound for Mackerras (from London's Henry
Wood Hall), is immediate and lively, with a wider dynamic range.
Additional recommendations ...
...No. 8. The wild dove. **Royal Scottish National Orchestra / Neeme Järvi.**
Chandos Ⓕ CHAN8666 (DDD: 8/89).
...No. 8. **Janáček** Sinfonietta, Op. 60. **New York Philharmonic Orchestra / Kurt Masur.**
Teldec Ⓕ 4509-90847-2 (63 minutes: DDD: 12/94).
...No. 8. The noon witch. **Berlin Philharmonic Orchestra / Claudio Abbado.**
Sony Classical Ⓕ SK64303 (51 minutes: DDD: 2/95).
...No. 8. *Coupled with works by various composers.* **Concertgebouw Orchestra / Karel Ančerl.**
Tahra Ⓕ TAH124/5 (two discs: 116 minutes: ADD: 3/96).

Dvořák Symphonies – No. 8 in G major, B163; No. 9 in E minor, B178, "From the New World".
Berlin Philharmonic Orchestra / Rafael Kubelík. DG The Originals Ⓜ 447 412-2GOR
(73 minutes: ADD). From 2720 066 (10/73). Recorded 1972. *Gramophone classical 100.*   ⒼⒼⒼ
These accounts are quite magnificent and their claims on the allegiance of collectors remain strong.
They have the kind of freshness and vigour that remind one of what it was like to hear these
symphonies for the first time. The atmosphere is authentic in feeling and the sense of nature seems to
be uncommonly acute. Kubelík has captured the enthusiasm of his players here and generates a sense
of excitement and poetry. The playing of the Berlin Philharmonic is marvellously eloquent
throughout and, as is so often the case, a joy in itself. The woodwinds phrase with great poetic feeling
and imagination though, come to that, all the departments of this great orchestra respond with
sensitivity and virtuosity. The recording has great dynamic range and encompasses the most
featherweight string *pianissimos* to the fullest orchestral tutti without discomfort. The listener is
placed well back in the hall so that the woodwind, though they blend beautifully, may seem a little too
recessed for some tastes, though it should be said that there is no lack of vividness, power or impact.
The balance and the timbre of each instrument is natural and truthful; nothing is made larger than
life and Kubelík has a natural warmth and flexibility. In so competitive a market as these, it would be
wrong to speak of any single recording as a first choice but this will always remain high in any list of
recommendations for it has a vernal freshness that is wholly reviving.
Additional recommendation ...
...Nos. 7-9[a]. The wild dove[b]. **Smetana** Má vlast – Vltava, B111[c]. [a]**Berlin Philharmonic Orchestra,**
[b]**Bavarian Radio Symphony Orchestra;** [c]**Boston Symphony Orchestra / Rafael Kubelík.**
DG Double Ⓜ 439 663-2GX2 (two discs: 146 minutes: ADD). *These are the same recordings*
as those reviewed above.   ⒼⒼⒼ

Dvořák Symphony No. 9 in E minor, B178, "From the New World"[a]. American Suite[b].
[a]**Vienna Philharmonic Orchestra / Kyrill Kondrashin;** [b]**Royal Philharmonic Orchestra /
Antál Dorati.** Decca Ⓜ 430 702-2DM (63 minutes: DDD: 8/91). Item marked [a] from
SXDL7510 (7/80), [b]410 735-2DH2 (3/85). Recorded 1979-83.   ⒼⒼ
Kondrashin's *New World* caused something of a sensation when originally transferred to CD. Here
was a supreme example of the clear advantages of the new medium over the old and the metaphor of
a veil being drawn back between listener and performers could almost be extended to a curtain: the
impact and definition of the sound is really quite remarkable and the acoustics of the Sofiensaal in
Vienna are presented as ideal for this score. The upper strings have brilliance without edginess, the
brass – with characteristically bright VPO trumpets – has fine sonority as well as great presence, the
bass is firm, full and rich and the ambience brings luminosity and bloom to the woodwind without
clouding.
Additional recommendations ...
...No. 9. My home. **Royal Scottish National Orchestra / Neeme Järvi.**
Chandos Ⓕ CHAN8510 (DDD).
...No. 9. My home. In nature's realm. **Czech Philharmonic Orchestra / Karel Ančerl.**
Supraphon Great Artists Series Ⓕ 11 1242-2 (64 minutes: ADD).
...No. 9. Symphonic Variations. **London Philharmonic Orchestra / Zdenek Macal.**
Classics for Pleasure Ⓑ CD-CFP9006 (66 minutes: DDD: 9/87).
...No. 9. **Suk** Serenade in E major, Op. 6. **Czech Philharmonic Orchestra / Václav Talich.**
Supraphon Historical mono Ⓜ 11 1899-2* (71 minutes: AAD: 2/94).

Dvořák Piano Quintet in A major, B155[a]. String Quintet in G major, B49[b]. **Gaudier Ensemble**
(Marieke Blankestijn, Lesley Hatfield, vns; Iris Juda, va; Christoph Marks, vc; [b]Stephen William,
db; [a]Susan Tomes, pf). Hyperion Ⓕ CDA66796 (66 minutes: DDD: 4/96). Recorded 1995.   ⒼⒼ
The Piano Quintet has received a high-powered performance from Menahem Pressler and the
Emerson Quartet. The pianist on the Gaudier's disc is Susan Tomes, who matches even Pressler in
imagination, encouraging a performance lighter than that for DG, full of mercurial contrasts that
seem entirely apt. For example, in the second movement *Dumka* there is more light and shade, and the
Scherzo sparkles even more, leading to a jaunty, exuberant finale. The G major String Quintet, the
earliest of the two which Dvořák wrote, the one with extra double-bass, is similarly lighter than the
Chilingirian Quartet. The Chilingirian is just as strongly characterized as the Gaudier, with a firmer,
fuller tone. Marieke Blankestijn's violin is thinner than Levon Chilingirian's, but it can be just as
beautiful, as in the lovely high-floating second subject of the slow movement. Altogether a fine disc,
if this coupling appeals.
Additional recommendation ...
...String Quintet. Serenade in D minor, B77. **Linos Ensemble.**
Capriccio Ⓕ 10 559 (65 minutes: DDD: 4/98).

Dvořák Piano Quintet in A major, B155[a]. Piano Quartet No. 2 in E flat major, B162.
Menahem Pressler (pf); **Emerson Quartet** (Eugene Drucker, [a]Philip Setzer, vns; Lawrence Dutton,
va; David Finckel, vc). DG Ⓕ 439 868-2GH (75 minutes: DDD: 9/94). Recorded 1993.   ⒼⒼ
If the Piano Quintet, with its wealth of memorable melody, is by far the better-known, Pressler and
the Emersons demonstrate how the Piano Quartet, sketched immediately after the other work and
completed two years later in 1889, is just as rich in invention, in some ways even more distinctive in
its thematic material. If there is one movement that above all proves a revelation, it is the *Lento* of the
Quartet. Opening with a duet for cello and piano, it is here played with a rapt, hushed concentration
to put it among the very finest of Dvořák inspirations. The following *grazioso* movement, almost like
a Viennese waltz, is then given a delicious schmaltzy flavour, with one whole-tone motif particularly
striking, not to mention another passage where the piano is made to sound like a musical-box. The
performance of the Quintet, too, is comparably positive in its characterization. Many will prefer the
easier, even warmer reading from Domus in the Piano Quartet (see below), which is neatly if not so
generously coupled with the much earlier Piano Quartet in D, B53. In this music it is not always the
high-powered reading that makes its mark most persuasively, and the Hyperion sound for Domus is
far warmer than the DG New York recording for this disc, which gives an unpleasant edge to
high violins, making the full ensemble rather abrasive. None the less, if the volume is curbed,
one can readily enjoy these passionate and intense accounts of two of Dvořák's most striking
chamber works.
Additional recommendations ...
...Piano Quintets – A major, B28; B155. **Rudolf Firkušný** (pf); **Ridge Quartet.**
RCA Victor Red Seal Ⓕ RD60436 (67 minutes: DDD: 7/92).
...Piano Quartets – No. 1 in D major, B53; No. 2. **Domus.**
Hyperion Ⓕ CDA66287 (70 minutes: DDD: 3/89).   Ⓖ
...Piano Quintet, B155. **Martinů** Piano Quintet No. 2. **Peter Frankl** (pf); **Lindsay Quartet.**
ASV Ⓕ CDDCA889 (70 minutes: DDD: 6/94).   Ⓖ
...Piano Quintet, B155[a]. String Quartet No. 9 in D minor, B75. [a]**Karl Engel** (pf); **Melos Quartet.**
Harmonia Mundi Ⓕ HMC90 1510 (72 minutes: DDD: 6/97).

Dvořák String Quintets – G major, B49[a]; E flat major, B180[b]. Intermezzo in B major, B49[c].
Chilingirian Quartet (Levon Chilingirian, Mark Butler, vns; Louise Williams, va;
Philip De Groote, vc); [b]**Simon Rowland-Jones** (va); [ac]**Duncan McTier** (db).
Chandos Ⓕ CHAN9046 (69 minutes: DDD: 11/92). Recorded 1990-91.

Dvořák's G major String Quintet is a thoroughly engaging affair. Originally in five movements, Dvořák subsequently removed the "Intermezzo" second movement, revising and publishing it separately eight years later as the haunting *Nocturne* for string orchestra. Enterprisingly, this Chandos disc includes that "Intermezzo" in its original string quintet garb. The E flat Quintet from 1893, on the other hand, is a wholly mature masterpiece. Completed in just over two months during Dvořák's American sojourn, it replaces the double-bass of the earlier Quintet with the infinitely more subtle option of a second viola. Brimful of the most delightfully fresh, tuneful invention, the score also shares many melodic and harmonic traits with the popular *American* Quartet – its immediate predecessor. The Chilingirian Quartet, ideally abetted by double-bassist Duncan McTier and violist Simon Rowland-Jones, are enthusiastic, big-hearted proponents of all this lovely material, and the excellent Chandos recording offers both a realistic perspective and beguiling warmth.

Additional recommendations ...
...String Quintet, B180. String Sextet in A major, B80. **Raphael Ensemble.**
  Hyperion Ⓕ CDA66308 (65 minutes: DDD: 8/89).
...String Quintet, B180. String Sextet, B80. **Josef Suk** (va); **Josef Chuchro** (vc); **Smetana Quartet.**
  Supraphon Ⓕ 11 1469-2 (68 minutes: DDD: 9/93).
...String Quintet, B180[a]. Terzetto. Bagatelles. [a]**Patrick Ireland** (va); **Lindsay Quartet.**
  ASV Ⓕ CDDCA806 (69 minutes: DDD: 9/93).
...String Quintet, B180[a]. Intermezzo[a]. String Sextet, B80[b]. **Panocha Quartet;** [b]**Josef Klusoň** (va);
  [b]**Michal Kaňka** (vc); [a]**Pavel Nejtek** (db). Supraphon Ⓕ 11 1461-2 (71 minutes: DDD: 5/94). **Ⓖ**
... String Quintet, B180. String Sextet, B80.**Vienna String Sextet.** EMI Ⓕ CDC7 54543-2
  (67 minutes: DDD: 10/94).
...String Quintet, B49. Serenade in D minor, B77. **Chamber Music Society of the Lincoln Center /
  David Shifrin.** Delos Ⓕ DE3152 (66 minutes: DDD: 8/95).

Dvořák String Quartets – No. 1 in A major, B8[a]; No. 2 in B flat major, B17[a]; No. 3 in D major, B18[a];
No. 4 in E minor, B19[a]; No. 5 in F minor, B37[a]; No. 6 in A minor, B40[a]; No. 7 in A minor, B45[a];
No. 8 in E major, B57[b]; No. 9 in D minor, B75[a]; No. 10 in E flat major, B92[b]; No. 11 in C major,
B121[a]; No. 12 in F major, B179, "American"[c]; No. 13 in G major, B192[d]; No. 14 in A flat major,
B193[c]; F major, B120 (Fragment)[a]. Cypresses, B152[a]. Quartettsatz[a]. Two Waltzes, B105[a].
Prague Quartet (Břetislav Novotny, Karel Přibyl, vns; Lubomír Malý, va; Jan Sírc, vc).
DG Ⓑ 429 193-2GCM9 (nine discs: 589 minutes: ADD: 8/90). Items marked [a] from
2740 177 (12/77), [b]2350 719 (11/76), [c]2350 632 (4/76), [d]2350 480 (4/75). **ⒼⒼⒼ**

Like Schubert, Dvořák turned to the string quartet early in his career, but in neither case is that a cue for lyrical flights on the subject of 'lifelong affinities'. Both had one sound practical reason for choosing this medium at the start of their careers: it was relatively easy to get quartet music played. The three complete quartets included in Vol. 1 (Nos. 1-3) show considerable facility in writing for strings (after all, Dvořák was a violinist), but it took him some time to arrive at a fully idiomatic quartet style: the first movement of No. 2 for instance wouldn't lose much by being orchestrated. Dvořák also had to learn to rein in his natural expansiveness: the Third Quartet spins out its modest material to an astonishing 70 minutes – the first movement alone is longer than the whole American Quartet! The outer movements of the No. 4 in E minor (Vol. 2) show him concentrating admirably, though the later shortened version of the central *Andante religioso* is a considerable improvement. So the interest of Vol. 1 (three discs) is largely musicological. Despite this, with playing so fresh and authoritative even the impossibly long-winded Third Quartet has rewards to offer. The Prague Quartet had played all these works in concert before making their recordings – it certainly sounds as though they have. Each performance has a strong sense of purpose, but that doesn't mean an inability to enjoy all those charming Dvořákian byways. Sometimes it's rather like being taken on a tour of a rich, fertile landscape by someone who knows and loves every tiny detail. Technically the playing is admirable, though you may be surprised at the scrunch at the climax of No. 1's slow movement – very untypical.

Nevertheless, the enjoyment increases strongly through Vol. 2. The violin cavatina in the *Andante* of the Fifth Quartet (disc 4, track 5) has just the right gentle lilt – recommended to the unconverted. Listening to the Prague in the fine first movement of No. 7 one realizes how what looks on the page like very simple music can come glowingly to life in the right hands – and the way they handle the slightly tricky *poco più mosso* at the second subject is very impressive. The finest work in Vol. 2 (discs 4-6) is undoubtedly the D minor Quartet, No. 9. According to Paul Griffiths in *The String Quartet* (Thames and Hudson: 1983) it was "written to impress Brahms"; it will certainly impress you. The Prague Quartet could perhaps have put a little more passion into the finale, but the performance as a whole has the combination of naturalness and concentration that characterizes almost everything in this set. Vol. 3 contains three gems: the E flat Quartet (No. 10), the *American* and No. 13 in G major – the outstanding work of the collection. The Prague are very sensitive to dynamic contrast (Dvořák's markings are often surprisingly detailed). Another good sample extract might be the opening of the G major's slow movement (disc 8, track 6); strong, intense playing here, and fine command of long phrasing – and what marvellous music! So don't let the size of this set put you off. There's plenty of fine music on these nine well-filled discs, all of it more than well performed. Recordings too are generally creditable – though the cello's sudden step backstage at the end of No. 4's *Andante* is perplexing; surely those elaborate runs should be the centre of attention? A minor detail. Buy and enjoy – only make sure you leave Vol. 1 until you've heard what Dvořák can really do.

Additional recommendations ...

...No. 12. Cypresses, B152 – No. 1. **Kodály** String Quartet No. 2, Op. 10. **Hagen Quartet.**
DG 419 601-2GH (DDD: 5/87).
...No. 12. **Schubert** String Quartet No. 14 in D minor, D810, "Death and the Maiden".
Borodin String Quartet No. 2 in D major – Notturno. **Quartetto Italiano.**
Philips Silver Line ⓜ 420 876-2PSL (75 minutes: ADD: 3/89).
...No. 12. *Coupled with works by* **Barber** *and* **Glass** Duke Quartet.
Collins Classics Ⓕ 1386-2 (61 minutes: DDD: 1/94).   Ⓖ
...No. 12. Piano Quintet in A major, B155ᵃ. **Janáček** String Quartet No. 1, "The Kreutzer
Sonata". ᵃ**Pavel Štěpán** (pf); **Smetana Quartet.** Testament Ⓕ SBT1074 (79 minutes: ADD: 3/96).
See review in the Collections section; refer to the Index.   ⒼⒼ
...No. 14. Terzetto in C major, B148. **Janáček** String Quartet No. 2, "Intimate Letters".
Smetana Quartet. Testament Ⓕ SBT1075 (77 minutes: ADD: 3/96). *See review in the Collections
section; refer to the Index.*   ⒼⒼ
...No. 12. *Coupled with works by* **Kodály** *and* **Smetana** Hollywood Quartet.
Testament Ⓕ SBT1072* (68 minutes: ADD/DDD: 5/96).
...Nos. 12 and 13. **Vlach Quartet, Prague.** Naxos Ⓢ 8 553371 (69 minutes: DDD: 4/96).
...Nos. 8 and 11. **Vlach Quartet, Prague.** Naxos Ⓢ 8 553372 (68 minutes: DDD: 9/96).
...No. 9ᵃ. Terzetto in C major, B148. **Vlach Quartet Prague.**
Naxos Ⓢ 8 553373 (59 minutes: DDD: 3/97).
...Nos. 10 and 14. **Vlach Quartet Prague.** Naxos Ⓢ 8 553374 (68 minutes: DDD: 6/97).

Dvořák String Quartets – No. 12 in F major, B179, "American"; No. 13 in G major, B192.
Vlach Quartet, Prague (Jana Vlachová, Ondřej Kukal, vns; Petr Verner, va; Mikael Ericsson, vc).
Naxos Ⓢ 8 553371 (69 minutes: DDD: 4/96).
On the face of it, the credentials of the Vlach Quartet of Prague would seem to be impeccable – the group's leader, Jana Vlachová, is the daughter of the great Josef Vlach – and, indeed, the players make a most pleasing impression on this vividly recorded Naxos coupling. They certainly produce a beguilingly rich, beautifully blended sound and bring to this music a big-hearted, songful fervour as well as textural mastery. What is more, Dvořák's characteristic, chugging cross-rhythms are handled with particular felicity. Interpretatively, their approach contrasts strongly with other readings in that the Vlach team adopt a coaxing, lyrically expressive stance (with the gorgeous slow movement of the *American* a highlight). In the case of the masterly G major Quartet, these gifted newcomers show fresh insights (they are especially perceptive in those wistful reminiscences at the heart of the finale).

Dvořák Piano Trios – No. 1 in B flat major, B51; No. 2 in G minor, B56. **Borodin Trio**
(Rotislav Dubinsky, vn; Yuli Turovsky, vc; Luba Edlina, pf). Chandos Ⓕ CHAN9172
(75 minutes: DDD: 11/93). Recorded 1992.   Ⓖ
Of Dvořák's six piano trios, only four survive, and only two are at all familiar to most listeners. These here are the other two, written in 1875 and 1876 when he was in his mid-thirties. They are delightful works, even if they cannot match the quality of the F minor Trio and the *Dumky*; and are given splendid advocacy by the Borodin Trio, who sense their quality while not overstating claims. That is to say, the players do not try to milk the fine slow movements for more emotion than they actually contain, and by playing them with sensitivity and a light touch manage to draw the most from them. The two scherzos are similarly given a lively spring but not any kind of forced hilarity: they are in fact quite gentle movements. Luba Edlina opens the B flat Trio with a beautifully delicate exposition of the melody arpeggiated in a manner instantly recognizable as by Dvořák.

Dvořák Piano Trios – No. 3 in F minor, B130; No. 4 in E minor, B166, "Dumky". **Florestan Trio**
(Anthony Marwood, vn; Richard Lester, vc; Susan Tomes, pf). Hyperion Ⓕ CDA66895
(68 minutes: DDD: 1/97). *Gramophone Editor's choice.*   Ⓖ
A favourite and appropriate pairing – Dvořák's most passionate chamber work in harness with one of his most genial. The F minor Piano Trio (1883) was contemporaneous with the death of Dvořák's mother; it anticipates something of the storm and stress that characterizes the great D minor Seventh Symphony (1884-5) and the Florestan Trio serve it well. All three players allow themselves plenty of expressive leeway and yet the musical line is neither distorted nor stretched too far. The second movement *Allegretto* is truly *grazioso* and the qualifying *meno mosso* perfectly judged. The finale is buoyant rather than especially rustic, whereas the more overtly colourful *Dumky* Trio inspires a sense of play and a vivid suggestion of local colour – 2'45" into the third movement, for example, or 1'25" into the fourth. Throughout the performance, the manifest 'song and dance' elements of the score (heartfelt melodies alternating with folk-style faster music) are keenly projected. The recordings are first-rate, as are the insert-notes. If you're after a subtle, musically perceptive coupling of these two works, then you could hardly do better.

Additional recommendations ...
...No. 4. **Smetana** Piano Trio in G minor, B104. **Rostislav Dubinsky** (vn); **Yuli Turovsky** (vc); **Luba Edlina** (pf). Chandos Ⓕ CHAN8445 (68 minutes: DDD: 5/86).
...Nos. 1-4. Romantic Pieces, B150. **Cohen Trio.**
CRD Ⓕ CRD3386/7 (two discs: 153 minutes: ADD: 10/97).

Dvořák Violin Sonata in F major, B106. Sonatina for Violin and Piano in G major, B183. Four Romantic Pieces, B150. **Gil Shaham** (vn); **Orli Shaham** (pf). DG Ⓕ 449 820-2GH (52 minutes: DDD: 5/97). Recorded 1995.
Here is some highly proficient, sensitive playing from the brother-and-sister partnership of Gil and Orli Shaham. Even today, the F major Sonata is scantily represented on disc. Its sublime *Poco sostenuto* centrepiece contains some of the noblest invention Dvořák ever penned and the Shahams do full justice to its eloquence and hushed concentration. Both outer movements also go with a will: the Brahmsian opening *Allegro ma non troppo* unfolds with dignified lucidity, while the high-spirited *Allegro molto* finale is playful and virtuosic. Likewise, the Shahams' advocacy of the *Sonatina* – one of the most captivating products of Dvořák's first American sojourn – has a youthful ardour and nimble assurance that communicate strongly. Apparently, this enchanting creation was the first piece discovered together by the then-teenage duo and their affection for it remains palpable. No grumbles, either, about the Shahams' expressive way with the equally appealing *Four Romantic Pieces*. The wistful concluding *Larghetto* is a delight. A lovely issue, in sum, excellently recorded.
Additional recommendation ...
...Violin Sonatina (arr. Lipka/Hallmann). *Coupled with works by* **Brahms** and **Hindemith** **Wilfried Strehle** (va); **Karina Wisniewska** (pf). Nimbus Ⓕ NI5473 (78 minutes: DDD: 9/96).

Dvořák Stabat mater[a]. Psalm 149. [a]**Lívia Aghová** (sop); [a]**Marga Schiml** (contr); [a]**Aldo Baldin** (ten); [a]**Luděk Vele** (bass); [a]**Prague Children's Choir; Prague Philharmonic Choir; Czech Philharmonic Orchestra / Jiří Bělohlávek.** Chandos Ⓕ CHAN8985/6 (two discs: 96 minutes: DDD: 2/92). Notes, texts and translations included. Recorded 1991.
The *Stabat mater* is a thirteenth-century Christian poem in Latin describing the Virgin Mary standing at the foot of the Cross. It has been set to music by many Catholic composers from Palestrina to Penderecki, and Dvořák's version, first heard in Prague in 1880, soon went on to other countries including Britain, where it had a number of cathedral performances and one in the Royal Albert Hall in London in 1884 that was conducted by the composer himself and used a choir of over 800 singers – "the impression of such a mighty body was indeed enchanting", he wrote. Its ten sections are well laid out for the different vocal and instrumental forces and so avoid the monotony which might seem inherent in a contemplative and deeply sombre text. This performance was recorded by Chandos with Czech forces in Prague Castle, and in it we feel the full dignity and drama of the work, an oratorio in all but name. The four solo singers convey genuine fervour and one feels that their sound, which is quite unlike that of British singers, must be akin to what the composer originally imagined. If they are a touch operatic, that doesn't sound misplaced and they perform well together, as in the second verse quartet "Quis est homo". The choral singing is no less impressive, and indeed the whole performance under Bělohlávek gets the balance right between reverent simplicity and intensity of feeling. Psalm 149 is a setting of "Sing unto the Lord a new song" for chorus and orchestra and its celebratory mood provides a fine complement to the other work.
Additional recommendations ...
...Stabat mater. Ten Legends, Op. 59[a]. **Soloists; Bavarian Radio Chorus and Symphony Orchestra;** [a]**English Chamber Orchestra / Rafael Kubelík.**
DG 2CD Series Ⓜ 453 025-2GTA2 (two discs: 128 minutes: ADD: 9/90).
...Stabat mater, B71. **Soloists; Oregon Bach Festival Choir and Orchestra / Helmuth Rilling.**
Hänssler Classic Ⓕ 98 935 (two discs: 87 minutes: DDD: 8/96).

Dvořák Mass in D major, Op. 86[a].
Eben Prague Te Deum 1989.
Janáček Our Father[b]. [a]**Dagmar Masková** (sop); [b]**Marta Benacková** (mez); [a]**Walter Coppola** (ten); [a]**Peter Mikulás** (bass); [b]**Lydie Härtelová** (hp); **Josef Ksica** (org); **Prague Chamber Choir / Josef Pancík.** ECM New Series Ⓕ 449 508-2 (59 minutes: DDD: 11/96). Texts and translations included. Recorded 1993.
This imaginative coupling brings together three fine pieces of Czech church music in skilled and sympathetic interpretations. Dvořák's Mass, the best known of them, has received a number of good recorded performances; this one, in the original 1887 version with organ, has a very well matched quartet of soloists who blend smoothly with each other and with the chamber choir. It is a private work, in that the commission for the consecration of the chapel of an architect and philanthropist Josef Hlávka, and the première with his and Dvořák's wives as soloists, led to a work of particular intimacy and charm. These qualities mark the present performance. Janáček's setting of the Lord's Prayer dates from 1906, and is in turn a meditative piece, not without vivid illustrative touches appropriate to a work originally designed to accompany a sequence of devotional pictures; and Petr Eben's *Prague Te Deum* coincided, in 1969, with a moment of apparent release from political oppression. It has something of Janáček's suddenness in the invention, and a graceful melodic

manner. Each of these works is in its way inward, personal and reflective, but they none the less share a Czech character; and this is well related to Czech history by Antonín Pešek in an exceptionally interesting, long essay setting the country's church music in its historical and religious context.

Dvořák Rusalka. **Milada Subrtová** (sop) Rusalka; **Eduard Haken** (bass) Watergnome;
Marie Ovčačíková (contr) Witch; **Ivo Zídek** (ten) Prince; **Alena Míková** (mez) Foreign Princess;
Jadwiga Wysoczanská (sop) First Woodsprite; **Eva Hlobilová** (sop) Second Woodsprite;
Věra Krilová (contr) Third Woodsprite; **Ivana Mixová** (sop) Turnspit; **Václav Bednář** (bar)
Hunter; **Prague National Theatre Chorus and Orchestra / Zdeněk Chalabala.**
Supraphon Ⓟ SU0013-2 (two discs: 149 minutes: ADD: 1/96). From SUAST50440/3 (9/64).
Notes, text and translation included. Recorded 1961.   Ⓖ

This excellent set boasts Eduard Haken, one of the great interpreters of the Watergnome, in robust voice, infusing the somewhat enigmatic character with a rueful gentleness as well as a firmness of utterance. Ivo Zídek as the Prince was in his mid-thirties and in his prime at the time of this recording, singing ardently and tenderly and with a grace of phrasing that matches him well to Milada Subrtová's Rusalka. Hers is a beautiful performance, sensitive to the character's charm as well as to her fragility and pathos. The Slavonic tradition of the old watersprite legend places her in the line of the suffering heroine and it is a measure of Dvořák's success that her delicate appeal holds throughout quite a long opera, and her sinuous but never oversensual lines and the piercing harmony associated with her give her a unique appeal. Subrtová sings the part with unfaltering sensitivity. Zdeněk Chalabala, who died only a couple of months after completing this recording, handles the score with great tenderness and an affection that shines through every bar. He was sometimes underrated as a conductor: this is a beautiful performance. The recording comes up remarkably well; and the booklet includes full text and translations into French, German, and – one or two unfortunate turns of phrase apart – quite reasonable English.

Additional recommendation ...

...**Soloists; Prague Philharmonic Chorus; Czech Philharmonic Orchestra / Václav Neumann.**
Supraphon Ⓟ 10 3641-2 (three discs: ADD: 7/86).

Dvořák The Jacobin. **Václav Zítek** (bar) Bohuš; **Vilém Přibyl** (ten) Jiří; **Daniela Sounová** (sop)
Terinka; **Karel Průša** (bass) Count Vilém; **René Tuček** (bar) Adolf; **Marcela Machotková** (sop)
Julie; **Karel Berman** (bass) Filip; **Beno Blachut** (ten) Benda; **Ivana Mixová** (mez) Lotinka;
Kantilena Children's Chorus; Kühn Chorus; Brno State Philharmonic Orchestra / Jiří Pinkas.
Supraphon Ⓟ 11 2190-2 (two discs: 155 minutes: ADD: 12/94). Notes, text and translation
included. From SUP2481/3 (2/80). Recorded 1977.

This was the first (and, so far, only) recording of Dvořák's charming village comedy – for the Jacobin of the title is not here a political activist but a young man, Bohuš, returning from exile in Paris to his stuffy old father, Count Vilém. The sub-plots include all manner of misunderstandings, and set in the middle of them is the touching figure of Benda, the fussy, rather pedantic but wholly moving music-master. Dvořák is known to have had in mind his own boyhood teacher, Antonín Liehmann, whose daughter gives her name, Terinka, to Benda's daughter. Beno Blachut celebrated his sixty-fourth birthday during the making of this set. His was a long career, as well as one of great distinction; he is still well able to get round the lines of this part, and gives an affecting picture of the old musician, never more so than in the rehearsing of the welcome ode. This is an idea that has cropped up in opera before, but it is charmingly handled here. Václav Zítek sings Bohuš pleasantly and Marcela Machotková trips away lightly as Julie. Vilém Přibyl sounds less than his most energetic, though his voice is in good fettle; and there is some lack of drive from Jiří Pinkas, who might have done more to bring out the often witty touches in Dvořák's scoring. Never mind: this revived version of a delightful piece can be safely recommended. There is a full libretto, with translations into French, German and rather stilted English.

Dvořák Kate and the Devil. **Anna Barová** (contr) Kate; **Richard Novák** (bass) Devil Marbuel;
Miloš Ježil (ten) Shepherd Jirka; **Daniela Suryová** (contr) Kate's mother; **Jaroslav Horáček** (bass)
Lucifer; **Jan Hladík** (bass) Devil the Gate-keeper; **Aleš Stáva** (bass) Devil the Guard;
Brigita Sulcová (sop) Princess; **Natália Romanová** (sop) Chambermaid; **Pavel Kamas** (bass)
Marshall; **Oldřich Polášek** (ten) Musician; **Brno Janáček Opera Chorus and Orchestra /
Jiří Pinkas.** Supraphon Ⓟ 11 1800-2 (two discs: 119 minutes: AAD: 9/94). Notes, text and
translation included. From 1116 3181/3 (3/82). Recorded 1979.

Kate and the Devil has never fared very well outside Czech lands. Record collectors have fared better, and it is high time to welcome back this version, originally recorded in 1979. Though this was never one of the best Supraphon recordings, it is perfectly serviceable. The plot is complicated, and broadly speaking concerns the bossy Kate who, finding herself a wallflower at the village hop, angrily declares that she would dance with the Devil himself. Up there duly pops a junior devil, Marbuel, who carries her off to hell, where her ceaseless chatter wearies Lucifer himself. The diabolical company is only too happy to allow the shepherd Jirka to remove her again. Jirka, attractively sung by Miloš Ježil, also manages to help the wicked but later repentant Princess to escape the Devil's clutches, and all ends well. The work has a proper coherence, and much good humour besides. Anna Barová's Kate is strong and full of character, but manages not to exclude the charm that should underlie her rantings at

Marbuel, who is handsomely sung by Richard Novák. Brigita Sulcová similarly makes much of the not very sympathetic Princess. Jaroslav Horáček enjoys himself hugely as Lucifer and Jiří Pinkas accompanies them well.

Further listening ...

...Piano Concerto in G minor, B63. *Coupled with* **Schubert** Fantasy in C major, D760, "Wanderer". **Sviatoslav Richter** (pf); **Bavarian State Orchestra / Carlos Kleiber.** EMI CDC7 47967-2 (11/87).

...Serenade in D minor, B77. *Coupled with works by* **Mysliveček** Sabine Meyer Wind Ensemble; **Manuel Fischer-Dieskau** (vc); **Christoph Schmidt** (db). EMI CDC5 55512-2 (9/96).

...Serenade in D minor, B77. *Coupled with* **Janáček** Mládí. Concertino. **Walter Boeykens Ensemble.** Harmonia Mundi Musique d'abord HMA190 1399 (7/97).

...Serenade in E major, B52. *Coupled with* **Suk** Serenade in E flat major, Op. 6. **Prague Chamber Philharmonic Orchestra / Jiří Bělohlávek.** Supraphon SU3157-2 (4/97).

...Slavonic Rhapsody No. 3 in A flat minor, B86. *Coupled with works by various composers.* **Montreal Symphony Orchestra / Charles Dutoit.** Decca 452 482-2DH (5/97). *See review in the Collections section; refer to the Index.*

...String Quartet No. 13 in G major, B192. *Coupled with works by* **Brahms** Alban Berg Quartet. Teldec 4509-95503-2 (2/95).

...String Sextet in A major, B80. *Coupled with* **Martinů** Serenade No. 2. String Sextet. **Academy of St Martin in the Fields Chamber Ensemble.** Chandos CHAN8771 (5/90).

...Ten Legends, B117. From the Bohemian Forest, B133. **Silke-Thora Matthies, Christian Köhn** (pf duet). Naxos 8 553137 (1/97).

...Four Romantic Pieces, B150. Songs my mother taught me, B104 No. 4 (arr. Kreisler). Slavonic Dances – E minor, B78 No. 8; G minor, B145 No. 2 (both arr. Kreisler); A flat major, B145 No. 8 (arr. Jacobson). Humoresques in G flat major, B187 No. 7 (arr. Jacobson). Rondo in G minor, B171 (arr. Jacobson). Violin Sonatina in G major, B183. **Susanne Stanzeleit** (vn); **Julian Jacobson** (pf). Meridian CDE84281 (3/96).

...Nine Moravian Duets, B62. *Coupled with works by various composers.* **Prague Chamber Choir / Josef Pancik.** Chandos CHAN9257 (12/95).

...13 Moravian Duets, B107. *Coupled with works by* **Brahms** and **Reger** Three Duets, Op. 111*a*. **Juliane Banse** (sop); **Brigitte Fassbaender** (mez); **Cord Garben** (pf). Koch Schwann 312592 (8/95).

...Requiem, B165[a]. Mass in D major, B153[b]. [a]**Pilar Lorengar** (sop); [b]**Neil Ritchie** (treb); [a]**Erzesébet Komlóssy** (contr); [b]**Andrew Giles** (alto); [a]**Robert Ilosfalvy**, [b]**Alan Byers** (tens); [a]**Tom Krause** (bar); [b]**Robert Morton** (bass); [b]**Nicholas Cleobury** (org); [a]**Ambrosian Singers;** [b]**Christ Church Cathedral Choir, Oxford / Simon Preston;** [a]**London Symphony Orchestra / István Kertész.** Double Decca 448 089-2DF2 (11/96). 🅖🅖

...Rusalka – O silver moon. *Coupled with works by various composers.* **Renée Fleming** (sop); **London Symphony Orchestra / Sir Georg Solti.** Decca 455 760-2DH (10/97). *Gramophone Editor's choice. See review in the Collections section; refer to the Index.*

...Songs my mother taught me, B104 No. 4. *Coupled with works by various composers.* **Renée Fleming** (sop); **English Chamber Orchestra / Jeffrey Tate.** Decca 458 858-2DH (3/98). *See review in the Collections section; refer to the Index. Selected by Soundings.*

...Songs my mother taught me, B104 No. 4. *Coupled with works by various composers.* **Angela Gheorghiu** (sop); **Malcolm Martineau** (pf). Decca 458 360-2DH (5/98). *See review in the Collections section; refer to the Index.*

...St Ludmila, B144. **Soloists; Prague Children's Choir; Prague Radio Chorus and Symphony Orchestra / Václav Smetáček.** Praga PR250 059/60 (7/95).

...Dimitrij. **Soloists; Prague Radio Chorus; Czech Philharmonic Chorus and Orchestra / Gerd Albrecht.** Supraphon 11 1259-2 (3/93).

...King and Charcoal Burner. **Soloists; Chorus and Orchestra of the National Theatre, Prague / Josef Chaloupka.** Supraphon SU3078-2 (9/97).

Sir George Dyson

British 1883-1964

Dyson The Canterbury Pilgrims[a]. In Honour of the City[b]. At the Tabard Inn. [a]**Yvonne Kenny** (sop); [a]**Robert Tear** (ten); [a]**Stephen Roberts** (bar); **London Symphony** [ab]**Chorus and Orchestra / Richard Hickox.** Chandos Ⓕ CHAN9531 (two discs: 118 minutes: DDD: 7/97). Texts included. Recorded 1996. *Gramophone Editor's choice. Gramophone Award Winner 1997.* 🅖

It seems extraordinary that Dyson's *Canterbury Pilgrims* had to wait so long for a première recording. This superb offering from Hickox of this full-length cantata based on the Prologue to Chaucer's *Canterbury Tales* bears out its reputation as Dyson's masterpiece. He misses the ironic side of the Prologue, Chaucer's delightful way of having a sly dig at his characters and even omits the delectable line about the French accent of the Prioress (here described simply as The Nun) being of "Stratford-atte-Bowe", not of Paris, but once that is said, this is a fresh, openly tuneful work, aptly exuberant in its celebration of Chaucer. Following the scheme of Chaucer's Prologue, Dyson in his 12 movements, plus Envoi, presents a sequence of portraits, deftly varying the forces used, with the three soloists well contrasted in their characterizations and with the chorus acting as both narrator and commentator, providing an emotional focus for the whole work in two heightened sequences, the sixth and twelfth movements, moving and noble portraits of the two characters who aroused Dyson's deepest sympathy, the Clerk of Oxenford and the Poor Parson of a Town. If the idiom is undemanding, with occasional echoes of Vaughan Williams's *A Sea Symphony* and with passages reminiscent of Rachmaninov's *The bells*, the cantata sustains its length well.

Sensibly, *At the Tabard Inn*, the concert overture which Dyson wrote in 1943, basing it on themes from the cantata, is given first. Outstanding among the soloists is Robert Tear who not only characterizes brilliantly but sings with admirable fullness and warmth. The beautiful, fading close, when Tear as the Knight begins the first tale, moving slowly off-stage, is most atmospherically done. Yvonne Kenny and Stephen Roberts sing well too, but are less distinctive both in timbre and expression. The London Symphony Chorus sing with incandescent tone, superbly recorded, and with the orchestra under Hickox – an ideal advocate – bring out the clarity and colourfulness of Dyson's instrumentation. *In Honour of the City* provides the perfect fill-up. Like the main work, it uses a modern-language version of a middle-English text, the poem by William Dunbar that William Walton set nine years later in 1937 in its original form in his coronation cantata of the same name. The idiom is very similar to that of the Chaucer work, music designed for a good amateur chorus, fresh, direct and tuneful, again with Hickox drawing glowing sounds from chorus and orchestra.

Further listening ...

...Concerto da camera. Concerto da chiesa. Concerto leggiero[a]. [a]**Eric Parkin** (pf); **City of London Sinfonia / Richard Hickox.** Chandos CHAN9076 (8/93).

...Symphony in G major. **City of London Sinfonia / Richard Hickox.** Chandos CHAN9200 (6/94). **ᴳ**

...Violin Concerto in E flat major[a]. Children's Suite, after De la Mare. [a]**Lydia Mordkovitch** (vn); **City of London Sinfonia / Richard Hickox.** Chandos CHAN9369 (9/95). *Gramophone Editor's choice.*   **ᴳ**

...Three Rhapsodies. *Coupled with* **Howells** String Quartet No. 3, "In Gloucestershire". **Divertimenti.** Hyperion CDA66139 (6/89).

...Evening Service in D major. *Coupled with works by various composers.* **Lichfield Cathedral Choir / Andrew Lumsden** with **Mark Shepherd, Nigel Potts** (orgs). Priory PRCD505 (10/95). *See review in the Collections section; refer to the Index.*

...Evening Service in D major. *Coupled with works by various composers.* **Ripon Cathedral Choir / Kerry Beaumont** with **Robert Marsh** (org). Priory PRCD555 (1/97).

...Evening Service in F major. *Coupled with works by various composers.* **Hereford Cathedral Choir / Roy Massey** with **Huw Williams** (org). Priory PRCD535 (7/96). *See review in the Collections section; refer to the Index.*

Petr Eben
Bohemian 1929

Suggested listening ...

...Homage to Dietrich Buxtehude. *Coupled with works by various composers.* **Peter King** (org). Priory PRCD618. *See review in the Collections section; refer to the Index.*

...Prague Te Deum 1989. *Coupled with works by* **Dvořák** and **Janáček** Soloists; Prague Chamber Choir / **Josef Pancík.** ECM New Series 449 508-2 (11/96). *See review under Dvořák; refer to the Index.*

Garth Edmundson
American 1900-1971

Suggested listening ...

...Toccata, "Vom Himmel hoch". *Coupled with works by various composers.* **Christopher Herrick** (org). Hyperion CDA66917 (8/97). *See review in the Collections section; refer to the Index.*

Edward Elgar
British 1857-1934

Elgar Cello Concerto in E minor, Op. 85[a]. Sea Pictures, Op. 37[b]. [a]**Jacqueline du Pré** (vc); [b]**Dame Janet Baker** (mez); **London Symphony Orchestra / Sir John Barbirolli.** EMI Ⓟ CDC5 56219-2 (54 minutes: ADD: 5/86). From ASD655 (12/65). Recorded 1965. *Gramophone classical 100.*   **ᴳᴳᴳ**

Issued in 1965 and one of EMI's best-sellers ever since, these Elgar recordings make the most cherishable of couplings. Though both Jacqueline du Pré and Dame Janet Baker were already well established and widely appreciated in 1965, this disc marked a turning point for both of them in their recording careers. With Barbirolli so warm-hearted and understanding an accompanist to each, these are both in every sense classic performances that can never be replaced. Jacqueline du Pré's Elgar has been all the more appreciated since her tragic illness took her away. In principle her *espressivo* may be too freely romantic, but the slow movement and epilogue remain supreme in their intensity, conveying in whispered *pianissimos* of daring delicacy an inner communion, while the bravura of the brilliant passages remains astonishing from an artist who was still only 20. Equally, the young Janet Baker translated the work into something greater than had been appreciated before. Until this recording,

Sea Pictures had tended to be underprized even among Elgarians; but the passion, intensity and sheer beauty of this performance with each of the five songs sharply distinct rebutted any idea that – in reflection of verse of varying quality – it had anything of sub-standard Elgar in it. It is a work which you will probably never be able to listen to again without hearing in your mind Dame Janet's deeply individual phrasing on this disc. What strikes you more than anything else is the central relevance to Dame Janet's whole career of the last stanza in "Sabbath morning at sea", a radiant climax. "He shall assist me to look higher" says the Barrett Browning poem, and the thrust of meaning as Dame Janet sings it invariably conveys a *frisson* such as you rarely get on record. The CD transfer is valuable for clarifying the sound, but it adds little to the original LP. The sound in the Cello Concerto exactly matches the LP sound, and the precise placing makes the soloist all the more vivid. The precision of CD makes more apparent the slight discrepancy between the sides, with *Sea Pictures* a degree fresher and fuller and with more bloom on the sound. The slight sibilant emphasis is not the fault of the transfer, but also comes on the LP.

Additional recommendations ...

...Cello Concerto. *Coupled with works by* **Haydn** *and* **Beethoven** Jacqueline du Pré (vc); **London Symphony Orchestra / Sir John Barbirolli.** EMI Studio Ⓜ CMS7 69707-2 (two discs: 107 minutes: ADD: 3/89). *The Cello Concerto is the same recording as the one reviewed above.*   ❹❹❹

...Cello Concerto[a]. The Dream of Gerontius, Op. 38[b]. [a]**Paul Tortelier** (vc); [b]**Soloists;** [b]**Huddersfield Choral Society;** [b]**BBC Symphony Orchestra;** [a]**Liverpool Philharmonic Orchestra / Sir Malcolm Sargent.** Testament mono Ⓕ SBT2025* (two discs: 120 minutes: ADD: 2/94). *See review further on in this section.*   ❹❹

...Cello Concerto[a]. Violin Concerto[b]. [a]**Lynn Harrell** (vc); [b]**Kyung-Wha Chung** (vn); [a]**Cleveland Orchestra / Lorin Maazel;** [b]**London Philharmonic Orchestra / Sir Georg Solti.** Decca Ⓜ 440 319-2DWO (78 minutes: ADD: 4/94).

...Cello Concerto. *Coupled with works by* **Milhaud** *and* **Respighi** Mstislav Rostropovich (vc); **Moscow Philharmonic Orchestra / Gennadi Rozhdestvensky.** Russian Disc Ⓕ RDCD11104 (52 minutes: ADD: 7/94).

...Cello Concerto. *Coupled with works by various composers.* **Jacqueline du Pré** (vc) with various artists and orchestras. EMI Ⓑ CZS5 68132-2 (six discs: 437 minutes: ADD: 8/94). *This is the same recording as the one reviewed above. Also see review in the Collections section; refer to the Index.*   ❹❹❹

...Cello Concerto. **Bloch** Schelomo. **Steven Isserlis** (vc); **London Symphony Orchestra / Richard Hickox.** Virgin Classics Ultraviolet Ⓜ CUV5 61125-2 (51 minutes: DDD: 11/94). *Selected by Sounds in Retrospect.*   ❹

...Cello Concerto[b]. **Dvořák** Cello Concerto in B minor, B191[a]. **Jacqueline du Pré** (vc); [a]**Chicago Symphony Orchestra / Daniel Barenboim;** [b]**London Symphony Orchestra / Sir John Barbirolli.** EMI Ⓕ CDC5 55527-2 (72 minutes: ADD: 11/95). *This is the same recording as the one reviewed above.*   ❹❹❹

...Cello Concerto[a]. "Enigma" Variations. Coronation March. Imperial March. Pomp and Circumstance. **Vaughan Williams** Fantasia on a Theme by Thomas Tallis. Fantasia on Greensleeves. [a]**Felix Schmidt** (vc); **London Symphony Orchestra / Barry Tuckwell.** Carlton Classics LSO Doubles Ⓜ 30368 01137 (two discs: 119 minutes: DDD: 1/98).

Elgar Violin Concerto in B minor, Op. 61.
Vaughan Williams The lark ascending. **Kennedy** (vn); **City of Birmingham Symphony Orchestra / Sir Simon Rattle.** EMI Ⓕ CDC5 56413-2 (72 minutes: ADD: 1/98). Recorded 1997.

Astonishingly, in the case of the first two movements at least, this release (recorded during the week following a live concert at Birmingham's Symphony Hall in July 1997) fully re-creates the heady excitement of that memorable event. From every conceivable point of view – authority, panache, intelligence, intuitive poetry, tonal eloquence and emotional maturity – Kennedy surpasses his 1985 *Gramophone* Award-winning EMI Eminence recording (currently out of the catalogue). The first movement is a magnificent achievement all round, with tension levels extraordinarily high for a studio project. Rattle launches the proceedings in exemplary fashion, his direction passionate, ideally flexible and texturally lucid (the antiphonally divided violins help). The CBSO, too, are on top form. But it's Kennedy who rivets the attention from his commanding initial entry onwards. There's no hiding in this of all scores and Kennedy penetrates to the very essence of "the soul enshrined within" in his melting presentation of the 'Windflower' theme – Elgar's *dolce semplice* realized to tear-spilling perfection. The slow movement is almost as fine. What poise and dedication these artists bring to this rapt meditation. Only the finale oddly dissatisfies. Not in terms of technical address or co-ordination (both of which are stunning); rather, for all the supreme accomplishment on show, the results are not terribly moving. The opening pages incline to a foursquare, slightly hectic brusqueness, while the great cadenza, so overwhelmingly intense in the concert-hall performance, has now acquired a whiff of calculation about it. Maybe it's a question of overpreparation? Despite any lingering doubts about this last movement we are still left with an enormously stimulating and marvellously well-engineered display which you are urged to experience for yourself. The fill-up is a provocative account of *The lark ascending*, which Kennedy (whose tone is ravishing) and Rattle spin out to a (surely unprecedented?) 17-and-a-half minutes.

Additional recommendations ...
...Violin Concerto[a]. Violin Sonata in E minor, Op. 82[b]. **Albert Sammons** (vn); [b]**William Murdoch**
(pf); [a]**New Queen's Hall Orchestra / Sir Henry Wood.** Pearl mono Ⓕ GEMMCD9496*.
...Violin Concerto. Cockaigne Overture, Op. 40. **Dong-Suk Kang** (vn); **Polish National Radio
Symphony Orchestra / Adrian Leaper.** Naxos Ⓢ 8 550489 (61 minutes: DDD: 4/92).
...Violin Concerto. Violin Sonata in E minor, Op. 82[b]. **Hugh Bean** (vn); [b]**David Parkhouse** (pf);
Royal Liverpool Philharmonic Orchestra / Sir Charles Groves.
Classics for Pleasure Ⓑ CD-CFP4632 (75 minutes: ADD: 9/93).

Elgar Violin Concerto in B minor, Op. 61[a]. Cello Concerto in E minor, Op. 85[b]. [a]**Yehudi Menuhin**
(vn); [b]**Beatrice Harrison** (vc); [a]**London Symphony Orchestra,** [b]**New Symphony Orchestra /
Sir Edward Elgar.** EMI Great Recordings of the Century mono Ⓜ CDH7 69786-2
(75 minutes: AAD: 11/89). Item marked [a] from DB1751/6 (11/62), recorded 1932;
[b]HMV D1507/09 (1/29), recorded 1928. *Gramophone classical 100.*   ⓖⓖⓖ
Elgar's conducting for Menuhin in the Violin Concerto's opening orchestral tutti is quite magnificent,
as is his solicitous, attentive accompaniment throughout the work. Menuhin's youthful, wonderfully
intuitive musicianship in fact needed little 'instruction', as is well known, and the success of the
recording may be judged from the fact that there have been few periods in the years since it was first
issued when it has not been available in some shape or form. Beatrice Harrison first studied the Cello
Concerto for an abridged, pre-electric recording with Elgar conducting. So impressed was the
composer then that he insisted that Harrison should be the soloist whenever he conducted the work
again. Their authoritative performance is deeply felt and highly expressive, but it has a quality of nobility and stoicism which comes as a refreshing change from some overindulgent modern performances.
After EMI had made the first LP transfer of the Menuhin Violin Concerto for the composer's centenary in 1957 the original matrices were destroyed. When Anthony Griffith made a fresh transfer in the
early 1970s using improved technology the results were at the same time better and worse, for Griffith
was obliged to work with commercial pressings. In going back to the 1957 tape for this transfer EMI's
engineers have on balance made the right decision, for although the 1957 engineers did not quite capture all the body of the originals there is an impressive clarity in their transfer, now brightened a little
more for CD. Griffith's 1970s transfer of the Harrison/Elgar Cello Concerto was impressively managed, and this reissue has given still more presence to the sound without any sense of falsification.

Elgar Falstaff, Op. 68[a]. Introduction and Allegro, Op. 47[b]. Serenade for Strings in E minor,
Op. 20[b]. [a]**London Symphony Orchestra,** [b]**New Symphony Orchestra / Anthony Collins.**
Beulah mono Ⓜ 1PD15* (59 minutes: ADD: 2/96). Item marked [a] from Decca LXT2940 (8/54),
[b]LXT2699 (9/52). Recorded 1952-54.
Even among the many recordings of *Falstaff*, few match Collins in the way his timing helps you to
visualize the story behind each incident. The reading is strong and purposeful yet not at all rushed,
with each section sharply characterized and with linking passages leading the ear on. Though the LSO
of 1954 was rather in the doldrums, the crisp ensemble would have done credit to the orchestra as
reconstituted later in the decade, not just in the woodwind and brass sections but in the strings too.
Plainly Collins inspired the players, who may well have been rediscovering the work, for that was a
period when Elgar's music, rather like the orchestra, was out of favour. The Beulah transfer does not
quite capture the full vividness of Decca's recording at the time, but there is a fair body in the sound
and the bite of the brass is splendid. What is irritating, however, is that there is only a single track for
the 34-minute work, with no sections separately indexed. In the *Serenade* and the *Introduction and
Allegro* Collins equally reveals his natural understanding of Elgarian timing and rubato. However, the
playing from what was then called the New Symphony Orchestra is not nearly as polished as in
Falstaff and the string sound tends to be fizzy. None the less, this is an invaluable offering, reminding
us of the mastery of a conductor whose achievement was never fully appreciated in his lifetime.
Additional recommendations ...
...Introduction and Allegro[a]. Serenade for Strings in E minor, Op. 20[b]. Pomp and Circumstance
Marches Nos. 1 and 4[c]. "Enigma" Variations – Nimrod[d]. The Dream of Gerontius – Praise to the
Holiest in the height[ae]. Salut d'amour[f]. There is sweet music[g]. [e]**Yvonne Minton** (sop); [e]**Sir Peter
Pears** (ten); [f]**Kyung-Wha Chung** (vn); [f]**Philip Moll** (pf); [g]**Louis Halsey Singers.** [a]**English Chamber
Orchestra /** [ae]**Benjamin Britten;** [b]**Academy of St Martin in the Fields / Sir Neville Marriner;**
[cde]**London Symphony Chorus and Orchestra / Sir Arthur Bliss,** [d]**Pierre Monteux.**
Decca Ⓑ 430 094-2DWO (66 minutes: ADD: 6/91).
...Cockaigne Overture. Introduction and Allegro. Serenade for Strings. "Enigma" Variations.
BBC Symphony Orchestra / Andrew Davis.
Teldec British Line Ⓕ 9031-73279-2 (74 minutes: DDD: 3/92).
...Introduction and Allegro. *Coupled with works by* **Barber** *and* **Tchaikovsky** **Boston Symphony
Orchestra / Charles Munch.** RCA Victor Gold Seal Ⓜ 09026 61424-2 (61 minutes: ADD: 9/93). ⓖⓖ
...Introduction and Allegro. *Coupled with works by various composers.* **English Chamber Orchestra /
Benjamin Britten.** Decca The Classic Sound Ⓜ 448 569-2DCS (58 minutes: ADD: 2/96).
...Falstaff. Nursery Suite. Dream children, Op. 43. Pomp and Circumstance March No. 3.
Bach Fantasia and Fugue in C minor, BWV537 (orch. Elgar). **London Philharmonic Orchestra /
Sir Adrian Boult.** Testament mono Ⓕ SBT1106* (77 minutes: ADD: 8/97).

...Serenade for Strings. Sospiri, Op. 70. Elegy, Op. 58. The spanish Lady – Burlesco: Allegro; Sarabande: Maestoso; Bourrée: Vivace. Introduction and Allegro, Op. 47. *Coupled with works by various composers.* **Academy of St Martin in the Fields / Sir Neville Marriner.** Decca Double Ⓑ 452 707-2DF2 (two discs: 8/97).

Elgar Variations on an Original Theme, Op. 36, "Enigma". Falstaff, Op. 68. Grania and Diarmid – Incidental Music; Funeral March. **City of Birmingham Symphony Orchestra / Sir Simon Rattle.** EMI British Composers Ⓕ CDC5 55001-2 (79 minutes: DDD: 3/95). Recorded 1992-93.   Ⓖ
Rattle gives us perhaps the most meticulously prepared and subtly blended *Falstaff* ever committed to disc. This conductor's keen intellect and almost fanatical fidelity to the letter of the score team up to produce the most invigorating, wittily observant results. It is, however, a bit like viewing a pristinely restored portrait of Shakespeare's fat knight, whereas Barbirolli presents us with the lovable, vulnerable creature of flesh and blood himself – his epilogue really does touch to the marrow every time. In *Enigma* the results are always enjoyable and refreshing, with myriad details in Elgar's lovingly-woven, orchestral canvas adroitly pinpointed. The sluggishness that so often blights the opening bars is mercifully absent and Rattle follows it up with a wonderfully transparent and affectionate "C.A.E.". Rattle brings an almost chamber-like intimacy and point to "R.B.T.", "Ysobel" and "W.N.", whilst his "Dorabella" is a veritable miracle of tripping delicacy. Both "Troyte" and "G.R.S." winningly combine athleticism and bluster. "Nimrod", too, is a success, its progress dignified and its noble climax unerringly well graduated (and we really do get a genuine *ppp* at the start). Overall, then, a fine, deeply-felt *Enigma*. The most completely successful item here is the glorious *Grania and Diarmid* incidental music: the magnificent "Funeral March" is one of Elgar's most inspired creations and Rattle gauges its brooding melancholy most eloquently. Balance is impeccable (and the transfer level comparatively low) in all three works, though the quality in *Falstaff* isn't quite as rich and glowing as elsewhere. An exceedingly stimulating release.
Additional recommendations ...
..."Enigma" Variations[a]. **Holst** The Planets, H125[b]. [a]**London Symphony Orchestra;** [b]**(Geoffrey) Mitchell Choir;** [b]**London Philharmonic Orchestra / Sir Adrian Boult.** EMI Studio Plus Ⓜ CDM7 64748-2 (78 minutes: ADD).
..."Enigma" Variations[a]. **Holst** The Planets, H125[b]. [a]**Royal Albert Hall Orchestra / Sir Edward Elgar;** [b]**London Symphony Orchestra / Gustav Holst.** EMI Composers in Person mono Ⓕ CDC7 54837-2* (70 minutes: ADD).
..."Enigma" Variations. Pomp and Circumstance Marches. **Royal Philharmonic Orchestra / Norman Del Mar.** DG Galleria Ⓜ 429 713-2GGA (58 minutes: ADD: 9/90).   Ⓖ
..."Enigma" Variations. Cockaigne Overture, Op. 40. Serenade for Strings in E minor, Op. 20. Salut d'amour, Op. 12. **Baltimore Symphony Orchestra / David Zinman.** Telarc Ⓕ CD80192 (62 minutes: DDD: 10/90).
..."Enigma" Variations. Cockaigne Overture. Serenade for Strings. Introduction and Allegro, Op. 47. **BBC Symphony Orchestra / Andrew Davis.** Teldec British Line Ⓕ 9031-73279-2 (74 minutes: DDD: 3/92).
..."Enigma" Variations. Froissart, Op. 19. Cello Concerto[a]. [a]**Robert Cohen** (vc); **Royal Philharmonic Orchestra / Sir Charles Mackerras.** Argo Ⓕ 436 545-2ZH (77 minutes: DDD: 6/93).
..."Enigma" Variations. **Debussy** Images. **Berlin Philharmonic Orchestra / James Levine.** Sony Classical Ⓕ SK53284 (67 minutes: DDD: 2/95).
..."Enigma" Variations[a]. **Holst** The Planets, H125[b]. [b]**New England Conservatory Chorus;** [a]**London Symphony Orchestra / Eugen Jochum;** [b]**Boston Symphony Orchestra / William Steinberg.** DG Ⓑ 439 446-2GCL (78 minutes: ADD: 3/95).
..."Enigma" Variations. *Coupled with works by* **Blacher** and **Kodály** Vienna Philharmonic Orchestra / Sir Georg Solti. Decca Ⓕ 452 853-2DH (68 minutes: DDD: 3/97).

Elgar Variations on an Original Theme, Op. 36, "Enigma"[a]. Falstaff, Op. 68[b]. [a]**Philharmonia Orchestra;** [b]**Hallé Orchestra / Sir John Barbirolli.** EMI Studio Ⓜ CDM7 69185-2 (65 minutes: ADD: 11/88). Item marked [a] from ASD548 (11/63), recorded 1962, [b]ASD610-11 (12/64), recorded 1964.   ⒼⒼ
Elgar Variations on an Original Theme, Op. 36, "Enigma"[a]. Pomp and Circumstance Marches, Op. 39[b]. [a]**London Symphony Orchestra,** [b]**London Philharmonic Orchestra / Sir Adrian Boult.** EMI Ⓜ CDM7 64015-2 (55 minutes: ADD: 4/92). Item marked [a] from HMV ASD2750 (11/71), recorded 1970, [b]ASD3388 (10/77), recorded 1976.   ⒼⒼ
The first EMI disc restores to the catalogue at a very reasonable price two key Elgar recordings of works which Sir John Barbirolli made very much his own. Barbirolli brought a flair and ripeness of feeling to the *Enigma* with which Elgar himself would surely have identified. Everything about his performance seems exactly right. The very opening theme is phrased with an appealing combination of warmth and subtlety, and variation after variation has a special kind of individuality, whilst for the finale Barbirolli draws all the threads together most satisfyingly. *Falstaff* is a continuous, closely integrated structure and again Barbirolli's response to the music's scenic characterization is magical while he controls the overall piece, with its many changes of mood, with a naturally understanding flair. The original recordings perhaps sounded more sumptuous but on CD there is more refined detail and greater range and impact to the sound.

As one might expect, Sir Adrian Boult's 1970 recording of the *Enigma* Variations offers similar riches to those of Barbirolli with the additional bonus of a slightly superior recorded sound. Boult's account has authority, freshness and a beautiful sense of spontaneity so that each variation emerges from the preceding one with a natural feeling of flow and progression. There is warmth and affection too coupled with an air of nobility and poise, and at all times the listener is acutely aware that this is a performance by a great conductor who has lived a lifetime with the music. One need only sample the passionate stirrings of Variation 1 (the composer's wife), the athletic and boisterous "Troyte" variation, or the autumnal, elegiac glow that Boult brings to the famous "Nimrod" variation to realize that this is a very special document indeed. The LSO, on top form, play with superlative skill and poetry and the excellent recording has been exceptionally well transferred to CD. The *Pomp and Circumstance* Marches, recorded six years later with the London Philharmonic Orchestra, are invigoratingly fresh and direct – indeed the performances are so full of energy and good humour that it is hard to believe that Boult was in his late eighties at the time of recording! A classic.

Elgar Symphony No. 1 in A flat major, Op. 55. In the South, Op. 50, "Alassio".
London Philharmonic Orchestra / Leonard Slatkin. RCA Victor Red Seal Ⓕ RD60380
(74 minutes: DDD: 6/91). Recorded 1989. ⒼⒼⒼ

Elgar's First Symphony was one of those rare pieces of music that seemed to attain full stature and admiration from the very first public hearing. At its première in Manchester in 1908 it caused a sensation, and Elgar was received by the audience very much in the same way that the pop stars of today are. The previous successes of the *Enigma* Variations, *Gerontius* and the masterly *Introduction and Allegro* had created high hopes in the public's mind for what they felt would be the first truly great English Symphony, and they were not disappointed. Its popularity has never waned and it still holds a special place in the affections of the public today. Leonard Slatkin is a conductor whose passion for British music has become something of a crusade, and a listener hearing him play Elgar's First Symphony without knowing the artists could well think that this was a performance under a conductor such as Sir Adrian Boult. But good music knows no bounds (after all, you don't have to be Austrian to play Mozart!) and Slatkin's understanding of this composer is abundantly clear throughout. There is no trace of sentimentality in the mighty first movement, for here is real grandeur and not just grandiose utterance while the noble sadness of the coda has special beauty. The other movements are hardly less fine, for the richly textured *Adagio* is most eloquently done and the finale is thrilling. Elgar's massive though subtle scoring can present problems for engineers; here they are magnificently solved and the sound is rich yet detailed with excellent bass. The Overture *In the South* which begins the disc is brilliantly vivid and dramatic.

Additional recommendations ...

...No. 1. Serenade for Strings. Chanson de nuit, Op. 15 No. 1. Chanson de matin, Op. 15 No. 2.
London Philharmonic Orchestra / Sir Adrian Boult. EMI British Composers Ⓜ CDM7 64013-2
(69 minutes: ADD). *Gramophone Award Winner 1977.* ⒼⒼⒼ

...No. 1. **London Philharmonic Orchestra / Vernon Handley.**
Classics for Pleasure Ⓑ CD-CFP9018 (52 minutes: ADD: 8/88). ⒼⒼ

...Nos. 1 and 2[a]. Falstaff[a]. The Dream of Gerontius[ab] – excerpts. The Music Makers[a] – excerpts.
Civic Fanfare[a]. **Anonymous** (arr. Elgar) The National Anthem[a]. [ab]**Soloists;**
[a]**London Symphony Orchestra;** [b]**Royal Albert Hall Orchestra / Sir Edward Elgar.**
EMI mono Ⓕ CDS7 54560-2*
(three discs: 211 minutes: ADD: 6/92). ⒼⒼⒼ

...No. 1. Pomp and Circumstance Marches Nos. 1 and 2. **Baltimore Symphony Orchestra /
David Zinman.** Telarc Ⓕ CD80310 (62 minutes: DDD: 11/92). Ⓖ

...No. 1. Imperial March, Op. 32. **BBC Philharmonic Orchestra / George Hurst.**
Naxos Ⓢ 8 550634 (54 minutes: DDD: 2/94).

...Nos. 1 and 2. Cockaigne Overture, Op. 40. In the South. **London Philharmonic Orchestra /
Sir Georg Solti.** Double Decca Ⓜ 443 856-2DF2 (two discs: 135 minutes: ADD: 7/95).

...No. 1. Introduction and Allegro, Op. 47. **BBC National Orchestra of Wales / Tadaaki Otaka.**
BIS Ⓕ CD727 (69 minutes: DDD: 1/96). *Selected by Soundings.*

...No. 1[a]. Pomp and Circumstance March No. 1[b]. Introduction and Allegro, Op. 47[c].
[a]**BBC Symphony Orchestra / Sir Colin Davis;** [b]**Boston Pops Orchestra / Arthur Fiedler;**
[c]**Boston Symphony Orchestra / Charles Munch.**
RCA Victor Classical Navigator Ⓑ 74321 24217-2* (71 minutes: ADD/DDD: 2/96).

...Nos. 1[a] and 2[b]. Pomp and Circumstance Marches[c]. Cockaigne, Op. 40[b].
[ac]**Royal Philharmonic Orchestra,** [b]**London Symphony Orchestra / André Previn.**
Philips Duo Ⓜ 454 250-2PM2 (two discs: 146 minutes: DDD: 10/97).

...Nos. 1[a] and 2[b]. Pomp and Circumstance March No. 5[c]. **Philharmonia Orchestra /
Bernard Haitink.** EMI Forte Ⓜ CZS5 69761-2 (two discs: 118 minutes: DDD: 10/97).

...In the South. **Brahms** Serenade No. 1 in D major, Op. 11. **La Scala Philharmonic Orchestra,
Milan / Riccardo Muti.** Sony Classical Ⓕ SK57973 (71 minutes: DDD: 2/95).

Elgar Symphony No. 2 in E flat major, Op. 63. In the South, Op. 50, "Alassio".
BBC Symphony Orchestra / Andrew Davis. Teldec Ⓕ 9031-74888-2 (70 minutes: DDD: 11/92).
Recorded 1992. *Selected by Sounds in Retrospect.* ⒼⒼⒼ

In what is unquestionably his finest achievement on record to date, Andrew Davis penetrates right to the dark inner core of this great symphony. In the opening *Allegro vivace e nobilmente*, for example, how well he and his acutely responsive players gauge the varying moods of Elgar's glorious inspiration: be it in the exhilarating surge of that leaping introductory paragraph or the spectral, twilight world at the heart of this wonderful movement, no one is found wanting. In fact, Davis's unerring structural sense never once deserts him, and the BBC Symphony Orchestra simply play their hearts out for their music director. Above all, though, it's in the many more reflective moments that Davis proves himself an outstandingly perceptive Elgarian, uncovering a vein of intimate anguish that touches to the very marrow; in this respect, his account of the slow movement is quite heart-rendingly poignant (just listen to those BBC strings at the final climax!) – undoubtedly the finest since Boult's incomparable 1944 performance with this very same orchestra – whilst the radiant sunset of the symphony's coda glows with luminous beauty. Prefaced by an equally idiomatic, stirring *In the South* (and aided throughout by some sumptuously natural engineering), this is an Elgar Second to set beside the very greatest. In every way a treasurable release.

Additional recommendations ...
...No. 2. Cockaigne Overture. **London Philharmonic Orchestra / Sir Adrian Boult.**
EMI British Composers Ⓜ CDM7 64014-2 (68 minutes: ADD).   ⒼⒼ
...No. 2. **London Philharmonic Orchestra / Vernon Handley.**
Classics for Pleasure Ⓑ CD-CFP4544 (54 minutes: ADD: 10/88).   Ⓖ
...No. 2. In the South. **London Philharmonic Orchestra / Sir Georg Solti.**
Decca Ⓜ 436 150-2DSP (72 minutes: ADD: 8/89).   Ⓖ
...No. 2. Serenade for Strings. **London Philharmonic Orchestra / Leonard Slatkin.**
RCA Victor Ⓕ 09026 60072-2 (67 minutes: DDD: 8/89).   ⒼⒼ
...No. 2ᵃ. Serenade for Strings ᵇ. ᵃ**Hallé Orchestra / James Loughran; ᵇAcademy of St Martin in the Fields / Sir Neville Marriner.** ASV Quicksilva Ⓢ CDQS6087 (70 minutes: ADD/DDD: 8/93).
...No. 2ᵃ. Sospiriᵇ. Elegyᵇ. ᵃ**Hallé Orchestra; ᵇNew Philharmonia Orchestra / Sir John Barbirolli.**
EMI British Composers Ⓜ CDM7 64724-2 (66 minutes: ADD: 2/94).   Ⓖ
...No. 2. **BBC Philharmonic Orchestra / Sir Edward Downes.**
Naxos Ⓢ 8 550635 (56 minutes: DDD: 6/94).
...No. 2. Sea Pictures, Op. 37ᵃ. ᵃ**Della Jones** (mez); **Royal Philharmonic Orchestra / Sir Charles Mackerras.** Argo Ⓕ 443 321-2ZH (74 minutes: DDD: 12/94).
...No. 2. Cockaigne (In London Town), Op. 40. Dream children, Op. 43 No. 1. **Hallé Orchestra / Sir John Barbirolli.** EMI British Composers mono Ⓜ CDM5 66399-2* (69 minutes: ADD: 6/97).
...Chanson de matin. Chanson de nuit. *Coupled with works by various composers.*
London Philharmonic Orchestra / Sir Adrian Boult.
Belart mono Ⓑ 461 354-2* (60 minutes: ADD: 9/97).   Ⓖ

Elgar/Payne Symphony No. 3 in C minor. **BBC Symphony Orchestra / Andrew Davis.**
NMC Ⓕ NMCD053 (56 minutes: DDD: 3/98). Recorded 1997. *Gramophone Editor's choice.*
Selected by Soundings.   ⒼⒼⒼ
Elgar Symphony No. 3 – sketches and commentary by Anthony Payne. **Robert Gibbs** (vn); **David Owen Norris** (pf); **BBC Symphony Orchestra / Andrew Davis.** NMC Ⓜ NMCD052 (70 minutes: DDD: 3/98). Recorded 1997.

Elgar left 130 pages of sketches for his Third Symphony and they have haunted the composer, author and critic, Anthony Payne, ever since he first gained access to them back in 1972. Longstanding opinion was that the ideas for the symphony (which occupied Elgar during 1933, the last full year of his life) showed a sad waning of his powers. Yet Payne utterly disproves this theory. The sweeping, almost grimly defiant opening paragraph with its gaunt parallel open fifths (the first 17 bars of which Elgar actually left in full score) is hard to dislodge from one's mind, as is the sublimely wistful second subject. After an unexpected exposition repeat (Elgar's, not Payne's, in case you were wondering), the development is launched with a magical new idea, whose incense-laden mystery and penetrating harmonic scope seem to cast a wistful glance back to the world of the oratorios. From a series of seemingly unpromising fragments, Payne proceeds to fashion a movement of great power and immensely satisfying proportions, while his idiomatic orchestration will surely win him many plaudits. The winsome main idea is drawn from Elgar's 1923 incidental score for Laurence Binyon's drama, *Arthur*. There are also two contrasting episodes, the second of which features a delectable little tune in A major. By contrast, the *Adagio solenne* slow movement wears a nobly tragic, world-weary demeanour. The mournful, daringly harmonized introduction immediately grips with its pain and anguish, yet the rapt D major second subject seems to offer new hope. Between these two themes comes another one of those visionary ideas which, as Payne asserts, "positively demands the sound of muted strings". The close could hardly be more chilling, a single solo viola note hanging in the air; it was this phrase, marked *fine*, that the dying composer gave to his dear friend, the violinist W.H. Reed, uttering the famous words: "Billy, this is the end." The finale begins with a rousing fanfare (in Elgar's scoring) and struts out in bustling fashion. All the same, the thematic invention is not quite on the same level as in the remainder (much of it is again drawn from the *Arthur* music), though the second subject has a *Cockaigne*-like swagger about it. Payne's resolution is intriguing, ingenious and, naturally, very personal. It is perhaps not terribly satisfying, but everyone will form their own view – and anyway, there is so much in the preceding 55 minutes for which to be exceedingly thankful.

All praise to Andrew Davis and the BBC SO for such an eloquent, profoundly involving performance and to the production team for obtaining such handsome sound. The companion issue is also beautifully realized, with over 50 musical examples, including the sketches for violin and piano that Elgar would play through on the piano with Billy Reed. There are excellent contributions here from David Owen Norris and Robert Gibbs (the latter uses Reed's own instrument). A fascinating and, above all, deeply rewarding pair of CDs which no Elgarian will want to miss.

Elgar Introduction and Allegro, Op. 47[a]. Chanson de nuit, Op. 15 No. 1 (arr. Fraser). Chanson de matin, Op. 15 No. 2 (arr. Fraser). Three Characteristic Pieces – No. 1, Mazurka, Op. 10. Serenade for Strings in E minor, Op. 20. Salut d'amour, Op. 12 (arr. Fraser). Elegy, Op. 58.
[a]**José-Luis Garcia**, [a]**Mary Eade** (vns); [a]**Quentin Ballardie** (va); [a]**Olga Hegedus** (vc);
English Chamber Orchestra / Sir Yehudi Menuhin. Arabesque ⓕ Z6563 (45 minutes: DDD: 6/87).
From ABQ6563 (1/87). Recorded 1982.

Elgar's pieces for string orchestra contain some of his greatest music and certainly the *Introduction and Allegro*, *Serenade* and *Elegy* included in this delightful programme embody quintessential Elgar. Sir Yehudi Menuhin's readings dig deep into the hearts of these works, drawing out the nostalgia and inner tragedy that underpins even some of the most seemingly high-spirited of Elgar's music. The lighter pieces allow relief from the intensity of the major works, thus making that intensity all the more effective. The English Chamber Orchestra is more than capable of providing first-rate soloists from its own ranks, and the quartet extracted for the *Introduction and Allegro* is suitably virtuosic. Both performers and engineers have produced an ideal integration of this solo group with the main string body, and the generally effervescent sound suits the celebratory nature of the piece.

Additional recommendations ...

...Chanson de matin,[c]. Beau Brummel – Minuet[c]. The Starlight Express[ac] – My old tunes; To the children. The Wand of Youth Suite No. 1, Op. 1*a* – Sun Dance[c]. Dream children, Op. 43[c]. Salut d'amour, Op. 12[c]. Minuet, Op. 21[d]. May song[d]. Rosemary, "That's for remembrance"[d]. Romance, Op. 62[bd]. Sevillana, Op. 7[d]. Sérénade lyrique[d]. Three Characteristic Pieces, Op. 10[d]. Carissima[d]. Mina[d]. [a]**Frederick Harvey** (bar); [b]**Michael Chapman** (bn); [c]**Royal Philharmonic Orchestra / Lawrance Collingwood**; [d]**Northern Sinfonia / Sir Neville Marriner**.
EMI British Composers Ⓜ CDM5 65593-2 (79 minutes: ADD).

...Salut d'amour (with Steven Isserlis, vc). Violin Sonata in E minor, Op. 82. Six Very Easy Melodious Exercises in the First Position, Op. 22. Mot d'amour, Op. 13. In the South – Canto popolare (In Moonlight). Sospiri, Op. 70. Chanson de nuit. Chanson de matin. **Nigel Kennedy** (vn); **Peter Pettinger** (pf). Chandos ⓕ CHAN8380 (55 minutes: DDD: 8/85).

...Salut d'amour. *Coupled with works by various composers*. **Gil Shaham** (vn); **Orpheus Chamber Orchestra**. DG ⓕ 449 923-2GH (58 minutes: DDD: 3/97).

Elgar String Quartet in E minor, Op. 83[a]. Canto popolare[b]. Piano Quintet in A minor, Op. 84[c].
[ab]**Piers Lane** (pf); [ac]**Vellinger Quartet** (Stephanie Gonley, Harvey de Sousa, vns; [b]James Boyd, va; Sally Pendlebury, vc). EMI Eminence Ⓜ CD-EMX2229 (65 minutes: DDD: 3/95).
Recorded 1994.

The Vellinger Quartet bring enormous heart, effortless technical accomplishment and (most importantly) genuine freshness of new discovery to the Quartet. In both outer movements their playing ideally combines propulsive excitement with passionate flexibility, yet, at the same time, they do not miss out on the vein of wistfulness and vulnerability coursing through Elgar's glorious inspiration. For the Piano Quintet they are joined by the excellent Piers Lane. Again, the emotional temperature is high, with these young performers extracting maximum drama from the opening movement in particular. The central *Adagio*, stately and very intense, could perhaps do with greater intimacy of feeling; their account of the finale generates all the edge-of-seat thrust of a live concert. Some Elgarians may baulk at the sheer physicality and unrelenting wholeheartedness of it all but their fervour has its place too. As a further appealing bonus, Lane partners the Vellinger's violist, James Boyd, for a generously sung rendering of *In Moonlight*, more familiar as the gloriously long-breathed *Canto popolare* theme from the central portion of *In the South*. Excellent recording.

Additional recommendations ...

...String Quartet. **Delius** String Quartet. **Brodsky Quartet**.
ASV ⓕ CDDCA526 (56 minutes: DDD: 7/89).

...String Quartet. **Walton** String Quartet in A minor. **Britten Quartet**.
Collins Classics ⓕ 1280-2 (56 minutes: DDD: 7/92).

...String Quartet. *Coupled with works by* **Bridge** *and* **Walton** Coull Quartet.
Hyperion ⓕ CDA66718 (73 minutes: DDD: 10/94).

...String Quartet. Piano Quintet[a]. [a]**Peter Donohoe** (pf); **Maggini Quartet**.
Naxos Ⓢ 8 553737 (62 minutes: DDD: 9/97).

Elgar The Black Knight, Op. 25. Scenes from the Bavarian Highlands, Op. 27. **London Symphony Chorus and Orchestra / Richard Hickox**. Chandos ⓕ CHAN9436 (61 minutes: DDD: 5/96).
Texts included. Recorded 1995. *Selected by Soundings.*

The Black Knight is a large-scale, red-blooded choral setting of Longfellow's translation of a German poem by Ludwig Uhland. Elgar completed it in 1893 and it provided him with his first big success –

especially in the Midlands, where it was gratefully taken up by many choral societies. The text tells of a sinister, unnamed "Prince of mighty sway", whose appearance at the King's court during the feast of Pentecost has disastrous consequences. Elgar's score boasts much attractive invention, some of it strikingly eloquent and prescient of greater offerings to come: for example, towards the end of track 8 (the section beginning with "Each the father's breast embraces"), Elgar's touching inspiration momentarily seems to look forward to "Nimrod" and even the First Symphony's sublime slow movement. The choral writing is always effective, the orchestration already vivid and assured. Richard Hickox and his combined London Symphony forces are dab hands at this kind of fare and their performance has great bloom and spaciousness. Similarly, in the tuneful, vernally fresh *Scenes from the Bavarian Highlands* (given here with the orchestral accompaniment Elgar supplied in 1896), Hickox and his colleagues respond with commendable spirit and pleasing polish. Truth to tell, in matters of interpretation there is little to choose between this account and the rival EMI version from Norman Del Mar (see below). Typical of Chandos, the recording is bright and clear, tonally beyond reproach and with just the right balance between choir and orchestra.

Additional recommendations ...
...Scenes from the Bavarian Highlands[a]. O salutaris hostia – three settings[b]. Tantum ergo[b]. Ecce sacerdos magnus[b]. The Light of Life, Op. 29[b] – Doubt not thy Father's care!; Light of the World. **Worcester Cathedral Choir / Christopher Robinson** with [a]**Frank Wibaut** (pf); [b]**Harry Bramma** (org). Chandos Collect Ⓜ CHAN6601 (51 minutes: ADD: 9/94).
...Scenes from the Bavarian Highlands[a]. **Stanford** Symphony No. 3 in F minor, Op. 28[a], "Irish". [a]**Bournemouth Symphony Chorus; Bournemouth Sinfonietta / Norman Del Mar.** EMI British Composers Ⓜ CDM5 65129-2 (70 minutes: ADD: 7/95). *See review under Stanford; refer to the Index.*

Elgar The Light of Life (Lux Christi), Op. 29. **Judith Howarth** (sop); **Linda Finnie** (mez); **Arthur Davies** (ten); **John Shirley-Quirk** (bar); **London Symphony Chorus and Orchestra / Richard Hickox.** Chandos Ⓔ CHAN9208 (63 minutes: DDD: 5/94). Text included. Recorded 1993.
Hickox's Elgarian credentials are immediately established in the glorious orchestral "Meditation", where his conducting demonstrates a noble flexibility, sensitivity to dynamic nuance and feeling for climax. Equally the engineering, sumptuous yet detailed, comes close to the ideal. The LSO and Chorus contribute to proceedings in exemplary, disciplined fashion. As The Blind Man, Arthur Davies could hardly be more ardent, but his slightly tremulous timbre will not be to all tastes. John Shirley-Quirk, so eloquent and firm-toned a Jesus for Groves back in 1980, now shows signs of unsteadiness in the same part. On the other hand, Linda Finnie and Judith Howarth make a creditable showing. Hickox's reading excels in precisely the areas where the Groves was deficient, and vice versa. If you already have the Groves reissue, hang on to it, for it is by no means outclassed by the Hickox. However, for anyone coming to this underrated score for the first time, Hickox's must now be the preferred version.

Additional recommendations ...
...Soloists; Liverpool Philharmonic Choir; Royal Liverpool Philharmonic Orchestra / Sir Charles Groves. EMI British Composers Ⓜ CDM7 64732-2 (64 minutes: ADD: 5/93).
...The Light of Life – Meditation. The Apostles[a]. [a]**Sheila Armstrong** (sop); [a]**Helen Watts** (contr); [a]**Robert Tear** (ten); [a]**Benjamin Luxon, John Carol Case** (bars); [a]**Clifford Grant** (bass); [a]**London Philharmonic Choir;** [a]**Downe House School Choir; London Philharmonic Orchestra / Sir Adrian Boult.** EMI Ⓜ CMS7 64206-2 (two discs: 127 minutes: ADD).

Elgar The Music Makers, Op. 69[a]. Dream children, Op. 43. Elegy, Op. 58. Sursum corda, Op. 11. Sospiri, Op. 70. Chanson de matin, Op. 15 No. 2. Chanson de nuit, Op. 15 No. 1. Salut d'amour, Op. 12. [a]**Jean Rigby** (mez); [a]**BBC Symphony Chorus and Orchestra / Andrew Davis.** Teldec British Line Ⓔ 4509-92374-2 (76 minutes: DDD: 2/95). Text included. Recorded 1993. ⒼⒼ
Gramophone Editor's choice.
Davis strikes right to the heart of *The Music Makers* and the results are profoundly idiomatic and enchanting. Indeed, 'special' moments abound in this performance: note the chilling hush of Elgar's prescribed *ppp* marking at the words "In the buried past of the earth" (7'24"); the ravishing tone Davis draws from his excellent choir for "A breath of our inspiration" (11'43"); and how touching is his handling of that sublime passage beginning at 25'52" ("O men! it must ever be/That we dwell, in our dreaming and singing,/A little apart from ye"), with its poignant intertwining of themes from the *Enigma* Variations and the Violin Concerto. Even more than the admirable Bryden Thomson, Davis underlines the intensely personal nature of Elgar's inspiration, whilst at the same time doing full justice to this underrated score's dreams and aspirations. The predominantly wistful atmosphere of the main work carries over into the two exquisite miniatures which comprise *Dream children*; Davis and the BBC orchestra capture their nostalgic mood to perfection, and prove to be no less affectionate advocates of the two *Chansons* and *Salut d'amour*. Similarly, both the *Elegy* and *Sospiri* find the BBC strings at their very finest. The sound is sumptuous.

Additional recommendation ...
...The Music Makers[a]. Sea Pictures, Op. 37. **Linda Finnie** (contr); **London Philharmonic** [a]**Choir and Orchestra / Bryden Thomson.** Chandos Ⓔ CHAN9022 (64 minutes: DDD: 3/92).

Elgar Sea Pictures, Op. 37. The Music Makers, Op. 69[a]. **Felicity Palmer** (mez);
London Symphony [a]Chorus and Orchestra / Richard Hickox. EMI British Composers
Ⓜ CDM5 65126-2 (62 minutes: DDD: 5/96). Texts included. From EL270589-1 (4/87).
These idiomatic Elgar performances from Richard Hickox well merit their mid-price resuscitation
within EMI's British Composers series. Strong competition for the coupling of *The Music Makers* and
Sea Pictures comes in the shape of Bryden Thomson's committed Chandos release. If Thomson has
the advantage of more lustrous engineering, Hickox's admirable London Symphony Chorus score
over Thomson's London Philharmonic voices in matters of intonation and diction. Felicity Palmer
(for Hickox) sings commandingly in both works, though her contribution in *The Music Makers*
doesn't always generate the tear-laden intensity the part requires. However, neither Hickox nor
Thomson quite match Andrew Davis's Teldec account – he in particular evinces a personal
identification with Elgar's inspiration that is rather special. In the *Sea Pictures*, however, Hickox and
Palmer form an intelligent, distinctive partnership, less endearing, perhaps, than many would like in
"In Haven" and "Where corals lie", yet tough and dramatic in "Sabbath morning at sea" and "The
swimmer". It is a thrusting, unsentimental view which is most refreshing. The orchestral playing is
excellent.

Elgar The Dream of Gerontius, Op. 38[a]. Cello Concerto in E minor, Op. 85[b]. [a]**Gladys Ripley**
(contr); [a]**Heddle Nash** (ten); [a]**Dennis Noble** (bar); [a]**Norman Walker** (bass); [b]**Paul Tortelier** (vc);
[a]**Huddersfield Choral Society;** [b]**BBC Symphony Orchestra;** [a]**Liverpool Philharmonic Orchestra /
Sir Malcolm Sargent.** Testament mono Ⓕ SBT2025* (two discs: 120 minutes: ADD: 2/94).   Ⓖ Ⓖ
Text included. Item marked [a] from HMV C3435/46 (6/45), [b]HMV BLP1043 (4/54).
This pioneering set of *Gerontius* has come up newly minted in these superbly engineered transfers
taken from 78rpm masters. That only enhances the incandescence and fervour of the reading itself, in
virtually all respects the most convincing the work has received. Sargent's conducting, influenced by
Elgar's, is direct, vital and urgently crafted with an inborn feeling for the work's ebb and flow and an
overall picture that comprehends the piece's spiritual meaning while realizing its dramatic leanness
and force. Heddle Nash's Gerontius is unrivalled in its conviction and inwardness. He was encouraged
by Elgar in 1930 to take the part and sang it under the composer's baton in 1932 to his satisfaction.
By 1945 the work was in Nash's being; he sang it from memory and had mastered every facet of
interpreting it. Such phrases as "Mary pray for me", "Novissima hora est" and "My soul is in my
hand, I have no fear" come from and go to the heart. "Take me away" is like a searing cry of pain
from the depth of the singer's soul. Gladys Ripley is a natural and communicative Angel throughout,
her flexible and appealing tone always a pleasure to hear. The Liverpool Philharmonic lives up to its
reputation at the time as the country's leading orchestra (in particular the sonorous string section) and
the Huddersfield Choral Society sing as though their lives depended on the outcome. Tortelier's Cello
Concerto presents the classical approach as compared with the romantic one of Du Pré, and is the
best of Tortelier's readings of the work on disc, with his tone and phrasing at their finest and most
telling. A considered and unaffected reading among the best ever committed to disc.
Additional recommendations ...
...The Dream of Gerontius[a]. **Holst** The Hymn of Jesus, Op. 37[b]. [a]**Yvonne Minton** (mez);
[a]**Sir Peter Pears** (ten); [a]**John Shirley-Quirk** (bar); [a]**Choir of King's College, Cambridge;**
[a]**London Symphony Chorus and Orchestra / Benjamin Britten;** [b]**BBC Chorus and Symphony
Orchestra / Sir Adrian Boult.**
Decca London Ⓜ 421 381-2LM2 (two discs: 113 minutes: ADD: 5/89).   Ⓖ
...The Dream of Gerontius[a]. Sea Pictures, Op. 37[b]. **Dame Janet Baker** (mez); [a]**Richard Lewis** (ten);
[a]**Kim Borg** (bass); [a]**Hallé Choir;** [a]**Sheffield Philharmonic Chorus;** [a]**Ambrosian Singers;**
[b]**London Symphony Orchestra;** [a]**Hallé Orchestra / Sir John Barbirolli.**
EMI Studio Ⓜ CMS7 63185-2 (two discs: 122 minutes: ADD: 12/89).
...The Dream of Gerontius[a]. Organ Sonata No. 1 in G major, Op. 28 (orch. Jacob). [a]**Soloists;**
[a]**Huddersfield Choral Society; Liverpool Philharmonic [a]Choir and Orchestra / Vernon Handley.**
EMI Eminence Ⓜ CD-EMXD2500 (two discs: 119 minutes: DDD: 10/93).

Elgar The Spirit of England, Op. 80[a]. Give unto the Lord, Op. 74. O hearken thou, Op. 64.
The Snow, Op. 26 No. 1. Land of Hope and Glory (arr. Fagge). [a]**Felicity Lott** (sop);
London Symphony Chorus; Northern Sinfonia / Richard Hickox. EMI British Composers
Ⓜ CDM5 65586-2 (52 minutes: DDD: 5/96). Texts included. From CDC7 49481-2 (1/89).
Hickox adopts a purposeful approach to the great wartime cantata, *The Spirit of England.* Many
collectors got to know this compassionate and moving score through Sir Alexander Gibson's
extremely fine 1976 recording (originally made for RCA, now reissued at mid price on Chandos).
Gibson's spacious and eloquent interpretation enshrined one of his very finest achievements in the
studio, and possibly this EMI rival doesn't match it in sheer depth of feeling. That said, Hickox draws
some magnificent singing from the London Symphony Chorus and his mobile reading compensates
with a fervour to which many will positively respond. The fillers are all worth having, especially
the sublime coronation Offertory from 1911, *O harken thou.* The production lacks nothing in
transparency and amplitude, though in *The Spirit of England* one ideally craves a more expansive
acoustic.

Additional recommendations ...

...The Spirit of England[b]. Coronation Ode, Op. 44[a]. [ab]Teresa Cahill (sop); [a]Anne Collins (contr); [a]Anthony Rolfe Johnson (ten); [a]Gwynne Howell (bass); **Scottish National Chorus and Orchestra / Sir Alexander Gibson.** Chandos Collect Ⓜ CHAN6574 (67 minutes: ADD: 11/92).

...Give unto the Lord[a]. O hearken Thou[a]. Ave verum corpus, Op. 2 No. 1[a]. Ave Maria, Op. 2 No. 2[a]. Ave maris stella, Op. 2 No. 3[a]. Vesper Voluntaries, Op. 14[b] – Introduction; Allegro. Angelus, Op. 56 No. 1[a]. Te Deum and Benedictus, Op. 34[a]. Organ Sonata No. 1 in G major, Op. 28[c]. [c]Herbert Sumsion (org); [a]**Worcester Cathedral Choir / Christopher Robinson** ([b]org) with [a]**Harry Bramma** (org). EMI British Composers Ⓜ CDM5 65594-2 (76 minutes: ADD: 11/96).

Elgar's Interpreters on Record, Volume 1. [e]Dora Labbette, [h]Alice Moxon (sops); [b]Dame Clara Butt, [c]Kathleen Ferrier (contrs); [b]Maurice d'Oisly, [d]Tudor Davies, [e]Hubert Eisdell (tens); [c]Dennis Noble, [e]Harold Williams, [h]Stuart Robertson (bars); [f]Peter Dawson (bass-bar); [e]Robert Easton (bass); [c]Gerald Moore (pf); [a]Black Diamonds Band; [b]New Queen's Hall Orchestra / Sir Henry Wood; [d]Symphony Orchestra / Sir Eugene Goossens; [e]Hallé Orchestra / Sir Hamilton Harty; [f]orchestra / Sir John Barbirolli; [g]St George's Chapel Choir, Windsor / Sir Walford Davies; [i]Light Symphony Orchestra / Haydn Wood; [j]Glasgow Orpheus Choir / Sir Hugh Roberton.** Dutton Laboratories Elgar Society mono Ⓜ CDAX8019* (76 minutes: ADD: 8/97). From Zonophone, Columbia and HMV originals; recorded 1912-48. Crown of India – March of the Mogul Emperors[a]. The Dream of Gerontius, Op. 38[b] – My work is done; I see not those false spirits; We now have passed the gate; Softly and gently. The Dream of Gerontius, Op. 38[c] – My work is done; It is because then thou didst fear. The Saga of King Olaf, Op. 30 – And King Olaf heard the cry![d]. The Apostles, Op. 49 – By the Wayside[e]. Caractacus, Op. 35[f] – Leap, leap to light; O my warriors. O hearken thou, Op. 64[g]. The Starlight Express[h] – O children, open your arms to me; There is a fairy hides in the beautiful eyes; I'm everywhere; My Old Tunes; Dustman, Laugher's Song. Songs (arr. Haydn Wood)[i] – Like to the damask rose; Queen Mary's song; Shepherd's Song, Op. 16 No. 1; Rondel, Op. 16 No. 3. The shower, Op. 71 No. 1[j].

The great composers, we know, are for all time, but there is still something special about them in their own era, especially if it should be close to that of the listener. This wonderful collection of recordings, made for the most part in Elgar's own lifetime, has not only authenticity of period; for those born into that time it is something to be played and savoured where no absurdity of unmeasured response will be wondered at, or, ever so kindly, derided. The voices of the soloists, for instance. A snigger at Dame Clara Butt's Angel in *The Dream of Gerontius* would incite thoughts of murder. Those five who sing the Beatitudes and commentary in *The Apostles*, they too are so wonderfully of their period, and fine singers too. Tudor Davies, fiery as a Welsh Martinelli in his declamation of Olaf's saga, or Peter Dawson, exponent of "singing that *was* singing" in *Caractacus*: these also are part of the sacred book. Kathleen Ferrier's test recording is movingly lovely to hear again, as, for that matter, is the Glasgow Orpheus Choir. In fact, not forgetting some of the less likely contents, this is an anthological treasure. Wondrously clean transfers have been mastered by Dutton Laboratories. Just hear that first track, the *Crown of India* March, and make a guess, without looking, at the date; or, listening with perfect clarity to that record from *The Apostles*, recall how the light blue label whizzed round amid the gunge and dust bequeathed by the second-hand shop whence it came. But everything is for congratulations here, including the admirable booklet-notes by John Knowles.

Further listening ...

...The Elgar Edition, Volume 2. **Sir Yehudi Menuhin** (vn); **London Symphony Orchestra; Royal Albert Hall Orchestra; New Symphony Orchestra; London Philharmonic Orchestra / Sir Edward Elgar.** EMI Elgar Edition mono CDS7 54564-2* (2/93).   ⒼⒼⒼ

...The Elgar Edition, Volume 3. **Sir Edward Elgar** (pf); **London Philharmonic Orchestra; Royal Albert Hall Orchestra; London Symphony Orchestra; New Symphony Orchestra; BBC Symphony Orchestra / Sir Edward Elgar, Lawrence Collingwood, Sir Landon Ronald. New Light Symphony Orchestra / J. Ainslie Murray. Light Symphony Orchestra / Haydn Wood.** EMI Elgar Edition mono CDS7 54568-2* (8/93). *Gramophone Editor's choice.*   ⒼⒼⒼ

...Three Bavarian Dances, Op. 27. *Coupled with works by* **Arnold** and **Walton**. **London Philharmonic Orchestra / Sir Adrian Boult.** Belart mono 461 359-2* (9/97).

...Carissima. *Coupled with works by various composers.* **The New London Orchestra / Ronald Corp.** Hyperion CDA66968 (5/97). *Gramophone Editor's choice.*   Ⓖ

...The Wand of Youth – Suites Nos. 1 and 2, Opp. 1a and 1b. Nursery Suite. **Ulster Orchestra / Bryden Thomson.** Chandos CHAN8318 (10/84).

...Organ Sonata No. 1 in G major, Op. 28. *Coupled with works by* **Bairstow** and **Harris**. **John Scott** (org). Priory PRCD401 (8/94).

...Organ Sonata No. 1 in G major, Op. 28. *Coupled with works by various composers.* **Christopher Herrick** (org). Hyperion CDA66778 (3/96). *See review in the Collections section; refer to the Index.*

...Violin Sonata in E minor, Op. 82. *Coupled with* **Walton** Violin Sonata. **Lorraine McAslan** (vn); **John Blakely** (pf). ASV Quicksilva CDQS6191 (11/96).

...The Apostles. **Soloists; London Symphony Chorus; London Symphony Orchestra / Richard Hickox.** Chandos CHAN8875/6 (12/90).   Ⓖ

...Ave verum corpus, Op. 2 No. 1. *Coupled with works by various composers.* **St Paul's Cathedral Choir / John Scott** with **Andrew Lucas** (org). Hyperion CDA66826 (7/96).

...Caractacus, Op. 35ª. Severn Suite, Op. 87*a.* ªJudith Howarth (mez); ªArthur Davies (ten); ªDavid Wilson-Johnson, ªStephen Roberts (bars); ªAlistair Miles (bass); **London Symphony ªChorus and Orchestra / Richard Hickox.** Chandos CHAN9156/7 (2/93).

...Partsongs – Opp. 18, 53, 71 and 73. Five Partsongs from the Greek Anthology, Op. 45. Death on the hills, Op. 72. How calmly the evening. Weary Wind of the West. Evening scene. The Prince of Sleep. Go, song of mine, Op. 57. **Finzi Singers / Paul Spicer.** Chandos CHAN9269 (1/95).

...Five Partsongs from the Greek Anthology. The Wanderer. Reveille, Op. 54. *Coupled with works by various composers.* **London Madrigal Singers / Christopher Bishop; Baccholian Singers of London; Philip Jones Brass Ensemble; English Chamber Orchestra / Ian Humphris.** EMI British Composers CMS5 65123-2 (2/96). *See review in the Collections section; refer to the Index.*

...Te Deum and Benedictus, Op. 34 – Te Deum. *Coupled with works by various composers.* **Norwich Cathedral Choir / Michael Nicholas** with **Neil Taylor** (org). Priory PRCD470 (10/94).

Maurice Emmanuel

French 1862-1938

Suggested listening ...

...Chansons bourguignonnes du Pays de Beaune, Op. 15 – Quand j'ai sôti de mon villaige; Il était une fille, une fille d'honneur; Le pommier d'Août; Noël; Complainte de Notre Dame; Aidieu, bargeire!. *Coupled with* **Canteloube** Chants d'Auvergne – excerpts. **Dawn Upshaw** (sop); **Orchestra of the Opéra de Lyon / Kent Nagano.** Erato 0630-17577-2 (10/97). *See review under Canteloube; refer to the Index.*

Juan del Encina

Spanish 1468-1529

Suggested listening ...

...Mi libertad en sosiego. Los sospiros no sosiegan. *Coupled with works by various composers.* **Gothic Voices / Christopher Page** with **Christopher Wilson** (vihuela) and **Andrew Lawrence-King** (hp). Hyperion CDA66653 (2/94). *See review in the Collections section; refer to the Index.* Ⓖ

...Más vale trocar. Si abrá en este baldrés! Qu'es de ti, desconsolado? Hoy comamos y bevamos. *Coupled with works by various composers.* **La Romanesca / José Miguel Moreno** (vihuela). Glossa GCD920203 (5/96). ✍ *See review in the Collections section; refer to the Index.* Ⓖ

...Triste España sin ventura! Antonilla es desposada. Tan buen ganadico. Mi libertad en sosiego. Pues que tú, Reina del cielo. Cucú, cucú, cucú. *Coupled with works by various composers.* **La Columbina.** Accent ACC95111D (11/96). *See review in the Collections section; refer to the Index.*

...Triste España sin ventura!. Cucú, cucú, cucú cú. Hoy comamos y be bamos. Mas vale trocar. *Coupled with works by various composers.* **The Hilliard Ensemble.** Virgin Classics Veritas VED5 61394-2 (11/97). *See review in the Collections section; refer to the Index.*

George Enescu

Romanian 1881-1955

Enescu Symphonies – No. 1 in E flat major, Op. 13; No. 2 in A major, Op. 17. **Monte-Carlo Philharmonic Orchestra / Lawrence Foster.** EMI Ⓕ CDC7 54763-2 (78 minutes: DDD: 9/93). Recorded 1990-92. *Gramophone Editor's choice.* Ⓖ

Brahmsian in colour the First Symphony may very well be, but the rhythmic vigour of its outer movements is quite unlike Brahms. Wagner? Well, any 24-year-old in 1905 writing a slow movement with moments of romantic yearning to it may be permitted to veer towards *Tristan.* Strauss may be the first name which springs to mind when listening to the Second Symphony, but by then Enescu's orchestration, highly individual and remarkably refined, had matured: 'Strauss', here, is merely a metaphor for richness of incident and colour. There is a flavour of Rachmaninov to the Second Symphony's slow movement, and an apparent kinship with Mahler, audible in the tense, martial finale, an apparent reaction to the outbreak of the First World War. Apart from the vividly imaginative orchestration, Enescu's own voice is heard most clearly in his extremely detailed and complex working of what is often basically bold and clear-cut melodic material. The symphonies are accomplished, immaculately crafted, and add up to distinctly more than the sum of their sometimes only apparent influences. Lawrence Foster's direction is brilliantly successful in ensuring that the wood is not obscured by all its luxuriant foliage; the recording is natural but very clear.

Additional recommendations ...

...No. 1. Overture on popular Romanian themes in A major, Op. 32. Study Symphony No. 4 in E flat major. **Romanian National Radio Orchestra / Horia Andreescu.** Olympia Ⓕ OCD441 (79 minutes: DDD: 11/94).

...No. 2. Romanian Rhapsodies, Op. 11. **Romanian National Radio Orchestra / Horia Andreescu.**
Olympia ℗ OCD442 (72 minutes: DDD: 11/94).
...No. 3 in C major, Op. 71. Poème roumain, Op. 1ᵃ. **Romanian National Radio** ᵃ**Chorus and
Orchestra / Horia Andreescu.** Olympia ℗ OCD443 (71 minutes: DDD: 11/94).
...No. 1. Suite No. 3 in D major, Op. 27, "Villageoise". **BBC Philharmonic Orchestra /
Gennadi Rozhdestvensky.** Chandos ℗ CHAN9507 (66 minutes: DDD: 3/97).
Further listening ...
...Romanian Rhapsody in A major, Op. 11 No. 1. *Coupled with works by various composers.*
Montreal Symphony Orchestra / Charles Dutoit.
Decca 452 482-2DH (5/97). *See review in the Collections section; refer to the Index.*
...Suites – No. 2 in C major, Op. 20; No. 3 in D major, Op. 27, "Villageoise". Andantino.
Romanian National Radio Orchestra / Horia Andreescu. Olympia OCD495 (11/95).
...Symphonie concertante, Op. 8ᵃ. Suite No. 1 in C major, Op. 9. Two Intermezzos, Op. 12.
ᵃ**Marin Cazacu** (vc); **Romanian National Radio Orchestra / Horia Andreescu.**
Olympia OCD444 (6/95).
...Impressions d'enfance, Op. 28ᵃ. *Coupled with works by various composers.* **Gidon Kremer** (vn);
Oleg Maisenberg (pf). Teldec 0630-13597-2 (7/97). *Gramophone Editor's choice. See review in the
Collections section; refer to the Index.*
...String Octet in C major, Op. 7. *Coupled with works by* **Shostakovich** and **R. Strauss**
Academy of St Martin in the Fields Chamber Ensemble. Chandos CHAN9131 (5/93).
...Violin Sonata No. 3 in A minor, Op. 25, "dans le caractère populaire roumain". *Coupled with
works by various composers.* **Sir Yehudi Menuhin** (vn); **Hepzibah Menuhin** (pf).
Biddulph mono LAB066* (6/93).   ⊛⊛⊛

Donald Erb   American 1927

Erb Remembrancesᵃ. Solo Violin Sonataᵇ. Sunlit Peaks and Dark Valleysᶜ. Harp Sonataᵈ.
Changesᵉ. ᵃ**David Spences, Ryan Anthony** (tpts); ᵇ**Gregory Fulkerson** (vn); ᶜ**Verdehr Trio;**
ᵈ**Yolanda Kondonassis** (hp); ᵉ**Ross Powell** (cl); ᵉ**Jo Boatright** (keybds). New World ℗ 80537-2
(72 minutes: DDD: 2/98).
This is a fascinating disc. Erb's voice can sometimes sound ungrateful in all-orchestral programmes,
but not so here in these instrumental works which date from 1994-95. Each piece is full of
extraordinary sonorities. Best of all are the Harp Sonata and *Remembrances*, though there is not a
single unappealing item and all are brilliantly played.

Pedro de Escobar   Portuguese c1465-1535

Suggested listening ...
...Clamabat autem mulier. Pásame por Dios barquero. Salve regina. *Coupled with works by various
composers.* **The Hilliard Ensemble.** Virgin Classics Veritas VED5 61394-2 (11/97). *See review in the
Collections section; refer to the Index.*

Edmund Eysler   Austrian 1874-1949

Suggested listening ...
...Bruder Straubinger – Küssen ist keine Sünd. Der lachende Ehemann – Weinlied. *Coupled with
works by various composers.* **Jerry Hadley** (ten); **Munich Radio Orchestra / Richard Bonynge.**
RCA Victor Red Seal 09026 68258-2 (9/97). *Gramophone Editor's choice. See review in the
Collections section; refer to the Index.*

Marco Facoli   Italian 16th century

Suggested listening ...
...Pass'e mezzo moderno. *Coupled with works by various composers.* **Rinaldo Alessandrini** (hpd).
Opus 111 OPS30-118 (4/95). ✔ *See review in the Collections section; refer to the Index.*

Leo Fall   Austrian 1873-1925

Suggested listening ...
...Die Rose von Stambul – Ein Walzer muss es sein; O Rose von Stambul. *Coupled with works
by various composers.* **Jerry Hadley** (ten); **Munich Radio Orchestra / Richard Bonynge.**
RCA Victor Red Seal 09026 68258-2 (9/97). *Gramophone Editor's choice. See review in
the Collections section; refer to the Index.*

Manuel de Falla

Falla El sombrero de tres picos[a]. Harpsichord Concerto[b]. [a]**Maria Lluisa Muntada** (sop);
[b]**Jaime Martin** (fl); [b]**Manuel Angulo** (ob); [b]**Joan-Enric Lluna** (cl); [b]**Santiago Juan** (vn);
[b]**Jorge Pozas** (vc); [b]**Tony Millan** (hpd); [a]**Spanish National Youth Orchestra / Edmon Colomer.**
Auvidis Valois Ⓕ V4642 (56 minutes: DDD: 9/92). Recorded 1989.

Falla's *El sombrero de tres picos* ("The three-cornered hat") started life as a 'mimed farce', but
Diaghilev then persuaded the composer to revise and enlarge it as a one-act ballet for his company
which had its première in London in 1919. Besides the orchestra, it features a soprano solo warning
wives to resist temptation and cries of "Olé" from men's voices representing a bullring crowd. Much
of the score consists of dances such as the fandango and seguidillas, while the finale is a jota. This
performance by Maria Lluisa Muntada and the Spanish National Youth Orchestra, playing under the
direction of their founder Edmon Colomer, brings to us all the vivid colours, intense melodies and
vigorous rhythms that together evoke that southernmost province of Spain which is Andalusia. These
artists clearly love and understand this music and they bring tremendous gusto to the famous
"Miller's Dance" (the longest single number) with its chunky chords getting louder and faster. The
Harpsichord Concerto, completed in 1926, shows us another side of Falla and was among the first
twentieth-century compositions for the instrument. It is less obviously Spanish in style and instead
more neo-classical – indeed, Stravinsky was probably the chief model – although we may detect an
Iberian element in its directness and even toughness. With just five instruments playing alongside the
soloist, it is really a chamber work, but the writing is so powerful that the composer's title is doubtless
justified. Here, too, the playing is fine and the recording of both these works is full-blooded and
atmospheric.

Additional recommendations ...

...El sombrero de tres picos. El amor brujo – ballet[b]. **Colette Boky** (sop); [b]**Huguette Tourangeau**
(mez); **Montreal Symphony Orchestra / Charles Dutoit.**
Decca Ⓕ 410 008-2DH (62 minutes: DDD: 8/83).

...Siete canciones populares españolas. El amor brujo – Canción del fuego fátuo. Soneto a
Córdoba. Harpsichord Concerto. *Coupled with works by various composers.* **Maria Barrientos,
Ninon Vallin** (sops); **Enrique Granados, Federico Mompou, Joaquin Nin** (pfs); **Manuel de Falla**
(pf/hpd); **instrumental ensemble.** EMI Composers in Person mono Ⓕ CDC7 54836-2*
(78 minutes: ADD: 11/93). *See review in the Collections section; refer to the Index.*

...El amor brujo – Suite. El sombrero de tres picos – Suites[b]. Noches en los jardines de España[a].
Dukas L'apprenti sorcier. [a]**Clifford Curzon** (pf); **National Symphony Orchestra,**
[b]**London Symphony Orchestra / Enrique Jordá.**
Dutton Laboratories mono Ⓜ CDK1202* (77 minutes: ADD: 12/96).

Falla El amor brujo – ballet (complete)[a]. Noches en los jardines de España[b].
Rodrigo Concierto de Aranjuez[c]. [a]**Huguette Tourangeau** (mez); [c]**Carlos Bonnell** (gtr);
[b]**Alicia de Larrocha** (pf); [ac]**Montreal Symphony Orchestra / Charles Dutoit;** [b]**London Philharmonic
Orchestra / Rafael Frühbeck de Burgos.** Decca Ovation Ⓜ 430 703-2DM
(71 minutes: DDD: 8/91). Item marked [a] from SXDL7560 (7/83), [b]410 289-2DH (10/84),
[c]SXDL7525 (7/81). Recorded 1980-83.   Ⓖ

Decca's hugely enjoyable disc of Spanish music includes Rodrigo's most famous work, the *Concierto
de Aranjuez* which has never lost its popularity since its Barcelona première in 1940 and here Carlos
Bonnell imparts a wistful, intimate feeling to the work, aided by a thoughtful accompaniment from
Charles Dutoit's stylish Montreal Orchestra. The famous string tune in the *Adagio* enjoys a fulsome
rendition. Dutoit's beautifully played interpretation of *El amor brujo* captures the wide range of
emotions that this fiery, mysterious piece requires and his performance of the famous "Ritual Fire
Dance" must be among the best in the catalogue. A cooler mood is captured in *Nights in the gardens
of Spain* with Alicia de Larrocha as the distinguished soloist. Her smooth, effortless playing matches
the mood of the piece exactly and de Burgos's accompaniment with the London Philharmonic is
equally sympathetic, with ripe tone colour and careful dynamics. Those unfamiliar with these great
Spanish works will be hard pressed to find a better introduction than this superbly recorded disc.

Additional recommendations ...

...El amor brujo[ac]. Siete canciones populares españolas[ab]. Serenata[b]. Serenata andaluza[b].
[a]**Martha Senn** (mez); [b]**Maria Rosa Bodini** (pf); [c]**Carme Ensemble / Luis Izquierdo.**
Nuova Era Ⓕ 6809 (57 minutes: DDD: 5/90).

...Noches en los jardines de España. *Coupled with works by* **Albéniz** and **Turina**
Alicia de Larrocha (pf); **London Philharmonic Orchestra / Rafael Frühbeck de Burgos.**
Decca Ⓕ 410 289-2DH (52 minutes: DDD: 10/84). *See review under Albéniz; refer to the Index.* Ⓖ

...Noches en los jardines de España. *Coupled with works by* **Ravel**
Francois-Joël Thiollier (pf); **Polish National Radio Symphony Orchestra / Antoni Wit.**
Naxos Ⓢ 8 550753 (44 minutes: DDD: 3/95).

...El amor brujo[a]. El sombrero de tres picos[b] – Dance of the Miller's Wife; Neighbours' Dance;
Miller's Dance; Final Dance. **Stravinsky** The Firebird – Concert Suite[c]. [a]**Grace Bumbry** (mez);
Berlin Radio Symphony Orchestra / Lorin Maazel.
DG The Originals Ⓜ 447 414-2GOR (65 minutes: ADD: 10/95).

Falla Quatre pièces espagnoles. Fantasía bética. La vida breve – Danse espagnoles No. 1.
Serenata andaluza. El Retablo de Maese Pedro – Sinfonia.
Montsalvatge Divagación. Three divertimentos on themes of forgotten composers. Si, à
Mompou. Berceuse a la memoria de Oscar Esplá. Sonatine pour Yvette. **Alicia de Larrocha** (pf).
RCA Victor Red Seal ℗ 09026 61389-2 (70 minutes: DDD: 9/94). Recorded 1992.   🅖🅖
It is odd of RCA to label this disc "Serenata andaluza" when half of it is occupied by music by a
Catalan composer with nothing Andalusian about him. The popularity of Montsalvatge's *Canciones
negras* has misled some commentators into exaggerating the West Indian calypso influence on his
output: a truer perspective on his style is offered by this selection of his piano music. From the
Divertimentos of 1942 only the habanera, with its echoes of Milhaud's *Saudades do Brasil*, falls into
the West Indian category. These pieces were dedicated to Alicia de Larrocha and the cheerful
Divagación was a wedding present to her. The *Sonatine* was written in 1962 for his then ten-year-old
daughter, obviously not for her to play (unless she was the most extraordinary child super-virtuoso of
all time) but as a musical portrait of her vivacious and temperamental moods. Larrocha takes the
first movement gently and quietly and the second with impassioned depth: the entertaining finale
(which quotes the most famous of nursery tunes) is as brilliant as ever. It then comes as a surprise to
find a very different, tougher idiom in the two *in memoriam* pieces (for left hand only) for older
contemporaries. In the Falla works Larrocha has surpassed herself. In the austere, penetrating and
incisive *Fantasía bética*, so elusive to bring off in performance, she displays great tonal imagination
throughout, confirming her status as the foremost interpreter today of Spanish keyboard music.
Additional recommendations ...
...La vida breve – Danses espagnoles Nos. 1 and 2. El amor brujo – Ritual Fire Dance. *Coupled
with works by various composers.* **Katia and Marielle Labèque** (pfs). Philips ℗ 438 938-2PH
(59 minutes: DDD: 9/94). *See review in the Collections section; refer to the Index.*
...La vida breve – Danses espagnoles Nos. 1 and 2 (arr. Samazeuilh). El amor brujo – Pantomime
(arr. Dougherty); Ritual Fire Dance (arr. Braggiotti). *Coupled with works by various composers.*
Sequeira Costa, Artur Pizarro (pfs). Collins Classics ℗ 1466-2 (62 minutes: DDD: 10/96).   🅖
See review in the Collections section; refer to the Index.
...(arr. Kreisler) La vida breve – Danse espagnole No. 1. *Coupled with works by various composers.*
Kennedy (vn); **John Lenehan** (pf). EMI ℗ CDC5 56626-2 (75 minutes: ADD: 5/98). *See review in
the Collections section; refer to the Index.*

Falla Atlántida (arr. E. Halffter)[a]. El sombrero de tres picos[b]. [a]**Enriqueta Tarrés,**
[b]**Victoria de los Angeles** (sops); [a]**Anna Ricci** (mez); [a]**Eduardo Giménez** (ten); [a]**Vincente Sardinero**
(bar); [a]**Children's Chorus of Our Lady of Remembrance;** [a]**Spanish National Chorus and Orchestra;**
[b]**Philharmonia Orchestra / Rafael Frühbeck de Burgos.** EMI Matrix Ⓜ CMS5 65997-2
(two discs, 146 minutes: DDD: 1/97). Texts and translations included.
Item marked [a] from HMV SLS5116 (5/78), [b]ASD604 (11/64).
Not even the devoted efforts of Falla's pupil Ernesto Halffter could succeed in making a convincing
whole of the oratorio his master left in a jumble of disorganized fragments. Both textually and
musically it remains a disparate collection of ideas that the composer, through ill-health and the
depression caused by the cumulative effects of the Spanish civil war, an unhappy refuge in Argentina
and then the great European war, was for over two decades unable to muster into order. Yet it was
conceived with the most elevated of aims – a mystic 're-emergence' of submerged Atlantis signifying
a celebration of Spain's extending the bounds of Christianity. There is much splendid music in the
widest diversity of styles, particularly for the chorus who, with a baritone narrator, carry the main
weight of the work. Sardinero is a noble-voiced narrator, Ricci brings pathos to her solo as the dying
Queen Pyrene; in the charmingly folk-like "Isabella's dream" a steadier line than Tarrés produces
would have been preferable. The chorus, who have some of the most impressive sections, are mostly
good, though once or twice showing signs of tiredness; and the orchestra provide useful support. In
view of its troubled genesis, the work is inevitably flawed, and some people might prefer merely a suite
of its finest sections; but the full Halffter reconstruction, now accepted as definitive, gives us a glimpse
of the masterpiece *Atlántida* might have been. There have been other excellent performances of the
ever-fresh *Three-cornered hat*, but none better than this imaginative and scintillating reading by
Frühbeck and the Philharmonia. So vivacious and idiomatic is the playing, so flexible and alive to all
the score's sly, witty allusions, and so subtle are the nuances, that the stage-pictures seem to be
conjured up before our eyes. The recording is as vivid as the performance. Terrific!

Falla El retablo de Maese Pedro[a]. **Matthew Best** (bass) Don Quijote; **Adrian Thompson** (ten) Maese
Pedro; **Samuel Linay** (treb) El Trujamán; **Maggie Cole** (hpd).
Milhaud Les Malheurs d'Orphée[b]. **Malcolm Walker** (bar) Orphée; **Anna Steiger** (sop) Eurydice;
Paul Harrhy (ten) Maréchal, Le sanglier; **Patrick Donnelly** (bass) Le charron; **Matthew Best**
(bass) Le vannier, L'ours; **Gaynor Morgan** (sop) Le renard, La soeur Jumelle; **Patricia Bardon**
(sop) Le loup, La soeur Ainée; **Susan Bickley** (mez) La soeur Cadette.
Stravinsky Renard[c]. Hugh Hetherington, Paul Harrhy (tens); **Patrick Donnelly, Nicolas Cavallier**
(basses); **Christopher Bradley** (cimbalom); [abc]**Matrix Ensemble / Robert Ziegler.**
ASV ℗ CDDCA758 (77 minutes: DDD: 7/91). Texts and translations included.

Three complete operas on one disc lasting 77 minutes must be good value, and especially so when they are important works from the first quarter of this century. One thing they have in common is that all were commissioned by the American-born Princess de Polignac, a patroness of music who exercised considerable flair in her choice of gifted artists in a Paris that was then full of them. The performances here by Robert Ziegler and his Matrix Ensemble are full of flair and his chosen singers for the three works sound at home in Spanish, French and Russian in turn. As presented here, Falla's puppet-opera is full of Iberian colour and verve, and although Milhaud's piece on the Orpheus legend is not so striking or dramatic it still has beauty and is elegantly and expressively sung and played. But the best music comes in Stravinsky's magnificently earthy and vivid 'barnyard fable' *Renard*, not a long work but a dazzling one, where this performance of great panache simply bursts out of one's loudspeakers to transport us instantly to a farmyard of old Russia. There's excellent cimbalom playing here from Christopher Bradley. The libretto of all three works is usefully provided in the booklet, together with an English translation. The recording is first class, being both immediate and atmospheric.

Further listening ...
...Homenaje, "Le tombeau de Claude Debussy". *Coupled with works by various composers.*
Pepe Romero (gtr). Philips 442 150-2PH (4/95).
...El paño moruno. *Coupled with works by various composers.* **Angela Gheorghiu** (sop);
Malcolm Martineau (pf). Decca 458 360-2DH (5/98). *See review in the Collections section; refer to the Index.*
...La vida breve. **Soloists; Ambrosian Opera Chorus; London Symphony Orchestra / Garcia Navarro.**
DG 435 851-2GH (10/92).

Giles Farnaby   British c1563-1640

Suggested listening ...
...Mal Sims. Muscadin. A Maske. The Old Spagnoletta. *Coupled with works by various composers.*
The Dufay Collective. Chandos New Direction CHAN9446 (10/96). *See review in the Collections section; refer to the Index.*

Robert Farnon   Canadian/British 1917

Suggested listening ...
...Portrait of a flirt. *Coupled with works by various composers.* **Studio Two Concert Orchestra /**
Reginald Kilbey. EMI British Composers CDM5 66537-2 (1/98). *See review in the Collections section; refer to the Index.*

David Farquhar   New Zealand 1928

Suggested listening ...
...Six Songs of Women. *Coupled with works by various composers.* **Tracey Chadwell** (sop);
Pamela Lidiard (pf). British Music Society BMS420/1CD (3/98). *See review in the Collections section; refer to the Index.*

Ernest Farrar   British 1885-1918

Suggested listening ...
...O mistress mine!. *Coupled with works by various composers.* **Ian Partridge** (ten); **Stephen Roberts**
(bar); **Clifford Benson** (pf). Hyperion CDA66015 (9/91). *See review in the Collections section; refer to the Index.*
...Call to remembrance, O Lord. *Coupled with works by various composers.* **St Paul's Cathedral**
Choir / John Scott with **Andrew Lucas** (org). Hyperion CDA66916 (A/97). *See review in the Collections section; refer to the Index.*

Carl Friedrich Fasch   German 1688-1758

Suggested listening ...
...Concerto for Trumpet, Oboe d'amore, Violin and Strings in E major. *Coupled with works by various composers.* **John Wallace** (tpt); **John Anderson** (ob d'amore); **Peter Thomas** (vn);
Philharmonia Orchestra / Christopher Warren-Green, Simon Wright. Nimbus NI7016 (2/95).
See review in the Collections section; refer to the Index.
...Trumpet Concerto. *Coupled with works by various composers.* **Niklas Eklund** (baroque tpt);
Drottningholm Baroque Ensemble / Nils-Erik Sparf. Naxos 8 553531 (11/96). *See review in the Collections section; refer to the Index.*

Gabriel Fauré

Fauré Pelléas et Mélisande, Op. 80 (with Chanson de Mélisande – orch. Koechlin)[a]. Three Songs, Op. 7 – Après un rêve (arr. vc/orch. Dubenskij)[b]. Pavane, Op. 50[c]. Elégie, Op. 24[b]. Dolly Suite, Op. 56 (orch. Rabaud). [a]**Lorraine Hunt** (sop); [b]**Jules Eskin** (vc); [c]**Tanglewood Festival Chorus; Boston Symphony Orchestra / Seiji Ozawa**. DG Ⓕ 423 089-2GH (56 minutes: DDD: 1/88). Texts and translations included. Recorded 1986.

Fauré's music for Maeterlinck's play *Pelléas et Mélisande* was commissioned by Mrs Patrick Campbell and to the usual four movement suite Ozawa has added the "Chanson de Mélisande", superbly sung here by Lorraine Hunt. Ozawa conducts a sensitive, sympathetic account of the score, and Jules Eskin plays beautifully in both the arrangement of the early song, *Après un rêve* and the *Elégie*, which survived from an abandoned cello sonata. The grave *Pavane* is performed here in the choral version of 1901. *Dolly* began life as a piano duet, but was later orchestrated by the composer and conductor Henri Rabaud. Ozawa gives a pleasing account of this delightful score and the recording is excellent.

Additional recommendations ...

...Pelléas et Mélisande. Pavane[a]. *Coupled with works by* **Chausson** [a]**Renaissance Singers; Ulster Orchestra / Paul Tortelier**. Chandos Ⓕ CHAN8952 (69 minutes: DDD: 12/91).

...(arr. C. Williams): Dolly – Berceuse. *Coupled with works by various composers.* **Reykjavik Wind Quintet**. Chandos Ⓕ CHAN9362 (63 minutes: DDD: 10/95).

...Pelléas et Mélisande – Prélude; Fileuse; Mort de Mélisande. *Coupled with works by various composers.* **Boston Symphony Orchestra / Serge Koussevitzky**. Biddulph mono Ⓕ WHL044* (70 minutes: ADD: 3/97).

Fauré Masques et bergamasques, Op. 112. Ballade, Op. 19[c]. Pavane, Op. 50. Fantaisie, Op. 79[a]. Pénélope – Overture. Elégie, Op. 24[b]. Dolly Suite, Op. 56. [a]**Richard Davis** (fl); [b]**Peter Dixon** (vc); [c]**Kathryn Stott** (pf); **BBC Philharmonic Orchestra / Yan Pascal Tortelier**. Chandos Ⓕ CHAN9416 (72 minutes: DDD: 5/96). Recorded 1995.

Fauré wrote surprisingly few orchestral works, and it was a good idea on the part of Chandos to assemble this selection. However, although the transcription of the celebrated cello *Elégie* is the composer's own, the *Dolly* suite, originally for piano duet, comes here in Henri Rabaud's arrangement and the flute *Fantaisie* is the transcription made by Louis Aubert for Jean-Pierre Rampal. The biggest *concertante* work here, the *Ballade* of 1881, is Fauré's orchestration of his piano piece of the same name; it is gentle music that persuades and cajoles in a very Gallic way. Though not an overtly virtuoso utterance, it makes its own exacting technical demands on the soloist, among them being complete control of touch and pedalling. The highly-regarded Fauréan Kathryn Stott meets these with consistent success. *Masques et bergamasques*, which takes its title from Verlaine's sad, mysterious poem *Clair de lune*, is a late stage work that the composer himself described as melancholy and nostalgic, but it is hardly romantic, being instead pointedly neo-classical in character and shape, recalling Bizet's youthful C major Symphony and Grieg's *Holberg Suite*. The playing here under Yan Pascal Tortelier is very satisfying, as are the elegant flute solos of the exquisitely delicate *Pavane*, performed here without the optional chorus, and in *Dolly*. The rarely heard Overture to the opera *Pénélope* is also effectively presented here. There's little rhetoric and no bombast in Fauré's art, but how civilized he was, and what sympathetic interpreters serve him here! The recording is warm yet delicate.

Fauré Ballade, Op. 19.
Franck Symphonic Variations, Op. 46.
d'Indy Symphonie sur un chant montagnard français in G major, Op. 25. **François-Joël Thiollier** (pf); **National Symphony Orchestra of Ireland / Antonio de Almeida**. Naxos Ⓢ 8 550754 (55 minutes: DDD: 1/95). Recorded 1993. *Gramophone Editor's choice.*

This is a disc of French works, all for piano and orchestra, and all from the late 1870s and 1880s. The renamed RTE Symphony Orchestra, a match for its more recorded counterpart in Ulster, taped the programme in their Dublin concert-hall (acoustically clean, bright and airy, but warm, if this disc's sound is representative). François-Joël Thiollier's playing is individual, often impulsive but always idiomatic, helped by the sensitive, guiding hand of a conductor obviously well acquainted with the music. A more high-profile production would probably have retaken those passages where piano and orchestra co-ordination is occasionally fractionally awry, such as in the last variation of the Franck, but then, it might also have seemed less spontaneous. Thiollier's rubato is always distinctive and attractive; the style, particularly and crucially in the Fauré, properly fluid. Both the piano and the orchestra's woodwind are discreetly prominent, but internal balances are generally excellent. There are no budget-price competitors in this repertoire that reproduce with such beauty of tone.

Additional recommendation ...

...Ballade, Op. 19. *Coupled with works by* **Ravel** Louis Lortie (pf); **London Symphony Orchestra / Rafael Frühbeck de Burgos**. Chandos Ⓕ CHAN8773 (57 minutes: DDD: 1/90).

Fauré Piano Quartets – No. 1 in C minor, Op. 15; No. 2 in G minor, Op. 45. **Domus** (Krysia Osostowicz, vn; Robin Ireland, va; Timothy Hugh, vc; Susan Tomes, pf). Hyperion Ⓕ CDA66166 (62 minutes: DDD: 10/86). From A66166 (10/86). *Gramophone Award Winner 1986.* Ⓖ

The First Piano Quartet reveals Fauré's debt to an earlier generation of composers, particularly Mendelssohn. Yet already it has the refined sensuality, the elegance and the craftsmanship which were always to be hallmarks of his style and it is a thoroughly assured, highly enjoyable work which could come from no other composer's pen. The Second Quartet is a more complex, darker work, but much less ready to yield its secrets. The comparatively agitated, quicksilver scherzo impresses at once, however, and repeated hearings of the complete work reveal it to possess considerable poetry and stature. Just occasionally one could wish that the members of Domus had a slightly more aristocratic, commanding approach to these scores, but overall the achievement is highly impressive, for their playing is both idiomatic and technically impeccable. The recording has an appropriately intimate feel to it and is faithful and well balanced.

Additional recommendation ...
...Piano Quartets. **Isaac Stern** (vn); **Jaime Laredo** (va); **Yo-Yo Ma** (vc) **Emanuel Ax** (pf).
   Sony Classical Ⓕ SK48066 (67 minutes: DDD: 9/93).

Fauré Piano Quintets – No. 1 in D minor, Op. 89; No. 2 in C minor, Op. 115. **Domus**
   (Krysia Osostowicz, vn; Timothy Boulton, va; Richard Lester, vc; Susan Tomes, pf);
   Anthony Marwood (vn). Hyperion Ⓕ CDA66766 (60 minutes: DDD: 7/95). Recorded 1994.
   Gramophone Award Winner 1995.

Having given us exemplary, *Gramophone* Award-winning performances of the two piano quartets, Domus continue with even more inspired recordings of the Quintets. However, not even the most ardent Fauréan or Francophile could admit that such music yields up its secrets easily. Indeed, despite pages pulsing with all of Fauré's sustained radiance and energy the abiding impression is of music of such profound introspection that the listener often feels like an interloper stumbling into an essentially private conversation. But perseverance reaps the richest rewards and moments like the opening of the D minor Quintet where Fauré achieves what is referred to in the insert-notes as a "rapt weightlessness", or the closing pages of the C minor Quintet's *Andante moderato* (starting at 6'25") send out resonances that finally embrace the entire work. The other-worldly dance commencing the finale of the First Quintet, the wild catch-as-catch-can opening and elfin close of the C minor Quintet's *Allegro vivo* or the grave serenity of the following *Andante moderato*; all these are surely at the heart of Fauré's simultaneously conservative and radical genius. Simply as a person Fauré remained conscious of an elusiveness that baffled and tantalized even his closest friends, companions who felt themselves gently but firmly excluded from his complex interior world. Domus fully suggest this enigma yet play with such ardour and *élan* that the composer himself would surely have been delighted ("people play me as if the blinds were down"). The recordings are superb.

Additional recommendations ...
...Nos. 1 and 2. **Peter Orth** (pf); **Auryn Quartet.** CPO Ⓕ CPO999 357-2 (62 minutes: DDD: 10/97).
...No. 1ᵃ. Piano Quartet No. 1 in C minor, Op. 15. **Pascal Rogé** (pf); **Ysaÿe Quartet.**
   Decca Ⓕ 455 149-2DH (64 minutes: DDD: 6/98).

Fauré Romance in A major, Op. 69ᵇ. Elégie, Op. 24ᵇ. Cello Sonatas – No. 1 in D minor, Op. 109ᵇ;
   No. 2 in G minor, Op. 117ᵇ. Allegretto moderatoᵃ. Sérénade, Op. 98ᵇ. Sicilienne, Op. 78ᵇ.
   Papillon, Op. 77ᵇ. Andanteᶜ. **Steven Isserlis,** ᵃ**David Waterman** (vcs); ᵇ**Pascal Devoyon** (pf);
   ᶜ**Francis Grier** (org). RCA Victor Red Seal Ⓕ 09026 68049-2 (62 minutes: DDD: 8/95).
   Recorded 1993-94.   Ⓖ

This, surely, is the most 'complete' of Fauré's complete works for cello yet to appear. Isserlis has unearthed the original version of the *Romance*, Op. 69 (entitled *Andante*, proudly hailed as a "world première recording"), with a sustained, chordal accompaniment for organ in place of the piano's broken chordal semiquavers, and a gracious flourish from the cello itself by way of adieu. Mystically accompanied by Francis Grier at the organ of Eton College Chapel, the cello's song, restored to the church, seems to acquire more depth. But let it be said at once that in the familiar version of this work, as throughout the disc, Pascal Devoyon is a partner in a thousand, keenly aware of Isserlis's respect for the "discretion, reticence and restraint" once hailed as the hallmarks of Fauré's style. In fact only in the noble *Elégie* do we discover the full breadth and richness of this cello's (a 1745 Guadagnini) tonal range. A world war, plus the private trauma of incipient deafness, helps to explain the yawning gulf between the miniatures and the two sonatas of 1918 and 1922. Skipping through the score of the First you notice that only once does Fauré use a dynamic marking above a *forte*, relying on the word *espressivo* to elicit just that little extra intensity at moments of climax. This is appreciated by both artists, most movingly in the central *Andante*. In the first movement, however, it is Devoyon's piquant accentuation that brings home the music's menace. The urgency and *Elégie*-evoking heart-throb of the G minor work again benefit from the immediacy of keyboard characterization, and the variety of keyboard colour, underpinning this poetically introspective cellist's fine-spun line.

Additional recommendations ...
...Fantaisie, Op. 79. Après un rêve, Op. 7 No. 1. Sicilienne. Pièce. *Coupled with works by various composers.* **Anna Noakes** (fl); **Gillian Tingay** (hp). ASV White Line Ⓜ CDWHL2101
   (76 minutes: DDD: 11/96). *See review in the Collections section; refer to the Index.*
...Elégie, Op. 24. Romance, Op. 69. Papillon, Op. 77. *Coupled with works by* **Chopin** *and* **Poulenc**
   Pieter Wispelwey (vc); **Paolo Giacometti** (pf).
   Channel Classics Ⓕ CCS10797 (67 minutes: DDD: 3/98).

Fauré Violin Sonatas – No. 1 in A major, Op. 13; No. 2 in E minor, Op. 108. Morceau de concours.
Andante in B flat major, Op. 75. Romance in B flat major, Op. 28. Berceuse, Op. 16.
Pierre Amoyal (vn); **Pascal Rogé** (pf). Decca Ⓕ 436 866-2DH (65 minutes: DDD: 2/95).
Recorded 1992. *Gramophone Editor's choice.*　　　　　　　　　　　　　　　　　　　　Ⓖ
These radiant early and late masterpieces are unforgettable reflections of Fauré's first romantic
ardour and his subsequent, deeply courageous journey through the most remote and interior regions
of both soul and mind. Fauré was a 'conservative' only in the richest, most inclusive sense, setting up
conventions only to challenge them with his unique mix of audacity and subtlety. Here, in the Second
Sonata, are turbulence and hyperactivity on a background of calm (to extend Copland's famous
description), the bitter fruit of Fauré's increasing deafness and lack of recognition (his publisher's
wife used the scores of his *Nocturnes* and *Barcarolles* as jam-jar covers). Amoyal and Rogé are
superbly challenging and authentic at every level. The opening *Allegro molto* from the First Sonata
becomes a tumultuous rush of events, a committed alternative to more 'classical' or staid readings,
while the *Andante* is kept firmly on the move (a qualifying *con moto*); a reminder, perhaps, of the
French fear of all possible sentimentality. Yet how stellar is Rogé's way with the *a tempo* and
dolcissimo at 2'36", and what an Elysium both players find as the music sinks to its final resting place.
The *Allegro vivo*, on the other hand, could hardly be more nimble, a true catch-as-catch-can with a
delightful relishing of Fauré's constantly shifting and mischievously altered phrase lengths. Again, in
the Second Sonata, both violinist and pianist play with rare individuality and unanimity, Amoyal's
sweet and slightly nasal tone complemented by Rogé's greater fullness. Their *Andante* is, again, coolly
paced but elsewhere there is a powerful recognition of Fauré's strength and delicacy and the way his
ceaseless flow of ideas is so often tinged with irony and unease. For their encores (distinguishing this
disc from some stylish alternative recordings of the sonatas) Amoyal and Rogé give us three
miniatures in which salon clichés are effortlessly and, indeed, magically transformed. Even the
Berceuse's passing resemblance to the *Eton Boating Song* seems sublime rather than unfortunate. The
recordings are excellent and the entire recital should do much to erase notions (sadly, still current) of
Fauré as a poor country cousin of Ravel and Debussy.

Additional recommendations ...
...Nos. 1 and 2. **Krysia Osostowicz** (vc); **Susan Tomes** (pf).
　Hyperion Ⓕ CDA66277 (50 minutes: DDD: 11/88).
...Nos. 1 and 2[a]. **Franck** Violin Sonata in A major[b]. **Arthur Grumiaux** (vn); [a]**Paul Crossley,**
　[b]**György Sebok** (pfs). Philips Musica da Camera Ⓜ 426 384-2PC (73 minutes: ADD: 7/90).　ⒼⒺ
...No. 1. *Coupled with works by* **Debussy** and **Poulenc** Isabelle van Keulen (vn);
　Ronald Brautigam (pf). Koch Schwann Ⓕ 315272 (56 minutes: DDD: 10/95).
...Nos. 1 and 2. Berceuse, Op. 16. Romance. Andante. **Dong-Suk Kang** (vn); **Pascal Devoyon** (pf).
　Naxos Ⓢ 8 550906 (62 minutes: DDD: 3/96).
...No. 1. *Coupled with works by various composers.* **Jacques Thibaud** (vn); **Alfred Cortot** (pf).
　Symposium mono Ⓕ 1156* (74 minutes: ADD: 1/97).

Fauré Five Impromptus. Impromptu, Op. 86. Thème et Variations in C sharp minor, Op. 73.
Romances sans paroles, Op. 17. Quatre Valses-caprices. 13 Barcarolles. Ballade in F sharp major,
Op. 19. 13 Nocturnes. Souvenirs de Bayreuth (with Martin Roscoe, pf). Pièces brèves, Op. 84.
Dolly, Op. 56 (Roscoe). Nine Préludes, Op. 103. Mazurka in B flat major, Op. 32. **Kathryn Stott**
(pf). Hyperion Ⓜ CDA66911/4 (four discs: 297 minutes: DDD: 5/95). Recorded 1994.
Gramophone Editor's choice.　　　　　　　　　　　　　　　　　　　　　　　　　　　　　Ⓖ
Fauré's piano works are among the most subtly daunting in all keyboard literature. Contradicting his
diffidence ("it seems that I repeat myself constantly") they possess, on the contrary, an astonishing
scope. Encompassing Fauré's entire creative life, they range through an early, finely wrought eroticism
via sporting with an aerial virtuosity as teasing and light as the elements themselves (the *Valses-
caprices*) to the final desolation of Fauré's last years. There, in his most powerful works (*Barcarolles*
Nos. 7-11, *Nocturnes* Nos. 11-13), he faithfully mirrors a pain that "scintillates in full consciousness"
a romantic agony prompted by increasing deafness and a lack of recognition that often seemed close
to oblivion. Few compositions have reflected a darker night of the soul, and Fauré's anguish, expressed
in both numbing resignation and unbridled anger, could surely only be exorcized by the articulation
of such profound and disturbing emotional complexity. The task for the pianist, then, is immense, but
in Kathryn Stott Fauré has a subtle and fearless champion. Her early Conifer albums were themselves
a vibrant and personal tribute. But, be warned, once your appetite is whetted you will want to move
on to Hyperion's sumptuously recorded, complete offering. Here, on four lavishly packaged CDs, are
the *Ballade* in its original solo version, the sixth *Impromptu* (transcribed from the harp), *Dolly* and
even the *Souvenirs de Bayreuth* where Fauré turns prankster and enjoys a night out with the boys.
　How thrilled Fauré would have been by the sheer immediacy of Stott's responses. Time and again
she throws convention to the winds, and although it would be surprising if all her performances were
consistent successes, disappointments are rare. Sometimes her rubato and luxuriant pedalling soften
the outlines of Fauré's starkest, most austere utterances. The Twelfth and Thirteenth *Nocturnes*, for
example, are surely too loosely controlled to achieve their fullest drama and focus, and here, in
particular, Paul Crossley is infinitely more concentrated and dramatic in his brightly lit CRD
recordings. She hurries rather than lingers over the effusiveness in the third of the *Romances sans*

paroles and the *Variations*, too, are not uniformly poised. A profounder sense of speculation in the *Molto adagio* of No. 6 would have been welcome, and an even greater sense of unearthly calm in No. 9. But such quibbles remain quibbles. How Stott relishes a modern Steinway's opulent transformation of the harp's thin and glittering textures in the Sixth *Impromptu*, and the *Mazurka* has rarely been spun off with such a truly virtuoso insouciance. The Third *Impromptu*'s missing *Molto meno mosso* (on the Conifer recording) is reinstated and the First *Impromptu*'s propulsion is even more urgently and richly inflected. The Fourth *Nocturne* is gloriously supple, and the 13 *Barcarolles* show Stott acutely responsive to passion and finesse alike. The *Pièces brèves*, too, are played with rare affection. Changes and developments in the interim period between the Conifer and Hyperion discs make for fascinating listening. A true and dedicated Francophile (though with an exceptionally wide repertoire), Stott is among the more stylish and intriguing of the younger generation of pianists. For *Souvenirs de Bayreuth* and *Dolly* she is robustly partnered by Martin Roscoe.

Additional recommendations ...
...Barcarolles Nos. 1-13. **Paul Crossley** (pf). CRD Ⓕ CRD3422 (64 minutes: DDD: 6/88).
...Nocturnes Nos. 1-7. **Paul Crossley** (pf). CRD Ⓕ CRD3406 (52 minutes: ADD: 6/88).
...Nocturnes Nos. 8-13. Eight Pièces brèves, Op. 84. **Paul Crossley** (pf).
　　CRD Ⓕ CRD3407 (51 minutes: ADD: 6/88).
...Nine Préludes, Op. 103. 13 Nocturnes – No. 1 in E flat minor, Op. 33 No. 1; No. 3 in A flat major, Op. 33 No. 3; No. 4 in E flat major, Op. 36; No. 6 in D flat major, Op. 63; No. 13 in B minor, Op. 119. Impromptu No. 3 in A flat major, Op. 34. Eight Pièces brèves – No. 1, Capriccio; No. 4, Adagietto; No. 5, Improvisation. Romances sans paroles, No. 3. Thème et Variations. **Albert Ferber** (pf). Saga Classics Ⓜ EC3397-2 (51 minutes: DDD: 3/94).　　ⒼⒼ
...Impromptus – No. 1 in E flat major, Op. 25; No. 2 in F minor, Op. 31; No. 3; D flat major, Op. 86 (arr. pf). Nocturnes – Nos. 1, 4 and 6; No. 8 in D flat major, Op. 84 No. 5; No. 9 in B minor/major, Op. 97; No. 10 in E minor, Op. 99; No. 11 in F sharp minor, Op. 104 No. 1. Three Romances sans paroles. Barcarolles – No. 1 in A minor, Op. 26; No. 2 in G, Op. 41; No. 4 in A flat major, Op. 44; No. 5 in F sharp minor, Op. 66; No. 6 in E flat major, Op. 70; No. 7 in D minor, Op. 90; No. 11 in G minor, Op. 105; No. 12 in E flat major, Op. 106. Mazurka, Op. 32. Valse-caprice No. 4 in A flat major, Op. 62. **Kathryn Stott** (pf).
　　Conifer Classics Ⓕ 75605 51751-2
　　(two discs: 129 minutes: DDD: 5/95).
...Dolly. *Coupled with works by various composers.* **Walter Klien, Beatriz Klien** (pfs).
　　Carlton Classics Turnabout Ⓑ 30371 0014-2 (78 minutes: ADD: 10/96).

Fauré Chansons, Volume 2. **Sarah Walker** (mez); **Malcolm Martineau** (pf). CRD Ⓕ CRD3477 (68 minutes: DDD: 8/93). Texts and translations included. Recorded 1991.
Le papillon et la fleur, Op. 1 No. 1. Op. 3 – No. 1, Seule!; No. 2, Sérénade toscane. L'absent, Op. 5 No. 3. Op. 8 – No. 1, Au bord de l'eau; No. 3, Ici-bas. Op. 10 – No. 1, Puisqu'ici-bas; No. 2, Tarentelle. La fée aux chansons, Op. 27 No. 2. Op. 39 – No. 1, Fleur jetée; No. 3, Le Pays des rêves; No. 4, Les roses d'Ispahan. Nocturne, Op. 43 No. 2. Clair de lune, Op. 46 No. 2. Op. 51 – No. 1, Larmes; No. 2, Au cimetière. Arpège, Op. 76 No. 2. Accompagnement, Op. 85 No. 3. Le plus doux chemin, Op. 87 No. 1. Le don silencieux, Op. 92. Chanson, Op. 94. C'est la paix!, Op. 114. Vocalise-étude. Pelléas et Mélisande – Chanson de Mélisande.
Starting with an early song, and a charmer, *Le papillon et la fleur* has the young Fauré with (so it seems) a head full of Schubert, as the piano enters with a ripple of *Die Forelle* and waltzes away into something more like *Seligkeit*. Here, that rather crusty quality in Sarah Walker's louder tones is something of a liability. Still, if this is the initial reaction it is not one that prevails for long. It is hard to imagine the *Nocturne* and *Au bord de l'eau* more beautifully sung, the first entering a very private world, the second catching perfectly the relaxed, reflective mood, and both benefiting from the softened, warmed tone of the singer and her excellent accompanist. The programme follows no chronological order. This has the advantage that the best-known songs can be distributed fairly evenly, with *Clair de lune*, *Les roses d'Ispahan* and *Aurore* mingled here with some from the 1870s and others that extend into the twentieth century. These include the frank emotion of the postwar *C'est la paix!* and *Le don silencieux* which Sarah Walker sings so affectionately to the haunting accompaniment of those wistfully unfulfilled harmonies. Most haunting of all, perhaps, is Mélisande's song, in English, written for Mrs Patrick Campbell and the London production of 1889.

Additional recommendations ...
...Automne, Op. 18 No. 3. Prison, Op. 83 No. 1. Soir, Op. 83 No. 2. Fleur jetée, Op. 39 No. 2. En sourdine, Op. 58 No. 2. Notre amour, Op. 23 No. 2. Mai, Op. 1 No. 2. La chanson du pêcheur, Op. 4 No. 1. Clair de lune, Op. 46 No. 2. *Coupled with works by various composers.* **Dame Janet Baker** (mez); **Gerald Moore** (pf). EMI Ⓜ CDM5 65009-2 (75 minutes: ADD: 11/94). *See review in the Collections section; refer to the Index.*
...Op. 18 – No. 2, Le voyageur; No. 3, Automne. Le secret, Op. 23 No. 3. Chanson d'amour, Op. 27 No. 1. Songs, Op. 39 – No. 1, Aurore; No. 2, Fleur jetée. Clair de lune, Op. 46 No. 2. Spleen, Op. 51 No. 3. Cinq mélodies, Op. 58. Prison, Op. 83 No. 1. *Coupled with works by* **Poulenc** and **Ravel** Thomas Allen (bar); **Roger Vignoles** (pf). Virgin Classics Ⓕ VC5 45053-2 (57 minutes: DDD: 5/95).

...Au bord de l'eau. Rêve d'amour, Op. 5 No. 2. Notre amour, Op. 23 No. 2. *Coupled with works by various composers.* **Sylvia McNair** (sop); **Roger Vignoles** (pf).
Philips Ⓕ 446 656-2PH (61 minutes: DDD: 5/97).
...Les roses d'Ispahan. Green, Op. 58 No. 3. *Coupled with works by various composers.*
Dame Felicity Lott (sop); **Graham Johnson** (pf). Hyperion Ⓕ CDA66937
(65 minutes: DDD: 10/97). *See review in the Collections section; refer to the Index.*

Fauré Requiem, Op. 48[a]. Messe basse[b]. Cantique de Jean Racine, Op. 11[b].
Vierne Pièces de fantaisie. Suite No. 1, Op. 51 – Andantino[c].
Séverac Tantum ergo[d]. [a]**Lisa Beckley** (sop); [a]**Nicholas Gedge** (bass-bar); [abd]**Oxford Schola Cantorum;** [a]**Oxford Camerata / Jeremy Summerly** with [abc]**Colm Carey** (org).
Naxos Ⓢ 8 550765 (60 minutes: DDD: 9/94). Texts and translations included. Recorded 1993.
One would say at once that this is a highly competitive recording of the Fauré Requiem but in fact it stands on its own because of the version it presents and the edition it uses. Most of the 30-odd available recordings are of the final 1901 and now somewhat discredited version; several more recent ones are of the 1894 score edited either by Nectoux and Delage or by John Rutter. This Naxos recording is of an edition by Denis Arnold (1983) based on the original version (1887) but incorporating the two additional movements. On first impulse, the word arising is 'austere'. Certainly the flashes of gold and scarlet made by the few but highly effective brass entries in the familiar versions are missed; the harp is notably absent from the *Sanctus*, and that wispy, high solo violin (1894) is now a less other-worldly presence at normal on-the-stave pitch. The instrumental colours are dark*ish*, yet not sombre, and are lightened by the sunlight stippling of the organ in the *In Paradisum*. With the voices added, the effect is of a subtler beauty, still more distinctively itself than even the 1894 score. The performance of the Requiem and the *Messe basse* is admirable, with excellent playing by Jeremy Summerly's Oxford Camerata, and fresh-voiced, sensitively attuned choral singing from Oxford Schola Cantorum. Authenticity extends now to French pronunciation of the Latin ("luceat eis" very French indeed). The rather flaccid organ solo by Vierne, written as a sight-reading exercise for his pupils, is finely played by Colm Carey. The *Tantum ergo* by Séverac is a haunting, carol-like little piece, beautifully sung, and Fauré's *Cantique de Jean Racine* makes a perfect conclusion to this lovely programme.

Additional recommendations ...
...Requiem (original version, ed. Rutter). Motets – Ave verum corpus; Tantum ergo; Ave Maria; Maria, Mater gratiae. Cantique de Jean Racine, Op. 11 (orch. Rutter). Messe basse. **Soloists; Cambridge Singers; City of London Sinfonietta / John Rutter.** Collegium Ⓕ COLCD109
(63 minutes: ADD/DDD: 1/89). *Gramophone Award Winner 1985.*   Ⓖ
...Requiem (original 1894 version)[a]. **Fauré/Messager** Messe des pêcheurs de Villerville[b].
[a]**Agnès Mellon** (sop); [a]**Peter Kooy** (bar); [b]**Jean-Philippe Audoli** (vn); [a]**Leo van Doeselaar** (org);
Petits Chanteurs de Saint-Louis; Paris Chapelle Royale Chorus; Musique Oblique Ensemble / Philippe Herreweghe. Harmonia Mundi Ⓕ HMC90 1292 (56 minutes: DDD: 4/89).   Ⓖ
...Requiem (1893 version)[a]. Cantique de Jean Racine[b]. Messe basse[b]. Motets[b] – Ave verum corpus; Tantum ergo. **Corydon Singers;** [a]**English Chamber Orchestra / Matthew Best** with [b]**John Scott** (org). Hyperion Ⓕ CDA66292 (58 minutes: DDD: 10/89).
...Requiem[a]. **Duruflé** Requiem, Op. 9[b]. [b]**Richard Eteson** (treb); [b]**Ann Murray** (sop); [b]**Olaf Bär** (bar); **King's College Choir, Cambridge; English Chamber Orchestra / Stephen Cleobury.** EMI Ⓕ CDC7 49880-2 (73 minutes: DDD: 12/89).
...Requiem[a]. Cantique de Jean Racine[b]. *Coupled with works by* **Duruflé** *and* **Messiaen**
[a]**Camilla Otaki** (sop); [b]**Mark Griffiths** (bar); **Trinity College Choir, Cambridge;**
[b]**Richard Pearce** (org); [a]**London Musici / Richard Marlow.**
Conifer Classics Ⓕ CDCF176 (73 minutes: DDD: 10/90).
...Requiem (revised version). Cantique de Jean Racine. Messe basse. *Coupled with works by* **Poulenc Soloists; Academy of St Martin in the Fields; Choir of St John's College, Cambridge / George Guest.** Decca Ovation Ⓜ 430 360-2DM (74 minutes: ADD: 9/91).
...Requiem[a]. Pavane, Op. 50. [a]**Robert Chilcott** (treb); [a]**John Carol Case** (bar);
[a]**King's College Choir Cambridge; New Philharmonia Orchestra / Sir David Willcocks.**
EMI Ⓜ CDM7 64715-2 (42 minutes: ADD: 7/93).
...Requiem. *Coupled with works by various composers.* **Catherine Bott** (sop); **Gilles Cachemaille** (bar); **Salisbury Cathedral Boys' Choir; Monteverdi Choir; Orchestre Révolutionnaire et Romantique / Sir John Eliot Gardiner.** Philips Ⓕ 438 149-2PH (70 minutes: DDD: 9/94). ✍
...Requiem[a]. Pavane, Op. 50. *Coupled with works by various composers.* [a]**Sylvia McNair** (sop);
[a]**Thomas Allen** (bar); **Academy of St Martin in the Fields** and [a]**Chorus / Sir Neville Marriner.**
Philips Ⓕ 446 084-2PH (54 minutes: DDD: 1/96).
...Cantique de Jean Racine (arr. Rutter). Requiem, Op. 48 – In paradisum. *Coupled with works by various composers.* **New College Choir, Oxford; Capricorn / Edward Higginbottom.**
Erato Ⓕ 0630-14634-2 (73 minutes: DDD: 1/97).
...Requiem[a]. **Duruflé** Requiem, Op. 9[b]. [b]**Dame Kiri Te Kanawa**, [a]**Lucia Popp** (sops); **Siegmund Nimsgern** (bass-bar); **Ambrosian Singers;** [a]**Desborough School Choir;** [a]**Philharmonia Orchestra,**
[b]**New Philharmonia Orchestra / Andrew Davis.** Sony Classical Essential Classics Ⓑ SBK67182
(79 minutes: ADD: A/97). *See review under Duruflé; refer to the Index.*

...Requiem – Pie Jesu. *Coupled with works by various composers.* **Lesley Garrett** (sop);
  Britten Sinfonia / Ivor Bolton. Conifer Classics Ⓕ 75605 51329-2 (73 minutes: DDD: 12/97).
  See review in the Collections section; refer to the Index.
...Requiem – Pie Jesu; Libera me. Ave verum, Op. 65 No. 1 (arr. Higginbottom). *Coupled with works*
  by various composers. **New College Choir, Oxford; Capricorn / Edward Higginbottom.**
  Erato Ⓕ 3984-21659-2 (66 minutes: DDD: 6/98). *Gramophone Editor's choice. See review in the*
  Collections section; refer to the Index.

Further listening ...
...String Quartet in E minor, Op. 121. *Coupled with works by* **Debussy** and **Ravel**
  Pro Arte Quartet. Biddulph mono LAB105*.   Ⓖ
...String Quartet in E minor, Op. 121. *Coupled with* **Saint-Saëns** String Quartets – No. 1 in
  E minor, Op. 112; No. 2 in G major, Op. 153. **Miami Quartet.** Conifer Classics 75605 51291-2
  (3/98). *Gramophone Editor's choice.*
...Pénélope – dram lyrique. **Soloists; Jean Laforge Vocal Ensemble; Monte-Carlo Philharmonic**
  Orchestra / Charles Dutoit. Erato Libretto 2292-45405-2 (4/92).

Robert Fayrfax   British 1464-1521

Fayrfax Missa Albanus. O Maria. Ave lumen gratiae. Aeternae laudis lilium (all ed. Skinner).
  Deo grata (ed. Sandon). **The Cardinall's Musick / Andrew Carwood.** ASV Gaudeamus
  Ⓕ CDGAU160 (75 minutes: DDD: 7/97). Texts included. Recorded 1995-96.
The centrepiece of this disc is the *Missa Albanus*, a work probably composed for St Alban's Abbey
with which the composer is known to have had close ties. It is not presented with chant propers – only
a 33-second snatch of a fragment of a Matins antiphon for the rhymed office of St Alban from which
Fayrfax draws his *cantus firmus* – in any kind of reconstruction, but is followed by an antiphon motet
which was probably also originally composed in honour of the saint but which survives in a version
with the text reworked for more general use as a homage to the Virgin.There is no denying the quality
of the music, both in this extended but always engaging piece, in *Aeternae laudis lilium*, another
massively conceived motet, and in the setting of the Mass itself. Like many of the other composers
represented in the Eton Choirbook, Fayrfax is direct and prolix by turn, the text being broken up into
contrasted sections, often substantial in themselves, but which explore different vocal combinations
and styles. The overall texture is consistently translucent, with The Cardinall's Musick appropriately
sonorous in the tuttis, and graceful in the elaborate passages for solo voices. Most striking are the
many passages for tenors and basses, the voices as rich and smooth as the purest, darkest chocolate.

Additional recommendation ...
...Missa Albanus. Aeternae laudis lilium. **The Sixteen / Harry Christophers.**
  Hyperion Ⓕ CDA66073 (50 minutes: DDD: 12/89).

Further listening ...
...Missa O quam Glorifica. Ave Dei patris filia. Somewhat musing. To complayne me, alas. *Coupled*
  with **Anonymous** That was my joy. **Sarum Chant** Kyrie Orbis factor; O quam Glori fica.
  The Cardinall's Musick / Andrew Carwood. ASV Gaudeamus CDGAU142 (6/95). ✒
  Gramophone Award Winner 1995.
...(ed. Skinner) Missa "Tecum principium"[b]. Maria plena virtute[b]. Recorder Works[a] – Mese tenor;
  O lux beata trinitas; Paramese tenor. [a]**Frideswide Consort** (Caroline Kershaw, Jane Downer,
  Christine Garratt, Jean McCreery, recs); [b]**The Cardinall's Musick / Andrew Carwood.**
  ASV Gaudeamus CDGAU145 (1/96). ✒ *Gramophone Editor's choice.*
...Paramese tenor. Mese tenor. *Coupled with works by various composers.* **Concordia.**
  Metronome METCD1012 (3/97). *Gramophone Editor's choice.*   ⒼⒼ

Philip Feeney   British 1954

Feeney (arr. Longstaff) Cinderella – ballet suite.
Muldowney The Brontes – ballet suite.
Carl Davis (arr. Longstaff) A Christmas Carol – ballet suite. **Northern Ballet Theatre Orchestra /**
  John Pryce-Jones. Naxos Ⓢ 8 553495 (73 minutes: DDD: 3/96). Recorded 1995.
A programme such as this, presenting music from three modern British ballets otherwise unavailable
on disc, is hardly the sort of fare one expects from a super-bargain label. For ballet enthusiasts it is
particularly pleasing to find it at such a modest price. However, even for someone who has neither
seen the ballets concerned nor is a ballet lover, it makes most agreeable listening. It is all richly scored,
with modern touches that are never such as to frighten off more timid listeners but, rather, create
some marvellously atmospheric sounds to portray the action described in the excellent accompanying
notes. It is tuneful stuff, and not just in the Carl Davis suite which quotes Christmas carols but in the
other two suites too. These seem much more interesting all round, both using a wide range of effects,
including keyboard and more exotic percussion instruments. The Feeney suite is very likeable: try, for
instance, the movement in which Cinderella prepares for the ball, with a shimmering gown to wear
and white doves helping her to dress. Performance and recording alike are excellent.

Jindřich Feld
Czechoslovakian 1925

Suggested listening ...
...Flute Sonata. *Coupled with works by various composers.* **Leslie Newman** (fl); **Amanda Hurton** (pf).
Cala CACD88026 (6/96). *See review in the Collections section; refer to the Index.*

Morton Feldman
American 1926-1987

Feldman Palais de Mari.
Wuorinen Piano Sonata No. 3. Bagatelle. Capriccio. **Alan Feinberg** (pf).
Koch International Classics ℗ 37308-2 (65 minutes: DDD: 9/96). Recorded 1994.
The Wuorinen works, all from the 1980s, are in the tough New York dialect of the post-Webern school but, with playing like this from Alan Feinberg, and so vividly recorded, they provide some scintillating listening. Whatever the music, he brings his own kind of commitment and panache to bear – a winning combination. The often cataclysmic Sonata No. 3 was written for Feinberg but the *Bagatelle*, if you can imagine anything by Wuorinen being a mere bagatelle, at least starts in poetic mode, quietly. So does the *Capriccio*, which starts with a Brahmsian expressiveness, albeit via Schoenberg: by the end the piano sounds under attack. The very late Feldman piece is a bonus, a relentlessly quiet oasis thrown into sharp relief in such a welter of hyperactivity. *Palais de Mari* was commissioned by Bunita Marcus, but it is only a third the length of *For Bunita Marcus* written in the previous year. Feinberg's performance of *Palais* has every detail of the score in place and he brings his unique qualities to this mesmerizingly rapt meditation, where events take the form of the occasional dry chord in a liquid landscape. This disc comes strongly recommended to Feldman enthusiasts.
Further listening ...
...For Christian Wolff. **Eberhard Blum** (fl); **Nils Vigeland** (pf/celesta).
Hat-Hut Hat Now Series ARTCD3-6120 (three discs: 7/94).
...For Philip Guston. **Eberhard Blum** (fls); **Nils Vigeland** (pf/celesta); **Jan Williams** (perc).
Hat-Hut Hat Now Series ARTCD4-6104 (four discs: 4/94).
...Intermission 1. Intermission 2. Intermission 5. Intermission 6. Piano Piece. Four Last Pieces.
Five Pianos[a]. **Steffen Schleiermacher**, [a]**Isabel Mundry**, [a]**Mats Persson**, [a]**Kristine Scholz**, [a]**Nils Vigeland** (pfs). Hat-Hut Hat Now Series ARTCD6143 (12/95).
...Only. *Coupled with works by various composers.* **The Hilliard Ensemble.**
ECM New Series 453 259-2 (1/97). *See review in the Collections section; refer to the Index.*
...Patterns in a Chromatic Field. **Rohan de Saram** (vc); **Marianne Schroeder** (pf).
Hat-Hut Hat Now Series ART2CD6145 (2/96).
...Piano Quintet. **Kronos Quartet; Aki Takahashi** (pf). Elektra Nonesuch 7559-79320-2 (2/94).
...String Quartet. **Group for Contemporary Music.** Koch International Classics 37251-2 (8/94).

Barry Ferguson
British 1942

Suggested listening ...
...South and West Suite. *Coupled with works by various composers.* **Roger Sayer** (org).
Priory PRCD495 (4/96). *See review in the Collections section; refer to the Index.*

Howard Ferguson
British 1908

Suggested listening ...
...Piano Sonata in F minor, Op. 8. *Coupled with works by various composers.*
Dame Myra Hess (pf). Biddulph mono LHW025* (3/96). *See review in the Collections section; refer to the Index.*

John Axel Fernström
Swedish 1897-1961

Suggested listening ...
...Wind Quintet, Op. 59. *Coupled with works by* **Kvandal** and **Nielsen Oslo Wind Ensemble.**
Naxos 8 553050 (3/95). *See review under Nielsen; refer to the Index.*

Alfonso Ferrabosco I
Italian 1543-1588

Suggested listening ...
...Hexachord fantasy. *Coupled with works by various composers.* **Fretwork.**
Virgin Classics VC5 45217-2 (12/97). *See review in the Collections section; refer to the Index.*

Alfonso Ferrabosco II

British before 1578-1628

Suggested listening ...

...Pavan and Alman. *Coupled with works by various composers.* **Parley of Instruments Renaissance Violin Band / Peter Holman.**
Hyperion CDA66806 (6/96). ☞ *See review in the Collections section; refer to the Index.*   Ⓖ

Oscar Fetrás

German 1854-1931

Suggested listening ...

...Mondnacht auf der Alster. *Coupled with works by various composers.* **New London Orchestra / Ronald Corp.** Hyperion CDA66998 (3/98). *See review in the Collections section; refer to the Index.*

Zdeněk Fibich

Bohemian 1850-1900

Fibich Moods, Impressions and Reminiscences, Op. 41 – 40 excerpts. **William Howard** (pf).
Chandos Ⓕ CHAN9381 (71 minutes: DDD: 9/95). Recorded 1993.
Fibich's Op. 41 is the sequence of short piano pieces, most of them lasting somewhere between two and three minutes, written in response to his love for Anežka. In all, 376 survive, and an unknown number more of them are thought to have been lost or destroyed, while some were absorbed into other works, including operas, from which clues can be found to their original association. The story has now become quite well known; and though a good many of the pieces are either mysteriously titled or left without allusion, they chart, in music of warmth, charm and emotional delight, Fibich's tenderness for Anežka, his enraptured passion for every aspect of her body, his deep love for a woman who gave him a movingly complete emotional, physical and intellectual devotion. The moods include not only delight but jealousy and regret at having caused her pain; the impressions often have highly erotic associations; the reminiscences refer to shared experiences through which their lives grew and deepened. Their course can be followed from Graham Melville-Mason's helpful note; but once the outline and some of the associations are grasped, it is as a loose suite of short, impressionistic pieces that such a programme is best heard, Schumannesque in nature and sometimes in manner. William Howard plays them with a careful attention to detail, to the deft manner in which a memorable idea can be created in only a page, and with affectionate phrasing of their warm melodies. Fibich is, here, a romantic miniaturist to set beside Schumann and perhaps even more Tchaikovsky, whose short piano pieces can be as apt in their creation of a mood. Touchingly, the sequence of pieces has unity as well as diversity. Anežka must indeed have been a fascinating woman.

Additional recommendation ...

...Moods, Impressions and Reminiscences, Opp. 41, 44, 47 and 57 – excerpts. Studies of Paintings, Op. 56. **Radoslav Kvapil** (pf). Unicorn-Kanchana Ⓕ DKPCD9149 (70 minutes: DDD: 10/94).   Ⓖ

Further listening ...

...Symphonies – No. 2 in E flat major, Op. 38; No. 3 in E minor, Op. 53.
Detroit Symphony Orchestra / Neeme Järvi. Chandos CHAN9328 (12/94).
...Quintet in D major, Op. 42. *Coupled with* **Dohnányi** Sextet in C major, Op. 37.
Endymion Ensemble. ASV CDDCA943 (2/96). *See review under Dohnányi; refer to the Index.*   Ⓖ
...Sonata in B flat major, Op. 28. *Coupled with works by* **Goetz** and **Moscheles** Anthony Goldstone, Caroline Clemmow (pf duet). Meridian CDE84237 (7/93).
...The Bride of Messina. **Soloists; Prague Radio Chorus; Prague National Theatre Chorus and Orchestra / František Jílek.** Supraphon 11 1492-2 (12/94).
...Šárka. **Soloists; Brno Janáček Opera Chorus; Brno State Philharmonic Orchestra / Jan Stych.**
Supraphon SU0036-2 (2/97).

John Field

Irish 1782-1837

Field Piano Concertos – No. 1 in E flat major, H27; No. 3 in E flat major, H32. **Benjamin Frith** (pf); **Northern Sinfonia / David Haslam.** Naxos Ⓢ 8 553770 (52 minutes: DDD: 2/98).
Recorded 1996.   Ⓖ
In recent years Field's concertos have been in the hands of two dedicated compatriots selling at full price. Now along comes Benjamin Frith with a coupling of Nos. 1 and 3 presenting a very formidable challenge at super-budget price. Both works are played with effortless fluency, plus all the immediacy and freshness of new discovery. Comparison with O'Rourke in No. 1 reveals that both artists are acutely responsive to the delicate charm of the Scottish-inspired (*'Twas within a mile of Edinboro' Town*) slow movement. But it is Frith who makes one more aware of Field's teasing delight in the unexpected in the smiling outer movements, to which he brings a wider range of tone, and more piquant accentuation in the last. In No. 3 there is strong competition from John O'Conor, who as a bonus inserts a slow movement (a lightly accompanied version of the B flat *Nocturne* for solo piano) as Field himself was wont to do. Mackerras's bolder baton somehow gives the extended, opening

Allegro moderato a stronger sense of direction than we get from the otherwise warmly sympathetic Northern Sinfonia under David Haslam. However, both teams revel in the composer's surprises of modulation, rhythm and orchestral colouring, while from neither soloist is there a trace of the perfunctory in passagework. The recording (in a resonant venue) might be thought overforward and full, but it remains a true bargain.

Additional recommendations ...

...No. 1; No. 2 in A flat major, H31; No. 3; No. 4 in E flat major, H28; No. 5 in C major, H39, "L'incendie par l'orage"; No. 6 in C major, H49; No. 7 in C minor, H58. **John O'Conor** (pf); **New Irish Chamber Orchestra / Janos Furst.** Onyx Ⓕ ONYX CD101/3 (three discs: DDD).

...Nos. 2 and 3. **John O'Conor** (pf); **Scottish Chamber Orchestra / Sir Charles Mackerras.** Telarc Ⓕ CD80370 (64 minutes: DDD: 8/94).   Ⓖ

...Nos. 3 and 5. **Míceál O'Rourke** (pf); **London Mozart Players / Matthias Bamert.** Chandos Ⓕ CHAN9495 (60 minutes: DDD: 2/97).

Field Nocturnes – No. 1 in E flat major, H24. No. 2 in C minor, H25. No. 3 in A flat major, H26. No. 4 in A major, H36. No. 5 in B flat major, H37. No. 6 in F major, H40. No. 7 in C major, H45. No. 8 in A major, H14*E*. No. 9 in E flat major, H30. No. 10 in E minor, H46*B*. No. 11 in E flat major, H56*A*. No. 12 in G major, H58*D*. No. 13 in D minor, H59. No. 14 in C major. No. 15 in C major, H61. **Roberto Mamou** (pf). Pavane Ⓕ ADW7110 (64 minutes: DDD: 8/93).
Field Nocturnes – No. 1 in E flat major, H24. No. 2 in C minor, H25. No. 3 in A flat major, H26. No. 4 in A major, H36. No. 5 in B flat major, H37. No. 6 in F major, H40. No. 7 in C major, H45. No. 8 in A major, H14*E*. No. 9 in E flat major, H30. No. 10 in E minor, H46*B*. No. 11 in E flat major, H56*A*. No. 12 in G major, H58*D*. No. 13 in D minor, H59. No. 14 in C major. No. 15 in C major, H61. No. 16 in F major, H62*A*. **Joanna Leach** (fp). Athene Ⓕ ATHCD1 (76 minutes: DDD: 10/93). ✏ Recorded 1990-91.

The Tunisian-born pianist Roberto Mamou achieves an often exemplary middle course between drama and understatement and he stresses Field's closeness to, rather than his remoteness from, Chopin. The recordings are satisfactory and although the last two *Nocturnes* are omitted this is an appealing issue. Joanna Leach forfeits only the last *Nocturne*. She performs on square pianos by Stodart, Broadwood and Thomas D'Almaine dating from 1823 to 1835 and, most persuasively, suggests an intimacy and transparency hard to parallel on more modern, brilliant and forceful instruments. The ear is quickly attuned to the sound, to the radically different pedalling Leach refers to in her excellent notes, and to a cloudy but appropriate and often hypnotic resonance. Melody and accompaniment (at the very heart of this music) are more closely entwined than on today's instruments, offering a greater sense of Field's harmonic subtlety. There are some extraneous noises, inseparable from period instruments, but so far from distracting attention they somehow add to the potent atmosphere of these performances. A fascinating pair of issues.

Additional recommendation ...

...Nocturnes Nos. 1-16. **John O'Conor** (pf). Telarc Ⓕ CD80199 (DDD: 5/90).

Further listening ...

...Air du bon roi Henri IV. Irish Dance, "Go to the Devil". Sehnsuchtswalzer. Fantaisie sur l'air de Martini. Rondeau écossais. Andante inédit in E flat major. Variations in D minor on a Russian song, "My dear bosom friend". Variations in B flat major on a Russian Air, "Kamarinskaya". Marche triomphale. Nouvelle fantaisie in G major. Nocturne in B flat major. Polonaise en rondeau. Fantaisie sur un air russe, "In the Garden". Two Album Leaves in C minor. Rondo in A flat major. **Míceál O'Rourke** (pf). Chandos CHAN9315 (3/95).

...Piano Sonatas, H8 – No. 1 in E flat major; No. 2 in A major; No. 3 in C minor; H17 – B major. Nocturnes – No. 3 in A flat major, H26; No. 7 in C major, H45; No. 17 in E major, H54*A*. **John O'Conor** (pf). Telarc CD80290 (11/92).

Michael Finnissy

British 1946

Suggested listening ...

...Stabat autem iuxta crucem. *Coupled with works by various composers.* **The Hilliard Ensemble.** ECM New Series 453 259-2 (1/97). *See review in the Collections section; refer to the Index.*

Gerald Finzi

British 1901-1956

Finzi Eclogue, Op. 10.
Delius Piano Concerto in C minor.
Vaughan Williams Piano Concerto in C major. **Piers Lane** (pf); **Royal Liverpool Philharmonic Orchestra / Vernon Handley.** EMI Eminence Ⓜ CD-EMX2239 (61 minutes: DDD: 11/95). Recorded 1994.

Piers Lane brings an exhilarating dash and bravura to Vaughan Williams's craggy concerto and the results are both clean-cut and refreshing. The balance obtained on EMI Eminence does not lack anything in naturalness, and the dynamic range is certainly satisfyingly wide (that brazen orchestral tutti towards the end of the *Fuga chromatica* opens out rivetingly), but the overall effect is perhaps just a little too distant. Howard Shelley is a rival for Lane in the lovely Finzi *Eclogue*. Although Handley's accompaniment positively glows, Shelley's limpid touch also pays great dividends. In the Delius Concerto, however, Lane's big-hearted gusto and genuine poetic insights prove something of a revelation. A memorable concentration and flexibility inform every bar of the central *Largo*, where Lane effortlessly sustains his measured initial tempo. Handley and the RLPO are exemplary partners in all of this (memorable solo contributions throughout); indeed, Handley's wonderfully clear-sighted conception makes for a glorious sense of home-coming at the close, with the clinching climax unerringly resolved. The piano sound, too, seems marginally more full-blooded than it was in the VW Concerto. All in all, the most rewarding version of Delius's endearing work currently available.

Additional recommendations ...

...Eclogue. *Coupled with works by* **Ferguson** Howard Shelley (pf); **City of London Sinfonia / Richard Hickox.** EMI Ⓜ CDM7 64738-2 (66 minutes: DDD: 2/88).

...Eclogue. *Coupled with works by* **Vaughan Williams** and **Foulds** Howard Shelley (pf); **Royal Philharmonic Orchestra / Vernon Handley.** Lyrita Ⓕ SRCD211 (57 minutes: DDD: 3/93). Ⓖ

Finzi. Love's Labour's Lost – Suite, Op. 28. Clarinet Concerto in C minor, Op. 31[a.] Prelude in F minor, Op. 25. Romance in E flat major, Op. 11. [a]**Alan Hacker** (cl); **English String Orchestra / William Boughton.** Nimbus Ⓕ NI5101 (65 minutes: DDD: 12/88). Recorded 1987. Ⓖ

There are several other Finzi issues available which include the Clarinet Concerto. Alan Hacker, however, encompasses all his colleagues' virtues, providing special insights and revelling in the brilliant writing. He also adds something extra – an almost mystical realization of the music's poetic vision which is deeply moving. This is in spite of the fact that the string-playing sometimes lacks polish and precision. Finzi wrote incidental music for a BBC production of *Love's Labour's Lost* and expanded it for a later open-air production. It is tuneful, graceful music, but one cannot feel that the stage was Finzi's world. The disc is completed by two interesting early pieces for strings, the *Prelude* and *Romance*, both wholly characteristic of the composer and very well played.

Additional recommendations ...

...Clarinet Concerto. **Stanford** Clarinet Concerto in A minor, Op. 80. **Thea King** (cl); **Philharmonia Orchestra / Alun Francis.** Hyperion Ⓕ CDA66001 (49 minutes: DDD: 6/87).

...Clarinet Concerto[a]. Five Bagatelles, Op. 23[b]. *Coupled with works by* **Stanford** Emma Johnson (cl); [b]**Malcolm Martineau** (pf); [a]**Royal Philharmonic Orchestra / Sir Charles Groves.** ASV Ⓕ DDCA787 (74 minutes: DDD: 6/92).

Finzi Dies natalis, Op. 8. Intimations of Immortality, Op. 29[a]. **John Mark Ainsley** (ten); **Corydon** [a]**Singers and Orchestra / Matthew Best.** Hyperion Ⓕ CDA66876 (67 minutes: DDD: 1/97). Texts included.

What is central, and essential, is the capacity of Finzi's music to grow in the listener's mind over long years, deepening in appeal, strengthening in the conviction of its purpose. Moreover, these performances are marvellously good at clarifying the strengths. Rather more than their predecessors, they clarify structure and texture. The soloist is more distinctly focused in the recording-balance, and this makes an important difference when the poet's words are as vital an element as they are here. Ainsley sings with grace and clarity, if not with such spiritual intensity as Langridge. The choir are a less full and immediate presence than in Hickox's recording of the *Intimations*; but for much of the time this kind of halo over the sound is appropriate, and in certain important passages the smaller numbers help to compensate with clearer definition. Highly recommended.

Additional recommendation ...

...Intimations of Immortality[a]. Grand Fantasia and Toccata in D minor, Op. 38[b]. [a]**Philip Langridge** (ten); [b]**Philip Fowke** (pf); [a]**Liverpool Philharmonic Choir and Philharmonic Orchestra / Richard Hickox.** EMI Digital Classics Ⓜ CDM7 64720-2 (61 minutes: DDD: 10/93).

Finzi All this night, Op. 33. Let us now praise famous men, Op. 35[a]. Lo, the full, final sacrifice, Op. 26[a]. Magnificat, Op. 36[a]. Seven Part-songs, Op. 17. Though did'st delight my eyes, Op. 32. Three Anthems, Op. 27[a]. Three Short Elegies, Op. 5[a]. White-flowering days, Op. 37. **Finzi Singers / Paul Spicer** with [a]**Harry Bicket** (org). Chandos Ⓕ CHAN8936 (79 minutes: DDD: 9/91). Texts included. Recorded 1990.

To the listener who seeks music in which the fastidious limitation of its means is itself some guarantee of the depth of its purposes, Finzi will always be rewarding. This is true of all the works collected here. Some, such as the first and last, *God is gone up* and *Lo, the full, final sacrifice*, are relatively well known, though not necessarily the most satisfying. There are some fine shorter pieces including the unaccompanied *Seven Poems of Bridges* and the *Three Drummond Elegies* that delight as word-settings. "White-flowering days", to words by Edmund Blunden, comes from *A Garland for the Queen*, the Coronation gift of ten composers in 1953, none happier than this in catching the fresh hopefulness of the time. Best of all perhaps is the *Magnificat*, which also had its first British performance in that year. It is heard here in its original version with organ, beautifully played on this disc and providing a more spiritual association than the orchestral accompaniment added later. The Finzi Singers are sensitive, assured and accurate; their tone is uniformly good, and they convey a sense of personal involvement in the music. The qualities of recorded sound and presentation are well up to the rest.

...Magnificat. Lo, the full, final sacrifice, Op. 26. God is gone up, Op. 27/2. *Coupled with works by* **Vaughan Williams** and **Bax** Soloists; King's College Choir, Cambridge / Stephen Cleobury. EMI British Composers Ⓜ CDM5 65595-2 (73 minutes: [a]ADD/DDD: 1/97).

...Cello Concerto, Op. 40. *Coupled with* **Leighton** Veris gratia – suite, Op. 9[a]. **Rafael Wallfisch** (vc); [a]**George Caird** (ob); **Royal Liverpool Philharmonic Orchestra / Vernon Handley.** Chandos CHAN8471 (10/86).

...Interlude in A minor, Op. 21 (arr. Ferguson). *Coupled with works by* **Howells** and **Patterson** **Nicholas Daniel** (ob); **Julius Drake** (pf). Léman Classics LC44801 (10/93).

...Let us garlands bring, Op. 18. Eclogue. *Coupled with works by* **Bryn Terfel** (bass-bar); **Malcolm Martineau** (pf). DG 445 946-2GH (8/95). *Gramophone Editor's record of the month.* *See review under Butterworth; refer to the Index.* ⒼⒼⒼ

Mateo Flecha   Spanish 1481-1553

...La bomba. La guerra. *Coupled with works by various composers.* **Ensemble Clément Janequin /** **Dominique Visse** (alto). Harmonia Mundi HMC90 1627 (4/98). *Gramophone Editor's choice.* *See review in the Collections section; refer to the Index.* ⒼⒼ

Benjamin Fleischmann   USSR c1919-c1942

Fleischmann Rothschild's Violin (orch. Shostakovich)[a].
Shostakovich From Jewish Folk Poetry, Op. 79[b]. [ab]**Marina Shaguch** (sop); [b]**Larissa Diadkova** (mez); [ab]**Konstantin Pluzhnikov**, [a]**Ilya Levinsky** (tens); [a]**Sergei Leiferkus** (bar); **Rotterdam Philharmonic Orchestra / Gennadi Rozhdestvensky.** RCA Victor Red Seal Ⓕ 09026 68434-2 (66 minutes: DDD: 4/97). Notes, texts and translations included.
Benjamin Fleischmann was among the most talented of Shostakovich's first pupils from the time of the latter's official rehabilitation in 1937. His opera on Chekhov's short story was completely composed but only two-thirds orchestrated by June 1941 when he was conscripted, and he died soon afterwards in battle. Shostakovich thought so highly of *Rothschild's Violin* that in February 1944 he completed the orchestration. The strongest parts of Fleischmann's score are the interludes and the postlude. These fully bear out his teacher's faith in him, and parts of them would not be out of place in Shostakovich's own *Lady Macbeth*. There are also hints of Stravinsky's *Symphony of Psalms*, which Shostakovich had been demonstrating to his pupils at the time. Here, the Rotterdam Philharmonic are on excellent form, and Leiferkus is in superb voice as the village coffin-maker/violinist nicknamed Bronze, who on his deathbed passes his instrument to his fellow amateur musician and former rival Rothschild. Shostakovich's 1949 song-cycle, *From Jewish Folk Poetry*, has proved a minefield for commentators. The essay in the booklet rightly reminds us that at the time it was composed it seemed to fulfil all the demands for Shostakovich's rehabilitation into the Socialist Realist fold. Yet you only have to read some of the texts and compare them with the musical setting to realize that there is an element of allegory at work. This is one of Shostakovich's most consistently fine song-cycles and the performance here is first-rate. However, the main point is that *Rothschild's Violin* is a worthwhile piece in its own right. Shostakovich's restoration was far more than a tribute to a tragically curtailed talent. It was a phenomenon without which the picture of his own development is seriously incomplete, and its first appearance on CD is a noteworthy event. RCA's well-balanced recording is also a plus.

Friedrich von Flotow   German 1812-1883

...Martha – 'Tis the last rose of summer. *Coupled with works with various composers.* **Renée Fleming** (sop); **English Chamber Orchestra / Jeffrey Tate.** Decca 458 858-2DH (3/98). *Selected by Soundings. See review in the Collections section; refer to the Index.*

Josef Foerster   Bohemian 1859-1951

Foerster Violin Concerto No. 1[a]. Cyrano de Bergerac[b]. [a]**Andrea Duka Löwenstein** (vn); [a]**Vienna Symphony Orchestra;** [b]**Czech Philharmonic Orchestra / Gerd Albrecht.** Orfeo Ⓕ C403971A (66 minutes: DDD: 1/98).
A man of wide artistic tastes and talents, Foerster was more than once captivated by the idea of setting dramatic ideas or portraits to music. Rostand's *Cyrano de Bergerac* touched him for the hero's predicament as he woos Roxane on another's behalf: the involvement with Shakespeare was more complicated. Foerster's sympathetic autobiography, *Der Pilger* (published in 1955, after his death),

describes how he imagined it first as a sequence portraying Imogen, Cordelia, Hamlet, Lear and Shylock. Touched by Perdita's 'winter's tale' he found his characters forming themselves into a new pattern in which music might express the inner nature of four aspects of love. Perdita remains the most vivid characterization of the four: she is lively, and forlorn yet merry. The others are Viola, a warm portrayal in rich orchestral garb, then Lady Macbeth, whose corrosion of love perhaps lies too far outside the experience of this gentle composer, and finally a movement entitled "Katherine, Petruchio and Eros", cheerfully rounding off an aggreable and expertly composed work. It contains much touching, noble inspiration, the idiom reminiscent of Suk, Strauss and Elgar. The amiable First Violin Concerto is less compelling, but will appeal to all with a sweet tooth. Warm-hearted performances under Albrecht, though Smetáček's 1978 recording of *Cyrano* is perhaps even more convincing. The sound is appealingly ripe.

Additional recommendation ...
...From Shakespeare, Op. 76[a]. Cyrano de Bergerac[b]. [a]**Prague Symphony Orchestra;** [b]**Czech Philharmonic Orchestra / Václav Smetáček.** Campion Ⓕ RRCD1319 (66 minutes: ADD/DDD: 11/93).

Further listening ...
...Wind Quintet in D major, Op. 95. *Coupled with works by* **Haas** *and* **Janáček** Aulos Wind Quintet. Koch Schwann Musica Mundi 310051 (6/93).

Pierre Fontaine   French ?1390/95-c1450

Suggested listening ...
...J'ayme bien celui. *Coupled with works by various composers.* **Gothic Voices / Christopher Page.** Hyperion CDA66783 (1/96). *See review in the Collections section; refer to the Index.*
...Pastourelle en un vergier. *Coupled with works by various composers.* **Alla Francesca.** Opus 111 OPS30-173 (7/98). *See review in the Collections section; refer to the Index.*   ⒼⒼⒼ

Arthur Foote   American 1853-1937

Suggested listening ...
...Cello Sonata, Op. 78. *Coupled with works by* **Bernstein** *and* **Barber** Andrés Díaz (vc); **Samuel Sanders** (pf). Dorian DOR90241 (2/98).
...Suite in E minor, Op. 63. *Coupled with works by various composers.* **Boston Symphony Orchestra / Serge Koussevitzky.** Pearl mono GEMMCD9492* (12/91). *See review in the Collections section; refer to the Index.*   ⒼⒼⒼ

Christoph Förster   German 1693-1745

Suggested listening ...
...Horn Concerto in E flat major. *Coupled with works by various composers.* **Barry Tuckwell** (hn); **Academy of St Martin in the Fields / Sir Neville Marriner.** EMI Forte CZS5 69395-2 (2/97). *See review in the Collections section; refer to the Index.*

Malcolm Forsyth   Canadian 1936

Suggested listening ...
...Electra Rising[a]. Tre Vie[b].Valley of a Thousand Hills. [a]**Amanda Forsyth** (vc); [b]**William H. Street** (sax); **Edmonton Symphony Orchestra / Grzegorz Nowak.** CBC Records SMCD5180 (2/98).

Stephen Foster   American 1826-1864

Suggested listening ...
...If you've only got a moustache. Gentle Annie. Don't bet your money at the Shanghai. *Coupled with works by various composers.* **Samuel Ramey** (bar); **Warren Jones** (pf). Sony Classical SK68339 (2/97). *See review in the Collections section; refer to the Index.*

Petronio Franceschini   Italian c1650-1680

Suggested listening ...
...Sonata for Two Trumpets, Strings and Continuo in D (Friedrich). *Coupled with works by various composers.* **Håkan Hardenberger** (tpt); **I Musici.** Philips 442 131-2PH (5/95). *See review in the Collections section; refer to the Index.*   Ⓖ

César Franck

Franck Symphony in D minor.
d'Indy Symphonie sur un chant montagnard français in G major, Op. 25[a]. [a]**Jean-Yves Thibaudet**
(pf); **Montreal Symphony Orchestra / Charles Dutoit.** Decca Ⓕ 430 278-2DH
(67 minutes: DDD: 1/92). Recorded 1989.

These two French masterpieces of the 1880s complement each other perfectly. The Franck is very much in the Austro-German symphonic tradition. Its language calls to mind the vaulted splendours and gothic interiors of many a Bruckner Symphony. d'Indy's Symphony, in reality more of a piano concerto, is based on a folk-song he heard whilst holidaying in the Cévennes mountains. Definitely outdoors music this, and far more recognizably French; indeed, with its echoes of Berlioz to its pre-echoes of Debussy and even 'Les Six', it occupies a central position in a century of French music. Dutoit's elegant, flowing way with the Franck (marvellously refined *espressivo* playing from the Montreal violins, and shining, incisive brass) is ideal for those who shy away from the Brucknerian monumentalism of the work; and Jean-Yves Thibaudet's eloquent solo-playing in the d'Indy is matched by exquisitely drawn instrumental solos from within the orchestra. Decca's spacious Montreal sound, too, proves just as apt for the organ-like timbres of the Franck, as for the d'Indy.

Additional recommendations ...

...Symphony in D minor. *Coupled with works by* **Berlioz** and **d'Indy** Chicago Symphony
Orchestra / Pierre Monteux. RCA Victor Papillon Ⓜ GD86805* (71 minutes: ADD: 3/89). ⒼⒼⒼ
...Symphony in D minor. Symphonic Variations[a]. [a]**Rudolf Firkušný** (pf); **Royal Philharmonic**
Orchestra / Claus Peter Flor. RCA Victor Red Seal Ⓕ RD60146 (60 minutes: DDD: 8/90).
...Symphony in D minor. Grande pièce symphonique in F sharp minor, Op. 17 – Andante. Panis
angelicus. *Coupled with works by various composers.* **Philadelphia Orchestra / Leopold Stokowski.**
Biddulph mono Ⓜ WHL011* (70 minutes: ADD: 8/95).
...Symphony in D minor. **Roussel** Symphony No. 3 in G minor, Op. 42. **French National**
Orchestra / Leonard Bernstein. DG Masters Ⓜ 445 512-2GMA (69 minutes: DDD: 10/95).
See review under Roussel; refer to the Index.
...Symphony in D minor. *Coupled with works by various composers.* **Concertgebouw Orchestra /**
Karel Ančerl. Tahra Ⓕ TAH124/5 (two discs: 116 minutes: ADD: 3/96).

Franck Psyché[a]. Le chasseur maudit. [a]**BBC Welsh Chorus; BBC National Orchestra of Wales /**
Tadaaki Otaka. Chandos Ⓕ CHAN9342 (65 minutes: DDD: 6/95). Texts and translations
included. Recorded 1994. Ⓖ

The goody-goody 'Pater seraphicus' image of Franck assiduously projected by his devoted pupils has worked to his disadvantage in these more cynical times, as has the common assertion that his orchestral writing is tied to conventions of organ style. The symphonic poem about the Rhenish Count who goes hunting on the Sabbath and is punished for his sacrilege by a curse condemning him to be pursued for all time by the flames and demons of Hell is worthy of Liszt (Franck's model), and as performed by the Welsh orchestra is vividly programmatic. The breadth of dynamic contrasts is a feature of the recording – as it also is of *Psyché*, the opening of which is almost on the edge of sound. Franck's disciple Vincent d'Indy was either grotesquely unperceptive or grossly overprotective in claiming that *Psyché* was devoid of "pagan spirit" and was an ethereal dialogue between the soul and a seraph. In fact the sensual nature of the music can scarcely be missed, particularly in the section depicting the union of Psyche and Eros (in which the cellos here shine) and in the final pardoning of Psyche for disobeying the order not to look at her lover. When, in the first of the choral passages (which are most often omitted from performance), the words run "Do you not feel a sweet desire unfolding in your agitated breast?", this is surely the emotional cry of the composer himself, who was then violently in love with his pupil Augusta Holmès. Tadaaki Otaka shapes the orchestral playing with tenderness and passion, and the chorus contribute sympathetic tone and clear articulation of the words: the women, however, particularly when alone, are apt to be slightly on the underside of notes.

Additional recommendation ...

...**Belgian Radio and Television Chorus; Liège Orchestra / Paul Strauss.**
EMI L'Esprit Français Ⓜ CDM5 65162-2 (47 minutes: ADD: 5/95).

Franck Symphonic Variations, Op. 46[b].
Grieg Piano Concerto in A minor, Op. 16[a].
Schumann Piano Concerto in A minor, Op. 54[c]. [ab]**Sir Clifford Curzon,** [c]**Friedrich Gulda** (pfs);
[a]**London Symphony Orchestra / Øivin Fjeldstad;** [b]**London Philharmonic Orchestra /**
Sir Adrian Boult; [c]**Vienna Philharmonic Orchestra / Volkmar Andreae.** Decca Headline Classics
Ⓑ 433 628-2DSP* (76 minutes: ADD: 1/92). Item marked [a]from LW5350 (7/59), [b]SXL2173
(1/60), [c]LXT5280 (5/57). ⒼⒼⒼ

Since the advent of the LP the Grieg and Schumann concertos have been ideally paired and here we have Sir Clifford Curzon's classic account of the Grieg from 1959 where he is sympathetically and idiomatically accompanied by Øivin Fjeldstad and the LSO. Curzon was at his finest in romantic piano concertos, and his playing achieves an exceptional balance between poetry and strength. This is a performance which clearly stakes a claim for the concerto as a work of genius. These same characteristics are also to the fore in the Franck *Symphonic Variations*, this time with Sir Adrian Boult conducting. Probably the finest performance of this popular work, it is imaginative and romantic with a perfect sense of style, and excellent rapport between conductor and soloist. As if these riches were not enough, and at bargain price, it is rounded off with another masterly reading of the Schumann Concerto by Friedrich Gulda, dating from 1956 and with Volkmar Andreae leading the Vienna Philharmonic. This reading is right in the centre of the authentic romantic style: extremely personal and authoritative. Decca's recorded sound for all three performances is more than acceptable, with true piano tone throughout. This is probably one of the finest bargain issues currently available.

Additional recommendations ...

...Symphonic Variations[a]. Violin Sonata in A major (trans. Delsart)[b]. Piano Quintet in F minor[c]. **Pascal Rogé** (pf); [c]**Richard Friedman, Steven Smith** (vns); [c]**Christopher Wellington** (va); [a]**London Festival Orchestra / Ross Pople** ([bc]vc). ASV ⓕ CDDCA769 (79 minutes: DDD: 11/91).

...Symphonic Variations. *Coupled with works by* **Fauré** *and* **d'Indy** François-Joël Thiollier (pf); National Symphony Orchestra of Ireland / Antonio de Almeida.
Naxos Ⓢ 8 550754 (55 minutes: DDD: 1/95). *Gramophone Editor's choice.*

...Symphonic Variations. *Coupled with works by* **Brahms** *and* **Litolff** Sir Clifford Curzon (pf); London Philharmonic Orchestra / Sir Adrian Boult. Decca The Classic Sound Ⓜ 425 082-2DCS (74 minutes: ADD: 4/95). *See review under Brahms; refer to the Index.*   ⒼⒼⒼ

...Symphonic Variations. *Coupled with works by* **Grieg** *and* **Liszt** Walter Gieseking (pf); London Philharmonic Orchestra / Sir Henry Wood. APR mono Ⓜ APR5513* (63 minutes: ADD: 3/96).

Franck Prélude, choral et fugue. Prélude, aria et final. Grand caprice. Les plaintes d'une poupée. Danse lente. Choral No. 3 in A minor (arr. Hough). **Stephen Hough** (pf). Hyperion ⓕ CDA66918 (68 minutes: DDD: 4/97). Recorded 1996. *Gramophone Editor's choice. Selected by Soundings.*   ⒼⒼ

To say that it is only the trappings of modern recording that enable Hough to stand shoulder to shoulder with interpretative giants of the past would be to underestimate his achievement. Of course a beautifully regulated Steinway and a near-ideal acoustic are a help. But Hough himself has a dream-ticket combination of virtues – astonishing agility, a faultless ear for texture, fine-tuned stylistic sensibility and an exceptional understanding of harmonic and structural tensions. He acknowledges all Franck's nuances, notated and implied, without ever disturbing the broader flow; he gives full rein to the heroic Lisztian cascades, without ever tipping over into melodrama. Perahia and Cherkassky are among the Franck exponents on CD who are comfortably surpassed. The only hint of a nit to be picked would be that the *fortissimo* arpeggiations in the "Choral" don't ring as resonantly as they might. One can't imagine the calm at the end of the "Aria" being better judged. In their very different ways the almost comical bravura of the *Grand caprice* and the salon charm of the *Danse lente* and *Les plaintes d'une poupée* are extremely difficult to bring off. Yet anyone who has followed Hough's recording career will know that this sort of thing is meat and drink to him. As for his own transcription of the A minor *Chorale*, the unavoidable adjective is 'awesome'.

Additional recommendations ...

...Prélude, choral et fugue. *Coupled with works by* **Liszt** Murray Perahia (pf).
Sony Classical ⓕ SK47180 (60 minutes: DDD: 10/91).   Ⓖ

...Prélude, chorale et fugue. Prélude, aria et final. Prélude, fugue et variation in B minor, Op. 18 (trans. Bauer). Danse lente. Les plaintes d'une poupée. L'organiste, Volume 1 – Chant de la Creuse; Vieux noël: Andantino; Vieux noël: Maestoso; Allegretto; Air béarnais; Chant béarnais; Vieux noël: Poco lento; Noël angévin: Allegretto; Noël angévin: Quasi allegro. **Robert Silverman** (pf). CBC Records Musica Viva ⓕ MVCD1061 (70 minutes: DDD: 6/94).

...Prélude, Fugue et Variation in B minor, Op. 18 (trans. Bauer). Prélude, Choral et Fugue. Danse lente. Prélude, Aria et Final. Choral No. 3 in A minor (trans. Crossley). **Paul Crossley** (pf). Sony Classical ⓕ SK58914 (74 minutes: DDD 2/95).

...Prélude, choral et fugue. *Coupled with works by* **Schumann** Shura Cherkassky (pf). Nimbus Ⓜ NI7705 (77 minutes: DDD: 3/95).   ⒼⒼ

...Prélude, choral et fugue. Les plaintes d'une poupée. Danse lente. Prélude, aria et final. *Coupled with works by* **Chausson** *and* **Dukas** Jean Hubeau (pf). Teldec Ⓑ 4509-96221-2 (two discs: 134 minutes: DDD: 4/96).

...Prélude, choral et fugue. *Coupled with works by* **Beethoven** *and* **Brahms** Evgeni Kissin (pf). RCA Victor Red Seal ⓕ 09026 68910-2 (57 minutes: DDD: 4/98). *Gramophone Editor's choice. See review under Beethoven; refer to the Index.*

Franck Pièce héroïque in B minor. Cantabile in B major. Fantaisie in A major. Grande pièce symphonique in F sharp minor, Op. 17. Pastorale in E major, Op. 19. Fantaisie in C major, Op. 16. Prélude, fugue et variation in B minor, Op. 18. Trois chorales – No. 1 in E major; No. 2 in B minor; No. 3 in A minor. Prière in C sharp minor, Op. 20. Final in B flat major, Op. 21. **Marie-Claire Alain** (org). Erato ⓕ 0630-12706-2 (two discs: 152 minutes: DDD: 7/96). Played on the Cavaillé-Coll organ, Saint-Etienne, Caen, France. Recorded 1995.

What makes this release exceptional? Many other recordings of Franck's organ works have also taken the trouble to locate a wholly authentic Cavaillé-Coll instrument – Michael Murray's set being the most distinguished. If Murray is a great communicator, presenting these large works in an endearingly direct and immediate way, Alain is a completely involved one. More than anyone else she delves into the very soul of these works. Thus we have an intensely prayerful *Prière*, a majestically statuesque *Grande pièce symphonique* while the *Chorales* are delivered with an unexpected degree of fervour; perhaps the Third is a shade overfervent since some of the semiquaver figurations lack absolute clarity – something which after one or two hearings serves to heighten the excitement but which might, after repeated listening, become irritating. This is a highly authoritative release not just in terms of playing but also in Alain's accompanying notes. The Caen organ is a particularly fine specimen of a Cavaillé-Coll, dating from 1884 – 25 years after the St Clotilde organ for which Franck wrote much of this music. The recording captures it, and the church's atmosphere, effectively. A word of warning: anyone seeking out Alain's memorable account of the *Pastorale* will find it on track 10 of the first disc, not track 9 as the tracking details on the box suggest.

Additional recommendations ...

...Fantaisie. Cantabile. Pièce héroïque. Fantaisie in C major. Grande pièce symphonique. Prélude, fugue et variation. Pastorale. Prière. Final. Chorales Nos. 1-3. **Michael Murray** (org). Telarc Ⓕ CD80234 (two discs: 149 minutes: DDD: 7/90).

...Chorale No. 3. *Coupled with works by various composers.* **Andrew Lucas** (org). Naxos Ⓢ 8 550955 (71 minutes: DDD: 11/94). *See review in the Collections section; refer to the Index.*

...Chorales Nos. 1-3. Pastorale. Pièce héroïque. *Coupled with works by* **Bach** and **Widor** **Fernando Germani** (org). EMI Forte Ⓜ CZS5 69328-2 (two discs: 134 minutes: DDD: 11/96).

...Prélude, fugue et variation. *Coupled with works by various composers. Coupled with works by various composers.* **Marie-Claire Alain** (org). Erato Ⓜ 0630-15343-2 (five discs: 351 minutes: ADD/DDD: 1/97).

...Fantaisie, Op. 16. Pastorale, Op. 19. Fantaisie in A major. Cantabile in B major. Pièce héroïque. Prière. Final, Op. 21. Prélude, fugue et variation. Grande pièce symphonique. Trois chorales. Andantino in G minor. **Gillian Weir** (org). Collins Classics Ⓕ 7044-2 (three discs: 160 minutes: DDD: 11/97).

Further listening ...

...Piano Concerto No. 2 in B minor, Op. 11. Variations brillantes sur la ronde favorite de Gustave III, Op. 8. **Jean-Claude Vanden Eynden** (pf); **RTBF New Symphony Orchestra / Edgar Doneux.** Koch Schwann Musica Mundi 311 111 (3/90).

...Piano Quintet in F minor. *Coupled with* **Shostakovich** Piano Quintet in G minor, Op. 57. **Victor Aller** (pf); **Hollywood Quartet.** Testament mono SBT1077* (5/96).

...Piano Quintet in F minor[a]. *Coupled with* **Chausson** String Quartet, Op. 35 (cpted d'Indy). [a]**Michaël Levinas** (pf); **Ludwig Quartet.** Naxos 8 553645 (6/98). *See review under Chausson; refer to the Index.*

...String Quartet in D major. *Coupled with* **Bartók** String Quartet No. 1, Sz40. **Pro Arte Quartet.** Biddulph mono LAB106*. Ⓖ

...Violin Sonata A major (arr. vc/pf). *Coupled with works by various composers.* **Jacqueline du Pré** (vc) with various artists and orchestras. EMI CZS5 68132-2 (8/94). *See review in the Collections section; refer to the Index.* ⒼⒼ

...Violin Sonata A major. *Coupled with works by* **Debussy** and **Ravel** Augustin Dumay (vn); **Maria-João Pires** (pf). DG 445 880-2GH (10/95). *See review under Debussy; refer to the Index.* Ⓖ

...Violin Sonata. *Coupled with* **Chausson** Concert for Violin, Piano and String Quartet in D major, Op. 21[a]. **Pierre Amoyal** (vn); **Pascal Rogé** (pf); [a]**Ysaÿe Quartet.** Decca 444 172-2DH (2/96). *See review under Chausson; refer to the Index.* Ⓖ

...Violin Sonata in A major[a]. *Coupled with* **Lalo** Symphonie espagnole, Op. 21[b]. **Zino Francescatti** (vn); [a]**Robert Casadesus** (pf); [b]**symphony orchestra / André Cluytens.** Pearl mono GEMMCD9250* (9/97). *Also contains short works by Bach, Debussy, Schumann, Shostakovich, Tartini and Wieniawski.*

...Violin Sonata in A major. **Brahms** Horn Trio in E flat major, Op. 40[a]. [a]**Barry Tuckwell** (hn); **Itzhak Perlman** (vn); **Vladimir Ashkenazy** (pf). Decca The Classic Sound 452 887-2DCS.

...Le mariage des roses. *Coupled with works by various composers.* **Dame Felicity Lott** (sop); **Graham Johnson** (pf). Hyperion CDA66937 (10/97). *See review in the Collections section; refer to the Index.*

...Panis angelicus. *Coupled with works by various composers.* **Lesley Garrett** (sop); **Britten Sinfonia / Ivor Bolton.** Conifer Classics 75605 51329-2 (12/97). *See review in the Collections section; refer to the Index.*

...Psalm 150. *Coupled with works by various composers.* **Judith Hancock** (org); [b]**St Thomas Church Choir / Gerre Hancock.** Koch International Classics 37228-2 (9/96).

...Les Béatitudes. **Soloists; Stuttgart Gächinger Kantorei and Radio Symphony Orchestra / Helmuth Rilling.** Hänssler Classic 98 964 (7/91).

Hernando Franco
Spanish 1532-1585

Suggested listening ...

...In ilhuicac cihuapille (attrib.). Memento mei, Deus. Dios itlazo nantzine (attrib.). *Coupled with works by various composers.* **The Hilliard Ensemble.** Virgin Classics Veritas VED5 61394-2 (11/97). *See review in the Collections section; refer to the Index.*

Benjamin Frankel

Frankel Violin Concerto, Op. 24[a]. Viola Concerto, Op. 45[b]. Serenata concertante, Op. 37[c].
[a]**Ulf Hoelscher,** [c]**Alan Smith** (vns); [b]**Brett Dean** (va); [c]**David Lale** (vc); [c]**Stephen Emmerson** (pf);
Queensland Symphony Orchestra, Brisbane / Werner Andreas Albert. CPO Ⓟ CPO999 422-2
(66 minutes: DDD: 4/98). Recorded [ac]1996 and [b]1997. *Gramophone Editor's choice.*

The Violin Concerto, which made Benjamin Frankel's name with the concert public when it was premièred in 1951 (he was already well known as a film composer), is inscribed "In memory of the six million"; it is 'about' the Holocaust. The slow movement of the concerto is a moving elegy, expressing deep sadness with beautiful lyricism, but there is nothing of horror or bitterness. There is an edge to the brilliant and witty, rather Walton-like scherzo and something of sobriety to the expressive first movement, and it is difficult to listen to the finale, in which a violin line of lovely, hovering grace turns into a light-hearted, even high-spirited waltz, without smiling. It is a work with a grieving centre, but not a Requiem. The Viola Concerto of 1967 is possibly even finer. It begins even more arrestingly than the earlier work with a long, lyrical melody over a lapping accompaniment and a deeper pulse. This theme is never literally repeated but it is recalled twice, after more angular music, and its last appearance is quite haunting. The serene slow movement is of similar form; so is the exuberant rondo finale, but Frankel was by now a past master at his own individual, highly tonal and melodious adaptation of serialism, and it gives the whole piece an audible logic and unity that is quite absorbing. You realize that a beautiful idea in the finale is a transformed variant of a spiky one from the first movement, and you want to play the whole work again to find out how it was done. Something similar happens in the delightful *Serenata concertante*. It is almost light music (Frankel described it as a 'street scene' in which passing traffic, a distant jazz band, lovers dancing and all manner of other things could be heard) but strictly ordered, all the episodes derived from a single 12-note row. For listeners who have never been able to get on with serialism the strange experience will not be discovering a serial work that is as engagingly tuneful as this one, but discovering that Frankel's manipulation of his row is perfectly audible. All three performances are fine, and the recordings very pleasing. If you still haven't tried Frankel's music this coupling is an ideal introduction to him.

Further listening ...
...Carriage and Pair. *Coupled with works by various composers.* **The New London Orchestra /**
  Ronald Corp. Hyperion CDA66968 (5/97). *Gramophone Editor's choice.*   Ⓖ
...Symphonies – No. 1, Op. 33; No. 5, Op. 67. May Day Overture, Op. 22.
  Queensland Symphony Orchestra / Werner Andreas Albert. CPO CPO999 240-2 (7/94).   Ⓖ
...Symphonies – No. 2, Op. 38; No. 3, Op. 40. **Queensland Symphony Orchestra, Brisbane /**
  Werner Andreas Albert. CPO CPO999 241-2 (8/95).
...Symphonies – No. 4, Op. 44; No. 6, Op. 46. Mephistopheles' Serenade and Dance, Op. 25.
  Queensland Symphony Orchestra / Werner Andreas Albert. CPO CPO999 242-2 (6/97).
...Clarinet Quintet, Op. 28[a]. Trio, Op. 10[b]. Pezzi pianissimi, Op. 41[b]. Bagatelles, Op. 35[c]. Early
  Morning Music[d]. [d]**Duncan Tolmie** (ob); [abd]**Paul Dean** (cl); [d]**Leesa Dean** (bn); [a]**Australian Quartet;**
  [b]**Markus Stocker** (vc); [b]**Kevin Power** (pf); [c]**Queensland Symphony Chamber Players.**
  CPO CPO999 384-2 (3/97).
...String Quartets – No. 1, Op. 14; No. 2, Op. 15; No. 3, Op. 18; No. 4, Op. 21; No. 5, Op. 43.
  Nomos Quartet. CPO CPO999 420-2 (6/97).
...The Aftermath, Op. 17[a]. Solemn Speech and Discussion, Op. 11. Three Sketches, Op. 2.
  Concertante Lirico, Op. 27. Youth Music, Op. 12. [a]**Robert Dan** (ten); **Seattle Northwest Chamber**
  Orchestra / Alun Francis. CPO CPO999 221-2 (2/95).

Frederick II, King of Prussia

Suggested listening ...
...Flute Concerto No. 3 in C major. *Coupled with works by various composers.* **Patrick Gallois** (fl);
  CPE Bach Chamber Orchestra / Peter Schreier. DG 439 895-2GH (11/94). *See review in the*
  Collections section; refer to the Index.

Girolamo Frescobaldi

Frescobaldi Il primo libro di madrigali. **Concerto Italiano / Rinaldo Alessandrini.** Opus 111
  Ⓟ OPS30-133 (53 minutes: DDD: 4/96). ✍ Texts and translations included. Recorded 1995.
  Gramophone Editor's choice.   Ⓖ

Frescobaldi, in Antwerp with his Roman patron in 1608, was commissioned by a local printer to produce his first and indeed only book of madrigals. The collection seems to have little impact on contemporaries. It was never reprinted and in our own times its existence gradually became submerged under the weight of Frescobaldi's reputation as a composer for the keyboard. Those interested in pursuing the matter discovered that the only known surviving copy lacks one of its voice-parts. Frescobaldi's *Primo libro* seemed set fair to remain a footnote in the textbooks rather than a musical reality. All that changed with the discovery of a complete set of partbooks, then in a private library, a challenge that Rinaldo Alessandrini has now taken up by both editing and recording the music. The distinctive sound and approach of his Concerto Italiano will be familiar to all enthusiasts for Italian music of the Monteverdi period (and above all for the music of Monteverdi himself), and their many admirers will not be disappointed with the result. Their instinctive feel for the diction, sound and sense of the Italian language married to a sophisticated and dynamic interpretational approach brings out all the rhetorical subtleties of Frescobaldi's extraordinary music, with its obvious parentage in the madrigals of Gesualdo and Monteverdi. This is virtuoso madrigal singing at its most exhilarating, all the more effective for being sometimes imaginatively underpinned by continuo instruments. The real revelation here is not so much the Concerto Italiano, whose powerful performances we have come to expect, but Frescobaldi's madrigals; no one with a soul should miss them.

Further listening ...
...Il primo libro di capricci. **Gustav Leonhardt** (hpd, ord) with **Harry van der Kamp** (bar).
   Deutsche Harmonia Mundi Ⓔ GD77071 (73 minutes: ADD: 1/91). 🗡
...Partite e toccate. **Pierre Hantaï** (hpd). Auvidis Astrée Ⓔ E8585 (78 minutes: DDD: 2/97). 🗡
...Partite – XIV, sopra l'aria della Romanesca; VI, sopra l'aria di Follia; Cento partite, sopra
   passacagli. Toccata in A minor. *Coupled with works by various composers.* **Sophie Yates** (hpd).
   Chandos Chaconne CHAN0601 (9/97). 🗡 *See review in the Collections section;*
   refer to the Index.
...Toccata. *Coupled with works by various composers.* **Rinaldo Alessandrini** (hpd).
   Opus 111 OPS30-118 (4/95). 🗡 *See review in the Collections section; refer to the Index.* ⒼⒼ
...Toccate e partite – Toccatas: prima, terza, settima, ottava; Partite: sopra Ruggiero sopra l'arria di
   Follia. Il primo libro di capricci – Capriccio di durezze. Il secondo libro di toccate e canzone –
   Toccatas: prima, seconda, settima, ottava, nona, undecima; Canzona terza. Il primo libro di
   toccate, partite e balletti – Cento partite sopra passacagli; Balletto e ciaccona. Il primo libro di
   capricci. **John Butt** (org). Harmonia Mundi Ⓔ HMU90 7178 (62 minutes: DDD: 2/97).

Peter Racine Fricker
British 1920-1990

Fricker Violin Sonatas – No. 1, Op. 12; No. 2, Op. 94.
Rawsthorne Violin Sonata.
Vaughan Williams Violin Sonata in A minor. **Susanne Stanzeleit** (vn); **Julian Jacobson** (pf).
   Cala United Ⓔ CACD88036 (78 minutes: DDD: 7/96). Recorded 1995.
This is the first commercial recording of the two violin sonatas by Fricker. In the late 1940s, he was regarded as one of the most promising young British composers of his generation. The First Sonata dates from 1951, the Second from 1986-87. Both are impressive achievements, unfailingly inventive and extremely well laid out. Though Fricker has a penchant for angular, arching melodic lines, there's a certain unyielding sternness of utterance which may put some listeners off: much as you appreciate the uncompromising integrity of Fricker's supremely accomplished writing, it's ultimately the kind of music to elicit respect rather than affection. Alan Rawsthorne's very fine Sonata (1958) is a typically resourceful, tightly knit affair. Indeed, inspiration runs high throughout, not least in the ghostly, hesitant waltz of the *Allegretto* second movement and the exhilarating headlong rush of the succeeding "Toccata". It is most assuredly a work which deserves to be far better known – as for that matter, does the Vaughan Williams. Its glorious opening "Fantasia" undoubtedly has something of the same questing spirit of his later Ninth Symphony, while the extended "Tema con variazioni" finale is another utterly characteristic, deeply thoughtful essay. Performances and recordings are persuasive.

Harold Friedell
British 1905-1958

Suggested listening ...
...Magnificat and Nunc dimittis in F major. *Coupled with works by various composers.*
   St Thomas Church Choir, New York / Gerre Hancock with **Patrick Allen** (org).
   Priory PRCD600 (1/98). *See review in the Collections section; refer to the Index.*

Robert Fuchs
German 1847-1927

Fuchs Clarinet Quintet in E flat major, Op. 102.
Romberg Quintet in E flat major, Op. 57ᵃ.
Stanford Two Fantasy Pieces. **Thea King** (cl); **Britten Quartet** (Peter Manning, vn; Keith Pascoe,
   vn/ᵃva; Peter Lale, va; Andrew Shulman, vc). Hyperion Ⓔ CDA66479 (80 minutes: DDD: 7/92).
   Recorded 1991.
Though the clarinet is a beautiful instrument, its solo repertory is small and we cannot afford to neglect any part of it, particularly as there are many fine players, among whom Thea King stands out as one of the finest. None of these three composers can claim to be among the musical greats, but each wrote sympathetically for the instrument and this sensitively played and well-recorded disc makes for pleasing listening. It should win friends for Andreas Romberg (a contemporary of

Beethoven and not the Romberg who composed *The Desert Song*), and the turn-of-the-century composers Robert Fuchs and Sir Charles Villiers Stanford – not least if we also gratefully remember two men for teaching, between them, Mahler, Sibelius, Vaughan Williams and Holst. Romberg's Quintet is fluent and unfailingly agreeable, if not more than that: listening to it, and not least the outer sections of the minuet second movement (the trio is more personal), one is reminded of Mozart in a genial yet elegant mood, and Romberg surely knew that composer's Clarinet Quintet and Concerto. Fuchs's work, written in 1917 when he was 70 and first performed at a concert to mark the occasion, is romantic in an almost Schubertian way although it was composed after the radical works of Stravinsky and Schoenberg had shaken the musical world. But we need not disagree with Brahms, who once said, "Fuchs is a splendid musician: all's so refined, skilled and delightfully inventive that we can always enjoy what we hear". The Two *Fantasy Pieces* by Stanford have similar civilized qualities plus occasional attractive touches of Irishness and complete a very enjoyable programme.

Further listening ...
...Cello Sonatas – No. 1 in D minor, Op. 29; No. 2 in E flat minor, Op. 83. Fantasiestücke, Op. 78. **Nancy Green** (vc); **Caroline Palmer** (pf). Biddulph LAW005 (4/93).
...20 Duos, Op. 55. *Coupled with* **Bartók** 44 Duos, Sz98. **Eugene Drucker, Philip Setzer** (vns). Biddulph Ⓜ LAW007 (74 minutes: DDD: 3/95).   ⒼⒼ
...Ten Fantasy Pieces, Op. 74[a]. Violin Sonata No. 6 in G minor, Op. 103[a]. Six Fantasy Pieces, Op. 117[b]. **Arnold Steinhardt** ([a]vn/[b]va); **Victor Steinhardt** (pf). Biddulph (special price) LAW012 (1/95).   Ⓖ
...Piano Sonatas – No. 1 in G flat major, Op. 19; No. 2 in G minor, Op. 88. **Daniel Blumenthal** (pf). Marco Polo 8 223377 (6/93).

Dyam Fumet   French 1867-1949

Suggested listening ...
...La nuit. *Coupled with works by* **Honegger** and **d'Indy**
Jean-Jacques Wiederker Chamber Orchestra / Frédéric Bouaniche.
Koch Schwann 310652 (6/95). *See review under d'Indy; refer to the Index.*

Andrea Gabrieli   Italian c1510-1586

Suggested listening ...
...Intonazioni – primo; settimo tono. Mass Movements – Kyrie a 5-12; Gloria a 16; Sanctus a 12; Benedictus a 12. O sacrum convivium a 5. Benedictus Dominus Deus sabbaoth. *Coupled with works by various composers.* **Gabrieli Consort and Players / Paul McCreesh.** Virgin Classics Veritas VC7 59006-2 (5/90). 🎖 *Gramophone* Award Winner 1990. *See review in the Collections section; refer to the Index.*   ⒼⒼ

Giovanni Gabrieli   Italian c1553/6-1612

G. Gabrieli Symphoniae sacrae (1615)[bc] – Jubilate Deo a 10; Misericordia tua a 12; Suscipe clementissime a 12; In ecclesiis a 14; Buccinate in neomenia a 19. Intonazioni[a] – del nono tono; duodecimo tono. Canzoni et Sonate[c] – Canzon XIV a 10; Sonata XVIII a 14; Sonata XIX a 15; Sonata XX a 22; Sonata XXI per tre violini. Timor et tremor a 6[ab]. Magnificat a 33 (arr. Keyte)[bc]. Domine Deus meus a 6[ab].
Barbarino Audi, dulcis amica mea[bc]. Ardens est cor meum[bc]. [a]**Timothy Roberts** (org); [b]**Gabrieli Consort** and [c]**Players / Paul McCreesh.** Archiv Produktion Ⓕ 449 180-2AH (78 minutes: DDD: 1/97). Texts and translations included. Recorded 1995. *Gramophone Editor's choice.*   Ⓖ
The words 'Venice' and 'splendour' were simply made to go together and are certainly brought together in this recording by the Gabrieli Consort and Players entitled "Music for San Rocco". It is dedicated to an exploration of the vocal and instrumental music of Giovanni Gabrieli, who composed many works for the Confraternity of San Rocco, with just a couple of contributions from the otherwise unknown Bartolomeo Barbarino. He was a virtuoso falsettist who is thought to have performed at the sumptuous feast of music held in honour of St Roch in 1608 of which a remarkably full eye-witness account survives among *Coryats Crudities* (1611). Indeed, Paul McCreesh and his team of advisers have taken Thomas Coryat's description of the 1608 festivities as the starting-point for this concert programme which was performed in the magnificent Scuola Grande di San Rocco, famous for its sequence of paintings by Tintoretto. The programme explores a wide range of works by Gabrieli, from the more intimate motets with organ accompaniment right through the spectrum to the extraordinary 33-part *Magnificat* reconstructed for the occasion by Hugh Keyte. The sheer magnificence of the sound of massed cornetts and sackbuts, blending so harmoniously with the voices, clearly struck Coryat, as is equally irresistible the best part of four centuries later. This is where the Gabrieli Consort and Players came in some years ago when one could only wonder at McCreesh's logistical abilities in bringing together the required number of chamber organs and so on.

The group have, of course, gone from strength to strength, and have explored a wide range of repertory, but they clearly retain a strong affinity with Gabrieli's music. The singing and playing are quite superb, securely and compellingly flamboyant. It's difficult to single out individuals but one must mention David Hurley who sings the remarkable solo motets by Barbarino with great poise. For the sheer splendour of the music, and the excellence of the performances, this recording is a must.

G. Gabrieli The 16 Sonatas and Canzonas from Sacrae symphoniae. Toccata quinti toni. Three Toccatas. Intonatione del noni toni. **His Majesties Sagbutts and Cornetts / Timothy Roberts** (org). Hyperion Ⓔ CDA66908 (75 minutes: DDD: 12/97). ✔ Recorded 1997.
Gramophone Editor's choice.
Giovanni Gabrieli is arguably the earliest composer to write a significant body of instrumental music to a formula which can be said to be truly idiomatic and timelessly palatable. The *Sacrae symphoniae* publication of 1597 is a mixed set of vocal and instrumental pieces and, in its grand design, preserves a glorious heyday of textural opulence, intimate and playful dialogue between galleries and unashamedly ostentatious virtuosity. His Majesties Sagbutts and Cornetts have augmented their chamber consort to form, as cornettist David Staff proudly proclaims, "the largest group of cornett and sagbutt players to have been assembled from one city since the 17th century". These wonderful 16 canzonas and sonatas make up the complete instrumental music of the 1597 collection. In essence it is the extensive juxtaposition between sombre blocks and glittering small-scale exchanges which gives the music its seminal quality of moving both inevitably and eventfully towards a self-assured resolution, befitting its aristocratic gait. Having a 'moderator' (in this case the fine keyboardist, Timothy Roberts), as opposed to an artistic director, is pragmatic and democratic but there is the odd moment where a strong artistic presence at the helm would have, ironically perhaps, empowered the musicians towards a more flexible and varied approach to articulation and colour. That said, there are some glorious and majestic sounds here: you can fly to the buzzing *Canzon duodecimi toni a 10*, bathe in the fragrant harmonic mosaic of the three-choir *Canzon quarti toni a 15* and relish elsewhere the peculiarly delicate and sweet sounds of this ensemble. Overall, a notable and distinctive achievement. Recommended to a broad listenership.

Additional recommendation ...
...Intonazioni – ottavo tono; terzo e quarto toni; quinto tono alla quarta bassa (James O'Donnell, org solo). Canzonas – XIII a 12; XVI a 15; IX a 10. Sonata VI a 8 pian e forte. Deus qui beatum. Marcum a 10. Omnes gentes a 16. *Coupled with works by various composers.* **Gabrieli Consort and Players / Paul McCreesh.** Virgin Classics Veritas Ⓔ VC7 59006-2 (71 minutes: DDD: 5/90). ✔
Gramophone Award Winner 1990. See review in the Collections section; refer to the Index. ⒼⒼ

Further listening ...
...Symphoniae sacrae – Exaudi me Domine. *Coupled with works by various composers.*
Huelgas Ensemble / Paul van Nevel. Sony Classical Vivarte SK66261 (4/96).
...Symphoniae sacrae – Canzon duodecimi toni a 10; Sonata piano e forte alla quarta bassa a 8; Canzon noni toni a 12; Canzon septimi e octavi toni a 12; Canzon primi toni a 8. Canzoni e sonata – Sonata XVIII a 14; Sonata XIX a 15; Canzon VII a 7; Canzon X a 8; Canzon XV a 10; Canzon XVI a 12; Canzon XII a 8; Sonata XX a 22. Canzon La Spiritata a 4. *Coupled with works by various composers.* **Wallace Collection / Simon Wright.** Nimbus NI5236 (11/90).

Gace Brulé
French c1160-after 1213

Suggested listening ...
...Les oxelés de mon païx. A la douçor de la bele seson. *Coupled with works by various composers.*
Paul Hillier (voc); **Andrew Lawrence-King** (psaltery/hp/org). Harmonia Mundi HMU90 7184 (4/97). *See review in the Collections section; refer to the Index.*

Niels Gade
Danish 1817-1890

Gade Symphony No. 1 in C minor, Op. 5. Hamlet Overture, Op. 37. Echoes from Ossian, Op. 1[a].
Danish National Radio Symphony Orchestra / Dmitri Kitaienko. Chandos Ⓔ CHAN9422 (61 minutes: DDD: 3/96). Item marked [a] from CHAN9075 (11/92), remainder new to UK. Recorded 1992-93.
Gade's First Symphony, which was turned down by the Copenhagen Music Society but accepted and championed in Leipzig by Mendelssohn, launched him on his long and successful career. Its subtitle, *On Sjøland's fair plains* ("Paa Sjølands fagre sletter"), alludes to one of the folk-songs collected and published by his teacher Andreas Peter Berggreen though it is not the only folk-song to figure in the score. The First Symphony comes from 1842 and is exactly contemporaneous with the *Sinfonia sérieuse* of Berwald. Although it may not have as individual a profile, it is eminently civilized, well-schooled music which deserves a place in the repertory. The performance is both vital and sensitive and the recording is splendidly natural, with a good perspective and front-to-back depth and no want of detail or presence. The *Echoes from Ossian* Overture is Gade's first opus, which he composed two years earlier. Like the symphony it is one of his most frequently recorded pieces, and its second group

has a charm that is difficult to resist. This performance, incidentally, has appeared before on the Chandos issue of *The Elf-king's Daughter*. The *Hamlet Overture* was written 21 years later under the influence of what Jens Cornelius calls "Leipzig-inspired ideals". It is beautifully crafted and fresh in its inspiration. The Järvi set is excellent and those who have it need not feel they are in any way short-changed but readers beginning a Gade collection could start here.

Additional recommendations ...

...Symphonies – No. 1; No. 8 in B minor, Op. 47. **Stockholm Sinfonietta / Neeme Järvi.** BIS Ⓕ CD339 (58 minutes: DDD: 11/87).

...Echoes from Ossian. *Coupled with works by various composers.* **Aarhus Royal Academy of Music Orchestra / Ole Schmidt.** Kontrapunkt Ⓕ 32194 (60 minutes: DDD: 7/95).

...Echoes from Ossian. Hamlet Overture. A Summer's Day in the Country, Op. 55. Holbergiana, Op. 61. **Rheinland-Pfalz Philharmonic Orchestra/ Ole Schmidt.** CPO Ⓕ CPO999 362-2 (69 minutes: DDD: 4/97).

Gade The Elf-king's Daughter, Op. 30[a]. Spring Fantasy, Op. 23[b]. [a]**Susanne Elmark,** [b]**Anne Margrethe Dahl** (sops); **Kirsten Dolberg** (mez); [b]**Gert Henning-Jensen** (ten); [a]**Guido Paëvatalu** (bar); [b]**Sten Byriel** (bass-bar); [b]**Elisabeth Westenholz** (pf); **Tivoli** [a]**Concert Choir and Symphony Orchestra / Michael Schønwandt.** Da Capo Ⓕ 8 224051 (63 minutes: DDD: 2/97). Texts and translations included. Recorded 1996.

Kitaienko's performance of *The Elf-king's Daughter* appeared on Chandos in 1992. To be frank it is not easy to choose between the two versions. Michael Schønwandt gives the brisker, fresher account of the score, an impression aided, perhaps, by the marginally more forward recording balance. He has the advantage of better singing, and those troubled by Anne Gjevang's vibrato on the Chandos disc will prefer Kirsten Dolberg, a lovely singer. Kitaicnko is always gentle and sometimes more poetic, though he rather drags the short Prologue, making it four as opposed to the three minutes or so here. This issue clearly scores over Kitaienko in one respect: its choice of coupling. The *Spring Fantasy* ("Forärs-Fantasi") was written in 1852 after Gade's return from Leipzig, where he had briefly succeeded Mendelssohn as conductor of the Gewandhaus Orchestra. By this time Gade was in his early thirties and held several key positions in Copenhagen both as a conductor and organist, and had just been knighted. So he felt secure enough to marry Sophie, the daughter of Denmark's senior composer, J.P.E. Hartmann. There was not only a difference in age and status between the two men but one of class too. The *Spring Fantasy* was a betrothal gift for his fiancée. An atmosphere of spring and happiness pervades the *Fantasy* which is one of the composer's sunniest works, though their happiness was cut short a few years later when Sophie died after having given birth to twins, one of whom also died. All four soloists here are admirable and there is a prominent part for the piano, expertly played here by Elisabeth Westenholz. It is a lovely work, its Mendelssohnian opening with clarinet and piano almost misleading one into thinking one has wandered into the wrong piece!

Additional recommendation ...

...The Elf-king's Daughter[a]. Echoes from Ossian[b]. Five Songs, Op. 13[c]. **Soloists;** [a]**Danish National Radio Choir;** [c]**Danish National Radio Chamber Choir / Stefan Parkman;** [ab]**Danish National Radio Symphony Orchestra / Dmitri Kitaienko.** Chandos Ⓕ CHAN9075 (77 minutes: DDD: 11/92).

Gade String Quartet in F major, "Wilkommen und Abschied". Allegro in A minor. Andante and Allegro molto in F minor[a]. Octet in F major, Op. 17[b]. **Kontra Quartet** (Anton Kontra, Boris Samsing, vns; Peter Fabricius, va; Morten Zeuthen, vc); [b]**Anne Egendal;** [b]**Per Lund Madsen** (vns); [b]**Sune Ranmo** (va); [ab]**Hans Nygaard** (vc). BIS Ⓕ CD545 (76 minutes: DDD: 3/96). Recorded 1992.

All these works date from 1836-48; the *Allegro* in A minor for string quartet from 1836, when Gade was 19; the F minor *Andante and Allegro molto* for string quintet from the following year; the F major Quartet, *Wilkommen und Abschied* from 1840 and the Octet from 1848, towards the end of his Leipzig period. All this music is fluent, urbane, civilized and inventive. In some ways its musical ideas are fresher than in Gade's mature pieces. The F minor Quintet is particularly delightful. But all this music has charm and is expertly and persuasively played by the Kontra Quartet and their musicianly colleagues. The recording is very acceptable, though there is a slight edge in tuttis. A useful supplement to the three mature Gade quartets already available and in some ways more enjoyable.

Further listening ...

...Symphonies – No. 2 in E major, Op. 10; No. 7 in F major, Op. 45. **Stockholm Sinfonietta / Neeme Järvi.** BIS CD355 (12/87).

...Symphonies – No. 3 in A minor, Op. 15; No. 4 in B flat major, Op. 20. **Stockholm Sinfonietta / Neeme Järvi.** BIS CD338 (7/87).

...Symphonies – No. 4 in B flat major, Op. 20; No. 6 in G minor, Op. 32. **Copenhagen Collegium Musicum / Michael Schønwandt.** Da Capo DCCD9202 (5/94).

...Symphonies – No. 5 in D minor, Op. 25[a]; No. 6 in G minor, Op. 32. [a]**Roland Pöntinen** (pf); **Stockholm Sinfonietta / Neeme Järvi.** BIS CD356 (12/87).

...String Quartets – F minor (1851); E minor (1877); D major, Op. 63. **Kontra Quartet.** BIS CD516 (10/92).

...Three Tone Pieces, Op. 22. *Coupled with works by* **Nielsen, Syberg** *and* **Nørgård** **Kevin Bowyer** (org). Nimbus NI5468 (7/96). *See review in the Collections section; refer to the Index.*

John Gay
British 1685-1732

Gay (arr. Britten). The Beggar's Opera. **Ann Murray** (mez) Polly; **Philip Langridge** (ten) Macheath;
Yvonne Kenny (sop) Lucy; **John Rawnsley** (bar) Lockit; **Robert Lloyd** (bass) Peachum;
Anne Collins (contr) Mrs Peachum; **Nuala Willis** (mez) Mrs Trapes; **Christopher Gillett** (ten)
Filch; **Declan Mulholland** (sngr) Beggar; **Aldeburgh Festival Choir and Orchestra /
Steuart Bedford.** Argo Ⓕ 436 850-2ZHO2 (two discs: 108 minutes: DDD: 9/93).
Notes and text included. Recorded 1992.

"Not a 'sport' among Britten's operas but an integral part of the totality of theatrical work, from *Paul
Bunyan* to *Death in Venice*": Donald Mitchell puts the claim well, and this first recording supports it
all the way. *The Beggar's Opera* was Britten's new work for the English Opera Group in 1948 but it
has had less than its due. Everything here is well set-up to make amends. The 12 players forming the
chamber orchestra are excellent individually and they respond sensitively to Steuart Bedford's
direction. The singer-actors are expertly assisted, and Michael Woolcock's production is vivid without
being obtrusive. At the very least, the speech causes no embarrassment; at best it is spirited, and the
full-fathom-five depth of Robert Lloyd's Peachum gives profound pleasure. The singing is probably
as good as it should be; in many of the numbers, character matters more than beauty of tone. But it
is to Britten's score that one has to return when making a recommendation. *The Beggar's Opera* can
also be obtained on records in very different forms. The starry version under Richard Bonynge is
more entertaining, but the gloss is thick and the enrichment of musical interest, when it occurs,
scarcely stretches the imagination. Britten's work is of a different order altogether. It is not mere
cleverness, though the sheer ingenuities of rhythm, counterpoint, harmony and orchestration keep the
ear fully occupied and delighted. Much more, the process is one of absorption and re-creation,
sometimes fierce or poignant, sometimes magical in its loveliness (the use of the chorus in "Cease your
funning", for example). The marvel is that the tunes themselves, so far from rejecting Britten's
treatment as the body might reject a transplant, seem to find themselves in their element. The
recording fills a gap in respect of Gay's masterpiece as surely as it fills another in the Britten *oeuvre*.
Additional recommendations ...
...**Soloists; London Voices; National Philharmonic Orchestra / Richard Bonynge.**
Decca Ⓕ 430 066-2DH2 (two discs: 125 minutes: DDD: 5/91).
...(ed. Turner, orch. Pearce-Higgins) **Soloists; 1968 London Cast / Neil Rhoden.**
Sony West End Ⓜ SMK66171 (59 minutes: ADD: 10/94).

Francesco Geminiani
Italian 1687-1762

Geminiani Concerti grossi, Op. 2 – No. 1 in C minor; No. 2 in C minor; No. 3 in D minor; No. 4
in D major; No. 5 in D minor; No. 6 in A major. Concerti grossi after Corelli's Op. 5 – No. 3 in
C major; No. 5 in G minor. **Tafelmusik / Jeanne Lamon** (vn). Sony Classical Vivarte Ⓕ SK48043
(59 minutes: DDD: 11/92). ✔ Recorded 1990.   Ⓖ
Imagine the scene. The year is 1715 and Francesco Geminiani is playing his violin for King George I,
accompanied on the harpsichord by none other than Handel. But Geminiani had not always enjoyed
the absolute favour of his colleagues; it is said that in Italy complaints were voiced regarding his
excessive use of rubato – a very unexpected phenomenon, especially when seen in the light of our own
attitudes to period performance. So, he left his workplace in Naples (where he was Concert Master),
came to London – his new 'base', so to speak – and additionally went on to work in Dublin and Paris.
The individual works in Geminiani's concerto-style Op. 2 set are forged in the *sonata da chiesa* (slow-
fast-slow-fast) format and contain much beautiful music, especially where, in chordal passages, there
is an overlapping of string lines. The faster movements set out on dancing feet – an aspect of the
music that Tafelmusik indulges with obvious relish – and the slower ones have a mildly sensuous
character. Nowhere, however, will you find as much as a hint of the wayward rubato about which
Geminiani's colleagues complained! Similar positive qualities apply to the performances of the two
Corelli violin sonata transcriptions, the second of which is particularly appealing. The recordings,
too, are warm and immediate, with plenty of space around them and impressive definition.
Additional recommendation ...
...Nos. 1-6. **Corelli** (trans. Geminiani) Sonata in D minor, Op. 5 No. 12, "La follia".
Europa Galante / Fabio Biondi (vn). Opus 111 Ⓕ OPS30-172 (61 minutes: DDD: 1/98).

Roberto Gerhard
Spanish/British 1896-1970

Gerhard Symphony No. 1. Violin Concerto[a]. [a]**Olivier Charlier** (vn); **BBC Symphony Orchestra /
Matthias Bamert.** Chandos Ⓕ CHAN9599 (72 minutes: DDD: 5/98). Recorded 1997.
Of the two works the Concerto – not only the first of Gerhard's four but one of his earliest orchestral
works in general – is much the more accessible, with its mingling of Spanish elements and a lyrical,
impressionistic dodecaphony most conspicuous in the central movement, intended as a tribute to his
teacher, Schoenberg, on his seventieth birthday and making use of the tone-row of his Fourth String
Quartet. The orchestra's tone, from the shimmeringly romantic, Szymanowskian opening onwards, is

seductive and brilliantly reproduced; Charlier throws off his spectacularly virtuosic part with abandon. The last movement is one of Gerhard's most dazzlingly attractive. The First Symphony is a tougher proposition, largely because of its athematicism (which the composer likened to non-representational painting) and absence of exact restatements ("as in bird-song", said Gerhard); and it is shot through with a sombre hue connected, so a thoughtful booklet-note argues, with his near-fatal heart attack in 1952. But its profusion of invention, both of material and of colour (including, in the central *Adagio*, an orchestral simulation of electronic 'white noise'), and its swings between tense, uneasy quiet and outbursts of almost uncontrollable violence are a constant fascination; and the huge, contrapuntally complex finale quite masterly.

Additional recommendation ...
...Symphonies – No. 1; No. 3, "Collages". **Tenerife Symphony Orchestra / Víctor Pablo Pérez.** Auvidis Montaigne Ⓕ MO782103 (59 minutes: DDD: 9/95).

Gerhard Pandora – suite. Soirées de Barcelone – suite (arr. Atherton). Ariel. **Barcelona Symphony Orchestra / Edmon Colomer.** Auvidis Montaigne Ⓕ MO782105 (72 minutes: DDD: 8/97). Recorded 1995.

It was through Antál Dorati, Musical Director for the de Basil Ballets Russes de Monte Carlo in the 1930s, that Roberto Gerhard was introduced to the company's choreographer, Massine, and in 1934 wrote *Ariel* for him, only to have it turned down as "too symphonic". Two years later, again for Massine, he started work on another ballet, inspired by Pyrenean summer-solstice fire festivals; but circumstances led him to abandon it after completing 80 per cent of the full score. At least *Pandora* saw the light in 1944 (even if originally in a two-piano version), when it was produced by the Ballets Jooss. Massine's reservation about *Ariel* does not seem unfair in view of the length of its lyrical central slow section. Elsewhere the music is sinewy and athletic, in a free tonality that becomes more neo-classical and ends in a resounding D major. *Soirées de Barcelone* is more Stravinskian in idiom, and would make an excellent introduction for anyone not yet familiar with Gerhard. The legendary opening of Pandora's box held an obvious symbolism for a Catalonian under the repressive regime of Franco, and so the ballet is not only saturated with Catalan folk references and the sinister medieval *Ad mortem festinamus* dance of death, but quotes the *Beer-barrel polka* and parodies a Falangist march; the epilogue, a lament for the dead and their mothers, is intensely moving. The orchestral playing, under Edmon Colomer, is first-class and the recording is of outstanding quality.

Additional recommendation ...
...Pandora – suite. Alegrías – suite. Cancionero de Pedrell[a]. Seven Haiku[a]. [a]**Josep Benet** (ten); **Teatre Lliure Chamber Orchestra, Barcelona / Josep Pons.** Harmonia Mundi Ⓕ HMC90 1500 (69 minutes: DDD: 11/94).

Gerhard Piano Trio[a]. Cello Sonata[b]. Chaconne[c]. Gemini[d]. [a]**Cantamen** ([cd]Caroline Balding, vn; [b]Jo Cole, vc; [bd]Timothy Lissimore, pf). Metier Ⓕ MSVCD92012 (9/97). Recorded 1995.

Between Gerhard's Piano Trio, written in 1918 at the age of 22, and *Gemini*, composed nearly half a century later, yawns a stylistic gulf that almost defies credence; but of the genuineness of his convictions in each case there is no question. The sensuous warmth of the Trio demonstrates the influence of Ravel, with clear reminiscences of the Frenchman's String Quartet in the finale. The second movement is exquisitely seductive, and Cantamen play the whole work with tenderness and sympathy. Five years later, everything was to change when Gerhard went to study in Vienna with Schoenberg; but his perpetually enquiring mind and ultra-sensitive ear, along with his strong sense of Catalan identity, led him to temper the dodecaphonic system, so that later works broke free of serial dogma and frequently incorporated references to Spanish turns of phrase. This is so in the 1956 Cello Sonata which, for all the trenchant energy of its outer movements, is never less than euphonious: its deeply lyrical slow movement is beautifully shaped by Jo Cole. The Chaconne for solo violin is rather more uncompromising in idiom but Caroline Balding fulfils its virtuosic demands with distinction. *Gemini*, with its plucked piano strings and keyboard clusters, its violin scurries and its frenetic outbursts, shows Gerhard's love of experimentation in sonorities and the two instruments are presented as antagonists rather than partners. The performance has real fire and conviction.

Additional recommendation ...
...Gemini[ab]. Libra[c]. Three Impromptus[b]. Concert for 8[c]. Leo[c]. [a]**Angel Gimeno** (vn); [b]**John Snijders** (pf); [c]**Nieuw Ensemble / Ed Spanjaard.** Largo Ⓕ 5134 (64 minutes: DDD: 2/97).

Further listening ...
...Don Quixote. Pedrelliana (En memoria). Albada, Interludi i Dansa.
Tenerife Symphony Orchestra / Victor Pablo Pérez. Auvidis Montaigne MO782104 (10/92).
...Symphonies – No. 2, "Métamorphoses"; No. 4, "New York".
Tenerife Symphony Orchestra / Victor Pablo Pérez. Auvidis Montaigne MO782102 (2/97).
...Symphony No. 3, "Collages". Piano Concerto[a]. Epithalamion.
[a]**Geoffrey Tozer** (pf); **BBC Symphony Orchestra / Matthias Bamert.**
Chandos CHAN9556 (A/97). *Selected by Soundings.*
...Dos apunts. Soirées de Barcelone. Dances from Don Quixote. Three Impromptus.
Coupled with **Homs** Piano Sonata No. 2. Jordi Masó (pf). Marco Polo 8 223867 (9/96).
...The Duenna (ed. Drew). **Soloists; Opera North Chorus; English Northern Philharmonia / Antoni Ros Marbà.** Chandos CHAN9520 (5/97).

Sir Edward German

British 1862-1936

German Richard III – Overture. Theme and Six Diversions. The Seasons. **Radio Telefis Eireann Concert Orchestra / Andrew Penny.** Marco Polo Ⓔ 8 223695 (65 minutes: DDD: 11/95). Recorded 1994.

This is a well-planned and impressively executed collection. Of course German could not match the passion or genius of Elgar; but the collection here proves that his music does not deserve the neglect that has been its lot. From the dark, brooding opening of the *Richard III* Overture this is music of real character, meticulously worked out, imaginatively scored, and more than once showing its Elgarian kinship. There may be something a little saccharine about the theme upon which German based the *Theme and Six Diversions* (1919) but the way he builds upon it shows his skills at their best, with some striking contrapuntal writing and a swirling waltz section. Perhaps best of all is the symphonic suite *The Seasons* (1899), in which the restful yearning of the "Autumn" movement is especially striking. Andrew Penny conducts the programme with a fine feel for the music's shape and dynamics, and he coaxes from the RTE Concert Orchestra the impression that this is music they have come to know and love. Listeners may do so too.

Further listening ...

...Nell Gwyn – Overture; Country Dance; Pastoral Dance; Merry-maker's Dance; Gipsy Suite. Henry VIII – Shepherds's Dance; Torch Dance; Morris Dance. The Conqueror – Berceuse. Romeo and Juliet – Pavane; Nocturne; Pastorale. Tom Jones – Waltz Song (arr. Tomlinson). Merrie England – Hornpipe; Minuet; Rustic Dance; Jig. **Bratislava Radio Symphony Orchestra / Adrian Leaper.** Marco Polo British Light Music 8 223419 (6/93).

...Symphony No. 2 in A minor, "Norwich". Symphonic Suite in D minor, "Leeds" – Valse gracieuse. Welsh Rhapsody. **National Symphony Orchestra of Ireland / Andrew Penny.** Marco Polo 8 223726 (1/96).

...Merrie England. **Soloists; Rita Williams Singers; Michael Collins Orchestra / Michael Collins.** Classics for Pleasure Silver Doubles CD-CFPSD4796 (4/96).

George Gershwin

American 1898-1937

Gershwin Piano Concerto in F major[a]. Porgy and Bess – symphonic suite. Second Rhapsody[a]. **Aalborg Symphony Orchestra / Wayne Marshall** ([a]pf). Virgin Classics Ⓜ VM5 61243-2 (72 minutes: DDD: 4/96). Recorded 1995.

Wayne Marshall makes his first entry in the Piano Concerto and, in the space of a bar or two, you hear a quick wit and a cool head, the ability to convey (just as Gershwin strove to do) the jazzman's freewheeling, rhapsodic manner alongside a concert pianist's formality. Where Gershwin sits back in the wee small hours spinning yet another of his blue tunes, Marshall is in no hurry to go anywhere. And yet there's a very real sense of the imperative, too, a 'something's coming' kind of feeling. When it comes, it's a special moment. So, too, is Gershwin's grandiose recapitulation (and Marshall goes all the way with that). Generally speaking, the Aalborg Symphony are well up on the style – no mean achievement when the orchestra can so easily sound like a dead-weight in this piece. But then, Marshall's 'Jack-be-nimble' approach is plainly infectious, encouraging reflexes from his band that are as quick and sparky as his own. The pulse of the Roaring Twenties was racy and capricious. But there was always time to dream. That's the tenor of Marshall's performance. The same is true of his dashing account of the *Second Rhapsody*. Again the contrasts are strong, the manner spontaneous – impulsive, Manhattan-brash to a degree – though Marshall never lets us forget that these are luxury goods. Gershwin's shot-silk climaxes (Hollywood dreams indeed), with all their audacious modulations and fruity horn counterpoints (nobody played with wrong-note harmonies like Gershwin), are played for all they're worth. There's also a spirited account of the Robert Russell Bennett *Porgy and Bess* Suite, as felicitous (real delicacy of atmosphere as "Clara" emerges from the opening street cries) as it is robust (that's quite a hurricane that blows through Catfish Row).

Additional recommendations ...

...Piano Concerto. Rhapsody in Blue[a]. An American in Paris. Variations on "I got rhythm". [a]**Earl Wild** (pf); **Boston Pops Orchestra / Arthur Fiedler.** RCA Victor Papillon Ⓜ GD86519 (70 minutes: ADD: 11/87). Ⓖ

...Piano Concerto[a]. Rhapsody in Blue. An American in Paris. [a]**Joanna MacGregor** (pf); **London Symphony Orchestra / Carl Davis.** Collins Classics Ⓕ 1139-2 (65 minutes: DDD: 11/91).

...Piano Concerto. Rhapsody in Blue. Second Rhapsody. **Howard Shelley** (pf); **Philharmonia Orchestra / Yan Pascal Tortelier.** Chandos Ⓕ CHAN9092 (64 minutes: DDD: 3/93).

Gershwin An American in Paris. Rhapsody in Blue[a].
Bernstein Candide – Overture. West Side Story – symphonic dances. **New York Philharmonic Orchestra / Leonard Bernstein** ([a]pf). Sony Classical Ⓜ SMK47529* (60 minutes: ADD: 11/92). From Philips SABL160 (10/60). Recorded 1958-59. ⒼⒼⒼ

Bernstein conducted and played the music of Gershwin with the same naturalness as he brought to his own music. Here, *An American in Paris* swings by with an instinctive sense of its origins in popular and film music; no stilted rhythms or four-squareness delay the work's progress, and where ripe schmaltz is wanted, ripe schmaltz is what we get, devoid of all embarrassment. *Rhapsody in Blue* is playful and teasing, constantly daring us to try to categorize its style, and then confounding our conclusions. Although the solo passages from individual players are beautifully taken, the orchestra capture the authentic flavour of Gershwin's and Bernstein's idiom, and Bernstein pushes them to transcend the printed scores. His own playing in the *Rhapsody* is tantalizingly unpredictable. The recording is clear and bright, perhaps a touch hard-edged, and a little of the richness of the original LP issue might have been preferred by some, especially as the editing is now made more obvious.

Additional recommendations ...
...Rhapsody in Blue. An American in Paris. Piano Concerto in F major. **London Symphony Orchestra / André Previn** (pf). EMI Ⓜ CDC7 47161-2 (ADD: 9/86).
...Rhapsody in Blue (arr. Dokshitzer). *Coupled with works by various composers.* **Timofei Dokshitzer** (tpt); **Bolshoi Theatre Orchestra / Alexander Lazarev.** Melodiya Ⓜ 74321 32045-2 (70 minutes: ADD: 2/97).

Gershwin Piano Rolls, Volume 2. [a]**George Gershwin**, [b]**Cliff Hess**, [c]**Rudy Erlebach**, [d]**Bert Wynn**, [e]**Fred Murtha** (pfs). Nonesuch Ⓕ 7559-79370-2 (42 minutes: DDD: 4/96). Derived from piano rolls cut between 1916 and 1921. Recorded 1992-93.
Gershwin La La Lucille – From now on[a]. Rialto Ripples[a]. **Frey** Havanola[a]. **Conrad** Singin' the Blues ('till My Daddy Comes Home)[a]. **Akst** Jaz-o-mine[a]. **Various** Greenwich Village Follies of 1920 – Just Snap Your Fingers at Care[a]. **Kern** Zip goes a Million – Whip-Poor-Will[a]. **Pinkard** Waitin' for Me[a]. **P. Wendling** Buzzin' the Bee[a]. **Schonberg** Darling[ab]. **Berlin** For Your Country and My Country[ac]. **M. Morris** Kangaroo Hop[a]. **Matthews** Pastime Rag No. 3[e]. **O. Gardner** Chinese Blues[d]. **Schonberger** Whispering[a]. **B. Grant** Arrah go on I'm gonna go Back to Oregon[a].

The first volume of three Gershwin piano rolls was a sensation, bringing his magnificent tunes to life from his own piano rolls, stunningly realized on the Yamaha Disklavier. If that volume was more of a revelation than this one, it is largely because it consisted entirely of Gershwin's own incomparable tunes. Most of his rolls were of popular songs of the day, rushed out to cash in on a hit. But there are some curiosities here and two numbers by Gershwin himself. The first of these is *Rialto Ripples*, a catchy rag Gershwin wrote in collaboration with Will Donaldson and put on to a roll in September 1916. At one time the piece was unknown, but there are now four recordings on CD and it is fascinating to compare Gershwin's own 1916 performance with the sheet music published a year later. The roll has much more of the ragtime idiom in oom-pah left-hand chords and even reveals a few misprints in the score. Another ragtime connection is the 1916 roll, under one of Gershwin's pseudonyms (Fred Murtha), of *Pastime Rag No. 3*, one of only five polished rags in different styles by black composer Artie Matthews. Again there are interesting differences between the sheet music published in the same year and Gershwin's roll – he doesn't play repeats but he returns to the A strain at the end. He doesn't seem to know what to do with the 'stoptime' effect (1'21") in Strain C and just holds the pedal down. The rest of the song arrangements, which sometimes employ two players, show the ragtime background of this piano style, especially in the earlier rolls. These are also good examples of the techniques of the roll arrangers, who hyped it all up by adding notes to create the effect of a whole team of pianists. It is excellent to have more of Gershwin's rolls on CD, but why so few? He recorded over 130, but whereas Vol. 1 was 61 minutes long this one is only 42. This is the only disappointment, however.

Gershwin Cuban Overture (arr. Stone). Rhapsody in Blue. Second Rhapsody. An American in Paris (all arr. cpsr).
Grainger Fantasy on George Gershwin's "Porgy and Bess". **Peter Donohoe, Martin Roscoe** (pfs). Carlton Classics Ⓜ 30366 0068-2 (77 minutes: DDD: 8/97). Recorded 1994.
Gramophone Editor's choice.

This is two-piano playing of superlative accomplishment and breathtaking bravura from Peter Donohoe and Martin Roscoe: the infectious zest and affectionate swagger of this music-making really do seem to leap out of the speakers. Thus the *Cuban Overture* has all the glitter and panache one could wish for, and much the same applies to *An American in Paris*. In the latter, note also the melting fantasy this partnership brings to that gorgeous episode where Gershwin prepares us for the arrival of that indelible trumpet tune. The wittily flexible and superbly co-ordinated realization of *Rhapsody in Blue* is another delight. It's not all barnstorming virtuosity, mind you. Donohoe and Roscoe lend thoughtful, exquisitely moulded advocacy to Percy Grainger's *Fantasy on George Gershwin's "Porgy and Bess"* and the hugely underrated *Second Rhapsody* blossoms in their poetic hands. The sound is rich and refined.

Gershwin Three Preludes. Sleepless Night. Rubato. Novelette in Fourths. Fragment. Blue Monday Suite. Three-quarter blues. Impromptu in two keys. Three Note Waltz. Romantic. Machinery Going Mad. Sleepless Night. Sutton Place. Rhapsody in Blue (all ed. Zizzo). **Alicia Zizzo** (pf). Carlton Classics Ⓜ 30366 0005-2 (56 minutes: DDD: 6/97).

Revisionism has hit Gershwin, whose manuscript affairs have needed sorting out ever since his death. Unscrupulous editors took a hand in preparing his scores for publication and he was always too busy to bother. So was everybody else until now. At last Alicia Zizzo has gained access to what material survives, or has recently been discovered, and she has made new editions of the music, which she performs here. This disc contains unknown short pieces which everyone interested in Gershwin will need to possess. It has always been known that there were more than the three published Preludes. No. 5 is the nifty 1919 *Novelette in Fourths*, anticipating both Confrey and Mayerl, which surfaced in the CD transfer of Gershwin's own piano roll performances which makes Zizzo's treatment seem tame. No. 7 is negligible since it is only a 25-second fragment but both Nos. 2 and 3, like most of the other short pieces, are really charming discoveries. Some are already familiar. As played by Zizzo the original manuscript of the *Irish waltz* (also known as *Three-quarter blues*) simply goes round its tune twice and so does the *Impromptu in two keys* – now in the higher key of E flat and a vast improvement on the 1973 score. Both have detailed rhythmic differences. The *Blue Monday Suite* is based on Gershwin's piano score for the unsuccessful 1922 one-act opera which is often regarded as a study for *Rhapsody in Blue* and *Porgy and Bess*. Although almost half the length of the opera, the suite provides further access to some characteristic Gershwin full of pre-echoes of things to come, including "The man I love".

Additional recommendation ...
...Three Preludes (arr. Gach). *Coupled with works by various composers.* **Richard Stoltzman** (cl); **Irma Vallecillo** (pf). RCA Victor Red Seal Ⓕ 09026 62685-2 (66 minutes: DDD: 9/96).

Gershwin Of Thee I Sing – Prelude[a]; Jilted. Second Rhapsody[a]. The Shocking Miss Pilgrim – For you, for me, for evermore. Cuban Overture[a]. Pardon My English – Isn't it a pity? Variations on "I got rhythm"[a]. Catfish Row[a]. Shall we dance? – Let's call the whole thing off[a]; They can't take that away from me[a]. Goldwyn Follies – Our love is here to stay. **Jack Gibbons** (pf).
ASV White Line Ⓜ CDWHL2082 (77 minutes: DDD: 3/95). Items marked [a] arr. Gibbons. Recorded 1992-93.
This disc is mostly comprised of Gibbons's own arrangements, based on Gershwin's film music, two-piano pieces, and in the case of the "Catfish Row" *Porgy and Bess* suite, his orchestrations. The longest work is the *Second Rhapsody*, composed for a scene in the Gershwins' first Hollywood movie, *Delicious* (from which the best-known song is "Blah, blah, blah"). The film starred Janet Gaynor and Charles Farrell, and in this sequence the heroine wanders frightened through Manhattan – it might be rechristened *A Scotswoman in New York*. George Gershwin referred to the main tune as his "Brahmsian theme" but today no one would mistake it for anything but Gershwin. "For you, for me", one of the melodies salvaged from their files by Ira Gershwin and used ten years after George's death, emerged in the 1947 film *The Shocking Miss Pilgrim*. Ira and Kay Swift hoped it would be a gold-mine and rated the tune higher than any among Gershwin's unpublished songs. The solo version of the *Cuban Overture* is Gibbons's own adaptation of Gershwin's four-hand arrangement; like the "Catfish Row" suite it makes formidable demands on the pianist and Gibbons gives them both virtuoso performances. The recital ends with three of the standards Gershwin wrote in Hollywood during the last months of his life. "They can't take that away from me" must be a strong contender for the great songs of the twentieth century, and no one hearing "Our love is here to stay" can doubt that a premonition of death lingered somewhere in the composer's heart in the autumn of 1936.

Gershwin Porgy and Bess. **Willard White** (bass) Porgy; **Cynthia Haymon** (sop) Bess; **Harolyn Blackwell** (sop) Clara; **Cynthia Clarey** (sop) Serena; **Damon Evans** (bar) Sportin' Life; **Marietta Simpson** (mez) Maria; **Gregg Baker** (bar) Crown; **Glyndebourne Chorus**; **London Philharmonic Orchestra / Sir Simon Rattle.** EMI Ⓕ CDS5 56220-2 (three discs: 189 minutes: DDD: 6/89). Notes and text included. Recorded 1988.
Gramophone classical 100. *Gramophone* Award Winner 1989. ⓆⓆⓆ
The company, orchestra and conductor from the outstanding 1986 Glyndebourne production re-create once more a very real sense of Gershwin's 'Catfish Row' community on EMI's complete recording. Such is the atmosphere and theatricality of this recording, we might easily be back on the Glyndebourne stage. From the very first bar it's clear just how instinctively attuned Simon Rattle and this orchestra are to every aspect of a multi-faceted score. The cast, too, are so *right*, so much a part of their roles, and so well integrated into the whole, that one almost takes the excellence of their contributions for granted. Here is one beautiful voice after another, beginning in style with Harolyn Blackwell's radiant "Summertime", which at Rattle's gorgeously lazy tempo, is just about as beguiling as one could wish. Willard White conveys both the simple honesty and inner-strength of Porgy without milking the sentiment and Haymon's passionately sung Bess will go wherever a little flattery and encouragement take her. As Sportin' Life, Damon Evans not only relishes the burlesque elements of the role but he really *sings* what's written a lot more than is customary. But the entire cast deliver throughout with all the unstinting fervour of a Sunday revivalist meeting. Sample for yourself the final moments of the piece – "Oh Lawd, I'm on my way" – if that doesn't stir you, nothing will.

Additional recommendations ...
...Excerpts. **Soloists; RCA Victor Chorus and Orchestra / Skitch Henderson.** RCA Victor Gold Seal Ⓜ GD85234 (48 minutes: ADD: 4/89).
...Porgy and Bess – Summertime; I loves you, Porgy. *Coupled with works by* **Barber** *and* **Previn**. **Kathleen Battle** (sop); **Orchestra of St Luke's / André Previn.** DG Ⓕ 437 787-2GH (46 minutes: DDD: 1/96). Ⓠ

Further listening ...

...Lady, Be Good! – Fascinatin' rhythm (arr. Wild); The Man I love (arr. Grainger).
Tip-Toes – That certain feeling (trans. Wodehouse). Oh, Kay! – Clap yo' hands (trans.
Wodehouse). *Coupled with works by various composers.* **Alan Feinberg** (pf); **Daniel Druckman**
(marimba). Argo 444 457-2ZH (11/95).

...Piano Rolls: Tip-Toes – Sweet and low-down; That certain feeling[a]. Novelette in Fourths[a]. Lady,
Be Good! – So am I[a]. Rhapsody in Blue[a]. Gershwin Songbook – Swanee[a]. When you want 'em,
you can't get 'em, when you've got 'em, you don't want 'em[a]. Tell me more – Tell me more[a].
George White's Scandals of 1920 – Idle dreams; My lady; On my mind the whole night long;
Scandal walk[a]. An American in Paris (trans. Milne)[b]. [a]**George Gershwin**, [b]**Frank Milne** (pfs).
Elektra Nonesuch 7559-79287-2 (4/94).

...Piano Transcriptions (arr. Wild) – Fantasy on "Porgy and Bess". Improvisation in the form of
a Theme and Three Variations on "Someone to watch over me". Seven Virtuoso Etudes: I got
rhythm; Lady be good; Liza; Embraceable you; Somebody loves me; Fascinatin' rhythm;
The man I love. **Earl Wild** (pf). Chesky CD32 (10/90).

...Nice work if you can get it. They all laughed. Embraceable you. Just another rhumba.
Coupled with works by various composers. **Samuel Ramey** (bar); **Warren Jones** (pf).
Sony Classical SK68339 (2/97). *See review in the Collections section; refer to the Index.*

...Girl Crazy. **Soloists; chorus and orchestra / John Mauceri.** Nonesuch 7559-79250-2 (2/91).

...Lady, Be Good!. **Soloists; chorus and orchestra / Eric Stern.**
Nonesuch 7559-79308-2 (7/93). *Gramophone Award Winner 1993.*

...Oh, Kay! **Soloists; chorus; Orchestra of St Luke's / Eric Stern.**
Nonesuch 7559-79361-2 (8/95). *Gramophone Award Winner 1996.*

...Pardon My English. **Soloists; chorus and orchestra / Eric Stern.** Nonesuch 7559-79338-2 (11/94).

...Strike Up the Band. **Soloists; chorus and orchestra / John Mauceri.** Nonesuch 7559-79273-2 (1/92).

Carlo Gesualdo   Italian c1561-1613

Gesualdo Responsoria et alia ad Officium Hebdonadae Sanctae spectantia. Benedictus. Miserere.
The Hilliard Ensemble. ECM New Series Ⓕ 843 867-2 (two discs: 124 minutes: DDD: 3/92). Texts
and translations included. ✒ Recorded 1990.   Ⓠ

To many, Gesualdo is known above all for the *crime passionnel* which left his wife and her lover
impaled on the same sword, but the notion that his highly-charged music is the product of a tortured
and unstable mind is, no doubt, over-romanticized. The exaggeratedly chromatic melodies and daring
harmonic style of his late music were fully in keeping with the experimental madrigal school of the
late sixteenth century. That said, Gesualdo's setting of the Responds for the Tenebrae of Holy Week
is surely one of the most intense and disturbing works of the entire period. The complex service of
Tenebrae is made up of the two offices, Matins and Lauds. Within Matins come the 27 responsories
that were the inspiration for Gesualdo's music, in addition to which he set the "Miserere" and
"Benedictus" from Lauds. At the beginning of the service the church is illuminated with candles, but
these are extinguished one by one, hence the name *tenebrae* (darkness). It is significant that Gesualdo
chose the most dramatic service of the church year, and one that is concerned with betrayal and death.
The Hilliard Ensemble has not missed one ounce of the profundity of this music, and their
performance is one of those rare artistic achievements that combines a heartfelt emotional response
with faultless technical control. Their phrases are perfectly shaped and directed, and while it is
virtually impossible to single out one particular contribution, David Beaven's ideally focused bass line
should not go unmentioned. The recording is excellent and every detail of the individual voices can
be heard. Texts and translations are included, together with an extract from Hildesheimer's *Tynset*,
but some explanatory notes would have been helpful.

Additional recommendations ...

...Responsoria et alia ad Officium Hebdonadae Sanctae spectantia – excerpts. Marian Motets –
Ave, dulcissima Maria; Precibus et meritis beatae Mariae; Ave, regina coelorum; Maria, mater
gratiae. **The Tallis Scholars / Peter Phillips.** Gimell Ⓕ 454 915-2PH (52 minutes: DDD: 12/87).

...Da pacem, Domine. Assumpta est Maria. Illumina nos misericordiarum (all cptd. Stravinsky).
Responsoria et alia ad Officium Hebdonadae Sanctae spectantia – Sicut ovis; Jerusalem; surge;
Plange quasi virgo; Recessit pastor noster; O vos omnes; Ecce quomodo moritur justus;
Astiterunt reges terrae; Aestimatus sum; Sepulto Domino. **Stravinsky** Mass[a]. Pater noster.
Ave Maria. The dove decending. **Trinity College Choir, Cambridge;** [a]wind players of
London Musici / Richard Marlow. Conifer Classics Ⓕ 75605-51232-2 (65 minutes: DDD: 6/95).

...Responsoria et alia ad Officium Hebdonadae Sanctae spectantia – Tenebrae factae sunt;
Caligaverunt oculi mei. *Coupled with works by various composers.* **Westminster Abbey Choir;**
Abbey Consort / Martin Neary.
Sony Classical Arc of Light Ⓕ SK66615 (77 minutes: DDD: 7/96).

Further listening ...

...Madrigali libro quinto. **Ensemble Métamorphoses / Maurice Bourbon.** Arion ARN68388 (3/98).

...Madrigals – Ahi, disperata vita. Sospirava il mio cor. O malnati messaggi. Non t'amo, o voce
ingrata. Luci serene e chiare. Sparge la morte al mio Signor nel viso. Arde il mio cor. Occhi del

mio cor vita. Mercè grido piangendo. Asciugate i begli ochi. Se la mia morte brami. Io parto. Ardita Zanzaretta. Ardo per te, mio bene. Instrumental works – Canzon francese. Io tacerò. Corrente, amanti. **Les Arts Florissants Vocal and Instrumental Ensemble / William Christie.** Harmonia Mundi HMC90 1268 (10/88). ✏   Ⓖ

...Canzon francese del Principe. *Coupled with works by various composers.* **Sophie Yates** (hpd). Chandos Chaconne CHAN0601 (9/97). ✏ *See review in the Collections section; refer to the Index.*

Johannes Ghiselin
Femish *fl* early 16th century

Suggested listening ...

...Ghy syt die wertste boven al. *Coupled with works by various composers.* **Early Music Consort of London / David Munrow.** Virgin Classics Veritas VED5 61334-2 (11/97). ✏ *See review in the Collections section; refer to the Index.*

Felice De Giardini
Italian 1716-1796

Suggested listening ...

...Quartets, Op. 21 – No. 2 in B flat major[c]; No. 5 in B flat major[c]; No. 6 in C major[c]. Quartets, Op. 25 – No. 3 in D major[a]; No. 5 in B flat major[b]. **L'Astrée.** Opus 111 OPS30-163 (10/97). ✏

Orlando Gibbons
British 1583-1625

Gibbons Preludes[a] – A minor, MBXX/1; G major, MBXX/2. Fancy, MBXX/3[b]. Fantasias – G major, MBXX/6[a]; D minor, MBXX/8[a]; G minor, MBXX/9[b]. Pavan, MBXX/15[a]. Pavins – MBXX/16[b]; MBXX/17[a]. Pavan and Galliard in A minor, "Lord Salisbury", MBXX/18-19[a]. Galliard, MBXX/22[a]. Galljardo, MBXX/23[b]. Ground in A minor, MBXX/26[b]. Whoope, doe me no harm, good man, MBXX/31[a]. French Ayre, MBXX/32[b]. Almayne, MBXX/33[b]. Alman, "The King's Jewel", MBXX/3[a]. Allmaine, MBXX/37[b]. French Coranto, MBXX/38[b]. French Allmaine, MBXX/41[b]. The Wellcome, MBXX/42[b]. **Richard Egarr** ([a]hpd/[b]virg). Globe Ⓟ GLO5168 (63 minutes: DDD: 5/98). ✏ Recorded 1997.

Gibbons was described by contemporaries as having "the best hand in England". Nevertheless, his considerable output for the keyboard is under-represented on disc as compared with that of his older contemporary, Byrd. Could this be because his virtuosity, unlike that of the exhibitionist John Bull, is less a matter of finger dexterity than of compositional technique (exploiting imitative counterpoint) and emotional depth – qualities less immediately captivating to the casual listener? The severe style of two substantial Fantasias here reflects Gibbons's austere nature – even his galliards are cast in a minor key; but all the pavans are remarkable for their expressive depth. A lighter vein, however, is struck in a group of French-inspired pieces, *The King's Jewel* and the brief variations on the popular tune *Whoope, doe me no harm, good man.* Presenting half this programme on a sweet-toned muselar (a Flemish virginal for domestic use) and half on a harpsichord – both Dutch copies of Ruckers instruments of 1640 – Egarr vigorously abjures the "sterile, metronomic approach of our time" and instead opts for flexible phrasing that responds to the music's inner stresses. In so doing he brings out admirably the individual character of a composer, the exploration of whom is richly rewarding to the thoughtful music-lover.

Gibbons O clap your hands. Great Lord of Lords. Hosanna to the Son of David. Prelude in G major[a]. Out of the deep. See, see, the word is incarnate. Preludes – No. 3 in D minor, MBXX/3[a]. Lift up your heads. Almighty and everlasting God. First (Short) Service – No. 6, Magnificat; No. 7, Nunc dimittis. Second Service – No. 3, Magnificat; No. 4, Nunc dimittis. Fantazia of four parts[a]. O God, the king of glory. O Lord, in Thy wrath rebuke me not. [a]**Laurence Cummings** (org); **Oxford Camerata / Jeremy Summerly.** Naxos Ⓢ 8 553130 (65 minutes: DDD: 8/96). Texts included. *Gramophone Editor's choice.*   Ⓖ

The Oxford Camerata provide us here with a representative selection of choral works by Orlando Gibbons, together with three of his organ pieces. The programme is introduced by a bright and busy performance of the eight-part *O clap your hands,* followed by the noble verse anthem *Great Lord of Lords* – and it is pleasing to hear in this piece, and in the other verse-anthems, the rich timbre of the countertenor Robin Blaze, a welcome acquisition for the Camerata. In fact the group have a great deal of vocal talent in their make-up and are strengthening their reputation all the time. They tackle the gently moving *See, see, the word is incarnate* with great confidence, together with the First and Second Services and the quiet collects with all the knowledge and aplomb of cathedral lay clerks or choral scholars from Oxford and Cambridge. We are obviously unable to tell what King's or Westminster Abbey's choirs would have sounded like in Gibbons's day, but what we have here is very much the sound of an Oxbridge choir today. Laurence Cummings plays two short preludes, the one in G major

– a real test of agility – from *Parthenia* and that in D minor from Benjamin Cosyn's *Virginal Book*. The *Fantazia of four parts* is a most extraordinary work, quite hard to steady and control. Nevertheless, it is a welcome addition to the programme.

Additional recommendations ...

...If ye be risen again with Christ. O Lord, in Thy wrath rebuke me not[a]. Almighty God, who by Thy Son. O clap your hands[a]. We praise Thee, O Father. So God loved the world. O God, the king of glory. 10 Fantasias[b]. Four Preludes[b] [a]**St John's College Choir, Cambridge / Christopher Robinson** with [b]**Robert Woolley** (org).
Chandos Chaconne Ⓕ CHAN0559 (79 minutes: DDD: 11/94).

...Hosanna to the Son of David. Almighty and everlasting God. Behold, Thou hast made my days. Blessed are all they that fear the Lord. Deliver us, O Lord, our God. Glorious and powerful God. I am the resurrection. Lift up your heads. O all true faithful hearts. O clap your hands. O Lord, how do my woes increase. O Lord, I lift my heart to thee. O Lord, in Thee is all my trust. O Lord, in Thy wrath rebuke me not. Out of the deep. Praise the Lord, O my soul. See, see, the Word is incarnate. This is the record of John. **Trinity College Choir, Cambridge; Fretwork / Richard Marlow.** Conifer Classics Ⓕ 75605 51231-2 (74 minutes: DDD: 8/95).

...O clap your hands. *Coupled with works by various composers.* **Choir of St Mary's Cathedral, Edinburgh / Timothy Byram-Wigfield.** Priory Ⓕ PRCD557 (64 minutes: DDD: 10/97).
See review in the Collections section; refer to the Index.

Gibbons Pavan and Galliard a 6[d]. Fantasia a 2 No. 1[d]. Go from my window[d]. Fantasias a 6 – Nos. 3 and 5[d]. Fantasia a 4 No. 1 "for the great double bass"[d]. Galliard a 3[d]. In Nomine a 4[d]. Pavan and Galliard in A minor, "Lord Salisbury"[b]. Prelude in G major[b]. Masks – Lincoln's Inn mask; The Fairest Nymph[b]. Alman in G major[b]. Behold, thou hast made my days[cd]. Glorious and powerful God[cd]. The First Set of Madrigals and Mottets[ad] – Daintie fine bird; Faire is the rose; I weigh not fortune's frown; I see ambition never pleased; I feign not friendship where I hate; The silver swanne. [a]**Tessa Bonner** (sop); [b]**Timothy Roberts** (keybds); [c]**Red Byrd; **[d]**Rose Consort of Viols.** Naxos Ⓢ 8 550603 (68 minutes: DDD: 2/95). Recorded 1992.   Ⓖ

Beautifully performed and finely recorded, this selection of Gibbons's music is especially attractive on account of the variety of its programme. At its richest it presents writing for voice and viols combined, five parts to each, or for viols alone, sometimes in six parts. In lightest, most transparent texture there is a charming piece for two viols. Three keyboard instruments are used for solos: virginals, harpsichord and organ. A soprano also sings solos to viol accompaniment. Moods and styles vary correspondingly. The *Masks* and *Alman* for virginals have a high-spirited, almost popular manner; the Fifth *Fantasia* includes some unusual chromaticism and harmonic developments that for a while almost anticipate Purcell. Tessa Bonner sings with unvibrant purity; but what will probably be found the most striking feature of the singing here is the pronunciation. It is one of the distinguishing marks of this curiously named group, Red Byrd, that they sing such music with vowel-sounds modified to fit theories about the English in which it would originally have been sung. Thus the "daintie fine bird" tells "oi sing and doy", and the 'u' acquires a sort of umlaut in *I weigh not fortune's frown*, "weigh" and "frown" also having a measure of rusticity. Perhaps it is a good idea, but it does increase the desirability of printed texts in the booklet. The instrumental music is all finely played, the viols avoiding any imputation of belonging to the squeeze-and-scrape school, and Timothy Roberts's keyboard solos are particularly skilful, both in legato and fluent passagework.

Further listening ...

...Two Fantasias a 4. 9 Fantasias a 3. Galliard a 3. *Coupled with works by* **Lupo**
The Parley of Instruments / Peter Holman. Hyperion CDA66395 (9/91). 〆

...Fantasias – D minor, MBXX/5; G major, MBXX/6; D minor, MBBXX/8; A minor, MBXX/11; A minor, MBXX/12; C major, MBXX/14. Preludes – A minor, MBXX/1; A minor, MBXX/4. Galliard, "Lady Hatton", MBXX/20. Ground in A minor, MBXX/26. French Coranto, MBXX/38. Pavan and Galliard in A minor, "Lord Salisbury", MBXX/18-19. The Italian ground, MBXX/27. The Queen's command, MBXX/28. *Coupled with works by* **Byrd** **Laurent Stewart** (hpd). Pierre Verany PV795051 (3/96). *See review under Byrd; refer to the Index.*

...Fantasia No. 6 in A minor. *Coupled with works by various composers.* **Sophie Yates** (virg). Chandos Chaconne CHAN0574 (12/95). 〆

...Canticles – Magnificat; Nunc dimittis, "Short Service"; Magnificat; Nunc dimittis, "Second Service". Full Anthems – Almighty and Everlasting God; Lift up your heads; Hosanna to the Son of David. Verse Anthems[a] – This is the record of John; See, see, the Word is incarnate; O Thou, the central orb. Hymns and Songs of the Church – Now shall the praises of the Lord be sung; O Lord of Hosts; A song of joy unto the Lord we sing; Come, kiss me with those lips of thine. Organ works – Voluntary; Fantasia for double organ; Fantasia. **King's College Choir, Cambridge / Philip Ledger** with **John Butt** (org) and [a]**London Early Music Group.** ASV Gaudeamus CDGAU123 (4/86). 〆

...Drop, drop slow tears. *Coupled with works by various composers.* **St Paul's Cathedral Choir / John Scott** with **Andrew Lucas** (org). Hyperion CDA66916 (A/97). *See review in the Collections section; refer to the Index.*

...First (Short) Service. *Coupled with works by various composers.* **Lichfield Cathedral Choir / Andrew Lumsden** with **Mark Shepherd, Nigel Potts** (orgs). Priory PRCD505 (10/95).

...Full Anthems – Hosanna to the Son of David; I am the resurrection; O clap your hands; O Lord, how do my woes increase; O Lord, I lift my heart to Thee; O Lord, in Thy wrath rebuke me not. Verse Anthems – Lord, we beseech Thee, pour Thy grace; Praise the Lord, O my soul; See, see, the Word is incarnate; Sing unto the Lord, o ye saints. Hymns and Songs of the Church – Come, kiss me with those lips of Thine; How sad and solitary now; Lord, I will sing to Thee; Lord, Thy answer I did hear; Now in the Lord my heart doth pleasure take; Now shall the praises of the Lord; O Lord of Hosts and God of Israel; O my love, how comely now; Sing praises Is'rel to the Lord; Song of joy unto the Lord we sing; The beauty, Israel, is gone; When one among the Twelve there was; Who's this, that leaning on her friend. Preces and Psalm 145.
The Clerkes of Oxenford / David Wulstan. Calliope CAL9611 (12/89).

...Second Service (ed. Higginbottom) – Te Deum Laudamus; Jubilate Deo; Magnificat; Nunc dimittis. Full Anthems – O clap your hands; O Lord, in Thy wrath rebuke me not. Verse Anthems – O God, the king of glory; Glorious and powerful God; Sing unto the Lord; See, see, the Word is incarnate. Organ works[a] – Fantasia of four parts; A Fancy in A major; Fantasia for double organ.
New College Choir, Oxford / Edward Higginbottom with [a]**David Burchell** (org).
CRD CRD3451 (12/88). ⓖ

...This is the record of John. *Coupled with works by various composers.* **St Paul's Cathedral Choir / John Scott** with **Andrew Lucas** (org).
Hyperion CDA66994 (12/97). *See review in the Collections section; refer to the Index.*

Alberto Ginastera

Argentinian 1916-1983

Ginastera Harp Concerto, Op. 25[a].
Glière Harp Concerto, Op. 74[a]. Concerto for Coloratura Soprano and Orchestra, Op. 82[b].
[b]**Eileen Hulse** (sop); [a]**Rachel Masters** (hp); **City of London Sinfonia / Richard Hickox.**
Chandos ⓕ CHAN9094 (65 minutes: DDD: 2/93). Recorded 1992.
Glière was among the comparatively few front-rank Russian composers who stayed on in their homeland after the 1917 Revolution. The music he composed there adopted a middle-of-the-road conservative style which helped him to steer clear of the more viscous controversies of the 1920s and 1930s. The Concertos for harp and coloratura sorano date from 1938 and 1942 respectively and are unashamedly ingratiating, high-grade mood-music, here played and recorded in a manner that those with a sweet tooth should find absolutely irresistible. The Harp Concerto by Ginastera is made of sterner stuff, but only slightly – it's Bartókian acerbities are tempered by an engaging Latin American swing. Once again the performance is crisp and bouncy, although in this instance the reverberant recording takes something of the edge off the rhythmic bite.

Additional recommendations ...
...Harp Concerto[a]. Piano Concerto No. 1, Op. 28[b]. Estancia – concert suite from ballet, Op. 8a.
[a]**Nancy Allen** (hp); [b]**Oscar Tarrago** (pf); **Mexico City Philharmonic Orchestra / Enrique Bátiz.**
ASV ⓕ CDDCA654 (64 minutes: DDD: 8/89). ⓖ

...Harp Concerto. **Mathias** Harp Concerto, Op. 50. **Ann Hobson Pilot** (hp); **English Chamber Orchestra / Isaiah Jackson.** Koch International Classics ⓕ 37261-2 (49 minutes: DDD: 12/94).

Further listening ...
...Concerto for Strings, Op. 33. *Coupled with works by* **Evangelista** *and* **Villa-Lobos**
I Musici de Montréal / Yuli Turovsky. Chandos CHAN9434 (5/96).

...Glosses on Themes of Pablo Casals, Op. 48[a]. Variaciones concertantes, Op. 23[b]. Glosses on Themes of Pablo Casals, Op. 46[c]. [ac]**London Symphony Orchestra,** [b]**Israel Chamber Orchestra / Gisèle Ben-Dor.** Koch International Classics 37149-2 (12/96).

...Cello Sonata, Op. 49[a]. Pampeana No. 2, Op. 21[a]. Triste, Op. 10 No. 2 (trans. Fournier)[a]. Danzas argentinas, Op. 2. Pequeña danza, Op. 8 No. 1. 12 American Preludes, Op. 12. Piano Sonata No. 1, Op. 22. [a]**Aurora Natola-Ginastera** (vc); **Alberto Portugheis** (pf).
ASV CDDCA865 (10/93). *Gramophone Editor's choice.*

...String Quartets – No. 1, Op. 20; No. 2, Op. 26; No. 3, Op. 40[a]. [a]**Olivia Blackburn** (sop); **Lyric Quartet.** ASV CDDCA944 (10/96).

...Dos Canciones, Op. 3[ad]. Canciones populares argentinas, Op. 10[ad]. Las horas de una estancia, Op. 11[ad]. Pampeana No. 1, Op. 16[bc]. Piano Quintet, Op. 29[cd]. [a]**Olivia Blackburn** (sop); [b]**Sherban Lupu** (vn); [c]**Alberto Portugheis** (pf); [d]**Bingham Quartet.** ASV CDDCA902 (3/95).

...Punena No. 2, Op. 45. *Coupled with works by various composers.* **Patrick Thomas Demenga** (vc).
ECM New Series 445 234-2 (8/95).

Umberto Giordano

Italian 1867-1948

Giordano Andrea Chénier. **Luciano Pavarotti** (ten) Andrea Chénier; **Leo Nucci** (bar) Gerard; **Montserrat Caballé** (sop) Maddalena; **Kathleen Kuhlmann** (mez) Bersi; **Astrid Varnay** (sop) Countess di Coigny; **Christa Ludwig** (mez) Madelon; **Tom Krause** (bar) Roucher; **Hugues Cuénod** (ten) Fleville; **Neil Howlett** (bar) Fouquier-Tinville, Major-domo; **Giorgio Tadeo** (bass) Mathieu; **Piero De Palma** (ten) Incredible; **Florindo Andreolli** (ten) Abate; **Giuseppe Morresi** (bass) Schmidt;

Ralph Hamer (bass) Dumas; **Welsh National Opera Chorus; National Philharmonic Orchestra /
Riccardo Chailly.** Decca Ⓕ 410 117-2DH2 (two discs: 107 minutes: DDD: 2/85). Notes, text and
translation included. From 411 117-1DH3 (11/84). Recorded 1982-84.

Andrea Chénier, set at the start of the French Revolution, is a potent blend of the social and the
emotional. The three main characters, the aristocratic Maddalena, the idealistic poet Chénier and the
fiercely republican Gerard, are caught up in a triangle that pits love against conscience, independence
against society. The opera has many well-known set numbers and high on any list of favourites must
be Chénier's so-called *Improviso* in Act 1 where he bursts out in a spontaneous poem on the power of
love, or Maddalena's glorious and moving "La mamma morta" in the Third Act where she describes
how her mother gave up her life to save her. Giordano had a real theatrical flair for the 'big moment'
and he paces the work masterfully. The tunes seem to flow endlessly from his pen and the characters
have real flesh and blood. The cast is strong, with Caballé and Pavarotti making a powerful central
pair. Riccardo Chailly conducts the excellent National Philharmonic with flair and feeling and the
whole opera is beautifully recorded.

Additional recommendations ...

...**Soloists; John Alldis Choir; National Philharmonic Orchestra / James Levine.**
RCA Victor Red Seal Ⓜ 74321 39499-2 (two discs: 114 minutes: ADD: 9/89).

...**Soloists; Rome Opera Chorus and Orchestra / Gabriele Santini.**
EMI Opera Ⓜ CMS5 65287-2 (two discs: 115 minutes: ADD: 7/95).

Giordano Fedora[a]. **Magda Olivero** (sop) Fedora; **Mario del Monaco** (ten) Loris; **Tito Gobbi** (bar)
de Siriex; **Leonardo Monreale** (bass) Lorek, Nicola; **Lucia Cappellino** (sop) Olga; **Virgilio
Carbonari** (bass) Borov; **Silvio Maionica** (bass) Grech; **Piero de Palma** (ten) Rouvel; **Peter Binder**
(bar) Kiril; **Dame Kiri Te Kanawa** (sop) Dmitri; **Riccardo Cassinelli** (ten) Desire; **Athos Cesarini**
(ten) Sergio; **Pascal Rogé** (pf) Boleslao Lazinski; **Monte-Carlo Opera Chorus and Orchestra /
Lamberto Gardelli.**
Zandonai Francesca da Rimini – excerpts[b]. [c]**Magda Oliviero** (sop) Francesca; [d]**Mario del Monaco**
(ten) Paolo; [e]**Annamaria Gasparini** (mez) Biancofiore; [f]**Virgilio Carbonari** (bass) Man-at-arms;
[g]**Athos Cesarini** (ten) Archer; **Monte-Carlo Opera Orchestra / Nicola Rescigno.**
Decca Grand Opera Ⓜ 433 033-2DM2 (two discs: 132 minutes: ADD: 3/92). Notes, texts and
translations included. Item marked [a] from SET435/6 (3/70), [b]SET422 (1/70). Recorded 1969.
Francesca da Rimini: Act 2 – E ancora sgombro il campo del comune? ... Date il segno, Paolo,
date ... Un'erba io m'avea, per sanare ... Onta et orrore sopra[cdfg]. Act 3 – No, Smadragedi, no! ...
Paolo, datemi pace! ... Ah la parola chi i miei occhi incontrano[cd]. Act 4 – Ora andate ... E così,
vada s'è pur mio destino[cde].

Today the name 'Fedora' may suggest a type of hat rather than an opera, but although Giordano was
overshadowed by his contemporary Puccini he was a successful composer. *Fedora* is based on a play
by Victorien Sardou, the French dramatist whose *La Tosca* provided Puccini with a plot. It is set in
the nineteenth century and variously in St Petersburg, Paris and Switzerland, and tells of the tragic
love between the Russian Count Loris Ipanov and the Princess Fedora Romazov (Romanov), but to
go into further detail of the plot, which disposes of various characters in turn and ends with the
heroine herself taking poison, would take up too much space and one admires the booklet writer who
has managed to produce a synopsis. *Fedora* has some Trivial Pursuits claim to be the first opera to
feature bicycles in the plot! The music is richly textured orchestrally and finely written for the voices,
and this recording made in 1969 is notable for the singing of Magda Olivero and Mario del Monaco,
who despite being in their mid-fifties bring tremendous verve, vocal resource and dramatic skill to
their roles. Tito Gobbi has less to do as the diplomat de Siriex, but gives him character, and another
plus is the playing of Pascal Rogé, who performs the non-singing role of the Polish pianist and spy
Boleslao Lazinski in Act 2 who, while performing, eavesdrops on a dialogue between Loris and
Fedora. This exchange is a marvellous example of verismo writing and singing, and so is their final
scene with her death. The set opens with excerpts from another opera, Zandonai's *Francesca da
Rimini* with the same two excellent principals. The recordings are as clear and fresh-sounding as they
were on the original releases.

Further listening ...

...**Madame Sans-Gêne. Soloists; RAI Chorus and Symphony Orchestra, Milan / Arturo Basile.**
Bongiovanni GB1129/30 (7/96).

Mauro Giuliani
Italian 1781-1829

Giuliani Choix de mes fleurs chéries, Op. 46 – Le jasmin; Le rosmarin; La rose. Etude in
E minor, Op. 100 No. 13. Grande ouverture, Op. 61. Leçons progressives, Op. 51 Nos. 3, 7 and
14. Minuetto, Op. 73 No. 9. Preludes, Op. 83 Nos. 5 and 6. Rondeaux progressives, Op. 14 Nos. 1
and 5. Six Variations, Op. 20. Variazioni sulla Cavatina favorita, Op. 101, "De calma oh ciel".
David Starobin (gtr). Bridge Ⓕ BCD9029 (48 minutes: DDD: 3/92). Recorded 1990.

Giuliani was born and died in Italy, in between which he lived for many years in Vienna, where he
achieved great success in salon-music circles with his guitar virtuosity and counted many
distinguished musicians amongst his friends and colleagues. He was in a sense the rival of Sor for the

guitar's nineteenth-century crown but the two were 'chalk and cheese'. Giuliani the more volatile, ebullient and (as a composer) loquacious – with over 200 works as against Sor's less than 70. Giuliani's incessant desire to please his public (and to make much-needed money in the process) led to the presence of much treadmill dross amongst the gold of his best works, a thing that has contributed to his chronic undervaluation. David Starobin, playing a nineteenth-century guitar, greatly helps to redress the balance in his unfailingly musical and technically fluent playing of a selection of Giuliani's best works. Some testify to Giuliani's contribution to the student literature, the titles of others reflect the salon tastes at which they were aimed; all show that, when he took the trouble, Giuliani could be charming, polished and ingenious, all at the same time. This is a disc to charm the ear without bruising the emotions, in the nicest possible way.

Further listening ...

...Guitar Concertos[a] – No. 1 in A major, Op. 30; No. 2 in A major, Op. 36; No. 3 in F major, Op. 70. Introduction, theme and variations and polonaise, Op. 65[b]. Six Variations on "I bin a Kohlbauern Bub", Op. 49. Gran Sonata Eroica in A major, Op. 150. Grande Ouverture, Op. 61. Giulianate, Op. 148 – La Melanconia. Variations on a Theme by Handel, Op. 107. Variazioni Concertanti, Op. 130[c]. **Pepe Romero**, [c]**Celedonio Romero** (gtrs); [ab]**Academy of St Martin in the Fields / Sir Neville Marriner.** Philips Duo 454 262-2PM2 (4/97).

...Duo concertant in E minor, "Grand Sonata", Op. 25. *Coupled with works by* **Paganini Monica Huggett** (vn); **Richard Savino** (gtr). Harmonia Mundi HMU90 7116 (5/95). ✒

...*CD411* – Duo for flute and guitar. Gran duetto concertante, Op. 52. Grand duo concertant, Op. 85. 12 Ländler samt Coda, Op. 75. Duetinno facile, Op. 77. *CD413* – Grand Pot-pourri, Op. 126. Grand Pot-pourri, Op. 53. Pièces faciles et agréables, Op. 74. Potpourri tiré de l'opéra Tancredi, Op. 76. Six Variations, Op. 81. **Mikael Helasvuo** (fl); **Jukka Savijoki** (gtr). BIS CD411 and CD413 (1/91).

...Ariette, Op. 95 – Quando sarà quel di; Le dimore amore non ama; Ad altro laccio. Cavatine, Op. 39 – Confuso, smarrito. Amor, perché m'accendi. Di tanti palpiti, Op. 79. Andantino sostenuto, Op. 71 No. 3. *Coupled with works by various composers.* **José Miguel Moreno** (gtr). Glossa GCD920202 (2/96). *See review in the Collections section; refer to the Index.*

Philip Glass

American 1937

Glass La Belle et la Bête. **Janice Felty** (mez) La Belle; **Gregory Purnhagen** (bar) La Bête, Avenant, Ardent, Port Official; **John Kuether** (bass) Father, Usurer; **Ana Maria Martinez** (sop) Felicie; **Hallie Neill** (sop) Adelaide; **Zheng Zhou** (bar) Ludovic; **Philip Glass Ensemble / Michael Riesman.** Nonesuch Ⓟ 7559-79347-2 (two discs: 89 minutes: DDD: 7/96). Notes, text and translation included. Recorded 1994.

This is one of Philip Glass's most innovative and impressive works. It isn't exactly an opera, nor is it film music; cantata is the nearest term, but even that won't really convey the idea. What Glass has done is to make a setting of the script for Jean Cocteau's 1946 film *La Belle et la Bête*, using every word as it is spoken in the film, but having it sung, the whole thing designed to be performed in concert, with a print of the film being projected silently. Of all Cocteau's movies, *La Belle et la Bête* is visually the most stylized, with its images of the Beast's castle, and the Vermeeresque settings for the family home of the merchant whose search for a rose to give to his youngest daughter sets off the nightmarish story. Cocteau described his film as "the illustration of the border that separates one world from the other". For all its surreal photography and extravagant décor by Christian Bérard (the apparently living, arms-bearing candelabra, poking out from the wall, have influenced hundreds of interior decorators), the dialogue in the film is delivered in a naturalistic way. The words are sung in an ethereal, other-worldly way, and the music trembles with typical Glass motifs. *La Belle et la Bête* hovers somewhere between genteel beat music and Messiaen-influenced *mélodie* and defies categorization. As Beauty, Janice Felty's voice matches the image of Josette Day in the film, but Gregory Purnhagen's light baritone would never suggest Jean Marais, whose smoky tones were such an inspiration to Cocteau. Most people prefer the Beast with his hairy face and claws to the rather effete-looking Prince Charming who emerges at the end, and Glass's music seems to make an ironic commentary on this transformation. Well worth investigating.

Further listening ...

...Itaipú[a]. The Canyon. **Atlanta Symphony** [a]**Chorus and Orchestra / Robert Shaw.** Sony Classical SK46352 (11/93). Ⓖ

...*"Low" Symphony.* **Brooklyn Philharmonic Orchestra / Dennis Russell Davies.** Point Music 438 150-2PTH (5/93). Ⓖ

...String Quartet No. 1. *Coupled with works by* **Barber** and **Dvořák** Duke Quartet. Collins Classics 1386-2 (1/94).

...Einstein on the Beach – Suite. *Coupled with works by various composers.* **Gregory Fulkerson** (vn). New World 80313-2 (6/94).

...Metamorphosis. Mad rush. Wichita vortex sutra. **Philip Glass** (pf). CBS SMK45576 (3/90).

...Anima Mundi. **Jeannie Gagné, Dora Ohrenstein** (sops); **Patricia Dunham, Linda November** (mezzos); **David Düsing, David Frye** (tens); **Alexander Blachly, Bruce Rodgers** (bars); **orchestra / Michael Riesman.** Nonesuch 7559-79329-2 (1/94).

...Hydrogen Jukebox. **Allen Ginsberg** (narr); **Vocal Ensemble**; **Carol Wincenc** (fl); **Andrew Sterman** (sax/bass cl); **Richard Peck** (sax); **Frank Cassara, James Pugliese** (perc); **Philip Glass** (pf) / **Martin Goldray** (keybds). Nonesuch 7559-79286-2 (1/94).
...Akhnaten. **Soloists; Stuttgart State Opera Chorus and Orchestra / Dennis Russell Davies.** Sony Classical M2K42457 (2/88). Ⓖ
...Einstein on the Beach. **Soloists; Philip Glass Ensemble / Michael Riesman.** CBS M4K38875 (9/86).
...Satyagraha. **NYC Opera Chorus and Orchestra / Christopher Keene.** CBS M3K39672 (9/86). Ⓖ

Alexander Glazunov

Russian/USSR 1865-1936

Glazunov Violin Concerto in A minor, Op. 82.
Tchaikovsky Violin Concerto in D major, Op. 35. **Maxim Vengerov** (vn); **Berlin Philharmonic Orchestra / Claudio Abbado.** Teldec Ⓕ 4509-90881-2 (55 minutes: DDD: 11/95). Recorded 1995. *Gramophone Editor's choice.*
This seems to be the only disc coupling what might reasonably be counted as the two greatest romantic Russian violin concertos: if Vengerov's reading of the Tchaikovsky emerges clearly as a leading contender among many superb versions, in the Glazunov he turns this warhorse concerto from a display piece into a work of far wider-ranging emotions. This Tchaikovsky immediately establishes itself as a big performance in the manner and in the range of dynamic of the playing. For all his power, and his youthfully eager love of brilliance, Vengerov is never reluctant to play really softly, and how magical that often is. Each theme in turn is sharply characterized, with dynamic contrasts cleanly established. The central Canzonetta is full of Russian temperament, with Vengerov freer in his rubato than most rivals, but conveying such natural unforced expressiveness there is nothing self-conscious about it. The finale is fast, light and sparkling, with articulation breathtakingly clean to match the transparency of the orchestral textures as controlled by Abbado. Vengerov rounds the performance off with an explosion of excitement such as one might expect in the concert-hall but not often in the recording studio. The Glazunov is if anything even more remarkable, with Vengerov making you appreciate afresh what a wonderful and varied sequence of melodies Glazunov offers. It is characteristic of Vengerov how he shades and contrasts his tone-colours. He reserves his big, romantic tone for the third theme, where most rivals let loose sooner with less subtle results. As in the Tchaikovsky, rubato is free but always spontaneous-sounding, and the lolloping fourth section brings some delicious portamento. Predictably the dashing final section is spectacular in its brilliance, again with each episode sharply contrasted and with orchestral textures fresh and clean.
Additional recommendations ...
...Violin Concerto[a]. The Seasons – ballet, Op. 67. [a]**Oscar Shumsky** (vn);
   Scottish National Orchestra / Neeme Järvi. Chandos Ⓕ CHAN8596 (57 minutes: DDD: 3/89).
...Violin Concerto. **Shostakovich** Violin Concerto No. 1 in A minor, Op. 99. **Itzhak Perlman** (vn);
   Israel Philharmonic Orchestra / Zubin Mehta. EMI Ⓕ CDC7 49814-2 (55 minutes: DDD: 1/90).
...Violin Concerto[a]. Piano Concerto No. 2 in B major, Op. 100[b]. Saxophone Concerto in E flat
   major, Op. 109[c]. [a]**Sergei Stadler** (vn); [b]**Dmitri Alexeev** (pf); [c]**Lev Mikhailov** (sax); [a]**Leningrad**
   Philharmonic Orchestra / Vladimir Ponkin; [b]**USSR Radio Symphony Orchestra / Yuri Nikolaevsky;**
   [c]**USSR Radio Symphony Orchestra Soloists Ensemble / Alexander Korneiev.**
   Olympia Ⓕ OCD165 (55 minutes: ADD/DDD: 2/90).
...Violin Concerto. **Dvořák** Violin Concerto in A minor, B108. **Frank Peter Zimmermann** (vn);
   London Philharmonic Orchestra / Franz Welser-Möst.
   EMI Ⓕ CDC7 54872-2 (52 minutes: DDD: 3/94). Ⓖ
...Violin Concerto. **Dvořák** Violin Concerto in A minor, B108. Romance in F minor, B39.
   Ilya Kaler (vn); **Polish National Radio Symphony Orchestra / Camilla Kolchinsky.**
   Naxos Ⓢ 8 550758 (63 minutes: DDD: 4/95).
...Violin Concerto. *Coupled with works by* **Prokofiev** and **Shchedrin** Anne-Sophie Mutter (vn);
   National Symphony Orchestra, Washington / Mstislav Rostropovich.
   Erato Ⓜ 0630-17722-2 (64 minutes: DDD: 9/97).
...Violin Concerto. *Coupled with works by* **Kabalevsky** and **Tchaikovsky** Gil Shaham (vn);
   Russian National Orchestra / Mikhail Pletnev. DG Ⓕ 457 064-2GH (62 minutes: DDD: 3/98).

Glazunov The Seasons – ballet, Op. 67.
Tchaikovsky The Nutcracker – ballet, Op. 71[a]. [a]**Finchley Children's Music Group;**
   Royal Philharmonic Orchestra / Vladimir Ashkenazy. Decca Ⓕ 433 000-2DH2
   (two discs: 131 minutes: DDD: 4/92). Recorded 1989-90. *Selected by Sounds in Retrospect.*
One cannot think of a happier coupling than Glazunov's complete *Seasons* – perhaps his finest and most successful score – with Tchaikovsky's *Nutcracker*. Glazunov's delightful ballet, with even the winter's "Frost", "Hail", "Ice" and "Snow", glamorously presented, and the bitterness of a Russian winter quite forgotten are, like the scenario of the *Nutcracker*, part of a child's fantasy world, for Tchaikovsky too, in Act 2, has a wintry fairy scene and a delectable "Waltz of the snowflakes" (featuring children's wordless chorus). Glazunov's twinklingly dainty scoring of the picturesque snowy characters is contrasted with the glowing summer warmth of the "Waltz of the cornflowers and poppies", and the vigorously thrusting tune (perhaps the most memorable theme he ever wrote)

of the Autumn "Bacchanale". Tchaikovsky's ballet opens with a children's Christmas party with the guests arriving, presents distributed and family dancing, in which everyone joins. Ashkenazy captures the atmosphere very engagingly; then night falls, the church clock outside strikes midnight and the magic begins. The drama of the spectacular mock battle between good and evil, the children's journey through the pine forest (to one of Tchaikovsky's most ravishing tunes) and the famous multi-coloured characteristic dances of the Act 2 Divertissement are all beautifully played by the RPO. There is much finesse and sparkle, and the lightest and most graceful rhythmic touch from Ashkenazy: the conductor's affection for the score and his feeling for Tchaikovsky's multi-hued orchestral palette is a constant delight to the ear. Yet the big *Pas de deux* brings a climax of Russian fervour. The recording is properly expansive here; made at Walthamstow, it sets everything within a glowing acoustic ambience. *The Seasons* was recorded in Watford Town Hall, and again the ear is seduced by the aural richness and the glowing woodwind detail. The one minor drawback is that in the *Nutcracker* the cueing is not generous and the action not precisely related to the narrative detail. But in every other respect this is marvellous entertainment.

Additional recommendations ...

...The Seasons. Scènes de ballet in A major, Op. 52. **Minnesota Orchestra / Edo de Waart.** Telarc Ⓕ CD80347 (66 minutes: DDD: 12/93).

...The Seasons[a]. **Prokofiev** Piano Concerto No. 3 in C major, Op. 26[b]. Visions fugitives, Op. 22[c] – excerpts. Suggestion diabolique, Op. 4 No. 4[d]. Symphony No. 1 in D major, Op. 25, "Classical" – Gavotte[e]. Piano Sonata No. 4 in C minor, Op. 29 – Andante assai[f]. Gavotte, Op. 32 No. 3[f].

[bcdef]**Sergey Prokofiev (pf);** [a]**orchestra / Alexander Glazunov;** [b]**London Symphony Orchestra / Piero Coppola.** EMI Composers in Person mono Ⓕ CDC5 55223-2* (79 minutes: ADD: 5/95). Ⓖ

Glazunov Complete Solo Piano Music, Volumes 3 and 4. **Stephen Coombs (pf).** Hyperion Ⓕ CDA66855, CDA66866 (two discs, oas: 60 and 70 minutes: DDD: 11/96). Recorded 1995. *CDA66855* – Four Preludes and Fugues, Op. 101. Prelude and Fugue in D minor, Op. 62. Prelude and Fugue in E minor (1926). *CDA66866* – Piano Sonata No. 2 in E minor, Op. 75. Prelude and Two Mazurkas, Op. 25. Two Impromptus, Op. 54. Idylle, Op. 103. Barcarolle sur les touches noires. Song of the Volga Boatmen, Op. 97 (arr. Siloti). In modo religioso, Op. 38. Triumphal March, Op. 40 (with Holst Singers / Stephen Layton). Pas de caractère, Op. 68 (all arr. cpsr).

After the delights of Stephen Coombs's Vols. 1 and 2, wonders unfold still further in the third disc of the series. Devoted to Glazunov's six essays in the form of the prelude and fugue, it begins and ends with intricately wrought homages to Bach – the first, of 1899, darker and much more chromatic than the last, a wholesome specimen revealing none of the problems of the composer's declining years. The Op. 101 set is both freer and more fantastical in its fugal treatments. Taken as a whole, it seems to be Glazunov's towering achievement in any field, working its way from the restless A minor No. 1, with its super-Elgarian sequences, and the capricious No. 2, to the C minor Prelude and Fugue – swooning Tchaikovskian romanticism within the perspectives of Bach and Chopin – and on to a thoroughly diatonic C major celebration – hard-earned victory indeed. Coombs meets the challenge as unflinchingly as he did the toughest pages encountered in his first two volumes; there's a little too much use of the sustaining pedal in the earlier chromatic welters, but the later stages are appropriately lucid and bright.

The fugue at the heart of the Second Sonata's finale does give us an extra taste of his contrapuntal genius, and it's all the more welcome in a sea of romantic rodomontade. That, though, is clearly what Glazunov felt the piano sonata was all about – and he does it with style: the E major transformation of the scherzo theme towards the end of this exhaustingly busy Second Sonata is a fine stroke. The rest of Vol. 4 either ties up loose ends, following Glazunov along the road of whimsical, radiant Chopin stylization, or throws in some enjoyable novelties. Coombs's orchestral thunder comes in useful for the weighty transcription of a *Triumphal March* for the Chicago Columbian Exposition; when the Holst Singers enter with their "Slava, Columbus"s, it's probably just as well that the recording presents them as a solid backdrop to the busy piano part, not a wall in front of it. Glazunov's handling of *John Brown's Body* here shows a surprising wit and spirit, and the serious transcription of the *Song of the Volga Boatmen* that follows, with its shades of Mussorgsky's "Bydlo", makes a surprising contrast – one of many that will surely raise this composer's status immeasurably.

Additional recommendations ...

...Suite on the name "Sacha", Op. 2. Two Pieces, Op. 22. Waltzes on the Theme "Sabela", Op. 23. Three Etudes, Op. 31. Petite valse, Op. 36. Nocturne, Op. 37. Grande valse de concert in E flat major, Op. 41. Three Miniatures, Op. 42. Prelude and Two Mazurkas. **Tatyana Franová (pf).** Marco Polo Ⓕ 8 223151 (69 minutes: DDD: 7/93).

...Etudes, Op. 31 – No. 2 in C minor; No. 3 in E minor. Prelude in D major, Op. 25 No. 1. *Coupled with works by various composers.* **Margaret Fingerhut (pf).** Chandos Ⓕ CHAN9218 (78 minutes: DDD: 4/94). *See review in the Collections section; refer to the Index.*

Further listening ...

...Album leaf in D flat major (orch. Rogal-Levitsky). *Coupled with works by various composers.* **Timofei Dokshitzer (tpt); Bolshoi Theatre Orchestra / Gennadi Rozhdestvensky.** Melodiya 74321 32045-2 (2/97).

...Chant du ménestrel, Op. 71. *Coupled with works by* **Kabalevsky** and **Khachaturian** Raphael **Wallfisch (vc); London Philharmonic Orchestra / Bryden Thomson.** Chandos CHAN8579 (6/88).

...From the middle ages, Op. 79. Scènes de ballet, Op. 52. *Coupled with* **Liadov** A musical snuffbox, Op. 31. **Scottish National Orchestra / Neeme Järvi.** Chandos CHAN8804 (10/90).

...Oriental Rhapsody in G major, Op. 29. *Coupled with works by various composers.* **Montreal Symphony Orchestra / Charles Dutoit.** Decca 452 482-2DH (5/97). *See review in the Collections section; refer to the Index.*

...Piano Concerto No. 1 in F minor, Op. 92. *Coupled with works by* **Rimsky-Korsakov** and **Prokofiev** Sviatoslav Richter (pf). **Moscow Youth Orchestra / Kyrill Kondrashin.** Melodiya mono 74321 29468-2* (6/96).

...Piano Concerto No. 1 in F minor, Op. 92; No. 2 in B major, Op. 100. *Coupled with* **Goedicke** Piano Concertstück in D major, Op. 11. **Stephen Coombs** (pf); **BBC Scottish Symphony Orchestra / Martyn Brabbins.** Hyperion CDA66877 (11/96).

...Raymonda, Op. 57. **Royal Scottish Orchestra / Neeme Järvi.** Chandos CHAN8447 (7/86).

...Raymonda, Op. 57. **Moscow Symphony Orchestra / Alexander Anissimov.** Naxos 8 553503/4 (8/96).

...The sea – fantasy, Op. 28. Spring, Op. 34. *Coupled with* **Kalinnikov** Symphony No. 1 in G minor. **Scottish National Orchestra / Neeme Järvi.** Chandos CHAN8611 (10/88).

...Symphonies – No. 1 in E major, Op. 5, "Slavyanskaya"; No. 5 in B flat major, Op. 55. **Bavarian Radio Symphony Orchestra / Neeme Järvi.** Orfeo C093101A (9/87).   ⓠ

...Symphony No. 2 in F sharp minor, Op. 16. Concert Waltz No. 1 in D major, Op. 47. **Bamberg Symphony Orchestra / Neeme Järvi.** Orfeo C148101A (11/90).   ⓠ

...Symphony No. 3 in D major, Op. 33. Concert Waltz No. 2 in F major, Op. 51. **Bamberg Symphony Orchestra / Neeme Järvi.** Orfeo C157101A (11/90).

...Symphony No. 3 in D major, Op. 33[a]. Stenka Razin, Op. 13[a]. Serenades[b] – No. 1 in A major, Op. 7; No. 2 in F major, Op. 11. [a]**London Symphony Orchestra,** [b]**Royal Philharmonic Orchestra / Yondani Butt.** ASV CDDCA903 (2/95).

...Symphonies – No. 4 in F sharp minor, Op. 16; No. 7 in F major, Op. 77, "Pastoral'naya". **Bamberg Symphony Orchestra / Neeme Järvi.** Orfeo C148201A (11/90).   ⓠ

...Symphony No. 6 in C minor, Op. 58. Lyric Poem, Op. 12. **Bamberg Symphony Orchestra / Neeme Järvi.** Orfeo C157201A (11/90).

...Symphony No. 8 in E flat major, Op. 83. Ouverture solennelle, Op. 73. Wedding procession, Op. 21. **Bavarian Radio Symphony Orchestra / Neeme Järvi.** Orfeo C093201A (9/87).

...Mazurka-Oberek in D major. Meditation, Op. 32. *Coupled with works by various composers.* **Itzhak Perlman** (vn); **Abbey Road Ensemble / Lawrence Foster.** EMI CDC5 55475-2 (1/96).

...Five Novelettes, Op. 15. *Coupled with works by* **Borodin** and **Tchaikovsky** Hollywood Quartet. Testament mono SBT1061* (8/95).

...Suite in C major, Op. 35. Elegy in D minor, Op. 105. Prelude and Fugue, "Les vendredis". *Coupled with works by various composers.* **Amati Ensemble of Munich / Attila Balogh.** Calig CAL50940 (11/95).

...Suite in C major, Op. 35. Elegy in D minor, Op. 105. String Quintet in A major, Op. 39[a]. **Shostakovich Quartet;** [a]**Alexander Kovalev** (vc). Olympia OCD542 (11/95).

...Three Etudes, Op. 31. Two Pieces, Op. 22. Trois morceaux, Op. 49. Nocturne, Op. 37. Miniature in C major. Easy Sonata. Sonatina. Two Prelude-improvisations. Theme and Variations, Op. 72. **Stephen Coombs** (pf). Hyperion CDA66844 (7/96).

...Piano Sonata No. 1 in B flat minor, Op. 74. Suite on the name "Sacha", Op. 2. Three Miniatures, Op. 42. Valse de salon, Op. 43. Grande valse de concert in E flat major, Op. 41. Waltzes on the Theme "Sabela", Op. 23. Petite valse, Op. 36. **Stephen Coombs** (pf). Hyperion CDA66833 (7/96).

...Tsar Iudeyskiy, Op. 95. **Russian State Symphony Chorus and Orchestra / Gennadi Rozhdestvensky.** Chandos CHAN9467 (10/96).

Reyngol'd Glière   Ukraine/USSR 1875-1956

Glière Symphony No. 2 in C minor, Op. 25. The Red Poppy – Ballet Suite, Op. 70. **New Jersey Symphony Orchestra / Zdenek Macal.** Delos Ⓕ DE3178 (73 minutes: DDD: 8/96). Recorded 1995.

Glière's colourful late-romantic Second Symphony is a fine choice for the first issue in the series. Just occasionally the woodwind detail sounds too good to be true, but otherwise the results are extremely satisfying, the blend of transparency and warmth being even finer than on the rival BBC Philharmonic recording on Chandos, who pride themselves on such things. Glière never puts a foot wrong, but that's because he's going along trails blazed for him by others long before 1908. Although the romantic parts of *Firebird* are audibly just round the corner, here the magic is tamed and the amount of repetition can even become slightly irksome. Between the two orchestras the honours are fairly even, though it has to be said that the New Jersey cor anglais plays with peerless refinement in the slow movement. In general Macal takes much the same view of the piece as Sir Edward Downes – the timings are very close indeed – though Macal coaxes slightly more suave phrasing from his musicians. Delos could have made their disc indispensable by choosing something less well known than the *Red Poppy* suite as a filler; but for newcomers to the composer this is certainly a more necessary work than the uninspired *Zaporozhy Cossacks* tone-poem on Chandos. Delos make a big pitch about their 'Virtual Reality' recording quality. Ultimately destined for Surround Sound Home Theatre reproduction, it involves, amongst other things, a careful choice of venue, slightly more than usual spatial separation of the players in the hall, and a pragmatic approach to multi-miking.

Additional recommendations ...
...No. 2. The Zaporozhy Cossacks, Op. 64. **BBC Philharmonic Orchestra / Sir Edward Downes.** Chandos Ⓕ CHAN9071 (64 minutes: DDD: 7/92).
...Symphony No. 1 in E flat major, Op. 8. The Red Poppy. **BBC Philharmonic Orchestra / Sir Edward Downes.** Chandos Ⓕ CHAN9160 (61 minutes: DDD: 7/93).   Ⓖ

Glière Symphony No. 3 in B minor, Op. 42, "Il'ya Mouromets". **Royal Philharmonic Orchestra / Harold Farberman.** Unicorn-Kanchana Souvenir Ⓜ UKCD2014/5 (two discs: 93 minutes: DDD: 3/89). From PCM500-1 (8/79). Recorded 1978.   Ⓖ

What happened to the Russian symphony between Tchaikovsky and Shostakovich? Scriabin and Rachmaninov were active of course, plus the solidly respectable Glazunov. But there was another distinctive voice, one whose interest lay in blending the heroic-saga tone of Borodin with the orchestral opulence of Wagner. This was Reyngol'd Glière, and his Third Symphony of 1912 is his undoubted masterpiece. It is a supremely late-romantic Technicolor score, extreme but never uncontrolled in its excess, and always directed towards vividness of narrative rather than self-display. Now usually performed without the once-standard cuts, its four movements are fairly protracted, the more so when taken at exceptionally spacious tempos as they are here by Harold Farberman (other more recent uncut recordings have clocked in at single-CD duration). But the spaciousness proves the making of the piece, giving the dimensions a truly epic feel and developing an unstoppable slow momentum. The recording quality no longer quite seems to justify the 'demonstration-class' praise originally accorded it, but it is still impressive enough.

Additional recommendations ...
...No. 3. **BBC Philharmonic Orchestra / Sir Edward Downes.** Chandos Ⓕ CHAN9041 (78 minutes: DDD: 5/92). *Selected by Sounds in Retrospect.*   Ⓖ
...No. 3. **Czech Radio Symphony Orchestra / Donald Johanos.** Naxos Ⓢ 8 550858 (76 minutes: DDD: 2/94).
...No. 3. **Loeffler** A Pagan Poem, Op. 14ᵃ. ᵃHouston Symphony Orchestra; ᵇLeopold Stokowski Symphony Orchestra / Leopold Stokowski. EMI Matrix Ⓜ CDM5 65074-2* (62 minutes: ADD: 7/94).
...No. 3. The Red Poppy – Ballet Suite, Op. 70 – Russian Sailors' Dance. *Coupled with works by* **Ippolitov-Ivanov** and **Stravinsky** Philadelphia Orchestra / Leopold Stokowski. Biddulph mono Ⓕ WHL005* (76 minutes: ADD: 7/94).

Further listening ...
...The Bronze Horseman – Concert Suite. Horn Concerto in B flat major, Op. 91ᵃ. ᵃRichard Watkins (hn); BBC Philharmonic Orchestra / Sir Edward Downes. Chandos CHAN9379 (12/95).
...Concerto for Coloratura Soprano, Op. 82ᵃ. Harp Concerto, Op. 74ᵇ. *Coupled with* **Ginastera** Harp Concerto, Op. 25ᵇ. ᵃEileen Hulse (sop); ᵇRachel Masters (hp); City of London Sinfonia / Richard Hickox. Chandos CHAN9094 (2/93). *See review under Ginastera; refer to the Index.*
...Concerto for Coloratura Soprano, Op. 82 (arr. Dunayev). *Coupled with works by various composers.* **Timofei Dokshitzer** (tpt); USSR Ministry of Defence Symphonic Band / Anatoly Maltsev. Melodiya 74321 32045-2 (2/97).
...Symphony No. 1 in E flat major, Op. 8. The Sirens, Op. 33. **Slovak Philharmonic Orchestra / Stephen Gunzenhauser.** Naxos 8 550898 (10/95).
...Taras Bulba – Ballet Suite. *Coupled with* **Stankovich** Rasputin – Ballet Suite. **Odessa Philharmonic Orchestra / Hobart Earle.** ASV CDDCA988 (4/97).

Mikhail Ivanovich Glinka   Russian 1804-1857

Glinka Ruslan and Lyudmila. **Vladimir Ognovienko** (bass-bar) Ruslan; **Anna Netrebko** (sop) Lyudmila; **Mikhail Kit** (bar) Svetozar; **Larissa Diadkova** (mez) Ratmir; **Gennadi Bezzubenkov** (bass) Farlaf; **Galina Gorchakova** (sop) Gorislava; **Konstantin Pluzhnikov** (ten) Finn; **Irina Bogachova** (mez) Naina; **Yuri Marusin** (ten) Bayan; **Chorus and Orchestra of the Kirov Theatre / Valery Gergiev.** Philips Ⓕ 446 746-2PH3 (three discs: 202 minutes: DDD: 5/97). Notes, text and translation included. Recorded live in 1995.   Ⓖ

There is a vast amount in this wonderful score to delight and fascinate. The previous recording of 'the father of Russian operas' (recorded in 1978) has an excellent, and superior, Ruslan in Evgeny Nesterenko but a needly Lyudmila in Bela Rudenko. Still, it is not so much in the solo singing as in recorded sound and the spark running through the orchestra that the distinction of this version lies. With Gergiev, the playing rises well above the reliability of long-practised routine; indeed, the Overture, always a winner, has quite exceptional brilliance and exhilaration. Later, the performance is just as remarkable for its refinement of detail and for sensitivity in the meditative, tender passages which enrich the musical score as they do the humanity of this operatic fairy-tale. The principals act with the professionalism of those brought up in a rigid school; they know their job and proceed accordingly. The Ruslan (Ognovienko) is an ample bass-baritone, the Farlaf (Bezzubenkov) a sturdy bass with a neat capacity for patter, Bayan (Marusin) a tenor with tense tone, slightly flat intonation, especially memorable as the bardic figure who holds in thrall an audience with a longer attention-span than might be counted on today. Larissa Diadkova's Ratmir made a strong impression in the 1995 Edinburgh Festival and it is good to hear her here. Gorchakova brings glamour of voice to her role of Gorislava, and the Lyudmila of Netrebko is outstanding.

Additional recommendations ...

...**Soloists; Chorus and Orchestra of the Bolshoi Theatre / Yuri Simonov.** Melodiya Ⓜ 74321 29348-2 (three discs: 187 minutes: ADD: 2/97).

...Ruslan and Lyudmila – Overture. *Coupled with works by various composers.* **Chicago Symphony Orchestra / Fritz Reiner.** RCA Victor Living Stereo Ⓜ 09026 61958-2 (71 minutes: ADD: 8/94). *See review in the Collections section; refer to the Index.* ⒼⒼⒼ

...Ruslan and Lyudmila – Overture. *Coupled with works by various composers.* **Baltimore Symphony Orchestra / David Zinman.** Telarc Ⓕ CD80378 (69 minutes: DDD: 12/95).

...Ruslan and Lyudmila – There is a desert country. *Coupled with works by various composers.* **Sergei Larin** (ten); **Philharmonia Orchestra / Gennadi Rozhdestvensky.** Chandos Ⓕ CHAN9603 (75 minutes: DDD: 5/98). *See review in the Collections section; refer to the Index.*

Further listening ...

...Grand Sextet in E flat major. *Coupled with* **Rimsky-Korsakov** Piano and Wind Quintet in B flat major. **Capricorn.** Hyperion CDA66163 (12/86). Ⓖ

...Jota aragonesa – Spanish Overture No. 1. *Coupled with works by various composers.* **London Symphony Orchestra / Sir Charles Mackerras.** Mercury Living Presence 434 352-2MM (12/95).

...Songs, Volume 1. A farewell to St Petersburg. Do not tempt me needlessly. The fire of longing burns in my blood. I recall a wonderful moment. Doubt. Mary. How sweet it is to be with you. Say not that it grieves the heart. **Sergei Leiferkus** (bar); **Semion Skigin** (pf). Conifer Classics 75605 51264-2 (4/96).

...A Life for the Tsar. **Soloists; Sofia National Opera Chorus and Festival Orchestra / Emil Tchakarov.** Sony Classical S3K46487 (9/91).

Christoph Gluck

Bohemian 1714-1787

Gluck Paride ed Elena – O del mio dolce ardor. Orfeo ed Euridice – Che puro ciel!; Che farò senza Euridice. Alceste – Non vi turbate.
Haydn Il mondo della luna – Una donna come me. Orlando Paladino – Ad un sguardo, a un cenno solo. La fedeltà premiata – Deh soccorri un'infelice.
Mozart Le nozze di Figaro – Voi che sapete. Don Giovanni – Batti, batti; Vedrai, carino; In quali eccessi ... Mi tradì quell'alma ingrata. Lucio Silla – Dunque sperar ... Il tenero momento. La finta giardiniera – Dolce d'amor compagna. La clemenza di Tito – Ecco il punto, oh Vitellia ... Non più di fiori. **Anne Sofie von Otter** (mez); **The English Concert / Trevor Pinnock** (hpd). Archiv Produktion Ⓕ 449 206-2AH (71 minutes: DDD: 10/97). 🖉 Texts and translations included. Recorded 1995.

For the sake of both vocal and family well-being, Anne Sofie von Otter has always followed the wise course of self-rationing in opera. This disc, an entirely personal selection of arias from the Viennese classical period, means all the more to her including, as it does, arias sung by dramatic and passionate women "most of whom", von Otter admits in the accompanying notes, "I have never performed on stage and, alas, probably never will". They include *La clemenza di Tito*'s Vitellia whom von Otter has irresistibly observed in her own role as Sesto: here she at last voices her guilt at implicating Sesto in her crime of passion, and expresses that unique fusion of sadness and desperation of "Non più di fiori" in the eloquent company of Colin Lawson's basset-horn, followed by Gluck's Alceste, again keenly observed by von Otter in a *comprimario* role. Her lyric mezzo is perfectly suited to that grave, Gluckian passion of "Non vi turbate". Gluck's Orfeo is, of course, familiar to von Otter at first hand, and here The English Concert's introduction to the accompanied recitative which precedes "Che farò" creates exquisitely the "nuova serena luce" of the Elysian fields against which von Otter's grief, affectingly ornamented, is the darker, the more plangent. The Mozart arias evoke memorable stage and concert performances by von Otter: a Cherubino whose phrasing combines with that of the wind soloists to create the warm breath of tender burgeoning sensuality in "Voi che sapete"; a Cecilio (*Lucio Silla*) whose coloratura captures the thrilled anticipation of that "tenero momento"; and a moustachioed Ramiro (*La finta giardiniera*) who pays ecstatic *cantabile* tribute to the power of love.

Gluck Iphigénie en Aulide. **Lynne Dawson** (sop) Iphigénie; **José van Dam** (bass) Agamemnon; **Anne Sofie von Otter** (mez) Clytemnestre; **John Aler** (ten) Achille; **Bernard Deletré** (bass) Patrocle; **Gilles Cachemaille** (bass) Calchas; **René Schirrer** (bass) Arcas; **Guillemette Laurens** (mez) Diane; **Ann Monoyios** (sop) First Greek woman, Slave; **Isabelle Eschenbrenner** (sop) Second Greek woman; **Monteverdi Choir; Lyon Opéra Orchestra / Sir John Eliot Gardiner.** Erato Ⓕ 2292-45003-2 (two discs: 132 minutes: DDD: 6/90). Notes, text and translation included. Recorded 1987.

Gluck's first reform opera for Paris has tended to be overshadowed by his other *Iphigénie*, the *Tauride* one. But it does contain some superb things, of which perhaps the finest are the great monologues for Agamemnon. On this recording, José van Dam starts a little coolly; but this only adds force to his big moment at the end of the second act where he tussles with himself over the sacrifice of his daughter and – contemplating her death and the screams of the vengeful Eumenides – decides to flout the gods and face the consequences. To this he rises in noble fashion, fully conveying the agonies Agamemnon suffers. The cast in general is strong. Lynne Dawson brings depth of expressive feeling to all she does and her Iphigénie, marked by a slightly grainy sound and much intensity, is very moving. John Aler's Achille too is very fine, touching off the lover and the hero with equal success, singing both with ardour and vitality. There is great force too in the singing of Anne Sofie von Otter as Clytemnestre, especially in her outburst "Ma fille!" as she imagines her daughter on the sacrificial altar. John Eliot Gardiner's Monteverdi Choir sing with polish, perhaps seeming a little genteel for a crowd of angry Greek soldiers baying for Iphigénie's blood. But Gardiner gives a duly urgent account of the score, pressing it forward eagerly and keeping the tension at a high level even in the dance music. A period-instrument orchestra might have added a certain edge and vitality but this performance wants nothing in authority or drama and can be securely recommended.

Additional recommendation ...
...**Soloists; Chorus and Orchestra of La Scala, Milan / Riccardo Muti.**
Sony Classical Ⓕ S2K52492 (two discs: 117 minutes: DDD).

Gluck Orfeo ed Euridice. **Derek Lee Ragin** (alto) Orfeo; **Sylvia McNair** (sop) Euridice;
Cyndia Sieden (sop) Amore; **Monteverdi Choir; English Baroque Soloists / Sir John Eliot Gardiner.**
Philips Ⓕ 434 093-2PH2 (two discs: 89 minutes: DDD: 2/94). ✍ Notes, text and translation
included. *Gramophone Editor's choice.*   Ⓖ
This version of *Orfeo*, played on period instruments and following the original text, has a degree of spiritual force to which other recordings scarcely aspire, and that is to the credit primarily of the conductor, John Eliot Gardiner. It begins with a taut, almost explosive account of the overture, moves to a deeply sombre opening chorus and then a *ballo* of intense expressiveness, finely and carefully moulded phrases (but plenty of air between them) and a lovely translucent orchestral sound. Every one of the numerous dances in this set, in fact, is the subject of thoughtful musical characterization, shapely execution and refined timing of detail. Derek Lee Ragin excels himself as Orpheus; the sound is often very beautiful, the phrasing quite extraordinarily supple and responsive for a countertenor voice. Eurydice is sung clearly and truly, and with due passion, by Sylvia McNair – she delivers "Che fiero momento" and some of the recitative, with considerable force – and the casting of Cyndia Sieden, with her rather pert, forward voice, as Amore is very successful.

Additional recommendations ...
...Orfeo ed Euridice. **Soloists; Ghent Collegium Vocale; La Petite Bande / Sigiswald Kuijken.**
Accent Ⓕ ACC48223/4D (two discs: 106 minutes: ADD: 1/90). ✍
...Orfeo ed Euridice. **Orphée et Eurydice – Air de furies; Ballet des ombres heureuses; Air vif;**
Menuet; Chaconne. Soloists; Berlin Radio Chorus; CPE Bach Chamber Orchestra /
Hartmut Haenchen. Capriccio Ⓕ 60 008-2 (two discs: 114 minutes: DDD: 1/90). ✍
...Orfeo ed Euridice. **Soloists; Stuttgart Chamber Choir; Tafelmusik / Frieder Bernius.**
Sony Classical Vivarte Ⓕ SX2K48040 (two discs: 83 minutes: DDD: 8/92). ✍
...Orphée et Euridice. **Soloists; Robert Blanchard Vocal Ensemble; Lamoureux Orchestra / Hans**
Rosbaud. Philips Opera Collector mono Ⓜ 434 784-2PM2* (two discs: 115 minutes: ADD: 5/93).
...Orphée et Eurydice. **Soloists; Glyndebourne Chorus; London Philharmonic Orchestra /**
Raymond Leppard. Erato Libretto Ⓜ 2292-45864-2 (two discs: 127 minutes: DDD: 5/93).
...Orphée et Eurydice – abridged recording[a]; J'ai perdu mon Eurydice. **Soloists;**
[a]**Alexis Vlassof Chorus; Paris Symphony Orchestra / Henri Tomasi.**
Pearl mono Ⓜ GEMMCD9169* (66 minutes: AAD: 12/95).   Ⓖ
...Orphée et Eurydice. **Soloists; Chorus and Orchestra of the San Francisco Opera /**
Donald Runnicles. Teldec Ⓕ 4509-98418-2 (two discs: 109 minutes: DDD: 7/96).   ⒼⒼ
...Orfeo ed Euridice – Che farò senza Euridice?. *Coupled with works by various composers.*
Vesselina Kasarova (mez). RCA Victor Red Seal Ⓕ 09026 68522-2 (64 minutes: DDD: 2/97).
Gramophone Editor's record of the month. See review in the Collections section; refer to
the Index.   ⒼⒼ
...Orfeo ed Euridice – Dance of the Blessed Spirits. **Philharmonic Symphony Orchestra of**
New York / Arturo Toscanini. Pearl mono Ⓕ GEMMCDS9373* (three discs: 230 minutes:
ADD: 3/90). *Gramophone classical 100. See review in the Collections section;*
refer to the Index.   ⒼⒼⒼ
...Orfeo ed Euridice – Dance of the Blessed Spirits. *Coupled with works by various composers.*
Vienna Philharmonic Orchestra / Rudolf Kempe.
Testament Ⓕ SBT1127* (78 minutes: ADD: 3/98).

Further listening ...
...Alessandro. *Coupled with works by* **Rebel** *and* **Telemann** Sonata (Septett) in E minor.
Cologne Musica Antiqua / Reinhard Goebel. Archiv Produktion 445 824-2AH (12/95). ✍
...Le Cinesi – opera-serenade. **Soloists; Munich Radio Orchestra / Lamberto Gardelli.**
Orfeo C178891A (1/90).
...Don Juan. Semiramis. **Tafelmusik / Bruno Weil.** Sony Classical SK53119 (10/93). ✍
...Alceste. **Soloists; Bavarian Radio Chorus; Bavarian Radio Symphony Orchestra / Serge Baudo.**
Orfeo C027823F (6/87).

...Iphigénie en Tauride. **Soloists; Monteverdi Choir; Lyon Opéra Orchestra / Sir John Eliot Gardiner.**
Philips 416 148-2PH2 (6/86). ✔
...Paride ed Elena. **Soloists; La Stagione Vocal Ensemble; La Statione / Michael Schneider.**
Capriccio 60 027-2 (6/93). ✔

Hermann Goetz
German 1840-1876

Suggested listening ...
...Lieder, Op. 12 – No. 1, Geheimnis; No. 2, Schliesse mir die Augen beide; No. 3, Wandervöglein.
Lieder, Op. 19 – No. 1, Ein Frühlingstraum; No. 2, Der Frühling kommt!; No. 3, Wandrers
Nachtlied, "Der du von dem Himmel bist". *Coupled with works by various composers.*
Olaf Bär (bar); **Helmut Deutsch** (pf).
EMI CDC5 55393-2 (1/96). *See review in the Collections section; refer to the Index.*

Károly Goldmark
Austrian/Hungarian 1830-1915

Goldmark Violin Concerto No. 1 in A minor, Op. 28[a].
Lalo Symphonie espagnole, Op. 21[b]. **Nathan Milstein** (vn); [a]**Philharmonia Orchestra / Harry Blech;**
[b]**St Louis Symphony Orchestra / Vladimir Golschmann.** Testament [a]stereo/[b]mono Ⓟ SBT1047*
(71 minutes: ADD: 11/95). Item marked [a] from HMV SXLP30193 (10/75. Recorded 1954-57.
Also includes unpublished session takes), [b]Capitol CTL7095 (10/55).
The Goldmark A minor Concerto inspired what was surely Nathan Milstein's finest hour in the
recording studio, a reading of the utmost refinement: warm, effortlessly brilliant and displaying that
unmistakably suave, silken tone. The work itself recalls both Reger and Dvořák, with wistful
melodies, lilting rhythms and much busy counterpoint. How delightful, therefore, to have – by way of
a bonus – a quarter-of-an-hour's worth of unpublished session takes, where Milstein exhibits the
utmost patience (and technical consistency) in playing and replaying even the most taxing passages.
Harry Blech directs a beautifully turned accompaniment, and one can only echo the sentiments of
Hugh Bean who, reminiscing about these sessions in the context of Testament's excellent booklet,
confesses "that if a visitor from an alien planet asked me, 'What does a violin sound like?', I would
want him to hear the second theme of the first movement – the innocence, the freshness and purity,
the sheer simplicity that takes a lifetime to achieve." That 'innocence, freshness and purity' are equally
apparent in the 1954 *Symphonie espagnole*, in spite of dry, NBC-style sound and an excessively close-
up solo image. Vladimir Golschmann's conducting is every bit as distinctive as Blech's, especially in
the *Andante*, where the St Louis strings exhibit impressive tonal lustre. This was Milstein's second
recording of the piece and, like its predecessor, omits the work's tangy "Intermezzo". As a
performance has real sparkle and provides a worthy companion for the superb Goldmark Concerto.
Additional recommendation ...
...No. 1. **Bruch** Violin Concerto No. 2 in D minor, Op. 44. **Nai-Yuan Hu** (vn);
Seattle Symphony Orchestra / Gerard Schwarz. Delos Ⓟ DE3156 (60 minutes: DDD: 12/95).
Further listening ...
...Rustic Wedding Symphony, Op. 26. Sakuntula Overture, Op. 13.
Royal Philharmonic Orchestra / Yondani Butt. ASV CDDCA791 (5/92).
...Rustic Wedding Symphony, Op. 26. Im Frühling, Op. 36. In Italien, Op. 49.
National Symphony Orchestra of Ireland / Stephen Gunzenhauser. Naxos 8 550745 (12/95).
...Der gefesselte Prometheus, Op. 38. Symphony No. 2 in E flat major, Op. 35. In Italien, Op. 49.
Philharmonia Orchestra / Yondani Butt. ASV CDDCA934 (11/95).

Berthold Goldschmidt
German 1903-1996

Goldschmidt Clarinet Concerto[a]. Violin Concerto[b]. Cello Concerto[c]. [a]**Sabine Meyer** (cl);
[b]**Chantal Juillet** (vn); [c]**Yo-Yo Ma** (vc); [a]**Berlin Komische Opera Orchestra / Yakov Kreizberg;**
[b]**Philharmonia Orchestra / Berthold Goldschmidt;** [c]**Montreal Symphony Orchestra / Charles Dutoit.**
Decca Entartete Musik Ⓟ 455 586-2DH (67 minutes: DDD: 1/98). Item marked [a]recorded 1997,
[b]1994, [c]live in 1996.
The oblivion into which these three concertos fell after their premières in the 1950s is puzzling. Their
style, even by the standards of 40-odd years ago, is not 'advanced', but they make highly original use
of traditional forms. The first movement of the Cello Concerto, for example, has half a dozen themes
instead of the expected two, but the ideas are subtly related so that the overall impression is of a richly
fertile but disciplined invention: there is not the slightest hint of garrulity, nor any sense that the music
is derived from Hindemith, whom at a few moments it superficially resembles. In the corresponding
movement of the Clarinet Concerto each idea grows out of its predecessor, all of them flowering from
a gently lyrical opening which repeatedly returns, sounding beautifully different at each recurrence. It
is partly this shrewd and practiced but quite unobtrusive craftsmanship that gives these pieces their
unmistakably personal flavour, their ability to encompass a wide range of mood and texture within a

short movement. The finale of the Clarinet Concerto includes nimbly pattering scherzo material, gracious lyricism, athletic energy and jovial exuberance, but they are unified, not merely juxtaposed. Goldschmidt's lyricism is firm and strong, and a fast movement does not have to relax to incorporate it. The slow movement of the Violin Concerto is marked *Andante amoroso*, but its beauty is grave and ample, not languishing. All three of these concertos, in fact, are strong and rich enough to repay repeated listening. The Violin Concerto was recorded after a series of performances by Chantal Juillet that so impressed Goldschmidt that he dedicated the neglected 40-year-old work to her. Although he did not live to see the release of that recording he had the satisfaction of knowing that it was being delayed until it could be coupled with his other two concertos. Juillet's reading of 'her' concerto is a splendid one, but the others here are no less fine, and all three are admirably recorded.

Additional recommendation ...
...Cello Concerto[a]. Ciaconna sinfonica. Chronica. [a]**David Geringas** (vc); **Magdeburg Philharmonic Orchestra / Mathias Husmann.** CPO Ⓕ CPO999 277-2 (55 minutes: DDD: 7/95).

Further listening ...
...Passacaglia, Op. 4[a]. The Comedy of Errors Overture[b]. Ciaccona sinfonica[c]. Chronica[d]. Les petits adieux[e]. Rondeau[f]. [e]**François Le Roux** (bar); [f]**Chantal Juillet** (vn); [abc]**City of Birmingham Symphony Orchestra / [ac]Sir Simon Rattle,** [b]**Berthold Goldschmidt;** [d]**Symphony Orchestra of the Komische Oper, Berlin / Yakov Kreizberg;** [e]**Montreal Symphony Orchestra / Charles Dutoit;** [f]**Berlin Radio Symphony Orchestra / Berthold Goldschmidt.** Decca 452 599-2DH (12/96).
...Retrospectrum[d]. Variations on a Palestinian Shepherd's Song, Op. 32[b]. Capriccio[a]. Capriccio, Op. 11[b]. Little Legend[b]. Scherzo[b]. From the Ballet[b]. Encore[bc]. String Quartet No. 4[e]. **Kolja Lessing** ([a]vn/[b]pf); [c]**Hansheinz Schneeberger** (vn); [d]**Gaede Trio;** [e]**Mandelring Quartet.** Largo 5128 (3/95).   Ⓖ
...String Quartets[a] – No. 2; No. 3. Belsatzar[d]. Letzte Kapitel[bcd]. [a]**Mandelring Quartet;** [b]**Jörg Gottschick** (narr); [c]**Alan Marks** (pf); [d]**Berlin Ars Nova Ensemble / Peter Schwarz.** Largo 5115 (11/91).
...Beatrice Cenci. **Soloists; Berlin Radio Chorus; Deutsches Symphony Orchestra, Berlin / Lothar Zagrosek. Goldschmidt** Clouds. Ein Rosenzweig. Nebelweben. Time. **Iris Vermillion** (mez) **Berthold Goldschmidt** (pf). Sony Classical S2K66836 (7/95). *Gramophone Editor's choice.*   Ⓖ
...Der gewaltige Hahnrei[a]. Mediterranean Songs[b]. [a]**Soloists;** [a]**Berlin Deutsches Symphony Orchestra;** [b]**John Mark Ainsley** (ten); [b]**Leipzig Gewandhaus Orchestra / Lothar Zagrosek.** Decca Entartete Musik 440 850-2DHO2 (3/94). *Gramophone Award Winner 1995. Gramophone Editor's choice.* Ⓖ
...Der Verflossene. *Coupled with works by various composers.* **Ute Lemper** (sop); **Matrix Ensemble / Robert Ziegler.** Decca Entartete Musik 452 601-2DH (12/96).

Nicolas Gombert   Flemish c1495-c1560

Gombert Missa Tempore paschali. Magnificat octavi toni. Adonai, Domine Iesu Christe. In illo tempore loquente Jesu. O Rex gloriae. **Henry's Eight / Jonathan Brown.** Hyperion Ⓕ CDA66943 (65 minutes: DDD: 7/97). Texts and translations included. Recorded 1996.
This disc reinforces the impression of Gombert as the most involving composer of his generation; the booklet-note aptly describes his music as a cross between the imitative processes of Josquin's generation and the seamless style of Ockeghem. The *Missa Tempore paschali* is thought to be a fairly early work, whereas the *Magnificat* is one of a set that probably dates from Gombert's last years. The Mass is most ambitious, culminating in a 12-voice *Agnus Dei* modelled on Brumel's Mass, *Et ecce terre motus*. When the first Gombert recording with Henry's Eight appeared one was inclined to give the Huelgas Ensemble's recital the edge; this time the two versions are more evenly matched. The Flemish ensemble perhaps shape the individual lines more distinctively but the English group have a surer grasp of large-scale form in the *Credo*, and the final *Agnus Dei* seems to crown the Mass in a more credible manner. An added feature is the more inventive, and highly convincing, use of false relations in the readings prepared for Henry's Eight by John O'Donnell. The result contains invigorating harmonic incident throughout. The Mass is complemented by some of the composer's most well-known works; the motet, *In illo tempore* is particularly lovely and Henry's Eight respond with some particularly sensitive singing. Those already familiar with their very English, yet full-bodied sound won't be disappointed; those who aren't can start here. In Henry's Eight Gombert has found worthy champions.

Additional recommendation ...
...Missa Tempore paschali. Regina caeli. In te Domine speravi. Media vita. Tous les regretz. Je prens congie. Magnificat Secundi toni. **Huelgas Ensemble / Paul van Nevel.** Sony Classical Vivarte Ⓕ SK48249 (76 minutes: DDD: 4/93).

Further listening ...
...Credo. Haec dies. Qui colis Ausoniam. Salve regina. O beata Maria. Vae, vae Babylon. Media vita. Lugebat David Absalon. *Coupled with* **Anonymous** Haec dies. Salve regina. Nunc dimittis. **Henry's Eight / Jonathan Brown.** Hyperion CDA66828 (10/96). *Gramophone Editor's choice.*   Ⓖ
...Mille regretz. A bien grant tort. Puisqu' ainsi est. Je prens congies. *Coupled with works by various composers.* **Clément Janequin Ensemble / Dominique Visse.** Harmonia Mundi HMC90 1453 (5/95).

Sir Eugene Goossens

British 1893-1962

Suggested listening ...
...Concertino, Op. 47. Phantasy Sextet, Op. 37. *Coupled with* **Bridge** String Sextet in E flat major,
H107. **Academy of St Martin in the Fields Chamber Ensemble.**
Chandos CHAN9472 (8/97). *See review under Bridge; refer to the Index.*

Samuel Gordon

American 20th century

Suggested listening ...
...Industry. *Coupled with works by various composers.* **Bang on a Can All-Stars.**
Sony Classical SK66483 (2/96). *See review in the Collections section; refer to the Index.*

Henryk Górecki

Polish 1933

Górecki Symphony No. 3, Op. 36, "Symphony of Sorrowful Songs". **Dawn Upshaw** (sop);
London Sinfonietta / David Zinman. Elektra Nonesuch Ⓕ 7559-79282-2 (54 minutes: DDD: 4/93).
Recorded 1991. *Gramophone Award Winner 1993.*   ⓆⓆ
Górecki's Third Symphony has become legend. Composed in 1976, it has always had its champions and
admirers within the contemporary music world, but in 1993 it found a new audience of undreamt-of
proportions. A few weeks after its release, this Elektra Nonesuch release not only entered the classical top-
ten charts, but was also riding high in the UK Pop Album charts. It has since become the biggest selling
disc of music by a contemporary classical composer. The Symphony, subtitled *Symphony of Sorrowful
Songs* was composed during a period when Górecki's musical style was undergoing a radical change from
avant-garde serialism to a more accessible style firmly anchored to tonal traditions. The Symphony's three
elegiac movements (or 'songs') form a triptych of laments for all the innocent victims of World War Two
and are a reflection upon man's inhumanity to man in general. The songs – including a poignant setting of
an inscription scratched by a girl prisoner on the wall of her cell in a Gestapo prison – are beautifully and
ethereally sung by Dawn Upshaw, and David Zinman and the London Sinfonietta provide an intense and
committed performance of the shimmering orchestral writing. The recording quality is excellent.
Additional recommendations ...
...No. 3. **Zofia Kilanowicz** (sop); **Polish State Philharmonic Orchestra / Jerzy Swoboda.**
Belart Ⓢ 450 148-2 (56 minutes: DDD).
...No. 3[b]. Three Pieces in Old Style[a]. [b]**Stefania Woytowicz** (sop); [a]**Warsaw Chamber Orchestra /
Karol Teutsch;** [b]**Berlin Radio Symphony Orchestra / Wlodzimierz Kamirski.**
Koch Schwann Musica Mundi Ⓕ 311041 (55 minutes: ADD: 4/93).
...No. 3[a]. Three Pieces in Old Style. [a]**Zofia Kilanowicz** (sop); **Katowice Radio Symphony Orchestra /
Antoni Wit.** Naxos Ⓢ 8 550822 (66 minutes: DDD: 10/94).

Górecki Kleines Requiem für eine Polka, Op. 66[a]. Harpsichord Concerto, Op. 40[b]. Good Night,
"In memoriam Michael Vyner", Op. 63[c]. [c]**Dawn Upshaw** (sop); [c]**Sebastian Bell** (fl);
[ac]**John Constable** (pf); [b]**Elisabeth Chojnacka** (hpd); [c]**David Hockings** (perc); [ab]**London Sinfonietta /
[a]David Zinman,** [b]**Markus Stenz.** Nonesuch Ⓕ 7559-79362-2 (59 minutes: DDD: 9/95).
Recorded 1993-94. *Gramophone Editor's choice.*
Like a small café huddled within the shadow of some ancient church, Górecki's *Kleines Requiem für
eine Polka* (1993) evokes feelings of paradox. The work's ground-springs are inscrutably personal, yet
the sum effect is one of overwhelming intensity. The opening movement suggests distracted
tranquillity. This is followed by a grating *Allegro* which approximates, at least in overall effect, the sort
of vicious 'knees-up' that Shostakovich penned whenever he bared his teeth at empty celebration.
Later, we are back within the tranquil interior of Górecki's imagination – and it's there that we stay
until the work ends. The *Kleines Requiem für eine Polka* displays a characteristic profundity expressed
via the simplest means. It is therefore a pity that the Harpsichord Concerto breaks the mood so
quickly: one's initial impression is of a further violent 'episode' from the first work, although the
stylistic contrast breaks the illusion soon enough. This is probably the most famous twentieth-century
harpsichord concerto after Falla's, and the most popular of Górecki's pieces after the Third
Symphony. Bach served as its creative prime mover, while Elisabeth Chojnacka is both its dedicatee
and its most celebrated interpreter. Here she revels in the piece's playful aggression. It's an unrelenting
display and in total contrast to *Good Night*, Górecki's deeply felt memorial to one of his staunchest
supporters, the late Michael Vyner. The language is sombre, but never merely mournful. Mostly quiet
and contemplative, *Good Night* is scored for alto flute, piano and tam-tam with Dawn Upshaw
intoning Hamlet's "flights of angels" in the closing movement. The work ends in a spirit of veiled
ritual with a sequence of quiet gong strokes. The performance and recording are consistently fine.
Additional recommendations ...
...Kleines Requiem für eine Polka[a]. Lerchenmusik, Op. 53[b]. [b]**Harmen de Boer** (cl);
[b]**Larissa Groeneveld** (vc); [a]**Schoenberg Ensemble / Reinbert de Leeuw** ([b]pf).
Philips Ⓕ 442 533-2PH (67 minutes: DDD: 5/96).

...Good Night[a]. Kleines Requiem für eine Polka[b]. Three Pieces in Old Style. [a]**Elzbieta Szmytka** (sop); [a]**Paul Edmund-Davies** (fl); [ab]**Mireille Gleizes** (pf); [a]**Huub Righarts** (perc); **I Fiamminghi / Rudolf Werthen.** Telarc Ⓕ CD80417 (57 minutes: DDD: 9/96).

Górecki Miserere, Op. 44[ab]. Amen, Op. 35[ab]. Euntes ibant et flebant, Op. 32[ab]. My Vistula, grey Vistula, Op. 46[c]. Broad waters, Op. 39[c]. [a]**Chicago Symphony Chorus;** [b]**Chicago Lyric Opera Chorus / John Nelson;** [c]**Lira Chamber Chorus / Lucy Ding.** Elektra Nonesuch Ⓕ 7559-79348-2 (67 minutes: DDD: 3/95). Texts and translations included. Recorded 1994.

Miserere is an intensely spiritual, imploringly prayerful work in which Górecki responds with heartfelt passion to the political events of 1981 (a sit-in by members of Rural Solidarity which ultimately led to the democratization of Poland). This is as intellectually demanding and emotionally compelling as anything by Górecki yet released on disc. Lovers of the Third Symphony will fall under its spell straight away, but it should gain respect from those less easily swayed by the opulent orchestral textures of that work, for here Górecki is using what is probably his favourite medium, the unaccompanied choir. The voices enter in a series of layered thirds until all ten parts commence an electrifying ascent through the word "Domine" to the work's climax which, with the first statement of "Miserere", suddenly bathes us in a quiet chord of A minor – a moment as devastatingly effective as an orchestra full of banging drums and crashing cymbals. John Nelson directs a hypnotic performance which wants for nothing in its impact, his choral forces both emotionally committed and technically excellent. The recording itself is certainly not technically excellent – there are a number of persistent background rattles and bangs, not to mention, at 3'42" in *Amen*, something which sounds like gunfire from the Chicago streets surrounding the church where the recording was made. That church suffers from a cloudy acoustic and there is a haze of surface noise. In the end, though, it only serves to reinforce this grainy aural picture of those dark, frightening times in Poland's recent history.

Further listening ...
...Piano Concerto, Op. 40. *Coupled with works by various composers.* **Alexei Lubimov** (pf); **Deutsche Kammerphilharmonie, Bremen / Heinrich Schiff.** Erato 0630-12709-2 (8/96).
...Symphony No. 2, Op. 31, "Copernican"[a]. Beatus vir, Op. 38. [a]**Emese Soós** (sop); **Tamás Altorjay** (bar); **Bartók Chorus; Fricsay Symphonic Orchestra / Tamás Pál.** Stradivarius STR33324 (7/94).
...Three Pieces in Old Style. *Coupled with works by* **Baird** and **Szymanowski** Polish Chamber Orchestra / Jerzy Maksymiuk. EMI Matrix CDM5 65418-2 (3/96).
...Epitafium, Op. 12[ab]. Scontri, Op. 17[b]. Genesis II: Canti strumentali, Op. 19 No. 2[b]. Refrain, Op. 21[b]. Old Polish music, Op. 24[c]. [a]**Polish National Philharmonic Choir;** [b]**Polish National Symphony Orchestra, Katowice / Jan Krenz;** [c]**Polish National Philharmonic Orchestra, Warsaw / Andrzej Markowski.** Olympia OCD385 (4/93).
...Euntes Ibant et Flebant, Op. 32. Totus tuus, Op. 60. Amen, Op. 35. *Coupled with works by* **Pärt** and **Tavener** Oxford Pro Musica Singers / Michael Smedley. Proud Sound PROUCD136 (12/94).
...Totus tuus, Op. 60. *Coupled with works by various composers.* **Vasari Singers / Jeremy Backhouse.** EMI Eminence CD-EMX2251 (8/96). *See review in the Collections section; refer to the Index.*
...Totus tuus, Op. 60. *Coupled with works by various composers.* **The King's Singers.** RCA Victor Red Seal 09026 68255-2 (8/96). *See review in the Collections section; refer to the Index.*
...Totus tuus, Op. 60. *Coupled with works by various composers.* **New College Choir, Oxford;** [a]**Capricorn / Edward Higginbottom.** Erato 0630-14634-2 (1/97).
...Totus tuus, Op. 60. *Coupled with works by various composers.* **Holst Singers / Stephen Layton.** Hyperion CDA66928 (8/97). *See review in the Collections section; refer to the Index.*

Jakov Gotovac
Yugoslavian 1895-1984

Suggested listening ...
...Ero the Joker – Dance. *Coupled with works by various composers.* **Vienna Philharmonic Orchestra / Rudolf Kempe.** Testament SBT1127* (3/98). *See review in the Collections section; refer to the Index.*

Louis Moreau Gottschalk
American 1829-1869

Gottschalk O ma charmante, épargnez-moi, RO182. Grande fantaisie triomphale sur l'hymne national brésilien, RO108. Melody in D flat major. Bamboula, RO20. The Dying Poet, RO75. Grande étude de concert, RO116, "Hercule". The last hope, RO133. Murmures éoliens, RO176. Symphony No. 1, RO5, "La nuit des tropiques" – Andante (arr. Napoleão). La chute des feuilles, RO55. Tournament Galop, RO264. **Philip Martin** (pf). Hyperion Ⓕ CDA66915 (73 minutes: DDD: 6/97). Recorded 1996.

It is not only the playing here which gives such satisfaction, but the whole package is stylishly produced – Rousseau on the booklet cover and fine notes from Jeremy Nicholas. The piano sound from the fastidious Hyperion team is absolutely flawless. Martin, operating in a context where some pianists can hardly play softly at all, has a really ravishing *pianissimo*. This makes *O ma charmante* and the perennial – but highly original – *The last hope* simply enchanting. Gottschalk is a real melodist. Martin understands the intimacies of the salon but he also lacks nothing in his transcendental virtuosity. The more flamboyant numbers, such as *Tournament Galop* prove this. About ten years after Gottschalk's death, his pianist colleague, Artur Napoleão, made a piano arrangement of the first movement of Symphony No. 1 (*Night in the tropics*) which Martin includes here. It is slightly drab compared with the orchestral version and soon feels repetitive. But don't let that put you off this outstanding continuation of Martin's Gottschalk series.

Further listening ...

...Grande fantaisie triomphale sur l'hymne national brésilien, RO108 (orch. Hazell). *Coupled with works by various composers.* **Cristina Ortiz** (pf); **Royal Philharmonic Orchestra / Moshe Atzmon.** Decca 414 348-2DH (9/86). *See review in the Collections section; refer to the Index.*   **Ⓖ**

...Suis-moi!, RO253. Berceuse, RO27. La jota aragonesa, RO130. Manchega, RO143. Marche de nuit, RO151. La Savane, RO232. Miserere du Trovatore, RO171. Souvenir d'Andalousie, RO242. Polkas – A flat major, RO275; B flat major, RO273. Ballade, RO271. Ynes, RO277. Caprice-Polka, RO44. Scherzo-romantique, RO233. Souvenir de Lima, RO247. Grand scherzo, RO114. Pasquinade, RO189. **Philip Martin** (pf). Hyperion CDA66697 (10/94).

Charles François Gounod
French 1818-1893

Gounod Symphonies – No. 1 in D major[a]; No. 2 in E flat major[b]. **Orchestra of St John's, Smith Square / John Lubbock.** ASV Ⓔ CDDCA981 (65 minutes: DDD: 1/97). Item marked [a] recorded 1996, [b]1993.

Gounod's symphonies are certainly not brow-furrowing and do not represent any advance in symphonic thought beyond Schumann and Mendelssohn, but they reveal Gounod in the Gallic tradition of elegantly crafted works with a light touch rather than in his familiar sentimental, sanctimonious image. The melodious, classically built and even witty First Symphony, with its delicate second-movement fugue and vivacious finale, is not to be peremptorily brushed aside. The longer Second Symphony makes an attempt to sound more serious, especially in the first movement and the dramatic scherzo – the cantilena of the *Larghetto* is beautifully shaped here – but high spirits return in the finale. John Lubbock and his St John's orchestra are adept at the crisply neat treatment that this music demands. His wind section is outstanding, but in the finale of No. 1 the violins too show real virtuosity. A warm but clean recorded sound adds to our pleasure. A happy disc.

Gounod Où voulez-vous aller?[a]. Le soir[a]. Venise[a]. Ave Maria[b]. Sérénade[b]. Chanson de printemps[a]. Au rossignol[b]. Ce que je suis sans toi[a]. Envoi de fleurs[a]. La pâquerette[b]. Boléro[b]. Mignon[a]. Rêverie[a]. Ma belle amie est morte[b]. Loin du pays[b]. Clos ta paupière[a]. Prière[b]. L'absent[a]. Le temps des roses[a]. Biondina[c]. The Worker[c]. A lay of the early spring[c]. My true love hath my heart[b]. Oh happy home! Oh blessed flower![c]. The fountain mingles with the river[a]. Maid of Athens[c]. Beware![a]. The Arrow and the Song[b]. Ilala: stances à la mémoire de Livingstone[c]. If thou art sleeping, maiden[c]. [a]**Felicity Lott** (sop); [b]**Ann Murray** (mez); [c]**Anthony Rolfe Johnson** (ten); **Graham Johnson** (pf). Hyperion Ⓕ CDA66801/02 (two discs: 136 minutes: DDD: 3/94). Texts and translations included. Recorded 1993.

This well-filled two-CD set is surely the most wide-ranging single issue ever devoted to Gounod's *mélodies*. The first of the discs confirms the commonly held view of Gounod. Almost without exception the songs are pleasing and sentimental, a sweetly-scented posy of hymns to flowers, of reveries and serenades. The selection includes two settings of poems that Berlioz had used in *Les nuits d'été*, plumbing the depths of the poetry, where Gounod is content to skim across the surface. Arranged in chronological order, the songs show how little Gounod's music deepened, but also how evergreen was his inspiration in melody and harmony. To turn to the second disc is to have all one's prejudices overturned. This comprises non-French settings, for which Gounod dons first Italian garb for the song-cycle *Biondina*, and then English for a group of ten songs written during his stay in London in the 1870s. The Italian cycle is a delight. It would be impossible to guess the composer, as Gounod exchanges his customary flowing themes and rippling arpeggios for an ardent, Tosti-like vocal line over dry staccato chords. Anthony Rolfe Johnson catches its mix of sunny lyricism and Gallic sensitivity to perfection. The English songs are even more unusual, ranging from the Victorian ballad style of *The Worker* to a bizarre musical tribute to Livingstone, entitled *Ilala*. All three singers are on their best form here, with Rolfe Johnson bringing an air of intimate seductiveness to Byron's *Maid of Athens*.

Gounod Faust. **Jerry Hadley** (ten) Faust; **Cecilia Gasdia** (sop) Marguerite; **Samuel Ramey** (bass) Méphistophélès; **Alexander Agache** (bar) Valentin; **Susanne Mentzer** (mez) Siébel; **Brigitte Fassbaender** (mez) Marthe; **Philippe Fourcade** (bass) Wagner; **Welsh National Opera Chorus and Orchestra / Carlo Rizzi.** Teldec Ⓕ 4509-90872-2 (three discs: 211 minutes: DDD: 7/94). Notes, text and translation included. Recorded 1993.

Where Gounod is at his most inspired this version of his most popular work is more than commendable. Most notable are the solos for Marguerite and Faust, the Garden scene, the vignette in Marguerite's room that used to be regularly cut, and the Prison scene (considerably extended by the restoration of passages cut – presumably – before the première: we are in controversial Oeser territory). Following the Oeser Edition means unusual variants and an alteration in the placing (later) of the Church scene. These are questionable decisions but not serious enough to cause a problem when making a choice of versions. The ballet music is rightly consigned to an appendix. The tender, sweet-toned and idiomatically French singing and style of Gasdia and Hadley quite exceed expectations in these days of homogenized and uniform interpretation. These two principals step outside those predictable parameters to give us readings of high individuality, favouring their grateful music with delicately etched line, varied dynamics and real involvement in their characters' predicaments – Faust's vain search for the elixir of renewal, Marguerite for the ideal man. Both their happiness and later remorse are eloquently expressed. Gasdia gives a well-nigh faultless performance – light-hearted, elated in the Jewel song, ardent in the Garden duet, ecstatic in the bedtime solo that follows, ineffably sad in her "Il ne revient pas". How can this exquisite solo have ever been omitted, we think, when Gasdia moves us so deeply? She is no less touching when she has lost her reason. Subtle timbres, poised high notes inform all her singing.

Hadley, with the ideal weight of voice for Faust, has done nothing better. "Je t'aime" at the first meeting with Marguerite is whispered in wonder. In the love duet he sings to her as a gentle lover, never bawling, caressing his music, and Gasdia replies in kind. The good news continues with Mentzer. She sings both Siébel's regular solos with vibrant, properly virile tone, the quick vibrato attractive. It's a real coup to have Fassbaender as Marthe, making so much of little. Ramey is the one singer to give a standardized performance. His Méphisto is as soundly and resolutely sung as one would expect from this sturdy bass, but it doesn't have the Francophone smoothness and subtlety of other interpretations. The only drawback is the often lax conducting. Rizzi conducts an often alarmingly slow account of the score and in compensation the more exciting passages are given rather too much verve. However, he is always aware of the sensuous nature of Gounod's scoring and the WNO Chorus and Orchestra are excellent. A choice between this and Plasson for a modern recording must rest on one or other singer. Haunted by the plaintive timbre of Gasdia and the artistry of Hadley one is persuaded that this is the version to have. The recording is by and large open, full of presence and well balanced.

Additional recommendations ...
...Soloists; Paris Opéra Chorus and Orchestra / André Cluytens.
EMI Ⓜ CMS7 69983-2 (three discs: 171 minutes: ADD: 7/89).
...Soloists; French Army Chorus; Toulouse Capitole Choir and Orchestra / Michel Plasson.
EMI Ⓕ CDS5 56224-2 (three discs: 204 minutes: DDD: 12/91).
...Faust (sung in English)[a]. Faust – Ballet Music[b]. Les nubiennes; Adagio (includes an introduction by Beecham). [a]Soloists; [a]BBC Choir; [a]symphony orchestra; [b]London Philharmonic Orchestra / [ab]Sir Thomas Beecham, [a]Clarence Raybould.
Dutton Laboratories mono Ⓜ 2CDAX2001* (two discs: 138 minutes: ADD: 5/94).
...Faust – Ballet Music. *Coupled with works by* **Delibes** Budapest Philharmonic Orchestra / János Sándor. Capriccio Ⓑ 15 616 (57 minutes: DDD: 5/90).
...Faust – O Dieu! que de bijoux! ... Ah! je ris. *Coupled with works by various composers.* **Renée Fleming** (sop); **English Chamber Orchestra / Jeffrey Tate.**
Decca Ⓕ 458 858-2DH (70 minutes: DDD: 3/98). *Selected by Soundings.*
See review in the Collections section; refer to the Index.
...Faust – Valse. *Coupled with works by various composers.* **Vienna Philharmonic Orchestra / Rudolf Kempe.** Testament Ⓕ SBT1127* (78 minutes: ADD: 3/98). *See review in the Collections section; refer to the Index.*

Gounod Roméo et Juliette. **Plácido Domingo** (ten) Roméo; **Ruth Ann Swenson** (sop) Juliette; **Alastair Miles** (bass) Frère Laurent; **Kurt Ollmann** (bar) Mercutio; **Susan Graham** (sop) Stephano; **Alain Vernhes** (bar) Capulet; **Sarah Walker** (mez) Gertrude; **Paul Charles Clarke** (ten) Tybalt; **Christopher Maltman** (bar) Paris; **Erik Freulon** (bar) Gregorio; **Toby Spence** (ten) Benvolio; **David Pittman-Jennings** (bar) Duc; **Dankwart Siegele** (bass) Frère Jean; **Bavarian Radio Chorus; Munich Radio Orchestra / Leonard Slatkin.** RCA Victor Red Seal Ⓕ 09026 68440-2 (two discs: 156 minutes: DDD: 6/96). Notes, text and translation included.
Gramophone Editor's choice. Recorded 1995.   Ⓖ

Thanks to the advocacy of Leonard Slatkin and his team, Gounod's romantic work, *Roméo et Juliette*, seems the epitome of the well-made French nineteenth-century opera. Swenson shows a true empathy for the shape and feeling of a Gounod phrase. At the start, in the famous Waltz song, she announces her gifts. Besides singing this showpiece with technical confidence, a full, rounded tone and refined delicacy in coloratura, she shows an understanding of the girl's youthful vivacity yet tempers that with inner feeling in the "Loin d'hiver" passage. The fear at having to enter the tomb of Tybalt in the solo at the end of Act 4, so often omitted in the opera house, is graphically expressed; as are the last, desperate utterances as she eagerly grasps the *poignard* to join her beloved in Elysium. Her French, though not perfect, is well learnt, and quite adequate to support her impressive portrayal. She seems to have inspired Domingo back to almost his best, youthful form. Roméo's famous aria is sung with growing ardour and full resonance. The outburst against Tybalt when he has killed Mercutio is heroic to a fault. But the golden tenor is still able to soften in the duets in response to this Juliette. Only once or twice the strain on high betrays the advancing years.

Two principals of such calibre deserve and, by and large, get worthy support and all are brought together into a firm ensemble by Slatkin's loving yet never lingering direction. He brings all the bitter-sweetness out of the Entr'actes by which Gounod obviously set so much store, cares for the composer's refined orchestration and shapes the set pieces with an unerring ear for matching tempos. What more can you ask for? Well, a chorus and orchestra that respond with a like mind, and that's what we have here. Most of the original 1873 score is in place, except for the first three movements of the Wedding tableau, often omitted. They are included in the more-or-less complete Plasson set, which in consequence runs to three discs. Their omission can easily be borne. To complete our pleasure the recording is well-nigh faultless. The voices are up-front where they should be but never to the detriment of the orchestra. The Plasson set is by no means outclassed. Catherine Malfitano is almost as appealing a Juliette as Swenson. Alfredo Kraus sometimes manages a finer line than Domingo though he sounds the older singer. The French support and more authentic version are also in its favour. But the recording is too resonant and fails to give the voices a proper presence.

Additional recommendations ...
...Soloists; **Midi-Pyrénées Regional Choir; Toulouse Capitol Chorus and Orchestra / Michel Plasson.**
    EMI Ⓕ CDS7 47365-8 (three discs: 166 minutes: DDD: 3/87).
...Roméo et Juliette – Je veux vivre; Dieu! quel frisson ... Amour, ranime mon courage. *Coupled with works by various composers.* **Kathleen Battle** (sop); **Chorus and Orchestra of the Opéra Bastille, Paris / Myung-Whun Chung.** DG Ⓕ 447 114-2GH (63 minutes: DDD: 7/96).

Further listening ...
...Marche funèbre d'une marionette. *Coupled with works by various composers.*
    Detroit Symphony Orchestra / Paul Paray. Mercury Living Presence 434 332-2MM (11/93).
    See review in the Collections section; refer to the Index.   ⒼⒼⒼ
...Marche funèbre d'une marionette. *Coupled with works by various composers.*
    Boston Pops Orchestra / Arthur Fiedler. RCA Victor Living Stereo 09026 68131-2 (12/95).
...Marche funèbre d'une marionette. *Coupled with works by various composers.*
    New London Orchestra / Ronald Corp.
    Hyperion CDA66998 (3/98). *See review in the Collections section; refer to the Index.*
...Messe solennelle de Sainte Cécile. **Soloists; French Radio National Chorus;**
    Nouvel Philharmonique / Georges Prêtre. EMI CDC7 47094-2 (5/85).
...Mors et Vita. **Barbara Hendricks** (sop); **Nadine Denize** (mez); **John Aler** (ten); **José van Dam** (bass-bar); **Orféon Donostiarra; Toulouse Capitole Orchestra / Michel Plasson.** EMI CDS7 54459-2 (2/93).
...Sappho. **Soloists; Saint-Etienne Lyric Chorus and Nouvel Orchestra / Patrick Fournillier.**
    Koch Schwann 313112 (7/94).

Percy Grainger
American/Australian 1882-1961

Grainger The Warriors.
Holst The Planets, H125[a]. [a]women's voices of the **Monteverdi Choir; Philharmonia Orchestra /**
    Sir John Eliot Gardiner. DG Ⓕ 445 860-2GH (68 minutes: DDD: 8/95). Recorded 1994.   Ⓖ
Grainger's *magnum opus*, *The Warriors*, was the "music for an imaginary ballet", a commission set up by Sir Thomas Beecham for Diaghilev's Ballets Russes, but one which failed to materialize. Grainger wrote it anyway, of course, his imagination running riot with visions of a great tribal pageant, a "wild sexual concert", the ghostly clans of all humankind spirited together in celebration of life's prime. Grainger bemoaned a world that he believed was "dying of 'good taste'". *The Warriors* was his corrective, a symphony of dissolution. It is excessive, vulgar, as strange as it is beautiful. Above all, it's the rhythmic excitement of the piece that is so totally irresistible. Gardiner's classical and pre-classical explorations have, by necessity of style, set great store by rhythmic matters, and what a boon they are in *The Planets*. It's Gardiner's insistence upon precise articulations that keeps fleet-footed "Mercury" so airborne, that brings the opening of "Jupiter" into such sharp relief, making it shine all the brighter. There are other moments where a little more theatrical rhetoric would not have gone amiss: is the controlled fury of "Mars" perhaps a shade too controlled? But the marmoreal beauty of "Venus" and "Neptune" (a ravishing texture descending from the gleam of celeste to an organ pedal sunk too deep to fathom), the sensitivity of the Philharmonia's playing, duly leave their impression. The recorded sound is superb.

Additional recommendation ...
...The Warriors. Hill-Song No. 1. Irish Tune from County Derry, BFMS20. Hill Song No. 2.
    Danish Folk-Music Suite. **Traditional Chinese** (harmonized Yasser, arr. Grainger,
    orch. Sculthorpe): Beautiful Fresh Flower. **Melbourne Symphony Orchestra / Geoffrey Simon.**
    Koch International Classics Ⓕ 37003-2 (67 minutes: DDD: 11/90).

Grainger In a Nutshell. Train Music (ed. Rathburn). The Warriors. Lincolnshire Posy.
    Country Gardens, BFMS22 (rev. 1950).
Debussy (orch. Grainger) Pagodes.
Ravel (orch. Grainger) La vallée des cloches[a]. **City of Birmingham Symphony Orchestra /**
    Sir Simon Rattle. EMI Ⓕ CDC5 56412-2 (70 minutes: DDD: 8/97). Item marked [a]
    from CDC7 54204-2 (8/91). Recorded [a]1990 and 1996. *Gramophone Editor's choice.*   ⒼⒼ

This is a marvellous Grainger anthology. Rattle surpasses Richard Hickox's commendable account of *In a Nutshell* in terms of rhythmic point and bracing character and makes us even more aware of the startling originality of Grainger's vision. *The Warriors* is handsomely served on CD by Geoffrey Simon and John Eliot Gardiner. Rattle's stunning version is the best one of all, possessing a mastery of texture and irresistible choreographic flair to remind us that the piece had its origins in a commission for Diaghilev's Ballets Russes. *Country Gardens* is quirkily scored, harmonically eventful and hugely entertaining. The delectable arrangements of Ravel's *La vallée des cloches* and Debussy's *Pagodes* are quite captivating in their imaginative sonorities and both receive exquisite treatment here. *Train Music* is an intriguing torso, dating from 1901, which the ambitious teenage composer began to score for an orchestra of about 150 players. It's heard here in a reduced orchestration by the American Grainger authority, Eldon Rathburn. Finally, we are given an exceptionally perceptive *Lincolnshire Posy*. Not only do the fabulous blend and immaculate intonation of the CBSO's wind and brass really take the breath away, but Rattle's interpretation is also full of insight. Most remarkable of all is "Rufford Park Poachers", full of tragic grandeur; "Lord Melbourne", too, is memorable, acquiring a fierce, hard-edged intensity. Both the recording and presentation are immaculate.

Additional recommendations ...
...In a Nutshell. The Duke of Marlborough Fanfare, BFMS36. Colonial Song, S1. English Dance. Shepherd's Hey, BFMS31. There were Three Friends. Fisher's Boarding House. We were Dreamers. Harvest Hymn. Blithe Bells. Walking Tune, RMTB3. Green Bushes, BFMS12.
BBC Philharmonic Orchestra / Richard Hickox. Chandos Grainger Edition Ⓕ CHAN9493 (72 minutes: DDD: 11/96). Recorded 1996. *Gramophone Editor's choice.*   Ⓖ
...Lincolnshire Posy[a]. Country Gardens[a]. In a Nutshell – The Gumsuckers' March[b]. Hill Song No. 2[b]. Ye Banks and Braes O' Bonnie Doon[b]. Faeroe Island Dance[b]. The lads of Wamphray[b]. Irish Tune from County Derry[a]. Shepherd's Hey![a]. The Merry King[b]. Molly on the Shore[b]. Colonial Song, S1[a]. **Royal Northern College of Music Wind Orchestra / [a]Timothy Reynish, [b]Clark Rundell.** Chandos Grainger Edition Ⓕ CHAN9549 (61 minutes: DDD: 9/97).

Grainger Youthful Suite. Molly on the Shore, BFMS1. Irish Tune from County Derry, BFMS15. Shepherd's Hey, BFMS16. Country Gardens. Early one Morning, BFMS unnum. Handel in the Strand, RMTB2. Mock Morris, RMTB1. Dreamery (ed. Ould). The Warriors (ed. Servadei).
BBC Philharmonic Orchestra / Richard Hickox. Chandos Grainger Edition Ⓕ CHAN9584 (75 minutes: DDD: 4/98). Recorded 1997.   ⒼⒼ
Featuring some ripe, beautifully clean-cut sonics, this collection represents a great success for all involved. As the opening, chest-swelling "Northern March" of the *Youthful Suite* immediately demonstrates, Hickox draws playing of infectious swagger from the ever-excellent BBC Philharmonic (marvellous brass sounds especially). The suite boasts some really striking invention, not least in the central "Nordic Dirge" (a hauntingly eloquent processional, incorporating plenty of "tuneful percussion") and a winsome, at times almost Ivesian "English Waltz". There follow seven of Grainger's most popular miniatures in the orchestrations Gershwin made for Leopold Stokowski. Hickox gives us Grainger's original thoughts and a delectable sequence they comprise, full of truly kaleidoscopic textural and harmonic variety. By the side of Rattle's CBSO version, Hickox's *Country Gardens* is perhaps marginally lacking in twinkling good humour and entrancing lightness of touch, but his infectious energy and evident affection more than compensate. *Dreamery*, described by Grainger as "Slow Tween-Play" (an epithet which, as annotator Barry Peter Ould suggests, "could be construed as his particular term for an intermezzo") appears here in the extended orchestral version. For *The Warriors*, Hickox uses a new critical edition prepared by the Australian Grainger authority, Alessandro Servadei. Grainger's orchestral palette has never sounded more gloriously extravagant than here. Then again, this impression is just as much a tribute to Hickox's performance, which is breathtaking in its virtuosic brilliance and stunning co-ordination.

Additional recommendation ...
...Country Gardens (orch. Schmid). Youthful Suite – Rustic Dance; Eastern Intermezzo. Blithe Bells (free ramble on a theme by Bach, "Sheep may safely graze"). Spoon River. My Robin is to the Greenwood Gone. Green Bushes. Mock Morris. Youthful Rapture[a]. Shepherd's Hey. Walking Tune. Molly on the Shore. Handel in the Strand (orch. Wood). **Philip Martin** (pf); [a]**Moray Welsh** (vc); **Bournemouth Sinfonietta / Kenneth Montgomery.**
Chandos Collect Ⓜ CHAN6542 (55 minutes: ADD: 2/92).

Grainger Piano music for four hands, Volumes 2 and 3. **Penelope Thwaites, John Lavender** (pfs). Pearl Ⓕ SHECD9623/31 (two discs, oas: 66 and 78 minutes: DDD: 1/94). Recorded 1989-91.
SHECD9623 – Children's March (Over the Hills and Far Away), RMTB4. Shepherd's Hey, BFMS16. Hill Song No. 1. Handel in the Strand, RMTB2. Harvest Hymn. The Widow's Party, KS7. The Lonely Desert Man Sees the Tents of the Happy Tribes. The Rival Brothers. Warriors II. Two Musical Relics of My Mother. Let's Dance Gay in Green Meadow, FI. Blithe Bells. Pritteling, Pratteling, Pretty Poll Parrot. *SHECD9631* – Rondo. Crew of the Long Dragon. Fantasy on George Gershwin's "Porgy and Bess". Ye Banks and Braes, BFMS32. Tiger-Tiger, KS4/JBC9. Walking Tune, RMTB3. **C. Scott** Three Symphonic Dances. **Delius** A Dance Rhapsody No. 1, RTVI/18. **Grieg** Knut Lurasens Halling II. **Addinsell** Festival. **Le Jeune** La Bel'aronde. **Gershwin** Girl Crazy – Embraceable you (all trans. Grainger).

Grainger's 'dishings-up' of his music for keyboard is often more satisfying than the better-known orchestral versions. Quite frequently his arrangements for two pianists are his last thoughts about music that has often gone through as many as half a dozen rethinkings already, so Vol. 2 of this highly accomplished series is something more than an anthology of pieces that many Graingerites will already have. *Shepherd's Hey*, for example, is equipped with a particularly exuberant new coda, and the bafflingly titled *Pritteling, Pratteling, Pretty Poll Parrot* turns out to be our old friend the *Gum-suckers' March* with an entirely new middle section and some affectionate sidelong glances at (apparently) Erik Satie. There is literally new music as well, most substantially *Warriors II*, which turns out to have rather little connection with the strange 'imaginary ballet' that we might now call *Warriors I*. Reconstructed from Grainger's sketches by no fewer than four hands it turns out to be one of his stronger pieces: ardently melodious, at times very close to Rachmaninov, big gestured and with more urgency than some of his works of this length. Volume 3 contains shorter original Grainger compositions and a number of his transcriptions. These latter are fascinating in their combination of scrupulous fidelity and creative rethinking for an entirely different medium. You wouldn't think that a transcription, even for *two* pianos, of Delius's First *Dance Rhapsody* could possibly work. In fact, it works so well that some may prefer Grainger's version to the original. In the *Porgy and Bess* Fantasy he treats the tunes with loving respect, but as a pianist can't help seeing different ways of presenting them: the very big gestures surrounding "My man's gone now"; a searching little prelude to "It ain't necessarily so" implying all sorts of interesting things Grainger could have done with that slithery little tune if he weren't obliged to play it straight – which he then does, with sparkling enjoyment.

Additional recommendations ...
...In a Nutshell Suite. Spoon River, AFMS1. When the World was Young. Molly on the Shore, BFMS1. Hill Song No. 2. Country Gardens, BFMS22. Mowgli's Song against People, KS15 and KJBC11. Eastern Intermezzo, RMTB5. English Waltz. The Wraith of Odin. Always Bright and Merry. The Duke of Marlborough's Fanfare. A Lincolnshire Posy, BFMS35. **Penelope Thwaites, John Lavender** (pfs). Pearl Ⓕ SHECD9611 (77 minutes: DDD: 10/89).
...Fantasy on George Gershwin's "Porgy and Bess". **Gershwin** Cuban Overture (arr. Stone). Rhapsody in Blue. Second Rhapsody. An American in Paris (all arr. cpsr). **Peter Donohoe, Martin Roscoe** (pfs). Carlton Classics Ⓜ 30366 0068-2 (77 minutes: DDD: 8/97).
Gramophone Editor's choice. See review under Gershwin; refer to the Index.

Grainger Jutish Medley, DFMS8. Colonial Song, S1. Molly on the Shore, BFMS1. Harvest Hymn. Spoon River, AFMS1. Country Gardens, BFMS22. Walking Tune, RMTB3. Mock Morris, RMTB1. Ramble on Themes from Richard Strauss's "Der Rosenkavalier". Shepherd's Hey, BFMS4. Irish Tune from County Derry, BFMS6. Handel in the Strand, RMTB2. The Hunter in his career, OEPM4. Scotch Strathspey and Reel, BFMS37. In a Nutshell Suite – No. 4, The Gum-suckers March. The Merry King, BFMS38. In Dahomey.
Stanford (arr. Grainger) Four Irish Dances, Op. 89 – No. 1, A March-Jig; No. 4, A Reel. **Marc-André Hamelin** (pf). Hyperion Ⓕ CDA66884 (73 minutes: DDD: 1/97).
Gramophone Editor's choice.   ⒼⒼ
Just when you think that you have heard all of Marc-André Hamelin's very considerable interpretative and pianistic faculties, along he comes to surprise us yet again with something completely unexpected. Here he turns his hand to Grainger's piano music, and brings what is perhaps one of the most riveting and satisfying anthologies of this music to date. Hamelin's superb control and artistry just about sweep the board if you're looking for a disc that not only brings you all the old favourites but also explores some of the less familiar music such as Grainger's arrangements of two of Stanford's *Irish Dances*, the Cakewalk Smasher, *In Dahomey* or some of the less familiar folk-music settings such as *The Merry King* – the latter a delightful discovery. The deceptive ease with which Hamelin presents these pieces is quite breathtaking. The *Irish Ttune from County Derry*, for instance, contains some exacting problems which call on the pianist to play *ppp* in the outer fingers and *mf* with the middle in order to bring out the melody which Grainger places almost entirely in the middle register of the piano, and yet Hamelin makes it sound incredibly natural. His subtle control of melodic voicing can also be heard in, among others, the marvellous *Scotch Strathspey and Reel* and the *Jutish Medley* and in the gorgeous *Ramble on Themes from Richard Strauss's "Der Rosenkavalier"*, Hamelin's mastery of the pedal (especially the seldom used middle pedal) is a real delight. All in all a very desirable Grainger anthology.

Additional recommendations ...
...Hill-song No. 1. 14 Songs of the North. Three Scotch Folksongs. Scotch Strathspey and Reel. **Ronald Stevenson** (pf). Altarus Ⓕ AIR-CD-9040 (45 minutes: DDD: 9/95).
...Danish Folk-Music Suite – The Power of Love; The Nightingale and the two Sisters; Jutish Medley. One More Day, my John, SCS1. Knight and Shepherd's Daughter, BFMS18. Near Woodstock Town. Country Gardens. Sussex Mummer's Christmas Carol, BFMS52. Shepherd's Hey. To a Nordic Princess. Love at First Sight. Over the Hills and Far Away. Bridal Lullaby. Handel in the Strand. Colonial Song. Paraphrase on the Waltz of the Flowers from Tchaikovsky's "The Nutcracker". *Coupled with works by* **Fauré** and **Dowland** **Penelope Thwaites** (pf). Unicorn-Kanchana Ⓕ DKPCD9127 (69 minutes: DDD: 3/93).
...In Dahomey. *Coupled with works by various composers.* **Alan Feinberg** (pf).
Argo Ⓕ 444 457-2ZH (76 minutes: DDD: 11/95).

Grainger I'm Seventeen Come Sunday, BFMS8. Brigg Fair, BFMS7. Love Verses from "The Song of Solomon". The Merry Wedding. Shallow Brown, SCS3. Father and Daughter. My Dark-Haired Maid, "Mo Nighean Dhu". The Bride's Tragedy. Irish Tune from County Derry, BFMS5. Scotch Strathspey and Reel, BFMS28. The Lost Lady Found, BFMS33. The Three Ravens, BFMS41. Danny Deever. Tribute to Foster. **Monteverdi Choir; English Country Gardiner Orchestra / Sir John Eliot Gardiner.** Philips Ⓕ 446 657-2PH (75 minutes: DDD: 4/96). Texts included. Recorded 1994-95. *Gramophone Award Winner 1996.* ⒼⒼ

The really startling thing about all these settings is the way in which Grainger unlocks the *inner* life of each text, each melody. He'll digest it, understand it, respect it, and then in his response – which is nothing if not personal – he'll elaborate, creating as little or as much subtext as is appropriate. Like Britten, in his folk-song settings, Grainger knew how and when to get out of the way. The plaintive *Brigg Fair* is no more, no less than the tenor solo and chiefly wordless chorus will allow us – a tune so precious to Grainger that even the harmony is almost an intrusion. Then there is the classic *Londonderry Air* – no words, just voices – a harmony that is so rich, so expressive, so integrated, that it always shrouds the melody in the imagination. Then what, you may ask, could be more extraordinary than the *Love Verses from "The Song of Solomon"*? Well, *Shallow Brown* for a start, which is astounding. A sea shanty with the reach of a spiritual, it is set as the sailors will have yelled it, the vocal line stretching and distorting, straining to be heard over furious oceanic *tremolandos* in guitars and strings. This is a fabulous disc. John Eliot Gardiner may well have inherited some of his joy in this music from his great-uncle, Balfour Gardiner (one of the 'Frankfurt Gang', which included Grainger). He is characteristically hot in his response to its rhythmic zest as are his wonderfully articulate, impeccably tuned, Monteverdi singers and players. The singing is, by turns, fleet, spry, fireside-cosy cathedral-rich – or plain raucous. Brilliant, revealing recorded sound.

Additional recommendations ...

...Jungle Book. Shallow Brown. Good-Bye to Love. Died for Love. The Power of Love. The Rival Brothers. Six Dukes Went Afishin'. The Sprig of Thyme. Willow, willow. Recessional. Lord Maxwell's Goodnight. The Three Ravens. The Running of Shindand. Early One Morning. The Love Song of Har Dyal. My Love's in Germanie. **Libby Crabtree** (sop); **John Mark Ainsley** (ten); **David Wilson-Johnson** (bar); **Polyphony; The Polyphony Orchestra / Stephen Layton.** Hyperion Ⓕ CDA66863 (74 minutes: DDD: 7/96). *Gramophone Editor's choice.* Ⓖ

...Shallow Brown[bde]. Marching Tune, BFMS9[de]. I'm Seventeen Come Sunday[de]. Shenandoah[bd]. Stormy[bd]. Molly on the Shore, BFMS1[e]. Brigg Fair[ad]. Early One Mmorning[be]. After-word[de]. There Was a Pig Went Out to Dig, BFMS18[d]. The Lonely Desert-man Sees the Tents of the Happy Tribes, RMTB9[ade]. Thou Gracious Power[d]. Irish Tune from County Derry[de]. Handel in the Strand, RMTB2[ce]. Six Dukes Went Afishin[d]. Anchor Song, KS6[d]. Ye Banks and Braes o' Bonnie Doon, BFMS30/1[de]. [a]**Mark Padmore** (ten); [b]**Stephen Varcoe** (bar); [c]**Penelope Thwaites** (pf); [d]**Joyful Company of Singers**; [e]**City of London Sinfonia / Richard Hickox.** Chandos Grainger Edition Ⓕ CHAN9499 (61 minutes: DDD: 1/97).

...Brigg Fair. *Coupled with works by various composers.* **Oxford Camerata / Jeremy Summerly.** Naxos Ⓢ 8 553088 (61 minutes: DDD: 5/97).

Further listening ...

...Sussex Mummers' Christmas Carol, BFMS17. Arrival Platform Humlet, RMTB1. *Coupled with works by various composers.* **Paul Coletti** (va); **Leslie Howard** (pf). Hyperion CDA66687 (10/94). *See review in the Collections Section; refer to the Index.*

...Bold William Taylor, BFMS43[d]. *Coupled with works by various composers.* **Sir Peter Pears** (ten); **Viola Tunnard** (pf). Belart 461 550-2 (12/97). *See review in the Collections section; refer to the Index.*

...Brigg Fair. *Coupled with works by* **A. C. Macleod** and **Molloy Philip Cave** (ten); **New College Choir, Oxford / Edward Higginbottom.** Erato 0630-19065-2 (3/98). *See review in the Collections section; refer to the Index.*

Enrique Granados
Spanish 1867-1916

Granados 12 Danzas españolas, Op. 37. 7 Valses poéticos. **Alicia de Larrocha** (pf). RCA Victor Red Seal Ⓕ 09026 68184-2 (68 minutes: DDD: 1/96). Recorded 1994.

Alicia de Larrocha, that incomparable interpreter of the Spanish repertoire, is revisiting many of her favourite musical haunts on RCA (this is at least her third recording of Granados's 12 *Danzas*, and her second of the *Valses poéticos*). And if some of her former edge and fire, her tonal and stylistic luxuriance are now replaced by more 'contained' and reflective qualities, her warmth and affection remain undimmed. Her rubato, while less lavishly deployed than before, is potent and alluring, as instantly recognizable as ever, and each and every dance is played with rare naturalness, ease and authority. But if a touch of sobriety occasionally blunts the fullest impact of these fascinating, most aristocratic idealizations of local Spanish life and colour, the actual playing is never less than masterly. The *Valses poéticos* are offered as an engaging encore. The recordings have much less range and reverberance than those on Decca; however, all lovers of this still misunderstood and neglected repertoire, played by one of the great pianists of our time, will want to add this to their collection.

Additional recommendations ...
...12 Danzas españolas. **Alicia de Larrocha** (pf). Decca Ⓕ 414 557-2DH (DDD: 10/85).
...Valses poéticos (trans. Williams). *Coupled with works by various composers.* **London Symphony Orchestra / Paul Daniel.** Sony Classical Ⓕ SK48480 (71 minutes: DDD: 7/92). *See review under Albéniz; refer to the Index.* Ⓖ
...12 Danzas españolas. Goyescas, Op. 11 – No. 4, Quejas o la maja y el ruiseñor; No. 7, El pelele. **Angela Hewitt** (pf). CBC Records Ⓕ MVCD1074 (66 minutes: DDD: 11/94).
...12 Danzas españolas – Villanesca; Andaluza (Playera). 7 Valses poéticos. Cuentos de la juventud – Dedicatoria. 15 Tonadillas – El majo Olvidado. *Coupled with works by* **Albéniz** *and* **Rodrigo. Julian Bream** (gtr). RCA Navigator Ⓢ 74321 17903-2 (77 minutes: DDD: 3/95). *See review under Albéniz; refer to the Index.* Ⓖ
...(arr. Breiner) 12 Danzas españolas. Escenas poéticas – Series 2. **Norbert Kraft** (gtr); **Razumovsky Sinfonia / Peter Breiner.** Naxos Ⓢ 8 553037 (72 minutes: DDD: 2/96).
...(arr. Kreisler) 12 Danzas españolas – Andaluza (Playera). *Coupled with works by various composers.* **Kennedy** (vn); **John Lenehan** (pf). EMI Ⓕ CDC5 56626-2 (75 minutes: ADD: 5/98). *See review in the Collections section; refer to the Index.*

Granados Goyescas. **Alicia de Larrocha** (pf). Decca Ⓕ 411 958-2DH (57 minutes: ADD: 3/89). From SXL6785 (12/77). Recorded 1976. Ⓖ
Granados Goyescas. El pelele. **Eric Parkin** (pf). Chandos Ⓕ CHAN9412 (61 minutes: DDD: 3/96). Recorded 1993.

The Granados *Goyescas* are profoundly Spanish in feeling, but the folk influence is more of court music than of the flamenco or *cante hondo* styles which reflect gipsy and Moorish influence. Alicia de Larrocha's set of seven pieces was given its first performance by the composer in 1911, and his own exceptional ability as a pianist is evident in its consistently elaborate textures. That performance took place in Barcelona, and as Granados's compatriot and a native of that very city de Larrocha fully understands this music in its richly varied moods; a fact which tells in interpretations that have a compelling conviction and drive. Thus, she can dance enchantingly in such a piece as "El Fandango de candil", while in the celebrated "Maiden and the nightingale", No. 4 of the set, we listen to a wonderful outpouring of Mediterranean emotion, all the more moving for its avoidance of excessive rubato and overpedalling. A splendid disc of one of the twentieth century's piano masterpieces.

A direction in the score at the beginning of the *Goyescas* is *con garbo y donaire* ("with charm and elegance"). The description aptly fits Parkin's performances. His readings have an element of free rubato about them, but this is not allowed to become excessive, and it serves to underline the essentially improvisatory nature of these pieces. Aided by a clean technique in this sometimes complex texture he gives persuasive performances that also contain much poetry. He captures the dignified flamboyance of the traditional dance in the "Fandango by candlelight", carefully observing the direction *avec beaucoup de rhythme*. Two of the hardest tests for a pianist in this collection of Goyesque studies are the preservation of coherence in the long "Serenata del espectro" and the avoidance of mawkishness in "La maja y el ruiseñor": Parkin emerges successfully from both. A piano with particularly bright top octaves was perhaps not the ideal instrument for this recording, but there is no lack of colour or nuance from the performer. Even measured against the formidable competition of Larrocha, this is a highly recommendable disc.

Additional recommendations ...
...Goyescas – El pelele. Danzas españolas, Op. 37 – No. 7, Valenciana; No. 10, Danza triste. *Coupled with works by various composers.* **Enrique Granados** (pf). EMI Composers in Person mono Ⓕ CDC7 54836-2* (78 minutes: ADD: 11/93). *See review in the Collections section; refer to the Index.*
...Goyescas. **Albéniz** Iberia. Navarra. **Alicia de Larrocha** (pf). Double Decca Ⓜ 448 191-2DF2 (two discs: 141 minutes: ADD: 4/96). *See review under Albéniz; refer to the Index. This performance is the same as the one reviewed above.* Ⓖ
...Goyescas – El pelele (arr. Longas). *Coupled with works by various composers.* **Sequeira Costa, Artur Pizarro** (pfs). Collins Classics Ⓕ 1466-2 (62 minutes: DDD: 10/96). *Gramophone Editor's choice. See review in the Collections section; refer to the Index.* Ⓖ
...Goyescas, Quejas o la maja y el ruiseñor. *Coupled with works by various composers.* **Dame Moura Lympany** (pf). Dutton Laboratories mono Ⓕ CDCLP4000* (77 minutes: ADD: 1/97). *See review in the Collections section; refer to the Index.*

Further listening ...
...Goyescas (choral version). **Soloists; Orfeón Donostiarra; Madrid Symphony Orchestra / Antoni Ros Marbà.** Auvidis Valois V4791 (5/97).

Carl Heinrich Graun

German 1703/4-1759

Suggested listening ...
...Montezuma – excerpts (ed. Bonynge). *Coupled with* **Bononcini** Griselda – excerpts. **Soloists; Ambrosian Singers; London Philharmonic Orchestra / Richard Bonynge.** Decca Grand Opera 448 977-2DMO2 (5/97).

Alexandr Grechaninov

Russian/American 1864-1956

Grechaninov Piano Trios – No. 1 in C minor, Op. 38; No. 2 in G major, Op. 128. **Bekova Sisters**
(Elvira Bekova, vn; Alfia Bekova, vc; Eleonora Bekova, pf). Chandos Ⓕ CHAN9461
(53 minutes: DDD: A/97). Recorded 1996.

Composed in 1906, Grechaninov's First Piano Trio is a typical product of Russia's 'Silver Age':
typical in its expert, school-of-Rimsky craftsmanship, typical in its languishing lyricism, typical in its
fundamental complacency. The first movement draws heavily on the figurations from Tchaikovsky's
Fourth Symphony but divests them of all emotional immediacy or dangerous intensity. This makes
for a pleasant, undemanding listening experience, and throws into relief the achievements of
Rachmaninov, Scriabin and Stravinsky. But don't expect any more than that. Grechaninov is one of
several candidates for the label of 'the Russian Brahms'. That fits him as unsatisfactorily as it does
Taneyev or Glazunov or anyone else it has been applied to, but the finale of his Second Trio at least
shows why its sticks. This playful, yet sturdy and always well-crafted music has a feel of 1881 rather
1931. Composed in California, at two removes from the Russia its composer had left once and for all
six years earlier, its childlike escapism is undoubtedly touching, and its sounds agreeable and
rewarding to play. Strong, enjoyable, upfront performances from the talented Bekova sisters;
Chandos's recording is well lubricated with resonance, but not absurdly so.

Additional recommendation ...
...Nos. 1 and 2. **Viktor Simčisko** (vn); **Jura Alexander** (vc); **Daniela Ruso** (pf).
Marco Polo Ⓕ 8 223416 (52 minutes: DDD: 6/93).

Further listening ...
...Symphony No. 1 in B minor, Op. 6[a]. Snowflakes, Op. 47[b]. Missa Sancti Spiritus, Op. 169[c].
[b]**Ludmilla Kuznetsova** (mez); [c]**Tatiana Jeranje** (contr); [c]**Russian State Symphony Cappella**
and [ab]**Orchestra / Valéry Polyansky**. Chandos New Direction CHAN9397 (12/95).
...Symphony No. 2 in A major, Op. 27, "Pastoral"[a]. Mass, Op. 166, "Et in terra pax"[b].
[b]**Anatoly Obraztsov** (bass); [b]**Russian State Symphonic Cappella and** [a]**Symphony Orchestra /**
Valéry Polyansky with [b]**Ludmilla Golub** (org). Chandos New Direction CHAN9486 (12/96).
...Symphony No. 4, Op. 102. Cello Concerto, Op. 8[a]. Missa festiva, Op. 154[b]. [a]**Alexander Ivashkin**
(vc); **Russian State** [b]**Symphonic Cappella and Symphony Orchestra / Valéry Polyansky.**
Chandos CHAN9559 (12/97).
...String Quartets – No. 2 in D minor, Op. 70; No. 4 in F major, Op. 124. **Moyzes Quartet.**
Marco Polo 8 223646 (10/94).
...Liturgia domestica, Op. 79. **Victor Radkevich** (ten); **Anatoli Obraztsov** (bass); **Ludmilla Golub**
(org); **Russian State Symphonic Cappella; Russian State Symphony Orchestra / Valéry Polyansky.**
Chandos New Direction CHAN9365 (8/95).
...The Liturgy of St John Chrysostom, Op. 13 No. 1. **Cantus Sacred Music Ensemble /**
Ludmilla Arshavskaya with **Archdeacon Valeri Shcheglov.** Olympia OCD447 (6/95).
...The Liturgy of St John Chrysostom, Op. 29 – The cherubic hymn; The Creed[a]; Our Father.
Coupled with works by various composers. [a]**James Bowman** (alto); **Holst Singers / Stephen Layton.**
Hyperion CDA66928 (8/97). *See review in the Collections section; refer to the Index.*
...Liturgy of St John Chrysostom, Op. 177 No. 4. **Cantus Sacred Music Ensemble /**
Ludmilla Arshavskaya. Olympia OCD480 (9/95).
...The Seven Days of the Passion. **Russian State Symphonic Cappella / Valéry Polyansky.**
Chandos CHAN9303 (1/95).

Will Gregory

20th century

Suggested listening ...
...Hoe down. *Coupled with works by various composers.* **Soloists; Apollo Saxophone Quartet.**
Argo 443 903-2ZH (8/95). *See review in the Collections section; refer to the Index.*

Nicolas Grenon

French *c*1380-1486

Suggested listening ...
...La plus belle. *Coupled with works by various composers.* **Alla Francesca.**
Opus 111 OPS30-173 (7/98). *See review in the Collections section; refer to the Index.* ⒼⒼⒼ

Edvard Grieg

Norwegian 1843-1907

Grieg Piano Concerto in A minor, Op. 16[a]. Piano Sonata in E minor, Op. 7[b].
Schumann Piano Concerto in A minor, Op. 54[a]. [a]**Stephen Kovacevich**, [b]**Zoltán Kocsis** (pfs);
[a]**BBC Symphony Orchestra / Sir Colin Davis.** Philips Solo Ⓜ 446 192-2PM (78 minutes:
[a]ADD/[b]DDD: 6/96). Items marked [a] from 6500 166 (3/72, recorded 1970-71),
[b]6514 115 (8/83, recorded 1982). ⒼⒼⒼ

Stephen Kovacevich's wholly natural, intimately poetic phrasing, his delicately glistening fingerwork and his bravura and rhythmic virility, too, when required (as in Grieg's finale) must of course be noted first. Yet it is difficult to recall any other performance in which pianist, conductor and orchestra are in closer or more subtly balanced and shaded accord than in this classic account. Each and every participant sounds as personally involved as they would in chamber music-making. The sound quality has not the forward brightness of present-day reproduction: you may need to turn up your volume control a little higher than usual. But its old-world mellowness seems just right for performances as loving as these. For good measure we're even given an encore – though curiously there is no mention of it in the accompanying booklet-notes – and from a totally different pianist. But Zoltán Kocsis's account of Grieg's early E minor Sonata is certainly sufficiently incisive and characterful to justify resurgence.

Additional recommendations ...

...Piano Concerto. **Schumann** Piano Concerto in A minor, Op. 54. **Krystian Zimerman** (pf);
Berlin Philharmonic Orchestra / Herbert von Karajan.
DG Karajan Gold Ⓕ 439 015-2GHS (64 minutes: DDD).

...Piano Concerto. **Schumann** Piano Concerto. **Radu Lupu** (pf); **London Symphony Orchestra /**
André Previn. Decca Ovation Ⓜ 417 728-2DM (61 minutes: ADD: 12/87).   Ⓠ

...Piano Concerto. **Schumann** Piano Concerto. **Pascal Devoyon** (pf); **London Philharmonic**
Orchestra / Jerzy Maksymiuk. Classics for Pleasure Ⓑ CD-CFP4574 (63 minutes: DDD: 2/91).

...Piano Concerto. Lyric Pieces, Book 8, Op. 65. **Liszt** Piano Concerto No. 2 in A major, S125.
Leif Ove Andsnes (pf); **Bergen Philharmonic Orchestra / Dmitri Kitaienko.**
Virgin Classics Ⓕ VC7 59613-2 (78 minutes: DDD: 4/91).

...Piano Concerto. *Coupled with works by* **Schumann** *and* **Franck** **Sir Clifford Curzon,**
Friedrich Gulda (pfs); **London Symphony Orchestra / Øivin Fjeldstad; London Philharmonic**
Orchestra / Sir Adrian Boult; Vienna Philharmonic Orchestra / Volkmar Andreae.
Decca Headline Classics Ⓑ 433 628-2DSP (76 minutes: ADD: 1/92). *See review under Franck;*
refer to the Index.   ⒼⒼⒼ

...Piano Concerto[b]. Peer Gynt – Suites Nos. 1 and 2[a]. Lyric Suite, Op. 54[c]. Holberg Suite, Op. 40[c].
Lyric Pieces – Book 1, Op. 12; Book 3, Op. 13[d]. Symphonic Dances, Op. 64[e].
[b]**Stephen Kovacevich,** [d]**Zoltán Kocsis** (pfs); [ac]**English Chamber Orchestra;** [e]**Philharmonia**
Orchestra / Raymond Leppard; [b]**BBC Symphony Orchestra / Sir Colin Davis.**
Philips Duo Ⓜ 438 380-2PM2 (two discs: 155 minutes: ADD: 8/93). *The performance*
of the Concerto is the same as the one reviewed above.   ⒼⒼⒼ

...Piano Concerto. **Schumann** Piano Concerto. **Lars Vogt** (pf); **City of Birmingham Symphony**
Orchestra / Sir Simon Rattle. EMI Ⓕ CDC7 54746-2 (62 minutes: DDD: 1/93).

...Piano Concerto *(orig. version)*[a]. **Larvik's Polka, CW102**[a]. 23 Short Pieces, CW105[a].
[a]**Love Derwinger** (pf); **Norrköping Symphony Orchestra / Jun'ichi Hirokami.**
BIS Ⓕ CD619 (62 minutes: DDD: 9/93).

...Piano Concerto. **Jean-Marc Luisada** (pf); **London Symphony Orchestra / Michael Tilson Thomas.**
DG Ⓕ 439 913-2GH (65 minutes: DDD: 12/94).

...Piano Concerto[a]. Lyric Pieces – French serenade, Op. 62 No. 3; Cradle song, Op. 68 No. 5.
Coupled with works by **Franck** *and* **Liszt** **Walter Gieseking** (pf); [a]**Berlin State Opera Orchestra /**
Hans Rosbaud. APR mono Ⓜ APR5513* (63 minutes: ADD: 3/96).

Grieg Holberg Suite, Op. 40. Two Elegiac Melodies, Op. 34. Peer Gynt – Suites Nos. 1 and 2,
Opp. 46 and 55. Two Lyric Pieces. **Academy of St Martin in the Fields / Sir Neville Marriner.**
Hänssler Classic Ⓕ 98 995 (66 minutes: DDD: 1/95). Recorded 1994.

The clean ruggedness of Grieg's music comes across well here. Indeed, there is much to praise: the sheer zest of the opening *Allegro vivace* of the *Holberg Suite* and, in the same five-movement work, the way Marriner and his players convey the necessary 'period' quality. The *Two Elegiac Melodies* are also fine; the second of them is the poignant "Last spring" and features some movingly hushed playing from the violins. The incidental music to *Peer Gynt*, which follows, has a similarly attractive freshness. One gets the impression that this is the kind of music that the ASMF can play beautifully at the drop of a hat, but beautiful playing it remains, with nothing routine about it. Even the well-worn "Morning" in Suite No. 1 sounds as fresh as if it were the morning of the world, and one could not ask for a more loving account of "Solveig's Song". The two transcriptions of the *Lyric Pieces* are also evocative, with fine oboe playing in the first, "Evening in the mountains". The recording is richly reverberant but permits detail to emerge.

Additional recommendations ...

...Peer Gynt – Suites Nos. 1 and 2. Holberg Suite. *Coupled with works by* **Sibelius**
Berlin Philharmonic Orchestra / Herbert von Karajan.
DG Karajan Gold Ⓜ 439 010-2GHS (78 minutes: DDD).

...Peer Gynt – Suites Nos. 1 and 2. *Coupled with works by various composers.*
Eileen Farrell (sop); **Boston Pops Orchestra / Arthur Fiedler.**
RCA Victor Living Stereo Ⓜ 09026 68131-2 (76 minutes: ADD: 12/95).

...Peer Gynt – Solveig's Song. *Coupled with works by various composers.*
Angela Gheorghiu (sop); **Malcolm Martineau** (pf). Decca Ⓕ 458 360-2DH
(75 minutes: DDD: 5/98). *See review in the Collections section; refer to the Index.*

Grieg Norwegian Dances, Op. 35. Lyric Suite, Op. 54. Symphonic Dances, Op. 64.
   Gothenburg Symphony Orchestra / Neeme Järvi. DG Ⓕ 419 431-2GH (68 minutes: DDD: 1/87).
Grieg's music has that rare quality of eternal youth: however often one hears it, its complexion retains
its bloom, the smile its radiance and the youthful sparkle remains undimmed. Though he is essentially
a miniaturist, who absorbed the speech rhythms and inflections of Norwegian folk melody into his
bloodstream, Grieg's world is well defined. Both the *Norwegian Dances* and the *Symphonic Dances*
were originally piano duets, which Grieg subsequently scored: Järvi conducts both with enthusiasm
and sensitivity. In the *Lyric Suite* he restores "Klokkeklang" ("Bell-ringing"), which Grieg omitted
from the final score: it is remarkably atmospheric and evocative, and serves to show how forward-
looking Grieg became in his late years. The recording is exceptionally fine and of wide dynamic range;
the sound is very natural and the perspective true to life.
Additional recommendations ...
...Norwegian Dances. Old Norwegian Romance with Variations, Op. 51. In Autumn, Op. 11.
   Lyric Pieces, Op. 43 – No. 5, "Erotik". **Svendsen** Two Icelandic Melodies. **Iceland Symphony
   Orchestra / Petri Sakari.** Chandos Ⓕ CHAN9028 (66 minutes: DDD: 8/92).
...Symphonic Dances. Sigurd Jorsalfar, Op. 56. Peer Gynt – Solveig's Song[a]; Solveig's Cradle Song[a].
   Six Romances, Op. 39 – From Monte Pincio[a]. A swan, Op. 25[a]. Spring, Op. 33[a]. Norway, Op. 58
   – Henrik Wergeland[a]. [a]**Solveig Kringleborn** (sop); **Royal Stockholm Philharmonic Orchestra /
   Gennadi Rozhdestvensky.** Chandos Ⓕ CHAN9113 (73 minutes: DDD: 3/93).

Grieg String Quartets – No. 1 in G minor, Op. 27; No. 2 in F major, CW146.
Schumann String Quartet No. 1 in A minor, Op. 41 No. 1. **Petersen Quartet** (Conrad Muck,
   Gernot Süssmuth, vns; Friedemann Weigle, va; Hans-Jakob Eschenburg, vc).
   Capriccio Ⓕ 10 476 (75 minutes: DDD: 1/94). Recorded 1993.
Grieg String Quartet No. 1 in G minor, Op. 27.
Mendelssohn String Quartet No. 2 in A minor, Op. 13. **Shanghai Quartet** (WeiGang Li, HongGang
   Li, vns; Zheng Wang, va; James Wilson, vc). Delos Ⓕ DE3153 (64 minutes: DDD: 6/94).
Since Grieg owed much to Schumann, coupling their quartets seems a good idea. These G minor and
A minor Quartets were written when the composers were in their thirties, although Grieg was a few
years older. Yet it is his work that sounds more youthfully passionate, while the Schumann is a rather
self-conscious homage to his friend Mendelssohn and classical models. The Petersens invest the Grieg
G minor Quartet with *gravitas* and are skilful in linking together the disparate sections of its
structure. Their recording has a very natural balance and an impressively wide dynamic range with
real *pianissimo*; it also copes well with Grieg's forceful, semi-orchestral string writing. The whole
performance has vigour and tenderness in good proportion, and a truly Scandinavian feeling. The
unfinished F major Quartet is another sensitively moulded performance and the work sounds no
more incomplete than Schubert's *Unfinished* Symphony. The Schumann is no less enjoyable; the
artists are fully inside his idiom and make a consistently beautiful and meaningful sound. The
Shanghai Quartet's brightly-lit account of the Mendelssohn suggests a rich store of interpretative
potential. Theirs is a sizzling, multi-coloured performance. The Grieg coupling is, if anything, even
finer, with an *Allegro molto* first movement that truly is *ed agitato*, a warming *Romanze* and a superbly
characterized *Intermezzo*. It is arguably the most compelling performance of this endearing score
since the original Budapest Quartet's trail-blazing HMV 78s from 1937. It is richly recorded.
Additional recommendation ...
...No. 1. *Coupled with works by* **Sibelius** and **Wolf** Budapest Quartet.
   Biddulph mono Ⓜ LAB098* (67 minutes: ADD: 4/95).

Grieg Cello Sonata in A minor, Op. 36.
Liszt Romance oubliée, S132. Elégies – No. 1, S130; No. 2, S131. Die Zelle in Nonnenwerth, S382.
   La lugubre gondola, S134.
Rubinstein Cello Sonata No. 1 in D major, Op. 18. **Steven Isserlis** (vc); **Stephen Hough** (pf).
   RCA Victor Red Seal Ⓕ 09026 68290-2 (76 minutes: DDD: 4/96). Recorded 1994.
With Steven Isserlis and Stephen Hough an inspired duo, natural recording artists both, it would be
a pity if the sentimental title, "Forgotten Romance", a translation of the shortest and least ambitious
piece in the collection, deterred any serious listener from investigating it. The logic of the grouping is
that the five cello pieces of Liszt, all of them brief and adapted from earlier works, are used to
frame the high romantic cello sonatas, by Grieg and Rubinstein, that are in danger of neglect. With
performances like these, as sharply disciplined as they are passionate, all the emotion is very well
founded, with sentimentality firmly kept at bay. The magnificent Grieg Sonata was written when he
was considering composing a second piano concerto and its material and manner very much reflect
the A minor Concerto, with the composer at his most richly distinctive. Compared with, say, Truls
Mørk and Jean-Yves Thibaudet on Virgin Classics, Isserlis and Hough are lighter and more
imaginative, choosing speeds that flow easily and naturally. Paradoxically that makes the result more
moving than any underlining of expression. One could say the same about all these performances. The
two *Elégies* – with Isserlis most persuasive in the improvisation-like passages – lead to the Rubinstein
First Sonata. It has the lyrical directness and honest four-square construction which make the
Mendelssohn cello sonatas so attractive. The disc is rounded off by two Liszt pieces slightly more

substantial than the others – *Die Zelle in Nonnenwerth* ("The Cell in Nonnenwerth") – a late adaptation of an early song, spare in texture, and Liszt's tribute to Wagner after his death, *La lugubre gondola*, one of many different adaptations.

Additional recommendations ...

...Cello Sonata. Intermezzo in A minor, CW118. *Coupled with works by* **Sibelius** Truls Mørk (vc); **Jean-Yves Thibaudet** (pf). Virgin Classics Ⓕ VC5 45034-2 (69 minutes: DDD: 10/94).

...Cello Sonataᵃ, Piano Sonata. Intermezzo in A minor, CW118ᵃ. ᵃ**Øystein Birkeland** (vc); **Håvard Gimse** (pf). Naxos Ⓢ 8 550878 (50 minutes: DDD: 11/94).

...Cello Sonata. Intermezzo in A minor, CW118. *Coupled with works by* **Delius** **Julian Lloyd Webber** (vc); **Bengt Forsberg** (pf). Philips Ⓕ 454 458-2PH (66 minutes: DDD: 4/98). *See review under Delius; refer to the Index.*

Grieg Violin Sonatas – No. 1 in F major, Op. 8; No. 2 in G major, Op. 13; No. 3 in C minor, Op. 45. **Augustin Dumay** (vn); **Maria-João Pires** (pf). DG Ⓕ 437 525-2GH (70 minutes: DDD: 9/93). Recorded 1993.　　　　　　　　　　　　　　　　　　　　　　　　　Ⓠ

Grieg Violin Sonatas – No. 1 in F major, Op. 8; No. 2 in G major, Op. 13; No. 3 in C minor, Op. 45. **Henning Kraggerud** (vn); **Helge Kjekshus** (pf). Naxos Ⓢ 8 553904 (67 minutes: DDD: A/97). Recorded 1996.

Grieg's violin sonatas span his creative life, the first two dating from his early twenties, before his Piano Concerto, and the Third Sonata of 1887 belonging to the last decade of his life. Augustin Dumay brings to this music a youthful *seigneur*, manifest in the impetuosity, charm and command of his playing. He and Maria-João Pires are at their considerable best in the G major Sonata, with its vivid first movement, lilting *Allegretto* and triumphant finale – whose conclusion they lift to the skies. The recording does full justice to Dumay's silky and resourceful tone. Pires is rightly an equal partner, and both artists bring an infectiously fresh response to the music. The finale of the C minor Sonata, music that anticipates Sibelius in its urgency and elemental force, is compellingly played.

The Naxos disc gives us consistently enjoyable performances. The two young Norwegians play with idiomatic style, and give the impression of absorbing and expressing every aspect of the music. The eagerness with which they set off at the start of Op. 8's first *Allegro* sets the tone; the *doloroso* opening of Op. 13, the delicacy and serenity of the E major section of that sonata's middle movement, and the exciting "Hall of the Mountain King" atmosphere they generate in the finale of Op. 45 – these are just a few of the places where Kraggerud and Kjekshus convince us they've found exactly the right sound and manner of expression. Of the considerable number of available recordings of the three sonatas, the one by Dumay and Pires is a front runner. They're magnificently recorded, causing one to regret the slight lack of brilliance in the new Naxos recording and wish that the violin in particular had been given a more glamorous presence. Their performances are outstanding, too; they're as deeply involved as the Norwegians but play with far greater freedom and a wonderfully uninhibited range of expression. They would remain the overall recommendation, but they do sometimes come dangerously close to guying the music. Kraggerud's account of the 'big tune' in the last movement of Op. 45, respecting all Grieg's marks of expression and phrasing, has a nobility that Dumay, more heart-on-sleeve and cavalier about dynamics and slurs, misses. The Naxos disc is, in short, highly recommendable – as a contrast to Dumay/Pires or simply as an excellent bargain.

Additional recommendations ...

...Nos. 1-3. **Lydia Mordkovitch** (vn); **Elena Mordkovitch** (pf). Chandos Ⓕ CHAN9184 (72 minutes: DDD: 9/93).

...Nos. 1-3. **Oscar Shumsky** (vn); **Seymour Lipkin** (pf). Biddulph Ⓕ LAW008 (63 minutes: DDD).

...Nos. 1-3. **Dong-Suk Kang** (vn); **Roland Pöntinen** (pf). BIS Ⓕ CD647 (69 minutes: DDD: 11/94).

Grieg Piano Works, Volumes 1-4. **Einar Steen-Nøkleberg** (pf). Naxos Ⓢ 8 550881/4 (four discs, oas: 72, 70, 64 and 71 minutes: DDD: 3/96). Recorded 1993.

8 550881 – Piano Sonata in E minor, Op. 7. Funeral March for Rikard Nordraak, CW117. Melodies of Norway – The sirens' enticement. Stimmungen, Op. 73. Transcriptions of Original Songs I, Op. 41 – No. 3, I love thee. Four Humoresques, Op. 6. Four Piano Pieces, Op. 1. *8 550882* (*Gramophone Editor's choice*) – Two Improvisations on Norwegian Folksongs, Op. 29. Melodies of Norway – A Ballad to Saint Olaf. 25 Norwegian Folksongs and Dances, Op. 17. Transcriptions of Original Songs II, Op. 52 – No. 2, The first meeting. 19 Norwegian Folksongs, Op. 66. *8 550883* – Four Album Leaves, Op. 28. Six Poetic Tone-pictures, Op. 3. Melodies of Norway – Iceland. Three Pictures from life in the country, Op. 19. Three Pieces from "Sigurd Jorsalfar", Op. 56 – Prelude. Ballade in G minor, Op. 24, "in the form of variations on a Norwegian melody". *8 550884* – Holberg Suite, Op. 40. Melodies of Norway – I went to bed so late. Six Norwegian Mountain Melodies, CW134. Peer Gynt Suite No. 1, Op. 46 – Morning. 17 Norwegian Peasant Dances, Op. 72.

These are the first four volumes of a complete Grieg cycle which stretches to no fewer than 14 discs. Since all of them are at super-budget price they make a very competitive alternative to other complete or near-complete surveys. Einar Steen-Nøkleberg came into prominence in the 1970s and won numerous Norwegian and other prizes. He was professor of the piano at the Hanover Musikhochschule for some years and is the author of a monograph on Grieg's piano music and its interpretation.

8 550881: The first disc juxtaposes early pieces, the Sonata, Op. 7, the Op. 6 *Humoresques* and the *Funeral March for Rikard Nordraak*, all written in the mid 1890s with his very last piano work, *Stimmungen* (or "Moods"), Op. 73. He plays these bold and original pieces with great flair and understanding. Whatever its limitations there is much greater range in Grieg's piano music than is commonly realized and Steen-Nøkleberg is attuned to the whole spectrum it covers, whether in the Bartókian "Mountaineer's Song" from the Op. 73 to the charm and innocence of the *Allegretto con grazia*, the third of the *Humoresques*, Op. 6. *8 550882*: The *19 Norwegian Folksongs* (1896) are remarkable pieces as Grieg himself knew. He wrote to the Dutch composer, Julius Röntgen, of having "put some hair-raising chromatic chords on paper. The excuse is that they originated not on the piano but in my mind." Readers will recognize No. 14 as the source of the theme for Delius's *On hearing the first cuckoo in spring*. Steen-Nøkleberg plays them with great tonal finesse and consummate artistry *8 550883*: The most substantial work on this disc is the *Ballade* which Grieg wrote on the death of his parents. This recording can hold its own with the best in this healthy area of the catalogue – even if there are moments where Steen-Nøkleberg seems too discursive. Yet what an imaginative colour he produces in the *Adagio* variation when the music suddenly melts *pianissimo*. *8 550884*: The *Norwegian Peasant Dances* are amazing pieces for their period, and though their audacity and dissonance were later overtaken by Bartók, they still retain their capacity to surprise. The playing conveys the extraordinary character and originality of these pieces as do few others. The smaller pieces on this record – and on its companions – are full of rewards. No collector should be without the celebrated Gilels anthology of *Lyric Pieces* and Leif Ove Andsnes's single disc containing the Sonata, which are more strongly profiled readings. However, the claims of these outstanding discs are strong.

Additional recommendation ...

...Norwegian Folksongs, Op. 66 – Cattle call; Tomorrow you marry; Cradle Song; I wander deep in thought. Norwegian Peasant Dances, Op. 72 – Halling from the hills; Prillar from the church-play; Gangar; Knut Luråsens Halling I; The goblin's bridal procession. *Coupled with works by various composers.* **Leif Ove Andsnes** (pf). EMI Ⓕ CDC5 56541-2 (68 minutes: DDD: 6/98). *See review in the Collections section; refer to the Index.*

Grieg Piano Sonata in E minor, Op. 7. Six Poetic Tone-pictures, Op. 3 – Nos. 4-6. Four Album Leaves, Op. 28 – No. 1 in A flat major; No. 4 in C sharp minor. Agitato. Lyric Pieces – Book 3, Op. 43; Book 5, Op. 54. **Leif Ove Andsnes** (pf). Virgin Classics Ⓕ VC7 59300-2 (72 minutes: DDD: 6/93). Recorded 1992.

Andsnes was 22 when he recorded Grieg's Sonata – exactly the composer's age when he wrote it. Despite the heroic opening, Andsnes does not save the first movement from sounding repetitive. It is the two inner movements that display real character and imagination and the pianist rises to the occasion in both. The finale is stunningly played. He is to be heard at his very best in the *Lyric Pieces*, Op. 43, which is the most familiar set of all. One relishes the glinting colours in "Butterfly", the simple heartfelt yearnings of "Solitary Wanderer" and the delightful twittering energy of the "Little Bird". Here is a pianist with sufficient insight and subtlety not to feel the need to prettify the music. This well-crafted CD has pleasant piano sound, not overclose in impact.

Additional recommendation ...

...Book 1, Op. 12 – No. 3, Watchman's Song; No. 5, Folksong; No. 7, Albumleaf; No. 8, National Song. Book 2, Op. 38 – No. 1, Berceuse; No. 3, Melody; No. 7, Waltz. Book 4, Op. 47. Book 5, Op. 54. Book 6, Op. 57. Book 7, Op. 62. Book 8, Op. 65. Book 9, Op. 68 – No. 1, Sailor's Song; No. 2, Grandmother's Minuet; No. 3, At your feet; No. 4, Evening in the Mountains; No. 5, Cradle Song. **Daniel Adni** (pf). EMI Forte CZS5 68634-2 (two discs: 145 minutes: ADD: 5/96).

Grieg Lyric Pieces – Arietta, Op. 12 No. 1. Berceuse, Op. 38 No. 1. Butterfly, Op. 43 No. 1. Solitary traveller, Op. 43 No. 2. Album Leaf, Op. 47 No. 2. Melody, Op. 47 No. 3. Norwegian Dance, "Halling", Op. 47 No. 4. Nocturne, Op. 54 No. 4. Scherzo, Op. 54 No. 5. Homesickness, Op. 57 No. 6. Brooklet, Op. 62 No. 4. Homeward, Op. 62 No. 6. In ballad vein, Op. 65 No. 5. Grandmother's Minuet, Op. 68 No. 2. At your feet, Op. 68 No. 3. Cradle Song, Op. 68 No. 5. Once upon a time, Op. 71 No. 1. Puck, Op. 71 No. 3. Gone, Op. 71 No. 6. Remembrances, Op. 71 No. 7. **Emil Gilels** (pf). DG The Originals Ⓜ 449 721-2GOR (56 minutes: ADD: 10/87). From 2530 476 (3/75). ⓰⓰⓰

This record is something of a gramophone classic. The great Russian pianist Emil Gilels, an artist of staggering technical accomplishment and intellectual power, here turns his attention to Grieg's charming miniatures. He brings the same insight and concentration to these apparent trifles as he did to towering masterpieces of the classic repertoire. The programme proceeds chronologically and one can appreciate the gradual but marked development in Grieg's harmonic and expressive language – from the folk-song inspired early works to the more progressive and adventurous later ones. Gilels's fingerwork is exquisite and the sense of total involvement with the music almost religious in feeling. This is a wonderful recording: pianistic perfection.

Additional recommendation ...

...Complete Works for Solo Piano. **Gerhard Oppitz** (pf). RCA Victor Red Seal Ⓕ 09026 61568/9-2 (two sets of three and four discs: 214 and 305 minutes: DDD: 4/94). *09026 61568-2:* Lyric Pieces – Book 1, Op. 12; Book 2, Op. 38; Book 3, Op. 43; Book 4, Op. 47; Book 5, Op. 54; Book 6, Op. 57; Book 7, Op. 62; Book 8, Op. 65; Book 9, Op. 68; Book 10, Op. 71. *09026 61569-2:*

Six Poetic Tone-pictures, Op. 3. 25 Norwegian Folksongs and Dances, Op. 17. Three Pictures from life in the country, Op. 19. Ballade in G minor in the form of Variations on a Norwegian Melody, Op. 24. Four Piano Pieces, Op. 1. Piano Sonata in E minor, Op. 7. Two Improvisations on Norwegian Folksongs, Op. 29. Transcriptions of Original Songs, Opp. 41 and 52. Four Humoresques, Op. 6. Four Album Leaves, Op. 28. Stimmungen, Op. 73. Three Piano Pieces. Holberg Suite, Op. 40. 19 Norwegian Folksongs, Op. 66. Funeral March for Rikard Nordraak, CW117. 17 Norwegian Peasant Dances, Op. 72.

Grieg Peer Gynt – The Bridal March passes by; Prelude; In the Hall of the Mountain King; Solveig's Song; Prelude; Arab Dance; Anitra's Dance; Prelude; Solveig's Cradle Song[a]. Symphonic Dances, Op. 64 – Allegretto grazioso[b]. In Autumn, Op. 11[c]. Old Norwegian Romance with Variations, Op. 51[d]. [a]**Ilse Hollweg** (sop); [a]**Beecham Choral Society; Royal Philharmonic Orchestra / Sir Thomas Beecham.** EMI Studio Plus ⓜ CDM7 64751-2* (76 minutes: ADD). Items marked [a] from HMV ASD258 (1/59), [b]HMV ASD518 (4/63), [cd]Columbia 22CX1363 (9/56). Recorded 1956-57.

Grieg's incidental music was an important integral part of Ibsen's *Peer Gynt* and from this score Grieg later extracted the two familiar suites. This recording of excerpts from *Peer Gynt* goes back to 1957 but still sounds well and is most stylishly played. He included the best known ("Anitra's Dance" is a delicate gem here) together with "Solveig's Song" and "Solveig's Cradle Song". Sir Thomas uses Ilse Hollweg to advantage, her voice suggesting the innocence of the virtuous and faithful peasant heroine. There is also an effective use of the choral voices which are almost inevitably omitted in ordinary performances of the two well-known orchestral suites: the male chorus of trolls in the "Hall of the Mountain King" are thrilling, and the women in the "Arab Dance" are charming. The other two pieces are well worth having too; *Symphonic Dances* is a later, freshly pastoral work, while the overture *In Autumn* is an orchestral second version of an early piece for piano duet. This reissue is further enhanced by the first release in stereo of the *Old Norwegian Romance*.

Additional recommendations ...

...Peer Gynt – complete. Sigurd Jorsalfar – incidental music, Op. 22. **Soloists; Gösta Ohlin's Vocal Ensemble; Pro Musica Chamber Choir; Gothenburg Symphony Orchestra / Neeme Järvi.** DG Ⓕ 423 079-2GH2 (two discs: 124 minutes: DDD: 2/88).   Ⓖ

...Peer Gynt – excerpts. **Soloists; San Francisco Symphony Chorus and Orchestra / Herbert Blomstedt.** Decca Ⓕ 425 448-2DH (73 minutes: DDD: 3/90).

...Peer Gynt Suites – No. 1, Op. 46; No. 2, Op. 55. Land Sighting, Op. 31[a]. Olav Trygvason, Op. 50[b]. [b]**Randi Stene** (mez); [b]**Anne Gjevang** (contr); [ab]**Håkan Hagegård** (bar); [ab]**Gothenburg Symphony Chorus; Gothenburg Symphony Orchestra / Neeme Järvi.** DG Grieg Edition Ⓕ 437 523-2GH (73 minutes: DDD: 6/93).

...Peer Gynt Suites Nos. 1 and 2. **Saeverud** Peer Gynt Suites Nos. 1[a] and 2. [a]**Anne-Margrethe Eikaas** (sop); **Norwegian Radio Orchestra / Ari Rasilainen.** Finlandia Ⓕ 0630-17675-2 (74 minutes: DDD: 5/98). *See review under Saeverud; refer to the Index.*

Grieg Haugtussa, Op. 67. Two brown eyes, Op. 5 No. 1. I love but thee, Op. 5 No. 3. A swan, Op. 25 No. 2. With a waterlily, Op. 25 No. 4. Hope, Op. 26 No. 1. Spring; Op. 33 No. 2. Beside the stream, Op. 33 No. 5. From Monte Pincio, Op. 39 No. 1. Six Songs, Op. 48. Spring showers, Op. 49 No. 6. While I wait, Op. 60 No. 3. Farmyard Song, Op. 61 No. 3. **Anne Sofie von Otter** (mez); **Bengt Forsberg** (pf). DG Grieg Anniversary Edition Ⓕ 437 521-2GH (68 minutes: DDD: 6/93). Texts and translations included. Recorded 1992. *Gramophone classical 100. Gramophone Editor's choice. Selected by Sounds in Retrospect. Gramophone* Award Winner 1993.   ⒼⒼⒼ

With performances like this, Grieg in his celebratory year emerged as a first-rank composer in this genre. Anne Sofie von Otter is at the peak of her powers, glorying in this repertoire which she obviously loves and knows intimately. Take the *Haugtussa* cycle, which Grieg considered his greatest achievement in this sphere of writing. Von Otter projects her imagination of the visionary herd-girl with absolute conviction. She is no less successful in the German settings that follow. The sad depths of *One day, my thought* from Six Songs, Op. 48, also set memorably by Wolf in his *Spanish Songbook*, the hopelessness of Goethe's *The time of roses* (Op. 48 No. 5), a setting of great beauty, are encompassed with unfettered ease, but so are the lighter pleasures of *Lauf der Welt*. Even the familiar *A dream* (Op. 48 No. 6) emerges as new in von Otter's daringly big-boned reading. Throughout, her readings are immeasurably enhanced by the imaginative playing of Bengt Forsberg. They breathe fresh life into *A swan* and in the almost as familiar *With a waterlily*, another superb Ibsen setting, the questing spirit expressed in the music is marvellously captured by the performers. And there are more pleasures to come. A superb account of *Hope*, a wistful, sweetly voiced and played account of *Spring*, the charming, teasing *While I wait* and a deeply poetic reading of the justly renowned *From Monte Pincio* are just three more definitive interpretations. This should be regarded as a 'must' for any collector of songs, indeed a collector of any kind.

Additional recommendations ...

...Six Songs with Orchestra[a]. The First Meeting, Op. 21 No. 1[a]. The Mountain Thrall[b]. Before a Southern Convent, Op. 20[c]. Bergljot, Op. 42[d]. [ac]**Barbara Bonney** (sop); [ac]**Randi Stene** (mez); [ab]**Håkan Hagegård** (bar); [d]**Rut Tellefsen** (narr); [c]**Gothenburg Symphony Chorus and Orchestra / Neeme Järvi.** DG Grieg Edition Ⓕ 437 519-2GH (61 minutes: DDD: 6/93).

...Two brown eyes; I love but thee. Op. 33 – No. 2, Last Spring; No. 9, At Rondane. Songs and
Ballads, Op. 9 – No. 4, Outward Bound. **Schubert** Die schöne Müllerin, D759. **Aksel Schiøtz**
(ten); **Gerald Moore, Folmer Jensen** (pfs). Danacord mono Ⓕ DACOCD452*
(75 minutes: ADD: 4/97). *See review in the Collections section; refer to the Index.*
...Songs, Op. 49 – No. 3, Kind greetings, fair ladies; No. 6, Spring showers. The Poet's farewell,
Op. 18 No. 3. *Coupled with works by various composers.* **Aksel Schiøtz** (ten) with various artists.
Danacord mono Ⓕ DACOCD453* (69 minutes: ADD: 4/97).
...Two brown eyes; I love but thee. Margaret's Cradle Song, Op. 15 No. 1. Four Songs, Op. 21.
Op. 25 – No. 2, A swan; No. 6, A bird-song. Op. 26 – No. 1, Hope; No. 2, I walked one balmy
summer eve; No. 4, With a primrose. Op. 33 – No. 2, Last Spring; No. 9, At Rondane. Op. 39 –
No. 1, From Monte Pincio; No. 3, Upon a grassy hillside. Six Songs, Op. 48. Spring showers,
Op. 49 No. 6. To her II, Op. 59 No. 4. While I wait, Op. 60 No. 3. Peer Gynt – Solveig's Song;
Solveig's Cradle Song. The Princess. **Bodil Arnesen** (sop); **Erling Eriksen** (pf).
Naxos Ⓢ 8 553781 (70 minutes: DDD: 5/97).

Further listening ...
...Funeral March in memory of Rikard Nordraak. In Autumn, Op. 11. Old Norwegian Romance
with Variations, Op. 51. Symphony in C minor. **Gothenberg Symphony Orchestra / Neeme Järvi.**
DG 427 321-2GH (6/89).   Ⓖ
...Holberg Suite, Op. 40. *Coupled with works by various composers.* **Israel Chamber Orchestra /**
Yoav Talmi. Chandos CHAN8593 (8/88).
...Lyric Pieces – Book 5, Op. 54; Book 6, Op. 57; Book 7, Op. 62. **Peter Katin** (pf).
Unicorn-Kanchana Souvenir UKCD2034 (11/90).
...Lyric Pieces – Book 8, Op. 65; Book 9, Op. 68; Book 10, Op. 71. **Peter Katin** (pf).
Unicorn-Kanchana Souvenir UKCD2035 (2/91).

Charles Griffes   American 1884-1920

Suggested listening ...
...Evening song. An old song re-sung. The lament of Ian the Proud. Song of the dagger.
Coupled with works by other composers. **Samuel Ramey** (bar); **Warren Jones** (pf).
Sony Classical SK68339 (2/97). *See review in the Collections section; refer to the Index.*

Wilhelm Grosz   Austrian 1894-1939

Suggested listening ...
...Afrika Songs, Op. 29[a]. Rondels, Op. 11[b]. Bänkel und Balladen, Op. 31[c]. Hit Songs (arr. Ziegler)[d]
– Harbour Lights; When Budapest was young; Along the Santa Fe trail; Isle of Capri; Red Sails
in the Sunset. [ab]**Cynthia Clarey** (sop); [a]**Jake Gardner** (bar); [c]**Andrew Shore** (bass-bar); [d]**Kelly**
Hunter (sngr); **Matrix Ensemble / Robert Ziegler.** Decca Entartete Musik 455 116-2DH (7/97).

Heinz Karl Gruber   Austrian 1943

Gruber Frankenstein!![a]. Nebelsteinmusik[b]. Three Mob Pieces[c]. Gomorra – Three songs[ac].
[b]**Ernst Kovacic** (vn); [ab]**Salzburg Camerata Academica / Franz Welser-Möst;** [c]**London Mob**
Ensemble / [c]**Heinz Karl Gruber** ([a]bar). EMI Ⓕ CDC5 56441-2 (64 minutes: DDD: A/97).
Texts and translations included. Recorded 1996-97.
Frankenstein!!, subtitled "a pan-demonium for baritone *chansonnier* and orchestra", is hugely
entertaining and devilishly clever, and it has proved very popular in the 20 years since Gruber wrote
it. It is a setting of children's rhymes, mostly comically scary or gruesome, by the Viennese poet
H.C. Artmann (here performed in an excellent English translation). The music touches all those areas
of culture to which the texts (in which Frankenstein and Dracula rub shoulders with James Bond and
Goldfinger) refer. So pop music and hints of folk-song, Kurt Weill and Hanns Eisler are all thrown
into the mix to fuse with Stravinskian neo-classicism and the Viennese cabaret tradition. The humour
is black but quizzically genial and Gruber's own performance is gleefully exuberant. The remarkable
Nebelsteinmusik is a violin concerto written for Ernst Kovacic. It is intended as a homage to Gruber's
teacher, Gottfried von Einem, and uses a brief melodic tag derived from the musical letter of his
name, as well as quotations from his works and from Berg's *Lyric Suite.* Gruber's mature music is as
tonal as von Einem's but using Bergian techniques in a tonal context is one of the ways, along with
copious reference to popular styles, in which he has contrived a style which is approachable, personal
and rich. The slow movement of *Nebelsteinmusik* is quite gorgeous, dreamily lyrical and with a wistful
quality that makes you expect it to reveal itself as based on a popular melody. No one but a hard-line
modernist could listen to the *Three Mob Pieces* without smiling from sheer pleasure. They are 'light'
music but not in the least trivial. The three songs from Gruber's long-gestated opera, *Gomorra,*
powerfully whet one's appetite for the complete work. Admirable performances, finely recorded. A
first-class introduction to a composer whose delightful wit should not blind one to his importance.

Further listening ...
...Der rote Teppich wird ausgerollt[c]. Violin Concerto No. 1[ac]. Sechs Episoden (aus einer
  unterbrochenen Chronik), Op. 20[b]. Four Pieces, Op. 11[a]. Bossa Nova, Op. 21e[ab]. [a]**Ernst Kovacic**
  (vn); [b]**Paul Crossley** (pf); [c]**London Sinfonietta / Heinz Karl Gruber**. Largo 5124 (9/94).

Sofia Gubaidulina   USSR/Russian 1931

Gubaidulina Chaconne. Piano Sonata. Musical Toys. Introitus: Concerto for Piano and
  Chamber Orchestra[a]. **Andreas Haefliger** (pf); [a]**North German Radio Philharmonic Orchestra /**
  Bernhard Klee. Sony Classical Ⓕ SK53960 (72 minutes: DDD: 5/95). Recorded 1993.   Ⓖ
This is an ideal disc for listeners who admire Gubaidulina's recent music and wonder where she
started from. The earlier works may be less 'polystylistic' than those of her near-contemporary Alfred
Schnittke, but there is a distinctive pluralism to be heard which makes her ability to give these
compositions an unmistakable coherence all the more remarkable. The *Chaconne* (1962) is a student
piece in which coherence is put at risk by a rather episodic form. What compensates is the energy of
invention, the presence of a powerful musical imagination which makes the Shostakovich of that
vintage seem relatively conventional. The Sonata (1965) has a dangerously diffuse first movement, but
a superb, darkly eloquent *Adagio* and an incisive finale rescue the piece and make the overall
experience a memorable one. The echoes of Prokofiev do nothing to dilute Gubaidulina's originality.
After the collection of delightfully direct and far-from-lightweight pieces for children entitled *Musical
Toys* (1969), *Introitus* (1978) offers a characteristically quirky mixture of the ritualistic and the
rhapsodic. Scale figures may be made to do more thematic work than a composition of this emotional
range can bear without strain, yet the work's striking textures and approachably radical variety of
harmonic contexts ensures that, in the end, all the diverse elements balance out. Andreas Haefliger
responds wholeheartedly to Gubaidulina's frequently demanding piano writing. The solo works are
very resonantly recorded, but there is no distortion and the immediacy of the sound seems apt.
Additional recommendation ...
...Introitus: Concerto for Piano and Chamber Orchestra. *Coupled with works by various composers.*
  Alexei Lubimov (pf); **Deutsche Kammerphilharmonie, Bremen / Heinrich Schiff.**
  Erato Ⓕ 0630-12709-2 (64 minutes: DDD: 8/96).

Gubaidulina String Quartet No. 2.
Kurtág String Quartet No. 1, Op. 1. Hommage à Milhály András, Op. 13. Officium breve in
  memoriam Andreae Szervánzky, Op. 28.
Lutosławski String Quartet. **Arditti Quartet** (Irvine Arditti, David Alberman, vns;
  Levine Andrade, va; Rohan de Saram, vc). Auvidis Montaigne Ⓕ MO789007
  (72 minutes: DDD: 4/92). Recorded 1990.
The need for a personal tone of voice is a quality all three of these eastern European composers well
understand. Lutosławski's quartet (1964) came at a crucial time in his development, as the first work
to relate his new technique of aleatory counterpoint (in which the pitches but not necessarily the
rhythms are prescribed) to a traditional, abstract genre. Compared to the best of his later works the
quartet is perhaps too long-drawn-out, but this highly expressive and strongly disciplined
performance makes an excellent case for it. Alongside the Lutosławski the three works by György
Kurtág sound remarkably intense and concentrated, yet with a lyricism that prevents their evident
austerity from growing merely arid, and which makes the reference to a tonal melody in the *Officium
breve* seem natural as well as touching. The world of consonant harmony is also evoked by
Gubaidulina, not as an expression of regret for the irretrievable past but as a way of extending her
own essentially modern language. There is a special sense of personal certainty and confidence about
all the music on this well-recorded disc. It needs no special pleading, but the commanding authority
of the Arditti Quartet's performance is still something to marvel at.
Further listening ...
...Concerto for Bassoon and Low Strings[a]. Concordanza. Detto II[b]. [a]**Harri Ahmas** (bn);
  [b]**Ilkka Pälli** (vc); **Lahti Chamber Ensemble / Osmo Vänskä**. BIS CD636 (6/94).
...Offertorium[a]. Hommage à T.S. Eliot[b]. [b]**Christine Whittlesey** (sop); [a]**Gidon Kremer**, [b]**Isabelle van**
  Keulen (vns); [b]**Tabea Zimmermann** (va); [b]**David Geringas** (vc); [b]**Alois Posch** (db); [b]**Eduard Brunner**
  (cl); [b]**Klaus Thunemann** (bn); [b]**Radovan Vlatkovič** (hn); [a]**Boston Symphony Orchestra /**
  Charles Dutoit. DG 427 336-2GH (9/89).   Ⓖ
...Pro et Contra. *Coupled with* **Firsova** Cassandra, Op. 60. **BBC National Orchestra of Wales /**
  Tadaaki Otaka. BIS CD668 (11/94).
...Silenzio[abc]. In Erwartung[de]. De profundis[a]. Classical Accordion Sonata, "Et expecto"[a].
  [a]**Geir Draugsvoll** (accordion); [b]**Arne Balk Møller** (vn); [c]**Henrik Brendstrup** (vc);
  [d]**Rascher Saxophone Quartet**; [e]**Kroumata Percussion Ensemble**. BIS CD710 (11/95).
...Symphony "Stimmen ... Verstummen". Stufen. **Royal Stockholm Philharmonic Orchestra /**
  Gennadi Rozhdestvensky. Chandos CHAN9183 (8/93).
...Allegro rustico. Sounds of the Forest. *Coupled with works by various composers.*
  Leslie Newman (fl); **Amanda Hurton** (pf).
  Cala CACD88026 (6/96). *See review in the Collections section; refer to the Index.*

...In croce[a]. Ten Preludes (Etudes). *Coupled with* **Ustvolskaya** Grand (Bolshoi) Duet[b].
Maya Beiser (vc); [a]**Dorothy Papadakos** (org); [b]**Christopher Oldfather** (pf).
Koch International Classics 37258-2 (11/95).
...In croce[a]. Seven Last Words[b]. Five Pieces, "Silenzio"[c]. [bc]**Kathrin Rabus** (vn); [ac]**Maria Kliegel** (vc);
[ac]**Elsbeth Moser** (accordion); [b]**Camerata Transsylvanica / György Selmeczi.** Naxos 8 553557 (6/96).
...Jetzt immer Schnee[ad]. Perception[bc]. [a]**Stella Kleindienst** (sop); [b]**Siegfried Lorenz** (bar); [c]**Leonid
Stasov** (spkr); [d]**Netherlands Chamber Choir; Schoenberg Ensemble / Reinbert de Leeuw.**
Philips 442 531-2PH (4/95). **Ⓠ**

Pierre Guédron
French ?1570/75-1619/20

Suggested listening ...
...Airs de cour. **Claudine Ansermet** (sop); **Paolo Cherici** (lte). Symphonia SY96153 (5/98).

Francisco Guerrero
Spanish 1528-1599

Guerrero Missa Sancta et immaculata. Hei mihi, Domine. Trahe me post te, Virgo Maria.
Magnificat septimi toni. Vexilla Regis. O lux beata Trinitas. Lauda mater ecclesia. **Westminster
Cathedral Choir / James O'Donnell.** Hyperion Ⓔ CDA66910 (65 minutes: DDD: 12/97). Texts
and translations included. Recorded 1997. **ⒼⒼ**
Quite why Guerrero has had to wait so long in the wings of musical history is a complicated story,
having partly to do with the inaccessibility of editions and partly the reputation with which he was
left, until recently, by music historians. This disc should help to introduce Guerrero as composer
whose music is exhilarating, full of variety and spiritually uplifting. The *Missa Sancta et immaculata,*
based as it is on Morales's sublime motet of that name, is magnificent. The motet's melodic contours
determine the character of the Mass, Guerrero finding infinitely subtle ways to vary and embellish his
model and fully exploiting his grasp of vocal colour. The two motets, *Hei mihi, Domine* and *Trahe me
post te,* show a more intimate, contemplative aspect of Guerrero, but what really brings one up with
a jolt are the three hymns, *Vexilla Regis, O lux beata Trinitas* and *Lauda mater ecclesia,* which have
been provided with the appropriate *alternatim* chants and which reveal themselves to be absolutely
wonderful music. *Vexilla Regis* is a miniature drama running the gamut of emotions and lasting
nearly 11 minutes. *Lauda mater ecclesia,* a magnificent text for the Feast of St Mary Magdalen, is a
flash of lightning. Westminster Cathedral Choir are on their very best form, incisive and thrilling.
Further listening ...
...Ave Virgo sanctissima. *Coupled with works by various composers.* **The Hilliard Ensemble.**
Virgin Classics Veritas VED5 61394-2 (11/97). *See review in the Collections section;*
refer to the Index.
...Maria Magdalene. *Coupled with works by* **Lobo** The Tallis Scholars / Peter Phillips.
Gimell 454 931-2PH (12/97). *Gramophone Editor's choice. See review under Lobo;*
refer to the Index.
...Niño Dios, d'amor herido. Prado verde y florido. Huyd, huyd. Si tu penas no pruevo. Todo
quanto pudo dar. *Coupled with works by various composers.* **La Columbina Ensemble.**
Accent ACC95111D (11/96). *See review in the Collections section; refer to the Index.*
...O Doctor optime. Instrumental and organ works by Cabézon, Rogier, Guerrero, Gombert and
Santa María. *Coupled with* **Morales** Mass for the feast of St Isidore of Seville. **Gabrieli Consort
and Players / Paul McCreesh.** Archiv Produktion 449 143-2AH (8/96). *Gramophone Editor's
record of the month. See review under Morales; refer to the Index.* **ⒼⒼ**
...Sacrae Cantiones. **La Capella Reial de Catalunya; Hespèrion XX / Jordi Savall.**
Auvidis Astrée E8766 (10/93). **✍**

Guillaume le Vinier
French c1190-1245

Suggested listening ...
...Pastourelle: Valuru, valuraine. *Coupled with works by various composers.* **Anne Azéma** (sop/spkr);
vocal and instrumental ensemble.
Erato 0630-17072-2 (12/97). **✍** *See review in the Collections section; refer to the Index.*

Alexandre Guilmant
French 1837-1911

Guilmant Organ Symphony No. 1 in D minor, Op. 42.
Poulenc Organ Concerto in G minor.
Widor Organ Symphony No. 5 in F minor, Op. 42 No. 1. **Ian Tracey** (org); **BBC Philharmonic
Orchestra / Yan Pascal Tortelier.** Chandos Ⓔ CHAN9271 (80 minutes: DDD: 11/94).
Played on the organ of Liverpool Cathedral. Recorded 1993. **ⒼⒼ**

As horoscope writers in some magazines might put it, with Yan Pascal Tortelier and the BBC Philharmonic in conjunction with Ian Tracey and the Liverpool Cathedral organ within the orbit of Chandos the earth is bound to move for you. And so it does. The Guilmant is one of those great spectaculars which thrives in just such a steamy acoustic environment, but Tortelier with his incisive, thrusting direction ensures that while there is vivid aural spectacle, musical integrity is preserved with quite remarkable clarity and co-ordination. The BBC Philharmonic are magnificent and Tracey plays this great hulking brute of an organ with a surety of touch which comes not only from years of intimate experience, but from a deep understanding of what is needed. As for the Poulenc, this is a splendid performance, combining high drama with spiritual intensity, but misplaced in these gargantuan Liverpudlian cavities. The sound is just too beefy and Poulenc's lightning changes of mood are largely masked by an all-enveloping acoustic. Tracey's true colours are shown off to the full in the Widor – and what an inspired piece of programme planning to include this famous solo organ symphony as the meat in the sandwich between works for organ and orchestra.

Further listening ...
...Deuxième Offertoire sur des Noëls, Op. 33. *Coupled with works by various composers.* **Peter King** (org).
   Christopher Herrick (org).
   Hyperion CDA66917 (8/97). *See review in the Collections section; refer to the Index.*
...Marche funèbre et chant séraphique, Op. 17 No. 3. *Coupled with works by various composers.*
   Gerard Brooks (org).
   Priory PRCD558 (4/98). *See review in the Collections section; refer to the Index.*

Jesús Guridi   Spanish 1886-1961

Suggested listening ...
...Triptico del Buen Pastor. *Coupled with works by various composers.* **Peter King** (org).
   Priory PRCD618. *See review in the Collections section; refer to the Index.*

Ivor Gurney   British 1890-1937

Suggested listening ...
...Sleep. Down by the salley gardens. Hawk and Buckle. *Coupled with works by various composers.*
   Ian Partridge (ten); **Stephen Roberts** (bar); **Clifford Benson** (pf).
   Hyperion CDA66015 (9/91). *See review in the Collections section; refer to the Index.*

Barry Guy   British 1947

Suggested listening ...
...Buzz. *Coupled with works by various composers.* **Fretwork.**
   Virgin Classics VC5 45217-2 (12/97). *See review in the Collections section; refer to the Index.*
...Un coup de dés. *Coupled with works by various composers.* **Barry Guy** (db); **The Hilliard Ensemble.**
   ECM New Series 453 259-2 (1/97). *See review in the Collections section; refer to the Index.*

Pavel Haas   Czechoslovakian 1899-1944

P. Haas String Quartets – No. 2, Op. 7, "From the Monkey Mountains"; No. 3, Op. 15.
Krása String Quartet. **Hawthorne Quartet** (Ronan Lefkowitz, Si-Jing Huang, vns; Mark Ludwig, va; Sato Knudsen, vc). Decca Ⓕ 440 853-2DH (76 minutes: DDD: 3/94). Recorded 1993.
   Gramophone Editor's choice. Gramophone Award Winner 1995.   ⓖⓖ
Like Haas, Hans Krása was influenced by the modern movement, including neo-classicism, jazz and 'the new tonality', and both entered Theresienstadt in 1941 to travel to their deaths (on the same day) three years later in the gas chambers of Auschwitz. Of all Janáček's pupils it was Haas who absorbed rather than merely imitated his ideas. Something of the master's aphoristic, questing manner remains, but other than that the Quartet represents the mature Haas. An air of tension pervades the three movements, alternating passages of lyricism with tightly intertwining parts of harmonic complexity. Krása's Quartet also reveals a voice of exceptional talent. As a product of his studies with Zemlinsky its harmonic world leans more towards *fin de siècle* Vienna than his homeland. The central movement contains a marvellous section of burlesque on a theme from the overture to Smetana's *The Bartered Bride*, whilst the slow finale opens up a magical, almost mystical, twilight world that Zemlinsky himself would have been proud to have penned. Excellent performances and superb recording.

Further listening ...
...Scherzo triste, Op. 5. Scharlatan – suite, Op. 14. Symphony (orch. Zouhar).
   Brno State Philharmonic Orchestra / Israel Yinon. Koch Schwann 31521-2 (4/97).
...Wind Quintet, Op. 10. *Coupled with works by* **Foerster** and **Janáček** Aulos Wind Quintet.
   Koch Schwann Musica Mundi 310051 (6/93).

Manos Hadjidakis

Greek 1925

Suggested listening ...
...Pai efiye to treno. *Coupled with works by various composers.*
Angela Gheorghiu (sop); **Malcolm Martineau** (pf).
Decca 458 360-2DH (5/98). *See review in the Collections section; refer to the Index.*

Patrick Hadley

British 1899-1973

Suggested listening ...
...La belle dame sans merci[ac]. One Morning in Spring. Lenten Meditations[abc]. **Sainton** Nadir.
The Dream of the Marionette. [a]**Neill Archer** (ten); [b]**Stephen Richardson** (bass);
Philharmonia [c]**Chorus and Orchestra / Matthias Bamert.** Chandos CHAN9539 (10/97).

Reynaldo Hahn

Venezuelan/French 1875-1947

Hahn Douze rondels[abde]. Etudes latines[cdef]. Si mes vers avaient des ailes[a]. Paysage[d]. Rêverie[a].
Offrande[b]. Mai[d]. Infidelité[a]. Seule[b]. Les cygnes[d]. Nocturne[a]. Trois jours de vendange[d]. D'une
prison[a]. Séraphine[d]. L'heure exquise[a]. Fêtes galantes[b]. Quand la nuit n'est pas étoilée[b]. Le plus
beau présent[d]. Sur l'eau[b]. Le rossignol des lilas[a]. A Chloris[d]. Ma jeunesse[b]. Puisque j'ai mis ma
lèvre[d]. La nymphe de la source[b]. Au rossignol[a]. Je me souviens[b]. Mozart – Air de la lettre[a].
O mon bel inconnu – C'est très vilain d'être infidèle[a]. Ciboulette – C'est sa banlieue[a]; Nous avons
fait un beau voyage[bd]. Une revue – La dernière valse[a]. [a]**Dame Felicity Lott** (sop); [b]**Susan Bickley**
(mez); [c]**Ian Bostridge** (ten); [d]**Stephen Varcoe** (bar); **Graham Johnson,** [f]**Chris Gould** (pfs);
[e]**London Schubert Chorale / Stephen Layton.** Hyperion Ⓕ CDA67141/2 (two discs: 134 minutes:
DDD: 10/96). Texts and translations included. Recorded 1995.   Ⓖ
The two cycles, *Douze rondels* and *Etudes latines*, are linked by a common fascination with the past.
The *Douze rondels* were composed to poems in a medieval metre, which allowed Hahn to try his hand
at pastiche madrigals and courtly ballads. The *Etudes latines* cast their gaze back still further in time
to classical antiquity. For Hahn, as for Debussy in his *Bilitis* songs and Ravel in *Daphnis et Chloé*, that
era seemed to represent the ultimate in purity and sensuality rolled into one. This collection of ten
songs is a real discovery and rivals late Fauré, both in its refinement and mesmerizing simplicity of
utterance. The three main singers divide the songs between them. Apart from a few moments when
one would like a more substantial tone, Stephen Varcoe's light baritone suits Hahn very well and he
is a refreshingly unaffected interpreter, who sings with grace and feeling. Susan Bickley is better at the
larger canvas of a piece like *Quand la nuit n'est pas étoilée* than the more intimate songs but the most
celebrated pair of all Hahn's *mélodies* goes to Dame Felicity Lott, whose sympathy for the French
style could have no happier outlet. Both *Si mes vers avaient des ailes* and *L'heure exquise* are included
here, the latter if not an hour, then at least two-and-a-half minutes that are truly exquisite. They are
both beautifully sung and are undisturbed by the discomfort around the top of the stave that
sometimes mars Lott's singing elsewhere. At the end, she offers four operetta solos as an encore.
Graham Johnson's accompaniments are as sensitive, and his essays as detailed and perspicacious, as
ever. The piano could have been placed a little closer, but the voices have been well captured. One
small point: the individual notes to each song in the booklet-notes precede the poem rather than
follow it, which may take purchasers by surprise.
Further listening ...
...Piano Concerto in E major. *Coupled with* **Massenet** Piano Concerto in E flat major.
Stephen Coombs (pf); **BBC Scottish Symphony Orchestra / Jean-Yves Ossonce.**
Hyperion CDA66897 (7/97).
...Le bal de Béatrice d'Este – ballet suite. *Coupled with* **Poulenc** Sinfonietta. Aubade[a].
[a]**Julian Evans** (pf); **New London Orchestra / Ronald Corp.** Hyperion CDA66347 (10/89).

Johan Halvorsen

Norwegian 1864-1935

Suggested listening ...
...Entry March of the Boyars. *Coupled with works by various composers.* **New London Orchestra /
Ronald Corp.** Hyperion CDA66998 (3/98). *See review in the Collections section; refer to the Index.*

George Frederic Handel

German/British 1685-1759

Handel Concerti grossi, Op. 3, HWV312-17. **Tafelmusik / Jeanne Lamon.** Sony Classical Vivarte
Ⓕ SK52553 (60 minutes: DDD: 7/93). ✍ Recorded 1991. *Gramophone Editor's choice.*   Ⓖ
This is a fine issue impressive both for its stylistic fluency and its infectious response to Handel's
music which could not conceivably disappoint anyone. Tafelmusik play only the six concertos of

which Handel's authorship is undisputed. Goodman, for example, further included the Concerto in F major (No. 4*b*) which, though not by Handel, is an attractive piece in its own right. Having said that, it is the Sony version which, in respect of finesse and vitality, has the edge over all the competition. Where Tafelmusik scores is in the sheer virtuosity of its playing and the easy gracefulness of its phrasing. Strong accents are not over emphasized and, though vigorous, there is nothing aggressive in this approach to the music. Tafelmusik include a plucked string instrument among their continuo colloquium; they have large reinforcements at the top and bottom of the string texture and the performances have great radiance. The disc is beautifully recorded.

Additional recommendations ...

...Op. 3. Op. 6, HWV319-30. **Academy of St Martin in the Fields / Sir Neville Marriner.**
  Decca Serenata Ⓜ 444 532-2DM3 (three discs: 221 minutes: ADD).   ⒼⒼ
...Op. 3. **English Baroque Soloists / Sir John Eliot Gardiner.**
  Erato Ⓜ 2292-45981-2 (60 minutes: DDD). ✒
...Op. 3. **Brandenburg Consort / Roy Goodman.** Hyperion Ⓕ CDA66633 (77 minutes: DDD: 6/93). ✒
...Op. 3. **Handel and Haydn Society Orchestra / Christopher Hogwood.**
  L'Oiseau-Lyre Florilegium Ⓜ 444 165-2OM (60 minutes: DDD: 9/85). ✒
...Op. 3. Op. 6. **Vienna Concentus Musicus / Nikolaus Harnoncourt.**
  Teldec Ⓑ 4509 95500-2 (four discs: 237 minutes: ADD/DDD: 2/96).

Handel Concerti grossi, Op. 6, HWV319-30. **The English Concert / Trevor Pinnock.**
  Archiv Produktion Ⓕ 410 897/9-2AH (three discs, oas: 42, 61 and 58 minutes:
  DDD: 5/84, 6/85 and 8/85). ✒ From 2742 002 (11/82).   ⒼⒼ
  410 897-2AH – No. 1 in G major; No. 2 in F major; No. 3 in E minor; No. 4 in A minor.
  410 898-2AH – No. 5 in D major; No. 6 in G minor; No. 7 in B flat major; No. 8 in C minor.
  410 899-2AH – No. 9 in F major; No. 10 in D minor; No. 11 in A major; No. 12 in B minor.
Handel's 12 *Concerti grossi*, Op. 6, have from four to six movements and are mostly in *da chiesa* form, i.e. without dance movements. They were written within one month in the autumn of 1739 (an average of two movements per day!) and when a great composer is thus carried on the tide of urgent inspiration it usually shows, as it does here in the flow of felicitous invention and memorable tune-smithing. The range of musical idioms used throughout is impressive and to them all Handel imparts his own indelible and unmistakable stamp. Trevor Pinnock's account contains much that is satisfying: polished ensemble, effectively judged tempos, a natural feeling for phrase, and a buoyancy of spirit which serves Handel's own robust musical language very well. Crisp attack, a judicious application of appoggiaturas and tasteful embellishment further enhance these lively performances. Pinnock varies the continuo colour by using organ and harpsichord and also includes Handel's autograph (though not printed) oboe parts for Concertos Nos. 1, 2, 5 and 6; where they occur a bassoon is sensibly added to fulfil the customary three-part wind texture of the period. Recorded sound is clear and captures well the warm sonorities of the instruments.

Additional recommendations ...

...Nos. 1-12. **Montreal I Musici / Yuli Turovsky.**
  Chandos Ⓕ CHAN9004/6 (three discs: 163 minutes: DDD: 9/92).
...Nos. 1-6. **Boston Baroque / Martin Pearlman.** Telarc Ⓕ CD80253 (76 minutes: DDD: 10/92). ✒
...Nos. 1-12. **Handel and Haydn Society Orchestra / Christopher Hogwood.**
  L'Oiseau-Lyre Ⓕ 436 845-2OH3 (three discs: 157 minutes: DDD: 8/93). ✒   Ⓖ
...Nos. 1-6. **Orpheus Chamber Orchestra.**
  DG Ⓕ 447 733-2GH3 (three discs: 164 minutes: DDD: 11/96).

Handel Concerti grossi, Op. 6 – No. 1 in G major; No. 2 in F major; No. 3 in E minor; No. 4 in
  A minor; No. 5 in D major. **Collegium Musicum 90 / Simon Standage** (vn). Chandos Chaconne
  Ⓕ CHAN0600 (62 minutes: DDD: 9/97). ✒ Recorded 1996. *Gramophone Editor's choice.*
This is one of the relatively few current recordings of Handel's ever-fresh Op. 6 *Concerti grossi* on period instruments, and includes the oboe parts that Handel later added to Nos. 1, 2, 5 and 6. The performances are brimful of vitality – the sheer sense of enjoyment in the penultimate *Allegro* of No. 5, for example, is irresistible – and the clean articulation and light, predominantly detached style give the music buoyancy and help to bring out Handel's often mischievous twinkle in the eye. In the final movement of No. 2 the crisp *détaché* bowing is effectively contrasted with the gently throbbing second thematic idea. Speeds are generally brisk, with boldly vigorous playing in, for example, the *Allegro* in No. 3 and the fugue in No. 4, but Standage's team can also spin a tranquil broad line in No. 4's *Largo*. There is solidity in the E minor's fugue and a proper pomposity in the opening of the Fifth Concerto (borrowed from the *Ode for St Cecilia's Day*). Dynamics, throughout, are subtly graded and natural-sounding, and except in one final cadence ornamentation is confined to small cadential trills. A small reservation concerns the *Polonaise* of No. 3: the heavy prominence of the drones, though emphasizing the rustic flavour, seems excessive and forces the movement to lumber. Otherwise this is an immensely enjoyable disc.

Handel Organ Concertos[a] – Op. 4: No. 1 in G minor; No. 2 in B flat major; No. 3 in G minor;
  No. 4 in F major; No. 5 in F major; Op. 7: No. 1 in B flat major; No. 2 in A major; No. 3 in
  B flat major; No. 4 in D minor; No. 5 in G minor; No. 6 in B flat major. Harp Concerto in

B flat major, Op. 4 No. 6[b]. [a]**Paul Nicholson** (org); [b]**Frances Kelly** (hp); **The Brandenburg Consort /** **Roy Goodman** (hpd). Hyperion Ⓕ CDA67291/2 (two discs: 154 minutes: DDD: 3/98). ✍
Recorded 1996.
This recording was made at St Lawrence Whitchurch on the organ which Handel must certainly have played. It has recently been admirably restored, so it was a happy notion to use the restored instrument here. Under Paul Nicholson's hands (and in just one concerto, his feet), the organ sounds well. There is plenty of brightly glittering passagework – in the second movement of Op. 4 No. 1, for example, or the *Allegro* of Op. 4 No. 2 – and rich diapason sound in such movements as the passacaglia-like first of Op. 7 No. 1; while the softer side of the instrument is particularly appealing in Op. 4 No. 5, where Nicholson, doubtless conscious that this is a transcription of a recorder sonata, draws from it some very sweet sounds. It has of course a mechanical action, and here and there the incidental noise may be rather disconcerting. Still, it is authentic, so possibly we should be grateful to have it so clearly reproduced. There is some very lively and at times virtuoso playing from Nicholson in the quick movements, with sturdy rhythms – in the second movement of Op. 4 No. 3, for example, or the first of Op. 7 No. 3. Some of the dance movements too go with a good swing, such as the Bourrée at the end of Op. 7 No. 1 or the Gavotte of Op. 4 No. 3, and the same applies to the 3/8 finale of Op. 7 No. 4. Nicholson gives good, precise accounts of the various solo fugues and the transcriptions and improvisatory movements used here when Handel offered merely an ad lib. He is a thoughtful player; his added ornamentation is always musical and intelligent, and stylish too, and his treatment of the natural caesuras in the music is always dictated by the structure. In several movements, however, overdeliberate orchestral phrasing or accentuation can be damaging. This happens quite often and it sometimes affects Nicholson's playing. Op. 4 No. 6 is played on the harp, with some very delicate timing from Frances Kelly. The recording is bright and clear, capturing happily the acoustic of this moderate-sized church.
Additional recommendations ...
...Complete Organ Concertos. **Rudolf Ewerhart** (org); **Collegium Aureum.**
Deutsche Harmonia Mundi Ⓜ 05472 77246-2 (three discs: 208 minutes: ADD: 3/93). ✍
...Op. 4 – No. 1[ac]; No. 6[ab]. *Coupled with works by various composers.* [a]**Harp Consort /**
Andrew Lawrence-King ([b]double harp/[c]org). Deutsche Harmonia Mundi Ⓕ 05472 77366-2 (70 minutes: DDD: 4/98). ✍ *See review in the Collections section; refer to the Index.*

Handel Music for the Royal Fireworks, HWV351. Concertos – F major, HWV331; D major, HWV335*a*. Passacaille, Gigue and Minuet in G major. Occasional Suite in D major (both arr. Pinnock). **The English Concert / Trevor Pinnock** (hpd). Archiv Produktion Ⓕ 453 451-2AH (60 minutes: DDD: 1/98). ✍ Recorded 1996.
Trevor Pinnock uses George II's preferred scoring rather than Handel's – that is, just wind and percussion. What we know about the first performances of the work seems to indicate that Handel had his way and strings were used, along with a massed wind; probably the wind version was never heard in Handel's day. Well, here it is, with 24 oboes, 12 bassoons, double bassoon, nine each of trumpets and horns and six percussion. It's certainly rousing stuff, and a noble noise. With his direct and unaffected rhythm, Pinnock sets up a sturdy momentum for the Overture and the effect is grand and imposing. The dances too receive straightforward performances, with plenty of spirit and energy. This disc offers some welcome rarities. The F major Concerto is made up of versions of two movements from the D major part of the *Water Music*, here in F major; one is the movement generally labelled in the eighteenth century "Mr Handel's Water Peice", again, with some interesting and very characteristic differences from the familiar version and the other is the *Alla Hornpipe*. In between Pinnock plays, as a slow movement, an *Adagio* from Op. 3 No. 5. The D major Concerto consists of what are probably early versions – less purposefully shaped, but again with some highly characteristic touches – of two movements from the *Fireworks Music* with a version of a movement from a violin sonata, on the organ, in between. The Passacaille, Gigue and Minuet come from a trio sonata and the *Occasional Suite* draws on the *Occasional Oratorio* overture, the *Ariodante* ballet and music composed for *Joshua* and *Alessandro Severo*. It all works pretty well, although some of the music in this last is not the most distinguished of Handel. But the concertos especially are well worth having, and certainly George II's vision of the *Fireworks Music* is to be relished in its way.
Additional recommendations ...
...Music for the Royal Fireworks. Concerto grosso in C major, HWV318, "Alexander's Feast".
Solomon, HWV67 – Sinfonia. Belshazzar, HWV61 – Overture. Alceste – Grand Entrée.
Saul, HWV53 – Overture. Samson, HWV57 – Overture. **The English Concert / Trevor Pinnock.**
Archiv Produktion Ⓜ 447 279-2AMA (62 minutes: DDD). ✍
...Music for the Royal Fireworks. Coronation Anthems[a] – Zadok the priest; The King shall rejoice;
My heart is inditing; Let thy hand be strengthened. [a]**New College Choir, Oxford; King's Consort /**
Robert King. Hyperion Ⓕ CDA66350 (57 minutes: DDD: 12/89). ✍

Handel Water Music, HWV348-50. Music for the Royal Fireworks, HWV351.
Le Concert des Nations / Jordi Savall. Auvidis Astrée Ⓕ E8512 (74 minutes: DDD: 3/94). ✍
Recorded 1993. *Gramophone Editor's choice.*
Handel Water Music, HWV348-50. Il pastor fido – Suite, HWV8*c*. **Tafelmusik / Jeanne Lamon** (vn). Sony Classical Vivarte Ⓕ Ⓞ SK68257 (76 minutes: DDD: 7/96). ✍ Recorded 1995.

Of the period-instrument couplings of these two 'elemental' suites, Savall's must be placed at or near the top of the list. It is, however, strange that though the booklet-notes acknowledge that the *Water Music* falls into "three suites" and that the Suite in G major was probably played during supper, the recorded performance ends with that in F major (described as "Suite II") preceded by the rest ("Suite I") – neither the published nor the 'logical' order. The 74-minute duration of the disc does not allow the movements from the earlier Concerto in F to be included. There is the familiar retitling and juggling with the order of movements, so that, *inter alia*, the "Coro" in Suite III becomes "Menuet I" and is followed by the Menuet in G major ("Menuet II"). By now we should be used to such manipulations, and those who like to follow the score will be grateful that they do not extend to the *Music for the Royal Fireworks*. What splendid performances these are though, spirited, clean-edged and elegantly embellished – by a solo trumpet in the *Adagio* of the Overture of the *Fireworks Music*, where the preceding section is repeated as marked. The orchestral force is substantial, and the comparatively high-level recording and generous acoustic give a deliberate sense of being close to the performers – just as, on the Thames, King George III may have been in a barge adjacent to the musicians – rather than of hearing them from the riverside. Should the order of play disturb you it will be worth the trouble to programme your player to recognize your preferred one.

The jubilant spirit of the *Water Music* is splendidly captured in Sony's version. This young Canadian group have a good grasp of Handelian style, and lots of energy; there is plenty of vigour to their playing but no roughness. There are many nicely and unobtrusively managed details of timing and accent, yet always perfectly natural and justified from within. Their tempos in the main are on the quick side but not hurried. Their flowing *Andante* for the famous Air, which so readily becomes sticky if done slowly, is particularly likeable; here it sounds just right and no less expressive than usual. Only the D major *Lentement* seems heavy and ponderous, and perhaps the *Bourrée* that follows is also a little clumsily done. The horn playing, recorded well forward, is particularly impressive – clean and clear, with a fine ring; it would have sounded well across the Thames. The movements are done here with the F major music first, then the D major and G major mixed, an unusual arrangement these days but one that probably has Handel's authority: and it works well. Tafelmusik get through the *Water Music* in some 52 minutes, and there is room for a substantial suite of dances from the second version of *Il pastor fido*, when Handel added ballet music for the French dancer Marie Sallé and her troupe. These are charming and lively pieces and the final Chaconne, with its inventive textures, is particularly appealing. The sound here is a shade middle- and bottom-heavy, rather more so than in *The Water Music*, but again the playing is splendidly fresh and spirited.

Additional recommendations ...

...Water Music. **Simon Standage, Elizabeth Wilcock** (vns); **The English Concert / Trevor Pinnock** (hpd). Archiv Produktion ⓕ 410 525-2AH (54 minutes: DDD: 2/84) ✍

...Water Music. Music for the Royal Fireworks. **Orpheus Chamber Orchestra.** DG ⓕ 435 390-2GH (66 minutes: DDD: 11/92).

...Water Music. **English Baroque Soloists / Sir John Eliot Gardiner.** Philips ⓕ 434 122-2PH (53 minutes: DDD: 5/93). ✍ *Gramophone Editor's choice.*

...Water Music. **Amsterdam Baroque Orchestra / Ton Koopman.** Erato ⓕ 4509-91716-2 (56 minutes: DDD: 10/94). ✍

...Water Music. **English Chamber Orchestra / George Malcolm.** ASV Quicksilva ⓢ CDQS6152 (52 minutes: DDD: 6/95).

...Water Music. **Telemann** Overture-Suite in C major, TWV55:C3, "Hamburger Ebb und Fluth". **The King's Consort / Robert King.** Hyperion ⓕ CDA66967 (70 minutes: DDD: 10/97). ✍

Handel Trio Sonatas – Op. 2, HWV386-91; Op. 5, HWV396-402. **London Baroque** (Ingrid Seifert, Richard Gwilt, vns; Charles Medlam, vc; Richard Egarr, hpd). Harmonia Mundi ⓕ HMC90 1379 and 1389 (two discs, oas: 58 and 69 minutes: DDD: 4/93). ✍ Recorded 1991.

HMC90 1379 – Op. 2: No. 1 in B minor; No. 2 in G minor; No. 3 in B flat major; No. 4 in F major; No. 5 in G minor; No. 6 in G minor. *HMC90 1389* – Op. 5: No. 1 in A major; No. 2 in D major; No. 3 in E minor; No. 4 in G major; No. 5 in G minor; No. 6 in F major; No. 7 in B flat major.   Ⓖ

Handel's publisher, Walsh, printed the six Trio Sonatas, Op. 2, in about 1730, following them up in 1739 with seven further trios which he published as the composer's Op. 5. In each set Handel offered a choice of melody instruments though the writing suggests that he had violins foremost in mind. This is the way in which all 13 sonatas are played on these two separately available discs and the decision is a good one. The performances by London Baroque are poised, well shaped and susceptible to the subtle nuances of Handel's part-writing. Ingrid Seifert and Richard Gwilt are partners of long standing and their even dialogue, sometimes grave, sometimes lively and at other times playful, serves the music effectively. Tempos are well judged and phrases are eloquently shaped and articulately spoken. In all this the violinists are sympathetically supported by the continuo players who make their own vital contribution to clear textures and overall balance. Recorded sound is appropriately intimate, serving the sound character of the instruments themselves and evoking a chamber music ambience. The music, it hardly need be said, maintains a high level of craftsmanship and interest which will surely delight listeners.

Additional recommendations ...
...Op. 2 – Nos. 1 and 4. *Coupled with works by various composers*. **Palladian Ensemble.**
Linn Records Ⓕ CKD050 (63 minutes: DDD: 5/97). ⟋ *See review in the collections section; refer to the Index.*
...Op. 2 – Nos. 1, 3 and 6. Pensieri notturni di Filli, H134, "Nel dolce dell'oblio"[a]. Agrippina condotta a morire, HWV110, "Dunque sarà pur vero"[a]. [a]**Johanna Koslowsky** (sop); **Musica Alta Ripa.**
Dabringhaus und Grimm Ⓕ MDGL3399 (63 minutes: DDD: 1/98). ⟋

Handel Sonatas for Recorder and Continuo – No. 1 in G minor, HWV360[ad]; No. 2 in A minor, HWV362[ac]; No. 3 in C major, HWV365[ac]; No. 5 in F major, HWV369[ad]; No. 6 in B flat major, HWV377[ad]. Sonata for Flute and Continuo No. 3 in B minor, HWV367*b*[bc]. **Marion Verbruggen** ([a]rec/[b]fl); **Jaap ter Linden** (vc); **Ton Koopman** ([c]hpd/[d]org). Harmonia Mundi Ⓕ HMU90 7151 (58 minutes: DDD: 3/96). ⟋ Recorded 1994.
These are very lively and musically intelligent performances of the Handel recorder sonatas. All six are played here: the four from the published Op. 1 set, one from a Fitzwilliam manuscript, and also – a shade perversely – a flute sonata as published in Op. 1, played here on a flute, although it does in fact exist in a recorder version in a different key (the booklet supposes that the recorder version in D minor is used, but it is actually the B minor flute one). Well, that's a minor point. The major one is that this is outstandingly fine recorder playing, sweet in tone, pointed in articulation, perfectly tuned, technically very fluent, and informed by a really good understanding of the art of ornamentation. Add to that the fact that Marion Verbruggen has a real command of Handel's language and you will realize that this CD is out of the ordinary. Some of Ton Koopman's accompaniments are a little busy (half are on the organ, half on the harpsichord), but it's all part of the sense of lively music-making that runs through this attractive disc.

Handel Flute Sonatas – No. 1 in E minor, HWV359*b*; No. 2 in G major, HWV363*b*; No. 3 in B minor, HWV367*b*; No. 4 in A minor, HWV374; No. 5 in E minor, HWV375; No. 6 in B minor, HWV376; No. 7 in D major, HWV378; No. 8 in E minor, HWV379. **Barthold Kuijken** (fl); **Wieland Kuijken** (va da gamba); **Robert Kohnen** (hpd). Accent Ⓕ ACC9180D (73 minutes: DDD: 11/93). ⟋ Recorded 1991.
In this recording of solo flute sonatas Barthold Kuijken plays pieces unquestionably by Handel as well as others over which doubt concerning his authorship has been cast in varying degrees. Three of the Sonatas (HWV359*b*, 363*b* and 367*b*) were published as part of Handel's Op. 1 by Walsh in about 1730. Three others (HWV374-6) were published in a collection of pieces by various composers at about the same time. The remaining two (HWV378 and 379) have been preserved in manuscript form. HWV378, though attributed to Johann Sigmund Weiss, brother of the celebrated lutenist – his name appears on the manuscript – is now thought to be the product of Handel's pen. HWV379 is an oddity in that it consists of a somewhat haphazard compilation and rearrangement of movements from other of Handel's solo sonatas. Certainly not all of the pieces here were conceived for transverse flute – there are earlier versions of HWV363*b* and 367*b*, for example, for oboe and treble recorder, respectively; but we can well imagine that in Handel's day most, if not all, of these delightful sonatas were regarded among instrumentalists as more-or-less common property. Barthold Kuijken, with his eldest brother Wieland and Robert Kohnen, gives characteristically graceful and stylish performances of the music. Kuijken is skilful in matters of ornamentation and is often adventurous, though invariably within the bounds of good taste. Dance movements are brisk and sprightly though he is careful to preserve their poise, and phrases are crisply articulated. This is of especial benefit to movements such as the lively *Vivace* of the B minor Sonata (HWV367*b*) which can proceed rather aimlessly when too legato an approach is favoured; and the virtuosity of these players pays off in the *Presto (Furioso)* movement that follows. In short, a delightful disc which should please both Handelians and most lovers of baroque chamber music.

Additional recommendation ...
...Nos. 1, 2 and 3. Recorder Sonatas (played on flute) – No. 1 in G minor, HWV360; No. 2 in A minor, HWV362; No. 3 in C major, HWV365; No. 5 in F major, HWV369. **Robert Stallman** (fl); **Karl Bennion** (vc); **Edwin Swanborn** (hpd).
VAI Audio Ⓕ VAIA1091 (71 minutes: DDD: 7/95).

Handel Keyboard Suites, HWV426-33 – No. 2 in F major; No. 3 in D minor; No. 5 in E major. Chaconne in G major, HWV435.
D. Scarlatti Keyboard Sonatas – B minor, Kk27; D major, Kk29; E major, Kk206; A major, Kk212; C sharp minor, Kk247; D major, Kk491; A major, Kk537. **Murray Perahia** (pf).
Sony Classical Ⓕ SK62785 (69 minutes: DDD: 5/97). Recorded 1996. *Gramophone Editor's record of the month. Selected by Soundings. Gramophone Award Winner 1997.* ⒼⒼ
In his projection of line, mass and colour Perahia makes intelligent acknowledgment of the fact that none of this is piano music, but when it comes to communicating the forceful effects and the brilliance and readiness of finger for which these two great player-composers were renowned, inhibitions are thrown to the wind. Good! Nothing a pianist does in the *Harmonious Blacksmith* Variations in Handel's E major Suite, or the Air and Variations of the D minor Suite could surpass in vivacity and cumulative excitement what the expert harpsichordist commands, and you could say the same of

Scarlatti's D major Sonata, Kk29; but Perahia is extraordinarily successful in translating these with the daredevil 'edge' they must have. Faster and yet faster! In the Handel (more than in the Scarlatti) his velocity may strike you as overdone; but one can see the sense of it. It is quite big playing throughout, yet not inflated. Admirable is the way the piano is addressed, with the keys touched rather than struck, and a sense conveyed that the music is coming to us through the tips of the fingers rather than the hammers of the instrument. While producing streams of beautifully moulded and inflected sound Perahia is a wizard at making you forget the percussive nature of the apparatus. There are movements in the Handel where the musical qualities are dependent on instrumental sound, or contrasts of sound, which the piano just can't convincingly imitate. And in some of the Scarlatti one might have reservations about Perahia's tendency to idealize, to soften outlines (hard to avoid, given the piano's capacity for nuance) and to make the bite less incisive. You could of course raise a more fundamental objection and say that it begs the question: why do it on the piano at all? If you can't bear to hear it on anything other than the harpsichord this record won't be for you. But Perahia is an artist, not just a pianist, and if you don't rule out of court the prospect of these composers *transcribed* for the piano, he has an experience to offer that is vivid and musically considered at the highest level – and not at all second-best. The virtuosity is special indeed, and there is not a note that hasn't been savoured, thought about and placed with affection.

Handel Keyboard Suites, HWV426-33 – No. 1 in A major[b]; No. 2 in F major[a]; No. 3 in D minor[a]; No. 4 in E minor[b]; No. 5 in E major[a]; No. 6 in F sharp minor[b]; No. 7 in G minor[b]; No. 8 in F minor[a]. [a]**Sviatoslav Richter,** [b]**Andrei Gavrilov** (pfs). EMI Forte Ⓜ CZS5 69337-2 (two discs: 119 minutes: ADD: 11/96). From HMV SLS5234 (2/83). Recorded live in 1979.
Handel Keyboard Suites, HWV434; HWV436-41 – No. 1 in G minor[b]; No. 2 in D minor[c]; No. 3 in D minor[c]; No. 4 in E minor[a]; No. 5 in B flat major[c]; No. 6 in G major[b]; No. 7 in D minor[c]; No. 8 in G minor[b].
Beethoven Piano Sonata No. 17 in D minor, Op. 31 No. 2, "Tempest"[a]. [ab]**Sviatoslav Richter,** [c]**Andrei Gavrilov** (pfs). EMI Forte Ⓜ CZS5 69340-2 (two discs: 119 minutes: ADD: 11/96). Items marked [a] from HMV ASD450 (10/61), [b]SLS5234 (2/83) and recorded live in 1979.

Even by Sviatoslav Richter's Tours Festival standards, 1979 was a red-letter year. Then, partnered by his dazzling young compatriot Andrei Gavrilov, he played Handel's 16 Suites, offering performances of such quality that long-familiar reservations concerning their provenance and overall success evaporated as if by magic. From Richter and Gavrilov these baroque chains of dances (Allemande, Courante, Sarabande and Gigue, with the addition of other lighter possibilities) emerge with an unforgettable wit and vitality. Listen to Gavrilov in the First Suite's opening Prelude and you will hear an authentic as well as spirited emulation of the extempore style. Yet it is in the slow movements that Gavrilov (a sometimes too fearless athlete of the keyboard) achieves his greatest effect. In such hands, the Sarabande from the Seventh Suite becomes Handel's 'black pearl', if you like, and in the same grave and ceremonial dances from Suites Nos. 11 and 13, the music emerges like great mysterious pools of light. Richter's genius has rarely sounded more imperturbable and, whether he is playful and resilient in, say, the Fifth Suite's Gigue or poised and tonally translucent – a model of sense and sensibility – in the *Air con Variazione* (the famous *Harmonious Blacksmith* Variations), you are always aware of the musical artist first and the transcendental pianist second. Tempos are judicious rather than extreme, and even the most determined Beckmesser will surely find himself abandoning pencil and paper and succumbing to the spell of such serenity and affection. Finally, as a further reminder of Richter's unique stature there is his legendary 1961 disc of Beethoven's D minor Sonata, Op. 31 No. 2. Rarely can Beethoven's suggestion that we should read Shakespeare's *The Tempest* (a metaphysical fantasy concerned with the mystery of death and rebirth) have seemed more teasing or obtuse. In any event, from Richter the music retains its mystery, its eloquence 'contained' to the point of enigma. Richter 'does' so little and the result is hauntingly pure and distilled. The recordings, though occasionally showing their age, have been beautifully transferred.

Additional recommendations ...
...HWV426-33 – Nos. 1-8. **Scott Ross** (hpd).
Erato Ⓕ 2292-45452-2 (two discs: 112 minutes: DDD: 2/90). 🎯
...HWV426-33 – Nos. 5 and 7. *Coupled with works by* **D. Scarlatti** Martin Souter (hpd). Isis Ⓕ ISISCD001 (75 minutes: DDD: 3/93). 🎯
...HWV426-33 – Nos. 1-5. **Martin Souter** (hpd). Isis Ⓕ ISISCD003 (79 minutes: 7/93). 🎯
...HWV426-33 – Nos. 1-8. **Kenneth Gilbert** (hpd).
Harmonia Mundi Musique d'abord Ⓜ HMA190 447/8 (two discs: 93 minutes: ADD: 12/95). 🎯
...HWV426-33 – No. 5. *Coupled with works by* **Mozart** Alicia de Larrocha (pf); [a]**Vienna Symphony Orchestra / Uri Segal.** Decca Eclipse Ⓜ 448 992-2DEC (77 minutes: DDD: 3/97).

Handel Keyboard Suites: HWV426-33 – No. 1 in A major; No. 7 in G minor; HWV438 – No. 4 in D minor. Chaconne in G major, HWV435. Prelude in D minor. The Lady's Banquet – Sonata in C major; Capriccio in F major, HWV481; Preludio ed Allegro in G minor, HWV574; Fantaisie in C major, HWV490. **Oliver Baumont** (hpd). Erato Ⓕ 0630-14886-2 (63 minutes: DDD: 5/97). 🎯 Recorded 1995.
A splendid disc, imbued with freshness and vitality. Employing three different instruments – a Flemish harpsichord (1652) by Couchet, a shallower, 'dustier'-toned anonymous Italian instrument

of 1677, and a wonderfully rich 1707 French instrument by Dumont – all tuned to a pitch a whole tone lower than that of today, Olivier Baumont presents two of Handel's 1720 "grand suites", the D minor Suite from the 1733 collection, which is seldom heard, the great C major Chaconne (one of Handel's own favourites), which Baumont plays with every variant repeated, and a handful of very early shorter pieces. Two things in particular are striking about these performances – Baumont's stylishness and spontaneous-sounding skilful free decorations of Handel's text (not only in repeats but, for example, in the minor-key variants of the Chaconne). Definitely a disc to raise one's spirits.

Handel Alcina – Mi lusinga il dolce affetto; Verdi prati, selve amene; Stà nell'Ircana. Ariodante – E vivo ancora? ... Scherza infida; Dopa notte. Giulio Cesare – Va tacito e nascosto; Se in fiorito ameno prato; Piangerò, la sorte mia; Dall' ondoso periglio ... Aure, deh, per pietà. Serse – Fronde tenere e belle ... Ombra mai fù; Se bramate d'amar, chi vi sdegna; Crude furie degl'orrido abissi. **Ann Murray** (mez); **Orchestra of the Age of Enlightenment / Sir Charles Mackerras.** Forlane Ⓟ UCD16738 (75 minutes: DDD: 8/95). 🖉 Texts and translations included. Recorded 1994.

The cautious tread of the watchful huntsman, with the lovely dialogue of voice and basset-horn in Caesar's first aria, makes a delightful beginning, and as the recital proceeds one realizes afresh what variety of mood and manner will be found in almost any collection of arias by Handel. These range from the simple ease and beneficence of "Verdi prati" to the florid outburst of the frustrated Xerxes in "Crude furie". In between are Cleopatra's lament, Caesar's love song, Ariodante's sadness and his new-found joy. The musical interest is unfailing wherever one likes to look for it, in rhythm, in harmonic poignancy, or in the scoring – the solo violin as woodbird in "Se in fiorito ameno prato" or in the basset-horn of "Va tacito". Handel and Sir Charles have long been associated, and with the Orchestra of the Age of Enlightenment he provides the singer with a stylish accompaniment that is never assertive or doctrinaire but scrupulous in its care for phrasing and texture. Ann Murray responds with singing which has not only her customary expressiveness and energy but also a generally well-preserved beauty of tone that has not always been so characteristic. Occasionally a harsher, less firmly placed tone threatens to emerge, as at the start and *da capo* of "Stà nell' Ircana", but such moments are short-lived and instead she encourages a mellower, warmer sound which also has the advantage of being precise in its focus. The voice is quite closely recorded.

Handel Judas Maccabaeus – I feel the Deity within ... Arm, arm, ye brave!. Te Deum in D major, "Dettingen" – Vouchsafe, O Lord. Samson – Honour and arms scorn such a foe. Berenice – Si, tra i ceppi e le ritorte. Alcina – Verdi prati, selve amene. Orlando – O voi del mio poter ... Sorge infausta una procella. Acis and Galatea – I rage, I melt, I burn! ... O ruddier than the cherry. Semele – Where'er you walk. Alexander's Feast – Revenge, revenge, Timotheus cries ... Behold a ghastly band. Giulio Cesare – Va tacito e nascosto. Serse – Fronde tenere ... Ombra mai fù. Messiah – Thus saith the Lord ... But who may abide?; Why do the nations?; Behold I tell you a mystery ... The trumpet shall sound. **Bryn Terfel** (bass-bar); **Scottish Chamber Orchestra / Sir Charles Mackerras.** DG Ⓟ 453 480-2GH (73 minutes: DDD: A/97). Texts and translations included. Recorded 1995.

"I feel", sings Terfel with assurance in his voice matching the solemnly, expectantly, ceremonious opening bars; and then, the second time, "I feel", but now with the awed conviction of one who has experienced "the Deity within". The adjustment, the change of expression, is small, and no doubt when described sounds obvious enough; but it is typical of the imaginative intelligence Terfel brings. Comparing recordings, one hears authority in early versions, something more mystical in recent ones, but never such alertness as in Terfel. And what of his singing, his voice-production, his care for legato? As to the latter, conflict always lurks as expressive emphasis, shading and verbal naturalism assert their rights in the face of pure beauty and the evenness of the singing-line. Terfel is one in whom the rival claims work their way to a compromise, though if one side has to win it will generally be the expressive element. A good example of the compromise is the second track, the "Vouchsafe, O Lord", quietly and simply sung, preserving the movement's unity and yet with a power of feeling that, at "let thy mercy lighten upon us", is as overtly emotional as an operatic aria. The adapted arias, "Where'er you walk", "Verdi prati" and "Ombra mai fù", justify their inclusion readily enough, and it is good to hear Terfel in the solos from *Messiah*. The singing here incorporates a good deal of embellishment, some of it of Sir Charles Mackerras's devising. He is an excellent conductor for Terfel, sharing with him an appreciation of the zest in Handel. The Scottish Chamber Orchestra appear to share it too, and the recording, though made in the resonant Usher Hall, is vivid and clean.

Additional recommendation ...

...Messiah – I know that my Redeemer liveth. *Coupled with works by various composers.* **Lesley Garrett** (sop); **Britten Sinfonia / Ivor Bolton.** Conifer Classics Ⓟ 75605 51329-2 (73 minutes: DDD: 12/97). *See review in the Collections section; refer to the Index.*

Handel Acis and Galatea, HWV49*b*. **Norma Burrowes** (sop) Galatea; **Anthony Rolfe Johnson** (ten) Acis; **Martyn Hill** (ten) Damon; **Willard White** (bass) Polyphemus; **Paul Elliot** (ten); **English Baroque Soloists / Sir John Eliot Gardiner.** Archiv Produktion Ⓟ 423 406-2AH2 (two discs: 95 minutes: ADD: 8/88). 🖉 Notes, text and translation included. From 2708 038 (9/78). Recorded 1978. *Gramophone Award Winner 1978.*

John Eliot Gardiner made this recording of Handel's masque during the late 1970s when the revival of period instruments was still in a comparatively early stage. Listeners may detect weaknesses both in intonation and in ensemble from time to time but, nevertheless, Gardiner's performance is lively and stylistically assured. He paces the work dramatically revealing nuances both in the text and in the music. The solo team is a strong one and there are especially fine contributions from Norma Burrowes and Anthony Rolfe Johnson. This is an enjoyable performance of an enchanting work.

Additional recommendation ...

...**Soloists; St Anthony Singers; Philomusica of London / Sir Adrian Boult.**
Decca Ⓜ 436 227-2DM2 (two discs: ADD).

Handel Alexander's Feast, HWV75[a]. Concerto grosso in C major, HWV318, "Alexander's Feast".
[a]**Donna Brown** (sop); [a]**Carolyn Watkinson** (contr); [a]**Ashley Stafford** (alto); [a]**Nigel Robson** (ten); [a]**Stephen Varcoe** (bar); [a]**Monteverdi Choir; English Baroque Soloists / Sir John Eliot Gardiner.**
Philips Ⓕ 422 053-2PH2 (two discs: 98 minutes: DDD: 11/88). ✍ Text included.
Recorded live in 1987.

Alexander's Feast was the first work Handel had set by a major English poet (Dryden) and it was also the first time he allotted the principal male part to a tenor instead of the castrato heroes of his Italian operas. These two factors, combined with much fine music, scored with great brilliance and imagination, ensured the immediate success of *Alexander's Feast*. It is strange that nowadays it is seldom performed so this recording would have been very welcome even had it not been so full of vitality and so stylishly performed (though perhaps with more sophisticated detail than the eighteenth century would have managed). The Monteverdi Choir and the soloists are all Gardiner regulars, though the pure-voiced Canadian soprano Donna Brown is a fairly recent (and welcome) acquisition; and the English Baroque Soloists have ample opportunities to shine – especially the violins, although the natural horns' lusty entry in the bucolic "Bacchus, ever fair and young" is exhilarating.

Additional recommendation ...

...**Alexander's Feast. Harp Concerto in B flat major, HWV294. Organ Concerto in G minor/major, HWV289. Soloists; Tragicomedia; The Sixteen Choir and Orchestra / Harry Christophers.**
Collins Classics Ⓕ 7016-2 (two discs: 116 minutes: DDD: 10/91). ✍

Handel Apollo e Dafne, HWV122, "La terra e liberata"[a]. Crudel tiranno amor, HWV97.
Nancy Argenta (sop); [a]**Michael George** (bass); **Collegium Musicum 90 / Simon Standage.**
Chandos Chaconne Ⓕ CHAN0583 (58 minutes: DDD: 4/96). ✍ Texts and translations included. Recorded 1994.

Handel's *Apollo e Dafne* is a difficult work to put in context. Completed in Hanover in 1710 but possibly begun in Italy, its purpose is not clear, while as secular cantatas go it is long (40 minutes) and ambitiously scored for two soloists and an orchestra of strings, oboes, flute, bassoon and continuo. But this is not just a chunk of operatic experimentation: it sets its own, faster pace than the leisurely unfolding of a full-length baroque stage-work, yet its simple Ovidian episode, in which Apollo's pursuit of the nymph Dafne results in her transformation into a tree, is drawn with all the subtlety and skill of the instinctive dramatic genius that Handel was. This recording features the by-now familiar expert Handelian voices of Nancy Argenta and Michael George, and both convey their roles convincingly. Argenta's hard, clear tone seems just the thing for the nymph, who is not required to be especially alluring but who does have to sound quick to anger and (literally) untouchable; and George strikes the right note as Apollo, bragging loudly at the opening of his superior skill in archery to Cupid before succumbing more gently, and in the end extremely touchingly, to Cupid's arts. The orchestra are bright and efficient (though without ever creating a very big sound), and the pacing of the work seems just right. This is superb Handel then, and as if that were not enough there is a bonus in the form of a shorter cantata for soprano and strings, *Crudel tiranno amor*. Of this no more need be said other than that it is a beautiful piece indeed, and that Argenta performs it well nigh perfectly.

Additional recommendation ...

...**Judith Nelson** (sop); **David Thomas** (bass); **Philharmonia Baroque Orchestra / Nicholas McGegan.**
Harmonia Mundi Musique d'abord Ⓑ HMA190 5157 (52 minutes: DDD: 11/96). ✍

Handel Alexander Balus, HWV65. **Lynne Dawson, Claron McFadden** (sops); **Catherine Denley** (mez); **Charles Daniels** (ten); **Michael George** (bass); **New College Choir, Oxford; The King's Consort and Choir / Robert King.** Hyperion Ⓕ CDA67241/2 (two discs: 156 minutes: DDD: A/97). ✍ Notes and text not included. Recorded 1997.

Alexander Balus has never been one of Handel's more popular oratorios. That is mainly because its plot is by modern standards lacking in drama and motivation, and accordingly does not call forth the vein of his music that nowadays has the strongest appeal. It tells a tale of treachery by Ptolomee, King of Egypt, against Alexander, King of Syria and the husband of his daughter Cleopatra (no relation to the famous one), who is allied to the Jews, under Jonathan. *Alexander Balus* is essentially a sentimental drama, one in which the interest centres on the various characters' emotional reactions to their situations, amatory, political and religious, and these are rather static in the first two acts but much more powerful in the more eventful third with the deaths of both Alexander and Ptolomee. To an eighteenth-century audience it would have had resonances in terms of contemporary politics and religion, and in particular it explains, by analogy with English Protestantism, the seemingly smug attitude taken up by the Jews: everything would have been all right if only they had the right religion. Understanding its background helps you to understand why the music is as it is, so it is a pity that the otherwise informative note here touches on none of this. Here we have a very capable, idiomatic, sensibly cast performance under Robert King. The choruses are especially accomplished. The New College Choir, supported by men from The King's Consort Choir, are confident, bright-toned and vigorous, clean in line and well balanced. Lynne Dawson sings beautifully in her firm and resonant soprano and her usual poised and unaffected style. She is one of the happiest features of this set, even if just occasionally there is a note that isn't an immediate bull's-eye. Her singing of the lamenting music in the final act is particularly moving. Cleopatra has a couple of duets, one with some attractive interplay with the secondary character Aspasia, sung with much assurance by Claron McFadden. As Alexander, Catherine Denley sings with much confidence and directness in music that isn't all of special individuality. Jonathan is sung fluently and warmly, but very plainly, by Charles Daniels. Lastly there is Michael George, ideally suited to the villainous Ptolomee, with his forceful (but always musical) manner and the touch of blackness in his tone. The orchestral playing is accomplished, often rather carefully shaped. The recitative moves at a steady but natural pace; ornamentation is generally modest. All Handelians will want this set, and others should not be put off by the indifferent press *Alexander Balus* has had from time to time: the master's voice is unmistakable, and always worth hearing.

Handel Clori, mia bella Clori, HWV92. Armida abbandonata, HWV105. Il delirio amoroso, HWV99. **Ann Murray** (mez); **Symphony of Harmony and Invention / Harry Christophers.** Collins Classics Ⓕ 1503-2 (67 minutes: DDD: 2/98). 🎵 Texts and translations included. Recorded 1997.

Handel's months in Rome during 1707 seem to have drawn from him some of his finest music – expansive in scale, original in ideas and often passionate in expression: you can sense him, a young man of 22, flexing his musical muscles. *Clori, mia bella Clori*, is the most orthodox work here, consisting simply of four arias each preceded by a recitative – but very fine arias, especially the truly gorgeous third one, an E flat miniature which gives Ann Murray opportunity for particular eloquence. *Armida abbandonata* strikes a highly original note right from the start, with its opening recitative accompanied not by continuo but by brilliant violin arpeggios, leading into "Ah! crudele", an *Adagio* aria with just continuo support (but very richly accompanied here by Alistair Ross) and sung with great intensity. Then comes a hectic *furioso* recitative as she calls on the elements to destroy her betrayer – but contradicts herself by trying to call them off in the desperate aria that follows. Possibly even more remarkable is *Delirio amoroso*, one of the largest in scale of all Handel's solo cantatas, with extended orchestral ritornellos. The first number, though a setting of tragic words, is a spacious piece in A major with demanding violin solos (finely done by Walter Reiter) and a virtuoso solo line too, with a darker-toned middle section in F sharp minor. Then the second is a lament for her beloved, with solo cello, the third a gentle aria with solo flute, evoking the zephyr that bears him down the Acheron to Hades. Ann Murray makes no pretensions to period-style singing and brings to this music a wide expressive range, from the drama of the first aria to the grief of the second, while the third and the closing minuets are done with gentle resignation. Harry Christophers paces the music well and accompanies securely and there is some excellent playing from his band.

Handel Deborah. **Yvonne Kenny, Susan Gritton** (sops); **Catherine Denley** (mez); **James Bowman** (alto); **Michael George** (bass); **New College Choir, Oxford; Salisbury Cathedral Choristers; King's Consort / Robert King.** Hyperion Ⓕ CDA66841/2 (two discs: 140 minutes: DDD: 2/94). 🎵 Text included. Recorded 1993.

Deborah, written in 1733, occupies an honoured place in the canon of Handel's oratorios as the first composed for the entertainment of London theatre audiences. It is also a compound of numerous earlier works, including the Chandos and Coronation Anthems, the *Brockes Passion* and the *Ode for the Birthday of Queen Anne*, and in putting *Deborah* together in this manner, Handel was less successful than he usually was in creating a unified work – though the librettist and indeed the Bible itself have to be assigned some of the blame. It is, however, worth revival, and this recording, the first on CD, is warmly welcome. It begins with an overture different from the one usually heard: a fine, stirring D major trumpety piece, with a concluding minuet that was to find a place in the *Fireworks* Music. There are some noble choruses, several of which are in five or even eight voices, giving Handel the opportunity for grand effects. In *Deborah*, the chief interest rests with the choruses. Here they are very well sung by the combined forces of 32 trebles, eight countertenors, six tenors and eight basses, who produce a lot more sound than you might expect. Robert King's control of this group and the polish he imparts to the choral singing, with its clearly projected lines and its firmness of tone is admirable as is Michael George's warm and resonant contribution as Abinoam and Catherine Denley's firm, direct and stylish singing of the music of the unfortunate Sisera. The orchestral playing is polished; the recorded sound is more reverberant than might be ideal.

Handel Dixit Dominus, HWV232[a]. Nisi Dominus, HWV238[b]. Salve Regina, HWV241[c]. [ac]**Arleen Auger**, [a]**Lynne Dawson** (sops); [ab]**Diana Montague** (mez); [a]**Leigh Nixon**, [b]**John Mark Ainsley** (tens); [ab]**Simon Birchall** (bass); **Choir and Orchestra of Westminster Abbey / Simon Preston.** Archiv Produktion Ⓕ 423 594-2AH (56 minutes: DDD: 2/89). 🎵 Texts and translations included.

Although *Dixit Dominus* is the earliest surviving large scale work by Handel (he was only 22 at the time of its composition in 1707) it displays a remarkable degree of competence and invention and also looks forward to the mature style to come. The vocal writing for both chorus and soloists is extremely ornate and embellished and requires a considerable amount of expertise and flair in order to do full justice to the music. Fortunately, Simon Preston and his team possess all the necessary requirements – indeed, this is one of the most energetic, exhilarating and purposeful performances of this work ever recorded. One need only single out the rhythmically incisive performances of the opening "Dixit Dominus Domineo meo" or the "Judicabit in nationibus" and the superbly crisp and articulate performances from the Orchestra of Westminster Abbey to realize that it is a very special recording indeed. The well thought out coupling of *Nisi Dominus* and *Salve Regina* are no less impressive, with the latter offering the listener another chance to sample the beautiful solo contributions of Arleen Auger. The recorded sound is also outstandingly fine. A delightful disc.

Additional recommendations ...

...Dixit Dominus. Coronation Anthems – Zadok the priest; The King shall rejoice; My heart is inditing; Let thy hand be strengthened. **Soloists; Monteverdi Choir and Orchestra / Sir John Eliot Gardiner.** Erato Ⓕ 2292-45136-2 (ADD). ✒

...Dixit Dominus[a]. Laudate pueri Dominum, HWV236/7[b]. Concerto for Organ and Strings in F major, HWV295, "Cuckoo and the Nightingale"[c]. [ab]**Soloists;** [c]**Peter Hurford** (org); [ab]**King's College Choir, Cambridge;** [ab]**English Chamber Orchestra / Stephen Cleobury;** [c]**Concertgebouw Chamber Orchestra / Joshua Rifkin.** Decca Eclipse Ⓑ 448 242-2DEC (74 minutes: DDD: 2/97).

Handel Israel in Egypt, HWV54. **Nancy Argenta, Emily Van Evera** (sops); **Timothy Wilson** (alto); **Anthony Rolfe Johnson** (ten); **David Thomas, Jeremy White** (basses); **Taverner Choir and Players / Andrew Parrott.** Virgin Classics Veritas Ⓜ VMD5 61350-2 (two discs: 135 minutes: DDD: 2/91). ✒ Text included. Recorded 1989.   Ⓖ

If anyone needs to assure themselves as to whether the English choral tradition is alive and well, they need only buy this CD. *Israel in Egypt*, of all Handel's works, is the choral one *par excellence* – so much so, in fact, that it was something of a failure in Handel's own time because solo singing was much preferred to choral by the audiences. Andrew Parrott gives a complete performance of the work, in its original form: that is to say, prefaced by the noble funeral anthem for Queen Caroline, as adapted by Handel to serve as a song of mourning by the captive Israelites. This first part is predominantly slow, grave music, powerfully elegiac; the Taverner Choir show themselves, in what is testing music to sing, to be firm and clean of line, well focused and strongly sustained. The chorus have their chance to be more energetic in the second part, with the famous and vivid Plague choruses – in which the orchestra too play their part in the pictorial effects, with the fiddles illustrating in turn frogs, flies and hailstones. And last, in the third part, there is a generous supply of the stirring C major music in which Handel has the Israelites give their thanks to God, in some degree symbolizing the English giving thanks for the Hanoverian monarchy and the Protestant succession. Be that as it may, the effect is splendid. The solo work is first-rate, too, with Nancy Argenta radiant in Miriam's music in the final scene and distinguished contributions from David Thomas and Anthony Rolfe Johnson.

Additional recommendation ...

...Israel in Egypt[a]. Chandos Anthem No. 10, HWV255, "The Lord is my light"[b]. [a]**Elizabeth Gale,** [a]**Lilian Watson,** [b]**April Cantelo** (sops); [a]**James Bowman** (alto); **Ian Partridge** (ten); [a]**Tom McDonnell** (bar); [a]**Alan Watt** (bass); [a]**Choir of Christ Church, Oxford;** [b]**Choir of King's College, Cambridge;** [a]**English Chamber Orchestra / Simon Preston;** [b]**Academy of St Martin in the Fields / Sir David Willcocks.** Double Decca Ⓜ 443 470-2DF2 (two discs: 131 minutes: ADD).

Handel Joseph and his Brethren. **Yvonne Kenny** (sop); **Catherine Denley** (mez); **Connor Burrowes** (treb); **James Bowman** (alto); **John Mark Ainsley** (ten); **Michael George** (bass); **New College Choir, Oxford; The King's Consort Choir; The King's Consort / Robert King.** Hyperion Ⓕ CDA67171/3 (three discs: 164 minutes: DDD: 12/96). ✒ Text included. Recorded 1996.

There has never been a complete, professional recording of *Joseph and his Brethren*, a neglect grotesquely out of proportion to the merits of its music. It is full of good and characteristic things, and there are several scenes, including the extended denouement in the last act, that are very moving. The work begins splendidly, with an unusual overture heralding a fine and deeply felt opening scene for Joseph, languishing in an Egyptian prison. The setting of his prophecy is effective, with seven bars of darting arpeggios for the years of plenty and seven of sparse harmonic writing, *adagio*, for the famine years. The rest of Act 1 is a celebration of Joseph's foresight, preferment and marriage to Asenath, Pharoah's daughter. The highlights of Act 2 include a prison scene for Simeon, an agonized G minor accompanied recitative and aria, a beautiful, nostalgic pastoral idyll for Joseph, and scenes for Joseph with his brothers which incorporate a splendid outburst from Simeon, an aria from Benjamin and a moving chorus from the brothers, a sustained prayer and a richly worked fugue. The soloists dispatch all this music with spirit and accuracy. Of course, the central figure is James Bowman in the very demanding title-role. He is in excellent voice, as full and rich as ever and duly agile in the rapid music. *Joseph* is well suited to Robert King's way of conducting Handel. This is not a specially dramatic performance, but carefully moulded, well balanced, intelligently paced. The choir produce a sound that is bright and firm, and the singing is resolute, although the attack is soft-edged rather than incisive. King is particularly good at shaping the dynamics in a natural and unanimous way.

Handel Messiah, HWV56. **Barbara Schlick, Sandrine Piau** (sops); **Andreas Scholl** (alto); **Mark Padmore** (ten); **Nathan Berg** (bass); **Les Arts Florissants Chorus and Orchestra / William Christie.** Harmonia Mundi Ⓕ HMC90 1498/9 (two discs: 143 minutes: DDD: 10/94). ✔ Text included. Recorded 1993. *Gramophone Editor's choice.* ⒼⒼⒼ

William Christie reaches the heart of Handel's masterpiece with great fluency, sure dramatic pacing and an intuitive feeling for the nobility of the piece. As Donald Burrows remarks in his accompanying essay, one of two included in the booklet, Christie's performance generally follows a pattern of the work close to that which Handel seems to have adhered to from the mid-1740s, thus incorporating the chorus, "Their sound is gone out into all lands" (Part 2). Additionally, Christie uses the later versions of the arias "But who may abide the day of his coming" (Part 1), and "Thou art gone up on high" (Part 2), for alto and soprano, respectively. Christie brings lively characterization to *Messiah,* allowing the text to determine the prevailing effect of each number. In this he is fully supported by a first-rate team of soloists, a responsive if not always impeccably drilled choir and a body of instrumentalists which sounds particularly strong. The vocal timbres of the two sopranos, Barbara Schlick and Sandrine Piau are a constant delight, the boy treble, Tommy Williams, is as reliable in his intonation as he is clear in declamation. Mark Padmore is impressive, too, for sensitive phrasing and a lyrical approach to the music. However it is perhaps Andreas Scholl who touches the heart most profoundly with his deeply felt singing of "He was despised". The choir of Les Arts Florissants is splendidly alert to the many nuances which Christie discovers in Handel's music. Last, but not least, there is the orchestra, crisp, incisive, warm in timbre and producing one of the most homogeneous sounds yet heard from its strings. In short, this is a triumph, Christie's concept of the oratorio enabling him to present a continuous drama in a manner which holds our attention from start to finish.

Handel Messiah, HWV56. **Dorothea Röschmann, Susan Gritton** (sops); **Bernarda Fink** (contr); **Charles Daniels** (ten); **Neal Davies** (bass); **Gabrieli Consort and Players / Paul McCreesh.** Archiv Produktion Ⓕ 453 464-2AH2 (two discs: 132 minutes: DDD: 12/97). ✔ Text included. Recorded 1996. *Gramophone Editor's record of the month. Selected by Soundings.* ⒼⒼⒼ

The Gabrieli Consort and Players are as responsive and professional a group as you will find these days. McCreesh has fastidiously assembled solo singers with broad mainstream experience and Handel's choruses encapsulate all the vitality and litheness of the modern English vocal consort at its best. More than that, McCreesh is a natural dramatist and all his singers respond magnificently to the evangelical fervour which Jennens, if one senses not always Handel, envisioned. McCreesh's expression is candid and immediate, if not imparted with the unfolding spirituality of Suzuki, or fragrancy of Christie; his is a particular type of musicianship which reaches out, quite Sargent-like in the robust swagger of "And the Glory", the grand leisurely "Amen" and almost elegiac enunciation in "Comfort ye" – perhaps too static for some but Charles Daniels's supreme control has us holding our breath. McCreesh, in employing, for the most part, the Foundling Hospital version of 1754, treats us to a second soprano. His casting serves him well with two incandescent performances: Susan Gritton is suitably unmollifiable in "a refiner's fire" though she turns on the intensity, if not exactly sweetness in "I know that my Redeemer liveth". Dorothea Röschmann provides a similarly bright edge and in both cases, we are treated to singing of considerable technical finesse. Bernarda Fink's heady and rasping contralto may not appeal to everyone but "He was despised" leaves one in little doubt of Jennens's starkest sentiments. Neal Davies is sure-footed and impressive. The energy and focused proclamation of this reading will surely win many friends: whilst tempos may appear hard-pushed, there is a consistency and rooted concentration to proceedings, always thoroughly engaged. Recorded sound is resonant but also close, and fairly compressed in its more rumbustious moments.

Additional recommendations ...

...**Soloists; Royal Philhrmonic Chorus and Orchestra / Sir Thomas Beecham.**
RCA Victor Gold Seal Ⓜ 09026-61266-2* (three discs: 161 minutes: ADD).

...**Soloists; Taverner Choir**; **Taverner Players / Andrew Parrott.**
Virgin Classics Veritas Ⓜ VMD5 61330-2 (two discs: 146 minutes: DDD). ✔

...**Soloists; Monteverdi Choir; English Baroque Soloists / Sir John Eliot Gardiner.**
Philips Ⓕ 434 297-2PH2 (two discs: 137 minutes: ADD: 1/84). ✔

...**Soloists; Christ Church Cathedral Choir, Oxford; Academy of Ancient Music / Christopher Hogwood.**
L'Oiseau-Lyre Florilegium Ⓕ 430 488-2OH2 (two discs: 137 minutes: ADD: 7/84). ✔ Ⓖ

...**Soloists; The English Concert Choir; The English Concert / Trevor Pinnock.**
Archiv Produktion Ⓕ 423 630-2AH2 (two discs: 150 minutes: DDD: 11/88). ✔ Ⓖ

...**Soloists; Collegium Musicum 90 Chorus; Collegium Musicum 90 / Richard Hickox.**
Chandos Chaconne Ⓕ CHAN0522/3 (two discs: 141 minutes: DDD: 3/92). ✔

...**The Scholars Baroque Ensemble / David van Asch** (bass).
Naxos Ⓢ 8 550667/8 (two discs: 161 minutes: DDD: 4/93). ✔

...**Soloists; Huddersfield Choral Society; Liverpool Philharmonic Orchestra / Sir Malcolm Sargent.**
Dutton Laboratories Essential Archive mono Ⓑ 2CDEA5010*
(two discs: 146 minutes: ADD: 12/96).

...**Soloists; Bach Collegium Japan / Masaaki Suzuki.**
BIS Ⓕ CD891/2 (two discs: 140 minutes: DDD: A/97). ✔

Handel The Occasional Oratorio, HWV62. **Susan Gritton, Lisa Milne** (sops); **James Bowman** (alto); **John Mark Ainsley** (ten); **Michael George** (bass); **New College Choir, Oxford; The King's Consort / Robert King.** Hyperion Ⓕ CDA66961/2 (two discs: 144 minutes: DDD: 6/95). ✔
Text included. Recorded 1994. Ⓖ

The occasion that called forth this work was the Jacobite rising of 1745 and its impending defeat. The Duke of Cumberland's victory at Culloden was yet to come. Handel, anticipating it, hit off the mood of the moment with a rousing piece full of appeals to patriotic feeling, partly through the traditional identification between the English Protestant culture of Hanoverian times with that of the biblical Hebrews. Much of the music comes from existing works, notably *Israel in Egypt* – the hailstone chorus does not seem to have much relevance to battles between the English and the Scots, but then of course English weather was always rather unpredictable. *The Occasional Oratorio* has usually had a bad press. Its 'plot' pursues the familiar route of Anxiety-Prayer-Victory-Jubilation, but the work lacks the unity of theme and purpose of the great dramatic oratorios; if, however, you value Handel primarily because the music is so splendid you will find a lot to relish here. Many of Robert King's performances excel more through their refinement than their vitality: but here he really rises to the challenge of this sturdier side of Handel's muse and produces playing and singing full of punch and energy, and with that command of the broad Handelian paragraph without which the music lacks its proper stature. The grand eight-part choruses, with the choir properly spaced, antiphonally, over the stereo span, make their due effect. King has a distinguished solo team. John Mark Ainsley's singing is particularly touching in the highly original "Jehovah is my shield", where the rocking figures in the orchestra eventually turn out to symbolize sleep. Also very enjoyable is Susan Gritton's soprano, a sharply focused voice with a fine ring and due agility in the lively music and handled with taste and a keen feeling for the shape of phrases in the contemplative airs. In all this is a very fine set.

Handel Samson, HWV57. **Lynne Dawson, Lynda Russell** (sops); **Catherine Wyn-Rogers** (contr); **Mark Padmore, Thomas Randle, Matthew Vine** (tens); **Jonathan Best, Michael George** (basses); **The Sixteen; Symphony of Harmony and Invention / Harry Christophers.** Collins Classics Ⓕ 7038-2 (three discs: 205 minutes: DDD: 8/97). ✔ Text included. Recorded 1996.

This complete recording of *Samson* gives a straightforward account of the work, in tune with styles of Handel performance favoured today, except for one in particular – the choice of tempos. This is a decidedly leisurely reading of the work; clearly Christophers has a sense of its magnitude, of the big issues with which it is involved and the nobility of its utterance, and he will not let himself be hurried. He has an excellent cast. Thomas Randle is well equipped for Samson, a firm, strong tenor, with a hint of baritonal quality in his middle and lower registers. There is no bombast here. "Total eclipse" has much of pathos but no heroics. "Why does the God of Israel sleep" is done with some power, and the renunciation of Dalila ("Your charms to ruin") is weightily sung; and there is plenty of fire in his rejection of the Philistine braggart, Harapha, but never at the cost of musical singing. Samson's father, Manoah is sung with characteristic warmth and depth of tone and feeling by Michael George; his bass contrasts aptly with the tauter, more focused one of Jonathan Best's Harapha. Mark Padmore contributes some well-placed singing as both the Israelite and the Philistine man. Lynne Dawson does the same as the woman from both camps; she contributes a vigorous "Let the bright seraphim" (which here has a brief choral section at the end, surviving in Handel's manuscript but probably never heard before). Lynda Russell's soft, seductive Dalila, a modest role, confined to Act 2, is enjoyable; but perhaps above all Catherine Wyn-Rogers excels as Micah, with beautifully intense singing and concentrated tone in all her music – her phrasing in "Then long eternity" and the heartfelt expression in "Return O God of hosts", for example, are quite outstanding. Stylistically the performance is cautious, with only modest added ornamentation and brief cadenzas, but of course the requisite appoggiaturas in the recitative. The Sixteen provide clear and spirited choral singing throughout, suitably jolly in the Philistine music, duly noble in that for the Hebrews, achieving unusual clarity of texture. A direct and faithful realization of this fine work.

Handel Saul, HWV53. **Lynne Dawson, Donna Brown** (sops); **Derek Lee Ragin** (alto); **John Mark Ainsley, Neil Mackie, Philip Salmon, Philip Slane** (tens); **Alastair Miles, Richard Savage** (basses); **Monteverdi Choir; English Baroque Soloists / Sir John Eliot Gardiner.** Philips Ⓕ 426 265-2PH3 (three discs: 159 minutes: DDD: 8/91). ✔ Recorded live in 1989.

Saul is considered by many to be one of the most arresting music dramas in the English language, even though it is officially classed as an oratorio. In it Handel explores in some psychological depth the motivation of his characters, most notably that of the eponymous anti-hero, whose tantrums caused by envy and his searching for supernatural intervention are all vividly delineated; as is the friendship of David and Jonathan and the different characters of Saul's daughters, Merab and Michal. In yet another compelling performance of Handel under his baton, John Eliot Gardiner – in this live recording made at the Göttingen Handel Festival in Germany – fulfils every aspect of this varied and adventurous score, eliciting execution of refined and biting calibre from his choir and orchestra. The young British bass Alastair Miles captures Saul in all his moods. John Mark Ainsley and Derek Lee Ragin are both affecting as Jonathan and David; so are Lynne Dawson and Donna Brown as Michal and Merab. There are a few cuts, but they aren't grievous enough to prevent a firm recommendation.

Handel Theodora, HWV68. **Lorraine Hunt** (sop); **Jennifer Lane** (mez); **Drew Minter** (alto); **Jeffrey Thomas** (ten); **Nigel Rogers** (ten); **David Thomas** (bass); **California University, Berkeley Chamber Chorus; Philharmonia Baroque Orchestra / Nicholas McGegan.** Harmonia Mundi
ⓕ HMU90 7060/2 (three discs: 170 minutes: DDD: 10/92). ✎ Text included. Recorded 1991. ⒢
"The Jews will not come to it ... because it is a Christian story, and the ladies will not come to it because it is a virtuous one" wrote Handel somewhat bitterly after the unfavourable reception of his sublime late oratorio, *Theodora*. If contemporary audiences were put off by its theme of martyrdom, we should be grateful that the self-righteous piety of Morell's libretto inspired some of Handel's finest music, complete for the first time on record with the added bonus of both the original and revised versions of "Symphony of Soft Musick". And at last it has a recording which can be wholeheartedly recommended. David Thomas as Valens, the Roman governor, opens the proceedings with a firm and resolute tone and later gives the bloodthirsty "Racks, gibbets, sword and fire" much menace. Lorraine Hunt was an inspired choice for the taxing title-role: the top notes of "Angels ever bright and fair" are celestially floated, while she finds great intensity in "With darkness deep", the emotional centre of the work. Drew Minter gives a mellifluous and characterful account of Didymus, a Roman officer recently converted to Christianity who attempts to save Theodora. Listen to their duet, "To Thee, Thou glorious Son" to hear how winningly they blend their voices. Praise too for Jeffrey Thomas as Septimius, particularly in his elegant ornamentation in the virtuoso aria "Dread the fruits of Christian folly", only occasionally showing strain in the wide leaps in "From virtue springs". Jennifer Lane is also impressive as Irene (described in the libretto simply as "A Christian") – despite being burdened with some of Morell's most trite utterances: "True Happiness is only found, where Grace and Truth and Love Abound, And pure religion feeds the Flame". Nicholas McGegan has at his command a highly skilled orchestra, chooses tempos which are unfailingly apt, supporting and giving weight to the vocal lines. Praise too, for the excellent University of California Chamber Chorus. Harmonia Mundi have provided an informative booklet with a full libretto in three languages and an illuminating essay from McGegan himself.

Handel Opera Arias and Duets. **Catherine Bott, Emma Kirkby** (sops); **Brandenburg Consort / Roy Goodman.** Hyperion ⓕ CDA66950 (76 minutes: DDD: 11/97). ✎ Texts and translations included. Recorded 1997. *Gramophone Editor's choice.*
Alessandro – Overture; Sinfonia; Che vidi?; No, più soffrir; Placa l'alma; Solitudine amate ... Aure, fonti; Pur troppo veggio ... Che tirannia d'Amor; Svanisci, oh reo timore ... Dica il falso. Admeto, Re di Tessaglia – Il ritratto d'Admeto; La sorte mia vacilla; Quest'è dunque la fede ... Vedrò fra poco. Riccardo Primo, Re di Inghilterra – Morte vieni ... A me nel mio rossere ... Quando non vede. Siroe, Re di Persia – A costei, che dirò?; L'aura non sempre; Si diversi sembianti ... Non vi piacque, ingiusti dei. Tolomeo, Re di Egitto – E dove, e dove mai ... Fonti amiche; Ti pentirai, crudel.
It was a happy idea to assemble a selection of Handel's arias written for the two sopranos whose famous rivalry coloured the last years of the first Royal Academy. Francesca Cuzzoni – impersonated here by Catherine Bott – was Handel's principal soprano from 1723, creating among other roles Cleopatra and Rodelinda. Faustina Bordoni – her roles here go to Emma Kirkby – arrived in 1726 and the two sang together in several operas including five new ones by Handel, all represented on this recording. Both were superlative singers and each had a characteristic style. Cuzzoni was praised for her clear and sweet high notes, her use of rubato, her control of volume and above all for her affecting expression. Bordoni, whose voice lay slightly lower, was admired for her fine articulation, her flexibility in divisions and ornamentation, and her passion and expression in slow arias. In his music composed for them, Handel clearly differentiated between their capacities, as this disc illustrates. The 'rival queens' first sang together in *Alessandro*, which is the opera most fully represented here. There are two of Cuzzoni's arias, one brilliant piece with rapid divisions, which Bott throws off in splendidly free fashion, and a pathetic one, a typical F minor *siciliano*, taken very slowly here, allowing plenty of time for some expressive (but restrained) elaboration in the *da capo*. Of Faustina's music we have the exquisite *scena* that opens Act 2, including the aria, "Aure, fonti", and the lively one with which the act closes. The aria typifies, in the way it demands and rewards precisely detailed singing, Handel's writing for her, and Kirkby's refinement of detail is remarkable. There is beautifully managed interplay between the singers in the *Alessandro* duet; they seem to feed one another with opportunities. The programme is imaginatively put together, offering a wide range of opportunities to each of the singers, which they seize avidly. Roy Goodman is a prompt and stylish accompanist. This CD is appealing on every level, as well as instructive about how Handel and his singers interacted.

Handel Agrippina. **Della Jones** (mez) Agrippina; **Derek Lee Ragin** (alto) Nero; **Donna Brown** (sop) Poppea; **Alastair Miles** (bass) Claudius; **Michael Chance** (alto) Otho; **George Mosley** (bar) Pallas; **Jonathan Peter Kenny** (alto) Narcissus; **Julian Clarkson** (bass) Lesbo; **Anne Sofie von Otter** (mez) Juno; **English Baroque Soloists / Sir John Eliot Gardiner.** Philips ⓕ 438 009-2PH3
(three discs: 217 minutes: DDD: 6/97). ✎ Notes, text and translation included.
Recorded 1991-92. *Gramophone Editor's choice.* ⒢⒢⒢
Agrippina is Handel's Venetian opera, composed in 1709 for the S. Giovanni Grisostomo theatre, where it was evidently and deservedly a great success; according to Handel's first biographer, the

audience were struck with the "grandeur and sublimity of its style". Handel drew on its music, but he never revived it: its scheme, with a large number of short and lightly accompanied arias, is very much of its time and its place – that amplitude of phrase and structure and indeed emotion, what we regard today as his "grandeur and sublimity", that distinguishes Handel's operas from those of his contemporaries, had yet to come. Yet *Agrippina* is a very effective piece, if directed with due vitality (as it certainly is here), and it is full of appealing music in a wide variety of moods. Any admirer of countertenor singing should be prepared to buy the set for Michael Chance's singing alone. But in fact there are two other countertenors here who are well worth hearing, especially Derek Lee Ragin, whose high-lying voice and sensitive, thoughtful phrasing serve Nero's music admirably. His last aria, a brilliant piece with colourful instrumental writing, as he renounces Poppea in expectation of the imperial crown, is breathtakingly done, fiery singing with very precise execution of the divisions. The third of the countertenors is Jonathan Peter Kenny as Narcissus, rather softer in tone and line, who provides some particularly musical singing in his aria near the end of Act 2.

Della Jones gives a masterful performance in the title-role. Her music is very varied in mood: there are several brief and catchy little pieces, which she throws off with spirit, but also some larger-scale numbers, such as the marvellous C minor aria near the end of Act 1 (although totally insincere in sentiment), which is done with great vigour, and the noble, invocation-like "Pensieri, voi mi tormentate", another of the opera's high points, to which she brings much intensity. Donna Brown as Poppea makes the most of a role with much lively and appealing music. Alastair Miles's full and resonant bass – the part goes down to cello C – brings due weight of authority to the emperor Claudius; Pallas is done by a clean, lightish but nicely firm baritone, George Mosley, and Julian Clarkson contributes some very neat singing in the role of Lesbo. Anne Sofie von Otter comes in as a *dea ex machina* at the every end, not to rescue the situation but to honour the marriage of Poppea and Otho – which of course she does in style. John Eliot Gardiner has not recorded many Handel operas, nor directed many in the theatre. But of course he is a fine and very experienced conductor of Handel and he has a sure feeling for tempo and for the character of each movement. The orchestral playing is beyond reproach. The text followed is that of the Chrysander edition which probably doesn't correspond too closely to Handel's own. This recording is comfortably among the half-dozen finest recordings of Handel operas.

Handel Ariodante. **Lorraine Hunt** (sop) Ariodante; **Juliana Gondek** (sop) Ginevra; **Lisa Saffer**
   (sop) Dalinda; **Jennifer Lane** (mez) Polinesso; **Rufus Müller** (ten) Lurcanio; **Nicolas Cavallier**
   (bass) King of Scotland; **Jörn Lindemann** (ten) Odoardo; **Wilhelmshaven Vocal Ensemble;**
   Freiburg Baroque Orchestra / Nicholas McGegan. Harmonia Mundi Ⓕ HMU90 7146/8
   (three discs: 202 minutes: DDD: 4/96). 📰 Notes, text and translation included. Recorded 1995.
   Gramophone Editor's choice. Gramophone Award Winner 1996.   Ⓖ

The Leppard performance of 1980 has Dame Janet Baker in superb voice, and for her commanding singing alone that set is more than worth having; but this version under Nicholas McGegan certainly surpasses it in almost every other way. This recording, made with the cast from the Göttingen Festival last year (largely American singers who have collaborated with McGegan in his Californian performances), seems at least the equal of the best he has done before. The quality of the music is of course a factor: *Ariodante* is one of the richest of the Handel operas. It begins with a flood of fine numbers, just like *Giulio Cesare*, mostly love music for the betrothed pair, Ariodante and the Scottish princess Ginevra – she is introduced in a wonderfully carefree aria, he in a gentle, exquisite slow arietta; then they have a very individual and beautiful love duet, and each goes on to a more jubilant aria. But the plot thickens and the music darkens with Polinesso's machinations, designed to impugn her fidelity: thus Act 2 contains music of vengeance and grief (above all the magnificent "Scherza infida!" for Ariodante, a G minor aria with muted upper and pizzicato lower strings, and soft bassoons), while the final act shows all the characters *in extremis*, until the plot is uncovered and equilibrium restored. This is also one of Handel's few operas with extensive ballet; each act includes some splendid and ingeniously tuneful dance music. McGegan directs in his usual spirited style. There is a real theatrical sense to his conducting: this is one of those opera sets where, after the overture, you find your spine tingling in expectation of the drama. Lorraine Hunt's soprano seems warm and full for a castrato part, but her line is always well defined and she has a delightfully musical voice which she uses gracefully and expressively. A fine set.

Additional recommendation ...

...**Soloists; London Voices; English Chamber Orchestra / Raymond Leppard.**
   Philips Ⓜ 442 096-2PM3 (three discs: 139 minutes: ADD: 12/94).

Handel Ariodante. **Anne Sofie von Otter** (mez) Ariodante; **Lynne Dawson** (sop) Ginevra;
   Veronica Cangemi (sop) Dalinda; **Ewa Podleś** (mez) Polinesso; **Richard Croft** (ten) Lurcanio;
   Denis Sedov (bass) King of Scotland; **Luc Coadou** (ten) Odoardo; **Choeur des Musiciens**
   du Louvre; Les Musiciens du Louvre / Marc Minkowski. Archiv Produktion Ⓕ 457 271-2AH3
   (three discs: 178 minutes: DDD: 2/98). 📰 Text and translation included. Recorded 1997.   ⒼⒼ

Lynne Dawson is the star of this show – and perhaps the leading Handel opera soprano today. In Act 2, where Ginevra finds herself inexplicably rejected and condemned by everyone, Dawson brings real depth of tone and feeling to her E minor lament, "Il mio crudel martoro"; in the final act she shines in the desolate miniature "Io ti bacio" and brings much fire to the outburst "Sì, morrò". But she never transgresses the canons of baroque style. Von Otter, too, has much marvellous music – the aria "Scherza infida", in G minor, with its sombre sustaining bassoons, is one of Handel's (or anyone's) greatest expressions of grief – and she sings it beautifully, but she is not really at one with this idiom and seems to lack a natural feeling for the amplitude of Handel's lines. She tries, perhaps, to do too much with them in terms of shaping and detailed expression. Yet of course there is much to enjoy here too, the beauty of the actual sound, the immaculate control, the many telling and musicianly touches of phrasing. But the noble, climactic triumphant aria, "Dopo notte" doesn't have quite the effect it should. For that, however, Minkowski is partly to blame. Carried away, it almost seems, by the passion of the music, he is often inclined to go at it baldheaded, too fast and with a ferocity of accent, especially in the bass lines, that seems foreign to the style and dangerously close to ugly. This happens in several of Ariodante's numbers, including this last aria, but also in the scene that opens Act 3, first in the dark-toned D minor Sinfonia and then, particularly, in the extraordinary C minor aria, "Cieca notte", with its extravagant leaps in the violin part and its jerky rhythms. Veronica Cangemi makes a charming Dalinda, light, spirited and duly agile, with some gently pathetic expression in the delightful *siciliana* song early in Act 2. Ewa Podles brings her large, resonant voice to Polinesso's music; the Lurcanio, Richard Croft, is a sturdy tenor, rather heavy in tone and at times almost baritonal. The King of Scotland's fatherly music is done with due fullness and warmth by Denis Sedov, who covers the two-octave range with comfort and resonance and brings due nobility to his *siciliana* aria in Act 2. Despite the driven quality of Minkowski's performance, especially in the high dramatic music of the latter part of the opera, the sheer passion of this set does give it claims to be considered first choice. The admirable McGegan performance is possibly a safer buy, and in some respects it is a more stylish performance, but the singing here, Lynne Dawson's above all, is on balance superior. And don't overlook the fine performance by Janet Baker on the Leppard set which otherwise sounds stylistically rather dated.

Handel Flavio. **Jeffrey Gall** (alto) Flavio; **Derek Lee Ragin** (alto) Guido; **Lena Lootens** (sop) Emilia; **Bernarda Fink** (contr) Teodata; **Christina Högman** (sop) Vitige; **Gianpaolo Fagotto** (ten) Ugone; **Ulrich Messthaler** (bass) Lotario; **Ensemble 415 / René Jacobs.** Harmonia Mundi Ⓕ HMC90 1312/3 (two discs: 156 minutes: DDD: 7/90). ✒ Notes, text and translation included. Recorded 1989.

Flavio is one of the most delectable of Handel's operas. Although it comes from his 'heroic' period, it is not at all in the heroic mould but rather an ironic tragedy with a good many comic elements. Does that sound confusing? – well, so it is, for you never know quite where you are when King Flavio of Lombardy starts falling in love with the wrong woman, for although this starts as an amusing idle fancy it develops into something near-tragic, since he imperils everyone else's happiness, ultimately causing the death of one counsellor and the dishonour of another. The delicately drawn amorous feeling is like nothing else in Handel, and in its subtle growth towards real passion and grief is handled with consummate skill. The opera, in short, is full of fine and exceptionally varied music, and it is enhanced here by a performance under René Jacobs that, although it takes a number of modest liberties, catches the moods of the music surely and attractively, with shapely, alert and refined playing from the admirable Ensemble 415. And the cast is strong. The central roles, composed for two of Handel's greatest singers, Cuzzoni and Senesino, eighteenth-century superstars, are sung by Lena Lootens, a delightfully natural and expressive soprano with a firm, clear technique, and the countertenor Derek Lee Ragin, who dispatches his brilliant music with aplomb and excels in the final aria, a superb minor-key expression of passion. The singers also include Bernarda Fink as the lightly amorous Teodata and Christina Högman, both fiery and subtle in the music for her lover, and the capable Jeffrey Gall as the wayward monarch. Altogether a highly enjoyable set, not flawless but certainly among the best ever Handel opera recordings.

Handel Giulio Cesare, HWV17. **Jennifer Larmore** (mez) Giulio Cesare; **Barbara Schlick** (sop) Cleopatra; **Bernarda Fink** (mez) Cornelia; **Marianne Rørholm** (mez) Sextus; **Derek Lee Ragin** (alto) Ptolemy; **Furio Zanasi** (bass) Achillas; **Olivier Lallouette** (bar) Curio; **Dominique Visse** (alto) Nirenus; **Concerto Cologne / René Jacobs.** Harmonia Mundi Ⓕ HMC90 1385/7 (four discs: 244 minutes: DDD: 4/92). ✒ Notes, text and translation included. Recorded 1991. *Gramophone Award Winner 1992.*

Handel's greatest heroic opera sports no fewer than eight principal characters and one of the largest orchestras he ever used. Undoubtedly this, and the singing of Francesca Cuzzoni (Cleopatra) and Senesino (Caesar), helped to launch *Giulio Cesare* into the enduring popularity that it enjoys to this day. But it is primarily the quality of the music, with barely a weak number in four hours of entertainment, that has made it such a favourite with musicians and audiences. Surprisingly, this is the only complete performance on period instruments currently available, an immediate advantage in giving extra 'bite' to the many moments of high drama without threatening to drown the singers in *forte* passages. This performance is a particularly fine one with an excellent cast; Caesar, originally sung by a castrato, is here taken by the young mezzo, Jennifer Larmore. She brings weight and a sense of integrity to the role (which surely couldn't be matched by a countertenor), seemingly untroubled by the demands of the final triumphant aria, "Qual torrente". Occasionally her vibrato becomes intrusive, particularly near the beginning of the opera, but that is a minor quibble in a performance of this stature. Handel could just as well have called his opera 'Cleopatra' as it is she who is the pivotal element in the drama, a role taken here by Barbara Schlick. One of Handel's most vividly developed characters, this many faceted woman is represented by Schlick with acuity and imagination, ranging from the haunting pathos of "Piangerò", where she occasionally seems stretched on the top notes, to the exuberant virtuosity of "Da tempeste" in the final act. If Cleopatra represents strength in a woman, then Cornelia is surely the tragic figure, at the mercy of events. Her first aria, "Priva son", here taken very slowly, shows Bernarda Fink to be more than equal to the role, admirable in her steady tone and dignity of character. Derek Lee Ragin's treacherous Ptolemy is also memorable, venom and fire injected into his agile voice. A first-rate cast is supported by René Jacobs and Concerto Cologne on fine form, though the continuo line is sometimes less than ideally clear. The recording is excellent.

Additional recommendations ...

...(sung in German). **Soloists; Stuttgart Radio Chorus; Munich Philharmonia Orchestra / Ferdinand Leitner.** Orfeo D'Or mono Ⓔ C351943D* (three discs: 215 minutes: ADD: 3/95).

...**Soloists; La Grande Ecurie et La Chambre du Roy / Jean-Claude Malgoire.** Auvidis Astrée Ⓔ E8558 (three discs: 221 minutes: DDD: 2/96).

Handel Orlando, HWV31. **Patricia Bardon** (mez) Orlando; **Rosemary Joshua** (sop) Angelica; **Hilary Summers** (contr) Medoro; **Rosa Mannion** (sop) Dorinda; **Harry van der Kamp** (bass) Zoroastro; **Les Arts Florissants / William Christie.** Erato Ⓕ 0630-14636-2 (three discs: 168 minutes: DDD: 9/96). ✍ Notes, text and translation included. Recorded 1996.   Ⓖ

There was already an excellent *Orlando* in the catalogue, but of course there is always room for more than one version and the present recording is rather different in character from Hogwood's. Christie is very much concerned with a smooth and generally rich texture and with delicacy of rhythmic shaping. His management of the recitative could hardly be bettered and moments of urgency or of other kinds of emotional stress are tellingly handled. Sometimes he favours a rather sustained style in the arias, making the textures seem airless and heavy, and the lines within them too smooth. However, to set against it there is his exceptional delicacy of timing, his careful but always natural-sounding moulding of cadences and other critical moments in the score. Not many Handel interpreters show this kind of regard for such matters and it is certainly a delight to hear Handel's music so lovingly nurtured; also, of course, it helps the singers to convey meaning. The cast is very strong, as is Hogwood's. While the older recording has a countertenor (James Bowman) in the title-role, this one has a mezzo, Patricia Bardon, who draws a very firm and often slender line, with that gleam in her tone that can so enliven the impact of a lowish mezzo – the famous Mad scene is magnificent. The Sleep scene, with very sweet, soft-toned playing of the *violette marine*, is lovely. Hilary Summers offers a very sensitively sung Medoro, pure and shapely in line. Harry van der Kamp makes a finely weighty Zoroastro, with plenty of resonance in his bottom register; the last aria in particular is done in rousing fashion. As Angelica, Rosemary Joshua's musicianship comes through in her attractive phrasing and timing. Rosa Mannion's Dorinda is no less full of delights, catching the character to perfection. The Hogwood set also has superlative singing from the sopranos, Arleen Auger and Emma Kirkby. There is really nothing to choose between these two sets vocally unless one has a decided preference for a mezzo as opposed to a countertenor. Hogwood's lighter orchestral textures are appealing but the refinement of detail in the newer set is equally admirable.

Additional recommendation ...

...**Soloists; Academy of Ancient Music / Christopher Hogwood.** L'Oiseau-Lyre Ⓕ 430 845-2OH3 (three discs: 158 minutes: DDD: 8/91). ✍   Ⓖ

Handel Radamisto, HWV12a. **Ralf Popken** (alto) Radamisto; **Juliana Gondek** (sop) Zenobia; **Lisa Saffer** (sop) Polissena; **Dana Hanchard** (sop) Tigrane; **Monika Frimmer** (sop) Fraarte; **Michael Dean** (bass-bar) Tiridate; **Nicolas Cavallier** (bass) Farasmane; **Freiburg Baroque Orchestra / Nicholas McGegan** (hpd). Harmonia Mundi Ⓕ HMU90 7111/3 (three discs: 190 minutes: DDD: 6/94). ✍ Notes, text and translation included. Recorded 1993.

Gramophone Editor's choice.   ⒼⒼ

Radamisto was Handel's first opera for the Royal Academy of Music, the company set up in 1719 under his musical directorship to put London opera on a secure basis (as optimistic a notion then as now). It is a tale of dynastic doings in post-classical Thrace, with King Tiridate of Armenia forsaking his wife Polissena because he becomes enamoured of Zenobia, Radamisto's queen; Radamisto and Zenobia go through various trials, but "after various Accidents, it comes to pass, that he recovers both Her and his Kingdom". It is easy enough to poke fun at plots such as these, but the score of *Radamisto*, one of Handel's richest, is its justification. Handel certainly knew how to 'wow' the London audiences on these big occasions. In the Second Act particularly, one arresting number follows another; Radamisto's "Ombra cara", which has been claimed (not without justice) as the finest aria Handel ever wrote, falls early in the act, and towards the end there is a wonderful sequence, chiefly of minor-key numbers, as the emotional tensions mount, culminating in a duet for the apparently doomed lovers. The Third Act, although dramatically less powerful, is also full of colourful and characterful music, including a noble quartet which Handel clearly remembered 30 years later when composing *Jephtha*. This performance is the best by far we have had from Nicholas McGegan. Any Handelian will relish the constantly alert playing, the strong dramatic pacing and the weight given to the orchestral textures, and he has the benefit of an excellent cast.

Handel Teseo. **Eirian James** (mez) Teseo; **Julia Gooding** (sop) Agilea; **Della Jones** (mez) Medea:
Derek Lee Ragin (alto) Egeo; **Catherine Napoli** (sop) Clizia; **Jeffrey Gall** (alto) Arcane;
François Bazola (bar) Sacerdote di Minerva; **Les Musiciens du Louvre / Marc Minkowski**.
Erato Ⓔ 2292-45806-2 (two discs: 148 minutes: DDD: 3/93). 🎵 Texts and translations included.
Recorded 1992. Ⓖ

Teseo was Handel's third opera for London, given at the beginning of 1713. Exceptionally, its libretto
was based on a French original, written by Quinault for Lully; it is a spectacular piece, in five acts,
with Medea (after the events of *Médée*) and Theseus (before the events of *Hippolyte* or the Ariadne
operas) as its central characters. It is Medea who, as slighted lover and jealous sorceress, provides the
principal musical thrills; but the score is, in any case, an unusually rich and inventive one, with much
colourful orchestral writing even before she turns up at the beginning of Act 2. When she does, she
introduces herself with a *Largo* aria, "Dolce riposo", of a kind unique to Handel in its depth of poetic
feeling, with a vocal line full of bold leaps above throbbing strings and an oboe obbligato; but, lest
we should think her docile, Medea hints at her true colours in the ensuing C minor aria, and by the
end of the act she is singing furious recitative and fiery, incisive lines – real sorceress music. Her
biggest scene comes at the start of the final act, a *Presto* vengeance aria, packed with raging rapid
semiquavers. Handel scored the opera for a more varied orchestra than usual; there are recorders,
flutes, oboes, bassoons and trumpets called for. The arias themselves tend to be rather shorter than
usual for Handel. The work needs first-rate singing, and by and large receives it here. The role of
Medea falls to Della Jones, a singer with a superb technique and a remarkable ability to identify with
the role; she truly lives Medea's part and brings to it great resources of spirit and technique. Except
when asked, or allowed, to play too fast, too loudly or too coarsely, the Musiciens du Louvre are an
impressive group, with an outstanding first oboist and some very capable violinists. Several numbers
are accompanied with only a continuo instrument, to good effect. The recitative always moves well,
and appoggiaturas are duly observed.

Further listening ...
...Airs from Vauxhall Gardens (arr. Steele-Perkins). *Coupled with works by various composers.*
Crispian Steele-Perkins (tpt); **Bournemouth Sinfonietta / Richard Studt** (vn).
Carlton Classics 30366 0038-2 (4/97). *See review in the Collections section; refer to the Index.*
...Chaconne in G major (arr. Nicholson). Concerto Movement for Organ and Orchestra in
D minor.*Coupled with works by various composers.* **The Parley of Instruments / Paul Nicholson**
(hpd/org/fp). Hyperion CDA66700 (8/94). 🎵
...Oboe Concertos – B flat major, HWV301; B flat major, HWV302*a*; G minor, HWV287.
Air in G minor. Rondo in G major (both orch. Camden). Suite in G minor (ed. Camden)[a].
Ottone – Overture[a]. **Anthony Camden**, [a]**Julia Girdwood** (obs); **City of London Sinfonia /
Nicholas Ward**. Naxos 8 553430 (5/97).
...Suite in D major.*Coupled with works by various composers.* **Niklas Eklund** (baroque tpt);
Drottningholm Baroque Ensemble / Nils-Erik Sparf. Naxos 8 553531 (11/96). 🎵 *See review
in the Collections section; refer to the Index.*
...20 Sonatas, 'Op. 1'. **Lisa Beznosiuk** (fl); **Rachel Beckett** (rec); **Paul Goodwin** (ob); **Elizabeth
Wallfisch** (vn); **Richard Tunnicliffe** (vc); **Paul Nicholson** (hpd). Hyperion CDA66921/3 (3/96). 🎵
...Coronation Anthems, HWV258-61[a]. Concerti a due cori, HWV332-4[b] – No. 2 in F major; No. 3
in F major. [a]**Westminster Abbey Choir; The English Concert / **[a]**Simon Preston, **[b]**Trevor Pinnock**.
Archiv Masters 447 280-2AMA (6/95). 🎵 Ⓖ
...Ode for St Cecilia's Day, HWV76. **Felicity Lott** (sop); **Anthony Rolfe Johnson** (ten);
Soloists; The English Concerto Choir; The English Concert / Trevor Pinnock.
Archiv Produktion 419 220-2AH (1/87). 🎵
...Te Deum in D major, HWV283, "Dettingham". Dettingham Anthem, HWV265,
"The King shall rejoice". **Soloists; Westminster Abbey Choir; The English Concert /
Simon Preston**. Archiv Produktion 410 647-2AH (9/84). 🎵
...Alceste, HWV45[a]. Comus[b]. [a]**Emma Kirkby, **[a]**Judith Nelson, **[b]**Patrizia Kwella** (sops);
Margaret Cable (mez); [a]**Paul Elliott** (ten); **David Thomas** (bass); **Academy of Ancient Music /
Christopher Hogwood**. L'Oiseau-Lyre Florilegium 443 183-2OM (11/94). 🎵
...Alcina, HWV34. **Soloists; Opera Stage Chorus; City of London Baroque Sinfonia /
Richard Hickox**. EMI CDS7 49771-2 (11/88). 🎵
...Alessandro. **Soloists; La Petite Bande / Sigiswald Kuijken**.
Deutsche Harmonia Mundi Editio Classica GD77110 (2/91). 🎵 Ⓖ
...L'Allegro, il Penseroso ed il Moderato, HWV55. **Soloists; Monteverdi Choir;
English Baroque Soloists / Sir John Eliot Gardiner.**
Erato 2292 45377-2 (7/85). 🎵 *Gramophone Award Winner 1987.*
...Almira. **Soloists; Fiori Musicali / Andrew Lawrence-King**. CPO CPO999 275-2 (7/96). 🎵
...Amadigi di Gaula. **Soloists; Les Musiciens du Louvre / Marc Minkowski.**
Erato 2292-45490-2 (9/91). 🎵 Ⓖ
...Athalia, HWV52. **Soloists; New College Choir, Oxford; Academy of Ancient Music /
Christopher Hogwood**. L'Oiseau-Lyre 417 126-2OH2 (2/87). 🎵
...Belshazzar, HWV61. **Soloists; The English Concert Choir; The English Concert / Trevor Pinnock**.
Archiv Produktion 431 793-2AH3 (10/91). 🎵

...Berenice, HWV38. **Soloists; Brewer Chamber Orchestra / Rudolph Palmer.**
Newport Classic NPD85620/3 (4/96). ✍

...Clori, Tirsi e Fileno, HWV96. **Soloists; Philharmonia Baroque Orchestra / Nicholas McGegan.**
Harmonia Mundi HMU90 7045 (2/93). ✍

...Floridante (abridged). **Soloists; Tafelmusik Baroque Orchestra / Alan Curtis.**
CBC Records SMCD5110 (1/93). ✍

...Giustino. **Soloists; Cantamus Chamber Choir, Halle; Freiburg Baroque Orchestra /
Nicholas McGegan.** Harmonia Mundi HMU90 7130/2 (12/95). ✍

...Jephtha, HWV70. **Soloists; Monteverdi Choir; English Baroque Soloists / Sir John Eliot Gardiner.**
Philips 422 351-2PH3 (6/89). ✍ *Gramophone* Award Winner 1989.   ⓖ

...Joshua, HWV64. **Soloists; New College Choir, Oxford; The King's Consort / Robert King.**
Hyperion CDA66461/2 (7/91). ✍

...Judas Maccabaeus, HWV63. **Soloists; New College Choir, Oxford; The King's Consort /
Robert King.** Hyperion CDA66641/2 (12/92). ✍

...Muzio Scevola (Act 3). *Coupled with works by* **Bononcini** **Soloists; Brewer Baroque Chamber
Orchestra / Rudolph Palmer.** Newport Classic Premier NPD85540 (3/93). ✍

...Ottone. **Soloists; Freiburg Baroque Orchestra / Nicholas McGegan.**
Harmonia Mundi HMU90 7073/5 (3/93). ✍

...Partenope. **Soloists; La Petite Bande / Sigiswald Kuijken.**
Deutsche Harmonia Mundi Editio Classica GD77109 (2/91). ✍   ⓖⓖ

...Poro, re dell'Indie. **Soloists; L'Europa Galante / Fabio Biondi.**
Opus 111 OPS30-113/5 (11/94). ✍

...Riccardo Primo, re d'Inghilterra, HWV23. **Soloists; Les Talens Lyriques / Christophe Rousset.**
L'Oiseau-Lyre 452 201-2OIIO3 (11/96). ✍   ⓖ

...Rinaldo, HWV7a – Or la tromba in suon festante. *Coupled with works by various composers.*
Vesselina Kasarova (mez). RCA Victor Red Seal 09026 68522-2 (2/97). *Gramophone* Editor's
record of the month. See review in the Collections section; refer to the Index.   ⓖⓖ

...Solomon, HWV67. **Soloists; Monteverdi Choir; English Baroque Soloists / Sir John Eliot Gardiner.**
Philips 412 612-2PH2 (12/85). ✍   ⓖ

...Susanna. **Soloists; Chamber Chorus of the University of California, Berkeley; Philharmonia
Baroque Orchestra / Nicholas McGegan.** Harmonia Mundi HMU90 7030/2 (10/90). ✍   ⓖ

...Tamerlano. **Soloists; English Baroque Soloists / Sir John Eliot Gardiner.** Erato 2292-45408-2. ✍

Jacob Handl-Gallus   Slovenian 1550-1591

Handl-Gallus Lamentationes Jeremiae Prophetae. **Czech Philharmonic Chorus, Brno / Petr Fiala.**
Supraphon Ⓕ SU3280-2 (58 minutes: DDD: 12/97). Recorded 1996.

Jacob Handl, or Gallus, after a time assimilating the ever-conflating styles of late renaissance
polyphony in central Europe, eventually settled in Prague in the mid-1580s. His *Lamentations of
Jeremiah* were probably composed in his last years there before his early death at the age of only 41.
These are patiently constructed pieces, whose triadically direct style belies a keen control of texture,
a firm grasp of tonal design and a self-confident response to textual challenges. Whilst much of the
music contains narrative declamation in simple diatonic patterns, special words are given distinctive
nuances, often a melismatic cadential pattern, a voice-leading peculiarity or simply, as in the opening
of *Lamentatio V*, a burst of raw sound. The meditative air which pervades these committed
performances is impressively sustained; each strand of sound is beautifully moulded by Petr Fiala.
Handl demonstrates a concern for an integrated *conceit* evolving a long-term, intense outpouring
strictly moderated. For those reared on equivalent Lamentations by Palestrina, White, Tallis, Lassus
and Victoria, such straight, homophonic statements of faith may seem relatively austere. Yet with
Fiala's remarkable pacing and the chorus's almost perfect intonation, this recording, especially if
listened to in a single sitting, is a rare joy. The rich sound of the choir – particularly in the liberating
"Pater noster" – is truly uplifting. Texts are provided, but only in Latin and Czech.
Further listening ...
...Ecce concipies. *Coupled with works by various composers.* **St Paul's Cathedral Choir / John Scott**
(org). Hyperion CDA66994 (12/97). *See review in the Collections section; refer to the Index.*

Howard Hanson   American 1896-1981

Hanson Symphonies – No. 2, Op. 30, "Romantic"; No. 4, Op. 34, "The Requiem". Elegy in
memory of Serge Koussevitzky. **Jena Philharmonic Orchestra / David Montgomery.**
Arte Nova Classics Ⓢ 74321 43306-2 (60 minutes: DDD: 12/97). Recorded 1996.

Here is enticingly off-the-beaten-track repertory from this new super-budget label. The Fourth
(*Requiem*) was apparently Hanson's own favourite of his seven symphonies. Inscribed "in memory of
my beloved father", it is a darkly intense, neo-Sibelian outpouring which won the composer the first
Pulitzer Prize ever given to music in 1944. The tuneful, opulently scored *Romantic* (No. 2) has
understandably remained a firm favourite with American orchestras and audiences since its première

in November 1930 under Serge Koussevitzky. More recently, its use on the soundtrack of the 1979 feature-film *Alien* won Hanson an entirely new band of admirers. The *Elegy* (1956) is a supremely touching memorial to a close friend and great conductor to whom American music this century owes an incontestably profound debt of gratitude. Performances are capable and shapely, and the sound is very good too. The orchestra respond with plenty of enthusiasm to David Montgomery who obviously knows his way round these scores. That said, there is nothing here which poses a serious challenge to Gerard Schwarz and the splendid Seattle Symphony in terms of orchestral finesse or interpretative insight: Montgomery's provincial band inevitably don't possess the ingratiating tonal lustre and sheer muscle of their American counterparts, while Schwarz's direction displays just that little bit of extra commitment to the cause. None the less, at its absurdly low price, this issue will find many new friends for Hanson's ripely romantic vision.

Additional recommendation ...
...Symphonies – No. 1 in D minor, "Nordic"; No. 2. Elegy in memory of Serge Koussevitzky.
   Seattle Symphony Orchestra / Gerard Schwarz. Delos Ⓕ DE3073 (71 minutes: DDD: 3/90).

Further listening ...
...Piano Concerto, Op. 36[a]. Symphonies – No. 5, Op. 43, "Sinfonia Sacra"; No. 7, "A Sea Symphony[b]. Mosaics. [a]**Carol Rosenberger** (pf); [b]**Seattle Symphony Chorale and Orchestra / Gerard Schwarz.** Delos DE3130 (3/93).
...Symphony No. 3 in A minor, Op. 63. *Coupled with works by various composers.*
   Boston Symphony Orchestra / Serge Koussevitzky. Biddulph mono WHL044* (3/97).
...Dies Natalis I[c]. The Mystic Trumpeter[abc]. Lumen in Christo[bc]. Lux aeterna, Op. 24[c]. [a]**James Earl Jones** (narr); [b]**Seattle Symphony Chorale and** [c]**Orchestra / Gerard Schwarz.** Delos DE3160 (5/95).

John H. Harbison

American 1938

Suggested listening ...
...Suite for Solo Cello. *Coupled with works by various composers.* **Richard Slavich** (vc).
   Crystal Records CD639 (5/98). *See review in the Collections section; refer to the Index.*
...Wind Quintet. *Coupled with works by various composers.* **Reykjavik Wind Quintet.**
   Chandos CHAN9174 (11/93). *See review in the Collections section; refer to the Index.* Ⓖ
...O Magnum Mysterium (two settings)[c]. Ave verum corpus[c]. Two Emmanuel Motets[c]. Communion Words[c]. Concerning Them Which Are Asleep[c]. Recordare[ad]. Violin Concerto[bd]. [a]**Roberta Anderson** (sop); [a]**Mary Westbrook-Geha** (mez); [a]**Frank Kelley** (ten); [a]**Donald Wilkinson** (bar); [b]**Rose Mary Harbison** (vn); [c]**Chorus and** [d]**Orchestra of Emmanuel Music / Craig Smith.**
   Koch International Classics 37310-2 (10/97).

Guy d'Hardelot

French/British 1858-1936

Suggested listening ...
...Because. *Coupled with works by various composers.*
   Lesley Garrett (sop); **Britten Sinfonia / Ivor Bolton.**
   Conifer Classics 75605 51329-2 (12/97). *See review in the Collections section; refer to the Index.*

Louis Hardin (aka Moondog)

American 1916

Suggested listening ...
...Synchrony No. 2. *Coupled with works by various composers.* **Judith Sherman** (drum);
   Kronos Quartet. Nonesuch 7559-79457-2 (12/97). *Gramophone* Editor's choice.
   See review in the Collections section; refer to the Index.

Clifford Harker

British 20th century

Suggested listening ...
...Magnificat and Nunc dimittis in A flat major. *Coupled with works by various composers.*
   Bristol Cathedral Choir / Christopher Brayne with **Ian Ball** (org).
   Priory PRCD528 (8/96). *See review in the Collections section; refer to the Index.*

Roy Harris

American 1898-1979

Suggested listening ...
...Symphonies Nos. 1 and 3. *Coupled with works by various composers.*
   Boston Symphony Orchestra / Serge Koussevitzky. Pearl mono GEMMCD9492* (12/91).
   See review in the Collections section; refer to the Index. ⒼⒼⒼ

Lou Harrison
American 1917

Harrison Symphony No. 3[a]. Grand Duo[b]. [b]**Romuald Tecco** (vn); [a]**Cabrillo Music Festival Orchestra / Dennis Russell Davies** ([b]pf). MusicMasters Ⓔ 7073-2 (68 minutes: DDD: 5/95).

The Third Symphony (1982) is a work of some substance and no little potential for widespread appeal. The boldly striding outer paragraphs of the opening *Allegro moderato* frame a more contemplative, raptly lyrical central section (with some beautiful writing for solo strings). Next follow three linked, nicely contrasted dance episodes, the first of which, a bouncy, good-natured "Reel in Honor of Henry Cowell" (one of Harrison's teachers), is particularly infectious. The slow movement comprises a gently swaying *Largo ostinato* of great dignity and slumbering power, whilst the finale is a joyous, finely-sustained *Allegro* of deceptive rigour and satisfying proportions. The *Grand Duo* for violin and piano from 1988 perhaps makes less consistently compelling listening, though its five movements also contain much characterful invention. Both the "Stampadé" and "Polka" offer plenty of opportunities (gratefully seized here) for vigorous violin double-stopping and piano cluster-chords, whereas a simple, trance-like euphony illuminates the tender, central "A Round". Moreover, Harrison's eloquent sense of dialogue similarly distinguishes the thoughtful extended slow movement and more declamatory initial "Prelude". Both works were commissioned by the Cabrillo Music Festival in California, whose eponymous orchestra perform with admirable discipline and total dedication under the ever-sympathetic guidance of Dennis Russell Davies. In the *Grand Duo*, the versatile Davies partners violinist Romuald Tecco with equally idiomatic, wonderfully assured results.

Further listening ...

...Symphony No. 2, "Elegiac". *Coupled with works by* **Hovhaness** American Composers Orchestra / Dennis Russell Davies. MusicMasters 7021-2 (5/93).

...Suite for Symphonic Strings. *Coupled with works by* **McPhee** and **Ung** American Composers Orchestra / Dennis Russell Davies. Argo 444 560-2ZH (4/96).

...Harp Suite[a]. Serenade[ac]. Perilous Chapel[cd]. Fugue[ce]. Song of Quetzalcoatl[ce]. May Rain[bc]. [b]**John Duykers** (ten); [a]**David Tanenbaum** (gtr); [b]**Julie Steinberg** (pf); [c]**William Winant** (perc); [d]**San Francisco Contemporary Music Players / Stephen Mosko**; [e]**Percussion Ensemble.** New Albion NA055CD (2/94).

...Mass (to St Anthony). *Coupled with* **Pärt** Berliner Messe[a]. **LeaAnne DenBeste** (sop); **Laura Crockett** (mez); [a]**David Vanderwal** (ten); [a]**Karl Blume** (bass); [a]**Marianne Lewis** (org); **Oregon Repertory Singers / Gilbert Seeley.** Koch International Classics 37177-2 (4/94).

Stephen Hartke
New Zealand 1952

...Caoine. *Coupled with works by various composers.* **Michelle Makarski** (vn). ECM New Series 449 957-2 (7/97). *See review in the Collections section; refer to the Index.*

Fred Hartley
British 1905-1991

Suggested listening ...

...Rouge et noir. *Coupled with works by various composers.* **Studio Two Concert Orchestra / Reginald Kilbey.** EMI British Composers CDM5 66537-2 (1/98). *See review in the Collections section; refer to the Index.*

Johan Peter Hartmann
Danish 1805-1900

Suggested listening ...

...Tell me, star of night, Op. 63. Little Christine – Sverkel's romance. *Coupled with works by various composers.* **Aksel Schiøtz** (ten) with various artists. Danacord mono DACOCD454* (5/97). *See review in the Collections section; refer to the Index.*

Karl Amadeus Hartmann
German 1905-1963

Hartmann Symphonies – No. 1[ac]; No. 2 – Adagio[d]; No. 3[e]; No. 4[d]; No. 5[d]; No. 6[d]; No. 7 (1957-8)[f]; No. 8[d]. Gesangsszene (1963)[b]. [a]**Doris Soffel** (contr); [b]**Dietrich Fischer-Dieskau** (bar); **Bavarian Radio Symphony Orchestra / **[c]**Fritz Rieger**, [d]**Rafael Kubelík**, [e]**Ferdinand Leitner**, [f]**Zdenek Macal**. Wergo Ⓔ WER60187-50 (four discs: 225 minutes: ADD: 5/90). From WER60086 (6/81). ❸❸❸

Stravinsky once remarked that Alban Berg was "synthetic, in the best sense" – the same could perhaps be said about Hartmann. In the 1930s he was beginning to establish a reputation, but was forced to withdraw himself and his works from public musical life as a known opponent of the Nazi regime. During the war he destroyed or radically revised most of his output up till then, and these eight symphonies (five of which are based on, or are revisions of, earlier works) appeared between 1946 and his death in 1963. Together they show his broad sympathies with the twentieth-century masters. As

Hartmann chose to write symphonies, he had to be mindful of the enormity of the tradition that preceded him, and you can hear the presence of Bruckner in the monumental sense of structure, of Reger in the densely chromatic counterpoint and an intense, tortured lyricism derived from Berg. There is a tribute to the neo-classical Stravinsky in the Fifth Symphony, and more than a hint of Bartók in the irresistible momentum of the fugues that conclude the Sixth. Mahler is present in the Whitman settings of the First Symphony, significantly entitled *Attempt at a Requiem*; also, in the upheavals of the first movement of the Eighth, the crisis near the end of the *Adagio* of Mahler's Tenth is vividly recalled (sustained high trumpets, screaming violins). The spectral Funeral March in Webern's *Pieces*, Op. 6, haunts sections of the First, Third and Eighth Symphonies. Whether, with Hartmann's synthesis of his models, he managed to forge a demonstrably personal idiom is open to question. What is indisputable is the power of Hartmann's music to communicate, and its capacity to fascinate as sheer sound. On the debit side, not all the vigorously contrapuntal sections of the later works avoid sounding academic. The dates of these live recordings are not given, but they are all naturally balanced, with excellent clarity – Hartmann's torrents of tuned percussion are thrillingly captured. The Bavarian Radio Symphony Orchestra play with polish and evident conviction.

Additional recommendations ...

...No. 1. *Coupled with works by various composers.* **Cornelia Kallisch** (contr); **Bamberg Symphony Orchestra / Ingo Metzmacher.** EMI Ⓕ CDC5 55424-2 (59 minutes: DDD: 3/97).
See review in the Collections section; refer to the Index.

...No. 2. Gesangsszene to words from Jean Giraudoux's "Sodom and Gomorrah"[a]. Sinfonia Tragica. [a]**Siegmund Nimsgern** (bar); **Bamberg Symphony Orchestra / Karl Anton Rickenbacher.** Koch Schwann Ⓕ 312952 (64 minutes: DDD: 5/94). *Gramophone Editor's choice.*

...No. 3. **Ives** Robert Browning Overture. **Bamberg Symphony Orchestra / Ingo Metzmacher.** EMI Ⓕ CDC5 55254-2 (52 minutes: DDD: 10/95).

Further listening ...

...Concerto funèbre. *Coupled with works by* **Berg** and **Janáček** Philharmonia Orchestra / Heinz Holliger; Deutsche Kammerphilharmonie / Thomas Zehetmair (vn/dir). Teldec 4509-97449-2 (6/95).

...String Quartets – No. 1, "Carillon"; No. 2. **Pellegrini Quartet.** CPO CPO999 219-2 (8/94).   Ⓖ

...Simplicius Simplicissimus. **Soloists; Munich Concert Choir; Bavarian Radio Symphony Orchestra / Heinz Fricke.** Wergo WER6259-2 (11/95).

Jonathan Harvey   British 1939

Harvey I love the Lord. Carols. Lauds (with Paul Watkins, vc). Sobre un éxtasis alte contemplación. Come, Holy Ghost. O Jesu, nomen dulce. Two Fragments. The Angels. Forms of Emptiness. **The Joyful Company of Singers / Peter Broadbent.** ASV Ⓕ CDDCA917 (63 minutes: DDD: 7/95). Texts and translations included. Recorded 1994.

Compare Jonathan Harvey's *Come, Holy Ghost* with one of his large-scale instrumental works and you might suspect that they are the work of different Jonathan Harveys, one providing short pieces for cathedral choirs, the other active on the avant-garde concert scene. So it is a particular virtue of this disc that by providing such a generous cross-section of Harvey's choral music it makes it easier to hear how the two Harveys are in fact one far-from-inconsistent composer. Since Harvey himself has progressed from choir school to electronic studio it is not so surprising that his music can relate to both worlds so effectively, and most of the compositions here take a fresh look at aspects of the English cathedral tradition without attempting to force those aspects into an unholy alliance with modernist techniques, and technologies. From the early *Fragments* (1966) to *The Angels* (1994) we can hear versions of the kind of contemplative intensity that informs some of Harvey's finest concert works (for example, *Bhakti*), and these choral pieces are never poor relations. The short *Sobre un éxtasis alte contemplación* works within its own essential sounds, and in exploring speech as well as song develops the more dramatic dialogue to be found in the larger-scale *Forms of Emptiness* (1986) and *Lauds* (1987). In such compositions, with their highly diverse textures, spiritual and sensual elements are brought into purposeful conjunction. The Joyful Company of Singers have the flexibility of tone as well as the strength of sonority to project all facets of this often challenging music.

Additional recommendation ...

...I love the Lord. Come, Holy Ghost. *Coupled with works by various composers.* **Ionian Singers / Timothy Salter; Thalia Myers** (pf); **Erik Jacobsen** (perc). Usk Recordings Ⓕ USK1216CD (67 minutes: DDD: 3/96).

Further listening ...

...Bhakti for Chamber Ensemble and Quadraphonic Tape. **Spectrum / Guy Protheroe.** NMC NMCD001 (9/89).

...Bhakti. **Nouvel Ensemble Moderne / Lorraine Vaillancourt.** Auvidis Montaigne MO782086 (7/96).

....From Silence[a]. Natajara[b]. Ritual Melodies[c]. [a]**Karol Bennett** (voc); [b]**Harrie Starreveld** (fl/picc); [a]**Lucy Chapman Stoltzman** (vn); [a]**Michael Thompson** (hn); [a]**Dean Anderson** (perc); [b]**René Eckhardt** (pf); [a]**Kathleen Supove,** [a]**John MacDonald,** [a]**Diana Dabby** (elec kbds); [ac]**David Atherton,** [ac]**Brent Koeppel,** [ac]**Ken Malsky,** [ac]**Philip Sohn** (computer/tape ops) / **Barry Vercoe.** Bridge BCD9031 (11/92).

...Fantasia. Laus Deo. *Coupled with works by* **Maxwell Davies** and **Williamson** Kevin Bowyer (org). Nimbus NI5509 (7/97).

...Song Offerings. *Coupled with works by* **G. Benjamin** and **Boulez** **Penelope Walmsley-Clark**
(sop); **Sebastian Bell** (fl); **London Sinfonietta / George Benjamin.** Nimbus NI5167 (10/89).
...Dum transisset Sabbatum. *Coupled with works by various composers.* **St Paul's Cathedral Choir /**
John Scott with **Andrew Lucas** (org). Hyperion CDA66826 (7/96).

Basil Harwood
British 1859-1949

Suggested listening ...
...O how glorious is the Kingdom. *Coupled with works by various composers.*
Choir of St Mary's Cathedral, Edinburgh / Timothy Byram-Wigfield with **Peter Backhouse** (org).
Priory PRCD557 (10/97). *See review in the Collections section; refer to the Index.*

Johannes Hasprois
French fl 1378-1428

Suggested listening ...
...Ma doulce amour. *Coupled with works by various composers.* **Hilliard Ensemble.**
Isis CD030 (7/97). *See review in the Collections section; refer to the Index.*

Johann Hasse
German 1699-1783

Hasse Overtures – Cleofide; Asteria. Salve regina in A major[b]. Chori angelici laetantes[b]. Fugue
and Grave in G minor. Salve regina in E flat major[ab]. [a]**Barbara Bonney** (sop); [b]**Bernarda Fink**
(contr); **Musica Antiqua Cologne / Reinhard Goebel** (vn). Archiv Produktion Ⓔ 453 435-2AH
(72 minutes: DDD: 9/97). ☛ Texts and translations included. Recorded 1996.
Hasse composed several settings of the *Salve regina* of which Reinhard Goebel has chosen two for his
interesting programme of vocal and instrumental pieces. The remaining pieces are two attractive
overtures for wind and strings, a motet for mezzo-soprano and an expressively intense, vibrant Fugue
in G minor of doubtful authenticity, but perhaps the work of the Mannheim composer, Franz Xaver
Richter. The greater part of the vocal music is for mezzo-soprano or contralto, in this instance
Bernarda Fink. These are full-bodied performances, vocally and instrumentally, and both the aural
luxuriance of Fink's warm, rounded tone and the richness of the accompanying string textures are
enjoyable. The motet, *Chori angelici laetantes* is a joyful, spirited and virtuoso composition with an
accompaniment of strings and continuo. Fink is on superb form here, attentive to the words of the
text and effortless in the delivery of her bravura passages. The motet is hugely appealing both for its
warmth of sentiment and, as so often with Hasse, for its ravishing melodies. The E flat *Salve regina* is
no less captivating, with a pair of oboes and a bassoon added to the string texture. Bonney and Fink
are evenly matched and blend together pleasingly in music which few will be able to resist. A delightful
programme, thoughtfully put together and very well executed.
Further listening ...
...Flute Concerto in G major. *Coupled with works by* **Agrell** and **Scheibe**
  Concerto Copenhagen / Andrew Manze. Chandos Chaconne CHAN0535 (6/93). ☛
...Keyboard Sonata in E flat major. *Coupled with works by various composers.*
  Christine Schornsheim (hpd/). Capriccio 10 424 (4/95). ☛
...La conversione di Sant' Agostino. **Soloists; Berlin RIAS Chamber Choir;**
  Berlin Ancient Music Academy / Marcus Creed. Capriccio 10 389/90 (7/93). ☛
...Quel vago seno, ò Fille[a]. Fille dolce, mio bene[a]. La conversione di Sant' Agostino – Ah Dio,
  ritornate[a]. Four Venetian ballads[a]. Trio Sonata in B minor, Op. 2 No. 6. Keyboard Sonata in
  C minor, Op. 7 No. 6. [a]**Julianne Baird** (sop); **Nancy Hadden** (fl); **Erin Headley** (va da gamba);
  [b]**Malcolm Proud** (hpd). CRD CRD3488 (11/94). *Gramophone Editor's choice.*   Ⓖ
...Requiem in C major[a]. Miserere in E minor. **Greta de Reyghere** (sop); **Susanna Moncayo von Hase**
  (contr); [a]**Ian Honeyman** (ten); **Dirk Snellings** (bass); **Il Fondamento Chorus and Orchestra /**
  Paul Dombrecht. Opus 111 OPS30-80 (11/93). ☛
...Piramo e Tisbe. **Soloists; Capella Clementina / Helmut Müller-Brühl.**
  Koch Schwann 310882 (4/94). ☛

Joseph Haydn
Austrian 1732-1809

Haydn Cello Concertos – No. 1 in C major, HobVII*b*/1; No. 2 in D major, HobVII*b*/2.
A. Kraft Cello Concerto in C major, Op. 4. **Anner Bylsma** (vc); **Tafelmusik / Jeanne Lamon.**
  Deutsche Harmonia Mundi Ⓔ RD77757 (67 minutes: DDD: 9/91). ☛ Recorded 1989.
At best, an 'authentic' performance can only aspire to return to the spirit, rather than the letter of the
period it strives to re-create, and yet the fine Dutch cellist Anner Bylsma comes as near as anyone to
convincing us that this is indeed the way Haydn might have wished these sunny, yet highly
sophisticated concertos, to be played. Haydn composed these works for the virtuoso cellist of the

Esterházy court orchestra, Anton Kraft, and the bold and adventurous solo writing reflects his fabled technical prowess and musical sensitivity. Bylsma offers a lithe, yet scrupulously classical and poised account of the C major Concerto, with a romantically inflected central *Adagio* followed by a dashingly brilliant, yet suitably witty finale. His rapid passagework in higher registers is astonishing, while he reveals the stately dignity of the D major work (long attributed to Kraft) in a cultured and attractively proportioned reading of rich intensity and variety. Bylsma includes his own revisions of period cadenzas, which are never less than apposite, and deftly executed. The real discovery here, though, is the Cello Concerto by Kraft himself, which combines the expected brilliant pyrotechnics with some effective melodic writing, in a work which anticipates the styles developed during the early nineteenth century. In fact, Kraft advised Beethoven on the cello part of his Triple Concerto, and his compositions exercised great influence in the genesis of modern cello technique. Bylsma is superbly supported by the excellent Tafelmusik, and the recording is first rate. A stunning collection.

Additional recommendations ...

...Nos. 1 and 2. [ab]. Violin Concertos[c] – C major, HobVIIa/1; A major, HobVIIa/3; G major, HobVIIa/4. Concerto for Violin, Keyboard and Strings in F major, HobXVIII/6[cd]. [a]**Christine Walevska** (vc); [d]**Bruno Canino** (hpd); **English Chamber Orchestra /** [b]**Edo de Waart,** [c]**Salvatore Accardo** (vn). Philips Duo Ⓜ 438 797-2PM2 (two discs: 142 minutes: ADD: 4/94).

...Nos. 1 and 2. **Truls Mørk** (vc); **Norwegian Chamber Orchestra / Iona Brown.** Virgin Classics Ⓕ VC5 45014-2 (50 minutes: DDD: 6/94).

...Nos. 1 and 2. *Coupled with works by various composers.* **Jacqueline du Pré** (vc); **London Symphony Orchestra / Sir John Barbirolli; English Chamber Orchestra / Daniel Barenboim.** EMI Ⓑ CZS5 68132-2 (six discs: 437 minutes: ADD: 8/94). *See review in the Collections section; refer to the Index.* ⒼⒼ

...Nos. 1 and 2. Symphony No. 104 in D major, "London". **Pieter Wispelwey** (vc); **Florilegium.** Channel Classics Ⓕ CCS7395 (73 minutes: DDD: 7/95).

...No. 2. *Coupled with works by various composers.* **János Starker** (vc); **Gerald Moore** (pf); **Philharmonia Orchestra / Carlo Maria Giulini, Walter Susskind.** EMI mono/stereo Ⓜ CZS5 68485-2 (six discs: 398 minutes: ADD: 12/95). *See review in the Collections section; refer to the Index.*

...No. 2 – Allegro moderato; Adagio (arr. Geraërt). *Coupled with works by various composers.* **Pablo Casals** (vc); **BBC Symphony Orchestra / Sir Adrian Boult.** Biddulph mono Ⓜ LAB144* (79 minutes: ADD: 1/98). *See review under Elgar; refer to the Index.*

...Nos. 1 and 2[a]. Lo speziale – Overture. [a]**Han-Na Chang** (vc); **Staatskapelle Dresden / Giuseppe Sinopoli.** EMI Ⓕ CDC5 56535-2 (58 minutes: DDD: 5/98).

Haydn Horn Concerto No. 1 in D major, HobXVII*d*/3.
Danzi Horn Concerto in E major.
Rosetti Horn Concerto in D minor. **Hermann Baumann** (hn); **Concerto Amsterdam / Jaap Schröder.** Teldec Das Alte Werk Ⓜ 0630-12324-2 (52 minutes: ADD: 8/96). Recorded 1968.

Hermann Baumann has always been one of the most impressive performers on the eighteenth-century hand horn and in his late 1960s recording of Haydn's splendid First Horn Concerto in D the characterful smoothness of his playing brings virtually no indications of the problems of hand 'stopping', and his intonation is absolutely true. The *Adagio* soars and there are also some wonderfully resonant low notes. The coupled Danzi Concerto is also appealing and brings ready bravura in its flowing opening movement, which is followed by a mellifluous central "Romance" and a perky finale. The third work here, a fine Bohemian Concerto by Antonio Rosetti, is *galant* in style, but with hints of high drama. The first movement is slightly reminiscent of Hummel's E major Trumpet Concerto and the slow movement is operatically romantic, the finale jolly. Jaap Schröder and his Concerto Amsterdam provide stylish accompaniments which maintain a firm late-eighteenth-century flavour, and the sound, fresh, warm and clear, is excellent.

Additional recommendation ...

...No. 1. *Coupled with works by various composers.* **Barry Tuckwell** (hn); **Academy of St Martin in the Fields / Sir Neville Marriner.** EMI Forte Ⓜ CZS5 69395-2 (two discs: 150 minutes: ADD: 2/97). *See review in the Collections section; refer to the Index.*

Haydn Keyboard Concertos – F major, HobXVIII/3; G major, HobXVIII/4; D major, HobXVIII/11. **Franz Liszt Chamber Orchestra / Emanuel Ax** (pf). Sony Classical Ⓕ SK48383 (59 minutes: DDD: 5/93). Recorded 1992.

Mozart's unique achievement in his 27 piano concertos has tended to overshadow the more modestly scored, less overtly virtuoso works by Haydn and only the D major Concerto is at all well known today. Whilst none of the three works recorded here could claim to add to the development of the form in the way that those of Mozart did, all three possess great charm: take for example the *Largo cantabile* of the early F major work to hear Haydn's melodic gift at its most endearing. The *Presto* finale of the same concerto recalls some of his later piano sonatas in its juxtaposition of knockabout comedy and theatrical minor-key drama. The G major, supposedly written for the blind pianist, composer and singer Maria Theresia von Paradis boasts an extended *Grave* slow movement. But it is the D major with its larger orchestra (horns and oboes added to strings) that works best and the *Rondo all'Ungarese* finale, with its myriad key changes and sparkling good humour, is predictably the highlight of the disc. Emanuel Ax (directing from the keyboard) gives performances of the utmost finesse and affection: if any performance were to help to restore the fortunes of these works then this is surely it. His playing throughout is deeply felt: graceful in the slow movements and dexterous in the outer ones. In addition, he plays his own charming cadenzas in the F and G major works. Sony's sound is spacious, with the piano forwardly placed and the notes are adequate, though no biographical information is included.

Additional recommendations ...
...D major; G major; F major; G major, HobXVIII /9. **Hae-won Chang** (pf); **Camerata Cassovia / Robert Stankovsky.** Naxos ⓖ 8 550713 (71 minutes: DDD).
...G major; F major, HobXVIII/7 (attrib.); D major. **Deutsche Kammerphilharmonie / Mikhail Pletnev** (pf). Virgin Classics ⓕ VC5 45196-2 (62 minutes: DDD: 11/96).

Haydn Trumpet Concerto in E flat major, HobVIIe/1[a]. Cello Concerto in D major, HobVIIb/2[b]. Violin Concerto No. 1 in C major, HobVII[c]. [a]**Wynton Marsalis** (tpt); [c]**Cho-Liang Lin** (vn); [b]**Yo-Yo Ma** (vc); [a]**National Philharmonic Orchestra / Raymond Leppard;** [b]**English Chamber Orchestra / José Luis Garcia;** [c]**Minnesota Orchestra / Sir Neville Marriner.** CBS Masterworks ⓕ MK39310 (59 minutes: DDD: 1/86). From IM39310 (1/85).

This compilation of three Haydn concertos has a different soloist and orchestra for each. The young American trumpeter Wynton Marsalis has all the fluency one could wish for and an instrument allowing a full three octaves to be displayed in his own cadenza to the first movement. Although this is an efficient performance, it in no way approaches the class of the next one. The cellist Yo-Yo Ma is very different as a performer: though equally a master of his instrument, and indeed a virtuoso who seems incapable of producing an ugly sound or playing out of tune, one feels a deep emotional involvement in all he does. In addition, the recording in the D major Cello Concerto is unusually faithful in blending the cello well into the ensemble without ever covering it. Ma is supported by the excellent English Chamber Orchestra and the qualities of integration and ensemble under their leader's direction are all that one could wish for. In the C major Violin Concerto the skilful Cho-Liang Lin has the benefit of a most sympathetic conductor in Sir Neville Marriner, but he cannot match Ma's subtlety and commitment.

Additional recommendations ...
...Trumpet Concerto. *Coupled with works by various composers.* **John Wallace** (tpt); **Philharmonia Orchestra / Christopher Warren-Green.** Nimbus ⓕ NI7016 (75 minutes: DDD: 2/95). *See review in the Collections section; refer to the Index.*
...Trumpet Concerto. *Coupled with works by various composers.* **Maurice André** (tpt); **Franz Liszt Chamber Orchestra / János Rolla.** EMI ⓕ CDC5 55231-2 (61 minutes: DDD: 7/95).
...Trumpet Concerto. *Coupled with works by various composers.* **Crispian Steele-Perkins** (tpt); **English Chamber Orchestra / Anthony Halstead.** Carlton Classics ⓜ 30366 0066-2 (63 minutes: DDD: 10/97). *See review in the Collections section; refer to the Index.*

Haydn Overtures – Acide e Galatea; Lo speziale; Le pescatrici; L'infedeltà delusa; Philemon und Baucis; Der Götterrath; Il ritorno di Tobia; Der Feuersbrunst; L'incontro improvviso; Il mondo della luna. **Haydn Sinfonietta, Vienna / Manfred Huss.** Koch Schwann ⓕ 317232 (61 minutes: DDD: 9/96). 📻 Recorded 1994.

The Haydn Sinfonietta's stylish, vigorous approach – enhanced by period instruments and exemplary recording – creates striking portrayals of the repertoire under review. Here, listeners are given the opportunity to sample overtures from Haydn's theatrical music composed between 1762 and 1777 in an absorbing illustration of life at Esterházy. The Sinfonietta's arresting vitality in *Acide e Galatea, Le pescatrici, Lo speziale* and *Il mondo della luna*, underlines this music's originally festive purpose; while suitably majestic performances of *L'infedeltà delusa* and *Philemon und Baucis* attest to their presentation before the Empress Maria Theresia. Increased intensity in minor-key pieces such as *Der Götterrath*, with its grand depiction of the 'Council of the Gods' (an allegory for the Hapsburg family), and *Il ritorno di Tobia* highlight Haydn's overtly dramatic writing. Brighter, more startling colours are brilliantly projected by these musicians in an aptly fiery account of *Der Feuersbrunst* and the exotic *L'incontro improvviso* which conjures up vivid images of a Turkish harem. With potent contrast between rhythmically taut energy in the fast movements and elegant sensitivity in the imaginatively scored slow ones, Huss and the Haydn Sinfonietta have surely produced a winner.

Haydn Six Scherzandos, HobII/33-8. **Vienna Haydn Sinfonietta / Manfred Huss.** Koch Schwann ⓕ 314432 (52 minutes: DDD: 11/95). Recorded 1993.

The *Six Scherzandos* which Haydn wrote in 1761 to impress his new patron, Prince Paul Anton Esterházy, exhibit all the typical characteristics of the composer's mature style. Each of these miniature symphonies presents the four movements of the classical symphony with a degree of thematic and formal concentration associated with Beethoven's Op. 126 *Bagatelles* and, ultimately, with the works of Anton Webern. Moreover, their sequence here creates a compelling musical cycle. The abounding vitality and subtle sensitivity with which Manfred Huss and the Vienna Haydn Sinfonietta perform this music emphasizes its remarkable formal and instrumental variety, highlighting the startling emotional intensity created by its sudden changes of mood. Sample the vivacious opening *allegros*, the rugged minuets (whose trios feature a solo flute, superbly played here by Reinhard Czasch), the affecting *adagios* – especially the operatic example in the Fourth *Scherzando* – scored for strings alone, and the brief, energetic finales. The set culminates in the Sixth *Scherzando*, in A major, whose opening movement's triadic principal theme, agitated repeated notes and elated interjections from the horns, signal the music's increased dramatic power. The rustic minuet is rhythmically more imaginative and its trio is melodically freer than in the other five works; the *Adagio*'s exquisite pathos is enhanced by tasteful contributions from the *basso continuo*, and the archetypal, witty finale simulates larger forces with its opposition of different instrumental groupings. Ensemble is impeccably balanced throughout, and the recorded sound is vividly clear and natural.

Haydn Symphonies. **Philharmonia Hungarica / Antál Dorati.** Decca Ⓑ 448 531-2LC33
(33 discs: ADD: 3/97). Recorded 1969-73.   ⒼⒼⒼ
No. 1 in D major. No. 2 in C major. No. 3 in G major. No. 4 in D major. No. 5 in A major. No. 6 in D major, "Le matin". No. 7 in C major, "Le midi". No. 8 in G major, "Le soir". No. 9 in C major. No. 10 in D major. No. 11 in E flat major. No. 12 in E major. No. 13 in D major. No. 14 in A major. No. 15 in D major. No. 16 in B flat major. No. 17 in F major. No. 18 in G major. No. 19 in D major. No. 20 in C major. No. 21 in A major. No. 22 in E flat major, "Philosopher". No. 23 in G major. No. 24 in D major. No. 25 in C major. No. 26 in D minor, "Lamentatione". No. 27 in G major. No. 28 in A major. No. 29 in E major. No. 30 in C major, "Alleluja". No. 31 in D major, "Hornsignal". No. 32 in C major. No. 33 in C major. No. 34 in D major minor. No. 35 in B flat major. No. 36 in E flat major. No. 37 in C major. No. 38 in C major. No. 39 in G minor. No. 40 in F major. No. 41 in C major. No. 42 in D major. No. 43 in E flat major, "Mercury". No. 44 in E minor major, "Trauersinfonie". No. 45 in F sharp minor, "Farewell". No. 46 in B major. No. 47 in G major, "Palindrome". No. 48 in C major, "Maria Theresia". No. 49 in F minor major, "La passione". No. 50 in C major. No. 51 in B flat major. No. 52 in C minor. No. 53 in D major, "Imperial". No. 54 in G major. No. 55 in E flat major, "Schoolmaster". No. 56 in C major. No. 57 in D major. No. 58 in F major. No. 59 in A major, "Fire". No. 60 in C major, "Il distratto". No. 61 in D major. No. 62 in D major. No. 63 in C major, "La Roxelane". No. 64 in A major, "Tempora mutantur". No. 65 in A major. No. 66 in B flat major. No. 67 in F major. No. 68 in B flat major. No. 69 in C major, "Loudon". No. 70 in D major. No. 71 in B flat major. No. 72 in D major. No. 73 in D major, "La chasse". No. 74 in E flat major. No. 75 in D major. No. 76 in E flat major. No. 77 in B flat major. No. 78 in C minor. No. 79 in F major. No. 80 in D minor. No. 81 in G major. No. 82 in C major, "L'ours". No. 83 in G minor, "La poule". No. 84 in E flat major. No. 85 in B flat major, "La reine". No. 86 in D major. No. 87 in A major. No. 88 in G major, "Letter V". No. 89 in F major. No. 90 in C major. No. 91 in E flat major. No. 92 in G major, "Oxford". No. 93 in D major. No. 94 in G major, "Surprise". No. 95 in C minor. No. 96 in D major, "Miracle". No. 97 in C major. No. 98 in B flat major. No. 99 in E flat major. No. 100 in G major, "Military". No. 101 in D major, "Clock". No. 102 in B flat major. No. 103 in E flat major, "Drumroll". No. 104 in D major, "London". "A" in B flat major. "B" in B flat major. Sinfonia concertante in B flat major, HobI/105, "No. 105".

Dorati's famous integral recording of all 104 of the published Symphonies now returns in a Decca bargain box containing 33 CDs. It still holds its place in the catalogue as the only complete set to contain everything Haydn wrote in this medium, including the Symphonies "A" and "B", omitted from the original numbering scheme simply because at one time they were not thought to be symphonies at all. The survey also encompasses additional alternative movements for certain works (notably Nos. 53 and 103) and alternative complete versions of the *Philosopher* Symphony and No. 63, which are fascinating. The remastering confirms the excellence of the vintage Decca sound. No more needs to be said, except that the one minus point in these very convincing modern-instrument performances is Dorati's insistence on measured, often rustic tempos for the minuets. Presentation is as a series of four CDs with consecutive numbering, with separate and highly illuminating notes for each group of works, written by H.C. Robbins Landon, who edited the scores and oversaw the whole project. This is good forward planning, for it means that further reissues are economically viable, using the current documentation. The six *Paris* Symphonies and 12 *London* Symphonies are already available separately on Decca Doubles (listed immediately below) and hopefully Decca have plans to make further additional piecemeal reissues. But for those who can run to the complete series this bargain box is self-recommending – a source of inexhaustible pleasure.

Additional recommendations ...
...Nos. 82-87. **Philharmonia Hungarica / Antál Dorati.**
    Decca Double Ⓜ 448 194-2DF2 (two discs: 148 minutes: ADD: 3/96).
...*Paris* Symphonies. **Philharmonia Hungarica / Antál Dorati.**
    Decca Double Ⓑ 448 195-2DF2 (two discs: ADD: 3/97).   ⒼⒼⒼ
...*London* Symphonies. **Philharmonia Hungarica / Antál Dorati.**
    Decca Double Ⓑ 452 256-2DF2 (two discs: ADD: 3/97).   ⒼⒼⒼ
...*London* Symphonies. **Philharmonia Hungarica / Antál Dorati.**
    Decca Double Ⓑ 452 259-2DF2 (two discs: ADD: 3/97).   ⒼⒼⒼ
...Nos. 13-16. **Hanover Band / Roy Goodman.** Hyperion Ⓕ CDA66534 (74 minutes: DDD: 3/94). 🎵
...Nos. 26, 35 and 49. **Northern Chamber Orchestra / Nicholas Ward.**
    Naxos Ⓢ 8 550721 (55 minutes: DDD: 1/94).

…Nos. 26, 42-44, 48 and 49. **Academy of Ancient Music / Christopher Hogwood.**
L'Oiseau-Lyre Ⓕ 440 222-2OH3 (three discs: 168 minutes: DDD: 11/94). ✏
…Nos. 42-44. **Hanover Band / Roy Goodman.** Hyperion Ⓕ CDA66530 (79 minutes: DDD: 2/93). ✏
…Nos. 41-43. **Tafelmusik / Bruno Weil.**
Sony Classical Vivarte Ⓕ SK48370 (66 minutes: DDD: 4/93). ✏
…No. 44, 51 and 52. **Tafelmusik / Bruno Weil.**
Sony Classical Vivarte Ⓕ SK48371 (62 minutes: DDD: 4/93). ✏
…Nos. 45, 48 and 102. **Capella Istropolitana / Barry Wordsworth.**
Naxos Ⓢ 8 550382 (73 minutes: DDD: 9/91).
…Nos. 70-72. **Hanover Band / Roy Goodman** (hpd).
Hyperion Ⓕ CDA66526 (76 minutes: DDD: 9/92). ✏
…No. 88. **Schubert** Symphony No. 9 in C major, D944, "Great". **Berlin Philharmonic Orchestra / Wilhelm Furtwängler.** DG The Originals mono Ⓜ 447 439-2GOR* (76 minutes: ADD: 12/95).
…Nos. 53, 73 and 79. **Orpheus Chamber Orchestra.** DG Ⓕ 439 779-2GH (63 minutes: DDD: 9/94).
…No. 92. *Coupled with works by* **Schubert Paris Conservatoire Orchestra / Bruno Walter.**
Dutton Laboratories Essential Archive mono Ⓑ CDEA5003* (79 minutes: ADD: 1/96).
…No. 92. *Coupled with works by various composers.* **Concertgebouw Orchestra / Karel Ančerl.**
Tahra Ⓕ TAH124/5 (two discs: 116 minutes: ADD: 3/96).
…Sinfonia concertante, HobI/105. Violin Concertos – C major, HobVIIa/1; G major, HobVIIa/4.
Orchestra of the Age of Enlightenment / Elizabeth Wallfisch (vn).
Virgin Classics Veritas Ⓜ VER5 61301-2 (59 minutes: DDD: 9/96). ✏

Haydn Symphonies – Nos. 1, 2, 4, 5, 10, 11, 18, 27, 32, 37 and 107. **Academy of Ancient Music / Christopher Hogwood.** L'Oiseau-Lyre Ⓕ 436 428-2OH3 (three discs: 172 minutes: DDD: 4/94). ✏
Recorded 1990-91.   Ⓖ
These very early symphonies, composed before Haydn moved to the Eszterházy court in 1761, may all too easily blur together in the mind: driving *allegros*, long on physical energy but short on memorable ideas, sparse-textured 'walking' *andantes* and breezy *buffo* finales. Superficially some of the opening movements and finales can seem virtually interchangeable. But even here there is more variety than you might at first suspect; and there is a world of difference between, say, the opening movement of No. 1, all quivering nervous energy, and that of No. 2, with its surprising amplitude and contrapuntal weight. If some of the slow movements are dull and arid, there is a melancholy, neo-baroque D minor *Andante* in No. 4 and a delicately expressive *Adagio, ma non troppo* in No. 32, probably the first in Haydn's long line of ceremonial C major symphonies with trumpets and timpani. But the two richest slow movements, both in texture and expression, stand at the head of works cast in church-sonata form (a sequence of slow, fast, minuet, fast): that in No. 5, with its high-lying *concertante* writing for horns; and the noble, processional *Adagio cantabile* of No. 11, whose eloquent violin writing foreshadows the well-known *Adagio* of No. 44. Hogwood's performances are pretty persuasive: crisp, precise, lightly and elegantly articulated, rhythmically spruce and almost invariably well tuned. Compared with the rival period-instrument versions from Goodman and the Hanover Band, Hogwood and the Academy are generally rather broader and more poised in quick movements, with more gracious, shapely phrasing, and in several of the slow movements Hogwood finds more in the music than Goodman, phrasing more considerately, with greater sensitivity to harmonic flux. Hogwood also has fuller presentation and slightly clearer, less reverberant recorded sound.
Additional recommendations ...
…Nos. 1-5. **Hanover Band / Roy Goodman** (hpd).
Hyperion Ⓕ CDA66524 (72 minutes: DDD: 3/92). ✏
…Nos. 9-12. **Hanover Band / Roy Goodman.** Hyperion Ⓕ CDA66529 (69 minutes: DDD: 12/92). ✏
…No. 1. La Canterina. **L. Hofmann** Flute Concerto in D major. **Soloists; Palmer Chamber Orchestra / Rudolf Palmer.** Newport Classic Ⓕ NPD85595 (70 minutes: DDD: 5/97).

Haydn Symphonies – Nos. 6-8. **The English Concert / Trevor Pinnock** (hpd). Archiv Produktion Ⓕ 423 098-2AH (65 minutes: DDD: 1/88). ✏
These symphonies represent the times of day; *Le matin* portrays the sunrise, and there is a storm in *Le soir*, but otherwise there is not a lot that could be called programmatic. But Haydn did take the opportunity to give his new colleagues in the princely band something interesting to do, for there are numerous solos here, not only for the wind instruments but for the section leaders – listen especially to the *Adagio* of No. 6, with solo violin and prominent flutes and cello, a delectable piece of writing. Inventively, the music is uneven; the concerto-like style was not wholly harmonious with Haydn's symphonic thinking. But there is plenty of spirited and cheerful music here, and that is well caught in these vivacious performances by Trevor Pinnock and his band, with their brisk tempos and light textures; the playing is duly agile, and the period instruments give a bright edge to the sound.
Additional recommendations ...
…Nos. 6-8. **Hanover Band / Roy Goodman.** Hyperion Ⓕ CDA66523 (69 minutes: DDD: 12/91). ✏
…Nos. 6-9, 12, 13, 16, 40 and 72. **Academy of Ancient Music / Christopher Hogwood.**
L'Oiseau-Lyre Ⓕ 433 661-2OH3 (three discs: 189 minutes: DDD: 6/93). ✏
…Nos. 6-8. **Northern Chamber Orchestra / Nicholas Ward.**
Naxos Ⓢ 8 550722 (59 minutes: DDD: 11/94).

Haydn Symphonies – Nos. 17-21. **Hanover Band / Roy Goodman.** Hyperion Ⓔ CDA66533
(79 minutes: DDD: 12/93). ✒ Recorded 1993.
The symphonies numbered 17-20 were among Haydn's very first; and while none is especially riveting in its invention they are all compact in design, with lean, economical orchestration and a characteristically high quota of nervous energy. The most colourful and ambitious work in this group, and the only one in four movements, is the ceremonial C major, No. 20, with its panoply of trumpets, timpani and horns. Symphony No. 21, the final work on the disc, dates from several years later (1764) and sounds it: the ideas in the fast movements are more striking in themselves and more tautly developed, while the opening *Adagio* is perhaps the most lyrically intense movement in all Haydn's early symphonies. Goodman allows the *Adagio* plenty of space, shaping the music sympathetically, with a firm sense of harmonic direction. Faster movements are rhythmically vital yet never overdriven, with Haydn's contrasts of colour and dynamics vividly realized (thrilling brass sonorities in No. 20). The minuets in Nos. 20 and 21 are neatly phrased, light on their feet (you may initially be thrown by that in No. 21, which opens exactly like the minuet in *Eine kleine Nachtmusik*). Delightful performances, stylish, spirited and deftly executed. Recording, documentation and playing time are all up to the standards set by other issues in the series.

Haydn Symphonies – Nos. 21-24, 28-31 and 34. **Academy of Ancient Music / Christopher Hogwood.**
L'Oiseau-Lyre Ⓔ 430 082-2OH3 (three discs: 190 minutes: DDD: 12/90). ✒ Recorded 1988-89.
Haydn Symphonies – Nos. 22-25. **Hanover Band / Roy Goodman.** Hyperion Ⓔ CDA66536
(75 minutes: DDD: 6/95). ✒ Recorded 1994.
Haydn Symphonies – Nos. 22, No. 29 and 60. **Northern Chamber Orchestra / Nicholas Ward.**
Naxos Ⓢ 8 550724 (60 minutes: DDD: 6/95). Recorded 1992-93.
The Academy of Ancient Music are usually a small orchestral body, supporting the contention expressed by Joseph Webster that Haydn's orchestra in 1764-65 was of about 13 to 16 players and that there was no keyboard continuo. In other words, there is no harpsichord to fill out textures, but although some listeners may miss it initially the playing soon convinces. The music itself cannot be summarized briefly, but as usual with Haydn, even these relatively unfamiliar pieces are inventive and often beautiful. The playing has zest, but however brisk the tempo chosen for quick movements they never degenerate into mere bustle, although other performers may take a less tense view than Christopher Hogwood. There are real discoveries to be made here, including the nervous, dramatic finale to Symphony No. 21 and minuets such as the enigmatic ones to Nos. 28 and 29. Similarly, slow movements have dignity, grace and often a quiet humour too, while phrasing is intelligent and affectionate and textures well balanced. Indeed, Hogwood's wind and string players alike are precise and stylish. Repeats are faithfully observed. Finally, the recording is clear and atmospheric.

Goodman and his orchestra give combustible performances, with pungent, earthy sonorities and terrific rhythmic vigour. They really lash into the repeated *fortissimos* in the development of the first movement of No. 24, the tension increased to breaking point, as Haydn surely intended. And the rollicking triple-time opening movement of No. 23, brilliantly coloured by high-pitched horns, goes with a lusty, infectious swing. In the opening movement of the *Philosopher*, the Hanover Band, typically, are rawer, starker and more sharply accented than the rival period-instrument version from Hogwood, with Goodman emphasizing the inexorably tramping bass line. In general Hogwood's readings are more urbane and light-footed; and he is definitely preferable in the slow movements of Nos. 23 and 24, which in Goodman's performances are vitiated by a plodding, graceless bass – the emphatic, upfront harpsichord continuo, sometimes effective in the quicker movements, may also be a problem. But Goodman's rugged, high-voltage readings of, say, the outer movements of Nos. 23 and 24 do lift the music off the page that much more vividly. Physically exciting performances, then, graphically captured in Hyperion's immediate, detailed recording.

In the *Philosopher*, Nicholas Ward and the Northern Chamber Orchestra (using modern instruments) present a spacious, elegantly phrased account of the title-character's personality. The incisive edge of the Hanover Band's period instruments gives the music's inherently austere tone a stronger profile, but Ward's idiomatic feeling for Haydn's style produces a subtly balanced, appealingly smooth-lined performance. The E major Symphony, No. 29 offers Ward and the NCO the opportunity to explore Haydn's attractive variety of instrumental forces and powerful opposition of major and minor. The programme culminates with the No. 60 (*Il distratto*). Here, Ward controls his orchestra with customary deftness to make the music's overtly descriptive elements especially telling. Haydn's comic depiction of the protagonist's absent-mindedness is vividly portrayed in the two outer movements, and distinctive thematic characterization effectively heightens the dramatic contrasts in the minuet and *Adagio*, in a winning performance that fully captures the composer's infectious wit.

Additional recommendations ...
...Nos. 31, 59 and 73. **Vienna Concentus Musicus / Nikolaus Harnoncourt.**
Teldec Das Alte Werk Ⓔ 4509-90843-2 (78 minutes: DDD: 4/95). ✒
...Nos. 30, 55 and 63. **Northern Chamber Orchestra / Nicholas Ward.**
Naxos Ⓢ 8 550757 (56 minutes: DDD: 5/95).

Haydn Symphonies – Nos. 22, 86 and 102. **City of Birmingham Symphony Orchestra /**
Sir Simon Rattle. EMI Ⓔ CDC5 55509-2 (68 minutes: DDD: 1/96). Recorded 1994.

Rattle establishes a middle path between traditional and period styles of performance. In addition, the idea of coupling symphonies from different periods of Haydn's career – not new but relatively rare – is refreshing, and has here produced an issue that one can warmly recommend to anyone simply wanting a representative Haydn symphony disc. The limited vibrato and light phrasing used by the strings throughout these performances set them apart from most others using modern instruments, giving them extra freshness and transparency. So in the *Adagio* of No. 102, elegant at a flowing speed, the solo cello is clearly defined, and the Minuet brings the strongest contrast of all with modern-instrument rivals, exuberantly turned into a scherzo at one-in-a-bar. No. 86, the fifth of the "Paris Symphonies", less appreciated only for lack of a nickname, is similarly refreshing, and here too Rattle refuses to rush his first movement in the name of authenticity. The main *Allegro* is marginally more relaxed than that of Dorati, whose pioneering Decca set still provides a useful yardstick in almost every work. By contrast Rattle's *Presto* for the finale is hectic, and one marvels at the agility of the Birmingham horns in their repeated triplets, though Dorati's tempo is only marginally less urgent. In the square rhythms of the opening *Adagio* of No. 22, Rattle manages to achieve elegance without sacrificing the chunky strength of the chorale on cor anglais, and this symphony, unlike the later ones, finds Rattle using harpsichord continuo. The helpful acoustic of Symphony Hall, Birmingham, sets the seal on the disc's success with warm, clear sound.

Haydn Symphonies – Nos. 50, 54-57 and 60. **Academy of Ancient Music / Christopher Hogwood.**
L'Oiseau-Lyre Ⓕ 443 781-2OH3 (three discs: 179 minutes: DDD: 5/98). ✍

All six symphonies on these discs date from 1773-74, when the intensity of Haydn's musical language during the preceding years was being tempered with a new urbanity and a deliberately calculated popular appeal. The older style is represented by the *Adagios* of Nos. 54 and 56, with their spacious lines and rarefied atmosphere. Typical of the newer, more 'accessible' manner is the obscurely nicknamed *Schoolmaster*, No. 55, with its droll, *faux-naïf* variation slow movement and its catchy finale, a deft and witty amalgam of variation, rondo and sonata forms. The little-known No. 57 also aims frankly at popular effect in its theme-and-variation slow movement, its stomping *Ländler*-Minuet and its *Prestissimo* finale suggesting a riotous comic opera imbroglio. The spirit of *opera buffa*, in fact, permeates several movements here, including the opening *Presto* of No. 54, a symphony Hogwood opts to perform in its original version – that is, without the slow introduction and the enhanced scoring for flutes, trumpets and timpani. Two of the other symphonies, both in C major with high horns, trumpets and timpani, have overt theatrical connections: No. 50 probably started life as the introduction to *Der Götterrath*, the lost prologue to the marionette opera *Philemon und Baucis*, while the burlesque six-movement *Il distratto*, No. 60, originated as incidental music to a farce centring on an 'absent-minded' hero – hence the music's frequent air of distractedness and comic inconsequentiality. Unlike, say, Norrington, Gardiner or Harnoncourt, Hogwood is not a conductor to impose a strikingly individual stamp on the music, but, as ever, there are no affectations, no eccentricities. Hogwood has thought carefully about the precise character of each movement, chooses his tempos shrewdly and is always alive to felicitous details of wind colour or inner string writing. Abetted by marvellously lithe, incisive playing from the Academy of Ancient Music, he gives a viscerally exciting reading of No. 56, the finale dispatched with phenomenal panache at the fastest possible tempo. Here and in Nos. 50 and 60 brass and timpani rasp and thunder to thrilling effect. The finale of No. 57 is likewise breathtaking, not only in its accuracy at high speed but also in its delicacy and point. Aided by notably sweet, refined string playing, the filigree writing in Nos. 54 and 57 is exquisitely realized. The recording is clean, immediate and well balanced.

Haydn Symphonies. **Tafelmusik / Bruno Weil.** Sony Classical Vivarte Ⓕ SK53985/6
(two discs, oas: 50 and 68 minutes: DDD: 11/94). ✍ Recorded 1993.
SK53985 – Nos. 50, 64 and 65. *SK53986* – Nos. 45-47.   ⓖⓖ

Whatever the numberings may suggest, the six symphonies on these discs cover a short chronological span. Nos. 45-47 belong to 1772, the climactic year of Haydn's first maturity that also saw the composition of the Op. 20 String Quartets; and the festive C major Symphony, No. 50, whose first two movements probably started life as the overture to a lost marionette opera, bears the date 1773, though the minuet and finale may just have been added later. Neither of the A major symphonies, Nos. 64 and 65, can be precisely dated, though circumstantial evidence suggests 1772-73. As H.C. Robbins Landon points out in his notes, No. 65, with its quirky, disjointed *Andante* and stomping, Brueghelian minuet, may have originally been composed as incidental music. He also proposes a theatrical connection – probably less likely – with the enigmatically titled No. 64, an altogether more searching, introspective work, with strange, almost Schubertian harmonic deflexions in the opening movement and a *Largo* of rare gravity and eloquence. The performances by the Toronto-based period-instrument orchestra under Bruno Weil offer playing of verve, flair and finesse allied to vital, decisive characterization are enhanced by unusually close attention to the composer's markings. In many ways the rival performances from Goodman are similarly conceived – generally spirited tempos, crisp articulation, incisive attack, clear, colourful textures, with pungent contributions from oboes and horns. But there are one or two obvious differences. Weil eschews a harpsichord continuo, which may influence you one way or the other. Goodman's continuo is, as ever, busy and forwardly balanced. As to interpretation, Goodman tends to be earthier and more rugged, though his direct, unvarnished manner can sometimes be prosaic in slow movements. But it is Weil, captured in vivid, immediate sound, who has the strongest feeling for long-range symphonic tensions, and conveys most consistently the reach and dramatic power of the sonata allegros, above all in his searing reading of the much-recorded *Farewell*.

Additional recommendations ...

...Nos. 48-50. **Hanover Band / Roy Goodman.** Hyperion Ⓕ CDA66531 (77 minutes: DDD: 7/93). ✔

...Nos. 45-47, 51, 52 and 64. **Academy of Ancient Music / Christopher Hogwood.** L'Oiseau-Lyre Ⓕ 443 777-2OH3 (three discs: 161 minutes: DDD: 10/96). ✔

...No. 45. *Coupled with works by various composers.* **London Symphony Orchestra / Sir Henry Wood.** Dutton Laboratories mono Ⓜ 2CDAX2002* (two discs: 138 minutes: ADD: 9/94).

Haydn Symphonies – Nos. 82-84. **Tafelmusik / Bruno Weil.** Sony Classical Vivarte Ⓕ SK66295 (73 minutes: DDD: 7/95). ✔ Recorded 1994. Recorded 1994. Ⓖ

Haydn Symphonies – Nos. 85-87. **Tafelmusik / Bruno Weil.** Sony Classical Vivarte Ⓕ SK66296 (71 minutes: DDD: 7/95). ✔ Recorded 1994.

Written in 1785-86 for the ample forces of the Concert de la Loge Olympique, Haydn's *Paris* symphonies were his grandest and most imposing works in the form to date. Bruno Weil and his brilliant period orchestra bring to the "Paris" Symphonies the same flair and finesse that distinguished the previous discs in their ongoing complete cycle. The blazing, far-reaching opening movement of *L'ours*, No. 82, augurs well: an urgent, though never rushed, tempo, keen texturing – some details more tellingly etched than ever heard before on disc – and lithe, vital rhythms. In the *Allegretto*, fleeter and more dapper than from either Goodman or Kuijken, Weil evokes the spirit of the corresponding movement of Beethoven's Eighth; and the finale, full of razor-sharp instrumental detailing, combines dancing grace with an exhilarating drive. Only in the minuet does one have reservations: Weil's very purposeful tempo here does underestimate the element of *ancien régime* opulence in this music; and as Goodman and Kuijken demonstrate, the trio responds better to a touch more charm and flexibility. In the opening movement of *La poule* Weil brings a real bite and trenchancy to the pervasive dotted rhythms and an exciting dramatic sweep to the development. The *Andante*, more flowingly paced than in the rival versions, is elegantly shaped, with long-breathed lyrical phrasing and beautifully poised woodwind playing. In the finale Weil drives rather fiercely (Kuijken is altogether more genial here). No. 84, the least consistently inspired of the "Paris" set, comes off well in all three versions. But in the opening *Allegro* Weil phrases more graciously than his rivals, and shapes the repeated-note bass lines with a stronger sense of direction. The beautiful *Andante* is ideally paced and full of subtle, delicately placed detail.

On the second disc Weil and his players are aggressively brisk in the *Adagio* introduction of No. 85. But they shape the main theme of the *Vivace* alluringly and bring plenty of fire to the tuttis, pointing Haydn's nervous, syncopated inner parts and ramming home the *sforzando* offbeat accents. Again, the trio of the minuet is short on wit and affection. But the finale is as spirited and gamesome as you could wish, and works up a fine lather in the central development; and the lightness and elegant ease of the *Allegretto* variations make the Kuijken version, in particular, seem distinctly sober. No. 86, the most imposing of the "Paris" Symphonies, seems less successful. The slow introduction is, again, uncomfortably brisk, while for all the eager athleticism of the playing the *Allegro spiritoso* rather lacks grandeur. In the *Capriccio* second movement Weil plays up Haydn's violent rhetorical outbursts; but at his controversially swift tempo the music's grave, majestic tread and intense, brooding harmonies go for comparatively little. Timings are revealing: Weil takes 5'47" to Kuijken's flowing but not inexpressive 6'30", while Goodman, less poised but more searching, weighs in at 7'44". The finale, on the other hand, combines ample symphonic breadth with terrific *élan*; and Weil brings a nice deadpan wit in the Rossini-ish second theme (0'54"). No. 87 is vividly done in all three recordings, though Weil again scores over his rivals both in his attention to detail and in his control of long-term tensions. In the *Adagio* he encourages warm, gracious phrasing, and shapes the violin sextuplets more eloquently than in the other readings. A final choice among the three period versions of these symphonies, all using an orchestra based on around 25 strings, cannot be clear-cut. Goodman is the least polished of the trio, and his interventionist harpsichord continuo can grow wearisome; but his high-adrenalin music-making is often compelling, especially in his brazen, sabre-rattling reading of No. 82. Honours are pretty evenly divided between the vital, affectionate, occasionally overleisurely Kuijken and the more tautly controlled Weil. And if Kuijken has the edge in No. 86, these Sony discs come out marginally ahead on points elsewhere, and score decisively in their more transparent recorded sound.

Additional recommendations ...

...Nos. 64, 84 and 90. **Nicolaus Esterházy Sinfonia / Béla Drahos.** Naxos Ⓢ 8 550770 (68 minutes: DDD: 3/95).

...Nos. 80, 87 and 89. **London Mozart Players / Jane Glover.** ASV Quicksilva Ⓢ CDQS6156 (70 minutes: DDD: 4/96).

...Nos. 82-84. **Orchestra of the Age of Enlightenment / Sigiswald Kuijken.** Virgin Classics Veritas Ⓕ VC7 59537-2 (78 minutes: DDD: 2/90). ✔

...Nos. 82-84. **Hanover Band / Roy Goodman.** Hyperion Ⓕ CDA66527 (79 minutes: DDD: 10/92). ✔

...Nos. 82-87. **Austro-Hungarian Haydn Orchestra / Adám Fischer.** Nimbus Ⓜ NI5419/20 (two discs: 148 minutes: DDD: 3/95).

...Nos. 83, 88 and 96. **Hallé Orchestra / Sir John Barbirolli.** Dutton Laboratories mono Ⓕ CDSJB1003* (65 minutes: ADD: 3/96).

...Nos. 83, 84 and 88. **London Mozart Players / Jane Glover.**
ASV Quicksilva ⓢ CDQS6167 (67 minutes: DDD: 7/96).
...Nos. 85-87. **Orchestra of the Age of Enlightenment / Sigiswald Kuijken.**
Virgin Classics Veritas Ⓕ VC7 59557-2 (79 minutes: DDD: 5/90). ⚞
...Nos. 85-87. **Hanover Band / Roy Goodman.** Hyperion Ⓕ CDA66535 (79 minutes: DDD: 11/94). ⚞

Haydn Symphonies – Nos. 90ᵃ, 91ᵇ and 92ᵇ. **Orchestra of the Eighteenth Century /**
Frans Brüggen. Philips Ⓕ 446 677-2PH (76 minutes: DDD). ⚞ Item marked ᵃ recorded
live in 1984 (from 422 022-2PH, 5/88), ᵇ1995.
Frans Brüggen's account of No. 90 is here recycled and logically coupled with the two other
symphonies. All three performances were recorded at public concerts and display Brüggen's familiar
hallmarks in this repertoire: colourful textures, strong, resilient rhythms, thoughtful, detailed
phrasing and a vivid feeling for the music's drama and glorious unpredictability. There are occasional
slight reservations about Brüggen's idiosyncrasies but these are small provisos to set against music-
making of real imagination and panache. He creates a marvellous sense of quizzical expectancy in the
introduction of the *Oxford*, for instance, and, at a cracking tempo, gives a thrilling account of the
finale. In the *Andante* of No. 90 Brüggen phrases more expressively than Kuijken, making more of
the chromaticism in the second half of the theme and the poetic turn to D flat in the coda. In the
corresponding movement of No. 91, he really lets rip in the raucous series of trills towards the end.
The finale of this symphony is a touch fierce and driven, missing the mellow gaiety characteristic of
Haydn in E flat (and well caught by Kuijken). However, at a spacious tempo Brüggen captures both
the lyrical grace and the taut symphonic drama of the opening movement and he gives a specially
delightful reading of the trio, pointing the 'oompah' accompaniment and relishing the rude off-beat
sforzandos from the horns. Kuijken's generally more relaxed way with Nos. 90 and 91 is
often persuasive, though it is stingy of Virgin to offer only a brace of symphonies. The recordings are
very acceptable (the audience remaining for the most part preternaturally quiet); the close
recording in Nos. 91 and 92 catches a fair amount of animated sniffing and teeth-sucking from the
conductor.
Additional recommendations ...
...Nos. 88-90. **Tafelmusik / Bruno Weil.**
Sony Classical Vivarte Ⓕ SK66253 (61 minutes: DDD: 10/95). ⚞
...Nos. 90 and 91. **La Petite Bande / Sigiswald Kuijken.**
Virgin Classics Veritas Ⓕ VC5 45068-2 (58 minutes: DDD: 10/95). ⚞

Haydn Symphonies – Nos. 95ᵃ, 97ᵃ and 101ᵇ. **Philharmonia Orchestra / Leonard Slatkin.**
RCA Victor Red Seal Ⓕ 09026 68426-2
(73 minutes: DDD: 6/98). Recorded ᵃ1993 and ᵇ1994.
This disc confirms Slatkin's credentials as an urbane and attentive Haydn interpreter. No. 95, the least
favoured of the set, and No. 97 come off particularly well. With no hint of ponderousness, Slatkin
brings an imposing breadth and weight to the first movement and Minuet of No. 95, while the
brilliant contrapuntal sallies in the finale gain much from the division of the violins left and right. The
aggressively extrovert *Vivace* that opens No. 97 has a fine snap and thrust to its rhythms, the mounting
tensions of the development powerfully realized; and Slatkin clearly relishes the strut and swagger of
the Minuet and the comic bravado of the finale. Here and elsewhere the playing of the Philharmonia
is alert and refined, with delectable work from the woodwind. In the slow movements of both these
symphonies Slatkin phrases warmly and graciously, bringing out the felicities of Haydn's part-
writing. Purists, though, may raise an eyebrow at the romantic liberties he occasionally takes with
tempo. The *Clock* is also enjoyable. However, abetted by a recording that gives a more incisive edge
to brass and timpani, Davis and the Concertgebouw (see below) bring a shade more *élan* and
excitement to the faster movements. Slatkin again scores, notably in the first and second movements
(the latter taken at a crisp, high-stepping *Andante*), by placing the violins on opposite sides. But if he
yields to Davis in the *Clock*, there is little to choose between the two conductors in Nos. 95 and 97,
where some may prefer Slatkin's rather more expansive, *espressivo* treatment of the slow movements.
Apart from the slightly too discreet brass and timpani, especially in No. 101, RCA's recordings
combine clarity with ample body and presence.
Additional recommendation ...
...No. 101. *Coupled with works by various composers.* **Philharmonic Symphony Orchestra of New**
York / Arturo Toscanini. Pearl mono Ⓕ GEMMCDS9373* (three discs: 230 minutes: ADD: 3/90).
Gramophone classical 100. *See review in the Collections section; refer to the Index.* ⊕⊕⊕

Haydn London Symphonies – Nos. 93 and 94 (both from 6514 192, 1/83); No. 97 (6514 074);
No. 99 (9500 139, 4/77); No. 100 (9500 510, 3/79); No. 101 (9500 679, 7/81). **Concertgebouw**
Orchestra / Sir Colin Davis. Philips Duo Ⓜ 442 614-2PM2 (two discs: ADD/DDD).
Recorded 1975-81. ⊕⊕⊕
Haydn London Symphonies – No. 95 (6514 074, 1/82); No. 96 (6725 010, 6/82); No. 98 (9500 678,
12/80); No. 102 (9500 679); No. 103 (9500 303, 7/78); No. 104 (9500 510). **Concertgebouw**
Orchestra / Sir Colin Davis. Philips Duo Ⓜ 442 611-2PM2 (two discs: ADD/DDD).
Recorded 1975-81. ⊕⊕⊕

Haydn Symphonies – Nos. 99 and 100. Overture in D major to Salomon's opera, "Windsor Castle". **London Classical Players / Sir Roger Norrington.** EMI Ⓕ CDC5 55192-2 (54 minutes: DDD: 12/94). ✦ Recorded 1993.
Haydn Symphonies – Nos. 101 and 102. **London Classical Players / Sir Roger Norrington.** EMI Ⓕ CDC5 55111-2 (53 minutes: DDD: 12/94). ✦ Recorded 1993.

A superb achievement all round – indeed, it's nigh on impossible to imagine better 'big-band' Haydn than one encounters here on Sir Colin Davis's four exceedingly well-filled CDs. His direction has exemplary sparkle (try the superb opening movement of the *Miracle* Symphony) and sensitivity (witness his eloquent moulding of No. 98's great *Adagio*). Minuets are never allowed to plod, outer movements have an ideal combination of infectious zip and real poise, and the humour (a commodity, of course, that is never absent for too long in Haydn's music) is always conveyed with a genial twinkle in the eye. Quite marvellous, wonderfully unanimous playing from the great Amsterdam orchestra, too (the woodwind contributions are particularly distinguished), with never a trace of routine to betray the six-year recording span of this critically acclaimed project. The Philips engineering, whether analogue or digital, is of the very highest quality throughout, offering a totally natural perspective, gloriously full-bodied tone and consistently sparkling textures within the sumptuous Concertgebouw acoustic. Invest in this set: it will yield enormous rewards for many years to come.

From Norrington come probing, often charismatic performances that play up the music's drama and rhetorical boldness. Nothing in these familiar works is ever taken for granted. After a swiftish, unsettling *Adagio* introduction (most conductors go for something more monumental here), No. 99's opening *Vivace assai* is unusually taut and urgent, the muscular cross-rhythms powerfully etched, the astringent harmonic clashes rammed home for all they're worth. Norrington's emphasis on the woodwind lines in Haydn's richly scored tuttis (clarinets are featured for the first time in his symphonies) not only makes for vivid, sharply differentiated colours but at salient moments also heightens the music's harmonic tension; and though the timpani are not ideally incisive, the valveless brass bray thrillingly in the movement's closing stages. The *Military* receives one of the most electrifying performances on disc. Both outer movements have a tremendous rhythmic fling, with sharp, precise articulation, not least from the cellos and basses. Haydn's flamboyant contrasts are thrillingly realized, and there is a real sense of abandon in the codas. The coupling of the *Clock* and No. 102 has a direct period rival from the Hanover Band, overseen from the fortepiano by Roy Goodman. Norrington's grander readings are ultimately more exhilarating, subtler in phrasing, more varied in articulation and accent and more commanding in their architectural reach.

Additional recommendations ...
...Nos. 72, 93 and 95. **Nicolaus Esterházy Sinfonia / Béla Drahos.**
Naxos Ⓢ 8 550797 (64 minutes: DDD: 12/95).
...Nos. 93-95. **Hanover Band / Roy Goodman.** Hyperion Ⓕ CDA66532 (66 minutes: DDD: 8/93). ✦
...Nos. 93-98. **Royal Philharmonic Orchestra / Sir Thomas Beecham.**
EMI Beecham Edition mono Ⓜ CMS7 64389-2* (two discs: 136 minutes: ADD: 9/93).
...Nos. 94, 98 and 104. **Philharmonia Orchestra / Leonard Slatkin.**
RCA Victor Red Seal Ⓔ 09026 62549-2 (79 minutes: DDD: 2/95).
...Nos. 97 and 98. **Nicolaus Esterházy Sinfonia / Béla Drahos.**
Naxos Ⓢ 8 550780 (59 minutes: DDD: 3/95).
...Nos. 99-104. **Royal Philharmonic Orchestra / Sir Thomas Beecham.**
EMI Beecham Edition Ⓜ CMS7 64066-2* (two discs: 156 minutes: ADD: 9/92).
...Nos. 101 and 102. **Hanover Band / Roy Goodman.**
Hyperion Ⓕ CDA66528 (52 minutes: DDD: 12/92).
...Nos. 98 and 100. Il mondo della luna – Overture. **Chamber Orchestra of Europe / Claudio Abbado.** DG Ⓕ 439 932-2GH (56 minutes: DDD: 10/95).
...Nos. 102 and 103. **Chamber Orchestra of Europe / Claudio Abbado.**
DG Ⓕ 449 204-2GH (54 minutes: DDD: 12/96).
... No. 104. *Coupled with works by various composers.* **Philharmonia Orchestra / Rudolf Kempe.**
EMI Profile Ⓑ CZS5 68736-2 (two discs: 156 minutes: ADD: 9/96).

Haydn Symphonies – Nos. 103 and 104. **La Petite Bande / Sigiswald Kuijken.**
Deutsche Harmonia Mundi Ⓕ 05472-77362-2 (57 minutes: DDD: 11/97). ✦ Recorded 1995.
The most obvious difference between Kuijken's readings of Haydn's last two symphonies and those of Norrington on the rival EMI disc lies in the slow movements. Ever the *agent provocateur*, Norrington takes an uncommonly brisk, brittle view of each of these *Andantes*; Kuijken is altogether more gracious and reflective, with affectionate touches of timing; and he leaves you in no doubt that the central *minore* section is the most awesome, physically powerful music in any eighteenth-century symphonic slow movement. Kuijken's grave, steady tread in the C minor-major theme and variations of No. 103 is also appealing, he brings a swaggering grandeur to the final C major variation and shapes with tenderness the quiet string phrases that usher in the coda – a sudden and magical change of atmosphere. In the minuets, conversely, Kuijken is appreciably faster than Norrington, especially in No. 103, where at his headlong tempo the flicking 'Scotch snap' figures tend to be blurred. There is less to choose between the two versions in the outer movements, though Kuijken is more genial and gamesome in the opening *Allegro con spirito* of No. 103 and broader, but hardly less thrilling, in the finale. No. 104 opens with a magnificently imposing, portentous introduction, and both the first

Allegro and the finale are strong and spirited, the urgent drama of the developments powerfully limned. The recorded sound has an attractive spaciousness and bloom, if not total clarity: inner string parts are not always ideally defined and both horns and bassoons at times seem underbalanced. Kuijken's interpretations, vividly realized by his 35-strong orchestra (particularly delectable work from first flute and first oboe), can be recommended to anyone seeking these symphonies in period performances that do ample justice to the music's boldness and imaginative reach.

Additional recommendation ...
...Nos. 103 and 104. **London Classical Players / Sir Roger Norrington.**
EMI Ⓕ CDC5 55002-2 (55 minutes: DDD: 7/94). ☞

Haydn Cassation in F major, HobII/20. Divertissement in B flat major, HobII/B4. Quartet for Flute and Strings in A major, HobII/A4. Notturno No. 1 in C major, HobII/25. **Linos Ensemble.**
Capriccio Ⓕ 10 719 (68 minutes: DDD: 9/96).
The Linos Ensemble's highly polished, enthusiastic performances in this programme of Haydn's chamber music for wind instruments and strings generate a compelling immediacy that is hard to resist. Moreover, the attractively diverse choice of pieces provides plenty of opportunity to demonstrate both the excellent soloistic skills of Linos's members and its deftly balanced ensemble, while suitably close recording throughout presents this group's eloquence and fresh vitality in fine, clear detail. The delightful, open-air qualities of this repertoire are exemplified by the F major *Cassation*, whose amiable good humour is captured with buoyant, cheerful vigour in the opening *Allegro*; with stately elegance in the two minuets, affecting melodiousness in the *Adagio*, and an engaging swing in the final rondo. The extrovert B flat *Divertissement* offers a charming display of fluent, conversational playing, a style which the Linos exploits to particular effect in the lively alternation of different instrumental groupings in the elegant A major Quartet for flute and strings. Sample the enchanting flute solo in the *Adagio* and fugal episode in the finale. Ultimately, the infectiously high-spirited, effervescent exchanges between flute and oboe in the witty C major *Notturno* (originally for *lira organizzata*) sum up the allure of this entertaining issue.

Haydn Divertimentos – F major, HobII/20; C major, HobII/11, "Der Geburtstag"; G major, HobII/G1; G major, HobII/1. **Linde Consort / Hans-Martin Linde.** Virgin Classics Veritas Ⓜ VER5 61163-2 (73 minutes: DDD: 2/96). From EMI CDC7 47941-2 (4/88). ☞
Recorded 1986.
Besides providing valuable insights into the composer's later symphonic style, Haydn's *Divertimentos* also offer delightful examples of Haydn's open-air music. Flautist Hans-Martin Linde directs his Consort with subtlety and sensitivity in highly engaging performances of four works. The two five-movement *Cassations*, HobII/20 and HobII/G1, are scored for nine instruments, including two horns. Here, the fast, outer movements are projected with lightness and elegance while lithe phrasing, supported by gently pulsating accompaniments in the *Adagio* (scored for strings alone), maximizes the music's expressive impact. The minuets and trios – which fully exploit the horns – show Haydn's potently imaginative instrumentation most vividly, and provide ideal settings for the Linde Consort's accomplished soloist skills and deftly blended ensemble. The two four-movement *Divertimentos*, HobII/1 and HobII/11, use only six instruments, and demonstrate a brilliant synthesis of unity and diversity. The two variation-form finales, in which successive variations present a different instrument as soloist, and the beguilingly comic "Mann und Weib" (HobII/11, second movement), whose bare octaves and opposition of violin and double-bass enchantingly illustrate both the unity of marriage and the difficulties of conjugal life, are particular highlights here. These eloquent expressions of Haydn's infectious wit, presented in excellently balanced recordings, should appeal to a wide audience.

Additional recommendation ...
...Divertimentos – G major, HobII/1; D major, HobII/ D22 Add; G major, HobII/9.
Vienna Haydn Sinfonietta / Manfred Huss. Koch Schwann Ⓕ 312862 (57 minutes: DDD: 1/96).

Haydn String Quartets, Volumes 1 and 2. **Pro Arte Quartet** (Alphonse Onnou, Laurent Halleux, vns; Germain Prévost, va; Robert Maas, vc). Testament mono Ⓕ SBT3055* and SBT4056* (two sets of three and four discs, oas: 229 and 243 minutes: ADD: 6/95).
From HMV Haydn Quartet Society issues; recorded 1931-38.
SBT3055 – No. 1 in B flat major, "La chasse". Op. 20: No. 2 in C major; No. 5 in F minor. E flat major, Op. 50 No. 3. Op. 54: No. 1 in G major; No. 2 in C major; No. 3 in E major. Op. 64: No. 3 in B flat major; No. 4 in G major. G minor, "Rider", Op. 74 No. 3. Op. 76: No. 3 in C major, "Emperor"; No. 4 in B flat major, "Sunrise". F major, Op. 77 No. 2. *SBT4056* – C major, Op. 1 No. 6. Op. 20: No. 1 in E flat major; No. 4 in D major. Op. 33: No. 2 in E flat major, "Joke"; No. 3 in C major, "Bird"; No. 6 in D major. D major, "Frog", Op. 50 No. 6. Op. 55: No. 1 in A major; No. 3 in B flat major. E flat major, Op. 64 No. 6. B flat major, Op. 71 No. 1. Op. 74: No. 1 in C major; No. 2 in F major. G major, Op. 77 No. 1.
Hoffstetter String Quartets, Op. 3 – No. 4 in B flat major; No. 5 in F major.   ⒼⒼ
The Pro Arte Quartet's first London appearance in 1925 prompted *The Times* to declare, "One has never heard them surpassed, and rarely equalled, in volume and beauty of tone, in accuracy of intonation and in perfection of balance between the parts" – and that could well be the verdict on these sets. Their tempos invariably seem just right and their phrasing has an inner life that is

extraordinarily potent. Alphonse Onnou and Laurent Halleux were superbly matched, and Halleux often led in their early days. Such virtuosity as the quartet exhibits is effortless and totally lacking in ostentation. Of course, the actual sound is dated – the string tone is wanting in bloom and freshness, particularly in some of the earlier recordings – but the ear soon adjusts, though one might wish that these transfers could have given us a little more space between movements. Ansermet tells how when the Pro Arte were asked to play his quartet pieces for Stravinsky, the composer, accustomed to scant understanding at that time, asked his visitors to listen first to the pianola transcriptions. After they had done so, modest and a little intimidated, they took up their instruments. From the very first note Stravinsky was won over, and at the end, greatly moved, all he could do was to exclaim, "I have nothing to say! It was perfect! I have never heard my music interpreted with such truth!"

Additional recommendation ...

...Complete String Quartets: E flat major, Op. 0. Op. 1 – No. 1 in B flat major, "La chasse"; No. 2 in E flat major; No. 3 in D major; No. 4 in G major; No. 6 in C major. Op. 2 – No. 1 in A major; No. 2 in E major; No. 4 in F major; No. 6 in B flat major. Six Quartets, Op. 9. Six Quartets, Op. 17. Six Quartets, Op. 20, "Sun". Six Quartets, Op. 33. D major, Op. 42. Six Quartets, Op. 50. Three Quartets, Op. 54, "Tost I". Three Quartets, Op. 55, "Tost II". Six Quartets, Op. 64, "Tost III". Three Quartets, Op. 71. Three Quartets, Op. 74. Six Quartets, Op. 76. Two Quartets, Op. 77. D minor, Op. 103[c]. The Seven Last Words, Op. 51 (with readings selected by Reginald Barrett-Ayres)[a]. [a]**Sir Peter Pears** (narr); **Aeolian Quartet**.
London ⓑ 455 261-2LC22 (22 discs: 24 hours 34 minutes: ADD: 4/98).

Haydn String Quartets, Op. 1 – No. 1 in B flat major, "Hunt"; No. 2 in E flat major; No. 3 in D major; No. 4 in G major; No. 5 in E flat major; No. 6 in C major. **Petersen Quartet** (Conrad Muck, Gernot Sussmuth, vns; Friedemann Weigle, va; Hans-Jakob Eschenburg, vc). Capriccio ⓕ 10 786/7 (two discs: 99 minutes: DDD: 12/97). Recorded 1995-96.
The history of the string quartet in effect began with these cheerful, compact *Divertimenti a quattro*, as the composer titled them; and though they contain only spasmodic hints of future glories, their freshness and exuberance make for highly pleasurable listening. All are in five movements, with two contrasted Minuets placed second and fourth, the former a leisurely *Minuetto galante*, the latter brisker and earthier, with the *sansculotte* two-part writing and octave doublings found in Haydn's later minuets right through to the Op. 76 Quartets. As in the early piano sonatas, the trios usually turn to the comic minor, often with striking effect – for example in the violins' canonic imitations in the fourth movement of No. 4, or the eloquent chromaticism in the second movement of No. 5. The slow movements are all accompanied arias for the first violin, often touching in their innocence and candour, while the ebullient *Presto* outer movements delight in quirkily irregular phrase-lengths, quick-fire repartee and sudden contrasts of texture and register – the kind of music that led po-faced North German critics to accuse Haydn of debasing the art with "comic fooling". The Petersen Quartet respond vividly to the music's youthful verve, with polished ensemble, keen attack and a wide spectrum of colour and dynamics. Purists may raise an eyebrow at the special effects the players deploy in repeats, especially in minuets – added touches of imitation, pizzicato and even *col legno*, a technique Haydn asks for once in a symphony (No. 67) but never in the quartets. But the young Haydn, famed for his mischievous humour, may well have enjoyed these liberties. No complaints about the recording, which combines clarity with an attractive church resonance.

Haydn String Quartets, Op. 9. **Kodály Quartet** (Attila Falváy, Tamás Szabó, vns; Gábor Fias, va; János Devich, vc). Naxos ⓢ 8 550786/7 (two discs, oas: 52 and 58 minutes: DDD: 11/94). Recorded 1993.
8 550786 – No. 1 in C major; No. 3 in G major; No. 4 in D minor.
8 550787 – No. 2 in E flat major; No. 5 in B flat major; No. 6 in A major.
Overshadowed by four dozen later masterpieces, Haydn's Op. 9 has usually received short shrift from both players and commentators. Least neglected of the set is the D minor, No. 4, described by Hans Keller as "the first great string quartet in the history of music". The minor mode at this period (1769-70) invariably drew something special from Haydn, and this work stands apart from the others for its intensity of expression, its mastery of texture and development and the sheer character of its ideas. The opening *Allegro moderato* could well have been at the back of Mozart's mind when he came to write his own great D minor Quartet, K421. "Boring" was Keller's unceremonious dismissal of the remaining five works of Op. 9. It is true that there are *longueurs*, nowhere more so than in the stiff, gawky opening movements of Nos. 1-3, with their neutral thematic material and overabundance of fussy violin figuration. The routine set of variations that opens No. 5 is also the kind of piece that has one's fingers itching for the fast-forward button. But there are compensations elsewhere: in the terse, resourceful and (especially in No. 3) witty finales; in the varied minuets, ranging from the high-stepping No. 5, with its alfresco octave doublings, to the suave, chromatically subtle No. 2; and in several of the slow movements, notably the tender *siciliano* in No. 1, the sorrowful, rather Gluckian C minor aria in No. 2 and the sensuous, rich-textured *Largo cantabile* in No. 5. The Kodály Quartet are, as ever, sympathetic Haydn exponents, impressing with their slightly old-fashioned warmth of sonority, the natural musicality of their phrasing and their care for blend, balance and intonation, though the rather boomy church acoustic hardly helps. However, in case you hadn't noticed, buying both discs should still leave you change from a tenner.

Haydn String Quartets, Op. 20, "Sun". **Quatuor Mosaïques** (Erich Höbarth, Andrea Bischof, vns; Anita Mitterer, va; Christophe Coin, vc). Auvidis Astrée Ⓔ E8784 (two discs: 147 minutes: DDD: 5/93). ✍ Recorded 1990. *Also available separately as detailed below. Gramophone Editor's choice. Gramophone Award Winner 1993.* ⒼⒼⒼ
E8785 – No. 1 in E flat major; No. 5 in F minor; No. 6 in A major.
E8786 – No. 2 in C major; No. 3 in G minor; No. 4 in D major.

Haydn was 40 when he completed his set of Op. 20 String Quartets in 1772. They therefore date from the composer's so-called *Sturm und Drang* period, though Haydn's increasingly frequent use of the more dramatic and 'serious' minor mode in these pieces can perhaps be attributed just as much to the fruitful influence of the three operatic projects he had been working on just a few years previously between 1766 and 1769. Moreover, these quartets also reveal a greater preoccupation with counterpoint than any of his music to that date, and the great fugal finales of Nos. 2, 5 and 6 clearly herald the arrival of the consummate craftsman so overwhelmingly displayed in the mature quartets to come. Incidentally, the Op. 20 set's nickname *Sun* derives from the illustration on the handsome title-page of the Hummel edition of this music, at the top of which peers out the sun-god's head. Admirable though the Salomon Quartet's readings are, they are surpassed by those of the superb Quatuor Mosaïques. These wonderfully flexible performances display an altogether breathtaking refinement, sensitivity and illumination. Indeed, in terms of expressive subtlety, imaginative intensity and sheer depth of feeling, the Mosaïques' achievement in these marvellous works is unmatched in the present catalogue and it is difficult to foresee it being surpassed for some considerable time to come. A stunning set in every way, with vividly realistic engineering to match.
Additional recommendation ...
...Nos. 4-6. **Salomon Quartet.** Hyperion Ⓔ CDA66622 (78 minutes: DDD: 2/93). ✍

Haydn String Quartets, Op. 20 – No. 1 in E flat major; No. 3 in G minor; No. 4 in D major.
Lindsay Quartet (Peter Cropper, Ronald Birks, vns; Robin Ireland, va; Bernard Gregor-Smith, vc). ASV Ⓔ CDDCA1027 (79 minutes: DDD: 6/98). Recorded 1997.
Gramophone Editor's choice.

The Lindsay Quartet are Haydn interpreters of rare understanding and communicative flair. Their characterization here is bold and decisive, enhanced by a scrupulous observation of the composer's expression and dynamic markings. Faster movements tend to be more urgent, less ruminative, than those from the Mosaïques (reviewed above). The *zingarese* cross-rhythms of No. 4's Minuet have an abrasive edge, and the *Presto e scherzando* finale is no mere frolic in the Lindsay's hands – its wit can scathe and sting, and the closing theme, with its gipsy *acciaccaturas*, has an almost manic insistence. Elsewhere the Lindsay bring an ideal warmth and lyricism to the opening movement of No. 1, characteristically phrasing in long, eloquent spans, and a quixotic energy to the outer movements of the G minor, No. 3, where the Mosaïques are broader and tougher. In the Minuet of No. 3 the Lindsay's singing line and flexibility of pulse realize to the full Haydn's searching harmonic progressions; and the lulling E flat Trio is exquisitely floated, with the players venturing an even more hushed, absorbed tone colour on the repeat. Each of the slow movements reveals dedication and profound identification. The players vindicate their dangerously slow tempo in the sublime *Affettuoso e sostenuto* of No. 1 with the breadth and intensity of their phrasing, their subtlety of colour and their feeling for harmonic flux. Conversely, the slow movements of No. 3 and, especially, No. 4 are more flowing than with the Mosaïques yet no less moving. As ever, the occasional moment of impure intonation and marginally imprecise ensemble is a small price to pay for performances of such colour, character and spontaneity. The Lindsay observe all the important marked repeats and the recording is vivid and truthful, though the close balance picks up a fair bit of sniffing. Choice between the generally bolder, more dramatic Lindsay and the more intimate, fluid and, at times, more whimsical Mosaïques is invidious. No serious Haydn collector will want to be without either.

Haydn String Quartets, Op. 33 – No. 1 in B minor; No. 2 in E flat major, "Joke"; No. 4 in B flat major. **Lindsay Quartet** (Peter Cropper, Ronald Birks, vns; Robin Ireland, va; Bernard Gregor-Smith, vc). ASV Ⓔ CDDCA937 (62 minutes: DDD: 3/96). Recorded 1994.
Gramophone Editor's choice.
Haydn String Quartets, Op. 33 – No. 1 in B minor; No. 4 in B flat major; No. 6 in D major.
Quatuor Mosaïques (Erich Höbarth, Andrea Bischof, vns; Anita Mitterer, va; Christophe Coin, vc). Auvidis Astrée Ⓔ E8570 (60 minutes: DDD: 6/97). ✍ Recorded 1996.

The Lindsay's is chamber-music-making of unusual recreative flair, untouched by the faintest hint of routine. In their uncommonly grave, inward readings of the slow movements of the E flat and B flat Quartets they sustain a daringly slow tempo magnificently, phrasing in long, arching spans, always acutely sensitive to harmonic movement, as in their subtle colouring of Haydn's breathtaking tonal excursions in No. 4. Beethoven is evoked in the Lindsay's swift, mordant reading of No. 1's epigrammatic *Scherzo*: rarely have the waspish part-writing and the abrupt, disconcerting contrasts in dynamics and articulation been so vividly realized. Typically, they make the most of the complete change of mood and texture in the major-key Trio, finding an almost Viennese sweetness of tone and phrase, complete with touches of portamento. The finale, fast, fierce, utterly un-comical, has a distinct whiff of the Hungarian *puszta* here, both in the wild gipsy figuration from 0'10" and the mounting passion of the sequence in the development. The Lindsay bring an ideal spaciousness and flexibility to the urban, quietly spoken first movement of the E flat Quartet, No. 2, taking due note of Haydn's *cantabile* marking. In the finales of this quartet and No. 4 they enter fully into the music's spirit with vital, inventively varied phrasing, palpably relishing Haydn's exuberance and comic sleight of hand. Here, as occasionally elsewhere, it's easy to overlook the odd moment of rhythmic unsteadiness or impure intonation for the sake of such involved and characterful music-making.

From the teasingly timed initial upbeat of the D major Quartet, No. 6, the Mosaïques' performances have all their familiar hallmarks: inventive phrasing, subtly varied colour, a sure sense of organic growth and a spontaneous-sounding delight in Haydn's inspired unpredictability. Their tempo and manner in the opening *Vivace assai* of No. 6 are, typically, gentler than that of the equally imaginative Lindsays, their articulation lighter and more delicate, as you would expect from period strings. They catch ideally the music's glancing *scherzando* spirit, with a delightfully eager, quick-witted give-and-take between the instruments. Like the Lindsays, the Mosaïques vividly play up the contrast between the perky, high-stepping D major theme and alternating D minor melody. But, characteristically, the Mosaïques flex the tempo more freely and play with the length of Haydn's upbeats, to witty or pathetic effect. In the *Andante* of the B minor Quartet the Mosaïques arguably overdo the whimsical hesitations. However, their unusually reflective way with this movement, and the sense of remoteness they bring to the strange, spare second theme (1'19"), the tone blanched, the octave doublings perfectly in tune, is very appealing. As for the undervalued B flat Quartet, it is a delight throughout, from the puckish opening movement, with its quasi-improvisatory freedom (the Lindsays are fiercer and more brittle here) to the comic exuberance of the finale; the vitality and point of the inner voices' semiquavers in the finale's G minor episode (2'32") are typical of the character the Mosaïques bring to seemingly routine accompanying figuration throughout these performances. In sum, this disc represents yet another winner from this period-instrument quartet. The recording has an attractive ambient warmth.

Haydn String Quartets, Op. 33 – No. 3 in C major, "The Bird"; No. 5 in G major; No. 6 in
   D major. **Lindsay Quartet** (Peter Cropper, Ronald Birks, vns; Robin Ireland, va;
   Bernard Gregor-Smith, vc). ASV Ⓕ CDDCA938 (61 minutes: DDD: 9/96). Recorded 1995.   Ⓖ
The Lindsay Quartet eclipse all-comers in range of colour, vital, creative phrasing and emotional penetration. They respond gleefully to the subversive comedy that pervades each of the three works – most overtly in the Slavonic-influenced finale of *The Bird*, and in the outrageous *Scherzo* of No. 5, where with explosive *sforzandos* and sly touches of timing they relish to the full Haydn's rhythmic and dynamic mayhem. But time and again in this music wit is suddenly suffused with poetry; and the Lindsay bring a glancing delicacy and grace of interplay to, say, the startling tonal deflexions in the opening *Vivace assai* of No. 6. With the Lindsay's slower-than-usual tempo and wonderfully tender, contained *sotto voce*, the second movement of No. 3, where Haydn transmutes the minuet-scherzo into a hymn, becomes the expressive core of the quartet. The variation finales of Nos. 5 and 6 can easily seem anticlimactic. Here, though, the players' rhythmic point and inventively varied phrasing and dynamics (repeats are never mere repetitions) make the music consistently compelling. The Lindsay play from the Henle Urtext edition, which corrects tempo markings and numerous details of phrasing in the unreliable Peters and Eulenburg editions; and they observe both repeats in sonata movements – particularly important in the first movement of *The Bird*, where the four-bar lead-back to the development adds yet another point of harmonic subtlety. Like the Quatuor Mosaïques, but few others, the Lindsay constantly provoke you to respond afresh to Haydn; to his wit and comic exuberance, his inexhaustible inventiveness and his often unsuspected profundity.

Additional recommendations ...
...Nos. 4-6. D major, Op. 42. **Salomon Quartet.**
   Hyperion Ⓕ CDA66682 (72 minutes: DDD: 9/93). 🎖
...Nos. 1-6. **Appónyi Quartet.** Ars Musici Ⓕ AM1083-2 (two discs: 108 minutes: DDD: 6/95).
...Nos. 2, 3 and 5. **Quatuor Mosaïques.** Auvidis Astrée Ⓕ E8569 (61 minutes: DDD: 6/96). 🎖
   Gramophone Editor's choice. Gramophone Award Winner 1996.   ⒼⒼ
...No. 3. *Coupled with works by* **Ravel** and **Schubert** Allegri Quartet.
   Naim Audio Ⓕ NAIMCD012 (62 minutes: DDD: 2/97).

Haydn String Quartet in D major, Op. 42.
Schumann String Quartet No. 3 in A major, Op. 41 No. 3.
Shostakovich String Quartet No. 3 in F major, Op. 73. **Allegri Quartet** (Peter Carter,
   David Roth, vns; Jonathan Barritt, va; Bruno Schrecker, vc). Naim Audio Ⓕ NAIMCD016
   (73 minutes: DDD: 4/98). Recorded 1996.
The beauty of these readings is that they mean what they say. There is no hint of any over-earnestness and the programme has been very carefully chosen. Haydn's exquisite Op. 42 is given an especially winning rendition, the *Andante ed innocentemente* first movement donning a degree of understatement that reflects its equivocal personality. Following Haydn's Op. 42 with Shostakovich's Op. 73 was an inspired idea: the former ends quietly and the latter opens with a sort of distracted innocence, marking time before the real drama starts. Sample 3'51" into the first movement and argument suddenly intensifies, playfully, provocatively, though characterization is cleverly differentiated. In the second movement, Prokofiev is an obvious point of reference and there has

rarely been a more delicately pointed account of the weird, tiptoe staccato passage that emerges out of the first idea. The third movement is a striking precursor of the Tenth Symphony's violent 'Stalin' *Scherzo*, the slow movement redolent of the Twelfth Symphony's noble opening and the long finale ending in a mood of veiled mystery. Above all, this is profoundly natural playing and the recordings maintain a realistic 'small concert-hall' ambience throughout. The disc ends with an affectionate, flexible performance of Schumann's loveliest string quartet. The opening *Andante espressivo* sets the mood while the ensuing second set (1'19") is limpid and rapturous, and the finale – which in some hands can seem repetitive – is given precisely the right degree of rhythmic emphasis. Again one senses wholehearted identification between the repertoire and its interpreters – and while one may question the wisdom of mixed-repertory CD programmes, this one is so well planned and well played, that it can be recommended even to those readers who already own recordings within cycles.

Haydn String Quartets, Op. 50, "Tost I". **Salomon Quartet** (Simon Standage, Micaela Comberti, vns; Trevor Jones, va; Jennifer Ward Clarke, vc). Hyperion Ⓕ CDA66821/2 (two discs, oas: 75 and 76 minutes: DDD: 9/94). ✍
CDA66821 – No. 1 in B flat major; No. 2 in C major; No. 3 in E flat major. *CDA66822* – No. 4 in F sharp minor; No. 5 in F major, "The Dream"; No. 6 in D major, "The Frog".
Commentators have sometimes detected Mozartian influences in Haydn's Op. 50, the first set he completed after the six quartets which Mozart dedicated to him. Perhaps the unusual weight and intensity of several of the Minuets and, even more unexpectedly, their Trios (especially in Nos. 4-6) can be seen as Haydn's response to the astonishing, subversive anti-minuet in Mozart's K387. But there is little of Mozart's expansive lyrical richness and harmonic sensuousness about Op. 50, which in its musical procedures is arguably Haydn's most ascetic, obsessive and intellectually rigorous set of quartets. There is wit here, of course, in abundance, but of a more subtle, ambivalent kind than the broad comedy of Haydn's previous set, Op. 33 – even in the finale of this set's most famous work, No. 6, whose quick-fire bariolage (repeated notes played alternately on adjacent strings) suggested to early listeners the croaking of a frog. This recording by the Salomon Quartet does ample justice to this masterly, intriguing, sometimes elusive music. The playing is confidently characterized, with strong, propulsive rhythms and lucid, carefully balanced textures; and despite the relative absence of vibrato they can produce a remarkably full-bodied sound where appropriate.

Haydn String Quartets, Op. 54 – No. 1 in G major. No. 2 in C major. No. 3 in E major.
Lindsay Quartet (Peter Cropper, Robin Ireland, vns; Ronald Birks, va; Bernard Gregor-Smith, vc). ASV Ⓕ CDDCA582 (66 minutes: DDD: 8/87).
All three quartets are in the usual four-movement form but with many surprises: in No. 1, the false recapitulation in the first movement, the dark modulations in the following sonata-form *Allegretto* and the Hungarian gipsy flavour (anticipated in the minuet) and mischievousness of the final rondo. No. 2 has a rhapsodic fiddler in its second movement, a nostalgic minuet with an extraordinarily anguished trio, and an *Adagio* finale in which a *Presto* section turns out to be no more than an episode. A notable feature of No. 3 is its ternary-form *Largo cantabile*, the centre of which is more like a mini-concerto for the first violin; 'Scotch snaps' pervade the minuet, and pedal points the finale. The performances (and the recording) are superb, marked by unanimity, fine tone, suppleness of phrasing, and acute dynamic shaping; in the second movement of No. 1 there are hushed passages whose homogeneity and quality of sound are quite remarkable. This recording is irresistible.
Additional recommendations ...
...No. 2. D major, Op. 64 No. 5, "The Lark". **Gabrieli Quartet.**
Chandos Ⓕ CHAN8531 (39 minutes: DDD: 11/87).
...Nos. 1-3. **Salomon Quartet.** Hyperion Ⓕ CDA66971 (71 minutes: DDD: 12/95). ✍

Haydn String Quartets, Op. 55, "Tost II" – No. 1 in A major; No. 2 in F minor; No. 3 in B flat major. **Lindsay Quartet** (Peter Cropper, Ronald Birks, vns; Robin Ireland, va; Bernard Gregor-Smith, vc). ASV Ⓕ CDDCA906 (64 minutes: DDD: 3/95). Recorded 1994.
Gramophone Editor's choice. Ⓖ
Most immediately striking of the trilogy is the F minor work, with its searching double variations on related minor and major themes (a favourite form in Haydn's later music), spiky, rebarbative second movement *Allegro* and strangely spare contrapuntal minuet. The A major, No. 1, has much of this key's traditional brilliance, with ample scope for the leader's creative virtuosity in the outer movements and the stratospheric trio of the minuet; in contrast the noble, wonderfully scored *Adagio cantabile* prefigures the profound slow movements of Haydn's final years. The more inward-looking No. 3 in B flat is specially remarkable for the varied recapitulations in the flanking movements, astonishingly free and inventive even for Haydn, and the subtle chromatic colouring in all four movements which may just owe something to the quartets Mozart had dedicated to Haydn three years earlier. Here and there the Lindsay's intonation is less than true, especially from the leader, but as so often with this group, this is a small price to pay for performances of such colour and penetration. The balance, as with many recent quartet recordings, is a shade closer than ideal but the overall sound-picture is very acceptable.
Additional recommendation ...
...Nos. 1-3. **Salomon Quartet.** Hyperion Ⓕ CDA66972 (69 minutes: DDD: 7/96). ✍

Haydn String Quartets, Op. 64, "Tost III". **Salomon Quartet** (Simon Standage, Micaela Comberti, vns; Trevor Jones, va; Jennifer Ward Clarke, vc). Hyperion Ⓕ CDA67011/12 (two discs, oas: 69 and 60 minutes: DDD: 12/96). ☛ Recorded 1995.
CDA67011 – No. 1 in C major; No. 2 in B minor; No. 3 in B flat major.
CDA67012 – No. 4 in G major; No. 5 in D major, "The Lark"; No. 6 in E flat major.
These are predictably stylish, clean-limbed readings of the quartets Haydn composed in his final months at Eszterházy, just before his first visit to London. As Peter Holman points out in his informative note, the Op. 64 works are generally less demonstrative, less 'public' in tone than the quartets that precede and follow them. The Salomon bring to them an aptly relaxed, intimate manner, with their familiar hallmarks of lucid textures, vital phrasing and a natural feeling for the music's conversational interplay. Tempos in the outer movements tend to be quite spacious, allowing the Salomon ample room for manoeuvre. The Salomon are particularly enjoyable in the set's one well-known quartet, No. 5, where Simon Standage shows an inventive variety of inflexion in the first movement's *Lark* theme – there's a beautiful sense of lyrical repose, for instance, when the theme appears for the only time in a full legato texture near the start of the development; and the unhurried tempo in the finale allows for much more meaningful phrasing than in the slick, virtuoso performances one often hears – again, the players' light, airy articulation is a delight here. The Salomon's observant, sympathetic readings, beautifully recorded, make a highly persuasive case for works that, the *Lark* apart, are still far too little heard.

Additional recommendations ...
...Nos. 1-3. **Kodály Quartet.** Naxos Ⓢ 8 550673 (64 minutes: DDD: 1/94).
Gramophone Editor's choice.
...Nos. 4-6. **Kodály Quartet.** Naxos Ⓢ 8 550674 (65 minutes: DDD: 1/94).
Gramophone Editor's choice.
...Nos. 1-6. **Festetics Quartet.** Harmonia Mundi Musique d'abord Ⓑ HMA190 3040/41 (two discs: 138 minutes: DDD: 12/95).

Haydn String Quartets, Opp. 71 and 74. **Kodály Quartet** (Attila Falvay, Tamás Szabo, vns; Gábor Fias, va; János Devich, vc). Naxos Ⓢ 8 550394 and 8 550396 (two discs, oas: 62 and 63 minutes: DDD: 2/91). Recorded 1989.
8 550394 – Op. 71: No. 1 in B flat major, No. 2 in D major; No. 3 in E flat major.
8 550396 – Op. 74: No. 1 in C major; No. 2 in F major; No. 3 in G minor, "The Rider".
The enterprising Kodály Quartet are working their way through the middle and late Haydn quartets and, rightly, taking their time about it. They rehearse together privately, and then every so often turn up at the Hungaroton Studios in Rottenbiller ready to record a new group. They play with self-evident joy in the music and an easy neatness of ensemble, which comes from familiarity with each other's company. There is never a hint of routine and the intercommunication is matched by enormous care for detail and clean ensemble. In short they play as one, and project this wonderful music with enormous dedication. Just sample the elegant *Andante* with variations which form the slow movement of Op. 71 No. 3, or the witty minuet which follows, or any of the consistently inspired Op. 74 set. The hushed intensity of playing in the *Largo assai* of Op. 74 No. 3 is unforgettable. The recordings are wholly natural and balanced within a well-judged acoustic; the sound is of the highest quality and documentation is excellent. At their modest price this pair of CDs is irresistible.

Additional recommendations ...
...Op. 74: Nos. 2 and 3. **Salomon Quartet.**
Hyperion Ⓕ CDA66124 (53 minutes: AAD: 3/87). ☛ *Selected by Sounds in Retrospect.*
...Op. 71 Nos. 1 and 2. **Salomon Quartet.** Hyperion Ⓕ CDA66065 (47 minutes: DDD: 12/87). ☛
...Op. 71 No. 3; Op. 74 No. 1. **Salomon Quartet.**
Hyperion Ⓕ CDA66098 (59 minutes: AAD: 12/87). ☛

Haydn String Quartets, Op. 76 – No. 2 in D minor, "Fifths"; No. 3 in C major, "Emperor"; No. 4 in B flat major, "Sunrise". **Alban Berg Quartet** (Günter Pichler, Gerhard Schulz, vns; Thomas Kakuska, va; Valentin Erben, vc). EMI Ⓕ CDC5 56166-2 (66 minutes: DDD: 3/97). Recorded 1993-94.
This disc of three of Haydn's most famous quartets are uncommonly fine, above all the performance of the D minor, No. 2. The Berg take both outer movements more spaciously than most of their rivals. In the opening *Allegro* the Berg are tougher and more austere, thinking and phrasing, as ever, in long spans, bringing an urgent sweep to the development and a true sense of climax to the coda, where the lower instruments' syncopated cross-rhythms scythe through the texture. And with their broader tempo the Berg realize more tellingly details like the repeated hairpin crescendos on the sequence of tied notes in the second group. In the Berg's hands the Hungarian-tinged finale has greater trenchancy and symphonic weight, with a more imaginative variety of colour and accent. The *Emperor* and the *Sunrise* are hardly less fine, marrying an impressive formal control with a vivid sense of character and felicity of detail: listen, for instance, to the Berg's subtle timing and hushed, veiled tone at the sudden dip to E flat in the first movement of No. 3; their rapt tenderness and breadth of phrase in the sublime *Adagio* of the *Sunrise*, the melody unfolding in a single unbroken span; or their deft management of the progressive speed increases in the finale of the same work, where they imbue the theme itself with

an infectious lilt. The leader's very fluid, ruminative phrasing in the Quartet's opening (from which it gets its nickname) makes it seem even more than usual like a slow introduction, with the first phrase stealing in magically from nowhere. At their best, and especially in No. 2, the Bergs bring a rare imaginative insight to this ever-astonishing, inexhaustible music; and for all the fire and brio of other readings, the Bergs could prove more enduring, not least since EMI's recording, despite a slight bias towards the first violin, is clear and sympathetic.

Additional recommendations ...
...Nos. 1-6. **Tokyo Quartet**. Sony Classical Ⓑ SB2K53522 (two discs: 130 minutes: ADD).
...Nos. 3 and 4. **Mozart** String Quartet No. 17 in B flat major, K458, "Hunt". **Amadeus Quartet**.
     DG Galleria Ⓜ 449 092-2GGA (67 minutes: ADD: 7/96).
...No. 2. *Coupled with works by* **Ravel** and **Schubert** Skampa Quartet.
     Supraphon Ⓕ SU3156-2 (61 minutes: DDD: 8/97).

Haydn String Quartets – Op. 77: No. 1 in G major; No. 2 in F major. D minor, Op. 103 (unfinished). **Quatuor Mosaïques** (Erich Höbarth, Andrea Bischof, vns; Anita Mitterer, va; Christophe Coin, vc). Auvidis Astrée Ⓕ E8799 (62 minutes: DDD: 2/90). ✧
Anyone who thinks that period-instrument performance means austerity and coolness should listen to this disc. Here is a group of youngish French players, using instruments of the kind Haydn would have heard, played (as far as we can know) in a style he would have been familiar with: the result is a disc full of expressive warmth and vigour. The opening of Op. 77 No. 1 is done duly gracefully, but with a sturdy underlying rhythm and the scherzo is as crisp and alive as one could ask for. Then the first movement of the F major work is very beautifully done, with many sensitive details; and the lovely second movement is ideally leisurely, so that the players have ample room for manoeuvre and the leader makes much of his opportunities for delicate playing in the filigree-like high music. The players show a real grasp of the structure and they know when to illuminate the key moments, with a touch of extra deliberation or a little additional weight of tone. These performances, clearly recorded, are competitive ones not merely within the protected world of 'early music' but in the bigger, 'real' world too!

Additional recommendation ...
...Nos. 1 and 2. **Berio** Notturno. **Alban Berg Quartet**.
     EMI Ⓕ CDC5 55191-2 (72 minutes: DDD: 10/95).

Haydn Seven Last Words, Op. 51. **Lindsay Quartet** (Peter Cropper, Ronald Birks, vns;
     Robin Ireland, va; Bernard Gregor-Smith, vc). ASV Ⓕ CDDCA853 (71 minutes: DDD: 6/93).
This performance by the Lindsay Quartet is magical and it confirms them as something a bit more special than just the leading British quartet. There are few groups who could sustain these seven slow movements, each lasting about ten minutes, and yet give them such variety of intensity, colour and mood. Haydn revealed himself as a visionary composer in the way he set about creating these seven miniature tone-poems for string quartet. The work is divided into nine sections comprising the seven slow movements each describing one of the final utterances of Christ on the Cross together with a slow introduction and a final *Presto con tutta la forza* which depicts the earthquake which occurred when "the veil of the temple was rent in twain".

Additional recommendations ...
...Seven Last Words. String Quartet in D minor, Op. 103 (unfinished). **Kodály Quartet**.
     Naxos Ⓢ 8 550346 (64 minutes: DDD: 2/91).
...Seven Last Words. **Borodin Quartet**. Teldec Ⓕ 4509-92373-2 (73 minutes: DDD: 4/95).

Haydn Flute Trios – No. 15 in G major, HobXV/15; No. 16 in D major, HobXV/16; No. 17 in
     F major, HobXV/17. **Konrad Hünteler** (fl); **Christophe Coin** (vc); **Patrick Cohen** (fp).
     Harmonia Mundi Ⓕ HMC90 1521 (62 minutes: DDD: 1/96). ✧ Recorded 1994.
"Nothing very special ... a simple bagatelle to amuse you in moments of extreme boredom", was Haydn's own offhand description of the F major Flute Trio in a letter to his friend Marianne von Genzinger. But for all their air of amiable insouciance, these three trios, composed the year before Haydn's first London visit, are highly sophisticated pieces, worked out with surprising breadth and harmonic freedom. Patrick Cohen and his partners are sympathetic interpreters, phrasing imaginatively and responding vividly to, say, the spirited exchanges between flute and keyboard in the first movement of No. 16, or the delightfully discursive, almost improvisatory progress of No. 17's opening *Allegro*. Throughout they create an engaging sense of intimacy and spontaneity. Though balanced a shade too forwardly, Konrad Hünteler's wooden period flute perfectly complements the delicate sonorities of the Walter fortepiano, with its notably sweet-toned treble; and Christophe Coin's gutty cello is always a telling presence, adding just the right degree of weight and intensity at climaxes. This disc can be recommended to anyone who fancies an hour of Haydn at his most genial.

Haydn Piano Trios. **Beaux Arts Trio** (Isidore Cohen, vn; Bernard Greenhouse, vc;
     Menahem Pressler, pf). Philips Ⓑ 454 098-2PB9 (nine discs: 394 minutes: ADD: 7/92).
     Recorded 1970-79. *Gramophone classical 100. Gramophone Award Winner 1979.* ⓖⓐⓐ
     G major, HobXV/25. F sharp minor, HobXV/26. C major, HobXV/27 (all from 6500 023, 6/71).
     E flat major, HobXV/29. E flat major, HobXV/30. E flat major, HobXV/31 (all from 6500 400,

3/73). C major, HobXV/21. D minor, HobXV/23. D major, HobXV/24. E major, HobXV/28 (all from 6500 401, 3/73). A major, HobXV/18. G minor, HobXV/19. E flat major, HobXV/22 (all from 6500 521, 6/74). B flat major, HobXV/20. G major, HobXV/32 (both from 6500 522, 11/73). G minor, HobXV/1. F major, HobXV/37. F major, HobXV/39. G major, HobXV/41. C major, HobXV/C1 (all from 6768 077). A flat major, HobXV/14. G major, HobXV/15 (both from 9500 034, 11/76). C minor, HobXV/13, D major, HobXV/16. F major, HobXV/17 (all from 9500 035, 2/77). G major, HobXIV/6. F major, HobXV/6. B flat major, HobXV/8. G major, XVI/6 (all from 9500 325, 3/78). F major, HobXV/2 (9500 325, 3/78). D major, HobXV/7. A major, HobXV/9. E minor, HobXV/12 (all from 9500 326, 8/77). G major, HobXV/5. E flat major, HobXV/10. E flat major, HobXV/f1 (all from 9500 327, 2/78). F minor, HobXV/11. E flat major, HobXV/36. C major, HobXIV/C1. D major, Hobdeest (all from 9500 472, 7/79). E major, HobXV/34. A major, HobXV/35. B flat major, HobXV/38. F major, HobXV/40 (all from 9500 473, 6/79).

Far more than Mozart's, Haydn's trios are essentially accompanied keyboard sonatas, with the cello wedded to the keyboard bass almost throughout; this lack of cello independence has deterred many groups from investigating their undoubted musical riches. Not, fortunately, the Beaux Arts, whose acclaimed complete cycle accumulated by stealth during the 1970s (when it was finally completed it received almost universal accolades, including *Gramophone*'s Record of the Year Award) and has now reappeared on nine mid-price discs. A dozen of the works date from the 1760s, or even earlier (which for a late developer like Haydn meant pre-puberty), and offer little more than rococo charm, though the G minor (No. 1 in Hoboken's catalogue), with its neo-baroque severity, is a notable exception. But the majority of the trios date from the 1780s and 1790s and contain some of Haydn's most imaginative, lyrical and harmonically adventurous music. Two outstanding works from the 1780s are the E minor, No. 12, with its passionate, closely worked opening *Allegro*, and No. 14 in A flat, with its exquisitely tender *Adagio* in a remote E major that leads without a break into one of Haydn's most hilariously quixotic finales.

The 14 magnificent trios of the 1790s range from relaxed, intimate pieces like the E flat, No. 29, through the sombre, almost tragic F sharp minor, No. 26, to the C major, No. 27, unsurpassed in the whole series for its intellectual and virtuoso brilliance. Finest of all, perhaps, are the E major, No. 28, with its radiant outer movements (wonderfully fanciful, delicate textures here) and its astonishing central E minor *passacaglia*; and the E flat, No. 30, with its noble, lyrically expansive first movement, its deep-toned, often richly chromatic *Andante* and its glorious German-dance finale. The Beaux Arts' playing throughout is vital, refined, and sharply responsive to the music's teeming richness and variety. The early trios were conceived for harpsichord, though such is the deftness and delicacy of Menahem Pressler's touch here that there is no question of the music being overpowered by the modern Steinway; and among individual delights in the group's performances of these early works mention should be made of their gentle, affectionate way with the central minuets, underlining their dual function as dances and surrogate slow movements. In the later trios they catch beautifully the leisurely, almost improvisatory feel of many of the opening movements, and bring a ruminative intensity, and a wonderful quality of soft playing to the great slow movements, while the finales have immense brio, wit and virtuosity, with ideally clean, crisp articulation from Pressler. Occasionally in the earlier works the Beaux Arts sound a touch oversophisticated for this guileless music – the opening violin solo in No. 2 is a case in point. And there are a few disappointments in the later trios – the first movement of the great F sharp minor, No. 26, sounds too lightweight, even skittish while, conversely, in the *passacaglia* of No. 28 they take a surprisingly ponderous view of Haydn's *Allegretto*. But there's a feast of superlative, little-known music here, most of the playing is extraordinarily felicitous, and the recording has Philips's customary warmth and refinement. £70 or so may seem a lot to fork out all at once, but no one is likely to regret the investment – this set will last a lifetime.

Haydn Piano Trios – E minor, HobXV/12; F sharp minor, HobXV/26;E major, HobXV/28; E flat major, HobXV/30. **Yuuko Shiokawa** (vn); **Boris Pergamenschikov** (vc); **András Schiff** (pf). Decca Ⓟ 444 861-2DH (69 minutes: DDD: 6/96). Recorded 1994.

With the outstandingly perceptive period-instrument performances of Haydn's E major Trio (No. 28) by the incisive and bracing Beths/Bylsma/Levin group (reviewed further on), András Schiff and his colleagues have to be on their mettle. Their performance of this work is a gentler creature altogether: it may not bite, but it is by no means muzzled. Shiokawa brings bright definition to the first movement with her buoyant violin playing, while the central *Allegretto*, forthright in the striding use of its stark, linear writing, is a match for anyone (and a minute quicker than most). Schiff's trio place this work in the context of an E minor Trio with a deliciously demure *siciliano*; the Trio No. 26 whose F sharp minor pathos is felt more in stern, penetrating accents than in leaning cadences; and finally the E flat Trio. The long and relaxed first movement is as lively with interpretative insight as it is with ideas, and the yearning chromaticisms of the slow movement are kept on a taut rein: with short, austere bow strokes, this is an *Andante* with plenty of compelling *moto*. These performances were warmly recorded in the Brahms Saal of the Vienna Musikverein.

Haydn Piano Trios – A flat major, HobXV/14; C major, HobXV/27; E flat major, HobXV/29; E flat minor, HobXV/31. **Yuuko Shiokawa** (vn); **Boris Pergamenschikov** (vc); **András Schiff** (pf). Decca Ⓟ 444 862-2DH (69 minutes: DDD: 1/96). Recorded 1994.

This disc gathers together four of Haydn's most inventive late keyboard trios, each one astonishing in its physical and intellectual energy, formal freedom and harmonic vision. The pianist is, of course, the motivating force in these works, above all in the C major Trio, which contains the most virtuosic keyboard writing in all Haydn. Schiff and his colleagues relish the wit, brilliance and sheer speed of Haydn's thoughts in the outer movements, with their comic off-beat accents, sudden changes of register and breathtaking harmonic scope. Rapid keyboard passagework is always imaginatively shaped and directed; and the pellucid, subtly coloured sonorities Schiff draws from his Bösendorfer are a constant source of delight. So, too, is the sharply etched cello of Boris Pergamenschikov, palpably relishing the mobility and vitality of Haydn's bass-lines – so much for the old view that the cello parts in these trios are virtually dispensable. The *Andante*, in the third-related key of A major (a favourite harmonic gambit in late Haydn), is swifter and lighter than the more romantically inflected reading from the Beaux Arts Trio, with more of a *siciliano* lilt – though there is plenty of weight and intensity in the A minor central section which breaks in rudely on Haydn's pastoral idyll. Occasionally, in this movement and elsewhere, Yuuko Shiokawa's tuning is slightly sour. And her phrasing of the soaring solo in the first movement of No. 31 is rather chilly, lacking the eloquence of the Beaux Arts' Isidore Cohen. However, she takes her chances in the German dance-style finale, where keyboard virtuosity is balanced by an unusually elaborate, high lying violin part. Here Shiokawa and Schiff really strike sparks off each other; and sudden moments of poetry are exquisitely handled. The far more riotous German dance that closes No. 29 (shades here of the boozy wine harvest in *The Seasons*) goes with a terrific swing, more abandoned and more pungently accented than the Beaux Arts' version. Decca's recording is intimate and finely balanced, with just the right degree of ambient warmth.

Haydn Piano Trios – A major, HobXV/18; D major, HobXV/24; G major, HobXV/25, "Gipsy Trio"; E flat major, HobXV/29. **Vienna Piano Trio** (Wolfgang Redik, vn; Marcus Trefny, vc; Stefan Mendl, pf). Nimbus Ⓕ NI5535 (60 minutes: DDD: 12/97). Recorded 1997.
Gramophone Editor's choice.
The *Gipsy* Trio may have been written in and for London, but this ensemble's short, snappy bowing, stomping piano accents and, above all, uniquely instinctive fluctuations of tempo and pulse in the finale, locate the work unmistakably in the grape-treading, Romany heart of the Burgenland. The steps of the dance shape and pervade the E flat Trio, too, in the jauntily sprung rhythms of the opening *Allegretto*, and the splendidly boisterous and cross-accented Allemande of its finale. Among countless other delights in these bold and addictive performances is the sensitivity to the power of silence, and the short, hushed half-tones within the long-breathed lines of the *Andante* of the A major Trio. And, not least, the perceptive understanding and judgement of the shifting qualities of an *Allegro* which so well supports the structure of the outer movements of the D major, as well as enabling many a clearly articulated yet fanciful variation in the *Gipsy* Trio. These recordings are close, sometimes breathy, but always thrillingly true.

Haydn Piano Trios – C major, HobXV/21; E flat major, HobXV/22; D minor, HobXV/23. **Erich Höbarth** (vn); **Christophe Coin** (vc); **Patrick Cohen** (fp). Harmonia Mundi Ⓕ HMC90 1400 (62 minutes: DDD: 9/93). 🎵 Recorded 1992.
Of the three works here, No. 21 is a generally lightweight, uncomplicated piece, with bucolic bagpipe effects in the gigue-like opening movement, an *Andante* built on a *Romanze*-type melody such as Mozart often favoured in his later music and a racy final *Presto*, a more compact counterpart to the finales in several of the "Salomon" symphonies. The D minor, No. 23, opening with a set of variations on Haydn's favourite plan of alternating minor and major themes, has a richly ornamented *Adagio ma non troppo* with a rhapsodic, almost improvisatory feel (a type of Haydn slow movement only found in these late trios) and a wiry, syncopated finale full of teasing cross-rhythms. Finest of the three works, though, is the E flat, No. 22, all of whose movements show Haydn's harmonic thinking at its most subtle and exploratory, above all, the haunting, pre-Schubertian G major *Poco adagio*. The performances from Patrick Cohen and his string colleagues are technically assured (string intonation well-nigh perfect throughout) and strongly characterized, with a wide spectrum of tone colour and dynamics; and the relatively light sonorities of period instruments make for consistently lucid textures. They are vividly recorded.

Haydn Piano Trios – D major, HobXV/24; G major, HobXV/25, "Tipsy Trio"; F sharp minor, HobXV/26. **Erich Höbarth** (vn); **Christophe Coin** (vc); **Patrick Cohen** (fp). Harmonia Mundi Ⓕ HMC90 1514 (47 minutes: DDD: 9/95). 🎵 Recorded 1994.
The Beaux Arts' slick, overskittish reading of the F sharp minor Trio's opening *Allegro* was one of the chief disappointments in their complete Philips cycle. Here Patrick Cohen and his colleagues realize far more fully the movement's sombre power, with a broader tempo, stronger yet more flexible rhythms and a much sharper response to the mounting harmonic tensions of the development. Cohen has the true measure of the music's emotional and intellectual force, judges rubato subtly and imbues his rapid passagework in the development and recapitulation with a real sense of dramatic urgency. If his fortepiano naturally dominates proceedings, the more egalitarian balance, easier to achieve on period instruments, allows both Erich Höbarth and Christophe Coin to make their mark. As Coin demonstrates, here and elsewhere, Haydn's cello writing is far less dull than it is often held to be. The

gipsy rondo of the popular G major Trio can hardly fail to bring the house down; but these players rip into the music with extraordinary flair and abandon, its devilry enhanced by Coin's boldly defined cello line. In the glorious D major Trio they capture beautifully the first movement's lyrical spaciousness and sense of inspired spontaneity, savouring each unexpected twist in harmony and melodic line, and bring an ideal fluidity and delicacy of interplay to the finale, gentlest and most poetic of the German dance movements found in many of Haydn's late trios. The Beaux Arts, with their rather suaver style, are fine in both the D major and the G major Trios, though Cohen and his partners seem to play with that much more fantasy and expressive variety. The recording, if a shade close (and catching a fair amount of sniffing), reproduces truthfully the ensemble's crisp, transparent textures.

Haydn Piano Trios – C major, HobXV/27; E major, HobXV/28; E flat major, HobXV/29; E flat major, HobXV/30. **Vera Beths** (vn); **Anner Bylsma** (vc); **Robert Levin** (fp).
Sony Classical Vivarte Ⓕ SK53120 (74 minutes: DDD: 6/94). 🖎
These are truly magnificent pieces, full of ideas of startling originality, and conceived on a grand scale – not simply long (though No. 42 certainly is that) but composed with a remarkable spaciousness to their ideas and their working-out. These performances do them ample justice, with their very brilliant and stylish pianism and a beautifully held instrumental balance (which, incidentally, gives the lie to the old notion that Haydn's cello parts are routine stuff: clearly Bylsma doesn't see them that way). Robert Levin, using a McNulty copy of a 1780 piano by J.A. Stein, produces playing of great vitality and delightful crispness, and puts across powerfully the intellectual force and the argumentative character of the music. Outstandingly keen and vital musicianship, excellently recorded.

Haydn Piano works. **John McCabe** (pf). Decca London Ⓑ 443 785-2LC12 (12 discs: 873 minutes: ADD: 12/95). From Decca HDN100/2 (10/75), HDN103/5 (5/76), HDN106/8 (9/76), HDN109/11 (4/77) and HDN112/5 (10/77). Recorded 1974-77.
Sonatas Nos. 1-62. Five Variations in D major, HobXVII/7. Seven Menuets from "Kleine Tänze für die Jugend", HobIX/8. Variations in F minor, HobXVII/6. Fantasia in C major, HobXVII/4. 12 Variations in E flat major, HobXVII/3. Adagio in F major, HobXVII/9. Six Variations in C major, HobXVII/5. 20 Variations in A major, HobXVII/2. Capriccio in G major, HobXVII/1. Seven Last Words.
Together with Schnabel's Beethoven sonatas and Klien's Mozart sonatas, McCabe's recordings of Haydn's piano sonatas represent one of the great recorded monuments of the keyboard repertoire. Sample any one of the discs in this budget-price set and you will immediately become aware of the immense treasures on offer. In addition to being a fine pianist, McCabe is also an accomplished composer, and the special qualities he brings to his performances benefit from his 'insider's' awareness of musical content, pursuing the structural argument in these pieces with the acute perceptions of a composer's ear. Thus, assisted by the rich resonance and tonal subtlety of the modern piano, McCabe provides a consistently stylish view of Haydn's developing musical persona that comprehensively exploits this repertoire's inherent expressive potential. Spare textures and astonishing formal concentration in the earliest works establish a perfect balance between structure and content, and McCabe's crisp, beautifully poised playing enables the music to make its own potently expressive impact. The middle-period sonatas demonstrate Haydn's further experimentation and consolidation of style and technique. Harpsichord textures, reminiscent of Scarlatti, are still apparent in works such as the A flat Sonata (No. 31), but so, too, are new influences. For instance, McCabe luxuriates in the *Sturm und Drang* characteristics of the G minor Sonata (No. 32), penetrating to the core of the musical fabric to release the full power of the score's passionate centre.
Haydn's piano sonatas reach a supreme level of refinement in the late works, and McCabe responds with suitably spacious playing, sensitive to the music's richer 'orchestral' colours. He brings a connoisseur's touch to the impressionistic harmonic effects in the first movement of the C major Sonata (No. 60); his sinuous phrasing underlines the Schubertian flavour of the opening *Andante* to the D major Sonata (No. 61); he charmingly points the Beethovenian syncopation in the same work's *Scherzo* and ultimately achieves the perfect balance between content and design in the magisterial E flat Sonata (No. 62). McCabe's consummate poise between foreground motivic activity and structural background is equally remarkable in the separate keyboard pieces, which add to the appeal of this set. His outstanding performances of both *Seven Last Words* and the ingeniously constructed F minor Variations are obvious highlights; but try, also, the enchanting *Adagio*, and the charming selection of dances, which provide further evidence of Haydn's mastery of miniature forms. The vividly clear 1970s recordings have retained all the clarity for which they are justly renowned and, as for comparisons, McCabe's performances here set the standards against which others will be judged.
Additional recommendation ...
...Piano Sonatas – C major, HobXVI/21; E major, HobXVI/22; F major, HobXVI/23; D major, HobXVI/24; E flat major, HobXVI/25; A major, HobXVI/26. **Jenö Jandó** (pf).
Naxos Ⓢ 8 553127 (67 minutes: DDD: 6/95).

Haydn Piano works. **Alfred Brendel** (pf). Philips Ⓕ 416 643-2PH4 (four discs: 205 minutes: ADD/DDD: 3/87). Booklet included. *Gramophone classical 100. Gramophone Award Winner 1987.*

Sonatas – C minor, HobXVI/20; E flat major, HobXVI/49 (both from 9500 774, 8/81); E minor,
HobXVI/34; B minor, HobXVI/32; D major, Hob XVI/42 (412 228-1PH, 8/85); C major,
HobXVI/48; D major, HobXVI/51; C major, Hob XVI/50 (6514 317, 11/83); E flat major,
HobXVI/52; G major, HobXVI/40; D major, HobXVI/37 (416 365-1PH, 12/86). Fantasia in
C major, HobXVI/4. Adagio in F major, HobXVI/9 (412 228-1PH, 8/85). Variations in F minor,
Hob XVI/6 (416 365-1PH, 12/86).　　　　　　　　　　　　　　　　　　　　　　　⊕⊕⊕
The sonatas collected in this set are some magnificent creations, wonderfully well played by Alfred
Brendel. Within the order and scale of these works Haydn explores a rich diversity of musical
languages, a wit and broadness of expression that quickly repays attentive listening. It is the
capriciousness as much as the poetry that Brendel so perfectly attends to; his playing, ever alive to the
vitality and subtleties, makes these discs a delight. The sophistication innate in the simple dance
rhythms, the rusticity that emerges, but above all, the sheer *joie de vivre* are gladly embraced. Brendel's
continual illumination of the musical ideas through intense study pays huge dividends. The recording
quality varies enormously between the different works and though the close acoustic on some of the
later discs could be faulted for allowing one to hear too much of the keyboard action, it certainly
brings one into vivid contact with the music.

Additional recommendations ...
...E minor, HobXVI/34. G major, HobXVI/40. B flat major, HobXVI/41. D major, HobXVI/42.
C major, HobXVI/48. Variations in F minor, HobXVII/6. **Jenö Jandó** (pf).
Naxos ⑤ 8 550845 (70 minutes: DDD: 8/94).
...E flat major, HobXVI/49. *Coupled with works by various composers.* **Vladimir Horowitz** (pf).
Sony Classical SK45818 (8/90). *See review in the Collections section; refer to the Index.*　⊕⊕⊕
...E flat major, HobXVI/49; C major, HobXVI/50; E flat major, HobXVI/52.
Variations in F minor, HobXVII/6. *Coupled with works by* **Mozart** Alfred Brendel (pf).
Philips ⓜ 446 921-2PM5 (five discs: 369 minutes: ADD/DDD: 2/96).

Haydn Piano Sonatas – A major, HobXVI/30; E flat major, HobXVI/52.
Schubert Piano Sonata No. 14 in A minor, D784. Marche militaire No. 1 in D major, D733
(arr. Tausig). **Evgeni Kissin** (pf). Sony Classical ⑤ SK64538 (62 minutes: DDD: 9/95).
Gramophone Editor's record of the month.　　　　　　　　　　　　　　　　　　⊕
Enormously enjoyable! This is Haydn playing of high style and verve – also affectionate, articulate,
colourful and expressive – and its vitality seems authentic even when Kissin asks you to admire the
means with which he achieves it. This is not wilful or eccentric playing. By the end of the A major
work, an engaging and (even by Haydn's standards) unconventional Sonata, you feel its stature has
been enhanced, which is just as it should be. Kissin meets the greater challenge of Haydn's last Sonata
of all (No. 62) equally well. The breadth as well as the brilliance of the first movement is there, and
its warmth; his tempo may be a little brisker than usual but it still allows for weight. The last
movement *Presto* really is breakneck, at a speed which would be unwise, not to say unrealistic, for
most others; once again, the impression is of allure allied to perfectly judged dramatic tension and
articulate speech. As someone remarked when we were listening to Kissin with the Boston Symphony
at Tanglewood a couple of summers ago, "it's not just that it's all there, but he makes it all happen at
the right time". Maybe he sustains the phrases of the *Adagio* with less success: they tend to emerge a
bar at a time, as with many players, instead of as an arching span. How difficult this is to do when
tone on the piano dies so quickly. But it is precisely this kind of growth and building through
sentences and long paragraphs – and through silences – that he manages so well in the first movement
of the Schubert sonata. It would be tedious to annotate everything, but admire here what you will:
the unforced, perfectly scaled range of dynamics and attacks; the motivating force of the left hand, so
often neglected by those who see interest only in the right; the sensitivity to harmonic movement,
again, and to the smallest shifts of colour and weight; the infallible timing and marvellous sense of
rhythm in all aspects; the voicing and vitality of the texture from top to bottom; a detail such as the
way the doubling of a melodic line at the octave produces not just a melody in octaves but an
intensification of the single line heard previously. Above all, there is a commanding vision of the
whole. The finale is equally fine. The recording balance is not too close and the sound is pleasingly
open and natural.

Haydn Piano Sonatas – B minor, HobXVI/32; E minor, HobXVI/34; G minor, HobXVI/44;
E flat major, HobXVI/49. **Emanuel Ax** (pf). Sony Classical ⓕ SK53635 (61 minutes: DDD: 7/95).
Recorded 1993.
Emanuel Ax's choice of piano sonatas focuses on the remarkable influence of C.P.E. Bach in this
repertoire. Of the three minor-key sonatas recorded here, the two-movement G minor work makes the
influences the most poignantly apparent. Ax's performance is finely proportioned, and his elegant,
sensitively shaped phrasing creates an arresting expression of the music's homogeneity and dramatic
intensity. Ax includes all repeats, which, in the finale of the one in B minor, for example, produces
startling results. In the finale of the E minor Sonata, by comparison, Ax's distinctive handling of
different textures, which enhances the contrast between sections, vividly reveals the movement's fusion
of rondo and variation forms. Ax ends his programme with the E flat major Sonata. Haydn himself
was especially proud of the *Adagio*, and Ax's performance of this movement's passionate minor-mode
middle section makes a dramatic impact. However, after panache and brilliance in the finale, Ax's

breathtakingly beautiful, gentle final cadence leaves the deepest impression. Ax's penetrating insights into the *Sturm und Drang* characteristics of these sonatas make an outstanding contribution to the appreciation of this aspect of the composer's keyboard sonata output.

Additional recommendation ...
...G minor, HobXVI/44. *Coupled with works by various composers.* **Sviatoslav Richter** (pf).
DG Double Ⓜ 447 355-2GDB2 (two discs: 150 minutes: ADD: 12/95).

Haydn Piano Sonatas – C major, HobXVI/35; C sharp minor, HobXVI/36; D major, HobXVI/37; E flat major, HobXVI/38; G major, HobXVI/39. **Jenö Jandó** (pf). Naxos Ⓢ 8 553128 (62 minutes: DDD: 7/95). Recorded 1993.
The exquisite, classical balance evident in these six keyboard sonatas makes them especially rewarding examples of the composer's exploitation of the piano's broad expressive range and rich textural variety. This latest volume in Jenö Jandó's complete edition presents these pieces in a compelling, modern-instrument version. For example, there is brilliance and sparkle in the opening movements of the D major and E flat Sonatas; warmth and dramatic intensity in the slow movements (most notably in the baroque echoes of the Sonatas in C major and D major), and an appealing blend of wit and elegance in finales such as the third movement of the D major Sonata, or the minuets which conclude the C sharp minor and E flat major Sonatas. Most remarkable, though, is the G major Sonata, where Jandó's customary precision and his sensitive balance of the music's linear and harmonic dimensions powerfully convey the work's concerto character and Haydn's imaginative approach to form. Try Jandó's engaging account of the opening *Allegro*, his deft balance of the slow movement's effective blend of major and minor, and his exuberant virtuosity in the finale.

Haydn Piano Sonatas – E flat major, HobXVI/49; C major, HobXVI/50; D major, HobXVI/51; E flat major, HobXVI/52. **Jenö Jandó** (pf). Naxos Ⓢ 8 550657 (62 minutes: DDD: 6/94).
The keyboard sonatas which Haydn originally intended for piano, such as the four considered here, show the composer's exploration of the instrument's capacity for greater dynamic variation. Jandó is sensitive to the relationship between motif and dynamics which is particularly evident in the E flat and D major Sonatas respectively. Aided by clear recorded sound, Jandó's satisfying warmth in the lyrical passages provides an effective dramatic contrast to his crisp, positive approach in the livelier music. Jandó's glittering technique has a high profile in the other two sonatas in the programme. Jandó's stylistically well-turned readings are uncontroversial, but they lack nothing in excitement. Sample the finale of the E flat Sonata, where the wealth of expressive detail at an extremely fast tempo is breathtaking.

Additional recommendation ...
...D major, HobXVI/24; A major, XVI/26; F major, XVI/29; C major, HobXVI/35; C sharp minor, HobXVI/36. **Julia Cload** (pf). Meridian Ⓕ CDE84210 (77 minutes: DDD: 3/93).

Haydn Missa Sancti Bernardi de Offida in B flat major, "Heiligmesse", HobXXII/10ᵃ.
Mare Clausum, HobXXIVa/9ᵇ. Insanae et vanae curae. Motetti de Venerabili Sacramento, HobXXIIIc/5a-d. Te Deum in C major, HobXXIIIc/2. ᵃ**Jörg Hering** (ten); ᵃᵇ**Harry van der Kamp** (bass); **Tölz Boys' Choir; Tafelmusik / Bruno Weil.** Sony Classical Ⓕ SK66260 (63 minutes: DDD: 7/96). 🎵 Texts and translations included. Recorded 1994. Ⓖ
A special attraction for Haydn lovers is the first-ever recording of the unfinished ode *Mare Clausum*, commissioned in 1794 by Haydn's colourful English friend Lord Abingdon, and evidently abandoned when the nobleman was imprisoned for libel. The gauche, crudely chauvinistic verses, trumpeting England's sovereignty of the sea, should make the most hardened Europhobe blush. But the two numbers Haydn completed are worthy of his ripest style: a noble F major bass aria with rich, inventive writing for woodwind, authoritatively sung by Harry van der Kamp, and a D major chorus whose verve and contrapuntal power presage the late Masses and oratorios. Under Bruno Weil's spirited direction both the Tölz Boys' Choir, with their bright-edged, slightly breathy tone, and the period orchestra, Tafelmusik, are on first-rate form here and throughout this enterprisingly planned disc. It includes the thrilling, majestic late *Te Deum* and the motet *Insanae et vanae curae*, adapted from a 'storm' chorus in the oratorio *Il ritorno di Tobia*. Weil's reading is eagerly responsive to the music's drama, with taut rhythms, sharp dynamic contrasts and keen instrumental detailing; and he maintains the initial pulse through the tranquil D major section. Between these masterpieces the four little *Motetti de Venerabili* from the 1750s (another recorded first) inevitably sound tame, for all their easy tunefulness and skilful marshalling of rococo cliché. The largest work on the disc is, of course, the so-called *Heiligmesse*, first of the six magnificent Mass settings of Haydn's old age. Like the shorter pieces, this receives an energetic, uplifting reading, with brisk tempos, fresh, incisive choral work and strongly etched orchestral colours. In one or two sections Weil can drive too hard and Harry van der Kamp sometimes overwhelms the excellent boy soloists. But there is no doubting the vigour and joyfulness of Weil's reading, nor the skill and commitment of his forces. Quite apart from its pioneering value, this is an inspiring Haydn collection whose appeal is enhanced by vivid sound.

Haydn Mass No. 1ᵇ, Missa sunt bona mixta malis, HobXXII/2ᵈ – Kyrie; part of Gloria.
Non nobis, Domine, HobXXIIIa/1ᵈ. Ave regina in A major, HobXXIIIb/3ᵃᶜ. Responsoria de Venerabilis, HobXXIIIc/4a-dˣ. Responsorium ad absolutionem in D minor, HobXXIIb/1ᶜ.

Salve regina in E major, HobXXIII*b*/1[be]. Mass No. 7 in B flat major, Missa brevis Sancti Johannis de Deo ("Kleine Orgelmesse"), HobXXII/7[e]. [a]**Marie-Claude Vallin,** [b]**Ann Monoyios** (sops); **Tölz Boys' Choir;** [c]**L'Archibudelli** (with [d]**Anner Bylsma,** vc; [d]**Anthony Woodrow,** db; [d]**Bob van Asperen,** org); [e]**Tafelmusik / Bruno Weil.** Sony Classical Vivarte Ⓕ SK53368 (60 minutes: DDD: 9/94). ☞ Texts and translations included. Recorded 1992-93.

This is the first appearance on disc of two recent Haydn discoveries, the brief Offertorium *Non nobis, Domine* and fragments (the *Kyrie* and part of the *Gloria*) of a Mass *Sunt bona mixta malis*. But its real charms lie in two works for solo soprano, choir and orchestra composed to mark the entry into convent life of Therese Keller whom Robbins Landon, in his characteristically earthy insert-note, suggests was Haydn's great love: "We must imagine the young Haydn, heartbroken, watching the love of his life taking the veil". Be that as it may, what seeps out of every pore is a warmth and sincerity, something akin to profound inner happiness, which makes one wonder just how deep Haydn's love was for the devout Therese Keller. Marie-Claude Vallin's captivating performance perfectly captures the essential innocence of the *Ave regina*. Her voice has a naïve, almost childlike quality, although in her ethereally soaring high notes and fluent trills there is no doubting her technical command. Ann Monoyios has an altogether fuller, more mature quality as befits the more intense *Salve regina* although, again, if this is Haydn heartbroken, he must have had superhuman powers of recuperation. Bruno Weil's support for these two delightful singers is as unobtrusive as it is sympathetic. His excellent team of musicians (not forgetting the splendid work from the Vivarte recording team) are allowed to relax in performances which seem almost to float on air, so graceful and effortless does it all sound. Add to this a performance of the *Little Organ* Mass (No. 7) of rare poise and elegance and you have a disc of real beauty.

Haydn Masses – No. 1*a* in G major, HobXXII/3, "Missal rorate coeli desuper"; No. 13 in B flat major, HobXXII/13, "Schöpfungsmesse"[a] (with alternative setting of the Gloria). [a]**Susan Gritton** (sop); [a]**Pamela Helen Stephen** (mez); [a]**Mark Padmore** (ten); [a]**Stephen Varcoe** (bar); **Collegium Musicum 90 Chorus; Collegium Musicum 90 / Richard Hickox.** Chandos Chaconne Ⓕ CHAN0599 (62 minutes: DDD: 1/97). ☞ Texts and translations included.
Gramophone Editor's record of the month.   ⒼⒼ

The *Creation* Mass is no less resplendent or searching than, say, the *Nelson* Mass or the *Harmoniemesse*, a glorious affirmation of Haydn's reverent, optimistic yet by no means naïve faith. Even by Haydn's standards, the work is startling in its exploitation of colourful and dramatic key contrasts, as in the sudden swerve from F major to an apocalyptic *fortissimo* D flat at "Judicare vivos"; the *Benedictus*, characteristically, moves from serene pastoral innocence (shades of "With verdure clad" from *The Creation*) to urgent intensity in its central development; and the sublime G major *Agnus Dei* has a profound supplicatory fervour extraordinary even among the composer's many memorable settings of this text. This reading eclipses previous recordings both in the quality of its choir and soloists, the subtlety of Hickox's direction and the vividness and transparency of the recorded sound. In faster movements like the *Kyrie* and the openings of the *Gloria* and *Credo* Hickox strikes just the right balance between dignity and happy, pulsing energy, relishing each of Haydn's dramatic *coups*; and he brings a marvellous clarity and verve, and a sure sense of climax, to the chromatically inflected fugues in the *Gloria* and at "Dona nobis pacem". Abetted by his first-rate orchestra, Hickox is always alive to the felicities of Haydn's scoring, while the 24-strong professional choir are superbly responsive throughout, firm and fresh of tone, maintaining a beautiful, even line in *piano* and *pianissimo*. The *Schöpfungsmesse* lasts under 44 minutes, leaving room for another substantial piece. But what we get is the alternative version of the *Gloria*, and the ultra-compressed (6'49") and instantly forgettable *Missa rorate coeli desuper*, which David Wyn Jones, in his excellent note, wryly describes as "a reminder of how perfunctory church music in eighteenth-century Austria could be". It is neatly dispatched by Hickox and his forces, but inevitably comes as an anticlimax.

Haydn Masses – No. 7 in B flat major, HobXXII/7[a], "Missa brevis Sancti Johannis de Deo"; No. 12 in B flat major, HobXXII/12, "Theresienmesse"[b]. **Janice Watson** (sop); [b]**Pamela Helen Stephen** (mez); [b]**Mark Padmore** (ten); [b]**Stephen Varcoe** (bar); **Collegium Musicum 90 Chorus; Collegium Musicum 90 / Richard Hickox.** Chandos Ⓕ CHAN0592 (60 minutes: DDD: 4/96). ☞ Texts and translations included. Recorded 1995. *Gramophone Editor's choice.*   Ⓖ

Hickox, with his expert period orchestra and 24-strong professional choir, generates the physical and spiritual elation essential to this music, calling to mind Haydn's own much-quoted remark that whenever he praised God his heart leapt with joy. In the glorious *Theresienmesse* of 1799 his manner is a shade brisker and more athletic than Trevor Pinnock's larger-scaled reading; but if Pinnock brings rather more breadth and grandeur to, say, the opening of the *Kyrie* or the *Sanctus*, Hickox is particularly fine in the exultant, springing *Gloria* and the rough-hewn vigour of the *Credo*. He understands, too, the Mass's dramatic and symphonic impetus, bringing a powerful cumulative momentum to the sonata-form "Dona nobis pacem" and thrillingly tightening the screws in the closing pages. Where Hickox has a decisive edge over Pinnock is first of all in the more forward placing of his choir (though never at the expense of orchestral detail, keenly observed by Hickox), and secondly in his uncommonly well-integrated solo quartet, who, framed by the sweet-toned Janice Watson and the gentle, mellifluous Stephen Varcoe, sing with a chamber-musical grace and refinement in the "Et incarnatus est" and the *Benedictus*. And their supplicatory tenderness in the

"Dona nobis pacem" (where Pinnock's solo quartet is more assertive and less subtle in phrasing) contrasts arrestingly with the choir's urgent demands for peace. Hickox also captures the peculiar serenity and innocence of the much earlier *Missa brevis Sancti Johannis de Deo*, or "Little Organ Mass", its intimacy enhanced here by the use of solo strings. A disc guaranteed to refresh the spirit.

Additional recommendations ...

...No. 12. *Coupled with works by* **M. Haydn** and **Mozart** Soloists; Choir of St John's College, Cambridge; Academy of St Martin in the Fields / George Guest.
Decca Ovation Ⓜ 430 159-2DM (56 minutes: ADD: 6/91).

...No. 6 in G major, HobXXII/6, "Missa Sancti Nicolai"; No. 12.
Soloists; The English Concert Choir; The English Concert / Trevor Pinnock.
Archiv Produktion Ⓕ 437 807-2AH (72 minutes: DDD: 1/94). ✍

Haydn Mass No. 11 in D minor, HobXXII/11, "Nelson"[a]. Te Deum in C major, HobXXIIIc/2.
[a]**Felicity Lott** (sop); [a]**Carolyn Watkinson** (contr); [a]**Maldwyn Davies** (ten); [a]**David Wilson-Johnson** (bar); **The English Concert and Choir / Trevor Pinnock**. Archiv Produktion Ⓕ 423 097-2AH (50 minutes: ADD: 2/88). ✍ Texts and translations included. *Gramophone Award Winner 1988.* Ⓖ

The British Admiral had ousted the Napoleonic fleet at the Battle of the Nile just as Haydn was in the middle of writing his *Nelson* Mass. Although the news could not have reached him until after its completion, Haydn's awareness of the international situation was expressed in the work's subtitle, "Missa in Augustiis", or "Mass in times of fear". With its rattle of timpani, its pungent trumpet calls, and its highly-strung harmonic structure, there is no work of Haydn's which cries out so loudly for recording on period instruments; and it is the distinctive sonority and highly charged tempos of this performance which set it apart from its competitors. The dry, hard timpani and long trumpets bite into the dissonance of the opening *Kyrie*, and the near vibrato-less string playing is mordant and urgent. The fast-slow-fast triptych of the *Gloria* is set out in nervously contrasted speeds, and the *Credo* bounces with affirmation. Just as the choral singing is meticulously balanced with instrumental inflexion, so the soloists have been chosen to highlight the colours in Pinnock's palette. This is an unusually exciting recording.

Haydn Mass No. 14 in B flat major, HobXXII/14[a], "Harmoniemesse". Salve regina in E major, HobXXIIIb/1. **Nancy Argenta** (sop); [a]**Pamela Helen Stephen** (mez); [a]**Mark Padmore** (ten); [a]**Stephen Varcoe** (bar); **Collegium Musicum 90 Chorus; Collegium Musicum 90 / Richard Hickox**. Chandos Chaconne Ⓕ CHAN0612 (59 minutes: DDD: 2/98). Texts and translations included. Recorded 1996. *Gramophone Editor's record of the month.* ⒼⒼⒼ

Haydn's first major work, the *Salve regina* of 1756, is here juxtaposed with his last, the *Harmoniemesse* of 1802, so-called because of its exceptionally full scoring for woodwind (*Harmonie* in German means wind band). The gulf between the two works, in sophistication, mastery and emotional range, is predictably vast. Yet, in their very different ways, both reconcile the formal liturgical conventions of their era with the expression of Haydn's own life-affirming religious faith. Hickox and his forces ideally capture this sense of celebratory spiritual energy. Tempos are lively yet never overdriven, rhythms alert and vital. In the Mass Hickox generates an exhilarating symphonic momentum in, say, the opening sections of the *Gloria* and *Credo*, and, aided by an outstandingly clear, well-balanced recording, realizes to the full such dramatic *coups* as the sudden swerve into A flat in the recapitulation of the "Benedictus" (2'31") and the martial fanfares that slew the music from D major to B flat at the start of the "Dona nobis pacem". The steely-edged valveless trumpets are thrilling here; and elsewhere the wind players do rich justice to Haydn's glorious, inventive writing, nicely balancing rusticity and refinement. Nancy Argenta's innocent, bell-like tones and graceful sense of line are heard to touching effect in the "Et incarnatus est" of the Mass. In the *Salve regina*, placed last on the disc but better taken as an aperitif, she also reveals her deft, fluent coloratura technique. No great depths in this youthful work, of course: but Haydn's setting of the Marian antiphon is elegant and affecting, with a command of shapely, Italianate melody and a feeling for dramatic contrast, as when in the second movement a vigorously affirmative chorus suddenly breaks off for a doleful, minor-key soprano solo. This is certainly the most memorable work of Haydn's from the 1750s and aptly complements Hickox's fervent, inspiring reading of the *Harmoniemesse*.

Additional recommendation ...

...No. 14. Te Deum in C major, HobXXIIIc/2. **Soloists; Namur Chamber Choir; La Petite Bande / Sigiswald Kuijken.** Deutsche Harmonia Mundi Ⓕ 05472 77337-2 (52 minutes: DDD: 2/97). ✍

Haydn Die Jahreszeiten. **Barbara Bonney** (sop); **Anthony Rolfe Johnson** (ten); **Andreas Schmidt** (bar); **Monteverdi Choir; English Baroque Soloists / Sir John Eliot Gardiner.** Archiv Produktion Ⓕ 431 818-2AH2 (two discs: 127 minutes: DDD: 5/92). ✍ Text and translation included. Recorded 1990.

The comparative unpopularity of Haydn's *The Seasons* when considered against his other great oratorio, *Die Schöpfung* ("The Creation"), is understandable perhaps, but it is not really all that well deserved. Less exalted its subject and libretto may be, but its depiction of the progress of the year amid the scenes and occupations of the Austrian countryside drew from its composer – then in his late sixties – music of unfailing invention, benign warmth and constant musical-pictorial delights. It is charming music written with great affection, and as such it is not only quintessentially Haydnesque, but also virtually guaranteed to raise a smile. As usual, John Eliot Gardiner and his forces turn in disciplined, meticulously professional performances. This is not one of those massive readings currently favoured even by period practitioners for Haydn's oratorios, though the orchestra are slightly larger – and consequently a tiny bit less lucid – than the sort you might nowadays find playing a classical symphony. The choir, however, perform with great clarity and accuracy, and bring, too, an enjoyable sense of characterization to their various corporate roles. The soloists all perform with notable poise and intelligence: Barbara Bonney's voice is pure and even, Anthony Rolfe Johnson sounds entirely at ease with the music, and Andreas Schmidt is gentle-voiced but certainly not lacking in substance. Perhaps in the end this is a performance which just lacks that last inch of necessary warmth to make it unbeatable, but it's a first-rate recommendation none the less.

Additional recommendations ...

...**Edith Mathis** (sop); **Siegfried Jerusalem** (ten); **Dietrich Fischer-Dieskau** (bar); **Chorus and Academy of St Martin in the Fields / Sir Neville Marriner.** Philips Duo Ⓜ 438 715-2PM2 (two discs: 134 minutes: ADD: 6/94).

...**Gundula Janowitz** (sop); **Peter Schreier** (ten); **Martti Talvela** (bass); **Vienna Singverein and Symphony Orchestra / Karl Böhm.** DG Double Ⓜ 437 940-2GX2 (two discs: 132 minutes: ADD: 5/95).

Haydn Die Schöpfung, HobXXI/2. **Sylvia McNair, Donna Brown** (sops); **Michael Schade** (ten); **Rodney Gilfry, Gerald Finley** (bars); **Monteverdi Choir; English Baroque Soloists / Sir John Eliot Gardiner.** Archiv Produktion Ⓕ 449 217-2AH2 (two discs: 101 minutes: DDD: 4/97). ✍ Text included. *Gramophone Editor's choice. Gramophone Award Winner 1997.* Ⓖ

With Gardiner's first down-beat it is obvious that Chaos's days are numbered. Not that 'days' (strictly speaking) are in question till the mighty words have been spoken, and then, in this performance, what an instantaneous blaze! No premonitory intimation (of pre-echo in the old days whereas now even the faintest stirring in the ranks of the choir will do it), but a single-handed switching-on of the cosmic power-grid and a magnificently sustained C major chord to flood the universe with light. This is one of the great characteristics here: the superbly confident, precise attack of choir and orchestra. Enthusiasm, then, in plenty; but how about the *mystery* of Creation? It is certainly part of the aim to capture this, for the bass soloist's "Im Anfange" ("In the beginning") with *pianissimo* chorus has rarely been so softly and so spaciously taken: the Spirit that moved upon the face of the waters is a veiled, flesh-creeping presence, felt again in the first sunrise and the "softer beams with milder light" of the first moon. Even so, others have incorporated this element more naturally. In particular, the fascinating performance under Weil on Sony conjures up, with rather less deliberation, some memorably distinctive tones. Weil's recording presents itself as a strong competitor, not only in its use of authentic instruments but also in that it sometimes comes closer to what one might have foretold of Gardiner than does Gardiner himself. Weil's tenor soloist, Jörg Hering, also compares well with Michael Schade, who sounded fresher in the fine version made in 1993 under Helmut Rilling (listed below). Gardiner has by far the better Raphael in Gerald Finley, and gains from having extra singers for Adam and Eve, especially as the Eve, Donna Brown, brings a forthright style doubly welcome after the somewhat shrinking-violet manner and breathy tone of Sylvia McNair's Gabriel. On the whole, Gardiner is sounder than Weil, who sometimes rushes: yet his is a fun *Creation* and a real enrichment of the library. Against others of comparable kind, Gardiner stands firm as an easy first choice: a re-creator of vision, a great invigorator and life-enhancer.

Additional recommendations ...

...(sung in English). **Soloists; Choir of New College, Oxford; Academy of Ancient Music Chorus; Academy of Ancient Music Orchestra / Christopher Hogwood.** L'Oiseau-Lyre Ⓕ 430 397-2OH2 (two discs: 99 minutes: DDD: 3/91). ✍

...**Soloists; Vienna Singverein; Berlin Philharmonic Orchestra / Herbert von Karajan.** DG Galleria Ⓜ 435 077-2GGA2 (two discs: 109 minutes: ADD: 12/91).

...**Soloists; Stuttgart Gächinger Kantorei; Stuttgart Bach Collegium / Helmuth Rilling.** Hänssler Classic Ⓕ 98 938 (two discs: 106 minutes: DDD: 12/94).

...**Soloists; Tafelmusik / Bruno Weil.** Sony Classical Vivarte Ⓕ SX2K57965 (two discs: 91 minutes: DDD: 2/95). ✍

...Die Schöpfung^a. Salve regina in E major, HobXXIII*b*/1^b. **Soloists;** ^a**Brighton Festival Chorus;** ^b**London Chamber Choir;** ^b**Argo Chamber Orchestra,** ^a**Royal Philharmonic Orchestra /** ^a**Antál Dorati,** ^b**Laszlo Heltay.** Double Decca Ⓜ 443 027-2DF2 (two discs: 129 minutes: ADD: 5/94).

Haydn Armida. **Jessye Norman** (sop) Armida; **Claes Hakon Ahnsjö** (ten) Rinaldo; **Norma Burrowes** (sop) Zelmira; **Samuel Ramey** (bass) Idreno; **Robin Leggate** (ten) Ubaldo; **Anthony Rolfe Johnson** (ten) Clotarco. **Lausanne Chamber Orchestra / Antál Dorati.** Philips Ⓕ 432 438-2PH2 (two discs: 140 minutes: ADD: 6/93). From 6769 021 (9/79).

Armida, widely considered Haydn's finest opera, is based on a familiar literary classic adopted for opera by numerous other composers: what is surprising is that in his setting Haydn reverted to *opera seria* style, with no *buffo* characters, very few ensembles and extensive *secco* recitatives. Dramatic action is minimal: for three acts Rinaldo lingers under the spell of the enchantress Armida despite all the efforts of fellow-Crusaders to recall him to his mission. The work's static nature, however, casts the emphasis on its musical qualities, and in this regard *Armida* is of the highest standard. The enchantress herself, personified by the redoubtable Jessye Norman, has the widest range of emotions to portray, from tenderness to rage; Ahnsjö as Rinaldo produces a fine legato and very accurate florid passagework, but his low register rather lets him down; Ramey shows laudable firmness and flexibility; and Burrowes's fresh youthful charm is very appealing. Another strength is the alert orchestral playing. The most notable features of the opera are three long through-composed sequences and imaginative scoring: the scene in the magic forest, where Rinaldo at last, to Armida's fury, breaks free from her spell, is masterly, and in itself is sufficient to compel a revision of the too common neglect of Haydn as an operatic composer.

Haydn L'anima del filosofo, ossia Orfeo et Euridice. **Uwe Heilmann** (ten) Orfeo; **Cecilia Bartoli** (mez) Euridice, Genio; **Ildebrando d'Arcangelo** (bass) Creonte; **Andrea Silvestrelli** (bass) Pluto; **Angela Kazimierczuk** (sop) Baccante; **Roberto Scaltriti** (bar) First Chorus; **Jose Fardilha** (bass) Second Chorus; **Colin Campbell** (bar) Third Chorus; **James Oxley** (ten) Fourth Chorus; **Chorus and Orchestra of the Academy of Ancient Music / Christopher Hogwood.**
L'Oiseau-Lyre Ⓕ 452 668-2OHO2 (two discs: 124 minutes: DDD: 4/97). ✒
Notes, text and translation included. Recorded 1996.   ⓐⓖ
At last, a truly searching, period-instrument performance of *L'anima del filosofo* is available. Christopher Hogwood builds his band on the model of those prevalent in late-eighteenth-century London theatres. Not only does his phrasing and articulation discover no end of both witty and poignant nuances, but the grave austerity of the string playing, and the plangency of the early woodwind instruments are eloquent advocates of an opera whose uncompromisingly tragic ending (even the seductive Bacchantes perish) owes more to Ovid and Milton than to operatic tradition. Hogwood also remembers that Haydn was writing for a Handelian London choral tradition: his chorus, be they cast as Cupids, Shades or Furies, have robust presence and sculpt their lines with firm muscle. Cecilia Bartoli takes the role of Euridice. In her very first aria, "Filomena abbandonata", she understands and eagerly re-creates the type of coloratura writing which simultaneously fleshes out the central nightingale simile and incarnates the single word "crudeltà". Her unmistakable, melting half-voice comes into its own as emotion first clouds reason, only to create the fatal emotional extremes to which she gives voice so thrillingly. Uwe Heilmann is just the tenor of rare agility and wide vocal range vital for this particular Orfeo. The minor parts are strongly profiled: Ildebrando d'Arcangelo is a stern, noble Creonte, Andrea Silvestrelli a fearsome, stentorian Pluto – and there's even a convincing *strepito ostile* off-stage as Euridice's abduction is attempted in Act 2. Beyond the detail, it is above all the unique poignancy of the musical drama at the heart of this strange, grave *Orfeo* which Hogwood discovers, not before time, and reveals with such sympathetic and compelling imaginative insight.

Additional recommendation ...
...**Soloists; Bavarian Radio Chorus; Munich Radio Orchestra / Leopold Hager.**
Orfeo Ⓕ C262932H (two discs: 125 minutes: DDD: 9/95).

Further listening ...
...Concerto for Violin, Keyboard and Strings in F major, HobXVIII/6. *Coupled with*
   Mendelssohn Concerto for Violin, Piano and Strings in D minor. **Ralf Gothóni** (pf);
   Kuhmo Virtuosi / Peter Csaba (vn). Ondine ODE810-2 (1/95).
...Violin Concertos – A major, HobVIIa/3; C major, HobVIIa/1; G major, HobVIIa/4.
   Concerto for Violin, Keyboard and Strings, HobXVIII/6ª. **Rainer Kussmaul** (vn);
   ªRobert Hill (hpd); **Amsterdam Bach Soloists.** Olympia OCD428 (6/94). ✒
...Divertimentos – G major, HobII/2; C major, HobII/17. Variations in E flat major, HobII/24.
   Haydn Sinfonietta, Vienna / Manfred Huss. Koch Schwann 314812 (4/96).
...Divertimento in B flat major, HobII/B4 (spurious). *Coupled with works by various composers.*
   Quintett Wien. Nimbus NI5479 (3/97).
...String Quartets – Op. 1: No. 5 in E flat major; No. 6 in C major. Op. 2: No. 1 in A major;
   No. 2 in E major. **Kodály Quartet.** Naxos 8 550399.
...Mass No. 10 in C major, HobXXII/9, "Missa in tempore belli". *Coupled with* **Mozart**
   Mass in C major, K317, "Coronation". **Soloists; Berlin RIAS Chamber Choir;**
   Berlin Philharmonic Orchestra / James Levine. DG 435 853-2GH (9/92).
...Il mondo della luna – Una donna come me. Orlando Paladino – Ad un sguardo, a un cenno solo.
   La fedeltà premiata – Deh soccorri un'infelice. *Coupled with works by* **Gluck** *and* **Mozart**
   Anne Sofie von Otter (mez); **The English Concert / Trevor Pinnock** (hpd).
   Archiv Produktion 449 206-2AH (10/97). *See review under Gluck; refer to the Index.*
...The Seven Last Words. **Soloists; Arnold Schönberg Choir; Vienna Concentus Musicus /**
   Nikolaus Harnoncourt. Teldec Das Alte Werk 2292-46458-2 (5/92). ✒
...Stabat mater. **Patricia Rozario** (sop); **Catherine Robbin** (mez); **Anthony Rolfe Johnson** (ten);
   Cornelius Hauptmann (bass); **The English Concert and Choir / Trevor Pinnock.**
   Archiv Produktion 429 733-2AH (9/90). ✒
...Esterházy Opera Cycle. – L'infedeltà delusa *(432 413-2PH2)*; L'incontro improvviso and opera
   arias *(432 416-2PH3)*; Il mondo della luna and opera arias *(432 420-2PH3)*; La vera constanza
   (432 424-2PH2); L'isola disabitata *(432 427-2PH2)*; La fedeltà premiata *(432 430-2PH2)*;
   Orlando Paladino *(432 434-2PH3)*; Armida *(432 438-2PH2)*.
   Soloists; Lausanne Chamber Orchestra / Antál Dorati. Philips (6/93).

Michael Haydn

M. Haydn Symphonies – B flat major, MH82 (P9); A major, MH152 (P6); G major, MH334 (P16); E flat major, MH473 (P26); F major, MH507 (P32). **London Mozart Players / Matthias Bamert.** Chandos Ⓕ CHAN9352 (69 minutes: DDD: 4/96). Recorded 1994.

Michael Haydn joined the orchestra of Oradea Cathedral as a violinist in 1757, before becoming *Kapellmeister* there. The first three movements of his A major Symphony (P6) began life as a ballet, while its finale comes from music previously used in the ballet-pantomime *Hermann*. Nevertheless, this tasteful reading by Bamert and the LMP presents a convincing structural unit. They offer great finesse and precision of ensemble in bright, fresher recordings. Dynamics and instrumental forces are strikingly opposed in the first movement, as are the major/minor contrasts in the minuet. The slow movement has an appropriately mannered stateliness, and the finale is engagingly vivacious. Like the A major Symphony, the B flat work (P9) has as its finale a later addition; but once again, the LMP's stylish playing, in a naturally lit recording, sounds thoroughly satisfying. The spacious acoustic, moreover, effectively highlights the ceremonial character of the G major Symphony, recalling its initial conception as part of the cantata for Nikolaus Hoffmann's installation as Abbot of Michaelbeuern.

Further listening ...

...Horn Concertino in D major (arr. Sherman). *Coupled with works by various composers.*
  Barry Tuckwell (hn); **English Chamber Orchestra / Sir Neville Marriner.**
  EMI Forte CZS5 69395-2 (2/97). *See review in the Collections section; refer to the Index.*
...Trumpet Concerto in C major, MH60. *Coupled with works by various composers.*
  Crispian Steele-Perkins (tpt); **English Chamber Orchestra / Anthony Halstead.**
  Carlton Classics 30366 0066-2 (10/97). *See review in the Collections section; refer to the Index.*
...Violin Concerto in B flat major, P53[a]. Clarinet Concerto in D major, P54[b]. Concerto for Harpsichord and Viola in C major, P55[c]. **Soloists;** [ac]**Oradea Philharmonic Orchestra / Ervin Acél;** [b]**Quodlibet Musicum Chamber Orchestra / Aurelian Octav Popa** (cl). Olympia OCD406 (10/90).
...String Quintets – Divertimento in B flat major, MH412; Notturno in C major, MH187; Notturno in G major, MH189. **L'Archibudelli.** Sony Classical Vivarte SK53987 (8/94). ✎
...Missa Sancti Aloysii, MH257. Missa sub titulo Sancti Leopoldi, MH837. Vesperae pro festo Sanctissimae innocentium, MH548. **Trinity College Choir, Cambridge; instrumental ensemble / Richard Marlow.** Conifer Classics CDCF220 (2/94).
...Partsongs for Male Voices – Hymne an Gott. Die Verwandlungen. Ständchen (two versions). Lied der Freiheit. Das Gebet. Monsieur Hans. Der Morgen im Lenz. Die Elfen. Coppia si tenera. Silenzio facciani. Der Obersulzer Wein. Die Wiedergenesung. Zu ihr, zu ihr. Abendlied. Rundgesang. Trinklied im Freien. Tischgebet. Abschiedslied. An den Wald. **Die Singphoniker.** CPO CPO999 333-2 (2/97).

Hayne van Ghizeghem

Suggested listening ...
...De tous biens plaine. De tous biens plaine (arr. Josquin). *Coupled with works by various composers.* **Early Music Consort of London / David Munrow.** Virgin Classics Veritas VED5 61334-2 (11/97). *See review in the Collections section; refer to the Index.*

Christopher Headington

Headington Piano Concerto[a]. The Healing Fountain (In Memoriam Benjamin Britten)[b]. Cello Serenade[c]. [b]**Andrew Carwood** (ten); [c]**Alexander Baillie** (vc); [a]**Gordon Fergus-Thompson** (pf); **Britten Sinfonia / Nicholas Cleobury.** ASV Ⓕ CDDCA969 (60 minutes: DDD: 9/97). Texts included. Recorded 1996.

The tragic death in a skiing accident of *Gramophone* contributor, Christopher Headington, robbed "British music of one of its most versatile and engaging talents of the post-war era" (to quote Terry Barfoot's sympathetic annotation). Apart from his reviewing commitments, Headington successfully combined a career as a composer, pianist, author, broadcaster, examiner and lecturer. The fastidious craft, lyrical restraint and pleasing proportions of the Piano Concerto attest to lessons well learnt from Headington's days as a composition student at the RAM under Sir Lennox Berkeley. As with the earlier Violin Concerto, the predominant influence is that of Britten (with whom Headington had briefly studied as a young man and whose music he admired enormously). Not surprisingly, given Headington's own considerable gifts as a pianist, the solo writing is always deft and idiomatic. The work as a whole exerts a ready appeal and never threatens to outstay its welcome. Written in 1978 as a direct response to Britten's death, *The Healing Fountain (In Memoriam Benjamin Britten)*, for high voice and chamber orchestra, welds eight settings of poems by Siegfried Sassoon, W.H. Auden, John Masefield, Wilfred Owen, Thomas Moore and Shelley into a deeply felt, 26-minute sequence. Headington's word-painting skills and compositional facility are not in doubt, though as one listens one can't help but draw unflattering comparisons with Britten's genius for this sort of thing – an impression which the work's sprinkling of quotations from *Peter Grimes, Death in Venice, Nocturne* and *A Midsummer Night's Dream* merely tends to reinforce. Commissioned by Julian Lloyd Webber and premièred by him in January 1995, the *Serenade* for cello and strings is cast in a single movement: not only is the writing civilized and resourceful, there's a luminosity and variety of texture that is really most beguiling. Performances and recording are exemplary; a worthy memento of a fine musician and composer.

Further listening ...
...Violin Concerto. *Coupled with* **R. Strauss** Violin Concerto, Op. 8. **Xue-Wei** (vn);
London Philharmonic Orchestra / Jane Glover. ASV CDDCA780 (12/91).   Ⓖ
...Ballade-Image. Cinquanta. *Coupled with works by various composers.* **Christopher Headington** (pf).
Kingdom KCLCD2017 (11/90).

Jake Heggie
American 1961

Suggested listening ...
...He's gone away. The leather-winged bat. Barb'ry Allen. To say before going to sleep. White in the moon. *Coupled with works by various composers.* **Jennifer Larmore** (mez); **Antoine Palloc** (pf). Teldec 0630-16069-2 (12/97). *See review in the Collections section; refer to the Index.*

Joseph Hellmesberger I
Austrian 1828-1893

Suggested listening ...
...Ballszene. *Coupled with works by various composers.* **New London Orchestra / Ronald Corp.** Hyperion CDA66998 (3/98). *See review in the Collections section; refer to the Index.*

Joseph Hellmesberger II
Austrian 1855-1907

Suggested listening ...
...Kleiner Anzeiger. *Coupled with works by* **members of the Strauss family**
Vienna Boys' Choir; Vienna Philharmonic Orchestra / Zubin Mehta.
RCA Victor Red Seal 09026 63144-2 (4/98). *See review under Strauss; refer to the Index.*

Johann David Heinichen
German 1683-1729

Suggested listening ...
...Concertos – C major, S211; G major: S213; S214, "Darmstadt"; S214, "Venezia"; S215; S217; F major: S226; S231; S232; S233; S234; S235. Serenata di Moritzburg in F major, S204. Sonata in A major, S208. Concerto Movement in C minor, S240. **Cologne Musica Antiqua / Reinhard Goebel.** Archiv Produktion 437 549-2AH2 (5/93). 🎖 *Gramophone Editor's choice. Gramophone Award Winner 1993.*   Ⓖ

Peter Heise
Danish 1830-1879

Heise When the swan dreaming. Springsong in Autumn. Springsong of the young lark. Summersong. Poems from the Middle Ages – Your father shall not scold. Love's Philosophy. The dreams of the Sleeping Beauty. The songs of Dyveke.
Lange-Müller Three Songs, Op. 4. Songs, Op. 6 – Sulamite's song in the Queen's garden. Folk-songs, Op. 18 – No. 4, Shine out, clear sunshine; No. 6, The willow bends. Spanish Students – The sun shines now (Juana's first song); Rose bushes! (Juana's second song). The shepherd pulls on his cape, Op. 34 No. 8. Cosmos Songs, Op. 57 – No. 3, The sun comes out like a rose; No. 4, I am singing of a King's son. Songs, Op. 64 – Vol. 2: No. 2, Oh, I own such lovely little fingers; No. 6, Speak quietly, young nightingale; Vol. 3: No. 2, Little birds are twittering in the sun.
Inger Dam-Jensen (sop); **Christen Stubbe Teglbjerg** (pf). Da Capo Ⓟ 8 224065 (65 minutes: DDD: 9/97). Texts and translations included. Recorded 1996.
Peter Heise and Peter Erasmus Lange-Müller represent the rapturous spring and the melancholy autumn of Danish romantic song. Heise, who wrote 300 songs in his short lifetime is the real standard-bearer of Danish song and this disc represents the best of his output: his exultant *Springsong in Autumn* and the *Springsong of the young lark* – a rippling paean of praise to the great Nordic thaw. Heise's seven *Songs of Dyveke* of 1879 – a brightly coloured pre-Raphaelite tapestry of Holger Drachmann's ballads about the ups and downs of falling in love with royalty (King Christian II in this case) – is a thrilling, inexplicably neglected cycle of constantly self-renewing melodic invention. Inger Dam-Jensen and her imaginative accompanist Christen Stubbe Teglbjerg show how superbly Heise writes for the voice. This disc also offers more of Lange-Müller's

sympathetic and poignant settings of his friend, Thor Lange's translations of Russian, Czech and Serbian poetry than does the recital from Sten Byriel and Ulrik Staerk. It is a natural selection for the collector and reinstates this neglected music into the recital repertoire.

Further listening ...
...Five Lenau Songs. Five Erotic Songs. The miner. In youth, when I did love. My Treasure. Arne's Song. A summer night. The kite. King and Marshall – Ingeborg, my soul, my heart. *Coupled with songs by* **Lange-Müller Sten Byriel** (bass-bar); **Ulrik Staerk** (pf). Da Capo 8 224033 (9/97).
...Drot og Marsk. **Soloists; Danish National Radio Choir; Danish National Radio Symphony Orchestra / Michael Schønwandt.** Chandos CHAN9143/5 (6/93).

Piers Hellawell

Suggested listening ...
...The Hilliard Songbook. *Coupled with works by various composers.* **The Hilliard Ensemble.** ECM New Series 453 259-2 (1/97). *See review in the Collections section; refer to the Index.*

Adolf von Henselt
German 1814-1889

Henselt Piano Concerto in F minor, Op. 16. Variations de concert, Op. 11, on "Quand je quittai la Normandie" from Meyerbeer's "Robert le diable".
Alkan Concerti da camera, Op. 10 – No. 1 in A minor; No. 2 in C sharp minor.
Marc-André Hamelin (pf); **BBC Scottish Symphony Orchestra / Martyn Brabbins.** Hyperion Ⓕ CDA66717 (70 minutes: DDD: 8/94). *Gramophone Editor's choice.* ⒼⒼ
Much of the credit for this disc must go to the phenomenal playing and superb musicianship of Marc-André Hamelin (whose account of the staggeringly difficult Henselt Concerto is quite breathtaking) but plaudits must also go to the imaginative programming and excellent booklet-notes. The main work of the disc, both in terms of quality and length, is of course the above-mentioned Henselt F minor Concerto, which, although once an active participant in the repertoire of most top league pianists during the late nineteenth century (at least those sufficiently technically equipped to approach it), dropped out of sight in the early part of this century until revived by those 'champions of the forgotten', Raymond Lewenthal and Michael Ponti. As a concerto it is particularly 'giving' to the listener and very *un*forgiving to the pianist, as the extreme technical difficulties are concealed in such a way that they become almost transparent to the ear – which probably accounts for its disappearance from the repertoire. Rubinstein once recounted that "I procured the concerto and his *études*, but after working on them for a few days I realised it was a waste of time, for they were based on an abnormal formation of the hand. In this respect Henselt, like Paganini, was a freak." Musically the concerto owes allegiance to Chopin (in the *Larghetto*) and Thalberg and Mendelssohn in the outer movements, but generally the overall Henseltian style has its own peculiar flavour which should win many friends through Hamelin's highly persuasive and thoroughly committed performance. The slightly earlier *Variations de concert* (on a theme from Meyerbeer's *Robert le diable*) is admittedly slighter fare but is nevertheless an attractive and enjoyable work which hails from the same stable as Chopin's *Là ci darem* Variations. The remainder of the disc consists of two 'mini' concertos by Henselt's exact contemporary and fellow 'reticent' Charles-Valentin Alkan (Henselt, like Alkan, gave very few public concerts due to stage-fright that bordered on the pathological). The two early *Concerti da camera* (the only surviving *concertante* pieces by Alkan) are not, it has to be said, 'major' Alkan works, but they are original in invention and full of melodic appeal, with more than a hint or two of the Alkan of later years. Hamelin, who has already proved himself a formidable Alkan exponent, delivers them with astonishing dexterity and panache and, as in the Henselt pieces, he is given equally committed support from the BBC Scottish Symphony Orchestra under the direction of Martyn Brabbins. A thoroughly enjoyable disc, well worth exploring.

Further listening ...
...Ballade in B flat major, Op. 31. Grande Valse, Op. 30, "L'aurore boréale". Impromptus – B flat minor, Op. 34; B minor, Op. 37; C minor, Op. 7; F minor, Op. 17. Introduction and Variations on a theme by Donizetti, Op. 1. Pensée fugitive, Op. 8. Rondo serioso. Scherzo in B minor, Op. 9. Toccatina in C minor, Op. 25. Valse mélancolique, Op. 36. **Rudiger Steinfatt** (pf). Koch Schwann 310023.

Hans Werner Henze
German 1926

Henze Symphony No. 9. **Berlin Radio Chorus; Berlin Philharmonic Orchestra / Ingo Metzmacher.** EMI Ⓕ CDC5 56513-2 (56 minutes: DDD: 6/98). Text and translation included. Recorded live in 1997. ⒼⒼ
Henze's Ninth Symphony deals with his experience of Nazi Germany and it is dedicated "to the heroes and martyrs of German anti-Fascism". All seven of its movements are choral, settings of poems by Hans-Ulrich Treichel, themselves based on the novel by Anna Seghers, *The Seventh Cross*.

The novel tells of seven prisoners, condemned to be crucified, who escape from a concentration camp. Six are recaptured; after a series of horrifying experiences the seventh manages to reach freedom by boarding a Dutch ship on the Rhine. The first movement, "The Escape", is not an exciting action scene but a portrayal of abject, pitiful terror; in its successor, "Among the Dead", the delirious prisoner finds himself in a no man's land of shadows. There is a brief, savage portrayal of the persecutors, then the trees from which the crosses will be made sing lyrically of their own beauty before they are ruthlessly hacked down. Now the fate of one of the other prisoners is described; he is an artist, and as he dies, "I … the wounded eagle, spread my wings and fly once more over the only land I have". At this point what is marked in the score as a *gran canto*, a grave, plangent string melody, rises with poignant eloquence in the strings. The penultimate movement, much the longest of the seven, is a hideous nightmare drama set in a cathedral, where the exhausted prisoner has hidden at night. Christ will not reply to his prayers; all he can hear is the voices of the dead (12 soloists, placed at the opposite end of the hall from the orchestra and choir), raptly and horribly praising the voluptuous pleasures of torture and martyrdom. "The Rescue", finally, provides the huge contrast of rich, calm, multilayered polyphony, but though the prisoner has survived, the horror remains. The extremest of emotions are explored and extremes are needed to express them. The lines are often tortuous or angular, the textures often dense. This is a live recording of the first performance and the chorus is not large and is placed well behind the main body of the orchestra. The recording balance does not always compensate for this, and at times it is difficult to follow both the choral counterpoint and the words, even with the text in front of you. Despite this the cumulative impact is shockingly powerful. It is a piece that one senses Henze has been steeling himself to write for years, and its eloquence catches you by the throat.

Henze Undine. **London Sinfonietta / Oliver Knussen** with **Peter Donohoe** (pf). DG Ⓕ 453 467-2GH2 (two discs: 103 minutes: DDD: 3/98). Recorded 1996. *Gramophone Editor's choice.*
Selected by Soundings. ⒼⒼⒼ
Henze's *Undine* (or *Ondine*, as Frederick Ashton's ballet for which it was written is called) is easily his most approachable score, filled with melody, magically delicate evocation and humour. When the ballet first appeared, in October 1958, the music was dismissed by some critics as an eclectic and derivative mish-mash, and indeed it makes no effort to disguise its indebtedness to, in particular, the neo-classical Stravinsky (the *Symphony in Three Movements* is briefly but almost literally quoted on more than one occasion). What we have been missing all these years, this enthusiastically committed performance demonstrates, is a score that pays homages to the whole tradition of classical dance and the music written for it, a score whose richness is out of all proportion to the chamber orchestra it uses. That richness ranges from a quite magnificently sonorous evocation of the sea, via the stately wedding music in Act 2, to the deliciously tongue-in-cheek miniature piano concerto that accompanies the quite irrelevant but entertaining *divertissement* in Act 3. The second *divertissement*, that is: disastrously for the otherwise poetic scenario about a water-nymph's fatal love for a human, Ashton insisted on two of them. But the heart of the ballet is the subtle, quietly iridescent music associated with Ondine herself. Ashton's ballet was described as a 'concerto' for Margot Fonteyn who was its inspiration, and much of Henze's score is a sort of portrait of "the radiant centre of the whole ballet … this wonder floating, almost, above the ground", as Henze described her at the time. It is his achievement that the concluding passacaglia, even after those interpolations, is so moving as Ondine, knowing that her kiss will kill her beloved, is nevertheless irresistibly drawn to embrace him. Knussen's performance is so good that you can almost imagine your own staging, and it is superbly recorded.

Further listening …
…Double Concerto for Oboe, Harp and Strings[a]. Fantasia for Strings. Sonata for Strings.
[a]**Heinz Holliger** (ob); [a]**Ursula Holliger** (hp); **Collegium Musicum, Zurich / Paul Sacher.**
DG 449 864-2GC (8/96).
…Symphonies – Nos. 1-5; No. 6[a]. **Berlin Philharmonic Orchestra,** [a]**London Symphony Orchestra /**
Hans Werner Henze. DG 449 861-2GC2 (8/96).
…Symphony No. 7. Barcarola. **City of Birmingham Symphony Orchestra / Sir Simon Rattle.**
EMI CDC7 54762-2 (11/93). Ⓖ
…El Cimarrón. **Paul Yoder** (bar); **Michael Faust** (fl); **Reinbert Evers** (gtr); **Mircea Ardeleanu** (perc).
Koch Schwann Musica Mundi 314030 (1/92).
…Wind Quintet. L'autunno. *Coupled with* **Hindemith** Kleine Kammermusik, Op. 24 No. 2.
Wind Septet. **Berlin Philharmonic Wind Quintet.** BIS CD752 (3/97).
…Capriccio. *Coupled with works by various composers.* **Matt Haimovitz** (vc).
DG 445 834-2GH (12/95).
…Sonatina. *Coupled with works by various composers.* **Håkan Hardenberger** (tpt).
Philips 446 065-2PH (11/96).
…Elegie für junge Liebende – excerpts: Act 1: Ah! Schnee fällt aufs Blütenmeer; Gut. Gut. Genau wie es mir passte; Wie reizend du bist!. Act 2: Nimm Platz, mein Kind; Du mein, ganz mein; Aus dem Garten, paradiesisch; Schon morgen von den Bergen; Bah! dieses Pack! welch ein schäbiger Bund!. Act 3: Grüss Gott. Auf ein Wort nur; Lina, Sie sieht schlecht aus; Interlude; Eins. Zwei. Drei. Vier. Wen bewundern wir?. members of the **Berlin Radio Symphony** and **Deutsche Oper Orchestras / Hans Werner Henze.** DG 449 874-2GC (8/96).

...Das Floss der Medusa. **Edda Moser** (sop); **Dietrich Fischer-Dieskau** (bar); **Charles Regnier** (spkr); **St Nicolai Boys Choir, Hamburg; Berlin Radio Chamber Chorus; Chorus and Orchestra of North German Radio / Hans Werner Henze.** DG 449 871-2GC (8/96).

...Requiem. **Ueli Wiget** (pf); **Håkan Hardenberger** (tpt); **Ensemble Modern / Ingo Metzmacher.** Sony Classical SK58972 (11/94). 🅖🅖

...Voices. **Roswitha Trexler** (mez); **Joachim Vogt** (ten); **Leipzig Symphony Orchestra / Horst Neumann.** Berlin Classics 0021802BC (12/95).

...Voices – excerpts. **Gudrun Pelker** (mez); **Frieder Lang** (ten); **Musikfabrik NRW / Johannes Kalitzke.** CPO CPO999 192-2 (12/95).

...Die Bassariden. **Soloists; Berlin Radio Chamber Choir; South German Radio Choir; Berlin Radio Symphony Orchestra / Gerd Albrecht.** Koch Schwann Musica Mundi 314 006 (10/91). 🅖

...The English Cat. **Soloists; Parnassus Orchestra / Markus Stenz.** Wergo WER6204-2 (12/92).

...Der junge Lord. **Soloists; Schoneberger Boys Choir; Chorus and Orchestra of the Deutsche Oper, Berlin / Christoph von Dohnányi.** DG 449 875-2GC2 (8/96).

Victor Herbert
American 1859-1924

Herbert Cello Concerto No. 2 in E minor, Op. 30.
Dvořák Cello Concerto in B minor, B191. **Yo-Yo Ma** (vc); **New York Philharmonic Orchestra / Kurt Masur.** Sony Classical Ⓔ SK67173 (61 minutes: DDD: 4/96). Recorded 1995. 🅖

The Victor Herbert Concerto here receives a high-powered performance, but one which does not overload the romantic element with sentiment, whether in the brilliant and vigorous outer movements or in the warmly lyrical slow movement. Ma's use of rubato is perfectly judged, with the slow movement made the more tender at a flowing speed. The finale is then given a quicksilver performance, both brilliant and urgent. This magnificent performance could not be more welcome, and when Herbert's concerto, first given in 1894, was almost certainly what prompted Dvořák to write his own concerto later that same year, triumphantly demonstrating the viability of the genre, the coupling could not be more apt either. Ma's and Masur's version of the Dvořák is among the very finest, matched by few and outshining most, including Ma's own previous version with Maazel and the Berlin Philharmonic (on Sony Classical SK42206). It is fascinating to compare Ma's two versions side by side, the newer one more readily conveying weight of expression despite the less spotlit placing of the soloist, more disciplined yet more spontaneous-sounding. This time Ma's expressiveness is simpler and more noble, and the recording (made in Avery Fisher Hall, New York), once a trouble-spot for engineers, is fuller and more open than the Berlin one, cleaner in tuttis, with only a touch of unwanted dryness on high violins. Ma and Masur together encompass the work's astonishingly full expressive range, making it the more bitingly dramatic with high dynamic contrasts.

Additional recommendation ...
...No. 2, Op. 30. *Coupled with works by* **Grofé Georges Miquelle** (vc); **Eastman-Rochester Orchestra / Howard Hanson.** Mercury Living Presence Ⓜ 434 355-2MM (66 minutes: ADD).

Louis Hérold
French 1791-1833

Hérold (arr. Lanchbery) La fille mal gardée – excerpts. **Orchestra of the Royal Opera House, Covent Garden / John Lanchbery.** Decca Ovation Ⓜ 430 196-2DM (51 minutes: ADD: 1/94). From SXL2313 (8/62). Recorded 1962. 🅖🅖

The Royal Ballet's *La fille mal gardée* remains a source of perpetual delight, not least for the music that John Lanchbery arranged largely from Hérold's patchwork score for the 1828 version. The Clog dance is the obvious highlight of the score; but there are felicitous moments throughout, with snatches of Rossini, Donizetti *et al* cropping up all over the place. This recording is the original one that Lanchbery conducted when the ballet proved such a success in the Royal Ballet's repertoire in 1960. More recently he has recorded the score complete; and ballet lovers will doubtless consider this fuller version essential. However, others will undoubtedly find that the complete score rather outstays its welcome by comparison with this constantly uplifting selection. At medium price and wearing its 30-odd years lightly, it makes a most compelling recommendation.

Additional recommendation ...
...La fille mal gardée – ballet[a]. **Lecocq** (arr. G. Jacob) Mam'zelle Angot – ballet[b]. [a]**Orchestra of the Royal Opera House, Covent Garden / John Lanchbery;** [b]**National Philharmonic Orchestra / Richard Bonynge.** Decca Ovation Ⓜ 430 849-2DM2 (two discs: 134 minutes: DDD: 12/91).

Johann Hertel
German 1727-1789

Suggested listening ...
...Trumpet Concerto in D major. *Coupled with works by various composers.*
Håkan Hardenberger (tpt); **Academy of St Martin in the Fields / Sir Neville Marriner.** Philips 420 203-2PH (12/87). *See review in the Collections section; refer to the Index.*

Jonny Heykens

Suggested listening ...
...Serenade No. 1. *Coupled with works by various composers.* **New London Orchestra / Ronald Corp.**
Hyperion CDA66998 (3/98). *See review in the Collections section; refer to the Index.*

Hildegard of Bingen

Hildegard of Bingen Favus distillans. Et ideo puelle. O tu illustrata. O vos angeli. Studium
divinitatis. O ignee Spiritus. O rubor sanguinis. O orzchis Ecclesia. O gloriosissimi lux vivens
angeli. Rex noster promptus est. Deus enim in prima muliere. De patria. Sed diabolus in invidia.
Nunc gaudeant materna viscera Ecclesia. **Sinfonye** (Jocelyn West, Vivien Ellis, Stevie Wishart,
Emily Levy, Vickie Couper, Julie Murphy); **members of the Oxford Girls' Choir.**
Celestial Harmonies Ⓕ 13127-2 (62 minutes: DDD: 9/96). Texts and translations included.
Gramophone Editor's choice.   Ⓖ
Stevie Wishart, in her enthusiastic discovery of Hildegard, has found fulfilment of an earlier student
ambition of hers to promote the musical genius of women. She succeeds in putting Hildegard's music
across, partly because she has benefited from the experiments of others, but chiefly by her imaginative
choice of singers, which includes quite young girls. The tuneful, unsophisticated timbre of the
youngest voices – as, for example, that of Vickie Couper in *Deus enim in prima muliere* – acts as a foil
to the sturdy chest voices of the older women – which have a quality of their own, somewhat akin to
that of Hungarian folk singers. Such contrasts seem to be typical of the whole Hildegardian picture.
Hildegard herself was made up of contrasts: she is ecstatic and at the same time quietly tender; she
can be passionate while maintaining a sense of decorum; she is erotic but also chaste. One could do
without the hurdy-gurdy and dispense with the drones and the improvised organum. What is left is an
understanding, a penetration of Hildegard's music, which rarely comes through in other
interpretations. One thinks particularly of the composer's portrayal of the mystery of the Incarnation
in *O tu illustrata* and also, particularly, of the remarkably sustained lines of ecstasy in *O vos angeli* –
this extraordinary outpouring ranging over two octaves, but which yet has shape and structure for all
Hildegard's protestations that she had never studied her art formally.
Additional recommendations ...
...O rubor sanguinis. Favus distillans. Laus Trinitati. In Matutinis Laudibus. O ecclesia oculi tui.
O viridissima virga. O aeterne Deus. O dulcissime amator. Rex noster promptus est. O cruor
sanguinis. Cum vox sanguinis. Instrumental Piece based on D modes of antiphon cycle. O virgo
ecclesia. Nunc gaudeant materna. O orzchis ecclesia. **Sequentia.**
Deutsche Harmonia Mundi Ⓕ 05472 77346-2 (77 minutes: DDD: 3/96).
...Deus in adjutorium meum intende. Studium divinitatis. Miserere mei Deus. Unde quocumque
venientes perrexerunt. Confitemini Domino quoniam bonus. De patria. Deus, Deus meus. Deus
enim in prima muliere. Benedicite omnia opera Domini Domino. Aer enim volat. Laudate
Dominum. Benedictio et claritas. Cum vox sanguinis. Diffusa est gratia in labiis tuis. Et ideo
puelle. Benedictus Dominus Deus Israël. Kyrie, Pater noster, Oratio. Benedicamus Domino.
Spiritui sancto. **Ensemble Organum / Marcel Pérès.**
Harmonia Mundi Ⓕ HMC90 1626 (79 minutes: DDD: 9/97).
...O Jerusalem aure civitas. Quia felix pueritia. O felix apparitio. O beatissime Ruperte. O tu
illustrata. Cum eruberint. Ave, generosa. O frondens virga. O quam pretiosa. O ignee Spiritus.
O quam magnum miraculum. Two instrumental pieces. **Sequentia / Barbara Thornton,
Benjamin Bagby.** Deutsche Harmonia Mundi Ⓕ 05472 77353-2 (67 minutes: DDD: 9/97).

Hildegard of Bingen Columba aspexit. Ave, generosa. O ignis spiritus Paracliti. O Jerusalem.
O Euchari, in leta vita. O viridissima virga. O presul vere civitatis. O Ecclesia.
Gothic Voices / Christopher Page with **Doreen Muskett** (symphony); **Robert White** (reed drones).
Hyperion Ⓕ CDA66039 (44 minutes: DDD: 7/85). Recorded 1981. *Gramophone classical 100.*
Gramophone Award Winner 1982-83.   ⒼⒼⒼ
This remarkable record contains a collection of choice gems from one of the greatest creative
personalities of the Middle Ages. Admittedly, we have limited means of assessing how these inspired
pieces were actually performed during the lifetime of Hildegard herself. But the refreshingly
unsophisticated timbre of the four sopranos and the reedy, almost boyish, vocal quality of the
contralto are convincing enough to transport the listener right back to the unpolluted atmosphere of
Hildegard's cloister. Most to be savoured are the unaccompanied items, amounting to 50 per cent of
the total. Indeed, since the notes go out of their way to tell us that "distractions such as the intrusion
of instrumental decorations" were to be avoided, why did the producer go out of his way to introduce
symphony and reed drones in the performance of the other 50 per cent? However, this is a delightful
recording. When it was first released it sparked new interest in the music of the Middle Ages by a
broader audience and it remains a jewel in Hyperion's crown.
Additional recommendations ...
...O vis aeternitatis. Nunc aperuit nobis. Quia ergo femina. Cum processit factura. Ave Maria,
O auctrix vitae. Spiritus Sanctus vivificans vite. O ignis Spiritus Paracliti. Caritas abundat in

omnia. O virga mediatrix. O viridissima virga. O pastor animarum. O tu suavissima virga.
O choruscans stellarum. O nobilissima viriditas. **Anonymous** Alma Redemptoris mater.
Instrumental Piece. **Sequentia.** Deutsche Harmonia Mundi Ⓕ 05472 77320-2
(73 minutes: DDD: 5/95). *Gramophone Editor's choice.*   Ⓖ
...O Euchari, in leta vita. O virga mediatrix. Ave generosa. Laus Trinitati. Kyrie eleison. O presul
vere civitatis. O ignis Spiritus Paracliti. Ordo virtutum – Procession. O pastor animarum.
O viridissima virga. O virga ac diadema. **Oxford Camerata / Jeremy Summerly.**
Naxos Ⓢ 8 550998 (59 minutes: DDD: 9/95).

Further listening ...
...O magne Pater. O aeterne Deus. Ave generosa. O frondens virga. O felix anima. Ave Maria,
O auctrix vitae. O quam mirabilis. O virtus sapientiae. O vis aeternitatis.
Coupled with works by **Abélard** and **Anonymous** Augsburg Early Music Ensemble.
Christophorus Musica Practica CHR74584 (3/93).
...O virtus sapientiae (arr. Pfau). *Coupled with works by various composers.* **Kronos Quartet.**
Nonesuch 7559-79457-2 (12/97). *Gramophone Editor's choice. See review in the Collections
section; refer to the Index.*

Paul Hindemith   German 1895-1963

Hindemith Cello Concerto[a]. The Four Temperaments[b]. [a]**Raphael Wallfisch** (vc); [b]**Howard Shelley**
(pf); **BBC Philharmonic Orchestra / Yan Pascal Tortelier.** Chandos Ⓕ CHAN9124
(52 minutes: DDD: 3/93). Recorded 1992.
These two concertos, both from Hindemith's maturity (1940), make a good pairing. The outwardly
conventional Cello Concerto contrasts a relatively small voice (the cello) which carries the work's
lyrical message, with a large orchestra used initially for active statements delivered with great power.
Hindemith's plan would seem to be gradually to reconcile these apparently contradictory modes of
address. *The Four Temperaments* is a concerto for piano and string orchestra, a much more evenly
balanced combination, using theme and variations form to integrate and relate the contrasted
'humours'. Hindemith's treatment of his material appears to argue that all temperaments, whatever
the dominant disposition, are closely related. His portraiture, in fact, reveals characterization of great
depth and dimension. Performances are superbly accomplished, indeed this is the finest of many
currently available recordings of *The Four Temperaments*. And Chandos have resisted the temptation
to move in on the soloist in the Cello Concerto. The sound is open and spacious.
Additional recommendations ...
...The Four Temperaments[a]. Symphony in B flat major. **Berg** Chamber Concerto for Piano, Violin
and 13 Wind Instruments[b]. [a]**Clara Haskil,** [b]**Carl Seemann** (pfs); [b]**Wolfgang Marschner** (vn);
Bavarian Radio Symphony Orchestra / Paul Hindemith.
Orfeo Ⓕ C197891A (76 minutes: ADD: 8/90).
...The Four Temperaments. Piano Concerto. **Siegfried Mauser** (pf); **Frankfurt Radio Symphony
Orchestra / Andreas Werner Albert.** CPO Ⓕ CPO999 078-2 (62 minutes: DDD: 12/91).

Hindemith Clarinet Concerto[a]. Horn Concerto[b]. Concerto for Trumpet, Bassoon and Strings[c].
Concerto for Flute, Oboe, Clarinet, Bassoon, Harp and Orchestra[d]. [d]**Walter Buchsel** (fl);
[d]**Liviu Varcol** (ob); [ad]**Ulrich Mehlhart** (cl); [cd]**Carsten Wilkening** (bn); [c]**Reinhold Friedrich** (tpt);
[b]**Marie Luise Neunecker** (hn); [d]**Charlotte Cassedanne** (hp); [b]**Brigitte Goebel** (spkr);
Frankfurt Radio Symphony Orchestra / Werner Andreas Albert. CPO Ⓕ CPO999 142-2
(70 minutes: DDD: 11/95). Recorded 1990-93.
Hindemith's four wind concertos (1947-49) have never enjoyed the success of the *Kammermusik*
concertos (with which they have much in common). That for clarinet came first, to a commission from
Benny Goodman. As was noted in *Music Survey* in 1950, it is "a musician's rather than a showman's
piece", and the lack of overt display may have militated against its popularity. Ulrich Mehlhart's
performance more than bears comparison with any rivals, and is served by the best sound. With the
1949 Horn Concerto, competition is concentrated in the definitive recording by the composer and
dedicatee, Dennis Brain (reviewed further on), which has rarely been out of the catalogue for long. If
not quite in Brain's class, Marie Luise Neunecker's is a fine, highly musical account. The declamation
of Hindemith's poem in praise of the horn, inscribed over its wordless setting, may be thought
intrusive. The other two concertos (both 1949) are rarities indeed, not until now commercially
available in the UK. In them, Hindemith most nearly approaches his 1920s manner, for instance in
the woodwinds and harp Concerto with the finale's quotations from Mendelssohn's *Wedding March*
(and perhaps fleeting allusions to Wagner's in the opening movement), occasioned by his silver
anniversary. In the Clarinet and Horn Concertos, Albert's tempos are brisker than the composer's
own; in all four works the soloists and Frankfurt orchestra prove committed advocates.
Additional recommendations ...
...Clarinet Concerto. *Coupled with works by* **Milhaud** and **Copland** Eduard Brunner (cl); **Bavarian
Radio Symphony Orchestra / Urs Schneider.** Koch Schwann Ⓕ 310352 (DDD: 62 minutes).
...Clarinet Concerto[a]. Cello Concerto[b]. [a]**George Pieterson** (cl); [b]**Tibor de Machula** (vc); **Royal
Concertgebouw Orchestra / Kyrill Kondrashin.** Etcetera Ⓕ KTC1006 (46 minutes: ADD: 6/88).

Hindemith Violin Concerto[a]. Symphonic Metamorphosis on Themes of Carl Maria von Weber[b]. Mathis der Maler[c]. [a]**David Oistrakh** (vn); [ab]**London Symphony Orchestra / **[a]**Paul Hindemith,** [b]**Claudio Abbado;** [c]**Suisse Romande Orchestra / Paul Kletzki.** Decca Enterprise Ⓜ 433 081-2DM (77 minutes: ADD: 9/92). Item marked [a] from SXL6035 (2/63), recorded 1962, [b]SXL6398 (5/69), [c]SXL6445 (12/70), both recorded 1968. ⒼⒼⒼ

Hindemithians who can afford to be choosy about the *Mathis der Maler* Symphony and the *Symphonic Metamorphosis* will immediately recognize the superiority of the full-price Blomstedt readings (reviewed further on). Consistently spectacular 1960s Decca sound adds allure to the merely proficient performances on offer here. What makes this medium-price disc indispensable is the 30-minute Violin Concerto with Oistrakh at his legendary best and the composer conducting. The late Deryck Cooke, in his original *Gramophone* review, wrote of Oistrakh as "superbly poised and eloquent ... and as performed here the Concerto shows that behind Hindemith's stony neo-classical facade beats a romantic German heart". Listening to this recording it's hard to understand the concerto's relative neglect – strange indeed are the tides of fashion – but easy to imagine current star violinists finding Oistrakh's an impossible act to follow. The 1962 sound gives Oistrakh a discreet dominance, and the engineers flatten out the slow movement's central climax, but thankfully no other allowances need be made for this preservation of a classic recording.

Additional recommendations ...

...Violin Concerto. Cello Concerto. **K.A. Hartmann** Concerto funèbre. **André Gertler** (vn); **Paul Tortelier** (vc); **Czech Philharmonic Orchestra / Karel Ančerl.** Supraphon Ⓕ 11 1955-2 (76 minutes: ADD).

...Symphonic Metamorphosis. **Reger** Variations and Fugue on a Theme of Mozart, Op. 132. **Bavarian Radio Symphony Orchestra / Sir Colin Davis.** Philips Ⓕ 422 347-2PH (55 minutes: DDD: 9/90).

...Mathis der Maler[a]. Symphonic Metamorphosis[b]. **Walton** Variations on a Theme by Hindemith[b]. [a]**Philadelphia Orchestra / Eugene Ormandy;** [b]**Cleveland Orchestra / George Szell.** Sony Classical Essential Classics Ⓑ SBK53258 (69 minutes: ADD: 4/94).

...Mathis der Maler[a]. String Trio No. 2[b]. String Quartet No. 3, Op. 22[c]. [b]**Szymon Goldberg** (vn); [b]**Emanuel Feuermann** (vc); [c]**Amar Quartet;** [a]**Berlin Philharmonic Orchestra / Paul Hindemith** ([b]va). Koch Schwann mono Ⓕ 311342* (70 minutes: ADD: 5/94).

...Violin Concerto[a]. Symphony in E flat major[b]. [a]**Joseph Fuchs** (vn); [a]**London Symphony Orchestra / Sir Eugene Goossens;** [b]**London Philharmonic Orchestra / Sir Adrian Boult.** Everest Ⓕ EVC9009 (57 minutes: ADD: 4/95).

...Violin Concerto[a]. Concerto for Orchestra, Op. 38. Kammermusik No. 4, Op. 36 No. 3[a]. Suite of French Dances. Rag Time (well-tempered). [a]**Michael Guttman** (vn); **Philharmonia Orchestra / José Serebrier.** ASV Ⓕ CDDCA945 (78 minutes: DDD: 3/96).

...Symphonic Metamorphosis. *Coupled with works by* **Janáček** *and* **Prokofiev** *and* **London Symphony Orchestra / Claudio Abbado.** Decca The Classic Sound Ⓜ 448 579-2DCS (79 minutes: ADD: 3/97).

Hindemith Mathis der Maler[a]. Trauermusik[a]. Symphonic Metamorphosis on Themes of Carl Maria von Weber. [a]**Geraldine Walther** (va); **San Francisco Symphony Orchestra / Herbert Blomstedt.** Decca Ⓕ 421 523-2DH (55 minutes: DDD: 10/88). Recorded 1987. ⒼⒼ

Hindemith Symphonic Metamorphosis on Themes of Carl Maria von Weber. Mathis der Maler. Nobilissima Visione. **Philadelphia Orchestra / Wolfgang Sawallisch.** EMI Ⓕ CDC5 55230-2 (71 minutes: DDD: 6/95). Recorded 1994. Ⓖ

The charge sometimes levelled against Hindemith of being dry and cerebral utterly collapses in the face of Blomstedt's disc. Masterly craftsmanship and virtuosity there is in plenty; but the powerful emotions of *Mathis der Maler* and the festive high spirits of the *Symphonic Metamorphosis* could not be denied except by those who wilfully close their ears. Each of the three movements of the *Mathis* Symphony is based on a panel of Grünewald's great Isenheim altar. The eventual glorious illumination of "The angels" folk-tune, the poignant slow movement and the blazing triumphant Alleluias after the desperate struggle with the demons in the finale have a searing intensity in Blomstedt's performance, which also presents Hindemith's elaborate web of counterpoints with the utmost lucidity. For brilliant and joyously ebullient orchestral writing few works can match that based on Weber's piano duets and his *Turandot* overture: here the San Francisco woodwind and brass have a field day. In addition, this warmly recommended disc includes a heartfelt performance of the very moving and beautiful elegy on the death of King George V, *Trauermusik*. It is tenderly played, with Geraldine Walther as a sweet-toned soloist and a full, rich sonority from the San Francisco strings.

The Philadelphia players for Sawallisch give taut performances that simply outclass most of the competition. Another by no means inconsiderable plus point is the unusual running order that achieves a better musical balance, starting with the most brilliant piece, the *Symphonic Metamorphosis*, and increasing in weight to the resounding brass Alleluias at the climax of the *Mathis* Symphony. Sawallisch's interpretations rank with Blomstedt in the *Mathis* Symphony and *Symphonic Metamorphosis*. Though many will prefer the leaner sound of the San Francisco Orchestra, EMI's sound for Sawallisch is relatively recessed. Given the spacious acoustic of Memorial Hall and the conductor's largeness of vision this is entirely apposite, there is no loss of detail.

Additional recommendations ...

...Mathis der Maler. Symphonic Metamorphosis. Konzertmusik for Strings and Brass, Op. 50.
Israel Philharmonic Orchestra / Leonard Bernstein.
DG Ⓕ 429 404-2GH (67 minutes: DDD: 5/91).   ⒼⒼ

...Symphony in E flat major. Nobilissima Visione. Neues vom Tage – overture. **BBC Philharmonic**
Orchestra / Yan Pascal Tortelier. Chandos Ⓕ CHAN9060 (60 minutes: DDD: 10/92).

...Symphonic Metamorphosis. Symphony in E flat major. Konzertmusik for Strings and Brass,
Op. 50. **New York Philharmonic Orchestra / Leonard Bernstein.**
Sony Classical Bernstein Royal Edition Ⓜ SMK47566 (70 minutes: ADD: 5/93).   Ⓖ

...Trauermusik. *Coupled with works by* **Schoenberg** *and* **Bartók** Cecil Aronowitz (va);
English Chamber Orchestra / Daniel Barenboim.
EMI Matrix Ⓜ CDM5 65079-2 (65 minutes: ADD: 12/94).   Ⓖ

Hindemith Hindemith plays and conducts Hindemith. [a]**Louis Cahuzac** (cl); [b]**Dennis Brain** (hn);
[c]**Szymon Goldberg** (vn); [d]**Emanuel Feuermann** (vc); [e]**Philharmonia Orchestra / Paul Hindemith**
([f]va). EMI Composers in Person mono/[e]stereo Ⓕ CDS5 55032-2*
(two discs: 157 minutes: ADD: 5/94). Recorded 1934-56.   ⒼⒼ
Solo Viola Sonata, Op. 25 No. 1[f] (from German Columbia LW10/12). Scherzo for Viola and
Cello[df] (LW12. Both recorded 1934). String Trio No. 2[cdf] (Columbia LX311/13, 8/34).
Nobilissima Visione[e] (EG291173-2, 4/87). Clarinet Concerto[ae] (Columbia 33CX1533, 5/58).
Symphonia serena[e] (33CX1676, 12/59; both stereo, appears for first time).
Horn Concerto[be] (HMV HLS7001, 3/72). Concert Music, Op. 50[e] (EG291173-2).
As a young man Hindemith played the viola professionally and is an excellent advocate of his own
Solo Viola Sonata, a work of considerable emotional depth. The orchestral items (all from 1956
sessions) include the Clarinet Concerto, with the veteran Louis Cahuzac a beautifully clear-toned
soloist, the *Symphonia serena,* Dennis Brain's unique, unmatchable account of the Horn Concerto,
and superlatively played performances of the masterly *Nobilissima Visione* suite and the *Concert
Music* for brass and strings, all in excellent stereo for the era. Common to all the interpretations here
is that very special directness of expression which is a unique feature of composer recordings.
Hindemith's clear, practical approach as a performer in a way reflects the symmetry and logic of his
own music. What is striking, however, is the degree of emotion that he also finds in it.

Additional recommendation ...

...Symphonia serena. Symphony, "Die Harmonie der Welt". **BBC Philharmonic Orchestra /**
Yan Pascal Tortelier. Chandos Ⓕ CHAN9217 (64 minutes: DDD: 11/94).   Ⓖ

Hindemith Kammermusiken – No. 1, Op. 24 No. 1; No. 2[a]; No. 3, Op. 36 No. 2[b]; No. 4, Op. 36
No. 3[c]; No. 5, Op. 36 No. 4[d]; No. 6, Op. 46 No. 1[e]; No. 7, Op. 46 No. 2[f]. Kleine Kammermusik
No. 1 for Wind Quintet, Op. 24 No. 2. [c]**Konstanty Kulka** (vn); [d]**Kim Kashkashian** (va);
[e]**Norbert Blume** (va d'amore); [b]**Lynn Harrell** (vc); [a]**Ronald Brautigam** (pf); [f]**Leo van Doeselaar**
(org); **Royal Concertgebouw Orchestra / Riccardo Chailly.** Decca Ⓕ 433 816-2DH2
(two discs: 138 minutes: DDD: 11/92). Recorded 1990. *Gramophone Award Winner 1993.*   Ⓖ
Even were the performances and recordings not outstanding (and they most certainly are) this would
be an extremely valuable set. Hindemith's series of *Kammermusik* ("Chamber Music") began in 1921
as an iconoclastic response to the hyper-intense emotionalism of German 'Expressionist' music over
the previous 15 years. It continued until 1927, at which point he began to rationalize both the
harmonic and the expressive foundations of his style. This, then, is neo-classicism with a German
accent and as such it was to be a vital force in sweeping away the cobwebs of musty late romanticism;
Walton, Prokofiev, Shostakovich and Britten were among those who, however indirectly, would feel
the benefit. The music is also immensely enjoyable in its own right. Hindemith cheekily throws
together disparate idioms and sheer force of personality is all that guards against total anarchy. All
this is done with more than half an eye on the performers' own enjoyment of recreation, and the fine
array of artists assembled by Chailly savour every detail. Recording quality is exemplary.

Additional recommendations ...

...Der Schwanendreher. Konzertmusik, Op. 48. Kammermusik No. 5. **Paul Cortese** (va);
Philharmonia Orchestra / Martyn Brabbins. ASV Ⓕ CDDCA931 (73 minutes: DDD: 9/95).

...Kammermusik No. 2. Wind Septet. **Henze** Wind Quintet. L'autunno.
Berlin Philharmonic Wind Quintet. BIS Ⓕ CD752 (65 minutes: DDD: 3/97).

...Kammermusik No. 2. *Coupled with works by various composers.* **Swiss Wind Quintet.**
Koch Discover International Ⓑ DICD920395 (65 minutes: DDD: 8/97).
See review in the Collections section; refer to the Index.

Hindemith Kammermusiken – No. 1, Op. 24 No. 1; No. 4, Op. 36 No. 3[a]; No. 5, Op. 36 No. 4[b].
[b]**Kolja Blacher** (vn); [a]**Wolfram Christ** (va); **Berlin Philharmonic Orchestra / Claudio Abbado.**
EMI Ⓕ CDC5 56160-2 (55 minutes: DDD: 12/96). Recorded 1996.
These performances are excellent. Where the *Gramophone* Award-winning Chailly underlines the
music's 1920s radicalism, Abbado takes a broader line, rather as the composer might have done in,
say, the 1940s. He is well served by his band and soloists – violinist Kolja Blacher especially has the
edge over any of his rivals – as well as the sound which varies its focus for each work. For example,

No. 1 (1922), scored for 12 instruments with no soloist, is closely miked to give a real chamber feel, while Nos. 4 and 5 (1924-25) sound more like orchestral works. For those readers already in possession of the Chailly, this disc may be redundant; if the thought of all seven at once is too daunting, then this is the place to start. Recommended with enthusiasm.

Hindemith String Quartet No. 3, Op. 22[a].
Prokofiev String Quartet No. 2 in F major, Op. 92[a].
Walton String Quartet in A minor[b]. **Hollywood Quartet** (Felix Slatkin, Paul Shure, vns;
Paul Robyn, va; Eleanor Aller, vc). Testament mono Ⓕ SBT1052* (74 minutes: ADD: 3/95).
Items marked [a] from Capitol CTL7016 (4/52), [b]CTL7004 (6/51). Recorded 1951.　　　　ⒼⒼ
Although numerous accounts of the Prokofiev have appeared over the years, none has approached, let alone surpassed, the Hollywood version of the Second Quartet. The same would no doubt apply to the Hindemith but for the fact that there have been fewer challengers. What a wonderful feeling for line these players had, what an incredible, perfectly matched and blended ensemble they produced – and how well these transfers sound! That goes for the Walton, too: there is no other account of the piece that makes so positive a case for it.
Additional recommendations ...
...No. 3, Op. 22. *Coupled with works by* **Schulhoff** and **Weill Brandis Quartet.**
Nimbus Ⓕ NI5410 (60 minutes: DDD: 3/95).
...No. 3, Op. 22; C major, Op. 2; No. 4, Op. 32; No. 5 in E flat major. Repertoire for Military Orchestra, "Minimax". Overture to the *Flying Dutchman* as played at sight by a spa band at seven o'clock in the morning. **Kocian Quartet.**
Praga Ⓕ PR250 093/4 (two discs: 144 minutes: DDD: 10/96).

Hindemith Violin Sonatas – E flat major, Op. 11 No. 1; D major, Op. 11 No. 2; E major (1935);
C major (1939). **Ulf Wallin** (vn); **Roland Pöntinen** (pf). BIS Ⓕ CD761 (56 minutes: DDD: 8/96).
It seems odd to think that, with several complete cycles on the market of Hindemith's sonatas for viola with and without piano, there are none of those for violin and piano. Only the E major of 1935 appears in recital or on disc, and then only fitfully. This is due to its brevity (under 10 minutes long – as is Op. 11 No. 1) and lack of complication (it is more of a *sonatina*), yet it is familiar Hindemith from first note to last. The C major work (1939) is more complex and grave, and probably the finest of them. The longest sonata – and most conservative in idiom – is that in D major. Both Op. 11 works were written in 1918 when Hindemith was on active service, and are remarkable for bearing few traces of either the grimness of the Great War or Hindemith's personal voice. Both deserve wider currency. This issue is also welcome in including the fragmentary abandoned finale of Op. 11 No. 1, a rustic dance not in keeping with the symmetry of the whole. Hindemith was right to omit it. The sweet-toned Ulf Wallin is fully attuned to Hindemith's wavelength and Roland Pöntinen as ever provides exemplary support. The recording is typical BIS (that is, excellent). A splendid disc.
Additional recommendation ...
...E flat major, Op. 11. *Coupled with works by various composers.* **Gidon Kremer** (vn);
Andrei Gavrilov (pf). EMI Forte Ⓜ CZS5 69334-2 (two discs: 151 minutes: ADD).
See review in the Collections section; refer to the Index.　　　　Ⓖ

Hindemith Viola Sonatas – F major, Op. 11 No. 4[a]; Op. 25 No. 4[a]; C major (1939). Nobilissima Visione – Meditation[a]. Trauermusik[b]. **Paul Cortese** (va); [a]**Jordi Vilaprinyó** (pf); [b]**Philharmonia Orchestra / Martyn Brabbins.** ASV Ⓕ CDDCA978 (70 minutes: DDD: 3/97).
The late-romantic lyricism of the early F major Sonata, Op. 11 No. 4, comes over as slightly saccharine, with a tendency for the extremes to be evened out – a common problem with works from Hindemith's most radical decade – whereas both Imai and Kashkashian (listed below) possess a much leaner sound. But in the more acerbic Second, Op. 25 No. 4 (1922), Cortese's warmth is very persuasive. He is at his best in No. 3 (1939), giving a performance of real depth that edges out Imai's and even the composer's own, revelatory though that is, from the top spot – though some might prefer a quicker pace. On balance, this can be recommended as first choice in the sonatas and *Meditation* (from *Nobilissima Visione*). The *Trauermusik* is a bonus, though it does not supplant the Walther-Blomstedt version and most coming to this disc will already have the Decca recording.
Additional recommendations ...
...Op. 11 No. 4; Op. 25 No. 4; C major. Meditation. **Nobuko Imai** (va); **Roland Pöntinen** (pf).
BIS Ⓕ CD651 (60 minutes: DDD: 9/94).　　　　Ⓖ
...Viola Sonatas – C major (1939)[a]; Op. 25 No. 1; Op. 25 No. 4[a]; Op. 11 No. 4[a]; Op. 11 No. 5;
Viola Sonata (1937). **Kim Kashkashian** (va); [a]**Robert Levin** (pf).
ECM New Series Ⓕ 833 309-2 (two discs: 128 minutes: DDD: 10/88).
...Op. 11 No. 4[a]. Trauermusik (arr. cpsr)[a]. Duett[b]. *Coupled with works by* **Brahms** and **Dvořák**
Wilfried Strehle (va); [b]**Wolfgang Boettcher** (vc); [a]**Karina Wisniewska** (pf).
Nimbus Ⓕ NI5473 (78 minutes: DDD: 9/96).

Hindemith Ludus tonalis.
Prokofiev Visions fugitives, Op. 22. **Olli Mustonen** (pf). Decca Ⓕ 444 803-2DH
(68 minutes: DDD: 5/96). Recorded 1994.

For a work that was once regarded as a landmark in twentieth-century piano music, Hindemith's *Ludus tonalis* has received scant attention in the way of recent studio recordings from pianists of note. To be fair, it is not an easy work for either audience or artist: its contrapuntal, angular and unforgiving textures pose demanding interpretative problems for the pianist, and at 50 minutes' duration its knotty sound-world can be difficult to digest for even the most enthusiastic of listeners. From an interpretative standpoint John McCabe and Olli Mustonen give very different performances. McCabe's strong points are structure, contrapuntal clarity (to the point of dryness at times) and a clear sense of something monumental unfolding. When compared with Mustonen he can seem a little impersonal and distant. In Mustonen's reading there is a real sense of journey as he traverses the 25 studies and there is greater tonal variation, expressive range and playfulness in his playing, which helps the listener to feel more involved in this music. Die-hard Hindemith enthusiasts may find McCabe's approach the more authoritative, but Mustonen is extremely persuasive in the way he sheds new light on this music, making it more accessible – ideal for winning new admirers to the work. Mustonen adds Prokofiev's *Visions fugitives* which makes an effective contrast. There's strong competition here but Mustonen acquits himself well, giving a fluid and beautifully shaped account of these "fleeting thoughts", and the recordings for both works are excellent.

Additional recommendation ...
...Ludus tonalis. Suite "1922", Op. 26. **John McCabe** (pf).
Hyperion Ⓟ CDA66824 (69 minutes: DDD: 5/96).

Hindemith Mass. Six Chansons. Eine lichte Mitternacht. Du musst dir Alles geben. Der Tod.
Nun da der Tag. Zwölf Madrigale – Mitwelt; Tauche deine Furcht in schwarzen Wein; Trink aus!; Frühling; Judaskuss; Du Zweifel an dem Sinn der Welt. **Netherlands Chamber Choir / Uwe Gronostay**. Globe Ⓟ GLO5125 (57 minutes: DDD: 5/96). Texts and translations included. Recorded 1994.
Hindemith Mass. Zwölf Madrigale – Eines Narren, eines Künstlers Leben; An eine Tote; An einen Schmetterling; Magisches Rezept; Es bleibt wohl, was gesagt wird; Kraft fand zu Form. Lieder nach alten Texten, Op. 33. **Danish National Radio Choir / Uwe Gronostay**. Chandos Ⓟ CHAN9413 (52 minutes: DDD: 5/96). Texts and translations included. Recorded 1995.
Given Hindemith's awareness of sometimes centuries-old traditions when writing his own music, it was almost inevitable that he should compose a Mass. The wonder is that it took him so long to get round to doing so, and he barely made it in time – dying in 1963, just six weeks after the first performance, having begun sketching a second. His tardiness can partly be explained by his view that Palestrina had had the last word with the Mass as a musical form. What is more important is the quality of the music, irrespective of why he wrote it. If not quite capturing the spirit of the missal, the Mass is still an evocative, exploratory setting, proving that he was far from being a spent force. Uwe Gronostay obviously has an affection for this work in particular, given that he has recorded it twice in as many years for two separate companies. There is little to choose between the performances, both being beautifully sung and shaped, qualities that are evident in the rest of each programme. Nor, indeed, are the couplings much help in the selection process, since the Mass is the sole duplication. Both discs contain six of the 12 deeply felt Madrigals Hindemith composed in 1958. The early *Lieder nach alten Texten* (1923) on Chandos are not really a sufficient makeweight, delightful though they are. Globe offer more in the lovely Rilke *Chansons* (1939) and the four male choruses, written between 1929 and 1939 to words by Whitman, Gottfried Benn, Hölderlin and Nietzsche. Chandos's sound is fuller, but Globe's is still very good. If you want just one disc of Hindemith's *a cappella* choral music, then go for Globe; but the Mass is worth having twice for its own sake, let alone in completing the Madrigal set.

Hindemith Mathis der Maler. **Roland Hermann** (bar) Mathis; **Josef Protschka** (ten) Albrecht; **Gabriele Rossmanith** (sop) Regina; **Sabine Hass** (sop) Ursula; **Harald Stamm** (bass) Riedinger; **Heinz Kruse** (ten) Hans Schwalb; **Victor von Halem** (bass) Lorenz von Pommersfelden; **Hermann Winkler** (ten) Wolfgang Capito; **Ulrich Hielscher** (bass) Truchsess von Waldberg; **Ulrich Ress** (ten) Sylvester von Schaumberg; **John Cogram** (ten) Der Pfeifer des Grafen von Helfenstein; **Marilyn Schmiege** (mez) Helfenstein; **North German Radio Chorus; Cologne Radio Chorus and Symphony Orchestra / Gerd Albrecht**. Wergo Ⓟ WER6255-2 (three discs: 166 minutes: DDD: 9/94). Notes and text included. Recorded 1990.
Hindemith Mathis der Maler. **Dietrich Fischer-Dieskau** (bar) Mathis; **James King** (ten) Albrecht; **Gerd Feldhoff** (bass) Lorenz von Pommersfelden; **Manfred Schmidt** (ten) Capito; **Peter Meven** (bass) Riedinger; **William Cochran** (ten) Schwalb; **Alexander Malta** (bass) Truchsess von Waldburg; **Donald Grobe** (ten) Sylvester von Schaumberg; **Rose Wagmann** (mez) Ursula; **Urszula Koszut** (sop) Regina; **Trudeliese Schmidt** (mez) Countess Helfenstein; **Bavarian Radio Chorus and Symphony Orchestra / Rafael Kubelík**. EMI Ⓟ CDS5 55237-2 (three discs: 183 minutes: ADD: 7/95). Notes, text and translation included. From SLS5182 (12/79). Recorded 1977.
The masterpiece, *Mathis der Maler,* is one of the pinnacles of twentieth-century German opera. It has become axiomatic to see in it a parable of the times, with Hindemith using the turbulent world of sixteenth-century Germany to mirror the Nazi Reich and his place in it. But in reality *Mathis* is a spiritual and historical opera, not a political one, even in the handling of the artist's relationship to

the society around him. Hindemith was at first equivocal in his feelings towards the regime, being by nature apolitical, even when his brother-in-law was dispatched to Oranienburg. The Nazi's antagonism towards Hindemith rested on a few iconoclastic works from the 1920s and the prudish outrage of Hitler and Goebbels at *Neues vom Tage*. Later, both Goebbels and Rosenberg tried to secure Hindemith's remaining in Germany by hinting at a staging of *Mathis* if its composer played their game. So full marks to Rudolf Stephan in his essay for Wergo for playing down the political angle; if Hitler had not risen to power until, say, 1936, one doubts that *Mathis* would have turned out much different. As his brief note declares, Gerd Albrecht's acquaintance with Hindemith's music, particularly the operas, goes back to the early 1960s, before the composer's death. Hindemith even sanctioned some retouching of the orchestration in *Mathis* made by Albrecht for a festival performance, though it is not made clear whether Albrecht has applied this here, nor to what extent. Rarely have Hindemith's often heavy textures sounded so clear. As to the music, is not the brief concluding "Alleluia" duet that crowns the sixth tableau one of *the* great moments in twentieth-century opera? You will be convinced from your very first hearing of it and any doubters on this point – or to the quality of the score as a whole – are urged to sample either of these accounts.

There are fine moments aplenty in Albrecht's reading, not least where familiar passages from the *Mathis* Symphony surface and precipitate some of the most intense music of the opera. Roland Hermann is, perhaps, a shade stolid in places as the painter (though his world-weariness in the final scene is just right); Josef Protschka makes a most authoritative Cardinal, acting as a perfect foil to Hermann's Mathis. They head a fine cast, supported by some lusty singing and playing from the combined forces of Cologne and North German Radios. Comparing the newer set with Kubelík's reissued version shows that honours are fairly even; choosing between them would depend largely on one's keenness for individual names. There is little to choose between the two versions; neither is perfect, but both are very fine. Albrecht, who makes one or two minor but noticeable cuts, has the benefit of more modern sound, but EMI's for Kubelík has transferred well. The choruses in particular are excellent, although Albrecht's seem tame in the famous "Temptation of St Antony" scene when set next to Kubelík's devilish-sounding Bavarians. Comparison of the casts yields a mixed picture; many readers will prefer Fischer-Dieskau as Mathis to the rather raw-voiced Hermann (except, as mentioned above, in the final tableau); for many this will be the crucial criterion, but Wergo do have the better of some other principals. The roles of Schwalb and his daughter encapsulate the predicament: for EMI, William Cochran is more imposing than Heinz Kruse as the peasant leader but Wergo's Gabriele Rossmanith is sweeter and younger-toned as Regina. For Albrecht, their first appearance seems to be a mid-afternoon stroll and not the convincing escape from pursuit that Kubelík effects here (first disc, track 4). Despite the urgings of sentiment, neither set outclasses the other. For most, choice will rest on preferences for specific cast members. Those who love this score will want both.

Further listening ...

...Der Dämon.*Coupled with works by* **Schreker** and **Schulhoff** Die Mondsüchtige. **Leipzig Gewandhaus Orchestra / Lothar Zagrosek.** Decca Entartete Musik 444 182-2DH (5/95). ⊖

...999 005-2ᵃ – Lustige Sinfonietta, Op. 4. Rag Time ("well-tempered"). Symphonische Tänze. 999 006-2ᵃ – Das Nusch-Nuschi – dance suite, Op. 20. Konzertmusik for strings and brass, Op. 50. Symphony, "Die Harmonie der Welt". CPO999 005-2, 999 006-2 (12/91).

...Octet. *Coupled with* **Beethoven** Septet in E flat major, Op. 20. **Berlin Philharmonic Octet.** Nimbus NI5461 (4/96).

...Der Schwanendreher. *Coupled with* **Bartók** Viola Concerto, Sz120. **Tabea Zimmermann** (va); **Bavarian Radio Symphony Orchestra / David Shallon.** EMI CDC7 54101-2 (3/93).

...Clarinet Sonata in B flat major. *Coupled with works by various composers.* **Jonathan Cohler** (cl); **Judith Gordon** (pf). Crystal CD733 (5/95).

...Horn Sonata. *Coupled with works by various composers.* **David Pyatt** (hn); **Martin Jones** (pf). Erato 3984-21632-2 (4/98). *See review in the Collections section; refer to the Index.*

...Die Serenaden, Op. 35ᵃᵇᵉᶠ. Cor Anglais Sonataᶜᵍ. Oboe Sonataᵇᵍ. Trio, Op. 47ᵈᵉᵍ. ᵃRuth Ziesak (sop); Lajos Lencsés (ᵇob/ᶜcor ang/ᵈheck); ᵉGunter Teuffel (va); ᶠAnsgar Schneider (vc); ᵍShoshana Rudiakov (pf). CPO Ⓕ CPO999 332-2 (58 minutes: DDD: 6/96).

...String Quartets – No. 2, Op. 16; No. 4, Op. 32. **Juilliard Quartet.** Wergo WER6283-2 (10/96).

...Wind Septet. *Coupled with works by* **Toch** and **Weill** Deutsche Kammerphilharmonie. Virgin Classics VC5 45056-2 (7/95).

...Organ Sonatas Nos. 1-3. *Coupled with works by* **Pepping** and **Schoenberg** Kevin Bowyer (org). Nimbus NI5411 (1/95).

...Tanzstücke, Op. 19. Klaviermusik, Op. 37. **Siegfried Mauser** (pf). Wergo WER6271-2 (5/97).

...Memories of Lincoln – Sing on there in the Swamp. *Coupled with works by various composers.* **Thomas Hampson** (bar); **Craig Rutenberg** (pf). EMI CDM5 55028-2 (10/97). *See review in the Collections section; refer to the Index.*

...When Lilacs Last in the Door-yard Bloom'd (Requiem for those we love). **Jan DeGaetani** (mez); **William Stone** (bar); **Atlanta Symphony Chorus and Orchestra / Robert Shaw.** Telarc CD80132 (7/87).

...Das Unaufhörliche. **Ulrike Sonntag** (sop); **Robert Wörle** (ten); **Siegfried Lorenz** (bar); **Berlin Radio Children's Choir; Berlin Radio Chorus and Symphony Orchestra / Lothar Zagrosek.** Wergo WER6603-2 (10/97).

Alun Hoddinott

British 1929

Hoddinott Symphonies – No. 2, Op. 29[a]; No. 3, Op. 61[b]; No. 5, Op. 81[c]. [ab]**London Symphony Orchestra /** [a]**Norman Del Mar,** [b]**David Atherton;** [c]**Royal Philharmonic Orchestra / Andrew Davis.** Lyrita Ⓕ SRCD331 (74 minutes: ADD: 2/97). Item marked [a] from TPLS13013 (4/68), [b]SXL6570 (4/73), [c]SXL6606 (3/74).

Alun Hoddinott is one of the best and most resourceful of living British symphonists, and the return to the catalogue of three demonstrations of that fact is welcome. What is meant by 'resourceful' is well illustrated by this coupling. The Second Symphony, from 1962, is apparently in a conventional four-movement layout, but in fact the outer movements investigate the arch-like or palindromic forms that Hoddinott was to make much use of later. Its successor is in two movements, but both are in two parts, with opening and closing *adagios* reflecting each other across the two intervening quick sections. The Fifth Symphony, most striking of all, has a finale of six panels, each slow section having a faster 'pair'. Its first movement (again there are only two) is described by the composer as an "interrupted passacaglia"; the effect is of craggy, splendidly stormy music continually encroaching upon lyricism. The performances are excellent, the recordings for the most part decent. There is only one regret. The original sleeves of these recordings carried reproductions of modern paintings, believed to have been chosen by the composer as striking analogues for the imagery of the works themselves. Unfortunately, the CD does not.

Further listening ...

...Passagio, Op. 94. The Heaventree of Stars, Op. 102[a]. Doubles, Op. 106[b]. Start Children, Op. 135. [a]**Hu Kun** (vn); [b]**David Cowley** (ob); [b]**Rosalie Armstrong** (hpd); **BBC Welsh Symphony Orchestra / Tadaaki Otaka.** Nimbus NI5357 (7/93).

...Quodlibet on Welsh Nursery Tunes. Chorales, Variants and Fanfares[a]. Ritornelli 2, Op. 100 No. 2. *Coupled with works by* **Mathias** [a]**Kevin Bowyer** (org); **Fine Arts Brass Ensemble.** Nimbus NI5466 (5/96).

...Organ Sonata. *Coupled with works by various composers.* **Jane Watts** (org). Priory PRCD389 (10/97). *See review in the Collections section; refer to the Index.*

...Piano Sonatas – No. 1, Op. 17; No. 2, Op. 27; No. 3, Op. 40; No. 4, Op. 49; No. 5, Op. 57. **Martin Jones** (pf). Nimbus NI5369 (12/93).

...Piano Sonatas – No. 6, Op. 78: No. 3; No. 7, Op. 114; No. 8, Op. 125; No. 9, Op. 134; No. 10, Op. 136. **Martin Jones** (pf). Nimbus NI5370 (5/95).

...Dives and Lazarus, Op. 39. Concertino for Viola and Chamber Orchestra, Op. 14. Nocturnes and Cadenzas, Op. 62. Sinfonia Fidei, Op. 95. **Soloists; Welsh National Opera Chorus; Philharmonia Chorus; New Philharmonia Orchestra / David Atherton; Philharmonia Orchestra / Sir Charles Groves.** Lyrita SRCD332 (2/97).

...The Lady and the Unicorn, Op. 110. *Coupled with works by various composers.* **Ionian Singers / Timothy Salter; Thalia Myers** (pf); **Erik Jacobsen** (perc).Usk Recordings USK1216 (3/96).

Georg Melchior Hoffmann

German 1685-1715

Suggested listening ...

...Meine Seele rühmt und preist (attrib.). *Coupled with works by* **Bach** *and* **Telemann.** **C.P.E. Bach Chamber Orchestra / Peter Schreier** (ten). Philips 442 786-2PH (5/98). *See review under J.S. Bach; refer to the Index.*

Paul Hofhaimer

Austrian 1459-1537

Suggested listening ...

...Ein fröhlich wesen. *Coupled with works by various composers.* **Early Music Consort of London / David Munrow.** Virgin Classics Veritas VED5 61334-2 (11/97). *See review in the Collections section; refer to the Index.*

Lee Hoiby

American 1926

Suggested listening ...

...Winter Song. A letter. *Coupled with works by various composers.* **Jennifer Larmore** (mez); **Antoine Palloc** (pf). Teldec 0630-16069-2 (12/97). *See review in the Collections section; refer to the Index.*

Antony Holborne

British *fl* 1584-1602

Suggested listening ...

...Hasellwoods Galliard. *Coupled with works by various composers.* **Paul O'Dette** (lte). Harmonia Mundi HMU90 7164 (7/97). *See review under Dowland; refer to the Index.*

Alfred Hollins

Suggested listening ...
...A Trumpet Minuet. *Coupled with works by various composers.* **Christopher Herrick** (org).
Hyperion CDA66778 (3/96). *See review in the Collections section; refer to the Index.*

Robin Holloway

Holloway Third Concerto for Orchestra, Op. 76. **London Symphony Orchestra /**
Michael Tilson Thomas. NMC Ⓕ NMCD039 (45 minutes: DDD: 2/98). Recorded live in 1996.
A North African holiday was the initial stimulus for Robin Holloway's *Second Concerto for Orchestra.*
The first ideas for No. 3 came during a trip through South America – sound pictures of Lake Titicaca,
riotous New Year's Day celebrations in the Bay of Bahia, the slow train-crossing of the Great
Brazilian Swamp and the huge, satanic slag heap at the Potosí Silver Mine. Holloway jotted them all
down on the spot: then his notebook was stolen, and it took another 13 years to recall them and finish
the piece. By then, of course, the alchemical processes of memory had transformed the original
musical impressions into something quite different. What might have been simply a descriptive tone-
poem finally emerged as a powerful and unusual musical argument – a huge slow movement, with a
moderately fast dance-like finale, which evolves from tiny scraps of motifs (hardly a 'theme' in sight).
And yet much of the original 'illustrative' character remains. String and woodwind textures recall
dense, overripe rain forest foliage; the dark, 'sluggish' first movement suggests the movement of a
vast, slow, muddy river; extravagant sensuousness contrasts with clangorous bells or craggy brass.
This recording, based on its 1996 première, is quite an achievement. It is rare for a conductor and an
orchestra to show such a compelling grasp of the shape and atmosphere of a work at its first
performance. Technically the sound has none of the usual problems of live recording – virtually no
intrusive noise, good balance, warm tone. The disc as a whole is a fine successor to NMC's
Gramophone Award-winning *Second Concerto.*

Further listening ...
...Second Concerto for Orchestra, Op. 40. **BBC Symphony Orchestra / Oliver Knussen.**
NMC NMCD015 (5/94). Recorded 1993. *Gramophone Editor's choice.*
Gramophone Award Winner 1994. ⒼⒼ
...Sea Surface Full of Clouds, Op. 28[a]. Romanza, Op. 31[b]. [a]**Penelope Walmsley-Clark** (sop);
[a]**Margaret Cable** (mez); [a]**Charles Brett** (alto); [a]**Martyn Hill** (ten); [b]**Erich Gruenberg** (vn); [a]**Richard**
Hickox Singers; City of London Sinfonia / Richard Hickox. Chandos CHAN9228 (9/94). Ⓖ

Vagn Holmboe

Holmboe Concertos – No. 11 for Trumpet and Orchestra, Op. 44[a]; No. 12 for Trombone and
Orchestra, Op. 52[b]; Tuba and Orchestra, Op. 127[c]. Intermezzo concertante, Op. 171[c].
[a]**Håkan Hardenberger** (tpt); [b]**Christian Lindberg** (tbn); [c]**Jens Bjørn-Larsen** (tuba);
Aalborg Symphony Orchestra / Owain Arwel Hughes. BIS Ⓕ CD802 (55 minutes: DDD: 3/97).
The Trumpet Concerto has a leanness of texture and neo-classical air that will surprise those familiar
with Holmboe's symphonies. It has been recorded twice before, though this is its first CD incarnation.
Fine though its predecessors were, this one outclasses them; Hardenberger's first entry creates an
electricity that is maintained throughout the work – indeed, the disc as a whole. No. 11's tripartite
design recurs, condensed into a single movement, in No. 12: a brief, expressively crucial slow section
framed by a large-boned *Allegro* (rather grave in character in the trombone work), and a good-
humoured, rollicking finale. The Tuba Concerto (1976), by contrast, requires a full orchestral
complement, its one integrated span bearing little semblance of traditional three-movement form. It
is the most dramatic and exploratory work here, both in mood and sonority, the demands of which
on tuba virtuosos over the years have occasioned it to be played in slightly differing versions (detailed
in the insert-notes), especially with regard to the taxing cadenza. The short *Intermezzo concertante*
(1987) reaffirms that, however ungainly it may seem, the tuba really can sing. This disc is a fitting
tribute to its composer: wonderful music, wonderfully performed and recorded.

Holmboe Symphonies – No. 11, Op. 144; No. 12, Op. 175; No. 13, Op. 192. **Aarhus Symphony**
Orchestra / Owain Arwel Hughes. BIS Ⓕ CD728 (63 minutes: DDD: 9/96). Recorded 1994.
Few who have invested in this series so far can have been left in any doubt that these are among the
most commanding symphonies to have emerged in post-war Europe. Some might even argue that they
are *the* finest since Sibelius and Nielsen. In a just world the best of them would be in the repertoire of
all the major symphony orchestras from Boston to Berlin. This CD includes the last three Holmboe
has composed. All credit to Owain Arwel Hughes and the Aarhus orchestra for their committed
advocacy and to BIS for recording them in such vivid, naturally balanced sound. Along with the
Seventh, the Eleventh, composed in 1980, is quintessential Holmboe, and its atmosphere resonates in
the mind long after you have heard it. To quote Knud Ketting's notes, "the symphony's climax in
dynamic and emotional terms comes in the second movement and it then slowly retreats within itself

... [it] is cast as a strong arch, which impresses at first hearing, and commands increasing admiration on closer acquaintance". The arabesque that opens the symphony seems to come from another world and the transparent, luminous textures communicate the sense of a spiritual quest that one rarely encounters in modern music. The Twelfth is a taut, well-argued piece, and is, like its two companions on this disc, in three movements. No one listening to the Thirteenth, written at the instigation of Owain Arwel Hughes, would think that it was the work of an 85-year-old. Of course, there have been other octogenarian symphonies but none that sounds quite so youthful or highly charged as this one. As this series reaffirms, the symphony is far from dead but is alive and kicking. The completion of this cycle is an important and above all exciting event that no music lover should miss.

Further listening ...

...Chamber Concertos – No. 1, Op. 17[a]; No. 2, Op. 20[b]; No. 3, Op. 21[c]. [b]**Eva Ostergaard** (fl); [c]**Niels Thomsen** (cl); [b]**Mikkel Futtrup** (vn); [a]**Anne Oland** (pf); **Danish Radio Concert Orchestra / Hannu Koivula.** Da Capo 8 224038 (4/97).

...Symphonies – No. 1, Op. 4; No. 3, Op. 25, "Sinfonia rustica"; No. 10, Op. 105. **Aarhus Symphony Orchestra / Owain Arwel Hughes.** BIS CD605 (11/94).

...Symphonies – No. 4, Op. 29, "Sinfonia sacra"[a]; No. 5, Op. 35. [a]**Jutland Opera Choir; Aarhus Symphony Orchestra / Owain Arwel Hughes.** BIS CD572 (6/93).

...Symphonies – No. 6, Op. 43; No. 7, Op. 50. **Aarhus Symphony Orchestra / Owain Arwel Hughes.** BIS CD573 (6/93).

...Symphonies – No. 8, Op. 56, "Sinfonia boreale"; No. 9, Op. 95. **Aarhus Symphony Orchestra / Owain Arwel Hughes.** BIS CD618 (8/95). ⓖ

...String Quartets – No. 1, Op. 46; No. 3, Op. 48; No. 4, Op. 63. **Kontra Quartet.** Marco Polo Da capo DCCD9203 (6/94).

...String Quartets – No. 2, Op. 47; No. 5, Op. 66; No. 6, Op. 78. **Kontra Quartet.** Da capo 8 224026 (7/96).

...String Quartets – No. 7, Op. 86; No. 8, Op. 87; No. 9, Op. 92. **Kontra Quartet.** Da Capo 8 224073 (12/97).

Gustav Holst

British 1874-1934

Holst A Somerset Rhapsody, H87. Beni Mora, H107. Invocation, H75[a]. A Fugal Overture, H151. Egdon Heath, H172. Hammersmith, H178. [a]**Tim Hugh** (vc); **Royal Scottish National Orchestra / David Lloyd-Jones.** Naxos Ⓢ 8 553696 (69 minutes: DDD: 6/98). Recorded 1996.
Gramophone Editor's choice. ⓖ

This superb recording was made in the Henry Wood Hall in Glasgow. Lloyd-Jones has as his two weightiest items the Hardy-inspired *Egdon Heath*, arguably Holst's finest work, as well as the prelude and fugue, *Hammersmith*, comparably dark and intense. In the latter he chooses the wind-band version, achieving a subtlety of shading in phrasing and dynamic amply to justify that striking choice. The Naxos sound is vividly atmospheric while letting one hear inner detail, particularly important in the fugue. Lloyd-Jones generally adopts flowing speeds close to those of Boult and is objective in his interpretation while bringing out to the full the tenderness and refinement of the writing. Particularly beautiful is the performance of *A Somerset Rhapsody* which opens the disc, with the cor anglais solo ravishingly played. Boult of course has unique authority in this music, and the Lyrita analogue recordings still sound superb, with clean focus and separation. Yet quite apart from the intrinsic quality of Lloyd-Jones's performances with the Scottish orchestra, and the formidable advantage of price, his grouping of works is more generous than the Boult disc. The six works are neatly balanced, three dating from before the climactic period of *The Planets* and *The Hymn of Jesus*, and three after. Particularly valuable – and not included on the Boult disc – is the atmospheric *Invocation* for cello and orchestra of 1911, rather dismissed by Imogen Holst, but here given a yearningly intense, deeply thoughtful performance with Tim Hugh as soloist. This is a highly recommendable offering, whether for the dedicated Holstian or the newcomer wanting to investigate this composer's more characteristic work outside *The Planets*.

Additional recommendations ...

...Beni Mora, H107[a]. A Fugal Overture, H151[b]. Hammersmith, H178[a]. Japanese Suite, H126[c]. Scherzo, H192[a]. A Somerset Rhapsody, H87[a]. [ab]**London Philharmonic Orchestra;** [c]**London Symphony Orchestra / Sir Adrian Boult.** Lyrita Ⓕ SRCD222 (62 minutes: ADD: 7/92). ⓖ

...St Paul's Suite, H118. A Fugal Concerto, H152[a]. Brook Green Suite, H190. A Somerset Rhapsody. The Perfect Fool – ballet music. [a]**Jonathan Snowden** (fl); [a]**David Theodore** (ob); **English Chamber Orchestra / Sir Yehudi Menuhin.** EMI Eminence Ⓜ CD-EMX2227 (48 minutes: DDD: 12/94).

Holst The Planets, H125. Women's voices of the **Montreal Symphony Chorus and Orchestra / Charles Dutoit.** Decca Ⓕ 417 553-2DH (53 minutes: DDD: 4/87). Recorded 1986.
Gramophone Award Winner 1987. ⓖⓖⓖ

Holst's brilliantly coloured orchestral suite, *The Planets*, is undoubtedly his most famous work and its success is surely deserved. The musical characterization is as striking as its originality of conception: the association of "Saturn" with old age, for instance, is as unexpected as it is perceptive.

Bax introduced Holst to astrology and while he wrote the music he became fascinated with horoscopes, so it is the astrological associations that are paramount, although the linking of "Mars" (with its enormously powerful 5/4 rhythms) and war also reflects the time of composition. Throughout, the work's invention is as memorable as its vivid orchestration is full of infinite detail. No recording can reveal it all but this one comes the closest to doing so. Dutoit's individual performance is in a long line of outstanding recordings.

Additional recommendations ...

...The Planets. **Berlin RIAS Chamber Choir; Berlin Philharmonic Orchestra / Herbert von Karajan.** DG Karajan Gold Ⓕ 439 011-2GHS (52 minutes: DDD). ⒼⒼ

...The Planets. **Geoffrey Mitchell Choir; London Philharmonic Orchestra / Sir Adrian Boult.** EMI Studio Ⓜ CDM7 64748-2 (49 minutes: ADD: 5/88). Ⓖ

...The Planets[a]. **Elgar** Variations on an Original Theme, Op. 36, "Enigma"[b]. [a]**London Symphony Orchestra / Gustav Holst;** [b]**Royal Albert Hall Orchestra / Sir Edward Elgar.** EMI Composers in Person mono Ⓕ CDC7 54837-2* (70 minutes: ADD: 10/93).

...The Planets[a]. Egdon Heath[b]. The Perfect Fool – ballet music[b]. **London Philharmonic Orchestra /** [a]**Sir Georg Solti,** [b]**Sir Adrian Boult.** Decca Ⓜ 440 318-2DWO (73 minutes: ADD: 4/94).

...The Planets[a]. St Paul's Suite, H118. [a]**Ambrosian Singers; Royal Philharmonic Orchestra / Vernon Handley.** Tring International Ⓢ TRP007 (62 minutes: DDD: 6/94).

...The Planets[a]. Egdon Heath, H172. **BBC Symphony** [a]**Chorus and Orchestra / Andrew Davis.** Teldec British Line Ⓕ 4509-94541-2 (64 minutes: DDD: 12/94). *Selected by Sounds in Retrospect.*

...The Planets[a]. **Grainger** The Warriors. [a]women's voices of the **Monteverdi Choir; Philharmonia Orchestra / Sir John Eliot Gardiner.** DG Ⓕ 445 860-2GH (68 minutes: DDD: 8/95). *See review under Grainger; refer to the Index.* Ⓖ

...The Planets. Coupled with works by **Vaughan Williams** and **Walton** BBC Symphony Orchestra / **Sir Adrian Boult.** Beulah mono Ⓜ 2PD12* (70 minutes: ADD: 12/96).

...The Planets (arr. Roberts)[a]. A Moorside Suite, H173. [a]**Hallé Choir; BlackDyke Mills Band / James Watson.** Doyen Master Series Ⓕ DOYCD050 (67 minutes: DDD: 2/97).

...The Planets[a]. St Paul's Suite, H118. [a]women's voices of the **New Queen's Hall Chorus; New Queen's Hall Orchestra / Roy Goodman.** Carlton Classics Ⓕ 30366 00432 (57 minutes: DDD: 4/97).

...The Planets. **Orff** Carmina Burana. **London Voices; London Symphony Orchestra / Richard Hickox.** Carlton Classics LSO Doubles Ⓜ 30368 01107 (two discs: 114 minutes: DDD: 1/98).

Holst Seven Partsongs, H162[a]. A Choral Fantasia, H177[b]. A Dirge for Two Veterans, H121[c]. Ode to Death, H144[d]. [ab]**Patricia Rozario** (sop); [d]**London Symphony Chorus;** [abc]**Joyful Company of Singers; City of London Sinfonia / Richard Hickox.** Chandos Ⓕ CHAN9437 (59 minutes: DDD: 6/96). Texts included. Recorded 1994.

It is the First World War that is the unnamed, ever-felt presence here. "I float this carol with joy, with joy to thee O Death" chants Walt Whitman with that willed mystical intoxication that proved so surprisingly attractive to both Holst and Vaughan Williams, composers who could face reality soberly enough and in Holst's case often with a bleak, spare beauty of sound that takes and bestows only a hard-won comfort. Listening even to the relatively 'light' and partially happy Bridges settings (the *Seven Partsongs*), one becomes aware of a hollow, half-anxious feeling, located in that mysterious area of midriff wherein these undefined apprehensions take their dwelling. With it comes a musician's cherishing of silence, as though the music which intrudes upon it must be most finely attuned if it is to justify the presumption. Death emerges from its temporary hiding place in the seventh ("Assemble, all ye maidens") and then, for the rest of the recital, comes into its kingdom. Most explicitly, the *Dirge for Two Veterans* takes up the "full-keyed bugles" of war, and that was written in the last months of 1914. In the *Ode to Death* (1931) and even the partsongs for women's voices, it is surely the dreadful sadness of that war which fills the hollow places and so, for comfort, enhances the apprehension of beauty in music. The programme has a very special value, and the performances are worthy of it. Comparisons work pretty regularly in favour of Hickox and his forces: in the *Partsongs*, for instance, the admirable Holst Singers are recorded with less sense of presence. With the *Dirge for Two Veterans* the Baccholian Singers with the Philip Jones Brass Ensemble from 1969 have the greater rhythmic vitality. Generally, however, this issue is the one to have.

Additional recommendations ...

...Two Psalms, H117[a]. Six Choruses, H186[a]. The Evening Watch, H159. Seven Partsongs, H162[a]. Nunc dimittis, H127. **Holst Singers and** [a]**Orchestra / Hilary Davan Wetton.** Hyperion Ⓕ CDA66329 (65 minutes: DDD: 1/90).

...The Homecoming, H120. Choral Hymns from the Rig Veda (Group 4), H100 – No. 3, Hymn to Manas. Canons, H187 – No. 3, The Fields of Sorrow; No. 4, David's Lament for Jonathan; No. 6, Truth of all Truth. Choral Folk Songs, H136 – No. 1, I Sowed the Seeds of Love; No. 3, Matthew, Mark, Luke and John; No. 4, The Song of the Blacksmith; No. 5, I Love my Love; No. 6, Swansea Town. Male Choruses, H186 – No. 1, Intercession; No. 2, Good Friday; No. 3, Drinking song; No. 4, A Love Song; No. 6, Before Sleep. A Dirge for Two Veterans. *Coupled with works by various composers.* **London Madrigal Singers / Christopher Bishop; Baccholian Singers of London; Philip Jones Brass Ensemble; English Chamber Orchestra / Ian Humphris.** EMI British Composers Ⓜ CMS5 65123-2 (two discs: 149 minutes: ADD: 2/96). *See review in the Collections section; refer to the Index.*

Holst The Cloud Messenger, Op. 30[a]. The Hymn of Jesus, Op. 37. [a]**Della Jones** (mez);
London Symphony Chorus and Orchestra / Richard Hickox. Chandos Ⓟ CHAN8901
(66 minutes: DDD: 5/91). Texts included. Recorded 1990.

When this CD was first released, the great talking point was *The Cloud Messenger*, a 43-minute work
of considerable imaginative power, virtually forgotten since its disastrous première under the baton of
Holst himself in 1913. It shows the composer already working on an epic scale – something which
casts light on the subsequent eruption of *The Planets*. It is marvellous to have the work on disc,
though it is, as you might expect, uneven. Those who admire the ascetic rigour of Holst's later music
may share the reservations of Imogen Holst and find the score disappointingly 'backward'. There are
certainly echoes of Vaughan Williams's *A Sea Symphony* and several older models. On the other
hand, the glittering approach to the sacred city on Mount Kailasa and the stylized orientalism of the
climactic dance are new to British music; another world, the world of "Venus", is foreshadowed in the
closing pages. The text is Holst's own translation from the Sanskrit. One of the few incontrovertible
masterpieces in Holst's output, the familiar *Hymn of Jesus* has seldom received a better performance
on disc, although the grand acoustics of London's St Jude's impart a certain warm imprecision – the
choral singing itself is splendidly crisp – which can blunt the impact of Holst's acerbic harmonies.

Additional recommendations ...
...The Hymn of Jesus[a]. **Elgar** The Dream of Gerontius[b]. [b]**Yvonne Minton** (mez); [b]**Sir Peter Pears**
(ten); [b]**John Shirley-Quirk** (bar); [b]**Choir of King's College, Cambridge;** [b]**London Symphony Chorus
and Orchestra / Benjamin Britten;** [a]**BBC Chorus and Symphony Orchestra / Sir Adrian Boult.**
Decca London Ⓜ 421 381-2LM2 (two discs: 113 minutes: ADD: 5/89).
...The Hymn of Jesus. *Coupled with works by various composers.* **Huddersfield Choral Society /
Sir Malcolm Sargent.** Dutton Laboratories mono Ⓜ CDAX8012* (75 minutes: ADD: 5/95).
...The Hymn of Jesus, H140[a]. First Choral Symphony, H155[b]. [b]**Felicity Palmer** (sop);
[a]**St Paul's Cathedral Choir;** [a]**London Symphony Chorus;** London Philharmonic [b]**Choir and
Orchestra /** [a]**Sir Charles Groves,** [b]**Sir Adrian Boult.**
EMI British Composers Ⓜ CDM5 65128-2 (72 minutes: ADD: 7/96).

Further listening ...
...A Fugal Concerto. St Paul's Suite. Morris Dance Tunes. Lyric Movement, H191. Brook Green
Suite. **Soloists; New Zealand Chamber Orchestra / Nicoholas Braithwaite.**
Koch International Classics 370582 (4/92).
...A Fugal Concerto. St Paul's Suite. Song without Words, H88. Lyric Movement, H191. Brook
Green Suite. **Soloists; City of London Sinfonia / Richard Hickox.** Chandos CHAN9270 (7/94).
...Invocation, Op. 19/2. *Coupled with works by* **Delius** *and* **Vaughan Williams**
Philharmonia Orchestra / Vernon Handley. RCA Victor Red Seal RD70800 (7/87).
...The Perfect Fool – ballet music. *Coupled with works by various composers.*
London Philharmonic Orchestra / Sir Adrian Boult. Belart mono 461 354-2* (9/97).   Ⓖ
...Two songs without words, H88[a]. Double Violin Concerto, H175[b]. The Golden Goose, H163 –
ballet music[a]. Capriccio for Orchestra, H185[a] (ed. I. Holst). A Fugal Concerto, H152[c].
A Moorside Suite, H173 – Nocturne[c]. Lyric Movement, H191[d]. Brook Green Suite, H190[d].
[c]**William Bennett** (fl); [c]**Peter Graeme** (ob); [b]**Emanuel Hurwitz,** [b]**Kenneth Sillito** (vns);
[d]**Cecil Aronowitz** (va); **English Chamber Orchestra / Imogen Holst.** Lyrita SRCD223 (4/93).
...A Winter Idyll, H31[c]. The Cotswolds, Symphony in F major, H47 – Elegy in memoriam William
Morris[c]. A Song of the Night, H74[ac]. Indra, H66[c]. Invocation for Cello and Orchestra, H75[bc].
Sita – Act 3, Interlude (ed. C. Matthews)[c]. Dances from "The Morning of the Year", H164
(ed. C. Matthews)[c]. The Lure, H149 (ed. C. Matthews and I. Holst)[d]. [a]**Lorraine McAslan** (vn);
[b]**Alexander Baillie** (vc); [c]**London Philharmonic Orchestra;** [d]**London Symphony Orchestra /
David Atherton.** Lyrita SRCD209 (6/93).
...Piano Quintet in A minor H11[b]. Wind Quintet in A flat major, H67[a]. *Coupled with* **Jacob**
Sextet, Op. 3[ab]. **Elysian Wind Quintet;** [b]**Anthony Goldstone** (pf). Chandos CHAN9077 (10/92).
...Short Piano Trio in E major. *Coupled with works by* **Bax** *and* **Stanford** Pirasti Trio.
ASV CDDCA925 (9/95). *See review under Bax; refer to the Index.*
...Toccata on the Northumbrian Pipe Tune, "Newburn Lads". Chrissemas Day in the Morning, on
a tune from "North Country Ballads", Op. 46 No. 1. Two Folk Song Arrangements, Op. 46
No. 2. Nocturne. Jig. Arpeggio Study. Two Pieces. A Piece for Yvonne. Dances (with
Caroline Clemmow, pf). *Coupled with works by* **C. Lambert** Anthony Goldstone (pf).
Chandos CHAN9382 (10/95).
...Choral Hymns from the Rig Veda – Group 3, H99. *Coupled with works by various composers.*
Netherlands Chamber Choir / John Alldis with **Manja Smits** (hp). Globe GLO5170 (2/98).
See review in the Collections section; refer to the Index.
...Partsongs – Ave Maria, H49. Of One that is so Fair, H130. Lullay My Liking, H129. Bring Us in
Good Ale, H131. Diverus and Lazarus, H137. This Have I Done for My True Love, H128. Songs
from The Princess, H80-81. O Spiritual Pilgrim, H188. Welsh Folk Songs, H183 – No. 9, My
Sweetheart's like Venus. Eastern Pictures, H112[c]. Light Leaves Whisper, H20. In Youth is
Pleasure, H76. Choral Folk Songs, H136. Carols, H91[ab]. Jesu, Thou the Virgin-born, H82.
[a]**David Theodore** (ob); [b]**Robert Truman** (vc); [c]**Sioned Williams** (hp); **Holst Singers /
Stephen Layton.** Hyperion CDA66705 (6/94).

...Songs, H174 – Persephone; Now in these Fairylands; A Little Music; The Floral Bandit; The Dream-city; Journey's End. *Coupled with works by various composers.* **Sarah Leonard** (sop); **Malcolm Martineau** (pf). Cala United CACD88016-2 (3/95).

...Sávitri, H96. **Soloists; Richard Hickox Singers; City of London Sinfonia / Richard Hickox.** Hyperion CDA66099 (2/88).

...The Golden Goose, H163. The Morning of the Year, H164. King Estmere, H70. **Guildford Choral Society; Philharmonia Orchestra / Hilary Davan Wetton.** Hyperion CDA66784 (4/96).

...At the Boar's Head[a]. The Wandering Scholar[b]. **Soloists;** [a]**Royal Liverpool Philharmonic Orchestra / David Atherton;** [b]**English Chamber Orchestra / Steuart Bedford.** EMI British Composers CDM5 65127-2 (4/96).

Simon Holt
British 1958

Suggested listening ...
...Banshee. *Coupled with works by* **Birtwistle** and **Maxwell** Melinda Maxwell (ob); **Richard Benjafield** (perc). NMC NMCD042S (10/97). *See review under Birtwistle; refer to the Index.*

Arthur Honegger
Franco/Swiss 1892-1955

Honegger Symphony No. 1. Pastorale d'été. Three symphonic movements – No. 1, "Pacific 231"; No. 2, "Rugby"; No. 3. **Bavarian Radio Symphony Orchestra / Charles Dutoit.** Erato Ⓕ 2292-45242-2 (55 minutes: DDD: 12/86). From NUM75254 (4/86). Recorded 1985. *Selected by Sounds in Retrospect.*

Honegger's First Symphony is a highly impressive work, concisely and effectively constructed in what might be generally described as a neoclassical style; and the scoring is attractive and skilful. His evocation of dawn on a summer's day in *Pastorale d'été*, scored for small orchestra with exquisite, quiet beauty, is surely a miniature masterpiece, and both *Pacific 231* (1924) and *Rugby* (1928) are brilliantly contrived essays in imaginative scoring and the use of cross-rhythms. Honegger was distressed by a critical notion that he was trying to imitate the sound of a steam locomotive and specific moves in a game of rugby: he insisted that the two scores conveyed only a general impression of a train journey and the atmosphere of Colombes stadium. So offended was he that he called the third companion piece merely *Mouvement symphonique No. 3*, but it is a little less effective than its two bedfellows. These vigorous performances are excellent.

Additional recommendations ...
...Symphonies Nos. 1-5. La tempête. Three symphonic movements – Nos. 1 and 3. **Czech Philharmonic Orchestra / Serge Baudo.** Supraphon Ⓕ 11 1566-2 (two discs: 146 minutes: ADD: 9/92).

...La tempête – Prélude. Pastorale d'été. Horace victorieux. Three symphonic movements – Nos. 1 and 2. La traversée des Andes. Le vol sur l'Atlantique. **Toulouse Capitole Orchestra / Michel Plasson.** DG Ⓕ 435 438-2GH (65 minutes: DDD: 9/93). Ⓖ

...Pastorale d'été. Cello Concerto. *Coupled with works by* **Poulenc** Maurice Maréchal (vc); **Paris Conservatoire Orchestra / Arthur Honegger;** [h]**Walther Straram Concerts Orchestra / Walther Straram.** EMI Composers in Person mono Ⓕ CDC5 55036-2* (76 minutes: ADD: 6/94).

...Symphonies Nos. 1-5. Pacific 231. Rugby. **Bavarian Radio Symphony Orchestra / Charles Dutoit.** Teldec Ultima Ⓑ 3984-21340-2 (two discs: 141 minutes: DDD: 5/98).

Honegger Symphonies[a] – No. 2 for Strings and Trumpet obbligato, H153; No. 3, H186, "Liturgique".
Stravinsky Concerto in D[b]. **Berlin Philharmonic Orchestra / Herbert von Karajan.** DG The Originals Ⓜ 447 435-2GOR (72 minutes: ADD: 12/95). Items marked [a] from 2530 068 (7/73), [b]2530 267 (8/72). Recorded 1969. *Gramophone classical 100.* ⒼⒼⒼ

Honegger Symphonies – No. 2; No. 3, "Liturgique". Three symphonic movements – No. 1, "Pacific 231". **Oslo Philharmonic Orchestra / Mariss Jansons.** EMI Ⓕ CDC5 55122-2 (66 minutes: DDD: 7/94). *Gramophone Editor's record of the month.* Ⓖ

Karajan's performances of these Honegger symphonies enjoy legendary status – and rightly so. Both the Second Symphony and the *Symphonie liturgique* are well represented in the current catalogue by a dozen or so versions, but there is no point in mentioning any of them individually as this recording remains in a class of its own for sheer beauty of sound and flawless ensemble. Only one exception need be made: Mariss Jansons and the Oslo Philharmonic, one of the best records of 1994 and arguably the Oslo's best disc to date. The French critic, Bernard Gavoty, once spoke rather flightily of Karajan "transcending emotions and imparting to them that furnace heat that makes a work of genius give off light if brought to the desired temperature" – but it's true! There is a luminous quality and an incandescence about these performances. The Stravinsky Concerto in D major was written within a year of the *Symphonie liturgique* and may perhaps be a little too 'cultured' and not spiky enough for some tastes. The lightness of touch, sprightliness of rhythm and flawless ensemble of the Berlin Philharmonic are a joy in themselves. This disc is a must for every music lover.

Additional recommendations ...

...Nos. 3 and 5. **Danish National Radio Symphony Orchestra / Neeme Järvi.**
Chandos Ⓕ CHAN9176 (57 minutes: DDD: 9/93). ⒼⒼ
...No. 2. *Coupled with works by* **R. Strauss** and **Webern** Seattle Symphony Orchestra Strings /
Gerard Schwarz. Delos Ⓕ DE3121 (71 minutes: DDD: 4/94).
...Nos. 3 and 5. Pastorale d'été. Chant de joie. Pacific 231. **Czech Philharmonic Orchestra /
Serge Baudo.** Supraphon Ⓜ 11 0667-2* (71 minutes: ADD).

Honegger Three Symphonic Movements – No. 1, "Pacific 231"[a]; No. 2, "Rugby"[a].
Milhaud Les choéphores[b].
Roussel Symphony No. 3 in G minor[c]. [b]**Vera Zorina** (spkr); [b]**Irene Jordan**, [b]**Virginia Babikian**
(sops); [b]**McHenry Boatwright** (bar); [b]**Schola Cantorum of New York; New York Philharmonic
Orchestra / Leonard Bernstein.** Sony Classical Masterworks Heritage Ⓜ MHK62352
(74 minutes: ADD: 10/97). Item marked [a] from CBS SBRG72453 (8/66), recorded 1962,
[c]SBRG72281 (11/67), recorded 1961, [b]recorded 1961, new to UK.
Les choéphores is one of Milhaud's most remarkable works and is the second part of Paul Claudel's
translation of the *Oresteia* of Aeschylus. It covers the same events as did Hofmannsthal and Strauss
in *Elektra*. Milhaud's score comprises seven scenes from the Claudel play and is written for large
forces including speaker, soloists, chorus and orchestra. Its use of polytonality, declamation and
choral speech, its boldness and dramatic intensity are striking or as the critic, Alfred Frankenstein is
quoted as saying, "absolutely sensational". *Les choéphores* is an important and exciting piece, and
these artists under Leonard Bernstein's direction give an electrifying account of it. This 1961
recording was never released in the UK, but the Honegger and Roussel pieces were. The late Trevor
Harvey, incidentally, was rather scathing about *Pacific 231* and thought *Rugby* "a horrid but
exceedingly difficult piece, here given a really virtuoso performance". The strident, over-resonant
recording may have taken its toll on Harvey's patience. It has been much improved in this transfer.
Bernstein's exhilarating account of the Roussel masterpiece was originally issued with Messiaen's
Trois petites liturgies de la Présence Divine on the reverse side. Felix Aprahamian complained of the
"rasp on the strings" and the studio reverberation; remastering has resulted in a distinct improvement:
there is greater clarity of texture and the strident edge on the upper strings has been tamed. The
presentation is exemplary.

Honegger Jeanne d'Arc au bûcher. **Françoise Pollet, Michèle Command** (sops); **Nathalie Stutzman**
(contr); **John Aler** (ten); **Marthe Keller, Georges Wilson, Pierre-Marie Escourrou, Paola Lenzi**
(narrs); **Chorus and Children's Voices of French Radio; French National Orchestra / Seiji Ozawa.**
DG Ⓕ 429 412-2GH (69 minutes: DDD: 4/91). Text and translations included.
Recorded live in 1989. *Selected by Sounds in Retrospect.* Ⓖ
Honegger described *Joan of Arc at the stake* as a "dramatic oratorio", but it is a work almost
impossible to categorize, the two chief characters – Joan and Brother Dominc – being speaking parts,
but with a chorus, a children's chorus, and a curiously constituted orchestra including saxophones
instead of horns, two pianos and, most notably, an ondes martenot which, with its banshee shriek,
bloodcurdlingly reinforces the climax as Joan breaks her earthly chains. The action is partly realistic,
partly symbolic, unfolding in quasi-cinematic flashbacks. The musical techniques and styles employed
by Honegger are extraordinarily varied, with humming and shouting besides singing, and with
elements of polyphony, folk-song, baroque dances and jazz rhythms; yet all is fused together in a
remarkable way to produce a work of gripping power and, in the final scenes, almost intolerable
emotional intensity: the beatific *envoi* "Greater love hath no man ..." is a passage that catches the
throat and haunts the mind. Ozawa fully captured the work's dramatic forces in this public
performance, which has been skilfully served by the recording engineers; Marthe Keller vividly
portrays Joan's bewilderment, fervour and agony, John Aler makes a swaggering Procus, and
Françoise Pollet is radiant-voiced as the Virgin. Even more than *Le Roi David*, this is Honegger's
masterpiece.

Further listening ...

...Concerto da camera. *Coupled with works by various composers.* **Jennifer Stinton** (fl);
Geoffrey Browne (cor ang); **Scottish Chamber Orchestra / Steuart Bedford.**
Collins Classics 1210-2 (8/91). *See review in the Collections section; refer to the Index.*
...Crime et Châtiment – Suite[a]. Le Déserteur ou Je t'attendrai. Farinet ou L'Or dans la Montagne –
Suite. le Grand Barrage. L'Idée. [a]**Jacques Tchamkerten** (ondes martenot);
Bratislava Radio Symphony Orchestra / Adriano. Marco Polo 8 223466 (6/94).
...Le dit des jeux du monde. *Coupled with works by* **Fumet** and **d'Indy** Jean Ferrandis (fl);
Hervé Noël (tpt); **Jean-Jacques Wiederker Chamber Orchestra / Frédéric Bouaniche.**
Koch Schwann 310652 (6/95). *See review under d'Indy; refer to the Index.*
...Les misérables – film score. **Bratislava Radio Symphony Orchestra / Adriano.**
Marco Polo 8 223181 (3/91).
...Clarinet Sonatina, H42. *Coupled with works by various composers.* **Jonathan Cohler** (cl);
Judith Gordon (pf). Crystal CD733 (5/95).
...Petit cours de morale, H148. *Coupled with works by various composers.* **Frederica von Stade** (mez);
Martin Katz (pf). RCA Victor Red Seal 09026 62711-2 (4/95).

...Les aventures du roi Pausole. **Soloists; Basle Madrigalists; Swiss Youth Philharmonic Orchestra /
Mario Venzago.** MGB Musiques Suisses CD6115 (9/94).

...Le Roi David. **Soloists; Philippe Cailard Chorale; instrumental ensemble / Charles Dutoit.**
Erato 2292-45800-2.

James Hook   British 1746-1827

Suggested listening ...

...Voluntary in C minor. *Coupled with works by various composers.* **Jennifer Bate** (org).
Unicorn-Kanchana DKPCD9106 (11/91). *Selected by Sounds in Retrospect. See review in the
Collections section; refer to the Index.*

Peter Hope   British 1930

Suggested listening ...

...The ring of Kerry – No. 1, Jaunting car. *Coupled with works by various composers.*
Light Music Society Orchestra / Sir Vivian Dunn. EMI British Composers CDM5 66537-2 (1/98).
See review in the Collections section; refer to the Index.

Mervyn Horder   1910-1997

Suggested listening ...

...White in the Moon. *Coupled with works by various composers.* **Anthony Rolfe Johnson** (ten);
Graham Johnson (pf). Hyperion CDA66471/2 (8/95). *See review in the Collections section;
refer to the Index.*

Joseph Horowitz   Austrian/British 1926

Suggested listening ...

...Variations on a Theme from Bizet's "Carmen". *Coupled with works by various composers.*
Arcadi Volodos (pf). Sony Classical SK62691 (10/97). *Gramophone Editor's choice.*
Selected by Soundings. See review in the Collections section; refer to the Index.   🅖🅖

Jacques Hotteterre   French 1674-1763

Hotteterre L'art de préluder – D major; G major; B minor; C major; C minor; G minor.
Première livre – Suite No. 3 in G major[a]. Deuxième livre – Suite No. 1 in G minor; Suite No. 2
in C minor[a]. Airs et Brunettes – Rochers, je ne veux point que votre eco fidelle; J'ay passé
deux jours sans vous voir; Dans ces deserts paisibles; Pourquoy, doux rossignol; Le beau
berger Tircis[a]. **Wilbert Hazelzet** (fl); [a]**Jaap ter Linden** (va da gamba); [a]**Konrad Junghänel**
(theorbo); [a]**Jacques Ogg** (hpd). Glossa Ⓔ GCD920801 (76 minutes: DDD: 3/97). 🖉
Recorded 1996.

At first sight a disc offering 76 minutes of music by the influential but not generally fêted French
baroque flautist, composer and teacher Jacques Martin Hotteterre can look like the kind of release
guaranteed to try many a listener's patience. Not so, however, when the musicianship on display is as
refined and thoughtful as that of the Dutchman, Wilbert Hazelzet, who here treats us to an enjoyable
programme of *préludes*, suites and song arrangements from a spread of Hotteterre's publications,
ranging from 1708 to 1723. Hazelzet plays on a copy of a flute made by a member of the Hotteterre
family itself (clearly this was a clan with wind-playing in their veins), and its unusually dark and fruity
sound is well matched to the music which, though it offers its fair share of lively moments, often
shows in addition a melancholy side which can be deeply moving. Try the haunting, brooding C minor
Suite on this disc, and see if you can still dismiss it as the product of a dry pedagogue. Hazelzet's
eloquent, unshowy playing does the music nothing less than excellent service, and he is helped by
discreet and nicely varied continuo accompaniments. This is an exquisite and surprising release, which
also happens to be one of the most attractively packaged discs of recent years. It should be a treat to
own.

Joachim van den Hove   Dutch 1567-1620

Suggested listening ...

...Pavana lachrimae. *Coupled with works by various composers.* **Paul O'Dette** (lte).
Harmonia Mundi HMU90 7164 (7/97). *See review under Dowland; refer to the Index.*

Alan Hovhaness

American 1911

Hovhaness Khrimian Hairig, Op. 49[a]. The Holy City, Op. 218[a]. Psalm and Fugue, Op. 40*a*.
Kohar, Op. 66. Symphony No. 17, Op. 203, "Symphony for Metal Orchestra".
[a]**Chris Gekker** (tpt); **Manhattan Chamber Orchestra / Richard Auldon Clark.**
Koch International Classics Ⓕ 37289-2 (53 minutes: DDD: 12/96). Recorded 1995.
The lengthiest offering here (at just over 20 minutes) is the *Symphony for Metal Orchestra* (the
seventeenth of Hovhaness's 67 symphonies to date) which was composed in 1963 shortly after a visit
to Japan. Scored for the singular combination of six flutes, three trombones and metallic percussion,
its four contemplative movements incorporate elements of Japanese gagaku music together with
sounds inspired by the Shó (a Japanese mouth-organ, here imitated by the flutes). Rather more
rewarding is *The Holy City*, a highly evocative, nine-and-a-half-minute essay for trumpet, harp,
chimes and strings dating from 1967 and full of atmospheric sonorities. Chris Gekker is the superb
trumpet soloist both here and in the serene, yet deceptively purposeful *Khrimian Hairig* (composed in
1944 and revised four years later), which takes its name from "a heroic Armenian priest" (though the
accompanying note doesn't reveal what the heroic deed was). The glowing string textures in the *Psalm
and Fugue* (1941) cast quite a spell, as do the hypnotic, mantra-like melodic lines of *Kohar* (1946),
another Armenian-inspired creation, scored for flute, cor anglais, timpani and strings. Richard
Auldon Clark and his New York group give outstandingly sympathetic performances. Really excellent
sound, too.

Hovhaness Symphony No. 2, Op. 132[a], "Mysterious Mountain".
Prokofiev Lieutenant Kijé – Suite, Op. 60[b].
Stravinsky Divertimento from "La baiser de la fée"[a]. **Chicago Symphony Orchestra / Fritz Reiner.**
RCA Victor Living Stereo Ⓜ 09026 61957-2 (64 minutes: ADD: 9/95). Items marked [a] new to
UK, [b]VICS1280 (2/68). Recorded 1957-58.
Reiner's mastery is everywhere in evidence, from the hymn-like cadences of Hovhaness's wholesome
though skilfully crafted Symphony to the fairy-tale excitement of *Kijé*'s "Troika". The Chicago
Symphony play like a generously augmented chamber ensemble, with delicately tapered strings, sweet-
toned woodwinds, impeccable brass (surely the most subtly voiced horns on disc) and a rhythmically
alert but never overzealous percussion section. Reiner's Straussian credentials are particularly telling
wherever musical lines converge – in Hovhaness's discursive celesta/harp embellishments, for example,
or the dreamlike review in *Kijé*'s "Burial" – while the *Fairy's Kiss* "Divertimento" has a positively
Mozartian elegance. Try, by way of sampling-points, Stravinsky's "Scherzo" and "Pas de deux"; or, if
you've ever doubted Reiner's capacity for tenderness, put on the closing half-minute of *Kijé*'s
"Romance". There's impressive virtuosity, too – especially in the Nielsenesque string flurries that
open Hovhaness's hectic *Allegro vivo*. Musically, this is a superb programme and the performance of
Mysterious Mountain – an American 'classic' – is unmissable. Similarly, the Stravinsky is in a class of
its own and *Lieutenant Kijé* is superbly executed. This RCA Living Stereo transfer is fairly good, save
for a momentary tape glitch 0'47" into Hovhaness's opening *Andante* and a fair degree of tape noise.
The overall sound is more hollow than one remembers from the old LPs, but there's ample clarity and
impressive channel separation. All in all, in a priceless CD – certainly from a musical stand-point.
Additional recommendations ...
…"Mysterious Mountain". Lousadzak, Op. 48[a]. **L. Harrison** Symphony No. 2, "Elegiac".
[a]**Keith Jarrett** (pf); **American Composers Orchestra / Dennis Russell Davies.**
MusicMasters Ⓕ 7021-2 (67 minutes: DDD: 5/93).
…"Mysterious Mountain". Prayer of St Gregory, Op. 62*b*. Prelude and Quadruple Fugue, Op. 128.
And God Created Great Whales, Op. 229 No. 1. Alleluia and Fugue, Op. 40*b*. Celestial Fantasy,
Op. 44. **Seattle Symphony Orchestra / Gerard Schwarz.** Delos Ⓕ DE3157 (63 minutes: DDD:
7/94).

Hovhaness Four Bagatelles, Op. 30. String Quartets – No. 1, Op. 8, "Jupiter"; No. 3, Op. 208
No. 1, "Reflections on my Childhood"; No. 4, Op. 208 No. 2, "The Ancient Tree". Suite from
String Quartet No. 2 – Gamelan in Sosi Style; Spirit Murmur; Hymn.
Z. Long Song of the Ch'in. **Shanghai Quartet** (WeiGang Li, HongGang Li, vns; Zheng Wang, va;
James Wilson, vc). Delos Ⓕ DE3162 (69 minutes: DDD: 3/95). Recorded 1994.   ⒼⒼ
The likeable First Quartet of 1936 boasts, like Mozart's *Jupiter* Symphony, a four-part fugue of
impressive rigour (hence the work's subtitle). In fact, this movement, along with the opening
"Prelude", was later reworked into for full orchestra into the *Prelude and Quadruple Fugue*, whilst the
vigorous fugue with which the quartet closes also crops up again in the latter half of the middle
movement of the Second Symphony, *Mysterious Mountain*. Next come three out of the seven pithy
movements that comprise the Second Quartet from 1952: the concluding "Hymn" is a particularly
affecting creation. Both the Third and Fourth Quartets share the same opus number (208) and were
inspired by childhood memories. The former basks in a soothing, supplicatory glow, with occasional
touches of Eastern promise (aural reminders of the composer's Armenian roots), whereas its more
nostalgic companion is a sweetly lyrical essay of beguiling euphony and striking resonance. Delos's
collection begins with the haunting, perfectly crafted *Four Bagatelles* (delightful miniatures, these)
and ends with *Song of the Ch'in* by the Chinese composer, Zhou Long: the 'ch'in' is a traditional

Chinese zither and this imaginative, fastidiously conceived piece from 1985 attempts to convey the piquant sounds of that ancient instrument through the 'modern' medium of the string quartet. These are consistently pure-toned, beautifully rapt performances from the talented young Shanghai Quartet, and Delos's sound is warm and true to match.

Further listening ...
...And God Created Great Whales, Op. 229 No. 1. Concerto No. 8, Op. 117. Elibris, Op. 50[a]. Alleluia and Fugue, Op. 40*b*. Anahid, Op. 57. [a]**Christine Messiter** (fl); **Philharmonia Orchestra / David Amos.** Crystal CD810 (4/95).
...Mountains and Rivers without End, Op. 225. Symphony No. 6, Op. 173, "The Celestial Gate". Prayer of St Gregory, Op. 62*b*[a]. Haroutiun, Op. 71 – Aria[a]. Return and Rebuild the Desolate Places, Op. 213[a]. [a]**Chris Gekker** (tpt); **Manhattan Chamber Orchestra / Richard Auldon Clark.** Koch International Classics 37221-2 (7/94).
...Requiem and Resurrection, Op. 224[a]. Symphony No. 19, Op. 217, "Vishnu"[b]. [a]**North Jersey Wind Symphony Orchestra;** [b]**Sevan Philharmonic Orchestra / Alan Hovhaness.** Crystal CD805 (4/95).
...Symphonies – No. 22, Op. 236, "City of Light"[a]; No. 50, Op. 360, "Mount St Helens"[b]. **Seattle Symphony Orchestra /** [a]**Alan Hovhaness;** [b]**Gerard Schwarz.** Delos DE3137 (12/93). *Gramophone Editor's choice. Selected by Sounds in Retrospect.*
...Symphonies – No. 39, Op. 321[a]; No. 46, Op. 347, "To the Green Mountains". *Coupled with* **Traditional** (arr. Kim Hee-jo) Milyang Arirang. [a]**Michael Long** (gtr); **KBS Symphony Orchestra / Vakhtang Jordania.** Koch International Classics 37208-2.

Herbert Howells
British 1892-1983

Howells Suite for Orchestra, "The B's". Three Dances[a]. In Green Ways[b]. [b]**Yvonne Kenny** (sop); [a]**Lydia Mordkovitch** (vn); **London Symphony Orchestra / Richard Hickox.** Chandos Ⓟ CHAN9557 (65 minutes: DDD: 12/97). Text and translation included. Recorded 1996. *Selected by Soundings.*
Both *The B's* (1914) and *Three Dances* (1915) are products of Howells's student days, when he was one of Stanford's favourite pupils at London's Royal College of Music. The former is a delightful orchestral suite celebrating Howells's circle of closest friends there. Each of the five movements bears as its subtitle the nickname of each: the "Overture" ("Bublum") is a swaggering self-portrait of Howells himself, and it's followed by a ravishing "Lament" ("Bartholomew" – Ivor Gurney), a "Scherzo" ("Blissy" – Arthur Bliss), a stately "'Mazurka' alias 'Minuet'" ("Bunny" – Francis Purcell Warren; a highly promising viola player who died at Mons) and a concluding rumbustious "March" ("Benjee" – Arthur Benjamin). As with so many of Howells's student offerings, the infectious confidence and sheer craft on show are remarkable. Richard Hickox and a finely prepared LSO turn in a big-hearted display, ripely captured by the Chandos engineers. Completed just a couple of months after *The B's*, the *Three Dances* for violin and orchestra reveal a similarly assured touch and engaging charm. *In Green Ways* exists in two versions, one with piano and another with orchestral backing. It takes its name from a collection of poetry by James Stephens, whose poem "The Goat Paths" forms the emotional kernel of the whole sequence in Howells's sublime treatment. Yvonne Kenny sings radiantly, with Hickox and the LSO as model partners. Chandos's airy recording complements another hugely enjoyable addition to Hickox's ongoing Howells series.

Additional recommendation ...
...Piano Concerto No. 2 in C minor[a]. Three Dances[b]. Concerto for Strings. [a]**Kathryn Stott** (pf); [b]**Malcolm Stewart** (vn); **Royal Liverpool Philharmonic Orchestra / Vernon Handley.** Hyperion Ⓟ CDA66610 (69 minutes: DDD: 3/93). Ⓖ

Howells King's Herald. Paradise Rondel. Fantasia[a]. Threnody[a]. Pastoral Rhapsody. Procession. [a]**Moray Welsh** (vc); **London Symphony Orchestra / Richard Hickox.** Chandos Ⓟ CHAN9410 (58 minutes: DDD: 3/96). Recorded 1995. *Gramophone Editor's choice.*
This delightful and moving disc offers a whole sequence of orchestral works which, for whatever reason, Howells hid from the world. One reason he was shy about offering such music for performance was that it often involved such deeply personal feelings. One remembers his reluctance even to allow the most ambitious of his works, the *Hymnus Paradisi*, to be performed, and here the two *concertante* works for cello similarly reflect Howells's anguish over the death of his ten-year-old son. He wrote the longer and more complex of the two, the *Fantasia*, in 1936-37, when he was still in deep mourning, and though the predominant mood is elegiac, with occasional echoes of the Elgar Cello Concerto, there are understandable flashes of violence and anger. The *Threnody* was sketched rather earlier, and is given here in the orchestration made by Christopher Palmer for the Howells centenary concert in 1992. More direct in style and structure, it is an effective pendant to the *Fantasia*, with the two movements together forming a rhapsodic concerto lasting almost half an hour. The other major piece is the *Pastoral Rhapsody* (1923), more conventionally English except for a radiant climax with anglicized echoes of *Daphnis* and *Petrushka*. In his note Lewis Foreman speculates that Howells may have allowed the piece to be forgotten after a couple of performances, feeling that Vaughan Williams's *Pastoral Symphony* was too close a model. In fact the *Rhapsody* is totally distinct, and so is the *Paradise Rondel*, named after a Cotswold village, a generally vigorous movement dating from 1925, which over a shorter span is full of sharp contrasts, including one passage

which in its addition of a piano offers clear echoes of the "Russian Dance" from *Petrushka*. Helped by rich, atmospheric sound, Richard Hickox draws performances both brilliant and warmly persuasive from the LSO, with Moray Welsh a movingly expressive soloist in the *concertante* works.

Howells Phantasy Quartet, Op. 25. String Quartet, "In Gloucestershire".
Delius String Quartet. **Britten Quartet** (Peter Manning, Keith Pascoe, vns; Peter Lale, va; Andrew Shulman, vc). EMI British Composers Ⓟ CDC5 55349-2 (73 minutes: DDD: 4/97).
This is chamber-music playing of exquisite poise and remarkable dedication. One of Stanford's star pupils at the RCM, Herbert Howells composed a wealth of outstanding music in his student years, not least the extraordinarily mature *Mass in the Dorian Mode* (1912), Piano Quartet (1916) as well as the present *Phantasy Quartet* (1917). The work won that same year's Cobbett Competition. The Britten Quartet accord the piece the blistering advocacy it deserves and reveal it as the youthful masterpiece it surely is. Far too long overlooked, Howells's *In Gloucestershire* is full of glorious nature music, yet always displays a formidable craft and organization. Of its four movements, the most personal comprises the deeply felt third (possibly another expression of Howells's grief in memory of his son, Michael, who was struck down by polio at the tender age of nine in 1935). The Britten Quartet deliver a reading of uncommon fervour, insight (listen to the way they gauge that sudden poignant switch from joyous revelry to darkness at the height of the finale) and thrilling (but never self-aware) technical brilliance. And what of the Delius Quartet? Amazingly, just one other version of this endearing piece is currently available, a satisfyingly straightforward rendering from the Brodsky Quartet in their pre-designer ASV days. Truth to tell, both the Brodsky and Britten give pleasure in their different ways, the latter perhaps having the edge in terms of beguiling flow and unanimity. Recording and balance throughout seem just about perfect.
Additional recommendation ...
...Phantasy Quartet. Piano Quartet in A minor, Op. 21[a]. Rhapsodic Quintet, Op. 31[b].
[b]**Michael Collins** (cl); [a]**Andrew West** (pf); **Lyric Quartet.**
Metier Ⓟ MSVCD92003 (52 minutes: DDD: 10/93).

Howells Organ Sonata No. 2. Six Pieces (1940-45). **Graham Barber** (org). Priory Ⓟ PRCD524 (67 minutes: DDD: 4/97). Played on the organ of Hereford Cathedral.
These are powerful and authoritative performances which ooze the spirit of Howells – that odd mixture of emotional detachment with a hint of deep personal passion, an undercurrent of tragedy and an almost improvisatory fluidity of structure. With Stephen Cleobury (who recorded the first disc in Priory's Howells series, listed further on) the music is a little difficult to extract from the atmosphere. That's not a problem with Barber, largely because his programme is rather more openly communicative than Cleobury's; the Sonata has a formal structure which makes it easy to follow while the *Six Pieces* present such a kaleidoscopic array of organ colours that the ear is continually enchanted. The Hereford organ is a lovely instrument. Certainly Priory have, in focusing their microphones on the organ, expunged much of the building's aural ambience, but the sound is an utter delight to the ear.

Howells Requiem[a]. Take him, earth, for cherishing.
Martin Mass for Double Chorus. [a]**Sally Barber** (sop); [a]**Julia Field** (mez); [a]**Mark Johnstone** (ten); [a]**Andrew Angus** (bass); **Vasari / Jeremy Backhouse.** Cala United Ⓟ CACD88033 (56 minutes: DDD: 12/94). Recorded 1994.   Ⓖ
Both pieces here are private works, not really intended for performance. Howells wrote the Requiem to exorcize his grief at the death of his son, and only at the very end of his life allowed it to be published. Martin described his Mass as "something between God and myself, and of no concern to anyone else". It should ideally be premièred, he thought, in a liturgical context and anonymously, though he wryly reflected that any such mystification would merely draw unsuitable attention to it; so he kept it to himself for close on 40 years. Both now look like crucial works in each composer's development. Howells's Requiem is not only the source of his masterpiece, the *Hymnus Paradisi*, but also of much that is characteristic in his later music, its radiance (sometimes shadowed) and its long expressive lines. Martin's Mass is not only a research laboratory into the problems of setting religious texts (how he enjoys 'dramatizing' the various sections of the *Credo*, using elaborate choral coloratura in the *Gloria*, inventing a surprising but effective staccato imagery to convey a heaven and earth filled with dazzling glory in the *Sanctus*!) but also into the neo-classical element that seasoned his later serialism. Although they make a fascinating coupling, they demand quite different types of singing; so again does Howells's much later motet, with its more public gestures and its broader span. Vasari succeed admirably. The difficulties of the Howells Requiem are exemplified in the image of light (a wonderful Howells chord, needing absolutely precise pitching and balance) and the expressive intensification of line that follows it in the fifth movement. It is beautifully done, but the singers also have the athletic virtuosity for Martin's twining melismas, the hurtling excitement of his "et resurrexit". This is choral singing of a high order, given a very spacious and natural recording.
Additional recommendations ...
...Requiem. Take him, earth, for cherishing. *Coupled with works by* **Vaughan Williams**
Mary Seers (sop); **Michael Chance** (alto); **Philip Salmon** (ten); **Jonathan Best** (bass); **Corydon Singers / Matthew Best.** Hyperion Ⓟ CDA66076 (60 minutes: ADD: 10/87).
See review under Vaughan Williams; refer to the Index.   ⒼⒼ

...Requiem. A Sequence for St Michael. The House of the Mind. *Coupled with works by*
Vaughan Williams Finzi Singers / Paul Spicer with **Harry Bickett** (org).
Chandos Ⓕ CHAN9019 (67 minutes: DDD: 5/92).

...Requiem. *Coupled with works by various composers.* **Netherlands Chamber Choir / John Alldis.**
Globe Ⓕ GLO5170 (59 minutes: DDD: 2/98). *See review in the Collections section;*
refer to the Index.

Further listening ...

...Violin Sonatas – No. 1, Op. 18; No. 2, Op. 26; No. 3, Op. 38. Cradle Song, Op. 9 No. 1. Three
Pieces, Op. 28. **Paul Barritt** (vn); **Catherine Edwards** (pf). Hyperion Ⓕ CDA66665 (3/94).

...Gadabout. Three Pieces, Op. 14. Sonatina. *Coupled with works by* **Stevens Jeremy Filsell** (pf).
Guild GMCD7119 (11/96). *See review under Stevens; refer to the Index.*

...Lambert's Clavichord, Op. 41. Howells' Clavichord, Books 1 and 2. **John McCabe** (pf).
Hyperion CDA66689 (8/94). *Gramophone Editor's choice.*

...Three Psalm-Preludes, Set 1, Op. 32. Three Psalm-Preludes, Set 2. Three Rhapsodies, Op. 17.
Rhapsody No. 4 in C major. **Stephen Cleobury** (org). Priory PRCD480 (6/95).

...Behold, O God our defender[a]. Three Carol-Anthems. Te Deum[a]. The Scribe. Thee will I love[a].
Blessed are the dead. Even such is time. Inheritance. Haec dies. God is gone up[a]. **Finzi Singers /**
Paul Spicer with [a]**Andrew Lumsden** (org). Chandos CHAN9458 (7/96). *Selected by Soundings.*

...Collegium Regale – Te Deum; Jubilate. *Coupled with works by various composers.*
Norwich Cathedral Choir / Michael Nicholas with **Neil Taylor** (org). Priory PRCD470 (10/94).

...A Dirge. *Coupled with works by various composers.* **London Madrigal Singers / Christopher Bishop;**
Baccholian Singers of London; Philip Jones Brass Ensemble; English Chamber Orchestra / Ian
Humphris. EMI British Composers CMS5 65123-2 (2/96). *See review in the Collections section;*
refer to the Index.

...Evening Service in G major. *Coupled with works by various composers.* **Lichfield Cathedral Choir /**
Andrew Lumsden with **Mark Shepherd, Nigel Potts** (orgs).
Priory PRCD505 (10/95). *See review in the Collections section; refer to the Index.*

...Evening Service in G major. *Coupled with works by various composers.* **Bristol Cathedral Choir /**
Christopher Brayne with **Ian Ball** (org).
Priory PRCD528 (8/96). *See review in the Collections section; refer to the Index.*

...Gavotte. Come sing and dance. King David. Girl's Song, Op. 22 No. 4. *Coupled with works by*
various composers. **Sarah Leonard** (sop); **Malcolm Martineau** (pf).
Cala United CACD88016-2 (3/95).

...Hymnus Paradisi[a]. An English Mass. [a]**Julie Kennard** (sop); [a]**John Mark Ainsley** (ten);
Royal Liverpool Philharmonic Choir and Orchestra / Vernon Handley. Hyperion CDA66488 (5/92).

...An Old Man's Lullaby[c]. Here she Lies[c]. O Garlands, Hanging by the Doors[c]. Two South African
Settings[b]. Upon a Summer's Day[b]. By the Hearth-stone[b]. Blaweary[b]. Three Folksongs[ad]. Sweet
Content[a]. A Garland for De la Mare[bcd]. Peacock Pie, Op. 33[d]. Four French Chansons, Op. 29[a].
In Green Ways, Op. 43[a]. Old Meg[a]. Three Children's Songs[a]. Four Songs, Op. 22[b]. Lost love[b].
O My Deir Hert[b]. Come Sing and Dance[b]. A Mugger's Song[d]. The Little Boy Lost[d]. The Restful
Branches[d]. Mally O![d]. Old Skinflint[d]. King David[d]. Gavotte[c]. Flood[c]. Goddess of the Night[c].
[a]**Lynne Dawson,** [b]**Catherine Pierard** (sops); [c]**John Mark Ainsley** (ten); [d]**Benjamin Luxon** (bar);
Julius Drake (pf). Chandos CHAN9185/6 (8/94). **Ⓖ**

...Mass in the Dorian Mode. Salve regina. O salutaris Hostia. Sweetest of Sweets. Come, My Soul.
Let All the World in Every Corner Sing. Nunc dimittis. Regina caeli. *Coupled with* **Stevens**
Mass for double choir. **Finzi Singers / Paul Spicer.** Chandos CHAN9021 (12/92).

...Missa Sabrinensis. **Janice Watson** (sop); **Della Jones** (mez); **Martyn Hill** (ten); **Donald Maxwell**
(bar); **London Symphony Chorus and Orchestra / Gennadi Rozhdestvensky.**
Chandos CHAN9348 (6/95). *Gramophone Editor's choice.*

...Salve regina. *Coupled with works by various composers.* **Choir of St Mary's Cathedral, Edinburgh /**
Timothy Byram-Wigfield. Priory PRCD557 (10/97). *See review in the Collections section;*
refer to the Index.

...Stabat mater. **Neill Archer** (ten); **London Symphony Chorus and Orchestra /**
Gennadi Rozhdestvensky. Chandos CHAN9314 (1/95).

Johann Hummel

Austrian 1778-1837

Hummel Concertino in G major, Op. 73. Piano Concerto No. 5 in A flat major, Op. 113.
Gesellschafts Rondo in D major, Op. 117. **London Mozart Players / Howard Shelley** (pf).
Chandos Ⓕ CHAN9558 (59 minutes: DDD: 1/98). Recorded 1997.
Although the music here is less enticing and substantial than Stephen Hough's *Gramophone* Award-
winning disc – the performances less exuberantly virtuosic and elegantly inflected – these are decorous
rarities played with an assured brilliance and affection. Hummel's Mozartian rather than
Chopinesque bias declares itself most obviously in his Op. 73 *Concertino*, though even here the
figuration has a recognizably Hummelian froth and sparkle. Too charming to be vacuous, such
surface brio has little in common with Mozart's depth and subtlety, and for music of greater romantic
range and ambition we turn to the A flat major Concerto, with its fuller scoring and lavishly

decorated solo part. Lovers of a finespun, operatic cantilena will warm to the central "Romanze". The *Gesellschafts Rondo* (offered here in a première recording) commences in solemn *Adagio* vein before turning to a more typically bustling and ceremonious *Vivace*. It may be that Hummel "puffed, blew and perspired" when he played but he won the admiration of Chopin (a hard master to please and one who turned Hummel's animation to rare poetic advantage) and his sheer style is infectious when projected with such unfailing expertise by Howard Shelley in his dual role as pianist and conductor of the London Mozart Players. The recordings are exceptionally well balanced, the acoustic pleasingly spacious.

Additional recommendation ...
...Concertino[a]. La Galante in E major (Rondo), Op. 120[b]. Bassoon Concerto in F major[c]. Septet militaire in C major, Op. 114[d]. [a]**Martin Galling** (pf); [c]**George Zuckerman** (bn); [ab]**Berlin Symphony Orchestra / Carl-August Bünte;** [cd]**Württemberg Chamber Orchestra / Jörg Faerber.**
Carlton Classics Turnabout Ⓑ 30371 0009-2 (77 minutes: ADD: 10/96).

Hummel Piano Concertos – A minor, Op. 85; B minor, Op. 89. **Stephen Hough** (pf);
English Chamber Orchestra / Bryden Thomson. Chandos Ⓕ CHAN8507
(66 minutes: DDD: 4/87). *Gramophone Award Winner 1987.*   ⒼⒼ
This is a staggering disc of Hummel's piano concertos played by Stephen Hough. The most obvious comparison is with the piano concertos of Chopin, but whereas those works rely on the grace and panache of the piano line to redeem an often lacklustre orchestral role, the Hummel works have finely conceived orchestral writing and certainly no shortage of original ideas. The piano part is formidable, combining virtuosity of a very high order indeed with a vigour and athleticism that does much to redress Hummel's somewhat tarnished reputation. The A minor Concerto is probably the better known of the two works here, with a thrilling rondo finale, but the B minor is no less inventive with some breath-taking writing in the piano's upper registers. This disc makes strong demands to be heard: inventive and exciting music, a masterly contribution from Stephen Hough, fine orchestral support from the ever sympathetic ECO under Thomson and, last but not least, a magnificent Chandos recording.

Hummel Piano Trios – E flat major, Op. 12; G major, Op. 35; G major, Op. 65; E flat major, Op. 96. **Beaux Arts Trio** (Ida Kavafian, vn; Peter Wiley, vc; Menahem Pressler, pf). Philips Ⓕ 446 077-2PH (69 minutes: DDD: 2/98). Recorded 1996. *Gramophone Editor's choice.*   Ⓖ
These are delightful, intelligent and witty performances of some very attractive music. The Op. 12 work is fresh and untroubled, taking delight in the easy mastery of counterpart that was one of Hummel's qualities, and the Beaux Arts Trio play it with a lively sense of enjoyment that suits it ideally. Hummel was not a profound composer, but he was an immensely talented one and the variety of his invention is remarkable. He never forgot Mozart, as can be heard in the G major Trio of 1811, and he kept an ear on current developments without changing his essentially classical approach to music. Romantic ideas were accommodated rather than imitated or seriously taken up. The Beaux Arts players understand the balance well, and do excellent justice to all these works. There is a great deal of pleasure to be had from these engaging performances of some charming music.

Additional recommendations ...
...Op. 12; F major, Op. 22; G major, Op. 35; G major, Op. 65; Op. 83; E flat major, Op. 93; Op. 96.
Parnassua Trio. Dabringhaus und Grimm Ⓕ L3307/08 (two discs: 120 minutes: DDD: 6/93).
...E flat major, Op. 12; E major, Op. 83; E flat major, Op. 96. **Borodin Trio.**
Chandos Ⓕ CHAN9529 (67 minutes: DDD: 6/97).

Further listening ...
...Trumpet Concerto in E flat major. *Coupled with works by various composers.*
Håkan Hardenberger (tpt); **Academy of St Martin in the Fields / Sir Neville Marriner.**
Philips 420 203-2PH (12/87). *See review in the Collections section; refer to the Index.*
...Trumpet Concerto in E flat major. *Coupled with works by various composers.* **Sergei Nakariakov**
(tpt); **Lausanne Chamber Orchestra / Jésus López-Cobos.** Teldec 4509-90846-2 (10/93).
See review in the Collections section; refer to the Index.
...Trumpet Concerto in E flat major. *Coupled with works by various composers.* **John Wallace** (tpt);
Philharmonia Orchestra / Christopher Warren-Green. Nimbus NI7016 (2/95). *See review in the Collections section; refer to the Index.*
...Trumpet Concerto in E flat major. *Coupled with works by various composers.* **Maurice André** (tpt);
Franz Liszt Chamber Orchestra / János Rolla. EMI CDC5 55231-2 (7/95).
...Trumpet Concerto in E flat major. *Coupled with works by various composers.* **Timofei Dokshitzer**
(tpt); **Moscow Chamber Orchestra / Rudolf Barshai.** Melodiya 74321 32045-2 (2/97).   Ⓖ
...Clarinet Quintet in E flat major. *Coupled with works by* **Reicha** and **Weber Charles Neidich** (cl);
L'Archibudelli. Sony Classical SK57968 (9/95). 🗲
...Septet in D minor, Op. 74. *Coupled with* **Berwald** Septet in B flat major. **Nash Ensemble.**
CRD CRD3344 (6/89).
...Violin/Flute Sonata in D major, Op. 50 (trans. Eichler). Viola Sonata in E flat major, Op. 5 No. 3
(trans. Eichler). **Ralph Holmes** (vn); **Richard Burnett** (fp); Amon Ra CD-SAR12 (7/87).
...Viola Sonata in E flat major, Op. 5 No. 3. *Coupled with works by various composers.*
Anna Barbara Duetschler (va); **Ursula Duetschler** (fp). Claves CD50-9502 (11/95). 🗲

Englebert Humperdinck

German 1854-1921

Humperdinck Hänsel und Gretel. **Jennifer Larmore** (mez) Hänsel; **Ruth Ziesak** (sop) Gretel; **Hildegard Behrens** (sop) Mother; **Bernd Weikl** (bar) Father; **Rosemary Joshua** (sop) Sandman; **Christine Schäfer** (sop) Dew Fairy; **Hanna Schwarz** (mez) Witch; **Tölz Boys' Choir; Bavarian Radio Symphony Orchestra / Donald Runnicles.** Teldec Ⓕ 4509-94549-2 (two discs: 103 minutes: DDD: 1/95). Notes, text and translation included. Recorded 1994.

Donald Runnicles here makes a very impressive recording début in a major opera set. Like EMI's version with Tate, this one was recorded by the Bavarian Radio Symphony Orchestra in the Herkulessaal in Munich, and with the Tölz Boys' Choir, yet thanks to Runnicles as well as to the engineers, the sound is noticeably different. In place of Tate's Brucknerian glow – as in the very opening – Runnicles has a lighter touch, regularly favouring faster speeds than other conductors. The lightness and refinement of the playing brings transparent textures and the most delicate *pianissimos*, with gentler markings observed more closely than usual, a point that comes out at the very start of the Overture. Far from reducing the impact of the performance, the lightness goes with an element of fantasy delightfully in keeping with the fairy-tale atmosphere. Though the choice of singers for the two title-roles in all the sets listed has been inspired, the emphasis here is more than ever on fresh, youthful voices. So it was too with Barbara Bonney and Anne Sofie von Otter on the Tate set, but here the distinction between boy and girl is if anything even more sharply drawn.

Ruth Ziesak as Gretel and Jennifer Larmore as Hänsel are, above all, natural-sounding, with little or no feeling of mature opera-singers pretending to be children, yet with no sense of strain and none of the edginess which occasionally afflicted the otherwise delightful partnership of Edita Gruberová and Ann Murray in the Davis/Philips set. Hanna Schwarz's Witch is sharply sinister without being too frightening. Schwarz was the Mother on the Tate set and here Hildegard Behrens is comparably strong and characterful, with Bernd Weikl firm and dark as the Father, while young voices are chosen for the two incidental roles of the Sandman and Dew Fairy. All the rival versions have points in their favour, with Davis more glowing than any, though with a less winning cast, and with Karajan subtler than the others in his rhythmic and tonal shading. Yet, this Teldec set for many will be a first recommendation. It brings, incidentally, a fascinating supplement in a brief orchestral coda, just over a minute long, which Humperdinck wrote in 1894 for a production of the opera in Dessau with Cosima Wagner as director. Ingeniously he has the Dessau national anthem set in counterpoint against various themes from the work, with toy trumpets providing a commentary.

Additional recommendations ...

...**Soloists; Tölz Boys' Choir; Bavarian Radio Symphony Orchestra / Jeffrey Tate.** EMI Ⓕ CDS7 54022-2 (two discs: 103 minutes: DDD).

...**Soloists; Loughton High School for Girls and Bancroft's School Choirs; Philharmonia Orchestra / Herbert von Karajan.** EMI mono Ⓜ CMS7 69293-2* (two discs: 108 minutes: ADD: 4/88).

...**Soloists; Cologne Opera Children's Chorus; Cologne Gurzenich Orchestra / Sir John Pritchard.** CBS Masterworks Ⓜ M2K79217 (two discs: 108 minutes: ADD: 11/88).

...**Soloists; Dresden Staatskapelle / Sir Colin Davis.** Philips Ⓕ 438 013-2PH2 (two discs: 103 minutes: DDD: 10/93). *Selected by Sounds in Retrospect.*

...Hänsel und Gretel[a]. **Weber** Abu Hassan[b]. **Soloists;** [a]**Mozart Chorus;** [a]women's voices of the **Deutsche Oper Chorus, Berlin;** [b]**chorus; Berlin Radio Symphony Orchestra /** [a]**Artur Rother,** [b]**Leopold Ludwig.** Preiser mono Ⓕ 90209* (two discs: 145 minutes: ADD: 3/96).

Further listening ...

...Shakespeare Suite Nos. 1 and 2. Overture No. 2 from "Die Heirat wider Willen". Humoresque in E major. **Bamberg Symphony Orchestra / Karl Anton Rickenbacher.** Koch Schwann 311972 (4/95). Ⓖ

...Hänsel und Gretel – Abends will ich schlafen gehn (sung in English). *Coupled with works by various composers.* **Lesley Garrett** (sop); **Britten Sinfonia / Ivor Bolton.** Conifer Classics 75605 51329-2 (12/97). *See review in the Collections section; refer to the Index.*

...Königskinder. **Soloists; Bavarian Radio Chorus; Munich Boys' Choir and Radio Orchestra / Fabio Luisi.** Calig CAL50968/70 (2/97).

John Humphries

British c1707-before c1740

Suggested listening ...

...Trumpet Concerto in D major, Op. 2 No. 12. *Coupled with works by various composers.* **Crispian Steele-Perkins** (tpt); **English Chamber Orchestra / Anthony Halstead.** Carlton Classics 30366 0066-2 (10/97). *See review in the Collections section; refer to the Index.*

Richard Hundley

American 1931

Suggested listening ...

...The Astronomers. *Coupled with works by various composers.* **Jennifer Larmore** (mez); **Antoine Palloc** (pf). Teldec 0630-16069-2 (12/97). *See review in the Collections section; refer to the Index.*

Henry Huss
American 1862-1953

Suggested listening ...
...Piano Concerto in B major, Op. 10. *Coupled with* **Schelling** Suite fantastique, Op. 7.
Ian Hobson (pf); **BBC Scottish Symphony Orchestra / Martyn Brabbins.**
Hyperion CDA66949 (A/97).

Lee Hyla
American 1952

Suggested listening ...
...Howl. *Coupled with works by various composers.* **Kronos Quartet.**
Nonesuch 7559-79372-2 (11/96). *See review in the Collections section; refer to the Index.*

Jacques Ibert
French 1890-1962

Ibert Divertissement.
Milhaud Le boeuf sur le toit, Op. 58. La création du monde, Op. 81.
Poulenc Les biches – Suite. **Ulster Orchestra / Yan Pascal Tortelier.** Chandos Ⓕ CHAN9023
(68 minutes: DDD: 9/92). Recorded 1991.
Here is 1920s French music directed by a conductor who is completely in the spirit of it, and plenty of spirit there is, too. Except for Ibert's *Divertissement*, this is ballet music, and that work too originated in the theatre as incidental music for Eugène Labiche's farce *The Italian Straw Hat*. Poulenc's suite from *Les biches*, written for Diaghilev's ballet company and first heard in Monte Carlo, is unfailingly fresh and bouncy and stylishly played here although Chandos's warm recording, good though it is, takes some edge off the trumpet tone; the genial nature of it all makes us forget that it is a unique mix of eighteenth-century *galanterie*, Tchaikovskian lilt and Poulenc's own inimitable street-Parisian sophistication and charm. As for Ibert's piece, this is uproariously funny in an unbuttoned way, and the gorgeously vulgar trombone in the Waltz and frantic police whistle in the finale are calculated to make you laugh out loud. Milhaud's *Le boeuf sur le toit* also has Parisian chic and was originally a kind of music-hall piece, composed to a scenario by Cocteau. It was while attending a performance of it in London in 1920 that the composer first heard the American jazz orchestra that, together with a later experience of New Orleans jazzmen playing "from the darkest corners of the Negro soul" (as he later expressed it) that prompted him to compose his masterly ballet, *La création du monde*, in which a deep-rooted African voice seems to speak through western instruments. Tortelier and his orchestra understand this strangely powerful music no less than the other pieces. This is a most desirable disc.
Additional recommendations ...
...Divertissement. *Coupled with works by various composers.* **Academy of St Martin in the Fields /**
Sir Neville Marriner. ASV Ⓕ CDDCA517 (60 minutes: ADD: 2/85).
...Divertissement. *Coupled with works by various composers.* **Paris Conservatoire Orchestra /**
Jean Martinon. Decca The Classic Sound Ⓜ 448 571-2DCS (64 minutes: ADD: 2/96).

Ibert Complete Chamber Music, Volumes 1 and 2. [a]**Eleonore Pameijer** (fl); [b]**Pauline Oostenrijk**
(ob); [c]**Hans Colbers** (cl); [d]**Peter Gaasterland** (bn); [e]**Herman Jeurissen** (hn); [f]**Peter Masseurs** (tpt);
[g]**Arno Bornkamp** (sax); [h]**Olga Franssen,** [i]**Helenus de Rijke** (gtrs); [j]**Ernestine Stoop** (hp);
Arnold Marinissen ([k]perc/[l]pipes); [m]**Menno van Delft** (hpd); [n]**Sepp Grotenhuis** (pf);
[o]**New Netherlands Quartet** ([p]Kees Hülsmann, Mieke Biesta, vns; Gerrit Oldeman, va;
[q]Marien van Staalen, vc). Olympia Ⓕ OCD468/9 (two discs, oas: 80 and 79 minutes: DDD: 2/97).
Recorded 1991-96.
OCD468 – Six pièces[j]. Deux mouvements[abcd]. Jeux[an]. Le jardinier de Samos[acfkpq]. Française[hi].
Aria[anp]. Trois pièces brèves[abcde]. Pastoral[l]. Paraboles[hi]. Cinq pièces en trio[bcd].
OCD469 – Entr'acte[ah]. Ariette[i]. L'âge d'or[gn]. Pièce[a]. String Quartet[o]. Trio[jpq]. Deux interludes[amp].
Etude-caprice pour un tombeau de Chopin[q]. Ghirlarzana[q]. Caprilena[p]. Impromptu[fn].
Carignane[dn].
Apart from the *Trois pièces brèves* for wind quintet, justly famous for their wit, Ibert's chamber music is little known and since most of this repertoire is new to the CD catalogue, this pair of CDs is to be warmly welcomed. The playing of these Dutch musicians is appealingly idiomatic. In addition to the *Pièces brèves* (1930), which are delightfully presented, the Trio for violin, cello and harp on the second disc, written 14 years later, is especially appealing. The *scherzando* finale in particular really fizzes! The second of the *Deux interludes* (1946) brings an unexpected Spanish gipsy flavour from the violin and then a ravishing flute solo. Less surprisingly, Spanish influences are also found in the music featuring the guitar, notably the *Entr'acte* for flute and guitar (1935), which even has some flamenco strumming. The two programmes are presented in order of composition and the first CD begins with the *Six pièces* (1916-17) for solo harp, of which the second ("Scherzetto") is the best known. These compositions are aural balm if not entirely characteristic; but the *Deux mouvements* (1921) for wind quartet certainly are representative, opening with trills before the flute takes flight like a bird, followed

by a pleasing oboe solo. *Jeux* could hardly be more deliciously French, and the start of *Le jardinier de Samos* (1924) reminds one a little of *Les biches*. The *Cinq pièces en trio* (1935) have a more pastoral flavour than the *Pièces brèves* and are most winning. The French write for the saxophone with special understanding, seldom allowing it to sound vulgar, and the melody of *L'âge d'or* (1935-36) has something of the character of a solemn chorale. The pieces for solo stringed instruments are full of character and the jolly trumpet *Impromptu* (1950) has a nice hint of jazz inflexion. Perhaps the key work on the second disc is the String Quartet (1937-42), which looks back to Ravel, especially in its pizzicato scherzo. The work is most impressively presented and the recording very naturally balanced with the acoustic . To sum up, over two-and-a-half hours of delightful entertainment.

Additional recommendations ...

...Trois pièces brèves. *Coupled with works by various composers.* **Reykjavik Wind Quintet.** Chandos Ⓕ CHAN9362 (63 minutes: DDD: 10/95).

...Aria[a]. Entr'acte[a]. Histoires[a]. Two interludes from "Le burlador"[a]. Jeux[a]. Deux mouvements[a]. Trois pièces brèves[a]. Pièce pour flûte seule. Le jardinier de Samos[a]. **Toke Lund Christiansen** (fl); [a]**Collegium Musicum Soloists.** Kontrapunkt Ⓕ 32202 (67 minutes: DDD: 12/95).

...Jeux. Aria. *Coupled with works by various composers.* **Emmanuel Pahud** (fl); **Eric Le Sage** (pf). EMI Ⓕ CDC5 56488-2 (66 minutes: DDD: 3/98). *See review in the Collections section; refer to the Index.*

Further listening ...

...Bacchanale. Bostoniana. Escales. Flute Concerto[a]. Louisville Concerto. Suite symphonique, "Paris". Hommage à Mozart. [a]**Timothy Hutchins** (fl); **Montreal Symphony Orchestra / Charles Dutoit.** Decca 440 332-2DH (6/94).

...Concertino da camera[a]. *Coupled with* **Bozza** Concertino[b]. **Marcel Mule** (sax); orchestra / [a]**Philippe Gaubert,** [b]**Eugene Bozza.** Clarinet Classics mono CC0013* (5/97).

...Film Suites – Macbeth; Golgotha[b]. Don Quichotte – Chanson de Sancho[a]. Chanson de Don Quichotte[a]. [a]**Henry Kiichli** (bass); [b]**Jacques Tchamkerten** (ondes martenot); **Bratislava Radio Symphony Orchestra / Adriano.** Marco Polo 8 223287 (3/91).

...Flute Concerto. *Coupled with works by various composers.* **Jennifer Stinton** (fl); **Scottish Chamber Orchestra / Steuart Bedford.** Collins Classics 1210-2 (8/91).

...Flute Concerto. *Coupled with works by various composers.* **Michael Faust** (fl); **Cologne Radio Symphony Orchestra / Serge Baudo.** Capriccio 10 495 (12/94).

...Trois pièces. **Gerard Brooks** (org). *Coupled with works by various composers.* Priory PRCD558 (4/98). *See review in the Collections section; refer to the Index.*

Vincent d'Indy

French 1851-1931

d'Indy Concerto for Piano, Flute, Cello and Strings, Op. 89[abde].
Fumet La nuit[c].
Honegger Le dit des jeux du monde[bce]. [a]**Patrick Dechorgnat** (pf); [b]**Jean Ferrandis** (fl); [c]**Hervé Noël** (tpt); [d]**Jean-Jacques Wiederker** (vc); [e]**Jean-Jacques Wiederker Chamber Orchestra / Frédéric Bouaniche.** Koch Schwann Ⓕ 310652 (56 minutes: DDD: 6/95).

Many collectors can remember when it was impossible to buy recordings of all Mahler's symphonies or Debussy's *Préludes*, so one cannot fail to wonder at the enterprise and perhaps financial boldness of today's smaller record companies. Indeed, the name of Fumet is probably unfamiliar to most people. A pupil of Franck, his radical politics seem to have hindered his career, although d'Indy supported his work. His symphonic poem for strings, *La nuit*, is atmospheric and the performance sensitive, although the rich textures are not fully served by the relatively small sound of this orchestra. Fumet reflects the more hothouse fervour of his teacher, and there is also some affinity with Szymanowski; if ultimately this music offers more sensuality than substance or shape, it has some interest and receives a committed performance. D'Indy's Concerto is surprisingly neo-classical, with little of the Franckian richness that one might expect, and this work of 1927 was his last orchestral piece. This again receives a sympathetic performance, although the music lacks weight and fails to make a strong impression. But admirers of this composer should snap up this disc while they can. The same applies to *aficionados* of Honegger, whose early (1918) incidental music to a mystery play called *Le dit des jeux du monde* receives its first recording in the form of a suite of six pieces. They are scored for 14 instruments including a bouteillophone (tuned bottles), and the third piece, "Mountain and Stones", is for percussion only. This suite is the most interesting music here and the performance is a strong one. The recording is clear, though not very atmospheric.

d'Indy Symphony No. 2 in B flat major, Op. 57. Souvenirs, Op. 52. **Monte Carlo Philharmonic Orchestra / James DePreist.** Koch International Classics Ⓕ 37280-2 (64 minutes: DDD: 8/96).

D'Indy's Second Symphony (1902-03) is a mighty utterance, epic in ambition and scale, yet tightly knit too. However, for all the intellectual strength of the writing, there is also plenty of tenderness and nobility on display (the first movement's secondary material has an almost Elgarian glow about it). D'Indy's scoring, too, is rich and colourful – in the *Modéré* third movement sample the two contrasting trio episodes, with their stylistic and melodic echoes of the composer's earlier *Symphonie sur un chant montagnard français*. D'Indy's Second is, in short, a most imposing and rewarding piece, and any reader who has ever fallen under the spell of the symphonies of, say, Chausson, Dukas or Magnard should hasten to make its acquaintance. The work's neglect both on record and in the concert-hall is to be regretted. The coupling on this Koch disc is *Souvenirs*, an eloquent and moving poem for orchestra from 1906 which d'Indy dedicated to the memory of his wife Isabelle, who had died the previous year. James DePreist presides over a finely prepared, characterful pair of performances and the Monte-Carlo Philharmonic, though not of the first rank, respond with striking commitment and evident understanding throughout, while the recording has great warmth and naturalness.

d'Indy Symphony No. 3, Op. 70, "de bello gallico". Saugefleurie, Op. 21. Souvenirs, Op. 62.
   Strasbourg Philharmonic Orchestra / Theodore Guschlbauer. Auvidis Valois Ⓕ V4686
   (72 minutes: DDD: 9/93). Recorded 1992.   Ⓖ

The real find here is *Souvenirs* (1906), a haunting, imaginatively scored tone-poem that starts with what sounds like a ghostly premonition of Shostakovich's Eleventh Symphony, then proceeds to varieties of chromatic lyricism that recall the Debussy of *Pelléas* and the lone Symphony of Ernest Chausson. The Third Symphony, a highly inventive commentary on aspects of the Great War, suggests a specific programme and is an ambiguous, loosely constructed piece that effectively extends one's limited experience of its composer. Theodore Guschlbauer's broadly sympathetic readings are more appreciative of the music's *lent et calm* than its *vif et agité*. Still, it's a gripping programme and essential listening for all incurable romantics.

Further listening ...
...L'étranger – Prélude, Act 2ᵃ. Six tableaux de voyage, Op. 36ᵃ. Fantaisie sur des thèmes populaires français, Op. 31ᵇ. Fervaal – Préludeᵃ. Saugefleurie, Op. 21ᵃ. ᵇ**Philippe Cousu** (ob); **Württemberg Philharmonic Orchestra / ᵃGilles Nopre, ᵇJean-Marc Burfin.** Marco Polo 8 223659 (1/95).
...Fervaal – Introduction. *Coupled with works by various composers.* **Columbia Symphony Orchestra / Thomas Schippers.** Sony Classical Masterworks Heritage MHK62837* (6/97).
...Symphonie sur un chant montagnard français in G major, Op. 25. *Coupled with works by* **Franck Jean-Yves Thibaudet** (pf); **Montreal Symphony Orchestra / Charles Dutoit.**
  Decca 430 278-2DH (1/92). *See review under Franck; refer to the Index.*   Ⓖ
...Symphonie sur un chant montagnard français in G major, Op. 25. *Coupled with works by* **Fauré** and **Franck François-Joël Thiollier** (pf); **National Symphony Orchestra of Ireland / Antonio de Almeida.** Naxos 8 550754 (1/95). *See review under Fauré; refer to the Index.*
...String Quartets – No. 1 in D major, Op. 35; No. 2 in E major, Op. 45. **Kodály Quartet.** Marco Polo 8 223140 (10/91).
...Prélude in E flat minor, Op. 66. *Coupled with works by various composers.* **Marie-Bernadette Dufourcet** (org). Priory PRCD422 (6/95). *See review in the Collections section; refer to the Index.*

Manuel Infante   Spanish 1883-1958

Suggested listening ...
...Trois danses andalouses. Musiques d'Espagne. *Coupled with works by various composers.*
  Sequeira Costa, Artur Pizarro (pfs). Collins Classics 1466-2 (10/96). *Gramophone Editor's choice.*
  See review in the Collections section; refer to the Index.   Ⓖ

John Ireland   British 1879-1962

Ireland A Downland Suite (arr. Ireland and Bush). Orchestral Poem in A minor. Concertino
  pastorale. Two Symphonic Studies (arr. Bush). **City of London Sinfonia / Richard Hickox.**
  Chandos Ⓕ CHAN9376 (64 minutes: DDD: 11/95). Recorded 1994.

There is little to choose between David Garforth's excellent 1983 version of the fresh-faced *Downland Suite* and Hickox's account, though it is the latter who extracts the slightly greater expressive intensity from the glorious second movement "Elegy". The *Concertino pastorale* is another fine work, boasting a most eloquent opening "Eclogue" and tenderly poignant "Threnody", towards the end of which Ireland seems to allow himself a momentary recollection of the haunting opening phrase of his much earlier orchestral prelude, *The Forgotten Rite*. In 1969 Ireland's pupil, Geoffrey Bush, arranged two sections of the score for the 1946 film *The Overlanders* which were not incorporated into the 1971 concert suite compiled by Sir Charles Mackerras. The resulting, finely wrought *Two Symphonic Studies* were recorded many years ago by Sir Adrian Boult for Lyrita – no longer available – and Hickox proves just as sympathetic an interpreter, whereas the *Orchestral Poem* in A minor is here receiving its recorded début. This is a youthful essay, completed in 1904, some three years after Ireland's studies with Stanford. It is a worthy rather than especially inspiring effort, with hardly a glimpse of the mature manner to come, save for some particularly beautiful string writing. Hickox makes out a decent enough case for it. However, with rich, refined Chandos sound, this is most enjoyable.

Additional recommendation ...
...A Downland Suite. The Holy Boy. Meditation on Keble's Rogotation Hymn. **Bridge** Suite, H93.
  English Chamber Orchestra / David Garforth. Chandos Ⓕ CHAN8390 (47 minutes: DDD: 5/87).

Ireland Violin Sonatas – No. 1 in D minor; No. 2 in A minor. Bagatelle. Berceuse. Cavatina.
The Holy Boy (arr. cpsr). **Paul Barritt** (vn); **Catherine Edwards** (pf). Hyperion ℗ CDA66853
(66 minutes: DDD: 11/96). Recorded 1995.
After many years of neglect by the record companies, Ireland's glorious Second Violin Sonata of 1917
(the work that established his reputation virtually overnight) at last appears to be coming into its own
once again. This Hyperion recording is perhaps the most completely satisfying of the three versions.
Paul Barritt and Catherine Edwards steer an intelligent middle course between the turbulent rhetoric
of Lydia Mordkovitch's epic account with Ian Brown on Chandos (part of a very desirable two-CD
set of Ireland's chamber music) and the more urgent, impulsive approach espoused by the youthful
partnership of Oliver Lewis and Jeremy Filsell on Guild. Here is a passionate, superbly disciplined
reading which communicates strongly, especially in the lovely *Poco lento quasi adagio* slow movement.
Nor do Barritt and Edwards put a foot wrong in the ambitious 1909 Cobbett Prize-winning First
Violin Sonata. The rest of the disc is filled out with all the four pieces which comprise the remainder
of Ireland's output for violin and piano. The good-humoured *Bagatelle* (1911) bears a dedication to
Marjorie Hayward, who participated in the belated 1913 première of the First Sonata (with Ireland
himself at the piano). Both the *Berceuse* (1902) and *Cavatina* (1904) are early miniatures – tuneful,
pretty and unpretentious offerings. Finally, *The Holy Boy* receives radiant advocacy, though,
somewhat surprisingly, this 1919 arrangement (made by the composer) was never published.
Recording quality is clean and intimate; balance seems eminently well judged.
Additional recommendations ...
...Violin Sonatas[ad] Nos. 1 and 2. Fantasy-Sonata in E flat major[ae]. Cello Sonata in G minor[cd]. The
Holy Boy[cd]. Phantasie Trio in A minor[bcd]. Trio No. 2 in E major[bcd]. Trio No. 3 in E major[bcd].
[a]**Gervase de Peyer** (cl); [b]**Lydia Mordkovitch** (vn); [c]**Karine Georgian** (vc); [d]**Ian Brown,**
[a] **Gwenneth Pryor** (pfs). Chandos ℗ CHAN9377/8 (two discs: 147 minutes: DDD: 12/95).
...Violin Sonata No. 2. *Coupled with works by* **Goossens** and **H. Ferguson** Oliver Lewis (vn);
Jeremy Filsell (pf). Guild ℗ GMCD7120 (60 minutes: DDD: 8/96).

Ireland Sarnia. London Pieces. In Those Days. Prelude in E flat major. Ballade. Columbine.
Month's Mind. **John Lenehan** (pf). Naxos Ⓢ 8 553700 (60 minutes: DDD: 3/98). Recorded 1995.
The pleasures here are many. John Lenehan is a very accomplished performer: not only is his technical
address impeccable, but he also possesses a strikingly wide dynamic range and sophisticated variety
of tone colour, both of which he uses to marvellously poetic (and never remotely self-conscious) effect
throughout. That Lenehan has a considerable affinity for Ireland's muse is immediately evident from
his raptly intimate delivery of the gentle opening diptych, *In Those Days*. Similarly, in the
extraordinarily imaginative, harmonically questing *Ballade* of 1929 Lenehan rises superbly to the
elemental fury of the remarkable central portion, with its brooding echoes of the 'Northern' Bax from
the same period. Elsewhere, *Columbine* is a treat, as is the ravishing *Month's Mind* (which the contents
on the back of the box misleadingly list as one of the *London Pieces*). The haunting Prelude in E flat,
too, is most affectingly realized. Eric Parkin's authoritative recordings will remain the connoisseur's
choice for this lovely repertoire, yet Lenehan's supremely affectionate and wonderfully articulate
advocacy will surely win Ireland many new friends and this finely engineered Naxos release clearly
represents exceptional value for money.
Additional recommendations ...
...Decorations. The Almond Tree. Four Preludes. Rhapsody. The Towing-Path. Merry Andrew.
Summer Evening. Piano Sonata in E minor. **Eric Parkin** (pf). Chandos ℗ CHAN9056
(72 minutes: DDD: 8/92).
...In Those Days. London Pieces. Leaves from a Child's Sketchbook. The Darkened Valley.
Two Pieces. Equinox. Sonatina. Prelude in E flat major. Ballade. Greenways. **Eric Parkin** (pf).
Chandos ℗ CHAN9140 (74 minutes: DDD: 6/93).
Further listening ...
...A London Overture. *Coupled with works by various composers.* **Liverpool Philharmonic Orchestra /
Sir Malcolm Sargent.** Dutton Laboratories mono CDAX8012* (5/95).
...Piano Concerto in E flat major[a]. Legend[a]. Mai-Dun. [a]**Eric Parkin** (pf);
London Philharmonic Orchestra / Bryden Thomson. Chandos CHAN8461 (1/87).
...Piano Concerto in E flat major. *Coupled with works by* **Bridge** and **Walton** Kathryn Stott (pf);
Royal Philharmonic Orchestra / Vernon Handley. Conifer Classics CDCF175 (1/90).   Ⓖ
...Piano Concerto in E flat major. *Coupled with* **Moeran** Symphony in G minor. Eileen Joyce (pf);
Hallé Orchestra / Leslie Heward. Dutton Laboratories mono CDAX8001* (5/93).   ⒼⒼⒼ
...Scherzo and Cortège (arr. G. Bush). Tritons – Symphonic Prelude. The Forgotten Rite – Prelude.
Satyricon – Overture. The Overlanders – Suite from the film (arr. Mackerras).
London Symphony Orchestra / Richard Hickox. Chandos CHAN8994 (2/92).
...Cello Sonata in G minor. *Coupled with works by* **Bridge** and **Stanford** Julian Lloyd Webber
(vc); **John McCabe** (pf). ASV CDDCA807 (2/93).
...Cello Sonata in G minor. *Coupled with works by* **Moeran** and **Rubbra** Raphael Wallfisch (vc);
John York (pf). Marco Polo 8 223718 (8/95). *See review under Moeran; refer to the Index.*
...Evening Service in F major. *Coupled with works by various composers.* **Ripon Cathedral Choir /
Kerry Beaumont** with **Robert Marsh** (org). Priory PRCD555 (1/97).

...Hawthorn Time. The Heart's Desire. The Lent Lily. Goal and Wicket. The Vain Desire. The Encounter. Epilogue. *Coupled with works by various composers.* **Anthony Rolfe Johnson** (ten); **Graham Johnson** (pf). Hyperion CDA66471/2 (8/95). *See review in the Collections section; refer to the Index.*

...The Land of Lost Content. The Trellis. *Coupled with works by various composers.* **Sir Peter Pears** (ten); **Benjamin Britten** (pf). Belart 461 550-2 (12/97). *See review in the Collections section; refer to the Index.*

...The Salley Gardens. The Trellis. Her Song. My True Love Hath My Heart. *Coupled with works by various composers.* **Sarah Leonard** (sop); **Malcolm Martineau** (pf). Cala United CACD88016-2 (3/95).

...Sea Fever. The Vagabond. The Bells of San Marie. *Coupled with works by various composers.* **Bryn Terfel** (bass-bar); **Malcolm Martineau** (pf). DG 445 946-2GH (8/95). *Gramophone Editor's record of the month. See review under Butterworth; refer to the Index.* 🅖🅖🅖

...A Sea Idyll. On a Birthday Morning. Soliloquy. April. Bergomask. Spring Will Not Wait. February's Child. Aubade. Ballade of London Nights. Month's Mind. Three Pastels. Columbine. Sarnia. **Eric Parkin** (pf). Chandos CHAN9250 (1/95). 🅖

Heinrich Isaac
Flemish c1450-1517

Suggested listening ...

...Angeli, Archangeli. *Coupled with works by various composers.* **The Clerks' Group / Edward Wickham.** ASV Gaudeamus CDGAU139 (3/95). *See review under Ockeghem; refer to the Index.*

...Carmen. In meinem Sinn (three versions). Greiner, zancker, schnöpffitzer. Mein Freud allein. Ich stund an einem Morgen. La mi la sol. Las rauschen. *Coupled with works by various composers.* **Convivium Musicum; Villanella Ensemble / Sven Berger.** Naxos 8 553352 (1/96). *Gramophone Editor's choice. See review in the Collections section; refer to the Index.* 🅖

...Donna di dentro dalla tua casa. Missa "La bassadanza". *Coupled with works by various composers.* **Early Music Consort of London / David Munrow.** Virgin Classics Veritas VED5 61334-2 (11/97). *See review in the Collections section; refer to the Index.*

...O decus ecclesiae. *Coupled with works by various composers.* **Fretwork.** Virgin Classics VC5 45217-2 (12/97). 🖉 *See review in the Collections section; refer to the Index.*

Grayston Ives
British 1948

Suggested listening ...

...Evening (Edington) Service. *Coupled with works by various composers.* **Lichfield Cathedral Choir / Andrew Lumsden** with **Mark Shepherd, Nigel Potts** (orgs). Priory PRCD505 (10/95). *See review in the Collections section; refer to the Index.*

Charles Ives
American 1874-1954

Ives Symphony No. 2. The Gong on the Hook and Ladder. Tone Roads – No. 1. A Set of Three Short Pieces – Largo cantabile, Hymn. Hallowe'en. Central Park in the Dark. The Unanswered Question. **New York Philharmonic Orchestra / Leonard Bernstein.** DG Ⓟ 429 220-2GH (68 minutes: DDD: 8/90). Recorded 1987-88. 🅖🅖🅖

Although Bernstein thought of Ives as a primitive composer, these recordings reveal that he had an undeniably deep affinity for, and understanding of, his music. The Second Symphony (written in 1902 and first performed in 1951) is a glorious work, still strongly rooted in the nineteenth century yet showing those clear signs of Ives's individual voice that are largely missing from the charming but lightweight First Symphony. Bernstein brings out all its richness and warmth without wallowing in its romantic elements, and he handles with utter conviction the multi-textures and the allusions to popular tunes and snatches from Bach, Brahms and Dvořák, to name but a few. The standard of playing he exacts from the NYPO, both here and in the disc's series of technically demanding shorter pieces, is remarkably high with the depth of string tone at a premium – and the engineers retain this to a degree unusual in a live recording. An essential disc for any collection.

Additional recommendations ...

...Orchestral Set No. 1. *Coupled with works by* **Schuman** and **Menin** Eastman-Rochester Orchestra **/ Howard Hanson.** Mercury Living Presence Ⓜ 432 755-2MM (77 minutes: ADD).

...Orchestral Set No. 1[a]. Symphony No. 4[b]. Central Park in the Dark[c]. [b]**Tanglewood Festival Chorus; Boston Symphony Orchestra /** [a]**Michael Tilson Thomas,** [bc]**Seiji Ozawa.** DG 20th Century Classics Ⓜ 423 243-2GC (57 minutes: ADD: 10/88).

...The Unanswered Question (orig. and rev. versions)[a]. Central Park in the Dark. Holidays[b]. [a]**Adolph Herseth** (tpt); **Chicago Symphony** [b]**Chorus and Orchestra / Michael Tilson Thomas.** Sony Classical Ⓟ SK42381 (63 minutes: DDD: 10/88).

...Central Park in the Dark. The Unanswered Question. Orchestral Set No. 1 – Three Places in New England. March No. 3, with My Old Kentucky Home. Fugue in four keys, on The Shining Shore. Symphony No. 3, "The Camp Meeting". **St Louis Symphony Orchestra / Leonard Slatkin.**
RCA Victor Red Seal Ⓕ 09026 61222-2 (63 minutes: DDD: 4/93).
...Orchestral Set No. 1, "A New England Symphony" – Three Places in New England. The Unanswered Question. Set for Theatre or Chamber Orchestra[a]. Symphony No. 3, "The Camp Meeting". Set No. 1[a]. [a]**Gilbert Kalish** (pf); **Orpheus Chamber Orchestra.**
DG Ⓕ 439 869-2GH (66 minutes: DDD: 10/94).
...Universe Symphony (realized L. Austin)[a]. Orchestral Set No. 2[b]. The Unanswered Question. [b]**C.C.M. Chamber Choir;** [a]**C.C.M. Percussion Ensemble; Cincinnati Philharmonia / Gerhard Samuel.** Centaur Ⓕ CRC2205 (62 minutes: DDD: 5/95). *Gramophone Editor's choice.*
...Symphony No. 1. The Unanswered Question. Robert Browning Overture. Orchestral Set No. 2. **Chicago Symphony Orchestra / Morton Gould.**
RCA Victor Navigator Ⓢ 74321 29246-2 (78 minutes: ADD: 6/96).
...Holidays – Symphony[a]. Orchestral Set No. 1, "A New England Symphony" – Three Places in New England. They are There![a]. **Baltimore Symphony** [a]**Chorus and Orchestra / David Zinman.** Argo Ⓕ 444 860-2ZH (6/96).

Ives Piano Sonata No. 1.
Barber Piano Sonata in E flat major, Op. 26. Excursions, Op. 20. **Joanna MacGregor** (pf).
Collins Classics Ⓕ 1107-2 (68 minutes: DDD: 3/92). Recorded 1990.
There are many fine recordings of the Barber Sonata since it is a work which has attracted well-equipped players right from the start. MacGregor stands up well, but the greater attraction is her Ives Sonata No. 1. The work, which waited 45 years for a first performance, is just as characteristic of Ives as the Second Sonata, and in some ways its mixture of hymn-tunes and ragtime makes a more coherent impact. The ragtime aspects are based on what Ives heard improvised or played that way himself: he went to a lot of trouble to catch the difference between playing the dots and swinging away. This informality is superbly caught by MacGregor, who risks all in truly Ivesian fashion in one or two places. She thoroughly understands the driving rhythms as well as the transcendental calm. By comparison anything by Barber is more polite. But the four *Excursions* come off well and show a different approach to popular idioms – more that of a tourist than an insider. But both composers know how to make use of sonata form in these two American classics, vividly played and recorded.

Ives Piano Sonata No. 2, "Concord, Mass., 1840-60". Three Quarter-tone Pieces[a]. **Alexei Lubimov,** [a]**Pierre-Laurent Aimard** (pfs). Erato Ⓕ 0630-14638-2 (60 minutes: DDD: 5/97). Recorded 1995.
Lubimov turns here to Ives, with sensational success. Everything is utterly idiomatic and the pacing of the four movements, each based on a different New England sage, is unexceptionable. Perhaps the first movement, "Emerson", is a little wearing to listen to in the slightly tight and close piano sound favoured by Erato. But the echo passages in "Hawthorne" are magical, especially the section starting at 5'23". Here and elsewhere Lubimov seems sensibly aware of the recordings by the original performer, John Kirkpatrick – all now sadly deleted. The simpler textures of "The Alcotts" are phrased immaculately and the more wayward last movement, "Thoreau", has all the atmosphere of its mystical setting at Walden Pond as well as a lovely flute solo. Lubimov has absolute fluency in delivering everything from the massed sonorities of "Emerson" through the rags in "Hawthorne" to the transcendental calm of "Thoreau". There are other recordings of this repertoire but the field is open to Lubimov as an all-Ives first choice. The significant bonus is the *Three Quarter-tone Pieces* for two pianos, which juxtaposes ragtime figures from the song *The Seer* in different tunings. This is hilarious Ives in a new idiom. The recorded sound here is very good. An essential Ives release.

Further listening ...
...Robert Browning Overture. *Coupled with* **Hartmann** Symphony No. 3.
Bamberg Symphony Orchestra / Ingo Metzmacher. EMI CDC5 55254-2 (10/95)
...Symphonies – No. 1; No. 4 (including original hymn settings).
Chicago Symphony Orchestra / Michael Tilson Thomas. Sony Classical SK44939 (2/91).
...Largo[a]. Trio for Violin, Clarinet and Piano[b]. Violin Sonatas – Nos. 2; No. 4, "Children's Day at the Camp Meeting". [a]**Stanley Drucker** (cl); **Glenn Dicterow** (vn); [b]**Alan Stepansky** (vc); **Israela Margalit** (pf). EMI Anglo-American Chamber Music Series CDC5 55406-2 (2/97).
...Trio for Violin, Clarinet and Piano. *Coupled with works by various composers.*
Yo-Yo Ma (vc); **Ronan Lefkowitz** (vn); **Gilbert Kalish** (pf).
Sony Classical SK53126 (4/94). *See review in the Collections section; refer to the Index.* Ⓖ
...Violin Sonata No. 4, "Children's Day at the Camp Meeting". *Coupled with works by various composers.* **Joseph Szigeti** (vn); **Andor Foldes** (pf). Biddulph mono LAB070/71*.
See review in the Collections section; refer to the Index. ⒼⒼ
...Violin Sonata No. 4, "Children's Day at the Camp Meeting". *Coupled with works by various composers.* **Anne Akiko Meyers** (vn); **André-Michel Schub** (pf). RCA Victor Red Seal 09026 68114-2 (8/96). *See review in the Collections section; refer to the Index.*
...My Native Land. The Things Our Fathers Loved. Memories. *Coupled with works by various composers.* **Jennifer Larmore** (mez); **Antoine Palloc** (pf).
Teldec 0630-16069-2 (12/97). *See review in the Collections section; refer to the Index.*

...Psalms – No. 54, Save me, O God, by Thy name[a]; No. 67, God be merciful to us[b]; No. 90, O Lord, Thou hast been our refuge[c]; No. 135[d]. Easter Carol[e]. Crossing the Bar[f].
The Celestial Country[g]. [dg]**Mark Calder** (tpt); [d]**Geoffrey Nash** (tbn); [g]**Kevin Morgan** (euph); [cdefg]**Christopher Hughes** (org); [c]**Stephen Lees**, [c]**Tony Lucas**, [c]**Nigel Shipway** (bells); [g]**Duke Quartet; BBC Singers / Stephen Cleobury.** Collins Classics 1479-2 (9/96).
...Walt Whitman. *Coupled with works by various composers.* **Thomas Hampson** (bar); **Craig Rutenberg** (pf). EMI CDM5 55028-2 (10/97). *See review in the Collections section; refer to the Index.*

Francis Jackson

British 1917

Suggested listening ...
...Evening Service in G major. *Coupled with works by various composers.*
Bristol Cathedral Choir / Christopher Brayne with **Ian Ball** (org).
Priory PRCD528 (8/96). *See review in the Collections section; refer to the Index.*

John James

British c1708-1746

Suggested listening ...
...Trumpet Concerto in D major, "The Four Seasons". *Coupled with works by various composers.*
Crispian Steele-Perkins (tpt); **Bournemouth Sinfonietta / Richard Studt** (vn).
Carlton Classics 30366 0038-2 (4/97). *See review in the Collections section; refer to the Index.*

Will James

Suggested listening ...
...Dark Water. *Coupled with works by* **Dett** and **Traditional London Adventist Chorale /**
Ken Burton. EMI Debut CDZ5 69707-2 (9/97). *See review in the Collections section; refer to the Index.*

Leos Janáček

Moravian 1854-1928

Janáček Sinfonietta, Op. 60[a]. Taras Bulba[a].
Shostakovich The Age of Gold – Suite, Op. 22[ab]. [a]**Vienna Philharmonic Orchestra /**
Sir Charles Mackerras; [b]**London Philharmonic Orchestra / Bernard Haitink.** Decca Ovation
Ⓜ 430 727-2DM (66 minutes: DDD: 12/91). Item marked [a] from 410 138-2DH (11/83),
recorded 1980, [b]D213D2 (11/80), recorded 1979.   ⒼⒼ
The Janáček items on this disc have long been a favourite coupling and in these thoroughly idiomatic performances the effect is truly spectacular. Of course these are far more than just orchestral show-pieces. Both works were fired by patriotic fervour – *Taras Bulba* by Czechoslovakia's struggle towards independence, the *Sinfonietta* by the city of Brno, the composer's adopted home town. Both works display a deep-seated passion for the basic elements of music and yield unprecedented levels of excitement. To get the most out of *Taras Bulba* you really need all its gory programmatic details (of battles, betrayal, torture and murder) to hand. The *Sinfonietta* on the other hand needs no such props; its impact is as irresistible and physically direct as a massive adrenalin injection. If the listener is to fully revel in this music a corresponding sense of abandon in the playing is even more important than attention to precision. The Vienna Philharmonic Orchestra here supply a good measure of both these and Sir Charles Mackerras's commitment and understanding of the music are second to none, while the high-level recording captures every detail in a vivid close-up sound image. Bernard Haitink's highly disciplined if somewhat straitlaced London Philharmonic Orchestra account of Shostakovich's *Age of Gold* suite is the coupling.

Additional recommendations ...
...Sinfonietta. Taras Bulba. Concertino[a]. [a]**Rudolf Firkušný** (pf); **Bavarian Radio Symphony**
Orchestra / Rafael Kubelík. DG Ⓑ 439 437-2GCL (61 minutes: ADD).   ⒼⒼ
...Sinfonietta. The Danube[a]. Violin Concerto, "Pilgrimage of the Soul"[b]. Schluk und Jau.
[a]**Karolina Dvořáková** (sop); [b]**Ivan Zenaty** (vn); **Brno State Philharmonic Orchestra /**
František Jílek. Supraphon Ⓕ 11 1522-2 (63 minutes: DDD: 9/93).   Ⓖ
...Taras Bulba. The Cunning Little Vixen – Suite. **Novák** Slovak Suite, Op. 32.
Czech Philharmonic Orchestra / Václav Talich.
Supraphon Historical mono Ⓜ 11 1905-2* (71 minutes: AAD: 1/94).   ⒼⒼ
...Sinfonietta. *Coupled with works by* **Bartók** Berlin Philharmonic Orchestra / Claudio Abbado.
DG Masters Ⓜ 445 501-2GMA (66 minutes: DDD: 12/94).   Ⓖ
...Taras Bulba. **Rachmaninov** Symphonic Dances. **North German Radio Symphony Orchestra /**
Sir John Eliot Gardiner. DG Ⓕ 445 838-2GH (56 minutes: DDD: 1/96).

...Sinfonietta[a]. Taras Bulba[b]. Lachian dances[c]. Suite[d]. Mládí[e]. Capriccio[f]. Concertino[g].
[efg]**Soloists;** [ab]**Vienna Philharmonic Orchestra / Sir Charles Mackerras;** [c]**London Philharmonic Orchestra / François Huybrechts;** [d]**Los Angeles Chamber Orchestra / Sir Neville Marriner;** [fg]**London Sinfonietta / David Atherton.**
Decca Double Ⓜ 448 255-2DF2 (two discs: 146 minutes: AAD/ADD: 7/96).
...Sinfonietta. *Coupled with works by* **Hindemith** and **Prokofiev London Symphony Orchestra / Claudio Abbado.** Decca The Classic Sound Ⓜ 448 579-2DCS (79 minutes: ADD: 3/97).

Janáček Pohádka[a]. Presto in E minor[b]. Violin Sonata[c]. Capriccio[d]. Concertino[d]. [c]**Pierre Amoyal** (vn); [ab]**Gary Hoffman** (vc); **Mikhail Rudy** (pf); members of [d]**L'Orchestre de l'Opéra National de Paris / Sir Charles Mackerras.** EMI Ⓕ Ⓘ CDC5 55585-2 (72 minutes: DDD: 2/97). Recorded 1995.
This is an odd assemblage of Janáček's late chamber music, but the music itself is capable of an oddity which does not dim with time. Mikhail Rudy contrasts well the eccentricity of the left-hand *Capriccio*, never losing sight of its contained lyricism, with the more approachable lyricism of the *Concertino*. In this he is ideally supported by Sir Charles Mackerras, whose expert judgement of the weight and pace and contrasts of the music never falters. Much of the secret in bringing off this difficult, haunting music lies in a sense of timing, together with something more, a long-acquired skill in contrasting textures dramatically which has itself something to do with timing, at any rate with a sense of dramatic cut and thrust. The violin and cello works, themselves very different in their more romantic natures, are finely handled by Amoyal and Hoffman, with Rudy a sympathetic and supportive partner. There are now many different versions of each of these works, none in this exact compilation. It is certainly one that can be strongly recommended.
Additional recommendations ...
...Mládí[a]. Concertino[b]. **Ligeti** Six Bagatelles[c]. Ten Pieces[d]. [abcd]**Claude Debussy Wind Quintet;** [a]**Bruno Martinez** (bass cl); [b]members of the **Parisii Quartet;** [b]**Philippe Cassard** (pf).
Harmonia Mundi Les Nouveaux Interprètes Ⓑ HMN91 1624 (61 minutes: DDD: 7/97).
...Concertino. Mládí. **Dvořák** Serenade in D minor, B77. **Walter Boeykens Ensemble.**
Harmonia Mundi Musique d'abord Ⓑ HMA190 1399 (63 minutes: DDD: 7/97).

Janáček String Quartets[a] – No. 1, "Kreutzer Sonata"; No. 2, "Intimate Letters". Along an Overgrown Path – Suite No. 1[b]. [b]**Radoslav Kvapil** (pf); [a]**Talich Quartet** (Petr Messiereur, Jan Kvapil, vns; Jan Talich, va; Evzen Rattai, vc). Calliope Ⓕ CAL9699
(73 minutes: DDD: 4/89). Items marked [a] from CAL1699 (1/86), [b]CAL9206 (8/88).   ⒼⒼ
Janáček's two string quartets stand with those of Bartók, Debussy and Ravel among the supreme masterpieces of the medium, composed during the first half of this century. Both are relatively late works: the *Kreutzer* Sonata dates from 1923 and was inspired by Tolstoy's tragic short story of the same title, depicting a women's disappointment in love both inside and outside marriage. Janáček translates the emotions of Tolstoy's story into music of intense passion. Even more immediate and personal is the Second Quartet entitled *Intimate Letters*, inspired by Janáček's infatuation at the age of 64 for his young pupil Kamila Slösslova. He poured into this quartet all his feelings for her: doubt, release, joy and despair are all graphically portrayed in Janáček's eliptical music. Inference and statement paradoxically give the quartet a wholeness which eludes other more forthright works. The Talich Quartet portray these two similar psycho-dramas with total commitment and devotion. The immense technical difficulties with which Janáček confronts his performers are set aside by the white heat of emotion clearly felt both by performers and composer. The insight of these readings fortunately even overcomes a recording perhaps too dry for Janáček's highly exposed string writing. As a bonus, Radoslav Kvapil gives an idiomatic reading of the first suite from *Along an Overgrown Path*, written between 1901 and 1908, and marked by the death of his daughter Olga in 1903. These short piano pieces display in embryo many of the stylistic features which were later to reappear in the two quartets. Again the performance is wholly authentic and committed, allowing Janáček's exceptional creativity to shine through without compromise. Again a rather dry recording.
Additional recommendations ...
...Quartets. *Coupled with works by* **Bartók** Tokyo Quartet.
RCA Victor Red Seal Ⓕ 09026 68286-2 (three discs: 199 minutes: DDD)
...Quartets. **Dvořák** Cypresses, B152. **Lindsay Quartet.**
ASV Ⓕ CDDCA749 (75 minutes: DDD: 11/91).   Ⓖ
...Quartets. **Dvořák** String Quartet No. 10 in E flat major, B92. **Vanbrugh Quartet.**
Collins Classics Ⓕ 1381-2 (73 minutes: DDD: 4/94).   Ⓖ
...Quartet No. 1. *Coupled with works by* **Dvořák** Smetana Quartet. Testament Ⓕ SBT1074
(79 minutes: ADD: 3/96). *See review in the Collections section; refer to the Index.*   ⒼⒼ
...Quartet No. 2. *Coupled with works by* **Dvořák** Smetana Quartet. Testament Ⓕ SBT1075
(77 minutes: ADD: 3/96). *See review in the Collections section; refer to the Index.*   ⒼⒼ

Janáček Pohádka.
Kodály Cello Sonata, Op. 4.
Liszt Elégies – No. 1, S130; No. 2, S131. La lugubre gondola, S134. **Anne Gastinel** (vc); **Pierre-Laurent Aimard** (pf). Auvidis Valois Ⓕ V4748 (50 minutes: DDD: 9/95).

This is an imaginative piece of programme planning, with arrangements of Liszt's *Elégies* and *La lugubre gondola* separated by Kodály's Sonata and Janáček's *Pohádka*. Liszt, writing in the 1870s and early 1880s, sounds as modern as either of the two composers writing in 1910; and indeed there is much in his augmented-chord harmony and his fondness for unusual scales that influenced Kodály, while Janáček also admired him and used his religious music for teaching purposes. This is romantic music outside the mainstream of European musical romanticism. Gastinel and Aimard give performances as intelligent as these juxtapositions suggest, oblique and dark in the linking figure of Liszt, especially with *La lugubre gondola*, one of the most extraordinary late piano pieces. Kodály's sonata is played with a quiet intensity, rhapsodic in manner but in fact strongly held together by the clarity of emphasis on the motto theme and its musical implications. Janáček's pieces can sound sharper and quirkier than here, and in such performances make their point more strongly; but this playing is of a piece with the whole approach in this recital. Gastinel has a clean, resinous tone, and a strong sense of line; she is well partnered by Aimard, and the recording is clear and well balanced.

Janáček Piano Sonata 1.X.1905, "From the Street". Along an Overgrown Path. In the Mists.
Thema con variazioni, "Zdenka". **Rudolf Firkušný** (pf). DG 20th Century Classics
Ⓜ 429 857-2GC (79 minutes: ADD: 3/91). From 2707 055 (6/72). Recorded 1971.   ⒼⒼⒼ
Janáček's only piano sonata has a history almost as dramatic as the events which inspired it. Its subtitle, *From the Street*, commemorates a student demonstration in which a 20-year-old worker was killed, an event which so outraged Janáček that he wrote a three-movement sonata as an expression of his feelings. Before the première in 1906 he burnt the third movement and after a private performance in Prague he threw the remaining movements into a river. It is only thanks to the pianist, Ludmil Tučkova, who had copied out the first two movements, that the work survives. The underlying theme of Firkušný's approach to this work (who may claim historical authenticity as he studied with Janáček) is anger, turning the first movement into a defiant roar of fury whilst the slow movement has an inherent restlessness, bitterness never far below the surface. Much of the same characteristics can be found in the other works – *Along an Overgrown Path* and the masterly *In the Mists* although he occasionally overloads these delicate little pieces with dramatic power. The early Theme and Variations are conventionally romantic but impeccably played. This disc represents playing of the highest class with full notes and tracking details.

Additional recommendations ...

...Piano Sonata. In the Mists. Along an Overgrown Path. **Leif Ove Andsnes** (pf).
Virgin Classics Ⓕ VC7 59639-2 (71 minutes: DDD: 10/91).

...Piano Sonata. Along an Overgrown Path – Suite No. 1. In the Mists. **Josef Páleníček** (pf).
Supraphon Ⓕ 10 1481-2 (54 minutes: ADD: 3/92).

Janáček Diary of one who disappeared (two versions). [a]**Nicolai Gedda**, [b]**Beno Blachut** (tens);
[a]**Véra Soukupová**, [b]**Stěpánka Stěpánová** (mezzos); [a]**Prague Radio Chamber Chorus**;
[b]**Czech Singers Chamber Chorus**; [ab]**Josef Páleníček** (pf). Supraphon [a]stereo/[b]mono Ⓜ SU0022-2*
(73 minutes: DDD/AAD: 2/96). Item marked [a] new to UK (recorded 1984), [b]from LPV319
(3/59, recorded 1956). Text and translation included.
Here is a highly interesting enterprise: two parallel performances of Janáček's song-cycle, both recorded in Prague, but one being the classic version with Beno Blachut made in 1956, the other hitherto unknown in this country and made in 1984 by Nicolai Gedda. Blachut, who despite his heroic use of his voice kept it in good order throughout a long career, was then in his early forties, and in his prime; Gedda, another singer who preserved his voice carefully, was in his sixtieth year. Any lover of Janáček's music is strongly urged to acquire this striking record. The commentary, by the distinguished scholar Jiří Vysloužil, makes no bones about preferring Blachut, observing that "what may have displeased some critics, including even those abroad, was the operatic style of Gedda's interpretation". It is easy enough to see what he means: for instance, in No. 6, translated as "Hey there my tawny oxen", as the young man ploughing has his head set afire by a glimpse of the gipsy girl in the bushes, Gedda gives the climactic phrase "v jednom je plameni" an Italianate fervour where Blachut develops the song's passion more steadily towards the phrase, which can therefore be less strenuously emphasized. Nevertheless, Gedda's vocal elegance and eloquence have their own appeal; and his Russian background has long helped him towards a deep understanding of music in the Slavonic repertory. His is a superb performance of a work that can well sustain a new approach, whatever loyalties there may be to Blachut's identification with the work. Listeners have a unique opportunity here for getting, literally, two for the price of one and enjoying the comparisons. A linchpin of both performances, as he so often was, is Josef Páleníček.

Janáček Glagolitic Mass[a]. Sinfonietta, Op. 60[b]. [a]**Felicity Palmer** (sop); [a]**Ameral Gunson** (mez);
[a]**John Mitchinson** (ten); [a]**Malcolm King** (bass); [a]**Jane Parker-Smith** (org); [a]**City of Birmingham
Chorus and Orchestra**; [b]**Philharmonia Orchestra / Sir Simon Rattle**. EMI Ⓕ CDC7 47504-2
(62 minutes: DDD: 10/88). Text and translation included. Item marked [a] from ASD4066 (5/82),
recorded 1981, [b]ASD143522-1 (10/83), recorded 1982.   Ⓖ
"I am not an old man, and I am not a believer – until I see for myself." Thus Janáček replied angrily to a critic after the première of his *Glagolitic Mass*. This is a gritty, masterful performance of a jagged, uncomfortable masterpiece. Its unusual title stems from the script of the ancient Slavonic text (*Glagol*)

which Janáček set to music. Rattle's is a full-blooded, urgent view of the work, with particularly fine solo contributions from Felicity Palmer and John Mitchinson. That the language is an unfamiliar one is occasionally evident in the chorus, though they, like the orchestra, give totally committed performances under Rattle's inspired leadership. Also included on this disc is the *Sinfonietta* (originally entitled "Military Sinfonietta", reflecting in the brass-heavy scoring of the work). It is as much a study in orchestration as form with the melody of the fourth movement appearing unaltered no less than 14 times, changed only in orchestral colour. It is brilliantly played here, with the 12 trumpets coming up gleaming in the final climax. An enticing proposition!

Additional recommendation ...
...Glagolitic Mass. **Poulenc** Gloria. **Soloists; Westminster Choir; New York Philharmonic Orchestra / Leonard Bernstein.**
Sony Classical Bernstein Royal Edition Ⓜ SMK47569 (65 minutes: ADD: 5/93).

Janáček (ed. Wingfield) Glagolitic Mass (original version)[a].
Kodály Psalmus Hungaricus, Op. 13[b]. [a]**Tina Kiberg** (sop); [a]**Randi Stene** (contr); **Peter Svensson** (ten); [a]**Ulrik Cold** (bass); [a]**Per Salo** (org); [b]**Copenhagen Boys' Choir; Danish National Radio Choir and Symphony Orchestra / Sir Charles Mackerras.** Chandos Ⓕ CHAN9310 (63 minutes: DDD: 12/94). Texts and translations included. Recorded 1994.
Mackerras's version of the *Glagolitic Mass* is of particular interest as it embodies one of the reconstructions that have been painstakingly made of Janáček's original intentions in different works as his stature has drawn greater scholarly interest. This one has been made by Paul Wingfield. He has gone into the nature of his restorations in great detail in his excellent monograph on the work in the Cambridge Music Handbooks series (CUP: 1992), and summarizes them in his note to this recording. Briefly, they involve the playing of the Intrada at the beginning and the end, in the Introduction a very complex rhythmic pattern and in the "Gospodi pomiluj" ("Kyrie") use of quintuple metre instead of the familiar four-in-a-bar (both far more effectively), and fierce timpani interjections in the wild organ solo. There are other points; but in any case, most interested listeners will care less for them in detail than for the heightened force and impact of the music. This it certainly now (or once again) has. These matters make it the more regrettable that, despite marvellous handling of the work by Mackerras, there are problems with a quartet of soloists that is less than exciting, and a recording that even with the most modern techniques can obscure the detail of the music and the clarity of the words. This should not detract from the interest of the disc, which every lover of the work will surely want to hear. Those who acquire it will have the additional benefit of a fine performance of Kodály's *Psalmus Hungaricus*, though the restored Mass is naturally the occasion here for recommendation and choice.

Janáček The Wild Duck. The Dove. Our Birch Tree. The Wandering Madman. Schoolmaster Halfar. Elegy on the Death of his Daughter Olga. The Wolf's Trail. Songs of Hradčany. Nursery Rhymes. **Netherlands Chamber Choir; Schoenberg Ensemble / Reinbert de Leeuw.**
Philips Ⓕ 442 534-2PH (60 minutes: DDD: 12/95). Texts and translations included.
Some of Janáček's most characteristic invention is to be found in the many choruses he wrote for local choirs who were moved by both a love of singing together and a demonstration of their national identity. There is a good selection here. Even the earliest, a touching little lament for a duck, has a quirkiness which saves it from sentimentality; the latest, the *Nursery Rhymes*, are marvellous little inventions from the dazzling evening of Janáček's life. One must resist any temptation to say that they take Stravinsky on at his own game: Janáček is his own man. In between comes a varied diet here. *Schoolmaster Halfar* (or *Cantor Halfar*) is set with a dazzling range of little musical ironies as the story unfolds of the teacher who ruined his life by insisting on speaking Czech. The *Elegy on the Death of his Daughter Olga* goes some way toward dignifying a conventional text with some heartfelt music, but the pressure of grief has not drawn the greatest of his music from him: perhaps more time was needed, and indeed the piano pieces he entitled *Along an Overgrown Path* re-enter ancient griefs more expressively. The performances are fluent and smooth; and perhaps this is not always a recommendation. Czech group brought to this music a sharpness, an oddity, a tang in the rhythms and phrasing that responded better to the music than these well-ironed performances. Nevertheless, for the best here there is enjoyment, and a most pleasurable reminder of Janáček's unquenchable individuality in whatever he set out to do.

Janáček The Cunning Little Vixen. The Cunning Little Vixen – orchestral suite (arr. V. Talich)[a].
Lucia Popp (sop) Vixen, Young vixen; **Dalibor Jedlička** (bass) Forester; **Eva Randová** (mez) Fox; **Eva Zikmundová** (mez) Forester's wife, Owl; **Vladimir Krejčik** (ten) Schoolmaster, Gnat; **Richard Novák** (ten) Priest, Badger **Václav Zítek** (bar) Harašta; **Beno Blachut** (ten) Pásek; **Ivana Mixová** (mez) Pásek's wife, Woodpecker, Hen; **Libuše Marová** (contr) Dog; **Gertrude Jahn** (mez) Cock, Jay; **Eva Hríbiková** (sop) Frantik; **Zuzana Hudecová** (sop) Pepik; **Peter Saray** (treb) Frog, Grasshopper; **Miriam Ondrášková** (sop) Cricket; **Vienna State Opera Chorus; Bratislava Children's Choir; Vienna Philharmonic Orchestra / Sir Charles Mackerras.**
Decca Ⓕ 417 129-2DH2 (two discs: 109 minutes: DDD: 11/86). Notes, text and translation included. From D257D2 (5/82). Item marked [a] new to UK. Recorded 1981.
Gramophone Award Winner 1983.   ⒼⒺⒼ

Janáček used the most unlikely material for his operas. For *The Cunning Little Vixen* his source was a newspaper series of drawings, with accompanying text, about the adventures of a vixen cub and her escape from the gamekeeper who raised her. The music is a fascinating blend of vocal and orchestral sound – at times ludicrously romantic, at others raw and violent. Sir Charles Mackerras's Czech training has given him a rare insight into Janáček's music and he presents a version faithful to the composer's individual requirements. In the title-role, Lucia Popp gives full weight to the text while displaying all the richness and beauty of her voice. There is a well-chosen supporting cast of largely Czech singers, with the Vienna Philharmonic to add the ultimate touch of orchestral refinement. Decca's sound is of demonstration quality, bringing out all the violent detail of Janáček's exciting vocal and orchestral effects.

Additional recommendations ...

...The Cunning Little Vixen (sung in English)[a]. Taras Bulba[b]. **Soloists; [a]Chorus and Orchestra of the Royal Opera House, Covent Garden; [b]Philharmonic Orchestra / Sir Simon Rattle.** EMI Ⓕ CDS7 54212-2 (two discs: 120 minutes: DDD: 3/92).

...The Cunning Little Vixen. **Soloists; Kuhn Children's Chorus; Czech Philharmonic Chorus and Orchestra / Václav Neumann.** Supraphon Ⓕ 10 3471-2 (two discs: 96 minutes: ADD: 4/93).

...The Cunning Little Vixen. **Soloists; Prague National Theatre Chorus and Orchestra / Bohumil Gregor.** Supraphon Ⓕ SU3071-2 (two discs: 102 minutes: AAD: 1/97).

Janáček Jenůfa. **Elisabeth Söderström** (sop) Jenůfa; **Wieslaw Ochman** (ten) Laca; **Eva Randová** (mez) Kostelnička; **Petr Dvorskü** (ten) Steva; **Lucia Popp** (sop) Karolka; **Marie Mrazová** (contr) Stařenka; **Václav Zitek** (bar) Stárek; **Dalibor Jedlička** (bass) Rychtar; **Ivana Mixová** (mez) Rychtarka; **Vera Soukopová** (mez) Pastuchyňa, Tetka; **Jindra Pokorná** (mez) Barena; **Jana Janasová** (sop) Jano; **Vienna State Opera Chorus; Vienna Philharmonic Orchestra / Sir Charles Mackerras.** Decca Ⓕ 414 483-2DH2 (two discs: 130 minutes: DDD: 12/85). From D276D3 (9/83). Recorded 1982. *Gramophone Award Winner 1984.*   ⒼⒼⒼ

Janáček's first operatic masterpiece is a towering work which blends searing intensity with heart-stopping lyricism. It tells of Jenůfa and the appalling treatment she receives as she is caught between the man she loves and another who eventually comes to love her. But dominating the story is the Kostelnička, a figure of enormous strength, pride and inner resource who rules Jenůfa's life and ultimately kills her baby. Randová's characterization of the role of the Kostelnička is frightening in its intensity but also has a very human core. The two men are well cast and act as fine foils to Söderström's deeply impressive Jenůfa. The Vienna Philharmonic play beautifully and Mackerras directs magnificently. The recording is all one could wish for and the booklet is a mine of informed scholarship.

Janáček Kátá Kabanová[a]. Capriccio[b]. Concertino[b]. **Elisabeth Söderström** (sop) Kátá Kabanová; **Petr Dvorský** (ten) Boris; **Naděžda Kniplová** (contr) Kabanicha; **Vladimír Krejčík** (ten) Tichon; **Libuše Márová** (mez) Varvara; **Dalibor Jedlička** (bass) Dikoj; **Zdeněk Svehla** (ten) Kudrjáš; **Jaroslav Souček** (bar) Kuligin; **Jitka Pavlová** (sop) Glaša; **Gertrude Jahn** (mez) Fekluša; **Vienna State Opera Chorus; Vienna Philharmonic Orchestra / Sir Charles Mackerras; [b]Paul Crossley** (pf); **[b]London Sinfonietta / David Atherton.** Decca Ⓕ 421 852-2DH2 (two discs: 140 minutes: ADD: 10/89). Notes, text and translation included. Item marked [a] from D51D2 (10/77), recorded 1976, [b]D223D5 (4/81), recorded 1978. *Gramophone classical 100. Gramophone Award Winner 1977.*   ⒼⒼⒼ

Janáček Kátá Kabanová. **Gabriela Beňačková** (sop) Kátá Kabanová; **Peter Straka** (ten) Boris; **Eva Randová** (mez) Kabanicha; **Ludek Vele** (bass) Dikoj; **Miroslav Kopp** (ten) Tichon; **Jozef Kundlák** (ten) Kudrjáš; **Dagmar Pecková** (mez) Varvara; **Zdeněk Harvánek** (bass) Kuligin; **Martina Bauerová** (mez) Glaša; **Dana Burešová** (mez) Fekluša; **Prague National Theatre Chorus; Czech Philharmonic Orchestra / Sir Charles Mackerras.** Supraphon Ⓕ SU3291-2 (two discs: 94 minutes: DDD: 2/98). Notes, text and translation included. Recorded 1997. *Gramophone Editor's choice.*   ⒼⒼ

Unlike the other three late operas, *Kátá Kabanová*'s story is one you would expect to see on the opera stage: Kátá, a free spirit, is imprisoned by marriage into, and domicile with, a family in a provincial Russian town on the Volga. The family is manipulated by her mother-in-law, a widow whose sole, obsessive concern is her status (familial and social). The only son (Kátá's husband) is understandably spineless, and Kátá looks for escape in love. She finds the love, but true escape only in suicide. Janáček focuses on his heroine, giving her at least two of the most moving scenes in opera: the first where, to music of shimmering, seraphic beauty he describes her childhood imagination given free rein by pillars of sunlight streaming through the dome in church; and the second in the last scene where, after her confession of adultery, she concludes that "not even God's own sunlight" gives her pleasure any more. Söderström has the intelligence and a voice which guarantees total credibility; and of the superb all-Czech supporting cast one might only have wished for a slightly younger-sounding sister-in-law. Mackerras obtains the finest playing from the Vienna Philharmonic; and Decca, true to their best operatic traditions, reproduce the whole with clarity, atmosphere, ideal perspectives and discernible stage movement – only a detectable levelling of the score's few extreme *fortissimos* points to the recording's vintage. As a bonus, Decca add the late chamber concertos, both excellently performed and engineered, and equally essential Janáček.

After 20 years it is a well-earned compliment that the Czechs should choose to return to Sir Charles, but understandable that they also should want to make a version with their own forces, and especially with their well-loved soprano, Gabriela Beňačková, who has been able to fill the National Theatre in Prague whenever she sings the role. She sings it beautifully here. From the outset she establishes, by tone and by subtle warmth of phrasing, the distinction between her nature and that of Eva Randová's prim Kabanicha. When it comes to her dream of the love that has already begun to burgeon in secret, she is confiding yet sensuous, with a contained passion that bursts out in the love scene. There are operatic heroines who scarcely seem to exist outside their love; Kátá is a real woman who is overcome by an emotion she does not consciously seek, and Beňačková makes her succumb with touching innocence to what she accepts will be guilt-burdened. Her last monologue is wonderfully affecting as the burden proves more than she can bear. Janáček's admirers will certainly want to hear this lovely performance, perhaps to add it to their collection beside Söderström's subtle, tender interpretation. It is chiefly for Beňačková that the set is to be recommended, though there is a mostly good set of supporting performances. Randová sings a firm if not particularly alarming Kabanicha. Dagmar Pecková sings a bright, tough little Varvara and her Kudrjáš is amiably, lightheartedly done by Jozef Kundlák. The two men competing for Kátá contrast well, Peter Straka an ardent Boris, phrasing with a warmth that matches him well to her, Miroslav Kopp a Tichon who manages to be genuinely touching even as he lies down under the Kabanicha's torrent of instructions. Ludek Vele a vigorous Dikoj. It is surprising that Sir Charles did not question the placing of the singers so that they are sometimes overwhelmed by the orchestra but he conducts a performance no less impassioned and lucid than before, perhaps even more precisely judged.

Additional recommendations ...

...Kátá Kabanová. **Soloists; Prague National Theatre Chorus and Orchestra / Jaroslav Krombholc.** Supraphon Ⓕ 10 8016-2* (two discs: 90 minutes: ADD: 11/93).

...Capriccio. *Coupled with works by* **Bartók** and **Martinů** Joela Jones (pf); **Cleveland Orchestra / Christoph von Dohnányi.** Decca Ⓕ 443 173-2DH (70 minutes: DDD: 4/95).

Further listening ...

...Violin Concerto, "Pilgrimage of the soul". *Coupled with works by* **Berg** and **Hartmann** Thomas Zehetmair (vn/dir); **Philharmonia Orchestra / Heinz Holliger; Deutsche Kammerphilharmonie.** Teldec 4509-97449-2 (6/95).

...Mládí. *Coupled with works by various composers.* **Nikita Cardinaux** (bass cl); **Swiss Wind Quintet.** Koch Discover International DICD920395 (8/97). *See review in the Collections section; refer to the Index.*

...Violin Sonata. *Coupled with works by* **Foerster** and **Novak** Josef Suk (vn); **Jan Panenka** (pf). Supraphon 11 0705-2 (5/90).

...I'm Waiting For You (two versions). War Song (first version). War Song (second version), "Blessing the flag". Fanfares – A major; D minor. Festival Chorus. Along an Overgrown Path – Our Evenings; A Blown-away Leaf; The Madonna of Frýdek; Good Night!; The Barn Owl Has Not Flown Away. Jealousy. Jenůfa – And That's How We Would Go ... Ah, He Was So Strong. Taras Bulba – original opening. The Excursions of Mr Brouček – Postlude to Part 1. The Living Corpse – fragment. March of the Blue Boys. **Soloists** (vocalists and instrumentalists); **Prague Philharmonic Chorus; Brno State Philharmonic Orchestra / Leoš Svárovský.** Supraphon 11 1878-2 (3/95).

...The Lord's Prayer[jghk]. Hail Mary[cehjk]. Mass in E flat major (ed. Wingfield)[abcdjik]. Adagios (ed. Reinberger)[i]. Exaudi Deus[jk]. Regnum mundi[jk]. Graduale in festo purificationis (Suscepimus Deus)[jk]. In nomine Jesu[jk]. *Coupled with works by* **Puccini** [a]Shelley Everall (sop); [b]Lynette Alcantara (contr); [c]William Kendall (ten); [d]Peter Harvey (bar); Douglas Paterson ([e]vn/[f]va); [g]Helen Cole (hp); [h]Christopher Monks, [i]Michael Phillips (orgs); [j]Gonville and Caius College Choir, Cambridge / [k]Geoffrey Webber ([l]org). ASV CDDCA914 (6/95).

...Moravian folk poetry in songs. **Zdena Kloubová** (sop); **Leo Marián Vodička** (ten); **Radoslav Kvapil** (pf). Unicorn-Kanchana DKPCD9154 (4/95). ⊚Ⓖ

...Nine Male-voice choruses[a]. Nursery Rhymes[b]. [a]Moravian Teachers' Choir / Antonín Tučapský; [b]Czech Philharmonic Chorus and Orchestra / Jan Kühn with Alfred Holeček (pf). Somm Recordings SOMMCD201 (2/96).

...Nursery Rhymes[ad]. Kašpar Rucký. The 70,000. The wolf's trail[d]. Songs of Hradčany[bc]. Elegy on the death of my daughter Olga[d]. Ave Maria. Our Father[ce]. [b]Will Sleath (fl); [c]Hugh Webb (hp); [d]Clive Williamson (pf); [e]Christopher Bowers-Broadbent (org); **New London Chamber Choir; [a]Critical Band / James Wood.** Hyperion CDA66893 (5/97).

...Our Father. *Coupled with works by* **Eben** and **Dvořák** Soloists; **Prague Chamber Choir / Josef Pancík.** ECM New Series 449 508-2 (11/96). *See review under Dvořák; refer to the Index.*

...Rákos Rákoczy[ab]. As we went to the feast[b]. I have sown green[b]. The grey falcon flew away[b]. Lachian Troják. The blessed dance. [a]Zuzana Lapčíková (sop); [a]Pavla Dittmannová (contr); [a]Petr Julíček (ten); [a]Ondřej Strejček (bass); [b]Brno Philharmonic Chorus; Brno State Philharmonic Orchestra / Leoš Svárovský. Supraphon SU3129-2 (4/97).

...The Excursions of Mr Brouček. **Soloists; Czech Philharmonic Chorus and Orchestra / František Jílek.** Supraphon 11 2153-2 (2/95)

...Fate (sung in English). **Soloists; Welsh National Opera Chorus and Orchestra / Sir Charles Mackerras.** EMI CDC7 49993-2 (9/90).

...From the House of the Dead[a]. Mládí[b]. Nursery Rhymes[c]. [b]**Soloists;** [bc]**Vienna State Opera Chorus;** [a]**Vienna Philharmonic Orchestra / Sir Charles Mackerras;** [b]**London Sinfonietta Chorus;** [ab]**London Sinfonietta / David Atherton.** Decca 430 375-2DH2 (10/91).   ⓐ

...The Makropoulos Affair. Lachian Dances[a]. **Soloists; Vienna State Opera Chorus; Vienna Philharmonic Orchestra / Sir Charles Mackerras;** [a]**London Philharmonic Orchestra / François Huybrechts.** Decca 430 372-2DH2 (10/91).   ⓐ

...The Makropoulos Affair. **Soloists; Prague National Theatre Chorus and Orchestra / Bohumil Gregor.** Supraphon 10 8351-2 (5/95).

...Osud. **Soloists; Brno Janáček Opera Chorus and Orchestra / František Jílek.** Supraphon SU0045-2 (1/96).

...Sárka. **Soloists; Brno Radio Symphony Chorus and Orchestra / Břetislav Bakala.** Multisonic mono 310154-2* (6/94).   ⓐ

Clément Janequin
French c1485-1558

Janequin Missa super "La bataille". Missa super "L'aveuglé dieu". Congregati sunt.
Clément Janequin Ensemble; Les Sacqueboutiers de Toulouse / Dominique Visse.
Harmonia Mundi Ⓕ HMC90 1536 (50 minutes: DDD: 1/96). ✎ Texts and translations included. Recorded 1994. *Gramophone Editor's choice.*
Janequin's reputation rests squarely on his secular music, in particular the fame of such descriptive compositions as *Le chant des oiseaux* and *La guerre*. His sacred output – all of two Masses, a single motet and a few psalms – seems pretty slim in comparison, but that is more likely to reflect Janequin's inability to secure any permanent ecclesiastical appointment than any lack of interest. This disc will therefore come as a revelation to quite a few. Take the Mass based on *La bataille*: the care with which Janequin doses his borrowings from the song bespeaks a masterly sense of pacing, even of drama. The first appearance of the 'battle sequence' impressively energizes those most problematic, lengthy expanses of text in the *Credo*: this is an inspired move, witty and original. The coupling of the two Masses has more than an anthological justification, for they could hardly be more contrasted. The Mass on *L'aveuglé dieu* appears to have been composed about 20 years after its companion, in the composer's old age. Its rich melodic vein bears the unmistakable stamp of his more serious, Ronsard song-settings, though many will find *La bataille* the more immediately compelling of the two. The Janequin Ensemble's customary panache is here reinforced by a judicious coupling of organ, cornet and sackbuts, but they also manage to communicate the considerable dignity emanating from both Masses. This ensemble's forays into sacred music are rare, but always memorable. In revealing an unsuspected facet of Janequin's genius, they yet again do their standard-bearer proud.
Further listening ...
...Chansons – Le chant des oiseaux. Toutes les nuictz. J'atens le temps. Il estoit une fillette. Ung jour Colin. O doulx regard, o parler. Or sus vous dormez trop (L'alouette). Quand contrement verras. Hellas mon Dieu, ton ire. Ma peine n'est pas grande. O mal d'aymer. Herbes et fleurs. A ce joly moys. Assouvy suis. Quelqu'un me disoit l'aultre jour. M'y levay par ung matin. M'ayme a eu de Dieu. Le chant du rossignol. Las on peult juger (arr. Morlaye). L'aveuglé dieu qui partout vole (arr. Alberto da Ripa). **Clément Janequin Ensemble.**
Harmonia Mundi HMC90 1099 (8/85).   ⓖ

John Jeffreys
British 1927

Jeffreys Merry eye. That ever I saw. Northumberland. I am the gilly of Christ. Jillian of Berry. The poacher's dog. Who is at my window?. 'Tis time, I think. What evil coil of Fate. Severn Meadows. In pride of May. Candlegate. Black Stichel. Stow-on-the-Wold. Otterburn. Yet will I love her. The little pretty nightingale. Ha'nacker Mill. The little milkmaid. My little pretty one. O mistress mine. It is winter. O my dere hert. Little trotty wagtail. **Ian Partridge (ten);**
Jennifer Partridge (pf). Meridian Ⓕ CDE84343 (70 minutes: DDD: 9/97). Texts included.
The list of compositions printed in the booklet shows John Jeffreys to be the writer of a large number of works, few, if any, having become widely known. He was born after the Great War but is of the age that was brought up in its shadow. The sound of bugles calling from sad shires was never far below the threshold of consciousness. He has a love of the English countryside, and that also runs deep in his music, which may seem to recall Vaughan Williams but is perhaps closer to Gerald Finzi and closer still to Peter Warlock. The songs have their own distinctive voice, and the style is that of a fastidious man who will neither seek originality for its own sake nor follow the fashion: who will write within the tradition he loves yet reject anything that is crudely obvious or ready-made. He is deservedly fortunate to have such delightful and sensitive artists as Ian and Jennifer Partridge to perform his songs. These are well written for both voice and piano, the vocal line serving the poem first but also the voice as a singing instrument. The special quality of Partridge's voice suits the thoughtful restraint of the composer's expression, most beautifully in his setting of Ivor Gurney's *Severn Meadows*, with its ghostly "he that dwells in shadows" and finely sustained *pianissimo* ending. The recording is clear and well balanced, the accompanying booklet attractively produced.

Jehannot de l'Escurel   French d 1304

Suggested listening ...
...*Bien se lace. Coupled with works by various composers.* **Anne Azéma** (sop/spkr);
vocal and instrumental ensemble.
Erato 0630-17072-2 (12/97). ✒ *See review in the Collections section; refer to the Index.*

John Jenkins   British 1592-1678

Jenkins Fantasias a 5 – No. 7 in C minor; No. 8 in C minor; No. 16 in D major. Fantasias a 4 –
No. 5 in F major; No. 6 in F major; No. 12 in D major. Fantasias a 6 – No. 3 in C minor; No. 8 in
A minor. Two In Nomines a 6. Pavan a 6 No. 2 in F major. Fantasia-Suite a 4 No. 4 in C major[a].
Fantasia-Suite a 4 No. 7 in D minor[a]. Divisions in D major. Pavan in A minor. Three Pieces for
Lyra Viol. [a]**Paul Nicholson** (org); **Fretwork** (Wendy Gillespie, Richard Campbell, Richard Boothby,
William Hunter, Julia Hodgson, Susanna Pell, viols). Virgin Classics Veritas Ⓕ VC5 45230-2
(78 minutes: DDD). ✒ Recorded 1995.   Ⓖ

Jenkins may be neither as dramatically striking nor as melodically individual as William Lawes but
his infectious lyricism, and control of broad spans of subtly inflected polyphony, is often masterful in
the very best of English traditions. Indeed, anyone who blithely insists that this is players' music had
better experience Fretwork's distinguished contribution to a fairly undistinguished discography. Not
all the works played here reach the peaks of which Jenkins was capable (lyra viol solos really are best
heard behind closed doors) but this is none the less an astutely compiled programme reflecting the
composer's versatility within fairly arcane idioms which Fretwork make accessible to a wide audience.
We now have Fretwork's keen ensemble and technical virtuosity for granted but they clearly identify
closely with Jenkins's undemonstrative and equable geniality. The sound is often dispassionately soft-
grained, sweet and fresh (as in the *Fantasia-Suite* No. 7 in D minor from the set of 28 fantasias for
treble, two basses and semi-obbligato organ) but still capable of an earthy warmth such as can be
heard in the *Pavan a 6*. Such eloquence is far closer to the mark than, for instance, Jordi Savall's
committed account. The price of such reserve – though it is less costly here than in the more intensely
searching chamber works of Lawes and Purcell – is that when Jenkins hauls a melodic idea over the
coals, we are often left wanting a more primal and broadly selected investigation by the player: a
recognition of an association through a darkening of the sound, an articulation re-articulated and
time taken to accentuate a particularly 'connected' dialogue. Such things are often just a matter of
taste and in this case should not detract from a disc which is one of Fretwork's finest achievements.

Further listening ...
...Pavan in F major in six parts. Fantasia in C minor in five parts. Divisions in C major. Fantasia in
C minor in four parts. Fantasia in F major, "All in a Garden Green". Pavan and Galliard,
"Newarke Seidge". Ayre, Almaine and Coranto in D minor. Fantasia-Suite in A minor in
two parts. Fantasias in three parts – C minor; D major; E minor. In Nomine in six parts in
G minor. **Rose Consort of Viols.** Naxos 8 550687 (8/94). ✒
...Two Pavans. 11 Fantasias. Two In Nomines. **Hespèrion XX; Michel Behringer** (org).
Auvidis Astrée E8724 (2/92). ✒
...Fantasia-Suites in four parts – F major; C major; E minor; A minor; F major; D major. Airs for
lyra consort – C major, "The Six Bells"; G major. **The Parley of Instruments / Peter Holman.**
Hyperion CDA66604 (12/92). ✒

Leon Jessel   German 1871-1942

Suggested listening ...
...Parade der Zinnsoldaten, Op. 123. *Coupled with works by various composers.*
New London Orchestra / Ronald Corp.
Hyperion CDA66998 (3/98). *See review in the Collections section; refer to the Index.*

David Johansen   Norwegian 1888-1974

Suggested listening ...
...Portraits, Op. 5. *Coupled with works by various composers.* **Leif Ove Andsnes** (pf).
EMI CDC5 56541-2 (6/98). *See review in the Collections section; refer to the Index.*

David Johnson   American 1922

Suggested listening ...
...Trumpet Tune in F major. *Coupled with works by various composers.* **Christopher Herrick** (org).
Hyperion CDA66917 (8/97). *See review in the Collections section; refer to the Index.*

Robert Johnson II
British c1583-1633

Suggested listening ...
...The Prince's Alman and Coranto. Air in G minor. The Temporiser a 4. The Witty Wanton.
Fantasia in G minor. *Coupled with works by various composers.*
Parley of Instruments Renaissance Violin Band / Peter Holman.
Hyperion CDA66806 (6/96). ☞ *See review in the Collections section; refer to the Index.*

Scott Johnson
American 1952

Suggested listening ...
...How It Happens (The Voice of I.F. Stone) – Cold War Suite.
Coupled with works by various composers. **Kronos Quartet.**
Nonesuch 7559-79372-2 (11/96). *See review in the Collections section; refer to the Index.*

André Jolivet
French 1905-1974

Jolivet Alla rustica[a]. Chant de Linos[b]. Pastorale de Noël[c]. Flute Concerto[d]. Suite en concert[e].
Fantaisie-caprice[f]. Cabrioles[f]. **Manuela Wiesler** (fl); [c]**Christian Davidsson** (bn); [abc]**Erica Goodman**
(hp); [b]**Patrik Swedrup** (vn); [b]**Håkan Olsson** (va); [b]**Helena Nilsson** (vc); [f]**Roland Pöntinen** (pf);
[e]**Kroumata Percussion Ensemble;** [d]**Tapiola Sinfonietta / Paavo Järvi.** BIS Ⓕ CD739
(64 minutes: DDD: 10/96). Item marked [d] from CD630 (6/94), [e]CD272, remainder new to UK.
Recorded 1992-95.
This wide-ranging collection contains short items for flute and piano or harp (the *Fantaisie-caprice*,
Cabrioles – "Capers" – both written around 1953, and *Alla rustica* from ten years later), two ensemble
pieces from the mid-1940s involving the harp (*Chant de Linos* and *Pastorale de Noël*), plus the two
concertos: the first with string orchestra (1949), and the second, *Suite en concert*, with percussion
(1965). Fine as are the rival readings, Manuela Wiesler is arguably preferable. This may be due partly
to her remarkable and commendable width of repertoire, but mainly to her wonderfully intuitive way
with Jolivet's music itself. Somehow she makes it sound just that bit more natural than anyone else,
and let's not forget that he is still a 'difficult' composer for many listeners. The BIS sound is splendid,
though it cannot hide the disparities in dates, venues and internal balance of the pieces recorded, so
volume adjustment between pieces is necessary for optimum playback.
Additional recommendations ...
...Poèmes pour l'enfant[a]. Chant de Linos[b]. Pastorales de Noël. Suite liturgique[a]. [a]**Barbara Rearick**
(mez); [b]**Karen Jones** (fl); **Britten-Pears Ensemble.** ASV Ⓕ CDDCA918 (68 minutes: DDD: 8/95).
...Petite suite[a]. Fantaisie-caprice[b]. Flute Sonata[c]. Sonatine for Flute and Clarinet[d]. Alla rustica[e].
Suite en concert[f]. **Anna Noakes** (fl); [d]**Leslie Craven** (cl); [a]**Jonathan Barritt** (va); [ae]**Gillian Tingay**
(hp); [bc]**Kathron Sturrock** (pf); [f]**Graham Cole,** [f]**Kate Eyre,** [f]**Rachel Gledhill,** [f]**Gary Kettel** (perc) /
[f]**Martin Yates.** ASV Ⓕ CDDCA948 (66 minutes: DDD: 8/96).
...Chant de Linos. *Coupled with works by various composers.* **Emmanuel Pahud** (fl);
Eric Le Sage (pf). EMI Ⓕ CDC5 56488-2 (66 minutes: DDD: 3/98). *See review in the Collections
section; refer to the Index.*
Further listening ...
...Epithalame. *Coupled with works by* **Messiaen** and **Daniel-Lesur The Sixteen /**
Harry Christophers. Collins Classics 1480-2 (11/96).
...Concertino for Trumpet, Piano and Strings. *Coupled with works by various composers.* **Sergei**
Nakariakov (tpt); **Alexander Markovich** (pf); **Lausanne Chamber Orchestra / Jésus López-Cobos.**
Teldec 4509-90846-2 (10/93). *See review in the Collections section; refer to the Index.*
...Hymne à l'Univers. *Coupled with works by various composers.* **Christopher Herrick** (org).
Hyperion CDA66457 (9/91). *See review in the Collections section; refer to the Index.*   ⒼⒼⒼ

Joseph Jongen
Belgian 1873-1953

Jongen Symphonie concertante, Op. 81[a]. Suite, Op. 48[b]. Allegro appassionato, Op. 79[b]
[a]**Hubert Schoonbroodt** (org); [b]**Therese-Marie Gilissen** (va); [a]**Liège Symphony Orchestra /**
René Defossez; [b]**RTBF Symphony Orchestra / Brian Priestman.** Koch Schwann Ⓕ 315 012
(70 minutes: DDD: 8/92). Recorded 1975-85.
Jongen's *Symphonie concertante* is a spectacular showpiece for organ and large orchestra, full of
thrilling effects, unforgettable tunes, spine-tingling climaxes and flashes of great beauty. Written in
1926 its rare performances today belie its sheer crowd-pulling potential, so it's very good to have the
work readily available on CD. Having said that it should be pointed out that while this is a perfectly
acceptable recording, it's neither the only one nor the best (see below for details of the Telarc
recording which is very much in the demonstration class). No, what makes this a "Good CD" are the
two works for viola and orchestra. The viola has little worthwhile concert repertory yet here is some

wonderful music (especially the ravishing "Poème élégiaque" from the *Suite*) which has been allowed to wallow in obscurity for the best part of a century. Hopefully this disc will change all that. Gilissen puts her all into this music, summoning up a vast array of emotions in the *Suite* and producing the kind of virtuoso playing in the *Allegro appassionato* more usually associated with the violin.

Additional recommendation ...
...Symphonie concertante. *Coupled with works by* **Franck** Michael Murray (org); San Francisco Symphony Orchestra / Edo de Waart. Telarc Ⓔ CD80096 (56 minutes: DDD: 3/85).

Further listening ...
...Pièce pour grand orgue. Two Pieces, Op. 53. Pieces, Op. 5 – No. 1, Andante cantabile; No. 2, Pastorale; No. 4, Offertoire; No. 5, Communion. Prélude et fugue, Op. 121. Elégie. Cantilène. Papillons noirs, Op. 69 No. 11. Two Pieces, Op. 47. Petite pièce. Petit prélude. Toccata, Op. 104. John Scott Whiteley (org). Priory PRCD324 (7/93).

Scott Joplin
American 1868-1917

Joplin Maple Leaf Rag[a]. The Entertainer[a]. The Ragtime dance[a]. Gladiolus Rag[a]. Fig Leaf Rag[a]. New Rag[a]. Euphonic Sounds[a]. Elite Syncopations[b]. Bethena[b]. Paragon Rag[b]. Solace[b]. Pine Apple Rag[b]. Weeping Willow[c]. The Cascades[c]. Country Club[c]. Stoptime Rag[c]. Magnetic Rag[a].
Joshua Rifkin (pf). Nonesuch Ⓜ 7559-79449-2 (71 minutes: ADD: A/97). Items marked [a] from H71248 (recorded 1970), [b]H71264 (1972), [c]H71305 (1974).

Joshua Rifkin based his whole approach on Joplin as a notated music in the classical tradition and not merely raw material for jazz musicians to knock about like any standard. After all, Joplin stated on most of his printed scores that it was "never right to play ragtime fast" and he clearly wanted to hear more or less what he wrote, as his own piano rolls show. Rifkin's approach is now totally vindicated. He brought the critical acumen of a musicologist to bear and it gave him the right answers. This collection of 17 rags is carefully balanced and invariably as musically conscientious as if he were playing Mozart. These performances of Rifkin's have stood repetition for some 25 years, whereas many more idiosyncratic treatments have become tiresome. *The Entertainer*, for example, sounds just as fresh here as when it was written. There are times when Rifkin's rare ornamentation in repeats seems slightly stilted, but he always respects the style of the period. There are other recordings of this repertoire but for the real thing – on the piano – there is no substitute for Rifkin, who provides the authentic Joplin experience. This is an important release and essentially the best buy now.

Josquin Desprez
French c1440-1521

Josquin Desprez Missa de beata virgine.
Mouton Nesciens mater. Ave Maria virgo serena. Ave sanctissima Maria. O Maria piissima.
Ave Maria gemma virginum. **Theatre of Voices / Paul Hillier.** Harmonia Mundi Ⓔ HMU90 7136 (53 minutes: DDD: 11/95). Texts and translations included. Recorded 1993.

Among the group of glorious composers who make the years around 1500 one of the richest eras in the history of music, Jean Mouton was one of the most successful; and he was the one who, in the eyes of sixteenth-century musicians, most successfully challenged the peerless Josquin Desprez. So it was a good idea to assemble a programme that juxtaposes the two composers: for Josquin it is his most successful Mass; and for Mouton a group of motets on the same theme – varied but all of them luscious and exhilarating. Effectively Paul Hillier divides up the Mass, as it would have been divided in a celebration, and puts Mouton's motets into the gaps. This works particularly well, the constant juxtaposition of the two similar yet contrasting styles clarifying one's perception of both composers. The music is also superbly performed. The 15 singers of the Theatre of Voices are effortlessly clear, wonderfully in tune and beautifully balanced. You hear the lines and spaces of Josquin just as you hear the immaculately modulated colours of Mouton; and that is partly because the singers have such good control of a range of vocal timbre. But beyond that there is an energy in the performances that keeps everything marvellously alive: even if you occasionally feel that Hillier takes the music a touch briskly, there is constant delight in the shapes that result. This is an issue of enormous distinction.

Additional recommendation ...
...Missa de beata virgine. O virgo prudentissima. Stabat mater dolorosa/Comme femme desconfortee. Ave Maria ... virgo serena (six-voice version). Inviolata integra et castra es, Maria. Tu solus qui facis mirabilia. **A Sei Voci / Bernard Fabre-Garrus.** Auvidis Astrée Ⓔ E8560 (59 minutes: DDD: 5/96).

Josquin Desprez Missa Ave maris stella. Motets – Illibata Dei virgo nutrix. Gaude virgo, mater Christi. Salve regina. In te Domine speravi (with Andrew Lawrence-King, hp). Plaine de dueil. Que vous madame. Regretz sans fin. Adieu mes amours. Je n'ose plus (both with Andrew Lawrence-King).
Anonymous Ave maris stella. **Taverner Consort and Choir / Andrew Parrott.**[b]
EMI Reflexe Ⓔ CDC7 54659-2 (77 minutes: DDD: 5/93). Texts and translations included. Recorded 1992. *Gramophone Editor's choice.*

Ⓖ

The customary glittering, steely sound of the Taverner Consort and Choir is here altered by the unexpected presence of countertenors, in an impressive programme of seldom-heard and seldom-recorded Josquin. The panorama it gives of Josquin's mastery of various techniques is fascinating: nobody could miss the contrast between *Illibata Dei virgo nutrix* and *Gaude virgo, mater Christi*. They are equally impressive, perfect examples of Josquin's contrapuntal and harmonic skill, and yet significantly different in their technical procedures and utterly different in the impression they make. Similarly, the *Missa Ave maris stella*, which stands midway between the earlier Mass settings and later works such as the *Missa Pange lingua*, offers points of comparison and contrast both because of its musical magnificence and because of its relative unfamiliarity. The performances are commensurate with the music, and though it is often something of a risk for an English group to record French-texted works (especially when experiments are involved), the *chansons* recorded here are also delightful.

Additional recommendations ...
...Missa Ave maris stella. Monstra te esse matrem (Ave maris stella). Salve regina. Gaude virgo, mater Christi. Alma Redemptoris mater. Ave regina celorum. Vultum tuum deprecabuntur. **A Sei Voci / Bernard Fabre-Garrus.**
Auvidis Astrée Ⓕ E8507 (63 minutes: DDD: 2/94).
...Scaramella va alla guerra. Allégez moy, doulce plaisant brunette. Allégez moy, doulce plaisant brunette (anonymous arrangement for two lutes). El grillo è buon cantore. De profundis clamavi a 5. Benedicta es, caelorum regina. Credo "De tous biens playne". Guillaume se va chauffeur. Adieu mes amours. Adieu mes amours (sixteenth-century anonymous arrangement for organ). Inviolata, integra et casta es, Maria. *Coupled with works by various composers.*
Early Music Consort of London / David Munrow.
Virgin Classics Veritas Ⓜ VED5 61334-2 (two discs: 132 minutes: ADD: 11/97).
See review in the Collections section; refer to the Index.

Josquin Desprez Missa Gaudeamus. Recordare virgo Mater. Regina caeli. Missa Ave maris stella. Virgo salutiferi/Ave Maria. **A Sei Voci; Maîtrise des Pays de Loire / Bernard Fabre-Garrus** (bass). Auvidis Astrée Ⓕ E8612 (68 minutes: DDD: 6/98). Texts and translations included. Recorded 1997.   ⒼⒼ
Bernard Fabre-Garrus has long been experimenting with different ways of performing renaissance polyphony. It seems that each of his recordings offers a new sound; and in this particular case his novelty is to use the children of the Maîtrise des Pays de Loire – both boys and girls – to sing the top line of Josquin's Mass *Gaudeamus*. This is one of Josquin's most rhythmically intricate works, so there is a major challenge here; just occasionally the rhythms slip a little. But to compensate for that there is a stirring energy to their singing; and part of the elegance of Fabre-Garrus performances has always been in his fluid, linear approach to polyphony, which works splendidly here. Moreover, with just six singers on the three lower lines, he always manages to produce a beautifully clear and balanced texture. This is a very successful and exciting performance of one of Josquin's most stunning masterpieces. His astonishingly varied treatment of the *Gaudeamus* melody ranges from straight imitation through unusually long-held tenor notes (that have a stunning effect on the work's harmonic rhythm), via bravura exercises in ostinato, to the heart-stopping modulations of the final *Agnus Dei*. The plainchants are sung with an unusual lucidity and energy. The motets include the rarely heard *Recordare virgo Mater*, which gives a special opportunity for the children to sing in three parts; and they end with a superlatively eloquent and clear performance of one of Josquin's most famous five-voice motets, *Virgo salutiferi*.

Josquin Desprez Missa L'homme armé super voces musicales. Missa L'homme armé sexti toni. **Anonymous** L'homme armé. **The Tallis Scholars / Peter Phillips.** Gimell Ⓕ 454 919-2PH (74 minutes: DDD: 7/89). Text and translation included.
Towards the end of the Middle Ages it became customary to use popular secular melodies instead of the usual plainchant themes as the basis for composing polyphonic Masses. One such was the fifteenth-century melody *L'homme armé* ("Beware of the armed man"), a melody that may have originated as a crusader song. These settings would provide endless opportunities for a composer to demonstrate his contrapuntal skills. In the first of Josquin's two settings, *Super voces musicales*, he uses the tune over and over again, beginning each time on successive ascending degrees of the six-note scale *Ut re mi fa sol la*, so that it rises higher and higher as the Mass progresses. Sometimes the melody appears back to front from halfway through the piece on to the end. In the *Sexti toni* Mass the tune is transposed so that F rather than G is the final note. The listener's enjoyment is in no way lessened by all this contrapuntal ingenuity. The music flows along with unsurpassed ease and beauty, displaying that unique quality of seeming inevitability which characterizes all great music. It is well matched by the expertise and enthusiasm of The Tallis Scholars and the first-class recording.

Josquin Desprez Missa Pange lingua. Missa La sol fa re mi. **The Tallis Scholars / Peter Phillips.** Gimell 454 909-2PH (3/87). *Gramophone Record Award Winner 1987.*
Gramophone classical 100.   ⒼⒼⒼ
This is absolutely superb. We must accept, of course, that Josquin is unlikely to have heard this music with two ladies on the top line, but they do it so well that only a fundamentalist would mark the disc

down for that. It should also be said that the least successful performance on the entire disc is in the opening *Kyrie* of this Mass where there is a certain brutality in the approach; and although The Tallis Scholars make much of the "Benedictus" and the last *Agnus Dei*, there may still be better ways of doing it. On the other hand, as just one example among many, these were the first musicians to make the "Osanna" truly successful and understand why Josquin should have chosen to compose it that way. But actually they sing even better in the Mass, *La sol fa re mi*. It is almost as though they recorded the works in the order in which they appear on the record and some special understanding of the music came to them in the course of the sessions. Again and again in the singing one has the feeling that Josquin's lines are projected with an understanding and clarity that have rarely been heard before. This is a Mass that performers and record companies have tended to avoid, because on paper it looks as though it couldn't possibly work. The *La sol fa re mi* of the title denotes (among other things) the melodic passage which appears over 200 times in the course of the work with its intervals unchanged – which may not seem a recipe for the kind of music one would want to hear. But Josquin treats his material with such astonishing sophistication that you are rarely aware of the melodic fragment as such; and Phillips is scrupulously careful never to emphasize the melody except in places – such as the end of the second "Osanna" – where it is clearly intended to work as an ostinato. This performance shows that the *La sol fa re mi* belongs with the greatest works of its era.

Additional recommendation ...

...Missa Pange lingua. Vultum tuum deprecabuntur. Planxit autem David. **Westminster Cathedral Choir / James O'Donnell.** Hyperion Ⓔ CDA66614 (76 minutes: DDD: 4/93).

Further listening ...

...Illibata Dei Virgo nutrix. *Coupled with works by various composers.* **The Clerks' Group / Edward Wickham.** ASV Gaudeamus CDGAU143 (3/96).

...Memor esto verbi tui. *Coupled with* **Ockeghem** Missa l'homme armé. Ave Maria. Alma redemptoris mater. **Oxford Camerata / Jeremy Summerly.** Naxos 8 554297 (4/98). *See review under Ockeghem; refer to the Index.*

...Missa Hercules dux Ferrarie. La déploration de Johannes Ockeghem, "Nymphes des bois". *Coupled with* **La Rue** Missa pro defunctis. **New London Chamber Choir / James Wood.** Amon Ra CDSAR24 (3/87).

...(attrib.) Qui habitat in adjutorio Altissimi. *Coupled with works by various composers.* **Huelgas Ensemble / Paul van Nevel.** Sony Classical Vivarte SK66261 (4/96). *See review in the Collections section; refer to the Index.*

...Victimae paschali laudes. *Coupled with works by various composers.* **Orlando Consort.** Metronome METCD1015 (4/97). *See review in the Collections section; refer to the Index.*

John Joubert

South African/British 1927

Suggested listening ...

...The Turning Wheel, Op. 95. *Coupled with works by various composers.* **Tracey Chadwell** (sop); **Pamela Lidiard** (pf). British Music Society BMS420/1CD (3/98). *See review in the Collections section; refer to the Index.*

Dmitry Kabalevsky

Russian/USSR 1904-1987

Kabalevsky Cello Concerto No. 2 in G major, Op. 77[a].
Khachaturian Cello Concerto[a].
Rachmaninov (trans. Rose) Vocalise, Op. 34 No. 14[b]. **Mats Lidström** (vc); [a]**Gothenburg Symphony Orchestra / Vladimir Ashkenazy** ([b]pf). BIS Ⓔ CD719 (65 minutes: DDD: 7/96).
Recorded live in 1995.

This BIS coupling is welcome in providing performances of two works which, if not masterpieces of the calibre of the Elgar or Dvořák concertos, are still sufficiently rewarding to be in the regular concert repertory. It certainly enables Ashkenazy to create an evocative opening atmosphere for the first movement of the Kabalevsky, when after mysterious string pizzicatos the soloist steals in with a gentle, singing tone. The soliloquy continues, for the work's unusual structure, with its three unbroken sections linked by cadenzas, invites an improvisational approach well understood by Mats Lidström. The *Allegro molto* centrepiece of the first movement brings unforced, yet exciting, virtuosity and then the opening mood is tenderly re-evoked. The *Poco marcato* scherzo features blazes of orchestral colour while the soloist swings along with splendid verve. Like the opening section, the third begins with another tender soliloquy, which continues with relatively minor interruptions from the wind and a burst of energetic passion shared by soloist and orchestra; then the mood again becomes tranquil. How differently the Khachaturian Concerto opens, with a flamboyantly coloured orchestral declamation before the cello sails off with vigorous animation. This is followed by a sinuous Armenian theme from the wind which the cello takes up ruminatively, with well-judged *espressivo*. Yet it is the energetic main theme that dominates and the soloist is carried along on its impetus, while ardently recalling the secondary material, finally leading to an exciting sequential coda. The finale offers the busy, rumbustious Khachaturian we know so well from the Violin Concerto. This composer's major works (with the exception of the Violin Concerto) can seem rather inflated, but it must be said that here the combined concentration of Lidström and Ashkenazy minimizes this impression. As an encore we are given a beautiful, restrained account of Rachmaninov's *Vocalise*. The recording is of high quality and well balanced, but a shade over-resonant, although the ear adjusts.

Additional recommendation ...

...Cello Concerto. *Coupled with works by* **Glazunov** and **Khachaturian**
  Raphael Wallfisch (vc); London Philharmonic Orchestra / Bryden Thomson.
  Chandos Ⓕ CHAN8579 (69 minutes: DDD: 6/88).   Ⓖ

Kabalevsky Symphony No. 2 in C minor, Op. 19[a].
Miaskovsky Symphony No. 21, Op. 51, "Fantasy in F sharp minor"[a].
Shostakovich Hamlet suite, Op. 116[a][b] – Introduction; Ball at the palace; The ghost;
  The poisoning; The players; Duel and death of Hamlet. [a]New Philharmonia Orchestra /
  David Measham; [b]National Philharmonic Orchestra / Bernard Herrmann. Unicorn-Kanchana
  Souvenir Ⓜ UKCD2066 (64 minutes: ADD: 2/95). Items marked [a] from RHS346 (4/78),
  [b]Decca PFS4315 (8/75). Recorded 1973-75.

Miaskovsky's twenty-first was for a long time the one symphony which kept his name alive in the West. The subtitle 'Fantasy' is rather a misnomer; nor is there any conspicuous sign of the times in which it was composed. But the themes are attractive in their friendly, neo-romantic-Waltonian way, and for the most part they are capable of standing up to the extensive repetition to which they are subjected – altogether an audience-friendly and rewarding piece. Kabalevsky's Second is no less indebted to the Rimsky-Korsakov academic line of symphonism – Russian romantic but without the emotional pressure. There is much sensitive phrasing from the New Philharmonia and the outer movements of the Kabalevsky go at a fine lick, while the hushed conclusion of his slow movement is beautifully handled. The only signs of short acquaintance are some scrabbly passages in the violins, which are also a drawback in the National Philharmonic Orchestra's playing of the Palace Ball movement in the Shostakovich *Hamlet* Suite. But never mind. This, too, is an idiomatic performance in its gritty determination, and rival versions certainly show no superior understanding of this bleak score. The recordings still sound first-rate.

Further listening ...

...Colas Breugnon – Overture. *Coupled with works by various composers.* **Chicago Symphony
  Orchestra / Fritz Reiner.** RCA Victor Living Stereo 09026 61958-2 (8/94). *See review in the
  Collections section; refer to the Index.*   ⒼⒼⒼ
...Suites – Colas Breugnon, Op. 24a; The Comedians, Op. 26; Romeo and Juliet, Op. 56.
  Moscow Symphony Orchestra / Vasily Jelvakov. Naxos 8 553411 (11/96).
...Violin Concerto in C major, Op. 48. *Coupled with works by* **Tchaikovsky** and **Glazunov**
  Gil Shaham (vn); Russian National Orchestra / Mikhail Pletnev. DG 457 064-2GH (3/98).
...Piano Sonatas – No. 1 in F major, Op. 6; No. 2 in E flat major, Op. 45; No. 3 in F major, Op. 46.
  Four Preludes, Op. 5. Recitative and Rondo, Op. 84. **Artur Pizarro** (pf).
  Collins Classics 1418-2 (12/94).
...Piano Sonata No. 3 in F major. *Coupled with works by various composers.* **Vladimir Horowitz** (pf).
  RCA Victor Gold Seal mono/[a]stereo GD60377* (6/92). *See review in the Collections section;
  refer to the Index.*   ⒼⒼⒼ

Victor Kalinnikov   Russian 1870-1927

Suggested listening ...
...Radiant light. *Coupled with works by various composers.* **Holst Singers / Stephen Layton.**
  Hyperion CDA66928 (8/97). *See review in the Collections section; refer to the Index.*

Imre Kalmán   Hungarian/American 1882-1953

Suggested listening ...
...Die Csárdásfürstin – Tanzen möcht'ich; Ganz ohne Weiber geht die Chose nicht. *Coupled with
  works by various composers.* **Jerry Hadley** (ten); **Munich Radio Orchestra / Richard Bonynge.**
  RCA Victor Red Seal 09026 68258-2 (9/97). *Gramophone Editor's choice. See review in the
  Collections section; refer to the Index.*

Giya Kancheli   Georgian 1935

Kancheli Symphony No. 3[a].
Pärt Symphony No. 3. [a]David James (alto); London Philharmonic Orchestra / Franz
  Welser-Möst. EMI Ⓕ CDC5 55619-2 (55 minutes: DDD: 8/96). *Gramophone Editor's choice.*   Ⓖ
This is a natural and effective coupling of spiritual-minimalist pieces from the Baltic and the Balkans. The benefits are clear in Kancheli's Third Symphony, with its extreme contrasts of solo vocal keening

and Stravinskian outbursts. Here the spaciousness of EMI's recording and the refinement of the LPO's playing are clear gains over the rival Georgian performance (which comes with the added drawback of having been transferred a whole tone too high by the original Melodiya team). The mesmeric folk-derived lament which punctuates the structure was sung on the earlier recording by Rustavi choir-member Gamlet Gonashvili, for whose unearthly tenor Kancheli conceived it. On this issue David James's ethereal countertenor, familiar from his work with the Hilliard Ensemble, is a valid alternative and one sanctioned by the composer. Franz Welser-Möst's basic tempo for the piece is less extreme than Kakhidze's; however, by the same token the impression of hypnotically sustained timelessness is slightly diminished. So for the fullest appreciation of this extraordinary music, both versions are needed. Pärt's Third Symphony, composed in 1971, two years before Kancheli's, is something of a half-way house in the composer's journey towards his now famous ascetic minimalism. Its chant-based archaisms sit rather oddly beside reminders of the twentieth-century mainstream, like a meditation annoyingly distracted by the outside world. Pärt's real breakthrough came with pieces like *Fratres*, which first appeared six years later, where the technical means are even slighter but the contemplative end is the more fully realized. *Fratres* is beautifully shaded and sustained by Welser-Möst and his players.

Additional recommendation ...

...Symphonies Nos. 3[a] and 6[b]. [a]**Gamlet Gonashvili** (ten); [b]**Archil Kharadze**, [b]**Giya Chaduneli** (vas); **Georgia State Symphony Orchestra / Dzansug Kakhidze.** Olympia Explorer OCD401 (9/90). Ⓖ

Kancheli Liturgy for Viola and Orchestra, "Mourned by the Wind"[a]. Bright Sorrow[b]. [b]**Ian Ford,** [b]**Oliver Hayes** (trebs); [a]**France Springuel** (vc); [b]**Cantate Domino Chorus; I Fiamminghi /** **Rudolf Werthen.** Telarc Ⓔ CD80455 (72 minutes: DDD: 10/97). Recorded 1996.

Givi Ordzhonikidze, the editor of a well-known book on Shostakovich, was one of Kancheli's closest friends and staunchest supporters, and it was the sense of loss after his death in 1984 that prompted the composition of the heart-rendingly beautiful *Liturgy* (subtitled *Mourned by the Wind*). The other inspiration was Yuri Bashmet, for this four-movement 40-minute lament was originally a Viola Concerto. It goes superbly on the cello too, thanks to France Springuel's passionate advocacy, and in this form it inevitably invites comparisons with Tavener's *The Protecting Veil*. A common feature of these two pieces is that they can seem almost unbearably moving if they catch you in the right mood and yet almost unbearably protracted if they don't. Yet for all the obvious gestures of lamentation and assuaging, *Liturgy* is not a tear-jerking piece. In fact the texture is for the most part quite transparent, and Kancheli constantly steers away from potentially manipulative clichés on to stonier paths. The more intense the urge towards consolation the more the sense of inconsolability grows; as a result the blind rage which erupts in the second and fourth movements is painfully intense. The Flemish orchestra give a wonderfully controlled performance and Telarc's recording quality is superb. *Bright Sorrow* again draws from the bottomless well of lamentation which is the ex-USSR composer's special curse and privilege. It bears the dedication, "To children, the victims of war", hence the choice of two boy soloists to intone phrases from Goethe, Shakespeare, Pushkin and the contemporary Georgian poet, Galaktion Tabidze, symbolizing the innocent victims of the last world war addressing themselves to the present-day generation. The soloists sing only slow, fragmented lines, marvellously conveying the fragility of innocence. The overall concept of polyglot texting and the fusion of pacifism and religiosity reflects a conscious admiration for Britten's *War Requiem*. The second half of the work seems to be gaining strength and optimism, but these are soon obliterated, leaving behind only a heart-broken crippled waltz. Highly recommended, whether or not you already have the Kancheli 'bug'.

Additional recommendation ...

...Liturgy for Viola and Orchestra, "Mourned by the Wind"[a]. *Coupled with* **Schnittke** Viola Concerto[b]. **Kim Kashkashian** (va); [a]**Bonn Beethovenhalle Orchestra;** [b]**Saarbrücken Radio Symphony Orchestra / Dennis Russell Davies.** ECM New Series Ⓔ 437 199-2 (68 minutes: DDD: 4/93). Ⓖ

Kancheli Bright Sorrow[a]. Mourned by the Wind[b]. [a]**Valentin Konstandi**, [a]**Konstantin Savochkin** (trebs); [b]**Yuri Bashmet** (va); [a]**Boys' Choir of the Moscow Choral School; State Symphony Orchestra of Georgia / Dzansug Kakhidze.** Melodiya Ⓜ 74321 49958-2 (74 minutes: [a]ADD/[b]DDD: 6/98). Item marked [a] recorded 1986, [b]1985.

These two works are every bit as haunting in these reissued Russian performances as in the Flemish ones on Telarc. That's not surprising when you have Bashmet as soloist in a piece written for and dedicated to him: his soaring, plangent tone seems to be made for Kancheli's music and vice versa. More surprising, perhaps, is that France Springuel, playing the cello version, is hardly less breathtaking (and the Telarc recording allows more subtlety of perspective than the Melodiya). There's also little to choose between the performances of *Bright Sorrow*. Kancheli's cantata in memory of child victims of war is a risky concept, consciously echoing Britten's *War Requiem*, but there's never a hint of sentimentality in its deeply felt memorializing. Dzansug Kakhidze is the conductor most closely associated with Kancheli over the years, but Rudolf Werthen has a wonderful instinct for the music too. Melodiya's recording, 1987 vintage, is fine, Telarc's even finer. Both issues have excellent booklet-essays; Melodiya give the more correct translation of *Bright* (rather than *Light*) *Sorrow*. Much inspiration to be had then, whichever issue you plump for.

Further listening ...
...Symphonies – No. 2, "Songs"; No. 7, "Epilogue". **Berlin Radio Symphony Orchestra /**
Michail Jurowski. CPO CPO999 263-2 (8/95).
...Symphonies – No. 4, "In Commemoration of Michaelangelo" (1975); No. 5 (1976).
Georgia State Symphony Orchestra / Dzansug Kakhidze. Olympia OCD403 (4/91).
...Symphonies – No. 6; No. 7, "Epilogue". **Tbilisi Symphony Orchestra / Ojansug Kakhidze.**
Sony Classical St Petersburg Classics SMK66590 (5/95).
...Exil. **Maacha Deubner** (sop); **Natalia Pschenitschnikova** (fl); **Catrin Demenga** (vn); **Ruth Killius**
(va); **Rebecca Firth** (vc); **Christian Sutter** (db) / **Wladimir Jurowski.**
ECM New Series 447 808-2 (12/95).
...Midday Prayers[a]. Night Prayers[b]. Caris Mere[c]. [b]**Vasiko Tevdorashvili** (voc); [ac]**Maacha Deubner**
(sop); [b]**Jan Garbarek** (sax); [a]**Eduard Brunner** (cl); [c]**Kim Kashkashian** (va); [ab]**Stuttgart Chamber**
Orchestra / Dennis Russell Davies. ECM New Series 449 198-2 (4/97).
...Morning Prayers[a]. Evening Prayers[b]. Abii ne viderem[c]. [a]**Vasiko Tevdorashvili** (voc);
[a]**Natalia Pschenitschnikova** (fl); [c]**Kim Kashkashian** (va); [b]**Hilliard Ensemble; Stuttgart Chamber**
Orchestra / Dennis Russell Davies. ECM New Series 445 941-2 (4/95).   ⓖⓔ

Johann Kapsberger
German/Italian c1580-1651

Kapsberger Libro IV d'intavolatura di chitarrone. Libro I d'intavolatura di chitarrone – Toccata
arpeggiata. **Rolf Lislevand** (theorbo); **Eduardo Eguez** (gtr); **Brian Feehan** (chitarrone);
Guido Morini (org/hpd); **Lorentz Duftschmid** (violone); **Pedro Estevan** (perc).
Auvidis Astrée Ⓕ E8515 (60 minutes: DDD: 4/95). Recorded 1993.   ⓖⓔ
Rolf Lislevand is one of the most interesting lutenists active today. He has dazzling technique (listen
to the last track), an extraordinarily wide dynamic range, an effortlessly infectious rhythmic style, and
he grasps hold of the music in a way that makes each piece very much his own. Briefly, he projects
with uncanny ease. He is a thoroughly idiosyncratic musician so one can unhesitatingly recommend
this as a disc for those who normally find lute music tedious and introverted: everything here sizzles
with life. Kapsberger generally has a reputation as an extremely interesting bad composer – a
reputation enthusiastically endorsed in Lislevand's quirky insert-note. But the performances here
bring the music very much to life. Taking his lead from Agazzari's treatise, Lislevand uses a five-man
continuo group to back the solos: a wonderfully flexible and exciting group. And, drawing hints from
some of the titles and styles as well as from the international ambience of Kapsberger's Venice, he
makes much use of oriental sources, not least in the colourful percussion playing of the virtuosic
Pedro Estevan: there is very sophisticated drumming here, and for the "Canario" he creates
an uncanny imitation of a canary. The only faint criticism is that there could have been a little more
documentation. Details of who is playing what would help the ear to understand the myriad
sounds.

Sigfrid Karg-Elert
German 1877-1933

Suggested listening ...
...Improvisation, Op. 81, "Nearer my God to Thee". *Coupled with works by various composers.*
Christopher Herrick (org). Hyperion CDA66917 (8/97). *See review in the Collections section;*
refer to the Index.

Minna Keal
British 1909

Keal Cello Concerto, Op. 5[a]. Ballade[b]. **Alexander Baillie** (vc); [b]**Martina Baillie** (pf);
[a]**BBC Scottish Symphony Orchestra / Martyn Brabbins.** NMC (special price) NMCD048S
(37 minutes: DDD: A/97). Recorded 1997.
It's not often that a disc can include two works by the same composer written more than 50 years
apart. But the point about Minna Keal's career is that its special circumstances (family commitments
that obliged her to abandon her ambitions to compose for so long) do not require special criteria to
be applied to the result. The *Ballade*, which Minna Keal wrote as a student in 1929, has personality
in abundance, with precisely the kind of confidence and strength of purpose needed to justify its
rather flamboyant gestures, reminiscent of John Ireland, Cyril Scott or even Frank Bridge. It must
have seemed quite something at the Royal Academy of Music in those days, and yet, inevitably, the
world of Keal's more recent music is very different. In the Cello Concerto (1988-94) emotional
intensity is more immediate, and as far as form is concerned, she now prefers terseness to elaboration.
Such strongly focused expressiveness might evoke a composer like Berthold Goldschmidt: or is it the
kind of music that Elisabeth Lutyens might have written had she lived for another decade? All kinds
of echoes can be heard here, and yet the music has its own unmistakable personality, using its forces
with an individual flair for sonority and structural proportion. This Cello Concerto is not a curiosity,
but a worthy addition to the repertory, and both performance and recording do it justice.

Keal String Quartet, Op. 1[a]. Wind Quintet, Op. 2[b]. Symphony, Op. 3[c]. Cantillation, Op. 4[cd]. [d]**Stephen Bryant** (vn); [a]**Archaeus Quartet** (Ann Hooley, Bridget Davey, vns; Elizabeth Turnbull, va; Joely Koos; vc); [b]**Lontano** (Ingrid Culliford, fl; Joseph Sanders, ob; David Rix, cl; Richard Skinner, bn; Alison Taylor, hn) / **Odaline de la Martinez;** [c]**BBC Symphony Orchestra / Nicholas Cleobury.** Lorelt Ⓜ LNT110 (68 minutes: DDD: 7/97). Recorded 1996.

Minna Keal studied composition at the Royal Academy of Music but due to family pressures she was forced to abandon her studies. Nearly 50 years later, a chance meeting with composer Justin Connolly reignited her creative spark and Keal produced the works gathered here, all of which abundantly proclaim a very real, late-flowering talent. The String Quartet of 1979 at once impresses in its formal concision, urgent sense of argument and most elegant craft – attributes also very much to the fore in the Op. 2 Wind Quintet. Keal's Symphony No. 3, some five years in gestation, is an ambitious creation, whose richly opulent garb, pleasing sense of architecture and high emotional quotient (especially in the eloquent *Sostenuto* slow movement) easily hold the listener's attention during its 30-minute span – a substantial achievement, well worth getting to know. Similarly the *Cantillation* for violin and orchestra represents another immensely likeable offering: beguilingly colourful, yet always purposeful and (above all) communicative. Performances, production-values and presentation are all beyond reproach. A most stimulating release, well worth investigating.

Albert Ketèlbey   British 1875-1959

Ketèlbey Bells Across the Meadows[b]. Chal Romano[b]. The Clock and the Dresden Figures[bf]. In a Chinese Temple Garden[ab]. In a Monastery Garden[ab]. In a Persian Market[ab]. In the Moonlight (Sous la lune)[b]. In the Mystic Land of Egypt[abe]. Sanctuary of the Heart[abd]. **Luigini** Ballet égyptien, Op. 12 – Suite[c]. [d]**Jean Temperley** (mez); [e]**Vernon Midgley** (ten); [f]**Leslie Pearson** (pf); [a]**Ambrosian Singers;** [b]**Philharmonia Orchestra / John Lanchbery;** [c]**Royal Philharmonic Orchestra / Anatole Fistoulari.** Classics for Pleasure Ⓑ CD-CFP4637 (69 minutes: ADD: 3/94). Items marked [abdef] recorded in 1977, [c]1958.

This Classics for Pleasure reissue gives us a captivating and indispensable budget-price Ketèlbey collection with the Philharmonia Orchestra playing with great style and hugely enjoying themselves. The Ambrosian Singers provide additional atmosphere in *In a Monastery Garden, In a Persian Market, In a Chinese Temple Garden* and *In the Mystic Land of Egypt,* and ensure the sentimental opulence of *Sanctuary of the Heart.* Ketèlbey programmes don't come much better than this. To make it even more enticing, CfP have added the superb 1958 RPO/Anatole Fistoulari recording of Luigini's *Ballet égyptien.* Like the Ketèlbey pieces it is a tuneful suite and has been in and out of the catalogue seemingly since the dawn of time, but has certainly never been better played than it is here. This CD also benefits from exceptionally informative notes.

Additional recommendations ...

...In a Monastery Garden. Wedgwood Blue. In the Mystic Land of Egypt. Bells Across the Meadows. In a Chinese Temple Garden. Sanctuary of the Heart. Cockney Suite – No. 5, Bank Holiday. Phantom Melody. In a Persian Market. *Coupled with works by various composers.* **Royal Philharmonic Choir and Orchestra / Eric Rogers.** Decca London Phase 4 Ⓜ 444 786-2LPF (77 minutes: ADD: 8/96).

...In a Monastery Garden[a]. The Adventurers. Chal Romano – Descriptive Overture. Suite romantique. Caprice pianistique. The Clock and the Dresden Figures. Cockney Suite – No. 3, At the Palais de Danse; No. 5, Bank Holiday. In the Moonlight. Wedgwood Blue. Bells Across the Meadows. Phantom melody. In a Persian Market[a]. [a]**Slovak Philharmonic Male Chorus; Bratislava Radio Symphony Orchestra / Adrian Leaper.** Marco Polo Ⓕ 8 223442 (74 minutes: DDD: 4/94).

...Bells Across the Meadows. *Coupled with works by various composers.* **New London Orchestra / Ronald Corp.** Hyperion Ⓕ CDA66868 (78 minutes: DDD: 7/96). *Gramophone Editor's record of the month.*   Ⓖ

...Sanctuary of the Heart. *Coupled with works by various composers.* **The New London Orchestra / Ronald Corp.** Hyperion Ⓕ CDA66968 (76 minutes: DDD: 5/97). *Gramophone Editor's choice.* Ⓖ

Aram Khachaturian   Russian/USSR 1903-1978

Khachaturian Violin Concerto in D minor. **Tchaikovsky** (arr. Glazunov) Méditation, Op. 42 No. 1. **Itzhak Perlman** (vn); **Israel Philharmonic Orchestra / Zubin Mehta.** EMI Ⓕ CDC7 47087-2 (46 minutes: DDD: 7/85). From EL270108-1 (3/85).

The twentieth century has had its share of great violin concertos. Khachaturian's is not quite that, in the sense that it never attempts the heights and depths we find in his Soviet colleagues, Prokofiev and Shostakovich; but is a work of considerable charm, beautifully written. Shostakovich once pointed out that a "natural and folk idiom" was evident in everything his friend wrote, and Khachaturian's Armenian origin is agreeably evident in the melodic and harmonic contours of the lilting second theme in the first movement and the *Andante sostenuto* that follows. It goes without saying that Itzhak Perlman plays this work with total technical command and persuasive feeling, and the result is most enjoyable, even if one feels in some places, such as the first movement's long cadenza, that musical inspiration is being spread rather thin. The finale, however, is predictably exciting. The Tchaikovsky *Méditation* coupling is well worth having, both for its intrinsic quality and also because it was originally planned as the slow movement of his own Violin Concerto. There is good accompaniment from Mehta and the Israel Philharmonic Orchestra and a bright recording.

Additional recommendation ...

...Violin Concerto in D minor. *Coupled with* **Kabalevsky** Violin Concerto in C major, Op. 48.
  Lydia Mordkovitch (vn); **Royal Scottish National Orchestra / Neeme Järvi.**
  Chandos Ⓕ CHAN8918 (53 minutes: DDD: 3/91).

Khachaturian Piano Concerto[a]. Dance Suite. Five Pieces for Wind Band – Waltz; Polka.
  [a]**Dora Serviarian-Kuhn** (pf); **Armenian Philharmonic Orchestra / Loris Tjeknavorian.**
  ASV Ⓕ CDDCA964 (59 minutes: DDD: 6/96). Recorded 1995.

In the Piano Concerto Dora Serviarian-Kuhn and her Armenian compatriot, Loris Tjeknavorian, are in every way first-class: both identify naturally with the sinuous oriental flavour of the melodic lines and understand that the outer movements need above all to convey thrusting vitality; here there is plenty of drive and rhythmic lift. But what primarily makes this performance memorable is Serviarian-Kuhn's sense of fantasy, so that her various cadential passages, for all their brilliance, are charismatically quixotic rather than merely bravura displays. The other works are very small beer. The "Waltz" for wind band has an engaging carousel flavour; the somewhat vulgar "Polka" which follows roisterously suggests the circus. The *Dance Suite* goes through the usual Khachaturian routines with which he likes to clothe his agreeable but at times rather insubstantial Armenian folk ideas. Easily the most memorable movement is the first and much the longer of the two Uzbek dances, which opens gently and touchingly: the reprise, with its haunting cor anglais solo, has a genial Nordic feeling. The closing "Lezghinka", too, is rather jolly, but repetitive. Excellent performances, vividly recorded.

Additional recommendation ...

...Symphony No. 2 in E minor, "The Bell"[a]. Piano Concerto[b]. Violin Concerto in D minor[c].
  Masquerade – Suite[d]. [c]**Ruggiero Ricci** (vn); [b]**Alicia de Larrocha** (pf); [a]**Vienna Philharmonic Orchestra / Aram Khachaturian;** [bc]**London Philharmonic Orchestra /** [b]**Raphael Frühbeck de Burgos,** [c]**Anatole Fistoulari;** [d]**London Symphony Orchestra / Stanley Black.**
  Double Decca Ⓜ 448 252-2DF2 (two discs: 146 minutes: ADD: 6/96).

Khachaturian Masquerade[a] – Waltz; Nocturne; Mazurka. Violin Concerto in D minor[b].
  Gayaneh[c] – Sabre Dance; Ayesha's Dance; Dance of the Rose Maidens; Lullaby; Lezghinka; Gayaneh's Adagio; Lyrical duo; Dance of the old people. [b]**David Oistrakh** (vn); **Philharmonia Orchestra / Aram Khachaturian.** EMI Composers in Person mono Ⓕ CDC5 55035-2*
  (79 minutes: ADD: 7/94). Item marked [a] from Columbia 33C1043 (11/55), [b]Columbia 33CX1303 (12/55), [c]33C1041 (10/55).

From the 1950s onwards Khachaturian made records quite regularly in the Soviet Union. There were also sessions in Vienna and London in 1954, 1961 and 1977. All the fruits of the 1954 sessions are here, with the exception of a short essay, *In memoriam*, for which there was no room on a very well-filled disc. The 1954 mono sound is not exactly state-of-the-art for its time, despite the expert attention of the remastering engineer, but it is more than good enough to convey the superb quality of the Philharmonia's playing at a vintage period in their existence. Khachaturian was a vigorous, effective conductor and the players respond to his uncomplicated, outgoing style as a composer with obvious enthusiasm. The recordings were sandwiched between Beethoven sessions with Klemperer and must have made a pleasant contrast. The Violin Concerto was written for Oistrakh in 1940 and he plays it with effortless, cheerful virtuosity in the outer movements and responds to the warmth of the central *Andante* in a particularly expressive, eloquent fashion. The three attractively romantic *Masquerade* pieces are very charmingly played, while in the seven numbers from *Gayaneh* the Philharmonia tear into the faster items with great gusto, and produce a particularly beautiful quality of string tone in the *Adagio*. None of the music on this disc is exactly first-rate, but it all comes to life very vividly and enjoyably through being played with such expertise and authority.

Khachaturian The Widow of Valencia – Suite. Gayaneh – Suite No. 2.
Tjeknavorian Danses fantastiques. **Armenian Philharmonic Orchestra / Loris Tjeknavorian.**
  ASV Ⓕ CDDCA884 (65 minutes: DDD: 3/94).   Ⓖ

Khachaturian's *The Widow of Valencia* is an early work (1940), yet already reveals the composer's fund of good tunes. He admitted its lack of authentic Spanishness and while the "Introduction" opens with flashing southern Mediterranean gusto, it soon makes way for a sultry Armenian melody of best local vintage. However, why worry? Altogether this is a most winning suite, without a dull bar, piquantly scored and brilliantly presented by an orchestra who are completely at home and clearly enjoying themselves. They also give us another suite, comprising six indelible numbers – for the most part little known – from Khachaturian's masterpiece, *Gayaneh*. Tjeknavorian's own *Danses fantastiques* frequently burst with energy and the gentler dances have that Armenian flavour so familiar in *Gayaneh*. Brilliant playing in glittering yet spacious sound.

Khachaturian Spartacus – Ballet suites Nos. 1-3. **Royal Scottish National Orchestra / Neeme Järvi.**
Chandos Ⓟ CHAN8927 (63 minutes: DDD: 5/91).
Khachaturian's ballet, *Spartacus*, first produced in 1956, was a judicious, and in the event a highly successful artistic response to the demands of Soviet populist realism. For its dramatic narrative of a Roman slave rebelling against his captors, eventually to be betrayed and killed, the composer created a score of striking vitality, at once full-blooded and crude, passionate and tuneful, and yet undoubtedly individual. The ballet's most famous number, the "Adagio of Phrygia and Spartacus", with its sweeping string tune, is justly popular and the theme returns nostalgically at the end in Phrygia's parting scene. Elsewhere there are many expressions of joyous extroversion and scenes of wild revelry, in which the music erupts with great physical energy, for example the "Entrance of the Merchants" and the wild "Dance of the Pirates", both in Suite No. 2. The scene of "The Market" which opens Suite No. 3 has enormous bustle. The romantic side of the score is full of languid sensuality: the Gaditanian Maidens (in the First Suite) are deliciously and decadently alluring, and the "Dance of the Egyptian Girl" is hardly less seductive in its sentient atmosphere. Those who enjoy the "Sabre Dance" from *Gayaneh* will respond to the vigorous "Dance of a Greek Slave" with its fiery rhythmic bite. Järvi and his Scottish players respond exuberantly to the near vulgarity of the unbuttoned animation and obviously revel in the lusher evocations. The resonant acoustics of the Henry Wood Hall, Glasgow, cast a rich ambient glow over Khachaturian's vivid primary colours and prevent the cruder climaxes from sounding too aggressive.

Further listening ...
...Cello Concerto. *Coupled with works by* **Kabalevsky** and **Glazunov** Raphael Wallfisch (vc);
London Philharmonic Orchestra / Bryden Thomson. Chandos CHAN8579 (6/88).
...Cello Concerto. *Coupled with works by* **Kabalevsky** and **Rachmaninov** Mats Lidström (vc);
Gothenburg Symphony Orchestra / Vladimir Ashkenazy (pf). BIS CD719 (7/96). *See review under Kabalevsky; refer to the Index.*
...Pepo. Undying Flame. Secret Mission. Admiral Ushakov. Prisoner No. 217.
Armenian Philharmonic Orchestra / Loris Tjeknavorian. ASV CDDCA966 (10/97).
...Symphonies – No. 1 in E minor; No. 3 in C major, "Simfoniya-poema".
Armenian Philharmonic Orchestra / Loris Tjeknavorian. ASV CDDCA858 (6/93).
...Symphony No. 3 in C major, "Simfoniya-poema". Triumphal Poem. *Coupled with*
Ippolitov-Ivanov Caucasian Sketches, Op. 10. **BBC Philharmonic Orchestra /**
Fedor Glushchenko. Chandos CHAN9321 (5/95).
...Trio for Clarinet, Violin and Piano. *Coupled with works by* **Kokai.** *and* **Prokofiev**
Walter Boeykens Ensemble. Harmonia Mundi HMC90 1419 (6/93).

Karen Khachaturian

USSR 1920

Suggested listening ...
...Violin Sonata in G minor, Op. 1. *Coupled with works by* **Prokofiev** *and* **Szymanowski**
David Oistrakh (vn); **Vladimir Yampolsky** (pf). Testament mono SBT1113* (2/98).
See review under Prokofiev; refer to the Index.
ⒼⒼⒼ

Wilhelm Kilmayer

German 1927

Suggested listening ...
...Trois études blanches. Douze études transcendentales. Drei verstreute Klavierstücke.
Rundgesänge und Morgenlieder. **Siegfried Mauser** (pf). Wergo WER6618-2 (2/98).

Leon Kirchner

American 1919

Suggested listening ...
...Music for Cello and Orchestra. *Coupled with works by* **Danielpour** and **Rouse**
Yo-Yo Ma (vc); **Philadelphia Orchestra / David Zinman.** Sony Classical SK66299 (3/97).
Gramophone Editor's choice. Selected by Soundings. See review under Danielpour;
refer to the Index. Ⓖ
...Triptych. *Coupled with works by various composers.* **Yo-Yo Ma** (vc); **Lynn Chang** (vn).
Sony Classical SK53126 (4/94). *See review in the Collections section; refer to the Index.* Ⓖ

Uuno Klami

Finnish 1900-1961

Suggested listening ...
...Whirls, Act 1 (arr. and orch. Aho). Violin Concerto, Op. 32[a]. Suomenlinna, Op. 30.
[a]**Jennifer Koh** (vn); **Lahti Symphony Orchestra / Osmo Vänskä.** BIS CD696 (1/98).

Gideon Klein

Klein String Trio. Fantasie a Fuga. Piano Sonata[a]. String Quartet, Op. 2.
Ullmann String Quartet No. 3, Op. 43. **Hawthorne Quartet** (Roman Lefkowitz, Si Jing Huang, vns; Mark Ludwig, va; Sato Knudsen, vc); [a]**Virginia Eskin** (pf). Channel Classics Ⓟ CCS1691 (68 minutes: DDD: 12/91). Recorded 1991.   ⒼⒼ
This CD is devoted to music by two Jewish musicians incarcerated in the Theresienstadt ghetto camp established by the Nazis in November 1941. Gideon Klein and Viktor Ullmann were substantial figures whose music needs no special pleading. In stylistic terms, Ullmann is perhaps the more predictable of the two. His Third Quartet shows him remaining true to Schoenbergian expressionism within a tonal context. Klein, deported to the camp at the age of 21, was by all accounts an astonishingly accomplished musician. His own music shows clear signs of potential greatness even if the major influences – including Schoenberg, Janáček and Bartók – are not fully assimilated. The invigorating String Trio, completed only nine days before Klein's disappearance, receives a magnificent performance from members of the Hawthorne Quartet, a group drawn from the Boston Symphony Orchestra. Virginia Eskin gives a powerful account of the Piano Sonata, humming along discreetly as she plays. High praise also for these ideally balanced recordings which document a form of spiritual resistance of an isolated and terrorized community which we can barely begin to comprehend.
Further listening ...
...Fantasie a Fuga[a]. String Trio[b]. Piano Sonata[c]. First Sin[d]. Two Madrigals[e]. Czech and Russian Folksongs[f]. [d]**Karel Kožušnik** (ten); [c]**Allan Sternfield** (pf); [ab]**The Group for New Music;** [ef]**Prague Philharmonic Choir / Pavel Kühn.** Koch International Classics 37230-2 (8/94).

Oliver Knussen

Knussen Flourish with Fireworks, Op. 22. The Way to Castle Yonder, Op. 21*a*. Two Organa, Op. 27. Horn Concerto, Op. 28[b]. Music for a Puppet Court, Op. 11. Whitman Settings, Op. 25[a]. "... upon one note", fantazia after Purcell. [a]**Lucy Shelton** (sop); [b]**Barry Tuckwell** (hn); **London Sinfonietta / Oliver Knussen.** DG Ⓟ 449 572-2GH (45 minutes: DDD: 1/97). Text included. Recorded 1995. *Gramophone Editor's choice. Selected by Soundings.*   ⒼⒼ
This is a sample of what Knussen has written since his two one-act operas *Where the Wild Things are* (1984) and *Higglety Pigglety Pop!* (1985), a period during which, he says, he has come to prefer being "bewitched for a few minutes than hypnotized for an hour". Bewitching these short pieces certainly are. The *Flourish* has lyrical substance as well as the appropriate 'occasional' brilliance. *The Way to Castle Yonder* is a very brief suite from *Higglety Pigglety Pop!*, but also a vivid orchestral tone-poem in its own right. The *Organa* are fine examples of his love of fantasy, ingenious pieces that use a twelfth-century technique to modern ends with such audible logic and lucid instrumentation that you want to hear both again immediately. Something similar happens in *Music for a Puppet Court*, two solutions to puzzle-canons by the Tudor composer John Lloyd flanking further developments of the same material. The lengthiest works here are both in a sense dreams. *"... upon one note"* is a day-dream from which Knussen is awoken by Purcell. The Horn Concerto is a beautiful, allusive dream about all the worlds that the solo horn can evoke, from woodland poetry to dark menace. Knussen is a masterly orchestrator. This disc will give unalloyed pleasure.
Further listening ...
...Symphonies – No. 2, Op. 7[a]; No. 3, Op. 18[b]. Trumpets, Op. 12[c]. Coursing, Op. 17[e]. Cantata, Op. 15[d]. Ophelia Dances, Book 1, Op. 18[b]. [a]**Elaine Barry,** [c]**Linda Hirst** (sops); [c]**Michael Collins,** [c]**Edward Pillinger,** [c]**Ian Mitchell** (clarinets); [d]**Nash Ensemble;** [b]**Philharmonia Orchestra / Michael Tilson Thomas;** [ae]**London Sinfonietta / Oliver Knussen.**
Unicorn-Kanchana Souvenir UKCD2010 (9/88).   Ⓖ

Sigurd von Koch

Suggested listening ...
...Exotic Songs – No. 1, In the month of Tjaitra; No. 3, Of lotus scent and moonlight. The wild swans – Spring night's rain; Mankind's lot; The wild swans. *Coupled with works by various composers.* **Anne Sofie von Otter** (mez); **Bengt Forsberg** (pf). DG 449 189-2GH (5/96). *Gramophone Editor's choice. See review in the Collections section; refer to the Index.*   ⒼⒼ

Zoltán Kodály

Kodály Symphony in C major. Summer Evening. Magyar Rondo[a]. [a]**Christopher Warren-Green** (vn); **Philharmonia Orchestra / Yondani Butt.** ASV Ⓟ CDDCA924 (54 minutes: DDD: 9/95). Recorded 1994.
Kodály's only Symphony has an engagingly pastoral quality, with mild but memorable thematic material, lively – even somewhat overwrought – musical arguments (probably the symphony's main

weakness) and notably scenic orchestration. Yondani Butt presents a volatile view of the piece, with weighty textures and a fairly intense delivery, especially in the first movement's emphatic development section. The slow movement, an elegiac *Andante* based on folk-style motives, is appealingly atmospheric, while the fresh-faced finale generates plenty of rustic excitement. As to available alternatives, the most obvious comparison has been issued as part of a mid-price Double Decca album which features two of the works programmed here – the Symphony and *Summer Evening* – in 1973 recordings by the Philharmonia Hungarica under Antál Dorati. The differences between the performances of the Symphony are quite significant, with Butt offering the broader paced, more momentous reading set within an imposing sound-frame, and Dorati (who is clearly, if less dynamically, recorded) scoring both in terms of superior orchestral execution and greater overall refinement. Both versions of *Summer Evening* underline the music's alternation of dance and reverie, whereas Butt's invigorating performance of the rarely heard but strangely more-ish *Magyar Rondo* (shades of Bartók's *Romanian Folk Dances*) has the Philharmonia playing like a generously augmented gipsy band, with stylish solo work from Christopher Warren-Green. Enthusiasm and sincerity are much in evidence throughout this well-recorded concert, while the odd spot of executive ruggedness is fairly appropriate to the music's outdoor character. A cordial recommendation.

Additional recommendation ...
...Symphony in C major. Háry János – concert suite. Dances from Galánta. Variations on a Hungarian folksong. Dances of Marosszék. Theatre Overture. Concerto for Orchestra. Summer Evening. **Philharmonia Hungarica / Antál Dorati.**
Double Decca Ⓜ 443 006-2DF2 (two discs: 150 minutes: ADD).

Kodály Magyar Rondo. Summer Evening.
Suk Serenade in E flat major, Op. 6. **Orpheus Chamber Orchestra.** DG Ⓕ 447 109-2GH
(52 minutes: DDD: 7/96).
The programme is winning, the playing spruce and the sound remarkably lifelike. Kodály's *Magyar Rondo* opens as if in imitation of Bartók's *Romanian Folkdances* (of two years earlier), though what actually emerges is a sequence of original Hungarian folk tunes – the recurring principal piece slow, the others fast – scored for strings, two clarinets and bassoons. It's a delightful work and a remarkable performance, not least for the way the Orpheus Chamber Orchestra come with gipsy slides and teasing rubato: once the action hots up, you could as well be listening to a top-class Hungarian folk band. *Summer Evening* also incorporates folk-style material, albeit with a certain formal ingenuity; the overall tone suggests an affectionate though unsentimental pastoral soundscape. Again, the scoring is relatively light (although the wind line-up is heavier than in the *Rondo*), which of course suits the Orpheus well. In Suk's *Serenade*, the playing itself is extremely well drilled, the tone silken, the phrasing effectively attenuated but the overall effect might have benefited from rather more in the way of dynamic shading and phrasal individuality. However, this is an enjoyable programme and the *Rondo* in particular is a real delight.

Kodály Háry János – concert suite. Dances of Marosszék. Variations on a Hungarian folksong, "The Peacock". Dances from Galánta. **Montreal Symphony Orchestra / Charles Dutoit.**
Decca Ⓕ 444 322-2DH (77 minutes: DDD: 4/96). Recorded 1994.
The Dorati disc (listed above), compiled from analogue recordings made in Marl in 1973, still sounds very impressive, though the CD transfer brings brightness that next to the Dutoit versions seems rather aggressive, almost glaring. The obvious merit of the Dorati reading of each piece is that, with Hungarian players as well as Hungarian conductor, they convey an extra idiomatic flair in the rhythms. So in the fifth movement "Intermezzo" of *Háry János* the big *tenutos* in this very nationalistic piece are even more winningly timed than with Dutoit, warmly persuasive though he is. Against that, the instrumental solos are often more imaginatively played by the Montreal principals, as for example the saxophone in the final Funeral March section of the fourth movement, the "Battle and Defeat of Napoleon". The *Peacock* Variations benefit even more than *Háry János* from the opulence of the Montreal sound, most of all in the glorious climax of the finale, which with Dutoit has tremendous panache. The Dorati version may be a degree more wild, but that climax is not nearly so rich. In the two sets of *Dances* Dutoit is not only warmly sympathetic in his springing of rhythms and moulding of phrases, he is more purposeful even than Dorati. For this apt and generous coupling of Kodály's four most popular orchestral pieces Dutoit stands as a clear first choice, though at mid price, with keenly idiomatic performances, the Dorati disc is still a strong contender.

Additional recommendations ...
...Háry János. Variations on a Hungarian folksong. **Ravel** Daphnis et Chloé – Suite No. 2. **Concertgebouw Orchestra / Willem Mengelberg.**
Archive Documents Mengelberg Edition mono Ⓕ ADCD115* (70 minutes: AAD: 3/96).
...Háry János – concert suite. Dances from Galánta. Dances of Marosszék. **London Philharmonic Orchestra / Walter Susskind.** Classics for Pleasure Ⓑ CD-CFP6029 (59 minutes: ADD: 5/98).

Kodály Solo Cello Sonata, Op. 8. Cello Sonata, Op. 4[a]. Three Chorale Preludes (after Bach)[a].
Maria Kliegel (vc); [a]**Jenö Jandó** (pf). Naxos Ⓢ 8 553160 (64 minutes: DDD: 3/97).
Maria Kliegel rises to the challenge of Kodály's Solo Sonata with considerable gusto: harmonics, *glissandos* (sometimes plucked with vibrato, as on a guitar), *sul ponticello*, fiery arpeggios – all are

expertly employed and delivered via a nicely rounded tone. Kliegel's lustrous account of the *Adagio* (to be played *con grand espressiono*) underlines harmonic similarities with late Liszt and the folky, one-man-band finale has plenty of panache. The appreciative booklet-note relates Bartók's enthusiasm for the Solo Sonata's "unusual and original style ... [and] surprising vocal effects". In fact, no other work by Kodály is so profoundly Bartókian in spirit (propulsive rhythms, novel tonalities, declamatory gestures, and so on). The Sonata, Op. 4 is a far milder piece, though forthright expressive declamation sits at the centre of the first movement and the second is infused with the spirit of folk music. Kliegel and Jenö Jandó are in obvious musical accord, and the recording is very good – although if you listen to the 'Bach-Kodály' tracks and wait for the Solo Sonata to start, you'll note a huge expansion in the cello's recorded profile. The three *Chorale Preludes* that open the programme are "attributed Bach" and enjoy the rich trimmings of a thunderous piano part (Busoni-cum-Liszt, with a snatch of Bartók added for good measure) and a warm flood of tone from Kliegel. A fine bargain, then, and a well-planned coupling.

Additional recommendations ...

...Solo Cello Sonata. *Coupled with works by* **Crumb** *and* **Escher** Pieter Wispelwey (vc). Globe Ⓕ GLO5089 (68 minutes: DDD: 12/94).

...Cello Sonata, Op. 4. *Coupled with works by* **Janáček** *and* **Liszt** Anne Gastinel (vc); **Pierre-Laurent Aimard** (pf). Auvidis Valois Ⓕ V4748 (50 minutes: DDD: 9/95). *See review under Janáček; refer to the Index.*

...Solo Cello Sonata. *Coupled with works by various composers.* **Matt Haimovitz** (vc). DG Ⓕ 445 834-2GH (69 minutes: DDD: 12/95).

...Solo Cello Sonata. *Coupled with works by various composers.* **János Starker** (vc); **Gerald Moore** (pf); **Philharmonia Orchestra / Carlo Maria Giulini, Walter Susskind.** EMI mono/stereo Ⓜ CZS5 68485-2 (six discs: 398 minutes: ADD: 12/95). *See review in the Collections section; refer to the Index.*

...Solo Cello Sonata. Cello Sonata, Op. 4[a]. **Lluis Claret** (vc); [a]**Rose-Marie Cabestany** (pf). Harmonia Mundi Musique d'abord Ⓑ HMA190 1325 (50 minutes: DDD: 2/96).

Kodály Háry János, Op. 15[a]. **Erzesébet Komlóssy** (contr) Orzse; **László Palócz** (bass-bar) Marczi; **György Melis** (bar) Háry János, Napoleon; **Zsolt Bende** (bar) Bombazine; **Olga Szönyi** (sop) Marie-Louise; **Margit László** (sop) Empress; **Sir Peter Ustinov** (narr).
Kodály Variations on a Hungarian folksong, "The Peacock"[b]. The Peacock[c]. Psalmus Hungaricus, Op. 13[d]. [d]**Lajos Kozma** (ten); [a]**Edinburgh Festival Chorus;** [d]**Brighton Festival Chorus;** [ad]**Wandsworth School Boys' Choir; London Symphony** [c]**Chorus and** [abd]**Orchestra / István Kertész.** Double Decca Ⓜ 443 488-2DF2 (two discs: 153 minutes: ADD: 10/95). Item marked [a] from SET399/400 (11/69), [bcd]SXL6497 (4/71).

An absolute must for children young and old, and certainly for all lovers of the Suite that Kodály extracted from his delightful musical-cum-opera-cum-pantomime. Peter Ustinov's dazzling, occasionally Goon-like characterizations of the entire speaking cast are inexhaustibly entertaining, and yet the kindly moral theme that underpins the libretto of *Háry János* – Hungarian nationalism benevolently respected by the Austrians – emerges intact. And if you're wondering whether the complete score harbours much in the way of worthwhile music that lovers of the Suite don't already know, then the answer is a resounding 'yes' – gipsy tunes, Hussar songs, colourful extensions of familiar material (the "Intermezzo", especially) and a substantial finale based on the Suite's "Song". Kertész's extrovert conducting is quite beyond criticism and Decca's 1968 recording is an experience in itself, with sundry sound effects (galloping steeds, gurgling liquids, crowd scenes, and so on) and a thrillingly aggressive presentation of brass and percussion. Decca's transfer is admirably up-front, and the odd audible edit or spot of rumble (tape or traffic, or both) hardly amount to adequate grounds for complaint. The fill-ups are both welcome and musically substantial. It was a good idea to preface the *Peacock* Variations with Kodály's choral arrangement of the original folk-song (a fine performance by the London Symphony Chorus), while the Variations themselves are given with considerable gusto and feeling for atmosphere. The *Psalmus Hungaricus* (arguably Kodály's masterpiece) receives a bright and forceful performance under Kertész, dramatically sung by tenor Lajos Kozma. This is a remarkably well-filled and well-planned set, although readers are warned that the otherwise excellent annotation includes neither texts nor translations.

Additional recommendation ...

...Psalmus Hungaricus[a]. Missa Brevis[b]. Pange Lingua[c]. Psalm 114[d]. [ab]**Elizabeth Gale,** [b]**Sally Le Sage,** [b]**Hannah Francis** (sops); [b]**Alfreda Hodgson** (contr); [a]**Lajos Kozma,** [b]**Ian Caley** (tens); [b]**Michael Rippon** (bass); [bc]**Christopher Bowers-Broadbent,** [d]**Gillian Weir** (orgs); [abcd]**Brighton Festival Chorus / László Heltay;** [a]**London Symphony Orchestra / István Kertész.** Decca Enterprise Ⓜ 433 080-2DM (70 minutes: ADD: 8/92).   Ⓖ

...Psalmus Hungaricus, Op. 13. *Coupled with works by* **Bartók** *and* **Weiner** Tamás Daróczy (ten); **Hungarian Radio and Television** [ab]**Chorus and** [b]**Children's Chorus;** [b]**Schola Cantorum Budapestiensis; Budapest Festival Orchestra / Sir Georg Solti.** Decca Ⓕ 458 929-2DH (59 minutes: DDD: 6/98). *Gramophone Editor's choice. See review under Weiner; refer to the Index.*

Further listening ...

...Intermezzo. **Dohnányi** String Quartets – No. 2 in D flat major, Op. 15; No. 3 in A minor, Op. 33. **Lyric Quartet.** ASV CDDCA985 (1/98). *See review under Dohnányi; refer to the Index.*

...String Quartet No. 2, Op. 10. *Coupled with works by* **Dvořák** **Hagen Quartet.**
DG 419 601-2GH (5/87).
...String Quartets – No. 1, Op. 2; No. 2, Op. 10. Gavotte. **Kontra Quartet.** BIS CD564 (1/95). ⓖ
...String Quartet No. 2, Op. 10. *Coupled with works by* **Dvořák** and **Smetana** **Hollywood Quartet.**
Testament mono/stereo SBT1072* (5/96).
...Laudes organi. Missa brevis. **Netherlands Chamber Choir / Uwe Gronostay**
with **Edgar Krapp** (org). Globe GLO5115 (1/95).
...Seven Pieces, Op. 11. *Coupled with works by various composers.* **Peter Frankl** (pf).
ASV CDDCA860 (6/93). *See review in the Collections section; refer to the Index.* ⓖⓖⓖ

Charles Koechlin
French 1867-1950

Koechlin Le livre de la jungle – Poèmes, Op. 18ᵃ. La course de printemps, Op. 95. La méditation
de Purun Bhagat, Op. 159. La loi de la Jungle, Op. 175. Les Bandar-Log, Op. 176. ᵃ**Iris Vermillion**
(mez); ᵃ**Johan Botha** (ten); ᵃ**Ralf Lukas** (bass); ᵃ**Berlin Radio Chamber Choir; Berlin Radio
Symphony Orchestra / David Zinman.** RCA Victor Red Seal (Special price) 09026 61955-2
(two discs: 90 minutes: DDD: 6/94). Texts and translations included. Recorded 1993.
Gramophone Award Winner 1994. ⓖⓖ
For 40 years, from his mid-thirties onwards, Koechlin, when he wasn't day-dreaming about goddesses
of the cinema screen, was obsessed with Kipling's two *Jungle Books*. This eventually materialized in
a large canvas of four symphonic poems, preceded by three songs (with chorus) that he then
orchestrated. The complete sequence, called *The Jungle Book*, appears for the first time on the present
disc; the Marco Polo disc contains only the orchestral works. RCA's inclusion of the Op. 18 songs
necessitates spreading to two discs, (though priced as a single disc): nevertheless the first song, the
lushly scored "Seal lullaby" (the only movement not sited in the Indian rain forest), is so seductively
beautiful that it would be a pity to miss it, especially as well sung as it is by Iris Vermillion. Of the
symphonic poems, only *The Bandar-Log* is at all known here. The title refers to the noisy, empty-
headed race of monkeys which gives Koechlin an opportunity to pillory parallelism, dodecaphony
and the sterile 'Back to Bach' movement then topical (in a fugato with each voice in a different key),
all in a dazzlingly virtuoso piece of scoring for a huge orchestra. Much the longest of the orchestral
pieces is *La course de printemps*, another virtuoso score, which falls into four sections – mysticism as
spring slowly stirs in the forest, Mowgli's urge finally to leave the animal companions with whom he
has lived and return to mankind, the painful following of unsettling "new trails" and "time of new
talk" (another metaphor for the world of musical composition), and night falling again (mainly an
immensely long monodic line over a pedal-note). Do not miss these remarkable scores, which reveal
a distinctly individual and boldly forward-looking mind with a wide stylistic vocabulary (generally
atonal), great dramatic sense and a stunning technical command. The orchestra rise fully to the
occasion and the sound is clear and vivid.
Additional recommendation ...
...**Rheinland-Pfalz State Philharmonic Orchestra / Leif Segerstam.**
Marco Polo Ⓕ 8 223484 (73 minutes: DDD: 6/94). ⓖ
Further listening ...
...Au loin, Op. 20 No. 2. Sur les flots lointains, Op. 130 (two versions). Le buisson ardent,
Op. 203/171. **Rheinland-Pfalz State Philharmonic Orchestra / Leif Segerstam.**
Marco Polo 8 223704 (8/95).
...Les heures persanes, Op. 65. **Rhineland-Pfalz State Philharmonic Orchestra / Leif Segerstam.**
Marco Polo 8 223504 (7/94).
...Seven Stars' Symphony, Op. 132. Quatre Interludes, Op. 214. L'Andalouse dans Barcelone,
Op. 134. **Deutsches Symphony Orchestra, Berlin / James Judd.**
RCA Victor Red Seal 09026 68146-2 (11/96).
...Horn Sonata, Op. 70. *Coupled with works by various composers.* **David Pyatt** (hn); **Martin Jones**
(pf). Erato 3984-21632-2 (4/98). *See review in the Collections section; refer to the Index.*
...14 Chants, Op. 157/2ᶜ. Premier album de Lilian, Op. 139ᵃᶜ. Second album de Lilian, Op. 149ᶜ –
Sérénade à l'étoile errante; Swimming; Les jeux du clown; Le voyage chimérique. Morceau de
lecture, Op. 218ᶜ. Flute Sonata, Op. 52ᶜ. Sonata for two flutes, Op. 75ᵇ. ᵃ**Jayne West** (sop);
Fenwick Smith, ᵇ**Leone Buyse** (fls); ᶜ**Martin Amlin** (pf). Hyperion CDA66414 (10/90).
...Choral sur le nom de Fauré. *Coupled with works by various composers.* **Academy of St Martin
in the Fields / Sir Neville Marriner.** Philips 446 084-2PH (1/96).

Erich Wolfgang Korngold
Austro/Hungarian 1897-1957

Korngold Piano Concerto for the Left Hand in C sharp major, Op. 17.
Marx Romantisches Klavierkonzert in E major. **Marc-André Hamelin** (pf); **BBC Scottish Symphony
Orchestra / Osmo Vänskä.** Hyperion Ⓕ CDA66990 (65 minutes: DDD: 4/98). Recorded 1997.
Lush as lush can be – that's the Joseph Marx *Romantisches Klavierkonzert*. It's all the most wildly
romantic concertos you can think of rolled into one huge pianistic feast. From the very first bar you

know why Joseph Marx gave the concerto the epithet *Romantic*. Though by no means a profound piece, it's a delight to listen to and a work of exceptional craftsmanship also. Its pianistic difficulties are legion and this could well be the reason for the work's neglect since the 1920s. As ever Marc-André Hamelin delivers the music with consummate ease. After a similar period of neglect Korngold's left-hand Piano Concerto is making a remarkable comeback on disc. Unlike many of the pieces composed for Paul Wittgenstein after he lost an arm in the First World War, this one actually makes a virtue out of all the inevitable spread-chords trickery required when writing for one hand. It's a splendid work that thoroughly deserves its current revival. Its gladiatorial solo part certainly emphasizes the 'struggle' inherent in the concerto form, but it is certainly not a concerto in the traditional sense, more, as Brendan Carroll suggests in the booklet-notes, a symphonic poem for piano and orchestra. Hamelin's reading has plenty of poetry and is allied to tremendous power and authority. The coupling with the marvellous Marx Concerto is inspired. The recorded sound is good and the accompaniment, from the BBC Scottish SO under Osmo Vänskä, superb.

Additional recommendation ...

...Piano Concerto[a]. Cello Concerto in C major, Op. 37[b]. Symphonic Serenade in B flat major, Op. 39. Military March in B flat major. [a]**Howard Shelley** (pf); [b]**Peter Dixon** (vc); **BBC Philharmonic Orchestra / Matthias Bamert.**
Chandos Ⓕ CHAN9508 (76 minutes: DDD: 3/97). *Gramophone Editor's choice.*

Korngold Violin Concerto, Op. 35[a].
Rózsa Violin Concerto, Op. 24[b]. Tema con variazioni, Op. 29a[c].
Waxman Fantasy on Bizet's "Carmen"[d]. **Jascha Heifetz** (vn); [c]**Gregor Piatigorsky** (vc); [c]**Chamber Orchestra;** [a]**Los Angeles Philharmonic Orchestra / Alfred Wallenstein;** [b]**Dallas Symphony Orchestra / Walter Hendl;** [d]**RCA Victor Symphony Orchestra / Donald Voorhees.**
RCA Victor Gold Seal [ad]mono/[bc]stereo Ⓜ GD87963* (70 minutes: ADD: 4/89). Item marked [a] from HMV ALP1233 (12/55), [b]SB6605 (4/65), [cd]new to UK. Recorded 1946-63.   ⓖⓖⓖ
Heifetz's legendary recording of the Korngold Concerto serves a double purpose: as an effective introduction to Korngold's seductive musical style, and as the best possible example of Heifetz's violin artistry. The work itself was written at the suggestion of Bronislaw Huberman, but it was Heifetz who gave the première in 1947. It calls on material that Korngold had also used in three of his film scores (he was at the time composing for Hollywood), although the way he welds the themes into a three-movement structure is masterly enough to suggest that the concerto came to him 'of a piece'. The very opening would be enough to seduce most listeners, unless – that is – they have an aversion to the film music of the period. Miklós Rózsa's Concerto has its roots in the composer's Hungarian soil, and echoes of Bartók are rarely absent. But whereas Korngold's score is taken from movie music, Rózsa's (or parts of it) became a film score – namely, *The Private Life of Sherlock Holmes*. Rózsa's self-possessed, skilfully written *Tema con variazoni* was taken, in 1962, from a much larger work then in progress, but Heifetz and Piatigorsky play it in a reduced orchestration. As to the *Carmen Fantasy* by Franz Waxman (another notable film composer), its luscious tunes and frightening technical challenges were written with the great violinist very much in mind. It's a stunning piece of playing, and wears its years lightly. The other recordings sound far better, and the Rózsa items are in stereo. Marvellous stuff!

Additional recommendations ...

...Violin Concerto[a]. Much ado about nothing, Op. 11[b] – The maiden in the bridal chamber; Dogberry and Verges; Intermezzo; Hornpipe. **Barber** Violin Concerto, Op. 14[a].
Gil Shaham (vn); [a]**London Symphony Orchestra / André Previn** ([b]pf).
DG Ⓕ 439 886-2GH (71 minutes: DDD: 9/94). *Gramophone Editor's choice.*   ⓖ
...Violin Concerto. *Coupled with works by* **Krenek** *and* **Weill Chantal Juillet** (vn); **Berlin Radio Symphony Orchestra / John Mauceri.**
Decca Entartete Musik Ⓕ 452 481-2DH (77 minutes: DDD: 4/97).

Korngold Symphony in F sharp major, Op. 40. Einfache Lieder, Op. 9[a] – No. 1, Schneeglöckchen; No. 3, Ständchen; No. 4, Liebesbriefchen; No. 6, Sommer. Die tote Stadt[a] – Glück, das mir verblieb. [a]**Barbara Hendricks** (sop); **Philadelphia Orchestra / Franz Welser-Möst.**
EMI Ⓕ CDC5 56169-2 (63 minutes: DDD: 12/96). Recorded 1995.
Gramophone Editor's choice.   ⓖ
Korngold Symphony in F sharp major, Op. 40. Much Ado About Nothing, Op. 11 – The Maiden in the Bridal Chamber; Dogberry and Verges; Intermezzo; Hornpipe. **London Symphony Orchestra / André Previn.** DG Ⓕ 453 436-2GH (63 minutes: DDD: 8/97). Recorded 1996.
Sir Edward Downes and the BBC Philharmonic Orchestra's superb account of Korngold's Symphony seemed pretty unassailable but both Welser-Möst and Previn give a different view of this magnificent work and are exceptionally strong contenders. For a start, Welser-Möst is less expansive than Downes, especially in the weighty *Adagio* slow movement, but he is no less impressive for that. Elsewhere, Welser-Möst also generates a greater degree of rhythmic incisiveness from his players – the fleet-footed *Scherzo* for instance, or the daring-do finale. Downes and his players also wear their hearts on their sleeves a little more, but again Welser-Möst's reading is not lacking in passion. Barbara Hendricks's ravishing accounts of four of the six *Einfache Lieder* and the famous Marietta's Lied from *Die tote Stadt* make an excellent foil to the symphony.

It takes a little time to adjust to Previn's reading on first hearing. He certainly eschews the sumptuous, Technicolor view of Downes. This is a much darker interpretation, with the first movement driven by a biting passion, and it's not surprising that the Mahlerian overtones are much less obvious here. Previn is slower, too, in the first movement, than Downes – by nearly two minutes. By comparison, Welser-Möst's account is more curvaceous and, more 'filmic' than Previn. One has less of an image of Errol Flynn sailing the high seas when that wonderful horn theme appears in the *Scherzo*, but Previn does tremendous things with this movement and he coaxes wonderful playing from the LSO. The sombre *Adagio* is superbly controlled and beautifully crafted, making it one of the most symphonic readings committed to disc, and in the finale Previn responds readily to the movement's optimistic spirit. Overall he achieves a very satisfying and balanced interpretation of this symphony. As a filler Previn gives us the short but genial *Much Ado About Nothing* suite. Once again Previn secures deftly shaped performances and reveals himself as a very fine Korngold conductor. It is difficult to choose between Downes and Previn in the symphony; both are equally satisfying for different, contrasting reasons. Welser-Möst sits somewhere between the two, and there are many things to admire in his recording, but for newcomers to this symphony the Previn receives a strong recommendation.

Additional recommendations ...

...Symphony. Theme and Variations, Op. 42. Straussiana. **North West German Philharmonic Orchestra / Werner Andreas Albert.** CPO Ⓕ 999 146-2 (68 minutes: DDD/ADD: 10/91).

...Symphony. Abschiedlieder, Op. 14ᵃ. ᵃ**Linda Finnie** (mez); **BBC Philharmonic Orchestra / Sir Edward Downes.** Chandos Ⓕ CHAN9171 (68 minutes: DDD: 9/93).　　　　　　Ⓠ

...Einfache Lieder, Op. 9 – No. 1, Schneeglöckchen; No. 2, Nachtwander; No. 3, Ständchen. Der Kranke, Op. 38 No. 2. *Coupled with works by* **Wolf Boje Skovhus** (bar); **Helmut Deutsch** (pf). Sony Classical Ⓕ SK57969 (62 minutes: DDD: 1/95). *See review under Wolf; refer to the Index.*

Korngold String Quartet No. 1 in A major, Op. 16.
Rezniček String Quartet No. 1 in C sharp minor. **Franz Schubert Quartet** (Florian Zwiauer, Helge Rosenkranz, vns; Hartmut Pascher, va; Attila Szekely, vc). Nimbus Ⓕ NI5506 (63 minutes: DDD: 1/98). Recorded 1996.

This disc brings us Korngold's First String Quartet, which is otherwise unavailable on disc at present. It was written in 1920, when the composer was 23. Although his music stemmed from the same late-romantic territory as the Austrian composer, Emil Rezniček, Korngold's writing for string quartet pushes the harmonic boundaries much further. It is much more wildly rhapsodic and lyrical in gesture, with moments of melting beauty juxtaposed with passages of stark dissonance in the first movement. The wonderful slow movement is a superb example of sustained melodic beauty, whilst the finale, with its jaunty rhythms and chirpy, lilting melodies, pre-echoes at times Korngold's music for the film, *The Adventures of Robin Hood*. The disc also gives us an all too infrequent opportunity to hear something other than the Overture to *Donna Diana* by Rezniček. His First String Quartet (he wrote four in all) was composed in 1921, when he was 60. Despite the date, however, the quartet is very much a product of the late-nineteenth century, rather than the early-twentieth century. It is unashamedly lyrical and romantic in utterance, and there is much to admire in its abundant melodic material and finely crafted movements – especially the slow movement. Though by no means a masterpiece it is nevertheless a discovery that should encourage further investigation into the works of a composer who has clearly been overlooked for far too long. The Franz Schubert Quartet provide the perfect guide to these seldom-heard works, and give performances of great conviction, charm and dazzling musicianship throughout. The recorded sound is very natural and well balanced.

Korngold String Quartet No. 3 in D major, Op. 34.
Kreisler String Quartet in A minor. **Angeles Quartet** (Kathleen Lenski, Steven Miller, vns; Brian Dembow, va; Stephen Erdody, vc). Koch International Classics Ⓕ 37325-2 (58 minutes: DDD: 11/96).

At first glance Kreisler and Korngold may not seem the most obvious of bedfellows; however, as contemporaries, both shared the same Viennese musical roots and, as the insert-note rightly points out, both fled Vienna for the United States to escape Nazi persecution. Also, both of the string quartets presented here possess a haunting Viennese nostalgia. Kreisler's only String Quartet was composed in 1921 and is a delightful discovery. Although the quartet contains much memorable melodic material, those expecting similar fare to his more well-known salon pieces may well be in for a pleasant surprise. The evidence here is that Kreisler was eminently capable of turning his hand to more complex, extended forms than the bon-bons (delightful though they are) that he is generally remembered for. Korngold's Third String Quartet is a later work, and here the nostalgia is of a Vienna gone for ever. Composed in 1945 it was one of the first works that broke that silence (in terms of his concert music) that Korngold had imposed on himself during the war. As ever, his melodic gifts are prolific throughout, and in the *Scherzo*, slow movement and finale Korngold reuses (much to our gain) melodies previously employed in his music to the films *Between Two Worlds*, *The Sea Wolf* and *Devotion*. The Angeles Quartet's performances of these rewarding works are exceptionally fine and committed and the recorded sound has an intimate and beautifully natural ambience.

Korngold Der Ring des Polykrates. **Endrik Wottrich** (ten) Arndt; **Beate Bilandzija** (sop) Laura; **Jürgen Sacher** (ten) Döblinger; **Kirsten Blanck** (sop) Lieschen; **Dietrich Henschel** (bar) Vogel; **Deutsches Symphony Orchestra, Berlin / Klauspeter Siebel.** CPO Ⓕ CPO999 402-2 (70 minutes: DDD: 3/97). Notes, text and translation included.

The thing that will astound most listeners approaching this opera for the first time will be the extraordinary mastery of both orchestration and vocal writing – not to mention the sheer melodic inventiveness – of a mere 17-year-old. The rather slight, though elegantly simple, plot is a classic case of mischief-making. Wilhelm Arndt, celebrating his supreme good fortune at landing the lucrative and prestigious post of court music director, a large monetary inheritance, and reflecting on a blissfully happy marriage, is visited by a long-lost friend, Peter Vogel, who, envious of his friend's good fortune (especially his marital bliss), goads Wilhelm into questioning his wife about any previous loves. Vogel's premise being that a sacrifice to the gods of good fortune is necessary in order to avert the bad luck that must surely follow in the wake of the good. To cut a short story even shorter, Vogel's plan fails, and he himself becomes the sacrifice as Wilhelm hands him his luggage and sends him on his way. In short *Der Ring des Polykrates* is a kind of comedic *Othello* with a happy ending. As for the music, the opera is extremely beautiful throughout but one or two moments are especially striking for their Straussian, even Mahlerian, beauty. But it's not just the beauty of the melodic and harmonic palette that impresses; Korngold shows us his superb grasp of pacing, plot control and structural cohesion too – as the booklet-notes point out one would normally only expect such skill from a more mature composer of operas. The performances from all the soloists are quite exceptional, and the Berlin orchestra under the direction of Klauspeter Siebel play as though this music were in their blood.

Further listening ...

...Baby Serenade, Op. 24[a]. Cello Concerto[b]. Symphonic Serenade[c]. [b]**Julius Berger** (vc); **North West German Philharmonic Orchestra / Werner Andreas Albert.** CPO 999 077-2 (10/91).

...Sinfonietta, Op. 5. Sursum corda, Op. 13. **BBC Philharmonic Orchestra / Matthias Bamert.** Chandos CHAN9317 (5/95). *Gramophone Editor's choice.*   ⒼⒼ

...Symphonic Serenade[b]. Between Two Worlds: Judgement Day[a]. Theme and Variations, Op. 42[b]. [a]**Alexander Frey** (pf); [a]**Berlin Radio Symphony Orchestra;** [b]**Deutsches Symphony Orchestra, Berlin / John Mauceri.** Decca Entartete Musik 444 170-2DH (7/97).

...Piano Trio in D major, Op. 1[a]. Violin Sonata in D major, Op. 6. **Glenn Dicterow** (vn); [a]**Alan Stepansky** (vc); **Israela Margalit** (pf). EMI Anglo-American Chamber Music Series CDC5 55401-2 (7/95). *Gramophone Editor's choice.*

...Piano Sonatas – No. 1 in D minor; No. 2 in E major, Op. 2; No. 3 in C major, Op. 25. **Matthijs Verschoor** (pf). Etcetera KTC1042 (7/87).

...Piano Sonatas – No. 1 in D minor; No. 2 in E major, Op. 2; No. 3 in C major, Op. 25. **Geoffrey Tozer** (pf). Chandos CHAN9389 (3/96).

...String Sextet in D major, Op. 10. *Coupled with* **Schoenberg** Verklärte Nacht. **Raphael Ensemble.** Hyperion CDA66425 (1/91).   Ⓖ

...Die tote Stadt. **Soloists; Tolz Boys' Choir; Bavarian Radio Chorus; Munich Radio Orchestra / Erich Leinsdorf.** RCA Opera Series GD87767 (11/89).   ⒼⒼ

...Die tote Stadt. **Soloists; Tomtberga School Children's Choir; Chorus and Orchestra of the Royal Opera, Stockholm / Leif Segerstam.** Naxos 8 660060/1 (9/97).

...Die tote Stadt – Glück, das mir verblieb. *Coupled with works by various composers.* **Dame Kiri Te Kanawa** (sop); **Philharmonia Orchestra / Julius Rudel.** MI CDC5 56417-2 (11/97). *See review in the Collections section; refer to the Index.*

...Die tote Stadt – Glück, das mir verblieb. *Coupled with works by various composers.* **Renée Fleming** (sop); **English Chamber Orchestra / Jeffrey Tate.** Decca 458 858-2DH (3/98). *See review in the Collections section; refer to the Index.*

...Die tote Stadt – Mein Sehnen, mein Wähnen. *Coupled with works by various composers.* **Thomas Hampson** (bar); **Pestalozzi Gymnasium Children's Choir; Munich Radio Orchestra / Fabio Luisi.** EMI CDC5 55233-2 (9/95). *See review in the Collections section; refer to the Index.*

...Violanta. **Soloists; Bavarian Radio Chorus; Munich Radio Orchestra / Marek Janowski.** CBS MK79229 (9/89).

...Das Wunder der Heliane. **Soloists; Berlin Radio Chorus; Berlin Radio Symphony Orchestra / John Mauceri.** Decca Entartete Musik 436 636-2DH3 (4/93). *Gramophone Award Winner 1995.*   ⒼⒼ

Leopold Koželuch   Bohemian/Austrian 1747-1818

Suggested listening ...

...Clarinet Concerto in E flat major. *Coupled with works by* **Crusell** *and* **Krommer** **Emma Johnson** (cl); **Royal Philharmonic Orchestra / Günther Herbig.** ASV CDDCA763 (9/91). *See review under Crusell; refer to the Index.*

Anton Kraft

Suggested listening ...
...Cello Concerto in C major, Op. 4. *Coupled with works by* **Haydn**
Anner Bylsma (bar vc); **Tafelmusik / Jeanne Lamon.**
Deutsche Harmonia Mundi RD77757 (9/91). ☞ *See review under Haydn; refer to the Index.*

Hans Krása

Suggested listening ...
...String Quartet. *Coupled with works by* **Haas Hawthorne Quartet.** Decca 440 853-2DH (3/94).
See review under Haas; refer to the Index. **Gramophon**e *Editor's choice.* ⒼⒼ

Joseph Martin Kraus

Kraus Symphonies – C major, VB139; C minor, VB142; E flat major, VB144. Olympie – Overture.
Swedish Chamber Orchestra / Petter Sundkvist. Naxos Ⓢ 8 553734 (62 minutes: DDD: 5/98).
Kraus was a German contemporary of Mozart's – the two men were born in the same year, but Kraus
lived one year longer – who spent most of his brief career at the court of Gustavus III in Stockholm.
He was induced to go there by contacts with a group of intellectuals he met at Göttingen; later he
belonged to a similar group in Stockholm, and he visited Vienna and Esterháza, Paris and London.
His music, admired by Haydn and Gluck, has a fiery, passionate quality that is often compared to the
Haydn of the early 1770s (the so-called *Sturm und Drang* period), but although there are resemblances
to Haydn, his music of the 1780s is stylistically more advanced; he is perhaps better seen as belonging
to the North German symphonic tradition, and certainly some of his gestures and his sense of drama
have a good deal in common with C.P.E. Bach. The latest work here is the overture for Voltaire's
Olympie, a fine D minor movement written in 1782 whose sombre slow introduction returns at the
end just when one might have expected the major-key second subject to be cheerfully recapitulated.
Kraus's music doesn't shirk true seriousness, and he was certainly no less ambitious, and scarcely less
successful, in the three symphonies here than were Mozart and Haydn at the same date, the early
1780s. The E flat work, nearly all in triple (or compound) metre, has powerful momentum as well as
elegant logic to its first movement, graceful melody in its *Larghetto* (especially the major section with
solo oboe) and energetic contrapuntal development in its finale. The C major Symphony starts as if
it is going to be a minor-key work, in its slow introduction, but is not quite such a consistently
impassioned piece. Last comes the C minor work that has justly won much admiration for Kraus – it
is full of interesting ideas and ingenious texture as well as vigorously argued development. The
performances are full of life and strongly committed to the music: there is plenty of tension in the
outer movements of the C minor work and shapely playing in the slow ones. All three symphonies,
and one more, are also available on the Capriccio disc by Concerto Köln, and some listeners may
prefer the cooler, vibrato-less sound of period instruments and the more abstract style of performance
there. This Swedish version offers what are clearly modern performances, but nevertheless stylish
ones, and is the more vividly recorded.

Additional recommendation ...
...Symphonies – C major; C minor; D major; E flat major. **Concerto Cologne.**
Capriccio Ⓕ 10 396 (72 minutes: DDD: 8/92). ☞

Further listening ...
...Sinfonia con fugato per la chiesa. Symphony in C major. Symphonie funèbre in C minor.
Sinfonia in C sharp minor. **Concerto Cologne.** Capriccio 10 430 (9/93). ☞

Fritz Kreisler

Kreisler Original Compositions and Arrangements – works by **Kreisler** and arrangements of
works by **Bach, Brandl, Dvořák, Falla, Glazunov, Heuberger, Poldini,**
Rimsky-Korsakov, Schubert, Scott, Tchaikovsky and **Weber** Fritz Kreisler (vn) with
various artists. EMI Références mono Ⓜ CDH7 64701-2* (78 minutes: ADD: 12/93).
From HMV Originals; recorded 1930-38. ⒼⒼⒼ
Kreisler Praeludium and Allegro in the style of Pugnani. Schön Rosmarin. Tambourin chinois,
Op. 3. Caprice viennois, Op. 2. Précieuse in the style of Couperin. Liebesfreud. Liebesleid. La
Gitana. Berceuse romantique, Op. 9. Polichinelle. Rondino on a theme by Beethoven. Tempo di
Menuetto in the style of Pugnani. Toy Soldier's March. Allegretto in the style of Boccherini.
Marche miniature viennoise. Aucassin and Nicolette, "Canzonetta medievale". Menuet in the
style of Porpora. Siciliano and Rigaudon in the style of Francoeur. Syncopation. **Joshua Bell**
(vn); **Paul Coker** (pf). Decca Ⓕ 444 409-2DH (63 minutes: DDD: 4/96). Recorded 1995.
Years of 'encore' employment have guaranteed the cult longevity of Kreisler's music – certainly
among violinists. And as light music goes, make no mistake that Kreisler's finest work vies with the

best of Eric Coates, Leroy Anderson or even Johann Strauss. The repertoire on the Kreisler's disc consists of his own pieces and a large number of arrangements. Some of the latter are pretty feeble musically, yet the great violinist's unique artistry and magical tone-quality shine through. Sometimes he does not land right in the middle of a note, but as always plays with the timing and phrasing of a great singer. Nothing is ever routine or set in his playing, which has a continual feeling of discovery and freshness. The transfers are excellent. Joshua Bell learned Kreisler from his teacher, the late Josef Gingold, and yet his approach is anything but 'old school'. He habitually avoids the pitfalls of imitation, flashiness and patronizing overkill, preferring instead to revisit the music with modern ears. His *Caprice viennois* is light years removed from the composer's own (whichever version you choose), a fresh-faced, strongly characterized reading that trades sentimentality for just a hint of jazz. And of course there's that inseparable twosome, *Liebesfreud* and *Liebesleid*, the latter in particular displaying Bell's tone at its most alluring. The longest piece on the disc is the *Praeludium and Allegro in the style of Pugnani* which Bell gives 'the full treatment', deftly pointing the *Allegro*, relishing passagework and double-stopping with impressive accuracy. This of course is one of numerous spoof baroque pieces that Kreisler passed off as edited originals but that were in fact his own compositions.

Some pieces seem indivisible from Kreisler's own very individual tone and phrasing, *Polichinelle*, for example, and *Marche miniature viennoise*, both of which paraded the sort of personalized rubato, timing and tone-production that have for so long seemed part of the music's very essence. Here and in a few other instances, Bell's brighter, more overtly virtuosic approach doesn't quite catch the music's period charm and yet a mini-masterpiece like the rarely heard *Berceuse romantique* (a sort of Fauré-Korngold synthesis) displays ample style, subtlety and affection of phrasing. Bell's smooth, witty and keenly inflected readings make for elevated entertainment: they may not replace the composer's own, but they do provide a youthful and in many ways illuminating alternative. The recordings are excellent, save that Coker's excellent accompaniments occasionally seem overprominent.

Additional recommendations ...

...Tempo di Menuetto in the style of Pugnani. *Coupled with works by various composers.*
  Sarah Chang (vn); **Sandra Rivers** (pf). EMI Ⓜ CDC7 54352-2 (51 minutes: DDD: 1/93).
  See review in the Collections section; refer to the Index.
...Schön Rosmarin. Tambourin chinois. Caprice viennois. *Coupled with works by various composers.*
  Maxim Vengerov (vn); **Itamar Golan** (pf). Teldec Ⓕ 9031-77351-2 (67 minutes: DDD: 4/94).
  See review in the Collections section; refer to the Index.
...Recitative and Scherzo-Caprice, Op. 6. *Coupled with works by various composers.*
  Leila Josefowicz (vn). Philips Ⓕ 446 700-2PH (62 minutes: DDD: 2/97).
...Liebesleid[a]. Tambourin chinois[a]. Praeludium and Allegro in the style of Pugnani[a]. String Quartet in A minor[b]. *Coupled with works by various composers.* **Kennedy,** [b]**Rosemary Furniss** (vns); [b]**Bill Hawkes** (va); [b]**Caroline Dale** (vc); [a]**John Lenehan** (pf). EMI Ⓕ CDC5 56626-2 (75 minutes: ADD: 5/98). *See review in the Collections section; refer to the Index.*

Further listening ...

...Violin Concerto in C major, "in the style of Vivaldi". *Coupled with* **Vivaldi** The Four Seasons, Op. 8 Nos. 1-4. **Gil Shaham** (vn); **Orpheus Chamber Orchestra.** DG 439 933-2GH (3/95).
...String Quartet in A minor. *Coupled with* **Korngold** String Quartet No. 3 in D major, Op. 34.
  Angeles Quartet.
  Koch International Classics 37325-2 (11/96). *See review under Korngold; refer to the Index.*
...(orch. McAlister): Schön Rosmarin. Liebesfreud. Liebesleid. *Coupled with works by various composers.* **Gil Shaham** (vn); **Orpheus Chamber Orchestra.** DG 449 923-2GH (3/97).

Ernst Krenek   Austro/American 1900-1991

Krenek O Lacrymosa, Op. 48. Stella's Monolog, Op. 57. Die Nachtigall, Op. 68. Fünf Lieder, Op. 82. Four Songs, Op. 112. The Flea, Op. 175. Wechselrahmen, Op. 189. **Christine Schäfer** (sop); **Axel Bauni** (pf). Orfeo Musica Rediviva Ⓕ C373951A (67 minutes: DDD: 2/96). Texts and translations included. Recorded 1994.
In this entertaining recital, the chronological arrangement of the songs affords a fair view of Krenek's stylistic development across nearly 40 years (1926-65). And quite a development it was, too, from the radiant *O Lacrymosa*, three further musings by Rilke on the Virgin Mary, to the near-volcanic *Wechselrahmen* ("Changing Settings"), to poems by Emil Barth. In terms of musical style, *O Lacrymosa* is clearly suggestive of Hindemith's *Das Marienleben*. More individual is *Stella's Monolog* (1928), on lines from Goethe's play *Stella*. Cast as a dramatic scene, this compositional *tour de force* has a wide range of moods, some of *buffa*-like airiness at odds with the text's romantic ardour, suggesting a send-up. When in 1937 Krenek came to set five brief stanzas by Kafka, he had finally embraced Schoenberg's 12-note method. The Kafka songs, Op. 82, as well as those of Op. 112 (1946-47, setting Gerard Manley Hopkins) show a concomitant spareness of texture, but his setting of Donne's *The Flea* (1960) is wonderfully exuberant, while *Wechselrahmen*'s extremity of expression is entirely apposite given Krenek's tirelessly adventurous spirit. Christine Schäfer is a sympathetic interpreter; a touch shrill in the topmost registers, her voice is big enough to cope with these songs' widely varying demands. Axel Bauni gives first-class support and the recording sounds bright and truthful. A must for anyone remotely interested in Lieder, of the twentieth century or any other.

Further listening ...
...Symphonic Elegy, "In memoriam Anton Webern". *Coupled with works by* **Berg** and **Schoenberg**
New York Philharmonic Orchestra / Dimitri Mitropoulos.
Sony Classical Masterworks Heritage mono MH2K62759* (2/98).
...Symphonies – No. 1, Op. 7; No. 5. **North-German Radio Philharmonic Orchestra, Hanover /**
Takao Ukigaya. CPO CPO999 359-2 (1/97).
...Symphony No. 2, Op. 12. **Hanover Radio Philharmonic Orchestra / Takao Ukigaya.**
CPO CPO999 255-2 (1/96).
...Piano Sonatas – No. 2, Op. 59; No. 3, Op. 92; No. 4. *Coupled with works by* **Berg** and **Webern**
Marcelo Bratke (pf). Olympia OCD431 (4/94).
...Lamentatio Jeremiae prophetae, Op. 93. **Berlin RIAS Chamber Choir / Marcus Creed.**
Harmonia Mundi HMC90 1551 (7/95).
...Jonny spielt auf. Soloists; Leipzig Opera Chorus; Chinchilla; Leipzig Gewandhaus Orchestra /
Lothar Zagrosek. Decca 436 631-2DH2 (4/93). *Gramophone Award Winner 1995.*

Conradin Kreutzer   German 1780-1849

Suggested listening ...
...Frühlingsglaube. Die Post. Nähe des Geliebten. Die Kapelle, Op. 64 No. 1. Nachtreise. Entschluss,
Op. 64 No. 2. *Coupled with works by various composers.* **Olaf Bär** (bar); **Helmut Deutsch** (pf).
EMI CDC5 55393-2 (1/96). *See review in the Collections section; refer to the Index.*

Franz Krommer   Bohemian 1759-1831

Suggested listening ...
...Clarinet Concerto, Op. 36. *Coupled with works by* **Crusell** and **Koželuch**
Emma Johnson (cl); **Royal Philharmonic Orchestra / Günther Herbig.**
ASV CDDCA763 (9/91). *See review under Crusell; refer to the Index.*

Ian Krouse   American 1956

Suggested listening ...
...Variations on a Moldavian Hora. *Coupled with works by various composers.* **Jason Vieaux** (gtr).
Naxos 8 553449 (11/97). *See review in the Collections section; refer to the Index.*

György Kurtág   Romanian 1926

Kurtág Aus der Ferne III. Officium breve, Op. 28. Ligatura, Op. 31b[a]. String Quartet, Op. 1.
Hommage à Mihály András (12 Microludes), Op. 13. **Keller Quartet** (András Keller, János Pilz,
vns; Zoltán Gál, va; Ottó Kertész, vc); [a]**Miklós Perényi** (vc); [a]**György Kurtág** (celesta).
ECM New Series Ⓟ 453 258-2 (49 minutes: DDD: 12/96).
This is the first disc to be devoted exclusively to Kurtág's music for string quartet. On musical grounds
alone it is of great significance, and both performance and recording are equal to the enterprise. The
Keller Quartet have secure technique as well as emotional commitment, while ECM have provided a
warm yet spacious acoustic for this expressive music. The journey begins with Kurtág's Op. 1 of 1959,
in a world, dominated by expressionistic fragmentation, of which he is clearly the master. Eighteen
years later, in the Op. 13 *Microludes*, Kurtág has perfected his own personal style, in which small,
separate forms are linked together, and the music's allusions – to Bartók and Webern, in particular –
are subsumed into a lyrical, dramatic discourse. The fruits of Kurtág's long apprenticeship are most
evident here in the superb *Officium breve* of 1988-89, a miracle of textural imagination and musical
thought whose richly varied language is distilled further into the two miniatures – *Ligatura* (also 1989)
and *Aus der Ferne* (1991). By now Kurtág's music is characterized by a concentrated homogeneity, and
by a harmony whose tensions, and stability, are the result of bringing convergence and divergence into
confrontation. The result is memorable and these fine recordings are immensely rewarding.
Additional recommendation ...
...String Quartet. Hommage à Milhály András. Officium breve in memoriam Andreae Szervánzky,
Op. 28. *Coupled with works by various composers.* **Arditti Quartet.** Auvidis Montaigne
Ⓟ MO789007 (72 minutes: DDD: 4/92). *See review under Gubaidulina; refer to the Index.*

Kurtág Játékok – excerpts from Books 1-5 and 8. Transcriptions from Machaut to Bach – No. 46,
Gottes Zeit ist die allerbeste Zeit (Bach: BWV106); No. 48, Aus tiefer Not (Bach: BWV687);
No. 50, Trio Sonata in E flat major (Bach: BWV525/1); No. 52, O Lamm Gottes unschuldig
(Bach: BWV*deest*). **György Kurtág, Márta Kurtág** (pf duet). ECM New Series Ⓟ 453 511-2
(50 minutes: DDD: 11/97). Recorded 1996.

If any contemporary composer can persuade the musical world that compositions of between 30 seconds and four minutes in length are the natural vehicle for progressive post-tonal music, and therefore for the music of the future, that composer is Kurtág. This sequence of compositions, the longest of which lasts just over five minutes, offers a very special experience. The disc contains a selection from Kurtág's ongoing sequence of 'games' (*Játékok*) for solo piano and piano duet. They are a mixture of studies and tributes, not explicitly pedagogic in *Mikrokosmos* mode, but ranging widely in technical demands and style, from fugitive fragments, in which even the smallest element tells, to the extraordinary flamboyance of a *Perpetuum mobile* containing nothing but *glissandos*. Most are sombre in tone, and even the more humorous items, like the furiously constrained "Beating – Quarrelling", have a bitter side to them. For access to another musical world, Kurtág has included four of his Bach transcriptions, music whose serenity and confidence speaks immediately of utter remoteness from the real present. Yet there is no nostalgia: Bach was then, Kurtág is now. The performances risk overprojection but they are supremely characterful, and the close-up recording reinforces the impression of music that is mesmerically persuasive in its imagination and expressiveness. If only even more of these pieces had been included!

Further listening ...
...Grabstein für Stephan, Op. 15*c*[a]. Stele, Op. 33. *Coupled with* **Stockhausen** Gruppen[b].
   [a]**Jürgen Ruck** (gtr); **Berlin Philharmonic Orchestra / Claudio Abbado**, [b]**Friedrich Goldman**,
   [b]**Marcus Creed**. DG 447 761-2GH (3/97).
...Kafka fragments, Op. 24. **Anu Komsi** (sop); **Sakari Oramo** (vn). Ondine ODE868-2 (11/96).
...Messages of the late Miss R.V. Troussova, Op. 17[a]. ... Quasi una Fantasia ... , Op. 27[b]. Scenes
   from a Novel, Op. 19[c]. [a]**Rosemary Hardy**, [c]**Christine Whittlesey** (sops); [c]**Mathias Tacke** (vn);
   [c]**Thomas Fichter** (db); [c]**Márta Fábián** (cimbalom); [b]**Hermann Kretzschmar** (pf);
   [ab]**Ensemble Modern / Peter Eötvös**. Sony Classical SK53290 (12/93).   Ⓖ
...Neun Stücke. Jelek, Op. 5. Hommage à R. Sch, Op. 15*d*. *Coupled with works by* **Schumann**
   Eduard Brunner (cl); **Kim Kashkashian** (va); **Robert Levin** (pf). ECM New Series 437 957-2 (1/96).
...Plays and Games for Piano, Book 3 – excerpts. *Coupled with works by various composers.* **Peter**
   Frankl (pf). ASV CDDCA860 (6/93). *See review in the Collections section; refer to the Index.* ⒼⒼⒼ

Johan Kvandal
Norwegian 1919

Suggested listening ...
...Wind Quintet, Op. 34. Three Sacred Folktunes, Op. 23*b*.
   Coupled with works by **Fernström** and **Nielsen Oslo Wind Ensemble.**
   Naxos 8 553050 (3/95). *See review under Nielsen; refer to the Index.*

Pierre de La Rue
Flanders c1460-1518

Suggested listening ...
...Missa "Ave sanctissima Maria". Ave sanctissima Maria. *Coupled with works by various composers.*
   Early Music Consort of London / David Munrow. Virgin Classics Veritas VED5 61334-2 (11/97).
   See review in the Collections section; refer to the Index.
...Fors seulement. *Coupled with works by* **Brumel** and **Ockeghem The Clerks' Group /**
   Edward Wickham. ASV Gaudeamus CDGAU168 (5/97). *Gramophone Editor's choice.*
   Gramophone Award Winner 1997. See review under Ockeghem; refer to the Index.   Ⓖ

La Voye-Mignot
French ?-1684

Suggested listening ...
...Suite in B flat major. *Coupled with works by* **Dumanoir** and **Mazuel Le Concert des Nations /**
   Jordi Savall. Auvidis Fontalis ES9908 (1/98). 🎵 *See review under Dumanoir; refer to the Index.*

Michel-Richard de Lalande
French 1657-1726

Lalande Trois Leçons de Ténèbres et le Miserere[a].
L. Couperin Tombeau de Monsieur de Blancrocher[d].
Marais Pièces de viole, Deuxième livre – Tombeau pour Monsieur de Lully;
   Tombeau de Monsieur de Sainte-Colombe[b].
Visée Tombeau des Mesdemoiselles de Visée[c]. [a]**Isabelle Desrochers** (sop); [abc]**Mauricio Buraglia**
   (theorbo); [ab]**Nima Ben David** (va da gamba); [abd]**Pierre Trocellier** (hpd/org). Auvidis Astrée
   Ⓟ E8592 (73 minutes: DDD: 12/96). 🎵 Texts and translations included. Recorded 1996.
   Gramophone Editor's choice.   Ⓖ
With Lalande's handsome settings of texts from the Lamentations of Jeremiah interspersed with eloquent instrumental *tombeaux* by Marais, Robert de Visée and Louis Couperin, this is an exquisite

and deftly planned programme which, unlike many a 70-minute CD, repays listening to from beginning to end. Like Couperin, Lalande left only three *Leçons de Ténèbres* out of the possible nine, scored for solo voices and continuo. Though they resemble the better-known Couperin settings in many ways, they probably predate them by several years, having reportedly been performed by his two daughters, who both died of smallpox in 1711. Compared to those of Couperin, Lalande's *Leçons* are more energetic and rhythmic; Lalande was a keen observer of text in his sacred music, and where Couperin achieves an aching but rather objective beauty, he is more gestural and in places more impassioned. It is an approach which is matched by the intelligent and expressive singing of Isabelle Desrochers, a soprano whose voice is pretty if slightly hard, but who really touches the heart with her ardent yet controlled delivery of this music. She is not always the most fluid or accurate of singers, but the urgency with which she implores Jerusalem to "turn to the Lord thy God" at the end of the third *Leçon* is not easily forgotten. The accompaniment is nicely varied throughout, and the instrumental items are well played. This is basically a beautiful, life-enhancing disc.

Further listening ...
...Sinfonies pour les soupers du Roi. **La Symphonie du Marais / Hugo Reyne.**
Harmonia Mundi HMC90 1337/40 (four discs: 7/91). ✔
...Cantate Domino, S72. De profundis, S23. Regina coeli, S53. **Ex Cathedra Chamber Choir and Baroque Orchestra / Jeffrey Skidmore.** ASV Gaudeamus CDGAU141 (7/95). ✔ ⓖ
...Dies irae, S31. Miserere mei Deus secundum, S27. **Linda Perillo, Patrizia Kwella** (sops); **Howard Crook** (alto); **Herve Lamy** (ten); **Peter Harvey** (bass); **Chorus and Orchestra of La Chapelle Royale / Philippe Herreweghe.** Harmonia Mundi HMC90 1352 (12/91). ✔ ⓖ
...Te Deum, S32. Super flumina. Confitebor tibi, Domine. **Véronique Gens, Sandrine Piau, Arlette Steyer** (sops); **Jean-Paul Fouchécourt, François Piolino** (tens); **Jérôme Corréas** (bass); **Les Arts Florissants / William Christie.** Harmonia Mundi HMC90 1351 (7/91). ✔

Edouard Lalo

French 1823-1892

Lalo Cello Concerto in D minor.
Massenet Fantaisie.
Saint-Saëns Cello Concerto No. 1 in A minor, Op. 33. **Sophie Rolland** (vc); **BBC Philharmonic Orchestra / Gilbert Varga.** ASV Ⓕ CDDCA867 (65 minutes: DDD: 12/93). Recorded 1993.
Gramophone Editor's choice. ⓖ
Sophie Rolland's performance of the Lalo Concerto is surely as fine as any recorded. It opens with great character, thanks to Gilbert Varga's strong accompaniment, and the solo playing is wonderfully songful. But Rolland is heard at her very finest as she plays her introduction to the finale with commanding improvisatory spontaneity. The orchestra burst in splendidly and she shows her technical mettle with some lovely bouncing bowing in the attractive closing Rondo. The Saint-Saëns Concerto brings similar felicities. Massenet's *Fantaisie* opens dramatically and is rhythmically vital, flowing onwards boldly to produce a winningly sentimental yearning melody which the soloist clearly relishes. A cadenza then leads to a charming, very French Gavotte (which has a flavour of *Manon*) and the piece ends jubilantly. It really is a find, and it could hardly be presented more persuasively. The balance is as near perfect as one could wish, the orchestral sound detailed, yet attractively full and resonant, and the cello placed in excellent perspective.

Additional recommendations ...
...Cello Concerto. *Coupled with works by* **Bruch** and **Saint-Saëns** Matt Haimovitz (vc); **Chicago Symphony Orchestra / James Levine.** DG Ⓕ 427 323-2GH (59 minutes: DDD: 6/89).
...Cello Concerto. *Coupled with works by* **Fauré** and **Saint-Saëns** Heinrich Schiff (vc); **New Philharmonia Orchestra / Sir Charles Mackerras.** DG Ⓑ 431 166-2GR (53 minutes: DDD: 8/91).
...Cello Concerto. *Coupled with works by* **Saint-Saëns** and **Schumann** János Starker (vc); **London Symphony Orchestra / Stanislaw Skrowaczewski.** Mercury Ⓜ 432 010-2MM (65 minutes: ADD: 4/92). ⓖⓖ
...Cello Concerto[a]. **R. Strauss** Don Quixote, Op. 35[b]. Jacqueline du Pré (vc); [b]Herbert Downes (va); [a]**Cleveland Orchestra / Daniel Barenboim;** [b]**New Philharmonia Orchestra / Sir Adrian Boult.** EMI Ⓕ CDC5 55528-2 (73 minutes: ADD: 11/95).
...Cello Concerto. *Coupled with works by* **Offenbach** Ofra Harnoy (vc); **Bournemouth Symphony Orchestra / Antonio de Almeida.** RCA Victor Red Seal Ⓕ 09026 68420-2 (65 minutes: DDD: 11/96).

Lalo Symphonie espagnole, Op. 21[a].
Vieuxtemps Violin Concerto No. 5 in A minor, Op. 37[b]. **Sarah Chang** (vn); [a]**Royal Concertgebouw Orchestra,** [b]**Philharmonia Orchestra / Charles Dutoit.** EMI Ⓕ CDC5 55292-2 (52 minutes: DDD: 5/96). Item marked [a]recorded live in 1995, [b]1994. *Gramophone Editor's choice.* ⓖ
Lalo Symphonie espagnole, Op. 21.
Saint-Saëns Violin Concerto No. 3 in B minor, Op. 61. **Chee-Yun** (vn); **London Philharmonic Orchestra / Jésus López-Cobos.** Denon Ⓕ CO-18017 (61 minutes: DDD: 9/97). Recorded 1996.
Vieuxtemps's Fifth Violin Concerto opens disarmingly, but the tutti gathers strength in Dutoit's hands before Chang steals in silkily and proceeds to dominate the performance with her warm lyricism and

natural, flowing rubato. In a performance like this it remains a small-scale work to cherish, for it hasn't a dull bar in it. The recording is warm and full, the balance treating the relationship between the violin and the excellent Philharmonia Orchestra as an equal partnership. The *Symphonie espagnole* is altogether more ambitious, as befitting its portentous title, but the Lalo's inventive Spanishry holds up well throughout the five movements. How attractive is the Concertgebouw acoustic for the fanfare-like opening – giving it weight as well as point. Again Dutoit's approach is full of impetus so that when the malagueña secondary theme arrives, presented with a special feminine allure, it makes a shimmering contrast. The delicious piping woodwind crescendo and decrescendo which begins the finale sets the scene for scintillating salterello fireworks from the soloist, with Dutoit's spirited orchestral interjections adding to the fun, and the solo lyrical interludes as seductive as ever. The dash into the home straight brings vociferous applause, which makes one realize that the concentration and spontaneity of the performance has been helped by the presence of an audience, who aren't apparent until this point. Certainly the splendidly resonant Concertgebouw sound and perfect balance would never have given the game away that this was not a recording made under studio conditions.

Chee-Yun is yet another of the formidable string-players to have emerged from South Korea in recent years. This disc bears witness to her artistry, built on a flawless technique, with immaculate intonation and exceptional sweetness of tone. Plainly she is a violinist to be judged by the highest standards, and fairly enough this attractive coupling of two favourite nineteenth-century French works comes into direct rivalry with Joshua Bell's outstanding Decca issue. It is partly due to the recording balance that Chee-Yun's performances sound less weighty than Bell's, but it's also a question of approach, for there is a degree of restraint and delicacy in her readings that contrasts with Bell's more extrovert, full-blooded manner. Many will prefer Chee-Yun's interpretation, and in her winning account of the Saint-Saëns the freshness and sweet lyricism mean that there is not the slightest hint of sentimentality or self-indulgence, with bright, clean attack in the first movement, purity in the interlude of the barcarolle-like slow movement and sparkle in the tarantella of the finale. For all the relative lightness there is no lack of bravura in the Lalo either, but in this colourful five-movement work you are more aware of understatement compared with, say, Chang, Bell or Little. Curiously, it is the very point on which one would have expected a Spanish conductor to shine that underlies that impression of understatement, for the LPO players seem reluctant to point Lalo's Spanish dance rhythms with quite the lift and emphasis they plainly require. Here the results sound a degree too literal, not sufficiently flexible, though that is hardly a criticism of the soloist, whose playing is as responsive here as in the Saint-Saëns. The cleanly focused recording is well suited to these readings.

Additional recommendations ...

...Symphonie espagnole. **Saint-Saëns** Violin Concerto No. 3 in B minor, Op. 61.
Itzhak Perlman (vn). **Orchestre de Paris / Daniel Barenboim.**
DG Ⓜ 445 549-2GMA (61 minutes: DDD).

...Symphonie espagnole. **Saint-Saëns** Violin Concerto No. 3 in B minor, Op. 61.
Joshua Bell (vn); **Montreal Symphony Orchestra / Charles Dutoit.**
Decca Ⓕ 425 501-2DH (62 minutes: DDD: 2/90).

...Symphonie espagnole. *Coupled with works by* **Saint-Saëns** and **Vieuxtemps**
Shlomo Mintz (vn); **Israel Philharmonic Orchestra / Zubin Mehta.**
DG Ⓕ 427 676-2GH (60 minutes: DDD: 3/92).

...Symphonie espagnole. **Bruch** Scottish Fantasy, Op. 46. **Anne Akiko Meyers** (vn);
Royal Philharmonic Orchestra / Jesús López-Cobos.
RCA Victor Red Seal Ⓕ RD60942 (60 minutes: DDD: 9/92).   Ⓖ

...Symphonie espagnole. *Coupled with works by* **Ravel** and **Sibelius** Itzhak Perlman (vn);
London Symphony Orchestra / André Previn.
RCA Gold Seal Masters Collection Ⓜ 07863 56520-2 (72 minutes: ADD: 7/93).

...Symphonie espagnole[a]. Cello Concerto[b]. **Saint-Saëns** Violin Concerto No. 1[a].
[a]**Kyung-Wha Chung** (vn); [b]**Lynn Harrell** (vc); [a]**Montreal Symphony Orchestra / Charles Dutoit;**
[b]**Berlin Radio Symphony Orchestra / Riccardo Chailly.**
Decca Ⓜ 436 483-2DM (74 minutes: DDD: 2/94).

...Symphonie espagnole. *Coupled with works by* **Berlioz** and **Saint-Saëns** Itzhak Perlman (vn);
Orchestre de Paris / Daniel Barenboim.
DG Digital Masters Ⓜ 445 549-2GMA (69 minutes: DDD: 7/95).

...Symphonie espagnole[a]. **Goldmark** Violin Concerto No. 1 in A minor, Op. 28[b]. **Nathan Milstein**
(vn); [a]**Philharmonia Orchestra / Harry Blech;** [b]**St Louis Symphony Orchestra /**
Vladimir Golschmann. Testament [a]stereo/[b]mono Ⓕ SBT1047* (71 minutes: ADD: 11/95).
See review under Goldmark; refer to the Index.

...Symphonie espagnole. **Bruch** Scottish Fantasy, Op. 46. **Tasmin Little** (vn); **Royal Scottish**
National Orchestra / Vernon Handley. EMI Eminence Ⓜ CD-EMX2277 (68 minutes: DDD: 6/97).
See review under Bruch; refer to the Index.

...Symphonie espagnole[a]. **Franck** Violin Sonata in A major[b]. **Zino Francescatti** (vn);
[b]**Robert Casadesus** (pf); [a]**symphony orchestra / André Cluytens.** Pearl mono Ⓜ GEMMCD9250*
(70 minutes: ADD: 9/97). *Also contains short works by Bach, Debussy, Schumann, Shostakovich,*
Tartini and Wieniawski.

Lalo Symphonie espagnole, Op. 21.
Dvořák Violin Concerto in A minor, B108. **Christian Tetzlaff** (vn); **Czech Philharmonic Orchestra /
Libor Pešek.** Virgin Classics Ⓕ VC5 45022-2 (63 minutes: DDD: 7/94). Recorded 1992-93.

This is a unique and generous coupling and if Virgin Classics' decision to record Tetzlaff in Prague
was dictated by the obvious advantage in having Dvořák's compatriots accompanying in his Violin
Concerto, the Czech Philharmonic's playing under Pešek proves just as idiomatic in the Spanish dance
rhythms of Lalo as in Czech dances, with crisp ensemble and rhythm deliciously sprung. What is
especially remarkable about Tetzlaff's performances of the *Symphonie espagnole* as well as the Violin
Concerto, is the quicksilver lightness of the passagework, which brings out the element of fantasy; in
that he is helped by a recording balance which does not spotlight the soloist as sharply as in most
other versions. In both works, each more episodic than most and hard to hold together, Tetzlaff's
concentration makes for a sense of spontaneity, leading one on just as magnetically as, for example,
Perlman in his more obviously weighty, more vibrato-laden readings of both pieces. Tetzlaff's sense
of fantasy consistently marks him out, so that with delectable pointing of rhythm and phrase he
makes the Lalo more subtly winning than it often is, less of a mere barnstorming showpiece, helped
by the extra transparency of textures.

Further listening ...
...Piano Trios – No. 1 in C minor, Op. 7; No. 2 in B minor; No. 3 in A minor, Op. 26. **Henry Trio.**
Pierre Verany PV794031 (8/94).   Ⓖ
...Symphony in G minor. Rapsodie. Scherzo. Divertissement. **Basle Symphony Orchestra /
Giancarlo Andretta.** CPO CPO999 296-2 (3/96).
...Piano Trios – No. 1 in C minor, Op. 7; No. 2 in B minor; No. 3 in A minor, Op. 26.
Barbican Piano Trio. ASV CDDCA899 (11/94).

David Lamb

Suggested listening ...
...Långdans efter Byfåns Mats. *Coupled with works by various composers.* **David Lamb** (bagpipes);
Kronos Quartet. Nonesuch 7559-79457-2 (12/97). *Gramophone Editor's choice. See review in the
Collections section; refer to the Index.*

Francesco Lambardi   Italian c1587-1642

Suggested listening ...
...Gagliarda. Partite sopra "Fidele". *Coupled with works by various composers.* **Rinaldo Alessandrini**
(hpd). Opus 111 OPS30-118 (4/95). ☞ *See review in the Collections section; refer to the Index.*

Walter Lambe   British c1450-c1499

Suggested listening ...
...Salve regina. *Coupled with works by various composers.* **The Sixteen / Harry Christophers.**
Collins Classics 1462-2 (3/96). *See review in the Collections section; refer to the Index.*
...Stella caeli. *Coupled with works by various composers.* **The Sixteen / Harry Christophers.**
Collins Classics 1342-2 (7/93). *See review in the Collections section; refer to the Index.*

Constant Lambert   British 1905-1951

Lambert Concerto for Piano and Nine Players[a]. Eight Poems[b]. Piano Sonata[c]. Mr Bear Squash-
you-all-flat[d]. [b]**Philip Langridge** (ten); [d]**Nigel Hawthorne** (narr); [ac]**Ian Brown** (pf);
[abd]**Nash Ensemble / Lionel Friend.** Hyperion Ⓕ CDA66754 (80 minutes: DDD: 7/95).
Texts included. Recorded 1994. *Gramophone Editor's choice.*   Ⓖ

The performance of the Piano Concerto is a rounded and deeply felt experience with the performers
scrupulously attentive to dynamic nuance; their playing also possesses immaculate polish,
irrepressible rhythmic vigour and heaps of panache – witness the exhilaratingly racy close to the first
movement. More crucially, this perceptive reading probes the unnerving strain of bleak melancholy
coursing through this poignant score. Nowhere is this more evident than in the elegiac finale, a tragic,
world-weary utterance which here attains an anguished climax of truly heartbreaking proportions.
Moreover, the ensuing coda is no less numbing in its inconsolable grief. Pianist Ian Brown acquits
himself as admirably in the Sonata as he does in the Concerto. This big-boned, daunting work calls
for a really strong technique which it duly receives. The tenderly affecting *Eight Poems* of Li-Po find
Philip Langridge in exquisite voice. These ravishing settings, given here with their rarely heard
accompaniment for flute, oboe, clarinet and string quintet, occupied Lambert on and off for a period
of four years (1926-29). In June 1924 Lambert completed his 'ballet' *Mr Bear Squash-you-all-flat*, the

earliest of his compositions currently known to us. This wittily anarchic entertainment, colourfully and confidently scored for chamber ensemble, more than likely also incorporated a part for narrator. Based on "a Russian children's tale" (a bedtime story from Lambert's St Petersburg-born father, perhaps, or just a leg-pulling piece of fiction?), the music reveals the influence of such contemporary continental figures as Satie, Milhaud, Honegger and, above all, Stravinsky. Assuming the voices and characters of Lambert's assorted menagerie (Mr Frog, Mr Mouse *et al*), Nigel Hawthorne enters into the fray with altogether infectious humour and enthusiasm. Featuring immaculate sound and excellent insert-notes, this anthology deserves the widest possible currency.

Additional recommendation ...

...Piano Sonata. Elegiac Blues. Elegy. *Coupled with works by* **Holst** Anthony Goldstone (pf). Chandos Ⓕ CHAN9382 (67 minutes: DDD: 10/95).

Further listening ...

...Horoscope. *Coupled with works by* **Bliss** and **Walton** English Northern Philharmonia / David Lloyd-Jones. Hyperion CDA66436 (3/91).

...Rio Grande[a]. Summer's Last Will and Testament[b]. Aubade héroïque. [a]Sally Burgess (mez); [b]William Shimell (bar); [a]Jack Gibbons (pf); [a]Opera North Chorus; [b]Leeds Festival Chorus; English Northern Philharmonia / David Lloyd-Jones. Hyperion CDA66565 (6/92).

Craig Sellar Lang
British 1891-1971

Suggested listening ...

...Tuba tune. *Coupled with works by various composers.* **Christopher Herrick** (org). Hyperion (3/96). *See review in the Collections section; refer to the Index.*

David Lang
American 1957

Suggested listening ...

...The Anvil Chorus. *Coupled with works by various composers.* **Bang on a Can All-Stars.** Sony Classical SK66483 (2/96). *Selected by Sounds in Retrospect. See review in the Collections section; refer to the Index.*

Peter Lange-Müller
Danish 1850-1926

Lange-Müller Fantasy, Op. 66. Soft Melodies, Op. 68. In Memoriam. Seven Woodland Pieces, Op. 56. **Morten Mogensen** (pf). Kontrapunkt Ⓕ 32228 (70 minutes: DDD: 9/96). Recorded 1995. This often touching and occasionally robust Danish composer was a conservative only in a subtle and inclusive sense. The booklet writer aptly evokes Fauré to define the intricate harmonic life of many of these works; also their elusive and recondite nature. The *Fantasy*, for example, is subtitled "Autumn" and a similarly seasonal haze hangs over *Soft Melodies. In Memoriam*, as its title declares, is a funeral elegy, while the *Seven Woodland Pieces* return us not so much to Schumann's *Waldszenen*, with their alternations of lightness (friendly landscape) and darkness (place of evil fame), but to Grieg's *Lyric Pieces*. Yet despite the evocation of such names, Lange-Müller's writing has a distinctive flavour and character. His *Fantasy* is a large-scale offering from a composer who clearly delighted in the miniature or lyric, and the title of Op. 68 is misleading when you consider the set's frequent blossoming into breadth and complexity. A Nordic introspection envelops the *Woodland Pieces* and it is sad to think of the composer's despair when he considered such music too tame and unadventurous to appeal to the taste of his time. Those who consider that Fauré showed little beyond a distinguished monotony (a tired yet familiar accusation) should steer clear, but others will surely find that Lange-Müller yields up riches and secrets on repeated hearings. One can imagine performances of greater pianistic colour and freedom (too often melody and accompaniment become one and the same thing) yet they have a cool authority. They are also finely recorded.

Further listening ...

...Once upon a time – Serenade; Midsummer Song. *Coupled with works by various composers.* **Aksel Schiøtz** (ten) with various artists. Danacord mono DACOCD454* (5/97). *See review in the Collections section; refer to the Index.*

...Serious Songs, Op. 27 – No. 2, Verzogen, verflogen; No. 3, Die du bist so schön und rein; No. 4, Nimm mich auf, uralte Nacht; No. 5, Der Zimmermann; No. 6, Die heil'gen drei Könige. The warrior's song, Op. 6 No. 1. At sunset, Op. 19 – No. 1, The sky softly glows flame-red. Songs of Russian origin, Op. 11 – No. 3, See, blue-grey cloud. At sunset, Op. 14 No. 1. The bear, Op. 23 No. 1. Songs, Op. 64 – Vol 1: No. 1, In the surf lies a rock; No. 2, There are two roses. The broad cloak of night, Op. 75 No. 9. Twilight, Op. 20 – No. 3, A fringe of misty heat. In the forest II, Op. 38 No. 3. Letizia – At the end of the flimsy train. *Coupled with songs by* **Heise** **Sten Byriel** (bass-bar); **Ulrik Staerk** (pf). Da Capo 8 224033 (9/97).

...Three Songs, Op. 4. Songs, Op. 6 – Sulamite's song in the Queen's garden. Folk-songs, Op. 18 – No. 4, Shine out, clear sunshine; No. 6, The willow bends. Spanish Students – The sun shines now (Juana's first song); Rose bushes! (Juana's second song). The shepherd pulls on his cape, Op. 34 No. 8. Cosmos Songs, Op. 57 – No. 3, The sun comes out like a rose; No. 4, I am singing of a King's son. Songs, Op. 64 – Vol. 2: No. 2, Oh, I own such lovely little fingers; No. 6, Speak quietly, young nightingale; Vol. 3: No. 2, Little birds are twittering in the sun. *Coupled with songs by* **Heise** Inger Dam-Jensen (sop); **Christen Stubbe Teglbjerg** (pf). Da Capo 8 224065 (9/97). *See review under Heise; refer to the Index.*

Alan Langford
British 1930

Suggested listening ...
...Waltz for strings. *Coupled with works by various composers.* **Pro Arte Orchestra / George Weldon.** EMI British Composers CDM5 66537-2 (1/98). *See review in the Collections section; refer to the Index.*

Rued Langgaard
Danish 1893-1952

Langgaard Music of the Spheres[a]. Four Tone Pictures. **Gitta-Maria Sjöberg** (sop); **Danish National Radio** [a]**Choir and Symphony Orchestra / Gennadi Rozhdestvensky.** Chandos Ⓕ CHAN9517 (53 minutes: DDD: 9/97). Recorded 1996.
Fitful though they have been, Chandos's issues devoted to the works of Langgaard have been especially welcome for their excellence of production. Now, with Rozhdestvensky at the helm, they have turned to what is probably this composer's most important – certainly most original – work, *Music of the Spheres* (1916-18). So radical did its sonic experiments seem even in the late-1960s that Ligeti no less, when inspecting the score, quipped that he had merely been a "Langgaard imitator" all along. The manipulation of blocks of sound rather than conventional thematic development does have much in common with trends in post-Second World War avant-garde composition (though stemming from impressionism), but other contemporaries of Langgaard's, such as Schoenberg and Scriabin, had traversed similar terrain at least in part. The main difference between Langgaard and Ligeti lies in the former's reliance on a fundamentally tonal language, however eccentrically deployed, and *Music of the Spheres* seems in hindsight to be a bridge between two other highly virtuosic scores with celestial connotations: Holst's *The Planets* and Ligeti's *Atmosphères*. The *Tone Pictures* (1917) were written alongside this extraordinary work, yet possess none of its stature: four charming songs, they seem effusive and outmoded by comparison. Chandos's sound is of demonstration quality.
Further listening ...
...Symphony No. 1, "Klippepastoraler". Fra Dybet[a]. [a]**Danish National Radio Choir; Danish National Radio Orchestra / Leif Segerstam.** Chandos CHAN9249.
...Symphonies – No. 4, "Fall of the Leaf"; No. 5, "Steppelands"; No. 6, "Heavens Asunder". **Danish National Radio Symphony Orchestra / Neeme Järvi.** Chandos CHAN9064 (12/92).

Jean Langlais
French 1907-1991

Langlais Symphonies – No. 1; No. 2, "Alla Webern". Suite française – Nazard; Arabesque sur les flûtes. Suite brève. Poem of Happiness. **Kevin Bowyer** (org). Nimbus Ⓕ NI5408 (68 minutes: DDD: 1/95). Played on the 1987 Carthy Organ of the Calgary Centre for the Performing Arts, Canada. Recorded 1992.
Langlais's First Symphony is an angry work, born out of the frustrations and horrors of the Nazi occupation of Paris. Bowyer has clearly gone for the emotive approach, venting his spleen at the microphones and uncompromisingly emphasizing Langlais's frequent outbursts of almost incoherent rage. It doesn't make for comfortable listening, but certainly underlines the starkness of the work. The most immediately obvious *alla Webern* aspects of the Second Symphony are its brevity – four movements totalling five minutes compared with 33 minutes for the First – and its desiccated, highly concentrated musical language. The profound Christian faith which was the driving force behind so much of Langlais's music finds an outlet here in the first nine notes, which spell out the words 'Dieu' and 'Marie'. The classical French organ composers of the seventeenth and eighteenth centuries seem poles apart from Webern, but Langlais absorbed their influence in equally distinctive ways, the most obvious results being the *Suite française* and the *Suite brève*. What all these works have in common is a restrained language almost devoid of emotional involvement. The crisp, sharp colours of this large but surprisingly intimate-sounding Canadian instrument, coupled with Bowyer's precise and fluent delivery, allow the music to speak with perfect clarity and impressive conviction.
Further listening ...
...Trois Paraphrases Grégoriennes, Op. 5. *Coupled with works by* **Alain** *and* **Messiaen Catharine Crozier** (org). Delos DE3147 (2/95).
...Poèmes évangéliques, Op. 2 – No. 2, La Nativité. Paraphrases grégoriennes, Op. 5 – Hymne d'actions de grâce. *Coupled with works by various composers.* **Andrew Lucas** (org). Naxos 8 550955 (11/94). *See review in the Collections section; refer to the Index.*

...Prelude and Fugue, Op. 1. *Coupled with works by various composers.* **Marie-Bernadette Dufourcet** (org). Priory PRCD422 (6/95). *See review in the Collections section; refer to the Index.*
...Triptyque. *Coupled with works by various composers.* **Roger Sayer** (org).
Priory PRCD495 (4/96). *See review in the Collections section; refer to the Index.*
...Messe solennelle. *Coupled with works by various composers.* **Judith Hancock** (org);
St Thomas Church Choir / Gerre Hancock. Koch International Classics 37228-2 (9/96).

Libby Larsen   American 1950

Larsen Symphonies – No. 1, "Water Music"; No. 3, "Lyric". Parachute Dancing. Ring of Fire.
London Symphony Orchestra / Joel Revzen. Koch International Classics Ⓟ 37370-2
(57 minutes: DDD: 2/98). Recorded 1996. *Gramophone Editor's choice.*
This is a terrific disc. Right from the very first bars of the invigorating *Water Music* Symphony (1984), one is drawn irresistibly into Larsen's sound world and left in no doubt that here is a composer who has made the art of symphonic writing very much her own. On the evidence of the present collection, her principal musical antecedents seem to be Sibelius, Stravinsky and the American symphonic composers of the mid-twentieth century (such as Schuman and Harris). But there is much more that is distinctively her own, and the result is a muse full of zest and vim. True, *Water Music* is more a sinfonietta than a symphony, but it is very accomplished none the less. One can almost 'hear liquid', as it were, and this is the finest water music since Respighi's *Fountains.* The Third Symphony (1991, not 1995 as listed on the cover) is an electric score. *Ring of Fire* (1995) is no less involving, a brilliant tone-poem inspired by lines from T.S. Eliot's *Little Gidding* (compare George Benjamin's *Ringed by the flat horizon*, deriving from *The Waste Land*). The performances from the LSO – on top form – take wing, with everyone clearly at home with the idiom.
Further listening ...
...Collage: Boogie. *Coupled with works by various composers.* **Baltimore Symphony Orchestra / David Zinman.** Argo 444 454-2ZH (7/95).
...Six Sonnets from the Portuguese. *Coupled with works by various composers.* **Arleen Auger** (sop); members of the **Saint Paul Chamber Orchestra** and the **Minnesota Orchestra / Joel Revzen** (pf). Koch International Classics 37248-2 (4/94). *See review in the Collections section; refer to the Index.*

Orlando Lassus   Franco/Flemish 1532-1594

Lassus Libro de villanelle, moresche, e altre canzoni. Madrigals – Tutto 'l dì piango; Sol'e pensoso i più deserti campi; O Lucia miau; Madonna mia pietà. **Concerto Italiano / Rinaldo Alessandrini.** Opus 111 Ⓟ OPS30-94 (59 minutes: DDD: 10/95). Texts and translations included.
Recorded 1994.
This wickedly funny disc was released to coincide with the commemoration of the quincentenary of Lassus's death. Hitherto, Concerto Italiano have concentrated on the highbrow end of Italian secular music. They have done so with style, and as much wit as the aesthetic of the late madrigal allows. Here at last they get a chance to let their hair down: the result is as hilarious as one could have hoped. They get inside both the meaning *and* the sound of the words, transfiguring musical texts that are (at times) purposefully naïve. They also capture the incipient, slightly worrying musical hysteria that pervades many of these pieces, and of which the French songs usually steer clear. Psychologically, this is well judged: as Lassus's letters show, Italian is the language of his manic phases, just as French corresponds to his depressive ones. This disc, then, completes the picture of the composer in his more unbuttoned moments. Apart from some indispensable anthology numbers such as "Matona mia cara" from the *Libro de villanelle* (performed with all the parody that the text demands), the most convincing performances are those of the *moresche*. A few more serious items are thrown in for the sake of contrast. These are the only disappointing pieces in the set, too slow for comfort by some margin – but then again, the rather archaic madrigal, *Madonna mia pietà* is delivered with real passion. Finally, a word about that packaging gimmick – a red banner that proclaims, "Everything you ever wanted to know about sex on CD!" A note of reassurance for those who might need it: the humour here is more often allusive than explicit, and as often lavatorial as genuinely bawdy. Those familiar with French *chanson* texts will probably have seen worse. Besides, one cannot help but respond to Lassus's evident relish at setting these dubious gems. Do follow the composer's and the singers' example, and let your hair down as well.

Lassus Lagrime di San Pietro. **Ensemble Vocal Européen / Philippe Herreweghe.** Harmonia Mundi Ⓟ HMC90 1483 (60 minutes: DDD: 8/94). Texts and translations included. Recorded 1993.   Ⓠ
Lassus Lagrime di San Pietro. **Huelgas Ensemble / Paul van Nevel.** Sony Classical Ⓟ SK53373
(63 minutes: DDD: 8/94). Texts and translations included. Recorded 1993.
Lassus completed his swan-song days before his death in 1594. The decision to set 20 stanzas from Luigi Tansillo's unfinished meditation on "the tears of St Peter" must have been a highly personal one. The poet's portrayal of a man driven nearly insane with remorse allowed Lassus to exorcize the

mental illness that engulfed him in his last years. The result is perhaps his most moving work, for there is in these *madrigali spirituali* a sense of distilled mannerism that calls to mind the understated passion of late-period Brahms. Philippe Herreweghe captures the detached expression of pain that makes this music so haunting. This is partly a matter of vocal timbre: individually the singers' tone is a shade cooler than that of the Huelgas Ensemble's members, but collectively they sound every bit as full-bodied as their rivals. However, it is in their interpretative acuteness that Herreweghe's singers gain a decisive edge. This is best illustrated by the groups' differing approaches to rubato: van Nevel uses *accelerandos* or straightforward shifts (usually to emphasize a textual illustration), but Herreweghe ever so slightly *stretches* the pulse when the voices achieve a poignant inflexion or come to a standstill. Such moments acquire an intensity that clearly identifies them as the key moments in a psychological drama, making the cycle as a whole compulsive listening. This is not to understate the many virtues of van Nevel's approach, but simply to say that Herreweghe's singers achieve something very, very special indeed.

Additional recommendation ...
...**Ars Nova / Bo Holten.** Naxos Ⓢ 8 553311 (55 minutes: DDD: 1/96).

Lassus Missa Vinum bonum. Missa Triste depart. Missa Quand'io pens'al martire. Vinum bonum et suave.
Arcadelt Quand'io pens'al martire.
Gombert Triste depart m'avoit. **King's College Choir, Cambridge / Stephen Cleobury.**
Decca London Ⓕ 444 335-2LH (70 minutes: DDD: 7/96). Texts and translations included.
Lassus Musica Dei donum optimi. Bicinia – Nos. 3, 9 and 14. Vinum bonum et suave. Missa Vinum bonum. Salve regina mater. Laudent Deum cythara. Justorum animae. Quam pulchra es. Agimus tibi gratias. Christus resurgens ex mortuis. Tristis est anima mea. Ave verum corpus. Bone Jesu verbum patris. Tui sunt coeli. Vide homo, quae pro te patior.
Ex Cathedra / Jeffrey Skidmore; His Majesties Sagbutts and Cornetts / Jeremy West (cornett).
ASV Gaudeamus Ⓕ CDGAU150 (69 minutes: DDD: 7/96). Texts and translations included.
Lassus's *Vinum bonum* Mass is one of a group of three double-choir cycles composed in the 1580s (the others being *Osculetur me* and the *Bell'amphitrit'altera*). Lassus's Masses have generally had a rather bad press, for reasons that have never really been spelt out. Nearly all are of the so-called 'parody' variety, that is, based on previously composed polyphonic pieces (by Lassus or by others), and it is fascinating to observe the skill with which he reworks his models, chosen most commonly from among Italian madrigals, French chansons and Latin motets; Stephen Cleobury's generous selection gives us one of each (the Masses on *Quand'io pens'al martire* and *Triste depart* are not to be found elsewhere). All three are sung immediately before the corresponding Mass, allowing the listener to explore the correspondences at leisure. These are fine performances, typical of the English treble tradition at its best; and if the four-voice Mass on *Quand'io pens'al martire* is a touch disappointing after the glorious promise of Arcadelt's madrigal, the two other cycles show Lassus on his best form. The King's College disc is (by definition) *a cappella*.

Ex Cathedra is a mixed choir and they are here joined for the *Vinum bonum* Mass by His Majesties Sagbutts and Cornetts. In that respect, they offer a clear alternative to King's. Their account of the motet *Vinum bonum* itself is more involving that that of King's, and for the Mass theirs is the more dynamic reading, and yet King's solemn account is not without grandeur. However, the balance in the mixed version favours the instruments ever so slightly more than than one might wish, sometimes to the detriment of the choral effect. Ex Cathedra present a contrasting series of motets for three to eight voices, and the wind ensemble round out the disc with a few *bicinia*, two-part pieces excerpted from his vocal music; so the two programmes are different enough for duplication scarcely to be an issue. In the final analysis, the choice largely depends on how you like your Lassus.

Lassus Missa Entre vous filles. Missa Susanne un jour. Infelix ego. **Oxford Camerata / Jeremy Summerly.** Naxos Ⓢ 8 550842 (68 minutes: DDD: 8/94). Text and translation of *Infelix ego* included. Recorded 1993.
The only Mass from this composer's considerable output to have found favour with record companies has been the eight-part *Bell'amfitrit altera*. This disc helps to dispel the still-current myth that Lassus's other Masses are of little interest. Both *Entre vous filles* and *Susanne un jour* show Lassus at his best, full of variety and invention, music of an immediate impact; in fact, they display exactly the same qualities as the better-known motets. The Oxford Camerata have understood this well, taking considerable care with the nuances of the text and really enjoying the music's rich sonorities. Sometimes a slight imprecision in the playing of chords is detectable, but this is more than outweighed by the sense of melodic contour and the powerful, somewhat dark and austere sound which conveys so well the spirit of the music. With over 68 minutes of some of the finest sixteenth-century polyphony available at such a low price, no one should hesitate to buy this disc.

Further listening ...
...**Lamentationes Hieremiae a 5. La Chapelle Royale European Ensemble / Philippe Herreweghe.** Harmonia Mundi HMC90 1299 (12/89).
...Missa Osculetur me. Motets – Osculetur me; Hodie completi sunt; Timor et tremor; Alma Redemptoris mater a 8; Salve regina mater a 8; Ave regina caelorum II a 6; Regina coeli a 7. **The Tallis Scholars / Peter Phillips.** Gimell 454 918-2PH (7/89).

...Motets – Regina coeli laetare (five versions). Laetentur coeli. Alma Redemptoris mater. Resonet in laudibus. Tui sunt coeli. Quem vidistis pastores. Omnes de Saba Venient. Peccantem me quotidie. Timor et tremor. Popule meus. Aurora lucis rutilat. Christus resurgens ex mortuis. Jesu nostra redemptio. Jam non dicam vos. Hodie completi sunt. Alleluja laus et gloria. Benedictio et claritas. Justorum animae. Exultate justi. **Trinity College Choir, Cambridge / Richard Marlow.** Conifer Classics CDCF230 (10/94).   Ⓖ
...Missa Bell'Amfitrit altera. Tui sunt coeli. *Coupled with works by various composers.* **The Sixteen / Harry Christophers** with [a]**Laurence Cummings** (org). Collins Classics 1360-2 (10/93). *See review in the Collections section; refer to the Index.*
...Missa Bell'Amfitrit' altera. *Coupled with works by various composers.* **Westminster Cathedral Choir; His Majesties Sagbutts and Cornetts / James O'Donnell** with **Timothy Roberts, Iain Simcock** (orgs). Hyperion CDA66688 (6/94).   Ⓖ
...Missa Qual donna attende à gloriosa fama. Tristis est anima mea. Exaltabo te Domine a 4. Psalmi Davidis poenitentiales – De profundis. Missa Venatorum. *Coupled with* **de Rore** Qual donna à gloriosa fama. **Christ Church Cathedral Choir, Oxford / Stephen Darlington.** Nimbus NI5150 (4/89).

Antonio Lauro   Venezuelan 1917-1986

Suggested listening ...
...Seis por derecho[a]. El marabino. Valses venezolanos – No. 3, Natalia[a]. *Coupled with works by various composers.* **Sharon Isbin** (gtr) with [a]**Gaudencio Thiago de Mello** (perc). Teldec 0630-19899-2 (7/98). *Gramophone Editor's choice. See review in the Collections section; refer to the Index.*   ⒼⒼ

William Lawes   British 1602-1645

Lawes Royall Consorts – No. 2 in D minor; No. 4 in D major; No. 5 in D major; No. 8 in C major; No. 10 in B flat major. **The Greate Consort** (Anne Schumann, vn; Emilia Benjamin, Reiko Ichise, va da gambas; Elizabeth Kenny, William Carter; theorbos) / **Monica Huggett** (vn). ASV Gaudeamus Ⓕ CDGAU147 (68 minutes: DDD: 6/97). 🖊 Recorded 1996.
Whilst Lawes's larger-scored *Fantasias* show us the theatricality of the composer's bold contrapuntal language and in the early 'violin' sets, the textural interplay typical of a more self-conscious *concertante* style, these formalized dances give us yet another view of the composer: the broody cavalier reflecting, in exquisitely fashioned thematic strains, the unequivocal decorum of musical conceits in Charles I's cultivated time-bomb of a court. The soft-grained and unforced string timbre of The Greate Consort is underpinned by delightfully subtle and undemonstrative theorbo playing. For some, the characterization in, say, the Aires of Consort No. 4 will seem a touch under-explored but given the Pavan's wonderful concentration of seamless allusions, gently passed back and forth, the sense of an integral suite is strongly and vitally projected. Maybe in such an obvious group-effort it is invidious to pick out individuals but English consort music is often more treble-dominated than we might think. Monica Huggett leads by example with tonal sweetness and exemplary musicianship. Rare qualities indeed, and treasure from which she has effected chamber music playing of the very highest quality.
Additional recommendations ...
...Consort Setts a 6[d] – G minor; C major; B flat major. Consort Setts a 5[d] – A minor; G minor. Dances for Lyra Viol[b] – The Countrey Coll, VdGS421; Jigg, VdGS422; Almaine, VdGS430; Corant, VdGS431; Saraband, VdGS432. Aires for Lyra Viol[b] – VdGS462; VdGS463. To Pansies, "Ah cruel love"[abc]. Gather ye rosebuds while you may[abc]. To the sycamore, "I'm sick of love"[abc]. On the Lillyes, "White though yee be"[abc]. [a]**Catherine Bott** (sop); [b]**Richard Boothby** (lyra viol); [c]**Paul Nicholson** (org); [d]**Fretwork.**
Virgin Classics Veritas Ⓕ VC5 45147-2 (67 minutes: DDD: 10/95). 🖊
...Royall Consorts. **Purcell Quartet; Nigel North, Paul O'Dette** (theorbos). Chandos Chaconne Ⓕ CHAN0584/5 (two discs: 127 minutes: DDD: 11/95). 🖊

Jean-Marie Leclair   French 1697-1764

Leclair Flute Concerto No. 3 in C major, Op. 7[a]. Violin Concertos[b] – Op. 7: No. 4 in F major; No. 6 in A major. No. 2 in A major, Op. 10. [a]**Rachel Brown** (fl); **Collegium Musicum 90 / Simon Standage** ([b]vn). Chandos Chaconne Ⓕ CHAN0564 (65 minutes: DDD: 2/95). 🖊 Recorded 1994.   ⒼⒼ
Of the violin concertos here, Op. 10 No. 2 is the richest harmonically. The solo instrument in Op. 7 No. 3 is Leclair's stated alternative of flute, the only one of his 12 violin concertos to be so designed. Accordingly, it lacks the double-stopping so much favoured by this greatly admired violinist-composer; but otherwise it exploits the graceful sequential passagework found in the other concertos,

though here with a fuller accompanying texture, with more movement in inner parts. Rachel Brown's playing throughout is deliciously cool and poised. Virtuoso violin fireworks abound in the vigorous first movements of the other two Op. 7 concertos here and the ebullient finale of the A major (the start of whose first movement has a Vivaldian resonance): as expected, Simon Standage throws off their difficulties with panache and an apparent ease that allows him also to add stylish embellishments of his own. The extensive multiple-stopping on which the elegant minuet-like Aria of Op. 7 No. 6 relies is performed with well-nigh impeccable intonation.

Leclair Violin Concertos – Op. 7: No. 1 in D minor; Op. 10: No. 3 in D major; No. 4 in F major; No. 6 in G minor. **Collegium Musicum 90 / Simon Standage** (vn). Chandos Chaconne
Ⓕ CHAN0589 (59 minutes: DDD: 11/95). ✍ Recorded 1995. *Gramophone Editor's choice.* ⒼⒼ
This disc contains Leclair's most vivacious and attractive works, played with great *élan*, sensitivity and neatness, and recorded with exemplary clarity and balance. The concertos represent a high-water mark in eighteenth-century violin technique, with extensive double-stopping (quite spectacular in the first *Allegro* of the F major Concerto and the *Andante* of the G minor), an extended range that soars up to heights scarcely ventured previously, rapid scales and flying arpeggios, and elaborate figurations of all kinds. To all of this Standage brings a seasoned virtuosity which he places completely at the service of the music's grace: his bowing in particular commands admiration. He shows an occasional urge to hurry, but the only movement that brings unease is the finale of the G minor, where his sudden changes of pace are unconvincing. From the stylistic viewpoint these concertos are interesting for their mingling of French and Italian elements. There are Vivaldian unisons, but French dance forms for the middle movements – a pair of minuets in the D minor, minuets *en rondeau* in the G minor, a pair of gavottes with unusual interplay between solo and tutti in the F major, and an ornate solo line over supporting reiterated chords in the D major. (Standage adds spontaneous embellishments of his own on repeats.) The first movements of Op. 10 Nos. 3 and 4 are more substantial than the others, with freer harmonic progressions, and the dotted rhythms of No. 6 impart a new dramatic flavour.
Additional recommendation ...
...Op. 7: No. 2 in D major; No. 5 in A minor. Op. 10: No. 1 in B flat major; No. 5 in E minor.
Collegium Musicum 90 / Simon Standage (vn).
Chandos Chaconne Ⓕ CHAN0551 (62 minutes: DDD: 8/94). ✍   ⒼⒼ

Leclair Ouverture in A major, Op. 13 No. 3. Deuxième Recréation de musique d'une execution facile in G minor, Op. 8.
Boismortier Sonata in G minor, Op. 34 No. 1[b].
Corrette Concerto comique No. 25, "Les Sauvages et la Furstemberg"[ab]. **Florilegium Ensemble** (Ashley Solomon, traverso; Rachel Podger, Anna McDonald, vns; Daniel Yeadon, vc; Elizabeth Kenny, theorbo/gtr; Neal Peres Da Costa, hpd); [a]**Jane Rogers** (va); [b]**Scott Pauley** (theorbo). Channel Classics Ⓕ CCS7595 (58 minutes: DDD: 12/95). ✍ Recorded 1994.
By far the greatest musical substance here lies in the two fine compositions by Leclair, the *Deuxième Recréation de musique* (Op. 8) and an *Ouverture* in A major (Op. 13 No. 3). In the *Ouverture*, above all, there is a pleasing *rapprochement* of Italian with French idioms – sequences, held under tighter rein than those typical of his Italian models, jostling with essentially French gestures such as those characterizing the distinctive *ouverture Française* itself. The *Recréation*, a suite of dances in all but name, is more consistently French while the pieces by Boismortier and Corrette reveal a marked bias towards the Italian sonata and concerto. Florilegium imbue all this music with a vitality which, at least in part, emanates from the players' effective application of appropriate ornament and their evident savouring of delicately wrought colours and textures. Perhaps there is occasionally a degree of self-consciousness or, at least, study in their playing which detracts from the light-hearted spirit which reigns, for example, in the "Forlane" of the *Recréation*, and the captivating first movement of the Corrette, based on Rameau's beguiling dance rondeau *Les sauvages*. But such reservations are the slightest of details when so much else here is endowed with graceful gesture, transparent textures and an evident affection for the music. Throughout, the continuo is imaginatively realized, with the constant presence of at least one theorbo or a baroque guitar in all but the Boismortier, where two theorbos are preferred. The recording itself is clear and resonant, perhaps a little lacking in intimacy.
Additional recommendation ...
...Première Récréation de musique, Op. 6. Deuxième Récréation de musique, Op. 8.
Les Nièces de Rameau. Pierre Verany Ⓕ PV794011 (57 minutes: DDD: 9/94).

Leclair Violin Sonatas, Op. 1 – No. 1 in A minor; No. 3 in B flat major; No. 8 in G major; No. 9 in A major. **François Fernandez** (vn); **Pierre Hantaï** (hpd); **Philippe Pierlot** (va da gamba).
Auvidis Astrée Ⓕ E8662 (64 minutes: DDD: 3/98). ✍ Recorded 1995.
Gramophone Editor's choice.   ⒼⒼ
Leclair's Op. 1 set was so successful when it was first published in 1723 that it had to be reprinted four times. Though the technical demands it makes on the violinist are considerable, the composer himself was at pains not to employ virtuosity as an end in itself and to condemn the "trivialisation" of players who exaggerated the speed of quick movements. Leclair also, like Couperin, was insistent that performers should not add ornamentation of their own – though in the four sonatas here only the initial *Adagio* of No. 3 is much decorated. Rather did he place emphasis on "le beau chant" –

expressive *cantabile*, which is well exemplified in the first movements of Nos. 1, 8 and 9. The crisp *Allegro*, with its rapid dipping across strings, and the *Largo* of No. 3 make play with multiple stopping, including double trills, and there is vigorous cross-string work too in the ebullient Giga of No. 1. Leclair shows himself fond of the rondeau form with long episodes, and the Sarabande of No. 9 is a set of variations. This last has an athletic gamba line, as does the whole of the G major Sonata; and the alert and positive continuo playing here (from both gamba and harpsichord) is a special pleasure. But naturally the main spotlight falls on François Fernandez, whose lively, pointed bowing, delicate and sprightly fast movements and graceful slow ones (like the gentle G major Musette) do full justice to Leclair's attractive invention.

Further listening ...

...Ouverture in G major, Op. 13 No. 1. *Coupled with works by various composers.* **Palladian Ensemble.** Linn Records CKD050 (5/97). *See review in the collections section; refer to the Index.*

...Première récréation de musique d'une exécution facile in D major, Op. 6ᵃ. Double Violin Sonata in D major, Op. 3 No. 6ᵇ. Trio in A major, Op. 14ᵃ. ᵇ**Micaela Comberti** (vn); ᵃ**Collegium Musicum 90 / Simon Standage** (ᵇvn). Chandos Chaconne CHAN0582 (5/97). 🎵

...Flute Sonatas: *ACC58435* – Op. 1: No. 2 in C major. Op. 2: No. 1 in E minor; No. 3 in C major; No. 5 in G major. *ACC58436* – Op. 1: No. 6 in E minor. Op. 2: No. 8 in D minor; No. 11 in B minor. Op. 9: No. 2 in E minor; No. 7 in G major. **Barthold Kuijken** (fl); **Wieland Kuijken** (va da gamba); **Robert Kohnen** (hpd). Accent ACC58435/6 (2/86). 🎵 🅶🅶

...Sonates en trio, Op. 4. **London Baroque.** Harmonia Mundi HMC90 1617 (12/97). 🎵

...Trio Sonatas – No. 1 in E minor, Op. 2; No. 7 in G major, Op. 9. *Coupled with works by various composers.* **Rachel Brown** (fl); **Mark Caudle** (viol); **James Johnstone** (hpd). Chandos Chaconne CHAN0544 (2/94).

...Trio Sonatas, Op. 4 – No. 1 in D minor; No. 2 in B flat major; No. 3 in D minor; No. 4 in F major; No. 5 in G minor; No. 6 in A major. **Purcell Quartet.** Chandos Chaconne CHAN0536 (7/93). 🎵

...Trio Sonatas, Op. 9 – No. 2 in E minor; No. 6 in D major; No. 8 in C major; No. 11 in G minor. **François Fernandez** (vn); **Pierre Hantaï** (hpd); **Philippe Pierlot** (va da gamba). Auvidis Astrée E8586 (7/97). 🎵

Nicola LeFanu
British 1947

Suggested listening ...

...I am Bread. A Penny for a Song. *Coupled with works by various composers.* **Tracey Chadwell** (sop); **Pamela Lidiard** (pf). British Music Society BMS420/1CD (3/98). *See review in the Collections section; refer to the Index.*

...Lullaby. Nocturne. *Coupled with works by various composers.* **Mühlfeld Ensemble.** Clarinet Classics CC0007 (10/94). *See review in the Collections section; refer to the Index.*

Louis Lefébure-Wély
French 1817-1869

Suggested listening ...

...Marche in F major, Op. 122 No. 4 *Coupled with works by various composers.* **Christopher Herrick** (org). Hyperion CDA66457 (9/91). *See review in the Collections section; refer to the Index.* 🅶🅶🅶

...Noël varié. *Coupled with works by various composers.* **Christopher Herrick** (org). Hyperion CDA66917 (8/97). *See review in the Collections section; refer to the Index.*

Johannes Legrant
French 15th century

Suggested listening ...

...Entre vous, nouviaux mariés. *Coupled with works by various composers.* **Alla Francesca.** Opus 111 OPS30-173 (7/98). *See review in the Collections section; refer to the Index.* 🅶🅶🅶

Franz Lehár
Austro/Hungarian 1870-1948

Lehár Giuditta (sung in English). **Deborah Riedel** (sop) Giuditta; **Jerry Hadley** (ten) Octavio; **Jeffrey Carl** (bar) Manuele Biffi; Antonio; **Andrew Busher** (spkr) Duke; **Naomi Itami** (sop) Anita; **Lynton Atkinson** (ten) Pierrino; **William Dieghan** (ten) Sebastiano; **English Chamber Orchestra / Richard Bonynge.** Telarc Ⓔ CD80436 (78 minutes: DDD: 11/97). Text included. Recorded 1996.

Giuditta was Lehár's last stage work and the peak of his compositional development. Written for the Vienna State Opera, it is a highly ambitious score, containing some fiendishly difficult vocal writing and using a large orchestra featuring mandolin and other exotic instruments. For this recording some two hours of music have been compressed into 78 minutes by means of snips here and there and the omission of a couple of subsidiary numbers. The piece has a *Carmen*-like story, about the disenchanted wife of an innkeeper who persuades a soldier to desert, before eventually abandoning and ruining him as she goes from lover to lover. The best-known number is Giuditta's "On my lips every kiss is like wine", here gloriously sung by Deborah Riedel; the leading male role was written for Tauber, and there are some marvellous and demanding tenor solos, equally superbly sung by the ever impressive Jerry Hadley. Despite writing for the opera-house, Lehár remained faithful to his formula of interspersing the music for the principal couple with sprightly dance numbers for a comedy pair, here in the hands of Naomi Itami and Lynton Atkinson. Assisted by Richard Bonynge's lilting conducting, these contribute richly to the appeal of the recording.

Lehár Das Land des Lächelns. **Anneliese Rothenberger** (sop) Lisa; **Harry Friedauer** (ten) Gustl; **Nicolai Gedda** (ten) Sou-Chong; **Renate Holm** (sop) Mi; **Jobst Moeller** (bar) Tschang; **Bavarian Radio Chorus; Graunke Symphony Orchestra / Willy Mattes.** EMI Ⓜ CMS5 65372-2 (two discs: 87 minutes: ADD: 2/95). From World Record Club SOC242/3 (8/71). Recorded 1967.
The great glory of this *Das Land des Lächelns*, Lehár's portrayal of the clash of western and eastern cultures, is the singing of Nicolai Gedda, who brings off "Dein ist mein ganzes Herz" and the other Richard Tauber favourites to splendid effect. Anneliese Rothenberger is on excellent form vocally and full of charm, and she and Gedda make an excellent partnership. Renate Holm is a smiling Mi and the other principals, chorus and orchestra all play their full parts. Willy Mattes is an experienced and sympathetic conductor of operetta. The score here is, of course, not identical with that given in London when the operetta was first produced there in 1931. Apparently, Tauber was in and out of the cast every other day, providing his understudy, Robert Naylor, with plenty of opportunities. The show only had a short run in London on its first appearance. It seems that it was Tauber rather than Lehár that people wanted to hear. This reissue should be in every Viennese operetta collection.
Additional recommendation ...
...(sung in English). **Soloists; London Voices; English Chamber Orchestra / Richard Bonynge.**
Telarc Ⓕ CD80419 (79 minutes: DDD: 1/97).
...Excerpts – Immer nur lächeln; Von Apfelblüten einen Kranz; Dein ist meines ganzes Herz.
Friederike – O Mädchen, mein Mädchen. Paganini – Gern hab'ich die Frau'n geküsst. Schön ist die Welt – Schön ist die Welt. Der Zarewitsch – Wolgalied. *Coupled with works by various composers.* **Jerry Hadley** (ten); **Munich Radio Orchestra / Richard Bonynge.**
RCA Victor Red Seal Ⓕ 09026 68258-2 (61 minutes: DDD: 9/97). *Gramophone Editor's choice.*
See review in the Collections section; refer to the Index.

Lehár Die lustige Witwe. **Cheryl Studer** (sop) Hanna; **Boje Skovhus** (bar) Danilo; **Bryn Terfel** (bass-bar) Zeta; **Rainer Trost** (ten) Camille; **Barbara Bonney** (sop) Valencienne; **Uwe Peper** (ten) Raoul; **Karl-Magnus Fredriksson** (bar) Cascada; **Heinz Zednik** (ten) Njegus; **Richard Savage** (bar) Bogdanowitsch; **Lynette Alcantara** (sop) Sylviane; **Philip Salmon** (ten) Kromow; **Constanze Backes** (mez) Olga; **Julian Clarkson** (bass) Pritschitsch; **Angela Kazimierczuk** (sop) Praškowia; **Wiener Tschuschkapelle; Vienna Philharmonic Orchestra / Sir John Eliot Gardiner.**
DG Ⓕ 439 911-2GH (80 minutes: DDD: 2/95). Notes, text and translation included.
Recorded 1994. *Gramophone Editor's record of the month.*   ⒼⒼ
This is one of those great operetta interpretations that is committed to record once in a generation if one is lucky. Gardiner's approach is on an altogether more inspired plane than his rivals. In the Viennese rhythms, he shows himself utterly at home – as in the Act 2 Dance scene, where he eases the orchestra irresistibly into the famous waltz. But there are also countless instances where Gardiner provides a deliciously fresh inflexion to the score. The cast of singers is uniformly impressive. If Cheryl Studer's "Vilja" isn't quite as assured as some others, her captivatingly playful "Dummer, dummer Reitersmann" is typical of a well-characterized performance. As Danilo, Boje Skovhus acquits himself well with a polished performance and he offers a natural, more human characterization than his rivals, while Barbara Bonney is superb. Not the least inspired piece of casting comes with Bryn Terfel, who transforms himself outstandingly well into the bluff Pontevedran ambassador. As for Gardiner's personally selected chorus, they make Monteverdi to Montenegro and Pontevedra seem the most natural transition in the world. DG's recorded sound has an astonishing clarity and immediacy, as in the way the piccolos shriek out at the Widow's Act 1 entrance or in the beautiful *pianissimo* accompaniment to the "Vilja-Lied".
Additional recommendations ...
...**Soloists; Philharmonia Chorus and Orchestra / Lovro von Matačić.**
EMI Ⓕ CDS7 47178-8 (two discs: 80 minutes: AAD: 4/86).   Ⓖ
...**Soloists; BBC Chorus; Philharmonia / Otto Ackermann.**
EMI mono Ⓜ CDH7 69520-2* (72 minutes: ADD: 11/88).
Further listening ...
...Gold und Silber, Op. 79. *Coupled with works by various composers.* **New London Orchestra / Ronald Corp.** Hyperion CDA66998 (3/98). *See review in the Collections section; refer to the Index.*
...Die lustige Witwe – Es lebt eine Vilja. *Coupled with works by various composers.*
Renée Fleming (sop); **English Chamber Orchestra / Jeffrey Tate.**
Decca 458 858-2DH (3/98). *See review in the Collections section; refer to the Index.*
...Der Zarewitsch (sung in English). **Soloists; London Voices; English Chamber Orchestra / Richard Bonynge.** Telarc CD80395 (1/97).

...Zigeunerliebe – Hör' ich Cymbalklänge. Friederike – Warum hast du mich wachgeküsst? Die lustige Witwe – Es lebt eine Vilja, ein Waldmägdelein. *Coupled with works by various composers.* **Lesley Garrett** (sop); **Crouch End Festival Chorus; Royal Philharmonic Concert Orchestra / James Holmes.** Silva Screen Classics SILKTVCD1 (2/96). *Gramophone Award Winner 1996.* *See review in the Collections section; refer to the Index.*

Liza Lehmann
British 1862-1918

Suggested listening ...

...The Daisy Chain – Fairies[b]; Keepsake Mill[d]; If no one ever marries me[a]; Stars[c]; The Swing[a]; Mustard and Cress[d]. Bird Songs[a] – The Woodpigeon; The Starling; The Yellowhammer; The Wren; The Owl. Magdalen at Michael's gate[a]. Evensong[b]. Endymion[a]. Music when soft voices die[d]. To a little red spider[d]. Dusk in the Valley[b]. The Lily of a Day[a]. When I am dead, my dearest[a]. Four Cautionary Tales and a Moral[bc]. Parody Pie – My true friend hath my hat[cd]. Nonsense Songs – Mockturtle Soup[c]; Will you walk a little faster[abcd]. **Horn** Cherry Ripe (arr. Lehmann)[a].
[a]**Janice Watson** (sop); [b]**Catherine Wyn-Rogers** (contr); [c]**Toby Spence** (ten); [d]**Neal Davies** (bar); **Steuart Bedford** (pf). Collins Classics 1508-2 (2/98).

Jón Leifs
Icelandic 1899-1968

Leifs Geysír, Op. 51. Trilogia piccola, Op. 1. Trois peintures abstraites, Op. 44. Icelandic Folk Dances, Op. 11. Overture to "Galdra-Loftur", Op. 10. Consolation, Op. 66. **Iceland Symphony Orchestra / Osmo Vänskä.** BIS Ⓕ CD830 (56 minutes: DDD: 7/97). Recorded 1996.
The orchestral prelude *Geysír* (1961) is a typical product of Jón Leifs's mature style: rough-hewn, granitic in sound, purged of everything inessential. Vänskä's account is slow overall but accentuates the eruptive central section tellingly. In the *Trois peintures abstraites* (1955) he secures tight ensemble and a good, focused performance. The same could be said for the *Galdra-Loftur* (1927); what Vänskä lacks in mystery he gains in tautness. It demonstrates that Leifs, not yet 30 at the time, had moved a good way towards his recognizable manner, especially when compared with the *Trilogia piccola*, composed in a somewhat polyglot fashion between 1919 and 1924. Here, as in the *Icelandic Folk Dances* of 1929, Leifs speaks with a more cosmopolitan accent (he was then working in Germany), whereas the later uncompromising pieces date from after his return home in 1945. Both works, and the elegiac *Consolation* for strings (1968; his last piece), are easier to handle than the bulk of his output though are no less atmospheric. This disc is an excellent general introduction to the composer and can be warmly commended to anyone even remotely interested in out-of-the-way repertoire.
Further listening ...

...Symphony No. 1, Op. 26, "Saga Symphony". **Iceland Symphony Orchestra / Osmo Vänskä.** BIS CD730 (3/96).

...Icelandic Overture, Op. 9[a]. Iceland Cantata, Op. 13[b]. Elegy, Op. 53. Fine I, Op. 55. Fine II, Op. 56. [ab]**Chorus of the Icelandic Opera;** [b]**Graduale Choir of Langholts Church; Iceland Symphony Orchestra / Petri Sakari.** Chandos New Direction CHAN9433 (5/96).

...String Quartets – No. 1, "Mors et vita", Op. 21; No. 2, "Vita et mors", Op. 36; No. 3, "El Greco", Op. 64. **Yggdrasil Quartet.** BIS CD691 (7/95).

Kenneth Leighton
British 1929-1988

Leighton God's Grandeur. What love is this of thine?. Give me wings of faith[a]. Crucifixus pro nobis, Op. 38[a]. Lully, lulla, thou little tiny child, Op. 25[b]. Mass, Op. 44[a]. Laudate pueri, Op. 68. **Finzi Singers / Paul Spicer** with [a]**Andrew Lumsden** (org). Chandos Ⓕ CHAN9485 (71 minutes: DDD: A/97). Texts and translations included. Recorded 1993.   ⒼⒼ
There is a fine unease in Kenneth Leighton, a sense that fulfilment, musical and spiritual, must be striven for. Every new phrase in these choral settings sounds like the outcome of innumerable rejections: nothing is facile. In several of them, comfort is found and with it a sweetness that means so much more when hard won out of bleakness. He is a composer for the pilgrimage – not joyless by any means, but serious. In this excellent programme never does anything compromise this integrity. In date the works range from a student composition, his fine, independent setting of the Coventry Carol, to the anthem, *What love is this of thine?*, written not very long before his death. In style, rhythm, melody, harmony, counterpoint and the expert management of choral sound, all contribute, taking turn as a principal source of life and interest. The performances have all that could be desired in textual responsiveness and technical control. Clearly all members are valuable singers, as is shown by the ample supply of soloists from the ranks. Of these, outstanding are Olive Simpson, whose lovely voice graces the carol, and James Oxley, soloist in *Crucifixus pro nobis*, a tenor of fine quality with apparently unflawed evenness of production. Most of the works here are sung *a cappella*, those that are not being accompanied with clarity and discretion by Andrew Lumsden. The acoustic of All Saints', Tooting, is resonant but not excessively so for such a programme as this.

Leighton Second Service, Op. 62[a]. Give me wings of faith[a]. O sacrum convivium. Solus ad victimam[a]. Crucifixus pro nobis, Op. 38[a].
Howells Chichester Service[a]. A Hymn for St Cecilia[a]. Salve regina. O salutaris hostia. My eyes for beauty pine[a]. Like as the hart[a]. **Queen's College Choir, Oxford / Matthew Owens** with [a]**David Went** (org). ASV Ⓕ CDDCA851 (74 minutes: DDD: 5/93). Texts included.
Herbert Howells was at Queen's College, Oxford, in 1916, and Kenneth Leighton read Classics there in 1947, so it is appropriate that they should be brought together by their college choir. A quality they had in common was their sure instinct for choral sound, and at the take-over point in this recital (the opening of Leighton's *Second Evening Service*) the succession is felt to be a very close and natural one. Both are well represented and the selection here overlaps very little with other desirable records: *Like as the hart* is the principal exception, and as this is a particularly lovely performance the duplication is easily justified. The Chichester Service has its first recording here: it is a fine work, rising in characteristic ecstasy. Leighton's Second Service is also impressive, the *Magnificat*'s "Gloria" swaying slowly, while that of the *Nunc Dimittis* ends in subdued fashion, beautiful in its quietness. The other major work here, the *Crucifixus pro nobis*, is probably better served by a tenor soloist, but this is a fine, urgent performance with excellent work by the choir, as indeed they provide throughout.
Additional recommendations ...
...Crucifixus pro nobis[a]. Second Service. Te Deum laudamus. Missa brevis, Op. 5. An Evening Hymn. Let all the world in every corner sing. **Traditional** (arr. Leighton) Lully, lulla (Coventry carol). [a]**Neil Mackie** (ten); **St Paul's Cathedral Choir / John Scott** with **Andrew Lucas** (org). Hyperion Ⓕ CDA66489 (74 minutes: DDD: 12/92).
...Second Service. *Coupled with works by various composers.* **Bristol Cathedral Choir / Christopher Brayne** with **Ian Ball** (org). Priory Ⓕ PRCD528 (73 minutes: DDD: 8/96). *See review in the Collections section; refer to the Index.*
Further listening ...
...Cello Concerto, Op. 31[a]. Symphony No. 3[b]. [a]**Raphael Wallfisch** (vc); [b]**Neil Mackie** (ten); **Royal Scottish Orchestra / Bryden Thomson.** Chandos CHAN8741 (10/89).
...Fantasy on an American Hymn Tune, Op. 70[a]. Alleluia Pascha Nostrum, Op. 85[b]. Piano Variations, Op. 30. Piano Sonata, Op. 64. [a]**Janet Hilton** (cl); [ab]**Raphael Wallfisch** (vc); **Peter Wallfisch** (pf). Chandos CHAN9132 (5/93).
...Evening (Magdalen) Service.**Lichfield Cathedral Choir / Andrew Lumsden** with **Mark Shepherd, Nigel Potts** (orgs).
Priory PRCD505 (10/95). *See review in the Collections section; refer to the Index.*

Edwin Lemare
British/American 1865-1934

Suggested listening ...
...Concert Fantasy on "Hanover", Op. 4. Marche héroïque in D major, Op. 74. *Coupled with works by various composers.* **Christopher Herrick** (org). Hyperion CDA66457 (9/91). *See review in the Collections section; refer to the Index.* ⒼⒼⒼ
...Concertstück in the form of a Polonaise, Op. 80. *Coupled with works by various composers.* **Christopher Herrick** (org). Hyperion CDA66778 (3/96). *See review in the Collections section; refer to the Index.*

Artur Lemba
Estonian 1885-1963

Lemba Piano Concerto No. 1 in G major.
Sumera Piano Concerto.
Tubin Concertino for Piano and Orchestra. **Lauri Väinmaa** (pf); **Estonian National Symphony Orchestra / Arvo Volmer.** Finlandia Ⓕ 3984-20684-2 (65 minutes: DDD: 5/98). Recorded 1997.
The main attraction of this enterprising recording is the earliest work here, the G major First Concerto (1910) by Artur Lemba. Tchaikovsky and Schumann clearly served as models, but in the first movement the grand virtuosic manner does not seem to sit quite right, though the last two movements contain much to enjoy. But then so does this disc as a whole. This recording of the Sumera Concerto bears comparison with Kalle Randalu's on BIS (both BIS discs referred to here are listed under their respective composers), despite the present account being of the 1997 revision, because the changes made are by and large very subtle; a touching-up rather than a rethink. If there is little to choose between these versions, the same can be said of the performances, which both capture its brooding intensity, although BIS's recording has the edge in clarity. Sumera was a pupil of Heino Eller; so, several decades earlier, was Eduard Tubin. His *Concertino* (1944-5) has several Prokofievian touches to it, though the big tune towards the end sounds like Rachmaninov. Pöntinen on BIS is more mercurial, better befitting the *Allegro vivace* and *Allegro giocoso* outer sections. Väinmaa takes over two minutes longer than his rival (over 23 minutes in all), though his interpretation is still fine.

John Anthony Lennon   American 1950

Suggested listening ...
...Zingari. *Coupled with works by* **Ruders** and **Crumb**
David Starobin (gtr); **SMU Meadows Symphony Orchestra / David Milnes.**
Bridge BCD9071 (6/97). *See review under Crumb; refer to the Index.*

Leonardo Leo   Italian 1694-1744

Suggested listening ...
...Concerto in D major for Four Violins and Strings. *Coupled with works by various composers.*
Cologne Musica Antiqua / Reinhard Goebel. Archiv Produktion 435 393-2AH (9/92). ☞
See review in the Collections section; refer to the Index.

Ruggiero Leoncavallo   Italian 1858-1919

Leoncavallo Pagliacci[a]. **Carlo Bergonzi** (ten) Canio; **Joan Carlyle** (sop) Nedda; **Giuseppe Taddei** (bar) Tonio; **Rolando Panerai** (bar) Silvio; **Ugo Benelli** (ten) Beppe.
Mascagni Cavalleria rusticana[a]. **Fiorenza Cossotto** (mez) Santuzza; **Adriane Martino** (mez) Lola; **Carlo Bergonzi** (ten) Turiddu; **Giangiacomo Guelfi** (bar) Alfio; **Maria Gracia Allegri** (contr) Lucia; **Chorus and Orchestra of La Scala, Milan / Herbert von Karajan.**Opera Intermezzos[b]. **Berlin Philharmonic Orchestra / Herbert von Karajan.** DG Ⓕ 419 257-2GH3 (three discs: 198 minutes: ADD: 10/87). Notes, texts and translations included. Items marked [a] from SLPM139205/07 (10/66), [b]SLPM139031 (6/69), both recorded 1965.
Verdi La traviata – Prelude, Act 3. **Puccini** Manon Lescaut – Intermezzo. Suor Angelica – Intermezzo. **Schmidt** Notre Dame – Intermezzo. **Massenet** Thaïs – Méditation (with Michel Schwalbé, vn). **Giordano** Fedora – Intermezzo. **Cilea** Adriana Lecouvreur – Intermezzo. **Wolf-Ferrari** I gioiello della Madonna – Intermezzo. **Mascagni** L'amico Fritz – Intermezzo.

Cav and Pag, as they are usually known, have been bedfellows for many years. Lasting for about 75 minutes each, both operas have certain similarities. Each work concerns the passions, jealousies and hatred of two tightly-knit communities – the inhabitants of a Sicilian town and the players in a travelling troupe of actors. *Cavalleria rusticana* ("Rustic chivalry") concerns the triangular relationship of mother, son and his rejected lover. Played against a rich musical tapestry, sumptuously orchestrated, the action is played out during the course of an Easter day. Bergonzi is a stylish, ardent Turiddu whose virile charms glitter in his every phrase and Fiorenza Cossotto makes a thrilling Santuzza motivated and driven by a palpable conviction; her contribution to the well-known Easter hymn scene is gripping. But the real hero of the opera is Karajan, whose direction of this powerful work is magnificent. Conviction and insight also instil *Pagliacci* with excitement and real drama. A troupe of actors arrive to give a performance of a *commedia dell'arte* play. The illustration of real love, life and hatred is portrayed in the interplay of Tonio, Silvio, Nedda and her husband Canio. As the two rivals, Caro Bergonzi and Giuseppe Taddei are superb. Taddei's sinister, hunch-backed clown, gently forcing the play-within-the-play closer to reality until it finally bursts out violently is a masterly assumption, and Karajan controls the slow build-up of tension with a grasp that few conductors could hope to equal. The Milan La Scala forces respond wholeheartedly and the 1965 recording sounds well. The third disc is filled by a selection of very rich, very soft-centred opera intermezzos.

Additional recommendations ...
...Cavalleria rusticana. **Soloists; Ambrosian Opera Chorus; National Philharmonic Orchestra / James Levine.** RCA Ⓕ 74321 39500-2 (71 minutes: ADD). *See review under Mascagni; refer to the Index.*
...Pagliacci. Cavalleria rusticana. **Soloists; Chorus and Orchestra of La Scala, Milan /Tullio Serafin.** EMI mono Ⓕ CDS5 56287-2* (two discs: 141 minutes: ADD).
...Pagliacci[a]. Cavalleria rusticana[b]. **Soloists; [a]London Voices; [a]Finchley Children's Music Group; [b]London Opera Chorus; [ab]National Philharmonic Orchestra / [a]Giuseppe Patanè, [b]Gianandrea Gavazzeni.** Decca Ⓕ 414 590-2DH2 (two discs: 143 minutes: ADD: 1/89).
...Pagliacci. Cavalleria rusticana. **Soloists; Ambrosian Opera Chorus; Philharmonia Orchestra / Riccardo Muti.** EMI Ⓜ CMS7 63650-2 (two discs: 150 minutes: ADD: 3/91).
...Pagliacci. **Soloists; Slovak Philharmonic Chorus; Bratislava Radio Symphony Orchestra / Alexander Ráhbari.** Naxos Ⓢ 8 660021 (70 minutes: DDD: 4/93).
...Pagliacci. **Soloists; Chorus and Orchestra of La Scala, Milan / Herbert von Karajan.** DG The Originals Ⓜ 449 727-2GOR (78 minutes: ADD: 1/97). *This is the same performance as the one reviewed above.*
...Mattinata. *Coupled with works by various composers.* **Angela Gheorghiu** (sop); **Malcolm Martineau** (pf). Decca 458 360-2DH (5/98). *See review in the Collections section; refer to the Index.*

Léonin
French *fl* c1163-9

Suggested listening...
...Et valde mane una sabbatorum; Alleluya – Assumpta est Maria; Alleluya – Video celos apertos. *Coupled with works by* **Pérotin** *and other composers.* **Orlando Consort; Westminster Cathedral Choir.** Archiv Produktion 453 487-2AH (2/98). *See review in the Collections sections; refer to the Index.*

Henry Ley
British 1887-1962

Suggested listening...
...Prayer of King Charles I. *Coupled with works by various composers.* **Choir of St Mary's Cathedral, Edinburgh / Timothy Byram-Wigfield.** Priory PRCD557 (10/97). *See review in the Collections section; refer to the Index.*

Anatoli Liadov
Russian 1855-1914

Liadov The Enchanted Lake, Op. 62.
Mussorgsky Boris Godunov – I am sick at heart[a].
Tchaikovsky Marche slave, Op. 31. Capriccio italien, Op. 45. Eugene Onegin – Waltz; Polonaise. **Kirov Theatre [a]Chorus and Orchestra / Valery Gergiev.** Philips Ⓕ 442 775-2PH (54 minutes: DDD: 7/95). This set includes a bonus sampler CD of previous previous recordings from the Kirov Theatre forces conducted by Gergiev.

Liadov's orchestral pieces have always had a tenuous hold on the repertory, and afford glimpses of an exceptional talent. His failure to realize more of this was partly due to a peculiarly Russian compulsive idleness. But he was also highly self-critical, and essentially a miniaturist who could probably never have achieved the full length ballet, *The Firebird*, commissioned from him by Diaghilev. Stravinsky always felt that Liadov was more relieved than hurt when the comission fell through, and would have defended the score that was the outcome. In the shifting harmonies and dissolving textures of *The Enchanted Lake*, which shimmers atmospherically, there is not only acknowledgement of *Siegfried's* Forest Murmurs but anticipation of Scriabin and even Schoenberg. It was a novel idea to have the Kirov orchestra's "Russian Spectacular", the title of this disc, open to the rich aural canvas of *Boris Godunov's* "Coronation Scene" as refashioned by Shostakovich, complete with tolling bells, weighty brass and generous cymbal spray. The sound is big and generalized, the conducting more majestic than excitable – which usefully serves to minimize the contrast with *Marche slave*, a comparatively lyrical statement with a notably sad-eyed account of the principal theme and lightweight, almost balletic sequences thereafter. Gergiev never drives too hard, while his artful shaping of *Eugene Onegin's* "Polonaise" incorporates particularly sensitive handling of the central section. Likewise in the Waltz, where the cello line is affectionately moulded. *Capriccio italien* is thoughtfully held together, with much deft passagework in the closing tarantella. There's a bonus CD too, made up of snippets from Gergiev's various Russian stage work recordings for Philips – nothing earth-shattering, but a nice cross-section to whet the appetite for more. This is a good, well-planned (if hardly generous) programme, warmly recorded and fairly representative of Gergiev's sympathetic and often dramatic conducting style.

Additional recommendations ...
...The Enchanted Lake. Baba-Yaga, Op. 56. Kikimora, Op. 63. Musical snuffbox, Op. 32. *Coupled with works by various composers.* **Philharmonia Orchestra; Royal Philharmonic Orchestra / Efrem Kurtz.** EMI Profile Ⓑ CZS7 67729-2 (two discs: 147 minutes: ADD: 9/93).
...The Enchanted Lake. *Coupled with works by various composers.* **Boston Symphony Orchestra / Serge Koussevitzky.** Biddulph mono Ⓕ WHL044* (70 minutes: ADD: 3/97).

Further listening ...
...Kikimora, Op. 63. *Coupled with works by various composers.* **Hallé Orchestra / Sir Adrian Boult.** Dutton Laboratories mono CDAX8010* (2/95).
...Atmosphères. *Coupled with works by various composers.* **Vienna Jeunesse Choir; Vienna Philharmonic Orchestra / Claudio Abbado.** DG 429 260-2GH (4/90).   Ⓖ
...Two Bagatelles, Op. 17. Prelude in B minor, Op. 11 No. 1. Prelude in F sharp minor, Op. 39 No. 4. *Coupled with works by various composers.* **Margaret Fingerhut** (pf). Chandos CHAN9218 (4/94).
...Three Pieces, Op. 11. Two Pieces, Op. 24. Little Waltz in G major, Op. 26. Marionettes, Op. 29. A musical snuffbox, Op. 32. Variations on a theme by Glinka in B flat major, Op. 35. Three Preludes, Op. 36. Barcarolle in F sharp major, Op. 44. Variations on a Polish folk theme, Op. 51. Three Pieces, Op. 57. Four Pieces, Op. 64. **Stephen Coombs** (pf). Hyperion CDA66986 (3/98).
...Preludes – C major, Op. 39 No. 4; F sharp minor, Op. 40 No. 2; D flat major, Op. 57 No. 1. *Coupled with works by various composers.* **Boris Berezovsky** (pf). Teldec 4509-96516-2 (7/96). *See review in the Collections section; refer to the Index.*

Gautier Libert
French 15th century

Suggested listening ...

...Se je me plains. *Coupled with works by various composers.* **Alla Francesca.** Opus 111 OPS30-173
(7/98). *See review in the Collections section; refer to the Index.*   ⓔⓔⓔ

Juan de Lienas
?Spanish/Mexican *fl* c1620-1650

Suggested listening ...

...Salve regina. *Coupled with works by various composers.* **The Hilliard Ensemble.** Virgin Classics
Veritas VED5 61394-2 (11/97). *See review in the Collections section; refer to the Index.*

Gyorgy Ligeti
Hungarian 1923

Ligeti Violin Concerto[a]. Cello Concerto[b]. Piano Concerto[c]. [a]**Saschko Gawriloff** (vn);
[b]**Jean-Guihen Queyras** (vc); [c]**Pierre-Laurent Aimard** (pf); **Ensemble InterContemporain /
Pierre Boulez.** DG Ⓕ 439 808-2GH (67 minutes: DDD: 1/95). Recorded 1992-93.
Gramophone Award Winner 1995.   ⓔⓔ
The Violin Concerto (1992) is music by a composer fascinated with Shakespeare's *The Tempest*:
indeed, it might even prove to be a substitute for Ligeti's long-mooted operatic version of the play.
There are plenty of "strange noises", the result not just of Ligeti's latter-day predilection for ocarinas,
but of his remarkable ability to play off natural and artificial tunings against each other. This work
is superior to the Piano Concerto because the solo violin is so much more volatile and poetic as a
protagonist, an animator who 'fires up' the orchestra, functioning as a leader at odds with the led.
Saschko Gawriloff is a brilliantly effective soloist, and well served by a sharply defined yet expressive
accompaniment – Boulez at his most incisive – and a totally convincing recording. The other works
are played and recorded with similar success. The Cello Concerto (1966) is a particularly powerful
reminder of the strengths of the earlier Ligeti, where simple, basic elements generate anything but
minimal consequences. Despite the virtues of the Sony Classical versions of the Cello and Piano
Concertos, the Violin Concerto gives DG the advantage: it's a major work, and a marvellous
demonstration of Ligeti's unique, and uniquely persuasive, angle on modern musical discourse.
Additional recommendation ...
...Cello Concerto[a]. Piano Concerto[b]. Chamber Concerto. [a]**Miklós Perényi** (vc); [b]**Ueli Wiget** (pf);
Ensemble Modern / Peter Eötvös. Sony Classical Ⓕ SK58945 (57 minutes: DDD: 6/94).   ⓔ

Ligeti Horn Trio[a]. Six Bagatelles[b]. Ten Pieces[b]. Sonata for Solo Viola[c]. [a]**Marie-Luise Neunecker**
(hn); [a]**Saschko Gawriloff** (vn); [c]**Tabea Zimmermann** (va); [a]**Pierre-Laurent Aimard** (pf);
[b]**London Winds** (Philippa Davies, fl; Gareth Hulse, ob; Michael Collins, cl; Robin O'Neill, bn;
Richard Watkins, hn). Sony Classical Ⓕ SK62309 (71 minutes: DDD: 4/98).   ⓔⓔ
Recorded 1994-96.
This issue presents music from the 1950s and 1960s (*Ten Pieces, Bagatelles*) to the 1980s and 1990s
(Horn Trio, Viola Sonata). Other similarly programmed volumes in this series have resulted in stylistic
schizophrenia, but here the works are more evenly matched than elsewhere. Those looking for a
specific reason to buy this disc need look no further than the account of the Horn Trio, Ligeti's
homage to Brahms, a work which has become a classic of its kind. What distinguishes this version is
the astonishing horn-playing of Marie-Luise Neunecker – the impression of near-effortlessness and
breadth of dynamic range she conveys are hardly likely to be bettered. As to her companions, they
have both recorded the Trio before, and their experience is audible. This interpretation is especially
effective at projecting the music's multiple levels and layers. As to its expressive power, even those who
find Ligeti's later music problematic can hardly deny the poignant, tragic beauty of the concluding
Lamento. The two sets of wind pieces are given polished, bravura performances by London Winds.
The *Bagatelles* are among the composer's most convincing music from his pre-Western period; as to
the *Ten Pieces*, they plough the same furrow as those two masterpieces from the same year (1968), the
Second String Quartet and *Continuum* for harpsichord (and the *Chamber Concerto*, begun the
following year); but they are altogether more lightweight, their brevity almost provocative when heard
against the broader canvas of those other works. Provocative in a very different way is the Viola
Sonata, completed in 1994. Listen to Tabea Zimmermann's commanding and expressive playing, and
hear a composer for whom confounding the critics' expectations has always been second nature.
Additional recommendations ...
...Ten Pieces[d]. Continuum[a]. Artikulation[e]. Glissandi[f]. Two Studies for Organ[b]. Volumina[c].
[a]**Antoinette Vischer** (hpd); [b]**Zsigmond Sathmáry**, [c]**Karl-Erik Welin** (orgs); [d]**South-West German
Radio Wind Quintet;** [ef]**Cologne Radio Studio for Electronic Music.**
Wergo Ⓕ WER60161-50 (54 minutes: ADD: 11/89).
...Ten Pieces[d]. Six Bagatelles[c]. **Janáček** Mládí[a]. Concertino[b]. [abcd]**Claude Debussy Wind Quintet;**
[a]**Bruno Martinez** (bass cl); [b]members of the **Parisii Quartet;** [b]**Philippe Cassard** (pf).
Harmonia Mundi Les Nouveaux Interprètes Ⓑ HMN91 1624 (61 minutes: DDD: 7/97).

Ligeti Etudes – Book 1; Book 2; Book 3. Musica ricercata. **Pierre-Laurent Aimard** (pf).
Sony Classical Ⓕ SK62308 (65 minutes: DDD: 1/97). Recorded 1995.
Gramophone Award Winner 1997.   Ⓖ

Let us salute Pierre-Laurent Aimard first – not just a modern music specialist but an artist of
phenomenal gifts, and excellently recorded here. First impressions of the music are likely to be of its
immediacy. The complexities are a problem only for the pianist – whatever the sources of Ligeti's
inspiration, his ideas serve only a musical/poetic purpose. Central to these dazzling pieces is his
longstanding interest in composing with layers of material in different metres or different tempos and
in producing what he calls "an illusion of rhythm"; evident, too, are his more recent preoccupations
with modern mathematics, in particular the young science of dynamical systems which seeks to
explain the precarious balance between pattern and chaos, order and disorder. Ligeti's powerful
imagination is fuelled by many things, but there is no question of having to have a special key to enter
his world. The music is enough. There are 15 *Etudes* so far, in two books plus the beginning of a
third, and as with the collections of Chopin and Debussy there is a good deal to be gained from
hearing each book in sequence. The example of Liszt might also come to mind, who opened up a
world of sound on the piano as Chopin before him had done, and as Debussy was to do. When we
reach the end of Ligeti's Book 2, apparently at the limits of pianistic possibilities and expression,
there can be no doubt that Ligeti's *Etudes* belong with the greatest piano music of this or any other
century. They are amazing.

Additional recommendations ...

...Etudes, Books 1 and 2. Invention. Due Capricci. Trois Bagatelles. Chromatische Phantasie.
Fredrik Ullén (pf). BIS Ⓕ CD783 (54 minutes: DDD: 1/97).

...March[ab]. Polyphonic étude[ab]. Three Wedding Dances[ab]. Sonatina[ab]. Allegro[ab]. Two Capriccios[a].
Invention[b]. Three Pieces[ab]. Passacaglia ungherese[c]. Hungarian Rock[c]. Continuum[c]. Ricercare:
Omaggio a Girolamo Frescobaldi[d]. Organ Studies Nos. 1 and 2[d]. Volumina[d]. [a]**Irina Kataeva,**
[b]**Pierre-Laurent Aimard** (pfs); [c]**Elisabeth Chojnacka** (hpd); [d]**Zsigmond Szathmáry** (org).
Sony Classical Ligeti Edition Ⓕ SK62307 (78 minutes: DDD: 7/97).

...Etudes, Books 1 and 2. *Coupled with works by various composers.* **Erika Haase** (pf).
Tacet Ⓕ Tacet53 (74 minutes: DDD: 2/98).

Ligeti Nonsense Madrigals[a]. Mysteries of the Macabre (arr. Howarth)[b]. Aventures[c]. Nouvelles
Aventures[d]. Der Sommer[e]. Three Weöres Songs[f]. Five Arany Songs[g]. Four Wedding Dances[h].
[b]**Sibylle Ehlert,** [cd]**Phyllis Bryn-Julson,** [e]**Christiane Oelze,** [fgh]**Rosemary Hardy,** [h]**Eva Wedin,**
[h]**Malena Ernman** (sops); [cd]**Rose Taylor** (contr); [cd]**Omar Ebrahim** (bar); [e]**Irina Kataeva,**
[fgh]**Pierre-Laurent Aimard** (pfs); [a]**King's Singers** (David Hurley, Nigel Short, altos;
Robert Chilcott, ten; Bruce Russell, Philip Lawson, bars; Stephen Connolly, bass);
[bcd]**Philharmonia Orchestra / Esa-Pekka Salonen.** Sony Classical Ⓕ SK62311
(72 minutes: DDD: 1/97). Texts and translations included.

This is a richly entertaining collection, in some ways a sort of autobiography, ranging from Ligeti's
early folk-song arrangements and settings of the safely 'classic' poet János Arany to the "non-tonal
but diatonic" *Nonsense Madrigals*, the most recent of them dating from 1993. These latter are hugely
inventive, sometimes very funny, but the second word of their title is as important as their first. In his
notes on them Ligeti writes of his interest in the "rhythmic-metrical complexity" of fourteenth- and
early fifteenth-century Franco-Flemish music, but it sounds as though he knows his Morley and his
Vautor pretty well, too. His inventiveness is also recognizable in some of the early pieces which, like
Nonsense Madrigals, could easily become very popular. *Aventures* and *Nouvelles Aventures*, those
abstract mini-operas to elaborately meaningless texts, still retain their power to amuse, but also to
challenge and provoke. In these excellent performances *Aventures* is clearly the comic opera of the
pair, *Nouvelles Aventures* the ancestor not only of Ligeti's preoccupation with 'clocks and clouds' but
of the climactic work of his first 20 years in the West, *Le grand macabre*. Ligeti himself acknowledges
that Elgar Howarth has reduced the three soprano arias from that opera "wonderfully" for chamber
ensemble. The arrangement points up their alarmingly manic humour and makes the hair-raising
difficulty of the vocal line even more obvious. Ligeti proudly claims that they are the most difficult
coloratura music ever written but Sibylle Ehlert's virtuosity is vivid. That, in fact, is the word for
pretty well all the performances here, save the Schumannesque Hölderlin setting *Der Sommer*, which
Christiane Oelze sings with touching gravity. The recordings are excellently clear and incisive.

Additional recommendation ...

...Night. Morning. Far from Home. Solitude. Two Canons. The Three Wise Men. Erring.
Lux aeterna. Wedding Dance. Songs from Inaktelke. Songs from Mátraszentimre. Widow Pápai.
Drei Phantasien. Hungarian Etudes. Youth!. Easter. Hortobágy. The Mighty Rock.
Double-Dance from Kálló. **London Sinfonietta Voices / Terry Edwards.**
Sony Classical Ⓕ SK62305 (65 minutes: DDD: 1/97).

Further listening ...

...Chamber Concerto[b]. Ramifications (versions for string orchestra[d] and solo strings[c]).
Lux aeterna[a]. Atmosphères[d]. [a]**Stuttgart Schola Cantorum / Clytus Gottwald;** [b]**Vienna Die Reihe
Ensemble / Friedrich Cerha;** [c]**Saar Radio Chamber Orchestra / Antonio Janigro;** [d]**South West
German Radio Symphony Orchestra / Ernest Bour.** Wergo WER60162-50 (10/89).

...Six Bagatelles. *Coupled with works by various composers.* **Swiss Wind Quintet.** Koch Discover International DICD920395 (8/97). *See review in the Collections section; refer to the Index.*

...String Quartets – No. 1, "Métamorphoses nocturnes"; No. 2. Homage to Hilding Rosenberg. Ballade and Dance. Two Pieces. **Arditti Quartet.** Sony Classical SK62306 (1/97).

...Die grosse Schildkröten. *Coupled with works by various composers.* **Håkan Hardenberger** (tpt). Philips 446 065-2PH (11/96).

...Le Grand Macabre. **Soloists; Austrian Radio Chorus; Arnold Schönberg Choir; Gumpoldskirchner Spartzen; Austrian Radio Symphony Orchestra / Elgar Howarth.** Wergo WER6170-2 (12/91).   Ⓖ

Douglas Lilburn   New Zealand 1915

Suggested listening ...

...Three Songs. **Tracey Chadwell** (sop); **Pamela Lidiard** (pf). *Coupled with works by various composers.* British Music Society BMS420/1CD (3/98). *See review in the Collections section; refer to the Index.*

Paul Lincke   German 1866-1946

Suggested listening ...

...Lysistrata – Glühwürmchen-Idyll. *Coupled with works by various composers.* **New London Orchestra / Ronald Corp.** Hyperion CDA66998 (3/98). *See review in the Collections section; refer to the Index.*

Franz Liszt   Hungarian 1811-1886

Liszt Piano Concertos – No. 1 in E flat major, S124[a]; No. 2 in A major, S125[a]. Piano Sonata in B minor, S178[b]. **Sviatoslav Richter** (pf); [a]**London Symphony Orchestra / Kyrill Kondrashin.** Philips Solo Ⓜ 446 200-2PM (69 minutes: ADD: 11/95). Items marked [a] from SABL207 (5/62, recorded 1961), [b]438 620-2PH3 (8/94). *Gramophone classical 100.*   ⒼⒼⒼ

A bargain in a million, albeit one that reflects two very different aspects of Richter's art. The concertos are strong, clear-headed, brilliantly executed and superbly accompanied. Philips confess Mercury engineering, and Wilma Cozart-Fine has herself remastered the original three-track tapes – which means that what started out as a clean-cut, judiciously balanced production, now sounds fuller, brighter and keener-edged than ever. The improvements are particularly telling where Kondrashin and the LSO are concerned: everything tells with more presence than before which, given the lofty standard of orchestral playing, is a real boon. As to Richter, his *pianissimos* are rapt, his running passages crystal-clear and the stormier elements in both concertos are given with immense force. The Sonata, a concert performance, was recorded almost 30 years later on a somewhat less well-tuned instrument. However, the mind behind the notes has lost none of its grip and the notes themselves, although occasionally blurred or botched, spring to life as in no other performance. The *Allegro energico* and final peroration rage mercilessly, while the closing *Lento assai* can rarely have sounded so calmly inevitable. In terms of sound, things aren't as well managed as in the concertos: there's the odd thump or cough and the piano tone is a mite shallow, but the performance is so compelling that you soon forget any sonic inadequacies.

Additional recommendations ...

...Nos. 1 and 2. Totentanz. **Krystian Zimerman** (pf); **Boston Symphony Orchestra / Seiji Ozawa.** DG Ⓔ 423 571-2GH (56 minutes: DDD: 11/88).   ⒼⒼ

...Nos. 1 and 2. S126. **Alfred Brendel** (pf); **London Philharmonic Orchestra / Bernard Haitink.** Philips Silver Line Ⓜ 426 637-2PSL (56 minutes: ADD: 11/90).   ⒼⒼ

...No. 2. **Grieg** Piano Concerto. Lyric Pieces, Book 8, Op. 65. **Leif Ove Andsnes** (pf); **Bergen Philharmonic Orchestra / Dmitri Kitaienko.** Virgin Classics Ⓔ VC7 59613-2 (78 minutes: DDD: 4/91).

...Nos. 1[a] and 2[b]. Hungarian Rhapsody No. 6 in D flat major, S244. Valse oubliée, S215 No. 1. Années de pèlerinage, Deuxième année, S160, "Italie" – No. 5, Sonetto 104 del Petrarca. *Coupled with works by various composers.* **Byron Janis** (pf); [a]**Moscow Philharmonic Orchestra / Kyrill Kondrashin;** [b]**Moscow Radio Symphony Orchestra / Gennadi Rozhdestvensky.** Mercury Living Presence Ⓜ 432 002-2MM (63 minutes: ADD: 9/91).

...No. 1[a]. Piano Sonata in B minor, B178[a]. Hungarian Rhapsody No. 6[a]. Les jeux d'eau à la Villa d'Este[b]. Vallée d'Oberman. [a]**Martha Argerich,** [b]**Lazar Berman** (pfs); [a]**London Symphony Orchestra / Claudio Abbado.** DG Ⓜ 439 409-2GCL (72 minutes: ADD: 1/94).

...No. 1[a]. Liebestraum in A flat major, S541 No. 3. Réminiscences de Don Juan (Mozart), S418. Hungarian Rhapsody No. 13 in A minor, S244. Faust (Gounod) – Waltz, S407. *Coupled with works by* **Saint-Saëns** and **Liadov** Shura Cherkassky (pf); [a]**Philharmonia Orchestra / Anatole Fistoulari.** Testament mono Ⓔ SBT1033* (62 minutes: ADD: 9/94).

See review in the Collections section; refer to the Index.   Ⓖ

…Nos. 1 and 2. Mazeppa, S100. Les Préludes, S97. [a]Geoffrey Tozer (pf); Suisse Romande Orchestra / Neeme Järvi. Chandos Ⓕ CHAN9360 (72 minutes: DDD: 9/95).
…Nos. 1 and 2. Danse macabre, Paraphrase on "Dies irae"[a]. Piano Sonata in B minor. Csárdás macabre. Valse oubliée No. 1. Années de pèlerinage – Première année: Deuxième année; Troisième année. Weinachtsbaum-Suite – No. 7, Schlummerlied. Nuages gris. Klavierstück in F sharp major, S192 No. 3. En rêve. R.W. – Venezia. Vexilla regis prodeunt. Mosonyis Grabgeleit. Schlaflos, Frage und Antwort. Unstern: Sinistre, distastro. La lugubre gondola – No. 1; No. 2 . Légendes. Harmonies poétiques et religieuses – No. 7, Funérailles. Fantasia and Fugue on the Theme B-A-C-H. Harmonies poétiques et religieuses – No. 1, Invocations; No. 3, Bénédiction de Dieu dans la solitude; Pensée des morts. Weinen, Klagen, Sorgen, Zagen. Isoldens Liebestod. Alfred Brendel (pf); [a]London Philharmonic Orchestra / Bernard Haitink. Philips Ⓜ 446 924-2PM5 (five discs: 361 minutes: ADD: 2/96).
…No. 1. Coupled with works by various composers. Walter Gieseking (pf); London Philharmonic Orchestra / Sir Henry Wood. APR mono Ⓜ APR5513* (63 minutes: ADD: 3/96).

Liszt Piano Concerto No. 1 in E flat major, S124.
Chopin Piano Concerto No. 1 in E minor, Op. 11. **Martha Argerich** (pf); **London Symphony Orchestra / Claudio Abbado.** DG The Originals Ⓜ 449 719-2GOR (56 minutes: ADD: 4/85). From 139383 (1/69). Recorded 1968. ⒼⒼ
Although 30 years old, these performances, in DG's beautifully refurbished sound, remain as fanciful and coruscating as the day they were made. Argerich's fluency and re-creative spark dazzle and dumbfound to a unique degree but, given her reputation for fire-eating virtuosity, it is perhaps necessary to say that both performances quiver with rare sensitivity as well as drama. Time and again she provides a telling and haunting poetic counterpoint to her, arguably, more familiar way of trailing clouds of virtuoso glory. Abbado partners his mercurial soloist as to the manner born, finding (in the Chopin in particular) a burgeoning sense of wonder where others sound dry and foursquare.

Liszt A Dante Symphony, S109[a]. Années de pèlerinage – deuxième année, S161, "Italie" – No. 7, Après une lecture du Dante – Fantasia quasi sonata[b]. [a]Berlin Radio Women's Chorus; [a]Berlin Philharmonic Orchestra / Daniel Barenboim ([b]pf). Teldec Ⓕ 9031-77340-2 (67 minutes: DDD: 7/94). Item marked [a] recorded at a performance in the Schauspielhaus, Berlin in 1992. Gramophone Editor's choice. Ⓖ
This disc proves conclusively that the Dante Symphony (a contemporary of the Faust Symphony) is no longer one that needs its apologists. Tone, full and rounded, firm and true, and rock-steady pacing elevate the symphony's opening ("Abandon all hope, ye who enter here") beyond its all too familiar resemblance to a third-rate horror-film soundtrack. As the symphony progresses, together with the countless examples of Berlin tone and artistry filling out, refining or shaping gestures in often revelatory ways, you become aware of Barenboim's skill in maintaining the large-scale tension he has created. And that is a very real achievement. As for the final choral Magnificat, if Liszt owed Wagner a debt of gratitude for persuading him to conclude the symphony with the "noble and softly soaring" bars that precede a more noisily affirmative appended coda, in Barenboim's Magnificat (and much else in the symphony), it is Wagner's debt to Liszt that is more readily apparent; the Parsifalian radiance of these final pages is unmistakable. More importantly, for once they sound convincingly conclusive. The Dante Sonata was recorded with the kind of risk-taking abandon and occasionally less than perfect execution that you might expect from a live event. Improvisatory, impulsive and full of extreme contrasts, Barenboim's Dante Sonata is vividly pictorial (with almost orchestral colourings). The instrument itself (closely miked and widely spaced) sounds larger than life. This recording is, in a word, riveting. The recording of the symphony is spacious, focused and expertly balanced.

Liszt A Faust Symphony, S108. **Hans-Peter Blochwitz** (ten); **Hungarian Radio Chorus; Budapest Festival Orchestra / Iván Fischer.** Philips Ⓕ 454 460-2PH (74 minutes: DDD: 4/98). Recorded 1996. ⒼⒼ
Iván Fischer here realizes the full breadth of Liszt's vision, forming anguish, Gretchen's tender modulations and the cynical thematic transformations that keep Mephistopheles alive and kicking. It is, above all, a profoundly authentic – or should one say authentically 'lived' – production, consistently animated (lightning shifts from piano to forte and back again are meticulously gauged), vividly recorded and with heavily scored tutti passages granted maximum impact. And yet Fischer is not beyond tweaking the odd instrumental line. At the passage starting at fig. X in "Faust", the espressivo horns are 'stopped'; while at the beginning of "Mephistopheles" Fischer has the bass and cello semiquavers bowed fairly near the bridge (almost sul ponticello, much as Bernstein does on his Boston recording. Flutes and clarinets at the outset of Gretchen suggest a chaste, winsome maiden and the Tristanesque passage, where the strings exchange affections over a fluid woodwind accompaniment, is beautifully phrased. As to Mephistopheles, no other performance experience projects the devilish, quick-witted variants of Faust's principal themes with as much keenness of attack as Fischer does here. The Budapest woodwinds are outstanding, and the strings have real bite. Select string portamentos sweeten the texture and there is no hint of the glutinous, excessively homogenized 'sound blanket' that evades the musical issue on so many

modern recordings. Furthermore, Iván Fischer affords us the rare opportunity of hearing Liszt's first (purely orchestral) ending, which Wagner so admired for its lack of "forced excitement or arousal of attention". It is impossible not to heartily agree with Wagner, though lovers of the better-known – and more extended – "Chorus mysticus" have the chance to enjoy that, too. The edited 'crossroads' occur at fig. Jj (after a brief musical rest), which means that you can programme your player to deliver either ending. Hans-Peter Blochwitz sings well, and so do the Hungarian Radio Chorus.

Additional recommendations ...

...**Charles Bressler** (ten); **New York Choral Art Society; New York Philharmonic Orchestra / Leonard Bernstein.**
Sony Classical Bernstein Royal Edition Ⓜ SMK47570 (72 minutes: ADD: 5/93).   Ⓐ

...**Peter Seiffert** (ten); **Ernst-Senff Chorus; Prague Philharmonic Chorus; Berlin Philharmonic Orchestra / Sir Simon Rattle.** EMI Ⓕ CDC5 55220-2 (69 minutes: DDD: 1/95).   Ⓐ

...**András Molnár** (ten); **Hungarian State Choir; Orchestra of the Franz Liszt Academy / András Ligeti.** Naxos Ⓢ 8 553304 (73 minutes: DDD: 10/95).

...**Vinson Cole** (ten); **Dresden State Opera Chorus; Staatskapelle Dresden / Giuseppe Sinopoli.**
DG Ⓕ 449 137-2GH (67 minutes: DDD: 7/96).   Ⓐ

...**Kenneth Riegel** (ten); **Tanglewood Festival Chorus; Boston Symphony Orchestra / Leonard Bernstein.** DG The Originals Ⓜ 447 449-2GOR (77 minutes: ADD: 7/96).   Ⓐ

Liszt Complete Symphonic Poems, Volumes 1 and 2. **London Philharmonic Orchestra / Bernard Haitink.** Philips Ⓜ 438 751/4-2PM2 (two sets of two discs: 127 and 131 minutes: ADD: 10/94). Recorded 1968-71.
438 751-2PM2 – Ce qu'on entend sur la montagne, S95 (from 6500 189, 1/72). Tasso, S96. Les Préludes, S97. Orpheus, S98 (SAL3750, 12/69). Prometheus, S99. Festklänge, S101 (6709 005, 9/72). Mazeppa, S100 (6500 046, 8/71). *438 754-2PM2* – Héroïde funèbre, S102. Die Ideale, S106. Mephisto Waltz No. 1, S514, "Der Tanz in der Dorfschenke"; No. 2, S110 (from 6709 005, 9/72). Hungaria, S103. Hamlet, S104 (6500 046, 8/71). Hunnenschlacht, S105. Von der Wiege bis zum Grabe, S107 (6500 189, 1/72).   ⒺⒺⒺ
The 12 'numbered' symphonic poems date from Liszt's rich maturity (the first, *Ce qu'on entend sur la montagne*, was composed during the late 1840s) with the lean, near-expressionist *Von der Wiege bis zum Grabe* ("From the Cradle to the Grave") following on after a period of some 25 years. Initial orchestration was invariably undertaken by Joachim Raff, although the composer himself always had the final say. When, in the early 1970s, Bernard Haitink galvanized the LPO into re-enacting these symphonic dramas, he had the field more or less to himself. Haitink's readings have an abundance of personality. In *Héroïde funèbre*, for example, his dangerously slow tempo exceeds Liszt's prescribed timing by some seven minutes: it is a terrifying vision, superbly sustained and beautifully played. He also copes manfully with the more explosive aspects of *Hamlet*, *Prometheus* and *Hunnenschlacht* (which he paces more securely than any other rival, past or present), and his way with the scores' many reflective episodes is entirely winning.

Elsewhere, he sorts through the complexities of Liszt's colourful orchestration with a cool head and a warm heart, etching the frequent examples of 'nature music' much as he does Wagner's and keeping abreast of each tone-poem's narrative trail. True, some of Liszt's *marcatos, impetuosos, appassionatos* and *agitatos* are occasionally brought to heel, but then others aren't – and we have Liszt's blessing for flexibility in what he himself terms "the degree of sympathy" that conductors employ for his work. What matters is that Haitink has us enter Liszt's world direct, rather than through the distorting mirror of the conductor's own ego. It is a volatile sequence, yes, and not without its *longueurs*, but it remains an essential musical confrontation for all students of the romantic orchestra and an accurate pointer to where Tchaikovsky, Smetana and countless others found significant musical sustenance. With excellent sound and commonsense documentation, these two sets will provide hours of aural adventure.

Additional recommendation ...

...*Prometheus, S99. Coupled with works by various composers.* **Soloists; Berlin Singakademie; Freiburg Soloists Choir; Berlin Philharmonic Orchestra / Claudio Abbado.**
Sony Classical Ⓕ SK53978 (75 minutes: DDD: 1/95). *Gramophone* Editor's choice. See review in the Collections section; refer to the Index.   ⒺⒺⒺ

...Les Préludes, S97. *Coupled with works by* **Sibelius** *and* **Smetana** Berlin Philharmonic Orchestra / Herbert von Karajan.
DG Digital Masters Ⓜ 445 550-2GMA (70 minutes: DDD: 9/83).

Liszt Tasso, S96. Trois Odes funèbres, S112[a]. [a]**Berlin Radio Men's Chorus; Berlin Radio Symphony Orchestra / Karl Anton Rickenbacher.** Koch Schwann Ⓕ 317682 (57 minutes: DDD: 11/96). Recorded 1994.
Tasso receives occasional hearings on record, most notably as part of Bernard Haitink's indispensable set of the complete symphonic poems with the LPO. Rickenbacher's is a strong, sombre reading that responds to the powerful opening – much the best music in a very uneven work – and does well with the minuet passage and with the later pages in which Liszt is at his most assertive and least creative. Nevertheless, the record has a claim on Lisztians for the inclusion, as what appears to be a first recording, of three very fine works that have lain neglected. Two are personal elegies. Though his

neglect of his children, and their committal to the 'care' of a dreadful governess, is one of the least appealing aspects of his normally benign and generous character, he felt the death of his son Daniel and his eldest daughter Blandine very deeply; and these are moving laments. "Les morts", a so-called Oration for Orchestra for Daniel, makes use of a chorus to intone, during the work, words by the Christian thinker who at one stage profoundly affected Liszt, the Abbé Lammenais. "La notte", for Blandine, is based on *Il penseroso*, from the Italian book of the *Années de pèlerinage*, but also includes some haunting Hungarian reminiscences. He asked for these two works to be played at his funeral. Dying half-ignored in Bayreuth, he went to his grave without any proper music. The *Odes* were not performed until 1912. The third is a kind of pendant to *Tasso*, and uses some of its themes. The *Odes* are strong, moving works, perhaps difficult to programme in concerts even individually. To have them available at last and in a recording that does well to clarify the generally sombre textures, in very sympathetic performances, is a cause for gratitude.

Liszt Piano Sonata in B minor, S178. Funeral Odes – No. 2, La notte, S699. Harmonies poétiques et réligieuses, S173 – No. 7, Funérailles. Nuages gris, S199. La Lugubre gondola, S200, No. 2.
Krystian Zimerman (pf). DG Ⓕ 431 780-2GH (66 minutes: DDD: 10/91).　　　Ⓖ

It is to be expected that an artist who has made one of the outstanding recordings of the Liszt concertos should also give us one of the finest ever B minor Sonatas. Whether you think it is *the* finest ever may depend on your priorities (and on whether you think it is sensible to venture such opinions). What can surely be said is that Zimerman brings to bear a combination of ardour, forcefulness, drive and sheer technical grasp which are tremendously exciting and for which it is difficult to think of a direct rival. However, others have achieved a subtler pacing and shading of climaxes, or a more philosophical inwardness, that make their readings equally, if not more rewarding. Pollini is perhaps the most nearly comparable in approach, but he is less overtly rhetorical from moment to moment and more concerned with long arcs of dramatic tension. DG have given Zimerman a very bright, close sound-image, as the very opening demonstrates. The release of tension at the first *fortissimo* has an almost startling vehemence. Zimerman's dramatic timing in the opening pages is wonderful, and the sternness which regulates the emotional pressure is close to ideal for the whole of the long *allegro energico*. This is playing in the grand manner, and if you automatically dislike 'conventional' hesitations and surges you will probably resist many of Zimerman's initiatives. It is with the *Andante sostenuto* slow movement that the inspiration wavers a little, not so much in the lyrical playing as in the building of the central climax. This comes to the boil too soon to clinch the crucial moment at 15'14" and it is the overall profile of climaxes which is the Achilles heel of the performance. Blame the music if you like but others have shown that a more convincing overall trajectory is possible. Richter and Brendel are two such. Although Zimerman's performance of "Funérailles" is curiously clinical, the central section emerging as a block-like episode rather than an integrated accumulation, memories from the rest of his recital linger in the mind. There is the magical evaporation at the end of *Nuages gris*, the passionate igniting towards the highpoint of *La notte* (a late reworking of "Il pensiero" from the second volume of *Années de pèlerinage*) and the subtle tonal shadings and high rhetorical charge of *La lugubre gondola II*. The instrument is superb and the sound quality, though not lacking impact, can be slightly tiring in the long run.

Additional recommendations ...

...Piano Sonata. Three Concert Studies, S144. **Louis Lortie** (pf).
　　Chandos Ⓕ CHAN8548 (52 minutes: DDD: 5/87).
...Piano Sonata. Mephisto Waltz No. 1, S514. Années de pèlerinage – Troisième année, S163: No. 4, Les jeux d'eau à la Villa d'Este; Deuxième année, S161, "Italie": No. 2, Il penseroso. Hungarian Rhapsody No. 15 in A minor, S244. **Mikhail Pletnev** (pf).
　　Olympia Ⓑ OCD172 (67 minutes: ADD: 12/87).　　　Ⓖ
...Piano Sonata. Piano Concerto No. 1 in E flat major (with orchestra / David Brockman). Années de pèlerinage, Deuxième année – Sonnetto 104 del Petrarca. Rapsodie espagnole. Two Concert Studies – No. 2, Gnomenreigen (two performances). Harmonies poétiques et religieuses – No. 7, Funérailles. Hungarian Rhapsody No. 12 in C sharp minor.
　　Gounod (trans. Liszt) Faust – Waltz. **Simon Barere** (pf).
　　APR Ⓦ APR7001* (two discs: 93 minutes: ADD: 11/03).
...Piano Sonata. Nuages gris, S199. Unstern: sinistre, disastro, S208. La lugubre gondola No. 1. R.W. – Venezia, S201. **Maurizio Pollini** (pf). DG Ⓕ 427 322-2GH (46 minutes: DDD: 7/90).　ⓊⒼ
...Piano Sonata. Two Légendes, S175. Scherzo and March, S177. **Nikolai Demidenko** (pf).
　　Hyperion Ⓕ CDA66616 (67 minutes: DDD: 2/93).　　　Ⓖ
...Piano Sonata. **Schubert** Piano Sonata in D major, D850. **Emil Gilels** (pf).
　　RCA Victor Living Stereo Ⓜ 09026 61614-2 (71 minutes: ADD: 4/94).　ⒼⒼ
...Piano Sonata. Polonaise in E major, S223 No. 2. Scherzo in G minor, S153. Nuages gris, S199. Consolations, S172 – No. 6, Allegretto sempre cantabile. Hungarian Rhapsody in A minor, S242 No. 17. Klavierstück in F sharp major, S193. Mephisto Polka, S217. Etudes d'exécution transcendante, S139 – No. 1, Preludio; No. 2, Molto vivace; No. 3, Paysage; No. 5, Feux follets; No. 7, Eroica; No. 8, Wilde Jagd; No. 10, Appassionata; No. 11, Harmonies du soir. Un sospiro, S144 No. 3. Gnomenreigen, S145 No. 2.
　　Coupled with works by **Chopin** Sviatoslav Richter (pf).
　　Philips Ⓕ 438 620-2PH3 (three discs: 202 minutes: DDD: 8/94).　　ⒼⒼ

…Piano Sonata. Fantasia and Fugue in G minor (Bach), S463. Hungarian Rhapsodies, S244 –
No. 2 in C sharp minor; No. 12 in C sharp minor; No. 13 in A minor; No. 15 in A minor,
"Rákóczy march". Liebesträum No. 3 in A flat major, "O lieb, so lang du lieben kannst", S541.
Shura Cherkassky (pf). Decca Ⓕ 433 656-2DH (79 minutes: ADD: 1/95).   ⒼⒼ

…Piano Sonata. Hungarian Rhapsody No. 6 in D flat major. *Coupled with works by various
composers.* **Martha Argerich** (pf). DG The Originals Ⓜ 447 430-2GOR (71 minutes: ADD: 6/95).
Gramophone Classical 100. See review in the Collections section; refer to the Index.   ⒼⒼⒼ

…Piano Sonata. Mephisto Waltz No. 1, S514. Un sospiro, S144 No. 3. Etudes d'exécution
transcendante d'après Paganini, S140 – No. 3, La campanella. *Coupled with works by*
Bartók and **Delibes/Dohnányi** Géza Anda (pf). Testament mono Ⓕ SBT1067*
(63 minutes: ADD: 10/95). *See review in the Collections section; refer to the Index.*   Ⓖ

…Piano Sonata. Mephisto Waltz No. 1, S514. Harmonies poétiques et religieuses, S173 –
Funérailles. Réminiscences de Don Juan (Mozart), S418. Etudes d'exécution transcendante
d'apres Paganini, S140 – La campanella. Hungarian Rhapsody No. 12 in C sharp minor, S244.
Consolations, S172 – No. 3, Lento placido. Années de pèlerinage – Première année, S160,
"Suisse"; Au bord d'une source; Deuxième année, S161: Sonetto 104 del Petrarca; Troisième
année, S163: Les jeux d'eau à la Villa d'Este. Concert Studies – Gnomenreigen, S145 No. 2;
Un sospiro, S144 No. 3. Rigoletto Paraphrase, S434. **Schubert/Liszt** Die Forelle, S564.
Erlkönig, S557a. **Jorge Bolet** (pf).
Double Decca Ⓜ 444 851-2DF2 (two discs 140 minutes: ADD/DDD: 1/96).

…Etudes d'exécution transcendante, S139 – No. 1, Preludio; No. 2, Etude; No. 3, Paysage; No. 5,
Feux follets; No. 11, Harmonies du soir. **Ravel** Miroirs. Valses nobles et sentimentales.
Sviatoslav Richter (pf). Praga mono/stereo Ⓑ CMX354009* (65 minutes: ADD: 6/96).   Ⓖ

…Piano Sonata. Liebestraum in A flat major, S541 No. 3. Valse oubliée, S215 No.1. Gnomenreigen,
S145 No. 2. Berceuse, S174. **Schubert** Impromptu in A flat major, D935 No. 2.
Sir Clifford Curzon (pf). Decca The Classic Sound Ⓜ 452 306-2DCS (58 minutes: ADD: 11/97).

…Harmonies poétiques et réligieuses – No. 1, Invocation; No. 2, Ave Maria; No. 3, Bénédiction de
Dieu dans la solitude; No. 4, Pensée des morts; No. 5, Pater noster; No. 6, Hymne de l'enfant à
son réveil. Les morts, S516. Resignazione, S187a. Ungarns Gott, S543a. **Philip Thomson** (pf).
Naxos Ⓢ 8 553073 (68 minutes: DDD: 11/97).

…Harmonies poétiques et réligieuses – No. 7, Funérailles; No. 8, Miserere, d'après Palestrina;
No. 9, Andante lagrimoso; No. 10, Cantique d'amour. Ave Maria in D flat major, S504.
Ave Maria in G major, S545. Ave Maria in E major, S182. Ave Maria d'Arcadelt, S183 No. 2.
Six Consolations, S172. Ungarns Gott, S543b. **Philip Thomson** (pf).
Naxos Ⓢ 8 553516 (64 minutes: DDD: 11/97).

Liszt Piano Sonata in B minor, S178[a]. La leggierezza, S144 No. 2[a]. Consolations, S172 – No. 3,
Lento placido[b]. Hungarian Rhapsody No. 12 in C sharp minor, S244[b]. Années de pèlerinage,
deuxième année, S161 – No. 5, Sonetto 104 del Petrarca; No. 6, Sonetto 123 del Petrarca[b].
Rigoletto (Verdi) – Paraphrase, S434[b]. Il trovatore (Verdi) – Miserere, S433[b]. Réminiscences de
Norma (Bellini), S394[b]. Tannhäuser (Wagner) – Overture, S442[b]. Die Meistersinger von
Nürnberg (Wagner) – Am stillen Herd, S448[b]. Tristan und Isolde (Wagner) – Liebestod, S447[b].
[a]**Bernard d'Ascoli**, [b]**Craig Sheppard** (pfs). Classics for Pleasure Silver Doubles Ⓢ CD-CFPSD4745
(two discs: 126 minutes: ADD/DDD: 2/96). Items marked [a] from CFP40380 (10/82), [b]CFP40051
(8/73). Recorded 1973-82.

True virtuosity is an elusive elixir. Far transcending mere accuracy or 'correctness' it sets the pulse
racing and the scalp tingling. Many will experience a similar twinge when they listen to Craig
Sheppard's recordings made in the early 1970s at the start of his meteoric, dangerously hectic career.
True, he can alternate passion and inwardness to memorable effect in the *Petrarch Sonnets*, or spin the
most delicate of lines in the D flat *Consolation*. But in page after page of the operatic paraphrases he
flaunts his hypnotic temperamental brio and brilliance. Listen to his concluding octaves in *Rigoletto*
(from him a burst of thunderous applause) or the final pages of *Tannhäuser* and you will witness an
astounding force and charisma; playing which rides on a knife edge between abandon and control. In
total contrast Bernard d'Ascoli, the blind French pianist, tempers Liszt's heroics with dignity and
poetic restraint. Those who yearn for a more swashbuckling B minor Sonata will find plenty of
alternatives, but for inner strength and refinement d'Ascoli is exceptional, particularly in the *Andante
sostenuto* where he so lucidly locates Liszt's mystical, still centre. *La leggierezza*, too, is spun off with
rare elegance, with a light, corruscating and *détaché* touch. But it is Craig Sheppard who has the lion's
share of the proceedings. You won't easily find more exciting or, indeed, more leonine Liszt playing.
The recordings cope superbly with his instantly recognizable lean and biting sonority.

Additional recommendations …

…Deuxième année – No. 4, Sonetto 47 del Petrarca; Nos. 5 and 6. Three Concert Studies, S144.
Liebestraüme, S541. **Kathryn Stott** (pf). Conifer Classics Ⓕ CDCF180 (63 minutes: DDD: 8/90).

…Rhapsodie espagnole, S254. Etudes de Concert, S145 – Gnomenreigen. Etudes de Concert, S144
– La leggierezza. Deuxième année – No. 5. Réminiscences de Don Juan, S418. Valse oubliée,
S215 No. 1. *Coupled with works by various composers.* **Simon Barere** (pf).
APR mono Ⓕ APR7001* (two discs: 126 minutes: ADD: 5/91). *See review in the
Collections section; refer to the Index.*   ⒼⒼⒼ

...La leggierezza, S144 No. 2. Waldesrauschen, S145 No. 1. Liebestraum in A flat major, S541
No. 3. Hungarian Rhapsody No. 12 in E minor, S242. Etude d'exécution transcendante No. 10,
"Appassionata", S139. *Coupled with works by* **Schumann** Evgeni Kissin (pf).
Revelation Ⓜ RV10031 (66 minutes: ADD: 6/97).
...Piano Sonata, S178. Funérailles, S173 No. 7. *Coupled with works by various composers.*
Vladimir Horowitz (pf). APR mono Ⓜ ① APR5516 (69 minutes: ADD: 5/98).
See review in the Collections section; refer to the Index.

Liszt 12 Etudes d'exécution transcendante, S139. **Jenö Jandó** (pf). Naxos Ⓢ 8 553119
(64 minutes: DDD: 11/97). Recorded 1994.
This is Vol. 2 in Naxos's project to record Liszt's complete piano music using a number of pianists.
Here, the indefatigable Jenö Jandó plays the 12 *Transcendental Etudes*, the ultimate test of quasi-
orchestral virtuosity and of the capacity to achieve nobility and true eloquence. Jandó perhaps lacks
diabolic *frisson* in the more ferocious numbers but his performances, overall, are much less disfigured
by wilful, sensational attributes or hysteria. No. 1 is dramatically pointed, an impressive curtain-
raiser, and he can hell-raise with assurance in "Mazeppa". His "Feux follets" hardly sparks with the
brilliance of, say, some of the full-blooded accounts of certain Russian artists, but even when it hardly
modulates from study to tone-poem it is still more than capable (higher praise than you might think
where such intricacy is concerned). He flashes an impressive rapier at the start of "Eroica" and there
is plenty of swagger and facility in the so-called "Appassionata" *étude*. "Chasse-neige", too, proceeds
with a fine sense of its menacing start to a howling, elemental uproar before returning to distant
thunder. Jandó is less assured in introspection, yet it has to be said that all-encompassing versions of
the *Transcendental Etudes* are hard to come by. Jandó is impressively recorded, though Naxos's
indecision as to whether the *Etudes* were composed in 1851 (their frontispiece) or 1852 (their inner
notes) confuses an already chequered history.

Liszt Impromptu in F sharp major, S191. Nuages gris, S199. La lugubre gondola, S200 Nos. 1 and 2.
Unstern: sinistre, disastro, S208. Totentanz, S525. Danse macabre (Saint-Saëns), S555.
Réminiscences des Huguenots (Meyerbeer), S412. **Arnaldo Cohen** (pf). Naxos Ⓢ 8 553852
(71 minutes: DDD: 6/97). Recorded 1996.
Arnaldo Cohen is as poetically and imaginatively intrepid as he is technically coruscating, and all
these performances offer refinement and ferocity in equal proportion. Few pianists could identify or
engage so closely with music which hovers on the edge of silence or extinction (*Nuages gris, La lugubre
gondola* Nos. 1 and 2), "grey with the pain of disillusion", or which sparks and sports with a truly
devilish intent (*Danse macabre, Totentanz* and so on). Try the build-up at 7'30" in the *Danse macabre*
where the music emerges from Cohen's fingers supercharged with malevolence. On the other hand he
can send the F sharp *Impromptu* spiralling into a true sense of its ecstasy, or momentarily inflect
Nuages gris (2'04") in a manner that accentuates rather than detracts from its abstraction and
economy. He makes something frighteningly bleak out of *Unstern* (or "Evil Star"), with its savagely
dissonant climax and unresolved hymnal solace, yet is no less at home in *Réminiscences des
Huguenots*, dismissing ambuscades of treacherous skips, octaves and every other technical terror with
a telling mix of verve and nonchalance. These, then, are performances of rare lucidity, virtuoso
voltage and trenchancy, and they have been excellently recorded.
Additional recommendation ...
...La lugubre gondola No. 1 (arr. Adams). *Coupled with works by* **J. Adams** and **Busoni**
London Sinfonietta / John Adams.
Nonesuch Ⓕ 7559-79359-2 (47 minutes: DDD: 4/97). *Gramophone Editor's choice.*   Ⓖ

Liszt Funérailles, S173 No. 7. Gnomenreigen, S145 No. 2. Liebesträume, S541 – No. 2 in E major;
No. 3 in A flat major. Valses oubliées, S215 – Nos. 1-3. Mephisto Waltz No. 1, S514, "Der Tanz
in der Dorfschenke". Troisième Année de pèlerinage, S163 – Aux cyprès de la Villa d'Este. Etudes
d'exécution transcendante, S139 – No. 5, Feux follets. Hungarian Rhapsody No. 17 in D minor,
S244. **Sviatoslav Richter** (pf). Revelation mono Ⓜ RV10011* (59 minutes: ADD: 10/96).
Recorded 1958.
The pianism on this disc is very special. The recital was recorded in concert in 1958, before Richter
had made his breakthrough in the West and at a time when his playing had a raw energy and a sense
of abandon that has become increasingly tempered over the years. There are places where the sheer
electricity and bravura carries one away (and occasionally – in the *Mephisto Waltz* No. 1, for example
– nearly carries Richter himself over the edge). However, equally awe-inspiring is the magical
pianissimo playing, where it is easy to forget that such sounds are being coaxed from an essentially
percussive instrument. In the monumental *Funérailles* one marvels at how Richter maintains such
intensity in playing seemingly so straightforward and understated. Pianism of such concentration and
inwardness draws the listener wholly into the artist's world. The recorded sound is variable and
generally rather claustrophobic (particularly at louder dynamics) and the endings of some tracks have
been faded out rather prematurely, presumably to omit the audience applause.
Additional recommendations ...
...12 Etudes d'exécution transcendante, S139. **Boris Berezovsky** (pf).
Teldec Ⓕ 4509-98415-2 (62 minutes: DDD: 3/97).

...Gnomenreigen. *Coupled with works by various composers.* **Murray Perahia** (pf).
  Sony Classical Ⓜ SX4K63380 (four discs: 270 minutes: DDD/ADD: 4/98).
  See review in the Collections section; refer to the Index.
...Mephisto Waltz No. 1. Venezia e Napoli , S162 – No. 3, Tarantella. Rhapsodie espagnole, S254.
  Harmonies poétiques et réligieuses, S173 – No. 3, Bénédiction de Dieu dans la solitude; No. 4,
  Pensée des morts. Deux Légendes, S175 – No. 1, St Francis of Assisi preaching to the birds.
  Ave Maria IV in G major, S545. Années de pèlerinage – Troisième année, S163 – Aux cyprès de la
  Villa d'Este (3-4); Aux cyprès de la Villa d'Este (4-4); Les jeux d'eau à la Villa d'Este.
  Recueillement, S204. Deux Lugubre gondola, S200. Années de pèlerinage – Deuxième année:
  Italie, S161 – Après une lecture du Dante – fantasia quasi sonata. Ave Maria in E, S182.
  Stephen Hough (pf). Virgin Classics Ⓑ VBD5 61439-2 (two discs: 142 minutes: DDD: 6/98).

Liszt Fantasia on two themes from Mozart's "Le nozze di Figaro", S697. Réminiscences de
  Don Juan (Mozart), S418. Réminiscences de Norma (Bellini), S394. Rigoletto (Verdi) –
  paraphrase, S434. Faust (Gounod) – Waltz, S407.
Rossini/Ginsburg Il barbiere di Siviglia – Largo al factotum. **Grigory Ginsburg** (pf).
  Melodiya mono Ⓜ 74321 33210-2* (70 minutes: ADD: 8/96). Recorded 1948-58.   ⒼⒼⒼ
What can be said of Grigory Ginsburg's Liszt transcriptions? They are already well known to piano
buffs, if only by reputation, since the LP versions have long been like gold-dust. From the stable of
Goldenweiser, and a long-time colleague of his at the Moscow Conservatoire, Ginsburg possessed a
jaw-dropping facility and lightness of touch which recall the piano rolls of Lhevinne and Rosenthal.
It's the kind of playing that sets you wondering if he was equally phenomenal in live performance and
whether such playing could perhaps only be achieved on light-touch instruments. Whatever the case,
his seemingly spontaneous eloquence and wit, heard at their most breathtaking in his own *Barber of
Seville* transcription, shine through the very shabby sound quality. This is about as 'must-have' as a
must-have can be for collectors of great piano recordings.

Liszt Hungarian Rhapsodies, S244 – No. 2 in C sharp minor[a]; No. 9 in E flat major[b]. Ballade
  No. 2 in B minor, S171[c]. Bénédiction de Dieu dans la solitude, S173 No. 3[d]. Berceuse, S174[e].
  Polonaise in C minor, S223 No. 1[f]. Scherzo and March, S177[g]. **Louis Kentner** (pf).
  APR mono Ⓜ APR5514* (79 minutes: ADD: 2/97). Item marked [a] from Columbia DX777
  (6/37), [b]DX987 (11/40), [c]DX851/2 (6/38), [d]DX879/80 (12/38), [e]DX1006 (4/41), [f]DX896 (1/41),
  [g]DX988/9 (12/40). Recorded 1937-41.
This glorious recital is a timely reminder of Louis Kentner's greatness, his richness and enterprise
during his heyday. Here is playing which in its life-affirming sweep and opulence makes accusations
concerning Liszt's theatricality doubly misleading. What expansiveness, what true *molto espressivo*
Kentner achieves in the Second *Hungarian Rhapsody*, what poetic warmth and freedom in the more
heartfelt, soaring melodies of the First *Polonaise* and Second *Ballade*. True, some may find him more
luxuriant than devotional in the *Bénédiction* (a reminder, perhaps, that the temporal and spiritual
aspects of Liszt's life were opposite sides of the same coin) but such personal charisma and
magnetism are in any case a far cry from our own age where one pianist is so easily mistaken for
another. In the *Scherzo and March* (played uncut), where the Abbé Liszt sardonically raises hell-fire,
Kentner's mastery is unassailable, and his elegance in the ravishing *Berceuse* (so closely modelled on
Chopin yet so far from that master's classic economy) again evokes a time when pianists were indeed
kings of the keyboard. Above all, these performances show a patrician ease that makes you sit back
and marvel, and forget a later period in Kentner's life when his playing so sadly became a parody of
its former quality. The transfers are superb.

Additional recommendations ...
...Hungarian Rhapsody No. 12. *Coupled with works by* **Brahms** *and* **Beethoven**
  Gina Bachauer (pf). Mercury Living Presence Ⓜ 434 340-2MM (77 minutes: ADD: 9/95).
...19 Hungarian Rhapsodies. Rhapsodie espagnole. **Roberto Szidon** (pf).
  DG Double Ⓜ 453 034-2GTA2 (two discs: 156 minutes: ADD: 11/96).   ⒼⒼ
...Hungarian Rhapsodies – No. 2 (including cadenza by Hamelin); No. 10 in E major; No. 13 in
  A minor. Apparition No. 1 in F sharp major, S155 No. 1. Waldesrauschen, S145 No. 1. Un
  sospiro, S144 No. 3. Nuages gris, S199. En rêve, S207. Réminiscences de Don Juan, S418.
  Marc-André Hamelin (pf). Hyperion Ⓕ CDA66874 (63 minutes: DDD: 4/97).
...Hungarian Rhapsody No. 2. *Coupled with works by various composers.*
  Montreal Symphony Orchestra / Charles Dutoit. Decca Ⓕ 452 482-2DH (70 minutes: DDD: 5/97).
  See review in the Collections section; refer to the Index.
...Hungarian Rhapsody No. 2 in C sharp minor, S244 (arr. Horowitz). Litanei, S562 No. 1.
  Schwanengesang, S560 – No. 3, Aufenthalt; No. 10, Liebesbotschaft. *Coupled with works by
  various composers.* **Arcadi Volodos** (pf). Sony Classical Ⓕ SK62691 (61 minutes: DDD: 10/97).
  *Gramophone Editor's choice. Selected by Soundings. See review in the Collections section;
  refer to the Index.*   ⒼⒼ

Liszt Années de pèlerinage – Première année, S160, "Suisse"; Deuxième année, S161, "Italie";
  Troisième année, S163. Venezia e Napoli, S162. **Lazar Berman** (pf). DG Ⓜ 437 206-2GX3
  (three discs: 176 minutes: ADD: 11/93). Recorded 1977.   ⒼⒼ

Liszt's three volumes of *Années de pèlerinage* are rarely recorded complete, largely because many pianists remain baffled by the dark-hued prophecy and romanticism of the third and final book. So it is particularly gratifying to welcome Lazar Berman's superb DG recordings back into the catalogue. Berman's resource here is remarkable and his performance of the entire book is hauntingly inward and sympathetic to both the radiance of "Les jeux d'eau à la Villa d'Este" and to Liszt's truly dark night of the soul (*lamentoso, doloroso* and so on), and to his desolate lack of spiritual solace elsewhere. He is hardly less persuasive in the first two books. "Chapelle de Guillaume Tell" is a true celebration of Switzerland's republican hero with alpine horns ringing through the mountains, while in "Au lac de Wallenstadt" Berman's gently undulating traversal is truly *pianissimo* and *dolcissimo egualamente*. His "Orage" is predictably breathtaking, and in the gloomy Byronic "Vallée d'Obermann" the severest critic will find himself mesmerized by Berman's free-wheeling eloquence. The 1977 recordings have been finely remastered.

Additional recommendations ...
...Première année. **Jorge Bolet** (pf). Decca Ⓕ 410 160-2DH (50 minutes: DDD: 12/84).   ⒼⒼ
...Deuxième année. **Jorge Bolet** (pf). Decca Ⓕ 410 161-2DH (51 minutes: DDD: 7/85).   ⒼⒼ
...Troisième année – No. 4, Les jeux d'eaux à la Villa d'Este. Harmonies poétiques et religieuses.
  Venezia e Napoli. Ballade No. 2 in B minor, S171. **Jorge Bolet** (pf).
  Decca Ⓕ 411 803-2DH (58 minutes: DDD: 12/85).   Ⓖ
...Deuxième année – No. 4, Sonetto 47 del Petrarca; No. 5, Sonetto 104 del Petrarca.
  Six Consolations, S172. Liebestraüme, S541. Rigoletto (Verdi) Paraphrase, S434.
  Daniel Barenboim (pf). DG Galleria Ⓜ 435 591-2GGA (61 minutes: DDD: 9/92).

Liszt Années de pèlerinage – Deuxième année, S161, "Italie". Venezia e Napoli, S162 – Gondoliera.
  Deux Légendes, S175. **William Kempff** (pf). DG Galleria Ⓜ 449 093-2GGA
  (57 minutes: ADD: 7/96). Recorded 1974.   Ⓖ
In the very early days of the mono LP era Wilhelm Kempff made a famous recording of Liszt's piano music for the Decca label. He re-recorded much of the same programme for DG in the Hannover Beethovensaal in 1974, adding "Sposalizio" to the other excerpts from the Deuxième année of the *Années de pèlerinage* – which included "Il penseroso" (a particularly haunting rendition), the "Canzonetta del Salvator Rosa" – and the three Petrarch Sonnets plus "Gondoliera" from *Venezia e Napoli*. But perhaps most famous of all were the *Deux Légendes* – wonderfully evocative and poetic readings. The opening bird-song of "St Francis of Assisi" is quite magical, and then the solemn tread of "St Francis de Paule walking on the water" is slowly built to an overwhelming climax. These are masterly and unforgettable performances and one finds oneself wondering why DG chose to reissue this outstanding recital – which is most realistically recorded – on their mid-price Galleria label rather than as an Original. However, this is a quite outstanding release and is certainly not to be missed.

Liszt Complete Solo Piano Music, Volume 15 – Song transcriptions. **Leslie Howard** (pf).
  Hyperion Ⓕ CDA66481/2 (two discs: 147 minutes: DDD: 4/92). Recorded 1990.
  Beethoven Adelaïde, S466. Sechs geistliche Lieder, S467. An die ferne Geliebte, S469.
  Lieder von Goethe, S468. **Mendelssohn** Lieder, S547. **Dessauer** Lieder, S485.
  Franz Er ist gekommen in Sturm und Regen, S488. Lieder, S489. **Rubinstein** Two songs, S554.
  Schumann Lieder von Robert und Clara Schumann, S569. Provenzalisches Lied, S570.
  Two songs, S567. Frühlingsnacht, S568. Widmung, S566.
Few composers have ever shown a more insatiable interest in the music of others than Liszt, or devoted more time to transcribing it for the piano. In this radio-cum-gramophonic age, such activity might even be deemed time wasted. But in Liszt's day it was a godsend for music-lovers and composers alike, and all praise to Leslie Howard for including it in his mammoth pilgrimage through the composer's complete keyboard works. Here, he plays 60 of Liszt's 100 or so song transcriptions, including several by the lesser-known Dessauer, Franz and (as composers) Anton Rubinstein and Clara Schumann, alongside Beethoven, Mendelssohn and Robert Schumann. The selection at once reveals Liszt's variety of approach as a transcriber no less than his unpredictability of choice. Sometimes, as most notably in Beethoven's concert aria, *Adelaïde*, the keyboard virtuoso takes over: he links its two sections with a concerto-like cadenza as well as carrying bravura into an amplified coda. Mendelssohn's *On wings of song* brings imitative subtleties all his own, while the fullness of heart of Schumann's *Dedication* and *Spring Night* is likewise allowed to expand and overflow. But after the dazzling pyrotechnics of many of his operatic arrangements, the surprise here is the self-effacing simplicity of so much included. The five songs from Schumann's *Liederalbum für die Jugend* are literal enough to be played by young children. Even his later (1880) fantasy-type transcriptions of Rubinstein's exotic *The Asra* has the same potent economy of means, characterizing his own original keyboard music in advancing years. Howard responds keenly to mood and atmosphere, and never fails, pianistically, to emphasize the 'singer' in each song – in response to the actual verbal text that Liszt was nearly always conscientious enough to write into his scores. The recording is clean and true.

Liszt Complete Solo Piano Music, Volume 21 – Soirées musicales, S424. Soirées italiennes, S411.
  Nuits d'été à Pausilippe, S399. Tre sonetti del Petrarca, S158. Venezia e Napoli, S159. La serenata

e L'orgia (Grande fantaisie sur des motifs des Soirées musicales), S422. La pastorella dell'Alpi e Li marinari (Deuxième fantaisie sur des motifs des Soirées musicales), S423. **Leslie Howard** (pf). Hyperion Ⓕ CDA66661/2 (two discs: 157 minutes: DDD: 7/93). Recorded 1991-92.

The two discs comprising Vol. 21 of Howard's enormous cycle remind us of the young Liszt's love affair with Italy, the spotlight now falling primarily – though not exclusively – on frolics with Rossini, Mercadante and Donizetti in lighter, lyrical vein. The special interest of the two original sets of pieces included, i.e. the three *Sonetti del Petrarca* and the four *Venezia e Napoli*, is that Howard introduces them as first written (c1839 and 1840 respectively) before Liszt's characteristically painstaking later revisions. There is much to enjoy in the playing itself, especially in simpler contexts when gondolas glide through calm waters, or lovers dream, or shepherds dance. Melody, so important throughout, is nicely sung. And whether in filigree delicacy or exuberant zest (as in excitable Venetian regattas) Howard invariably relishes Liszt's ear-catching ornamentation.

Additional recommendations ...

...Complete Solo Piano Music, Volume 25 – Cantico di San Francesco – Preludio per il Cantico del Sol, S499a. Cantico del sol di San Francesco, S499. Von der Wiege bis zum Grabe, S512. O sacrum convivium, S674a (two versions). Salve Regina, S669 No. 1. Ave maris stella, S669 No. 2. Gebet, S265. Ora pro nobis, S262. Resignazione, S187b. Il m'aimait tant, S533. Romance, "O pourquoi donc", S169. Ich liebe dich, S546a. Die Zelle in Nonnenswerth, S534. **Leslie Howard** (pf). Hyperion Ⓕ CDA66694 (77 minutes: DDD: 5/94).

...Complete Solo Piano Music, Volume 27 – Szózat und Ungarischer Hymnus, S486. God Save the Queen, S235. Canzone napolitana, S248. Ungarische Nationalmelodien, S243. Hussitenlied on a melody by J. Krov, S234. Glanes de Woronince, S249. La Marseillaise, S237. Vive Henri IV, S239. La cloche sonne, S238. Rákóczy March, S242a/1. **Leslie Howard** (pf). Hyperion Ⓕ CDA66787 (73 minutes: DDD: 9/94).

Liszt Complete Solo Piano Music, Volume 29. Hungarian Themes and Rhapsodies, S242. **Leslie Howard** (pf). Hyperion Ⓕ CDA66851/2 (two discs: 159 minutes: DDD: 4/95). Recorded 1993.

When listening to these 22 pieces, officially entitled *Magyar Dalok* and *Magyar Rapszódiák*, you at once realize you've heard many a snatch of them before. And not surprisingly, for they are in fact the source of most of what eventually emerged as Liszt's world-wide best-sellers, the *Hungarian Rhapsodies*. The composer revels in the lavishly decorative, cimbalom-coloured, improvisational style of the gipsies, in the process making demands on the pianist variously described by Leslie Howard in his insert-notes as "devil-may-care, frighteningly difficult, frenetic, hand-splitting" and so on. Whether due to Liszt's own waning interest in platform pyrotechnics, or the fact that only he could really bring them off, simplification and formal condensation seem to have been primary aims when recasting these first flings as *Hungarian Rhapsodies*. But as Howard reveals, there are losses as well as gains in the maturer Liszt. Despite moments of protracted rodomontade there is a vast amount to enjoy.

Liszt Complete Solo Piano Music, Volume 30. **Leslie Howard** (pf). Hyperion Ⓕ CDA66861/2 (two discs: 153 minutes: DDD: 4/95). Recorded 1993.

Weber/Liszt Oberon – Overture, S574. **Mozart/Liszt** Fantasia on themes from Le nozze di Figaro and Don Giovanni, S697. **Verdi/Liszt** Ernani Paraphrase, S432. Miserere du Trovatore, S433. Rigoletto Paraphrase, S434. Réminiscences de Boccanegra, S438. **Donizetti/Liszt** Valse de concert sur deux motifs du Lucia et Parisina, S214/3. **Meyerbeer/Liszt** Réminiscences de Robert le diable – Cavatine; Valse infernale, S413. **Gounod/Liszt** Les Adieux – Reverie sur un motif de Roméo et Juliette, S409. **Erkel/Liszt** Schwanengesang and Marsch from Hunyadi László, S405. **Wagner/Liszt** Lohengrin – Elsa's Bridal Procession, S445/2; Three Pieces, S446. Fantasy on themes from Rienzi, S439.

Liszt's operatic outings, ranging from literal transcriptions, such as the opening *Oberon* Overture, to the most free fantasias, like that on motives from *Rienzi* at the end of the disc. The sequence is artfully planned to provide the maximum contrast between Liszt as lion and dove, with four of the 16 items earmarked as "first recordings". Of these, the Gounod *Roméo et Juliette* Reverie is a tender, nocturne-like idyll that not for a second outstays its welcome. Liszt scholars may nevertheless be still more grateful for Howard's rescue of the other three, and first and foremost the nearly 22-minute long Fantasia on themes from *Le nozze di Figaro and Don Giovanni*, the "almost-complete" manuscript of which Howard has now himself completed for performance and publication. Though self-indulgently protracted (as Busoni surely realized when preparing his own shortened version), its thematic interweavings *en route* still take your breath away. With Verdi and Wagner we are on more familiar ground, where it goes without saying that Howard has formidable CD rivals. But throughout the disc there is a spaciousness in his characterization that far more often than not compensates for momentary technical strain or loss of finesse. His tonal range is certainly wide, ranging from the deep, dark, brooding intensity he finds for the *Ernani* and *Il trovatore* excerpts to his translucent delicacy in the upper reaches of Gounod's Reverie. Apart from a slightly metallic touch above a certain dynamic level in the treble, the recorded sound quality can best be described in a nutshell as ripe.

Liszt Complete Solo Piano Works, Volume 34. Douze Grandes Etudes, S137. Morceau de salon, S142. **Leslie Howard** (pf). Hyperion Ⓕ CDA66973 (76 minutes: DDD: 10/95). Recorded 1994.

In this first recording of the concert version of the *Douze Grandes Etudes* (1837), Leslie Howard brings his customary technical wizardry to bear on this outrageously difficult music in an arresting virtuoso display that demonstrates Liszt's consummate skill at transforming musical material. Moreover, despite Liszt's exhortation that only the later revisions of the studies should be played, there is a great deal to recommend the 1837 set, as these performances attest. The extreme technical demands of these pieces have led to critical scorn, but the challenges they contain are not designed merely for display, but are the result of the composer's comprehensive exploitation of the piano's expressive capabilities. Saint-Saëns said that "in Art a difficulty overcome is a thing of beauty" and, in the present instance, Howard's triumph over the monumental difficulties posed by these pieces compellingly reveals the astonishing beauty of Liszt's 'orchestral' use of tone colour and sparkling virtuosity.

Liszt Opera Transcriptions – Rigoletto (Verdi) – Paraphrase, S434. Lucia et Parisina (Donizetti) – Valse à capriccio, S401. Faust (Gounod) – Waltz, S407. Eugene Onegin (Tchaikovsky) – Polonaise, S429. Der Fliegende Holländer (Wagner) – Spinning Chorus, S440. Tannhäuser (Wagner) – Rezitativ und Romanze, S444. Lohengrin (Wagner) – Verweis an Elsa, S446. Tristan und Isolde (Wagner) – Liebestod, S447. Le nozze di Figaro (Mozart) – Fantasia, S697. **Jean-Yves Thibaudet** (pf). Decca Ⓕ 436 736-2DH (69 minutes: DDD: 2/94). Recorded 1992.

Surely no major composer ever did more to propagate the music of others than Liszt. But he was also a legendary virtuoso, not easily allowing himself to forget his own dazzling fingers in his innumerable transcriptions. In this operatic selection Jean-Yves Thibaudet artfully contrasts five of the more demonstrative kind with four in which faithfulness to the original text was Liszt's main concern – these latter, significantly, drawn from the music of his formidable son-in-law to be, Richard Wagner. The filigree delicacy of Thibaudet's effortlessly brilliant finger-work is very impressive, not least in the decorative flights of the first three Verdi, Donizetti and Gounod items. Sometimes it suggests the trickles of scintillating fairy lights in the sky after the bursting of a rocket, sometimes the liquidity of water itself though still with each note retaining its own pinpoint glisten. In the earlier Wagner items Thibaudet matches Wagner's comparative simplicity with a similar concern for the unadorned truth, again, with his light pedalling, drawing sounds of ear-catching translucency from the keyboard's upper reaches. He finds the full, close-woven intensity of the "Liebestod" harder to sustain but the piece is finely shaped as a whole. The recital ends heartily with the less frequently heard *Figaro* Fantasia completed in 1912 by no less a man than Busoni.

Additional recommendation ...
...Rigoletto (Verdi) – Paraphrase, S434; Der fliegende Holländer (Wagner) – Spinning Chorus, S440; Six Chants polonais (Chopin), S480; Widmung (Schumann), S566; Frühlingsnacht (Schumann), S568; Stabat mater (Rossini) – Cujus animam, S553 No. 1; The Nightingale (Alabiev), S250 No. 1; Die Loreley (Liszt), S532; Abschied (Russian folk-song), S251; Die Rose (Spohr), S571; Réminiscences de Norma (Bellini), S394. **Geoffrey Tozer** (pf). Chandos Ⓕ CHAN9471 (78 minutes: DDD: 4/97).

...Chants polonais, S480 – Frühling; Das Ringlein. **Chopin** Etudes. Impromptus Nos. 1-3. Piano Concerto No. 2 in F minor, Op. 21ᵃ. Waltzes Nos. 1-14. Preludes Nos 1-24. Piano Sonatas Nos. 2 and 3. Four Ballades. Berceuse in D flat major, Op. 57. Nocturnes Nos. 2, 4, 5, 7, 15 and 16. Polonaise No. 6 in A flat major, Op. 53, "Heroic". Fantasie in F minor, Op. 49. Tarantelle in A flat major, Op. 43. Barcarolle in F sharp major, Op. 60. Polish songs, Op. 74 – My darling. **Alfred Cortot** (pf); ᵃorchestra / **Sir John Barbirolli**. EMI mono Ⓜ CZS7 67359-2* (six discs: 429 minutes: ADD: 6/92).   Ⓖ Ⓖ

Liszt Excelsior!, S666. Am Grabe Richard Wagners, S267. Harmonies poétiques et réligieuses, S173 – Funérailles (trans. Kynaston). Two Recital Pieces, S268 – No. 2, Trauerode. Orpheus, S98. Fantasia und Fugue, S259, "Ad nos, ad salutarem undam". **Nicolas Kynaston** (org). IMP Masters Ⓕ 30366 0003-2 (75 minutes: DDD: 7/96). Played on the Klais organ of Ingolstadt, Münster, Germany. Recorded 1994. *Gramophone Editor's choice. Selected by Soundings.*   Ⓖ

As one of the wonders of the organ world the Ingolstadt Klais has frequently been the focus of record producers' attention. Similarly Liszt's organ music is no stranger to the catalogues, while Nicolas Kynaston has an impressive discography to his credit. Certainly we have here all the ingredients of a splendid release. It's not merely splendid, though: this disc is a true colossus among organ recordings. The instrument's vast dynamic range positively luxuriates in a sumptuous acoustic, vividly captured by a recording of true demonstration quality. Here's one to impress neighbours and friends with, whether or not they (or you, for that matter) enjoy organ music. Sometimes the Liszt of seemingly endless transcriptions and small programmatic organ pieces can pall, but it's in these very pieces – not least Kynaston's own perceptive transcription of "Funérailles" – that the real strengths of this disc lie and there is a thrilling account of the great *Ad nos, ad salutarem undam*. Kynaston handles the organ with matchless sensitivity, continually conjuring up ravishing sounds and making these performances intensely pleasurable. His astute interpretative insight reveals every bar of music with utter conviction.

Additional recommendation ...
...(trans. Schaab) Orpheus, S98. *Coupled with works by various composers.* **Peter King** (org). Priory Ⓕ PRCD618 (78 minutes: DDD). *See review in the Collections section; refer to the Index.*

Liszt Ihr Glocken von Marling, S328. Im Rhein, im schönen Strome, S272. Bist du!, S277. Vergiftet sind meine Lieder, S289. Jugendglück, S323. Freudvoll und leidvoll, S280. Wilhelm Tell, S292 – Der Fischerknabe; Der Hirt, Der Alpenjäger. Die drei Zigeuner, S320. Der Glückliche, S334. Kling leise, mein Lied, S301. Die Macht der Musik, S302. Wer nie sein Brot mit Tranen ass, S297. Ich möchte hingehn, S296. Die Vätergruft, S281. Ich scheide, S319. Uber allen Gipfeln ist Ruh, S306 (Wanderers Nachtlied II). **Philip Langridge** (ten); **John Constable** (pf).
Unicorn-Kanchana Ⓕ DKPCD9162 (71 minutes: DDD: 2/96). Recorded 1995.

Liszt's songs, a much underrated part of his output, find a most sympathetic interpreter in Philip Langridge. He has the intelligence and poetic sensibility to appreciate their very varied nature, and indeed without such qualities no singer is likely to make very much of them. He even comes close to persuading this listener that the setting of Goethe's *Wanderers Nachtlied* is a fair response to one of the most famous and exquisite lyrics in the German language, but not even his elegance of line can justify the interminable repetitions of the ending. Never mind: there is much here that is well chosen from quite a long list, and Langridge shows a striking ability to enter the world of each song and think it through with real perception. He can colour the graceful melodies of *Bist du!* and *Kling leise* with a sweetness of tone that is exactly judged to match his smooth line; he can, appropriately, seem to poison this for *Vergiftet sind meine Lieder* and darken it for *Die Vätergruft*; he can characterize the three gipsies colourfully (with Constable strutting out the proud Hungarian cadences); he can produce a remarkable burst of power for *Jugendglück*. Only in *Der Alpenjäger* does he seem rather overwhelmed, careful as Constable is at all times to do justice to Liszt's piano sonorities without unleashing too much sheer volume. Theirs is a sensitive partnership, and Constable is scrupulous in judging when the piano is supportive, when almost contradictory and when independent.

Additional recommendations ...

...Die Vätergruft, S281. Go not, happy day, S335. Es rauschen die Winde, S294. Ihr Auge, S310. Uber allen Gipfeln ist Ruh, S306. Am Rhein, in schönen Strome, S272. Es muss ein Wunderbares sein, S314. Vergiftet sind meine Lieder, S289. La Tombe et la rose, S285. Comment, dissaient-ils, S276. Oh! quand je dors, S282. *Coupled with works by* **Wagner** *and* **Berlioz**
Thomas Hampson (bar); **Geoffrey Parsons** (pf). EMI Ⓕ CDC5 55047-2 (77 minutes: DDD: 5/94).
...Freudvoll und leidvoll, S280. Uber allen Gipfeln ist Ruh. Mignons Lied I, S275. Der du von dem Himmel bist, S279. *Coupled with works by various composers.* **Dame Margaret Price** (sop); **Graham Johnson** (pf). Forlane UCD16728 (71 minutes: DDD: 2/95). *See review in the Collections section; refer to the Index.*

Liszt Christus, S3. **Henriette Bonde-Hansen** (sop); **Iris Vermillion** (mez); **Michael Schade** (ten); **Andreas Schmidt** (bar); **Cracow Chamber Choir; Stuttgart Gächinger Kantorei; Stuttgart Radio Symphony Orchestra / Helmuth Rilling.** Hänssler Classic Exclusive Series Ⓕ CD98 121 (three discs: 162 minutes: DDD: 6/98). Text and translation included. Recorded live in 1997.

Christus is essentially a contemplative work and so could really be said to exist in a different time-scale to most music. Much of the opening part, the "Christmas Oratorio", uses very simple melody and harmony, and is studiously undramatic. The comparison it seems to invite, with Berlioz and *L'enfance du Christ*, is misleading. Helmuth Rilling does well not to charge it with too much colour, and, if listened to as meditation rather than drama, what can seem static takes on a positive atmosphere as a group of long reflections on the Christmas events. This is a far cry from the sensational Liszt of the early virtuoso years, even from the creative ventures of the previous decade, not yet reaching the terse, inward pieces of the last years. There is greater drama in the middle part, "After Epiphany", especially in the superb scene of Christ walking on the water. Although there is still the suggestion that a wonder is being contemplated, Liszt stirs up a terrific storm. This part also includes the beautiful setting of the Beatitudes, sung by Andreas Schmidt with a degree of uncertainty which he entirely sheds when he comes to pronounce the sentences in Part 3 ("Passion and Resurrection") for the scene of the Agony in the Garden. Liszt here turns to his most intense chromatic idiom, one which has tempted commentators to call the movement Wagnerian, even *Tristan*esque; it was, of course, Liszt who set the example. The long setting of the *Stabat mater* is beautifully controlled by Rilling. His soloists support him well, though Iris Vermillion can seem rather operatic; Henriette Bonde-Hansen sings with a beautiful, clear tone. The recording does excellent justice to Liszt's wide-ranging orchestration, especially considering its live performances. *Christus* is not a work for every day, nor for every conductor. It is done justice in this sympathetic, patient performance.

Further listening ...

...Totentanz. *Coupled with works by various composers.* **Chicago Symphony Orchestra / Fritz Reiner.** RCA Victor Living Stereo 09026 61250-2 (4/93).
...Elégies – No. 1, S130; No. 2, S131. La lugubre gondola, S134. *Coupled with works by* **Janáček** *and* **Kodály** Anne Gastinel (vc); Pierre-Laurent Aimard (pf). Auvidis Valois V4748 (9/95). *See review under Janáček; refer to the Index.*
...Grand duo concertant on Lafont's "Le marin", S128[a]. La lugubre gondola, S134[a]. Soirées de Vienne – Valse caprice d'après Schubert in A minor, S427 (trans. Oistrakh)[a]. Erlkönig, S558 No. 4[a]. *Coupled with works by* **Ernst** *and* **Schubert** Gidon Kremer (vn); [a]Oleg Maisenberg (pf). DG 445 820-2GH (10/95).

...Romance oubliée, S132. *Coupled with works by various composers.* **Leslie Howard** (pf).
Hyperion CDA66683 (11/93).
...Romance oubliée, S132. Elégies – No. 1, S130; No. 2, S131. Die Zelle in Nonnenwerth, S382.
La lugubre gondola, S134. *Coupled with works by* **Grieg** *and* **Rubinstein**
Steven Isserlis (vc); **Stephen Hough** (pf).
RCA Victor Red Seal 09026 68290-2 (4/96). *See review under Grieg; refer to the Index.*
..."Weinen, Klagen, Sorgen, Zagen", Präludium, S179.
Coupled with works by various composers. **Vladimir Horowitz** (pf).
Sony Classical SK45818 (8/90). *See review in the Collections section; refer to the Index.* 🅖🅖🅖
...Complete Solo Piano Music, Volume 31. The Schubert Transcriptions – Soirées de Vienne: Valses
caprices, S427. Mélodies hongroises (Divertissement à l'hongroise), S425. Two Transcriptions for
Sophie Menter. Three Marches, S426. Marche militaire, S426*a*. Ave Maria, S557*d*. La sérénade,
S559*a*. Erlkönig, S557*a*. Die Rose, S556*i*. Der Gondelfahrer, S559. **Leslie Howard** (pf).
Hyperion CDA66951/3 (8/95).
...Complete Solo Piano Music, Volume 45. Grosse Concert-Phantasie über spanische Weisen, S253.
La romanesca, S252 (two versions). Rapsodie espagnole, S254. Feuille morte – Elégie d'après
Soriano, S428. Rondeau fantastique, S232. **Leslie Howard** (pf). Hyperion CDA67145 (A/97).
...Oh! quand je dors, S282. *Coupled with works by various composers.*
Angela Gheorghiu (sop); **Malcolm Martineau** (pf).
Decca 458 360-2DH (5/98). *See review in the Collections section; refer to the Index.*

Gaston Litaize

French 1909-1991

Suggested listening ...
...Variations sur un Noël angevin. *Coupled with works by various composers.* **Christopher Herrick**
(org). Hyperion CDA66917 (8/97). *See review in the Collections section; refer to the Index.*

Antonio Literes

Spanish 1673-1747

Suggested listening ...
...Ah del rustico pastor. *Coupled with works by various composers.* **Al Ayre Español / Eduardo López
Banzo.** Deutsche Harmonia Mundi 05472 77325-2 (8/95). 🖉 *See review in the Collections
section; refer to the Index.* 🅖

Henry Litolff

British/French 1818-1891

Suggested listening ...
...Concerto symphonique No. 4 in D minor, Op. 102 – Scherzo. *Coupled with works by various
composers.* **Cristina Ortiz** (pf); **Royal Philharmonic Orchestra / Moshe Atzmon.**
Decca 414 348-2DH (9/86). *See review in the Collections section; refer to the Index.* 🅖
...Concerto symphonique No. 4 in D minor, Op. 102 – Scherzo. *Coupled with works by* **Brahms**
and **Franck Sir Clifford Curzon** (pf); **London Philharmonic Orchestra / Sir Adrian Boult.**
Decca The Classic Sound 425 082-2DCS (4/95). *Gramophone* classical 100. *See review under
Brahms; refer to the Index.* 🅖🅖🅖

George Lloyd

British 1913

Lloyd Iernin. **Marilyn Hill Smith** (sop) Iernin; **Geoffrey Pogson** (ten) Gerent; **Henry Herford** (bar)
Edryn; **Malcolm Rivers** (bass-bar) Bedwyr; **Jonathon Robarts** (bass) Priest; **Jeremy White** (bass)
Saxon Thane; **Stephen Jackson** (bar) Huntsman; **Claire Powell** (mez) Cunaide; **BBC Singers and
Concert Orchestra / George Lloyd.** Albany Ⓜ TROY121/3 (three discs: 173 minutes: ADD: 9/94).
Notes and text included. Also includes an interview with George Lloyd. Recorded 1985.
The heart goes out to this opera. Some of the causes may be suspect. Perhaps it is sentimental to allow
knowledge of the composer's age at the time of writing (George Lloyd was 21) to influence one's
response, but it does. Then there is the pleasure of seeing the work which enjoyed so much success
followed by such complete neglect convincingly revived, with the composer, now as conductor,
renewing acquaintance with his own music half a century later. At the London première in 1935 *The
Times* found the opera "spontaneous in invention and almost consistently effective ... the only
exception [being] the choral writing which, conceived along unusual lines and largely unisonous, does
not quite achieve the composer's intentions and might well be revised". Whether the hint was taken
we are not told, but the score has not been revised for this performance, and most of the choral
writing (not all that "unisonous") works well. More important is the writing for soloists, and on the
whole this seems instinctively expert: for instance, the high notes are sparingly required, so that when
they occur they have maximum effect. The heroine's role wants a coloratura soprano who also has a

substantial middle and lower-middle register. That should not be too much to ask, but one can only guess at the kind of Italianate full-bodied sound that was probably in the composer's ear when he wrote the work. Marilyn Hill-Smith is more successful with the higher, more agile and less dramatic parts of the role. All the male principals have splendidly singable music, but the best performance comes from Claire Powell, sumptuous of voice and noble of manner.

Further listening ...
...Piano Concerto No. 3. **Kathryn Stott** (pf); **BBC Philharmonic Orchestra / George Lloyd.** Albany TROY019-2 (3/90).
...Symphonies – No. 2; No. 9. **BBC Philharmonic Orchestra / George Lloyd.** Albany TROY055-2 (6/87).
...Symphonies – No. 6[a]; No. 10, "November Journeys"[b]. John Socman – Overture[a]. [b]**BBC Philharmonic Brass;** [a]**BBC Philharmonic Orchestra / George Lloyd.** Albany TROY015-2 (8/89).
...Symphony No. 8. **Philharmonia Orchestra / George Lloyd.** Albany TROY230 (6/97).
...Aubade. Eventide. The road through Samarkand. **Anthony Goldstone, Caroline Clemmow** (pfs). Albany TROY248 (11/97).
...Hereford Service. *Coupled with works by various composers.* **Hereford Cathedral Choir / Roy Massey** with **Huw Williams** (org). Priory PRCD535 (7/96).
...A Litany. **Janice Watson** (sop); **Jeremy White** (bass); **Guildford Choral Society; Philharmonia Orchestra / George Lloyd.** Albany TROY200-2 (11/96).
...A Symphonic Mass. **Brighton Festival Chorus; Bournemouth Symphony Orchestra / George Lloyd.** Albany TROY100-2 (12/93). *Gramophone Editor's choice.*
...The Vigil of Venus. **Carolyn James** (sop); **Thomas Booth** (ten); **Welsh National Opera Chorus and Orchestra / George Lloyd.** Albany TROY170-2 (1/96).
...John Socman – Act 1 scenes 1 and 2; Act 2 scene 1; Act 3. **Soloists; London Voices; Trinity Boys' Choir; Philharmonia Orchestra / George Lloyd.** Albany TROY131-2 (1/95).

Richard Lloyd
British 1933

Suggested listening ...
...Drop down, ye heavens. *Coupled with works by various composers.* **St Paul's Cathedral Choir / John Scott** with **Andrew Lucas** (org). Hyperion CDA66994 (12/97). *See review in the Collections section; refer to the Index.*

William Lloyd Webber
British 1914-1982

W. Lloyd Webber Viola Sonatina[a]. Nocturne[b]. Two Pieces for Cello and Piano[c]. Badinage de Noël[d]. Song Without Words[d]. Scherzo in G minor[d]. Arabesque[d]. Presto for Perseus[d]. Romantic Evening[d]. Explanation[e]. Five Songs[f]. Missa Sanctae Mariae Magdalenae[g]. [f]**John Graham-Hall** (ten); [a]**Philip Dukes** (va); [bc]**Julian Lloyd Webber** (vc); [a]**Sophia Rahman,** [bcde]**John Lill,** [f]**Philip Ledger** (pfs); [g]**Ian Watson** (org); [g]**Richard Hickox Singers / Richard Hickox.** ASV Ⓕ CDDCA961 (59 minutes: DDD: 9/96). Texts included. Items marked [cdfg] from CDDCA5904 (9/87). Recorded 1995.
The composer was also a distinguished organ scholar, respected teacher, and father of you know who. The fluent *Sonatina* has three pithy, beautifully crafted movements which contain much resourceful, attractively idiomatic writing. The wistful *Nocturne* for cello and piano derives from Lloyd Webber's 1948 oratorio *St Francis of Assisi*, while the (undated) piano miniature entitled *Explanation* possesses a similar, innocent charm (it certainly fits very happily into the sequence of piano pieces here). The five songs are really very pretty indeed (suggesting comparisons with Roger Quilter) as, indeed, are the two were cello and piano offerings, "In the half-light" and the "Air varié" (based on César Franck's *Tantum ergo*). That just leaves the immensely assured, five-movement *Missa Sanctae Mariae Magdalenae*, a substantial late work dating from 1979. Performances and recordings are beyond reproach.

Alonso Lobo
Spanish c1555-1617

Lobo Missa Maria Magdalene. O quam suavis est, Domine. Quam pulchri sunt. Ave regina caelorum. Versa est in luctum. Credo quod Redemptor. Vivo ego, dicit Dominus. Ave Maria.
Guerrero Maria Magdalene. **The Tallis Scholars / Peter Phillips.** Gimell Ⓕ 454 931-2PH (63 minutes: DDD: 12/97). Texts and translations included. *Gramophone Editor's choice.*
As with so many masters of the renaissance, Alonso Lobo has mainly become known for one work, his setting of the funerary *Versa est in luctum*. This is undoubtedly a masterpiece of its kind but to have it placed alongside other pieces from Lobo's 1602 collection (one of the six Masses in the volume, and all seven motets) affords a welcome chance to assess his composition skills more fully. Furthermore, to have a group as internationally presitigious as The Tallis Scholars dedicate a whole CD to his music is a well-deserved accolade. Lobo's music is sonorous in a manner that is direct and

unfussy in effect, though often highly expressive, and always structured with the utmost technical control. Take, for example, Lobo's *Ave Maria*, an 8-in-4 canon (in other words, four more voices are generated from the original quartet) which emanates a sense of absolute serenity. In fact, each of the motets explores a different aspect of the compositional techniques brought to the genre, and the Mass is equally fine, Lobo making the spacious textures of the motet, *Maria Magdalene* by his teacher Guerrero a distinguishing feature of his own setting of the Ordinary. The Tallis Scholars are on superb form, the overall sound vibrant and immediate with solo sections providing contrast through a more introspective approach. Even if you've never heard of Lobo, or have never bought a CD of late-Renaissance polyphony before, try this one – you'll be bowled over.

Additional recommendation ...
...O quam suavis est, Domine. *Coupled with works by various composers.* **The Hilliard Ensemble.** Virgin Classics Veritas ⑬ VED5 61394-2 (two discs: 126 minutes: DDD: 11/97). *See review in the Collections section; refer to the Index.*

Pietro Locatelli

Italian 1695-1764

Locatelli 10 Sonatas, Op. 8. **Locatelli Trio** (Elizabeth Wallfisch, vn; Richard Tunnicliffe, vc; Paul Nicholson, hpd); **Rachel Isserlis** (vn). Hyperion ⑤ CDA67021/2 (two discs: 116 minutes: DDD: 8/96). 🎵
There is a sense of the decadent about the music of Locatelli. But decadence, we all know, can be quite fun, and it would be an austere spirit that took little pleasure in these sonatas and especially the playing of them here. This two-disc set of his Op. 8 (published in 1744) contains six violin sonatas and four trio sonatas, three for two violins and continuo and one using the much less common combination of violin, cello and continuo. A number of them then have a slowish movement and most end with a quick triple-metre piece, again in brilliant violinistic style. The most attractive is No. 5, with its interesting gestures and hints of wit in the second movement. The most demanding is No. 6 with its final minuet with variations, quite breathtaking (and improbably set in E flat, a perverse gesture): here Elizabeth Wallfisch clambers unruffled through the technical thickets, which include an extraordinary variation with trills on one string and moving parts on another and dashes from one end of the compass to the other and back again, and much more besides. This is amazing violin playing of a kind of virtuosity rarely heard from a period instrument player. The three trio sonatas for two violins are not of course virtuoso music in quite the same way, and musically not generally very inventive. The performances are altogether admirable; no one who admires good violin playing will want to miss Wallfisch's crisp, rhythmic playing on this disc.

Further listening ...
...12 Concerti grossi, Op. 1. **Raglan Baroque Players / Elizabeth Wallfisch** (vn), **Nicholas Kraemer** (hpd/org). Hyperion CDA66981/2 (1/96). 🎵
...Concerti grossi – Op. 1: C minor; D major; G minor; Op. 7: E flat major, "Il pianto d'Arianna". Sinfonia in F minor, "Composta per le esequie della sua Donna che si celebrarono in Roma". **Europa Galante / Fabio Biondi** (vn). Opus 111 OPS30-104 (1/96). 🎵
...12 Concertos, Op. 3, "L'Arte del Violino". **Elizabeth Wallfisch** (vn); **Raglan Baroque Players / Nicholas Kraemer.** Hyperion CDA66721/3 (1/95). 🎵
...Introduttioni Teatrali and Concerti, Op. 4 – No. 12 in F major. *Coupled with works by various composers.* **Cologne Musica Antiqua / Reinhard Goebel.** Archiv Produktion 435 393-2AH (9/92). 🎵 *See review in the Collections section; refer to the Index.*

Matthew Locke

British 1621-1677

Locke Consort of Fower Parts. Duos – No. 1 in D major; No. 2 in C major. **Fretwork** (Wendy Gillespie, Richard Campbell, William Hunt, Julia Hodgson, Susanna Pell, Richard Boothby, viols); ᵃ**Nigel North** (lte); **Paul Nicholson** (org/spinet). Virgin Classics Veritas ⑤ VC5 45142-2 (67 minutes: DDD: 11/96). 🎵 Recorded 1990.
Although we do not know for certain whether Matthew Locke taught Purcell, the *Consort of Fower Parts* explains much of the peculiarly concentrated devices which gave Purcell the means to instil the so-called antiquated *Fantasias* with the experimental tonal and idiomatic spice which makes them so unique in English chamber music. On their own terms, Locke's Consorts are collectively no match, though, as they are suites not fantasias, the comparison is perhaps unfair. That said, Locke is capable of some exquisite music and Fretwork here are loving advocates. Experienced as they are in the performance of so much of the finest English consort music of the seventeenth century from Byrd to Purcell, Fretwork are particularly well placed to discriminate between the elusive properties in an age of subtle, abstract ideals. In the Ayre of No. 4 and the equivalent in Suites Nos. 2 and 6, there is a simplicity of utterance entirely appropriate to Locke's delightful tunefulness, as does the disarming warmth of expression in the opening movements of the major-key works. As ever with Fretwork, the intonation is well-nigh perfect. There is a considered and deft use of a variety of continuo instruments and mention must be made also of two attractive *Duos* for bass viols, which break up the prevalent quartet texture. Locke's special language shines as brightly here as one can remember.

Further listening ...

...Sacred Choral Music – Descende caelo cincta sororibus (The Oxford Ode). How doth the city sit solitary. Super flumina Babylonis. O be joyful in the Lord, all ye lands. Audi, Domine, clamantes ad te. Lord let me know mine end. Jesu auctor clementie. Be Thou exalted, Lord. **New College Choir, Oxford; The Parley of Instruments / Edward Higginbottom** with **Peter Holman** (org). Hyperion CDA66373 (9/91).

...Psyche. **Soloists; New London Consort Chorus; New London Consort / Philip Pickett.** L'Oiseau-Lyre 444 336-2OH (2/96). *Gramophone Editor's choice.* Ⓖ

Charles Martin Loeffler

French/American 1861-1935

Suggested listening ...

...Two Rhapsodies. *Coupled with* **Nielsen** Wind Quintet, FS100. **Prokofiev** Quintet in G minor, Op. 39. **Chamber Music Northwest / David Shifrin** (cl). Delos DE3136 (12/93).

...Quatre poèmes, Op. 5. *Coupled with works by various composers.* **Mitsuko Shirai** (mez); **Tabea Zimmermann** (va); **Hartmut Höll** (pf). Capriccio 10 462 (9/95). *See review in the Collections section; refer to the Index.* Ⓖ

Carl Loewe

German 1796-1869

Loewe Die drei Lieder, Op. 3 No. 3. Elvershöh, Op. 118 No. 2. Der Woywode, Op. 49 No. 1. Die nächtliche Heerschau, Op. 23. Der letzte Ritter, Op. 124. Tom der Reimer, Op. 135. Odins Meeresritt, Op. 118. Waffenweihe Kaiser Heinrich's IV, Op. 122. **Andreas Schmidt** (bar); **Cord Garben** (pf). CPO Ⓕ CPO999 253-2 (65 minutes: DDD: 11/96).

To embark upon the complete performance of Carl Loewe's Lieder and Ballads is an ambitious venture, as there are some 375 of them. This opening volume contains only one really well-known ballad, *Tom der Reimer*, familiar from Fischer-Dieskau's powerful performances and sung here with something of that master's devotion to words and their dramatic import. This is an essential quality for the ballads on this opening volume, and Andreas Schmidt's control of the portrayal of character and of the often sensational unfolding of events is superb. He and his pianist, Cord Garben (sometimes set rather far back and not sufficiently clear in articulation), have a sure instinct for Loewe's structures, for the movement from one section or tempo into another, for the telling surprise modulation, for the decorative touches in the melody, so that these fine works are not merely a string of events but a dramatic experience. Apart from the spooky ballads, such as *Elvershöh* and others which were said to have gripped Loewe's listeners as he sang them himself at the piano, a strong vein which he explored was the historical narrative. There is a chilling delivery of the ballad embodying that popular nineteenth-century image, the dead troops reviewed by their dead general – in this case, Napoleon. This is an excellent beginning to a major enterprise.

Additional recommendation ...

...Herr Oluf, Op. 2 No. 2. Graf Eberstein, Op. 9, Book 6, No. 5. Die Gruft der Liebenden, Op. 21. General Schwerin, Op. 61 No. 2. Landgraf Ludwig, Op. 67 No. 3. Drei Balladen, Op. 97. Der Pilgrim vor St Just, Op. 99 No. 3. Hueska, Op. 108 No. 2. Kaiser Ottos Weihnachtsfeier, Op. 121 No. 1. Gesänge, Op. 123 – No. 2, Trommelständchen; No. 3, Die Uhr. **Andreas Schmidt** (bar); **Cord Garben** (pf). CPO Ⓕ CPO999 305-2 (78 minutes: DDD: 8/97).

Loewe Kleiner Haushalt, Op. 71. Die Heinzelmännchen, Op. 83. Heinrich der Vogler, Op. 56 No. 1. Das Vaterland, Op. 125 No. 2. Der Nöck, Op. 129 No. 2. Fünf Lieder, Op. 145. Prinz Eugen, der edle Ritter, Op. 92. Archibald Douglas, Op. 128. **Kurt Moll** (bass); **Cord Garben** (pf). CPO Ⓕ CPO999 306-2 (58 minutes: DDD: 5/97). Texts and translations included.

Kurt Moll has all the attributes that go to make a fine Loewe singer, not only the splendidly flexible bass voice that can darken the grim songs (plunging to a strong low E), brighten the cheerful ones and colour all the detail of the ballads vividly, but nimbleness of wit as well as gravity, a sense of comedy as well as dignity, a sense of being on stage. He has been a witty Osmin and a noble Sarastro; such dramatic gifts are priceless here. The delightful Rückert *Kleiner Haushalt* is a real comic *tour de force*; at the other end of his recital, *Archibald Douglas* has an impetus that is dramatic but adroitly skirts the melodramatic. He makes a compelling narrative of *Heinrich der Vogler*, changing tone and manner for the lyrical songs that make up the *Fünf Lieder*, Op. 145 and in "Der Feind" deftly sketching the animals who all shy away from their common enemy approaching through the wood – a man. This is one of the best discs yet to appear in CPO's Loewe Edition, well worth considering by those who do not want to follow the whole series.

Loewe Drei Balladen, Op. 1ᵇ – Edward; Erlkönig. Drei Balladen, Op. 2ᵇ – Herr Oluf. Drei Balladen, Op. 3ᶜ – Elvershöh; Die drei Lieder. Lieder, Gesänge, Romanzen und Balladen, Op. 9ᵃ – Book 1: Wandrers Nachtlied; Book 3: Ich denke dein; Book 8: Türmwächter Lynkeus zu den Füssen der Helena; Lynkeus, der Türmer, auf Fausts Sternwarte singend; Gutmann und Gutweib. Drei Balladen, Op. 20ᵃ. Die Gruft der Liebenden, Op. 21ᶜ. Zehn Geistliche Gesang,

Op. 22[a] – Book 1: Gottes ist der Orient!. Drei Balladen, Op. 44[a] – Der getreue Eckart; Der Totentanz. Drei Balladen, Op. 56[c] – Heinrich der Vogler. Drei Balladen, Op. 59[b] – Der Schatzgräber. Zwölf Gedichte, Op. 62[b] – Book 1: Süsses Begräbnis; Hinkende Jamben. Kleiner Haushalt, Op. 71[b]. Vier Legenden, Op. 75[c] – Der heilige Franziskus. Sechs Gesänge, Op. 79[a] – Frühzeitiger Frühling. Fünf Lieder, Op. 81[a] – In Vorübergehen. Prince Eugen, Op. 92[a.] Drei Balladen, Op. 97[b] – Der Mohrenfürst auf der Messe. Odins Meeresritt, Op. 118[c]. Drei Gesänge, Op. 123[c] – Trommelständchen; Die Uhr. Archibald Douglas, Op. 128[b]. Drei Balladen, Op. 129[c] – Der Nöck. Tom der Reimer, Op. 135[a][c]. Fünf Lieder, Op. 145[b] – Meeresleuchten. Canzonette[a]. Freibeuter[a]. Wenn der Blüten Frühlingsregen[a]. **Dietrich Fischer-Dieskau** (bar); **Jörg Demus** (pf). DG Ⓜ 449 516-2GX2 (two discs: 156 minutes: ADD: 10/96). Texts and translations included. Items marked [a] from 2530 052 (7/71), [b]2531 376 (7/82), [c]recorded 1968 (new to UK).

Loewe is remembered above all as a ballad composer – but Fischer-Dieskau championed a wider range of his vast output. All the best-known ballads are included here, magnificently sung by a great artist at the height of his powers. *Edward, Herr Oluf, Heinrich der Vogler, Prince Eugen, Der Zauberlehrling*: these and others are sung with a wonderful sense of the graphic, conveyed through an appreciation of the colour of the words that never descends into overemphasis and that is beautifully attuned to Loewe's illustrative manner. Fischer-Dieskau and Demus are ideal partners, Demus responding quickly and with an ear for the sinister that often marks the piano writing and its subtle use of motive. Wagner praised Loewe's setting of *Erlkönig*, a song which a number of good judges preferred to Schubert's. But Loewe was also a Lieder writer in the great German tradition, and this is too often overlooked; but not by Fischer-Dieskau, whose vastly ranging forays into the repertory did so much to rescue reputations. Two songs alone, from this magisterial collection, are witness to Loewe's stature. They are settings of the wonderful poems from the second part of *Faust* in which Lynceus, the lynx-eyed watcher on the tower, sees the magical appearance, from the depths of Homeric antiquity, of Helen of Troy herself. He, incarnating the gift of the perception of visual beauty, after a life of watching from his tower can conceive of nothing that could surpass this wonder; and, in the second song, hymns his gratitude to the gift of sight. Loewe's two settings are beautiful responses to the poetry of a great artist with the gift of an ideal simplicity. There is a wide range to explore here; these two songs alone should persuade the responsive listener to make the exploration.

Further listening ...
...Wirkung in der Ferne, Op. 59 No. 1. Das Milchmädchen, Op. 36 No. 1. Drei Legenden, Op. 37 – No. 1, Das Muttergottesbild; No. 2, Moosröslein. Die Mutter an der Wiege. Die Gottesmauer, Op. 140. Der Traum der Witwe, Op. 142. Spirito santo, Op. 143. Mein Geist ist trüb, Op. 5 No. 5. Die Sonne der Schlaflosen, Op. 13 No. 6. Die Braut von Corinth, Op. 29. **Iris Vermillion** (mez); **Cord Garben** (pf). CPO CPO999 318-2 (1/97).
...Die schwarzen Augen, Op. 94 No. 2. Die Junggesell. Urgrossvaters Gesellschaft, Op. 56 No. 3. Der gefangene Admiral, Op. 115. Gruss vom Meere, Op. 103 No. 1. Der Graf von Habsburg, Op. 98. Der seltne Beter, Op. 141. Kaiser Karl V, Op. 99 – No. 1, Das Wiegenfest zu Gent; No. 4, Die Leiche zu St Just. Der Bettler, Op. 44 No. 1. **Roman Trekel** (bar); **Cord Garben** (pf). CPO CPO999 304-2 (1/97).
...Mein Herz, ich will dich fragen, Op. 86. Traumlicht. Gesammelte Lieder, Gesänge, Romanzen und Lieder, Op. 9 – Book 2: No. 2, Lied der Desdemona. Book 4: No. 4, Frühlingserwachen. Book 8: No. 4, Mädchenwünsche. Book 10: No. 2, Die Sylphide; No. 4, Niemand hat's gesehn. Des fremden Kindes heiliger Christ, Op. 33 No. 3. Der Blumen Rache, Op. 68 No. 3. Gedichte, Op. 62. Bienenweben. Ganymed, Op. 81 No. 5. Das vergessene Lied, Op. 65 No. 1. O, meine Blumen, ihr meine Freude!. Walpurgisnacht, Op. 2 No. 3. **Gabriele Rossmanith** (sop); **Cord Garben** (pf). CPO CPO999 260-2 (1/97).

Zhou Long   Chinese 20th century

Suggested listening ...
...Song of the Ch'in. *Coupled with works by* **Hovhaness** Shanghai Quartet.
Delos DE3162 (3/95). *See review under Hovhaness; refer to the Index.*

Antonio Lotti   Italian c1667-1740

Lotti Duetti, terzetti e madrigali a più voci, Op. 1 – Inganni dell'umanità; Lamento di tre amanti; La vita caduca; Moralità d'una per la; Incostanza femminile; Lontananza insopportabile; Funerale della speranza; Crudeltà rimproverata; Giuramento amorosa; Querela amorosa; Incostanza della sorte Scherzo d'amore; Capriccio; Supplica ad amore. **Il Complesso Barocco / Alan Curtis** (hpd). Virgin Classics Veritas Ⓔ VC5 45221-2 (78 minutes: DDD: 2/98).
Texts and translations included. Recorded 1996.
Mention Antonio Lotti and most people will think of the *Crucifixus*, and little if anything else. A Venetian contemporary of Vivaldi, his association with St Mark's lasted all of his working life, nearly 60 years, until his death. In addition, his music was performed and published all over Europe, arousing the enthusiasm of no less a patron than the Emperor Leopold I. That the compositions

recorded here are best described as madrigals may come as a surprise; but though the madrigal's heyday was by then long gone, it did enjoy a revival at the turn of the eighteenth century. Certainly these pieces meet the genre's basic definition, being mainly through-composed and scored for no more than a handful of voices and continuo. What fascinates here is the music's hybrid nature and its flexibility. The texture is largely imitative, with each text-line having its own melodic point; but alongside this convention are Lotti's very contemporary-sounding harmonic touches. Interestingly, these attracted the disapproval of at least one theorist, exactly as had Monteverdi's a century before. Today, they are a source of unexpected delight, especially in this vivacious and spirited interpretation. There should no longer be any need to praise the confidence with which Italian ensembles have taken hold of their native repertory – and Il Complesso Barocco is not the least of them (its director, Alan Curtis, being the only foreigner among them). This is music of high vocal virtuosity, requiring the utmost agility in execution and deftness of characterization: on that count the ensemble can hardly be faulted, though admittedly the higher voices are perhaps slightly less sure-footed in their extreme registers. The continuo, spearheaded by Curtis himself, is equally natural and unfussy (though in the more richly scored pieces, as in *La vita caduca*, the organ may be a touch too obtrusive). There can be few better opportunities to broaden (or to make) one's acquaintance with Lotti.

Further listening ...

...Crucifixus a 8. *Coupled with works by various composers.* **Soloists; Westminster Cathedral Choir / James O'Donnell.** Hyperion CDA66850 (5/96). *See review in the Collections section; refer to the Index.*

...Crucifixus a 8. *Coupled with works by various composers.* **Choir of St Mary's Cathedral, Edinburgh / Timothy Byram-Wigfield.** Priory PRCD557 (10/97). *See review in the Collections section; refer to the Index.*

...Crucifixus a 8. *Coupled with works by various composers.* **St Paul's Cathedral Choir / John Scott** with **Andrew Lucas** (org). Hyperion CDA66916 (A/97). *See review in the Collections section; refer to the Index.*

...Crucifixus a 8. *Coupled with works by various composers.* **New College Choir, Oxford / Edward Higginbottom.** Erato 3984-21659-2 (6/98). *Gramophone Editor's choice.* *See review in the Collections section; refer to the Index.*

Arthur Lourié   Russian 1892-1966

Lourié String Quartets[a] – No. 1; No. 2; No. 3, "Suite". Duo for Violin and Viola[b].
[a]**Utrecht Quartet** ([b]Eeva Koskinen, Katherine Routley, vns; [b]Daniel Raiskin, va; Sebastian Koloski, vc). ASV Ⓕ CDDCA1020 (62 minutes: DDD: 5/98). Recorded 1996.

Here is a comprehensive examination of the mysterious Arthur Lourié, and it could hardly be more intriguing. Lourié was a provoking and imaginative creative mind, and a real original. He was known, if at all, for having been Commissar of Music during the immediately post-revolutionary phase in Soviet Russia and, later, for being first very close to Stravinsky, then unmentionable in his presence (it seems that he may have intrigued against Stravinsky's second wife). There is not much of the Soviet Union and not much more of Stravinsky in these three absorbingly odd quartets. Indeed the most striking thing about them is their remarkable range of musical imagery and the sheer rapidity with which Lourié was developing over the mere three years that they span. The First Quartet is a big, half-hour piece, packed with vividly imaginative ideas which are, however, for the most part simply juxtaposed, with little or no sense of progression, let alone development. The language is basically lyrical, and becomes more expressive as the work continues, but Lourié rarely allows any key to register for long. One idea will suggest another to him, a brief unifying motive may emerge, but again not for long. At times there is an odd sort of resemblance to Janáček, but the overall impression is of a gifted composer pouring ideas on to paper and hoping that sheer urgency will hold the result together. The Second Quartet is a bizarre development from this. Dense textures open to reveal a demure little tune, which becomes quite jovial before plainer harmonies and a hint of Stravinskian neo-classicism lead to a return of the opening and some curious recollections of pre-classical music, to which spiky dissonances are added as an almost dismissive coda. It is all over in a single movement of eight minutes. The Third Quartet, only a year later, begins with two juxtaposed ideas, but now they are genuinely worked together into an oddly gripping two-minute (!) "Prelude", which is followed by a grave "Chorale", an urgently serious "Hymn" and a shadowed "Funeral March", fraught with harmonic tension. Where all this is leading seems to be the brief, epigrammatic "Duo", the music now pared down to essentials and clearly revealing either roots in or deep nostalgia for Russian folk music. The fine Utrecht players are obviously fascinated by this music, and they play it for all it is worth.

Donato Lovreglio   Italian 1841-1907

Suggested listening ...

...Fantasia on Verdi's "La traviata", Op. 45. *Coupled with works by various composers.* **Michael Collins** (cl); **Kathryn Stott** (pf). EMI Eminence Virtuosi CD-EMX2287 (9/92). *See review in the Collections section; refer to the Index.*

Alexandre Luigini

French 1850-1906

Suggested listening ...
...Ballet égyptien, Op. 12 – Suite. *Coupled with works by* **Ketèlbey** **Royal Philharmonic Orchestra /**
Anatole Fistoulari. Classics for Pleasure CD-CFP4637 (3/94). *See review under Ketèlbey;*
refer to the Index.

Jean-Baptiste Lully

Italian/French 1632-1687

Lully Phaëton. **Howard Crook** (ten) Phaëton; **Rachel Yakar** (sop) Clymène; **Jennifer Smith** (sop)
Théone; **Véronique Gens** (sop) Libye; **Gérard Thervel** (bar) Epaphus; **Jean-Paul Fouchécourt** (ten)
Triton, Sun, Earth, Goddess; **Philippe Huttenlocher** (bar) Mérops; **Laurent Naouri** (bar) Saturn,
Protée; **Virginie Pochon** (mez) Astrée, Hour of the Day; **Jérôme Varnier** (sop) Autumn, Jupiter;
Florence Couderc (sop) Shepherdess, Hour of the Day; **Sagittarius Vocal Ensemble;**
Les Musiciens du Louvre / Marc Minkowski. Erato Ⓔ 4509-91737-2 (two discs: 144 minutes: ⒼⒼ
DDD: 8/94). ✍ Notes, text and translation included. Recorded 1993.
In 1688 *Phaëton* was chosen to inaugurate the new Royal Academy of Music at Lyon where, as
Jérôme de la Gorce remarks in his excellent introduction, it was so successful "that people came to
see it from forty leagues around". The libretto is based on the famous legend in Ovid's *Metamorphoses*
and afforded composer and librettist ample opportunity for evocative and colourful writing. The
score is generously endowed with *divertissements*, an invigorating overture and a supple swiftly
moving chaconne. The casting is effective, by and large, and notably for the stylish, alluring and
impassioned singing of Véronique Gens. Jennifer Smith is authoritative as the hapless princess
Théone; her diction is excellent and her careful placing of notes comparably so. The exchanges with
Phaëton are passionately sung, with Howard Crook in the title-role engaging vigorously in the
dialogue. Third in this impressive triumvirate of princesses is Rachel Yakar who, as Clymène,
Phaëton's mother, is affectionate yet forceful. Her Act 1 air, "D'une amoureuse ardeur un grand
Coeur peut brûler" ("A mighty heart can burn with amorous ardour"), with its fleeting resemblance
to Henry Lawes's "Sufferance", is beautifully done with the dual emphasis on heroism and love
skilfully balanced. There are fine contributions from the remaining dramatis personae, too. Last,
but in French opera certainly not least, are the choral and instrumental contributions; both make a
strong impression, the orchestra especially so with a resonant basso continuo team affording constant
pleasure. Minkowski sets a cracking pace for the drama and there are few if any flagging moments.
In short, all this is engaging music, imaginatively performed and thoroughly entertaining. Recorded
sound is excellent and the booklet, give or take a few small errors, all that one could wish for.
Strongly recommended; the cover illustration alone, one of a group of seventeenth-century
wooden panels depicting Phaëton, horses and chariot plunging to earth invites further investigation.

Further listening ...
...Alceste. **Soloists; Sagittarius Vocal Ensemble; La Grande Ecurie et La Chambre du Roy /**
Jean-Claude Malgoire. Auvidis Astrée E8527 (4/93). ✍
...Armide. **Soloists; Collegium Vocale; La Chapelle Royale Chorus and Orchestra /**
Philippe Herreweghe. Harmonia Mundi HMC90 1456/7 (8/93). ✍
...Atys. *Prologue. Tragédie-lyrique.* **Soloists; Les Arts Florissants Chorus and Orchestra /**
William Christie. Harmonia Mundi HMC90 1257/9 (7/87). ✍
...Le bourgeois gentilhomme – incidental music. *Coupled with* **Campra** L'Europe galante –
ballet suite. **Soloists; Tölz Boys' Choir; La Petite Bande / Gustav Leonhardt.**
Deutsche Harmonia Mundi Editio Classica GD77059 (2/91). ✍
...Le bourgeois gentilhomme. Cadmus et Hermione. Les noces de village. *Coupled with* **A. Philidor**
Le mariage de la grosse Cathos. **Marie-Ange Petit** (perc); **London Oboe Band / Paul Goodwin.**
Harmonia Mundi HMU90 7122 (4/95). ✍
...Dies irae. Miserere. *Coupled with* **Du Mont** Memorare **Soloists; Parish Chappelle Royale Chorus**
and Orchestra / Philippe Herreweghe. Harmonia Mundi HMC90 1167 (5/86). ✍

David Lumsdaine

Australian 1931

Suggested listening ...
...A Norfolk Songbook. *Coupled with works by various composers.* **Tracey Chadwell** (sop);
John Turner (recs). British Music Society BMS420/1CD (3/98). *See review in the*
Collections section; refer to the Index.

John Lurie

American 1952

Suggested listening ...
...Stranger than Paradise. *Coupled with works by various composers.* **Balanescu Quartet.**
Argo 436 565-2ZH (3/93). *See review in the Collections section; refer to the Index.*   Ⓖ

Witold Lutosławski

Lutosławski Concerto for Orchestra. Funeral Music. Mi-parti. **BBC Philharmonic Orchestra /
Yan Pascal Tortelier.** Chandos Ⓕ CHAN9421 (55 minutes: DDD: 4/96). Recorded 1993.
Selected by Soundings.
                                                             Ⓖ
All three phases of Lutosławski are here, with two of his finest orchestral works flanking a
'transitional' score whose historical importance outweighs its purely musical interest. Tortelier's
virtues as a conductor – expressive warmth allied to a special rhythmic buoyancy – are generously
apparent in a sizzling account of the *Concerto for Orchestra*. The musical flow is firmly controlled, yet
the effect is never inflexible, and the technical precision and alertness of the playing throughout is
something for the listener to revel in. The sound is bright, well differentiated dynamically, and even if
the BBC's Manchester studio lacks some of the depth and atmosphere of Chicago's Orchestra Hall,
as caught in Barenboim's rival version on Erato, the Chandos recording is generally more vivid, in
keeping with a performance which has precisely the kind of bite and energy that the score demands.
It is good that Chandos and Tortelier chose *Mi-parti* to complete the disc, since of all Lutosławski's
later instrumental works this one makes out the best possible case for his radical change of technique
around 1960. Although the composer's own Polish recordings of *Mi-parti* (and of the *Concerto*)
remain in the catalogue, and are naturally of some historical interest, the music-making on this
Chandos release is superior, making this the primary recommendation of these works.
Additional recommendation ...
...Funeral music. Symphony No. 4. Partita[a]. Interlude. Chain 2[a]. [a]**Krzysztof Bakowski** (vn); **Polish
National Radio Symphony Orchestra / Antoni Wit.** Naxos Ⓢ 8 553202 (77 minutes: DDD: 10/96).

Lutosławski Concerto for Orchestra. Symphony No. 3. **Chicago Symphony Orchestra /
Daniel Barenboim.** Erato Ⓕ 4509-91711-2 (58 minutes: DDD: 8/93). Recorded live in 1992.
Gramophone Editor's choice.   ⒼⒼ
Lutosławski's Third Symphony was commissioned by the Chicago SO and first performed by them
under Sir Georg Solti in 1983, but only nine years later did the orchestra record the work. None of
the versions made in the interim can equal Barenboim's blend of refined detail and cumulative power,
and the Erato recording is also more faithful to the dynamics marked in the score. The *Concerto for
Orchestra*, completed almost 30 years before the symphony, is comparatively conservative in style, but
it has ample substance to match its panache. It also remains a formidable challenge to an orchestra.
As with the symphony, Barenboim's strength is the large-scale creation and sustaining of tension, and
the Erato recording contains the heavy climaxes without draining them of clarity or impact.
Additional recommendations ...
...Symphonies Nos. 3 and 4. Les espaces du sommeil[a]. [a]**John Shirley-Quirk** (bar);
Los Angeles Philharmonic Orchestra / Esa-Pekka Salonen.
Sony Classical Ⓕ SK66280 (68 minutes: DDD: 11/94).
...Concerto for Orchestra. Jeux vénitiens. Livre pour Orchestre. Mi-Parti.
Polish National Radio Symphony Orchestra / Witold Lutosławski.
EMI Matrix Ⓜ CDM5 65305-2 (78 minutes: ADD: 7/95).

Lutosławski Symphonies – No. 1; No. 2. Symphonic Variations. Funeral music.
Polish National Radio Symphony Orchestra / Witold Lutosławski. EMI Matrix Ⓜ CDM5 65076-2
(71 minutes: ADD: 2/95). From 1C 165 03231/6 (7/79). Recorded 1976-77.   ⒼⒼ
All four works included on this superbly refurbished CD share an acute sense of texture, with the
Symphonic Variations (1938) serving as a sort of changing room where the composer busily
experiments with all manner of musical dress. The *Funeral music* for Bartók (1956-58) is a powerful
synthesis of original thought and active homage, with plentiful reminders of the master himself –
especially of his *Divertimento* for strings. The real ground-breaker, however, is the Second Symphony,
a seething, structured mass in two parts: the first, nervous and diffuse (with strikingly original
passagework for piano and percussion), the second – which arrives without a break – initially
dense, but ultimately ethereal. All in all, this must surely count as *the* introduction to
Lutosławski's symphonic world, and helpful notes offer the uninitiated plenty of useful musical
signposts.
Additional recommendation ...
...No. 2. Piano Concerto[a]. Chantefleurs et Chantefables[b]. Fanfare for Los Angeles Philharmonic.
[b]**Dawn Upshaw** (sop); [a]**Paul Crossley** (pf); **Los Angeles Philharmonic Orchestra /
Esa-Pekka Salonen.** Sony Classical Ⓕ SK67189 (74 minutes: DDD: 6/96).

Lutosławski Chantefleurs et Chantefables[a]. Preludes and Fugue. Five Songs[a]. Chain 1.
[a]**Solveig Kringelborn** (sop); **Norwegian Chamber Orchestra / Daniel Harding.**
Virgin Classics Ⓕ VC5 45275-2 (73 minutes: DDD: 5/98). Texts and translations included.
Chantefleurs et Chantefables, Lutosławski's penultimate work, was heard as a late and exquisite
flowering of lyricism, prompted in part by the French language, in part by the delicately fresh
evocations of childhood wonder that he found in Robert Desnos's poems. It was by no means
unheralded: it has obvious ancestors in the *Five Songs* to Polish texts that Lutosławski wrote over 30
years earlier but which have seldom been heard since, no doubt because of their language. They are

very beautiful, with gratefully lyrical vocal lines over strikingly evocative orchestral textures (strings, two harps, piano, timpani and percussion) that are complex in technique but lucidly 'readable' to the ear. Solveig Kringelborn, who gave the first performance of *Chantefleurs et Chantefables* under the composer's direction, sounds just as much at home in Polish as in French. The two purely instrumental works here are quite as absorbingly coupled. The seven Preludes are played in the order in which they are printed in the score, but for all the disparate material they contain it is obvious that Lutosławski composed them with great care so that they would make equal but different sense played in any order. The extended "Fugue" (quotation marks inserted because although it isn't really a fugue it has the feeling of one), a remarkable work from 1972, is clearly an ancestor of the three *Chains* that followed in the 1980s. *Chain I*, for 14 instruments, progresses from a sequence of crisp, lively, at times almost neo-classical 'events' to a climax of density (ultimately a 12-note chord) in which until the very last moment every line is clearly distinguishable. These are quite admirable performances and recordings, the Norwegian Chamber Orchestra responding with enthusiasm and warmth to Lutosławski's implicit demands that they should play like an ensemble of soloists. Daniel Harding's love for this music is apparent in his care for balance, vivid sonority and the sheer range (from eloquent intensity to touching tenderness) of Lutosławski's lyricism.

Additional recommendation ...
...Chantefleurs et Chantefables[a]. Symphony No. 3. [a]**Valdine Anderson** (sop);
   BBC National Orchestra of Wales / Tadaaki Otaka. BIS Ⓕ CD743 (54 minutes: DDD: 8/96).

Further listening ...
...Chain 2[a]. *Coupled with* **Schnittke** Viola Concerto[b]. **Isabelle van Keulen** ([a]vn/[b]va);
   Philharmonia Orchestra / Heinrich Schiff. Koch Schwann 31523-2 (11/95).
...Dances Preludes. *Coupled with works by* **Copland** and **Nielsen** Janet Hilton (cl);
   Royal Scottish Orchestra / Mattias Bamert. Chandos CHAN8618 (10/88).
...Partita for Violin, Orchestra and Obbligato Solo Piano[a]. Chain 2[b]. *Coupled with* **Stravinsky**
   Violin Concerto in D major[c]. **Anne-Sophie Mutter** (vn); [a]**Phillip Moll** (pf); [ab]**BBC Symphony**
   Orchestra / Witold Lutosławski; [c]**Philharmonia Orchestra / Paul Sacher.**
   DG 423 696-2GH (2/89). *See review under Stravinsky; refer to the Index.*   Ⓖ
...Piano Concerto[a]. Chain 3. Novelette. [a]**Krystian Zimerman** (pf); **BBC Symphony Orchestra /**
   Witold Lutosławski. DG 431 664-2GH (4/92).
...Variations on a Theme of Paganini (arr. Ptasazynska). *Coupled with works by* **Helweg** and
   Bartók Safri Duo; Slovak Duo. Chandos New Direction CHAN9398 (9/96).

Agnes Elisabeth Lutyens
British 1906-1983

Suggested listening ...
...Six Bagatelles. O saisons, o châteaux, Op. 13. *Coupled with works by various composers.*
   Teresa Cahill (sop); **Brunel Ensemble / Christopher Austin.**
   Cala The Edge CACD77005 (6/97). *See review in the Collections section; refer to the Index.*
...Trio, Op. 135. *Coupled with works by various composers.* **Mühlfeld Ensemble.**
   Clarinet Classics CC0007 (10/94). *See review in the Collections section; refer to the Index.*

Edward MacDowell
American 1860-1908

MacDowell Piano Sonata No. 4 in E minor, Op. 59, "Keltic". Forgotten Fairy Tales, Op. 4.
   Six Poems after Heine, Op. 31. 12 Virtuoso Etudes, Op. 46. **James Barbagallo** (pf).
   Marco Polo Ⓕ 8 223633 (65 minutes: DDD: 2/96).
Edward MacDowell's star may have faded to near oblivion over the years. Yet even when his very personal and oddly touching voice seems stifled by deference to outmoded European ideals he provides enough poetic and psychological interest to make James Barbagallo's affectionate tribute more than worthwhile. The rough-and-tumble of academic life, with its hard-nosed jockeying for position, was ill-suited to MacDowell's gentle nature and his professorship at Columbia was short-lived. A romantic escapist, he retreated to his "House o' Dreams" in idyllic New Hampshire, where he indulged his passion for "the Gaelic world ... of bards and heroes of great adventure", a "love of other times". Significantly, the gems of this disc in this ongoing and excellently recorded series are surely the six Op. 31 *Poems after Heine*, their charm and piquancy evoking Scottish castles, nightingales and a shepherd boy "crowned with golden sunshine". The *Forgotten Fairy Tales*, too, have their moments but the 12 *Virtuoso Etudes* are less interesting than their title implies: the "Polonaise" is truly awful and the "Valse triste" an unengaging mixture of whimsy and complacency. But "Wilde Jagd", with its sinister chromatic undertow, is effective and there is much homely lyricism elsewhere. The larger forms, however, seem to have defeated a composer who was essentially a miniaturist. Although the *Keltic* Sonata urges us on with instructions such as "with tragic pathos", the music is overwhelmed by Grieg's influence and by too many tub-thumping, inflated gestures. Overall, Barbagallo is more persuasive in intimacy than in brilliance. However, if he is hard-pressed by some of MacDowell's more hectoring demands he is unfailingly warm-hearted in his approach.

Further listening ...
...Piano Concertos[a] – No. 1 in A minor, Op. 15; No. 2 in D minor, Op. 23. Woodland Sketches, Op. 51[c]. Piano Sonata No. 1 in G minor, Op. 45, "Tragica"[c]. *Coupled with* **Chávez** Piano Concerto[b]. [ab]**Eugene List**, [c]**Vivian Rivkin** (pfs); [ab]**Vienna State Opera Orchestra / Carlos Chávez.** Millennium Classics MCD80086 (5/97).
...Woodland Sketches, Op. 51. Sea Pieces, Op. 55. Fireside Tales, Op. 61. New England Idylls, Op. 62. **James Barbagallo** (pf). Marco Polo 8 223631 (4/95).

James MacMillan
British 1959

MacMillan The Confession of Isobel Gowdie. Tryst. **BBC Scottish Symphony Orchestra / Jerzy Maksymiuk.** Koch Schwann Ⓟ 310502 (54 minutes: DDD: 10/92).
Gramophone Award Winner 1993. Ⓖ
This time the publicity doesn't exaggerate. The première of *The Confession of Isobel Gowdie* at the 1990 Proms was a "spectacular triumph" – nothing less – and this with an audience drawn largely (one presumes) by Beethoven's Fourth Symphony and Sibelius's Violin Concerto. But success can fade with alarming rapidity. What matters now is that several years later, away from the uplift of that extraordinary reception, *The Confession of Isobel Gowdie* tells its story as stirringly as ever. If MacMillan's programme (the martyrdom of a Scottish Catholic 'witch') seems overpictorial, no problem; the progression from rapt modal string threnody (complete with keening *glissandos*) through mounting violence to the re-emergence and transformation of the modal lament is as easy to follow as the 'narrative' of a Mahler symphony – and the after-effect isn't all that dissimilar. Others may be bothered by undisguised echoes of other composers: Copland, Messiaen, Stravinsky, Ives, the famous single-note crescendo from Berg's *Wozzeck* ... but the fact that they are undisguised is part of their strength – that and the way they are so obviously drawn into the argument. Of course the quality of the performance matters, and Maksymiuk and his orchestra give the kind of penetrating performance which (usually) only comes from long involvement. *Tryst* also emerges well: the forces may be smaller, but the head-on confrontation of violence with calmer, more humane sounds again generates a compelling musical drama, and the ending, though less spectacular than Isobel Gowdie's final one-tone immolation, works both as an imaginative conclusion and a challenge to go back and dig deeper. Away with caution! Give this a try.
Further listening ...
...The Berserking[a]. Sowetan Spring[b]. Britannia[b]. Sinfonietta[b]. [a]**Peter Donohoe** (pf); **Royal Scottish National Orchestra / [a]Markus Stenz, [b]James MacMillan.** RCA Victor Red Seal 09026 68328-2 (7/96). *Gramophone Editor's choice.* Ⓖ
...Seven Last Words from the Cross[a]. Cantos Sagrados[b]. **Polyphony; [b]Christopher Bowers-Broadbent** (org); [a]**London Chamber Orchestra / James MacMillan.** Catalyst 09026 68125-2 (5/95). *Gramophone Editor's choice.* Ⓖ
...Veni, veni, Emmanuel[a]. After the tryst[b]. "...as others see us..."[c]. Three Dawn Rituals[c]. Untold[c]. [a]**Evelyn Glennie** (perc); [b]**Ruth Crouch** (vn); [b]**Peter Evans** (pf); [ac]**Scottish Chamber Orchestra / [a]Jukka-Pekka Saraste, [c]James MacMillan.** Catalyst 09026 61916-2 (9/93). *Gramophone Editor's choice.* Ⓖ
...Visitatio Sepulchri[a]. Búsqueda[b]. **Soloists; Scottish Chamber Orchestra / [a]Ivor Bolton, [b]James MacMillan.** Catalyst 09026 62669-2 (4/95).
... ... here in hiding ... . *Coupled with works by various composers.* **The Hilliard Ensemble.** ECM New Series 453 259-2 (1/97). *See review in the Collections section; refer to the Index.*

John McCabe
British 1939

Suggested listening ...
...Red leaves. *Coupled with works by various composers.* **Brunel Ensemble / Christopher Austin.** Cala The Edge CACD77005 (6/97). *See review in the Collections section; refer to the Index.*

Sir Paul McCartney
British 1942

McCartney Standing Stone. **London Symphony Chorus and Orchestra / Lawrence Foster.** EMI Ⓟ CDC5 56484-2 (75 minutes: DDD: 11/97). Recorded 1997.
McCartney's 'symphonic poem' has a frank, artless, experimental character that will not be to all tastes. Themes are varied and tried out in different combinations without much sense of 'development' or uniformity of style. Whatever his aspirations, he sounds most comfortable when operating within the sort of closed structural units that show off his melodic gift. His long-range thinking rarely embraces the harmonic, but there is plenty of textural variety, nicely realized by McCartney's collaborators. *Standing Stone* aspires to the cachet of through-composed entity (there are four movements) so it was sensible of EMI to provide 19 tracks which allow the uncommitted listener selective access. The first woodwind entries announce that, for good or ill, *Standing Stone* will

be more exploratory in idiom than anything in McCartney's previous output. The second section, "Cell growth", is notable for its iridescent scoring and for the fact that the music, despite oscillating in quasi-Sibelian fashion, isn't ever likely to develop beyond the amoeba stage. The third, the "'Human' theme" is more successful: a striking, grandly aspirational melody in the Bernstein/Lloyd Webber/Vangelis manner, sung by the chorus over a droning accompaniment that thickens into Hollywood schmaltz. There are more attractive melodic ideas in "Sea Voyage" (track 6) even if the treatment is overstated – a problem throughout. It is the modest sections that are most likely to impress. The "Fugal celebration" of track 16, while not exactly fugal, is more carefully wrought than is sometimes the case elsewhere. A highlight is the touching "Love duet" (track 18), not at all inflated and beautifully articulated by the LSO are on fine form throughout. In the concluding "Celebration" McCartney's Victorian hymn pulls the threads together with a certain nobility before turning (temporarily) saccharine and loud. How to sum up? It may be difficult to regard *Standing Stone* as anything other than a footnote to McCartney's 'popular' work, and one would have to stretch the definition of 'classical' music to include it. It is, perhaps unavoidably, derivative. And yet it would be as foolish to look for 'originality' here as in a (McCartney-derived) Oasis song – that is scarcely the point of either. The sound and packaging are suitably opulent.

Harl McDonald
American 1899-1955

Suggested listening ...
...San Juan Capistrano. *Coupled with works by various composers.*
Boston Symphony Orchestra / Serge Koussevitzky. Pearl mono GEMMCD9492* (12/91).
See review in the Collections section; refer to the Index. ⓖⓖⓖ

Michael McGlynn
Irish 1958

Suggested listening ...
...From Nowhere to Nowhere. *Coupled with works by various composers.*
Gerard McChrystal (sax); **London Musici / Mark Stephenson.**
Silva Classics SILKD6010 (6/96). *See review in the Collections section; refer to the Index.*

A.C. Macleod
Scottish 19th century

Suggested listening ...
...(arr. Statham) Skye Boat Song. *Coupled with works by* **Grainger** and **Molloy**
New College Choir, Oxford / Edward Higginbottom.
Erato 0630-19065-2 (3/98). *See review in the Collections section; refer to the Index.*

Guillaume de Machaut
French c1300-1377

Machaut Messe de Nostre Dame. Je ne cesse de prier (Lai "de la fonteinne"). Ma fin est mon commencement. **Hilliard Ensemble / Paul Hillier.** Hyperion ⓕ CDA66358
(54 minutes: DDD: 2/90). Texts and translations included. ⓖ
Machaut's *Messe de Nostre Dame* is the earliest known setting of the Ordinary Mass by a single composer though we cannot be certain either that Machaut wrote it at one time or even that he initially intended to bring its six movements together. Paul Hillier avoids a full reconstruction: his deference to 'authenticity' restricts itself to the usage of fourteenth-century French pronunciation of the Latin. His ensemble sing two to a part, with prominent countertenors. It is arguable whether the group sing the chant at too fast a tempo but they are smooth and flexible and the performance as a whole is fluid and light in texture. Also included are two of Machaut's French compositions. The wonderful *Lai "de la fonteinne"* is admirably sung by three tenors and is pure delight – food for the heart as well as the intellect. The more familiar *Ma fin est mon commencement,* with its retrograde canon, is a final happy addition to this admirable disc.

Additional recommendations ...
...Messe de Nostre Dame (including plainchant appropriate for the Feast of Purification of the BVM). **Ensemble Organum / Marcel Pérès.**
Harmonia Mundi ⓕ HMC90 1590 (57 minutes: DDD: 2/97).
...Hareu! hareu! le feu/Helas! ou sera pris confors. Amours me fait desirer. Trop plus est belle/Biaute paree/Je ne sui mie certeins. Se ma dame m'a guerpy. Se je souspir. Dame se vous m'estes lointeinne. Quant je sui mis. Mes esperis se combat. Ma fin est mon commencement. Douce dame jolie. De Bon Espoir/Puis que la douce rousee. De toutes flours. Quant Theseus/ Ne quier veoir. Quant j'ay l'espart. Phyton le mervilleus serpent. *Coupled with works by various composers.* **Early Music Consort of London / David Munrow.**
Virgin Veritas Edition ⓜ VER5 61284-2 (two discs: 156 minutes: ADD: 9/96).

Further listening ...
...Dame, de qui toute ma joie vient. Foy porter, honneur garder. Dame, je sui cilz/Fins cuers doulz. Tuit mi penser. Dame, mon cuer en vous temaint. Dame a qui m'ottri. Biauté qui toutes autres pere. Je vivroie liement. Rose, liz. Dame, a vous sans retollir. Amours me fait desirer. Douce dame jolie. Felix virgo/Inviolata/Ad te suspiramus. **Gothic Voices / Christopher Page.** Hyperion CDA66087 (1/84).   ⓖ

...Dame, je suis cilz/Fins cuer. Trop plus/Biauté paree/Je ne suis. Tres bonne et belle. Se mesdisans. Dame, je vueil endurer. *Coupled with works by various composers.* **Gothic Voices / Christopher Page.** Hyperion CDA66619 (6/93). *See review in the Collections section; refer to the Index.*

...Kyries I-III (arr. Kronos). *Coupled with works by various composers.* **Marja Mutru** (harmonium); **Kronos Quartet.** Nonesuch 7559-79457-2 (12/97). *Gramophone Editor's choice. See review in the Collections section; refer to the Index.*

Jarbas Maciel   Brazilian 1929

Suggested listening ...
...A Pedra do Reino. *Coupled with works by various composers.* **Quinteto da Paraíba.** Nimbus NI5483 (10/96). *See review in the Collection section; refer to the Index.*

Elizabeth Maconchy   British 1907-1994

Suggested listening ...
...Concertinos – Nos. 1 and 2. *Coupled with works by* **Arnold** and **Britten** **Thea King** (cl); **English Chamber Orchestra / Barry Wordsworth.** Hyperion CDA66634 (12/93). *See review under Arnold; refer to the Index.*

...Sun, Moon and Stars. Three Songs. *Coupled with works by various composers.* **Tracey Chadwell** (sop); **Pamela Lidiard** (pf). British Music Society BMS420/1CD (3/98). *See review in the Collections section; refer to the Index.*

Giovanni de Macque   Flemish ?1548-1614

Suggested listening ...
...Seconde Stravaganze. *Coupled with works by various composers.* **His Majestys Sagbutts and Cornetts.** Hyperion CDA66847 (11/96). *See review in the Collections section; refer to the Index.*

...Seconde stravaganze. *Coupled with works by various composers.* **Sophie Yates** (hpd). Chandos Chaconne CHAN0601 (9/97). 🖉 *See review in the Collections section; refer to the Index.*

Antônio Madureira   Brazilian

Suggested listening ...
...Toré. Aralume. Preguiça. O Guerreiro. Baque de Luanda. Toada e Dobrado da Cavalhada. *Coupled with works by various composers.* **Quinteto da Paraíba.** Nimbus NI5483 (10/96). *See review in the Collection section; refer to the Index.*

Alberic Magnard   French 1865-1914

Magnard Cello Sonata in A major, Op. 20. Piano Trio in F minor, Op. 18[a]. [a]**Régis Pasquier** (vn); **Xavier Phillips** (vc); **Hüseyin Sermet** (pf). Auvidis Valois Ⓟ V4807 (63 minutes: DDD: 2/98). Recorded 1997.

Albéric Magnard's chamber music is something of a closely guarded secret. To be sure, it isn't music that dresses up to attract the listener, but the finely integrated textures and forms, and the strong, memorable ideas, go together to create a musical experience that's quite intense. This disc is a good starting-point for exploration, coupling two works of Magnard's maturity, the grand and expansive Trio of 1904 and the more concise and concentrated Sonata of 1910. The playing has a confident, direct, unexaggerated quality that's very appealing and, in most cases, does full justice to Magnard's invention. It's particularly convincing in the faster pieces – the scherzo and finale of the Cello Sonata, and the Trio's first movement. In the Cello Sonata Xavier Phillips and Hüseyin Sermet sound a touch laboured in the finale. In the Trio, Phillips and Régis Pasquier could have made the lyrical passages more alluring. But, even if Pasquier, Phillips and Sermet haven't produced an outright winner, their performances, of considerable distinction and superior sound, make this a most welcome addition to the Magnard discography.

Alma Mahler

A. Mahler Fünf Lieder[bc]. Vier Lieder[abc]. Fünf Lieder[ac].
Zemlinsky Fünf Gesänge, Op. 7[abc]. [a]**Ruth Ziesak** (sop); [b]**Iris Vermillion** (mez);
[c]**Christian Elsner** (ten); **Cord Garben** (pf). CPO Ⓕ CPO999 455-2 (59 minutes: DDD: 1/98).
Texts and translations included. Recorded 1996.

The songs of Alma Schindler-Mahler-Werfel, as the booklet to this disc calls her, would be of interest even if they were bad. Bad they are not: her teacher Zemlinsky found "very much talent but little skill" in the compositions she showed him. He taught her skill, as these 14 songs show; they are all that survive of a once voluminous portfolio of works, virtually all of them written before, at the age of 22, she married Mahler on condition that she give up composing. He relented eventually, and she wrote two or three more songs, but seems to have composed nothing after 1916, when she was in her mid thirties. For the most part they are likeable rather than impressive, providing incidental pleasures rather than consistent ones. Her ideas themselves are often excellent but she cannot always sustain them. Her melody for Hartleben's *In my father's garden*, for example, is both a good tune and a shrewd response to the fact that each verse contains pairs of repeated phrases. But the poem does have six verses and her setting seems protracted at six minutes. Much the same is true of Falke's *Harvest Song*, but at its very end she writes a beautiful, bold melisma which is arresting. There are signs of her range expanding in the later songs, most of which call for big gestures, and she can provide them even for such difficult texts as two *Hymns* by Novalis and (perhaps her finest song) Bierbaum's *Ecstasy*. It probably seemed a good idea to couple them with Zemlinsky's Op. 7, which he dedicated to her. In their restraint and control, however, the Zemlinsky settings exemplify those qualities that Alma seldom achieved. The most moving piece in the recital is his gentle reproof to her, a setting of Jacobsen's *Irmelin Rose*: "But Princess Steel-Heart chased all her lovers away, finding some blemish [Alma had never hidden the fact that she found Zemlinsky ugly] in all of them". But we would not be listening to this recital if she had not acquired all those hyphens; even merely talented songs are fascinating from such a woman as she was. They are admirably sung and accompanied, and the recording is excellent.

Additional recommendation ...
...(orch. Colin and David Matthews)[a]: Die stille Stadt. Laue Sommernacht. Bei dir ist es traut. Licht in der Nacht. Waldeinsamkeit. Emtelied. *Coupled with* **Zemlinsky** Eine florentinische Tragödie[b]. [ab]**Iris Vermillion** (mez); [b]**Heinz Kruse** (ten); [b]**Albert Dohmen** (bar); [ab]**Royal Concertgebouw Orchestra / Riccardo Chailly.**
Decca Entartete Musik Ⓕ 455 112-2DH (71 minutes: DDD: 12/97). *Gramophone Editor's choice.*
See review under Zemlinsky; refer to the Index.

Gustav Mahler

Mahler Symphonies. [bh]**Cheryl Studer**, [c]**Jessye Norman**, [h]**Sylvia McNair**, [h]**Andrea Rost** (sops); [b]**Waltraud Meier**, [d]**Frederica von Stade**, [h]**Anne Sofie von Otter** (mezzos); [h]**Rosemarie Lang** (contr); [h]**Peter Seiffert** (ten); [h]**Bryn Terfel** (bass-bar); [h]**Jan-Hendrik Rootering** (bass); [c]**Vienna Boys' Choir**; [h]**Tölz Boys' Choir**; [b]**Arnold Schoenberg Choir**; [c]**Vienna State Opera Chorus**; [h]**Berlin Radio Chorus**; [h]**Prague Philharmonic Chorus**; [aeh]**Berlin Philharmonic Orchestra**; [bcdij]**Vienna Philharmonic Orchestra**; [fg]**Chicago Symphony Orchestra / Claudio Abbado**. DG Ⓜ 447 023-2GX12
(12 discs: 718 minutes: ADD/DDD: 12/95). Texts and translations included. Item marked [a] from 431 769-2GH (10/91), [b]439 953-2GH2 (5/94), [c]2741 010 (7/82), [d]2530 966 (6/78), [e]437 789-2GH (12/93), [f]2707 117 (11/80), [g]413 773-2GH2 (3/85), [h]445 843-2GH2 (6/95), [ij]423 564-2GH2 (8/88). Recorded 1977-94.
No. 1 in D major[a] (recorded live in 1989); No. 2 in C minor, "Resurrection"[b] (1992); No. 3 in D minor[c]; No. 4 in G major[d]; No. 5 in C sharp minor[e] (1993 – *Gramophone Editor's choice.*); No. 6 in A minor[f]; No. 7 in E minor[g]; No. 8 in E flat major, "Symphony of a Thousand"[h] (1994); No. 9 in D major[i] (1987); No. 10 in F sharp minor – Adagio[j] (1985).

The current pre-eminence of Gustav Mahler in the concert-hall and on disc is not something that could have been anticipated – other than by the composer himself. Hard now to believe that his revival had to wait until the centenary celebrations of his birth in 1960. And yet by 1980 he was more widely esteemed than his longer-lived contemporaries Sibelius and Strauss and could suddenly be seen to tower over twentieth-century music much as Beethoven must have done in a previous age. (Not that he hadn't been there all along: the music of Berg, Shostakovich, Britten and even Copland bears witness to this, disparately but resonantly Mahlerian.) By this time too, a new generation of conductors had come to the fore, further transforming our perceptions of the composer. Claudio Abbado is arguably the most distinguished of this group and, while his interpretations will not satisfy every listener on every occasion, they make an excellent choice for the library shelves, when the price is reasonably competitive and the performances so emblematic (and arguably central to our understanding) of Mahler's place in contemporary musical life.

Of the alternatives, Haitink's package has the fewest expressive distortions while Bernstein's is of course the most ceaselessly emotive of them all; neither has Abbado's particular combination of qualities. It is probably no accident that Donald Mitchell's notes for this set are focused on the nature of Mahler's 'modernity'. For it is that ironic, inquisitive, preternaturally aware young composer who haunts this conductor's performances. Not for Abbado the heavy, saturated textures of nineteenth-century romanticism, nor the chilly rigidity of some of his own 'modernist' peers. Instead an unaffected warmth and elegance of sound allows everything to come through naturally – in so far as the different venues and DG's somewhat variable technology will permit – even in the most searingly intense of climaxes. Increasingly these days, Abbado is presenting Mahler as a fluent classicist, less concerned to characterize the surface battle of conflicting emotions than to elucidate the underlying symphonic structure. The lack of Solti's brand of forthright theatricality can bring a feeling of disappointment. But even where he underplays the drama of the moment, sufficient sense of urgency is sustained by a combination of well-judged tempos, marvellously graduated dynamics and precisely balanced, ceaselessly changing textures. The propulsion comes from within. For those still put off by Mahler's supposed vulgarity the unhurried classicism of these readings may well be the most convincing demonstration of the composer's absolute integrity.

It was in November 1907 that Mahler famously told Sibelius that "the symphony must be like the world. It must embrace everything." And perhaps it is only today that we see this as a strength rather than a weakness in his music. He wrote music that is 'about' its own past while at the same time probing into all our futures, music that is so all-embracing and communicates with such directness that we can make it 'mean' whatever we want it to, confident that we alone have really understood the code. Abbado lacks Bernstein's desire to explore these limitless possibilities every time he mounts the podium, but some will count that a blessing. These are committed and authoritative performances.

Additional recommendations ...

...Nos. 1-9. No. 10 – Adagio. **Soloists; Bavarian Radio Chorus; Tölz Boys' Choir; Regensburg Cathedral Boys' Choir; Munich Motet Choir; North German Radio Chorus; West German Radio Chorus; Bavarian Radio Symphony Orchestra / Rafael Kubelík.** DG Ⓑ 429 042-2GX10 (ten discs: 651 minutes: ADD: 5/90).   ⒼⒼ

...Nos. 1-9. No. 10 – Adagio. **Soloists; Brooklyn Boys' Choir; Vienna Boys' Choir; Westminster Choir; New York Choral Artists; Vienna Singverein; Vienna State Opera Chorus; New York Philharmonic Orchestra; Royal Concertgebouw Orchestra; Vienna Philharmonic Orchestra / Leonard Bernstein.** DG Ⓜ 435 162-2GX13 (13 discs: 764 minutes: ADD/DDD: 2/92).   ⒼⒼ

...Nos. 1-9. **Soloists; Chicago Chorus and Symphony Orchestra / Sir Georg Solti.** Decca Ⓑ 430 804-2DC10 (ten discs: 672 minutes: DDD/ADD: 4/92).   Ⓖ

...Nos. 1-9. No. 10 – Adagio. **Soloists; Southend Boys's Choir; Tiffin Boys' School Choir; London Philharmonic Choir and Orchestra / Klaus Tennstedt.** EMI Mahler Edition available as follows: Nos. 1-4: Ⓜ CMS7 64471-2 (four discs: 295 minutes: ADD/DDD: 4/93). Nos. 6-8: Ⓜ CMS7 64476-2 (four discs: 254 minutes: ADD/DDD: 4/93). Nos. 5, 9 and 10 – Adagio: Ⓜ CMS7 64481-2 (189 minutes: ADD/DDD: 4/93).   Ⓖ

...Nos. 1-9. **Concertgebouw Orchestra / Bernard Haitink.** Philips Bernard Haitink Symphony Edition Ⓜ 442 050-2PB10 (ten discs: 692 minutes: ADD: 11/94).   ⒼⒼ

Mahler Symphony No. 1 in D major.
Berg (orch. Verbey) Piano Sonata, Op. 1. **Royal Concertgebouw Orchestra / Riccardo Chailly.** Decca Ⓕ 448 813-2DH (70 minutes: DDD: 1/97). Recorded 1995.
Gramophone Editor's choice.   ⒼⒼ

Chailly gives us a straightforward symphonic overview in which the more overtly programmatic elements are never allowed to threaten the work's structural integrity. Lest it be thought that this implies 'worthy but dull', two things give this performance a very special appeal: the quality of the orchestral playing and the scrupulous attention paid to phrasing and dynamics. The first movement is particularly fresh. How often do we get a genuine *ppp* from the horns before the *cantabile* melody of the cellos and the active part of the development. No doubt the two middle movements will be too emotionally reticent for some: that second movement hardly evokes a peasants' merrymaking, while the third is purged of rusticity, its more bizarre and hysterical elements reduced to a series of incidental if novel orchestral effects. And yet, where a lesser orchestra might have sounded plain, the Royal Concertgebouw imbue the music with real character. The ending goes very well, the horns correctly prominent, the all-too-common percussive thwack on the final crotchet conscientiously eschewed. Chailly's enterprising coupling is much more convincing than you might suppose and much more relevant than another *Blumine*. The recording quality is excellent.

Additional recommendations ...

...No. 1. **Berlin Philharmonic Orchestra / Bernard Haitink.** Philips Ⓕ 420 936-2PH (57 minutes: DDD: 10/88).   ⒼⒼ

...No. 1. **Royal Concertgebouw Orchestra / Leonard Bernstein.** DG Ⓕ 427 303-2GH (56 minutes: DDD: 3/89).   ⒼⒼ

...No. 1. **London Symphony Orchestra / Jascha Horenstein.** Unicorn-Kanchana Souvenir Ⓜ UKCD2012 (57 minutes: ADD: 4/89).   Ⓖ

...No. 1. **Berlin Philharmonic Orchestra / Claudio Abbado.** DG Ⓕ 431 769-2GH (55 minutes: DDD: 10/91).   ⒼⒼ

...No. 1. **Blumine. City of Birmingham Symphony Orchestra / Sir Simon Rattle.** EMI Ⓕ CDC7 54647-2 (65 minutes: DDD: 12/92).   Ⓖ

...Nos. 1ª and 2ᵇ. ᵇ**Sheila Armstrong** (sop); ᵇ**Dame Janet Baker** (mez); ᵇ**Edinburgh Festival Chorus;**
ᵃ**New York Philharmonic Orchestra,** ᵇ**London Symphony Orchestra / Leonard Bernstein.**
Sony Classical Bernstein Royal Edition Ⓜ SM2K47573 (two discs 142 minutes: ADD: 5/93).   Ⓖ
...No. 1. Blumine. **Danish National Radio Symphony Orchestra / Leif Segerstam.**
Chandos Ⓕ CHAN9242 (67 minutes: DDD: 3/94).   Ⓖ
...No. 1. Blumine. **Florida Philharmonic Orchestra / James Judd.**
Harmonia Mundi Ⓕ HMU90 7118 (66 minutes: DDD: 9/94).   Ⓖ
...No. 1. Lieder eines fahrenden Gesellenª. ª**Dietrich Fischer-Dieskau** bar);
Bavarian Radio Symphony Orchestra / Rafael Kubelík.
DG The Originals Ⓜ 449 935-2GOR (66 minutes: ADD: 2/97).   ⒼⒼⒼ

Mahler Symphony No. 2 in C minor, "Resurrection". **Arleen Auger** (sop); **Dame Janet Baker**
(mez); **City of Birmingham Symphony Chorus and Orchestra / Sir Simon Rattle.**
EMI Ⓕ CDS7 47962-8 (two discs: 86 minutes: DDD: 12/87). Text and translation included.
From EX270598-3 (10/87). *Gramophone Award Winner 1988.*   ⒼⒼⒼ
Mahler Symphony No. 2 in C minor, "Resurrection". **Cheryl Studer** (sop); **Waltraud Meier** (mez);
Arnold Schoenberg Choir; Vienna Philharmonic Orchestra / Claudio Abbado.
DG Ⓕ 439 953-2GH2 (two discs: 87 minutes: DDD: 5/94). Recorded live in the Musikverein,
Vienna in 1992. *Selected by Sounds in Retrospect.*   ⒼⒼ
The folk-poems from *Des Knaben Wunderhorn*, with their complex mixture of moods and strong
ironic edge, formed the basis of Mahler's inspiration for the Second Symphony. It is a work of huge
scope, emotionally as well as physically taxing, and from Rattle it receives a performance that
remarkably rekindles the feeling of a live performance with a quite breathtaking immediacy. The
CBSO play magnificently and Rattle's attention to the letter of the score never hinders his overall
vision of this masterpiece. The recording is superb. As has often been suggested in these pages, a live
performance should have a headstart in tapping the vital component of spiritual uplift. Abbado
presents the score directly with the maximum clarity and precision. In this he is assisted by playing of
astounding accuracy and beauty of tone, captured in a recording of (impractically?) wide dynamic
range and exquisite detail. Rattle's more radical rethink is not on the agenda; neither is his slow and
deliberate treatment of the curious staccato nose-dive at the end of the first movement. Abbado's
funeral march is relatively contained, the quiet passages very atmospheric. The deft, restrained
manner works well enough in the inner movements, especially the *Andante moderato*. He launches
into the third movement *Scherzo* with the audience restive (elsewhere they are pleasingly inaudible);
there follows charm but perhaps insufficient sense of threat. The "Urlicht" is again on the cool side,
though Waltraud Meier, beautifully controlling her legato while conscientiously projecting to a real
public in a large hall, is suddenly impassioned at "Ich bin von Gott". The massive finale, conceived
here on the very grandest scale, goes well but not quite well enough: the choir are backwardly
balanced and do not efface memories of the Philharmonia Chorus for Klemperer or the City of
Birmingham chorus for Rattle. More seriously, there are some agogic touches which impede the
natural flow. However, as a document of a great occasion, the Abbado set stands up very well indeed.
Additional recommendations ...
...**Barbara Hendricks** (sop); **Christa Ludwig** (mez); **Westminster Choir; New York Philharmonic**
Orchestra / Leonard Bernstein. DG Ⓕ 423 395-2GH2 (two discs: 94 minutes: DDD: 7/88).   ⒼⒼ
...**Elisabeth Schwarzkopf** (sop); **Hilde Rössl-Majdan** (mez); **Philharmonia Chorus and Orchestra /**
Otto Klemperer. EMI Studio Ⓜ CDM7 69662-2 (79 minutes: ADD: 1/90).   ⒼⒼⒼ
...**Sylvia McNair** (sop); **Jard van Nes** (contr); **Ernst-Senff Chorus; Berlin Philharmonic Orchestra /**
Bernard Haitink. Philips Ⓕ 438 935-2PH2 (two discs: 86 minutes: DDD: 11/94).   ⒼⒼ
...**Ruth Ziesak** (sop); **Charlotte Hellekant** (mez); **San Francisco Symphony Chorus and Orchestra /**
Herbert Blomstedt. Decca Ⓜ 443 350-2DX2 (two discs: 80 minutes: DDD: 12/94). *Selected by*
Sounds in Retrospect.   Ⓖ
...No. 2ª. **Beethoven** (arr. Mahler) String Quartet No. 11 in F minor, Op. 95, "Serioso".
ª**Tina Kilberg** (sop); ª**Kirsten Dolberg** (mez); ª**Danish National Radio Choir;**
Danish National Radio Symphony Orchestra / Leif Segerstam.
Chandos Ⓕ CHAN9266/7 (two discs: 116 minutes: DDD: 10/95).
...Nos. 2ª and 4ᵇ. ª**Carol Neblett** (sop); ᵇ**Frederica von Stade**, ª**Marilyn Horne** (mezzos);
ª**Chicago Symphony Chorus and Orchestra,** ᵇ**Vienna Philharmonic Orchestra / Claudio Abbado.**
DG Ⓜ 453 037-2GTA2 (two discs: 138 minutes: ADD: 11/96).
...**Corinne Frank** (sop); **Ann O'Malley Gallogly** (contr); **Twin City Symphony Chorus; Minneapolis**
Symphony Orchestra / Eugene Ormandy. Biddulph mono Ⓜ WHL032* (77 minutes: ADD: 7/97).

Mahler Symphony No. 3 in D minor. **Norma Procter** (contr); **Wandsworth School Boys' Choir;**
Ambrosian Singers; London Symphony Orchestra / Jascha Horenstein. Unicorn-Kanchana
Souvenir Ⓜ UKCD2006/7 (two discs: 97 minutes: ADD: 11/88). Text and translation included.
From RHS302/03 (12/70).   Ⓖ
Every now and again, along comes a Mahler *performance* that no serious collector can afford to be
without. Horenstein's interpretation of the Third Symphony is an outstanding example and its reissue
on CD at mid price is a major addition to the Mahler discography. No other conductor has surpassed
Horenstein in his total grasp of every facet of the enormous score. Even though the LSO strings of

the day were not as powerful as they later became, they play with suppleness and a really tense sound, especially appropriate in the kaleidoscopic first movement, where changes of tempo and mood reflect the ever-changing face of nature. Horenstein gives the posthorn solo to a flügelhorn, a successful experiment. His light touch in the middle movements is admirable, and Norma Procter is a steady soloist in "O Mensch! Gib acht!", with the Wandsworth School Boys' Choir bimm-bamming as if they were all Austrian-born! Then comes the *Adagio* finale, its intensity and ecstasy sustained by Horenstein without dragging. The recording is not as rich as more recent ones, but it is still a classic.

Additional recommendations ...

...No. 3[a]. Four Rückert Lieder[b]. Seven Lieder und Gesänge aus dre Jugendzeit[b]. [a]**Martha Lipton** (mez); [b]**Dietrich Fischer-Dieskau** (bar); [a]womens' chorus of the **Schola Cantorum;** [a]**Boys' Choir of the Transfiguration;** [a]**New York Philharmonic Orchestra / Leonard Bernstein** (pf[b]).
Sony Classical Ⓕ SM2K47576 (two discs: 142 minutes: ADD: 12/86).　　　　　　　　ⒺⒺ

...**Jessye Norman** (sop); **Vienna Boys' Choir; Vienna State Opera Concert Choir; Vienna Philharmonic Orchestra / Claudio Abbado.**
DG Ⓕ 410 715-2GH2 (two discs: 103 minutes: DDD: 11/88).　　　　　　　　　　ⒺⒺ

...**Christa Ludwig** (mez); **Brooklyn Boys' Chorus; New York Choral Artists; New York Philharmonic Orchestra / Leonard Bernstein.** DG Ⓕ 427 328-2GH2 (two discs: 106 minutes: DDD: 6/89).　　Ⓔ

...**Jard van Nes** (contr); **Tölz Boys' Choir; women's voices of the Ernst-Senff Choir; Berlin Philharmonic Orchestra / Bernard Haitink.**
Philips Ⓕ 432 162-2PH2 (two discs: 103 minutes: DDD: 4/92).　　　　　　　　ⒺⒺ

Mahler Symphony No. 4 in G major. **Angela Maria Blasi** (sop); **Bavarian Radio Symphony Orchestra / Sir Colin Davis.** RCA Victor Red Seal Ⓕ 09026 62521-2 (61 minutes: DDD: 7/96). Text and translation included.　　　　　　　　　　　　　　　　　　　　Ⓔ

Sir Colin Davis's Fourth is enormously enjoyable. Maybe his Mahler is too restless, too blatantly 'conducted' for some tastes, but that is at least symptomatic of a desire to communicate a personal vision of, and affection for, Mahler's score. Both playing and recording are of exceptional standard, even if the lack of ironic edge to the sound lends the music-making a somewhat old-fashioned air. Davis's scherzo is warm and characterful in a rather cumbersome sort of way, but his slow movement is a marvel – elevated in feeling and blessedly free of the intrusive inflexions which mar an otherwise refreshing account of the opening movement. No more affecting account has appeared for a decade. After this, the finale disappoints just a little. The 'operatic' soloist does not really point her words with sufficient poignancy – nor does she seem willing or able to sing quietly in her upper register – and Sir Colin again insists on playing up the composer's expressive hesitations, adding one or two of his own. This may not be wholly idiomatic Mahler and yet it has abundant humanity and an extraordinary lack of artifice. The sympathetic acoustic of the Herkulessaal, well caught, is a great asset.

Additional recommendations ...

...No. 4. **Kathleen Battle** (sop); **Vienna Philharmonic Orchestra / Lorin Maazel.**
Sony Classical Ⓕ SMK39072 (61 minutes: DDD: 3/85).　　　　　　　　　　　Ⓔ

...No. 4. Lieder eines fahrenden Gesellen. **Judith Raskin** (sop); **Cleveland Orchestra / George Szell.**
Sony Classical Essential Classics Ⓕ SBK46535 (75 minutes: ADD: 11/88).　　ⒺⒺ

...No. 4. **Helmut Wittek** (treb); **Concertgebouw Orchestra / Leonard Bernstein.**
DG Ⓕ 423 607-2GH (57 minutes: DDD: 8/88).　　　　　　　　　　　　　　ⒺⒺ

...No. 4. **Barbara Hendricks** (sop); **Los Angeles Philharmonic Orchestra / Esa-Pekka Salonen.**
Sony Classical Ⓕ SK48380 (58 minutes: DDD: 8/92).　　　　　　　　　　　Ⓔ

Mahler Symphony No. 4 in G major. **Amanda Roocroft** (sop); **City of Birmingham Symphony Orchestra / Sir Simon Rattle.** EMI Ⓕ CDC5 56563-2 (59 minutes: DDD: 6/98). Recorded 1997. *Selected by Soundings.*　　　　　　　　　　　　　　　　Ⓔ

Rattle springs two big surprises in the first four bars. The first tempo might initially strike you as *over*cautious, but check Mahler's score, and note the words: *Bedächtig – Nicht eilen* ("Cautious; prudent – don't hurry"). In keeping with the accepted view among seasoned Mahlerians that the *poco ritard* in the third bar does not apply to the sleigh bells, Rattle then effects a fleeting moment of disarray as the bells jangle roughshod over this elegant turn into the first theme. A gauche, childlike moment. But then comes the real surprise. The tempo for this charming theme-with-airs (marked *gemächlich* – "leisurely") is faster, not slower, than the opening tempo. Leisurely, yes, but eager too. The adventure playground of Mahler's youth is up and running. The benefits of this become plainer as the movement unfolds. The second subject sounds completely new (the CBSO cellos manage to persuade us that they've only just discovered it). The first horn is youth's magic horn, the woodwinds beckon raucously. And all the while those startling swings of mood and manner just happen – no rhyme, no reason; just a child's fancy. But beware the bogeyman fiddler. His dance of death – all the sharper, all the more sour (remember he's tuned up a tone) for being so flatly dispatched – comes as a timely reminder that childhood fears are no less real for being the stuff of fairy-tales. Rattle contrasts this beautifully with the rubicund Trio. The transfiguration at its heart, swathed in woozy portamento, is simply gorgeous. So, too, the opening of the slow movement, the cellos' legato so fine as to suggest little or no contact with the strings. Rattle now joins Maazel, Salonen and Sir Colin Davis as the versions of Mahler's Fourth most likely to please, to stimulate and to endure. His reading is perhaps the most inquisitive (and thus the most intriguing) of them.

Mahler Symphony No. 5 in C sharp minor. **New Philharmonia Orchestra / Sir John Barbirolli.**
EMI Ⓜ CDM7 64749-2 (74 minutes: ADD: 11/88). From ASD2518/9 (12/69). Recorded 1969.
Gramophone classical 100. ⒼⒼⒼ
Sir John Barbirolli's Fifth occupies a special place in everybody's affections: a performance so big in spirit and warm of heart as to silence any rational discussion of its shortcomings. Some readers may have problems with one or two of his sturdier tempos. He doesn't make life easy for his orchestra in the treacherous second movement, while the exultant finale, though suitably bracing, arguably needs more of a spring in its heels. But against all this, one must weigh a unity and strength of purpose, an entirely idiomatic response to instrumental colour and texture (the dark, craggy hues of the first two movements are especially striking); and most important of all that very special Barbirollian radiance, humanity – call it what you will. One point of interest for collectors – on the original LP, among minor orchestral mishaps in the *Scherzo*, were four bars of missing horn obbligato (at nine bars before fig. 20). Not any more! The original solo horn player, Nicholas Busch, has returned to the scene of this momentary aberration (Watford Town Hall) and the absent bars have been ingeniously reinstated. There's even a timely grunt from Sir John, as if in approval. Something of a classic, then, though one, it is suggested, to be regarded as a supplement, particularly in the case of first-time buyers, to the best of more recent versions (the Bernstein disc is stunning. EMI's remastering is splendid.

Additional recommendations ...
...**Vienna Philharmonic Orchestra / Leonard Bernstein.**
DG Ⓕ 423 608-2GH (75 minutes: DDD: 8/88). ⒼⒼ
...**Berlin Philharmonic Orchestra / Claudio Abbado.**
DG Ⓕ 437 789-2GH (69 minutes: DDD: 12/93). Ⓖ
...**Berlin Philharmonic Orchestra / Herbert von Karajan.**
DG The Originals Ⓜ 447 450-2GOR (74 minutes: ADD: 7/96).
...**Royal Concertgebouw Orchestra / Riccardo Chailly.**
Decca Ⓕ 458 860-2DH (72 minutes: DDD: 4/98).

Mahler Symphony No. 5 in C sharp minor. **Royal Philharmonic Orchestra / Daniele Gatti.**
Conifer Classics Ⓕ 75605 51318-2 (70 minutes: DDD: 5/98). Recorded 1997.
Gramophone Editor's choice. Ⓖ
Don't let the very opening put you off. Daniele Gatti's Mahler is an expertly prepared eruption of youthful enthusiasm, a display of heart-on-sleeve lyricism. He takes his cue from Mahler's injunction that the upbeat triplets of the trumpet theme should be played somewhat hurriedly, in the manner of military fanfares, and throughout the movement he is wont to place the material in inverted commas. In the subsequent movements, no one is likely to confuse Gatti's flexible rubato with mere mannerism. The wide dynamic range is impressive but subtlety of inflexion is the conductor's trump card. So while the second movement is an almost frantic and at times formidably loud *tour de force*, the famous *Adagietto* is uncommonly slow and sensitive. For the most part, too, Gatti coaxes a properly middle-European sound out of his wind and brass, and, if the RPO's strings cannot yet match those of Vienna, Berlin or Amsterdam, their sound is surprisingly full and rich. Indeed, the musicians sound so grandly confident that the few lapses seem worse than they are. The finale is again thrillingly extrovert, quite without heaviness. In short, this is something of a triumph for all concerned. The production team makes the very best of London's Henry Wood Hall. Above all, Gatti deserves high praise for what must be counted the freshest, most natural-sounding Fifth we have had for a long time.

Mahler Symphony No. 6 in A minor. Kindertotenlieder[a]. [a]**Thomas Hampson** (bar);
Vienna Philharmonic Orchestra / Leonard Bernstein. DG Ⓕ 427 697-2GH2
(two discs: 115 minutes: DDD: 1/90). Recorded live in 1988. ⒼⒼ
Mahler's tragic Sixth Symphony digs more profoundly into the nature of man and Fate than any of his earlier works, closing in desolation, a beat on the bass drum, a coffin lid closing. Bernstein's reading was at a concert, with all the electricity of such an occasion, and the VPO respond to the conductor's dark vision of Mahler's score with tremendous bravura. Fortunately, the achingly tender slow movement brings some relief, but with the enormous finale lasting over 30 minutes we must witness a resumption of a battle to the death. The coupling is a logical one, for the *Kindertotenlieder* takes up the theme of death yet again. But it is in a totally different, quieter way: these beautiful songs express a parent's grief over the loss of a child, and although some prefer a woman's voice, the sensitive Thomas Hampson makes a good case here for a male singer. The recording of both works is so good that one would not know it was made 'live', particularly as the applause is omitted.

Additional recommendations ...
...No. 6. Five Rückert-Lieder[a]. [a]**Hanna Schwarz** (mez); **Chicago Symphony Orchestra /
Claudio Abbado.** DG Galleria Ⓜ 423 928-2GGA2 (two discs: 104 minutes: ADD/DDD: 3/89). Ⓖ
...No. 6. **City of Birmingham Symphony Orchestra / Sir Simon Rattle.**
EMI Ⓕ CDS7 54047-2 (two discs: 86 minutes: DDD: 11/90).
...Nos. 6[a] and 8[b]. [b]**Soloists;** [b]**Leeds Festival Chorus;** [b]**London Symphony Chorus;** [b]**Orpington Junior
Singers;** [b]**Highgate School Choir;** [b]**Finchley Children's Music Group;** [a]**New York Philharmonic
Orchestra,** [b]**London Symphony Orchestra / Leonard Bernstein.** Sony Classical Bernstein Royal
Edition Ⓜ SM3K47581 (three discs: 157 minutes: ADD: 5/93). *Gramophone classical 100.* ⒼⒼⒼ

...No. 6. **Vienna Philharmonic Orchestra / Pierre Boulez.**
DG Ⓕ 445 835-2GH (79 minutes: DDD: 6/95).
...No. 6. **R. Strauss** Ein Heldenleben, Op. 40. **New Philharmonia Orchestra;**
London Symphony Orchestra / Sir John Barbirolli.
EMI Forte Ⓜ CZS5 69349-2 (two discs: 135 minutes: ADD: 10/96).

Mahler Symphonies – No. 6 in A minor[a]; No. 7 in E minor[b]. **London Philharmonic Orchestra /**
Klaus Tennstedt. EMI Ⓕ CDS5 55294-2 (three discs: 180 minutes: DDD: 9/95). Recorded live
in [a]1991 and [b]1993.

In spite of the difficulties, Klaus Tennstedt always thrived on the tensions of live performance and
this disc receives a particularly warm welcome in the wake of his retirement from the podium. They
present the conductor at his most single-minded in music that always brought out the best in him. Not
that the results will be to all tastes. This is not all-embracing, world-view Mahler. The sight-lines are
too limited for that, the outlook sometimes constrictingly bleak. Despite Tennstedt's inspirational
approach there is a lack of tonal variety and the London Philharmonic can sound penny plain for all
the dour strength of the brass. This is partly because the conductor is indifferent to the finer points
of stylization. You won't find Bernstein's flexibility and emotional range: Tennstedt's rubato, similarly
extreme, has a coarser grain and is intended neither to console nor to play up Mahler's sticky Viennese
lyricism. What Tennstedt brings to these scores is an aura of integrity and a fierce intensity of
expression finally unencumbered by the technical flaws that have sometimes detracted from his
achievement. In both works, EMI have obtained good results from the tapes given the acoustic
attributes of the venue. The Sixth is the more impressive of the two readings, executed with splenetic
zeal at broader tempos than Tennstedt at one time favoured in this music. The Seventh sounds a little
less confident. The main body of the movement has the grittily determined demeanour of the Sixth,
its second section most obviously emotive, dripping with rubato. In music so reliant on colour and
texture there isn't really enough gradation of dynamic: the more sparsely orchestrated passages sound
insufficiently hushed and the sluggish alpine reveries offer no refuge from anxious monochrome. The
rest of the performance is not uninteresting – the central *Scherzo* incisive, the second *Nachtmusik*
carefully prepared and notable for the dusky veiled tone of the strings, the vigorous finale solid rather
than crisp. And yet, in attempting to push home every nuance, Tennstedt could in the end be
destroying what it is he is trying to create, rocking the boat so much that forward momentum is lost.
If you take the Seventh to be an inherently contradictory search for an unrealized ideal of expression,
you might find Tennstedt's disruptive manner just the ticket – he never seems quite sure which way to
turn. Go elsewhere – to Bernstein above all – if you want the music to make more conventional sense.
What we have here are two expertly captured performances by a Mahlerian with a singular vision –
ungainly and uncomfortable perhaps, but for many unforgettable.

Mahler Symphony No. 7 in E minor.
Diepenbrock Im grossen Schweigen[a]. [a]**Håkan Hagegård** (bar); **Royal Concertgebouw Orchestra /**
Riccardo Chailly. Decca Ⓕ 444 446-2DH2 (two discs: 108 minutes: DDD: 5/95).
Text and translation included.   ⒼⒼ

With Rattle complete on one disc, Chailly's two-CD coupling looks ungenerous but is by no means
ill-chosen. Diepenbrock's original version of *Im grossen Schweigen* was premièred in May 1906,
making it a close contemporary of Mahler's Seventh, a composition whose 'meaning' is at least as
elusive as that of the Nietzsche prose poem set by Diepenbrock. Where some commentators hear
Mahler anatomizing a musical language on the brink of collapse, others note parallels with Strauss's
Nietzsche-inspired *Also sprach Zarathustra* in the first movement, followed thereafter by "music
embodying a romanticism that we thought had been overcome" (Bruno Walter). The raucous finale
has everyone foxed. Be it a strength or a weakness, Chailly is not one to dwell on the darker side. His
account is an opulent, positive, comfortably Straussian affair in which every detail is wonderfully
articulated by the players, mostly without the brittle edges one might think implicit in those self-
conscious stylistic allusions and precisely imagined sonorities. As for the recording, Decca have
surpassed themselves.

Additional recommendations ...
...No. 7. **Chicago Symphony Orchestra / Sir Georg Solti.**
Decca Ovation Ⓜ 425 041-2DM (78 minutes: ADD: 5/86).
...No. 7. **New York Philharmonic Orchestra / Leonard Bernstein.**
DG Ⓕ 419 211-2GH2 (two discs: 83 minutes: DDD: 12/86).   ⒼⒼ
...No. 7. **City of Birmingham Symphony Orchestra / Sir Simon Rattle.**
EMI Ⓕ CDC7 54344-2 (77 minutes: DDD: 9/92).   Ⓖ
...Nos. 7 and 9; 10 – Adagio. **New York Philharmonic Orchestra / Leonard Bernstein.**
Sony Classical Bernstein Royal Edition Ⓜ SM3K47585 (three discs: 185 minutes: ADD: 5/93).
...No. 7; No. 10 – Adagio. **Russian State Symphony Orchestra / Evgeni Svetlanov.**
CdM Russian Season Ⓕ RUS288 117/8 (two discs: 117 minutes: DDD: 3/96).

Mahler Symphony No. 8 in E flat major. **Elizabeth Connell, Edith Wiens, Felicity Lott** (sops);
Trudeliese Schmidt, Nadine Denize (contrs); **Richard Versalle** (ten); **Jorma Hynninen** (bar);
Hans Sotin (bass); **Tiffin Boys' School Choir; London Philharmonic Choir and Orchestra /**

Klaus Tennstedt. EMI Ⓕ CDS7 47625-8 (two discs: 82 minutes: DDD: 5/87). Notes, text and translation included. From EX270474-3 (3/87). Recorded 1986. *Gramophone Award Winner 1987. Selected by Sounds in Retrospect.*   ⒼⒼ

Mahler Symphony No. 8 in E flat major. **Heather Harper, Lucia Popp, Arleen Auger** (sops); **Yvonne Minton** (mez); **Helen Watts** (contr); **René Kollo** (ten); **John Shirley-Quirk** (bar); **Martti Talvela** (bass); **Vienna Boys' Choir; Vienna State Opera Chorus; Vienna Singverein; Chicago Symphony Orchestra / Sir Georg Solti.** Decca Ⓕ 448 293-2DH (80 minutes: ADD: 5/96). Text and translation included. From SET534/5 (10/72). Recorded 1971.   ⒼⒼ

Mahler's extravagantly monumental Eighth Symphony, often known as the *Symphony of a Thousand*, is the work that raises doubts in even his most devoted admirers. Its epic dimensions, staggering vision and sheer profligacy of forces required make it a 'difficult work'. Given a great live performance it will sway even the hardest of hearts; given a performance like Tennstedt's, reproduced with all the advantages of CD, home-listeners, too, can be mightily impressed (and so, given the forces involved, will most of the neighbourhood!) – the sheer volume of sound at the climax is quite overwhelming. The work seeks to parallel the Christian's faith in the power of the Holy Spirit with the redeeming power of love for mankind and Tennstedt's performance leaves no doubt that he believes totally in Mahler's creation. It has a rapt, almost intimate, quality that makes his reading all the more moving. The soloists are excellent and the choruses sing with great conviction.

Of the so-called classic accounts, it is Solti's which most conscientiously sets out to convey an impression of large forces in a big performance space, this despite the obvious resort to compression and other forms of gerrymandering. Whatever the inconsistencies of Decca's multi-miking and overdubbing, the overall effect remains powerful even today. The remastering has not eradicated all trace of distortion at the very end, despite some cautious clipping of levels and, given the impressive flood of choral tone at the start of the "Veni creator spiritus", it still seems a shame that the soloists and the Chicago brass are quite so prominent in its closing stages. As for the performance itself, Solti's extrovert way with Part 1 works tremendously without quite erasing memories of Bernstein's ecstatic fervour. In Part 2, it may be the patient Wagnerian mysticism of Tennstedt that sticks in the mind. Less inclined to delay, Solti makes the material sound more operatic. And yet for its combination of gut-wrenching theatricality and great solo singing, Solti's version makes a plausible first choice – now more than ever. Also, it has been squeezed onto a single CD, albeit at premium price.

Additional recommendations ...

...Nos. 6-8. **Soloists; Tiffin Boys' School Choir; London Philharmonic Choir and Orchestra / Klaus Tennstedt.** EMI Mahler Edition Ⓜ CMS7 64476-2 (four discs: 254 minutes: ADD/DDD: 4/93). *No. 8 is the same recording as the one reviewed above.*   ⒼⒼ

...No. 8. **Soloists; Tölz Boys' Choir; Berlin Radio Chorus; Prague Philharmonic Chorus; Berlin Philharmonic Orchestra / Claudio Abbado.** DG Ⓕ 445 843-2GH2 (two discs: 81 minutes: DDD: 6/95).   Ⓖ

...No. 8. **Soloists; Berlin Radio Chorus; Sudfunkchor, Stuttgart; Tölz Boys' Choir; Bavarian Radio Chorus and Symphony Orchestra / Sir Colin Davis.** RCA Victor Red Seal Ⓕ 09026 68348-2 (two discs: 83 minutes: DDD: 6/97).

Mahler Symphony No. 9 in D major[a]. Kindertotenlieder[b]. Five Rückert-Lieder[c]. [bc]**Christa Ludwig** (mez); **Berlin Philharmonic Orchestra / Herbert von Karajan.** DG Double Ⓜ 453 040-2GTA2 (two discs: 132 minutes: ADD: 12/96). Items marked [a] from 2707 125 (5/81), [b]2707 081 (6/75), [c]2707 082 (12/75). Recorded 1979-80. *Gramophone Award Winner 1981.*   ⒼⒼ

Mahler Symphony No. 9 in D major. **Berlin Philharmonic Orchestra / Herbert von Karajan.** DG Karajan Gold Ⓕ Ⓘ 439 024-2GHS2 (two discs: 85 minutes: DDD: 4/96). Recorded live in 1982. From 410 726-2GH2 (7/84). *Gramophone classical 100.*
Gramophone Award Winner 1984.   ⒼⒼⒼ

Mahler's Ninth is a death-haunted work, but is filled, as Bruno Walter remarked, "with a sanctified feeling of departure". Rarely has this symphony been shaped with such understanding and played with such selfless virtuosity as it was by Herbert von Karajan and the BPO in a legendary series of concerts in 1982. Karajan came late to Mahler and yet, until the release of his (rather more fiercely recorded) 1982 concert relay, he seemed content to regard this studio performance as perhaps his finest achievement on disc. The attractions of earlier recording are greatly enhanced by Christa Ludwig's carefully considered Mahler performances of the mid-1970s. The voice may not be as fresh as it was when she recorded the songs in the late-1950s, but there are few readings of comparable nobility. Dame Janet Baker and Brigitte Fassbaender are perhaps more responsive to the mood of each song, the one intimate, almost self-communing, the other more bitingly dramatic. Nevertheless, Ludwig articulates the text with unrivalled clarity and "In diesem Wetter" at least is positively operatic. How much of the grand scale should be attributed to Karajan? It is difficult to say; the voice *is* sometimes strained by the tempos. Despite the absence of texts, this collection is not to be missed. One-disc Ninths are not exactly commonplace but, with both Walter's celebrated 1938 recording and Barbirolli's 1964 Berlin version also in the running, the field is not short of distinguished contenders.

Choice between the 1982 Karajan classic and the analogue studio recording is by no means easy. Both versions won *Gramophone* Awards in their day, but, whereas the low-profile, low-price reissue of the analogue LP has Christa Ludwig's magisterial *Kindertotenlieder* and *Rückert-Lieder*, this live account preserves the look and price bracket of the original package. There is no extra music. The performance remains a remarkable one, the thrills and spills of the (subsequently unearthed) Bernstein concert relay of 1979 replaced by a commitment to lucidity of sound and certainty of line. There is nothing dispassionate about the way the Berlin Philharmonic tear into the *Rondo-Burleske*, the agogic touches of the analogue version ironed out without loss of intensity. True, Karajan does not seek to emulate the passionate immediacy of a Barbirolli or Bernstein, but in his broadly conceived, gloriously played *Adagio* the sepulchral hush is for once as memorable as the eruptive climax. The finesse of the playing is of course unmatched. For this Karajan Gold reissue, the tapes have been picked over in order to open up the sound and do something about the early-digital edginess of the strings. There is still some occlusion at climactic points; and if those strings now seem more 'plasticky' than fierce, it is impossible to say whether the conductor would have approved.

Additional recommendations ...

...No. 9. **Berlin Philharmonic Orchestra / Sir John Barbirolli.**
   EMI Studio Ⓜ CDM7 63115-2 (78 minutes: ADD: 11/89).   Ⓖ
...No. 9ᵃ· **Wagner** Siegfried Idyllᵇ. ᵃ**New Philharmonia Orchestra; ᵇPhilharmonia Orchestra /
   Otto Klemperer.** EMI Studio Ⓜ CMS7 63277-2 (two discs: 105 minutes: ADD: 1/90).
...No. 9. **Berlin Philharmonic Orchestra / Leonard Bernstein.**
   DG Ⓕ 435 378-2GH2 (two discs: 82 minutes: ADD: 5/92).
...No. 9. **Chicago Symphony Orchestra / Carlo Maria Giulini.**
   DG Double Ⓜ 437 467-2GX2 (two discs: 88 minutes: ADD: 12/94).
...No. 9. **Philharmonia Orchestra / Giuseppe Sinopoli.**
   DG Ⓕ 445 817-2GH2 (two discs: 83 minutes: DDD: 3/95).

Mahler Symphony No. 9 in D major. **Vienna Philharmonic Orchestra / Bruno Walter.**
Dutton Laboratories Essential Archive mono Ⓑ CDEA5005* (70 minutes: ADD: 8/96).
Recorded live in 1938. From HMV DB3613/22 (1/39).   ⒼⒼⒼ
Of course, there is no such thing as a 'definitive' performance but this is as near as one can get to it. Bruno Walter conducted the first performance of the Ninth Symphony in 1912 (it is dedicated to him) as well as this, its first commercial recording. It bestrode no fewer than ten 78rpm discs and consumed many fibre needles! Although later performances (including Walter's) have offered more polished orchestral playing and more vivid recording, none brings one closer to its world of feeling or takes one more deeply into its spirit. For all its blemishes, it has a unique authority and atmosphere. Its fires are white-hot and there is a blazing intensity that has never been surpassed on the gramophone. There is a demonic passion to the *Rondo-Burlesque* (the orchestra play as if their corporate life is at stake) and the final *Adagio* has a poignancy that once heard is not easily forgotten. Even younger readers unencumbered by nostalgia will recognize the authenticity of feeling here, and everyone who cares about Mahler is urged to listen to it. Although this has appeared in various manifestations (this is the same performance as the EMI Références set listed below), the superiority in every respect of the present transfer is in no doubt. The image is better defined and has both body and presence.

Additional recommendation ...

...No. 9. **Vienna Philharmonic Orchestra / Bruno Walter.**
   EMI Références mono Ⓜ CDH7 63029-2* (70 minutes: ADD: 8/89). *Gramophone Award
   Winner 1989. This is the same recording as the one reviewed above.*   ⒼⒼⒼ

Mahler (ed. Cooke) Symphony No. 10 in F sharp minor. **Bournemouth Symphony Orchestra /
Sir Simon Rattle.** EMI Ⓕ CDC7 54406-2 (76 minutes: DDD: 5/92). From HMV SLS5206
(12/80).   ⒼⒼ
Rattle's superb interpretation of Cooke's performing version of the Tenth Symphony now sweeps the board. His achievement is in a special class, empowering the music with such emotional clout that you forget the scholarly debates. There are in fact several adjustments to Schirmer's published score which Rattle explained in the splendid booklet which accompanied the original LP issue. Unfortunately, this has not been included with this CD reissue. One example of his innovatory approach is his merging of the drum stroke which ends the fourth movement with the one which triggers the fifth; furthermore the opening pages of the finale are truly awesome here. Tempos are unfailingly appropriate and the orchestra are second to none. With excellent sound this is altogether an essential purchase.

Additional recommendations ...

...(ed. Cooke). **Schoenberg** Verklärte Nacht, Op. 4. **Berlin Radio Symphony Orchestra /
   Riccardo Chailly.** Decca Ⓕ 444 872-2DX2 (two discs: 110 minutes: DDD: 3/88).   Ⓖ
...(recons. R. Mazzetti Jnr). **St Louis Symphony Orchestra / Leonard Slatkin.**
   RCA Victor Red Seal Ⓕ 09026 68190-2 (75 minutes: DDD: 4/96).

Mahler Das Lied von der Erde. **Kathleen Ferrier** (contr) **Julius Patzak** (ten) **Vienna Philharmonic
Orchestra / Bruno Walter.** Decca Ⓕ 414 194-2DH* (ADD: 1/85). From LXT2721/2 (10/52).
Recorded 1952. *Gramophone classical 100.*   ⒼⒼⒼ
Mahler (trans. Schoenberg and Riehn) Das Lied von der Erde. **Monica Groop** (mez); **Jorma Silvasti**
(ten); **Lahti Chamber Ensemble / Osmo Vänskä.** BIS Ⓕ CD681 (61 minutes: DDD: 7/95).
Texts and translations included. Recorded 1994.   ⒼⒼ
"A finer performance than this would not be a song of earth", wrote the *Record Guide* (Collins, 1955) of Decca's legendary performance. The authors also added, "and the recording is excellent", a view

which LP collectors might not have subsequently endorsed but which this altogether superb, historically important transfer to CD in some measure approves. High tessitura string and vocal contributions are occasionally somewhat shrill and lacking in body when set alongside modern recordings but, astonishingly, one might be in the hall with the VPO and these remarkable artists. If what we hear on this transfer from the master tapes in the fifth song is significantly different from what Bruno Walter heard as tenor, solo violin and flute raptly commune, it would be surprising. Equally astounding is the way the transferred recording conveys the sheer weight and body of the Vienna Philharmonic's tone. How easily can we now appreciate the passion, drive, and guile of Walter's conducting, with its subtle colourings and many barely perceptible rubatos. The opening song is especially thrilling, with Patzak quite persuasively 'there' in the musical picture. The post-war VPO winds, the oboe especially, may strike some as curiously nasal. Yet it is the very complexity and idiosyncrasy of the orchestral timbres which help give this reading its special interest. No one has conducted or played the elusive third movement better than this; the pace is ideal, and Patzak, though no longer in his prime, outpoints every rival except possibly Wunderlich on the Klemperer recording. And beyond this there is Ferrier, an artist born to sing this music and singing it here at a time so close to her own death as to make this a real, truly harrowing song of farewell.

Osmo Vänskä's reading is nothing short of superb in every respect. A recording of demonstration quality, it lets us hear every strand of the translucent scoring; its range and focus are quite remarkable and the balance ideal. All this displays Vänskä's dedicated interpretation and the finely chiselled playing of his ensemble to the greatest advantage. The Swedish team are superior even to Herreweghe's excellent group, each individual executing his or her part with the utmost refinement and sensibility. Vänskä takes an even brisker view of tempo than Herreweghe, and the work, especially the final movement, is all the more cohesive and forward-moving as a result, avoiding any hint of sentimentality; nor can one imagine the third movement sounding more effervescent or the fourth more heady. The soloists just about surpass the achievements of their counterparts for Herreweghe. Silvasti has the ideal tenor for this version of the work: it has a silvery sheen yet with a touch of metal in it. As long as you don't mind the occasional use of a fast vibrato, Silvasti is sure to please because he has the words and the music at his command, projecting everything with great aplomb. Groop, better known than her tenor colleague, further enhances her growing reputation with an impassioned performance of the alto's songs, quite a match for the also excellent Remmert (Herreweghe), and perhaps just that bit richer in timbre. She rises magnificently to all the challenges of the "Abschied", declaiming with extraordinary Baker-like urgency.

Additional recommendations ...

...**Dame Janet Baker** (mez); **James King** (ten); **Royal Concertgebouw Orchestra / Bernard Haitink.**
Philips Silver Line ⓜ 432 279-2PSL (66 minutes: ADD).   ⓖ
...**Brigitte Fassbaender** (mez); **Francisco Araiza** (ten); **Berlin Philharmonic Orchestra /**
Carlo Maria Giulini. DG ⓕ 413 459-2GH (DDD: 10/84).
...**Christa Ludwig** (mez); **Fritz Wunderlich** (ten); **Philharmonia Orchestra; New Philharmonia**
Orchestra / Otto Klemperer. EMI ⓕ CDC7 47231-2 (64 minutes: ADD: 12/85).   ⓖ
...**Christa Ludwig** (mez); **René Kollo** (ten); **Berlin Philharmonic Orchestra / Herbert von Karajan.**
DG Galleria ⓜ 419 058-2GGA (66 minutes: ADD: 4/88).
...**Maureen Forrester** (contr); **Richard Lewis** (ten); **Chicago Symphony Orchestra / Fritz Reiner.**
RCA Victor Gold Seal ⓜ GD60178 (63 minutes: ADD: 10/91).   ⓖⓖ
...**Agnes Baltsa** (mez); **Klaus König** (ten); **London Philharmonic Orchestra / Klaus Tennstedt.**
EMI ⓕ CDC7 54603-2 (67 minutes: DDD: 2/93).
...(trans. Schoenberg and Riehn) **Birgit Remmert** (contr); **Hans Peter Blochwitz** (ten);
Ensemble Musique Oblique / Philippe Herreweghe.
Harmonia Mundi ⓕ HMC90 1477 (63 minutes: DDD: 12/94).   ⓖ
...**Ruxandra Donose** (mez); **Thomas Harper** (ten); **National Symphony Orchestra of Ireland /**
Michael Halász. Naxos ⓢ 8 550933 (59 minutes: DDD: 11/95).
...Das Lied von der Erde[a]. Rückert Lieder – No. 1 (sung in English)[b]; No. 4[c]. Symphony No. 5 –
Adagietto[d]. [ac]**Kirsten Thorborg** (mez); [ab]**Charles Kullman** (ten); [acd]**Vienna Philharmonic Orchestra**
/ Bruno Walter; [b]**orchestra / Sir Malcolm Sargent.**
Dutton Laboratoires Essential Archive mono ⓑ CDEA5014* (74 minutes: ADD: 8/97).
...Das Lied von der Erde[a]. Lieder eines fahrenden Gesellen[b]. Kindertotenlieder[c]. Rückert-Lieder[d].
Lieder aus "Des Knaben Wunderhorn"[e] – Wer hat dies Liedlein erdacht?; Des Antonius von
Padua Fischpredigt; Wo die schönen Trompeten blasen; Revelge; Der Tamboursg'sell.
[a]**Murray Dickie** (ten); [a]**Dietrich Fischer-Dieskau** (bar); [bcd]**Dame Janet Baker** (mez);
[e]**Lucia Popp** (sop); [e]**Bernd Weikl** (bar); [ad]**Philharmonia Orchestra;** [bc]**Hallé Orchestra;**
[e]**London Philharmonic Orchestra /** [a]**Paul Kletzki,** [bcd]**Sir John Barbirolli,** [e]**Klaus Tennstedt.**
EMI ⓜ CZS5 69665-2 (two discs: 154 minutes: ADD: 2/98).

Mahler Lieder aus "Des Knaben Wunderhorn". **Jard van Nes** (contr); **John Bröcheler** (bass);
Arnhem Philharmonic Orchestra / Roberto Benzi. Ottavo ⓕ OTRC79238
(55 minutes: DDD: 2/94). Texts included. Recorded 1992.
Jard van Nes is a natural for Mahler, both from the vocal and interpretative point of view. Particularly admirable is the fresh, spontaneous way in which she approaches her contributions, free from both the long shadow of past performance or awe before such familiar songs. She catches ideally the folk-

like charm of "Rheinlegendchen" and "Wer hat dies Liedlein erdacht?". She is also appropriately earthy in "Das irdische Leben", then marvellously tender as the distant lover in "Des Schildwache Nachtlied". Her unadorned mastery of word and tone cannot be praised too highly – listen to the *keck* delivery of "Verlor'ne Muh": just right – and she crowns her performance with her grave utterance in "Urlicht". Bröcheler is among the best, characterizing "Lob des hohen Verstandes" with enthusiastic vivacity and revelling in St Antony's sermon. Benzi and his orchestra never make the mistake of some more noted performers of over-egging the pudding. Although the detail is all clearly projected and keenly played, in a perfectly balanced recording, the music is kept on the move.

Additional recommendations ...

...**Dame Elisabeth Schwarzkopf** (sop); **Dietrich Fischer-Dieskau** (bar); **London Symphony Orchestra /**
  George Szell. EMI Ⓕ CDC7 47277-2 (48 minutes: ADD: 11/88).   Ⓖ
...No. 2, Verlorne Müh; No. 7, Rheinlegendchen; No. 9, Wo die schönen Trompeten blasen; No. 10,
  Lob des hohen Verstands. Lieder und Gesang – No. 1, Frühlingsmorgen. No. 2, Erinnerung.
  No. 4, Serenade aus Don Juan. No. 5, Phantasie aus Don Juan No. 7, Ich ging mit Lust durch
  einen grünen Wald. No. 8, Aus! Aus!. *Coupled with works by* **Wolf Anne Sofie von Otter** (mez);
  Ralf Gothóni (pf). DG Ⓕ 423 666-2GH (59 minutes: DDD: 6/89).
...Excerpts[a] – Das irdische Leben; Des Antonius von Padua Fischpredigt. **Bruckner** Symphony
  No. 7 in E major[b]. [a]**Brigitte Fassbaender** (mez); [a]**Deutsches Symphony Orchestra, Berlin,**
  [b]**Berlin Radio Symphony Orchestra / Riccardo Chailly.**
  Decca Eclipse Ⓑ 448 710-2DEC (76 minutes: DDD: 8/96).   Ⓖ

Mahler Das klagende Lied (complete version including "Waldmärchen"). **Susan Dunn** (sop);
  Markus Baur (alto); **Brigitte Fassbaender** (mez); **Werner Hollweg** (ten); **Andreas Schmidt** (bar);
  Städtischer Musikverein Düsseldorf; Berlin Radio Symphony Orchestra / Riccardo Chailly.
  Decca Ⓕ 425 719-2DH (64 minutes: DDD: 2/92). Text and translation included.
  Recorded 1989.   ⒼⒼ
Even the musically acute listener would be unlikely to realize that *Das klagende Lied* is the work of a teenager. Mahler's first significant work is as self-assured as anything he was to write in later life. Indeed enthusiastic Mahlerians will recognize here passages which crop up in other works, most notably the Second Symphony. Those same enthusiastic Mahlerians might not recognize much of this recording, however, since only two movements of *Klagende Lied* are usually performed: the 30-minute first movement is considered too rambling. But no one could possibly arrive at that conclusion from this tautly directly, electrifying performance, and it contains some wonderfully imaginative music, including some delightful forest murmurs, which it seems tragic to miss out. For this movement alone this CD is a must for any Mahler fan, but more than that this is a spectacular recording of a one-in-a-million performance. The soloists, choir and orchestra achieve near perfection under Chailly's inspired direction, and the decision to substitute for the marvellous Brigitte Fassbaender a boy alto (Markus Baur) to represent the disembodied voice of the dead brother is a stroke of pure genius. His weird, unnatural voice provides a moment of sheer spine-tingling drama.

Additional recommendations ...

...**Soloists; Bath Festival Chorus; Waynflete Singers; Bournemouth Symphony Orchestra /**
  Richard Hickox. Chandos Ⓕ CHAN9247 (71 minutes: DDD: 5/94).
...**Soloists; San Francisco Symphony Chorus and Orchestra / Michael Tilson Thomas.**
  RCA Victor Red Seal Ⓕ 09026 68599-2 (67 minutes: DDD: 9/97).

Mahler Kindertotenlieder[a]. Rückert-Lieder[b]. Lieder eines fahrenden Gesellen[a]. **Dame Janet Baker**
  (mez); [a]**Hallé Orchestra;** [b]**New Philharmonia Orchestra / Sir John Barbirolli.**
  EMI Ⓕ CDC7 47793-2 (65 minutes: ADD: 12/87). Texts and translations included.
  Items marked [a] from ASD2338 (2/68), [b]ASD2518/19 (12/69).   ⒼⒼⒼ
Mahler Kindertotenlieder. Rückert-Lieder. Lieder eines fahrenden Gesellen. Lieder aus Des
  Knaben Wunderhorn – Das irdische Leben; Des Antonius von Padua Fischpredigt; Urlicht.
  Brigitte Fassbaender (mez); **Deutsches Symphony Orchestra, Berlin / Riccardo Chailly.**
  Decca Ⓕ 425 790-2DH (71 minutes: DDD: 4/94). Texts and translations included.
  Recorded 1988-89.   Ⓖ
The songs of the *Lieder eines fahrenden Gesellen* ("Songs of a Wayfarer") are directly quoted from Mahler's First Symphony and the same fresh, springtime atmosphere is shared by both works. The orchestration has great textural clarity and lightness of touch. The *Kindertotenlieder*, more chromatically expressive than the earlier work, tap into a darker, more psychologically complex vein in Mahler's spiritual and emotional make-up. The *Rückert-Lieder* are not a song-cycle as such but gather in their romantic awareness and response to the beauties of the poetry a unity and shape that acts to bind them. Together, Baker and Barbirolli reach a transcendental awareness of Mahler's inner musings. Barbirolli draws from the Hallé playing of great delicacy and precision and establishes a clear case for having this CD in your collection.

  Fassbaender's emotionally charged way of singing is ideally matched to Mahler yet she is just as able to smile and sing gently, wittily. It is the dramatic declamation, however, that the true flavour of her singing is caught. Throughout the *Fahrenden Gesellen* it is the immediacy, fearlessness of attack and her particular intensity, that makes these readings so arresting. The swiftish speeds throughout ensure that sentimentality is kept at bay; so does Chailly's and the orchestra's biting precision and light touch. Similar characteristics inform a deeply eloquent interpretation of *Kindertotenlieder*. Right from the start the world-weary tone and verbal illumination in the first song catch at the heart and suggest palpably the sense of personal responsibility for the children's deaths on the part of the protagonist. Baker/Barbirolli, with the singer in lovely voice, must be a 'safer' recommendation than the more daring Fassbaender, but the latter is an inviting proposition – and a searing experience.

Additional recommendations ...

...Lieder eines fahrenden Gesellen[a]. Kindertotenlieder[b]. Rückert-Lieder[b]. **Dietrich Fischer-Dieskau** (bar); [a]**Bavarian Radio Symphony Orchestra / Rafael Kubelík;** [b]**Berlin Philharmonic Orchestra / Karl Böhm.** DG Ⓕ 415 191-2GH (60 minutes: ADD: 9/85).

...Lieder eines fahrenden Gesellen. Lieder und Gesange. Im Lenz (1880). Winterlied (1880). **Dame Janet Baker** (mez); **Geoffrey Parsons** (pf). Hyperion Ⓕ CDA66100 (58 minutes: DDD: 4/87). Ⓖ

...**Catherine Robbin** (mez); **Kitchener-Waterloo Symphony Orchestra / Raffi Armenian.** CBC Records Ⓕ SMCD5098 (55 minutes: DDD: 5/92).

...**Das Lied von der Erde**[a]. Lieder eines fahrenden Gesellen[b]. Kindertotenlieder[b]. Rückert-Lieder[c]. Lieder aus Des Knaben Wunderhorn – Wer hat dies Liedlein erdacht?[d]; Des Antonius von Padua Fischpredigt[e]; Wo die schönen Trompeten blasen[d]; Revelge[e]; Der Tambourg'sell[e]. [d]**Lucia Popp** (sop); [bc]**Dame Janet Baker** (mez); [a]**Murray Dickie** (ten); [a]**Dietrich Fischer-Dieskau,** [e]**Bernd Weikl** (bars); [a]**Philharmonia Orchestra / Paul Kletzki;** [b]**Hallé Orchestra;** [c]**New Philharmonic Orchestra / Sir John Barbirolli;** [de]**London Philharmonic Orchestra / Klaus Tennstedt.** EMI Rouge et NoirⓂ CZS7 62707-2 (two discs: 155 minutes: ADD/DDD: 8/92).

...**Andreas Schmidt** (bar); **Cincinnati Symphony Orchestra / Jésus López-Cobos.** Telarc Ⓕ CD80269 (56 minutes: DDD: 5/93).

...Lieder eines fahrenden Gesellen. Im Lenz. Winterlied[a]. Maitanz im Grünen. Lieder und Gesänge[a] – Serenade aus Don Juan; Aus! Aus!' Starke Einbildungskraft; Selbstgefühl. Lieder und Gesänge[a] – Erinnerung; Um schlimme Kinder artig zu machen; Zu Strassburg auf der Schanz; Ablösung im sommer; Nicht wiedersehen!. Lieder und Gesänge (orch. Berio)[b] – Frühlingsmorgen; Erinnerung; Hans und Grethe; Phantasie aus Don Juan; Ich ging mit Lust durch einen grünedn Wald; Scheiden und Meiden. **Thomas Hampson** (bar); [a]**David Lutz** (pf); [b]**Philharmonia Orchestra / Luciano Berio.** Teldec Ⓕ 9031-74002-2 (68 minutes: DDD: 8/94).

...Lieder eines fahrenden Gesellen. Rückert-Lieder. **Zemlinsky** Sechs Gesänge, Op. 13. **Anne Sofie von Otter** (mez); **North German Radio Symphony Orchestra / Sir John Eliot Gardiner.** DG Ⓕ 439 928-2GH (56 minutes: DDD: 3/97). *Gramophone Editor's choice. See review under Zemlinsky; refer to the Index.* Ⓖ

Further listening ...

...Quartet in A minor. *Coupled with works by various composers.* **Gidon Kremer** (vn); **Veronika Hagen** (va); **Clemens Hagen** (vc); **Oleg Maisenberg** (pf). DG 447 112-2GH (4/96). *See review in the Collections section; refer to the Index.*

...Lieder und Gesänge – No. 1, Frühlingsmorgen; No. 2, Erinnerung; No. 3, Hans und Gretche; No. 6, Um schlimme Kinder artig zu machen; No. 7, Ich ging mit Lust durch einen grünen Wald; No. 9, Starke Einbildungskraft; No. 11, Ablösung im Sommer; No. 12, Scheiden und Meiden; No. 13, Nicht wiedersehen!. *Coupled with songs by* **Brahms** Lucia Popp (sop); **Geoffrey Parsons** (pf). Arts Music 47367-2 (A/97). *See review under Brahms; refer to the Index.*

Guillaume Malbecque   French c1400-1465

Suggested listening ...

...Adieu vous di, mes seigneurs et amis. Quant de la belle me parti. Dieu vous doinst bon jour. *Coupled with works by various composers.* **Hilliard Ensemble.** Isis CD030 (7/97). *See review in the Collections section; refer to the Index.*

Albert Malotte   American 1895-1964

Suggested listening ...

...The Lord's Prayer. *Coupled with works by various composers.* **Lesley Garrett** (sop); **Britten Sinfonia / Ivor Bolton.** Conifer Classics 75605 51329-2 (12/97). *See review in the Collections section; refer to the Index.*

Pierre de Manchicourt   French c1510-1564

Manchicourt Missa Veni Sancte Spiritus. Chansons – Long temps mon cueur languissoit; Faulte dargent cest douleur non pareille; O cruaulté logée en grand beaulté. Reges terrae. O virgo virginum. Maria Magdalene. Usquequo piger dormies. **Huelgas Ensemble / Paul van Nevel.** Sony Classical Vivarte Ⓕ SK62694 (63 minutes: DDD: 1/98). Texts and translations included. Recorded 1996.

Paul van Nevel has a rare gift of nosing out little-recorded composers, and convincing you that the neglect is wholly undeserved. Here he brings us Pierre de Manchicourt, a Franco-Flemish composer working (like Nicolas Gombert, whose works van Nevel has also recorded – see the listing under Gombert) in the Hapsburg orbit during the mid-sixteenth century. Like Gombert, he favours thick textures (six voices being the norm) in which all the parts are active most of the time. His imitative practice is slightly less restrictive than Gombert's, and his melodic lines are more florid. Van Nevel himself calls them "flamboyant", and links Manchicourt's style with late gothic architecture. Within a highly circumscribed idiom, Manchicourt negotiates the differing demands of Mass, motet and chanson most skilfully. The three songs recorded here are particularly lovely, and there are real finds among the motets: *Usquequo piger dormies* sets a weird biblical text exhorting layabouts to take example from the industrious ant. As for the disc's centrepiece, the Mass, *Veni Sancte Spiritus*, it is a superb example of late Franco-Flemish handiwork at its most involving. The performances represent the Huelgas Ensemble at their most beguiling, with fewer eccentricities than they sometimes exhibit, and they are beautifully captured by Sony's engineering team.

Further listening ...
...Laudate Dominum. *Coupled with works by various composers.* **Huelgas Ensemble / Paul van Nevel.** Sony Classical Vivarte SK66261 (4/96). *See review in the Collections section; refer to the Index.*

Francesco Mancini Italian 1672-1737

Suggested listening ...
...Sonata for Recorder, two Violins and Continuo in D minor. *Coupled with works by various composers.* **Giardino Armonico / Giovanni Antonini** (rec). Teldec Das Alte Werk 4509-93157-2 (11/94). *See review in the Collections section; refer to the Index.*   **ⒼⒼ**

Giovanni de Maque Italian 1550-1614

Suggested listening ...
...Due Gagliarde. Seconde Stravaganze. *Coupled with works by various composers.* **Rinaldo Alessandrini** (hpd). Opus 111 OPS30-118 (4/95). *See review in the Collections section; refer to the Index.*   **ⒼⒼ**

Dumisani Maraire Rhodesian 1943

Suggested listening ...
...Mai Nozipo. *Coupled with works by various composers.* **Dumisani Maraire** (ngoma/hosho); **Astor Piazzolla** (bandoneon); **Patty Manning, John Taylor, Larry Caballero** (vocs); **Djivan Gasparian** (duduk); **Kronos Quartet.** Nonesuch 7559-79394-2 (2/96). *See review in the Collections section; refer to the Index.*

Marin Marais French 1656-1728

Marais La gamme et autres morceaux de simphonies – la gamme en forme d'un petit opéra; Sonata à la marésienne. **London Baroque / Charles Medlam.** Harmonia Mundi Musique d'abord Ⓑ HMX290 1105: 47 minutes: DDD: 9/97). *Recorded 1983.*
The attention of the wider public was drawn to the music of Marais by the enthralling French film (*Tous les matins du monde*) about this virtuoso viola da gamba player/composer's relationship with his mentor, Sainte-Colombe, who is portrayed as a recluse, in contrast with his more flamboyant pupil. This reissue in Harmonia Mundi's bargain Musique d'abord series gives us an inviting entry into Marais's sound world. The main work is *La gamme*, of which the full translated title is "The scale in the form of a little opera". It was described by a contemporary as "a *pièce de symphonie* that imperceptibly ascends the steps of the octave; one then descends, thereby going through harmonious songs and melodious tones, the various sounds of music". The scoring makes the most of a trio sonata group of violin, a pair of violas da gamba and harpsichord continuo, with plenty of opportunities for soloists to shine with the solo line or obbligatos. The music introduces the scalic pattern in lively and expressive, even humorous fashion, and then in a continuous sequence centres on each note in turn. The performance by Charles Medlam and London Baroque is first-rate and the recording is smooth, well detailed, but without the abrasive edge that accompanies some recordings featuring gambas.

Marais Alcyone – Suites. **Le Concert des Nations / Jordi Savall.** Auvidis Astrée Ⓔ E8525 (53 minutes: DDD: 2/95). *Recorded 1993.*   **Ⓖ**
As one of the greatest exponents of the solo viol tradition perfected by Marais, Savall focuses his insights upon this music and interprets the scoring as Marais might have done. He experiments with

all the chamber-music combinations of the day and, typically, hazards some of his own, particularly in the Chaconne. Occasionally, Savall uses winds and occasionally miscalculates his effects, as in the "Bourrée pour les Bergers et Bergères". His command of Maraisian ornamentation is, however, everywhere evident and indeed very welcome because of the constant melodic echoes of the solo repertoire in the opera score. With chamber music come more transparent textures, revealing the harmonic and textural richness of the post-Lullian style; cross-rhythms, syncopations and sequences have more impact. By contrast, the opera performances can often sound sluggish and four-square. Savall also includes music that was left out of the opera recording, including the delicately syncopated "Air pour les Faunes et les Driades" from the Prologue, the exquisitely scored Sarabande, with its beautifully shaded cadences, and the Gigue from Act 1 as well as the "Sarabande pour les Prêtresses de Junon" from Act 2. In the Prologue and the March and Air "pour les Matelots" in Act 3, Savall orchestrates passages that were once vocal solos to maintain the proportions of the movements.

Marais Pièces de viole, Première livre. **Philippe Pierlot** (va da gamba); **Ricercar Consort.**
  Ricercar Ⓜ 205842 (three discs: 223 minutes: DDD: 4/98). ✍
This is the first instalment of a projected series, to include all of Marais's music for viols. It is music of exquisite refinement, dream-like and reserved, with just those qualities of interpretation from Philippe Pierlot and the Ricercar Consort. Some of the livelier pieces might have been treated more robustly; here, little disturbs the placid surface, but it is ravishing playing for all that. There are nine suites in all, and two occasional pieces (not to be taken in at one sitting, preferably, but savoured individually). This three-CD set (for the price of two) offers excellent value.
Further listening ...
...Pièces en Trio – Suites: B flat major; C minor; E minor. Suite d'un goût étranger – La rêveuse; Le badinage. **Ensemble Fitzwilliam.** Auvidis Valois V4638 (11/92).
...Pièces de viole, Deuxième livre – Tombeau pour Monsieur de Lully; Tombeau de Monsieur de Sainte-Colombe. *Coupled with works by various composers.* **Mauricio Buraglia** (theorbo); **Nima Ben David** (va da gamba); **Pierre Trocellier** (hpd/org). Auvidis Astrée E8592 (12/96). ✍
Gramophone Editor's choice. *See review under Lalande; refer to the Index.*   Ⓖ
...Pièces de Viole, Troisième Livre – Suites: E minor; D major; G major. **Jordi Savall** (va da gamba); **Hopkinson Smith** (theorbo); **Ton Koopman** (hpd). Auvidis Astrée E8761 (12/92). ✍   Ⓖ
...Pièces de Viole, Quatrième Livre: Suite d'un goût étranger – Marche Tartare; La Tartarine and Double; Les festes champêtre; Le toubillon; Le labyrinthe; L'arabesque; Allemande la superbe; La rêveuse; Marche; Gigue; Le badinage. **Jordi Savall** (va da gamba); **Ton Koopman** (hpd); **Hopkinson Smith** (baroque gtr; theorbo). Auvidis Astrée E7727 (9/88). ✍   Ⓖ
...Pièces de Viole, Cinquième Livre – Suites: G minor; E minor/major. Le tableau de l'opération de la taille. Le tombeau pour Marais le cadet. **Jordi Savall** (bass viol); **Hopkinson Smith** (theorbo); **Ton Koopman** (hpd) with **Jean-Michael Damian** (spkr). Auvidis Astrée E7708 (2/88). ✍   Ⓖ

Alessandro Marcello   Italian 1684-1750

Suggested listening ...
...Oboe Concerto in D minor. *Coupled with works by various composers.* **Håkan Hardenberger** (tpt); **I Musici.** Philips 442 131-2PH (5/95). *See review in the Collections section; refer to the Index.*   Ⓖ

John March   British 1752-1828

Suggested listening ...
...Quartetto in B flat major in imitation of the Stile of Haydn's Opera Prima. *Coupled with works by various composers.* **Salomon Quartet.** Hyperion CDA66780 (3/96). *See review in the Collections section; refer to the Index.*

Czeslaw Marek   Polish/Swiss 1891-1986

Marek Capriccio, Op. 15. Serenade in D major, Op. 24[a]. Sinfonietta in D major, Op. 17.
[a]**Ingolf Turban** (vn); **Philharmonia Orchestra / Gary Brain.** Koch Schwann Ⓕ 364402
(67 minutes: DDD: A/97). Recorded 1996.
This is the second volume of Gary Brain's complete Marek series and features beautifully assured playing from the Philharmonia in scores that are a technical minefield for the players. Brain's firm direction and ear for detail secure performances that are near ideal, yet his control is admirably unobtrusive, Marek's music being allowed to breathe at its own often unhurried pace. The *Allegretto grazioso* of the Serenade (1916-18) is a case in point: Brain's restrained tempo at first seems too relaxed and many conductors would want to push the music on; however, that could seriously undermine the precisely judged balance between the four movements, and the appositeness of Brain's choice becomes clear in the context of the whole. The excellent Ingolf Turban is perfectly cast in the solo role, his sweet tone and clear intonation spot on. The Serenade is a pure delight, a sunny, lyrical

concerto in all but name. The style is broadly central European, which holds true for its companions, the lively and aptly named *Capriccio* (1914-15) and fine *Sinfonietta* (1914-16), unlike the works on the first disc which were very varied in manner. Yet there is no lack of contrast between the pieces here, even the Serenade and *Sinfonietta*, the finale of the former being a reworking of that of the latter; in fact, the stylistic and thematic links make for an integrated programme.

Further listening ...
...Suite, Op. 25. Méditations, Op. 14. Sinfonia, Op. 28. **Philharmonia Orchestra / Gary Brain.** Koch Classics 36439-2 (12/96).

Luca Marenzio

Italian 1553/4-1599

Marenzio Madrigali a 4vv ... libro primo. **Concerto Italiano** (Rossana Bertini, sop; Claudio Cavina, alto; Giuseppe Maletto, ten; Sergio Foresti, bass; Mara Galassi, hp; Andrea Damiani, lte) / **Rinaldo Alessandrini.** Opus 111 Ⓕ OPS30-117 (62 minutes: DDD: 10/94).
    Texts and translations included. Recorded 1994.   Ⓖ

What Concerto Italiano reveal to us is that four-part writing in this expressive and varied milieu makes a virtue out of its limitations: Marenzio capitalizes on exposed dialogues between voices and textural brittleness. Classicism (in the broadest musical sense synonymous with four-part writing long before Bach chorales or Haydn quartets) is what Alessandrini is seeking to impart in this clear juxtaposition of fluent canzonets with intimate rhetoric. The music is so subtly shaded, both by Marenzio and the singers, that unless you are a reincarnated madrigalist this should be experienced in small doses. There is just the same commitment and concentration to the extensive detail in the music. Just observe how much care has gone into *Chi vol udire i miei sospiri in rime* with its beautifully paced crescendo on the word "sospiri" (sighs), the almost imperceptible sketching of the pulse and other wonderful liberties with rhythmic inflexion. So much of this innate understanding is of course expressed through the singers' native tongue (what life those watery vowels bring to Petrarch's later-to-be-famous *Zefiro torna*) and a warm changeable Mediterranean breeze which unselfconsciously manipulates the temperature. None of this would count for much were the ensemble not highly refined in purely abstract terms and this is perhaps the best yet in that respect. Only rarely does the soprano's rich and penetrating tone cause one to worry and when it does this is usually because of a slight tendency to flatness. A small concern in a very fine release.

Biagio Marini

Italian c1587-1685

Suggested listening ...
...Sinfonia grave: La Zorzi. Sonata a quattro. Sonata a 6.
    Coupled with works by various composers. **His Majestys Sagbutts and Cornetts.**
    Hyperion CDA66847 (11/96). *See review in the Collections section; refer to the Index.*

Igor Markevitch

Russian/Italian 1912-1983

Markevitch Complete Orchestral Music, Volumes 1-3. **Arnhem Philharmonic Orchestra / Christopher Lyndon-Gee.** Marco Polo Ⓕ 8 223653, 8 223666 and 8 223724 (three discs, oas: 55, 55 and 54 minutes: DDD: A/97, 1/98). Recorded 1995-96.
8 223653 – Le nouvel âge. Sinfonietta in F major. Cinéma Ouverture.
8 223666 – Cantique d'amour. L'envol d'Icare. Concerto grosso. *8 223724* – Rébus. Hymnes.
Rated highly by his contemporaries, Markevitch's music was widely performed and enthusiastically received from around 1929 to the outbreak of the Second World War. Inexplicably, and still only in his late twenties, he abandoned composition and began to forge a new career as a distinguished conductor. Towards the end of his life he allowed his works to be performed and published again, but although several have attracted widespread acclaim these are première recordings. The *Sinfonietta*, written when he was 16, and the *Concerto grosso* both owe a debt to Hindemith; but throughout both works you get a distinct impression that this is an already mature composer. In the *Cinéma Ouverture*, one might ascribe the use of whistles and car-horns to the influence of Satie, but Markevitch uses them quite differently and very strikingly, as part of a highly original exercise in polyrhythm. Apart from his individuality the most impressive thing about Markevitch is the absolute certainty of his ear. In *L'envol d'Icare* ("The Flight of Icarus") the sound world of the piece is defined by the presence within the orchestra of a small solo group playing in quarter-tones, precisely imagined to produce harmonies of shimmering radiance. The final section of the work, "The death of Icarus", will strike many listeners as a prediction of minimalism; in fact its repetitive *moto perpetuo* is subject to constant rhythmic change, and there is a strange magic to the gradual suggestion that Icarus has been reborn after his destruction. *Le nouvel âge*, a strong, bold, ultimately rather disconcertingly machine-like symphony from an abortive opera, suggests that though Markevitch left Russia at the age of two, he was well aware of the 'constructivist' aesthetic promoted there. The *Cantique d'amour*, on the other hand, reminds us that his language was French: it is luxuriant in colour and texture and rises to a full

and impassioned climax. He is a fascinating composer, at times an inspired one, and all his music is vividly communicative and approachable. Perhaps he abandoned composing because he found the fierce, even mechanistic energy that dominates so much of his music limiting or restrictive.

Volume 3 suggests that he was aware of this possibility, and sought means to expand his style. Written at the age of 19 the ballet, *Rébus*, caused Henri Prunières in the *New York Times* to declare Markevitch a genius. Much of it is in his machine-like manner, but although it encompasses a good deal of variety, the 25-minute piece seldom relaxes. It is brilliantly scored and quite haunting in its combination of ferocious rhythmic impetus and irresistible harmonic movement. *Hymnes*, in its original version begun only a year later, is nevertheless an advance. It does not retreat from Markevitch's mechanistic manner, indeed it intensifies it – there is huge excitement to the wildly barbarous second movement, scored with even more brazen splendour than *Rébus*. And both here and in the fourth movement, the exploration of complex rhythm is more methodical than in the earlier work. But in *Hymnes* (which despite its title is a purely instrumental work, and a secular one) we have a genuine slow movement, of an almost improvisatory lyrical grace, and in the final section ("Hymn to Death", added to the work three years later) a deepening of Markevitch's lyrical language towards gravity, mystery and shadow. It is an even more impressive work than *Rébus*. Markevitch has found a convinced and convincing exponent in Christopher Lyndon-Gee, who draws performances of high quality from the excellent Arnhem Philharmonic. The recordings are decent, too.

Further listening ...
...Galop[a]. Noces[b]. Serenade[c]. L'envol d'Icare[d]. [c]**Wolfgang Meyer** (cl); [c]**Dag Jensen** (bn); **Kolja Lessing** ([c]vn/[bd]pf); [d]**Christopher Lyndon-Gee** (pf); [d]**Franz Lang**, [d]**Jens Gagelmann**, [d]**Raphael Haeger** (perc); [a]**Markevitch Ensemble, Cologne.** Largo 5127 (10/95).

Heinrich Marschner
German 1795-1861

Suggested listening ...
...Rheinromanzen, Op. 128 – No. 1, Die sieben Freier. Gesänge und Balladen, Op. 160 – No. 1, Der König von Thule; No. 2, Die Rache. Das Flämmchen auf der Heide, Op. 80 No. 12. Die Monduhr, Op. 102 No. 2. Das Lied von alten König, Op. 82 No. 2. Der betrogene Teufel, Op. 87 No. 1. *Coupled with works by various composers.* **Olaf Bär** (bar); **Helmut Deutsch** (pf). EMI CDC5 55393-2 (1/96). *See review in the Collections section; refer to the Index.*
...Hans Heiling – An jenam Tag. Der Vampyr – Ha! Noch einen ganzen Tag. *Coupled with works by various composers.* **Thomas Hampson** (bar); [a]**Pestalozzi Gymnasium Children's Choir; Munich Radio Orchestra / Fabio Luisi.** EMI CDC5 55233-2 (9/95). *See review in the Collections section; refer to the Index.*
...Bagatelles, Op. 4 – E major; A minor; A major; G major; A major; F major. *Coupled with works by* **Sor** *and* **Werthmüller** Tilman Hoppstock (gtr). Signum SIGX75-00 (2/98). *See review in the Collections section; refer to the Index.*

Roger Marsh
British 1949

Suggested listening ...
...Ferry Music. *Coupled with works by various composers.* **Mühlfeld Ensemble** Clarinet Classics CC0007 (10/94). *See review in the Collections section; refer to the Index.*

Istvan Marta
Hungarian 1952

Suggested listening ...
...Doom. A sigh. *Coupled with works by various composers.* **Kronos Quartet.** Nonesuch 7559-79242-2 (4/91). *See review in the Collections section; refer to the Index.*

Frank Martin
Swiss 1890-1974

Martin Concerto for Seven Wind Instruments, Timpani, Percussion and Strings[a]. Etudes for String Orchestra[a]. Petite Symphonie concertante[b]. Passacaglia for String Orchestra[c]. Violin Concerto[d]. In terra pax[e]. [e]**Ursula Buckel** (sop); [e]**Marga Höffgen** (contr); [e]**Ernst Haefliger** (ten); [e]**Pierre Mollet** (bar); [e]**Jakob Stämpfli** (bass); [d]**Wolfgang Schneiderhan** (vn); [b]**Pierre Jamet** (hp); [b]**Germaine Vaucher-Clerc** (hpd); [b]**Doris Rossiaud** (pf); [e]**Lausanne Choral Union;** [c]**Stuttgart Chamber Orchestra / Karl Münchinger;** [abde]**Suisse Romande Orchestra / Ernest Ansermet.** Double Decca [bcd]mono/[ae]stereo Ⓜ 448 264-2DF2 (two discs: 147 minutes: ADD: 8/96). Items marked [a] from SXL2311 (6/62), [b]LXT2631 (12/51), [c]LXT5153 (8/57), [d]LX3146 (2/56), [e]SXL6098 (6/64).
This invaluable issue restores not only the pioneering recording of Martin's masterpiece, the *Petite Symphonie concertante* for harp, harpsichord, piano and double string orchestra, but also that of the Violin Concerto. They have great authority and a sense of atmosphere that is very special. The Violin

Concerto is an inspired and noble piece, and Schneiderhan's mono recording makes its first appearance since the mid-1950s. In reviewing the original Vox LP the reviewer spoke of the work's "clarity, restraint and dignity". Anyone who responds to the Prokofiev D major Concerto or the Bartók and Walton will feel at home here. The *Concerto for seven wind instruments* and the *Etudes* for string orchestra were recorded in the early 1960s and the sound is very fresh. *In terra pax* is a strong work but is here showing its age (see the Chandos review further on). In any event this package is well worth having for the sake of the Violin Concerto.

Additional recommendation ...
...Concerto for Seven Wind Instruments. Erasmi Monumentum. Etudes for String Orchestra.
London Philharmonic Orchestra / Matthias Bamert.
Chandos Ⓕ CHAN9283 (67 minutes: DDD: 7/94).

Martin Symphonie concertante. Symphonie. Passacaglia. **London Philharmonic Orchestra /
Matthias Bamert.** Chandos Ⓕ CHAN9312 (67 minutes: DDD: 1/95). Recorded 1993.
Gramophone Editor's choice.

Frank Martin's *Symphonie concertante* is a transcription of the *Petite symphonie concertante* for harp, harpsichord, piano and double string orchestras, made in 1945-46, a year after the original. As one would expect from so imaginative a master, the orchestration is characteristically resourceful and intelligent. Melodic ideas, previously associated with the three soloists, are generally assigned to the wind and effective use is made of muted trumpets. Successful though it is, one can understand why it has not supplanted its predecessor, whose sonorities are so subtle and original. The *Symphonie* (1936-37) is a great rarity. Although scored for large orchestra, the instrumentation is of consistent lightness and delicacy, almost chamber-like in its subtlety. The slow movement, suffused with the muted colours and moonlit landscapes of some shadowy *Pelléas* country, is the most haunting movement of the four. At first the overall structure of the symphony seems somewhat amorphous, but the logic of Martin's thought processes emerges as one immerses oneself in the piece. This luminous and beautiful score deserves a warm welcome and is well served by the LPO under Matthias Bamert, and the Chandos team. The recording is truthfully balanced and has a natural concert-hall perspective. Both these are first recordings and the *Passacaglia*, too, is a first modern recording. An invaluable and rewarding issue.

Martin Der Sturm – Overture; Mein Ariel, hast du, der Luft nur ist; Ein feierliches Lied; Hin sind meine Zauberei'n[a]. Maria-Triptychon[b]. Sechs Monologe aus Jedermann[c]. [b]**Linda Russell** (sop);
[ac]**David Wilson-Johnson** (bar); [c]**Duncan Riddell** (vn); **London Philharmonic Orchestra /
Matthias Bamert.** Chandos Ⓕ CHAN9411 (68 minutes: DDD: 3/96). Recorded 1994.
Gramophone Editor's choice.

The *Maria-Triptychon* was written in the late 1960s in response to a request from Wolfgang Schneiderhan for a work for violin, soprano and orchestra that he could perform with his wife, Irmgard Seefried. Although the alternative recording with Seefried and Schneiderhan under the composer himself emanating from a Swiss Radio tape is authoritative, it does not match this Chandos recording in sheer beauty of sound. Linda Russell sings the solo part with great sympathy and intelligence, and Duncan Riddell assumes the mantle of Schneiderhan with no mean success. The transparency of texture that the Chandos team achieve shows this visionary score in the most favourable light. It makes a stronger impression than in any earlier performance and much of its success is due to the dedication of the LPO and their conductor Matthias Bamert. He distils a strong atmosphere and sense of mystery in all these scores. David Wilson-Johnson is on impressive form in the *Jedermann* Monologues (one of the great song-cycles of the century). His is as perceptive and moving an account as any – and he is no less impressive in *Der Sturm*, and what a magical score that is! The recording is well balanced.

Additional recommendation ...
...Petite symphonie concertante[a]. Maria-Triptychon[b]. Passacaglia (transc. comp.)[c].
[b]**Irmgaard Seefried** (sop); [b]**Wolfgang Schneiderhan** (vn); [a]**Eva Hunziker** (hp);
[a]**Germaine Vaucher-Clerc** (clavecin); [a]**Doris Rossiaud** (pf); [ab]**Suisse Romande Orchestra;**
[c]**Berlin Philharmonic Orchestra / Frank Martin.**
Jecklin Disco mono Ⓕ JD645-2* (57 minutes: ADD: 10/91).

Martin Der Cornet. **Jard van Nes** (contr); **Nieuw Sinfonietta Amsterdam / Reinbert de Leeuw.**
Philips Ⓕ 442 535-2PH (61 minutes: DDD: 11/95). Text and translation included.
Recorded 1993.   Ⓖ

Der Cornet is among Martin's greatest compositions and one of the most powerful works of its kind that our war-torn century has produced. *Der Cornet*, or to give it its full title, *Die Weise von Liebe und Tod des Cornets Christoph Rilke* ("The Song of the Love and Death of Cornet Christoph Rilke"), to Rainer Maria Rilke's celebrated text, strikes chilling resonances today. Briefly speaking it tells of a youthful ensign who fell in 1660 under "the sabres of the Turks into an ocean of flowers", and at times of war – and in particular Balkan wars – the story inevitably makes poignant reading. Later in life Rilke thought the poem "highly second-rate" though second-rate is the last thing one could say about Frank Martin's setting. The work is a rarity, which is understandable considering that *Der Cornet* takes nearly an hour, and makes great demands not only on the contralto but on the emotional tranquillity of the listener. This very fact, as well as the concentration of the piece, has militated against its wider dissemination. The setting comprises all but four of the 27 stanzas and the conductor and patron, Paul Sacher, encouraged Martin to score them for small chamber orchestral resources. The narrative is very much in command and the orchestral colouring is economical. Martin's responsiveness to the rhythm and music of the words is almost Debussian in its subtlety (German was not his first tongue). Each of the songs encapsulates a different aspect of the drama that unfolds in the prose poems, and in each the composer sought a musical form as close as possible to its literary form. The chamber forces involved are used with the utmost economy and to maximum effect. In addition to the strings, there are some winds, harp, piano and percussion but the textures have the lucidity and transparency that mark the Hofmannsthal *Everyman* settings which were composed in the same year (1943). Jard van Nes gives a dedicated and moving account of the cycle and Reinbert de Leeuw and the Nieuw Sinfonietta Amsterdam are sensitive and supportive. The sound is clean and well focused. Readers who have the Lipovšek recording need not feel impelled to change. Both performances cast so strong a spell that it is difficult to choose between them. If you find one not in stock, you can safely acquire the other. Buy neither and you will be missing a powerful musical experience.

Additional recommendation ...

...Der Cornet. **Marjana Lipovšek** (mez); **Austrian Radio Symphony Orchestra / Lothar Zagrosek.** Orfeo Ⓕ C164881A (59 minutes: DDD: 10/88).   ⒼⒼ

Martin Piano Quintet[a]. Ballade for Flute and Piano[b]. Piano Sonata[c]. Ballade for Cello and Piano[d]. Quatre Sonnets à Cassandre[e]. [abcd]**Ian Burnside** (pf); **Britten-Pears Ensemble** ([e]Barbara Rearick, mez; [be]Karen Jones, fl; [ac]Laurence Jackson, [a]Celia Waterhouse, vns; [ae]Susan Knight, va; [ae]Paul Watkins, vc). ASV Ⓕ CDDCA1010 (75 minutes: DDD: 3/98). Text and translation included. Recorded 1996.

Although there have been several alternative accounts of the *Ballade* for flute and piano and even one of the Piano Quintet and the *Quatre Sonnets à Cassandre*, this appears to be the first on disc of the Violin Sonata, so this release fills an important gap in the catalogue. Martin was a late developer and all these pieces, apart from the two *Ballades*, come from the period before he found his real voice in *Der Cornet*, *Le vin herbé* and the six *Everyman* Monologues in the late-1930s to early-1940s. The earliest work is the Piano Quintet (1919), written while the composer was still in his twenties. Ravel is the strongest influence here, particularly in the Trio section of the second movement, though in the first movement the musical language is much closer to Fauré. It is a work of haunting and sustained eloquence and is played with great feeling by these accomplished artists. They are a good deal brisker than their Zurich rivals in both the first movement and the *Adagio*. The best-known piece here, composed by Martin for the Concours de Genève in 1939, is the *Ballade* for flute, of which Karen Jones gives a brilliant account. The Violin Sonata comes from the same decade and is a short, three-movement work from 1932, which at one point pays direct homage to the Debussy sonata which would have been some 15 years old and 'new music' at the time Martin embarked on his piece. As is the case with the *Ballades*, the solo instrument is a bit too forwardly balanced. The post-war *Ballade* for cello and piano is a powerful piece, finely characterized and well projected by Paul Watkins and Ian Burnside. There is much more space round the sound in the *Quatre Sonnets à Cassandre*, settings of Ronsard written two years after the Piano Quintet. This is delightful music to which Barbara Rearick brings charm and finesse. A valuable and welcome issue.

Additional recommendation ...

...Pavane couleur du temps[a]. Piano Quintet[b]. String Trio[c]. Trio sur des mélodies populaires irlandaises[d]. **Zurich Chamber Ensemble** (Brenton Langbein, [ab]Andreas Pfenninger, vns; [a]Cornel Anderes, [bc]Jürg Dähler, vas; Raffaele Altwegg, [a]Luciano Pezzani, vcs); [bd]**Hanni Schmid-Wyss** (pf). Jecklin Disco Ⓕ JD646-2 (66 minutes: ADD: 10/91).

...Passacaille. *Coupled with works by various composers.* **John Scott** (org). Priory Ⓕ PRCD485 (74 minutes: DDD: 8/96). *Selected by Soundings.*

Martin In terra pax[a]. Les quatre éléments. [a]**Judith Howarth** (sop); [a]**Della Jones** (contr); [a]**Martyn Hill** (ten); [a]**Roderick Williams** (bar); [a]**Stephen Roberts** (bass); [a]**Brighton Festival Chorus; London Philharmonic Orchestra / Matthias Bamert.** Chandos Ⓕ CHAN9465 (67 minutes: DDD: 8/96). Text and translations included.

Sometime in 1944, towards the end of the Second World War, Swiss Radio approached Frank Martin with a commission for a work to be performed at the conclusion of the hostilities. The result was *In terra pax*, which Ernest Ansermet conducted in 1945 and which he eventually recorded in the 1960s. (this is the reissue reviewed at the beginning of this section). Matthias Bamert has now put us in his debt with his impressive ongoing survey of Martin's output, to which this disc is a distinguished addition. *In terra pax* is an eloquent and noble work, in every way characteristic of the master. The singers are not always quite as impressive as in the Ansermet set, but in every other respect the present recording is superior. Ansermet was a lifelong and loyal champion of Martin's music and the composer paid him a handsome tribute with *Les quatre éléments*, written in 1963 to celebrate the great conductor's eightieth birthday the following year. It is a work of vibrant imaginative force. As usual the textures are pale but luminous, translucent and subtle; the invention is highly personal and distinctive. As with most of Martin's music, the rewards are richer on each occasion one returns to it.

Martin Mass for Double Choir[a]. Passacaille[b].
Pizzetti Messa di requiem[a]. De profundis[a]. [a]**Westminster Cathedral Choir / James O'Donnell**
([b]org). Hyperion Ⓕ CDA67017 (71 minutes: DDD: 3/98). Texts and translations included.
Recorded 1997.   ⒼⒼⒼ
These are magnificent performances. Written in 1922, the *Agnus Dei* being added four years later, the
Mass is one of Martin's most sublime compositions. Surprisingly it gains enormously from using
boys' rather than female voices and although one might think women naturally score over boys in
terms of understanding and maturity, it is a measure of James O'Donnell's achievement with
Westminster Cathedral Choir that the gain in purity and beauty is at no time at the expense of depth
and fervour. This is an altogether moving and eloquent performance, often quite thrilling and always
satisfying. This disc brings us a fine performance by O'Donnell of the *Passacaille* and the Pizzetti
Messa di Requiem, also composed in 1922. The received wisdom is that it is in his *a cappella* music
that Pizzetti is at his finest and in his 1951 monograph Guido Gatti spoke of his setting as "the most
serene and lyrical of all ... from Mozart's to Gabriel Fauré's". Serene and lyrical it most certainly is,
and it will come as a revelation to those encountering it for the first time. Intending no disrespect to
the expert Danish performance on Chandos, this is in a different league. There is a fervour and a
conviction about the Westminster performances of both the Requiem and the 1937 *De profundis*.
The luminous tone this choir produce in both these inspired and masterly works will ring in your ears
long after you have finished playing this splendidly recorded disc.

Additional recommendations ...
...Mass for Double Choir. *Coupled with works by* **Howells** Vasari / Jeremy Backhouse.
Cala United Ⓕ CACD88033 (56 minutes: DDD: 12/94).
See review under Howells; refer to the Index.   Ⓖ
...Mass for Double Choir. Fünf Gesänge des Ariel. Ode à la musique[a]. Cantate pour le 1er août.
Quatre Chansons. Trois Chansons. [a]**Simon Birchall** (bar); **The Sixteen / Harry Christophers.**
Collins Classics Ⓕ 1467-2 (67 minutes: DDD: 9/96). *Gramophone Editor's choice.*   Ⓖ
...Mass for Double Choir – Agnus Dei. *Coupled with works by various composers.* **New College
Choir, Oxford / Edward Higginbottom.** Erato Ⓕ 3984-21659-2 (66 minutes: DDD: 6/98).
Gramophone Editor's choice. See review in the Collections section; refer to the Index.

Further listening ...
...Ballade for Piano and Orchestra. Piano Concertos Nos. 2 and 4. **Jean-François Antonioli** (pf);
Turin Philharmonic Orchestra / Marcello Viotti. Claves CD50-8509 (3/87).
...Ballade for Piano and Orchestra[a]. Ballade for Trombone and Orchestra[b]. Concerto for
Harpsichord and Small Orchestra[c]. [a]**Sebastian Benda** (pf); [b]**Armin Rosin** (tbn);
[c]**Christiane Jaccottet** (hpd). Jecklin Disco JD5292 (9/89).
...Ballade (arr. Ansermet). *Coupled with works by various composers.* **Michael Faust** (fl);
Cologne Radio Symphony Orchestra / Alun Francis, Serge Baudo.
Capriccio 10 495 (12/94). *See review in the Collections section; refer to the Index.*
...Three Danses. Petite complainte. Pièce brève *Coupled with works by* **Martinů** and **Honegger**
Aurèle Nicolet (fl); Heinz Holliger (ob/cor ang); Ursula Holliger (hp); **Academy of St Martin in the
Fields / Sir Neville Marriner.** Philips 434 105-2PH (9/93).
...Requiem. **Elisabeth Speiser** (sop); **Ria Bollen** (contr); **Eric Tappy** (ten); **Peter Lagger** (bass);
**Lausanne Women's Chorus; Union Chorale; Ars Laeta Vocal Ensemble;
Suisse Romande Orchestra / Frank Martin.** Jecklin Disco JD631-2 (1/90).

Johann Martini   German 1741-1816

Suggested listening ...
...Plaisir d'amour. *Coupled with works by various composers.*
Angela Gheorghiu (sop); **Malcolm Martineau** (pf).
Decca 458 360-2DH (5/98). *See review in the Collections section; refer to the Index.*

Johannes Martini   Burgundian c1440-1498

Suggested listening ...
...Magnificat tertii toni. Ave Maris stella. O beate Sebastiane. Salve regina.
Coupled with works by **Obrecht The Clerks' Group / Edward Wickham.**
ASV Gaudeamus CDGAU171 (5/98). *See review under Obrecht; refer to the Index.*

Bohuslav Martinů   Bohemian 1890-1959

Martinů Cello Concertos – No. 1; No. 2. Cello Concertino. **Raphael Wallfisch** (vc);
Czech Philharmonic Orchestra / Jiří Bělohlávek. Chandos Ⓕ CHAN9015
(76 minutes: DDD: 4/92). Recorded 1991.

As the composer of almost 30 concerto-type works, Bohuslav Martinů cannot always escape the charge of flatulent note-spinning that attaches itself to such fertility. On the present disc, his unique imaginative vision is most obvious in the Cello Concerto No. 1. The central slow movement in particular finds Martinů at his best, a deeply moving threnody with a potent nostalgic quality which will be instantly recognizable to admirers of the later symphonies. There is an improvisatory freedom about the Second Concerto which makes it harder to grasp and the thematic material has rather too much in common with other, better scores. The much earlier *Concertino* is in Martinů's playful, more overtly neoclassical vein. You may notice some vamp-until-ready eighteenth-century scrubbing in the concertos, but here the younger composer is preoccupied with the lighter aspects of the style. There's a Stravinskian wit and elegance about the writing and the chamber scoring reflects both the fashionable trends and the economic constraints of life in 1920s Paris. In the First Concerto, Raphael Wallfisch is rather backwardly balanced *vis-à-vis* the Czech Philharmonic, whose regular conductor, Jiří Bělohlávek, is of course totally inside this music. At the same time, the resonant Spanish Hall of Prague Castle provides an agreeable ambient glow which does not mask too much detail. Make no mistake: this is a most attractive proposition for those already familiar with the idiom. Adventurous beginners should perhaps start elsewhere.

Martinů Piano Concertos – No. 2; No. 3; No. 4, "Incantation". **Rudolf Firkušný** (pf);
   Czech Philharmonic Orchestra / Libor Pešek. RCA Victor Red Seal Ⓕ 09026 61934-2
   (67 minutes: DDD: 4/95). Recorded 1993. *Gramophone Editor's choice.*   Ⓖ
These performances not only have special authority but are in a class of their own. Although the five piano concertos are not of comparable importance to the Martinů symphonies, they are not of negligible interest. Martinů returned to the medium throughout his career: the First and weakest dates from 1925 and the last, the *Fantasia concertante* in B flat, from 1957, two years before his death. The disc bears the title "Tribute to Rudolf Firkušný" and the jewel-case reminds us that he gave the first performance of all three concertos. The Fourth, *Incantation*, is undoubtedly the finest of them all, highly imaginative in its exotic sound-world, with what sound like wild Aztec bird calls and war cries, and full of luminous and subtle sonorities. Firkušný's account is a revelation to those who have heard only the Páleníček, Leichner or Havlíková recordings. There is the right sense of pace – and space: phrases have time to breathe and make their point. The Czech PO under Libor Pešek give Firkušný dedicated and sympathetic support. The recording is very good and allows one to hear more orchestral detail than ever before. In Firkušný's hands the Second Concerto has a real sense of warmth and delight. The Third, too, emerges in superlatively fresh and vivid colours. What is also astonishing is that at no time does Firkušný's playing betray his years: he was 81 when these performances were given! He was an aristocrat among pianists and this is a worthy memorial to him.

Martinů Symphonies. **Bamberg Symphony Orchestra / Neeme Järvi.**
   BIS Ⓕ CD362, CD363 (*Selected by Sounds in Retrospect*) and CD402
   (three discs, oas: 61, 63 and 59 minutes: DDD: 9/87, 12/88).
   CD362 – Nos. 1 and 2. *CD363* – Nos. 3 and 4. *CD402* – Nos. 5 and 6.   Ⓖ
Despite his travels throughout his formative years as a composer, Martinů remained a quintessentially Czech composer and his music is imbued with the melodic shapes and rhythms of the folk-music of his native homeland. The six symphonies were written during Martinů's years in America and in all of them he uses a large orchestra with distinctive groupings of instruments which give them a very personal and unmistakable timbre. The rhythmic verve of his highly syncopated fast movements is very infectious, indeed unforgettable, and his slow movements are often deeply expressive, most potently, perhaps, in that of the Third Symphony which is imbued with the tragedy of war. The Bamberg orchestra play marvellously and with great verve for Järvi, whose excellently judged tempos help propel the music forward most effectively. His understanding of the basic thrust of Martinů's structures is very impressive and he projects the music with great clarity. The BIS recordings are beautifully clear, with plenty of ambience surrounding the orchestra, a fine sense of scale and effortless handling of the wide dynamic range Martinů calls for. Enthusiastically recommended.

Additional recommendations ...
...Nos. 1 and 2. **Berlin Symphony Orchestra / Claus Peter Flor.**
   RCA Victor Red Seal Ⓕ RD60154 (62 minutes: DDD: 11/90).
...No. 6. **Janáček.** Sinfonietta. **Suk** Fantasticke scherzo, Op. 25. **Czech Philharmonic Orchestra /**
   Jiří Bělohlávek. Chandos Ⓕ CHAN8897 (65 minutes: DDD: 1/91).
...Nos. 3 and 4. **Royal Scottish National Orchestra / Bryden Thomson.**
   Chandos Ⓕ CHAN8917 (60 minutes: DDD: 6/91).
...Nos. 1-6. **Czech Philharmonic Orchestra / Václav Neumann.**
   Supraphon Ⓕ 110382-2 (three discs: 181 minutes: AAD: 1/92).
...No. 5. Memorial to Lidice. Les fresques de Piero della Francesca[a].
   Czech Philharmonic Orchestra / Karel Ančerl.
   Supraphon Historical mono/[a]stereo Ⓕ 11 1931-2* (77 minutes: AAD: 3/93).   Ⓖ
...No. 4. Field Mass[a]. Memorial to Lidice. [a]**Ivan Kusnjer** (bar); **Czech Philharmonic** [a]**Chorus and**
   Orchestra / Jiří Bělohlávek. Chandos Ⓕ CHAN9138 (65 minutes: DDD: 5/93).   ⒼⒼⒼ
...Nos. 3 and 4. **Czech Philharmonic Orchestra / Václav Neumann.**
   Supraphon Ⓜ 11 1967-2 (62 minutes: DDD: 12/95).

Martinů Trio for Flute, Violin and Piano[abc]. Promenades[abd]. Flute Sonata[ac]. Five Madrigal
Stanzas[bc]. Scherzo[ac]. Madrigal Sonata[abc]. [a]**Alain Marion** (fl); [b]**Angèle Dubeau** (vn);
Marc-André Hamelin ([c]pf/[d]hpd). Analekta fleurs de lys Ⓜ FL2 3031 (71 minutes: DDD: 9/97).
Recorded 1993. *Gramophone Editor's choice.*
This is a most enjoyable record. The performances are fresh and exhilarating, vital and intelligent; the
recording natural and alive, and the music unfailingly delightful and inventive. The Trio for flute,
violin and piano and the *Promenades* were written in Paris just before the war; the Flute Sonata comes
from 1945 and the *Madrigal Stanzas* and *Madrigal Sonata* are wartime pieces written in 1942 and
1943 – at about the time of the First Symphony. They are both sunny and full of life, betraying none
of the turbulence of the times. These artists give consistent pleasure and delight; the cheeky *Scherzo*
of 1929 has rarely been played with quite so much character.
Additional recommendations ...
...Flute Sonata. *Coupled with works by various composers.* **Jean-Pierre Rampal** (fl); **John Steele
Ritter** (pf). Sony Classical Ⓕ SK53106 (77 minutes: DDD: 9/94).
...Flute Sonata. *Coupled with works by various composers.* **Leslie Newman** (fl); **Amanda Hurton** (pf).
Cala United Ⓕ CACD88026 (76 minutes: DDD: 6/96). *See review in the Collections section;
refer to the Index.*

Martinů Piano Quartet (1942)[a]. Quartet for Oboe, Violin, Cello and Piano (1947)[b]. Viola Sonata
(1955)[c]. String Quintet (1927)[d]. [b]**Joel Marangella** (ob); [a]**Isabelle van Keulen**, [bd]**Charmian Gadd,**
[d]**Solomia Soroka** (vns); [acd]**Rainer Moog**, [d]**Theodore Kuchar** (vas); [ad]**Young-Chang Cho,**
[b]**Alexander Ivashkin** (vcs); [ac]**Daniel Adni**, [b]**Kathryn Selby** (pfs). Naxos Ⓢ 8 553916
(73 minutes: DDD: 2/97). Recorded 1994.
The Quartet for oboe, violin, cello and piano is a highly attractive piece in the busy yet unfussy neo-
classical style that Martinů made so much his own. Its opening theme is quite captivating, but all three
movements have charm. It alone is well worth the modest price of the disc. The other music on this
CD is hardly less delightful. The Viola Sonata is an eloquent work from the mid 1950s, composed
three years after the *Rhapsody-Concerto* for the same instrument and orchestra. These were vintage
years in Martinů's creativity and it is surprising that more players have not taken it up. The String
Quintet is the earliest work, dating from his Paris years, and shows the influence of Roussel. Although
the first movement is perhaps not top-drawer Martinů, the slow movement is most imaginative. The
performances are often touched with distinction and are never less than eminently serviceable. Daniel
Adni could perhaps be a little more supple in the Piano Quartet of 1942 though in general he plays
with spirit. There is plenty of air round the players and the recording is lifelike and well balanced.
Further listening ...
...Three Czech Dances. *Coupled with works by* **Bennett** and **Poulenc**
  Jennifer Micallef, Glen Inanga (pfs). Royal Over-Seas League CD2000 (2/98).
...Concerto for String Quartet and Orchestra. *Coupled with works by* **Janáček** and **Bartók**
  Cleveland Orchestra / Christoph von Dohnányi. Decca 443 173-2DH (4/95).
...Estampes. The parables. Overture. La rhapsodie, "Allegro symphonique".
  Czech Philharmonic Orchestra / Jiří Bělohlávek. Supraphon 10 4140-2 (6/91).
...Memorial to Lidice. *Coupled with works by various composers.* **Bamberg Symphony Orchestra /
  Ingo Metzmacher.** EMI CDC5 55424-2 (3/97). *See review in the Collections section; r
  efer to the Index.*
...Violin Concertos Nos. 1 and 2. Rhapsody-Concerto for Viola and Orchestra. **Josef Suk** ([a]vn/[b]va);
  Czech Philharmonic Orchestra / Václav Neumann. Supraphon 11 1969-2 (11/95).
...Cello Sonatas Nos. 1-3. **Steven Isserlis** (vc); **Peter Evans** (pf). Hyperion CDA66296 (7/89).
...String Quartets Nos. 1–7. **Panocha Quartet.** Supraphon 11 0994-2 (9/95).
...String Sextet. Three Madrigals. *Coupled with* **Schulhoff** String Sextet. **Raphael Ensemble.**
  Hyperion CDA66516 (7/92).
...Three Czech Dances. Borová. 12 Esquisses. Four Mouvements. Les ritournelles. Windows on the
  garden. **Radoslav Kvapil** (pf). Unicorn-Kanchana DKPCD9140 (12/93).
...The Butterfly that stamped. Women's voices of the **Kühn Chorus; Prague Symphony Orchestra /
  Jiří Bělohlávek.** Supraphon 11 0380-2 (9/95).
...Echec au Roi[a]. The Revolt. [a]**Vladimír Olexa** (spkr); [a]**Kateřina Kachlíkova** (contr);
  Prague Symphony Orchestra / Jiří Bělohlávek. Supraphon 11 1415-2 (5/94).
...The Epic of Gilgamesh. **Eva Depoltová** (sop); **Stefan Margita** (ten); **Ivan Kusnjer** (bar);
  Ludek Vele (bass); **Milan Karpíšek** (spkr); **Slovak Philharmonic Choir; Slovak Philharmonic
  Orchestra / Zdeněk Košler.** Marco Polo 8 223316 (4/91).
...The Greek Passion. **Soloists; Kuhn Children's Chorus; Czech Philharmonic Chorus;
  Brno State Philharmonic Orchestra / Sir Charles Mackerras.** Supraphon 10 36112 (3/91).
...Julietta. **Soloists; Prague National Theatre Chorus and Orchestra / Jaroslav Krombholc.**
  Supraphon 10 8176-2 (6/93).
...The Opening of the Wells. Legend of the Smoke from Potato Fires. Mikeš of the Mountains.
  Soloists; Kühn Chorus / Pavel Kühn. Supraphon 11 0767-2 (5/94).
...Spalíček. The Romance of the Dandelions. Primrose. **Soloists; Kantilena Children's Chorus;
  Kuhn Chorus; Brno State Philharmonic Orchestra / František Jílek.** Supraphon 11 07522 (4/93).

Giuseppe Martucci

Martucci Piano Concerto No. 2 in B flat minor, Op. 66[a]. La canzone dei ricordi[b].
[b]**Mirella Freni** (sop); [a]**Carlo Bruno** (pf); **Orchestra Filarmonica della Scala / Riccardo Muti.**
Sony Classical Ⓕ SK64582 (72 minutes: DDD: 11/96). Text and translation included.
Recorded 1995. *Gramophone Editor's choice.*
Here is an ideal coupling for anyone who has been meaning to investigate Martucci, but has not yet
got round to doing so; or for anyone who has, and wants a couple of his indisputably major works in
performances of great distinction. Both the Piano Concerto and *La canzone dei ricordi* ("The song of
memories") date from Martucci's full maturity; they show, however, quite distinct sides of his talent.
The concerto is huge, boldly romantic and intensely Brahmsian, but also much more assured and
original than most concertos to which such a description might be applied. The first movement, for
example, is laid out with great confidence in an ingenious expansion of sonata form, yet with enough
variety of incident and splendidly virtuoso pianism to earn every second of its 23 minutes. The slow
movement has abundant romantic melody (at times almost recalling – or rather predicting –
Rachmaninov) and achieves noble eloquence before its tranquil conclusion. The finale is an
entertainingly and resourcefully ingenious sonata rondo with especially brilliant piano writing. Bruno
is in fiery and eloquent command of it. *La canzone dei ricordi* is no less opulent but more intimate and
much more Italian: a song-cycle of poignant regret for lost love, in a language that owes as much to
Martucci's Italian forebears and contemporaries in its vocal writing as it does to Wagner in its
harmony. And yet it is also individual, not least in its subtle use of recurring motives and of string
textures of great richness. It is a most appealing and effective piece, and Freni seizes all its
opportunities for ample lyricism and impassioned gesture with gratitude. Both she and the orchestra
gain from a warmly sympathetic acoustic.
Further listening ...
...Symphony No. 1 in D minor, Op. 75. Novelletta, Op. 82 No. 2. Notturno in G flat major, Op. 70
No. 1. Tarantella, Op. 44 No. 6. **Philharmonia Orchestra / Francesco d'Avalos.**
ASV CDDCA675 (12/89).
...Symphony No. 2 in F major, Op. 81. Andante in B flat major, Op. 69 No. 2[a]. Colore orientale,
Op. 44 No. 3. [a]**George Ives** (vc); **Philharmonia Orchestra / Francesco d'Avalos.**
ASV CDDCA689 (5/90).
...Notturno in G flat major, Op. 70 No. 1. Novelletta, Op. 82 No. 2. Giga, Op. 61 No. 3. *Coupled
with works by* **Busoni** and **Casella La Scala Philharmonic Orchestra, Milan / Riccardo Muti.**
Sony Classical SK53280 (4/94). *See review under Busoni; refer to the Index.* ⒼⒼ

Joseph Marx

Suggested listening ...
...Durch Einsamkeiten. *Coupled with works by various composers.*
Mitsuko Shirai (mez); **Tabea Zimmermann** (va); **Hartmut Höll** (pf).
Capriccio 10 462 (9/95). *See review in the Collections section; refer to the Index.* Ⓖ
...Romantisches Klavierkonzert in E major. *Coupled with* **Korngold** Concerto for Piano
(Left Hand) and Orchestra in C sharp major, Op. 17. **Marc-André Hamelin** (pf);
BBC Scottish Symphony Orchestra / Osmo Vänskä. Hyperion CDA66990 (4/98).

Pietro Mascagni

Mascagni Cavalleria rusticana. **Renata Scotta** (sop) Santuzza; **Plácido Domingo** (ten) Turiddu;
Isola Jones (mez) Lola; **Pablo Elvira** (bar) Alfio; **Jean Kraft** (mez) Mamma Lucia;
Ambrosian Opera Chorus; National Philharmonic Orchestra / James Levine.
RCA Ⓕ 74321 39500-2 (71 minutes: ADD). Notes, text and translation included. Recorded 1978.
This was a strong contender in an overcrowded field when it was first released and this welcome
reissue confirms this opinion. You would be hard put to find a more positive or a more intelligent
Turiddu or Santuzza than Domingo or Scotto. Scotto manages to steer a precise course between being
too ladylike or too melodramatic. She suggests all the remorse and sorrow of Santuzza's situation
without self-pity. Her appeals to Turiddu to reform could hardly be more sincere and heartfelt, her
throbbing delivery to Alfio, "Turiddi mi tolse l'honore", expresses all her desperation when forced to
betray her erstwhile lover, and her curse on Turiddu, "A te la mala pasqua", while not resorting to the
lowdown vigour of some of her rivals, is filled with venom. Not since Callas (for Serafin on EMI),
have so many aspects of the character been so vividly encompassed. Domingo proved how committed
he was to his role when the part was first given to him at Covent Garden in the mid-1970s. He gives
an almost Caruso-like bite and attack to Turiddu's defiance and (later) remorse, and finds a more
appropriate timbre than Bergonzi (for Karajan on DG, reviewed under Leoncavallo). He also delivers
the Brindisi with an appropriately carefree manner, oblivious of the challenge awaiting him. Pablo
Elvira's Alfio is no more than adequate, and the other American support is indifferent. Levine's
direction, as positive as Karajan's, is yet quite different. He goes much faster, and time and again

catches the passion if not always the delicacy of Mascagni's score. He is well supported by the superb National Philharmonic Orchestra. With a recording that is bright and forward, there is altogether a theatrical dimension to this reading that is wholly arresting. For anyone wanting *Cavalleria* on a single disc, or for those with a *Pagliacci* but no *Cavalleria* in their collection, this set is a definite recommendation. Others who already have the famous Karajan may like to consider this as an addition on an altogether different and equally valid plane of interpretation.

Additional recommendations ...

...Cavalleria rusticana. **Leoncavallo** Pagliacci. **Soloists; Chorus and Orchestra of La Scala, Milan /
Tullio Serafin.** EMI mono Ⓕ CDS5 56287-2* (two discs: 141 minutes: ADD).

...Cavalleria rusticana. **Leoncavallo** Pagliacci. **Soloists; Chorus and Orchestra of La Scala, Milan /
Herbert von Karajan.** DG Ⓕ 419 257-2GH3 (three discs: 198 minutes: ADD: 10/87).
See review under Leoncavallo; refer to the Index.

...Cavalleria rusticana[a]. **Leoncavallo** Pagliacci[b]. **Soloists;** [a]**London Opera Chorus;** [b]**London Voices;**
[b]**Finchley Children's Music Group;** [ab]**National Philharmonic Orchestra /** [a]**Gianandrea Gavazzeni,**
[b]**Giuseppe Patanè.** Decca Ⓕ 414 590-2DH2 (two discs: 143 minutes: ADD: 1/89).

...Cavalleria rusticana. **Leoncavallo** Pagliacci. **Soloists; Ambrosian Opera Chorus; Philharmonia
Orchestra / Riccardo Muti.** EMI Ⓜ CMS7 63650-2 (two discs: 150 minutes: ADD: 3/91).

...Cavalleria rusticana (in English). **Soloists; Geoffrey Mitchell Choir; London Philharmonic
Orchestra / David Parry.** Chandos Opera in English Ⓕ CHAN3004 (79 minutes: DDD).

...Cavalleria rusticana – Regina coeli ... Inneggiamo, il Signor. *Coupled with works by various
composers.* **Lesley Garrett** (sop); **Britten Sinfonia / Ivor Bolton.** Conifer Classics Ⓕ 75605 51329-2
(73 minutes: DDD: 12/97). *See review in the Collections section; refer to the Index.*

...Cavalleria rusticana – Intermezzo. *Coupled with works by various composers.*
Vienna Philharmonic Orchestra / Rudolf Kempe. Testament Ⓕ SBT1127*
(78 minutes: ADD: 3/98). *See review in the Collections section; refer to the Index.*

Mascagni Iris. **Daniella Dessì** (sop) Iris; **José Cura** (ten) Osaka; **Roberto Servile** (bar) Kyoto;
Nicolai Ghiaurov (bass) Blind Man; **Michiè Nakamaru** (sop) Geisha; **Ezio di Cesare** (ten)
Ragpicker; **Corrado Amici** (ten) Pedlar; **Chorus and Orchestra of the Rome Opera /
Gianluigi Gelmetti.** Ricordi Ⓕ 74321 51544-2 (two discs: 126 minutes: DDD: 3/98).
Notes, text and translation included. Recorded live in 1996.

Do persevere with this one. It begins disconcertingly badly: the backwardly-placed chorus in the opening scene are muffled, the orchestra brightly tinny in anything above *forte* and when Daniella Dessì is first heard it sounds as though she's having an off-day, too, her upper notes spreading under pressure. Everything rapidly improves, however. Within ten minutes or so the engineers have sorted out their balance difficulties and Dessì has recovered. Mascagni's problem is said to have been that he never quite managed to repeat the success of *Cavalleria rusticana*. His subsequent operas seem to demonstrate that for the most part he made determined efforts *not* to repeat *Cavalleria*. Apart from its expected wealth of melody, *Iris* might almost be by a different composer. Quite apart from its dramatic ingenuities it contains musical innovations that one hardly expects either from the composer of *Cavalleria* or the rather embittered conservative that Mascagni eventually became – almost impressionist harmony, for a start, and a striking and accomplished use of the whole-tone scale. Then there is his use of 'light' music, often of an oriental cast, for sinister ends. And that strange, almost repulsively gripping monologue that Italians call "La piovra" ("The octopus" – Iris recounts her dream of an octopus engulfing the naked body of a beautiful woman, who smiles as she dies: the octopus is the image of pleasure and of death) – one assumes that Mascagni and his librettist Illica have been overdosing on Freud, but no: *Iris* appeared two years before *The Interpretation of Dreams*. Dessì is very good at "La piovra" and movingly evokes the pathos of Iris's nostalgia for the little garden she once tended. Indeed, after that opening scene the entire performance matures into just the sort of reading this opera needs. The role of Osaka, the wealthy nobleman at whose behest Iris is kidnapped but who is soon bored by her childish innocence, must be frustrating for an intelligent tenor: it is shortish, with very little room to suggest subtlety of character. Cura responds with warm, robust tone, quite recalling the young Plácido Domingo or indeed the young Franco Corelli, but also demonstrating that he has a lovely *mezza voce* available. Servile as the odious procurer is excellent. Ghiaurov is very reliable as Iris's old, blind father, and the small but crucial role of the Geisha is well taken by Nakamaru. Gelmetti obviously believes in this score and he handles its delicacies as well as its occasional crudities with great sympathy. The recording, once past its teething troubles, is not at all bad, with a good sense of the stage.

Additional recommendation ...

...**Soloists; Bavarian Radio Chorus; Munich Radio Orchestra / Giuseppe Patanè.**
Sony Classical Ⓕ M2K45526 (two discs: 124 minutes: DDD: 9/89).

Benedict Mason
British 1954

Suggested listening ...

...Lighthouses of England and Wales. **BBC Symphony Orchestra / Lothar Zagrosek.**
Collins Classics 2004-2 (3/92). *See review in the Collections section; refer to the Index.* Ⓖ Ⓖ

John Mason
British d 1548

Suggested listening ...
...Vae nobis miseris. Quales sumus. *Coupled with works by* **Sheppard** and **Davy**
The Magdalen Collection / Harry Christophers.
Collins Classics 1511-2 (7/97). *See review under Sheppard; refer to the Index.*

Jules Massenet
French 1842-1912

Massenet Don Quichotte[a]. Scènes alsaciennes[b]. **Nicolai Ghiaurov** (bass) Don Quichotte;
Régine Crespin (sop) Dulcinée; **Gabriel Bacquier** (bar) Sancho Panza; **Michèle Command** (sop)
Pedro; **Annick Duterte** (sop) Garcias; **Peyo Garazzi** (ten) Rodriguez; **Jean-Marie Fremeau** (ten)
Juan; [a]**Suisse Romande Chorus and Orchestra / Kazimierz Kord;** [b]**National Philharmonic**
Orchestra / Richard Bonynge. Decca Ⓜ 430 636-2DM2 (two discs: 133 minutes: ADD: 4/92).
Notes, text and translation included. Item marked [a] from D156D3 (11/79),
[b]SXL6827 (12/77). Recorded 1978.
This heroic comedy, which was Massenet's last big success (in 1910, when he was 68), is most welcome.
People who think of him as only a salon composer, lacking the vigour and depth of a Berlioz or a
Debussy, should listen to the start of Act 1, set in a Spanish town square at fiesta time; the opening
music bursts out of the loudspeakers like that of Verdi's *Otello*, although here the mood is joyous,
with tremendous rhythmic verve and gusto. In fact, this opera is closer to Verdi's *Falstaff*, with the
same admixture of gentler serious moments amidst the comic bustle and intrigue, and of course, here
again the central character is a comic yet lovable figure. The recording, made by a British team in
Geneva in 1978, still sounds well although orchestral detail could be clearer. As for the performance
by mainly Swiss forces under Kazimierz Kord, and with a Bulgarian bass in the title role (written for
Chaliapin), one can only praise it for its idiomatic realization of a 'Spanish' opera by a gifted French
composer for the theatre. Though Régine Crespin may be too mature vocally for Dulcinée, the object
of the elderly Don Quixote's adoration, she sings splendidly and few will find this a serious weakness.
Nicolai Ghiaurov rightly makes Quixote himself a real person, touching and dignified as well as
comic, and Gabriel Bacquier gives a rounded portrayal of his servant Sancho Panza, so that Quixote's
death scene in the company of his old friend is particularly strong. The booklet provides a synopsis
plus the French text and a translation. This is a fine mid-price issue, and the lively and tuneful *Scènes
alsaciennes* with a British orchestra under Richard Bonynge make a fine fill-up.
Additional recommendation ...
...**Soloists; Toulouse Capitole Chorus and Orchestra / Michel Plasson.**
EMI Ⓕ CDS7 54767-2 (two discs: 115 minutes: DDD: 12/93).

Massenet Hérodiade. **Nadine Denize** (mez) Hérodiade; **Cheryl Studer** (sop) Salomé; **Ben Heppner**
(ten) Jean; **Thomas Hampson** (bar) Hérode; **José van Dam** (bass-bar) Phanuel; **Marcel Vanaud**
(bar) Vitellius; **Jean-Philippe Courtis** (bass) High Priest; **Martine Olmeda** (mez) Young
Babylonian; **Jean-Paul Fouchécourt** (ten) Voice in the Temple; **Toulouse Capitole Chorus and**
Orchestra / Michel Plasson. EMI Ⓕ CDS5 55378-2 (three discs: 166 minutes: DDD: 2/96).
Notes, text and translation included. Recorded 1994. *Gramophone Editor's choice.*   Ⓖ
Written in 1880, *Hérodiade* is typical of the early grand operas with which Massenet courted
popularity. In its final version, which is the one used for this recording, it offers five magnificent roles
to singers who have the wherewithal to make the most of them. It is no wonder that Studer and
Heppner want to sing the opera, when their solo scenes are such glorious show-pieces and – as always
with Massenet – gratefully written for the voice. There is little point in making biblical comparisons.
Forget Strauss's *Salome* for a moment and think instead of Verdi and *Aida*. It is impossible to say
whether Massenet consciously took Verdi's masterpiece as a model, but we do know that he put in his
request for tickets to see the first performance of *Aida* at the Palais Garnier while he was orchestrating
Hérodiade. The similarities are inevitable, as both operas are descendants of Meyerbeer. There are
copious ballets, mystic off-stage chanting, grand choral finales and exotic settings of Eastern promise.
Michel Plasson conducts the opera uncut and has the advantage of a good studio recording. He is not
one for taking an objective view of the music and there are times when he rushes frenetically ahead,
as if he is as possessed by the lurid goings-on in the drama as the characters on stage. The sense of
atmosphere is palpable. In Plasson's hands the heavy chords at the opening of Act 3 resound with a
potent mysticism that presages Klingsor's castle (Massenet knew his Wagner too). In fact, we are at
the dwelling of Phanuel the sorcerer, a less threatening proposition. José van Dam is marvellous in
this big solo, leaning on the opening words of "Dors, ô cité perverse" with a sinister gleam in his voice
that sends shivers down one's back. Silvery pure in tone, Studer's Salomé throws herself into the
drama with lustful abandon and Heppner phrases the music with remarkable breadth and seems to
have heroic top notes to spare.

Massenet Manon. **Ileana Cotrubas** (sop) Manon; **Alfredo Kraus** (ten) Des Grieux; **Gino Quilico**
(bar) Lescaut; **José van Dam** (bass-bar) Comte des Grieux; **Jean-Marie Frémeau** (bar)
De Brétigny; **Charles Burles** (ten) Guillot; **Ghyslaine Raphanel** (sop) Poussette;

Colette Alliot-Lugaz (sop) Javotte; **Martine Mahé** (mez) Rosette; **Jacques Loreau** (bar)
Innkeeper; **Toulouse Capitole Chorus and Orchestra / Michel Plasson.** EMI Ⓕ CDS7 49610-2
(three discs: 154 minutes: DDD: 11/88). Notes, text and translation included.
From SLS173141-3 (11/83). Recorded 1982.

Massenet's most popular opera has had surprisingly few recordings, and at present this is the only
modern version listed on the *Gramophone* Database. At least that relieves the collector from the
responsibilities of choice (for the opera is certainly not one to be without), regardless of the countless
number of available recordings containing excerpts, and anyway Plasson's version would be hard to
improve upon. The performance is a genuine piece of company-work, particularly welcome as the
company is French and can call upon such gifted singers as Colette Alliot-Lugaz and Charles Burles
to take principal supporting roles. Excellent are the brother and father, frequently underestimated as
both singing and acting parts but here played with distinction of voice and style by Gino Quilico and
José van Dam. It is with the two leading roles that some qualifications have to be introduced among
the general praise. Manon and Des Grieux, whatever their sins, have youth on their side, which is
something Ileana Cotrubas and Alfredo Kraus in 1982 could not quite claim. Kraus is still
marvellously clear in tone, firm in production and resonant throughout his extensive rnge, but he has
developed a way of allowing the emotion (as in "Ah, fuyez, douce image") to take too external a form
of expression and occasionally the music requires a somewhat richer timbre. Cotrubas is usually fine
until a high note approaches, affecting the ease and steadiness – and sometimes the charm – of her
singing. Even so, both give deeply felt, extressively nuanced performances, presenting genuine
characers and not stereotypes. Plasson conducts a performance that is both vigorous and delicate, and
production and recorded sound are excellent.

Additional recommendations ...

...Manon – Allons! il le faut! ... Adieu, notre petite table; Suis-je gentille ainsi? ... Obéissons, quand
leur voix appelle. *Coupled with works by various composers.* **Kathleen Battle** (sop);
Chorus and Orchestra of the Opéra Bastille, Paris / Myung-Whun Chung.
DG Ⓕ 447 114-2GH (63 minutes: DDD: 7/96).

...Manon – excerpts[a]. **Gounod** Mireille – Mon coeur ne peut changer ... A toi mon âme.
Emma Luart (sop); [a]**Charles Friant**, [a]**Gaston Micheletti** (tens); [a]**Roger Bourdin,**
[a]**Jean Vieuille** (bars); orchestra / Gustave Cloez.
Vintage Music Company mono Ⓕ VM1002* (68 minutes: AAD: 4/97).

...Manon – Obéissons quand leur voix appelle. *Coupled with works by various composers.*
Renée Fleming (sop); **English Chamber Orchestra / Jeffrey Tate.**
Decca Ⓕ 458 858-2DH (70 minutes: DDD: 3/98). *Selected by Soundings.*
See review in the Collections section; refer to the Index.

Massenet Werther. Georges Thill (ten); **Ninon Vallin** (mez) Charlotte; **Marcel Roque** (bar)
Albert; **Germaine Féraldy** (sop) Sophie; **Armand Narçon** (bass) Bailli; **Henri Niel** (ten) Schmidt;
Louis Guenot (bass) Johann; **Cantoria Children's Choir; Chorus and Orchestra of the
Opéra-Comique, Paris / Elie Cohen.** EMI Références mono Ⓜ CHS7 63195-2*
(two discs: 121 minutes: ADD: 3/90). Notes, text and translation included.
From French Columbia LFX151/65. Recorded 1931. *Gramophone* classical 100.   ⒼⒼⒼ

If you want to hear just how thoroughly prepared, technically secure, idiomatic and deeply felt French
singing could be between the wars, you need only listen to this wonderful performance, here brought
to new life on this excellent EMI transfer. The reading shows the benefits of singers sticking to their
own language and singing repertory they knew through and through. Vallin develops her portrayal
unerringly from a comparatively cool and contained start to the emotional outpouring of the *Air des
lettres*, the *Air des larmes* and Prayer, where all the desperate emotions of Charlotte pour out of her
in sympathy with Massenet's impassioned writing. The placing of her tone, the way she moves
naturally with the music and the consistently warm and steady tone – these are things to treasure.
Thill's tone is just as glorious and true as his partner's, his enunciation of the text pleasing and
unaffected. Each of Werther's many solos receive a near-ideal reading, with the voice at once plangent
and virile. Perhaps what one marvels at more than anything is the way both singers scrupulously
follow Massenet's copious markings of feeling and dynamics, and how rewarding are the results.
Nowhere is this more significant than in the final scene. In lesser hands it can seem an anti-climax:
here it is infinitely moving. Listen to Thill at "Je meurs en te disant que je t'adore!" – all Werther's
happiness at being close to Charlotte as he lies dying is there expressed. The singers surrounding this
sovereign pair are no less pleasing. Roque provides a mellow baritone and just the right amount of
concern as the solid Albert. Narçon starts off the opera splendidly as a jovial Bailli. Féraldy is pert
and lively as Sophie, with the light, airy soprano the role calls for but so seldom gets. Elie Cohen's
conducting has elegance, balance and passion – but passion that never becomes overheated as it does
in some modern interpretations. Tempos are all perfectly judged and Cohen avoids heavy-handed
lingering that doesn't allow Massenet to speak for himself. All in all, a classic set that is unlikely to be
equalled. The sound for its time is more than adequate.

Massenet Werther. **Jerry Hadley** (ten) Werther; **Anne Sofie von Otter** (mez) Charlotte;
Gérard Théruel (bar) Albert; **Dawn Upshaw** (sop) Sophie; **Jean-Marie Frémeau** (bar) Magistrate;
Gilles Ragon (ten) Schmidt, Brühlmann; **Frédéric Caton** (bass) Johann; **Geneviève Marchand** (sop)

Kätchen; **Chorus and Orchestra of the Opéra National de Lyon / Kent Nagano.**
Erato Ⓕ 0630-17790-2 (two discs: 121 minutes: DDD: A/97). Notes, text and translation
included. Recorded 1995.
The opening scene of this recording promises very well; the orchestra certainly know how to play
Massenet and Nagano avoids the extremes of quasi-*verismo* style that can mar this essay in
masochistic, unrequited passion. Jerry Hadley suggests convincingly the impulsive, romantic young
poet. He has the power in his upper register for the later outbursts, but one feels that this role stretches
him to the limits of his resources. No such problem with Carreras for Davis, but here the worry is that
he sounds like Turiddu in *Cavalleria rusticana*. As Charlotte, Anne Sofie von Otter has just the right
balance between sounding young (she's meant to be 20) but emotionally mature. She and Federica von
Stade (for Davis) are among the finest interpreters of the role. Ninon Vallin in the historic Cohen
recording is superb, although the sound, of course, is fairly remote. Like Vallin, Von Stade and von
Otter are both singers who alternate between soprano and mezzo. Dawn Upshaw makes a very
positive, flirty Sophie and Gérard Théruel a good Albert. There is a grandeur about the Davis
recording which the Erato version doesn't quite attain. However, von Otter and Hadley sound every
bit as dramatic, but in a more intimate, neurotic way. In brief, this recording can be recommended
warmly; it doesn't replace the Davis version but offers an alternative.
Additional recommendation ...
...**Soloists; Children's Choir; Royal Opera House Orchestra, Covent Garden / Sir Colin Davis.**
Philips Ⓕ 416 654-2PH2 (two discs: 131 minutes: ADD: 2/87).
Further listening ...
...Fantaisie. *Coupled with works by* **Lalo** and **Saint-Saëns** Sophie Rolland (vc);
BBC Philharmonic Orchestra / Gilbert Varga. ASV CDDCA867 (12/93). *See review under Lalo;*
refer to the Index. **Gramophone** *Editor's choice.*   Ⓖ
...Hérodiade – Ballet music. Orchestral Suites – No. 1, Op. 13. No. 2, "Scènes hongroises"; Suite
No. 3, "Scènes dramatiques". **New Zealand Symphony Orchestra / Jean-Yves Ossonce.**
Naxos 8 553124 (9/95).
...Orchestral Suites – No. 4, "Scènes pittoresques"; No. 5, "Scènes napolitaines"; No. 6, "Scènes de
féerie"; No. 7, "Scènes alsaciennes". **New Zealand Symphony Orchestra / Jean-Yves Ossonce.**
Naxos 8 553125 (9/95).
...Piano Concerto in E flat major. *Coupled with* **Hahn** Piano Concerto in E major. **Stephen Coombs**
(pf); **BBC Scottish Symphony Orchestra / Jean-Yves Ossonce.** Hyperion CDA66897 (7/97).
...Thaïs – Méditation. *Coupled with works by various composers.* Itzhak Perlman (vn);
Abbey Road Ensemble / Lawrence Foster. EMI CDC5 55475-2 (1/96).
...Chérubin. **Soloists; Bavarian State Opera Chorus; Munich Radio Orchestra / Pinchas Steinberg.**
RCA Victor Red Seal 09026-60593-2 (12/92).
...Le Cid. **Soloists; Byrne Camp Chorale; New York Opera Orchestra / Eve Queler.**
Sony Classical M2K79300 (2/90).
...Esclarmonde. **Soloists; Finchley Children's Music Group; John Alldis Choir;**
National Philharmonic Orchestra / Richard Bonynge. Decca 425 651-2DM3 (8/90).
...Grisélidis. **Soloists; Lyon National Choir; Lyon Opéra Chorus; Franz Liszt Symphony Orchestra,**
Budapest / Patrick Fournillier. Koch Schwann 312702 (12/94).
...Le Roi de Lahore. **Soloists; London Voices; National Philharmonic Orchestra / Richard Bonynge.**
Decca Grand Opera 433 851-2DMO2 (2/93).
...Thérèse. **Soloists; Linden Singers; New Philharmonia Orchestra / Richard Bonynge.**
Decca 448 173-2DHO (10/96).

William Mathias

British 1934-1992

Mathias Ave Rex, Op. 45[a]. Elegy for a Prince, Op. 59[b]. This Worlde's Joie, Op. 67[c]. [c]**Janet Price**
(sop); [c]**Kenneth Bowen** (ten); [b]**Sir Geraint Evans** (bar); [c]**Michael Rippon** (bass); [a]**Welsh National**
Opera Chorus; [c]**Bach Choir;** [c]**St George's Chapel Choir, Windsor Castle;** [ab]**London Symphony**
Orchestra / David Atherton; [c]**New Philharmonia Orchestra / Sir David Willcocks.**
Lyrita Ⓕ SRCD324 (79 minutes: ADD: 2/95). Texts included. Item marked [a] from
Decca SXL6607 (12/73), [b]Argo ZRG882 (6/78), [c]HMV ASD301 (12/76). Recorded 1973.
Here are three works for voice and orchestra, two choral, one for soloist, written between 1969 and
1974. They have a good deal in common yet enough separate identity for them to comprise a varied
programme, the *Elegy for a Prince* forming a relatively tough and tangy item to be sandwiched in
between the choral collections. Of these, *Ave Rex* is a set of carols, "Sir Christmas" being now by far
the best known, and *This Worlde's Joie* a cantata in four movements, nearly 50 minutes long,
employing a boys' choir as well as the usual forces of soloists, mixed choir and orchestra. This, of
course, makes us think of Britten, and indeed it is difficult not to think of him, and to a lesser extent
Tippett, throughout the disc. In his useful booklet-note, Geraint Lewis acknowledges this but
expresses it in terms of "occasional points of contact and homage", which is probably excessively
diplomatic. *This Worlde's Joie* moves delightfully from one good setting to another, always contriving
to unify the structure and work effectively towards climax and contrast. The Prince of the *Elegy* is
Llywelyn ap Gruffudd, killed by English soldiers in 1282: a stern mood prevails, the orchestral writing

harder and more austere than the composer's usual style, though it yields to some tender expression in the last section. Sir Geraint Evans sings with authority and dark coloration. The soloists in the cantata are excellent and one wonders why more was not heard on record of Janet Price. Willcocks and Atherton conduct with vigour and care for detail, and the recordings are admirably clean.

Additional recommendation ...
...Ave Rex. I will celebrate. O how amiable, Op. 90 No. 3. Rex Gloriae – Four Latin Motets, Op. 83. Missa Aedis Christi, Op. 92. Jesus College Service, Op. 53. A Grace, Op. 89 No. 3. As truly as God is our Father. Let the people praise Thee, O God, Op. 87. Organ Fantasy, Op. 78 – No. 2, Canzonetta. **Simon Lawford** (org); **Christ Church Cathedral Choir / Stephen Darlington.** Nimbus Ⓕ NI5243 (76 minutes: DDD: 9/90).

Further listening ...
...Clarinet Concerto, Op. 68; Harp Concerto, Op. 50; Piano Concerto No. 3, Op. 40. **Gervase de Peyer** (cl); **Osian Ellis** (hp); **Peter Katin** (pf); **London Symphony Orchestra; New Philharmonia Orchestra / David Atherton.** Lyrita SRCD325 (7/95).
...Harp Concerto, Op. 50. *Coupled with* **Ginastera** Harp Concerto, Op. 25. **Ann Hobson Pilot** (hp); **English Chamber Orchestra / Isaiah Jackson.** Koch International 37261-2 (12/94).
...String Quartets – No. 1, Op. 38; No. 2, Op. 84; No. 3, Op. 97. **Medea Quartet.** Metier MSVCD92005 (10/95).
...Summer Dances. Soundings. *Coupled with* **Hoddinott** Quodlibet on Welsh Nursery Tunes. Chorales, Variants and Fanfares[a]. Ritornelli 2, Op. 100 No. 2. [a]**Kevin Bowyer** (org); **Fine Arts Brass Ensemble.** Nimbus NI5466 (5/96).
...Fanfare. Processional. Invocations, Op. 35. Fantasy, Op. 78. Berceuse, Op. 95 No. 3. Jubilate, Op. 67 No. 2. Antiphonies, Op. 88 No. 2. Fenestra. Recessional, Op. 96 No. 4. Chorale. **John Scott** (org). Nimbus NI5367 (6/93).
...Variations on a Hymn Tune, Op. 20. Canzonetta, Op. 78 No. 2. Jubilate, Op. 67 No. 2. Chorale. Toccata giocosa, Op. 36 No. 2. *Coupled with works by various composers.* **Jane Watts** (org). Priory PRCD389 (10/97). *See review in the Collections section; refer to the Index.*

Nicola Matteis
Italian/British died 1707 or later

Suggested listening ...
...Setts of Ayres – Book 2: No. 10, Preludio in ostinatione; No. 12, Andamento malincolico; Book 3: No. 7, Preludio-Prestissimo; No. 8, Sarabanda-Adagio; No. 9, Gavotta con divisioni; Book 4: No. 27, Bizzararrie sopra un basso malinconico; No. 28, Aria amorosa-Adagio. *Coupled with works by various composers.* **Palladian Ensemble.** Linn Records CKD041 (5/96). ☞ *See review in the Collections section; refer to the Index.*

Colin Matthews
British 1946

Suggested listening ...
...11 Studies in Velocity. *Coupled with works by various composers.* **Nicholas Unwin** (pf). Metier MSVCD92009 (1/96). *See review in the Collections section; refer to the Index.*

Nicholas Maw
British 1935

Maw Odyssey (1972-85, rev. 1989-90). **City of Birmingham Symphony Orchestra / Sir Simon Rattle.** EMI Ⓕ CDS7 54277-2 (two discs: 95 minutes: DDD: 9/91). Recorded live in 1990.
Gramophone classical 100. ⒼⒼⒼ
Nicholas Maw's *Odyssey* is a musical voyage of extraordinary emotional conviction. Given its well-nigh 20-year gestation, it is also a composition of remarkable coherence, a super-symphony in a single span which sustains its forward movement and sense of direction over an hour and a half with formidable skill. The listener is undoubtedly helped by a formal design that sets up plentiful associations with the grand symphonic structures of the late romantic era, particularly Mahler and Strauss. But Maw is no parodist: he is a late twentieth-century affirmation of belief in certain fundamental musical truths, especially the need for contrast between consonance and dissonance, and the consequently inescapable relevance of tonality. The whole enterprise could have yielded an embarrassing pretentiousness. Yet the actual effect is rather to reinforce awareness of the difficulties the composer had to surmount in bringing *Odyssey* to a convincing conclusion – a conclusion that seems to express fulfilment and apprehension in equal measure. Simon Rattle, the CBSO and the EMI recording team are all equal to the composer's imaginative vision. A studio recording might have managed an even richer sound, but the impact of this live event is overwhelming in a very special way.

Maw Ghost Dances. La Vita Nuova[a]. Roman Canticle[b]. [a]**Carmen Pelton** (sop); [b]**William Sharp** (bar); **Twentieth Century Consort / Christopher Kendall.** ASV Ⓕ CDDCA999 (65 minutes: DDD: 10/97). Texts and translations included. Recorded 1995.

Maw's originality may not be the kind that leaps up and yells in your face; but original he certainly is. He can draw on influences as diverse as Britten and Richard Strauss in *La Vita Nuova*, blend elements of Schoenberg's *Pierrot* and Stravinsky's *Petrushka* with the sounds of Latin American and African folk instruments in *Ghost Dances*, and still come up with something that feels like nobody else. The sound of the soprano's sultry tonal phrases in *La Vita Nuova* is a long way from the eerie tone of the African Kalimba at the end of *Ghost Dances* – beautifully described by Malcolm MacDonald in his notes as "like a phantom piano played with a bony finger". And yet in context they are obviously the same composer: a romantic with a fertile imagination and a superb technical palate, who clearly delights in enticing and surprising the ear. The performances are of outstanding warmth and finesse. The sound world of *La Vita Nuova* emerges with such richness and depth that it's hard to believe that only ten instruments are playing and Carmen Pelton has a strong sense of the way the vocal lines soar and dip over long periods. William Sharp is eloquent and quite distinct throughout the short *Roman Canticle*. And everything in *Ghost Dances* seems as clear as it should be, with no loss of atmosphere – an excellent recording. It adds up to a near-perfect introduction to a composer who offers genuine, long-term rewards, not instant, transient gratification.

Further listening ...

...Dance Scenes. **Philharmonia Orchestra / Daniel Harding.**
EMI British Composers MDS8 82648-2 (7/96).   ⒢

...Life Studies. Sonata notturna[a]. [a]**Raphael Wallfisch** (vc); **English String Orchestra /
William Boughton.** Nimbus NI5471 (8/96).

...Flute Quartet. Piano Trio. **Judith Pearce** (fl); **Paul Coletti** (va); **Monticello Trio.**
ASV CDDCA920 (6/95). *Gramophone Editor's choice.*   ⒢

Melinda Maxwell   British 20th century

Suggested listening ...

...Elegy. *Coupled with works by* **Holt** and **Birtwistle** Melinda Maxwell (ob); **Jan Gruithuyzen** (pf).
NMC NMCD042S (10/97). *See review under Birtwistle; refer to the Index.*

Sir Peter Maxwell Davies   British 1934

Maxwell Davies Symphony No. 6. Time and the Raven. **Royal Philharmonic Orchestra /
Sir Peter Maxwell Davies.** Collins Classics ⒻⒺ 1482-2 (63 minutes: DDD: 1/97). Recorded 1996.
The finale of Peter Maxwell Davies's Sixth is perhaps the most sheerly beautiful symphonic movement he has yet written. Its beauty is not unshadowed but under threat, and there is a climax of plangent urgency before a grim pounding fades to silence. The symphony begins and ends with an earnest string melody which, according to the composer, "is subjected to continuous transformations in between". That theme is based on an Australian aboriginal song which Maxwell Davies has previously used in *Time and the Raven*, a 14-minute orchestral movement commissioned by the RPO to mark the fiftieth anniversary of the United Nations. In *Time and the Raven* the conflict is a simple one, between nationalist images and one drawn from a people whose words for 'world' and 'tribal community' are the same. A symphonic conflict is far more complex, of course, and to lumber Maxwell Davies's Sixth with an internationalist programme would be an impertinence. For anyone approaching his symphonies for the first time the Sixth would make a good introduction, while for those who already know the others its shows him continuing to explore the possibilities of symphonic form. After the complex single-movement Fifth, a 'finale-directed' symphony in three movements might seem something of a retreat, but in fact the argument powerfully bridges pauses between movements and changes of tempo within them. Collins Classics were commendably prompt in recording the Sixth within six months of its première. By now it almost goes without saying that the performance and the recorded sound are both first-class.

Maxwell Davies Strathclyde Concertos – No. 3[a]; No. 4[b]. [a]**Randall Cook** (hn); [b]**Lewis Morrison**
(cl); [a]**Peter Franks** (tpt); **Scottish Chamber Orchestra / Sir Peter Maxwell Davies.**
Collins Classics ⒻⒺ 1239-2 (61 minutes: DDD: 10/92). Recorded 1991.
Maxwell Davies's plan to write a sequence of no fewer than ten *Strathclyde* Concertos (now completed) for the principals of the Scottish Chamber Orchestra turned into a research project into the nature of the concerto, the relationship between soloist and orchestra. His solo parts are always satisfying, even virtuoso, but the orchestra seldom adopt an accompanying or antagonistic role. In the double concerto for trumpet and horn, for example, the flutes and strings also play a very important part, with material of their own that the soloists hardly touch, but the effect is to emphasize the 'flute-ness' of the flutes and the 'string-ness' of the strings: they become, in effect, co-soloists themselves. Maxwell Davies is also interested of course, in this concerto, in the 'trumpet-ness' and 'horn-ness' of his two principal soloists, and in the beautiful slow movement they dramatize this by eventually exchanging functions, the trumpet becoming lyrical, the horn martial. One of the functions of the clarinet, in its concerto, is to point up the sober beauty, the 'un-clarinet-ness', of the textures against which its cool solo line moves; it has an especially fruitful relationship with that section of the

orchestra with which it is in greatest contrast, the low strings. Both works require intent listening; both reward it with readily perceptible formal ingenuity (the way in which the clarinet concerto's main theme is only gradually revealed as a haunting folk-song is especially absorbing) and a fascinating interplay of instrumental character. Both concertos are vividly performed and very cleanly recorded.

Maxwell Davies Corpus Christi, with Cat and Mouse. House of Winter. Sea Runes. Lullabye for
Lucy. Apple-Basket: Apple-Blossom. One star, at last. A Hoy Calendar. Westerlings.
BBC Singers / Simon Joly. Collins Classics Ⓟ 1463-2 (71 minutes: DDD: 2/96).
Texts and translation included. Recorded 1995.

You might think unaccompanied voices would cramp Maxwell Davies's style. Far from it: the range of colour and texture here is remarkable, all the more so since, with a single exception, all these pieces sound challenging but grateful to sing. The exception is *Westerlings*, which calls for a chorus of virtuosos. Like all this music, save *Corpus Christi*, it uses poems by the late George Mackay Brown, in this case a narrative of the Norse settlement of Orkney, interspersed with magical wordless 'seascapes' and concluding with a setting of the Lord's Prayer in the Orkney dialect of Old Norse: a solemn thanksgiving for a safe landfall. It is closely related to the sea music of Maxwell Davies's symphonies, but the texts and a brilliantly resourceful use of vocal effect and vocal 'scoring' (the illusion of flutes, strings, even an organ, is consummate) make it both dramatic and pictorially evocative. *House of Winter* portrays both the frozen stillness and the violent storms of an Orkney winter, but with poetry and luminous colour rather than onomatopoeia; like its companion piece, *Sea Runes*, its lines are kind to voices. Some of the smaller works here – the very pure melody over rocking "lullays" of *Lullabye for Lucy, A Hoy Calendar* – would not tax a good amateur choir, though some pages of *Corpus Christi* most certainly would. The choral singing, as one would expect of this ensemble and this conductor, is superfine; the recording is both clean and pleasingly spacious.

Maxwell Davies The Beltane Fire. Caroline Mathilde – suite from Act 2. [a]**Carys Lane,**
[a]**Carolyn Sampson** (sops); [a]**Deborah Miles-Johnson,** [a]**Sally Bruce-Payne** (mezzos);
BBC Philharmonic Orchestra / Sir Peter Maxwell Davies. Collins Classics Ⓟ 1464-2
(70 minutes: DDD: 6/96). Recorded 1995.

You would expect a pronounced Scottish element in the ballet score that is actually set in Scotland; in fact a touching and distinctly Scottish melody, associated with the unfortunate princess, recurs throughout the *Caroline Mathilde* suite as well, though it isn't heard in its 'pure' form until the very end when Caroline is sent into exile. Elsewhere Maxwell Davies shows a remarkable ability to adapt his style – one of his styles, at all events – to the needs of ballet, writing what any ballet-goer will recognize as a real *pas-de-deux* in the form of a passacaglia which rises to impassioned lyricism and then sombre gravity. Elements of paraphrase rather than pastiche are present in a menacing courtly gavotte and a dance of grotesque violence in which the people mock Caroline's doomed affair with a court doctor. No less sinister, there is a scene in which a conspiracy against the hated foreign princess is represented in quiet, rather hymn-like music with conventional harmonies (it is also rather like – can this be a coincidence? – one of Carl Nielsen's patriotic songs): consonance itself curdles and becomes nightmarish. At one time Maxwell Davies would have raucously parodied this; here he no longer needs to. Similar elements are present in *Beltane Fire*, and again the destructive elements are not mocked: the music of the minister and the elders whose influence eventually destroys a folk fiddle-player is quiet, often sinisterly so, but it is never caricatured. The folk music references here are overt. Maxwell Davies writes Orkney fiddle tunes of total authenticity, but also expands their expressive range, in this instance to a wild pagan vigour for the fertility dance around the Beltane flames and to the pathos of the fiddler's son remembering a destroyed way of life as the curtain falls. As Maxwell Davies's major concert works move closer towards tonal reference so the pieces in his other style take on deeper seriousness and eloquence. Could the two be moving towards each other? Excellent performances, as by now we would expect, from the Maxwell Davies/BBC Philharmonic partnership; the recordings are clean and vivid.

Further listening ...

...Strathclyde Concertos – No. 5[a]; No. 6[b]. [b]**David Nicholson** (fl); [a]**James Clark** (vn);
[a]**Catherine Marwood** (va); **Scottish Chamber Orchestra / Sir Peter Maxwell Davies.**
Collins Classics 1303-2 (5/94).
...Strathclyde Concertos – No. 7[a]; No. 8[b]. A Spell for Green Corn: The MacDonald Dances[c].
[a]**Duncan McTier** (db); [b]**Ursula Leveaux** (bn); [c]**James Clark** (vn); **Scottish Chamber Orchestra /
Sir Peter Maxwell Davies.** Collins Classics 1396-2 (9/94).
...Strathclyde Concertos – No. 9; No. 10. Carolísima. **Scottish Chamber Orchestra /
Sir Peter Maxwell Davies.** Collins Classics 1459-2 (5/97).
...Symphony No. 1. **BBC Philharmonic Orchestra / Sir Peter Maxwell Davies.**
Collins Classics 1435-2 (12/95).
...Symphony No. 2 in B minor. **BBC Philharmonic Orchestra / Sir Peter Maxwell Davies.**
Collins Classics 1403-2 (9/94). *Gramophone Editor's choice.*   Ⓖ
...Symphony No. 3. **BBC Philharmonic Orchestra / Sir Peter Maxwell Davies.**
Collins Classics 1416-2 (1/95).
...Symphony No. 4. Trumpet Concerto[a]. [a]**John Wallace** (tpt); [a]**Scottish Chamber Orchestra /
Sir Peter Maxwell Davies.** Collins Classics 1181-2 (6/91).

...Symphony No. 5[a]. Five Klee Pictures[a]. Chat Moss[b]. Cross Lane Fair[b]. [a]**Philharmonia Orchestra;**
  [b]**BBC Philharmonic Orchestra / Sir Peter Maxwell Davies.** Collins Classics 1460-2 (6/95).   Ⓖ
...Vesalii icones[a]. The Bairns of Brugh[b]. Runes from a Holy Island[c]. **The Fires of London /**
  Sir Peter Maxwell Davies. Unicorn-Kanchana Souvenir UKCD2068 (2/95).
...O magnum mysterium – Fantasia. Three Organ Voluntaries. Reliqui Domum meum.
  Organ Sonata. *Coupled with works by* **J. Harvey** and **Williamson** Kevin Bowyer (org).
  Nimbus NI5509 (7/97).
...Ave maris stella. Image, Reflection, Shadow[a]. Runes from a Holy Island[b].
  [a]**Gregory Knowles** (cimbalom); **The Fires of London /** [b]**Sir Peter Maxwell Davies.**
  Unicorn-Kanchana Souvenir UKCD2038 (3/91).   Ⓖ
...Black Pentecost[a]. Stone Litany. **Della Jones** (mez); [a]**David Wilson-Johnson** (bar);
  BBC Philharmonic Orchestra / Sir Peter Maxwell Davies. Collins Classics 1366-2 (8/93).
...Le jongleur de Notre Dame[a]. Movement for String Quartet[b]. [a]**Edward Albert** (bar);
  [b]**Arditti Quartet;** [a]**Opera Sacra, Buffalo / Charles Peltz.** Mode Records MODE59 (2/98).
...Miss Donnithorne's Maggot[a]. Eight Songs for a Mad King[b]. [a]**Mary Thomas** (sop);
  [b]**Julius Eastman** (bar); **The Fires of London / Sir Peter Maxwell Davies.**
  Unicorn-Kanchana DKPCD9052 (3/88).
...An Orkney Wedding, with Sunrise. Kinloche, his Fantassie[b]. Seven Songs Home[a]. Yesnaby
  Ground[c]. Dances from "The Two Fiddlers"[b]. Jimmack the Postie[b]. Farewell to Stromness[c].
  Lullaby for Lucy[a]. Renaissance Scottish Dances[b]. [a]**St Mary's Music School Choir;**
  [b]**Scottish Chamber Orchestra / Sir Peter Maxwell Davies** ([c]pf).
  Unicorn-Kanchana DKPCD9070 (12/88).
...Job. **Soloists; Vancouver Bach Choir; CBC Vancouver Orchestra / Sir Peter Maxwell Davies.**
  Collins Classics 1516-2 (12/97).
...The Lighthouse. **Soloists; BBC Philharmonic Orchestra / Sir Peter Maxwell Davies.**
  Collins Classics 1415-2 (1/95).
...The Martyrdom of St Magnus. **Soloists; Scottish Chamber Opera Ensemble / Michael Rafferty.**
  Unicorn-Kanchana DKPCD9100 (3/91).
...Resurrection. **Soloists; BBC Philharmonic Orchestra / Sir Peter Maxwell Davies.**
  Collins Classics 7034-2 (8/95).

Billy Mayerl   British 1902-1959

Mayerl Crystal Clear. Orange Blossom. Piano Exaggerations. Pastorale Exotique.
  Wistaria. Canaries' Serenade. Shy Ballerina. Puppets Suite, Op. 77. Piano Transcriptions – Body
  and Soul; Deep Henderson; Tormented; Sing, you sinners; Cheer up; Have you forgotten?;
  The object of my affection; Is it true what they say about Dixie?; I need you; Love was born;
  I'm at your service.
Parkin Mayerl Shots, Sets 1 and 2. A Tribute to Billy Mayerl. **Eric Parkin** (pf).
  Priory Ⓟ PRCD544 (80 minutes: DDD: 12/96). Recorded 1995.
This disc of mainly Mayerl must be bringing Parkin close to having recorded the complete works. So
much the better, as there is nobody since the master himself who has come anywhere near Parkin's
easy technical mastery and fastidious musicianship in this delightful music. It is especially good to
have together all four of the *Piano Exaggerations*, Mayerl's second set of pieces from 1926 – and what
a good group they make. So do Mayerl's other suites. Some pianists hit the more demanding pieces
quite hard: Parkin, like Mayerl, knows better and his playing is consistently light and subtle. This has
always been his approach, allied to a faultless sense of pace and rhythm. However, Mayerl, apart from
perfecting the piano novelty, also contributed to the English pastoral tradition, which Parkin knows
equally well. *Shy Ballerina* is charmingly done with rubato which would be quite out of place in
Mayerl's rhythmic numbers. The three-movement *Puppets Suite* is a *tour de force*. There are more
transcriptions too, based on standards we still know, as well as on some of Mayerl's own songs, which
sadly we still don't. As a bonus on this generous 80-minute CD Parkin puts in two sets of his own
pieces called *Mayerl Shots*. He explains that, as a result of practising lots of Mayerl, further ideas
surfaced spontaneously in a similar idiom. These are all fluent tributes and there are even quotations
for the specialists. The piano sound is sharp and clear. Essential listening.

Mayerl Scallywag. Jasmine. Oriental. Minuet for Pamela. Fascinating Ditty. Funny Peculiar.
  Chopsticks. Carminetta. Mignonette. Penny Whistle. Piano Transcriptions – Me and my girl;
  Blue velvet; Sittin' on the edge of my chair; The pompous gremlin; My heaven in the pines;
  Alabamy bound; Stardust; Please handle with care; Two lovely people; Two hearts on a tree;
  You're the reason why. Studies in Syncopation, Op. 55 – Nos. 7, 10, 14, 15 and 18.
Parkin Mayerl Shots, Set 3. **Eric Parkin** (pf). Priory Ⓟ PRCD565 (76 minutes: DDD: 7/97).
  Recorded 1995.
This release, "Scallywag", has its own discoveries, notably the *Studies in Syncopation*, which parallel
Bartók's *Mikrokosmos* in this field. There are three books of six pieces each, dating from 1930-31, and
Parkin plays five of them, proving that they are not just exercises but real music. There are gems in
yet more transcriptions – Carmichael's *Stardust*, Mayerl's own "You're the reason why" from his 1934

show *Sporting Love*, and a forgotten but lovely tune by Peter York called *Two hearts on a tree*. The Spanish *Carminetta* is Mayerl's equivalent of Joplin's *Solace*. And there is real comedy – totally appreciated and effectively realized by Parkin – in *Chopsticks* and *Penny Whistle*. As in the previous volume Parkin gives us his own response to Mayerl in a similar idiom – a third set of what he has aptly called *Mayerl Shots*. The recording is adequate although there is occasionally some background noise.

Mayerl Piano Transcriptions, Volume 3 – There's a small hotel; The mood that I'm in; So rare; I'm always in the mood for you; Turkey in the straw; For only you; Thanks for the memory; The Highland Swing; I got love; Amoresque; There's rain in my eyes; Patty cake, patty cake, baker man; Blame it on my last affair; I have eyes; Like a cat with a mouse; Phil the Fluter's Ball; Fools rush in; Peg o' my heart; All the things you are; The Musical Earwig; Transatlantic Lullaby; Tell me I'm forgiven; Japanese Juggler; Poor little rich girl. **Eric Parkin** (pf). Priory Ⓕ PRCD468 (63 minutes: DDD: 7/95). Recorded 1993. *Gramophone Editor's choice.*   ⒼⒼ
This is pure 1930s music. This is not Mayerl as the lightning-fingered whizz-kid of the 1920s, although many of the transcriptions are tricky enough: it's the style he taught through the Billy Mayerl School of Music, a success story here and abroad until the war. The war killed nostalgia and well before Mayerl died in 1959 a teenage pop culture was on the rampage. But these transcriptions – popular songs of the period arranged in Mayerl's inimitable English accent – are a wonderful encapsulation of an era and they transcend it – as long as they are played like this. The demands on the performer are similar to studying the style of the period at any time. Classically trained pianists have to work hard to play Joplin, Gershwin and Mayerl. But Mayerl belongs to them, as long as their left hand is strong enough, because this is basically a notated tradition rather than an improvised one. Parkin understands it all – the effortless lilt, the light touch, not too much pedal, nothing overdone, everything speaking for itself.
Further listening ...
...Marigold[a]. A Lily Pond. Four Aces[a]. From a Spanish lattice[a]. Minuet by Candlelight. Aquarium Suite[a]. Autumn Crocus[a]. Bats in the Belfry[a]. Pastoral Sketches. Fireside Fusiliers[a]. The Parade of the Sandwich-Board Men[a]. Waltz for a lonely heart. Busybody. [a]**Andrew Ball** (pf); **Bratislava Radio Symphony Orchestra / Gary Carpenter.** Marco Polo 8 223514 (12/94).
...Piano Works, Volume 2 – Four Aces Suite – No. 1, Ace of Clubs; No. 4, Ace of Spades. Mistletoe. Autumn crocus. Hollyhock. White heather. Three Dances in Syncopation, Op. 73. Sweet William. Parade of the Sandwich-Board Men. Hop-O'-My-Thumb. Jill all alone. Aquarium Suite. *Coupled with* **Mayerl/Croom-Johnson** Bats in the Belfry. Green tulips. **Eric Parkin** (pf). Chandos CHAN8848 (11/90).
...Piano works, Volume 3 – Filigree. Three Miniatures in syncopation, Op. 76. Siberian lament. In my Garden: Summertime. Three Japanese Pictures, Op. 25 – A Temple in Kyoto; The Cherry Dance. Beguine Impromptu. The Big Top. The Legends of King Arthur – The Sword Excalibur; Guinevere. Honky-tonk. In my Garden: Autumntime. Romanesque. Four insect Oddities. Leprechaun's Leap. **Eric Parkin** (pf). Chandos CHAN9141 (9/93).   Ⓖ
...Piano Transcriptions, Volume 1 – Did you ever see a dream walking?; Thanks; Love locked out; On the other side of Lovers' Lane; I cover the waterfront; Weep no more my baby; We belong together; Close your eyes; Masquerading in the name of love; Two cigarettes in the dark; Oceans of time; April in Paris; Arlene; Love thy neighbour; Say it. Balloons; Other people's babies; June in January; Imaginary Foxtrot; The Continental; With my eyes wide open I'm dreaming; Chasing shadows; The girl with the dreamy eyes; Cheek to cheek. **Eric Parkin** (pf). Priory PRCD466 (1/95).
...Piano Transcriptions, Volume 2 – Smoke gets in your eyes; You hit the spot; Anything goes; I feel like a feather in the breeze; Love me forever; Please believe me; Evr'thing's been done before; I breathe on windows; Without a word of warning; There's a star in the sky; Fatal fascination; Limehouse Blues; Will I ever know?; A penny in my pocket; Turn on the taps; The dance goes on; I'm in a dancing mood; Without rhythm; My first thrill; Stranger in a cup of tea; You're not too bad yourself; Lambeth Walk; At the Balalaika; Everything's in rhythm with my heart. **Eric Parkin** (pf). Priory PRCD467 (5/95).

Ascanio Mayone
Italian c1565-1627

Suggested listening ...
...Partite sopra "Fidele". *Coupled with works by various composers.* **Rinaldo Alessandrini** (hpd). Opus 111 OPS30-118 (4/95). ☞ *See review in the Collections section; refer to the Index.*   ⒼⒼ

Michel Mazuel
French 1603-1676

Suggested listening ...
...Suite in G major. *Coupled with works by* **Dumanoir** *and* **La Voye-Mignot**
Le Concert des Nations / Jordi Savall.
Auvidis Fontalis ES9908 (1/98). ☞ *See review under Dumanoir; refer to the Index.*

Nikolay Medtner

Medtner Piano Concerto No. 1 in C minor, Op. 33[a]. Piano Quintet in C major, Op. posth[b].
Dmitri Alexeev (pf); [b]**New Budapest Quartet** (András Kiss, Ferenc Balogh, vns;
Laszlo Barsony, va; Karoly Botvay, vc); [a]**BBC Symphony Orchestra / Alexander Lazarev.**
Hyperion Ⓕ CDA66744 (59 minutes: DDD: 3/95). Recorded 1994.

Medtner would have been both grateful and astonished by his present and ever-increasing recognition. Once dismissed as an unsatisfactory betwixt-and-between composer, one without a convincing personal voice who was overshadowed by Rachmaninov's greater glamour and accessibility, his time has truly come. For Dmitri Alexeev the First Concerto is Medtner's masterpiece, an argument he sustains in a performance of superb eloquence and discretion. Even the sort of gestures later vulgarized and traduced by Tinseltown are given with an aristocratic quality, a feel for a love of musical intricacy that takes on an almost symbolic force and potency, but also for Medtner's dislike of display. You may occasionally miss Igor Zhukov's more blustering, devil-may-care virtuosity, yet time and again Alexeev makes you pause to reconsider Medtner's quality, and his reserve brings its own distinctive reward. The early *Abbandonamente ma non troppo* has a haunting improvisatory inwardness and later, as the storm clouds gather ominously at 11'55", his playing generates all the necessary electricity. How thankful one is, too, for Alexeev's advocacy of the Piano Quintet where, together with his fully committed colleagues, the New Budapest Quartet, he recreates music of the strangest, most unworldly exultance and introspection. Instructions such as *poco tranquillo (sereno)* and *Quasi Hymn* take us far away from the turbulence of the First Concerto (composed in the shadow of the First World War) and the finale's conclusion is wonderfully uplifting. The recordings are judiciously balanced in both works, and the BBC Symphony Orchestra under Lazarev are fully sympathetic.

Additional recommendation ...

...Piano Concertos Nos. 1-3[a]. Sonata-Ballade in F sharp major, Op. 27. **Geoffrey Tozer** (pf);
[a]**London Philharmonic Orchestra / Neeme Järvi.** Chandos Ⓕ CHAN9040 (two discs: 127 minutes:
DDD: 4/92).

Medtner Piano Concertos – No. 2 in C minor, Op. 50; No. 3 in E minor, Op. 60.
Nikolai Demidenko (pf); **BBC Scottish Symphony Orchestra / Jerzy Maksymiuk.**
Hyperion Ⓕ CDA66580 (74 minutes: DDD: 4/92). Recorded 1991.
Gramophone Award Winner 1992. ⒼⒼ

Medtner Piano Concertos – No. 2 in C minor, Op. 50[a]; No. 3 in E minor, Op. 60[b]. Arabesque in
A minor, Op. 7 No. 2[c]. Fairy Tale in F minor, Op. 26 No. 3[d]. **Nikolay Medtner** (pf);
[ab]**Philharmonia Orchestra / Issay Dobrowen.** Testament mono Ⓕ SBT1027*
(77 minutes: ADD: 4/94). Item marked [a] from HMV DB6559/63 (2/48), [b]DB6718/22 (8/48),
[c]DB6563, [d]DB6564 (both 2/48). Recorded 1947. ⒼⒼ

Hyperion's splendid disc is given a fine recording, good orchestral playing from a Scottish orchestra under a Polish conductor and, above all, truly coruscating and poetic playing from the brilliant young Russian pianist Nikolai Demidenko. It also did a splendid rehabilitation job for Nikolay Medtner who is steadily coming in from the cold after half a century of neglect. He was a contemporary and friend of Rachmaninov who settled in Britain in the 1930s, and like Rachmaninov (to whom the Second Concerto is dedicated and who returned the compliment with his own Fourth) he was an excellent pianist. But while the other composer became immensely popular, Medtner languished in obscurity, regarded (if thought about at all) as an inferior imitation of Rachmaninov who wrote gushing music that was strong on gestures but weak on substance. The fact is that he can be diffuse (not to say long-winded) and grandiose, and memorable tunes are in short supply, so that his music needs to be played well to come off. But when it is there's much to enjoy and the strong Russian flavour of the ornate writing is evident, as is the composer's masterly understanding of the piano. Listening to the composer himself in the Second's first *molto cantabile a tempo, ma expressivo* or the Third's *dolce cantabile* is to be made doubly aware of his haunting and bittersweet lyricism. The streaming figuration in the Second Concerto's *Romanza* is spun off with deceptive ease, a reminder that while Medtner despised obvious pyrotechnics he was a superlative pianist. So here, surely, is an ideal complement to Demidenko's hypnotically fiery and articulate accounts. Two exquisitely played encores are included (the ambiguous poetry of the A minor *Arabesque* could be by no other composer), and the 1947 recordings have been superbly remastered.

Medtner Violin Sonatas – No. 1 in B minor, Op. 21; No. 2 in G major, Op. 44. **Lydia Mordkovitch**
(vn); **Geoffrey Tozer** (pf). Chandos Ⓕ CHAN9293 (60 minutes: DDD: 11/94).

Lydia Mordkovitch and Geoffrey Tozer faced stiff competition in this repertoire from Alexander Shirinsky and Dmitri Galynin (on the currently unavailable Mezhdunarodnaya Kniga label), not only because they offered exceptionally fine performances, but also because their two-CD set offered all three violin sonatas plus the remaining (very attractive) shorter works that make up Medtner's total output for violin and piano. In general, Mordkovitch's readings emphasize a more lyrical and relaxed approach, and this is particularly so in the lyrical first movement of the short, attractive First Sonata – a little too relaxed perhaps in the outer sections of the lilting second movement "Danza". Elsewhere (for instance the *Allegro appassionato* and Finale-Rondo of the Second Sonata), Mordkovitch has a more intuitive grasp of structure, allowing the music to unfold with a degree more ease and direction. Nevertheless, in their own way, both artists are persuasive interpreters of these works and can be strongly recommended to the first-time explorer. The recorded sound is warm and well balanced.

Medtner Violin Sonata No. 3 in E minor, Op. 57, "Epica".
Ravel Violin Sonata. **Vadim Repin** (vn); **Boris Berezovsky** (pf).
Erato Ⓕ 0630-15110-2 (61 minutes: DDD: 2/97). Recorded 1996.

The Medtner sonata is the principal work here. Of the three that he wrote this is perhaps the most intricately worked and, at over 40 minutes, certainly the most substantial. At times it seems almost too long for its own good and for that reason it needs a very persuasive and masterly performance in order to project its strengths. Fortunately Vadim Repin's and Boris Berezovsky's performance here is about as persuasive as you can get – Repin is lyrical and passionate and has plenty of fiery temperament for this music, and he is ideally complemented by Berezovsky's equally splendid playing. Much is made of the sonata's lyrical and melodic abundance (the *Scherzo* is delivered with great panache) and Repin's choice of tempo for all movements is expertly judged. Those with only an interest in the Ravel will probably content themselves with one of the many other fine, more aptly coupled recordings available (see under Ravel; refer to the Index), which is a pity, as Repin and Berezovsky are perhaps even more impressive here than in the Medtner. As a vehicle for Repin's talent it shows what a marvellous colourist he is, what exceptional subtlety and nuance he brings to the music and, in the "Blues" movement especially, the sheer *frisson* he is capable of generating. One cannot understate the superb ensemble playing either, with Berezovsky perfectly attuned to every twist and turn of Repin's playing. The recorded sound throughout is very realistic and naturally balanced.

Medtner The Angel, Op. 1*a*. Winter Evening, Op. 13 No. 1. Songs, Op. 28 – No. 2, I cannot hear that bird; No. 3, Butterfly; No. 4, In the Churchyard; No. 5, Spring Calm. The Rose, Op. 29 No. 6. I loved thee well, Op. 32 No. 4. Night, Op. 36 No. 5. Sleepless, Op. 37 No. 1. Songs, Op. 52 – No. 2, The Raven; No. 3, Elegy; No. 5, Spanish Romance; No. 6, Serenade. Noon, Op. 59 No. 1. Eight Songs, Op. 24. **Ludmilla Andrew** (sop); **Geoffrey Tozer** (pf).
Chandos Ⓕ CHAN9327 (60 minutes: DDD: 12/95). Texts and translations included.

Musical Opinion, reviewing the newly published Op. 52 in 1931, concluded that, "very accomplished musician" as he undoubtedly was, Medtner could hardly be considered "a born song writer": "These restless, feverish compositions with their incessant chromaticism and modulations are essentially unvocal, though they are dramatic and rhapsodical enough." It says something for the achievement of Ludmilla Andrew that the 'unvocal' character of Medtner's writing is hardly evident at all, though, to be fair, the first three songs from Op. 52 are perhaps the very ones in which the voice is most hard-pressed and in which it is even possible to feel that they might do very well as piano solos. In the "Serenade" (No. 6 in the set), the piano part *is* an accompaniment, and the singer brings to it a charm and delicacy worthy of its dedicatee, Nina Koshetz. Geoffrey Tozer is an excellent accompanist (he is in any case a highly experienced Medtner pianist). His playing of "Winter Evening", with its evocative rustling start, is superb; but always, along with the sheer virtuosity, there is a responsive feeling for mood and coloration. In his written notes he mentions critics who complain that Medtner's songs are "sonatas in disguise", and the balance of recording might have helped to stifle such objections if it had allowed the singer more presence. Certainly there are songs in which the piano takes over. Yet in many the interest is evenly distributed, and these are among the most delightful in the repertoire.

Further listening ...
...Russian Round Dance (A Tale), Op. 58 No. 1. Knight Errant, Op. 58 No. 2.
Coupled with works by **Rachmaninov** **Dmitri Alexeev, Nikolai Demidenko** (pfs).
Hyperion CDA66654 (10/94). *Gramophone Editor's choice.*
...Danza festiva, Op. 38 No. 3. *Coupled with works by various composers.*
Marc-André Hamelin (pf). Hyperion CDA66765 (3/95). *See review under Alkan; refer to the Index. Gramophone Editor's choice.* Ⓖ Ⓖ
...Forgotten Melodies, Op. 38 – Sonata reminiscenza; Canzona serenata. Sonaten-Triade, Op. 11 – Sonata elegia. Forgotten Melodies, Op. 39 – Canzona matinata; Sonata tragica. Scazka (Fairy Tale) in B flat minor, Op. 20 No. 1. Theme and Variations in C sharp minor, Op. 55. Dithyramb in E flat major, Op. 10 No. 2. **Nikolai Demidenko** (pf). Hyperion CDA66636 (9/93).
Gramophone Editor's choice. Selected by Sounds in Retrospect.
...Four Fairy Tales, Op. 34 – No. 2 in E minor; No. 3 in A minor. Fairy Tale in B flat minor, Op. 20 No. 1. Fairy Tale in D minor, Op. 51 No. 1. Romantic Sketches for the Young, Op. 65 – Book 2: Tale. *Coupled with works by various composers.* **Boris Berezovsky** (pf).
Teldec 4509-96516-2 (7/96). *See review in the Collections section; refer to the Index.*

Diogo Melgás
Portuguese 1638-1700

Melgás Popule meus. Lamentaçao de Quinta Feira Santa. Salve regina.
Rebelo Super aspidem. Ecce nunc. In te, Domine, speravi. Qui habitat. Fratres sobrii. Educes me. Panis angelicus. Magnificat. **The Sixteen; His Majesties Sagbutts and Cornetts /**
Harry Christophers. Collins Classics Ⓕ 1465-2 (68 minutes: DDD: 12/96). Recorded 1996.

The latest recording from The Sixteen explores the little-known world of sacred choral music from seventeenth-century Portugal through works by two of the leading composers of the time: João Lourenço Rebelo and Diogo Dias Melgás. The singers are joined for some of the pieces by His Majesties Sagbutts and Cornetts and/or a continuo team of theorbo, harp and organ. The result is a fascinating insight into the musical life in the western extremity of Europe at a time when Italian developments have traditionally been held to represent the mainstream. The blend of vocal and instrumental writing, for example in Rebelo's *Super aspidem*, is just as assured and colourful as Gabrieli's, while the more virtuoso vocal idiom of the Portuguese composer's *Qui habitat* owes much to the later Venetian style, as does the instrumental elaboration of chant in Rebelo's setting of Psalm 31, *Educes me* (plenty of resonances of the 1610 Vespers here). Alongside these more 'modern' works are impressive polychoral pieces and the more restrained polyphonic idiom of Melgás's setting of the Improperia, *Popule meus*. All the music is of a high quality, and it is excellently performed. His Majesties Sagbutts and Cornetts have already successfully joined forces with Westminster Cathedral Choir, and the result on this recording with The Sixteen is just as compelling. The singers are quite superb, and particularly admirable is the sustained intensity of the *a cappella* singing in Melgás's *Popule meus*. This is one of the best and most interesting discs by The Sixteen in recent years, and the sound is excellent.

Additional recommendation ...
...Salve regina. Lamentationes. In Monte Oliveti. O vos omnes. Pia et dolorosa Mater. In ieiunio et fletu. Memento homo. Ecce ascendimus. Adiuva nos. Ille homo. Ego sum resurrectio. Magister volumus. Rex tremendae maiestatis. Recordare Virgo Mater. *Coupled with works by* **Morago**
Pro Cantione Antiqua / Mark Brown with **Robert Aldwinckle** (org), **Celia Harper** (hp); **Andrew Watts** (dulcian). Hyperion Ⓕ CDA66715 (62 minutes: DDD: 11/94).

Felix Mendelssohn   German 1809-1847

Mendelssohn Piano Concertos – No. 1 in G minor, Op. 25; No. 2 in D minor, Op. 40. Capriccio brillant in B minor, Op. 22. Rondo brillant in E flat major, Op. 29. Serenade and Allegro giocoso, Op. 43. **Stephen Hough** (pf); **City of Birmingham Symphony Orchestra / Lawrence Foster.**
Hyperion Ⓕ CDA66969 (75 minutes: DDD: 9/97). Recorded 1997.   ⒼⒼ
With Stephen Hough's Mendelssohn we enter a new dimension. The soft, stylish arpeggios that open the first work here, the *Capriccio brillant*, announce immediately that something special is on the way. But this is just a preparation for the First Concerto. Here again, 'stylish' is the word. One can sense the background – especially the operatic background against which these works were composed (Weber is very much present). The first solo doesn't simply storm away, *fortissimo*; one hears distinct emotional characteristics: the imperious, thundering octaves, the agitated semiquavers, the pleading appoggiaturas. The revelation is the First Concerto's slow movement: not a trace of stale sentimentality here, rather elegance balanced by depth of feeling. Some of the praise must go to the CBSO and Lawrence Foster; after all it's the CBSO violas and cellos that lead the singing in that slow movement. Foster and the orchestra are also effective in the opening of the Second Concerto – too often dismissed as the less inspired sequel to No. 1. The first bars are hushed, sombre, a little below the main tempo, so that it's left to Hough to energize the argument and set the pace – all very effective. Hough is now clearly the first recommendation in the concertos. If you still doubt that Mendelssohn could be possessed by genuine creative fire, discs like this should be enough to show you how wrong you are.

Additional recommendations
...Nos. 1 and 2. **András Schiff** (pf); **Bavarian Radio Symphony Orchestra / Charles Dutoit.**
Decca Ⓕ 414 672-2DH (DDD: 5/86).
...Nos. 1 and 2. Capriccio brillant. **London Mozart Players / Howard Shelley** (pf).
Chandos Ⓕ CHAN9215 (55 minutes: DDD: 4/94).   Ⓖ
...Nos. 1 and 2. Capriccio brillant. Rondo brillant. **Benjamin Frith** (pf); **Košice State Philharmonic Orchestra / Robert Stankovsky.** Naxos Ⓢ 8 550681 (70 minutes: DDD: 4/94).   Ⓖ

Mendelssohn Piano Concerto in E minor (reconstr. Todd)[a].
Mendelssohn-Hensel Das Jahr – February; March; May; September; December.
Schumann Konzertsatz in D minor (1839)[a].
C. Schumann Piano Sonata in G minor. **Jennifer Eley** (pf); [a]**English Chamber Orchestra / Sayard Stone.** Koch International Classics Ⓕ 37197-2 (64 minutes: DDD: 10/96). Recorded 1994-95.
What a delightful disc this is. Mendelssohn's E minor Piano Concerto fragment (sympathetically reconstructed by R. Larry Todd and recorded here for the first time) makes a compelling opener. Ably supported by the ECO, Jennifer Eley deploys her athletic virtuosity with taste and precision in the dramatic *Allegro*, while piano and orchestra are winningly expressive in the sweetly melodious *Andante*. As Todd points out in the insert-notes, this E minor Concerto offers valuable insights into the Violin Concerto with which it shares common thematic and design features, and a performance as authoritative as this one will prove irresistible to collectors. Likewise, Robert Schumann's *Konzertsatz* for piano and orchestra – an important landmark in the composer's progress towards his A minor Piano Concerto – is played dynamically by these musicians. Most notable, though, are the

two works for solo piano – Clara Schumann's G minor Sonata and excerpts from Fanny Mendelssohn-Hensel's *Das Jahr* – where Eley's feeling for this repertoire is at its most alluring and evocative. She articulates the Sonata's first movement with astonishing clarity, produces aptly rich *cantabile* in the *Adagio*, neat precision in the scherzo and builds to an exciting climax in the finale. Eley also shows her own vivid musical imagination to be an ideal match for Fanny Mendelssohn's in the selections from *Das Jahr*. There is elfin grace in the scherzo of "February", satisfying warmth in "March", radiant exhilaration in "May", beautifully liquid melody in "September" ("Am Flusse") and, finally, impressive swirling musical imagery in "December".

Mendelssohn Double Piano Concertos – E major; A flat major. **Benjamin Frith, Hugh Tinney** (pfs); **RTE Sinfonietta / Prionnsías O'Duinn.** Naxos Ⓢ 8 553416 (74 minutes: DDD: 2/97). Recorded 1995.

Mendelssohn was 14 when he completed his first two-piano Concerto in E major, and still only 15 when he followed it with a considerably longer (rather too long) and more ambitious second in A flat. Both concertos were first heard at the Sunday morning music parties regularly given at the cultivated Mendelssohns' Berlin home, with the composer's much-loved, slightly older sister, Fanny, at the second piano. As her talents were akin to his own, the two solo parts are indistinguishable in their challenges. And it is to the great credit of Benjamin Frith and Hugh Tinney that without a score at hand, you would be hard-pressed to guess who was playing what. You will be as impressed by their attunement of phrasing in lyrical contexts as by their synchronization in all the brilliant semiquaver passagework in which both works abound. Their uninhibited enjoyment of the imitative audacities of the later work's finale is a real *tour de force*. Under Prionnsías O'Duinn the RTE Sinfonietta play with sufficient relish to allow you to forget that the recording is perhaps just a little too close. In short, a not-to-be-missed opportunity to explore the precocious young Mendelssohn at super-bargain price.

Additional recommendation ...

...E major; A flat major. **Stephen Coombes, Ian Munro** (pfs); **BBC Symphony Orchestra / Jerzy Maksymiuk.** Hyperion Ⓕ CDA66567 (72 minutes: DDD: 9/92).   Ⓖ

Mendelssohn Violin Concertos – E minor, Op. 64; D minor. **Kyoko Takezawa** (vn); **Bamberg Symphony Orchestra / Claus Peter Flor.** RCA Victor Red Seal Ⓕ 09026 62512-2 (53 minutes: DDD: 2/95). Recorded 1994.   Ⓖ

Kyoko Takezawa and Claus Peter Flor offer performances which consistently reflect the joy of the performers in the music. Many of the other performances listed below are faster in all but one of the six movements but Takezawa uses that additional elbow-room to give the music an extra sense of fantasy, often of fun, entirely apt for this composer. In the central *Andante* Takezawa, at her relatively slow speed, is just as fresh and unsentimental as the competition. Rather than power and weight, Takezawa in the outer movements finds a muscular resilience which in context is just as compelling. In the D minor Concerto such qualities are if anything even more striking, and one keeps registering moments of delight, whether in the Mozartian lightness of the first movement, full of fantasy, the Schubertian lyricism of the second, raptly done, with its musing little cadenzas for the soloist, or the Hungarian point of the finale.

Additional recommendations ...

...E minor. **Tchaikovsky** Violin Concerto in D major, Op. 35. **Takako Nishizaki** (vn); **Slovak Philharmonic Orchestra / Kenneth Jean.** Naxos Ⓢ 8 550153 (67 minutes: DDD).

...E minor. **Bruch** Violin Concerto No. 1 in G minor, Op. 26. **Anne-Sophie Mutter** (vn); **Berlin Philharmonic Orchestra / Herbert von Karajan.** DG Ⓕ 400 031-2GH (57 minutes: DDD: 3/83).

...E minor. **Tchaikovsky** Violin Concerto in D major, Op. 35. **Nathan Milstein** (vn); **Vienna Philharmonic Orchestra / Claudio Abbado.** DG Galleria Ⓜ 419 067-2GGA (DDD: 8/87).

...E minor. *Coupled with works by* **Bruch** and **Schubert** Nigel Kennedy (vn); **English Chamber Orchestra / Jeffrey Tate.** EMI Ⓕ CDC7 49663-2 (71 minutes: DDD: 1/89).

...D minor. Violin and Piano Concerto in D minor. **Gidon Kremer** (vn); **Martha Argerich** (pf). DG Ⓕ 427 338-2GH (59 minutes: DDD: 9/89).   ⒼⒼ

...E minor[a]. **Beethoven** Violin Concerto in D major, Op. 61[b]. **Yehudi Menuhin** (vn); [a]**Berlin Philharmonic Orchestra;** [b]**Philharmonia Orchestra / Wilhelm Furtwängler.** EMI Références mono Ⓜ CDH7 69799-2* (71 minutes: ADD: 10/89).   ⒼⒼ

...E minor[a]. **Bruch** Violin Concerto[b]. [a]**Miklós Szenthelý,** [b]**Emmy Verhey** (vns); [a]**Budapest Philharmonic Orchestra / János Sándor;** [b]**Budapest Symphony Orchestra / Arpád Joó.** LaserLight Ⓑ 15 615 (52 minutes: DDD: 3/91).

...E minor. **Brahms** Violin Concerto in D major, Op. 77. **Xue-Wei** (vn); **London Philharmonic Orchestra / Ivor Bolton.** ASV Ⓕ CDDCA748 (67 minutes: DDD: 4/91).

...E minor; D minor. **Viktoria Mullova** (vn); **Academy of St Martin in the Fields / Sir Neville Marriner.** Philips Ⓕ 432 077-2PH (50 minutes: DDD: 5/91).

...E minor. **Beethoven** Violin Concerto in D major, Op. 61. **Kyung-Wha Chung** (vn); **Vienna Philharmonic Orchestra / Kyrill Kondrashin.** Decca Ⓜ 430 752-2DM (71 minutes: DDD: 2/93).

...E minor[a]. Symphony No. 4 in A major, Op. 90, "Italian". The Hebrides, Op. 26. [a]**Pinchas Zukerman** (vn); **New York Philharmonic Orchestra / Leonard Bernstein.** Sony Classical Bernstein The Royal Edition Ⓜ SMK47592 (73 minutes: DDD: 8/93).   Ⓖ

...E minor[b]. **Elgar** Violin Concerto in B minor, Op. 61[a.] **Alfredo Campoli** (vn);
London Philharmonic Orchestra / Sir Adrian Boult.
Beulah [a]mono/[b]stereo Ⓜ 1PD10* (73 minutes: ADD 10/94).
...E minor. *Coupled with works by* **Mozart** and **Vieuxtemps** Jascha Heifetz (vn);
Royal Philharmonic Orchestra / Sir Thomas Beecham.
EMI Références mono Ⓜ CDH5 65191-2* (69 minutes: ADD: 10/94).
...E minor. **Brahms** Violin Concerto in D major, Op. 77. **Dmitry Sitkovetsky** (vn);
Academy of St Martin in the Fields / Sir Neville Marriner.
Hanssler Classic Ⓕ 98 934 (69 minutes: DDD: 7/96).
...E minor. **Brahms** Double Concerto in A minor, Op. 102[a].
Itzhak Perlman (vn); [a]**Yo-Yo Ma** (vc); **Chicago Symphony Orchestra / Daniel Barenboim.**
Teldec Ⓕ 0630-15870-2 (59 minutes: DDD: 7/97).

Mendelssohn String Symphonies – No. 1 in C major; No. 2 in D major; No. 3 in E minor;
No. 4 in C minor; No. 5 in B flat major; No. 6 in E flat major; No. 7 in D minor; No. 8 in
D major; No. 9 in C major; No. 10 in B minor; No. 11 in F major; No. 12 in G minor; No. 13 in
C minor, "Sinfoniesatz". **Hanover Band / Roy Goodman.** RCA Victor Red Seal Ⓕ 09026 68069-2
(three discs: 225 minutes: DDD: 1/96). Recorded 1992-93.
Mendelssohn's extraordinary precocity is nowhere more comprehensively shown than in the 13 early
string symphonies, and though it is extraordinary that these were unknown until 1960, it is scarcely
less so that there are still works in Berlin awaiting editing and performance. The symphonies are
exceptional, though, in that the range of their invention far exceeds what might be expected of even
so prodigiously talented a boy. The inventiveness remains dazzling, as with (to take only two
examples) the chorale idea in the Minuet of the Sixth Symphony or the brilliant contrapuntal writing
in the Eighth Symphony, in which the more immediate inspiration was Mozart, and in particular the
Jupiter Symphony. Roy Goodman makes use of the version with wind instruments for this symphony,
which Mendelssohn made within three days of having written the original, and (with one reservation)
accepts Mendelssohn's astonishingly fast tempo markings. He brings them off brilliantly, even the
helter-skelter bass pizzicatos in the Trio of the Minuet. He also shows, with the use of period string
techniques, how quick Mendelssohn's ear was for novel sonorities. An affection for the still
underprivileged viola may have come from Mozart, but Mendelssohn would also have heard these
sounds pioneered by Weber (who otherwise barely influenced him in these works). There are beautiful
string sonorities even in the very earliest works, especially in the often darkly-hued slow movements;
and the finales have all the pace and wit of the more mature Mendelssohn (that is to say, when he was
in his teens). Goodman judges tempo well, which is to say he has a shrewd sense of weight as well as
of pace. He also directs from the keyboard, which it is certain Mendelssohn himself would have done
at those famous Sunday morning concerts in his parents' Berlin house, and he permits himself the
occasional contribution: both in theory and in practice, this is entirely in style. This is an excellent set,
intelligently assembled, scrupulously prepared, lucidly recorded, played with a freshness and wit that
serve these delightful pieces well.

Additional recommendations ...
...Nos. 1-6. **English String Orchestra / William Boughton.**
Nimbus Ⓕ NI5141 (60 minutes: DDD: 3/89).
...Nos. 7, 8 and 10. **English String Orchestra / William Boughton.**
Nimbus Ⓕ NI5142 (52 minutes: DDD: 3/89).
...Nos. 9, 11 and 12. **English String Orchestra / William Boughton.**
Nimbus Ⓕ NI5143 (71 minutes: DDD: 3/89).
...Nos. 1-12. **London Festival Orchestra / Ross Pople.**
Hyperion Ⓕ CDA66561/3 (three discs: 203 minutes: DDD: 12/91).   Ⓖ
...Nos. 2, 3, 9 and 10. **Nieuw Sinfonietta, Amsterdam / Lev Markiz.**
BIS Ⓕ CD643 (60 minutes: DDD: 6/94).
...Nos. 8-10. **Concerto Cologne.**
Teldec Das Alte Werk Ⓕ 4509-94565-2 (67 minutes: DDD: 12/94). ✍
...Nos. 1, 4, 6, 7 and 12. **Concerto Cologne.**
Teldec Das Alte Werk Ⓕ 4509-98435-2 (68 minutes: DDD: 7/96). ✍
...Nos. 8 and 11. **Nieuw Sinfonietta Amsterdam / Lev Markiv.**
BIS Ⓕ CD748 (70 minutes: DDD: 11/96).
...Nos. 4, 5, 8 and 13. **Nieuw Sinfonietta Amsterdam / Lev Markiz.**
BIS Ⓕ CD798 (59 minutes: DDD: 11/97).
...Nos. 1- 12[a]. Piano Concertos Nos. 1 and 2[bc]. The Hebrides[c]. A Midsummer Night's Dream[c].
Symphonies Nos. 3[c] and 4[d]. Violin Concerto, Op. 64de. Meeresstille und glückliche Fahrt[d].
[b]**Joseph Kalichstein** (pf); [e]**Benjamin Hudson** (vn); [a]**English String Orchestra / William Boughton;**
[c]**Scottish Chamber Orchestra / Jaime Laredo;** [d]**Hanover Band / Roy Goodman.**
Nimbus Ⓜ NI1765 (six discs: 375 minutes: DDD: 1/98).

Mendelssohn String Symphonies – No. 1 in C major; No. 6 in E flat major; No. 7 in D minor;
No. 12 in G minor. **Nieuw Sinfonietta Amsterdam / Lev Markiz.** BIS Ⓕ CD683
(70 minutes: DDD: 9/95). Recorded 1994.

Amazing stuff, brilliantly performed. The first of the symphonies fair bursts from the staves, with a chuckling finale that would surely have delighted Rossini. And although the Sixth Symphony's finale harbours hints of miracles to come, Mendelssohn's mature personality is more comprehensively anticipated in the Seventh. Again, the finale suggests the ebullient, life-affirming manner of the orchestral symphonies, albeit sobered by a spot of fugally formal writing later on. The Twelfth Symphony opens with a Handelian sense of ceremony, goes on to incorporate a characteristically tender *Andante* and ends with a finale that, to quote Stig Jacobsson's enthusiastic notes, "dies away to *pizzicato* and a subsequent *accelerando* which recalls Rossini". This is truly delightful music, a product of natural genius and destined to remain unique (at least in terms of youthful precocity) until Wolfgang Korngold penned his *Sinfonietta* and Piano Trio some 90 years later. Competing claims of versions from other performers (many of whom are excellent) are unlikely to upstage this latest volume of Nieuw Sinfonietta Amsterdam's ongoing cycle. The playing is both sensitive and exciting (No. 6's finale is dispatched with maniacal zeal), while BIS's sound is impressively full-bodied. Lev Markiz was the first leader of Rudolf Barshai's magnificent Moscow Chamber Orchestra and readers who recall that group's greatest recordings can anticipate a parallel level of distinction here.

Mendelssohn String Symphonies – No. 2 in D major; No. 3 in E minor; No. 5 in B flat major;
    No. 11 in F major; No. 13 in C minor, "Sinfoniesatz". **Concerto Cologne.**
    Teldec Ⓔ 0630-13138-2 (73 minutes: DDD: 6/97). ✔ Recorded 1996.
With this third disc, Concerto Cologne complete their cycle of Mendelssohn's youthful symphonies. As before, the players have an excellent sense of spontaneity, and of the chamber music element which is part of the style of these works. They listen acutely, and respond sensitively to Mendelssohn's vivid sense of string colour, especially to his love of viola tone (as at the start of No. 11). They also have a just sense of tempo, and never appeal to sensation by playing the fastest movement as fast as they can: cases in point, where a little less than a flat out speed makes far more musical sense, are the *Allegro di molto* that opens No. 3 and the *Presto* concluding No. 5. There are now plenty of choices for cycles of these highly enjoyable pieces, notable among them Roy Goodman's Hanover Band, the Nieuw Sinfonietta Amsterdam, the English String Orchestra and the London Festival Orchestra. There is really very little to choose between performances by expert string players of music that does not make very subtle interpretative demands, but the Hanover Band is excellent, with, in the same class, the present set, which places a particular emphasis on tone colour.

Mendelssohn Symphonies – No. 1 in C minor, Op. 11; No. 5 in D major, Op. 107,
    "Reformation". **Deutsches Symphony Orchestra, Berlin / Vladimir Ashkenazy.**
    Decca Ⓔ 444 428-2DH (60 minutes: DDD: 6/95). Recorded 1994.   Ⓖ
Ashkenazy conducts the former Radio Symphony Orchestra in fresh, finely moulded readings of Symphonies Nos. 1 and 5. He allows himself a spacious approach, phrasing affectionately in slow movements marked by consistently gentle *pianissimos*, not just a question of recording balance. So the second movement *Andante* of No. 1 is tender and the slow introductions of the *Reformation* Symphony has plenty of mystery. The *pianissimo* statements of the Dresden Amen introduction to the first movement have you catching your breath, as will the warmth of the initial statement of the *Ein' feste Burg* in the finale, on unaccompanied flute. By contrast Ashkenazy's *allegros* are often faster than other readings, with the Minuet of No. 1 becoming almost a scherzo, as does the second movement of the *Reformation*. There are moments in the first movements of both symphonies, where he comes near to sounding too hectic, but he compensates with springing rhythms. What is slightly disappointing is the relative thinness of the string sound, not as sweet as it could be. It is a minor reservation, and anyone to whom the coupling and Ashkenazy's approach appeal can safely go ahead.
Additional recommendations ...
...No. 1; No. 2 in B flat major, Op. 52, "Hymn of Praise" (with Elizabeth Connell, Karita Mattila, sops; Hans-Peter Blochwitz, ten); No. 3 in A minor, Op. 56, "Scottish"; No. 4 in A major, Op. 90, "Italian"; No. 5. Overtures – The Hebrides, Op. 26; A Midsummer Night's Dream, Op. 21. The Fair Melusina, Op. 32. Octet in E flat major, Op. 20 – Scherzo. **London Symphony Orchestra / Claudio Abbado.** DG Ⓔ 415 353-2GH4 (four discs: 245 minutes: DDD: 1/86).   ⒼⒼ
...Nos. 1-5. **New Philharmonia Orchestra / Wolfgang Sawallisch.**
Philips Ⓑ 432 598-2PB3 (three discs: 194 minutes: ADD: 8/91).   Ⓖ
...Nos. 1-5. **Berlin Philharmonic Orchestra / Herbert von Karajan.**
DG Ⓜ 429 664-2GSE3 (three discs: 202 minutes: ADD: 8/91).
...Nos. 1 and 5. **Milton Keynes Chamber Orchestra / Hilary Davan Wetton.**
Unicorn-Kanchana Ⓔ DKPCD9117 (63 minutes: DDD: 2/93).
...Nos. 1 and 5. The Hebrides. **Philharmonia Orchestra / Walter Weller.**
Chandos Ⓔ CHAN9099 (75 minutes: DDD: 2/93).
...Nos. 1-5. The Hebrides. **Soloists; Philharmonia Chorus and Orchestra / Walter Weller.**
Chandos Enchant Ⓜ CHAN7090 (three discs: 218 minutes: DDD: 2/98).

Mendelssohn Symphony No. 2 in B flat major, Op. 52, "Hymn of Praise". **Soile Isokoski** (sop);
    Mechthild Bach (sop); **Frieder Lang** (ten); **Cologne Chorus Musicus; Das Neue Orchester /**
    Christoph Spering. Opus 111 Ⓔ OPS30-98 (65 minutes: DDD: 9/94). ✔ Text and translation
    included. Recorded 1993.

This is one of Mendelssohn's lesser-known but highly rewarding symphonies. The *Hymn of Praise* stands under the shade of Beethoven's *Choral* Symphony, with its considerable length and choral and solo contributions, but it does not reach similar heights of sublimity. What it does possess is an unassuming lyricism, vitality and elegance throughout that is highly attractive. Christoph Spering is relaxed in his choice of tempos. In no way, however, does he let the music drag or become sentimental. With clean, crisp textures this is a most refreshing performance, full of incidental beauties. In the main *Allegro* of the first movement as well as in the opening section of the big choral cantata-finale, Spering's speeds are fast but refreshing. The rest is different, not just slower in its speeds, but often more affectionate. The duet for the two soprano soloists, "Ich harrete des Herrn" ("I waited on the Lord"), is especially beautiful, with Soile Isokoski and Mechthild Bach both angelically sweet yet nicely contrasted. The tenor soloist too, Frieder Lang, is exceptionally sweet-toned. The chorus, as recorded in a warm acoustic, are not always ideally clear in inner definition, but the freshness of their singing matches that of the whole performance. Anyone attracted by the advance of period performance into nineteenth-century repertory should certainly not miss this issue.

Additional recommendations ...

...No. 2. **Cynthia Haymon, Alison Hagley** (sops); **Peter Straka** (ten); **Philharmonia Chorus and Orchestra / Walter Weller.** Chandos Ⓕ CHAN8995 (73 minutes: DDD: 5/92).

...No. 2 – Ich harrete des Herrn (sung in English). *Coupled with works by various composers.*
St Paul's Cathedral Choir / John Scott with **Andrew Lucas** (org). Hyperion Ⓕ CDA66916 (71 minutes: DDD: A/97). *See review in the Collections section; refer to the Index.*

Mendelssohn Symphonies – No. 3 in A minor, Op. 56, "Scottish"[a]; No. 4 in A major, Op. 90, "Italian"[b]. **San Francisco Symphony Orchestra / Herbert Blomstedt.** Decca Ⓕ 433 811-2DH (67 minutes: DDD: 4/93). Item marked [a] recorded 1989, [b]1991. ⒼⒼ

Recent years have seen a number of competitive releases of this popular coupling, not least a treasurable Teldec CD featuring Nikolaus Harnoncourt at the helm of the remarkably responsive Chamber Orchestra of Europe, full of that conductor's special brand of re-creative insight. Enter Herbert Blomstedt and his splendid San Francisco orchestra, in matters of interpretation more traditionally solid and less daring than that Teldec partnership, perhaps, but with considerable virtues of their own. Blomstedt's *Scottish* impresses most by dint of its joyous vigour (outer movements go with a will), rhythmic bounce (perky winds and razor-sharp strings in the *Scherzo*) and unaffected eloquence (as in his affectionately flowing yet never short-winded third movement *Adagio*). This *Italian*, too, is first-rate. Under Blomstedt the opening *Allegro vivace* positively fizzes along, aided by some quite beautifully sprung string playing, whilst the *Saltarello* finale is articulated with real panache. The middle movements are perhaps marginally less memorable, though again the stylish orchestral response yields much pleasure. Although the symphonies were actually set down some 17 months apart, Decca's admirably consistent sound-picture possesses the exemplary clarity and sheen we have now come to expect from this particular sound-source. No one can go far wrong with this disc.

Additional recommendations ...

...Nos. 4 and 5. **London Symphony Orchestra / Claudio Abbado.**
DG Ⓕ 415 974-2GH (DDD: 9/86). ⒼⒼ

...Nos. 3 and 4. **Orchestra of St John's, Smith Square / John Lubbock.**
ASV Quicksilva Ⓢ CDQS6004 (71 minutes: ADD: 12/87).

...No. 3. Die erste Walpurgisnacht[a]. [a]**Christine Cairns** (mez); [a]**Jon Garrison** (ten);
[a]**Tom Krause** (bar); **Cleveland Orchestra and** [a]**Chorus / Christoph von Dohnányi.**
Telarc Ⓕ CD80184 (67 minutes: DDD: 3/89).

...Nos. 3 and 4. **London Symphony Orchestra / Claudio Abbado.**
DG 3-D Classics Ⓑ 427 810-2GDC (71 minutes: DDD: 2/90). ⒼⒼ

...Nos. 3 and 4. **Chamber Orchestra of Europe / Nikolaus Harnoncourt.**
Teldec Ⓕ 9031-72308-2 (69 minutes: DDD: 5/92). ⒼⒼⒼ

...Nos. 4 and 5. A Midsummer Night's Dream[b] – Scherzo. Octet in E flat major,
Op. 20 – Scherzo. **NBC Symphony Orchestra / Arturo Toscanini.**
RCA Victor Gold Seal mono Ⓜ GD60284* (64 minutes: ADD: 6/92). ⒼⒼ

...No. 4[a]. Overture – The Hebrides, Op. 26[a]. A Midsummer Night's Dream[b] – Overture; Scherzo;
Nocturne; Wedding March. [a]**Israel Philharmonic Orchestra;** [b]**Bavarian Radio Symphony Orchestra
/ Leonard Bernstein.** DG Classikon Ⓑ 439 411-2GCL (67 minutes: ADD: 3/94). Ⓖ

...Nos. 3 and 4. **Leipzig Gewandhaus Orchestra / Kurt Masur.**
Teldec Digital Experience Ⓜ 4509-92148-2 (67 minutes: DDD: 4/94). ⒼⒼⒼ

...Nos. 3 and 4. **Academy of St Martin in the Fields / Sir Neville Marriner.**
Philips Ⓕ 442 130-2PH (69 minutes: DDD: 10/94).

...No. 4. **Shostakovich** Symphony No. 5 in D minor, Op. 47. **Vienna Philharmonic Orchestra /
Sir Georg Solti.** Decca Ⓕ 440 476-2DH (71 minutes: DDD: 10/94).

Mendelssohn Symphony No. 3 in A minor, Op. 56, "Scottish"[a]. The Hebrides, Op. 26[a].
A Midsummer Night's Dream[b] – Overture and incidental music, Opp. 21 and 61: Scherzo;
Nocturne; Wedding March. **London Symphony Orchestra / Peter Maag.**
Decca The Classic Sound Ⓜ 443 578-2DCS* (76 minutes: ADD: 7/95). Items marked [a] from
SXL2246 (12/60), [b]SXL2060 (3/59). Recorded 1957-60. *Gramophone classical 100.* ⒼⒼⒼ

The Hebrides and the *Scottish* Symphony offer 'Classic' Decca engineering at its best: airy 1960 Kingsway Hall sound with a real sense of perspective drawing the ear in (woodwind set behind strings but without loss of clarity – how flat is the layout of many a modern recording), pin-point instrumental positioning yet no impression of instruments sealed off from each other, and, for the pre-Dolby period, a remarkable dynamic range, accomplished with low hiss levels and no audible overloading. There is, perhaps, a slight thinness of tone in the middle register, a characteristic that is far more pronounced in the 1957 *Midsummer Night's Dream* excerpts (calling to mind, if memory serves correctly, one critic's charge, decades ago, that Decca were recording in "zinc tanks"), but the high-key clarity and fizzing presence readily compensate. At the time, Maag would probably have earned the description of a classically oriented Mendelssohnian, but his intelligent balancing of the orchestra and gauging of the work's proportions and rhetoric do not preclude imaginative handling of their illustrative poetry; in other words, he is a superb Mendelssohnian stylist. Personal rhythmic and dynamic inflexions abound (no doubt eyebrows will rise at such things as his sudden broad delivery of the Mechanicals' clowning in the *Midsummer Night's Dream* Overture). Singing lines are all beautifully wrought, especially that of the symphony's *Adagio* (rather more leisurely than we are used to nowadays), and its 'martial' sections benefit from discreetly balanced timpani. In *The Hebrides*, the balance and range of the sound allow all those swells (superbly observed) to register in proper proportion – here is both delicate impressionism and all the stormy drive and drama that you could want, putting many more recent rivals in the shade. At the heart of this disc's success is, of course, the playing of the revitalized LSO, responding to some challenging tempos with mainly knife-edge precision of ensemble and superb attack, producing heart-easing warmth in the symphony's *Adagio*, and shining in all solo opportunities – truly vintage LSO champagne.

Additional recommendations ...

...A Midsummer Night's Dream – Scherzo (two versions); Nocturne.
Philharmonic Symphony Orchestra of New York / Arturo Toscanini.
Pearl mono Ⓕ GEMMCDS9373* (three discs: 230 minutes: ADD: 3/90).
Gramophone classical 100. See review in the Collections section; refer to the Index. ⊖⊖⊖
...Nos. 3-5. Overtures – The Hebrides, Op. 26; Meeresstille und glückliche Fahrt, Op. 27.
Orchestra of the Eighteenth Century / Frans Brüggen.
Philips Ⓕ 456 267-2PH2 (two discs: 120 minutes: DDD: 9/97). ✍

Mendelssohn Symphonies – No. 3 in A minor, Op. 56, "Scottish"; No. 4 in A major,
Op. 90, "Italian". The Hebrides, Op. 26. **Ulster Orchestra / Dimitry Sitkovetsky.**
Classic fM Ⓜ 75605 57013-2 (77 minutes: DDD: 6/98). Recorded 1997.
Violinist-turned-conductor, Dimitry Sitkovetsky, here draws from the orchestra superb performances of both symphonies as well as the overture, helped by the outstandingly full and rich recording, made in the Ulster Hall. In a way that challenges and generally outshines the many rival discs coupling the *Scottish* and *Italian* Symphonies, Sitkovetsky consistently conveys the feeling of live performances caught on the wing. With speeds beautifully chosen and with rhythms crisp and well sprung, his readings are full of light and shade, warmly dramatic, demonstrating an expressive freedom – notably in pressing ahead – which always sounds natural, never self-conscious. With refined playing from every section, at once tense and polished, textures are exceptionally clear and transparent, so that inner details are brought out that are often obscured. In that, the full and immediate recording adds to the impact and vivid sense of presence. The strings in particular produce some magical *pianissimos*, reflecting Sitkovetsky's own mastery as an instrumentalist, yet the stormy passages in the first movement of the *Scottish* also have a physical impact that brings out the inspiration from nature to an exceptional degree. Similarly in the *Hebrides* Overture, after a restrained opening, the atmospheric beauty of the writing comes out vividly. A very generous and apt coupling, with the exposition repeat observed in the *Italian* Symphony (important because of the long lead-back) but not in the *Scottish*.

Mendelssohn Overtures – Die Hochzeit des Camacho, Op. 10; A Midsummer Night's Dream,
Op. 21 (from RD87764, 10/88); Meeresstille und glückliche Fahrt, Op. 27; Ruy Blas, Op. 95;
Athalie, Op. 74; The Hebrides, Op. 26. **Bamberg Symphony Orchestra / Claus Peter Flor.**
RCA Victor Red Seal Ⓕ RD87905 (59 minutes: DDD: 1/89). Recorded 1987-88. ⊖
Die Hochzeit des Camacho ("The Marriage of Camacho") Overture was written in 1825, two years before the masterly evocation of *A Midsummer Night's Dream*, with its gossamer fairies, robust mortals and pervading romanticism, and already demonstrates the teenage composer's enormous musical facility and organizational skills, together with the high quality of his invention. *Meeresstille und glückliche Fahrt* ("Calm sea and prosperous voyage" of 1828) anticipates *The Hebrides* of a year later, and celebrates an ocean voyage on a sailing ship. *Ruy Blas* is a jolly, slightly melodramatic, but agreeably tuneful piece and *Athalie* is also attractive in its melodic ideas. *Fingal's Cave* with its beauty and dramatic portrayal of Scottish seascapes matches the Shakespearian overture in its melodic inspiration (the opening phrase is hauntingly unforgettable) and shows comparable skill in its vivid orchestration. Flor directs wonderfully sympathetic and spontaneous performances, with the Bamberg Symphony Orchestra playing gloriously. There is abundant energy and radiant lyrical beauty in the playing and each piece is unerringly paced and shaped. The glowing recording gives a wonderful bloom to the orchestral textures without preventing a realistic definition.

Additional recommendation ...
...The Hebrides. *Coupled with works by* **Brahms** and **Schubert** Chicago Symphony Orchestra /
Fritz Reiner. RCA Victor Gold Seal Ⓜ 09026 61793-2 (69 minutes: ADD: 9/95).
See review under Brahms; refer to the Index.

Mendelssohn A Midsummer Night's Dream, Opp. 21 and 61[a]. Symphony No. 4 in A major,
Op. 90, "Italian". [a]**Kenneth Branagh** (spkr); [a]**Sylvia McNair** (sop); [a]**Angelika Kirchschlager** (mez);
[a]**Women of the Ernst-Senff Chorus; Berlin Philharmonic Orchestra / Claudio Abbado.**
Sony Classical Ⓕ SK62826 (78 minutes: DDD: 5/97). Text included. Recorded live in 1995.
Gramophone Editor's choice.   ⒼⒼ
It makes an attractive package having Mendelssohn's *A Midsummer Night's Dream* music,
dramatically presented (with Kenneth Branagh taking every role from Titania to Puck), and then very
generously coupled with Mendelssohn's most popular symphony. Sony have managed to squeeze in
50 minutes of the *Midsummer Night's Dream* music, which means that the only omissions are the
fragmentary reprise of the "Wedding March" and the two little comic pieces, "Bergomask" and
"Funeral March", intended for the Rude Mechanicals' Pyramus and Thisbe episodes. Some may resist
Branagh's style – burring his 'r's for a Mummerset Puck, coming near to an Olivier imitation in
Oberon's final speech – but in his versatility he is very persuasive. Having speech over music in
melodrama certainly makes sense of the more fragmentary passages of the score in a way they do not,
for example, in André Previn's EMI presentation of the music down to the last note. Abbado's
performances are a delight, fresh and transparent in the fairy music, with generally fast speeds made
exhilarating, never breathless. The chorus are atmospherically balanced, with the two excellent
soloists, Sylvia McNair and Angelika Kirchschlager, set more forwardly. The recording, made in the
Philharmonie in Berlin, is rather more vivid, a degree less recessed than in the symphony, where the
orchestra are placed at a slight distance, an effect one gets used to. In the *Italian* Symphony Abbado's
reading has changed little since his more recent LSO version of 1985 (listed earlier), though here and
there, as in the third movement, the phrasing is this time a little more moulded. By any reckoning he
remains one of the most persuasive interpreters of this delectable work.

Additional recommendations ...
...A Midsummer Night's Dream. **Lillian Watson** (sop); **Delia Wallis** (mez);
    Finchley Childrens' Music Group; London Symphony Orchestra / André Previn.
    EMI Ⓕ CDC7 47163-2 (58 minutes: DDD: 9/86).
...A Midsummer Night's Dream. **Edith Wiens** (sop); **Sarah Walker** (mez);
    London Philharmonic Choir and Orchestra / Andrew Litton.
    Classics for Pleasure Ⓑ CD-CFP4593 (50 minutes: DDD: 9/92).
...A Midsummer Night's Dream[a]. Die erste Walpurgisnacht, Op. 60[b]. [a]**Pamela Coburn** (sop);
    [a]**Elisabeth von Magnus** (contr/narr); [b]**Birgit Remmert** (contr); [b]**Uwe Heilmann** (ten);
    [b]**Thomas Hampson** (bar); [b]**René Pape** (bass); [a]**Christoph Bantzer** (narr);
    [b]**Arnold Schoenberg Choir; Chamber Orchestra of Europe / Nikolas Harnoncourt.**
    Teldec Ⓕ 9031-74882-2 (78 minutes: DDD: 2/94).
...A Midsummer Night's Dream. **Kathleen Battle** (sop); **Frederica von Stade** (mez);
    Dame Judi Dench (narr); **Tanglewood Festival Chorus; Boston Symphony Orchestra / Seiji Ozawa.**
    DG 439 897-2GH (56 minutes: DDD: 10/94).   Ⓖ
...A Midsummer Night's Dream[a]. The Hebrides, Op. 26. [a]**Sandrine Piau**, [a]**Delphine Collot** (sops);
    [a]**La Chapelle Royale Choir; [a]Collegium Vocale; Champs Elysées Orchestra / Philippe Herreweghe.**
    Harmonia Mundi Ⓕ HMC90 1502 (55 minutes: DDD: 4/95).
...A Midsummer Night's Dream – Nocturne. *Coupled with works by* **Mozart** and **Rossini**
    Philharmonia Orchestra / Otto Klemperer. Testament Ⓕ SBT1102 (72 minutes: ADD: 7/97).

Mendelssohn Piano Trios – No. 1 in D minor, Op. 49; No. 2 in C minor, Op. 66.
    Vienna Piano Trio (Wolfgang Redik, vn; Marcus Trefny, vc; Stefan Mendl, pf).
    Nimbus Ⓕ NI5553 (55 minutes: DDD: 6/98). Recorded 1997.
In Stefan Mendl the Vienna Piano Trio has an exceptionally brilliant pianist. Perhaps the spotlight
ought not to be quite so much on the keyboard in the first of these two works, in D minor, but his
fingerwork is delectably light and frothy. The composer himself, as an effortless prestidigitator, is of
course much to blame in giving it so unrelentingly breathless a stream of notes. In the intervening six
years before the C minor Trio, Mendelssohn learnt a lot – no doubt never forgetting his friend Hiller's
comment that some of the patterned, arpeggio-type figuration in the earlier work was "old-
fashioned". You need only compare the elfin scherzos of both to appreciate the infinitely subtler
scoring of the latter. Subject-matter is likewise more affirmatively contrasted throughout, notably in
the chorale-inspired triumphs of the finale. A more forwardly projected, richer cello song would have
helped, but general balance in Nimbus's resonant concert-hall is better here than in the D minor. And
the enthusiastic freshness and vitality of this young team is a constant stimulus (note their daringly
fast tempo risked in both scherzos). In sum, plenty to enjoy here.

Mendelssohn Octet in E flat major, Op. 20. String Quintet No. 2 in B flat major, Op. 87.
    Academy of St Martin in the Fields Chamber Ensemble. Philips Ⓕ 420 400-2PH
    (63 minutes: ADD: 11/87). From 9500 616 (3/80). Recorded 1978.   Ⓖ

Mendelssohn was as remarkable a prodigy as Mozart and one can only speculate with sadness what marvels he might have left us had he lived longer. Had death claimed him at 20 we would still have this glorious Octet, a work of unforced lyricism and a seemingly endless stream of melody. The Academy Chamber Ensemble, all fine soloists in their own right, admirably illustrate the benefits of working regularly as an ensemble for they play with uncommon sympathy. The string quintet is a work of greater fervour and passion than the Octet but it is characterized by the same melodiousness and unfettered lyricism with plenty of opportunities for virtuoso playing, which are well taken. The recordings, made in 1978, give a pleasant and warm sheen to the string colour of the ensemble.

Additional recommendation ...
...Octet. **Bargiel** Octet in C minor, Op. 15*a*. **Divertimento.**
Hyperion CDA66356 (67 minutes: DDD: 4/90).

Mendelssohn String Quintet No. 2 in B flat major, Op. 87. String Quartet No. 2 in A minor,
Op. 13. **Hausmusik** (Monica Huggett, Pavlo Besnoziuk, vns; Roger Chase, Simon Whistler, vas;
Richard Lester, vc). Virgin Classics Veritas Ⓕ VC5 45104-2 (60 minutes: DDD: 5/95). ✍

Mendelssohn's A minor Quartet, Op. 13, is an uncharacteristically serious work. Its quotation from Mendelssohn's song *Ist es wahr*, and the music's Beethovenian tone convey a prevailing mood of stress and anxiety. In a finely judged, excellently recorded version of the work, the Coull Quartet reveal a wealth of detail, through deftly controlled ensemble and perceptive structural observation. Nevertheless, the keener edge of Hausmusik's period instruments gives the quartet's dramatic contrasts more bite and makes the emotional content more potent. Resonant, sensitively blended harmonies and closely argued counterpoint in the first movement evolve into subtly balanced oppositions of minor (fugato) and major (lyrical calm) in the second movement, and delicate, gossamer textures in the *Intermezzo* (evocative of the fairy music in *A Midsummer Night's Dream*), emphasize the finale's expressive intensity, with its poignant echoes of the quartet's opening. By contrast, Mendelssohn's Second Quintet, Op. 87, is a gloriously exultant piece that still remains sadly neglected. Written in 1845, only a few months after the Violin Concerto, the quintet has suffered from accusations that it shows a decline in Mendelssohn's creative powers. However, the engaging freshness of Hausmusik's vividly recorded, period-instrument account powerfully brings out the work's instrumental brilliance and *joie de vivre*. The exuberance of the outer movements is expressed with boundless energy; crisp precision highlights the second movement's contrapuntal detail, and Hausmusik's attentive playing in the slow movement arrestingly conveys the music's ardently impassioned mood.

Mendelssohn String Quartets – E flat major (1823); No. 1 in E flat major, Op. 12; No. 2 in
A minor, Op. 13; No. 3 in D major, Op. 44 No. 1; No. 4 in E minor, Op. 44 No. 2; No. 5 in E flat
major, Op. 44 No. 3; No. 6 in F minor, Op. 80. Andante, Scherzo, Capriccio and Fugue, Op. 81
Nos. 1-2. **Melos Quartet** (Wilhelm Melcher, Gerhard Voss, vns; Hermann Voss, va; Peter Buck,
vc). DG Ⓜ 415 883-2GCM3 (three discs: 199 minutes: ADD: 12/87). From 2740 267 (11/82).
Recorded 1976-81.   ⓐⓐⓐ

The familiar and misleading cliché of Mendelssohn as the cheerful chappie of early romanticism vanishes at the sound of the F minor Quartet, Op. 80. Here is the intensity, anguish and anger that everyone thought Mendelssohn incapable of. His beloved sister Fanny died in May 1847 (his own death was merely months away), and the ensuing summer saw him leave Berlin for Switzerland, where he began to "write music very industriously". And what remarkable music it is. Right from the opening *Allegro assai* one senses trouble afoot, an unfamiliar restlessness mixed in with the more familiar busyness. Furthermore the second movement is surely the most fervent and punishing that Mendelssohn ever wrote – wild, insistent and unmistakably tragic in tone. This gradual intensification and darkening that occurs throughout Mendelssohn's quartet cycle makes it a most revealing guide to his creative development. But of course much of the earlier music is in fact profoundly 'Mendelssohnian' in the accepted sense of that term: fresh, dynamic, light-textured, beautifully crafted and full of amiable melodic invention. The very early E flat Quartet, Op. posth (composed when Mendelssohn was only 14), although fashioned very much in the style of Haydn and Mozart, points towards imminent developments – a song-like A minor Quartet, already taking its lead from late Beethoven in the same key, the E flat, Op. 12, with its delightful Canzonetta (once popular as a separate 'encore') and the eventful Op. 44 set, three of Mendelssohn's most concentrated full-scale works. And DG also add the four separate pieces, Op. 81, thus treating us to the entire Mendelssohn string quartet canon (the chronology of which, incidentally, is very much at odds with that suggested by the published opus numbers). The Melos Quartet come up trumps with a really superb set of performances – technically immaculate, transparent in tone and full of enthusiasm. The recordings, too, although analogue, report their playing with great presence and clarity.

Additional recommendations ...
...Nos. 1 and 2. **Gabrieli Quartet.** Chandos Ⓕ CHAN8827 (59 minutes: DDD: 1/92).
...Nos. 1 and 2. Andante in E major, Op. 81 No. 1. Scherzo in A minor, Op. 81 No. 2.
Coull Quartet. Hyperion Ⓕ CDA66397 (62 minutes: DDD: 1/92).
...Nos. 4 and 6. E flat major (1823). **Coull Quartet.**
Hyperion Ⓕ CDA66579 (80 minutes: DDD: 11/92).
...Nos. 1-6. **Cherubini Quartet.** EMI Ⓕ CDS7 54514-2 (three discs. 125 minutes: DDD: 8/93).   Ⓖ

...Nos. 1-6. Four Pieces for String Quartet, Op. 81 – Andante in E major; Scherzo in A minor; Capriccio in E minor; Fugue in A flat major. **Coull Quartet.**
Hyperion Ⓜ CDS44051/3 (three discs: 222 minutes: DDD: 6/94).
...Nos. 2 and 5. Andante in E major, Op. 81 No. 1. Scherzo in A minor, Op. 81 No. 2.
Aurora Quartet. Naxos Ⓢ 8 550861 (70 minutes: DDD: 12/94).
...Nos. 3 and 6. Capriccio in E minor, Op. 81 No. 3. Fugue in A flat major, Op. 81 No. 4.
Aurora Quartet. Naxos Ⓢ 8 550861 (65 minutes: DDD: 12/94).

Mendelssohn Cello Sonatas – No. 1 in B flat major, Op. 45; No. 2 in D major, Op. 58. Variations concertantes, Op. 17. Assai tranquillo. Song without words, Op. 109. **Steven Isserlis** (vc);
Melvyn Tan (fp). RCA Victor Red Seal Ⓕ 09026 62553-2 (62 minutes: DDD: 3/95). ✍
Recorded 1994. *Gramophone Editor's choice.*
Isserlis and Tan offer idiomatic, well-turned performances full of freshness and vigour. Try the First Sonata in B flat major (which Mendelssohn wrote for his brother, Paul, in 1838), where the second movement's dual function as scherzo and slow movement is convincingly characterized, and the music's passionate outbursts sound arrestingly potent. The *Variations concertantes*, Op. 17, were also written for Paul Mendelssohn and here, too, Isserlis's and Tan's fine blend of subtlety and panache affectingly conveys the music's nostalgic mood, and culminates powerfully in the work's conclusion. In the D major Second Sonata, Isserlis's and Tan's spontaneity and energy in the outer movements, skilfully controlled variety of timbre and touch in the scherzo, and dramatic opposition of chorale (piano) and recitative (cello) in the third movement sound immensely compelling. The *Assai tranquillo*, written during a journey from Dusseldorf to Leipzig in 1835, bears a touching dedication from the composer to his friend, Julius Rietz. Here, as in the charming *Song without words*, Op. 109, sympathetic tonal balance between cello and fortepiano in the softly lit recording poignantly brings out the music's sentiment. Isserlis and Tan effectively draw out the work's inconclusive ending to create a telling analogy of the eternal nature of friendship. Excellent balance and crisp, restrained recording helps vividly to evoke this music's romantic atmosphere.
Additional recommendation ...
...Nos. 1 and 2. Variations concertantes. Song without words – Op. 19 No. 1; Op. 109.
Lynn Harrell (vc); **Bruno Canino** (pf). Decca Ⓕ 430 198-2DH (67 minutes: DDD: 10/92).

Mendelssohn Piano Sonata in E major, Op. 6. Variations sérieuses in D minor, Op. 54.
Three Preludes, Op. 104*a*. Three Studies, Op. 104*b*. Kinderstücke, Op. 72, "Christmas Pieces".
Gondellied in A major. Scherzo in B minor. **Benjamin Frith** (pf). Naxos Ⓢ 8 550940
(65 minutes: DDD: 5/96). Recorded 1994-5.
The multiplicity of notes in Mendelssohn's piano music sometimes lays him open to the charge of 'note-spinning'. So what higher praise for Frith than to say that thanks to his fluency, tact and fancy, not a single work in this second volume seems to outstay its welcome. The unchallengeable masterpiece, of course, is the *Variations sérieuses*, so enthusiastically taken up by Clara Schumann, and still a repertory work today. Frith characterizes each variation with telling contrasts of tempo and touch without sacrificing the continuity and unity of the whole. Equally importantly, never for a moment does he allow us to forget the *sérieuses* of the title. No less impressive is his sensitively varied palette in the early E major Sonata (unmistakable homage to Beethoven's Op. 101) so often helped by subtle pedalling. But surely the recitative of the *Adagio* at times needs just a little more intensity and underlying urgency. Of the miniatures the six *Kinderstücke* ("Christmas Pieces" – written for the children of a friend) emerge with an unforced charm. As music they lack the romance of Schumann's ventures into a child's world, just as the *Three Studies* do of Chopin's magical revelations in this sphere. However, Frith's fingers never let him down. In the first B flat Study he even seems to acquire a third hand to sustain its middle melody. For sheer seductive grace, the independent *Gondellied* haunts the memory most of all. With pleasantly natural sound, too, this disc is quite a bargain.
Additional recommendations ...
...Piano Sonatas – Op. 6; G minor, Op. 105; B flat major, Op. 106. Andante and Rondo capriccioso in E minor, Op. 14. **Frederic Chiu** (pf). H
armonia Mundi Ⓕ HMU90 7117 (67 minutes: DDD: 5/94).
...Six Preludes and Fugues, Op. 35. Rondo capriccioso in E major, Op. 14. Variations sérieuses.
String Quartet No. 1 in E flat major, Op. 12 – Canzonetta (trans. F. Le Couppey).
Danielle Laval (pf). Auvidis Valois Ⓕ V4729 (68 minutes: DDD: 7/95). Ⓖ
...Kinderstücke. Songs without Words. Gondellied. Zwei Klavierstücke. Albumblatt in E minor,
Op. 117. **Daniel Barenboim** (pf).
DG Double Ⓜ 453 061-2GTA2 (two discs: 133 minutes: ADD: 11/96). Ⓖ
...Piano Sonata in B flat major, Op. 106. Three Fantaisies, Op. 16. Albumblatt in E minor, Op. 117.
Andante cantabile and Presto agitato in B major. Variations in E flat major, Op. 82. Rondo capriccioso in E major, Op. 14. **Benjamin Frith** (pf). Naxos Ⓢ 8 553186 (57 minutes: DDD: 1/98).

Mendelssohn Lieder – Op. 8: No. 4, Erntelied; No. 8, And'res Maienlied. Op. 9: No. 6, Scheidend. Op. 19*a*: No. 1, Frühlingslied; No. 2, Das erste Veilchen; No. 3, Winterlied; No. 4, Neue Liebe; No. 5, Gruss; No. 6, Reiselied. Op. 34: No. 1, Minnelied; No. 2, Auf Flügeln des Gesanges; No. 3, Frühlingslied; No. 6, Reiselied. Op. 47: No. 1, Minnelied; No. 2, Morgengrüss;

No. 3, Frühlingslied; No. 4, Volkslied; No. 6, Bei der Wiege. Op. 57: No. 1, Altdeutsches Lied; No. 2, Hirtenlied; No. 4, O Jugend; No. 5, Venetianisches Gondellied; No. 6, Wanderlied. Op. 71: No. 1, Tröstung; No. 3, An die Entfernte; No. 4, Schilflied; No. 5, Auf der Wanderschaft; No. 6, Nachtlied. Op. 84: No. 1, Da lieg' ich unter den Bäumen; No. 3, Jagdlied. Op. 86: No. 1, Es lauschte das Laub; No. 4, Allnächtlich im Traume; No. 5, Der Mond. Op. 99: No. 1, Erster Verlust; No. 5, Wenn sich zwei Herzen Scheiden. Op. posth.: Das Waldschloss; Pagenlied; Der Blumenkranz; Warnung vor dem Rhein; Schlafloser Augen Leuchte. **Dietrich Fischer-Dieskau** (bar); **Wolfgang Sawallisch** (pf). EMI Ⓜ CMS7 64827-2 (two discs: 95 minutes: ADD: 12/93). Texts included. From HMV SLS805 (7/72). Recorded 1970. ⓔⓔ

Mendelssohn's Lieder offer a challenge all their own, and Fischer-Dieskau takes it up with characteristic alacrity. As the majority of these songs are primarily accompanied melody, with little inherent teasing out or biting on the words, the singer is presented with a comparatively empty stage for his recreative imagination to design and pace. There are passing moments (in the Op. 47 *Morgengrüss*, for example) when the simplicity and ingenuousness of Mendelssohn's settings seems to frustrate Fischer-Dieskau. These moments, though, are rare. His voice, here in its prime, can draw on an extraordinarily wide palette of colour within the legato of the most timeworn strophic song. Both Fischer-Dieskau and Sawallisch, whose light-filled piano playing shows his real sympathy and understanding for this composer, know just when to move into the salon with Mendelssohn. The four Lenau settings and the little drama of mortality offered in *Das erste Veilchen* are re-created with a perfectly-scaled sense of fleeting ardour and melancholy. Best of all, perhaps, are those little vignettes of the dark mythology of the German folk-soul, those diabolic night rides into the forest which find Mendelssohn at his witchy best, and Fischer-Dieskau at his most virtuosic. This revelatory boxed set comes with gracefully detailed notes by Philip Radcliffe, full song texts but no translations.

Additional recommendations ...
...Scheidend. Frühlingslied. Winterlied. Neue liebe. Gruss. Auf Flügeln des Gesanges. Reiselied. Das Waldschloss. Pagenlied. Morgengrüss. Frühlingslied. Volkslied. Bei der Wiege. Venetianisches Gondellied. An die Entfernte. Schilflied. Herbstlied, Op. 84 No. 2. Allnächtlich im Traume. Der Mond. Lieblingsplätzchen, Op. 99 No. 3. **Wolfgang Holzmair** (bar); **Anna Wagner** (pf). Preiser Ⓔ 93368 (53 minutes: ADD: 7/91).

...Op. 19*a* – No. 4, Neue Liebe; No. 5, Gruss. Lieder, Op. 34 – No.2, Auf Flügeln des Gesanges; No. 6, Reiselied. Morgengruss, Op. 47 No. 2. Allnächtlich im Träume, Op. 86 No. 4. **Schubert** Schwanengesang, D957 – Der Atlas; Ihr Bild; Das Fischermädchen; Die Stadt; Am Meer; Der Doppelgänger. **Schumann** Dichterliebe, Op. 48. **Christoph Prégardien** (ten); **Andreas Staier** (fp). Deutsche Harmonia Mundi Ⓔ 05472 77319-2 (57 minutes: DDD: 12/94). ☞ *See review under Schumann; refer to the Index.*

...Op. 9 – No. 5, Im Herbst[a]; No. 6, Scheidend[ab]; No. 9, Ferne[a]. Op. 19*a* – No. 1, Frühlingslied[b]; No. 2, Das erste Veilchen[a]; No. 6, Reiselied[b]. Op. 34 – No. 1, Minnelied[b]; No. 6, Reiselied[b]. Op. 47 – No. 3, Frühlingslied[a]; No. 6, Bei der Wiege[a]. Venetianisches Gondellied, Op. 57 No. 5[b]. Six Duets, Op. 63[ab]. Op. 71 – No. 2, Frühlingslied[a]; No. 5, Auf der Wanderschaft[b]. Op. 84 – No. 1, Da lieg' ich unter den Bäumen[b]; No. 3, Jagdlied[b]. Altdeutsches Frühlingslied, Op. 86 No. 6[b]. Op. 99 – No. 3, Lieblingsplätzchen[a]; No. 5, Wenn sich zwei Herzen scheiden[a]. Op. posth – Pagenlied[a]; Der Blumenkranz[b]. **Fanny Mendelssohn** Op. 9 – No. 10, Verlust[b]; No. 12, Die Nonne[a]. [a]**Sophie Daneman** (sop); [b]**Nathan Berg** (bar); **Eugene Asti** (pf). Hyperion Ⓔ CDA66906 (65 minutes: DDD: 5/98).

Mendelssohn Lieder – Op. 8: No. 8, And'res Maienlied; No. 10, Romanze. Op. 9: No. 1, Frage; No. 5, Im Herbst; No. 7, Sehnsucht; No. 8, Frühlingsglaube; No. 9, Ferne; No. 10, Verlust; No. 12, Die Nonne. Op. 19*a*: No. 3, Winterlied; No. 4, Neue Liebe. Op. 34: No. 2, Auf Flügeln des Gesanges; No. 3, Frühlingslied; No. 4, Suleika; No. 5, Sonntagslied. Op. 47: No. 3, Frühlingslied; No. 5, Der Blumenstrauss; No. 6, Bei der Wiege. Op. 57 No. 3, Suleika. Op. 71: No. 2, Frühlingslied; No. 6, Nachtlied. Op. 86: No. 3, Die Liebende schreibt; No. 5, Der Mond. Op. 99: No. 1, Erster Verlust; No. 5, Wenn sich zwei Herzen Scheiden; No. 6, Es weiss und rät es doch keiner. Pagenlied, Op. posth. **Barbara Bonney** (sop); **Geoffrey Parsons** (pf). Teldec Ⓔ 2292-44946-2 (60 minutes: DDD: 2/93). Texts and translations included. Recorded 1991.

The charm of these songs lies in their simple style and almost endless stream of delightful melody. Unlike other Lieder composers Mendelssohn avoided blatant word-painting or vivid characterizations and certainly the most satisfying songs here tend to be settings of texts which do not on the surface of it offer much scope for musical expression. But while this disc may not give us the very best of Mendelssohn, or indeed the finest examples of nineteenth-century Lied, the singing of Barbara Bonney makes this a CD not to be missed. Here is a rare example of a singer caught on record at the very height of her technical and artistic powers, able to exercise seemingly effortless vocal control in portraying the subtle colours and understated moods of each songs. The partnership with that ever-sensitive accompanist Geoffrey Parsons is inspired. Listen to how Bonney seems to float ethereally above the rippling piano figures in that most famous of all Mendelssohn songs, *Auf Flügeln des Gesanges* ("On wings of song") – a performance which can surely never have been bettered on record. An interesting footnote is that three of these songs are by Fanny Mendelssohn but have by convention always been ascribed to her brother.

Mendelssohn Lieder – Op. 8: No. 7, Maienlied; No. 8, And'res Maienlied, Op. 9: No. 1, Frage;
No. 2, Geständnis; No. 8, Frühlingsglaube; Op 19*a*: No. 4, Neue Liebe; No. 5, Gruss; Op. 34:
No. 2, Auf Flügeln des Gesanges; No. 3, Frühlingslied; No. 4, Suleika; Op. 47: No. 1, Minnelied;
No. 4, Volkslied; Op. 57: No. 3, Suleika; No. 6, Wanderlied; Op. 71: No. 4, Schilflied; No. 6,
Nachtlied; Op. 86: No. 3, Die Liebende schreibt; No. 5, Der Mond; Op. 99: No. 1, Erster Verlust;
No. 6, Es weiss und rät es doch keiner. Op. posth.: Mädchens Klage; Das Waldschloss. Romances
(Byron) – There be none of beauty's daughters; Sun of the sleepless. **Dame Margaret Price** (sop);
Graham Johnson (pf). Hyperion Ⓕ CDA66666 (59 minutes: DDD: 3/94). Texts and translations
included. Recorded 1993. *Gramophone Editor's choice.*
This recital wholly dispels any lingering doubts there may be about Mendelssohn as a composer of
Lieder. He surpassed even Schubert and Brahms in his understanding of Heine's *Die Liebende
schreibt*. At the heart of the recital are the settings of Goethe. Besides *Die Liebende schreibt* the pair
include the poignant *Erster Verlust* and the two Suleika settings, neither quite a match for Schubert's
inspired versions but valid in their own right, particularly when sung with Price's uninhibited,
Lehmannesque ardour. Another facet of the performances, a free-ranging *Schwung*, can be heard in
Frühlingslied and the familiar *Neue Liebe*. The real discoveries here are the two Byron settings
uncovered by Johnson. Mendelssohn understood and knew how to set English and the accentuations
here are wholly idiomatic. The recording has great presence. Both singer and pianist are in the room
with us, anxious and able to please.

Mendelssohn Die erste Walpurgisnacht, Op. 60[a]. Songs without Words (orch. Matthus)[b] –
Andante con moto, Op. 19 No. 1; Allegro di molto, Op. 30 No. 2; Adagio, Op. 53 No. 4; Andante
grazioso, Op. 62 No. 6. Lieder (orch. Matthus)[c] – Op. 34: No. 2, Auf Flügeln des Gesanges;
No. 6, Reiselied. Op. 19*a*: No. 4, Neue Liebe; No. 5, Gruss. And'res Maienlied, Op. 8 No. 8.
Pagenlied, Op. posth. Schilflied, Op. 71 No. 4. Der Mond, Op. 86 No. 5. [a]**Jadwiga Rappé** (contr);
[ac]**Deon van der Walt** (ten); [a]**Anton Scharinger** (bar); [a]**Matthias Hölle** (bass); **Bamberg Symphony
[a]Chorus and Orchestra / Claus Peter Flor.** RCA Victor Red Seal Ⓕ 09026 62513-2
(61 minutes: DDD: 2/98). Texts and translations included. Recorded 1994.   Ⓠ
The idea of pagans outwitting their Christian oppressors inspired Mendelssohn to pen some of his
most mischievous musical invention: Berlioz was extremely impressed and the rumpus that erupts
when Druid guards "come with prods and pitchforks" (track 8) matches the sailors' choruses from
The Flying Dutchman for visceral excitement. The lighter Mendelssohn has doughty men tiptoe
through a woodland retreat to a Puckish scherzo while the closing 'hymn to faith' recalls the Second
Symphony and *Elijah*. Claus Peter Flor directs a performance notable above all for its delicacy, its
warmth of texture, its excellent solo singing and the energetic drive of the big choruses. The Overture
in particular shows Flor's skill at creating a three-dimensional sound stage, shaping and blending,
allowing due prominence to salient musical lines without spoiling the overall balance. The fill-ups are
eight delightful Lieder interspersed with four of the *Songs without Words*, piquantly scored by
Siegfried Matthus with especially imaginative use of harp and high percussion. "Spring Song"
becomes an oboe solo; "May Breezes" is shared among solo strings and harp; No. 20 is passed to the
solo horn (alluding unmistakably to *A Midsummer Night's Dream*); "On Wings of Song" incorporates
fluid harp writing, and "Traveller's Song" restlessly shimmering strings (to fit the autumn wind). Deon
van der Walt is the pleasingly mellifluous soloist and Flor is as considerate, authoritative and
imaginative as he is in the main work. All in all, a super disc, beautifully engineered.

Mendelssohn Paulus, Op. 36. **Juliane Banse** (sop); **Ingeborg Danz** (mez); **Michael Schade** (ten);
Andreas Schmidt (bar); **Stuttgart Gächinger Kantorei; Prague Chamber Choir; Czech Philharmonic
Orchestra / Helmuth Rilling.** Hänssler Classic Ⓕ 98 926 (two discs: 131 minutes: DDD: 6/96).
Text and translation included. Recorded 1994.
Rilling gives dramatic life to a work that can all too easily ramble episodically. His own Stuttgart
choir, such a revered group, and the Czech forces partnering them make certain that their conviction
comes across to us boldly. Each section is firmly integrated into the whole and offers great clarity.
Schmidt is excellent with his steady, warm voice and he is completely inside the role. His singing of
"Gott sei gnädig" is both firmly phrased and movingly interpreted. Young Juliane Banse sings her
recitatives and solos, especially "Jerusalem", with notable beauty of tone. The youthful German-
Canadian tenor Michael Schade is an artist of the utmost refinement and intelligence. If you already
have the Kurt Masur version on Philips (now deleted) you need not feel you have second-best but if
you're a newcomer to the work Schmidt will probably win you over to Rilling.

Mendelssohn Elijah (sung in German). **Christine Schäfer** (sop); **Cornelia Kallisch** (contr);
Michael Schade (ten); **Wolfgang Schöne** (bass-bar); **Stuttgart Gächinger Kantorei; Stuttgart Bach
Collegium / Helmuth Rilling.** Hänssler Classic Ⓕ 98 928 (two discs: 128 minutes: DDD: 9/95).
Text and translation included. Recorded 1994. *Gramophone Editor's choice.*
Rilling has recorded *Elijah* before with his Stuttgart forces, a 1981 account not without merits but
wholly superseded by this one. Above all he brings out arrestingly the drama of the piece, turning it
into a well-varied, exciting quasi-opera, a far from traditional view of the oratorio and rivalling, in
that respect, Sawallisch and even more Masur. The vicissitudes of the prophet's eventful life, his

reaction to events, the challenge to Baal, the encounter with Jezebel, have never sounded so electrifying. For that we have to thank Rilling's disciplined chorus, as biting in diction, precise and convincing in attack, and firm in tone as Sawallisch's, as involving as Masur's. Yet they can also provide the most sensitive, ethereal tone, as in Nos. 28 and 29, trio and chorus, "Siehe, der Hüter Israels". In general, every strand of the complex writing for chorus is made clear yet the overall effect is one of spontaneous combustion. The orchestral playing is no less arresting. Furthermore no Elijah since Theo Adam has so unerringly or authoritatively captured his many moods than Schöne. Here is the courageous man of action as he confronts Baal's followers and ironically taunts them, the sense of fiery conviction in "Ist's nichts des Herrn Wort", of doubt in "Es ist genug", and finally the wonderful Bachian serenity in "Ja, es sollen wohl Berge weichen", all evoked in the most positive and imaginative delivery of the text. The voice itself, a firm, expressive bass-baritone, is ideal for the role, one on which the singer has obviously lavished much time and consideration – to excellent effect. The same can be said for Schäfer, the soprano sensation from Germany, who brings a Silja-like conviction to all her work, nowhere more so than in "Höre Israel". Anyone hearing her declaim "Weiche nicht" would never be afraid again. The voice itself is interesting, gleaming yet not without warmth in the tone. Kallisch is almost as convincing in the mezzo solos and gives us a wonderfully malign portrayal of Jezebel. Schade is a fresh-voiced, communicative Obadiah, not quite in the Schreier class (Sawallisch) but close to it and he's another who is vivid with his words, especially so in the juniper tree recitative. Drawbacks? Just two. The recording is slightly too reverberant, but on this occasion the added space around the voices doesn't preclude immediacy of impact. Then the booklet has an incredibly pretentious and impenetrable note plus a confusing layout for the text.

Additional recommendations ...
...Soloists; **London Symphony Chorus; London Symphony Orchestra / Richard Hickox.**
Chandos Ⓕ CHAN8774/5 (two discs: 131 minutes: DDD: 2/90).
...Soloists; **Leipzig Radio Chorus; Israel Philharmonic Orchestra / Kurt Masur.**
Teldec Ⓕ 9031-73131-2 (two discs: 110 minutes: DDD: 5/93).
Gramophone Award Winner 1993. Selected by Sounds in Retrospect.   ⒼⒼ
...Soloists; **Leipzig Radio Chorus; Leipzig Gewandhaus Orchestra / Wolfgang Sawallisch.**
Philips Duo Ⓜ 438 368-2PM2 (two discs: 131 minutes: ADD: 8/93).   ⒼⒼ
...Soloists; **Collegium Vocale; La Chapelle Royale Choir and Orchestra;**
Champs Elysées Orchestra / Philippe Herreweghe.
Harmonia Mundi Ⓕ HMC90 1463/4 (two discs: 127 minutes: DDD: 11/93).   Ⓖ
...Soloists; **Figuralchor Frankfurt; Singakademie; Frankfurt Opera House and Museum Orchestra /**
Sylvain Cambreling. Arte Nova Ⓢ 74321 43324-2 (two discs: 123 minutes: DDD: 1/98).

Mendelssohn Elijah (sung in English). **Renée Fleming, Libby Crabtree** (sops); **Patricia Bardon,**
Sara Fulgoni (mezzos); **Matthew Munro** (treb); **John Mark Ainsley, John Bowen** (tens);
Neal Davies (bar); **Bryn Terfel** (bass-bar); **Geoffrey Moses** (bass); **Edinburgh Festival Chorus;**
Orchestra of the Age of Enlightenment / Paul Daniel. Decca Ⓕ 455 688-2DH2
(two discs: 131 minutes: DDD: 9/97). ✏ Text included. Recorded 1996.
Gramophone Editor's record of the month.   ⒼⒼ

Paul Daniel and Bryn Terfel ensure that this is one of the most dramatic performances of the oratorio on disc. The young conductor, with the advantage of a period instrument orchestra and an excellent one at that, has looked anew at the score and as a consequence reveals much of the rhythmic and dynamic detail not always present in other performances, at least those available on CD in English. His accomplishment in terms of pacing and of balance is also praiseworthy, and he earns further marks for using the trio, quartet and double quartet of soloists Mendelssohn asks for in specific pieces, so as to vary the texture of the music. Terfel simply gives the most exciting and vivid account of the prophet's part yet heard. His range, in terms of vocal register and dynamics, is huge; his expression, mighty and immediate, befits a man of Elijah's temperament. As the score demands, anguish, anger and sympathy are there in full measure, displayed in exceptional definition of words, and when this Elijah calls on the Lord for the saving rain, the Almighty could hardly resist such a commanding utterance. Yet there is always the inwardness part of the role demands, not least in "It is enough": you sense a man at the end of his tether. If, however, you find his interpretation too grandiloquent, then Thomas Allen on the Marriner version is a more than acceptable alternative, a smoother, more amenable but also deeply felt performance. Where the other soloists are concerned, there is not much to choose between the two sets. For the concerted numbers Daniel has chosen voices that nicely match each other in timbre. The chorus are alert and unanimous in both attack and well thought-through phrasing, but their actual sound is often a little soft-centred, partly because all-important consonants are ignored. In every respect the orchestral playing on Daniel's version is exemplary. For anyone wanting the work in the vernacular, this set should, by a small measure, be the primary recommendation.

Additional recommendations ...
...(Sung in English). **Soloists; Academy of St Martin in the Fields Chorus and Orchestra /**
Sir Neville Marriner. Philips Ⓕ 432 984-2PH2 (two discs: 127 minutes: DDD: 10/92).   Ⓖ
...(Sung in English). **Soloists; Wandsworth School Boys' Choir; New Philharmonia Chorus;**
New Philharmonia Orchestra / Rafael Frühbeck de Burgos.
EMI Forte Ⓑ CZS5 68601-2 (two discs: 140 minutes: ADD: 5/96).

Further listening ...
...Concerto for Violin, Piano and Strings in D minor. *Coupled with* **Haydn** Concerto for Violin, Keyboard and Strings in F major, HobXVIII/6. **Ralf Gothóni** (pf); **Kuhmo Virtuosi / Peter Csaba** (vn/dir). Ondine Ⓕ ODE810-2 (58 minutes: DDD: 1/95).
...Clarinet Sonata in E flat major. *Coupled with works by* **Danzi** *and* **Weber** **Charles Neidich** (cl); **Robert Levin** (fp). Sony Classical SK64302 (9/95). 🏮
...Piano Duets – Piano Trio No. 2 in C minor, Op. 66. Variations in B flat major, Op. 83*a*. Andante and Allegro brillant in A major, Op. 92. *Coupled with* **Mendelssohn-Hensel** Three pieces for Piano Duet. **Yaara Tal, Andreas Groethuysen** (pf duet). Sony Classical SK48494 (6/93).   ⒼⒼ
...Piano Quartets – No. 2 in F minor, Op. 2; No. 3 in B minor, Op. 3.[a]**Andra Darzins** (va); [a]**Wolfgang Wagner** (db); **Bartholdy Piano Quartet.** Naxos 8 550967 (10/94).
...Piano Trio No. 1 in D minor, Op. 49. *Coupled with* **Brahms** Piano Trio No. 1 in B major, Op. 8. **Chung Trio.** Decca Ⓕ 421 425-2DH (65 minutes: DDD: 4/95).   Ⓖ
...Sextet in D major, Op. 110[a]. Piano Quartet No. 1 in C minor, Op. 1. **Bartholdy Piano Quartet.** Naxos 8 550966 (10/94).
...Organ works, Volume 1 – Sonatas, Op. 65: No. 1 in F minor; No. 2 in C minor. Fugue in D minor. Chorale variations on "Wie gross ist des Allmächt'gen Güte". Andante in D major. Trio in F major. Prelude and Fugue in G major. Andante with variations. Allegro in D minor/major. **Peter Planyavsky** (org). Motette CD11271 (10/92).
...Six Preludes and Fugues, Op. 35. Three Caprices, Op. 33. Perpetuum mobile in C major, Op. 119. **Benjamin Frith** (pf). Naxos 8 550939 (11/95).
...Christus, Op. 97 – Say where is He born; There shall a Star. *Coupled with works by various composers.* **Chichester Cathedral Choir / Alan Thurlow** with **James Thomas** (org). Priory PRCD539 (5/96).
...Sacred Choral Works: Verleih uns Frieden gnädiglic[c]. Kyrie eleison. Three sacred pieces – Ehre sei Gott; Heilig ist Gott. Three sacred choruses, Op. 23 – Ave Maria[bcd]; Mitten wir. Six Anthems, Op. 79. Three Psalms, Op. 78. Hör mein Biten Herr[ad]. [a]**Anne Dawson** (sop); [b]**Rogers Covey-Crump** (ten); **Corydon Singers;** [c]**English Chamber Orchestra / Matthew Best** with [d]**John Scott** (org). Hyperion CDA66359 (4/90).
...Oedipus at Colonos, Op. 93. **Soloists; Berlin Radio Chorus; Carl Maria von Weber Men's Choir; Bavarian Radio Symphony Orchestra / Stefan Soltesz.** Capriccio 10 393 (1/95).   Ⓖ

Fanny Mendelssohn-Hensel
German 1805-1847

Suggested listening ...
...Das Jahr – February; March; May; September; December. *Coupled with works by various composers.* **Jennifer Eley** (pf). Koch International Classics 37197-2 (10/96). *See review under Mendelssohn; refer to the Index.*

José Merlin
Argentinian 20th century

Suggested listening ...
...Suite del recuerdo. *Coupled with works by various composers.* **Jason Vieaux** (gtr). Naxos 8 553449 (11/97). *See review in the Collections section; refer to the Index.*

Tarquinio Merula
Italian 1594/5-1665

Merula Madrigali, libro secondo, Op. 10 – Aria di Ciaccona, "Su la cetra amorosa". Curtio precipitato, libro secondo, Op. 13 – Folle è ben che si crede; Chi vuol ch'io m'inamori; Un bambin chi va alla scola; Quando gli uccelli portaranno i zoccoli; Sentirete una canzonetta; Menti lingua bugiarda; Ho ch'è tempo di dormire. Capriccio cromatico[a]. Toccata del secondo tono[b]. **Montserrat Figueras** (sop); **Jean-Pierre Canihac** (cornet); **Lorenz Duftschmid** (vn); [b]**Andrew Lawrence-King** (hp); **Rolf Lislevand** (theorbo/baroque gtr); **Jordi Savall** (va da gamba); [a]**Ton Koopman** (hpd). Auvidis Astrée Ⓕ E8503 (56 minutes: DDD: 1/94). 🏮 Texts and translations included. Recorded 1992.
Tarquinio Merula is barely represented in the catalogue except as a composer of distinctive instrumental music. This release shows that Merula's secular vocal style is if anything even more interesting. The 1638 book of solo songs, from which most of this disc is taken, is an expressive and ingenious collection which displays amongst other things Merula's mature handling of Monteverdi's *stile concitato* and a highly attractive treatment of popular songs. Figueras's approach in the intricate and colourful melodic strands of the 'concerted' pieces is impetuous but effectively paced too. The result is at times little short of spellbinding: *Su la cetra amorosa* is executed with all the considerable virtuosity, energy and emotional intensity it deserves, complemented moreover by an exciting and fluent dialogue with a solo cornett. Also impressive is her ability to judge the fine line between comedy

and despair in *Quando gli uccelli portaranno i zoccoli* ("When birds wear clogs"), where Merula's slightly bizarre sense of humour and a proven sense of irony are exhibited to the full. Ensemble can be a little ropey, but the overall richness of musical timbre and freedom of expression is what ultimately prevails. Well worth investigating.

Further listening ...

...Chiacona. *Coupled with works by various composers.* **His Majesties Sagbutts and Cornetts.** Hyperion CDA66847 (11/96). *See review in the Collections section; refer to the Index.*

Claudio Merulo   Italian 1533-1604

Merulo Toccate, Ricercare, Canzoni d'Intavolatura d'Organo. **Fabio Bonizzoni** (hpd/org). ✐
Arcana Ⓕ A30 (69 minutes: DDD: 2/98).

Claudio Merulo is one of the earlier representatives of the great Italian line of keyboard virtuosos. As always with Arcana, the sound recording and the choice of instruments are superb, allowing one to hear one of the oldest surviving Italian organs (a splendid sixteenth-century harpsichord is also featured). The music is perhaps not quite so consistently impressive, though it is never uninspired; devotees of this repertory need not hesitate.

Further listening ...

...Susanne un jour. *Coupled with works by various composers.* **Sophie Yates** (hpd). Chandos Chaconne CHAN0601 (9/97). ✐ *See review in the Collections section; refer to the Index.*

Olivier Messiaen   French 1908-1992

Messiaen Concert à quatre[a]. Les offrandes oubliées. Un sourire. Le tombeau resplendissant.
[a]**Catherine Cantin** (fl); [a]**Heinz Holliger** (ob); [a]**Mstislav Rostropovich** (vc); [a]**Yvonne Loriod** (pf);
Orchestra of the Opéra-Bastille, Paris / Myung-Whun Chung. DG Ⓕ 445 947-2GH
(66 minutes: DDD: 8/95). Recorded 1994.

Messiaen's musical testament is the great hour-long orchestral cycle *Eclairs sur l'au-delà.* If the late works on this disc, *Un sourire* and the *Concert à quatre*, lack the visionary grandeur, still strong in *Eclairs*, they both embody that spirit of joyous serenity which sets the composer apart from virtually all his contemporaries. *Un sourire*, inspired by what Messiaen felt to be the 'smiling' quality of Mozart's music, involves the familiar contrast between other-worldly meditation and more mundane exuberance (birdsong), with a well-balanced formal design in which contrast matters more than continuity. *Concert à quatre* similarly juxtaposes reflective and lively materials, but the stylistic range is unusually wide, since Messiaen based the delightful second movement on a *Vocalise* of 1935. The pianist tends to dominate, especially in the finale (in whose completion Yvonne Loriod was actively involved) but the three other soloists also make their presence felt in a vivid and affectionate performance. The two early orchestral scores that complete the disc belong to Messiaen's pre-birdsong world. Contrasts are already extreme, but here the celestial meditations are offset by explosive episodes whose provenance reaches back to the Witches Sabbaths of Berlioz, Liszt and Franck. The youthful composer can even be forgiven his excessive use of the bass drum in *Le tombeau resplendissant* when the total effect of the piece is so absorbing and original. These are state-of-the-art recordings of performances given in the fraught days of Chung's final appearances with the orchestra. The atmosphere is suitably apocalyptic, but the playing remains superbly disciplined.

Messiaen Un sourire[c]. Et exspecto resurrectionem mortuorum[c]. Oiseaux exotiques[ab].
La ville d'en-haut[ac]. Un Vitrail et des oiseaux[ac]. [a]**Yvonne Loriod** (pf); [b]**Bavarian Radio Symphony Orchestra;** [c]**Berlin Radio Symphony Orchestra / Karl Anton Rickenbacher.**
Koch Schwann Ⓕ 311232 (70 minutes: DDD: 12/94). Recorded 1993.

This performance of *Oiseaux exotiques* was recorded by Bavarian Radio in 1985; Messiaen admired it and apparently suggested the four other works on this CD as a coupling. Very shrewd. In *Oiseaux exotiques* Messiaen creates a bower-bird's nest of extravagant, endearingly ramshackle ornateness. *Et exspecto resurrectionem mortuorum*, on the other hand, is one of his grandest and simplest structures, with its litany-like repetitions and responses. Placed between these, the three shorter pieces can be seen both as a useful way of programming works that fit awkwardly in concerts or as a series of further illustrations of Messiaen's use of what one might call 'strophic form'. *Un Vitrail et des oiseaux* ("A stained-glass window and birds"), for example, splits a typical chorale-like theme into four strophes, follows each with a varied 'antistrophe' of birdsong, and each of those with a progressively embellished cadenza, ending with a coda and a solemn restatement of all four strophes of the chorale. It is disarmingly simple and yet audibly related to the cumulative nobility of *Et exspecto*. That tiny but lovely homage to Mozart, *Un sourire*, is a miniature example of the same process; so is *La ville d'en-haut*, which can now be heard as a sort of sketch for Messiaen's last vision of eternity, *Eclairs sur L'au-delà.* He was right, in short: these five disparate pieces do make a satisfying and illuminating programme. *Oiseaux exotiques* (a cheerful racket of a piece) is rather drily recorded; there's more space around the other pieces in the collection. All are very well played, with proper regard to Messiaen's all-important silences and near-silences as well as his precisely judged juxtapositions.

Additional recommendation ...
...Oiseaux exotiques[a]. Sept Haïkaï[b]. Couleurs de la cité céleste[c]. La ville d'en-haut[d]. Un Vitrail et des oiseaux[e]. Et exspecto resurrectionem mortuorum[f]. [abc]**Peter Donohoe** (pf);
Netherlands Wind Ensemble / Reinbert de Leeuw.
Chandos New Direction Ⓕ CHAN9301/02 (two discs: 102 minutes: DDD: 1/95).

Messiaen Des canyons aux étoiles. **Marja Bon** (pf); **Hans Dullaert** (hn); **Ger de Zeeuw**
(xylorimba); **Wim Vos** (glockenspiel); **Asko Ensemble; Schoenberg Ensemble;**
The Hague Percussion Ensemble / Reinbert de Leeuw. Auvidis Montaigne Ⓕ MO782035
(two discs: 91 minutes: DDD: 4/95). Recorded 1990.
This is one of Messiaen's most vivid scores, new and magnificent landscapes, as so often with him, drawing his imagination to further extremes of instrumental sonority. In this case the landscapes were the cliffs and towers of red, orange and violet rock that he marvelled at in Bryce Canyon, Utah ("the most beautiful thing that exists in the United States"), the huge natural amphitheatre of Cedar Breaks and, endearing itself to Messiaen by its name as well as its "limpid waters", its "rock walls of pink, white, mauve, red, black", the river gorge of Zion Park. (A steep rock pinnacle in the area was later named Mount Messiaen.) The orchestra to evoke all this is modest in size (44 players, including solo piano, horn, xylorimba and glockenspiel), with only 13 solo strings set against quadruple woodwind, triple brass and much percussion. But within this already dazzlingly bright ensemble Messiaen calls for such extra effects as wind machine and géophone (a shallow drum with lead shot inside), cellos and double-bass playing on the wrong side of the bridge, a trumpeter using the mouthpiece of his instrument only, a high clarinet with the reed restrained by the player's teeth, and so on. Although extreme, these sounds are calculated with great care. After an invocation of Bryce Canyon has twice led to a contemplation of "chasms of darkness, terror of the abyss" (rasping trombones and pounding drums) the third cycle achieves a brazen splendour over which the song of the white-winged dove, played by solo horn, piano and strings, hovers just as Messiaen describes it. And in the ensuing eighth movement one of his hushed, motionless string melodies has each of its phrases embellished at the end with *glissandos* in harmonics from a solo violin and with the double-bass quietly bouncing the bow stick on the strings: "droplets of water and silken rustlings", said Messiaen, and the effect is magically precise. This performance exults in such details and in the fearsome scale of many of the score's gestures. It was recorded live (though apparently without an audience) and is fully worthy of the work, and the excellent recording (the instruments are audibly arranged according to the layout printed in the score) gives the music space to resound in.

Messiaen Chronochromie. La ville d'en-haut. Et exspecto resurrectionem mortuorum. **Cleveland**
   Orchestra / Pierre Boulez. DG Ⓕ 445 827-2GH (58 minutes: DDD: 4/95). Recorded 1993.   Ⓖ
Boulez has spoken of his pleasure at performing Messiaen with an orchestra relatively unfamiliar with his music. It sounds as though the Cleveland Orchestra must have enjoyed it too. You would expect them to, perhaps, in such a passage as that in the fourth movement of *Et exspecto*, where the two superimposed plainchant melodies return together with the noble "theme of the depths" – it has great splendour, as does the chorale melody of the finale, rising at the end to a satisfyingly palpable *fffff*. And in this performance of *Chronochromie* you can hear why Messiaen said that certain pages of it were "a double homage to Berlioz and Pierre Schaeffer [the French pioneer of electronic music]". Absolute rhythmic precision and the clarity of colour that comes from meticulous balance are among the other pleasures of these performances. They make a most satisfying coupling, too. The recordings are excellent: clean but not clinical and ample in dynamic range.

Messiaen Turangalîla-symphonie[a]. Quatuor pour la fin du temps[b]. [b]**Saschko Gawriloff** (vn);
   [b]**Siegfried Palm** (vc); [b]**Hans Deinzer** (cl); [b]**Aloys Kontarsky,** [a]**Peter Donohoe** (pfs);
   [a]**Tristan Murail** (ondes martenot); [a]**City of Birmingham Symphony Orchestra / Sir Simon Rattle.**
   EMI Ⓕ CDS7 47463-8 (two discs: 130 minutes: DDD/ADD: 12/87). Item marked [b] from
   Deutsche Harmonia Mundi 065 99711 (8/79).   Ⓖ
No longer a rarity in the concert-hall, Messiaen's epic hymn to life and love has been lucky on record too, with Rattle's performance staying just ahead of the pack. Messiaen's luxuriant scoring presents a challenge for the engineers as much as the players and the EMI team come through with flying colours. Tristan Murail's ondes martenot is carefully balanced here – evocative and velvety, neither reduced to inaudibility nor overmiked to produce an ear-rending screech. Peter Donohoe's piano obbligato is similarly integrated into the orchestral tapestry yet provides just the right kind of decorative intervention. Rattle is at his best in the work's more robust moments like the jazzy fifth movement and the many rhythmic passages which recall Stravinsky's *Le Sacre*. But those unfamiliar with Messiaen's extraordinary score should perhaps start with the central slow movement, the beautiful *Jardin du sommeil d'amour*, exquisitely done by the Birmingham team. Unlike at least one rival account, this *Turangalîla* spills on to a second CD, which leaves room for a distinguished *Quatuor pour la fin du temps*. The music-making here lacks the youthful spontaneity of the main work, but is notable for an unusually slow and sustained performance of the movement with cello solo.
Additional recommendations ...
...Turangalîla-symphonie. **Soloists; Royal Concertgebouw Orchestra / Riccardo Chailly.**
   Decca Ⓕ 436 626-2DH (77 minutes: DDD: 11/93).   Ⓖ

...Quatuor pour la fin du temps. **Bartók** Contrasts, Sz111. **Chamber Music Northwest.**
Delos Ⓕ DE3043 (63 minutes: ADD: 6/87).
...Quatuor pour la fin du temps. **Krauze** Quatuor pour la Naissance. **David Campbell** (cl);
Madeline Mitchell (vn); **Christopher van Kampen** (vc); **Joanna MacGregor** (pf).
Collins Classics Ⓕ 1393-2 (65 minutes: DDD: 6/94).
...Turangalîla-symphonie. **Poulenc** Concert champêtre[a]. Concerto for Organ, Strings
and Timpani[b]. **Soloists; Michel Béroff** (pf); **Jeanne Loriod** (ondes martenot);
Simon Preston ([a]hpd/[b]org); **London Symphony Orchestra / André Previn.**
EMI Forte Ⓜ CZS5 69752-2 (two discs: 129 minutes: ADD: 8/97).

Messiaen Eclairs sur L'Au-Delà. **Polish Radio National Symphony Orchestra, Katowice /
Antoni Wit.** Jade Ⓕ JADC099 (63 minutes: DDD: 6/94). Recorded live in 1993.
Messiaen Eclairs sur l'Au-Delà. **Orchestra of the Opéra-Bastille, Paris / Myung-Whun Chung.**
DG Ⓕ 439 929-2GH (66 minutes: DDD: 12/94).   ⊚⊚
Eclairs sur L'Au-Delà ("Illuminations of the Beyond") was Olivier Messiaen's last major work. It is
almost a summary, musical and spiritual, of the preoccupations of his preceding 60 years but shows
him delightedly discovering not only new birds but also entrancingly new sounds: he has not made
such startling use before of the contrabass clarinet (in the huge and complex eighth movement, which
culminates in a Great Messiaen Tune of sonorous nobility), nor employed (to evoke the Lyrebird)
such vertiginous leaps between sections of the orchestra. In one way, then, it is a series of nostalgic
revisits. In the fourth movement, for example, there's a sort of two-minute summary of the extremely
dense counterpoint of *Chronochromie*; the sixth recalls the "Dance of fury for the seven trumpets" in
the *Quartet for the end of time*. But there's also a touching sense of Messiaen in his eighties preparing
to contemplate the beyond. In the ninth of the 11 movements he writes his last birdsong piece, no
fewer that 25 birds impersonated simultaneously by 18 woodwind instruments: the image is of Christ
as the Tree of Life, the birds are the souls of the blessed, and of course they are all singing at once.
He then considers "The path to the invisible", and if we were expecting a rapt meditation we do not
know Messiaen: it is a clamorous and insistent piece, one of his great angular toccatas, expressing the
very difficulty of keeping to that path. And finally, most movingly, one of his almost motionless,
beginningless and endless string chorales, "Christ, Light of Paradise". The live Jade recording has
remarkably few signs of how very difficult a piece it is to play. The recording is pleasantly spacious,
the audience only makes its presence felt by a certain amount of coughing between movements; it is,
in short, the sort of 'première recording' in which one can safely concentrate on the music.
    Chung has distinct advantages, mark you, including an arguably finer orchestra and the
comparative leisure of a studio recording; in fact it was made in the Opéra-Bastille itself, and
impressively spacious it sounds. Where these advantages show is in small but quite important details
of balance and sheer finesse. In the very opening wind chorale, for example, Chung's chording is a
touch more precise, and on many pages he has obviously worked very hard to ensure clarity of texture
and polished playing. Yet the sense that the Polish orchestra is excitedly discovering this score is no
less absorbing than the Parisians' meticulous and loving care of it. Chung takes a little more time over
the piece, most noticeably in the way that he allows silences their full measure. He also explores a finer
range of very quiet sounds than Wit (perhaps a studio and the absence of an audience helped). These
together might tip the balance in Chung's direction but then, listening again to Messiaen's discovery
of a (to him) new and vociferous bird in the third movement, you sense the Polish players sharing his
pleasure and seasoning that emotion with relief that this frighteningly difficult music is coming off
without a hitch. In short, Chung's is an obvious first choice: it's beautifully played, immaculately
recorded and vividly expressive. But once in a while a live recording of a difficult score gets pretty well
everything right and manages as well to communicate the excitement of a first performance.
Additional recommendation ...
...Eclairs sur L'Au-Delà. **Sydney Symphony Orchestra / David Porcelijn.**
ABC Classics Ⓕ 8 770011 (62 minutes: DDD: 11/96).   Ⓖ

Messiaen Six Petites Esquisses d'Oiseaux. Cantéyodjayâ. Quatre Etudes de rythme. Pièce pour le
Tombeau de Paul Dukas. **Gloria Cheng** (pf). Koch International Classics Ⓕ 37267-2
(49 minutes: DDD: 9/95).
Gloria Cheng is a pianist much in demand as a specialist in taxing contemporary scores, and you can
easily hear why: she is technically fearless and meticulously attentive to complex rhythms, she can
sustain a bold melodic line splendidly, and her playing has powerful attack. She is just what the
exhilarating but exhausting *Cantéyodjayâ* needs, and she gives it a performance of great *élan* and
exciting drama. Similar qualities are needed, of course, in the outer sections of the *Quatre Etudes*,
which have all the ferocity that Messiaen asks for. If there is any criticism it is that she tends to mark
up Messiaen's quieter dynamics. Thus the famous "Mode de valeurs et d'intensités", which has a
'mode' of seven degrees of intensity, from *ppp* to *fff*, seems to lack a couple of degrees at the bottom
end. However, rarely does one hear this piece sound quite so coherent, and Cheng's concentration in
the austere "Neumes rythmiques" is remarkable. There is admirable precision in the *Petites Esquisses*,
but again a slight lack of dynamic range at the quieter end of the spectrum means that each bird does
not quite, as Messiaen insists, "have its own aesthetic". Still, an enjoyable if rather short recital,
ending with an impressively austere account of Messiaen's elegy for his teacher

Additional recommendations ...

...Pièce pour le Tombeau de Paul Dukas. Fantaisie burlesque. Rondeau. Six Petites Esquisses d'Oiseaux. Visions de l'Amen[a]. **Peter Hill,** [a]**Benjamin Frith** (pfs).
Unicorn-Kanchana Ⓕ DKPCD9144 (79 minutes: DDD: 6/94).

...Etudes de rythme – Ile de feu II. Préludes – No. 1, La colombe; No. 3, Le nombre léger; No. 6, Cloches d'angoisse et larmes d'adieu. Cantéyodjayâ. Catalogue d'oiseaux – La traquet rieur; Le courlis cendré. Vingt regards sur l'enfant Jésus – Regard du Père; Par Lui a été fait; Regard des prophètes, des bergers et des Mages. **Rolf Hind** (pf).
Cala United Ⓕ CACD88019 (69 minutes: DDD: 12/94).

...Etudes de rythme – Ile de feu I et II. *Coupled with works by various composers.*
Shura Cherkassky (pf). Decca Ⓕ 433 657-2DH (79 minutes: ADD: 2/96).   Ⓖ

...Etudes de rythme. *Coupled with works by various composers.* **Erika Haase** (pf).
Tacet Ⓕ Tacet53 (74 minutes: DDD: 2/98).

Messiaen Vingt regards sur l'enfant Jésus. **Joanna MacGregor** (pf). Collins Classics Ⓕ 7033-2 (two discs: 128 minutes: DDD: 5/96). Recorded 1995.

Joanna MacGregor is a pianist who combines fearless technique with great intelligence and imagination. When these qualities are matched by stunningly beautiful piano sound the likelihood of a distinguished account of the *Vingt regards sur l'enfant Jésus* is strong, and so it proves. MacGregor knows very well that some of these pieces require exquisitely vivid colour while others need a narrower chromatic range but one of absolute clarity (the crystalline glistening of the first variation in No. 15, "La baiser de l'Enfant-Jésus", the cycle's 'slow movement'). But she has few problems with the sheer strength needed elsewhere and only a couple of times do you get a slight impression that either she or the piano had reached its limits (at the height of No. 6, the tumultuous "Par Lui tout a été fait") or that a little more dynamic variation would have aided her brilliant colour contrasts (in the second development section of No. 10, "Regard de l'esprit de joie"). Elsewhere, not least in the huge finale, her playing has commanding power and grandeur. Her precision, too, is admirable. Above all, perhaps, she communicates a real love for the sound-world of this cycle, which is just as often sensuous and pianistic as it is mystical. We are not short of good recordings of the *Vingt regards*, but MacGregor's is probably the most sheerly beautiful of them all. Yvonne Loriod has great authority and a tireless strength that MacGregor cannot match on one or two pages, but she also has an occasional tendency to hurry, and the recorded sound is a touch hard. Peter Hill finds at times subtler shadings and occasionally allows silences to register more magically, but his instrument is not quite as superb nor so finely recorded as MacGregor's. The same is true of Håkon Austbø's performance, otherwise exceptionally good and exceptionally cheap. MacGregor's version was made in the concert-hall at Snape on an extremely fine Steinway but the central achievement here is her perception of Messiaen's prodigal invention of sonorities.

Additional recommendations ...

...Vingt regards. **Peter Hill** (pf).
Unicorn-Kanchana Ⓕ DKPCD9122/3 (two discs: 142 minutes: DDD: 9/92).   ⒼⒼ

...Vingt regards. **Mélisande Chauveau** (pf).
Forlane Ⓕ UCD16709/10 (two discs: 140 minutes: DDD: 7/94).

...Vingt regards. **Håkon Austbø** (pf).
Naxos Ⓢ 8 550829/30 (two discs: 133 minutes: DDD: 12/94). *Gramophone Editor's choice.*   Ⓖ

...Vingt regards. Petites Esquisses d'Oiseaux. Préludes. Etudes de rythme – Ile de feu I and II.
Yvonne Loriod (pf). Erato Ⓜ 4509-96222-2 (three discs: 185 minutes: ADD: 12/94).   ⒼⒼ

Messiaen La nativité du Seigneur[a]. Le banquet céleste[b]. **Jennifer Bate** (org). Unicorn-Kanchana Ⓕ DKPCD9005 (62 minutes: DDD: 2/88). Played on the organ of Beauvais Cathedral.
Item marked [a] from DKP9005 (6/82), [b]DKP9018 (2/83).   ⒼⒼⒼ

La nativité du Seigneur comprises nine meditations on themes associated with the birth of the Lord. Messiaen's unique use of registration gives these pieces an extraordinarily wide range of colour and emotional potency and in Jennifer Bate's hands (and feet) it finds one of its most persuasive and capable advocates. Bate was much admired by the composer and is so far the only organist to have recorded his complete works for the instrument. *Le banquet céleste* was Messiaen's first published work for the organ and is a magical, very slow-moving meditation on a verse from St John's Gospel (VI, 56). The very faithful recording captures both the organ and the large acoustic of Beauvais Cathedral to marvellous effect.

Additional recommendations ...

...La nativité du Seigneur. Diptyque. Les corps glorieux. Verset pour la fête de la dédicace. Le banquet céleste. Apparition de l'église éternelle. Livre d'orgue. Nine Méditations sur le mystère de la Sainte Trinité. L'Ascension. Messe de la Pentecôte. Livre du Saint Sacrement.
Gillian Weir (org). Collins Classics Ⓜ 7031-2 (seven discs: 418 minutes: DDD: 12/94).   Ⓖ

...Le banquet celeste[a]. La nativité du Seigneur[a]. Diptyque[b]. Les corps glorieux[c]. L'Ascension[c]. Messe de la Pentecôte[c]. Apparition de l'église éternelle[d]. Livre d'orgue[d]. Verset pour la fête de la dédicace[d]. Neuf Méditations sur le mystère de la Sainte Trinité[e]. Livre du Saint-Sacrement[f]. Les corps glorieux[b]. [a]**Jennifer Bate,** [b]**Jon Gillock,** [c]**Naji Hakim,** [d]**Louis Thiry,** [e]**Thomas Daniel Schlee,** [f]**Hans-Ola Ericsson** (org). Jade Ⓜ 74321-29491-2 (seven discs: 430 minutes: DDD: 7/96).

Messiaen Apparition de l'église éternelle[a]. La nativité du Seigneur[b]. **Olivier Messiaen** (org).
EMI Composers in Person mono Ⓕ CDC5 55222-2* (72 minutes: ADD: 6/95).
Item marked [a] from Ducretet-Thomson DUC4/5, [b]DUC2/3 (both recorded 1956).
Played on the organ of Sainte-Trinité, Paris.   Ⓖ

During 1956 Messiaen recorded what was up to that date his complete organ *oeuvre* at Sainte-Trinité
– the church where he had been organist since 1931. This pairing of two famous works, written shortly
after his appointment to Sainte-Trinité, is more than a simple reissue, for it has been newly edited and
digitally remastered by Simon Gibson and Andrew Walter. The most obvious benefit is the vivid aural
picture it gives of the instrument which so inspired Messiaen – listen to the sense of utter calm created
by the voix céleste in "Desseins éternels", or that peculiar luminosity which bathes "Les mages" (both
from *La nativité*) as they trudge along following the night star. No recording process yet invented
could recapture that hypnotic mixture of vision, utter conviction and virtuosity which were the
hallmarks of Messiaen's playing in the flesh, but this CD does come very close and coupled with Felix
Aprahamian's fascinating notes, makes an issue of considerable musical as well as historic value.

Messiaen Livre du Saint Sacrement. **Jennifer Bate** (org). Unicorn-Kanchana Ⓕ DKPCD9067/8
(two discs: 129 minutes: DDD: 10/87). Played on the organ of L'Eglise de la Sainte-Trinité, Paris.
Selected by Sounds in Retrospect.   ⒼⒼ

The crowning achievement of Messiaen's unique cycle of music for the organ, the *Livre du Saint
Sacrement* is also his largest work for the instrument. It is an intensely personal score based on the
cornerstone of his faith, the Blessed Sacrament, and spans a wide range of emotions from hushed,
private communion to the truly apocalyptic. Jennifer Bate gave the British première of the work in
1986, following which Messiaen invited her to record it using his own organ at the Trinity Church in
Paris. He was on hand throughout the sessions as he so often was. The recording is a model of clarity
and it is hard to imagine the complex and often very subtle textures of this music being better
conveyed. This is a magnificent achievement.

Messiaen L'Ascension. Apparition de l'église éternelle. Diptyque. Messe de la Pentecôte.
Thomas Trotter (org). Decca Ⓕ 436 400-2DH (75 minutes: DDD: 9/93). Played on the organ
of the Eglise-Collégiale Saint-Pierre de Douai, France. Recorded 1991.
Gramophone Editor's choice.   ⒼⒼ

Even if the shelf is buckling under the weight of Messiaen recordings this one just has to be included.
Trotter proves to be in the top rank of Messiaen interpreters. Both the vision and language of *Messe
de la Pentecôte* are remote and too often performers fight shy of such musical intensity by
concentrating on dazzling registration or displays of technical bravado. Not so Trotter whose
sensitivity and self-control are never in doubt. There's nothing remotely silly or contrived about the
birdsong element here – it seems a natural and musical expression of joy and peace: which is what we
all know Messiaen intended but which so rarely works in performance. The choice of instrument is
inspired. Its warm colours glow like sunlight seen through a stained glass window down the length of
a dark, incense laden nave. Perhaps the action noise can be a little distracting at first but this is quickly
forgotten in these intense and deeply-moving performances.

Additional recommendations ...
...Méditations. L'Ascension. Messe de la Pentecôte. **Jennifer Bate** (org).
Unicorn-Kanchana Ⓕ DKPCD9024/5 (two discs: 134 minutes: DDD: 5/89).
...L'Ascension. Le banquet céleste. Apparition de l'église éternelle. Diptyque.
Hans-Ola Ericsson (org). BIS Ⓕ CD409 (64 minutes: DDD: 9/89).

Messiaen Poèmes pour Mi[a]. Réveil des oiseaux[b]. Sept Haïkaï[c]. [a]**Françoise Pollet** (sop);
[b]**Pierre-Laurent Aimard,** [c]**Joela Jones** (pfs); **Cleveland Orchestra / Pierre Boulez.**
DG Ⓕ 453 478-2GH (72 minutes: DDD: 2/98). Texts and translations included.
Recorded [a]1994, [bc]1996.

Since all the performances here are excellent, virtuoso indeed, and the recordings are first-class, this
can be confidently recommended to any Messiaen enthusiast who happens to want these three works.
But it would also make an ideal next step for anyone who has recently been bowled over by
Turangalîla, say, or the *Catalogue d'oiseaux*, and wants to explore Messiaen methodically. For that
listener the *Poèmes pour Mi* would represent him at his most lyrically passionate and sensuous, the
Réveil des oiseaux his 'bird style' at its most intransigent, while the *Sept Haïkaï* stand both for
Messiaen's love-affair with Asia and his attempts to convey vivid colour in music. And in Françoise
Pollet the *Poèmes* get as close as any reading has to Messiaen's specification of a *grand soprano
dramatique* as the ideal solo voice. She can sustain a long arch of melody splendidly and, assisted by
Boulez's firm control, generates great rhythmic excitement in the fourth and ninth songs of the set.
This latter quality gives exhilaration to *Réveil des oiseaux*, as the tangle of exuberant melodies grows
ever more complex; Aimard is glitteringly precise here. But it is the *Sept Haïkaï* that are most crucial
to Messiaen's later development, with their pairs of movements reflecting each other, their searing
saturated colours, their use of juxtaposed 'refrains' and their central homage to the sound of a
Japanese orchestra. Boulez has expressed reservations about some of his great teacher's theories, but
evidently has few if any about the fantastic sound world imagined by his astonishingly precise ear.

Further listening ...

...Thème et Variations. *Coupled with works by various composers.*
Isabelle van Keulen (vn); **Ronald Brautigam** (pf).
Koch Classics 36416-2 (5/97). *See review in the Collections section; refer to the Index.*

...Catalogue d'oiseaux. Petites Esquisses d'Oiseaux. **Håkan Austbø** (pf). Naxos 8 553532/4.

...Catalogue d'oiseaux, Books 1-3. **Peter Hill** (pf). Unicorn-Kanchana DKPCD9062 (5/88).

...Catalogue d'oiseaux – Books 4-6. **Peter Hill** (pf). Unicorn-Kanchana DKPCD9075 (9/89).

...Catalogue d'oiseaux – Book 7. La Fauvette des jardins. **Peter Hill** (pf).
Unicorn-Kanchana DKPCD9090 (8/90).

...Le merle noir. *Coupled with works by various composers.* **Emmanuel Pahud** (fl); **Eric Le Sage** (pf).
EMI CDC5 56488-2 (3/98). *Selected by Soundings. See review in the Collections section; refer to the Index.*

...Méditations sur le mystère de la Sainte Trinité. **Hans-Ola Ericsson** (org). BIS CD464 (3/92).

...Cinq Rechants. *Coupled with works by* **Daniel-Lesur** and **Jolivet** The Sixteen /
Harry Christophers. Collins Classics 1480-2 (11/96).

...Harawi. **Jane Manning** (sop); **David Miller** (pf).
Unicorn-Kanchana Souvenir Series UKCD2084 (9/97).

...O sacrum convivium. *Coupled with works by* **Duruflé** and **Fauré** Trinity College Choir,
Cambridge with **Richard Pearce** (org). Conifer Classics CDCF176 (10/90).

...O sacrum convivium. *Coupled with works by* **Daniel-Lesur** BBC Symphony Chorus /
Stephen Jackson with **Jeremy Filsell** (org). ASV CDDCA900 (1/95).

...O sacrum convivium. *Coupled with works by various composers.* **St Thomas Church Choir /
Gerre Hancock.** Koch International Classics 37228-2 (9/96).

...Pourquoi?. Le sourire. La fiancée perdue. *Coupled with works by various composers.*
Frederica von Stade (mez); **Martin Katz** (pf). RCA Victor Red Seal 09026 62711-2 (4/95).

...Pourquoi?. Le sourire. La fiancée perdue. *Coupled with works by various composers.*
Sylvia McNair (sop); **Roger Vignoles** (pf). Philips 446 656-2PH (5/97).

J.W. Metcalf

Suggested listening ...

...Music for the Star of the Sea. *Coupled with works by various composers* **The Hilliard Ensemble.**
ECM New Series 453 259-2 (1/97). *See review in the Collections section; refer to the Index.*

Giacomo Meyerbeer
German 1791-1864

Meyerbeer Dinorah. **Deborah Cook** (sop) Dinorah; **Christian du Plessis** (bar) Hoël; **Alexander
Oliver** (ten) Corentin; **Della Jones** (mez) Goatherd; **Marilyn Hill Smith** (sop) Goatgirl; **Roderick
Earle** (bass) Huntsman; **Ian Caley** (ten) Reaper; **Geoffrey Mitchell Choir; Philharmonia Orchestra
/ James Judd.** Opera Rara Ⓟ ORC005 (three discs: 151 minutes: ADD: 4/94). Notes, text and
translation included. From OR5 (8/80). Recorded 1979.

The day after its première at the Opéra-Comique, Meyerbeer wrote to his wife to say that everybody,
including the Emperor and Empress, seemed to have liked his opera but that with a Paris first-night
you could never really be sure. In the event, success pursued it till the taste for such things lapsed.
There is nothing second-rate about the singing here, simply that it lacks star-quality (which does not
necessarily mean big names). Deborah Cook is fluent and likeable in the title-role; Christian du Plessis
competent in his (the grief-stricken ending of his aria having fine effect); and Alexander Oliver, an
excellent comedian, brings a happy touch to the simple but not entirely witless Corentin. Della Jones
does admirably in her supporting role, and the Geoffrey Mitchell Choir sing as well as ever. The
playing of the Philharmonic Orchestra is of a quality that makes appreciation of Meyerbeer's scoring
no problem at all, and James Judd conducts without too much of the rigidity of some modern
maestros. As always in Opera Rara's record productions, the presentation is exemplary, and
recorded sound, if afflicted in this outdoor opera with distinctly indoor resonance, is clear and well
balanced. The opera itself is hampered by an awkward plot (involving, for one thing, almost
as much retrospective narration as *The Ring*), but the music has a genuine lyric charm. More than
that, its strands are skilfully interwoven, with a delightful ending. Meyerbeer and his librettists
planned originally a short opera in three scenes; if they had had their way it might have been a
masterpiece.

Further listening ...

...Komm!. Der Garten des Herzens. Lied des venezianischen Gondoliers. Hör' ich das Liedchen
klingen. Die Rose, die Lilie, die Taube. Sie und ich. Menschenfeindlich. Chant des moissonneurs
vendéens. La barque légère. La chanson de Maître Floh. Sicilienne. La poète mourant.
Coupled with works by **Rossini** Thomas Hampson (bar); **Geoffrey Parsons** (pf).
EMI CDC7 54436-2 (4/92).

...Les Huguenots. **Soloists; Ambrosian Opera Chorus; New Philharmonic Orchestra /
Richard Bonynge.** Decca 430 549-2DM4.

Mezzetti

Suggested listening ...
...Cântec se sirenă. *Coupled with works by various composers.*
Angela Gheorghiu (sop); **Malcolm Martineau** (pf).
Decca 458 360-2DH (5/98). *See review in the Collections section; refer to the Index.*

Nikolay Miaskovsky   Russian 1881-1950

Miaskovsky Cello Concerto in C minor, Op. 66.
Prokofiev Symphony-Concerto for Cello and Orchestra in E minor, Op. 125 (also includes
alternative finale). **Truls Mørk** (vc); **City of Birmingham Symphony Orchestra / Paavo Järvi.**
Virgin Classics Ⓕ VC5 45310-2 (two discs: 83 minutes: DDD: 5/98).   ⒼⒼ
Whichever way you view it – as attractive repertoire, as dynamic sound, or as distinctive interpretation
– this CD is a sure-fire winner. Neither work yields its strongest virtues without encouragement: the
Prokofiev responds best to focused solo phrasing and firm handling from the rostrum, while
Miaskovsky's concerto can too easily sound discursive. Here, however, musical impact takes effect
right from Prokofiev's introductory bars: Paavo Järvi and his players cut a commanding profile and
the recording conveys a startlingly realistic sound stage, especially from the lower strings. Truls Mørk
might be tagged a 'communicative introvert': his tone is firm and even, his phrasing refined and his
poetic musicianship especially suits the Miaskovsky concerto, with its subtle asides and winding
musical lines. Again, Järvi comes up trumps with a sympathetic accompaniment and the recording is
spectacularly good.
Additional recommendations ...
...Cello Concerto. **Shostakovich** The Limpid Stream, Op. 39 – Adagio. **Tchaikovsky**
Variations on a Rococo Theme in A minor, Op. 33. Nocturne, Op. 19 No. 4.
Julian Lloyd Webber (vc); **London Symphony Orchestra / Maxim Shostakovich.**
Philips Ⓕ 434 106-2PH (63 minutes: DDD: 5/92).
...Cello Concerto. **Prokofiev** Symphony-Concerto. **Mischa Maisky** (vc);
Russian National Orchestra / Mikhail Pletnev.
DG Ⓕ 449 821-2GH (70 minutes: DDD: 4/97). *Gramophone Editor's choice.*   Ⓖ

Miaskovsky Sinfonietta No. 1 in B minor, Op. 32 No. 2. Theme and Variations. Two Pieces,
Op. 46 No. 1. Napeve. **St Petersburg Chamber Ensemble / Roland Melia.** ASV Ⓕ CDDCA928
(56 minutes: DDD: 10/95). Recorded 1994.
The dignity and solid craftsmanship of Nikolay Miaskovsky make him a likeable figure; and the
circumstances in which he maintained those values make him rather more than likeable. The
Variations are consistently attractive, as are the shorter works, despite disconcerting reminiscences of
the *Skye Boat Song* in the first of the Op. 46 Pieces. That's not to say that the music 'holds' you in the
way that Stravinsky, Martinů, Honegger or Tippett do. And, as so often with Miaskovsky, there are
slack moments where ideas seem to be coming back for no better reason than to fill out a pre-
allocated space. The fact remains that if you have got the Miaskovsky bug, or if you want the fullest
possible picture of middle-of-the-road Soviet music, you will find confident, full-bodied performances
here which are the equal of any.

Miaskovsky Symphony No. 6 in E flat minor, Op. 23, "Revolutionary". **Yurlov Russian Choir;**
USSR Symphony Orchestra / Kyrill Kondrashin. Russian Disc mono Ⓕ RDCD15008*
(65 minutes: ADD: 10/94). Recorded 1959.   Ⓖ
This is not a flawless performance and the sound is on the thinnish side. But then no other recording
of this work has anything approaching the fire, the expressive ebb and flow, or the sheer dramatic
sweep of Kondrashin. When it first appeared in the early 1920s Miaskovsky's Sixth was hailed as the
first Soviet symphony – not the first composed on Soviet soil, but the first to embody the cataclysmic
experiences, the conflicts and aspirations of Revolution. Of course that begs all sorts of questions.
For instance, does the finale's turn from heroic optimism to funereal tragedy represent solidarity with
past martyrdom or present betrayal of ideals? And what, apart from the emblematic tunes in that
finale, distinguishes the essential message of this music from, say, Rachmaninov's Second or Glière's
Third, to mention two comparable pre-revolutionary Russian symphonies? Not that it is really
necessary to agonize over such things. This is a musically self-sufficient symphonic drama of
aspiration, yearning, frustration and wistfulness, all held in a tense state of becoming by a squared-
off but masterly Wagnerian chromaticism and lit up from time to time by moments of immensely
touching poetic inwardness. If you are sufficiently curious to give Miaskovsky a try and are unsure
where to start with the 13 out of 27 symphonies currently available on CD, do go for this one in this
recording.

Miaskovsky String Quartets. **Taneyev Quartet** (Vladimir Ovcharek, Grigory Lutzky, vns;
Vissarion Solovyev, va; Josef Levinzon, vc). Russian Disc Ⓕ RDCD11013 and
RDCD11031/4 (five discs, oas: 284 minutes: AAD: 12/96). Recorded 1982-84.

RDCD11013 (58 minutes) – No. 1 in A minor, Op. 33 No. 1; No. 4 in F minor, Op. 33 No. 4.
RDCD11031 (66 minutes) – No. 2 in C minor, Op. 33 No. 2; No. 6 in G minor, Op. 49; No. 10 in
F major, Op. 67 No. 1. *RDCD11032* (52 minutes) – No. 3 in D minor, Op. 33 No. 3; No. 5 in
E minor, Op. 47. *RDCD11033* (54 minutes) – No. 7 in F major, Op. 55; No. 8 in F sharp minor,
Op. 59. *RDCD11034* (53 minutes) – No. 9 in D minor, Op. 62 No. 1; No. 11 in E flat major,
Op. 67 No. 2.

Outside Russia, Miaskovsky is probably best known, and then only by repute, as the composer of a
long series of symphonies – 27 in all, of which 11 are currently available on record. In his own
country, his reputation remains secure for qualities of musical integrity that meant much to his
colleagues, one of the most admiring of whom was Prokofiev, and to his pupils, who included
Kabalevsky and Khachaturian. With the very earliest, there is music that explores new approaches to
tonality, as in the very opening of No. 1 and in its *Andante sostenuto*, where the violin sets off with a
wide-ranging melody that owes a good deal of its nature to Russian folk example. In later works, there
is a similar tonal ambiguity, sometimes suggesting knowledge of Bartók, sometimes reflecting the
harmonic side-slips and novel tonal polarities of Hindemith, exceptionally – in the Trio to the *Scherzo
fantastico* of No. 7 – bringing the music under bitonal pressures. The lyricism is constant; so are
several other characteristics running through these works. One is melancholy, manifest most overtly
in the Quartet No. 8 written in memory of a friend but recurring as a distinguishing feature in a
number of them, with movements that are marked *malincolico, lugubre, lagrimabile*. Perhaps
connected to this is a somewhat enigmatic manner in many of the faster movements, with music
attracting the qualifications *inquieto, misterioso, pensieroso, tenebroso, fantastico, sussurando*.
Proposals of *scherzando* or *energico* or *giocoso e festivo* are rarer; and even then, the music bears a
sense of effort. Miaskovsky's sheer musical skill – agreeably shown in the long set of variations on a
Grieg lullaby which concludes the two-movement No. 3 – sees to it that this is music unfailingly
crafted, approachable and effective. For those who are curious, perhaps a reasonable sampler would
be the record containing No. 2 (1930), a well-contrasted piece, No. 6 (1940), with its capricious
burlesque movement and one of the composer's most heartfelt lamentations, and No. 10 (1945). The
Taneyev Quartet give performances that clearly reflect great faith in the music, and the recordings are
level and clear.

Further listening ...
...Serenade in E flat major, Op. 32 No. 1. Sinfonietta in B minor, Op. 32 No. 2. Lyric Concertino in
G major, Op. 32 No. 3. Salutation Overture in D major, Op. 48. **Moscow New Opera Orchestra /
Yevgeny Samoilov.** Olympia OCD528 (7/94).
...Symphonies – No. 1 in C minor, Op. 3[a]; No. 19 in E flat major, Op. 46[b]. [a]**USSR Ministry of
Culture Symphony Orchestra / Gennadi Rozhdestvensky;** [b]**Russian State Brass Orchestra /
Nikolai Sergeyev.** Russian Disc RDCD11007 (3/94).
...Symphonies – No. 5 in D major, Op. 18; No. 9 in E minor, Op. 28. **BBC Philharmonic Orchestra /
Sir Edward Downes.** Marco Polo 8 223499 (7/94).
...Symphony No. 21, Op. 51, "Fantasy in F sharp minor". *Coupled with works by* **Kabalevsky** and
Shostakovich New Philharmonia Orchestra / David Measham; National Philharmonic
Orchestra / Bernard Herrmann. Unicorn-Kanchana Souvenir UKCD2066 (2/95).
See review under Kabalevsky; refer to the Index.
...Cello Sonatas[a] – No. 1 in D major, Op. 12; No. 2 in A minor, Op. 81. Cello Concerto in C minor,
Op. 66[b]. **Marina Tarasova** (vc); [a]**Alexander Polezhaev** (pf); [b]**Moscow New Opera Orchestra /
Yevgeny Samoilov.** Olympia OCD530 (12/94).
...Cello Sonata No. 1 in D major, Op. 12. *Coupled with works by* **Rachmaninov** Truls Mørk (vc);
Jean-Yves Thibaudet (pf). Virgin Classics ℗ VC5 45119-2 (72 minutes: DDD: 11/96).
...Piano Sonatas – No. 1 in D minor, Op. 6; No. 2 in F sharp minor, Op. 13; No. 3 in C minor,
Op. 19; No. 6 in A flat major, Op. 64 No. 2. **Murray McLachlan** (pf). Olympia OCD214 (12/88).
...Piano Sonata No. 3 in C minor, Op. 19. *Coupled with works by* **Scriabin** and **Prokofiev**
Sviatoslav Richter (pf). Melodiya mono 74321 29470-2* (6/96).
...Piano Sonatas – No. 4 in C minor, Op. 27; No. 5 in B major, Op. 64 No. 1. Sonatine in E minor,
Op. 57. Prelude, Op. 58. **Murray McLachlan** (pf). Olympia OCD217 (3/89).

Robin Milford
British 1903-1959

Suggested listening ...
...If it's ever spring again. The colour. So sweet love seemed. *Coupled with works by various
composers.* **Ian Partridge** (ten); **Stephen Roberts** (bar); **Clifford Benson** (pf).
Hyperion CDA66015 (9/91). *See review in the Collections section; refer to the Index.*

Darius Milhaud
French 1892-1974

Milhaud Harp Concerto, Op. 323[a]. Le boeuf sur le toit, Op. 58. La création du monde, Op. 81.
[a]**Frédérique Cambreling** (hp); **Lyon Opéra Orchestra / Kent Nagano.**
Erato MusiFrance ℗ 2292-45820-2 (59 minutes: DDD: 2/93). Recorded 1992.   Ⓖ

Here is music to delight, with performances to match. Milhaud's ballet *Le boeuf sur le toit* was written for Jean Cocteau in 1919 and is set in an American bar during the Prohibition period (forbidding the manufacture and sale of alcohol) that was then just beginning. Some performances of this vivid French score lay the humour on too thick, but this one under Kent Nagano has more Gallic taste and sophistication and the playing is above all musicianly, while the more uproarious moments come over all the more effectively for this very reason. The playing by the accomplished Lyon orchestra is excellent, not least the wind players who have plenty to do. Written four years later, *La création du monde* was one of the first works by a European composer to take its inspiration from African folklore and the raw black jazz that Milhaud heard in New Orleans. This ballet on the creation myth ends with a mating dance and the whole work is powerfully and darkly sensual. Nagano and his French orchestra bring out all the character of this music and take the jazz fugue in Scene 1 more urgently than usual, to excellent effect. The Harp Concerto dates from 1953, three decades further on into Milhaud's career, and inevitably it has a brighter character, though here, too, there is some jazz influence, though of a far gentler kind. Cambreling is a fine player and the radiant good spirits that emerge by the finale are typical of this uneven but nearly always fascinating composer.

Additional recommendations ...

...Le boeuf sur le toit. *Coupled with works by various composers.* **London Symphony Orchestra / Antál Dorati.** Mercury Ⓜ 434 335-2MM (67 minutes: ADD).   Ⓖ

...Le boeuf sur le toit. Le carnaval d'Aix, Op. 83*b*[a]. Le carnaval de Londres, Op. 172. L'Apothéose de Molière, Op. 286. [a]**Jack Gibbons** (pf); **New London Orchestra / Ronald Corp.** Hyperion Ⓕ CDA66594 (77 minutes: DDD: 12/92).

...Le boeuf sur le toit. La création du monde. Scaramouche, Op. 165*b*. Saudades do Brasil, Op. 67. Suite provençale, Op. 152*b*. **Marcelle Meyer** (pf); **Concerts Arts Orchestra; Champs Elysées Theatre Orchestra / Darius Milhaud.** EMI Composers in Person [a]mono Ⓕ CDC7 54604-2* (77 minutes" ADD: 4/93).

...Le boeuf sur le toit. La création du monde. Trois opéras-minute. Piano Concerto No. 1[a]. La fête de la musique, Op. 159. [a]**Marguerite Long** (pf); **Darius Milhaud** (pf/cond); various artists. Classical Collector mono Ⓕ 150 122* (three discs: 256 minutes: ADD: 9/93).

...La création du monde. *Coupled with works by* **Poulenc** and **Saint-Saëns** Ani Kavafian, Julie Rosenfeld (vns); Toby Hoffman (va); Carter Brey (vc); André Previn (pf). RCA Victor Red Seal Ⓕ 09026 68181-2 (50 minutes: DDD: 11/95).

Milhaud Symphony No. 3, Op. 271, "Te Deum". Les cloches – Symphonic Suite, Op. 259. Saudades do Brasil, Op. 67 – Botafogo; Leme; Tijuca; Laranjeiras. **Russian State Symphony Cappella / Gennadi Rozhdestvensky.** Olympia Ⓕ OCD452 (61 minutes: DDD: 6/96). Recorded live in 1993.

A couple of first recordings here are useful in filling gaps in the discography of the compulsively productive Milhaud. Don't let the existence of Rachmaninov's famous choral setting of *The Bells*, or the fact that Russian forces are involved here, mislead you into false expectations: this is not a setting of Poe's poem but a ballet score based on it. Written in 1946, it was well received at its première in Chicago but was a disaster when performed in New York by an ill-prepared Ballets Russes de Monte-Carlo: Milhaud was obliged to substitute a simpler finale for subsequent performances, but restored the original for the Symphonic Suite now recorded. The work, about a young bride and her groom, begins joyously and melodiously, but at the "Bronze bells" section the atmosphere becomes heavy with menace, and the hysterical final bacchanale depicts the King of the Ghouls spiriting the bridegroom away. The resonance of the hall in which this live recording was made creates a slightly thick sound, though detail is mostly clear. Rozhdestvensky adopts slower speeds for the "Silver" and "Golden" sections than the composer indicates and makes heavy cuts in the finale. The Third Symphony (the only one of Milhaud's first ten not hitherto recorded) was commissioned by French radio to celebrate the ending of the Second World War. Starting with a vigorous, tough movement that could be interpreted as symbolizing wartime struggles, it passes to a meditative, prayerfully intense slow movement (in which a wordless chorus is imaginatively used): a jubilant *Pastorale* suggests the coming of peace, which is finally hailed in a choral *Te Deum*. Again there are marked divergences from Milhaud's printed timings, but the performance is persuasive and exudes great confidence and the two middle movements, at least, represent Milhaud at his best.

Further listening ...

...Cello Concerto No. 1, Op. 136. *Coupled with works by* **Elgar** and **Respighi** USSR TV and Radio Large Orchestra / **Gennadi Rozhdestvensky.** Russian Disc RDCD11104 (7/94).

...Cello Concerto No. 1, Op. 136. *Coupled with works by various composers.* **János Starker** (vc); [a]**Gerald Moore** (pf); **Philharmonia Orchestra / Carlo Maria Giulini, Walter Susskind.** EMI mono/stereo CZS5 68485-2* (12/95). *See review in the Collections section; refer to the Index.*

...Clarinet Concerto, Op. 230. Scaramouche, Op. 165*c*. *Coupled with works by* **Copland** and **Hindemith** Eduard Brunner (cl); **Bavarian Radio Symphony Orchestra / Urs Schneider.** Koch Schwann 310352.

...Little Symphonies and Little Operas – No. 1, Op. 43, "Le printemps"; No. 2, Op. 49, "Pastoral"; No. 3, Op. 71, "Serenade"; No. 4, Op. 74, "Dixtuour"; No. 5, Op. 75; No. 6, Op. 79. L'enlèvement d'Europe. L'abandon d'Ariane. La deliverance de Thésée. **Capella Cracoviensis / Karl Anton Rickenbacher.** Koch Schwann 311392 (5/93).

...Symphonies – No. 1, Op. 210; No. 2, Op. 247. Suite provençale, Op. 152*b*.
Toulouse Capitole Orchestra / Michel Plasson. DG 435 437-2GH (7/92).
...Symphonies – No. 6, Op. 343; No. 7, Op. 344. Overture méditerranéenne, Op. 330.
Toulouse Capitole Orchestra / Michel Plasson. DG 439 939-2GH (6/95).
...Symphonies – No. 7, Op. 344; No. 8, Op. 362, "Rhodanienne"; No. 9, Op. 380.
Basle Radio Symphony Orchestra / Alun Francis. CPO CPO999 166-2 (6/95).
...Symphonies – No. 10, Op. 382; No. 11, Op. 384, "Romantique"; No. 12, Op. 390, "Rurale".
Basle Radio Symphony Orchestra / Alun Francis. CPO CPO999 354-2 (11/96).
...Duo concertante, Op. 351. Caprice, Op. 335*a*. *Coupled with works by various composers.*
Jonathan Cohler (cl); **Judith Gordon** (pf). Crystal CD733 (5/95).
...Saudades do Brasil, Op. 67. La muse ménagère, Op. 245[a]. Madame Bovary, Op. 128[a].
Alexandre Tharaud (pf); [a]**Madeleine Milhaud** (spkr). Naxos 8 553443 (65 minutes: DDD: 5/96).
...Sonatine, Op. 100. Duo Concertant, Op. 351. *Coupled with works by various composers.*
Victoria Soames (cl); **Julius Drake** (pf). Clarinet Classics CC0001 (9/92).
...String Quartets[a] – No. 1, Op. 5; No. 2, Op. 16. Quatre poèmes de Léo Latil, Op. 20[b].
Trois poèmes de Jean Cocteau, Op. 59[b]. [b]**Ulrike Sonntag** (sop); [b]**Rudolf Jansen** (pf);
[a]**Fanny Mendelssohn Quartet.** Troubadisc TRO-CD01409 (5/95).
...String Quartets – No. 3, Op. 32[a], "Latil"; No. 4, Op. 46[b]; No. 5, Op. 64[b]. Machines agricoles,
Op. 56[c]. Catalogue de fleurs, Op. 60[d]. [acd]**Ulrike Sonntag** (sop); [cd]**Irmela Nolte** (fl);
[cd]**Deborah Marshall** (ob); [cd]**Michael Weigel** (bn); [cd]**Arpat György** (db); [ab]**Fanny Mendelssohn**
Quartet ([cd]Renate Eggebrecht, Mario Korunić, vns; [cd]Stefan Berg, va; [cd]Friedemann Kupsa, vc) /
[d]**Linda Horowitz.** Troubadisc TRO-CD01410 (6/96).
...Violin Sonata No. 2, Op. 40. *Coupled with works by various composers.*
Isabelle van Keulen (vn); **Ronald Brautigam** (pf).
Koch Classics 36416-2 (5/97). *See review in the Collections section; refer to the Index.*
...Quatre esquisses, Op. 227. Madame Bovary, Op. 128. Three Rag Caprices, Op. 78. Saudades
do Brasil, Op. 67. Les charmes de la vie, Op. 360. Polka, Op. 95. Tango des Fratellini, Op. 58*c*.
Coupled with **Satie** (arr. Milhaud) Cinq grimaces. **Boaz Sharon** (pf).
Unicorn-Kanchana DKPCD9155 (5/95).
...Printemps – Volume 1, Op. 25; Volume 2, Op. 66.
Coupled with works by various composers. **Marcelo Bratke** (pf).
Olympia Explorer OCD487 (12/96). *See review in the Collections section; refer to the Index.*
...Segoviana, Op. 366. *Coupled with works by various composers.* **Elliot Fisk** (gtr).
MusicMasters 67174-2 (4/97). *See review in the Collections section; refer to the Index.*
...Les choéphores. *Coupled with works by* **Honegger** and **Roussel** Soloists; Schola Cantorum of
New York; New York Philharmonic Orchestra / **Leonard Bernstein.** Sony Classical Masterworks
Heritage MHK62352 (10/97). *See review under Honegger; refer to the Index.*

Francisco Millán   Spanish 16th century

Suggested listening ...
...O dulce y triste memoria. *Coupled with works by various composers.* **The Hilliard Ensemble.**
Virgin Classics Veritas VED5 61394-2 (11/97). *See review in the Collections section;
refer to the Index.*

Mitake

Suggested listening ...
...Kawa no Nagare no yô ni. *Coupled with works by various composers.*
Angela Gheorghiu (sop); **Malcolm Martineau** (pf).
Decca 458 360-2DH (5/98). *See review in the Collections section; refer to the Index.*

Ernest Moeran   British 1894-1950

Moeran String Quartets – No. 1 in A minor; No. 2 in E flat major. String Trio in G major[a].
Maggini Quartet ([a]Laurence Jackson, David Angel, vns; [a]Martin Outram, va;
[a]Michal Kaznowski, vc). Naxos Ⓢ 8 554079 (59 minutes: DDD: 10/97). Recorded 1995.
Gramophone Editor's choice.
The A minor Quartet dates from 1921 when Moeran was a pupil of John Ireland at the Royal College
of Music. It is an enormously fluent, folk-song-inspired creation, full of Ravelian poise; indeed the
last movement of the three (an exhilarating rondo) owes much to the finale of the French master's
F major Quartet. Not surprisingly, Moeran himself always retained his affection for this piece, and
the Maggini Quartet accord it wonderfully assured, flexible advocacy. Discovered among Moeran's
papers by his widow after his death in 1950, the E flat Quartet appears to be another comparatively
early effort. It is cast in just two movements, the second of which is an ambitious linked slow

movement and finale, full of ambition and tender fantasy, and containing some truly magical inspiration along the way. Perhaps this movement's intrepid thematic and emotional diversity engendered sufficient niggling doubts in Moeran's mind for him to suppress the whole work. Certainly, in a performance as convinced and convincing as the one here, its melodic fecundity and unpretentious, 'out of doors' charm will endear it to many. That leaves the masterly String Trio of 1931, which, in its impeccable craft, rhythmic pungency (the opening *Allegretto giovale* boasts a time-signature of 7/8), gentle sense of purpose and unerring concentration (above all in the deeply felt slow movement), represents one of Moeran's finest achievements. The members of the Maggini Quartet reveal a relish for Moeran's exquisitely judged part-writing and give an admirably polished, affectionate rendering. Sound and balance are excellent throughout this enterprising, hugely enjoyable collection.

Moeran Cello Sonata.
Ireland Cello Sonata in G minor.
Rubbra Cello Sonata in G minor, Op. 60. **Raphael Wallfisch** (vc); **John York** (pf).
   Marco Polo Ⓔ 8 223718 (59 minutes: DDD: 8/95). Recorded 1994.
Unlike the concerto, examples of the English cello sonata are not particularly thick on the ground (one thinks also of those by Britten, Rawsthorne, Bax and Truscott) but one would be hard put to it to select a finer trio than the three recorded here. All are products of full maturity, each composer being in his forties or fifties at the time. Moeran's solitary Sonata is arguably his finest and most satisfying work. The music has a dramatic and passionate demeanour – Moeran composed it for his wife of two years, Peers Coetmore, in 1947 – yet its three movements are very diverse, the vigorous finale even seeming to glance towards Bartók. Rubbra's, composed the previous year, bears a more thoughtful aspect, not least in the fast-faster-slow disposition of its three movements. None the less, for all the work's serenity it too possesses an inner steel. Ireland's Sonata (1923) has not perhaps the same intellectual rigour but is still an object lesson in musical construction and balance. Raphael Wallfisch has an appealing warmth of tone and his playing is always deeply musical. He also wears his technique rather more lightly than some of his more abrasive, higher-profile rivals, though he does sound a shade raw in the uppermost register. Pianist John York provides able support, and Gary Cole's recording is clean and natural. Well worth investigating.

Moeran Songs of Springtime. Phyllida and Corydon.
Warlock A Cornish Carol. I saw a fair maiden. Benedicamus Domino. The full heart. The rich
   cavalcade. Corpus Christi. All the flowers of the Spring. As dew in Aprylle. Bethlehem Down.
   A Cornish Christmas Carol. **Finzi Singers / Paul Spicer.** Chandos Ⓔ CHAN9182
   (76 minutes: DDD: 10/93). Texts included. Recorded 1992. *Gramophone Editor's choice.*   Ⓖ
The Peter Warlock we all know and love from the evergreen *Capriol Suite* and the boisterous songs seems a world away from the introverted and intense artist of these unaccompanied choral carols. Perhaps Warlock's real genius was an ability to create profound expression in short musical structures, but even the more outgoing pieces – the joyful *Benedicamus Domino* and the Cornish Christmas Carol with its gentle hint at "The First Nowell" – have an artistic integrity which raises them high above the level of the syrup of modern day carol settings. Given performances as openly sincere and sensitive as these few could remain unmoved. In the two Moeran madrigal suites there is an indefinable Englishness – the result of a deep awareness of tradition and love of the countryside. The Finzi Singers' warm-toned, richly expressive voices capture the very essence of this uniquely lovely music.

Additional recommendation ...
...Songs of Springtime. Weep you no more, sad fountains. Gather ye rosebuds. Robin Hood
   borne on his bier. The jolly carter. The sailor and young Nancy. Irish elegy.
   Coupled with works by various composers. **City Chamber Choir of London / Stephen Jones.**
   British Music Society Ⓔ BMS417CD (50 minutes: DDD: 10/96).

Further listening ...
...Cello Concerto[a]. Sinfonietta. [a]**Raphael Wallfisch** (vc); **Bournemouth Sinfonietta /**
   Norman Del Mar. Chandos CHAN8456 (9/87).
...Serenade in G major. Nocturne. *Coupled with works by* **Warlock** Hugh Mackey (bar);
   Renaissance Singers; Ulster Orchestra / Vernon Handley. Chandos CHAN8808 (3/91).
...Symphony in G minor. Overture to a Masque. **Ulster Orchestra / Vernon Handley.**
   Chandos CHAN8577 (4/88).
...Symphony in G minor. *Coupled with* **Ireland** Piano Concerto in E flat major[a]. [a]**Eileen Joyce** (pf);
   Hallé Orchestra / Leslie Heward. Dutton Laboratories mono CDAX8001* (5/93).   ⒼⒼⒼ
...Violin Concerto[a]. Lonely Waters. Whythorne's Shadow. [a]**Lydia Mordkovitch** (vn);
   Ulster Orchestra / Vernon Handley. Chandos CHAN8807 (9/90).
...Violin Concerto[a]. Two Pieces for Small Orchestra[b]. Cello Concerto[c]. [a]**Lydia Mordkovitch** (vn);
   [c]**Raphael Wallfisch** (vc); [ab]**Ulster Orchestra**; [c]**Bournemouth Sinfonietta /** [ab]**Vernon Handley**,
   [c]**Norman Del Mar.** Chandos Enchant CHAN7078 (4/98).
...Three Piano Pieces. On a May Morning. Three Fancies. Two Legends. Theme and Variations.
   Stalham River. Toccata. Irish Love Song. Summer Valley. The White Mountain. Two Pieces.
   Bank Holiday. **Eric Parkin** (pf). J. Martin Stafford JMSCD2 (5/96).

...Evening Service in D major. *Coupled with works by various composers.* **St Edmundsbury Cathedral Choir / Mervyn Cousins** with **Scott Farrell** (org). Priory PRCD554 (1/97).

...Far in a western brookland. O fair enough are sky and plain.
Coupled with works by various composers. **Anthony Rolfe Johnson** (ten); **Graham Johnson** (pf).
Hyperion CDA66471/2 (8/95). *See review in the Collections section; refer to the Index.*

...The merry month of May. *Coupled with works by various composers.*
Sir Peter Pears (ten); **Viola Tunnard** (pf).
Belart 461 550-2 (12/97). *See review in the Collections section; refer to the Index.*

...Te Deum and Jubilate in E flat major. *Coupled with works by various composers.*
Norwich Cathedral Choir / Michael Nicholas with **Neil Taylor** (org). Priory PRCD470 (10/94).

James Molloy   British 1839-1909

Suggested listening ...
...(arr. Rowley) Kerry dance. *Coupled with works by* **Grainger** and **A.C. Macleod**
New College Choir, Oxford / Edward Higginbottom.
Erato 0630-19065-2 (3/98). *See review in the Collections section; refer to the Index.*

Johann Molter   German 1696-1765

Suggested listening ...
...Trumpet Concerto No. 1 in D major, MWV4:12. *Coupled with works by various composers.*
Niklas Eklund (baroque tpt); **Drottningholm Baroque Ensemble / Nils-Erik Sparf.**
Naxos 8 553531 (11/96). 🎵 *See review in the Collections section; refer to the Index.*

Federico Mompou   Spanish 1893-1987

Mompou Música callada. **Herbert Henck** (pf). ECM New Series Ⓟ 445 699-2
(63 minutes: DDD: 9/95). Recorded 1993. *Gramophone Editor's choice.*
Listening to this disc is rather like entering a retreat. There is a rapt, contemplative atmosphere around these 28 miniatures (only two run for as long as three minutes) written between 1959 and 1967 as an attempt to express St John of the Cross's mystic ideal of "the music of silence". Practically all slow-moving, using repetition as a structural device but avoiding keyboard virtuosity, and rarely rising even to a *forte*, they seem to acknowledge descent from Erik Satie via the impressionists, though harmonically much freer and sometimes harsher – even, occasionally, stepping inside the area of atonality. No. 3 has a childlike innocence in its folkloric theme: Mompou's fascination with bell-sounds finds echoes in Nos. 5, 17 and 22. Overall there is a sense of tranquil self-communion which, paradoxically, exerts a strange spell on the listener. Herbert Henck, a specialist in twentieth-century music, plays this collection with a tender sensitivity and an ideally suited luminosity of tone, and he is finely recorded. An exceptional and haunting issue, whose sounds seem to hang in the air, as it were.

Mompou Cançons i danses – Nos. 1, 3, 5, 7, 8 and 9. Preludes – Nos. 1, 5, 6, 7, 9 and 10.
Cants màgics. Charmes. Variations. Dialogues. Paisajes. **Stephen Hough** (pf).
Hyperion Ⓟ CDA66963 (77 minutes: DDD: 9/97). Recorded 1996. *Gramophone Editor's choice. Selected by Soundings.*   ⒼⒼⒼ
The music of Federico Mompou may appear at first to consist of little more than charming, delicately scented but dilettantish salon near-improvisations with marked overtones of Erik Satie; but it is significant that his earliest works (in the 1920s) are imbued with a sense of mystery and wonder. Later he was to progress from an ingenuous lyricism (in the *Songs and dances*) to a profounder contemplation and mysticism, to greater harmonic and keyboard complexity (*Dialogues*) and finally, in the 1946-60 *Paisajes* ("Landscapes"), to a more experimental, less tonal idiom. In the hands of an imaginative pianist like Stephen Hough this other-worldly quality becomes revelatory. Hough's command of tonal nuance throughout is ultra-sensitive, he catches Mompou's wistful moods to perfection, and on the rare occasions when the music lashes out, as in *Prelude* No. 7, he is scintillating. In the more familiar *Songs and dances* he is tender in the (mostly melancholy) songs and exhilaratingly crisp rhythmically in the dances. He treats the "Testament d'Amelia" in No. 8 with a good deal of flexibility, and because Mompou declared (and demonstrated in his own recordings) that "it's all so free", he takes the fullest advantage of the marking *senza rigore* in No. 5, which reflects Mompou's lifelong fascination with bell-sounds.

Additional recommendations ...
...Cançons i danses Nos. 5-8. Paisajes – No. 1, La fuente y la campana. Scènes d'enfants – No. 5, Jeunes filles au jardin. Suburbis – No. 1, El carrer, el guitarrista i el vell cavall.
Coupled with works by various composers. **Federico Mompou** (pf); **instrumental ensemble.**
EMI Composers in Person mono Ⓟ CDC7 54836-2* (78 minutes: ADD: 11/93).
See review in the Collections section; refer to the Index.

...Cançons i danses. Preludes – Nos. 5, 6, 7, "Fireworks" and 11. **Alicia de Larrocha** (pf).
RCA Victor Red Seal Ⓕ 09026 62554-2 (60 minutes: DDD: 11/94). ⓆⒼ
...Cançons i danses No. 6 – Canción. *Coupled with works by various composers.* **Arturo Benedetti Michelangeli** (pf). Testament mono Ⓕ SBT2088* (two discs: 130 minutes: ADD: 12/96).
See review in the Collections section; refer to the Index.
...Cançons i danses. Impresiones intimas. **Gustavo Romero** (pf).
Koch International Classics Ⓕ 37185-2 (67 minutes: DDD: 4/97).

Alonso de Mondéjar
Spanish *fl* 1502-1505

Suggested listening ...
...Ave rex noster. *Coupled with works by various composers.* **The Hilliard Ensemble.**
Virgin Classics Veritas VED5 61394-2 (11/97). *See review in the Collections section; refer to the Index.*

Jean-Joseph de Mondonville
French 1711-1772

Mondonville Six Sonates en symphonies, Op. 3. **Les Musiciens du Louvre / Marc Minkowski.**
Archiv Produktion Ⓕ 457 600-2AH (58 minutes: DDD: 7/98). ✍
Gramophone Editor's choice. ⓆⒼⒼ
These pieces show Mondonville on ground closest to his heart, and indeed in a position to offer something unique. He was a violinist first and foremost, and his most important legacy is his Op. 3 set of six sonatas for violin and obbligato keyboard of 1734 – among the first of their kind – of which these *Sonates en symphonies* are orchestrations, made by the composer himself and performed with great success in Paris 15 years later. To put it simply, they are pure enjoyment from beginning to end, breathing as they do that spirit of almost pure hedonism which characterizes the most beguiling of mid-eighteenth-century French art. All the symphonies are in three movements, the outer ones being brisk and animated with much busy passagework surviving the transition from solo violin music very effectively, and the middle ones tuneful miniatures evoking the hushed atmosphere of a balmy night scene from a French baroque opera. Marc Minkowski's own dramatic skills help him to create a magical atmosphere in these, while his customary galvanizing energy lends irrepressible and boisterous life to the quick movements. The orchestra play superbly, and all in all, these are utterly delightful recordings.

Mondonville Grands motets – Dominus regnavit; In exitu Israel; De profundis. **Sophie Daneman, Maryseult Wieczorek** (sops); **Paul Agnew, François Piolino** (tens); **Maarten Koningsberger** (bar); **François Bazola** (bass); **Les Arts Florissants / William Christie.** Erato Ⓕ 0630-17791-2
(72 minutes: DDD: 10/97). ✍ Texts and translations included. Recorded 1996.
Gramophone Editor's record of the month. ⓆⒼ
Mondonville's *grands motets* were enormously popular for many years at the Concert Spirituel in Paris (of which he was a director for a time). They follow the pattern laid down by Delalande and continued by Rameau, but with more independent instrumental parts and incorporating Italian influences (e.g. *da capo* arias) and operatic elements. These three on psalm texts are deeply impressive. *Dominus regnavit* (1734) was perhaps the earliest of Mondonville's *grands motets* and, besides its polyphonic opening chorus, is notable for two verses entirely for high-register voices and instruments, an operatic *tempête*, and a stunning complex "Gloria patri". *De profundis* (1748), written for the funeral of a Chapel Royal colleague, is by its nature sombre, and ends not with the usual "Gloria patri" but with "Requiem aeternam" and a fugue. The initial chorus was praised to the sky by contemporaries as "sublime": other highlights are a baritone aria over a free chaconne bass, and a chorus illustrating "morning" and "night" by high and low voices respectively. There is even more illustrative music in the 1755 *In exitu Israel*: what amounts to a dramatic scena, with agitated strings and rushing voices for the "fleeing sea", dotted figures for the mountains "skipping like rams", and tremolos and vocal melismas for the "trembling earth". The present performances are vivid, with very good soloists, an alertly responsive chorus and a neat orchestra.

Mondonville Grands motets – Caeli enarrant; Venite exultemus; Jubilate Deo. **Catherine Padaut** (sop); **Guillemette Laurens** (mez); **Rodrigo del Pozo** (alto); **Jérôme Corréas** (bass); **Les Chantres de la Chapelle; Limoges Baroque Ensemble / Christophe Coin.** Auvidis Astrée Ⓕ E8614 (60 minutes: DDD: 12/97). ✍ Texts and translations included. Recorded 1997. Ⓖ
Of the three examples of Mondoville's *grands motets* presented here, the most substantial, and the most famous, is *Venite exultemus.* Hailed by a contemporary as "unquestionably his masterpiece", it was subsequently received with such enthusiasm by the Concert Spirituel audience that it had to be repeated annually for more than 20 years. It contains some overtly pictorial music – rushing violins representing the waves in the bass aria "The sea is His", general agitation in the virtuoso "Forty years I was grieved" (a spectacular performance by Rodrigo del Pozo); also noteworthy are two soprano arias, the first slow and affecting, with a solo recorder part, the second with an oboe and no bass.

There is a lengthy joyful doxology. *Jubilate Deo*, though perhaps less striking, also illustrates Mondonville's fresh and varied instrumental writing (admirably performed here by this Limoges group). An oboe-and-bassoon duet vies with one simultaneously for soprano and bass; jubilant instruments and a violin obbligato add to the impact of an ornate soprano solo (another is accompanied only by the upper instruments and chorus voices, yet another by a forceful dotted figure first heard in instrumental unison). The *Gloria Patri* is brilliant. The 1750 *Caeli enarrant* gives more scope to the (five-part) chorus, with a majestically full-voiced opening, "The heavens declare", and a particularly florid "As it was in the beginning". And what a good choral group this is – alert and spirited, with fresh and accurately placed voices.

Further listening ...
...Violin Sonata in G major, Op. 3 No. 5. *Coupled with works by various composers.*
  Simon Standage (vn); **Lars Ulrik Mortensen** (hpd).
  Chandos Chaconne CHAN0531 (6/93). *See review under Leclair; refer to the Index.*
...Les fêtes de Paphos. **Soloists; Accentus Chamber Choir; Les Talens Lyriques / Christophe Rousset.**
  L'Oiseau-Lyre 455 084-2OHO3 (7/97).

Moniot d'Arras

French *fl* 1213-1239

Suggested listening ...
...Ce fu en mai. *Coupled with works by various composers.*
  Paul Hillier (voc); **Andrew Lawrence-King** (psaltery/hp/org).
  Harmonia Mundi HMU90 7184 (4/97). *See review in the Collections section; refer to the Index.*
...Ce fu en mai. *Coupled with works by various composers.*
  Anne Azéma (sop/spkr); **vocal and instrumental ensemble.**
  Erato 0630-17072-2 (12/97). *See review in the Collections section; refer to the Index.*

Matthias Monn

Austrian 1717-1750

Suggested listening ...
...Cello Concerto in G minor (arr. Schoenberg). *Coupled with works by various composers.*
  Jacqueline du Pré (vc); **London Symphony Orchestra / Sir John Barbirolli.**
  EMI CZS5 68132-2 (six discs: 8/94). *See review in the Collections section; refer to the Index.* **GG**

Gentil Montaña

Columbian 20th century

Suggested listening ...
...Porro. *Coupled with works by various composers.* **Sharon Isbin** (gtr)
  with **Gaudencio Thiago de Mello** (perc). Teldec 0630-19899-2 (7/98).
  Gramophone Editor's choice. See review in the Collections section; refer to the Index. **GG**

Phillippus de Monte

Dutch 1521-1603

Suggested listening ...
...Quand de ta lèvre. Si trop souvent. Le premier jour du mois de mai.
  Coupled with works by various composers. **Clément Janequin Ensemble / Dominique Visse** (alto).
  Harmonia Mundi HMC90 1491 (2/95). *See review in the Collections section; refer to the Index.*

Claudio Monteverdi

Italian 1567-1643

Monteverdi Vespro della Beata Virgine (ed. Parrott/Keyte). **Taverner Consort; Taverner Choir; Taverner Players / Andrew Parrott.** Virgin Classics Veritas Ⓜ VMD5 61347-2
  (two discs: 106 minutes: DDD: 10/85). Recorded 1984. From HMV EX270129-3 (5/85). *✍* **G**
The technical and interpretative problems of the Monteverdi *Vespers* of 1610 are legion. Should the entire volume be performed as an entity, or just the psalms, or perhaps a mixture of psalms and motets? Since the vocal lines in the original publication are heavily ornamented, does this preclude the addition of further embellishment after the manner of contemporary instruction books? Which portions should be sung chorally (and how large should such a 'choir' be?), and which by the soloists? How should the continuo be realized? Many of these difficulties stem from the ambiguities of the original publication of the *Vespers* which remains the source from which all modern performing editions must be made. Others are caused by uncertainties surrounding seventeenth-century liturgical practice. In both these areas this recording offers new ideas. Firstly the liturgy. The central controversy raised by the *Vespers* concerns five non-liturgical compositions inserted among the Marian psalms, hymn and *Manificat: Nigra sum, Pulchra es, Duo Seraphim, Audi coelum* and the

Sonata sopra Sancta Maria. These, the sacred *concerti* described on the title-page as "suitable for the chapels or private chambers of princes", do not conform textually to any known Marian office but occur in Monteverdi's collection in positions normally occupied by psalm antiphons. These apparent contradictions have led some editors to suggest that they should not be performed as part of the *Vespers.* More convincing is the view, followed here, that the *concerti* are substitutes for the antiphons missing from Monteverdi's collections. And this view is taken even further by seeing them as antiphon-repeats and inserting plainchant for the missing first strain. This is done for three of the psalms; for the remaining two, contemporary instrumental sonatas by Giovanni Paolo Cima are performed. One effect is to make this version feel more unified, more monumental.

Both physically and emotionally the *concerti* are presented here as the focal points of the *Vespers,* the jewels in the crown. Certainly they are the occasion for some of the most spectacular singing on this recording. The essential ingredient here is the performance of Nigel Rogers, surely the most accomplished and convincing singer of the early seventeenth-century Italian virtuoso repertory to be found anywhere. He gives persuasive and seemingly effortless performances in three of the *concerti* in his highly characteristic melifluous, dramatic yet perfectly controlled manner. In two cases, *Audi coelum* and *Duo Seraphim,* he is well matched with Andrew King and Joseph Cornwell. By comparison *Pulchra es,* sung by Tessa Bonner and Emma Kirkby, seems rather understated, certainly too much so for this deliberately and deliciously ambiguous text. One important feature of Andrew Parrott's interpretation is its fundamental conception, historically accurate, of the *Vespers* as chamber work rather than a 'choral' one. Thus only one instrument is used per part, the harpsichord is employed very sparingly, and the basic continuo group is restricted to organ and chitarrone. Following the same principle, one voice per part is taken as the norm. The result is a clarity of texture, evident from the opening bars, which allows correct tempos to be used without stifling the often intricate rhythmic features of the writing. *Nisi Dominus,* for example, is taken at a lively speed but does not end up sounding rushed as so often happens. *Lauda Jerusalem* proceeds at a jaunty pace without loss of detail, and *Laetatus sum* sounds stately without being leaden-footed. That these effects can be achieved is largely due to decisions about the size and balance of forces.

Finally, mention should be made of another fundamental choice which represents something of a novelty. Both *Lauda Jerusalem* and the *Magnificat* are transposed down a fourth here, as indeed they should be according to the convention relating to the clef combinations in which they were originally notated. This brings all the vocal parts into the tessitura of the rest of the work, and also restores the instruments to their normal ranges. Whether or not the result is less 'exciting' than the version we are used to hearing has only partly to do with questions of musicality. For the rest, in this respect as in others, one of the lasting virtues of this well-balanced, unobtrusive recording is that it allows us to hear the *Vespers* sounding something along the lines that Monteverdi intended.

Additional recommendations ...

...Vespro della Beata Virgine (ed. Gardiner). Exultent caeli. *Coupled with works by* **G. Gabrieli** and **G. Bassano Soloists; Salisbury Cathedral Boys' Choir; Philip Jones Brass Ensemble; Munrow Recorder Ensemble; Monteverdi Choir and Orchestra / Sir John Eliot Gardiner.** Decca Double Ⓜ 443 482-2DF2 (two discs: 141 minutes: ADD). ♪   Ⓖ

...Vespro della Beata Virgine. Magnificat II a 6. **Soloists; Monteverdi Choir; London Oratory Junior Choir; His Majesties Sagbutts and Cornetts; English Baroque Soloists / Sir John Eliot Gardiner.** Archiv Produktion Ⓕ 429 565-2AH2 (two discs: 106 minutes: DDD: 1/91). ♪   Ⓖ

...Vespro della Beata Virgine. Missa in illo tempore. **Soloists; Regensburg Cathedral Choir; Hamburg Wind Ensemble for Early Music / Hans-Martin Schneidt.** Archiv Produktion Ⓕ 447 719-2AX2 (two discs: 142 minutes: ADD: 4/96). ♪

...Vespro della Beata Virgine – Domine ad adiuvandum; Dixit Dominus; Laudate pueri; Laetatus sum; Nisi Dominus; Lauda Jerusalem (with plainchant antiphons). Magnificat II. Motets – quam pulchra es. Domine, ne in furore. Ego flos campi. Adoramus te, Christe. Laudate Dominum omnes gentes. Ego dormio, et cor meum vigilat. Christe, adoramus te. Cantate Domino. **Concerto Italiano / Rinaldo Alessandrini.** Opus 111 Ⓕ OPS30-150 (75 minutes: DDD: 7/96). ♪ *Gramophone Editor's choice.*   Ⓖ

...Selva morale e spirituale – Beatus vir; Dixit Dominus I; Laudate Dominum; Laudate pueri; Magnificat. Messa et salmi, concertati, e parte da capella – Confitebor tibi, Domine. **Anonymous** Gregorian Chant for Ascension Day – Vespers. **Schütz Academy / Howard Arman.** Capriccio Ⓕ 10 521 (62 minutes: DDD: 2/97).

Monteverdi Il primo libro de madrigali. Settimo libro de madrigali – Tempro la cetra; Tirsi e Clori. **The Consort of Musicke / Anthony Rooley.** Virgin Classics Veritas Ⓕ VC5 45143-2 (57 minutes: DDD: 8/96). Texts and translations included.

This is a 'first' in more ways than one. To begin with, Monteverdi's *Primo libro* of 1587 is, even by the standards of the sixteenth century, a youthful publication. The composer was then just 19 years old. This collection, preceded by the precocious *Sacrae cantiunculae* of five years earlier, and the *Canzonette* of 1584, presents a detailed map of his absorption of contemporary madrigalian styles, and above all of his command of the lighter repertories that had become so popular in Italy during the 1580s. At the same time, there is a bittersweet quality about these pieces, for all that they are so episodically structured. This presages the later books when Monteverdi had moved to the Gonzaga court at Mantua, and had become acquainted with the more adventurous music then being written by composers both there and at Ferrara, inspired by the poetry of Guarini and Tasso. This is a 'first' also in the sense that it is the first recording to treat the book in its entirety. Few madrigals from the *Primo libro* have attracted other ensembles who, inevitably, have been drawn to the later madrigals, and above all to the contents of the last two books. Here The Consort of Musicke are on fine form, turning in sensitively wrought and carefully considered accounts, with perfect ensemble and tuning, and the textual details sensitively registered. The disc is rounded off with a number of pieces from the *Settimo libro*, clearly more dramatic in conception and effect, which provide an instructive and dramatic contrast with the madrigals from the first book. The continuo grouping here provides a sturdy and richly textured accompaniment to the soloists, and both instrumentalists and vocalists apply discreet and appropriate ornamentation with style.

Monteverdi Il secondo libro de madrigali. **Concerto Italiano** (Rossana Bertini, sop; Rosa Dominguez, mez; Claudio Cavina, alto; Giuseppe Maletto, Sandro Naglia, tens; Marco Radaelli, bar; Daniele Carnovich, bass) / **Rinaldo Alessandrini.** Opus 111 Ⓟ OPS30-111 (58 minutes: DDD: 8/95). Texts and translations included. 🎯 *Gramophone Editor's choice.* ⒼⒼ
Captivation begins with the very opening of the first piece on the disc, *Non si levav'anchor l'alba novella*, whose gently growing sense of the awakening dawn is itself a delicately drawn metaphor for transition from the urgent desire of the lovers' final embrace after a night of lovemaking to the gentle pain of their parting. The exquisite bittersweet pathos of the scene, whose every nuance and ambiguity is superbly caught in Alessandrini's vision of Monteverdi's music, sets both the standard and the tone for much of what follows in a number of important ways. First, with the exception of *S'andasse amor a caccia* and *Non giacinto o narcisi*, there are no examples here of the lighter *canzonetta*, such a prominent feature of the musical picture in Italy during the 1580s and a strong presence in the composer's own *Primo libro* of 1587. Secondly, and crucially, almost half the contents of the *Secondo libro* of three years later are settings of poetry by Torquato Tasso, whose *Gerusalemme liberata* was the most significant and influential epic to have been written in Italy since Ariosto's *Orlando furioso*, first published in the early decades of the century. Packed with strong images and bright colours, Tasso's verse was much drawn upon by many composers, including Monteverdi who continued to set it throughout his career. In Rinaldo Alessandrini and the Concerto Italiano, the intimate fusion of words and music which the composer embarks upon in this Second Book, and which was to remain a lifelong preoccupation, is delineated with charm, skill and profound understanding.

Monteverdi Il quarto libro de madrigali. **Concerto Italiano / Rinaldo Alessandrini.**
Opus 111 Ⓟ OPS30-81 (62 minutes: DDD: 12/93). 🎯 Texts and translations included.
Recorded 1993. *Gramophone* Award Winner 1994. *Gramophone Editor's choice.*   ⒼⒼ
Monteverdi's Fourth Book of Madrigals, first published in 1603, is a wide-ranging collection of pieces written during the previous ten years. Originally written for performance before a select audience by an ensemble of professional virtuoso singers, these madrigals, many of which are set to the sensuous, emotional and epigrammatic verses of Guarini and Tasso, demonstrate Monteverdi's seemingly inexhaustible ability to unite words and music in expressively effective ways. A complete and profound understanding of textual nuance is, then, central to any successful performance and here the Concerto Italiano begins with an obvious and considerable advantage over any group of non-Italians. Some of the finest madrigals in the Fourth Book are those involving direct speech, which allowed Monteverdi to make full use of the court virtuosi, famed for their abilities to combine clear declamation with dramatic gestures and subtle shadings of dynamics and speed. In general the Concerto Italiano have taken the combined messages of music and history to heart; these are performances infused with a flexible approach to tempo and strong projection of text geared to a determination to allow each detail of the words to speak with due force. The singing style itself is muscular without losing its ability to move into a gentler mood, the vocal balance good, the overall sound rich in its lower registers and bright and clear in the upper ones. At its best this record is simply without equal.

Monteverdi Il quinto libro de madrigali. **Concerto Italiano / Rinaldo Alessandrini.**
Opus 111 Ⓟ OPS30-166 (65 minutes: DDD: 5/97). 🎯 Texts and translations included.
Recorded 1996. *Gramophone Editor's choice.*   Ⓖ
There is a modernity about Monteverdi's poetic choices in the Fifth Book which is in turn reflected in an adventurous harmonic and gestural language which pushes the madrigalian vocabulary of Giaches de Wert and Luca Marenzio to new boundaries. As always with Monteverdi, his main preoccupation here is with an intimate bonding of words and music in a way which goes beyond the illustrative and pictorial manoeuvres of traditional madrigalian styles. This aesthetic priority, which remained with the composer throughout his life, is one which Rinaldo Alessandrini and the Concerto Italiano have done so much to understand and reveal, above all in a series of highly acclaimed recordings that have transformed our perceptions of both the sound and the sense of Monteverdi's music. Enthusiasts for the Concerto's highly dramatic, yet sensitive and subtle approach, the rich fruit of a winning combination of a true understanding of the textual complexities of Guarini's verse allied to a high order of technical control, will not be disappointed by this disc. The opening diptych, "Cruda Amarilli/O Mirtillo", sets the tone and style for much of what follows; the pace is stately, the passion being generated by those extraordinary dissonances that so offended Artusi, delineated here

with a lingering attention that is truly spine-chilling while still retaining its erotic undertow. Here and elsewhere on this recording, the exactness of the voicing, the gentle underscoring of rhythm and meaning, the authentic sound of the Italian language and the sheer musicality of the final result are united in performances of great expressive power and integrity.

Monteverdi Il ottavo libro de madrigali – Sinfonia; Altri canti d'amor; Non havea Febo ancora, "Lamento della ninfa"; Vago augelletto; Perchè t'en fuggi, O Fillide?; Altri canti di Marte; Ogni amante è guerrier; Hor ch'el ciel e la terra; Gira il nemico insidioso Amore; Dolcissimo uscignolo; Ardo, ardo, avvampo, mi struggo. **Concerto Italiano / Rinaldo Alessandrini.** Opus 111 ℗ OPS30-187 (75 minutes: DDD: 11/97). ✒ Texts and translations included. Recorded 1997.   ⓰⓰⓰

Monteverdi's Eighth Book of Madrigals, issued with the eye-catching title of *Madrigali guerrieri et amorosi* ("Madrigals of Love and War"), was published in 1638. Taking their cue from the prominent position allocated to his cherished *genere concitato* in both the preface and contents of the collection, Rinaldo Alessandrini has made an unusual selection of pieces in which this kind of writing, which in practice involves much rapid chordal repetition, triadic formulas and scale passages to imitate the sounds of war, is prominent. It is a brave choice. The rhetorical gestures of the *genere concitato* are few, simple, obvious and rapidly pall when overused. Nor are they confined to the *madrigali guerrieri* alone, since the agitation caused by the pains of love can also call them up. The real interpretative difficulty is to invest these moments with sufficient drama and character that they emerge from their somewhat textbook status and come to life. The Concerto Italiano's dramatic readings of these texts involve the deployment of all the familiar devices of severe contrast, occasional changes of pace, subtle underscorings at cadences and the highlighting of dissonant moments. The star performance of the disc is "Hor ch'el ciel e la terra" which begins with a magically poetic evocation, through exquisitely voiced repeated chords, of the stillness of the night before settling into a depiction of the lover's pain, achieved here through sharp stabbing motions of almost mannerist exaggeration. The Concerto's account of the second part ("Cosi soil d'una chiara fonte viva") is remarkable, not least for its inspired isolation of vocal lines of great lyrical power passed between the voices; the result is a revelation. There are now a good number of recordings of the pieces from the Eighth Book available, but no serious Monteverdian can afford to be without this one.

Monteverdi Chamber Duets – Chiome d'oro, bel tesoro; Io son pur vezzosetta pastorella; Non è di gentil core; Non è mai le stelle; O come sei gentile, caro augellino; Ohimè, dovè il mio ben?; O viva fiamma; S'el vostro cor, madonna; Soave libertate; Tornate, o cari baci; Vorrei baciarti, O Filli; Book 8: Mentre vaga Angioletta ogn'anima; O sia tranquill'il mare; Book 9: Bel pastor dal cui bel guardo. Scherzi musicali – Zefiro torna. Non vedrò mai le stelle. **Complesso Barocco / Alan Curtis** (hpd/org). Virgin Classics Veritas ℗ VC5 45293-2 (68 minutes: DDD: 5/98). ✒ Texts and translations included. Recorded 1996.

It is indeed surprising (as Alan Curtis observes in the essay accompanying this disc) that no one had yet hit upon the idea of gathering all of Monteverdi's chamber duets in a single collection. The rationale for so doing is audible throughout the recording: Monteverdi's essays in the genre are of a consistently high quality and include some of his most popular pieces (such as *Zefiro torna*, or the ravishing *Chiome d'oro*). The opening track wonderfully sets the tone, and showcases another of the recording's distinctive features, a particularly full continuo group. As one expects of Complesso Barocco, the standard of interpretation throughout is very high, although some of the more extended pieces seem to lose the thread of the argument, and the male soloists seem almost breathless at the tail-end of certain *passaggi*. The native singers' ease with the language is an essential asset: *Bel pastor*, one of the few duets for unequal voices, is particularly telling in this regard. Moving beyond interpretation, this project brings to the fore Monteverdi's astonishing resourcefulness and diversity of expression: what generous, essential music this is!

Monteverdi L'incoronazione di Poppea. **Sylvia McNair** (sop) Poppea; **Dana Hanchard** (sop) Nerone; **Anne Sofie von Otter** (mez) Ottavia, Fortune, Venus; **Michael Chance** (alto) Ottone; **Francesco Ellero d'Artegna** (bass) Seneca; **Catherine Bott** (sop) Drusilla, Virtue, Pallas Athene; **Roberto Balcone** (alto) Nurse; **Bernarda Fink** (contr) Arnalta; **Mark Tucker** (ten) Lucano, First Soldier; **Julian Clarkson** (bass) Lictor, Mercury; **Marinella Pennicchi** (sop) Love; **Constanze Backes** (sop) Valleto; **Nigel Robson** (ten) Liberto, Second Soldier; **English Baroque Soloists / Sir John Eliot Gardiner.** Archiv Produktion ℗ 447 088-2AH3 (three discs: 191 minutes: DDD: 7/96). ✒ Notes, text and translation included. Recorded live in 1993.   ⓰

The central question was always about how much needs to be added to the surviving notes in order to make *Poppea* viable on stage. Gardiner and his advisers believe that nothing needs adding and that the 'orchestra' indeed played only when explicitly notated in the score but that it was a very small group. To some ears this will have a fairly ascetic effect but it is firmly in line with current scholarly thinking about the opera. To compensate for that asceticism Gardiner has a rich group of continuo players and they play with wonderful flexibility. And Gardiner's spacious reading of the score bursts with the variety of pace that one might expect from a seasoned conductor of early opera. (Much of this material is thought not to be by Monteverdi, but that is another story.) Sylvia McNair is a gloriously sensuous Poppea: from her sleepy first words to the final duet she is always a thoroughly devious character, with her breathy, come-hither tones. Complementing this is Dana Hanchard's angry-brat Nerone, less even in voice than one might hope, but dramatically powerful. Whether they quite challenge Helen Donath and Elisabeth Söderström for Harnoncourt must remain a matter of opinion, but they certainly offer a viable alternative. The strongest performances here, though, come from Michael Chance and Anne Sofie von Otter as Ottone and Ottavia, both of them offering superbly rounded portrayals. Again they face severe challenges from Harnoncourt's unforgettable Paul Esswood and Cathy Berberian, but here the challenge is more equal, being on roughly the same grounds. Francesco Ellero d'Artegna is perhaps the most vocally skilled Seneca to date, with a resonant low C, though Michael Schopper for René Jacobs comes closer to the character of the oddball philosopher with clear political views for which he is happy to die. Catherine Bott is a wonderfully lively Drusilla; and the remainder of the cast are, as one might expect from Gardiner, consistently strong. The fact that this was recorded at a public concert is noticeable only from occasional superfluous noises.

Additional recommendations ...
...Soloists; **Vienna Concentus Musicus / Nikolaus Harnoncourt.**
   Teldec Ⓕ 2292-42547-2 (four discs: ADD: 9/86). ✎   Ⓖ
...Soloists; **Concerto Vocale / René Jacobs.**
   Harmonia Mundi Ⓕ HMC90 1330/32 (three discs: 197 minutes: DDD: 4/91). ✎

Monteverdi L'Orfeo. **Laurence Dale** (ten) Orfeo; **Efrat Ben-Nun** (sop) Euridice, Music;
   Jennifer Larmore (mez) Messenger; **Andreas Scholl** (alto) Hope; **Paul Gérimon** (bass) Charon;
   Bernarda Fink (contr) Proserpina; **Harry Peeters** (bass) Pluto; **Nicolas Rivenq** (bar) Apollo;
   Concerto Vocale / René Jacobs. Harmonia Mundi Ⓕ HMC90 1553/4
   (two discs: 120 minutes: DDD: 12/95). ✎ Notes, text and translation included. Recorded 1995.
It is clear right from the start, with the almost aggressive snarling brass and thudding drums of the opening Toccata, that René Jacobs's reading of L'Orfeo is a full-blooded one. The tone is set almost immediately by Efrat Ben-Nun, whose approach to the two roles that she sings is refreshingly direct and dramatic; her lines are sensitively shaped and phrased, and only the improvised embellishments to the part of Music, at times quite elaborate, could possibly cause any controversy. Among the other soloists Bernarda Fink delivers a convincingly urgent account of Proserpina's appeal at the opening of the Fourth Act, while Harry Peeters's Pluto presents his measured responses with an attractively lyrical authority. Charon's strangely angular lines, with their air of menace appropriate to one who spends time in contact with the Underworld, are expertly managed by Paul Gérimon, who shows himself to be a true Monteverdi bass. René Jacobs's approach to the thorny question of orchestration is robust. The score is notoriously difficult to interpret in this respect, often contradictory in its indications and in the end any solution can only be judged against some notion of what Monteverdi's sound-world might have been. Jacobs's version was originally given at the Salzburg Festival in 1993, and his instrumental resources, based around three continuo instruments spatially separated, are more a reflection of the acoustical properties of a modern pit rather than those of the sort of room in the Ducal Palace in which L'Orfeo was first performed. There is nothing necessarily wrong with that, and it has to be said that the result is successful, discriminating and only rarely over-elaborate. In Laurence Dale in the title-role, Jacobs has found a powerful protagonist, a singer capable of negotiating convincingly the sudden changes of emotional state that characterize the part at some of its most critical moments. More to the point, "Possente spirto" is something of a *tour de force*, conveying the central conception of the power of song with true rhetorical understanding. This is a version of L'Orfeo to be reckoned with.

Additional recommendations ...
...Soloists; **Munich Capella Antiqua; Vienna Concentus Musicus / Nikolaus Harnoncourt.**
   Teldec Das Alte Werk Ⓜ 2292-42494-2 (two discs: 108 minutes: ADD: 7/85). ✎
...Soloists; **New London Consort / Philip Pickett.**
   L'Oiseau-Lyre Ⓕ 433 545-2OH2 (two discs: 108 minutes: DDD: 2/93). ✎
...Soloists; **Chiaroscuro; London Cornett and Sackbutt Ensemble / Theresa Caudle; London Baroque /**
   Charles Medlam. EMI Ⓜ CMS7 64947-2 (two discs: 104 minutes: DDD: 4/94). ✎   Ⓖ

Monteverdi Il Ritorno d'Ulisse in Patria. **Christoph Prégardien** (ten) Ulisse; **Bernarda Fink** (contr)
   Penelope; **Christina Högmann** (sop) Telemaco, Siren; **Martyn Hill** (ten) Eumete; **Jocelyne Taillon**
   (mez) Ericlea; **Dominique Visse** (alto) Pisandro, Human Fragility; **Mark Tucker** (ten) Anfinomo;
   David Thomas (bass) Antinoo; **Guy de Mey** (ten) Iro; **Faridah Subrata** (mez) Melanto; **Jörg**
   Dürmüller (ten) Eurimaco; **Lorraine Hunt** (sop) Minerva, Fortune; **Michael Schopper** (bass)
   Nettuno, Time; **Olivier Lallouette** (bass) Giove; **Claron McFadden** (sop) Giunone; **Martina Bovet**
   (sop) Siren, Love; **Concerto Vocale / René Jacobs.** Harmonia Mundi Ⓕ HMC90 1427/9
   (three discs: 179 minutes: DDD: 3/93). ✎ Notes, text and translation included. Recorded 1992.
The only surviving manuscript score of this major musical drama, preserved in Vienna, presents an incomplete version of three acts. For this recording, René Jacobs has, within the spirit of seventeenth-century music-making, added more music by Monteverdi and others to expand the work to a satisfying five-act structure suggested by some surviving librettos. He has also considerably expanded the scoring, very much enlivening the instrumental palette that Monteverdi would have had available to him for his original production in Vienna in 1641. For some, this will rule this recording out of

consideration. However, the result, even though weakly argued for in the insert-notes, is so powerful and effective that it is to be hoped that most would not be prey to such reservations. The extensive cast, led by Christoph Prégardien in the title role, is excellently chosen, not only for vocal quality but also for a convincing awareness of Monteverdi's idiom. Without that, the performance could have seemed tame, and that is nowhere better exemplified than in Act 1, Scene 7 where Ulysses awakes, wondering where he is and what is to happen to him. Prégardien here manages to convey as much depth of feeling as a Pagliaccio yet stays clearly within the bounds of Monteverdi's expressive style. The result is a *tour de force*, one of the many within this production. The adept instrumental contribution certainly helps to maintain variety throughout the work, and an accompaniment suited to the sentiments expressed by the vocalists is always possible with these resources. Ultimately, this production is very much one for our time. It presents a practical solution to the problems of performing music of another age – this realization was, in fact, for a 1992 Montpellier production – and one that turns out to be inspired, moving and totally compelling.

Additional recommendation ...
...**Soloists; Vienna Concentus Musicus / Nikolaus Harnoncourt.**
Teldec Das Alte Werk Ⓜ 2292-42496-2 (three discs: 193 minutes: ADD). 🎖

Further listening ...
...Il Combattimento di Tancredi e Clorinda. Il ballo della ingrate. Altri canti d'amor. Volgendo il ciel. **Red Byrd; The Parley of Instruments / Peter Holman.** Hyperion CDA66475 (9/92). 🎖
...Il Combattimento di Tancredi e Clorinda[a]. Il ballo della ingrate[b]. Tirsi e Clori[c]. **Catherine Bott,** [b]**Tessa Bonner** (sops); [ac]**Andrew King,** [a]**John Mark Ainsley** (tens); [b]**Michael George** (bass); **New London Consort / Philip Pickett.** L'Oiseau-Lyre 440 637-2OH (6/95). 🎖
...Selva morale e spirituale – Beatus vir. *Coupled with works by various composers.* **New College Choir, Oxford; Capricorn / Edward Higginbottom.** Erato Ⓕ 3984-21659-2 (66 minutes: DDD: 6/98). *Gramophone Editor's choice. See review in the Collections section; refer to the Index.*
...Su le penne de' venti[a]. Selva morale e spirituale – Nos. 1, 6, 7, 10, 16 and 21[b]. Messa et salmi, concertati, e parte da capella – Nos. 4 and 13[c]. [bc]**Emma Kirkby** (sop); [bc]**Ian Partridge** (ten); [ab]**David Thomas** (bass); **Parley of Instruments.** Hyperion CDA66021 (11/87). 🎖   Ⓖ

Xavier Montsalvatge
Spanish 1912

Suggested listening ...
...Divagación. Three divertimentos on themes of forgotten composers. Si, à Mompou. Berceuse a la memoria de Oscar Esplá. Sonatine pour Yvette. *Coupled with works by* **Falla Alicia de Larrocha** (pf). RCA Victor Red Seal 09026 61389-2 (9/94). *See review under Falla; refer to the Index.*   ⓖⓖ
...Canto negro. *Coupled with works by various composers.* **Angela Gheorghiu** (sop); **Malcolm Martineau** (pf). Decca 458 360-2DH (5/98). *See review in the Collections section; refer to the Index.*

Ivan Moody
British 1964

Suggested listening ...
...Endechas y Canciones. Canticum Canticorum I. *Coupled with works by various composers.* **The Hilliard Ensemble.** ECM New Series 453 259-2 (1/97). *See review in the Collections section; refer to the Index.*

Philip Moore
British 1943

Suggested listening ...
...Canterbury Service. *Coupled with works by various composers.* **Bristol Cathedral Choir / Christopher Brayne** with **Ian Ball** (org). Priory PRCD528 (8/96). *See review in the Collections section; refer to the Index.*

Cristóbal de Morales
Spanish c1500-1553

Morales Mass for the feast of St Isidore of Seville. **Gabrieli Consort and Players / Paul McCreesh.** Archiv Produktion Ⓕ 449 143-2AH (76 minutes: DDD: 8/96). Texts and translations included. *Gramophone Editor's record of the month.*   ⓖⓖ
Morales Missa "Mille regretz". Emendemus in melius. **Guerrero** O Doctor optime.
Instrumental and organ works by Cabézon, Rogier, Guerrero, Gombert and Santa María.
It must have been difficult to find a suitable programme to follow the Gabrieli Consort's triumphant recording of Victoria's Requiem (refer to the Index), but with this disc of Morales's *Missa Mille regretz* this has certainly been achieved, and with a logical connection to the previous release. To begin

at the beginning, expecting that the instrumental *canciones* by Guerrero and Rogier (transcribed from the Lerma manuscript by Douglas Kirk) which open the disc would be merely padding, it is delightful to hear playing of such sensitivity: one can understand why instrumentalists were so prized in Spanish cathedrals at this time if they played like this. Morales's Mass itself (performed, like the Victoria, by an all-male consort) is sung splendidly. There is a real feeling for the work's direction (not easily discerned in music so seamlessly polyphonic as Morales) which, in combination with the seductively rich sonority of the choir, make it a performance of genuine stature. The only reservations concern the stodgy singing of the "Hosanna" which would surely benefit from a lighter, more rhythmic approach. The plainchant is for the feast of St Isidore of Seville, taken from unspecified sixteenth- and seventeenth-century sources by Robert Snow. It is sung (again as on the Victoria disc) accompanied by a dulcian, as indeed is the polyphony, common Spanish practice of the time. Instruments and choir come together only in Guerrero's motet, *O Doctor optime*, sung at the Offertory, which is an object lesson in how to achieve blend and balance. Another *canción* by Rogier acts as a recessional, and the disc closes with a short piece by Tomás de Santa María followed by a magnificent performance of Morales's motet *Emendemus in melius*. This disc is a must!

Morales Missa "Queramus cum pastoribus". Andreas Christi famulus. Sancta Maria, succurre miseris. Clamabat autem mulier. O sacrum convivium. Regina coeli.
Mouton Queramus cum pastoribus. **Westminster Cathedral Choir / James O'Donnell.** Hyperion
ⓟ CDA66635 (65 minutes: DDD: 1/96). Texts and translations included. Recorded 1992.
In the *Missa Queramus cum pastoribus* the *divisi* basses of Westminster provide the ideal counterweight to the warm forthright tone of the boys. James O'Donnell adopts generally unhurried tempos that allow the counterpoint to unfold with seamless ease, but the choral sound is of such intensity and focus that the ear is constantly arrested. At its most punchy, as in the "Osannas", this could become wearing, but in the more sustained movements it is just what is needed to bring the music alive. Parts of this recording have an almost tactile quality and these occur precisely where the tactus is at its most spacious. Westminster Cathedral Choir supplement their Mass, preceded by the Mouton motet on which it is based, with five marvellous motets by Morales, of which the simplest but perhaps the most effective is *Sancta Maria, succurre miseris*. The *Regina coeli*, with its running quaver figures, could have done with a little more lightness of touch, but what a thrilling sound this choir makes when in full cry.
Further listening ...
...Missa Pro defunctis a 5. Officium defunctorum a 5. **La Capella Reial de Catalunya;**
 Hespèrion XX / Jordi Savall. Auvidis Astrée E8765. 🎵   Ⓖ
...Pater noster. Parce mihi, Domine. Magnificat a 6. *Coupled with works by various composers.*
 The Hilliard Ensemble. Virgin Classics Veritas VED5 61394-2 (11/97). *See review in the Collections section; refer to the Index.*

Robert Moran   American 1937

Suggested listening ...
...Music from the Towers of the Moon. *Coupled with works by various composers.*
 Balanescu Quartet. Argo 436 565-2ZH (3/93). *See review in the Collections section;*
 refer to the Index.   Ⓖ

Jorge Morel   Mexican 1931

Suggested listening ...
...Chôro. Danza Brasileira. Danza in E minor.
 Coupled with works by various composers. **Jason Vieaux** (gtr).
 Naxos 8 553449 (11/97). *See review in the Collections section; refer to the Index.*

Landgrave of Moritz   German 1572-1632

Suggested listening ...
...Pavin (arr. Dowland?). *Coupled with works by various composers.* **Paul O'Dette** (lte).
 Harmonia Mundi HMU90 7164 (7/97). *See review under Dowland; refer to the Index.*

Thomas Morley   British 1557/8-1602

Suggested listening ...
...First Evening Service. Canterbury Service. *Coupled with works by various composers.*
 Bristol Cathedral Choir / Christopher Brayne with **Ian Ball** (org).
 Priory PRCD528 (8/96). *See review in the Collections section; refer to the Index.*

Moritz Moszkowski

Moszkowski Fantaisie Impromptu, Op. 6. Trois Etudes de Concert, Op. 24. Trois Morceaux, Op. 42. Trois Morceaux, Op. 73. Grande Valse de Concert, Op. 88. Isoldens Tod – Concert Paraphrase after Wagner. **Seta Tanyel** (pf). Collins Classics Ⓕ 1473-2 (65 minutes: DDD: 12/96). Recorded 1996. *Gramophone Editor's choice.*   Ⓖ

When Paderewski claimed "after Chopin he best understands how to write for the piano" he paid Moszkowski a shrewd and ingenious compliment. Although Moszkowski could be limited and facile he wrote superbly for his chosen instrument, decking out one charming melody after another with the most grateful and scintillating virtuosity. The items presented here span most of Moszkowski's creative career and the full range of his artistry, from the gentle innocence of his salon music (the *Morceaux* of Opp. 42 and 73) to the extrovert virtuosity of the *Etudes de Concert* and the wonderfully pianistic transcription of the final scene from Wagner's *Tristan und Isolde.* Tanyel's playing is gracious, affectionate and polished. The technical demands (often considerable) are surmounted with nonchalant ease and fluency. She tends to eschew idiosyncrasy, but reveals a naturally refined stylishness. The most impressive piece offered here is the paraphrase of Wagner's *Isoldens Tod*, which is in many ways superior to Liszt's famous transcription, and is among Moszkowski's finest piano writing. Tanyel's colourful account is beautifully moulded, giving a sense of inevitability to the ever-intensifying chromaticism, and of climactic culmination to the diatonic release and aftermath. This is a set all enthusiasts of super-virtuosity should investigate. The recording is impeccable.

Further listening ...

...Piano Concerto in E major, Op. 59. *Coupled with* **Paderewski** Piano Concerto in A minor, Op. 17. **Piers Lane** (pf); **BBC Scottish Symphony Orchestra / Jerzy Maksymiuk.** Hyperion CDA66452 (2/92).

...Aus aller Herren Ländern, Op. 23. *Coupled with* **Dvořák** Ten Legends, B117. **Isabel Beyer, Harvey Dagul** (pf duet). Four Hands Music FHMD9671 (5/97).

...Etincelles, Op. 36 No. 6. *Coupled with works by various composers.* **Pavel Nersessian** (pf). Bel Air Music BAM9725 (3/98). *See review in the Collections section; refer to the Index.*

Jean Mouton

Suggested listening ...

...Nesciens mater. Ave Maria virgo serena. Ave sanctissima Maria. O Maria piissima. Ave Maria gemma virginum. *Coupled with* **Josquin Desprez** Missa de beata virgine. **Theatre of Voices / Paul Hillier.** Harmonia Mundi HMU90 7136 (11/95). *See review under Josquin Desprez; refer to the Index.*

...Nesciens mater. *Coupled with works by various composers.* **Early Music Consort of London / David Munrow.** Virgin Classics Veritas VED5 61334-2 (11/97). *See review in the Collections section; refer to the Index.*

...Queramus cum pastoribus. *Coupled with works by* **Morales** Westminster Cathedral Choir / James O'Donnell. Hyperion CDA66635 (1/96). *See review under Morales; refer to the Index.*

Leopold Mozart

Suggested listening ...

...Horn Concerto in D major. *Coupled with works by various composers.* **Barry Tuckwell** (hn); **Academy of St Martin in the Fields / Sir Neville Marriner.** EMI Forte CZS5 69395-2 (2/97). *See review in the Collections section; refer to the Index.*

...Trumpet Concerto in D major. *Coupled with works by various composers.* **Niklas Eklund** (baroque tpt); **Drottningholm Baroque Ensemble / Nils-Erik Sparf.** Naxos 8 553531 (11/96). ☞ *See review in the Collections section; refer to the Index.*

Wolfgang Amadeus Mozart

Mozart Flute Concertos – No. 1 in G major, K313/K285*c*; No. 2 in C major, K314/K285*d*. Andante in C major, K315/K285*e*. Flute and Harp Concerto in D major, K299/K297*c*[a]. **Konrad Hünteler** (fl); [a]**Helga Storck** (hp); **Orchestra of the Eighteenth Century / Frans Brüggen.** Philips Ⓕ 442 148-2PH (78 minutes: DDD: 8/96). ☞

Mozart Flute Concertos – No. 1 in G major, K313/K285*c*; No. 2 in D major, K314/K285*d*. Flute and Harp Concerto in C major, K299/K297*c*[a]. **Emmanuel Pahud** (fl); [a]**Marie-Pierre Langlamet** (hp); **Berlin Philharmonic Orchestra / Claudio Abbado.** EMI Ⓕ CDC5 56365-2 (71 minutes: DDD: 7/97). Recorded 1996. *Gramophone Editor's choice.*

Mozart's splendid flute music provides the strongest proof that his supposed dislike for the instrument was only to justify his failure to complete the famous commission from the Dutch amateur musician DeJean. On the Philips disc, Konrad Hünteler and Frans Brüggen shape the elegant lines of the

G major Concerto with appropriate finesse, enhanced by an exceptionally attractive blend between Hünteler's c1720 Denner flute and the orchestra's pleasingly fine-grained sound. Susan Palma's eloquent alternative with the Orpheus Chamber Orchestra is one of the finest versions of this piece played on modern instruments; however, Hünteler's softer flute sound (atmospherically evoking the human voice) and the orchestra's more distinctive period instruments bring added dramatic intensity to this music. Likewise, Hünteler and the orchestra capture the direct charm of the C major *Andante*. To appease DeJean, Mozart offered an arrangement for flute of his Oboe Concerto. For this recording, the eighteenth-century flute parts have been compared with those for oboe for a more 'authentic' text, and the resulting exquisitely balanced account makes a wholly convincing masterpiece for the flute. Mozart was prompt with the commission for a flute and harp concerto for Comte de Guines, who "played the flute matchlessly" and whose daughter "played the harp magnificently". Hünteler and Storck, aided by the orchestra's subtle playing, highlight vividly the music's perfect match of technical and instrumental resources.

Where RCA record the superstar of the flute, James Galway, in the latest of his many versions, EMI turn to one of his successors as principal flute of the Berlin Philharmonic. One notable contrast between their readings is that the Galway performances take over six minutes longer. While Galway's cadenzas are consistently longer and generally more elaborate than Pahud's, the difference of tempo in fast movements is relatively little, at least in the solo concertos. Where there is a significant contrast is in the slow movements, of which Galway takes a far more expansive view. The marginally faster speeds in the Berlin performance are a degree more in tune with latter-day taste, and generally in the outer movements Pahud's touch is lighter than Galway's, well matched against a modest-sized Berlin Philharmonic, no larger in its string section, than the Academy. Many will feel that the more flowing speeds for the slow movements are more apt, for Pahud, like Galway, is a natural soloist, pointing phrases and rhythms with poetic individuality, never just a conformist orchestral player. Overall, this disc will give much enjoyment.

Additional recommendations ...

...No. 1. Andante. Flute and Harp Concerto. Bassoon Concerto. **Soloists; Academy of Ancient Music / Christopher Hogwood.** L'Oiseau-Lyre Ⓕ 417 622-2OH (74 minutes: DDD: 5/88). 🎖

...No. 1. Andante. Flute and Harp Concerto. **Irena Grafenauer** (fl); **Maria Graf** (hp); **Academy of St Martin in the Fields / Sir Neville Marriner.** Philips Ⓕ 422 339-2PH (58 minutes: DDD: 7/89).

...Nos. 1 and 2. Flute and Harp Concerto. Andante. Rondo in D major for Flute and Orchestra, K373 (arr. Galway). Divertimento in D major, K334 – Menuetto (arr. Galway). Serenade No. 13 in G major, K525, "Eine kleine Nachtmusik". **Marisa Robles** (hp); **Chamber Orchestra of Europe / James Galway** (fl). RCA Victor Red Seal Ⓕ RD87861 (two discs: 109 minutes: DDD: 7/89).

...No. 1. Andante. Flute and Harp Concerto[a]. **Susan Palma** (fl); [a]**Nancy Allen** (hp); **Orpheus Chamber Orchestra.** DG Ⓕ 427 677-2GH (58 minutes: DDD: 3/90).

Mozart Clarinet Concerto in A major, K622[a]. Clarinet Quintet in A major, K581[b].
Thea King (basset cl); [b]**Gabrieli String Quartet** (Kenneth Sillito, Brendan O'Reilly, vns; Ian Jewel, va; Keith Harvey, vc); [a]**English Chamber Orchestra / Jeffrey Tate.**
Hyperion Ⓕ CDA66199 (64 minutes: DDD: 9/86). From A66199 (3/86).
Mozart Clarinet Concerto in A major, K622[a].
Spohr Clarinet Concerto No. 1 in C minor, Op. 26.
Weber Clarinet Concerto No. 2 in E flat major, J118. **Ernst Ottensamer** (cl/[a]basset cl);
Vienna Philharmonic Orchestra / Sir Colin Davis. Philips Ⓕ 438 868-2PH
(72 minutes: DDD: 6/94). Recorded 1992.

The two works on the Hyperion disc are representative of Mozart's clarinet writing at its most inspired; however, the instrument for which they were written differed in several respects from the modern clarinet, the most important being its extended bass range. Modern editions of both the Clarinet Concerto and the Quintet have adjusted the solo part to suit today's clarinets, but Thea King reverts as far as possible to the original texts, and her playing is both sensitive and intelligent. Jeffrey Tate and the ECO accompany with subtlety and discretion in the concerto, and the Gabrielli Quartet achieve a fine sense of rapport with King in the Quintet. Both recordings are clear and naturally balanced, with just enough distance between soloist and listener.

Ernst Ottensamer is a virtuoso with a real sense of style, that is to say a musician with an instinct for the difference between the contained romanticism of Mozart's concerto and the overt but differing romanticism of Spohr and Weber. His tone is rich and warm, with a beautiful depth in the lower registers of the basset clarinet in the Mozart, but also a brilliance that has a bit of a wicked glint to it in Weber's finale compared to the dancing ease of Mozart's. Mozart's *Adagio* is beautifully judged in tempo, a song with a seamless line, while Weber's *Romanza* is taken quite differently, like a wordless operatic aria. Spohr's short *Adagio,* a touchingly simple, direct piece, is charmingly delivered, and elsewhere Ottensamer listens with a careful ear to the woodwind and other lines which in this work intermingle so subtly: he is an old Philharmoniker who shows a proper attention to his colleagues. He is given close, sympathetic support by orchestra and conductor. One of Davis's particular qualities is his ear for the telling simplicities in Mozart, so that here a plain arpeggio springs to life with the clarinet's melody, or a set of repeated notes has a sense of direction towards a cadence. Anyone acquiring this record should take note of just how musically the 'accompaniment' is all done. The VPO respond with complete understanding, and the recording engineers have missed nothing.

Additional recommendations ...

...Clarinet Concerto[a]. Flute and Harp Concerto in C major, K299/K297c[b]. [a]**Emma Johnson** (cl); [b]**William Bennett** (fl); [b]**Osian Ellis** (hp); **English Chamber Orchestra / Raymond Leppard.** ASV Ⓕ CDDCA532 (54 minutes: DDD).

...Clarinet Concerto. Oboe Concerto in C major, K314/K285. **Antony Pay** (basset cl); **Michael Piguet** (ob); **Academy of Ancient Music / Christopher Hogwood** (fp/hpd). L'Oiseau-Lyre Ⓕ 414 339-2OH (47 minutes: DDD: 5/86). ✍

...Clarinet Concerto. Oboe Concerto. **Jack Brymer** (cl); **Neil Black** (ob); **Academy of St Martin in the Fields / Sir Neville Marriner.** Philips Ⓕ 416 483-2PH (50 minutes: ADD: 10/88). Ⓖ

...Clarinet Quintet. Oboe Quartet. Horn Quintet. **Anthony Pay** (cl); **Neil Black** (ob); **Timothy Brown** (hn); **Academy of St Martin in the Fields Chamber Ensemble.** Philips Musica da Camera Ⓜ 422 833-2PC (69 minutes: ADD: 10/89).

...Clarinet Concerto[b]. Oboe Concerto[c]. Bassoon Concerto in B flat major, K191/[g]. Flute and Harp Concerto[ah]. Flute Concerto in G major, K313[a]. Horn Concertos – No. 1 in D major, K412/K386b[e]; No. 2 in E flat major, K417[f]; No. 3 in E flat major, K447[f]; No. 4 in E flat major, K495[e]. Andante for Flute and Orchestra in C major, K315/K284e. Sinfonia concertante in E flat major, KAnh9/K297B[bf]. [b]**Susan Palma** (fl); [b]**Stephen Taylor**, [c]**Randall Wolfgang** (obs); [b]**David Singer** (cl); [d]**Charles Neidich** (basset cl); [b]**Steven Dibner**, [g]**Frank Morelli** (bns); [e]**David Jolley**, [f]**William Purvis** (hns); [h]**Nancy Allen** (hp); **Orpheus Chamber Orchestra.** DG Ⓑ 431 665-2GX3 (three discs: 113 minutes: DDD: 7/91).

...Clarinet Concerto[a]. Oboe Concerto[b]. Bassoon Concerto[c]. [a]**Jacques Lancelot** (cl); [b]**Pierre Pierlot** (ob); [c]**Paul Hongne** (bn); [a]**English Chamber Orchestra / Jean-Pierre Rampal**; [b]**Jean-François Paillard Chamber Orchestra / Jean-François Paillard**; [c]**Bamberg Symphony Orchestra / Theodore Guschlbauer.** Erato Bonsai Ⓑ 2292-45937-2 (67 minutes: ADD: 6/93).

...Clarinet Quintet. Divertimento in D major, K136. **Thea King** (cl); **Aeolian Quartet.** Saga Classics Ⓜ EC3387-2 (51 minutes: ADD: 3/94).

...Clarinet Quintet. **Brahms** Clarinet Quintet in B minor, Op. 155. **Harold Wright** (cl); **Boston Symphony Chamber Players.** Philips Ⓕ 442 149-2PH (72 minutes: DDD: 9/94). *See review under Brahms; refer to the Index.*

...Clarinet Concerto[a]; Oboe Concerto in C major, K314/K271k[b]; Bassoon Concerto[c]. [b]**John Mack** (ob); [a]**Franklin Cohen** (cl); [c]**David McGill** (bn); **Cleveland Orchestra / Christoph von Dohnányi.** Decca Ⓕ 443 176-2DH (69 minutes: DDD: 2/96).

Mozart Horn Concertos – No. 1 in D major, K412; No. 2 in E flat major, K417; No. 3 in E flat major, K447; No. 4 in E flat major, K495. Rondos for Horn and Orchestra – D major, K514; E flat major, K371, "Concert Rondo". **Anthony Halstead** (hn); **Academy of Ancient Music / Christopher Hogwood.** L'Oiseau-Lyre Ⓕ 443 216-2OH (60 minutes: DDD: 8/95). ✍
Recorded 1993. Ⓖ

Mozart Horn Concertos[a] – No. 1 in D major, K412; No. 2 in E flat major, K417; No. 3 in E flat major, K447; No. 4 in E flat major, K495. Horn Quintet in E flat major, K407/K386c[b]. **David Pyatt** (hn); [b]**Kenneth Sillito** (vn); [b]**Robert Smissen**, [b]**Stephen Tees** (vas); [b]**Stephen Orton** (vc); [a]**Academy of St Martin in the Fields / Sir Neville Marriner.** Erato Ⓜ 0630-17074-2 (70 minutes: DDD: 7/97). Recorded 1996. *Gramophone Editor's record of the month.* ⒼⒼ

These horn concertos, mostly written for Mozart's family friend, Joseph Leutgeb, are full of humour: phrases turning in unexpected directions, surprising exploitations of the horn's special capacities and incapacities, and so on. A particular charm of Anthony Halstead's disc lies in cool, understated performances, which are in the best traditions of British horn playing and in the variety in his approach to the different concertos: the broader phrasing and longer lines he brings to the more consciously expansive and symphonic K495, for example, the chamber musical playing in K447 (easily the finest of the concertos), and the gentle lyricism in K417. Everywhere, however, he excels with his shapely moulding of the music and his natural, musical way of rounding off phrases. Playing a period horn, valveless, of course, he 'makes' the notes that are not natural harmonics by deft movements of his hand in the bell. Sometimes this technique can lead to the chromatic notes differing sharply in quality from the open ones, but Halstead seems to have more control over tone quality than most natural horn players: the stopped notes sometimes slip in unobtrusively, but where he wants to use colour to stress them or pick them out, he does so very effectively, with the occasional touch of brassiness or muffling. Clearly his special skill allows him extra options. For the D major Concerto, the last of the four (the correct chronological order is K417, K495, K447, K412), we are given here both the Süssmayr version of the finale (the familiar one, written during the Easter after Mozart's death and including a Lamentation plainsong) and a very capable filling-out of Mozart's incomplete autograph version by John Humphries, who also supplies the skilful completion of the skeletal K371 *Rondo*. With the Academy of Ancient Music under Christopher Hogwood on lively form, with well pointed ritornellos and attentive accompaniments, this is a thoroughly enjoyable and musicianly account of these endearing works.

David Pyatt, *Gramophone*'s Young Artist of the Year in 1996, has provided performances in which calm authority and high imagination fuse; and this disc is ideally placed in the catalogue between the nobility and urbanity of Dennis Brain, and the more relaxed, plain-speaking Barry Tuckwell. Although there can be no direct comparison with Anthony Halstead, Pyatt's is very much in that mode of supple, understated and often witty playing, accompanied by truly discriminating orchestral forces. Soloist and orchestra create a constantly shifting and lively pattern of dynamic relationships. Pyatt makes the music's song and meditation very much his own. Compared with the dark, dream-like *cantabile* of Brain, he offers in the Second Concerto an *Andante* of cultivated conversation and, in the Third, a *Romanza* of barely moving breath and light. His finales trip the light fantastic. The Second Concerto's springing rhythms reveal wonderfully clear high notes; the Third is nimble and debonair without being quite as patrician as Brain's; and the Fourth creates real mischief in its effervescent articulation. The cadenzas by Terry Wooding (to the first movements of the Third and Fourth Concertos) epitomize Pyatt's performances as a whole: longer and more daringly imaginative than those of either Brain or Tuckwell, while remaining sensitively scaled and fancifully idiomatic. The concertos are, uniquely, coupled with a fine performance of the Horn Quintet in E flat, with members of the ASMF.

Additional recommendations ...

...Horn Concertos. **English Chamber Orchestra / Barry Tuckwell** (hn).
Decca Ⓕ 410 284-2DH (52 minutes: DDD: 9/85).

...Horn Concertos. Fragment for Horn and Orchestra in E major, K494*a*. **Anthony Halstead**
(natural hn); **Hanover Band / Roy Goodman.** Nimbus Ⓕ NI5104 (55 minutes: DDD: 8/88). ✍

...Horn Concertos. Rondo (cptd. Tuckwell). **Barry Tuckwell** (hn); **Academy of St Martin
in the Fields / Sir Neville Marriner.** EMI Studio Ⓜ CDM7 69569-2 (60 minutes: ADD: 1/89).

...Horn Concertos. Rondo, K371 (rev. Levin). **Ab Koster** (hn); **Tafelmusik / Bruno Weil.**
Sony Classical Vivarte Ⓕ SK53369 (64 minutes: DDD: 2/94). ✍ Ⓖ

...Horn Concertos. Rondo, K371 (cptd. Tuckwell). **R. Strauss** Horn Concerto No. 1
in E flat major, Op. 11. **Radovan Vlatković** (hn); **English Chamber Orchestra / Jeffrey Tate.**
EMI Studio Plus Ⓜ CDM7 64851-2 (76 minutes: DDD: 10/94).

...Horn Concertos. Fragment for Horn and Orchestra in E major, K494*a* (ed. Humphries).
Rondo, K371 (cptd. Humphries). **Swann** Ill wind[a]. **Eric Ruske** (hn); [a]**Richard Suart** (bass);
Scottish Chamber Orchestra / Sir Charles Mackerras.
Telarc Ⓕ CD80367 (64 minutes: DDD: 10/94).

...Horn Concertos. *Coupled with works by* **Mendelssohn** and **Rossini** Alan Civil (hn);
Philharmonia Orchestra / Otto Klemperer. Testament Ⓕ SBT1102 (72 minutes: ADD: 7/97).

Mozart Horn Concertos – No. 1 in D major, K412; No. 2 in E flat major, K417; No. 3 in E flat major, K447; No. 4 in E flat major, K495. Piano Quintet, K452. **Dennis Brain** (hn); **Philharmonia Orchestra / Herbert von Karajan.** EMI mono Ⓕ CDC5 55087-2* (55 minutes: ADD: 2/88).
From Columbia 33CX1140 (10/54). Recorded 1954. *Gramophone classical 100.* ⒼⒼⒼ
Dennis Brain was the finest Mozartian soloist of his generation. Again and again Karajan matches the graceful line of his solo phrasing (the *Romance* of No. 3 is just one ravishing example), while in the *Allegros* the crisply articulated, often witty comments from the Philharmonia violins are a joy. The glorious tone and the richly lyrical phrasing of every note from Brain himself is life-enhancing in its radiant warmth. The *Rondos* are not just spirited, buoyant, infectious and smiling, although they are all of these things, but they have the kind of natural flow that Beecham gave to Mozart. There is also much dynamic subtlety – Brain doesn't just repeat the main theme the same as the first time, but alters its level and colour. His legacy to the next generation of horn players (and those that have followed on afterwards) was to show them that the horn – a notoriously difficult instrument – could be tamed absolutely and that it could yield a lyrical line and a range of colour to match any other solo instrument. He was tragically killed, in his prime, in a car accident while travelling home overnight from the Edinburgh Festival – his driving was as legendary as his playing. He left us this supreme Mozartian testament which may be approached by others but rarely, if ever, quite equalled, for his was uniquely inspirational music-making, with a quality something like innocence to make it the more endearing. It is a pity to be unable to be equally enthusiastic about the recorded sound. The mono master is, rightly, not given spurious stereo treatment, but the remastering – although the horn timbre, with full Kingsway Hall resonance, is unimpaired – has dried out the strings: added clarity is no fair exchange for loss of amplitude and bloom. But this remains a classic recording.

Mozart Oboe Concerto in C major, K314/K271*k*.
R. Strauss Oboe Concerto in D major. **Douglas Boyd** (ob); **Chamber Orchestra of Europe /
Paavo Berglund.** ASV Ⓕ CDCOE808 (44 minutes: DDD: 11/87). From COE808 (7/87).
Mozart Oboe Concerto in C major, K314/K271*k*[a]; Flute Concerto in G major, K313/K285*c*[b];
Clarinet Concerto in A major, K622[c]. [a]**Nicholas Daniel** (ob); [b]**Kate Hill** (fl); [c]**Joy Farrall**
(basset cl); **Britten Sinfonia / Nicholas Cleobury.** Classic fM Ⓜ 75605 57001-2
(73 minutes: DDD: 1/98). Recorded 1997.
ASV's coupling links two of the most delightful oboe concertos ever written. Mozart's sprightly and buoyant work invests the instrument with a chirpy, bird-like fleetness encouraging the interplay of lively rhythm and elegant poise. Boyd's reading of this evergreen work captures its freshness and spontaneity beautifully. If the Mozart portrays the sprightly side of the instrument's make-up the Strauss illustrates its languorous ease and tonal voluptuousness. Again Boyd allows himself the freedom and breadth he needs for his glowing interpretation; he handles the arching melodies of the opening movement and the witty staccato of the last with equal skill. Nicely recorded.

Classic fM's collection of Mozart's finest solo woodwind concertos is a winner. All the soloists are distinguished British orchestral players, each having a distinct personality in his or her own right. Joy Farrall's clarinet style combines an easy freedom with warm classical directness. Her performance of the Clarinet Concerto is totally seductive, with Nicholas Cleobury's gracefully phrased opening ritornello setting the scene for the lightly pointed solo entry. Her delicacy of feeling and velvety, luminous timbre immediately cajole the ear, as does the subtlety of her wistful dynamic nuancing. Her fluid line is heard at its most ravishing in the *Adagio*, richly echoed by the strings of the Britten Sinfonia; and the delicacy of the reprise is particularly magical. It is followed by a delicious, bubbling finale with lilting secondary material. Nicholas Daniel is hardly less appealing in the more petite Oboe Concerto and his reedy sweetness of timbre never cloys. He, too, is at his finest in the slow movement, while in the infectious closing *Rondo* finale he provides a neatly succinct cadenza. The Flute Concerto is equally delectable, especially the tender *Adagio* which Cleobury moves forward at exactly the right measured pace and which Kate Hill carols so touchingly. The neatly pointed minuet finale is captivating. Recorded sound is excellent and well balanced.

Additional recommendations ...
...Oboe Concerto. Clarinet Concerto in A major, K622. **Michael Piguet** (ob); **Antony Pay** (basset cl); **Academy of Ancient Music / Christopher Hogwood** (fp/hpd). L'Oiseau-Lyre Ⓕ 414 339-2OH (DDD: 5/86). ✐
...Oboe Concerto. Clarinet Concerto. **Neil Black** (ob); **Jack Brymer** (cl); **Academy of St Martin in the Fields / Sir Neville Marriner.** Philips Ⓕ 416 483-2PH (50 minutes: ADD: 10/88).

Mozart Piano Concertos – No. 1 in F major, K37; No. 2 in B flat major, K39; No. 3 in D major, K40; No. 4 in G major, K41; No. 5 in D major, K175; No. 6 in B flat major, K238; No. 8 in C major, K246; No. 9 in E flat major, K271, "Jeunehomme"; No. 11 in F major, K413/K387*a*; No. 12 in A major, K414/K385*p*; No. 13 in C major, K415/K387*b*; No. 14 in E flat major, K449; No. 15 in B flat major, K450; No. 16 in D major, K451; No. 17 in G major, K453; No. 18 in B flat major, K456; No. 19 in F major, K459; No. 20 in D minor, K466; No. 21 in C major, K467; No. 22 in E flat major, K482; No. 23 in A major, K488; No. 24 in C minor, K491; No. 25 in C major, K503; No. 26 in D major, K537, "Coronation"; No. 27 in B flat major, K595. **English Chamber Orchestra / Murray Perahia** (pf). Sony Classical Ⓜ SX12K46441 (12 discs: 608 minutes: ADD/DDD). Recorded 1975-84. *Gramophone classical 100.* ⒼⒼⒼ

Mozart concertos from the keyboard remain unbeatable. There is a rightness, an effortlessness, about doing the concertos this way which makes for heightened enjoyment. Not that it is the only way; and yet so many of them seem to gain in vividness when the interplay of pianist and orchestra is realized by musicians listening to each other in the manner of chamber music. Provided the musicians are of the finest quality, of course. We now just take for granted that, corporately and individually, the members of the English Chamber Orchestra will match the sensibility of the soloist. They are on top form here, as is Perahia, and the finesse of detail is breathtaking. Just occasionally Perahia communicates an 'applied' quality – a refinement which makes some of his statements sound a little too good to be true, even brittle. But this is to be pernickety. The line of his playing, appropriately vocal in style, is exquisitely moulded; and the only reservations one can have are that a hushed, 'withdrawn' tone of voice, which he is little too ready to use, can bring an air of self-consciousness to phrases where ordinary, radiant daylight would have been even more illuminating; and that here and there a robuster treatment of brilliant passages would have been in place. However, the set is entirely successful on its own terms – whether or not you want to make comparisons with other favourite recordings. Indeed, we now know that records of Mozart piano concertos don't come any better played than here.

Additional recommendations ...
...Nos. 1-27. **Salzburg Mozarteum Orchestra / Géza Anda** (pf). DG Ⓜ 429 001-2GX10 (ten discs: 670 minutes: ADD: 6/90).
...Nos. 1-27. Rondo in D major, K382 (ASD2838). **English Chamber Orchestra / Daniel Barenboim** (pf). EMI Ⓜ CZS7 62825-2 (ten discs: 661 minutes: ADD: 6/90).
...Nos. 1-27. Concertos after J.C. Bach, K107 – D major; G major; E flat major. Double Piano Concertos – K242; K365/K316*a*. Concerto in F major for Three Pianos, K242, "Lodron". Rondos – K382; A major, K386. **Alfred Brendel, Imogen Cooper, Katia** and **Marielle Labèque** (pfs); **Ingrid Haebler** (fp); **Academy of St Martin in the Fields / Sir Neville Marriner; Berlin Philharmonic Orchestra / Semyon Bychkov** (pf); **Vienna Capella Academica / Eduard Melkus; Amsterdam Baroque Orchestra / Ton Koopman** (hpd). Philips Mozart Edition Ⓜ 422 507-2PME12 (12 discs: 755 minutes: ADD/DDD: 5/91).
...No. 13 in C major, K415/K387*b*; No. 24 in C minor, K491. **London Mozart Players / Howard Shelley** (pf). Chandos Ⓜ CHAN9326 (57 minutes: DDD: 1/95).
...No. 14[a]. Serenade No. 6 in D major, K239, "Serenata notturna". Adagio and Fugue in C minor, K546. Violin Concerto No. 5 in A major, K219, "Turkish"[b]. [a]**Rudolf Serkin** (pf); **Busch Chamber Players / Adolf Busch** ([b]vn). Pearl mono Ⓜ GEMMCD9278* (69 minutes: ADD: 6/97).
...Nos. 21 and 22. **Homero Francesch** (pf); **Nice Philharmonic Orchestra / Klaus Weise.** Kontrapunkt Ⓕ 32189 (60 minutes: DDD: 2/95).
...Nos. 21 and 22. **London Mozart Players / Howard Shelley** (pf). Chandos Ⓕ CHAN9404 (63 minutes: DDD: 2/96).

...Nos. 21 and 25. **Stephen Kovacevich** (pf); **London Symphony Orchestra / Sir Colin Davis.**
Philips Concert Classics Ⓑ 426 077-2PCC (59 minutes: ADD: 2/90).
...No. 22. **Beethoven** Piano Sonata No. 5 in C minor, Op. 10 No. 1. **Till Fellner** (pf);
ªLausanne Chamber Orchestra / Uri Segal. Claves Ⓕ CD50-9328 (62 minutes: DDD: 9/94).
...Nos. 22 and 23. **Mitsuko Uchida** (pf); **English Chamber Orchestra / Jeffrey Tate.**
Philips Insignia Ⓜ 434 164-2PM (60 minutes: DDD).
...Nos. 22 and 23. **Berlin Philharmonic Orchestra / Daniel Barenboim** (pf).
Teldec Ⓕ 9031-75711-2 (63 minutes: DDD: 11/92).
...Nos. 22 and 24. **English Chamber Orchestra / Murray Perahia** (pf).
CBS Masterworks Ⓕ SK42242 (67 minutes: DDD: 8/87). ⒼⒼⒼ
...Nos. 23 and 24. **Wilhelm Kempff** (pf); **Bamberg Symphony Orchestra / Ferdinand Leitner.**
DG Galleria Ⓜ 423 885-2GGA (56 minutes: ADD: 12/88). Ⓖ
...Nos. 23 and 24. **Jenö Jandó** (pf); **Concentus Hungaricus / Mátyás Antal.**
Naxos Ⓢ 8 550204 (63 minutes: DDD: 10/90).
...Nos. 23 and 24. **Mitsuko Uchida** (pf); **English Chamber Orchestra / Jeffrey Tate.**
Philips Solo Ⓜ 442 648-2PM (58 minutes: DDD: 7/95).
...Nos. 23 and 26. Piano Sonata No. 13 in B flat major, K333/315c. **Alfred Brendel** (pf);
Academy of St Martin in the Fields / **ªᵇSir Neville Marriner.**
Philips Complete Mozart Edition Ⓜ 446 230-2PM (78 minutes: DDD/ADD: 5/91).
...No. 26. Rondos – D major, K382; A major K386. **English Chamber Orchestra / Murray Perahia**
(pf). Sony Classical Ⓕ SK39224 (DDD: 11/85).

Mozart Piano Concertos – No. 9 in E flat major, K271, "Jeunehomme"; No. 12 in A major,
K414/K385p. **Robert Levin** (fp); **Academy of Ancient Music / Christopher Hogwood.**
L'Oiseau-Lyre Ⓕ 443 328-2OH (56 minutes: DDD: 7/94). Ⓖ
As Robert Levin starts with the one concerto in which the piano enters at once, K271, you don't have
long to wait before you hear his crisp tone, precise articulation and spruce rhythms. His pianism is
athletic, alert and very neatly pointed. He makes much of the quicksilver changes of mood in the
music, emphasizing them by rhythmic means rather than stressing continuity of line. In the slow
movement of K271 he shows a keen sensitivity to the ebb and flow of tension in the music; he has,
and he conveys, a strong sense of the direction each phrase is taking, its destiny implicit from its
beginning. The articulation in the finale is delightfully clear. The cadenzas are improvised, and (in the
best sense) sound it. Levin's accompanying note argues that using new cadenzas preserves the spirit
of spontaniety, especially as we all know the old ones backwards by now; that is true, although anyone
who plays this disc repeatedly will soon know the new ones too. But the policy seems an intelligent
one, and there is indeed a sense of something fresh and exciting about the performances. In K414, too,
there is the same emphasis on characterizing the music strongly, even at the cost of rhythmic flow
from time to time. In the slow movement he draws a beautifully clear line, with his very precise
fingerwork; in the finale too the detail is carefully placed. Again, the cadenzas here follow Mozart's
design but are his own. Levin's instrument is bright-toned and exceptionally even in quality, and he
stands out sharply from the orchestra. The support offered by Christopher Hogwood and the AAM
is lively and rhythmically alert, with some nicely shaped detail and a proper touch of swagger to the
tuttis. Altogether a very impressive and enjoyable disc, with a happy air of adventure.
Additional recommendations ...
...No. 9ª. Piano Sonata No. 17 in B flat major, K570. **Beethoven** Piano Concerto No. 1 in
C major, Op. 15ª. **Walter Gieseking** (pf); ªBerlin State Opera Orchestra / Hans Rosbaud.
APR mono Ⓜ APR5511* (75 minutes: ADD).
...Nos. 9 and 21. **English Chamber Orchestra / Murray Perahia** (pf).
CBS Masterworks Ⓕ SK34562 (59 minutes: DDD: 6/87). ⒼⒼⒼ
...Nos. 9 and 17. **London Mozart Players / Howard Shelley** (pf).
Chandos Ⓕ CHAN9068 (61 minutes: DDD: 11/92).

Mozart Piano Concertos – No. 9 in E flat major, K271, "Jeunehomme"; No. 17 in G major, K453.
Cologne Concerto / Andreas Staier (fp). Teldec Das Alte Werk Ⓕ 4509-98412-2
(61 minutes: DDD: 3/96). ✍ Recorded 1995. *Gramophone* Editor's choice. Ⓖ
Andreas Staier, speaking of the use of period instruments in this outstanding recording of Mozart's
G major Concerto, K453, declares the piece has "more of the farmyard about it" that way – and he's
absolutely right. From the braying and bellowing of the mid-phrase crescendos, the snuffling and
snorting of the bassoons and the hee-hawing of the alternating loud and soft chords, Staier appears
throughout as the delighted child with a favourite picturebook. Conductorless, the string playing
in the outer movements of both this and the E flat Concerto is buoyant with daring. The impetus and
excitement of both dialogue and modulations in the slow movement of K453 is thrilling – and so is
the dialogue within the orchestral writing itself in the finale. In K271 the music-making has a bracing
immediacy as the almost percussive string playing cuts into the fortepiano's rhetoric, so imaginatively
developed in Staier's fingers.
Additional recommendations ...
...Nos. 8 and 9. **Mitsuko Uchida** (pf); **English Chamber Orchestra / Jeffrey Tate.**
Philips Ⓕ 432 086-2PH (55 minutes: DDD: 7/92).

…Nos. 9 and 17. **Berlin Philharmonic Orchestra / Daniel Barenboim** (pf).
Teldec Ⓕ 9031-73128-2 (63 minutes: DDD: 11/92).
…Nos. 9 and 27. **Jenö Jandó** (pf); **Concentus Hungaricus / András Ligeti.**
Naxos Ⓢ 8 550203 (58 minutes: DDD: 10/90).
…Nos. 17 and 18. **Jenö Jandó** (pf); **Concentus Hungaricus / Mátyás Antal.**
Naxos Ⓢ 8 550205 (57 minutes: DDD: 10/90).

Mozart Piano Concertos – No. 9 in E flat major, K271; No. 20 in D minor, K466.
Deutsche Kammerphilharmonie / Mikhail Pletnev. Virgin Classics Ⓕ VC5 45130-2
(66 minutes: DDD: 6/96). Recorded 1995.
Pletnev's K271 raises no alarms, though he certainly enjoys the piano's early entry into some high-stepping *staccato* which draws a *marcato* string riposte. There's a degree of audacity, too, in the interplay of one hand with another, and both with the woodwind soloists in the development. The strings of the Deutsche Kammerphilharmonie play with restrained vibrato which makes the slow movement even darker, more austere; and Pletnev's probing rubato makes it more of a debate than an aria. The finale is a true *Presto*, made lucid by the rigour of its rhythmic definition, and constantly unpredictable in Pletnev's pacing of its cadenzas and of the perverse little minuet. The K466 is not too quick off the mark to deprive the snarling upbeats of their full fury, the syncopations from tugging hard, and the descending chords from digging deep. The deliberation of Pletnev's own playing can verge on the ponderous (especially when the recorded sound is on the constricted side); but then this is a deeply pondered performance of real *gravitas*, using Beethoven's cadenzas and making a weighty argument out of the *Rondo* right until its final return.
Additional recommendation ...
…Nos. 9, 15, 22, 25 and 27. **Alfred Brendel** (pf); **Academy of St Martin in the Fields /
Sir Neville Marriner.** Philips Duo Ⓜ 442 571-2PM2 (two discs: 155 minutes: 4/95).

Mozart Piano Concertos – No. 11 in F major, K413/K387*a*; No. 13 in C major, K415/K387*b*.
Rondo in A major, K386. **Robert Levin** (fp); **Academy of Ancient Music / Christopher Hogwood.**
L'Oiseau-Lyre Ⓕ 444 571-2OH (57 minutes: DDD: 9/95). ✔ Recorded 1994.
The first impression, at the beginning of the F major Concerto, is of a performance very much in chamber-music style: a neat, compact body of strings, playing attentively in crisp and springy rhythms, with the faint clang of the fortepiano continuo in the background adding sharpness and definition. Robert Levin performs this concerto, one of the less familiar among Mozart's, most beautifully and unassumingly. He draws very precise articulation and sweet tone from the instrument; there is a delightful sense of the brilliance arising naturally and spontaneously rather than as self-conscious virtuosity. Although chamber musical in approach, the performance has its moments of drama too, with hints of the opera house in its characterization and its surprises. Mozart wrote cadenzas for these concertos, but Levin, true to the practice of the time, improvises his own. The music of K415 is thematically less interesting than the other two in the set and possibly the ideas cannot quite support the larger canvas on which Mozart was evidently trying to work. Some of the bravura material seems just a shade empty. Still, this is a very sympathetic reading, with a really splendid improvised cadenza, and again there is some lovely melodic shaping in the slow movement. Mozart used material from his original slow movement draft within the finale, and these sections are handled here with considerable drama. Levin, of course, adds a certain amount of decoration to the lines throughout both concertos, especially in repeated material, and does so with impeccable taste and style and at exactly the points where it seems to be needed. The lone *Rondo*, K386, a charming piece, completes this distinguished disc.

Mozart Piano Concertos – No. 12 in A major, K414/K385*p*; No. 19 in F major, K459.
London Mozart Players / Howard Shelley (pf). Chandos Ⓕ CHAN9256 (52 minutes: DDD: 6/94).
Recorded 1993.
These are clear and stylish readings. The playing of both the Shelley and the London Mozart Players is assured, relaxed and unfailingly enjoyable, allowing the music to unfold very naturally. Shelley demonstrates his fine judgement of tempo, and textures are also well served; the recording gives quite a bold sound to his modern piano, but its overall immediacy and warmth are not excessive and the balance is just right. Phrasing is another area deserving praise: Shelley and his expert team manage to shape the music gracefully without falling into the slightly mannered delivery which can affect other artists in this repertory. Finally, cadenzas have the right balance of freedom and formality. Perhaps the two 'slow' movements here – the quotes are because that of K414 is an *Andante* and K459's is an *Allegretto* – are richer in style than will suit some tastes: they do not sound authentic in period-performance terms, but then this is another kind of performance and perfectly convincing. The recordings are of the high quality we have come to expect from the Chandos team.
Additional recommendations ...
…Nos. 19[a] and 27[b]. Piano Sonata No. 2 in F major, K280/K189*e*. **Clara Haskil** (pf);
[a]**Berlin Philharmonic Orchestra;** [b]**Bavarian State Orchestra / Ferenc Fricsay.**
DG The Originals Ⓜ 449 722-2GOR* (70 minutes: ADD/mono).
…Nos. 19 and 23. **Maurizio Pollini** (pf); **Vienna Philharmonic Orchestra / Karl Böhm.**
DG Ⓕ 413 793-2GH (ADD: 1/86).

...Nos. 12 and 14. **Louis Lortie** (pf); **I Musici de Monteal / Yuli Turovsky.**
Chandos Ⓕ CHAN8455 (48 minutes: DDD: 1/87).
...Nos. 12 and 15. **Mozartian Players / Steven Lubin** (fp).
Arabesque Ⓕ Z6552 (48 minutes: DDD: 3/87). ✒
...Nos. 19 and 27. **András Schiff** (pf); **Salzburg Mozarteum Camerata Academica / Sándor Végh.**
Decca Ⓕ 421 259-2DH (59 minutes: DDD: 3/89).
...Nos. 19 and 26. **Salzburg Mozarteum Camerata Academica / Géza Anda** (pf).
DG Privilege/Panorama Classics Ⓑ 427 209-2GR (57 minutes: ADD: 6/90).
...Nos. 19-21 and 24. Rondos – D major, K382; A major K386 (ed E. Smith & A. Brendel).
Alfred Brendel (pf); **Academy of St Martin in the Fields / Sir Neville Marriner.**
Philips Duo Ⓜ 442 269-2PM2 (two discs: 159 minutes: DDD: 10/94).
...Nos. 14, 15, 19, 21, 26 and 27. Double Piano Concerto in E flat major, K365 (with Imogen
Cooper, pf). Piano Sonatas – No. 8 in A minor, K310; No. 11 in A major, K331; No. 13 in B flat
major, K333; No. 14 in C minor, K457. Fantasia in C minor, K475. Rondo in A minor, K511.
Adagio in B minor, K540. *Coupled with works by* **Haydn** Alfred Brendel (pf);
Academy of St Martin in the Fields / Sir Neville Marriner.
Philips Ⓜ 446 921-2PM5 (five discs: 369 minutes: ADD/DDD: 2/96).
...Nos. 19 and 22. **Handel** Keyboard Suite No. 5 in E major, HWV430.
Alicia de Larrocha (pf); [a]**Vienna Symphony Orchestra / Uri Segal.**
Decca Eclipse Ⓜ 448 992-2DEC (77 minutes: DDD: 3/97).

Mozart Piano Concertos – No. 15 in B flat major, K450; No. 16 in D major, K451.
English Chamber Orchestra / Murray Perahia (pf). Sony Classical Ⓕ SK37824
(50 minutes: DDD). *Gramophone Award Winner 1984.* ⒼⒼⒼ
This is an interpretation of the highest calibre: Perahia's delicious shaping of even the longest and
most elaborate phrases, his unfailingly clear and arresting articulation, and his delicacy and
refinement of tone are without parallel. Perahia's attention is, moreover, by no means restricted to the
solo parts: even the tiniest details of the orchestral writing are subtly characterized, and the piano and
orchestra take on the character of a dialogue – sometimes poignant, often witty or sparklingly
humorous. The two works are admirably contrasted: the Fifteenth on the whole light and high-
spirited, while the first movement of the Sixteenth is almost Beethovenian in its grandeur and
purposefulness, and both concertos have typically beautiful slow movements. Recordings are superb:
an overly attentive microphone could have done irreparable damage to Perahia's legato, but here the
distance is expertly judged and the soloist/orchestra balance is exemplary.

Mozart Piano Concertos – No. 15 in B flat major, K450; No. 26 in D major, K537, "Coronation".
Robert Levin (fp); **Academy of Ancient Music / Christopher Hogwood.**
L'Oiseau-Lyre Ⓕ 455 814-2OH (62 minutes: DDD: 1/98). ✒ Recorded 1997.
Gramophone Editor's choice. Selected by Soundings. ⒼⒼ
This disc is particularly interesting for several reasons. Firstly, the fortepiano employed (unsigned)
belonged to Mozart himself. Secondly, an earlier version of K450's *Andante* – whose existence is not
even mentioned by Köchel, Einstein, Hutchings or *Grove* – with significant differences in the shape of
the theme, is included besides the usual one. Thirdly, Robert Levin – by playing along in tuttis,
improvising cadenzas, lead-ins and liberal embellishments, providing new left-hand parts for K537
and adopting some of Mozart's original, more difficult readings in K450 – has boldly opted for
performances with an element of spontaneity and non-familiarity such as Mozart's own audiences
would have experienced. The results are delightfully fresh and vital. The wind are excellent, the finale
of K450 is splendidly light-footed; but in K537 Hogwood might have heeded Richard Strauss's advice
not to look encouragingly at the trumpets, who in the first movement are somewhat overenthusiastic.
The biggest surprise comes in the slow movement of K537, where Levin often offers a free, but stylish
paraphrase of the solo part. There is an A just below middle C on this fortepiano that gives off a
curious tinkle whenever it is struck, and in the initial *Allegro* of K537 this can be a bit obtrusive; but
it's not enough to put you off a thoroughly illuminating performance.

Mozart Piano Concertos – No. 17 in G major, K453[a]; No. 21 in C major, K467.
Maria-João Pires (pf); **Chamber Orchestra of Europe / Claudio Abbado.** DG Ⓕ 439 941-2GH
(58 minutes: DDD: 2/96). Recorded [a]live in 1993. *Gramophone Editor's choice.*
It is clear from the opening of the G major Concerto that Claudio Abbado and the Chamber
Orchestra of Europe were on good form at this concert in Italy. It springs along, yet unhastily, and
the orchestral sound, while full-bodied, has none of the heaviness that detracts from good Mozartian
style. Playing what sounds like a modern piano of unusual tonal crispness, Maria-João Pires also
satisfies, with shapely phrasing and lovely sonorities, and this whole first movement proceeds with
both a keen sense of purpose and unmannered grace, the exchanges of the development section being
delightfully done. The cadenza here is Mozart's own and, of course, a model of what cadenzas in his
concertos should be but often are not, in other words suiting the music and not overlong. After these
unalloyed pleasures, the touching *Andante* is no less satisfying, elegantly sculptured and with
marvellous woodwind playing. The playful, variation-form finale is again perfectly judged, and indeed
the performance of the whole concerto offers truly outstanding Mozart playing, among the best on

disc and unquestionably in the Perahia class. The recording is worthy of it: beautifully balanced and clear for one taken live while also being refreshingly free of audience noise and applause. The C major Concerto is also excellent, the first movement strong yet not pompous, with all concerned thankfully never forgetting that this is Mozart and not Beethoven. The famous 'Elvira Madigan' slow movement is not at all romanticized but admirably poised, and the finale springs along.

Additional recommendation ...

...Nos. 21[a] and 26[b]. 12 Variations in C major on "Ah, vous dirai-je, Maman", K265/K300e[c].

   [ab]**Robert Casadesus** (pf); [c]**André Previn** (pf); [a]**Cleveland Orchestra**; [b]**Columbia Symphony Orchestra / George Szell**. Sony Classical Essential Classics ⑧ SBK67178 (66 minutes: ADD: 5/96).

Mozart Piano Concertos – No. 17 in G major, K453; No. 20 in D minor, K466. **Robert Levin** (fp); **Academy of Ancient Music / Christopher Hogwood**. L'Oiseau-Lyre ⑨ 455 607-2OH (61 minutes: DDD: 9/97). ✍ Recorded 1996.

The performance of the D minor Concerto is a major achievement, one of those recordings that has about it a sense of occasion, a feeling that the artists are creating the music afresh. Well, so they are, to a rather greater extent than usual: Robert Levin improvises the cadenzas and quite a lot else besides. The first-movement cadenza here is a particular triumph. Hogwood and Levin take quite a measured tempo for this movement, and it works very well, giving Levin just the space he needs to shape the music pointedly and with meaning. Here and there he does vary the text more than one might expect. Of course, that is well within his rights, historically speaking, and he never transgresses the boundaries of good taste but at times one might feel there is a little too much ornamentation. In the *Romance*, there are one or two moments where the elaboration of the main theme seems restless, though others, for example the final statement, with a witty touch anticipating Mozart's own variation in the orchestra, are entirely persuasive. In the lighter G major Concerto Levin is truly on sparkling form, playing the outer movements gracefully and wittily – the finale is especially fine, with the basic speed maintained, to brilliant effect. There is some attractive varying of repeats, which is surely what the music asks for. There is elaboration here too, occasional in the first movement, more generous in the *Andante*. The central issue, however, is that these are very fine performances, with much sensitive and delicate playing from Levin, with admirable support from Hogwood and the AAM musicians; and the balance between piano and orchestra seems particularly happily managed with the glittering fortepiano sound coming clearly through the textures but so translucent as to allow the woodwind details to be heard very sharply too.

Mozart Piano Concertos – No. 18 in B flat major, K456; No. 19 in F major, K459. **Robert Levin** (fp); **Academy of Ancient Music / Christopher Hogwood**. L'Oiseau-Lyre ⑨ ① 452 051-2OH (59 minutes: DDD: 11/96). ✍ Recorded 1995.

These are thoughtful and strongly characterized performances which make much of the individuality of the works. K456 is taken at rather steady tempos, with soft and sustained textures and gentle colours, and Levin plays it with rare tenderness and delicacy – there are many sensitive touches of timing in the first movement and less of self-conscious brilliance or assertiveness than the music might permit. This rather inward view is very compelling, and it harmonizes happily with the view he and Hogwood take of the slow movement, a G minor set of variations, which on modern instruments is apt to sound decoratively pathetic but not deeply felt, which it certainly does here. There is a good deal of intensity, and of darker colouring: partly the result of the superior blend of sound resulting from the use of the fortepiano. And some of the solo woodwind playing is of a very high order. Then the finale is taken at quite a measured tempo, not at all as a jolly hunting piece, giving Levin opportunities (which he eagerly takes) to shape and shade individual phrases effectively. Levin improvises the cadenzas, although sets by Mozart survive for both concertos: his argument that a cadenza should have an element of the unexpected is a strong one. The F major, K459 is a lighter work, in a sense; its airy orchestral textures are quite unlike those of the other concertos, especially K456. This is a lively, almost jaunty performance, but in no way superficial; there are countless delectable touches in Levin's playing as well as lightness and elegance, and the effect is very appealing. Similarly, the slow movement, here an *Allegretto*, is quite relaxed, and there is some lovely woodwind playing, counterpointing gracefully with the piano, all exquisitely audible in this aurally translucent recording; at the end you are left under no illusions about the seriousness and stature of the music.

Mozart Piano Concertos – No. 18 in B flat major, K456; No. 20 in D minor, K466. **Richard Goode** (pf); **Orpheus Chamber Orchestra**. Nonesuch ⑨ 7559-79439-2 (58 minutes: DDD: 4/97). Recorded 1996. *Gramophone Editor's record of the month. Selected by Soundings.*   ⑤⑤⑤

With a first-rate balance and quality of sound, here is a Mozart concerto record to transcend considerations of style and stance. The excellence of Richard Goode's playing is not surprising, but the quality of his collaboration with the Orpheus Chamber Orchestra is special: and the beautiful thing about Mozart performance of this calibre is that the two seem inseparable. Of course the freshness and placing of the detail are to be savoured, but it is the long view which holds and persuades. In the D minor Concerto's first movement the brilliant piano writing is so thrilling here because it's projected as being essential to the expression, not just a decoration of it. Goode is particularly impressive in the way he handles the three successive solo statements at the start of the development without slackening pace. They are subtly different in feeling, one from the other, and although he's not the first player to have noticed this, it's characteristic of his distinction to have kept the detail and the overview in balance. He plays his own cadenza in the finale, in place of Beethoven's. He has some good ideas about dynamics in this last movement, and the lightening of mood at the turn to the major key towards the end has rarely sounded such an inspiration – on Mozart's part, of course. The B flat Concerto, K456, is equally enjoyable. The outer movements are brisk and light on their feet, even balletic, but all the colours – and the shadows which pass over the face of the music – are there, just as one wants. Paciness makes for vivacity but never brittleness. At the end, you feel you have had glorious entertainment, and a discourse that has touched on the deepest things. You may well be slightly puzzled as to how Goode achieves so much while appearing to do so little – perhaps it's a question of being so focused, of keeping his eye on the ball! In this the orchestra match him, as they also match his spontaneity and relish for the task.

Mozart Piano Concertos. **English Chamber Orchestra / Murray Perahia** (pf).
CBS Masterworks Ⓕ SK42241 and SK42243 (two discs, oas: 63 and 70 minutes: ADD/DDD: 9/87). Items marked [a] from 76651 (4/78), [b] 76731 (5/80), [c] 76481 (5/76).
SK42241 – No. 20 in D minor, K466[a]; No. 27 in B flat major, K595[b]. *SK42243* – No. 11 in F major, K413[a]; No. 12 in A major, K414/K385p[b]; No. 14 in E flat major, K449[c].   ⒼⒼⒼ
These discs happily epitomize some of the best qualities of the complete Perahia/ECO set. Always intelligent, always sensitive to both the overt and less obvious nuances of this music, Perahia is firstly a true pianist, never forcing the instrument beyond its limits in order to express the ideas, always maintaining a well-projected singing touch. The superb ECO reflect his integrity and empathy without having to follow slavishly every detail of his articulation or phrasing. K414 and K413 are charming and typically novel for their time, but do not break new ground in quite the way that K449 does. Here, Mozart's success in the theatre may have suggested a more dramatic presentation and working of ideas for this instrumental genre. K595 is a work pervaded by a serenity of acceptance that underlies its wistfulness. Mozart had less than a year to live, and the mounting depression of his life had already worn him down, yet there is still a sort of quiet joy in this music. The vast range of styles, emotions, and forms that these few works encompass are evocatively celebrated in these performances, and admirably captured in civilized recordings.

Additional recommendations ...
...Nos. 12 and 20. Rondo in D major, K382. **Evgeni Kissin** (pf); **Moscow Virtuosi / Vladimir Spivakov.** RCA Victor Red Seal Ⓕ 09026 60400-2 (67 minutes: DDD: 2/93).
...Nos. 13 and 20. **Jenö Jandó** (pf); **Concentus Hungaricus / András Ligeti.**
Naxos Ⓢ 8 550201 (56 minutes: DDD: 10/90).
...Nos. 12, 14 and 21. **Jenö Jandó** (pf); **Concentus Hungaricus / András Ligeti.**
Naxos Ⓢ 8 550202 (71 minutes: DDD: 10/90).
...Nos. 14 and 27. **London Mozart Players / Howard Shelley** (pf).
Chandos Ⓕ CHAN9137 (55 minutes: DDD: 6/93).
...Nos. 14-16. **English Chamber Orchestra / Daniel Barenboim** (pf).
EMI Studio Ⓜ CDM7 69124-2 (74 minutes: ADD: 12/88).
...Nos. 20, 21, 23 and 27. Piano Sonata No. 18 in D major, K576. Rondo in A minor, K511.
Philharmonia Orchestra / Vladimir Ashkenazy (pf).
Double Decca Ⓜ 436 383-2DF2 (two discs: 149 minutes: ADD).   Ⓖ
...Nos. 20 and 21. **Mitsuko Uchida** (pf); **English Chamber Orchestra / Jeffrey Tate.**
Philips Ⓕ 416 381-2PH (62 minutes: DDD: 7/86).
...Nos. 20 and 25. **Alicia de Larrocha** (pf); **English Chamber Orchestra / Sir Colin Davis.**
RCA Victor Red Seal Ⓕ 09026 68399-2 (62 minutes: DDD: 12/96).
...Nos. 20 and 27. **Sir Clifford Curzon** (pf); **English Chamber Orchestra / Benjamin Britten.**
Decca Ⓕ 417 288-2DH (65 minutes: ADD: 10/86).
...Nos. 20 and 21. **Berlin Philharmonic Orchestra / Daniel Barenboim** (pf).
Teldec Ⓕ 9031-75710-2 (61 minutes: DDD: 11/92).
...Nos. 26 and 27. **Mitsuko Uchida** (pf); **English Chamber Orchestra / Jeffrey Tate.**
Philips Ⓕ 420 951-2PH (65 minutes: DDD: 11/88).
...No. 27. Double Piano Concerto in E flat major, K365/K316a[a]. **Emil Gilels, [a]Elena Gilels** (pfs);
Vienna Philharmonic Orchestra / Karl Böhm.
DG Galleria Ⓜ 419 059-2GGA (59 minutes: ADD: 1/87).   Ⓖ
...Nos. 19[a] and 27[b]. Piano Sonata No. 2 in F major, K280/K189e[c]. **Clara Haskil** (pf);
[a]**Berlin Philharmonic Orchestra / [b]Bavarian State Orchestra / Ferenc Fricsay.**
DG The Originals [ab]mono/[c]stereo Ⓜ 449 722-2GOR* (70 minutes: ADD: 12/97).
...No. 27. *Coupled with works by various composers.* **Chamber Orchestra of Europe / Murray Perahia** (pf). Sony Classical Ⓜ SX4K63380 (four discs: 270 minutes: DDD/ADD: 4/98).
See review in the Collections section; refer to the Index.

Mozart Piano Concerto No. 20 in D minor, K466[a]. Symphony No. 38 in D major, K504, "Prague"[b]. Serenade No. 13 in G major, K525, "Eine kleine Nachtmusik"[c]. Three German Dances, K605[d]. **Vienna Philharmonic Orchestra / Bruno Walter** ([a]pf). Pearl mono Ⓜ GEMMCD9940* (72 minutes: AAD: 3/94). Item marked [a] from HMV DB3273/6 (10/38), [b]DB3112/14, [c]DB3075/6, [d]HMV DA1570, 9/37).

Bruno Walter was an accomplished pianist, and his solo work in Mozart's D minor Concerto is full of personality. The first movement cadenza by Reinecke is boring, but otherwise there's much to enjoy in this romantic and subjective interpretation. The VPO plays beautifully both here and in the other Mozart works. The *Prague* Symphony has lots of muscle as well as grace and elegance. If a romantic approach to *Eine kleine Nachtmusik* is sought by the listener then Walter's affectionate interpretations will surely give great pleasure, and the little *German Dances* are charmingly played. Pearl have used commercial pressings for their issue, and a certain amount of surface noise is present. Colin Attwell has reproduced the original sound-quality very faithfully and straightforwardly, and his transfers are much kinder to the ears than most others from this period.

Additional recommendation ...
...Eine kleine Nachtmusik. *Coupled with works by various composers.* **Louis Zimmerman, Ferdinand Hellmann** (vns); **Concertgebouw Orchestra / Willem Mengelberg.**
Pearl mono Ⓜ GEMMCD9154* (76 minutes: ADD: 3/96).

Mozart Violin Concertos[b] – No. 1 in B flat major, K207; No. 2 in D major, K211; No. 3 in G major, K216; No. 4 in D major, K218 (all from 6706 011-1/4, 10/70); No. 5 in A major, K219; D major, K271*a*/K271*i* (both from SAL3588, 2/67). Rondos[b] – B flat major, K269/K261*a*; C major, K373 (6707 011-1/4). Concertone in C major, K190/K186*E* (6707 011-1/4)[abce]. Adagio in E major, K261 (6500 036, 1/72)[b]. Sinfonia concertante in E flat major, K364/K320*d*[dlh]. Piano and Violin Concerto in D major, KAnh56/K315*f*[gh]. Sinfonia concertante in A major, KAnh104/K320*e*[dfh] (all new to UK). [a]**Richard Morgan** (ob); [b]**Henryk Szeryng,** [c]**Gérard Poulet** (vns); [d]**Nobuko Imai** (va); [e]**Norman Jones,** [f]**Stephen Orton** (vcs); [g]**Howard Shelley** (pf); [b]**New Philharmonia / Sir Alexander Gibson;** [h]**Academy of St Martin in the Fields / Iona Brown** (vn). Philips Mozart Edition Ⓜ 422 508-2PME4 (four discs: 265 minutes: ADD/DDD: 6/91). Recorded 1966-70.   ⓖⓖ

Leaving aside works of doubtful authenticity, there are five Mozart violin concertos. They belong to his late teenage years in Salzburg and were composed in 1775. They have been somewhat overshadowed by the piano concertos which, of course, are not only five times as numerous but also span the composer's whole career and include many mature masterpieces. While this is understandable, it would be a pity to miss out on these violin concertos which are surprisingly refreshing, youthful works of great charm. They agreeably reflect their creator's love and understanding of an instrument which he himself played more than capably. It is believed that his father Leopold, who was an authority on violin playing as well as a performer, may have encouraged him to compose them and then play them himself. The concertos have much in common with Mozart's cassations, divertimentos and serenades, which also highlight the solo violin and have other concerto-like elements in them. But their lightweight means of expression in no way diminishes their long-term appeal, for Mozart filled them to the brim with wonderful ideas. Henryk Szeryng has a relaxed way with these works and the orchestral contribution from the New Philharmonia under Sir Alexander Gibson is alert yet sensitive. Szeryng's tone is unfailingly beautiful with a sweetness that is greatly appealing. His evident affection for these works makes for pleasing listening and the vivid and witty 'Turkish' episode in the finale of No. 5 has great spirit. This disc also includes the 'doubtful' but agreeable solo Concerto in D major, K271*a*, together with a rather laid-back account of the *Sinfonia concertante* with Iona Brown and Nobuko Imai as the soloists (beautifully matched and well blended). In addition we have the reconstructions of the incomplete projected Concerto for piano and violin and the single-movement *Sinfonia concertante* in A major for string trio and orchestra. The recordings are satisfying.

Additional recommendations ...
...Sinfonia concertante, K364/K320*d*. Concertone, K190/K186*E*. **Itzhak Perlman** (vn); **Pinchas Zukerman** (va/vn); **Chaim Jouval** (ob); **Marcel Bergman** (vc); **Israel Philharmonic Orchestra / Zubin Mehta.** DG Ⓕ 415 486-2GH (60 minutes: DDD: 12/85).
...Nos. 3 and 5. Adagio, K261. **Cho-Liang Lin** (vn); **English Chamber Orchestra / Raymond Leppard.** CBS Masterworks Ⓕ SK42364 (62 minutes: DDD: 12/87). *Selected by Sounds in Retrospect.*
...Nos. 3-5. **Christian Altenburger** (vn); **German Bach Soloists / Helmut Winscherman.** LaserLight Ⓑ 15 525 (75 minutes: DDD: 5/90).
...Sinfonias concertante – K364/K320*d*; E flat major, KAnh9/C14.01/K297*b*[a]. **Todd Phillips** (vn); **Maureen Gallagher** (va); [a]**Stephen Taylor** (ob); [a]**David Singer** (cl); [a]**Steven Dibner** (bn); [a]**William Purvis** (hn); **Orpheus Chamber Orchestra.** DG Ⓕ 429 784-2GH (63 minutes: DDD: 4/91).
...Nos. 1-5[a]. Rondo, K373[b]. Adagio, K261[b]. Sinfonia concertante, K364/K320*d*[c]. **Arthur Grumiaux** (vn). [c]**Arrigo Pelliccia** (va); [a]**London Symphony Orchestra / Sir Colin Davis;** [b]**New Philharmonia Orchestra / Raymond Leppard.** Philips Duo Ⓜ 438 323-2PM2 (two discs: 153 minutes: ADD: 9/93).
...Nos. 3 and 5. Sinfonia concertante, K364/K320*d*[a]. **Stephanie Chase** (vn); [a]**Roger Chase** (va); **Hanover Band / Roy Goodman.** Cala Ⓜ CACD1014 (two discs: 82 minutes: DDD: 12/93). ✏
...Sinfonia concertante, K364/K320*d*. *Coupled with works by various composers.* **Albert Spalding** (vn); **William Primrose** (va); **New Friends of Music Orchestra / Fritz Stiedry.** Biddulph mono Ⓜ LAB088* (58 minutes: ADD: 9/94).
...No. 5. *Coupled with works by* **Mendelssohn** *and* **Vieuxtemps** **Jascha Heifetz** (vn); **London Philharmonic Orchestra / Sir John Barbirolli.** EMI Références mono Ⓜ CDH5 65191-2* (69 minutes: ADD: 10/94).

...Nos. 1-5. Sinfonia concertante, K364/K320*d*[a]. [a]**Rudolf Barshai** (va); **Bath Festival Orchestra /**
Yehudi Menuhin (vn). EMI Seraphim Ⓢ CES5 68530-2 (two discs: 172 minutes: ADD: 1/96).
...Nos. 1-5. Adagio, K261. Rondos – K269/K261*a*; K373. **Frank-Peter Zimmermann** (vn);
Württemberg Chamber Orchestra / Jörg Faerber.
EMI Forte Ⓜ CZS5 69355-2 (two discs: 116 minutes: ADD: 2/97).
...Nos. 1-5. Rondo – K269/K261*a*; K373. Adagio, K261. **Simon Standage** (vn);
Academy of Ancient Music / Christopher Hogwood.
L'Oiseau-Lyre Double Decca Ⓜ 455 721-2OF2 (two discs: 128 minutes: DDD: 3/98).

Mozart Violin Concertos – No. 1 in B flat major, K207; No. 2 in D major, K211; No. 5 in A major,
K219. **Orchestra of the Age of Enlightenment / Monica Huggett** (vn). Virgin Classics Veritas
Ⓕ VC5 45010-2 (77 minutes: DDD: 9/94). ☞ Recorded 1991.
These fresh, appealing performances stand up well in an awesomely crowded field. With her gut-
strung Amati, Monica Huggett does not, of course, rival modern-instrument virtuosos like
Grumiaux, Szeryng and Perlman in brilliance and dynamic range. But these concertos gain much
from her sweet, slender tone, her light, buoyant articulation and her beautiful control of colour in
piano dynamics. The passagework in the opening movements of the first two concertos can often seem
tedious in high-powered traditional performances; but the lighter period bow and Huggett's deft
touches of timing and shading invariably lend wit and point to Mozart's sequences of triplets and
semiquavers. The finales of both these concertos are delightfully lithe and airy, while the closing
minuet of No. 5 is unusually delicate – though there is plenty of gusto in the A minor 'Turkish'
episode (from 3'59"). In the three slow movements other performances may be more overtly
expressive, freer with rubato; but Huggett's purity and poise, her subtle graduations of vibrato and
her gentle eloquence of phrase are very persuasive. These performances share with the rival period
readings from Simon Standage a keen feeling for the music's dance rhythms and a sure sense of style
in cadenzas (aptly brief) and ornamentation. The orchestral contribution in both versions, too, is
crisp, transparent and nicely detailed. Standage is generally the more assertive player, brighter of tone,
sharper of attack but lacking Huggett's tenderness and imagination. Huggett, too, has the edge in
purity of intonation. Clear, warm sound, naturally balanced.
Additional recommendation ...
...Nos. 1-5. Adagio, K261. Rondos – K269/K261*a*; K373. **Simon Standage** (vn);
Academy of Ancient Music / Christopher Hogwood.
L'Oiseau-Lyre Ⓕ 433 045-2OH2 (two discs: 128 minutes: DDD: 4/92). ☞

Mozart Violin Concerto No. 3 in G major, K216.
Brahms Violin Concerto in D major, Op. 77[a]. **Frank Peter Zimmermann** (vn); **Berlin Philharmonic**
Orchestra / Wolfgang Sawallisch. EMI Ⓕ CDC5 55426-2 (60 minutes: DDD: 5/96).
Item marked [a] recorded live in 1995.
With the string complement of the Berlin Philharmonic reduced, and Sawallisch at his most
sparkling, the Mozart is a delight throughout, with a quicksilver lightness in the outer movements
very different from the big bow-wow approach that virtuoso violinists used to adopt. More than in
the Brahms Zimmermann finds a vein of fantasy, and in the central *Adagio* he plays with a repose and
concentration markedly greater than in his live account of the Brahms slow movement. Curiously, it
is not until the finale of the Brahms, where Zimmermann seems to acquire an extra degree of daring,
that the advantages of live recording come home at all clearly. Till then, his performance seems just a
little too well mannered, with his silvery tone pointing a lack of bravura, however brilliant the playing
is technically. Yet in the finale not only does the performance take wing, but Zimmermann becomes
more individual, less plain in his manners, as in the little commas of expression he inserts each time
in the main Hungarian dance theme.

Mozart Serenade No. 3 in D major, K185/K167*a*[a]. March in D major, K189/K167*b*.
Five Contredanses, K609. Notturno in D major, K286/K269*a*. [a]**Arvid Engegard** (vn);
Salzburg Mozarteum Camerata Academica / Sándor Végh. Capriccio Ⓕ 10 302
(66 minutes: DDD: 10/91). Recorded 1988-89.
The main work here is the big *Serenade*, K185, commissioned by the Antretter family of Salzburg and
first performed in August 1773 to celebrate the end of the university year. Like other works of its kind
it incorporates a miniature two-movement violin concerto within a loose symphonic framework: an
Andante designed to display the instrument's powers of cantilena, and a brisk *contredanse* with plenty
of opportunities for ear-catching virtuosity. There is also a violin solo in the glum D minor trio of the
second minuet. But perhaps the finest movements are the sensuous A major *Andante grazioso*, with
its *concertante* writing for flutes and horns, and the rollicking 6/8 finale, preceded by an unexpectedly
searching *Adagio* introduction. The performance by Végh and his hand-picked Salzburg players is
affectionate, rhythmically alive and beautifully balanced, with an imaginative, subtly coloured solo
violin contribution from Arvid Engegard. The tempo and specific character of each movement is
shrewdly judged: the two minuets, for example, are vividly differentiated, the first properly
swaggering, with a nice lilt in the trio, the second spruce and quick-witted. Only in the finale is Végh
arguably too leisurely, though here too the style and rhythmic lift of the playing are infectious. Végh
follows the serenade with deft, colourful readings of five contredanses from Mozart's last year and a

beguiling performance of the *Notturno* for four orchestras, exquisitely imagined open-air music, with its multiple echoes fading into the summer night. All in all a delectable disc, offering a varied concert of Mozart's lighter music performed with exceptional flair and finesse. The recording, too, is outstandingly vivid, with the spatial effects in the *Notturno* beautifully managed.

Mozart Serenade No. 10 in B flat major, K361/K370, "Gran Partita"[a]. **Berlin Philharmonic Orchestra Wind Ensemble / Zubin Mehta.** Sony Classical Ⓕ SK58950 (50 minutes: DDD: 9/95). Recorded 1993.

A big work, this, written for the kind of wind ensemble that became popular during the 1780s at the Austrian imperial court and its aristocratic imitators. In fact, the usual combination was of pairs of oboes, clarinets, horns and bassoons, but here Mozart adds two more horns, a pair of bassett horns and a double-bass; the effect is thus even more massive, although his mastery of texture is such that it never feels overblown and a contemporary described this piece as "herrlich und gross, trefflich und her", which the insert-note here translates as "glorious and grand, excellent and sublime". Since the 13 players here are of the highest quality and Mehta is a sympathetic conductor, everything unfolds impressively, and there is a sense of joy in the music-making, the playing natural, easy without slickness and expressive (sometimes even passionate) without mannerism. To experience the blend of weight and grace that the music and performance offer, listen to the first Minuet, the second of the five movements. The tempo is just right and the shaping of phrases (not least in the delicately scored first trio and the bouncy second one) elegant. Altogether, this is playing of distinction. As for the sound of the *Adagio* which follows, the music which awed Salieri in Shaffer's play *Amadeus*, this is no less poised. Indeed, here is an excellent performance that is complemented by a clear and atmospheric recording made in the Berlin Philharmonie. Strongly recommended and earning first place among current versions.

Additional recommendations ...

...Nos. 6, 12 and 13. **Orpheus Chamber Orchestra.**
DG Galleria Ⓜ 439 524-2GGA (54 minutes: DDD: 12/86).
...No. 10. **Chamber Orchestra of Europe Wind Soloists / Alexander Schneider.**
ASV Ⓕ CDCOE804 (52 minutes: DDD: 4/87).
...No. 10. **Academy of St Martin in the Fields Wind Ensemble / Sir Neville Marriner.**
Philips Ⓕ 412 726-2PH (49 minutes: DDD: 5/87).
...Nos. 10 and 11. Adagio in F major, K410/K484*d*[a]. [a]**Holliger Wind Ensemble;**
Academy of St Martin in the Fields / Sir Neville Marriner.
Philips Complete Mozart Edition Ⓜ 446 227-2PM (76 minutes: DDD: 5/87).
...Complete Edition, Volume 3 – Serenades, Marches and Cassations for Orchestra. Serenades:
No. 3 in D major, K185/K167*a*; No. 4 in D major, K203/K189*b*; No. 5 in D major, K204/K231*a*;
No. 6 in D major, K239, "Serenata notturna"; No. 7 in D major, K250/K248*b*, "Haffner"; No. 9 in D major, K320, "Posthorn"; No. 13 in G major, K525, "Eine kleine Nachtmusik". Marches:
D major, K62; D major, K189/K167*b*; D major, K215/K213*b*; D major, K237/K189*c*; K249;
D major, K335/K320*a* No. 1; D major, K335/K320*a* No. 2. Cassations: G major, K63; B flat major, K99/K63*a*; D major, K100/K62*a*. Divertimento in D major, K131. Notturno in D major, K286/K269*a*. Galimathias musicum, K32.
Soloists; Academy of St Martin in the Fields / Sir Neville Marriner.
Philips Mozart Edition Ⓜ 422 503-2PME7 (seven discs: 404 minutes: DDD: 12/90).
...No. 10. **St Luke's Orchestra / Sir Charles Mackerras.** Telarc Ⓕ CD80359 (51 minutes: DDD: 8/94).
...Nos. 10 and 12. **Budapest Wind Ensemble / Zoltán Kocsis.**
Harmonia Mundi Musique d'abord Ⓑ HMA190 3051 (69 minutes: DDD: 8/94).
...No. 10. Divertimento No. 12 in E flat major, K252/K240*a*. **Linos Ensemble.**
Capriccio Ⓕ 10 472 (60 minutes: DDD: 7/95).
...No. 9 in D major, K320, "Posthorn". Two Marches, K335/K320*a*. Idomeneo – Ballet Music, K367. **Academy of Ancient Music / Christopher Hogwood.**
L'Oiseau-Lyre Ⓕ 452 604-2OH (76 minutes: DDD: 3/97). ✍

Mozart Serenade No. 11 in E flat major, K375. Harmoniemusik on "Die Zauberflöte" (arr. Stumpf)[a]. **Nachtmusique** (Alf Hörberg, cl/[a]basset hn; Danny Bond, Donna Agrell, bns; Claude Maury, Teunis Van der Zwart, hns) / **Eric Hoeprich** (cl/[a]basset horn).
Glossa Ⓕ GCD920601 (65 minutes: DDD: 1/98). ✍ Recorded 1996.

This recording of K375 uses the relatively rare original version, without oboes. In some ways it makes better sense – the later one with oboes never quite justifies their presence. This performance is thoughtful, euphonious (the chording purer than is usual with period instruments) and very musicianly. The opening movement is taken rather deliberately, the central *Adagio* rather more quickly than usual and flowing very gracefully. Eric Hoeprich, who directs from the first clarinet, has a beautifully full and round tone and provides many happy details of expressive timing. In both Minuets (the lighter second taken in lively fashion) the tempo is slightly relaxed for the Trio, to good effect, both at the Trio itself and at the *da capo*. There is some very neat and spirited playing in the finale; the clarinets in particular are tested and show themselves duly agile. If some of the emphatic chords in the opening movement are a little too loudly played, leading to some coarsening of tone, this is nevertheless one of the best available versions of the work, certainly in its sextet form. The

Zauberflöte wind arrangements are less familiar than those of the Da Ponte operas and particularly enjoyable; more than once the transcription virtually reproduces the original scoring. They follow the same formulae as the others, offering shortened versions of the overture and 13 favourite numbers. The arrangements are mainly by J.C. Stumpf though two pieces are done in other versions, for smaller ensemble, to create variety.

Additional recommendations ...

...No. 11. No. 12 in C minor, K388/K384*a*. Wind soloists of the **Chamber Orchestra of Europe /
Alexander Schneider.** ASV Ⓕ CDCOE802 (47 minutes: DDD: 5/88).
...Nos. 11 and 12. **Pleyel** Sextet in E flat major. **Mozzafiato / Charles Neidich** (cl).
Sony Classical Ⓕ SK64306 (73 minutes: DDD: 9/95). ⚐
...Nos. 11 and 12. Overtures – Le nozze di Figaro, K492; Don Giovanni, K527; Die Zauberflöte,
K620. **English Concert Wind.** Hyperion Ⓕ CDA66887 (63 minutes: DDD: 3/97).

Mozart Serenade No. 13 in G major, K525, "Eine kleine Nachtmusik". Divertimentos – E flat
major, K252/K240*a*; D major, K131. **Orpheus Chamber Orchestra.** DG Ⓕ 419 192-2GH
(64 minutes: DDD: 12/86).

There are many worthy recorded performances of Mozart's most famous *Serenade*, the one that is now universally called *Eine kleine Nachtmusik,* but this one by the string section of the Orpheus Chamber Orchestra has qualities of refinement and alertness, even enthusiasm, that make it rather special. These players clearly enjoy the music, but bring to it a delightful precision as well as the necessary *joie de vivre* and spontaneity, and each of the four movements is beautifully shaped and characterized, so that this very familiar music comes up as fresh as anyone could wish for. The two early *divertimentos* which accompany the serenade provide a pleasing complement and contrast. Each has a different instrumentation, the one in D (written when Mozart was 16, but sounding more mature) being for flute, oboe, bassoon, four horns and strings while the one in E flat is for just six instruments, these being pairs of oboes, bassoons and horns. Here, too, the Orpheus players are of the highest calibre both technically and artistically and their sound is well captured, as is that of the strings in *Eine kleine Nachtmusik.*

Additional recommendations ...

...Eine kleine Nachtmusik. Serenade No. 6 in D major, K239, "Serenata notturna".
Coupled with works by **Elgar** *and* **Grieg Serenata of London.**
IMP Classics Ⓜ PCD1108 (65 minutes: DDD: 11/87).
...Eine kleine Nachtmusik. Overtures – Idomeneo; Die Entführung aus dem Serail; Der
Schauspieldirektor; Le nozze di Figaro; Don Giovanni; Così fan tutte; La clemenza di Tito;
Die Zauberflöte. **Tafelmusik / Bruno Weil.** Sony Classical Vivarte Ⓕ SK46695
(60 minutes: DDD: 5/92). ⚐
...Eine kleine Nachtmusik. **Tchaikovsky** Symphony No. 5 in E minor, Op. 64.
Vienna Philharmonic Orchestra / David Oistrakh. Orfeo Ⓕ C302921B (67 minutes: ADD: 6/93).
...Eine kleine Nachtmusik. Divertimentos for Strings – D major, K136; B flat major, K137;
F major, K138. ª**Alois Posch** (db); **Hagen Quartet.** DG Ⓕ 439 940-2GH (58 minutes: DDD: 4/95).
...Eine kleine Nachtmusik. *Coupled with works by various composers.*
Agi Jambor, Marinus Flipse (pfs); **Concertgebouw Orchestra / Willem Mengelberg.**
Archive Documents Mengelberg Edition mono Ⓕ ADCD112* (69 minutes: AAD: 5/95).

Mozart Divertimentos – B flat major, K287/K271*h*; D major, K205/K167*a*. **Salzburg Mozarteum
Camerata Academica / Sándor Végh.** Capriccio Ⓕ 10 271 (59 minutes: DDD: 11/89). ⓆⓆⓆ

Mozart's Divertimento, K287 is a six-movement work cast on quite a large scale, and is scored for two violins, viola, two horns and bass, a combination which presents some difficulties of balance. One solution is to use a full orchestral string section, but this can bring its own problems, for Mozart demands playing of virtuoso standard in this score, and anything less than this is ruthlessly exposed. Sandor Végh's smallish string band is of high quality, and has a pleasantly rounded tone quality. The engineers have managed to contrive a satisfactory balance which sounds not at all unnatural, and the sound quality itself is very good. Végh directs an attractive, neatly-pointed performance of the work, one which steers a middle course between objective classicism and expressive warmth. The Divertimento, K205, has five movements, but none of them lasts longer than five minutes, and the work is much shorter and more modest than K287. Scoring in this case is for violin, viola, two horns, bassoon and double bass, to provide another difficult but well resolved problem for the engineers. Végh directs another characterful, delightful performance, to round off a very desirable disc.

Additional recommendations ...

...Complete Edition, Volume 4 – Divertimentos and Marches. Divertimentos: E flat major, K113;
D major, K136/K125*a*; B flat major, K137/K125*b*; F major, K138/K125*c*; K205/167*a*; F major,
K247; D major, K251; K287/K271h; D major, K334/K320*b*. Marches: F major, K248; D major,
K290/K167*ab;* D major, K445/K320*c*. Eine kleine Nachtmusik. Ein musikalischer Spass, K522.
Academy of St Martin in the Fields / Sir Neville Marriner.
Philips Mozart Edition Ⓜ 422 504-2PME5 (five discs: 271 minutes: DDD: 12/90).
...D major, K131; K287/K271*h*. **Capella Istropolitana / Harald Nerat.**
Naxos Ⓢ 8 550996 (73 minutes: DDD: 6/95).

Mozart Ein musikalischer Spass, K522. Contredanses – C major, K587, "Der Sieg vom Helden
Koburg"; D major, K534, "Das Donnerwetter"; C major, K535, "La Bataille"; G major, K610,
"Les filles malicieuses"; E flat major, K607/K605a, "Il trionfo delle donne". Gallimathias
musicum, K32. German Dances – K567; K605; C major, K611, "Die Leyerer". March in
D major, K335 No. 1. **Orpheus Chamber Orchestra.** DG Ⓕ 429 783-2GH
(69 minutes: DDD: 4/91). Recorded 1989.

After all the Mozart with which we were bombarded during his bicentenary year, it is a mark of his
greatness that an issue such as this comes up with an incomparably engaging freshness. The celebrated
Musikalischer Spass ("Musical Joke") which begins the disc is never so crudely funny that it wears
thin, but make no mistake, the jokes are there in just about every passage, whether they are parodying
third-rate music or wobbly playing, and oddly enough sound still more amusing when the
performance is as stylishly flexible as this one by the conductorless Orpheus Chamber Orchestra. One
of the tunes here (that of the finale on track four) is that of the BBC's *Horse of the Year* programme
– and what a good tune it is, even at the umpteenth repetition as the hapless composer finds himself
unable to stop. The rest of this programme is no less delightful and includes miniature pieces
supposedly describing a thunderstorm, a battle, a hurdy-gurdy man and a sleigh-ride (with piccolo
and sleigh-bells). There is also a *Gallimathias musicum*, a ballet suite of dainty little dances averaging
less than a minute in length, which Mozart is supposed to have written at the age of ten. Whatever
the case this CD, subtitled "A Little Light Music", provides proof of his genius, though differently
from his acknowledged masterpieces. The recording is as refined as anyone could wish yet has plenty
of impact.

Mozart Symphonies – No. 1 in E flat major, K16; No. 4 in D major, K19; No. 5 in B flat major,
K22; No. 6 in F major, K43; No. 7 in D major, K45; No. 7a in G major, K45a/KAnh221, "Alte
Lambach"; No. 8 in D major, K48; No. 9 in C major, K73; No. 10 in G major, K74; No. 11 in
D major, K84/K73q; No. 12 in G major, K110/K75b; No. 13 in F major, K112; No. 14 in
A major, K114; No. 15 in G major, K124; No. 42 in F major, K75; No. 43 in F major, K76/K42a;
No. 44 in D major, K81/K731; No. 45 in D major, K95/K73n; No. 46 in C major, K96/K111b;
No. 47 in D major, K97/K73m; No. 55 in B flat major, K45b; F major, KAnh223/K19a; B flat
major, K74g/KAnh216/C11.03. **The English Concert / Trevor Pinnock.** Archiv Produktion
Ⓕ 437 792-2AH4 (four discs: 297 minutes: DDD: 11/93). 🎞 Recorded 1992.
Gramophone Editor's choice.

Pinnock's Mozart symphony cycle is only the second to use period instruments, and the performances
on these four discs are outstandingly vital and stylish, making the most persuasive case for this music.
Hogwood's pioneering period cycle from the early 1980s, with its revelations of articulation and
sonority, is often exciting, but suffers from intermittent roughness of execution and an often stiff,
austere approach to the slow movements. In both these respects Pinnock and The English Concert are
far preferable, reflecting the advance in all facets of period performance in the intervening decade.
The string sound is recognizably 'authentic' in its bright edge and restrained use of vibrato, but is
altogether smoother, sweeter and more subtly coloured than on the Hogwood discs. Ensemble is more
polished, tuning (especially of the oboes) far more precise. And Pinnock is not only more elegant and
affectionate in the slow movements, but often shapes the *Allegros* more purposefully, with more
considered phrasing and surer long-term control. The first contains six works (Köchel Nos. 16, 19,
19a, 22, 43 and 45a) written between 1764, when Mozart was eight, and late 1767, just before his
twelfth birthday. Though the invention here is often rudimentary, Mozart already reveals himself as
a precocious musical mimic, adeptly manipulating the clichés of the contemporary *galant* style.
Textures are, as always, ideally transparent, and violins divided on opposite sides so that the many
antiphonal passages make their proper effect. The second disc covers the years 1768-70, and begins
with Mozart's first symphony with trumpets and drums, K45, unremarkable in its actual ideas but
shrewdly laid out for maximum orchestral brilliance. Most of the works on the third disc were written
on Mozart's first two Italian journeys, in the spring and summer of 1770 and the autumn of 1771;
and they are distinctly Italianate in their harmonic and textural simplicity and easy *buffo* brilliance.
Not surprisingly, the final disc, with five symphonies from 1771 and early 1772, contains the most
consistently memorable music in this set. Finest of all these symphonies is the very Viennese K114 in
A major, a key that invariably drew something out of the ordinary from Mozart. The first movement,
with its luminous textures (high horns complemented by flutes rather than oboes), has a particularly
expressive second theme in imitation, shaped by Pinnock with a vocal eloquence. This superb set,
recorded with truthful immediacy, becomes the prime recommendation for these juvenile symphonies.
Additional recommendations ...
...Complete Edition, Volume 1 – Early Symphonies: No. 1 in E flat major, K16; No. 4 in D major,
K19; F major, KAnh223/K19a; No. 5 in B flat major, K22; No. 6 in F major, K43; No. 7 in
D major, K45; G major, K*deest*, "Neue Lambacher" (attrib. L. Mozart); No. 7a in G major,
K45a/KAnh221, "Alte Lambacher"; (No. 55) in B flat major, K45b/KAnh214; No. 8 in D major,
K48; No. 9 in C major, K73; No. 10 in G major, K74; (No. 42) in F major, K75; (No. 43) in
F major, K76/K42a; (No. 44) in D major, K81/K73l; No. 11 in D major, K84/K73q; (No. 45) in
D major, K95/K73n; (No. 46) in C major, K96/K111b; (No. 47) in D major, K97/K73m; No. 12
in G major, K110/K75b; No. 13 in F major, K112; No. 14 in A major, K114 (with additional

alternative minuet); No. 15 in G major, K124; No. 16 in C major, K128; No. 17 in G major, K129; No. 18 in F major, K130; No. 19 in E flat major, K132 (with additional alternative slow movement); No. 20 in D major, K133; (No. 50) in D major, K141*a* (K161 and K163); (No. 48) in D major, K111*a* (K111 and K120); (No. 51) in D major, K207*a* (K196 and K121); (No. 52) in C major, K213*c* (K208 and K102). Minuet in A major, K61*g* No. 1.
Academy of St Martin in the Fields / Sir Neville Marriner.
Philips Mozart Edition Ⓜ 422 501-2PME6 (six discs: 399 minutes: ADD/DDD: 12/90).

...Complete Edition, Volume 2 – Middle and Late Symphonies: No. 21 in A major, K134; No. 22 in C major, K162; No. 23 in D major, K181/K162*b*; No. 24 in B flat major, K182/K173*dA*; No. 25 in G minor, K183/K173*dB*; No. 26 in E flat major, K184/K161*a*; No. 27 in G major, K199/K161*b*; No. 28 in C major, K200/K189*k*; No. 29 in A major, K201/K186*a*; No. 30 in D major, K202/K186*b*; No. 31 in D major, K297/K300*a*, "Paris" (with additional alternative slow movement); No. 32 in G major, K318; No. 33 in B flat major, K319; No. 34 in C major, K338; No. 35 in D major, K385, "Haffner"; No. 36 in C major, K425, "Linz"; No. 38 in D major, K504, "Prague"; No. 39 in E flat major, K453; No. 40 in G minor, K550; No. 41 in C major, K551, "Jupiter". Minuet in C major, K409/K383*f*. Adagio maestoso in G major, K444/K425*a*.
Academy of St Martin in the Fields / Sir Neville Marriner.
Philips Mozart Edition Ⓜ 422 502-2PME6 (six discs: 402 minutes: ADD: 12/90).

...*CD80256* – No. 1 in E flat major, K16; F major, K19*a*; No. 4 in D major, K19; No. 5 in B flat major, K22; No. 6 in F major, K43; B flat major, K45*b*/KAhn214; No. 7 in D major, K45. *CD80272* – No. 8 in D major, K48; No. 9 in C major, K73/K75*a*; D major, K73*l*/K81; D major, K73*m*/K97; D major, K75*n*/K95; D major, K73*n*/K95; D major, K73*q*/K84. *CD80273* – No. 10 in G major, K74/K73*p*; C major, K111*b*/K96; F major, K75; G major, K75*b*/K110; No. 13 in F major, K112. **Prague Chamber Orchestra / Sir Charles Mackerras.**
Telarc Ⓕ CD80256, CD80272/3 (three discs, oas: 83, 61 and 58 minutes: DDD: 11/91).
...*8 550113* (65 minutes): No. 25 in G minor, K183/K173*dB*; No. 32 in G major, K318; No. 41 in C major, K551, "Jupiter". *8 550119* (69 minutes): No. 29 in A major, K201/K186*a*; No. 30 in D major, K202/K186*b*; No. 38 in D major, K504, "Prague". *8 550164* (61 minutes): No. 28 in C major, K200/K189*k*; No. 31 in D major, K297/K300*a*, "Paris"; No. 40 in G minor, K550. *8 550186* (62 minutes): No. 34 in C major, K338; No. 35 in D major, K385, "Haffner"; No. 39 in E flat major, K543. *8 550264* (65 minutes): No. 27 in G major, K199/K161*b*; No. 33 in B flat major, K319; No. 36 in C major, K425, "Linz". *8 550299* (62 minutes): No. 40 in G minor, K550; No. 41 in C major, K551, "Jupiter". **Capella Istropolitana / Barry Wordsworth.**
Naxos Ⓢ (six discs, oas: 384 minutes: DDD: 4/91).
...Nos. 31, 33 and 34. **Prague Chamber Orchestra / Sir Charles Mackerras.**
Telarc Ⓕ CD80190 (65 minutes: DDD: 3/90).
...Nos. 31–41. **The English Concert / Trevor Pinnock.**
Archiv Produktion Ⓕ 447 043-2AH4 (four discs: 256 minutes: DDD: 12/95). ✍
...Nos. 13–24. D major (No. 48), K120/K111*a*; D major (No. 50), K141*a*/K161, K163; D major (No. 51), K121/K207*a*; C major (No. 52), K102/K213*c*. **English Chamber Orchestra / Jeffrey Tate.** EMI Ⓕ CDS5 55480-2 (three discs: 201 minutes: DDD: 1/96).
...Nos. 1-36; Nos. 38-41; (Nos. 42-47); (No. 7a) in G major, K45*a*/KAnh221, "Alte Lambach"; G major, "Neue Lambach". **Berlin Philharmonic Orchestra / Karl Böhm.**
DG Ⓑ 453 231-2GX10 (ten discs: 749 minutes: ADD: 5/97).

Mozart Symphonies. **Northern Chamber Orchestra / Nicholas Ward.** Naxos Ⓢ 8 550871/2 (59 and 56 minutes, oas: DDD: 12/95).
8 550871 – No. 1 in E flat major, K16; No. 2 in B flat major, K17 (attrib. L. Mozart); No. 4 in D major, K19; No. 5 in B flat major, K22. **Abel** (formerly attrib. Mozart) Symphony, Op. 7 No. 3. *8 550872* – No. 6 in F major, K43; No. 7 in D major, K45; No. 8 in D major, K48; No. 9 in C major, K73; No. 10 in G major, K74.
These two discs of Mozart's first ten symphonies offer a unique view of the composer's earliest years of apprenticeship as a symphonist. Ward and his orchestra demonstrate a sensitive response to the wealth of stylistic influences apparent in these works. Purists may question the inclusion of two of the symphonies, Nos. 2 and 3, since neither work is actually by Mozart. The former is attributed to the composer's father, Leopold, while the latter is Mozart's orchestration of C.F. Abel's E flat Symphony, Op. 7 No. 3. However, when they are played with such engaging style and elegance as here, these two works add a further important dimension to Mozart's early symphonic output. Where J.C. Bach's influence is most powerful (Symphonies Nos. 1, 4, 5 and 6), the NCO present the music's contrasting thematic characters with fine clarity, balancing the music's beautifully transparent textures with appropriate lightness of touch. The inclusion of trumpets and drums in the next three symphonies (Nos. 7, 8 and 9) announces the young composer's growing brilliance and stature. In these pieces, the NCO move into a suitably higher gear, revealing Mozart's new and potent originality, with powerfully dramatic tuttis and expressively sung *andantes*. Mozart made his first trip to Italy in 1770, and the symphony he wrote in Milan that year (No. 10) shows his enthusiastic incorporation of Italian stylistic models. Here the NCO's deliciously spacious orchestral playing demonstrates Mozart's ravishing originality, with dramatic opposition of gesture and instrumentation in the exuberant *allegros* and a beguilingly graceful slow movement that winningly displays a keen awareness of the

composer's innovative touches. These are indeed splendid performances, admirably complemented by vivid recordings (made in the spacious acoustic of the Concert Hall, New Broadcasting House, Manchester).

Mozart Symphonies – No. 15 in G major, K124; No. 16 in C major, K128; No. 17 in G major, K129; No. 18 in F major, K130. **Northern Chamber Orchestra / Nicholas Ward.**
Naxos Ⓢ 8 550874 (58 minutes: DDD: 12/95). Recorded 1994.

After Mozart returned from his first extended tour of Italy in 1771, he embarked on a number of symphonic projects that show his astonishing assimilation and transformation of the Italian overture, with crisp, transparent orchestration and suppleness of expression. The influence of Sammartini and J.C. Bach – whose music could be heard at concerts in Salzburg during 1772 when these pieces were written – is especially apparent in the bold thematic gestures and civilized discourse between wind and strings. Nicholas Ward and the NCO bring their customary style and eloquence to this music in performances that evocatively portray its blend of formal unity, radiant vitality and occasionally – as in the rhythmically imaginative finale of the C major Symphony – rustic charm. Opening *allegros* are suitably vivacious, *andantes* are graceful and poignant and the vigorous finales bristle with energy. The first movement of the C major Symphony offers a more potent dramatic formula, with subtly poetic triplets and tense tremolos; however, the highlight of the programme is the F major Symphony (No. 18), which Saint-Foix described as "the first of [Mozart's] great symphonies". Here, Ward's and the NCO's dramatically compelling account, beautifully presented in a natural, spacious recording, brilliantly highlights the music's operatic qualities.

Mozart Salzburg Symphonies – No. 16 in C major, K128; No. 17 in G major, K129; No. 18 in F major, K130; No. 19 in E flat major, K132; No. 20 in D major, K133; No. 21 in A major, K134; No. 22 in C major, K162; No. 23 in D major, K181/K162b; No. 24 in B flat major, K182/K173dA; No. 25 in G minor, K183/K173dB; No. 26 in E flat major, K184/K161a; No. 27 in G major, K199/K161b; No. 28 in C major, K200/K189k; No. 29 in A major, K201/K186a; No. 30 in D major, K202/K186b. **The English Concert / Trevor Pinnock.** Archiv Produktion Ⓕ 439 915-2AH4 (four discs: 264 minutes: DDD: 1/95). ✒   Ⓖ

This is the second of the projected three boxes making up Trevor Pinnock's more or less comprehensive cycle of the Mozart symphonies and includes all the symphonies Mozart wrote between the spring of 1772 and the end of 1774, his most prolific period of symphony composition. Trevor Pinnock's are the first period-instrument performances of most of these works since Christopher Hogwood's pioneering recordings of the late 1970s and early 1980s. Techniques of handling these instruments have improved greatly over the last decade, and what is exciting about this set is the sweetness of the sound (not at all the same as the sweetness of a modern chamber orchestra) and the suppleness and flexibility The English Concert bring to the music. They play, much of the time, as if it were chamber music, particularly in second subjects – the lyrical passages, that is, where they shape the phrases with a warmth and refinement you hardly expect in orchestral music. Timing is quietly witty, yet not at all contrived or artificial: it is the sort of expressive refinement that depends on listening to one another, not on the presence of a conductor. There is large-scale playing too. The opening of the brilliant D major work, K133 has a splendid swing, with its prominent trumpets, and a real sense of a big, symphonic piece. K184 is duly fiery and its accents are neatly judged. The two final symphonies are both very impressively done: an eloquent rather than a fiery account (though something of that too) of the opening movement of K201, with a particularly euphonious and shapely *Andante*, and the finales of both are done with exceptional vitality and the rhythmic resilience that is characteristic of these performances. In short, quite outstanding performances, unfailingly musical, wholly natural and unaffected, often warmly expressive in the slow music and always falling very happily on the ear, with no trace of the harshness that some people think is inevitable with period instruments. They are excellently recorded, with the properly prominent wind balance helping to characterize the sound-world of each work.

Additional recommendations ...

...Nos. 23 and 36. Sinfonia concertante in E flat major, K364/K320dª. ªRainer Kussmaul (vn); ªWolfram Christ (va); **Berlin Philharmonic Orchestra / Claudio Abbado.**
Sony Classical Ⓕ SK66859 (75 minutes: DDD: 9/96).

...Nos. 24, 26, 27 and 30. **Prague Chamber Orchestra / Sir Charles Mackerras.**
Telarc Ⓕ CD80186 (58 minutes: DDD: 8/89).

...No. 29. *Coupled with works by various composers.* **Leipzig Gewandhaus Orchestra / Hermann Abendroth.** Tahra mono Ⓕ TAH106/07* (two discs: 154 minutes: AAD: 9/94).

Mozart Symphonies – No. 21 in A major, K134; No. 22 in C major, K162; No. 23 in D major, K181/K162b; No. 24 in B flat major, K182/K173dA; No. 26 in E flat major, K184/K161a. **Northern Chamber Orchestra / Nicholas Ward.** Naxos Ⓢ 8 550876 (53 minutes: DDD: 1/96). Recorded 1993.

This is an opportunity to enjoy Mozart's inexhaustibly imaginative assimilation and transformation of Italian operatic models. To begin, Ward's sensitively balanced orchestral textures reveal Mozart's fragrant orchestration with great clarity in the A major Symphony. Sample the second movement's deftly handled interplay of strings, woodwind and horns, and buoyantly stately Menuetto that culminates effectively in the finale's restless drive. The complete musical satisfaction provided by the four Italian-overture symphonies that comprise the remainder of the programme is due both to the fullness and vigour of the orchestration itself, and to the NCO's lively performances. The opening *allegros* and cheerfully effervescent finales bubble with infectious vitality, while the slow movements provide the opportunity for more intimate instrumental ensembles. Most impressive, however, is the E flat major work, which originated as the overture to the play *Lanassa*. Here, Ward and the NCO compellingly portray the dramatic violence of the opening *Presto*, the profound despair of its minor-key *Andante* and the exuberant rhythms of its finale. The recording is atmospheric.

Additional recommendation ...

...Nos. 23 and 34. *Coupled with works by* **Brahms** and **Debussy** Dresden Philharmonic Orchestra / Carl Schuricht. Berlin Classics mono Ⓜ 0090732BC* (50 minutes: ADD: 7/96).

Mozart Symphonies – No. 25 in G minor, K183/K173*dB*; No. 31 in D major, K297/K300*a*, "Paris"; D major, K320. Maurerische Trauermusik in C minor, K477/K479*a*.
Berlin Philharmonic Orchestra / Claudio Abbado. Sony Classical Ⓕ SK48385
(75 minutes: DDD: 5/95). Recorded 1992.

These are exhilarating accounts of Mozart using modern instruments in performances which marry sweetness and purity to crisp rhythms and dramatic bite. What the title above fails to underline is the fact that the third of the three symphonies, K320 in D major, on the disc is the one which Mozart adapted from that same *Posthorn Serenade*, selecting just the first, fifth and seventh movements. It is astonishing that though the three-movement symphony is so much briefer than the seven-movement Serenade, it seems much bolder and more powerful in its arguments. This version of the *Paris* Symphony has the alternative, earlier slow movement as a supplement, as well as the later one in its usual place. No. 29 is presented, as most recent versions have been, as a large-scale structure, with both halves of the outer movements repeated. Anyone wanting performances on modern instruments is unlikely to find the approach too massive for Mozart, for although the string band is substantial, the purity and clarity of the playing aerates textures. Woodwind doubling is always clearly audible, as with the bassoons in the second movement of No. 29. Abbado's underlining of light and shade regularly makes for delectable moments, for example in the woodwind trio for the Minuet where the descending scales are made to sound like laughter. The recording also captures very tellingly the intensely serious, lugubrious timbres of the *Maurerische Trauermusik* ("Masonic Funeral Music" of 1785, composed a year after he became a Mason), made dark with extra weight of wind set against a string section without cellos.

Additional recommendations ...

...Masonic Funeral Music – Maurerische Trauermusik[f]; Lobegesang auf die feierliche Johannisloge, K148[ae]; Dir, Seele des Weltalls, K429/K468*a*[acf]; Lied zur Gesellenreise, K468[ae]; Die Maurerfreude, K471[acf]; Zerfliesset heut', geliebte Brüder, K483[acd]; Ihr unsre neuen Leiter, K484[acd]; Die ihr des unermesslichen Weltalls, K619[ae]; Laut verkünde unsre Freude, K623[abcf]; Lasst uns mit geschlungnen Händen, K623*a*[cd]. [a]**Werner Krenn** (ten); [b]**Tom Krause** (bar); [c]**Edinburgh Festival Chorus; György Fischer** ([d]org/[e]pf); [f]**London Symphony Orchestra /** István Kertész. Decca Serenata Ⓜ 425 722-2DM (53 minutes: ADD: 11/90).

...Maurerische Trauermusik. *Coupled with works by* **Brahms** and **R. Strauss** Vienna Philharmonic Orchestra / Herbert von Karajan.
EMI Karajan Edition mono Ⓜ CDM5 66390-2* (72 minutes: ADD: 9/97).

Mozart Symphonies – No. 25 in G minor, K183/K173*dB*; No. 28 in C major, K200/K189*k*; No. 29 in A major, K201/K186*a*. **Prague Chamber Orchestra / Sir Charles Mackerras.**
Telarc Ⓕ CD80165 (78 minutes: DDD: 9/88).

Here are three symphonies from Mozart's late teens, written in his native Salzburg, in crisply articulated performances. The first of them is a *Sturm und Drang* piece in a key that the composer reserved for moods of agitation. Mackerras takes the orchestra through the big opening *Allegro con brio* of No. 25 with drive and passion, although it is unlikely that Mozart would have expected a Salzburg orchestra in the 1770s to play as fast as this skilful body of Czech players. The gentle *Andante* comes therefore as a relief, though here too Mackerras keeps a firm rhythmic grasp on the music, and indeed a taut metrical aspect is a feature of all three symphonies as played here, so that minuets dance briskly and purposefully and finales bustle. However, the sunlit warmth of the beautiful A major Symphony, No. 29, comes through and the bracing view of the other two symphonies is a legitimate one, though giving little or nothing in the direction of expressive lingering, much less towards sentimental indulgence. The Prague Chamber Orchestra are an expert ensemble, not overlarge for this style of music and the recording is admirably clear although a little reverberant.

Additional recommendation ...

...Nos. 28 and 29. No. 35 in D major, K385, "Haffner". **Berlin Philharmonic Orchestra /** Claudio Abbado. Sony Classical Ⓕ SK48063 (74 minutes: DDD: 3/92).

Mozart Symphonies – No. 29 in A major, K201/K186*a*[a]; No. 31 in D major, K297/K300*a*, "Paris"[b]; No. 32 in G major, K318[c]; No. 33 in B flat major, K319[a]; No. 34 in C major, K338[b]; No. 35 in D major, K385, "Haffner"[c]; No. 36 in C major, K425, "Linz"[c]; No. 38 in D major, K504, "Prague"[d]; No. 39 in E flat major, K543[d]; No. 40 in G minor, K550[e]; No. 41 in C major,

K551, "Jupiter"[e]. **English Baroque Soloists / Sir John Eliot Gardiner.** Philips Ⓜ 442 604-2PH5 (five discs: 309 minutes: DDD: 3/95). Items marked [a] from 420 736-2PH (8/86), [b]420 937-2PH (7/88), [c]422 419-2PH (9/89), [d]426 283-2PH (2/91), [e]426 315-2PH (11/92). 🎘 ⓖⓖ

Gardiner took his pilgrimage through the late Mozart symphonies more or less in chronological order over a span of six years. The first disc contains appealing performances of Nos. 29 and 33, the former particularly lyrical and shapely, with an eloquent account of the *Andante*, the latter distinguished for its refinement of line and the properly spirited opening movement. Then comes the *Paris*, No. 31, a piece designed to show off a virtuoso orchestra, which it duly does in this alert and shapely reading, coupled with No. 34, another large-scale piece, in which Gardiner again provides a specially graceful slow movement. In the *Haffner, Linz* and *Prague* Symphonies Gardiner is possibly more concerned with classical grandeur than with strong characterization of the ideas. The G minor is the outstanding achievement of the set: the first movement performed with great drive and spaciousness, the second shapely and intense in expression, the finale done with immense vitality, the strings' arpeggios leaping vividly through the texture. The *Jupiter* is almost equally splendid, if slightly flawed by some *piano* effects in the first movement tuttis (this happens too in No. 39) where they do not belong, but the crowning glory, the finale, contains many thrilling things. This is probably the version to choose, under any conductor, of these symphonies on period instruments – indeed perhaps on any instruments.

Additional recommendations ...

...Nos. 40 and 41. **Prague Chamber Orchestra / Sir Charles Mackerras.**
Telarc Ⓕ CD80139 (71 minutes: DDD: 5/87).
...Nos. 34, 35 and 39. **London Mozart Players / Jane Glover.**
ASV Ⓕ CDDCA615 (74 minutes: DDD: 7/88).
...Nos. 38 and 39. **English Baroque Soloists / Sir John Eliot Gardiner.** Philips Ⓕ 426 283-2PH (66 minutes: DDD: 2/91). 🎘 *These are the same recordings as those reviewed above.*
...Nos. 40 and 41. **English Baroque Soloists / Sir John Eliot Gardiner.**
Philips Ⓕ 426 315-2PH (75 minutes: DDD: 11/92). 🎘
...No. 40. **Tchaikovsky** Symphony No. 5 in E minor, Op. 64. **North German Radio Symphony Orchestra / Günter Wand.** RCA Victor Red Seal Ⓕ 09026 68032-2 (73 minutes: DDD: 6/95).
...Nos. 35, 36, 38-41. **Berlin Philharmonic Orchestra / Karl Böhm.**
DG The Originals Ⓜ 447 416-2GOR2 (two discs: 146 minutes: ADD: 11/95).
...Nos. 40 and 41. **The English Concert / Trevor Pinnock.**
Archiv Produktion Ⓕ 447 048-2AH (73 minutes: DDD: 12/95). 🎘
...Nos. 35, 36 and 38. **London Philharmonic Orchestra / Sir Thomas Beecham.**
Dutton Laboratories Essential Archive mono Ⓑ CDEA5001* (71 minutes: ADD: 1/96).
...Nos. 29, 31 and 33. **Orchestra of the Eighteenth Century / Frans Brüggen.**
Philips Ⓕ 446 104-2PH (71 minutes: DDD: 10/96). 🎘
...Nos. 40 and 41. La clemenza di Tito – Overture. **Salzburg Mozarteum Camerata Academica / Sándor Végh.** Decca Ⓕ 448 062-2DH (64 minutes: DDD: 10/96).
...Nos. 29, 31 and 34. **London Philharmonic Orchestra / Sir Thomas Beecham.**
Dutton Essential Archive mono Ⓑ CDEA5008* (62 minutes: ADD: 5/97).
...Nos. 35, 36, 38, 39, 40 and 41. **Berlin Philharmonic Orchestra / Herbert von Karajan.**
DG Double Ⓜ 453 046-2GTA2 (two discs: 148 minutes: ADD: 7/97).
...Nos. 39-41. **London Philharmonic Orchestra / Sir Thomas Beecham.**
Dutton Laboratories Essential Archive mono Ⓑ CDEA5012* (77 minutes: ADD: 9/97).

Mozart Symphonies – No. 29 in A major, K201/K186*a*; No. 33 in B flat major, K319; No. 40 in G minor, K550. **Orpheus Chamber Orchestra.** DG Ⓕ 453 425-2GH (73 minutes: DDD: 8/97). Recorded 1995.

The reading of the great G minor symphony here is impressively strong and positive and defies the idea that a corporate interpretation necessarily lacks individuality. The first movement is genuinely *Molto allegro*, very fast indeed but full of detail and not at all breathless sounding, with full, immediate sound heightening the sharp dynamic contrasts. The third and fourth movements bring fast speeds too and crisp attack, while the *Andante*, on the slow side for a latter-day performance, is yet similarly dramatic in its contrasts. It is a powerful, compelling account, and equally recommendable is the Orpheus's reading of No. 33, again with exhilaratingly fast speeds for the outer movements, and with the slow movement relatively expansive and smoother than the others. Though the very opening of No. 29 brings playing a little less tautly compelling, the same qualities quickly emerge in a reading at once fresh and highly polished. And again the immediate, full-bodied sound adds to the impact, with braying horn vividly caught, not least in the exuberant, superbly articulated account of the finale. The Orpheus omit second-time repeats, but until conductors such as Mackerras observed them, few would have expected them anyway in a modern-instrument performance.

Mozart Symphony No. 33 in B flat major, K319. Serenade No. 9 in D major, K320, "Posthorn". **Academy of St Martin in the Fields / Iona Brown.** Hänssler Classic Ⓕ CD98 129 (59 minutes: DDD: 3/98). Recorded 1997.

Mozart Symphony No. 35 in D major, K385, "Haffner". Serenade No. 7 in D major, K250/K248*b*, "Haffner". **Academy of St Martin in the Fields / Iona Brown** (vn). Hänssler Classic Ⓕ CD98 173 (72 minutes: DDD: 3/98). Recorded 1997.

Quite apart from the originality of the couplings – each disc bringing together a middle-period symphony and a contemporaneous Serenade – Iona Brown and the Hänssler recording team between them certainly provide a clear contrast to Marriner's well-known recordings with the same orchestra (see the listed recommendations above). The sound recording has a sharpness of focus and sense of presence more often associated with the finest analogue recordings of the 1960s and 1970s. It is also surprising to find that the venue was Henry Wood Hall, for this sounds rather more intimate than most recordings made there, with plenty of bloom but no excessive reverberation. This is Mozart sound, using modern instruments but with some concern for the crisper manners encouraged by period performance, that in its freshness and beauty makes one want to go on listening. The performances are consistently brisker and fresher than Marriner's. The finale of the Symphony No. 33, for example, brings a hectic speed which does not sound at all breathless, with featherlight triplets, and similarly in the finale of the *Posthorn* Serenade with which it is coupled. Exceptionally in that Serenade Iona Brown opts for a more relaxed speed and more moulded style in the lovely minor-key *Andantino* of the fifth movement. The posthorn in the Trio of the second Minuet is this time much more brazen and more forwardly balanced than before. The coupling of the *Haffner* Symphony and *Haffner* Serenade is specially apt. In the Symphony Brown, unlike Marriner, follows the autograph in omitting an exposition repeat. Iona Brown herself is the virtuoso soloist in the Serenade, as she was in the Marriner version on Philips, lighter than ever in the *moto perpetuo* scurryings of the fourth-movement Rondo. For those who continue to resist period performances in this repertory these are very refreshing discs.

Mozart Symphonies – No. 36 in C major, K425, "Linz"; No. 38 in D major, K504, "Prague".
Prague Chamber Orchestra / Sir Charles Mackerras. Telarc Ⓕ CD80148
(66 minutes: DDD: 10/87).
Mozart wrote his *Linz* Symphony in great haste (five days to be precise), but needless to say there is little evidence of haste in the music itself, except perhaps that the first movement has all the exuberance of a composer writing on the wing of inspiration. The slow movement with its siciliano rhythm certainly has no lack of serenity, although it has drama too. The *Prague* Symphony was written only three years later, yet Mozart's symphonic style had matured and the work is altogether more ambitious and substantial. A glorious spaciousness surrounds Sir Charles's performances. The recording venue is reverberant, yet there is no loss of detail, and the fullness of the sound helps to add weight to climaxes without going beyond the bounds of volume that Mozart might have expected. Sir Charles captures the joy and high spirits that these symphonies embody without in any way undermining their greatness. This vivacity is emphasized by the East European sound of the Prague Chamber Orchestra, with the out-of-doors timbre of its winds which provides a pleasing contrast both with those of the standard British and Germanic orchestras and specialist, authentic ensembles. Mackerras does, however, adopt some aspects of the modern approach to Mozart performance: he includes harpsichord continuo, his minuets are taken trippingly, one-to-a-bar, and he prefers bowing that is crisper, more detached, and pointed. Phrasing and articulation are taken with a natural grace and without overemphasis, dynamics being graded to provide drama at the right moments. The very rightness of the result is recommendation enough.

Additional recommendation ...
...No. 38. **Beethoven** Mass in D major, Op. 123, "Missa solemnis". **Philharmonia Orchestra / Herbert von Karajan.** Testament Ⓕ SBT2126 (two discs: 157 minutes: ADD: 6/98).

Mozart Symphonies – No. 38 in D major, K504, "Prague"[a]; No. 39 in E flat major, K543[b].
The English Concert / Trevor Pinnock. Archiv Produktion Ⓕ 449 142-2AH
(63 minutes: DDD: 3/98). From 447 043-2AH4 (12/95). Recorded [a]1993, [b]1994.   Ⓖ
The *Prague* has a sombre opening, catching the sense of mystery in that remarkable slow introduction, which leads to a bright and spirited account of the main *Allegro*, its structure nicely articulated. The *Andante*, also attentively shaped, has its proper hints of darkness, as well as pastoral grace; and Pinnock offers a reading of the finale with plenty of weight as well as vivacity. The special character of the work as a whole is well captured. The same goes for the great E flat Symphony: what is especially appealing is the sturdiness and the fire of the tuttis in the first movement and the way Pinnock and his orchestra convey the anger, almost despair, in those astonishing tuttis in the *Andante*. There is plenty of lyricism too; but this is not simply a gentle and lyrical symphony, as some conductors would have it – here even the Minuet is done with urgency and intensity. For anyone wanting these two works, a more satisfying version would be hard to find.

Mozart Complete Edition, Volume 14 – Piano Quintet in E flat major, K452[a] (from 420 182-2PH, 8/87). Clarinet Trio in E flat major, K498, "Kegelstatt"[b] (6500 073, 2/71). Adagio and Rondo in C minor, K617[c] (9500 397, 5/78). Adagio in C major, K356/K617a[d]. Piano Quartets[e] – No. 1 in G minor, K478; No. 2 in E flat major, K493 (both from 410 391-1PH, 10/84). Piano Trios[f] – B flat major, K254; D minor, K442 (cptd. Stadler and Marguerre); No. 1 in G major, K496; No. 3 in B flat major, K502; No. 4 in E major, K542; No. 5 in C major, K548; No. 6 in G major, K564 (all from 422 079-2PH3, 11/88). [a]**Aurèle Nicolet** (fl); [ac]**Heinz Holliger** (ob); [a]**Eduard Brunner,** [b]**Jack Brymer** (cls); [a]**Hermann Baumann** (hn); [a]**Klaus Thunemann** (bn);

^{cd}**Bruno Hoffmann** (glass harmonica); ^b**Patrick Ireland**, ^c**Karl Schouten**, ^e**Bruno Giuranna** (vas); ^c**Jean Decroos** (vc); ^{ef}**Beaux Arts Trio** (Isidore Cohen, vn; Bernard Greenhouse, vc; Menahem Pressler, pf); ^a**Alfred Brendel**, ^b**Stephen Kovacevich** (pfs).
Philips Mozart Edition Ⓜ 422 514-2PME5 (five discs: 274 minutes: ADD/DDD: 9/91).
Gramophone Award Winner 1991.   Ⓖ
These recordings come from different locations and dates, ranging from 1969 to 1987. Four discs out of the five offer the two piano quartets and seven piano trios, played by the Beaux Arts Trio who are joined in the quartets by the viola player Bruno Giuranna; these are clearly the centrepiece of the issue and the playing of this fine ensemble is strongly characterful yet thoughtful. These are alert, direct and yet refined performances and earn only praise, although the recording in Philips's favoured Swiss location of La-Chaux-de-Fonds could have placed a little more distance between the players and the listener (we also hear the odd intake of breath). But otherwise this clear sound suits the music, and Menaham Pressler's piano tone is well captured. The D minor Trio which ends the series is not wholly authentic, being mainly Maximilian Stadler's compilation from existing material found by Mozart's widow Constanze after his death. Before we come to the piano quartets and piano trios, the first disc also has important works in fine performances in which Alfred Brendel and Heinz Holliger are just two of the artists involved (the Quintet for piano and wind was among the composer's favourite works). The first disc also offers two pieces featuring the ravishing sound of the glass harmonica (musical glasses), which is played by its leading exponent, Bruno Hoffmann, and the solo *Adagio* in C major is quite ethereally beautiful, if rather closely recorded. This unique instrument is usefully described and illustrated in the booklet.

Additional recommendations ...

...Piano Quartets Nos. 1 and 2^a. Horn Quintet in E flat major, K407^b. ^a**Sir Clifford Curzon** (pf); ^amembers of the **Amadeus Quartet**; ^b**Dennis Brain** (hn); ^bmembers of the **Griller Quartet**. Decca Historic mono Ⓜ 425 960-2DM* (62 minutes: ADD: 4/90).   Ⓖ
...Piano Quartets Nos. 1 and 2. **Mozartean Players.**
Harmonia Mundi Ⓕ HMU90 7018 (64 minutes: DDD: 3/91).
...Piano Quintet, K452. **Beethoven** Piano and Wind Quintet in E flat major, Op. 16.
Hansjörg Schellenberger (ob); **Larry Combs** (cl); **Dale Clevenger** (hn); **Daniele Damiano** (bn); **Daniel Barenboim** (pf). Erato Ⓕ 4509-96359-2 (49 minutes: DDD: 12/94).
...Piano Quintet, K452^b. Piano Concerto No. 26 in D major, K537, "Coronation"^a. ^b**Heinz Holliger** (ob); ^b**Elmar Schmid** (cl); ^b**Klaus Thunemann** (bn); ^b**Radovan Vlatkovic** (hn); **András Schiff** (pf); ^a**Salzburg Mozarteum Camerata Academica / Sándor Végh.**
Decca Ⓕ 443 877-2DH (56 minutes: DDD: 4/95).
...Piano Quartet No. 1. **Schubert** Piano Quintet in A major, D667, "Trout"^a.
Thomas Zehetmair (vn); **Tabea Zimmermann** (va); **Richard Duven** (vc); ^a**Peter Riegelbauer** (db); **Alfred Brendel** (pf). Philips Ⓕ 446 001-2PH (75 minutes: DDD: 1/96). *See review under Schubert; refer to the Index.*
...Clarinet Trio, K498. **Bruch** Acht Stücke, Op. 83. **Ludmila Peterková** (cl); **Josef Suk** (va); **Josef Hála** (pf). Supraphon Ⓕ SU3014-2 (57 minutes: DDD: 2/97).
...Piano Quintet, K452^a. Sinfonia concertante in E flat major, K297b^b. **Beethoven** Piano Quintet in E flat major, Op. 16^a. ^a**Walter Gieseking** (pf); **Philharmonia Wind Quartet;** ^b**Philharmonia Orchestra / Herbert von Karajan.** Testament mono Ⓕ SBT1091*
(80 minutes: ADD: 3/97). *See review under Beethoven; refer to the Index.*   ⒼⒼⒼ

Mozart Complete Edition, Volume 11 – String Quintets: No. 1 in B flat major, K174; No. 2 in C minor, K406/K516*b*; No. 3 in C major, K515; No. 4 in G minor, K516; No. 5 in D major, K593; No. 6 in E flat major, K614. **Arthur Grumiaux, Arpad Gérecz** (vns); **Georges Janzer, Max Lesueur** (vas); **Eva Czako** (vc). Philips Mozart Edition Ⓜ 422 511-2PME3 (three discs: 170 minutes: ADD: 9/91). From 6747 107 (1/76). Recorded 1973.
Gramophone classical 100. Gramophone Award Winner 1991.   ⒼⒼⒼ
Of the six works which comprise Mozart's complete *oeuvre* for string quintet, that in B flat major, K174, is an early composition, written at the age of 17. It is a well-made, enjoyable work, but not a great deal more than that. The C minor work, K406, is an arrangement by Mozart of his Serenade for six wind instruments, K398. It is difficult not to feel that the original is more effective, since the music seems to sit a little uncomfortably on string instruments. But the remaining four works, written in the last four years of Mozart's life, are a different matter. The last string quintets from Mozart's pen were extraordinary works, and the addition of the second viola seems to have encouraged him to still greater heights. It has been suggested that Mozart wrote K515 and K516 to show King Friedrich Wilhelm II of Prussia that he was a better composer of string quintets than Boccherini, whom the King had retained as chamber music composer to his court. There was no response, so he offered these two quintets for sale with the K406 arrangement to make up the usual set of three. K593 and K614 were written in the last year of his life. Arthur Grumiaux and his colleagues recorded their survey in 1973. Refinement is perhaps the word that first comes to mind in discussing these performances, which are affectionate yet controlled by a cool, intelligent sensitivity. The recordings have been well transferred, the quality is warm and expansive and Grumiaux's tone, in particular, is a delight to the ear but all the playing is alert and stylish. In all, this Philips release is one to earn a strong recommendation, offering as it does Mozart playing of fine quality allied to very decent sound.

Additional recommendations ...

...K515. K516. K593. K614. **Simon Whistler** (va); **Salomon Quartet.**
Hyperion Ⓕ CDD22005 (two discs: 129 minutes: DDD: 11/91). ✍

...K406/K516*b. Coupled with works by* **R. Strauss** Vienna String Sextet.
EMI Ⓕ CDC5 55108-2 (61 minutes: DDD: 2/95).

...K174 (including two rejected movements); K515. **Eder Quartet; János Fehérvári** (va).
Naxos Ⓢ 8 553103 (67 minutes: DDD: 4/95).

...K516ª. String Quartet No. 14 in G major, K387. **Lindsay Quartet;** ªPatrick Ireland (va).
ASV Ⓕ CDDCA923 (73 minutes: DDD: 6/95). ✍   Ⓖ

...K515. K516. **L'Archibudelli.** Sony Classical Vivarte Ⓕ SK66259 (63 minutes: DDD: 9/95). ✍

...K406/K516*b*. K516. **Eder Quartet; János Fehérvári** (va).
Naxos Ⓢ 8 553104 (56 minutes: DDD: 1/96).

Mozart String Quintet No. 3 in C major, K515ª. String Quartet No. 16 in E flat major, K428.
ªLouise Williams (va); **Lindsay Quartet.** ASV Ⓕ CDDCA992 (67 minutes: DDD: 8/97).
Recorded 1995.   Ⓖ

Here's a really fine performance of the great C major Quintet. The Lindsays take the first movement at a true *Allegro*, so that it bowls along in top gear, the details vivid and sharply etched. Much of this grandest and most spacious movement in Mozart's chamber output is marked to be played softly: in the Lindsays' hands the wonderful counterpoint in the development section can be heard with exceptional clarity as the tension builds up, but not the dynamic. The *Andante* sounds the more touching for never being overplayed, and it's a special pleasure to hear how the most florid passages for first violin and first viola fit effortlessly into the rhythmic scheme. In the finale, Peter Cropper introduces some beautifully played portamentos in the main theme, and the whole movement sounds delightfully witty and happy. The E flat Quartet, K428 is cool and stylish, which suits this enigmatic work rather well. The Lindsays' way of using Mozart's marks of expression and articulation to make the music speak feels absolutely right, especially in their delicate, refined *Andante*, and it's good to hear the quartet played with all its repeats. The recording has a nice intimate quality.

Mozart Flute Quartet No. 1 in D major, K285ª. Oboe Quartet in F major, K370/K368*b*ᵇ. Clarinet
Quintet in A major, K581ᶜ. ªJaime Martin (fl); ᵇJonathan Kelly (ob); ᶜNicholas Carpenter (cl);
Brindisi Quartet (ᵇᶜJaqueline Shave, ªᶜPatrick Kiernan, vns; Katie Wilkinson Krososhunin, va;
Anthony Pleeth, vc). EMI Debut Ⓕ CDZ5 69702-2 (64 minutes: DDD: 9/97). Recorded 1996.

Do you like your Mozart refined and graceful? Or robust and spontaneously expressive? A combination of both would be perfect, you may think, but in practice it's not always easy to achieve. The Brindisi Quartet and their three colleagues play with exceptional finesse, and excellent balance and blend, well captured by the recording. These are predominantly light-toned performances, with the phrases shaped convincingly and with unfailing elegance. Their approach seems just about ideal in the Flute Quartet, where the joyful, vivacious atmosphere of the outer movements is enhanced by thoughtful attention to detail. Jaime Martin's sensitive, sensuous flute-playing in the *Adagio* provides a delightful contrast. There are many good things in the other two pieces, too. Jonathan Kelly's virtuosity in the Oboe Quartet's finale is really exciting, as is the brilliant, superbly balanced development section in the Clarinet Quintet's first movement. But there are places where you might long for something less cool and detached. The recording of the Oboe Quartet by Nicholas Daniel and members of the Lindsay Quartet (reviewed further on with the String Quartet No. 17 and the Horn Quintet) really does manage to combine stylishness with strong expression.

Additional recommendations ...

...Flute Quartets – No. 1; No. 2 in G major, K285*a*; No. 3 in C major, K285*b*/KAnh171; No. 4 in
A major, K298. Oboe Quartet (arr. Galway)ª. ªJames Galway (fl); **Tokyo Quartet.**
RCA Victor Red Seal Ⓕ 09026 60442-2 (69 minutes: DDD: 6/93).

...Flute Quartets Nos. 1-4. **Irena Grafenauer** (fl); **Gidon Kremer** (vn); **Veronika Hagen** (va);
Clemens Hagen (vc). Sony Classical Ⓕ SK66240 (55 minutes: DDD: 6/96).

...Oboe Quartetª. Oboe Quintet in C minor, K406/K516*b*ᵇ. Adagio in F major, KAnh94/K580*a*ᶜ.
String Quartet No. 22. ªᵇᶜLajos Lencsés (ob/ᶜcor ang); **Stamitz Quartet.**
Capriccio Ⓕ 10 525 (68 minutes: DDD: 6/96).

...Flute Quartet No. 3 (trans. Fuchs). Oboe Quartet. Adagio for Cor Anglais, Violin, Viola and
Cello in C major, K580*a*. Divertimento for Oboe, Two Horns and Strings in D major, K251.
Simon Fuchs (hn); **Novšak Trio;** mbrs of the **Zurich Tonhalle Orchestra.**
Tudor Ⓕ TUDOR7049 (67 minutes: DDD: 5/98).

Mozart Piano Quartets – No. 1 in G minor, K478; No. 2 in E flat major, K493. **Isaac Stern** (vn);
Jaime Laredo (va); **Yo-Yo Ma** (vc); **Emanuel Ax** (pf). Sony Classical Ⓕ SK66841
(56 minutes: DDD: 8/97). Recorded 1994.

There is no shortage of good recordings of this favourite coupling of two Mozart masterpieces, and this grouping of star names offers performances of comparable imagination and insight. In the E flat Quartet, K493, it is not just Isaac Stern and Yo-Yo Ma whose solo entries have one sitting up, but also Jaime Laredo in the rare moments when Mozart gives a solo opportunity to his own instrument, the viola. Speeds are beautifully chosen, and in both works the performances consistently convey a sense of happy spontaneity. Emanuel Ax shows what a natural, individual Mozartian he is. The G minor work is in many ways parallel to the great piano concertos of the period, with the piano regularly set against the strings in ensemble, and Ax readily establishes the sort of primacy plainly required, even in such company as this. He is a shade robust at the start of the central *Andante* but in fast music as in slow his gift of pointing rhythms and moulding phrases is consistently persuasive and imaginative. The recording, made in the Manhattan Center, New York, is a degree drier than in many of the current rival versions, but there is ample bloom on the sound, fitting very well in a domestic listening room.

Mozart Complete Edition, Volume 12 – String Quartets: No. 1 in G major, K80/K73*f*; No. 2 in
   D major, K155/K134*a*; No. 3 in G major, K156/K134*b* (with additional original Adagio); No. 4
   in C major, K157 (all from 6500 142, 12/71); No. 5 in F major, K158; No. 6 in B flat major,
   K159; No. 7 in E flat major, K160/K159*a*; No. 8 in F major, K168 (6500 172, 12/72); No. 9 in
   A major, K169; No. 10 in C major, K170; No. 11 in E flat major, K171; No. 12 in B flat major,
   K172; No. 13 in D minor, K173 (6747 097, 9/74); No. 14 in G major, K387; No. 15 in D minor,
   K421/K417*b* (SAL3632, 10/67); No. 16 in E flat major, K428/K421*b*; No. 17 in B flat major,
   K458, "Hunt" (SAL3633, 10/67); No. 18 in A major, K464; No. 19 in C major, K465,
   "Dissonance" (SAL3634, 10/67); No. 20 in D major, K499, "Hoffmeister"; No. 21 in D major,
   K575 (6500 241, 7/72); No. 22 in B flat major, K589; No. 23 in F major, K590 (6500 225, 7/73).
   Quartetto Italiano (Paolo Borciani, Elisa Pegreffi, vns; Piero Farulli, va; Franco Rossi, vc).
   Philips Mozart Edition Ⓜ 422 512-2PME8 (eight discs: 474 minutes: ADD: 8/91).
   Recorded 1966-1973. *Gramophone Award Winner 1991.*   Ⓖ
These are classic performances which have won praise ever since they began to appear back in 1967. Admittedly, a little allowance has to be made for the sound since the recordings date from between 1966 and 1973. For example, it is a touch heavy and close in the 1966 recording of the D minor Quartet that is one of the wonderful set of six that Mozart dedicated to Haydn. In a way, this accords to some extent with the playing of the Quartetto Italiano, which is at times rather earnest – and in the first movement of this work, rather deliberate in its pace. But these are really the only criticisms of a generally splendid issue, and the innate seriousness of these fine Italian artists is almost always a plus feature: indeed, they bring an overall intelligence, refinement and, above all, range of interpretative values to this often superb and always attractive music. As for quality of ensemble, they are impeccable. This is undeniably still the best general survey of Mozart's string quartets available, and at mid price the eight discs represent a safe investment that should yield many years of pleasure.

Additional recommendations ...
...Nos. 7, 8, 9 and 22. **Eder Quartet.** Naxos Ⓢ 8 550544 (67 minutes: DDD: 9/93).
...Nos. 10, 11 and 15. **Eder Quartet.** Naxos Ⓢ 8 550546 (62 minutes: DDD: 2/95).
...Nos. 12, 13 and 21. **Eder Quartet.** Naxos Ⓢ 8 550545 (57 minutes: DDD: 2/95).

Mozart String Quartets – No. 15 in D minor, K421/K417*b*; No. 16 in E flat major, K428/K421*b*;
   No. 17 in B flat major, K458, "Hunt"; No. 20 in D major, K499, "Hoffmeister". **Franz Schubert
   Quartet** (Florian Zwiauer, Helge Rosenkranz, vns; Hartmut Pascher, va; Vincent Stadlmair, vc).
   Nimbus Ⓕ NI5455/6 (two discs: 115 minutes: DDD: 3/96). Recorded 1994.   Ⓖ
Mozart's profound debt to Haydn in the six string quartets he dedicated to the composer (of which the Franz Schubert Quartet here play K421 and K428) is most evident in their innovative approach to texture. Moreover, the true equality between the four parts – demonstrating a critical relationship between instrumentation and musical substance – has inspired startlingly different interpretative approaches. The Chilingirian Quartet's elegantly refined, charmingly understated accounts of the D minor and E flat Quartets convincingly present the music in an intimate, private context. By contrast, like the Alban Berg Quartet, the Franz Schubert Quartet offer more dramatic readings, whose wider dynamic range projects the music in a more public manner. Nimbus's impressively truthful recording reveals the music's varied textures with pellucid clarity in the opening *allegros*, and relatively fast *andantes* imbue the performers' lush ensemble with appropriately increased animation. The minuets are more passionate than those of the Chilingirian, and the finales are likewise bold and dramatic, with the variation finale of the D minor work, in particular, confirming a satisfying sense of overall unity. Despite their striking contrasts, though, the Franz Schubert Quartet do not quite achieve the extremes of the Alban Berg, whose powerfully arresting 1979 recording of the *Hunt* Quartet (K458) still sounds exceptionally fresh. The Franz Schubert Quartet's comparatively relaxed approach to the first movement, for example, fails to match the Berg's exhilarating evocation of the chase. Nevertheless, for those who find the latter too highly charged, the Franz Schubert Quartet here offer an alternative whose beautiful textural clarity and vivid thematic detail many will find irresistible. The Eder Quartet's remarkably robust, fluent version of the *Hoffmeister* Quartet, whose greater formal and expressive scope is everywhere apparent, represents excellent value. However, the Franz Schubert Quartet bring greater delicacy and finesse to their performance, most notably in their dynamic control and contrapuntal clarity. Try them in the first movement's development section, their lucid counterpoint in the second movement's introspective trio (in the tonic minor), their heartfelt expression in the *Adagio*, and their enthralling, symphonic conception of the finale. These distinguished accounts deserve an assured place among the very best alternatives.

Additional recommendations ...
...Nos. 14-23. **Alban Berg Quartet.** Teldec Ⓜ 4509-95495-2 (four discs: 265 minutes: ADD).
...Nos. 17 and 19. **Alban Berg Quartet.** Teldec Ⓕ 2292-43037-2 (57 minutes: ADD: 7/86).
...Nos. 20 and 21. **Chilingirian Quartet.** CRD Ⓕ CRD3427 (53 minutes: DDD: 2/87).
...Nos. 14 and 15. **Chilingirian Quartet.** CRD Ⓕ CRD3362 (59 minutes: ADD: 9/90).
...Nos. 16 and 17. **Chilingirian Quartet.** CRD Ⓕ CRD3363 (56 minutes: ADD: 9/90).
...Nos. 18 and 19. **Chilingirian Quartet.** CRD Ⓕ CRD3364 (68 minutes: ADD: 9/90).
...Nos. 21 and 23. **Salomon Quartet.** Hyperion Ⓕ CDA66355 (61 minutes: DDD: 4/91). ✏
...Nos. 18 and 19. **Quatuor Mosaïques.** Auvidis Astrée Ⓕ E8748 (76 minutes: DDD: 8/92). ✏   Ⓖ
...No. 19. Divertimentos – K136-8. **Eder Quartet.** Naxos Ⓢ 8 550543 (66 minutes: DDD: 9/93).
...Nos. 20 and 23. Adagio and Fugue in C minor, K546. **Eder Quartet.**
Naxos Ⓢ 8 550547 (62 minutes: DDD: 4/95).
...No. 19. **Beethoven** String Quartet No. 12 in E flat major, Op. 127. **Amadeus Quartet.**
Orfeo mono Ⓕ C358941B* (63 minutes: ADD: 10/95)
...Nos. 20 and 23. Adagio and Fugue in C major, K546. **Eder Quartet.**
Naxos Ⓢ 8 550547 (62 minutes: DDD: 5/95).
...No. 17. *Coupled with works by* **Haydn Amadeus Quartet.**
DG Galleria Ⓜ 449 092-2GGA (67 minutes: ADD: 7/96).
...Nos. 15 and 21. **Hagen Quartet.** DG Ⓕ 449 136-2GH (55 minutes: DDD: 2/97).
...No. 15. String Quintet No. 5 in D major, K593[a]. [a]**Louise Williams** (va); **Lindsay Quartet.**
ASV Ⓕ CDDCA1018 (65 minutes: DDD: 4/98).
...Nos. 17 and 19. **Lindsay Quartet.** Classics for Pleasure Ⓢ CD-CFP6034 (54 minutes: ADD: 5/98).

Mozart String Quartet No. 17 in B flat major, K458, "Hunt"[a]. Oboe Quartet in F major,
K370/K368b[b]. Horn Quintet in E flat major, K407/K386c[c]. [b]**Nicholas Daniel** (ob); [c]**Stephen Bell**
(hn); **Lindsay Quartet** (Peter Cropper, vn; Ronald Birks, [a]vn/[c]va; Robin Ireland, va;
Bernard Gregor-Smith, vc). ASV Ⓕ CDDCA968 (68 minutes: DDD: 1/97). Recorded 1995.
The Lindsays really make the *Hunt* Quartet sparkle. One could describe their approach as middle-of-
the-road; they're as meticulous as many period-instrument groups about details of phrasing, and
avoid excessive accents and vibrato, yet their sound is modern, and the care over detail doesn't
preclude a very spontaneous approach in which the music's feeling is compellingly communicated. In
the Oboe Quartet Nicholas Daniel matches the string players' care over articulation and detailed
expression, and plays with exceptional technical polish and brilliance. His gleaming tone is capable of
great expressive range. The Horn Quintet is perhaps not quite such an individual or remarkable work
as the two quartets. And you may find yourself longing for the extra character and beauty that a fine
performance with the natural horn would have had. Yet this is a highly recommendable reading, too.
The recording is very lifelike, with clear spacing of the instruments. All in all, a disc that deserves to
become a bestseller.

Mozart Piano Trios – No. 1 in G major, K496; No. 3 in B flat major, K502. Divertimento in B flat
major, K254. **Augustin Dumay** (vn); **Jian Wang** (vc); **Maria João Pires** (pf). DG Ⓕ 449 208-2GH
(73 minutes: DDD: 10/97). Includes bonus CD featuring short works by Brahms, Franck, Grieg,
Mozart and Ravel. Recorded 1995. *Gramophone Editor's choice.*   ⒼⒼ
This disc of early Mozart trios is radiant with the discriminating, fanciful and exuberant music-
making which characterizes this rare trio of friends. A crescendo of joy shooting up through the
opening scalic and arpeggio figures of K496 is answered by finely tapered violin playing and a cello
which draws the ear to its contributions long before the true dialogue of the *Andante*. This ensemble
finds a truly lilting 6/8 (rather than the illusion of a sturdier 3/4) for the second movement, and the
finale is full of a sense of wonder, in its platinum-tipped violin and the drawing back into finely
nuanced tones of grey for the sombre fifth variation. For K502, Pires picks up on the sense of forward
impetus inherent in the rhythm of the opening theme and in the slow movment her phrasing makes
its melody more shapely above the unsurpassed beauty of sustained tone in violin and cello. A
delicious performance of the little *Divertimento*, K254 reveals the ancestry of these two trios; and
there is yet another bonus in a 48-minute disc of extracts from the six recordings of Mozart, Brahms,
Franck, Ravel and Grieg made over six years by the incomparable duo of Pires and Dumay.
Additional recommendation ...
...Nos. 1 and 3; No. 4 in E major, K542; No. 5 in C major, K548; No. 6 in G major, K564.
Divertimento, K254. **Mozartean Players.**
Harmonia Mundi Ⓕ HMU90 7033/4 (two discs: 136 minutes: DDD: 8/93). ✏

Mozart Complete Edition, Volume 17 – Complete Piano Sonatas: No. 1 in C major, K279/K189*d*
(from 412 617-1PH, 1/86); No. 2 in F major, K280/K189*e*; No. 3 in B flat major, K281/K189*f*;
No. 4 in E flat major, K282/K189*g*; No. 5 in G major, K283/K189*h* (all from 420 186-2PH, 4/88);
No. 6 in D major, K284/K205*b* (420 185-1PH, 7/87); No. 7 in C major, K309/K284*b*; No. 8 in
A minor, K310/K300*d*; No. 9 in D major, K311/K284*c* (412 174-1PH, 4/86); No. 10 in C major,
K330/K300*h* (412 616-1PH, 4/85); No. 11 in A major, K331/K300*i*; No. 12 in F major,
K332/K300*k* (412 123-1PH, 7/84); No. 13 in B flat major, K333/K315*c* (412 616-1PH);
No. 14 in C minor, K457 (412 617-1PH); No. 15 in F major, K533/K494; No. 16 in C major,

K545 (412 122-1PH, 11/84); No. 17 in B flat major, K570 (420 185-1PH); No. 18 in D major, K576 (420 617-1PH). Fantasia in C minor, K475 (412 617-1PH). **Mitsuko Uchida** (pf).
Philips Mozart Edition Ⓜ 422 517-2PME5 (five discs: 325 minutes: DDD: 9/91).
Gramophone Award Winner 1989.   ⊖⊖⊖
By common consent, Mitsuko Uchida is among the leading Mozart pianists of today, and her recorded series of the piano sonatas won critical acclaim as it appeared and finally *Gramophone* Awards in 1989 and 1991. Here are all the sonatas, plus the *Fantasia* in C minor, K475, which is in some ways a companion piece to the sonata in the same key, K457. This is unfailingly clean, crisp and elegant playing, that avoids anything like a romanticized view of the early sonatas such as the delightfully fresh G major, K283. On the other hand, Uchida responds with the necessary passion to the forceful, not to say *Angst*-ridden, A minor Sonata, K310. Indeed, her complete series is a remarkably fine achievement, comparable with her account of the piano concertos. The recordings were produced by Erik Smith in the Henry Wood Hall in London and offer excellent piano sound; thus an unqualified recommendation is in order for what must be one of the most valuable volumes in Philips's Complete Mozart Edition. Do not be put off by critics who suggest that these sonatas are less interesting than some other Mozart compositions, for they are fine pieces written for an instrument that he himself played and loved.

Additional recommendations ...
...Complete Sonatas. Fantasia, K475. **Maria João Pires** (pf).
  DG Ⓕ 431 760-2GH6 (six discs: 397 minutes: DDD: 2/92).   ⊖⊖⊖
...Complete Sonatas. Fantasia, K475. **Christoph Eschenbach** (pf).
  DG Ⓜ 419 445-2GX5 (five discs: 339 minutes: ADD: 3/94).
...Nos. 2-5. **Mitsuko Uchida** (pf).
  Philips Ⓕ 420 186-2PH (54 minutes: DDD: 4/88). *Part of the five-disc set reviewed above.*   ⊖⊖⊖
...Nos. 8, 11 and 15. **Murray Perahia** (pf). Sony Classical Ⓕ SK48233 (64 minutes: DDD: 12/92).
...Nos. 3, 4 and 15. **Maria João Pires** (pf). DG Ⓕ 437 546-2GH (62 minutes: DDD: 7/93).   ⊖⊖⊖
...Nos. 2, 5, 13, 14 and 15. Fantasia, K475. **Sviatoslav Richter** (pf).
  Philips Ⓕ 438 480-2PH2 (two discs: 138 minutes: 8/94).   ⊖
...No. 8. K614. *Coupled with works by various composers.* **Dinu Lipatti** (pf).
  EMI Références mono Ⓜ CDH5 65166-2* (73 minutes: ADD: 12/94).
  See review in the Collections section; refer to the Index.   ⊖⊖⊖
...No. 10. *Coupled with works by various composers.* **Glenn Gould** (pf).
  Sony Classical mono Ⓜ SMK53474* (76 minutes: ADD: 9/95).
  See review under J.S. Bach; refer to the Index.
...Nos. 1-8. **Mieczysław Horszowski** (pf).
  Arbiter mono Ⓜ ARBITER101* (two discs: 128 minutes: ADD: 4/97).
...No. 17. *Coupled with works by* **Chopin** and **Shostakovich Emil Gilels** (pf).
  Testament mono Ⓕ SBT1089* (64 minutes: ADD: 5/97).
...Nos. 4-18. Fantasia, K475. **Ronald Brautigam** (fp).
  BIS Ⓕ CD836/40 (five discs, oas: 61, 58, 71, 60 and 74 minutes: DDD: 2/98). ✏
...Nos 1-14; Nos. 16-18. Fantasias – K475; C minor, K396; D minor, K397/K385g. 12 Variations in
  E flat major on "La belle Françoise", K353/K300f. Six Variations in F major on Paisiello's
  "Salve tu, Domine", K398/K416e. Eight Variations in A major on Sarti's "Come un agnello",
  K460/K454a. Allegro in G minor, K312/K590d. Minuet in D major, K355/K567b. Rondo in
  A minor, K511. Adagio in B minor, K540. Gigue in G major, K574. **Lili Kraus** (pf).
  Music & Arts mono Ⓜ CD1001* (five discs: 374 minutes: AAD: 6/98).

Mozart Piano Sonatas – No. 1 in C major, K279/K189d; No. 2 in F major, K280/K189e; No. 3 in
B flat major, K281/K189f. **Ronald Brautigam** (fp). BIS Ⓕ CD835 (58 minutes: DDD: 8/97). ✏
Recorded 1996.
Ronald Brautigam brings uncommon energy and excitement to these sonatas, playing them with a freshness and sense of novelty that few manage to produce for music familiar to most pianists from their schoolroom days. One might find the first movement of K279 a little breathless, perhaps wanting in elegance; Brautigam doesn't always bother to round off a phrase gracefully. But the *Andante* is beautifully played, with much delicacy of timing, just the right vein of sentiment and a fine command of the textures available on the fortepiano. He is indeed masterly in all the slow movements here. In the beautiful F minor middle movement of K280 his understanding of the expressive nature of Mozart's harmony is particularly telling, and in the recapitulation especially he produces an almost Chopinesque poetry with the soft-textured left hand against a right-hand melody: let no one say this isn't Mozartian, for if you can do it as tastefully as this, on the instrument Mozart used, you may be sure Mozart would have done something like it. Mozart might have made the repeats (all of which are observed) a little more elaborate; Brautigam ornaments very little but he does play the music slightly differently second time round in details of timing and shading. There are few recordings of these sonatas on the fortepiano, and these are extremely musical and imaginative performances.

Mozart Piano Sonatas – No. 5 in G major, K283/K189h; No. 6 in D major, K284/K205b;
No. 10 in C major, K330/K300h. **Maria João Pires** (pf). DG Ⓕ 437 791-2GH
(73 minutes: DDD: 3/94).   ⊖⊖⊖

Maria João Pires presents these sonatas with clear yet lightly pedalled textures and an overall directness that still allows room for tonal and rhythmic flexibility – which, generally speaking, is not overdone. Largely, her playing seems to let the music speak for itself, although of course just offering the notes is not enough and what we here appreciate is the art that conceals art. However, one might question the occasional detail: for example, less than a minute into the G major Sonata, Pires's longish trill on the D preceding the second subject is questionable, which gives us a bar with four beats in it instead of three. The *Andante* of the same work begins with repeated Cs that seem too emphatically staccato, and its central section is a little overdramatized. The dance movement called *Rondeau en Polonaise* in K284 is on the slow side, though it still holds together, and the variation-form finale varies considerably in pace. Pires consistently observes repeats, including the second halves of movements (thus we get virtually every note of K283 twice), as is indicated. These are clear, commendable performances, and the kind of grace that Pires brings to this music, in which other pianists can sound a touch severe, is most appealing. The recording is pleasing and admirably faithful.

Additional recommendation ...

...Nos. 5 and 11. Fantasia in D minor, K397/K385g. **Ivo Pogorelich** (pf).
DG Ⓕ 437 763-2GH (48 minutes: DDD: 8/95).

Mozart Complete Edition, Volume 18 – Piano Variations: G major, K24[a]; D major, K25[a]; C major, K179/K189a[a]; G major, K180/K173c[a]; C major, K264/K315d[a]; C major, K265/K300e[a]; F major, K352/K374c[a]; E flat major, K353K/300f[a]; E flat major, K354/K299a[a]; F major, K398/K416e[a]; G major, K455[a] (all from 6747 380, 6/79); A major, K460/K454a[c] (new to UK); B flat major, K500[a]; D major, K573[a]; F major, K613[a] (6747 380). Minuets – F major, K1d[c]; G major/C major, K1/K1e/K1f[c]; F major, K2[c]; F major, K4[c]; F major, K5[c]; D major, K94/K73h[c]; D major, K355/K576b[b] (all new to UK). Fantasia in D minor, K397/K385g[b] (412 123-1PH, 7/84). Rondos – D major, K485[b] (420 185-2PH, 7/87); A minor, K511[b] (412 122-1PH, 11/84). Adagio in B minor, K540[b]. Gigue in G major, K574[b] (both from 412 616-1PH, 4/85). Klavierstück in F major, K33B[c]. Capriccio in C major, K395/K300g[c]. March No. 1 in C major, K408/K383e[c]. Prelude and Fugue in C major, K394/K383a[c]. Allegros – C major, K1b[c]; F major, K1c[c]; B flat major, K3[c]; C major, K5a[c]; G minor, K312/K590d[c]; B flat major, K400/K372a (cpted Stadler)[c]. Suite in C major, K399/K385i[c]. Kleine Trauermarsch in C minor, K453a[c]. Andante in C major, K1a[c]. Fugue in G minor, K401/K375e[c] (with Tini Mathot, hpd. All new to UK). [a]**Ingrid Haebler**, [b]**Mitsuko Uchida** (pfs); [c]**Ton Koopman** (hpd). Philips Mozart Edition Ⓜ 422 518-2PME5 (five discs: 274 minutes: ADD/DDD: 10/91). *✍ Gramophone Award Winner 1991.* ⓖⓖⓖ
These five mid-price discs offer music of fine and often superb quality in a convenient format. The piano was Mozart's own instrument (though he also played the violin) and he composed much music for it besides the sonatas and concertos. Of the three artists here, two are generally fine and satisfying, though the third is more controversial. Ingrid Haebler was recorded back in 1975, but the piano sound is good and little tape background remains. Her performances of the variation sets, which take up the first three discs, are delicate without cuteness, effortlessly encompassing the music's wide range of moods. Mitsuko Uchida, on the fourth disc, performs individual pieces including the two rondos and the beautiful *Adagio* in B minor (the only piece Mozart wrote in this key) in a highly refined manner, a touch oversophisticated perhaps but still beautiful and expressive and taking full, unashamed advantage of the sound of a modern grand. By contrast, Ton Koopman's disc of minuets and other miscellaneous things is played on a harpsichord at a semitone below modern concert pitch and offers a recording of such immediacy that some listeners will regard it as too bright. Koopman puts gusto into everything he does, but not always to good effect. However, even if grace is in short supply in his performances, they undeniably offer ample personality and such reservations as one may have about his playing should not affect the desirability of the set as a whole.

Mozart (arr. Grieg) Keyboard Sonatas – No. 15 in F major, K533/K494; No. 16 in C major, K545. Fantasia in C minor, K475. **Sviatoslav Richter, Elisabeth Leonskaja** (pfs).
Teldec Ⓕ 4509-90825-2 (62 minutes: DDD: 2/96). Recorded 1993.
Now this really is something to tickle the fancy of transcription-fanciers. When Grieg added an accompaniment for a second piano to Mozart's keyboard sonatas, he did it primarily with teaching in mind. It was apparently common practice in the 1880s for teachers to accompany their pupils on a second piano. But the resulting compositions soon found their way into the concert-hall where, according to Grieg, "the whole thing sounded surprisingly good". And so it does today. In trying to "impart to several of Mozart's sonatas a tonal effect appealing to our modern ears" Grieg left a telling little document or two on just what those late nineteenth-century Norwegian ears expected. If the C major 'Sonata facile' seems to sit even more sedately in the drawing-room, then it soon becomes clear that the light glinting through its windows is not a million miles away from that bouncing off the fjord waters which lap around Troldhaugen. The C minor *Fantasia* becomes a dark salon melodrama (shades of *Bergljot*) which moves from conversation with not a little chromatic prevarication to the hanging of whimsical icicles of figuration around the major-key section. Gently exuberant harmonies cross-weave their way through the sparse trio-sonata-like textures of the opening F major before a trotting bass makes a high-stepping mountain horse of the rondo-finale. These are Mozart-Kugeln with a *bonne bouche* or two of the finest Gravadlax on the side. And if these fond tributes are good enough for Elisabeth Leonskaja and Sviatoslav Richter, who could resist tasting them?

Mozart Violin Sonatas – No. 1 in C major, K6. No. 2 in D major, K7. No. 3 in B flat major, K8. No. 4 in G major, K9. No. 5 in B flat major, K10. No. 6 in G major, K11. No. 7 in A major, K12. No. 8 in F major, K13. No. 9 in C major, K14. No. 10 in B flat major, K15. No. 11 in E flat major, K26. No. 12 in G major, K27. No. 13 in C major, K28. No. 14 in D major, K29. No. 15 in F major, K30. No. 16 in B flat major, K31. **Gérard Poulet** (vn); **Blandine Verlet** (hpd). Philips Duo ⓜ 438 803-2PM2 (two discs: 135 minutes: ADD: 4/94). ✍ From 422 515-2PME7 (9/91). Recorded 1975.

The early keyboard and violin sonatas include the boy composer's first works to appear in print: K6-9 were composed during his five-month Paris stay of 1763-4; K10-15 followed in 1765, when the Mozarts resided in London's Belgravia for over a year. The Sonatas, K26-31 appeared a month or two later when the family moved to The Hague. The precociously lively invention is consistently ear-catching, especially in the spunky violin part in the *allegros* and the often graceful lyrical writing. Even if the keyboard dominates the musical partnership, the violinist is always contributing attractive comments. The performances here are very well played, being vital and fresh, and very spontaneous sounding; moreover, they are well balanced and naturally recorded. There is much to intrigue here and many of these miniature works are extremely rewarding in their simplicity and direct melodic appeal.

Additional recommendations ...
...Nos. 17, 32 and 35. **Isaac Stern** (vn); **Yefim Bronfman** (pf).
Sony Classical SK53972 (70 minutes: DDD: 9/94).
...Nos. 19, 20, 22, 24 and 28. **Isaac Stern** (vn); **Yefim Bronfman** (pf).
Sony Classical Ⓕ SK64309 (72 minutes: DDD: 11/95).

Mozart Suite in the style of Handel in C major, K399 – Overture. Adagio and Allegro in F minor, K594 (ed. Trotter). Londoner Notenskizzenbuch, KAnh109*b* – Allegro in F major, K15*a*; Andante in E major, K15*o*; Andante in B flat major, K15*q*. Andante in B flat major, K15*ii*. Adagio in B minor, K540. Allegro in G major, K72*a*. Fugue in G minor, K401/K375*e*. Gigue in G major, K574. Prelude and Fugue in C major, K394/K383*a*. Andantino in E flat major, K236. Andante für eine Walze in eine kleine Orgel in F major, K616. Adagio in C major, K356/K617*a*. Fantasia für eine Uhr, K608 (ed. Trotter). **Thomas Trotter** (org). Decca London Ⓕ 443 451-2LH (66 minutes: DDD: 10/95). Played on the organ of the Nederlandse Hervormde Kerk, Farmsum, The Netherlands. Recorded 1993.

It takes much scratching around in the dirt to find enough Mozart organ music to fill a CD. It wasn't that Mozart was unfamiliar with the organ: far from it – Robin Langley's absorbing insert-notes quote a conversation between Vincent Novello and Mozart's widow in which she says "Mozart's favourite instrument was the organ – upon which he played with incomparable skill". It was this "incomparable skill" which meant Mozart left so little organ music for posterity; he was such a fluent improviser that he never really needed to write anything down. So what we have here, apart from pieces for other instruments which probably wouldn't get much of an airing if they weren't played on the organ (K594 and K608, originally for mechanical clock, are, ironically, generally considered to be the greatest organ works between Bach and Mendelssohn), are fragments and miniatures, tantalizing crumbs from the table of a genius, which in the hands of most players would seem little more than worthwhile curiosities. Thomas Trotter is an openly communicative player and while his discography to date centres around the extensive romantic repertoire, he proves himself here to be equally compelling in both classical repertoire and in short musical structures. Helped by a ravishing instrument which he handles with admirable fluency (although the action noise is horribly obtrusive), Trotter's Mozart truly comes to life. The big pieces (including a breathtakingly virtuosic account of K608) sit comfortably alongside the miniatures and the whole disc presents a thoroughly rewarding musical experience – required listening to anyone who would dismiss the classical era as anti-organ.

Additional recommendation ...
...Adagio in B minor, K540. Six German Dances, K509. *Coupled with works by various composers.*
Murray Perahia (pf). Sony Classical ⓜ SX4K63380 (four discs: 270 minutes: DDD/ADD).
See review in the Collections section; refer to the Index.

Mozart Concert Arias – Ah! se in ciel, benigne stelle, K538; Vorrei spiegarvi, oh Dio!, K418; No, no che non sei capace, K419; Se tutti i mali miei, K83/K73*p*; Popoli di Tessaglia! ... Io non chiedo, eterni Dei, K316/K300*b*; Mia speranza adorata ... Ah, non sai qual pena sia, K416; Alcandro, lo confesso ... Non so d'onde viene, K294; Ma che vi fece, o stelle ... Sperai vicino il lido, K368. **Natalie Dessay** (sop); **Orchestra of the Opéra de Lyon / Theodor Guschlbauer.** EMI Ⓕ CDC5 55386-2 (64 minutes: DDD: 8/96). Texts and translations included.

Natalie Dessay is a charming singer, with almost all the endowments of art and nature which these arias so exactly require. Her range extends upward far into the leger lines yet without incurring breathiness of a pallid coloration in the lower notes. She has a sylph's grace and lightness, and yet the timbre or character of her voice is thoroughly human. The profusion of scales and more intricate passagework common in some degree to all these pieces finds in her an unostentatious virtuoso, mind and breath giving well-regulated support, and a sensitive feeling for phrase and line making good musical sense throughout. Where vehemence and a dramatic quality of voice are in demand, as in the opening of *Popoli di Tessaglia*, we can find some reassurance in their absence because at least the young singer does not try to force an effect. In less strenuous attack, as in *No, no che non sei capace*, she conveys the energy of a determined spirit yet still has some way to develop as an expressive artist. The more sorrowful and tender phrases of *Se tutti i mali miei*, for example, evoke only a mild response in her. Occasionally, too, Dessay's purity forfeits normal resonance and for what seems to be an involuntary note or two the voice flutes with a kind of disembodied hollowness. An instance occurs just before the second part of *Vorrei spiegarvi*, yet this is such a lovely performance, so graceful in its leisurely interplay of voice and instruments, that grumbling really is out of order. Orchestra, conductor and recorded sound all make their contributions. In all of these marvellous incidental compositions the listener has one essential occupation, which is the discovery of delight.

Mozart Mass in C major, K257, "Credo". Litaniae de venerabili altaris sacramento, K243.
 Angela Maria Blasi (sop); **Elisabeth von Magnus** (contr); **Deon van der Walt** (ten); **Alistair Miles** (bass); **Arnold Schoenberg Choir; Vienna Concentus Musicus / Nikolaus Harnoncourt.**
 Teldec Das Alte Werk Ⓕ 9031-72304-2 (61 minutes: DDD: 6/93). ☞
 Notes, texts and translations included. Recorded 1991. ⓖⓖⓖ
The *Litaniae de venerabili altaris sacramento* of 1775 has powerful claims to be reckoned the finest of Mozart's church works before the C minor Mass and Requiem; but it has never quite had the recognition it deserves. Or the performance: until now, that is. It is clearly a deeply felt work, from the grave, warm opening of the "Kyrie", through the imposing "Verbum caro factum" and the graceful "Hostia" that succeeds it, the "Tremendum" with its almost Verdian menace and the appealing "Dulcissum convivium" (a soprano aria with soft textures supplied by flutes and bassoons), the highly original "Viaticum" and the resourcefully and lengthily developed "Pignus" to the "Agnus", a beautiful soprano aria with solo writing for flute, oboe and cello. The performance here under Nikolaus Harnoncourt rightly sees no need to apologize for the stylistic diversity of the work. The issue is made still more attractive by the inclusion of a Mass setting of the same year, one of Mozart's most inventive and original in its textures and its treatment of words. Altogether a very attractive record.

Mozart Mass in C major, K317, "Coronation". Vesperae solennes de confessore in C major, K339. Epistle Sonata in C major, K278/K271e[a]. **Emma Kirkby** (sop); **Catherine Robbin** (mez); **John Mark Ainsley** (ten); **Michael George** (bass); **Winchester Cathedral Choir; Winchester Quiristers; Academy of Ancient Music / Christopher Hogwood** with [a]**Alastair Ross** (org). L'Oiseau-Lyre
 Ⓕ 436 585-2OH (54 minutes: DDD: 4/93). ☞ Texts and translations included. Recorded 1990.
It is difficult to think of many recordings of Mozart's church music that so happily captures its character – the particular mixture of confidence, jubilation and contemplation – as Hogwood's. His unfussy direction, his broad phrasing, his lively but generally unhurried tempos and his happy details of timing serve splendidly in the *Coronation* Mass, the finest of Mozart's completed mass settings; the solemnity of the *Kyrie*, the fine swing of the *Gloria* and the energy of the *Credo*, with due pause for its rapt moment at the "Et incarnatus", all these come over with due effect. Arguably the "Osanna" is rather quick, but its jubilation is splendid. And the sweetness of the *Benedictus* is ravishing. Not more so, however, than the *Agnus*, for there, at a decidedly slow tempo, Hogwood allows Emma Kirkby to make the most of this very sensuous music, which she duly most beautifully does. The soloists are altogether an excellent team, with two refined voices in the middle and Michael George a firm and sturdy bass. The inclusion of the K278 Epistle Sonata is a happy notion. The *Vesperae solennes de confessore* is a setting of the five vesper psalms and the *Magnificat*, made in 1780, a year after the Mass, for some church feast in Salzburg. With admirable singing from the choir, a fresh-voiced group whose boys have a fine bright ring, and a spacious recording with exceptionally good stereo separation that properly conveys the ecclesiastical ambience, this is a disc to treasure.

Additional recommendations ...

...K317[a]. C minor, K427/K417a, "Great"[b]. D minor, K626[c], "Requiem". **Soloists;** [ac]**John Alldis Choir; London Symphony** [b]**Chorus and** [ab]**Orchestra,** [c]**BBC Symphony Orchestra / Sir Colin Davis.**
 Philips Duo Ⓜ 438 800-2PM2 (two discs: 135 minutes: ADD: 3/94). ⓖ

...K317. Exsultate, jubilate, K165/K158a. Vesperae solennes de confessore.
 Soloists; The English Concert and [a]**Choir / Trevor Pinnock.**
 Archiv Produktion Ⓕ 445 353-2AH (68 minutes: DDD: 10/94). ☞

...K317[a]. Ave verum corpus[b]. Vesperae solennes de confessore[a]. Exsultate, jubilate, K165/K158a[c].
 [ac]**Barbara Schlick** (sop); [a]**Elisabeth von Magnus** (contr); [a]**Paul Agnew** (ten); [a]**Matthijs Mesdag** (bass); **Amsterdam Baroque** [ab]**Choir and Orchestra / Ton Koopman.**
 Erato Ⓕ 0630-10705-2 (72 minutes: DDD: 2/96).

...K317. **Beethoven** Mass in D major, Op. 123, "Missa Solemnis".
 Soloists; Vienna Singverein; Berlin Philharmonic Orchestra / Herbert von Karajan.
 DG Double Ⓜ 453 016-2GTA2 (two discs: 111 minutes: ADD: 7/97).

Mozart (ed. Maunder) Mass in C minor, K427/K417a, "Great". **Arleen Auger, Lynne Dawson** (sops); **John Mark Ainsley** (ten); **David Thomas** (bass); **Winchester Cathedral Choir; Winchester College Quiristers; Academy of Ancient Music / Christopher Hogwood.** L'Oiseau-Lyre Florilegium
 Ⓜ 425 528-2OH (51 minutes: DDD: 7/90). ☞ Text and translation included. Recorded 1988.

Mozart left unfinished the work that ought to have been the choral masterpiece of his early Viennese years but there is enough of it to make up nearly an hour's music – music that is sometimes sombre, sometimes florid, sometimes jubilant. Christopher Hogwood avoids any charge of emotional detachment in his steady and powerful opening *Kyrie*, monumental in feeling, dark in tone; and he brings ample energy to the big, bustling choruses of the *Gloria* – and its long closing fugue is finely sustained. The clarity and ring of the boys' voices serve him well in these numbers. There is a strong solo team, headed by the late Arleen Auger in radiant, glowing voice and, as usual, singing with refined taste; Lynne Dawson joins her in the duets, John Mark Ainsley too in the trio. But this is essentially a "soprano mass" – Mozart wrote it, after all, with the voice of his new wife (and perhaps thoughts of the much superior one of her sister Aloysia) in his mind – and Auger, her voice happily stealing in for the first time in the lovely "Christe", excels in the florid and expressive music of the "Et incarnatus" (where Richard Maunder has supplied fuller string parts than usual, perhaps fuller than Mozart would have done had he finished the work). Hogwood directs with his usual spirit and clarity.

Additional recommendations ...

...Mass in C minor. **Soloists; Monteverdi Choir; English Baroque Soloists / Sir John Eliot Gardiner.** Philips Ⓕ 420 210-2PH (54 minutes: DDD: 5/88). 🌊

...Mass in C minor. **Beethoven** Missa solemnis. **Soloists; Atlanta Symphony Chorus and Orchestra / Robert Shaw.** Telarc Ⓕ CD80150 (two discs: 139 minutes: DDD: 11/88).

...Mass in C minor. **Soloists; Berlin Radio Chorus; Berlin Philharmonic Orchestra / Claudio Abbado.** Sony Classical Ⓕ SK46671 (53 minutes: DDD: 10/91).

...Mass in C minor. Masonic Funeral Music, K477. **Soloists; Collegium Vocale; La Chapelle Royale Choir; Champs Elysées Orchestra / Philip Herreweghe.** Harmonia Mundi Ⓕ HMC90 1393 (60 minutes: DDD: 9/92). 🌊

...Mass in C minor. Ave verum corpus in D major, K618. **Soloists; Academy of St Martin in the Fields Chorus and Orchestra / Sir Neville Marriner.** Philips Ⓕ 438 999-2PH (55 minutes: DDD: 12/94).

Mozart (cptd. Süssmayr) Mass in D minor, K626, "Requiem". **Sylvia McNair** (sop); **Carolyn Watkinson** (contr); **Francisco Araiza** (ten); **Robert Lloyd** (bass); **Chorus and Academy of St Martin in the Fields / Sir Neville Marriner.** Philips Ⓕ 432 087-2PH (50 minutes: DDD: 12/91). Text and translation included. Recorded 1990.

Mozart Mass in D minor, K626, "Requiem" (cptd. Süssmayr)[a]. Ave verum corpus in D major, K618. [a]**Anna Maria Panzarella** (sop); [a]**Nathalie Stutzmann** (contr); [a]**Christoph Prégardien** (ten); [a]**Nathan Berg** (bass); **Les Arts Florissants / William Christie.** Erato Ⓕ 0630-10697-2 (54 minutes: DDD: 11/95). 🌊 Texts and translations included. Recorded 1994.

Alongside those old musical teasers, "Who wrote Haydn's *Toy* Symphony?" (Leopold Mozart) and "Who wrote Purcell's Trumpet Voluntary?" (Jeremiah Clarke) can be added "Who wrote Mozart's Requiem?". Mozart's pupil Süssmayr was responsible for much of the work as most modern audiences would recognize it, but exactly how much was Mozart's, how much Süssmayr's, and how much anybody else's is anyone's guess. But performers don't seem unduly perturbed by this masterpiece's less than certain provenance, and there is no shortage of first-rate CD versions. Sir Neville Marriner's interpretation stands out as one of towering authority with a nobility and emotional impact few performances outside the concert-hall could expect to muster. From the stately opening "Requiem aeternam" to the Requiem's emotional climax, the "Agnus Dei", Marriner's musicians produce superlative performances. The chorus is remarkably well disciplined (just listen to the beautifully incisive singing with its dramatic dynamic contrasts in the "Domine Jesu"), and from the soloists Robert Lloyd's resonant "Tuba mirum" is a stunning contribution to a disc of exceptional quality.

Les Arts Florissants provide a substantial, dramatic reading: the tempo for the "Requiem aeternam" is slow, but malleable, and Christie is ready to make the most of the changes in orchestral colour or choral texture and indeed to dramatize the music to the utmost. Clearly he has little truck with any notion that this is an austere piece: he sees it as operatic, almost romantic – and the result is very compelling. There are surprising things: "Quantus tremor", in a very weighty account of the "Dies irae", for example, is hushed rather than terrifying; the "Recordare" is slow to the point of stickiness; there are rather mannered crescendos in the *Sanctus*; and often cadences are drawn out, for example in the "Hostias". The powerful choruses of the Sequence are imposingly done, and the grave "Lacrimosa" wonderfully catches the special significance not only of the music itself but also of the fact that this is the moment where Mozart's last autograph trails off. The choral singing is sharply etched and generally distinguished: the choir give a vigorous yet finely dovetailed *Kyrie* fugue and the "Quam olim Abrahae" is splendidly sturdy. Although the solo singing is not uniformly outstanding the soprano's melting tone is sometimes very appealing, and Prégardien is an excellent stylist; the *Benedictus* is particularly impressive, very shapely and refined. In short, this is a reading full of character and imaginative ideas, very much a conscious modern interpretation of the work and very finely executed. The disc is completed by perhaps the only piece which can reasonably follow the Requiem, the *Ave verum corpus*, in a slow, hushed, rather romantic reading that is undeniably moving.

Additional recommendations ...
...Requiem. Kyrie in D minor, K341. Soloists; Monteverdi Choir; English Baroque Soloists /
Sir John Eliot Gardiner. Philips Ⓕ 420 197-2PH (54 minutes: DDD: 11/87). ✔
...Requiem. Soloists; St John's College Choir, Cambridge; English Chamber Orchestra /
George Guest. Chandos Ⓕ CHAN8574 (54 minutes: DDD: 2/88).
...Requiem. Soloists; John Alldis Choir; BBC Symphony Orchestra / Sir Colin Davis.
Philips Silver Line Ⓜ 420 353-2PM (54 minutes: ADD: 2/88).
...Requiem (ed. Druce). Ave verum corpus, K618. Maurerische Trauermusik, K477/K479. Soloists;
Schütz Choir of London; Schütz Consort; London Classical Players / Sir Roger Norrington.
EMI Ⓕ CDC7 54525-2 (58 minutes: DDD: 11/92). ✔
...Requiem. Symphony No. 25 in G minor, K183/K173dB. Soloists;
Vienna State Opera Concerto Choir; Vienna Philharmonic Orchestra / Bruno Walter.
Orfeo D'Or mono Ⓕ C430961B* (76 minutes: ADD: 10/96).
...Requiemᵃ. Kyrie, K341. ᵃSoloists; La Chapelle Royale; Collegium Vocale;
Orchestra of the Champs-Elysées, Paris / Philippe Herreweghe.
Harmonia Mundi Ⓕ HMC90 1620 (54 minutes: DDD: 5/97). ✔

Mozart Così dunque tradisci, K432. Alcandro, lo confesso, K512. Mentre ti lascio, K513. Per
questa bella mano, K612. Rivolgete a lui lo sguardo, K584. Die Zauberflöte – Der Vogelfänger
bin ich ja; In diesen heil'gen Hallen; Ein Mädchen oder Weibchen. Le nozze di Figaro – Hai già
vinta la causa! ... Vedrò mentr'io sospiro. Don Giovanni – Madamina, il catalogo è questo; Deh!
vieni alla finestra. **Thomas Quasthoff** (bar); **Württemberg Chamber Orchestra / Jörg Faerber.**
RCA Victor Red Seal Ⓕ 09026 61428-2 (56 minutes: DDD: 10/97). Texts and translations
included. Recorded 1996.
With a voice hovering usefully between bass and baritone, and a rich, vibrant tone, the greatly
talented Quasthoff reminds one of Ramey at his most convincing but with more colouring in his tone.
In what is a taxing recital devoted to concert and opera arias, there is virtually nothing to criticize.
Quasthoff has the versatility and imagination to move easily between roles in the same opera; thus
after the Sarastro aria, he shows himself a wholly delightful Papageno, singing with a ready smile in
his tone and a nice variety between verses of the bird-catcher's two songs. Then a suave, seductive
Serenade from his Giovanni is followed by an appropriately oily "Madamina" from his Leporello. In
Figaro he undertakes only the Count and changes coats again, as it were, to exhibit anger and
command. From *Così fan tutte* he chooses Guglielmo's discarded aria, "Rivolgete", which can sound
too long, but not when sung with such relish as here. It's particularly rewarding to have modern
recordings of the four concert arias unaccountably neglected by basses, especially when sung with
such warm tone, firm line and pointed diction. Quasthoff couldn't have better partners than the
experienced, seemingly ageless Faerber and his orchestra, prompt in rhythm and well balanced with
the voice.
Additional recommendations ...
...Le nozze di Figaro – Voi che sapete. Don Giovanni – Batti, batti; Vedrai, carino; In quali eccessi
... Mi tradì quell'alma ingrata. Lucio Silla – Dunque sperar ... Il tenero momento. La finta
giardiniera – Dolce d'amor compagna. La clemenza di Tito – Ecco il punto, oh Vitellia ... Non
più di fiori. *Coupled with works by* **Haydn** and **Gluck** Anne Sofie von Otter (mez);
The English Concert / Trevor Pinnock (hpd). Archiv Produktion Ⓕ 449 206-2AH
(71 minutes: DDD: 10/97). *See review under Gluck; refer to the Index.*
...Le nozze di Figaro – Porgi, amor; E Susanna non vien! ... Dove sono. *Coupled with works by*
various composers. **Renée Fleming** (sop); **London Symphony Orchestra / Sir Georg Solti.**
Decca Ⓕ 455 760-2DH (72 minutes: DDD: 10/97). *Gramophone Editor's choice.*
See review in the Collections section; refer to the Index.
...Die Zauberflöte – Ach, ich fühl's. *Coupled with works by various composers.* **Dame Kiri Te Kanawa**
(sop); **Philharmonia Orchestra / Julius Rudel.** EMI Ⓕ CDC5 56417-2 (57 minutes: DDD: 11/97).
See review in the Collections section; refer to the Index.

Mozart Così fan tutte – Ah, scostati! ... Smanie implacabili. Le nozze di Figaro – Non so più cosa
son. Idomeneo – Non ho colpa; Il padre adorato; March of the priests. Mitridate, rè di Ponto –
Venga pur, minacci; Già dagli occhi. Don Giovanni – Vedrai, carino; In quali eccessi ... Mi tradì
quell'alma ingrata. Lucio Silla – Il tenero momento. La clemenza di Tito – Marcia; Deh per
questo istante; Non più di fiori. Io ti lascio, o cara, addio, KAnh245/K621a. **Vesselina Kasarova**
(mez); **Staatskapelle Dresden / Sir Colin Davis.** RCA Victor Red Seal Ⓕ 09026 68661-2
(74 minutes: DDD: 9/97). Texts and translations included. *Gramophone Editor's choice.*
Kasarova is a most exciting young singer. Being the questing, individual spirit she is, she can be
controversial as she breaks new ground in interpretation. She does nothing by halves, so some of these
performances could divide lovers of Mozart singing. However, most of the arias in this vivid recital
are thrilling in all the right kinds of ways. Defiant Dorabella, despondent Elvira and confused Vitellia
are all unerringly portrayed, but it is in the great castrato roles that Kasarova excels most of all. Both
sides of Farnace's character in *Mitridate* are explored in his arias, the first fiercely proud, the single
word "barbaro" saying it all. Then in the second we hear the gently palpitating voice of repentance,
"son pentito". In Cecilio's aria from *Lucio Silla*, another aspect of Kasarova's singing brings a smile

of pleasure – the wonderful variety she brings to her runs. The aria, *Io ti lascio* displays her grave beauty of tone, enhanced by the slightest of vibrations, revealing a singer of high intelligence with the means to fulfil her earnest intents. Who better to partner such an elevated singer than Sir Colin? He provides the know-how of a loving Mozartian, prompt in every phrase, and singer and conductor are seconded by playing of idiomatic firmness from the Dresden orchestra. Everything is admirably recorded.

Mozart Così fan tutte – In uomini, in soldati; Temerari! ... Come scoglio; Ei parte ... Per pietà, ben mio. Le nozze di Figaro – E Susanna non vien! ... Dove sono; Giunse alfin il momento ... Al desio (K577*a*). Don Giovanni – Batti, batti, o bel Masetto; In quali eccessi ... Mi tradì quell' alma ingrata. Davidde penitente, K469 – Lunghi le cure ingrate. Exsultate, jubilate, K165/K158*a*. **Cecilia Bartoli** (mez); **Vienna Chamber Orchestra / György Fischer.** Decca Ⓕ 443 452-2DH (61 minutes: DDD: 11/94). Texts and translations included. Recorded 1993.

On disc anything is possible: taking this selection of arias together with her other Mozart/da Ponte recordings, we can now hear Bartoli in all three female roles in *Così fan tutte*, three in *Le nozze di Figaro* and two in *Don Giovanni* – versatility unbounded. There are relatively few Italian mezzos, or sopranos for that matter, who sing a lot of Mozart and Bartoli's very Italian characteristics are immediately identifiable: brilliance of execution, vitality of words, sharpness of mind. She tears into the recitative before Donna Elvira's "Mi tradì" with a blistering fury that leaves most interpreters of the role standing and has no problems with the *fioriture* of the aria itself. Her Fiordiligi has the bite for "Come scoglio", but comparisons with a variety of lyric sopranos show up a want of depth to the tone, both here and in "Per pietà". Her Countess delivers her lines with appropriately aristocratic weight, though one senses her natural temperament being suppressed with difficulty. However much she tries to disguise herself, the real Bartoli is likely to pop her head out. There are unlikely to be any complaints about her effervescent Despina or Zerlina, both portrayals for which she has stage experience. In the concert-hall she is also a spirited interpreter of *Exsultate, jubilate*. From the opening line Bartoli makes other singers seem bland by comparison, getting the Latin words to tingle with a sense of elation that only an Italian-speaker would dare. The orchestral sound might be more firmly focused (the sound picture in "Batti, batti" has the solo cello close, while the wind struggle to be heard from some deep recess) but Fischer accompanies his soloist with energy and tact.

Additional recommendations ...

...Exsultate, jubilate – Alleluia. Regina coeli, K108/K74*d* – Ora pro nobis Deum. Ascanio in Alba – Al mio ben mi veggio avanti. Lucio Silla – Dunque sperar poss'io ... Il tenero momento. *Coupled with works by various composers.* **Aris Christofellis** (sop); **Ensemble Seicentonovecento / Flavio Colusso.** EMI Ⓕ CDC5 56134-2 (65 minutes: DDD).

...Die Entführung aus dem Serail[a]. Exsultate, jubilate[b]. **Soloists;** [a]**Berlin RIAS Chamber Choir and Orchestra;** [b]**Berlin Radio Symphony Orchestra / Ferenc Fricsay.** DG Dokumente [a]mono/[b]stereo Ⓜ 445 412-2GDO2* (two discs: 125 minutes: ADD 7/95).

...Exsultate, jubilate. Ergo interest in G major, K143/K73*a. Coupled with works by* **Pergolesi** and **J.C. Bach** **Ruth Ziesak** (sop); **La Stagione / Michael Schneider.** Deutsche Harmonia Mundi Ⓕ 05472 77335-2 (57 minutes: DDD: 11/96).

...Le nozze di Figaro – Voi che sapete. Don Giovanni – Batti, batti, o bel Masetto. *Coupled with works by various composers.* **Vesselina Kasarova** (mez). RCA Victor Red Seal Ⓕ 09026 68522-2 (64 minutes: DDD: 2/97). *Gramophone Editor's record of the month. See review in the Collections section; refer to the Index.* ⒼⒼ

...Zaïde – Ruhe sanft, mein holdes Leben. Don Giovanni – Batti, batti, o bel Masetto. Idomeneo – Rè di Creta – Zeffiretti lusinghieri. Ah, lo previdi ... Ah, t'invola, K272. Voi avete un cor fedele, K217. Exsultate, jubilate, K165/K158*a*. **María Bayo** (sop); **Galicia Symphony Orchestra / Victor Pablo Pérez.** Auvidis Valois Ⓕ V4790 (53 minutes: DDD: 6/97).

...Exsultate, jubilate – Alleluia. Vesperae solennes de confessore in C major, K339– Laudate Dominum. Mass No. 18 in C minor, "Great Mass" – Laudamus te. *Coupled with works by various composers.* **Lesley Garrett** (sop); **Britten Sinfonia / Ivor Bolton.** Conifer Classics Ⓕ 75605 51329-2 (73 minutes: DDD: 12/f97). *See review in the Collections section; refer to the Index.*

...Lucio Silla – Ah, corri, vola ... Quest'improvviso tremito. Don Giovanni – Or sai chi l'onore; Crudele! Ah no, mo bene ... Non mi dir. Idomeneo – Idol mio, se ritroso; Oh smania! oh furie! ... D'Oreste, d'Aiace. **R. Strauss** Salome – Ach, du wolltest mich nicht deinen Mund küssen lassen. Guntram – Fass'ich sie bang. Ariadne auf Naxos – Es gibt ein Reich. Arabella – Mein Elemer!. Die Aegyptische Helena – Zweite Brautnacht!. **Jane Eaglen** (sop); **Israel Philharmonic Orchestra / Zubin Mehta.** Sony Classical Ⓕ SK60042 (65 minutes: DDD: 6/98).

Mozart Le nozze di Figaro – Giunse alfin il momento ... Deh, vieni; Giunse alfin il momento ... Al desio di chi t'adora, K577*a*. Don Giovanni – In quali eccessi ... Mi tradì. Die Entführung aus dem Serail – Ach, ich liebte. Il rè pastore – L'amerò, sarò costante[a]. Die Zauberflöte – Ach, ich fühl's. La finta giardiniera – Geme la tortorella; Crudel, Oh Dio! fermate; Ah, dal pianto, dal singhiozzo. Zaïde – Ruhe sanft, mein holdes Leben. Il sogno di Scipione – Lieve son al par del vento. Nehmt meinen Dank, ihr holden Gönner, K383. **Renée Fleming** (sop); [a]**Krista Bennion Feeney** (vn); **Orchestra of St Luke's / Sir Charles Mackerras.** Decca Ⓕ 452 602-2DH (60 minutes: DDD: 10/96). Recorded 1995. *Gramophone Editor's choice.*

Renée Fleming's exceptionally beautiful voice has a depth to it which first reminds you of de los Angeles in her prime and then, in the context of *Le nozze di Figaro*, of the mistress rather than the maid. It also points up the slight oddity that as regards tessitura (or the 'lie' of the voice) the two roles differ very little, while the voice-characters are nevertheless quite distinct. It suggests also good reasoning on the part of Fleming, who is quoted in an article on the disc as saying "I wanted to do this high-lying Mozart before it's too late." She does indeed mingle "high-lying Mozart" with the medium. In several items she faces the heights and takes them with zest and success. The Germanic use of head-voice in "Ach, ich liebte" (*Die Entführung*), for instance, is forsworn in favour of a full-bodied voice in the upper notes. In La Fortuna's aria from *Il sogno di Scipione* not only are the C major scales similarly brave and full, but the cadenza is topped with a staccato E and G, both *in alt*. But this is the record of more than a singer. Mackerras and the St Luke's Orchestra contribute greatly towards its distinction. The playing of the big scene for Sandrina in *La finta gardiniera*, for instance, is something very special. In the *Zauberflöte* and *Zaïde* arias a fast tempo is chosen, with a loss of the more luxurious loveliness and a gain in eighteenth-century refinement. In everything, orchestral parts as well as the voice, the sound is suited to the sense, and both give plentiful delight.

Mozart Die Entführung aus dem Serail – Martern aller Arten. Die Zauberflöte – Ach, ich fühl's. Vorrei spiegarvi, oh Dio, K418. No, che non sei capace, K419. Ah, se in ciel, benigne stelle, K538. Il rè pastore – L'amerò, sarò costante. Voi avete un cor fedele, K217. Chi sà, chi sà, qual sia, K582. Le nozze di Figaro – Deh vieni, non tardar. Der Schauspieldirektor – Bester Jüngling. Nehmt meinen Dank, ihr holden Gönner, K383. Schon lacht der holde Frühling, K580.
Sumi Jo (sop); **English Chamber Orchestra / Kenneth Montgomery**. Erato Ⓕ 0630-14637-2 (65 minutes: DDD: 1/97). Texts and translations included.

Sumi Jo's disc naturally begs comparison with Renée Fleming's (reviewed above). Both singers give delightful performances, and if a contrast claims attention it lies rather more in the instrumental work and perhaps that of the conductors. In "Ach, ich fühl's" (*Die Zauberflöte*) Mackerras, conducting for Fleming, takes an unusually fast tempo, while Kenneth Montgomery, still quick compared with what became the norm, avoids the suspicion of didacticism. Interestingly, it is Sumi Jo who forfeits elegance in the difficult high run on "Herzen", while Fleming, at the faster speed, uses her technique to more secure advantage. In *Nehmt meinen Dank* comparison focuses more exclusively upon the singers, for here Fleming is distinctly the more expressive: warmer ("bleibt immer dar"), more responsive ("so feurig, als mein Herz ihn sprich"). Delights abound. Sumi Jo has the apt Susanna voice, and her "Deh vieni" is delicious. In *Vorrei spiegarvi* the delicate charm is winningly captured, with a beautifully judged interplay between voice and instruments. "Martern aller Arten" has its scales and broad intervals clearly articulated, with plenty of spirit and never a harsh note. Throughout the recital this lovely singer shows herself a worthy exponent of the tradition handed on from Mozart's own time.

Margaret Price sings Mozart Dame Margaret Price (sop); [a]**English Chamber Orchestra;**
[b]**London Philharmonic Orchestra / James Lockhart** ([c]pf). RCA Victor Gold Seal Ⓜ 09026 61635-2 (two discs: 151 minutes: ADD: 5/95). Items marked [a] from SER5675 (10/73), [b]LRL1 5077 (10/75), [c]LSB5001 (4/71). Texts and translations included.
Mozart La clemenza di Tito – Parto, parto (with Thea King, cl)[a]. Le nozze di Figaro – Voi che sapete[a]; E Susanna non vien! ... Dove sono[a]; Giunse alfin il momento ... Deh vieni, non tardar[a]. Die Entführung aus dem Serail – Martern aller Arten[a]. Il rè pastore – L'amerò, sarò costante[a] (Jose-Luis Garcia, vn)[a]. Don Giovanni – In quali eccessi ... Mi tradì quell' alma ingrata[a]; Crudele! Ah no mio bene ... Non mi dir[a]. Idomeneo – Parto, e l'unico ... Idol mio, se ritroso[b]. Concert arias – Vado, ma dove? oh Dei!, K583[b]; Vorrei spiegarvi, oh Dio, K418[b]; Ch'io me scordi di te ... Non temer, amato bene, K490 (Dennis Simons, vn)[b]; Al desio, K577[b]; Bella mia fiamma ... Resta, oh cara, K528[b]. Ch'io mi scordi di te ... Non temer, amato bene, K505[b]; Nehmt meinen Dank, ihr holden Gönner, K383[b]. Eine kleine deutsche Kantate, K619[c].
Mussorgsky The Nursery[c]. **Liszt** Sonetti di Petrarca, S270[c]. Ⓖ

Margaret Price's early recordings announced to the world a unique singer: nobody could mistake that purity of tone or the way she has of moving from note to note, as though each is a separate gem in a row of pearls. Although complete recordings followed of some of the Mozart operas, this disc of individual arias holds its own. "Idol mio" from *Idomeneo* has never been more ravishing; the Countess's "Dove sono" is an example of the purest classical poise, despite some plummy Italian vowels. A touch of breathiness intrudes in fast passages where the voice is asked to move around, but even mentioning it seems unfair, when there is so much beauty on all sides. At this stage of her career Margaret Price was not the kind of artist to inject drama into Mozart's more formal concert arias, but that disc also contains some favourite tracks. Her *Nehmt meinen Dank* lights upon an unexpectedly sweet tone and *Vorrei spiegarvi* seems even more spectacular today than it did at the time, given that the young Mozartian soprano has subsequently gone on to sing Aida. The fillers are taken from Price's "Wigmore Hall" song recital. There is no room for the Italian songs, but we do get her fearless singing of Liszt's Petrarch Sonnets, accompanied in a drily unromantic fashion by James Lockhart. The verdict is clear-cut: not to be missed.

Mozart Ah, lo previdi ... Ah, t'invola, K272. A questo seno ... Or che il cielo, K374. Alma grande e nobil core, K578. Grabmusik, K42a/K35a – Betracht dies Herz und frage mich[a]. Vado, ma dove?

oh Dei!, K583. Bella mia fiamma ... Resta, o cara, K528. Misera! dove son ... Ah! non son io, K369. **Gundula Janowitz** (sop); **Vienna Symphony Orchestra / Wilfried Boettcher.**
DG The Originals Ⓜ 449 723-2GOR (61 minutes: ADD: 2/97). Texts and translations included.
From SLPM139198 (8/67), except [a] new to UK (recorded 1966).   Ⓖ
An 'original' is exactly what this disc is, as it reproduces Janowitz's first solo recital record, issued in 1967. Listening back, we can marvel not just at the purity of tone and silken vocal line, but also a refinement of style that marks out a fully formed artist. The highlights include a delicate *Vado, ma dove?* and a performance of *Bella mia fiamma* which lights up the music with the subtlest of colours from within. Some of the recitatives might have been more dramatic, but Wilfried Boettcher and the Vienna Symphony Orchestra provide alert accompaniment. There is also a bonus: the original LP did not have room for the ravishing G minor lament "Betracht dies Herz" from the *Grabmusik*, K42, and that is now issued for the first time here, a minor treasure in its own right.

Mozart Exsultate, jubilate, K165/K158a. Zaïde – Ruhe sanft, meine holdes Leben. Nehmt meinen Dank, ihr holden Gönner, K383. Mia speranza adorata ... Ah non sai qual pena sia, K416. Vorrei spiegarvi, oh Dio, K418. Ch'io mi scordi di te ... Non temer, amato bene, K505a.
R. Strauss Morgen, Op. 27 No. 4. Liebeshymnus, Op. 32 No. 3. Der Rosenband, Op. 36 No. 1. Wiegenlied, Op. 41 No. 1. Das Bächlein, AV118. **Christine Schäfer** (sop); [a]**Maria João Pires** (pf); **Berlin Philharmonic Orchestra / Claudio Abbado.** DG Ⓕ 457 582-2GH (65 minutes: DDD: 4/98). Texts and translations included. Recorded 1997. *Gramophone Editor's choice.*   Ⓖ
Schäfer must now be rated in the royal line of Schwarzkopf, Seefried, Ameling, Popp and most recently Bonney as an interpreter of Mozart and Strauss. Yet, she is, like those renowned singers, very much her own person with her own distinctive voice and style. Her almost vibrato-less, at times slightly acerbic tone won't be to all tastes but her unadorned, clear and imaginative singing of all the Mozart arias demands and holds attention. In *Nehmt meinen Dank*, the single word "Geduld" carries a wealth of meaning; the whole of K416 – Mozart at his most pained and searching – has an intense feeling of farewell as Schäfer delivers it and again a single word, "addio" at the end of the recitative, is drenched in sadness. In *Non temer, amato bene*, with Pires providing an ideal counterpoint to the singer, Schäfer etches into the mind the full import of the emotions being expressed, without a hint of sentimentality. *Ruhe sanft* disarms criticism, so touchingly, simply, is it sung, with the little cadenza before the reprise deftly touched in. The more extrovert pieces, *Exsultate, jubilate* and *Vorrei, spiegarvi* are, appropriately enough, sung more objectively. Abbado and the Berlin Philharmonic support Schäfer in the most refined fashion possible, all the instrumental detail finely honed. They are just as ingratiating in Strauss. Most recent interpreters have had richer, warmer voices than Schäfer's. She is a throwback to, say, Elisabeth Schumann, who sang *Wiegenlied* with just the same kind of artless, silvery beauty, combined with a pure, keen line – a real winner. But so is each of these beautifully composed and sung pieces, the texts fully understood so that the words are ideally melded with their settings: note especially the extra tranche of intensity at the climax of *Liebeshymnus* and the ideal delineation of the elegiac *Morgen*'s reflective mood, the tempo for once not too slow. Indeed it's in this last song, that one hears, as well as anywhere, the soprano's special gift of plaintive eloquence. The recording could not be better balanced.

Mozart Le nozze di Figaro – Non so più; Voi che sapete; Giunse alfin il momento ... Deh vieni. Così fan tutte – E'amore un ladroncello. Don Giovanni – Vedrai, carino. La clemenza di Tito – Parto, partob; Deh, per questo; Ecco il punto, o Vitellia ... Non piu di fioric. Concert Arias – Chi sa, chi sa, qual sia, K582; Alma grande e nobil core, K578; Ch'io mi scordi di te?, K505a.
Cecilia Bartoli (mez); [a]**András Schiff** (pf); **Peter Schmidtl** ([b]basset cl and [c]basset hn); **Vienna Chamber Orchestra / György Fischer.** Decca Ⓕ 430 513-2DH (58 minutes: DDD: 12/91). Texts and translations included. Recorded 1989-1990.
Mozart wrote some of his most appealing music for the mezzo-soprano voice with the roles of Cherubino and Susanna in *Le nozze di Figaro*, Dorabella in *Così fan tutte* and Zerlina in *Don Giovanni* each boasting at least one memorable aria. Alongside these this disc includes a handful of concert arias including *Ch'io mi scordi di te?* which was written for the farewell performance of the great mezzo Nancy Storace with Mozart himself playing the concertante piano role. Here with as innate an interpreter of Mozart's piano writing as András Schiff and a voice so remarkably self-assured as Cecilia Bartoli's the electricity of that first, historic performance seems almost to be recreated. And, here as elsewhere, György Fischer directs the splendid Vienna Chamber Orchestra with disarming sensitivity while the recording is wonderfully warm and vibrant. Cecilia Bartoli boasts a voice of quite extraordinary charm and unassuming virtuosity: her vocal characterizations would be the envy of the finest actresses and her intuitive singing is in itself a sheer delight. But she also brings to these arias a conviction and understanding of the subtleties of the language which only a native Italian could. Listen to the subtle nuances of "Voi che sapete", the depth of understanding behind Dorabella's seemingly frivolous "E'amore un ladroncello"; these are not mere performances, but interpretations which penetrate to the very soul of the music. No Mozart lover should be without this CD.

Additional recommendation ...

...Alma grande e nobil core, K578. Ah, lo previdi ... Ah, t'invola, K272. A questo seno ... Or, che il chielo, K374. Vado, ma dove? oh Dei!, K583. Bella mia fiamma ... Resta, oh cara, K528. Misera! dove son ... Ah! non son io, K369. *Coupled with works by various composers.*

Gundula Janowitz (sop); Irwin Gage (pf); Vienna Symphony Orchestra / Wilfried Boettcher; Orchestra of the Deutsche Staatsoper, Berlin / Ferdinand Leitner.
DG Double Ⓜ 447 352-2GDB2 (two discs: 152 minutes: ADD: 12/95).

Mozart La clemenza di Tito. Uwe Heilmann (ten) Tito; Della Jones (mez) Vitellia; Cecilia Bartoli (mez) Sesto; Diana Montague (mez) Annio; Barbara Bonney (sop) Servillia; Gilles Cachemaille (bar) Publio; Academy of Ancient Music Chorus; Academy of Ancient Music / Christopher Hogwood. L'Oiseau-Lyre Ⓔ 444 131-2OHO2 (two discs: 137 minutes: DDD: 3/95). 🎵
Notes, text and translation included.Recorded 1993. *Gramophone Editor's choice.*
Mozart La clemenza di Tito. Gösta Winbergh (ten) Tito; Carol Vaness (sop) Vitellia; Delores Ziegler (mez) Sesto; Martha Senn (mez) Anno; Christine Barbaux (sop) Servilia; László Polgár (bass) Publio; Vienna State Opera Chorus; Vienna Philharmonic Orchestra / Riccardo Muti. EMI Ⓕ CDS5 55489-2 (two discs: 136 minutes: ADD: 10/95). Notes, texts and translation included. Recorded live in 1988. *Gramophone Editor's choice.*

The appeal of *La clemenza di Tito*, if less immediate and less obvious than that of the other operas of Mozart's maturity, is still very powerful and very individual. Hogwood has assembled a quite remarkable cast, with certainly two, perhaps three, outstanding interpretations. First among them must be Cecilia Bartoli, who rightly establishes Sextus as the central character, the one whose actions and whose feelings are the focal point of the drama. The opening number is the duet "Come ti piace, imponi", where the firm and pure sound of Bartoli's voice, in contrast with the contained hysteria of Vitellia's, at once defines the opera's basis. It is clear from her singing that she reads Sextus, for all his weakness in giving way to Vitellia, as a man of integrity, one of the noblest Romans of them all. Then there is Della Jones's remarkable Vitellia. There are lots of interesting and emotionally suggestive touches in her singing, which is very committed and very passionate, if not perhaps immaculately tidy – but then, tidiness is no part of Vitellia's persona. Her rich bottom register is magnificent and the top Bs have no fears for her. Uwe Heilmann's Titus is marked by much subtle and finely shaped singing and a keen awareness of how phrasing conveys sense. Occasionally the tone is inclined to be nasal, but that does not interfere with a very sympathetic and often moving reading. Hogwood's keen awareness of what, expressively speaking, is going on in the music, and his refusal to be tied to a rigid rhythmic pulse in order to make it manifest, is one of the strengths of this recording. The recitatives are sung with a great deal of life and awareness of meaning, not simply gabbled through at maximum speed. These, of course, are not Mozart's own work and are usually heavily cut; Gardiner on his Archiv version cuts them extensively. While some may feel that the inclusion of every note, as in the present version, is an advantage to the opera, others may not unreasonably take the opposite view. At any rate, the discs' tracking is arranged so that a new track begins for each aria, which enables the listener to make their own cuts without difficulty. There are now two very fine recordings of this opera with period instruments. On balance, the Hogwood is better sung, whereas Gardiner has the advantage of a stronger sense of continuity, derived no doubt from the fact of its having been recorded more or less live.

Muti, oblivious to or at least putting aside attempts at period practice, interprets the work unashamedly as a grand, incisive near-tragedy. Nor is he averse to the players of the Vienna Philharmonic drawing the most sensuous sounds from the score, something that Gardiner, even more Hogwood, eschew, yet he never indulges Mozart, favouring swiftish, though flexible tempos and sharp rhythms. Muti is also notable for catching the *tinta*, the individual colour, of this work. Listen to the trio of contrasted feeling, "Quello di Tito", in Act 2 and you'll divine the calibre of this reading, or a little earlier to the way Muti persuades the chorus into the most mellifluous sounds in "Ah, grazie si rendamo". Muti's approach is admirably seconded by the generous voices taking the three central roles: Vaness is in her element as Vitellia, alternately amorous, vindictive, scheming and forgiving. Hers is not as verbally detailed nor so keenly vituperative an account as Varady's for Gardiner and Böhm, or indeed Baker's for Davis, but it is boldly and confidently sung throughout a longish evening. As Sextus, Ziegler is fully the equal of her/his loved one, encompassing both her arias with richly contoured tone and courageously delivered coloratura, all tending to convey Sesto's torture of the mind. The only drawback is a certain similarity in the two singers' refulgent tone. At the centre of the emotional chasm stands Winbergh's commanding, concerned Tito, perhaps the most heroically sung on any version yet sufficiently flexible for his arias' runs (given a few unwanted aspirates). If the other singers aren't quite in the same category, they are all well in the vocal and dramatic picture. It is good to hear the true sound of a theatre acoustic on this live recording. Of course, on the other hand you have to cope with applause at the end of many numbers and one intrusion, happily only in dry recitative, of an audible aeroplane. So, a formidable addition to the work's discography, totally engrossing on its own terms and recommendable as a contender to any newcomer to the piece on disc.

Additional recommendations ...
...Soloists; Leipzig Radio Choir; Dresden Staatskapelle / Karl Böhm.
DG Ⓜ 429 878-2GX2 (two discs: 140 minutes: ADD: 12/90).
...Soloists; Monteverdi Choir; English Baroque Soloists / Sir John Eliot Gardiner.
Archiv Produktion Ⓕ 431 806-2AH2 (two discs: 118 minutes: DDD: 12/91). 🎵
...Soloists; Chorus and Orchestra of the Royal Opera House, Covent Garden / Sir Colin Davis.
Philips Mozart Edition Ⓜ 422 544-2PME2 (two discs: 128 minutes: ADD: 4/92).

Mozart Così fan tutte. **Dame Elisabeth Schwarzkopf** (sop) Fiordiligi; **Christa Ludwig** (mez)
Dorabella; **Hanny Steffek** (sop) Despina; **Alfredo Kraus** (ten) Ferrando; **Giuseppe Taddei** (bar)
Guglielmo; **Walter Berry** (bass) Don Alfonso; **Philharmonia Chorus and Orchestra / Karl Böhm.**
EMI Ⓜ CMS7 69330-2 (three discs: 165 minutes: ADD: 11/88). Notes, text and translation
included. From SAN103/6 (5/63). Recorded 1962.   Ⓖ

Mozart Così fan tutte. **Amanda Roocroft** (sop) Fiordiligi; **Rosa Mannion** (sop) Dorabella;
Eirian James (mez) Despina; **Rainer Trost** (ten) Ferrando; **Rodney Gilfry** (bar) Guglielmo;
Carlos Feller (bass) Don Alfonso; **Monteverdi Choir; English Baroque Soloists /
Sir John Eliot Gardiner.** Archiv Produktion Ⓕ 437 829-2AH3
(three discs: 134 minutes: DDD: 2/94). ☞ Recorded live in 1992.

Mozart Così fan tutte. **Soile Isokoski** (sop) Fiordiligi; **Monica Groop** (mez) Dorabella;
Nancy Argenta (sop) Despina; **Markus Schäfer** (ten) Ferrando; **Per Vollestad** (bar) Guglielmo;
Huub Claessens (bass) Don Alfonso; **La Petite Bande and Chorus / Sigiswald Kuijken.**
Accent Ⓕ ACC9296/8 (three discs: 181 minutes: DDD: 2/94). ☞
Notes, text and translation included. Recorded live in 1992.

Così fan tutte is the most balanced and probing of all Mozart's operas, formally faultless, musically
inspired from start to finish, emotionally a matter of endless fascination and, in the second act,
profoundly moving. It has been very lucky on disc, and besides this delightful set there have been
several other memorable recordings. However, Böhm's cast could hardly be bettered, even in one's
dreams. The two sisters are gloriously sung – Schwarzkopf and Ludwig bring their immeasurable
talents as Lieder singers to this sparkling score and overlay them with a rare comic touch. Add to that
the stylish singing of Alfredo Kraus and Giuseppe Taddei and the central quartet is unimpeachable.
Walter Berry's Don Alfonso is characterful and Hanny Steffek is quite superb as Despina. The pacing
of this endlessly intriguing work is immaculate. The emotional control of the characterization is
masterly and Böhm's totally idiomatic response to the music is arguably without peer. However, two
modern recordings, using period instruments, do offer stimulating alternative views.

Gardiner's is a *Così* with a heart, and a heart in the right place. It comes from a stage performance
given in the Teatro Comunale at Ferrara – the city from which, of course, the sisters in the story hail
– in 1992. The vitality and the communicativeness of the recitative is one result of recording a live
performance; it is flexible, conversational and lively, as it ought to be, and the Italian pronunciation
is remarkably good considering there isn't a single Italian in the cast. Amanda Roocroft makes a
capable Fiordiligi, with a big, spacious "Come scoglio", and shows real depth of feeling in what is a
very beautiful account of "Per pietà"; her tone is bright and forward. Rosa Mannion, as Dorabella,
acts effectively with her voice in "Smanie implacabili" and is full of life in her Act 2 aria. The
Guglielmo, Rodney Gilfry, is quite outstanding for his light, warm and flexible baritone, gently
seductive in Act 1, showing real brilliance and precision of articulation in "Donne mie". Eirian
James's Despina is another delight, spirited, sexy and rich-toned, and full of charm without any of
the silliness some Despinas show. Period instruments notwithstanding, this is a fairly traditional
performance. Gardiner often uses quite generous rubato to highlight the shape of a phrase, and he is
alert, as always, to how the orchestral writing can underline the sense.

The Kuijken, another live recording, is lighter in mood than Gardiner's. Nearly all the tempos are
quicker and there is more sense of spontaneity. Mozart very rarely wrote dynamic or accentuation
marks into his singers' parts; the singers were expected to learn their music from a repetiteur (or
Mozart himself) and take their cues from what they heard in performance. Gardiner has his singers
follow, meticulously, the orchestral dynamics; Kuijken leaves them, more or less, to sing with what
they hear. This is a symptomatic difference: one performance is highly wrought, the other freer and
more natural. The sisters in the Kuijken version are excellently done by Soile Isokoski, even in voice
and with an attractive ring, and Monica Groop, again a pleasing and even voice intelligently and
musically used. Their duets are both very appealing, with a happy sense in "Prenderò quel
brunettino" that they might be getting up to a little mischief. The Alfonso here, Huub Claessens, more
baritone than bass, is particularly successful in the recitative, which here again is done with much care
for its meaning. A pleasing and lively *Così*, it would be a good recording with which to get to know
the opera, whereas the Gardiner is a connoisseur's performance, subtle and sophisticated, and
communicating important things about the opera.

Additional recommendations ...
...**Soloists; Glyndebourne Chorus; London Philharmonic Orchestra / Bernard Haitink** with
Martin Isepp (hpd). EMI Ⓕ CDS7 47727-8 (three discs: 186 minutes: DDD: 7/87).
...**Soloists; Philharmonia Chorus and Orchestra / Herbert von Karajan.**
EMI Références mono Ⓜ CHS7 69635-2* (three discs: 157 minutes: ADD: 12/88).
...**Soloists; Ambrosian Opera Chorus; Academy of St Martin in the Fields / Sir Neville Marriner.**
Philips Ⓕ 422 381-2PH3 (three discs: 191 minutes: DDD: 11/90).
...**Soloists; Glyndebourne Festival Chorus and Orchestra / Fritz Busch.**
EMI Références Ⓜ CHS7 63864-2* (two discs: 153 minutes: ADD: 9/91).
...**Soloists; Chorus and Orchestra of the Royal Opera House, Covent Garden / Sir Colin Davis.**
Philips Mozart Edition Ⓜ 422 542-2PME3 (three discs: 183 minutes: ADD: 1/92).
...**Soloists; Edinburgh Festival Chorus; Scottish Chamber Orchestra / Sir Charles Mackerras.**
Telarc Ⓕ CD80360 (three discs: 188 minutes: DDD: 4/94). *Gramophone Editor's choice.*

...Excerpts. **Soloists; Glyndebourne Festival Orchestra / Fritz Busch; Philharmonia Orchestra /**
Walter Susskind. Testament mono Ⓕ SBT1040* (73 minutes: ADD: 6/94).

...**Soloists; Vienna State Opera Chorus; Vienna Philharmonic Orchestra / Karl Böhm.**
Orfeo mono Ⓕ C357942I* (two discs: 137 minutes: ADD: 2/95).

...**Soloists; London Voices; Chamber Orchestra of Europe / Sir Georg Solti.**
Decca Ⓕ 444 174-2DHO3 (three discs: 179 minutes: DDD: 3/96).

...**Soloists; Berlin RIAS Chamber Choir; Berlin Philharmonic Orchestra / Eugen Jochum.**
DG Ⓜ 449 580-2GX3 (three discs: 181 minutes: ADD: 8/96).

Mozart Don Giovanni. **Eberhard Waechter** (bar) Don Giovanni; **Dame Joan Sutherland** (sop)
Donna Anna; **Dame Elisabeth Schwarzkopf** (sop) Donna Elvira; **Graziella Sciutti** (sop) Zerlina;
Luigi Alva (ten) Don Ottavio; **Giuseppe Taddei** (bar) Leporello; **Piero Cappuccilli** (bar) Masetto;
Gottlob Frick (bass) Commendatore; **Philharmonia Chorus and Orchestra / Carlo Maria Giulini.**
EMI Ⓕ CDS5 56232-2* (three discs: 162 minutes: ADD: 12/87). Notes, text and translation
included. From Columbia SAX2369/72 (2/61). Recorded 1959. *Gramophone classical 100.* ⒼⒼⒼ

Mozart Don Giovanni. **Rodney Gilfry** (bar) Don Giovanni; **Luba Orgonasova** (sop) Donna Anna;
Charlotte Margiono (sop) Donna Elvira; **Eirian James** (mez) Zerlina; **Christoph Prégardien** (ten)
Don Ottavio; **Ildebrando d'Arcangelo** (bass) Leporello; **Julian Clarkson** (bass) Masetto;
Andrea Silvestrelli (bass) Commendatore; **Monteverdi Choir; English Baroque Soloists /**
Sir John Eliot Gardiner. Archiv Produktion Ⓕ 445 870-2AH3 (three discs: 176 minutes:
DDD: 8/95). ✒ Notes, text and translation included. Recorded 1994.   Ⓖ

Mozart Don Giovanni. **Bo Skovhus** (bar) Don Giovanni; **Christine Brewer** (sop) Donna Anna;
Dame Felicity Lott (sop) Donna Elvira; **Nuccia Focile** (sop) Zerlina; **Jerry Hadley** (ten)
Don Ottavio; **Alessandro Corbelli** (bar) Leporello; **Umberto Chiummo** (bass) Masetto,
Commendatore; **Scottish Chamber Chorus and Orchestra / Sir Charles Mackerras.**
Telarc Ⓕ CD80420 (three discs: 183 minutes: DDD: 11/96). Notes, text and translation included.
Recorded 1995. *Gramophone Editor's choice.*   Ⓖ

Although the EMI set is over 38 years old, none of its successors is as skilled in capturing the piece's
drama so unerringly. It has always been most recommendable and Giulini captures all the work's most
dramatic characteristics, faithfully supported by the superb Philharmonia forces of that time. At this
stage of Giulini's career, he was a direct, lithe conductor, alert to every turn in the story and he
projects the nervous tension of the piece ideally while never forcing the pace, as can so easily happen.
Then he had one of the most apt casts ever assembled for the piece. Waechter's Giovanni combines
the demonic with the seductive in just the right proportions, Taddei is a high-profile Leporello, who
relishes the text and sings with lots of 'face'. Elvira was always one of Schwarzkopf's most successful
roles: here she delivers the role with tremendous intensity. Sutherland's Anna isn't quite so full of
character but it is magnificently sung. Alva is a graceful Ottavio. Sciutti's charming Zerlina,
Cappuccilli's strong and Italianate Masetto and Frick's granite Commendatore are all very much in
the picture. The recording still sounds well.

The Gardiner set has a great deal to commend it. The recitative is sung with exemplary care over
pacing so that it sounds as it should, like heightened and vivid conversation, often to electrifying
effect. As an adjunct, ensembles, particularly the Act 1 quartet, are also treated conversationally, as if
one were overhearing four people giving their opinions on a situation in the street. The orchestra,
perfectly balanced with the singers in a very immediate acoustic, supports them, as it were 'sings' with
them. That contrasts with, and complements, Gardiner's expected ability to empathize with the
demonic aspects of the score, as in Giovanni's drinking song and the final moments of Act 1, which
fairly bristle with rhythmic energy without becoming rushed. The arrival of the statue at Giovanni's
dinner-table is tremendous, the period trombones and timpani achieving an appropriately brusque,
fearsome attack. Throughout this scene, Gardiner's penchant for sharp accents is wholly appropriate;
elsewhere he is sometimes too insistent. As a whole, tempos not only seem right on their own account
but also, all-importantly, carry conviction in relation to each other. Where so many conductors today,
including Norrington on EMI, rush "Mi tradi", Gardiner prefers a more meditative approach,
allowing his soft-grained Elvira to make the most of the aria's expressive possibilities.

As in his other Mozart opera recordings, Gardiner benefits from working with singers whom he
knows well. Gilfry's Giovanni is lithe, ebullient, keen to exert his sexual prowess; an obvious charmer,
at times surprisingly tender yet with the iron will only just below the surface. Suave and appealing,
delivered in a real baritone timbre, his Giovanni is as accomplished as any on disc. Ildebrando
d'Arcangelo was the discovery of these performances: this young bass is a lively foil to his master and
on his own a real showman, as "Madamina" indicates, a number all the better for a brisk speed.
Orgonasova once more reveals herself a paragon as regards steady tone and deft technique – no need
here to slow down for the coloratura at the end of "Non mi dir" – and she brings to her recounting
of the attempted seduction a real feeling of immediacy. In "Or sai chi l'onore" she manages just the
right kind of supple urgency. As Anna, Margiono sometimes sounds a shade stretched technically, but
consoles us with the luminous, inward quality of her voice and her reading of the role, something
innate that cannot be learnt. Nobody in their right senses is ever going to suggest that there is one,
ideal version of *Don Giovanni*; the work has far too many facets for that, but for sheer theatrical *élan*
complemented by the live recording, Gardiner is among the best, particularly when one also takes into
account a recording that is wonderfully truthful and lifelike.

The Mackerras set has no astonishing or brilliant individual interpretations here, but the whole is full of life and energy and freshness. The Scottish Chamber Orchestra are not a period-instrument group, but Mackerras, as he explains in his thoughtful note in the accompanying booklet (and as we hear), uses valveless horns and trumpets and something close to period timpani – hence the alarming sound of the opening chords. He also calls for sharper attack and quicker decay from the string players and a very forward wind balance. Tempos are often but by no means always on the fast side. But he also allows his singers plenty of time to phrase their music expressively, for example in the Giovanni-Zerlina scene in the first finale, in the trio at the beginning of Act 2 (some wonderfully sensual orchestral colours here), in Giovanni's serenade, in the great sextet (very powerfully done) and in the cemetery scene, which has a proper sense of the hieratic and yet a knife-edge tension too. In sum, it is a highly theatrical interpretation, one that constantly has you on the edge of your seat. Umberto Chiummo makes a good, incisive Masetto and (perhaps with a little help) a truly formidable Commendatore in the final scenes. Nuccia Focile provides a beguiling Zerlina, with a sweet upper range and more than a touch of sensuousness and charm. Alessandro Corbelli, the Leporello, is a lively, lowish baritone who uses the sound of the words to advantage and can phrase with just the right hint of elegance. His voice is very close, arguably too close, in general sound to that of the Giovanni, Bo Skovhus, yet the master-servant relationship is conveyed convincingly. Skovhus's sharp vitality (listen to "Metà di voi"), his virile Champagne Aria and his deeply sensual portamentos in the Serenade stress those aspects of Giovanni's character that underlie the plot. Jerry Hadley offers an Ottavio of some intensity, not the smoothest or most graceful, but stronger in expression than most and Dame Felicity is in full, creamy voice in a role she has often sung with distinction.

On the question of versions, Mackerras gives the Prague original first (with "Dalla sua pace" inserted in Act 1), so if you play the second disc through to the end, you should then skip the first ten tracks of the third disc to continue; or, if you want the Vienna version, you should skip the last six of the second and pick up at the beginning of the third, where you will hear the rare (and rather silly, though musically agreeable) Zerlina-Leporello duet and Elvira's scene (but not "Il mio tesoro"). This is an excellent solution for listeners who can be bothered to press a couple of buttons. Lazy ones will hear some of the music twice over. All round, an immensely enjoyable version of *Don Giovanni*.

Additional recommendations ...

...**Soloists; Glyndebourne Festival Chorus; London Philharmonic Orchestra / Bernard Haitink.**
EMI Ⓕ CDS7 47037-8 (three discs: 172 minutes: DDD: 12/84). Ⓔ

...**Soloists; Glyndebourne Festival Chorus and Orchestra / Fritz Busch.**
EMI Références mono Ⓜ CHS7 61030-2* (three discs: 172 minutes: ADD: 3/89). Ⓔ

...**Soloists; Vienna State Opera Chorus; Vienna Philharmonic Orchestra / Josef Krips.**
Decca Ⓜ 411 626-2DM3 (three discs: 166 minutes: ADD: 9/89).

...**Soloists; Drottningholm Theatre Chorus and Orchestra / Arnold Oestman.**
L'Oiseau-Lyre Ⓕ 425 943-2OH3 (three discs: 171 minutes: DDD: 12/90). 🖉

...**Soloists; Vienna State Opera Chorus; Vienna Philharmonic Orchestra / Wilhelm Furtwängler.**
EMI Références mono Ⓜ CHS7 63860-2* (three discs: 182 minutes: ADD: 7/91).

...**Soloists; Chorus and Orchestra of the Royal Opera House, Covent Garden / Sir Colin Davis.**
Philips Mozart Edition Ⓜ 422 541-2PME3 (three discs: 164 minutes: ADD: 1/92).

...**Soloists; Schütz Choir of London; London Classical Players / Sir Roger Norrington.**
EMI Ⓕ CDS7 54859-2 (three discs: 195 minutes: DDD: 10/93). 🖉

...**Soloists; Vienna State Opera Chorus; Vienna Philharmonic Orchestra / Dimitri Mitropoulos.**
Sony Classical mono Ⓕ SM3K64263* (three discs: 154 minutes: ADD: 11/94). ⒼⒼ

...**Soloists; Collegium Compostellanum; La Petite Bande / Sigiswald Kuijken.**
Accent Ⓕ ACC95116/8 (three discs: 153 minutes: DDD: 4/97).

Mozart Die Entführung aus dem Serail[a]. Exsultate, jubilate, K165/K158a[b]. [ab]**Maria Stader** (sop) Constanze (Beate Guttmann); **Rita Streich** (sop) Blonde; **Ernst Haefliger** (ten) Belmonte (Sebastian Fischer); **Martin Vantin** (ten) Pedrillo (Wolfgang Spier); **Josef Greindl** (bass) Osmin; **Walter Franck** (spkr) Bassa Selim; [a]**Berlin RIAS Chamber Choir and Orchestra,** [b]**Berlin Radio Symphony Orchestra / Ferenc Fricsay.** DG Dokumente [a]mono/[b]stereo Ⓜ 445 412-2GDO2* (two discs: 125 minutes: ADD: 7/95). Notes, texts and translations included.
Item marked [a] from DGM18184/5 (7/55), [b]SLPEM136291 (11/62).

The 1954 Fricsay set, at mid price, is an excellent buy. Fricsay was an advocate of crisp, zestful, pared-down Mozart *avant la lettre*. This was the first in his distinguished series of Mozart opera recordings, throughout which he used Berlin Radio forces and singers familiar with his work. They prove formidable advocates. The orchestra, recorded in resonant, honest mono, play superbly throughout for their conductor. Stader was a particular favourite with Fricsay. If not the most refulgent of sopranos, she had both the consistency of voice and thoroughness of technique to cope with almost all the demands of Constanze's music. Although one ideally wants a more dramatic singer in the part, her feeling for the shape of a Mozart phrase is always admirable. She is suitably partnered by the fluent, lyrical Haefliger, who also sang Belmonte at Glyndebourne in the 1950s. Although his voice hasn't quite the bite and positive characteristics of other Belmontes, it is used with consummate style. Rita Streich is the ideal Blonde, singing with pure tone and spirited attack: she has the individuality of voice, the hint of vibrato most attractive, to please the most fastidious listener. Vantin is a more than adequate Pedrillo, who sings his Serenade in an appropriate *mezza voce*. Greindl brings a fully fledged bass to bear on Osmin's music and fills it with a nice combination of vicious sadism leavened by comedy. Although his singing is occasionally marred by intrusive aspirates, he is among the most enjoyable Osmins on disc. Happily he and Streich are allowed to speak their own dialogue so that their Act 2 encounter goes particularly well. As was a dubious custom with DG at the time, the other singers are doubled by speaking voices that hardly match their own. Those who have come to appreciate Fricsay's many attributes as a conductor will not be disappointed by this reissue, and will gain as a generous bonus Stader's delightful account of *Exsultate, jubilate*. In absolute terms those without *Die Entführung* in their collection should hear this one. If they are not wedded to stereo sound, it may be the answer, as evenly cast and well conducted as any.

Mozart Die Entführung aus dem Serail. **Ingrid Habermann** (sop) Constanze; **Donna Ellen** (sop) Blonde; **Piotr Bezcala** (ten) Belmonte; **Oliver Ringelhahn** (ten) Pedrillo; **Franz Kalchmair** (bass) Osmin; **Harald Pfeiffer** (spkr) Bassa Selim; **Linz Landestheater Choir; Linz Bruckner Orchestra / Martin Sieghart.** Arte Nova Classics Ⓢ 74321 49701-2 (two discs: 115 minutes: DDD: 1/98). Notes, text and translation included. Recorded live at the Linz Opera in 1996-1997.

This is a real bargain, just about as enjoyable as any performance given by more prominent artists on better-known labels. Recorded live, it is not surprising to find such a natural sense of ensemble among the principals or such a well-integrated account of the score from Sieghart, who is also aware of the latest research on this score in terms of orchestration and small embellishments. His reading is a shade strict and unsmiling, but it has the virtue of keeping the drama on the move in a work that can outstay its welcome in more self-indulgent performances, and the playing of the small band is exemplary. Dialogue is included but kept to the minimum essential to clarify the action. Ingrid Habermann has the dramatic coloratura, the technique and all the notes to encompass the fearful demands of Constanze's role and shows the dramatic resolution it requires. The Polish tenor Piotr Bezcala has also been judiciously cast for his part: his voice is firm and sappy, and he discloses an ability to make his four taxing arias sound relatively simple. One or two unwanted lachrymose moments apart, he is a model of Mozartian style. The Canadian soprano, Donna Ellen, is a mettlesome Blonde, happy in the dizzy heights reached in her first aria. Her Pedrillo is a lively singer but one prone to questionable pitch, particularly in his Serenade. Best of all is the native Austrian, Franz Kalchmair as an Osmin with a rotund, pleasing bass, as happy at the bottom as at the top of his range and he is obviously a formidable actor. The Bassa Selim's role has been severely curtailed; what remains of it is spoken with the appropriate blend of menace and authority by Harald Pfeiffer. The recording is reasonably good, but there is a disturbing discrepancy between the acoustic used for respectively the sung and spoken sections of the piece. But that is not a drawback serious enough to prevent a strong recommendation.

Additional recommendations ...
...Soloists; Zurich Opera House Chorus and Orchestra / Nikolaus Harnoncourt.
  Teldec Ⓕ 2292-42643-2 (three discs: 135 minutes: DDD: 5/88).
...Soloists; Leipzig Radio Choir; Dresden Staatskapellle / Karl Böhm.
  DG Ⓜ 429 868-2GX2 (two discs: 131 minutes: ADD: 12/90).
...Soloists; Academy of Ancient Music Chorus and Orchestra / Christopher Hogwood.
  L'Oiseau-Lyre Ⓕ 430 339-2OH2 (two discs: 144 minutes: DDD: 11/91). ✍
...Soloists; John Alldis Choir; Academy of St Martin in the Fields / Sir Colin Davis.
  Philips Mozart Edition Ⓜ 422 538-2PME2 (two discs: 128 minutes: DDD: 4/92).
...Soloists; Vienna State Opera Chorus; Vienna Symphony Orchestra / Bruno Weil.
  Sony Classical Ⓕ S2K48053 (two discs: 123 minutes: DDD: 5/92).

Mozart Idomeneo, Rè di Creta. **Anthony Rolfe Johnson** (ten) Idomeneo; **Anne Sofie von Otter** (mez) Idamante; **Sylvia McNair** (sop) Ilia; **Hillevi Martinpelto** (sop) Elettra; **Nigel Robson** (ten) Arbace; **Glenn Winslade** (ten) High Priest; **Cornelius Hauptmann** (bass) Oracle; **Monteverdi Choir; English Baroque Soloists / Sir John Eliot Gardiner.** Archiv Produktion Ⓕ 431 674-2AH3 (three discs: 211 minutes: DDD: 6/91). ✍ Notes, text and translation included. Recorded 1990. *Gramophone classical 100. Gramophone Award Winner 1991.* ⒼⒼⒼ
Mozart Idomeneo, Rè di Creta. **Plácido Domingo** (ten) Idomeneo; **Cecilia Bartoli** (mez) Idamante; **Heidi Grant Murphy** (sop) Ilia; **Carol Vaness** (sop) Elettra; **Thomas Hampson** (bar) Arbace; **Frank Lopardo** (ten) High Priest; **Bryn Terfel** (bass-bar) Oracle; **Chorus and Orchestra of the Metropolitan Opera, New York / James Levine.** DG Ⓕ 447 737-2GH3 (three discs: 176 minutes: DDD: 1/97). Notes, text and translation included. *Gramophone Editor's choice.* ⒼⒼⒼ

Gardiner's is unquestionably the most vital and authentic account of the opera to date on disc. We have here what was given at the work's first performance in Munich plus, in appendices, what Mozart wanted, or was forced, to cut before that première and the alternative versions of certain passages, so that various combinations of the piece can be programmed by the listener. Gardiner's direct, dramatic conducting catches ideally the agony of Idomeneo's terrible predicament – forced to sacrifice his son because of an unwise row. This torment of the soul is also entirely conveyed by Anthony Rolfe Johnson in the title role to which Anne Sofie von Otter's moving Idamante is an apt foil. Sylvia McNair is a diaphanous, pure-voiced Ilia, Hillevi Martinpelto a properly fiery, sharp-edged Elettra. With dedicated support from his own choir and orchestra, who obviously benefited from a long period of preparation, Gardiner matches the stature of this noble *opera seria*. The recording catches the excitement which all who heard the live performances will recall.

After Gardiner's lithe, slimline *Idomeneo*, Levine brings us back to a 'traditional' reading, with a big orchestra and a cast starry enough to make the Golden Horseshoe thoroughly happy. There can be little question that this must be the most recommendable recording for those not wanting a period-instrument 'authentic' version. First, however, a word of explanation is needed, in view of the great divergences among current recordings of the opera, to clarify what this consists of. It is more or less the Munich first performance version: we get both arias for Arbace (particularly welcome in view of Thomas Hampson's fine singing), Idamante's acceptance of death "No, la morte" and Elettra's final venomous "D'Oreste, d'Aiace", but not Idomeneo's "Torna la pace" and only the shorter version of his "Fuor del mar" (with a changed ending). Recitatives are given almost complete, and though words are most expressively coloured throughout, this results in many recitatives almost turning into *ariosos*. Appoggiaturas are applied, if not very consistently, but only one artist, Heidi Grant Murphy, ventures to ornament an aria, in the reprise section of "Se il padre perdei". Murphy's Ilia is a gentle, youthful, sweet-voiced *ingénue*; her *fioriture* in "Zeffiretti" are sung with delicious purity and clarity. Bartoli as Idamante is utterly convincing and deeply involved in every nuance of the character's emotions, and her "No, la morte" is memorable. Carol Vaness may be forgiven for a rather screamy "D'Oreste, d'Aiace" but her earlier "Tutto nel cor" shows the right bitterness and fury, and she persuasively softens her tone when Elettra feels that fate seems to be favouring her. As Idomeneo, Plácido Domingo gives a reading of the nobility and intelligence we might expect from him, one which makes him an outstanding interpreter of the role. Aided by a well-judged production that successfully conveys the various perspectives in the opera, Levine presides over a coherently planned performance satisfying both from the dramatic and the lyrical viewpoints.

Additional recommendations ...

...Soloists; Leipzig Radio Choir; Dresden Staatskapelle / Karl Böhm.
DG Ⓜ 429 864-2GX3 (three discs: 170 minutes: ADD: 12/90).
...Soloists; Vienna State Opera Chorus; Vienna Philharmonic Orchestra / Ferenc Fricsay.
DG mono Ⓜ 447 662-2GX3* (three discs: 155 minutes: ADD: 9/95).

Mozart Le nozze di Figaro. **Bryn Terfel** (bass-bar) Figaro; **Alison Hagley** (sop) Susanna;
Rodney Gilfry (bar) Count Almaviva; **Hillevi Martinpelto** (sop) Countess Almaviva; **Pamela Helen Stephen** (mez) Cherubino; **Susan McCulloch** (sop) Marcellina; **Carlos Feller** (bass) Bartolo;
Francis Egerton (ten) Don Basilio, Don Curzio; **Julian Clarkson** (bass) Antonio; **Constanze Backes** (sop) Barbarina; **Monteverdi Choir; English Baroque Soloists / Sir John Eliot Gardiner.**
Archiv Produktion Ⓕ 439 871-2AH3 (three discs: 179 minutes: DDD: 8/94). ✍
Notes, text and translation included. Recorded live in 1993. Ⓖ

The catalogue of *Figaro* recordings is a long one, and the cast lists are full of famous names. In this version there is only one principal with more than a half-dozen recordings behind him, and some have none at all. It is a commentary on the times, on the astuteness of the casting here and on the capacity of a strong conductor to make the whole so much more than the sum of its parts that this version can stand comparison with any, not only for its grasp of the drama but also for the quality of its singing. It is, of course, a period-instrument recording, more evidently so than many under Gardiner. The string tone is pared down and makes quite modest use of vibrato, the woodwind is soft-toned (but happily prominent). The voices are generally lighter and fresher-sounding than those on most recordings of the opera and the balance permits more than usual to be heard of Mozart's instrumental commentary on the action and the characters. The recitative is done with quite exceptional life and feeling for its meaning and dramatic import, with a real sense, during much of it, of lively and urgent conversation, especially in the first half of the work. Bryn Terfel and Alison Hagley make an outstanding Figaro and Susanna. Terfel is quite a deep bass-baritone with enough darkness in his voice to sound pretty menacing in "Se vuol ballare" as well as bitter in "Aprite un po' quegli occhi"; it is an alert, mettlesome performance – and he also brings off a superlative "Non più andrai", done with tremendous spirit to its rhythms and richly and pointedly coloured. Hagley offers a reading of spirit and allure. The interplay between her and the woodwind in "Venite inginocchiatevi" is a delight, and her cool but heartfelt "Deh vieni" is very beautiful. Once or twice her intonation seems marginally under stress but that is the price one pays for singing with so little vibrato, and it's worth it. Hillevi Martinpelto's unaffected, youthful-sounding Countess is enjoyable; both arias are quite lightly done, with a very lovely, warm, natural sound in "Dove sono" especially. Some may prefer a more polished, sophisticated reading, of the traditional kind, but this is closer to what Mozart would have wanted and expected.

Rodney Gilfry provides a Count with plenty of fire and authority, firmly focused in tone; the outburst at the *Allegro assai* in "Vedrò mentr'io sospiro" is formidable. Pamela Helen Stephen's Cherubino sounds charmingly youthful and impetuous; "Voi che sapete" is taken a good deal quicker than usual, and with a touch of comedy, and benefits from it. There is no want of dramatic life in Gardiner's direction. His tempos are marginally quicker than most, and the orchestra often speaks eloquently of the drama. Gardiner adopts the Moberly/Raeburn order of events in Act 3. This involves placing "Dove sono" before, instead of after, the sextet and in the last Act he places Susanna's aria before, instead of after, Figaro's. Tempos are marginally faster on the Oestman version, which also offers a valuable appendix of alternative numbers. It is a very difficult choice: Gardiner's is the more dramatic, Oestman's the livelier and the more Italianate and giving a remarkable sense of everyone enjoying themselves.

Additional recommendations ...
...**Soloists; London Opera Chorus; London Philharmonic Orchestra / Sir Georg Solti.**
Decca Ⓕ 410 150-2DH3 (three discs: 169 minutes: DDD: 4/84).
...**Soloists; Glyndebourne Chorus; London Philharmonic Orchestra / Bernard Haitink**
with **Martin Isepp** (hpd). EMI Ⓕ CDS7 49753-2 (three discs: 178 minutes: DDD: 7/88).
...**Soloists; Chorus and Orchestra of the Drottningholm Court Theatre / Arnold Oestman**
with **Mark Tatlow** (hpd cont).
L'Oiseau-Lyre Ⓕ 421 333-2OH3 (three discs: 186 minutes: DDD: 12/88). ✍
...**Soloists; Glyndebourne Festival Chorus and Orchestra / Vittorio Gui.**
Classics for Pleasure Ⓑ CD-CFPD4724* (two discs: 158 minutes: ADD: 9/91).
...**Soloists; Netherlands Opera Chorus; Royal Concertgebouw Orchestra / Nikolaus Harnoncourt.**
Teldec Ⓕ 4509-90861-2 (three discs: 185 minutes: DDD: 10/94). ✍
...**Soloists; Vienna State Opera Chorus; Vienna Symphony Orchestra / Karl Böhm.**
Philips Opera Collector mono Ⓜ 438 670-2PM3* (three discs: 167 minutes: ADD: 10/94).
...**Soloists; Scottish Chamber Chorus and Orchestra / Sir Charles Mackerras.**
Telarc Ⓕ CD80388 (three discs: 209 minutes: DDD: 8/95).
...**Soloists; Vienna State Opera Chorus; Vienna Philharmonic Orchestra / Claudio Abbado.**
DG Ⓕ 445 903-2GH3 (three discs: 170 minutes: DDD: 10/95).
...(sung in German). **Soloists; Vienna State Opera Chorus;**
Vienna Philharmonic Orchestra / Wilhelm Furtwängler.
EMI Festspieldokumente mono Ⓕ CHS5 66080-2* (three discs: 176 minutes: ADD: 11/96).
...**Soloists; Chorus and Orchestra of the Deutsche Oper, Berlin / Karl Böhm.**
DG The Originals Ⓜ 449 728-2GOR3 (three discs: 172 minutes: ADD: 3/97).
...**Overtures** – Le nozze di Figaro; Don Giovanni; Die Zauberflöte. *Coupled with works by various*
composers. **London Philharmonic Orchestra; Berlin Philharmonic Orchestra /**
Sir Thomas Beecham. Dutton Laboratories mono Ⓑ CDLX7009* (75 minutes: ADD: 10/94).
See review in the Collections section; refer to the Index.
...**Overture.** *Coupled with works by* **Wagner, Verdi, Weber** and **R. Strauss** Hallé Orchestra /
Sir John Barbirolli. Dutton Laboratories mono Ⓜ CDSJB1004* (75 minutes: ADD: 11/96).

Mozart Le nozze di Figaro. **Cesare Siepi** (bass) Figaro; **Hilde Gueden** (sop) Susanna; **Alfred Poell**
(bar) Count Almaviva; **Lisa della Casa** (sop) Countess Almaviva; **Suzanne Danco** (sop)
Cherubino; **Hilde Rössl-Majdan** (contr) Marcellina; **Fernando Corena** (bass) Bartolo;
Murray Dickie (ten) Don Basilio; **Hugo Meyer-Welfing** (ten) Don Curzio; **Harald Pröglhöf** (bass)
Antonio; **Anny Felbermayer** (sop) Barbarina; **Vienna State Opera Chorus;**
Vienna Philharmonic Orchestra / Erich Kleiber. Decca Grand Opera Series Ⓜ 417 315-2DM3*
(three discs: 172 minutes: ADD: 2/90). From SXL2087/90 (3/59). Recorded 1955.
Gramophone classical 100.   ⒼⒼⒼ
Erich Kleiber's *Figaro* is a classic of the classics of the gramophone: beautifully played by the Vienna
Philharmonic, conducted with poise and vitality and a real sense of the drama unfolding through the
music. It's very much a Viennese performance, not perhaps as graceful or as effervescent as some but
warm, sensuous and alive to the interplay of character. At the centre is Hilde Gueden, whose Susanna
has echoes of Viennese operetta singing although she remains a true Mozartian stylist – her "Deh
vieni" is impeccably graceful and perfectly timed. Lisa della Casa's Countess may not be one of the
most dramatic but the voice is full yet focused, and "Dove sono" is a delight in particular. Suzanne
Danco's Cherubino is not exactly impassioned, and is really as much girlish as boyish, but it is still
neat and musical singing. The balance among the men is affected by the casting of Figaro with a
weightier singer than the Count. But Alfred Poell's Count makes up in natural authority and
aristocratic manner what he lacks in sheer power, and he shows himself capable, too, of truly sensual
singing in the Act 3 duet with Susanna. There are excellent performances, too, from Corena's verbally
athletic Bartolo and Dickie's alert, ironic Basilio. However, the true star is Erich Kleiber. The
beginning of the opera sets your spine a-tingling with theatrical expectation. Act 1 goes at pretty
smart tempos, but all through he insists on full musical value. There is no rushing in the
confrontations at the end of Act 2 – all is measured and properly argued through. And everything is
truly sung: the singers are never allowed, even had they wanted to, to skimp on the music to convey
the drama, and they have rather to use the music to convey it. With Kleiber and the VPO behind
them, they do so utterly convincingly. The transfer to CD presents the sound as well as one could hope
for from a set made nearly 45 years ago – no lover of this opera should be without it.

Mozart Zaïde. **Lynne Dawson** (sop) Zaïde; **Hans-Peter Blochwitz** (ten) Gomatz; **Olaf Bär** (bar)
Allazim; **Herbert Lippert** (ten) Sultan Soliman; **Christopher Purves** (bass) Osmin; **Academy of**
Ancient Music / Paul Goodwin. Harmonia Mundi Ⓕ HMU90 7205 (75 minutes: DDD: 6/98). ✍
Notes, text and translation included. Recorded 1997.   ⒼⒼ
Mozart began composing the work known as *Zaïde* in 1779-80, but left it unfinished, ostensibly
because no performance was in prospect, but perhaps also because, very soon after he broke off, he
came to see that this rather static kind of musical drama was not the sort of piece he wanted to write.
Moreover, the character relationships are difficult to deal with: the libretto and the music (as far as it
goes) imply a powerful attraction at the beginning of the opera between Zaïde and Gomatz, but

ultimately, in the final scene, which Mozart never reached, they turn out to be brother and sister: very touching, and well attuned to the sensibilities of the time, but cramping to the composer. Nevertheless, the music of *Zaïde* is full of fine things, often foreshadowing not only the similar *Entführung* but also *Idomeneo*. This recording captures its beauties and its depth of feeling beautifully. This is partly because of the sympathetic conducting of Paul Goodwin, who paces it with excellent judgement, bringing to it just the right degree of flexibility, and achieves orchestral textures that are both clear and warm – much more so than usual from period-instrument groups. The melodramas, tellingly shaped, perfectly catch the tone of passion. The AAM play at their best for him (notably, and understandably, the principal oboist). It is hard to imagine a better cast. Lynne Dawson sings the title-role with a frail beauty that is very appealing. Hans-Peter Blochwitz's shapely lines and full, eloquent tone make Gomatz's arias a delight, too; and Herbert Lippert, the second tenor, as the Sultan (in love, or lust, with Zaïde), is almost his match in evenness and lyrical quality. It is also a luxury to have Olaf Bär as Allazim: the music is sung with a refinement of tone and ease of articulation that you don't imagine it has often had before. Christopher Purves sings Osmin cleanly without perhaps quite fully realizing the comedy. In sum, this far excels any previous recording.

Mozart Die Zauberflöte. **Rosa Mannion** (sop) Pamina; **Nathalie Dessay** (sop) Queen of Night; **Hans-Peter Blochwitz** (ten) Tamino; **Anton Scharinger** (bass) Papageno; **Reinhard Hagen** (bass) Sarastro; **Willard White** (bass) Speaker; **Steven Cole** (ten) Monostatos; **Linda Kitchen** (sop) Papagena; **Anna Maria Panzarella** (sop) First Lady; **Doris Lamprecht** (mez) Second Lady; **Delphine Haidan** (contr) Third Lady; **Damien Colin** (treb) First Boy; **Patrick Olivier Croset** (treb) Second Boy; **Stéphane Dutournier** (treb) Third Boy; **Christopher Josey** (ten) First Armed Man, First Priest; **Laurent Naouri** (bass) Second Armed Man, Second Priest; **Les Arts Florissants / William Christie.** Erato Ⓕ 0630-12705-2 (two discs: 150 minutes: DDD: 5/96). ✏
Notes, text and translation included. Recorded 1995.

With a background primarily in the French baroque, William Christie comes to *Die Zauberflöte* from an angle quite unlike anyone else's; yet this is as idiomatic and as deeply Mozartian a reading of the work as any. Interviewed in the booklet-note, Christie says wise things about the work and ways of performing it, and in particular remarks on the unforced singing that is one of his objectives, much more manageable with the gentler sound of period instruments. All of this is borne out by the performance itself, which falls more sweetly and lovingly on the ear than any other. All this gives Christie opportunities to shape the work subtly and sensitively, with finer levels of nuance than are available to most modern performances. Mozartians will relish it, and it will prompt fresh thought about the work. His tempos, for example, often set tradition aside. Many are quickish, but not all: "Der Hölle Rache" is distinctly slower than usual, deliberate rather than fiery; so in particular is the union of Pamina and Tamino in the second finale, which gives it a *gravitas* that establishes it as the true emotional climax of the work. Yet overall the performance is quick and light-textured – and often quite dramatic. These light and soft textures and graceful phrasing are what above all characterize this recording. Some may find Christie less responsive than many more traditional interpreters to the music's quicksilver changes in mood, yet this is a part of his essentially broad and gentle view of *Die Zauberflöte*. His cast has few famous names. There is of course Hans-Peter Blochwitz, probably the finest Tamino around these days. As Pamina, Rosa Mannion has much charm and a hint of girlish vivacity but blossoms into maturity and indeed passion in "Ach, ich fühl's" – the final phrases, as the wind instruments fall away and leave her alone and desolate, are very moving. Natalie Dessay's Queen of Night is forthright, clean and well tuned, with ample weight and tonal glitter. The orchestral playing from Les Arts Florissants is as polished as always, and the translucent sound is a joy on the ear. You may find the Oestman particularly appealing for its exceptional pointedness and vivacity; Christie is quite different in character and offers a very satisfying, acutely musical view of the work.

Additional recommendations ...
...**Soloists; Bavarian Radio Chorus and Symphony Orchestra / Bernard Haitink.**
EMI Ⓕ CDS7 47951-8 (three discs: 159 minutes: DDD: 3/88).
...**Soloists; Vienna Boys' Choir; Vienna State Opera Concert Choir; Vienna Philharmonic Orchestra / Sir Georg Solti.** Decca Ⓕ 433 210-2DH2 (two discs: 152 minutes: DDD: 10/91).
...**Soloists; Schütz Choir of London; London Classical Players / Sir Roger Norrington.**
EMI Reflexe Ⓕ CDS7 54287-2 (two discs: 139 minutes: DDD: 11/91). ✏
...**Soloists; Scottish Chamber Chorus and Orchestra / Sir Charles Mackerras.**
Telarc Ⓕ CD80302 (two discs: 153 minutes: DDD: 12/91).
...**Soloists; Dresden Kreuzchor; Leipzig Radio Chorus; Dresden Staatskapelle / Sir Colin Davis.**
Philips Mozart Edition Ⓜ 422 543-2PME3 (three discs: 162 minutes: DDD: 4/92).
...**Soloists; Drottningholm Court Theatre Chorus and Orchestra / Arnold Oestman.**
L'Oiseau-Lyre Ⓕ 440 085-2OHO2 (two discs: 156 minutes: DDD: 2/94). ✏
Gramophone Editor's choice. Selected by Sounds in Retrospect. Ⓖ
...**Soloists; Hungarian Festival Chorus; Budapest Failoni Orchestra / Michael Halász.**
Naxos Opera Classics Ⓢ 8 660030/31 (two discs: 149 minutes: DDD: 7/94).
Gramophone Editor's choice.
...**Soloists; Vienna State Opera Chorus; Vienna Philharmonic Orchestra / Wilhelm Furtwängler.**
EMI Salzburg Festival Edition mono Ⓜ CHS5 65356-2* (three discs: 176 minutes: ADD: 1/96).

...Soloists; **Monteverdi Choir; English Baroque Soloists / Sir John Eliot Gardiner.**
Archiv Produktion Ⓔ 449 166-2AH2 (two discs: 158 minutes: DDD: 10/96). ⚹
...Soloists; **Vienna Boys' Choir; Vienna State Opera Chorus; Vienna Philharmonic Orchestra /
George Szell.** Orfeo mono Ⓜ C455972I* (two discs: 156 minutes: ADD: 2/98).

Mozart Die Zauberflöte. **Tiana Lemnitz** (sop) Pamina; **Erna Berger** (sop) Queen of Night;
Helge Roswaenge (ten) Tamino; **Gerhard Hüsch** (bar) Papageno; **Wilhelm Strienz** (bass) Sarasto;
Walter Grossmann (bass) Speaker, Second Armed Man; **Heinrich Tessmer** (ten) Monostatos,
First Armed Man; **Irma Beilke** (sop) Papagena, First Boy; **Hilde Scheppan** (sop) First Lady;
Elfriede Marherr-Wagner (sop) Second Lady; **Rut Berglund** (contr) Third Lady, Third Boy;
Carla Spletter (sop) Second Boy; **Ernest Fabbry** (ten) Priest; **Favres Solisten Vereinigung;
Berlin Philharmonic Orchestra / Sir Thomas Beecham.** EMI Références mono
Ⓜ CHS7 61034-2* (two discs: 130 minutes: ADD: 3/90). Notes, texts and translation included.
From HMV DB3465/73 (7/38). Recorded 1937-1938. Also available on Pearl mono
Ⓔ GEMMCDS9371* (two discs: 130 minutes: ADD: 3/90). *Gramophone classical 100.* ❻❻❻
Beecham's feeling for both the grandeur and the delicacy, and the evident command he has of his
forces, ensure attentiveness and delight at every turn. Every appearance of Gerhard Hüsch is a joy:
we have had good Papagenos since this, the first of all complete recordings of *Die Zauberflöte*, but he
surely remains the best. Tiana Lemnitz sings with such surpassing beauty for so much of the time that
the occasional scoop is forgiven. Erna Berger's Queen of Night is firm and technically accomplished,
and there are splendid performances by the Three Ladies. The Tamino is not well cast: Roswaenge
lacks finesse though he is a positive enough character. Wilhelm Strienz is literally out of his depth,
producing nasty, unresonant low notes and generally sounding more like a Hans Sachs than a
Sarastro. Walter Grossmann is a woolly Speaker, and Heinrich Tessmer, perfect as Monostatos, is no
use as First Armed Man. The absence of dialogue, as the anonymous writer of EMI's admirable
sleeve-note says, "turns music-drama into a sort of song-cycle". Altogether a set to pick one's way
through, essential though it is to have it at hand. And this also applies to the Pearl, warily
recommending it over its rival with the caution that there is surface-sound (however reduced) and,
alas, no text and translation. The Pearl transfer provides the greater enjoyment, although it is true that
EMI have all but eliminated the surface-sound; true also that the EMI transfer has greater sharpness
of sibilants and 't's with all that that may imply about frequency range.
Further listening ...
...Cassations – G major, K63, "Final-Musik"; B flat major, K99/K63*a*. Adagio and Fugue in
C minor, K546. **Salzburg Mozarteum Camerata Academica / Sándor Végh.**
Capriccio 10 192 (3/88). ❻❻
...Cassations – G major, K63, "Final-Musik"; B flat major, K99/K63*a*; D major, K100/K62*a*.
Salzburg Chamber Orchestra / Harald Nerat. Naxos 8 550609 (4/93).
...17 Church Sonatas. **Ian Watson** (org); **Classical Orchestra of the King's Consort / Robert King**
(org). Hyperion CDA66377 (11/90). ⚹
...Dances, Marches and Overtures – Five Minuets, K461K/K448*a*[b]. Contredanses[b] – Six,
K462/K448*b*; D major, K534, "Das Donnerwetter"; C major, K535, "La Bataille"; C major,
K587, "Der Sieg vom Helden Koburg"; Two, K603. Two Minuets with Contredanses
(Quadrilles), K463[b]. German Dances[b] – Six, K509; Six, K600; Three, K605. Marches[b] – D major,
K52; D major, K189/K167*b*; C major, K214; D major, K215/K213*b*; D major, K237/K189*c*;
F major, K248; D major, K249; Two in D major, K335/K320*a*; C major, K408 No. 1/K383*e*;
D major, K408 No. 2/K385*a*; C major, K408 No. 3/K383*F*; D major, K445/K320*c*. Overtures[a] –
Die Zauberflöte; Le nozze di Figaro; Ascanio in Alba; Idomeneo; Der Schauspieldirektor; Così
fan tutte; Die Entführung aus dem Serail; La Finta Giardiniera; Lucio Silla; La clemenza di Tito;
Don Giovanni. Idomeneo – Marches[b]: Nos. 8, 14 and 25. Le nozze di Figaro: March[b]: No. 23.
[a]**Dresden Staatskapelle / Hans Vonk;** [b]**Salzburg Mozarteum Orchestra / Hans Graf.**
Capriccio 10 809 (three discs: 10/91).
...Symphonies after Serenades – D major: K100/K62*a*; K185/K167*a*; K203/K198*b*; K204/K213*a*;
K250/K248*b*; K320. **Tafelmusik / Bruno Weil.** Sony Classical S2K47260 (12/92). ⚹
...Clarinet Quintet in A major, K581. *Coupled with* **Brahms** Clarinet Quintet in B minor, Op. 115.
David Campbell (cl); **Bingham Quartet.** Olympia OCD637 (6/98).
...Divertimento in E flat major for String Trio, K563. Six Preludes and Fugues (after Bach), K404*a*
– No. 1 in D minor; No. 2 in G minor; No. 3 in F major; No. 6 in F minor. **L'Archibudelli Trio.**
Sony Classical Vivarte SK46497. ⚹
...Divertimento in F major, K213. Die Zauberflöte – Duets for flute and clarinet (arr.
Schmeiser/Hödl). *Coupled with works by various composers.* **Quintett Wien.**
Nimbus NI5479 (3/97).
...Double Piano Sonata in D major, K448/K375*a*. Andante and Variations in G major, K501.
Coupled with **Schubert** Fantasie in F minor, D940. **Louis Lortie, Hélène Mercier** (pf duet).
Chandos CHAN9162 (7/93).
...Apollo and Hyacinthus. **Soloists; Salzburg Chamber Choir; Salzburg Mozarteum Orchestra /
Leopold Hager.** Philips Mozart Edition 422 526-2PME2 (11/91).
...Ascanio in Alba. **Soloists; Choir of the Sorbonne, Paris; Concerto Armonico / Jacques Grimbert.**
Naxos 8 660040/41 (12/95).

...La finta semplice. **Soloists; C.P.E. Bach Chamber Orchestra / Peter Schreier.**
Philips Mozart Edition 422 528-2PME2 (11/91).
...La finta giardiniera. **Soloists; Salzburg Mozarteum Orchestra / Leopold Hager.**
Philips Mozart Edition 422 533-2PME3 (5/92).
...Mitridate. **Soloists; Salzburg Mozarteum Orchestra / Leopold Hager.**
Philips Mozart Edition 422 529-2PME3 (2/92).
...Il rè pastore. **Soloists; Academy of St Martin in the Fields / Sir Neville Marriner.**
Philips Mozart Edition 422 535-2PME2 (4/92).
...Il rè pastore. **Soloists; Vienna Concentus Musicus / Nikolaus Harnoncourt.**
Teldec 4509-98419-2 (2/97). ✍
...Thamos, König in Aegypten. **Alastair Miles** (bass); **Monteverdi Choir; English Baroque Soloists /
Sir John Eliot Gardiner.** Archiv Produktion 437 556-2AH (2/94). ✍

Alonso Mudarra   Spanish c1510-1580

Suggested listening ...
...Fantasias – primer tono; quarto tono; quinto tono. *Coupled with works by various composers.*
Ensemble Clément Janequin / Dominique Visse (alto). Harmonia Mundi HMC90 1627 (4/98).
Gramophone Editor's choice. See review in the Collections section; refer to the Index.   ⓖⓖ
...Tres libros de musica en cifras para vihuela – Si me llaman a mi; Ysabel, perdiste la tu faxa;
Guárdame las vacas. *Coupled with works by various composers.*
La Romanesca / José Miguel Moreno (vihuela). Glossa GCD920203 (5/96). ✍
Gramophone Editor's choice. See review in the Collections section; refer to the Index.   ⓖ

Dominic Muldowney   British 1952

Suggested listening ...
...The Brontes – ballet suite. *Coupled with works by* **Feeney** and **Carl Davis**
Northern Ballet Theatre Orchestra / John Pryce-Jones.
Naxos 8 553495 (3/96). *See review under Feeney; refer to the Index.*

Henri Mulet   French 1878-1967

Suggested listening ...
...Carillon-sortie in D major. *Coupled with works by various composers.* **Christopher Herrick** (org).
Hyperion CDA66676. *See review in the Collections section; refer to the Index.*

Herbert Murrill   British 1909-1952

Suggested listening ...
...Carillon. *Coupled with works by various composers.* **Andrew Lucas** (org).
Naxos 8 550955 (11/94). *See review in the Collections section; refer to the Index.*

Colin Muset   French fl c1200-1250

Suggested listening ...
...En mai, quant li rossignolez. *Coupled with works by various composers.* **Paul Hillier** (voc);
Andrew Lawrence-King (psaltery/hp/org). Harmonia Mundi HMU90 7184 (4/97).
See review in the Collections section; refer to the Index.
...En mai, quant li rossignolez. *Coupled with works by various composers.* **Anne Azéma** (sop/spkr);
vocal and instrumental ensemble.
Erato 0630-17072-2 (12/97). ✍ *See review in the Collections section; refer to the Index.*

Modest Mussorgsky   Russian 1839-1881

Mussorgsky Pictures at an Exhibition (orch. Ravel). A Night on the Bare Mountain
(arr. Rimsky-Korsakov).
Ravel Valses nobles et sentimentales. **New York Philharmonic Orchestra / Giuseppe Sinopoli.**
DG ⓟ 429 785-2GH (67 minutes: DDD: 5/91).
Sinopoli's recording of *Pictures at an Exhibition* has great panache and is full of subtle detail and
sharply characterized performances. Of course none of this would be possible without the marvellous
virtuosity of the NYPO, whose brass section play with a wonderful larger-than-life sonority and

whose woodwind section produce playing of considerable delicacy and finesse, as for example in "Tuileries" and the "Ballet of the Unhatched Chicks". Sinopoli clearly revels in the drama of this work and this is nowhere more noticeable than in his sinister readings of "Catacombs" and "Baba-Yaga". *A Night on the Bare Mountain* is no less impressive, where again the flair and virtuosity of the orchestra have an almost overwhelming impact. Less successful are Ravel's *Valses nobles et sentimentales* which are perhaps too idiosyncratic for an individual recommendation despite some superb performances and moments of great beauty. The sound is very well balanced and engineered.

Additional recommendations ...

...Pictures at an Exhibition. A Night on the Bare Mountain. **Cleveland Orchestra / Lorin Maazel.** Telarc Ⓕ CD80042 (41 minutes: DDD: 11/84).

...Pictures at an Exhibition (orig. piano version)[a]. Pictures at an Exhibition (orch. Ashkenazy)[b]. [b]**Philharmonia Orchestra / Vladimir Ashkenazy** ([a]pf). Decca Ⓕ 414 386-2DH (67 minutes: DDD: 5/86).

...Pictures at an Exhibition (orch. Funtek). Songs and Dances of Death (arr. Aho)[a]. [a]**Martti Talvela** (bass); **Finnish Radio Symphony Orchestra / Neeme Järvi.** BIS Ⓕ CD325 (67 minutes: DDD: 6/87).

...Pictures at an Exhibition. **Stravinsky** Petrushka[a]. [a]**Leslie Howard** (pf); **London Symphony Orchestra / Claudio Abbado.** DG Ⓕ 423 901-2GH (68 minutes: DDD: 3/89).

...Pictures at an Exhibition. A Night on the Bare Mountain. Khovanshchina – Prelude. **Oslo Philharmonic Orchestra / Mariss Jansons.** EMI Ⓕ CDC7 49797-2 (49 minutes: DDD: 1/90).

...Pictures at an Exhibition. **Stravinsky** The Firebird – concert suite. **Royal Concertgebouw Orchestra / Carlo Maria Giulini.** Sony Classical Ⓕ SK45935 (61 minutes: DDD: 12/90).

...A Night on the Bare Mountain[a]. **Prokofiev** Romeo and Juliet – concert suites[b]. [a]**London Symphony Orchestra / Antál Dorati;** [b]**Minneapolis Symphony Orchestra / Stanislaw Skrowaczewski.** Mercury Ⓜ 432 004-2MM (67 minutes: ADD: 3/91).

...Pictures at an Exhibition (orig. piano version). **Tchaikovsky** (arr. Pletnev) The Sleeping Beauty, Op. 66 – excerpts. **Mikhail Pletnev** (pf). Virgin Classics Ⓕ VC7 59611-2 (64 minutes: DDD: 4/91). Ⓖ

...Pictures at an Exhibition. A Night on the Bare Mountain. *Coupled with works by* **Borodin** **Slovak Philharmonic Orchestra / Daniel Nazareth.** Naxos Ⓢ 8 550051 (68 minutes: DDD: 7/91).

...Pictures at an Exhibition. **Stravinsky** The Rite of Spring. **Philadelphia Orchestra / Riccardo Muti.** EMI Ⓜ CDM7 64516-2 (64 minutes: DDD: 11/92).

...Pictures at an Exhibition. A Night on the Bare Mountain. Khovanshchina – Prelude. **Atlanta Symphony Orchestra / Yoel Levi.** Telarc Ⓕ CD80296 (50 minutes: DDD: 4/92).

...Pictures at an Exhibition. *Coupled with works by* **Respighi** **Chicago Symphony Orchestra / Fritz Reiner.** RCA Victor Gold Seal Ⓜ 09026 61401-2 (70 minutes: ADD: 8/93). ⒼⒼ

...Pictures at an Exhibition. **Tchaikovsky** Piano Concerto No. 1 in B flat minor, Op. 23[a]. **Vladimir Horowitz** (pf); [a]**NBC Symphony Orchestra / Arturo Toscanini.** RCA Victor Gold Seal Ⓜ GD60321* (61 minutes: ADD: 9/93). Ⓖ

...Pictures at an Exhibition (arr. Leonard)[a]. A Night on the Bare Mountain (orch. Rimsky-Korsakov). Sorochinsky Fair – Gopak (orch. Liadov). Pictures from the Crimea (orch. Goehr). Khovanshchina – Prelude (orch. Stokowski). From my tears (orch. Kindler). Scherzo in B flat major (orch. Rimsky-Korsakov). [a]**Tamás Ungár** (pf). **Philharmonia Orchestra / Geoffrey Simon.** Cala Ⓕ CACD1012 (77 minutes: DDD: 11/93).

...Pictures at an Exhibition. A Night on the Bare Mountain. *Coupled with works by various composers.* **Chicago Symphony Orchestra / Fritz Reiner.** RCA Victor Living Stereo Ⓜ 09026 61958-2 (71 minutes: ADD: 8/94). ⒼⒼⒼ *See review in the Collections section; refer to the Index.*

...A Night on the Bare Mountain (arr. Rimsky-Korsakov and Stokowski). Boris Godunov – Symphonic Synthesis (arr. Stokowski). Pictures at an Exhibition (omitting Nos. 3 and 7; orch. Stokowski). Khovanshchina – Prelude, Act 4 (orch. Stokowski). Borodin Prince Igor – Dance of the Polovtsi Maidens (orch. Glazunov, Rimsky-Korsakov and Stokowski). **Philadelphia Orchestra / Leopold Stokowski.** Dutton Laboratories mono Ⓜ CDAX8009* (79 minutes: ADD: 11/94).

...Pictures at an Exhibition. *Coupled with works by* **Debussy** and **Ravel** **Berlin Philharmonic Orchestra / Herbert von Karajan.** DG The Originals Ⓜ 447 426-2GOR (75 minutes: ADD: 12/95).

...Pictures at an Exhibition (piano version[a]; orch. Ravel[b]). *Coupled with works by* **Chopin** [a]**Byron Janis** (pf); [b]**Minneapolis Symphony Orchestra / Antál Dorati.** Mercury Living Presence Ⓜ 434 346-2MM (66 minutes: ADD: 2/96). Ⓖ

...Pictures at an Exhibition (piano version[a]; orch. Ravel[b]). [a]**Alfred Brendel** (pf); [b]**Vienna Philharmonic Orchestra / André Previn.** Philips Solo Ⓜ 442 650-2PM (67 minutes: DDD: 2/96).

...A Night on the Bare Mountain (arr. Tchernov). *Coupled with works by various composers.* **Boris Berezovsky** (pf). Teldec Ⓕ 4509-96516-2 (61 minutes: DDD: 7/96). *See review in the Collections section; refer to the Index.*

...A Night on the Bare Mountain (arr. Stokowski). Pictures at an Exhibition. Boris Godunov – Symphonic synthesis. Khovanshchina – Act IV entr'acte. **BBC Philharmonic / Matthias Bamert.** Chandos Ⓕ CHAN9445 (69 minutes: DDD: 9/96).

Mussorgsky Pictures at an Exhibition[a].
Tchaikovsky Piano Sonata in G major, Op. 37[b]. **Sviatoslav Richter** (pf).
 Melodiya mono Ⓜ 74321 29469-2* (61 minutes: ADD: 6/96). Item marked [a] recorded 1958, [b]1956.
The blend of German and Russian backgrounds must have something to do with the unique power
of Richter at his best. Certainly that comes across in the tempering of rhetoric with structural insight
which elevates the Tchaikovsky Sonata beyond any other performance of this unwieldy piece; again
Richter's sweeping panache and volcanic sense of flow make for a colossal Mussorgsky *Pictures*
(Moscow, 1958), far better recorded than the famous, though currently unavailable, live Sofia
account. Richter's interpretations in these years had an elemental power and unselfconscious
abandon that was refined and tempered in later life. The mono sound is acceptable.
Additional recommendation ...
...Pictures at an Exhibition. **William Kapell** (pf).
 Arbiter mono Ⓕ ARBITER108* (71 minutes: ADD: 5/98).

Mussorgsky Complete Songs. **Boris Christoff** (bass); **Alexandre Labinsky, Gerald Moore** (pfs);
 French Radio National Orchestra / Georges Tzipine. EMI Références mono Ⓜ CHS7 63025-2
 (three discs: 191 minutes: ADD: 8/89). From ALP1652/5 (1/59) and DB21383 (2/52).
 Notes, texts and translations included. Recorded 1951-1956.*Gramophone classical 100.*   ⒼⒶⒼ
This set is undoubtedly one of the all-time glories of the gramophone and should be in any
worthwhile song collection. This is unquestionably Boris Christoff's most important legacy. Even on
the first disc, in the earlier and slightly less remarkable songs, Mussorgsky offers a range of
personalities and emotions as then unknown in Russian song. There are the war-like King Saul, the
sad figure of Wilhelm Meister in the *Song of the Old Man* (what we know as "An die Türen"), the
desolate landscape of *The Wind Howls*, the folk-hero, Calistratus. Then we hear a wide variety of
styles from the recitative-like *Cast-off Woman* to the gentle lyricism of *Night*. In this last song
Christoff produces that magical *mezza voce* of his to suggest the intimacy of the loved one portrayed
within. But, by then – the eleventh song – he has already given us an amazing palette of sound
colours, everything from the utterly ferocious to the gentlest whisper. With the second disc, we come
to many of the better-known songs but few of them have ever been better interpreted than here. In
Hopak, the bass has a rollicking time of it, relishing every word. In *Savishna*, a wonderfully vivid
song, he subtly portrays the idiot. He catches the bitter satire of *The Classicist* and the humour of *The
Seminarist*, where the Latin recitation is gleefully projected. The rather weak *Puppet Show* is almost
saved here by Christoff's identity with its twists of irony. Then he can change style again to produce
a hypnotically sweet tone for *Evening Song*, a tender lyric built on only five notes. But the centrepiece
of this disc is, of course, the *Nursery* cycle, where Christoff manages to adapt his big tone for a
convincing impersonation of a small boy. He finds yet other voices for the Nurse and for the Mother.
This is a *tour de force*. Similarly rewarding are his performances of the *Sunless* and *Songs and Dances
of Death* cycles. He catches all the bleak gloom of the first, the histrionic force of the second, where
his variety of timbre is once more astonishing, but in the *Songs and Dances* he uses a corrupt
orchestration. After these two cycles, Mussorgsky's inspiration seemed to falter, though *On the
Dnieper*, a lyrical piece of surpassing beauty, and the ever-popular *Song of the flea*, which ends the
set, are remarkable achievements in their way and are here excellently interpreted. Labinsky and
Moore are vivid and imaginative partners, although the recording (quite rightly) favours the voice.

Mussorgsky Songs and Dances of Death. The Nursery. The Peep-show. Forgotten.
 The Seminarist. Darling Savishna. The he-goat: A worldly story. Mephistopheles' song of the
 flea. **Sergei Leiferkus** (bar); **Semeon Skigin** (pf). Conifer Classics Ⓕ CDCF229 (66 minutes:
 DDD: 2/95). Texts and translations included. Recorded 1993. *Gramophone Editor's choice.* ⒼⒶ
Few have interpreted Mussorgsky with the kind of confidence, understanding and sheer vocal bravura
that Leiferkus shows here. He has all the necessary *gravitas*, vocal presence and tonal nuance.
Leiferkus has recorded *Songs and Dances of Death* before with orchestra but the version with piano
is to be preferred because their very intimacy in this form makes the pieces that much more
frightening. At present there is no version with piano in the catalogue to rival Leiferkus's for intensity
of expression or breadth of characterization. Here Death in all its terrifying guises as so arrestingly
depicted by the composer, comes starkly into your home, courtesy of the singer, his vivid partner and
an ideal recording. The accomplishment in *The Nursery* cycle is, if possible, even more astonishing as
the baritone completely changes the character of his tone for impersonating the child. Usually
assigned to a soprano, it has been attempted in the past on disc, and successfully so, by Christoff.
Leiferkus at once emulates his great predecessor's achievement yet manages to give these delightful
songs his own, very definite profile. More delights follow. The satire of *The Peep-show* is brilliantly
realized. In the rest of the songs Mussorgsky's gift for strongly flavoured story-telling and figure-
painting is conveyed in abundance through Leiferkus's ebullient delivery, closing with a rollicking but
never overdone *Song of the flea*.
Additional recommendations ...
...Songs and Dances of Death. *Coupled with works by various composers.* **Dmitri Hvorostovsky** (bar);
 Kirov Theatre Orchestra / Valery Gergiev. Philips Ⓕ 438 872-2PH (62 minutes: DDD: 5/94).
 See review in the Collections section; refer to the Index.

...Songs and Dances of Death[a]. **Tchaikovsky** Symphony No. 5 in E minor, Op. 64.
[a]**Anatoly Kotscherga** (bass); **Berlin Philharmonic Orchestra / Claudio Abbado.**
Sony Classical Ⓕ SK66276 (65 minutes: DDD: 3/95).
See review under Tchaikovsky; refer to the Index.

...The Nursery. Songs and Dances of Death. *Coupled with works by* **Rachmaninov**
and **Tchaikovsky** Ewa Podles (contr); **Graham Johnson** (pf).
Forlane UCD16683 (5/95). *See review in the Collections section; refer to the Index.*

...The Nursery. *Coupled with works by* **Mozart** and **Liszt** Dame Margaret Price (sop);
James Lockhart (pf). RCA Victor Gold Seal Ⓜ 09026 61635-2
(two discs: 151 minutes: ADD: 5/95). *See review under Mozart; refer to the Index.*   Ⓖ

...The Nursery. Sunless. Songs and Dances of Death. Hebrew Song.
Mephistopheles' song of the flea. Gopak. **Marjana Lipovšek** (mez); **Graham Johnson** (pf).
Sony Classical Ⓕ SK66858 (63 minutes: DDD: 9/96).

...Songs and Dances of Death (orch. Shostakovich)[a]. **Shostakovich** Symphony No. 10 in
E minor, Op. 93. [a]**Robert Lloyd** (bass); **Philadelphia Orchestra / Mariss Jansons.**
EMI Ⓕ CDC5 55232-2 (72 minutes: DDD: 6/95). *See review under Shostakovich;*
refer to the Index.

...Where art thou, little star?. Hour of jollity. Sadly rustled the leaves. I have many palaces and
gardens. A Prayer. Tell me why, o maiden. What are words of love to you?. The wild wind blows.
But if I could meet thee again. Dear one, why are thine eyes sometimes so cold?. Old man's song.
King Saul. Night. Kalistratushka. The outcast. Lullaby. Salammbô – Balearic song. **Sergei**
Leiferkus (bar); **Semion Skigin** (pf). Conifer Classics Ⓕ 75605 51265-2 (58 minutes: DDD: 12/96).

...Songs and Dances of Death. *Coupled with works by various composers.* **Sergei Larin** (ten);
Eleonora Bekova (pf). Chandos Ⓕ CHAN9547 (67 minutes: DDD: 6/97). *See review in the*
Collections section; refer to the Index.

Mussorgsky Epitaph. The sphinx. Not like thunder, trouble struck. Softly the spirit flew up to
heaven. Pride. Is spinning man's work?. The vision. It scatters and breaks. On the Dnieper.
Eremushka's lullaby. The feast. The classicist. From my tears. Sunless. **Sergei Leiferkus** (bar);
Semion Skigin (pf). Conifer Classics Ⓕ 75605 51248-2 (59 minutes: DDD: 12/95).
Texts and translations included. Recorded 1995. *Gramophone Editor's choice.*

Leiferkus so much *enjoys* singing. That's evident from first to last on this, the second instalment of his
absolutely riveting account of Mussorgsky's songs. His success is based on his amazing variety of tone
colour and textual inflexion. The singer who is so embittered, so biting in a big, baritonal manner for
projecting the harshness in *Not like thunder* dissolves into the warm, all-enveloping, bass-like
interpreter of *Softly the spirit flew up to heaven*, one of the composer's most melodically inspired
songs. Then in the next song, another voice, another character is met as Leiferkus catches to
perfection the heroic irony of *Pride*. In *The vision*, and again in the Schumannesque *From my tears*,
we hear a lyrically vibrant baritone, dispensing an appropriately erotic charge so strongly contrasting
with the deliberately light, almost mincing tone employed to convey the sharp satire of *The classicist*.
The grand passion of that Cossack lament, *On the Dnieper*, and the extrovert good cheer of *The feast*
are further triumphs – and all that is before we reach his reading of the *Sunless* cycle, where Leiferkus
sounds suitably world-weary as he plumbs the depths of this profoundly depressing work. In
everything his confident and pointed delivery of the text is exemplary yet verbal histrionics never get
in the way of good singing. With Skigin once again a wonderfully responsive partner and a recording
that improves, in terms of intimacy, on that of Vol. 1, no more need be said except to recommend this
disc unreservedly and urge you to acquire it.

Mussorgsky *Songs*[a] – Where are thou, little star? Night. Gopak. The nettle mountain. You
drunken sot! The orphan. The magpie. Child's song. The ragamuffin. Evening song. Gathering
mushrooms. The wanderer. The garden by the Don. Hebrew song. Meines Herzens Sehnsucht.
Ich wollt' meine Schmerzen ergössen. *Piano Pieces*[b] – Méditation. On the southern shore of the
Crimea. Au village. Intermezzo in modo classico. Une larme. Gopak. Impromptu passionne.
[a]**Sergei Leiferkus** (bar); [a]**Semion Skigin**, [b]**Vovka Ashkenazy** (pfs). Conifer Classics
Ⓕ 75605 51274-2 (74 minutes: DDD: 5/97). Texts and translations included.

Leiferkus enjoys himself immensely with Mussorgsky's songs; and this is infectious. The range of
colour he displays would be self-indulgent, were it not for the fact that the nature of many of them
demands a dramatic identification. Moreover, the artist who can lull the senses with such beautiful
warmth of tone in *Night* or *Evening song* or *The wanderer* has not only the right but really the duty
to throw it to one side for the bawling of the energetically faithless wife in *Gopak* (with wonderfully
exuberant playing by the ever-admirable Semion Skigin), or the termagant's screeching tirade of
"Akh, ti" at the homecoming drunkard. There is a sharper edge and a lightening of tone for *The*
magpie, and a very cleverly judged irony in the sweetness as in *Gathering mushrooms* it dawns on the
listener that the crop being picked is poisoned, and destined for use in the near future. The taunting
of the old woman in *The ragamuffin*, one of Mussorgsky's most brilliant *tours de force*, is a real piece
of virtuosity. With the towering exception of *Pictures at an Exhibition*, Mussorgsky's piano music is
of little account, consisting of either salon musings like *Une larme* and *Méditation* or genre pieces
with some Russian melodic colouring. The most interesting is the *Intermezzo in modo classico*,

inspired by a peasant scene and demonstrating that he was only really inspired by words or imagery. Vovka Ashkenazy plays them gracefully and lightly. But it is for the songs that this splendid record is to be enjoyed.

Mussorgsky Scherzo in B flat major. Intermezzo "in modo classico". Khovanshchina – Dance of the Persian Slave Girls; Intermezzo; Golitsyn's journey. Boris Godunov – Introduction and Polonaise (all orch. Rimsky-Korsakov). Sorochinsky Fair – Overture; Gopak (both orch. Liadov); Parassia's Song[a]. Sunless (orch. Svetlanov)[a]. [a]**Natalia Gerasimova** (sop); **Russian State Symphony Orchestra / Evgeni Svetlanov.** RCA Victor Red Seal Ⓕ 09026 68406-2 (71 minutes: DDD: 10/97). Recorded 1994.

Mussorgsky by name, but not necessarily by nature. Virtually everything on this musically varied CD has been orchestrated by another hand. Svetlanov's performances are unforced and malleable, while the recordings have considerable impact: the double-basses at the start of *Khovanshchina*'s Entr'acte are virtually tangible. The "Dance of the Persian Slave Girls" is very much 'pre-*Polovtsi*' and Liadov's felicitous orchestrations of music from *Sorochinsky Fair* are appealing. The performances are nicely judged and Natalia Gerasimova – a stylish, brittle-voiced soprano with a pronounced Slavic vibrato – gives a winning account of Parassia's schizoid "Dumka". However, the disc's highlight is Svetlanov's sensitive orchestration of the *Sunless* cycle. Here Gerasimova tames her exuberance for an appropriately inward performance, and the recording keeps her in perfect aural perspective with the orchestra. The first and fourth songs are scored for strings, the second for woodwind, the third for brass and woodwind, whereas the fifth makes economical use of larger forces (including percussion) and the sixth – "On the river" – recalls the world of Rachmaninov's *The isle of the dead*. Svetlanov's mastery of mood and texture suggests active parallels with the superb Mussorgsky orchestrations of Shostakovich and Markevitch. The recordings are excellent, and the sound uniformly first-rate. There are no full texts for the vocal items, just English synopses.

Mussorgsky St John's Night on the Bare Mountain. Pictures at an Exhibition (orch. Ravel). The destruction of Sennacherib[a]. Salammbô – Chorus of priestesses[a]. Oedipus in Athens – Chorus of people in the temple[a]. Joshua[b]. [b]**Elena Zaremba** (mez); [a]**Prague Philharmonic Chorus; Berlin Philharmonic Orchestra / Claudio Abbado.** DG Ⓕ 445 238-2GH (65 minutes: DDD: 2/95). Texts and translations included. Recorded live in 1993.   Ⓖ Ⓖ

St John's Night on the Bare Mountain is the original version of *A Night on the Bare Mountain*. Abbado obviously relishes the odd grotesque spurts of colour from the woodwind, and the Mussorgskian ruggedness. The composer's structural clumsiness is not shirked and the lack of the smooth continuity found in the Rimsky arrangement does not impede the sense of forward momentum; indeed at the close the Russian dance element is emphasized, rather than the sinister pictorialism. (Of course the luscious slow ending is not here at all – that was added by Rimsky.) The choral pieces are gloriously sung and again Abbado brings out their Russian colour, especially in the glowing yet sinuous "Chorus of priestesses". *Joshua* is made to seem a minor masterpiece with its lusty opening (hints of Borodin's Polovtsians) and its touching central solo ("The Amorite women weep"). This is most eloquently sung by Elena Zaremba and the theme is then movingly taken up first by the women of the chorus and then the men, before the exultant music returns. The performance of *Pictures at an Exhibition*, like the choral items, gains from the spacious ambience and sumptuous overall textures. It is not, perhaps, an electrifying performance, but it is dramatic in its contrasts and very beautifully played.

Additional recommendation ...

...Joshua[ab]. St John's Night on the Bare Mountain. Salammbô – Chorus of priestesses[b]. The destruction of Sennacherib[b]. Oedipus in Athens – Chorus of people in the temple[b]. Khovanshchina – Prelude; Galitsin's journey (Introduction, Act 4). Scherzo in B flat major. Triumphal march, "The capture of Kars". [a]**Zehava Gal** (contr); **London Symphony** [b]**Chorus and Orchestra / Claudio Abbado.** RCA Gold Seal Master Series Ⓜ 09026 61354-2 (54 minutes: ADD: 6/93).

Mussorgsky St John's Night on the Bare Mountain[bc]. Scherzo in B flat major. Intermezzo "in modo classico" in B minor. Khovanshchina – Prelude, Act 1, "Dawn over the Moscow River"; Mysterious powers[a]; In the Streltsy quarter all are sleeping[b]; Dance of the Persian Slave Girls; The departure of Prince Golizyn. Mlada – Festive March. [a]**Marianna Tarasova** (mez); [b]**Anatoly Kotcherga** (bass); [c]**Berlin Radio Chorus;** [c]**Südtiroler Kinderchor; Berlin Philharmonic Orchestra / Claudio Abbado.** Sony Classical Ⓕ SK62034 (60 minutes: DDD: 1/98). Texts and translations included. Recorded 1995-1996.

No work of Mussorgsky's has a more tangled history than *St John's Night on the Bare Mountain*. To cut a long story short, in 1867 Mussorgsky wrote the orchestral *Bare Mountain*, but, dismayed by Balakirev's withering comments, shelved it. Then, to the opera-ballet *Mlada*, commissioned in collaboration with Rimsky-Korsakov, Cui and Borodin, he contributed a scene, based on the orchestral piece and now lost, sometimes known as "The Sabbath of the Black Goat". This he adapted for the never-to-be-finished opera, *Sorochintsy Fair*, for chorus and orchestra, as "The Young Peasant's Dream". Despite the title given it on the record (as above), it is this operatic vocal and choral scene which is here recorded. Based on it, Rimsky-Korsakov made the orchestral transcription which has been so widely performed and recorded. There is more to it than that; but all that need be added here is that there have been various versions of the opera: Cui (1917) and Tcherepnin (1923) took a hand, but the best known performing score is by Shebalin (1931). Abbado gives the piece a formidable charge of energy here, strong, potent and dynamic. It is a powerful piece, especially in the original operatic scene rather than in the more appealing Rimsky-Korsakov orchestral guise which we know so well. He also gives a gentle, evocative performance of the *Khovanshchina* Prelude depicting dawn over the River Moscow, and accompanies his singers well in the two scenes from the opera, with Kotcherga a gloomy Shaklovity and Tarasova powerfully conjuring up the spirits of darkness in one of Mussorgsky's greatest arias. There is also a lively performance of the dance, and a vivid one of the *Intermezzo* which Mussorgsky half-pretended was symphonic but was really a lively response to a scene he witnessed of some peasants blundering through the snow.

Mussorgsky Boris Godunov. **Anatoly Kotcherga** (bass) Boris; **Sergei Larin** (ten) Grigory; **Marjana Lipovšek** (mez) Marina; **Samuel Ramey** (bass) Pimen; **Gleb Nikolsky** (bass) Varlaam; **Philip Langridge** (ten) Shuisky; **Helmut Wildhaber** (ten) Missail; **Sergei Leiferkus** (bar) Rangoni; **Liliana Nichiteanu** (mez) Feodor; **Valentina Valente** (sop) Xenia; **Yevgenia Gorokhovskaya** (mez) Nurse; **Eléna Zaremba** (mez) Hostess; **Alexander Fedin** (ten) Simpleton; **Albert Shagidullin** (bar) Shchelkolov; **Wojciech Drabowicz** (ten) Mitukha, Krushchov; **Slovak Philharmonic Chorus; Berlin Radio Chorus; Tölz Boys' Choir; Berlin Philharmonic Orchestra / Claudio Abbado.**
Sony Classical Ⓕ S3K58977 (three discs: 200 minutes: DDD: 5/94). Notes, text and translation included. ⊙⊙

Mussorgsky (arr. Rimsky-Korsakov) Boris Godunov. **Boris Christoff** (bass) Boris, Pimen, Varlaam; **Nicolai Gedda** (ten) Grigory; **Eugenia Zareska** (mez) Marina, Feodor; **André Bielecki** (ten) Shuisky, Missail, Krushchov; **Kim Borg** (bass) Rangoni, Shchelkalov; **Ludmila Lebedeva** (sop) Xenia; **Lydia Romanova** (mez) Nurse, Hostess; **Wassili Pasternak** (ten) Simpleton; **Raymond Bonte** (ten) Lavitsky; **Eugène Bousquet** (bass) Chernikovsky; **Choeurs Russes de Paris; French Radio National Orchestra / Issay Dobrowen.** EMI Références mono Ⓜ CHS5 65192-2* (three discs: 178 minutes: ADD: 12/94). From HMV ALP1044/7 (4/53). Recorded 1952.
Nobody has been more diligent than Abbado in seeking the truth about this vast canvas. Here we have the latest fruits of his efforts. He chooses the definitive 1872-74 version, adding scenes, including the complete one in Pimen's cell and the St Basil's scene from 1869. His is a taut, tense reading, grand, virtuosic, at times hard-driven, favouring extremes of speed and dynamics. The orchestra is very much in the foreground, sounding more emphatic than would ever be the case in the opera house. Kotcherga has a superb voice, firmly produced throughout an extensive register. His is a Boris avoiding conventional melodrama and concerned to show the loving father. The ambitious lovers are well represented. Indeed, Larin is quite the best Grigory yet on disc, sounding at once youthful, heroic and ardent, and quite free of tenor mannerisms. Lipovšek characterizes Marina forcefully: we are well aware of the scheming Princess's powers of wheeler-dealing and of erotic persuasion. The recording is of demonstration standard: most potent in the way it captures the incisive and pointed singing of the combined choruses in their various guises. Here all is vividly brought before us by conductor and producer in the wide panorama predicated by Mussorgsky's all-enveloping vision.

Dobrowen's lean, vivid, acutely shaped direction, benefiting from taut rhythms and fastish tempos, is as vital as that on any version since, certainly making this set the recommendation for the Rimsky recension. Its other main attribute is, of course, Christoff's first complete reading on disc of the tortured Tsar, whose role he sings with an enviable combination of firm tone, vital diction and concentrated histrionics, never overstepping the mark. His assumption of two other parts has always been frowned on, but he so subtly varies his tone – softer, greyer for Pimen, rotundly rollicking for Varlaam – that the tripling only worries in the final scene when Pimen comes face to face with the dying ruler. The contrast of his finely shaded Pimen with Ramey's one-dimensional singing on the Abbado version is most marked. If that were not enough, there is the beauty and ardour of the young Gedda as Grigory to please the ear and Zareska's seductive, vocally appealing Marina. She also sings a likeable Feodor. Kim Borg doubles successfully as Shchelkalov and an oily Rangoni. The choral singing is good. We have heard much better on disc since, but few orchestras, in the West at least, have sounded so Russian as these French players but then few have had the benefit of being tutored by Dobrowen. The digital transfers bring out the excellence of the original engineering.

Mussorgsky Boris Godunov. **Ivan Petrov** (bass) Boris Godunov; **Vladimir Ivanovsky** (ten) Grigory; **Irina Arkhipova** (mez) Marina; **Mark Reshetin** (bass) Pimen; **Alexey Geleva** (bass) Varlaam; **Georgy Shulpin** (ten) Shuisky; **Nikolay Zakharov** (ten) Missail; **Yevgeny Kibkalo** (bass) Rangoni; **Valentina Klepatskaya** (mez) Feodor; **Tamara Sorokina** (sop) Xenia; **Yevgeniya Verbitskaya** (mez) Nurse; **Veronika Borisenko** (mez) Innkeeper; **Anton Grigoryev** (bass) Simpleton, Nikitich; **Alexey Ivanov** (bar) Shchelkalov; **Vladimir Valaitis** (bar) Lavitsky; **Yury Galkin** (bass) Chernikovsky; **Leonid Ktitorov** (bass) Mityukha; **Anatoly Mishutin** (ten) Krushchov, Boyar; **Chorus and Orchestra of the Bolshoi Theatre, Moscow / Alexander Melik-Pashayev.**
Melodiya Ⓜ 74321 29349-2 (three discs: 175 minutes: ADD: 12/96). Notes, text and translation included. Recorded 1962.
This is the first time this desirable set has been generally available in this country and it has been well worth the wait. It is certainly the most authentic-sounding version of the Rimsky arrangement so far recorded. Under Melik-Pashayev's conducting, which combines discipline, an innate understanding

of the score's rhythmic and melodic requirements and sheer experience in directing the work, it flows onwards in a steady stream of musical and dramatic consistency. Nowhere else will you hear such a cast of singers, steeped in the best tradition of performing the work at the Bolshoi, and at the same time so apt for their given roles. Petrov isn't at all in the Chaliapin or Christoff (Dobrowen) mould of performing the work: his performance is entirely free of melodrama and is sung with all the vocal verities observed in a rounded, warm bass. In his more modest way, Petrov invests his role with just as much feeling and drama as his more histrionic rivals – his is a richly rewarding portrayal on all counts. Even better is the Marina of the young Arkhipova. In her case, one can assert with certainty that she has no peer, let alone a better on any other set. The proud carriage of her voice and the finely nuanced character of her loud and soft singing are just what one wants from the ambitious Polish Princess. Her Grigory, Ivanovsky, isn't vocally quite in her class – the voice sounds strained under pressure – but, like everyone else in the cast, he is very much inside his role and declaims it with real passion. In the Polish act Kibkalo makes an ideally insinuating Rangoni. Reshetin is perfectly cast as grave old Pimen; he is another bass whose tone is well supported and easily produced. Shulpin has one of those sharp-edged tenors that many British ears abhor, but it seems to be absolutely the right voice for that crepuscular, two-faced boyar. Grigoryev is a plangent, touching Simpleton. Most of the supporting cast is in the same mould, peculiarly Russian, and therefore idiomatic in timbre. Some may baulk at the backward recording of the orchestra. The excellent singing of the chorus is also vividly caught. The stereo spread is a trifle too marked. If you enjoy Rimsky's admittedly inauthentic scoring, you should seriously consider this well-remastered Melodiya set.

Additional recommendation ...
...**Soloists; Bodra Smyana Representative Children's Choir; Sofia National Opera and Festival Orchestra / Emil Tchakarov.**
Sony Classical Ⓕ S3K45763 (three discs: 210 minutes: DDD: 4/92).

Mussorgsky Khovanshchina. **Aage Haugland** (bass) Ivan Khovansky; **Vladimir Atlantov** (ten) Andrey Khovansky; **Vladimir Popov** (ten) Golitsin; **Anatolij Kotscherga** (bar) Shaklovity; **Paata Burchuladze** (bass) Dosifey; **Marjana Lipovšek** (contr) Marfa; **Brigitte Poschner-Klebel** (sop) Susanna; **Heinz Zednik** (ten) Scribe; **Joanna Borowska** (sop) Emma; **Wilfried Gahmlich** (ten) Kouzka; **Vienna Boys' Choir; Slovak Philharmonic Choir; Vienna State Opera Chorus and Orchestra / Claudio Abbado.** DG Ⓕ 429 758-2GH3 (three discs: 171 minutes: DDD: 11/90). Ⓖ
Notes, text and translation included. Recorded live in 1989.
The booklet-essay suggests that Mussorgsky's music constantly poses a question to his Russian compatriots: "What are the causes of our country's continuing calamities, and why does the state crush all that is good?". Anyone who follows today's news from Russia and then experiences this opera will understand what is meant, and while we observe with sympathy we seem no nearer than the citizens of that great, tormented country to finding solutions for its endemic problems. However, Mussorgsky was not the least of those Russian musicians who found lasting beauty in her history and he expressed it in a powerfully dramatic idiom that drew on folk-music and had both epic qualities and deep humanity as well as an occasional gentleness. There is also an element here of Russian church music, since *Khovanshchina* has a political and religious theme and is set in the 1680s at the time of Peter the Great's accession. Since the work was unfinished when Mussorgsky died, performances always involve conjectural work, and the version here – which works convincingly – is mostly that of Shostakovich with the choral ending that Stravinsky devised using Mussorgsky's music. The cast in this live recording is not one of star opera singers, but they are fully immersed in the drama and the music, as is the chorus and the orchestra under Claudio Abbado, and the result is deeply atmospheric. The booklet has the Russian text and a translation as well as informative essays on the music.

Additional recommendations ...
...**Soloists; Kirov Theatre Chorus and Orchestra / Valery Gergiev.**
Philips Ⓕ 432 147-2PH3 (three discs: 196 minutes: DDD: 6/92).
...Prelude, Act 1 (arr. Rimsky-Korsakov). *Coupled with works by various composers.*
Boston Symphony Orchestra / Serge Koussevitzky.
Biddulph mono Ⓕ WHL044*(70 minutes: ADD: 3/97).

Further listening ...
...What are words of love to you?. Night. *Coupled with works by various composers.*
Olga Borodina (mez); **Larissa Gergieva** (pf). Philips 442 780-2PH (8/95).
...The Marriage (orch. Rozhdestvensky). **Soloists; USSR Ministry of Culture Symphony Orchestra / Gennadi Rozhdestvensky.** *Coupled with* **Rimsky-Korsakov** Mozart and Salieri.
Soloists; Bolshoi Theatre Orchestra / Mark Ermler. Olympia OCD145 (9/93).

John Musto   American 1954

Suggested listening ...
...Triolet. The Rose Family. *Coupled with works by various composers.* **Dame Felicity Lott** (sop); **Graham Johnson** (pf). Hyperion CDA66937 (10/97). *See review in the Collections section; refer to the Index.*

Charles Naginski

American 1909-1940

...Look down fair moon. *Coupled with works by various composers.* **Thomas Hampson** (bar);
Craig Rutenberg (pf).
EMI CDM5 55028-2 (10/97). *See review in the Collections section; refer to the Index.*   ⊕⊕⊕
...Richard Cory. *Coupled with works by various composers.* **Jennifer Larmore** (mez); **Antoine Palloc**
(pf). Teldec 0630-16069-2 (12/97). *See review in the Collections section; refer to the Index.*

Conlon Nancarrow

Mexican 1912-1997

Nancarrow Three Canons for Ursula. Studies for Player Piano Nos. 3*c*, 6 and 11.
Bach The Art of Fugue, BWV1080. **Joanna MacGregor** (pf). Collins Classics Ⓕ 7043-2
(two discs: 108 minutes: DDD: 10/96). Recorded 1995.
In her witty and incisive notes, MacGregor compels us to hear a vital relationship between eighteenth-
and twentieth-century composers who see fugue and canon as the highest musical good, a "sounding
mathematics" which "achieves a depth and simplicity and at times a luminous serenity" and the
performances testify to her sense of Bach's richness and intellectual grace. Immaculate, lucid and
sensitive she reveals *The Art of Fugue* as an incomparable act of meditation. MacGregor has recorded
Bach and Nancarrow before but here the juxtaposition is the thing. Using multi-track techniques she
emulates and excels Nancarrow's original player piano capacity for intricacy. Very short quaver-
durations in Study No. 11 end in a fantastic virtuoso uproar and remind one of a related complexity
in "Canon B", the second of the *Three Canons for Ursula*. The difficulties are immense but in Joanna
MacGregor such music has a superlative champion. All her performances in their power and
eloquence positively beg you to share her sense of discovery and exhilaration. This is an indispensable
issue all musicians who relish a supreme play of the mind and. The recordings are magnificent.
Additional recommendation ...
...Studies for Player Piano (arr. Mikhashoff) – Nos. 1, 2, 3*c*, 5, 6, 7, 9, 12, 14, 18, 19. Tango?
(arr. Mikhashoff). Toccata (arr. Mikhashoff). Piece No. 2. Trio. Sarabande and Scherzo.
Ensemble Modern / Ingo Metzmacher.
RCA Victor Red Seal Ⓕ 09026 61180-2 (73 minutes: DDD: 11/93).   ⓖ
Further listening ...
...Studies for Player Piano – Nos. 42, 45*a*, 45*b*, 45*c*, 48*a*, 48*b*, 48*c*, 49*a*, 49*b*, 49*c*. **Conlon Nancarrow.**
Wergo WER60165-50 (8/89).

Luys de Narváez

Spanish fl 1530-1550

...Paseávase el rey moro. Lós Seys libros del Delphin – Diferencias de Guardame las vacas.
Coupled with works by various composers. **La Romanesca / José Miguel Moreno** (vihuela).
Glossa GCD920203 (5/96). 🎵 *Gramophone Editor's choice. See review in the Collections
section; refer to the Index.*   ⓖ

Stephen Nau

French/British ?-1647

...Suite in F major. Ballet in F major. Pavan and Galliard in D minor. *Coupled with works by
various composers.* **Parley of Instruments Renaissance Violin Band / Peter Holman.**
Hyperion CDA66806 (6/96). 🎵 *See review in the Collections section; refer to the Index.*   ⓖ

Juan de Navas

Spanish fl 1659-1709

...Tono di Miserere, "Si mis hierros os tienen pendiente". *Coupled with works by* **Durón** and
Torres Al Ayre Español / Eduardo López Banzo. Deutsche Harmonia Mundi 05472 77376-2
(7/97). 🎵 *Gramophone Editor's choice. See review under Durón; refer to the Index.*

William Neidlinger

1863-1924

...Memories of Lincoln. *Coupled with works by various composers.*
Thomas Hampson (bar); **Craig Rutenberg** (pf).
EMI CDM5 55028-2 (10/97). *See review in the Collections section; refer to the Index.*   ⊕⊕⊕

Johann Neruda
Czechoslovakian/German c1707-c1780

Suggested listening ...
...Trumpet Concerto in E flat major. *Coupled with works by various composers.*
John Wallace (tpt); **Philharmonia Orchestra / Christopher Warren-Green.**
Nimbus NI7016 (2/95). *See review in the Collections section; refer to the Index.*
...Trumpet Concerto in E flat major (ed. Steele-Perkins). *Coupled with works by various composers.*
Crispian Steele-Perkins (tpt); **English Chamber Orchestra / Anthony Halstead.**
Carlton Classics 30366 0066-2 (10/97). *See review in the Collections section; refer to the Index.*

Otto Nicolai
German 1810-1849

Suggested listening ...
...Die Lustigen Weiber von Windsor – Nun eilt herbei.
Coupled with works by various composers. **Maria Ivogün** (sop) with various artists.
Nimbus Prima Voce NI7832* (8/92). *See review in the Collections section; refer to the Index.*

Carl Nielsen
Danish 1865-1931

Nielsen Flute Concerto, FS119[a]; Clarinet Concerto, FS129[b]. Maskarade[c] – Overture; Magdalone's dance scene; Prelude, Act 2; Dance of the cockerels. [a]**Holger Gilbert-Jespersen** (fl); [b]**Ib Erikson** (cl); **Danish State Radio Symphony Orchestra /** [ac]**Thomas Jensen,** [b]**Mogens Wöldike.** Dutton Laboratories mono Ⓜ CDLXT2505* (62 minutes: ADD: 2/96). Items marked [ab] from Decca LXT2979 (12/54), [c]Decca LW5132 (12/54).   ❋❋

In the early 1920s Nielsen heard the Copenhagen Wind Quintet rehearsing some works by Mozart and was moved to compose his enchanting Wind Quintet. He subsequently planned to write each of its members a concerto but only lived long enough to compose the two recorded here – the Flute Concerto of 1926 and the Clarinet Concerto of two years later. The soloist at the former's première was Holger Gilbert-Jespersen and it was he who made its first recording over a quarter of a century later. Gilbert-Jespersen was by all accounts an artist of refined taste and strong Gallic sympathies, and much of the piece was inspired by his temperament. The burlesque gestures of the trombone at the end are a joke which Nielsen made at his expense. Unless it is discreetly handled, the affectionate little jest can itself sound crude; but here all is perfection, particularly in such a superb CD transfer as this. These concertos and the four excepts from *Maskarade* were all recorded in April 1954, albeit with Mogens Wöldike conducting the Clarinet Concerto. Aage Oxenvad, who was the original dedicatee, was to have recorded it but died shortly before the sessions were due to take place. At the time, Ib Erikson was Principal Clarinet of the Danish State Radio Symphony Orchestra, which throughout the 1950s was without question the finest orchestra in Scandinavia. This version conveys better than so many more modern ones the unearthly quality of the Concerto, its rarefied and bracing air. These performances carry a special authority and cannot be too strongly recommended.

Additional recommendations ...
...Clarinet Concerto. *Coupled with works by* **Copland** and **Lutosławski Janet Hilton** (cl); **Royal Scottish Orchestra / Matthias Bamert.** Chandos Ⓜ CHAN8618 (51 minutes: DDD: 10/88).
...Concertos – Clarinet, FS129[b]; Flute, FS119[a]; Violin, FS61[c]. [a]**Patrick Gallois** (fl); [b]**Olle Schill** (cl); [c]**Dong-Suk Kang** (vn); **Gothenburg Symphony Orchestra / Myung-Whun Chung.** BIS Ⓕ CD616 (79 minutes: DDD: 7/93).   ❋
...Flute Concerto[a]. Clarinet Concerto[b]. Rhapsody Overture: an imaginary trip to the Faroe Islands, FS123. Saul and David – Prelude to Act 2. Springtime in Funen (Fynsk Forår), FS96[c]. [c]**Asa Bäverstam,** [c]**Linnéa Ekdahl** (sops); [c]**Andreas Thors** (treb); [c]**Kjell Magnus Sandvé** (ten); [c]**Per Høyer** (bar); [a]**Per Flemström** (fl); [b]**Håken Rosengren** (cl); [c]**Swedish Boys' Choir;** [c]**Swedish Radio Choir; Swedish Radio Symphony Orchestra / Esa-Pekka Salonen.** Sony Classical Ⓕ SK53276 (75 minutes: DDD: 4/94).   ❋

Nielsen Violin Concerto, FS61[a].
Sibelius Violin Concerto in D minor, Op. 47[b]. **Cho-Liang Lin** (vn); [a]**Swedish Radio Symphony Orchestra,** [b]**Philharmonia Orchestra / Esa-Pekka Salonen.** Sony Classical Ⓕ SK44548 (69 minutes: DDD: 1/89). Recorded 1987-8. *Gramophone Award Winner 1989.*   ❋❋
Nielsen Violin Concerto, FS61[a]. Flute Concerto, FS119[b]. Clarinet Concerto, FS129[c]. [d]**Toke Lund Christiansen** (fl); **Niels Thomsen** (cl); [a]**Kim Sjøgren** (vn); **Danish National Radio Symphony Orchestra / Michael Schønwandt.** Chandos Ⓕ CHAN8894 (80 minutes: DDD: 4/91). Recorded 1990.   ❋

The CBS offering was the best recording of the Sibelius Concerto to have appeared for more than a decade and probably the best ever of the Nielsen. Cho-Liang Lin brings an apparently effortless virtuosity to both concertos. He produces a wonderfully clean and silvery sonority and there is no lack of aristocratic finesse. Only half-a-dozen years separate the two concertos, yet they breathe a totally different air. Lin's perfect intonation and tonal purity excite admiration and throughout them both there is a strong sense of line from beginning to end. Esa-Pekka Salonen gets excellent playing from the Philharmonia Orchestra in the Sibelius and almost equally good results from the Swedish Radio Symphony Orchestra. This should take its place among the classic concerto recordings of the century. The well-filled Chandos CD brings all three concertos together: the Violin Concerto comes from the period of the Third Symphony and the two wind concertos were written after the Sixth during the last years of his life. Nielsen planned to write five concertos, one for each member of the Copenhagen Wind Quintet.

Kim Sjøgren may not command the purity of tone of Cho-Liang Lin but he has the inestimable advantage of totally idiomatic orchestral support: Michael Schønwandt has an instinctive feeling for this music – and this shows throughout the whole disc. The perspective between soloist and orchestra is well judged (Sjøgren is never larger than life) and so is the internal balance. In the Flute Concerto, which veers from Gallic wit to moments of great poetic feeling, Toke Lund Christiansen is an excellent soloist. He has no want of brilliance or authority and his performance also has plenty of character. Niels Thomsen's account of the Clarinet Concerto is one of the very finest now before the public. If there is any music from another planet, this is it! There is no attempt to beautify the score nor to overstate it: every dynamic nuance and expressive marking is observed by both the soloist and conductor. Thomsen plays as if his very being is at stake and Michael Schønwandt secures playing of great imaginative intensity from the Danish Radio Orchestra.

Additional recommendations ...

...Flute Concerto. *Coupled with works by various composers.* **Jennifer Stinton** (fl); **Scottish Chamber Orchestra / Steuart Bedford.** Collins Classics Ⓕ 1210-2 (66 minutes: DDD: 8/91).

...Flute Concerto[a]. Clarinet Concerto[b]. **Hindemith** Violin Concerto[c]. [a]**Julius Baker** (fl); [b]**Stanley Drucker** (cl); [c]**Isaac Stern** (vn); **New York Philharmonic Orchestra / Leonard Bernstein.** Sony Classical Bernstein Royal Edition Ⓜ SMK47599 (73 minutes: ADD: 7/93). ⒼⒼ

...Flute Concerto. *Coupled with works by various composers.* **Michael Faust** (fl); **Cologne Radio Symphony Orchestra / Alun Francis.** Capriccio Ⓕ 10 495 (64 minutes: DDD 12/95).

...Violin Concerto. **Sibelius** Violin Concerto in D minor, Op. 47. **Maxim Vengerov** (vn); **Chicago Symphony Orchestra / Daniel Barenboim.** Teldec Ⓕ 0630-13161-2 (70 minutes: DDD: 9/96).

Nielsen Symphonies – No. 1 in G minor, FS16; No. 6, FS116, "Sinfonia semplice". **San Francisco Symphony Orchestra / Herbert Blomstedt.** Decca Ⓕ 425 607-2DH (67 minutes: DDD: 2/90). Recorded 1989. ⒼⒼⒼ

Nielsen always nurtured a special affection for his First Symphony – and rightly so, for its language is natural and unaffected. It has great spontaneity of feeling and a Dvořákian warmth and freshness. Blomstedt's recording is one of the best to have appeared for some years. It is vital, beautifully shaped and generally faithful to both the spirit and the letter of the score. The recording, too, is very fine: the sound has plenty of room to expand, there is a very good relationship between the various sections of the orchestra and a realistic perspective. Blomstedt gives a powerful account of the Sixth, too, with plenty of intensity and an appreciation of its extraordinary vision. It is by far the most challenging of the cycle and inhabits a very different world from early Nielsen. The intervening years had seen the cataclysmic events of the First World War and Nielsen himself was suffering increasingly from ill health. Blomstedt and the fine San Fransisco orchestra convey the powerful nervous tension of the first movement and the depth of the third, the *Proposta seria.* A splendid issue.

Additional recommendations ...

...No. 1. Flute Concerto[a]. An imaginary journey to the Faroe Islands, FS123. [a]**Patrick Gallois** (fl); **Gothenburg Symphony Orchestra / Myung-Whun Chung.** BIS Ⓕ CD454 (63 minutes: DDD: 8/90). ⒼⒼ

...No. 1. No. 2 in B minor, FS29, "The four temperaments", FS29. **Royal Scottish Orchestra / Bryden Thomson.** Chandos Ⓕ CHAN8880 (63 minutes: DDD: 6/92).

...Nos. 1-6. Gothenburg Symphony Orchestra / Neeme Järvi. DG Ⓕ 437 507-2GH3 (three discs: 202 minutes: DDD: 12/93).

...No. 1[a]; No. 2[b]; No. 3, FS60, "Sinfonia espansiva"[c]; No. 4, FS76, "The inextinguishable"[c]; No. 5, FS97[a]; No. 6, FS116, "Sinfonia semplice"[c]. **Danish Radio Symphony Orchestra /** [a]**Erik Tuxen,** [b]**Launy Grøndahl,** [c]**Thomas Jensen.** Danacord mono Ⓕ DACOCD351/3* (three discs: 203 minutes: ADD: 4/95).

...Nos. 1 and 5. Helios Overture[a]. **Danish State Radio Symphony Orchestra / Thomas Jensen,** [a]**Erik Tuxen.** Dutton Laboratories mono Ⓜ CDLXT2502* (79 minutes: ADD: 7/95). Ⓖ

...Nos. 1 and 6. **National Symphony Orchestra of Ireland / Adrian Leaper.** Naxos Ⓢ 8 550826 (68 minutes: DDD: 12/95).

...No. 1 **Sibelius** Symphony No. 7 in C major, Op. 105. **Copenhagen Philharmonic Orchestra / Okko Kamu.** Classico Ⓕ CLASSCD115 (52 minutes: DDD: 9/96).

Nielsen Symphonies – No. 2, FS29, "The Four Temperaments"; No. 3, FS60, "Sinfonia espansiva"[a]. [a]**Nancy Wait Fromm** (sop); [a]**Kevin McMillan** (bar); **San Francisco Symphony Orchestra / Herbert Blomstedt.** Decca Ⓕ 430 280-2DH (67 minutes: DDD: 8/90). *Gramophone Award Winner 1991.* ⒼⒼⒼ

This disc couples two of Nielsen's most genial symphonies, both of which come from the earliest part of the century, in performances of the very first order. The Second (1902), inspired by the portrayal of *The Four Temperaments* (Choleric, Phlegmatic, Melancholic, Sanguine) that he had seen in a country inn, has splendid concentration and fire and, as always, from the right pace stems the right character. Moreover the orchestra sounds inspired, for there is a genuine excitement about their playing. Indeed Blomstedt's accounts are by far the most satisfying to have appeared for some time. The Third *Espansiva*, is even more personal in utterance than *The Four Temperaments*, for during the intervening years Nielsen had come much further along the road of self-discovery. His melodic lines are bolder, the musical paragraphs longer and his handling of form more assured. It is a glorious and richly inventive score whose pastoral slow movement includes a part for two wordless voices. Blomstedt gives us an affirmative, powerful reading and in the slow movement, the soprano produces the required ethereal effect. The Decca sound is very detailed and full-bodied, and in the best traditions of the company. Blomstedt's *Espansiva* has greater depth than most rival accounts; the actual sound has that glowing radiance that characterizes Nielsen, and the tempo, the underlying current on which this music is borne, is expertly judged – and nowhere better than in the finale. Blomstedt is an experienced guide in this repertoire and this shows, while his orchestra play with refreshing enthusiasm.

Additional recommendations ...

...No. 2. Aladdin – Orchestral Suite, Op. 34. **Gothenburg Symphony Orchestra /
Myung-Whun Chung.** BIS Ⓕ CD247 (56 minutes: DDD: 5/84).   ⒢⒢

...Nos. 2[a] and 4[b]. **Danish State Radio Symphony Orchestra /** [a]**Thomas Jensen,** [b]**Launy Grøndahl.**
Dutton Laboratories mono Ⓑ CDCLP4001* (68 minutes: ADD: 12/96).

...Nos. 2 and 6. Maskarade – Overture; Prelude, Act 2. **Philadelphia Orchestra / Eugene Ormandy.**
Sony Classical Essential Classics Ⓑ SBK63040 (74 minutes: ADD: 1/98).

Nielsen Symphonies – No. 2, FS29, "The Four Temperaments"; No. 3, FS60, "Sinfonia espansiva". **National Symphony Orchestra of Ireland / Adrian Leaper.** Naxos Ⓢ 8 550825 (68 minutes: DDD: 11/95).

The vital current on which every phrase must be borne in Nielsen needs to flow at higher voltage. This is music which needs to be played at white heat. Well, there is no lack of electricity in Leaper's reading of the Second. He sets a cracking pace for the first movement, the choleric temperament, and hardly puts a foot wrong in its three companions. His tempos in the *Sinfonia espansiva* are well judged and sensible throughout all four movements. The finale, where many conductors get it wrong, seems to be just right. These are more than just serviceable performances: they are very good indeed and the Irish orchestra sound well rehearsed and inside the idiom. You can pay more and do worse although some collectors will be inclined to think the additional polish one gets from Blomstedt or Myung-Whun Chung is worth the extra outlay. These latter performances continue to grow in stature, and it is no mean compliment to the Naxos versions to say that they give them a very good run for their money. Naxos do not identify the singers in the slow movement of the *Espansiva*. No one investing in this issue and then going on to either of the Blomstedt accounts is going to feel that they have been let down. The recording team secure a very decent balance: well laid-back wind and brass, with good front-to-back perspective and transparency of texture.

Nielsen Symphonies – No. 3, FS60, "Sinfonia espansiva"[a]; No. 5, FS97. [a]**Catherine Bott** (sop); [a]**Stephen Roberts** (bar); **Royal Scottish Orchestra / Bryden Thomson.** Chandos Ⓕ CHAN9067 (71 minutes: DDD: 2/93). Recorded 1991.

Bryden Thomson and the Royal Scottish Orchestra give fresh and direct readings of the *Espansiva* and the Fifth which are eminently satisfying. At no point are we aware of the conductor interposing himself between composer and listener, and one can sense an evident enthusiasm on the part of the players. This is Nielsen plain and unadorned without any frills. Thomson has a very good feeling for Nielsen's tempos and his account of the finale feels just right. All in all, a splendidly sane performance with good singing from the fine soloists in the slow movement. The Fifth Symphony is another unaffected and straightforward performance that has a great deal going for it – not least the beautiful clarinet playing in the coda, and the thoroughly committed second movement. One is, perhaps, more aware of the beat in the first movement than in Blomstedt's Decca account and it rarely seems to float or sound disembodied as it does with him. However, Thomson gets very spirited playing from all departments of the orchestra and the recordings are very good and present, even if the sound lacks the transparency Decca achieved for Blomstedt. These are eminently enjoyable, ardent performances that can hold their head high amongst any competition.

Additional recommendations ...

...No. 3. Clarinet Concerto, FS129[a]. Maskarade – Overture. **Pia Raanoja** (sop); **Knut Skram** (bar); [a]**Olle Schill** (cl); **Gothenburg Symphony Orchestra / Myung-Whun Chung.**
BIS Ⓕ CD321 (68 minutes: DDD: 8/86).

...Nos. 3 and 5. **New York Philharmonic Orchestra / Leonard Bernstein.**
Sony Classical Bernstein Royal Edition Ⓜ SMK47598 (71 minutes: ADD: 7/93).   ⒢⒢

...Nos. 3[a] and 4. At the bier of a young artist, FS58. [a]**Kirsten Schultz** (sop);
[a]**Peter Rasmussen** (bar); **Danish Radio Symphony Orchestra / Herbert Blomstedt.**
EMI Matrix Ⓜ CDM5 65415-2 (75 minutes: ADD: 12/95).

Nielsen Symphonies – No. 4, FS76, "The inextinguishable"; No. 5, FS97. **San Francisco Symphony Orchestra / Herbert Blomstedt.** Decca Ⓕ 421 524-2DH (72 minutes: DDD: 10/88).   ⒺⒼⒼ
Nielsen Symphonies – No. 4, FS76, "The inextinguishable"; No. 6, FS116, "Sinfonia semplice".
Royal Scottish National Orchestra / Bryden Thomson. Chandos Ⓕ CHAN9047
(70 minutes: DDD: 3/93). Recorded 1991.
These are two of Nielsen's most popular and deeply characteristic symphonies. Blomstedt's are good performances that can hold their own with any in the current catalogue, and as recordings they surpass the competition. The Fourth Symphony occupied Nielsen between 1914 and early 1916 and reveals a level of violence new to his art. The landscape is harsher; the melodic lines soar in a more anguished and intense fashion (in the case of the remarkable slow movement, "like the eagle riding on the wind", to use the composer's own graphic simile). Blomstedt's opening has splendid fire and he is not frightened of letting things rip. The finale with its exhilarating dialogue between the two timpanists comes off splendidly. The Fifth Symphony of 1922 is impressive, too: it starts perfectly and has just the right glacial atmosphere. The climax and the desolate clarinet peroration into which it dissolves are well handled. The recording balance could not be improved upon: the woodwind are well recessed (though clarinet keys are audible at times), there is an almost ideal relationship between the various sections of the orchestra and a thoroughly realistic overall perspective. Blomstedt has a good rapport with his players who sound in excellent shape and respond instinctively to these scores.
Bryden Thomson's accounts of the Fourth and Sixth calls to mind the ardent intensity of the pioneering Danish recordings (no longer available) by Launy Gróndahl and Thomas Jensen, such are their fire. The orchestra play with total commitment and the underlying violence of No. 4 makes a powerful impact, both at the opening and in the finale. But his Sixth is arguably the very finest version of the work on disc, notwithstanding the cultured and splendidly recorded account by Herbert Blomstedt (reviewed above with the First Symphony). Thomson strikes exactly the right tempo for the first movement and the problematic "Humoreske" has never made better sense. He takes it at a steadier pace than most rival conductors, so that its questioning spirit registers. The third movement, the "Proposta seria", is both eloquent and searching. Even in a strongly competitive field this splendidly recorded Chandos account brings one closer to this extraordinary work than any other.

Additional recommendations ...
...No. 5. Violin Concerto, Op. 33[a]. [a]**Dong-Suk Kang** (vn); **Gothenburg Symphony Orchestra / Myung-Whun Chung.** BIS Ⓕ CD370 (68 minutes: DDD: 12/87).
...No. 4[a]. Pan and Syrinx, FS87[a]. **Sibelius** Symphony No. 5 in E flat major, Op. 82[b].
[a]**City of Birmingham Symphony Orchestra;** [b]**Philharmonia Orchestra / Sir Simon Rattle.**
EMI Ⓜ CDM7 64737-2 (78 minutes: DDD: 11/93).
...Nos. 4 and 5. **National Symphony Orchestra of Ireland / Adrian Leaper.**
Naxos Ⓢ 8 550743 (74 minutes: DDD: 10/94).
...No. 5[a]. Sibelius Luonnotar, Op. 70[b]. Night Ride and Sunrise, Op. 55[c]. The Oceanides, Op. 73[c].
[b]**Dame Gwyneth Jones** (sop); [a]**Danish National Radio Symphony Orchestra / Rafael Kubelík;**
[bc]**London Symphony Orchestra / Antál Dorati.**
EMI Studio Plus Ⓜ CDM5 65182-2 (73 minutes: ADD: 10/94).
...Nos. 4 and 6. **Gothenburg Symphony Orchestra / Neeme Järvi.**
BIS Ⓕ CD600 (67 minutes: DDD: 7/93).
...No. 4. Little Suite in A minor, FS6. Hymnus amoris, FS21[a]. [a]**Soloists;** [a]**Copenhagen Boys' Choir;**
Danish National Radio [a]**Choir and Symphony Orchestra / Ulf Schirmer.**
Decca Ⓕ 452 486-2DH (72 minutes: DDD: 1/97).
...Nos. 5 and 6. **Danish Radio Symphony Orchestra / Herbert Blomstedt.**
EMI Matrix Ⓜ CDM5 65867-2 (71 minutes: ADD: 9/96).

Nielsen Aladdin – Suite, FS89. Maskarade – Overture; Prelude, Act 2; The Cockerels' Dance.
Rhapsody Overture: An imaginary journey to the Faroe Islands, FS123. Helios Overture, FS32.
Saga-Drøm, FS46. Pan and Syrinx, FS87. **Gothenburg Symphony Orchestra / Neeme Järvi.**
DG Ⓕ 447 757-2GH (72 minutes: DDD: 9/96). Recorded 1995.
Järvi gets totally committed playing from his fine orchestra; they convey the feeling that they all believe in every note they utter. *Aladdin* is given with great spirit and spontaneity. The recording, made by the same team and in the same venue as the orchestra's earlier recording of the work, under Myung-Whun Chung (listed above), is excellent, though the 1983 BIS account has marginally greater depth and transparency. In only one instance does Järvi get it wrong and that is in the *Helios Overture*, which is too fast for its sunrise to cast its spell! Thoughts turn to Jupiter where the sun rises every ten hours. Järvi gets through this piece, admittedly not top-drawer Nielsen, in 9'31". Erik Tuxen (also listed earlier) who, after all, should know about these matters, struck the right balance in 1952 at 11'42". Everything else here calls for straightforward applause.

Nielsen Wind Quintet, FS100.
Fernström Wind Quintet, Op. 59.
Kvandal Wind Quintet, Op. 34. Three Sacred Folktunes, Op. 23b. **Wind Ensemble** (Tom Ottar Andreasson, fl; Lars Peter Berg, ob; Arild Stav, cl; Jan Olav Marthinsen, hn; Hans Peter Aasen, bn). Naxos Ⓢ 8 553050 (70 minutes: DDD: 3/95). Recorded 1993.

This is a thoroughly entertaining CD, combining three very different and unfamiliar works with what is probably the finest wind quintet ever penned. The major item here, of course, is the Nielsen: a glorious work which achieves the rare combination of seriousness of expression as well as being utterly relaxed in tone. The Oslo Ensemble are a little slower than usual, but their measured tempos are most convincing; indeed, in the finale they highlight musical connections with Nielsen's Fifth and Sixth Symphonies in ways rarely heard elsewhere. The Swede John Axel Fernström was undeniably a minor composer; his Twelfth Symphony has been available briefly in this country (conducted by Vernon Handley, no less). If his music does not possess many visionary qualities it is certainly well crafted and his 1943 Quintet is an engaging and worthwhile concert opener. Johan Kvandal from Norway is a weightier proposition and better-known outside of his native country than is Fernström. Kvandal's Quintet, Op. 34 (1971), was written for the Oslo ensemble (apparently for a couple of cases of wine!) and is serious and high-minded in tone, contrasting effectively with both the Fernström and Kvandal's own *Sacred Folktunes* of 1963. In the Quintet's fast second movement Kvandal adopts a rather Shostakovichian manner, even alluding to the Soviet master's Twelfth Symphony, though to what purpose (if deliberate at all) is unexplained. The idiomatic playing is reproduced in a slightly flat recording (made in the studios of Norwegian Radio), although the Naxos sound has great immediacy. The Bergen Quintet on BIS must remain the first choice but this disc, with its welcome couplings, makes a fine alternative.

Additional recommendations ...
...Wind Quintet. *Coupled with works by various composers.* **Aulos Wind Quintet.**
Koch Schwann Musica Mundi Ⓕ 310100 (71 minutes: DDD).   Ⓖ
...Wind Quintet[a]. Fantasy Piece for Clarinet and Piano, FS3h[b]. Fantasy Pieces for Oboe and Piano, FS8[c]. Canto serioso for Horn and Piano, FS132[d]. Serenata in vano, FS68[e]. The Mother, FS94 – The fog is lifting[f]; The children are playing[g]; Faith and Hope are playing[h]. Allegretto for Two Recorders, FS157[i]. [a]**Bergen Wind Quintet** (Gro Sandvik, fl[fgh], rec[i]; [c]Steinar Hannevold, ob; [be]Lars Kristian Holm Brynildsen, cl; [de]Vidar Olsen, hn; Per Hannevold, bn[e], rec[i]); [f]**Turid Kniejski** (hp); [h]**Lars Anders Tomter** (va); [e]**Sally Guenther** (vc); [e]**Torbjorn Eide** (db); [bcd]**Leif Ove Andsnes** (pf). BIS Ⓕ CD428 (56 minutes: DDD: 9/89).
...Wind Quintet. *Coupled with works by* **Loeffler** *and* **Prokofiev Chamber Music Northwest.**
Delos Ⓕ DE3136 (71 minutes: DDD: 12/93).
...Wind Quintet. *Coupled with works by various composers.* **Swiss Wind Quintet.**
Koch Discover International Ⓑ DICD920395 (65 minutes: DDD: 8/97).
See review in the Collections section; refer to the Index.

Nielsen String Quartets – No. 1 in G minor, FS4; No. 2 in F minor, FS11; No. 3 in E flat major, FS23 (Op. 14); No. 4 in F major, FS36. Movements for String Quartet, FS3c. **Danish Quartet** (Tim Frederiksen, Arne Balk-Møller, vns; Claus Myrup, va; H. Brendstrup, vc). Kontrapunkt Ⓕ 32150/1 (two discs: 138 minutes: DDD: 10/93).   Ⓖ
Nielsen composed two quartets and a string quintet during his student years. There was a gap of eight years between the F minor Quartet and the Third, in E flat, Op. 14 (FS23) during which Nielsen had written his First Symphony, and another eight before the F major, Op. 44 (FS36) saw the light of day. By this time he had written his opera, *Saul and David* and the best part of *Maskarade* as well as the Second Symphony. The Danish Quartet do not have the thrust or, perhaps, the finish of the Kontra Quartet on BIS, but they are very sensitive to dynamic nuance, phrase more imaginatively, and are generally speaking more involving. Of course, the F major Quartet goes deeper than the Third. There is a grace, an effortless fluency and a marvellous control of pace. Ideas come and go just when you feel they should; yet its learning and mastery is worn lightly. Though the earlier quartets are not such perfect works of art, they are nevertheless always endearing. The Danish Quartet is completely inside this music and is totally persuasive. In spite of the closely balanced recording this set gives real pleasure and can be recommended with enthusiasm.

Additional recommendation ...
...Nos. 1-4. String Quintet in G major, FS5[a]. At the bier of a young artist, FS58[b].
Kontra Quartet; [a]**Philipp Naegele** (va); [b]**Jan Johannsson** (db).
BIS Ⓕ CD503/04 (two discs: 150 minutes: DDD: 4/92).

Nielsen Five Pieces, FS10. Humoresque Bagatelles, FS22. Chaconne, FS79. Suite, FS91. Three Pieces, FS131. **Leif Ove Andsnes** (pf). Virgin Classics Ⓕ VC5 45129-2 (54 minutes: DDD: 8/96).
Gramophone Editor's choice.   Ⓖ
This music on this disc is quite wonderful and deserves the widest dissemination. Although the *Suite* (*Suite luciferique*) was dedicated to Schnabel, the great pianist never played it in public. On record the finest advocate of the piano music was Arne Skjold Rasmussen, whose three-LP set appeared fleetingly in this country in a Vox box during the 1960s. Without the slightest disrespect to him, it now has to be said that this music has at last found its true interpreter in the Norwegian Leif Ove Andsnes. He has the measure both of the fresh and charming early pieces, FS10 and 22, and the later more searching, other-worldly *Suite* and the *Three Pieces*. The *luciferique* of the former alludes, incidentally, to the messenger of light, not the prince of darkness, and Nielsen subsequently withdrew the title. This is music of great substance and a deep and powerful originality. Andsnes has such a natural feeling for it that you will probably never find yourself questioning his interpretative

judgements. He brings wit and subtlety to pieces like the "Spinning Top" and "Jumping Jack" from FS10, and there is always a splendid rhythmic grip, tonal sensitivity and variety of keyboard colour. He communicates real conviction to the listener, a feeling that this is the only way this music can sound. There is an impressive eloquence and nobility here, and the recorded sound is in every respect exemplary. It is 'present', natural and lifelike. Because this music is unfamiliar, collectors may be cautious or slow in exploring it. To judge from his BBC Proms performance in 1995, Andsnes has quite a following and it is to be hoped that he will lead his admirers on to this music which he has here served so well.

Nielsen Aladdin. **Mette Ejsing** (contr); **Guido Paevatalu** (bar); **Danish National Radio Chamber Choir; Danish National Radio Symphony Orchestra / Gennadi Rozhdestvensky.**
Chandos Ⓕ CHAN9135 (79 minutes: DDD: 5/93). Text and translation included.
Recorded 1992. *Gramophone Editor's choice.*   Ⓖ

So far Nielsen's music to Adam Oehlenschläger's *Aladdin* has been known only from the seven-movement suite. However, the suite only comprises about 20 minutes of music, which is little more than a quarter of Nielsen's original score. *Aladdin* comes from 1917-18, and was commissioned for a particularly lavish production of the play at the Royal Theatre in Copenhagen. More than half the music consists of orchestral interludes to accompany processions and dances, most of which come in the Third Act. Many are delightful and endearing, and once heard difficult to get out of one's head. Robert Simpson summed the work up in his Nielsen monograph: "The market-square in Isfahan where four orchestras play in four different tempos suggesting marvellously the clashing colours, movements and sounds of an eastern market-place in undoubtedly the most striking and original part of the music. Some of it is not very interesting (the rather commonplace Blackamoors' Dance, for instance) but most is intensely perceptive and colourful." It is full of characteristic Nielsenesque touches, and although it is not the composer at his very best, it offers many irresistible delights. Performance and recording are superb.

Further listening ...
...Helios Overture, FS32. Symphonic Rhapsody, FS7. Saga-drøm, FS46. An evening on Giske, FS9. Paraphrase on "Nearer my God to Thee", FS63. Bohemian-Danish Folk tune. FS130. Rhapsody Overture: An imaginary journey to the Faroe Islands, FS123. Pan and Syrinx, FS87. **Danish National Radio Symphony Orchestra / Gennadi Rozhdestvensky.**
Chandos CHAN9287 (9/94).
...String Quintet in G major, FS5. *Coupled with works by* **Svendsen**
Academy of St Martin in the Fields Chamber Ensemble. Chandos CHAN9258 (5/94).   Ⓖ
...Violin Sonatas – No. 1 in A major, FS20; No. 2, FS64. **Lydia Mordkovitch** (vn);
Clifford Benson (pf). Chandos CHAN8598 (9/89).
...Commotio, FS155. *Coupled with works by various composers.* **Christopher Herrick** (org).
Hyperion CDA66676 (8/94). *See review in the Collections section; refer to the Index.*
...Commotio, FS155. *Coupled with works by various composers.* **Kevin Bowyer** (org).
Nimbus NI5468 (7/96). *See review in the Collections section; refer to the Index.*
...Saul and David. **Soloists; Danish National Radio Choir and Symphony Orchestra / Neeme Järvi.**
Chandos CHAN8911/12 (3/91).

John Niles   American 1892-1980

Suggested listening ...
...Black is the color of my true love's hair. Fee Simple. *Coupled with works by various composers.*
Jennifer Larmore (mez); **Antoine Palloc** (pf).
Teldec 0630-16069-2 (12/97). *See review in the Collections section; refer to the Index.*

Joaquín Nin   Cuban 1879-1949

Suggested listening ...
...Cantos populares españolas – No. 3, Tonada de la niña perdida; No. 4, Montañesa; No. 6, Malagueña; No. 7, Granadina; No. 19, Canto Andaluz; No. 20, Polo. *Coupled with works by various composers.* **Joaquin Nin** (pf); **instrumental ensemble.**
EMI Composers in Person mono CDC7 54836-2* (11/93). *See review in the Collections section; refer to the Index.*

Guillaume Nivers   French c1632-1714

Suggested listening ...
...Antiphonarium Monasticum, Antiennes I-VI. *Coupled with works by* **Charpentier**
Le Concert Spirituel / Hervé Niquet.
Naxos 8 553174 (3/96). *See review under Charpentier; refer to the Index.*   Ⓖ

Thomas Noble

British/American 1867-1953

Suggested listening ...
...Evening Service, Op. 6. *Coupled with works by various composers.*
Bristol Cathedral Choir / Christopher Brayne with **Ian Ball** (org).
Priory PRCD528 (8/96). *See review in the Collections section; refer to the Index.*

Luigi Nono

Italian 1924-1990

Nono Prometeo. **Ingrid Ade-Jesemann, Monika Bair-Ivenz** (sops); **Peter Hall** (ten);
Freiburg Soloists Choir; Ensemble Modern / Ingo Metzmacher. EMI Ⓕ CDS5 55209-2
(two discs: 134 minutes: DDD: 12/95). Notes, text and translation included. Recorded live in 1993.
Prometeo is a challenge to the faculty of listening; at least part of the meaning of its subtitle, "tragedia
dell'ascolto", is that it is a tragedy to be perceived through the hearing only. It is a two-and-a-quarter-
hour opera without staging or action, in which few if any of the words are intended to be
distinguishable and whose dynamic level is often at the very limit of audibility. You could add "and
proceeds at a tempo of *adagissimo* almost throughout", but even when, as often happens, the basic
tempo is very slow indeed there are often two or more musics of different degrees of slowness going
on at once, thus colour, texture and harmony change more rapidly than pulse. The effect, even so, is
of a very long piece of very slow, very quiet music. It is in nine sections; two of them give a clear
indication of Nono's intentions. The fourth, *Interludio primo*, is for solo contralto, flute, clarinet and
tuba, the instruments mostly doubling the voice, so that the whole piece can be heard as a monody in
which the function of the instruments is to 'colour' the voice expressively. The text hints, with the aid
of a single line from Hesiod's *Theogony*, at a vision of a new Prometheus. It was Nono's intention,
one suspects, that having previously read the text (it is very short) we should perceive its meaning
through the music alone. It is like a sort of ritual 'still centre' to the entire work, inviting you to
suspend your sense of time and listen to every change of pitch and timbre with an unaccustomed
intensity: the musicians are instructed never to rise above *ppppp*, and in this performance they are
admirably faithful to that instruction.
A different kind of challenge is posed by the sixth section, in which three very fragmentary
'movements', each for a different vocal and instrumental combination, are played simultaneously,
punctuated by a separate chorus intoning six 'distant memories' from the Prologue. This time you will
need the texts in front of you, since there are not three but seven of them and here they have fused
with the music, as the voice and the instruments fused in *Intermedio primo*. The effort of hearing and
making sense of three different, intermittent musical strands is great but one is aware of a strange
poetry, a grave beauty. One of the reasons for this is the extraordinary care with which Nono planned
every aspect of what he called his 'acoustic dramaturgy', including its complex yet subtle electronic
transformations. The performance maintains a remarkable control over this huge span of hushed
concentration. The recording, too, is exceptional, revealing gradations of quietness that you will
rarely before have been asked to perceive. A challenging redefinition of how music may encompass
myth and drama (oh yes: you are aware of a compelling drama taking place, one which only your ears
can interpret).
Additional recommendation ...
...Prometeo – suite. *Coupled with works by various composers.* **Soloists; Berlin Singakademie;**
Freiburg Soloists Choir; Berlin Philharmonic Orchestra / Claudio Abbado.
Sony Classical Ⓕ SK53978 (75 minutes: DDD: 1/95). *Gramophone Editor's choice.*
See review in the Collections section; refer to the Index.   ⒼⒼⒼ
Further listening ...
...Il canto sospeso. *Coupled with works by* **Mahler** Soloists; Berlin Radio Chorus;
Berlin Philharmonic Orchestra / Claudio Abbado. Sony Classical SK53360 (10/93).
...Canti di vita e d'amore. *Coupled with works by various composers.* **Sarah Leonard** (sop);
Thomas Randle (ten); **Bamberg Symphony Orchestra / Ingo Metzmacher.**
EMI CDC5 55424-2 (3/97). *See review in the Collections section; refer to the Index.*
...Liebeslied. *Coupled with works by various composers.* **Vienna Jeunesse Choir;**
Vienna Philharmonic Orchestra / Claudio Abbado. DG 429 260-2GH (4/90).

Per Nørgård

Danish 1932

Nørgård Symphony No. 3[a]. Piano Concerto[b]. [b]**Per Salo** (pf); **Danish National Radio** [a]**Choir**
and Symphony Orchestra / Leif Segerstam. Chandos New Direction Ⓕ CHAN9491
(73 minutes: DDD: 7/97). Text and translation included. Recorded 1996.
Chandos have provided typically opulent sound for this rich, variegated score of Symphony No. 3
(1972-5), and in the depth and presence of their recording one finds a wealth of detail that could
otherwise be missed. Although in the first movement some sonorities could be projected more
prominently in the half-hour-long second movement the disc comes into its own, both sonically and
as a performance. Segerstam's experience as a Mahler conductor enables him to weld the disparate

elements most convincingly, though one feels bound to say that the music is never really symphonic. Nørgård's Piano Concerto is more recent, having been completed in 1996. Readers who know his viola and cello concertos *Between* and *Remembering Child* will find that this concerto approaches the genre from a quite different tack. Gone is the traditionally confrontational nature of the form: here the keyboard is first amongst equals, an ally of the orchestra whose concern it is to fuse and reconcile the opposing tempos. In fact, two entirely new ones emerge, but along the way Nørgård traverses some extraordinary terrain, as for instance in the weird cadenza in the piano's lowest register just over half-way through. Per Salo is undaunted by the technical difficulties, giving us a fascinating disc.

Further listening ...
...Twilight. *Coupled with works by various composers.* **Aarhus Royal Academy of Music Orchestra / Ole Schmidt.** Kontrapunkt 32194 (7/95).
...Echo Zone I-III. *Coupled with works by various composers.* **Safri Duo.**
Chandos New Direction CHAN9330 (4/95).
...Partita concertante, Op. 23. *Coupled with works by various composers.* **Kevin Bowyer** (org).
Nimbus NI5468 (7/96). *See review in the Collections section; refer to the Index.*
...Trio, Op. 15[a]. Spell[a]. Cao Shu. Lin[a]. **LINensemble.** Kontrapunkt 32211 (3/96).
...And time shall be no more. *Coupled with works by various composers.*
Danish National Radio Choir / Stefan Parkman. Chandos CHAN9264 (4/95).
...Siddharta[a]. Percussion Concerto, "For a Change"[b]. [a]Soloists; [b]**Gert Mortensen** (perc);
Danish National Radio [a]**Choir;** [a]**Childrens' Choir and Symphony Orchestra / Jan Latham-Konig.**
Da Capo 8 224031/2 (12/95).

Ib Nørholm   Danish 1931

Nørholm Symphonies – No. 4, Op. 76[a], "De-creation"; No. 5, Op. 80, "The Elements".
[a]**Nina Pavlovski** (sop); [a]**Stefan Dahlberg** (ten); [a]**Per Høyer** (bar); [a]**Ib Nørholm** (narr);
[a]**Danish National Radio Choir; Odense Symphony Orchestra / Eduard Serov.**
Kontrapunkt Ⓕ 32212 (74 minutes: DDD: 10/95). Recorded 1995.
Like Per Nørgård, Ib Nørholm was a pupil of Vagn Holmboe and is currently Professor of Composition in Copenhagen. His early music was in a lyrical Nordic style very much in the tradition of Nielsen and Holmboe. But unlike his master, who "without glancing to left or right, without regard to fashions or trends, goes his own way" (as Klemperer said of Sibelius), Nørholm has looked very much to left and right, and has been keenly responsive to the European avant-garde and has, perhaps, embraced "the new internationalism" too eagerly. The very titles of some of his works betray their self-consciousness: the Sixth Symphony is called "Moralities, or There may be many miles to the nearest spider". Nørholm possesses a sophisticated aural imagination and a fine ear for texture. Both symphonies offer us moments of considerable beauty and many others that are not. Basically the Fourth Symphony is deficient in thematic vitality and although there is a great deal of activity, there is little real musical movement. The Fifth Symphony is the more interesting of the two pieces. The opening of its third movement, *Poco fluente*, is quite beautiful but there is, arguably, too much neo-expressionistic hysteria and too little sense of momentum. The performances are dedicated and the recording copes admirably with the complex textures and reproduces them with lucidity.

Further listening ...
...Symphonies – No. 1, Op. 10; No. 3, Op. 57, "Day's Nightmare".
Odense Symphony Orchestra / Eduard Serov. Kontrapunkt 32132 (9/93).   Ⓖ
...Symphonies – No. 6, Op. 85, "Moralities, or There may be many miles to the nearest spider"[a].
No. 8, Op. 114, "Faith and Longing"[b]. [a]**Majken Bjerno** (sop); [ab]**Per Høyer** (bar); [a]**Uffe Henriksen,**
[a]**Ulla Seel** (narrs); **Odense Symphony Orchestra / Edward Serov.** Kontrapunkt 32162 (2/94).   Ⓖ
...Symphonies – No. 7, Op. 88, "Ecliptic Instincts"; No. 9, Op. 116, "The Sun Garden in Three
Shades of Light". **Odense Symphony Orchestra / Eduard Serov.** Kontrapunkt 32112 (9/93).   Ⓖ
...Violin Concerto, Op. 60[a]. Cello Concerto, Op. 108[b]. [a]**Kishiko Suzumi** (vn); [b]**Erling Blöndal
Bengtsson** (vc); **Aalborg Symphony Orchestra / Tamás Vetö.** Kontrapunkt 32099 (9/93).   Ⓖ

Angelo Notari   Italian 1556-1663

Suggested listening ...
...Variations on the "Ruggiero". *Coupled with works by various composers.*
Parley of Instruments Renaissance Violin Band / Peter Holman.
Hyperion CDA66806 (6/96). ☞ *See review in the Collections section; refer to the Index.*   Ⓖ

Vítezslav Novák   Bohemian 1870-1949

Novák In the Tatra Mountains, Op. 26. Eternal Longing, Op. 33. Slovak Suite, Op. 32.
Royal Liverpool Philharmonic Orchestra / Libor Pešek. Virgin Classics Ⓕ VC5 45251-2
(68 minutes: DDD: 6/97). Recorded 1996.   Ⓖ

Libor Pešek's latest Slavonic excursion with the RLPO for Virgin Classics will surely win many new friends for the music of Dvořák-pupil, Vítězslav Novák. Aided by luminous, supremely affectionate orchestral playing and rich, beautifully refined sound, the *Slovak Suite* (1903) creates a delightful impression here – but then again, given its wealth of glorious melody and felicitous orchestral colour how could it not? Pešek's unhurried manner imparts a stately, glowing dignity to the opening "At Church", while the ensuing "Children's Scene" goes with refreshing snap and clean-limbed vigour. Elsewhere, the ravishing portrait of "The Lovers" is sweetly drawn, evincing a gentle, unaffected ardour that is most touching, "The Ball" nicely combines earthiness and humour, and the concluding "The Night" has exactly the right sense of wide-eyed, pantheistic wonder and fragrant tenderness. Enthusiasts won't need reminding just how good both rival versions are, especially Karel Sejna's irresistibly tangy Brno account. Pešek's account may not be as capable of activating the tear-ducts to quite the same degree as do Sejna's or Talich's, but it remains a thoroughly pleasing achievement all the same. The symphonic poems *In the Tatra Mountains* and *Eternal Longing* date from 1902 and 1904 respectively. Both inhabit a headily evocative, neo-Straussian landscape – indeed, it's remarkable just how much of the former strikingly pre-echoes *An Alpine Symphony*. Of the two, *Eternal Longing* is the more visionary and subtly coloured; its slightly earlier partner, on the other hand, displays the stronger melodic profile and more satisfying formal ruggedness. Throughout, Novák's orchestral command is total and both works are undoubtedly superior examples of *fin de siècle* decadence which many listeners will lap up. Collectors will, of course, always cherish Sejna's marvellous performances from 1966, but Pešek matches his countryman's formidable interpretative prowess, particularly in the extra sense of peril and drama he brings to the central portion of *In the Tatra Mountains*. Moreover, the admirable Liverpool orchestra respond with all the freshness and enthusiasm of new discovery.

Additional recommendations ...

...Slovak Suite[a]. Eternal Longing, Op. 33[b]. In the Tatra Mountains[a].
[a]**Brno State Philharmonic Orchestra;** [b]**Czech Philharmonic Orchestra / Karel Sejna.**
Supraphon Crystal Collection Ⓜ 11 0682-2 (65 minutes: ADD: 6/93). 🔊🔊

...Slovak Suite. *Coupled with works by* **Janáček** Czech Philharmonic Orchestra / **Václav Talich.**
Supraphon Historical mono Ⓜ 11 1905-2* (71 minutes: AAD: 1/94). 🔊🔊

Further listening ...

...Pan, Op. 43. **Slovak Philharmonic Orchestra / Zdenek Bílek.** Marco Polo 8 223325 (10/91).
...Serenades – F major, Op. 9; D major, Op. 36. **Ukrainian Chamber Orchestra / Andrew Mogrelia.** Marco Polo 8 223649 (3/96).

Michael Nyman
British 1944

Nyman The Piano Concerto[a]. MGV (Musique à Grande Vitesse)[b]. [a]**Kathryn Stott** (pf);
[a]**Royal Liverpool Philharmonic Orchestra;** [b]**Michael Nyman Band; orchestra / Michael Nyman.**
Argo Ⓕ 443 382-2ZH (59 minutes: DDD: 9/94). Recorded 1994.

Considering the international success of Jane Campion's film *The Piano*, it seems quite logical that Nyman should adapt his celebrated score into a concert piece. Though performed uninterrupted, the 32-minute concerto is divided into four clear-cut sections. The Scottish folk-songs on which much of the score is based imbue the piece with a yearning, heartfelt quality not usually associated with this composer. Indeed, the whole concerto, as so convincingly advocated by Kathryn Stott and the RLPO, throbs with an unbridled romantic fervency (the second movement and the end of the third almost Rózsa-like in their ardour) that may come as something of a shock to hardened Nymanites or those who appreciate the less grandiose scoring for the film. More recognizably Nymanesque is *MGV*, a sort of *Pacific 231* for the 1990s, composed for the inauguration of the TGV North-European line in France. Here the composer's abstract style is eminently suited to describing a non-stop, imaginary railway journey through five regions between Paris and Lille; his repeated phrases and chugging, insistently propulsive rhythms create an effect that is totally spellbinding, with the strings adding an especially effective sense of speed and visual sweep. A rewarding disc that will appeal to Nyman fans old and new.

Additional recommendation ...

...The Piano Concerto[a]. On the Fiddle[b]. Prospero's Books – Prospero's curse;
Prospero's magic; Miranda; Cornfield. [a]**Peter Lawson** (pf);
Royal Philharmonic Orchestra / Jonathan Carney ([b]vn).
Tring International Royal Philharmonic Collection Ⓢ TRP097 (68 minutes: DDD: 2/97).

Nyman Noises, Sounds and Sweet Airs. **Catherine Bott** (sop); **Hilary Summers** (contr);
Ian Bostridge (ten); **Basse-Normandie Instrumental Ensemble / Dominique Debart.**
Argo Ⓕ 440 842-2ZH (73 minutes: DDD: 4/95). Text included. Recorded 1993.

Nymanites will rejoice. The pulse, the raunchy textures and the restless alternation of metre (either between 'numbers' or within them) all hail from a familiar work-bench: this is miniaturist minimalism taken to epic extremes. The sound is unmistakable: hear it at your local record store and you'll either be reaching for your wallet, or racing for the door. A 'Prospero Express', with 20 carriages (musical sections), each housing a different slice of the action – hyperactive, restless, moody (the score is far darker than various of its concert or film-based predecessors) and featuring some imaginative word-painting. Not that Shakespeare's *The Tempest* could possibly serve you as a libretto – not unless you have scissors and paste handy. "Very heavily and idiosyncratically edited", admits the composer. And how! *Prospero's Books*, incidentally, is a totally separate score. The performance itself seems fairly expert, save for one or two instances where the soprano's relatively high tessitura gives Catherine Bott cause for some strain. The recording is excellent.

Further listening ...

...Double Concerto for Saxophone and Cello[a]. Trombone Concerto[b]. Harpsichord Concerto[c].
[a]**John Harle** (sax); [b]**Christian Lindberg** (tbn); [a]**Julian Lloyd Webber** (vc); [c]**Elisabeth Chojnacka** (hpd); [a]**Philharmonia Orchestra**, [b]**BBC Symphony Orchestra**, [c]**Michael Nyman String Orchestra /**
Michael Nyman. EMI CDC5 56487-2 (11/97).

...Where the Bee Dances. *Coupled with works by various composers.*
Gerard McChrystal (sax); **London Musici / Mark Stephenson.**
Silva Classics SILKD6010 (6/96). *See review in the Collections section; refer to the Index.*

...Four Songs for Tony. *Coupled with works by various composers.* **Apollo Saxophone Quartet.**
Argo 443 903-2ZH (8/95). *See review in the Collections section; refer to the Index.*

...String Quartets Nos. 1-3. **Balanescu Quartet.** Argo 433 093-2ZH (8/91).

...Prospero's Books (music from the film by Peter Greenaway). **Sarah Leonard, Ute Lemper,**
Marie Angel (sops); **Deborah Conway** (sngr); **Michael Nyman Band / Michael Nyman.**
Decca 425 224-2DH (11/91).

Gösta Nystroem

Swedish 1890-1966

Suggested listening ...

...The Arctic Ocean. Viola Concerto, "Hommage à la France"[a]. Sinfonia concertante[b].
[a]**Nobuko Imai** (va); [b]**Niels Ullner** (vc); **Malmö Symphony Orchestra / Paavo Järvi.**
BIS CD682 (4/95).

Jacob Obrecht

Dutch *c*1450-1505

Obrecht Missa Caput. Salve regina a 4. Salve regina a 6. Venit ad Petrum. **Oxford Camerata /**
Jeremy Summerly. Naxos Ⓢ 8 553210 (69 minutes: DDD: 6/98). Texts and translations included.
Obrecht enthusiasts can look forward to 2005 and the opportunity it offers to lavish the same kind of attention on Obrecht as happened with Ockeghem in 1997. In the *Caput* Mass, Obrecht literally builds on the works of Ockeghem. In such reworkings it was incumbent on the composer to find some new twist; Obrecht's solution is to present the plainchant on a different pitch in each movement (in the *Kyrie*, that of the English setting, and in the *Agnus*, that of Ockeghem). This is Obrecht in an expansive, note-spinning mode, with his customary fullness of sonority (try the beginning of the *Credo*) and what a normally terse critic like Gustave Reese called "sheer loveliness". If Oxford Camerata do not always match the composer for invention and inspiration, they produce a clean and faithful reading none the less. Alongside the plainsong from which the *Caput* melisma is drawn (thoughtfully included for reference) and the well-known six-voice *Salve regina* is a lesser known but very fine four-voice setting. The super-budget price should allay any hesitation, whether for the curious or the dedicated collector.

Obrecht Missa Malheur me bat. Laudes Christo redemptori.
J. Martini Magnificat tertii toni. Ave Maris stella. O beate Sebastiane. Salve regina.
The Clerks' Group / Edward Wickham. ASV Gaudeamus Ⓔ CDGAU171
(68 minutes: DDD: 5/98). Texts and translations included. Recorded 1997.
Obrecht's *Malheur me bat* uses the technique of 'segmentation', so called because the borrowed tune is divided into segments, each of which is repeated several times with increasing speed over the course of a section of the Mass (the final *Agnus Dei* rounds things off by restoring the tune's integrity). In *Malheur me bat* the tune appears in the top voice throughout, so the procedure is especially easy to follow; and the beginning of the *Agnus Dei* shows how brilliantly Obrecht succeeded in integrating the borrowed material into its new context. The Clerks approach this movement in their most mellifluous mode, a trait that distinguishes their interpretation of the Mass – indeed, the disc – as a whole. Though the technical accomplishment of The Clerks' reading is audible, the interpretative acuteness that characterizes their recordings seems strangely muted in comparison with other discs, as though the singers had not quite got the measure of the music. Surely the astonishing parallel chords of the last *Agnus* call forth a bolder exposition: such harmonies would have stopped fifteenth-century listeners dead in their tracks, and are just the sort of gesture one might have expected The Clerks to emphasize. However, one must concede that the polish and beauty of the sound-image here has a charm all its own, which many will prefer to The Clerks in sharper-edged mode. Ultimately it is Obrecht's music that demands to be heard and sung. Johannes Martini's motets, however, are restricted by a certain short-windedness. The most engaging is the one where there are the fewest interruptions: *O beate Sebastiane*.

Further listening ...
...Quod Chorus Vatum/Haec Deum Caeli. *Coupled with works by various composers.*
The Clerks' Group / Edward Wickham.
ASV Gaudeamus CDGAU139 (3/95). *See review which follows, under Ockeghem.*
...Salve regina. *Coupled with works by* **Ockeghem** and **Josquin Desprez**
The Clerks' Group / Edward Wickham. Proud Sound PROUCD133 (10/93). *See review which follows, under Ockeghem.*
...(attrib.) Humilium decus. *Coupled with works by various composers.* **The Clerks' Group /**
Edward Wickham. ASV Gaudeamus CDGAU143 (3/96). *Gramophone Editor's choice.*
See review which follows, under Ockeghem.
...Salve crux. *Coupled with works by various composers.* **Orlando Consort.**
Metronome METCD1015 (4/97). *See review in the Collections section; refer to the Index.*
...Missa Maria Zart. **The Tallis Scholars / Peter Phillips.**
Gimell 454 932-2PH (3/96). *Gramophone Editor's choice.*
...Ein fröhlich wesen. Haec Deum caeli. Laudemus nunc Dominum. *Coupled with works by various composers.* **Early Music Consort of London / David Munrow.**
Virgin Classics Veritas VED5 61334-2 (11/97). *See review in the Collections section; refer to the Index.*

Turlough O'Carolan
Irish 1670-1738

Suggested listening ...
...Carolan's Concerto. *Coupled with works by various composers.* **The Irish Band /**
Andrew Lawrence-King (hp). Deutsche Harmonia Mundi 05472 77366-2 (4/98). ✄
See review in the Collections section; refer to the Index.

Johannes Ockeghem
Flanders c1410-1497

Ockeghem Missa prolationum.
Fifteenth-Century Choral Works The Clerks' Group / Edward Wickham. ASV Gaudeamus
℗ CDGAU143 (65 minutes: DDD: 3/96). Recorded 1995. *Gramophone Editor's choice.*
Obrecht (attrib.) Humilium decus. **Busnois** Gaude coelestis Domina. In hydraulis.
Pullois Flos de spina. **Josquin Desprez** Illibata Dei Virgo nutrix.
This recording focuses on one of the most astonishing compositional feats of the second half of the fifteenth century: Ockeghem's *Missa prolationum*. The successive movements of the Ordinary of the Mass are based on double canons that progress from the unison to the octave, while at the same time the composer also exploits the inherent ambiguity of the mensural system (hence the work's title) of the later Middle Ages so that the rhythmic relationships between the voices are constantly being transformed. The astonishing thing is how effortlessly Ockeghem weaves his complex polyphonic web, and this is reinforced here by the unfettered, direct way in which The Clerks' Group approach the music. Although there are only eight singers in the group (so a maximum of two voices to a part), they bring a very satisfactory mix of the vocal agility one might expect from a small ensemble and the ability to sing through the long-breathed lines favoured by Ockeghem, without ever sounding strained or thin. The overall sound is immediate, crystal clear and closely recorded, but it never lacks for richness or blend – much credit to the ASV production team, too, in this respect. Although at first sight the five motets on the disc seem only loosely related to each other and to the Mass (the works date variously from the 1460s through to the 1490s), there are potentially illuminating links: several of the composers appear to pay homage, whether directly or indirectly, to one another's pieces and in general they all opt for quite self-consciously complex structures yet create a musical idiom that is lucid and full of emotional responses to the texts (mostly Marian) they chose to set. This recording allows the listener fully to appreciate the Franco-Netherlandish school at its best.

Ockeghem Missa Ecce ancilla Domini. Intemerata Dei mater. Ave Maria.
Josquin Desprez Déploration sur la mort de Johannes Ockeghem, "Nymphes des bois".
Obrecht Salve regina. **The Clerks' Group / Edward Wickham.** Proud Sound ℗ PROUCD133
(64 minutes: DDD: 10/93). Texts and translations included. Recorded 1993.
This astonishing music poses a considerable challenge in performance. With formal and stylistic conventions being flouted at every turn, matters of phrasing and pacing acquire a crucial importance, and much depends on the performers' ability to render local details intelligently. That is what makes this recording so special. *Missa Ecce ancilla*, though one of Ockeghem's most impressive Mass-cycles, is hardly an obvious choice for an ensemble making its recording début, but the Clerks' Group have absorbed Ockeghem's idiom to an extent that has scarcely been achieved hitherto, and command the technical means to match: balance and richness of tone, registral security and dynamic flexibility are all spot on. As a result, one makes sense of details which seemed baffling in previous recordings. Better still, such moments acquire the dramatic impact that is their ultimate justification. It is a joy to hear such an intelligent reading delivered with such confidence.

Ockeghem Missa l'homme armé. Ave Maria. Alma redemptoris mater.
Josquin Desprez Memor esto verbi tui.
Plainchant Alma redemptoris mater. Immittet angelus Domini.
Anonymous L'homme armé. **Oxford Camerata / Jeremy Summerly.** Naxos Ⓢ 8 554297
(57 minutes: DDD: 4/98). Texts and translations included.

The centrepiece of this recording is Ockeghem's *L'homme armé* Mass. Oxford Camerata's choice for the Ockeghem quincentenary is most apt because, although this isn't the first recording of Ockeghem's Mass on CD, it is far and away the most accomplished. *L'homme armé* may be one of Ockeghem's earliest Masses, dating perhaps from the early 1450s. It is also one of his most curious. For the most part it lies in a relatively high register, belying the composer's usual predilection for low bass ranges; but every now and again the basses descend in spectacular fashion. In the third *Agnus*, they hold down the tune in very long notes, with the other voices seeming to float above them. Seldom before in the history of music can the articulation of time have been so clear a feature of a piece's design: it seems almost to have been suspended altogether. It is an extraordinary moment, and extraordinarily difficult to pull off in performance, but here the singers seem to have got it right. Elsewhere, Summerly's approach is nicely varied, but on the whole more meditative than emphatic; one might say that the performance grows in stature with each movement, as though keeping pace with the cycle's ambition. In its details the reading is not without the odd glitch, but taken as a whole it is a fine achievement. The accompanying motets work very well but it is a shame that the choir's richness of sound is not quite matched by the acoustic. They deserve a more inspiring venue. But the overall impression is resoundingly positive: those who didn't hear any Ockeghem during his anniversary year should find this super-budget disc too good an opportunity to pass up.

Additional recommendation ...
...Missa sine nomine a 4. Missa L'homme armé a 4. Peccantem me quotidie. Sicut cervus desiderat. Super flumina Babylonis. **Soloists of the San Petronio Cappella Musicale / Sergio Vartolo.** Naxos Ⓢ 8 553314 (DDD: 9/97).

Ockeghem Missa, "Mi-Mi" (quarti toni). Salve regina I. Alma redemptoris mater.
Busnois Victimae Paschali laudes.
Obrecht Quod Chorus Vatum/Haec Deum Caeli.
Isaac Angeli, Archangeli. **The Clerks' Group / Edward Wickham.**
ASV Gaudeamus Ⓕ CDGAU139 (63 minutes: DDD: 3/95). Recorded 1994.

The Clerks are setting a powerful chord in favour of Ockeghem, up to now shamefully under-recorded. In the *Mi-Mi* Mass, which includes only men's voices, the dark sonorities achieved by The Clerks seem just right for this most mysterious of Ockeghem's Masses. Also, the accompanying motets find them on their strongest form. These are crisp, clever, truly imaginative performances, delivered with a confidence bordering on arrogance. The sopranos' robust delivery is a welcome contrast to the brooding abstraction of Ockeghem's Mass. Listen to the hint of bells in Isaac's *Angeli, Archangeli*: this is an astonishing piece that you won't find recorded elsewhere. Why mince words? This is superb.

Ockeghem Mass, De plus en plus. Presque transi. Prenez sur moi vostre exemple. O rosa bella o dolce anima mia. Aultre Venus estés. Petite camusette. Tant fuz gentement. Mort tu as navré.
Orlando Consort (Robert Harre-Jones, alto; Charles Daniels, Angus Smith, tens; Donald Greig, bar). Archiv Produktion Ⓕ 453 419-2AH (73 minutes: DDD: 8/97). Texts and translations included. Recorded 1996. ⒼⒼⒼ

This superb recording of Ockeghem's Mass, *De plus en plus*, by the Orlando Consort offers another constrasting view to add to those of The Clerk's Group and The Tallis Scholars. The Orlandos' mixed programme of sacred and secular music offers perhaps the most rounded picture of Ockeghem's art. In the Mass, the Orlandos are the obvious choice for those who prefer a soloistic approach, or for whom anything other than countertenors on top lines smacks of heresy. Each ensemble uses a different edition, and the Orlandos seem to have the edge – the strikingly different colouring from around the five-minute mark of the *Gloria* is one example of clear contrast between Jaap van Benthem's edition and those of Andrew Kirkman (Clerks) and John Milsom (The Tallis Scholars). But they won't have only the purists on their side. The Orlandos, like The Tallis Scholars, are more experienced singers than The Clerks, which translates here into more logical phrasing and breathing in solo passages; but they share with The Clerks a greater interpretative acuteness, and a quality of ensemble that is of itself more expressive. To sum up, the Orlandos on the whole achieve more with less: that is part of the magic of hearing Ockeghem sung this way. The accompanying songs certainly makes the case for Ockeghem's versatility as a song composer, a point emphasized by the differences of scoring to which they are especially sensitive. If this recording demonstrates anything, it is that the sacred and the secular are very different worlds. If the Orlandos seem to have trouble shifting gears between the two they are certainly not alone, either in England or abroad.

Additional recommendations ...
...Mass, De plus en plus. Credo. Gaude Maria (attrib.).
Coupled with works by various composers **The Clerks' Group / Edward Wickham.**
ASV Gaudeamus Ⓕ CDGAU153 (72 minutes: DDD: 1/97).

...Mass, De plus en plus. Au travail suis. Au travail suis. **Binchois** De plus en plus.
The Tallis Scholars / Peter Phillips. Gimell Ⓕ 454 935-2PH (64 minutes: DDD: 2/97).
...Prenez sur moi vostre exemple. Ma bouche rit. Intemerata Dei mater.
Coupled with works by various composers. **Early Music Consort of London / David Munrow.**
Virgin Classics Veritas Ⓜ VED5 61334-2 (two discs: 132 minutes: ADD: 11/97).
See review in the Collections section; refer to the Index.

Ockeghem Requiem. Fors seulement. Missa, "Fors seulement".
Brumel Du tout plongiet/Fors seulement.
La Rue Fors seulement. **The Clerks' Group / Edward Wickham.** ASV Gaudeamus Ⓕ CDGAU168
(71 minutes: DDD: 5/97). Texts and translations included. Recorded 1996.
Gramophone Editor's choice. Gramophone Award Winner 1997.   Ⓖ
Top billing goes to the Requiem, Ockeghem's most widely recorded work and perhaps his most
enigmatic piece, stylistically very wide-ranging and diverse. Aesthetic judgement is hard to pass, since
it may well be incomplete; but the surviving movements contain some of his most arresting
inspirations. This is the first version of any quality to feature sopranos on the top lines. Incidentally,
no recording of the Requiem is uniformly excellent; on the other hand, the words of the Mass for the
dead conjure up many associations, and The Clerks deserve praise for the verve and imagination with
which they respond to the work's interpretative challenges. The fillers are the works built on
Ockeghem's song *Fors seulement* (which includes Antoine Brumel's *Du tout plongiet*). It is difficult to
decide which to praise more highly: the pieces themselves, which are incomparable, or the singing,
which represents The Clerks' finest achievement to date. *Fors seulement* inspired a flowering of
astonishing pieces scored for very low voices (initiated, it appears, by the composer himself): in both
the Mass and in *Du tout plongiet*, the basses descend to written low Cs. In addition, these pieces are
exceptionally richly scored (the Mass and the La Rue song are five-voice works), creating polyphony
as dense and as dark as a strong Trappist ale. The Clerks achieve almost miraculous linear definition
here, without losing an iota of the music's sensuous appeal: quite a feat, given the low pitch and
awesome contrapuntal complexity involved. Enough superlatives: this is a major achievement.
Further listening ...
...(attrib.) Deo gratias. *Coupled with works by various composers.* **Huelgas Ensemble / Paul van Nevel.**
Sony Classical Vivarte SK66261 (4/96). *See review in the Collections section; refer to the Index.*
...Ut heremita solus. *Coupled with works by various composers.* **Fretwork.**
Virgin Classics VC5 45217-2 (12/97). *See review in the Collections section; refer to the Index.*

Jacques Offenbach   German/French 1819-1880

Offenbach (arr. M. Rosenthal) Gaîté parisienne.
Rossini (arr./orch. Respighi) La boutique fantasque. **Boston Pops Orchestra / Arthur Fiedler.**
RCA Victor Living Stereo Ⓜ 09026 61847-2* (64 minutes: ADD: 2/94). Recorded 1954-1956.   Ⓖ
Arthur Fiedler and the Boston Pops, for so long the guardians of traditional concert-hall light music
in America, never made a better stereo recording than the amazing early (1954) complete
Offenbach/Rosenthal *Gaîté parisienne* ballet score. It scintillates with effervescence and vitality, has
just the right degree of brash vulgarity, yet the richly embracing acoustics of Symphony Hall ensure
that the entry of the great "Barcarolle" has warmth as well as allure. This transfer makes the very
most of the outstanding masterpiece. The coupling comprises some 27 minutes from the hardly less
delectable Rossini/Respighi *La boutique fantasque* also brightly and atmospherically played and again
given first-class sound from two years later. A real collector's item, not to be missed by anyone who
cares about the history of stereo reproduction and also for the sheer *joie de vivre* of the music.
Additional recommendation ...
...Gaîté parisienne. *Coupled with* **Gounod** Faust – ballet music. **Montreal Symphony Orchestra /**
Charles Dutoit. Decca Ovation Ⓜ 430 718-2DM (59 minutes: DDD: 8/91).

Offenbach Les contes d'Hoffmann. **Plácido Domingo** (ten) Hoffmann; **Dame Joan Sutherland**
(sop) Olympia, Giulietta, Antonia, Stella; **Gabriel Bacquier** (bar) Lindorf, Coppélius, Dapertutto,
Dr Miracle; **Huguette Tourangeau** (mez) La Muse, Nicklausse; **Jacques Charon** (ten) Spalanzani;
Hugues Cuénod (ten) Andrès, Cochenille, Pitichinaccio, Frantz; **André Neury** (bar) Schlemil;
Paul Plishka (bass) Crespel; **Margarita Lilowa** (mez) Voice of Antonia's Mother; **Roland Jacques**
(bar) Luther; **Lausanne Pro Arte Chorus; Du Brassus Chorus; Suisse Romande Chorus and**
Orchestra / Richard Bonynge. Decca Ⓕ 417 363-2DH2 (two discs: 143 minutes: 11/86).
Notes, text and translation included. Recorded 1968.
This is a wonderfully refreshing set, made the more sparkling in the CD transfer, which enhances the
sense of presence and immediacy in the often-complicated action. The story emerges crystal-clear,
even the black ending to the Giulietta scene in Venice, which in Bonynge's text restores the original
idea of the heroine dying from a draught of poison, while the dwarf, Pitichinaccio shrieks in delight.
One also has to applaud his rather more controversial decision to put the Giulietta scene in the middle
and leave the dramatically weighty Antonia scene till last. That also makes the role of Stella the
more significant, giving extra point to the decision to have the same singer take all four heroine roles.

With Dame Joan available it was a natural decision, and though in spoken dialogue she is less comfortable in the Giulietta scene than the rest, the contrasting portraits in each scene are all very convincing, with the voice brilliant in the doll scene, warmly sensuous in the Giulietta scene and powerfully dramatic as well as tender in the Antonia scene. Gabriel Bacquier gives sharply intense performances, firm and dark vocally, in the four villain roles, Hugues Cuénod contributes delightful vignettes in the four *comprimario* tenor roles, while Domingo establishes at the very start the distinctive bite in his portrait of Hoffmann; a powerful and a perceptive interpretation. The recording is vivid, and with first-class playing from the Suisse Romande Orchestra this will, arguably, always be first choice for this opera.

Additional recommendations ...

...Soloists; Chorus and Orchestra of the Opéra-Comique, Paris / André Cluytens.
EMI mono Ⓜ CMS5 65260-2* (two discs: 130 minutes: ADD: 9/95).

Further listening ...

...Cello Concerto in G major, "Concerto militaire" (cpted. J-M. Clément). Cello Concerto in G major, "Concerto militaire" – Andante (arr. cpsr). *Coupled with* **Lalo** Cello Concerto in D minor. **Ofra Harnoy** (vc); **Bournemouth Symphony Orchestra / Antonio de Almeida.** RCA Victor Red Seal 09026 68420-2 (11/96).

...Concerto-rondo. *Coupled with works by* **Saint-Säens** and **Tchaikovsky** Ofra Harnoy (vc); **Cincinnati Symphony Orchestra / Erich Kunzel; Victoria Symphony Orchestra / Paul Freeman.** RCA Victor Red Seal RD71003 (11/86).

...Belle Lurette – On s'amuse, on applaudit. *Coupled with works by various composers.* **Kathleen Battle** (sop); **Chorus and Orchestra of the Opéra Bastille, Paris / Myung-Whun Chung.** DG 447 114-2GH (7/96).

...La belle Hélène. **Soloists; Toulouse Capitole Chorus and Orchestra / Michel Plasson.** EMI CDS7 47157-8 (9/86).

...La belle Hélène – On me nomme Hélène la Blonde. Orphée aux enfers – J'ai vu le Dieu Bacchus; Ce bal est original. *Coupled with works by various composers.* **Lesley Garrett** (sop); ᵃ**Crouch End Festival Chorus; Royal Philharmonic Concert Orchestra / James Holmes.** Silva Screen Classics SILKTVCD1 (2/96). *Gramophone Award Winner 1996.* *See review in the Collections section; refer to the Index.*

...Christopher Columbus. **Soloists; Geoffrey Mitchell Choir; London Mozart Players / Alun Francis.** Opera Rara ORC002 (4/93).

...Les contes d'Hoffmann – Les oiseaux dans la charmille. *Coupled with works by various composers.* **Inessa Galante** (sop); **Latvian National Opera Orchestra / Alexander Vilumanis.** Campion RRCD1344 A/97). *See review in the Collections section; refer to the Index.*

...Orphée aux enfers. **Soloists; Les Petits Chanteurs à la Croix Potencée; Toulouse Capitole Chorus and Orchestra / Michel Plasson.** EMI CDS7 49647-2 (1/89).

...Orphée aux enfers (sung in English). **Soloists; D'Oyly Carte Opera Chorus; D'Oyly Carte Opera Orchestra / John Owen Edwards.** Sony Classical S2K66616 (2/95). *Selected by Sounds in Retrospect.*

...Orphée aux enfers – Overture. *Coupled with works by various composers.* **London Symphony Orchestra / Sir Charles Mackerras.** Mercury Living Presence 434 352-2MM (12/95).

...Orphée aux enfers – Overture. *Coupled with works by various composers.* **Vienna Philharmonic Orchestra / Rudolf Kempe.** Testament SBT1127 (3/98). *See review in the Collections section; refer to the Index.*

...La Périchole. **Soloists; Rhine Opera Chorus; Strasbourg Philharmonic Orchestra / Alain Lombard.** Erato Libretto 2292-45686-2 (5/92).

...Robinson Crusoe (sung in English). **Soloists; Geoffrey Mitchell Choir; Royal Philharmonic Orchestra / Alun Francis.** Opera Rara ORC007 (8/94).

Julián Orbón

Cuban 1925-1991

Suggested listening ...

...Preludio y Danza. *Coupled with works by various composers.* **Jason Vieaux** (gtr). Naxos 8 553449 (11/97). *See review in the Collections section; refer to the Index.*

Carl Orff

German 1895-1982

Orff Carmina Burana. **Gundula Janowitz** (sop); **Gerhard Stolze** (ten); **Dietrich Fischer-Dieskau** (bar); **Schönberg Boys' Choir; Chorus and Orchestra of the Deutsche Oper, Berlin / Eugen Jochum.** DG The Originals Ⓜ 447 437-2GOR (56 minutes: ADD: 12/95). Text and translation included. From SLPM139362 (7/68). Recorded 1967. 🅖🅖

Orff Carmina Burana. **Beverly Hoch** (sop); **Stanford Olsen** (ten); **Mark Oswald** (bar); **F.A.C.E. Treble Choir; Montreal Symphony Chorus and Orchestra / Charles Dutoit.** Decca Ⓕ 455 290-2DH (59 minutes: DDD: 1/98). Texts and translations included. Recorded 1996.

Since its original release, Jochum's performance has consistently been a prime recommendation for this much-recorded piece. Listening to it again in the superbly remastered sound, one can easily hear why. He pays great attention to detail – particularly with regard to tempo and articulation – yet the performance as a whole has a tremendous cogent sweep and the choruses have terrific power. The more reflective sections are not neglected, however, and movements such as "Stetit Puella", with Janowitz sounding alluring and fey, have surely never been more sensitively handled. Stolze is ideal as the roasted swan and Fischer-Dieskau encompasses the very varied requirements of the baritone's music with ease. This distinguished performance, authorized by the composer and here sounding better than ever, retains its place at the head of the queue.

Dutoit's is the most satisfying and sheerly enjoyable modern performance of *Carmina Burana* to have appeared for some time. He is scrupulous in his attention to the many markings to be found in the score and ensures that details of articulation and orchestration are clearly audible, without obtruding from the overall texture. His tempos, almost without exception, feel just right, and Dutoit has conveyed his evident enthusiasm for the music to his performers, who respond accordingly. Stanford Olsen's roasted swan song is appropriately weird – helped by Orff's strange accompaniment being superbly pointed, whilst Beverly Hoch compensates for some thinness of tone with expressive phrasing, including a sensuous portamento in her "In trutina" solo. Apart from his first number, which is somewhat ponderous, Mark Oswald delivers the baritone's music with an equal measure of sensitivity and gusto. The choral singing is exceptionally fine, and it is particularly good to hear No. 19, "Si puer cum puellula" sung by soloists from the chorus, as directed in the score. The recording, clear and full-bodied, leads to the conclusion that, in a very crowded field, this release is the most recommendable of digital versions.

Additional recommendations ...

...Soloists; London Symphony Chorus and Orchestra / Eduardo Mata.
  RCA Victor Classical Navigator ⑬ 74321 17908-2 (60 minutes: DDD).
...Soloists; Rutgers University Choir; Philadelphia Orchestra / Eugene Ormandy.
  Sony Classical Ⓜ SBK47668* (58 minutes: ADD).
...Soloists; St Clement Danes Grammar School Boys' Choir; London Symphony Chorus
  and Orchestra / André Previn. EMI Ⓕ CDC5 56444-2 (63 minutes: DDD: 12/86).
...Soloists; Shinyukai Choir; Berlin Cathedral Boys' Choir; Berlin Philharmonic Orchestra /
  Seiji Ozawa. Philips Ⓕ 422 363-2PH (60 minutes: DDD: 7/89).
...Soloists; San Francisco Girls' Chorus; San Francisco Boys' Chorus; San Francisco Symphony
  Chorus and Orchestra / Herbert Blomstedt. Decca Ⓕ 430 509-2DH (59 minutes: DDD: 12/91).
...Soloists; Southend Boys' Choir; London Philharmonic Choir and Orchestra / Zubin Mehta.
  Teldec Ⓕ 9031-74886-2 (60 minutes: DDD: 2/94).
...Soloists; St Louis Symphony Chorus and Orchestra / Leonard Slatkin.
  RCA Victor Red Seal Ⓕ 09026 61673-2 (60 minutes: DDD: 4/95).
...Carmina Burana[a]. **Holst** The Planets, H125. [a]Soloists; [a]Southend Boys' Choir;
  London Symphony Chorus and Orchestra / Richard Hickox.
  Carlton Classics LSO Doubles Ⓜ 30368 01107 (two discs: 114 minutes: DDD: 1/98).
...Carmina Burana – In trutina. *Coupled with works by various composers.* Renée Fleming (sop);
  English Chamber Orchestra / Jeffrey Tate. Decca Ⓕ 458 858-2DH (70 minutes: DDD: 3/98).
  See review in the Collections section; refer to the Index.

Orff Trionfi – Carmina Burana[a]; Catulli Carmina[b]; Trionfo di Afrodite[c]. [a]**Barbara Hendricks**,
[bc]**Dagmar Schellenberger**, [c]**Lisa Larson**, [c]**Eva Maria Nobauer** (sops); [c]**Barbara Reiter** (contr);
[a]**Michael Chance** (alto); [bc]**Lothar Odinius**, [c]**Robert Swensen** (tens); [c]**Klaus Kuttler**, [a]**Jeffrey Black**
(bars); [c]**Alfred Reiter** (bass); [a]**St Albans Abbey Choir**; [a]**London Philharmonic Choir**; [bc]**Linz Mozart
Choir**; [a]**London Philharmonic Orchestra**; [bc]**Munich Radio Orchestra / Franz Welser-Möst.**
EMI Ⓕ CDS5 55519-2 (two discs: 137 minutes: DDD: 5/96). Texts and translations included.
Item marked [a] from CDC7 54054-2 (11/90). Items marked [b] and [c] are also available on
CDC5 55517-2 (79 minutes: DDD). Recorded 1989.

This is a most welcome issue, since *Catulli Carmina* and *Trionfo di Afrodite* are under-represented in the current catalogue, unlike *Carmina Burana* which is here given a lithe and vigorous reading with spectacular playing from the LPO and fine singing from the choruses. Barbara Hendricks's vibrato may not be to all tastes and Jeffrey Black is too genial, lacking the requisite *slancio* quality his part demands, whilst Michael Chance's beautiful tone is not what was intended by the composer since a tenor singing in his highest register is specified. Nevertheless, this performance is more than the sum of its parts and Welser-Möst's attention to detail is evidence of his careful and considered approach. In the central section of *Catulli Carmina*, the unaccompanied settings of Catullus are well realized with secure intonation and variety of expression and the prologue, with its insistent ostinatos for four pianos and percussion, is quite electrifying. *Trionfo di Afrodite* receives a thrilling and compelling performance and the final, orgiastic shouts of the chorus greeting the appearance of the goddess, make it the climax of the whole triptych. As bride and bridegroom, Dagmar Schellenberger and Lothar Odinius rise to the challenges of their parts with their wide-ranging and melismatic melodic lines, although the soprano eschews the top E which concludes the duet representing their wedding-night. A pity, too, that the voices were not placed off-stage as the score requires at this point. The other soloists and chorus sing with conviction and enthusiasm, supported by colourful and confident orchestral playing. Just occasionally, Welser-Möst presses ahead when Orff directs otherwise, but he draws out the dramatic qualities inherent in these works which were conceived for the theatre and despite blemishes, this set is now the preferred version of *Trionfo*. The single disc, pairing the less familiar pieces, with excellent notes and translations, is highly recommended to those willing to discover that Orff was by no means a 'one work' composer.

Additional recommendation ...
...Catulli Carmina. **Stravinsky** Les noces. Soloists / **Wolfgang Schäfer.**
Koch Schwann Musica Mundi Ⓕ 314021 (65 minutes: DDD: 7/91).

Further listening ...
...Antigone. **Soloists; Bavarian Radio Chorus and Symphony Orchestra / Ferdinand Leitner.**
DG 20th Century Classics 437 721-2GC3 (8/93).
...De temporum fine comoedia – symbolic drama. **Soloists; Cologne Radio Chorus; Tölz Boys' Choir; Berlin RIAS Chamber Chorus; Cologne Radio Symphony Orchestra / Herbert von Karajan.**
DG 20th Century Classics 429 859-2GC.
...Die Kluge. Der Mond. **Soloists; Rudolf Kiermeyer Children's Choir; Bavarian Radio Chorus; Munich Radio Orchestra / Kurt Eichhorn.** Eurodisc GD69069 (3/91).
...Orff-Schulwerk. **Godela Orff-Büchtemann** (spkr); **Tolz Boys' Choir / Gerhard Schmidt-Gaden; Munich Hochschule Chamber Choir / Fritz Schieri; Stuttgart Sprechchor / Heinz Mende;** instrumental ensemble / **Carl Orff.** RCA Victor Red Seal 09026 68031-2 (8/95).

Charles Wilfred Orr
British 1893-1976

Suggested listening ...
...When I watch the living meet. Hughley steeple. Into my heart. O see how thick the goldcup flowers. The Isle of Portland. This time of year. *Coupled with works by various composers.*
Anthony Rolfe Johnson (ten); **Graham Johnson** (pf).
Hyperion CDA66471/2 (8/95). *See review in the Collections section; refer to the Index.*

Diego Ortiz
Spanish c1510-c1570

Suggested listening ...
...Trattado de glosas – Recercarda segunda sobre el passamezzo moderno; Recercada tercera para viola de gamba sola; Recercada quarta sobre la folia; Recercada quinta sobre el passamezzo antiguo; Recercada settima sobre la Romanesca. *Coupled with works by various composers.*
La Romanesca / José Miguel Moreno (vihuela). Glossa GCD920203 (5/96). 🎵
Gramophone Editor's Choice. See review in the Collections section; refer to the Index. Ⓖ

Leslie Osborne
British 20th century

Suggested listening ...
...Lullaby for Penelope. *Coupled with works by various composers.*
Studio Two Concert Orchestra / Reginald Kilbey. EMI British Composers CDM5 66537-2 (1/98).
See review in the Collections section; refer to the Index.

Jack Ossewaarde
American 1918

Suggested listening ...
...Magnificat and Nunc dimittis in C major. *Coupled with works by various composers.*
St Thomas Church Choir, New York / Gerre Hancock with **Patrick Allen** (org).
Priory PRCD600 (1/98). *See review in the Collections section; refer to the Index.*

Jaime Ovalle
Brazilian 1894-1955

Suggested listening ...
...Azulão. *Coupled with works by various composers.* **Angela Gheorghiu** (sop); **Malcolm Martineau** (pf). Decca 458 360-2DH (5/98). *See review in the Collections section; refer to the Index.*

Johann Pachelbel
German 1653-1706

Pachelbel Musicalische Ergötzung. **Les Cyclopes** (Manfred Kraemer, Laura Johnson, vns; Nina Diehl, vc; Bibiane Lapointe, hpd; Thierry Maeder, org). Pierre Verany Ⓕ PV794111 (53 minutes: DDD: 7/95). 🎵 Recorded 1994.
This recording is a sobering reminder that the likes of Pachelbel and Muffat from the German-speaking world are on the same level and sometimes even better than, for example, the likes of Biber.

Indeed, it is most likely that Biber published his partitas for *scordatura* violins, *Harmonia artificioso–ariosa*, as a direct consequence of this very set, which Pachelbel sent to the press in 1691. One can quite believe it, judging by the way Biber articulates and circumnavigates the contours of the sarabande as Pachelbel does equally well in the third *Partie*. But there is more to it than that: it is the freedom of the polyphonic textures and coloration achieved through the special *scordatura* tuning of the violins (an elaborate system to facilitate double- and triple-stopping and diversify the tonal properties of the instrument) which both composers share. The relatively restricted structure of the dance, the chaconne and the suite as a whole gives the spirit of free invention and variation a context in which Pachelbel would seem to have set a trend for his Moravian colleague to contemplate. Pachelbel's *scordatura* music is arguably more instantly appealing than Biber's more arcane examples, though less intricate and rhetorically concentrated. Pachelbel was, after all, a more cosmopolitan figure by the very nature of his geographical situation, a world of less maverick virtuosity than Biber's though one which exhibits a greater range of up-to-date sonata techniques from Italy and mature dance movements from France. As with Muffat, and so many other Germans, the marriage is fortuitous and, as the sonata *allegro* of the third *Partie* shows, the rigours of indigenous counterpoint blend effortlessly into the merry hybrid. In all the six suites – each one for two violins and basso continuo – Les Cyclopes are admirably forthright, yet capable, too, of portraying with a rich palette an intensity of feeling and immediacy which few baroque chamber ensembles achieve so effortlessly. The character of the dances is clearly and often humorously communicated and the passagework is always executed with precision and a sleight of hand, even if the tuning is occasionally a touch wayward. These committed performances can be safely recommended to those searching for attractive and finely wrought music of the pre-Bach period.

Additional recommendation ...

…Musicalische Ergötzung – Suite No. 4 in E minor. Suite in G major. Aria con variazoni in
  A major. Canon and Gigue in D major. *Coupled with works by* **Buxtehude**
  Cologne Musica Antiqua / Reinhard Goebel.
  Archiv Produktion Galleria Ⓜ 427 118-2AGA (63 minutes: ADD: 6/89). ✍

Further listening ...

…Hexachordum Apollinis. Ciacconas – D major; F minor. **John Butt** (org).
  Harmonia Mundi HMU90 7029 (5/91).
…Prelude, "Vom Himmel hoch". *Coupled with works by various composers.* **Christopher Herrick**
  (org). Hyperion CDA66917 (8/97). *See review in the Collections section; refer to the Index.*
  Arthur Fiedler. Elan CD82266 (7/96).   Ⓔ

José Padilla

Spanish 1889-1960

Suggested listening ...

…El relicario. *Coupled with works by various composers.* **New London Orchestra / Ronald Corp.**
  Hyperion CDA66998 (3/98). *See review in the Collections section; refer to the Index.*
…Transfige, dulcissime Domine. *Coupled with works by various composers.*
  The Hilliard Ensemble. Virgin Classics Veritas VED5 61394-2 (11/97).
  See review in the Collections section; refer to the Index.

Nicolò Paganini

Italian 1782-1840

Paganini Violin Concertos – No. 1 in E flat major, Op. 6; No. 2 in B minor, Op. 7, "La
  campanella". **Salvatore Accardo** (vn); **London Philharmonic Orchestra / Charles Dutoit.**
  DG Ⓕ 415 378-2GH (69 minutes: ADD: 2/87). From 2740 121 (11/75).
Paganini Violin Concerto No. 1 in E flat major, Op. 6.
Saint-Saëns Havanaise in E major, Op. 83. Introduction and Rondo capriccioso in A minor,
  Op. 28. **Sarah Chang** (vn); **Philadelphia Orchestra / Wolfgang Sawallisch.**
  EMI Ⓕ CDC5 55026-2 (55 minutes: DDD: 1/95). Recorded 1993-1994.

Paganini's violin music was at one time thought quite inaccessible to lesser mortals among the violin-playing fraternity, but as standards of technique have improved master technicians are now able to do justice to such works as these concertos. Salvatore Accardo is certainly among them, and we can judge his skill as early as the opening violin solo of the First Concerto. This is typical of the style, with its authoritative and rhetorical gestures and use of the whole instrumental compass, but so is the second theme which in its refinement and songlike nature demands (and here receives) another kind of virtuosity expressed through a command of tone, texture and articulation. Dutoit and the London Philharmonic Orchestra have a mainly subordinate role, certainly when the soloist is playing, but they fulfil it well and follow Accardo through the kind of rhythmic flexibilities which are accepted performing style in this music and which for all we know were used by the virtuoso performer-composer himself. The 1975 recording is faithful and does justice to the all-important soloist.

  Paganini would surely have been utterly astonished at Sarah Chang's version of his No. 1. She made her début with the piece in the Avery Fisher Hall at the age of eight(!), but had reached more advanced years (12) when she recorded it in Philadelphia for EMI. The performance is dazzling, particularly the finale where her light rhythmic touch and deliciously pert sliding "harmonized harmonics" are a wonder of technical assurance. Note too, in the first movement, the relaxed ease of the decorated bouncing bow passages and the gently tender reprise of the second subject. The slow movement is not overtly romantic, but the freshness is never in doubt. One does not expect her to sound maturely sophisticated like Perlman (who remains unsurpassed in this repertoire) and she slightly understates the sultry atmosphere of the Saint-Saëns *Havanaise* to pleasing effect, yet manages the coda with spruce flexibility of phrase and the most subtle graduations of timbre. The *Introduction and Rondo capriccioso* has plenty of dash and she catches the Spanish sunlight in the *Introduction* without an overtly sensuous response. She is not flattered by the recording: balanced close. Sawallisch directs with plenty of verve and he supports his soloist admirably.

Additional recommendations ...

...No. 1. **Saint-Saëns** Violin Concerto No. 3 in B minor, Op. 61ᵃ. **Zino Francescatti** (vn); **Philadelphia Orchestra / Eugene Ormandy.**
CBS Masterworks Portrait mono Ⓜ MPK46728* (51 minutes: ADD: 12/91).

...Nos. 1 and 2. **Ilya Kaler** (vn); **Polish National Radio Symphony Orchestra / Stephen Gunzenhauser.**
Naxos Ⓢ 8 550649 (67inutes: DDD: 12/93).

...No. 1. *Coupled with works by various composers.* **Itzhak Perlman** (vn); **Royal Philharmonic Orchestra / Lawrence Foster.** EMI Ⓜ CMS7 64922-2 (three discs: 211 minutes: ADD/DDD: 4/94).

...Nos. 1 and 2. **Ilya Grubert** (vn); **Moscow Chamber Orchestra / Constantine Orbelian.**
Chandos Ⓕ CHAN9492 (67 minutes: DDD: 12/96).

Paganini Centone di sonate – Nos. 7-12. **Moshe Hammer** (vn); **Norbert Kraft** (gtr).
Naxos Ⓢ 8 553142 (72 minutes: DDD: 2/96).

The *Centone di sonate* (a "hotchpotch of sonatas") consists of 18 'sonatas' which are really salon works with a variety of movements – none of them in sonata form. Whether Paganini, who wrote them sometime after 1828, intended these pieces for public performance or merely for the use of the then abundant amateur musicians is not known. As usual in his works of this genre, it is the violin which hogs the limelight while the guitar remains a humble bag-carrier. The guitar parts are indeed so simple that they would have been within the reach of any amateur who was capable of keeping his end up with another musician; Segovia considered them beneath his dignity and refused many invitations to play them with famous partners! Nothing is harder than to be 'simple': Mozart managed it whilst at the same time being deceptively complex; Paganini did it at a far less sublime level, with sentimental, cheerful and pert tunes. Truth to tell, they are not the kind of works which impel one to listen to them at one sitting except for the most devoted *aficionado* of Paganini's violinistic voice or of hearing the guitar in an unremittingly subservient though genuinely complementary role. These splendid performances on modern instruments make no claim to 'authentic' status, but they are no less appealing for that. They squeeze every last drop from the music with (inauthentically) full sound, and a Siamese-twin tightness of ensemble that was probably rare amongst those who played these works in Paganini's own time. In the end, these works have a charm that is hard for any but the most straitlaced to resist. It is unlikely that the *Centone* will ever be better played and/or recorded.

Paganini Music for Violin and Guitar, Volumes 1 and 2. **Scott St John** (vn); **Simon Wynberg** (gtr).
Naxos Ⓢ 8 550690/759 (two discs, oas: 54 and 59 minutes: DDD: 12/94). Recorded 1993.
8 550690 – Six Sonatas for Guitar and Violin, Op. 3. Sonata concertata in A major, Op. 61.
60 Variations on "Barucabà", Op. 14. Cantabile in D major, Op. 17. *8 550759* – Six Sonatas for Guitar and Violin, Op. 2. Cantabile e Valtz, Op. 19. Variazioni di bravura on Caprice No. 24.
Duetto amoroso. Sonata per le gran viola e chitarra.

Many legends were attached (and they still are) to the life of Paganini. Those concerning his alleged relationships with the devil and with women (more probable) would have made rich pickings for today's tabloids. Several of the violin/guitar duos testify to Paganini's amorous inclinations: the sections of the *Duetto amoroso* spell out the course of an affair, from beginning to separation, and may have been aimed (unsuccessfully, one imagines) at the Princess Elisa Baciocchi in Lucca. His conservative harmonic vocabulary springs few surprises and his melodies sometimes verge on banality, but by dint of sheer charm and technical ingenuity he somehow gets away with it; only the po-faced could resist an admiring smile at his effrontery. Collectively, these works present the full range of Paganini's technical armoury – the left-hand pizzicatos, high harmonics, double-stopping, 'sneaky' chromatic runs and the rest, and Scott St John betrays no difficulty in dealing with every googly that comes his way. More than that, in the daunting *Sonata per le gran viola e chitarra* (celebrating Paganini's acquisition of a Stradivarius instrument) cocks a snook at every viola joke that ever was. The guitar's role in the action varies from purely supportive subservience to more equal (though at a lower acrobatic level) partnership, as in the *Sonata concertata* and from time to time in the Op. 3 Sonatas. Wynberg proves as well matched a partner as St John could have wished for. Violinists, guitarists and lovers of winsomeness for its own sake should revel in these very well recorded discs and will find much information in the booklet.

Additional recommendations ...

...Sonata concertata. Six Sonatas for Guitar and Violin, Op. 3 – No. 1 in A major; No. 4 in A minor; No. 6 in E minor. Grand Sonata for Violin and Guitar in A major, Op. posth. Centone

di Sonate, Op. 64 – No. 2 in D major; No. 4 in A major. Cantabile. Sonata a preghiera (arr. Hannibal). Moto perpetuo in C major (Allegro di concert), Op. 11.
Gil Shaham (vn); **Göran Söllscher** (gtr). DG Ⓕ 437 837-2GH (61 minutes: DDD: 4/94).
…Grand Sonata for Violin and Guitar in A major, Op. posth. Sonata concertata, Op. 61. **Giuliani** Duo concertant in E minor, Op. 25, "Grand Sonata". **Monica Huggett** (vn); **Richard Savino** (gtr). Harmonia Mundi Ⓕ HMU90 7116 (69 minutes: DDD: 5/95). 🗲

Paganini 24 Caprices, Op. 1. **Itzhak Perlman** (vn). EMI Ⓕ CDC7 47171-2
(72 minutes: ADD: 7/88). From SLS832 (6/72).   ᎶᎶ
This electrifying music with its dare-devil virtuosity has long remained the pinnacle of violin technique, and they encapsulate the essence of the composer's style. For a long time it was considered virtually unthinkable that a violinist should be able to play the complete set; even in recent years only a handful have produced truly successful results. Itzhak Perlman has one strength in this music that is all-important, other than a sovereign technique – he is incapable of playing with an ugly tone. He has such variety in his bowing that the timbre of the instrument is never monotonous. The notes of the music are dispatched with a forthright confidence and fearless abandon that are ideal. The frequent double-stopping passages hold no fear for him. Listen to the fire of No. 5 in A minor and the way in which Perlman copes with the extremely difficult turns in No. 14 in E flat; this is a master at work. The set rounds off with the famous A minor Caprice, which inspired Liszt, Brahms and Rachmaninov, amongst others, to adapt it in various guises for the piano.
Additional recommendations …
…**Salvatore Accardo** (vn). DG Galleria Ⓜ 429 714-2GGA (75 minutes: DDD: 9/90).
…**Leonidas Kavacos** (vn). Dynamic Ⓕ CDS66 (77 minutes: DDD: 9/93).
…**Michael Rabin** (vn). EMI Ⓜ CDM7 64560-2 (69 minutes: ADD: 9/93).   ᎶᎶ
…**Ilya Kaler** (vn). Naxos Ⓢ 8 550717 (79 minutes: DDD: 9/93).
…**Ruggiero Ricci** (vn). Biddulph Ⓕ LAW016 (76 minutes: DDD: 11/96).
…Nos. 1-23 (arr. Schumann)[a]; No. 24. **David Garrett** (vn); [a]**Bruno Canino** (pf).
DG Ⓕ 453 489-2GH (79 minutes: DDD: 8/97).
Further listening …
…Grand Sonata in A major, Op. posth. – second and third movements. Ghiribizzi, MS43 – No. 20, Andante in C major on Mozart's "Là ci darem la mano"; No. 37, Adagietto con espressione in A major. Sonatina No. 1 in C. *Coupled with works by various composers.* **Tom Kerstens** (gtr). Conifer Classics CDCF518 (9/94).
…Grand Sonata in A major, Op. posth (arr. Bream). *Coupled with works by* **José** and **Castelnuovo-Tedesco** Julian Bream (gtr). EMI CDC5 55362-2 (11/96).
…Centone di sonate Nos. 1-6. **Moshe Hammer** (vn); **Norbert Kraft** (gtr). Naxos 8 553141 (5/95).
…Introduction and Variations on "Nel cor più non mi sento" from Paisiello's "La Molinara". *Coupled with works by various composers.* **Leila Josefowicz** (vn). Philips 446 700-2PH (2/97).

Giovanni Palestrina

Italian *c*1525/6-1594

Palestrina The Palestrina 400 Collection. **The Tallis Scholars / Peter Phillips.**
Gimell Ⓜ 454 890-2PM4 (four discs: 249 minutes: ADD/DDD: 1/94). Items marked [a] from 1585-01 (11/81), [b]1585-03 (4/83), [c]CfP CFP40339 (10/80), [d]CDGIM008 (1/87), [e]CDGIM020 (9/90). Recorded 1980-1989. *Gramophone Award Winner 1991.*
Selected by Sounds in Retrospect.
Palestrina Missa Benedicta es[a]. Missa Nigra sum[b]. Missa Papae Marcelli[c]. Missa brevis[d]. Missa Nasce la gioia mia[d]. Missa Assumpta est Maria[e]. Missa Sicut lilium inter spinas[e]. Nigra sum[b]. Assumpta est Maria[e]. Sicut lilium inter spinas I[e]. **Anonymous** Benedicta es[a]. Assumpta est Maria in caelum[e]. **Josquin Desprez** Benedicta es, celorum regina[a]. **Lheritier** Nigra sum[b]. **Primavera** Nasce la gioia mia[d].
From the 100-plus Masses that he could have recorded, Peter Phillips has chosen so shrewdly that the selection here offered appears as comprehensive a cross-section of Palestrina's achievement as you could possibly wish in the space of four hours. The Palestrina enthusiast will very likely have bought all these performances as they appeared. But does the non-specialist need more than a couple of Palestrina Masses to represent the composer? Would not seven of them prove … well, not to put too fine a point upon it, a bit same-y? The answers are an emphatic 'yes' and a firm 'no' respectively. The variety of texture and audible technique among these Mass settings is quite remarkable. Among the seven Masses collected here, a profound development takes place between the massive sonority of the *Missa Benedicta es*, audibly both Palestrina's homage to, and his measuring of himself against, his great predecessor Josquin Desprez (Josquin's motet and its plainchant base are included, to make the point crystal-clear), and the division of the voices in the *Missa Assumpta est Maria* into two dissimilar, antiphonal choirs, projecting and dramatizing the text with urgent force as well as beauty. The music is most beautifully but not too beautifully sung. Balance, intonation, chording and clarity of texture are all immaculate, but the performances respond to the changes of emotional temperature between the Masses also; they are expressively sung, in the best sense of that word. The recordings, in ample but not obscuring acoustics, are very fine.

Additional recommendations ...
...Missa Assumpta est Maria. Missa Sicut lilium inter spinas. Motets – Assumpta est Maria a 6;
Sicut lilium inter spinas I. **Plainchant** Assumpta est Maria. **The Tallis Scholars / Peter Phillips.**
Gimell Ⓕ 454 920-2PH (72 minutes: DDD: 9/90).
...Assumpta est Maria. Missa Assumpta est Maria. Ave Maria. Beata es virgo Maria. Hodie beato
virgo. Rorate coeli. Magnificat. **Clare College Choir, Cambridge / Timothy Brown.**
EMI Debut Ⓑ CDZ5 69703-2 (67 minutes: DDD: 8/97).
...Missa Papae Marcelli. Stabat mater. **Pro Cantione Antiqua / Mark Brown.**
Carlton Classics Ⓜ 30366 0070-2 (59 minutes: DDD: 11/97).

Palestrina Ave Maria. Alma Redemptoris mater a IV. Veni sponsa Christi. Surge, propera amica
mea. Quae est ista. Magnificat IV toni. Hodie beata virgo. Ave regina coelorum a IV. Magnificat
VII toni. Ave Maria a V. Ave maris stella. **Camerata Nova / Luigi Taglioni.** Stradivarius
Ⓕ STR33375 (59 minutes: DDD: 6/97). Texts and translations included. Recorded 1996.
This is the new Italian sound of renaissance church music: a gentle vibrato, but a wonderfully loose
and relaxed sound with a kind of breathy production. In the normal four-voice Palestrina texture
both the two top voices are taken by women; but the sopranos are extremely light in their sound so
they never dominate the texture, and the altos are of that wonderful variety that one usually only
hears from Italians, with a firm and infinitely attractive chest register that goes confidently down to a
low F. If the texture here is quite unlike what we are used to hearing from the best British ensembles,
that is partly because there is an emphasis on line rather than on sonority. It's a sound of tremendous
restraint, as though none of the singers is attempting to project a 'voice'. If one can say with
confidence that this was not the sound Palestrina was expecting (any more than he was expecting the
sound of The Tallis Scholars and their like), one can say with equal confidence that the Camerata
Nova bring across the spirit and the polyphonic vitality of his music with astonishing power.
Considerable credit must go to Luigi Taglioni for producing such a gentle and controlled ensemble.
The music is also nicely chosen: a group of Marian motets, two Magnificat settings and a Marian
hymn to form a neatly contrasted programme, with several pieces gloriously sung by four solo
women's voices. If you thought that Palestrina was a composer of seamless and immaculate textures
with just a touch too much surface gloss for comfort, this may be a record to help you to hear one of
the world's most influential composers in a different light.
Additional recommendation ...
...Vergine bella. Motets – Ave Maria; Salve regina; Sub tuum praesidium; Ave regina coelorum;
Salve regina; Ave mundi spes; Alma Redemptoris mater; Regina coeli. Magnificat.
  Akademia / Françoise Lasserre with **Laurent Stewart** (org).
  Pierre Verany Ⓕ PV794041 (56 minutes: DDD: 9/94).   Ⓖ

Palestrina Surge, illuminare Jerusalem. Missa Papae Marcelli. Stabat mater. Alma Redemptoris
mater. Magnificat Primi Toni. Nunc dimittis.
Allegri Miserere mei. **The Tallis Scholars / Peter Phillips.** Gimell Ⓕ 454 994-2PH
(73 minutes: DDD: 9/94). Texts and translations included. Recorded live in 1994.
The sense of a memorable occasion is quite tangible here. The largely Italian audience, assembled in
Palestrina's own great Basilica of Santa Maria Maggiore to mark the 400th anniversary of his death,
is clearly impressed by The Tallis Scholars' virtuosity. The *Missa Papae Marcelli* is in fact a good four
minutes faster than in their previous recording, made in 1980. No doubt they know the piece even
better now, and no doubt Phillips has changed his view of it. But it really seems as though the building
and its acoustic both had an effect, firstly in encouraging the singers really to sing out (the *Sanctus*
has an extraordinary full-throated fervour), but perhaps also the knowledge that this was the very
spot where Palestrina worked with his choir prompted an even greater awareness of the music's
eloquence. The Allegri *Miserere* doesn't really belong in this collection, of course; it was written for
another building entirely (the Sistine Chapel) decades after Palestrina's death. It may have been
included because Peter Phillips, alongside his scholarship and his gifts as a choir-trainer, has a feeling
for drama and the spatial effects of this music could not be rendered nearly so spectacularly in the
Sistine. It is stunning, with Deborah Roberts in the florid solo soprano part floating high Cs and
roulades up into the vast space with luminous clarity. The Palestrina pieces have their own drama, and
they are shrewdly programmed. It was a good choice to begin the disc with the almost rollicking
jubilation of *Surge, illuminare*, wise to follow the showy *Miserere* with Palestrina at his most sublime
in the *Stabat mater*. To follow that with the hymn-like, homophonic *Alma Redemptoris mater*, and
that with the joyous *Magnificat* (for two choirs, but sounding like at least six, of quite different
colours) is programme-building of a very high order. To add the eight-part *Nunc dimittis* as an encore,
with its wonderful arching lines and a firework-display of counterpoint at the end, has a touch of
genius to it. The recorded sound is splendid, the acoustic always perceptible but the singers never lost
in it.
Additional recommendations ...
...Missa Aeterna Christi munera. Sicut cervus. Super flumina Babylonis a 4. Vidi turbam magnam.
Quae est ista. Duo ubera tua. Nigra sum, sed formosa. Surge, amica mea. Magnificat Primi Toni.
  Anonymous Aeterna Christi munera. **Westminster Cathedral Choir / James O'Donnell.**
  Hyperion Ⓕ CDA66490 (67 minutes: DDD).

...Missa Papae Marcelli. Tu es Petrus. *Coupled with works by various composers.* **Westminster Abbey Choir / Simon Preston.** Archiv Produktion Ⓕ 415 517-2AH (59 minutes: DDD: 5/86).   Ⓖ
...Missa Papae Marcelli. *Coupled with works by* **Allegri** and **W. Mundy**
The Tallis Scholars / Peter Phillips. Gimell Ⓕ 454 939-2PH (69 minutes: ADD: 7/86).   Ⓖ

Palestrina Masses – Viri Galilaei; O Rex gloriae. Motets – Viri Galilaei; O Rex gloriae.
Westminster Cathedral Choir / James O'Donnell. Hyperion Ⓕ CDA66316
(68 minutes: DDD: 1/90). Texts and translations included. Recorded 1988.
This is music in which Westminster Cathedral Choir excel: their response to the richly reverberant acoustic is warm and generous; they perform with the ease and freedom of kinship – a far cry from the studied perfection of many other choirs. Each motet is heard before its reworking as a Mass. The six-part scoring of *Viri Galilaei* (two trebles, alto, two tenors and bass) invites a variety of combinations and textures, culminating in the joyful cascading Alleluias at the end of Part I and the jubilant ascending series in Part II. In the Mass the mood changes from triumph to quiet pleading – a change partly due to revised scoring: the two alto parts beneath the single treble produce a more subdued sound. The Choir clearly relishes this exploration of the deeper sonorities: in the *Creed* one entire section is entrusted to the four lowest voices. The four-part motet *O Rex gloriae* is lithe and fast-moving. The corresponding Mass, largely syllabic in style, gives the Choir the chance to demonstrate their superb command of phrasing and accentuation: the Latin comes over with intelligibility and subtlety. Listen, also, to the wonderful solo boys' trio in the "Crucifixus", and for the carefully crafted canons in the *Benedictus* and the *Agnus Dei.*
Further listening ...
...Coelestis urbs Jerusalem *Coupled with works by various composers.*
   Vienna Hofburgkapella Schola; Concerto Palatino; Gradus ad Parnassum / Konrad Junghänel.
   Deutsche Harmonia Mundi 05472 77326-2 (7/95).
...Exsultate Deo. Sicut cervus desiderat. *Coupled with works by various composers.*
   Soloists; Westminster Cathedral Choir / James O'Donnell.
   Hyperion CDA66850 (5/96). *See review in the Collections section; refer to the Index.*
...Matins Responsory. Vesper Responsory. *Coupled with works by various composers.*
   St Paul's Cathedral Choir / John Scott.
   Hyperion CDA66994 (12/97). *See review in the Collections section; refer to the Index.*
...Missa brevis. Missa Nasce la gioia mia. *Coupled with* **Primavera** Nasce la gioia mia.
   Tallis Scholars / Peter Phillips. Gimell 454 908-2PH (1/87).
...Missa Dum complerentur. Motets – Super flumina Babylonis; Exsultate Deo; Sicut cervus;
   O bone Jesu, exaudi me a 8; Dum complerentur a 6.
   Christ Church Cathedral Choir, Oxford / Stephen Darlington. Nimbus NI5100 (11/88).
...Missa in festis Apostolorum I and II. Missa sine nomine. Missa in Semiduplicibus Maioribus I
   and II. **Soloists of San Petronio Cappella Musicale Nova Schola Gregoriana / Sergio Vartolo**
   with **Liuwe Tamminga** (org). Bongiovanni GB5544/5-2 (5/95).
...Missa sine nomine a 4. Missa L'homme armé a 4. Peccantem me quotidie. Sicut cervus desiderat.
   Super flumina Babylonis. **Soloists of the San Petronio Cappella Musicale / Sergio Vartolo.**
   Naxos 8 553314 (9/97).
...Missa Ut re mi fa sol la. Ecce, nunc benedicite a 12. *Coupled with* **Victoria** Ave Maria, gratia
   plena. Omnis pulchritudo Domini. Salve regina. Alma Redemptoris mater.
   Montreal Studio Ancienne Choir. Analekta Fleurs de Lys FL2 3120 (4/98).
...Motets – Stabat mater a 8. Hodie beata virgo. Senex puerum portabat. Magnificat a 8. Litaniae
   de Beata Vergine Mariae I a 8. *Coupled with* **Allegri** Miserere mei. **Roy Goodman** (treb);
   King's College Choir, Cambridge / Sir David Willcocks. Decca Ovation 421 147-2DM (5/89).   Ⓖ

Sir Andrzej Panufnik   Polish/British 1914-1991

Panufnik Sinfonia concertante[a]. Concerto for Timpani, Percussion and Strings[b]. Harmony.
   [a]**Karen Jones** (fl); [a]**Rachel Masters** (hp); [b]**Richard Benjafield** (perc); [b]**Graham Cole** (timp);
   London Musici / Mark Stephenson. Conifer Classics Ⓕ CDCF217 (55 minutes: DDD: 8/94).
   Recorded 1993.
All of the works recorded here, as with most of Andrzej's Panufnik's later music, are quite rigorously built from spare basic resources (*Harmony* and the *Sinfonia concertante* from two three-note cells, the *Concertino* from a single motif of four notes). They ought to sound 'same-y', and in a sense they do, in that all three have a certain serenity at their core, with frequent recourse to quietness, and all three are harmonically transparent. That is Panufnik's idiom, and one wouldn't complain of two Mozart symphonies that they both sound Mozartian. But all three pieces are also 'about' the unification of dissimilarity. The basic material of the *Sinfonia concertante* is put to lyrical, meditative, tranquil use in the first of its main movements but is shown in the second to be just as capable of generating abrupt discontinuity, swift movement and vigorous rhythm; the brief concluding "Postscriptum" reflects on how very simple the raw material for such contrast can be. The 'method' is tested more severely in the five-movement *Concertino*, which was written as a test-piece, and, since the two soloists are percussionists, as something of a display vehicle as well. *Harmony* takes the

unifying of dualities a step further: here we have two instrumental groups (wind octet and a small string ensemble without double-basses) that engage in serene dialogue until they eventually merge and the music intensifies through angular stress to passionate but austere tenderness. It is a memorable image, surely not coincidentally dedicated to Panufnik's wife on the occasion of their silver wedding; it is subtitled "Poem", and is indeed poetic, but the poetry and severity of the technique are inseparable. All three works are beautifully played and very cleanly recorded.

Additional recommendation ...
...Concerto festivo[a]. Landscape[a]. Katyń Epitaph[a]. Concerto for Timpani, Percussion and Strings[ab]. Sinfonia sacra[c]. [b]**Kurt-Hans Goedicke** (timp); [b]**Michael Frye** (perc); [a]**London Symphony Orchestra;** [c]**Monte Carlo Opera Orchestra / Andrzej Panufnik.**
Unicorn-Kanchana Souvenir Ⓜ UKCD2020 (69 minutes: DDD/ADD: 8/89).

Panufnik String Quartets – No. 1; No. 2, "Messages"; No. 3. Song to the Virgin Mary[a]. String Sextet[a]. **Chilingirian Quartet** (Levon Chilingirian, Charles Stewart, vns; Simon Rowland, va; Philip de Groote, vc); [a]**Roger Chase** (va); [a]**Stephen Orton** (vc). Conifer Classics Ⓕ CDCF218 (72 minutes: DDD: 12/93). Recorded 1993.

While the Second Quartet (1980) recalls the outdoor nocturnals of Bartók and Szymanowski, the First (1976) – opens with urgent, strongly differentiated chatter and then switches to luminous, long-breathed lines; subdued, shifting and rising to an ethereal height. The Third Quartet (1991) serves as a concentrated résumé of Panufnik's quartet style. The *Song to the Virgin Mary* was transcribed from an *a cappella* choral piece of the same name and conjures up something of Dvořák's steadfast, simple piety. "Trains of Thought" was inspired by the hypnotic rhythm of wheels on a track and the thoughts suggested by them; it is based on a three-note cell, "constantly rotated and frequently transposed and reflected". But the effect is more like a dream one might have of the train floating off the tracks and careering up into the firmament: the rhythm remains gently insistent, the harmonic language subtle and suggestive. The Chilingirian Quartet perform well, the sound is excellent and the notes are both appetizing and informative. A most engaging release.

Additional recommendation ...
...Song to the Virgin Mary. *Coupled with works by various composers.*
King's College Choir, Cambridge / Stephen Cleobury. EMI Ⓕ CDC5 56439-2 (64 minutes: DDD: 10/97). *See review in the Collections section; refer to the Index.*

Further listening ...
...Symphony No. 8, "Sinfonia Votiva". *Coupled with* **Sessions** Concerto for Orchestra.
Boston Symphony Orchestra / Seiji Ozawa. Hyperion CDA66050 (7/89).
...Symphony No. 9, "Sinfonia della Speranza". Piano Concerto[a]. [a]**Ewa Poblocka** (pf);
London Symphony Orchestra / Sir Andrzej Panufnik. Conifer Classics CDCF206 (5/92).   Ⓖ
...Sinfonia sacra[a]. Arbor cosmica[b]. [a]**Royal Concertgebouw Orchestra;** [b]**New York Chamber Symphony / Sir Andrzej Panufnik.** Elektra Nonesuch 7559-79228-2 (5/91).   Ⓖ
...Tragic Overture[a]. Autumn Music[a]. Heroic Overture[a]. Nocturne[a]. Sinfonia rustica[b].
[a]**London Symphony Orchestra / Jascha Horenstein;** [b]**Monte Carlo Opera Orchestra / Andrzej Panufnik.** Unicorn-Kanchana Souvenir UKCD2016 (4/89).

Alessandro Parisotti Italian 1835-1913

Suggested listening ...
...Se tu m'ami, C xxii, 68. *Coupled with works by various composers.*
Angela Gheorghiu (sop); **Malcolm Martineau** (pf).
Decca 458 360-2DH (5/98). *See review in the Collections section; refer to the Index.*

Eric Parkin British 1924

Suggested listening ...
...Mayerl Shots, Sets 1 and 2. A Tribute to Billy Mayerl. *Coupled with works by* **Mayerl**
Eric Parkin (pf). Priory PRCD544 (12/96). *See review under Mayerl; refer to the Index.*
...Mayerl Shots, Set 3. *Coupled with works by* **Mayerl**
Eric Parkin (pf). Priory PRCD565 (7/97). *See review under Mayerl; refer to the Index.*

Sir Hubert Parry British 1848-1918

Parry Piano Concerto in F sharp major.
Stanford Piano Concerto No. 1 in G major, Op. 59. **Piers Lane** (pf); **BBC Scottish Symphony Orchestra / Martyn Brabbins.** Hyperion Ⓕ CDA66820 (73 minutes: DDD: 2/96). Recorded 1995.

Parry's Piano Concerto (1879) is a resourceful, imposing creation, stylistically most obviously indebted to Brahms's D minor Concerto (there's also an endearing crib from the Tchaikovsky B flat minor Concerto in the coruscating solo writing towards the very close of the work). The writing is assured, fluent and harmonically often quite daring: within 50 seconds of the piece's F sharp major opening, for instance, we find ourselves plunged into an amazingly distant G major! By contrast, Stanford's First Concerto in G, composed 14 years after its companion here, has an altogether less weighty demeanour. This tuneful, unpretentious and beautifully crafted essay, which Stanford intended to be "of a bright and butterfly nature", though longer than the Parry, actually feels shorter, so charming are Stanford's melodic gifts and felicitous sense of colour. The limpid central *Adagio molto* is especially appealing. Piers Lane proves a fearlessly secure, eloquent exponent of all this material, whilst Martyn Brabbins elicits polished and responsive playing from the BBC Scottish SO. The sound is clean and true.

Parry Orchestral works. **London Philharmonic Orchestra / Matthias Bamert.**
Chandos Ⓜ (four discs, oas: 53, 52, 76 and 57 minutes: DDD: 7/92, 10/91, 1/91 and 9/91). Recorded 1990-1992.
CHAN9062 – Symphony No. 1 in G minor. Concertstück in G minor.
CHAN8961 – Symphony No. 2 in F major, "Cambridge". Symphonic Variations.
CHAN8896 – Symphonies: No. 3 in C major, "English"; No. 4 in E minor (*Selected by Sounds in Retrospect*). *CHAN8955* – Symphony No. 5 in B minor, "Symphonic Fantasia 1912".
From Death to Life. Elegy for Brahms.   Ⓖ

Written in its composer's thirty-second year, Parry's First Symphony witnessed the realization of several decades of aspiration and dedication toward this grandest of musical objectives. Despite its obvious Germanic, and more specifically Brahmsian affiliations, the symphony reflects much of the comfortable optimism of the Victorian era. Even so, there's little in the way of Gothic excess, and not a trace of inflated jingoism here. The symphony is ably constructed and tastefully orchestrated, with several of its most powerful statements returning in the finale. Matthias Bamert's performance is assured and totally committed, as he makes out the strongest possible case for the work from its very opening bars. He also includes an ardently reasoned account of Parry's *Concertstück* in G minor, hardly music of the calibre of the symphony, but worth hearing, none the less. This is a revelatory issue and it is difficult to imagine these triumphant offerings being superseded for a very long time to come. The same forces score another important first with their fine recordings of the *Cambridge* Symphony and the *Symphonic Variations*. This disc also offers some surprises, for it seems incredible that this music has remained virtually unknown for the best part of a century! The Second Symphony has no particular link with Cambridge, save for the fact that it received its première there in 1883. Bamert and the LPO offer a revelatory performance here in which the real qualities of the music are allowed to shine through any reverential backward glances at the works of Brahms, Dvořák and Schumann. Parry was enthusiastic, however, about Dvořák's *Symphonic Variations* and Brahms's *Haydn* Variations, and followed the example of both in his own set for orchestra. The London Philharmonic are captured here on vibrant form and the sound is especially full-bodied and resonant.

The discovery on the third disc is the Fourth Symphony, first performed (conducted by Hans Richter) in 1889, revised in 1910, performed twice in its new version and then forgotten for nearly 80 years. It is a deeply personal work, almost confessional in its repressed passion. The first movement (16 minutes) is on an immense scale, covering an emotional range comparable with Elgar's Second (which it preceded). The Third Symphony is more conventional, an English equivalent of Schumann's *Rhenish*. Its sunny exuberance and the lightness of the scoring make it highly attractive. Performance and recording are both admirable. Parry's Fifth Symphony dates from 1912 and like so much of his output this substantial work reveals the composer's enduring devotion to the music of Brahms. However, Parry was fascinated by the idea of writing a programmatic symphony, in the Lisztian mould, and thus each of the four linked movements have titles which relate strongly to his personal ethical outlook. The finale, entitled "Now" culminates with an expansive review of material from earlier in the work, and here it is clearly a sense of confidence and affirmation, expressed in grandiose Edwardian musical rhetoric, which concludes Parry's symphonic cycle. The remaining movements, "Stress", "Love" and "Play" also serve to remind us of the clear romantic origins of this splendid and inexplicably neglected British symphony. Also included here are two shorter, although no less weighty Parry rarities, and the Symphonic Poem *From Death to Life* shares much common ground with the Fifth Symphony, at least in terms of its general subject matter. The LPO again respond with tremendous conviction and brilliance. In conclusion, all these recordings are highly recommended.

Additional recommendations ...
...No. 1. From Death to Life. **English Symphony Orchestra / William Boughton.**
Nimbus Ⓕ NI5296 (64 minutes: DDD: 5/92).
...No. 2. Overture to an Unwritten Tragedy. Symphonic Variations. **Royal Scottish National Orchestra / Andrew Penny.** Naxos Ⓢ 8 553469 (59 minutes: DDD: 10/96).
...No. 5. Symphonic Variations. Elegy for Brahms. Ode at a Solemn Music, "Blest Pair of Sirens"[a].
[a]**London Philharmonic Choir; London Philharmonic Orchestra / Sir Adrian Boult.**
EMI Ⓜ CDM5 65107-2 (58 minutes: ADD: 11/87).

Parry Shulbrede Tunes. Theme and 19 Variations in D minor. Hands across the Centuries.
Peter Jacobs (pf). Priory Ⓕ PRCD451 (73 minutes: DDD: 10/95). Recorded 1992.
This likeable anthology usefully expands our appreciation of a figure best known for his choral and symphonic offerings. The three works gathered here span some 38 years. Nearly three decades

separate the publication dates of the *Theme and 19 Variations* and Parry's next piano work, the charming ten-movement suite of 1914 entitled *Shulbrede Tunes*. The twelfth-century Shulbrede Priory in Sussex was the home of Parry's elder daughter, Dorothea, her husband, Arthur Ponsonby, and their two children, Elizabeth and Matthew. Each family member, as well as the house and grounds, is lovingly evoked by Parry in this winsome, nicely contrasted series of character pieces. Indeed, Dorothea (or "Dolly", as she is named here) is represented by two portraits, the second of which comprises the emotional core of the series. Parry's seven-movement suite from 1916, *Hands across the Centuries*, instantly recalls his earlier *Lady Radnor's Suite* (and the *English Suite* to come) in its easy tunefulness and reliance on baroque dance forms. Peter Jacobs's playing here betokens total commitment and idiomatic warmth. The engineering, too, is eminently truthful (if just a touch hissy).

Parry English Lyrics[a]: Set 2 – O mistress mine; Take, O take those lips away; No longer mourn for me; Blow, blow, thou winter wind; When icicles hang by the wall. Set 4 – Thine eyes still shine for me; When lovers meet again; When we two parted; Weep you no more; There be none of beauty's daughters; Bright star. Set 5 – A Welsh lullaby. Set 6 – When comes my Gwen; And yet I love her till I die; Love is a bable. Set 7 – On a time the amorous Silvy. Set 8 – Marian; Looking backward. Set 9 – There. Set 10 – From a city window.
Vaughan Williams Songs of Travel[b]. Linden Lea[b]. **Robert Tear** (ten); **Philip Ledger** (pf).
Belart ⑧ 461 493-2 (77 minutes: ADD: A/97). Items marked [a] from Argo ZK44 (10/79), [b]Argo ZRG732 (3/73).
This selection of Parry's songs is very welcome in these fine and intelligent performances by Robert Tear and Philip Ledger. Parry does not always measure up to his texts (in the sonnets of Keats and Shakespeare especially), and is best when renouncing his teatime-Brahms style in favour of a more personal and imaginative idiom, as in "When icicles hang by the wall" and "From a city window". Vaughan Williams's great song-cycle, *Songs of Travel*, has a freshness partly deriving from the comparative rarity of hearing it in higher keys for the tenor voice. Both artists give the impression of having studied the songs as it were 'from scratch'. Tear's phrasing is a delight, showing exceptional sensitivity to the words, and Ledger's playing, with very sparing use of pedal, is scrupulously clean and careful over detail. The recorded sound is fine. No texts are included but it hardly matters: the diction is so clear you are unlikely to miss a word.

Further listening ...
...Nonet in B flat major (ed J. Dibble). *Coupled with* **Stanford** Serenade (Nonet) in F major, Op. 95. **Capricorn.** Hyperion CDA66291 (9/89).
...Violin Sonata in D major. 12 Short Pieces. Fantasie-sonata in B minor.
Erich Gruenberg (vn); **Roger Vignoles** (pf). Hyperion CDA66157 (9/91).
...Blest Pair of sirens. I was glad (orch. Jacob). Jerusalem (orch. Elgar). Judith – Long since in Egypt's plenteous land. *Coupled with works by various composers.* **Winchester Cathedral Choir; Waynflete Singers; Bournemouth Symphony Orchestra / David Hill** with **Timothy Byram-Wigfield** (org). Argo 430 836-2ZH (4/92).
...The Soul's Ransom – Sinfonia Sacra[a]. Choric song from Tennyson's "The Lotos Eaters".
Della Jones (mez); [a]**David Wilson-Johnson** (bar); **London Philharmonic Choir and Orchestra / Matthias Bamert.** Chandos CHAN8990 (1/92).
...Sunset. *Coupled with works by various composers.* **Chichester Cathedral Choir / Alan Thurlow** with **James Thomas** (org). Priory PRCD539 (5/96).

Robert Parsons I

British c1530-1570

Suggested listening ...
...Ave Maria. *Coupled with works by various composers.* **St Paul's Cathedral Choir / John Scott.** Hyperion CDA66994 (12/97). *See review in the Collections section; refer to the Index.*

Arvo Pärt

Estonian 1935

Pärt Fratres (seven versions). Festina Lente. Cantus in Memory of Benjamin Britten. Summa.
Peter Manning (vn); **France Springuel** (vc); **Mireille Gleizes** (pf); **I Fiamminghi.** Telarc Ⓕ CD80387 (79 minutes: DDD: 6/95). Recorded 1994.   Ⓖ
Telarc's *Fratres-Fest* proves beyond doubt that good basic material can be reworked almost *ad infinitum* – if the manner of its arrangement is sufficiently colourful. The present sequence is particularly imaginative in that it alternates two varied pairs of *Fratres* with atmospheric original string pieces, then separates the last two versions with the sombre pealing of *Festina Lente*. The first *Fratres* opens to a low bass drone and chaste, ethereal strings: the suggested image is of a slow oncoming processional – mourners, perhaps, or members of some ancient religious sect – with drum and xylophone gradually intensifying until the percussive element is so loud that it resembles Copland's *Fanfare for the Common Man*. One envisages aged protagonists who have been treading the same ground since time immemorial, whereas the frantically propelled, arpeggiated opening to the version for violin, strings and percussion leaves a quite different impression. Still, even here the music

does eventually calm and Peter Manning provides an expressive solo commentary. All six arrangements share a common 'approach-and-retreat' formula, with ideas that arrive from – and subsequently retreat to – some distant horizon. Next comes the gentle cascading of Pärt's *Cantus in Memory of Benjamin Britten*, with its weeping sequences and lone, tolling bell. The eight-cello *Fratres* uses eerie harmonics (as does the cello and piano version that ends the programme), whereas *Fratres* for wind octet and percussion is cold, baleful, notably Slavonic-sounding and occasionally reminiscent of Stravinsky. The alternation of *Summa* (for strings) and the quartet version of *Fratres* works nicely, the former more animated than anything else on the disc; the latter, more intimate. The performances are consistently sympathetic, and the recordings are excellent.

Additional recommendations ...

...Fratres[a]. Fratres[b]. Cantus in memory of Benjamin Britten[c]. Tabula rasa[d]. [bd]**Gidon Kremer** (vn); [b]**Keith Jarrett** (pf); [d]**Tatjana Grindenko** (vn); [d]**Alfred Schnittke** (prepared pf); [a]**Berlin Philharmonic Cellists;** [c]**Stuttgart State Orchestra / Dennis Russell Davies;** [d]**Lithuanian Chamber Orchestra / Saulius Sondeckis.** ECM New Series Ⓕ 817 764-2 (DDD).   Ⓖ

...Cantus in Memory of Benjamin Britten. *Coupled with works by various composers.* **Royal Scottish Orchestra / Neeme Järvi.** Chandos Ⓕ CHAN8656 (74 minutes: DDD: 11/89).

...Fratres. *Coupled with works by* **Tubin** and **Tüür Tallinn Quartet; Love Derwinger** (pf). BIS Ⓕ CD574 (67 minutes: DDD: 1/94).

...Fratres[ab]. Cantus in Memory of Benjamin Britten[c]. Summa[c]. Spiegel im Spiegel[ab]. Festina lente[c]. Tabula Rasa[abcd]. [a]**Tasmin Little** (vn); [b]**Martin Roscoe** (pf); [c]**Bournemouth Sinfonietta / Richard Studt** ([d]vn). EMI Eminence Ⓜ CD-EMX2221 (64 minutes: DDD: 6/94).   Ⓖ

...Fratres. Spiegel im Spiegel. *Coupled with works by various composers.* **Rusné Mataityté** (vn); **Margrit-Julia Zimmermann** (pf). Proud Sound Ⓕ PROUCD139 (57 minutes: DDD: 7/96).

...Fratres. *Coupled with works by* **Vasks** and **Tüür** Duke Quartet. Collins Classics Ⓕ 1475-2 (55 minutes: DDD: 7/96).

...Fratres. Symphony No. 3. **Kancheli** Symphony No. 3[a]. [a]**David James** (alto); **London Philharmonic Orchestra / Franz Welser-Möst.** EMI Ⓕ CDC5 55619-2 (55 minutes: DDD: 8/96). *Gramophone Editor's choice. See review under Kancheli; refer to the Index.*

...Summa. The Beatitudes[a]. Seven Magnificat Antiphons. *Coupled with works by various composers.* [a]**John Keys** (org); **Vasari Singers / Jeremy Backhouse.** EMI Eminence Ⓜ CD-EMX2251 (74 minutes: DDD: 8/96). *See review in the Collections section; refer to the Index.*

...Summa. And One of the Pharisees ... . *Coupled with works by various composers.* **The Hilliard Ensemble.** ECM New Series Ⓕ 453 259-2 (two discs: 120 minutes: DDD: 1/97). *See review in the Collections section; refer to the Index.*

...Collage teemal BACH. Fratres. Cantus in memory of Benjamin Britten. Summa. Festina lente. Tabula Rasa[a]. [a]**Jan Söderblom**, [a]**Tero Latvala** (vns); [a]**Jouko Laivuori** (prepared pf); **Tapiola Sinfonietta / Jean-Jacques Kantorow.** BIS Ⓕ CD834 (62 minutes: DDD: 4/97). *Selected by Soundings.*

...Fratres. *Coupled with works by various composers.* **Gidon Kremer** (vn); **Deutsche Kammerphilharmonie.** Teldec Ⓕ 0630-14654-2 (79 minutes: DDD: 11/97). *Gramophone Editor's choice. See review in the Collections section; refer to the Index.*

Pärt Kanon pokajanen. **Estonian Philharmonic Chamber Choir / Tõnu Kaljuste.** ECM New Series Ⓜ 457 834-2 (two discs: 83 minutes: DDD: 6/98). Texts and translations included. Recorded 1997. *Gramophone Editor's choice.*

Kanon pokajanen is music of transition, best heard at break of day or at eventide. The 83-minute *a cappella* masterpiece divides into eight 'Odes', with "Kontakion" and "Ekos" – both of them fairly brief – at the start of the second CD. Those who would rather sample first are directed to the concluding "Prayer after the Canon" (disc 2, track 6), the work's longest – and possibly most beautiful – movement. The "Prayer" opens among small groups of voices answering one another, then embraces the full choir before fading to a serene close. The text implores Christ to effect a sweetening of the Soul, whereas the preceding Odes alternate bitter contrition with gentle entreaties for mercy. The structure is, by Pärt's own admission, based on 'the word'. "I wanted the word to be able to find its own sound," he writes in a unique but brief insert-note, "... to draw its own melodic line." After a radiant celebration of the Israelites' triumph over Pharaoh, *Kanon* continues with a quietly pulsing "Have Mercy on me, O God", darkens for a chant-like lament of the burdened sinner, has the "Mercy" motif return, graduates to the higher voices for more repentance, proclaims "Glory to the Father", sees the male singers return for "bitter weeping" and, after another brief response, closes in the treble for a prayer to "The Most Pure Mother of God". That, roughly speaking, is the pattern for all eight Odes: a prayer-stanza, a plea for mercy, another prayer-stanza, and so on. *Kanon pokajanen* recalls the tintinnabulation of Pärt's recent creative past, but on a grand scale: here the repeated segments are larger, more widely spaced, more subtly varied. The text is crucial, and the process of following it in translation essential for a full appreciation of how Pärt feels and experiences the *Kanon*'s meaning. Of course, one also has the 'soft option' of letting *Kanon pokajanen* waft thoughtlessly into the ether (the glorious singing of the Estonian Philharmonic Chamber Choir suggests ethereal weightlessness), but this isn't recommended. Pärt's profound marriage of word, music and spirit sits at the very apex of the current religio-musical revival, and deserves some measure of our attention in payment for the two years it took to complete. The recording is faultless.

Pärt Litany[a]. Psalom[b]. Trisagion[c]. [a]**Hilliard Ensemble;** [a]**Estonian Philharmonic Chamber Choir;** [a]**Talinn Chamber Orchestra / Tõnu Kaljuste;** [bc] **Lithuanian Chamber Orchestra / Saulius Sondeckis.**
ECM New Series Ⓕ 449 810-2 (42 minutes: DDD: 9/96). Text and translation included.
Recorded 1995. *Gramophone Editor's choice.*
Pärt's mature work remains profoundly minimalist, not in the 'repeated patterns' sense of early Reich, but in its economy of means and purity of sound. *Litany*, or "Prayers of St John Chrysostom for each Hour of the Day and Night" consists, like so much of Pärt's work, entirely of essentials. The high string writing that opens the piece prompts ethereal solo voices and the quiet, Sibelian rumble of a big drum *tremolando*. Within minutes the mood intensifies and the instruments – rather more of them than we're used to from this composer (including select brass and woodwind) – congregate to heighten the drama. At 11'06", the mood changes with a pulsing drum and a gently insistent rhythm. Again, volume and mood intensify, but this time the principal climax – which mushrooms suddenly to almost Wagnerian proportions – summons gongs, bells, bass-drum and timpani for what sounds like a solemn ritual chiming. In terms of length and sonority, *Litany* is the biggest work on the disc, whereas *Psalom* and *Trisagion* – both of which call on a string orchestra – revisit the quietistic atmosphere of *Fratres*. *Psalom* relies as much on rests as on manifest notes, and recalls, in mood if not structure, the unpeopled terrains of Liszt's *Von der Weige bis zum Grabe* ("From the Cradle to the Grave"). *Trisagion* features sudden declamations midway, aching dialogue between upper and lower voices and a brief, propulsive ending based on a single repeated chord. Both works suggest wordless meditations in a space somewhere outside of time and rely heavily on the sustained concentration of their interpreters. This they receive in abundance, not only from the players themselves but from the recording team, who have negotiated the various acoustics with immense skill. Heard simply as sound, all three works ravish the ear. Playing-time is less than average and yet *Litany*, *Psalom* and *Trisagion* leave an aural aftertaste that resonates far beyond the allotted time-span of a single well-filled CD, indeed of 20.
Additional recommendation ...
...Psalom. *Coupled with works by various composers.* **Kronos Quartet.**
Nonesuch Ⓕ 7559-79457-2 (69 minutes: DDD: 12/97). *Gramophone Editor's choice.*
See review in the Collections section; refer to the Index.

Pärt Te Deum[a]. Silouans Song, "My soul yearns after the Lord ... "[a]. Magnificat. Berliner Messe[a].
Estonian Philharmonic Chamber Choir; [a]**Tallinn Chamber Orchestra / Tõnu Kaljuste.**
ECM New Series Ⓕ 439 162-2 (66 minutes: DDD: 11/93). Texts and translations included.
Recorded 1993. *Gramophone Editor's choice.*   ⒼⒼ
Pärt's *Te Deum* sets the standard liturgical text to a wide range of nuances, shades and dynamics; brief string interludes provide heart-rending wordless commentaries, and the work's closing pages provide a serenely moving affirmation of holiness. Although relatively static in its musical narrative, Pärt's *Te Deum* is both mesmerizing and enriching. *Silouans Song* (1991), an eloquent study for strings, is as reliant on silence as on sonority. It is again austere and chant-like, although its dramatic interpolations approximate a sort of sacral protest. The brief *Magnificat* for a cappella choir (1989) positively showers multi-coloured resonances. However, the *Te Deum*'s closest rival – in terms of substance and appeal – is surely the 25-minute *Berliner Messe* (1990-92). Here again Pärt employs the simplest means to achieve the most magical ends: "Veni Sancte Spiritus" weaves a luminous thread of melodic activity either side of a constant, mid-voice drone, while the weighted phrases of the *Sanctus* take breath among seraphic string chords. And how wonderful the gradual darkening of the closing *Agnus Dei*, where tenors initially answer sopranos and an almost imperceptible mellowing softens the work's final moments. Beautiful sounds, these – gripping yet remote, communicative yet deeply personal in their contemplative aura, while the all-round standard of presentation – performance, engineering, documentation – serves Pärt as devotedly as Pärt serves the Divine Image.
Additional recommendations ...
...Magnificat. Summa. *Coupled with works by* **Górecki** and **Tavener** Oxford Pro Musica Singers / **Michael Smedley.** Proud Sound Ⓕ PROUCD136 (77 minutes: DDD: 12/94).
...Magnificat. *Coupled with works by various composers.* **Holst Singers / Stephen Layton.**
Hyperion Ⓕ CDA66928 (79 minutes: DDD: 8/97). *See review in the Collections section; refer to the Index.*

Pärt Statuit et Dominus[a]. Missa Sillabica. Beatus Petronius. Seven Magnificat Antiphons.
De profundis[a]. Memento mori. Cantate Domino[a]. Solfeggio. **Estonian Philharmonic Chamber Choir / Tõnu Kaljuste** with [a]**Christopher Bowers-Broadbent** (org). Virgin Classics Ⓕ VC5 45276-2 (61 minutes: DDD: 1/98). Texts and translations included. Recorded 1995-1996.
Gramophone Editor's choice
Pärt's demands on the organ as an accompaniment to voices are neither particularly complex nor technically demanding but do require exceptional sensitivity from the player. It is largely through skilful use of registration that Bowers-Broadbent displays his profound understanding of the music. He balances his role admirably, keeping a discreet distance from the singers for the most part and measuring the long drawn-out crescendo of *De profundis* to perfection. However, this is, of course, a disc devoted to Pärt's choral music and it is the choir, rather than the organist, who are the real heroes.

Unlike the Theatre of Voices, the Estonian Philharmonic Choir don't sound as if they've studied the music long and hard. Just because they are Estonian doesn't give them any particular interpretative advantage over non-Estonian singers. But these performances feel as if they come from the heart; there is a tangible sense of spiritual empathy which Paul Hillier's American singers can't emulate. Compare the magical, ethereal quality of the singing in the divine *Gloria* from the *Missa Sillabica* which Tõnu Kaljuste draws from his singers with Hillier's rather studied approach. And in the magical *Magnificat Antiphons* the Estonian choir reveal an even greater depth of feeling. The recording is gloriously atmospheric.

Additional recommendation ...
...De profundis[ab]. Missa Sillabica[a]. Solfeggio. And one of the Pharisees. Cantate Domino[a]. Summa. Seven Magnificat Antiphons. The Beatitudes. Magnificat. [a]**Christopher Bowers-Broadbent** (org); [b]**Daniel Kennedy** (perc); **Theatre of Voices / Paul Hillier** (bass). Harmonia Mundi Ⓕ HMU90 7182 (76 minutes: DDD: 4/97).

Pärt Annum per annum[a]. Pari intervalli[a]. Mein Weg hat Gipfel und Wellentäler[a]. Trivium I-III[a].
Cage Souvenir[a].
Scelsi In nomine lucis[b]. **Christoph Maria Moosmann** (org). New Albion Ⓕ NA074CD
(64 minutes: DDD: 2/96). Items marked [a] played on the organ in St Martin's Cathedral, Rottenburg, [b]Collegiate Church of St Hippolyte, Poligny, France.

The pieces by Pärt constitute his complete organ output to date. *Pari intervalli*, originally written for woodwind as a memorial tribute, and *Trivium I-III* are the earliest, dating from 1976 when Pärt broke a three-year composing silence. Then came *Annum per annum* (1980) where five movements representing sections of the Mass are framed by one long sustained chord of D – loud going down to soft in the prelude and the opposite in the postlude. The latest piece, *Mein Weg* (1989), is closely based on a poem about the spiritual journey through life. Most of the Pärt works have a veritable fixation on D, which comes up resplendently in the loud second piece of *Trivium* which, like the first one, is on a pedal. This is the organ music of spiritual minimalism, restrained but powerful if you are on the right wavelength. The Cage and Scelsi are first recordings. Cage's *Souvenir* (1984), commissioned by the American Guild of Organists, at times sounds like an improvisation on a recurrent theme suggesting plainsong. But, being Cage, the piece contains irreverent squawks and eruptions of clusters to put things into perspective. The interaction between textures is – for Cage – unusually structured and satisfying. *In nomine lucis* (1974) by the eccentric Italian Giacinto Scelsi, who died in 1988, is in memory of his younger colleague Franco Evangelisti. This is a most unusual, atmospheric piece, where Moosmann uses assistants to operate the organ's mechanical stops very precisely to obtain microtones. *In nomine lucis* seems to be Scelsi's only organ work and there is nothing quite like it. The organ at Rottenburg (on which everything here is performed except the Scelsi), although modern, sounds exactly right for the neo-medievalism of Pärt's timeless message, and the recording is outstanding.

Additional recommendation ...
...Pari Intervalli. *Coupled with works by various composers.* **John Scott** (org). Priory Ⓕ PRCD485 (74 minutes: DDD: 8/96). *Selected by Soundings.*

Further listening ...
...Cello Concerto, "Pro et contra"[a]. Perpetuum mobile, Op. 10. Symphonies – No. 1, "Polyphonic"; No. 2; No. 3. [a]**Frans Helmerson** (vc); **Bamberg Symphony Orchestra / Neeme Järvi.** BIS CD434 (9/89). Ⓖ
...Symphony No. 1, "Polyphonic". Nekrolog, Op. 3. *Coupled with works by* **Tubin** and **Tüür Royal Stockholm Philharmonic Orchestra / Paavo Järvi.** Virgin Classics VC5 45212-2 (5/97).
...Adagio. *Coupled with works by various composers.* **Jaime Laredo** (vn); **Sharon Robinson** (vc); **Joseph Kalichstein** (pf). Arabesque Z6676 (2/97).
...Variations for the healing of Arinushka. *Coupled with works by various composers.* **Kalle Randalu** (pf). Catalyst 09026 68331-2 (2/96).
...Miserere[a]. Festina lente[b]. Sarah was ninety years old[c]. [a]**Western Wind Choir;** [ac]**Hilliard Ensemble / Paul Hillier;** [b]**Bonn Beethovenhalle Orchestra / Dennis Russell Davies.** ECM New Series 847 539-2 (1/92). ⒼⒼ
...Passio Domini nostri Jesu Christi secundum Johannem. **Michael George** (bass); **John Potter** (ten); **Hilliard Ensemble; Western Wind Chamber Choir / Paul Hillier.** ECM New Series 837 109-2 (2/89). ⒼⒼⒼ

Harry Partch
American 1901-1974

Suggested listening ...
...Eight Hitchhikers' Inscriptions from a Highway Railing at Barstow, California (arr. Johnston). *Coupled with works by various composers.* **Ben Johnston** (voc); **Kronos Quartet.** Nonesuch 7559-79372-2 (11/96). *See review in the Collections section; refer to the Index.*
...Two Studies on Ancient Greek Scales (arr. Johnson). *Coupled with works by various composers.* **Kronos Quartet.** Nonesuch 7559-79457-2 (12/97). *Gramophone Editor's choice.* *See review in the Collections section; refer to the Index.*

Paullet
French 15th century

Suggested listening ...
...J'aim. Qui?. *Coupled with works by various composers.* **Hilliard Ensemble.**
Isis CD030 (7/97). *See review in the Collections section; refer to the Index.*
...J'aim. Qui?. *Coupled with works by various composers.* **Alla Francesca.**
Opus 111 OPS30-173 (7/98). *See review in the Collections section; refer to the Index.* ⒼⒼⒼ

John Pavlett
British late 14th century

Suggested listening ...
...A Toye. *Coupled with works by various composers.* **Mhairi Lawson** (sop); **Circa 1500.** ASV
Gaudeamus CDGAU163 (12/97). ✒ *See review in the Collections section; refer to the Index.*

Anthony Payne
British 1936

Suggested listening ...
...Symphony No. 3 in C minor (Elgar/Payne). **BBC Symphony Orchestra / Andrew Davis.**
NMC NMCD053 (3/98). *Gramophone Editor's choice. See review under Elgar,*
refer to the Index. ⒼⒼⒼ

Teodorico Pedrini
Italian 1671-1746

Suggested listening ...
...Sonate a Violono Solo col Basso del Nepridi, Op. 3 – No. 1 in A major; No. 4 in G minor; No. 5
in G major; No. 7 in B flat major; No. 10 in C minor. *Coupled with* **Amiot** *Divertissements*
chinois. **XVIII-21, Musique des Lumières.** Auvidis Astrée E8609 (10/97). *See review under Amiot.*

Martin Peerson
British 1571/3-1651

Suggested listening ...
...Blow out the trumpet. *Coupled with works by various composers.*
St Paul's Cathedral Choir / John Scott with **Andrew Lucas** (org).
Hyperion CDA66994 (12/97). *See review in the Collections section; refer to the Index.*

Georgs Pelécis
Latvian 1947

Suggested listening ...
...Violin and Piano Concerto, "Nevertheless". *Coupled with works by various composers.* **Gidon**
Kremer (vn); **Vadim Sacharov** (pf); **Deutsche Kammerphilharmonie.** Teldec 0630-14654-2 (11/97).
Gramophone Editor's choice. See review in the Collections section; refer to the Index.

Francisco de Peñalosa
Spanish c1470-1528

Suggested listening ...
...Inter vestibulum et altare. Magnificat quarti toni. *Coupled with works by various composers.*
The Hilliard Ensemble. Virgin Classics Veritas VED5 61394-2 (11/97). *See review in the*
Collections section; refer to the Index.
...O Domina sanctissima. *Coupled with works by various composers.* **His Majestys Sagbutts and**
Cornetts. Hyperion CDA66847 (11/96). *See review in the Collections section; refer to the Index.*
...Por las sierras de Madrid. Ne reminiscaris, Domine. Precor te, Domine. Sancta Maria.
Coupled with works by various composers. **Gothic Voices / Christopher Page**
with **Christopher Wilson** (vihuela) and **Andrew Lawrence-King** (hp).
Hyperion CDA66653 (2/94). *See review in the Collections section; refer to the Index.* Ⓖ

Krzysztof Penderecki
Polish 1933

Penderecki St Luke Passion – Stabat mater; Miserere; In pulverem mortis. Magnificat – Sicut
locutus est. Agnus Dei. Song of Cherubim. Veni creator. Benedicamus Domino. Benedictus.
Tapiola Chamber Choir / Juha Kuivanen. Finlandia Ⓔ 4509-98999-2 (52 minutes: DDD: 3/96).
Texts and translations included. *Selected by Soundings.*

There is a neat correspondence in the way the earliest and most recent pieces included here – *Stabat mater* (1962) and *Benedictus* (1992) – both move to resolutions on simple major triads. The difference is in the extent to which the triads in the later work govern the musical fabric throughout. In the 1960s such common chords had to be fought for, and could even seem tacked on rather arbitrarily. In general, however, it is another kind of consistency that makes this disc musically worthwhile. Although all the works tend to be reflective and devotional in character, the contrapuntal medium of the unaccompanied chorus inspires the composer to an economical intensity all too often absent from his later instrumental works. Indeed, it is as part of that intensity that elements of his early, much more dissonant style, so powerfully represented in the three extracts from the *St Luke Passion* and the fragment from the *Magnificat*, re-emerge within the more traditional harmonic world of the later pieces – especially the *Veni creator*. Yet it should also be said that Penderecki's austere response to this celebratory text seems more than a little strange. Of the later works *Song of Cherubim* is the most powerful, ending as it does with remarkably rapt "Alleluias". A note tells us that the composer regards the *Benedictus* as a draft to be reworked at a later stage. These performances are on the whole models of pure-toned clarity, although the sound of the choir can harden into harshness at higher dynamic levels. The recordings are full of atmosphere but well balanced and not excessively resonant.

Additional recommendation ...
...Agnus Dei. The Cherubic Hymn. *Coupled with works by various composers.*
King's College Choir, Cambridge / Stephen Cleobury. EMI Ⓟ CDC5 56439-2
(64 minutes: DDD: 10/97). *See review in the Collections section; refer to the Index.*

Penderecki Anaklasis[a]. Threnody for the victims of Hiroshima[b]. Fonogrammi[c]. De natura sonoris I[d]. Capriccio[e]. Canticum canticorum Salomonis[f]. De natura sonoris II[g]. Dream of Jacob[h]. [e]**Wanda Wilkomirska** (vn); [f]**Cracow Philharmonic Chorus;** [bcdefgh]**Polish National Radio Symphony Orchestra;** [a]**London Symphony Orchestra / Krzysztof Penderecki.** EMI Matrix Ⓜ CDM5 65077-2 (75 minutes: ADD: 10/94). Items marked [a] from HMV EMD5507 (1/74), [bdfh] EMD5529 (6/76), [ceg] HMV SLS850 (8/74). Recorded 1972-1975. ⒼⒼ

Krzysztof Penderecki's creative heyday (1950s-1970s) prompted a release of dramatic aural ingenuity the like of which had not been heard before and has rarely been heard since. Works such as the *St Luke Passion*, the *Dies irae* and, most especially, the *Threnody for the victims of Hiroshima* featured on this CD, delve deep within the recesses of collective memory, often triggering disturbing images. Even that master musical psychologist Alban Berg could hardly have approximated the *Threnody's* chamber of horror – the blinding light of its opening bars, the aural swerve as trees bend and houses shatter, the jittery aftermath as fall-out spreads its poisonous message, and the myriad gestures and effects that amount to a terrifying experience. No other twentieth-century instrumental work quite equals the *Threnody* for graphic impact and no other composer has provided the victims of Hiroshima and Nagasaki with such a dramatic or telling memorial. The trouble is that the *Threnody* accounts for just 9'55" on a 75'25" CD – so what of the rest? Penderecki's invariable preference for slow motion, dense tonal clusters, roaring sonorities (*De natura sonoris II* rises to a deafening primeval groan), wailing vocalizations and sundry instrumental effects (tapping and screeching, not to mention a virtual absence of melody and definable rhythm, make for a pretty draining listening session. One wonders whether the musical metaphors that Penderecki used during this phase of his career are actually capable of expressing anything brighter than *Angst*, terror, fear, disorientation and – very occasionally – black humour. Yet it is a fascinating sound-world for all that, and the *Threnody* is surely its most profound justification. The recordings report all with merciless clarity.

Further listening ...
...String Quartets Nos. 1[b] and 2[b]. Prelude[a]. Der unterbrochene Gedanke[b]. String Trio[cef]. Clarinet Quartet[acdf]. [a]**Martin Fröst** (cl); [b]**Tale Quartet.** BIS CD652 (5/95).
...St Luke Passion (Passio et mors Domini nostri Jesu Christi secundum Lucam). **Soloists; Cracow Boys' Choir; Warsaw National Philharmonic Chorus; Polish Radio National Symphony Orchestra / Krzysztof Penderecki.** Argo 430 328-2ZH (3/91). ⒼⒼ

Clovis Pereira
Brazilian 1942

Suggested listening ...
...Three Northeastern pieces. Variations on a theme of Guerra Peixe.
Coupled with works by various composers. **Quinteto da Paraíba.**
Nimbus NI5483 (10/96). *See review in the Collection section; refer to the Index.*

Giovanni Pergolesi
Italian 1710-1736

Pergolesi Stabat mater[a]. Salve regina in C minor. **Emma Kirkby** (sop); [a]**James Bowman** (alto); **Academy of Ancient Music / Christopher Hogwood.** L'Oiseau-Lyre Florilegium Ⓟ 425 692-2OH (52 minutes: DDD: 2/90). 🎵 Texts and translations included. Recorded 1988.
Pergolesi's *Stabat mater*, written in the last few months of his brief life, enjoyed a huge popularity throughout the eighteenth century. But modern performances often misrepresent its nature, either

through over-romanticizing it or by transforming it into a choral work. None of these are qualities overlooked in this affecting performance, for Emma Kirkby and James Bowman are well versed in the stylistic conventions of baroque and early classical music – and their voices afford a pleasing partnership. Both revel in Pergolesi's sensuous vocal writing, phrasing the music effectively and executing the ornaments with an easy grace. Singers and instrumentalists alike attach importance to sonority, discovering a wealth of beguiling effects in Pergolesi's part writing. In the *Salve regina* in C minor Emma Kirkby gives a compelling performance, pure in tone, expressive and poignant, and she is sympathetically supported by the string ensemble. The recording is pleasantly resonant and does justice to Pergolesi's translucent textures. Full texts are included.

Additional recommendations ...

...Stabat mater. **Margaret Marshall** (sop); **Lucia Valentini Terrani** (mez); **London Symphony Orchestra / Claudio Abbado.** DG Ⓕ 415 103-2GH (43 minutes: DDD: 4/85).

...Stabat mater[ab]. Salve regina[a]. In coelestibus regnis[b]. [a]**Gillian Fisher** (sop); [b]**Michael Chance** (alto); **King's Consort / Robert King.** Hyperion Ⓕ CDA66294 (54 minutes: DDD: 11/88). 🗡

...Salve regina in A minor. Salve regina in C minor. *Coupled with works by* **Leo** and **Gallo** **Barbara Schlick** (sop); **Europa Galante / Fabio Biondi** (vn). Opus 111 Ⓕ OPS30-88 (59 minutes: DDD: 4/94). 🗡

...Stabat mater[a]. Orfeo. **Regina Klepper** (sop); [a]**Martina Borst** (mez); **Bamberg Quartet; Stefan Adelmann** (db); **Berthold Höps** (hpd/org). Capriccio Ⓕ 10 517 (52 minutes: DDD: 7/95).

...Stabat mater[a]. Orfeo. **Julie Faulkner** (sop); [a]**Anna Gonda** (mez); **Budapest Camerata / Michael Halász.** Naxos Ⓢ 8 550766 (52 minutes: DDD: 9/95).

...Salve regina. *Coupled with works by* **Mozart** and **J.C. Bach** **Ruth Ziesak** (sop); **La Stagione / Michael Schneider.** Deutsche Harmonia Mundi Ⓕ 05472 77335-2 (57 minutes: DDD: 11/96).

Pergolesi Livietta e Tracollo[a]. La serva padrona[b]. [a]**Nancy Argenta** (sop) Livietta; [a]**Werner van Mechelen** (bass) Tracollo; [b]**Patricia Biccire** (sop) Serpina; [b]**Donato di Stefano** (bass) Uberto; **La Petite Bande / Sigiswald Kuijken** (vn). Accent Ⓕ ACC96123D (80 minutes: DDD: 11/97). 🗡 Notes and texts included. Recorded live in 1996.

La serva padrona, most famous of *intermezzi*, is given here with a rare but comparable companion-piece. *Livietta e Tracollo* is also for two characters, light soprano and *buffo* bass, with two sections, originally to be played in the intervals of the evening's *opera seria*. Rather more complicated and improbable than *La serva padrona*, it tells of a girl disguised as a French peasant (male) seeking vengeance on a robber who in turn appears disguised as a pregnant Pole. She succeeds in the first half, while in the second the man, now disguised as an astrologer, has more luck and they agree to get married. Musically it is not so very inferior to the *Serva*. Both have more wit in the music than in the libretto, with deft parodies of *opera seria* and a popular appeal in the repeated phrases of their arias, catchy without being coarse. The performance here is a lively one with Nancy Argenta as a resourceful and not too pertly soubrettish Livietta. Kuijken's Petite Bande play with a distinctively 'period' tone; the speeds are sprightly and the rhythms light-footed. In both works, the women are better than the men, who (on this showing) lack the comic touch. Patricia Biccire sings attractively, especially in her 'sincere' aria, "A Serpina penserate", and she paces her recitatives artfully. A lower baroque pitch is used and the final number is the short duet, "Per te io ho nel core", as in the original score. The booklet contains both librettos (in Italian) and summaries of the plots, as well as Kuijken's thoughts on the project.

Additional recommendation ...

...La Serva Padrona[a]. L'Olimpiade – Overture (arr. anon). [a]**Isabelle Poulenard** (sop); [a]**Philippe Cantor** (bass); **Nice Baroque Ensemble / Gilbert Bezzina.** Pierre Verany Ⓕ PV795111 (52 minutes: DDD: 4/96). 🗡

Further listening ...

...Confitebor tibi Domine. *Coupled with works by* **Durante** and **Astorga** **Ann Monoyios** (sop); **Balthasar Neumann Choir; Freiburg Baroque Orchestra / Thomas Hengelbrock.** Deutsche Harmonia Mundi 05472 77369-2 (10/97). 🗡 *See review under Durante; refer to the Index.*

Pérotin   French *c*1160-*c*1225

Perotin Viderunt omnes. Alleluia, Posui Adiutorium. Dum sigillum summi Patris. Alleluia, Nativitas. Beata viscera. Sederunt principes. **Anonymous** Veni creator spiritus. O Maria virginei. Isias cecinit. **Hilliard Ensemble** (David James, alto; John Potter, Rogers Covey-Crump, Mark Padmore, Charles Daniels, tens; Gordon Jones, bar) / **Paul Hillier** (bar). ECM New Series Ⓕ 837 751-2 (68 minutes: DDD: 2/90). Texts included.   Ⓠ

This is a superb and original recording. It gives musical individuality to a group of works that have hitherto tended to sound much the same. Moreover, as a special attraction for those wanting to see artistic individuality in early composers, it includes all but one of the identifiable works of Pérotin. Inevitably his two grand four-voice organa take up much of the record. At nearly 12 minutes each they may have been the most ambitious polyphonic works composed up to the end of the twelfth century. The Hilliard Ensemble adopt a wonderfully suave and supple approach to both *Viderunt* and *Sederunt*, softening the pervasive rhythms that can make them a shade oppressive and showing a clear view of the entire architecture of each piece. They surge irrepressibly from one section to another, creating a musical momentum that belies the admirably slow speeds they generally adopt. They also beautifully underline the musical differences between the two works, producing a sound which seems a credible reflection of what one might have heard at Notre Dame in the late twelfth century. What is particularly exciting here is the way in which the musicians grasp at the individual dynamic of each work: the enormous open spaces they create to project the text of the magical *O Maria virginei*; the breakneck virtuosity in their swirling performance of *Dum sigillum*, the ever so gently modulated rhythms in the strophic *Veni creator*; the harder edge in their tone for *Alleluia Nativitas*; and so on. With a splendidly judged note by Paul Hillier, this is a recording of the highest distinction.

Additional recommendations ...
...Mors. Beata viscera. *Coupled with works by various composers.*
   Paul Elliott (ten); **Alan Bennett** (sngr); **Theatre of Voices / Paul Hillier** (bass).
   Harmonia Mundi Ⓕ HMU90 7157 (77 minutes: DDD: 1/97).
...Sederunt principes. *Coupled with works by various composers.* **Orlando Consort;**
   Westminster Cathedral Choir. Archiv Produktion Ⓕ 453 487-2AH (76 minutes: DDD: 2/98).
   See review in the Collections sections; refer to the Index.
...Viderunt omnes (arr. Kronos). *Coupled with works by various composers.* **Kronos Quartet.**
   Nonesuch Ⓕ 7559-79457-2 (69 minutes: DDD: 12/97). *Gramophone Editor's choice.*
   See review in the Collections section; refer to the Index.

Wilhelm Peterson-Berger   Swedish 1867-1942

Suggested listening ...
...Nothing is like the time of waiting. Swedish folk ballads, Op. 5 – No. 1, When I go myself in the dark forest; No. 3, Like stars in the heavens. Three Marit's Songs, Op. 12. Böljeby Waltz. Return. Aspåkers Polka. *Coupled with works by various composers.* **Anne Sofie von Otter** (mez); **Bengt Forsberg** (pf). DG 449 189-2GH (5/96). *Gramophone Editor's choice. See review in the Collections section; refer to the Index.*   ⒼⒼ

Allan Pettersson   Swedish 1911-1980

Pettersson Symphonies – No. 3; No. 15. **Norrköping Symphony Orchestra / Leif Segerstam.**
BIS Ⓕ CD680 (71 minutes: DDD: 1/96). Recorded 1993-1994.
The first difference that strikes the casual ear when comparing Leif Segerstam's account of Pettersson's Fifteenth Symphony (1978) with that by Peter Ruzicka on CPO is tempo; so pronounced is it, that Segerstam takes six minutes less (at 32'20") than his rival. In CPO's notes, Andreas Meyer and Ruzicka make a virtue of their more relaxed paces (the work is built around three principal and interacting speeds), which arose from the alleged impracticality of certain passages. Segerstam and his Swedish forces take these in their stride to come much closer to the composer's timing of 31'00" (he never heard the work performed). Repeated hearings reinforce Segerstam's superiority. His vision of the work is more clearly focused, the interpretation tauter and more compelling than Ruzicka's, and the excellent BIS sound ensures that the orchestral detail comes through still more clearly. Yet Ruzicka knows Pettersson's music probably better than anyone; perhaps it is just that Segerstam is able to translate his own understanding into actual sound rather better. The BIS coupling, of No. 3 (1954-1955), is a further advantage, though here competition is somewhat stiffer. Again, Segerstam is quicker, though only by two minutes, largely accounted for by the treatment of the introduction to the first movement. There is little to choose between the two versions (Francis's coupling of No. 4 is a fine one), but in the final analysis BIS and Segerstam must be first choice for both symphonies.

Additional recommendations ...
...Nos. 3 and 4. **Saarbrücken Radio Symphony Orchestra / Alun Francis.**
   CPO Ⓕ CPO999 223-2 (78 minutes: DDD: 12/95).
...No. 15. **Ruzicka** "... das Gesegnete, das Verfluchte". **Berlin Radio Symphony Orchestra /**
   Peter Ruzicka. CPO Ⓕ CPO999 095-2 (52 minutes: DDD: 12/95).

Pettersson Symphonies – No. 5; No. 16[a]. [a]**John-Edward Kelly** (sax); **Saarbrücken Radio Symphony Orchestra / Alun Francis.** CPO Ⓕ CPO999 284-2 (65 minutes: DDD: 11/96). Recorded 1995.
The orchestral playing is full of commitment, the account of the 40-minute Fifth (1960-1962) sounding tremendously vivid; if some details come off marginally better in Atzmon's pioneering performance, Francis has the edge where it counts, in his overall view of this magnificent work. Yet the coupling – the last symphony the Swede managed to complete – is better still. No. 16 was written in 1979 for the American saxophonist Frederik Hemke. Here Kelly, who has made some minor modifications to the solo part for reasons explained in the booklet (the ailing composer appears to have been uncertain of the instrument's range), glides through the hair-raising virtuosity with breathtaking ease. This is the kind of advocacy Pettersson, who never heard the work, can only have dreamed of. An excellent disc.

Additional recommendation ...
...No. 5[a]. Viola Concerto[b]. [b]Nobuko Imai (va); Malmö Symphony Orchestra / [a]Moshe Atzmon, [b]Lev Markiz. BIS Ⓕ CD480 (71 minutes: DDD: 2/91).

Pettersson Symphonies Nos. 7 and 11. **Norrköping Symphony Orchestra / Leif Segerstam.**
BIS Ⓕ CD580 (70 minutes: DDD: 4/94). Recorded 1992.
Most of Pettersson's major works are constructed as large, unified movements (although he was an accomplished miniaturist) and Nos. 7 and 11, respectively 46 and 24 minutes in length, are no exceptions. The former in some ways is unrepresentative of the composer; the obsessiveness of mood and hectoring tone are present, especially in the *Angst*-ridden first and third spans, but the range of expression is much wider than in most of his other works. Composed in 1967-68, it has a unique atmosphere, both haunting and haunted, which will stay with you for a long time. His melodic genius is confirmed in the long and heartfelt central threnody, as well as by the beautiful quiet coda, truly music to "soften the crying of a child"; its delivery by the Norrköping players has just the right amount of detachment. Segerstam's tempos permit the work to breathe and resonate not unlike Mahler. The Eleventh Symphony (1974) is less combative in tone, although it has its moments, and is not on the same elevated plane as the Seventh. As usual from BIS, the recording quality is first-rate, allowing both the devastating power and delicate fine detail of these scores to emerge equally well.
Additional recommendation ...
...No. 7. **Hamburg Philharmonic Orchestra / Gerd Albrecht.**
CPO CPO999 190-2 (45 minutes: DDD: 10/94).

Pettersson Concerto for Violin and String Quartet No. 1[a]. Four Improvisations[b]. Fuga in E major[c]. Fantasy[d]. Lamento[e]. [c]**Christiane Dimigen** (ob); [c]**Johannes Peitz** (cl); [c]**Eckart Hübner** (bn); [a]**Ulf Hoelscher** (vn); [e]**Volker Banfield** (pf); [ab]**Mandelring Quartet** (Sebastian Schmidt, Nanette Schmidt, vns; [d]Michael Scheitzbach, va; Bernhard Schmidt, vc).
CPO Ⓕ CPO999 169-2 (60 minutes: DDD: 1/96).
This is a revelatory issue. Readers of a nervous disposition regarding Pettersson's music should start this disc with the *Four Improvisations* (1936). The opening's rusticity will come as a surprise; the remainder oscillates between Bartók in folk-mode and Hindemith. Like the other shorter items, the *Improvisations* are stylistically anonymous, unrecognizable when set against the monumental, *Angst*-driven output of the composer's maturity, and strangely patchy in quality. When vast symphonic canvases could later be erected from the sparest of material, the two-and-a-half-minute *Fantasy* (1936) seems prodigal by comparison in achieving so little with so much. On a similar scale, *Lamento* (1945) – Pettersson's only surviving piano work – is quite forgettable. At over 14 minutes in duration, the 1948 wind *Fuga* is certainly no trifle; its obsessive reliance on pure counterpoint is suggestive of the later symphonist. Yet it just does not *sound* like Pettersson, making the vibrancy of personality evident in every bar of the Concerto of a year later all the more extraordinary. This really is a masterpiece, albeit a discomfiting one, written by a composer who was also a master string player. Hoelscher and the Mandelring Quartet give a fine performance and CPO's sound has very little glare, softening edges that are unnaturally severe with no loss of impact.
Further listening ...
...Symphony No. 2. Symphonic Movement. **BBC Scottish Symphony Orchestra / Alun Francis.**
CPO CPO999 281-2 (9/95).
...Symphony No. 8. **Berlin Radio Symphony Orchestra / Thomas Sanderling.**
CPO CPO999 085-2 (10/94).
...Symphony No. 9. **Deutsches Symphony Orchestra / Alun Francis.** CPO CPO999 231-2 (9/95).
...Symphony No. 14. **Berlin Radio Symphony Orchestra / Johan Arnell.** CPO CPO999 191-2 (10/94).

Hans Pfitzner
German 1869-1949

Pfitzner Palestrina – Preludes, Acts 1, 2 and 3. Das Herz – Liebesmelodie.
Das Käthchen von Heilbronn, Op. 17 – Overture.
R. Strauss Guntram – Overture. Capriccio – Prelude. Feuersnot – Liebesszene. **Orchestra of the Deutsche Oper, Berlin / Christian Thielemann.** DG Ⓕ 449 571-2GH (75 minutes: DDD: 3/97).
Gramophone Editor's choice. ⓖⓖ
For a still relatively young man (he is 37) Christian Thielemann shows a marked fondness for broad tempos: even more obviously he loves big gestures and sumptuously rich sound. You can hear both tendencies in Pfitzner's *Käthchen von Heilbronn* Overture. On the face of it this is a problematic piece: very long (16 minutes) and with especially leisured transitions between its sections. After the big, bold, martial music of the opening you might expect a conductor to be a little nervous of the fact that Pfitzner allows a particularly lengthy transition to ensue before he even begins to prepare for his 'second subject', in fact the superbly romantic melody that represents Käthchen herself. Quite admirably, Thielemann does not hurry nor does he overstate the Käthchen theme: full, impassioned eloquence is reserved for its grandiose return. Although he allows the overture's big moments ample space to expand, there is no sense of mere waiting between them: he shows great care and sensitivity in Pfitzner's quieter pages. He obviously loves this music, and that is still more obvious in the

Palestrina preludes, where the luminously pure textures of the first Prelude receive no less scrupulous attention than the nobly baying brass in the second or the velvety denseness of string sonority in some pages of the last. Thielemann's Strauss is no less effective. He finds a genuine Straussian line and ardour even in the not yet wholly mature *Guntram* Overture, builds a huge climax from the exquisite string sounds that begin the *Feuersnot* love scene and only falters just a little in the *Capriccio* Sextet; here he allows his solo strings to play just a little too forcefully. A distinguished début marked by ravishing orchestral playing. The recording is richly ample: you can almost reach out and stroke it.

Additional recommendation ...

...Das Christ-Elflein – Overture[c]. Palestrina – Preludes, Acts 1, 2 and 3[c]. Duo for Violin, Cello and Small Orchestra, Op. 43[bc]. 1938). Lieder[a] – Hast du von den Fischerkindern, Op. 7 No. 1; Der Gärtner, Op. 9 No. 1; Die Einsame, Op. 9 No. 2; Zum Abschied meiner Tochter, Op. 10 No. 3; Michaelskirchplatz, Op. 19 No. 2; In Danzig, Op. 22 No. 1; Nachts, Op. 26 No. 2; Abbitte, Op. 29 No. 1; Hussens Kerker, Op. 32 No. 1; Säerspruch, Op. 32 No. 2 (originally unpublished); Leuchtende Tage, Op. 40 No. 1; Herbstgefühl, Op. 40 No. 4. [a]**Gerhard Hüsch** (bar); [b]**Max Strub** (vn); [b]**Ludwig Hoelscher** (vc); [c]**Berlin State Opera Orchestra / Hans Pfitzner** ([a]pf). EMI Composers in Person mono Ⓟ CDC5 55225-2* (75 minutes: ADD: 5/95).

Pfitzner Palestrina. **Nicolai Gedda** (ten) Palestrina; **Dietrich Fischer-Dieskau** (bar) Borromeo; **Gerd Nienstedt** (bass) Master of Ceremonies; **Karl Ridderbusch** (bass) Christoph Madruscht, Pope Pius IV; **Bernd Weikl** (bar) Morone; **Herbert Steinbach** (ten) Novagerio; **Helen Donath** (sop) Ighino; **Brigitte Fassbaender** (mez) Silla; **Renate Freyer** (contr) Lukrezia; **Victor von Halem** (bass) Cardinal of Lorraine; **John van Kesteren** (ten) Abdisu; **Peter Meven** (bass) Anton Brus; **Hermann Prey** (bar) Count Luna; **Friedrich Lenz** (ten) Bishop of Budoja; **Adalbert Kraus** (ten) Theophilus; **Franz Mazura** (bass) Avosmediano; **Tölz Boys' Choir; Bavarian Radio Chorus and Symphony Orchestra / Rafael Kubelík.** DG 20th Century Classics Ⓜ 427 417-2GC3 (three discs: 206 minutes: ADD: 7/89). Notes, text and translation included. From 2711 013 (2/74).   ⓰⓰⓰

Rafael Kubelík's magnificent, sumptuously cast DG recording of *Palestrina* is an almost impossible act to follow, indeed it's hard to imagine such an extravagance of vocal riches being encountered in a German opera recording nowadays: Brigitte Fassbaender ardently impulsive in the brief role of Palestrina's pupil Silla, Helen Donath pure-voiced and touching as his son Ighino, and an absolute constellation of superb basses and baritones, often doubling quite small parts: Karl Ridderbusch, Bernd Weikl, Hermann Prey, Franz Mazura, with at their head Dietrich Fischer-Dieskau as a surely unsurpassable Borromeo: dangerously powerful, intensely concerned and in magnificent voice. And those are just the 'secondary' roles! Pfitzner's text is one of the finest librettos ever written, and Gedda's singing gives the impression that the beauty of the words and their portrayal of Palestrina's dignity and suffering are more important to him than concern for his own voice. Kubelík's urgent conducting has a visionary quality, with a marvellous ear for the lucid radiance of this wonderful score.

Further listening ...

...Cello Concertos – G major, Op. 42; A minor, Op. 52; A minor, Op. posth. **David Geringas** (vc); **Bamberg Symphony Orchestra / Werner Andreas Albert.** CPO CPO999 135-2 (4/94).

...Das Fest auf Solhaug – Three Preludes. Kleine Symphonie in G major, Op. 44. Symphony in C major, Op. 46. **Bamberg Symphony Orchestra / Werner Andreas Albert.** CPO CPO999 080-2 (5/91).

...Piano Concerto in E flat major, Op. 31. **Volker Banfield** (pf); **Munich Philharmonic Orchestra / Werner Andreas Albert.** CPO CPO999 045-2.

...Violin Concerto in B minor, Op. 34. Duo for Violin, Cello and small orchestra, Op. 43. Scherzo in C minor. **Saschko Gawriloff** (vn); **Julius Berger** (vc); **Bamberg Symphony Orchestra / Werner Andreas Albert.** CPO CPO999 079-2 (5/91).

...Abbitte, Op. 29 No. 1. *Coupled with works by various composers.* **Mitsuko Shirai** (mez); **Hartmut Höll** (pf). Capriccio 10 534 (12/94).

...Das dunkle Reich, Op. 38[a]. Der Blumen Rache[b]. Fons salutifer, Op. 48[c]. [a]**Yvonne Wiedstruck** (sop); [b]**Yvi Jänicke** (contr); [a]**Yaron Windmüller** (bar); [ac]**Sigurd Bruns** (org); **Berlin Radio** [bc]**Chorus and Symphony Orchestra / Rolf Reuter.** CPO CPO999 158-2 (4/95).

Achille Philip   French 1878-1959

Suggested listening ...

...Toccata and Fugue in A minor. *Coupled with works by various composers.* **Gerard Brooks** (org). Priory PRCD558 (4/98). *See review in the Collections section; refer to the Index.*

Peter Philips   British 1560/1-1628

Suggested listening ...

...Ecce vicit Leo. *Coupled with works by various composers.* **St Paul's Cathedral Choir / John Scott** with **Andrew Lucas** (org). Hyperion CDA66916 (A/97). *See review in the Collections section; refer to the Index.*

Astor Piazzolla
Argentinian 1921-1992

Piazzolla Concerto for Bandoneon, Strings and Percussion[a]. Tres movimientos tanguísticos porteños. Tangos (arr. Vidal)[a] – Decaríssimo; Invierno porteño; Adiós nonino; Milonga del ángel; La muerte del ángel. [a]**Pablo Mainetti** (bandoneón); **Lluís Vidal** (pf); **Chamber Orchestra of the Teatre Lliure, Barcelona / Josep Pons.** Harmonia Mundi Ⓕ HMC90 1595 (67 minutes: DDD: 11/96). Recorded 1995. *Gramophone Editor's record of the month.* ⒼⒼ

Astor Piazzolla is practically unique in creating a sophisticated bridge between popular and 'intellectual' styles; and this disc will come as an eye-opener to those so far unacquainted with his music. Try the separate tangos, from the jazzy *Decaríssimo*, through the melancholy *Milonga del ángel* and the miniature tone-poem of *Invierno porteño* ("Winter in Buenos Aires") to the agitated fugato of the strongly syncopated *Muerte del ángel*. There is then a big step to the *Tres movimientos tanguísticos porteños* ("Three Buenos Aires movements"), which present radical sublimations of the tango, the first in a very free harmonic idiom, the second with a deeply poetic opening but becoming increasingly diverse in character and pace, and the third notable for its irregular rhythms and contrapuntal texture. If the Bandoneon Concerto is ultimately less than totally convincing, it is due to its mixture of styles, ranging from something like a cross between Copland and Villa-Lobos to Ponce-like sentimentality, and to a disappointingly diffuse finale; but the slow movement contains some genuinely moving moments. Performance and recording throughout are of the highest standard.

Additional recommendation ...

...Revirado. Fuga y misterio. Milonga del ángel. Decaríssimo. Soledad. La muerte del ángel. Adiós nonino. Libertango. Verano porteño. Michelangelo '70. Buenos Aires hora cero. Tangata. **Emanuel Ax, Pablo Ziegler** (pfs). Sony Classical Ⓕ SK62728 (60 minutes: DDD: 4/97).

Piazzolla Libertango (arr. Calandrelli)[abdil]. Tango Suite (arr. S. Assad)[ef] – Andante; Allegro. Le Grand Tango (arr. Calandrelli)[j]. Sur – Regreso al amor[bil]. Fugata[abdij]. Mumuki[abdik]. Tres minutos con la realidad[abdgij]. Milonga del ángel[bhm]. Histoire du Tango – Café 1930 (all arr. Calandrelli)[b].
Calandrelli Tango Remembrances[c]. **Yo-Yo Ma** (vc); [a]**Antonio Agri** (vn); [b]**Nestor Marconi,** [c]**Astor Piazzolla** (bandoneón); [d]**Horacio Malvicino,** [e]**Odair Assad,** [f]**Sérgio Assad,** [g]**Oscar Castro-Neves** (gtrs); [h]**Edwin Barker,** [i]**Héctor Console** (db); [j]**Kathryn Stott,** [k]**Gerardo Gandini,** [l]**Leonardo Marconi,** [m]**Frank Corliss** (pfs). Sony Classical Ⓕ SK63122 (64 minutes: DDD: 2/98). Recorded 1987-1997.

Yo-Yo Ma is the latest international artist to surrender to the spell of the Argentinian dance: he can also be heard on the soundtrack of the film, *The Tango Lesson*. Here, surrounded by a brilliant group of experts in the genre, he presents with wholehearted commitment a well-varied programme of Piazzolla pieces. They range from the melancholy or sultry to the energetic or fiery. Among the latter, *Fugata* is ingenious, *Mumuki* richly eloquent, and *Tres minutos con la realidad* nervily edgy: in this last, Kathryn Stott understandably earned the admiration of her Argentinian colleagues. She also shines with Yo-Yo Ma in an exciting performance of *Le Grand Tango*: his playing in the *Milonga del ángel* is outstandingly beautiful. Special mention must also be made of some spectacular virtuosity by the Assad brothers in the *Tango Suite*. The characteristic bandoneón is featured with the cellist in *Café 1930*; and by technological trickery Yo-Yo Ma partners Piazzolla himself (recorded in 1987) in a confection called *Tango Remembrances*. Those who are already fans of this genre will be in no need of encouragement to procure this disc: others will find it perhaps the most persuasive demonstration yet of the extent to which this dance has transcended its low-class Buenos Aires origins.

Additional recommendations ...

...Histoire du Tango[ab]. Five Pieces[b]. Six Etudes tanguistiques[a]. [a]**Mikael Helasvuo** (fl); [b]**Jukka Savijoki** (gtr). Ondine Ⓕ ODE781-2 (64 minutes: DDD: 12/92).

...Histoire du Tango. Estaciones Porteñas (arr. Carlevaro)[b]. Six Etudes tanguistiques[a]. Tango Suite – Tango No. 2 (arr. Gallois/Söllscher). [a]**Patrick Gallois** (fl); [b]**Göran Söllscher** (gtr). DG Ⓕ 449 185-2GH (63 minutes: DDD: 7/97).

Further listening ...

...Asleep. *Coupled with works by various composers.* **Dumisani Maraire** (ngoma/hosho); **Astor Piazzolla** (bandoneon); **Patty Manning, John Taylor, Larry Caballero** (vocs); **Djivan Gasparian** (duduk). **Kronos Quartet.**
Nonesuch 7559-79394-2 (2/96). *See review in the Collections section; refer to the Index.*

Giovanni Picchi
Italian fl 1575-1630

Suggested listening ...

...Balli – Ballo ongaro; Ballo alla polacha; Ballo ditto il Picchi. *Coupled with works by various composers.* **Rinaldo Alessandrini** (hpd). Opus 111 OPS30-118 (4/95). ✏ *See review in the Collections section; refer to the Index.*

...Toccata. Intavolatura di Balli d'Arpicordo – Ballo ongaro; Ballo alla polacha; Todesca; Ballo ditto il Picchi. *Coupled with works by various composers.* **Sophie Yates** (hpd). Chandos Chaconne CHAN0601 (9/97). ✏ *See review in the Collections section; refer to the Index.*

Gabriel Pierné

French 1863-1937

Suggested listening ...
...Violin Sonata, Op. 36. *Coupled with works by* **Ravel** and **Debussy** Gérard Poulet (vn); Noël Lee (pf). Arion ARN68228 (9/94). *Gramophone Editor's choice. See review under Ravel; refer to the Index.*

Diego Pisador

Spanish 1509/10-after 1557

Suggested listening ...
...Libro de música – En la fuente del rosel; La manana de Sant Juan. *Coupled with works by various composers.* **La Romanesca / José Miguel Moreno** (vihuela). Glossa GCD920203 (5/96). ✔ *Gramophone Editor's choice. See review in the Collections section; refer to the Index.* Ⓖ

Walter Piston

American 1894-1976

Piston Symphony No. 6. The Incredible Flutist – Suite. Three New England Sketches. **St Louis Symphony Orchestra / Leonard Slatkin.** RCA Victor Red Seal Ⓕ RD60798 (57 minutes: DDD: 1/92). Recorded 1989-1990.

The Incredible Flutist's title is perhaps misleading, for there is no solo flute part, and in fact the score consists of a series of short, attractive dance movements. The original music was written for a 1938 ballet: two years later Piston used about half the material for a concert suite which soon became quite popular. The *Three New England Sketches* date from 1959. They comprise "Seaside", a mostly peaceful, evocative essay, "Summer Evening", a wispy, delicate scherzo and "Mountains", whose very grand, portentous outer sections surround a central episode of busy counterpoint. Piston's Sixth Symphony is generally regarded as his best. Written in 1955, it is typically direct in expression, and has no programme. The first movement is very American in its suggestion of wide-open space and in its rhythmic irregularities. A quicksilver scherzo forms the second movement, and then a serene *Adagio* is followed by a cheerful finale, with strident brass, rushing strings, and bubbling woodwind. Leonard Slatkin always conducts music of his own country with great sympathy and insight, as he does here. His orchestra has exactly the right timbre, which is important in American repertoire of this kind, and the engineering is very good.

Piston The Incredible Flutist – Suite[a]. Fantasy for English Horn, Harp and Strings[b]. Suite for Orchestra. Concerto for String Quartet, Wind Instruments and Percussion[c]. Psalm and Prayer of David[d]. [a]**Scott Goff** (fl); [b]**Glen Danielson** (hn); [b]**Theresa Elder Wunrow** (hp); [c]**Juilliard Quartet** (Robert Mann, Joel Smirnoff, vns; Samuel Rhodes, va; Joel Krosnick, vc); **Seattle Symphony** [d]**Chorale and Orchestra / Gerard Schwarz.** Delos Ⓕ DE3126 (68 minutes: DDD: 2/94). Recorded 1991-1992.

Gerard Schwarz's flutist fixes you with his limpid tone. However, it will always be known as the score with the Tango. Schwarz goes with the flow, the sway of the melody, but it can never linger long enough. The *Fantasy* enters darkened Elysian fields – Piston's lyricism sits well with this distinctive voice of sorrow and regret. We can trace their kinship right back to the composer's first published work – the orchestral *Suite* of 1929. At its heart is a long and intense pastorale: the cor anglais is there at the inception. Framing it, motoric syncopations carry us first to a kind of drive-by the blues with bar-room piano and Grappelli violin. The finale is essentially a fugal work-out: high-tech Hindemith. Piston's very last work, the *Concerto*, is ten eventful minutes where the imperative is once again pitted against the contemplative. The mixing of timbres is masterly, a fleck of woodwind or a brush of tambourine or antique cymbal speaking volumes. But at the centre of gravity is the Juilliard Quartet, moving in mysterious ways, leading on to a closing viola solo – another dark voice posing both unanswered question and valediction. In fact, the last words uttered here are those of the *Psalm and Prayer of David* – a rare vocal setting for Piston, and as such, refreshingly open, unhackneyed, unhieratical. Performance and recording values make the strongest possible case for this music.

Further listening ...
...Violin Sonatina. *Coupled with works by various composers.* **Anne Akiko Meyers** (vn); **André-Michel Schub** (pf). RCA Victor Red Seal 09026 68114-2 (8/96). *See review in the Collections section; refer to the Index.*

Ildebrando Pizzetti

Italian 1880-1968

Suggested listening ...
...Messa di requiem[a]. De profundis[a]. *Coupled with* **Martin** Mass for Double Choir[a]. Passacaille[b]. [a]**Westminster Cathedral Choir / James O'Donnell** ([b]org). Hyperion CDA67017 (3/98). *See review under Martin; refer to the Index.* ⒼⒼⒼ

Peteris Plakidis

Suggested listening ...
...Two Grasshopper Dances. *Coupled with works by various composers.* **Gidon Kremer** (vn).
Teldec 0630-13597-2 (7/97). **Gramophone** *Editor's choice. See review in the Collections section;*
refer to the Index.
...Two Grasshopper Dances. **Gidon Kremer** (vn); **Vadim Sacharov** (pf). Teldec 0630-14654-2 (11/97).
Gramophone *Editor's choice. See review in the Collections section; refer to the Index.*

John Playford I

Suggested listening ...
...The English Dancing Master: Part 1 – Halfe Hannikin; Goddesses. Part 2 – Aye me; Saturday
night and Sunday morn; Pauls Wharfe. Appendix – The Indian Queen; On the cold ground; Of
noble race was Shinkin; A Morisco; Jamaica; The Waits; Ham House; Pell Mell; Kettledrum;
Johnny, Cock thy Beaver *Coupled with works by various composers.* **The Dufay Collective.**
Chandos New Direction CHAN9446 (10/96). *See review in the Collections section;*
refer to the Index.

John Plummer

Suggested listening ...
...Tota pulchra es. Anna mater matris Christi. *Coupled with works by various composers.*
The Sixteen / Harry Christophers.
Collins Classics 1462-2 (3/96). *See review in the Collections section; refer to the Index.*

Manuel Ponce

Ponce Piano Concerto[a]. Violin Concerto[b]. Concierto del sur[c]. [b]**Henryk Szeryng** (vn),
[c]**Alfonso Moreno** (gtr); [a]**Jorge Federico Osorio** (pf); [b]**Royal Philharmonic Orchestra,** [ac]**State of**
Mexico Symphony Orchestra / Enrique Bátiz. ASV Ⓟ CDDCA952 (78 minutes: DDD: 8/96).
Item marked [a] from CDDCA916 (1/96), [b]HMV EL270151-1 (8/85), [c]HMV ESD165105-1 (8/83).
Manuel Ponce has been called the "father of Mexican musical nationalism"; but in his Piano
Concerto (his first sizeable work) there is little, if any, trace of local colour. This is a showy,
conventional late-romantic work of the barnstorming variety, and despite a great deal of bravura
piano writing – Ponce himself was the soloist in its first performance in 1912 – its sound and fury
do not amount to much musically. Osorio (who made an agreeable record of Ponce's solo piano music
for ASV) is suitably exhibitionist: the orchestral sound is a bit shrill. By 1941, the year of the
Concierto del sur, Ponce's style had changed and matured, he having meanwhile studied in Paris with
Dukas; and this is one of the best guitar concertos in the repertory; its Mexican character is evident
in the festive finale. Moreno's performance is strong in urgency and intensity though it could have had
a greater sense of poetry in the *Andante*. Ponce's only other concerto, that for violin two years later,
is his best-known thanks to the championship of Szeryng, its dedicatee, and through the inclusion in
its melancholy second movement of references to his famous song *Estrellita* (whose rights he had
unwittingly surrendered to an astute publisher). Szeryng plays the virtuoso solo part – which
includes a lengthy cadenza, as does the guitar concerto – brilliantly, but in the acoustic of the
Mexican hall used for this mid-1980s recording the tuttis are somewhat thick and rowdy.

Further listening ...
...Sonatina meridional. Thème varié et finale. Sonata III. Variations and Fugue on "La Folia de
España". **Timo Korhonen** (gtr). Ondine ODE770-2 (7/92).
...Balada mexicana. Arrulladora. Tema mexicano variado. Romanza de amor. Preludio y Fuga
sobre un tema de Handel. Mazurkas Nos. 1, 2, 4-7 and 10. Scherzino mexicano. Gavota.
Intermezzo No. 1. Rapsodia cubana No. 1. **Jorge Federico Osorio** (pf). ASV CDDCA874 (5/95).
...Prelude y Fuga sobre un tema de Handel. Suite Cubana – Penilunio. Cuatro danzas Mexicanas.
Intermezzo No. 1. Introduccíon, Preludio y Fuga sobre un tema de J.S. Bach. Malgré tout.
Scherzino Mexicano. Preludio y Fuga para la mano izquierda sola. Dos Estudios de Concierto.
Notturno. Balada Mexicana. **David Witten** (pf). Marco Polo 8 223609 (5/96).

Amilcare Ponchielli

Ponchielli La Gioconda. **Maria Callas** (sop) La Gioconda; **Fiorenza Cossotto** (mez) Laure
Adorno; **Pier Miranda Ferraro** (ten) Enzo Grimaldo; **Piero Cappuccilli** (bar) Barnaba; **Ivo Vinco**
(bass) Alvise Badoero; **Irene Companeez** (contr) La Cieca; **Leonardo Monreale** (bass) Zuane;
Carlo Forte (bass) A Singer, Pilot; **Renato Ercolani** (ten) Isepo, First Distant Voice; **Aldo Biffi**

(bass) Second Distant Voice; **Bonaldo Giaiotti** (bass) Barnabotto; **Chorus and Orchestra of La Scala, Milan / Antonio Votto.** EMI mono Ⓜ CDS5 56291-2* (three discs: 167 minutes: DDD: 2/88). Notes, text and translation included. From Columbia SAX2359/61 (11/60). Recorded 1959.

Ponchielli's old warhorse has had a bad press in recent times, which seems strange in view of its melodic profusion, his unerring adumbration of Gioconda's unhappy predicament and of the sensual relationship between Enzo and Laura. But it does need large-scale and involved singing – just what it receives here on this now historic set. Nobody could fail to be caught up in its conviction. Callas was in good and fearless voice when it was made, with the role's emotions perhaps enhanced by the traumas of her own life at the time. Here her strengths in declaiming recitative, her moulding of line, her response to the text are all at their most arresting. Indeed she turns what can be a maudlin act into true tragedy. Ferraro's stentorian ebullience is most welcome. Cossotto is a vital, seductive Laura. Cappuccilli gives the odious spy and lecher Barnaba a threatening, sinister profile, whilst Vinco is a suitably implacable Alvise. Votto did nothing better than this set, bringing out the subtlety of the Verdi-inspired scoring and the charm of the "Dance of the Hours" ballet. The recording sounds excellent for its age.

Additional recommendations ...

...Soloists; Chorus and Orchestra of the Accademia di Santa Cecilia, Rome / Lamberto Gardelli. Decca Grand Opera Ⓜ 430 042-2DM3 (three discs: 155 minutes: ADD).

...Soloists; London Opera Chorus; Finchley Children's Music Group; National Philharmonic Orchestra / Bruno Bartoletti. Decca Ⓕ 414 349-2DH3 (three discs: 151 minutes: ADD: 7/85).

...La Gioconda – Dance of the Hours. *Coupled with works by various composers.* Vienna Philharmonic Orchestra / Rudolf Kempe. Testament Ⓕ SBT1127* (78 minutes: ADD: 3/98). *See review in the Collections section; refer to the Index.*

Geoffrey Poole
British 20th century

Suggested listening ...

...Wymondham Chants. *Coupled with works by various composers.* **The King's Singers.** RCA Victor Red Seal 09026 68255-2 (8/96). *See review in the Collections section; refer to the Index.*

Gavriil Popov
Russian/USSR 1904-1972

Popov Symphonies – No. 1, Op. 7[a]; No. 2, Op. 39, "Motherland"[b]. [a]**Moscow State Symphony Orchestra;** [b]**USSR TV and Radio Symphony Orchestra / Gennadi Provatorov.** Olympia Ⓕ OCD576 (78 minutes: [a]DDD/[b]ADD: 2/96). Item marked [a] recorded 1989, [b]1961. *Gramophone Editor's choice.*

Gavriil Popov is something of a mystery man of twentieth-century Russian music. His First Symphony was much admired by musicians including Shostakovich, to whose youthful, rebellious vigour it owes something in manner if not a great deal in idiom. The opening *Allegro energico* must rank as one of the most powerful symphonic movements to come out of Russia in the twentieth century, well able to hold its place beside Shostakovich and Prokofiev. The harmony is bitter, the rhythmic impetus relentless, the orchestration violent, the sense of form brilliant in its control of this harsh, compelling music. The *Largo* is a tormented piece of introspection, beautifully scored and enigmatic in mood; the finale is a scherzo and coda, balancing what has gone before with some passages that seem sardonic but which are genuinely absorbed into a glowing conclusion. The Soviet authorities, already in a state of muddle when he played it to them in 1932, were thrown into disarray. It *was* played, however, and was taken up in the West by conductors including Malko, Klemperer, Scherchen and Kleiber. We have heard too little of it since, and this fine performance should do much to awaken interest. Then came a Second Symphony, simpler in mood and written out of a deep sense of patriotism in the middle of the war. It is also excellently composed, and genuinely symphonic despite its fashioning out of film music. The first movement excludes wind and brass in a long, powerful exordium for strings and timpani. There follow a lively *Presto*, somewhat in *Petrushka* vein, a beautifully sustained *Largo*, and a cheerfully optimistic finale. No doubt with some relief, the authorities gave it a Stalin Prize in 1946. Two years later came Zhdanov and rejection. Popov's later career never really recovered. He drank himself to death, eventually, in 1972. It is only just that there should be so much passion and conviction in these performances, by a conductor who has clearly taken great trouble to master this difficult music and convey his belief in it to his two orchestras.

Further listening ...

...Symphonic Suite No. 1[a]. Symphony No. 5 in A major, Op. 77, "Pastoral"[b]. [a]**Rimma Glushkova** (sop); [a]**Alexander Polyakov** (bar); [a]**Moscow Radio and Television Symphony Orchestra / Edvard Chivzhel;** [b]**USSR State Symphony Orchestra / ** [b]**Gurgen Karapetian.** Olympia OCD598 (8/97).

...Symphony No. 6, Op. 99, "Festive"[a]; Chamber Symphony in C major, Op. 2[b]. [a]**USSR Radio Symphony Orchestra / Eduard Chivzhel;** [b]**Moscow Chamber Ensemble / Alexander Korneyev.** Olympia OCD588 (7/96).

Richard Popplewell

Suggested listening ...
...Suite for Organ. Elegy. *Coupled with works by various composers.* **Jane Watts** (org).
Priory PRCD389 (10/97). *See review in the Collections section; refer to the Index.*

Constanza Porta

Italian c1529-1601

Suggested listening ...
...Missa Ducalis – Sanctus; Agnus Dei. *Coupled with works by various composers.*
Huelgas Ensemble / Paul van Nevel. Sony Classical Vivarte SK66261 (4/96).
See review in the Collections section; refer to the Index.

Cole Porter

American 1891-1964

Suggested listening ...
...Paris – Let's do it. Gay Divorce – Night and Day. Leave it to Me – My heart belongs to daddy.
Miss Otis Regrets. Nymph Errant – The Physician. *Coupled with works by* **Britten** Jill Gomez
(sop); **Martin Jones** (pf); **instrumental ensemble.** Unicorn-Kanchana DKPCD9138 (9/93).
Gramophone Editor's choice. See review under Britten; refer to the Index.   **Ⓖ**
...Blow, Gabriel, blow. Begin the Beguine. Ev'ry time we say goodbye. The tale of the oyster.
Coupled with works by various composers. **Samuel Ramey** (bar); **Warren Jones** (pf).
Sony Classical SK68339 (2/97). *See review in the Collections section; refer to the Index.*

Francis Poulenc

French 1899-1963

Poulenc Sinfonietta. Concert champêtre[a]. Pièce brève sur le nom d'Albert Roussel. Bucolique.
Fanfare. Deux Marches et un Intermède. Suite française. [a]**Pascal Rogé** (hpd);
French National Orchestra / Charles Dutoit. Decca Ⓕ 452 665-2DH (78 minutes: DDD: 3/97).
The *Concert champêtre* is a difficult work to bring off, and Poulenc himself is largely to blame: owing
to his unfamiliarity with the then little-known harpsichord he seriously miscalculated the balance,
employing far too large an orchestra, and his many hesitations and delays in completing the work
make themselves manifest in the bitty structure, with abrupt and inconsequential changes of pace in
the outer movements that few performances manage to make convincing. On record the concerto has
usually suffered from too puny a harpsichord sound, and even here the instrument could with
advantage have been more closely recorded to make its full effect; but this is the best version of the
work now available. Poulenc was equally dilatory in finishing the *Sinfonietta*. Though the work is
considerably more substantial than its title suggests, it does not outstay its welcome, at least in this
engaging reading, which Dutoit shapes with vitality and sensitive phrasing, though even he cannot
make the finale sound other than a patchwork. This is a vigorous and alert interpretation. The
pleasurably neat and characterful performances of the *Suite française* for wind, percussion and
harpsichord, based on themes by the sixteenth-century Claude Gervaise of the three-movement
musique de table for a banquet at the 1937 Exposition Universelle, and of the tributes for the sixtieth
birthday of Roussel and the seventy-fifth of his friend Marguerite Long add to the disc's attractions.
Additional recommendation ...
...Concert champêtre[a]. Concerto for Organ, Strings and Timpani in G minor[b]. *Coupled with*
Messiaen Turangalîla-symphonie[c]. [c]**Soloists;** [c]**Michel Béroff** (pf); [c]**Jeanne Loriod**
(ondes martenot); **Simon Preston** ([a]hpd/[b]org); **London Symphony Orchestra / André Previn.**
EMI Forte Ⓜ CZS5 69752-2 (two discs: 129 minutes: ADD: 8/97).

Poulenc Les Biches[a]. Bucolique[b]. Pastourelle[b]. Matelote provençale[b] (all from ASD4067, 9/81).
Les Mariés de la Tour Eiffel[c] – Discours; La baigneuse de Trouville. Suite française, d'après
Claude Gervaise[c] (all from ASD2450, 6/69). Les animaux modèles[d] (ASD2316, 7/67).
Sinfonietta[c]. Marches et un intermède[c] (both from ASD2450, 6/69). Concert champêtre[de].
Double Piano Concerto in D minor[df] (both from ASD517, 4/63). [e]**Aimée van de Wiele** (hpd);
[f]**Francis Poulenc,** [f]**Jacques Février** (pfs); [a]**Ambrosian Singers;** [ab]**Philharmonia Orchestra,**
[c]**Orchestre de Paris;** [d]**Paris Conservatoire Orchestra / Georges Prêtre.** EMI Rouge et Noir
Ⓜ CZS7 62690-2 (two discs: 156 minutes: ADD/DDD: 3/92). Recorded 1962-1980.
Now here's a bargain not to be missed – over two-and-a-half hours of Poulenc's inimitably frothy art
crammed on to just two CDs. The highlight has to be Georges Prêtre's marvellous 1980 recording of
the complete *Les Biches* ballet music: with the Philharmonia on sparkling form and a suitably lusty
contribution from the Ambrosian Singers, it makes for deliciously inconsequential entertainment.
This item, as well as a trio of shorter purely orchestral offerings (the graceful *Pastourelle*, cheeky
Matelote provençale and sublimely haunting *Bucolique: Hommage à Marguerite Long*), are captured
here in a stunningly vivid Abbey Road recording – unquestionably one of EMI's very finest early

digital efforts. In fact, Prêtre directs proceedings with no little flair throughout, though the robust response of the two Paris-based groups may come as something of a shock after the silky refinement of our own Philharmonia. Vintage accounts of the winsomely skittish *Concert champêtre* (with harpsichordist Aimée van de Wiele) and elegant Concerto for two pianos (featuring Jacques Février and the composer himself) are joined by lively readings of the engagingly anachronistic *Suite française*, *Sinfonietta* and the rarely-heard wartime ballet *Les Animaux modèles*. This last item suffers most from orchestral imprecision (and is rather dully engineered into the bargain), though the actual music is well worthy of further investigation: both outer tableaux ("Le petit jour" and "Le repos de midi") are supremely touching in their wistful nobility. In sum, an irresistible package.

Additional recommendation ...

...Sinfonietta. Aubade[a]. **Hahn** Le Bal de Béatrice d'Este – ballet suite. [a]**Julian Evans** (pf);
　New London Orchestra / Ronald Corp. Hyperion Ⓕ CDA66347 (64 minutes: DDD: 10/89).

Poulenc Piano Concerto[a]. Double Piano Concerto in D minor[b]. Organ Concerto in G minor[c].
　[ab]**Pascal Rogé,** [b]**Sylviane Deferne** (pfs); [c]**Peter Hurford** (org); **Philharmonia Orchestra /**
　Charles Dutoit. Decca Ⓕ 436 546-2DH (60 minutes: DDD: 12/93). Recorded 1992.　　　Ⓖ

The Piano Concerto has the right blend of melodic and textural richness, wit and warmth in the hands of performers who understand the music well enough to bring out all its felicitous detail without exaggeration. The mood of its expansive first movement is more tender than usual here, with its incisive wit and spiky Stravinskian instrumentation being correspondingly less in evidence. But the music can take this approach, and the climaxes are not underplayed, while the ecstatically chorale-like music towards the end of the movement is done to perfection. In the gentle *Andante con moto*, Rogé and Dutoit are in their element, but here again the powerful passages make their impact, while the romp of a finale has the right *joie de vivre*. The Double Piano Concerto comes over with great vivacity, with Deferne and Rogé (playing second piano) skilfully unanimous and crisply recorded. The Organ Concerto, recorded in St Alban's Cathedral, is also successful; Peter Hurford's mastery in Bach serves him well in its more darkly baroque aspects, but he is equally idiomatic in the uninhibitedly bouncy passages.

Additional recommendations ...

...Double Piano Concerto[a]. Sonata for Piano Duet. Capriccio. L'embarquement pour Cythère.
　Elégie. **Milhaud** Scaramouche. **Katia and Marielle Labèque** (pfs); [a]**Boston Symphony Orchestra /**
　Seiji Ozawa. Philips Ⓕ 426 284-2PH (50 minutes: DDD: 8/91).
...Organ Concerto. *Coupled with works by* **Guilmant** *and* **Widor** **Ian Tracey** (org);
　BBC Philharmonic Orchestra / Yan Pascal Tortelier. Chandos Ⓕ CHAN9271
　(80 minutes: DDD: 11/94). *See review under Guilmant; refer to the Index.*　　　　　ⒼⒼ
...Double Piano Concerto. **Saint-Saëns** Le carnaval des animaux.
　Güher and Süher Pekinel (pfs); **French Radio Philharmonic Orchestra / Marek Janowski.**
　Teldec Ⓜ 4509-97445-2 (38 minutes: DDD: 2/96).
...Double Piano Concerto[a]. Aubade[b]. Sinfonietta.
　[ab]**Jean Bernard Pommier,** [a]**Anne Queffélec** (pfs); **City of London Sinfonia / Richard Hickox.**
　Virgin Classics Ⓕ VC5 45028-2 (68 minutes: DDD: 9/96).
...Piano Concerto[a]. Concerto for Organ, Strings and Timpani[b]. Concert champêtre[c]. [a]**Jean Bernard**
　Pommier (pf); [b]**Gillian Weir** (org); [c]**Maggie Cole** (hpd); **City of London Sinfonia / Richard Hickox.**
　Virgin Classics Ⓕ VC5 45067-2 (69 minutes: DDD: 9/96).
...Organ Concerto. *Coupled with works by various composers.* **Marie-Claire Alain** (org).
　ORTF National Orchestra / Jean Martinon. Erato Ⓜ 0630-15343-2
　(five discs: 351 minutes: ADD/DDD: 1/97).

Poulenc Sextet for Piano and Wind Quintet[a].
Milhaud La création du monde[b].
Saint-Saëns Septet in E flat major, Op. 65[c]. [a]**Elizabeth Mann** (fl); [a]**Stephen Taylor** (ob);
　[a]**David Shifrin** (cl); [a]**Dennis Godburn** (bn); [a]**Richard Todd** (hn); [c]**Thomas Stevens** (tpt);
　[bc]**Ani Kavafian,** [bc]**Julie Rosenfeld** (vns); [bc]**Toby Hoffman** (va); [bc]**Carter Brey** (vc); [c]**Jack Kulowitsch**
　(db); **André Previn** (pf). RCA Victor Red Seal Ⓕ 09026 68181-2 (50 minutes: DDD: 11/95).
　Recorded 1993.

Predictably, one feels that Previn is the moving spirit behind these performances of three vivid French pieces for biggish chamber ensembles, and that it is especially his *joie de vivre* that informs Poulenc's sextet, where his charming solo at 2'13" in the first movement is just the first of many delights that help us to forget that its construction is not of the tightest. His colleagues also deserve every credit, and this crisply recorded account of the work is admirable, sparkling without glare. This version of Milhaud's ballet score, *La création du monde*, is a five-movement suite for piano plus string quartet that the composer made at his publisher's request. This is hard on its primitive elements, and indeed is no substitute for the original, but the performers offer all the vigour and sexiness that they can and it comes across well enough. After the uninhibited Poulenc and Milhaud, the programming of Saint-Saëns makes one fear a let-down in musical temperature, but the composer of the *Carnival of the Animals* had five years before already penned a jolly, witty and busy score in his Septet of 1881, whose scoring includes a trumpet and double-bass. This is another sparkling performance and rounds off an excellent, enterprising disc.

Additional recommendation ...
...Sextet[a]. Sonatas – Oboe[b]; Violin[d]; Clarinet[e]. Elégie[c]. [d]**Gérard Poulet** (vn); [e]**Pascal Moraguès** (cl); [abc]**Ivan Klánský**, [de]**Pascal Devoyon** (pfs); [a]**Prague Wind Quintet.**
Praga Digitals Ⓕ PRD250 109 (73 minutes: DDD: 4/98).

Poulenc Capriccio[c]. Sonata for Two Pianos[c]. Elégie[c]. Sonata for Piano Duet[c]. L'embarquement
pour Cythère[c]. Violin Sonata[a]. Elégie[b]. [a]**Chantal Juillet** (vn); [b]**André Cazalet** (hn); **Pascal Rogé,**
[c]**Jean-Philippe Collard** (pfs). Decca Ⓕ 443-968-2DH (70 minutes: DDD: 10/95).
Recorded 1989-1994.   Ⓖ Ⓖ
Few records could be more haunting or thought-provoking than this. For the lasting and predominant
impression is of how Poulenc's music is so frequently clouded by a sense of elegy, by an uneasy if
richly fruitful truce between levity and despair. The presence of two *Elégies*, and by implication, a
third, is therefore hardly insignificant. Yet how typical of Poulenc, given so sombre a setting, to ring
the changes with infinite elegance and poetry. The *Elégie* for horn and piano, composed in memory
of Dennis Brain's tragic death in 1957, sounds the darkest note, the *Elégie* for two pianos, on the other
hand, is intended to evoke the aroma of cognac and Gauloises, while the Violin and Piano Sonata's
central "Intermezzo" and "Presto tragico" luxuriantly and tersely recall the death of Federico Garcia
Lorca, murdered by Franco's minions in 1936 for his combined liberalism and homosexuality.
Elsewhere the light shines through. *L'embarquement pour Cythère* is classic Poulenc, mischievously
linking Watteau's painting of idealized love and the comforting world of seaside chips, accordions
and cheap perfume (both Watteau and Poulenc were frequent holiday visitors to Nogent-sur-Marne).
Here is witty and dazzling relief indeed. Both performances and recording are superb. Pascal Rogé,
who has the lion's share of the proceedings, could hardly sound more authentically Gallic, more
stylishly aware of the composer's tears and laughter. Jean-Philippe Collard, Chantal Juillet and André
Cazalet are distinguished partners.

Additional recommendations ...
...Violin Sonata. *Coupled with works by* **Fauré** and **Debussy** Isabelle van Keulen (vn);
Ronald Brautigam (pf). Koch Schwann Ⓕ 315272 (56 minutes: DDD: 10/95).
...Violin Sonata. *Coupled with works by* **Debussy** and **Ravel** Tasmin Little (vn); **Piers Lane** (pf).
EMI Eminence Ⓜ CD-EMX2244 (61 minutes: DDD: 12/95). *Gramophone Editor's choice.*   Ⓖ Ⓖ
...Violin Sonata. *Coupled with works by* **Debussy** and **Ravel** Cho-Liang Lin (vn);
Paul Crossley (pf). Sony Classical Ⓕ SK66839 (77 minutes: DDD: 7/96).
...Sonata for Two Pianos. Elégie. L'embarquement pour Cythère.
Coupled with works by **Bennett** and **Martinů** Jennifer Micallef, Glen Inanga (pfs).
Royal Over-Seas League Ⓕ CD2000 (60 minutes: DDD: 2/98).

Poulenc Les soirées de Nazelles. Deux Novelettes – No. 1 in C major; No. 2 in B flat minor.
Novelette "sur un thème de M de Falla". Pastourelle (arr. pf). Trois mouvements perpétuels.
Valse. 15 Improvisations – No. 1 in B minor; No. 2 in A flat major; No. 3 in B minor; No. 6 in
B flat major; No. 7 in C major; No. 8 in A minor; No. 12 in E flat major, "Hommage à
Schubert"; No. 13 in A minor; No. 15 in C minor, "Hommage à Edith Piaf". Trois Pièces.
Pascal Rogé (pf). Decca Ⓕ 417 438-2DH (67 minutes: DDD: 7/87). Recorded 1986.   Ⓖ Ⓖ
Gramophone Award Winner 1988. Selected by Sounds in Retrospect.
Poulenc Humoresque. Nocturnes. Suite in C major. Thème varié. 15 Improvisations – No. 4 in
A flat major; No. 5 in A minor; No. 9 in D major; No. 10 in F major, "Eloge des gammes";
No. 11 in G minor; No. 14 in D flat major. Two Intermezzos. Intermezzo in A flat major.
Villageoises. Presto in B flat major. **Pascal Rogé** (pf).
Decca Ⓕ 425 862-2DH (63 minutes: DDD: 4/91). Recorded 1989.   Ⓖ
These beautifully recorded and generously filled discs offer a rich diversity of Poulenc's output. On
the first disc, the masterly *Soirées de Nazelles* were improvised during the early 1930s at a country
house in Nazelles as a memento of convivial evenings spent together with friends. It paints a series of
charming portraits – elegant, witty and refined. The *Trois mouvements perpétuels* are, like so many of
the works represented here, lighthearted and brief, improvisatory in flavour and executed with a
rippling vitality. The *Improvisations* constantly offer up echoes of the piano concertos with their inf
ectious rhythmic drive – the "Hommage à Schubert" is a tartly classical miniature in three-time played
with just the right amount of nonchalant ease by Pascal Rogé. The "Hommage à Edith Piaf" is a
lyrical and touching tribute – obviously deeply felt. The *Humoresque* which opens the second recital
is open-air and open-hearted in style, yet songlike too in its melodic richness. The simplicity of this
music is deceptive, as is that of the warmly caressing C major Nocturne that follows, for both pieces
need subtle phrasing, rubato and the kind of textures only obtainable through the most refined use
of the sustaining pedal. Rogé has these skills, and he is also fortunate in having an excellent piano at
his disposal as well as a location (the Salle Wagram in Paris) that gives the sound the right amount of
reverberation. There are many delights in this music and the way it is played here: to mention just one,
listen to the masterly way that the composer and pianist together gradually bring around the flowing
freshness of the C major Nocturne towards the deeply poignant feeling of the close. Both discs hold
the listener's attention effortlessly from one piece to the next. They should especially delight, and to
some extent reassure, anyone who deplores the absence of charm and sheer romantic feeling in much
of our century's music.

Additional recommendations ...
...Suite in C major. Les Biches – Adagietto. Trois mouvements perpétuels. Les soirées de Nazelles.
  Intermezzo No. 3 in A flat major. Valse-improvisation sur le nom de Bach. Trois Pièces.
  Badinage. Napoli. **Eric Parkin** (pf). Chandos Ⓕ CHAN8637 (59 minutes: DDD: 10/88).
...Humoresque. Deux Novelettes. Novelette "sur un thème de M de Falla". Villageoises. 15
  Improvisations. Intermezzos – No. 1 in C major; No. 2 in D flat major. Suite française. Presto.
  Mélancolie. Thème varié. **Eric Parkin** (pf). Chandos Ⓕ CHAN8847 (72 minutes: DDD: 12/90).
...Trois Mouvements perpétuels. Trois Pièces. *Coupled with works by various composers*
  Marcelo Bratke (pf). Olympia Explorer Ⓜ OCD487 (62 minutes: DDD: 12/96).
  See review in the Collections section; refer to the Index.
...Nocturnes – No. 1 in C major; No. 5 in D minor; No. 6 in G major. Presto in B flat major.
  Improvisations – No. 10 in F major, Eloge des gammes; No. 12; No. 15. Intermezzo No. 2 in
  D flat major (1934). Trois mouvements perpétuels. *Coupled with works by* **Debussy** and **Satie**
  Kun Woo Paik (pf). Virgin Classics Ultraviolet Ⓜ CUV5 61327-2 (76 minutes: DDD: 2/97).
...Pastourelle. Toccata. *Coupled with works by various composers.* **Vladimir Horowitz** (pf).
  APR mono Ⓜ APR5517* (71 minutes: ADD: 5/98). *See review in the Collections section;
  refer to the Index.*

Poulenc Un soir de neige. Chansons françaises. Sept chansons. Chanson à boire. Petites voix.
  Figure humaine. **New London Chamber Choir / James Wood.** Hyperion Ⓕ CDA66798
  (67 minutes: DDD: 12/95). Texts and translations included. Recorded 1995.
Except for the charming miniature *Petites voix*, all the works here exist in recordings by The Sixteen,
whose performances have rightly been much praised. But the versatile James Wood and his choir have
never shrunk from challenges, and they give The Sixteen a good run for their money. Poulenc's
unaccompanied secular choral works, which demand virtuoso choirs, evidently hold no terrors for
them. The major work here is the wartime *Figure humaine*, whose finale, "Liberté", became an
inspiration to the Resistance movement. The choir at once impresses by the vividness with which it
treats words and by its intelligent verbal phrasing (though some vowels, especially nasal ones, are not
entirely native-sounding): it commands a wide dynamic range, thrilling at climaxes, with perceptive
tonal nuances; and the chording of the difficult chromaticisms is commendably assured. The most
characteristic movement of the cantata, "Toi ma patiente", is beautifully shaped, and the final
cadence of "En chantant" is perfectly 'placed', thanks to the bright-voiced sopranos. In faster-moving
pieces The Sixteen are rather neater, but the New London's accelerating passion in "Liberté"
is scarifying, and the final cry (complete with a blood-curdling top E) is overwhelming. The other
wartime work, *Un soir de neige*, is finely moulded throughout, with a movingly deep appreciation of
its mood of melancholy contemplation. These all illustrate Poulenc's serious side. In the earlier
Sept chansons there is a mixture of moods, which are well caught, though the nimble "Marie" could
have been better defined. There is energy and obvious enjoyment in the performance of the eight
folk-song arrangements, especially "Les tisserands", but also quiet pathos in "La belle se sied au pied
de la tour".
Additional recommendations ...
...Figure humaine. Quatre motets pour un temps de pénitence. Laudes de Saint Antoine de Padoue.
  Quatre motets pour le temps de Noël. Quatre petites prières de Saint François d'Assise.
  The Sixteen / Harry Christophers. Virgin Classics Ⓕ VC7 59192-2 (62 minutes: DDD: 3/90).
...Mass. Salve regina. Ave verum corpus. Exultate Deo. Un soir de neige. Chansons françaises.
  Chanson à boire. Sept Chansons. **The Sixteen / Harry Christophers.**
  Virgin Classics Ⓕ VC7 59311-2 (69 minutes: DDD: 12/93).

Poulenc Le Bestiaire ou Cortège d'Orphée. Cocardes. Trois Poèmes de Louise Lalanne.
  A sa guitare. Tel jour, telle nuit. Miroirs brûlants – Tu vois le feu du soir. Banalités.
  Métamorphoses. Voyage. Le Souris. La Dame de Monte-Carlo. **Felicity Lott** (sop);
  Graham Johnson (pf). Forlane Ⓕ UCD16730 (64 minutes: DDD: 8/94).
  Texts and translations included. Recorded 1994.
This programme of *mélodies* is perfectly chosen and balanced. Juxtaposing song cycles and single
numbers from the whole of Poulenc's career, putting them in chronological order, it highlights the
extreme modernity of Poulenc's choice of poetry with his universal appeal as a songwriter. *Le
Bestiaire* from 1918, to Apollinaire's verses, is his earliest substantial group and it is remarkable how
vivid and strong the Poulenc sound already was, when he was just 19. Of the three early Cocteau
settings, *Cocardes*, Poulenc said he wanted "the smell of French fried, the accordion, Piver perfume"
– once one has that in mind, both pianist and singer do splendidly, with lines such as "Lionoléum en
trompe-l'oeil. Merci. Cinéma, nouvelle muse". *Tel jour, telle nuit* was, of course, one of the great cycles
composed for Pierre Bernac but the brighter colours of Lott's voice make it more romantic than, for
instance, Souzay's interpretation. Graham Johnson as accompanist is the worthy successor to Dalton
Baldwin and the composer himself as the perfect interpreter of Poulenc's *mélodies*.
Additional recommendations ...
...Le bal masqué[a]. Le Bestiaire ou Cortège d'Orphée[a]. Trio for Oboe, Bassoon and Piano.
  Piano and Wind Sextet. [a]**Thomas Allen** (bar); **Nash Ensemble.**
  CRD CRD3437 Ⓕ (55 minutes: DDD: 10/86).

...La courte paille. Banalités – Hôtel; Voyage à Paris. Métamorphoses – C'est ainsi que tu es. Poèmes – Fêtes galantes. A sa guitare. *Coupled with works by various composers.* **Frederica von Stade** (mez); **Martin Katz** (pf).
RCA Victor Red Seal Ⓕ 09026 62711-2 (70 minutes: DDD: 4/95).
...Bleuet. Banalités – Hôtel; Voyage à Paris. Trois Métamorphoses.
Coupled with works by various composers. **Sylvia McNair** (sop); **Roger Vignoles** (pf).
Philips Ⓕ 446 656-2PH (61 minutes: DDD: 5/97).
...Trois Poèmes de Louise Lalanne. Montparnasse. La courte paille. Deux Poèmes (1943). Chansons pour enfants. La grenouillère. Le portrait. Bleuet. Airs chantés. Priez pour paix. Toréador. Fancy. **Dame Felicity Lott** (sop); **Pascal Rogé** (pf). Decca Ⓕ 458 859-2DH (63 minutes: DDD: 4/98).

Poulenc Le bal masqué[bcd]. Le bestiaire[bd]. Rapsodie nègre[bcd]. Cocardes[bd]. Trois mouvements perpétuels[c]. Le gendarme incompris[abd]. Quatre poèmes de Max Jacob[bd]. [a]**Dominique Visse** (alto); [b]**François Le Roux** (bar); [a]**Lambert Wilson** (narr); [c]**Pascal Rogé** (pf); [d]**Soloists of the French National Orchestra / Charles Dutoit.** Decca Ⓕ 452 666-2DH (76 minutes: DDD: 3/97).
Texts and translations included.

This is a disc that fans of the early *gamin* Poulenc will fall on with cries of joy. The biggest surprise is probably the four poems by Max Jacob, here recorded for the first time: it was thought that Poulenc had discarded them, but four years ago Milhaud's widow found the manuscript among the papers of her husband, who had conducted the first performance. The surprise is not this reappearance but Poulenc's musical language: while the second and fourth poems are set in his familiar frolicsome madcap style, the other two, largely atonal, reveal that in 1921 he had been toying with Schoenbergian ideas. The other near novelty (its first modern recording) is the "playlet interspersed with songs" *Le gendarme incompris*, a farce about a marquise cross-dressed as a priest who is arrested by a periphrastic gendarme and brought before an easily corruptible police chief. The whole piece is wildly hilarious (quite apart from the literary joke of cocking a snook at Mallarmé and Verlaine). On rather more familiar ground Le Roux, as usual, shines with his subtle sense of style – Poulenc insisted that even his most frivolous pieces should be treated *au grand sérieux* – and his exemplary enunciation. Pascal Rogé sparkles in the "Intermède" of the impudent *Bal masqué* (as does a solo violinist in its "Bagatelle"), performed with zest by all, and equally gambols in the "Ronde" of that *blague*, Poulenc's first work to be publicly performed, the *Rapsodie nègre* (here presented in its original 1917 version). On the other hand, the popular *Mouvements perpétuels* are given in a later instrumentation, possibly by another hand than Poulenc's own. Le Roux's versatility is again demonstrated in the circus/fairground atmosphere of the *Cocardes* and the epigrammatic *Bestiaire.* The excellent soloists from the French National Orchestra are recorded with great clarity; and James Harding, braving Jacob's and Cocteau's minefield of puns, Joycean wordplay and surrealist juxtapositions, provides spirited translations.

Poulenc Gloria. Stabat mater. **Janice Watson** (sop); **BBC Singers; BBC Philharmonic Orchestra / Yan Pascal Tortelier.** Chandos Ⓕ CHAN9341 (56 minutes: DDD: 8/95). Texts and translations included. Recorded 1994.

We are immediately struck, at the start of the *Gloria*, by the radiantly warm but clean orchestral sonority: only later does an uneasy suspicion arise that, apparently seduced by the sound, the recording engineers may be favouring it at the expense of the chorus, especially at orchestral *fortes* (this is more evident in the *Gloria* than the *Stabat mater*, for example at the burst of joy of "Domine Fili unigenite"). But it is committed and thoroughly secure choral singing, perhaps most easily appreciated in some of the unaccompanied passages – tender in the almost mystic "O quam tristis" and firm-toned at "Fac ut ardeat" (both in the *Stabat mater*); it gives real attack at "Quis est homo" (just holding its own against the orchestra); the sopranos can produce a bright, ringing tone; and only the very first line of the *Stabat mater*, lying low in the basses, needed to be a bit stronger (as in most performances). Janice Watson is a sweet-voiced soloist with very pure intonation; but she could with advantage have strengthened her consonants throughout. Tortelier gives intensely felt readings of both works – the murmurous ending of the *Stabat mater* and the thrilling *fortissimo* chords at "Quoniam" in the *Gloria* spring to mind – and fortunately he keeps the vocal "Domine Deus" entry moving at the same pace as at its introduction (a debatable moment in the Hickox version). He takes the Stravinskian "Laudamus te" fast and lightly; the only questionable speed is of "Quae moerebat", which sounds too cheerful for the words ("mourning and lamenting"). Taken all in all, these are performances of undoubted quality.

Additional recommendations ...
...Gloria[a]. Stabat mater[a]. Litanies à Vierge noire. [a]**Catherine Dubosc** (sop);
Westminster Singers; City of London Sinfonia / Richard Hickox.
Virgin Classics Ⓕ VC7 59286-2 (68 minutes: DDD: 2/93).
...Gloria. **Janáček** Glagolitic Mass. **Soloists; Westminster Choir;**
New York Philharmonic Orchestra / Leonard Bernstein.
Sony Classical Bernstein Royal Edition Ⓜ SMK47569 (65 minutes: ADD: 5/93).
...Gloria[a]. Stabat mater[a]. Litanies à la vierge noire[b]. [a]**Françoise Pollet** (sop); [a]**French Radio Choir;**
[b]**Maîtrise de Radio France; French National Orchestra / Charles Dutoit.**
Decca Ⓕ 448 139-2DH (62 minutes: DDD: 4/96).

Poulenc Mass in G major. Quatre motets pour le temps de Noël. Quatre petites prières de Saint François d'Assise. Quatre motets pour un temps de pénitence. Laudes de Saint Antoine de Padoue. Salve regina. Ave verum corpus. Exultate Deo. **Trinity College Choir, Cambridge / Richard Marlow.** Conifer Classics Ⓕ CDCF151 (70 minutes: DDD: 10/88). Texts and translations included. ⒼⒼ

The lusciously chromatic harmony of the Mass in G major can easily cloy but the bright, radiant textures of the singing of the Trinity College Choir avoids this entirely. Readers unfamiliar with this work will be surprised how potent it is. The *Ave verum corpus* for high high voices is quite exquisite and in the St Francis *Prières* Marlow is assured and musically aware. The choir does, however, produce occasional curious French pronunciation, with some very odd mute "e"s. An interesting personal sidelight on these graceful and expressive pieces for male voices is revealed by the dedication to Frère Jérome of Champfleury "in memory of his grandfather, my uncle Camille Poulenc". The interpretation of the Penitential Motets is very dramatic and the short motet *Salve regina* is graceful and serene. Caution needs to be taken not to listen to too many of these works – virtually entirely homophonic, and nearly all characterized by Poulenc's special brand of tartly sweet harmonies – one after the other. The performances, with fine balance, expressive dynamic shadings, pure intonation, intelligent phrasing and excellent enunciation, are very impressive. Marlow, of course, is operating on home ground, in the almost ideal acoustics of Trinity College Chapel in Cambridge. The accompanying notes are interesting and informative.

Additional recommendations ...
...Gloria[ab]. Salve regina. Ave verum corpus. Exultate Deo. Litanies à la Vierge Noire[b]. Quatre motets pour un temps de pénitence[c]. Quatre motets pour le temps de Noël. [a]**Donna Deam,** [c]**Mary Seers** (sops); **Cambridge Singers;** [b]**City of London Sinfonia / John Rutter.** Collegium Ⓕ COLCD108 (67 minutes: DDD: 10/88).
...Mass. Quatre petites prières. Salve regina. **Martin** Mass for double chorus. **Christ Church Cathedral Choir, Oxford / Stephen Darlington.** Nimbus Ⓕ NI5197 (59 minutes: DDD: 12/89).
...Mass. Salve regina. *Coupled with works by* **Fauré** Jonathon Bond (treb); **Choir of St John's College, Cambridge / George Guest.** Decca Ovation Ⓜ 430 360-2DM (74 minutes: ADD: 9/91).
...Mass in G major. Salve regina. Exultate Deo. Litanies à la vierge noire. *Coupled with works by* **Duruflé** and **Fauré** Soloists; **St John's College Choir, Cambridge; Academy of St Martin in the Fields / George Guest** with **Stephen Cleobury** (org). Double Decca Ⓜ 436 486-2DF2 (two discs: 149 minutes: ADD: 7/94). *See review under Duruflé; refer to the Index.* Ⓖ
...Exultate Deo. *Coupled with works by various composers.* **St Thomas Church Choir / Gerre Hancock.** Koch International Classics Ⓕ 37228-2 (53 minutes: DDD: 9/96).

Poulenc Mass in G major. Quatre motets pour un temps de pénitence. Quatre motets pour le temps de Noël. Exultate Deo. Salve regina. **Berlin RIAS Chamber Choir / Marcus Creed.** Harmonia Mundi Ⓕ HMC90 1588 (52 minutes: DDD: 8/96). Texts and translations included. ⒼⒼ

We seem to be in danger of becoming spoilt by the number of fine recordings of Poulenc's *a cappella* religious works; but this latest disc bids fair to go to the top of the list of contenders. There has never been a more beautiful performance of the *Salve regina*. And elsewhere this virtuoso choir display, beyond impeccably pure intonation and chording (chorus-masters everywhere will note with envy the sopranos' clean, dead-sure attacks on high notes), a sensitivity to verbal meaning, dynamics and vocal colour that argues not only skilful direction but a complete ease and absorption into the music's often chromatic nature by all the singers. They bring a bright-eyed tone to the *Exultate Deo*, awe to "O magnum mysterium" (in the Christmas motets), and a striking diversity of timbre to "Tristis est anima mea" (in the penitential motets); in the mass they interpret to perfection the *doucement joyeux* indication of the *Sanctus*. Like the Shaw Singers on Telarc, they appear to have been recorded in some large church, but without the problems of resonance occasionally found in that earlier issue: words are extremely clear throughout. (If one were to be ultra-critical, one might feel, in the Christmas motets, that words were being separated rather too much.) The excellent Westminster Cathedral disc contains the *Litanies à la vierge noire* and the *Petites prières* in addition to the same programme as here; but it has something of a preponderance of the treble voices, and here the use of women rather than boys results in a more sophisticated tone and a truer balance. A first-class disc.

Additional recommendations ...
...Mass[a]. Quatre motets pour le temps de Noël. Quatre motets pour un temps de pénitence. Quatre petites prières[b]. [a]**Donna Carter** (sop); [b]**Christopher Cock** (ten); **Robert Shaw Festival Singers / Robert Shaw.** Telarc Ⓕ CD80236 (52 minutes: DDD: 10/90).
...Mass[a]. Quatre petites prières. Quatre motets pour un temps de pénitence[b]. Quatre motets pour le temps de Noël. Salve regina. Exultate Deo. Litanies à la vierge noire[c]. [a]**Mark Kennedy,** [b]**Eamonn O'Dwyer** (trebs); **Westminster Cathedral Choir / James O'Donnell** with [c]**Ian Simcock** (org). Hyperion Ⓕ CDA66664 (70 minutes: DDD: 6/94).

Poulenc Dialogues des Carmelites. **Catherine Dubosc** (sop) Blanche de la Force; **Rachel Yakar** (sop) Madame Lidoine; **Rita Gorr** (mez) Madame de Croissy; **Brigitte Fournier** (sop) Soeur Constance; **Martine Dupuy** (mez) Mère Marie; **José van Dam** (bass-bar) Marquis de la

Force; **Jean-Luc Viala** (ten) Chevalier de la Force; **Michel Sénéchal** (ten) L'Aumônier;
François Le Roux (bar) Le geôlier; **Lyon Opéra Chorus and Orchestra / Kent Nagano.**
Virgin Classics Ⓕ VCD7 59227-2 (two discs: 152 minutes: DDD: 9/92). Notes, text and
translation included. *Gramophone Award Winner 1993.*   ⒼⒼ
Once more in a work out of the ordinary (following that given to them in 1990 for Prokofiev's *Love
for Three Oranges*) the dedication of Kent Nagano and his Opéra de Lyon forces resulted in the 1993
Gramophone Record Award for best opera recording. Poulenc's *chef d'oeuvre* is one of the few operas
written since *Wozzeck* that has survived in the repertory – and deservedly so. It is written from, and
goes to, the heart, not in any extrovert or openly histrionic way but by virtue of its ability to explore
the world of a troubled band of Carmelite nuns at the height of the terrors caused by the French
Revolution, and do so in an utterly individual manner. Poulenc unerringly enters into their psyches as
they face their fatal destiny. Nagano responds keenly to the sombre, elevated mood and intensity of
Poulenc's writing and unfailingly delineates the characters of the principals as they face their everyday
martyrdom. The magisterial authority of Martine Dupuy's Mère Marie, the agony of Rita Gorr's Old
Prioress, the inner torment of Catherine Dubosc's Sister Blanche, the restraint of Rachel Yakar's
Madame Lidoine, the eager charm of Brigitte Fournier's Sister Constance are only the leading players
in a distribution that is admirable in almost every respect. The score is for once given complete. The
recording is atmospheric and suggests stage action without exaggeration.

Poulenc La voix humaine[a].
Cocteau Le bel indifférent[b]. [a]**Denise Duval** (sop) La Femme; [b]**Edith Piaf** (spkr);
[a]**Paris Opéra-Comique Orchestra / Georges Prêtre**; [b]**instrumental ensemble.**
EMI L'Esprit Français Ⓜ CDM5 65156-2* (69 minutes: ADD: 10/94).
Item marked [a] from Vox OPL160 (8/63), recorded 1959, [b]recorded 1953, new to UK.
Auteuil 04 virgule 7 is on the line again. But one shouldn't make jokes. Poor woman, the situation is
real and dreadful, with Cocteau's script never betraying itself into the cheapness which lies waiting,
available at the drop of a word or a receiver, and with the music capturing mood, pace and
development in such sympathy with the text that one marvels both were not written by the same man.
It conjures up the image of her agonized one-sided conversation, over a maddeningly frustrating
telephone line, as a woman driven suicidal by her lover's desertion for another woman. Imagination,
of course, can do much on its own, as it certainly did with the original singer, Denise Duval, for whom
the role was written, whose performance, skilfully judged and varied, provides a genuine dramatic
experience. She is incomparably sure in her feeling for the idiom, and Prêtre, who conducted the
première, is a strong ally, never overindulgent in the sickly-sweet torments of memory and desire, but
keeping the piece moving and rightly tense. The recording took full advantage of the then recent
advent of stereo, so that the singer carries the telephone across from (perhaps) table to bed, in a way
that might now be found disconcerting or too self-conscious a feature of production. It is coupled
here with another Cocteau monologue-play, but this time in its original form. *Le bel indifférent* was a
tour de force for Edith Piaf, and the recording magnificently catches her in all her moods, sardonic,
murderous or tearful. EMI may be congratulated on the issue; not, however, on its presentation,
which is quite inadequate – no printed texts are given.

Poulenc Les mamelles de Tirésias[a]. **Denise Duval** (sop) Thérèse, Fortune-teller;
  Marguérite Legouhy (mez) Marchande de journaux, Grosse Dame; **Jean Giraudeau** (ten)
  Husband; **Emile Rousseau** (bar) Policeman; **Robert Jeantet** (bar) Director; **Julien Thirache** (bar)
  Presto; **Frédéric Leprin** (ten) Lacouf; **Serge Rallier** (ten) Journalist; **Jacques Hivert** (sngr) Son;
  Gilbert Jullia (sngr) Monsieur Barbu; **Chorus and Orchestra of the Opéra-Comique, Paris /
  André Cluytens.**
Poulenc Le bal masqué[b]. **Jean-Christoph Benoit** (bar); **Maryse Charpentier** (pf);
  Paris Conservatoire Orchestra / Georges Prêtre. EMI L'Esprit Français [a]mono/[b]stereo
  Ⓜ CDM5 65565-2* (70 minutes: ADD: 12/95). Item marked [a] from Columbia 33CX1218
  (2/55), recorded 1953, [b]HMV ASD2296 (1/67), recorded 1965.
Apollinaire's play, written in the 1900s, did not reach the stage until 1917. Poulenc was at the first
performance – which gave the word "sur-réaliste" to the language – but he did not compose the opera
until 25 years later, during the Second World War. *Les mamelles de Tirésias* is Poulenc's *Così fan tutte*;
the story is absurd, naïve, although the puns and rhymes of Apollinaire's poetry are a constant
delight. (Mostly untranslatable, Thérèse-française-fraises-Zanzibaraise, it goes on throughout the
piece.) What Poulenc has done is to express a whole range of deep emotion in the music, the
homesickness of the exile, the longing for children, the mystery of masculine/feminine desires. He
described the music as "producing laughter while still allowing tenderness and real lyricism". Poulenc
found his ideal interpreter in Denise Duval, who created the role of Thérèse in 1947, and went on to
sing it wherever the opera was given right up until the time of its first American (concert) performance
in 1960. Duval combines the "wild touch of vaudeville", as Ned Rorem put it, with her typically
forward, slightly nasal, French soprano. "The work that is dearest to me" was how Poulenc described
Mamelles at the time of this recording in 1953, and he judged Cluytens's conducting "sensational"
and wrote, "it is one of the greatest joys of my life". What can one add? It is one of the greatest
recordings of French opera, unchallenged and unsurpassed for 40 years. The filler, Poulenc's early
cantata *Le bal masqué* is an ephemeral work, but it is done with style and vigour by Jean-Christoph

Benoit and Prêtre. No libretto, nor even a synopsis, is included with this CD, which is a great shame, since the text is of such a complicated pattern. Highly recommended, nevertheless.

Further listening ...

...Cello Sonata. *Coupled with works by* **Chopin** and **Fauré** Pieter Wispelwey (vc);
Paolo Giacometti (pf). Channel Classics CCS10797 (3/98).

...Flute Sonata. *Coupled with works by various composers.* **Emmanuel Pahud** (fl); **Eric Le Sage** (pf).
EMI CDC5 56488-2 (3/98). *See review in the Collections section; refer to the Index.*

...Oboe Sonata. L'invitation au château. Villanelle^e. Sonata for Two Clarinets. Trio for Oboe,
Bassoon and Piano. Sextet for Piano and Wind Quintet. Clarinet and Bassoon Sonata. Rapsodie
nègre. Clarinet Sonata. Mouvements perpétuels. Flute Sonata. *Coupled with works by*
Ravel Various soloists. Cala CACD1018 (2/95).

...Oboe Sonata. Trio for Oboe, Bassoon and Piano. *Coupled with works by* **Britten**
Jean-François Duquesnoy (bn); **Emmanuel Strosser** (pf). Harmonia Mundi Les Nouveaux
Interprètes HMN91 1556 (2/96). *See review under Britten; refer to the Index.*   Ⓖ

...Banalités – Chanson d'Orkenise; Hôtel. La courte paille – Le carafon; La reine de coeur.
Chansons villageoises – Les gars qui vont à la fête. Deux poèmes de Louis Aragon.
Coupled with works by various composers. **John Wustman** (pf).
Decca 417 813-2DH (11/88). *See review in the Collections section; refer to the Index.*

...Les chemins de l'amour. *Coupled with works by various composers.*
Angela Gheorghiu (sop); **Malcolm Martineau** (pf).
Decca 458 360-2DH (5/98). *See review in the Collections section; refer to the Index.*

Roy Powell

20th century

Suggested listening ...

...Bow out. *Coupled with works by various composers.* **Apollo Saxophone Quartet; Roy Powell** (keybds).
Argo 443 903-2ZH (8/95). *See review in the Collections section; refer to the Index.*

Leonel Power

British c1370-1445

Power Ave regina. Gloria and Credo. Beata viscera. Sanctus. Agnus Dei. Salve regina. Mass Cycle:
Alma redemptoris mater. Ibo michi ad montem. Quam pulchra es. **Hilliard Ensemble**
(David James, Ashley Stafford, altos; Paul Elliott, Leigh Nixon, Rogers Covey-Crump, tens;
Paul Hillier, Michael George, basses). Virgin Classics Veritas Ⓜ VER5 61345-2 (53 minutes:
ADD: 10/97). Texts and translations included. From EMI CDM7 63064-2 (11/89).
Recorded 1980.

This is a very fine recording of works by John Dunstable's contemporary, Leonel Power. These are spontaneous readings, in tune perhaps with Power's more wayward personality. His occasional eccentricities include polyrhythms, and a more striking use of dissonance than Dunstable evinces. The disc boasts a real show-stopper in the rollicking five-voice *Gloria*, and a more subtle but equally rewarding find in the Mass, *Alma redemptoris mater*, thought by some to be the very first extant *cantus firmus* Mass. Marian pieces and a couple of settings from the Song of Songs complete a varied and invigorating programme. Since no other comparable recording has since appeared in Power's discography, this reissue is all the more welcome. The slightly dry ambience rarely detracts from the performances.

Further listening ...

...Gloria. *Coupled with works by various composers.* **Gothic Voices / Christopher Page.**
Hyperion Ⓕ CDA66783 (67 minutes: DDD: 1/96). *See review in the Collections section;
refer to the Index.*

Anthony Powers

British 1953

Suggested listening ...

...Trio. *Coupled with works by various composers.* **Mühlfeld Ensemble.**
Clarinet Classics CC0007 (10/94). *See review in the Collections section; refer to the Index.*

Michael Praetorius

German 1571-1621

Praetorius Lutheran Christmas Mass. **Roskilde Cathedral Boys' Choir and Congregation;
Gabrieli Consort; Gabrieli Players / Paul McCreesh.** Archiv Produktion Ⓕ 439 250-2AH
(79 minutes: DDD: 12/94). ✍ Text and translation included.   ⒼⒼ

The aesthetic of contrast, so central to early baroque spectacle (sacred or profane), is inspired here by the traditional part played by the congregation in Lutheran worship. Praetorius's music for the *figuraliter* (the vocal/instrumental choirs) is greatly influenced by fashionable Venetian techniques.

But what is striking is the way the old *alternatim* practices of the Protestant church blend so naturally with the intricate textures and scorings of a colourful Italian-style canvas, ranging from intimate dialogues to full grandiloquent sonority. What is more, the centrality of the chorale is never compromised. Despite all these ingredients, it is McCreesh's research and imagination that make this service such a powerful testament to the faith expressed by Lutherans of Praetorius's generation, and indeed by subsequent generations to which Bach was so indebted. The service follows, to all intents and purposes, the Mass of the Roman rite (sung with distinction by the Gabrieli Consort though the sopranos seem a little unsure in the *Kyrie*) interspersed with a versatile array of motets, hymns, prayers, intoned readings, a superbly conceived and suitably mysterious Pavan by Schein for the approach to Communion and several rhetorically positioned organ preludes. For a congregation, the Gabrieli Consort and players are joined by the boys of Roskilde Cathedral, Denmark and a some local amateur choirs. The effect is remarkable for its fervour in the hymns; now one can see why *Von Himmel hoch da komm ich her* inspired so many settings in the seventeenth century. Other familiar tunes include *Quem pastores, Wie schon leuchtet der Morgenstern* in a shimmering prelude by Scheidt followed by a delicately nuanced motet on the same tune. *In dulci jubilo* is treated to a flamboyant setting by Praetorius featuring six trumpets. The spacious acoustic of the cathedral exhibits McCreesh's acute timbral sense; definition is not ideally sharp but this is a small price to pay for a natural perspective which embraces the sense of community worship essential for this project.

Further listening ...
...Magnificat per omnes versus. Aus tiefer Not à 4. Der Tag vertreibt die finster Nacht.
  Venite exultemus Domino. Maria Magdalena. Peccavi fateor. Psalm 116.
  Huelgas Ensemble / Paul van Nevel. Sony Classical Vivarte SK48039.
...Magnificat Primi Toni. *Coupled with works by various composers.* **Kristian Olesen** (org).
  Priory PRCD444 (5/97).
...Terpsichore – excerpts. **New London Consort / Philip Pickett.**
  L'Oiseau-Lyre Florilegium 414 633-2OH (11/86).
...Terpsichore – Nine dances. Eulogodia Sionia – Resonet in laudibus. Polyhymnia caduceatrix –
  Erhalt uns Herr bei deinem Wort[a]. Musae Sioniae – Gott der Vater wohn uns bei[a]. Aus tiefer
  Not. Allein Gott in der Hoh sei Ehr. Christus der uns selig macht[a]. [a]**Boys' voices of St Alban's
  Cathedral and Abbey Church; Early Music Consort of London / David Munrow.**
  Virgin Veritas Edition VER5 61289-2 (9/96).
...Wachet auf, ruft uns die Stimme. Nun kommt der Heiden Heiland. In dulci jubilo. Vom Himmel
  hoch. Resonet in laudibus. Wie schön leuchtet der Morgenstern. Puer natus in Bethlehem.
  Trinity College Choir, Cambridge / Richard Marlow. Conifer Classics Ⓟ 75605 51256-2 (3/96).

Henry Prentes

British c1450-1514

Suggested listening ...
...Magnificat. *Coupled with works by* **Cornysh** *and* **Turges**
  The Cardinall's Musick / Andrew Carwood.
  ASV Gaudeamus CDGAU164 (9/97). *See review under Cornysh; refer to the Index.*

Simon Preston

British 1938

Suggested listening ...
...Vox Dicentis. *Coupled with works by various composers.* **Jane Watts** (org).
  Priory PRCD389 (10/97). *See review in the Collections section; refer to the Index.*

André Previn

German/American 1929

Suggested listening ...
...Sallie Chisum remembers Billy the Kid. Vocalise. *Coupled with works by various composers.*
  Barbara Bonney (sop); **Sato Knudsen** (vc); **André Previn** (pf).
  Decca 455 511-2DH (2/98). *See review in the Collections section; refer to the Index.*

Sergey Prokofiev

Russian/USSR 1891-1953

Prokofiev Symphony-Concerto (Sinfonia concertante) for Cello and Orchestra in E minor,
  Op. 125.
Tchaikovsky Variations on a Rococo Theme for Cello and Orchestra, Op. 33. Andante cantabile
  for Cello and Strings. **Yo-Yo Ma** (vc); **Pittsburgh Symphony Orchestra / Lorin Maazel.**
  Sony Classical Ⓟ SK48382 (68 minutes: DDD: 11/92).
The *Symphony-Concerto* – a reworking of Prokofiev's earlier Cello Concerto – states that "the title was prompted by the enhanced role of the orchestra which sounds at par in the ensemble with the solo

cello". It is sometimes called *Sinfonia concertante* (as it is on this disc). This revision, like that of the Fourth Symphony, has its detractors; those who feel Prokofiev's second (even third) thoughts were not necessarily an improvement. However, you are likely to come away from this performance less aware of patchwork and padding and more excited about what this music is capable of expressing. Take the last half of the finale: the theme rings out slowly and majestically on full brass, then, in an instant, confidence withers at the icy *sul ponticello* from orchestral cellos, and we are transported to the nursery accompanied by a funereal tread from timpani and basses. The solo cello rises from this to fix on the home key with a fast and furious ostinato while the brass intone an outline of the theme – menacing, like the *Dies Irae*. At the end we are left with the cello hanging on to his ostinato for grim life and a final peremptory chord from the orchestra – "grim life"? Yes, if the cello is any more forwardly placed the notion of a single voice at the mercy of ... well, at the mercy of whatever, is upset; and when this work was substantially recast, for Prokofiev (both body and soul) in his final years, times were pretty grim. It's tempting to say that Ma and Maazel emphasize the lyrical and elegiac elements at the expense of the dramatic and sardonic ones, but their reading is not that easily pigeon-holed. In the second movement there is a marvellous wit, fantasy and playfulness from Ma, and refined tone of great beauty for the *cantabile* at 3'13", without a doubt one of Prokofiev's loveliest melodies. Mindful of the work's dedicatee, Rostropovich's special authority in this work, Ma's is the version to be recommended as a basic library choice. Was there restricted session time for the *Rococo* Variations? The woodwind seem too loud for their *piano* markings in the fifth bar, and at 1'53" the oboist thinks there's no repeat of the second half of the theme. The slower woodwind refrain isn't too convincing, which prior to the second variation, draws attention to the fact that Ma and Maazel race off here 50 per cent faster (the marking is *tempo della thema*). Despite all of this, Ma lends his playing a blend of aristocratic finesse, caprice and elevated lyricism. The *Andante cantabile* is slow, almost a lullaby and quite hypnotic – even the silences soothe. As to the recording, quite apart from the truthful perspectives which allow the listener to perceive details of orchestration normally obscured, the soundstage has openness and coherence.

Additional recommendations ...
...Symphony-Concerto. **Borodin** Symphony No. 2 in B minor. **Mstislav Rostropovich** (vc);
   Leningrad Philharmonic Orchestra / Kurt Sanderling.
   Multisonic Russian Treasure Ⓜ 310188-2 (67 minutes: ADD).
...Symphony-Concerto. **Miaskovsky** Cello Concerto in C minor, Op. 66. **Mischa Maisky** (vc);
   Russian National Orchestra / Mikhail Pletnev.
   DG Ⓕ 449 821-2GH (70 minutes: DDD: 4/97). *Gramophone Editor's choice.*   Ⓖ
...Symphony-Concerto (also includes alternative finale). **Miaskovsky** Cello Concerto in C minor,
   Op. 66. **Truls Mørk** (vc); **City of Birmingham Symphony Orchestra / Paavo Järvi.**
   Virgin Classics Ⓕ VC5 45310-2 (two discs: 83 minutes: DDD: 5/98).
   See review under Miaskovsky; refer to the Index.   Ⓖ
...Symphony-Concerto[a]. Cello Concertino in G minor, Op. 132[b]. Cello Sonata in C major, Op. 119[c].
   Mstislav Rostropovich (vc); [c]**Sviatoslav Richter** (pf); [ab]**USSR State Symphony Orchestra /
   Gennadi Rozhdestvensky.** Revelation mono Ⓜ RV10102 (77 minutes: ADD: 6/98).

Prokofiev Piano Concertos – No. 1 in D flat major, Op. 10; No. 2 in G minor, Op. 16; No. 3 in
   C major, Op. 26; No. 4 in B flat major, Op. 53 (left-hand); No. 5 in G major, Op. 55.
   Vladimir Ashkenazy (pf); **London Symphony Orchestra / André Previn.** Decca Ⓜ 452 588-2DF2
   (two discs: 126 minutes: ADD: 3/90). From 15BB 218 (10/75). Recorded 1974-1975.   ⒼⒼ
While it's true that the Prokofiev piano concertos are an uneven body of work, there's enough imaginative fire and pianistic brilliance to hold the attention even in the weakest of them; the best, by common consent, Nos. 1, 3 and 4, have stood the test of time very well. As indeed have these Decca recordings. The set first appeared in 1975, but the sound is fresher than many contemporary digital issues, and Ashkenazy has rarely played better. Other pianists have matched his brilliance and energy in, say, the Third Concerto, but very few have kept up such a sure balance of fire and poetry. The astonishingly inflated bravura of the Second Concerto's opening movement is kept shapely and purposeful and even the out-of-tune piano doesn't spoil the effect too much. And the youthful First has the insouciance and zest its 22-year-old composer plainly intended. Newcomers to the concertos should start with No. 3: so many facets of Prokofiev's genius (including that wonderfully piquant lyricism) are here, and Ashkenazy shows how they all take their place as part of a kind of fantastic story. But there are rewards everywhere, and the effort involved in finding them is small. Why hesitate?

Additional recommendations ...
...Nos. 1, 2 and 4. **London Symphony Orchestra / André Previn** (pf).
   Decca Ovation Ⓜ 448 126-2DM (72 minutes: ADD).   ⒼⒼ
...Nos. 1, 3 and 4. **Kun Woo Paik** (pf); **Polish National Radio Symphony Orchestra / Antoni Wit.**
   Naxos Ⓢ 8 550566 (72 minutes: DDD: 11/92).   Ⓖ
...No. 1. Suggestion diabolique, Op. 4 No. 4. *Coupled with works by* **Tchaikovsky** and **Balakirev**
   Andrei Gavrilov (pf); **London Symphony Orchestra / Sir Simon Rattle.**
   EMI Studio Ⓜ CDM7 64329-2 (74 minutes: DDD: 11/92).   Ⓖ
...Nos. 2 and 5. **Kun Woo Paik** (pf); **Polish National Radio Symphony Orchestra / Antoni Wit.**
   Naxos Ⓢ 8 550565 (57 minutes: DDD: 11/92).

...Nos. 1-5. **Vladimir Krainev** (pf); **Frankfurt Radio Symphony Orchestra / Dmitri Kitaienko.**
Teldec Ⓕ 9031-73257-2 (two discs: 123 minutes: DDD: 7/93). ⒼⒼ
...No. 1. *Coupled with works by* **Glazunov** and **Rimsky-Korsakov** **Sviatoslav Richter** (pf).
Moscow Youth Orchestra / Kyrill Kondrashin.
Melodiya mono Ⓜ 74321 29468-2* (57 minutes: ADD: 6/96).
...Nos. 1-5. **Alexander Toradze** (pf); **Kirov Orchestra / Valery Gergiev.**
Philips Ⓕ 462 048-2PH2 (two discs: 134 minutes: DDD: 4/98).

Prokofiev Piano Concertos – No. 1 in D flat major, Op. 10; No. 3 in C major, Op. 26[a].
Evgeni Kissin (pf); **Berlin Philharmonic Orchestra / Claudio Abbado.** DG Ⓕ 439 898-2GH
(42 minutes: DDD: 12/94). Item marked [a] recorded live in 1993. Ⓖ
Kissin always seems to have time to acknowledge the implications of Prokofiev's harmony, to allow the left hand to converse with the right (always naturally, never tricksily), and to gauge the relationship of his part to the orchestra. He is also scrupulous with dynamics. At the first entry in the C major Concerto he manages, as few pianists do, the *piano* contrast after the first three notes without losing soloistic presence. And he resists the temptation to shout out *forte* passages, so that Prokofiev's *fortissimos* stand in proper relief, as do his carefully placed accents (hear the opening theme of the same concerto's finale). Perhaps none of that strikes you as exceptional, but it is so in Prokofiev, where the sheer athletic demands are extreme and refinement seems like too much to ask. With a technique like his and an orchestra as responsive as the Berlin Philharmonic there are just a few places in the C major Concerto, such as the final pages, where Kissin might have allowed himself to be a bit more carried away. But there is no shortage of exhilaration in the youthful D flat Concerto, which is a model blend of attack, wit, poetry and drive. In fact there is little discernible difference between this studio recording and the live C major, either in accuracy or in excitement. It would be wrong to say that Kissin surpasses Ashkenazy (reviewed above), whose performances of all five concertos on a two-disc, mid-price Decca set still sound breathtakingly vivid. Bronfman on Sony Classical is virtually a match for him and offers the Fifth Concerto in addition. But DG's recording is clearer than the 20-year-old Decca set, and Abbado and the Berliners are far superior to Mehta and the Israel Philharmonic. Full price for 42 minutes of music may seem a bit steep; but what Kissin and Abbado have to offer is certainly in the luxury class.

Additional recommendations ...
...Nos. 1, 4 and 5. **Boris Berman** (pf); **Royal Concertgebouw Orchestra / Neeme Järvi.**
Chandos Ⓕ CHAN8791 (64 minutes: DDD: 10/90).
...No. 3[a]. Visions fugitives, Op. 22 – Nos. 3, 5, 6, 9-11 and 16-18. Suggestion diaboloque, Op. 4
No. 4. Tales of an old grandmother, Op. 31 – Nos. 2 and 3. Three Pieces, Op. 59 – Nos. 2 and 3.
Gavotte. Piano Piece, Op. 52 No. 3. Sonata No. 4 in C minor, Op. 29 – Andante. Four Pieces,
Op. 32 – No. 3. **Sergey Prokofiev** (pf); [a]**London Symphony Orchestra / Piero Coppola.**
Pearl Ⓕ GEMMCD9470* (57 minutes: ADD: 11/91).
...Nos. 1 and 3. Piano Sonata No. 7 in B flat major, Op. 83. **Mari Kodama** (pf);
Philharmonia Orchestra / Kent Nagano. ASV Ⓕ CDDCA786 (64 minutes: DDD: 4/92).
...Nos. 1, 3 and 5. **Yefim Bronfman** (pf); **Israel Philharmonic Orchestra / Zubin Mehta.**
Sony Classical Ⓕ SK52483 (66 minutes: DDD: 12/93). Ⓖ
...No. 3[a]. Violin Concerto No. 1 in D major, Op. 19[b]. Lieutenant Kijé – Suite, Op. 60[b].
[a]**Martha Argerich** (pf); [b]**Shlomo Mintz** (vn); [a]**Berlin Philharmonic Orchestra;**
[b]**Chicago Symphony Orchestra / Claudio Abbado.**
DG Classikon Ⓑ 439 413-2GCL (69 minutes: ADD/DDD: 1/94). ⒼⒼ
...No. 3[b]. Visions fugitives, Op. 22[c] Nos. 3, 5, 6, 9-11 and 16-18. Suggestion diabolique, Op. 4
No. 4[d]. Symphony No. 1 in D major, Op. 25, "Classical" – Gavotte[e]. Piano Sonata No. 4 in
C minor, Op. 29 – Andante assai[f]. Gavotte, Op. 32 No. 3[f]. **Glazunov** The Seasons[a].
[bcdef]**Sergey Prokofiev** (pf); [a]**orchestra / Alexander Glazunov;** [b]**London Symphony Orchestra /
Piero Coppola.** EMI Composers in Person mono Ⓕ CDC5 55223-2* (79 minutes: ADD: 5/95). Ⓖ

Prokofiev Piano Concertos[a] – No. 2 in G minor, Op. 16; No. 4 in B flat major, Op. 53 (left-hand).
Overture on Hebrew Themes in C minor, Op. 34[b]. **Yefim Bronfman** (pf); [b]**Giora Feidman** (cl);
[b]**Juilliard Quartet** (Robert Mann, Joel Smirnoff, vns; Samuel Rhodes, va; Joel Krosnick, vc);
[a]**Israel Philharmonic Orchestra / Zubin Mehta.** Sony Classical Ⓕ SK58966
(65 minutes: DDD: 5/95). Recorded 1993-1994. *Gramophone Editor's choice.* ⒼⒼ
Bronfman's technical facility makes light of the Second Concerto's massive first movement cadenza, and when the Israeli brass break through at 9'45" – all brawn and thunder – the effect is quite overwhelming. The *Scherzo* is neat and mechanized, the *Intermezzo*'s initial 'fee-fi-fo-fum' brisk but grimly intimidating, while the long, dizzyingly eventful finale is effectively held in check. As to the Fourth (left-hand) Concerto, this is, perhaps, the work's finest recording to date. The first movement has an appropriately cool demeanour, with nimble pianism and precise orchestral support. Then there is the *Andante*, one of Prokofiev's most introspective narratives, here given with just the right balance of mobility and restraint. The *Moderato*, too, has great charisma, its quick-fire mood changes (from menace to laughter, and back again) inspiring from these players a combination of energy, poise and finesse. It is a beautifully recorded, trim, dapper and above all stylish account of Prokofiev's most underrated concerto. As if that were not enough, Sony throw in an extraordinary rendition of the

tangy *Overture on Hebrew Themes*, where the Juilliard Quartet mimic and humour Giora Feidman's saucy, Klezmer-style clarinet playing, an authentic flashback to old-time Yiddish theatre or street song: caustic, lovable and primary-coloured in the manner of Chagall. It makes a wonderful encore.
Additional recommendation ...
...No. 4. *Coupled with works by* **Britten** and **Ravel** Leon Fleisher (pf); **Boston Symphony Orchestra / Seiji Ozawa.** Sony Classical Ⓕ SK47188 (68 minutes: DDD: 4/93).

Prokofiev Piano Concerto No. 3 in C major, Op. 26[a].
Ravel Piano Concerto in G major[a]. Gaspard de la nuit[b]. **Martha Argerich** (pf); [a]**Berlin Philharmonic Orchestra / Claudio Abbado.** DG The Originals Ⓜ 447 438-2GOR (71 minutes: ADD: 12/95).
  Items marked [a] from SLPM139349 (2/68), recorded 1967, [b]2530 540 (8/75), recorded 1974.
There have been others to match the bustle and brilliance of Argerich's Prokofiev, her coloristic range, her drive, her flashiness, her straining at the leash; but none who has so satisfyingly combined all those qualities, who has given us such a rocket-launched recapitulation in the first movement, such circus-routine vividness in the following variations, or such monstrous, hyperbolic fairy-tale imagery in the finale, and all done with the most engaging reckless abandon. The Ravel Concerto is another bundle of energy. Yet how miraculous is the blend and interplay of piano and orchestra, and how ecstatically Argerich weaves around the cor anglais restatement in the slow movement. *Embarras de richesses* indeed: Argerich's *Gaspard* is a version of Ravel's devilish triptych which is unusually faithful to his subdued dynamic markings, quite apart from its breathtaking agility. The results ring poetically true at the same time as defying criticism in pianistic terms.
Additional recommendations ...
...Nos. 3[a] and 5[a]. Autumnal, Op. 8[b]. Overture on Hebrew Themes, Op. 34[c]. [c]**Keith Puddy** (cl); [c]**Gabrieli Quartet; London Symphony Orchestra /** [a]**André Previn,** [b]**Vladimir Ashkenazy** ([ac]pf). Decca Ovation Ⓜ 448 127-2DM (72 minutes: ADD).
...No. 3. **Schumann** Piano Concerto in A minor, Op. 54.
  Van Cliburn (pf); **Chicago Symphony Orchestra /** [a]**Walter Hendl,** [b]**Fritz Reiner.** RCA Victor Living Stereo 09026 62691-2 (61 minutes: ADD: 8/96).

Prokofiev Piano Concerto No. 5 in G major, Op. 55[a].
Rachmaninov Piano Concerto No. 2 in C minor, Op. 18[b]. **Sviatoslav Richter** (pf); **Warsaw Philharmonic Orchestra /** [a]**Witold Rowicki,** [b]**Stanislaw Wislocki.** DG Ⓕ 415 119-2GH* (58 minutes: ADD: 6/85). Item marked [a] from 138075 (3/60), [b] 138076 (1/60). Recorded 1959. ⒼⒼⒼ
Prokofiev was to find no more dedicated an advocate for his keyboard works than Richter. So how good that this artist's now legendary account of the Fifth Piano Concerto has been granted a new lease of life on CD. Although it has never enjoyed the popularity of Prokofiev's Nos. 1 and 3, here, however, attention is riveted from first note to last. Richter delights in the music's rhythmic vitality and bite, its melodic and harmonic unpredictability. Both piano and orchestra are so clearly and vividly reproduced that it is difficult to believe that the recording is 35 years old. Though betraying its age slightly more, notably in the sound of the keyboard itself, Rachmaninov's No. 2 is no less gripping. Not all of Richter's tempos conform to the score's suggested metronome markings, but his intensity is rivalled only by his breathtaking virtuosity. Never could the work's opening theme sound more laden, more deeply and darkly Russian.

Prokofiev Violin Concertos[a] – No. 1 in D major, Op. 19; No. 2 in G minor, Op. 63. Solo Violin Sonata in D major, Op. 115. **Gil Shaham** (vn); [a]**London Symphony Orchestra / André Previn.** DG Ⓕ 447 758-2GH (60 minutes: DDD: 6/96). *Gramophone Editor's choice.* Ⓖ
Rarely, if ever, have there been performances where soloist, orchestra and conductor connect with such unerring intuition, where the music is treated so naturally. Previn ushers in the First Concerto's crystalline opening with gentle intensity, raising the curtain for Gil Shaham's warmly tended first entry. Both make great play with the march theme that follows. The effect is like spicy gossip shared between friends while the *Scherzo* is equally rich in dialogue. Shaham's tone is at its most expressive at the beginning of the third movement, and at its most delicate just prior to the last big climax. This natural exegesis extends to the darker Second Concerto, even where Shaham or Previn linger about a particular phrase. The recording, too, is extremely impressive, with well defined string lines and a fine body of winds, brass and percussion (the all-important bass drum especially). Note how, beyond the raucous happenings of the second movement's central episode, the violins waft back with the principal theme (at 6'56"). Similar felicities occur regularly throughout both concertos, while the Second's finale – a riotous, slightly tongue-in-cheek *danse macabre* – is here sensibly paced and very well articulated. And as if all that weren't enough, Shaham treats us to a substantial encore in the lively Solo Sonata that Prokofiev intended to be performed in unison by a group of young players.
Additional recommendations ...
...Nos. 1 and 2. Itzhak Perlman (vn); **BBC Symphony Orchestra / Gennadi Rozhdestvensky.** EMI Ⓕ CDC7 47025-2 (DDD: 9/84).
...No. 2. **Shostakovich** Violin Concerto No. 1 in A minor, Op. 99.
  Viktoria Mullova (vn); **Royal Philharmonic Orchestra / André Previn.** Philips Ⓕ 422 364-2PH (60 minutes: DDD: 6/89). ⒼⒼ

...Nos. 1 and 2. **Stravinsky** Violin Concerto in D major.
Kyung-Wha Chung (vn); **London Symphony Orchestra / André Previn.**
Decca Ovation Ⓜ 425 003-2DM (72 minutes: ADD: 7/90). Ⓖ
...No. 1ª. Violin Sonata No. 1 in F minor, Op. 80ᵇ. Five Melodies, Op. 35ᵇ.
David Oistrakh (vn); ᵇ**Frida Bauer** (pf); ª**Moscow Philharmonic Orchestra / Yuri Temirkanov.**
Praga Ⓕ PR250 041 (61 minutes: ADD: 9/93).
...No. 1ª. Piano Concerto No. 3 in C major, Op. 26ᵇ. ª**Shlomo Mintz** (vn); ᵇ**Martha Argerich** (pf);
ª**Chicago Symphony Orchestra;** ᵇ**Berlin Philharmonic Orchestra / Claudio Abbado.**
DG Classikon Ⓑ 439 413-2GCL (69 minutes: ADD/DDD: 1/94). ⒼⒼ
...Nos. 1 and 2ª. The Love for Three Oranges – Les ridicules; Scène infernale; Marche; Scherzo; Le
Prince et la Princesse; La fruite. ª**Joshua Bell** (vn); **Montreal Symphony Orchestra / Charles
Dutoit.** Decca Ⓕ 440 331-2DH (65 minutes: DDD: 1/94).
...No. 1. **Shostakovich** Violin Concerto No. 1 in A minor, Op. 99. **Maxim Vengerov** (vn); **London
Symphony Orchestra / Mstislav Rostropovich.** Teldec Ⓕ 4509-92256-2 (62 minutes: DDD: 2/95).
Includes bonus sampler disc. *Gramophone Award Winner 1995.*
Gramophone Editor's choice. See review under Shostakovich; refer to the Index. ⒼⒼⒼ
...Nos. 1 and 2. **Stravinsky** Violin Concerto in D major.
Cho-Liang Lin (vn); **Los Angeles Philharmonic Orchestra / Esa-Pekka Salonen.**
Sony Classical Ⓕ SK53969 (70 minutes: DDD: 3/95). Ⓖ
...No. 1. **Tchaikovsky** Violin Concerto in D major, Op. 35. **Julian Rachlin** (vn); **Moscow Radio
Symphony Orchestra / Vladimir Fedoseyev.** Sony Classical Ⓕ SK66567 (58 minutes: DDD: 8/95).
...No. 2. *Coupled with works by various composers.* **Jascha Heifetz** (vn); **Boston Symphony
Orchestra / Serge Koussevitzky.**
Pearl Ⓜ GEMMCDS9167* (two discs: 157 minutes: ADD: 11/95).
...No. 2. **Shostakovich** Violin Concerto No. 1 in A minor, Op. 99. **Vadim Repin** (vn);
Hallé Orchestra / Kent Nagano. Erato Ⓕ 0630-10696-2 (59 minutes: DDD: 1/96).
See review under Shostakovich; refer to the Index.
...Nos. 1ª and 2ª. Solo Violin Sonata in D major, Op. 115. **Tedi Papavrami** (vn); ª**Polish National
Radio Symphony Orchestra / Antoni Wit.** Naxos Ⓢ 8 553494 (62 minutes: DDD: 5/97).
...No. 2. **Stravinsky** Violin Concerto in D major. **Itzhak Perlman** (vn); **Chicago Symphony
Orchestra / Daniel Barenboim.** Teldec Ⓕ 4509-98255-2 (46 minutes: DDD: 7/97).
...No. 1. *Coupled with works by* **Glazunov** and **Shchedrin**
Anne-Sophie Mutter (vn); **National Symphony Orchestra, Washington / Mstislav Rostropovich.**
Erato Ⓜ 0630-17722-2 (64 minutes: DDD: 9/97).
...No. 2. **Shostakovich** Violin Concerto No. 2 in C sharp minor, Op. 129. **Maxim Vengerov** (vn);
London Symphony Orchestra / Mstislav Rostropovich. Teldec Ⓕ 0630-13150-2
(62 minutes: DDD: A/97). *See review under Shostakovich; refer to the Index.*
...Nos. 1ª and 2ᵇ. Solo Violin Sonata in D major, Op. 115. Sonata for Two Violins in C major,
Op. 56. Violin Sonatas Nos. 1 and 2ᶜ. The Love for Three Oranges – March (trans. Heifetz)ᶜ.
Five Melodies, Op. 35bᶜ. **Frank Peter Zimmermann** (vn); ᶜ**Alexander Lonquich** (pf);
ª**Berlin Philharmonic Orchestra / Lorin Maazel;** ᵇ**Philharmonia Orchestra / Mariss Jansons.**
EMI Ⓜ CMS5 66605-2 (two discs: 144 minutes: DDD: 1/98).

Prokofiev Peter and the wolf, Op. 67ª. Symphony No. 1 in D major, Op. 25, "Classical". March in
B flat minor, Op. 99. Overture on Hebrew Themes, Op. 34*bis*ᵇ. ª**Sting** (narr); ᵇ**Stefan Vladar** (pf);
Chamber Orchestra of Europe / Claudio Abbado. DG Ⓕ 429 396-2GH (50 minutes: DDD: 4/91).
Recorded 1986-1990. Ⓖ
Abbado and the multi-talented Sting offer a lively and beautifully crafted account of Prokofiev's ever
popular *Peter and the wolf.* Any fears that the original freshness of Prokofiev's creation may be lost
in favour of a less formal approach are soon dispelled – Sting is an effective and intelligent storyteller
capable of capturing the imagination of adults and children alike, and there is never a feeling of
contrivance or mere gimmickry. The orchestral playing is a real delight too; sharply characterized and
performed with great affection. The *Overture on Hebrew Themes* is more commonly heard in its drier,
more acerbic version for clarinet, piano and string quartet, but makes a welcome and refreshing
appearance on this disc in Prokofiev's own arrangement for small orchestra. Abbado's elegant and
graceful reading of the *Classical* Symphony is one of the finest in the catalogue, and is particularly
notable for its beautifully shaped phrasing, clarity of inner detail and crisp articulation.
Additional recommendations ...
...Peter and the wolf. *Coupled with works by* **Britten** **Royal Philharmonic Orchestra / André Previn**
(narr). Telarc Ⓕ CD80126 (55 minutes: DDD: 10/87).
...Peter and the wolfª. Symphony No. 1 in D major, Op. 25, "Classical"ᵇ. Lieutenant Kijé-Suite,
Op. 60ᶜ. The Love for Three Oranges – Suiteᵈ. ª**Sir Ralph Richardson** (narr);
ᵇ**London Symphony Orchestra / Sir Malcolm Sargent;** ᶜ**Paris Conservatoire Orchestra /
Sir Adrian Boult;** ᵈ**London Philharmonic Orchestra / Walter Weller**
Decca Headline Classics Ⓑ 433 612-2DSP (76 minutes: ADD: 1/92).
...Peter and the wolf. *Coupled with works by* **Bizet** and **Saint-Saëns** ᶠ**Sir John Gielgud** (narr);
Royal Philharmonic Orchestra / Andrea Licata. Tring International Royal Philharmonic
Collection Ⓢ TRP046 (69 minutes: DDD: 11/95).

Prokofiev Peter and the Wolf, Op. 67[a].
Debussy La boîte à joujoux. [a]**Patrick Stewart** (narr); **Orchestra of Opéra de Lyon / Kent Nagano.**
Erato Ⓕ 4509-97418-2 (61 minutes: DDD: 8/95). Text included.
Choosing the 'right' *Peter and the Wolf* is particularly difficult in that the versions that most please young children tend to drive parents mad, while the more urbane productions can challenge a child's concentration span. *Star Trek* veteran Patrick Stewart manages to straddle the borders with a narration that is both involving and restrained, an intimate yet lively reading, beautifully integrated into the orchestral score – which is itself superbly played by the Orchestra of Opéra de Lyon. Kent Nagano's roster of insights is far too substantial to itemize individually, so suffice to say that anyone in search of a stylishly tailored, tastefully phrased account is unlikely to complain. The recording, too, is exceptionally well balanced, albeit in the slightly cavernous acoustic of the Opéra de Lyon; whereas the location chosen for *La boîte à joujoux* – Lyon's Auditorium Maurice Ravel – is near ideal. This, too, is a performance of rare refinement and poise – a keenly inflected, tender and texturally luminous reading, with graphic characterization and phrasing that suggests lightning reflexes all round. However, as each of the four movements is positively crammed with dramatic incident, anyone interested in following the storyline will need some sort of synopsis – either as prescribed by the composer (if such a thing exists) or as imagined by a skilful annotator. Regrettably, all Erato give us is the bare text for *Peter and the Wolf*, plus essential recording details. There are no notes on Prokofiev's music and absolutely nothing whatsoever about the Debussy. This is ridiculous, especially as the disc is aimed primarily at youngsters. After all, here was a golden opportunity to realize, via tracking or indexing, the power of words in relation to music. Kent Nagano's conducting is superb, the recordings are generally excellent, Patrick Stewart tells a mean tale – it's just a shame that Erato's presentation is inadequate.

Prokofiev Cinderella, Op. 87. Summer Night – Suite, Op. 123. **Russian National Orchestra /**
Mikhail Pletnev. DG Ⓕ 445 830-2GH2 (two discs: 138 minutes: DDD: 6/95).
Gramophone Editor's record of the month.   Ⓖ Ⓖ
This is an outstanding release. If Pletnev launches *Summer Night* somewhat brusquely, what follows is beyond reproach. Most striking of all is the radical clarity of texture which makes Prokofiev's modest suite seem at once unprecedentedly modern and that much more shrewdly realized in terms of colour. The score was extrapolated from the opera *The Duenna* (or *Betrothal in a Monastery*) in 1950 and its neglect, as Pletnev shows, is unaccountable. It is curious that a ballet as familiar as *Cinderella* should be so seldom heard in its entirety. Like *Romeo and Juliet*, *Cinderella* gives an impression of immense assurance, belying the obvious hazards of cultural production under Stalin. It is strong without being daring, colourful without being extravagant, and once again exhibits an emotional involvement often hidden in the past. This sounds reassuringly Tchaikovskian and yet there is also something pale and elusive in its make-up, perhaps designed to reflect the character of its main protagonist. The motif of Cinderella repressed, first heard at the very start of the ballet, is given a heavy tread, the orchestra dragging their metaphorical feet to intensify the pensive mood. As for the second motto theme, anticipating her eventual happiness with her dream prince, it is not so much broad and impassioned as achingly beautiful. Nor is the conducting without humour. The sisters' "dancing lesson" has never been more vividly evoked, their unruly behaviour and slow learning curve precisely delineated in the truculent attack of the two solo violins. "The Prince's first galop" (thrice he rushes off impetuously in search of his beloved) is as light as a feather, executed with matchless finesse by the Russian strings. The sound is good, the orchestral playing superb.
Additional recommendations ...
...Cinderella[a]. Symphony No. 1 in D major, Op. 25, "Classical"[b]. **London Symphony Orchestra /**
André Previn. EMI Forte Ⓜ CZS5 68604-2 (two discs: 127 minutes: [a]DDD/[b]ADD: 7/96).
...Pieces from Cinderella – Gavotte, Op. 95 No. 2; Oriental dance, Op. 97 No. 6; Grand waltz,
Op. 107 No. 1. *Coupled with works by various composers.* **Arcadi Volodos** (pf).
Sony Classical Ⓕ SK62691 (61 minutes: DDD: 10/97). *Gramophone Editor's choice.*
See review in the Collections section; refer to the Index.

Prokofiev Romeo and Juliet, Op. 64 – Suites Nos. 1-3: excerpts. Chout, Op. 21 – ballet suite.
London Symphony Orchestra / Claudio Abbado. Decca Ovation Ⓜ 425 027-2DM
(54 minutes: ADD: 6/91). From SXL6286 (5/67). Recorded 1966.   Ⓖ
It was an excellent idea to couple nine items from the familiar *Romeo and Juliet* ballet score with a similar sequence from the unjustly neglected *Chout* – the blackly comic tale of a village trickster, the Buffoon of the alternative title. *Romeo and Juliet* is more popular than ever these days, but Abbado's mid-1960s selection – less predictable than most – retains its freshness and appeal; only his sluggish *Dance of the girls with lilies* lacks something in charm. The sound is pretty good, the brass very immediate. While *Chout* has that rather sadistic plot – and the audiences of 1921 had ultra-modern cubist sets, costumes and choreography to object to – its neglect seems unaccountable today, given the quality of the music. Here, Prokofiev was clearly inspired by Stravinsky's *Petrushka*. Even if there remains some loosely-written connective tissue, there is also a fund of melodic invention that could only have come from the younger man. The orchestration glitters throughout, sharp-edged and totally distinctive. Decca's analogue recording remains impressive with clearly defined scintillating textures.

Additional recommendations ...

...Romeo and Juliet – excerpts. **Phiharmonia Orchestra / Claus Peter Flor.**
RCA Victor Red Seal Ⓕ 09026 61388-2 (58 minutes: DDD: 10/93).
...Romeo and Juliet – excerpts. **Royal Liverpool Philharmonic Orchestra / Libor Pešek.**
Virgin Classics Ⓕ VC7 59278-2 (71 minutes: DDD: 10/93). *Gramophone Editor's choice.*
...Romeo and Juliet[b]. **Rimsky-Korsakov** Scheherazade, Op. 35[a].
[a]**Berlin Radio Symphony Orchestra,** [b]**Leipzig Gewandhaus Orchestra / Karel Ančerl.**
Tahra mono Ⓕ TAH119* (68 minutes: DDD: 11/95).
...Romeo and Juliet – Suite No. 2. *Coupled with works by various composers.*
Bernard Zighera (pf); **Boston Symphony Orchestra / Serge Koussevitzky** (db).
Biddulph mono Ⓕ WHL045* (78 minutes: ADD: 2/97).

Prokofiev Romeo and Juliet, Op. 64 – Introduction; Romeo; The street awakens; Morning Dance;
The Quarrel; The Fight; The Prince gives his order; Juliet, as a young girl; Arrival of the guests;
Mask; Dance of the Knights; Romeo and Juliet; Folk Dance; Friar Laurence; Dance; Tybalt and
Mercutio fight; Mercutio dies; Romeo decides to avenge Mercutio's death; Romeo fights Tybalt;
Introduction to Act 3; The last farewell; Dance of the girls with the lilies; Juliet's funeral; Death
of Juliet. **Montreal Symphony Orchestra / Charles Dutoit.** Decca Ⓕ 430 279-2DH
(75 minutes: DDD: 9/91). Recorded 1989.
The melodic invention, always consistently inspired, the harmonic flavour, often pungent, and the
individual and brilliantly colourful orchestration of *Romeo and Juliet* bring the ear constant diversity
and stimulation. Charles Dutoit's 1991 recording is extremely attractive: by judicious selection he
compresses the epic span of the ballet into 24 separate items from the original score. The playing of
the Montreal Symphony Orchestra is spectacular with very fleet strings and brass playing of imposing
weight and tragic pungency. Dutoit's interpretation is highly theatrical: the lighter excerpts from the
score are pointed and witty, while the more romantic elements are given full expression and the variety
of Shakespeare's and Prokofiev's dramatic vision is most expertly recreated by Dutoit. The recording
is top class, not only expertly balanced but capturing the wide dynamic range and finesse of the
splendidly virtuoso Montreal orchestra.

Additional recommendations ...
...Romeo and Juliet. **Cleveland Orchestra / Lorin Maazel.**
Decca Ⓕ 417 510-2DH2 (two discs: 141 minutes: ADD: 2/87). ⒼⒼ
...Romeo and Juliet. **Orchestra of the Royal Opera House, Covent Garden / Mark Ermler.**
Royal Opera House Records Ⓕ ROH309/10 (two discs: 145 minutes: DDD: 11/94).
...Romeo and Juliet – excerpts. **Royal Concertgebouw Orchestra / Myung-Whun Chung.**
DG Ⓕ 439 870-2GH (63 minutes: DDD: 10/94).
...Romeo and Juliet – Suites Nos. 1 and 2: excerpts. **Cleveland Orchestra / Yoel Levi.**
Telarc Ⓕ CD80089 (50 minutes: DDD: 2/87).
...Romeo and Juliet – Suites Nos. 1 and 2. **Oslo Philharmonic Orchestra / Mariss Jansons.**
EMI Ⓕ CDC7 49289-2 (59 minutes: DDD: 5/89).
...Romeo and Juliet – Suites Nos. 1-3[a]. **Mussorgsky** A Night on the Bare Mountain[b].
[a]**Minneapolis Symphony Orchestra / Stanislav Skrowaczewski;** [b]**London Symphony Orchestra /
Antál Dorati.** Mercury Living Presence Ⓜ 432 004-2MM (67 minutes: ADD: 3/91). Ⓖ
...Romeo and Juliet – Suites Nos. 1-3. **Royal Scottish National Orchestra / Neeme Järvi.**
Chandos Ⓕ CHAN8940 (78 minutes: DDD: 9/91).
...Romeo and Juliet – Suites Nos. 1-3: excerpts. **Czecho-Slovak State Philharmonic Orchestra,
Košice / Andrew Mogrelia.** Naxos Ⓢ 8 550380 (55 minutes: DDD: 9/91).
...Romeo and Juliet – excerpts. **San Francisco Symphony Orchestra / Michael Tilson Thomas.**
RCA Victor Red Seal Ⓕ 09026 68288-2 (78 minutes: DDD: 5/96).
...Romeo and Juliet. **London Symphony Orchestra / André Previn.**
EMI Forte Ⓜ CZS5 68607-2 (two discs: 149 minutes: ADD: 7/96).
...Romeo and Juliet. **Cleveland Orchestra / Lorin Maazel.**
Decca Double Decca Ⓜ 452 970-2DF2 (two discs: 141 minutes: ADD: 6/98).

Prokofiev Symphonies – No. 1 in D major, Op. 25, "Classical" (from CHAN8400, 3/86); No. 2 in
D minor, Op. 40 (CHAN8368, 10/85. *Selected by Sounds in Retrospect*); No. 3 in C minor, Op. 44;
No. 4 in C major, Op. 47 (original 1930 version, both from CHAN8401, 5/86); No. 4 in C major,
Op. 112 (revised 1947 version, from CHAN8400, 3/86); No. 5 in B flat major, Op. 100
(CHAN8450, 7/86); No. 6 in E flat minor, Op. 111 (CHAN8359, 7/85); No. 7 in C sharp minor,
Op. 131 (CHAN8442, 7/86). **Royal Scottish National Orchestra / Neeme Järvi.**
Chandos Ⓕ CHAN8931/4 (four discs: 260 minutes: DDD). *Gramophone Award Winner 1985.* Ⓖ
Prokofiev was not a natural symphonist. Albeit successful in emulating Haydn in the *Classical*
Symphony, the Sixth Symphony is his only undisputed integrated symphonic structure (and an epic-
tragic utterance as intense as any by Shostakovich). It has been suggested that his symphonies all have
a sense of some unstaged scenario, and the Third and Fourth (and to a lesser extent, the Seventh)
Symphonies actually rework material from his music for the stage. The Fourth (in both versions) in
particular fails to convince as a symphony owing to the profusion and individuality of its often
strikingly beautiful thematic ideas – it's a real patchwork quilt of a piece. Enter Neeme Järvi, nothing

if not a man of the theatre, to give maximum dramatic intensity and character to all Prokofiev's ideas, whether they add up symphonically or not; capable of overawing his Scottish forces into playing of aerial lightness and easeful lyricism in the *Classical* Symphony, and pulling no punches where Prokofiev's inspiration (as in the Second and Third Symphonies) is at is most strident, violent and hysterical. Make no mistake, though, these are also readings of real stature: where there is symphonic 'line', Järvi unerringly finds it. Drawbacks? Some may feel the need for a deeper pile of string sound, particularly in the Fifth Symphony; and these typically spacious Chandos productions do not always ensure adequate projection for the woodwind, but more often than not one cannot fail to be impressed by the coherence and co-ordination, both musically and technically, of some of this century's most fabulous and fraught orchestral essays. As a cycle, this is unlikely to be challenged for some time.

Additional recommendations ...

...Nos. 1 and 7. The Love for Three Oranges – suite, Op. 33a[b]. **Philharmonia Orchestra / Nicolai Malko.** Classics for Pleasure ⑧ CD-CFP4523* (57 minutes: ADD).   Ⓖ

...Nos. 5 and 7. **London Symphony Orchestra / André Previn.** EMI Ⓜ CDM5 65181-2 (77 minutes: ADD).

...No. 6. Waltz Suite, Op. 110 – Nos. 1, 5 and 6. **Scottish National Orchestra / Neeme Järvi.** Chandos Ⓕ CHAN8359 (57 minutes: DDD: 7/85).

...No. 2. Romeo and Juliet – Suite No. 1. **Scottish National Orchestra / Neeme Järvi.** Chandos Ⓕ CHAN8368 (61 minutes: DDD: 10/85).

...No. 1. No. 4 (revised 1947 version). **Scottish National Orchestra / Neeme Järvi.** Chandos Ⓕ CHAN8400 (52 minutes: DDD: 3/86). *Selected by Sounds in Retrospect.*

...No. 3; No. 4 (original 1930 version). **Scottish National Orchestra / Neeme Järvi.** Chandos Ⓕ CHAN8401 (59 minutes: DDD: 5/86).

...No. 7. Sinfonietta in A major, Op. 48. **Scottish National Orchestra / Neeme Järvi.** Chandos Ⓕ CHAN8442 (51 minutes: DDD: 7/86).

...No. 1. *Coupled with works by* **Bizet** and **Britten** Orpheus Chamber Orchestra. DG Ⓕ 423 624-2GH (64 minutes: DDD: 1/89).

...No. 1. Peter and the wolf, Op. 67a. March in B flat major, Op. 99. Overture on Hebrew Themes, ...Nos. 1[a] and 5[b]. [a]**London Philharmonic Orchestra;** [b]**Saint Louis Symphony Orchestra / Leonard Slatkin** RCA Masters Collection Ⓜ 09026 61350-2 (57 minutes: DDD: 3/93).

...No. 6. **Stravinsky** Petrushka (1911 version). **Leningrad Philharmonic Orchestra / Evgeny Mravinsky.** Multisonic Russian Treasure mono Ⓜ 310189-2* (76 minutes: ADD: 8/94).

...Nos. 1 and 5. **Los Angeles Philharmonic Orchestra / André Previn.** Philips Solo Ⓜ 442 399-2PM (57 minutes: DDD: 9/94).

...No. 6. Waltz Suite, Op. 110. **National Symphony Orchestra of Ukraine / Theodore Kuchar.** Naxos Ⓢ 8 553069 (70 minutes: DDD: 1/96).

...No. 3. **Hindemith** Symphonic Metamorphosis on Themes of Carl Maria von Weber. **Janáček** Sinfonietta. **London Symphony Orchestra / Claudio Abbado.** Decca The Classic Sound Ⓜ 448 579-2DCS (79 minutes: ADD: 3/97).

Prokofiev Symphony No. 5 in B flat major, Op. 100. Scythian Suite, Op. 20. **City of Birmingham Symphony Orchestra / Sir Simon Rattle.** EMI Ⓕ CDC7 54577-2 (64 minutes: DDD: 6/93). Recorded 1992.   Ⓖ

Here is a Prokofiev Fifth as vibrant, intelligent and meticulously prepared as you'd expect from this partnership. In the mighty opening movement, there's real mystery about those fairy-tale slumberings at the start of the development, and how naturally Rattle quickens the pulse during the pages which follow, the sense of expectancy and adventure palpably conveyed. Enter the coda, and Rattle's expertly-graduated dynamics ensure a riveting succession of spectacular climaxes. Here, too, EMI's impressive recording opens out magnificently. Rattle's scherzo is a marvellously quick-witted conception, the slow movement etched with genuine tenderness and bustling good humour reigns supreme in the admirably spirited finale. The coupling is a stunning *Scythian Suite*, combining foundation-threatening pagan spectacle and heart-stopping beauty in ideal equilibrium. Brilliant!

Additional recommendations ...

...Scythian Suite. Alexander Nevsky, Op. 78a. [a]**Linda Finnie** (sop); **Scottish National** [a]**Chorus and Orchestra / Neeme Järvi.** Chandos Ⓕ CHAN8584 (60 minutes: DDD: 5/88).

...Scythian Suite[b]. Alexander Nevsky, Op. 78a. Lieutenant Kijé – Suite, Op. 60[b]. [a]**Elena Obraztsova** (mez); [a]**London Symphony Chorus and Orchestra;** [b]**Chicago Symphony Orchestra / Claudio Abbado.** DG The Originals Ⓜ 447 419-2GOR (79 minutes: ADD: 6/95).

Prokofiev Symphonies – No. 5 in B flat major, Op. 100[b]; No. 1 in D major, Op. 25, "Classical"[a]. Romeo and Juliet – Suite No. 2[c]. The Tale of the Buffoon (Chout) – Danse finale[a]. **Boston Symphony Orchestra / Serge Koussevitzky.** RCA Victor Gold Seal mono Ⓜ 09026 61657-2* (73 minutes: ADD: 4/95). Items marked [a] recorded 1947, [bc]from VL71077, 7/77, recorded 1945-1947. *Gramophone classical 100.*   ⒼⒼⒼ

Although there have been many fine and some thrilling performances of Prokofiev's Fifth Symphony since it first appeared on record, this is one of the best. Another is the perfectly proportioned and beautifully played Karajan recording on DG. Of course, there are many more modern and better recorded versions that can be recommended but (to put an unwelcome scenario) were the bomb about to drop, and one had only time to play one version of the Fifth, for many people it would be this one. Not even the Berlin Philharmonic under Karajan can match the strings of the Boston Symphony in sheer power and eloquence under Koussevitzky. They possess a lyrical intensity matched by few others. Above the stave they sing with unerring purity of intonation: the sound is marvellously clean and their tone can only be called luminous. The wind and brass are of comparable excellence. This account dates from February 6th and 7th, 1946, yet the musicians sound as if they have known this music all their lives. The *Classical* is both vivacious and enchanting. Superb performances, then, in a class of their own, which produce even better results now than they did on vinyl.

Additional recommendation ...
...Nos. 1 and 5. **Berlin Philharmonic Orchestra / Herbert von Karajan.**
DG Galleria Ⓜ 437 253-2GGA (71 minutes: ADD: 1/93). ⒼⒼ

Prokofiev String Quartets – No. 1 in B minor, Op. 50; No. 2 in F major, Op. 92. **American Quartet** (Mitchell Stern, Laurie Carney, vns; Daniel Avshalomov, va; David Geber, vc). Olympia Ⓜ OCD340 (50 minutes: ADD: 2/90). Recorded 1982. ⒼⒼ
Prokofiev's wider popularity has never extended to his chamber music. Of his two quartets, the Second is by far the better-known and comes from the war years when Prokofiev was evacuated to the Caucasus, where he made a study of the musical folklore of Kabarda – indeed, it is sometimes known as the "Kabardinian" Quartet. Although the material is folk-derived, it is completely absorbed into Prokofiev's own melodic bloodstream and doesn't sound in the least bit 'folksy'. The second movement quotes a Kabardinian love song of great lyrical beauty, and at one point in the slow movement, the accompaniment imitates a Caucasian stringed instrument, the kamancha. It is a work of real quality which has the astringent flavouring and poetic flair that characterizes Prokofiev at his best. Although the First Quartet, written at the behest of the Library of Congress in 1930, is not so immediately appealing it, too, is a work of substance which grows on the listener. Prokofiev's friend and colleague, Nikolay Miaskovsky, who composed 13 string quartets and more than twice as many symphonies, particularly admired the last movement, and encouraged Prokofiev to score it for full strings. The American Quartet communicate conviction and belief in this music: theirs is a persuasive account, sensitive and yet full-blooded, and they are very well recorded.

Additional recommendations ...
...Nos. 1 and 2. Sonata in C major for Two Violins, Op. 56. **Emerson Quartet.**
DG Ⓕ 431 772-2GH (59 minutes: DDD: 10/91). Ⓖ
...No. 2. *Coupled with works by* **Hindemith** and **Walton** Hollywood Quartet. Testament mono
Ⓕ SBT1052* (74 minutes: ADD: 3/95). *See review under Hindemith; refer to the Index.* ⒼⒼ
...Nos. 1[a] and 2[a]. Cello Sonata in C major, Op. 119[b]. [a]**Aurora Quartet;** [b]**Michael Grebanier** (vc); [b]**Janet Guggenheim** (pf). Naxos Ⓢ 8 553136 (69 minutes: DDD: 6/95).

Prokofiev Piano Sonatas – No. 1 in F minor, Op. 1; No. 4 in C minor, Op. 29; No. 6 in A major, Op. 82. **Yefim Bronfman** (pf). Sony Classical Ⓕ SK52484 (52 minutes: DDD: 11/94). Ⓖ
Recorded 1991. *Gramophone Editor's choice.*
These are performances which are highly considered, thoroughly idiomatic, possessed of exceptionally clean fingerwork and articulation and rich in subtleties and expressive nuance. Bronfman opens the disc with a particularly impressive and bold-hearted account of the Sixth Sonata; one of those interpretations that seizes and holds the listener's attention from the first to last bar. There's a real sense of dramatic narration about this performance, as opposed to the sometimes overtly (and exclusively) virtuosic readings of some pianists. That's not to deny the virtuosic elements of Bronfman's performance, of which there are plenty, though more impressive is the deceptive ease and finesse with which he traverses some of Prokofiev's excessive demands. In the Fourth Sonata every mood change is superbly caught, and Bronfman's lyricism and delicacy in the tender, probing central section of the slow movement is particularly memorable. The short, youthful First Sonata, always a difficult work to bring off successfully, is played with great verve and panache. Good recorded sound.

Additional recommendations ...
...No. 1; No. 4; No. 5 in C major (revised version), Op. 135; No. 9 in C major, Op. 103; No. 10 in E minor, Op. 137. **Murray McLachlan** (pf). Olympia Ⓜ OCD255 (70 minutes: DDD: 3/90).
...No. 4. Music for Children, Op. 65. Six Pieces, Op. 52. **Boris Berman** (pf).
Chandos Ⓕ CHAN8926 (65 minutes: DDD: 6/91). Ⓖ
...No. 1. Gavotte No. 4 from "Hamlet", Op. 77*bis*. Three Pieces, Op. 96. Sonatinas, Op. 54 – No. 1 in E minor; No. 2 in G major. Four Pieces, Op. 4. **Buxtehude** (arr. Prokofiev) Organ Prelude and Fugue in D minor. **Boris Berman** (pf). Chandos Ⓕ CHAN9017 (57 minutes: DDD: 11/92).
...Piano Sonata No. 3 in A minor, Op. 28. Three Pensées, Op. 62. Three Pieces from "Cinderella", Op. 95. Ten Pieces, Op. 12. **Boris Berman** (pf). Chandos Ⓕ CHAN9069 (56 minutes: DDD: 11/92).
...No. 1. No. 8 in B flat major, Op. 84. Four Pieces, Op. 3. Three Pieces, Op. 59. The tales of an old grandmother, Op. 31. **Oleg Marshev** (pf). Danacord Ⓕ DACOCD392 (64 minutes: DDD: 1/94).
...Nos. 4 and 6. Legend, Op. 12 No. 6. Visions fugitives, Op. 22 Nos. 3-6, 8, 9, 11, 14, 15 and 18. Pieces, Op. 32 – No. 1, Danse; No. 4, Waltz. Pieces from "Cinderella" – Op. 95: No. 2, Gavotte; Op. 97: No. 3, Autumn fairy, No. 6, Oriental dance; Op. 102: No. 1, Grand waltz, No. 3, Quarrel. *Coupled with works by* **Scriabin** and **Shostakovich** Sviatoslav Richter (pf). Philips Ⓕ 438 627-2PH2 (two discs: 152 minutes: DDD: 8/94). ⒼⒼ

Prokofiev Piano Sonatas – No. 2 in D minor, Op. 14; No. 7 in B flat major, Op. 83. The Love for Three Oranges, Op. 33*ter* – March. Ten Pieces from "Cinderella", Op. 97 – No. 10, Waltz. Six Pieces from "Cinderella", Op. 102 – No. 4, Amoroso. Three Pieces, Op. 96 – No. 1, Waltz from "War and Peace". **Barry Douglas** (pf). RCA Victor Red Seal Ⓕ RD60779 (56 minutes: DDD: 3/92). Recorded 1991.   Ⓖ

Prokofiev Ten Pieces from "Romeo and Juliet", Op. 75. Ten Pieces from "Cinderella", Op. 97. The Love for Three Oranges, Op. 33*ter* – March; Scherzo. **Tedd Joselson** (pf). Olympia Ⓕ OCD453 (62 minutes: DDD: 10/92). Recorded 1991.

There has often been a tendency with Prokofiev's piano music for pianists to overplay the percussive, steely qualities of the piano writing at the expense of the lyrical aspects. Barry Douglas, however, attains the perfect blend – muscular and athletic where power and agility are called for, but ever alert to the lyricism which lies beneath the surface. The Second Sonata is a prime example. Douglas has the full measure of this youthful, energetic masterpiece, and one feels that he has fully assimilated this piece before committing it to disc. The first movement with its restless oscillation between expressive melody and ruminative figuration is thoughtfully fashioned, and the knockabout scherzo and fleet-footed energetic finale are delivered with much vigour and flair. The Seventh Sonata (the central work of Prokofiev's "War Trilogy") is impressive too, with Douglas fully in command of its bristling difficulties. As for the rest of the disc, Douglas offers some of the less frequently heard piano transcriptions, of which the delirious 'love' Waltz from *Cinderella* and the March from *The Love for Three Oranges* crave particular attention. The recording is beautifully engineered and balanced.

Crisp, clean finger-work and a fine sense of rhythmic buoyancy can also be found on the very recommendable Olympia disc featuring the American pianist Tedd Joselson. Joselson made a considerable impact in 1976 with his recording of Prokofiev's Sonatas Nos. 2 and 8 (no longer available), and his special empathy with this composer can be heard further in his readings of Prokofiev's own transcriptions from the ballets *Cinderella* and *Romeo and Juliet*. Both collections contain some of the composer's most delightful and engaging numbers: from the charming character portrait "Juliet as a young girl" (brilliantly characterized here by Joselson) and the famous "Montagues and "Capulets" found in *Romeo and Juliet*, to the capricious "Grasshoppers and Dragonflies" and miniature "Four Seasons" suite from *Cinderella*. Joselson displays a keen talent for story-telling and atmosphere throughout, and has been provided with a clear and vivid recording.

Additional recommendations ...

...No. 5. Ten Pieces from "Romeo and Juliet", Op. 75. Four Pieces, Op. 32. March and Scherzo from "The Love for Three Oranges", Op. 33*ter*. **Boris Berman** (pf). Chandos Ⓕ CHAN8851 (65 minutes: DDD: 2/91).

...No. 7. Toccata in D minor, Op. 11. *Coupled with works by various composers.* **Vladimir Horowitz** (pf). RCA Victor Gold Seal mono/stereo Ⓜ GD60377* (65 minutes: ADD: 6/92). *See review in the Collections section; refer to the Index.*   ⒼⒼⒼ

...No. 2. Dumka. Three Pieces, Op. 59. Six Pieces from "Cinderella", Op. 102. Waltzes Suite (Schubert). **Boris Berman** (pf). Chandos Ⓕ CHAN9119 (65 minutes: DDD: 4/93).

...Nos. 2 and 7. Visions fugitives, Op. 22. **Laurent Cabasso** (pf). Auvidis Valois Ⓕ V4655 (58 minutes: DDD: 11/92).

...No. 7. *Coupled with works by various composers.* **Maurizio Pollini** (pf). DG The Originals Ⓜ 447 431-2GOR (68 minutes: ADD: 6/95). *Gramophone Classical 100. See review in the Collections section; refer to the Index.*   ⒼⒼⒼ

...No. 7. *Coupled with works by* **Scriabin** and **Miaskovsky** Sviatoslav Richter (pf); Melodiya monoⓂ 74321 29470-2* (68 minutes: ADD: 6/96).

...Ten Pieces from "Romeo and Juliet". War and Peace – Waltz, Op. 96 No. 1. The Love for Three Oranges – March; Scherzo. Six Pieces from "Cinderella". **Vladimir Ashkenazy** (pf). Decca Ⓕ 452 062-2DH (60 minutes: DDD: 9/96).

...No. 8 in B flat major, Op. 84. *Coupled with works by* **Rachmaninov** and **Scriabin** Sergio Fiorentino (pf). APR Fiorentino Edition Ⓜ APR5552 (63 minutes: DDD: 9/96).

...Nos. 2, 3, 5 and 9. Yefim Bronfman (pf). Sony Classical Ⓕ SK53273 (66 minutes: DDD: 10/96).

...Nos. 2, 7 and 8. **Mikhail Pletnev** (pf). DG Ⓕ 457 588-2GH (69 minutes: DDD: 6/98).

Prokofiev Piano Sonatas – No. 6 in A major, Op. 82; No. 7 in B flat major, Op. 83. Dumka. Visions fugitives, Op. 22. **Oleg Marshev** (pf). Danacord Ⓕ DACOCD391 (74 minutes: DDD: 1/94). Recorded 1991.   Ⓖ

Oleg Marshev is a charismatic performer whose dynamic, full-throated volcanic approach (though he is certainly not afraid to allow lyricism into the music when called upon to do so), provides great involvement for the listener. This, Volume One of his complete survey, opens with a commanding, virtuosic performance of the Sixth Sonata which simply teems with detail and subtle nuance. The second movement *Allegretto* is delivered with tremendous flair and *élan* in the outer sections, and the phlegmatic third movement is beautifully paced and crafted. Marshev unleashes the full power of his formidable armoury in the tumultuous finale, where in the closing bars he almost hits boiling-point in terms of sheer virtuosity; his performance may not quite reach those of Kissin or Pogorelich but it is certainly a recording that anyone would be happy to live with. In contrast, the early *Dumka* is given a beautifully poised and effortless reading, and the same can be said of Marshev's extremely fine account of the *Visions fugitives*. Marshev concludes the first volume with a stunning account of the Seventh Sonata, which approaches Pollini's classic recording for its breadth of vision, dynamic control and sheer virtuosity; pianistically it has all one could wish for – superb rhythmic impetus, tremendous force, wonderful phrasing and in the slower, more reflective moments beautiful tonal control and expressive nuance. The fearsome, toccata finale can only be compared to Pollini's scorching reading for its accuracy and heart-pounding excitement. The recording is full bodied.

Additional recommendations ...

...No. 6. **Ravel** Gaspard de la nuit. **Ivo Pogorelich** (pf).
DG Ⓕ 413 363-2GH (52 minutes: DDD: 11/84). ⒼⒼ

...No. 6. *Coupled with works by various composers.* **Evgeni Kissin** (pf). Sony Classical Ⓕ SK45931 (73 minutes: DDD: 11/90). *See review in the Collections section; refer to the Index.* ⒼⒼ

...No. 6. Etude in C minor, Op. 2 No. 3. *Coupled with works by various composers.* **Evgeni Kissin** (pf). RCA Victor Red Seal Ⓕ RD60443 (two discs: 103 minutes: DDD: 3/91). ⒼⒼ

...Visions fugitives – Nos. 1, 2, 3, 6, 7, 9, 10, 11, 12, 13, 14, 16. *Coupled with works by various composers.* **Artur Rubinstein** (pf). RCA Victor Gold Seal Ⓜ 09026 61445-2 (64 minutes: ADD: 10/93). *See review in the Collections section; refer to the Index.* ⒼⒼⒼ

...Visions fugitives. **Hindemith** Ludus tonalis. **Olli Mustonen** (pf).
Decca Ⓕ 444 803-2DH (68 minutes: DDD: 5/96).

Prokofiev Piano Sonata No. 8 in B flat major, Op. 84[a]. Visions fugitives, Op. 22 – Nos. 3, 6 and 9[a].
Debussy Estampes[b]. Préludes, Book 1[b] – Voiles; Le vent dans la plaine; Les collines d'Anacapri.
Scriabin Piano Sonata No. 5 in F sharp major, Op. 53[b]. **Sviatoslav Richter** (pf).
DG Dokumente Ⓜ 423 573-2GDO (67 minutes: ADD: 9/88). Items marked [a] from SLPM138950 (8/65), [b]SLPM138849 (4/63). Recorded 1963. ⒼⒼ
Richter has long been acclaimed as one of the most dedicated champions of Prokofiev's keyboard music, with the Eighth Sonata always particularly close to his heart. It would certainly be hard to imagine a more profoundly and intensely experienced performance than the one we get here, or one of greater keyboard mastery. After the yearning introspection of the temperamental opening movement and the *Andante*'s evocation of a more gracious past, the rhythmic tension and sheer might of sonority he conjures in the finale make it easy to understand why the composer's biographer, I.V. Nestyev, suspected some underlying programme culminating in "heroic troops resolutely marching ahead, ready to crush anything in their path". In the uniquely Prokofievian fantasy of the three brief *Visions fugitives* he is wholly bewitching. As for the Fifth Sonata of Scriabin, his impetuous start at once reveals his understanding of its manic extremities of mood. For just these Russian performances alone, this excellently refurbished disc can be hailed as a collector's piece. And as a bonus there is Debussy too, with infinite subtleties of tonal shading to heighten atmospheric evocation.

Additional recommendation ...

...Visions fugitives. *Coupled with works by* **Scriabin** Nikolai Demidenko (pf).
Conifer Classics Ⓕ CDCF204 (73 minutes: DDD: 8/91). Ⓖ

Prokofiev Violin Sonatas – No. 1 in F minor, Op. 80; No. 2 in D major, Op. 94a. Five Melodies, Op. 35b. **Vadim Repin** (vn); **Boris Berezovsky** (pf). Erato Ⓕ 0630-10698-2 (63 minutes: DDD: 1/96). Recorded 1995. *Gramophone Editor's choice.* Ⓖ
A clear first choice in this repertoire and heartening confirmation of the young Vadim Repin's considerable violinistic skills. Tension sets in right from the First Sonata's opening bars: the tone is bright, sweet, tremulous and warmly expressive, while the music's sombre mood is precisely gauged. Repin phrases with considerable sensitivity and his attack in the work's faster episodes – the *Allegro brusco*'s outer sections and most of the finale – has a Heifetzian 'edge'. Nervous energy is also much in evidence, while the *Andante* – one of Prokofiev's most haunting creations – has a wistfully distracted air that Boris Berezovsky matches with some notably perceptive piano playing. The *Allegrissimo* finale, too, is arresting: deftly fingered, percussively insistent and with a truly heartfelt projection of the work's tender closing phrase. One of Repin's leading qualities is his obvious interpretative sincerity; nowhere does one sense the suave affectation that afflicts some of his contemporaries, a fact that registers with particular force in the Second Sonata's opening *Moderato*. Here lesser artists often sound either matter-of-fact or uninterested, and even superior ones opt for relative coolness. Repin and Berezovsky, on the other hand, are both tender and relaxed; phrasal 'crossfire' and keen inflexion keep sparks flying in the *Scherzo*, the *Allegretto leggiero e scherzando* is appropriately limpid, and although the finale could have swaggered rather more freely, there are magical moments to spare. Both players achieve an impressive range of colour throughout and the five delightful *Melodies* make for a welcome sequence of encores. Very well recorded.

Additional recommendations ...

...Violin Sonata No. 2. *Coupled with works by* **Ravel** and **Stravinsky** Viktoria Mullova (vn); Bruno Canino (pf). Philips Ⓕ 426 254-2PH (61 minutes: DDD: 8/90).

...Violin Sonatas. Five Melodies, Op. 35b. **Gidon Kremer** (vn); **Martha Argerich** (pf). DG Ⓕ 431 803-2GH (66 minutes: DDD: 10/92). Ⓖ

...Violin Sonatas[b]. Violin Concerto No. 2 in G minor, Op. 63[a]. **Itzhak Perlman** (vn); [b]**Vladimir Ashkenazy** (pf); [a]**Boston Symphony Orchestra / Erich Leinsdorf.** RCA Victor Gold Seal Ⓜ 09026 61454-2 (78 minutes: ADD: 9/94). Ⓖ

...Violin Sonatas. Five Melodies. **Nikolai Madojan** (vn); **Elisabeth Westenholz** (pf).
Kontrapunkt Ⓕ 32185 (68 minutes: DDD: 9/94).
...Violin Sonatas. **Ravel** Violin Sonata in G major. **Shlomo Mintz** (vn); **Yefim Bronfman** (pf).
DG Masters Ⓜ 445 557-2GMA (74 minutes: DDD: 11/95).

Prokofiev Violin Sonata No. 2 in D major, Op. 94a[a].
K. Khachaturian Violin Sonata, Op. 1[a].
Szymanowski Violin Sonata in D minor, Op. 9[b]. **David Oistrakh** (vn); **Vladimir Yampolsky** (pf).
Testament mono Ⓕ SBT1113* (65 minutes: ADD: 2/98). Items marked [a] from
Columbia 33CX1342 (4/56), [b]33CX1201 (3/55). Recorded 1955.   Ⓔ Ⓔ Ⓔ
David Oistrakh's playing is, at its best, a calming force in an agitated world – intelligent, considered
(just occasionally overcalculated), invariably poised, big-toned and confident. You know what to
expect and are rarely disappointed, and these excellent refurbishments of key Oistrakh performances
from the 1950s lend a characteristic narrative quality to a wide variety of repertoire. Best perhaps is
the Prokofiev sonata, which Oistrakh himself instigated in reaction to hearing the flute-and-piano
original. The playing is quietly confidential in the first and third movements, pert in the scherzo and
exuberant in the closing *Allegro con brio*. Oistrakh's phrasing is incisive without sounding aggressive
(most notes retain their full measure of tone, even at speed), while his handling of rhythm is both
supple and muscular. Szymanowski's post-romantic Op. 9 is lusciously full-toned and expertly
negotiated by Yampolsky, while the reading of Karen Khachaturian's Op. 1 – a pleasant piece
reminiscent of Kabalevsky, the lighter Shostakovich and, very occasionally, Gershwin – is another
masterly performance, especially in the delightful *Andante*. All in all, this is a superb disc, expertly
annotated and very well presented. The Prokofiev Second Sonata is as near 'definitive' as anyone has
a right to expect, while the rest is typical of a violinist whose aristocratic playing and artistic
diplomacy were – and remain – an inspiration to us all.

Prokofiev Ivan the Terrible, Op. 116. **Liubov Sokolova** (mez); **Nikolai Putilin** (bar);
Chorus of the Kirov Opera; Rotterdam Philharmonic Orchestra / Valery Gergiev.
Philips Ⓕ 456 645-2PH (65 minutes: DDD: 2/98). Text and translation included.
Recorded 1996.   Ⓔ Ⓔ
Gergiev has been an immensely effective musical director of the Kirov company. In non-dramatic
music he can seem less than electrifying, but this studio account of *Ivan* ranks with the best of his
opera recordings. Of course, recommending just one version for the collection is not easy when the
work, rather like the film itself, does not exist in a definitive form. Part 1 of Eisenstein's masterpiece
was released in 1946 to worldwide acclaim, although Stravinsky for one did not care for its mix of
iconography and melodrama. Prokofiev's health was so poor that he recommended that Gavriil Popov
take over as composer for Part 2. Later he was able to resume work on the project – only to find it
withheld from distribution. Soviet officials found its portrayal of Ivan's psychological decline too
negative and, no doubt, too close to home. Which is not to say that Prokofiev intended to encode any
criticism of Stalin in the notes. The film was released in the USSR in 1958 by which time plans to
complete the trilogy had been abandoned, its prime movers long dead. Prokofiev thought highly
enough of the score to reuse sections of it, but he left no guidelines for presenting it in the concert-
hall. Reshaping the music to fit a chronological narrative, Abram Stasevich fabricated an overlong
oratorio. Gergiev's version is based on Stasevich; only here the music is left to fend for itself without
the interpolated Russian texts. The Russian choir and some notably forward timpani help Gergiev
build the right atmosphere. The wide vibrato of his young mezzo is nothing if not authentic and there
will be no complaints about the robust singing of Nikolai Putilin. James Agee acclaimed the film as
"A visual opera, with all of opera's proper disregard of prose-level reality" but if you want the music
divorced from the images, Gergiev's account is among the most sheerly dramatic.
Additional recommendation ...
...Ivan the Terrible (ed. Lankester). Alexander Nevsky, Op. 78. **Soloists;**
New London Children's Choir; London Symphony Chorus and Orchestra / Mstislav Rostropovich.
Sony Classical Ⓕ S2K48387 (two discs: 153 minutes: DDD: 4/93).

Prokofiev The Fiery Angel. **Galina Gorchakova** (sop) Renata; **Sergei Leiferkus** (bar) Ruprecht;
Vladimir Galusin (ten) Agrippa; **Konstantin Pluzhnikov** (ten) Mephistopheles; **Sergei Alexashkin**
(bass) Faust; **Vladimir Ognovanko** (bass) Inquisitor; **Evgeni Boitsov** (ten) Jakob Glock;
Valery Lebed (bass) Doctor; Yuri Laptev (ten) Mathias; **Mikhail Kit** (bar) Servant; **Evgenia
Perlasova** (mez) Landlady; **Larissa Diadkova** (mez) Fortune teller; Olga Markova-Mikhailenko
(contr) Mother Superior; **Yevgeny Fedotov** (bass) Innkeeper; **Mikhail Chernozhukov** (bass)
First Neighbour; **Andrei Karabanov** (bar) Second Neighbour; **Gennadi Bezzubenkov** (bass)
Third Neighbour; **Tatiana Kravtsova** (sop) First Nun; **Tatiana Filimoniva** (sop) Second Nun;
Chorus and Orchestra of the Kirov Opera / Valery Gergiev. Philips Ⓕ 446 078-2PH2
(two discs: 119 minutes: DDD: 1/96). Recorded live in 1993. Notes, text and translation included.
Recorded 1993. *Gramophone Editor's choice*. *Gramophone Award Winner 1996*.   Ⓔ Ⓔ
At last we have something close to the music's full potential revealed. The opera is no blameless
masterpiece – Prokofiev's indulgence in lurid sensationalism sometimes gets the better of his artistic
judgement. But that sounds a pretty po-faced judgement in the face of the overwhelming power which

so much of this score exudes. This Maryinsky performance comes live from what is clearly a highly-charged occasion in one of the world's great opera houses. That brings with it the disadvantage of a constrained opera-pit acoustic, which makes some of Prokofiev's over-the-top scoring seem pretty congested. But the immediacy and clarity of the sound, plus the orchestra's rhythmic grasp, ensures that the effect is still properly blood-curdling. If Leiferkus's distinctive rich baritone at first sounds a touch microphoney, the ear can soon adjust to that too, and Gorchakova brings intense beauty as well as intensity to Renata's hysterics, taking us right inside the psychological drama. The supporting roles are filled with distinction and this makes a huge difference to the sustaining of dramatic tension, the crescendo which Prokofiev aimed to build through his five acts. Considering the extent of the stage goings-on there is remarkably little audience distraction on the recording.

Prokofiev The Love for Three Oranges (sung in French). **Gabriel Bacquier** (bar) King of Clubs; **Jean-Luc Viala** (ten) Prince; **Hélène Perraguin** (mez) Princess Clarissa; **Vincent Le Texier** (bass-bar) Leandro; **Georges Gautier** (ten) Truffaldino; **Didier Henry** (bar) Pantaloon, Farfarello, Master of Ceremonies; **Gregory Reinhart** (bass) Tchelio; **Michèle Lagrange** (sop) Fata Morgana; **Consuelo Caroli** (mez) Linetta; **Brigitte Fournier** (sop) Nicoletta; **Catherine Dubosc** (sop) Ninetta; **Jules Bastin** (bass) Cook; **Béatrice Uria Monzon** (mez) Smeraldina; **Chorus and Orchestra of Lyon Opéra / Kent Nagano.** Virgin Classics Ⓕ VCD7 59566-2 (two discs: 102 minutes: DDD: 12/89). Notes, text and translation included. *Gramophone Award Winner 1990.*   Ⓠ

This is a wonderfully zany story about a prince whose hypochondriac melancholy is lifted only at the sight of a malevolent witch tumbling over, in revenge for which she casts on him a love-spell for three oranges: in the ensuing complications he encounters an ogre's gigantic cook who goes all gooey at the sight of a pretty ribbon, princesses inside two of the oranges die of oppressive desert heat, and the third is saved only by the intervention of various groups of 'spectators' who argue with each other on the stage. The music's brittle vivacity matches that of the plot, and though there are no set-pieces for the singers and there is practically no thematic development – the famous orchestral March and Scherzo are the only passages that reappear – the effervescent score is most engaging. The performance, conducted by the musical director of the Lyon Opéra, is full of zest, with lively orchestral playing and a cast that contains several outstanding members and not a single weak one; and the recording is extremely good. Those desirous of so doing can delve into the work's symbolism and identify the objects of its satire – principally Stanislavsky's naturalistic Moscow Arts Theatre: others can simply accept this as a thoroughly enjoyable romp.

Prokofiev War and Peace. **Lajos Miller** (bar) Prince Andrei Bolkonsky; **Galina Vishnevskaya** (sop) Natasha Rostova; **Katherine Ciesinski** (mez) Sonya; **Maria Paunova** (mez) Maria Akhrosimova; **Dimiter Petkov** (bass) Count Ilya Rostov; **Wieslaw Ochman** (ten) Count Pytor Bezukhov; **Stefania Toczyska** (mez) Helena Bezukhova; **Nicolai Gedda** (ten) Anatol Kuragin; **Vladimir de Kanel** (bass-bar) Dolokhov; **Mira Zakai** (contr) Princess Maria Bolkonsky; **Malcolm Smith** (bass) Colonel Vasska Denisov; **Nicola Ghiuselev** (bass) Marshal Mikhail Kutuzov; **Eduard Tumagian** (bar) Napoleon Bonaparte; **Radio France Chorus; French National Orchestra / Mstislav Rostropovich.** Erato Libretto Ⓜ 2292-45331-2 (four discs: 247 minutes: DDD: 4/92). Notes, text and translation included. From ECD75480 (1/89). Recorded 1986.   Ⓠ

Over four hours long, 72 characters, 13 scene changes: is it any wonder that Prokofiev's *War and Peace*, adapted from Tolstoy's famously epic novel, has had few performances and even fewer forays into the recording studio? At the front of the booklet Rostropovich recalls how, as Prokofiev lay dying, he reiterated one wish, that Rostropovich should make this opera known to the world. It comes as no surprise, then, to find a deeply committed performance from both soloists (only 45 of them due to some adroit doubling), chorus and orchestra. Prokofiev adapted the novel into seven 'peace' and six 'war' tableaux, thus sustaining drama through contrast throughout its Wagnerian length. With few exceptions the multinational cast sing in good Russian and among them Lajos Miller is particularly affecting as Prince Andrei, pleasingly ardent in his opening moonlit aria. The central female role of Natasha is taken by Galina Vishnevskaya. She sang the role in the 1959 première and inevitably no longer sounds like an innocent 16 year old. Unfortunately, problems are compounded by a hardness in her tone and a lack of attention to detail in some of the quieter sections – particularly in her exchanges with Helena where the asides sound like part of the normal conversation. Stefania Toczyska as the treacherous Helena makes a great impression, as does Katherine Ciesinski as Natasha's confidante, Sonya. Of the men, Nicolai Gedda as Prince Anatol sings with character and great style and Eduard Tumagian is a suitably heroic and steadfast Napoleon. An added attraction of the recording are the sound effects, particularly in the war scenes, convincing but never overly obtrusive. Good translations are provided in three languages, crowning a laudable achievement.

Additional recommendation ...

...War and Peace – Symphonic Suite (arr. Palmer). Summer Night – Suite, Op. 123. Russian Overture, Op. 72. **Philharmonia Orchestra / Neeme Järvi.** Chandos Ⓕ CHAN9096 (64 minutes: DDD: 3/93).

Further listening ...

...Cantata for the 20th Anniversary of the October Revolution, Op. 74[a]. The tale of the stone flower – excerpts. [a]**Gennadi Rozhdestvensky** (spkr); **Philharmonia** [a]**Chorus and Orchestra / Neeme Järvi.** Chandos CHAN9095 (3/93).

...Lieutenant Kijé – Suite, Op. 60. *Coupled with* **Rimsky-Korsakov** Scheherazade, Op. 35.
London Philharmonic Orchestra / Takuo Yuasa. EMI Eminence CD-EMX2214 (12/93).
...Lieutenant Kijé – Suite, Op. 60. *Coupled with works by* **Hovhaness** and **Stravinsky**
Chicago Symphony Orchestra / Fritz Reiner. RCA Victor Living Stereo 09026 61957-2 (9/95).
See review under Hovhaness; refer to the Index.
...Lieutenant Kijé – Suite, Op. 60. *Coupled with works by various composers.* **Boston Symphony**
Orchestra / Serge Koussevitzky. Dutton Laboratories mono CDAX8015* (1/97).
...Semyon Kotko – symphonic suite, Op. 81*bis*. Four Portraits and Denoument from
"The Gambler", Op. 49. **Royal Scottish Orchestra / Neeme Järvi.** Chandos CHAN8803 (9/90).
...Flute Sonata in D major, Op. 94. *Coupled with works by various composers.*
Jennifer Stinton (fl); **Scott Mitchell** (pf). Collins Classics 1103-2 (12/91).
...Toccata in D minor, Op. 11. *Coupled with works by various composers.* **Martha Argerich** (pf).
DG The Originals 447 430-2GOR (6/95). *Gramophone Classical 100. See review in the*
Collections section; refer to the Index.   ⓖⓖⓖ
...Alexander Nevsky, Op. 78. *Coupled with* **Rachmaninov** The Bells, Op. 35.
Soloists; London Symphony Chorus and Orchestra / André Previn.
EMI Studio CDM7 63114-2 (10/89). *See review under Rachmaninov; refer to the Index.*   ⓖⓖ
...Eugene Onegin. **Timothy West, Samuel West, Niamh Cusack** (narrs);
New Company; Sinfonia 21 / Sir Edward Downes. Chandos CHAN9318/9 (11/94).

Giacomo Puccini
Italian 1858-1924

Puccini Opera Arias: La rondine – Chi il bel sogno di Doretta. La bohème – Sì, mi chiamano
Mimì; Donde lieta uscì. Gianni Schicchi – O mio babbino caro. Manon Lescaut – In quelle trine
morbide; Sola, perduta, abbandonata. Suor Angelica – Senza mamma, O bimbo. Tosca – Vissi
d'arte. Madama Butterfly – Un bel di vedremo; Che tua madre; Tu, tu, piccolo iddio.
Turandot – Signore, ascolta!; In questa reggia; Tu, che di gel sei cinta. **Julia Varady** (sop);
Berlin Radio Symphony Orchestra / Marcello Viotti. Orfeo ⓔ C323941A
(52 minutes: DDD: 5/95). Recorded 1993.

A lovely and somewhat surprising record by the most fascinating and patrician lyric soprano of the
present age: 'surprising' because, though Varady is associated closely enough with Verdi, the Puccini
connection is less readily made, 'lovely' because the voice is still so pure, the style so musical and
(above all) the response so intelligent, immediate and full-hearted. She adjusts wonderfully well to the
Italian idiom, lightening the vowels, freeing the upper range, allowing more portamento than she
would probably do in other music, yet employing in its use the finest technical skill and artistic
judgement. Her singing of Magda's song in *La rondine* opens the record and introduces a singer who
sounds (give or take a little) half her actual age: Varady's début dates back to 1962, and these
recordings were made in 1993. In Mimì's narrative she sings with so fine a perception of the character
– the hesitancies, the joy in "mi piaccion quelle cose" – that Schwarzkopf's exquisite recording came
to mind, just as, from time to time, and especially in the *Madama Butterfly* excerpts, the finely
concentrated, tragic restraint of Meta Seinemeyer was recalled. It is good to hear, too, how sensitively
Varady differentiates between characters, Manon Lescaut having that essential degree of additional
sophistication in tone and manner. What runs as a thread through all of these characterizations is a
feeling for their dignity. Mimì does not simper. Sister Angelica does not sob. Lauretta has resolution
in her pleading. Butterfly, Liù and Tosca are what they should be: women whose pathos lies not in
their weakness but in a passionate, single-minded fidelity. That leaves Turandot which is a mistake.
That is, she is outside the singer's scope and should remain so: it is not merely a matter of vocal thrust,
weight and stamina, but also of voice-character. The performance of her aria has clear merits (the
imperiousness of "Mai nessun m'avrà" for instance), but a little more of Manon ("L'ora, o Tirsi") or
Tosca ("Non lo sospiri la nostra casetta") or the solos from *Le Villi* and *Edgar* would have been more
welcome. Welcome too would have been printed texts, though it is true the excerpts are all pretty well
known. None of that should deter purchase; this is singing to treasure.

Additional recommendations ...
...La bohème – Quando m'en vo' soletta. Tosca – Vissi d'arte. *Coupled with works by various*
composers. **Inessa Galante** (sop); **Latvian National Opera Orchestra / Alexander Vilumanis.**
Campion ⓔ RRCD1344 (63 minutes: AAD/DDD: A/97). *See review in the Collections section;*
refer to the Index.
...La rondine – Chi il bel sogno di Doretta. *Coupled with works by various composers.*
Renée Fleming (sop); **English Chamber Orchestra / Jeffrey Tate.** Decca ⓔ 458 858-2DH
(70 minutes: DDD: 3/98). *See review in the Collections section; refer to the Index.*

Puccini Opera Arias: Turandot – Non piangere, Liù!; Nessun dorma!. Gianni Schicchi – Avete
torto! Firenze è come un albero fiorito. Il Tabarro – Hai ben ragione; Io voglio la tua bocca ...
Folle di gelosia!. La rondine – Parigi! è la citta dei desideri ... Forse, come la rondine; Dimmi che
vuoi seguirmi. La fanciulla del West – Una parola sola! ... Or son sei mesi; Risparmiate lo
scherno ... Ch'ella mi creda libero. Madama Butterfly – Dipende dal grado di cottura ... Amore o
grillo; Addio, fiorito asil. Tosca – Recondita armonia; E lucevan le stelle. La bohème – Che gelida

manina. Manon Lescaut – Tra voi, belle; Donna non vidi mai; Ah! Manon, mi tradisce; Ah! non v'avvicinate!; Manon ... senti, amor mio ... Vedi, son io che piango. Edgar – Orgia, chimera dall'occhio vitreo. Le villi – Ecco la casa ... Torna ai felici dì. **José Cura** (ten); **Philharmonia Orchestra / Plácido Domingo.** Erato Ⓕ 0630-18838-2 (71 minutes: DDD: 11/97). Texts and translations included. Recorded 1997. ⒼⒼ

For those of us who can feast on a good tenor voice as if there were no tomorrow, this is (to put it crudely) the goods. First, however, a peculiarity of this programme is that it goes backwards. It starts with *Turandot* and recedes along a strict chronological line to *Le villi*. That of itself is an attractive idea, but it means that the terminus is a long and somewhat inconclusive excerpt, while the starting-point is "Nessun dorma!". We all know what that means these days, and it looks suspiciously like making a bid for the market if not for the kingdom. A dark, rather throaty, big and uncharming voice reiterates the famous command. As it takes the high As we realize that this is special, rising easily and thrillingly out of the baritonal middle register; Cura holds his high B ("vincerò") for the maximum length compatible with holding on to the succeeding A for even longer. But he is a man with surprises in store. "Non piangere, Liù!" begins quietly and is thoughtfully phrased. Similarly he shows his unpredictability in the *Tosca* arias: "Recondita armonia" is stolid, almost routine, but then "E lucevan le stelle" becomes the real expression of a man facing the prospect of imminent execution, and writing a poem. Throughout, Cura displays a thrilling voice with an individual timbre. His 'face' wears too much of a scowl and he does not give the impression of thinking about the person he is nominally addressing, but this is a solo recital and perhaps it would be different in a complete opera. He is accompanied here with uncommon sympathy by a conductor who has a good deal more experience of singing than has the singer himself.

Puccini La bohème. Jussi Björling (ten) Rodolfo; **Victoria de los Angeles** (sop) Mimì; **Robert Merrill** (bar) Marcello; **Lucine Amara** (sop) Musetta; **John Reardon** (bar) Schaunard; **Giorgio Tozzi** (bass) Colline; **Fernando Corena** (bass) Benoit, Alcindoro; **William Nahr** (ten) Parpignol; **Thomas Powell** (bar) Customs Official; **George del Monte** (bar) Sergeant; **Columbus Boychoir; RCA Victor Chorus and Orchestra / Sir Thomas Beecham.** EMI mono Ⓕ CDS5 56236-2* (two discs: 108 minutes: ADD: 6/87). Notes, text and translation included.
From ALP1409/10 (1/57). *Gramophone classical 100.* ⒼⒼⒼ

To recommend a 37-year-old mono recording of *La bohème* over all the more glamorously star-studded and sumptuously recorded versions that have appeared since may seem perverse, but the Beecham version is a true classic which has never been surpassed. This intimate opera is not about two superstars showing off how loudly they can sing their top Cs, but about a poverty-stricken poet's love for a mortally-ill seamstress. De los Angeles's infinitely-touching Mimì and Björling's poetic, ardent Rodolfo are backed by consistently fine and characterful ensemble work making this the most realistic version ever recorded. The recording of course shows its age, but this is scarcely noticeable as page after page of the score come freshly alive again: not a *tour de force* of vocalism, not a sequence of famous arias with bits of dialogue between but a lyric tragedy of wrenching pathos and truth.

Additional recommendations ...

...Soloists; Sainta Cecilia Academy Chorus, Rome; Santa Cecilia Academy Orchestra, Rome / Alberto Erede. Decca mono Ⓜ 440 233-2LF2* (two discs: 105 minutes: ADD). Ⓖ

...Soloists; Chorus and Orchestra of La Scala, Milan / Antonino Votto. EMI mono Ⓜ CDS5 56295-2* (two discs: 106 minutes: ADD: 11/87).

...Soloists; Schöneberger Boys' Choir; Berlin German Opera Chorus; Berlin Philharmonic Orchestra / Herbert von Karajan. Decca Ⓕ 421 049-2DH2 (two discs: 110 minutes: ADD: 11/87). Ⓖ

...Act 4. Heddle Nash (ten) with various artists. London Philharmonic Orchestra / Sir Thomas Beecham. Dutton Laboratories mono Ⓑ CDLX7012* (69 minutes: ADD: 2/95). *See review in the Collections section; refer to the Index.* Ⓖ

...Soloists; Chorus and Orchestra of La Scala, Milan / Carlo Sabajno. VAI mono Ⓕ VAIA1078* (two discs: 104 minutes: ADD: 3/95).

...Soloists; Chorus and Orchestra of La Scala, Milan / Umberto Berrettoni. Nimbus mono Ⓜ NI7862/3* (two discs: 102 minutes: ADD: 3/95).

...Soloists; Chorus and Orchestra of the Santa Cecilia Academy, Rome / Tullio Serafin. Double Decca Ⓜ 448 725-2DF2* (two discs: 112 minutes: ADD: 1/97).

Puccini La Fanciulla del West. Carol Neblett (sop) Minnie; **Plácido Domingo** (ten) Dick Johnson; **Sherrill Milnes** (bar) Jack Rance; **Francis Egerton** (ten) Nick; **Robert Lloyd** (bass) Ashby; **Gwynne Howell** (bass) Jake Wallace; **Paul Hudson** (bass) Billy Jackrabbit; **Anne Wilkens** (sop) Wowkle; **Chorus and Orchestra of the Royal Opera House, Covent Garden / Zubin Mehta.** DG Ⓕ 419 640-2GH2 (two discs: 130 minutes: ADD: 11/87). Notes, text and translation included. From 2709 078 (9/78). Recorded 1977. *Gramophone Award Winner 1978.*

This opera depicts the triangular relationship between Minnie, the saloon owner and 'mother' to the entire town of gold miners, Jack Rance, the sheriff and Dick Johnson (alias Ramerrez), a bandit leader. The music is highly developed in Puccini's seamless lyrical style, the arias for the main characters emerge from the texture and return to it effortlessly. The vocal colours are strongly polarized with the cast being all male except for one travesti role and Minnie herself. The score bristles with robust melody as well as delicate scoring, betraying a masterly hand at work. Carol Neblett is a strong Minnie, vocally distinctive and well characterized, whilst Plácido Domingo and Sherrill Milnes make a good pair of suitors for the spunky little lady. Zubin Mehta conducts with real sympathy for the idiom and the orchestra respond well.

Additional recommendation ...

...**Soloists; Santa Cecilia Academy Chorus and Orchestra, Rome / Franco Capuana.**
Decca Grand Opera Ⓜ 421 595-2DM2 (two discs: 133 minutes: ADD: 1/89).

Puccini Madama Butterfly. **Renata Scotto** (sop) Madama Butterfly; **Carlo Bergonzi** (ten) Pinkerton; **Rolando Panerai** (bar) Sharpless; **Anna di Stasio** (mez) Suzuki; **Piero De Palma** (ten) Goro; **Giuseppe Morresi** (ten) Prince Yamadori; **Silvana Padoan** (mez) Kate Pinkerton; **Paolo Montarsolo** (bass) The Bonze; **Mario Rinaudo** (bass) Commissioner; **Rome Opera House Chorus and Orchestra / Sir John Barbirolli.** EMI Ⓜ CMS7 69654-2 (two discs: 142 minutes: ADD: 5/89).
Notes, text and translation included. From SAN184/6 (9/67). Recorded 1966. Ⓖ

This is not quite the best sung *Butterfly* available but Barbirolli ensures that it is the most richly and enjoyably Italianate. Italian opera was in his blood and as a cellist at Covent Garden, playing under Puccini's direction, and as a conductor whose formative years were spent in the theatre (his Covent Garden début was in this very opera), Barbirolli's pleasure in returning to the world of opera is audible throughout this recording. The rapport between him and the Italian orchestra is close and affectionate; it is a heartwarming performance, subtle and supple in the pacing of the love duet, urgently passionate in the great outbursts. Scotto is a touching Butterfly, with all the tiny and crucial details of characterization delicately moulded. There have been more dashing Pinkertons than Bergonzi, but not many who have so effectively combined suavity of sound with neatness of phrasing and good taste. Panerai is a first-class Sharpless and di Stasio a sympathetic Suzuki; there are no weak links elsewhere, and the recording is decent enough for its date, if a bit narrow in perspective and with the singers rather forwardly placed. Barbirolli's *Butterfly* has several distinguished rivals on CD, but for a performance that will remind you of the first time you fell in love with this opera it has permanent value and great eloquence.

Additional recommendations ...

...**Soloists; Vienna State Opera Chorus; Vienna Philharmonic Orchestra / Herbert von Karajan.**
Decca Ⓕ 417 577-2DH3 (three discs: 145 minutes: ADD: 6/87). Ⓖ

...**Soloists; Chorus and Orchestra of La Scala, Milan / Herbert von Karajan.**
EMI mono Ⓜ CDS5 56298-2* (two discs: 139 minutes: ADD: 10/87).

...**Soloists; Ambrosian Opera Chorus; Philharmonia Orchestra / Giuseppe Sinopoli.**
DG 423 567-2GH3 (three discs: 154 minutes: DDD: 12/88).

...**Soloists; Rome Opera Chorus and Orchestra / Gabriele Santini.**
EMI Studio Ⓜ CMS7 63634-2 (two discs: 137 minutes: ADD: 3/91).

...**Soloists; Slovak Philharmonic Chorus; Czecho-Slovak Radio Symphony Orchestra, Bratislava / Alexander Rahbari.**
Naxos Ⓢ 8 660015/6 (two discs: 141 minutes: DDD: 5/92). ⒼⒼ

...**Soloists; Choruses of Radio France; Orchestre de Paris / James Conlon.**
Sony Classical Ⓕ S2K69258 (two discs: 133 minutes: DDD: 4/97).

...**Soloists; Chorus and Orchestra of the Santa Cecilia Academy, Rome / Tullio Serafin.**
Double Decca Ⓑ 452 594-2DF2* (two discs: 144 minutes: ADD: 9/97).

Puccini Manon Lescaut. **Mirella Freni** (sop) Manon Lescaut; **Luciano Pavarotti** (ten) Des Grieux; **Dwayne Croft** (bar) Lescaut; **Giuseppe Taddei** (bar) Geronte; **Ramon Vargas** (ten) Edmondo; **Cecilia Bartoli** (mez) Singer; **Federico Davia** (bass) Innkeeper, Captain; **Anthony Laciura** (ten) Dancing Master; **Paul Groves** (ten) Lamplighter; **James Courtney** (bass) Sergeant; **Chorus and Orchestra of the Metropolitan Opera / James Levine.** Decca Ⓕ 440 200-2DHO2 (two discs: 120 minutes: DDD: 11/93). Notes, text and translation included. Recorded 1992.

With Luciano Pavarotti as a powerful Des Grieux, James Levine conducts a comparably big-boned performance of *Manon Lescaut*, bringing out the red-blooded drama of Puccini's first big success, while not ignoring its warmth and tender poetry in exceptionally full, vivid sound with the voices well in front of the orchestra. In the title-role Freni's performance culminates in an account of the big Act 4 aria, more involving and passionate than any of the others on the versions listed below with the voice showing no signs of wear, and with her sudden change of face at the words "terra di pace" ("a land of peace") bringing a magical lightening of tone. That aria makes a thrilling climax, when too often this act can seem a letdown. In this as in so much else, Levine conveys the tensions and atmosphere of a stage performance in a way that owes much to his experience at the Metropolitan. More completely than the other versions, each with very great merits, it avoids the feeling of a studio performance. Reactions to Pavarotti as Des Grieux will differ widely. The closeness of balance means that in volume his singing rarely drops below *mezzo forte*, but there is little harm in having so passionate a portrait of Des Grieux as Pavarotti's. Needless to say, the hero's big emotional climaxes in each of the first three acts come over at full force. The rest of the cast is strong too, with Dwayne Croft a magnificent Lescaut who, as well as singing with rich, firm tone, brings out the character's wry humour. Many collectors will count this a clear first choice among current versions. For the sheer power of Puccinian drama, vividly conveyed, it will be hard to beat.

Additional recommendations ...
...Soloists; Chorus of the Royal Opera House, Covent Garden; Philharmonia Orchestra /
Giuseppe Sinopoli. DG Ⓕ 413 893-2GH2 (two discs: DDD: 3/85).
...Soloists; Chorus and Orchestra of La Scala, Milan / Tullio Serafin.
EMI mono Ⓕ CDS5 56301-2* (two discs: 120 minutes: 9/86).
...Soloists; Jack Gregoor Choir; Belgian Radio and TV Philharmonic Chorus and Orchestra /
Alexander Rahbari. Naxos Ⓢ 8 660019/20 (two discs: 126 minutes: DDD: 12/92).

Puccini La rondine[a]. Le Villi[b] – Prelude; L'Abbandono; La Tregenda; Ecco la casa ... Torna ai
felice dì. Morire![c]. [a]**Angela Gheorghiu** (sop) Magda; **Roberto Alagna** (ten) Ruggero;
[a]**Inva Mula-Tchako** (sop) Lisetta; [a]**William Matteuzzi** (ten) Prunier; [a]**Alberto Rinaldi** (bar)
Rambaldo; [a]**Patricia Biccire** (sop) Yvette; [a]**Patrizia Ciofi** (sop) Bianca; [a]**Monica Bacelli** (mez)
Suzy; [a]**Riccardo Simonetti** (bar) Périchaud; [a]**Toby Spence** (ten) Gobin; [a]**Enrico Fissore** (bar)
Crébillon; [ab]**London Voices**; [ab]**London Symphony Orchestra** / Antonio Pappano ([c]pf).
EMI Ⓕ CDS5 56338-2 (two discs: 131 minutes: DDD: 5/97). Texts and translations included.
Recorded 1996. *Gramophone Editor's choice. Gramophone Award Winner 1997.* 🅖🅖

It could not be more welcome when a recording transforms a work, as this one does, setting it on a
new plane. *La rondine* ("The Swallow"), Puccini's ill-timed attempt to emulate Lehár in the world of
operetta, completed during the First World War, has long been counted his most serious failure, "a
bird with half-broken wings" as Mosco Carner called it. Puccini's cunning has never been in doubt
either, for he and his librettists cleverly interweave elements not just of *La traviata* but of *The Merry
Widow* and *Die Fledermaus*, not to mention earlier Puccini operas. His melodic style may for the most
part be simpler than before, but one striking theme follows another with a profusion that any other
composer might envy. What Pappano reveals far more than before is the subtlety with which Puccini
interweaves his themes and motifs, with conversational passages made spontaneous-sounding in their
flexibility. Above all, Pappano consistently brings out the poetry, drawing on emotions far deeper
than are suggested by this operetta-like subject, thanks also to Gheorghiu's superb performance,
translating her mastery as Violetta to this comparable character. Magda's first big solo, "Che il bel
sogno di Doretta" (neatly forecast by the poet, Prunier, in the preceding section) finds Gheorghiu at
her most ravishing, tenderly expressive in her soaring phrases, opening out only at the final climax.
From first to last, often with a throb in the voice, her vocal acting convinces you that Magda's are
genuine, deep emotions, painful at the end, intensified by the ravishing beauty of her voice.

As Ruggero, the hero, Alagna has a far less complex role, winningly characterizing the ardent young
student. What will specially delight Puccinians in this set is that he is given an entrance aria about
Paris, "Parigi e un citta", which transforms his otherwise minimal contribution to Act 1. The
partnership of Gheorghiu and Alagna highlights the way that Puccini in the melodic lines for each of
his central characters makes Ruggero's more forthright, Magda's more complex. Among much else,
the role of the poet, Prunier, is transformed thanks to the clear-toned William Matteuzzi in what is
normally a *comprimario* role. Not only is his relationship with Magda beautifully drawn, his
improbable affair with the skittish maid, Lisetta, is made totally convincing too, mirroring Magda's
affair. The fill-ups are welcome too, particularly as neither of the rival sets has any. The excerpts from
Le Villi, warm and the dramatic, make one wish that Pappano could go on to record that first of
Puccini's operas, with Alagna giving a ringing account of Roberto's aria, as he does of the song,
Morire! – with Pappano at the piano. Originally an album-piece written for a wartime charity, Puccini
used it, transposed up a semitone, with different words, as the entrance aria for Ruggero. Altogether
a set to treasure for bringing out the full genius of a tenderly moving work too long discounted.

Additional recommendations ...
...Le Villi. Soloists; Ambrosian Opera Chorus; National Philharmonic Orchestra / Lorin Maazel.
CBS Masterworks Ⓕ MK76890 (DDD: 5/88).
...La rondine. Soloists; Ambrosian Opera Chorus; London Symphony Orchestra / Lorin Maazel.
CBS Ⓕ M2K37852 (DDD: 10/85).

Puccini Il Tabarro[a]. **Tito Gobbi** (bar) Michele; **Margaret Mas** (sop) Giorgetta; **Giacinto Prandelli**
(ten) Luigi; **Piero De Palma** (ten) Tinca; **Plinio Clabassi** (bas) Talpa; **Miriam Pirazzini** (mez)
Frugola.
Puccini Suor Angelica[b]. **Victoria de los Angeles** (sop) Suor Angelica; **Fedora Barbieri** (mez)
Princess; **Mina Doro** (mez) Abbess, Mistress of the novices; **Corinna Vozza** (mez) Sister Monitor;
Lidia Marimpietri (sop) Suor Genovieffa, Almoner Sister I; **Santa Chissari** (sop) Suor Osmina,
Almoner Sister II, Novice; **Anna Marcangeli** (sop) Suor Dolcina; **Teresa Cantarini** (mez)
Infirmary Sister; **Silvia Bertona** (sop) Lay Sister I; **Maria Huder** (mez) Lay Sister II.
Puccini Gianni Schicchi[c]. **Tito Gobbi** (bar) Gianni Schicchi; **Victoria de los Angeles** (sop) Lauretta;
Carlo del Monte (ten) Rinuccio; **Anna Maria Canali** (Zita); **Adelio Zagonara** (ten) Gherardo;
Lidia Marimpietri (sop) Nella; **Claudio Cornoldi** (ten) Gherardino; **Saturno Meletti** (bass) Betto
di Signa; **Paolo Montarsolo** (bass) Simone; **Fernando Valentini** (bar) Marco; **Giuliana Raymondi**
(sop) La Cieca; **Rome Opera Chorus; Rome Opera Orchestra** / [a]**Vincenzo Bellezza**, [b]**Tullio Serafin**,
[c]**Gabriele Santini**. EMI mono/[c]stereo Ⓜ CMS7 64165-2* (three discs: 161 minutes: ADD: 6/93).
Texts and translations included. Item marked [a] from HMV ALP1355 (5/56), [b]ALP1577 (6/58),
[c]ASD295 (12/59).

Unless you insist on the most up-to-date recorded sound, or on buying the individual operas of Puccini's trilogy separately (and that, regrettably, is becoming harder to do these days; most available recordings come as indivisible boxed sets) this is the classic *Trittico*, and the obvious first recommendation. Gobbi's blackly authoritative but pitiful Michele in *Il Tabarro* and his genially authoritative Schicchi (the two outer panels of the triptych *do* match, in an odd sort of way) have seldom been equalled, let alone surpassed. De los Angeles's Angelica is more purely and movingly sung than any other on record, and her Lauretta in *Gianni Schicchi* is enchanting. Could it be said, even so, that *Il Tabarro* is the weak link in this trilogy? It is a three-hander, surely, and neither the soprano nor the tenor are quite in Gobbi's league? Mas is a bit plummy and mezzoish, true, but the slight implication this gives that Giorgetta's liaison with the young stevedore Luigi is her last chance at escape from a hateful life and a marriage that has soured adds an extra twinge of pain to a plot in which all three principals are victims. And in this context Prandelli's slightly strenuous rawness of tone characterizes Luigi rather well. In *Gianni Schicchi*, Carlo del Monte as Rinuccio also looks like under-casting but in fact he's one of the few tenors who've recorded the part who sounds convincingly young, and his ardent praise of Florence and the 'new men' who are reinvigorating the city is proudly sung. Here, too, Gobbi is surrounded by a constellation of pungent character actors, and de los Angeles in *Suor Angelica* is teamed with a charmingly girlish, impulsive Genovieffa and with Fedora Barbieri's rigidly implacable Princess (is there another parallel here, with the stiff-necked Zita, 'La Vecchia', in *Gianni Schicchi*?). With generally very stylish conducting throughout (only Belezza in *Il Tabarro* is a touch staid, and he omits nearly all of Puccini's off-stage sound effects) only the rather elderly recordings might be seen as a drawback. EMI boldly label the whole set 'stereo', but both *Il Tabarro* and *Suor Angelica* sound like minimally 'processed' mono: a touch congested in fuller pasages, a hint of fizzy brightness here and there but nothing that's not abundantly worth putting up with for such performances as these.

Additional recommendations ...

...Suor Angelica. **Soloists; Munich Children's Choir; Bavarian Radio Chorus; Munich Radio Orchestra / Giuseppe Patanè.** RCA Victor Classics ⑧ 74321 40575-2 (56 minutes: ADD: 9/97).

...Il Tabarro. **Soloists; Jaak Gregoor Choir; Belgian Radio and TV Philharmonic Chorus and Orchestra, Brussels / Alexander Rahbari.** Koch International Classics ⑤ DICD920209 (48 minutes: DDD: 4/95).

...Il Tabarro. **Soloists; Bavarian Radio Chorus; Munich Radio Orchestra / Giuseppe Patanè.** RCA Victor Classics ⑧ 74321 40581-2 (51 minutes: ADD: 9/97).

Puccini Tosca. **Maria Callas** (sop) Floria Tosca; **Giuseppe di Stefano** (ten) Mario Cavaradossi; **Tito Gobbi** (bar) Baron Scarpia; **Franco Calabrese** (bass) Cesare Angelotti; **Angelo Mercuriali** (ten) Spoletta; **Melchiorre Luise** (bass) Sacristan; **Dario Caselli** (bass) Sciarrone, Gaoler; **Alvaro Cordova** (treb) Shepherd Boy; **Chorus and Orchestra of La Scala, Milan / Victor de Sabata.** EMI mono ⒻCDS5 56304-2* (two discs: 108 minutes: ADD: 9/85). Notes, text and translation included. From Columbia 33CX1094/5 (12/53). Recorded 1953. *Gramophone classical 100.* ⓺⓺⓺

In the course of *Tosca*'s history there have been many notable interpreters, but few have been able to encompass so unerringly the love, jealousy and eventual courage of Tosca as well as Maria Callas. Her resinous, sensuous tone, her wonderful diction, and her inborn passion filled every phrase of the score with special and individual meaning. In 1953 she was in her early prime, the tone seldom prey to those uneasy moments on high that marred her later recordings, and with the vital, vivid conducting of Victor de Sabata, her performance has rightly attained classic status. Giuseppe di Stefano is the ardent Cavaradossi, his tone forward and vibrant in that way peculiar to Italians. Tito Gobbi's cynical, snarling Scarpia, aristocratic in manner, vicious in meaning, remains unique in that part on record. The mono recording stands up well to the test of time.

Additional recommendations ...

...**Soloists; Vienna State Opera Chorus; Vienna Philharmonic Orchestra / Herbert von Karajan.** Decca Grand Opera Ⓜ 421 670-2DM2 (two discs: 114 minutes: ADD: 1/89).

...**Soloists; Paris Opéra Chorus and Conservatoire Orchestra / Georges Prêtre.** EMI Ⓜ CMS7 69974-2 (two discs: 112 minutes: DDD: 8/89).

...**Soloists; Slovak Philharmonic Chorus; Czecho-Slovak Radio Symphony Orchestra, Bratislava / Alexander Rahbari.** Naxos ⑤ 8 660001/2 (two discs: 116 minutes: DDD: 10/91).

...**Soloists; Chorus and Orchestra of the Royal Opera House, Covent Garden / Sir Colin Davis.** Philips Duo Ⓜ 438 359-2PM2 (two discs: 118 minutes: ADD: 8/93).

Puccini Tosca (sung in English). **Jane Eaglen** (sop) Tosca; **Dennis O'Neill** (ten) Cavaradossi; **Gregory Yurisich** (bar) Scarpia; **Peter Rose** (bass) Angelotti; **John Daszak** (ten) Spoletta; **Andrew Shore** (bass) Sacristan; **Christopher Booth-Jones** (bass) Sciarrone; **Ashley Holland** (bass) Gaoler; **Charbel Michael** (mez) Shepherd Boy; **Peter Kay Children's Choir; Geoffrey Mitchell Choir; Philharmonia Orchestra / David Parry.** Chandos Ⓕ CHAN3000 (two discs: 118 minutes: DDD: 6/96). Notes and text included. Recorded 1995.

This is an issue to delight far more than devotees of opera in English, a gripping account of Puccini's red-blooded drama. Above all, it offers the first major recording to demonstrate the powers of Jane Eaglen at full stretch in one of the most formidable, vocally satisfying portrayals of the role of Tosca in years. David Parry here demonstrates his full understanding of Puccini and the bite and energy in the playing of the Philharmonia, not to mention the expressive warmth in the love music, will have you riveted as though hearing the music for the first time. The opulent Chandos sound, cleanly focused with plenty of atmosphere and presence, adds to the impact, whether in the power of the big tuttis or in the subtlety of whispered string *pianissimos*. Off-stage effects are nicely evocative, though the sequence of bell-sounds at the start of Act 3 is so clear it suggests an orchestra rather than a Roman landscape. Otherwise, the slightly forward balance of voices against orchestra is very well judged for a set in which the audibility of words is paramount. The translation is Edmund Tracey's as used by ENO at the Coliseum and generally very good because unobtrusive, even if you get occasional awkwardnesses. Eaglen is well matched by Dennis O'Neill as Cavaradossi, aptly Italianate in every register, and betraying only a slight unevenness occasionally, not a wobble, on high notes under pressure. Gregory Yurisich makes a powerful Scarpia, younger-sounding than most, and therefore a more plausible lover. The others are well cast too, notably Peter Rose as an outstanding, fresh-voiced Angelotti.

Puccini Turandot. **Dame Joan Sutherland** (sop) Princess Turandot; **Luciano Pavarotti** (ten) Calaf; **Montserrat Caballé** (sop) Liù; **Tom Krause** (bar) Ping; **Pier Francesco Poli** (ten) Pang, Prince of Persia; **Piero De Palma** (ten) Pong; **Sir Peter Pears** (ten) Emperor Altoum; **Nicolai Ghiaurov** (bass) Timur; **Sabin Markov** (bar) Mandarin; **Wandsworth School Boys' Choir; John Alldis Choir; London Philharmonic Orchestra / Zubin Mehta.** Decca Ⓕ 414 274-2DH2 (two discs: 117 minutes: ADD: 5/85). From SET561 (9/73). Notes, text and translation included. Recorded 1972. ❻Ⓖ❻

Turandot is a psychologically complex work fusing appalling sadism with self-sacrificing devotion. The icy Princess of China has agreed to marry any man of royal blood who can solve three riddles she has posed. If he fails his head will roll. Calaf, the son of the exiled Tartar king Timur, answers all the questions easily and when Turandot hesitates to accept him, magnanimously offers her a riddle in return – "What is his name?". Liù, Calaf's faithful slave-girl, is tortured but rather than reveal his identity kills herself. Turandot finally capitulates, announcing that his name is Love. Dame Joan Sutherland's assumption of the title role is statuesque, combining regal poise with a more human warmth, whilst Montserrat Caballé is a touchingly sympathetic Liù, skilfully steering the character away from any hint of the mawkish. Pavarotti's Calaf is a heroic figure in splendid voice and the chorus is handled with great power, baying for blood at one minute, enraptured with Liù's nobility at the next. Mehta conducts with great passion and a natural feel for Puccini's wonderfully tempestuous drama. Well recorded.

Additional recommendations ...

...Soloists; **Chorus and Orchestra of La Scala, Milan / Tullio Serafin.**
EMI Ⓜ CDS5 56307-2* (two discs: 118 minutes: ADD: 11/87).

...Soloists; **Rome Opera Chorus and Orchestra / Francesco Molinari-Pradelli.**
EMI Ⓜ CMS7 69327-2* (two discs: 112 minutes: ADD).

Further listening ...

...Crisantemi. *Coupled with works by* **Donizetti** and **Verdi** Alberni Quartet CRD CRD3366 (5/89).

...Messe di Gloria in A flat major[a]. *Coupled with* **Mozart** Vesperae solennes de confessore – Laudate Dominum[b]. [a]Soloists; [b]**Dame Kiri Te Kanawa** (sop); [a]**West German Radio Chorus;** [b]**London Symphony Chorus;** [a]**Frankfurt Radio Symphony Orchestra / Eliahu Inbal;** [b]**London Symphony Orchestra / Sir Colin Davis.** Philips 434 170-2PM (1/93).

...Salve del ciel regina. Requiem. Vexilla regis. *Coupled with works by* **Janáček** Shelley Everall (sop); **William Kendall** (ten); **Peter Harvey** (bar); **Douglas Paterson** (va); **Christopher Monks** (org); **Gonville and Caius College Choir, Cambridge / Geoffrey Webber.** ASV CDDCA914 (6/95).

Máximo Pujol

Argentinian 1957

Pujol Five Preludes. Elegía por la muerte de un tanguero. Sonatina. Suite Buenos Aires[a]. Tangata de Agosto[b]. **María Isabel Siewers** (gtr); [a]**Amiram Ganz** (vn); [b]**Stamitz Quartet** (Vitězslav Cernoch, Josef Kekula, vns; Jan Pěruška, va; Vladimir Leixner, vc). ASV Ⓕ CDDCA970 (76 minutes: DDD: 9/97). Recorded 1995-1996.

The music of Máximo Diego Pujol is deeply imbued with his native country's traditions. His Five Preludes were written when he was 20, and their improvisatory character may partly be due to the fact that at that time he had had no formal musical education: nevertheless the reflective "Tristón" reveals a genuine talent and sensitivity, and "Candombe en mi" has rhythmic vitality. The *Sonatina* he wrote two years later shows greater resource in its layout and its harmony, and while conspicuously utilizing Argentinian dance forms is fairly sparing of clichés. The other work here for solo guitar, the elegy for Piazzolla, dates from a decade later. Its second movement exploits an obsessive figure, but its deeply felt conclusion is impressive: the finale openly espouses tango rhythm, perhaps implying faith in its capacity to endure even after the death of one of its great interpreters. The suite with violin depicts various *barrios* of Buenos Aires: both the first movement, a lively classical tango with melancholy interludes, and the third, a *candombe*, are catchy, and the romantic second movement shows a decided melodic gift. María Isabel Siewers is an admirable guitarist, with a clean technique, subtle nuances of rhythm and tone, and in the *Elegy* her differentiation of simultaneous tonal planes is exemplary. She is well partnered by the other players; and the recording is excellent, beautifully clear and resonant.

Additional recommendation
...Preludios – Nos. 2, 3 and 5. *Coupled with works by various composers.* **Jason Vieaux** (gtr).
Naxos Ⓢ 8 553449 (64 minutes: DDD: 11/97). *See review in the Collections section;
refer to the Index.*

Giovanni Punto
Bohemian 1746-1803

Suggested listening ...
...Horn Concertos – No. 5 in F major; No. 6 in E flat major; No. 10 in F major;
No. 11 in E major. *Coupled with works by various composers.*
Barry Tuckwell (hn); **English Chamber Orchestra / Sir Neville Marriner.**
EMI Forte CZS5 69395-2 (2/97). *See review in the Collections section; refer to the Index.*

Henry Purcell
British 1659-1695

Purcell Complete Ayres for the Theatre – The History of Dioclesian, or The Prophetess, Z627[b].
King Arthur, Z628[b]. The Fairy Queen, Z629[b]. The Indian Queen, Z630[b]. The Married Beau,
Z603[a]. The Old Bachelor, Z607[b]. Amphitryon, Z572[a]. The Double Dealer, Z592[a]. Distressed
Innocence, Z577[a]. The Gordian Knot Unty'd, Z597[a]. Abdelazer, Z570[a]. Bonduca, Z574[a].
The Virtuous Wife, Z611[a]. Sonata While the Sun Rises in "The Indian Queen"[b]. Overture in
G minor[a]. Sir Anthony Love, Z588 – Overture[a]. Timon of Athens, Z632[a]. The Indian Queen,
Z630 – Symphony[b]. [a]**The Parley of Instruments;** [b]**The Parley of Instruments Baroque Orchestra /
Roy Goodman.** Hyperion Ⓕ CDA67001/3 (three discs: 209 minutes: DDD: 10/95). Recorded 1994.
Gramophone Editor's choice.   Ⓖ
The difference between this latest 'completist' project and the others is that all these works were
published within 18 months of Purcell's death. The 13 suites of choice movements from plays and
semi-operas, entitled *A Collection of Ayres, compos'd for the Theatre, and upon other occasions,* may
well have been the editing work of Purcell's brother, Daniel. Whoever it was had a rare combination
of musical integrity and commercial flair: the pieces lifted from Purcell's interpolations to plays are
often reordered and arranged with a deftness and charm which conveys the spirit of the theatre as
well as heightening the loss and poignancy of Purcell's passing. How moving the Rondeau Minuet
from *The Gordian Knot Unty'd* must have seemed to those who knew and loved Purcell. As a major
retrospective of Purcell's life in the theatre, the *Ayres for the Theatre* mainly comprise instrumental
dances from their original sources, though there are several movements readapted from sung airs,
such as "Fairest isle" from *King Arthur* and "If love's a sweet passion" from *The Fairy Queen.*
    The tunes are wonderful and varied, the inner part-writing as skilful as Muffat and Rameau
(to name two other composers who bring fine counterpoint to slight forms) and the rhythmic
imagination knows no bounds. Even so, this is not music where more than a suite at a time can be
recommended for ultimate satisfaction: stop while you still want more. And more you will most
certainly want with Roy Goodman's alert and distinctive direction. About a decade ago, Goodman
and Peter Holman recorded this music in a series of programmes for the BBC alongside suites by
Purcell's peers. There is a greater aplomb and colour nowadays, a far keener sense of shape and
understanding to Purcell's blend of elusive side-glances and uninhibited bravura. If a few of the
movements sound a touch mundane and lack dynamism as one follows on from another, the positive
side is that the performances are never forced and rarely mannered. For the semi-opera 'suites',
Goodman employs a full orchestra. What The Parley of Instruments have in abundance is a cordiality
of expression which seems so absolutely right, especially in the slower airs. A most welcome release.
Additional recommendations ...
...Ayres for the Theatre – Suites: Dioclesian; King Arthur; The Fairy Queen; The Indian Queen.
Tafelmusik / Jeanne Lamon. Sony Classical Vivarte Ⓕ SK66169 (71 minutes: DDD: 2/96). ✍
...The Indian Queen – Symphony[ac]. Yorkshire Feast Song, Z333 – Symphony in D major[bcd].
King Arthur – Symphony in C major[abd]. *Coupled with works by various composers.*
[a]**Frank de Bruine** (ob); [b]**Mark Bennett,** [c]**Michael Laird** (tpts); [d]**Judy Tarling** (vn);
The Parley of Instruments / Peter Holman. Hyperion Ⓕ CDA66817 (70 minutes: DDD: 7/96).
...Abdelazar – Rondeau. Trumpet Sonata No. 2 in D major, Z850. *Coupled with works by various
composers.* **Wynton Marsalis** (tpt); **English Chamber Orchestra / Anthony Newman.**
Sony Classical Ⓕ SK66244 (58 minutes: DDD: 11/96).
...Ayres for the Theatre (arr. Steele-Perkins). *Coupled with works by various composers.*
Crispian Steele-Perkins (tpt); **Bournemouth Sinfonietta / Richard Studt** (vn). Carlton Classics
Ⓜ 30366 0038-2 (76 minutes: DDD: 4/97). *See review in the Collections section; refer to the Index.*

Purcell Fantasia in F major, Z745, "Upon one note". Three Fantasias, Z732-4. Nine Fantasias,
Z735-43. In Nomines – G minor Z746; G minor, Z747, "Dorian". **Hespèrion XX**
(Sophie Watillon, Eunice Brandao, Sergi Casademunt, Wieland Kuijken, Marianne Müller,
Philippe Pierlot, viols) **/ Jordi Savall** (treb viol). Auvidis Astrée Ⓕ E8536
(54 minutes: DDD: 9/96). ✍ Recorded 1994.

Purcell's music for viols represents the final flowering of the English consort tradition. While we know when many of them were composed (the four-part *fantasias* date from the summer of 1680 when Purcell was in residence with the court at Windsor Castle) no one has yet satisfactorily explained why they exist and for whom they were composed. Viol consorts had been out of fashion for at least 20 years, ousted by the Italian violin sonatas and French ballet music. Purcell's polished essays in this antique form were neither published nor, apparently, widely circulated. Nevertheles, we cherish them today for their sublime expressiveness and craftsmanship. It would have been surprising if Hespèrion XX had not recorded the complete Purcell *Fantasias* to mark the recent tercentenary. Jordi Savall and his group have achieved a state of abstraction seldom experienced in music. It almost goes without saying that Hespèrion's playing is always extremely beautiful: the music demands it. But any need to be rhetorical, to lean on a dissonance or pronounce a cadence, has been outgrown and discarded. The scale within which these features and more (most notably the rhythmic life of the music) are articulated is so minimal, so subtle and yet ultimately so compelling, that from the first track the listener is transported into a rarefied aural dimension usually reserved for single movements or even phrases. Don't miss it.

Additional recommendation ...

...Fantasia in B flat major, Z736. *Coupled with works by various composers.* **Kronos Quartet.**
Nonesuch Ⓕ 7559-79457-2 (69 minutes: DDD: 12/97). *Gramophone Editor's choice.*
See review in the Collections section; refer to the Index.

Purcell Fantasias – three part, Z732-4; four part, Z735-43; five part, "upon one note", Z745[a].
In Nomines – G minor, Z746[b]; G minor, "Dorian", Z747[c]. [abc]**Joanna Levine,** [bc]**Susanna Pell,**
[c]**Catherine Finnis** (viols); **Phantasm** (Laurence Dreyfus, Wendy Gillespie, Jonathan Manson,
Markku Luolajan-Mikkola, viols). Simax Ⓕ PSC1124 (51 minutes: DDD: 2/97). ✍
Recorded 1994. *Gramophone Award Winner 1997.* ⒼⒼ

Purcell's contrapuntal mastery is dazzling, with the points of imitation in the various sections of each fantasia treated in double or triple counterpoint, inversion, augmentation and all other technical devices – for instance, the initial subjects of fantasias Z739, 742 and 743 at once appear in mirror images of themselves – but the music's deep expressiveness and the dramatic tension created by its chromaticisms and unpredictable harmonies make it clear that he certainly had performance in mind (a matter of some dispute), even if, because of the king's dislike of such intellectual pursuits, only privately by conservative-minded music-lovers. It is this expressiveness which Phantasm emphasize in this recording, both in their varied dynamics and in their use of vibrato. They are, if anything, even more striking than Fretwork. Fretwork's approach is, on the whole, plainer – one might even say more severe: speeds here are in general faster and there is rather more variety of bowing and hence of articulation. If it weren't that rival versions inevitably affect each other's sales, one could rejoice that such fine, though differing, readings of these superb works were available.

Additional recommendation ...

...Fantasias – three part, Z732-34; four part, Z735-43; five part, Z745; A minor (incomplete).
In Nomines – Z746; Z747[a]. **Fretwork;** [a]**Imogen Seth-Smith** (viol).
Virgin Classics Veritas Ⓕ VC5 45062-2 (55 minutes: DDD: 5/95). ✍ *Gramophone Editor's record of the month.* Ⓖ

Purcell 12 Sonatas of Three Parts, Z790-801 – No. 1 in G minor; No. 2 in B flat major; No. 3 in D minor; No. 4 in F major; No. 5 in A minor; No. 6 in C minor; No. 7 in E minor; No. 8 in G major; No. 9 in C minor; No. 10 in A minor; No. 11 in F minor; No. 12 in D major.
Pavlo Beznosiuk, Rachel Podger (vns); **Christophe Coin** (bass viol); **Christopher Hogwood** (org).
L'Oiseau-Lyre Ⓕ 444 449-2OH (72 minutes: DDD: 4/96). Recorded 1994.

If the lyrical refinement and other-worldliness of the *Fantasias* is largely absent, Purcell manipulates the flighty drama of the Italian spirit with a seasoned individuality. For a start he never entirely rejects the Englishness of the *Fantasias*, both in terms of harmonic unpredictability and the contrapuntal texture which forced Roger North to describe the sonatas as "clog'd with somewhat of an English vein". Sonata No. 5 is a case in point and one which the performers here relish with an imploring legato and doleful accentuation, plentifully endowed with rhetorical detail. Indeed, characterization – and just how far one goes in music whose gestures are mapped out with great clarity – is what makes this such an interesting recording. There is a grandeur and interpretational scope which gives each sonata its own measure of distinction. The violin playing of Pavlo Beznosiuk and Rachel Podger is beautifully matched and coloured, warm-toned in the opening of the Corellian Sixth Sonata but 'just and quick', crisp and precise in the canzona-style *allegros* of Sonatas Nos. 2 and 12. Hogwood performs on a chamber organ throughout (often in tandem – when Purcell decrees it – with Christophe Coin's eloquent if slightly restrained gamba), unlike Richard Egarr in London Baroque's polished and finely-crafted accounts who varies the texture with a harpsichord. However, youthful abandon and effervescent personality are what makes this disc such an infectious addition to the catalogue. We have distinguished performances from the Purcell Quartet but this is chamber music playing which seeks out new territory.

Additional recommendations ...

...Nos. 1-7. Pavans – G minor, Z752[a]; B flat major, Z750; A minor, Z749. [a]**Risa Browder** (vn);
Purcell Quartet. Chandos Ⓕ CHAN8591 (51 minutes: DDD: 1/89). ✍

...Nos. 8-12. Ten Sonatas in Four Parts, Z802-11 – No. 1 in B minor; No. 2 in E flat major. Fantasia upon a Ground in D and F major[a]. Pavans – A major, Z748; G minor, Z751. Chacony in G minor, Z730[a]. [a]**Risa Browder** (vn); **Purcell Quartet.** Chandos Ⓟ CHAN8663 (53 minutes: DDD: 10/89). ✏

Purcell A Choice Collection of Lessons – Suites: No. 1 in G major, Z660; No. 2 in G minor, Z661; No. 3 in G major, Z662; No. 4 in A minor, Z663; No. 5 in C major, Z666; No. 6 in D major, Z667; No. 7 in D minor, Z668; No. 8 in F major, Z669; Chaconne in G minor, Z T680. Ground in Gamut in G major, Z645. Ground in C minor, Z D221. Ground in D minor, Z D222. Prelude in G minor. The Second Part of Musick's Hand-maid – A New Ground in E minor, Z T682; Suite in C major, Z665. Sarabande with Division, Z654. Hornpipe in D minor, "Round O", Z T684. **Sophie Yates** (hpd). Chandos Chaconne Ⓟ CHAN0587 (70 minutes: DDD: 3/96). ✏ Recorded 1994.
Purcell A Choice Collection of Lessons – Suites: No. 1 in G major, Z660; No. 2 in G minor, Z661; No. 3 in G major, Z662; No. 4 in A minor, Z663; No. 5 in C major, Z666; No. 6 in D major, Z667; No. 7 in D minor, Z668; No. 8 in F major, Z669. The Second Part of Musick's Hand-maid – March in C major, Z647; Minuet in A minor, Z649; A New Scotch Tune in G major, Z655; A New Ground in E minor, Z T682; A New Irish Tune in G major, Z646; Sefauchi's Farewell in D minor, Z656. Ground in Gamut in G major, Z645. Ground in C minor, Z T681. Ground in D minor, Z D222. Air in G major, Z641. Air in D minor, Z T675. Hornpipe in D minor, "Round O", Z T684. Hornpipe in E minor, Z T685. **Olivier Baumont** (hpd). Erato Ⓟ 0630-10695-2 (64 minutes: DDD: 3/96). ✏ Recorded 1995.

Considering Purcell's long involvement with keyboard instruments, it is curious, and certainly disappointing, that he wrote so little of any substance for them. So far, they have attracted little attention, but these two recommendable discs go far to redress the balance. Not many are likely to echo the late Professor Westrup's claim that the eight three- or four-movement suites are "worthy predecessors of Bach's"; but they do contain fine individual movements, such as the Almands of Nos. 8 and, particularly, 7. Other than the suites, the harpsichord works consist of brief dance movements, popular tunes (including the satiric anti-English Irish *Lilliburlero*, unaccountably adopted by the BBC for their World Service news bulletins), grounds (of which Purcell was a supreme master) and transcriptions from his theatre music. There is a good deal of overlap between these two discs – the suites, three grounds and the *Round O* Hornpipe which Britten used as the basis for his virtuosic orchestral *tour d'horizon*.

Sophie Yates, playing on a copy of a 1681 Vaudry harpsichord, takes it at Britten's sturdily stately pace; Olivier Baumont, on the 1664 Hatley virginals at Fenton House in London (though employing that collection's 1752 Kirckman harpsichord for the suites) takes it up-tempo as a real hornpipe, to startling effect. Features of Yates's playing, throughout, are its freshness and neatness (especially of ornaments), and she is always stylish – her unmeasured preludes convey a true improvisatory feeling – but overall her readings are more sober than Baumont's and have less sense of fantasy. He shows more boldness, more dash in the energetic Preludes to Suites Nos. 2, 3 and 5, is more springy in all the corants, and almost everywhere adopts faster speeds which tend to give the miniature movements more character. In two of the grounds, particularly the moving E minor "Here the deities approve", he also makes the melody line stand out better. (Incidentally, there is a confusion in Chandos's notes, which state that a C minor ground from the ode *Ye tuneful Muses* – given a mixed-up catalogue number too! – is included, though in fact it isn't.) Baumont extends the Fifth Suite with a skippety Jigg taken from the 1689 volume which was the only one to be printed in Purcell's lifetime, and is daring enough to precede the Seventh Suite (which has no prelude) with a Prelude from a seventeenth-century manuscript now in Oxford which he has transposed for the occasion.

Additional recommendation ...

...A Choice Collection of Lessons – Suites: Nos. 1-8. Ground in C minor, T D221. The Second Part of Musick's Hand-maid – A New Scotch Tune in G major, Z655; A New Ground in E minor, Z T682. Hornpipe in E minor, Z T685. **Kenneth Gilbert** (hpd). Harmonia Mundi Ⓟ HMC90 1496 (67 minutes: DDD: 5/95). ✏

Purcell Complete Anthems and Services, Volume 7 – I was glad when they said unto me[a]. I was glad when they said unto me, Z19[b]. O consider my adversity, Z32[c]. Beati omnes qui timent Dominum, Z131[d]. In the black dismal dungeon of despair, Z190[e]. Save me, O God, Z51[f]. Morning and Evening Service in B flat major, Z230 – Te Deum; Jubilate[g]. Thy Way, O God, is Holy, Z60[h]. Funeral Sentences for the death of Queen Mary II[i] – Drum Processional; March and Canzona in C minor, Z860; Man that is born of Woman, Z27; In the midst of Life, Z17b; Thou know'st Lord, Z58b; Thou know'st Lord, Z58c. [dfgi]**Mark Kennedy,** [dg]**Eamonn O'Dwyer,** [fg]**James Goodman** (trebs); [e]**Susan Gritton** (sop); [fg]**James Bowman,** [g]**Nigel Short** (altos); [bcdi]**Rogers Covey-Crump,** [bcfghi]**Charles Daniels,** [g]**Mark Milhofer** (tens); [bcdfghi]**Michael George,** [g]**Robert Evans** (basses); [b]**New College Choir, Oxford;** [acfi]**King's Consort Choir; King's Consort /** **Robert King.** Hyperion Ⓟ CDA66677 (70 minutes: DDD: 6/94). ✏ Recorded 1993.

This recording is made up predominantly of anthems, devotional songs and a morning service (a functional, though not perfunctory, setting of the *Te Deum* and *Jubilate*) most of which disclose the range and quality of the composer's sacred *oeuvre* near its best. Of the two settings of *I was glad*, the first was, until not long ago, thought to be the work of John Blow. This full anthem more than whets our appetite with its agreeable tonal and melodic twists; when the *Gloria* arrives, we are assured that this is vintage Purcell by the sensitive pacing as much as an exquisite contrapuntal denouement. The earlier setting is more poignant. Opening with a string symphony in the spirit of a Locke consort, the music blossoms into a deliciously Elysian melodic fabric. Good sense is made of the overall shape and the soloists are, as ever, excellent. *Beati omnes* is a positive gem; this may well have been written for the composer's wedding. Of the small-scale pieces, *In the black dismal dungeon* is the real masterpiece and it is delivered astutely by the secure and musicianly voice of Susan Gritton. Finally to the funeral pieces. Here we have an ominous procession from the Guild of Ancient Fifes and Drums and the first appearance of four 'flatt' trumpets – as opposed to two plus two sackbuts; the effect of this subtle timbral change makes extraordinary sense of the music, engendering a new grandeur and uncompromising clarity as would have befitted such an occasion. The vocal performances are earthy and impassioned.

Additional recommendations ...

...Complete Anthems and Services, Volume 8 – In thee, O Lord, do I put my trust, Z16. Blessed is the man that feareth the Lord, Z9. Morning and Evening Service in B flat major, Z230 – Benedicite. Jehova, quam multi sunt hostes mei, Z135. Full of wrath, his threatening breath, Z185. Bow down thine ear, O Lord, Z11. Evening Service in G minor, Z231. Be merciful unto me, Z4. They that go down to the sea in ships, Z57. **Soloists; King's Consort and [i]Choir / Robert King.** Hyperion CDA66686 (65 minutes: DDD: 10/94). 🎵   🄶

...Te Deum in D major, Z232. Funeral Sentences – Man that is born of Woman; In the midst of life. Thou know'st Lord. March and Canzona, Z860, The Bell Anthem, "Rejoice in the Lord alway". Z49. Remember not, Lord, our offences, Z50. Blow up the trumpet in Sion, Z10. Hear my prayer, O Lord, Z15. My heart is inditing, Z30. O Lord God of hosts, Z37.
Soloists; Ghent Collegium Vocale / Philippe Herreweghe.
Harmonia Mundi Ⓕ HMC90 1462 (68 minutes: DDD: 2/94). 🎵

...Complete Anthems and Services, Volume 9 – The Lord is my light, Z55[a]. The Lord is King, the earth may be glad thereof, Z54[b]. Blessed is he whose unrighteousness is forgiven, Z8[c]. O Lord God of hosts, Z37[d]. Let God arise, Z23[e]. Morning and Evening Service in B flat major, Z230 – Cantate Domino; Deus misereatur[f]. Blessed be the Lord my strength, Z6[g]. O Lord our governor, Z141[h]. In guilty night (Saul and the Witch of Endor), Z134[i]. [i]**Susan Gritton** (sop); [c]**Connor Burrowes**, [cdfh]**Eamonn O'Dwyer**, [dh]**Mark Kennedy**, [f]**Aaron Webber** (trebs); [cdf]**James Bowman** (alto); [afgi]**Rogers Covey-Crump**, [acdefg]**Charles Daniels**, [ceh]**Mark Padmore**, [d]**Mark Milhofer** (tens); [abcdfghi]**Michael George** (bass); **King's Consort Choir; King's Consort / Robert King.** Hyperion Ⓕ CDA66693 (65 minutes: DDD: 12/94).

...Harmonia Sacra –Lord, what is man?, Z192. O Solitude! my sweetest choice, Z406. In the black dismal dungeon of despair, Z190. Lord, I can suffer Thy rebukes, Z136. Saul and the Witch of Endor, "In guilty night", Z134. Plung'd in the confines of despair, Z142. Awake, ye dead, Z182. The Earth trembled, Z197. My op'ning eyes are purg'd, ZD72. With sick and famish'd eyes, Z200. O, I'm sick of life, Z140. Close thine eyes and sleep secure, Z184. Funeral Sentences for the death of Queen Mary II – Man that is born of woman, Z27. Voluntaries – C major, Z717; G major, Z720[a]. Ground in C minor, T D221[b]. **Gabrieli Consort and Players / Paul McCreesh; Timothy Roberts** ([a]org/[b]hpd). Archiv Produktion Ⓕ 445 829-2AH (70 minutes: DDD: 7/95). 🎵
Gramophone Editor's choice.

...Morning and Evening Service in B flat major, Z230 – Benedicite; Evening Service: Te Deum and Jubilate in D major, Z232. Evening Service in G minor, Z231. O God, thou hast cast us out, Z36. O Lord God of hosts, Z37. Remember not, Lord, our offences, Z50. Lord, how long wilt thou be angry?, Z25. O God, thou art my God, Z35. Funeral Sentences for the death of Queen Mary II – Man that is born of Woman, Z27; Thou know'st Lord, Z58. Jehova, quam multi sunt hostes mei, Z135. My heart is inditing, Z30. O sing unto the Lord, Z44. My beloved spake, Z28. They that go down to the sea in ships, Z57. Praise the Lord, O Jerusalem, Z46. **Various soloists; The English Concert / Simon Preston.** Archiv Produktion The Purcell Collection Ⓜ 447 150-2AP2 (two discs: 157 minutes: DDD: 7/95). 🎵

Purcell The Second Part of Musick's Handmaid – Suite in C major, Z665. A Choice Collection of Lessons, Suites – G major, Z660; G minor, Z661; A minor, Z663; D minor, Z668. **The Harp Consort** (Ellen Hargis, sop; Douglas Nasrawi, alto; Rodrigo Del Pozo, ten; Harry van der Kamp, bass; David Douglass, vn; Nancy Hadden, fls; Hille Perl, lira/bass viol; Jane Achtman, bass viol; Paul O'Dette, lte/gtr; Pat O'Brien, banduria/gtr; Thomas Ihlenfeldt, theorbo/gtr; Steve Player, gtr; Lee Santana, chitarrone/theorbo) **/ Andrew Lawrence-King** (hp/org/hpd/perc). Auvidis Astrée Ⓕ E8564 (75 minutes: DDD: 1/96). Texts and translations included. Recorded 1995.
Andrew Lawrence-King's name is synonymous with many of the most exotic and beguiling recorded sounds of the pre-classical harp, whether as soloist or within a continuo battery. On this occasion he directs a delightful programme of Purcell's songs and instrumental music drawn from the second part of *Musick's Hand-maid* (1687), Playford's attractively titled publication, and the later *Choice Collection of Lessons* (1696). Self-made suites of sung and non-sung airs are indeed an ingenious way of relieving the beautifully opaque but fairly uncompromising sound of the harp, though Lawrence-King's instinctive control of line and delicate embellishment – heard most poignantly in "A New

Ground" (a transcription of "Here the deities approve") – makes a very strong case for an extended recital. He does not chance his arm (except in the delightful way the improvisatory spirit raises its head above the parapet, as in the "Round-O") and breaks up the solo numbers with his own succinct playing on a selection of keyboards, as well as agreeable contributions from a small band of obbligato instrumentalists and four solo singers. Each of the latter is adequate for the task without taking the breath away, although Ellen Hargis's atmospheric "Evening Hymn" comes closer than any with its supple phrasing and crystalline accompaniment on the harp. The longest piece, "Begin the song and strike the living lyre", demonstrates the prowess, in purely vocal terms, of Harry van der Kamp. None of the instrumental music was written specifically for the harp, though Lawrence-King explains in his note how harpists were ever-present at court and one can easily imagine how this instrument could add exotic spice to an evening entertainment; the D minor *Suite* is especially atmospheric, capped only by a wonderfully intimate and finite, "Thou knowest, Lord, the secrets of our hearts". A colourful and inventive Purcell recital, then, quite unlike anything else we have heard in these days of inexhaustible Purcelliana.

Purcell Funeral Sentences for the death of Queen Mary II – Man that is born of woman, Z27; In the midst of life, Z17 (first version); Thou knows't Lord, Z58 (second and third settings). The Queen's Epicedium, "Incassum, Lesbia, rogas", Z383 (with Carys-Anne Lane, sop). March and Canzona in C minor, Z860. Jehova, quam multi sunt hostes mei, Z135 (Andrew Carwood, ten; Michael MCarthy, bass). Remember not, Lord, our offences, Z50. I will sing unto the Lord, Z22. O God, thou art my God, Z35. O God, the King of Glory, Z34. Lord, how long wilt thou be angry?, Z25. Hear my prayer, O Lord, Z15. Blow up the trumpet in Sion, Z10. O God, thou hast cast us out, Z36. Organ Music[a] – Three Voluntaries: C major, Z717, D minor, Z718; G major, Z720. **Oxford Camerata / Jeremy Summerly** with [a]**Laurence Cummings** (org). Naxos Ⓢ 8 553129 (72 minutes: DDD: 2/95). Recorded 1994.

This release enters a growing field with a mouthwatering selection of the best of the anthems with just organ accompaniment. However, some of them are gathered together into a little sequence misleadingly titled "Funeral Music for Queen Mary", for which extra flavour is provided by the *March and Canzona* (Z860) and, in this case, one of the solo elegies, *Incassum, Lesbia*. It's great stuff, but not much of it was actually composed for Queen Mary. Put the Queen from your mind, however, and there are few obstacles to enjoyment. The Oxford Camerata are a young-sounding group, sharply defined and clear if not always as expertly balanced as some of today's chamber choirs. Jeremy Summerly extracts loving and, in the main, convincing performances from them. There are plenty of good things, including an impressive general crescendo in *Hear my prayer*, and indeed it is in longer-range effects such as this that the main successes are scored; smaller details, by contrast – the first dissonance in *Jehova, quam multi sunt hostes mei* for instance, or the odd moment where a little more time is needed – tend to disappoint. But these are small worries; any disc which offered such a 24-carat Purcell selection in performances even half as good as these would be hard to resist.

Additional recommendations ...

...Jehova, quam multi sunt hostes mei, Z135. Miserere mei, Z109. Funeral Sentences for the death of Queen Mary II – Man that is born of woman, Z27; In the midst of life, Z17; Thou know'st Lord, Z58 (first and second settings). The Queen's Epicedium, "Incassum, Lesbia, rogas", Z383. Birthday Ode, "Love's goddess sure was blind', Z331. O dive custos Auriacae domus, Z504. March and Canzona in C minor, Z860. *Coupled with works by various composers.* **The Sixteen Choir and Orchestra / Harry Christophers.** Collins Classics Ⓕ 1425-2 (80 minutes: DDD: 1/95). 🎯

...Funeral Sentences for the death of Queen Mary II[b]. Ode for St Cecilia's Day, 1683, "Welcome to all the pleasures", Z339[a]. Come ye sons of art away, Z323[c]. March and Canzona in C minor, Z860[d]. Funeral Music for the death of Queen Mary[b]. [c]**Emily Van Evera** (sop); [c]**Timothy Wilson** (alto); [ac]**John Mark Ainsley**, [ac]**Charles Daniels** (tens); [c]**David Thomas** (bass); [abc]**Taverner Consort**, [abc]**Choir and Players / Andrew Parrott.** Virgin Classics Veritas Ⓕ VC5 45159-2 (55 minutes: DDD: 12/95). 🎯

...Hear my prayer, O Lord, Z15. *Coupled with works by various composers.* **New College Choir, Oxford / Edward Higginbottom.** Erato Ⓕ 3984-21659-2 (66 minutes: DDD: 6/98). *Gramophone Editor's choice. See review in the Collections section; refer to the Index.*

Purcell Music for the Funeral of Queen Mary – March and Canzona in C minor, Z860[c]. Funeral Sentences for the death of Queen Mary II[a]. The Bell Anthem, "Rejoice in the Lord alway", Z49[ad]. Remember not, Lord, our offences, Z50[a]. Give sentence with me, O Lord, Z12[a]. Jehova, quam multi sunt hostes mei, Z135[ab]. O, I'm sick of life, Z140[a]. My beloved spake, Z28[ad]. Hear my prayer, O Lord, Z15[a]. O God, thou art my God, Z35[ab]. Voluntaries[e] – No. 1 in C major, Z717; No. 4 in G major, Z720. [a]**Winchester Cathedral Choir;** [b]**Hilary Brooks** (vc); [c]**Baroque Brass of London;** [d]**The Brandenburg Consort / David Hill** ([e]org) with **David Dunnett** (org). Argo Ⓕ 436 833-2ZH (66 minutes: DDD: 6/94). 🎯 Texts included. Recorded 1992.

David Hill is a master of long-breathed melody and sustained intensity and he brings to Purcell's anthems a breadth of vision inspired by the time-span of earlier genres. Indeed, it is the range of anthems skilfully chosen from amongst Purcell's finest church music which distinguishes this disc as much as the funeral pieces. *Jehova, quam multi sunt hostes mei* is particularly effective, exemplifying not only Hill's astute pacing but also his vigorous sense of the dramatic declamatory style which

Purcell must have gleaned from continental sources. The open-throated treble sound is equally appropriate and characterizes the vocal colouring of almost all the works. The soloists for the verse anthems are drawn both from the ranks of the choir and a pool of professional soloists. Between them they shape the music with spirit and eloquence as can be relished in the abundant fruits of *My beloved spake*. The strings of The Brandenburg Consort balance the buoyant vocal style here with sparkling rhythmic exchanges. Winchester benefits from that fragility and loneliness which a solo treble can give to "In the midst of life", especially in a gothic acoustic. The Baroque Brass of London capture the doleful strains with finesse and make wonderful musical sense of the Canzona. The same players on 'flat' trumpets reappear on all current versions. There is good reason for this: only the truly dedicated are prepared to spend hours practising an instrument which splits notes as soon as you look at it, for a complete repertoire lasting no more than ten minutes.

Additiona Irecommendation ...
...Four Voluntaries, Z717-20. Verse in F major, Z716. A Choice Collection of Lessons – March in C major, Z T687; Chaconne in G minor, Z T680; Trumpet Tune in C major, Z T678, "Cibell". Grounds – Gamut in G major, Z645; C minor, T D221. Voluntary in A major (on the Old 100th), Z721. Trumpet Voluntary in D major. O Solitude! my sweetest choice, Z406. If music be the food of love, Z379 No. 1. **Blow** Six Organ Voluntaries. **Locke** Seven Voluntaries. **John Butt** (org). Harmonia Mundi Ⓜ HMX290 1528/33 (65 minutes: DDD: 7/95).

Purcell Ode for St Cecilia's Day, 1692, Hail, bright Cecilia, Z328. My beloved spake, Z28. O sing unto the Lord, Z44. **Gabrieli Consort and Players / Paul McCreesh.** Archiv Produktion Ⓕ 445 882-2AH (70 minutes: DDD: 10/95). Texts included. Recorded 1994.
Gramophone Editor's record of the month.   Ⓖ
Purcell Ode for St Cecilia's Day, 1683, Z339, "Welcome to all the pleasures"[a]. Funeral Sentences for the death of Queen Mary[b]. Birthday Ode, Z323, "Come ye sons of art away"[c]. March and Canzona in C minor, Z860[d]. Funeral Music for the death of Queen Mary[b]. [c]**Emily Van Evera** (sop); [c]**Timothy Wilson** (alto); [ac]**John Mark Ainsley**, [ac]**Charles Daniels** (tens); [c]**David Thomas** (bass); [abc]**Taverner Consort**, [abc]**Choir and Players / Andrew Parrott.** Virgin Classics Veritas Ⓕ VC5 45159-2 (55 minutes: DDD: 12/95). From EMI CDC7 49635-2 (2/90).

The Archiv performance of the 1692 Ode for St Cecilia's Day is exceptionally receptive to the brilliance of the score. The trumpets are bold and brassy (only occasionally overblown) and the ensemble as a whole moves effortlessly from discretion and intimacy to the imposing timbral homogeneity of McCreesh's most extrovert Venetian exploits. His tempos – especially in the grand opening instrumental sinfonia – are irrepressible and invigorating; there is a danger that this eight-section introduction can seem too much of a good thing, if not briskly negotiated. The solo singing is almost uniformly outstanding: Peter Harvey is the busiest of the basses and he delivers his splendid music, including "Wondrous machine!", with authority and variety of colour. Charles Daniels must, by now, have sung almost everything by Purcell but there is no sign of flagging: "'Tis Nature's voice" has a magical sense of unfolding as the music's captivating charms are gradually exposed. His duet with Mark le Brocq, "In vain the am'rous flute" has its moments, though the intonation of the recorders is languorous to say the least. Susan Hemington Jones sounds bright and alert though she seems just a touch unsettled and she is guilty of the occasional rather ugly 'early-musicy' swell, though to pick out a couple of bars there should certainly not detract attention from some notable singing in the verse anthem, *O sing unto the Lord*, especially in an extraordinarily moving close where the Gabrieli Consort's warmth of tone is exquisitely caught. *My beloved spake* is the other filler: a wonderful work and again very well performed. It is the Ode, above all, which takes the plaudits here. Whilst McCreesh makes the score sparkle with his energetic view of tempos, Andrew Parrott parades his smooth and integrated forces with less instant theatricality. Instead we have a typically homogeneous and unfolding scenario which complements McCreesh's more effervescent and lush reading.   The reappearance of Parrott's recordings of Purcell's earlier Cecilian ode, *Welcome to all the pleasures* and the time-honoured and particularly accessible *Come ye sons of art away* is also received with open arms. Some may distrust the low pitch (A=392) but the high tenor of Charles Daniels and the satisfying registral blend of Timothy Wilson and John Mark Ainsley in "Sound the trumpet" are more than adequate recompense and the former's mellifluous rendering of "Here the deities approve" is a real gem to be savoured. King has much to say about all these odes too. Blessed on almost all fronts.

Additional recommendations ...
...Hail, bright Cecilia, Z328. **Taverner Consort, Choir and Players / Andrew Parrott.** Virgin Classics Veritas Ⓕ VC5 45160-2 (57 minutes: DDD: 12/95).
...Te Deum and Jubilate in D major, Z232[a]. The Noise of Foreign Wars[a]. Odes for St Cecilia's Day – Raise, raise the voice, Z334[a]; Welcome to all the pleasures[a]. Trumpet Sonata No. 1 in D major[b]. [a]**Jeni Bern**, [a]**Susan Bisatt** (sops); [a]**Christopher Robson**, [a]**William Purefoy** (altos); [a]**Ian Honeyman** (ten); [a]**Thomas Guthrie** (bass); [b]**David Staff** (tpt); [a]**Choir and Orchestra of the Golden Age / Robert Glenton.** Naxos Ⓢ 8 553444 (63 minutes: DDD: 7/96).

Purcell Secular Solo Songs, Volume 3. [a]**Barbara Bonney**, [b]**Susan Gritton** (sops); [c]**James Bowman** (alto); [d]**Rogers Covey-Crump**, [e]**Charles Daniels** (tens); [f]**Michael George** (bass); [g]**Mark Caudle**, [h]**Susanna Pell** (vas da gamba); **David Miller** (lte/theorbo) / **Robert King** (org/hpd).

Hyperion Ⓔ CDA66730 (76 minutes: DDD: 1/95). 🖉 Texts included. Recorded 1993-94.
She loves, and she confesses, Z413[bh]. Amintas, to my grief I see, Z356[dh]. Corinna is divinely fair,
Z365[ag]. Amintor, heedless of his flocks, Z357[eg]. He himself courts his own ruin, Z372[cg]. No, to
what purpose, Z468[bfg]. Sylvia, 'tis true you're fair, Z512[efg]. Lovely Albina's come ashore, Z394[ag].
Spite of the godhead, pow'rful love, Z417[dg]. If music be the food of love, Z379/3[ag]. Phyllis, I can
ne'er forgive it, Z408[eg]. Bacchus is a pow'r divine, Z360[fg]. Bess of Bedlam, "From silent shades",
Z370[bh]. Let formal lovers still pursue, Z391[cg]. I came, I saw, and was undone, Z375[ag]. Who can
behold Florella's charms?, Z441[eg]. Cupid, the slyest rogue alive, Z367[dh]. If prayers and tears,
Z380[bh]. In Chloris all soft charms agree, Z384[dg]. Let us, kind Lesbia, give away, Z466[afg]. Love is
now become a trade, Z393[eg]. Ask me to love no more, Z358[cg]. O Solitude! my sweetest choice,
Z406[bg]. Olinda in the shades unseen, Z404[ag]. Pious Celinda goes to prayers, Z410[dg]. When
Strephon found his passion vain, Z435[afg]. The fatal hour comes on apace, Z421[bh]. Sawney is a
bonny lad, Z412[dh]. Young Thirsis' fate, ye hills and groves, deplore, Z473[fg].   Ⓖ

This third and last volume of Purcell's non-theatrical secular songs consummates a most rewarding
survey of 87 songs with more of the same: a vocal palette of six singers who are by now so steeped in
the nuances of Purcell's strains that even the slightest offering sparkles with something memorable.
The treasure is shared between Barbara Bonney and Susan Gritton who complement each other
superbly. Gritton, becoming more refined in characterization and tonal colour by the day, is allotted
the free-style and dramatic pieces whilst to Bonney's fluid and sensual melisma is designated the more
strophic or *cantabile* settings. *Lovely Albina's come ashore*, at one time thought to be "the last song
that Mr. Henry Purcell sett before he Dy'd", is at any rate one of the composer's most mature
creations, tantalizingly hinting at a new, tautly designed and classically balanced type of song. This
work, *If music be the food of love* (the best of the three versions) and *I came, I saw* are striking
examples of how exceptionally Bonney negotiates Purcell's skipping and curling contours and makes
these songs sound even finer creations than we previously thought. *From silent shades* ("Bess of
Bedlam") is Purcell's quintessential mad-song and Gritton has the measure of it all the way; packed
full of incident, imagery and musical detail, her narration is clear and finely judged, reporting the tale
with irony and change of colour, thereby never resorting to the more usual overexaggeration which
tends to lessen the impact of Bess's condition. The CD is beautifully and thoroughly documented but
prepare to rip the booklet to shreds getting it back in the jewel-case.

Additional recommendation ...

...Secular Solo Songs, Volume 1 – Draw near, you lovers, Z462[af]. While Thyrsis, wrapt in downy
sleep, Z437[c]. Love thou can'st hear, tho' thou art blind, Z396[e]. I lov'd fair Celia, Z381[d]. What
hope for us remains now he is gone?, Z472[bf]. Pastora's beauties when unblown, Z407[a]. A
thousand sev'ral ways I tried, Z359[d]. Urge me no more, Z426[b]. Farewell, all joys, Z368[c]. If music
be the food of love, Z379a[d]. Amidst the shades and cool refreshing streams, Z355[a]. They say
you're angry, Z422[e]. Let each gallant heart, Z390[e]. Anacreon's Defeat, "This poet sings the
Trojan wars", Z423[f]. Ah! how pleasant 'tis to love, Z353[a]. My heart, whenever you appear,
Z399[d]. On the brow of Richmond Hill, Z405[c]. Rashly I swore I would disown, Z411[e]. Since the
pox or the plague, Z471[ef]. Beneath a dark and melancholy grove, Z461[bf]. Musing on cares of
human fate, Z467[af]. Whilst Cynthia sung, all angry winds lay still, Z438[d]. How I sigh when
I think of the charms, Z374[b]. Ye happy swains, whose nymphs are kind, Z443[a]. Beware, poor
shepherds, Z361[e]. See how the fading glories of the year, Z470[af]. Cease, anxious world, your
fruitless pain, Z362[b]. O! fair Cedaria, hide those eyes, Z402[e]. [a]**Barbara Bonney,** [b]**Susan Gritton**
(sops); [c]**James Bowman** (alto); [d]**Rogers Covey-Crump,** [e]**Charles Daniels** (tens); [f]**Michael George**
(bass); **Mark Caudle** (viol); **David Miller** (lte/theorbo); **Robert King** (org/hpd).
Hyperion Ⓔ CDA66710 (70 minutes: DDD: 9/94). 🖉   Ⓖ

Purcell Welcome, viceregent of the mighty king, Z340[a]. O dive custos Auriacae domus, Z504[b].
Raise, raise the voice, Z334[c]. The Fairy Queen – O let me weep[d]. The Queen's Epicedium,
"Incassum, Lesbia, rogas", Z383[e]. Why, why are all the Muses mute?, Z343[f]. Young Thirsis' fate,
ye hills and groves, deplore, Z473[g]. [abdf]**Suzette Leblanc,** [abcf]**Barbara Borden** (sops); [af]**Steve
Dugardin** (alto); [acef]**Douglas Nasrawi** (ten); [af]**Harry van der Kamp,** [acfg]**Simon Grant** (basses);
Tragicomedia / Stephen Stubbs, Erin Headley. Teldec Das Alte Werk Ⓕ 4509-95068-2
(76 minutes: DDD: 7/95). Texts included. Recorded 1994.

The music chosen here is all out of Purcell's top drawer, with Tragicomedia combining works with
ravishing string ritornellos and extrovert paeans to the King, such as the gloriously crystalline and
breezy *Welcome, viceregent*, with the more intimate elegies on the death of Queen Mary which have
the capacity to melt marble. The ensemble in the larger works is always fresh and immediate and how
Tragicomedia relish the rich glowing textures of this first Welcome Song. The solo singing of Suzette
Leblanc and Barbara Borden is particularly striking: bright though never uniformly, they produce a
glistening yet suitably threnodizing reading of the deliciously poignant *O dive custos*. Douglas
Nasrawi is a naturally dramatic and effective singer though apart from favouring a soprano in
Incassum, Lesbia, his tone is rather wearingly projected. The most significant work to be included is
the unjustly little-known but outstanding Ode, *Why, why are all the Muses mute?*. This was the first
Welcome Ode which Purcell composed for King James II in 1685. The usual array of solos, duets,
choruses and so on is framed by an unusually rhetorical opening in a declamatory quasi-recitative
where the musicians have to be awakened from their slumber and, at the close, by a harmonically

devastating setting of the words, "His fame shall endure till all things decay, His fame and the world together shall die, Shall vanish together away". In between, we are blessed with one of Purcell's most affecting ground bass arias, "Britain, thou now art great", which is sung acceptably by Steve Dugardin, though there is really no touching James Bowman on Hyperion in this song as the latter curls himself with such effortless nobility around the seamless melodic strand. Elsewhere, Tragicomedia provide an altogether different approach to Robert King, a tighter, more shapely consort with an attractive vibrancy and immediacy throughout. The recorded sound is spacious.

Purcell Odes and Welcome Songs, Volumes 6-8. **Gillian Fisher, Mary Seers, Susan Hamilton, Tessa Bonner** (sops); **James Bowman, Nigel Short, Michael Chance** (altos); **Mark Padmore, Andrew Tusa, Rogers Covey-Crump, Charles Daniels, John Mark Ainsley** (tens); **Michael George, Robert Evans** (basses); **New College Choir, Oxford; King's Consort / Robert King.** Hyperion Ⓟ CDA66494, CDA66587 and CDA66598 (three discs, oas: 68, 66 and 68 minutes: DDD: 3/93). ✍ Texts included. Recorded 1991.
CDA66494 – Love's goddess sure was blind, Z331. Raise, raise the voice, Z334. Laudate Ceciliam, Z329. From those serene and rapturous joys, Z326. *CDA66587* – Of old, when heroes thought it base, Z333. Swifter, Isis, swifter flow, Z336. What, what shall be done on behalf of the man?, Z341. *CDA66598* – Come ye sons of art, away, Z323. Welcome, viceregent of the mighty king, Z340. Why, why are all the Muses mute?, Z343.
These three CDs represent the final instalments in Hyperion's complete recording of Purcell's Odes and Welcome Songs. Purcell composed a number of these celebratory works between 1680 and 1695, and 24 survive. They were written for a considerable range of events: most of them for royal birthdays, of King James II and Queen Mary, but also for a royal wedding, educational celebrations, and the 'Yorkshire Feast' of 1689. This cornucopia of wonderful music has largely been ignored, and Hyperion's edition is to be warmly welcomed, not only for bringing to the catalogue such magnificent music, but also for the extremely sympathetic and musical performances by the King's Consort under the direction of Robert King. Of all the works on these discs, probably the most well known is *Come ye sons of art, away* written for Queen Mary in 1694 (Volume 8). This joyous work contains some of Purcell's most ebullient music, typified by the duet for two countertenors, "Sound the trumpet". Like all of the works in the set this is surrounded by a well contrasted group of solos and duets for individual voices, instrumental interludes, and the occasional chorus. Less famous, but equally full of Restoration pomp and ceremony is the Yorkshire Feast song (Volume 7). Like many of the odes, the text for this is second-rate, ostensibly telling the story of York from the Roman occupation to the seventeenth century. However, this is merely the pretext for a splendidly varied set of vocal and instrumental items, the climax of which might be more fitting for a coronation than for a dinner of Yorkshire worthies! Volume 6 contains four of the least well known if no less rich and varied odes, two of which are dedicated to the patron saint of music, St Cecilia. While composed for slightly smaller forces than the more ceremonial odes, these contain music which is equally jaunty and exhilarating. Throughout all three volumes the most striking fact is Purcell's extraordinary inventiveness, and his incredible facility at word setting: even the most lame texts come alive in his hands, and the variety of expression throughout is astonishing. That such fine music should have lain unrecognized and unplayed for so long is cause for some amazement, but no less rejoicing that at last it has been restored in such understanding performances. Robert King's direction is always sensitive to both the broad span and individual nuances of Purcell's kaleidoscopic writing for voice and instruments. The King's Consort play with great understanding throughout and has clearly wholly absorbed the often elusive style of this music, in which many influences, most notably those from France, are combined. The vocal soloists are uniformly excellent, but special mention must be made of the ravishing soprano Gillian Fisher, and the versatile countertenor James Bowman. Hyperion's recordings throughout are without fault, achieving both excellent internal balance and appropriate atmosphere and perspective.
Additional recommendation ...
...Come ye sons of art away. Funeral Sentences for the death of Queen Mary II.
Soloists; English Baroque Soloists / Sir John Eliot Gardiner.
Erato Ⓜ 4509-96553-2 (44 minutes: ADD/DDD: 7/95). ✍

Purcell O Solitude! my sweetest choice, Z406[a]. Not all my torments can your pity move, Z400[ac]. Stript of their green our groves appear, Z444[abc]. The Blessed Virgin's Expostulation – Tell me, some pitying Angel, Z196[abc]. If music be the food of love, Z379/1[bc]. The fatal hour comes on apace, Z421[a]. The Queen's Epicedium – Incassum, Lesbia, rogas, Z383[ac]. Cupid, the slyest rogue alive, Z367[abc]. Bess of Bedlam – From silent shades, Z370[abc]. An Evening Hymn on a Ground – Now that the sun hath veiled his light, Z193[c]. O Solitude! my sweetest choice, Z406[b]. Tyrannic Love – Ah! how sweet it is to love[bc]. The Fairy Queen – Hark! the echoing air[abc]. Pausanias – Sweeter than roses[ab]. The Tempest – Dear pretty youth[ab]. The Comical History of Don Quixote – From rosy bow'rs[abc]. Sophonisba – Beneath the poplar's shadow[ab]. The Indian Queen – I attempt from love's sickness[c]. The History of Dioclesian – Let us dance, let us sing[abc]. King Arthur – Fairest isle[a]. **Nancy Argenta** (sop); [a]**Nigel North** (lte/gtr); [b]**Richard Boothby** (va da gamba); [c]**Paul Nicholson** (hpd/org). Virgin Classics Veritas Ⓟ VC7 59324-2 (74 minutes: DDD: 6/94). ✍ Texts included. Recorded 1992. *Gramophone Editor's choice.* Ⓖ Ⓖ

Here we can delight in one of the best recordings of Purcell's songs (mainly taken from *Orpheus Britannicus*) to have emerged in recent times and arguably the most literary-sensitive accounts since Alfred Deller. Nancy Argenta proves that declamatory and strophic songs (and many sub-genres in between) can be negotiated in the same recital with supreme technical finesse, profound understanding of the texts and the type of inventive nuances which enhance the implied conceits of an extraordinary range of songs. Moreover, she has the technical and temperamental control to explore the expressive gamut, from impish and deliberately impersonal no-nonsense texts (such as "Stript of their green", where the singer's rolling spontaneity is just what is called for) to the impulsive gestures and psychological tensions in "Tell me, some pitying Angel" and "From rosy bow'rs". The former is an especially fine portrayal with its sustained organ continuo commentating alongside sundry plucks (always astutely gauged by Nigel North, Richard Boothby and Paul Nicholson) whilst Argenta delivers the Virgin's touching and anxious expostulation with a rare understanding and empathy. Sheer technical bravura, however, is what performances of these songs too frequently lack and the quality of pitching (notoriously awkward leaps abound) and tuning sets this disc in a class of its own; only very occasionally does shrillness or a rather lifeless vibrato detract from an otherwise exquisite release – one which should sit on the shelves of all those who need convincing that Purcell's solo vocal music of this ilk is anything but a glorious testament to the human voice.

Additional recommendations ...

...Harmonia – Sacra Lord, what is man?, Z192. O Solitude! my sweetest choice, Z406; In the black dismal dungeon of despair, Z190; Lord, I can suffer Thy rebukes, Z136; Saul and the Witch of Endor, "In guilty night", Z134; Plung'd in the confines of despair, Z142; Awake, ye dead, Z182; The Earth trembled, Z197; My op'ning eyes are purg'd, ZD72; With sick and famish'd eyes, Z200; O, I'm sick of life, Z140; Close thine eyes and sleep secure, Z184. Funeral Sentences for the death of Queen Mary II – Man that is born of Woman, Z27. Voluntaries – C major, Z717; G major, Z720[a]. Ground in C minor, T D221[b]. **Gabrieli Consort and Players / Paul McCreesh; Timothy Roberts** ([a]org/[b]hpd). Archiv Produktion Ⓕ 445 829-2AH (70 minutes: DDD: 7/95). ☞

...The Staircase Overture. Suite of Instrumental Pieces (arr. Hogwood) – Cebell; Slow Air; We Come to Sing; Trumpet Tune; Jig; Hear, mighty Love. If music be the food of love, Z379C[a]. The Libertine – To arms, heroic prince[a]. Tell me, some pitying Angel, Z196[a]. Bonduca – O lead me to some peaceful gloom[a]. O Solitude! my sweetest choice, Z406[a]. The Fairy Queen[a] – Hark! the echoing air; O let me weep. Pausanias – Sweeter than roses[a]. King Arthur – Fairest isle[a]. She that would gain a faithful lover, Z414[a]. Cupid, the slyest rogue alive, Z367[a]. The Indian Queen – I attempt from love's sickness[a]. Oedipus – Music for a while[a]. The fatal hour comes on apace, Z431[a]. Chaconne in G minor, Z730.[a]**Sylvia McNair** (sop); **Academy of Ancient Music / Christopher Hogwood.** Philips Ⓕ 446 081-2PH (63 minutes: DDD: 9/95).

...The Fairy Queen – Thrice happy lovers; O let me weep ("The Plaint"). The History of King Richard II – Retir'd from any mortal's sight. King Arthur – Fairest isle. Sir Anthony Love – Pursuing Beauty. Oedipus – Music for a while. Henry the Second, King of England – In vain 'gainst love I strove. Rule a Wife and Have a Wife – There's not a swain. The Married Beau – See where repenting Celia lies. Timon of Athens – The cares of lovers. Tyrannic Love – Ah! how sweet it is to love. The Tempest – Dear pretty youth. Bonduca – O lead me to some peaceful gloom. Pausanias – Sweeter than roses. *Coupled with works by various composers.* **Catherine Bott** (sop); **Pamela Thorby** (rec); **Anthony Robson** (ob); **Pavlo Beznosiuk, Rachel Podger** (vns); **Paula Chateauneuf** (theorbo/gtr); **Richard Egarr** (hpd); **Mark Levy** (bass viol). L'Oiseau-Lyre Ⓕ 443 699-2OH (58 minutes: DDD: 4/96). ☞

Purcell Dioclesian Acts 1-4. **Catherine Pierard** (sop); **James Bowman** (alto); **John Mark Ainsley, Mark Padmore** (tens); **Michael George** (bass); **Collegium Musicum 90 Chorus; Collegium Musicum 90 / Richard Hickox.** Chandos Chaconne Ⓕ CHAN0568 (54 minutes: DDD: 7/95). ☞ Text included.

It was *Dioclesian*, the least known of the four semi-opera masterpieces of Purcell, for which the composer initially earned a reputation for writing stage music. The 'opera' was by all accounts a roaring success, though music played a less important part in the stage works of the 1690s than it did in the masque-related works of the previous decades – ironically just at the time when England could at last boast a dramatic master who could stand tall amongst the 'greats' of France and Italy. If the paucity of tableaux means a less atmospheric scenic context, such as we experience in *The Fairy Queen* or *King Arthur*, there is still much fine music which deserves to be highly regarded. Hickox is evidently committed to this score: the instrumental movements are all disciplined and yet display the buoyancy and variety of expression of one who senses the freshness of Purcell's first foray into the theatre. His soloists are authoritative Purcellians and they never disappoint. Hickox manages to sustain the tension and climate he sets from the start which is arguably what Gardiner never quite manages.

Purcell Dido and Aeneas. **Catherine Bott** (sop) Dido; **John Mark Ainsley** (ten) Aeneas; **Emma Kirkby** (sop) Belinda; **David Thomas** (bass) Sorceress; **Elizabeth Priday** (sop) First Witch; **Sara Stowe** (sop) Second Witch; **Julianne Baird** (sop) Second Woman; **Daniel Lochmann** (treb) First Sailor; **Michael Chance** (alto) Spirit; **Academy of Ancient Music Chorus and Orchestra / Christopher Hogwood.** L'Oiseau-Lyre Ⓕ 436 992-2OHO (52 minutes: DDD: 7/94). ☞ Ⓖ Ⓖ Notes and text included. Recorded 1992.

Purcell Dido and Aeneas. **Véronique Gens** (sop) Dido; **Nathan Berg** (bass-bar) Aeneas; **Sophie Marin-Degor** (sop) Belinda; **Claire Brua** (sop) Sorceress; **Sophie Daneman** (sop) Second Woman, First Witch; **Gaëlle Mechaly** (sop) Second Witch; **Jean-Paul Fouchécourt** (ten) Spirit, Sailor; **Les Arts Florissants / William Christie.** Erato Ⓕ 4509-98477-2 (52 minutes: DDD: 6/95). ☛ Notes and text included. Recorded 1994. Ⓖ

Emma Kirkby (whose Dido, for Parrott, remains one of the finest on record) sings Belinda for Hogwood; David Thomas (whose Aeneas, on the same recording, was outstanding) sings the Sorceress; Michael Chance takes the tiny part of the Spirit, thereby putting its moment into centre stage as the gloriously conceived turning-point of the story. A few innovations, too. Following the arguments that the Sorceress could be a man, Hogwood's choice of Thomas has offered us perhaps the most eloquent version on disc so far. Thomas gives full value to the words and the music. Less convincing is the use of a boy for the sailor's song; despite direct and spirited singing, its text is quite inappropriate for a boy. Much more successful is the use of the Drottningholm wind-machines to interpret the various stage-instructions and give the entire performance a real sense of verisimilitude. Catherine Bott is a fine Dido, even-voiced across the range and powerfully expressive if occasionally a touch free with the rhythms. John Mark Ainsley easily stands as the finest Aeneas since David Thomas. This is a very difficult role to handle dramatically, because its moods change so fast; and Ainsley handles all this with heartbreaking ease. This is a classic interpretation. So too is Hogwood's reading of the score, with his faultless sense of the right speed and the right rhythm as well as his ability to see the moment when everything must be interrupted to give space to the drama.

William Christie's reading of *Dido* is very much in terms of the reputed French influence on Purcell. Overdotting, reverse dotting and *inégalité* are used throughout; the lines are often heavily embellished in the manner of Lully. This is a perfectly justifiable approach to the music, since there is little direct evidence to say exactly how much the French style dominated in England. This version – with single strings, an excellent small choir and a slightly obtrusive harpsichord – stands well alongside what is otherwise available: if you prefer *Dido* in the French manner this is the record you will want; if not, you will probably still want it as an very different view of a major work. Apart from a few moments' inattention in Belinda's "Haste, haste to town", you would hardly notice that most of the cast are Francophone, except in that Nathan Berg's imposing bass-baritone finds it slightly easier to exploit the colour and the meaning of Aeneas's words. Véronique Gens is a lucid and sensible Dido, partnered by a sprightly Belinda from Sophie Marin-Degor and a good Second Woman from Sophie Daneman. Claire Brua's Sorceress is a splendidly insinuating conception, with a slithering melodic style that neatly characterizes her evil. Perhaps the main musical distinction of this version is the way Christie presents the final paragraphs. Up to this point he has taken generally quick speeds, and he runs the final confrontation of Dido and Aeneas at a headlong tempo, which works very well. Then he comes almost to a standstill at the moment when Aeneas leaves the stage, choosing an unusually slow speed for the chorus "Great minds against themselves conspire". This makes way for a dangerously slow Lament, which is heart-stopping, and the final chorus, which is not.

Additional recommendations ...

...Soloists; **St Anthony Singers; English Chamber Orchestra / Anthony Lewis.**
    Decca Serenata Ⓜ 425 720-2DM* (53 minutes: ADD: 12/90).
...Soloists; **Taverner Choir and Players / Andrew Parrott.**
    Chandos Chaconne Ⓕ CHAN0521(56 minutes: DDD: 11/91). ☛
...Soloists; **The Scholars Baroque Ensemble.** Naxos Ⓢ 8 553108 (58 minutes: DDD: 10/97).

Purcell King Arthur. **Véronique Gens, Claron McFadden, Sandrine Piau, Susannah Waters** (sops); **Mark Padmore, Iain Paton** (tens); **Jonathan Best, Petteri Salomaa, François Bazola-Minori** (basses); **Les Arts Florissants Chorus and Orchestra / William Christie.** Erato Ⓕ 4509-98535-2 (two discs: 90 minutes: DDD: 6/95). ☛ Notes and text included. Recorded 1995.
Gramophone Award Winner 1995. *Gramophone* Editor's choice. ⒼⒼⒼ

If the co-operation with John Dryden led to a unity of vision in terms of music's expressive role in the overall drama, Purcell was limited to a historical patriotic fantasy with little room for the magic and pathos of, say, the superior *Fairy Queen*. Yet in the context of a stage presentation, Purcell's music shines through strongly. On disc though, with just the music, not even the dramatic powers of William Christie can restore its place in the overall scheme. But never mind, this is a score with some magnificent creations and Christie is evidently enchanted by it. The choral singing is richly textured, sensual and long-breathed, yet always alert to a nuance which can irradiate a passage at a stroke, as Christie does in the bittersweet close of "Honour prizing" – easily the best moment in Act 1. The instrumental movements are finely moulded so that sinewy counterpoint and rhythmic profile are always strongly relayed. The songs, too, have been acutely prepared and are keenly characterized without resorting to excess. All the basses deliver their fine music with aplomb. If there is one drawback to extracting the musical numbers from the 'opera' when they have so clearly been delivered within a theatrical context, it is that the highly contextual characterizations lend themselves less well to the musical continuity of a CD. But *King Arthur* without the play is dramatically a nonsense so why try to pretend? Christie does not but makes the strongest case for this music to date.

Additional recommendation ...

...Soloists; **Monteverdi Choir; English Baroque Soloists / Sir John Eliot Gardiner.**
    Erato Ⓕ 4509-96552-2 (two discs: 90 minutes: DDD: 7/95). ☛

Purcell The Indian Queen. **Tessa Bonner, Catherine Bott** (sops); **Rogers Covey-Crump** (ten); **Peter Harvey** (bass); **Purcell Simfony Voices; Purcell Simfony / Catherine Mackintosh** (vn). Linn Records ⓔ CKD035 (60 minutes: DDD: 9/95). Recorded 1994.

Purcell The Indian Queen. **Emma Kirkby, Catherine Bott** (sops); **John Mark Ainsley** (ten); **Gerald Finley** (bar); **David Thomas** (bass); **Tommy Williams** (sngr); **Chorus and Orchestra of the Academy of Ancient Music / Christopher Hogwood.** Also includes additional Act by Daniel Purcell. L'Oiseau-Lyre ⓔ 444 339-2OHO (73 minutes: DDD: 1/96). Notes and text included. Recorded 1994.

Although until the Linn disc, there had been no new version of *The Indian Queen* since Gardiner's (now unavailable) 1979 recording, this is no reflection on the quality of the work. If *The Indian Queen* is less ambitious than the other three 'operas' there is the sure touch here of the composer at his most mature and adept (as his last great work for the theatre, there is a strong possibility that Purcell may never have lived to hear it). The Prologue, in which he had the rare opportunity to set an extended dialogue, is beautifully balanced, the humour in Act 2 delicate and inimitably charming, and the music in Act 3 – when Zempoalla's ill-fated love is prophesied by Ismeron the magician in "Ye twice ten hundred deities" – ranks alongside the finest moments in Purcell's output and was praised by Dr Burney nearly 100 years later. The small-scale character of the work, compared to its siblings, is taken a stage further by the Purcell Simfony, who employ a minute chamber-size group of four strings, doubling oboe and recorder, single trumpet and drums. The soloists sing with airy restraint but each responds to these Hilliardesque proportions with a rhythmic buoyancy and direct intimacy which projects a finely gauged overall conception of the work. If the expressive power of the music is at times rather glazed, there is a sure atmosphere which is captured by a delightful perspective on the recorded sound, ensuring that the light puff-pastry of "I come to sing great Zempoalla's story" and "I attempt from love's sickness" is both warm and yet never imposing. The ensemble is not always first-rate but there is nothing too worrisome and the instrumental numbers are elegantly shaped. Tessa Bonner gets the lion's share of the solo soprano numbers, ahead of the more colourful Catherine Bott, though the former's comparatively brittle sound has a crystalline quality which suits director Catherine Mackintosh's consistent, if austere strategy. To sum up, the Linn release is consistently touching, one which in a paradoxical way gets under the skin despite the recessed emotional climate it conveys.

The difference between the Purcell Simfony's graceful and intimate performance and the account from Christopher Hogwood is that the latter makes us realize that for all the constraints, the score is not inherently small-scale and that it warrants all the subtlety of colour that can be achieved using 12 soloists and a decent sized choir and orchestra. Needless to say, Hogwood conveys a consistent, logical and meticulous understanding of the score. The orchestral playing is crisp and transparent, the Academy of Ancient Music's articulation allowing the integrity of the inner parts to be heard to the full without compromising blend. Amongst a distinguished line-up of singers, John Mark Ainsley gets the lion's share and is perhaps marginally more effective as the Indian Boy than as Fame, but such gloriously mellifluous and controlled singing can only enhance the reputation of this work. Emma Kirkby is in fine fettle and she executes the justly celebrated song "I attempt from love's sickness" with her usual communicative panache. Then comes the pleasurably contrasted voice of Catherine Bott: "They tell us that your mighty powers" could not be in better hands. David Thomas as Envy, with his two followers in the Act 2 masque, highlights this brilliant scene as the work of a true connoisseur of the theatre. Mature Purcell is most strongly felt in the deftly ironic invocation by the conjurer, Ismeron, whose "Ye twice ten thousand deities" is delivered authoritatively by Gerald Finley, though the lulling to sleep, before the God of Dream's gloomy non-prediction, is strangely unconvincing. Taken as a whole, the quality of music shines very brightly in Hogwood's reading. It is perhaps a touch calculated in places. The Purcell Simfony's melting chorus "While thus we bow before your shrine" is preferable; but Hogwood's new version has to stand as the current favourite. His inclusion of Daniel Purcell's Act 5 masque is interesting but not much more than that.

Purcell The Fairy Queen. **Gillian Fisher, Lorna Anderson** (sops); **Ann Murray** (mez); **Michael Chance** (alto); **John Mark Ainsley, Ian Partridge** (tens); **Richard Suart, Michael George** (basses); **The Sixteen Choir and Orchestra / Harry Christophers.** Collins Classics ⓕ 7013-2 (two discs: 133 minutes: DDD: 4/92). ✒ Text included. Recorded 1990.   ⓖ

Purcell The Fairy Queen. **Lorraine Hunt, Catherine Pierard** (sops); **Susan Bickley** (mez); **Howard Crook, Mark Padmore** (tens); **David Wilson-Johnson** (bar); **Richard Wistreich** (bass); **Schütz Choir of London; London Classical Players / Roger Norrington.** EMI ⓕ CDS5 55234-2 (two discs: 122 minutes: DDD: 2/95). ✒ Notes and text included. Recorded 1993.

Of Purcell's four semi-operas in which extended musical set pieces or masques are mixed with substantial dialogue, it is *The Fairy Queen* that stands the best chance of catching the public's imagination, not only because of its superb music but also on account of its foundation in such a well-loved part of England's literary heritage as *A Midsummer Night's Dream*. Much has been made of the liberties taken by Purcell's anonymous librettist for this work, but no one who has heard the music could deny that the composer conjures just as truthfully as Shakespeare the pains and pleasures of love, the interludes of low comedy, and the magical atmosphere of the fairy wood. Harry Christophers has assembled a strong cast for his recording. With singers like Gillian Fisher, Michael Chance, John

Mark Ainsley and Ian Partridge aboard, things are unlikely to go far astray, while the contribution of the always excellent Sixteen Choir means, too, that this is a performance without any serious weakness. The orchestra, it's true, could sound more committed at times, while Ann Murray seems a little out of place in this particular company; but in general there is a refreshing lightness, an authentic Englishness, to this recording that serves the music well. Perhaps the highlight is the gentle Second Act Masque which lulls Titania to sleep, but also highly enjoyable are the comic scenes, such as the one in which a drunken poet suffers an uncomfortable encounter with some fairies. This is not a recording which has everything – it lacks sheer splendour for one thing – but it is among the best.

Roger Norrington clearly identifies with Purcell's refined characterization. There is a great sense throughout that each gesture in the music has been thoroughly absorbed and filtered. This makes for an extraordinarily tidy and persuasively articulated account: the instrumental dances contain a luminosity which is at times revelatory and the attention to detail gives the marvellously fleeting nuance of Purcell's part-writing the chance to be noticed; no one has produced such a mesmerically crafted evocation in "A Dance for the Followers" of Oberon sprinkling magic flower juice into Titania's eyes. The vocal numbers boast a skilfully chosen array of singers, each of whom evidently suits Norrington's highly focused view of the music. Unlike Christophers's if not more celebrated then more recognizably diverse group of soloists, we have here an easy and pleasing contrast between different voices. Norrington's 'state of the art' Purcell and the price for such intricate and poised expression is that the whole feels rather studio-made. On a less fundamental level, the keen edge of his vision denies a more yielding approach at times. For all that, this is a splendid achievement.

Additional recommendations ...

...**Soloists; Monteverdi Choir; English Baroque Soloists / Sir John Eliot Gardiner.**
Archiv Produktion Ⓕ 419 221-2AH2 (two discs: 138 minutes: DDD: 8/87). ✍

...**Soloists; Les Arts Florissants / William Christie.**
Harmonia Mundi Ⓕ HMC90 1308/9 (two discs: 128 minutes: DDD: 1/90). ✍

...**Soloists; Ambrosian Opera Chorus; English Chamber Orchestra / Benjamin Britten.**
Decca Serenata Ⓜ 433 163-2DM2 (two discs: 96 minutes: ADD: 5/92).

...**The Scholars Baroque Ensemble.** Naxos Ⓢ 8 550660/1 (two discs: 129 minutes: DDD: 7/94).

Further listening ...

...Chacony in G minor for strings, Z730. *Coupled with works by various composers.*
English Chamber Orchestra / Benjamin Britten. Decca The Classic Sound 448 569-2DCS (2/96).

...Suites – The Fairy Queen; Dido and Aeneas; King Arthur; Abdelazer; Chaconne in G minor, Z730. **Freiburg Baroque Orchestra / Thomas Hengelbrock.**
Deutsche Harmonia Mundi RD77231 (3/92). ✍

...Trumpet Sonata No. 2 in D major, Z850. *Coupled with works by various composers.* **Niklas Eklund** (baroque tpt); **Drottningholm Baroque Ensemble / Nils-Erik Sparf.** Naxos 8 553531 (11/96). ✍
See review in the Collections section; refer to the Index.

...Ten Sonatas in Four Parts, Z802-11 – No. 3 in A minor; No. 4 in D minor; No. 5 in G minor; No. 6 in G minor; No. 7 in C major; No. 8 in G minor (with two variant movements); No. 9 in F major; No. 10 in D major. Organ Voluntaries, Z717-20 – No. 2 in D minor; No. 4 in G major. Prelude for Solo Violin in G minor, ZN773. **Purcell Quartet.**
Chandos CHAN8763 (12/89). ✍

...Organ Works – Four Voluntaries, Z717-20. Verse in F major, Z716. A Choice Collection of Lessons: March in C major, ZT687; Chaconne in G minor, ZT680; Trumpet Tune in C major, "Cibell", ZT678; Trumpet Tune in C major, ZT698. Ground in Gamut in G major, Z645. Ground in C minor, TD221. Voluntary in A major on the Old Hundredth, Z721. Trumpet Voluntary in D major. *Coupled with* **Blow** Six Voluntaries. **Locke** Seven Voluntaries from Melothesia. **John Butt** (org). Harmonia Mundi HMU90 7103 (6/94). ✍

...Songs from Orpheus Britannicus: The Rival Sisters, Z609 – Calia has a thousand charms. Fly swift, ye hours, Z369. Gentle shepherds, you that know, Z464. Aureng-Zebe, Z573 – I see, she flies me. Pausanias, Z585 – Sweeter than roses. I came, I saw, and was undone, Z375. If music be the food of love, Z379/3. Bess of Bedlam, "From silent shades", Z370. Timon of Athens, Z632 – Love in their little veins. The Comical History of Don Quioxte, Z578 – From rosy bow'rs. King Arthur, Z628 – Fairest isle. Tyrannic Love, Z613 – Ah! how sweet it is to love. The Fatal hour comes on apace, Z421. O Solitude! my sweetest choice, Z406. The history of Dioclesian, Z627 – Since from my dear Astrea's sight. Bonduca, Z574 – O lead me to some peaceful gloom. The Fairy Queen, Z629 – Thrice happy lovers. Solo Harpsichord: The Second Part of Musick's Handmaid – A New Ground in E minor, Z T682. Ground in D minor, Z D222. Hornpipe in D minor, "Round O", Z T684. A Choice Collection of Lessons – Chaconne in G minor, Z T680. **Agnès Mellon** (sop); **Wieland Kuijken** (va da gamba); **Christophe Rousset** (hpd). Auvidis Astrée E8757 (9/93). ✍

...The Symphony Songs – Hark, Damon, hark, Z541. How pleasant is this flowery plain, Z543. We reap all the pleasures, Z547. Hark how the wild musicians sing, Z542. Weeping, "See where she sits", Z508. Oh! what a scene does entertain my sight, Z506. A Serenading Song, "Soft notes and gently raised", Z510. If ever I more riches did desire, Z544. Four Pavans, Z748-51. **Red Byrd; The Parley of Instruments / Peter Holman.** Hyperion CDA66750 (8/95). ✍

...Hail, bright Cecilia, Z328. **Equale Brass; Monteverdi Choir and Orchestra / Sir John Eliot Gardiner.** Erato 4509 96554-2 (7/95). ✍

...The Tempest. **Soloists; English Baroque Soloists / Sir John Eliot Gardiner.**
Erato 4509-96555-2 (7/95). 🖊

...Timon of Athens – Masque. The History of Dioclesian – Masque. **Soloists;**
Collegium Musicum 90 / Richard Hickox. Chandos Chaconne CHAN0558 (11/94). 🖊

...Timon of Athens. The History of Dioclesian. **Soloists; English Baroque Soloists /**
Sir John Eliot Gardiner. Erato 4509 96556-2 (7/95). 🖊

Johann Quantz

German 1697-1773

Suggested listening ...
...Flute Concerto in G major. *Coupled with works by various composers.* **Patrick Gallois** (fl);
CPE Bach Chamber Orchestra / Peter Schreier. DG 439 895-2GH (2/95). *See review in the*
Collections section; refer to the Index.

...Trio Sonata in C major. *Coupled with works by various composers.* **Palladian Ensemble.**
Linn Records CKD050 (5/97). *See review in the collections section; refer to the Index.*

Roger Quilter

British 1877-1953

Quilter Shakespeare Songs, Op. 23 – No. 3, It was a lover and his lass[abc]; No. 4, Take, o take those
lips away[bc]. O mistress mine, Op. 6 No. 2[bc]. How shall I your true love know?, Op. 30 No. 3[ac].
Orpheus with his lute, Op. 32 No. 1[bc]. Hark! Hark! the lark![bc]. The Arnold Book of Old Songs[ac]
– Ye banks and braes; Charlie is my darling; Ca'the yowes to the knowes. I arise from dreams of
thee, Op. 29[bc]. Songs, Op. 25 – No. 3, An old carol[bc]; No. 5, Music, when soft voices die[ac]. Songs,
Op. 3 – No. 1, Love's philosophy[bc]; No. 2, Now sleeps the crimson petal[ac]. Spring is at the door,
Op. 18 No. 4[ac]. Passing dreams, Op. 10 No. 2[bc]. Three Pastoral Songs, Op. 22[ace]. Go, lovely rose,
Op. 24 No. 3[bc]. Songs, Op. 14[ac] – No. 1, Autumn evening; No. 3, A last year's rose. Amaryllis at
the fountain, Op. 15 No. 2[ac]. I dare not ask a kiss, Op. 28 No. 3[bc]. To Julia, Op. 8[bcd]. Rosmé –
Love calls through the summer night[abc]. [a]**Lisa Milne** (sop); [b]**Anthony Rolfe Johnson** (ten);
[c]**Graham Johnson** (pf); [d]**Duke Quartet** ([e]Louisa Fuller, Rick Koster, vns; John Metcalfe, va;
[e]Ivan McCready, vc). Collins Classics Ⓕ 1512-2 (70 minutes: DDD: 5/98). Texts included.
Recorded 1997.

When Quilter sat down at the piano, did he always put his hands on the keyboard in the same kinds
of place? And did he sometimes get tired of those places and want to compose like somebody else,
Ravel or Holst or Lehár? The wonder is that, in this small output, and output of small things, he was
almost always, utterly and unmistakably, himself. 'Almost always': two items in this programme
prompt that. One is the very last, a duet with a waltz-refrain, dated 1940. He hadn't quite the courage
to carry on and make a real big thing of it, adding the bold banality that might have ensured success.
The other is the setting of Shelley's *Indian Serenade* ("I arise from dreams of thee"). The longest of
the songs and the most elaborate, it is also the furthest from the drawing-room and nearest to art-
song; and it is the least characteristic. The delicacy and restrained passion of Quilter's characteristic
writing finds a sensitive exponent in Graham Johnson. Both singers bring an affectionate touch. Lisa
Milne is delightful in the Ophelia song, *How shall I your true love know?* and in the spirited *Charlie is*
my darling. Anthony Rolfe Johnson is most gratefully heard in the quieter songs such as *An old carol*
("I sing of a maiden"). It is interesting to hear the Herrick cycle, *To Julia,* in the arrangement Quilter
made for accompaniment by piano quintet. Also moving and fascinating to hear again the song in
which he really did extend – and remain – himself: his arrangement of *Ca'the yowes to the knowes.*

Further listening ...
...A Children's Overture, Op. 17. Where the Rainbow Ends – Suite. As you like it – Suite,
Op. 21. Country Pieces. The Rake – Suite. Three English Dances, Op. 11. Julia – Concert Waltz
from "Rosmé". **Bratislava Radio Symphony Orchestra / Adrian Leaper.**
Marco Polo British Light Music 8 223444 (8/94).

...Three Songs, Op. 3 – No. 1, Love's Philosophy; No. 2, Now Sleeps the Crimson Petal. At Close of
Day. Three Shakespeare Songs, Op. 6. To Julia, Op. 8. Four Songs, Op. 14. Seven Elizabethan
Lyrics, Op. 12. Three Songs of William Blake, Op. 20. Go, Lovely Rose, Op. 24 No. 3. Arab Love
Song, Op. 25 No. 4. Music, When Soft Voices Die, Op. 25 No. 5. In the Bud of the Morning-o,
Op. 25 No. 6. I Arise from Dreams of Thee, Op. 29. **Benjamin Luxon** (bar); **David Willison** (pf).
Chandos CHAN8782 (3/90).

...Four Songs of Mirza Schaffy, Op. 2. Three Songs, Op. 3 – No. 1, Love's philosophy; No. 2, Now
sleeps the crimson petal. Four Child Songs, Op. 5 – No. 1, A Good Child; No. 2, The
Lamplighter; No. 3, Where Go the Boats?. Three Shakespeare Songs, Op. 6. Seven Elizabethan
Lyrics, Op. 12. Four Songs, Op. 14 – No. 1, Autumn Evening; No. 3, A Last Year's Rose. Five
Shakespeare Songs, Op. 23. Go, lovely rose, Op. 24 No. 3. Six Songs, Op. 25 – No. 4, Arab love
song; No. 5, Music, when soft voices die. Four Shakespeare Songs, Op. 30. The Arnold Book of
Old Songs – No. 1, Drink to me only with thine eyes; No. 2, Over the mountains; No. 13,
Barbara Allen. Two September Songs. June. **John Mark Ainsley** (ten); **Malcolm Martineau** (pf).
Hyperion CDA66878 (11/96).

Sergey Rachmaninov

Rachmaninov The Complete Recordings. [a]**Fritz Kreisler** (vn); [b]**Sergey Rachmaninov** (pf); **Philadelphia Orchestra** / [c]**Leopold Stokowski,** [d]**Eugene Ormandy,** [e]**Sergey Rachmaninov.** RCA Victor Gold Seal mono Ⓜ 09026 61265-2* (ten discs: 640 minutes: ADD: 3/93). Recorded 1919-1942. *Gramophone classical 100. Gramophone Award Winner 1993.*
Rachmaninov Piano Concertos[b] – No. 1 in F sharp minor, Op. 1[d]; No. 2 in C minor, Op. 18[c]; No. 3 in D minor, Op. 30[d]; No. 4 in G minor, Op. 40[d]. Rhapsody on a Theme of Paganini, Op. 43[bc]. The isle of the dead, Op. 29[e]. Vocalise, Op. 34 No. 14[e]. Symphony No. 3 in A minor, Op. 44[e]. Solo Piano works[b] – Daisies. Nine Etudes tableaux, Op. 33 – No. 2 in C major; No. 7 in E flat major. Nine Etudes tableaux, Op. 39 – No. 6 in A minor. Lilacs (two versions, recorded in 1923 and 1942). Six Moments musicaux, Op. 16 – Allegretto. Five Morceaux de fantaisie, Op. 3 – No. 5, Sérénade in B flat minor. Seven Morceaux de salon, Op. 10 – No. 5, Humoresque in G major. Oriental Sketch in B flat major. Polka de W.R. (three versions, recorded in 1919, 1921 and 1928). Preludes – C sharp minor, Op. 3 No. 2 (three versions, recorded in 1919, 1921 and 1928); G minor, Op. 23 No. 5; G flat major, Op. 23 No. 10; E major, Op. 32 No. 3; G major, Op. 32 No. 5; F minor, Op. 32 No. 6; G sharp minor, Op. 32 No. 12. **Beethoven** Violin Sonata No. 8 in G major, Op. 30 No. 3[ab]. 32 Variations on an original theme in C minor, WoO80[b]. **Schubert** Violin Sonata in A major (Duo), D574[ab]. **Grieg** Violin Sonata No. 3 in C minor, Op. 45[ab]. **Schumann** Carnaval, Op. 9[b]. **Chopin** Piano Sonata No. 2 in B flat minor, Op. 35[b]. Also includes solo piano works by other composers. ⒼⒼⒼ
Here, on RCA's superbly remastered ten-disc set, is awe-inspiring and scintillating confirmation of Rachmaninov's greatness; as composer, pianist, chamber musician and conductor. Controversy over his stature as a composer may live on in the dustier corners of academia, but today once confident assertions that his music would never last, that it lacked the regenerative force of true tragedy or that it was, in essence, little more than a precursor of Hollywood, have been triumphantly erased. Works such as the Second Symphony, the Third Piano Concerto and the Second Piano Sonata are played without the once acceptable and debilitating cuts so sadly sanctioned by the composer, and innovative as well as traditional elements in Rachmaninov's writing are celebrated. What is indisputable, however, is Rachmaninov's quality as a pianist. Alternatively teasing and granitic in other composer's music (his way with Schumann's *Carnaval* and Chopin's Second Sonata, to name but two, will always incite argument) his performances of his own works are, quite simply, inimitable, imbued with a brio and aristocracy entirely his own. The most immediately appealing include all four concertos and the Paganini *Rhapsody*, Handel's *Harmonious Blacksmith* Variations (pure pianistic sorcery) and Rachmaninov's own second *Moment musical* and *Mélodie*, Op. 3 No. 2; the former of a mind-bending virtuosity, the latter aglow with the *cantabile* and rubato of another, far-off age. But everything is absorbing, nothing without interest. These recordings blazen out Rachmaninov's stature both as creator and re-creator in every golden bar.

Additional recommendations ...

...Nos. 1-4. Rhapsody on a Theme of Paganini. **Rafael Orozco** (pf); **Royal Philharmonic Orchestra /** **Edo de Waart.** Philips Ⓜ 438 326-2PM2 (two discs: 150 minutes: ADD).

...Nos. 1-4. Rhapsody on a Theme of Paganini. **Earl Wild** (pf); **Royal Philharmonic Orchestra /** **Jascha Horenstein.** Chandos Ⓕ CHAN8521/2 (two discs: 134 minutes: ADD: 9/87). ⒼⒼⒼ

...Nos. 1-4. **Vladimir Ashkenazy** (pf); **Concertgebouw Orchestra / Bernard Haitink.** Decca Ⓕ 421 590-2DH2 (two discs: 134 minutes: DDD: 4/89).

...Nos. 1 and 4. **Vladimir Ashkenazy** (pf); **London Symphony Orchestra / André Previn.** Decca Ⓜ 425 004-2DM (55 minutes: ADD: 7/90). Ⓖ

...Nos. 1-4. Rhapsody on a Theme of Paganini. **Howard Shelley** (pf); **Royal Scottish National Orchestra / Bryden Thomson.** Chandos Ⓕ CHAN8882/3 (two discs: 154 minutes: DDD: 4/91).

...Lilacs, Op. 21 No. 5. Etudes tableaux, Op. 39 – No. 1 in C minor; No. 5 in E flat minor. *Coupled with works by various composers.* **Evgeni Kissin** (pf). Sony Classical Ⓕ SK45931 (73 minutes: DDD: 11/90). *See review in the Collections section; refer to the Index.* ⒼⒼ

...Nos. 2[a] and 3[b]. [a]**Sergei Rachmaninov,** [b]**Vladimir Horowitz** (pfs); [a]**Philadelphia Orchestra /** **Leopold Stokowski;** [b]**London Symphony Orchestra / Albert Coates.** Biddulph Ⓜ LHW036* (65 minutes: ADD: 11/97). ⒼⒼⒼ

Rachmaninov Piano Concerto No. 1 in F sharp minor, Op. 1[a]. Rhapsody on a Theme of Paganini, Op. 43[b]. **Vladimir Ashkenazy** (pf); [a]**Concertgebouw Orchestra;** [b]**Philharmonia Orchestra / Bernard Haitink.** Decca Ⓕ 417 613-2DH (52 minutes: DDD: 12/87). Ⓖ
Showpiece that it is, with its lush romantic harmonies and contrasting vigorous panache, the First Concerto has much to commend it in purely musical terms and although its debts are clear enough (most notably perhaps to Rimsky-Korsakov), it stands on its own two feet as far as invention, overall design and musical construction are concerned. The *Paganini* Rhapsody is one of the composer's finest works and arguably the most purely inventive set of variations to be based on Paganini's catchy tune ever written. The wealth of musical invention it suggested to Rachmaninov is truly bewildering and his control over what can in lesser hands become a rather laboured formal scheme is masterly indeed. Ashkenazy gives superb performances of both works and the Concertgebouw and the

Philharmonia are in every way the perfect foils under Bernard Haitink's sympathetic direction. There is weight, delicacy, colour, energy and repose in equal measure here and it is all conveyed by a full-bodied and detailed recording.

Additional recommendations ...

...No. 1. Rhapsody on a Theme of Paganini **Mikhail Pletnev** (pf); **Philharmonia Orchestra / Libor Pešek**. Virgin Classics Ⓜ VC7 59506-2 (51 minutes: DDD: 12/88).

...No. 1. **Prokofiev** Piano Concerto No. 3 in C major, Op. 26. Toccata in C major, Op. 11. **Pinto** Three Scenes from Childhood. **Byron Janis** (pf); **Moscow Philharmonic Orchestra / Kyrill Kondrashin**. Mercury Ⓜ 434 333-2MM (69 minutes: ADD: 7/94).

...Nos. 1 and 3. **Jean-Yves Thibaudet** (pf); **Cleveland Orchestra / Vladimir Ashkenazy**. Decca Ⓕ 448 219-2DH (71 minutes: DDD: 10/95).

...Nos. 1[a] and No. 2[b]. **Sviatoslav Richter** (pf). [a]**USSR Radio Symphony Orchestra, [b]Leningrad Philharmonic Orchestra / Kurt Sanderling**. Melodiya mono Ⓜ 74321 29467-2* (62 minutes: ADD: 6/96).

Rachmaninov Piano Concertos – No. 1 in F sharp minor, Op. 1; No. 2 in C minor, Op. 18; No. 3 in D minor, Op. 30; No. 4 in G minor, Op. 40. **Vladimir Ashkenazy** (pf); **London Symphony Orchestra / André Previn**. Double Decca Ⓜ 444 839-2DF2 (two discs: 135 minutes: ADD: 2/96). From SXLF6565/7 (9/72). Recorded 1990-1991.   Ⓖ

This reissue dates from 1972 yet the sound and balance are superb and there is nothing to cloud or impede one's sense of Ashkenazy's greatness in all these works. From him every page declares Rachmaninov's nationality, his indelibly Russian nature. What nobility of feeling and what dark regions of the imagination he relishes and explores in page after page of the Third Concerto in particular. Significantly his opening is a very moderate *Allegro ma non tanto*, later allowing him an expansiveness and imaginative scope hard to find in other more 'driven' or hectic performances. His rubato is as natural as it is distinctive and his way of easing from one idea to another shows him at his most intimately and romantically responsive. There are no cuts, and his choice of the bigger of the two cadenzas is entirely apt, given the breadth of his conception. Even the skittering figurations and volleys of repeated notes just before the close of the central *Intermezzo* cannot tempt Ashkenazy into display and he is quicker than any other pianist to find a touch of wistfulness beneath Rachmaninov's occasional outer playfulness (the *scherzando* episode in the finale).

Such imaginative fervour and delicacy are just as central to Ashkenazy's other performances. His steep unmarked *decrescendo* at the close of the First Concerto's opening rhetorical gesture is symptomatic of his romantic bias, his love of the music's interior glow. And despite his prodigious command in, say, the final pages of both the First and Fourth Concertos, there is never a hint of bombast or a more superficial brand of fire-and-brimstone virtuosity. Previn works hand in glove with his soloist. Clearly, this is no one-night partnership but the product of the greatest musical sympathy, of a mutual skill and affection. The opening of the Third Concerto's *Intermezzo* (where the orchestra momentarily step into the limelight) could hardly be given with a more idiomatic, brooding melancholy, a perfect introduction for all that is to follow. Naturally, you will have your own favourite individual performances but if you want playing which captures Rachmaninov's always elusive, opalescent centre then Ashkenazy is hard to beat. His are probably the most personal and deeply felt performances available.

Additional recommendations ...

...No. 2[a]. **Prokofiev** Piano Concerto No. 5 in G major, Op. 55[b]. **Sviatoslav Richter** (pf); **Warsaw Philharmonic Orchestra / [a]Stanislaw Wislocki, [b]Witold Rowicki**. DG Ⓕ 415 119-2GH* (58 minutes: ADD: 6/85). *See review under Prokofiev; refer to the Index.*   Ⓖ Ⓖ Ⓖ

...No. 2. Coupled with works by various composers. **Cristina Ortiz** (pf); **Royal Philharmonic Orchestra / Moshe Atzmon**. Decca Ⓕ 414 348-2DH (58 minutes: DDD: 9/86). *See review in the Collections section; refer to the Index.*   Ⓖ

...No. 2. Rhapsody on a Theme of Paganini, Op. 43. **Vladimir Ashkenazy** (pf); **London Symphony Orchestra / André Previn**. Decca Ovation Ⓜ 417 702-2DM (58 minutes: ADD: 7/87). *The Concerto is the same recording as the one reviewed above.*   Ⓖ

...No. 2. Rhapsody on a Theme of Paganini. **Philip Fowke** (pf); **Royal Philharmonic Orchestra / Yuri Temirkanov**. EMI Eminence Ⓜ CD-EMX9509 (59 minutes: DDD: 10/87).

...Nos. 2[a] and 3[b]. **Sergei Rachmaninov** (pf); **Philadelphia Orchestra / [a]Leopold Stokowski, [b]Eugene Ormandy**. RCA Red Seal mono Ⓕ RD85997* (66 minutes: ADD: 10/88).   Ⓖ Ⓖ Ⓖ

...No. 3[a]. Preludes[b] – C sharp minor, Op. 3 No. 2; B flat major, Op. 23 No. 2; G minor, Op. 23 No. 5; B minor, Op. 32 No. 10; D flat major, Op. 32 No. 13. **Vladimir Ashkenazy** (pf); [a]**London Symphony Orchestra / André Previn**. Decca Ovation Ⓜ 417 764-2DM (70 minutes: ADD: 10/88). *The Concerto is the same recording as the one reviewed above*   Ⓖ

...No. 2. Rhapsody on a Theme of Paganini. **Jenő Jandó** (pf); **Budapest Symphony Orchestra / György Lehel**. Naxos Ⓢ 8 550117 (58 minutes: DDD: 10/90).

...Nos. 2 and 3. **Earl Wild** (pf); **Royal Philharmonic Orchestra / Jascha Horenstein**. Chandos Collect Ⓜ CHAN6507 (66 minutes: ADD: 2/91).   Ⓖ Ⓖ

...No. 3. Coupled with works by **Saint-Saëns** and **Shostakovich** Emil Gilels (pf); **Paris Conservatoire Orchestra / André Cluytens**. Testament mono Ⓕ SBT1029* (65 minutes: ADD: 2/94). *See review under Saint-Saëns; refer to the Index.*   Ⓖ Ⓖ

...Nos. 2 and 3. **Lilya Zilberstein** (pf); **Berlin Philharmonic Orchestra / Claudio Abbado.**
DG Ⓕ 439 930-2GH (76 minutes: DDD: 2/95).
...No. 2[a]. **Tchaikovsky** Piano Concerto No. 1 in B flat minor, Op. 23[b]. **Sviatoslav Richter** (pf);
[a]**Warsaw Philharmonic Orchestra / Stanislaw Wislocki;** [b]**Vienna Symphony Orchestra /
Herbert von Karajan.** DG The Originals Ⓜ 447 420-2GOR (71 minutes: ADD: 7/95).   ⒼⒼ
...No. 2[a]. Rhapsody on a Theme of Paganini[b]. Preludes – C sharp minor, Op. 3 No. 2; G minor,
Op. 23 No. 5; G major, Op. 32 No. 5; B minor, Op. 32 No. 10; G sharp minor, Op. 32 No. 12.
Moment musical in E minor, Op. 16 No. 4. **Mendelssohn** (arr. Rachmaninov) A Midsummer
Night's Dream – Scherzo. **Benno Moiseiwitsch** (pf); **London Philharmonic Orchestra /**
[a]**Walter Goehr,** [b]**Basil Cameron.** APR Signature mono Ⓜ APR5505* (78 minutes: ADD: 10/95).
...No. 2[a]. Preludes – G minor, Op. 23 No. 5; G major, Op. 32 No. 5. **Tchaikovsky** Piano Concerto
No. 1 in B flat minor, Op. 23[a]. **Géza Anda** (pf); [a]**Philharmonia Orchestra / Alceo Galliera.**
Testament mono Ⓕ SBT1064* (76 minutes: ADD: 10/95). *See review in the Collections section;
refer to the Index.*   Ⓖ

Rachmaninov Piano Concertos[a] – No. 1 in F sharp minor, Op. 1; No. 4 in G minor, Op. 40.
Rhapsody on a Theme of Paganini, Op. 43[b]. **Zoltán Kocsis** (pf); **San Francisco Symphony
Orchestra / Edo de Waart.** Philips Solo Ⓜ 446 582-2PM (72 minutes: DDD: 7/96).
Items marked [a] from 6514 377 (2/84), [b]412 738-1PH. Recorded 1982.
Rachmaninov Piano Concertos – No. 2 in C minor, Op. 18[a]; No. 3 in D minor, Op. 30[b].
Vocalise, Op. 34 No. 14 (arr. Kocsis)[c]. **Zoltán Kocsis** (pf); [ab]**San Francisco Symphony Orchestra /
Edo de Waart.** Philips Solo Ⓜ 446 199-2PM (75 minutes: DDD: 7/96). Item marked [a] from
412 738-1PH (5/86), [b]411 475-2PH (8/85), [c]412 213-1PH (1/86). Recorded 1978-1984.
Few if any readings of the piano concertos and the *Paganini* Rhapsody spark or scintillate with such
daredevilry, are of such unapologetic virtuoso voltage, as these. True, Kocsis can sometimes be more
voluble than poised, breezing through the Third Concerto's haunting opening theme at the fastest
flowing tempo and – for lovers of the ever-romantic Variation No. 18 from the *Paganini* Rhapsody, in
particular – sometimes sacrificing heart's-ease for high-octane bravura. Again, you may question his
near *allegretto* spin through the Second Concerto's central *Adagio*, eagerly glimpsing so many
dazzling athletic opportunities ahead. Even so, try him in the Third Concerto's cadenza (the slimmer
and better of the two) and you will hear it topped and tailed with a ferocious and almost palpable
aplomb. Listen to him snapping off phrase ends in the intricate reel of the *Paganini* Rhapsody's
Variation No. 15 or flashing fire in the *Allegro leggiero* from the First Concerto's finale and you may
well wonder when you last encountered such fearless brilliance, pace and relish. Even those attuned
to the darker, more introspective Rachmaninov of Ashkenazy will surely pause to wonder. Edo de
Waart and the San Francisco Symphony Orchestra are no match for the LSO for Previn; yet, overall,
this is the most propulsive and exciting set of the complete concertos. Kocsis's whirlwind tempos even
allow him time for an encore – his own ardent elaboration of the *Vocalise*, a performance sufficiently
ecstatic to set even the least susceptible heart a-flutter.

Additional recommendations ...
...No. 3. Rhapsody on a theme of Paganini. **Mikhail Rudy** (pf); **St Petersburg Philharmonic
Orchestra / Mariss Jansons.** EMI Ⓕ CDC7 54880-2 (66 minutes: DDD: 11/93).
...No. 3[a]. Piano Sonata No. 2 in B flat minor, Op. 36. **John Lill** (pf); [a]**BBC National Orchestra of
Wales / Tadaaki Otaka.** Nimbus Ⓕ NI5348 (72 minutes: DDD: 10/94).
...Vocalise (trans. Rose). *Coupled with works by* **Kabalevsky** *and* **Khachaturian** Mats Lidström
(vc); **Gothenburg Symphony Orchestra / Vladimir Ashkenazy** (pf). BIS Ⓕ CD719
(65 minutes: DDD: 7/96). *See review under Kabalevsky; refer to the Index.*
...Vocalise. Cello Sonata in G minor, Op. 19. Two Pieces, Op. 2. **Miaskovsky**
Cello Sonata No. 1 in D major, Op. 12. **Truls Mørk** (vc); **Jean-Yves Thibaudet** (pf).
Virgin Classics Ⓕ VC5 45119-2 (72 minutes: DDD: 11/96).

Rachmaninov Piano Concerto No. 3 in D minor, Op. 30[a].
Tchaikovsky Piano Concerto No. 1 in B flat minor, Op. 23[b]. **Martha Argerich** (pf); [a]**Berlin Radio
Symphony Orchestra / Riccardo Chailly;** [b]**Bavarian Radio Symphony Orchestra / Kyrill Kondrashin.**
Philips Ⓕ 446 673-2PH (73 minutes: DDD: 8/95). Item marked [a] recorded live in 1982,
new to UK; [b]1980, from 6514 118 (7/82). *Gramophone Editor's choice.*   ⒼⒼⒼ
Here, at long last, is Martha Argerich's legendary 1982 Rachmaninov Third Concerto with Chailly
coupled with a reissue of her famously volatile 1980 Tchaikovsky First with Kondrashin. To describe
both performances as 'live' is to deal in understatement, for rarely in her entire and extraordinary
career has Argerich sounded more exhaustingly restless and quixotic, her mind and fingers flashing
with reflexes merely dreamt of by other less phenomenally endowed pianists. Yet her Rachmaninov is
full of surprises, her opening *Allegro* almost convivial until she meets directions such as *più vivo* or
veloce, where the tigress in her shows her claws and the music is made to seethe and boil at a white-
hot temperature. The cadenza (the finer and more transparent of the two) rises to the sort of climax
that will make all pianists' hearts beat faster and her first entry in the "Intermezzo" interrupts the
orchestra's musing with the impatience of a hurricane. But throughout these pages it is almost as if
she is searching for music that will allow her virtuosity its fullest scope. In the finale she finds it,
accelerating out of the second movement with a sky-rocketing propulsion. Here the music races like

wildfire, with a truly death-defying turn of speed at 7'21" and an explosive energy throughout that must have left audience, conductor and orchestra feeling as if hit by some seismic shock-wave. The Tchaikovsky, too, finds Argerich at her most inflammatory. Those of a nervous disposition or, more precisely, those who like their Tchaikovsky to be more magisterial and composed will, of course, look elsewhere but who would miss volleys of octave spun off like single notes, or a second movement central *Prestissimo* dispatched at a scarcely credible tempo? A performance, then, for those who like life in the fast lane, though it has to be said that such incandescence is hardly flaunted, more a "spontaneous overflow of powerful feelings" of emotion recollected not so much in tranquillity as in a cloud of fire and fury. The recordings, given the tricky circumstances, are remarkably successful.

Rachmaninov Piano Concerto No. 3 in D minor, Op. 30[a].
Tchaikovsky Piano Concerto No. 1 in B flat minor, Op. 23[b]. **Vladimir Horowitz** (pf);
 New York Philharmonic Symphony Orchestra / Sir John Barbirolli. APR mono Ⓔ APR5519*
 (66 minutes: ADD: 6/97). Item marked [a] recorded live in 1941, [b]1940.   ⒼⒼⒼ
Yes, the pundits were right. This is the Rachmaninov Third to end all Rachmaninov Thirds, a performance of such super-human pianistic aplomb, pace and virtuosity that it makes all comparisons, save with Horowitz himself (expertly charted in the accompanying essay by Michael Glover) a study in irrelevance. It was Horowitz's 1930 recording with Albert Coates that made Artur Rubinstein pale with envy before he turned very nasty indeed; goodness knows how he would have reacted had he heard Horowitz and Barbirolli! Taken from a 1941 New York broadcast (with apologies from the producer for snaps, crackles, pops and the like) Horowitz's tumultuous, near-apocalyptic brilliance includes all his unique and tirelessly debated attributes; his swooning rubato, thundering bass and splintering treble, his explosive attack, his super-erotic inflexions and turns of phrase. Try the skittering *scherzando* variation just before the close of the central *Intermezzo* and note how the pianist's velocity eclipses even his legendary recording with Fritz Reiner. This ultimate wizard of the keyboard is in expansive mood in the Tchaikovsky. There are ample rewards, too, for those who rejoice in Horowitz at his most clamorous, for the thunder and lightning of this 'Tornado from the Steppes'. The performance ends in what can only be described as a scream of octaves and an outburst by an audience driven near to hysteria. Barbirolli and the New York Philharmonic Symphony Orchestra are equal to just about every twist and turn of their volatile soloist's argument and so these performances (and most notably the finale of the Rachmaninov) are, quite simply, beyond price.

Rachmaninov Piano Concerto No. 4 in G minor, Op. 40.
Ravel Piano Concerto in G major. **Arturo Benedetti Michelangeli** (pf); **Philharmonia Orchestra /
 Ettore Gracis.** EMI Ⓔ CDC7 49326-2* (47 minutes: ADD: 9/88). From ASD255 (10/58).
 Recorded 1957. *Gramophone classical 100.*   ⒼⒼⒼ
The continuing presence of Michelangeli's classic account of the Fourth Concerto and of Richter in the Second (on DG, coupled with the Fifth Prokofiev Concerto) are almost unfair to all other accounts; but they are enormously helpful to the reviewer, since they cut straight through what might otherwise be a tedious list of minor pros and cons. In crude and subjective terms Michelangeli makes the spine tingle in a way none of the others can approach. How does he do it? Of course this is the secret every pianist would love to know, and which no writer can ever pin down. But it is possible to give some general indications. It is not a question of technique, at least not directly, because Ashkenazy, for example (on Decca) can match their most virtuosic feats; indirectly, yes, it is relevant, in that there are dimensions in Michelangeli's pianism which allow musical conceptions to materialize which might not dawn on others. It is not a question of structure, in the narrow sense of the awareness of overall proportions, judicious shaping of paragraphs, continuity of thought; but the way structure is projected and the way it is transmuted into emotional drama; of course these things are critical. In one way or another most of the recordings in this section respond vividly to the excitement of Rachmaninov's dramatic climaxes; but with Michelangeli these climaxes seem to burst through the music of their own volition, as though an irresistible force of nature has been released. It is this crowning of a structure by release, rather than by extra pressure, which gives the performance a sense of exaltation and which more than anything else sets it on a different level. It enables him to be freer in many details (some of which may not be universally approved) and yet seem more inevitable as a whole. The impact of all this would be negligible without a sympathetically attuned conductor and orchestra. Fortunately that is exactly what Michelangeli has. Michelangeli's Ravel is open to cricicism, partly because many listeners feel uncomfortable with his persistent left-before-right mannerism in the slow movement and with his unwarranted textual tinkerings (like changing the last note). But there is no doubt that he is as finely attuned to this aloof idiom as to its temperamental opposite in the Rachmaninov. And although the recording cannot entirely belie its vintage, it does justice to one of the finest concerto records ever made.

Rachmaninov Symphonies – No. 1 in D minor, Op. 13; No. 2 in E minor, Op. 27; No. 3 in
 A minor, Op. 44[c]. Symphonic Dances, Op. 45[a]. The isle of the dead, Op. 29[a]. Vocalise, Op. 34
 No. 14[b] (arr. composer). Aleko[c] – Intermezzo; Gipsy Girls' Dance. **London Symphony Orchestra /
 André Previn.** EMI Ⓑ CMS7 64530-2 (three discs: 227 minutes: ADD: 10/93). Items marked
 [a] from ASD3259 (9/76), [b] ASD3284 (12/76), [c] ASD3369 (8/77). Recorded 1974-1976.   ⒼⒼ

Rachmaninov Symphonies – No. 1 in D minor, Op. 13[a]; No. 2 in E minor, Op. 27[b]; No. 3 in A minor, Op. 44[c]. **Concertgebouw Orchestra / Vladimir Ashkenazy.** Double Decca Ⓜ 448 116-2DF2 (two discs: 140 minutes: DDD: 7/96). Item marked [a] from SXDL7603 (11/83), [b]SXDL7563 (7/82), [c]SXDL7531 (6/83). Recorded 1980-1982. ⒼⒼ

Rachmaninov's three symphonies reflect three very different phases in his creative development: the first (1895) is a stormy synthesis of contemporary trends in Russian symphonic music, the Second (1906-07), an epic study in Tchaikovskian opulence, and the third (1935-36) a seemingly unstoppable stream of original ideas and impressions. The Second was the first to gain wide acceptance, and with good reason. It shares both the key and general mood of Tchaikovsky's Fifth. Cast in E minor, its initial gloom ultimately turns to triumph, and the symphony includes enough glorious melodies to keep Hollywood happy for decades. The First Symphony had a difficult birth, largely through the incompetent musical midwifery of Alexander Glazunov whose conducting of the work's première apparently left much to be desired. It is, however, an immensely promising piece and although undeniably the product of its times, prophetic not only of the mature Rachmaninov, but of other Northern voices, including – occasionally – the mature Sibelius. Both the Third Symphony and its near-contemporary, the *Symphonic Dances* find Rachmaninov indulging a fruitful stream of musical consciousness, recalling motives and ideas from earlier compositions, yet allowing gusts of fresh air to enliven and rejuvenate his style. Both works have yet to receive their full due in the concert-hall, although the strongly evocative *Isle of the dead* is more securely embedded in the repertory. What with these and a trio of warming shorter pieces, André Previn's mid-1970s LSO package makes for an excellent bargain package. The performances are entirely sympathetic, avoiding familiar interpretative extremes such as slickness, bombast and emotional indulgence. Previn shows particular understanding of the Third Symphony, the *Symphonic Dances* and *The isle of the dead,* works that represent Rachmaninov at his most innovative and assured. The Second Symphony is played without cuts (not invariably the case, even today) and the recordings are generous in tone and revealing of detail, especially among the woodwinds.

Ashkenazy has made few more distinguished discs as conductor than his Rachmaninov symphony recordings of the early 1980s. They are to that decade what Ormandy's were to the 1960s or Previn's to the 1970s and their appearance in this two-disc format has the obvious attraction of economy. The downside of the repackaging is that you have to put up with a change of disc half-way through the Second Symphony and lose the shorter orchestral works included in the Previn set. Previn is the most natural but not always the most electrifying of Rachmaninov interpreters and many will find Ashkenazy preferable, particularly in No. 1. Although some of Ashkenazy's speeds seem unnaturally pressed – he fairly tips us into the first movement reprise having declined to cap the climax with unvalidated bells – the excitement is infectious. Previn's LSO are not at their best in the *Larghetto* (placed third), but in the corresponding movement of the Second Symphony the boot is on the other foot. Not that Ashkenazy isn't convincing too – so long as you can forget the Previn. Ashkenazy's volatile approach is at its most extreme in the Third, the mood much less autumnal than it usually is (and perhaps should be), with the fruity Concertgebouw brass unconstrained. Such an unashamedly episodic rendering of the score has its drawbacks, but the virtuosic energy and romantic gush are hard to resist. Throughout the cycle, the players are unfailingly alert and the recordings sound very well indeed. While the big acoustic muddles some detail, hall resonance helps distract the ear from the slightly steely quality of the strings (most noticeable in No. 2). An exceptional bargain.

Additional recommendations ...

...Nos. 1-3. Vocalise. **Philadelphia Orchestra / Eugene Ormandy.**
CBS Maestro Ⓜ M2YK45678 (two discs: 137 minutes: ADD: 8/90).
...Symphonic Dances. *Coupled with works by* **Smetana** and **Offenbach** Philadelphia Orchestra / Eugene Ormandy. Sony Classical Essential Classics Ⓑ SBK48279 (76 minutes: ADD: 6/93).
...The isle of the dead. Vocalise. *Coupled with works by various composers.*
Bernard Zighera (pf); **Boston Symphony Orchestra / Serge Koussevitzky** (db).
Biddulph mono Ⓕ WHL045* (78 minutes: ADD: 2/97).

Rachmaninov Symphony No. 2 in E minor, Op. 27. The Rock, Op. 7. **Russian National Orchestra / Mikhail Pletnev.** DG Ⓕ 439 888-2GH (64 minutes: DDD: 6/94). Recorded 1993.
Gramophone Editor's choice. Selected by Sounds in Retrospect. ⒼⒼ

Mikhail Pletnev's achievement is to make us hear the music afresh: a performance characterized by relatively discreet emotionalism, strong forward momentum and a fanatical preoccupation with clarity of articulation. When there is no Slavic wobble, it scarcely matters that his winds display an individuality which once or twice fails to transcend mere rawness – so much the better in this music! The strings, forceful and husky (with separated violin desks) are beyond reproach. The most remarkable playing comes in the finale. The lyrical effusions are superbly characterized without undermining the sense of inexorability, the climaxes not just powerful but affecting too. The closing pages bring a rush of adrenalin of the kind rarely experienced live, let alone in the studio. This is great music-making, the rubato always there when required, the long phrases immaculately tailored yet always sounding spontaneous. DG's unexpected coupling is *The Rock*, an early, rather bitty piece which is however very deftly scored and intriguingly Scriabinesque in places. In Pletnev's hands, the central climax is surprisingly powerful, with just a hint of the buzz-saw in the brass playing. The fabulous delicacy elsewhere is alone worth the price of admission.

Additional recommendations ...
...No. 2. Vocalise. **BBC Welsh Symphony Orchestra / Tadaaki Otaka.**
Nimbus Ⓕ NI5322 (66 minutes: DDD: 5/92).
...No. 2. Vocalise[a]. [a]**Sylvia McNair** (sop); **Baltimore Symphony Orchestra / David Zinman.**
Telarc Ⓕ CD80312 (68 minutes: DDD: 10/92). *Selected by Sounds in Retrospect.*
...No. 2. The Rock, Op. 7. **St Petersburg Philharmonia Academic**
Symphony Orchestra / Alexander Dmitriev.
Sony Classical St Petersburg Classics Ⓜ SMK57650 (63 minutes: DDD: 2/95).
...No. 2. The Rock, Op. 7. **Philadelphia Orchestra / Charles Dutoit.**
Decca Ⓕ 440 604-2DH (72 minutes: DDD: 6/95).

Rachmaninov Symphony No. 3 in A minor, Op. 44. Symphonic Dances, Op. 45. **St Petersburg**
Philharmonic Orchestra / Mariss Jansons. EMI Ⓕ CDC7 54877-2 (72 minutes: DDD: 12/93).
Recorded 1992. **Gramophone** *Editor's choice.*   ⓖⓖ
This is one of the more distinguished Rachmaninov issues of recent years. While no Rachmaninov
Third unfolds as inexorably as Previn's (reviewed above), it is refreshing to hear the opening 'motto'
theme played perfectly in tune by an orchestra on even more dazzling form than the LSO, and Jansons
unearths such exquisite details of sonority and texture that criticism is all but silenced. There have
been more haunting, more fundamentally pessimistic accounts, but none with such an ear for
Rachmaninov's sometimes risky orchestral effects. The *Symphonic Dances* are even more impressive.
The insinuating waltz movement is irresistible, very free with idiomatic-sounding rubato, while the
dynamic outer portions of the finale are superbly articulated, dazzling in the closing stages. EMI's
close-miking of instrumental lines may inhibit the sort of tonal blend implied by Rachmaninov's
scoring, but the distinctive heft and huskiness of Mravinsky's string section is not betrayed. In its lush,
extrovert way, this disc is unbeatable.
Additional recommendations ...
...No. 3. **Shostakovich** Symphony No. 6 in B minor, Op. 54[b]. **London Symphony Orchestra /**
André Previn. EMI Studio Ⓜ CDM7 69564-2 (75 minutes: ADD: 12/88).   ⓖⓖ
...No. 3. The isle of the dead, Op. 29. Vocalise (arr. composer). **Philadelphia Orchestra /**
Sergey Rachmaninov. Pearl Ⓕ GEMMCD9414* (59 minutes: AAD).   ⓖⓖ
...No. 3. The isle of the dead. **BBC Welsh Symphony Orchestra / Tadaaki Otaka.**
Nimbus Ⓕ NI5344 (64 minutes: DDD: 4/93).
...No. 3. Symphonic Dances, Op. 45. **Concertgebouw Orchestra / Vladimir Ashkenazy.**
Decca Ovation Ⓜ 436 481-2DM (76 minutes: DDD: 2/94).   ⓖⓖ
...No. 3. Symphonic Dances, Op. 45. **Baltimore Symphony Orchestra / David Zinman.**
Telarc Ⓕ CD80331 (74 minutes: DDD: 1/95).

Rachmaninov Symphony No. 3 in A minor, Op. 44. Morceaux de fantaisie, Op. 3 – No. 3,
Mélodie in E major; No. 4, Polichinelle in F sharp minor (both orch. anon.). **National Symphony**
Orchestra of Ireland / Alexander Anissimov. Naxos Ⓢ 8 550808 (52 minutes: DDD: 6/98).
Recorded 1996.   ⓖ
Can Anissimov hope to compete in a field that includes Ashkenazy's high-octane digital accounts in
sundry bargain formats, not least a Double Decca two-pack offering all three symphonies? Perhaps
surprisingly the answer turns out to be yes, for the conductor produces a highly distinctive
performance of the Third, inspiring his orchestra to playing of considerable warmth and flair. Sound
quality is excellent too. String tone is crucially important with this composer, and here again any
worries proved unfounded. Not for Anissimov the 'neurotic' Russian-ness of Ashkenazy's
Rachmaninov. Like Jansons, he disregards the first-movement exposition repeat, but he makes the
orchestral voices speak with an altogether gentler tone. There are shattering climaxes when the music
calls for them, and the symphony ends in rousing style; elsewhere the sophisticated languor and
careful phrasing recall André Previn's famous recording. Although some will be disappointed with the
generally slow tempos (relaxed even further for those succulent second subjects), there is, as with the
Previn on EMI, an unusual wholeness of musical vision and pacing which never sacrifices the needs
of the larger structure to the lure of momentary thrills. The couplings are somewhat mysterious as no
arranger is cited. Despite the short measure, this is thoroughly recommendable at the price.

Rachmaninov Symphonic Dances, Op. 45[a].
Janáček Taras Bulba[b]. **North German Radio Symphony Orchestra / Sir John Eliot Gardiner.**
DG Ⓕ 445 838-2GH (56 minutes: DDD: 1/96). Recorded live in 1993.
Rachmaninov's *Symphonic Dances* are played with great sharpness here, emphasizing the
extraordinary originality of his last completed work and serving as a reminder that the original title
was *Fantastic Dances*: this might be more suitable for a performance that, though not lacking in
lyrical grace, sets some familiar characteristics in a novel, strange and even somewhat disquieting
context. The waltz of the central movement (once to have been called "Twilight") has a rhythmic
fluency that suggests not so much elegance as a faintly uncertain atmosphere; and there are shadows
lying across the urgency of the finale. A fascinating score, intelligently and imaginatively read. *Taras
Bulba* is also very well played. Here, the problems include unusual instrumental balance but, still
more, getting the relationships between the many tempo changes into the right perspective. Gardiner

is sensitive to these, without always following the instructions in the score to the letter. For the most part, his reading justifies this, though in the first movement, "The Death of Andri", the move into the *Allegro vivo* is not done *accelerando* but abruptly, three bars early, which seems to go against the nature of the melodic phrases. But this is a small point, and for the rest the performance is admirably detailed and well judged; and in both works the orchestral playing is full of virtuosity and clarity.

Additional recommendations ...

...Symphonic Dances. 14 Songs, Op. 34 – Vocalise (rev. 1915)[a]. **Stravinsky** Jeu de cartes.
[a]**Nelli Lee** (sop); **Novosibirsk Philharmonic Orchestra / Arnold Kaz.**
Sony Classical St Petersburg Classics Ⓜ SMK57660 (65 minutes: DDD: 2/95).

...Symphonic Dances. The bells, Op. 35[a]. [a]**Elizaveta Shumskaya** (sop); [a]**Mikhail Dovenman** (ten);
[a]**Alexei Bolshakov** (bar); [a]**Russian Republican Chamber Choir; Moscow Philharmonic Orchestra /
Kyrill Kondrashin.** Melodiya Ⓜ 74321 32046-2 (69 minutes: ADD: 10/96).

Rachmaninov Trios élégiaques – G minor; D minor, Op. 9. **Copenhagen Trio** (Søren Elbaek, vn;
Troels Svane Hermansen, vc; Morten Mogensen, pf). Kontrapunkt Ⓕ 32187 (65 minutes: DDD:
12/94). Recorded 1994.

The shade of Tchaikovsky haunts both these works. In the first, there are turns of phrase from his Trio, and much of the style and the textural approach to the problems derive from his example – not always a very good one, when it came to dealing with a virtuoso piano part against the weaker sound of the strings. Rachmaninov is ingenious, and handles his material expertly in a long, shapely movement. Tchaikovsky is more consciously the exemplar of the second trio. Deeply impressed by the younger composer's *The Rock*, he had agreed to conduct the first performance in January 1894, a rare gesture of appreciation. On Tchaikovsky's death in October, the shocked Rachmaninov wrote his Trio "in memory of a great artist", just as Tchaikovsky had once written a Trio in memory of another great artist, Nikolay Rubinstein. And here, too, there is a substantial variation movement, on a theme from *The Rock*. It is lyrically varied, not with conscious allusions after the manner of Tchaikovsky's elegy but with a sense of indebtedness that is unmistakable. Rachmaninov initially intended to have the opening statement of the theme played on the harmonium; he later revised the work, removing this appalling idea, and it is the second version which is recorded here, and well recorded in a fine performance that does full justice to a lengthy but affecting piece.

Additional recommendation ...

...**Borodin Trio.** Chandos Ⓕ CHAN8341 (60 minutes: DDD: 3/85).

Rachmaninov Complete Solo Piano Music. **Howard Shelley** (pf). Hyperion Ⓜ CDS44041/8
(eight discs: 449 minutes: DDD: 3/94). From CDA66081, CDA66082, CDA66184, CDA66047,
CDA66009 (all 10/88), CDA66198 (9/87), CDA66091 (8/88) and CDA66486 (3/92).
Variations on a Theme of Chopin, Op. 22. Variations on a Theme of Corelli, Op. 42. Mélodie in
E major, Op. 3 No. 3. Piano Sonatas – No. 1 in D minor, Op. 28; No. 2 in B flat minor, Op. 36
(orig. version); No. 2 in B flat minor, Op. 36 (rev. version). Ten Preludes, Op. 23. 13 Preludes,
Op. 32. Prelude in D minor. Prelude in F major. Morceaux de fantaisie, Op. 3. Morceau de
fantaisie in G minor. Song without words in D minor. Pièce in D minor. Fughetta in F major.
Fragments in A flat major. Oriental Sketch in B flat major. Three Nocturnes – No. 1 in F sharp
minor; No. 2 in F major; No. 3 in C minor. Quatre Pièces – Romance in F sharp minor; Prélude
in E flat minor; Mélodie in E major; Gavotte in D major. 17 Etudes-tableaux, Opp. 33 and 39.
Transcriptions – **Rimsky-Korsakov** The Tale of Tsar Saltan – The flight of the bumble-bee.
Kreisler Liebesleid. Liebesfreud. **Bizet** L'Arlésienne Suite No. 1 – Menuet. **Schubert** Die
schöne Müllerin, D957 – Wohin? **Mussorgsky** Sorochinsky Fair – Gopak. **Bach** Solo Violin
Partita No. 3 in E major, BWV1006 – Preludio, Gavotte, Gigue. **Rachmaninov** Daisies, Op. 38
No. 3. Lilacs, Op. 21 No. 5. Vocalise, Op. 34 No. 14 (arr. Kocsis). **Mendelssohn** A Midsummer
Night's Dream, Op. 61 – Scherzo. **Behr** Lachtäubchen, Op. 303 (pubd. as Polka de VR).
Tchaikovsky Cradle Song, Op. 16 No. 1. Recorded 1978-91.   Ⓖ

This Hyperion set is a significant testament to Howard Shelley's artistry. Pianistically impeccable, he understands what Rachmaninov was about. The original piano works span some 45 years of the composer's life. The earliest pieces here, the *Nocturnes*, strangely owe allegiance neither to Field nor Chopin, but are very much in the mid-to-late nineteenth-century Russian salon style. The Third, in C minor, has nothing whatever to do with its title. Nicely written too, but still uncharacteristic, are four pieces from 1888, which amply demonstrate that from his early teens the composer had something individual to say. The *Mélodie* in E major (not to be confused with that from Op. 3) is memorable for its hypnotic use of piano tone. Hyperion's recording quality can be heard at its very best here; there is real bloom and colour. Written shortly after his First Piano Concerto in the early 1890s, the *Morceaux de fantaisie*, Op. 3 bring us to familiar Rachmaninov. The ubiquitous Prelude in C sharp minor is the second number but Shelley tries to do too much with it; he is more effective in the *Sérénade* with its Spanish overtones. In the E flat minor *Moments musicaux*, Op. 16 one feels that he is able to master Rachmaninov's swirling accompaniments idiomatically. In Variation No. 15 of the seldom-heard *Variations on a Theme of Chopin* (the theme is the Prelude in C minor from Op. 28) Shelley succeeds in bringing the notes to life, getting his fingers around the fleet *scherzando* writing. The first set of Preludes is, of course, mainstream repertoire and, as such, easier to assess. In the warmly expressive D major Prelude he lends the piece a strong Brahmsian feel and it emerges as very well focused, especially since the voices are so subtly separated. He manages to transform the C minor into a restless mood picture. The First Sonata is coventionally dismissed as being unwieldy but Shelley gives it a symphonic stature and allows it to be seen in conjunction more with the composer's orchestral writing. Within a couple of years Rachmaninov was at the height of his powers and shortly after the Third Concerto he wrote the Op. 32 Preludes. Shelley conjures up an exquisite moonlit scene for the G major, but he is not as impressive in the B minor. However, with him it is always the music that dictates the course of the interpretation. In the two sets of *Etudes-tableaux* he excels as he does too in the Second Sonata. He draws together the disparate elements of the finale with terrific mastery and shows himself the equal of the 'Horowitz clones' in matters of technique. In the *Corelli* Variations he is not quite in tune with the scope of the work but is outstanding in the transcriptions, if a little straight-faced. The recorded sound is never less than serviceable and is sometimes excellent.

Additional recommendations ...

...Preludes – B flat major, Op. 23 No. 2; G minor, Op. 23 No. 5; C minor, Op. 23 No. 7; C major, Op. 32 No. 1; B flat minor, Op. 32 No. 2. **Tchaikovsky** Piano Concerto No. 1 in B flat minor[a]. **Sviatoslav Richter** (pf); [a]**Vienna Symphony Orchestra / Herbert von Karajan.** DG Galleria Ⓜ 419 068-2GGA (50 minutes: ADD: 8/87).

...Piano Sonata No. 2. Morceau de fantaisie. Song without words. Pièce in D minor. Fughetta. Fragments. Oriental Sketch. Three Nocturnes. Quatre Pièces – Romance; Prélude; Mélodie; Gavotte. **Howard Shelley** (pf). Hyperion Ⓕ CDA66198 (59 minutes: DDD: 9/87). *This is the same recording as the one reviewed above.*

...Preludes – C sharp minor, Op. 3 No. 2; B flat major, Op. 23 No. 2; G minor, Op. 23 No. 5; B minor, Op. 32 No. 10; D flat major, Op. 32 No. 13. Piano Concerto No. 3 in D minor, Op. 30[a]. **Vladimir Ashkenazy** (pf); [a]**London Symphony Orchestra / André Previn.** Decca Ovation Ⓜ 417 764-2DM (70 minutes: ADD: 10/88).

...Preludes, Op. 23. Morceaux de fantaisie. **Howard Shelley** (pf). Hyperion Ⓕ CDA66081 (60 minutes: ADD: 10/88). *This is the same recording as the one reviewed above.*

...Preludes, Op. 32. Preludes – F major; D minor. **Howard Shelley** (pf). Hyperion Ⓕ CDA66082 (48 minutes: ADD: 10/88).

...Flight of the bumble-bee (arr. Malcolm). *Coupled with works by various composers.* **George Malcolm** (hpd). Decca Ⓜ 444 390-2DWO (75 minutes: ADD: 11/95). 🖎

...Morning, Op. 4 No. 2 (arr. Volodos). Melody, Op. 21 No. 9 (arr. Volodos). *Coupled with works by various composers.* **Arcadi Volodos** (pf). Sony Classical Ⓕ SK62691 (61 minutes: DDD: 10/97). *Gramophone* Editor's choice. Selected by Soundings. *See review in the Collections section; refer to the Index.* ⒼⒺ

...Prelude in G minor, Op. 23 No. 5. *Coupled with works by various composers.* **Pavel Nersessian** (pf). Bel Air Music Ⓕ BAM9725 (65 minutes: DDD: 3/98). *See review in the Collections section; refer to the Index.*

...Prelude in G minor, Op. 23 No. 5. *Coupled with works by various composers.* **Vladimir Horowitz** (pf). APR mono Ⓜ APR5517* (71 minutes: ADD: 5/98). *See review in the Collections section; refer to the Index.*

Rachmaninov Piano Sonata No. 1 in D minor, Op. 28.
Scriabin Piano Sonatas – No. 1 in F minor, Op. 6; No. 4 in F sharp, Op. 30. **Sergio Fiorentino** (pf). APR Ⓜ APR5556 (72 minutes: DDD: 7/97). Recorded 1995.

Sergio Fiorentino's reading of Scriabin's Fourth Piano Sonata is more intense and focused than most recent recordings. The delineation between melody and accompaniment in the opening movement is brilliantly accomplished and the winged *Prestissimo volando* which follows is exhilarating and superbly controlled. The First Sonata is no less impressive. His reading has youthful impetuosity in the first movement coupled with a powerful, tragic undertone in the second and fourth, and there is an imperious authority in his interpretation. Rachmaninov's First Piano Sonata has immense authority too, especially in the opening movement which is given a forceful, yet finely controlled, reading. Fiorentino strides through its formidable demands with consummate ease, and in the *Lento* there is much to be admired in his *cantabile* and beautiful phrasing. A very rewarding disc from a pianist of tremendous stature. Recorded sound is good.

Additional recommendations ...

...Piano Sonatas – No. 1; No. 2 (original version). **Gordon Fergus-Thompson** (pf). Kingdom Ⓕ KCLCD2007 (73 minutes: DDD: 6/89).

...Piano Sonata No. 1. Variations on a Theme of Chopin. **Boris Berezovsky** (pf). Teldec Ⓕ 4509-90890-2 (66 minutes: DDD: 7/94).

...Piano Sonata No. 1. 13 Preludes, Op. 32. **Santiago Rodriguez** (pf). Elan Ⓕ 82244 (73 minutes: DDD: 3/96).

Rachmaninov Piano Sonata No. 2 in B flat minor, Op. 36 (original version). Preludes – Op. 23: No. 1 in F sharp minor; No. 7 in C minor; Op. 32: No. 2 in B flat minor; No. 6 in F minor; No. 9 in A major; No. 10 in B minor. Etudes-tableaux – Op. 39: No. 2 in B minor; No. 7 in C minor; F minor, Op. 33 No. 1. Morceaux de fantaisie, Op. 3 – No. 3 in E major, "Mélodie"; No. 5 in B flat minor, "Sérénade". **Zoltán Kocsis** (pf). Philips Ⓕ 446 220-2PH (61 minutes: DDD: 2/96). Recorded 1994. *Gramophone* Editor's choice. ⒼⒺ

This richly exploratory recital – far removed from a popular or commercial programme – contradicts at every turn stale, still prevailing notions concerning Rachmaninov. For not only is the Second Sonata played in its original 1913 version rather than the stitched-together 1931 revision, but the shorter items include many of the composer's finest works. The seventh rather than the first C minor *Etude-tableau*, Op. 39, for example, is an elegy of the most startling modernity with its *lamentoso* outcries, its memory of the Russian liturgy and its massive central carillon. How refreshing, too, to open with the Brahmsian syncopation and expressive richness of the A major Prelude, Op. 32 No. 9 and to mix mood and key to such kaleidoscopic and dazzling effect. Throughout, Kocsis's performances are as bold and stimulating as his choice of works, gloriously free-spirited and of an immense pianistic brio and command. Indeed his performance of the Second Sonata is as fulminating and rhapsodic as any on record. Action-packed in an exhausting and enthralling way, his reading never sounds arch or contrived in a way that so often disfigures Horowitz's famous account. Kocsis possesses a stupendous technique, stepping out in dazzling style in the ultra-Russian *Etude-tableau*, Op. 33 No. 1 and clarifying the Siberian whirlwind of the F minor Prelude, Op. 32 No. 6 with a breathtaking clarity and focus. Kocsis's accompanying essay is no less stimulating and astringent than his playing (he is unsparing over the 1931 revision of the Sonata) and he has been magnificently recorded.

Additional recommendations ...
...Piano Sonata No. 2. Morceaux de fantaisie, Op. 3. Variations on a theme of Chopin, Op. 22.
 Santiago Rodriguez (pf). Elan Ⓕ 82248 (73 minutes: DDD: 3/96).
...Piano Sonata No. 2. *Coupled with works by* **Prokofiev** and **Scriabin** Sergio Fiorentino (pf).
 APR Fiorentino Edition Ⓜ APR5552 (63 minutes: DDD: 9/96)

Rachmaninov 24 Preludes, Opp. 23 and 32. Prelude in D minor. Morceaux de fantaisie, Op. 3. Lilacs. Daisies. Mélodie in E major. Oriental Sketch in B flat major. Moments musicaux, Op. 16. **Dmitri Alexeev** (pf). Virgin Classics Ⓕ VCD7 59289-2 (two discs: 138 minutes: DDD: 5/94). Recorded 1987-1989.

Alexeev's all-Russian mastery has seldom been heard to such advantage and his technical force and authority throughout are unarguable. True, he hardly wears his heart on his sleeve in the quixotic minuet of Op. 23 No. 3, is less than poetically yielding in the Chopinesque tracery of Op. 23 No. 4. He does, however, capture the Slavonic malaise of No. 1 with rare insight and his punishing weight and rhetoric in Op. 23 Nos. 2 or 7 will make even the most sanguine listener's pulse beat faster. He unleashes the central build-up of Op. 32 No. 7 with the impact of a Siberian whirlwind and time and again his icy, determinedly unsentimental approach gives added strength and focus to the composer's brilliant fury. Alexeev is more convincing in the more vertiginous numbers from the *Moments musicaux*, in Nos. 2, 4 and 6 rather than in the opening rhythmic play of No. 1 where he sounds altogether too literal and austere. Yet you only have to hear his way of making even *Polichinelle's* well-worn phrases come up as fresh as paint or his trenchancy in *Oriental Sketch* to realize that you are in the presence of a master pianist. The recordings are of demonstration quality and the accompanying essay mirrors the rare toughness and integrity of these performances; the essential nobility of Rachmaninov's genius.

Additional recommendation ...
...Preludes – Op. 23: No. 1 in F sharp minor; No. 2 in B flat; No. 5 in G minor; No. 6 in E flat major; Op. 32: No. 12 in G sharp minor. Etudes-tableaux, Op. 39 – No. 3 in F sharp minor; No. 5 in E flat minor. Moments musicaux, Op. 16 – No. 3 in B minor; No. 4 in E minor; No. 5 in D flat major; No. 6 in C major. Elégie in E flat minor, Op. 3 No. 1. *Coupled with works by* **Scriabin** **Andrei Gavrilov** (pf). EMI Eminence Ⓜ CD-EMX2237 (72 minutes: DDD: 12/95).

Rachmaninov Etudes-tableaux: Op. 33[a] – No. 5 in D minor (new to UK. 1983); No. 6 in E flat minor; No. 9 in C sharp minor (610 075, 10/84); Op. 39 – No. 1 in C minor; No. 2 in A minor; No. 3 in F sharp minor; No. 4 in B minor; No. 7 in C minor; No. 9 in D major (all 610 075). Preludes: Op. 23 – No. 1 in F sharp minor; No. 2 in B flat major; No. 4 in D major; No. 5 in G minor; No. 7 in C minor; No. 8 in A flat major; Op. 32 – No. 1 in C major; No. 2 in B flat minor; No. 6 in F minor; No. 7 in F major; No. 9 in A major; No. 10 in B minor; No. 12 in G sharp minor (all new to UK. 1971). **Sviatoslav Richter** (pf). Olympia Ⓕ OCD337 (74 minutes: DDD/ADD: 1/94). Items marked [a] recorded 1983, others 1971. ⒼⒼ

As in previous volumes in this valuable series, sound quality is on the dry side. But Richter's is the sort of playing which positively benefits from close analytical scrutiny, and serious collectors of piano recordings should need no further encouragement. Recorded between 1971 and 1983 they show a Richter in transition. Still in evidence is the prime-of-life virtuoso who burst on to the Western scene in the 1960s; but increasingly taking over is the uncompromising, ascetic philosopher-pianist of the 1980s. Metaphysics in Rachmaninov? Certainly. And not just the apparently superhuman fingerwork in the E flat minor *Etude-tableau* or the first C minor of Op. 39. What comes across is something beyond expression. It is an overriding fatalism, a sense of the immense sadness of Russia, broken only by moments of heroic resistance. The Preludes are more resonantly recorded, with a rather disappointing tubby bass. If you can live with that there is a quite unique Rachmaninov to be heard here – a brave, noble spirit, expressed in writing of an unquenchable fervour and orchestral solidity.

Rachmaninov Etudes-tableaux, Opp. 33 and 39. **John Lill** (pf). Nimbus Ⓕ NI5439
(64 minutes: DDD: 9/95). Recorded 1995.

The *Etudes-tableaux* are known to be musical evocations of various pictorial or perhaps narrative
ideas, though quite rightly Rachmaninov did not let on where the stimuli came from; there is certainly
no sign that John Lill is much preoccupied with such matters. He is a powerful keyboard technician,
which is the first necessity in approaching these virtuoso studies, and this puts him in a strong position
for dealing with the bold assertiveness of some of them, for instance the first piece of all. He also has
a very vivid sense of tempo (balancing speed and texture sympathetically), and equally a sense for the
slight lifting of pressure as well as slowing up, or the reverse, which is the essence of true romantic
rubato. Where he can seem less responsive than some of his colleagues is with the more delicate pieces,
whose fantasy he perhaps underrates. But if he also loses something in introspection, he can
command admiration with his magisterial delivery. In sum, a very strong set of performances of some
fascinating music.

Additional recommendations ...

...Op. 39 – No. 3 in F sharp minor; No. 4 in B minor; No. 7 in C minor; No. 9 in D major.
Coupled with works by various composers. **Boris Berezovsky** (pf). Teldec Ⓕ 4509-96516-2
(61 minutes: DDD: 7/96). *See review in the Collections section; refer to the Index.*
...Op. 39 – No. 5 in E flat minor; No. 6 in A minor. *Coupled with works by various composers.*
Murray Perahia (pf). Sony Classical Ⓜ SX4K63380 (four discs: 270 minutes: DDD/ADD: 4/98).
See review in the Collections section; refer to the Index.

Rachmaninov Etudes-tableaux: Op. 33 – No. 2 in C major; No. 8 in G minor. Op. 39 – No. 3 in
F sharp minor; No. 4 in B minor; No. 5 in E flat minor. Preludes: Op. 23 – No. 1 in F sharp
minor; No. 3 in D minor; No. 5 in G minor; No. 7 in C minor; No. 10 in G flat major. Preludes:
Op. 32 – No. 6 in F minor; No. 8 in A minor; No. 10 in B minor; No. 12 in G sharp minor.
Five Morceaux de fantaisie, Op. 3. **Nikolai Demidenko** (pf). Hyperion Ⓕ CDA66713
(70 minutes: DDD: 10/94). Recorded 1994.

Nikolai Demidenko's performances couple immense pianistic tact and skill, though the rushes of
adrenalin, when they come (the searing central climax of the Op. 3 "Elégie" or the A minor Prelude,
Op. 32 where a tiny motif is tempest-tossed seemingly in all directions at the same time) are almost
palpable. The C major *Etude-tableau*, Op. 23 No. 2 rises and falls with supreme naturalness and
impetus and the absence of all lushness or luxuriance in the G minor *Etude-tableau*, Op. 32 No. 8 is
a pointed reminder of Rachmaninov's serious, religious inspiration. Demidenko creates a magnificent
carillon of Moscow bells in the great B minor Prelude and his E flat minor *Etude-tableau*, Op. 39 is
arrestingly sombre and dry-eyed, its conclusion articulated with a rare sense of ebbing drama, of all
passion spent. If you prefer Rachmaninov's emotional storms viewed acutely but from a distance then
Demidenko is your man. The recordings faithfully mirror this pianist's very distinctive sound-world.

Rachmaninov The Bells, Op. 35[a].
Prokofiev Alexander Nevsky, Op. 78[b]. [a]**Sheila Armstrong** (sop); [b]**Anna Reynolds** (mez);
[a]**Robert Tear** (ten); [a]**John Shirley-Quirk** (bar); **London Symphony Chorus and Orchestra /
André Previn.** EMI Studio Ⓜ CDM7 63114-2 (78 minutes: ADD: 10/89). Item marked [a]
from ASD3284 (12/76), [b]ASD2800 (7/72).   ⒼⒼ

This is an ideal coupling with first-rate soloists in both works. Sheila Armstrong is especially fine in
The Bells and Anna Reynolds provides genuine Slavonic intensity in her contribution to the Prokofiev.
The chorals singing too, if without the special vocal timbre and enunciation of a Russian group, has
undoubted fervour, while in the famous "The Battle on the Ice" sequence in *Alexander Nevsky*, the
orchestral playing has thrilling pungency and bite. The orginal analogue recordings, made in
London's Kingsway Hall, were exceptionally well balanced and on LP the combination of ambient
effect and sharpness of detail was ideally judged. Undoubtedly the remastering increases the clarity
and projection of the sound with, perhaps, a slight loss of warmth and atmosphere. However, the
ovrall effect is certainly vividly spectacular and compulsively dramatic. This disc is a very real bargain
for the performances are both very fine indeed.

Additional recommendation ...

...The Bells. Vocalise. *Coupled with works by* **Tchaikovsky** Suzanne Murphy (sop); **Keith Lewis**
(ten); **David Wilson-Johnson** (bar); **Scottish National Chorus and Orchestra / Neeme Järvi.**
Chandos Ⓕ CHAN8476 (63 minutes: DDD: 2/87). *Selected by Sounds in Retrospect.*
...(arr. Braden) Vocalise. *Coupled with works by various composers.* **Renée Fleming** (sop);
English Chamber Orchestra / Jeffrey Tate. Decca Ⓕ 458 858-2DH (70 minutes: DDD: 3/98).
Selected by Soundings. See review in the Collections section; refer to the Index.

Rachmaninov Vespers, Op. 37. **Olga Borodina** (mez); **Vladimir Mostowoy** (ten); **St Petersburg
Chamber Choir / Nikolai Korniev.** Philips Ⓕ 442 344-2PH (56 minutes: DDD: 11/94).
Texts and translations included. Recorded 1993.

The St Petersburg Chamber Choir sing the *Vespers*, or *All-Night Vigil*, dramatically. Korniev follows
the composer's markings carefully, but he is evidently concerned to give a concert performance of
vivid immediacy, and there are places where this departs from the reflective or celebratory nature of

music that is so strongly grounded in Orthodox tradition. This is most marked with Olga Borodina, who is not the first fine singer to bring too operatic a note to her solo in "Blagoslovi, dushe moya" ("Bless the Lord, O my soul"); Vladimir Mostowoy is more discreet in "Blagosloven esi" ("Blessed art Thou"). The choir itself is excellent, with particularly fine sopranos who can chant high above the others in beautifully pitched thirds; while there is, as ever in Russian church choirs, a splendid bass section that can underpin the textures with effortlessly rich low Cs, and find no difficulty with the famous descending scale down to a sonorous bottom B flat at the end of "Nyne otpushchayeshi" (the *Nunc dimittis*). The recording is not always as clear as it could be with the textures and especially the words. A strength of the issue, which distinguishes it from almost all others available, is the booklet, which includes not only the full text in transliteration (with English, German and French translations), but also excellent essays.

Additional recommendations ...

...Vespers. **Corydon Singers / Matthew Best.** Hyperion CDA66460 (66 minutes: DDD: 7/91). Ⓖ

...Vespers. **St Petersburg Cappella / Vladislav Chernushenko.**
  CDM Russian Season Ⓕ LDC288 050 (62 minutes: DDD: 5/93).

...Vespers. **Swedish Radio Choir / Tönu Kaljuste.**
  Virgin Classics Ⓕ VC5 45124-2 (54 minutes: DDD: 9/95).

...Vespers[a] – Bless the Lord, O my soul; Blessed is the man. Liturgy of St John Chrysostom, Op. 31 – Cherubic Hymn; The Lord's Prayer. *Coupled with works by various composers.* [a]**Paul Nicholson** (alto); **King's College Choir, Cambridge / Stephen Cleobury.** EMI Ⓕ CDC5 56439-2 (64 minutes: DDD: 10/97). *See review in the Collections section; refer to the Index.*

Rachmaninov Songs, Volume 2 – 12 Songs, Op. 21[abcd]. 15 Songs, Op. 26[abcd]. Were you hiccoughing?[d]. Night[b]. [a]**Joan Rodgers** (sop); [b]**Maria Popescu** (mez); [c]**Alexandre Naoumenko** (ten); [d]**Sergei Leiferkus** (bar); **Howard Shelley** (pf). Chandos Ⓕ CHAN9451 (72 minutes: DDD: 8/96). Texts and translations included. Items marked [d] from CHAN9374 (10/95). Recorded 1994-1995.

Two figures in particular haunt this second volume of Chandos's survey of Rachmaninov's songs (the first volume is listed below) – Feodor Chaliapin and Rachmaninov himself. They had become friends in the years when they worked together in an opera company and when Rachmaninov was concentrating on developing his piano virtuosity. As a result the Op. 21 songs are dominated by an almost operatic declamatory manner coupled with formidably difficult accompaniments. Leiferkus rises splendidly to the occasion, above all in "Fate" (Op. 21 No. 1), and so throughout the songs does Howard Shelley. He is unbowed by the technical problems and he understands the novel proportions of songs in which the piano's participation has an unprecedented role. He also enjoys himself in the roisterous exchanges with Leiferkus in what is really Rachmaninov's only lighthearted song, *Were you hiccoughing?* The songs for the other voices are less powerful, in general more lyrical and intimate. Alexandre Naoumenko only has five songs, and they are not, on the whole, among the more striking examples, but he responds elegantly to "The fountain" (Op. 26 No. 11). Maria Popescu gives a beautiful account of one of the most deservedly popular of them all, "To the children" (Op. 26 No. 7), and of the remarkable Merezhkovsky setting, "Christ is risen" (Op. 26 No. 6), no outburst of Orthodox jubilation but a grieving for the sorry state of the world into which a reborn Christ would now come. Joan Rodgers is enchanting in "The Lilacs" (Op. 21 No. 5) and moving in the song acknowledging that love is slipping away, "Again I am alone" (Op. 26 No. 9). She has complete mastery of the style, and nothing here is finer than her arching phrase ending "How peaceful" (Op. 21 No. 7) – "da ty, mechta moya" (and you, my dream) – with Shelley gently articulating Rachmaninov's reflective piano postlude from the world of Schumann.

Additional recommendations ...

...At the gate of the holy abode[d]. I shall tell you nothing[d]. Again you leapt, my heart[a]. April! A festive Spring[c]. Twilight has fallen[c]. Song of the disillusioned[d]. The flower has faded[b]. Do you remember the evening[b]. Six Songs, Op. 4[abcd]. Six Songs, Op. 8[abcd]. 12 Songs, Op. 14[abcd]. [a]**Joan Rodgers** (sop); [b]**Maria Popescu** (mez); [c]**Alexander Naoumenko** (ten); [d]**Sergei Leiferkus** (bar); **Howard Shelley** (pf). Chandos Ⓕ CHAN9405 (76 minutes: DDD: 4/96).

...Songs[b] – Sing not to me, beautiful maiden, Op. 4 No. 4. 12 Songs, Op. 21 – No. 4, They answered; No. 7, How fair this spot. Before my window, Op. 26 No. 10. **Goldins** 18 Jewish Folk Songs[a]. **Inessa Galante** (sop); [a]**Janis Bulvas** (vn); [a]**Vladimir Choclov**, [a]**Ingmars Zemzars**, [b]**Inta Villerusa** (pfs). Campion Ⓕ RRCD1340 (63 minutes: ADD: 8/96).

...Songs, Op. 21 – No. 7, How fair this spot. Six Songs, Op. 38 – No. 3, Daisies. Songs, Op. 34 – No. 14, Vocalise. *Coupled with works by* **Stravinsky** *and* **Tchaikovsky** Itzhak Perlman (vn); Samuel Sanders (pf). EMI Perlman Edition Ⓜ CDM5 66061-2 (79 minutes: ADD/DDD: 3/97).

Rachmaninov Letter to K. S. Stanislavsky[d]. 14 Songs, Op. 34[abcd]. From the Gospel of St John[d]. Six Songs, Op. 38[a]. A prayer[a]. All wish to sing[a]. [a]**Joan Rodgers** (sop); [b]**Maria Popescu** (mez); [c]**Alexandre Naoumenko** (ten); [d]**Sergei Leiferkus** (bar); **Howard Shelley** (pf). Chandos Ⓕ CHAN9477 (68 minutes: DDD: 11/96). Texts and translations included. Items marked [d] from CHAN9374 (10/95). Recorded 1994-1995.

The final volume of this series of the complete Rachmaninov songs opens with a powerful dramatic outpouring. It is in fact a formal letter of apology, for unavoidable absence from a gathering, which he sent for Chaliapin to sing to Stanislavsky; and one of the most touchingly elegant phrases is simply the date on the letter, October 14th, 1908. Perhaps he was showing a rare touch of irony in using his full lyrical powers in such a context; but at any rate, the piece nicely prefaces the two collections of his last phase of song-writing, before he left Russia for exile. Some of his greatest songs are here, coloured in their invention by the four great singers whose hovering presence makes the disposition of this recital between four similar voices a highly successful idea. The Chaliapin songs go to Sergei Leiferkus, occasionally a little overshadowed by this mighty example (as in "The raising of Lazarus", Op. 34 No. 6) but much more often his own man, responding to the subtly dramatic, sometimes even laconic melodic lines with great sympathy for how they interact with the words, as with the strange Afanasy Fet poem "The peasant" (Op. 34 No. 11). Alexandre Naoumenko inherits the mantle of Leonid Sobinov, and though he sometimes resorts to a near-falsetto for soft high notes, he appears to have listened to that fine tenor's elegance of line and no less subtle feeling for poetry. Pushkin's "The muse" (Op. 34 No. 1) is most tenderly sung, and there is a sensitive response to line with "I remember this day". Maria Popescu only has two songs this time, "It cannot be" and "Music" (Op. 34 Nos. 7 and 8), but she has the light tone and bright manner which can also be heard on records from her exemplar, Antonina Nezhdanova. Joan Rodgers is, as before, exquisite in the most rapturous and inward of the songs (the great Felia Litvinne was the original here). Of the Op. 38 set, Rachmaninov was particularly fond of "The rat-catcher" (No. 4), and especially of "Daisies" (No. 3), which she sings charmingly, but it is hard to understand why he did not add "Sleep". He might have done had he heard Rodgers's rapt performance with Howard Shelley, the music delicately balanced in the exact way he must have intended between voice and piano as if between sleep and waking.

Rachmaninov Aleko. **Sergei Leiferkus** (bar) Aleko; **Maria Gulegina** (sop) Zemfira;
 Anatoly Kocherga (bass) Old Gipsy; **Ilya Levinsky** (ten) Young Gipsy; **Anne Sofie von Otter** (mez) Old Gipsy Woman.
Rachmaninov The Miserly Knight. **Anatoly Kocherga** (bass) Servant; **Sergei Aleksashkin** (bass) Baron; **Sergei Larin** (ten) Albert; **Ian Caley** (ten) Jew; **Vladimir Chernov** (bar) Duke.
Rachmaninov Francesca da Rimini. **Sergei Leiferkus** (bar) Lanciotto Malatesta; **Maria Gulegina** (sop) Francesca; **Ilya Levinsky** (ten) Dante; **Sergei Aleksashkin** (bass) Virgil; **Sergei Larin** (ten) Paolo; **Gothenburg Opera Chorus and Orchestra / Neeme Järvi.** DG Ⓔ 453 452-2GH3 (three discs: 174 minutes: DDD: 5/98). Notes, texts and translations included. Recorded 1996.
Rachmaninov's three one-act operas that survive give evidence of real dramatic talent. Who else has written so accomplished a graduation exercise as *Aleko*? Tchaikovsky was dazzled, no doubt also flattered, by some suggestions of imitation. It is a number opera, based on Pushkin's dramatic poem *The Gipsies*, warning that the urban sophisticate cannot recapture pristine wildness, and has at its centre a superb soliloquy of lost love. Leiferkus takes a lyrical approach; this is a beautiful, tragic performance, ironically set against Ilya Levinsky's carelessly superficial charm as the Young Gipsy. Zemfira is sung with fierce spirit by Maria Gulegina, especially in her cruel 'Old husband' song, and at the end with a lingering caress that seems to be for neither man but for Death itself. The other operas are different matters, both tinged with Bayreuth experiences that Rachmaninov had absorbed more thoroughly than is sometimes allowed. *The Miserly Knight* is one of the 'little tragedies' in which Pushkin presents a moral issue but does not offer a solution. Here, it is the contrast between the old knight, claiming that his devotion to gold has taken him beyond passion into a realm of serenity, and his son, who merely needs the ready. The long central soliloquy, perhaps Rachmaninov's finest piece of dramatic writing, is superbly delivered by Sergei Aleksashkin, with the wide range of his eloquence drawing sympathy to the miser. Sergei Larin portrays his son Albert as a selfish extrovert; and Ian Caley does what he can to make the Jewish moneylender more human than an unpleasant caricature.

Francesca da Rimini requires Rachmaninov to triumph over an inept libretto by Modest Tchaikovsky. This he does to a remarkable degree, using Modest's inability to produce a text for the chorus of the damned to good advantage with wordless wails, and filling out the sketchy love duet with some 50 bars of a sensuous orchestral kiss. However, he should have rejected the banal placing of the final line, about the lovers reading no more that day, in favour of its breathtaking place in Dante, when their poring over Lancelot and Guinevere reveals their own love to them. Ilya Levinsky brings a more intensely lyrical line and manner to this than in *Aleko*, and Maria Gulegina ranges from docility before Lanciotto (Leiferkus again a jealous husband) to rapture in the love duet. Neeme Järvi leads all three operas, as the orchestra should do for much of the time, and the beautiful playing he draws from the Gothenburg orchestra helps to make these three records a set extolling Rachmaninov's operatic talent. It is an excellent 'trilogy', excellently presented with a transliteration and good translations into English.
Additional recommendation ...
...The Miserly Knight. **Soloists; Bolshoi Theatre Orchestra / Andrey Chistiakov.**
 CdM Russian Season Ⓔ LDC288 080 (60 minutes: DDD: 10/94).
Further listening ...
...Boris Godunov – One last story. *Coupled with works by various composers.*
 Sergei Larin (ten); **Philharmonia Orchestra / Gennadi Rozhdestvensky.**
 Chandos CHAN9603 (5/98). *See review in the Collections section; refer to the Index.*
...Cello Sonata in G minor, Op. 19. *Coupled with* **R. Strauss** Cello Sonata in F major, Op. 6.
 Anne Gastinel (vc); **Pierre-Laurent Aimard** (pf). Auvidis Valois V4692 (12/93).

...Cello Sonata in G minor, Op. 19[a]. *Coupled with* **Shostakovich** Cello Sonata in D minor,
Op. 40[b]. **Daniil Shafran** (vc); [a]**Yakov Flier**, [b]**Dmitry Shostakovich** (pfs).
Revelation mono RV10017* (10/96).
...Suite No. 2, Op. 17. Russian Rhapsody, Op. posth. Symphonic Dances, Op. 45. *Coupled with
works by* **Medtner** Dmitri Alexeev, Nikolai Demidenko (pfs). Hyperion CDA66654 (10/94).
Gramophone Editor's choice.
...At the gate of the holy abode. Do you remember the evening. From the Gospel of St John. I shall
tell you nothing. Letter to K.S. Stanislavsky. Song of the disillusioned. Were you hiccoughing?
Songs, Op. 4 – Oh no, I beg you, forsake me not; Morning; In the silence of the secret night; Sing
not to me, beautiful maiden. Songs, Op. 8 – Child, thou art as beautiful as a flower; Brooding.
Songs, Op. 14 – I was with her; How everyone loves thee; She is as lovely as the moon; Spring
waters; 'Tis time. Songs, Op. 21 – Fate; By the fresh grave; Lilacs; Before the icon; No prophet I.
Songs, Op. 26 – He took all from me; Let us rest; Christ is risen; When yesterday we met; All
things pass by. Songs, Op. 34 – In the soul of each of us; The raising of Lazarus; You knew him;
The peasant. **Sergei Leiferkus** (bar); **Howard Shelley** (pf). Chandos CHAN9374 (10/95).
...Six Songs, Op. 4 – No. 1, Oh no, I beg you, forsake me not; No. 3, In the silence of the secret
night; No. 4, Sing not to me, beautiful maiden. Six Songs, Op. 8 – No. 5, The dream. 12 Songs,
Op. 14 – No. 9, She is as lovely as the noon. 12 Songs, Op. 21 – No. 6, Fragment from Musset.
15 Songs, Op. 26 – No. 2, He took all from me; No. 6, Christ is risen; No. 13, When yesterday we
met. *Coupled with works by* **Tchaikovsky** Dmitri Hvorostovsky (bar); **Oleg Boshniakovich** (pf).
Philips 432 119-2PH (10/91).
...Six Songs, Op. 4[a]. Six Songs, Op. 8[a]. 12 Songs, Op. 14[a]. 12 Songs, Op. 21[a]. 15 Songs, Op. 26[a].
14 Songs, Op. 34[a]. Six Songs, Op. 38[a]. At the gate of the holy abode[a]. Song of the disillusioned[a].
The flower has faded[a]. Do you remember the evening?[a]. Were you hiccoughing?[a]. I shall tell you
nothing[a]. Again you leapt, my heart[a]. April! A festive Spring[a]. Twilight has fallen[a]. Powdered
paint[a]. Night[a]. Letter to K. S. Stanislavsky[a]. From the Gospel of St John[a]. Daisies. Lilacs.
[a]**Elisabeth Söderström** (sop); **Vladimir Ashkenazy** (pf). London 436 920-2LM3 (5/94).
...Six Songs, Op. 4 – No. 2, Morning; No. 3, In the silence of the secret night. Op. 14 – No. 1, I wait
for thee; No. 8, Oh, do not grieve; No. 9, She is as lovely as the moon; No. 11, Spring waters.
Op. 26 No. 6, Christ is risen. *Coupled with works by* **Mussorgsky** and **Tchaikovsky**
Ewa Podles (contr); **Graham Johnson** (pf).
Forlane UCD16683 (5/95). *See review in the Collections section; refer to the Index.*
...Liturgy of St John Chrysostom, Op. 31. **Soloists; Bulgarian National Radio Chorus /
Mikhail Milkov.** EMI Forte CZS5 68664-2 (5/96).
...Vocalise, Op. 34 No. 14. *Coupled with works by various composers.*
Inessa Galante (sop); **Latvian National Opera Orchestra / Alexander Vilumanis.**
Campion RRCD1344 (A/97). *See review in the Collections section; refer to the Index.*

Jean-Philippe Rameau   French 1683-1764

Rameau Ouvertures – Les fêtes de Polymnie; Les indes galantes; Zäis; Castor et Pollux; Naïs;
Platée; Les fêtes d'Hébé; Zoroastre; Dardanus; Les paladins; Hippolyte et Aricie; Le temple de
la gloire; Pygmalion; Les surprises de l'Amour; Les fêtes de l'Hymen et de l'Amour; Acante et
Céphise. **Les Talens Lyriques / Christophe Rousset.** L'Oiseau-Lyre Ⓕ 455 293-2OH
(70 minutes: DDD: 7/97). ✒ Recorded 1996. *Gramophone Editor's choice.*   ⓖⓖⓖ
Rameau was an orchestrator of rare and individual genius and his operas, ballets and smaller
entertainments are generously provided with some of the most original and alluring dance music to
emerge from the eighteenth century. Roughly speaking, the music on this disc was written between
1733, the date of Rameau's first opera *Hippolyte et Aricie*, and 1761, when he produced his *comédie-
lyrique*, *Les Paladins*. Lovers of Rameau's music will be thoroughly familiar with most of the music
played on the disc but will be delighted to find some rarities, too. The most remarkable of these is the
overture to the *pastorale-héroique*, *Acante et Céphise*. It was commissioned to celebrate the birth of
the Duke of Burgundy in 1751. Adulatory prologues were out of fashion by the 1750s but instead
Rameau attempted something entirely new – a portrayal in music of the good wishes of the nation,
and the public rejoicing at the news of the Prince's birth. Rameau experimented with programmatic
elements and vivid tone-painting elsewhere in his overtures, notably in those of *Platée* (1745), and
Zaïs (1748). The overture to *Acante et Céphise* is different again, with its inclusion of specific
'occasional' references. Its three sections are marked "Voeux de la Nation", "Feu d'Artifice" (whose
bass-line is punctuated by cannon-fire – thunderously captured in the recording) and "Fanfare". Les
Talens Lyriques respond admirably to this music, relishing every bar of it in performances which are
refined in ensemble and articulate in speech. Rousset has proved himself a fine exponent of this
hugely rewarding repertoire.

Rameau Premier livre de pièces de clavecin. Pièces de clavecin en concerts. Nouvelles suites de
pièces de clavecin. Les petits marteaux de M Rameau. La Dauphine. **Christophe Rousset** (hpds).
L'Oiseau-Lyre Ⓕ 425 886-2OH2 (two discs: 129 minutes: DDD: 12/91). ✒ Recorded 1989.
Gramophone Award Winner 1992.

This recording of Rameau's solo harpsichord music outdistances most of the competition. Rousset does not include everything that Rameau wrote for the instrument but he does play all the music contained in the principal collections of 1706, 1724 and c1728 as well as *La Dauphine*. Rousset's phrasing is graceful and clearly articulated, the inflexions gently spoken and the rhythmic pulse all that one might wish for. Tempos are, for the most part, well judged and the playing admirably attentive to detail and delightfully animated. Only occasionally does Rousset perhaps just miss the mark with speeds that are uncomfortably brisk and lacking that choreographic poise which is such a vital ingredient in French baroque music. But he is at his strongest is irresistible and this is how we find him in "Les niais de Sologne" and its variations, the reflective "L'entretien des Muses", the animated "Les cyclopes", "La poule", "L'enharmonique" and the dazzling A minor Gavotte and variations. In these and in many other of the pieces, too, Rousset's impeccable taste and seemingly effortless virtuosity provide the listener with constant and intense delight. The quality of the recording is ideal as are the two instruments which Rousset has chosen to play.

Additional recommendations ...

...Pièces de clavecin en concerts. **Robert Kohnen** (hpd); **Barthold Kuijken** (fl); **Sigiswald Kuijken** (vn); **Wieland Kuijken** (va da gamba). Accent Ⓕ ACC9493D (61 minutes: DDD: 8/95). 🗝 Ⓖ
...Nouvelles suites de pièces de clavecin – A minor. Pièces de clavècin – Suite in E minor.
  Trevor Pinnock (hpd). CRD Ⓕ CRD3310 (52 minutes: ADD: 8/88). 🗝
...Premier livre de pièces de clavecin – Suite in A minor. La Dauphine. Cinq pièces pour clavecin seull. Pièces de clavecin en concerts. La pantomime. **Trevor Pinnock** (hpd).
  CRD Ⓕ CRD3320 (43 minutes: ADD: 8/88). 🗝
...Pièces de clavecin – Suite in D minor/major. Nouvelles suites de pièces de clavecin – G major/minor. **Trevor Pinnock** (hpd). CRD Ⓕ CRD3330 (52 minutes: ADD: 8/88). 🗝
...Pièces de clavecin en concerts. **Ryo Terakado** (vn); **Kaori Uemura** (va da gamba);
  Christophe Rousset (hpd). Harmonia Mundi Ⓕ HMC90 1418 (74 minutes: DDD: 4/93). 🗝
...Pièces de clavecin en concerts – Cinquième concert. *Coupled with works by various composers.*
  Rachel Brown (fl); **Mark Caudle** (viol); **James Johnstone** (hpd).
  Chandos Chaconne Ⓕ CHAN0544 (71 minutes: DDD: 2/94). 🗝
...L'enharmonique. L'Egyptienne. La Dauphine. *Coupled with works by various composers.*
  Sophie Yates (hpd). Chandos Chaconne Ⓕ CHAN0545 (71 minutes: DDD: 11/93). 🗝
  See review in the Collections section; refer to the Index.
...Pièces de clavecin en concerts. **Catherine Mackintosh** (vn); **Laurence Dreyfus** (va da gamba);
  Ketil Haugsand (hpd). Simax Ⓕ PSC1095 (69 minutes: DDD: 6/94). 🗝
  Gramophone Editor's choice.

Rameau Anacréon[a]. Le berger fidèle. **Véronique Gens**, [a]**Annick Massis** (sops); [a]**Rodrigo del Pozo** (ten); [a]**Thierry Félix** (bar); **Les Musiciens du Louvre / Marc Minkowski.** Archiv Produktion Ⓕ 449 211-2AH (57 minutes: DDD: 4/97). 🗝 Texts and translations included. Recorded 1995.
Anacréon dates from 1757 when it took its place as a freshly composed *entrée* for a revival of Rameau's opéra-ballet, *Les surprises de l'Amour*. The text by Pierre Joseph Bernard is entertaining, but Rameau's music is much more so. The story, as recounted by Bernard, has little or nothing to do with Anacreon's prowess as a poet, but focuses on his amorous and bibulous reputation acquired as a result of his famous love poems. The action centres round a *contretemps* between Bacchus and Cupid who, respectively, represent the interests of wine and women or, rather, in this instance, a particular woman, Lycoris. Eventually, Anacreon and Lycoris are reunited as, indeed, are Bacchus and Cupid: Bacchus allows us to love and Cupid allows us to drink. All very accommodating. The performance is mainly excellent, the instruments and ensemble voices of Les Musiciens du Louvre under Marc Minkowski's direction are sharply focused and the music is forcefully projected. Most of the solo contributions are convincing, but Thierry Félix, who sings the role of Anacreon, is disappointing. He is too much of the time, quite simply out of tune. Notwithstanding this reservation, the performance generally works well. The disc also offers an enchanting performance of Rameau's chamber cantata, *Le berger fidèle*. The soloist is Véronique Gens, who gives a touchingly poignant account of the very fine opening "Air plaintif". Thorough documentation and pleasing recorded sound.

Additional recommendation ...

...Anacréon. **Soloists; Les Arts Florissants Vocal Ensemble; Les Arts Florissants Instrumental Ensemble / William Christie.**
  Harmonia Mundi Musique d'abord Ⓜ HMA190 1090 (45 minutes: ADD: 12/87). 🗝

Rameau Deus noster refugium. In convertendo. Quam dilecta. **Sophie Daneman, Noémi Rime** (sops); **Paul Agnew** (ten); **Nicolas Rivenq** (bar); **Nicolas Cavallier** (bass); **Les Arts Florissants / William Christie.** Erato Ⓕ 4509-96967-2 (70 minutes: DDD). 🗝 Texts and translations included. Recorded 1994. *Gramophone Award Winner 1995.*
Rameau's three examples of the *grand motet* form were not much respected in his own day, and that was in the 1750s, when his reputation as a composer, built on the success of his operas, could hardly have been higher. Today, it is that very reputation which inclines us more towards Rameau's church music than that of his contemporaries. This recording was an auspicious start to William Christie's association with Erato. Erato have considerably improved their insert-note information and

presentation in general, and they've been repaid with bright, eventful performances. All three motets date from relatively early in Rameau's career, before he had really made a name for himself, yet all show to a certain extent some of the characteristics that 20 years or so later would so thrillingly illuminate his operas. *Deus noster refugium*, for instance, features impressive depictions of nature in turmoil that would not sound out of place in *Hippolyte et Aricie*, and all three begin with long, expressive solos not unlike the opening of an act from a *tragédie-lyrique*. *Quam dilecta* does sound a little more 'churchy' than the others, with its impressive, rather Handelian double fugue, but *In convertendo* – a work which Rameau heavily revised well into his operatic Indian summer in 1751 – absolutely reeks of the theatre. Drop anyone familiar with the composer's operas into the middle of this piece, and surely only its Latin text would give away that this is church music. It comes as no surprise to find Christie going to town on this dramatic element. The slightly dry acoustic of the Radio France studio is a help, as are the forceful, penetrating qualities of the solo and choral singers. But it is Christie's command of gesture, pacing and contrast which really gives these performances such an invigorating character.

Rameau Castor et Pollux. **Howard Crook** (ten) Castor; **Jérôme Corréas** (bass) Pollux; **Agnès Mellon** (sop) Télaïre; **Véronique Gens** (sop) Phebe; **René Schirrer** (bar) Mars; Jupiter; - **Sandrine Piau** (sop) Venus, Happy Spirit, Planet; **Mark Padmore** (ten) Love, High Priest; **Claire Brua** (sop) Minerve; **Sophie Daneman** (sop) Follower of Hebe; Celestial Pleasure; **Adrian Brand** (ten) Athlete I; **Jean-Claude Sarragosse** (bass) Athlete II; **Les Arts Florissants and Orchestra / William Christie.** Harmonia Mundi Ⓕ HMC90 1435/7 (three discs: 173 minutes: DDD: 7/93). ✍ Notes, text and translation included. Recorded 1992. ⒼⒼ

Castor et Pollux was Rameau's second *tragédie en musique*. Its first performance took place in October 1737 but the opera was greeted with only moderate enthusiasm. It was only with the composer's thoroughly revised version of 1754 that the opera enjoyed the popularity that it unquestionably deserved. The revision tautened a drama which had never been weak but it dispensed with a very beautiful Prologue. Christie and Les Arts Florissants perform Rameau's first version complete with its Prologue. The librettist, Pierre-Joseph Bernard, was one of the ablest writers with whom Rameau collaborated and his text for *Castor et Pollux* has been regarded by some as the best in the history of eighteenth-century French opera. Bernard focuses on the fraternal love of the 'heavenly twins' and specifically on the generosity with which Pollux renounces his immortality so that Castor may be restored to life. Christie's production was staged at Aix-en-Provence in the summer of 1991 and recorded by Harmonia Mundi a year later. This performance realizes the element of tragedy, above all in the First Act, and Christie's singers sound very much at home with French declamation. A very beautiful score, affectionately and perceptively interpreted that will afford deep and lasting pleasure.

Additional recommendation ...
...**Soloists; English Bach Festival Chorus and Baroque Orchestra / Charles Farncombe.** Erato Ⓜ 4509-95311-2 (two discs: 137 minutes: DDD: 5/95). Ⓖ

Rameau Les fêtes d'Hébé. **Sophie Daneman** (sop) Hébé, Une Naïde, Eglé; **Gaëlle Méchaly** (sop) L'amour; **Paul Agnew** (ten) Momus, Le ruisseau, Lycurgue; **Sarah Connolly** (mez) Sapho, Iphise; **Jean-Paul Fouchécourt** (ten) Thélème, L'oracle, Mercure; **Luc Coadou** (bass) Alcée; **Laurent Slaars** (bar) Hymas; **Matthieu Lécroart** (bar) Le fleuve; **Maryseult Wieczorek** (mez) Une Lacédémonienne, Une bergère; **Thierry Félix** (bar) Tirtée, Eurilas; **Les Arts Florissants / William Christie.** Erato Ⓕ 3984-21064-2 (two discs: 148 minutes: DDD: 4/98). Notes, text and translation included. Recorded 1997. *Gramophone Editor's choice.* ⒼⒼⒼ

Rameau produced one of his most engaging scores for *Les fêtes d'Hébé*. The entertainment comprises a prologue and three *entrées*. All is prefaced with a captivating two-movement Overture whose playful second section has much more in common with a Neapolitan *sinfonia* than a traditional opera overture in the French mould. The dances belong to one of the composer's fruitiest vintages and Christie has capitalized upon this with a sizeable band which includes, where appropriate, a section of musettes, pipes and drums. The singers are carefully chosen for their contrasting vocal timbres and the line-up, by and large, is strong. The leading roles in each of the opera's four sections are fairly evenly distributed between Sophie Daneman, Sarah Connolly, Jean-Paul Fouchécourt, Paul Agnew and Thierry Félix. The first three of this group are consistently engaging; their feeling for theatre, and their intuitive ability to seek out those aspects of Rameau's vocal writing which enliven it, seldom fail, and they bring considerable charm to their performances. Agnew, too, is on strong form though in the lower end of his vocal tessitura, required for the role of Momus in the Prologue, he sounds less secure than in his more accustomed *haute-contre* range. That can be heard to wonderful effect elsewhere and, above all, in a duet for a Stream and a Naiad (first *Entrée*) in which he is joined by Daneman. This beguiling little love-song is proclaimed with innocent fervour and tenderness. Félix has a rounded warmth and resonance and his occasional weakness of poorly focused tone has here been largely overcome. *Les fêtes d'Hébé* contains a wealth of inventive, instrumentally colourful and evocative dances. Small wonder that audiences loved it so much in the 1720s: with music of such vital originality, how could it be otherwise? Christie and Les Arts Florissants have possibly never been on crisper, more disciplined form than here, revelling in Rameau's beguiling pastoral images, tender and high-spirited in turn. A ravishing entertainment, from start to finish.

Rameau Hippolyte et Aricie. **Mark Padmore** (ten) Hippolyte; **Anne-Maria Panzarella** (sop) Aricie; **Lorraine Hunt** (sop) Phèdre; **Laurent Naouri** (bass) Thésée; **Eirian James** (mez) Diane; **Gaëlle Mechaly** (sop) L'Amour, Female Sailor; **Nathan Berg** (bass) Jupiter, Pluton, Neptune; **Katalin Károlyi** (mez) Oenone; **Yann Beuron** (ten) Arcas Mercure; **François Piolino** (ten) Tisiphone; **Christopher Josey** (ten) Fate I; **Matthieu Lécroart** (bar) Fate II; **Bertrand Bontoux** (bass) Fate III; **Mireille Delunsch** (sop) High Priestess; **Patricia Petibon** (sop) Priestess, Shepherdess; **Les Arts Florissants / William Christie.** Erato Ⓕ 0630-15517-2 (three discs: 182 minutes: DDD: 6/97). ✏
Notes, text and translation included. Recorded 1996. *Gramophone Award Winner 1997.* ⊙⊙

Unlike Marc Minkowski, who was tempted by the 1757 revision of the start of Act 2, with its reorchestration and baritone Tisiphone, William Christie adheres throughout to Rameau's 1733 original, in so doing opening up some passages previously omitted. He uses an orchestra with more string weight than his predecessor, and they play with rather greater security both of ensemble and intonation, and with splendidly crisp rhythms. Despite the opera's title, the main protagonists are Theseus and his queen Phaedra, whose guilty passion for his son Hippolytus precipitates the tragedy. In all three recordings Phaedra is strongly cast, none more so than in the present case, with Lorraine Hunt even more passionate than Dame Janet Baker was on the Decca recording, and particularly impressive in the superb aria, "Cruelle mère des amours", which begins Act 3. Throughout the opera, indeed, one is also struck alike by the profusion of invention, the unobtrusive contrapuntal skill, the charm and colour of the instrumentation and the freedom allotted to the orchestra. The work's final scene, for example, set in a woodland, is filled with a truly enchanting atmosphere, ending, after the customary chaconne, with "Rossignols amoureux" (delightfully sung by Patricia Petibon). Anna-Maria Panzarella makes an appealingly youthful Aricia (to whom Rameau allocates surprisingly little on her own), and Mark Padmore is easily the best Hippolytus of the three recordings, making the most of his despairing Act 4 aria, "Ah, faut-il, en ce jour, perdre tout ce que j'aime?". Pains have been taken with the whole cast over the expressive delivery of words and over neatness of ornamentation; and production values such as the proper perspective for the entry of the crowd rejoicing at Theseus's return have been well considered. All told, this is one of William Christie's best achievements, an obvious labour of love for a masterpiece which, he confesses, has entranced him for 30 years.

Additional recommendations ...

...**Soloists; Sagittarius Vocal Ensemble; Les Musiciens du Louvre / Marc Minkowski.** Archiv Produktion Ⓕ 445 853-2AH3 (three discs: 167 minutes: DDD: 9/95). ✏
...**Soloists; St Anthony Singers; English Chamber Orchestra / Sir Anthony Lewis.** Decca Serenata Ⓜ 444 526-2DMO2 (two discs: 146 minutes: ADD: 5/96).
...Hippolyte et Aricie – Orchestral Suite. **La Petite Bande / Sigiswald Kuijken.** Deutsche Harmonia Mundi Editio Classica Ⓜ GD77009 (52 minutes: 7/90). ✏

Rameau Les Indes galantes – Prologue: **Claron McFadden** (sop) Hébé; **Jérôme Corréas** (bar) Bellone; **Isabelle Poulenard** (sop) L'Amour. Le Turc généreux: **Nicolas Rivenq** (bass) Osman; **Miriam Ruggieri** (sop) Emilie; **Howard Crook** (ten) Valère. Les Incas du Pérou: **Bernard Deletré** (bass) Huascar; **Isabelle Poulenard** (Phanie); **Jean-Paul Fouchécourt** (ten) Carlos. Les fleurs: **Fouchécourt** (Tacmas); **Corréas** (Ali); **Sandrine Piau** (sop) Zaïre; **Noémi Rime** (sop) Fatime. Les sauvages: **Rivenq** (Adario); **Crook** (Damon); **Deletré** (Don Alvar); **McFadden** (Zima); **Les Arts Florissants / William Christie.** Harmonia Mundi Ⓕ HMC90 1367/9 (three discs: 203 minutes: DDD: 2/91). ✏ Notes, text and translation included.

Les Indes galantes was Rameau's first *opéra-ballet*. He completed it in 1735 when it was performed at the Académie Royale in Paris. *Opéra-ballet* usually consisted of a prologue and anything between three and five entrées or acts. There was no continuously developing plot but instead various sections might be linked by a general theme, often hinted at in the title. Such is the case with *Les indes galantes* whose linking themes derives from a contemporary taste for the exotic and the unknown. Following a prologue come four entrées, "Le Turc généreux", "Les Incas du Pérou", "Les fleurs" and "Les sauvages". William Christie and Les Arts Florissants give a characteristically warm-blooded performance of one of Rameau's most approachable and endearing stage works. Christie's control of diverse forces – his orchestra consists of some 46 players – his dramatic pacing of the music, his recognition of Rameau's uniquely distinctive instrumental palette and his feeling for gesture and rhythm contribute towards making this a lively and satisfying performance. The choir are alert and well disciplined and the orchestra a worthy partner in respect of clear textures and technical finesse; this can be readily appreciated in the splendid, spaciously laid out and tautly constructed orchestral Chaconne which concludes the work. The booklet contains full texts in French, English and German and the music is recorded in a sympathetic acoustic.

Additional recommendations ...

...**Soloists; Valencia Vocal Ensemble; Jean-François Paillard Chamber Orchestra / Jean-François Paillard.** Erato Ⓜ 4509-95310-2 (three discs: 205 minutes: ADD: 5/95).
...Les Indes galantes – Suite. **Orchestra of the Eighteenth Century / Frans Brüggen.** Philips Ⓕ 438 946-2PH (44 minutes: DDD: 8/94). ✏   ⊙⊙
...Les Indes galantes – Suite[a]. Dardanus – Suite[b].
Collegium Aureum / [a]Gustav Leonhardt, [b]Reinhard Peters. Deutsche Harmonia Mundi Editio Classica Ⓜ 05472 77269-2 (70 minutes: ADD: 8/93). ✏

Rameau Naïs. **Linda Russell** (sop) Naïs; **Ian Caley** (ten) Neptune; **Ian Caddy** (bass) Jupiter, Telenus; **John Tomlinson** (bass) Pluton; **Richard Jackson** (bass) Tiresie; **Brian Parsons** (ten) Asterion; **Antony Ransome** (bar) Palemon; **Ann Mackay** (sop) Flore, Second Shepherdess; **Jennifer Smith** (sop) First Shepherdess; **English Bach Festival Chorus and Orchestra / Nicholas McGegan.** Erato Ⓑ 4509-98532-2 (two discs: 106 minutes: ADD: 11/95).
Notes, text and translation included. From STU71439 (10/81). Recorded 1980.

Naïs was commissioned to celebrate the Treaty of Aix-la-Chapelle in 1748, and first performed the following year. Thus it was a vocal counterpart to Handel's *Music for the Royal Fireworks*, both pieces marking the conclusion of the War of the Austrian Succession. The present recording was made in 1980 following performances at London's Old Vic Theatre and at Versailles under the auspices of Lina Lalandi's enterprising English Bach Festival. Though, dramatically, *Naïs* is unremarkable, Rameau and his librettist, Louis de Cahusac, with whom he collaborated on many occasions, made a special point of establishing a strong relationship between dance and action. As Graham Sadler, editor of the edition and author of an informative introduction points out, Cahusac himself provided detailed choreographic outlines for the dances which feature so prominently in this piece. And Rameau responded with music which, of its kind, is much closer to the spirit of *opéra-ballet* than heroic opera, and is representative of his finest.

Nicholas McGegan has an effective understanding of French baroque style and brings out much that is graceful and enlivening in Rameau's score. Only the Prologue bears any relevance to the Treaty which occasioned the work, and this in strictly allegorical terms. Here, John Tomlinson and Ian Caddy are especially effective. In the opera itself Linda Russell is appealing in the title-role with Ian Caley an ardent Neptune in love with her. But, as so often with Rameau's vocal music in the tenor register, the uppermost notes sometimes betray a hint of strain. For the most part in the purely instrumental numbers the participants seem to revel in Rameau's uniquely colourful orchestral palette. Who wouldn't? From the moment that we hear the superbly inventive overture, through to the sparkling tambourins which occur towards the end of Acts 1 and 3, Rameau never for a second lets us down; there is nothing like hearing the wonderful dances in their dramatic context so carefully considered by composer and librettist. Only the choral singing occasionally fails to measure up to the solo and instrumental contributions. But this is, notwithstanding, a welcome reappearance of an exhilarating score.

Additional recommendation ...

...Naïs – Suite. Le temple de la gloire – Suite. **Philharmonia Baroque Orchestra / Nicholas McGegan.** Harmonia Mundi Ⓕ HMU90 7121 (71 minutes: DDD: 7/95). 🗡 ⒼⒼ

Rameau La Princesse de Navarre. **Marilyn Hill Smith, Eiddwen Harrhy, Frances Chambers, Judith Rees** (sops); **Michael Goldthorpe** (ten); **Peter Savidge** (bar); **Ian Caddy, Richard Wigmore** (basses); **English Bach Festival Singers and Baroque Orchestra / Nicholas McGegan.** Erato Ⓜ 0630-12986-2 (56 minutes: ADD: 9/96). Text and translation included. From STU71283. Recorded 1979.

Here is another precious Rameau recording, the composer's only *comédie-ballet*. The event which occasioned it was the marriage of the Dauphin to Princess Maria-Theresa of Spain in 1745. Rameau was to be responsible for all the music while Voltaire would provide the libretto. It was an uneasy partnership, attested to by Voltaire on several occasions in correspondence with various officials concerned with the wedding arrangements. What we have here is the musical side of the entertainment without the spoken dialogue. The solution is not a bad one since, though the opera, with its effective blend of tragedy and comedy, pleased the court, it is perhaps less likely to beguile the audiences of today. The present performance, together with some of the spoken dialogue, was staged at Covent Garden by Lina Lalandi's English Bach Festival in 1978 and the musical items were recorded, with much the same cast, in the following year under Nicholas McGegan's direction. A *galant*-sounding overture, with horns, in the three-movement Italian *sinfonia* manner, is followed by a sequence of airs, choruses and *symphonies de ballet* grouped into three acts. McGegan brings vitality to the performances and any shortcomings of interpretative finesse are compensated for by vocal and instrumental *élan*. Rather unhelpfully, neither box nor booklet makes it clear who is singing what, though eventually a degree of surmise can sort out the worst of the problem. It is the dances, though, which enjoy the lion's share of Rameau's score and some of these are of considerable merit. Especially attractive is a Menuet (track 8) for pairs of oboes and bassoons, better known as Menuet II in Rameau's keyboard version (*Nouvelles suites de pièces de clavecin*, c1729). Among the vocal numbers the ariette "Vents furieux" (track 11) is impressive for its declamatory vigour and vocal athleticism. But these are just finials on a musical folly which offers much else to please the senses and is full of Rameau's customary playful musical caprice.

Further listening ....

...Abaris (Les Boréades) – Orchestral Suite. Dardanus – Ouverture; Entrée pour les Guerriers; Bruit de guerre; Premier Air: Grave; Deuxième Air: Vivement; Tambourins; Les songes; Chaconne. **Orchestra of the Eighteenth Century / Frans Brüggen.** Philips 420 240-2PH (5/87). 🗡

...Les Paladins – Suite. **Orchestra of the Age of Enlightenment / Gustav Leonhardt.** Philips 432 968-2PH (9/92). 🗡 ⒼⒼ

...Grand Motets: Deus noster refugium; In convertendo[b]; Quam dilecta. **Soloists; Les Arts Florissants Chorus and Orchestra / William Christie.** Erato 4509-96967-2. 🗡 ⒼⒼⒼ

...Pièces de clavecin – Suites: A minor (1706); E minor (1724);
D major (1724); A minor (*c*1729); G major (*c*1729). Quatre Pièces en concert.
Coupled with works by various composers. **Marcelle Meyer** (pf).
EMI mono CZS5 68092-2* (6/95). *See review in the Collections section; refer to the Index.* 🅖🅖🅖
...La rappel des oiseaux. Tambourin. La poule. *Coupled with works by various composers.*
George Malcolm (hpd). Decca 444 390-2DWO (11/95). 🖉
...Platée. **Soloists; Françoise Herr Vocal Ensemble; Musiciens du Louvre / Marc Minkowski.**
Erato MusiFrance 2292-45028-2 (9/90). 🖉   🅖🅖
...Pygmalion. Nélée et Myrthis. **Soloists; Les Arts Florissants Chorus and Orchestra /**
William Christie. Harmonia Mundi HMC90 1381 (7/92). 🖉

Ture Rangström
Swedish 1884-1947

Suggested listening ....
...Poems by Bo Bergman – No. 1, Wings in the night; No. 3, Melody.
The Dark Flower – No. 2, Prayer to the night; No. 4, Farewell. Pan. Old Swedish.
Coupled with works by various composers. **Anne Sofie von Otter** (mez); **Bengt Forsberg** (pf).
DG 449 189-2GH (5/96). *See review in the Collections section; refer to the Index.*   🅖🅖

Raulin de Vaux
French 15th century

Suggested listening ....
...Savés pour quoy suy sy gay. *Coupled with works by various composers.* **Alla Francesca.**
Opus 111 OPS30-173 (7/98). *See review in the Collections section; refer to the Index.*   🅖🅖🅖

Einojuhani Rautavaara
Finnish 1928

Rautavaara Symphony No. 7, "Angel of Light". Annunciations[a]. [a]**Kari Jussila** (org);
Helsinki Philharmonic Orchestra / Leif Segerstam. Ondine Ⓟ ODE869-2
(65 minutes: DDD: 6/96). Recorded 1995. *Gramophone Editor's choice. Selected by Soundings.* 🅖
The Seventh Symphony's opening *Tranquillo* evokes a calm though powerful atmosphere, with many
Sibelian points of reference – most especially in recognizable echoes of the *Largo* fourth movement
from Sibelius's Fourth Symphony, whereas the closing *Pesante-cantabile* is more in line with the
symphonic world of Alan Hovhaness. The Angel idea originates in a series that already includes a
number of other works (*Angels and Visitations* and *Angel of Dusk*, for instance), the reference being
(as the composer himself explains) to "an archetype, one of mankind's oldest traditions and perennial
companions". This Jungian axis is reflected in monolithic chords, ethereal harmonic computations
(invariably broad and high-reaching) and an unselfconscious mode of musical development. Readers
schooled in the more contemplative works of Górecki, Pärt and Tavener will likely respond to this
spatially generous essay, though Rautavaara's language is more a celebration of nature and her works
than of any specific religious ritual. Comparisons with the *Annunciations* (for organ, brass quintet,
wind orchestra and percussion) find the earlier work far harsher in tone, much more demanding
technically (it calls for a formidable organ virtuoso) and more radical in its musical language. Here
the style ranges from the primeval drone that opens the work through canon, 'bird forest' activity (a
recurring strategy in Rautavaara's music) and the novel effect of having the "notes of a dense chord
weirdly circulating in the room" when the organ motor is switched off. Kari Jussila rises to the various
challenges set for him with what sounds like genuine enthusiasm (his fast fingerwork is amazing) while
Leif Segerstam and the Helsinki Philharmonic fully exploit the tonal drama of both works. The
recordings are warm and spacious.

Rautavaara Departure. The bride. Praktisch Deutsch. With joy we go dancing. Summer night.
The cathedral. Suite de Lorca, Op. 72. Ludus verbalis, Op. 10. Nirvana Dharma[a]. Die erste
Elegie. [a]**Petri Alanko** (fl); **Finnish Radio Chamber Choir / Eric-Olof Söderström.**
Ondine Ⓟ ODE851-2 (61 minutes: DDD: 6/96). Texts and translations included.   🅖
Rautavaara's compositional career has been one of exploration rather than outright experimentation,
its goal the evolution of his personal fusion of the serial and the tonal. The impressive quality and
diversity of Rautavaara's output for mixed chorus, leaving aside the huge cantata *The Myth of Sampo*,
are laid out for close inspection on this disc, ranging from the folk-based partsongs *Departure*, *The
bride* and *Summer night* (all 1975), to the collage-like absurdism of *Praktisch Deutsch* ("Practical
German", 1969; the text derives from a dictionary and phrase book), to the grand canvas of *The
cathedral* (1983) which is in fact a tone-poem for unaccompanied voices rather than a large-scale
motet. Tone-painting is used again in the 1979 *Nirvana Dharma*, with its enchanting flute solo
depicting the god Krishna. This, *The cathedral* and the concluding *Die erste Elegie* (1993, setting the
first of Rilke's *Duino* elegies) are major compositions by any standard. The most familiar work here
is the exuberant *Suite de Lorca* (1973). Söderström's performances are fine. A cracking disc.

Rautavaara Vigilia. **Pia Freund** (sop); **Lilli Paasikivi** (mez); **Topi Lehtipuu** (ten); **Petteri Salomaa** (bar); **Jyrki Korhonen** (bass); **Finnish Radio Chamber Choir / Tino Nuoranne.**
Ondine ℗ ODE910-2 (64 minutes: DDD: 5/98). Text and translation included.
Recorded 1997. *Gramophone Editor's choice.* 🅖🅖
Although grounded in the faith of the Finnish Orthodox Church, *Vigilia* somehow manages to excavate a spiritual path beyond the confines of denominational dogma. Rautavaara's delicious blend of ancient and modern modes is pointedly exemplified in the "First Katisma", where soprano and contralto, then tenor and baritone, proclaim "Blessed is the man that walketh not in the counsel of the ungodly". There, the harmonic drift is decidedly 'post-renaissance', whereas the "Alleluias" that follow update to 'post-romantic' and the subsequent assurance that "the Lord knoweth the way of the righteous" brings us on line with the wistful, nature-loving Rautavaara of the Seventh Symphony and *Cantus arcticus.* The *a cappella Vigilia* was a joint commission from the Helsinki Festival and the Finnish Orthodox Church; the original Evening and Morning Services date from 1971 and 1972, respectively, with this concert version following on later. Possible influences include Bartók, Stravinsky and Messiaen, though early music is a more palpable prompt and Rautavaara himself is always the leading voice. Rautavaara's employment, or rather absorption, of ancient modes runs roughly parallel with Steve Reich's in works such as *Tehillim* and *Proverb*, though by contrast with Reich, harmonic colouring takes its lead from poetic imagery rather than from the sounds of specific words. *Vigilia* uses variation technique to impressive effect; it is a refreshingly open-hearted piece, one that – whether sombre or celebratory, traditional or innovative – grants ritual narrative a vibrant voice and should earn its composer wide-scale recognition. The performance is beautifully sung and the recording bold and realistic.

Further listening ....
...Cantus arcticus, Op. 61[a]. Symphony No. 5[a]. String Quartet No. 4, Op. 87[b]. [b]**Sirius Quartet;**
[a]**Leipzig Radio Symphony Orchestra / Max Pommer.** Catalyst 09026 62671-2.
...Dances with the winds, Op. 69. *Coupled with works by various composers.*
Petri Alanko (fls); **Lahti Symphony Orchestra / Osmo Vänskä.** BIS CD687 (5/97).
...Violin Concerto[a]. Isle of bliss. Angels and Visitations.
[a]**Elmar Oliveira** (vn); **Helsinki Philharmonic Orchestra / Leif Segerstam.**
Ondine ℗ ODE881-2 (55 minutes: DDD: 4/97). Recorded 1996. *Gramophone Editor's choice.*
...The Myth of Sampo. **Tom Nyman** (ten); **Sauli Tiilikainen** (bar); **Antti Suhonen** (bass);
Helsinki University Chorus / Matti Hyökki. Ondine ODE842-2 (12/95).
...Suite de Lorca, Op. 72. *Coupled with works by various composers.*
Danish National Radio Choir / Stefan Parkman. Chandos CHAN9264 (4/95).

Oreste Ravanello

Italian 19th Century

Suggested listening ....
...Theme and Variations in B minor. *Coupled with works by various composers.* **Keith John** (org).
Priory PRCD370 (11/92). *Selected by Sounds in Retrospect. See review in the Collections section;*
refer to the Index. 🅖🅖🅖

Maurice Ravel

French 1875-1937

Ravel Piano Concerto in G major[a]. Piano Concerto for the Left Hand[a]. Menuet antique.
Une barque sur l'océan. Fanfare pour "L'éventail de Jeanne". [a]**Pascal Rogé** (pf);
Montreal Symphony Orchestra / Charles Dutoit. Decca ℗ 410 230-2DH (57 minutes: DDD: 3/84).
From SXDL7592 (8/83). 🅖
Ravel Ma mère l'oye. Pavane pour une infante défunte. Le tombeau de Couperin. Valses nobles et sentimentales. **Montreal Symphony Orchestra / Charles Dutoit.** Decca ℗ 410 254-2DH
(67 minutes: DDD: 11/84). *Gramophone Award Winner 1985.* 🅖
It is, of course, possible to build a satisfying Ravel library from different sources, but that would bring unavoidable duplication of repertoire. Yet collections like these are rarely consistent in quality. This is that rare case: not one of these recordings is seriously outclassed, either interpretatively or sonically. Dutoit and his Montreal orchestra are superb stylists; Ravel was just as much of a musical magpie as Stravinsky, with few historical, contemporary, or popular styles remaining exempt from a sophisticated Ravelian transformation (in some works they rub shoulders, for example, the *Valses nobles et sentimentales*). Dutoit ensures that the styles register, but without labouring the point – the result is always pure Ravel. There is also a consistent elegance, both of execution and expression, though Dutoit has a cunning (or sixth sense) in knowing when to let the players off the leash, and by how much (the G major Piano Concerto abounds in examples). A balletic stance goes hand in hand with rare departures from Ravel's suggestions of pace; for example, the virtuosity of his orchestra allows him to take the mercurial "Prélude" to *Le tombeau de Couperin* at Ravel's marking, without loss of composure. One radical departure from the score is his slow tempo for the strings' melody as we enter the "Jardin féerique" in *Ma mère l'oye*, but even the most fastidious Ravelian will surely

succumb to the rapt beauty of the result. Ravel, the time traveller, from the childhood, fairy-tale world of *Ma mère l'oye* to *Le tombeau de Couperin*'s homage to the French baroque, also benefits from an acoustic setting where space can add an extra dimension, a depth for, say, the horn fanfares at the "once upon a time" start of *Ma mère l'oye* or the last post resonances that the trumpet imparts in the Trio of *Le tombeau*'s Minuet. St Eustache in Montreal has just such an acoustic, where the perspective laid out by the different planes draws you in and envelops you. Unlike so many recordings made in churches these days, there's no blurring of detail, or ungainly weight in *fortissimos*; and microphone placement gives a discreet presence to all that glitters.

Additional recommendations ...

...Piano Concerto in G major. Gaspard de la nuit. Sonatine.
   Martha Argerich (pf); **Berlin Philharmonic Orchestra / Claudio Abbado.**
   DG Galleria Ⓜ 419 062-2GGA (54 minutes: ADD: 12/87).   Ⓖ
...Piano Concerto in G major. **Rachmaninov** Piano Concerto No. 4 in G minor, Op. 40.
   Arturo Benedetti Michelangeli (pf); **Philharmonia Orchestra / Ettore Gracis.**
   EMI Ⓕ CDC7 49326-2* (47 minutes: ADD: 9/88). *Gramophone classical 100.*
   See review under Rachmaninov; refer to the Index.   ⒼⒼⒼ
...Piano Concerto in G major[a]. Piano Concerto for the Left Hand[b]. Fanfare pour "L'éventail de
   Jeanne". Menuet antique. Le tombeau de Couperin. [a]**Martha Argerich,** [b]**Michel Béroff** (pfs);
   London Symphony Orchestra / Claudio Abbado. DG Ⓕ 423 665-2GH (65 minutes: DDD: 2/89). Ⓖ
...Piano Concerto in G major. Piano Concerto for the Left Hand.
   Louis Lortie (pf); **London Symphony Orchestra / Rafael Frühbeck de Burgos.**
   Chandos Ⓕ CHAN8773 (57 minutes: DDD: 1/90).
...Piano Concerto for the Left Hand[ab]. Menuet antique[c]. La valse[c]. Ma mère l'oye[c]. Daphnis et
   Chloé[c]. Shéhérazade – fairy overture[c]. Valses nobles et sentimentales[c]. Le tombeau de Couperin[c].
   Une barque sur l'océan[c]. Alborada del gracioso[b]. Pavane pour une unfante défunte[b]. Rapsodie
   espagnole[b]. Fanfare pour "L'éventail de Jeanne"[c]. Boléro[c]. [a]**Philippe Entremont** (pf);
   [b]**Cleveland Orchestra,** [c]**New York Philharmonic Orchestra / Pierre Boulez.**
   Sony Classical Ⓜ SM3K45842 (three discs: 223 minutes: ADD: 2/91).
...Piano Concerto in G major[a]. Piano Conferto for the left hand[a]. **Falla** Noches en los jardines de
   España. [a]**François-Joël Thiollier** (pf); **Polish National Radio Symphony Orchestra / Antoni Wit.**
   Naxos Ⓢ 8 550753 (64 minutes: DDD: 3/95).

Ravel Le tombeau de Couperin. Pavane pour une infante défunte. Ma mère l'oye . Une barque sur
   l'océan. Alborada del gracioso. **Orchestra of the Opéra National de Lyon / Kent Nagano.** Erato
   Ⓕ 0630-14331-2 (69 minutes: DDD: 6/97). Recorded 1994. *Gramophone Editor's choice.*   ⒼⒼ
The fairytale wonders and crystalline textures of *Ma mère l'oye* rarely fail to bring out the best in performers and sound engineers. And Nagano joins the score's other master magicians of the past decade, namely, Dutoit, Rattle and Boulez. But no consideration would be complete without putting into the frame Monteux's 1964 recording – it takes but a few seconds to hear 'through' a moderate degree of tape hiss to a group of crack musicians gathered around the revered *maître* and producing sublime chamber music, with the most finely gauged seeking out and savouring of expressive colour, character and period *charme*. Nagano enjoys perhaps the most present and tactile recorded sound of all (a distinctively 'hairy' contrabassoon in "Beauty and the Beast"), with a fine bloom, if not quite the depth of the Dutoit or Boulez, or the comprehensive focus for detail of the Rattle. Interpretatively, Nagano shares most with Rattle, preferring a wide variety of tempo; not as slow as him in Beauty's "Pavane", though one might complain that "Tom Thumb" suggests more movement than Nagano's tempo allows (he turns it into a dreamy woodland interlude). "Pagodaland", by contrast, is more lively than usual, with the opening piccolo solo nicely inflected.

Both the Boulez and Nagano discs offer *Une barque sur l'océan*, and Nagano's account is one of the most most gripping ever heard. It is a piece whose transcription tends to find more apology than advocacy among Ravel commentators, and is a less frequent inclusion among Ravel anthologies on disc. A pity, as its alternating gentle sunlit sway (and what enchantment lies in the dappled detailing) and the huge waves of sound that arise from it are a gift to conductors who fancy themselves as Poseidon for eight minutes. The "Prelude" of *Le tombeau de Couperin* is reminiscent of water music (an enchanted babbling brook?). Here Nagano eschews Dutoit's gentle rapids (and the score's challengingly fast metronome mark), facilitating more precise articulation and lovely colouring (wonderfully liquid woodwinds, so well caught by the recording). And in the "Forlane", precise accentuation and articulation give the main theme a real lift. Questions of balance in *Le tombeau* between baroque manners and romantic warmth tend to find different answers from different interpreters, and different expectations from listeners. And some may feel that Nagano's 'expressive' haltings in the central sections of the "Forlane" and "Rigaudon" are more affectation than affection. Still, it would be wrong to end with a complaint. This is a distinguished Ravel collection.

Additional recommendations ...

...Le tombeau de Couperin. Boléro. Shéhérazade[a]. Tzigane[b]. [a]**Dame Margaret Price** (sop);
   [b]**Salvatore Accardo** (vn); **London Symphony Orchestra / Claudio Abbado.**
   DG Classikon Ⓑ 439 414-2GCL (58 minutes: ADD/DDD: 6/94).
...Ma mère l'oye. Boléro. Rapsodie espagnole. Une barque sur l'océan. Alborada del gracioso.
   Berlin Philharmonic Orchestra / Pierre Boulez. DG Ⓕ 439 859-2GH (76 minutes: DDD: 9/94). Ⓖ

...La valse. Ma mère l'oye. Boléro. *Coupled with works by various composers.* **London Symphony Orchestra / Pierre Monteux.** Philips The Early Years Ⓜ 442 544-2PM5 (five discs: 311 minutes: ADD: 12/94). *See review in the Collections section; refer to the Index.* ⒼⒼⒼ
...La valse. Rapsodie espagnole. Boléro. **Debussy** Images. **Boston Symphony Orchestra / Charles Munch.** RCA Victor Living Stereo Ⓜ 09026 61956-2* (74 minutes: ADD: 12/94). *See review under Debussy; refer to the Index.* Ⓖ
...Rapsodie espagnole. *Coupled with works by* **Debussy Philadelphia Orchestra / Leopold Stokowski.** Biddulph mono Ⓜ WHL013* (77 minutes: ADD: 8/95).
...Boléro. *Coupled with works by* **Mussorgsky** and **Debussy Berlin Philharmonic Orchestra / Herbert von Karajan.** DG The Originals Ⓜ 447 426-2GOR (75 minutes: ADD: 12/95).
...Introduction and Allegro for flute, clarinet, harp and string quartet[a]. Ma mère l'oye[b] – Pavane de la Belle au bois dormant; Les entretiens de la belle et la bête; Petit Poucet; Laideronette, Impératrice des Pagodes. Pavane pour une infante défunte[c]. La valse[d]. *Coupled with works by* **Debussy** *and* **Satie.** [a]**Alice Chalifoux** (hp); [a]**Maurice Sharp** (fl); [a]**Robert Marcellus** (cl); [ac]**Cleveland Orchestra;** [cd]**Philharmonia Orchestra /** [a]**Louis Lane,** [b]**Michael Tilson Thomas,** [c]**George Szell,** [d]**Eugene Ormandy.** Sony Classical Essential Classics Ⓑ SBK63056 (68 minutes: ADD: 4/98).

Ravel Fanfare pour "L'éventail de Jeanne". Shéhérazade[a]. Alborada del gracioso. Miroirs – La vallée des cloches (arr. Grainger). Ma mère l'oye. La valse. [a]**Maria Ewing** (mez); **City of Birmingham Symphony Orchestra / Sir Simon Rattle.** EMI Ⓕ CDC7 54204-2 (75 minutes: DDD: 8/91). Text and translation included. Recorded 1989. ⒼⒼ
In the past there have been instances of Rattle's intensive preparation for setting down a much loved masterpiece precluding spontaneity in the end result. Not here. Along with the customary refinement and revelation of texture, there is a sense of Rattle gauging the very individual fantasy worlds of this varied programme with uncanny precision: an aptly childlike wonder for *Ma mère l'oye*'s fairy tale illustrations; the decadence and decay that drive *La valse* to its inevitable doom; and the sensual allure of the Orient in *Shéhérazade* providing a vibrant backdrop for soprano Maria Ewing's intimate confessions. The three shorter items that make up this indispensable (and generously filled) disc are equally successful, all recorded with stunning realism.

Additional recommendations ...

...Shéhérazade. *Coupled with works by various composers.* **Régine Crespin** (sop); **John Wustman** (pf); **Suisse Romande Orchestra / Ernest Ansermet.** Decca Ⓕ 417 813-2DH (68 minutes: ADD: 11/88). *See review in the Collections section; refer to the Index.*
...La valse. *Coupled with works by various composers.* **Philharmonia Orchestra / Igor Markevitch.** Testament mono Ⓕ SBT1060* (77 minutes: ADD: 2/96).
...La valse (arr. cpsr). *Coupled with works by* **Dukas** and **R. Strauss Martha Argerich, Alexandre Rabinovitch** (pfs). Teldec 4509-96435-2 (7/96). *Gramophone Editor's choice. See review under Dukas; refer to the Index.* ⒼⒼ
...La vallée des cloches (orch. Grainger). *Coupled with works by* **Debussy** and **Grainger City of Birmingham Symphony Orchestra / Sir Simon Rattle.** EMI Ⓕ CDC5 56412-2 (70 minutes: DDD: 8/97). *Gramophone Editor's choice. See review under Grainger; refer to the Index.*

Ravel Daphnis et Chloé[a]. La valse. [a]**Berlin Radio Chorus; Berlin Philharmonic Orchestra / Pierre Boulez.** DG Ⓕ 447 057-2GH (71 minutes: DDD: 12/95). Recorded 1993-1994. *Gramophone Editor's choice. Selected by Soundings.* Ⓖ
Increasingly, for considering modern recordings of *Daphnis*, it seems you must banish memories of 1959 Monteux; put behind you the most playful, mobile, texturally diaphanous, rhythmically supple account of the score ever recorded; one that is uniquely informed by history and selfless conductorial wisdom. For some, Monteux's view may remain a rather moderate one – certainly in terms of basic tempo and basic dynamic range; and Ravel's score suggests tempos and dynamics which modern performances, and especially recordings, have more faithfully reproduced (not necessarily to its advantage). Boulez has, of course, acquired a vast wealth of experience of conductorial wisdom (not least in subtle accommodations of pace and general phrasing) since his first New York recording of *Daphnis*. And here he has the Berlin Philharmonic Orchestra – on top form – to sustain and shape melody within some of his strikingly slow tempos (such as the opening, and Part 3's famous "Daybreak"), and who remain 'composed' in his daringly fast ones (the "Dance of the young girls around Daphnis" and the "Danse guerrière" – one of the most exciting on disc). Just occasionally, you feel that there are parts of the work that interest him less than others (Chloé's "Danse suppliante", and the 'amours' of the "Pantomime"). But anyone who doubts Boulez's ability to achieve, first, a sense of ecstasy should hear this "Daybreak"; secondly, a refined radiance (rather than ripe refulgence), should try the first embrace (track 5, 2'49"; at this point, this is also one of the very few recordings where you can hear the chorus); or, thirdly, to characterize properly the supernatural, listen to the 'flickering' accents he gives the start of the string *tremolo* chords in the "Nocturne".

The chorus work, not least in the so-called "Interlude", is outstanding; the harmonic boldness of this passage was just as startling in New York, but the Berlin chorus, unlike the New York one, are here properly set back. Vowel sounds are varied; the dynamics are just as powerfully graded and the passage builds superbly to the "Danse guerrière", with off-stage brass perfectly placed and timed. In general, DG's recording – a sumptuous Jesus-Christus Kirche production – strikes exactly the right compromise between clarity and spaciousness, much as Decca's did for Dutoit. Finer details, dynamic extremes and internal balances aren't quite as consistently observed as in the Rattle, either from the podium or from the mixing desk, but that production sounds comparably studio-bound. With the added lure of an expansive and often massively powerful *La valse* (spectacular timpani), this is now the most recommendable modern *Daphnis* available.

Ravel Daphnis et Chloé[a]. Rapsodie espagnole[b]. Pavane pour une infante défunte[b]. [a]**Chorus of the Royal Opera House, Covent Garden; London Symphony Orchestra / Pierre Monteux.** Decca The Classic Sound Ⓜ 448 603-2DCS* (74 minutes: ADD: 9/96). Item marked [a] from SXL2164 (12/59), recorded 1959, [b]SXL2312 (7/62), recorded 1961. *Gramophone classical 100.*   ⒢⒢⒢

Ravel Daphnis et Chloé. **New England Conservatory Choir; Boston Symphony Orchestra / Charles Munch.** RCA Victor Living Stereo Ⓜ 09026 61846-2* (54 minutes: ADD: 3/94). From VICS1297 (12/70). Recorded 1955.   ⒢⒢

Diaghilev's ballet *Daphnis et Chloé*, based on a pastoral romance by the ancient Greek poet Longus, was first produced in June 1912, with Nijinsky and Karsavina in the title roles and choreography by Mikhail Fokine. Pierre Monteux conducted the first performance, and 47 years later he recorded his peerless interpretation for Decca. Though the Second Suite from the ballet is familiar to concert-goers and makes an effective piece in its own right, the full score, with wordless chorus, conveys still greater atmosphere and magic. No work of more sheer sensual beauty exists in the entire orchestral repertoire, and Monteux was its perfect interpreter. He conducts with a wonderful sense of clarity and balance: every important detail tells, and there is refinement of expression, yet inner strength too. The LSO play with superlative poetry and skill, and the chorus is magnificent in its tonal blend and colour. The *Rapsodie espagnole* and *Pavane* are also given ideal performances, and the recordings show off Decca's exceedingly high standards during the late 1950s and early 1960s. Another landmark *Daphnis*, Munch's with the Boston Symphony Orchestra made in stereo, sounds equally astonishing in RCA's transfer. Robert Layton, writing in *Gramophone*, and comparing Monteux with Munch "succumbed more readily to the heady intoxication, the dazzling richness of colour and virtuosity" of the Munch. Both Monteux and Munch (along with Ansermet and more recently Dutoit) understood the dangers of extremes and excessive lingering in this score; of sentiment turning into syrup and Ravel's "Choreographic Symphony" (his own term) falling apart. It should be noted that, though their recordings balance Ravel's complex score more skilfully and imaginatively than most modern contenders, the score's huge range of dynamics could not be fully realized by the technology of the time.

Additional recommendations ...

...Daphnis et Chloé. **Montreal Symphony Chorus and Orchestra / Charles Dutoit.** Decca Ⓕ 400 055-2DH (56 minutes: DDD: 3/83).   ⒢

...Daphnis et Chloé – Suite No. 2. Boléro. *Coupled with works by* **Debussy Berlin Philharmonic Orchestra / Herbert von Karajan.** DG Galleria Ⓜ 427 250-2GGA (64 minutes: ADD: 7/89).   ⒢⒢

...Alborada del gracioso. Rapsodie espagnole. Valses nobles et sentimentales. Pavane pour une infante défunte. **Debussy** Images. **Chicago Symphony Orchestra / Fritz Reiner.** RCA Victor Gold Seal Ⓜ GD60179* (68 minutes: ADD: 1/90).   ⒢⒢

...Alborada del gracioso. Rapsodie espagnole. La valse. Pavane pour une infante défunte. Le tombeau de Couperin. **Ibert** Escales. **Detroit Symphony Orchestra / Paul Paray.** Mercury Living Presence Ⓜ 432 003-2MM* (67 minutes: ADD: 4/91).   ⒢

...Daphnis et Chloé[a]. **Debussy** Khamma. [a]**Het Groot Omroepkoor; Royal Concertgebouw Orchestra / Riccardo Chailly.** Decca Ⓕ 443 934-2DH (74 minutes: DDD: 10/95). *See review under Debussy; refer to the Index.*

...Pavane pour une infante défunte. *Coupled with works by various composers.* **Academy of St Martin in the Fields** and [a]**Chorus / Sir Neville Marriner.** Philips Ⓕ 446 084-2PH (54 minutes: DDD: 1/96).

...Daphnis et Chloé – Suite No. 2. *Coupled with works by* **Kodály Concertgebouw Orchestra / Willem Mengelberg.** Archive Documents Mengelberg Edition mono Ⓕ ADCD115* (70 minutes: AAD: 3/96).

...Pavane pour une infante défunte. Ma mère l'oye – Suite. *Coupled with works by* **Debussy Royal Concertgebouw Orchestra / Carlo Maria Giulini.** Sony Classical Ⓕ SK66832 (64 minutes: DDD: 11/95).

...Daphnis et Chloé[a]. Ma mère l'oye[b]. [a]**Dallas Symphony Orchestra / Eduardo Mata;** [b]**Boston Symphony Orchestra / Charles Munch.** RCA Victor Classical Navigator Ⓢ 74321 29257-2 (76 minutes: DDD/ADD: 6/96).

...Daphnis et Chloé – Suite No. 2. *Coupled with works by* **Petrov** and **Stravinsky Leningrad State Academy Boys' Choir; Leningrad Symphony Orchestra / Yuri Temirkanov.** Melodiya Ⓜ 74321 32044-2 (69 minutes: ADD: 2/97).

Ravel String Quartet in F major.
Vaughan Williams On Wenlock Edge[ab]. String Quartet No. 1 in G minor. [a]**Philip Langridge** (ten); [b]**Howard Shelley** (pf); **Britten Quartet** (Peter Manning, Keith Pascoe, vns; Peter Lale, va; Andrew Shulman, vc). EMI Ⓕ CDC7 54346-2 (78 minutes: DDD: 2/92). Recorded 1990-1991.
This outstanding disc from the Britten Quartet brings together several works which have far more in common than one might at first imagine. Vaughan Williams spent a short study vacation in Paris

during 1908 hoping, on his own admission, to acquire "a little French polish" from Ravel, who himself took part in the French première of his student's song cycle, *On Wenlock Edge*. Ravel's String Quartet receives a provocative, and yet totally convincing reading from the Britten Quartet, who choose to dwell upon the polarization of tonal and melodic content in this work to a greater degree than any of their rivals on disc, most of whom offer the more usual coupling in the shape of the Debussy Quartet. *On Wenlock Edge*, a setting of six poems selected from A.E. Housman's set of 63 poems, *A Shropshire Lad*, is heard here in a quite exceptional performance from the tenor, Philip Langridge, joined by pianist Howard Shelley and the Britten Quartet. Langridge recognizes the irony and understatement of Housman's verse, whilst exploiting its more sinister undertones with searching skill, as he does in the uncanny dialogue between the living and the dead, in "Is my team ploughing", bringing chilly pallor to his delivery of the opening stanza in particular. It would be difficult to match the communicative power of this performance even in the concert-hall. The Brittens also excel in a crystalline and devoted account of Vaughan Williams's underrated G minor Quartet, which sounds more than usually weighty and musically coherent in this fluid and sharply perceived reading. The technical aspects of the playing are second to none, while its added sensitivity contributes to an involving and frequently moving musical experience. The recorded sound is brilliant and immediate.

Additional recommendations ...

...String Quartet. *Coupled with works by* **Debussy** and **Fauré** Pro Arte Quartet.
  Biddulph mono Ⓜ LAB105* (78 minutes: ADD).   Ⓖ
...String Quartet. **Debussy** String Quartet in G minor, Op. 10. **Quartetto Italiano.**
  Philips Silver Line Ⓜ 420 894-2PSL (57 minutes: ADD: 10/88).   Ⓖ
...String Quartet. *Coupled with works by* **Beethoven** and **Mozart** Sharon Quartet.
  Koch International Classics Ⓢ DICD920171 (74 minutes: DDD: 10/94).
...String Quartet. *Coupled with works by* **Debussy** and **Menu** Parisii Quartet.
  Auvidis Valois Ⓕ V4730 (68 minutes: DDD: 10/95).
...String Quartet. *Coupled with works by* **Debussy** and **Stravinsky** Lindsay Quartet.
  ASV Ⓕ CDDCA930 (61 minutes: DDD: 12/95).
...String Quartet. *Coupled with works by* **Haydn** and **Schubert** Allegri Quartet.
  Naim Audio Ⓕ NAIMCD012 (62 minutes: DDD: 2/97).
...String Quartet. *Coupled with works by* **Haydn** and **Schubert** Skampa Quartet.
  Supraphon Ⓕ SU3156-2 (61 minutes: DDD: 8/97).

Ravel Violin Sonatas[b] – 1897; 1927. Tzigane[c]. Pièce en forme de Habanera[b]. Berceuse sur le nom de Gabriel Fauré[b]. Sonata for Violin and Cello[a]. Kaddisch (trans. Garban)[b]. **Chantal Juillet** (vn); [a]**Truls Mørk** (vc); **Pascal Rogé** ([b]pf/[c]pf luthéal). Decca Ⓕ 448 612-2DH (78 minutes: DDD: 12/96). Recorded 1995. *Gramophone Award Winner 1997.* ⒼⒼ
The piano luthéal, used at the Paris première of *Tzigane*, is an instrument modified to sound like a cimbalom. Its timbre isn't quite the same, but Pascal Rogé produces a wonderful range of sparkling metallic sounds, lending an exciting and exotic atmosphere to the performance. The violin playing in *Tzigane* is special too – Chantal Juillet's gipsy style is absolutely convincing, the opening solo passage delivered with brilliantly characterized rhythms and a fine sense of timing. If *Tzigane* is the most striking item on the disc, the other performances aren't far behind. The short pieces are especially enjoyable – the velvety tone Juillet produces for *Kaddisch*, the elegant variations of tone (from both players) in the *Pièce en forme de Habanera*, and the delicate textures and gentle phrasing of the *Berceuse*. In the two Violin Sonatas with piano the playing is fastidious and very well balanced. Rogé never dominates – in the loudest passages he produces a clear sound, with resonance carefully controlled. In the 'big' passages of the 1927 Sonata there's no attempt to rival the barnstorming excitement or the romantic warmth and urgency of some of the many other recommendable versions. Juillet's and Rogé's playing is cooler, but always expressive, with imaginative and beautiful variations of tone colour. Juillet and Mørk match each other excellently in the Sonata for Violin and Cello. Again, there's a wide range of sonorities, including some suitably grotesque sounds in the second movement, and infectious rhythmic *élan* in the finale. The recording is clear and bright.

Additional recommendations ...

...Violin Sonata (1927). *Coupled with works by* **Prokofiev** and **Stravinsky** Viktoria Mullova (vn); **Bruno Canino** (pf). Philips Ⓕ 426 254-2PH (61 minutes: DDD: 8/90).
...Tzigane. Berceuse sur le nom de Gabriel Fauré. Pièce en forme de habanera. *Coupled with works by* **Franck** and **Debussy** Augustin Dumay (vn); **Maria João Pires** (pf).
  DG Ⓕ 445 880-2GH (56 minutes: DDD: 10/95). *See review under Debussy; refer to the Index.* Ⓖ
...Violin Sonata (1927). **Prokofiev** Violin Sonatas – No. 1 in F minor, Op. 80; No. 2 in D major, Op. 94*a*. **Shlomo Mintz** (vn); **Yefim Bronfman** (pf).
  DG Masters Ⓜ 445 557-2GMA (74 minutes: DDD: 11/95).
...Violin Sonatas – 1897; 1927. Tzigane. Berceuse sur le nom de Gabriel Fauré. *Coupled with works by* **Poulenc** and **Debussy** Cho-Liang Lin (vn); **Paul Crossley** (pf).
  Sony Classical Ⓕ SK66839 (77 minutes: DDD: 7/96).
...Violin Sonatas[b] – 1897; 1927. Tzigane[c]. Pièce en forme de Habanera[b]. Berceuse sur le nom de Gabriel Fauré[b]. Sonata for Violin and Cello[a]. Kaddisch (trans. Garban)[b]. **Chantal Juillet** (vn); [a]**Truls Mørk** (vc); **Pascal Rogé** ([b]pf/[c]pf luthéal).
  Decca Ⓕ 448 612-2DH (78 minutes: DDD: 12/96).

...Violin Sonata (1927). *Coupled with works by various composers.* **Isabelle van Keulen** (vn); **Ronald Brautigam** (pf). Koch Classics Ⓕ 36416-2 (64 minutes: DDD: 5/97). *See review in the Collections section; refer to the Index.*

...Violin Sonata (1927). **Medtner** Violin Sonata No. 3 in E minor, Op. 57, "Epica". **Vadim Repin** (vn); **Boris Berezovsky** (pf). Erato Ⓕ 0630-15110-2 (61 minutes: DDD: 2/97). *See review under Medtner, refer to the Index.*

...Tzigane. *Coupled with works by various composers.* **Zino Francescatti** (vn); **M. Faure** (pf). Symposium mono Ⓕ 1156* (74 minutes: ADD: 1/97).

Ravel Violin Sonatas – 1897; 1927.
Debussy Violin Sonata.
Pierné Violin Sonata, Op. 36. **Gérard Poulet** (vn); **Noël Lee** (pf). Arion Ⓕ ARN68228 (65 minutes: DDD: 9/94). Recorded 1993. *Gramophone Editor's choice.*

The special significance of this performance of Debussy's Sonata – his last work – is that it was written for the violinist's father Gaston Poulet, who gave the première in 1917 with the composer at the piano; a second performance by the same artists in the same year was Debussy's last public appearance. Gérard Poulet is very impressive in this beautiful, mercurial and ultimately melancholy piece – which, he says, his father taught him "in every detail". This performance, therefore, is probably as close as we can get to the authentic preservation of the composer's intentions. His tone is warm yet delicate, and the lilt and fantasy of the sonata emerge strikingly, with an idiomatic flexibility of tempo and dynamics. The recording, too, is a good one, with just the right amount of atmosphere, although the piano could have been placed a bit more forwardly, not least because Lee is such a fine artist: Nadia Boulanger called him "one of the finest musicians I have ever met". Ravel's Violin Sonata of 1927 also gets a strong performance. Rightly, the playing style is quite different here, and the edgy lyricism of the first movement is perfectly caught, as is the bittersweet quality of the Blues and the barely suppressed hysteria of the *Perpetuum mobile.* As for Ravel's one-movement Sonata of 1897, which remained unplayed until 1975, this performance brings out its naïve charm, though it reveals little of the composer we know. Pierné's Sonata (1900) is a welcome addition to the current catalogue, passionate and brilliant and in every way rewarding. Altogether, an outstanding disc.

Ravel Gaspard de la nuit[a]. Valses nobles et sentimentales[b]. Jeux d'eau[c]. Miroirs[c]. Sonatine[b]. Le tombeau de Couperin[b]. Prélude[a]. Menuet sur le nom de Haydn[a]. A la manière de Borodine[a]. Menuet antique[a]. Pavane pour une infante défunte[a]. A la manière de Chabrier[a]. Ma mère l'oye[d]. **Pascal Rogé,** [d]**Denise-Françoise Rogé** (pfs). Double Decca Ⓜ 440 836-2DF2 (two discs: 142 minutes: ADD: 10/94). Items marked [a] from SXL6700 (3/75), [b]SXL6674 (11/74), [cd]SXL6715 (11/75). Recorded 1973-1994. ⒼⒼ

Everything is expressed with a classic restraint, elegance and economy, an ideal absence of artifice or idiosyncrasy. Rogé, exemplifying the finest French pianism, knows precisely where to allow asperity to relax into lyricism and vice versa, and time and again he finds that elusive, cool centre at the heart of Ravel's teeming and luxuriant vision. True, those used to more Lisztian but less authentic Ravel may occasionally find Rogé diffident or *laissez-faire.* But lovers of subtlety will invariably see him as illuminating and enchanting. How often do you hear *Ma mère l'oye* given without a trace of brittleness or archness, or *Jeux d'eau* presented with such stylish ease and tonal radiance? Rogé may lack something of Thibaudet's menace and high-flying virtuosity in "Scarbo" (also on Decca) but how memorably he re-creates Ravel's nocturnal mystery. Even if one misses a touch of cruelty behind Ondine's entreaty, few pianists can have evoked her watery realm with greater transparency. Arguably one of the finest Ravel recordings available.

Additional recommendations ...

...Gaspard de la nuit. **Prokofiev** Piano Sonata No. 6 in A major, Op. 82. **Ivo Pogorelich** (pf). DG Ⓕ 413 363-2GH (52 minutes: DDD: 11/84). ⒼⒼ

...Ma mère l'oye. *Coupled with works by* **Fauré** and **Bizet** Katia and Marielle Labèque (pfs). Philips Ⓕ 420 159-2PH (56 minutes: DDD: 11/87).

...Gaspard de la nuit. Sonatine. Piano Concerto in G major[a]. **Martha Argerich** (pf); [a]**Berlin Philharmonic Orchestra / Claudio Abbado.** DG Galleria Ⓜ 419 062-2GGA (54 minutes: ADD: 12/87). ⒼⒼ

...Pavane. Le tombeau de Couperin. Sérénade. Jeux. Valses nobles et sentimentales. La valse. **Louis Lortie** (pf). Chandos Ⓕ CHAN8620 (66 minutes: DDD: 5/89).

...Gaspard de la nuit. Menuet antique. Menuet sur le nom de Haydn. A la manière de Borodine. A la manière de Chabrier. Prélude. Miroirs. Sonatine. **Louis Lortie** (pf). Chandos Ⓕ CHAN8647 (74 minutes: DDD: 10/89).

...Miroirs – Alborada del gracioso. *Coupled with works by various composers.* **Dinu Lipatti** (pf). EMI Références mono Ⓜ CDH7 63038-2* (66 minutes: ADD: 11/89). ⒼⒼⒼ

...Boléro. Introduction and Allegro. La valse. Ma mère l'oye. Rapsodie espagnole. **Louis Lortie, Hélène Mercier** (pfs). Chandos CHAN8905 (65 minutes: DDD: 3/91).

...Sérénade grotesque. Menuet antique. Pavane pour une infante défunte. Jeux d'eau. Sonatine. Miroirs. Gaspard de la nuit. Menuet sur le nom de Haydn. Valses nobles et sentimentales. Prélude. A la manière de Borodine. A la manière de Chabrier. Le tombeau de Couperin. **Jean-Yves Thibaudet** (pf). Decca Ⓕ 433 515-2DH2 (two discs: 130 minutes: DDD: 11/92).

...Gaspard de la nuit. Jeux. Le tombeau de Couperin. Valses nobles. **Gordon Fergus-Thompson** (pf).
ASV Ⓕ CDDCA805 (72 minutes: DDD: 12/92).

...A la manière de Borodine. A la manière de Chabrier. Menuet antique. Menuet sur le nom de
Haydn. Miroirs. Pavane pour une infante défunte. Prélude. Sérénade grotesque. Sonatine.
Gordon Fergus-Thompson (pf). ASV Ⓕ CDDCA809 (68 minutes: DDD: 10/93).

...(arr. Sadlo) Ma mère l'oye – Pavane de la Belle au bois dormant; Les entretiens de la belle et la
bête; Petit Poucet; Laideronette, Imperatrice des Pagodes; Le jardin féerique. Rapsodie espagnole.
Bartók Sonata for Two Pianos and Percussion, Sz110. **Martha Argerich, Nelson Freire** (pfs);
Peter Sadlo, Edgar Guggeis (perc). DG Ⓕ 439 867-2GH (56 minutes: DDD: 10/94).
Gramophone Editor's choice. See review under Bartók; refer to the Index.   ⓆⒼⓆ

...La parade. Pavane pour une infante défunte. Sérénade grotesque. A la manière de Chabrier.
A la manière de Borodine. Menuet antique. Jeux d'eau. Menuet sur le nom de Haydn. Prélude.
Sonatine. Miroirs. **François-Joël Thiollier** (pf). Naxos Ⓢ 8 550683 (75 minutes: DDD: 2/95).

...Miroirs. Sonatine. Jeux d'eau. **Debussy** Pour le piano. Estampes. **Lilya Zilberstein** (pf).
DG Ⓕ 439 927-2GH (74 minutes: DDD: 2/95).

...Gaspard de la nuit. Sonatine. Valses nobles et sentimentales. La valse. **Boris Berezovsky** (pf).
Teldec Ⓕ 4509-94539-2 (57 minutes: DDD: 3/95).

...Jeux d'eau. *Coupled with works by various composers.* **Martha Argerich** (pf).
DG The Originals Ⓜ 447 430-2GOR (71 minutes: ADD: 6/95). *Gramophone Classical 100.*
See review in the Collections section; refer to the Index.   ⓆⒼⓆ

...Miroirs. Valses nobles et sentimentales. *Coupled with works by* **Liszt** Sviatoslav Richter (pf).
Praga mono/stereo Ⓑ CMX354009* (65 minutes: ADD: 6/96).

...Gaspard de la nuit. Prélude. Menuet sur le nom de Haydn. Jeux d'eau. Le tombeau de Couperin.
Huseyin Sermet (pf). Auvidis Valois Ⓕ V4755 (59 minutes: DDD: 7/96).

...Ma mère l'oye. *Coupled with works by various composers.*
Carlton Classics Turnabout Ⓑ 30371 0014-2 (78 minutes: ADD: 10/96).

...Pavane pour une infante défunte. *Coupled with works by various composers.* **Anna Noakes** (fl);
Gillian Tingay (hp). ASV White Line Ⓜ CDWHL2101 (76 minutes: DDD: 11/96).
See review in the Collections section; refer to the Index.

...Valses nobles et sentimentales. **Mussorgsky** Pictures at an Exhibition. **Ivo Pogorelich** (pf).
DG Ⓕ 437 667-2GH (62 minutes: DDD: 6/97). *Selected by Soundings. See review under*
Mussorgsky; refer to the Index.   ⓆⒼⓆ

Ravel L'enfant et les sortilèges. **Françoise Ogéas** (sop) Child; **Jeanine Collard** (contr) Mother,
Chinese cup, Dragonfly; **Jane Berbié** (sop) Sofa, She Cat, Squirrel, Shepherd; **Sylvaine**
Gilma (sop) Fire, Princess, Nightingale; **Colette Herzog** (sop) Bat, Little Owl, Shepherdess;
Heinz Rehfuss (bar) Armchair, Tree; **Camille Maurane** (bar) Grandfather Clock, Tom Cat;
Michel Sénéchal (ten) Teapot, Little Old Man (Mr Arithmetic), Frog; **Chorus and Children's**
Voices of French Radio; French Radio National Orchestra / Lorin Maazel. DG Ⓕ 423 718-2GH*
(43 minutes; ADD: 3/89). Notes, text and translation included. From SLPM138675 (6/61).
Recorded 1960. *Gramophone Award Winner 1989. Selected by Sounds in Retrospect.*   ⓆⒼⓆ
This is a Desert Island Disc if ever there was one. Every musical and verbal point in Ravel's brilliantly
ingenious, deliciously witty and entirely enchanting score is brought out by a well-nigh perfect cast,
backed by first class orchestral playing; and the recording is as vivid as anyone could wish. The story
is that of a petulant brat who breaks the china, pulls the cat's tail, pricks the pet squirrel with a pen-
nib, puts the fire out by upsetting the kettle on it, tears the wallpaper and his books and snaps off the
pendulum of the grandfather clock – only to find that all these come to life and turn on him. Their
anger is appeased only when he tends the squirrel's paw; and finally the naughty child, having seen the
error of his ways, falls tearfully into his mother's arms. Everyone will have their own favourite
passages but the last pages of the opera, in particular, are hauntingly beautiful. This disc is a gem.
Additional recommendation ...
...L'enfant et les sortilèges. **Soloists; Maîtrise, Chorus and National Orchestra of French Radio /**
Ernest Bour. Testament mono SBT1044* (43 minutes: ADD: 2/95).
Gramophone Award Winner 1995.   Ⓖ

Ravel L'enfant et les sortilèges[a]. Shéhérazade[b]. Shéhérazade – fairy overture. [a]**Colette Alliot-Lugaz**
(sop) Child; [ab]**Catherine Dubosc** (sop) Sofa, Bat, Owl, Princess; [a]**Marie-Françoise Lefort** (sop)
Shepherdess, Fire, Nightingale; [a]**Odette Beaupré** (mez) Squirrel, Dragon-fly, She-cat;
[a]**Claudine Carlson** (mez) Mother, Chinese cup, Shepherd; [a]**Georges Gautier** (ten) Teapot, Little
Old Man, Frog; [a]**Didier Henry** (bar) Clock, Tom-cat; [a]**Lionel Sarrazin** (bass) Armchair, Tree;
Montreal Symphony Orchestra / Charles Dutoit. Decca Ⓕ 440 333-2DH
(73 minutes: DDD: 10/95). Notes, texts and translations included. Recorded 1992.
The sound quality of this fine Decca recording of Ravel's intoxicating opera is of such splendid
clarity that every nuance of this witty and highly emotional score can be heard, without any
sacrifice where the voices and text are concerned. Dutoit and the Montreal forces play with obvious
care and affection. Of all operas, this is one where orchestral texture and balance is of the utmost
importance. Among the soloists, Odette Beaupré is a sensual and characterful Dragon-fly and
Squirrel. Marie-Françoise Lefort is lively as the Fire and contributes to the ensemble of the Shepherds

and Shepherdesses – perhaps the saddest, most typical Colette-Ravel moment, it seems to describe in music all the mixed grief and joy at the loss of innocence and childhood. Catherine Dubosc is better as the Sofa, Bat and Owl than she is in the song of the Princess – how one longs for the security of the old-time French singers on the three classic versions (Martha Angelici for Bour, Sylvaine Gilma for Maazel and, the best of all, Suzanne Danco for Ansermet). Colette Alliot-Lugaz does what she can with the role of the Child – it is mostly an acting, not singing, part but she gets the little solo about the heart of the rose, and deals with it gently. Only the Maazel set – incredibly, nearly 34 years old – comes anywhere near the sound quality of this recording. However, the Dutoit must now be the standard recommendation, with either the Bour or Ansermet as a reminder of the past glories of the French style. The fill-up is generous, with a sumptuous account of the early *Shéhérazade* Overture, contrasting with the better-known song-cycle. Dubosc performes this, making a strong impression, but of course it is a work that has attracted every great singer, including Suzanne Danco herself.

Additional recommendation ...

...Shéhérazade[bl]. Vocalise en forme de habanera[dj]. Chants populaires[abdefj]. Sur l'herbe[ej]. Histoires naturelles[ej]. Cinq mélodies populaires grécques[bj]. Tripatos[bj]. Ballade de la reine morte d'aimer[bj]. Manteau de fleurs[bj]. Rêves[bj]. Don Quichotte à Dulcinée[fj]. Ronsard à son âme[fj]. Sainte[fj]. Les grands vents venus d'outre-mer[fj]. Un grand sommeil noir[fj]. Deux mélodies hébraïques[fj]. Trois poèmes de Stéphane Mallarmé[al]. Noël des jouets[aj]. Deux épigrammes de Clément Marot[aj]. Chansons madécasses[cgh]. Chanson du rouet[cj]. Si morne[cj]. [a]**Dame Felicity Lott,** [b]**Mady Mesplé,** [c]**Jessye Norman** (sops); [d]**Teresa Berganza** (mez); [e]**Gabriel Bacquier** (bar); [f]**José van Dam** (bass); [g]**Michel Debost** (fl); [h]**Renaud Fontanarosa** (vc); [j]**Dalton Baldwin** (pf); [k]**Toulouse Capitole Orchestra,** [l]**Orchestre de Paris Chamber Ensemble / Michel Plasson.** EMI Rouge et Noir Ⓜ CZS5 69299-2 (two discs: 136 minutes: DDD: 2/97).

Further listening ...

...Introduction and Allegro. Pièce en forme habanera. *Coupled with works by* **Poulenc** Soloists. Cala CACD1018 (2/95).

...Introduction and Allegro. *Coupled with works by various composers.* **Arthur Gleghorn** (fl); **Mitchell Lurie** (cl); **Ann Mason Stockton** (hp); **Hollywood Quartet; Concert Arts Strings / Felix Slatkin.** Testament mono SBT1053* (3/95). *See review in the Collections section; refer to the Index.* Ⓖ Ⓖ

...Piano Trio in A minor. *Coupled with* **Chausson** Piano Trio in G minor, Op. 3. **Beaux Arts Trio.** Philips 411 141-2PH (4/85).

...Piano Trio in A minor. *Coupled with works by* **Debussy** and **Schmitt** Joachim Trio. Naxos 8 550934 (8/95).

...L'aurore. Matinée de Provence. Tout est lumière. Les bayadères. La nuit. *Coupled with works by* **Debussy** and **Caplet** Brigitte Desnoues, Gaële Le Roi (sops); Marc Duguay (ten); **Chorus and Orchestra of the Sorbonne, Paris / Jacques Grimbert.** Marco Polo 8 223755 (10/95).

...Chants populaires – Chanson française; Chanson espagnole; Chanson italienne; Chanson hébraïque. Vocalise en forme de Habanera. Deux mélodies hébraïques. Tripatos. *Coupled with works by various composers.* **Cecilia Bartoli** (mez); **Myung-Whun Chung** (pf). Decca 452 667-2DH (12/96). *Gramophone Editor's Record of the month. See review in the Collections section; refer to the Index.*

...Chants populaires – Chanson française; Chanson espagnole; Chanson italienne. *Coupled with works by various composers.* **Lisa della Casa** (sop); **Arpad Sándor** (pf). EMI Salzburg Festival Edition mono CDH5 66571-2* (2/98). *See review in the Collections section; refer to the Index.*

...L'heure espagnole. **Soloists; French Radio National Orchestra / Lorin Maazel.** DG 423 719-2GH (3/89).

...L'heure espagnole. **Soloists; Orchestra of the Opéra-Comique, Paris / André Cluytens.** EMI mono CDM5 65269-2* (9/95).

Thomas Ravenscroft   British *c*1582-*c*1635

Suggested listening ...

...There were three ravens[abc]. New oysters. Jolly Shepherd[a]. A wooing song of a Yeoman of Kents Sonne[ab]. Come follow me[a]. Of all the birds that I ever see[a]. *Coupled with works by various composers.* [a]**John Potter** (sngr); [b]**Richard Campbell** (viol/bandora/gtr); [c]**David Miller** (lte/theorbo/gtr/cittern); **The Dufay Collective.** Chandos New Direction CHAN9446 (10/96). *See review in the Collections section; refer to the Index.*

Alan Rawsthorne   British 1905-1971

Rawsthorne String Quartets – No. 1, "Theme and Variations"; No. 2; No. 3. String Quartet (1935). **Flesch Quartet** (Philippa Ibbotson, Mark Denman, vns; Robert Gibbs, va; David Newby, vc). ASV Ⓕ CDDCA983 (75 minutes: DDD: 7/97). Recorded 1996.
The unpublished 1935 String Quartet receives its first recording here and a very pleasing discovery it proves to be, for its four movements already display the superior finish, tangy harmonic sense and clear-headed logic one immediately associates with Rawsthorne. His First Quartet proper dates from

1939. Cast in one movement, it comprises a theme and six variations, and Rawsthorne's resourceful inspiration inevitably calls to mind the inventiveness and impeccable craft of his own exhilarating *Symphonic Studies* (completed the previous year). As it happens, the fourth (and last) movement of the Second Quartet also uses variation form. It's another high quality offering, which demands and well repays close concentration and study: here is music of considerable substance, rigour and fastidious refinement. Like its predecessor, the Third Quartet is meaty, formally elegant and contains not one wasted note or gesture. It is also the most searching of the three quartets. One senses a definite stylistic and emotional kinship between its touching slow movement and the noble Sarabande of Rawsthorne's extremely fine Third Symphony of 1964. These are highly committed, eloquent and consistently purposeful performances from the Flesch Quartet. The rather close, occasionally wiry sound is a bit disconcerting at first, but turn down the volume just a touch and the ear soon adjusts.

Further listening ...

...Clarinet Concerto. *Coupled with works by* **Jacob** and **Cooke** Thea King (cl);
 Seattle Northwest Chamber Orchestra / Alun Francis. Hyperion CDA66031 (10/89).
...Piano Concerto No. 2. Concerto for Piano, Strings and Percussion No. 1. Double Piano
 Concerto[a]. **Geoffrey Tozer,** [a]**Tamara-Anna Cislowski** (pfs); **London Philharmonic Orchestra /**
 Matthias Bamert. Chandos CHAN9125 (4/93).
...Symphonies – No. 1[a]; No. 2, "Pastoral"[b]; No. 3[c]. [b]**Tracey Chadwell** (sop); [ab]**London Philharmonia**
 Orchestra / [a]**Sir John Pritchard,** [b]**Nicholas Braithwaite;** [c]**BBC Symphony Orchestra / Norman Del**
 Mar. Lyrita Ⓕ SRCD291 (75 minutes: ADD/DDD: 2/96).
...Clarinet Quartet. *Coupled with works by* **Bliss** and **Routh** Nicholas Cox (cl); **Nicholas Ward,**
 Peter Pople (vns); **Ivo-Jan van der Werff** (va); **Paul Marleyn** (vc).
 Redcliffe Recordings RR010 (11/96). *See review under Bliss; refer to the Index.*
...Violin Sonata. *Coupled with works by* **Fricker** and **Vaughan Williams** Susanne Stanzeleit (vn);
 Julian Jacobson (pf). Cala United CACD88036 (7/96).

Jean-Féry Rebel French 1661-1747

Rebel Les élémens. Les caractères de la danse. Le tombeau de Monsieur de Lully.
 Les Musiciens du Louvre / Marc Minkowski. Erato Ⓕ 2292-45974-2
 (48 minutes: DDD: 11/93). 🎵 Recorded 1992. ⓖⓖ
Jean-Féry Rebel, a contemporary of Couperin, was among those composers who lent real distinction to the comparatively unsung period of French baroque music between Lully's death and the full flowering of Rameau's genius. In *Les élémens* (1737) the composer, in accordance with intellectual trends of the time, evokes Nature in many of its movements; and at times it is quite startlingly vivid as you will hear at once in the harmonically confused opening measures of the overture. Each element is allotted its own distinctive character, Earth recognizable by its tied bass notes, Water by upward and downward scale passages on the flutes, Air by reiterated piccolo trills and Fire by brilliant upper string passagework. The second of the suites on this delightful disc, like *Les élémens*, has both a programmatic and choreographic purpose. *Les caractères de la danse* (1715) consists of a compendium of some of the most popular dances of the time, skilfully interlocked to form a single unit. Third on the disc is a touching and beautifully written three-part sonata *Le tombeau de Monsieur de Lully*. Italian and French manners interweave rewardingly in this heartfelt lament for Louis XIV's redoubtable "surintendant de la musique". Here and throughout the programme the performances are first-rate. All is well documented and superbly recorded.

Additional recommendation ...

...Les elémens. *Coupled with works by* **Gluck** and **Telemann** Cologne Musica Antiqua /
 Reinhard Goebel. Archiv Produktion Ⓕ 445 824-2AH (63 minutes: DDD: 12/95). 🎵
 Gramophone Editor's choice.

João Rebelo Portuguese 1610-1661

Suggested listening ...

...Super aspidem. Ecce nunc. In te, Domine, speravi. Qui habitat. Fratres sobrii.
 Educes me. Panis angelicus. Magnificat. *Coupled with works by* **Melgás** The Sixteen;
 His Majesties Sagbutts and Cornetts / Harry Christophers.
 Collins Classics 1465-2 (12/96). *See review under Melgás; refer to the Index.*

Max Reger German 1873-1916

Reger Suite im alten Stil, Op. 93. Serenade in G major, Op. 95. **Bamberg Symphony Orchestra /**
 Horst Stein. Koch Schwann Ⓕ 315662 (66 minutes: DDD: 11/97). Recorded 1993.
 Gramophone Editor's choice.
There are few orchestral works composed during the last 100 years that have been more unfairly neglected than Reger's delightful Serenade, Op. 95. And what a beauty it is! The opening theme is

unalloyed delight, while the first movement's expansive workings are eventful, affectionately discursive and formally well crafted. The second subject is one of Reger's loveliest melodies and the harp chimes that signal the melting return of the opening idea spell genuine magic. The contrapuntal finale is full of fun and the work ends – in thematic terms – from whence it began, in a mood of pastoral reverie. As to the orchestra, Reger employs winds, brass and timpani framed by two separate string groups, one playing with mutes (the one placed on the right-hand side of the stage), the other without, so that antiphonal interplay between them is underlined. Lovers of mainstream romantic repertory cannot fail to respond and Stein's performance is, viewed overall, the most polished we have had so far. The *Suite in the Olden Style* started life as a duo for violin and and piano but the orchestral version dates from the very end of Reger's tragically short career. The rumbustious first movement opens in the manner of Bach's Third *Brandenburg Concerto*; the *Largo* hints at Bruckner and the fugal finale is built on a puckish theme that seems to wind on into infinity. Here, then, is an excellent CD to counter all those unfounded rumours about Reger's 'dry, dull, academic' composing style. If you love Bach, Brahms, Bruckner or Dvořák – then you have the potential to love at least Reger's Serenade virtually as much.

Additional recommendation ...

...Suite im alten Stil. 93. Piano Concerto, Op. 114ᵃ. ᵃ**Love Derwinger** (pf); **Norrköping Symphony Orchestra / Leif Segerstam.** BIS Ⓕ CD711 (67 minutes: DDD: 5/96).

Reger Four Symphonic Poems after Arnold Böcklin, Op. 128. Variations and Fugue on a Theme of J.A. Hiller, Op. 100. **Royal Concertgebouw Orchestra / Neeme Järvi.** Chandos Ⓕ CHAN8794 (67 minutes: DDD: 3/90). Recorded 1989. ⒼⒼ

Reger Variations and Fugue on a Theme of Beethoven, Op. 86. Eine Ballettsuite in D major, Op. 130. Four Symphonic Poems after Arnold Böcklin, Op. 128. **Norrköping Symphony Orchestra / Leif Segerstam.** BIS Ⓕ CD601 (72 minutes: DDD: 6/94). Recorded 1993. Ⓖ

Mention of Reger's name in 'informed' circles is likely to produce a conditioned reflex: "Fugue!". In his day he was the central figure of the 'Back to Bach' movement, but he was also a romantic who relished all the expressive potential of the enormous post-Wagnerian orchestra. Then came the slender acerbities of the next generation of neo-classicists, and Reger's backward glances were deemed inflated and in shocking taste. Until relatively recently he has proved largely unexportable from his native Germany. Chandos, not surprisingly, exploit the open spaces of the Amsterdam Concertgebouw, forsaking some of the healthy transparency of the Davis recording on Orfeo for an extra spatial dimension; a more sumptuous glow. With Järvi's instinct for pacing in late romantic music, and his great orchestra's evident delight in the copious riches of the discovery, for the *Hiller* Variations, this disc is very tempting. Anyone who warms to Vaughan Williams's *Tallis Fantasia* will immediately respond to the "Hermit playing the violin", the first of the four *Böcklin* tone-poems; Debussy's "Jeux de vagues" from *La mer* was obviously in Reger's mind for the second poem "At play in the waves"; and the "Isle of the dead" is Reger's no less doom- and gloom-laden response to the painting that so captured Rachmaninov's imagination. The final painting, "Bacchanal", was described as a Munich beer festival in Roman costume – an entirely fitting description for Reger's setting of it!

Segerstam's disc is well programmed to show off the contrasting sides of orchestral Reger: firstly, the familiar champion of absolute music and the German tradition in the Variations; secondly, in *Eine Ballettsuite*, the unlikely purveyor of a relatively lightly scored *divertissement* of six dance or character portraits "for musical epicures"; and finally, in the *Böcklin* Poems, one who succumbed to the lure of programme music and 'impressionist' colour and timbre. Maybe the epicurean pleasures of *Eine Ballettsuite* are savoured by Sir Colin Davis with a little more humour, and, as recorded, brighter timbres, but Segerstam's Swedish orchestra in every way match Davis's Bavarians' evident love for the music. In both the first and third *Böcklin* Poems Segerstam is closer to Reger's metronome markings than the faster, more freewheeling Järvi. Segerstam is also, throughout the Poems, more acutely responsive to the extremes – and the minutest gradations in between – of both pace and dynamics. For the first and third poems (and parts of the second) this means that you are now aware just how much of this music dwells in the regions of *pianissimo* and beyond, and also how fine an impressionist Reger was. In the Poems, Järvi, it has to be said, has the advantage of a great orchestra, rather than a very good one, and a more accommodating acoustic. BIS give Segerstam another of their textbook recordings, that is to say: an ears only, halfway back in an average size, modern concert-hall experience (levels are lower for the *Böcklin* Poems).

Additional recommendations ...

...Hiller Variations. Eine Ballettsuite, Op. 130. **Bavarian Radio Symphony Orchestra / Sir Colin Davis.** Orfeo Ⓕ C090841A (59 minutes: DDD; 4/87). Ⓖ

...Hiller Variations. **Zemlinsky** Gesänge nach Maeterlinck, Op. 13ᵃ. ᵃ**Hedwig Fassbender** (mez); **Czech Philharmonic Orchestra / Václav Neumann.** Supraphon Ⓕ 11 1811-2 (60 minutes: DDD: 7/93).

...Hiller Variations. Mozart Variations, Op. 32. **New Zealand Symphony Orchestra / Franz-Paul Decker.** Naxos Ⓢ 8 553079 (72 minutes: DDD: 7/95).

Reger Six Morceaux, Op. 24. Silhouetten, Op. 53. Blätter und Blüten, Op. 58. **Jean Martin** (pf). Naxos Ⓢ 8 550932 (79 minutes: DDD: 10/95). Recorded 1994.

A valuable treat for all inquisitive piano buffs and dedicated Regerians, even if some of the music is of variable quality. Least impressive, perhaps, are the *Six Morceaux*, Op. 24 (1898) – all of them fairly derivative, especially of Chopin (No. 2), Schubert (No. 4) and Brahms (No. 5). Whether they quite repay their taxing demands is open to some doubt, whereas the *Silhouetten* Op. 53 (1900) and *Blätter und Blüten* Op. 58 (1900-02) are quite another matter. Both sets are rich in playful modulations and lyrical ideas. Op. 53's opening "Ausserst lebhaft" anticipates the mischievous Reger of the *Hiller Variations*; the Ninth recalls the Grieg of the *Lyric Pieces*, the Tenth, Reger's own *Ballettsuite* (of some 13 years later), and the Twelfth, Brahms's late *Intermezzos*. All could enrich any programme of late-romantic piano music, while the more aphoristic (and technically simpler) *Blätter und Blüten* are lighter in tone, their high-points being (at least on first acquaintance) a charming "Frühlingslied" and a thoughtful pair of "Romanzen", the second of which recalls Smetana's piano music at its finest. Seventy-nine minutes constitute a fair chunk out of anyone's leisure timetable but, with the present context, 44 of them (that is, Op. 53 and 58) could be very happily spent listening. And certainly Jean Martin plays well and is realistically recorded.

Reger Six Preludes and Fugues, Op. 131*a*. Preludes and Fugues, Op. 117 – No. 1 in B minor; No. 2 in G minor; No. 3 in E minor; No. 5 in G major; No. 6 in D minor; No. 7 in A minor; No. 8 in E minor. **Mateja Marinković** (vn). ASV Ⓜ CDDCA876 (two discs: 82 minutes: DDD: 9/94). Recorded 1993.
Reger's knowledge of, and feeling for, the violin were all-embracing, and although his winding melodic lines can sometimes prove maddeningly discursive, there is much beauty in the writing – the A minor Prelude, or the E minor Prelude, Op. 131*a* providing particularly good sampling points. Bach is of course an overwhelming presence: quite apart from direct quotations there is the all-pervasive influence of the unaccompanied Sonatas and Partitas, especially with regard to Reger's fugues, which invariably start with a hint of Bachian *déjà-vu* before modulating way beyond the baroque's customary orbit. All 13 works here are surprisingly varied in theme and tone, although even the most enthusiastic listener is advised not to take in more than a few at a time. The prize-winning violinist Mateja Marinković is professor at both the Royal Academy of Music and the Guildhall School of Music, and his warm-centred, tonally true performances serve Reger handsomely. A major addition to the solo violin repertory on CD, and a must for all Regerians.

Reger Drei geistliche Gesänge, Op. 110. Drei Gesänge, Op. 39. **Danish National Radio Choir / Stefan Parkman**. Chandos Ⓕ CHAN9298 (56 minutes: DDD: 10/94). Texts and translations included. Recorded 1993-1994.																												Ⓠ
Visions of myriad notes covering the page would frighten most choirs away, but these singers are made of sterner stuff. For them complex contrapuntal structures, devious chromatic harmonies and textures so thick you need a forage knife to get through them, hold no terrors. Rather they not only weave their way through Reger's characteristically tangled scores without a moment's doubt, but illuminate the paths so clearly one hardly notices the dense musical undergrowth all around. Parkman has a clear-sighted view of what is wanted and, aided by singers whose pure, perfectly blended tone is in itself a joy to hear, he follows his vision unfalteringly: everything falls neatly into place making real musical sense. The hefty Op. 110 Motets (ostensibly in five, but often diverging into as many as nine independent parts) can, and usually do, sound oppressively heavy, but here offer some of the most sublimely beautiful moments yet captured on CD. A triumph of skill over adversity.

Further listening ...
...Konzert im alten Stil, Op. 123[a]. Sinfonietta in A major, Op. 90. **Peter Rosenberg, [a]Harold Orlovsky** (vns); **Bamberg Symphony Orchestra / Horst Stein**. Koch Schwann 313542 (8/94).
...Piano Concerto. **Gerhard Oppitz** (pf); **Bamberg Symphony Orchestra / Horst Stein**. Koch Schwann 311058.																												ⒼⒼ
...Variations and Fugue on a Theme of Mozart, Op. 132. *Coupled with* **Hindemith** Symphonic Metamorphosis on Themes of Carl Maria von Weber. **Bavarian Radio Symphony Orchestra / Sir Colin Davis**. Philips 422 347-2PH (9/90).																												ⒼⒼ
...Serenades[a] – D major, Op. 77*a*; G major, Op. 141*a*. Three Suites for Viola, Op. 131*d* – G minor; D major; E minor. [a]**Anna Noakes** (fl); [a]**Barry Wilde** (vn); **George Robertson** (va). ASV CDDCA875 (9/94).																												Ⓠ
...Pieces, Op. 59 – No. 5, Toccata in D minor; No. 6, Fugue in D major; No. 9, Benedictus. *Coupled with works by various composers.* **Andrew Lucas** (org). Naxos 8 550955 (11/94). *See review in the Collections section; refer to the Index.*
...Violin Sonata in A minor, Op. 91 No. 7 – Chaconne. *Coupled with works by various composers.* **Michelle Makarski** (vn). ECM New Series 449 957-2 (7/97). *See review in the Collections section; refer to the Index.*
...An die Hoffnung, Op. 124. *Coupled with works by various composers.* **Karita Mattila** (sop); **Berlin Philharmonic Orchestra / Claudio Abbado**. Sony Classical SK53975 (3/95).
...Three Duets, Op. 111*a*. *Coupled with works by* **Dvořák** *and* **Brahms Juliane Banse** (sop); **Brigitte Fassbaender** (mez); **Cord Garben** (pf). Koch Schwann 311592 (8/95).
...Es schläft ein stiller Garten, Op. 98 No. 4. Lieder, Op. 4 – No. 3, Winterahnung; No. 4, Im April. Ein Paar, Op. 55 No. 9. Nelken, Op. 15 No. 3. Gesänge, Op. 75 – No. 11, Aeolsharfe; No. 12, Hat gesagt – bleibt's nicht dabei; No. 18, Einsamkeit. Die bunten Kühe, Op. 70 No. 4. Schlummerlied.

Flötenspielerin, Op. 88 No. 3. Totensprache, Op. 62 No. 12. Lieder, Op. 97 – No. 2, Wiegenlied; No. 3, Ein Drängen ist in meinem Herzen; No. 4, Der bescheidene Schäfer. Schlichte Weisen, Op. 76 – No. 3, Waldeinsamkeit; No. 13, Der verliebte Jäger; No. 32, Von der Liebe; No. 35, Mittag. Traum durch die Dämmerung, Op. 35 No. 3. An die Hoffnung, Op. 124.
Iris Vermillion (mez); **Peter Stamm** (pf). CPO CPO999 317-2 (5/97).
...Latin Requiem, Op. 145a. Requiem, Op. 144b. **Soloists; North German Radio Chorus and Symphony Orchestra / Roland Bader.** Koch Schwann 313004.

Steve Reich
American 1936

Reich Proverb[a]. Nagoya marimbas[b]. City life[c]. [b]**Bob Becker,** [b]**James Preiss** (marimbas); [a]**Theatre of Voices** (Andrea Fullington, Sonja Rasmussen, Allison Zelles, sops; Alan Bennett, Paul Elliott, tens); [ac]**Steve Reich Ensemble /** [a]**Paul Hillier;** [c]**Bradley Lubman.** Nonesuch
Ⓕ 7559-79430-2 (42 minutes: DDD: 2/97). Recorded 1996. *Gramophone Editor's choice.*   Ⓖ
The Wittgenstein quotation ("How small a thought it takes to fill a whole life") serves as the basis of *Proverb* for three sopranos, two tenors, vibraphones and two electric organs, a composition that was premièred as a partial work 'in progress' at a 1995 Prom. The complete piece (it plays for some 14 minutes) holds together very well. Three sopranos "sing the original melody of the text in canons that gradually augment, or get longer", whereas Perotin's influence can be heard in the tenor parts. Reich's skill at inverting, augmenting and generally transforming his material has rarely sounded with such immediacy. After a virtuosic, pleasantly up-beat *Nagoya marimbas* lasting four-and-a-half minutes comes *City life*, probably Reich's best piece since *Different Trains*. The sound-frame includes air brakes, pile drivers, car alarms, boat horns and police sirens, all of which are loaded into a pair of sampling keyboards and played alongside the instrumental parts (two each of flutes, oboes, clarinets and pianos, plus string quartet and bass). The first movement opens with what sounds like a distant relation of Stravinsky's *Symphonies of Wind Instruments* then kicks into action on the back of a Manhattan street vendor shouting "Check it out". The second and fourth movements witness gradual acceleration – the second to a pile driver, the fourth to a heartbeat – and the third has the two sampling keyboards engaging in top-speed crossfire based on speech samples. The last and most dissonant movement utilizes material taped when the World Trade Centre was bombed in 1993. *City life* is a tightly crafted montage, formed like an arch (A-B-C-B-A), lean, clever, catchy and consistently gripping. In fact the whole disc (all 42 minutes of it) should thrill dyed-in-the-wool Reichians and preach convincingly to the as-yet unconverted. The sound is excellent.

Additional recommendation ...
...Come Out[a]. Piano Phase[b]. It's Gonna Rain[c]. Four Organs[d]. Drumming[e]. Music for Mallet Instruments, Voices and Organ[f]. Clapping Music[g]. Six Marimbas[h]. Music for 18 Musicians[i]. Eight lines[j]. Tehillim[k]. The Desert Music[l]. New York Counterpoint[m]. Sextet[n]. The Four Sections[o]. Different Trains[p]. Electric Counterpoint[q]. Three Movements[r]. The Cave[s]. Proverb[t]. Nagoya Marimbas[u]. City Life[v]. [k]**Barbara Borden,** [k]**Tannie Willemstijn** (sops); [k]**Yvonne Benschop,** [k]**Ananda Goud** (mezzos); [m]**Evan Ziporyn** (cl); [q]**Pat Metheny** (gtr); [p]**Kronos Quartet** (David Harrington, John Sherba, vns; Hank Dutt, va; Joan Jeanrenaud, vc); [b]**Nurit Tilles,** [b]**Edmund Niemann** (pfs); [d]**Michael Gordon,** [d]**Lisa Moore,** [d]**Mark Stewart,** [d]**Evan Ziporyn** (elec kbds); [g]**Steve Reich,** [du]**James Preiss,** [gn]**Russell Hartenberger,** [nu]**Bob Becker** (perc); [efhiln]**Steve Reich and Musicians;** [j]**Bang on a Can All-Stars /** [jv]**Bradley Lubman;** [k]**Hague Percussion Ensemble,** [k]**Schoenberg Ensemble /** [k]**Reinbert de Leeuw;** [stv]**Steve Reich Ensemble;** [t]**Theatre of Voices /** [st]**Paul Hillier;** [l]**Brooklyn Philharmonic Chorus and Orchestra,** [or]**London Symphony Orchestra /** [lor]**Michael Tilson Thomas.** Nonesuch Ⓜ 7559-79451-2 (ten discs: 559 minutes: DDD: 9/97).

Further listening ...
...Drumming. Six Pianos. Music for Mallet Instruments, Voices and Organ.
Steve Reich and Musicians. DG 20th Century Classics 427 428-2GC2 (9/89).   ⒼⒼ
...Four Organs. *Coupled with works by various composers.* **Piano Circus.** Argo 440 294-2ZH (1/94).   Ⓖ
...The Four Sections[a]. Music for Mallet Instruments, Voices and Organ[b].
[b]**Steve Reich and Musicians;** [a]**London Symphony Orchestra / Michael Tilson Thomas.** Elektra Nonesuch 7559-79220-2 (6/91).   ⒼⒼ
...Six Pianos. *Coupled with* **Riley** In C. **Piano Circus.** Argo 430 380-2ZH (6/91).
...Tehillim (Psalms) for Women's Voices and Instruments.
Vocal ensemble; instrumental ensemble / George Manahan. ECM New Series 827 411-2.   Ⓖ
...The Cave. **The Steve Reich Ensemble / Paul Hillier.** Nonesuch 7559-79327-2 (3/96).

Antoine-Joseph Reicha
Bohemian/French 1770-1836

Suggested listening ...
...Clarinet Quintet in B flat major, Op. 89. *Coupled with works by* **Hummel** and **Weber**
Charles Neidich (cl); **L'Archibudelli.** Sony Classical SK57968 (9/95). 🏅
...Wind Quintets – D minor, Op. 88 No. 4; G major, Op. 99 No. 6.
Michael Thompson Wind Quintet. Naxos 8 553528 (A/97).

Henriette Renié   French 1875-1956

Suggested listening ...
...Contemplation. *Coupled with works by various composers.* **Naoko Yoshino** (hp).
Philips 446 064-2PH (2/96). *See review in the Collections section; refer to the Index.*

Ottorino Respighi   Italian 1879-1936

Respighi Piano Concerto in A minor. Toccata. Fantasia slava. **Konstantin Scherbakov** (pf); **Slovak
Radio Symphony Orchestra / Howard Griffiths.** Naxos Ⓢ 8 553207 (51 minutes: DDD: 11/95).
Recorded 1994.
All these pieces are otherwise available in decent performances, but at this price how could anyone
with the slightest weakness for Respighi hesitate? Scherbakov and Griffiths do a good deal more than
dutifully go through the motions, the soloist in particular playing with delicacy and affection, grateful
for the (quite frequent) opportunities to demonstrate how well he would play Liszt or Rachmaninov,
but in the *Toccata* he is interested as well in Respighi's more characteristic modal vein; as a Russian,
he demonstrates that this too, like so much in Respighi, was influenced by the time he spent in Russia.
Russian soloist, English conductor and Slovak orchestra all enjoy the moment in the *Fantasia slava*
where Respighi presents a morsel of Smetana in the evident belief that it's a Russian folk-dance, but
the Concerto and the *Fantasia*, both very early Respighi, are not patronized in the slightest. The
central slow section of the Concerto, indeed, achieves something like nobility, and although there is
a risk of the pianism in this work seeming overblown and rhetorical, Scherbakov's fondness for
Respighi's more fleet-footed manner doesn't let this happen often. The *Toccata* is not so much an
exercise in the neo-baroque, often though its dotted and florid figures promise it, more of an essay on
how far one can be neo-baroque without giving up a post-Lisztian keyboard style and comfortable
orchestral upholstery. But in a slow and florid central section, a rather melancholy aria that passes
from the soloist to the oboe, to the strings and back again, there is a real quality of Bachian utterance
translated not unrecognizably into a late romantic language (you may be momentarily reminded of
Gerald Finzi). Scherbakov sounds touched by it, and obviously wants us to like it. Indeed these are
likeable performances of music that needs that sort of help, but repays it. The recordings are more
than serviceable, but each work is given only a single track.
Additional recommendations ...
...Piano Concerto. Concerto in modo misolidio. **Geoffrey Tozer** (pf); **BBC Philharmonic Orchestra /
Sir Edward Downes.** Chandos Ⓕ CHAN9285 (65 minutes: DDD: 8/94).
...Toccata[a]. Tre corali. Fantasia slava[a]. Belfagor – overture. [a]**Geoffrey Tozer** (pf); **BBC Philharmonic
Orchestra / Sir Edward Downes.** Chandos Ⓕ CHAN9311 (60 minutes: DDD: 1/95).

Respighi Concerto gregoriano. Poema autunnale.
Saint-Saëns Violin Concerto No. 3 in B minor, Op. 61. **Pierre Amoyal** (vn); **French National
Orchestra / Charles Dutoit.** Decca Ⓕ 443 324-2DH (69 minutes: DDD: 7/95). Recorded 1993. ⓆⒶ
This is big, bold, romantic violin playing, just what both concertos need. The Respighi especially,
perhaps: he had recently discovered Gregorian chant and modality, and the *Concerto gregoriano* was
the first big work to exploit these. But Respighi was a violinist long before he discovered plainchant,
and the noun of the work's title is at least as important as its adjective. Moreover in numerous of his
compositions he shows himself well acquainted with Saint-Saëns, who also knew about chant and the
modes, as the 'third subject' of his Third Concerto's finale demonstrates. The two concertos make a
good coupling, in short, and an excellent demonstration that the manner appropriate to Saint-Saëns's
work, conceived for a great virtuoso (Sarasate), pays dividends in the Respighi as well. The *Concerto
gregoriano*'s problem is that its first two movements are both rhapsodic and relatively slow. A
performance that reticently takes the description 'Gregorian' too seriously risks differentiating them
inadeqately. "Quelques longeurs en ce Concerto?" asks the author of the French notes on this
coupling. Not in a performance as sumptuous as this, one which finds strength and drama in what
can seem dulcet meandering; and when the finale arrives and is given suitable vigour we seem to be
hearing another of Respighi's Roman pictures, a jubilant and richly coloured one. The Saint-Saëns is
just as good: Amoyal's tone is sweetly seductive in legato playing, opening out admirably to the more
flamboyant gestures, never becoming hectic in the virtuoso passages. That 'third subject' in the finale
is not played ethereally, as some violinists take it: Amoyal knows very well that its function is to return
triumphantly in the brass (Saint-Saëns might well have subtitled it, as Respighi did his finale,
"Alleluia") and he plays it firmly and brightly. Both Amoyal and Dutoit seem to be enjoying
Respighi's richly coloured, warmly elegaic *Poema autunnale*, discovering maybe that a work dutifully
chosen as an appropriate filler is perhaps the best music here. The recording manages both to place
Amoyal in a flatteringly forward perspective and to allow a satisfying fullness to orchestral tuttis.
Additional recommendations ...
...Concerto gregoriano[a]. Poema autunnale. Ballata delle gnomidi. [a]**Lydia Mordkovitch** (vn); **BBC
Philharmonic Orchestra / Sir Edward Downes.** Chandos Ⓕ CHAN9232 (64 minutes: DDD: 4/94).
...Concerto gregoriano. Concerto all'antica. **Andrea Cappelletti** (vn); **Philharmonia Orchestra /
Matthias Bamert.** Koch Schwann Ⓕ 311242 (63 minutes: DDD: 8/94).

Respighi Pines of Rome. Fountains of Rome. Roman Festivals. **Pittsburgh Symphony Orchestra /
Lorin Maazel.** Sony Classical Ⓕ SK66843 (64 minutes: DDD: 6/97). Recorded 1994-96.
Respighi Pines of Rome. Fountains of Rome. Roman Festivals. **Orchestra dell'Accademia di Santa
Cecilia / Daniele Gatti.** Conifer Classics Ⓕ 75605 51292-2 (66 minutes: DDD: 7/97).
Recorded 1996.

Respighi's three orchestral showpieces inspired by Rome have often been dismissed as merely musical
picture postcards, but in ripely committed performances like Maazel's, there are few works to match
them in showing off the glories of a modern orchestra in full cry. Maazel's is an exceptionally fine
recording. The orchestral sound is perfectly natural and perfectly believable; the acoustic is both
perceptible and credible; Respighi's textures are satisfyingly rich but always comprehensible;
instruments are in the right perspective, and when a solo line is prominent there is no sense that it has
been artificially spotlit or moved forward. Once you've got over the pleasurable relief of hearing such
a sound again, you notice of course what a splendid orchestra this is: in *Pines* alone, what wonderfully
velvety strings to evoke the shadows of the pines near a catacomb, what sensitive woodwind soloists
as companions to the nightingale (poetically distant but beautifully clear) on the moonlit Janiculum!
And then, trusting the balances as Maazel's own and not half-wondering whether your compliments
ought not to be awarded to the engineers, you enjoy not only the fine control of his big crescendos in
the second and fourth movements, but the fact that you don't have to fiddle with the volume controls
to appreciate both the quiet and the loud ends of those crescendos. Sony's booklet, artfully, is in
monochrome; the sound is not only in full colour but in three-dimensional relief. It is quite stunning.

The Conifer recording is Daniele Gatti's début as an orchestral conductor and it is an auspicious
one. Although Respighi's trilogy might not seem ideal repertory for the purpose, nor perhaps the
Santa Cecilia the ideal orchestra, both orchestra and repertoire have in fact been rather shrewdly
chosen. The recording documents the results of a five-year, obviously happy, relationship with the
orchestra and they play quite beautifully for him in music that they must know backwards – they gave
the first performances of *Pines* and *Fountains* and the European première of *Festivals*. The reputation
of these works as orchestral showpieces means that there are quite precise expectations of every
performance, but Gatti fulfils these expectations admirably but there are many signs that he has his
own ideas about this music, and they are convincing as well as refreshing. "The fountain of Valle
Giulia at dawn", for example, is slower than usual, making for an attractively gentle pastoral. The
breathless hush at the end of "The Medici fountain at sunset" is very beautiful, too, and in the pitfall-
ridden "Pines of the Janiculum" pretty well everything is right: the appearance of the recorded
nightingale magically timed and placed, against a softly warm string background (but with ardent
solo playing), the rubato and phrasing finely judged, the piano and clarinet poetically evoking
moonlight. At the other end of the dynamic spectrum there is a huge and satisfying crescendo to
conclude "Epiphany" (No. 4 of *Festivals*) and a magnificent blare of extra brass at the end of "Pines
of the Appian Way". The recording is also first-class: realistically spacious and atmospheric, with a
huge dynamic range.

Additional recommendations ...

...Pines of Rome. Fountains of Rome. Roman Festivals. **Philadelphia Orchestra / Riccardo Muti.**
EMI Ⓕ CDC7 47316-2 (3/86). Ⓖ

...Pines of Rome. Fountains of Rome. Roman Festivals. **NBC Symphony Orchestra /
Arturo Toscanini.** RCA Victor Gold Seal mono Ⓜ GD60262* (60 minutes: ADD: 1/91). Ⓖ

...Pines of Rome. Fountains of Rome. Roman Festivals. **Philadelphia Orchestra / Eugene Ormandy.**
RCA Victor Silver Seal Ⓑ VD60486 (62 minutes: ADD: 2/91).

...Pines of Rome. Fountains of Rome. Roman Festivals. **Academy of St Martin in the Fields /
Sir Neville Marriner.** Philips Ⓕ 432 133-2PH (64 minutes: DDD: 4/92).

...Pines of Rome; Fountains of Rome; Roman Festivals. **Royal Philharmonic Orchestra /
Enrique Bátiz.** Naxos Ⓢ 8 550539 (61 minutes: DDD: 8/92).

...Pines of Rome. Fountains of Rome. Roman Festivals. **Mussorgsky** Pictures at an Exhibition. **Chicago Symphony
Orchestra / Fritz Reiner.** RCA Victor Ⓑ 09026 61401-2* (70 minutes: ADD: 8/93).   ⒼⒼ

...Pines of Rome. Fountains of Rome. Roman Festivals. **Montreal Symphony Orchestra /
Charles Dutoit.** Decca Ovation Ⓜ 430 729-2DM (60 minutes: DDD: 8/94).

...Fountains of Rome. *Coupled with works by various composers.*
Santa Cecilia Academy Orchestra, Rome / Victor de Sabata.
EMI Références mono Ⓜ CHS5 65506-2* (two discs: 148 minutes: ADD: 9/95).

...Pines of Rome. Fountains of Rome. **Debussy** La mer. **Chicago Symphony Orchestra /
Fritz Reiner.** RCA Victor Living Stereo Ⓜ 09026 68079-2 (62 minutes: ADD: 9/95).

...Pines of Rome[a]. Fountains of Rome[a]. Gli uccelli[b]. Trittico botticelliano[b]. Antiche danze ed arie
per liuto[c]. Belfagor – overture[a]. [a]**London Symphony Orchestra / Lamberto Gardelli;**
[b]**Academy of St Martin in the Fields,** [c]**Los Angeles Chamber Orchestra / Sir Neville Marriner.**
EMI Forte Ⓜ CZS5 69358-2 (two discs: 135 minutes: ADD: 2/97).

...Pines of Rome. Fountains of Rome. Roman Festivals. **Oslo Philharmonic Orchestra /
Mariss Jansons.** EMI Ⓕ CDC5 55600-2 (65 minutes: DDD: 3/97).

...Fountains of Rome. **Debussy** La mer. Jeux. Nocturnes – Nuages; Fêtes.
Orchestra of the Santa Cecilia Academy, Rome / Victor de Sabata.
Testament mono Ⓕ SBT1108* (70 minutes: ADD: 4/98).

Respighi Church Windows. Brazilian Impressions. Roman Festivals. **Cincinnati Symphony Orchestra / Jesús López-Cobos.** Telarc Ⓕ CD80356 (71 minutes: DDD: 7/94). Recorded 1993.
Gramophone Editor's choice.
One could easily argue that neither *Church Windows* nor *Brazilian Impressions* is quite as successful as the 'essential' Respighi of *Pines, Fountains* and *Festivals* (and that *Festivals* is the weakest of the Roman trilogy anyway). The only answer to that, López-Cobos seems to suggest, is to take the music perfectly seriously and pay scrupulous attention not just to its potential for sonorous spectacle but to its wealth of beautifully crafted detail. The gong at the end of the second movement of *Church Windows* is magnificently resonant, as is the organ in the finale, and the work is given an extra inch or two of stature by sensitive handling of those moments that need but don't always get delicacy. He pays such care to character and detail in "Butantan", that creepy depiction of a snake-farm in *Brazilian Impressions*, that you can not only recapture the real, crawling horror that Respighi experienced there, but discover in the music also a queer sort of Debussian grace as well. And as for *Roman Festivals*, well, what's wrong with 20-odd minutes of wide-screen spectacular once in a while? But if every colour is precisely rendered, the quiet passages as affectionately turned as they are here, what skill there is to be found in it, what a gift for immaculately precise instrumental detail. With that sort of handling all three pieces sound quite worthy of sharing shelf space with *Pines* and *Fountains*. The recording is spectacular.
Additional recommendation ...
...Church Windows. Brazilian Impressions. **Philharmonia Orchestra / Geoffrey Simon.**
Chandos Ⓕ CHAN8317 (45 minutes: DDD: 8/84).

Respighi Gli uccelli. Antiche danze ed arie per liuto – Suites Nos. 1 and 3. Trittico botticelliano.
Orpheus Chamber Orchestra. DG Ⓕ 437 533-2GH (69 minutes: DDD: 7/93).
Recorded 1991. ⒼⒼⒼ
This is astonishing playing. To do without a conductor when performing Respighi might seem an easier task than in an authentic masterpiece, but these suites require so much care over details of phrasing, colour, balance and articulation that not a few skilled conductors have failed to distil their freshness and charm unalloyed. But there are no conducted performances that excel these in their immaculate care over texture, delicacy of nuance and precision of tuning. Nor do they lack character, by any means: the orchestra's method of rehearsal, democracy tempered by the authority of a leader elected for each work, seems to have ensured a pretty well ideal balance between unanimity and soloistic individuality. If you add an infectious sense of enjoyment (the not quite respectable enjoyment of Respighi's hand-colouring of his monochrome originals) and solo playing of great refinement, it becomes hard to imagine how these readings could be improved on. Excellent recording.
Additional recommendations ...
...Gli uccelli. Antiche danze ed arie per liuto – Suites Nos. 1 and 3. Trittico botticelliano.
Saint Paul Chamber Orchestra / Hugh Wolff. Teldec Ⓕ 4509-91729-2 (70 minutes: DDD: 1/95). Ⓖ
...Ballata delle gnomidi. Adagio con variazioni[a]. Trittico botticelliano. Suite in G major for Strings and Organ[b]. [a]**Alexander Baillie** (vc); [b]**Leslie Pearson** (org); **Philharmonia Orchestra / Geoffrey Simon.** Cala Ⓕ CACD1007 (69 minutes: DDD: 3/93).
...Antiche danze ed arie per liuto. Aria. Berceuse. **Sinfonia 21 / Richard Hickox.**
Chandos Ⓕ CHAN9415 (63 minutes: DDD: 2/96).

Respighi Cinque canti all'antica. Sei liriche. Deità silvane. Ballata alla luna. Stornello.
Stornellatrice. Contrasto. Tanto bella. Invito alla danza. L'ultima ebbrezza. Notturno. Luce.
Leonardo de Lisi (ten); **Reinild Mees** (pf). Channel Classics Ⓕ CCS9396 (60 minutes: DDD: 9/97).
Texts and translations included. Recorded 1996.
Leonardo de Lisi is a discovery, a lyric tenor of real quality with a Lieder singer's subtlety, taste and responsiveness to words. In fact by the colour of the voice you might not take him to be an Italian and his French diction is almost impeccable in the two settings by Respighi (among the *Sei liriche*) of French texts, the quite magical "Le repos en Egypte" and the striking "Noël ancien". If you have not so far thought of Respighi as a song composer you are in for a surprise. Sopranos quite often programme his charming *Stornellatrice* as an encore but it has equals and indeed superiors here. *Tanto bella*, for example: ample grateful melody over a lilting accompaniment, with a haunting middle section. The *Canti all'antica* are fresh and very simple, sometimes rather like a Monteverdian *arioso*. But with the *Sei liriche* of 1912 we reach audible French influence as well as French texts and by 1917 and *Deità silvane* Respighi's smooth lines have become flexible and his idiomatic keyboard writing is now filled with vivid imagery. Reinild Mees is obviously as fond of *Deità silvane* as de Lisi is. Both are excellently recorded, the voice a little close but not disturbingly so.
Additional recommendations ...
...Notturno. Storia breve. Tanto bella. Lagrime. L'ultima ebbrezza. Luce. *Coupled with works by various composers.* **Rebecca Evans** (sop); **Michael Pollock** (pf).
EMI Debut Ⓑ CDZ5 69706-2 (69 minutes: DDD: 5/97).
...Nebbie. *Coupled with works by various composers.* **Angela Gheorghiu** (sop); **Malcolm Martineau** (pf). Decca Ⓕ 458 360-2DH (75 minutes: DDD: 5/98). *See review in the Collections section; refer to the Index.*

Respighi Deità silvane[a]. Nebbie[b]. Aretusa[b]. La sensitiva[b]. [a]**Ingrid Attrot** (sop); [b]**Linda Finnie** (mez); **BBC Philharmonic Orchestra / Richard Hickox.** Chandos Ⓕ CHAN9453 (60 minutes: DDD: 11/96). Texts and translations included. Recorded 1995.

In some of Respighi's comparatively neglected pieces, his accustomed richness and subtlety of orchestral colour go with a certain lack of melodic individuality. Once or twice in *Deità silvane* ("Woodland gods"), for example, one wishes that the poems' classical imagery would lead him towards an evocation or even a direct quotation from Italian music's 'classical' past of the kind that so often renders his better-known music so memorable. In *La sensitiva* ("The sensitive plant"), however, his care for the imagery and especially the prosody of Shelley's poem (in Italian translation) was so responsive that really striking melodic invention was the result. The orchestral colour of the piece is exquisite, the succession of ideas (the sensitive plant is image both of unhappy lover and spurned artist) a good deal more than merely picturesque. In a performance as expressive as this it seems one of Respighi's best works, and a good deal more sophisticated than he is generally given credit for. *Aretusa* is fine, too, with bigger dramatic gestures, even richer colour and some magnificent sea music. The much better-known *Nebbie* ("Mists"; though seldom heard in its rich orchestral dress) is another example of Respighi finding a genuinely sustained melodic line in response to a text which obviously meant a great deal to him. Everything here is played with a real care for Respighi's line as well as his sumptuous but never muddy colours. The recording is first-class.

Respighi Aretusa[a]. Il tramonto[a]. Lauda per la natività del Signore[b]. Trittico botticelliano. [b]**Patricia Rozario** (sop); [a]**Dame Janet Baker**, [b]**Louise Winter** (mezzos); [b]**Lynton Atkinson** (ten); [b]**Richard Hickox Singers; City of London Sinfonia / Richard Hickox.** Collins Classics Ⓕ 1349-2 (72 minutes: DDD: 9/92). Texts and translations included. Recorded 1991.

Aretusa and *Il tramonto* are set to translations of poems by Shelley: colourful works with a wide range of expression, stimulating just that kind of boldness and generosity of utterance in which Dame Janet is expert. She is in fine voice here, and at the end of *Il tramonto* ("The tomb of the dead self") her tone is stern, strong and dark, intensely personal. Even so, coming to the disc initially for these tone-poems for solo voice and orchestra, one may eventually be most glad of the purchase for its introduction to the choral *Lauda per la natività del Signore.* This is a most lovely work. It has solo parts for Mary, the Angel and a shepherd (all well taken), but the great joy lies in the choral and orchestral writing, rich and imaginative, showing evident delight in the medievalism. The better-known *Trittico botticelliano* is very enjoyable too, and all are fine in performance and recorded sound.

Additional recommendations ...

...Il tramonto[a]. **Martucci** Canzone dei Ricordi[a]. Nocturne, Op. 70 No. 1.
[a]**Carol Madalin** (mez); **English Chamber Orchestra / Alfredo Bonavera.**
Hyperion Ⓕ CDA66290 (56 minutes: DDD: 7/88).
...Poema autunnale[a]. Suite in G major[b]. Il tramonto[c]. **Menotti** Cantilena e scherzo[d].
[c]**Christopher Trakas** (bar); [a]**Igor Gruppman** (vn); [b]**Hollace C. Koman** (org); [d]**Marian Rian Hays** (hp); [c]**Quartetto di Venezia;** [abd]**San Diego Chamber Orchestra / Donald Barra.**
Koch International Classics Ⓕ 37215-2 (63 minutes: DDD: 8/94).

Further listening ...

...Adagio con variazioni. *Coupled with works by* **Elgar** and **Milhaud** Mstislav Rostropovich (vc); **Moscow Philharmonic Orchestra / Gennadi Rozhdestvensky.** Russian Disc RDCD11104 (7/94).
...Belkis, Queen of Sheba – orchestral suite. Metamorphosen modi XII.
Philharmonia Orchestra / Geoffrey Simon. Chandos CHAN8405 (5/86).   Ⓖ
...Sinfonia drammatica. **BBC Philharmonic Orchestra / Sir Edward Downes.**
Chandos CHAN9213 (1/94).   Ⓖ
...Violin Sonata. *Coupled with works by* **Franck** and **Poulenc** Josef Suk (vn); Josef Hála (pf).
Supraphon 11 0710-2 (5/90).
...La primavera[a]. Quattro Liriche su poesie popolari armene[ab]. [ab]**Soloists;** [a]**Slovak Philharmonic Chorus;** [a]**Bratislava Radio Symphony Orchestra /** [ab]**Adriano.** Marco Polo 8 223595 (5/95).
...La bella dormente nel bosco. **Soloists; Slovak Philharmonic Chorus; Slovak Radio Symphony Orchestra (Bratislava) / Adriano.** Marco Polo 8 223742 (7/96).
...Semirama. **Soloists; Hungarian Radio and Television Chorus; Hungarian State Orchestra / Lamberto Gardelli.** Hungaroton HCD31197/8 (7/93).

Julius Reubke   German 1834-1858

Reubke Piano Sonata in B flat minor.
Schumann Kreisleriana, Op. 16. **Till Fellner** (pf). Erato Ⓕ 0630-12710-2
(63 minutes: DDD: 10/96). Recorded 1996.   Ⓖ

Reubke's B flat minor Piano Sonata was completed just before his untimely death at 24 and here Till Fellner's performance has outstanding imaginative sympathy and pianistic command. The prime inspirational source for his expansive, thematically metamorphosed and interlinked three-movement work was undoubtedly Liszt's B minor Sonata, not only in form but in so much of its general style of keyboard expression and its emotional questings and conflicts. Not a note played here sounds second-hand. One is lost in admiration at the concentrated intensity Fellner brings to arresting challenges, soul-searching recitative, spiritual repose and majestic grandeur. For the triumphant home-coming he draws a near organ-like fullness and depth of sonority from his instrument. "A positively wild love is in some of the movements, and your life and mine, and the way you look." So Schumann wrote to Clara about *Kreisleriana*, dashed off in a mere four days during their enforced separation. Here there is not quite the same immediacy or urgency of response as in the Reubke Sonata. Perhaps Fellner is more closely attuned to the visionary Eusebius than the impulsive Florestan. The two dreams of Clara (Nos. 4 and 6) are questionably slow here. That said, it is a deeply thoughtful, poetic performance, carried out with exemplary keyboard refinement and tonal beauty.

Further listening ...

...Sonata on the 94th Psalm in C minor. *Coupled with* **Schumann** Six Fugues on B-A-C-H, Op. 60. **Kevin Bowyer** (org). Nimbus NI5361 (2/94).

...Sonata on the 94th Psalm in C minor. *Coupled with works by various composers.* **Christopher Herrick** (org). Hyperion Ⓕ CDA66917 (70 minutes: DDD: 8/97). *See review in the Collections section; refer to the Index.*

Herman Reutter
German 1900-1985

Suggested listening ...

...Fünf antike Oden, Op. 57. *Coupled with works by various composers.* **Mitsuko Shirai** (mez); **Tabea Zimmermann** (va); **Hartmut Höll** (pf). Capriccio 10 462 (9/95). *See review in the Collections section; refer to the Index.* Ⓖ

Emil Rezniček
Austrian 1860-1945

Suggested listening ...

...String Quartet No. 1 in C sharp minor. *Coupled with* **Korngold** String Quartet No. 1 in A major, Op. 16. **Franz Schubert Quartet.** Nimbus NI5506 (1/98). *See review under Korngold; refer to the Index.*

Johannes Rezon
French 15th century

Suggested listening ...

...Il est temps que je me retraye. *Coupled with works by various composers.* **Hilliard Ensemble.** Isis CD030 (7/97). *See review in the Collections section; refer to the Index.*

Alan Ridout
British 1934-1996

Suggested listening ...

...Litany. *Coupled with works by various composers.* **Andrew Angus** (bass); **Vasari Singers / Jeremy Backhouse.** EMI Eminence CD-EMX2251 (8/96). *See review in the Collections section; refer to the Index.*

Wolfgang Rihm
German 1952

Suggested listening ...

...Gesungene Zeit. *Coupled with* **Berg** Violin Concerto. **Anne-Sophie Mutter** (vn); **Chicago Symphony Orchestra / James Levine.** DG 437 093-2GH (1/93). *Selected by Sounds in Retrospect. See review under Berg; refer to the Index.* ⒼⒼ

...Kolchis[a]. Antlitz[b]. Klavierstück No. 6, "Bagatellen"[c]. Von weit[d]. Dritte Musik[e]. [e]**Gottfried Schneider** (vn); [a]**Frank Reinecke** (db); [a]**Sarah O'Brien** (harp); [abcd]**Ensemble Recherche;** [e]**South West German Radio Symphony Orchestra / Michael Gielen.** Wergo Ⓕ WER6623-2 (63 minutes: DDD: 5/98).

Knudage Riisager
Danish 1897-1974

Suggested listening ...

...Etudes – ballet. Qarrtsiluni, Op. 36. Erasmus Montanus, Op. 1. **Danish National Radio Symphony Orchestra / Gennadi Rozhdestvensky.** Chandos CHAN9432 (7/97).

...Mother Denmark. *Coupled with works by various composers.* **Aksel Schiøtz** (ten) with various artists. Danacord mono DACOCD454* (5/97). *See review in the Collections section; refer to the Index.*

Nicolay Rimsky-Korsakov   Russian 1844-1908

Rimsky-Korsakov Scheherazade, Op. 35. Capriccio espagnol, Op. 34. **London Symphony Orchestra / Sir Charles Mackerras.** Telarc Ⓕ CD80208 (60 minutes: DDD: 10/90). Recorded 1990.

Rimsky-Korsakov Scheherazade, Op. 35[a]. Capriccio espagnol, Op. 34[b]. Russian Easter Festival Overture, Op. 36[b]. [a]**Herman Krebbers** (vn); [ac]**Concertgebouw Orchestra / **[a]**Kyrill Kondrashin;** [b]**London Symphony Orchestra / **[bc]**Igor Markevitch.** Philips Solo Ⓜ 442 643-2PM (74 minutes: ADD: 6/95). Item marked [a] recorded 1980, [b]1963, [c]1965.   ⒼⒼ

Sir Charles Mackerras throws himself into this music with expressive abandon, but allies it to control so that every effect is realized and the London Symphony Orchestra play these familiar works as if they were discovering them afresh. Together they produce performances that are both vivid and thoughtful, while the solo violin in *Scheherazade*, who represents the young queen whose storytelling skills prolong and finally save her life in the court of the cruel Sultan Shahriar (portrayed by powerful brass), is seductively and elegantly played by Kees Hulsmann, not least at the wonderfully peaceful end to the whole work. The finale featuring a storm and shipwreck is superbly done, the wind and brass bringing one to the edge of one's seat and reminding us that Rimsky-Korsakov served in the Russian Navy and well knew the beauty and danger of the sea. This sensuous and thrilling work needs spectacular yet detailed sound, and that is what it gets here, the 1990 recording in Walthamstow Town Hall being highly successful and giving us a CD that many collectors will choose to use as a demonstration disc to impress their friends. The performance and recording of the *Capriccio espagnol* is no less of a success, and this issue is worth every penny of its price.

Kondrashin's performance of *Scheherazade* is one of the very finest made of Russian music in the Concertgebouw; it has glamour and brilliance, and the resonance brings a wonderful feeling of spaciousness in the first movement and adds a thrill to the spectacle of the finale. Kondrashin has the full measure of this colourful score, while the finale builds up to a feeling of excitement which leads to a riveting climax at "The Shipwreck". Of course, any performance of this masterpiece stands or falls by the portrayal of Scheherazade herself by the solo violin, and here the Concertgebouw's leader, Herman Krebbers dominates the action from the gentle, beguiling opening to his exquisite closing solo, suggesting that all is well at last between the Sultan and his bewitching Sultana. A brilliant performance of Rimsky's *Capriccio espagnole* follows, very well played by the LSO under Igor Markevitch; indeed, the 1963 recording sounds far more lustrous than it did on LP. It is upstaged, however, by Markevitch's performance of the composer's *Russian Easter Festival Overture*, made two years later, when again the aura of the Concertgebouw ambience adds a glow to more remarkable playing from this great orchestra. Altogether a superb disc, and generously full.

Additional recommendations ...

...Scheherazade. **Debussy** La mer. **Chicago Symphony Orchestra / Fritz Reiner.** RCA Victor Gold Seal Ⓜ GD60875* (69 minutes: ADD).   ⒼⒼ

...Scheherazade. **Borodin** Prince Igor – Polovtsian Dances[a]. [a]**Beecham Choral Society; Royal Philharmonic Orchestra / Sir Thomas Beecham.** EMI Ⓕ CDC7 47717-2* (58 minutes: ADD: 9/87).   ⒼⒼ

...Scheherazade. **Prokofiev** Lieutenant Kijé – Suite, Op. 60. **London Philharmonic Orchestra / Takuo Yuasa.** EMI Eminence Ⓜ CD-EMX2214 (68 minutes: DDD: 12/93).

...Scheherazade. Russian Easter Festival Overture, Op. 36. **Vienna Philharmonic Orchestra / Seiji Ozawa.** Philips Ⓕ 438 941-2PH (58 minutes: DDD: 6/94).

...Scheherazade. The tale of Tsar Saltan, Op. 57 – Tsar's farewell and departure; Tsarina in a barrel at sea; The three wonders. **Philharmonia Orchestra / Enrique Bátiz.** Naxos Ⓢ 8 550726 (61 minutes: DDD: 6/94).

...Scheherazade. **Stravinsky** Scherzo fantastique, Op. 3. **Royal Concertgebouw Orchestra / Riccardo Chailly.** Decca Ⓕ 443 703-2DH (59 minutes: DDD: 10/94).   Ⓖ

...Scheherazade[a]. **Prokofiev** Romeo and Juliet[b]. [a]**Berlin Radio Symphony Orchestra,** [b]**Leipzig Gewandhaus Orchestra / Karel Ančerl.** Tahra mono Ⓕ TAH119* (68 minutes: DDD: 11/95).

Rimsky-Korsakov Scheherazade, Op. 35. Capriccio espagnol, Op. 34. **London Philharmonic Orchestra / Mariss Jansons.** EMI Ⓕ CDC5 55227-2 (62 minutes: DDD: 7/95).   Ⓖ

The first point to distinguish this powerful coupling of *Scheherazade* and *Capriccio espagnol*, from Jansons and the LPO, is the weight and richness of the recording. It has got to be one of EMI's finest, not as analytically transparent as some but vivid and immediate with a thrillingly wide dynamic range. Not that detail is lacking: it is fascinating to register the castanets very clearly at the end of the final "Fandango" of the *Capriccio*, normally obscured in the general hubbub. As to Jansons's interpretation of the main work, he follows up the big bold, brassy opening with a surprisingly restrained account of the main theme as it develops, keeping power in reserve, building up more slowly than usual. What then is consistently striking in all four movements is Jansons's pointing of rhythm, lilting, bouncy and affectionate in a way that distinguishes this from most other versions. This is a *Scheherazade* that dances winningly, less earnest than usual, often suggesting a smile on the face. That is very welcome in a work that, for all its exotic colour and memorable themes, needs persuasive handling if it is not to seem like a lot of introductions leading to introductions, and codas leading to codas, with little meat in the middle. Jansons's control of structure leads to a masterly sense of resolution at the great climax towards the end of the finale, as the main theme returns *fortissimo*. Nowhere does this seem like a virtuoso exercise, brilliant as the playing of the LPO is, not least that of the warmly expressive violin soloist, Joakim Svenheden. Rather, emotionally involved, Jansons finds a rare exuberance in Rimsky-Korsakov's stream of ideas and colours, leading compellingly from one to another. The *Capriccio espagnol* brings a similar combination of expressive warmth and exuberance. In the brilliant "Alborada" at the beginning of the *Capriccio* Jansons's speed is less hectic than some, and with springy rhythms it is made to sound relaxed, jolly rather than fierce. Not that in either work is there any shortage of biting excitement. Particularly in *Scheherazade* choice between versions leaves many options open, but this warmly distinctive account with its opulent sound clearly stands among the strongest contenders.

Rimsky-Korsakov Symphonies – No. 1 in E minor, Op. 1; No. 2 (Symphonic Suite), Op. 9, "Antar"; No. 3 in C major, Op. 32. Russian Easter Festival Overture, Op. 36. Capriccio espagnol, Op. 34. **Gothenburg Symphony Orchestra / Neeme Järvi.** DG ⓕ 423 604-2GH2 (two discs: 125 minutes: DDD: 2/89).   ⓖⓖ

No one is going to claim Rimsky's First and Third Symphonies to be neglected masterpieces. He came to refer to his First (partly written whilst the young naval officer was on duty!) as a "disgraceful composition", and along with the other two symphonies, it was subjected to extensive revision by the later learned master of musical technique. As the equally learned, entertaining and informative essay accompanying this set points out, the opening of the symphony could have been a trial run for the opening of Schumann's Fourth (and a very fine one, too!). It's the beautifully lyrical second theme which reminds us that Rimsky was reared in the country and had the early advantage of a good soaking in folk-song. Though the debt to Glinka is obvious, to our ears classical concerns seem uppermost throughout, and the music is free from anything that could be called exoticism. Not so the Second. Rimsky was a member of the 'Mighty Five', a group of composers (including Mussorgsky, Balakirev and Borodin) sworn to the nationalist cause, professing horror at anything tinged with German academicism and ever searching for subjects on which they could lavish a preference for orchestral colour above form. Rimsky's *Antar* combined these ideals, and more. Our hero of the title is allocated a Berliozian *idée fixe*, an oriental location (the desert of Sham) and the joys of vengeance, power and love from the grateful fairy Gul-Nazar as a gift for saving her from a winged monster. It is, in every way, an antecedent of *Sheherazade* and, after hearing Järvi's rich and eloquently descriptive account, one wonders why it has never attained anything like the same popularity. His Third Symphony reverts to a more academic manner. In 1871 he was invited to join the theory and composition faculty at the St Petersburg Conservatory and, in Tchaikovsky's words, "from contempt of schooling he had turned all at once to the cult of musical technique". Despite a paucity of truly memorable ideas, it is a symphony to admire for its construction and light-as-air orchestration. The set is completed with urgent, vibrant accounts of the *Capriccio espagnol* and the *Russian Easter Festival Overture*, quite the most colourful and exciting versions on disc, and they confirm that the less familiar symphonies could not be in better hands. DG's engineers resist the temptation to glamorize the music and offer a lucid and spacious panorama of sound.

Additional recommendations ...

...Russian Easter Festival Overture. Capriccio espagnol. *Coupled with works by* **Borodin** and **Tchaikovsky** Gothenburg Symphony Orchestra / Neeme Järvi. DG ⓕ 429 984-2GH (76 minutes: DDD: 3/91).

...Russian Easter Festival Overture. *Coupled with works by various composers.* **Baltimore Symphony Orchestra / David Zinman.** Telarc ⓕ CD80378 (69 minutes: DDD: 12/95).

...Nos. 1 and 2. Capriccio espagnole, Op. 34. **Bergen Philharmonic Orchestra / Dmitri Kitaienko.** Chandos CHAN9178 (11/93).

...Nos. 1 and 2. **Russian State Symphony Orchestra / Evgeni Svetlanov.** RCA Victor Red Seal ⓕ 09026 62558-2 (67 minutes: DDD: 11/94).

Rimsky-Korsakov Symphony No. 3 in C major, Op. 32. Sadko, Op. 5. Mlada – Procession of the Nobles. The Maid of Pskov – Overture. The Tale of Tsar Saltan – The three wonders. The Tsar's Bride – Overture. **Russian State Symphony Orchestra / Evgeni Svetlanov.** RCA Victor Red Seal ⓕ 09026 62684-2 (76 minutes: DDD: 10/95). Recorded 1993.

Borodin and Tchaikovsky were both hostile to Rimsky-Korsakov's Third Symphony when they heard it in its first version, but not as critical as the composer himself. What we have here is its third and final revision, purged of the excesses of technique that, he wrote in his memoirs, made it all too dry. In this version, which has had several recordings, it is enjoyable less as the solemn exercise to which Borodin objected than as a piece of vivid orchestral writing with some attractive ideas guiding it. It therefore fits easily into a programme of Korsakov orchestral show-pieces, of which the most substantial is the musical picture *Sadko*. Svetlanov is an old hand with this music, and he draws properly colourful performances from the orchestra, clearly and brightly recorded. Serious collectors of Rimsky-Korsakov's symphonies will no doubt have acquired the fine set by Neeme Järvi with the Gothenburg Symphony Orchestra on DG (reviewed above). For those following Svetlanov's series or for what might be called a Rimsky-Korsakov taster, even if not of his best music, the present disc is very acceptable.

Rimsky-Korsakov Sadko. **Vladimir Galusin** (ten) Sadko; **Valentina Tsidipova** (sop) Volkhova;
Sergei Alexashkin (bass) Okean-More; **Marianna Tarassova** (mez) Lyubava Buslayevna;
Larissa Diadkova (contr) Nezhata; **Bulat Minjelkiev** (bass) Viking Merchant; **Gegam Grigorian**
(ten) Indian Merchant; **Alexander Gergalov** (bar) Venetian Merchant; **Vladimir Ognovenko** (bass)
Duda; **Nikolai Gassiev** (ten) Sopel; **Nikolai Putilin** (bar) Apparition; **Yevgeny Boitsov** (ten) Foma
Nazarich; **Gennadi Bezzubenkov** (bass) Luka Zinovich; **Kirov Opera Orchestra / Valery Gergiev.**
Philips Ⓟ 442 138-2PH3 (three discs: 173 minutes: DDD: 1/95). Notes, text and translation
included. Recorded live in 1993.   Ⓖ

Rimsky-Korsakov's operas are not so well represented in the catalogue that one can afford to give
anything but a welcome to this complete version from the Maryinsky company, for all its drawbacks.
Sadko is a panoramic work, packed with numbers, rather less packed with event or with character.
The various characters delivering themselves of a song or a ballad or an address are reasonably well
contrasted, partly because of Rimsky-Korsakov's skills in drawing on different Russian influences
and in differentiating between a simple tonal language for the real world and a more chromatic idiom
for the seductive realm of the Sea King (Okean-More) and his daughter Volkhova. It needs a
numerous and strong cast who can make the most of its opportunities. Sadko himself is sung by
Vladimir Galusin pretty steadily at full volume. He settles down a little as the opera proceeds, and by
Act 3 is finding a somewhat more pacific manner. Valentina Tsidipova returns his advances, and
makes her own, with a good feeling for line, if one can overcome resistance to the steady vibrato. The
Sea King is strongly sung by Sergei Alexashkin, truculent at first but warming his tone somewhat as
he comes to accept Sadko. But it is a pity that the best-known number from the opera, the song of the
Indian Merchant, should be sung as half-heartedly as it is by Gegam Grigorian. Valery Gergiev leads
his forces well, and draws some vigorous, colourful singing from the choruses in their various
manifestations. There is, however, a good deal of noise occasioned by the many stage comings and
goings, with clumpings and hoarse whisperings as well as tunings-up and applause. The recording has
difficulty in catching all the singers equally in their various peregrinations across the stage, but for the
most part this is a fair representation of a score that is nothing if not colourful.

Further listening ...
...May Night – Overture. Orchestral Suites – Snow Maiden; Christmas Eve; Mlada; Invisible City
of Kitezh; The Golden Cockerel. The Tale of Tsar Saltan. **Royal Scottish Orchestra /**
Neeme Järvi. Chandos CHAN8327/9.   Ⓖ
...Orchestral Suites – The Golden Cockerel; The Tale of Tsar Saltan; Christmas Eve.
Armenian Philharmonic Orchestra / Loris Tjeknavorian. ASV CDDCA772 (9/92).   Ⓖ
...Piano Concerto in C sharp minor, Op. 30. *Coupled with works by* **Balakirev**
Malcolm Binns (pf); **English Northern Philharmonia / David Lloyd-Jones.**
Hyperion CDA66640 (7/93). *See review under Balakirev; refer to the Index.*   ⒼⒼ
...Piano Concerto in C sharp minor, Op. 30. *Coupled with works by* **Glazunov** and **Prokofiev**
Sviatoslav Richter (pf). **Moscow Youth Orchestra / Kyrill Kondrashin.**
Melodiya mono 74321 29468-2* (6/96).
...(arr. Kreisler) The Golden Cockerel – Hymn to the Sun. *Coupled with works by various composers.*
Kennedy (vn); **John Lenehan** (pf). EMI CDC5 56626-2 (5/98). *See review in the Collections section;*
refer to the Index.
...Piano Quintet in B flat major. *Coupled with* **Glinka** Grand Sextet in E flat major. **Capricorn.**
Hyperion CDA66163 (12/86).   Ⓖ
...The tale of Tsar Saltan – Flight of the bumble-bee (arr. Cziffra). *Coupled with works by various*
composers. **Arcadi Volodos** (pf). Sony Classical SK62691 (10/97). *Gramophone Editor's choice.*
Selected by Soundings. See review in the Collections section; refer to the Index.   ⒼⒼ
...(arr. Rachmaninov) The tale of Tsar Saltan – Flight of the bumble-bee. *Coupled with works by*
various composers. **Vladimir Horowitz** (pf).
APR mono APR5517* (5/98). *See review in the Collections section; refer to the Index.*
...May Night – Hey there! Boys!a; How calm, how cool is it here. Sadko – Song of the Indian guest.
Coupled with works by various composers.
Sergei Larin (ten); **Philharmonia Orchestra / Gennadi Rozhdestvensky.**
Chandos CHAN9603 (5/98). *See review in the Collections section; refer to the Index.*
...The octave, Op. 45 No. 3. The clouds begin to scatter, Op. 42 No. 3. Of what I dream in the quiet
sky, Op. 40 No. 3. Enslaved by the rose, the nightingale, Op. 2 No. 2. In spring, Op. 43 – No. 1,
The lark sings louder; No. 2, Not the wind, blowing from the heights. *Coupled with works by*
various composers. **Olga Borodina** (mez); **Larissa Gergieva** (pf). Philips 442 780-2PH (8/95).
...Songs: Op. 43 – No. 1, The lark sings louder; No. 2, Not the wind, blowing from the heights.
The octave, Op. 45 No. 3. The nymph, Op. 56 No. 1. The clouds begin to scatter, Op. 42 No. 3.
On the hills of Georgia, Op. 3 No. 4. Of what I dream in the quiet sky, Op. 40 No. 3. Enslaved
by the rose, the nightingale, Op. 2 No. 2. Silence descends on the golden cornfields, Op. 39
No. 3. Withered flower, Op. 51 No. 3. *Coupled with works by various composers.*
Sergei Larin (ten); **Eleonora Bekova** (pf). Chandos CHAN9547 (6/97). *See review in the*
Collections section; refer to the Index.
...The Maid of Pskov. **Soloists; Chorus and Orchestra of the Kirov Opera / Valery Gergiev.**
Philips 446 678-2PH2 (11/97).

...Mozart and Salieri. **Soloists; Bolshoi Theatre Orchestra / Mark Ermler.** *Coupled with*
Mussorgsky The Marriage (orch. Rozhdestvensky). **Soloists; USSR Ministry of Culture**
Symphony Orchestra / Gennadi Rozhdestvensky. Olympia OCD145 (9/93).
...Sadko – The paragon of cities; Beautiful city! Kashchey the Immortal – In this, night's darkest
hour. Snow Maiden (second version) – Under the warm blue sea. The Tsar's Bride – Still the
beauty haunts my mind. *Coupled with works by various composers.*
Dmitri Hvorostovsky (bar); **Kirov Theatre Orchestra / Valery Gergiev.**
Philips 438 872-2PH (5/94). *See review in the Collections section; refer to the Index.*
...Snow Maiden – Love duet. *Coupled with works by various composers.* **Inessa Galante** (sop);
Samsons Izjumovs (bar); **Latvian National Opera Orchestra / Alexander Vilumanis.**
Campion RRCD1344 (A/97). *See review in the Collections section; refer to the Index.*
...The Tsar's Bride. **Soloists; Sveshnikov Russian Academy Choir; Bolshoi Theatre Orchestra /**
Andrey Tchistiakov. CdM Russian Season LDC288 056/7 (8/93).
...The Tsar's Bride – Thoughts of the beautiful girl[b]; What do you want? ... It seems that you no
longer love your Lyubasha; This is what life has come to[a]. *Coupled with works by various*
composers. [a]**Olga Borodina** (mez); [b]**Dmitri Hvorostovsky** (bar);
English Chamber Orchestra / Patrick Summers.
Philips 454 439-2PH (6/98). *See review in the Collections section; refer to the Index.*

Martin de Rivafrecha
Spanish d 1528

Suggested listening ...
...Vox dilecti mei. *Coupled with works by various composers.* **The Hilliard Ensemble.**
Virgin Classics Veritas VED5 61394-2 (11/97). *See review in the Collections section;*
refer to the Index.

George Rochberg
American 1918

Suggested listening ...
...Caprice Variations (excerpts). *Coupled with works by various composers.* **Michelle Makarski** (vn).
ECM New Series 449 957-2 (7/97). *See review in the Collections section; refer to the Index.*
...Ricordanza. *Coupled with works by various composers.* **Richard Slavich** (vc); **Alice Rybak** (pf).
Crystal Records CD639 (5/98). *See review in the Collections section; refer to the Index.*

Joaquin Rodrigo
Spanish 1901

Rodrigo Concierto de Aranjuez[a]. Fantasía para un gentilhombre[a]. Un tiempo fue Itálica famosa.
Zarabanda lejana. Adela[b]. Villancicos[b] – Pastorcito Santo; Coplillas de Belén. Coplas del pastor
enamorado[b]. **Manuel Barrueco** (gtr); [a]**Philharmonia Orchestra / Plácido Domingo** ([b]ten).
EMI Ⓕ CDC5 56175-2 (67 minutes: DDD: 4/98). Texts and translation included.
Recorded 1995-1997.
Rodrigo Concierto de Aranjuez. Fantasía para un gentilhombre. Concierto para una fiesta.
David Russell (gtr); **Naples Philharmonic Orchestra (Florida) / Erich Kunzel.** Telarc Ⓕ CD80459
(72 minutes: DDD: 4/98). Recorded 1997.
Both these discs contain amongst the very best recordings of the *Concierto de Aranjuez* and *Fantasia*
para un gentilhombre. Barrueco and Russell are members of the guitar's top-drawer élite – giving
performances of crystalline clarity – and they are both excellently supported by their orchestras. In
both these recordings the guitar is foregrounded to the extent that it achieves greater dominance than
it ever does in the concert-hall. One might regard this as a distortion, but as it more faithfully
represents what was/is in the composer's inner ear it should be enjoyed in its own right. Neither do
these comments apply only to the guitar and orchestra works of Rodrigo. If you already have top-
rated versions of either or both of these pieces you may rest content with them, but if you decide (for
whatever reason) to add one of these new recordings to your collection then your choice may depend
on the other items they contain. In Russell's case it is the *Concierto para una fiesta.* The thought
"where have I heard this before?" may cross your mind – in relation to both musical elements and the
mode of orchestration. But you may find these familiar echoes lovably welcome. Barrueco adds two
solos, neither one yet dulled by overfamiliarity. The *Zarabanda lejana* is given with the utmost
expressivity, and *Un tiempo fue Itálica famosa* is delivered with panache; rapid passages in Rodrigo's
guitar works are almost invariably scales, appropriately testifying to the influence of flamenco.
Barrueco has one more trump card to play – his partnership with Plácido Domingo in four songs,
selected from those for which Rodrigo himself has made adaptations for the guitar of the original
piano accompaniments (the texts are given in four languages). Both are longstanding devotees of
Rodrigo's music, and it shows. The partnership extends through the whole of this recording, in which
Domingo also conducts the orchestra, an exercise in which both parties demonstrate their happy
meeting of minds.

Additional recommendations ...

...Concierto de Aranjuez. Fantasía para un gentilhombre. **John Williams** (gtr); **Philharmonia Orchestra / Louis Frémaux.** CBS Masterworks Ⓕ SK37848 (53 minutes: DDD: 7/85).

...Concierto de Aranjuez. Fantasía para un gentilhombre. **Villa-Lobos** Guitar Concerto. **Göran Söllscher** (gtr); **Orpheus Chamber Orchestra.** DG Ⓕ 429 232-2GH (65 minutes: DDD: 6/90).

...Concierto de Aranjuez[a]. **Falla** El amor brujo[b]. Noches en los jardines de España[c]. [a]**Carlos Bonnell** (gtr); [c]**Alicia de Larrocha** (pf); [ab]**Montreal Symphony Orchestra / Charles Dutoit;** [c]**London Philharmonic Orchestra / Rafael Frühbeck de Burgos.** Decca Ovation Ⓜ 430 703-2DM (71 minutes: DDD: 8/91). *See review under Falla; refer to the Index.*

...Invocación y Danza. En los trigales. *Coupled with works by various composers.* **John Williams** (gtr); **London Symphony Orchestra / Paul Daniels.** Sony Classical Ⓕ SK48480 (71 minutes: DDD: 7/92). *See review under Albéniz; refer to the Index.*   Ⓖ

...Concierto de Aranjuez. *Coupled with works by* **Arnold** and **Takemitsu** Julian Bream (gtr); **City of Birmingham Symphony Orchestra / Sir Simon Rattle.** EMI Ⓕ CDC7 54661-2 (58 minutes: DDD: 7/93).   Ⓖ

...Concierto de Aranjuez[a]. Fantasía para un gentilhombre[b]. Tres piezas españolas. Invocacíon y danza. **Julian Bream** (gtr); [a]**Chamber Orchestra of Europe / Sir John Eliot Gardiner;** [b]**RCA Victor Chamber Orchestra / Leo Brouwer.** RCA Victor Gold Seal Ⓜ 09026 61611-2 (69 minutes: DDD: 2/94).

...Concierto de Aranjuez. *Coupled with works by* **Castelnuovo-Tedesco** and **Villa-Lobos** **Norbert Kraft** (gtr); **Northern Chamber Orchestra / Nicholas Ward.** Naxos Ⓢ 8 550729 (60 minutes: DDD: 4/94). *See review under Castelnuovo-Tedesco; refer to the Index.*

...Concierto de Aranjuez. *Coupled with works by* **Bennett** and **Arnold** Julian Bream (gtr); **Melos Ensemble / Sir Colin Davis.** RCA Victor Julian Bream Edition Ⓕ 09026 61598-2 (62 minutes: ADD: 6/94). *See review under Bennett; refer to the Index.*

...Concierto de Aranjuez[ac]. Fantasía para un gentilhombre[ac]. Cançoneta[bc]. Invocacíon y Danza[a]. Tres Pequeñas piezas[a]. [a]**Pepe Romero** (gtr); [b]**Augustín Léo Ara** (vn); [c]**Academy of St Martin in the Fields / Sir Neville Marriner.** Philips Ⓕ 438 016-2PH (64 minutes: DDD: 8/94).   Ⓖ

Further listening ...

...Concierto pastoral. *Coupled with* **Khachaturian** (arr. Gallois) Flute Concerto in D minor. **Patrick Gallois** (fl); **Philharmonia Orchestra / Ion Marin.** DG 435 767-2GH (10/92).

...Zarabanda lejana y villancico. *Coupled with works by* **Montsalvatge** **Madrid Symphony Orchestra / Antoni Ros Marbà.** Marco Polo 8 223753.

...Tres Piezas españolas. *Coupled with works by* **Albéniz** and **Granados** Julian Bream (gtr). RCA Navigator 74321 17903-2 (3/95). *See review under Albéniz; refer to the Index.*   Ⓖ

...Por tierras de Jerez. *Coupled with works by various composers.* **Pepe Romero** (gtr). Philips 442 150-2PH (4/95).

...Suite. Preludio al gallo mañanero. Zarabanda lejana. Pastorale. Bagatela. Serenata española. Sonada de adiós (Hommage à Paul Dukas). Tres Danzas de España. Danza de la Amapola. Tres Evocaciones. Preludio de Añoranza. Cinco Sonatas de Castilla con Toccata a modo de pregón. Berceuse de printemps. Berceuse d'automne. Air de Ballet sur le nom d'une Jeune Fille. El Album de Cecilia (Seis Piezas para manos pequeñas). A l'ombre de Torre Bermeja. Cuatro Piezas. Cuatro Estampas andaluzas. Cinco Piezas infantiles[a]. Sonatiuna para dos Munecas[a]. Gran Marcha de los Subsecretarios[a]. Atardecer[a]. **Gregory Allen,** [a]**Anton Nel** (pfs). Bridge BCD9027 (7/92).

Johan Helmich Roman   Swedish 1694-1758

Suggested listening ...
...Drottningholm Music, "Royal Wedding Music". Little Drottningholm Music. **Uppsala Chamber Orchestra / Anthony Halstead.** Naxos 8 553733 (2/98).

Andreas Romberg   German 1767-1821

Suggested listening ...
...Quintet in E flat major, Op. 57. *Coupled with works by* **Fuchs** and **Stanford** Thea King (cl); **Britten Quartet.** Hyperion CDA66479 (7/92). *See review under Fuchs; refer to the Index.*

Cipriano de Rore   Italian 1515/16-1565

Rore Missa Praeter rerum seriem. Motets – Infelix ego; Parce mihi; Ave regina; Descendi in hortum meum.
Josquin Desprez Praeter rerum seriem. **The Tallis Scholars / Peter Phillips.** Gimell Ⓕ 454 929-2PH (72 minutes: DDD: 6/94). Texts and translations included. *Gramophone Award Winner 1994.*   Ⓖ

This record begins with a magisterially concentrated and evocative account of one of Josquin's most inspired and tightly-constructed motets, the six-voice *Praeter rerum seriem*. This in turn is the starting-point for Rore's Mass – which takes as its cue Josquin's antiphonal approach – wherein the song on which the Mass is based is passed from the upper to the lower voices in succession. Rore, whose piece is in one sense an act of homage to Josquin was, if briefly, Josquin's successor at the d'Este court at Ferrara. It is in this context that Rore's work is an act of homage in a second sense, since to Josquin's already rich texture Rore adds an additional soprano part, while the first alto voice carries throughout a *cantus firmus* to the text "Hercules secundus dux Ferrarie quartus vivit et vivet". Around this structural scaffolding the remaining voices weave an endlessly inventive sequence of carefully-worked motives reminiscent of Josquin's original. This performance is characterized by great sensitivity to textual inflexion and to the many moments of exquisite bonding of words and music. Nevertheless, in the end it is Peter Phillips's ability to control the overall architecture of the music, as well as its detail, that provides the basis for a reading of such conviction; his direction, combined with The Tallis Scholars's strongly-focused singing and well-balanced ensemble, results in a gripping performance of rare beauty, intelligence and power. No less fine is the group of four motets that completes the recording, and which reveals Rore as one of the greatest and last exponents of the Franco-Flemish tradition.

Further listening ...

...Io canterei d'amor. Non è ch'il duol. Non gemme non fin oro. Signor mio caro. Vergine bella.
Coupled with works by various composers. **Labyrinto / Paolo Pandolfo** (va da gamba).
Harmonia Mundi HMC90 5234 (6/97). 🏊.

...Il quinto libro de madrigali. Le vive fiamme – Alma real, se come fida stella; Alma Susanna;
Amor che t'ho fatt'io; Di l'estrem' orizonte; Fera gentil; Vaghi pensieri. O voi che sotto.
The Consort of Musicke / Anthony Rooley. Musica Oscura 070991 (1/94).

Ned Rorem

American 1923-

Rorem Piano Concerto for the Left Hand[a]. Eleven Studies for Eleven Players[b]. [b]**Kathy Lord** (ob); [b]**Gregory Raden** (cl); [b]**Elizabeth Ostling** (fl); [b]**Katerina Englichova** (hp); [b]**Jack Sutte** (tpt); [b]**Anthony Lafargue**, [b]**Ryan Leveille** (perc); [b]**Steven Copes** (vn); [b]**Choong-Jin Chang** (va); [b]**Jeffrey Lastrapes** (vc); [a]**Gary Graffman**, [b]**Reiko Uchida** (pfs) / **Rossen Milanov**; [a]**Curtis Institute Student Orchestra / André Previn.** New World Ⓔ 80445-2 (62 minutes: DDD: 2/95). Recorded 1993.

In an appealingly candid booklet-essay, Ned Rorem describes his Left-Hand Concerto (his fourth for piano so far) as an "entertainment" – an entirely apt epithet, as it turns out, but one even more well suited to the earlier companion work on this valuable New World offering, namely the austerely titled *Eleven Studies for Eleven Players*. Dating from 1959-60, this charming suite is full of sparkling invention, nostalgic and witty by turns, and everywhere Rorem's scoring displays a very Gallic refinement. The Left-Hand Concerto of 1991 is another multi-movement work, eight in all, spread across three varying sections. Again, Rorem's inspiration impresses by dint of its appealing lyrical fervour and colourful, assured instrumentation, nowhere more so than in the strikingly beautiful "Hymn" and "Duet" which together form the emotional core of the concerto. The *Eleven Studies* receive a thoroughly sensitive, polished rendering from New World's *ad hoc* ensemble. In the concerto, Gary Graffman is a committed exponent (though his chosen instrument is not in the best of health) and André Previn draws an enthusiastic orchestral response from the students of the Curtis Institute.

Further listening ...

...Winter pages[a]. Bright music[b]. [b]**Marya Martin** (fl); [a]**Todd Palmer** (cl); [a]**Frank Morelli** (bn); **Ida** and [b]**Ani Kavafian** (vns); **Fred Sherry** (vc); [a]**Charles Wadsworth**, [b]**André-Michel Schub** (pfs). New World 80416-2 (10/92).

...After Reading Shakespeare. *Coupled with works by various composers.* **Alice Rybak** (pf). Crystal Records CD639 (5/98). *See review in the Collections section; refer to the Index.*

...A Childhood Miracle[a]. Three Sisters Who Are Not Sisters[b]. **Singers;** [b]**John van Buskirk** (pf); [a]**Magic Circle Chamber Orchestra / Ray Evans Harrell.** Newport Classic NPD85594 (10/95).

...As Adam early in the morning. Look down fair moon. Sometimes with one I love. That shadow, my likeness. *Coupled with works by various composers.* **Thomas Hampson** (bar); **Craig Rutenberg** (pf). EMI CDM5 55028-2 (10/97). *See review in the Collections section; refer to the Index.* 🅖🅖🅖

...Miss Julie. **Soloists; Manhattan School of Music Opera Chorus and Orchestra / David Gilbert.** Newport Classic NPD85605 (5/96).

Johann Rosenmüller

German 1619-1684

Rosenmüller Vespro della beata Vergine. **Canticum; Cantus Cölln; Concerto Palatino / Konrad Junghänel.** Harmonia Mundi Ⓔ HMC90 1611/2 (two discs: 131 minutes: DDD: 2/97). Texts and translations included. Recorded 1996. *Gramophone Editor's choice.* 🅖🅖

The Marian cycle of devotions set by Johann Rosenmüller continues Cantus Cölln's important mission of illuminating Germany's finest seventeenth-century offerings, and this is a magnificent vindication of their efforts. His style is something of a godsend to Cantus Cölln, and vice versa. Here is a composer with an exemplary command of the Venetian aesthetic. As a fluent and brilliant colourist of the most grandiloquent styles, he also never forsakes Teutonic contrapuntal discipline; the combination, at its best, produces a meticulously voiced control of texture and tautness of conception. These are attributes long admired in the performances of this eminent vocal ensemble also, and they are heard with concentrated fervour in five Psalms and a Magnificat, interspersed with plainsong, motets (with texts expertly reworked to fit the Vespers) and two fine instrumental sonatas. Whilst "Dixit Dominus", in terms of scale (it is over 600 bars long), is a memorable compendium of glistening scoring, rhythmic vitality, snappy declamation and textual characterization, often of a masterly kind, there are other works – less structurally ambitious – where the totality of Rosenmüller's invention flatters rather more. "Laudate pueri" evolves mesmerizingly, capped by a thrilling extended "Sicut erat" (so too in the C minor Magnificat, whose opening chords resemble an early romantic opera overture). Cantus Cölln give a virtuoso performance of this work – "He raiseth the poor out of the dust" is punctuated wonderfully by the instrumental commentary – and also "Laetatus sum", where the singers' invigorating dialogue distracts the listener from D major overkill, a small Achilles' heel in Rosenmüller's dazzling armoury. "Laude Jerusalem" is in the same vein, yet with a rolling sarabande momentum and an unusual *obbligato* combination of trumpet and cornetto. Cantus Cölln and Concerto Palatino demonstrate how a relatively small consort can sound majestic through extreme care in all matters of ensemble and intonation. A fine achievement.

Further listening ...

...Jubilent aethera. In te, Domine, speravi. Ach Herr, strafe mich nicht in deinem Zorn. Lieber Herre Gott, wecke uns auf. Studentenmusick – Suite in C major. Sonatas – No. 3 à 2; No. 4 à 3; No. 7 à 4; No. 10 à 5; No. 11 à 5.**The King's Noyse / David Douglass** (vn). Harmonia Mundi HMU90 7179 (4/97).

...12 Sonate a 2, 3, 4 e 5 stromenti da arco e altri e Basso continuo – Nos. 2, 7, 9 and 11. Sonate da Camera – Nos. 1, 2 and 4. Student-Music – Suite in C major. **Hespèrion XX / Jordi Savall.** Auvidis Astrée E8709. ✍

Antonio Rosetti
Bohemian c1750-1792

Rosetti Sinfonias – C major, A9/KI:21; D major, A12/KI: 12; F major, A33/KI: 24; G major, A40/KI: 22. **London Mozart Players / Matthias Bamert.** Chandos Ⓟ CHAN9567 (67 minutes: DDD: 3/98). Recorded 1996.

Rosetti's way was not all that different from Haydn's or Mozart's, but you will perceive an individual, and interesting, voice. His music is graceful in line, he has a spirited vein of minuet composition, and his slow movements combine a gentle lyricism with real seriousness and warmth of feeling. He has quite a wry wit and an odd way of ending movements somewhat enigmatically, with an oblique little gesture. Most fascinating of all, he uses contrapuntal writing, mainly but not exclusively in his first movements, to enrich and add weight to the music – just as Haydn and Mozart were doing at the same time. Listen in particular to the C major Symphony with its contrapuntal touches in the opening music growing fuller and more purposeful in the development: it is ingenious, attractive and effective. The finale here too, headed *Capriccio*, has some charmingly capricious counterpoint, and it also shows Rosetti's predilection for major-minor changes (not the only feature that hints at Schubert); and the slow movement is a *Romanze*, of eloquence and grace but quite unpretentious. The F major Symphony is another of particular interest, with a delightfully playful first movement and more contrapuntal writing, of quite an original sort, in the finale. Enjoyable too is the G major work for its lyrical opening movement and its appealing *Andante*, with muted strings. The London Mozart Players are certainly on excellent form, under the gifted Matthias Bamert, and these are subtler, more polished, more beguilingly phrased performances than those of Concerto Köln. And the first D major Symphony, with its variation slow movement and its snappy, Haydnish finale, is one to relish. The Cologne musicians' use of period instruments achieves a kind of intimacy, almost a chamber-music style, that perhaps eludes the English group. However, their performances convey something more of the special character of Rosetti's writing. He is not Haydn or Mozart: there are the odd moments where foursquare rhythms and too many cadences remind you that he is a Grade B man. But there is fine music and good entertainment here too and anyone curious about the context of the great Viennese masters should give this disc a hearing.

Additional recommendation ...

...C major; G major; D major, A13/KI: 30; D major, A20/KI, "La Chasse": 18; D major, A13/KI: 30. **Concerto Köln.** Teldec Das Alte Werk Ⓟ 0630-18301-2 (66 minutes: DDD: 3/98). ✍

Further listening ...

...Horn Concerto in D minor. *Coupled with works by* **Haydn** and **Danzi** Hermann Baumann (hn); **Concerto Amsterdam / Jaap Schröder.** Teldec Das Alte Werk 0630-12324-2 (8/96). *See review under Haydn; refer to the Index.*

...Sinfonias – G minor, K1:27; E flat major, K1:23; B flat major, K1:25; E flat major, K1:32. **Concerto Köln.** Teldec Das Alte Werk 4509-98420-2 (12/95). ✍

...Piano Sonata No. 2 in E flat major. *Coupled with works by various composers.* **Naoko Yoshino** (hp). Philips 446 064-2PH (2/96). *See review in the Collections section; refer to the Index.*

Nikolay Roslavets

Russian 1881-1944

Suggested listening ...
...Piano Sonatas Nos. 1, 2 and 5. Three Compositions. Three Etudes. Prelude. Two Compositions. Two Poems. Five Preludes. **Marc-André Hamelin** (pf). Hyperion CDA66926 (9/97).

Salamone Rossi

Italian 1570-c1630

M. Rossi Madrigals, Book 1[a]. Così foss'io creduto[a]. Occhi piangete e intenerite il core[a]. Toccate e Correnti – Toccata quarta; Toccata settima; Corrente terza; Corrente sesta; Corrente decima.
[a]**Il Complesso Barocco / Alan Curtis** (hpd). Virgin Classics Veritas Ⓕ VC5 45220-2
(74 minutes: DDD: 3/98). Texts and translations included. Recorded 1995-96.
The Italian madrigal of the early-seventeenth century enjoyed an extended run which lasted well into the 1620s and 1630s. Of course, by around 1620 – when the majority of Rossi's examples were probably composed – the madrigal had many visages; Janus-faced, the *oeuvre* of Monteverdi sets the seal on the range of idioms with his eight books. What this collection of a complete unpublished First Book conveys above all is a genre which occupied such musicians as Wert, Gesualdo and Marenzio: an essentially polyphonic style, purposely and perversely undermined by extravagant dissonance, chromatic harmony and declamatory rhythm. Such image-laden, descriptive and text-governed music ultimately needs pure musical technique for it not to become a game for amateurs. What is so attractive about his music is Rossi's eloquent way with the human voice. The individual timbres of each voice of Il Complesso Barocco are used with striking penetration to reveal every sinew of meaning. In the highly characterized counterpoint of *Langue al vostro*, depicting a statutory Guarini sentiment of heartache infused with sensual pain, each voice finds the most apt inflexion and, even in the bizarre Sonetto *Hor che la notte*, language-inspired nuance comes home to roost in the lap of the ensemble; such intoxicating qualities are compounded by Italian singers who vindicate the idea of full-throated Latin singing as highly desirable for this repertoire. The rhetorical freedom and naturalness of Alan Curtis's singers are partly mirrored by his instrumental consort of two violins, two violas and continuo. This group does not play a *concertato* role but is an alternative for voices in four of the madrigals. The process of presenting such literarily inspired works in a wordless medium, and therefore bringing a degree of abstraction to proceedings, can be supported historically but it is a curious exercise nevertheless. This is a powerfully presented disc of fine madrigals, even if Rossi is only intermittently equipped to deliver Monteverdi's noble consummation of a prevailing mood. Rossi is certainly a most intriguing figure.
Additional recommendation ...
...Toccata settima. *Coupled with works by various composers.* **Sophie Yates** (hpd).
Chandos Chaconne Ⓕ CHAN0601 (64 minutes: DDD: 9/97). ☞ *See review in the Collections section; refer to the Index.*

Gioachino Rossini

Italian 1792-1868

Rossini Overtures[a] – Tancredi; L'italiana in Algeri; L'inganno felice; La scala di seta; Il barbiere di Siviglia; Il Signor Bruschino; La cambiale di matrimonio; Il turco in Italia. Introduction, Theme and Variations in E flat (attrib.)[b]. [b]**Charles Neidich** (cl); **Orpheus Chamber Orchestra.**
DG Masters Ⓜ 445 569-2GMA (66 minutes: DDD: 10/96). Items marked [a] from 415 363-2GH
(10/85), [b]435 875-2GH. ⒼⒼ
This is one of the finest of all collections of Rossini overtures to have been recorded in recent decades. The superbly stylish playing apart, one of the reasons for the disc's success is the fact of its working within shrewdly appointed boundaries of chronology and style. All the overtures are early, dating from the years in which Rossini put his own indelible mark on the operatic overture (or "musical visiting card" as Gino Roncaglia so elegantly expressed it). They also date from the time, pre-Naples, when Rossini was writing for smallish orchestras; no danger here of us being ricocheted from early Rossini to late by some grand maestro and his souped-up symphony orchestra. It is also nice to hear overtures that do not normally get a look-in in such anthologies. One can imagine a few collectors being disturbed by the dryness of the recording and the fierce brilliance of the playing. But that, too, is part of the disc's allure; its ability to conjure afresh the aggressive radicalism of the young Rossini. It is doubtful wehther the clarinet piece (attributed to Rossini, and certainly using music by him) adds greatly to the disc's value. The melodies sound better on the voice; though, inevitably, the Orpheus players soon have the whole thing fizzing as appetizingly as a glass of sharply chilled champagne.

Rossini Overtures – Armida; Il barbiere di Siviglia; Bianca e Falliero; Demetrio e Polibio; La gazza ladra; Guillaume Tell; L'inganno felice; Matilde di Shabran; Semiramide; Il Signor Bruschino. **Orchestra of La Scala, Milan / Riccardo Chailly.** Decca Ⓕ 448 218-2DH
(75 minutes: DDD: 5/96). Recorded 1995. *Gramophone Editor's choice.* Ⓖ
This collection is a truly memorable day out at the Rossini fair. Musically everything is top notch. Chailly's conducting is characteristically full-blooded, but stylish and witty too. Milan's La Scala

orchestra respond to his masterly direction with playing of tremendous colour, verve and corporate virtuosity. And Decca's engineers have achieved a sound whose mixture of warmth, brilliance and immediacy ensures that all the overtures, big and small, come up in a razor-sharp focus. For the most part, the collection juxtaposes the familiar with the rather less familiar. Nor are the less familiar pieces of lesser interest. The overture to *Armida*, with its solemn drum-beats and vertiginous warbling horns, is a case in point. And it was a very clever move indeed to include the overture to *Bianca e Falliero* which is itself a kind of guided tour of the later Neapolitan operas, containing as it does themes for *La donna del lago*, *Ricciardo e Zoraide* and *Ermione*. This is one of those discs when everything goes right. It offers an hour-and-a-quarter of untrammelled pleasure.

Rossini Overtures – Guillaume Tell; La scala di seta; Il Signor Bruschino; Il barbiere di Siviglia; La gazza ladra; La Cenerentola. **Chicago Symphony Orchestra / Fritz Reiner.** RCA Victor Gold Seal Ⓜ GD60387* (47 minutes: ADD: 9/90). From SB2075 (7/60). Recorded 1958.   ⒼⒼⒼ

This is one of the most famous of all collections featuring this sparkling repertoire. By the time of this recording, Fritz Reiner had built the Chicago Symphony into one of the world's greatest ensembles, and their swaggering yet supremely flexible virtuosity is heard to superb effect on this survey. Not that these accounts are in any sense overdriven or that Rossini's music is used merely as an excuse for high-powered orchestral display; far from it: Reiner's direction possesses elegance, genial high-spirits and (at times) an almost Beechamesque wit – sample, say, the pointed woodwind dialogue in the scintillating reading of *La Cenerentola* to hear this. In fact, the only regret one could possibly have about this simply marvellous music-making is that, with a total duration of just under 47 minutes there isn't more of it! Despite some (inevitable) residual hiss, the RCA transfer engineers have worked wonders with these elderly tapes, producing a far more full-blooded, transparent sound-picture than one would have thought possible. At mid-price, this is unmissable. Buy it!

Additional recommendations ...

...Il barbiere di Siviglia. La Cenerentola. La gazza ladra. L'italiana in Algeri. Il Signor Bruschino. Le siège de Corinthe. **London Symphony Orchestra / Claudio Abbado.** DG Galleria Ⓜ 419 869-2GGA (47 minutes: DDD: 5/88).

...Il barbiere di Siviglia. L'italiana in Algeri. Semiramide. **Philharmonic Symphony Orchestra of New York / Arturo Toscanini.** *Coupled with works by various composers.* Pearl mono Ⓕ GEMMCDS9373* (three discs: 230 minutes: ADD: 3/90). *Gramophone classical 100. See review in the Collections section; refer to the Index.*   ⒼⒼⒼ

...La scala di seta; Il Signor Bruschino; L'italiana in Algeri; Il barbiere di Siviglia; La gazza ladra; Semiramide; Guillaume Tell. **London Classical Players / Roger Norrington.** EMI CDC7 54091-2 (60 minutes: DDD: 4/91). 🖉   Ⓖ

...Complete Overtures – La cambiale di matrimonio. La scala di seta. Il barbiere di Siviglia. Tancredi. L'italiana in Algeri. Il Signor Bruschino. Il turco in Italia. L'inganno felice. Guillaume Tell. Semiramide. Le siège de Corinthe. La Cenerentola. La gazza ladra. Il viaggio a Reims. Maometto II. Ricciardo e Zoriade. Otello. Armida. Ermione. Torvaldo e Dorliska. Bianca e Falliero. Demetrio e Polibio. Eduardo e Cristina. Edipo a Colono. Sinfonia al Conventello. Sinfonia di Bologna. **Academy of St Martin in the Fields / Sir Neville Marriner.** Philips Ⓜ 434 016-2PM3 (three discs: 209 minutes: ADD: 10/92).   ⒼⒼ

...La scala di seta. *Coupled with works by various composers.* **London Philharmonic Orchestra; Berlin Philharmonic Orchestra / Sir Thomas Beecham.** Dutton Laboratories mono Ⓑ CDLX7009* (75 minutes: ADD: 10/94). *See review in the Collections section; refer to the Index.*

...Guillaume Tell. *Coupled with works by* **Wolf-Ferrari, Respighi** and **Verdi** Santa Cecilia Academy Orchestra, Rome / Victor de Sabata. EMI Références mono Ⓜ CHS5 65506-2* (two discs: 148 minutes: ADD: 9/95).

...Il barbiere di Siviglia; Guillaume Tell; La Cenerentola; L'italiana in Algeri; La scala di seta; La gazza ladra; Semiramide; Il Signor Bruschino; Il turco in Italia. **Academy of St Martin in the Fields / Sir Neville Marriner.** Philips Ⓜ 446 196-2PM (76 minutes: ADD: 12/95).

Rossini Sonate a quattro – No. 1 in G major; No. 2 in A major; No. 3 in C major; No. 4 in B flat major; No. 5 in E flat major; No. 6 in D major.
Bellini Oboe Concerto in E flat major[a].
Cherubini Horn Sonata in F major[b].
Donizetti String Quartet in D major (1828). [a]**Roger Lord** (ob); [b]**Barry Tuckwell** (hn); **Academy of St Martin in the Fields / Sir Neville Marriner.** Double Decca Ⓜ 443 838-2DF2 (two discs: 112 minutes: ADD: 7/95). Recorded 1964-1968.

Rossini's six string sonatas are usually heard performed by a string orchestra, although they were in fact composed for a quartet of two violins, cello and double bass. The sonatas, which display amazing musical dexterity and assurance, may date from as early as 1804. The world of eighteenth-century opera is never far away, with the first violin frequently taking the role of soprano soloists, particularly in the slow movements. Written for Rossini's friend Agostino Triosso, who was a keen double bass player, the sonata's bass parts are full of wit and suavity. There are other thoroughly recommendable modern digital versions, including the Hyperion issue using original instruments, and the performances by the Serenata of London, full of elegance and polish, which give us for the first time on CD the original instrumentation. Yet there is something very special about Marriner's Academy set, made for Argo in the late 1960s. The playing has an elegance and finesse, a sparkle and touch of humour that catches the full character and charm of these miraculous examples of the precocity of the 12-year-old composer. The Double Decca format here is ideal because of the substantial bonuses. Donizetti's String Quartet sounds elegant in its string-orchestra version, Bellini's Oboe Concerto is played stylishly by Roger Lord and Cherubini's mini-concerto for horn and strings is dispatched with aplomb by by Barry Tuckwell. Highly recommendable.

Additional recommendations ...
...Nos. 1-6. **Serenata of London.** ASV Ⓕ CDDCA767 (78 minutes: DDD: 10/91).
...Nos. 1-6. **Elizabeth Wallfisch, Marshall Marcus** (vns); **Richard Tunnicliffe** (vc); **Chi-Chi Nwanoku** (db). Hyperion Ⓕ CDA66595 (80 minutes: DDD: 10/92). ◢

Rossini Péchés de vieillesse – Book 2, "Album français"; Book 3, "Morceaux réservés" – Chant funèbre à Meyerbeer; Les amants de Séville; Ave Maria; Le chant des titans. **Maryse Castets** (sop); **Mechthild Georg** (mez); **Jean-Luc Maurette** (ten); **Michel Brodard** (bar); **Raimund Nolte** (bass); **Elzbieta Kalvelage** (pf); **Marcel Jorand** (perc); **Chorus Musicus / Christoph Spering** (harm). Opus 111 Ⓕ OPS30-70 (74 minutes: DDD: 7/93). Text and translations included. Recorded 1992.

This is a very collectable CD. In the first place, it gives us not some arbitrary and ill-matched selection from Rossini's *Péchés de vieillesse*, but a charming gallimaufry of pieces that make up the *Album français*, plus four striking items from Rossini's *Morceaux réservés*. For the most part, it is Gallic music played and sung with in an authentic Gallic style. And that includes a splendid period Erard piano, expertly played by Elzbięta Kalvelage. There is also an Alexandre harmonium joining the piano in Rossini's exquisite *pastorale* "La Nuit de Noël" and in a spirited orchestra-less rendering of his strangely belligerent "Le chant des titans". The disc begins with the firefly brilliance of the *a cappella* "Toast pour le nouvel an" and ends with an exquisite short "Requiem". On the way, we have the desperate brilliance of "Roméo", a musical soliloquy Berlioz might have been proud to own. Flirtatiousness and pathos sit side by side in "La grande Coquette" and the famous tenor and baritone duo "Un sou". And if that seems too lachrymose, relief is at hand in the form of a charming musical sorbet, "Chanson de Zora". Each of the soloists seems to be a natural Rossinian and Christoph Spering's Chorus Musicus are stylish and disciplined in the five choral pieces.

Additional recommendations ...
...**Soirées musicales** – La promessa; Il rimpròvero; La partenza; L'orgia; La gita in gondola; La danza. Péchés de vieillesse – Book 1: La lontananza; Il fanciullo smarrito. Book 2: Roméo; Le dodo des enfants; La lazzarone. Book 3: L'esule; Au chevet d'un mourant; Le sylvain; Ariette à l'Ancienne. La dichiarazione. Sorzico. Mi lagnerò tacendo (eight versions). Nizza. Duetto buffo di due gatti[a]. **Rockwell Blake** (ten); [a]**Gérard Lesne** (alto); **Antonio Pappano** (pf). EMI Ⓕ CDC5 55614-2 (72 minutes: DDD: 10/96).
...**Péchés de vieillesse:** Book 3 – L'esule; Book 11 – A ma belle mère; Aragonese. La passeggiata. Mi lagnerò tacendo – Boléro. Soirées musicales – La danza. *Coupled with works by* **Bellini** and **Donizetti** Cecilia Bartoli (mez); James Levine (pf). Decca Ⓕ 455 513-2DH (67 minutes: DDD: 11/97). *Gramophone Editor's choice. See review in the Collections section; refer to the Index.*

Rossini Petite messe solennelle. **Helen Field** (sop); **Anne-Marie Owens** (mez); **Edmund Barham** (ten); **John Tomlinson** (bass); **David Nettle, Richard Markham** (pfs); **Peter King** (harm); **City of Birmingham Symphony Orchestra Chorus / Simon Halsey.** Conifer Classics Ⓕ CDCF184 (78 minutes: DDD: 10/90). Text and translation included. Recorded 1989. *Selected by Sounds in Retrospect.*

Rossini Petite messe solennelle. **Daniella Dessì** (sop); **Gloria Scalchi** (mez); **Giuseppe Sabbatini** (ten); **Michele Pertusi** (bass); **Chorus and Orchestra of the Teatro Comunale, Bologna / Riccardo Chailly.** Decca Ⓜ 444 134-2DX2 (two discs: 82 minutes: DDD: 2/95). Text and translation included. *Gramophone Editor's choice.*

Of Rossini's later works, none has won such affection from the general listening public as the *Petite messe solennelle*. He called it "the final sin of my old age" and, as with the other of his *péchés de vieillesse*, he declined to have it published. Editions issued in 1869, the year after his death, failed to retain his original scoring and contained numerous inaccuracies, yet these have been the basis of most subsequent recordings of the work. The Conifer disc presents the Mass in a revelatory Oxford University Press edition by Nancy Fleming, using two pianos in addition to a fine, French harmonium. That alone would mark it out for prime consideration, even if the reading were only passable, but here we have the bonus of dedicated, heartfelt performances from all involved. Above all, the scale of the work is finely captured – it was intended for chamber performance and both writing and scoring reflect the intimacy of Rossini's ideas. Much praise must go to Simon Halsey for so clearly establishing the parameters for this performance, and to the recording engineers for making it all seem so convincing. The whole issue establishes a benchmark for assessing recordings of this work.

A properly representative of the orchestrated version has been long overdue. Chailly's performance is a glorious heart-warming affair. Not that you are likely to be convinced right away. To ears accustomed to the *Kyrie* in its original form, the texturing here is pure suet. Nor does the sound of the largish and here rather distantly placed choir seem especially well focused in the *Christe eleison*. Gradually, though, the ear adjusts, the musicians warm to their task, the performance gets into its stride. The Bologna Chorus sing the *Gloria* and *Credo* with passion, clarity and love. The tenor is adequate, the bass superb, the two girls absolutely fabulous. (The *Qui tollis* is sung with near-shameless allure.) If the *Crucifixus* can never be as painful as it is in the sparer original version, this is amply offset by the sheer beauty of Daniella Dessì's singing and by the hair-raising force of the "Et resurrexit" (superbly recorded) as Chailly and his choir realize it. By the end, after Gloria Scalchi's deeply affecting account of the *Agnus Dei*, you begin to wonder whether the orchestral version wasn't more than a match for the original. It isn't, but it is an indication of the cumulative eloquence of this utterly inspired performance that it comes to seem so.

Rossini Stabat mater. **Luba Orgonasova** (sop); **Cecilia Bartoli** (mez); **Raúl Giménez** (ten); **Roberto Scandiuzzi** (bass); **Vienna State Opera Concert Choir; Vienna Philharmonic Orchestra / Myung-Whun Chung.** DG Ⓕ 449 178-2GH (59 minutes: DDD: 2/97). Text and translation included. Recorded 1995. *Gramophone Editor's choice.* ⒼⒼ

Chung's conducting of *Stabat mater* is somewhat Karajanesque: extremely beautiful orchestral playing; a choir who sing expressively but who yield something in focus and clarity of sound to the best rival English choirs; a strong dramatic sense with some unusual tempos that lead to the performance occasionally seeming mannered; and much fine solo singing, the singers encouraged to sing with great inwardness, with a special kind of *quiet* beauty. This is where the performance differs markedly from the Hickox, until now the prime recommendation. There the soloists sing their solo numbers in far more open and extrovert manner. In the case of the tenor this works to Hickox's disadvantage, since Arthur Davies in extrovert mood merely sounds coarse and is no match for Raúl Giménez when he is being encouraged by Chung to husband his rescources and sing with honeyed charm. Hickox has the better bass in Roderick Earle, but, again, Chung sees his soloist through very effectively. Between Della Jones and Cecilia Bartoli there is simply no comparison; for Jones and Hickox "Fac ut portem" is a dramatic oration, for Bartoli and Chung it is a private meditation. You pay your money and you take your choice. The soloists are as fine as any on record and the text is nursed with special care by both soloists, choir, and conductor. The integration of singers, orchestra and acoustic is not quite as well managed as on the Chandos recording where we have a church acoustic (St Jude's, Hampstead) as opposed to the more secular sounding Golden Hall of the Vienna Musikverein. Nor is Chung's reading as straightforward, as right-sounding as Hickox's. There are things in the Chung – the rather too jaunty "Sancta mater", the rather too protracted "Quando corpus morietur" – that seem irksome on a first hearing, let alone on repetition. In the absence of one outright recommendation, this latest recording can be regarded as first among equals among what is currently a distinguished trio of runners-up.

Additional recommendations ...

...Soloists; Philharmonia Chorus and Orchestra / Carlo Maria Giulini. DG Ⓕ 410 034-2GH (65 minutes: ADD: 9/83).

...Soloists; London Symphony Chorus and Orchestra / István Kertész. Decca Ovation Ⓜ 417 766-2DM (54 minutes: ADD: 7/89).

...Soloists; London Symphony Chorus; City of London Sinfonia / Richard Hickox. Chandos Ⓕ CHAN8780 (59 minutes: DDD: 3/90).

...Soloists; Bavarian Radio Chorus and Symphony Orchestra / Semyon Bychkov. Philips Ⓕ 426 312-2PH (65 minutes: DDD: 3/91).

...Petite messe solennelle[a]. Stabat mater[b]. **Soloists; [a]Choir of King's College, Cambridge / Stephen Cleobury; [b]Chorus and Orchestra of the Maggio Musicale, Florence / Riccardo Muti.** EMI Forte Ⓜ CZS5 68658-2 (two discs: 147 minutes: DDD: 7/96).

Rossini Otello – Che ascolto? ... Ah come mai non senti pietà. Guillaume Tell – Ne m'abandonne pas ... Asile héréditaire. Stabat mater – Cujus animam gementem. L'italiana in Algeri – Languir per una bella; Ah, come il cor di giubilo. Le siège de Corinthe – Avançons, oui ces murs ... Grand Dieu faut-il qu'un peuple qui t'adore. **Donizetti** La favorite – Un ange, une femme inconnue; Je ne méritais pas ... Qui ta voix m'inspire; La maîtresse du roi? ... Ange si pur. Messa da Requiem – Ingemisco. Gabriella di Vergy – Si compia il sacrificio ... Io l'amai. **Justin Lavender** (ten); **Bournemouth Symphony Orchestra / Howard Williams.** IMP Classics Ⓢ 30367 0010-2 (73 minutes: DDD: 3/96). Recorded 1994.

Rodrigo's long and incredibly difficult aria from Rossini's *Otello* announces Lavender's ability both to spin a secure legato and negotiate divisions with facility. But it is the second item that places him in the forefront of Rossini singing today. Every note of Arnold's strenuous outpouring is hit dead centre; up to the high C near the aria's close, the runs are cleanly delivered, the tone is clear and unfettered. Lavender's kind of tenor with its keen, pointed head voice may well be very much the sound Rossini had in mind for that part – and for Néocles in *Siège*, whose Act 3 scena is interpreted with the involvement possible only to an artist who has already sung the part on stage. In both these pieces Lavender's French is idiomatic. *La favorite* is at last being restored to the original language and Lavender demonstrates how much smoother Fernand's arias sound in French. Note also his long breath and his feeling for the shape of a Donizettian phrase. His Italian is no less excellent than his French. Perhaps there isn't enough light and shade in Lindoro's pieces from *L'italiana* but Raoul's romantic outpouring from *Gabriella* goes well. One piece in Latin from each composer finds Lavender full of the right conviction, the top D flat in "Cuius animam" taken fearlessly. Howard Williams is the

ideal partner, breathing life into every bar of the orchestration, especially notable in the Rossini pieces. The only reservations concern the recording – too much air around the voice – and the insertnotes which are inadequate. Let neither prevent you hearing a notable and fascinating début recital.
Additional recommendations ...
...La Cenerentola – Nacqui all'affano (with soloists). Il barbiere di Siviglia – Una voce poco fa. L'italiana in Algeri – Pronti abbiamo e ferri e mani ... Amici in ogni evento ... Pensa alla patria. *Coupled with works by various composers.* **Vesselina Kasarova** (mez); **Bavarian Radio Chorus; Munich Radio Orchestra / Friedrich Haider.**
RCA Victor Red Seal Ⓕ 09026 68522-2 (64 minutes: DDD: 2/97). *Gramophone Editor's record of the month. See review in the Collections section; refer to the Index.* ⒼⒼ
...Il viaggio a Reims – Arpa gentil. *Coupled with works by various composers.* **Inessa Galante** (sop); **Latvian National Opera Orchestra / Alexander Vilumanis.** Campion Ⓕ RRCD1344 (63 minutes: AAD/DDD: A/97). *See review in the Collections section; refer to the Index.*
...Il barbiere di Siviglia – Largo al factotum[b]; Una voce poco fa ... Io son docile[a]; Dunque io son?. *Coupled with opera arias and duets by various composers.* [a]**Olga Borodina** (mez); [b]**Dmitri Hvorostovsky** (bar); **English Chamber Orchestra / Patrick Summers.** Philips Ⓕ 454 439-2PH (66 minutes: DDD: 6/98). *See review in the Collections section; refer to the Index.*

Rossini Zelmira – Riedi al soglio[a]. Le nozze di Teti e di Peleo – Ah, non potrian reistere. Maometto II – Ah! che invan su questo ciglio; Giusto ciel, in tal periglio[a]. La donna del lago – Tanti affetti in tal momento[a]. Elisabetta, Regina d'Inghilterra – Quant' è grato all'alma mia[a]; Fellon, la penna avrai[a]. Semiramide – Serenai vaghirai ... Bel raggio lusinghier[a]. **Cecilia Bartoli** (mez); [a]**Chorus and Orchestra of the Teatro La Fenice, Venice / Ion Martin.** Decca Ⓕ 436 075-2DH (59 minutes: DDD: 2/92). Recorded 1991. Texts and translations included.
This sparkling disc brings together a collection of arias composed by Rossini for one of the great prima donnas of the nineteenth century, who was also his wife, Isabella Colbran. It is tempting to wonder whether even she had a voice to match that of Cecilia Bartoli, one of the most luscious, most exciting voices in opera. All those dazzling chromatic runs, leaps, cadenzas and cascading coloraturas are handled with consummate ease. Throughout, Bartoli sounds as if she's enjoying the music; there is always an engaging smile in the voice, although she is properly imperious in the extracts from *Elisabetta* and disarmingly simple in the prayerful "Giusto ciel, in tal periglio" ("Righteous heaven in such danger") from *Maometto II.* The orchestral and choral forces bring a delightful intimacy to the proceedings, with some cheeky woodwind solos and fruity brass passages. The recording, produced at the Teatro La Fenice by Decca veteran Christopher Raeburn, favours the voices but gives it just enough distance to accommodate high Cs and astounding A flats at the bottom of the range. The orchestral perspective is changeable but satisfactory. For Rossini and Bartoli fans, this disc is a must.

Rossini Il barbiere di Siviglia. **Roberto Servile** (bar) Figaro; **Sonia Ganassi** (mez) Rosina; **Ramon Vargas** (ten) Almaviva; **Angelo Romero** (bar) Doctor Bartolo; **Franco de Grandis** (bass) Don Basilio; **Ingrid Kertesi** (sop) Berta; **Kázmér Sarkany** (bass) Fiorello; **Hungarian Radio Chorus; Failoni Chamber Orchestra, Budapest / Will Humburg.** Naxos Ⓢ 8 660027/9 (three discs: 158 minutes: DDD: 3/94). Notes and text included. *Gramophone Editor's choice.* ⒼⒼ
Not everyone will approve, but there are ways in which this super-budget recording of *Il barbiere di Siviglia* puts to shame just about every other version of the opera there has yet been. Those it may not please are specialist vocal collectors for whom *Il barbiere* is primarily a repository of vocal test pieces, a kind of musical Badminton. If, on the other hand, you regard *Il barbiere* (Rossini, ex-Beaumarchais) as a gloriously subversive music drama – vibrant, scurrilous, unstoppably vital – then this set is guaranteed to give a great deal of pleasure. 'Performance' is the key word here. Humburg is described in the Naxos booklet as "Conductor and Recitative Director"; and for once the recitatives really are part of the larger drama. The result is a meticulously produced, often very funny, brilliantly integrated performance that you will almost certainly find yourself listening to as a stage play – rather than an opera with eminently missable (often arbitrarily abbreviated) recitatives. With a virtually all-Italian cast, the results are a revelation. The erotic allure of the duet "Dunque io son" is striking, arising as it does here out of the brilliantly played teasing of Rosina by Figaro about her new admirer. Similarly, Don Basilio's Calumny aria, superbly sung by Franco de Grandis, a black-browed bass from Turin who was singing for Karajan, Muti and Abbado while still in his twenties. This takes on added character and colour from the massive sense of panic created by de Grandis and the admirable Dr Bartolo of Angelo Romero when Basilio comes in with news of Almaviva's arrival in town. The Overture is done with evident relish, the playing of the Failoni Chamber Orchestra (a group from within the Hungarian State Opera Orchestra) nothing if not articulate. Aided by a clear, forward recording, a *sine qua non* with musical comedy, the cast communicates the Rossini/ Sterbini text – solo arias, ensembles, recitatives – with tremendous relish. They are never hustled by Humburg, nor are they spared: the *stretta* of the Act 1 finale is a model of hypertension and clarity. It would have been nice to have an English version of the libretto, but you can't have everything at rock-bottom prices and Naxos do provide an excellent track-by-track synopsis. Super-Scrooges might complain that 158 minutes of music could have been shoe-horned on to two CDs, but three CDs is a fair deal for a complete *Il barbiere*, and the layout is first-rate. This *Il barbiere* jumps to the top of the pile in a single leap. As operatic pole-vaulters, this puts Naxos in the Olympic class.

Additional recommendations ...

...Soloists; **Ambrosian Opera Chorus; Academy of St Martin in the Fields / Sir Neville Marriner**
with **Nicholas Kraemer** (fp). Philips Ⓕ 446 448-2PH2 (three discs: 147 minutes: DDD: 4/84).

...Soloists; **Philharmonia Chorus and Orchestra / Alceo Galliera.**
EMI Ⓜ CDS5 56310-2* (two discs: 130 minutes: ADD: 6/87).

...Soloists; **Chorus and Orchestra of La Scala, Milan / Riccardo Chailly.**
CBS Masterworks Ⓕ S3K37862 (three discs: 155 minutes: DDD: 9/88).

...Soloists; **Chorus and Orchestra of the Teatro Communale, Bologna / Giuseppe Patanè.**
Decca Ⓕ 425 520-2DH3 (three discs: 161 minutes: DDD: 9/89).

...Soloists; **Glyndebourne Festival Chorus; Royal Philharmonic Orchestra / Vittorio Gui.**
EMI Rossini Edition Ⓜ CMS7 64162-2 (two discs: 141 minutes: ADD: 5/92).

...Soloists; **Chorus of the Teatro La Fenice, Venice; Chamber Orchestra of Europe / Claudio Abbado.**
DG Ⓕ 435 763-2GH2 (two discs: 155 minutes: DDD: 12/92).

...Soloists; **Chorus; Orchestra della Toscana / Gianluigi Gelmetti.**
EMI Ⓕ CDS7 54863-2 (three discs: 140 minutes: DDD: 11/93).

...Soloists; **Chorus and Orchestra of the Metropolitan Opera, New York / Erich Leinsdorf.**
RCA Victor Living Stereo Ⓜ 09026 68552-2 (three discs: 160 minutes: ADD: 5/97).

Rossini La Cenerentola. **Teresa Berganza** (mez) Angelina; **Luigi Alva** (ten) Don Ramiro;
Renato Capecchi (bar) Dandini; **Paolo Montarsolo** (bar) Don Magnifico; **Margherita Guglielmi**
(sop) Clorinda; **Laura Zannini** (contr) Tisbe; **Ugo Trama** (bass) Alidoro; **Scottish Opera Chorus;**
London Symphony Orchestra / Claudio Abbado. DG Ⓕ 423 861-2GH2 (two discs: 144 minutes:
ADD: 9/86). Notes, text and translation included. From 2709 039 (6/72). Recorded 1971.   **Ⓔ**

Rossini's Cinderella is a fairy-tale without a fairy, but no less bewitching for the absence of a magic
wand. In fact the replacement of the winged godmother with the philanthropic Alidoro, a close friend
and adviser of our prince, Don Ramiro, plus the lack of any glass slippers and the presence of a
particularly unsympathetic father character, makes the whole story more plausible. *La Cenerentola*,
Angelina, is more spunky than the average pantomime Cinders, not too meek to complain about her
treatment or to beg to be allowed to go to the ball. She herself gives Don Ramiro one of her pair of
bracelets, charging him to find the owner of the matching ornament and thus taking in hand the
control of her own destiny. Along the way, Don Ramiro and his valet Dandini change places, leading
to plenty of satisfyingly operatic confusion and difficult situations. This recording, when originally
transferred to CD, was spread across three discs, but it has now been comfortably fitted into two. It
gives a sparkling rendition of the score with a lovely light touch and well-judged tempos from Abbado
and the London Symphony Orchestra and virtuoso vocal requirements are fully met by the cast. The
chief delight is Teresa Berganza's Angelina, gloriously creamy in tone and as warm as she is precise.
The supporting cast is full of character, with Luigi Alva a princely Don Ramiro, Margherita
Guglielmi and Laura Zannini an affected and fussy pair of sisters, and Renato Capecchi as Dandini,
gleeful and mischievous as he takes on being prince for a day. Although the recording was made in
1972 it has survived its technological transfers more than usually well.

Additional recommendations ...

...Soloists; **West German Radio Choir; Cappella Coloniensis / Gabriele Ferro.**
Sony Classical Ⓕ S2K46433 (two discs: 148 minutes: ADD: 6/91).

...Soloists; **Glyndebourne Festival Chorus and Orchestra / Vittorio Gui.**
EMI Rossini Edition mono Ⓜ CMS7 64183-2* (two discs: 117 minutes: ADD: 5/92).

...Soloists; **Bologna Teatro Communale Chorus and Orchestra / Riccardo Chailly.**
Decca Ⓕ 436 902-2DHO2 (two discs: 148 minutes: DDD: 11/93).

Rossini L'inganno felice. **Annick Massis** (sop) Isabella; **Raúl Giménez** (ten) Bertrando;
Rodney Gilfry (bar) Batone; **Pietro Spagnoli** (bass) Tarabotto; **Lorenzo Regazzo** (bar) Ormondo;
Le Concert des Tuileries / Marc Minkowski. Erato Ⓕ 0630-17579-2 (78 minutes: DDD: 11/97).
Notes, text and translation included. Recorded live in 1996.

This is a fine and tremendously enjoyable recording of an exquisite early Rossini one-acter that in the
first flush of Rossini's national and international success in the years 1812-24 was, without question,
one of his most popular operas. The plot resembles that of a late Shakespearian comedy. Set in a
seaside mining community, it is concerned with the discovery and rehabilitation of Isabella, Duke
Bertrando's wronged and, so he thinks, long-dead wife. It is a work that is comic and serious, witty
and sentimental; and there, perhaps, lies the rub. Rossini, especially early Rossini, is meant to be all
teeth and smiles, yet *L'inganno felice* is not quite like that. The very *mise-en-scène* is odd: 'seaside' and
'mining' being, in such a context, strangely contradictory concepts. This is a splendid performance,
using a chamber ensemble of about 30 players. It is a live performance, recorded with pleasing
immediacy, that begins bullishly but settles to intimacy when the drama requires. The score is full of
vocal pitfalls, not least for the tenor and for the baritone Batone. But Giménez and Gilfry cope more
than adequately,with enough in reserve to produce moments of genuine ease and beauty. Annick
Massis is a charming Isabella, good in her first aria, ravishing in her second. The final scene of
L'inganno felice, its finest sequence, is set at night amid the mining galleys and is beautifully performed
here, looking forward in some respects to the wonderful Act 2 Nocturne of *Le comte Ory;* they are,
indeed, works of similar pedigree, albeit an age apart.

Rossini L'italiana in Algeri. **Marilyn Horne** (mez) Isabella; **Ernesto Palacio** (ten) Lindoro; **Domenico Trimarchi** (bar) Taddeo; **Samuel Ramey** (bass) Mustafà; **Kathleen Battle** (sop) Elvira; **Clara Foti** (mez) Zulma; **Nicola Zaccaria** (bass) Haly; **Prague Philharmonic Chorus; I Solisti Veneti / Claudio Scimone.** Erato Libretto Ⓜ 2292-45404-2 (two discs: 140 minutes: ADD: 1/92). Notes and text included. From STU71394 (3/81). Recorded 1980.

Written within the space of a month during the spring of 1813, and with help from another anonymous hand, Rossini's *L'italiana in Algeri* was an early success, and one which went on to receive many performances during the nineteenth century, with an increasingly corrupt text. A complete reconstruction was undertaken by Azio Corghi and published in 1981; this recording uses this edition which corresponds most closely to what was actually performed in Venice in 1813. *L'italiana* is one of Rossini's wittiest operas, featuring as did a number of his most successful works a bewitching central character, in this case Isabella, who makes fun of her various suitors, with the opera ending with a happy escape with her beloved, Lindoro, a typical *tenorino* role. This fine recording on Erato has plenty of vocal polish. Scimone's biggest asset is Marilyn Horne as Isabella: possibly the finest Rossini singer of her generation and a veteran in this particular role, she sings Rossini's demanding music with great virtuosity and polish. Her liquid tone and artful phrasing ensure that she is a continuous pleasure to listen to. She is strongly supported by the rest of the cast: Kathleen Battle is a beguiling Elvira, Domenico Trimarchi a most humorous Taddeo, and Samuel Ramey a sonorous Bey of Algiers – Isabella's opponent and pursuer. Ernesto Palacio's Lindoro, however, has patches of white tone and is correct rather than inspiring. Scimone's conducting is likewise efficient if at times slightly lacking in sparkle. It is, however, guaranteed to give considerable pleasure.

Additional recommendation ...
...Soloists; **Vienna State Opera Chorus; Vienna Philharmonic Orchestra / Claudio Abbado.** DG Ⓕ 427 331-2GH2 (two discs: 127 minutes: DDD: 10/89).

Rossini Semiramide. **Dame Joan Sutherland** (sop) Semiramide; **Marilyn Horne** (mez) Arsace; **Joseph Rouleau** (bass) Assur; **John Serge** (ten) Idreno; **Patricia Clark** (sop) Azema; **Spiro Malas** (bass) Oroe; **Michael Langdon** (bass) Ghost of Nino; **Leslie Fryson** (ten) Mitrane; **Ambrosian Opera Chorus; London Symphony Orchestra / Richard Bonynge.** Decca Ⓜ 425 481-2DM3 (three discs: 168 minutes: ADD: 2/90). Notes, text and translation included. From SET317/19 (10/66). Recorded 1966. ⒼⒼ

Wagner thought it represented all that was bad about Italian opera and Kobbe's *Complete Opera Book* proclaimed that it had had its day – but then added what looked like second thoughts, saying that "were a soprano and contralto to appear in conjunction in the firmament the opera might be successfully revived". That was exactly what happened in the 1960s, when both Sutherland and Horne were in superlative voice and, with Richard Bonynge, were taking a prominent part in the reintroduction of so many nineteenth-century operas which the world thought it had outgrown. This recording brought a good deal of enlightenment in its time. For one thing, here was vocal music of such 'impossible' difficulty being sung with brilliance by the two principal women and with considerable skill by the men, less well known as they were. Then it brought to many listeners the discovery that, so far from being a mere show-piece, the opera contained ensembles that possessed quite compelling dramatic intensity. People who had heard of the duet "Giorno d'orrore" (invariably encored in Victorian times) were surprised to find it remarkably unshowy and even expressive of the ambiguous feelings of mother and son in their extraordinary predicament. It will probably be a long time before this recording is superseded, admirably vivid as it is in sound, finely conducted and magnificently sung.

Rossini Il Signor Bruschino. **Samuel Ramey** (bass) Gaudenzio; **Claudio Desderi** (bar) Bruschino padre; **Kathleen Battle** (sop) Sofia; **Frank Lopardo** (ten) Florville; **Michele Pertusi** (bass) Filiberto; **Jennifer Larmore** (mez) Marianna; **Octavio Arévalo** (ten) Bruschino figlio, Commissario; **English Chamber Orchestra / Ion Marin.** DG Ⓕ 435 865-2GH (76 minutes: DDD: 12/93). Notes, text and translation included. Recorded 1991.

Witty and sentimental but also at times hair-raisingly cruel, *Il Signor Bruschino* is the last, and arguably the best, of the one-acters Rossini wrote for the tiny Teatro San Moisè in Venice between 1810 and January 1813. These early *farse* can get by on tolerably good singing. What they absolutely can't do without is first-rate conducting – and, on record, clear, sharply defined orchestral sound. Choosing between the conducting of DG's Ion Marin and Claves's Marcello Viotti isn't all that difficult. Marin is far more vital; and what a cast there is on DG – a cast so expert and experienced they can't fail to bring the score wonderfully to life. Central to the whole enterprise is the Bruschino of Desderi, a superbly rounded portrait of a man who, despite the sweltering heat and the machinations of everyone around him, finally gives as good as he gets. Ramey's portrait of Gaudenzio is masterly, acted with relish and richly sung. Battle gives a ravishing account of Sofia's aria "Ah!, donate il caro sposo" with its cor anglais colourings. This *Bruschino* is probably the one to have. Whatever reservations one may occasionally have about the conducting and the focus of the recording, it is difficult to imagine a better-cast account.

Additional recommendations:
...Soloists; **Turin Philharmonic Orchestra / Marcello Viotti.**
Claves Ⓕ CD50-8904/5 (two discs: 84 minutes: DDD: 10/89).

...**Soloists; Warsaw Chamber Opera Orchestra / Jacek Kaspszyk.**
Pavane Ⓟ ADW7158 (72 minutes: DDD: 5/93).

Rossini Tancredi. **Ewa Podles** (contr) Tancredi; **Sumi Jo** (sop) Amenaide; **Stanford Olsen** (ten)
Argirio; **Pietro Spagnoli** (bar) Orbazzano; **Anna Maria di Micco** (sop) Isaura; **Lucretia Lendi**
(mez) Roggiero; **Capella Brugensis; Collegium Instrumentale Brugense / Alberto Zedda.**
Naxos Ⓢ 8 660037/8 (two discs: 147 minutes: DDD: 11/95). Notes and Italian text included.
Recorded 1994. *Gramophone Editor's choice.*   Ⓖ

Tancredi is a seminal work in the Rossini canon, a work which mingles a new-found reach in the
musical architecture with vocal and instrumental writing of rare wonderment and beauty. Philip
Gossett's new Critical Edition of the score. is the one used here, albeit somewhat pragmatically, by
Alberto Zedda. The singing is splendid throughout, with a cast that is unusually starry. Podles herself
has sung the role of Tancredi (to acclaim) at La Scala, Milan; and the Amenaide, Sumi Jo, is a touch
cool at first, too much the pert coloratura but this is not an impression that persists. Hers is a
performance of wonderful vocal control and flowering sensibility. Podles, a smoky-voiced Pole, likes
to go her own way at times. In recitatives, rests are ignored and emphases freely redistributed. In arias,
it is not unusual to find the pulse beating faster or slower as the musical temperature rises or falls. In
the event, though, she and Sumi Jo work well together, and they sound marvellous. Podles also
manages, chameleon-like, to adjust to the purer, more obviously stylish Rossini manner of a singer
who is very unlike herself, the young American tenor Stanford Olsen. His portrait of the conscience-
stricken father Argirio matches singing of grace and impetus with great fineness of dramatic
sensibility. As a result, something like the scene of the signing of his daughter's death-warrant
emerges here as the remarkable thing it is. Zedda is lucky to have at his disposal another of those
wonderfully stylish chamber orchestras and chamber choirs that Naxos seem able to conjure at will.
The aqueously lovely preface to Tancredi's first entrance is a fairly representative example of the
players' ear for Rossini's delicately-limned tone-painting. And the recording itself is beautifully
scaled. As usual with Naxos, you get a multilingual synopsis plus an original-language libretto
without translation; but in the case of an opera like *Tancredi*, where it is very much a case of 'Prima
la musica', this is not a great disincentive to buy. All in all, then, this is a fine set; the first-ever studio
recording of *Tancredi*, and a palpable hit.

Additional recommendations ...
...**Soloists; Chorus and Orchestra of La Fenice, Venice / Ralf Weikert.**
Sony Classical Ⓟ S3K39073 (three discs: 169 minutes: DDD: 8/88).
...**Soloists; Bavarian Radio Chorus; Munich Radio Orchestra / Roberto Abbado.**
RCA Victor Red Seal Ⓟ 09026 68349-2 (three discs: 208 minutes: DDD: 12/96).

Rossini Il turco in Italia. **Michele Pertusi** (bass) Selim; **Cecilia Bartoli** (mez) Fiorilla;
Alessandro Corbelli (bar) Don Geronio; **Ramón Vargas** (ten) Don Narciso; **Laura Polverelli** (mez)
Zaida; **Francesco Piccoli** (ten) Albazar; **Roberto de Candia** (bar) Prosdocimo; **Chorus and
Orchestra of La Scala, Milan / Riccardo Chailly.** Decca Ⓟ 458 924-2DHO2 (two discs:
142 minutes: DDD: 5/98). Notes, text and translation included. Recorded 1997.   ⒼⒼⒼ

It was only natural that, with a star mezzo of Cecilia Bartoli's stature on their books, Decca should
have turned to Rossini's *Il turco in Italia*, an obvious role for a singer of her temperament. Add to that
a conductor of Riccardo Chailly's sympathies and the opera was asking to be recorded. Chailly, of
course, has recorded the work before – for CBS back in 1981 – but in the years since, he has matured
as a Rossini conductor and the Scala orchestra have this music under their collective fingers; indeed
there is an energy and vitality to this playing that is wholly infectious. For Chailly's earlier recording,
Montserrat Caballé was a very underpowered Fiorilla; Bartoli is full of fire and mettle (her "Sqallido
veste bruna" is sensational). Michele Pertusi is a fine Selim and his performance seems to breathe
stage experience – it is a characterization that is as vocally fine as it is theatrically adept. Alessandro
Corbelli, reinforcing his credentials as a Rossini singer of flair and panache, is a strongly
characterized Geronio. This is a recording that smacks of the theatre, and unlike so many so-called
comic operas, has lost nothing in its transfer to disc. Under Chailly's baton it fizzes and crackles like
few other sets – recitatives are dispatched with the assurance of native Italian speakers and with a
genuine feeling for the meaning of the text. Decca's recording is beautifully judged and the set makes
a fine modern alternative to the now classic (but cut) 1954 recording under Gavazzeni with Maria
Callas incomparable as Fiorilla.

Additional recommendations ...
...**Soloists; Chorus and Orchestra of La Scala, Milan / Gianandrea Gavazzeni.**
EMI mono Ⓜ CDS5 56313-2* (two discs: 113 minutes: ADD: 12/87).
...**Soloists; Ambrosian Opera Chorus; National Philharmonia Orchestra / Riccardo Chailly.**
CBS Masterworks Ⓟ S2K37859 (two discs: 146 minutes: DDD: 9/89).
...**Soloists; Ambrosian Opera Chorus; Academy of St Martin in the Fields / Sir Neville Marriner.**
Philips Ⓟ 434 128-2PH2 (two discs: 154 minutes: DDD: 12/92).

Rossini Il viaggio a Reims. **Sylvia McNair** (sop) Corinna; **Cheryl Studer** (sop) Madama Cortese;
Luciana Serra (sop) Contessa di Folleville; **Lucia Valentini Terrani** (mez) Marchesa Melibea;
Raúl Giménez (ten) Cavalier Belfiore; **William Matteuzzi** (ten) Conte di Libenskof; **Samuel Ramey**

(bass) Lord Sidney; **Ruggero Raimondi** (bass) Don Profondo; **Enzo Dara** (bar)
Barone di Trombonok; **Giorgio Surian** (bar) Don Prudenzio; **Lucio Gallo** (bar) Don Alvaro;
Berlin Radio Chorus; Berlin Philharmonic Orchestra / Claudio Abbado.
Sony Classical Ⓕ S2K53336 (two discs: 135 minutes: DDD: 12/93). Notes, text
and translation included. Recorded live in 1992.   ❸❸❸
The rediscovery of Rossini's dazzling, sophisticated coronation entertainment *Il viaggio a Reims* was
one of the musical highlights of the 1980s; and it was Abbado's DG recording that brought the work
to the public at large (it was voted *Gramophone*'s Record of the Year in 1986). No one who already
has the DG recording need feel compelled to go out and buy the Sony. After all, the music is the same,
and so are no fewer than six of the 11 principal singers. Of the singers who are repeating their roles,
both Ramey and Dara now surpass their already superb earlier performances. Dara has transformed
the aria in which Baron Trombonok catalogues national foibles. What was previously more or less a
straight recitation is now a miracle of subversive inflexion, with Abbado and the Berlin players
adding wonderful new colours that seem to lie dormant in the earlier recording. When it comes to the
singers, the Sony set has its weaknesses. Not Gallo. His Don Alvaro is less cumbersome than Nucci's
on DG. Nor perhaps Serra as the fashion-crazed young French widow. But for Count Libenskof DG's
Francisco Araiza is far more in command of the role than William Matteuzzi. On balance, though,
collectors will be better off with the Sony, and it is better recorded.

Additional recommendation ...
...**Soloists; Prague Philharmonic Chorus; Chamber Orchestra of Europe / Claudio Abbado.**
DG Ⓕ 415 498-2GH2 (two discs: 136 minutes: DDD: 1/86). *Gramophone classical 100.*
Gramophone Award Winner 1986.   ❸❸❸

Further listening ...
...Introduction, Theme and Variations in B flat major. *Coupled with works by various composers.*
Emma Johnson (cl); **English Chamber Orchestra / Sir Charles Groves.**
ASV CDDCA559 (11/86).   ❸❸
...Wind Quartet No. 6. *Coupled with works by various composers.* **Aulos Quintet.**
Koch Schwann Musica Mundi 310087 (10/91).   ❸
...Péchés de Vieillesse, Book 5, "Album pour les enfants adolescents" – Ouf! les petits pois;
Un sauté; Book 8, "Album de château" – Un regret, un espoir; Prélude prétentieux;
Book 9 – La savoie aimante. *Coupled with works by various composers.* **Marcelle Meyer** (pf).
EMI mono CZS5 68092-2* (6/95). *See review in the Collections section; refer to the Index.* ❸❸❸
...Péchés de vieillesse, Book 9 – Prélude, thème et variations. *Coupled with works by* **Mozart**
and **Mendelssohn** Gerald Moore (pf). Testament SBT1102 (7/97).
...Messa di gloria. **Sumi Jo** (sop); **Ann Murray** (mez); **Raúl Giménez, Francisco Araiza** (tens);
Samuel Ramey (bass); **Academy of St Martin in the Fields Chorus and Orchestra /**
Sir Neville Marriner. Philips 434 132-2PH (12/92).
...Giovanna d'Arco. Songs – Ariette à l'ancienne. Beltà crudele. Canzonetta spagnuola.
Il risentimento. Il trovatore. L'âme délaissée. L'Orpheline du Tyrol. La Grande Coquette.
La légende de Marguerite. La pastorella. La regate veneziana. Mi lagnerò. Nizza.
Cecilia Bartoli (mez); **Charles Spencer** (pf). Decca 430 518-2DH (4/91).
...Soirées musicales – La promessa; L'invito; La pastorella dell'Alpi.
Coupled with works by various composers. **Rebecca Evans** (sop); **Michael Pollock** (pf).
EMI Debut CDZ5 69706-2 (5/97).
...Le Comte Ory. **Soloists; Chorus and Orchestra of Lyon Opera / Sir John Eliot Gardiner.**
Philips 422 406-2PH2 (10/89).
...Le Comte Ory. **Soloists; Glyndebourne Festival Chorus; Glyndebourne Festival Orchestra /**
Vittorio Gui. EMI mono CMS7 64180-2* (5/92).
...Demetrio e Polibio. **Soloists; Sluk Chamber Choir of Bratislava; Graz Symphony Orchestra /**
Massimiliano Carraro. Dynamic CDS171 (4/97).
...La donna del lago. **Soloists; Prague Philharmonic Chorus; Chamber Orchestra of Europe /**
Maurizo Pollini. CBS Masterworks S2K39311 (8/88).
...Elisabetta, Regina d'Inghilterra. **Soloists; Ambrosian Singers; London Symphony Orchestra /**
Gian-Franco Masini. Philips 432 453-2PM2 (12/92).
...Ermione. **Soloists; Prague Philharmonic Chorus; Monte Carlo Philharmonic Orchestra /**
Claudio Scimone. Erato 2292-45790-2.
...La gazza ladra. **Soloists; Prague Philharmonic Choir; Turin Radio Symphony Orchestra /**
Gianluigi Gelmetti. Sony Classical S3K45850 (10/90).
...Guillaume Tell. **Soloists; Ambrosian Opera Chorus; National Philharmonic Orchestra /**
Riccardo Chailly. Decca 417 154-2DH4 (2/87).
...Mosè in Egitto. **Soloists; Ambrosian Opera Chorus; Philharmonia Orchestra / Claudio Scimone.**
Philips 420 109-2PM2 (12/92).
...L'occasione fa il ladro. **Soloists; English Chamber Orchestra / Marcello Viotti.**
Claves 50-9208 (5/93).
...Otello. **Soloists; Ambrosian Opera Chorus; Philharmonia Orchestra / Jesús López-Cobos.**
Philips 432 456-2PM2 (12/92).
...Ricciardo e Zoraide. **Soloists; Geoffrey Mitchell Choir; Academy of St Martin in the Fields /**
David Parry. Opera Rara ORC14 (4/97).

Nino Rota

Rota Film Music – The Godfather. Il gattopardo. Prova d'orchestra. La dolce vita.
Otto e mezzo. Rocco e i suoi fratelli. **La Scala Philharmonic Orchestra / Riccardo Muti.**
Sony Classical Ⓕ SK63359 (71 minutes: DDD: 4/98). Recorded 1979.

The influences on Nino Rota's music for *The Godfather* aren't hard to identify – Stravinsky, Ravel, Puccini. It's an ironic commentary on the sordid story to back it with surging neo-romantic symphonic music. Coppola's two-part epic of Italian immigrants in the USA and the drift into mob rule was probably the biggest assignment of Rota's long career. The score made a huge contribution to the film's success – so much so that after his death the studio returned to his music for *Godfather III*. Its mixture of Neapolitan folk-song spattered with jazzy honky-tonk makes for a pleasant opening to this second CD of Rota's music by Riccardo Muti and the Scala Philharmonic. Rota's career was inextricably bound up with those of the two most influential Italian film-makers of the 1950s and 1960s – Fellini and Visconti. Fellini's two big successes of the early 1960s, *La dolce vita* and *Otto e mezzo* are represented by brief extracts – the open-air circus-parade finale of the latter score still has a mysterious, exuberant feel. The sources Rota drew on for this are similar to those in *The Godfather* but his use of them is surer and more original. The last collaboration with Fellini was the comedy about a rehearsal – *Prova d'orchestra*. Time is not being kind to a lot of Fellini's work which now seems self-indulgent, but conversely Visconti's films have a massive grandeur that is overwhelming. *Il gattopardo* ("The Leopard") remains one of the most startling and ambitious films ever made. Muti's first screen use of Rota had the ballroom sequence; here there is a brief suite of themes from the film. *Rocco e i suoi fratelli* caused a scandal in Italy in 1960 with its depiction of organized crime and corruption and it led to Visconti's rift with La Scala because of government interference. He would surely have smiled to think, nearly 40 years later, of the orchestra playing Rota's score for the film. Anyone who enjoyed the disc listed below will be pleased with this follow-up, but those who have not yet heard *La strada* should start with that.

Further listening ...

...La strada – ballet suite. Il Gattopardo – dances. Concerto for Strings. **La Scala Philharmonic Orchestra / Riccardo Muti.** Sony Classical Ⓕ SK66279 (62 minutes: DDD: 8/95).
Gramophone Editor's choice.   Ⓖ

...Piccola offerta musicale[a]. Sarabanda e Toccata[b]. Trio[c]. Ippolito gioca[d]. Il presepio[e]. Difficult pieces for children[f] – Cantilena; Puccettino nella giungha. Intermezzo[g]. Nonetto[h]. [e]**Anna Maria Pammer** (sop); [a]**Felix Renggli**, [ch]**Sharon Bezaly** (fls); [a]**Heinz Holliger**, [h]**Markus Deuter** (obs); [a]**Elmar Schmid**, [h]**Bernhard Zachhuber** (cls); [a]**Klaus Thunemann**, [h]**Lorelei Dowling** (bns); [a]**Radovan Vlatkovič**, [h]**Volker Altmann** (hns); [c]**Gidon Kremer**, [h]**Hanna Weinmeister** (vns); [g]**Gérard Caussé**, [h]**Firmiam Lermer** (vas); [h]**Howard Penny** (vc); [h]**Erich Hehenberger** (db); [b]**Maria Graf** (hp); [c]**Oleg Maisenberg**, [d]**Marino Formenti**, [f]**Mascha Smirnov**, [g]**Alena Chernushenko** (pfs); [e]**Hagen Quartet.** BIS CD870 (A/97).

Christopher Rouse

Rouse Trombone Concerto, "In memoriam Leonard Bernstein"[a]. Gorgon. Iscariot. [a]**Joseph Alessi** (tbn); **Colorado Symphony Orchestra / Marin Alsop.** RCA Victor Red Seal Ⓕ 09026 68410-2 (62 minutes: DDD: 8/97). Recorded 1995. *Gramophone Editor's choice.*

These striking pieces by Christopher Rouse, one of the more genuinely individual composers working in America today, are performed with impressive commitment and authority by Marin Alsop and her orchestra. Originally an acolyte of George Crumb, Rouse has since gone his own way, incorporating elements of rock music in a series of energetic orchestral pile-drivers before striking out into the symphonic mainstream with Shostakovich an increasingly powerful presence. There is a none-too-subtle quality about the invention, the resort to musical allusion and (intimidating to some) the pop-inspired dynamic range. And yet, as Rouse's music has become increasingly conservative, he has avoided the cute and if anything grown bolder. The longest work here, the Trombone Concerto of 1992, packs a formidable punch in a virtuosic, concentrated performance from Joseph Alessi, with solid if occasionally slightly ragged accompaniment from the orchestra. Mahler, Copland, Shostakovich (the Fourth Symphony) and, principally, Leonard Bernstein are raided for archetypes: the work borrows a theme from the latter's *Kaddish* Symphony. *Gorgon* is an earlier piece, a startling demonstration of the energy that informed Rouse's previous creative phases, conclusive proof that concert music can explode with the volume and drive of rock. Alsop secures a real performance and the recording gives impressive weight to the percussion section. Play loud or not at all. *Iscariot* is a complete contrast, slow moving and lightly scored (which is not to say quiet). There is consoling balm but scepticism too in those post-Ivesian string sonorities, attacked with relish by the players. The recording as such seems rather more successful here than in the Trombone Concerto, with greater detail achieved. This is an invigorating and accessible programme.

Further listening ...

...Cello Concerto. *Coupled with works by* **Kirchner** *and* **Danielpour** Yo-Yo Ma (vc); **Philadelphia Orchestra / David Zinman.** Sony Classical SK66299 (3/97).
Gramophone Editor's choice. See review under Danielpour; refer to the Index.

...Symphony No. 2. Flute Concerto[a]. Phaethon. [a]**Carol Wincenc** (fl); **Houston Symphony Orchestra /
Christoph Eschenbach.** Telarc CD80452 (8/97).

Albert Roussel

French 1869-1937

Roussel Bacchus et Ariane, Op. 43. Le festin de l'araignée, Op. 17. **BBC Philharmonic Orchestra /
Yan Pascal Tortelier.** Chandos Ⓕ CHAN9494 (68 minutes: DDD: 8/96).
Gramophone Editor's choice.   ⒼⒼ
As compared to his contemporary Dukas, Roussel has been somewhat sidelined as a "connoisseur's
composer". That presumably means that he did not write fat, lush tunes that could be exploited in
television commercials, but produced works of vigorous ideas and more subtle quality. Record
companies used to fight shy of his music – the Third and Fourth Symphonies have indeed maintained
a foothold, but with the ballet *Bacchus et Ariane*, which is closely linked with the Third, we have
mostly been given only its second half. Here are alert, rhythmically vital performances of Roussel's
two most famous ballets, which even at the most exuberantly excited moments (like the "Bacchanale"
in *Bacchus*) preserve a truly Gallic lucidity, and which Tortelier marks by a captivating lightness of
touch; and when it comes to quiet passages one could not ask for greater tenderness than in the
beautiful end of Act 1 of *Bacchus* (shame on those conductors who neglect this for the more extrovert
Act 2), when Bacchus puts Ariadne to sleep. *Le festin de l'araignée*, written 18 years earlier, is in a
quite different style. Where *Bacchus*'s trenchant idiom at times makes one think of Stravinsky's
Apollon Musagète, *Le festin* (which had the misfortune to be overshadowed by *The Rite of Spring*,
produced only eight weeks later) is atmospheric and more impressionistic (in the same vein as
Roussel's First Symphony). It is a score full of delicate invention, whose one weakness is that for its
full appreciation a knowledge of its detailed programme is needed – and that is provided here in the
booklet. The BBC Philharmonic play it beautifully. If this is 'connoisseur's music', then be happy to
be called a connoisseur: you will find it delectable.

Roussel Symphony No. 3 in G minor, Op. 42[b].
Franck Symphony in D minor[a]. **French National Orchestra / Leonard Bernstein.**
DG Masters Ⓜ 445 512-2GMA (69 minutes: DDD: 10/95). Recorded live in 1981.
Item marked [a] from 2532 050 (12/82), [b]previously unpublished.
This 1981 Roussel Third is recognizably via Bernstein, and is more kaleidoscopic and meaningful than
you are likely to have heard it, unless you possess his first New York account (CBS, 11/67 – never
reissued on CD). The *Rite of Spring*-cum-*Age of Steel* stamping rhythms of the first movement are
now a little slower, the effect possibly a little relaxed until you arrive at the central climax (astonishing
'whooping' horns and crashing metal) and the coda (now superbly emphatic with ringing trumpets
and lots more crashing metal). The slow movement's songful yearning is, as it was before, slow,
sublime and intensely searching in the manner of its counterpart in Mahler's Sixth, though the
contrasting *più mosso* is not now fast enough and has its limp moments. That said, the general control
is superior, particularly at and around the movement's now awesome final climax. Bernstein's New
Yorkers were uninhibitedly rowdy and brash in the finale; the finale's moments of brashness are now
offset by rather more sophistication (at, again, a slower tempo). The recording, which has a less than
ideally focused bass drum, is both spacious and present, with an appropriate touch of astringency on
top. Bernstein's Franck is atmospheric, big on rhetoric, extreme in its range of tempo and dynamics
and typically intense. His control is again superb, with the orchestra's winds mellifluous in tone.
Additional recommendations ...
...No. 3. Bacchus et Ariane – ballet suite No. 2. **Detroit Symphony Orchestra / Neeme Järvi.**
Chandos Ⓕ CHAN8996 (68 minutes: DDD: 10/95).
...No. 1, Op. 7, "Le poème de la forêt"; No. 2 in B flat major, Op. 23; No. 3; No. 4 in A major,
Op. 53. **French Radio Philharmonic Orchestra / Marek Janowski.**
RCA Victor Red Seal Ⓕ 09026 62511-2 (two discs: 119 minutes: 6/96).
...No. 3. *Coupled with works by* **Honegger** and **Milhaud** New York Philharmonic Orchestra /
Leonard Bernstein. Sony Classical Masterworks Heritage Ⓜ MHK62352 (74 minutes: ADD: 10/97).
See review under Honegger; refer to the Index.
...Symphonies Nos. 1-4. **French National Orchestra / Charles Dutoit.**
Teldec Ultima Ⓑ 3984-21090-2 (two discs: 119 minutes: DDD: 5/98).

Roussel Impromptu, Op. 21[a]. Deux Poèmes de Ronsard, Op. 26[b]. Joueurs de flûte, Op. 27[c]. Violin
Sonata No. 2 in A major[d]. Segovia, Op. 29[e]. Sérénade, Op. 30[f]. Duo[g]. Vocalises – Aria No. 2[h].
[b]**Irene Maessen** (sop); [bcf]**Paul Verhey** (fl); [h]**Hans Roerade** (ob); [gh]**Jos de Lange** (bn); [d]**Jean-Jacques
Kantorow** (vn); [af]**Erika Waardenburg** (hp); [e]**Jan Goudswaard** (gtr); [g]**Quirijn van Regteren Altena**
(db); [cdh]**Jet Röling** (pf); [f]**Schoenberg Quartet** (Janneke van der Meer, Wim de Jong, vns; Henk
Guittart, va; Viola de Hoog, vc). Olympia Ⓕ OCD459 (65 minutes: DDD: 9/95). Recorded 1994.
While Roussel's orchestral music has won a following in this country, his chamber music still, for the
most part, enjoys only cult status here. This excellent second volume covers the period from 1919 to
1928, when Roussel, firmly rejecting the impressionism of his contemporary Ravel, had adopted what
is often (though loosely) referred to as neo-classical style. Try as one may, it is difficult to avoid the

use of the adjective "astringent" commonly applied to his music; but along with its clean-cut clarity (like that of a good dry wine) and a rhythmic alertness often manifested in unusual time-signatures and changeable tempos goes a dry humour – as in the comic *Duo* for bassoon and double-bass, the fourth piece of the *Joueurs de flûte* (in the vein of Debussy's *Prélude*, "General Lavine, eccentric") or the angular finale (mostly in 10/8) of the Second Violin Sonata. What is in short supply, however, except in the Aria played here on the oboe, is lyricism: Roussel can be seductive (the charmingly sung Ronsard songs, with their elaborate flute arabesques) or exotic ("Krishna", the third of the "flute players"), he can even indulge in pastiche, as in the guitar *Segovia*, but – even if this sounds like heresy – his themes remain obstinately unmemorable and he lacks purely melodic invention. Throughout the disc the performances merit the highest praise but special mention must be made of Erika Waardenburg's beautiful playing, with superfine tonal gradations, of the *Impromptu* for harp.

Additional recommendation ...

...Segovia. *Coupled with works by various composers.* **Elliot Fisk** (gtr). MusicMasters Ⓟ 67174-2 (76 minutes: DDD: 4/97). *See review in the Collections section; refer to the Index.*

Further listening ...

...Piano Concerto in G major, Op. 36[a]. Concertino, Op. 57[b]. Pour une fête de printemps, Op. 22. Suite in F major, Op. 33. [b]**Albert Tétard** (vc); [a]**Danielle Laval** (pf); **Orchestre de Paris / Jean-Pierre Jacquillat.** EMI L'Esprit Français CDM5 65154-2 (7/95).

...Symphony No. 4 in A major, Op. 53. Sinfonietta, Op. 52. *Coupled with works by* **Debussy** and **Milhaud** Detroit Symphony Orchestra / Neeme Järvi. Chandos CHAN9072 (12/92).

...Suite in F major, Op. 33. *Coupled with works by* **Chabrier** Detroit Symphony Orchestra / Paul Paray. Mercury 434 303-2MM*. *See review under Chabrier; refer to the Index.* ⒼⒼⒼ

...Trio, Op. 40[afg]. String Quartet in D major, Op. 45[g]. Andante and Scherzo, Op. 51[ae]. Pipe in D major[ae]. Trio, Op. 58[g]. Elpénor, Op. 59[ag]. Andante[bcd]. [a]**Paul Verhey** (fl); [b]**Hans Roerade** (ob); [c]**Frank van den Brink** (cl); [d]**Jos de Lange** (bn); [e]**Jet Röling** (pf); [f]**Herre-Jan Stegenga** (vc); [g]**Schoenberg Quartet.** Olympia OCD460 (11/95).

...Andante and Scherzo, Op. 51. *Coupled with works by various composers.* **Peter Lloyd** (fl); **Rebecca Holt** (pf). IMP Classics PCD991 (9/92).

...Prelude and Fughetta, Op. 41. *Coupled with works by various composers.* **Marie-Bernadette Dufourcet** (org). Priory PRCD422 (6/95). *See review in the Collections section; refer to the Index.*

Francis Routh   British 1927

Suggested listening ...

...Clarinet Quintet. *Coupled with works by* **Rawsthorne** and **Bliss** Nicholas Cox (cl); **Nicholas Ward, Peter Pople** (vns); **Ivo-Jan van der Werff** (va); **Paul Marleyn** (vc). Redcliffe Recordings RR010 (11/96). *See review under Bliss; refer to the Index.*

Miklós Rózsa   Hungarian/American 1907-1995

Rózsa Cello Concerto, Op. 32[a].
Schurmann The Gardens of Exile. [a]**Peter Rejto** (vc); **Pecs Hungarian Symphony Orchestra / Howard Williams.** Silva Classics Ⓟ SILKD6011 (60 minutes: DDD: 9/96). Recorded 1995.
Rózsa's Cello Concerto (1969) is substantial, concentrated and accomplished. What is immediately striking is not so much the beguilingly tangy harmonic resource and rhythmic flair of his inspiration (the composer's native Hungarian roots shine through in every bar) as the effortless technical assurance and irresistible colour of it all (Rózsa's expert scoring is a real treat throughout). The eventful, beautifully proportioned first movement is rich in strong ideas, persuasively worked out, and features a cadenza which combines eloquence and riveting virtuosity. By contrast, the central *Lento con grand espressione* is songful and tinged with anguish, whereas the *Allegro vivo* finale, save for a brief, shadowy slower episode, positively swaggers with spiky energy and (again) terrific rhythmic *élan*. Like Rózsa, Gerard Schurmann has gained a reputation as a composer of both film and 'serious' music. Scored for cello obbligato and orchestra, *The Gardens of Exile* (1991) bears a dedication to Sir Michael Tippett. In an introductory note the composer explains: "The condition of exile referred to in the title of this piece is internal, while the metaphorical gardens in which to dwell contain cultivated memories of the past, back to childhood. Superimposed on this idea were my recollections of a vast expanse of semi-wild tropical gardens in Java. Elegantly structured and the product of a sophisticated aural imagination (the orchestration is exotic, luscious even), Schurmann's music has something of the craft and angular lyricism of his teacher, Alan Rawsthorne. In fact *The Gardens of Exile* is a most beguiling score. Rejto is a commanding, highly articulate soloist and his contribution has both discipline and tonal lustre to commend it. The accompaniment is watchful and dedicated and although balance is well judged, the overall sound could have done with more bloom. A most enjoyable pairing.

Rózsa Variations on a Hungarian Peasant Song, Op. 4[a]. North Hungarian Peasant Songs and Dances, Op. 5[a]. Duo, Op. 7[a]. Solo Violin Sonata, Op. 40. **Isabella Lippi** (vn); [a]**John Novacek** (pf). Koch International Classics Ⓟ 37256-2 (62 minutes: DDD: 11/95). Recorded 1994.

In his autobiography, *A Double Life* (Midas Books: 1982) Rózsa proudly declares that "the music of Hungary is stamped indelibly ... on virtually every bar I have ever put on paper", and nowhere are the fervent, rustic rhythms of the composer's beloved homeland more vividly assimilated than in his music for solo violin. This is especially true of Opp. 4 and 5, two early successes from 1929, both of which blaze with potent memories of the Magyar peasant music that Rózsa felt was all around him, and which he would jot down "in a kind of delirium" during his youth on the family estate. Op. 7 was written two years later and marked the end of his term as a student in Leipzig. Though evoking once again the gipsy fiddlers of his boyhood, the themes here are actually Rózsa's own and reveal some of the surging romanticism that would later characterize his film scores. Following his memorable career in Hollywood, Rózsa made a satisfying return to 'pure' music with the Solo Violin Sonata of 1986. Dedicated to his friend Manuel Compinsky, this passionate, energetic piece pays another loving tribute to the mother country that provided Rózsa with a "living source of inspiration". Isabella Lippi is a highly expressive soloist. She tackles the many fiendishly animated passages with great panache but also displays a keen understanding of the music's pastoral colouring and darkly romantic fervour. Sympathetic support from her accompanist and clear, warm sound.

Further listening ...

...Viola Concerto, Op. 37[a]. Sinfonia concertante for Violin, Cello and Orchestra, Op. 29[b]. [b]**Igor Gruppman** (vn); [a]**Paul Silverthorne** (va); [b]**Richard Boch** (vc); **New Zealand Symphony Orchestra / James Sedares**. Koch International Classics 37304-2 (10/96).

...Violin Concerto, Op. 24. Tema con variazioni, Op. 29a. *Coupled with works by* **Korngold** and **Waxman** Jascha Heifetz (vn); Gregor Piatigorsky (vc); **Chamber Orchestra / Alfred Wallenstein**. RCA Victor Gold Seal GD87963 (4/89). *See review under Korngold; refer to the Index.* ⊕⊕⊕

...Theme, Variations and Finale, Op. 13a. Hungarian Nocturne, Op. 28. Three Hungarian Sketches, Op. 14. Overture to a Symphony Concert, Op. 26a. **New Zealand Symphony Orchestra / James Sedares**. Koch International Classics 37191-2 (9/93). *Gramophone Editor's choice.*

...Symphony in Three Movements, Op. 6a. The Vintner's Daughter, Op. 23a. **New Zealand Symphony Orchestra / James Sedares**. Koch International Classics 37244-2 (6/94).

Edmund Rubbra
British 1901-1986

Rubbra Violin Concerto, Op. 103[a]. Viola Concerto, Op. 75[b]. [a]**Tasmin Little** (vn); [a]**Rivka Golani** (va); **Royal Philharmonic Orchestra / Vernon Handley**. Conifer Classics Ⓕ CDCF225 (54 minutes: DDD: 10/94). Recorded 1994. ⊕⊕

The Viola Concerto, a première recording, is a work of striking euphony and depth. There are none of the piquant dissonances of, say, the Bartók or Walton concertos; the Rubbra concentrates on linear development; the satisfaction this concerto gives resides primarily in the subtlety with which its lines evolve and grow. The pensive, rhapsodic opening puts one immediately under its spell. The most poetic of the three movements is the finale, subtitled *Collana musicale* or "musical necklace", nine linked sections, each of them self-contained and offering thoughts on the theme rather than conventional variations. Rivka Golani gives a fine account of the solo part, her playing committed and intelligent even though her tone could at times do with greater opulence. The Violin Concerto, too, is a three-movement piece, though here it is the middle movement, *Poema,* that is the emotional centre of gravity; it has both depth and serenity. The invention unfolds seemlessly and organically, each idea growing out of and developing from the preceding one. Tasmin Little's playing is thoughtful and eloquent and her virtuosity conveys a sense of effortless ease. Moreover, in Vernon Handley she is supported by a conductor who both knows what this music is about, and has its measure.

Rubbra Symphony No. 1, Op. 44. Sinfonia concertante, Op. 38[a]. A tribute, Op. 56. [a]**Howard Shelley** (pf); **BBC National Orchestra of Wales / Richard Hickox.** Chandos Ⓕ CHAN9538 (71 minutes: DDD: 10/97). Recorded 1995-1996. *Gramophone Editor's choice.*

An important issue. With it Richard Hickox turns to the Rubbra of the 1930s. The First Symphony dates from 1935-1937 and the *Sinfonia concertante* precedes it, though in the form in which we know it dates from the early-1940s. At its first performance in 1937 parallels were drawn between the First Symphony and Vaughan Williams's Fourth and Walton's B flat minor, for like them this is powerful and at times angry music. Robert Simpson described it as a "severe, even stringent piece ... [whose] dogged power is not meant to endear itself to the listener". Harold Truscott wrote of it demanding "enormous concentration of the listener" and spoke of its orchestration as "persistently thick and without relief". In fact, he went so far as to say "it's not primarily an orchestral sound at all and you have to forget colour and concentrate on line development". You could say that evolution rather than development in the conventional sense lies at the heart of its musical processes. It is a tribute to the orchestral balance that Richard Hickox has achieved and the expertise of the Chandos team that the texture sounds as lucid as it does. The tempestuous first movement comes off very well, so does the charming second movement, *Perigourdine*, a French dance whose eight-bar tune runs through the whole movement like a sort of *moto perpetuo*. However, it is the powerful slow finale, which is longer than the other two put together, that leaves the strongest and most enduring impression. The *Sinfonia concertante* is hardly less substantial or indeed symphonic. Its beautiful and reflective opening almost foreshadows the later Piano Concerto in G major but, as with the Symphony, it is the last movement which resonates longest in the memory. This is a prelude and fugue dedicated to the memory of his teacher, Gustav Holst who had died in 1934. It is a searching, thoughtful movement, eloquently and sensitively performed. Both the Symphony and the *Sinfonia concertante* have taken 60 years to reach the catalogue, and the fact that they are long overdue does not diminish the warmth of their welcome.

Rubbra Symphonies – No. 2 in D major, Op. 45; No. 6, Op. 80. **BBC National Orchestra of Wales / Richard Hickox.** Chandos Ⓕ CHAN9481 (68 minutes: DDD: 11/96). Recorded 1996.

By scrupulously observing every dynamic nuance and ensuring that accents are light and articulation is alive, Richard Hickox and his orchestra succeed in making the Second Symphony sound more lucid than before. He takes particular care with the violin line which Rubbra so often doubled at the octave, and which when phrased with the right weight does not sound as thick as it can so easily do. Even the admittedly overscored *Scherzo* gains by his lighter accentuation. But the heart of the work is its slow movement, a serene and moving meditation. Good though Vernon Handley's recording was, Hickox comes even closer to the tranquillity and at the same time the power that this music enshrines, and builds the movement with masterly control. The Sixth Symphony dates from the 1950s at a time when Rubbra enjoyed something approaching fame. The slow movement, *Canto*, is wonderfully serene and one of the most beautiful he ever wrote. It grows out of an open fifth and in its purity and tranquillity of spirit it calls to mind the world of the *Missa in honorem Sancti Dominici* written five years earlier. Hickox prepares every change in mood so naturally; he always allows the space in which the argument can unfold. Particularly striking is the coda of the first movement (track 1, 8'02") which sounds even more effective here than on Norman Del Mar's excellent Philharmonia disc. The carolling figure on harp, celesta and clarinets in the *Scherzo* is also beautifully done. All praise for Hickox's perceptive interpretation, the players' dedication and sensitivity and the exemplary recorded sound.

Additional recommendations ...

...No. 2 [a]; No. 7 in C major, Op. 88[b]. Festival Overture, Op. 62[c]. [ac]**New Philharmonia Orchestra / Vernon Handley;** [b]**London Philharmonic Orchestra / Sir Adrian Boult.** Lyrita Ⓕ SRCD235 (78 minutes: ADD: 12/92).

...No. 6[a]; No. 8, Op. 132, "Hommage à Teilhard de Chardin". Soliloquy, Op. 57[b]. [b]**Rohan de Saram** (vc); [b]**London Symphony Orchestra / Vernon Handley;** [a]**Philharmonia Orchestra / Norman Del Mar.** Lyrita Ⓕ SRCD234 (73 minutes: ADD: 10/92).

Rubbra Symphonies – No. 4, Op. 53; No. 10, Op. 145, "Sinfonia da camera"; No. 11, Op. 153. **BBC National Orchestra of Wales / Richard Hickox.** Chandos Ⓕ CHAN9401 (58 minutes: DDD: 1/96). Recorded 1993-1994.

Rubbra's music lacks the kind of surface allure that captivates the ear at first acquaintance. Nor does he possess the dramatic power of Vaughan Williams or his immediate contemporary Walton, but he does have a sense of organic continuity that is both highly developed and immediately evident to the listener. Wilfrid Mellers put it in a nutshell when he said of the symphonies, there is "nothing abstruse about their tonality and harmony, which is basically diatonic", but they are difficult because "the continuity of their melodic and polyphonic growth is logical and unremitting. The orchestration shows scarcely any concern for the possibilities of colour, nothing on which the senses can linger and the nerves relax. Second subjects are hardly ever contrasting ideas but rather evolutions from or transfigurations of the old." The opening of the Fourth Symphony is one of the most beautiful things not just in Rubbra but in the English music of our time. These pages are free from any kind of artifice, and their serenity and quietude remain with the listener for a long time. The Fourth (1940-42) was a wartime work, though no one would ever guess so. The Tenth and Eleventh Symphonies are late works from 1974 and 1979 respectively. Both symphonies are highly concentrated one-movement affairs which unfold with the seeming inevitability and naturalness so characteristic of the composer. To sum up, this is music made to last. Richard Hickox has the measure of its breadth and serenity, and secures a sense of total commitment and dedication from his excellent players. The Chandos recording is in the best traditions of the house.

Additional recommendations ...

...Symphonies – No. 3, Op. 49; No. 4, Op. 53. A Tribute, Op. 56. Resurgam – Overture, Op. 149. **Philharmonia Orchestra / Norman Del Mar.** Lyrita Ⓕ SRCD202 (73 minutes: DDD: 11/90). *Selected by Sounds in Retrospect.*

...No. 10. Improvisations on Virginal Pieces by Giles Farnaby, Op. 50. A Tribute, Op. 56. **Bournemouth Sinfonietta / Hans-Hubert Schönzeler.** Chandos Collect Ⓜ CHAN6599 (40 minutes: ADD: 11/93).

Further listening ...

...Symphony No. 5 in B flat major, Op. 63. *Coupled with works by* **Bliss** *and* **Tippett** Melbourne Symphony Orchestra / Hans-Hubert Schönzeler. Chandos Collect CHAN6576 (6/92).

...Symphony No. 5 in B flat major, Op. 63. Improvisations on Virginal Pieces by Giles Farnaby, Op. 50 – No. 4, Loth to depart. *Coupled with works by* **Britten** *and* **Heming** Theo Olof (vn); Hallé Orchestra / Sir John Barbirolli. EMI British Composers mono CDM5 66053-2* (5/97). *See review under Britten; refer to the Index.*

...Symphony No. 9, Op. 140, "Sinfonia sacra"[a]. The Morning Watch, Op. 55. [a]**Lynne Dawson** (sop); [a]**Della Jones** (mez); [a]**Stephen Roberts** (bar); **BBC National Chorus and Orchestra of Wales / Richard Hickox.** Chandos CHAN9441 (6/96). *Gramophone Editor's choice.* Ⓖ

...Cello Sonata in G minor, Op. 60. *Coupled with works by* **Moeran** and **Ireland Raphael Wallfisch**
(vc); **John York** (pf). Marco Polo 8 223718 (8/95). *See review under Moeran; refer to the Index.*
...Cello Sonata in G minor, Op. 60. *Coupled with works by* **Britten** and **Mayer Timothy Gill** (vc);
Fali Pavri (pf). Guild GMCD7114 (4/96).
...String Quartets – No. 1 in F minor, Op. 35; No. 2 in E flat major; No. 3, Op. 112; No. 4, Op. 150.
Sterling Quartet. Conifer Classics 75605 51260-2 (5/96).
...String Quartet No. 2 in E flat major. *Coupled with works by* **Tate** and **P. Wishart**
English Quartet. Tremula TREM102-2 (12/93).
...Evening Service in A flat major. *Coupled with works by various composers.* **St Edmundsbury**
Cathedral Choir / Mervyn Cousins with **Scott Farrell** (org). Priory PRCD554 (1/97).

Anton Rubinstein

Russian 1829-1894

Rubinstein Piano Concerto No. 4 in D minor, Op. 70[a].
Encores Shura Cherkassky (pf); [a]**Royal Philharmonic Orchestra / Vladimir Ashkenazy.**
Decca Ⓕ 448 063-2DH (76 minutes: [a]DDD/[b]ADD: 3/96). Items marked [b] from L'Oiseau-Lyre
DSLO7 (6/75). Items marked [a]recorded 1994, [b]1974.
Encores[b]: **Rubinstein** Melody in F major, Op. 3 No. 1. **J. Strauss II/Godowsky** Wein, Weib
und Gesang. **Godowsky** Waltz-poem No. 4 (for left hand). Triakontameron – Alt Wien.
Saint-Saëns/Godowsky Le carnaval des animaux – No. 13, The swan. **Schubert/**
Godowsky Moment musical in F minor, D780 No. 3. **Tchaikovsky** Nocturne in C sharp
minor, Op. 19 No. 4. **Glazunov** Valse in D major, Op. 42 No. 3. **Chaminade** Autrefois, Op. 87
No. 4. **Moszkowski** Caprice espagnole, Op. 37.
What other pianist possessed so succulent or teasing a sense of sophistication? Every glistening strand
of Godowsky's *Wein, Weib und Gesang*, his polyphonic, poly-rhythmic maze, is highlighted with
uncanny virtuoso resource, and even Sir Clifford Curzon – that incomparable Schubertian – might
have smiled rather than frowned over Cherkassky's Schubert-Godowsky, an arrangement he
abhorred. Glazunov's *Valse* in D is spun off with a delicate, vertiginous brilliance entirely Cherkassky's
own and Chaminade's *Autrefois* is a charming pastiche. Then there is Rubinstein's Fourth Concerto,
another work for long at the centre of Cherkassky's affections. That august publication, *The Record
Guide* (Collins: 1951) may have offered a sniping estimate ("the swelling introduction promises great
things, but what emerges is perhaps only a rather large mouse") but played with Cherkassky's musical
commitment even the most outwardly conventional gestures take wing. A passing sense of frailty is
instantly erased by Cherkassky's tip-toe delicacy in the whirlwind finale, by a shot-silk tonal finesse
in the central *Andante*, and by a capacity to take all the time in the world to make his points, whether
piquantly or expressively. Ashkenazy's partnership with his quicksilver soloist could hardly be more
sympathetic and the recordings capture Cherkassky's tonal bloom and colour to perfection.
Additional recommendation ...
...Piano Concertos – No. 3 in G major, Op. 45; No. 4. **Joseph Banowetz** (pf);
Košice State Philharmonic Orchestra / Robert Stankovsky. Marco Polo 8 223382.

Rubinstein Piano Concerto No. 5 in E flat major, Op. 94. Caprice russe, Op. 102. **Joseph Banowetz**
(pf); **Bratislava Radio Symphony Orchestra / Robert Stankovsky.** Marco Polo Ⓕ 8 223489
(67 minutes: DDD: 2/95). Recorded 1993.
This disc brings to a conclusion Joseph Banowetz's admirable survey of Rubinstein's complete music
for piano and orchestra for Marco Polo. The Fifth Concerto (dating from 1874) is by far the most
monumental, both in terms of duration – it spans some 46 minutes – and in the virtuosic demands
that it places on any pianist brave enough to undertake a performance. Although it certainly has its
flaws (its length being one) there is still a great deal to admire, not least its abundance of warmly
lyrical melodies. The technical difficulties of the solo part may largely account for the concerto's
absence from the repertoire (the work is dedicated to the high priest of super-virtuosity, Alkan, and
contains chordal spans of gigantic proportions); but there is certainly more to this work than mere
showy virtuosity. The *Caprice russe* was composed four years after the Fifth Concerto and is a single
movement *concertante* work based on three Russian folk-songs whose origins, as Banowetz writes, are
somewhat dubious. He clearly has faith in the piece, to judge by his brilliant, engaging performance.
Further listening ...
...Don Quixote, Op. 87. Ivan the Terrible, Op. 79. **Russian State Symphony Orchestra /**
Igor Golovchin. Russian Disc RDCD11397 (9/95).
...Piano Concertos – No. 1 in E major, Op. 25; No. 2 in F major, Op. 35. **Joseph Banowetz** (pf);
Košice State Philharmonic Orchestra / Alfred Walter. Marco Polo 8 223456 (7/93).
...Symphony No. 4 in D minor, Op. 95, "Dramatic". **Russian State Symphony Orchestra /**
Igor Golovchin. Russian Disc RDCD11357 (6/95).
...Cello Sonata No. 1 in D major, Op. 18. *Coupled with works by* **Liszt** and **Grieg**
Steven Isserlis (vc); **Stephen Hough** (pf).
RCA Victor Red Seal 09026 68290-2 (4/96). *See review under Grieg; refer to the Index.*
...Barcarolles – No. 3 in G minor; No. 4 in G major. Valse-caprice in E flat major. *Coupled with
works by* **Liszt Artur Rubinstein** (pf). RCA Victor Gold Seal mono 09026 61860-2* (1/94).

...The Demon. **Soloists; Wexford Festival Chorus; National Symphony Orchestra of Ireland /
Alexander Anissimov.** Marco Polo 8 223781/2 (3/96).
...The Demon – Do not weep, my child; On the airy ocean; I am he whom you called. Nero –
Vindex's Epithalamium: I sing to you, Hymen divine!. *Coupled with works by various composers.*
Dmitri Hvorostovsky (bar); **Kirov Theatre Orchestra / Valery Gergiev.**
Philips 438 872-2PH (5/94). *See review in the Collections section; refer to the Index.*

Poul Ruders

Danish 1949

Ruders Violin Concerto No. 1[a]. Etude and Ricercare[b]. The Bells[c]. The Christmas Gospel[d]. [c]**Lucy
Shelton** (sop); [a]**Rolf Schulte** (vn); [c]**Speculum Musicae / David Starobin** ([b]gtr); [a]**Riverside Symphony
Orchestra / George Rothman;** [d]**Malmö Symphony Orchestra / Ola Rudner.** Bridge Ⓕ BCD9057
(62 minutes: DDD: 2/96). Texts included. Recorded 1994-95. *Gramophone Editor's choice.*   Ⓖ
Ruders's First Violin Concerto (from 1981) begins as routine minimalist auto-hypnosis. But it
develops some wonderfully inventive ways of disrupting and reassembling itself. Admittedly the last
movement, with its chaconne based on Vivaldi and Schubert, tiptoes on the border of sensationalism.
Otherwise the work could join Schnittke's Fourth as one of the few contemporary violin concertos
with a strong claim to standard-repertoire status. Rebecca Hirsch on Unicorn-Kanchana was superb;
now Rolf Schulte gives an even more intense account of the solo part; the Riverside orchestra are even
tighter in discipline, and the recording is a fraction closer. All these factors help to make the overall
musical impression even more vivid. Less persuasive is Ruders's vocal writing in *The Bells* (the same
Edgar Allen Poe texts as set by Rachmaninov), and there is something not quite convincing about the
instrumental setting too – perhaps too uniform an intensity, too much frantic heterophony. Oliver
Knussen has done this sort of thing rather more successfully. *The Christmas Gospel*, tossed off in two
weeks for a mixed animation and live-action film, is darkly impressive – necessarily simple and direct,
but still rewarding, even when divorced from the visual images. Superb performances and recordings
throughout.
Additional recommendation ...
...Violin Concerto No. 1[a]. Concerto for Clarinet and Twin-orchestra[b]. Drama-Trilogy –
Cello Concerto, "Polydrama"[c]. [a]**Rebecca Hirsch** (vn); [b]**Niels Thomsen** (cl); [c]**Morten Zeuthen** (vc);
Odense Symphony Orchestra / Tamás Vető.
Unicorn-Kanchana Ⓕ DKPCD9114 (60 minutes: DDD: 4/92).

Ruders Violin Concerto No. 2[a]. Dramaphonia[b]. [a]**Rebecca Hirsch** (vn); [b]**Poul Rosenbaum** (pf);
[a]**Copenhagen Collegium Musicum / Michael Schønwandt;** [b]**Lontano / Odaline de la Martinez.**
Da Capo Ⓕ DCCD9308 (61 minutes: DDD: 9/84). Recorded 1992.
The Second Violin Concerto was composed in 1990-91. It opens with two contrasting but tranquil
movements, the first inspired by the sight of an Andean eagle, seen by the composer whilst on holiday
in Chile. The imagery of a bird in flight, soaring, wheeling, diving, now still, permeates the music, the
last two movements of which are more impassioned. *Dramaphonia* (1987), played here by the
ensemble for whom it was composed (Lontano and Odaline de la Martinez), is of a more radical cast,
having no particular programme. The music charts a cumulatively compelling course through three
movements (played without a break) depicting a wide range of emotional states and atmospheres,
such as "Sinister", "Nervous", "Bleak", "Frantic" and so on. Both works receive committed and well-
prepared performances and the disc has been well engineered.
Further listening ...
...Psalmodies. *Coupled with works by* **Crumb** *and* **J.A. Lennon** David Starobin (gtr); **Speculum
Musicae / Donald Palma.** Bridge BCD9071 (6/97). *See review under Crumb; refer to the Index.*
...Psalmodies[a]. Vox in Rama[b]. [a]**David Starobin** (gtr); [a]**Speculum Musicae /
David Palma;** [bc]**Capricorn /** [c]**Oliver Knussen.** Bridge BCD9037 (5/93).
...Solar Trilogy – Gong; Zenith; Corona. **Odense Symphony Orchestra / Michael Schønwandt.**
Da Capo 8 224054 (6/97).
...Solar Trilogy – Gong. Symphony "Himmelhoch Jauchzend – zum Tode Betrübt".
Thus saw Saint John. Tundra. **Danish National Radio Symphony Orchestra / Leif Segerstam.**
Chandos CHAN9179 (10/93).   Ⓖ
...Second Set of Changes. *Coupled with works by various composers.* **Fretwork.**
Virgin Classics VC5 45217-2 (12/97). *See review in the Collections section; refer to the Index.*
...String Quartets – No. 2; No. 3, "Motet". *Coupled with* **Abrahamsen**
String Quartets Nos. 1 and 2. **Kontra Quartet.** Da Capo DCCD9006.

William Russell

British 1777-1813

Suggested listening ...
...Voluntary in F major. *Coupled with works by various composers.* **Jennifer Bate** (org).
Unicorn-Kanchana DKPCD9106 (11/91). *Selected by Sounds in Retrospect. See review in the
Collections section; refer to the Index.*   Ⓖ

John Rutter

British 1945

Rutter Requiem[ac]. Hymn to the Creator of Light. God be in my head. A Gaelic Blessing[c]. Psalmfest – No. 5, Cantate Domino. Open thou mine eyes[b]. A Prayer of St Patrick. A Choral Fanfare. Birthday Madrigals – No. 2, Draw on, sweet night; No. 4, My true love hath my heart. The Lord bless you and keep you[c]. [a]**Rosa Mannion,** [b]**Libby Crabtree** (sops); **Polyphony;** [c]**Bournemouth Sinfonietta / Stephen Layton.** Hyperion Ⓕ CDA66947 (69 minutes: DDD: 8/97). Texts and translations included. Recorded 1997. *Gramophone Editor's choice.*

Here is music finely crafted, written with love for the art and an especial care for choral sound. It is melodious without being commonplace, harmonically rich without being sticky, modern in the graceful way of a child who grows up responsive to newness but not wanting to kick his elders in the teeth. He gives us, in large measure, the heart's desire: we listen saying "Ah yes!" and with a half-foreseen satisfaction "Yes, of course! Lovely!" But he's on too familiar terms with our heart's desires, doesn't extend them, or surprise us into realizing that they were deeper and subtler than we thought. This is by way of cautiously savouring a remembered taste, which could readily be indulged without perceived need for an interval: one item leads to another and before we know it the pleasurable hour is over. The Requiem itself lasts for 36 minutes; the other pieces vary from under two minutes to just over six. Most are unaccompanied and show the choir of 25 voices as another of those expert groups of assured and gifted professionals that are among the principal adornments of modern musical life. Their capacity as a virtuoso choir is tested in the *Cantate Domino* and *Choral Fanfare*, but Rutter writes for real singers (not just singer-musicians) and their tone is unfailingly beautiful. Rosa Mannion and Libby Crabtree are excellent soloists. In the accompanied works the balance between singers and players is well judged, and the booklet is produced with Hyperion's customary good taste and helpfulness.

Additional recommendations ...

...Requiem. I will lift up mine eyes – Psalm 121. **Caroline Ashton, Donna Deam** (sops); **Cambridge Singers; City of London Sinfonia / John Rutter.** Collegium Ⓕ COLCD103 (44 minutes: DDD: 11/86).

...Gloria for chorus and orchestra. Anthems – All things bright and beautiful; The Lord bless you and keep you; The Lord is my shepherd; O clap your hands; Open thou mine eyes; Praise ye the Lord; A Prayer of St Patrick. **Cambridge Singers; Philip Jones Brass Ensemble / John Rutter.** Collegium Ⓕ COLCD100 (45 minutes: DDD: 6/87).

...Hymn to the Creator of Light. *Coupled with works by various composers.* **St Paul's Cathedral Choir / John Scott.** Hyperion Ⓕ CDA66994 (71 minutes: DDD: 12/97). *See review in the Collections section; refer to the Index.*

...Requiem[c]. Veni Sancte Spiritus[a]. What sweeter music[a]. Hymn to the Creator of Light. Cantate Domino. Cantus[b]. Te Deum[bc]. **King's College Choir, Cambridge / Stephen Cleobury** with [a]**Robert Quinney** (org); [b]**The Wallace Collection;** [c]**City of London Sinfonia.** EMI Ⓕ CDC5 56605-2 (74 minutes: DDD: 5/98).

Rutter Five Traditional Songs.
Vaughan Williams Five English Folksongs.
Traditional (arr. Rutter) I know where I'm going. Down by the sally gardens. The bold grenadier. The keel row. The cuckoo. She's like the swallow. Willow song. The willow tree. The miller of Dee. O can ye sew cushions? Afton water. The sprig of thyme. She moved through the fair (arr. Runswick). The lark in the clear air (arr. Carter). **Cambridge Singers; City of London Sinfonia / John Rutter.** Collegium Ⓕ COLCD120 (66 minutes: DDD: 11/93). Texts included. Ⓖ

Pleasure in singing is almost the *raison d'être* of this disc. John Rutter not only provides those of us over 30 with a healthy dollop of nostalgia, but gives these songs a whole new lease of life in some characteristically scrumptious arrangements. He is not attempting to follow in the footsteps of the great folk-song arrangers (he pays tribute to this tradition by including Vaughan Williams's *Five English Folksongs*). His arrangements belong more to the light music tradition; what Messrs Binge, Coates and Tomlinson achieved with orchestral colours Rutter finds primarily through vocal ones – and it's significant that the very finest arrangements here (including a ravishing "Golden Slumbers") are unaccompanied. He is supported throughout by an outstanding group of singers.

Further listening ...

...Fancies[a]. Suite antique[b]. Five Childhood Lyrics[c]. When icicles hang[a]. [b]**Duke Dobing** (fl); [b]**Wayne Marshall** (hpd); [ac]**Cambridge Singers;** [ab]**City of London Sinfonia / John Rutter.** Collegium COLCD117 (3/93).

Kaija Saariaho

Finnish 1952

Saariaho Verblendungen[a]. Jardin secret I[b]. Laconisme de l'aile[c]....sah den Vögeln[d]. NoaNoa[e]. [b]**Kaija Saariaho** (tape operator); [ce]**Camilla Hoitenga** (fl); [d]**Tuula-Marja Tuomela** (sop); [d]**Tapio Laivaara** (fl); [d]**Jouko Teikari** (ob); [d]**Eira Ojanen** (vc); [d]**Margit Rahkonen** (pf); [de]**Kaija Saariaho** (electronics); [a]**Finnish Radio Symphony Orchestra / **[a]**Esa-Pekka Salonen,** [d]**Atso Almila.** BIS Ⓕ CD307 (59 minutes: DDD/ADD: 1/98). Texts included. Recorded 1982, 1984 and 1996.

This is a fascinating profile largely of Saariaho's compositions from the early 1980s. Included on this welcome reissue are the rugged textures of *Verblendungen*, which is still among the most pungent of electroacoustic works, and the hermetic sound world of *Jardin Secret I*. However, *NoaNoa*, dating from 1991, and happily added for this reissue, demonstrates just how far her music has progressed in sophistication and tonal allure.

Further listening ...
...Du cristal[a]. ... à la fumée[b]. Nymphea, "Jardin secret III"[c]. [b]**Petri Alanko** (alto fl); [b]**Anssi Karttunen** (vc); [c]**Kronos Quartet;** [ab]**Los Angeles Philharmonic Orchestra / Esa-Pekka Salonen.** Ondine ODE804-2 (10/93).
...Nymphea. *Coupled with works by various composers.* **Kari Kriikku** (cl); **Jukka Tiensuu** (hpd); **Arditti Quartet.** Auvidis Montaigne MO782033 (9/96).

Nicholas Sackman
British 1950

Suggested listening ...
...Hawthorn. **BBC Symphony Orchestra / Andrew Davis.** NMC NMCD027S (7/96).
...Piano Sonata. *Coupled with works by various composers.* **Steven Neugarten** (pf).
Metier MSVCD92008 (1/96). *See review in the Collections section; refer to the Index.*

Harald Saeverud
Norwegian 1897-1992

Saeverud Peer Gynt, Op. 28 – Suites Nos. 1[a] and 2.
Grieg Peer Gynt Suites Nos. 1 and 2, Opp. 46 and 55. [a]**Anne-Margrethe Eikaas** (sop); **Norwegian Radio Orchestra / Ari Rasilainen.** Finlandia Ⓕ 0630-17675-2 (74 minutes: DDD: 5/98). Recorded 1996.

To juxtapose the *Peer Gynt* music of Grieg and Saeverud on record is such an obvious idea that it is astonishing that no one has thought of it before. It was inevitable that there should be a reaction against the pictorialism and romanticism of Grieg's *Peer Gynt*, particularly after the upheaval of the Second World War and the Nazi occupation of Norway, and when Saeverud was approached by Hans Jacob Nilsen to compose his incidental music, it was for a realistic production shorn of sentiment and glamour. Saeverud's score for the play has no vestige of romanticism, not a trace of gentility, and its musical language is robust and uncouth. It is full of character, whether it is in "Peerludium", the portrayal of the cocky Peer himself, the wild and lascivious "Anitra" (nothing demure about her) or the splendidly earthy "Devil's Five-hop" and the equally brilliant "Dovretroll jog". The Norwegian Radio Orchestra are a highly accomplished body with great refinement of colour and tone, and Ari Rasilainen draws splendid, well-characterized playing from them. The familiar Grieg suites are hardly less fine. The recording is refined, most realistic in perspective and ideally balanced.

Additional recommendation ...
...Peer Gynt, Op. 28 – Suites Nos. 1 and 2. Symphony No. 6, Op. 19, "Sinfonia dolorosa". Galdreslåtten, Op. 20. Kjempeviseslåtten, Op. 22*a* No. 5 (orch. cpsr). **Stavanger Symphony Orchestra / Alexander Dmitriev.** BIS Ⓕ CD762 (67 minutes: DDD: 12/96).

Further listening ...
...Tunes and Dances from Siljustøl: Suite No. 2, Op. 22 – Ballad of revolt. Suite No. 3, Op. 24 – Winflowers twiddle the moonbeam fiddle; Thor the hammerer. Suite No. 4, Op. 25 – Tone's cradle-song. *Coupled with works by various composers.* **Leif Ove Andsnes** (pf).
EMI CDC5 56541-2 (6/98). *See review in the Collections section; refer to the Index.*

Camille Saint-Saëns
French 1835-1921

Saint-Saëns Cello Concerto No. 1 in D minor[a].
Lalo Cello Concerto[b].
Schumann Cello Concerto No. 1 in A minor, Op. 129[b]. **János Starker** (vc); **London Symphony Orchestra /** [a]**Antál Dorati,** [b]**Stanislaw Skrowaczewski.** Mercury Ⓜ 432 010-2MM (65 minutes: ADD: 4/92). Item marked [a] from SAL3559 (7/66), [b]Philips SAL3482 (3/65).   ⒼⒼ

János Starker recorded for the Mercury label on several occasions during the 1960s, and the results provide a vivid document of an extraordinary artist heard at the peak of his career. The First Cello Concerto – which the composer completed in 1872 - is possibly Saint-Saëns's most fluent of all his concertos. However, he found the technical means of the instrument so restrictive that he vowed never to write another one, a vow he failed to keep. It has a pleasing, symmetrical design, full of engaging music. Starker succeeds in making it sound a good deal more substantial than it really is, in a reading of exemplary mastery coupled with scrupulous attention to every requirement of the score. His outward intensity belies a formidable intellectual mastery of Schumann's Cello Concerto, a work whose tangible mood of paranoia and mingled heroism has perplexed generations of players and listeners alike. Interpretations as zealous and charismatic as this are certainly to be treasured, as much for a clarification of the composer's intention, as for the valiant heroism of Starker's playing. He brings a similar clear-sighted gravity of purpose to the Lalo concerto, with a suitably massive opening movement contrasted effectively by a charmingly realized intermezzo and a finale of quicksilver brilliance. The sheer dynamism and drama of this reading has never been bettered. Mercury's original masters traditionally set new standards of fidelity and dynamic range, but in their refurbished form it seems scarcely possible that these classic performances are over 30 years old, whilst from a musical standpoint, these individual and occasionally provocative readings remain as enthralling as ever.

Additional recommendations ...

...Cello Concerto. *Coupled with works by* **Bruch** and **Lalo** Matt Haimovitz (vc); **Chicago Symphony Orchestra / James Levine.** DG Ⓕ 427 323-2GH (59 minutes: DDD: 6/89).

...Cello Concerto. *Coupled with works by* **Fauré** and **Lalo** Heinrich Schiff (vc); **New Philharmonia Orchestra / Sir Charles Mackerras.** DG Privilege Ⓑ 431 166-2GR (53 minutes: ADD: 8/91).

...Cello Concerto. *Coupled with works by* **Lalo** and **Massenet** Sophie Rolland (vc); **BBC Philharmonic Orchestra / Gilbert Varga.** ASV Ⓕ CDDCA867 (65 minutes: DDD: 12/93). *Gramophone Editor's choice. See review under Lalo; refer to the Index.* Ⓖ

...Cello Concerto. Le carnaval des animaux – The swan[a]. Romance in F major, Op. 36[b]. Romance in D major, Op. 51[b]. Cello Sonata No. 1 in C minor, Op. 32[b]. Chant saphique in D major, Op. 91[b]. Gavotte in G minor, Op. posth[b]. Allegro appassionato in B minor, Op. 43[b]. Prière, Op. 158[c]. **Steven Isserlis** (vc); **Dudley Moore**, [b]**Pascal Devoyon** (pfs); [c]**Francis Grier** (org); **London Symphony Orchestra / Michael Tilson Thomas.** RCA Victor Red Seal Ⓕ 09026 61678-2 (59 minutes: DDD: 12/93). Ⓖ

...Cello Concerto. *Coupled with works by various composers.* **Jacqueline du Pré** (vc) with various artists and orchestras. EMI Ⓑ CZS5 68132-2 (six discs: 437 minutes: ADD: 8/94). *See review in the Collections section; refer to the Index.* ⓒⓒ

...Cello Concerto. *Coupled with works by various composers.* **Mstislav Rostropovich** (vc); **Philharmonia Orchestra / Sir Malcolm Sargent.** Testament Ⓕ SBT1101* (79 minutes: ADD: 5/97).

...Cello Concertos – No. 1; No. 2 in D minor, Op. 119. Suite, Op. 16 (arr. vc/orch). Allegro appassionato in B minor, Op. 43. Le carnaval des animaux – Le cygne. **Maria Kliegel** (vc); **Bournemouth Sinfonietta / Jean-François Monnard.** Naxos Ⓢ 8 553039 (62 minutes: DDD: 11/97).

Saint-Saëns Piano Concertos – No. 1 in D major, Op. 17[a]; No. 2 in G minor, Op. 22[b]; No. 3 in E flat major, Op. 29[c]; No. 4 in C minor, Op. 44[a]; No. 5 in F major, Op. 103, "Egyptian"[b]. **Pascal Rogé** (pf); [a]**Philharmonia Orchestra;** [b]**Royal Philharmonic Orchestra;** [c]**London Philharmonic Orchestra / Charles Dutoit.** Double Decca Ⓜ 443 865-2DF2 (two discs: 140 minutes: ADD: 7/95). From D244D3 (10/81). ⓒⓒ

Saint-Saëns's First Concerto was written when the composer was 23 years old, and it is a sunny, youthful, happy work conventionally cast in the traditional three-movement form. A decade later he wrote the Second Concerto in a period of only three weeks. This concerto begins in a mood of high seriousness rather in the style of a Bach organ prelude; then this stern mood gives way to a jolly fleet-footed scherzo and a *presto* finale: it is an uneven work, though the most popular of the five concertos. The Third Concerto is perhaps the least interesting work, whilst the Fourth is the best of the five. It is in effect a one-movement work cast in three ingeniously crafted sections. Saint-Saëns wrote his last, the *Egyptian*, in 1896 to mark his 50 years as a concert artist. Mirroring the sights and sounds of a country he loved, this is another brilliant work. Pascal Rogé has a very secure, exuberant sense of rhythm, which is vital in these works, as is his immaculate, pearly technique. Dutoit is a particularly sensitive accompanist and persuades all three orchestras to play with that lean brilliance which the concertos demand. The recordings are true and well balanced.

Additional recommendations ...

...No. 2. *Coupled with works by various composers.* **Artur Rubinstein** (pf); **Philadelphia Orchestra / Eugene Ormandy.** RCA Digital Red Seal Ⓜ RD85666 (63 minutes: ADD: 10/87). Ⓖ

...Nos. 2 and 4. **Idil Biret** (pf); **Philharmonia Orchestra / James Loughran.** Naxos Ⓢ 8 550334 (55 minutes: DDD: 12/90).

...No. 2[a]. Le carnaval des animaux[b]. **Brahms** Seven Piano Pieces, Op. 116[c]. **Emil Gilels**, [b]**Yakov Zak** (pfs); [ab]**USSR State Symphony Orchestra /** [a]**Kyrill Kondrashin,** [b]**Karl Eliasberg.** Revelation [ab]mono/[c]stereo Ⓜ RV10014* (69 minutes: ADD: 10/96). Ⓖ

Saint-Saëns Piano Concerto No. 2 in G minor, Op. 22[b].
Rachmaninov Piano Concerto No. 3 in D minor, Op. 30[a].
Shostakovich Prelude and Fugue in D major, Op. 87 No. 5[c]. **Emil Gilels** (pf); [ab]**Paris Conservatoire Orchestra / André Cluytens.** Testament mono Ⓕ SBT1029* (65 minutes: ADD: 2/94). Item marked [a] from Columbia 33CX1323 (1/56), [b]33CX1217 (3/55), [c]33CX1364 (9/56). Recorded 1954-1956. ⓒⓒ

Gilels was a true king of pianists and these Paris and New York based recordings can only strengthen and confirm his legendary status. Here, once more, is that superlative musicianship, that magisterial technique and, above all, that unforgettable sonority; rich and sumptuous at every level. What breadth and distinction he brings to the first movement of the Saint-Saëns, from his fulmination in the central octave uproar to his uncanny stillness in the final pages. High jinks are reserved for the second and third movements, the former tossed off with a teasing lightness, the latter's whirling measures with infinite brio. An approximate swipe at the *Scherzo's* flashing double-note flourish, a false entry and a wrong turning five minutes into the finale offer amusing evidence of Gilels's high-wire act; this performance was, after all, recorded before today's obsession with a gleaming and artificial perfection. No performance of this concerto is more 'live', and it is small wonder that Claudio Arrau included it among his desert island favourites.

Gilels's Rachmaninov is altogether more temperate yet, once more, this is among the few truly great performances of this work. His tempo is cool and rapid, and maintained with scintillating ease through even the most formidable intricacy. The cadenza – the finer and more transparent of the two – billows and recedes in superbly musical style and the climax is of awe-inspiring grandeur and the central *scherzando* in the finale is as luminous as it is vivacious. The finale's *meno mosso* variation is excluded (a beautiful passage that Gilels would doubtless have reinstated in our more enlightened times) and, it has to be said, Cluytens's partnership is distant and run of the mill. But the recordings hardly show their age in such admirably smooth transfers. Gilels's 'encore', Shostakovich's piquant Prelude and Fugue No. 5 shines like a brilliant shaft of light after the Rachmaninov. The performance is perfection, entirely justifying Artur Rubinstein's comment after hearing him play in Russia: "If that boy comes to the West, I shall have to shut up shop".

Saint-Saëns Violin Concerto No. 3 in B minor, Op. 61.
Wieniawski Violin Concerto No. 2 in D minor, Op. 22. **Julian Rachlin** (vn); **Israel Philharmonic Orchestra / Zubin Mehta**. Sony Classical Ⓕ SK48373 (52 minutes: DDD: 12/92). Recorded 1991.
Saint-Saëns's expansive Third Violin Concerto has the rare distinction of providing a showcase for virtuosos without compromising purely musical values. In terms of thematic material and orchestration, it has all the gracefulness and restraint of a classical concerto (as well it might, given its composer's admiration for Beethoven), but, additionally, it manages to find space for passion (first movement) and tenderness (second), as well as encourage a highly musical brand of technical display (third). Written for Sarasate in the early 1880s, the Concerto has long attracted the attention of leading players, yet has still to achieve the popularity of Saint-Saëns's more celebrated shorter works for violin and orchestra, his *Havanaise* and *Introduction and Rondo capriccioso*. Tchaikovsky was much taken with Henryk Wieniawski's Second Concerto (1862), a less ambitious piece than the Saint-Saëns but one that, over the years, has proved more popular. A great violinist himself, Wieniawski knew how to challenge his interpreters with devilishly difficult passagework and gorgeous melodies (such as we encounter at the heart of this D minor Concerto), and it is a pleasure to encounter a young player who so fully understands its idiom. Lithuanian-born Julian Rachlin has a smooth, velvety tone and a lightning left hand; his playing has something of the cultured refinement of the late Nathan Milstein; yet it has its own personality and on this particular CD enjoys the added advantage of superb accompaniments, beautifully recorded. Incidentally, in the Wieniawski, the orchestral tutti passages are played complete – a bonus that you won't find on either of Jascha Heifetz's classic recordings!

Additional recommendations ...
...Violin Concerto No. 3. **Lalo** Symphonie espagnole, Op. 21. **Itzak Perlman** (vn).
   Orchestre de Paris / Daniel Barenboim. DG Masters Ⓜ 445 549-2GMA (61 minutes: DDD).
...Violin Concerto No. 3. **Lalo** Symphonie espagnole, Op. 21. **Joshua Bell** (vn);
   Montreal Symphony Orchestra / Charles Dutoit. Decca Ⓕ 425 501-2DH (62 minutes: DDD: 2/90).
...Violin Concerto No. 3. Caprice andalous in G major, Op. 122. Introduction and Rondo
   capriccioso in A minor, Op. 28. Morceau de concert in G major, Op. 62. Romance in C major,
   Op. 48. **Dong-Suk Kang** (vn); **Katowice Radio Symphony Orchestra / Antoni Wit.**
   Naxos Ⓢ 8 550752 (64 minutes: DDD: 10/94).
...Violin Concerto No. 3. *Coupled with works by* **Lalo** *and* **Berlioz** Itzhak **Perlman** (vn); **Orchestre
   de Paris / Daniel Barenboim.** DG Digital Masters Ⓜ 445 549-2GMA (69 minutes: DDD: 7/95).
...Violin Concerto No. 3. *Coupled with works by* **Respighi** Pierre Amoyal (vn); **French National
   Orchestra / Charles Dutoit.** Decca Ⓕ 443 324-2DH (69 minutes: DDD: 7/95).
   See review under Respighi; refer to the Index.   ⒼⒼ
...Violin Concerto No. 3. **Lalo** Symphonie espagnole, Op. 21.
   Chee-Yun (vn); **London Philharmonic Orchestra / Jésus López-Cobos.**
   Denon Ⓕ CO-18017 (61 minutes: DDD: 9/97). *See review under Lalo; refer to the Index.*

Saint-Saëns Danse macabre in G minor, Op. 40. Phaéton in C major, Op. 39. Le rouet d'Omphale in A major, Op. 31. La Jeunesse d'Hercule in E flat major, Op. 50. Marche héroïque in E flat major, Op. 34. Introduction and Rondo capriccioso in A minor, Op. 28[a]. Havanaise in E major, Op. 83[a]. [a]**Kyung-Wha Chung** (vn); [a]**Royal Philharmonic Orchestra; Philharmonia Orchestra / Charles Dutoit.** Decca Ⓜ 425 021-2DM (66 minutes: ADD).   Ⓖ
It's enough to make you weep – at the age of three, Saint-Saëns wrote his first tune, analysed Mozart's *Don Giovanni* from the full score when he was five, and at ten claimed he could play all of Beethoven's 32 piano sonatas from memory. There is some consolation in the fact that, according to a contemporary, physically "he strangely resembled a parrot", and perhaps even his early brilliance was a curse rather than a blessing, as he regressed from being a bold innovator to becoming a dusty reactionary. In his thirties (in the 1870s) he was at the forefront of the Lisztian avant-garde. To Liszt's invention, the 'symphonic poem' (Saint-Saëns was the first Frenchman to attempt the genre, with César Franck hard on his heels), he brought a typically French concision, elegance and grace. Charles

Dutoit currently has few peers in this kind of music; here is playing of dramatic flair and classical refinement that exactly matches Saint-Saëns intention and invention. Decca's sound has depth, brilliance and richness.

Additional recommendations ...

...Introduction and Rondo capriccioso. Havanaise. *Coupled with works by various composers.*
Maxim Vengerov (vn); **Israel Philharmonic Orchestra / Zubin Mehta.**
Teldec Ⓕ 9031-73266-2 (63 minutes: DDD: 5/92).

...Marche héroïque. Suite algérienne in C major, Op. 60 – March militaire française. *Coupled with works by various composers.* **Detroit Symphony Orchestra / Paul Paray.**
Mercury Living Presence Ⓜ 434 332-2MM* (66 minutes: ADD: 11/93). *See review in the Collections section; refer to the Index.* ⒼⒼⒼ

...Introduction and Rondo capriccioso. Havanaise. **Paganini** Violin Concerto No. 1 in E flat major, Op. 6. **Sarah Chang** (vn); **Philadelphia Orchestra / Wolfgang Sawallisch.**
EMI Ⓕ CDC5 55026-2 (55 minutes: DDD: 1/95). *See review under Paganini; refer to the Index.*

...Danse macabre. Le rouet d'Omphale. *Coupled with works by various composers.*
Paris Conservatoire Orchestra / Jean Martinon.
Decca The Classic Sound Ⓜ 448 571-2DCS (64 minutes: ADD: 2/96).

Saint-Saëns Symphonies – A major; F major, "Urbs Roma"; No. 1 in E flat major, Op. 2; No. 2 in A minor, Op. 55; No. 3 in C minor, Op. 78, "Organ"[a]. [a]**Bernard Gavoty** (org); **French Radio National Orchestra / Jean Martinon.** EMI Ⓜ CZS5 69683-2 (two discs: 156 minutes: ADD: 5/91). Recorded 1972-1975. Ⓖ

Saint-Saëns's four early symphonies have rather tended to be eclipsed by the popularity of his much later *Organ* Symphony. It's easy to see why the latter, with its rich invention, its colour and its immediate melodic appeal has managed to cast an enduring spell over its audiences, but there is much to be enjoyed in the earlier symphonies too. The A major dates from 1850 when Saint-Saëns was just 15 years old and is a particularly attractive and charming work despite its debt to Mendelssohn and Mozart. The Symphony in F major of 1856 was the winning entry in a competition organized by the Societé Sainte-Cécile of Bordeaux but was immediately suppressed by the composer after its second performance. The pressures of writing for a competition no doubt contribute to its more mannered style but it nevertheless contains some impressive moments, not least the enjoyable set of variations that form the final movement. The Symphony No. 1 proper was in fact written three years before the *Urbs Roma* and shares the same youthful freshness of the A major, only here the influences are closer to Schumann and Berlioz. The Second Symphony reveals the fully mature voice of Saint-Saëns and in recent years has achieved a certain amount of popularity which is almost certainly due in part to this particularly fine recording. Inevitably we arrive at the *Organ* Symphony, and if you don't already have a recording then you could do a lot worse than this marvellously colourful and flamboyant performance. Indeed, the performances throughout this generous set are persuasive and exemplary. A real bargain and well worth investigating.

Additional recommendations ...

...No. 2. Suite algérienne in C major, Op. 60. Phaéton in C major, Op. 39.
London Symphony Orchestra / Yondani Butt. ASV Ⓕ CDDCA599 (54 minutes: DDD: 5/88).

...Nos. 2 and 3[a]. [a]**Gillian Weir** (org); **Ulster Orchestra / Yan Pascal Tortelier.**
Chandos Ⓕ CHAN8822 (56 minutes: DDD: 7/90).

...Nos. 1-3; A major; F major, "Urbs Roma".
Bernard Gavoty (org); **French Radio National Orchestra / Jean Martinon.**
EMI Rouge et Noir Ⓜ CZS5 69683-2 (two discs: 156 minutes: ADD: 1/98).

Saint-Saëns Symphony No. 3 in C minor, Op. 78, "Organ"[a]. Le carnaval des animaux[b].
[a]**Peter Hurford** (org); [b]**Pascal Rogé**, [b]**Christina Ortiz** (pfs); [a]**Montreal Symphony Orchestra;** [b]**London Sinfonietta / Charles Dutoit.** Decca Ovation Ⓜ 430 720-2DM (58 minutes: DDD: 12/91). Ⓖ

Saint-Saëns Symphony No. 3 in C minor, Op. 78, "Organ"[a].
Debussy La mer[b].
Ibert Escales[b]. [a]**Berj Zamkochian** (org); **Boston Symphony Orchestra / Charles Munch.** RCA Living Stereo Ⓜ 09026 61500-2* (73 minutes: ADD: 4/93). Item marked [a] recorded 1959, [b]1956. ⒼⒼ

Let's face it, 'motto' themes and their transformations rarely produce good singable tunes. This Symphony uses a unifying motto theme, but it is fertile enough to produce two unforgettable melodies: the sensuous, arching string cantilena in the slow movement, and the grandly striding theme of the finale (so singable it was even borrowed for a pop chart-topping hit in the 1970s). In 1886 Saint-Saëns poured his considerable experience as an unequalled virtuoso of the organ, piano and practitioner of Lisztian unifying techniques into his *Organ* Symphony; it instantly put the French Symphony on the map, and provided a model for Franck and many others. With its capacity for grand spectacle (aside from the organ and a large orchestra, its scoring includes two pianos) it has suffered inflationary tendencies from both conductors and recording engineers. Dutoit's (and Decca's) achievement is the restoration of its energy and vitality. The private and affectionate portraits in the 'zoological fantasy', *The carnival of the animals,* benefit from more intimate though no less spectacular sound, and a direct approach that avoids obvious clowning.

The famous Charles Munch recording of this Symphony was made in Symphony Hall, Boston. To get round the problems of the hall resonance the RCA engineers moved many of the seats from the body of the hall so that the orchestra could spread out, while the organ (situated behind the stage) was miked separately. The result was a wonderfully rich, sumptuous sound which at the same time achieved internal clarity – one notices that in the *Scherzo* and the filigree passages for piano in the introduction to the finale. However, it is the spectacular moments that one remembrs: the rich bonding of organ and strings in the *Poco adagio* and the full-blooded organ entry from Berj Zamkochian in the finale. Munch's superb reading moves forward with a powerful lyrical impulse in a single sweep from the first note to the last. To make this issue even more enticing Munch's 1956 versions of Debussy's *La mer* and Ibert's *Escales* ("Port of call") have been included. There is some marvellous playing in both, especially from the lustrous Boston violins. Here, however, the original recordings were more closely balanced and the effect is less rich, the dynamic range less wide. Yet the adrenalin runs high in both performances and the picturesque imagery of *Escales* is vividly conveyed.

Additional recommendations ...

...Le carnaval des animaux[a]. **Ravel** Ma mère l'oye. [a]**Joseph Villa, Patricia Jennings** (pfs); **Pittsburgh Symphony Orchestra / André Previn.** Philips Ⓕ 400 016-2PH (49 minutes: 4/83).

...No. 3. **Daniel Chorzempa** (org); **Berne Symphony Orchestra / Peter Maag.** IMP Classics Ⓜ PCD2010 (37 minutes: DDD: 4/87).

...No. 3[a]. Samson et Dalila – Bacchanale[b]. Le déluge – Prélude[b]. Danse macabre[b]. [a]**Gaston Litaize** (org); [a]**Chicago Symphony Orchestra;** [b]**Orchestre de Paris / Daniel Barenboim.** DG Galleria Ⓜ 415 847-2GGA (56 minutes: DDD: 4/87).   ⒼⒼ

...No. 3. **Dukas** L'apprenti sorcier. **Simon Preston** (org); **Berlin Philharmonic Orchestra / James Levine.** DG Ⓕ 419 617-2GH (47 minutes: DDD: 8/87). *See review under Dukas; refer to the Index.*   Ⓖ

...No. 3[a]. Phaéton, Op. 39. [a]**Michael Murray** (org); **Royal Philharmonic Orchestra / Christian Badea.** Telarc Ⓕ CD80274 (46 minutes: DDD: 12/91).

...No. 3[a]. **Paray** Mass for the 500th Anniversary of the Death of Joan of Arc[b]. [a]**Marcel Dupré** (org); [b]**Soloists; [b]Rackham Symphony Choir; Detroit Symphony Orchestra / Paul Paray.** Mercury Living Presence Ⓜ 432 719-2MM (73 minutes: ADD: 9/92).

...Le carnaval des animaux (with Olga Barabini, Mary Binney Montgomery, pfs). Danse macabre, Op. 40. Samson et Dalila – Bacchanale. *Coupled with works by* **Bizet** Philadelphia Orchestra / **Leopold Stokowski.** Biddulph mono Ⓜ WHL012* (72 minutes: ADD: 8/95).

...Le carnaval des animaux. *Coupled with works by* **Bizet** and **Prokofiev** **Royal Philharmonic Orchestra / Andrea Licata.** Tring International Royal Philharmonic Collection Ⓢ TRP046 (69 minutes: DDD: 11/95).

...Le carnaval des animaux. *Coupled with works by various composers.* **Hugh Downs** (narr); **Leo Litwin, Samuel Lipman** (pfs); **Boston Pops Orchestra / Arthur Fiedler.** RCA Victor Living Stereo Ⓜ 09026 68131-2 (76 minutes: ADD: 12/95).

...Le carnaval des animaux. **Poulenc** Double Piano Concerto in D minor. **Güher and Süher Pekinel** (pfs); **French Radio Philharmonic Orchestra / Marek Janowski.** Teldec Ⓜ 4509-97445-2 (38 minutes: DDD: 2/96).

...No. 3[a]. Cyprès et Lauriers, Op. 156[a]. La Foi, Op. 130. [a]**Matthias Eisenberg** (org); **Toulouse Capitole Orchestra / Michel Plasson.** EMI Ⓕ CDC5 55584-2 (two discs: 84 minutes: DDD: 12/97).

Saint-Saëns String Quartets – No. 1 in E minor, Op. 112; No. 2 in G major, Op. 153. **Fauré** String Quartet in E minor, Op. 121. **Miami Quartet** (Ivan Chan, Cathy Meng Robinson, vns; Chauncey Patterson, va; Keith Robinson, vc). Conifer Classics Ⓕ 75605 51291-2 (75 minutes: DDD: 3/98). Recorded 1997. *Gramophone Editor's choice.*   ⒼⒼ

Saint-Saëns was 64 when he wrote the First Quartet, a closely argued, intense piece, and didn't follow it up for another 20 years; the Second Quartet is not dissimilar in style to those far more popular fruits of his old age, the three woodwind and piano sonatas. Though neither quartet has the melodic memorability of his best-known music, the neglect is hard to understand – there's an effortless mastery of string textures, inventive and original use of counterpoints, and a delightfully fresh approach to form, with continual surprises enlivening the overall unity. The Miami Quartet are a brilliant ensemble. Exceptionally well balanced, there's an uncomplicated, unexaggerated *élan* to their playing, which seems just right for this music, in which intellectual playfulness is an important ingredient. The contrapuntal fun and games of No. 2's finale has a stunning light-fingered virtuosity, yet the more serious moments are just as effective – the sweet serenity of the opening of No. 1's *Adagio*, for instance. The Miami are highly recommended, even without taking into account their beautiful performance of the Fauré; the subtle harmonic and emotional shifts of this unique piece are captured in the most convincing way, with wonderfully affecting changes of tone colour. All round it's an outstanding disc. The Conifer recording is admirably realistic; its clarity highlights the exceptional precision of the playing.

Saint-Saëns Piano Trios – No. 1 in F major, Op. 18; No. 2 in E minor, Op. 92. **Joachim Trio** (Rebecca Hirsch, vn; Caroline Dearnley, vc; John Lenehan, pf). Naxos Ⓢ 8 550935 (65 minutes: DDD: 12/95). Recorded 1993. *Gramophone Editor's choice.*

1863 and 1892 are the dates of these trios, of which No. 1 was written by a composer not yet 30 but already a confident master of his craft. Bland his voice may be, but it is intelligent and agreeable: a French Brahms without genius, one dares suggest, although Mendelssohn also comes to mind. At the same time, there are passages unlike either of these composers, such as the bare and angular main theme of the A minor slow movement in No. 1, though Grieg might have written it. Such music needs sympathetic, unfussy interpretation and the skilful and sensitive Joachim Trio give it just that; as for the First Trio as a whole, the work is charming (try the fleet scherzo for a sample) and the booklet-essay rightly notes the "delicate brilliance" of the piano writing by a composer who was also an expert player. The E minor Trio, a more dramatic five-movement piece is played here with fine judgement and thus warmly expressive without sentimentality or mannerism. The recording is excellent.

Saint-Saëns Chanson (Nouvelle chanson sur un vieil air). Guitare. Rêverie. L'attente. Le chant de ceux qui s'en vont sur la mer. Le pas d'armes du Roi Jean. La coccinelle. A quoi bon entendre. Si vous n'avez rien à me dire. Dans ton coeur. Danse macabre. Mélodies persanes, Op. 26 – La brise; Sabre en main; Au cimetière; Tournoiement. Marquise, vous souvenez-vous?. La Cigale et la Fourmi. Chanson à boire du vieux temps. Nocturne. Violons dans le soir[a]. Guitares et mandolines. Une flûte invisible[b]. Suzette et Suzon. Aimons-nous. Temps nouveau. Le vent dans la plaine. Grasselette et Maigrelette. **François Le Roux** (bar); [a]**Krysia Ososlowicz** (vn); [b]**Philippa Davies** (fl); **Graham Johnson** (pf). Hyperion Ⓟ CDA66856 (78 minutes: DDD: 5/97). Recorded 1996. Texts and translations included.

This is the most resounding blow yet to be struck for the *mélodies* of Saint-Saëns. François Le Roux with his incisive diction and ability to characterize each song, is a real champion for the man, once so successful, who became, as Graham Johnson puts it in the booklet, "a footnote" rather than a chapter in the history of French music. Many of the poems that Saint-Saëns set were used by other composers, for instance *Dans ton coeur*, which became Duparc's *Chanson triste*, by "Jean Lahor" (Henri Cazalis). Graham Johnson playfully suggests what a fortune Saint-Saëns might have made if he had survived long enough to write for the movies a bit more. The first song of the *Mélodies persanes,* "La brise", is full of eastern promise, the second, "Sabre en main" a rollicking bit of toy-soldier galloping away, but just as one is beginning to think that Johnson is shooting himself in the foot by being so ironic about the music they're performing comes the hauntingly beautiful fifth song, "Au cimetière", with its quietly rippling accompaniment and the languorous poem about the lovers sitting on a marble tomb and picking the flowers. Le Roux sings this with controlled, quiet intensity. Johnson makes the point that it is of little importance from which part of the composer's life the songs come, he embodies that totally French nineteenth-century style, sometimes anticipating Hahn and Massenet, sometimes harking back to Boieldieu. If a setting of La Fontaine's fable about the cicada and the ant is pure salon charm, then the final "Grasselette et Maigrelette" Ronsard *chanson*, composed when Saint-Saëns was 85 in 1920, is a vivacious *café-concert*-style evocation of old Paris. On the concert platform François Le Roux is one of the most charismatic performers of our time, his flashing eyes and total involvement making each recital memorable. Though he has recorded a wide range of music, from Couperin to Birtwistle, he has not always made the impact one would expect on disc, but this is certainly one of the best things he has done so far. A double welcome, for performers and rare repertory.

Saint-Saëns Samson et Dalila. **Carlo Cossutta** (ten) Samson; **Marjana Lipovšek** (mez) Dalila; **Alain Fondary** (bar) Priest; **Yves Bisson** (bar) Abimelech; **Harald Stamm** (bass) Old Hebrew; **Constantin Zaharia** (ten) Messenger; **Jerôme Engramer** (ten) First Philistine; **Ionel Pantea** (bass) Second Philistine; **Sofia Chamber Choir; Bregenz Festival Chorus; Vienna Volksoper Chorus; Vienna Symphony Orchestra / Sylvain Cambreling**. Koch Schwann Ⓟ 317742 (two discs: 127 minutes: DDD: 4/96). Notes, text and translation included. Recorded live in 1988.

Cambreling draws as much sensuousness and delicacy from the score as any, and also attends to its pagan element with suitable brio. Though like some of his predecessors, such as Barenboim and Davis, he is inclined to linger unduly against the composer's express wishes, as in the marginally too slow tempo for "Mon coeur s'ouvre à ta voix", he uses the gained time to underline the refinement of the scoring, helped by some lovely playing from his orchestra, which is in true theatrical balance with the singers. Although by rights the polyglot cast should tell against the set, the French is in fact as idiomatic as any apart from that on the reissued Fourestier set. While Lipovšek sometimes, like Baltsa (Davis) and Meier (Chung), indulges in dramatic gestures strictly outside the realm of style appropriate to the piece, she sings for the most part with a more luscious tone than either of those rivals, is certainly more pleasing to listen to than Meier and instils the whole role, by vocal means alone, with a sense of Dalila's dangerous powers of seduction. Working in a live performance she has an advantage over all her rivals in creating theatrical intensity.

She is matched in that by Cossutta. The then 56-year-old tenor has just the kind of *élan* in his attack that sometimes eludes Domingo (Barenboim and Chung). In that he comes close to matching Luccioni on the old Fourestier version. Some may find the vibrato that is part and parcel of Cossutta's timbre disturbing. Once that is taken on board, Cossutta's is as vigorous, pliable and musically attentive a Samson as any. Vickers, *chez* Prêtre, is something else again, highly individual, but occasionally exaggerated in expression in a way Cossutta avoids. Cossutta matches Luccioni and Vickers in the concentrated pathos of "Vois ma misère" and the declamatory attack called for at "Et!

je proclame ta justice!", which has an Otello-like power to it. Fondary was Chung's High Priest, and here he repeats his formidable assumption, matched on disc only by Blanc (Prêtre) and Cabanel (Fourestier). The smaller roles are adequately taken and the choral singing equals the excellence of that on the other recent sets. Stage noises are minimally distracting even during the dances; applause is confined to ends of acts. As a whole the recording has more presence than the backwardly recorded Chung set. The work has been reasonably fortunate on disc. For all its merits as regards solo singing, the Fourestier is too dimly recorded for a first recommendation. Barenboim has a poor Dalila, and Davis's Baltsa is something of an acquired taste. Prêtre is still highly competitive (with Gorr a superb Dalila). Of the two most recent versions, Chung is undoubtedly the safer recommendation, Cambreling the more exciting both because it is taken live and because of the special *frisson* the two principals give to their music. Do hear one or other version of this superbly integrated score.

Additional recommendations ...

...Soloists; **René Duclos Choir; Paris Opéra Orchestra / Georges Prêtre.**
EMI Ⓕ CDS7 47895-8 (two discs: 121 minutes: ADD: 7/88).
...Soloists; **Bavarian Radio Symphony Chorus and Orchestra / Sir Colin Davis.**
Philips Ⓕ 426 243-2PH2 (two discs: 123 minutes: DDD: 1/91).
...Soloists; **Chorus and Orchestra de Paris / Daniel Barenboim.**
DG Ⓜ 413 297-2GX2 (two discs: 126 minutes: ADD: 11/91).
...Soloists; **Chorus and Orchestra of the Bastille Opera, Paris / Myung-Whun Chung.**
EMI Ⓕ CDS7 54470-2 (two discs: 124 minutes: DDD: 2/93).   Ⓖ
...Soloists; **Chorus and Orchestra of the Paris Opéra / Louis Fourestier.**
EMI mono Ⓜ CMS5 65263-2* (two discs: 116 minutes: ADD: 9/95).
...Samson et Dalila – J'ai gravi la montagne ... La victoire facile. *Coupled with works by various composers.* **Olga Borodina** (mez); **Dmitri Hvorostovsky** (bar); **English Chamber Orchestra / Patrick Summers.** Philips Ⓕ 454 439-2PH (66 minutes: DDD: 6/98). *See review in the Collections section; refer to the Index.*

Further listening ...

...Henry VIII – Ballet-divertissement. *Coupled with* **Delibes** Sylvia.
Razumovsky Sinfonia / Andrew Mogrelia. Naxos 8 553338/9 (6/96).
Gramophone Editor's choice. See review under Delibes; refer to the Index.
...Morceaux de concert – Op. 62[a]; Op. 154[b]; Op. 94[c]. Romance, Op. 36. Caprice andalou, Op. 122. Romance, Op. 48. Spartacus. [a]**Olivier Charlier** (vn); [b]**Marielle Nordmann** (hp); [c]**Radovan Vlatkovič** (hn); **Ensemble Orchestral de Paris / Jean-Jacques Kantorow.**
EMI CDC5 55587-2 (9/96).
...Allegro appassionato in B minor, Op. 43. *Coupled with works by various composers.*
Mischa Maisky (vc); **Daria Hovora** (pf). DG 439 863-2GH (9/94).   Ⓖ
...Odelette, Op. 162. Clarinet Sonata in E flat major, Op. 167. Feuillet d'album, Op. 81. Bassoon Sonata in G major, Op. 168. Caprice sur des airs danois et russes, Op. 79. Oboe Sonata in D major, Op. 166. Romance in D flat major, Op. 37. Tarantelle in A minor, Op. 6. *Coupled with works by* **Debussy**
Various soloists. Cala CACD1017 (2/95).
...Septet in E flat major, Op. 65. *Coupled with works by* **Milhaud** and **Poulenc Thomas Stevens** (tpt); **Ani Kavafian, Julie Rosenfeld** (vns); **Toby Hoffman** (va); **Carter Brey** (vc); **Jack Kulowitsch** (db); **André Previn** (pf). RCA Victor Red Seal 09026 68181-2 (11/95).
...Violin Sonata No. 1 in D minor, Op. 75. *Coupled with works by various composers.*
Isabelle van Keulen (vn); **Ronald Brautigam** (pf). Koch Classics 36416-2 (5/97).
See review in the Collections section; refer to the Index.
...Fantaisie in D flat major, Op. 101. *Coupled with works by various composers.* **Peter King** (org).
Priory PRCD618. *See review in the Collections section; refer to the Index.*
...Trois Prélude et Fugues, Op. 99. Trois Préludes et Fugues, Op. 109. *Coupled with* **Harwood**
Organ Sonata No. 1 in C sharp minor, Op. 5. **Adrian Partington** (org).
Priory PRCD384 (8/94).
...Henry VIII. **Soloists; Rouen Théâtre des Arts Chorus; French Lyrique Orchestra / Alain Guingal.**
Le Chant du Monde LDC278 1083/5 (4/93).

Philip Sainton   British 1891-1967

Suggested listening ...
...Nadir. The Dream of the Marionette. *Coupled with* **Hadley** La belle dame sans merci[ac].
One Morning in Spring. Lenten Meditations[abc]. [a]**Neill Archer** (ten); [b]**Stephen Richardson** (bass);
Philharmonia [c]**Chorus and Orchestra / Matthias Bamert.** Chandos CHAN9539 (10/97).

Antonio Salieri   Italian 1750-1825

Suggested listening ...
...Falstaff. **Soloists; Milan Madrigalists; Guido Cantelli Orchestra, Milan / Alberto Veronesi.**
Chandos CHAN9613 (6/98).

Aulis Sallinen

Sallinen Variations for Orchestra, Op. 8. Violin Concerto, Op. 18[a]. Some aspects of Peltoniemi Hintrik's funeral march, Op. 19[b]. The nocturnal dances of Don Juanquixote, Op. 58.
[a]**Eeva Koskinen** (vn); [b]**Torleif Thedéen** (vc); **Tapiola Sinfonietta / Osmo Vänskä**. BIS Ⓕ CD560 (63 minutes: DDD: 6/93). Recorded 1992.

Sallinen's operas and symphonies have stolen the limelight in recent years at the expense of other works fully worthy of attention as this well-played and well-recorded disc proves. Whereas the Variations (1963) are somewhat anonymous if deftly written, the Violin Concerto (1968) is an altogether maturer work, unusually sombre for so bright a solo instrument. The Third String Quartet (1969) is subtitled *Some aspects of Peltoniemi Hintrik's funeral march*. This arrangement for string orchestra dates from 1981. *The nocturnal dances of Don Juanquixote* is an extended fantasia for cello and strings, the title being the only parody of Strauss (although a solo violin enters late as Sancho Panza-leporello!). Sallinen is fond of playing games and all is never as it seems: one can almost hear the collective thud of critics' jaws falling open at this Arnold-like spoof, yet there are darker moments too: bravo to Sallinen and BIS for this intriguing issue.

Sallinen Songs of Life and Death, Op. 69[a]. The Iron Age – Suite, Op. 55b[b]. [b]**Margit Papunen** (sop); [a]**Jorma Hynninen** (bar); **Opera Festival Chorus;** [b]**East Helsinki Music Institute Choir; Helsinki Philharmonic Orchestra / Okko Kamu**. Ondine Ⓕ ODE844-2 (75 minutes: DDD: 12/95). Texts and translations included. Recorded 1995.

Listening to these two works by Aulis Sallinen is a bit like looking at two different photographs of the composer: the face is undeniably the same but not the perspective. *Songs of Life and Death* (1993-94) arose, rather by mischance, from a failed effort to compose a Requiem on verses by Lassi Nummi. Although title and outward form suggest Mahlerian associations, the conservative musical language rather brings Verdi to mind, and in a very real sense this cycle is a twentieth-century equivalent of the latter's Requiem: both are symphonic in construction and operatic in idiom, composed from spiritual rather than religious standpoints, and make use of secular elements. There are differences, of course, not least in scale and conception, which serve to underline a similarity of purpose and stature relative to their epochs. And while Sallinen's songs are also very much songs of *life*, death is not here perceived as a grim or tragic end, and this imparts to the whole a peculiarly late twentieth-century aspect. Here at last is the choral-and-orchestral masterpiece Sibelius should have written, Finnish to the core yet international in appeal. It is one of the very finest compositions Sallinen has yet produced. Where in the *Songs of Life and Death* voices are the principal element, in the *Iron Age* Suite (1978-82) the focus is rather on the orchestra, the chorus being an important but more colouristic extra. The suite originated in music written for a series of prize-winning Finnish TV documentaries and in it the more familiar Sallinen of the symphonies and early operas is on display. Both works receive terrific performances from Sallinen's long-standing champion, Okko Kamu, and his forces.

Further listening ...
...Symphonies – No. 4, Op. 49; No. 5, Op. 57, "Washington Mosaics". Shadows, Op. 52.
   Malmö Symphony Orchestra / James DePreist. BIS CD607 (12/94).
...String Quartets – No. 1, Op. 14; No. 2, "Canzona"; No. 3, "Aspects of Peltoniemi Hintrik's Funeral March", Op. 19; No. 4, "Silent Songs"; No. 5, "Pieces of Mosaic". **Jean Sibelius Quartet.** Ondine ODE831-2 (12/95).
...Chamber Music II, Op. 41. *Coupled with works by various composers.* **Petri Alanko** (fls); **Lahti Symphony Orchestra / Osmo Vänskä.** BIS CD687 (5/97).
...The Horseman. **Soloists; Savonlinna Opera Festival Chorus and Orchestra / Ulf Söderblom.** Finlandia 1576-51101-2 (2/97).
...Kullervo. **Soloists; Finnish National Opera Chorus; Finnish National Opera Orchestra / Ulf Söderblom.** Ondine ODE780-2 (8/92).
...The Palace. **Soloists; Savonlinna Opera Festival Chorus and Orchestra / Okko Kamu.** Koch Classics 36465-2 (1/97).

Giovanni Salvatore

Suggested listening ...
...Toccata prima. Canzon Francese terza. Due Correnti.
   Coupled with works by various composers. **Rinaldo Alessandrini** (hpd).
   Opus 111 OPS30-118 (4/95). 🖙 *See review in the Collections section; refer to the Index.* ⒼⒼ

Giuseppe Sammartini

Giovanni Battista Sammartini

G. Sammartini Recorder Concerto in F major[a]. Concerti grossi – No. 6 in E minor; No. 8 in G minor.

G.B. Sammartini Symphonies – G major; D major. String Quintet in E major.
[a]**Conrad Steinmann** (rec); **Ensemble 415 / Chiara Banchini** (vn). Harmonia Mundi Musique
d'abord ⑧ HMA190 1245 (63 minutes: DDD: 4/87). Recorded 1986. ✎   ⊕⊕⊕
Giuseppe Sammartini, the elder brother and virtuoso oboist, here contributes a recorder concerto and
two concerti grossi sandwiched between two symphonies and a quintet for strings by the more
progressive Giovanni Battista. The differences in style – one emanating from London and bearing the
stamp of the conservative English taste, the other from Milan and one of the instigators of an
important new genre – are unmistakable. Giuseppe's restless E minor "Spiritoso" from the Sixth
Concerto Grosso, the G minor *French Overture* and graceful minuets belong to a different musical
world from that of G.B.'s brash symphonies. Under the capable and lively direction of Chiara
Banchini, Ensemble 415 present these works at their best: lightly textured with brisk tempos,
articulated with unusual precision (which the resonant church acoustic only slightly blunts) and
sympathetically read; for though the quality of the music varies – the Symphony in G major is
especially appealing, that in D major embarrassingly thin with its empty Vivaldian *arpeggios* – the
performance never falters. Giuseppe's recorder concerto, rescued from a manuscript in Sweden, is
nicely played by Conrad Steinmann. Banchini's solo in the *Largo* of GB's late String Quintet is most
affecting, showing herself to be equally at home on the platform and in the front desk.
Additional recommendation ...
...Recorder Concerto in F major. Oboe Concerto in E flat major. Concerto for Piccolo Cello,
   Strings and Continuo in C major. Trio for Two Recorders and Continuo in F major.
   G.B. Sammartini Trio for Two Flutes and Continuo in D major. Sonata for Flute, Two Violins
   and Continuo in D major. **Cologne Camerata.** Deutsche Harmonia Mundi ⑤ 05472 77323-2
   (59 minutes: DDD: 8/95).   ⊕

John Sanders   British 1933

Suggested listening ...
...The Reproaches. *Coupled with works by various composers.*
   St Paul's Cathedral Choir / John Scott with **Andrew Lucas** (org).
   Hyperion CDA66916 (A/97). *See review in the Collections section; refer to the Index.*

Pierre Sancan   French 1916

Suggested listening ...
...Sonatine. *Coupled with works by various composers.* **Emmanuel Pahud** (fl); **Eric Le Sage** (pf).
   EMI CDC5 56488-2 (3/98). *Selected by Soundings. See review in the Collections section;
   refer to the Index.*

Pablo Sarasate   Spanish 1844-1908

Suggested listening ...
...Zigeunerweisen, Op. 20. *Coupled with works by various composers.* **Joshua Bell** (vn);
   Royal Philharmonic Orchestra / Andrew Litton. Decca 433 519-2DH (1/92). *See review in the
   Collections section; refer to the Index.*
...Zigeunerweisen, Op. 20[c]. *Coupled with works by various composers.* **Sergei Nakariakov** (tpt);
   Alexander Markovich (pf). Teldec 4509-94554-2 (6/95). *See review in the Collections section;
   refer to the Index.*   ⊕⊕
...Zigeunerweisen, Op. 20. Introduction and Tarantella, Op. 43. *Coupled with works by
   various composers.* **Itzhak Perlman** (vn); **Abbey Road Ensemble / Lawrence Foster.**
   EMI CDC5 55475-2 (1/96).

Erik Satie   French 1866-1925

Satie Parade. Trois Gymnopédies – Nos. 1 and 3 (orch. Debussy); No. 2 (orch. Corp). Mercure.
   Three Gnossiennes (orch. Corp). Relâche. **New London Orchestra / Ronald Corp.**
   Hyperion ⑤ CDA66365 (66 minutes: DDD: 2/90). Recorded 1989.
In 1918, the year after Diaghilev's Russian Ballet staged Satie's *Parade* in Paris, Poulenc wrote that "to
me, Satie's *Parade* is to Paris what *Petrushka* is to St Petersburg" (André Gide, however, commented
on its poverty-stricken pretentiousness). Satie was thenceforth adopted as the spiritual father of "Les
Six", whose ideal was the marriage of serious music with jazz, vaudeville, and the circus. Those who
only know Satie from his early *Gymnopédies* and *Gnossiennes* – take heed: *Parade* shuffles along its
apparently aimless, deadpan and wicked way with interjections from typewriters, lottery wheels,
pistols and sirens. What does it all mean? Ronald Corp could be accused of retaining a slightly stiff
upper lip, but there may well be a seriousness of purpose behind Satie's balletic miniatures. Certainly,

there is little here of the uproarious debunking of some of "Les Six". His orchestrations of the *Gnossiennes* and the remaining *Gymnopédie* are idiomatic, and his performances of all six have the requisite cool beauty. Hyperion's sound is spacious and natural.

Additional recommendations ...

...Parade. *Coupled with works by various composers.* **London Symphony Orchestra / Antál Dorati.** Mercury Ⓜ 434 335-2MM (67 minutes: ADD). Ⓖ

...Parade. *Coupled with works by various composers.* **Philharmonia Orchestra / Igor Markevitch.** Testament mono Ⓕ SBT1060* (77 minutes: ADD: 2/96).

Satie Six Gnossiennes. Ogives. Petite ouverture à danser. Sarabandes. Trois Gymnopédies.
Reinbert de Leeuw (pf). Philips Ⓕ 446 672-2PH (67 minutes: DDD: 2/96). Recorded 1992.
Tender, solemn, droll, silly and occasionally plain boring, Satie's piano music has certainly proved its appeal for performers and record collectors, judging from the number of recitals devoted to it. But this one is out of the ordinary, for unlike the majority of artists, who offer a mixed bag of pieces, Reinbert de Leeuw has chosen music that is entirely solemn and even hieratic in utterance. He begins with the archaically beautiful *Gnossiennes*, taking the first of them unusually slowly but with compelling concentration. The composer's devotees will be thrilled, though you have to surrender completely to get the message of this repetitive, proto-minimalist music. The four *Ogives* derive their name from church architecture and their unbarred, diatonically simple music has clear affinities with plainchant although unlike chant it is richly harmonized. Monotonous it may be, but that is part of its charm, if that term can apply to such a contemplative style. The very brief *Petite ouverture à danser* is a mere meandering sketch in lazy waltz-time, but all Satie is sacred to the converted and the writer of the booklet-essay accords it four lines, finding in it (as translated here) "a suggestion of indifference, vacillating between a melancholy melody and indecisive harmony". (Not exactly Beethoven, one might say.) The two pensively sad triptychs of *Sarabandes* and *Gymnopédies* – here very slow yet tonally most refined – complete this finely played and recorded disc, which offers nothing whatsoever of the bouncier *café-concert* Satie.

Satie Sports et divertissements. Enfantillages pittoresques. Valse-ballet. Fantaisie-valse. Le piège de Méduse. Petite musique de clown triste. Première pensée Rose + Croix. Le fils des étoiles – La vocation; L'initiation. Carnet d'esquisses et de croquis. Petit prélude de "La Mort de Monsieur Mouche". Gambades. Caresse. Trois Peccadilles importunes. La diva de l'Empire. Les pantins dansent. Danse de travers. Petite ouverture à danser. Rêverie du pauvre. **Pascal Rogé** (pf).
Decca Ⓕ 455 370-2DH (61 minutes: DDD: 1/98). Recorded 1996.
This unusual collection displays a broader diversity of style and expression than we expect from Satie. It contains the rarely heard *Sports et divertissements*, comprising 20 snap-shots, none lasting more than a minute or so, each evoking a sport or recreational activity. This is surely one of Satie's finest works, and it ought to be better known. Also recorded are early pieces, including the *Valse-ballet* and *Fantaisie-valse*, published in 1885. Much of this music displays a childlike innocence and simplicity, but here we also find wit, pastiche and evocation. Pascal Rogé has already consolidated his reputation as a performer of French repertoire. His responses are generally cool and reserved; this undoubtedly suits the ethereal timelessness of much of Satie's output, but occasionally one wishes, if only for contrast in the context of the disc as a whole, that Rogé would let himself go a bit more (the "Esquisses et Sketch montmartrois" from the *Carnet d'esquisses et de croquis*, for example). That said, his playing is wholly idiomatic and vividly captures the spirit of Satie's idiosyncratic imagination. This collection of miniatures (the disc has 60 tracks) allows for selective listening, although each work, especially the *Sports et divertissements*, should be heard in full. Recorded with a wonderfully natural, if very close, piano sound, this is one of the most enjoyable and varied Satie recitals on disc.

Satie Trois Gymnopédies. Six Gnossiennes. Cinq Nocturnes. Trois Embryons desséchés. Trois avant-dernières pensées. Valse-ballet. Fantaisie-valse. Je te veux. **Ronan O'Hora** (pf).
Tring International Ⓢ TRP069 (61 minutes: DDD: 7/96).
Ronan O'Hora is a sensitive pianist in this repertory, where there are now many recorded contenders and a fair range of interpretative styles, and the sad tenderness of the *Gymnopédies* comes across, although he is brisker than some artists with the meltingly beautiful flow of Nos. 1 and 3. If O'Hora is justifiably concerned to eschew an inappropriately romantic approach, this is not at the expense of the occasional discreet rubato (as towards the end of No. 2) without which the music would lack humanity. Not all this music has the gravity of this triptych, or the *Gnossiennes*. Elsewhere Satie gives us his characteristic caperings and banalities, and O'Hora responds neatly and wittily, doing the best he can with the silly repetitive endings of at least two pieces. Indeed, his programme is well played and planned. As suggested, there are many rival Satie pianists on disc but there is so much of Satie's piano music now available that you can purchase several discs without duplicating repertory, save perhaps for the ubiquitous *Gymnopédies*. O'Hora's disc offers a pleasingly intimate, atmospheric recording.

Additional recommendations ...

...Avant-dernières pensées. Caresse. Chapitres tournés en tous sens. Trois Gymnopédies. Jack-in-the-box. Six Pieces. Trois Préludes flasques. Deux Rêveries nocturnes. Sonatine bureaucratique. Sports et divertissements. **Michel Legrand** (pf). Erato Ⓕ 4509-92857-2 (54 minutes: DDD: 12/93).

...Chapitres tournés en tous sens. Croquis et agaceries d'un gros bonhomme en bois. Je te veux valse. Le Picadilly. Pièces froides. Le piège de Méduse. Poudre d'or. Trois préludes du fils des étoiles. Prélude en tapisserie. Sonatine bureaucratique. Sports et divertissements. Trois Gymnopédies. Véritables préludes flasques (pour un chien). Vexations. **Peter Dickinson** (pf). Conifer Classics Ⓜ CDCF512 (77 minutes: DDD: 5/93).

...Croquis et agaceries d'un gros bonhomme en bois. Trois descriptions automatiques. Trois valses du précieux dégoûté. Petite ouverture à danser. Valse-ballet. Fantaisie-valse. Les pantins dansent. Caresse. Danse de travers. Deux pièces froides. Première pensée Rosé + Croix. Prélude de la Porte heroique du ciel. Passacaille. Prélude en tapisserie. Poudre d'or. Trois morceaux en forme de poire[a]. La belle excentrique. **Anne Queffélec**, [a]**Cathérine Collard** (pfs). Virgin Classics Ⓕ VC7 59296-2 (72 minutes: DDD: 8/93).

...Six Gnossiennes. Véritables préludes flasques (pour un chien). Vieux séquins et vieilles cuirasses. Chapitres tournés en tous sens. Trois Gymnopédies. Embryons desséchés. Je te veux valse. Sonatine bureaucratique. Heures séculaires et instantanées. Le Picadilly. Avant-dernières pensées. Sports et divertissements. **Anne Queffélec** (pf). Virgin Classics Ⓕ VC7 59515-2 (76 minutes: DDD: 5/89).

...Six Gnossiennes. Avant-dernières pensées. Première pensée Rose + Croix. Trois préludes du fils des étoiles. Chapitres tournés en tous sens. Trois Gymnopédies. Le Piège de Méduse. Rêverie du pauvre. Je te veux valse. Prélude de la Porte héroïque du ciel. **John Lenehan** (pf). Earthsounds Ⓕ CDEASM003 (63 minutes: DDD: 5/93).

...Cinq grimaces (arr. Milhaud). *Coupled with works by* **Milhaud** Boaz Sharon (pf). Unicorn-Kanchana Ⓕ DKPCD9155 (71 minutes: DDD: 5/95).

...Trois Gymnopédies. Je te veux valse. Quatre préludes flasques. Prélude en tapisserie. Nocturne No. 4. Vieux séquins et vieilles cuirasses. Embryons desséchés. Six Gnossiennes. Sonatine bureaucratique. Le Piccadilly. **Pascal Rogé** (pf). Decca Ⓕ 410 220-2DH (61 minutes: DDD: 5/89).

...Trois Gymnopédies. Gnossiennes – 1891; 1889. Ogives Nos.1 and 2. Descriptions automatiques – Sur un vaisseau; Sur un casque. Chapitres tournés en tous sens – Celui qui parle trop. Croquis et agaceries d'un gros bonhomme en bois – Españaña. Trois Embryons desséchés – d'Edriophthalma; de Podophthalma. *Coupled with works by* **Poulenc** and **Debussy** **Kun Woo Paik** (pf). Virgin Classics Ultraviolet Ⓜ CUV5 61327-2 (76 minutes: DDD: 2/97).

...Gymnopédies – Lent et douloureux; Lent et grave. *Coupled with works by* **Debussy** *and* **Ravel** Cleveland Orchestra / Louis Lane. Sony Classical Essential Classics Ⓑ SBK63056 (68 minutes: ADD: 4/98).

...Je te veux. *Coupled with works by various composers.* **Angela Gheorghiu** (sop); **Malcolm Martineau** (pf). Decca Ⓕ 458 360-2DH (75 minutes: DDD: 5/98). *See review in the Collections section; refer to the Index.*

Further listening ...

...Les aventures de Mercure[a]. Socrate[b]. Messe des Pauvres[c]. Gymnopédies[d] – Lent et douloureux; Lent et grave. Geneviève de Brabant[e]. Les pantins dansent[f]. Le piège de Méduse[g]. Choses vues à droite et à gauche [h]. **Soloists;** [c]**René Duclos Choir;** [e]**Paris Opera Chorus;** [ab]**Orchestre de Paris;** [d]**Paris Conservatoire Orchestra;** [fg]**Lamoureux Concerts Orchestra /** [abe]**Pierre Dervaux,** [c]**Jean LaForge,** [d]**Louis Auriacombe,** [fg]**Aldo Ciccolini.** EMI Rouge et Noir CZS5 69686-2 (2/98).

Emil von Sauer

German 1862-1942

Sauer Piano Concerto No. 1 in E minor.
Scharwenka Piano Concerto No. 4 in F minor, Op. 82. **Stephen Hough** (pf); **City of Birmingham Symphony Orchestra / Lawrence Foster.** Hyperion Ⓕ CDA66790 (70 minutes: DDD: 11/95). Recorded 1994. *Gramophone Editor's record of the month. Gramophone Award Winner 1996.* Ⓖ

In Scharwenka's Fourth Piano Concerto grand, Lisztian ambitions are fulfilled and embellished in writing of the most ferocious intricacy and the tarantella finale throws everything at the pianist, seemingly simultaneously. It is therefore hardly surprising that after early triumphs the Fourth Concerto fell into neglect. At its second performance, given in 1910 with Scharwenka as soloist and Mahler as conductor, it was described as being of a "truly Dionysian and bewildering brilliancy", a phrase that, lifted into our own times, encapsulates Stephen Hough's astonishing performance. Then there is Sauer's First Concerto, its key a warm, over-the-shoulder memory of Chopin's E minor Concerto, yet with a style and content to make even the least susceptible listeners' heads nod and feet tap. The *Cavatina* is as luscious and enchanting as the finale is teasingly brief and light-hearted. Throughout, haunting melodies are embroidered with the finest pianistic tracery and, once again, the performance is bewitching. In the *Cavatina* Hough's caressing, fine-spun tone and long-breathed phrasing are a model for singers as well as pianists, and in the finale there is a lightly deployed virtuosity that epitomizes his aristocratic style. Naturally, the spotlight falls unashamedly on the soloist in such music, but the orchestra have no small part in the proceedings, and Lawrence Foster and the City of Birmingham Symphony Orchestra are superbly resilient and enthusiastic, with strings that sing their hearts out, notably in the third movement of the Sauer. These are both première recordings, and the sound and balance are exemplary.

Isias Savio
Brazilian 1900-1977

Suggested listening ...
...Batucada. *Coupled with works by various composers.* **Sharon Isbin** (gtr) with
Gaudencio Thiago de Mello (perc). Teldec 0630-19899-2 (7/98). *Gramophone Editor's choice.*
See review in the Collections section; refer to the Index. 🅖🅖

Robert Saxton
British 1953

Suggested listening ...
...Piano Sonata. *Coupled with works by various composers.* **Nicholas Unwin** (pf).
Metier MSVCD92009 (1/96). *See review in the Collections section; refer to the Index.*
...Chacony. *Coupled with works by various composers.* **Steven Neugarten** (pf).
Metier MSVCD92008 (1/96). *See review in the Collections section; refer to the Index.*
...Birthday Piece for Richard Rodney Bennett. Elijah's Violin. *Coupled with works by various
composers.* **Brunel Ensemble / Christopher Austin.** Cala The Edge CACD77005 (6/97).
See review in the Collections section; refer to the Index.

Alessandro Scarlatti
Italian 1660-1725

A. Scarlatti Cantatas, Volume 1. Già lusingato appieno da Zeffiri. Arianna. Poi che riseppe Orfeo.
Bella madre de'fiori. **Christine Brandes** (sop); **Arcadian Academy** (Elizabeth Blumenstock,
Lisa Weiss, vns; Mary Springfels, va da gamba; David Tyler, archlte/theorbo; Nicholas McGegan,
hpd). Conifer Classics Ⓕ 75605 51293-2 (72 minutes: DDD: 6/97). ☞ Texts and translations
included. Recorded 1996. *Gramophone Editor's record of the month.* 🅖🅖
Alessandro Scarlatti wrote some 700 cantatas: so it's four down in this first Volume, around 690-odd
to go. Not that there'll be any complaint if they are all as delectable as this. Scarlatti's range of
invention is as wide as his technical diversity, which even in this one genre – and he also wrote about
60 operas – is astonishing. Introductory sinfonias can be, as here, in one, two or three movements or
absent altogether (*Orfeo*); arias can be in *da capo* form (his favourite) or *devisen* ("motto") or strophic,
with midway and final ritornellos, as in *Bella madre de'fiori*, or without, accompanied only by
continuo (as throughout in *Orfeo*) or with imitative or independent violin lines; recitatives are either
accompanied or *secco*, but always expressive, often dramatic. Possessed of an Emma Kirkby-like light
and pure-toned voice, Christine Brandes invests all her words with meaning, colouring her tone and
dynamics in accordance with the mood, and able to convey fury as well as heartache. Technically, too,
she is ideally suited to this repertoire: she is at ease with florid writing, demonstrates a finely
controlled *messa di voce* at the words "Al trono" in *Già lusingato* and elsewhere, and is stylish in
ornamenting repeat sections. The vitality, freshness and character brought by the Arcadian Academy
to their playing earns this disc an enthusiastic recommendation.

A. Scarlatti Humanità e Lucifero[a].
Corelli Trio Sonatas – B flat major, Op. 3 No. 3; C major, Op. 4 No. 1. [a]**Rossana Bertini** (sop);
[a]**Massimo Crispi** (ten); **Europa Galante / Fabio Biondi** (vn). Opus 111 Ⓕ OPS30-129 (61 minutes:
DDD: 3/96). Text and translation included. ☞
Alessandro Scarlatti's oratorio, *Humanità e Lucifero*, here receives its first recording. It dates from
1704 when it was first performed at the Collegio Nazareno in Rome on the Feast of the Blessed Virgin
Mary. The text is written in the Italian vernacular, more widely understood than Latin. It takes the
form of a dispute between Humanity – who celebrates the birth of the Virgin – and Lucifer, who
struggles with her for supremacy. Eventually, Lucifer recognizes that in Humanity he has more than
met his match and he returns to Lake Avernus and the nether regions "neither prince nor king". The
imagery evoked by the unidentified librettist is charmingly naïve and sometimes colourful, both
aspects of which are characteristically capitalized upon by Scarlatti. This is a vibrant score of instant
melodic and harmonic appeal, very well sung by Rossana Bertini (Humanity) and marginally less so
by Massimo Crispi (Lucifer). Bertini has a particularly bright vocal timbre which suits her role
admirably. Her intonation is deadly accurate and her performance radiates light throughout. Crispi is
more variable in the success with which he negotiates some of Scarlatti's exacting passagework. The
voice is less refined in tone quality than Bertini's and, while this is appropriate to his Stygian role,
there is a tendency towards bluster which adversely affects tonal focus. The music itself holds the
attention throughout and, as so often with Scarlatti, there are moments of outstanding beauty,
enhanced by delicate scoring perhaps for solo violin, cello or sopranino recorder. In contrast with
these delicate touches are passages of resonant scoring for solo trumpet. The insertion of two trio
sonatas by Scarlatti's contemporary, Corelli, from Opp. 3 and 4 are also very affecting in context.
They are sensitively played by Biondi and his instrumentalists who bring a rare sense of poetry to the
slow movements. In summary, this is a rewarding issue and one which readers so far unacquainted
with Scarlatti's vocal music are likely to find a very enjoyable introduction. Recorded sound is
excellent and full texts with translations are included.

Further listening ...

...Abramo, il tuo semblante. *Coupled with* **Corelli** String Sonata No. 1 in G minor, WoO2.
Soloists; Stagione / Michael Schneider. Deutsche Harmonia Mundi 05472 77291-2. ✍

...Abramo, il tuo sembiante[a]. *Coupled with* **Corelli** Concerto grosso in G minor, Op. 6 No. 8,
"Christmas Concerto". [a]**Soloists; Concerto Italiano / Rinaldo Alessandrini.**
Opus 111 OPS30-156 (3/97).

...Agar et Ismaele esiliati (Ishmael). Sonatas for Recorder and Strings – C minor; A minor[a].
Soloists; [a]**Elissa Berardi** (rec); **Brewer Chamber Orchestra / Rudolph Palmer.**
Newport Classic Premier NPD85558 (7/94).

...Cain overo Il Primo Omicidio. **Concerto Italiano; L'Europa Galante / Fabio Biondi.**
Opus 111 OPS30-75/6. ✍   Ⓖ

...Sinfonie di concerto grosso Nos. 7-12. Concerti grossi Nos. 1-3. **I Musici.** Philips 434 160-2PM.

...Sonata for Recorder, Two Violins and Continuo in A minor. *Coupled with works by various
composers.* **Giardino Armonico / Giovanni Antonini** (rec). Teldec Das Alte Werk 4509-93157-2
(11/94). *See review in the Collections section; refer to the Index.*   ⒼⒼ

...Toccata per il cembalo. *Coupled with works by various composers.* **Rinaldo Alessandrini** (hpd).
Opus 111 OPS30-118 (4/95). ✍ *See review in the Collections section; refer to the Index.* ⒼⒼ

...Dixit Dominus II. *Coupled with* **Vivaldi** Gloria in D major. **Soloists; The English Concert Choir;
The English Concert / Trevor Pinnock.** Archiv Produktion 423 386-2AH (5/88). ✍

...Infirmata, vulnerata. De tenebroso lacu. Salve regina in F minor[a]. Totus amore languens.
[a]**Véronique Gens** (sop); **Gérard Lesne** (alto); **Il Seminario Musicale.**
Virgin Classics Veritas VC5 45103-2 (6/95). ✍

...Lamentazioni per la Settimana Santa. **Noémi Rime, Martina Lins** (sops);
Le Parlement de Musique / Martin Gester. Opus 111 OPS30-66 (8/93). ✍

...Questo silenzio ombroso[a]. Filli che esprime la sua fede a Fileno. Marc'Antonio e Cleopatra[a].
E pur vuole il cielo e amore[a]. Ero e Leandro. Clori e Mirtillo[a]. [a]**Sandrine Piau** (sop);
Gérard Lesne (alto); **Il Seminario Musicale.** Virgin Veritas VC5 45126-2 (5/97).

...Il trionfo della grazia (La Maddalena). **Silvia Piccollo** (sop); **Rossana Bertini** (sop);
Gloria Banditelli (contr); **L'Europa Galante / Fabio Biondi.** Opus 111 OPS30-96 (10/94). ✍ Ⓖ

...Variations on "La folia"[a]. Cantatas[b] – Correa nel seno amato; Già lusingato appieno.
[b]**Lynne Dawson** (sop); **Purcell Quartet.** Hyperion CDA66254 (3/90). ✍

Domenico Scarlatti

Italian 1685-1757

D. Scarlatti Missa Breve, "La Stella". Te Deum in C major. Stabat mater in C minor[a]. Iste
Confessor[b]. **The Sixteen / Harry Christophers** with **Ian Watson** (org); [a]**Siobhan Armstrong** (hp);
[ab]**Robin Jeffrey,** [a]**Elizabeth Kenny** (theorbos). Collins Classics Ⓕ 1504-2
(60 minutes: DDD: 11/97). Texts and translations included. Recorded 1997.

Domenico Scarlatti's church music is often unfairly underrated because we cannot dismiss from our
minds the harmonic and rhythmic exuberance that characterize his keyboard sonatas; it dates from
earlier, mostly from his time in Rome, before he flowered in the heady atmosphere of Spain, where he
was to spend most of his life. Judged on their merits and without reference to Domenico's mature
Spanish output, a couple of these works, at least, are by no means without depth and tension, as The
Sixteen make abundantly clear in these committed and technically splendidly assured performances.
The Mass is stylistically mixed, as if Domenico was still feeling his way into an idiom in which he
could feel at home; nevertheless, it is quite impressive. But after the smooth, richly chordal *Kyrie* and
an unexpectedly restrained *Gloria* the bold harmonies at "Et incarnatus est" in the *Credo* pull one up
with a jerk. A surprise of another kind is the omission of the *Benedictus* in favour of "Cibavit eos
Dominus"; then the *Agnus Dei* refers back to the *Sanctus*. Admittedly *Iste Confessor* is no more than
a simple melodious hymn in five verses alternating between solo soprano and chorus, and the *Te
Deum*, very diatonic until the final "Non confundar", is little more than a generalized elation. The
Stabat mater, however, is on a far more distinguished level; Harry Christophers's admirable singers
invest it with a compelling passion and intensity. The appropriately ecclesiastical acoustic of the
recording venue has been cleanly captured.

Additional recommendation ...

...Stabat mater[a]. *Coupled with* **Esteves** Mass for Eight Voices. [a]**Elisabeth Hermans** (sop);
[a]**Jan Van Elsaker** (ten); **Currende Vocal Ensemble / Erik Van Nevel**
with **Jacques Van Der Meer** (va da gamba); **Lidewij Scheifes** (vc); **Herman Stinders** (org).
Accent Ⓕ ACC9069D (48 minutes: DDD: 5/92). ✍

D. Scarlatti Keyboard Sonatas – C major (manuscript – Yale University); G major; D major;
C major (all three ed. Henle); G major (ed. Sociedad Española de Musicología, Madrid);
D minor; A major; G major (all ed. Unión Musical Española, Madrid); A major (ed. Musica
Antiqua, Lisbon); A major; E major (both MS – Biblioteca de Catalunya, Barcelona); A major
(MS – British Library, London); A major (MS – Real Conservatorio de Música, Madrid).
Fandango in D minor. **Mayako Soné** (hpd). Erato Ⓕ 4509-94806-2
(51 minutes: DDD: 10/94). ✍

Ⓖ

It's a bit silly of Erato to label this disc "Unpublished sonatas" when the publishers of eight of the present 14 are actually listed: if they meant 'recently discovered sonatas', why not say so? Apart from this, however, a certain scepticism is called for by the claim that these are by Scarlatti. A few may well be by him; the majority, to differing extents, are of doubtful authenticity. The most convincing 'possibles' are the robustly exuberant Yale C major and three sonatas (two of them longer than usual) found in Valladolid and published by UME in Madrid. The *Fandango* has been worked up by the player here from a sketch (an impression of Scarlatti's improvisation?) in a private collection in Tenerife: shorter than the famous example attributed to Soler but closely resembling it in style. It is played with tremendous gusto – like everything else on this disc – on a Blanchet copy by Mayako Soné, a young harpsichordist who is making quite a name for herself. Her experience as a continuo player has doubtless been a contributory factor in her splendidly strong rhythmic sense; and her crisp articulation is a pleasure to hear. Regardless of the authenticity or otherwise of these pieces, this is a very attractive disc.

D. Scarlatti Keyboard Sonatas – Kk1; Kk3; Kk8; Kk9; Kk11; Kk17; Kk24; Kk25; B minor, Kk27; Kk29; Kk87; Kk96; Kk113; Kk141; Kk146; Kk173; Kk213; Kk214; Kk247; Kk259; Kk268; Kk283; Kk284; Kk380; Kk386; Kk387; Kk404; Kk443; Kk519; Kk520; Kk523.
Mikhail Pletnev (pf). Virgin Classics Ⓔ VCD5 45123-2 (two discs: 140 minutes: DDD: 3/96).
Recorded 1994. *Gramophone Editor's choice. Gramophone Award Winner 1996.*　　　　　　Ⓖ

Every so often a major pianist reclaims Scarlatti for the piano with an outstanding recording and this is certainly such an occasion. As Ralph Kirkpatrick put it, Scarlatti's harpsichord, while supremely itself, is continually menacing a transformation into something else. True, the relation of the music to harpsichord sound could hardly be closer – you can't argue on that point! – and of course it wouldn't have been composed the way it is for a different instrument. Enter Mikhail Pletnev. A two-CD album seems hardly sufficient to contain the feast of thrilling and imaginative playing he offers here. But let's put the music first; 140 minutes of Scarlatti is hardly enough to display the full range of this inexhaustibly surprising composer. He is marvellous at suggesting imaginary orchestrations and stimulating our own imagination. He makes us aware of the different vantage points as the music passes before us, of the different tones of voice and rhetorical inflexions – as various in these sonatas as the events in them are unpredictable. There are dances and fiestas and processions here, serenades and laments, and evocations of everything from the rudest folk music to courtly entertainments and churchly polyphony; and as the kaleidoscope turns you marvel at the composer who could embrace such diversity and shape it and put it all on to the keyboard. No wonder Chopin found Scarlatti a kindred spirit.

This is strongly individual playing, be warned. Pletnev's free-ranging poetic licence may not be to your taste, and admittedly it does beg a few questions. Not that his spectacular virtuosity is likely to be controversial: this really is *hors de catégorie* and enormously enjoyable. And the evocations of the harpsichord are often very witty – only a fool would play Scarlatti on the piano as if the harpsichord had never existed. But Pletnev doesn't shrink from using the full resources of the piano, sustaining pedal included, and if you baulk at the prospect of that as the means to an end he will probably not be for you. The sustaining pedal is indeed dangerous in music which is almost wholly to do with lines, not washes of colour; its effect is to make us see Scarlatti as if through Mendelssohn's eyes. Yet moments of such falsification are rare. As often as not when Pletnev appears to be on the verge of stepping outside Scarlatti's world, or reinventing a little bit of it, it's because of some shaft of insight vouchsafed to his extraordinary musical mind that is well worth having. Characterization is everything, and though he can be a mite coy in the reflective sonatas he generally goes straight to the heart of the matter. The vigorous, full tone in the quick numbers is a joy to have, and most admirable of all is the way he makes sound immediately command character. That is something only the best artists are able to do. There are no doubts about the recorded sound: this is one of the best piano recordings available.

D. Scarlatti Keyboard Sonatas – Kk69; Kk113; Kk114; Kk115; Kk116; Kk208; Kk209; Kk215; Kk216; Kk246; Kk247; Kk394; Kk395; Kk414; Kk415; Kk426; Kk427; Kk513. **Andreas Staier** (hpd). Teldec Das Alte Werk Ⓔ 0630-12601-2 (74 minutes: DDD: 7/96). ⟋

Staier's previous Scarlatti records aroused a keen anticipation for more, which at long last has been fulfilled. He is adept at capturing the mercurial changes of mood and still surprising harmonic quirks of that unpredictable genius, and even when we disagree with his readings they always hold the interest. In particular, he manages to convey the spirit of Scarlatti's spur-of-the-moment inventive powers, not merely by adding spontaneous extra ornaments or inserting buckshee pauses-for-thought, but by his very flexible pace – which may take some getting used to. Kk427, which is marked "as fast as possible", has never been played faster than here, but Kk114 – one of two sonatas including the direction *Tremulo* to indicate a continuous trill – sounds rushed, and Kk208 is preternaturally slow, drawing attention to a left-hand-before-right mannerism that also affects the pensive Kk69. Staier makes big variations within Kk394 and Kk395, for example, and starts the second half of the bright Kk414 at a new tempo. Yet he only does it to tease, and he can, when he wants to, maintain an admirably direct forward impulse, as in the C sharp minor Sonata, Kk246, his wonderfully springy Kk209, or in Kk113, with its exhilarating cross-hand leaps. Scarlatti styles exemplified here range from the Neapolitan three-section Pastorale, Kk513 to the savage Spanish scrunches of Kk215, and from continuity – even isorhythm in Kk415 – to constant stop-and-start tactics, as in Kk426 (which, together with its companion Kk427, calls for an instrument with a top G, which this Keith Hill copy of a mid-eighteenth-century German harpsichord evidently has). For some unfathomable reason Teldec's booklet totally ignores the programme and instead prints a completely irrelevant short story.

D. Scarlatti Keyboard Sonatas – Kk213; Kk214; Kk318; Kk319; Kk347; Kk348; Kk356; Kk357; Kk380; Kk381; Kk454; Kk455; Kk478; Kk479; Kk524; Kk525; Kk526; Kk527.
Ralph Kirkpatrick (hpd). DG Classikon Ⓜ 439 438-2GCL (52 minutes: ADD: 9/96). ✍
From 2533 072 (9/71). Recorded 1970.

An infectious zest characterizes these attractive performances of Scarlatti sonatas, most of them among the less well known. And Scarlatti's own zest is manifest in their wonderfully imaginative diversity: unmistakable, for example, is the sheer glee with which he constantly plunges from one end of the keyboard to the other in Kk356 and K357 (to write which he resorted to the use of four staves), indulges in bold modulations (Kk526 and K319), and writes a couple of sonatas in the then *ultima Thule* key of F sharp major. Kirkpatrick's presentation accords with the theory that the sonatas were intended to be paired; and the insert-note, informative as to the background but silent about the works selected, rightly disagrees with the absurd theory that the 500-plus sonatas were all written in the composer's last few years. The bright-toned instrument employed here (and vividly recorded) was by Rainer Schütze of Heidelberg. An exhilarating disc.

Additional recommendations ...

...555 Keyboard Sonatas. **Scott Ross** (hpd) with **Monica Huggett** (vn); **Christophe Coin** (vc); **Michael Henry** (ob); **Marc Vellon** (bn). Erato Ⓕ 2292-45309-2 (34 discs: DDD: 6/88). ✍
...Kk1; Kk8; Kk9; Kk11; Kk13; Kk20; Kk87; Kk98; Kk119; Kk135; Kk159; Kk380; Kk450; Kk487; Kk529. **Ivo Pogorelich** (pf). DG Ⓕ 435 855-2GH (60 minutes: DDD: 1/93).
...Kk7; Kk84; Kk185; Kk187; Kk193; Kk208; Kk491; Kk492. *Coupled with works by* **Soler**
Virginia Black (hpd). Cala United Ⓕ CACD88005-2 (58 minutes: DDD: 8/94). ✍
See review under Soler; refer to the Index.
...Kk9; Kk13; Kk17; Kk27; Kk29; Kk30; Kk32; Kk64; Kk69; Kk87; Kk96; Kk114; Kk119; Kk125; Kk159; Kk175; Kk202; Kk245; Kk279; Kk377; Kk380; Kk427; Kk430; Kk432; Kk446; Kk450; Kk474; Kk478; Kk492; Kk519; Kk523; Kk533. *Coupled with works by various composers.*
Marcelle Meyer (pf). EMI mono Ⓜ CZS5 68092-2* (four discs: 275 minutes: ADD: 6/95).
See review in the Collections section; refer to the Index.   ⒼⒼⒼ
...Kk9; Kk27; Kk30; Kk33; Kk69; Kk87; Kk96; Kk159; Kk193; Kk247; Kk492; Kk531.
Anne Queffélec (pf). Erato Ⓜ 4509-96960-2 (51 minutes: ADD: 3/95).   ⒼⒼ
...Kk10; Kk20; Kk23; Kk24; Kk25; Kk28; Kk56; Kk60; Kk64; Kk104; Kk126; Kk146; Kk179; Kk180; Kk181; Kk182; Kk192; Kk193; Kk256; Kk257; Kk260; Kk334; Kk341; Kk342; Kk443; Kk444; Kk462; Kk463; Kk474; Kk475; Kk505; Kk506; Kk513; Kk528; Kk529.
Gilbert Rowland (hpd). Kingdom Ⓜ KLCD5009/10 (two discs: 150 minutes: DDD: 10/96). ✍
...Kk14. *Coupled with works by various composers.* **Dame Myra Hess** (pf). Biddulph mono
Ⓜ LHW025* (76 minutes: ADD: 3/96). *See review in the Collections section; refer to the Index.* Ⓖ
...Kk27; Kk29; Kk206; Kk212; Kk247; Kk491; Kk537. *Coupled with works by* **Handel**
Murray Perahia (pf). Sony Classical Ⓕ SK62785 (69 minutes: DDD: 5/97). *Gramophone Editor's record of the month.* **Gramophone** *Award Winner 1997. Selected by Soundings. See review under Handel; refer to the Index.*   ⒼⒼ
...Kk27; Kk212. *Coupled with works by various composers.* **Murray Perahia** (pf).
Sony Classical Ⓜ SX4K63380 (four discs: 270 minutes: DDD/ADD: 4/98). *See review in the Collections section; refer to the Index.*
...Kk30, "Cat's Fugue"; Kk46; Kk87; Kk119; Kk132; Kk133; Kk208; Kk213; Kk215; Kk259; Kk260; Kk278; Kk380; Kk429; Kk517; Kk544; Kk545. **Colin Booth** (hpd).
Olympia Ⓜ OCD251 (74 minutes: DDD: 3/95).
...Kk32; Kk109; Kk234; Kk296; Kk259; Kk440; Kk490; Kk515. **Wanda Landowska** (hpd).
EMI Références mono Ⓜ CDH7 64934-2* (69 minutes: ADD: 8/94).
...Kk33; Kk54; Kk96; Kk146; Kk162; Kk198; Kk391; Kk466; Kk474; Kk481; Kk491; Kk525.
Vladimir Horowitz (pf). Sony Classical Ⓕ SK53460 (72 minutes: ADD: 7/94).
...Kk52; Kk211; Kk212; Kk248; Kk249; Kk261; Kk262; Kk263; Kk264; Kk318; Kk319; Kk347; Kk348; Kk416; kk417; kk490; Kk491; Kk492. **Elaine Thornburgh** (hpd). Koch International
Classics Ⓕ 37014-2 (72 minutes: DDD: 10/91). ✍   ⒼⒼ
...Kk64; Kk87; Kk96; Kk132; Kk133; Kk175; Kk202; Kk213; Kk214; Kk263; Kk264; Kk277; Kk278; Kk420; Kk421; Kk460; Kk461. **Andreas Staier** (hpd). Deutsche Harmonia Mundi
Ⓕ 05472-77274-2 (71 minutes: DDD: 3/93). ✍   ⒼⒼⒼ
...Kk87; Kk125. *Coupled with works by various composers.* **Vladimir Horowitz** (pf). APR mono
Ⓜ APR5517* (71 minutes: ADD: 5/98). *See review in the Collections section; refer to the Index.*
...Kk108; Kk118; Kk119; Kk141; Kk198; Kk203; Kk454; Kk455; Kk490; Kk491; Kk492; Kk501; Kk502; Kk516; Kk517; Kk518; Kk519. **Andreas Staier** (hpd).
Deutsche Harmonia Mundi Ⓕ RD77224 (70 minutes: DDD: 2/92). ✍   ⒼⒼⒼ
...Kk113; Kk380; Kk381; Kk213; Kk119; Kk120; Kk501; Kk502; Kk466; Kk146; Kk318; Kk319; Kk24. **Virginia Black** (hpd). CRD Ⓕ CRD3442 (60 minutes: DDD: 6/87). ✍   Ⓖ

...Kk124; Kk99; Kk201; Kk87; Kk46; Kk95; Kk204a; Kk490; Kk491; Kk492; Kk520; Kk521; Kk513. **Trevor Pinnock** (hpd). CRD Ⓕ CRD3368 (61 minutes: ADD: 12/86). ✐   Ⓖ
...Kk380. *Coupled with works by various composers.* **Pavel Nersessian** (pf).
Bel Air Music Ⓕ BAM9725 (65 minutes: DDD: 3/98). *See review in the Collections section; refer to the Index.*

Further listening ...
...Sonata for Mandolin and Continuo in D minor, Kk90. *Coupled with works by various composers.*
Il Giardino Armonico / Giovanni Antonini (rec). Teldec Das Alte Werk 4509-93157-2 (11/94).
See review in the Collections section; refer to the Index.   ⒼⒼ

Giacinto Scelsi
Italian 1905-1988

Suggested listening ...
...In nomine lucis. *Coupled with works by* **Pärt** *and* **Cage** Christoph Maria Moosmann (org).
New Albion NA074CD (2/96). *See review under Pärt; refer to the Index.*

Franz Xaver Scharwenka
Polish 1850-1924

Scharwenka Piano Concertos – No. 2 in C minor, Op. 56; No. 3 in C sharp minor, Op. 80.
Seta Tanyel (pf); **Hanover Radio Philharmonic Orchestra / Tadeusz Strugała.**
Collins Classics Ⓕ 1485-2 (79 minutes: DDD: 5/97).
Scharwenka would surely have been heartened by Seta Tanyel's admirable campaign on his behalf. Here, she continues with the Second and Third Piano Concertos, once again surmounting every ferocious obstacle with an ease that allows her an unblemished freedom to concentrate on the composer's musical character. Those with a taste for full-blown rhetoric in an ultra-nineteenth-century style and for some notably beguiling slow movements (the *Adagio* from the Third is hard to resist) will, of course, hardly need persuading, but other more sceptical listeners will surely be convinced when the performances temper an enviable fluency and expertise with discretion. True, Tanyel's playing does not always scintillate with the most concentrated virtuoso aplomb (try Earl Wild in the First Concerto or the Fourth by Stephen Hough, listed overleaf, yet in the Third Concerto's massive cadenza she is as impressive in octave thunder as in filigree delicacy. Tadeusz Strugala's partnership is suitably enthusiastic and the recordings, as always from this source, are exemplary.

Scharwenka Four Polish Dances, Op. 47. Menuet, Op. 65 No. 1. Scherzo, Op. 65 No. 2.
Six Waltzes, Op. 28. Variations on a Theme by C. H., Op. 57. Drei Klavierstücke, Op. 86.
Erzählungen am Klavier (Legends), Op. 5. **Seta Tanyel** (pf). Collins Classics Ⓕ 1474-2
(72 minutes: DDD: 8/96). Recorded 1995.
Chopin's spirit may hover over the *Polish Dances* (all four are *mazurkas*), Brahms over the *Waltzes* and Schumann over large sections of Opp. 5, 57 and 86, with terms such as *langsam-innig* or *langsam und zart* telling their own affectionate tale. Yet by the time Scharwenka reached his *Drei Klavierstücke*, Op. 86 he felt increasingly free of the past; able to venture into a greater harmonic subtlety, modulatory ease and cunning. The "Nocturne" is more impressionistic than Chopinesque and, after the sprightly "Serenade", "Marchen" blossoms into considerable expressive richness. The *Variations on a Theme by C. H.*, too, increase in interest and although Vars. 9 and 11 are haunted by Schumann's *Faschingsschwank aus Wien* and *Davidsbundler-tänze* respectively, they transform their bias into music of a special distinction and freshness. So, far from scraping the barrel there is much here to surprise and enliven, even if there is nothing as immediately attractive as the *Eglantine Waltz* and *Valse-Caprice*; both sufficiently charming to entice even the least susceptible dancer on to the ballroom floor. Tanyel's performances are beyond reproach. Strong, sensitive and stylish, she is warmly sympathetic. The recordings, while closer than the earlier ones, are excellent.

Further listening ...
...Piano Concerto No. 1 in B flat minor, Op. 32. *Coupled with* **Chopin** Piano Concerto No. 1
in E minor, Op. 11. **Seta Tanyel** (pf); **Philharmonia Orchestra / Yuri Simonov.**
Collins Classics 1263-2.   Ⓖ
...Piano Concerto No. 1 in B flat minor, Op. 32. *Coupled with works by* **Balakirev** and
Paderewski Earl Wild (pf); **Boston Symphony Orchestra / Erich Leinsdorf.**
Elan CD82266 (7/96).
...Piano Concerto No. 4 in F minor, Op. 82. *Coupled with* **Sauer** Piano Concerto No. 1 in E minor.
Stephen Hough (pf); **City of Birmingham Symphony Orchestra / Lawrence Foster.**
Hyperion CDA66790 (11/95). *Gramophone Editor's record of the month.* **Gramophone Award**
Winner 1996. See review under Sauer; refer to the Index.   Ⓖ
...Piano Quartet in F major, Op. 37. Piano Trio in A minor, Op. 45. **Levon Chilingirian** (vn); **Ivo-Jan van der Werff** (va); **Garbis Atmacayan** (vc); **Seta Tanyel** (pf). Collins Classics 1419-2 (3/95).
...Piano Trio No. 1 in F sharp minor, Op. 1[ab]. Violin Sonata in D minor, Op. 2[a]. Cello Sonata in
E minor, Op. 46[a][b]. Serenade, Op. 70[a]. [a]**Lydia Mordkovitch** (vn); [b]**Colin Carr** (vc);
Seta Tanyel (pf). Collins Classics 1448-2 (10/95).

...Five Polish Dances, Op. 3. Piano Sonata No. 1 in C sharp minor, Op. 6. First Polonaise, Op. 12. Impromptu, Op. 17. Valse-Caprice, Op. 31. Polonaise, Op. 42. Eglantine Waltz, Op. 84. **Seta Tanyel** (pf). Collins Classics 1325-2 (9/92).

Samuel Scheidt

German 1587-1654

Scheidt Ludi Musici – Alamande a 4; Canzon ad imitationem Bergamas angl a 5; Canzon super Cantionem Gallicam a 5; Canzon super O Nachbar Roland a 5; Five Courants a 4; Courant dolorosa a 4; Two Galliards a 4; Galliard a 5; Galliard battaglia a 5; Three Paduanas a 4. **Hespèrion XX / Jordi Savall** (viol). Auvidis Fontalis Ⓕ ES8559 (62 minutes: DDD: 8/97). ✍ Recorded 1995.

Scheidt's *Ludi Musici* reflects the fusion of English and German traditions in the emergent world of instrumental music in early seventeenth-century Germany and is a mouth-wateringly diverse and inventive mixture of dance, canzona and variation. These are works which brim over with character and nonchalantly brilliant craftsmanship. Scheidt has that rare knack, for the 1620s and 1630s, of sustaining an instrumental piece for more than two minutes without bombarding us with a new idea every ten bars; the longer pieces such as the Paduanas and the brilliant Canzon a 5 *ad imitationem Bergamas angl*, with its thrilling close, convey admirable long-term direction amid a concentrated love of ephemeral effect. This is a cocktail which Hespèrion XX relish. The Pavans are, as you would expect from Jordi Savall, eventful. There are moments when an indulgence from Savall's treble viol stifles the potential for a more reflective allusion, but the overriding effect is of a performer striving to find a meaningful discourse, not content just to 'let the music play itself'; the colour and shape he brings to line and texture is often beguiling (disarmingly poignant in the stillness of the final Paduana), at times too much of a good thing but always engaging.

Additional recommendations ...
...Ich glaub und weiss. Paduan a 4. Lobet, ihr Himmel, den Herren. *Coupled with works by* **Zachow** and **Handel Stadtsingechor, Halle; Berolina Quartet.** Berlin Classics Ⓕ 0011 312BC (61 minutes: DDD: 6/96).
...Canzona super Cantionem Gallicam. Galliard battaglia a 5. *Coupled with works by various composers.* **His Majestys Sagbutts and Cornetts.** Hyperion Ⓕ CDA66847 (69 minutes: DDD: 11/96). *See review in the Collections section; refer to the Index.*

Johann Hermann Schein

German 1586 1630

Schein Israelis Brünnlein. **Ensemble Vocal Européen / Philippe Herreweghe.** Harmonia Mundi Ⓕ HMC90 1574 (79 minutes: DDD: 3/97). Texts and translations included.
Anyone who hears this sympathetic account of *Israelis Brünnlein* ("The Fountains of Israel" – 26 sacred madrigals in five and six parts with a *basso seguente*) from Ensemble Vocal Européen will undoubtedly be convinced that this is one of the great pillars of German baroque music. It is fascinating not only as a demonstration of how the best German music incorporates foreign styles within indigenous techniques but also for Schein's discovery of his own unique expressive horizons, in ways which cannot directly be attributed to either Mantua or Leipzig. As in the *Lagrime di St Pietro* of Lassus (a composer whose poised contrapuntal craft is transmuted with profound respect by Schein), secular idioms successfully serve the sacred vision. Herreweghe, whose cool and collected reading of the Lassus masterpiece (see review under Lassus; refer to the Index) is vocally peerless, finds fresh priorities here. The exposed solo context draws out a greater sense of quasi-spontaneous attention, particularly in upbeat examples like "Freue dich des Weibes" and the concentrated brilliance of "Ist nicht Ephraim?". Emotional intensity is, however, inclined to sound overmeasured in works like "Die mit Tränen säen" and "Was betrübst", where dramatic urgency is required above the restrained shapeliness and refinement that is Herreweghe's hallmark. This is where Cantus Cölln steal the odd march in their choice of 11 madrigals from this collection (recorded alongside examples from *Opella Nova II*). However, there are some fine singers here (underpinned by the splendid Peter Kooy), even if the tenor tuning is not always beyond reproach; as an almost comprehensive – five pieces are left out – volume of 80-odd minutes, this is a commendable achievement and further assures Schein's reputation as a master of exquisite characterization.

Additional recommendation ...
...Unser Leben währet siebnzig Jahr. Ach Herr, ach meiner schone. Mach dich auf, werde Licht. Da Jakob vollendet hatte. Ich lasse dich nicht. Magnificat. Die mit Tränen säen. O Herr, ich bin dein Knecht. Vom Himmel hoch da komm ich her. Vom Himmel hoch da komm ich her. Herr, lass meine Klage. Ist nicht Ephraim mein teurer Sohn. Warum betrübst du dich, mein Herz. Ich bin die Wurzel des Geschlechtes David. Ich freue mich im Herren. Was betrübst du dich, meine Seele. Vater unser, der du bist im Himmel. Nun danket alle Gott. **Cantus Cölln / Konrad Junghänel** (lte). **La Fenice / Konrad Junghänel.** Deutsche Harmonia Mundi Ⓕ 05472 77359-2 (75 minutes: DDD).

Further listening ...
...Vocal Works – O Amarilli zart. Aurora schön mit ihrem Haar. Frischauf, ihr Klosterbrüder mein. Ringstum mich schwebet Trauerigkeit. Als Filli schön und fromm. In Filli schönen Augelein.

O Scheiden, o bitter Scheiden. Unlängst dem blinden Gröttelein. Wie kommst's, o zarte Filli mein. Kickehihi, kakakanei. Cupido blind, das Venuskind. Wenn Filli ihre Liebesstrahl. O Amarilli, schönste Zier. Heulen und schmerzlichs Weinen. All wilden Tier im grünen Wald. O Venus und Cupido blind. Amor, das liebe Räuberlein. O seidene Härelein. Ihr Brüder, lieben Brüder mein. Mirtillo hat ein Schäfelein. Die Vöglein singen. Mein Schifflein lief im wilden Meer. **Cantus Cölln / Konrad Junghänel.** Deutsche Harmonia Mundi RD77088 (10/90). ✐

Ernest Schelling

American 1876-1939

Suggested listening ...
...Suite Fantastique, Op. 7. *Coupled with* **Huss** Piano Concerto in B major, Op. 10. **Ian Hobson** (pf); **BBC Scottish Symphony Orchestra / Martyn Brabbins.** Hyperion CDA66949 (A/97).

Johann Heinrich Schmelzer

Austrian c1620/23-1680

Schmelzer Sonatae unarum fidium – Nos. 1-6. Sonata for Violin and Continuo in A minor, "Il cucù".
Biber (arr. A. Schmelzer) Sonata for Violin and Continuo, "Victori der Christen".
Romanesca (Andrew Manze, vn; Nigel North, theorbo; John Toll, hpd/org).
Harmonia Mundi Ⓕ HMU90 7143 (67 minutes: DDD: 10/96). ✐ Also includes a free sampler disc of Biber violin sonatas. Recorded 1995. Performances of works from the indigenous Austrian seventeenth-century 'school' have made a significant impact on the *status quo* of mainstream baroque instrumental music of late. This is not to say that the more formalized Italian traditions, that dominated in Vienna until Schmelzer's gradual and unspectacular rise to Kappelmeister of the imperial court in 1679, have been in any way shown up; rather that the distinctive rhetorical flavour of *Mittel Europa* has both broadened our horizons and encouraged players and listeners to think more flexibly about the unique language of composers such as Biber and Schmelzer. These are men who have left a remarkable amount to the imagination: and yet, a step of faith, technical brilliance and a commitment to find the dramatic and emotional heart of these solo works reaps untold rewards. Whilst Biber has enjoyed the most marked renaissance of those in the employ of the imperial court, Schmelzer is the spiritual father of this colourful native expression. Coming to these recordings (the first to include all six of Schmelzer's pioneering *Sonatae unarum fidium*, or "Sonatas for one violin" of 1644) from Biber's extravagant and incomparably theatrical sonatas, one is immediately struck by common stylistic threads but also by Schmelzer's studied lyricism, a searing and disarming feel for melodic progression (heard in the close of the *Cucù* Sonata) and the sense of a man who, when he is not following his tail with ostinato basses, has thoroughly mastered the canzona-sonata mentality and takes full advantage of its freedom. All Biberian features certainly, but as Andrew Manze both explains in his note and demonstrates in his playing, there is less overall ostentation here; whilst the extraordinary Sonata No. 4 latterly contains gloriously extended and potent outbursts, it is the patient arching direction of Schmelzer's melodic frame which draws one into his web. Manze and his accomplished continuo players (the contribution of the theorbo is both exquisite and distinctive) are wonderful exponents in this mesmerizing baroque byway.
Further listening ...
...Sonata a 3 in B minor, "Lamento. Duodena selectarum sonatarum – No. 2 in A minor; No. 8 in B flat major. Sonata sopra la morte Ferdinand III. Lamento a 3 in B flat major. Harmonia a 5 in B flat major. *Coupled with works by* **Biber Freiburg Baroque Orchestra Consort.** Deutsche Harmonia Mundi 05472 77348-2 (7/96). ✐ *See review under Biber, refer to the Index.*
...Sonatas – Lamento sopra la morte Ferdinandi III; Sonata a tre violini. Sonata a tre; Sonata a tre "Lanterly"; Duodena selectarum sonatarum – No. 9. *Coupled with works by* **Muffat London Baroque / Charles Medlam.** Harmonia Mundi HMA190 1220 (11/87). ✐
...Vesperae sollennes[ab]. Sonata per Chiesa et Camera. Sacro-Profanus Concentus Musicus – Sonata XII. *Coupled with works by various composers.* **Vienna Hofburgkapella Schola;** [b]**Concerto Palatino; Gradus ad Parnassum / Konrad Junghänel.** Deutsche Harmonia Mundi 05472 77326-2 (7/95). ✐

Franz Schmidt

Czechoslovakian/Austrian 1874-1939

Schmidt Symphony No. 4 in C major. Variations on a Hussar's Song. **London Philharmonic Orchestra / Franz Welser-Möst.** EMI Ⓕ CDC5 55518-2 (72 minutes: DDD: 1/96).
Recorded 1994. *Gramophone Editor's choice. Gramophone Award Winner 1996.* ⒼⒼⒼ
Writing in *The Symphony* (ed. Robert Simpson, Penguin Books: 1967) the late Harold Truscott made out a strong case for Franz Schmidt. He robustly dismissed the notion that his music does not travel. "It 'travels' very well, when allowed to do so, and I will go so far as to say that anyone who claims a love and understanding of Beethoven, Brahms or Sibelius, should have no difficulty with Schmidt. There could," he went on, "scarcely be a more positive work than No. 4, whose confidence is complete

and without bombast" and it is obvious that Schmidt's mastery of the art of symphonic thinking and of the orchestra is everywhere in evidence. The symphony is in one unbroken span whose material derives from the haunting opening 21-bar theme on solo trumpet – in itself an idea of remarkable originality. Unlike Reger, whose influence can at times be clearly heard, Schmidt was a late developer and far from prolific. Indeed apart from the four symphonies, there is only one other orchestral work, the *Variations on a Hussar's Song* recorded here. For those who have never encountered his music, it is perhaps best if loosely described as rich in palette, in much the same way as Elgar, chromatic in its harmonic language yet never cloying, and above all it has an innate nobility, an elegiac dignity of utterance and a sense of vision. Not without reason did Truscott call Schmidt the "only real successor to Bruckner – in so far as there is one at all". Welser-Möst shows great feeling for and sympathy with this music and carries his fine players with him. Theirs is playing of eloquence and dedication, and the recording team produce truthful and well-detailed sound.

Schmidt Das Buch mit sieben Siegeln. **Hilde Gueden** (sop); **Ira Malaniuk** (contr); **Anton Dermota, Fritz Wunderlich** (tens); **Walter Berry** (bass-bar); **Vienna Singverein; Vienna Philharmonic Orchestra / Dimitri Mitropoulos.** Sony Classical Festspieldokumente mono Ⓜ SM2K68442* (two discs: 111 minutes: ADD: 3/96). Text included. Recorded live in 1959.

Franz Schmidt's oratorio combines learned, Bruckner-like contrapuntal artifice with a vivid sense of drama that at times recalls the naïve peasant baroque of some Austrian and South German carved altarpieces, at others the horrific realism of Matthias Grünewald. As a composer himself and a man of deep religious conviction Mitropoulos responded to both these aspects, and such haunting passages as the duet for two survivors of the pestilence and death spread by the horsemen of the Apocalypse, or the tremendous earthquake chorus that follows the breaking of the seventh seal have a powerful sense of drama which is emphasized by Mitropoulos's precise care for contrapuntal and instrumental detail. Yes, in this live performance there are a few untidinesses but the impact and the devout urgency of the reading are not in the least diminished by them. In the hugely taxing central role of St John, Dermota is deeply impressive. Although the part is often given to a dramatic tenor it responds to a lyric voice that is capable at times of ringing fullness. Dermota matches Mitropoulos's urgency, and clearly means every word of the role. At one point, where a descending vocal line illustrates the text's reference to the four beasts and the elders falling down before the Lamb, it is obvious that the bottom note of the phrase is not within his range. Instead, quietly and reverently, he speaks it, and the expressive effect of this is characteristic of his whole performance. The other soloists, Gueden and Berry especially, are distinguished, and both chorus and orchestra audibly respond to Mitropoulos's conviction. The mono recording is a little constricted at times, with patches of acid string tone, but it improves and gains impact as it proceeds. *Das Buch mit sieben Siegeln* still has the reputation of a piece that the Austrians regard as a classic but which doesn't travel. This recording refutes that view with inspiriting eloquence.

Additional recommendation ...
...Soloists; Vienna Singverein and Symphony Orchestra / **Horst Stein.**
Calig Ⓕ CAL50978/9 (two discs: 113 minutes: DDD: 9/97).

Further listening ...
...Symphony No. 1 in E major. *Coupled with* **R. Strauss** Intermezzo – symphonic interludes.
Detroit Symphony Orchestra / Neeme Järvi. Chandos CHAN9357 (4/96).
...Symphony No. 2 in E flat major. **Chicago Symphony Orchestra / Neeme Järvi.**
Chandos CHAN8779 (3/90).
...Symphony No. 4 in C major. *Coupled with* **Mahler** Symphony No. 2, "Resurrection".
Vienna Philharmonic Orchestra / Zubin Mehta. Double Decca 440 615-2DF2 (5/94).
...Drei Phantasiestücke nach ungarischen Nationalmelodien. *Coupled with* **Brahms** (arr. Piatti)
21 Hungarian Dances. **Nancy Green** (vc); **Frederick Moyer** (pf). Biddulph LAW010 (5/95).
...String Quartets – No. 1 in A major; No. 2 in G major. **Franz Schubert Quartet of Vienna.**
Nimbus NI5467 (6/96).
...Chaconne in C sharp minor *Coupled with works by various composers.* **Keith John** (org).
Priory PRCD370 (11/92). *Selected by Sounds in Retrospect. See review in the Collections section; refer to the Index.* ⒼⒼⒼ
...Notre Dame. **Soloists; Choir of St Hedwig's Cathedral, Berlin; Berlin RIAS Chamber Choir; Berlin Radio Symphony Orchestra / Christof Perick.** Capriccio 10 248/9 (5/89).
...Notre Dame – Intermezzo. *Coupled with works by various composers.*
Vienna Philharmonic Orchestra / Rudolf Kempe.
Testament SBT1127* (3/98). *See review in the Collections section; refer to the Index.*

Florent Schmitt
French 1870-1958

Schmitt La tragédie de Salomé. **Marie-Paule Fayt** (sop); **Rhineland-Pfalz State Philharmonic Orchestra / Patrick Davin.** Marco Polo Ⓕ 8 223448 (59 minutes: DDD: 12/93). Recorded 1991.

This is a real rarity. We have had recordings of the large-orchestra suite from *La tragédie de Salomé* before but here, apparently for the first time, is the complete ballet which runs to twice the length of the suite and calls for only a chamber orchestra (the theatre couldn't accommodate more). Schmitt's virtuosity in drawing rich sonorities and a voluptuous, barbaric atmosphere from it is astonishing. Unlike the treatments of the biblical story by Strauss or Massenet, in the scenario here there is no question of Salome being in love with John the Baptist. Schmitt composed a well-structured score of exotic and sensual colour that includes broad lyrical episodes as well as vividly orgiastic sections. Compared to the suite for full orchestra, these lose nothing in impact or impressiveness by the smaller forces employed – indeed, the music gains in clarity and pungency thereby. It is not surprising that Stravinsky, to whom the work was dedicated, described it as "one of the greatest masterpieces of modern music". The performance, and the recording, are deserving of the highest commendation.

Further listening ...
...La danse d'Abisag, Op. 75. Habeyssée, Op. 110[a]. Rêves, Op. 65. Symphony No. 2, Op. 137.
[a]**Hannele Segerstam** (vn); **Rheinland-Pfalz State Philharmonic Orchestra / Leif Segerstam.**
Marco Polo 8 223689 (3/95).
...In memoriam Gabriel Fauré, Op. 72 – Scherzo. *Coupled with works by various composers.*
Academy of St Martin in the Fields and [a]**Chorus / Sir Neville Marriner.**
Philips 446 084-2PH (1/96).
...Symphonie concertante, Op. 82[a]. Rêves, Op. 65. Soirs, Op. 5. [a]**Huseyin Sermet** (pf);
Monte-Carlo Philharmonic Orchestra / David Robertson. Auvidis Valois V4687 (9/94).
...Deux mirages. *Coupled with works by* **Dutilleux** and **Dukas** John Ogdon (pf).
EMI Matrix CDM5 65996-2 (11/96). *See review under Dukas; refer to the Index.*

Alfred Schnittke

USSR 1934

Schnittke Concerto grosso No. 1[a]. Quasi una sonata[b]. Moz-Art à la Haydn[c]. [ac]**Tatiana Grindenko** (vn); **Yuri Smirnov** ([a]hpd/[a]prep pf/[b]pf); **Chamber Orchestra of Europe /** [a]**Heinrich Schiff,** [bc]**Gidon Kremer** ([a]vn). DG Ⓜ 439 452-2GCL (62 minutes: DDD: 9/90). Recorded live in 1988.
For a single representative of Alfred Schnittke's work you could choose nothing better than the first *Concerto grosso* of 1977. Here are the psychedelic mélanges of baroque and modern, the drastic juxtapositions of pseudo-Vivaldi with pseudo-Berg, producing an effect at once aurally exciting and spiritually disturbing. The piece has had many recordings, but never with the panache of Kremer and friends and never with the vivid immediacy of this live DG recording (in fact the solo violins are rather too closely miked for comfort, but that's only a tiny drawback). *Quasi una sonata* was originally composed in 1968 for violin and piano and it was something of a breakthrough piece for Schnittke as he emerged from what he called "the puberty rites of serialism", letting his imagination run riot for the first time. No one could call it a disciplined piece, but if that worries you, you should leave Schnittke alone anyway. The transcription for solo violin and string orchestra is an ingenious one and Kremer again supplies all the requisite agonized intensity. *Moz-Art à la Haydn* is a very slight piece of work, and it really depends on visual theatricality to make its effect. Still, it complements the other two pieces well enough, and this disc makes another excellent introduction to this composer.

Additional recommendation ...
...Concerto grosso No. 1[a]. Viola Concerto[b]. Concerto for Piano and Strings[c]. Monologue[d].
Praeludium in memoriam Dmitri Shostakovich[e]. Suite in the Old Style[f]. [a]**Gidon Kremer,**
[a]**Tatjana Grindenko,** [e]**Sasha Rozhdestvensky** (vns); [c]**Vladimir Krainev,** [e]**Sergei Bezrodny** (pfs);
[ab]**London Symphony Orchestra /** [a]**Gennadi Rozhdestvensky,** [b]**Mstislav Rostropovich;**
[cf]**Moscow Virtuosi /** **Vladimir Spivakov** ([e]vn); [d]**Moscow Soloists /** [d]**Yuri Bashmet** ([b]va).
RCA Victor Ⓜ 74321 24894-2 (two discs: 127 minutes: ADD/DDD: 5/95). Ⓖ

Schnittke Violin Concertos[a] – No. 2; No. 3. Stille Nacht[b]. Gratulations rondo[b]. **Gidon Kremer** (vn); [a]**Chamber Orchestra of Europe / Christoph Eschenbach** ([b]pf). Teldec Ⓕ 4509-94540-2 (61 minutes: DDD: 2/95). Recorded 1994. ⒼⒼ
Schnittke's Second Violin Concerto opens with the kind of jagged, convulsive, Webern-crossed-with-Shostakovich cadenza that is a trademark of his string writing. Does the rest of the concerto live up to this opening? And what is all the curious writing for the solo double-bass supposed to mean? Jürgen Köchel's accompanying note reveals all – or at least something startling. It turns out that the structure is based on Christ's life, death and resurrection, and that the double-bass is a Judas figure, an anti-soloist (shades of Liszt's Faust/Mephistopheles perhaps). That may or may not affect one's reactions to the music. Do Berg's Violin Concerto and Chamber Concerto, for instance, stand by their hidden programmes or by the notes composed as a result of them? And the Third Concerto is certainly not a piece to be trifled with. Its unusual scoring for 13 winds and four strings is partly modelled on Berg's Chamber Concerto, and at one stage the composer was toying with another Biblical subtitle, *The Song of Songs*. But the musical invention seems more self-sufficient, more concentrated and more finished than that of the Second Concerto. The violin's trills convey the alarm of a whole psychic world tottering, and all three movements have their nerve-endings exposed. The Mahlerian chorale of the finale carries bittersweetness to the *n*th degree. Throughout the disc Kremer's personality is a compelling presence, and the Chamber Orchestra of Europe are terrific in their support. Eschenbach's contribution is perhaps less overt but certainly no less vital, and in the two contrasted miniatures (in many ways the outstanding compositions in the programme) his discretion is the ideal foil for his charismatic partner. Recording quality is of the very finest.

Additional recommendations ...
...Violin Concertos Nos. 1 and 2. **Mark Lubotsky** (vn); **Malmö Symphony Orchestra / Eri Klas.** BIS Ⓕ CD487 (61 minutes: DDD: 4/91).
...Violin Concerto No. 3[a]. Piano Concerto[b]. Violin Sonata No. 3[c]. [ac]**Mark Lubotsky** (vn); [c]**Irina Schnittke** (pf); [a]**Sibelius Academy Wind Players;** [ab]**Virtuosi di Kuhmo / Ralf Gothóni** ([b]pf). Ondine Ⓕ ODE893-2 (60 minutes: DDD: 10/97).

Schnittke Esquisses. **Orchestra of the Bolshoi Theatre / Andrey Chistiakov.** CdM Russian Season
   Ⓕ RUS288 155 (54 minutes: DDD: 6/98). Recorded 1996.   Ⓖ
Esquisses ("Sketches") was a ballet based on a conflation of Gogol's best-known stories, put on at the Bolshoi in 1975 for the 175th anniversary of the author's birth. Schnittke had already supplied music for the Taganka theatre's Gogol adaptations in 1978, arranged by Rozhdestvensky as the *Gogol Suite*. For the ballet he fleshed out this work with a dozen new numbers, around 20 minutes of music. The result is one of his most entertaining pieces, playful, memorable, laconic, packed with sly grotesqueries: ideal for the theatre, in other words. The performance and recording do it full justice. The booklet-essay would have been more useful had it included outlines of the Gogol stories involved.

Schnittke Symphony No. 1. **Russian State Symphony Orchestra / Gennadi Rozhdestvensky.**
   Chandos Ⓕ CHAN9417 (68 minutes: DDD: 7/96). Recorded live in 1988.
Sporadic aggressive bravos and mild applause greet this performance of Schnittke's First Symphony, given in the Great Hall of the Moscow Conservatory in 1988. Which seems about right. The bravos salute the courage it took to produce such an iconoclastic piece from the depths of Brezhnevian stagnation around 1970, and all that meant to Russian composers at the time. The muted applause reflects the obvious fact that the symphony's intrinsic merits are slight, plus perhaps the realization that its symbolic value as a kind of musical dissidence was nullified by the freedoms instituted under Gorbachov. It had already become non-contemporary, in other words. That does not prevent Rozhdestvensky from motivating his orchestra to a performance of considerably more immediacy than Segerstam's Stockholmers (who were no shrinking violets themselves). That's hardly surprising, given Rozhdestvensky's involvement with the work – as dedicatee and as the man responsible for the rewrite of its conclusion, for its notorious première in Gorky and for its first recording on Melodiya (never made widely available). As with that Melodiya version, the recording quality on this disc makes up in directness and impact what it loses to BIS in warmth and clarity. At times you fancy you can hear the audience discussing the show – a not inappropriate addition, given the deliberately provocative nature of Schnittke's collage techniques. The main point is that coarseness and blatancy are the manner to which interpretations of this symphony need to be born, and this is what is on offer.
Additional recommendation ...
...Symphony No. 1. **Ben Kallenberg** (vn); **Ake Lännerholm** (tbn); **Carl-Axel Dominique** (pf); **Royal Stockholm Philharmonic Orchestra / Leif Segerstam.** BIS Ⓕ CD577 (72 minutes: DDD: 11/93).

Schnittke Quasi una sonata[a]. Piano Trio[b]. Piano Sonata No. 2[c]. [ab]**Mark Lubotsky** (vn); [bc]**Irina Schnittke** (pf); [a]**English Chamber Orchestra / Mstislav Rostropovich** ([b]vc). Sony Classical
   Ⓕ SK53271 (63 minutes: DDD: 4/94). Recorded 1992. *Gramophone Editor's choice.*   Ⓖ
The opening bars of Schnittke's *Quasi una sonata* grab you by the throat here and the rest of the piece never lets go. It is one of the earliest examples of Schnittke's polystylistic manner and its raw, agonized inspiration and marvellous sense of dramatic timing make it one of his most durable works. Mark Lubotsky's playing is spellbinding. The orchestration of the piano part, dating from 1986, also works extremely well. The Second Piano Sonata (1990) was written for, and is here marvellously played by, the composer's wife. Like so many of Schnittke's recent works it largely avoids the Gothic horror effects which made so much of his earlier output immediately appealing. In purging his reliance on them he occasionally flounders in search of a comparable intenity of communication through the notes alone. All the same, the fake-Brahms-cum-Franck siciliano which underpins the last of the three movements is a haunting idea. The 1992 Piano Trio is another reworking, this time of the String Trio of 1985. The chillng eruptions and dumbstruck responses come across well enough in the piano trio medium, and like everything on the disc it is played with intensity and dedication. Beautiful recorded sound, too.
Additional recommendation ...
...Quasi una Sonata. *Coupled with works by various composers.* **Gidon Kremer** (vn); **Andrei Gavrilov** (pf). EMI Forte Ⓜ CZS5 69334-2 (two discs: 151 minutes: ADD).   Ⓖ

Schnittke String Quartet No. 3. Piano Quintet[a].
Mahler/Schnittke Piano Quartet[a]. **Borodin Quartet** (Mikhail Kopelman, Andrei Abramenkov, vns; Dmitri Shebalin, va; Valentin Berlinsky, vc); [a]**Ludmilla Berlinsky** (pf). Virgin Classics
   Ⓕ VC7 59040-2 (66 minutes: DDD: 12/91). Recorded 1990.
Schnittke's chamber music does not have the high public profile of some of his symphonies and concertos, but in many ways it is more fastidiously composed and it certainly makes for equally rewarding listening at home. The Piano Quintet is the outstanding feature of this disc. Predominantly slow and mournful (it is dedicated to the memory of the composer's mother) and with a haunting waltz on the notes of the BACH monogram, it is here played with compelling intensity, especially by

the pianist Ludmilla Berlinsky, daughter of the Borodin Quartet's cellist. The Piano Quartet is a conflation of the 16-year-old Mahler's first movement with his incomplete second movement in Schnittke's own paraphrase – another haunting experience, beautifully played and recorded. Less satisfying as a performance, because slightly glossed over, is the Third Quartet; but this is perhaps the finest and undoubtedly the most often performed of Schnittke's chamber works, and as a whole the disc can be warmly recommended to those looking for a representative sample of Schnittke rather than a comprehensive library.

Additional recommendation ...
...String Quartets Nos. 1-3. **Tale Quartet.** BIS Ⓔ CD467 (62 minutes: DDD: 7/90).

Schnittke String Trio[a]. Violin Sonatas[b] – No. 1; No. 2, "Quasi una sonata". **Mateja Marinković** (vn); [a]**Paul Silverthorne** (va); [a]**Timothy Hugh** (vc); [b]**Linn Hendry** (pf). ASV Ⓔ CDDCA868 (65 minutes: DDD: 8/94).

This performance is extremely satisfying. It is atmospherically recorded, and convincingly reinforces the Trio's claims to be considered one of Schnittke's major works. The music is surely to be preferred in this original version, rather than as the 'Trio Sonata' of Yuri Bashmet's orchestral arrangement. Dating from 1985, and written in response to a commission from the Alban Berg Society of Vienna, the Trio is notable for the extent to which its reminiscences and re-creations are far less contrived and self-indulgent than is often the case with this composer. They are not merely backward-looking, nostalgic gestures, but suggest a blueprint for a new, romantically tinged post-modernism. Whether or not you go along with this analysis, it is difficult to deny that the Trio puts the pair of early violin sonatas into the shade. They are not negligible pieces, even so, and these performances have much to commend them. True, Mark Lubotsky's version on Ondine has particular authority – he is the dedicatee of both sonatas – and Lubotsky is an arrestingly muscular player, but the dry, close sound on the Ondine disc is inferior to the more spacious, better balanced ASV. Marinković and Hendry make a first-rate duo: even the most piano-bashing bits of the Second Sonata are not deprived of all musical sense, and the urgent interplay between the instruments is authentically intensity.

Additional recommendations ...
...Violin Sonatas. Suite in the Old Style. **Mark Lubotsky** (vn); **Ralf Gothóni** (pf). Ondine Ⓔ ODE800-2 (53 minutes: DDD: 4/94).
...String Trio. Concerto for Three[a]. Minuet. **Berg** (trans. Schnittke) Four-part Canon[a]. **Gidon Kremer** (vn); **Yuri Bashmet** (va); **Mstislav Rostropovich** (vc); [a]**Moscow Soloists.** EMI Ⓔ CDC5 55627-2 (55 minutes: DDD: 5/96).
...Violin Sonata No. 1. *Coupled with works by various composers.* **Rusné Mataityté** (vn); **Margrit-Julia Zimmermann** (pf). Proud Sound Ⓔ PROUCD139 (57 minutes: DDD: 7/96).

Schnittke Suite in the Old Style[c]. Moz-Art à la Haydn[a]. Praeludium in memoriam Dmitri Shostakovich[a]. A Paganini. Stille Musik[b]. Stille Nacht[c]. Madrigal in Memoriam Oleg Kagan. Gratulations rondo[c]. **Mateja Marinković,** [a]**Thomas Bowes** (vns); [b]**Timothy Hugh** (vc); [c]**Linn Hendry** (pf). ASV Ⓔ CDDCA877 (68 minutes: DDD: 4/95).

At first glance, this disc presents a rather scrappy impression. It contains no large-scale pieces, and the largest work – the early *Suite in the Old Style* – is for the most part an uneventful exercise in dutiful imitation. It is what the *Suite* only hints at that the other works realize more fully. In the *Gratulations rondo* Schnittke again wears the mask of conformity to an old, easygoing classicism. When the mask begins to slip, we wonder what to think. Is this a serious lesson about the potential banality of classicism's familiar formulas? Are the distortions of those formulas expressive of affection or hostility? These issues come most fully into focus in *Stille Nacht*, as Gruber's sweet little tune, with its obediently basic harmony, is subjected to quiet but ruthlessly dissonant deconstruction. "Silent Night" acquires the connotations of Rachel Carson's *Silent Spring*, suggesting an environmental disaster rather than a cosy spirituality. Schnittke's ability to create memorable musical laments is well displayed here, in the Shostakovich and Kagan memorial pieces, in *Stille Musik* and even in *A Paganini*, which traces an absorbing contest between an apparent distaste for virtuosity and a celebration of it. The impact of these compositions is the greater for their relative concentration – not an invariable virtue in Schnittke – and Mateja Marinković is a player of admirable technical refinement. The recording is first-class, and the disc can serve as an ideal introduction to Schnittke for listeners who may have doubts about his larger-scale works. 'Scrappy' it is not.

Additional recommendations ...
...Moz-Art[ab]. Praeludium[ab]. A Paganini[a]. Stille Musik[ac]. Madrigal – violin version[a]; cello version[c]. Trio[acd]. [a]**Oleh Krysa**, [b]**Alexander Fischer** (vns); [c]**Torleif Thedéen** (vc); [d]**Tatiana Tchekina** (pf). BIS Ⓔ CD697 (78 minutes: DDD: 11/95).
...Cello Sonata No. 1. Improvisation[a]. Five Aphorisms[b]. Madrigal in memoriam Oleg Kagan[a]. Klingende Buchstaben[a]. [a]**Alexander Ivashkin** (vc); [b]**Tamas Vesmas** (pf). Ode Manu Ⓔ CDMANU1480 (53 minutes: DDD: 11/96).

Further listening ...
...Cello Concerto No. 2[a]. In memoriam. [a]**Mstislav Rostropovich** (vc); **London Symphony Orchestra / Seiji Ozawa.** Sony Classical SK48241 (7/92).
...Choir Concerto. **Russian State Symphonic Cappella / Valéry Polyansky.** Chandos New Direction CHAN9332 (3/95).

...Concerti grossi – No. 3; No. 4/Symphony No. 5. **Royal Concertgebouw Orchestra /
Riccardo Chailly.** Decca 430 698-2DH (2/92).
...Concerto grosso No. 5[a]. *Coupled with* **Glass** Violin Concerto. **Gidon Kremer** (vn);
[a]**Rainer Keuschnig** (invisible pf); **Vienna Philharmonic Orchestra / Christoph von Dohnányi.**
DG 437 091-2GH (10/93).
...Concerto grosso No. 6[a]. Symphony No. 8. [a]**Sasha Rozhdestvensky** (vn); [a]**Viktoria Postnikova** (pf);
Royal Stockholm Philharmonic Orchestra / Gennadi Rozhdestvensky. Chandos CHAN9359 (7/95).
...Minnesang. Choir Concerto. **Danish National Radio Choir / Stefan Parkman.**
Chandos CHAN9126 (2/93).
...Peer Gynt. **Stockholm Royal Opera Orchestra / Eri Klas.** BIS CD677/8 (4/95).
...Symphony No. 4[a]. Three Sacred Hymns. [a]**Iaroslav Zdorov** (alto); [a]**Dmitri Pianov** (ten);
Russian State Symphony Cappella; [a]**Russian State Symphony Orchestra / Valéry Polyansky.**
Chandos CHAN9463 (7/96).
...Symphonies Nos. 6 and 7. **BBC National Orchestra of Wales / Tadaaki Otaka.**
BIS CD747 (8/96).
...Viola Concerto[a]. *Coupled with* **Lutosławski** Chain 2[b]. **Isabelle van Keulen** ([a]va[b]vn/);
Philharmonia Orchestra / Heinrich Schiff. Koch Schwann 31523-2 (11/95).
...String Quartet No. 2. *Coupled with works by* **Shostakovich** and **Tchaikovsky** Duke Quartet.
Collins Classics 1450-2 (2/96). *See review under Shostakovich; refer to the Index.*
...Piano Sonata (1987). *Coupled with works by* **Stravinsky** Boris Berman (pf).
Chandos CHAN8962 (10/91).
...Collected songs where every verse is filled with grief (arr. Kronos). *Coupled with works by various
composers.* **Kronos Quartet.** Nonesuch 7559-79457-2 (12/97). *Gramophone Editor's choice.*
See review in the Collections section; refer to the Index.
...Penitential Psalms. Voices of Nature[a]. [a]**Gert Sørensen** (vibr); **Danish National Radio Choir /
Stefan Parkman.** Chandos CHAN9480 (2/97).

Othmar Schoeck

Swiss 1886-1957

Schoeck Penthesilea. **Helga Dernesch** (sop) Penthesilea; **Jane Marsh** (sop) Prothoe;
Mechtild Gessendorf (sop) Meroe; **Marjana Lipovšek** (mez) High Priestess; **Gabriele Sima** (sop)
Priestess; **Theo Adam** (bass-bar) Achilles; **Horst Hiestermann** (ten) Diomede; **Peter Weber** (bass)
Herold; **Austrian Radio Chorus and Symphony Orchestra / Gerd Albrecht.** Orfeo Ⓟ C364941B
(80 minutes: ADD: 3/95). Notes and text included. Recorded live in 1982.
Gramophone Editor's choice.   Ⓖ

Schoeck's one-act opera, *Penthesilea* is an astonishing and masterly score. It seems barely credible that
a work so gripping in its dramatic intensity, and so powerful in atmosphere, should be so little known.
It has the listener on the edge of the seat throughout its 80 short minutes and, like any great opera, it
continues to cast a spell long after the music has ended. In the *Grove Dictionary of Opera*, Ronald
Crichton wrote that "at its most intense, the language of *Penthesilea* surpasses in ferocity Strauss's
Elektra, a work with which it invites comparison". In so far as it is a one-act work, set in the Ancient
World, highly concentrated in feeling and with strongly delineated characters, it is difficult not to
think of Strauss's masterpiece. Yet its sound-world is quite distinctive. Though he is a lesser figure,
Schoeck similarly renders the familiar language of Straussian opera entirely his own. The vocabulary
is not dissimilar yet the world is different. We are immediately plunged into a vivid and completely
individual world, packed with dramatic incident: off-stage war cries and exciting, dissonant trumpet
calls. There is an almost symphonic handling of pace, but the sonorities are unusual: for example,
there is a strong wind section, some ten clarinets at various pitches, while there are only a handful of
violins; much use is made of two pianos in a way that at times almost anticipates Britten. The present
performance emanates from the 1982 Salzburg Festival; Helga Dernesch in the title-role commands
the appropriate range of emotions as Penthesilea and the remainder of the cast, including the Achilles
of Theo Adam, rise to the occasion. The important choral role and the orchestral playing under Gerd
Albrecht are eminently committed and the recording is good without being state-of-the-art. There is
a useful essay and libretto, though in German, not English or French.

Further listening ...
...Prelude for Orchestra, Op. 48. Horn Concerto, Op. 65[a]. Serenade for Oboe, Cor anglais and
Strings, Op. 27[b]. Suite for Strings in A flat major. [b]**Silvia Zabarella** (ob); [b]**Martin Zurcher**
(cor ang); [a]**Bruno Schneider** (hn); **Musikcollegium Winterthur / Werner Andreas Albert.**
CPO CPO999 337-2 (2/97).
...Violin Sonatas – D major, Op. 16; E major, Op. 46; D major, WoO22. Albumblatt, WoO70.
Paul Barritt (vn); **Catherine Edwards** (pf). Guild GMCD7142 (4/98).
...Der Sänger, Op. 57. **Frieder Lang** (ten); **Ruth Lang-Oester** (pf). Koch Schwann 310912 (10/94).
...Venus. Soloists; **Heidelberg Chamber Choir; Basle Boys' Choir; Swiss Youth Philharmonic
Orchestra / Mario Venzago.** MGB Musikszene Schweiz CD6112 (10/94).
...Sieh' mich, Heil'ger, wie ich bin. Mit einem gemalten Bande. *Coupled with works by various
composers.* **Lisa della Casa** (sop); **Arpad Sándor** (pf). EMI Salzburg Festival Edition mono
CDH5 66571-2* (2/98). *See review in the Collections section; refer to the Index.*

Arnold Schoenberg

Schoenberg Verklärte Nacht, Op. 4 (arr. string orch). Variations for Orchestra, Op. 31. **Berlin Philharmonic Orchestra / Herbert von Karajan.** DG Ⓕ 415 326-2GH (52 minutes: ADD: 3/86). From 2711 014 (3/75).   ⒼⒼ

The decadence of German culture in the 1920s and 1930s is already very apparent in the saturated romanticism of *Verklärte Nacht* (1899), the most lusciously sentient work ever conceived for a string group. By comparison the *Variations for Orchestra* comes at the peak of the composer's atonal period and is perhaps the most impressive and imaginative demonstration of the possibilities of this compositional method. Thus the two works on this CD are pivotal in Schoenberg's career and Karajan and the Berlin Philharmonic make the very best case for both works. It is impossible not to respond to the sensuality of *Verklärte Nacht* in their hands, while the challenging *Variations* also make a profound impression. The recording matches the intensity of the playing brilliantly.

Additional recommendations ...

...Verklärte Nacht. **Mahler** Symphony No. 10. **Berlin Radio Symphony Orchestra / Riccardo Chailly.** Decca Ⓜ 444 872-2DX2 (two discs: 110 minutes: DDD: 3/88).

...Verklärte Nacht. Variations for Orchestra. Pelleas und Melisande, Op. 5. *Coupled with works by* **Berg** and **Webern Berlin Philharmonic Orchestra / Herbert von Karajan.** DG Ⓜ 427 424-2GC3 (three discs: 181 minutes: ADD: 9/89).   ⒼⒼ

...Variations for Orchestra. Cello Concerto in D major. Five Orchestral Pieces, Op. 16. **Modern Psalm. Soloists / Bratislava Philharmonic Choir; South-West German Radio Symphony Orchestra / Michael Gielen.** Wergo Ⓕ WER60185-50 (60 minutes: DDD: 10/90).

...Verklärte Nacht. Suite in E flat major, Op. 29. Three Pieces. **Ensemble InterContemporain / Pierre Boulez.** Sony Classical Ⓜ SMK48465 (61 minutes: ADD: 12/93).

The original version of Verklärte Nacht is reviewed further on in this section.

Schoenberg Verklärte Nacht[a]. Five Orchestral Pieces, Op. 16[a]. Three Piano Pieces, Op. 11[b]. Six Piano Pieces, Op. 19[b]. Piano Piece, Op. 11 No. 2 (arr. Busoni)[b]. [a]**Chicago Symphony Orchestra / Daniel Barenboim** ([b]pf). Teldec Ⓕ 4509-98256-2 (77 minutes: DDD: 8/95). Recorded 1995.

Like Barenboim's 1967 EMI Matrix reissue of *Verklärte Nacht* with the English Chamber Orchestra, this version begins with the evident belief that Schoenberg's initial marking of *Sehr langsam* is not an invitation to linger lovingly over every last semiquaver. The newer performance is far from a mere re-run, however. The verdict on the 1967 account was that "weight of expression tends to impede rather than further the musical flow". In 1995 the expressive trajectory of the whole is magnificently natural and persuasive, as one might expect from the experienced Wagnerian that Barenboim has now become. Only at the very end does he risk too weighty an articulation and too broad a tempo, a tendency confirming that his reading is still stronger in passion than it is in tenderness. The recorded sound is also spacious in the extreme, so many collectors will prefer the more intimate effect of the kind achieved by the Sinfonia Varsovia or the Orpheus Chamber Orchestra. Barenboim's superbly played account is nevertheless a superior example of the kind of 'wide screen' approach to Schoenberg's early masterwork favoured by conductors like Karajan and Sinopoli. The appeal of this disc is greatly enhanced by the other items. There is a marvellously vivid performance of the Op. 16 *Pieces* which, for clarity of texture and depth of expression, counts – along with Robert Craft's – as one of the most convincing of current versions. And we also hear Barenboim as pianist in the Op. 11 and Op. 19 *Pieces*. There are minor idiosyncracies in Op. 19 – for example, a rather brisk tempo for No. 6 – but Op. 11 is excellent. As a bonus Barenboim also plays Busoni's 'amplification' (perhaps 'dilution' is a better term) of Op. 11 No. 2. This is one of the more pointless attempts by one talent to render another, very different talent more 'comprehensible', but it provides a distinctive and far from insignificant footnote to a Schoenberg disc of unusual substance and distinction.

Additional recommendations ...

...Verklärte Nacht. *Coupled with works by* **Hindemith** and **Bartók English Chamber Orchestra / Daniel Barenboim.** EMI Matrix Ⓜ CDM5 65079-2 (65 minutes: DDD: 12/94).   Ⓖ

...Verklärte Nacht. Pelleas und Melisande, Op. 5. **Philharmonia Orchestra / Giuseppe Sinopoli.** DG Ⓕ 439 942-2GH (79 minutes: DDD: 6/95).

Schoenberg Variations for Orchestra, Op. 31. Pelleas und Melisande, Op. 5. **Chicago Symphony Orchestra / Pierre Boulez.** Erato Ⓕ 2292-45827-2 (62 minutes: DDD: 4/93). Recorded 1991.   Ⓖ

The two faces of Schoenberg could scarcely be more starkly juxtaposed than they are on this superbly performed and magnificently recorded disc – Boulez and the CSO at their formidable best. *Pelleas und Melisande* can be taken not only as Schoenberg's 'answer' to Debussy's opera (also based on Maeterlinck's play) but as his challenge to Richard Strauss's supremacy as a composer of symphonic poems. It is indeed an intensely symphonic score in Schoenberg's early, late-romantic vein, with an elaborate single-movement structure and a subtle network of thematic cross-references. Yet none of this is an end in itself, and the music is as gripping and immediate a representation of a tragic love story as anything in the German romantic tradition. To move from this to the abstraction of the 12-note Variations, Op. 31 may threaten extreme anticlimax. Yet from the delicate introduction of the work's shapely theme to the turbulent good humour of the extended finale Schoenberg proves that his new compositional method did not drain his musical language of expressive vitality. The elaborate counterpoint may not make for easy listening, but the combination of exuberance and emotion is irresistible – at least in a performance like this.

Additional recommendations ...

...Pelleas und Melisande. **Webern** Passacaglia for Orchestra, Op. 1. **Scottish National Orchestra / Matthias Bamert.** Chandos Ⓕ CHAN8619 (54 minutes: DDD: 10/88).

...Pelleas und Melisande, Op. 5. Verklärte Nacht. **Philharmonia Orchestra / Giuseppe Sinopoli.** DG Ⓕ 439 942-2GH (79 minutes: DDD: 6/95).

Schoenberg Chamber Symphony No. 1, Op. 9[a]. Erwartung[b]. Variations for Orchestra, Op. 31[c]. [b]**Phyllis Bryn-Julson** (sop); [a]**Birmingham Contemporary Music Group;** [bc]**City of Birmingham Symphony Orchestra / Sir Simon Rattle.** EMI Ⓜ CDC5 55212-2 (75 minutes: DDD: 4/95). Text and translation included. Recorded 1993. *Gramophone Award Winner 1995.*
Gramophone Editor's choice.   ⒼⒼ

This well-filled disc offers an unusually comprehensive survey of the essential Schoenberg – the irascible late-romantic of the *Chamber Symphony* (1906), the radical expressionist of *Erwartung* (1909) and, in the *Variations* (1928), the synthesizer of expressionist moods with techniques that set up neo-classical associations. Rattle's account of the *Chamber Symphony* may well come to displace that of the Orpheus Chamber Orchestra (reviewed below) from its favoured position, if only for the demonstration quality of the sound, which has remarkable depth and realism. Rattle ensures a superbly well characterized and integrated performance, which only veers towards over-emphasis at the very end. There is also ample refinement where that is called for, and this quality is no less abundant in *Erwartung*. Here the almost impressionistic sheen of the orchestral sound fits well with Phyllis Bryn-Julson's generally restrained approach to the vocal line. When it comes to the *Variations for Orchestra*, Rattle and the CBSO are supreme. This recording may well be the first to convey the full, astonishing range of the work's textures, from the most delicate chamber music to dense tuttis, without a hint of artificiality. But it is the interpretation which counts for most. Rattle brings all these textures to rhythmic and expressive life, avoiding the lumpiness and stridency which occasionally afflict other conductors. He has evidently taken enormous care to follow Schoenberg's detailed markings, yet the result has a sovereign spontaneity. Despite strong competition from Boulez this performance is a triumph.

Additional recommendations ...

...Chamber Symphony No. 1, Op. 9[b]. Die Jakobsleiter[a]. Begleitmusik zu einer Lichtspielszene, Op. 34[c]. [a]**Soloists.** [a]**BBC Singers;** [b]**Ensemble InterContemporain;** [ac]**BBC Symphony Orchestra / Pierre Boulez.** Sony Classical Ⓜ SMK48462 (76 minutes: ADD: 12/93).   Ⓔ

...Erwartung. *Coupled with works by* **Berg** and **Krenek** Dorothy Dow (sop); **New York Philharmonic Orchestra / Dmitri Mitropoulos.** Sony Classical Masterworks Heritage mono Ⓜ MH2K62759* (two discs: 134 minutes: ADD: 2/98).

Schoenberg Chamber Symphonies – No. 1, Op. 9; No. 2, Op. 38. Verklärte Nacht, Op. 4 (arr. string orch). **Orpheus Chamber Orchestra.** DG Ⓕ 429 233-2GH (69 minutes: DDD: 7/90). Recorded 1989.   ⒼⒼ

In the late twentieth century there's increasing evidence that the early twentieth century's most radical music is becoming so easy to perform that it may at last be losing its terrors for listeners as well as players. This can only be welcomed, provided that performances do not become bland and mechanical, and the conductorless Orpheus Chamber Orchestra triumphantly demonstrate how to combine fluency with intensity. If you like your Schoenberg effortful – to feel that the players are conquering almost insuperable odds – these recordings may not be for you. But if you like spontaneity of expression that is never an end in itself, and communicates Schoenberg's powerfully coherent forms and textures as well as his abundant emotionalism, you should not hesitate. The DG disc is the first to place Schoenberg's two Chamber Symphonies alongside *Verklärte Nacht*. The First Chamber Symphony shows Schoenberg transforming himself from late-romantic into expressionist, while in the Second the recent American immigrant, in the 1930s, looks back to his romantic roots and forges a new, almost classical style. With superb sound, this is a landmark in recordings of twentieth-century music.

Additional recommendations ...

...Symphony No. 1. Pierrot lunaire, Op. 21[a]. [a]**Marianne Pousseur** (sop); **Musique Oblique Ensemble / Philippe Herreweghe.** Harmonia Mundi Ⓕ HMC90 1390 (58 minutes: DDD: 8/92).

...Symphony No. 2. *Coupled with works by* **Busoni** and **Weill** New Philharmonia Orchestra / **Frederik Prausnitz / Gary Bertini.** EMI Matrix Ⓜ CDM5 65869-2 (79 minutes: ADD: 4/96).

Schoenberg String Quartets – No. 1, Op. 7; No. 2 in F sharp minor, Op. 10[a]; No. 3, Op. 30; No. 4, Op. 37. [a]**Dawn Upshaw** (sop); **Arditti Quartet** (Irvine Arditti, David Alberman, vns; Garth Knox, va; Rohan de Saram, vc). Auvidis Montaigne Ⓕ MO782024 (two discs: 139 minutes: DDD: 1/95). Recorded 1993.   ⒼⒼ

These recordings were made in London, in collaboration with the BBC, and the sound is consistently spacious, with a natural clarity and an even balance; the details of Schoenberg's complex counterpoint, as evident in No. 1 as in No. 4, can be heard with a minimum of stress and strain.

Although one occasionally gets the impression that the Arditti are relatively cool in their response to this often fervent music, the overall mood they create is far from anti-romantic, and they call on a remarkably wide range of dynamics and tone-colours. Even if every nuance in Schoenberg's markings is not followed, this is warmly expressive playing. Dawn Upshaw's contribution to the Second Quartet also helps to heighten the sense of drama although she misses some of that mysterious, ecstatic quality which makes this music so haunting. In fact, for an unambiguously romantic reading of the two early quartets you need to brave the grinding surface noise of the marvellously vibrant Kolisch performances (recorded in 1936). It is in the Third and Fourth Quartets that the superior sound-quality of the Auvidis Montaigne issue pays the greatest dividends. Textural clarity is vital here, and although even the Arditti struggle to sustain the necessary lightness in the long second movement of No. 4, their wider dynamic range brings you consistently close to the toughly argued, emotionally expansive essence of this music. Yet the performance of No. 3 is the finest achievement of the set: clarity of form and emotional conviction combine to create an absorbing account of a modern masterwork. It sets the seal on a most distinguished enterprise.

Additional recommendations ...

...Nos. 1-4. **Clemence Gifford** (sop); **Kolisch Quartet.**
Archiphon mono Ⓕ ARC103/04* (two discs: 140 minutes: ADD: 1/94).　　　　　　Ⓖ
...No. 2. *Coupled with works by* **Berg** *and* **Webern Christiane Oelze** (sop); **Brindisi Quartet.**
Metronome Ⓕ METCD1007 (70 minutes: DDD: 6/95).

Schoenberg String Quartet in D major. String Trio, Op. 45[b].
Zemlinsky Two Movements for String Quintet[a]. Two Movements for String Quartet. [a]**Andrea Wennberg** (va); **Corda Quartet** ([b]Olga Nodel, Christiane Plath, vns; [b]Frauke Tometten-Molino, va; [b]Edith Salzmann, vc). Stradivarius Ⓕ STR33438 (79 minutes: DDD: 10/97). Recorded 1996.
While it is no longer necessary to introduce Zemlinsky as Schoenberg's brother-in-law and musical mentor, rather than as a composer in his own right, it is still interesting to hear programmes which compare and contrast their compositional developments. This well-performed disc confirms that, although after a similar start the two grew ever further apart, Zemlinsky's later music was much more than the unadventurous outpouring of a lesser talent. Written in the mid-1890s, Zemlinsky's Two Movements for string quintet are accomplished and personable studies whose obvious echoes of various late-romantic masters enhance rather than diminish their appeal. Much the same can be said (though the influences are slightly different) of Schoenberg's D major Quartet of 1897, even more impressive as a student piece in avoiding any hint of that diffuseness in which Zemlinsky occasionally indulged. By 1929, the date of the Two Movements for string quartet, Zemlinsky was still a late-romantic, though with an intensity suggesting familiarity with Berg's more recent pieces, like the *Lyric Suite* (dedicated to Zemlinsky). At that time, Schoenberg was already well on the road that would lead to the fragmented, atonal expressionism of the String Trio, exceptional though that work is in its impatience with the kind of links to classical and romantic traditions that Schoenberg usually admitted. The Corda Quartet convey the full emotional range of these works.

Schoenberg Verklärte Nacht, Op. 4[a] (orig. version).
Schubert String Quintet in C major, D956[b]. [a]**Alvin Dinkin** (va); **Kurt Reher** (vc); **Hollywood Quartet** (Felix Slatkin, Paul Shure, vns; Paul Robyn, va; Eleanor Aller, vc). Testament mono Ⓕ SBT1031* (73 minutes: ADD: 4/94). Item marked [a] from Capitol CCL7507 (4/51), [b]Capitol CTL7011 (1/52). Item marked [a] recorded 1950, [b]1951. *Gramophone Award Winner 1994.* ⒼⒼⒼ
This was the first ever recording of *Verklärte Nacht* in its original sextet form and it remains unsurpassed. When it was first reviewed in *Gramophone*, Lionel Salter wrote of it as being "beautifully played with the most careful attention to details of dynamics and phrasing, with unfailing finesse, with consistently sympathetic tone, and, most important, with a firm sense of the basic structure". The Schubert too fully deserves its classic status. The tranquillity of the slow movement has never been conveyed with greater nobility or more perfect control. The Hollywood Quartet made music for the sheer love of it and as a relaxation from their duties in the film-studio orchestras, for which they were conspicuously overqualified. They have incomparable ensemble and blend; and their impeccable technical address and consummate tonal refinement silence criticism. The transfers could not be better.

Schoenberg Five Orchestral Pieces, Op. 16[a]. A Survivor from Warsaw, Op. 46[b]. Begleitmusik zu einer Lichtspielszene, Op. 34[a]. Herzgewächse, Op. 20[c]. Serenade, Op. 24[d]. [c]**Eileen Hulse** (sop); [d]**Stephen Varcoe** (bar); [b]**Simon Callow** (narr); [b]**London Voices**; [d]**Twentieth Century Classics Ensemble**; [abc]**London Symphony Orchestra / Robert Craft.**
Koch International Classics Ⓕ 37263-2 (69 minutes: DDD: 6/95). Recorded 1994.
This is an absorbing issue, not least for the sheer variety of works that it contains. The two largest compositions, Op. 16 and Op. 24, define the disc's range. The *Five Orchestral Pieces*, in which expressionism can be heard emerging from the chrysalis of late romanticism, are played with supreme finesse by the LSO, and Robert Craft probes the richly diverse textures with exemplary concentration and precision. The downside is some loss of immediacy, a general feeling of caution. There are also slight reservations about the balance in *A Survivor from Warsaw*, where Simon Callow is, one imagines, placed behind the orchestra, depriving this harrowing work of its visceral impact. Since

Callow's style can veer in a flash from the conversational to the melodramatic, a closer focus would have been preferable. *Herzgewächse* and *Begleitmusik zu einer Lichtspielszene* are both well performed, the latter with a recessed perspective, similar to that in Op. 16, which ensures an extremely well-blended texture without loss of detail. Nevertheless, there is no doubt that the finest performance here is that of the *Serenade*, Op. 24, where the sound (recorded in New York, not in London) is cleaner, and the characterization is superb from beginning to end. Stephen Varcoe is a rather breathy singer in the dauntingly angular and wide-ranging "Sonnet", but the performance as a whole makes a convincing case for the work's high level of musical thought and purely technical mastery. With this outstanding account, Craft's latest Schoenberg series is well and truly launched.

Additional recommendations ...

...Serenade[a]. Five Orchestral Pieces[b]. Ode to Napoleon, Op. 41[c]. [a]**John Shirley-Quirk** (bar); [bc]**David Wilson-Johnson** (bar); [ac]**Ensemble InterContemporain; BBC Symphony Orchestra / Pierre Boulez.** Sony Classical Ⓜ SMK48463 (66 minutes: ADD: 12/93).

...A Survivor from Warsaw. *Coupled with works by various composers.* **Udo Samel** (spkr); **men's voices of the Bamberg Symphony Chorus; Bamberg Symphony Orchestra / Ingo Metzmacher.** EMI Ⓕ CDC5 55424-2 (59 minutes: DDD: 3/97). *See review in the Collections section; refer to the Index.*

Schoenberg Cabaret Songs – No. 1, Galathea; No. 2, Gigerlette; No. 3, Der genügsame Liebhaber. Drüben geht die Sonne scheiden. Vier Lieder, Op. 2. Die Aufgeregten, Op. 3 No. 2. Lieder, Op. 6 – No. 1, Traumleben; No. 4, Verlassen; No. 8, Der Wanderer. Gedenken. Jane Grey, Op. 12 No. 1. Zwei Lieder, Op. 14. Folksong arrangements – Der Mai tritt ein mit Freuden; Es gingen zwei Gespielen gut; Mein Herz ist mir gemenget; Mein Herz in steten Treuen. **Mitsuko Shirai** (mez); **Hartmut Höll** (pf). Capriccio Ⓕ 10 514 (63 minutes: DDD: 5/95). Texts and translations included. Recorded 1993.

Mitsuko Shirai has pretty well the ideal voice for these songs. It's not large, but her subtle control of dynamics enables her to encompass surprisingly big gestures. Her intimacy and deft way with words bring great rewards, too. Most of these songs are early Schoenberg, still within hailing distance of Brahms or Wolf (who would not have been ashamed of the long, lyrical line of "Traumleben", with its overt quotation from Wagner's *Tristan*). Even in Op. 14, where atonality is in sight, close motivic working and, in "In diesen Wintertagen", a graceful vocal line, retain a close kinship to the nineteenth-century Lied, and Shirai's easy negotiation of awkward intervals prevents them from ever sounding ungrateful. The strangest pieces here, but oddly attractive, are Schoenberg's folk-song arrangements (who would ever have thought he had much time for such things?). Much later than any of the original songs in this collection, in their close and sometimes busy counterpoint they are a touching homage to Brahms (who loved, collected and arranged such songs himself) and even to Bach: they are 'chorale preludes' in all but name. Shirai, very properly, sings them beautifully but plainly. Her husband is an ideally responsive partner; the recording is satisfactory, if a bit too close.

Schoenberg Gurrelieder. **Susan Dunn** (sop); **Brigitte Fassbaender** (mez); **Siegfried Jerusalem, Peter Haage** (tens); **Hermann Becht** (bass); **Hans Hotter** (narr); **St Hedwig's Cathedral Choir, Berlin; Dusseldorf Musikverin Chorus; Berlin Radio Symphony Orchestra / Riccardo Chailly.** Decca Ⓕ 430 321-2DH2 (two discs: 101 minutes: DDD: 3/91). Text and translation included. Recorded 1985. *Selected by Sounds in Retrospect.*   Ⓖ

Schoenberg Gurrelieder. **Deborah Voigt** (sop); **Jennifer Larmore** (mez); **Thomas Moser, Kenneth Riegel** (tens); **Bernd Weikl** (bar); **Klaus Maria Brandauer** (spkr); **Dresden State Opera Chorus; Leipzig Radio Chorus; Prague Mens' Chorus; Staatskapelle Dresden / Giuseppe Sinopoli.** Teldec Ⓕ 4509-98424-2 (two discs: 113 minutes: DDD: 8/96). Texts and translations included. Recorded live in 1995

"Every morning after sunrise, King Waldemar would have a realization of the renewing power of nature, and would feel the love of Tove within the outward beauty of Nature's colour and form" (thus said Leopold Stokowski, who made the first-ever recording of *Gurrelieder*). This vast cantata, a direct descendant of Wagnerian music-drama, was for the turn-of-the-century musical scene in general, more the ultimate gorgeous sunset. Schoenberg started work on it in 1899, the same year as his *Verklärte Nacht*, but delayed its completion for over a decade, by which time some of his more innovatory masterpieces were already behind him. Schoenberg's forces are, to put it mildly, extravagant. As well as the six soloists and two choruses, the orchestra sports such luxuries as four piccolos, ten horns and a percussion battery that includes iron chains; and so complex are some of the textures that, to achieve a satisfactory balance, a near miracle is required of conductor and recording engineers. Decca have never been mean with miracles where large scale forces are concerned and this set is no exception. Chailly gives us a superbly theatrical presentation of the score. The casting of the soloists is near ideal. Susan Dunn's Tove has youth, freshness and purity on her side. So exquisitely does she float her lines that you readily sympathize with King Waldemar's rage at her demise. Siegfried Jerusalem has the occasional rough moment but few previous Waldemars on disc have possessed his heroic ringing tones and range of expression. And Decca make sure that their trump card, the inimitable Hans Hotter as the speaker in "The wild hunt of the summer wind", is so tangibly projected that we miss not one single vowel or consonant of his increasing animation and excitement at that final approaching sunrise.

Sinopoli's account is more luxurious, he is more likely than Chailly to let his orchestra rip (the Staatskapelle Dresden letting rip is an awesome sound) and he is more generous with ample rubato. These qualities, together with Teldec's sumptuous live recording (if an audience were present they must have been bound and gagged: not a single intrusive sound) count for a great deal in this piece, and for their sake you might be prepared to put up with one or two less than ideal soloists. Deborah Voigt's voice is bright, vibrant, fearless in *ff* and in the upper register, but needing hard work to fine it down to really expressive, quiet singing. But when she does work hard she is impressive. So is Thomas Moser, sometimes a stalwartly baritonal Waldemar, once or twice a little unsteady, but with ringing, heroic top notes. Larmore is even brighter than Voigt, with a penetrating fast vibrato: strongly dramatic, but not as gravely moving as the best Waldtaube ever, Chailly's Brigitte Fassbaender. No actor in the Speaker's role, not even one as distinguished as Brandauer, will ever surpass Chailly's Hans Hotter, much richer of voice and rising to a splendidly full-throated (and *sung!*) final word, but Brandauer has wit and character on his side. The choral singing in the later scenes is opulent. Sinopoli takes 12 minutes longer over the piece than Chailly. Yes, his speeds are generally slower, and the long sequence of love-songs in Part 1 occasionally loses urgency as a result, but a good deal of the difference of timing is accounted for by flexible rubato, which will strike anti-Sinopolists as fussy but others as voluptuous.

Additional recommendation ...

...Gurrelieder. Four Lieder, Op. 11. **Soloists; BBC Singers; BBC Choral Society; Goldsmith's Choral Union; London Philharmonic Choir; BBC Symphony Orchestra / Pierre Boulez.**
Sony Classical Ⓜ SM2K48459 (two discs: 129 minutes: ADD: 12/93).

Schoenberg Moses und Aron. **David Pittman-Jennings** (narr) Moses; **Chris Merritt** (ten) Aron; **László Polgár** (bass) Priest; **Gabriele Fontana** (sop) Young Girl, First Naked Woman; **Yvonne Naef** (mez) Invalid Woman; **John Graham Hall** (ten) Young Man, Naked Youth; **Per Lindskog** (ten) Youth; **Henk de Vries** (bar) Young Man; **Siegfried Lorenz** (bar) Another Young Man; **Chorus of the Netherlands Opera; Royal Concertgebouw Orchestra / Pierre Boulez.**
DG Ⓕ 449 174-2GH2 (two discs: 106 minutes: DDD: 10/96). Notes, text and translation included. Recorded 1995. *Selected by Soundings.*   Ⓖ

Moses und Aron is respected rather than loved, with the reputation of being a tough assignment for all concerned. One of the essays in the booklet accompanying this recording calls it a didactic opera. Pierre Boulez, however, is a conductor in whom didacticism is close to a passion, and he is obviously passionate about this opera (this is his second recording of the piece). We take it for granted that in any work to which he feels close, every detail will be both accurate and audible. But for Schoenberg *Moses und Aron* was a warning as well as a homily, and as much a confession of faith as either. Boulez, often himself a Moses preaching against anti-modern backsliding, is at one with Schoenberg here. Some such reason, surely, has led to this being not only a performance of immaculate clarity, but of intense and eloquent beauty and powerful drama too. The recording was made during a run of stage performances, but in the Concertgebouw in Amsterdam, not in the theatre. In the beautiful acoustic of their own hall, the orchestra play with ample richness as well as precision, and the at times complex textures benefit enormously from a perceptible space around them. The choral singing matches the orchestral playing in quality: beautiful in tone, eloquently urgent, vividly precise in the difficult spoken passages. The soloists are all admirable, with no weak links. Merritt in particular seems to have all that the hugely taxing role of Aron demands: a fine control of long line, intelligently expressive use of words, where necessary the dangerous demagogue's glamour. Pittman-Jennings is a properly prophetic Moses, grand of voice. But the set is Boulez's achievement above all: he is as good at dramatic excitement (the transformations of Moses's staff) as at soberly or poignantly expressive melody (the memorably beautiful closing scene), and the long, orgiastic worship of the Golden Calf has all that one hopes for from it: power, menace, hysteria, the grotesque, but also a queerly impressive sensuous lyricism which is disturbingly alluring. This is one of Boulez's finest achievements, a compelling argument for *Moses und Aron* as an anything but coldly didactic opera.

Further listening ...

...Drei Klavierstücke, Op. 11. Sechs Klavierstücke, Op. 19. Funf Klavierstücke, Op. 23. Suite, Op. 25. Klavierstücke, Op. 33*a*. Klavierstücke, Op. 33*b*. Piano Concerto, Op. 42[a]. Phantasy, Op. 47[b]. Ode to Napoleon, Op. 41[c]. Pierrot lunaire, Op. 21[d]. [d]**Patricia Rideout** (spkr); [c]**John Horton** (narr); [b]**Israel Baker** (vn); **Glenn Gould** (pf); [c]**Juilliard Quartet;** [a]**CBC Symphony Orchestra / Robert Craft.** Sony Classical Glenn Gould Edition SM2K52664 (4/95).
...Drei Klavierstücke, Op. 11. *Coupled with works by* **Decaux** *and* **Ravel** Frederic Chiu (pf). Harmonia Mundi HMU90 7166 (1/96).
...Sechs Klavierstücke, Op. 19. Ode to Napoleon, Op. 41. *Coupled with works by* **Ullmann** Günther Herzfeld, Frank-Immo Zichner (pfs). Edition Abseits EDA008-2 (11/95).
See review under Ullmann; refer to the Index.
...Piano Concerto, Op. 42. *Coupled with* **Schumann** Piano Concerto in A minor, Op. 54. **Maurizio Pollini** (pf); **Berlin Philharmonic Orchestra / Claudio Abbado.**
DG 427 771-2GH (7/90).   Ⓖ
...Piano Concerto, Op. 42[a]. Drei Klavierstücke, Op. 11. Suite, Op. 25. *Coupled with works by* **Berg** *and* **Webern** Glenn Gould (pf). [a]**CBC Symphony Orchestra / Jean-Marie Beaudet.**
CBC Records Perspective Series mono PSCD2008* (1/96).

...Piece in D minor. String Trio, Op. 45. Phantasy, Op. 47. *Coupled with works by various composers.*
Gidon Kremer (vn); **Veronika Hagen** (va); **Clemens Hagen** (vc); **Oleg Maisenberg** (pf).
DG 447 112-2GH (4/96). *See review in the Collections section; refer to the Index.*
...Wind Quintet. *Coupled with works by* **Berg** and **Webern** Houston Symphony Chamber Players /
Christoph Eschenbach. Koch International Classics 37337-2 (12/96).
...Three Piano Pieces, Op. 11. Six Little Piano Pieces, Op. 19. Five Piano Pieces, Op. 23.
Piano Suite, Op. 25. Piano Pieces, Opp. 33*a* and 33*b*. **Maurizio Pollini** (pf).
DG 20th Century Classics 423 249-2GC (6/88).   🅖🅖
...Suite, Op. 25. *Coupled with works by various composers.* **Glenn Gould** (pf).
Sony Classical mono SMK53474* (9/95). *See review under Bach; refer to the Index.*
...Variations on a Recitative, Op. 40. Two Fragments of an Organ Sonata. *Coupled with works by*
Pepping and **Hindemith Kevin Bowyer** (org). Nimbus NI5411 (1/95).
...Choral Works – Friede auf Erden, Op. 13; Kol nidre, Op. 39; Drei Volkslieder, Op. 49.
Zwei Kanons – Wenn der schwer Gedrückte klagt; O dass der Sinnen doch so viele sind!.
Drei Volkslieder – Es gingen zwei Gespielen gut; Herzlieblich Lieb, durch Scheiden; Schein uns,
du liebe Sonne. Vier Stücke, Op. 27. Drei Satiren, Op. 28. Sechs Stücke, Op. 35. Dreimal tausen
Jahre, Op. 50*a*. De profundis (Psalm 130), Op. 50*b*. Modern Psalm (Der erste Psalm), Op. 50*c*.
A Survivor from Warsaw, Op. 46. **John Shirley-Quirk, Günter Reich** (narrs); **BBC Singers;
BBC Chorus and Symphony Orchestra; London Sinfonietta / Pierre Boulez.**
Sony Classical SM2K44571 (8/90).
...Pierrot lunaire, Op. 21ᵃ. *Coupled with* **Webern** Concerto, Op. 24. ᵃ**Jane Manning** (sop);
Nash Ensemble / Sir Simon Rattle. Chandos Collect CHAN6534 (8/92).

Franz Schreker   Austrian 1878-1934

Schreker Die Gezeichneten. **Heinz Kruse** (ten) Alviano Salvago; **Elizabeth Connell** (sop)
Carlotta; **Monte Pederson** (bar) Count Vitelozzo Tamare; **Alfred Muff** (bass) Duke Adorno/
Capitaneo di Giustizia; **Lászlo Polgar** (bass) Lodovico Nardi, Podesta; **Christiane Berggold**
(mez) Martuccia; **Martin Petzold** (ten) Pietro; **Robert Wörle** (ten) Guidobald Usodimare;
Endrik Wottrich (ten) Menaldo Negroni; **Oliver Widmer** (bar) Michelotto Cibo; **Matthias Goerne**
(bass-bar) Gonsalvo Fieschi; **Kristin Sigmundsson** (bass) Julian Pinelli; **Petteri Salomaa** (bass)
Paolo Calvi; **Marita Posselt** (sop) Ginevra Scotti; **Reinhard Ginzel** (ten) First Senator;
Jörg Gottschick (bass) Second Senator; **Friedrich Molsberger** (bass) Third Senator;
Herbert Lippert (ten) A youth; **Berlin Radio Chorus; Deutsches Symphony Orchestra, Berlin /
Lothar Zagrosek.** Decca Entartete Musik Ⓔ 444 442-2DHO3 (three discs: 171 minutes:
DDD: 6/95). Notes, text and translation included. Recorded 1993-1994.
Gramophone Editor's choice.   🅖🅖
The mingling in *Die Gezeichneten* of post-*Salome* opulence (Strauss with rich admixtures of Scriabin,
Szymanowski, Korngold and Puccini) with post-*Salome* gaminess of subject matter is indeed strong
stuff. Carlotta, a beautiful but gravely ill painter knows that her health would never withstand
physical love. She is loved, he believes hopelessly, by the monstrously ugly nobleman Alviano; she is
desired by the licentious Count Tamare. Drawn by the beauty of Alviano's soul she at first declares
her love for him, but then deserts him for Tamare. On learning that she gave herself to Tamare
voluntarily, knowing the fatal consequences, Alviano first kills his rival, then goes mad. Schreker's
sheer resourcefulness is breathtaking. Each character seems to have not merely an identifying theme
but a whole sound-world. Scenes of extreme complexity are handled with total assurance. The score
is melodious, fabulously multi-coloured and has great cumulative power. One reservation was hinted
at by Alban Berg's reaction to the libretto: he found it superb but "a bit kitschy". It is, and this quality
is intensified in the music by a curious impassivity, as though Schreker were observing his characters
from outside. Carlotta's 'conversion' from spiritual to physical love is not accompanied by much
change in her alluringly mysterious music; her characterization is fantastically detailed but has no
depth. She, Alviano and Tamare are ideas, not people. It is an opera in which richness of detail,
complexity of texture and sheer glamour replace humanity. The end is 'effective' but not tragic.
Nevertheless, as a document of its time (1918) and as a score of unprecedented richness it abundantly
deserves recording. Edo de Waart's performance on Marco Polo was a splendid achievement, all the
more so for being recorded live. Indeed choice between his version and the newer set would be trickier
were it not for the fact that de Waart makes several lengthy cuts (about 20 minutes of music in all) in
the last act and his tenor is under painfully audible strain. Zagrosek's reading is superb, his cast
almost without flaw. Connell has all Carlotta's glamour, together with a purity of tone and a subtle
response to words and phrasing that come close to giving her a soul. Kruse is less imaginative, one or
two of Alviano's high notes give him trouble, but he sings strongly and lyrically; Pederson makes a
grippingly formidable, physical opponent. The precision and detail of the subsidiary characters are
praiseworthy throughout; even very small roles have been cast from strength. The recording is
remarkably fine, spacious and sumptuous, with not a single detail out of focus.
Additional recommendation ...
...**Soloists; Dutch Radio Philharmonic Chorus and Orchestra / Edo de Waart.**
Marco Polo 8 223328/30 (three discs: 147 minutes: DDD: 12/91).

Further listening ...
...Chamber Symphony[a]. Prelude to a Drama[a]. Valse lente[b]. Die Ferne Klang – Night Interlude[b].
   Berlin Radio Symphony Orchestra / [a]Michael Gielen, [b]Karl Anton Rickenbacher.
   Koch Schwann 311078 (11/88).   Ⓔ
...Der Geburtstag der Infantin – Suite. *Coupled with works by* **Hindemith** and **Schulhoff**
   Leipzig Gewandhaus Orchestra / Lothar Zagrosek.
   Decca Entartete Musik 444 182-2DH (5/95).   Ⓔ
...Der Ferne Klang. **Soloists; Berlin RIAS Chamber Chorus; Berlin Radio Chorus
   and Symphony Orchestra / Gerd Albrecht.** Capriccio 60 024-2 (12/91).
...Der ferne Klang – In einem Lande ein bleicher König. *Coupled with works by various composers.*
   Thomas Hampson (bar); **Pestalozzi Gymnasium Children's Choir; Munich Radio Orchestra /
   Fabio Luisi.** EMI CDC5 55233-2 (9/95). *See review in the Collections section; refer to the Index.*
...Irrelohe. **Soloists; Vienna Singverein; Vienna Symphony Orchestra / Peter Gülke.**
   Sony Classical S2K66850 (12/95).
...Irrelohe – Prelude, Acts 1, 2 and 3. Vom ewigen Leben[a]. Four Little Pieces. Vorspiel zu einer
   grossen Oper. [a]**Claudia Barainsky** (sop); **Deutsches Symphony Orchestra, Berlin / Peter Ruzicka.**
   Koch Schwann 364542 (1/98).

Franz Schubert   Austrian 1797-1828

Schubert Overtures – Der Teufel als Hydraulicus; Der Spiegelritter; Des Teufels Lustschloss;
   Der vierjährige Posten; Claudine von Villa Bella; Die Freunde von Salamanka;
   Die Zwillingsbrüder; Alfonso und Estrella; Die Verschworenen; Fierrabras. **Haydn Sinfonietta,
   Vienna / Manfred Huss.** Koch Schwann Ⓕ 311212 (68 minutes: DDD: 4/98). ✒ Recorded 1997.
The works here cover a span of some dozen years, ranging from the jaunty, bustling *Der Teufel als
Hydraulicus* and the more ambitious *Der Spiegelritter*, both composed around the time of Schubert's
fifteenth birthday, to the overtures to his richest and grandest stage works, *Alfonso und Estrella* (1821)
and *Fierrabras* (1823). The teenage overtures, while giving few hints of Schubert's melodic genius, are
full of striking dramatic gestures. There are intermittent echoes of Mozart and affinities between two
effervescent operetta overtures of 1815, *Der vierjährige Posten* and *Claudine von Villa Bella*, and the
contemporary Second Symphony. The boldest and most colourful of these early overtures is that to
Schubert's first completed opera, *Des Teufels Lustschloss*, a grisly Gothic horror tale whose hero
undergoes blood-curdling ordeals worthy of Indiana Jones. Schubert evidently relished the
opportunity for orchestral grotesquerie, whether in the eerie chorale for horns and trombones in the
development or the screeching, cackling coda, with its piercing woodwind and high trumpets. Of the
later overtures, those to the one-act *Singspiels*, *Die Zwillingsbrüder* and *Die Verschworenen*, are
delightfully conspiratorial, with a nod to Mozart's *Figaro* in the former and a strong dash of Rossini
in the latter. *Alfonso und Estrella* and *Fierrabras* are altogether more imposing affairs. Each opens
with a brooding, atmospherically scored slow introduction, while the main *Allegro* of *Alfonso* has a
tremendous cumulative rhythmic force that points ahead to the *Great* C major Symphony. With his
Viennese-based Manfred Huss does ample justice to Schubert's exhilarating invention. Tempos are
lively, rhythms strong and propulsive and textures sharply etched, with Huss making the most of the
composer's theatrical contrasts. The recording has admirable clarity and impact.

Schubert Symphonies – No. 1 in D major, D82; No. 2 in B flat major, D125; No. 3 in D major,
   D200; No. 4 in C minor, D417, "Tragic"; No. 5 in B flat major, D485; No. 6 in C major, D589;
   No. 8 in B minor, D759, "Unfinished". No. 9 in C major, D944, "Great". **Royal Concertgebouw
   Orchestra / Nikolaus Harnoncourt.** Teldec Ⓕ 4509-91184-2 (four discs: 284 minutes: DDD: 12/93).
   Recorded live in 1992. *Gramophone Editor's choice.*   ⒼⒼⒼ
Harnoncourt, like Abbado on DG, has researched Schubert's own manuscripts, and corrected many
unauthentic amendments that found their way into the printed editions of the symphonies, such as
the eight bars later added to the Fourth Symphony's first movement exposition; but the differences
between Harnoncourt's interpretative Schubert and Abbado's are startling. The Ninth's finale, unlike
Abbado's, a whirling, spinning *vivace* – is borne aloft on astonishingly precise articulation of its
rhythms and accents, and a springy delivery of the triplets. Characteristics, of course, one has come
to expect from an Harnoncourt performance. Still, what a joy to hear this *Allegro*, and those of most
of the earlier symphonies, seized with such bright and light-toned enthusiasm. Here is urgent, virile
and vehement playing, never over-forceful, over-emphatic or burdened with excessive weight. What
came as a surprise was the consistent drawing out of these scores' potential for sadness and
restlessness. Harnoncourt does not set apart the first six symphonies as merely diverting, unlike
Abbado (out-and-out charm is seldom part of Harnoncourt's Schubertian vocabulary): their
bittersweet ambiguities and apparent affectations of anxiety here acquire a greater significance, and
the cycle, as a whole, a greater continuity. Up to a point, the darker, more serious Schubert that
emerges here, derives from the type of sound Harnoncourt fashions from his orchestra; not least, the
lean string tone and incisive brass. And maybe, up to a point, from the corrections: Harnoncourt
refers to the manuscripts as often being "harsher and more abrupt in tone [than the printed editions],
juxtaposing extreme dynamic contrasts", though you can't help feeling that contrasts in general have

been given a helping hand. Trios are mostly much slower than the urgent minuets/scherzos that frame them (with pauses in between the two). And Schubert's less vigorous moments are very noticeable as such, and are inflected with varying degrees of melancholy – it is uncanny how the string playing, in particular, often suggests a feeling of isolation (along with the sparing vibrato is an equally sparing use of that enlivening facility: *staccato*). The *Unfinished* Symphony's first movement is a stark, harrowing experience (yet it remains a well-tempered musical one: gestures are never exaggerated); the opening is as cold as the grave itself; the second subject knows its song is short-lived. In both movements, the elucidation and balance of texture can only be described as masterly: just listen to the trombones casting shadows in both codas. This, then, is as seriously pondered, coherent and penetrating a view of the complete cycle as we have had. Whether or not you feel Harnoncourt focuses too much on Schubert's darker side, you have to marvel at his ability to realize his vision. The recorded sound offers that inimitable Concertgebouw blend of the utmost clarity and wide open spaces.

Additional recommendations ...
...Nos. 1-6. No. 7 in E major, D729. Nos. 8 and 9. No. 10 in D major, D936A (realized Newbould). Symphonic fragments – D major, D615 (orch. Newbould); D major, D708A (cptd and orch. Newbould). **Academy of St Martin in the Fields / Sir Neville Marriner.**
Philips Ⓕ 412 176-2PH6 (six discs: DDD: 3/85).
...Nos. 1-6, 8 and 9. Rosamunde – incidental music, D797. Entr'acte No. 3 in B flat major. Ballet Music – No. 1 in B minor; No. 2 in G major. **Cologne Radio Symphony Orchestra / Günter Wand.**
RCA Victor Gold Seal Ⓜ GD60096 (five discs: 267 minutes: ADD/DDD: 2/89).
...Nos. 1-6, 8 and 9. **Chamber Orchestra of Europe / Claudio Abbado.**
DG Ⓕ 423 651-2GH5 (five discs: 320 minutes: DDD: 2/89).   ⒼⒼⒼ
...Nos. 1 and 2. **Chamber Orchestra of Europe / Claudio Abbado.**
DG Ⓕ 423 652-2GH (59 minutes: DDD: 9/89).
...No. 4. *Coupled with works by* **Debussy** and **Tchaikovsky** New York Philharmonic Symphony **Orchestra / Sir John Barbirolli.**
Dutton Laboratories Essential Archive mono Ⓑ CDEA5000* (69 minutes: ADD: 1/96).
...Nos. 4 and 8. **Bavarian Radio Symphony Orchestra / Carlo Maria Giulini.**
Sony Classical Ⓕ SK66833 (64 minutes: DDD: 12/96).
...Nos. 1-9. **Sinfonia Varsovia / Yehudi Menuhin.**
G.I.B. Classics Ⓜ GIB7905-2 (four discs: 239 minutes: DDD: 1/98).

Schubert Symphonies – No. 1 in D major, D82; No. 2 in B flat major, D125; No. 3 in D major, D200; No. 4 in C minor, D417, "Tragic"; No. 5 in B flat major, D485; No. 6 in C major, D589; No. 8 in B minor, D759, "Unfinished"; No. 9 in C major, D944, "Great". **Staatskapelle Dresden / Sir Colin Davis.** RCA Victor Red Seal Ⓕ 09026 62673-2 (four discs: 269 minutes: DDD: 3/97).
Recorded 1994.   ⒼⒼⒼ
Back in 1981, Davis (in Boston on Philips, 7/81 – no longer available) was the first to give us a Ninth with 'all' the repeats, as he does here. Since 1981, we've had Ninths that have also given us the repeats in the *da capo* of the *Scherzo* (which Davis didn't then, and doesn't now). But, with repeat-extended recordings of the Ninth, there is a fine line between being borne along by it, and, to be frank, becoming bored by it. Drive and energy play their part, but there are many other influencing factors – contrasts of tempo and dynamics, consistently spirited and incisive accentuation and articulation, and weight of orchestral sound, to which you might feel Davis has not quite enough of the first two, and maybe a touch too much of the third. Perhaps the jury needs further deliberation on the Davis Ninth; sample it extensively and you will continue to be impressed by the general magnificence of playing (trombones are never blatant), and by the beauty and airy articulacy of the sound (bass-lines are particularly well defined). The cumulative effect of Davis's maintained tempos is heard to greater advantage in his *Unfinished*, among the finest of recent recordings, as are the Abbado and Harnoncourt. In Davis's first movement, there is none of their hastening for the dramatic and energetic moments and the benefit is heard in the coda's "incomparable song of sorrow" (Einstein). There must be no doubt that Davis's achievement in the first six symphonies will have collectors cherishing this set. The delights are far too numerous to mention, and if reservations in the Ninth Symphony have caused alarm, not one of them applies here. His instincts never desert him: for the general pacing and weighting of the music (slow introductions with an old-world patience, but no false grandeur); for knowing when to charm with a small slowing; and for knowing when to leave well alone (the serene and steady progress of the Fifth's *Andante*) and when to intervene (the gradual increase of tempo in the Sixth's finale). And where Abbado is scrupulous about dynamics, Davis is more selective; the Fourth's *Andante* is properly sublime and shapely, and the wind-down from the agitated second idea, with all those dying falls, has never been more affectingly done.

The First Symphony's first movement immediately announces a satisfyingly rich and varied spectrum of tone-colour allied to a lightness of touch, and then a beautifully sung second subject, the whole informed with a blithe Mozartian grace. What more could one ask for? Well, perhaps for the small adjustments in balance and dynamics that Davis makes in the movement's coda that speak volumes about the kind of preparation (study or experience; probably both) that has obviously gone into the majority of these realizations. And then there is the orchestra itself, retaining a few features of its former self. The horns have lost the old Eastern European vibrato, but it is still a warm sound;

one, in the balance here, always clearly in the picture. The clarinets remain an acquired taste; their characteristic 'hoot' is very likeable (a joy in the yodelling which opens the *Allegro con brio* of the Third Symphony's first movement); their tone always individual enough to remain a distinct feature of the woodwind choir, indeed of tuttis in general. String tone is not full-bodied in the Berlin manner, but sweet, the playing always possessed of grace of movement (and when called on, power), their famed articulation rarely deserting them. Much is made of the spacious Lukaskirche acoustic; there are only a few places where it prevents an ideally focused image (the same could be said of the Harnoncourt Concertgebouw set) and one can't imagine many collectors foregoing the bloom for something more clinical. It must be said, though, that Abbado's cycle set new standards of textural clarity which are unlikely ever to be equalled on either modern or period instruments.

Schubert Symphony – No. 3 in D major, D200[a]; No. 5 in B flat major, D485[a]; No. 6 in C major, D589[b]. **Royal Philharmonic Orchestra / Sir Thomas Beecham.** EMI Studio Ⓜ CDM7 69750-2* (78 minutes: ADD: 8/90). Items marked [a] from HMV ASD345 (6/60), [b]Columbia 33CX1363 (9/56). *Gramophone classical 100.*　　　　　　　　　　　　　　　　　　　　ⒼⒼⒼ
Beecham was well into his seventies when he made these recordings with the Royal Philharmonic, the orchestra he had founded in 1946. His lightness of touch, his delight in the beauty of the sound he was summoning, the directness of his approach to melody, and his general high spirits will all dominate our memory of these performances. But listening again, we may be reminded that Beecham could equally well dig deep into the darker moments of these works. Schubert's elation was rarely untroubled and the joy is often compounded by its contrast with pathos – Beecham had that balance off to a tee. It should be noted that he does not take all the marked repeats and he doctored some passages he considered over-repetitive. However, these recordings may also serve as a reminder of the wonderful heights of musicianship that his players achieved, as in the trio of the Third Symphony's minuet, where a simple waltz-like duet between oboe and bassoon attains greatness by the shapeliness, ease and poignancy of its execution. Despite some signs of age, these recordings still preserve the brilliance of their readings and the tonal quality of this orchestra. Altogether, a disc to lift the heaviest of spirits.

Additional recommendations ...
...Nos. 3 and 4. **Chamber Orchestra of Europe / Claudio Abbado.**
DG Ⓕ 423 653-2GH (58 minutes: DDD: 9/89).　　　　　　　　　　　　　　　　ⒼⒼⒼ
...No. 3. **Schumann** Symphony No. 3 in E flat major, Op. 97, "Rhenish".
North German Radio Symphony Orchestra / Günter Wand.
RCA Victor Red Seal Ⓕ 09026 61876-2 (56 minutes: DDD: 2/94).　　　　　　　　　　ⒼⒼ
...Nos. 5 and 6. Overture in C major in the Italian style, D591. **Stockholm Sinfonietta / Neeme Järvi.**
BIS Ⓕ CD387 (72 minutes: DDD: 9/88).
...Nos. 5 and 6. **Chamber Orchestra of Europe / Claudio Abbado.**
DG Ⓕ 423 654-2GH (61 minutes: DDD: 9/89).
...Nos. 5 and 8. **Royal Concertgebouw Orchestra / Leonard Bernstein.**
DG Ⓕ 427 645-2GH (57 minutes: DDD: 1/90).
...No. 5.*Coupled with works by* **Brahms** and **Mendelssohn** Chicago Symphony Orchestra / **Fritz Reiner.** RCA Victor Gold Seal Ⓜ 09026 61793-2 (69 minutes: ADD: 9/95).
See review under Brahms; refer to the Index.　　　　　　　　　　　　　　　　　　Ⓖ
...No. 5. **Beethoven** Symphony No. 6 in F major, Op. 68, Pastoral". **Vienna Philharmonic Orchestra / Karl Böhm.** DG The Originals Ⓜ 447 433-2GOR (74 minutes: ADD: 1/96).
Gramophone classical 100. See review under Beethoven; refer to the Index.　　　　　ⒼⒼⒼ
...Nos. 2, 3 and 5. **Orchestra of the Eighteenth Century / Frans Brüggen.**
Philips Ⓕ 446 100-2PH (78 minutes: DDD: 7/96). 🎵
...Nos. 5 and 8. Rosamunde – Overture, "Die Zauberharfe". **Netherlands Radio Chamber Orchestra / Ton Koopman.** Erato Ⓕ 0630-15518-2 (67 minutes: DDD: 8/97).
...No. 5. **London Philharmonic Orchestra / Sir John Pritchard.**
Classics for Pleasure Ⓢ CD-CFP6036 (53 minutes: ADD: 5/98).

Schubert Symphonies – No. 8 in B minor, D759, "Unfinished"; No. 9 in C major, D944, "Great". **Berlin Philharmonic Orchestra / Günter Wand.** RCA Victor Red Seal Ⓜ 09026 68314-2 (two discs: 85 minutes: DDD: 1/96). Recorded live in 1995.
The advantages of these Berlin readings over Wand's 1991 Hamburg Musikhalle/North German RSO recordings (also live) are, often, as you might expect: greater facility (in, say, the infamous string triplets in the Ninth's last movement), generally richer string sonority (a proper 'heft' for those stamping C major chords also in the Ninth's finale), sweeter, more vibrant and more focused woodwind (wonderful solos in the Eighth's second movement second subject), a generally wider (though far from excessive) range of dynamics in the Eighth, more expansive phrasing, and accents more consistently placed (and recorded sound with marginally greater presence). The ground-plans remain the same, in other words, the basic tempo and its modification (and what ingenious and effective plans they are, and how marvellous it has been to re-encounter Wand's sublimely wrought rubato); as does the conductor's views on repeats (taken in the Eighth's first movement, but not in the Ninth's outer movements). It is pointless to speculate whether the small details that *have* changed (for example, the now truly *pianissimo* second subject of the Eighth's first movement) are due to Wand's

further four years' thoughts on the works, or changes brought about by the Berlin orchestra's own musical collective, or just 'another time, another place'. Probably a bit of all three. If you already own the Hamburg recordings, there is no need to rush out and buy this package (and, of course, you will also be the proud owner of the finest Schumann Fourth of the last two decades – the Hamburg Schubert Eighth's coupling). But if you don't, this set is an obvious choice. Wand's Schubert is informed by a very special devotion, wisdom and insight, and a very individual spirit of adventure.

Additional recommendations ...
...No. 8. Sonata for Piano Duet in C major, D812, "Grand Duo" (orch. Joachim).
Chamber Orchestra of Europe / Claudio Abbado. DG Ⓕ 423 655-2GH (71 minutes: DDD).
...No. 8 in B minor, D759, "Unfinished". **Schumann** Symphony No. 4 in D minor, Op. 120.
North German Radio Symphony Orchestra / Günter Wand. RCA Victor Red Seal Ⓕ RD60826
(57 minutes: DDD: 5/92). *See review under Schumann; refer to the Index.* ⓋⒼ
...No. 8. *Coupled with works by various composers.* **Concertgebouw Orchestra / Pierre Monteux.**
Philips The Early Years Ⓜ 442 544-2PM5 (five discs: 311 minutes: ADD: 12/94).
See review in the Collections section; refer to the Index. ⓋⒼⒼ
...No. 8. Marche militaire in D major, D733 No. 1. *Coupled with works by various composers.*
Louis Zimmerman, Ferdinand Hellmann (vns); **Concertgebouw Orchestra / Willem Mengelberg.**
Pearl mono Ⓜ GEMMCD9154* (76 minutes: ADD: 3/96).
...No. 9. **Vienna Philharmonic Orchestra / Sir Georg Solti.**
Decca Ⓕ 430 747-2DM (55 minutes: DDD: 3/83). Ⓖ
...No. 9. **Royal Concertgebouw Orchestra / Leonard Bernstein.**
DG Ⓕ 427 646-2GH (50 minutes: DDD: 1/90).
...No. 9. **North German Radio Symphony Orchestra / Günter Wand.**
RCA Victor Red Seal Ⓕ RD60978 (53 minutes: DDD: 1/92).
...No. 9. **Bavarian Radio Symphony Orchestra / Carlo Maria Giulini.**
Sony Classical Ⓕ SK53971 (57 minutes: DDD: 8/95).
...No. 9. **Haydn** Symphony No. 88 in G major, "Letter V". **Berlin Philharmonic Orchestra /
Wilhelm Furtwängler.** DG The Originals mono Ⓜ 447 439-2GOR* (76 minutes: ADD: 12/95).
...No. 9. Rosamunde, D797[b] – Ballet in B minor; Ballet in G major. **Haydn** Symphony No. 92 in
G major, "Oxford"[a]. [a]**Paris Conservatoire Orchestra,** [b]**London Symphony Orchestra / Bruno
Walter.** Dutton Laboratories Essential Archive mono Ⓑ CDEA5003* (79 minutes: ADD: 1/96).
...Nos. 8 and 9. Marche militaire in D major, D733 No. 1. **Concertgebouw Orchestra /
Willem Mengelberg.** Biddulph mono Ⓜ WHL039 (78 minutes: ADD: 4/98).

Schubert Symphony No. 10 in D major, D936a (realized Newbould). Symphonic fragments –
D major, D615; D major, D708a (orch. Newbould). **Scottish Chamber Orchestra /
Sir Charles Mackerras.** Hyperion Ⓕ CDA67000 (54 minutes: DDD: 11/97). Recorded 1997.
Someone will have to find another name for Schubert's *Unfinished* Symphony (the B minor) before too long. In fact there are six unfinished Schubert symphonies: there are two whole movement expositions for D615, torsos of three movements and a nearly complete *Scherzo* for D708a, and enough sketch material for Brian Newbould to attempt a complete conjectural reconstruction of D936a, the symphony Schubert began writing in the last weeks of his life. Inevitably some will ask, why bother? Well, apart from the increase in the sense of wonder at Schubert's sheer productivity, there is some wonderful music here, especially the slow movement of D936a, desolate and warmly consoling by turns. As a whole, D936a suggests that, even at this late stage, Schubert was still thinking in terms of new developments. The concluding third movement, contrapuntally fusing elements of scherzo and finale, is like nothing else in Schubert – or in any other composer of the classical period. Of course, Newbould has had to do some guessing here, but the results are on the whole strikingly authoritative. The performances carry plenty of conviction and the recordings are atmospheric while allowing one to hear all significant detail. Altogether this is a fascinating disc – and not just for musicologists.

Schubert Octet in F major, D803. Minuet and Finale in F major, D72[a]. **Vienna Octet;**
[a]**Vienna Wind Soloists.** Decca Eclipse Ⓑ 448 715-2DEC (72 minutes: DDD: 8/96).
From 430 516-2DH (2/93). Ⓖ
Over the years Decca have made a speciality of recording the Schubert Octet in Vienna, and this budget-priced reissue of their latest version by the Vienna Octet, captured within the glowing acoustics of the Mozartsaal of the Vienna Konzerthaus, and ideally balanced by Christopher Raeburn, is the most winning of all. The enticing warmth of the opening *Adagio* catches the listener's attention at once, and the central movements – the *Scherzo* bustling with vitality and the deliciously played *Andante con variazioni* – are unforgettable. Then comes the lovingly Schubertian *Menuetto*, and after an arresting *tremolando* introduction, the joyfully bucolic finale rounds things off in sparkling fashion. At its price, this Vienna version is now in a class of its own. As a bonus we are offered the *Minuet and Finale*, D72, two engaging miniatures from the composer's youth, nicely elegant in the hands of the Vienna Wind Soloists. The demonstration-standard recording makes this a bargain not to be passed by.

Additional recommendations ...
...Octet. **Gaudier Ensemble.** ASV Ⓕ CDDCA694 (64 minutes: DDD: 5/90).

...Octet. **Budapest Schubert Ensemble.** Naxos Ⓢ 8 550389 (68 minutes: DDD: 8/93).
...Octet. **Berlin Soloists.** Teldec Digital Experience Ⓜ 4509-91448-2 (63 minutes: DDD: 11/93).
...Octet. **Mozzafiato; L'Archibudelli.** Sony Classical Ⓕ SK66264 (61 minutes: DDD: 9/96).   Ⓖ

Schubert Piano Quintet in A major, D667, "Trout"[a]. String Quartet No. 14 in D minor, D810,
"Death and the Maiden"[b]. [a]**Sir Clifford Curzon** (pf); [a]members of the **Vienna Octet**
(Willi Boskovsky, vn; Gunther Breitenbach, va; Nikolaus Hübner, vc; Johann Krump, db);
[b]**Vienna Philharmonic Quartet** (Willi Boskovsky, Otto Strasser, vns; Rudolf Streng, va;
Robert Scheiwein, vc). Decca Ⓜ 417 459-2DM* (71 minutes: ADD: 6/88).
Item marked [a] from SXL2110 (6/59), recorded 1957, [b]SXL6092 (5/64), recorded 1963.   Ⓖ
Schubert composed the *Trout* Quintet in his early twenties for a group of amateur musicians in the
town of Steyr in Upper Austria, which lies upon the River Enns which was then noted for its fine
fishing and keen fishermen. The Quintet was certainly tailored for special circumstances, but like all
great occasional music it stands as strongly as ever today, with its freshly bubbling invention and
sunny melodiousness. Willi Boskovsky's gentle and cultured mind is very much responsible for the
success of these performances of Schubert's two best-known chamber works. In the delectable *Trout*
Quintet there is real unanimity of vision between the players, as well as an immaculate attention to
the details of the scoring. Clifford Curzon's part in the performance is memorable especially for his
quiet playing – the atmosphere is magical in such moments. Everywhere there is a great awareness of
the delicacy and refinement of Schubert's inventiveness. The *Death and the Maiden* Quartet is no less
successful. Schubert's strikingly powerful harmonies, together with a sustained feeling of intensity, all
go to heighten the urgency of the first movement. Despite this, string textures are generally kept light
and feathery. In the *Andante* all is subtly understated and although a mood of tragedy is always
lurking in the background, never is it thrown at the listener. Boskovsky's understanding of the music
is very acute and the performance cannot fail to satisfy even the most demanding. These are two
vintage recordings and in the quartet the quality of sound is quite remarkable.
Additional recommendations ...
...Piano Quintet. **Clemens Hagen** (vn); **Veronika Hagen** (va); **Lukas Hagen** (vc); **Alois Posch** (db);
  András Schiff (pf). Decca Ⓕ 411 975-2DH (44 minutes: DDD: 4/85).
...Piano Quintet. String Trios[a] – B flat major, D471; B flat major, D581.
  [a]**Grumiaux Trio; Jacques Cazauran** (db); **Ingrid Haebler** (pf).
  Philips Musica da Camera Ⓜ 422 838-2PC (63 minutes: ADD: 10/89).
...Piano Quintet[a]. Adagio and Rondo concertante in F major, D487. **Kodály Quartet;**
  [a]**István Tóth** (db); **Jenö Jandó** (pf). Naxos Ⓢ 8 550658 (53 minutes: DDD: 4/93).
...Piano Quintet[b]. Lieder[a] – Die Forelle, D550; Am Strome, D539; Auf dem see, D543; Erlafsee,
  D586; An eine Quelle, D530; Der Jüngling am Bache, D192; Der Schiffer, D536.
  [a]**John Mark Ainsley** (ten); [b]**Steven Lubin** (fp); [b]**Academy of Ancient Music Chamber Ensemble.**
  L'Oiseau-Lyre Ⓕ 433 848-2OH (60 minutes: DDD: 9/93). ✒
...Piano Quintet[a]. Quartet in G major for Guitar, Flute, Viola and Cello, D96[b].
  [b]**Wolfgang Schulz** (fl); [a]**Georg Hetzel** (vn); [ab]**Wolfram Christ** (va); [ab]**Georg Faust** (vc);
  [a]**Alois Posch** (db); [b]**Göran Söllscher** (gtr); [a]**James Levine** (pf).
  DG Ⓕ 431 783-2GH (65 minutes: DDD: 1/94). *Gramophone Editor's choice.*
...Piano Quintet[a]. Violin Sonatina in D major, D384[b]. Violin Sonatina in A minor, D385[c].
  Violin Sonatina in G minor, D408[d]. Octet in F major, D803[e]. [a]**Steven Lubin** (fp); [bcd]**Jaap
  Schröder** (vn); [bcd]**Christopher Hogwood** (fp); [ae]**Academy of Ancient Music Chamber Ensemble.**
  L'Oiseau-Lyre Double Decca Ⓜ 455 724-2OF2 (two discs: 156 minutes: DDD/ADD: 3/98).

Schubert Piano Quintet in A major, D667, "Trout"[a].
Mozart Piano Quartet in G minor, K478. **Thomas Zehetmair** (vn); **Tabea Zimmermann** (va);
  Richard Duven (vc); [a]**Peter Riegelbauer** (db); **Alfred Brendel** (pf). Philips Ⓕ 446 001-2PH
  (75 minutes: DDD: 1/96). Recorded 1994.
"The Schubert of this quintet is not the great Schubert, but the one whom we cannot help but love."
Pertinent sentiments (Alfred Einstein quoted by William Kinderman) although listening to this
particular performance of the *Trout* suggests something of a compromise between 'lovable' and
'great'. Brendel is of course the lynchpin and, as ever, balances heart and mind with innate good taste.
Time and again you find yourself overhearing detail that might otherwise have passed for nothing:
every modulation tells (needless to say, this *Andante* probes deeper than most); every phrase of
dialogue has been polished, pondered and carefully considered. And yet it *is* a dialogue, with the
loose-limbed Thomas Zehetmair leading his supremely accomplished colleagues through Schubert's
delightful five-tier structure. The *Scherzo* and *Allegro giusto* frolic within the bounds of propriety
(some will favour an extra shot of animal vigour), whereas the first, second and fourth movements are
rich in subtle – as opposed to fussy – observations. The recording, too, is exceedingly warm, with only
the occasional want of inner detail to bar unqualified enthusiasm. As ever, Philips achieve a well-
rounded, almost tangible piano tone. Mozart's G minor Quartet makes for an unexpected, though
instructive, coupling, treading as it does on the *Trout*'s playful tail. Here again there is much to learn
and enjoy, especially in terms of phrasal dovetailing and elegant articulation (Brendel's opening
flourish is a model of Mozartian phrase-shaping). Still, you may sometimes crave rather more in the
way of *Sturm und Drang* – a fiercer, more muscular attack, most especially in the first movement. Yet

there will be times when the conceptual unity and executive refinement of this performance – its articulate musicality – will more than fit the bill. Both works include their respective first movement repeats.

Schubert String Quintet in C major, D956. **Melos Quartet** (Wilhelm Melcher, Ida Bieler, vns; Hermann Voss, va; Peter Buck, vc); **Wolfgang Boettcher** (vc). Harmonia Mundi Ⓕ HMC90 1494 (57 minutes: DDD: 8/94). Includes free sampler disc of other Melos Quartet recordings. Recorded 1993.
Schubert String Quintet in C major, D956. **Borodin Quartet** (Mikhail Kopelman, Andrei Abramenkov, vns; Dmitri Shebalin, va; Valentin Berlinsky, vc); **Mikhail Milman** (vc). Teldec Ⓕ 4509-94564-2 (52 minutes: DDD: 4/95). Recorded 1994.

In his programme notes, Christian Girardin compares Schubert's String Quintet with the composer's *Great* C major Symphony: both works share the same key, involve a profound investigation of tone-colour and exhibit a kind of transcendency which derives not from the quantity, but from the quality of musical time. The Melos Quartet's playing is broad and expansive, and their sensational string tone sounds extraordinarily resonant in their rich recording. Relaxed speeds and sensitively balanced textures allow internal voices to make their full impact. However, it is the dramatic intensity which this group achieves in the music's silences that is most remarkable. Prospective buyers are further enticed by a free sampler of other Melos recordings which, aside from music by Janáček, Bruckner and Brahms, includes a fine performance of Schubert's *Quartettsatz*.

Decades of experience has taught the Borodin Quartet that there is more to late Schubert than resignation and dream. In each movement, it is harmonic instability, suddenness of dynamic contrast, harshness of rhythm and texture which are emphasized – and all caught faithfully in the outstanding engineering and production. Comparison in the case of this work, and this performance, really is odious. But surely there are few other accounts with a longer, more intense inner crescendo at the very core of those opening chords, or a more starkly rhythmic cut-off? The fierceness of those ever-tautening sequences and imitations at the start do away with any need for over-sweetness in the second, lyrical subject: it simply becomes set into gentle, natural relief. The great slow movement convinces entirely in its pulse-rate and pacing, with great dignity drawn from the full, sustained dotted note values in the violin parts. The *presto* of the *Scherzo* is restrained by a certain heavy-heeled ballast, so that the velocity of every note counts, and this most sober of Trios is given a frame of fitting substance. Few quartets capture so movingly the anxious tremor in the heart of the finale, as it lunges savagely between major and minor. But then few quartets have learned to look so far away from themselves and so deep into the very centre of the music.

Additional recommendations ...
...String Quintet. **Aeolian Quartet; Bruno Schrecker** (vc).
  Saga Classics Ⓜ EC3368-2* (54 minutes: ADD: 4/92).
...String Quintet. **Emerson Quartet; Mstislav Rostropovich** (vc).
  DG Ⓕ 431 792-2GH (53 minutes: DDD: 9/92).   ⒼⒼ
...String Quintet[a]. String Quartet No. 12 in C minor, D703, "Quartettsatz". **Takács Quartet;**
  [a]**Miklos Perényi** (vc). Decca Ⓕ 436 324-2DH (64 minutes: DDD: 6/93).
...String Quintet. **Brandis Quartet; Wenn-Sinn Yang** (vc).
  Nimbus Ⓕ NI5313 (54 minutes: DDD: 6/93).
...String Quintet. **Schoenberg** Verklärte Nacht, Op. 4[a] (orig. version).
  Hollywood Quartet; [a]**Alvin Dinkin** (va); **Kurt Reher** (vc).
  Testament mono Ⓕ SBT1031* (73 minutes: ADD: 4/94). *See review under Schoenberg;*
  refer to the Index. Gramophone *Award Winner 1994.*   ⒼⒼⒼ
...String Quintet[a]. Symphony No. 5 in B flat major, D485[b]. [a]**Isaac Stern,** [a]**Alexander Schneider**
  (vns); [a]**Milton Katims** (va); [a]**Paul Tortelier** (vc); [b]**Prades Festival Orchestra / Pablo Casals** ([a]vc).
  Sony Classical Casals Edition mono Ⓜ SMK58992* (76 minutes: ADD: 5/94).   ⒼⒼⒼ
...String Quintet[a]. **Beethoven** Grosse Fuge in B flat major, Op. 133.
  Hagen Quartet; [a]**Heinrich Schiff** (vc). DG Ⓕ 439 774-2GH (68 minutes: DDD: 11/94).
...String Quintet. String Trio in B flat major, D471. **Raphael Ensemble.**
  Hyperion Ⓕ CDA66724 (65 minutes: DDD: 12/95).
...String Quintet. **Boccherini** String Quintet No. 5 in E major, G275.
  Isaac Stern, Cho-Liang Lin (vns); **Jaime Laredo** (va); **Yo-Yo Ma, Sharon Robinson** (vcs).
  Sony Classical Ⓕ SK53983 (76 minutes: DDD: A/97).

Schubert String Quartets – No. 10 in E flat major, D87; No. 13 in A minor, D804. Quartettsatz in C minor, D703. **Artis Quartet** (Peter Schuhmayer, Johannes Meissl, vns; Herbert Kefer, va; Othmar Muller, vc). Sony Classical Ⓕ SK66720 (66 minutes: DDD: 2/97). Recorded 1994.

The Artis Quartet have all the right Viennese qualifications to play Schubert – their playing is graceful and stylish, with genuine warmth of tone and expression. In the A minor Quartet they take their cue from Schubert's many expression marks – making the accents and crescendos sound absolutely spontaneous; pointers to the underlying emotion. It helps that they play the many soft passages so delicately; by contrast the more intense, dramatic moments come over strongly without any hint of overplaying, using imaginative variations of tone-colour to point the different shades of feeling. The flowing *Andante* is a delight, and the restrained lilt of the Minuet, maintaining the melancholic mood, is equally successful. Only in the finale are some of the rhythms not ideally poised, but even here there's much to admire. They play the early E flat Quartet beautifully too; in the finale the leader's elegant portamentos, and the rhythmic fizz of the opening, remind us that the young Schubert was writing in the era of both Spohr and Rossini. The C minor *Quartettsatz* is less pleasing. Though in essence it's another fine and brilliant performance, the frequent hold-ups for accents start to sound rather contrived.

Additional recommendations ...

...Quartettsatz (cpted. Newbould). *Coupled with works by* **Haydn** and **Ravel** Allegri Quartet.
  Naim Audio Ⓕ NAIMCD012 (62 minutes: DDD: 2/97).
...No. 4 in C major, D46; No. 7 in D major, D94; No. 10. **Coull Quartet.**
  Upbeat Classics Ⓕ URCD126 (72 minutes: DDD: 9/97).

Schubert String Quartets – No. 10 in E flat major, D87; No. 13 in A minor, D804.
  Quatuor Mosaïques (Erich Höbarth, Andrea Bischof, vns; Anita Mitterer, va; Christophe Coin, vc). Auvidis Astrée Ⓕ E8580 (68 minutes: DDD: 10/96). 🎯 Recorded 1995.
  Gramophone Editor's choice. ⒼⒼ

Listening to this recording of the A minor Quartet, the first ever on period instruments, one is put in mind of Schubert's own verdict on the Schuppanzigh Quartet's performance of the work in March 1824: "Rather slow, but very pure and tender". With unusually broad tempos, the Mosaïques consistently stress the music's pathos, loneliness and fatalism. The Hungarian-flavoured finale is normally seen as a stoically cheerful reaction to the pain that has gone before. But here it steals in as if in a dream from the spectral close of the minuet, the opening melody delicately floated, its off-beat accents barely flicked; where the Alban Berg and the Lindsay bring a faintly military strut to the C sharp minor melody (2'11"), the Mosaïques, suppressing any hint of swagger in the dotted rhythms, distil a doleful balletic grace. In the *Andante* of the *Rosamunde* the Mosaïques, while slower than either of their rivals, never lose sight of the *gehende Bewegung*, the walking motion that underlies so many of Schubert's *andantes*.

They match the Lindsay in their tender, sentient phrasing, subtly flexing the pulse in response to harmonic movement. The minuet, with its glassy, vibratoless *pianissimos*, is more eerily remote, less human in its desolation, than from the Alban Berg or Lindsay. For their coupling the Mosaïques offer the early E flat Quartet, written when Schubert was just 16. Not even their affectionate, considered advocacy can do much for the dull, harmonically stagnant opening movement. But they relish the raw energy of the *Scherzo*, with its braying donkey evocations, and bring a delicious demure wit to the Rossinian second theme of the finale (0'58"). And, as in the absorbing, moving reading of the A minor Quartet, the delicacy of nuance and clarity of texture, easier to obtain from the sparer-toned period instruments, is often revelatory. The recording is clean, vivid and immediate. In sum, yet another outstanding disc from the Mosaïques, comparable with the finest modern-instrument readings, in musical insight and expressive subtlety.

Schubert String Quartets. **Alban Berg Quartet** (Günther Pichler, Gerhard Schulz, vns; Thomas Kakuska, va; Valentin Erben, vc). EMI Ⓕ CDC5 56470/1-2 (two discs, oas: 57 and 60 minutes: DDD: 2/98). Item marked [a] recorded live in 1994, [bc]1997. ⒼⒼ
  CDC5 56470-2 – No. 10 in E flat major, D87[c]; No. 13 in A minor, D810[a]. "Death and the Maiden". *CDC5 56471-2* – No. 12 in C minor, D703[c], "Quartettsatz"; No. 15 in G major, D887[b].

The Alban Berg Quartet's policy of making recordings at concert performances certainly produces impressive results: interpretations that avoid any feeling of routine or of being overcareful. What impresses above all is the flexibility and sensitivity of these performances. In the first movement of D887 the Alban Berg, by subtly drawing our attention to the precise emotional colour of all Schubert's magical harmonic shifts, find a touching, intimate quality within the grand design. And it's certainly an advantage for any group performing this quartet to be able to produce such a magnificent *tremolando* – whether it's the forest murmurs of the first movement or the Gothic shuddering of the *Andante*'s middle section. The G major Quartet is the outstanding performance on these discs, but *Death and the Maiden* isn't far behind, particularly the con fuoco *Scherzo* and finale. For the first movement, though, you may well prefer the forceful and dramatic account (complete with the rarely played exposition repeat) of the Melos Quartet. In the *Andante*, the Melos make a beautifully balanced sound but by the side of the Alban Berg they seem emotionally uncommitted; the major-key variation, especially, lacks the poignancy that the Viennese group bring to it (though the Alban Berg play this movement without repeats). There are also a few places, where Schubert is straightforwardly tuneful (in D703 and in the outer movements of D87, especially) where one wishes Günther Pichler would play in a simpler, more direct manner. The Busch Quartet's 1930s recordings of D810 and D887 are smoother, less emphatic than that of modern groups, and this enables them to convey the emotional nuances, particularly of the D minor Quartet, in a more inward and profound way. And the two quartets are available (with some repeats missing) on a single CD. But it's a measure of the Alban Berg Quartet's exceptional quality to realize that they are in the same league, with the same sense of players totally absorbed in the music. And of course the recorded sound is immeasurably more vivid and lifelike.

Additional recommendations ...

...Nos. 13 and 14. **Alban Berg Quartet.** EMI Ⓕ CDC7 47333-2 (72 minutes: DDD: 7/86).

...Nos. 12 and 14. **Lindsay Quartet.** ASV Ⓕ CDDCA560 (52 minutes: DDD: 3/87).
...No. 8 in in B flat major, D112; No. 13. **Lindsay Quartet.**
ASV Ⓕ CDDCA593 (65 minutes: ADD: 4/88).
...Nos. 12-15. **Melos Quartet.**
Harmonia Mundi Ⓕ HMC90 1408/9 (two discs: 134 minutes: DDD: 12/92).   ⒼⒼ
...No. 2 in C major, D32. No. 14.
Artis Quartet. Sony Classical Ⓕ SK52582 (59 minutes: DDD: 6/93).
...Nos. 13 and 14. **Takács Quartet.** Decca Ⓕ 436 843-2DH (75 minutes: DDD: 12/93).
...No. 8 in B flat major, D112[a]; Nos. 14[a] and 15[a]. Fantasy in C major, D934[ab]. Piano Trio No. 2[ab].
[b]**Rudolf Serkin** (pf); [a]**Busch Quartet.**
Pearl mono Ⓜ GEMMCDS9141* (two discs: 158 minutes: AAD: 7/95)
...Nos. 13 and 14. **Brandis Quartet.** Nimbus Ⓕ NI5438 (79 minutes: DDD: 12/95).
...No. 12. *Coupled with works by* **Haydn** *and* **Ravel** Skampa Quartet.
Supraphon Ⓕ SU3156-2 (61 minutes: DDD: 8/97).
...Nos. 12-15. String Quintet in C major, D956[a]. [a]**Wen-Sinn Yang** (vc); **Brandis Quartet.**
Nimbus Ⓜ NI1770 (three discs: 185 minutes: DDD: 10/97).
...Nos. 12[a], 14[b] and 15[c]. String Quintet in C major, D956[d]. [d]**Dietfried Gürtler** (vc); [a]
[d]**Weller Quartet;** [b]**Vienna Philharmonic Quartet;** [c]**Gabrieli Quartet.**
Double Decca Ⓑ 452 396-2DF2 (two discs: 138 minutes: ADD: 10/97).
...Nos. 8 and 13. **Coull Quartet.** Upbeat Classics Ⓕ URCD134 (68 minutes: DDD: 5/98).

Schubert String Quartets—No. 14 in D minor, D810, "Death and the Maiden"[a]; No. 15 in
G major, D887[b]. **Busch Quartet** (Adolph Busch, Gösta Andreasson, vns; Karl Doktor, va;
Hermann Busch, vc). **Busch Quartet.** EMI Références mono Ⓜ CDH7 69795-2*
(73 minutes: ADD: 5/89). Item marked [a] recorded 1936, [b]1938. *Gramophone classical 100.* ⒼⒼⒼ
Death and the Maiden is the best served of Schubert's quartets on CD. The Busch Quartet's account
is now 62 years old but it still brings us closer to the heart of this work than any other. The slow
movement, in particular, has an unmatched and marvellous eloquence. The same must also be said of
the G major Quartet, a performance of surpassing beauty which reveals more of the depth and
humanity of the score than any subsequent recording. Such are these performances that the music is
quick to engross your thoughts to the exclusion of any consideration of the age of the recordings. The
present recording is, on on the whole, good: exceptionally so in the quieter passages.

Schubert Piano Trios[a] – B flat major, D28 (Sonata in one movement); No. 1 in B flat major, D898;
No. 2 in E flat major, D929. Notturno in E flat major, D897[a]. String Trios[b] – B flat major, D471;
B flat major, D581. [a]**Beaux Arts Trio** (Menahem Pressler, pf; Daniel Guilet, vn;
Bernard Greenhouse, vc); [b]**Grumiaux Trio** (Arthur Grumiaux, vn; Georges Janzer, va,
Eva Czako, vc). Philips Duo Ⓜ 438 700-2PM2 (two discs: 127 minutes: ADD: 4/94).
Items marked [a] recorded 1966, [b]1969.   ⒼⒼ
These performances are polished, yet the many solo contributions from each of the players emerge
with a strong personality. The Beaux Arts cellist brings lovely phrasing and a true simplicity of line,
so right for Schubert – memorably in the lovely slow movement melody of the Trio No. 2 in E flat. In
addition to the great piano trios (B flat, D898 and E flat, D929) the set includes the extremely
personable, very early Sonata in B flat, D28, where the lyrical line already has the unmistakable
character of its young composer. Also included is the *Notturno*, D897, a raptly emotive short piece
played here with a remarkable depth of feeling that recalls the gentle intensity of the glorious slow
movement of the String Quintet. The recording is naturally balanced, although a little dry in the
treble. Of the two rarer string trios, also early works, the four-movement Trio, D581 is totally
infectious, with that quality of innocence that makes Schubert's music stand apart. Given such
persuasive advocacy, and vivid recording, both pieces cannot fail to give the listener great pleasure.

Schubert Piano Trios[ab] – No. 1 in B flat major, D898; No. 2 in E flat major, D929.
Sonata in A minor, D821, "Arpeggione"[b]. Notturno in E flat major, D897[ac].
[a]**Yuuko Shiokawa** (vn); [b]**Miklos Perényi** (vc); **András Schiff** (pf). Teldec Ⓕ 0630-13151-2
(two discs: 127 minutes: DDD: 12/97). Recorded 1995.
These discs begin with an outstanding performance of the *Arpeggione* Sonata. The recording is clear
and spacious, and the outer movements have an effortless sense of momentum that is not too
inflexible to allow for some expressive rubato and pointing of the phrases. There's no hint in Perényi's
playing that this is a difficult work for the cello, and he produces a most beautiful, warm, serene tone
for the *Adagio*. Schiff's special feeling for Schubert is apparent even in the most subsidiary details of
the piano part and particularly in the more dominating roles of the trios and the *Notturno*. These
three well-matched players find exactly the right tone and feeling. In the first *Allegro* of the B flat Trio
the superior recording helps them to convey the music's grandeur and the following *Andante* is played
with a flowing, evocative style. Shiokawa's clear-toned, elegant violin playing is a great asset here. In
the *Notturno*, too, a flowing tempo doesn't spoil the tranquillity of the opening melody, but allows the
contrasting episode to emerge triumphantly. At this point, the Beaux Arts seem, by contrast, quite
ponderous. In the monumental E flat Trio Schiff, Shiokawa and Perényi seem sometimes a little polite
and decorous but their interpretation is certainly not lacking in vitality or variety. The finale in this

performance lasts nearly 20 minutes: the players have gone back to the original version of the movement – Schubert made cuts when preparing the trio for publication. If you're an admirer of Schubert's "heavenly length" you'll hear it as the true culmination of one of his greatest instrumental works.

Additional recommendations ...

...No. 1. **Borodin Trio.** Chandos Ⓕ CHAN8308 (43 minutes: DDD: 3/84).

...No. 2. **Borodin Trio.** Chandos Ⓕ CHAN8324 (DDD: 11/84).

...Nos. 1 and 2; B flat major, D28. Notturno. **Vienna Haydn Trio.**
Teldec Ⓑ 0630-12337-2 (two discs: 96 minutes: DDD: 1/97).

...Nos. 1 and 2. Notturno. Sonata in B flat major, D28. **Fontenay Trio.**
Teldec Ⓕ 4509-94558-2 (two discs: 106 minutes: DDD: 2/97).

...Nos. 1 and 2. **Pinchas Zukerman** (vn); **Lynn Harrell** (vc); **Vladimir Ashkenazy** (pf).
Decca Ⓜ 455 685-2DX2 (two discs: 91 minutes: DDD: 12/97).

...No. 2; B flat major, D28. **La Gaia Scienza.**
Winter & Winter Basic Edition Ⓕ 910 006-2 (55 minutes: DDD: 12/97). 🎶

Schubert Piano Music for Four Hands, Volume 1. Overture in F major, D675. Eight Variations on a theme from Hérold's "Marie", D908. Rondo in D major, D608. Marches héroïques, D602. Fantasie in F minor, D940. Variations in B flat major, D603/D968*a*. Divertissement à la hongroise, D818. Six Polonaises, D824. **Yaara Tal, Andreas Groethuysen** (pf duet).
Sony Classical Ⓕ S2K58955 (two discs: 137 minutes: DDD: 9/94). Recorded 1993.

The first thing one notices about this issue is the very clear and firm sound; Tal and Groethuysen explain that they have used a Fazioli Model 308 piano and thank their recording team for its "exceptional abilities". Indeed, an impressive sound comes from this big instrument, which the artists consider necessary to re-create the "symphonic ambitions" and "extremes" of the music, although it is unlike anything Schubert could have heard, and they play with a fine tonal and dynamic range which allows intimacy as well as power. The treble is bright yet not glaring, as we hear in the closing page of the *Overture*. The recording is fairly reverberant but produces a satisfying aural picture. The performances are strong and compelling, with plenty of momentum, yet flexible. The *Rondo* has a winning *galanterie*, and the players know that *Allegretto* marking here applies to style as well as tempo. The F minor *Fantasie* is Schubert's best-known keyboard duet and, of course, inhabits a more private world in which despair features strongly. Tal and Groethuysen's basic tempo is a genuine *Allegro molto moderato*, and they know how to make transitions from one mood to the next, as when approaching the doom-laden F sharp minor section at 4'55". Furthermore, they rightly bring out the 'smiles through tears' aspect of the more lyrical music, do not hurry the scherzo (which is consequently all the stronger) and shape the fugue finely. They are very impressive and one is reminded of the performance by Louis Lortie and Hélène Mercier which is equally magisterial.

Additional recommendations ...

...Fantasie. *Coupled with works by* **Mozart Louis Lortie, Hélène Mercier** (pfs).
Chandos Ⓕ CHAN9162 (50 minutes: DDD: 7/93).

...Divertissement. Trois Marches Militaires, D733. Grandes marches, D819 – No. 2 in G minor; No. 3 in B minor. **Isabel Beyer, Harvey Dagul** (pf duet).
Four Hands Music Ⓕ FHMD894 (69 minutes: DDD: 4/95).

...Polonaises. Divertissement, D823. **Isabel Beyer, Harvey Dagul** (pf duet).
Four Hands Music Ⓕ FHMD895 (70 minutes: DDD: 12/95).

...Divertissement. Fantasie. 4 Ländler, D814. Allegro in A minor, D947, "Lebensstürme". Divertissement, D823. Sonata for Piano Duet in C major, D812, "Grand Duo".
Christoph Eschenbach, Justus Frantz (pf duet).
EMI Forte Ⓜ CZS5 69770-2 (two discs: 154 minutes: ADD: 8/97).

Schubert Divertissements – à la hongroise, D818; sur des motifs originaux français, D823.
Andreas Staier, Alexei Lubimov (fp duet). Teldec Ⓕ 0630-17113-2 (66 minutes: DDD: 6/98). 🎶
Recorded 1997. 🏆🏆

Schubert's *Divertissement à la hongroise*, his most flamboyant essay in the Hungarian vernacular style, has always overshadowed the *Divertissement* on French themes. Yet the less favoured work is in some ways the more compelling. Its profoundly un-divertimento-like first movement has a haunting, quintessentially Schubertian second theme and one of the composer's most turbulent and tonally audacious developments. The *Andantino*, a set of variations on a glum little theme that sounds more plausibly French than anything else in the work, is transfigured by its ravishing final variation in the major; and the finale is a sprawling, colourful rondo, built on a theme that equivocates between G major and E minor and permeated by Schubert's favourite driving dactylic rhythms. This is the first recording of either work on a fortepiano. And using a fine copy by Christopher Clarke of an 1826 Graf instrument, Staier and Lubimov give performances which, in poetry, *élan* and sheer relish have never been surpassed. One immediate advantage of a fortepiano in this music is the way it clarifies the textures, especially in the bass regions, which can too easily sound murky on a modern grand. Then there is the unique array of colours available through the use of no fewer than five pedals – the harp-like sonorities of the *una corda* pedal, for instance, or the 'bassoon' pedal, with its buzzing lower strings. The instrument's *coup de grâce* is its so-called Turkish pedal, attached to bass drum, bells and cymbals, which the players unleash at strategic points with swashbuckling effect. If you're still sceptical about the merits of a fortepiano in such repertoire, then these hugely enjoyable performances, vividly recorded, should convert you.

Schubert Piano Music for Four Hands, Volume 2. Allegro in A minor, D947, "Lebensstürme".
  Four Polonaises, D599. Variations in E minor on a French song, D624. Divertissement, D823.
  Grandes marches, D819. Rondo in A major, D951. **Yaara Tal, Andreas Groethuysen** (pf duet).
  Sony Classical Ⓕ S2K66256 (two discs: 153 minutes: DDD: 4/96). Recorded 1994.
The first discs in the Schubert series from Tal and Groethuysen is reviewed above. This pair of discs features the same Fazioli Model 308 grand piano, its big modern sound clearly unauthentic but surprisingly effective in conveying what the artists call the 'symphonic' aspects of the music. The recording is splendidly clear yet atmospheric, with a fine dynamic range. As for the playing, it is wonderfully controlled, affectionate while subtly poised and textured, with flexible tone and tempo – a model of Schubert duet style and ultimately surpassing the Isabel Beyer/Harvey Dagul series, good though that is, because of the younger artists' greater responsiveness and refinement. With Beyer and Dagul one cannot quite forget that some of this music is the lesser Schubert: Tal and Groethuysen are just that bit more persuasive, and winningly so. However, the little-known "Lebensstürme" *Allegro* that opens the first disc here is of a higher quality than that, a vivid and intense piece in Schubert's tragic key of A minor that is not unworthy of comparison with the *Fantasie* and was composed a month after that masterpiece of the composer's final year. The *Four Polonaises* of 1818 are more ordinary, but still delightful when played as elegantly as this, and the same may be said of the E minor *Variations on a French song* – a work from the same year that the young Schubert dedicated to Beethoven. The later *Divertissement* ("sur des motifs originaux français"), a three-movement suite in all but name, is in the same key of E minor but more striking: its central variation-form *Andantino* is among the best and most personal music that Schubert wrote, with subtleties of every kind that Tal and Groethuysen respond to consistently.All this music is on the first disc. The second offers the same mixed bag: medium to highest quality in the music but outstanding playing. Thus the six *Grandes marches* are frankly conventional despite their occasional Hungarian flavour; they also last far too long, occupying well over an hour in all and with No. 5 alone lasting nearly 20 minutes – though the latter, funereal and in the unusual key of F flat minor, is rather special and was later transcribed for orchestra by Liszt. However, the very late *Rondo* in A is rich in invention and emotionally deep.

Schubert Sonata for Piano Duet in C major, D812, "Grand Duo". Eight Variations in
  A flat major, D813. Trois marches militaires, D733. **Daniel Barenboim, Radu Lupu** (pf duet).
  Teldec Ⓕ 0630-17146-2 (77 minutes: DDD: 8/97). Recorded 1993. *Gramophone Editor's choice.*
One might expect this combination of artists playing Schubert to produce winning results, and so it does. Rarely will you hear duet playing of such refined elegance and multicoloured animation. Here, the playing is more vivid and glamorous than one finds from Isabel Beyer and Harvey Dagul; whereas the Beyer/Dagul duo invoke the intimacy of the nineteenth-century salon, the dynamic and coloristic range of Barenboim's and Lupu's performances suggests a more public environment. After the spirited brio of the familiar *Marches militaires*, the remainder of the disc contains music of greater seriousness and architectural breadth. The Variations in A flat are beautifully played, with subtle and discerning pianism. The largest work on this disc is the C major Sonata: here it runs to 43 minutes, longer than any of Schubert's solo sonatas. It can reasonably be classed alongside Schubert's two other late masterpieces in C, the *Great* Symphony and the String Quintet. The *Grand Duo* is symphonic in scope and expression, although the writing is innately pianistic. The fine detail of Barenboim's and Lupu's account, their diversity of colour and attack and their voicing of melodic and inner lines, suggests an image of suitably orchestral depth and variety. Furthermore, the surface gloss of these performances is underpinned by the most crystalline lucidity and poetry. The recording is excellent.

Additional recommendations ...
...Sonata for Piano Duet, D812. Eight Variations, D813.
  Grande Marche in E flat major, D819 No. 1. **Isabel Beyer, Harvey Dagul** (pf duet).
  Four Hands Music Ⓕ FHMD893 (75 minutes: DDD: 6/94).
...Piano Music for Four Hands, Volume 3. Sonatas for Piano Duet – B flat major, D617; D812.
  Trois marches militaires. Eight Variations, D813. Grande marche funèbre, D859. Grande marche
  héroïque, D885. Deux marches caratéristiques, D968*b*. **Yaara Tal, Andreas Groethuysen** (pf duet).
  Sony Classical Ⓕ S2K68240 (two discs: 134 minutes: DDD: 11/96).
...Trois marches militaires. Grandes marches, D819. German Dance in G major, D618. Grande
  marche funèbre in C minor, D859. Grande marche héroïque in A minor, D885. March, D928.
  Deux Marches caractéristiques in C major, D968b. Marches héroïques, D602. Rondo in
  A major, D951. **Christoph Eschenbach, Justus Frantz** (pf duet).
  EMI Forte Ⓜ CZS5 69764-2 (two discs: 156 minutes: ADD: 8/97).

Schubert Violin Sonatas[a] – D major, D384; A minor, D385; G minor, D408.
Mendelssohn Violin Sonata in F minor, Op. 4[b]. **Jaap Schröder** (vn); **Christopher Hogwood** (fp).
  L'Oiseau-Lyre Florilegium Ⓜ 443 196-2OM (76 minutes: ADD: 9/94). Items marked [a] from
  DSLO565 (11/80), [b]DSLO571 (4/81). ✒

Schubert Violin Sonatas – D major, D384; A minor, D385; G minor, D408. **Angèle Dubeau** (vn); **Anton Kuerti** (pf). Analekta fleurs de lys Ⓜ FL2 3042 (55 minutes: DDD: 10/97). Recorded 1990.
In the first of Schubert's three violin sonatas of 1816, the violin and piano are deployed on equal terms and, in L'Oiseau-Lyre's recording, the instruments themselves (a Stradivarius violin of 1709 and a c1825 Haschka fortepiano) sound ideally matched. The Second Sonata's more introspective character offers the opportunity for the artists to demonstrate more comprehensively the special abilities of their instruments. In the first movement, subtle pedal effects produce a textural variety which amply compensates for any lack of power compared with the modern piano, while the second movement shows most vividly the violin's astonishing tonal variety in different registers. Despite this duo's remarkably robust sound at times, the Third Sonata's defiant opening achieves a vehemence which modern instruments are possibly better able to express. Nevertheless, Schröder's and Hogwood's true Schubertian feeling makes theirs an arresting and valuable period-instrument alternative. A sensitive and intelligent performance of Mendelssohn's F minor Sonata, Op. 4 completes this excellent reissue's thoroughly satisfying programme.
The performances on the Analekt fleurs de lys disc are really impressive performances. Angèle Dubeau and Anton Kuerti are at one in maintaining the intimate tone of these works; they manage to make each detail expressive, yet keeping to a natural, unforced utterance. It helps, in such memorably tuneful music, that they both know exactly how to present a singing, legato melodic line. Even when playing very quietly, Dubeau keeps some tension in the way the notes are joined together; this art, which many modern string-players seem to have forgotten, enables her to convey effortlessly the feeling behind the notes – the sweet melancholy of the minor episode in D384's *Andante*, for instance. The lively music, such as the finales of D384 and D408, is played with splendid verve, and they're aware, too, of the more dramatic moments. The major drawback of this issue is the recording quality. By comparison, for instance, with DG's vivid, beautifully balanced recording of Kremer and Maisenberg, this sounds dim and distant and the violin, especially, lacks presence. Recording quality aside, however, Dubeau and Kuerti give by far the more winning, affecting interpretation.

Additional recommendations ...
...D384; D385; D408; D574. **Gidon Kremer** (vn); **Oleg Maisenberg** (pf).
DG Ⓕ 437 092-2GH (62 minutes: DDD: 4/93). ❽❽❽
...D384. *Coupled with works by various composers.* **Joseph Szigeti** (vn); **Andor Foldes,**
Béla Bartók (pfs). Biddulph mono Ⓜ LAB070/71* (two discs: 129 minutes: ADD: 7/94).
See review in the Collections section; refer to the Index. ❽❽
...D384; D385; D408; A major, D574. **Fabio Biondi** (vn); **Olga Tverskaya** (fp).
Opus 111 Ⓕ OPS30-126 (79 minutes: DDD: 10/95). 🗡

Schubert Violin Sonata in A major (Duo), D574. Rondo brillant in B minor, D895. Fantasy in C major, D934. **Gidon Kremer** (vn); **Valery Afanassiev** (pf). DG Ⓕ 431 654-2GH (67 minutes: DDD: 3/92). Recorded 1990. ❽❽❽
Few recitals can offer the listener such unalloyed pleasure as this gloriously played and generously conceived Schubert recording from Gidon Kremer and Valery Afanassiev. Rarer yet by far, though, are releases capable of generating the kind of communicative ambience more normally revealed by the intimacy of live music making. The very opening bars of Afanassiev's piano introduction at the start of the *Duo* in A major, D574, with its restrained yet expectant dignity of utterance would mesmerize the heart of the sternest critic, whilst Kremer exhibits charm, wit, understatement and sheer delight in this work. The B minor Rondo and the magnificent Fantasy in C major were written a decade after the *Duo* and were both intended to display the talents of the composer's friend, the Czech violinist, Josef Slavic, who had settled in Vienna during 1826. Neither work found favour at the time, and quite possibly the dark premonitions of the Rondo, whose emotional sympathies recalled those of the *Unfinished* Symphony, were unsuited to Viennese popular tastes. However, although Kremer's approach avoids mere rhetoric here, this superb recording is surely crowned by a magisterial performance of the *Fantasy*. It combines bravura, elegance and a deep affinity with the Schubertian genre, captured with splendid realism by a recording which is technically beyond criticism.

Schubert Sonata in A minor, D821, "Arpeggione".
Schumann Märchenbilder, Op. 113. Adagio and Allegro in A flat major, Op. 70.
Bruch Kol nidrei, Op. 47.
Enescu Konzertstück. **Yuri Bashmet** (va); **Mikhail Muntian** (pf). RCA Victor Red Seal
Ⓕ RD60112 (73 minutes: DDD: 12/90). Recorded 1989.
The booklet tells us that Yuri Bashmet, aged 38 at the time of this recording, had already 30 new works for the viola dedicated to him. Perhaps thanks should go to this Russian artist, with his glorious tone, and his closely attuned pianist, Mikhail Muntian, for enriching the CD catalogue with Georges Enescu's rarely heard *Konzertstück*, written in Paris in the composer's impressionable early twenties, and played here with intuitive understanding of its fantasy and lyrical rapture. Like that work, the four miniatures of Schumann's *Märchenbilder* of 1851 were also inspired by the viola itself, whereas Schumann's *Adagio and Allegro*, Bruch's *Kol nidrei* (based on one of the oldest and best-known synagogue melodies) and Schubert's charming A minor Sonata were originally written for valve-horn, cello and the now obsolete arpeggione respectively. But with his wide range of colour and his "speaking" phrasing Bashmet makes them all entirely his own, only causing the occasional raised

eyebrow with slower tempos for slow numbers (such as Schumann's lullaby-like Op. 113, No. 4 and the *Adagio* of Schubert's Sonata) than could be enjoyed from players without his own fine-spun, intimately nuanced line. Strongly recommended.

Additional recommendations ...

...Sonata, D821. *Coupled with works by* **Debussy** and **Schumann** Mstislav Rostropovich (vc); **Benjamin Britten** (pf). Decca Ⓕ 417 833-2DH (59 minutes: ADD: 9/88). *See review under Debussy; refer to the Index.*   ⒼⒼⒼ

...Sonata, D821. *Coupled with works by* **Schumann** and **Mendelssohn** Friedrich-Jürgen Sellheim (vc); Eckart Sellheim (pf). Sony Classical Essential Classics Ⓑ SBK48171 (72 minutes: ADD: 10/92).

...Sonata, D821. *Coupled with works by* **Schumann** Maria Kliegel (vc); **Kristin Merscher** (pf). Naxos Ⓢ 8 550654 (68 minutes: DDD: 7/93).

...Sonata, D821. *Coupled with works by* **Bridge** Mstislav Rostropovich (vc); **Benjamin Britten** (pf). Decca The Classic Sound Ⓜ 443 575-2DCS (52 minutes: ADD: 4/95).   ⒼⒼ

Schubert Andante in C major, D29. Minuet in A minor, D277*a*. Minuet in A major, D334. 13 Variations in A minor on a theme by Anselm Hüttenbrenner, D576. Andante in A major, D604. Fantasy in C major, D605*a*, "Grazer Fantasie". Three Impromptus, D946. **James Lisney** (pf). Olympia Ⓕ OCD479 (65 minutes: DDD: 2/96). Recorded 1995.

James Lisney's unusual Schubert recital offers an illuminating programme of lesser-known works, demonstrating the composer's exploitation of tonal colour and keyboard sonority. After a sensitive performance of the enchanting C major *Andante*, D29, Lisney plays a group of pieces that exploit the expressive potential of A major/minor tonality. Two minuets establish the emotional contrast between these tonal colours: the A minor one is bold and defiant, with a tranquil F major trio, while the carefree, amiable A major work is balanced by a poignantly lyrical trio in E major. The *Variations on a theme by Anselm Hüttenbrenner* demonstrates a more complex and dramatic A major/minor dichotomy, which Lisney here presents beautifully with subtle control of the theme's different transformations and telling modal shifts. In addition, Lisney offers a thoroughly absorbing, searching account of the brooding, introspective A major *Andante* and a poetically romantic, finely conceived performance of the *Grazer Fantasie*. To conclude, carefully observed interpretations of the three *Impromptus*, D946, whilst perhaps lacking the spontaneity of Brendel's reissued versions (on a two-disc set), nevertheless confirm Lisney as a thoughtful and perceptive Schubertian. This fascinating concert, which benefits from satisfyingly faithful recorded sound, should attract a wide audience.

Schubert Fantasy in C major, D760, "Wandererfantasie"[a].
Schumann Fantasie in C major, Op. 17[b]. **Maurizio Pollini** (pf). DG The Originals Ⓜ 447 451-2GOR (52 minutes: ADD: 6/96). Item marked [a] from 2530 473 (1/75), [b]2530 379 (5/74). Recorded 1973.

The cover shows Caspar David Friedrich's familiar *The Wanderer above the Sea of Fog*. Pollini, on the other hand, is a wanderer in a transparent ether or crystalline light and both of these legendary performances, recorded in 1973 and beautifully remastered, are of a transcendental vision and integrity. In the Schubert his magisterial, resolutely un-virtuoso approach allows everything its time and place. Listen to his flawlessly graded triple *piano* approach to the central *Adagio*, to his rock-steady octaves at 5'23" (where Schubert's merciless demand is so often the cause of confusion) or to the way the decorations in the *Adagio* are spun off with such rare finesse, and you may well wonder when you have heard playing of such an unadorned, unalloyed glory. Pollini's Schumann is no less memorable. Doubting Thomases on the alert for alternating touches of imperiousness and sobriety will be disappointed, for, again, Pollini's poise is unfaltering. The opening *Moderato* is *sempre energico*, indeed, its central *Etwas langsamer* is so sensitively and precisely gauged that all possible criticism is silenced. The coda of the central march (that *locus classicus* of the wrong note) is immaculate and in what someone once called the finale's "shifting sunset vapour" Pollini takes us gently but firmly to the shores of Elysium. Here is a record that should grace every musician's shelf.

Additional recommendations ...

...Fantasy. **Schumann** Fantasie in C major, Op. 17. **Murray Perahia** (pf). CBS Masterworks Ⓕ MK42124 (52 minutes: DDD: 12/86).   Ⓖ

...Fantasy. **Dvořák** Piano Concerto in G minor, B63. **Sviatoslav Richter** (pf); **Bavarian State Orchestra / Carlos Kleiber.** EMI Ⓕ CDC7 47967-2 (59 minutes: ADD: 11/87).

Schubert Impromptus – D899; D935. Drei Klavierstücke, D946. Allegretto in C minor, D915. **Maria João Pires** (pf). DG Ⓕ 457 550-2GH2 (two discs: 108 minutes: DDD: 5/98). Recorded 1997.   ⒼⒼⒼ

This is something very special indeed. Maria João Pires's two-disc set of Schubert's *Impromptus*, significantly dedicated to Sviatoslav Richter, contains a booklet in which standard notes are replaced by carefully chosen extracts from Pires's own reading: reflections on time, space and wilderness from Yves Simon's *Le voyageur magnifique*; meditations on Schubert as Wanderer; and thoughts from a neuroscientist on the "physiology" of great music. Like so many prefaces, these words are best read afterwards, when certain fragments, different for each listener, may well close-focus in the mind elements still resonating in the ear. Pires's characteristic impassioned absorption in all she plays – that concentration which makes the listener appear to be eavesdropping on secrets shared between friends – could hardly find a truer soul mate than in the sensibility of Schubert. Each *Impromptu* has a rare sense of integrity and entirety, born of acute observation and long-pondered responses. Pires's instinct for tempo and pacing brings a sense of constant restraint, a true *molto moderato* to the *Allegro* of the C minor work from D899, created by a fusion of right-hand *tenuto* here with momentary left-hand rubato there. Then there is the clarity of contour within the most subtly graded undertones of the G flat major of D899 which re-creates it as a seemingly endless song. Or an *Andante* just slow, just nonchalant enough for the *Rosamunde* theme of the D935 B flat major to give each variation space and breath enough to sing out its own sharply defined character. The *Allegretto*, D915 acts as a *Pause* between the two discs, a resting place, as it were, for reflection and inner assessment on this long journey. Its end – which could as well be its beginning – is in the *Drei Klavierstücke*, D946 of 1828. The first draws back from the fiery impetuousness within the *Allegro assai*'s tautly controlled rhythms, to an inner world with its own time scale; the second, more transpired than played, has an almost unbearable poignancy of simplicity. The paradox of these totally unselfregarding performances is how unmistakably they speak and sing out Pires and her unique musicianship. To draw comparisons here would be not so much odious as simply to miss the point.

Additional recommendations ...
...D899. D935. **Radu Lupu** (pf). Decca Ⓕ 411 711-2DH (DDD: 10/84).
   D899 – No. 2 in E flat major; No. 3 in G flat major. *Coupled with works by various composers.*
   Dinu Lipatti (pf). EMI Références mono Ⓜ CDH5 65166-2* (73 minutes: ADD: 12/94).
   See review in the Collections section; refer to the Index.   ❸❸❸
...D899; D935. **Alfred Brendel** (pf). Philips Ⓕ 422 237-2PH (61 minutes: DDD: 10/89).
...D899; D935. **Krystian Zimerman** (pf). DG Ⓕ 423 612-2GH (65 minutes: DDD: 5/91).
...D899; D935. **Peter Katin** (fp). Athene Ⓕ ATHCD5 (64 minutes: DDD: 1/95). ✍
...D899; D935. Allegretto in C minor, D915. 11 Ecossaises, D781. Ungarische Melodie in B minor,
   D817. **Alfred Brendel** (pf). Philips Solo Ⓜ 442 543-2PM (74 minutes: ADD: 1/96).
...D899; D935. Fantasy, D760. **Edwin Fischer** (pf). APR mono Ⓜ APR5515* (74 minutes: ADD: 3/97).
...D899; D935. Fantasy, D760. **Edwin Fischer** (pf).
   Pearl mono Ⓜ GEMMCD9216* (74 minutes: ADD: 3/97).
...D899; D935. **Mitsuko Uchida** (pf). Philips Ⓕ 456 245-2PH (66 minutes: DDD: 5/97).
   Gramophone Editor's choice.   ❸❸
...D935 – No. 2. **Liszt** Piano Sonata in B minor, S178 Liebestraum in A flat major, S541 No. 3.
   Valse oubliée, S215 No. 1. Gnomenreigen, S145 No. 2. Berceuse, S174. **Sir Clifford Curzon** (pf).
   Decca The Classic Sound Ⓜ 452 306-2DCS (58 minutes: ADD: 11/97).
...D899 – No. 2 in E flat major; No. 4 in A flat major. Moment musical No. 1 in C major D780.
   Coupled with works by various composers. **Pavel Nersessian** (pf). Bel Air Music Ⓕ BAM9725
   (65 minutes: DDD: 3/98). *See review in the Collections section; refer to the Index.*
...D899 – No. 4. *Coupled with works by various composers.* **Murray Perahia** (pf).
   Sony Classical Ⓜ SX4K63380 (four discs: 270 minutes: DDD/ADD: 4/98).
   See review in the Collections section; refer to the Index.

Schubert Drei Klavierstücke, D946. 12 Waltzes, D969. Six Moments musicaux, D780.
   Peter Katin (fp). Athene Ⓕ ATHCD7 (74 minutes: DDD: 6/96). ✍ Recorded 1995.
One of the most attractive features of Katin's Schubert disc is its comfortable intimacy, conjuring images of the composer's own domestic music-making. The Clementi square piano sounds wholly appropriate in the *Waltzes*, highlighting Schubert's magical blend of Viennese gaiety and warmer harmonic shades. In the *Drei Klavierstücke*, Katin further underlines his relaxed approach with some beautifully atmospheric effects and the inclusion of all repeats. Witness the timeless quality in the slower sections of the first piece; the menacing tremolos of the C minor music and the ethereal upper register of the A flat minor music in the second piece, and the subtly coloured textures and boldly projected voice-leading in the third one.

Schubert Piano Sonatas – No. 1 in E major, D157; No. 3 in E major, D459; No. 13 in A major,
   D664. **András Schiff** (pf). Decca Ⓕ 440 311-2DH (71 minutes: DDD: 11/95).
   Recorded 1992-1993.
This seventh volume in Schiff's Schubert sonata cycle spotlights the young composer, starting with the E major work (D157) which, at the age of 18, he chose as his official No. 1. Schiff plays it with a delectable, springlike freshness and tonal charm – banishing every vestige of the "impersonality" the insert-note writer warns us to expect in the opening *Allegro ma non troppo*. His delicate keyboard 'orchestration' is no less a delight in the slow movement, with its plaintive reminders of Mozart's Barbarina and her lost pin. It is easy to understand why the E major Sonata (D459) of the following year first appeared in print, posthumously, as *Fünf Klavierstücke*. Each of the five movements inhabits a world of its own. And each is as unpredictable in sequence of ideas and modulation as in actual keyboard texture. Schiff himself revels in the music's romantic pre-echoes, not least in the demonstrative finale unusually headed *Allegro patetico*. The disc is completed by the A major Sonata of 1819, the last of Schubert's youthful essays in the genre before a four-year break, but the first of these early works to find a regular place in the repertory. Its gracious, lyrical charm is caught by Schiff in a reading of winning simplicity. No detail is overlooked (there are endless subtleties to enjoy just

from his left hand) but never does his point-making intrude. Even in the spirited final *Allegro* his relaxed approach suggests not a hard-working concert pianist but a Schubert playing at home for the delectation of his friends.

Additional recommendations ...

...Nos. 17, 20 and 21. March in E major, D606. Six Moments musicaux, D780. **Artur Schnabel** (pf). EMI Références Ⓜ CHS7 64259-2* (two discs: 138 minutes: ADD: 5/92).

...No. 13. Fantasy in C major, D760, "Wanderer". *Coupled with works by various composers.* **Sviatoslav Richter** (pf). EMI Ⓜ CMS7 64429-2 (four discs: 273 minutes: ADD: 3/93).

...No. 13; No. 20. **Elisabeth Leonskaja** (pf). Teldec Ⓕ 9031-74865-2 (71 minutes: DDD: 10/93).

...Nos. 13 and 21. **Radu Lupu** (pf). Decca Ⓕ 440 295-2DH (59 minutes: DDD: 11/94).

...Nos. 13 and 14. Ungarische Melodie in B minor, D817. 12 Waltzes, D145.
Vladimir Ashkenazy (pf). Decca The Classic Sound Ⓜ 443 579-2DCS (57 minutes: ADD: 4/95).

...Nos. 13 and 21. **Jeremy Menuhin** (pf). Dinemec Classics Ⓕ DCCD004 (57 minutes: DDD: 10/96).

...Nos 1 and 21. Variations in F major, D156. **James Lisney** (pf). Olympia Ⓜ OCD560 (72 minutes: DDD: 10/96).

Schubert Piano Sonatas – No. 2 in C major, D279; No. 12 in F minor, D625; No. 21 in B flat major, D960. **András Schiff** (pf). Decca Ⓕ 440 310-2DH (78 minutes: DDD: 6/95). Recorded 1992.

In his own contribution to the insert-notes, Schiff writes, "[Schubert's] music is most sensitive to tonal quality, especially in soft and softest dynamics. He's also a quintessentially Viennese composer, and for this reason a Bösendorfer Imperial has been chosen." The C major Sonata, D279, eloquently reinforces Schiff's argument. Despite its strong Beethovenian flavour, most notably in the first two movements, Schiff is undemonstrative with the music's overt virtuosity, preferring to allow his sensitive *cantabile*, attractively enhanced by the Bösendorfer's delicate edge, to express Schubert's radiant lyricism. Schubert left the first movement of the F minor Sonata, D625, incomplete and Schiff poignantly breaks off where the composer did. His graceful, elegant playing charmingly conveys the music's Biedermeier character in the second movement, and he shows a profound sympathy for Schubert's musical and expressive language through effective opposition of the finale's dramatic forces in a performance that matches Richter's affectionately attentive account. Brendel's omission, on his two-disc set (listed further on), of the exposition repeat in the first movement of the B flat major Sonata, D960, conveys a fluid sense of organic development within a prevailing mood of calm and serenity. By contrast, Schiff's inclusion of the exposition repeat emphasizes the music's discontinuities for a more potent expression of the underlying unease, first apparent in the bass trills. Subtle shifts of key and colour are powerfully effective in both the slow movement and the finale, and deft control in the *Scherzo* yields much revelatory detail – further evidence of the appropriateness of the Bösendorfer sound.

Additional recommendation ...

...Complete Piano Sonatas. **Wilhelm Kempff** (pf). DG Ⓜ 423 496-2GX7 (seven discs: 461 minutes: ADD).

Schubert Piano Sonatas. **Martino Tirimo** (pf). EMI Eminence Ⓜ CD-EMX2278/9 (two discs: 78 and 70 minutes: DDD: 12/96). Recorded 1995.
CD-EMX2278: No. 3 in E major, D459; No. 5 in A flat major, D557; No. 18 in G major, D894.
CD-EMX2279: No. 2 in C major, D279 with Allegretto, D346 (cptd. Tirimo); No. 17 in D major, D850. Menuetto (Allegro) in A minor, D277a.

Martino Tirimo's cycle of *all* Schubert's piano sonatas will be keenly sought after by collectors. His interpretation of the A flat Sonata is particularly interesting. After the opening *Allegro*, his leisurely pace in the slow movement accentuates the boldness of his reading, which he further reinforces by repeating the second part of the finale instead of the first as Schiff does. Tirimo's performance of the C major Sonata (including the *Allegretto* as finale) is also arresting. Schubert-scholar Walter Rehberg first suggested (in 1928) the fragmentary *Allegretto* as a possible fourth movement, and Tirimo's completion of it convincingly reveals its mirroring of the first movement's thematic gestures. Tirimo's slow tempo in the *Andante* creates a wistful quality that is less striking than with Schiff; but, since Schiff makes no attempt to complete the sonata, this can easily be understood as an appropriate difference in structural emphasis. The inclusion of the earlier version of the minuet (D277a) is valuable for those wishing to make comparisons. Schubert possessed a fantastic ability to create hybrid forms and his sonatas often exhibit a remarkably fluid, through-composed quality. The E major Sonata was originally published in 1843 as *Fünf Klavierstücke*. Nevertheless, Tirimo highlights the structural coherence in this work's five movements with sensitivity and idiomatic elegance. The opening *Allegro* flows naturally into the graceful first scherzo (here marked *Andante*). Tirimo's heartfelt emotion in the *Adagio* gives moment for pause before the second scherzo's opposition of light, graceful dance and dark-hued atmosphere (in the trio). He concludes with a winning account of the finale's delightful interplay of operatic and balletic characters. The first movement of the G major Sonata was entitled *Fantasie* in the first printed edition, and the Bösendorfer piano's unique tonal palette enhances Schiff's presentation of its melodic threads to magical effect. Tirimo gives an eloquent reading of this work's broad, introspective moods; yet there are slight reservations in the scherzo, where Schiff plays with a good deal more gusto, and, in the finale, where Tirimo's faster speed encourages a plainer presentation of the music's contrasts. Also Tirimo's weighty playing in the scherzo of the D major Sonata lacked Schiff's persuasive style. Ultimately, though, Tirimo's blend of thoughtful scholarship, technical precision and fresh spontaneity remains compelling.

Schubert Piano Sonatas – No. 4 in A minor, D537; No. 20 in A major, D959. **Malcolm Bilson** (fp). Hungaroton Ⓕ HCD31587 (59 minutes: DDD: 8/96). ☞

Bilson's is not the first disc to highlight the close affinity between Schubert's A minor Piano Sonata, composed in March 1817, and the great A major Sonata from the composer's final year. In a recording of the same two works, Schiff – aided by the modern Bösendorfer piano's capacity for sustained serene tone – perceptively reveals the A minor Sonata's voice-leading threads in a compelling blend of romantic, dance-like grace and lyrical warmth. With judicious use of the moderator pedal, Bilson here effectively exploits the 1815 Lagrassa fortepiano's robust tone in a reading which, though less dramatic than Schiff's, atmospherically opposes different tonal regions. Schubert miraculously transformed the duple-metre theme of the A minor Sonata's slow movement into the flowing lines of the A major Sonata's rondo finale. Schiff's concentration on detail throughout this later work could be seen to be impeding the music's natural impetus. However, the spaciousness of his account does successfully convey the music's broad landscape. Bilson's blend of spontaneity and distinctive contrasts of tonal colour in all movements winningly conveys both the music's potently dramatic use of motivic material and its large-scale psychological spans.

Additional recommendation ...
…Nos. 4 and 20. **Andras Schiff** (pf). Decca Ⓕ 440 309-2DH (65 minutes: DDD: 1/95).

Schubert Piano Sonatas – No. 4 in A minor, D537; No. 15 in C major, D840, "Relique".
Ralf Gothóni (pf). Ondine Ⓕ ODE797-2 (56 minutes: DDD: 1/95). Recorded 1991.

When Schubert's C major Piano Sonata, D840 was first published in 1861, it was given the title *Relique* in the mistaken belief that it was the composer's last work. In fact, it was composed in April 1825, around the same time as Schubert began work on the *Great* C major Symphony. Usually, only the first two completed movements are played, but like Richter (reviewed further on), Gothóni also includes the fragmentary third and fourth ones. Gothóni's is a thoughtful performance that shows a sympathetic response to Schubert's harmonic language and the various tonal colours associated with it. Richter's characteristically profound concentration creates an exceptionally broad landscape – notably in the first movement – but Gothóni's account, though less challenging intellectually, offers a comparable technical and expressive range and he gives a vivid and powerful performance of the work's dramatic extremes. The reverberant recording adds emphasis to the music's volcanic outbursts.

Additional recommendations ...
…Nos. 4 and 13. **Alfred Brendel** (pf). Philips Ⓕ 410 605-2PH (11/83).
…Nos. 15 and 20. **Imogen Cooper** (pf). Ottavo Ⓕ OTRC58714 (65 minutes: DDD: 12/88).
…Nos. 4, 13 and 14. Impromptus, D899 – No. 2 in E flat major. **Sviatoslav Richter** (pf). Olympia Ⓕ OCD288 (50 minutes: DDD: 10/92).
…Nos. 4 and 13. Fantasy in C major, D760, "Wanderer". **Jenö Jandó** (pf). Naxos Ⓢ 8 550846 (59 minutes: DDD: 3/95).
…Nos. 5, 6, 9 and 13. **Michael Endres** (pf). Capriccio Ⓕ 10 553 (74 minutes: DDD: 9/95).
…Nos. 4, 7 and 15. **Michael Endres** (pf). Capriccio Ⓕ 10 717 (78 minutes: DDD: 5/96).

Schubert Piano Sonatas – No. 5 in A flat major, D557; No. 9 in B major, D575; No. 18 in G major, D894. **András Schiff** (pf). Decca Ⓕ 440 307-2DH (76 minutes: DDD: 6/94). Recorded 1992.

Schubert's piano music from András Schiff always lifts the spirits, and this time quite a bit higher than most comparable available versions. Typically, he chooses his favourite Bösendorfer Imperial with its Viennese accent and writes in an introduction to the notes of its Schubertian sensitivity to tone-quality, particularly in the softest dynamics. Schiff cites the opening of the G major Sonata, D894 as an example and, indeed, this movement, which the composer originally called a Fantasy, has a gentle luminosity about it. Schiff's approach to the vast first movement more closely resembles Lupu's (reviewed further on) in its meditative, long-sighted qualities; but Schiff again triumphs, in coaxing both a wider and a more finely controlled tone palette out of his instrument. Schiff's greatest achievement here, though, is his organic view of the inner and outer worlds of this sonata. As in the song, "Der Lindenbaum" (from *Winterreise*), images of both tender dream and harsh reality seem to shape the piece. Schiff makes them seem simply different sides of the same persona. One flows into and out of another, with the dark concentration of rhythm in the eye of the storm. In the last movement, Schiff outdoes Lupu in the dance of constantly shifting weights and measures, lights and half-lights which dapple the rondo's returns. Schiff seems to play through the childlike ears and eyes of Schubert himself. This outstanding performance of D894 is nicely balanced by a deliciously understated D557, the most classically conceived of all Schubert's sonatas, and by the more adventurous D575. Here, Schiff continues to exploit the qualifying *ma non troppo* of the opening *Allegro* to create a sense of a plethora of ideas and energies being held back within an unquiet serenity. If the slow movement is a little over-deliberate, the finale again seems to be constantly surprising itself with the new ideas which sing out as if they had only just been imagined.

Additional recommendations ...

...No. 5. Two Scherzos, D593. *Coupled with works by* **Brahms** Radu Lupu (pf).
  Decca Ovation Ⓜ 448 129-2DM (74 minutes: DDD/ADD: 9/96).

...Nos. 9 and 11. Six Moments musicaux, D780 – No. 1 in C major; No. 3 in F minor; No. 6 in
  A flat major. **Sviatoslav Richter** (pf). Olympia Ⓕ OCD286 (65 minutes: DDD: 10/92).   Ⓐ

Schubert Piano Sonatas – No. 7 in E flat major, D568; No. 19 in C minor, D958.
  András Schiff (pf). Decca Ⓕ 440 308-2DH (61 minutes: DDD: 10/94).

Those who like their C minor Sonata bulging with Byronic sentiment or exploding with theatrical
sparks will no doubt find Schiff's unshowy approach intolerably ascetic though the absorption, the
inner penetration of his playing here is worth the loss of a few histrionic thrills. His understanding is
revealed in tiny, delicate touches – the way the C minor's first movement eases gently into the second
subject, or the nicely timed silences in the Menuetto, with the *Allegro* finale arising after another short
but pregnant pause. At the same time there's a profound grasp of the Schubertian pulse: the tension
between subtle rubato and what Theodor Adorno called the "somnambulistic" forward tread. It's
beautifully judged, whether in minute details (the slight holding back in the running quavers near the
start of the E flat Sonata is a perfect example) or in the longer term – the way D568's Minuet resumes
the first movement's basic pulse. Schiff is emphatically not one of those pianists that wants to show
you at every stage what a fabulously rich palette he possesses, but the sound he coaxes from his
Bösendorfer is hauntingly lovely, and the Decca recording captures it, and the Vienna Musikverein
Brahms-Saal's intimate warmth, superbly.

Additional recommendations ...

...Nos. 7 and 17. **Malcolm Bilson** (fp). Hungaroton Ⓕ HCD31586 (64 minutes: DDD: 5/96). 🖋
...No. 19. Impromptus, D899. 12 German Dances, D790. **Alain Planès** (pf).
  Harmonia Mundi Ⓕ HMC90 1564 (71 minutes: DDD: 10/96).

Schubert Piano Sonatas – No. 9 in B major, D575; No. 15 in C major, D840, "Relique";
  No. 18 in G major, D894. **Sviatoslav Richter** (pf). Philips Ⓕ 438 483-2PH2
  (two discs: 117 minutes: ADD: 8/94). Recorded live in1979.   ⒼⒼⒼ

Facts first. The G major Sonata, D894 takes up an entire CD, in comparison with the average 16 or
17 minutes. Richter's first movement is no less than 26'51" long. Then the C major, D840 appears not
unvollendet at all, but with its little unfinished Menuetto and Rondo taking their own eye- and ear-
opening place. Behind these facts lie the concepts which set these performances apart. The heavenly
length of the first movement of D894 is created out of Richter's relationship with time itself. The
more one listens to his late Schubert, the more one realizes that movement and momentum are not
conceived as linear. Rather they are cyclical, very much in the spirit of the final song of *Winterreise*
in which the Leiermann's turning melody could be eternal. No wonder that it is to Richter that singers
like Peter Schreier turn when working out the when and the how of their Schubert. The opening
Molto moderato is read as extremely slow: the ear begins by being on tenterhooks for what might
come next – then shocked by the sudden, harsh brightening of tone as the first temporary modulation
is prepared. As the movement progresses, the opening motif becomes like a mantra in an extended
meditation in which the listener must go through the same discipline of private pacing as the
performer. At a practical level, Richter's tempo allows the mood of *Molto moderato e cantabile* to be
unbroken by busy-ness even as the theme metamorphoses into quaver figuration. The *Andante*, when
at last it arrives, moves with a contrastingly lithe, blithe ease, more songlike, more forceful at its centre.
The simplicity and clarity of movement created by Richter's fingers in the bright dance of weight and
measure which is the final *Allegretto* (and which makes for an archaic, hymn-like *Andante* in D575) is
Schubert's sweetness and light. His dark side, in both these sonatas, is explored uncompromisingly by
Richter in modulations of key and dynamics abrupt enough to hurt. Richter's complete incomplete
Sonata, D840 is another extraordinary journey. Another endless *Moderato* (22 minutes) is this time
relentless in the bare, unbeautiful resonance of its repeated figures which, all the more miraculously,
become song accompaniment. It is followed by a strange, minimalist Menuetto and an almost surreal
sense of bleakness as the pirouetting Rondo melts into thin air.

Schubert Piano Sonatas – No. 14 in A minor, D784; No. 17 in D major, D850.
  Alfred Brendel (pf). Philips Ⓕ 422 063-2PH (63 minutes: DDD: 11/88).   ⒼⒼ

There is an extraordinary amount of highly experimental writing in Schubert's piano sonatas. The
essence of their structure is the contrasting of big heroic ideas with tender and inner thoughts; the
first impresses the listener, the second woos him. The two works on this CD are in some ways on a
varying scale. The D major lasts for 40 minutes, the A minor for around 23. However, it is the latter
that contains the most symphonically inspired writing – it sounds as if it could easily be transposed
for orchestra. Alfred Brendel presents the composer not so much as the master of Lieder-writing, but
more as a man thinking in large forms. Although there are wonderful quiet moments when intimate
asides are conveyed with an imaginative sensitivity one remembers more the urgency and the power
behind the notes. The A minor, with its frequently recurring themes, is almost obsessive in character
whilst the big D major Sonata is rather lighter in mood, especially in the outer movements. The
recorded sound is very faithful to the pianist's tone, whilst generally avoiding that insistent quality
that can mar his loudest playing.

Additional recommendations ...

...No. 14. Six Moments musicaux, D780. Scherzos, D593. **Maria João Pires** (pf).
  DG Ⓕ 427 769-2GH (63 minutes: DDD: 2/90).
...Nos. 14, 16, 18 and 20. **Trudelies Leonhardt** (fp).
  Jecklin Ⓕ J4420/1-2 (two discs: 141 minutes: ADD: 11/91). ✍
...Nos. 1, 14 and 20. **Radu Lupu** (pf). Decca Ovation Ⓜ 425 033-2DM (73 minutes: ADD: 2/92).
...Nos. 6, 14 and 17. **András Schiff** (pf). Decca Ⓕ 440 306-2DH (75 minutes: DDD: 12/93).
...No. 17ᵃ. Impromptus, D899ᵃ – No. 3 in G flat major; No. 4 in A flat major.
  Six Moments musicaux, D780ᵇ. **Sir Clifford Curzon** (pf).
  Decca The Classic Sound Ⓜ 443 570-2DCS (77 minutes: ADD: 4/95).
...No. 14 . Marche Militaire No. 1 in D major, D733 (arr. Tausig). *Coupled with works by* **Haydn**
  Evgeni Kissin (pf). Sony Classical Ⓕ SK64538 (62 minutes: DDD: 9/95).
  Gramophone Editor's record of the month. See review under Haydn; refer to the Index.   Ⓖ
...No. 14. Six Moments musicaux, D780. 12 Grazer Walzer, D924. **Till Fellner** (pf).
  Erato Ⓕ 0630-17869-2 (63 minutes: DDD: 4/98).

Schubert Piano Sonatas – No. 15 in C major, D840, "Relique"; No. 18 in G major, D894.
  Mitsuko Uchida (pf). Philips Ⓕ 454 453-2PH (70 minutes: DDD: 12/97). Recorded 1996.
Schubert's G major Sonata, D894, is the ultimate *Frühlingstraum*. Pervading the entire work is that oscillation between light-filled dream and stark waking reality. These may be juxtaposed in dramatic motivic contrast, but they are, quintessentially, twin sides of a single consciousness; and it is Mitsuko Uchida's supreme achievement to understand and re-create precisely this quality. Brendel, of course, knows it too: like him, Uchida creates a true opening *molto moderato* of profound stillness and long distances. Chords really resonate and breathe out, yet her quick intakes of breath as the second subject steps into dance are tempered with the more flexible, whimsical intimacy of a Schiff. Uchida's gentleness of touch is ballasted by a firmly delineated bass and a weight of rhythmic articulation equal to Brendel's, though actually surpassing him in resonance. She finds an easy, instinctive pace for the *Andante*, creating compacted shocks in the ringing chords of its minor-key episodes. These chords announce a Menuetto in which the Trio slinks in as the merest spectre of a Ländler, and leads to a finale in which Uchida creates a dance of the spirit within a deep inner stillness. The *Relique* Sonata, D840, one of Schubert's great and tantalizingly unfinished works, sounds entire, fully achieved in Uchida's hands. She shares with Schiff a leisured playing-out of the first movement – a quite different response from the urgent, less 'private' playing of Brendel here. And her *Andante* is no less intimate in its *bel canto* of minute nuance and inflexion, starker and bleaker still than Schiff's masterpiece.

Additional recommendations ...

...Nos. 15 and 18. **Alfred Brendel** (pf). Philips Ⓕ 422 340-2PH (64 minutes: DDD: 10/89).
...Complete Piano Sonatas. **András Schiff** (pf).
  Decca Ⓜ 448 390-2DM7 (seven discs: 498 minutes: DDD: 3/97).

Schubert Piano Sonata No. 16 in A minor, D845. Impromptus, D946. **Alfred Brendel** (pf).
  Philips Ⓕ 422 075-2PH (61 minutes: DDD: 10/89).
Schubert Piano Sonatas – No. 16 in A minor, D845ᵃ; No. 18 in G major, D894ᵇ. **Radu Lupu** (pf).
  Decca Ⓕ 417 640-2DH (74 minutes: ADD: 6/87). Item marked ᵃ from SXL6931 (12/79),
  ᵇSXL6741 (5/76).
Though love of the music alone, as pianists know, is not enough to master these pieces, it is essential, and in this big A minor Sonata Brendel presents us with a drama that is no less tense for being predominantly expressed in terms of shapely melody. There is a flexibility in this playing that reminds us of the pianist's own comment that in such music "we feel not masters but victims of the situation": he allows us plenty of time to savour detail without ever losing sight of the overall shape of the music, and the long first movement and finale carry us compellingly forwards, as does the scherzo with its urgent energy, while the *Andante* second movement, too, has the right kind of spaciousness. In the *Impromptus* which date from the composer's last months, Brendel is no less responsive or imaginative. Richly sonorous digital recording in a German location complements the distinction of the playing on this fine disc. Radu Lupu also understands Schubert's style as do few others and the way in which he is able to project this essentially private world is outstanding. His tone is unfailingly clear, and this adds substantially to the lucidity of the readings. The simplicity of the opening themes of the A minor Sonata is a marvel of eloquence and when it is reset in the development section of the first movement one is amazed to hear Lupu transforming it into something far more urgent and full of pathos. The G major Sonata again fires Lupu's imagination and in the Minuet third movement he uses a considerable amount of rubato for the dance; its solid rhythmic pulse is an ideal foil to offset the extraordinary transitions of the finale that follows. The recorded sound is excellent.

Additional recommendations ...

...No. 16. Fantasy in C major, D760, "Wanderer". **Maurizio Pollini** (pf).
  DG Ⓕ 419 672-2GH (58 minutes: DDD: 8/87).   ⒼⒼ
...Nos. 8, 15 and 16. **András Schiff** (pf). Decca Ⓕ 440 305-2DH (71 minutes: DDD: 12/93).

Schubert Piano Sonata No. 16 in A minor, D845. Impromptus, D946. **Andreas Staier** (fp). ✍
  Teldec Das Alte Werk Ⓕ 0630-11084-2 (62 minutes: DDD: 7/96).

Once again, it is Andreas Staier's imagination and insight as a musician, rather than Staier-as-fortepianist, which comes to the fore in this rich recital. In the Sonata, for instance, Staier sets up a wide gulf between the two poles of Schubert's musical material – the sustained and lyrical, and the percussive and propulsive – in metaphysical terms, if you like, between the inner and outer, the contemplative and active life of this movement. Then he starts to paint with the pedal: there is a choice of four on this 1825 Viennese Johann Fritz fortepiano, and his changing use of them as the hands wander through the development creates a wide landscape for the journey, reminiscent of some of the piano writing in *Winterreise*. Here, and in the even more far-reaching expressive palette of the E flat major *Impromptu*, Staier really does realize the truth of his own statement that this – unlike the multi-purpose modern concert grand – is truly a "specifically Romantic instrument". In the slow movement's variations, the shifting balance between the hands are uniquely tailored to the resonating scale of the instrument, to uniquely revelatory effect. None of this could happen, of course, without Staier's own exceptionally sensitive imagination. At the start of the E flat minor *Impromptu* he creates a wide area of open space for the *Andante*, with the little, high, cadenza-like scalic figure appearing, as a sudden and wonderful bright light, as time is momentarily suspended.

Schubert Piano Sonata No. 19 in C minor, D958. Impromptus, D899. Deutsche Tänze, D783.
  Imogen Cooper (pf). Ottavo Ⓕ OTRC78923 (70 minutes: DDD: 2/92). Recorded 1989.   ⓖⓖ
This is in fact the last of Imogen Cooper's six-disc cycle of the piano music of Schubert's last six years, a cycle launched in 1988 hard on the heels of similar cycles given on the concert platform in both London and Amsterdam. Like its predecessors, it confirms her as a Schubert player of exceptional style and finesse. Intuitively perceptive phrasing and a willingness to let the music sing within a wholly Schubertian sound-world are prime virtues. And though (like her erstwhile mentor, Alfred Brendel) she is no slave to the metronome when contrasting first and second subjects in sonata expositions, she still makes the music her own without the self-consciously mannered kind of interpretation heard from one or two more recent rivals in this strongly competitive field. Her urgent yet poised performance of the late C minor Sonata certainly confirms her admission (in a 1988 *Gramophone* interview) that the comparatively clinical atmosphere of an audience-less recording venue worries her not at all. In London's Henry Wood Hall her Yamaha is as clearly and truthfully reproduced (save for a slight suspicion of pedal-haze in the sonata's demonically driven finale) as most else in the series. The *Impromptus* reveal an acutely sensitive response to Schubert's dynamic subtleties and surprises of key, while the 16 *German Dances* tell their own simple Viennese tale.
Additional recommendation ...
...No. 19. Moments musicaux, D780. **Jeremy Menuhin** (pf).
  Dinemec Classics Ⓕ DCCD002 (61 minutes: DDD: 10/96).

Schubert Piano Sonatas – No. 19 in C minor, D958; No. 21 in B flat major, D960.
  Sviatoslav Richter (pf). Olympia Ⓕ OCD335 (78 minutes: ADD: 1/94). Recorded 1972.   ⓖⓖ
As any follower of Richter's Schubert knows, you have to allow his sense of time to take over. Resist it and you will draw a blank. Submit to it and you will pass through an unsuspected doorway into an inner world of timeless inevitability. The C minor first movement is all fierce concentration and bleakness, the second all intense inner singing, the third deceptive simplicity with silences weighted as if hovering over the music's own demise, and the finale has a hellish drive to it – an utterly compelling experience. Monumental as ever, the first movement of the B flat Sonata is immensely slow, the tempo chosen not with the opening theme in mind but with a view to the G flat trill and the following silence, reminders of the chasm beneath. Don't expect any consolation from the slow movement or Grecian lightness from the scherzo; all is directed towards the controlled desperation of the finale. Any duffer (to paraphrase Goethe) can make this sonata touching; but with Richter it becomes (to risk malicious misunderstanding) appalling. It bores into the soul.
Additional recommendations ...
...Nos. 19 and 21. **Jenö Jandó** (pf). Naxos Ⓢ 8 550475 (69 minutes: DDD).
...Nos. 19-21. Impromptus, D946. Allegretto in C minor, D915. **Maurizio Pollini** (pf).
  DG Ⓕ 419 229-2GH2 (two discs: 142 minutes: DDD: 4/88).
...Nos. 19-21. Three Impromptus, D946. **Alfred Brendel** (pf).
  Philips Duo Ⓜ 438 703-2PM2 (two discs: 128 minutes: ADD: 5/94).

Schubert Piano Sonatas – No. 19 in C minor, D958; No. 20 in A major, D959;
  No. 21 in B flat major, D960. **Andreas Staier** (fp). Teldec Das Alte Werk Ⓕ 0630-13143-2
  (two discs: 119 minutes: DDD: 7/97). ⌖ Recorded 1996.   ⓖⓖ
The harpsichord has all but replaced the concert grand in baroque keyboard music. But resistance to the fortepiano is still strong; that clattery tone, the lack of sustaining power in high registers – it just doesn't sing like a modern piano. However, there are many instances where the sound of the 1825 Johann Fritz piano, and especially Andreas Staier's handling of it, are simply revelatory. Staier uses the fortepiano's moderator pedals and the *una corda* pedal, which shifts the hammers so that they strike only one string each, to great effect. Staier's use of these tools never seem excessive or misplaced, and it's hard to believe that Schubert wouldn't have made similar use of them. It isn't only in the special effects department that the fortepiano scores. In the middle of the slow movement of D959 there's a remarkable, violent cadenza-like passage which is rarely effective on modern concert

pianos. On the fortepiano you can strain and pound for all you're worth, and yet the *scale* of the sound feels absolutely right. The later recitative-like contrast of the *ffz* chords and short, pleading *piano* phrases at the climax of the second movement of D959 works wonderfully here. Similarly, Staier can play the *fzp* and *ffzp* accents in the trio section of D960's *Scherzo* with due emphasis without destroying the music's prevailing lightweight character. But it is Staier's handling of the instrument, not the instrument itself, that makes these recordings so exceptional. In matters of tempo, phrasing and so on, his approach is thoroughly modern; in fact his performances would probably translate very effectively to a modern piano without any – or much – sense of incongruity. This is a most impressive fortepiano recording. And that goes for the sound quality too. A strong recommendation for anyone who isn't terminally prejudiced.

Schubert Piano Sonata No. 20 in A major, D959. Moments musicaux, D780.
  Stephen Kovacevich (pf). EMI Ⓔ CDC5 55219-2 (66 minutes: DDD: 1/96). Recorded 1994.   ❻

Here is Schubert playing as compulsive and single-minded as any on record. Formidably serious and concentrated this is not for lovers of 'lilac time' or of softly focused, lyrical options. Indeed, it is often as if the Grim Reaper himself had cut a swathe through Schubert, forbidding at a glance even a touch of solace, let alone *Gemütlichkeit*. Yet the force and authenticity of such an outwardly controversial view is made unarguable and few pianists have penetrated more deeply to the dark, restlessly beating heart beneath Schubert's outwardly genial surface. The ferocity of Kovacevich's *fortissimo* chording in the development section of the sonata's first movement is wholly typical of his refusal of all polite circumspection, and rarely can the *Andantino*, with its central elemental uproar, have sounded more spare or disconsolate. Even the *Scherzo* becomes both a memory of Beethoven's fierce whimsy and a presage of Chopin's irony, and more than touch of unease erases much chance of a conventionally meandering or leisurely view of the finale. For Kovacevich, then, this is surely Schubert's sonata equivalent of *Winterreise*; a savage journey into oblivion. Many will look for light relief in the *Moments musicaux*, but once again Kovacevich refuses all obvious sentiment or enticement. His tone remains lean and acidulous, and he possesses a rare ability to drain his sonority of all colour substance, accentuating the hectic flush of No. 5 and achieving an extreme sense of desolation in No. 6. This record, then, is for those who concede that Schubert could be "full of sorrow/And leaden eyed despair", a composer who had more than his share of life's vicissitudes. Competition from other great Schubertians (Schnabel, Brendel, Pollini, Lupu and Imogen Cooper, to name but five!) is intense, yet Kovacevich's Schubert surely inhabits a world of its own and is in a sense beyond compare; an extraordinary achievement. The recordings are spectacularly bold.

Additional recommendations ...
...No. 20. Ungarische Melodie in B minor, D817. 16 Deutsche Tanze and Two Ecossaises, D783.
  Allegretto in C minor, D915. **Alfred Brendel** (pf).
  Philips Ⓕ 422 229-2PH (56 minutes: DDD: 2/89).
...Nos. 4 and 20. **Laurent Cabasso** (pf). Auvidis Valois Ⓕ V4630 (64 minutes: DDD: 4/91).
...No. 20. Six Moments musicaux, D780. **Olga Tverskaya** (fp).
  Opus 111 Ⓔ OPS30-139 (74 minutes: DDD: 3/96). ✒
...No. 20. Impromptus, D935. **Jeremy Menuhin** (pf).
  Dinemec Classics Ⓕ DCCD003 (77 minutes: DDD: 10/96).

Schubert Piano Sonata No. 21 in B flat major, D960. Allegretto in C minor, D915. 12 Ländler,
  D790. **Stephen Kovacevich** (pf). EMI Ⓕ CDC5 55359-2 (58 minutes: DDD: 7/95). Recorded 1994.
  Gramophone Editor's choice.   ❻

Kovacevich creates his own ambience with such force and fidelity that he achieves an ultimate musical illusion: a definitive and unarguable statement indelibly and disturbingly true to Schubert's always ambiguous genius. Of course, those wedded to a less savage sense of experience, to a lightness and civility that are part of Schubert's appeal, will look elsewhere. For even in his selection of encores, Kovacevich retreats at every opportunity into a crepuscular, near hallucinatory world, his sense of elegy all pervasive. In the sonata's first-movement repeat (the nine bars despised by Brendel but, clearly, relished by Kovacevich) the distant thunder of the opening erupts in a violent upheaval. The outwardly innocent quaver flourish at 4'03" flashes with sudden anger, a startling gesture, yet one wholly in keeping with a work where desperation so easily surfaces through autumnal sadness and resignation. The *Andante*, too, is a marvel of the most concentrated musical thinking, there are some swingeing *sforzandos* in the finale to remind us, once more, of underlying menace and even the *Scherzo's* brightly tripping outer sections are shadowed by an unusually dark-hued way with the central trio. Throughout, the effort of interpretation is immense and so although you will doubtless return to deeply cherished recordings by Pollini (magisterially detached), Kempff, with his more whimsical poetry or Brendel with his intellectual rigour and refinement Philips you will probably find a special place for Kovacevich. No more darkly questing performance exists. The recordings faithfully capture Kovacevich's awe-inspiring dynamic range, from the merest whisper to an elemental uproar.

Additional recommendations ...
...No. 21. Fantasy in C major, D760, "Wanderer". **Alfred Brendel** (pf).
  Philips Silver Line Ⓜ 420 644-2PM (57 minutes: ADD: 8/87).
...No. 21. Allegretto in C minor, D915. Impromptus, D946. **Maurizio Pollini** (pf).
  DG Ⓕ 427 326-2GH (71 minutes: DDD: 5/89).

…No. 21. Fantasy. **Alfred Brendel** (pf). Philips Ⓕ 422 062-2PH (58 minutes: DDD: 1/90).
…No. 21. **Schumann** Fantasie in C major, Op. 17. **Sir Clifford Curzon** (pf).
Orfeo D'Or Ⓜ C401951B (66 minutes: ADD: 4/96).

Schubert Stabat mater – oratorio, D383[a]. Magnificat in C major, D486[b]. Offertorium in B flat
major, D963[c]. [ab]**Sheila Armstrong** (sop); [ab]**Hanna Schaer** (mez); [ac]**Alejandro Ramirez** (ten);
[ab]**Philippe Huttenlocher** (bar); **Lausanne Vocal Ensemble; Lausanne Chamber Orchestra /
Michel Corboz.** Erato Ⓜ 4509 96961-2 (59 minutes: ADD: 3/95). Recorded 1979.
Schubert's strikingly fresh setting of the *Stabat mater* (in a German translation) was written in the
composer's nineteenth year, yet it displays clear anticipations of his later music, especially in the
terzetto (No. 11) for soprano, tenor, baritone and chorus and the striking chorus "Wer wird Zähren
sanflen Mitleids" (No. 5) with its superb horn writing. There is a beautiful tenor aria with oboe
obbligato, in which Alejandro Ramirez is very stylish, while the bass aria "Sohn des Vaters" is dark
and strong. Here Philippe Huttenlocher may not be quite sombre enough, yet his contribution is still
most enjoyable. The singing of the Lausanne Vocal Ensemble, with the Lausanne CO under Corboz,
combines clarity of focus with a firm sonority, and Schubert's lively, if somewhat uncharacteristic,
fugues certainly have plenty of vigour. The two shorter Schubert pieces that make up the rest of the
disc, the Magnificat (again with a fine contribution from Ramirez) and the Offertorium, are also given
strong performances from Corboz. The recording, although not crystal clear, has transferred vividly.
Additional recommendation …
…Kyrie in D minor, D31[a]; Kyrie in F major, D66[b]. Salve Regina in B flat major, D106[c]. Offertory:
Totus in corde langueo in C major, D136[d]. Stabat Mater in G minor, D175[e]. Offertory: Tres sunt
in A minor, D181[f]. Gradual in C major, D184[g]. Salve Regina (Offertorium) in F major, D223[h].
Tantum ergo in C major, D461[i]; Tantum ergo in C major, D460[j]. Magnificat in C major, D486[k].
Auguste jam coelestium in G major, D488[l]. Salve Regina in A major, D676[m]. Six Antiphons for
Palm Sunday, D696[n]. Psalm 23, D706[o]. Tantum ergo in C major, D739[p]; Tantum ergo in
D major, D750[q]. Salve Regina in C major, D811[r]. Deutsche Messe, D872[s]. Psalm 92, D953[t].
Hymnus an den Heiligen Geist (second version), D964[u]. Lazarus, D689, "Der Feier der
Auferstehung"[v]. [aklv]**Lucia Popp** (sop); [akl]**Adolf Dallapozza** (ten); [c]**Francisco Araiza** (ten);
[dhmv]**Helen Donath** (sop); [ij]**Erika Rüggerberg** (sop); [i]**Juliana Falk** (mez); [i]**Albert Gassner** (ten);
[i]**Peter Lika** (bass-bar); [k]**Brigitte Fassbaender** (mez); [ktv]**Dietrich Fischer-Dieskau** (bar);
[o]**Wolfgang Sawallisch** (pf); [v]**Maria Venuti** (sop); [v]**Josef Protschka** (ten); [v]**Robert Tear** (ten);
[abefgijknpqsv]**Bavarian Radio Chorus;** [abcdefghijklmpqsuv]**Bavarian Radio Symphony Orchestra;**
[ortu]**Capella Bavariae /** [abcdefghijklmnpqrstuv]**Wolfgang Sawallisch.**
EMI Sawallisch Edition Ⓜ CMS7 64783-2 (three discs: 217 minutes: AAD/ADD: 8/94).

Schubert Mass No. 5 in A flat major, D678[a]. Deutsche Messe, D872[b]. [a]**Stefan Preyer** (treb);
[a]**Thomas Weinhappel** (alto); [a]**Jörg Hering** (ten); [a]**Harry van der Kamp** (bass); [b]**Arno Hartmann**
(org); **Vienna Boys' Choir; Chorus Viennensis; Orchestra of the Age of Enlightenment /
Bruno Weil.** Sony Classical Vivarte Ⓕ SK53984 (60 minutes: DDD: 8/94). 🎵
Texts and translations included.   Ⓖ
In the *Deutsche Messe* Bruno Weil makes no attempt to impose interpretative individuality on music
designed purely for liturgical use: he is content merely to oversee neat ensemble and balance. The
orchestra, consisting mainly of wind instruments, double the chorus parts and while their role might
seem largely superfluous they do provide a comfortable cushion on which the choir can relax while
making their way effortlessly through such unchallenging music. It's a different story with the
sparkling A flat major Mass, but again Bruno Weil's understated direction results in an immensely
satisfying performance. There is a youthful vigour and infectious enthusiasm here. Of course, much
of that comes from the superb singing of the Vienna Boys' Choir. Their exuberant 'Hosanna's in the
Sanctus and *Benedictus* are more unashamedly joyful than such music has a right to be. The two boy
soloists sing with a musical maturity way beyond their years. That is not to belittle the splendid
contribution from the adult voices nor the exquisite playing of the Orchestra of the Age of
Enlightenment. Weil achieves the perfect tonal blend: nothing disturbs the open-hearted honesty of
this genuinely sincere performance.
Additional recommendations …
…No. 2 in G major, D167. Salve regina in A major, D676. **Haydn** Missa brevis Sancti Joannis
de Deo, "Kleine Orgelmesse". Flute-clock pieces, HobXIX – Nos. 6, 9, 15, 20 and 32.
Soloists; Haydn Society Chorus and Orchestra / Denis McCaldin.
Meridian Duo Ⓜ DUOCD89003 (55 minutes: ADD: 2/90).
…No. 2[a]; No. 6[b]. [a]**Dawn Upshaw,** [b]**Benita Valente** (sops); [b]**Marietta Simpson** (mez); [a]**David Gordon,**
[b]**Jon Humphrey,** [b]**Glenn Siebert** (tens); [a]**William Stone** [b]**Myron Myers** (bars); **Atlanta Symphony
Chamber Chorus; Atlanta Symphony Chorus and Orchestra / Robert Shaw.**
Telarc Ⓕ CD80212 (78 minutes: DDD: 9/90).
…*CMS7 64778-2* – Masses: No. 1 in F major, D105[a]; No. 2[b]; No. 3 in B flat major, D324[c]; No. 4 in
C major, D452[d]; No. 5[e]; No. 6[f]. Stabat mater, D383[g]. Also contains six other short works.
CMS7 64783-2 – Lazarus, D689[h]. Deutsche Messe. Also contains 20 other short works.
[abcdh]**Lucia Popp,** [abefgh]**Helen Donath,** [h]**Maria Venuti** (sops); [acdef]**Brigitte Fassbaender** (mez);
[abcd]**Adolf Dallapozza,** [a]**Peter Schreier,** [ef]**Francisco Araiza,** [gh]**Josef Protschka** (tens); [h]**Robert Tear** (ten);

Dietrich Fischer-Dieskau (bar); **Bavarian Radio Chorus; Bavarian Radio Symphony Orchestra /
Wolfgang Sawallisch.** EMI Sawallisch Edition Ⓜ CMS7 64778-2 and CMS7 64783-2 (two sets of
four and three discs: 297 and 217 minutes: ADD/DDD: 8/94). Ⓠ
...No. 5. **Soloists; Vienna Boys' Choir; Chorus Viennensis; Orchestra of the Age of Enlightenment /
Bruno Weil.** Sony Classical Vivarte Ⓕ SK53984 (60 minutes: DDD: 5/97).

Schubert Mass No. 6 in E flat major, D950. **Benjamin Schmidinger** (treb); **Albin Lenzer** (alto);
  Jörg Hering (ten); **Kurt Azesberger** (ten); **Harry van der Kamp** (bass); **Vienna Boys' Choir;
  Chorus Viennensis; Orchestra of the Age of Enlightenment / Bruno Weil.** Sony Classical Vivarte
  Ⓕ SK66255 (48 minutes: DDD: 8/95). 🎵 Text and translation included. Recorded 1994.
The most striking thing about this disc is the recording balance. It is as if there's a microphone behind
every music-stand. The effect is of a group of disparate musicians more than a conglomerate whole
but, with individual playing as good as this, it does provide a real listening treat, although it won't be
to everyone's taste. To even fewer tastes will be the unequivocal bias towards orchestral playing. After
all, what is a Schubert Mass if not primarily a choral work? There is some lovely singing here, not
least from the quintet of soloists; yet all the voices are relegated to play second fiddle to the orchestra.
Of all his Masses the E flat work (Schubert's last) is the least concerned with expressing a belief or in
presenting fundamental Christian texts (although it wasn't the only Mass from which he unilaterally
omitted unpalatable sections of the *Credo*) and its intricate orchestral textures and delightful
instrumental writing are worthy of the closest inspection. Bruno Weil has already proved himself to
be a deeply sympathetic Schubertian with a clear sense of what works, and what on first hearing
comes as something of a shock is shown on repeated listening to make perfectly good musical sense.
This view of Schubert may be from an unusual angle, but it is an infinitely rewarding approach to this
unutterably beautiful music.
Additional recommendations ...
...**Soloists; Vienna State Opera Concerto Choir; Vienna Philharmonic Orchestra / Claudio Abbado.**
  DG Ⓕ 423 088-2GH (57 minutes: DDD: 8/88).
...**Soloists; Arnold Schoenberg Choir; Chamber Orchestra of Europe / Nikolaus Harnoncourt.**
  Teldec Ⓕ 0630-13163-2 (52 minutes: DDD: 5/97).

Schubert Psalm 23, D706[b]. Gott in der Natur, D757[b]. Gesang der Geister über den Wassern –
  D538; D714[a]. Nachtgesang im Walde, D913[a]. Gondelfahrer, D809[b]. Psalm 92, D953. Nachthelle,
  D892[b]. Der Tanz, D826. Mondenschein, D875. Ständchen, D920. Die Geselligkeit, D609[b].
  Mailied, D202[a]. Lützows wilde Jagd, D205[a]. Sehnsucht, D636. **BBC Singers / Jane Glover;**
  [a]members of the **City of London Sinfonia;** [b]**Susan Tomes** (pf). Collins Classics Ⓕ 1499-2
  (74 minutes: DDD: 10/97). Texts and translations included. Recorded 1996. ⒼⒼ
Of all the hundreds of settings of Psalm 23 ("The Lord is my shepherd") surely none exudes such
calm and inner peace as Schubert's. And few recordings have ever yielded such sublime beauty from
this setting as does this dreamily shaped, exquisitely moulded account from the BBC Singers under
the wonderfully relaxed hand of Jane Glover. It sets the scene for a disc of exceptional beauty and
charm. The BBC Singers have been criticized for sounding like a collection of 28 solo voices. There's
certainly more than a grain of truth in that, but in this repertoire that's exactly what's needed. These
are part-songs rather than choral pieces, with each part demanding both the musical and technical
skill of a full-fledged soloist. That individual voices are discernible only enhances the sense of
intimacy, but where a solo voice is projected above the others, as in the enchanting setting of
Ständchen where an effectively fresh-voiced Jacqueline Fox is given the most exquisite support from
the male voices (and the ever-sensitive Susan Tomes, whose piano playing throughout is an absolute
treasure), Jane Glover has no problems achieving the ideal balance. These performances capture
perfectly the essential spirit of the music. Enhanced by a top-notch recording this is a truly
exceptional disc.
Additional recommendation ...
...D538. D53. D51. D54. D57. D58. D60. D656. D55. D61. D62. D64. D63. D983*a*. D338. D43.
  D69. D71. D67. **Singphoniker.** CPO Ⓕ CPO999 398-2 (51 minutes: DDD: A/97).

Schubert Complete Secular Choral Works. **Elisabeth Flechl, Ruth Ziesak** (sops); **Martina Steffl,
  Angelika Kirchschlager** (mezs); **Birgit Remmert** (contr); **Franz Leitner, Thomas Künne,
  Christoph Prégardien, Herbert Lippert** (tens); **Oliver Widmer** (bar); **Karl Heinz Lehner,
  Hiroyuki Ijichi, Edgard Loibl, Robert Holl** (basses); **Barbara Moser, András Schiff, Andreas Staier,
  Werner Schröckmayr** (pfs); **Arnold Schoenberg Choir; Vienna Concert-Verein / Erwin Ortner.**
  Teldec Ⓕ 4509-94546-2 (seven discs: 480 minutes: DDD: 8/97). Texts and translations
  included. Recorded 1995-1996.
The scheme of presentation here is both sensible and imaginative. Each of the discs has a subject-
heading and each has its share of the treasures. The first, "Transience", opens with the setting of
Goethe's *Gesang der Geister über den Wassern* for men's voices and string quartet (without violins),
probably the supreme masterpiece of the whole collection. The fascinating contrapuntal treatment of
Schiller's *Dreifach ist der Schritt der Zeit* in its male-voice setting, and the gentle melancholy of Scott's
Coronach are also memorable. The love-songs on the second disc begin and end with the *Ständchen*,
"Zögernd leise", its second version, with male-voice chorus, being so much the more attractive in these

performances. Under the heading of "Eternity" (third disc) comes much that has perhaps a questionable place in a secular anthology: good to have, nevertheless, the anthem known to British choristers as *Where Thou reignest* as *Schiksalslenker, blicke nieder*. The fourth disc has "Heroism" as its theme, with *Mirjams Siegesgesang* as its lengthiest work. "Nature" (fifth disc) produces several masterpieces, including Kleist's *Gott in der Natur* and the magical *Nachthelle*. The sixth, devoted to "Celebration", has some longer occasional pieces, none so delightful as the brief cantata written for his father's birthday in 1813, with guitar accompaniment. The last disc, "Circle of Friends", begins, beguilingly, with *Der Tanz* and ends with *Zur guten Nacht*. Ortner's soloists do well, but it is in the choral singing that the great merit of these performances lies. The Arnold Schoenberg Choir is a fine body of musicians and here they show a virtually unflawed beauty and opulence of tone. The pianists, headed by András Schiff, are excellent.

Additional recommendation ...

...Lied im Freien, D572[a]. Die Bürgschaft[b]. Die Advokaten, D37[c]. Trinklied, D148[d]. Wilkommen, lieber schöner Mai, D244[e]. Fischerlied, D364[f]. Trinklied, D267[g]. Trinklied, D356[h]. Bergknappenlied, D268[i]. Ruhe, schönstes Glück der Erde, D657[j]. Trinklied im Winter, D242[k]. Gott in der Natur, D757[l]. Naturgenuss, D422[m]. Der Schnee zerrinnt, D130[n]. Frühlingsgesang, D740[o]. Trinklied im Mai, D427[p]. Frühlingslied, D243[q]. Widerspruch, D865[r]. Mondenschein, D875[s]. Nachtmusik, D848[t]. Goldner Schein, D357[u]. Frühlingslied, D914[v]. Nachtgesang im Walde, D913[w]. Die Nacht, D983c[x]. Gondelfahrer, D809[y]. Nachthelle, D892[z]. Die Nachtigall, D724[A]. Lacrimoso son io, D131b[B]. Der Entfernten, D331[C]. Mailied, D129[D]. Zum Rundetanz, D983b[E]. Wein und Liebe, D901[F]. Geist der Liebe, D747[G]. Liebe säuseln die Blätter, D988[H]. Andenken, D423[I]. Leise, leise, lasst uns singen, D635[J]. Erinnerungen, D424[K]. Widerhall, D428[L]. Lacrimoso son io, D131a[M]. Gesang der Geister über den Wassern, D714[N]. Nur wer die Sehnsucht kennt, D656[O]. Im Gegenwärtigen Vergangenes, D710[P]. Bootgesang, D835[Q]. Bardengesang, D147[R]. Trinklied aus dem 16 Jahrhundert, D847[S]. La pastorella al prato, D513[T]. Klage um Ali Bey, D140[U]. Schlachtgesang, D912[V]. Der Geistertanz, D494[W]. Ständchen, D920, "Zögernd leise"[X]. Das Dörfchen, D641[Y]. Mailied, D202[Z]. Trinklied, D75. Dreifach ist der Schritt der Zeit, D69. Vöruber die stöhnende Klage, D53. Unendliche Freude, D51. Hier strecket der wallende Pilger, D57. Dessen Fahne Donnerstürme wallte, D58. Hier umarmen sich getreue Gatten, D60. Unendliche Freude, D54. An den Frühling, D338. Frisch atmet des Morgens lebendiger Hauch, D67. Punschlied, D277. Selig durch die Liebe, D55. Ein Jugendlicher Maienschwung, D61. Thronend auf erhab'nem Sitz, D62. Majestätsche Sonnenrosse, D64. Wer die steile Sternenbahn, D63. Liebe, D983a. Die Zwei Tugendwege, D71. Dreifach ist der Schritt der Zeit, D43. Lützows wilde Jagd, D205. Die Einsiedelei, D337. Totengräberlied, D38. Mailied, D199. Flucht, D825b. Der Morgenstern, D203. Coronach, D836. Wehmut, D825. Grab und Mond, D893. Ewige Liebe, D825a. Zur guten Nacht, D903. Mirjams Siegesgesang, D942. Jünglingswonne, D983a. Das Stille Lied, D916. [cekqDIM]**Albert Gassner** (ten); [cekqxDEILM]**Anton Rosner** (ten); [cxEIL]**Peter Schranner** (ten); [dhsz]**Peter Schreier** (ten); [eBHU]**Karin Hautermann** (sop); [eH]**Irmgard Lampart** (sop); [eBHU]**Erika Rüggeberg** (sop); [eM]**Heinrich Weber** (ten); [kqxDEL]**Josef Weber** (bass); [uUZ]**Gudrun Greindl-Rosner** (mez); [u]**Adelheid Schiller** (sop/cont); [u]**Renate Freyer** (mez); [w]**Olaf Klamand** (hn); [wZ]**Ernst Dörflinger** (hn); [w]**Willy Beck** (hn); **Günther Weber** (hn); [xEO]**Peter Lika** (bass-bar); [B]**Isolde Mitternacht-Geissendörfer** (sop); [UZ]**Juliana Falk** (contr); [X]**Brigitte Fassbaender** (mez); [Z]**Kurt Richter** (hn); [Hildegard Behrens (sop); **Paul Hansen** (bass); **Dietrich Fischer-Dieskau** (bar); **Johannes Ritzkowski** (hn); [afjklnptvFKNRSVW]**Bavarian Radio Chorus**; [dghimorswyzACGJOPQTUXY]**Capella Bavariae**; [b]**Bavarian Radio Orchestra**, [N]**Bavarian Radio Symphony Orchestra / Wolfgang Sawallisch**[cdghilmorsyzAGPQTXY](pf).
EMI Ⓜ CMS5 66139-2 (four discs: 265 minutes: DDD/ADD: 2/82).

Schubert Lieder, Volumes 1-3. **Dietrich Fischer-Dieskau** (bar); **Gerald Moore** (pf).
DG Ⓑ 437 214-2GX21 (21 discs: 1463 minutes: ADD: 3/93). Volumes also available separately, as detailed below. Recorded 1966-1972. *Gramophone classical 100*.
437 215-2GX9 (Volume 1: nine discs: 404 minutes): 234 Lieder, written between 1811 and 1817 (from 2720 022, 12/70). *437 225-2GX9* (Volume 2: nine discs: 395 minutes): 171 Lieder, written between 1817 and 1828 (from 643547/58, 1/70). *437 235-2GX3* (Volume 3: three discs: 184 minutes): Die schöne Müllerin, D795. Winterreise, D911. Schwanensgesang, D957 (2720 059, 1/73). 🅖🅖🅖

Twenty-one discs at under £100 bringing together two of this century's greatest Lieder interpreters – it sounds like a recipe for success, as indeed it is, fulfilling the highest expectations. The recordings were made when Dietrich Fischer-Dieskau was at his peak and Gerald Moore could draw on a lifetime's experience and love of this repertoire. Though the set makes no claims to completeness (in the way that Graham Johnson's ongoing Schubert series on Hyperion does), most of the songs for male voice are included here. The use of a single singer and pianist gives the set a unity that allows the listener to gasp anew at the composer's wide-ranging inspiration and imagination. Fischer-Dieskau brings a unique understanding, an elegant line and a diction that renders the text clear without resort to the written texts. If occasionally he imparts an unnecessary weightiness to the lighter songs, this quibble is as nothing when his historic achievement is taken as a whole. And though he made many recordings of the song cycles these are perhaps the finest, with Moore the ideal partner.

Try for example, the bleakness of "Ihr Bild" from *Schwanengesang* or the hallucinatory happiness of "Der Lindenbaum" from *Winterreise*. The songs themselves are basically in chronological order (but with the three song cycles collected together in the final box). It is unfortunate there is no index – trying to find individual songs can be frustrating. It should also be added that the translations are distinctly quirky in places; better to use Richard Wigmore's excellent book *Schubert: The Complete Song Texts* (Gollancz: 1988) if you have a copy to hand. This is undoubtedly one of the greatest bargains in the *Guide*. Buy, without fear of disappointment.

Additional recommendations ...

...D433. D686. D917. D777. D300. D774. D828. Die Verschworenen (Der hausliche Krieg) – Ich schleiche bang und stilla. Claudine von Villa Bella – Liebe schwarmt auf allen Wegen. D800. D827. D788. D965ᵃ. D881. D257. D891. D558. D547. **Edith Wiens** (sop); ᵃ**Joaquin Valdepeñas** (cl); **Rudolf Jansen** (pf). CBC Records Musica Viva Ⓕ MVCD1053 (66 minutes: DDD: 5/93).

...D720. D717. D257 (includes a false start). D367. D544. D118. D882. D839. *Coupled with works by various composers*. **Irmgard Seefried** (sop); **Erik Werba** (pf). Orfeo D'Or mono Ⓕ C297921B* (71 minutes: ADD: 9/93). *See review in the Collections section; refer to the Index.* ⒼⒼ

...D138. D118. D877 No. 4. D720. D715. D768. D544. D296. *Coupled with works by various composers*. **Dawn Upshaw** (sop); **Richard Goode** (pf). Nonesuch Ⓕ 7559-79317-2 (53 minutes: DDD: 8/94). *Gramophone Editor's choice. See review in the Collections section; refer to the Index.* Ⓖ

...D504. D806. D691. D677. D808. D807. *Coupled with works by various composers*. **Dame Janet Baker** (mez); **Gerald Moore** (pf). EMI Ⓜ CDM5 65009-2 (75 minutes: ADD: 11/94). *See review in the Collections section; refer to the Index.*

...Op. 25 – No. 2; No. 5; No. 6. *Coupled with works by various composers*. **Dietrich Fischer-Dieskau** (bar); **Karl Engel** (pf). Orfeo D'Or mono Ⓕ C389951B (72 minutes: ADD: 2/96).

Schubert Lieder – Gretchen am Spinnrade, D118ᵃ. Was bedeutet die Bewegung?, D720ᵃ. Ach, um deine feuchten Schwingen, D717ᵃ; Schwestergruss, D762ᵃ. Schlummerlied, D527ᵃ. An die untergehende Sonne, D457ᵃ. Heiss' mich nicht reden, D877 No. 2ᵃ. So lasst mich scheinen, D877 No. 3ᵃ. Nur wer die Sehnsucht kennt, D877 No. 4ᵃ. Kennst du das Land, D321ᵃ. Berthas Lied in der Nacht, D653ᵃ. Epistel an Herrn Josef Spaun, D749ᵃ. Raste, Krieger, D837ᵃ. Jäger, ruhe von der Jagd, D838ᵃ. Hin und wieder, D239ᵃ. Lieber schwärmt, D239 No. 6ᵃ. An die Nachtigall, D497ᵃ. Schlafe, schlafe, D498ᵃ. Delphine, D857ᵃ. Wiegenlied, D867ᵃ. Die Männer sind méchant, D886 No. 3ᵃ. Iphigenia, D573ᵃ. Das Mädchen, D652ᵃ. Die junge Nonne, D828ᵃ. Am Grabe Anselmos, D504ᶜ. Abendstern, D806ᶜ. Die Götter Greichenlands, D677ᶜ. Gondelfahrer, D808ᶜ. Auflösung, D807ᶜ. Die Forelle, D550ᵇ. Rastlose Liebe, D138ᵇ. Auf dem Wasser zu singen, D774ᵇ. Der Tod und das Mädchen, D531ᵇ. An die Musik, D547ᵇ; Frühlingsglaube, D686ᵇ. Der Musensohn, D764ᵇ. An Sylvia, D891ᵇ. Litanei, D343ᵇ. Heidenröslein, D257ᵇ. Nacht und Träume, D827ᵇ. Du bist die Ruh', D776ᵇ. **Dame Janet Baker** (mez); ᵃᶜ**Gerald Moore,** ᵇ**Geoffrey Parsons** (pfs). EMI Forte Ⓜ CZS5 69389-2 (two discs: 155 minutes: ADD: 10/96). Items marked ᵃ from HMV SLS812 (9/71), ᵇASD4054 (7/81), ᶜASD2431 (1/69).

When the major part of this issue, the first 25 songs, appeared in 1971 under the title "A Schubert Evening", the reviewer gave it a glowing review in *Gramophone*. EMI provided a lavish booklet with annotations on each song, texts and translations, and illustrations of the artists and of Schubert. Virtually nothing of that remains. The briefest summary of the notes, no pictures (just fancy and irrelevant artwork), no words. In a spectacular piece of mis-marketing, EMI seem to be setting out to frighten away those at whom this mid-price issue is aimed – among them many newcomers to Lieder. That is a great shame as this set has some of the most glorious Schubert singing you can imagine. "A Schubert Evening" was in part instigated as a complementary issue to Fischer-Dieskau's contemporaneous recording of all Schubert's songs suited to a male interpreter. Dame Janet chose those he had abjured, ones specifically written for a female protagonist. She fulfils almost every aspect of her riveting selection in terms of vibrant tone, immaculate line, control of dynamics, insights into the poems' meaning and lively storytelling, where that's called for. EMI, in their documentation, seem to have overlooked the fact that five of the songs, Nos. 7-11 on the second CD, come from an earlier recital (our title compilers have made no such error). They are in fact five of the songs that Baker often sang at recitals from the start of her career and to which she was particularly attached; *Am Grabe Anselmos* and *Gondelfahrer*, two superb pieces, are perhaps the most telling of a wonderful group. The remainder of the recordings from a 1980 recital with Parsons, showing no deterioration in the mezzo's singing, offer several of the composer's most popular pieces, all sung *con amore*. Even with such inadequate packaging, this is an issue to treasure.

Schubert An den Mond, D193. Wandrers Nachtlied I, D224. Der Fischer, D225. Erster Verlust, D226. Heidenröslein, D257. Erlkönig, D328. Litanei auf das Fest Allerseelen, D343. Seligkeit, D433. Ganymed, D544. An die Musik, D547. Die Forelle, D550. Frühlingsglaube, D686. Im Haine, D738. Der Musensohn, D764. Wandrers Nachtlied II, D768. Der Zwerg, D771. Auf dem Wasser zu singen, D774. Du bist die Ruh, D776. Nacht und Träume, D827. Fischerweise, D881. Im Frühling, D882. An Silvia, D891. **Ian Bostridge** (ten); **Julius Drake** (pf). EMI Ⓕ CDC5 56347-2 (69 minutes: DDD). Texts and translations included. *Gramophone Editor's choice.* Ⓖ

Bostridge's growing band of devoted admirers are sure to be satisfied by this selection from Schubert's most popular songs. They will once more wonder at his famed engagement with the text in hand and his innate ability both to sing each piece in an entirely natural manner and at the same time to search out its inner meaning, everything achieved without a vocal or technical mishap within hearing. His gift for finding the right manner for each song is exemplified in the contrast between the easy simplicity he brings to such apparently artless pieces as *Fischerweise, Frühlingsglaube* and the less familiar *Im Haine* (this a wondrous performance of a song that is the very epitome of Schubert the melodist) and the depth of feeling found in *Erster Verlust* (a properly intense reading), *Nacht und Traüme, Wandrers Nachtlied* I and II, *Du bist die Ruh* (so elevated in tone and style) and *Litanei.* Bostridge also characterizes spine-chillingly the intense, immediate drama of *Erlkönig* and *Der Zwerg*, though here some may prefer the weight of a baritone. In the latter piece Drake is particularly successful at bringing out the originality of the piano part, and in a much simpler song, *An Sylvia*, he gives to the accompaniment a specific lift and lilt that usually goes unheard. *An die Musik* might have benefited from a slightly simpler treatment and the piano in *Fischerweise* is a touch heavy, but the faults are marginal, and in these songs, as in everything else, the ear responds eagerly to the tenor's fresh, silvery tone and his ever-eager response to words. The recording and notes are faultless.

Schubert Der Musensohn, D764*b*. Schwanengesang, D957 – Liebesbotschaft; Abschied; Die Stadt; Die Taubenpost. Der Schiffer, D536. Die Forelle, D550*e*. An eine Quelle, D530. Auf der Bruck, D853. Das Rosenband, D280. Rastlose Liebe, D138. Winterreise, D911 – Der Lindenbaum. Auf dem Wasser zu singen, D774. Im Freien, D880. Im Abendrot, D799. Wandrers Nachtlied II, D768. Im Frühling, D882. An den Mond, D296. Auf dem Strom, D943[a].
Hans-Peter Blochwitz (ten); [a]**Marie-Luise Neunecker** (hn); **Rudolf Jansen** (pf).
Philips Ⓕ 438 932-2PH (64 minutes: DDD: 3/95). Texts and translations included. Recorded 1992.
This choice of songs gives a true and rewarding conspectus of Schubert's genius as a writer of Lieder. Here is Schubert's world, its emotions and mysteries, encapsulated in miniature. On the other hand, even if you are a collector well versed in Schubert, and perhaps investing in the Hyperion Edition, and/or with Fischer-Dieskau by your side, you could still profit by the purchase of this one-off CD, simply because Blochwitz's voice is exactly right for this repertoire: a silvery, easily produced tenor, owned by an artist who sings German as a natural speaker and as an unaffected musician. Every piece makes its point yet with the kind of innate art that conceals art. As he has the ever-perceptive and musically faultless Jansen, so pellucid in his playing, as his partner, this is a delight from start to finish; and that finish, a fitting climax to an intelligently planned programme, is the grandly romantic *Auf dem Strom*, beautifully balanced and clearly recorded, completing one's pleasure in this CD.

Schubert Im Frühling, D882. Die Blumensprache, D519. Die gefangenen Sänger, D712. Der Schmetterling, D633. An den Mond, D259. An den Mond, D296. Die Gebüsche, D646. Der Fluss, D693. Der Knabe, D692. Nacht und Träume, D827. Im Abendrot, D799. Glaube, Hoffnung und Liebe, D955. Vom Mitleiden Mariä, D632. Beim Winde, D669. Des Mädchens Klage , D6. Blanka, D631. Das Mädchen, D652. Die Rose, D745. Die junge Nonne, D828. Nähe des Geliebten, D162. **Christine Schäfer** (sop); **Irwin Gage** (pf). Orfeo Ⓕ C450971A (79 minutes: DDD: 2/98). Texts and translations included. Recorded 1997.
What makes Schäfer such a special artist is the candid, plaintive, natural quality of her tone and her simplicity of phrasing. These are combined with clear, unaffected diction, and a sense of vulnerability in the timbre, to evoke the pure spirit of each song. Some, used to more vibrant, luscious voices, may find Schäfer's tone too narrow or they may be troubled by moments when she is deliberately on the flat side of a note but they are part of her vocal personality and perhaps nearer to what was heard in Schubert's day. Her attributes as a Schubertian, already disclosed in her contributions to the Hyperion Edition, are confirmed by her discerning choice of songs in this generously filled programme. Whether the pieces are grave or cheerful, Schäfer finds the right expression. The simplicity at the start of *An den Mond* (D296) is succeeded by heightened intensity at just the appropriate moment, in the fifth stanza. In that underrated Schlegel setting, *Der Fluss*, she adds special urgency to the last line. In better-known songs, such as *Nacht und Träume* and *Im Abendrot*, which succeed one another here, the soprano refreshes the familiar through a new draught of feeling, simple yet inward, and that is the epithet that comes most readily to mind in those two melancholic songs, *Das Mädchen* and *Die Rose*, the one about an unloved girl, the other about a flower speaking of its mortality. To end she catches the perfect Schubert/Goethe accord of *Nähe des Geliebten*, where "Ich denke dein" and "Ich bin bei dir" are affirmations of a deep love. Irwin Gage partners his singer with many touches of subtle, finely shaded phrasing. Add a surely balanced recording and Lieder lovers are in for a generous treat.

Schubert Ave Maria (Ellens Gesang III), D839. Ganymed, D544. Kennst du das Land, D321; Heiss mich nicht reden, D877 No. 2; So lasst mich scheinen, D877 No. 3; Nur wer die Sehnsucht kennt, D877 No. 4. Liebhaber in allen Gestalten, D558. Heidenröslein, D257. Nahe des Geliebten, D162. Die Forelle, D550. Auf dem Wasser zu singen, D774. Im Abendrot, D799. Ständchen, D889. Du bist die Ruh, D776. Gretchen am Spinnrade, D118. Gretchens Bitte, D564. Der Hirt auf dem Felsen, D965[a]. **Barbara Bonney** (sop); [a]**Sharon Kam** (cl); **Geoffrey Parsons** (pf). Teldec Ⓕ 4509-90873-2 (73 minutes: DDD: 3/95). Texts and translations included. Recorded 1994.

Ⓖ

Bonney's programme is most carefully planned. She begins with a substantial selection of Goethe settings, going to the heart of the matter in all the Mignon songs, singing *Ganymed* with exemplary legato and breath control. Then she makes a well-varied selection from many of the better-known pieces. She crosses paths with Blochwitz only in *Die Forelle* and *Auf dem Wasser zu singen*. Both take the same time over each, but it is worth noting that Jansen, for Blochwitz, finds more variety and lift in the barcarolle-like accompaniment of the latter song that does Parsons. Vocally speaking, both versions are enjoyable in their natural accomplishments. Bonney's line and breath are again remarkable in *Du bist die Ruh*, which also demonstrates, as do all the other offerings, the purity of her tone – more North American clear-aired than Viennese creamy – yet that is never allowed to exclude depth of feeling. Indeed when she returns to the Goethe settings with *Gretchen am Spinnrade* she shows particular eloquence in the way that, at a deliberate pace, she builds the song unerringly to its climaxes and also catches the inwardness of Gretchen's state of mind. The recording is faultless.

Additional recommendations ...

...D965. D433. D118. D756. D922. D882. D691. D300. D764.
Coupled with works by various composers. **Elly Ameling** (sop); **Various soloists.**
Deutsche Harmonia Mundi Ⓕ 74321 26617-2 (four discs: 239 minutes: ADD: 12/95).
See review in the Collections section; refer to the Index.
...D839. *Coupled with works by various composers.*
Lesley Garrett (sop); **Britten Sinfonia / Ivor Bolton.** Conifer Classics Ⓕ 75605 51329-2
(73 minutes: DDD: 12/97). *See review in the Collections section; refer to the Index.*

Schubert Heidenröslein, D257. Wonne der Wehmut, D260. Der Jüngling an der Quelle, D300. Erntelied, D434. Im Walde, D708. Geheimes, D719. Suleika I, D720. Dass sie hier gewesen, D775. Viola, D786. Im Abendrot, D799. Abendstern, D806. Ave Maria, D839. Totengräbers Heimweh, D842. Bei dir allein, D866 No. 2. Der Wanderer an den Mond, D870. Im Frühling, D882. An Silvia, D891. Ständchen, D920[a]. **Anne Sofie von Otter** (mez); **Bengt Forsberg** (pf) with [a]**Swedish Radio Chorus.** DG Ⓕ 453 481-2GH (69 minutes: DDD: 5/98).
Texts and translations included. Recorded 1996.   ⒼⒼ
Anne Sofie von Otter has been waiting with some trepidation to make her first Schubert disc, conscious of the high degree of both literary awareness and musical commitment necessary for such an undertaking. In songs such as *An Silvia* and *Geheimes* the wide-eyed wonder of her own discovery incarnates that of the songs' own subjects. Tiny moments of gentle emphasis, and a little spring on each note of its rising sequences adds to the wondering incredulity of *An Silvia*'s questionings; and von Otter's vocal heritage of the baroque and of Mozart have, of course, schooled her voice to articulate perfectly the tapering phrases and shy note-pairs that convey the glancing secrets of *Geheimes*. The recital grows gradually darker, moving, by way of *Ständchen*, D920, to the twilight of *Im Abendrot*. Here, long, firmly-grounded vowels are backlit by the afterglow of Forsberg's piano line before some deep, passionate digging into the *Angst* of *Totengräbers Heimweh*, and a wonderfully breathless, intimately urgent imprecation of an *Ave Maria*.

Schubert Schiller Lieder – Die Bürgschaft, D246; Hoffnung, D637; Hektors Abschied, D312; An Emma, D113; Des Mädchens Klage, D191; Gruppe aus dem Tartarus, D583; Der Pilgrim, D794; Der Alpenjäger, D588; Leichenfantasie, D7; Die Götter Griechenlands, D677; Sehnsucht, D636. **Christoph Prégardien** (ten); **Andreas Staier** (fp). Deutsche Harmonia Mundi Ⓕ 05472 77296-2 (74 minutes: DDD: 1/94). Texts and translations included. Recorded 1993. ✍
Gramophone Editor's choice.   Ⓖ
In *Die Götter Griechenlands*, Prégardien encompasses all the most compelling aspects of such notable tenor interpreters of Lieder as Patzak, Pears and Schreier. The plangent timbre is perfect for this elegiac lament, the legato ideal, the phraseology touching. Because this is perhaps Schubert's most telling setting of Schiller, to whose poetry the disc is devoted, it heads the main reasons for buying it. The performance of a quite different song, the ballad *Die Bürgschaft*, is another, as here Prégardien brings to bear quite different attributes – a darker tone, a powerful sense of the song's drama and an innate feeling for the pulse of this long but ultimately rewarding piece. Over and above that, the singer makes every word tell. The same is true of the jejune but entertaining *Leichenfantasie*. All the other songs, even the more intractable ones, are interpreted with the high intelligence and sense of style one would expect. Staier is both an alert and persuasive player, but once or twice, such as in *Der Pilgrim*, one longs for the softer timbre of a modern instrument instead of a fortepiano. Recording is first-rate.

Schubert Lieder, Volume 23 – Der Tod Oscars, D375. Das Grab, D377[a]. Der Entfernten, D350. Pflügerlied, D392. Abschied von der Harfe, D406. Der Jüngling an der Quelle, D300. Abendlied, D382. Stimme der Liebe, D412. Romanze, D144. Geist der Liebe, D414. Klage, D415. Julius an Theone, D419. Der Leidende, D432. Der Leidende (second version), D432b. Die frühe Liebe, D430. Die Knabenzeit, D400. Edone, D445. Die Liebes-götter, D446. An Chloen, D363. Freude der Kinderjahre, D455. Wer sich der Einsamkeit ergibt, D478. Wer nie sein Brot mit Tränen ass, D480. An die Türen, D479. Der Hirt, D490. An ersten Maimorgen, D344. Bei dem Grabe meines Vaters, D496. Mailied, D503. Zufriedenheit, D362. Skolie, D507. **Christoph Prégardien** (ten); [a]**London Schubert Chorale; Graham Johnson** (pf). Hyperion Ⓕ CDJ33023 (78 minutes: DDD: 7/95). Texts and translations included. Recorded 1994.

When the Hyperion Schubert Edition is completed, this latest wondrous offering will rank among its most precious jewels. Prégardien is a prince among tenor interpreters of Lieder at present, on a par with Blochwitz in instinctive, natural and inevitably phrased readings. Johnson, besides, of course, finding exactly the right performers for these songs, surpasses even his own high standard of playing in this series. Then there is Schubert himself, the Schubert of 1816 by and large, who was, Johnson tentatively suggests in his notes, going through a phase of "bringing himself under control". That means, largely but far from entirely, writing gently lyrical strophic songs, most of them of ineffable beauty and simplicity, starkly contrasting with the Harfenspieler settings from *Wilhelm Meister*, two of which were written in 1816, the other in 1822. In such an outright masterpiece as *Der Jüngling an der Quelle*, Prégardien and Johnson confirm the latter's view that this piece "makes time stand still". They emphasize, in *Stimme der Liebe*, how Schubert uses shifting harmonies to indicate romantic obsession. They show in the two similar but subtly different versions of *Der Leidende* ("The suffering one") what Johnson calls "two sides of the same coin", with the tenor's plangent, tender singing, line and text held in perfect balance, an unalloyed delight. The two Hölty songs that follow, *Die frühe Liebe* and *Die Knabenzeit*, evince a wonderful affinity with thoughts of childhood on the part of poet and composer, again ideally captured here. So is the "chaste and wistful" mood of Klopstock's *Edone*. These are just a few of many discoveries on this generously timed disc. Ideally balanced recording.

Additional recommendations ...
...Volume 1 – D30. D73. D121 (first version). D162 (second version). D216. D195. D159
(second version). D224. D225 (second version). D226. D260. D296. D250. D284. D402. D587
(second version). D588 (second version). D794. D636 (second version). **Dame Janet Baker** (mez);
Graham Johnson (pf). Hyperion Ⓕ CDJ33001 (70 minutes: DDD: 10/88).   Ⓖ
...Volume 6 – D534 (completed by Anton Diabelli). D521 (with chorus). D806. D235. D237. D579.
D856. D767. D927. D906. D933. D939. D904. D905. D903 (chorus). **Anthony Rolfe Johnson**
(ten); **Graham Johnson** (pf). Hyperion Ⓕ CDJ33006 (73 minutes: DDD: 6/90).
...Volume 7 – D152. D192. D187. D188. D191. D186. D193. D196. D210 (Klärchens Lied). D215a.
D227. D228. D231. D247. D261. D283. D280. D298. D317. D319. D305. D321. D310
(two versions). **Elly Ameling** (sop); **Graham Johnson** (pf).
Hyperion Ⓕ CDJ33007 (71 minutes: DDD: 8/90).
...Volume 8 – D259. D114. D418. D289. D290. D238. D614. D208. D462. D463. D464. D465.
D466. D495. D498. D920 (with chorus). D653. D328. **Sarah Walker** (mez); **Graham Johnson** (pf).
Hyperion Ⓕ CDJ33008 (72 minutes: DDD: 10/90).
...Volume 10 – D149. D151. D160. D161. D177. D197. D198. D201. D207. D211. D213. D214.
D271. D302. D303. D325. **Martyn Hill** (ten); **Graham Johnson** (pf).
Hyperion Ⓕ CDJ33010 (74 minutes: DDD: 5/91).
...Volume 11 – D518. D774. D807. D753. D801. D584. D116. D367. D474. D672.
Schwanengesang, D744. D433. D727. D595. D531. D59. D989. D871. **Brigitte Fassbaender**
(mez); **Graham Johnson** (pf). Hyperion Ⓕ CDJ33011 (65 minutes: DDD: 8/91).
...Volume 14 – D737. D166. D396. D583. D890. D541. D450. D540. D554. D312. Antigone und
Oedip, D542 (both with Marie McLaughlin, sop). D360. D548. D699. D707. D700. D677.
Thomas Hampson (bar); **Graham Johnson** (pf). Hyperion Ⓕ CDJ33014 (80 minutes: DDD: 4/92).
...Volume 15 – D457. D141. D436. D194. D713. D270. D264. D217. D403. D808. D938. D870.
D880. D878. D833. D828. **Dame Margaret Price** (sop); **Graham Johnson** (pf).
Hyperion Ⓕ CDJ33015 (72 minutes: DDD: 2/93).
...Volume 16 – D7. D388. Die Entzückung an Laura – first version, D390, second version
(completed van Hoorickx), D577. D189. D113. D117. D793. D246.D638. D391. D52. D794.
Thomas Allen (bar); **Graham Johnson** (pf). Hyperion Ⓕ CDJ33016 (78 minutes: DDD: 3/93).
...Volume 17 – D373 (Mutter geht durch ihre kammern). D150. D371. D376. D405. D393. D404.
D416. D398. D401. D429. D458 (Ilmerine). D467. D468. D343. D491 (An Franz Schubert).
D504. D497. D496a. D500. D502. D508. D509. D342. **Lucia Popp** (sop); **Graham Johnson** (pf).
Hyperion Ⓕ CDJ33017 (71 minutes: DDD: 6/93).
...Volume 18 – D219. D358. D477. D431. D399. D434. D394. D456. D499. D765. D770. D851.
D853. D862. D874 (cpted. R. Van Hoorickx). D861. D876 (Im Jänner 1817). D834. D882. D883.
D884. D860. **Peter Schreier** (ten); **Graham Johnson** (pf).
Hyperion Ⓕ CDJ33018 (76 minutes: DDD: 7/93). *Gramophone Editor's choice.*   Ⓖ
...Volume 21 – D527. D516. D522. D550. D513a. D515. D523. D514. D532. D530. D547. D517.
D552. D559. D558. D578. D586. D596. D607. D711. D616. D622. D626. D632.
Edith Mathis (sop); **Graham Johnson** (pf).
Hyperion Ⓕ CDJ33021 (65 minutes: DDD: 8/94). *Gramophone Editor's choice.*   ⒼⒼ
...Volume 22 – D148[efgh]. D266[a]. D288[e]. D252[g]. D221[d]. D277[efgh]. D272[a]. D269[abd]. D329 (cpted
Hoorickx)[d]. D229[e]. D236[ach]. D143[d]. D315[e]. D316[e]. D155[e]. D285[g]. D306[e]. D263[d]. D313[e].
D248[efgh]. D287[a]. D171[g]. D322[ag]. D286[ae]. D327 (cpted Hoorickx)[d]. D282[ag]. D232[bceh]. D330[efgh].
[a]**Lorna Anderson**, [a]**Patricia Rozario** (sops); [c]**Catherine Denley** (mez); [d]**Catherine Wyn-Rogers**
(contr); [e]**Jamie MacDougall**, [f]**John Mark Ainsley** (tens); [g]**Simon Keenlyside** (bar);
[h]**Michael George** (bass); **Graham Johnson** (pf). Hyperion Ⓕ CDJ33022 (78 minutes: DDD: 1/94).
...Volume 29 – D650[a]. D651[a]. D637[a]. Hymnen[a] – I, D659; II, D660; III, D661; IV, D662. D687[a].
D620[b]. D626[a]. D671[a]. D673[a]. D685[a]. D686[a]. D702[a]. D708[a]. [a]**Marjana Lipovšek** (mez);
[b]**Nathan Berg** (bar); **Graham Johnson** (pf). Hyperion Ⓕ CDJ33029 (78 minutes: DDD: 11/97).

Schubert Lieder, Volume 24 – Schäfers Klagelied, D121[be]. An Mignon, D161[ae]. Geistes-Gruss, D142 (two versions)[de]. Rastlose Liebe, D138[be]. Der Gott und die Bajadere, D254[abde]. Tischlied, D234[ce]. Der Schatzgräber, D256[de]. Der Rattenfänger, D255[ce]. Bundeslied, D258[bcde]. Erlkönig, D328[abde]. Jägers Abendlied, D215[ce]. Jägers Abendlied, D368[ce]. Wer nie sein Brot mit Tränen ass, D480 (two versions)[be]. Nur wer die Sehnsucht kennt, D359[ae]. So lasst mich scheinen, D469a and D469b (two fragments)[ae]. Nur wer die Sehnsucht kennt, D481[ae]. Nur wer die Sehnsucht kennt, D656[f]. An Schwager Kronos, D369[ce]. Hoffnung, D295[de]. Mahomets Gesang, D549 (cptd. R. Van Hoorickx)[be]. Ganymed, D544[ae]. Der Goldschmiedsgesell, D560[ce]. Gesang der Geister über den Wassern, D484 (cptd. R. Van Hoorickx)[de]. Gesang der Geister über den Wassern, D705 (cptd. E. Asti)[ef]. [a]**Christine Schäfer** (sop); [b]**John Mark Ainsley** (ten); [c]**Simon Keenlyside** (bar); [d]**Michael George** (bass); [e]**Graham Johnson** (pf); [f]**London Schubert Chorale / Stephen Layton.** Hyperion Ⓟ CDJ33024 (79 minutes: DDD: 1/96). Texts and translations included. Recorded 1993-1994.

Renewed praise first of all for Graham Johnson. This volume is as cogent an example as any of his method, a masterly exposition, in written words and musical performance, of the crucial relationship between Goethe and Schubert upon which Johnson throws a good deal of new light. As ever here the familiar happily rubs shoulders with the unfamiliar. Not all is notable Schubert, but the lesser songs, among them one or two hearty occasional pieces, merely serve to place in perspective the greater ones. The CD begins with one of the latter, *Schäfers Klagelied*, in a finely honed, dramatic performance by Ainsley, who is heard later on the disc always to advantage. Track 2 introduces Christine Schäfer, a kind of amalgam of Popp and Silja, if you can imagine such a singer. Good as she is in this first version of *An Mignon*, she is better in the sadly neglected *Der Gott und die Bajadere*, as Johnson avers. This is the only song in the genre about prostitution, and a haunting one too, even though, throughout its appreciable length, it relies on just one melody, and Schäfer precisely catches its haunting atmosphere. But the climax of her contribution comes in *Ganymed* – w.ith Johnson providing exactly the right rhythmic lilt at the piano, her voice conveys all the elation of poem and music. Schäfer is the child in a three-voice rendering of *Erlkönig*, a manner of performing the piece that has the composer's blessing. Johnson has surely never surpassed his account here of the hair-raisingly difficult piano part. Then he is just as accomplished with Keenlyside in a thrilling account of another masterpiece engendered by response to Goethe's genius, *An Schwager Kronos*. George, who perhaps has the least ingratiating songs to perform, sings with feeling and style but sometimes an excess of vibrato. A short review can only touch on the most significant delights in what is an engrossing and invaluable addition to this series.

Schubert Lieder, Volume 26 – Der Einsame, D800[c]. Des Sängers Habe, D832[c]. Lied der Delphine, D857 No. 1[a]. Lied des Florio, D857 No. 2[c]. Mondenschein, D875[d]. Nur wer die Sehnsucht kennt, D877 No. 1[ab]. Heiss mich nicht reden, D877 No. 2[a]. So lasst mich scheinen, D877 No. 3[a]. Nur wer die Sehnsucht kennt, D877 No. 4[a]. Totengräberweise, D869[c]. Das Echo, D990C[a]. An Silvia, D891[b]. Horch, horch! die Lerch', D889[a]. Trinklied, D888[c]. Wiegenlied, D867[a]. Widerspruch, D865[d]. Der Wanderer an den Mond, D870[c]. Grab und Mond, D893[d]. Nachthelle, D892[bd]. Abschied von der Erde, D829[c]. [a]**Christine Schäfer** (sop); [b]**John Mark Ainsley** (ten); [c]**Richard Jackson** (bar); [d]**London Schubert Chorale; Graham Johnson** (pf). Hyperion Ⓟ CDJ33026 (76 minutes: DDD: 12/96). Texts and translations included. Recorded 1995. *Gramophone Editor's choice.* 🅖🅖

As another wondrous addition to this unique venture, it is hard to know where to begin in its praise. It has several centres of excellence, the first being Schäfer's beseeching, urgent account of the Mignon settings from Goethe's *Wilhelm Meister* that make plain her pre-eminence today among sopranos in Lieder. Next comes Ainsley's winningly fresh account of *An Silvia*. You may be as surprised at how wholly new-minted Ainsley's ardent tones and Johnson's elating piano manage to make of such a hackneyed song. Schäfer and Johnson do the same service for *Horch, horch! die Lerch'*. Then comes the extraordinary discovery of this volume. As a rule, Johnson has excluded unaccompanied vocal pieces from his project; happily, he has made an exception in the case of the astonishingly original Seidl setting *Grab und Mond*, which touches on eternal matters, or rather the permanence of death, a message starkly expressed in typically daring harmony. The London Schubert Chorale give it a spellbinding interpretation and also contribute positively to a performance of another Seidl setting, the better-known *Nachthelle*, where the high-lying tenor lead provides no problems for Ainsley. There have to be reservations over the work of Richard Jackson. No amount of creative intelligence can mask the fact that his dried-out tone is inadequate to the demands of *Der Einsame*, the unjustly neglected *Totengräberweise* and *Der Wanderer an den Mond*, which call for a richer palette of sound. Throughout, Johnson's playing and, of course, his admirable notes are their customary sources of pleasure and enlightenment. The recording is well-nigh faultless.

Schubert Lieder, Volume 27 – Lob der Tränen, D711[a]. Lebensmelodien, D395[a]. Sprache der Liebe, D410[a]. Wiedersehn, D855[a]. Sonett I, D628[a]. Sonett II, D629[a]. Sonett III, D630[a]. Abendröte, D690[a]. Die Berge, D634[a]. Die Vögel, D691[a]. Der Fluss, D693[b]. Der Knabe, D692[a]. Die Rose, D745[b]. Der Schmetterling, D633[a]. Der Wanderer, D649[a]. Das Mädchen, D652[b]. Die Sterne, D684[a]. Die Gebüsche, D646[a]. Blanka, D631[b]. Der Schiffer, D694[a]. Fülle der Liebe,

D854[a]. Im Walde, D708[a]. [a]**Matthias Goerne** (bar); [b]**Christine Schäfer** (sop); **Graham Johnson** (pf). Hyperion Ⓕ CDJ33027 (78 minutes: DDD: 1/97). Texts and translations included.

Goerne's brief is Schubert's settings of the brothers Schlegel, whose volatile character and life are amply and fascinatingly described in Johnson's introduction to the booklet. As ever in this series, there are songs that we should curse ourselves for neglecting for so long. Among the few settings of August von Schlegel is the interesting *Lebensmelodien*, where the Swan and the Eagle engage in a colloquy – the one all tranquil, the other all disturbed – and are observed by doves on whom Schubert lavishes his most beautiful music. In the formal *Wiedersehn*, as Johnson avers, Schubert imitates the style of a Handelian aria. The second of three Petrarch translations prefigures, arrestingly, the mood of *Winterreise*. When we come to brother Friedrich and the quasi-cycle *Abendröte* we are in an even more exalted world where *Der Fluss*, another of Schubert's miraculous water songs, *Der Knabe*, above all *Die Rose*, where the fading of the rose is a metaphor for lost virginity (this, movingly done by Schäfer), and *Der Wanderer* show just how willingly Schubert responded to Schlegel's imagery. About Goerne's singing as such, ably assisted by Johnson's playing, there need be no reservations, particularly in the visionary *Die Sterne*, but as the CD progresses his interpretations begin to seem a shade soporific; one wonders if he has lived long enough with these songs to penetrate to their heart. His easily produced, slightly vibrant and mellifluous baritone and sense of Schubertian style make him, by and large, a rewarding interpreter. The recording is excellent.

Schubert Lieder – Gruppe aus dem Tartarus, D583. Litanei auf das Fest Allerseelen, D343. Die Forelle, D550. An die Leier, D737. Lachen und Weinen, D777. Schwanengesang, D957 – No. 4, Ständchen; No. 10, Das Fischermädchen; No. 14, Die Taubenpost. Meerestille, D216. Der Wanderer, D489 (formerly D493). Erlkönig, D328. Der Tod und das Mädchen, D531. Heidenröslein, D257. Wandrers Nachtlied II, D768. An die Musik, D547. Auf der Bruck, D853. Schäfers Klagelied, D121. An Silvia, D891. Du bist die Ruh', D776. An die Laute, D905. Rastlose Liebe, D138. Ganymed, D544. Der Musensohn, D764. **Bryn Terfel** (bass-bar); **Malcolm Martineau** (pf). DG Ⓕ 445 294-2GH (69 minutes: DDD: 10/94). Texts and translations included. Recorded 1994. *Gramophone Award Winner 1995. Gramophone Editor's choice.* ⒼⒼ

Terfel's gift, now well known, is a generous, individual voice, a natural feeling for German and an inborn ability to go to the heart of what he attempts. His singing here is grand in scale – listen to any of the dramatic songs and the point is made – but like Hotter, whom he so often resembles, he is able to reduce his large voice to the needs of a sustained, quiet line, as in *Meerestille*. When the two come together as in *Der Wanderer*, the effect can be truly electrifying, even more so, perhaps, in *Erlkönig* where the four participants are superbly contrasted. Yet this is a voice that can also smile, as in *An die Laute* and "Die Taubenpost" or express wonder, as in *Ganymed*, a most exhilarating interpretation, or again explode in sheer anger as in the very first song, the strenuous *Gruppe aus dem Tartarus*. Terfel is not afraid to employ rubato and vibrato to make his points and above all to take us right into his interpretations rather than leave us admiring them, as it were, from afar. Throughout, Martineau's at once vigorous and subtle playing is an apt support: his accompaniment in *Erlkönig* is arrestingly clear and precise.

Additional recommendations ...

...D259. D369. D216. D328. D719. D764. *Coupled with works by various composers.* **Dietrich Fischer-Dieskau** (bar); **Karl Engel** (pf). Orfeo D'Or mono Ⓕ C389951B* (72 minutes: ADD: 2/96).

...D777. D882. D776. D118. *Coupled with works by various composers.* **Lisa della Casa** (sop); **Arpad Sándor** (pf). EMI Salzburg Festival Edition mono Ⓜ CDH5 66571-2* (64 minutes: ADD: 2/98). *See review in the Collections section; refer to the Index.*

Schubert Heidenröslein, D257. Die Forelle, D550. An die Nachtigall, D497. Im Frühling, D882. Die junge Nonne, D828. Nacht und Träume, D827. Auf dem Wasser zu singen, D774. Ave Maria, D839. Frühlingsglaube, D686. Gretchen am Spinnrade, D118. Du bist die Ruh, D776. Der Tod und das Mädchen, D531. Viola, D786. Die Männer sind méchant, D866 No. 3. **Renée Fleming** (sop); **Christoph Eschenbach** (pf). Decca Ⓕ 455 294-2DH (66 minutes: DDD: 4/97). Texts and translations included. Recorded 1996. *Gramophone Editor's choice.* Ⓖ

When yet another recital of Schubert Lieder appears, composed in the main of well-known songs, one looks for some special attributes to set it off from what has gone before in such profusion. Renée Fleming frequently supplies just those touches of individual response and high art which the ear is seeking. Like Dame Margaret Price she brings considerable stage experience to bear on her readings in terms of dramatic immediacy. That is particularly true of *Die junge Nonne* and *Gretchen am Spinnrade*, both of which carry the charge of emotions made manifest at the moment of recording. There is almost as much to enjoy and appreciate in the more reflective, inward pieces. *Im Frühling*, in both voice and piano, catches very precisely the sense of longing evoked by the spring, with Eschenbach pointing up the poignancy of alternating major-minor. In *An die Nachtigall*, Fleming's tone is poised, finely controlled. Even more so in the more difficult *Du bist die Ruh*, where she shades the end of the final two couplets with a ravishing *piano*. *Nacht und Träume*, still harder to sustain, is as time-stopping as it should be. In the sadly neglected flower-ballad *Viola* the pair suggest a true partnership of thought and execution. At least three other songs, *Auf dem Wasser zu singen*, *Ave Maria* and *Frühlingsglaube* seem marginally too slow. Here, and sometimes elsewhere, a shade more rhythmic verve, a greater attention to consonants, would improve on what is already a formidable array of virtues, and Eschenbach's habit of indulging in *ritenutos* sometimes becomes a distraction. These small points apart, this is a Liederabend to savour and it has been faultlessly recorded.

Schubert Im Abendrot, D799. Die Sterne, D939. Nacht und Träume, D827. Der liebliche Stern, D861. Der Vollmond strahlt, D797 No. 3*b*. Der Einsame, D800. Schlaflied, D527. An Silvia, D891. Das Mädchen, D652. Minnelied, D429. Die Liebe hat gelogen, D751. Du liebst mich nicht, D756. An die Laute, D905. Der Blumenbrief, D622. Die Männer sind méchant, D866 No. 3. Seligkeit, D433 (all from ᵃ6500 704, 1/76). Nachtviolen, D752. Du bist die Ruh, D776 (both from ᵃ9500 350, 6/78). Das Lied im Grünen, D917. Der Schmetterling, D633. An die Nachtigall, D497. An die Nachtigall, D196. Der Wachtelschlag, D742. Im Freien, D880. Die Vögel, D691. Fischerweise, D881. Die Gebüsche, D646. Im Haine, D738 (ᵃ6500 706, 10/75). Kennst du das Land, D321. Nur wer die Sehnsucht kennt, D877 No. 4. Heiss mich nicht reden, D877 No. 2. So lasst mich scheinen, D877 No. 3. Die Liebende schreibt, D673. Nähe des Geliebten, D162. Heidenröslein, D257. Liebhaber in allen Gestalten, D558 (6500 515, 7/74). Die junge Nonne, D828. Der König in Thule, D367. Gretchen am Spinnrade, D118. Gretchens Bitte, D564. Szene aus Goethes Faust, D126 (with Anand Kraak, ten; chorus and org). Suleika I, D720. Suleika II, D717. Raste Krieger!, D837. Jäger, ruhe von der Jagd, D838. Ave Maria, D839 (ᵃ9500 169, 4/78). An die Musik, D547. Schwestergrüss, D762. Sei mir gegrüsst, D741. Die Blumensprache, D519. An den Mond, D296. Abendbilder, D650. Frühlingssehnsucht, D957 No. 3. Erster Verlust, D226. Nachthymne, D687. Die Sterne, D684. Der Knabe, D692. Wiegenlied, D498. Berthas Lied in der Nacht, D653 (ᵃ6514 298, 6/83). Ganymed, D544. Die Götter Griechenlands, D677. Der Musensohn, D764. Fülle der Liebe, D854. Sprache der Liebe, D410. Schwanengesang, D744. An den Tod, D518. Die Forelle, D550. Am Bach im Frühling, D361. Auf dem Wasser zu singen, D774. Der Schiffer, D694. An die Entfernte, D765. Sehnsucht, D516. An die untergehende Sonne, D457. Abendröte, D690 (ᵇ416 294-2PH, 8/87). **Elly Ameling** (sop); ᵃ**Dalton Baldwin,** ᵇ**Rudolf Jansen** (pfs). Philips The Early Years Ⓜ 438 528-2PM4 (four discs: 260 minutes: ADD/DDD: 4/94). Texts included. Recorded 1972-1984.

The first *Im Abendrot* (the Lappe setting) introduces the smiling Ameling of 1973, her voice basking in the images of golden shafts of light, and rapt in an easeful legato. In the shorter vowels and pulsing pianistic light of *Die Sterne*, she still finds serenity, just as in *Der Einsame* the poet's solitude is sensed at the heart of a tingling, sentient world. The expressive subtlety of these performances comes from an unique fusion of response between Ameling and Baldwin during this period. In the second disc, their creative empathy is turned to Schubert's settings of Goethe. Ameling focuses on the vulnerability and childlike eagerness of Mignon, missing, perhaps, the nervous feverishness which lies just below the surface of these songs, and which Wolf was to exploit to the full. After one of the most perfectly-scaled performances of *Heidenröslein* on disc, Ameling and Baldwin turn to Goethe's Gretchen and Suleika, and to Scott's Ellen. Gretchen's searing vision at the spinning-wheel is answered by the rarely heard *Szene aus Goethes Faust* in which Ameling finds herself in the company of an anonymous and very spooky *Böser Geist*, as well as a ghostly choir who seem piped in from another planet. Seven years later, Ameling turns to a still stranger spirit world. The third disc, recorded in 1982, includes the lunar beauty of Schubert's Bruchmann setting, *Schwestergrüss*, articulated by a voice bleached of any colour. It is almost impossible to detect any sense of ageing in the voice here. Characterized by songs which search out the most elusive of soul moods, this third recital reveals Ameling's soprano at its most finely nuanced, in songs such as *Abendbilder* and the Novalis *Nachthymne*. In the final disc, at the age of 50, Ameling took on the challenge of some of Schubert's most visionary songs: facing Schiller's Greek gods, Goethe's *Ganymed*, Schlegel's *Der Schiffer* and moving through Mayrhofer's longing to Schlegel's final sunset. These songs stretch the voice and the mind to its very limits, yet Ameling's artistry seems to grow with the music itself. The set includes full texts but no translations. In the end, though, Ameling's singing renders them all but redundant.

Additional recommendations ...

...D720. D717. D776. D762. D550. D837. D838. D839. *Coupled with works by various composers.*
Gundula Janowitz (sop); **Irwin Gage** (pf); **Vienna Symphony Orchestra / Wilfried Boettcher; Orchestra of the Deutsche Staatsoper, Berlin / Ferdinand Leitner.**
DG Double Ⓜ 447 352-2GDB2 (two discs: 152 minutes: ADD: 12/95).

Schubert Songs to poems by Goethe. Am Flusse, D160. Trost in Tränen, D120. Schäfers Klagelied, D121. Meeres Stille, D216. Heidenröslein, D257. Jägers Abendlied, D368. Sehnsucht, D123. Die Liebe, D210. Rastlose Liebe, D138. Nähe des Geliebten, D162. Der Fischer, D225. Erster Verlust, D226. Der König in Thule, D367. Wer sich der Einsamkeit ergibt, D478. An die Türen, D479. Wer nie sein Brot mit Tränen ass, D480. An Schwager Kronos, D369. An Mignon, D161. Ganymed, D544. An die Entfernte, D765. Versunken, D715. An den Mond, D259. Der Musensohn, D764. Auf dem See, D543. Geistes-Gruss, D142. **Christoph Prégardien** (ten); **Andreas Staier** (fp). Deutsche Harmonia Mundi Ⓔ 05472 77342-2 (70 minutes: DDD: 6/96). Texts and translations included. Recorded 1994.

Prégardien proves himself just as adept at such a light piece as *Heidenröslein* as in the still, solemn thoughts of *Meeres Stille*, or the forceful challenge of *An Schwager Kronos*; the eager striving of

Ganymed, or the spring-like joy of *Der Musensohn*, adapting his flexible tone to the varying requirements of each. The reading of the *Harfenspieler Lieder* forms the centrepiece of the recital, the singer catching the melancholy and mystery so unerringly suggested by the composer himself. The books speak unkindly of *Sehnsucht*, but Prégardien, a superb Bach interpreter, brings out the connection with the older composer in the recitative of this cantata-like song. Staier again seems the ideal partner for this singer. His luminous playing of his fortepiano, notably in such a piece as *An den Mond*, exactly matches the ethereal beauty of the tenor's performance. Once or twice we may wish for the more substantial tones of a Fischer-Dieskau or a Schreier with their attendant 'modern' pianists, but the older interpreters' gifts are, in a sense, complementary to and different from the younger artists. The natural, well-balanced recording allows us to hear all the subtleties to be found in these performances, which pay homage, in their verbal detailing, as much to poet as to composer.

Schubert Der Einsame, D800. Ständchen, D889. An Silvia, D891. Der Jüngling an der Quelle, D300. Lied eines Schiffers, D360. Gruppe aus dem Tartarus, D583. Die Götter Griechenlands, D677. Im Walde, D708. Der Wanderer an den Mond, D870. Freiwilliges Versinken, D700. Himmelsfunken, D651. Prometheus, D674. Gondelfahrer, D808. Die Sterne, D939. Auf der Bruck, D853. Heidenröslein, D257. Im Haine, D738. Nachtviolen, D752. Bei dir allein, D866/2. Du bist die Ruh, D776. **Simon Keenlyside** (bar); **Malcolm Martineau** (pf).
EMI Eminence Ⓜ CD-EMX2224 (71 minutes: DDD: 8/94). Texts and translations included.
Gramophone Editor's choice.   Ⓖ

Simon Keenlyside is the best baritone singer and interpreter of Schubert this country has ever had and is fully the equal of such Austro-German coevals as Holzmair and Schmidt. Hyperbole? Anyone who hears this enriching recital will not think so. Keenlyside has just about all the attributes needed by a Schubert interpreter: a magnificent tone, firm and natural, rounded throughout an extensive register, an inborn sense of line, perfect German, and in addition to all that an instinctive intelligence that carries him confidently through his long and taxing programme with hardly a phrase that could be bettered in terms of colour or word-painting. You can sit back without a qualm knowing that he will have the reserves and the trenchancy of purpose to conquer such Everests of the Schubert repertory as *Prometheus* and *Gruppe aus dem Tartarus* where his vocal means are fully equal to the defiance the songs proclaim. *Auf der Bruck* is filled with the ongoing energy Schubert calls for. Then there's the thoughtfulness to fulfil the demands of such a philosophical and forward-looking song as *Freiwilliges Versinken*, the sense of questing romanticism for *Im Walde*. Among the reflective pieces, *Die Götter Griechenlands* is notable for plangent feeling and tone – just right. *Gondelfahrer*, that marvellous evocation of bells heard at night, is full of nocturnal mystery. *Heidenröslein* is delicate in its subtle timbres and smiling tone; so is *Die Sterne* while *Bei dir allein* has a Fischer-Dieskau enthusiasm. And the recital is crowned by the final offering, *Du bist die Ruh*, where the voice opens out in its full beauty. These successes make the one or two failures mystifying. They come at the start of the disc so perhaps the performers weren't yet into their stride. *Der Einsame* plods at an unduly slow tempo. *Ständchen* lacks airiness, Martineau's foursquare accompanying thereabouts doesn't help. Later he provides many inspired moments (try *Im Haine*, where he so charmingly supports the baritone's *mezzo voce*), and he never over-eggs the pudding in the heavier songs. The recording is ideally balanced and judged but the texts and translations have been carelessly read. However, any trifling drawbacks don't prevent an outright recommendation for this well chosen and absorbing mid-price disc.

Schubert Lieder on Record, Volumes 1 and 2. Various artists. EMI mono Ⓜ CHS5 66150-2*, CHS5 66154-2* (two sets of three discs each: 205 and 202 minutes: ADD: 7/97). Texts and translations included. From G&T, HMV Columbia, Parlophone and Odeon originals. Recorded 1898-1952.
Sopranos – Pauline Cramer, Ursula van Diemen, Elise Elizza, Kirsten Flagstad, Marta Fuchs, Dusolina Giannini, Ria Ginster, Frieda Hempel, Lilli Lehmann, Lotte Lehmann, Frida Leider, Minnie Nast, Flora Nielsen, Aaltje Noordewier-Reddingius, Margaret Ritchie, Lotte Schöne, Elisabeth Schumann, Dame Elisabeth Schwarz-kopf, Irmgard Seefried, Meta Seinemeyer, Susan Strong. *Mezzo-sopranos* – Therese Behr-Schnabel, Julia Culp, Elena Gerhardt, Marie Götze, Susan Metcalfe-Casals, Edyth Walker. *Contraltos* – Edith Clegg, Ottilie Metzger, Maria Olszewska, Sigrid Onegin. *Tenors* – Friedrich Brodersen, Karl Erb, Heinrich Hensel, John McCormack, Franz Naval, Julius Patzak, Sir Peter Pears, Aksel Schiøtz, Leo Slezak, Richard Tauber, Georges Thill, Gustav Walter. *Baritones* – David Bispham, Leopold Demuth, Hans Duhan, Dietrich Fischer-Dieskau, Sir George Henschel, Gerhard Hüsch, Herbert Janssen, Charles Panzéra, Bernhard Sonnerstedt, Harold Williams. *Bass-baritones* – Harry Plunkett Greene, Hans Hotter, Friedrich Schorr. *Basses* – Feodor Chaliapin, Wilhelm Hesch, Alexander Kipnis, Paul Knüpfer, Endré Koréh, Lev Sibiriakov, Vanni-Marcoux, Ernst Wachter.

Much has happened to the interpretation of Lieder since 1952 and quite a bit since 1982 when this issue first appeared on LP. Yet there is still much to be learnt from listening to these 93 songs interpreted by 64 singers in a total of 129 performances. Styles have changed radically since the early decades of the century. Nowadays we insist on accuracy over every aspect of interpretation; in these older performances the text and its meaning takes precedence over almost everything else: nearly all these singers are keen to tell an urgent message and never mind if that involves excessive rubato, *ritardandos*, playing about with note values. Practically every singer is an individualist, the voice and style immediately recognizable. Today the manner is more uniform, the personal, eccentric approach often frowned upon. The transfers are almost identical with those made by Keith Hardwick for the LP set, very many taken off vinyl, giving you the singers in very present form, no scratch intervening. The oldest discs – many rarities – are intractable: 1990s technology might has not improved on what we encounter here. These are fascinating and rewarding issues that no lover of Schubert and/or Lieder should be without.

Schubert Schwanengesang, D957. Herbst, D945. Der Wanderer an den Mond, D870. Am Fenster, D878. Bei dir allein, D866 No. 2. **Peter Schreier** (ten); **András Schiff** (pf). Decca Ⓕ 425 612-2DH (63 minutes: DDD: 6/90). Texts and translations included. Recorded 1989.
Gramophone Award Winner 1990.   ⒼⒼⒼ
Schubert Schwanengesang, D957. Sehnsucht, D879. Der Wanderer an den Mond, D870. Wiegenlied, D867. Am Fenster, D878. Herbst, D945. **Brigitte Fassbaender** (mez); **Aribert Reimann** (pf). DG Ⓕ 429 766-2GH (68 minutes: DDD: 6/92). Texts and translations included. Recorded 1989-1991. *Gramophone Award Winner 1992.*   Ⓖ
Though *Schwanengesang* is not a song-cycle but a collection of Schubert's last (or 'swan') songs by their first publisher, it is generally felt to form a satisfying sequence, with a unity of style if not of theme or mood. This is certainly not weakened by the addition on the Decca disc of the four last songs which were originally omitted, all of them settings of poems by Johann Seidl. Seidl is one of the three poets whose work Schubert used in these frequently sombre songs and it is strange to think that all concerned in their creation were young men, none of the poets being older than Schubert. The listener can scarcely be unaware of a shadow or sometimes an almost unearthly radiance over even the happiest (such as "Die Taubenpost", the last of all) and that is particularly true when the performers themselves have such sensitive awareness as here. Peter Schreier is responsive to every shade of meaning in music and text; graceful and charming in "Das Fischermädchen", flawlessly lyrical in "Am Meer", he will sometimes risk an almost frightening raw-boned cry as in the anguish of "Der Atlas" and "Der Doppelgänger". András Schiff's playing is a miracle of combined strength and delicacy, specific insight and general rightness. One of the great Lieder recordings, and not merely of recent years. Fassbaender and Reimann offer something equally compelling but rather different in their account of *Schwanengesang*. Fassbaender's interpretation, idiosyncratic in every respect, pierces to the heart of the bleak songs with performances as daring and challenging as the playing of her partner. More than anyone, these two artists catch the fleeting moods of these mini-dramas, and their searing originality of concept. Even the lighter songs have a special individuality of utterance. This is a starkly immediate interpretation that leaves the listener shattered. The extra Seidl settings, rarely performed, are all worth hearing. Both of these notable partnerships are superb in their own ways.
Additional recommendations ...
...Schwanengesang. **Bryn Terfel** (bass-bar); **Malcolm Martineau** (pf).
  Sain Ⓕ SCDC4035 (57 minutes: DDD: 5/92).
...Schwanengesang. Die schöne Müllerin. Winterreise. **Dietrich Fischer-Dieskau** (bar);
  Gerald Moore (pf). DG Ⓑ 437 235-2GX3 (three discs: 184 minutes: ADD: 3/93).
...Schwanengesang[a]. D547[b]. D216[b]. D882[b]. D361[c]. D583[d]. D719[e]. D741[e].D799[e]. D224[c]. D768[c].
  Hans Hotter (bass-bar); **Gerald Moore** (pf).
  EMI Références mono Ⓜ CDH5 65196-2* (78 minutes: ADD: 10/94).
...Schwanengesang – Der Atlas; Ihr Bild; Das Fischermädchen; Die Stadt; Am Meer;
  Der Doppelgänger. *Coupled with works by* **Mendelssohn** *and* **Schumann**
  Christoph Prégardien (ten); **Andreas Staier** (fp). Deutsche Harmonia Mundi Ⓕ 05472 77319-2
  (57 minutes: DDD: 12/94). ☞ *See review under Schumann; refer to the Index.*   Ⓖ
...Schwanengesang – Abschied. D369. D295. D553. D565. D649. D677. D700. D771. D772. D842.
  D853. D832. D878. D881. D871. D932. D933. D939. D800. D799. **Dietrich Fischer-Dieskau**
  (bar); **Hartmut Höll** (pf). Erato Ⓕ 4509-98493-2 (77 minutes: DDD: 9/95).

Schubert Die schöne Müllerin, D795, with a reading of six poems not set by Schubert.
  Ian Bostridge (ten); **Dietrich Fischer-Dieskau** (narr); **Graham Johnson** (pf).
  Hyperion Ⓕ CDJ33025 (73 minutes: DDD). Text and translation included. Recorded 1994-1995.
  Gramophone Editor's choice. Gramophone Award Winner 1996.   ⒼⒼⒼ
Schubert Die schöne Müllerin, D795. **Wolfgang Holzmair** (bar); **Jörg Demus** (pf).
  Preiser Ⓕ 93337 (68 minutes: ADD: 3/89). Recorded 1984.
Schubert Die schöne Müllerin, D795. **Håkan Hagegård** (bar); **Emanuel Ax** (pf). RCA Victor Red
  Seal Ⓕ 09026 61705-2 (61 minutes: DDD: 2/95). Texts and translations included. Recorded 1987.
The 20 songs of *Die schöne Müllerin* portray a Wordsworthian world of heightened emotion in the pantheistic riverside setting of the miller. The poet, Wilhelm Müller, tells of solitary longings, jealousies, fears and hopes as the river rushes by, driving the mill-wheel and refreshing the natural world. Bostridge and Johnson go to the heart of the matter, the young tenor in his aching tones and naturally affecting interpretation, the pianist in his perceptive, wholly apposite playing – and, of course, in his extensive notes. The sum of their joint efforts is a deeply satisfying experience. Bostridge shares with Partridge the right timbre for the protagonist and a straightforward approach, with Schreier a deeper journey into the meaning of each song, with Prégardien a liquid, refined line, and

with all three an instinctive rightness of phrasing. Bostridge's peculiarly beseeching voice enshrines the vulnerability, tender feeling and obsessive love of the youthful miller, projecting in turn the young lover's thwarted passions, self-delusions and, finally, inner tragedy. Nowhere does he stretch beyond the bounds of the possible, as even Schreier just occasionally does, everything expressed in eager then doleful tones. Johnson suggests that "Ungeduld" mustn't be "masterful and insistent" or the youth would have won the girl, so that even in this superficially buoyant song the sense of a sensitive, sad, introverted youth is maintained. The daydreaming strophic songs have the smiling, innocent, intimate sound that suits them to perfection, the angry ones the touch of stronger metal that Bostridge can now add to his silver, the tragic ones, before the neutral "Baches Wiegenlied", an inner intensity that rends the heart as it should. An occasional moment of faulty German accenting matters not at all when the sense of every word is perceived. As a bonus we have here, as on the Fassbaender recording, a recitation of the Prologue and Epilogue and of the Müller poems not set by Schubert: Fischer-Dieskau, who for various reasons set out by Johnson, didn't, regretfully, have a part in this series as a singer, now graces it with his speaking voice. The ideal Hyperion recording catches everything in very present terms, as it does Johnson's own adumbration in his playing of what he writes in his notes. In all musical matters, everything Johnson writes only enhances one's enjoyment, if that is the right word, of a soul-searching interpretation which now ranks with those tenor versions listed below as a recommendation.

Simply as a voice Hagegård is perhaps superior to that of any of those singers reviewed and listed here. It is, paradoxically, a light yet heroic sound, typically Swedish in timbre, flexible throughout its range and – relevant to the work in hand – tenor-like in tone. Its owner uses it with marked attention to vocal verities, never disturbing a sure legato, placing his words firmly and naturally on it. The eager youth of the early songs is unerringly enacted, perhaps without quite the sense of vulnerability suggested by Holzmair and other tenor interpreters, although by the same token he suggests an appropriately open-air, fresh youth. When sorrow, jealousy and eventually heartbreak enter the lad's life, Hagegård projects these with as much conviction yet without a hint of exaggeration or sentimentality. He, and the sensitive but never obtrusive Ax, allow Schubert to speak for himself in sensible, moderate speeds and discreet phrasing: in the context of frequent repetitions, this has undoubted advantages. Holzmair and Demus, Schmidt and Jansen do much the same. It would be hard to choose among these three versions if you wanted a straightforward reading, but the sheerly beautiful sound of Hagegård's voice places him marginally in front. Bär and, most of all, Fischer-Dieskau peer deeper into the songs and the youth's psychology – but Hagegård and his partner probably come closer to a truly Schubertian ideal. The recording is ideally balanced.

Additional recommendations ...

...*Coupled with* D550. D686. D257. **Fritz Wunderlich** (ten); **Hubert Giesen** (pf).
    DG The Originals Ⓜ 447 452-2GOR (72 minutes: ADD).
...**Dietrich Fischer-Dieskau** (bar); **Gerald Moore** (pf). DG Ⓕ 415 186-2GH (62 minutes: ADD: 9/85). Ⓠ
...**Josef Protschka** (ten); **Helmut Deutsch** (pf). Capriccio Ⓕ 10 082 (66 minutes: DDD: 6/87).
...**Olaf Bär** (bar); **Geoffrey Parsons** (pf). EMI Ⓕ CDC7 47947-2 (65 minutes: DDD: 8/87).
...**Siegfried Lorenz** (bar); **Norman Shetler** (pf). Capriccio Ⓕ 10 220 (68 minutes: DDD: 5/90).
...**Peter Schreier** (ten); **András Schiff** (pf).
    Decca Ⓕ 430 414-2DH (63 minutes: DDD: 5/91). *Selected by Sounds in Retrospect.*   ⓠⓠ
...**Christoph Prégardien** (ten); **Andreas Staier** (fp).
    Deutsche Harmonia Mundi Ⓕ 05472 77273-2 (60 minutes: DDD: 12/92). 🖋
...*Coupled with* **Beethoven** An die ferne Geliebte, Op. 98. **Gerhard Hüsch** (bar); **Hanns Udo Müller** (pf). Preiser Lebendige Vergangenheit mono Ⓕ 89202* (two discs: 137 minutes: AAD: 12/92).
...**Ian Partridge** (ten); **Jennifer Partridge** (pf).
    Classics for Pleasure Ⓑ CD-CFP4672 (63 minutes: ADD: 9/95).   ⓠ
...**Peter Schreier** (ten); **Konrad Ragossnig** (gtr).
    Berlin Classics Ⓕ 0011 232BC (65 minutes: ADD: 3/96).
...*Coupled with works by* **Grieg** Aksel Schiøtz (ten); **Gerald Moore** (pf).
    Danacord mono Ⓕ DACOCD452* (75 minutes: ADD: 4/97). *See review in the Collections section; refer to the Index.*
...Excerpts. *Coupled with works by various composers.* **Aksel Schiøtz** (ten) with various artists.
    Danacord mono Ⓕ DACOCD454* (72 minutes: ADD: 5/97). *See review in the Collections section; refer to the Index.*
...Die schöne Müllerin[a]. Also contains short items [b] by Arne, Handel and Pessard.
    Richard Crooks (ten); [a]**Frank la Forge**, [b]**Frederic Schauwecker** (pfs).
    Claremont mono Ⓜ CDGSE78-50-67* (62 minutes: ADD: 5/97).

Schubert Winterreise, D911. **Peter Schreier** (ten); **András Schiff** (pf).
    Decca Ⓕ 436 122-2DH (72 minutes: DDD: 5/94). Text and translation included.
    Recorded 1991. *Gramophone Editor's choice.*   ⓠⓠ
Schubert Winterreise, D911. **Bernd Weikl** (bar); **Helmut Deutsch** (pf). Nightingale Classics Ⓕ NC070960-2 (70 minutes: DDD: 5/95). Text and translation included. Recorded 1993.
Schubert Winterreise, D911. **Dietrich Fischer-Dieskau** (bar); **Jörg Demus** (pf).
    DG The Originals Ⓜ 447 421-2GOR (71 minutes: ADD: 8/95). Text and translation included.
    From SLPM139201/2 (6/66). Recorded 1965.

Schubert Winterreise, D911. **Wolfgang Holzmair** (bar); **Imogen Cooper** (pf).
Philips Ⓕ 446 407-2PH (70 minutes: DDD: 5/96). Text and translation included. Recorded 1994.
Schubert Winterreise, D911. **Christoph Prégardien** (ten); **Andreas Staier** (fp).
Teldec Das Alte Werk Ⓕ 0630-18824-2 (74 minutes: DDD: 12/97). 🖝 Texts and
translations included. Recorded 1996.

Winterreise can lay claim to be the greatest song cycle ever written. It chronicles the sad, numbing
journey of a forsaken lover, recalling past happiness, anguishing over his present plight, commenting
on how the snow-clad scenery reflects or enhances his mood. Schreier himself, in his note in the
booklet accompanying his recording, refers to the unique density and spiritual concentration of the
songs; that, and their hallucinatory nature, inform this riveting performance from start to finish,
nowhere more so than in "Wasserflut" and "Einsamkeit". The latter is a paradigm of the whole
searing, almost unbearable experience. If you can tolerate it you will be engaged and surely moved by
the whole. In this song, Schreier leans into the words and notes of "Ach, das die Luft so ruhig!"
suggesting the cry of a desperate, tormented soul – as does the emphatic enunciation of the single
word "Bergstroms" earlier, in "Irricht". Also arresting is the curiously daring way Schreier asks the
question at the end of "Die Post", as if it were a spontaneous afterthought. These make the moments
of calm and repose all the more eerie. The sad delicacy of Schiff's playing at the start of
"Frühlingstraum" sets the scene of the imagined May to perfection, and the flowing lift of his left
hand in "Täuschung" is as deceptively friendly as the light described by the singer. "Das Wirtshaus"
is all false resignation: voice and piano tell us of the man's tired emptiness. Anger and defiance, as in
the earlier performance, are registered in raw, chilling tone and phraseology. Then, in the pair's
revelatory way, they draw attention anew to the originality of concept of "Letzte Hoffnung". The
final songs taken simply, speak beautifully of acceptance. The disc further benefits from the warm yet
clear acoustic of the recording. Viewing the whole scene, it matches Fassbaender in its unbridled
involvement. Fischer-Dieskau is still there as another kind of benchmark for those who prefer a lower,
more amenable voice in this cycle.

For those who prefer a baritone, Weikl seriously challenges the hegemony, among lower-voiced
singers, of the versions listed below. Indeed it is the absolute vocal security and evenness of Weikl's
actual singing that so impresses even before one considers his view of the work, and in that he recalls
Schmidt on DG. Nowhere is there any sign of strain, over-emphasis, faltering in pitch, or failure of
nerve in executing a phrase with a long breath, and as the singer has such a strong voice one feels
throughout that there is always something held in reserve. As a reading the Weikl unerringly keeps
that balance between detachment and subjectivity. Tempos are in every case perfectly judged – and
here Deutsch's well-observed and well-balanced playing makes a significant contribution – a
wonderful frozen feeling in "Auf dem Flusse", for instance. Weikl displays many gradations of tone
to enhance his thought-through reading – "Gefrorne Tränen" is a good example – but he uses vocal
emphases more sparingly, reserving his most pointed verbal accents for such things as "Gras" in
"Erstarrung", "Hähne" in "Frühlingstraum" and "Hunde" in "Im Dorfe", but even these never upset
the verities of line and firm tone, and the sheer beauty of the singing, as in "Der Lindenbaum", is
balm to the ear. For those who find Fischer-Dieskau's more agonized, psychological readings too
much to bear, or find his style too interventionist, Weikl is the obvious choice. A superb recording.

The issue in the DG Originals series of Fischer-Dieskau's *Winterreise* was recorded in 1965. On the
verge of his fifth decade, the singer was in his absolute prime – and it shows. Indeed listening to his
interpretation is like coming home to base after many interesting encounters away from the familiar.
Indeed, it is possibly the finest of all in terms of beauty of tone and ease of technique – and how
beautiful, how smooth and velvety was the baritone's voice at that time. That this is the most interior,
unadorned and undemonstrative of Fischer-Dieskau's readings perhaps arises from the fact that
Demus, a discerning musician and sure accompanist, is the most reflective of all the singer's many
partners in the cycle. Demus never strikes out on his own, is always there unobtrusively and subtly
supportive, with the right colour and phrasing, literally in hand. Given an intimate, slightly dry
recording, finely remastered, the whole effect is of a pair communing with each other and stating the
sad, distraught message of Schubert's bleak work in terms of a personal message to the listener in the
home. A deeply rewarding performance. Certainly if you want Fischer-Dieskau in the cycle you need
look no further.

As far as Holzmair is concerned, we are at the opposite extreme from Fischer-Dieskau's big-scale
approach with its huge variety of tonal colour and expression, much nearer to Schmidt, who has a
more rounded tone than Holzmair but doesn't match the Austrian's personal involvement. Bär and
Weikl lie somewhere in between Holzmair and Fischer-Dieskau, their readings bigger in scale than
Holzmair's but not as overtly dramatic as the older baritone's. Among the pianists, Demus and Jansen
come closest to Cooper's penetrating *aperçus*. Absolute recommendations are simply not possible. Yet
Holzmair and Cooper give us such a natural, unvarnished view of the great work, that their CD
deserves to stand as recommendation, among baritone interpretations, with the others.

Prégardien and Staier have something new and important to offer. From the very first song, we are
in the presence of a sensitive, inward man in fear of his fate. Something is actually happening to this
sufferer's soul at the second "des ganzen Winters Eis"; indeed the whole final verse of the second song
expresses the youth's anguish. Just as memorable as the stab of pain in the repeated final line "Da ist
meiner Liebstens Haus" at the end of "Wasserflut", the introverted misery of the ice-carving of the
loved one's name in "Auf dem Flusse" and the almost mesmeric feeling in the final verse as the torrent

rages in the protagonist's heart. This is what the singing of this cycle is about: the exposing of raw nerves. Staier is just as revelatory. Using his fortepiano to maximum effect, he finds so many fresh perceptions in his part, as in the precise weighting at the start of "Einsamkeit" and, as important, ones that accord perfectly with those of his regular partner. Here you have the sense of performers who have lived together with the cycle and conceived a unified, thought-through vision. Listen to the way the pair mesh together to searing effect at the end of "Irrlicht", or how they make use of the pregnant pause to increase the work's drama as at the start of "Rast", in which Prégardien displays an unexpected range of dynamics. The ineffable sadness of "Frühlingstraum" (the text ideally articulated, the close quite properly trance-like), the raw blast of winter in "Der stürmische Morgen", the tense weariness of "Der Wegweiser", the weary half-voice of "Das Wirtshaus" – these and so much else contribute to the impression of a truly great performance. The recording is very finely balanced.

Additional recommendations ...

...**Peter Schreier** (ten); **Sviatoslav Richter** (pf). Philips Ⓕ 442 360-2PH (77 minutes: DDD: 9/94).
...**Dietrich Fischer-Dieskau** (bar); **Alfred Brendel** (pf).
　Philips Ⓕ 411 463-2PH (70 minutes: DDD: 12/86).
...**Robert Holl** (bass-bar); **Konrad Richter** (pf). Preiser Ⓕ 93317 (72 minutes: ADD: 8/89).
...**Olaf Bär** (bar); **Geoffrey Parsons** (pf). EMI Ⓕ CDC7 49334-2 (75 minutes: DDD: 11/89).
...**Brigitte Fassbaender** (mez); **Aribert Reimann** (pf). EMI Ⓕ CDC7 49846-2 (70 minutes: DDD: 7/90).
...**Sir Peter Pears** (ten); **Benjamin Britten** (pf). Decca Ⓜ 417 473-2DM (73 minutes: ADD: 10/91).
...**Max van Egmond** (bar); **Jos van Immerseel** (fp).
　Channel Classics Ⓕ CCS0190 (67 minutes: DDD: 3/92). ☞
...**Dietrich Fischer-Dieskau** (bar); **Daniel Barenboim** (pf).
　DG Classikon Ⓑ 439 432-2GGL (73 minutes: ADD: 9/94).
...**Matthias Goerne** (bar); **Graham Johnson** (pf).
　Hyperion Schubert Edition Ⓕ CDJ33030 (74 minutes: DDD: 1/98). *Selected by Soundings.*

Schubert Die Verschworenen, oder Der häusliche Krieg. **Soile Isokoski** (sop) Countess Ludmilla; **Peter Lika** (bass) Count Heribert von Lüdenstein; **Rodrigo Orrego** (ten) Astolf von Reisenberg; **Andreas Fischer** (ten) Garold von Nummen; **Christian Dahm** (bass) Friedrich von Trausdorf; **Thomas Pfützner** (bass) Knight; **Mechthild Georg** (mez) Udolin; **Anke Hoffmann** (sop) Isella; **Lisa Larsson** (sop) Helene; **Susanne Behnes** (sop) Luitgarde; **Marion Steingötter** (sop) Camilla; **Iris Kupke** (sop) Woman; **Chorus Musicus; Das Neue Orchester / Christoph Spering.**
Opus 111 Ⓕ OPS30-167 (64 minutes: DDD: 2/97). ☞ Notes, text and translation included. Recorded 1996.

Ignaz Castelli's neatly wrought text, loosely based on Aristophanes' *Lysistrata*, prompted, early in 1823, Schubert's most dramatically viable stage-work, a one-act *Singspiel*. Aristophanes' story of aggrieved womenfolk withholding their favours until their husbands abandoned their warmongering is transposed here to Vienna during the Crusades and softened with a liberal injection of Biedermeier sentiment. Schubert's parodistic martial music for the macho warriors can occasionally grow wearisome, especially in the finale. Otherwise, though, he scarcely puts a foot wrong. His dramatic pacing is sure and lively, his invention witty, touching and colourful, with its intermittent echoes of Mozart. The opera's gem is Helene's bittersweet F minor *Romanze*, with its sinuous clarinet obbligato (beautifully played here) and haunting modulation to the major in the very last bars. With his polished orchestra and fresh-toned chorus Christoph Spering gives a sympathetic, shrewdly paced account of the score, allowing the lyrical numbers plenty of breathing space and revealing a light, pointed touch in the comic ensembles. Of the singers, Peter Lika's Count has plenty of 'face', though his bass can become coarse under pressure. Rodrigo Orrego, as the knight Astolf, displays an agreeable, soft-grained tenor; and all four principal female roles are well taken, with Lisa Larsson showing a bright, pure tone and a shapely sense of phrase as Helene, and Soile Isokoski bringing real distinction to the role of the Countess, her warm, vibrant soprano, with its hint of mezzo richness and depth, more than once reminiscent of Schwarzkopf. The recording is vivid and well balanced, giving ample presence to the voices while allowing Schubert's felicitous scoring its due.

Further listening ...

...Rosamunde, D797 – No. 1, Die Zauberharfe Overture, D644; No. 5, Entr'acte in B flat major; No. 9, Ballet in G major. *Coupled with works by various composers.*
　Vienna Philharmonic Orchestra / Rudolf Kempe.
　Testament SBT1127* (3/98). *See review in the Collections section; refer to the Index.*
...Introduction and Variations in E minor on "Trockne Blumen" from "Die schöne Müllerin", D802. *Coupled with works by* **Liszt** *and* **Ernst** Gidon Kremer (vn); Oleg Maisenberg (pf). DG 445 820-2GH (10/95).
...Psalm 23, D706 (all arr. Cameron). *Coupled with works by various composers.*
　New College Choir, Oxford; Capricorn / Edward Higginbottom. Erato 3984-21659-2 (6/98).
　Gramophone Editor's choice. See review in the Collections section; refer to the Index.
...Stabat Mater, D175. Masses – No. 2 in G major, D167; No. 3 in B flat major, D324. Salve regina in A major, D676. **Greta De Reyghere** (sop); **Lieve Maertens** (mez); **Toby Spence** (ten); **Jan Van der Crabben** (bar); **Collegium Instrumentale Brugense; Capella Brugensis / Patrick Peire.** René Gailly CD87 140 (4/98).

...Ständchen, D957 No. 4. *Coupled with works by various composers.*
Angela Gheorghiu (sop); **Malcolm Martineau** (pf).
Decca 458 360-2DH (5/98). *See review in the Collections section; refer to the Index.*
...Fierrabras. **Soloists; Arnold Schönberg Choir; Chamber Orchestra of Europe / Claudio Abbado.**
DG 427 341-2GH2 (10/90).
...Lazarus, D689 (cpted. Denisov). **Soloists; Stuttgart Gächinger Kantorei;**
Stuttgart Bach Collegium / Helmuth Rilling. Hänssler Classic 98 111 (4/97). ✍

Ervin Schulhoff   Bohemian 1894-1942

Schulhoff Symphonies – No. 3; No. 5. **Prague Radio Symphony Orchestra / Vladimír Válek.**
Supraphon Ⓕ 11 2161-2 (53 minutes: DDD: 10/96).
Posthumous premières of these works in the 1950s aroused little interest, but Schulhoff has acquired quite a following in recent years and this latest addition to his discography should not be overlooked. As always in music where there is no performance tradition to speak of, the range of interpretative possibilities is wide. On this showing, Vladimír Válek is the most deft and neo-classical of Schulhoff conductors, offering well-prepared, notably fluent accounts of both pieces; his aim seems to be to reconcile their blatant Communistic idiom with the lighter, Roaring Twenties manner of the composer's previous creative period. In Israel Yinon's recording of the Third Symphony, you sense that the music is not just being given room to breathe; it can only be considered in the light of the composer's death in a Nazi concentration camp. Accordingly, Yinon adopts a much weightier tempo in the first movement, its ostinato unrelenting, its drums militantly thwacked. Albrecht's idea of *moderato* is yet more funereal, suggesting that it is the Czech conductor who is out of line. Nevertheless, Válek's account is arguably the most persuasive of the three, executed with commendable crispness. In the Fifth Symphony, risking some loss of *gravitas*, Válek is again nothing if not urgent. The music makes better sense in his hands and any lack of clarity in the orchestral textures would seem to derive from deficiencies in the writing. Even the lack of a clinching melodic idea is made to appear less important. This is a valuable disc, decently annotated.
Additional recommendations ...
...Nos. 1-3. **Philharmonia Hungarica / George Alexander Albrecht.**
CPO Ⓕ CPO999 251-2 (70 minutes: DDD: 1/95).
...Nos. 2 and 3. Concerto for String Quartet and Orchestra[a]. [a]**Kyncl Quartet; Czech State**
Philharmonic Orchestra, Brno / Israel Yinon. Koch Schwann Ⓕ 315432 (62 minutes: DDD: 2/96).

Schulhoff Sextet[a]. String Quartet in G major, Op. 25[b]. Duo[c]. Solo Violin Sonata[d].
[a]**Rainer Johannes Kimstedt** (va); [a]**Michael Sanderling** (vc); [ab]**Petersen Quartet**
([d]Conrad Muck, [c]Gernot Sussmuth, vns; Friedemann Weigle, va; [c]Hans-Jakob Eschenburg, vc).
Capriccio Ⓕ 10 539 (77 minutes: DDD: 11/95). Recorded 1994.
As Schulhoff enthusiasts will have come to expect, the works represented are not at all uniform in style. The early quartet is prematurely neo-classical. It was conceived in 1918 when the composer was still serving in the Austrian Army. The German group certainly give it their all. Taut and tough, they seem intent on radicalizing the discourse whether through a heightened response to its finer points or a profound understanding of the Beethovenian models that lurk beneath the surface invention. As a result, the Quartet emerges as a witty, substantial piece. The string Sextet was completed six years later but sounds quite different, its Schoenbergian first movement well integrated with the more eclectic idiom of the rest. Whatever the outward manner, Schulhoff's rhythmic phraseology is metrically conceived. Even if you already know the Sextet the Petersen make a plausible first choice. The aggressive communication of their playing is emphasized by the bright, not quite top-heavy sound balance. The Janáček-Bartók-Ravel axis of the *Duo* is equally well served. The Sonata for solo violin (1927) is at least as interesting as similar works by Hindemith, less emotionally wrenching than the Bartók. That work was composed a couple of years after Schulhoff's premature death. A thoroughly distinguished issue by an ensemble seemingly incapable of giving a dull performance.
Additional recommendation ...
...Violin Sonata No. 1, Op. 7[a]. Cello Sonata, Op. 17[d]. Solo Violin Sonata[b]. Duo[c].
[abc]**Oleh Krysa** (vn); [cd]**Torleif Thedéen** (vc); [a]**Tatiana Tchekina**, [d]**Stefan Bojsten** (pfs).
BIS Ⓕ CD679 (73 minutes: DDD: 3/97).

Schulhoff String Quartet No. 1.
Hindemith String Quartet No. 3, Op. 22.
Weill String Quartet. **Brandis Quartet** (Thomas Brandis, Peter Brem, vns; Wilfried Strehle, va;   Ⓖ
Wolfgang Boettcher, vc). Nimbus Ⓕ NI5410 (60 minutes: DDD: 3/95). Recorded 1992.
All three works bear witness to a culture that, in terms of tempo and sensation, was in the process of excited transformation. The period covered is 1923-1924, the time of rocketing German inflation, the establishment of the USSR, Rilke's *Duino Elegies* as well as major Kafka (who died in 1924), Mann, Musil, Cocteau and Bréton (his Surrealist manifesto). This music is full of it all. Hindemith's bold Third Quartet – one of the composer's most arresting and accessible pieces – launches its explorations within a relatively formal framework, certainly in comparison with Schulhoff and Weill. Rich

invention is tempered by a sense of outward propriety. Weill's Quartet opens with considerable expressive warmth, although it soon busies itself with a whole range of interesting ideas (the finale is particularly rich in incident), with a hoot of a *Scherzo* that suddenly swerves to a Reger-like March, then waltzes gently forth in a manner that suggests Shostakovich before embarking on further discursive episodes and scurrying off to a cheeky *diminuendo*. Granted, one feels that Weill is in search of something he never quite finds, but the very act of searching makes for an absorbing adventure. Even more compelling, however, is Schulhoff's dazzling First Quartet, the last piece in the programme and a highly dramatic musical mystery tour. Urgency rules right from the opening bars, while Schulhoff's tonal palette is both wide-ranging and ingeniously employed: pizzicato, *col legno*, *sul ponticello*, harmonics (wonderfully effective in the finale), dense harmonic computations and a rhythmic vitality that recalls Bartók at full cry (most especially in the third movement). The work's pale, equivocal coda recalls the parallel quartet mysteries of Schulhoff's fellow Holocaust victims Krása and Haas, while the work as a whole is far more than the sum of its restless and endlessly fascinating parts. A fine programme, lustrously recorded.

Additional recommendation ...
...String Quartets Nos. 1 and 2. Five Pieces for String Quartet. **Petersen Quartet.**
Capriccio Ⓕ 10463 (47 minutes: DDD: 5/93).

Further listening ...
...Die Mondsüchtige. *Coupled with works by* **Schreker** *and* **Hindemith**
Leipzig Gewandhaus Orchestra / Lothar Zagrosek. Decca Entartete Musik 444 182-2DH (5/95). Ⓖ
...Piano Concerto No. 2[a]. Concerto for Flute and Piano[b]. Concertino for String Quartet and Orchestra[c]. Jazz Etudes – Blues; Chanson; Tango[d]. Esquisses de jazz – Blues; Charleston[d]. Partita – Tango-Rag; Tempo di Fox à la Hawai; Tango; Shimmy-Jazz[d].
[b]**Bettina Wild** (fl); [ab]**Aleksandar Madzar,** [d]**Erwin Schulhoff** (pfs);
[c]**Hawthorne Quartet;** [abc]**Deutsche Kammerphilharmonie / Andreas Delfs.**
Decca Entartete Musik [d]mono/stereo 444 819-2DH (12/95).
...Symphony No. 1. Suite for Chamber Orchestra. Flammen – festive overture.
Brno State Philharmonic Orchestra / Israel Yinon. Koch Schwann 314372 (8/95). Ⓖ
...Violin Sonata No. 2. *Coupled with works by various composers.* **Gidon Kremer** (vn);
Oleg Maisenberg (pf). Teldec 0630-13597-2 (7/97). *Gramophone Editor's choice.*
See review in the Collections section; refer to the Index.
...Flammen. **Soloists; Berlin RIAS Chamber Choir; Berlin Deutsches Symphony Orchestra /**
John Mauceri. Decca Entartete Musik 444 630-2DHO2 (1/95). Ⓖ

Gunther Schuller
American 1925

Suggested listening ...
...Magnificat and Nunc dimittis (St Thomas Service). *Coupled with works by various composers.*
St Thomas Church Choir, New York / Gerre Hancock with **Patrick Allen** (org).
Priory PRCD600 (1/98). *See review in the Collections section; refer to the Index.*
...Suite. *Coupled with works by various composers.* **Reykjavik Wind Quintet.**
Chandos CHAN9174 (11/93). *See review in the Collections section; refer to the Index.* Ⓖ

Clara Schumann
German 1819-1896

Suggested listening ...
...Piano Sonata in G minor. *Coupled with works by various composers.* **Jennifer Eley** (pf).
Koch International Classics 37197-2 (10/96). *See review under Mendelssohn; refer to the Index.*

Robert Schumann
German 1810-1856

Schumann Cello Concerto in A minor, Op. 129[a]. Adagio and Allegro in A flat major, Op. 70[b].
Fantasiestücke, Op. 73[b]. Funf Stücke im Volkston, Op. 102[b]. **Heinrich Schiff** (vc);
[b]**Gerhard Oppitz** (pf); [a]**Berlin Philharmonic Orchestra / Bernard Haitink.**
Philips Ⓕ 422 414-2PH (60 minutes: DDD: 6/93). Item marked [a] recorded 1988,
[b] arr. Grützmacher, recorded 1991. *Gramophone Editor's choice.* ⒼⒼ
Schumann Cello Concerto in A minor, Op. 129[a]. Adagio and Allegro in A flat major, Op. 70[b].
Fantasiestücke, Op. 73[b]. Fünf Stücke im Volkston, Op. 102[b]. Mass in C minor, Op. 147 –
Offertorium[c].
Bargiel Adagio in G major, Op. 38[a]. **Steven Isserlis** (vc); [c]**Dame Felicity Lott** (sop); [c]**David King**
(org); [a]**Deutsche Kammerphilharmonie / Christoph Eschenbach** ([b]pf). RCA Victor Red Seal
Ⓕ 09026 68800-2 (75 minutes: DDD: 12/97). 🎗 Recorded 1996. *Gramophone Editor's choice.*
Selected by Soundings.
Schumann's Cello Concerto is a fairly dark, troubled work, and sometimes cellists are tempted to adopt a somewhat overwrought approach when playing it. In fact, it responds best to a more balanced

approach, as exemplified in the performance by Heinrich Schiff. His playing is very eloquent, and quite strong, but there is also a feeling of dignity and refinement in his response to the music. Everything is perfectly in scale, and the work's essential nobility is allowed to emerge in a most moving fashion. Schiff's technique is faultless, and his tonal quality is very beautiful. Haitink and the BPO seem totally in sympathy with the soloist, and the recording is warm and well detailed. The three items with piano accompaniment comprise a series of short pieces which are for the most part sunnier in outlook than the Concerto, and they make an effective contrast to the larger-scale work. Again Schiff's playing is expressive, but his phrasing is full of subtlety and poetry, and Oppitz is a highly responsive partner.

Only two of the works in RCA's fully and forwardly recorded anthology – the *Fünf Stücke im Volkston* of 1840 and the Concerto of a year later – were originally inspired by the cello. But in closely attuned, super-sensitive partnership with Eschenbach as both conductor and pianist, Steven Isserlis somehow persuades us that no instrument better revealed "the beloved dreamer whom we know as Schumann", as Tovey once put it. Helped by unhurried tempos and a lovely-voiced *c*1745 Guadagnini cello, Isserlis draws out the rich, nostalgic poetry of the concerto's first two movements with the eloquence of speech. And with his buoyancy of heart and bow he silences all criticism of the finale – even its low-lying cadenza (this he subsequently plays again with the composer's surely less effective flourish for the soloist in the closing bars). The five engaging *Volkston* pieces with piano are vividly characterized and contrasted in mood. And the Op. 73 and Op. 70 miniatures lose nothing through transfer from clarinet and horn respectively to one of the composer's two optional alternatives. The *Adagio and Allegro* for horn surely gains in expressive intimacy and vitality when bowed rather than blown. The *Offertorium* (with its telling accompanying cello thread) is sung by Felicity Lott with heart-easing beauty. The inclusion of a hitherto unrecorded, noble *Adagio* by Clara Schumann's gifted half-brother, Woldemar Bargiel, also helps to make this disc something of a collector's piece.

Additional recommendations ...

...Cello Concerto. *Coupled with works by* **Lalo** *and* **Saint-Saëns** János Starker (vc);
London Symphony Orchestra / Stanislaw Skrowaczewski. Mercury Ⓜ 432 010-2MM
(65 minutes: ADD: 4/92). *See review under Saint-Saëns; refer to the Index.*   Ⓖ Ⓖ

...Cello Concerto[a]. Piano Concerto in A minor, Op. 54[b]. Introduction and Allegro appassionato,
Op. 92[c]. [a]Jacqueline du Pré (vc); [a]New Philharmonia Orchestra / Daniel Barenboim ([b]pf);
[bc]London Philharmonic Orchestra / Dietrich Fischer-Dieskau.
EMI Ⓜ CDM7 64626-2 (74 minutes: ADD: 3/93).

...Cello Concerto[a]. Piano Trio No. 1 in D minor, Op. 63[b]. Funf Stücke im Volkston[c].
[b]Alexander Schneider (vn); Pablo Casals (vc); [b]Mieczyslaw Horszowski, [c]Leonard Mannes (pfs);
[a]Prades Festival Orchestra / Eugene Ormandy.
Sony Classical Casals Edition Ⓜ SMK58993 (74 minutes: ADD: 5/94).   Ⓖ Ⓖ

...Cello Concerto. *Coupled with works by various composers.* **Jacqueline du Pré** (vc)
with various artists and orchestras. EMI Ⓑ CZS5 68132-2 (six discs: 437 minutes: ADD: 8/94).
See review in the Collections section; refer to the Index.   Ⓖ Ⓖ

...Cello Concerto. **Brahms** Double Concerto in A minor, Op. 102[a]. [a]Ilya Kaler (vn);
Maria Kliegel (vc); **National Symphony Orchestra of Ireland / Andrew Constantine.**
Naxos Ⓢ 8 550938 (59 minutes: DDD: 10/95). *Gramophone Editor's choice.*
See review under Brahms; refer to the Index.

...Cello Concerto. **Hindemith** Cello Concerto. János Starker (vc); Bamberg Symphony Orchestra /
Dennis Russell Davies. RCA Victor Red Seal Ⓕ 09026 68027-2 (52 minutes: DDD: 10/95).

...Cello Concerto. *Coupled with works by various composers.* **János Starker** (vc);
Gerald Moore (pf); **Philharmonia Orchestra / Carlo Maria Giulini, Walter Susskind.**
EMI mono/stereo Ⓜ CZS5 68485-2 (six discs: 398 minutes: ADD: 12/95)
See review in the Collections section; refer to the Index.

...Romanze in A minor, Op. 94 No. 1. *Coupled with works by various composers.*
Mischa Maisky (vc); **Daria Hovora** (pf). DG Ⓕ 439 863-2GH (67 minutes: DDD: 9/94).   Ⓖ

...Cello Concerto[a]. Symphony No. 4 in D minor, Op. 120. [a]Christophe Coin (vc);
Orchestre des Champs-Elysées / Philippe Herreweghe.
Harmonia Mundi Ⓕ HMC90 1598 (56 minutes: DDD: 9/97). 🖉

Schumann Piano Concerto in A minor, Op. 54[a]. Introduction and Allegro appassionato in
D minor (Concertstück), Op. 92[a]. Violin Concerto in D minor, Op. posth[b]. Cello Concerto in
A minor, Op. 129[c]. Konzertstücke in F major, Op. 86[d]. [d]Gerd Seifert, [d]Norbert Hauptmann,
[d]Christopher Kohler, [d]Manfred Klier (hns); [b]Gidon Kremer (vn); [c]Paul Tortelier (vc);
[a]Daniel Barenboim (pf); [a]London Philharmonic Orchestra / Dietrich Fischer-Dieskau;
[b]Philharmonia Orchestra / Riccardo Muti; [c]Royal Philharmonic Orchestra / Yan Pascal Tortelier;
[d]Berlin Phiharmonic Orchestra / Klaus Tennstedt. EMI Rouge et Noir Ⓜ CZS7 67521-2
(two discs: 121 minutes: ADD: 8/93). Items marked [a] from HMV ASD3053 (3/75),
[b]ASD143519-1 (10/83), [c]ASD3728 (10/79), [d]ASD3724 (12/79).   Ⓖ

If ever a performance of Schumann's Piano Concerto stressed the principle of dialogue between soloist and conductor, then this is it. True, the Philharmonia's string ensemble isn't as water-tight under Fischer-Dieskau as it might have been under some other conductors; and poetry is invested at the premium of relatively low-level drama. Orchestral textures are absolutely right for Schumann –

warm yet transparent, full-bodied yet never stodgy – and poetry is a major priority. Add Barenboim's compatible vision and keyboard finesse, and you indeed have a memorable reading. The more discursive *Introduction and Allegro appassionato* has plenty of interest, but remembering that this isn't exactly top-drawer Schumann, the performance could be more arresting. Conversely, the *Konzertstücke* has as much forthrightness as it could possibly take, certainly in terms of engineering: the four magnificent horns ring out with Olympian force, keenly supported by an animated BPO. The Cello Concerto is more smoothly recorded, but although Tortelier *père* had the measure of this fragile masterpiece's troubled spirit, his son was, at least at this stage in his career, less comprehensively perceptive. As for the Violin Concerto, one finds oneself frequently moved by Kremer's solo playing – his handling of the slow movement has a tonal richness – but less than happy with Muti's indulgent accompaniment. The repetitions in this work are frequently misunderstood as symptoms of creative decline rather than as the trenchant rhetorical devices that they in fact are, and Muti gives the impression of being unconvinced by them. Nevertheless, Kremer and Muti are, within the useful context of this competitively-priced set, certainly up to the task of communicating what is still a scandalously underrated work. They also have the benefit of good engineering.

Additional recommendations ...

...Konzertstück. Symphonies Nos. 1-4. Overture, Scherzo and Finale, Op. 52. Etudes symphoniques, Op. 13 – Variation No. 11; Finale (arr. Tchaikovsky). Piano Concerto in A minor, Op. 54. Manfred – Overture. **Bella Davidovich** (pf); **Seattle Symphony Orchestra / Gerard Schwarz.** Delos Ⓜ DE3146 (four discs: 231 minutes: DDD: 7/95).

...Violin Concerto. **Brahms** Violin Concerto in D, Op. 77.
Joshua Bell (vn); **Cleveland Orchestra / Christoph von Dohnányi.**
Decca Ⓕ 444 811-2DH (68 minutes: DDD: 5/96). *See review under Brahms; refer to the Index.*

...Violin Concerto. *Coupled with works by various composers.* **Gidon Kremer** (vn);
Philharmonia Orchestra / Riccardo Muti. EMI Forte Ⓜ CZS5 69334-2
(two discs: 151 minutes: ADD). *See review in the Collections section; refer to the Index.* Ⓖ

Schumann Piano Concerto in A minor, Op. 54.
R. Strauss Burleske in D minor, AV85. **Hélène Grimaud** (pf); **Deutsches Symphony Orchestra, Berlin / David Zinman.** Erato Ⓕ 0630-11727-2 (52 minutes: DDD: 2/96). Recorded 1995.
Such is Grimaud's immediacy of response to every change of mood in the opening *Allegro affettuoso* of Schumann's concerto that some listeners may think it a little too excitable – at the expense of maturer composure and poise. But never in this movement, nor in a finale of unflagging vitality and *joie de vivre*, is there any hint of mere keyboard display. You could certainly never hope to hear the first movement's nostalgic main theme played with a more eloquent simplicity. Piano and orchestra are in exceptionally close accord throughout, and not least in the intimate conversational exchanges of the *Andantino grazioso*. Written when Strauss was a mere 22, the *Burleske* cries out for youthful virtuosity, volatility, caprice and charm – which we're given here with effortless fluency by all concerned. In what could vaguely be described as lyrical 'second subject' territory (from the start of track 5, *tranquillo*) who could fail to enjoy those amazing pre-echoes of irresistibly seductive, smiling (*con amore*) things-to-come a quarter of a century later in *Der Rosenkavalier*? The Erato sound is clear-cut rather than lusciously cushioned, but never hard-edged: it falls agreeably on the ear.

Additional recommendations ...

...Piano Concerto. **Grieg** Piano Concerto. **Radu Lupu** (pf); **London Symphony Orchestra / André Previn.** Decca Ovation Ⓜ 417 728-2DM (61 minutes: ADD: 12/87). Ⓖ

...Piano Concerto[a]. Davidsbündlertänze, Op. 6. Kinderszenen, Op. 15. **Fanny Davies** (pf); [a]**Royal Philharmonic Society Orchestra / Ernest Ansermet.**
Pearl mono Ⓕ GEMMCD9291* (65 minutes: ADD: 5/88).

...Piano Concerto. **Schoenberg** Piano Concerto, Op. 42. **Maurizio Pollini** (pf);
Berlin Philharmonic Orchestra / Claudio Abbado. DG Ⓕ 427 771-2GH (51 minutes: DDD: 7/90).

...Piano Concerto. *Coupled with works by* **Franck** *and* **Grieg** Friedrich Gulda (pf);
Vienna Philharmonic Orchestra / Volkmar Andreae. Decca Headline Classics Ⓑ 433 628-2DSP*
(76 minutes: ADD: 1/92). *See review under Franck; refer to the Index.* ⒷⒼⒼ

...Piano Concerto. **Grieg** Piano Concerto. **Lars Vogt** (pf);
City of Birmingham Symphony Orchestra / Sir Simon Rattle.
EMI Ⓕ CDC7 54746-2 (62 minutes: DDD: 1/93).

...Piano Concerto. **Grieg** Piano Concerto in A minor, Op. 16.
Jean-Marc Luisada (pf); **London Symphony Orchestra / Michael Tilson Thomas.**
DG Ⓕ 439 913-2GH (65 minutes: DDD: 12/94).

...Piano Concerto[b]. Kreisleriana, Op. 16. Kinderszenen, Op. 15. Fantasiestücke, Op. 12. Fantasie in C major, Op. 17. Etudes symphoniques, Op. 13. Drei Romanzen, Op. 94[c]. Abendlied, Op. 85 No. 12[c]. Adagio und Allegro in A flat major, Op. 70[c]. Fantasiestücke, Op. 73[c]. Funf Stücke in Volkston, Op. 102. *Coupled with works by* **Brahms** Alfred Brendel (pf); Heinz Holliger (ob); **London Symphony Orchestra / Claudio Abbado.**
Philips Ⓜ 446 925-2PM5 (five discs: 334 minutes: ADD/DDD: 2/96).

...Piano Concerto. *Coupled with works by* **Grieg** Stephen Kovacevich (pf); **BBC Symphony Orchestra / Sir Colin Davis.** Philips Solo Ⓜ 446 192-2PM (78 minutes: ADD/DDD: 6/96).
See review under Grieg; refer to the Index. ⒼⒼⒼ

Schumann Piano Concerto in A minor, Op. 54. Introduction and Allegro appassionato in
G major, Op. 92. Introduction and Allegro in D minor, Op. 134. **Murray Perahia** (pf); **Berlin
Philharmonic Orchestra / Claudio Abbado.** Sony Classical Ⓕ SK64577 (57 minutes: DDD: 1/98).
Recorded 1994.   ⒼⒼ
With a considerable number of versions already available, the Piano Concerto needs no special
pleading. From Perahia and Abbado it comes across with refreshing eagerness, as if Schumann could
scarcely pause for breath in an uprush of inspiration. But unflagging strength of direction by no
means excludes the personal. The first movement, in particular, brings intimately revealing nuances
of phrasing from Perahia, with a finely shaped, richly expressive cadenza before a delectably light-
fingered, effervescent coda. Free of coy cosseting the *Andante* has a natural, gracious flow. However,
a more expansive melodic glow in the middle section would not have gone amiss, not least when the
violins soar into the upper reaches (a masterstroke of orchestration) near its end. Piquantly crunched
acciaccaturas at the start inject the finale with inexhaustible rhythmic buoyancy. Recorded in Berlin's
Philharmonie the sound quality is vibrantly full and forward. Perahia adds Schumann's two later
works for piano and orchestra as couplings, of which the sorely neglected last in D minor was part of
his birthday present for Clara barely six months before his breakdown. Though less immediately ear-
catching than the Mendelssohnian G major work (where Perahia's exhilarating homecoming silences
often heard accusations of protraction), Schumann's farewell to the genre – as played here – is striking
as by far the more intense and laden of the two, with eventual major-key victory won after deeper
internal struggle.

Schumann Piano Concerto in A minor, Op. 54[a].
Prokofiev Piano Concerto No. 3 in C major, Op. 26[b]. **Van Cliburn** (pf); **Chicago Symphony
Orchestra /** [a]**Fritz Reiner,** [b]**Walter Hendl.** RCA Victor Living Stereo Ⓜ 09026 62691-2
(61 minutes: ADD: 8/96). Item marked [a] from SB2113 (8/61), [b]RA13002 (12/60).   Ⓖ
The outright winner of the first Tchaikovsky Competition, Van Cliburn's playing left an indelible
mark and an enduring legend. Returning to these two wholly characteristic performances is to be
forcibly reminded of his cardinal and unique qualities. Here, captured in RCA's magnificent
remastering, is that sumptuously rich and burnished tone, that generous elasticity of phrase and
rhythm, that open-hearted rhetorical splendour. Tempos, as so often with Cliburn, are expansive,
allowing him an imperial breadth and majesty. Listen to the fullness and clarity he finds in
Schumann's first movement *passionato* elaboration, or the way he sweeps all before him in the finale's
exultant conclusion. On the other hand Cliburn's romantic generosity would probably have angered
Prokofiev, whose austere performance of his own Third Concerto was bleak and angular. Yet even he
would surely have marvelled at the way every note is made audible in his scintillating score. Given such
superb assurance the final variation in the second movement sounds more than ever like two different
forms of motion proceeding simultaneously and, all in all, both performances provide awe-inspiring
evidence of Cliburn's once towering genius. In these too often lean times, when emotional aridity is
often applauded highly, such magnificence is doubly rewarding.

Schumann Symphonies – No. 1 in B flat major, Op. 38, "Spring"; No. 2 in C major, Op. 61;
No. 3 in E flat major, Op. 97, "Rhenish"; No. 4 in D minor, Op. 120.
Overture, Scherzo and Finale, Op. 52. **Dresden Staatskapelle / Wolfgang Sawallisch.**
EMI Sawallisch Edition Ⓜ CMS7 64815-2 (two discs: 148 minutes: ADD: 11/93).
From HMV SLS867 (2/74). Recorded 1972.   ⒼⒼⒼ
Schumann Symphonies. **Bavarian Radio Symphony Orchestra / Rafael Kubelík.**
Sony Classical Essential Classics Ⓑ SBK48269/70 (two discs, oas: 74 and 76 minutes: ADD: 7/93).
From CBS 79324 (10/79). Recorded 1978-1979.
SBK48269 – No. 1 in B flat major, Op. 38, "Spring"; No. 2 in C major, Op. 61.
SBK48270 – No. 3 in E flat major, Op. 97, "Rhenish"; No. 4 in D minor, Op. 120.
Manfred, Op. 115 – Overture.   ⒼⒼⒼ
Schumann's symphonies come in for a lot of criticism because of his supposed cloudy textures and
unsubtle scoring, but in the hands of a conductor who is both skilful and sympathetic they are most
engaging works. Sawallisch's recordings, brightly transferred, provide us with a much admired set. His
style, fresh and unforced, is not as high powered as some other conductors but it is sensible, alert and
very pleasing. He achieves great lightness in the First and Fourth Symphonies – there's always a sense
of classical poise and control but never at the expense of the overall architecture of the pieces. The
Second and Third Symphonies, larger and more far-reaching in their scope, again benefit from
Sawallisch's approach. The playing of the Staatskapelle Dresden is superlative in every department,
with a lovely veiled string sound and a real sense of ensemble. These are real bargains and with the
Overture, Scherzo and Finale thrown in for good measure, definitely not to be missed.
It is difficult to understand why Kubelík's wonderful cycle failed to make an impact when it was first
issued. His sensitivity to detail, his refusal to bully Schumann's vulnerable structures and his ability
to penetrate occasional thickets of orchestration, make these especially memorable. Just listen to the
cheeky bassoon backing clarinet, 1'44" into the *Spring* Symphony's fourth movement, the limpid
phrasing of the *Rhenish* Symphony's *Nicht schnell* third movement, or the to-ing and fro-ing between
first and second violins (usefully separated, as virtually always with Kubelík) in the last movement of

the Second. Only the first movement of the Fourth seems a little heavy-handed, but then the poetry of the *Romanze* and the exuberance of the finale more than make amends. First movement repeats are observed and the playing throughout is rich in felicitous turns of phrase. The sound, though, is a minor stumbling block: violins are thin (one of the few disadvantages of having them separated is that their massed tone becomes mildly diluted), brass a little fuzzy and the whole production less focused than Sawallisch's set. But Kubelík's insights are too varied and meaningful to miss, and there is much pleasure to be derived from them. What with a stirring *Manfred* Overture added for good measure, they also constitute exceptional value for money.

Additional recommendations ...

...Nos. 1-4. Overtures – Genoveva; Manfred. **Berlin Philharmonic Orchestra / Rafael Kubelík.**
DG Double Ⓜ 437 395-2GX2 (two discs: 153 minutes: ADD).

...Nos. 1-4. **Suisse Romande Orchestra / Armin Jordan.**
Erato Duo Bonsai Ⓑ 4509-95357-2 (two discs: 131 minutes: DDD).

...Nos. 1-4. **Berlin Philharmonic Orchestra / Herbert von Karajan.**
DG Symphony Edition Ⓜ 429 672-2GSE2 (two discs: 132 minutes: ADD: 7/90).

...Nos. 1 and 4. **Vienna Philharmonic Orchestra / Riccardo Muti.**
Philips Ⓕ 442 121-2PH (65 minutes: DDD: 1/95).

...Nos. 1-4. **Staatskapelle Dresden / Giuseppe Sinopoli.**
DG Ⓕ 439 923-2GH2 (two discs: 135 minutes: DDD: 9/95).

...Nos. 1-4. **Chamber Orchestra of Europe / Nikolaus Harnoncourt.**
Teldec Ⓕ 0630-12674-2 (two discs: 124 minutes: DDD: 11/96).

...Nos. 1-4. **Cologne Radio Symphony Orchestra / Hans Vonk.**
EMI Forte Ⓜ CZS5 69370-2 (two discs: 130 minutes: DDD: 11/96).

...Nos. 1 and 3. **Polish National Radio Symphony Orchestra / Antoni Wit.**
Naxos Ⓢ 8 553082 (65 minutes: DDD: 11/96).

...Nos. 1-4. Manfred, Op. 115 – Overture. **Cleveland Orchestra / George Szell.**
Sony Classical Heritage Ⓜ MH2K62349 (two discs: 135 minutes: ADD: 2/97).

Schumann Symphonies – No. 1 in B flat major, Op. 38, "Spring"; No. 2 in C major, Op. 61; No. 3 in E flat major, Op. 97, "Rhenish"; No. 4 in D minor, Op. 120 (1841 and 1851 versions); G minor, WoO29, "Zwickauer". Overture, Scherzo and Finale, Op. 52. Konzertstück in F major, Op. 86[a].
[a]**Roger Montgomery,** [a]**Gavin Edwards,** [a]**Susan Dent,** [a]**Robert Maskell** (hns);
Orchestre Révolutionnaire et Romantique / Sir John Eliot Gardiner. Archiv Produktion
Ⓕ 457 591-2AH3 (three discs: 202 minutes: DDD: 1997). Recorded 1996. 🎧
Gramophone Editor's choice.   ⊖⊖⊖

The first point to note is how much more comprehensive this is than previous cycles, even the outstanding RCA set of period performances from Roy Goodman and the Hanover Band. That offers the *Overture, Scherzo and Finale* in addition to the four numbered symphonies, but No. 4 comes in the rare first version of 1841. Gardiner offers both versions, 1841 and 1851, and his performances of them are very well geared to bringing out the contrasts. Still more fascinating is the inclusion of both the early, incomplete Symphony in G minor, and the *Konzertstück* of 1849 for four horns, with the ORR soloists breathtaking in their virtuosity in the outer movements, using horns with rotary valves crooked in F. Otherwise, except in three specified movements, natural horns are used, braying clearly through orchestration which always used to be condemned as too thick. In his note, Gardiner fairly points out the merits of the 1841 version in transparency and other qualities, suggesting, as others have, that the doublings in the later version make it safer and more commonplace. Paradoxically in performance, Gardiner is if anything even more electrifying in the later, more thickly upholstered version, as ever clarifying textures and building up to a thrilling conclusion. Even the *Zwickauer* Symphony of 1832 emerges as very distinctive of Schumann. It is, incidentally, a merit of the layout of this set on three well-filled discs that the eight works appear in chronological order. The contrasts between Gardiner and Goodman in their approach to the numbered works are not as marked as expected, often as much a question of scale and recording quality as of interpretative differences, with Goodman's orchestra more intimate, and with the RCA sound a degree less brightly analytical. Both prefer fast speeds, with Goodman a shade more relaxed and Gardiner more incisive, pressing ahead harder, with syncopations – so important in Schumann – more sharply dramatic. One advantage that Gardiner has in his slightly bigger scale is that he brings out more light and shade, offering a wider dynamic range. Hence the solemn fourth movement of the *Rhenish* Symphony inspired by Cologne Cathedral – as with Goodman taken at a flowing speed – builds up more gradually in a bigger, far longer crescendo, in the end the more powerful for being held back at the start. Though the Goodman set still holds its place in presenting an intensely refreshing view of these masterpieces, Gardiner not only goes a degree further in that process, but offers a conspectus of Schumann as symphonist that is all the richer and more illuminating for the inclusion of the extra rarities.

Additional recommendations ...

...Nos. 3 and 4. **London Classical Players / Sir Roger Norrington.**
EMI Ⓕ CDC7 54025-2 (57 minutes: DDD: 3/91). 🎧

...No. 3. **Schubert** Symphony No. 3 in D major, D200. **North German Radio Symphony Orchestra / Günter Wand.** RCA Victor Red Seal Ⓕ 09026 61876-2 (56 minutes: DDD: 2/94).

...No. 3; No. 4 (1841 version). **Chamber Orchestra of Europe / Nikolaus Harnoncourt.**
Teldec Ⓕ 4509-90867-2 (57 minutes: DDD: 2/95).
...Nos. 1-4. Overture, Scherzo and Finale, Op. 52. **Hanover Band / Roy Goodman.**
RCA Victor Red Seal Ⓕ 09026 61931-2 (two discs: 134 minutes: DDD: 3/95). ✔   Ⓖ
...Nos. 2 and 4. **Polish National Radio Symphony Orchestra / Antoni Wit.**
Naxos Ⓢ 8 550923 (68 minutes: DDD: 3/95).
...No. 4. **Bartók** Piano Concerto No. 3, Sz119[a].[a]**Géza Anda** (pf); **Staatskapelle Dresden /**
Herbert von Karajan. DG Ⓜ 447 666-2GDO (55 minutes: ADD: 10/95).
Gramophone Editor's choice. See review under Bartók; refer to the Index.   Ⓖ

Schumann Symphony No. 2 in C major, Op. 61. Konzertstück in F major, Op. 86. Manfred,
Op. 115 – Overture. **Philharmonia Orchestra / Christian Thielemann.** DG Ⓕ 453 482-2GH
(76 minutes: DDD: 1/98). Recorded 1996. *Gramophone Editor's record of the month.*   Ⓖ
This programme is brilliantly designed for continuous listening. Thielemann is his own man, making
no stylistic concessions to 'historically informed' performance. The disc begins with the *Manfred*
Overture: its opening three chords are very smoothly delivered (they are usually incisive and strong),
but they are justified by the spacious gravity and dignity of what follows. You may find this *Manfred*
too ready to yield to introspective slower motion (a feature of the performance of the Second
Symphony). Then *Manfred*'s interior world is blown away by "something quite curious" as Schumann
described his *Konzertstück* for four horns and orchestra. Replace "curious" with "dazzling", even
"reckless", and you might gain a better idea of the piece. Here is playing of great brilliance and
bravado. We've not had a performance of the Second Symphony as satisfying since Karajan's and
Sawallisch's from the early 1970s. On first hearing, one occasionally feels that Thielemann had lost his
sense of proportion, principally in the *Scherzo*, whose much slower Trios can sound self-conscious.
But, more often than not, a few bars further on, and the nature of the expression released by that
slower tempo makes clear the reason for its choice. And in the Symphony's outer *Allegros* Thielemann
always ensures enough urgent propulsion and springing energy to make workable his many slowings.
Never do you feel the tension sagging as a result of a slowing; on the contrary, the contrasts invariably
intensify the drama. The Symphony's *Adagio* (over 12 minutes of it; Goodman is 8'20" and ten
minutes is the average) is the disc's principal glory: a wondrously sustained and shaped *cantabile*, with
the essential bass-line well defined. It might be thought a risky business recording Schumann in a
church, but the microphones are close and this ample sound offers a convincing focus and proportion.
Additional recommendation ...
...No. 2. Piano Concerto in A minor, Op. 54[a]. [a]**Andreas Staier** (fp);
Orchestra of the Champs-Elysées, Paris / Philippe Herreweghe.
Harmonia Mundi Ⓕ HMC90 1555 (68 minutes: DDD: 9/96). ✔

Schumann Symphony No. 4 in D minor, Op. 120.
Schubert Symphony No. 4 in C minor, D417, "Tragic".
Mendelssohn Die schöne Melusine, Op. 32. **Berlin Philharmonic Orchestra /**
Nikolaus Harnoncourt. Teldec Ⓕ 4509-94543-2 (77 minutes: DDD: 5/96). Recorded live in 1995.
"I think of it as one of the greatest symphonic poems" Harnoncourt has said of *Die schöne Melusine*.
A bold claim, but here indeed is a bold and beauteous performance. Beauty first, "the beauty of calm
waters" as Tovey described the opening: upwardly curling mother-of-pearl Berlin winds and strings.
Then boldness: and here the strongly rhythmic second theme is subjected to such a dramatic *animato*
that its definition may strike you as initially blurred (a momentary impression though, and the
Overture as a whole benefits from Harnoncourt's tempo contrasts). The Berliners' musical collective
would appear to have had a profound (and positive) effect on Harnoncourt in the Schubert. Compare
the slow movement with his Concertgebouw recording (part of a cycle: see the review under Schubert;
refer to the Index to Reviews): there, the *Andante*'s relatively detached period manners are here (at a
slower tempo, though still an *Andante*) transformed into a very real beauty and eloquence of phrase
and expression. Very startling, if you don't know the Abbado (listed under the Schubert/Harnoncourt
review) or Harnoncourt's Amsterdam recording, is the removal of eight bars (from the printed
editions) in the first movement's exposition, and Harnoncourt's fateful ('Tragic'?) half-tempo delivery
of the finale's closing unison C chords. Dramatic delaying tactics – whether tiny hesitations, or huge
fermatas – have always been a feature of Harnoncourt's conducting. Together with his insistent
accentuation, sudden contrasts of dynamics, texture and tempo (for example, *Scherzo*/Trio tempos),
you may feel that this Schumann Fourth (the familiar revision) sets out to contradict the symphony's
apparent continuity, certainly compared to a performance like Wand's on RCA. But then, this is a
performance that can catch fire spectacularly in a way that few others do, especially in the symphony's
closing stages. The Berliners' playing is magnificent, and the sound is both present and spacious.

Schumann Symphony No. 4 in D minor, Op. 120.
Schubert Symphony No. 8 in B minor, D759, "Unfinished". **North German Radio Symphony**
Orchestra / Günter Wand. RCA Victor Red Seal Ⓕ RD60826 (57 minutes: DDD: 5/92).
Recorded live in 1991.   ⒼⒼ
Wand's Schumann Fourth has impressive cumulative power; something the composer obviously
intended with all four movements linked and sharing common themes. Wand's purposeful manner

does not preclude many individual touches early in the work (the *Romanze* is darkly coloured and beautifully phrased), but as Schumann's thematic unity in continuity becomes more established, so Wand tightens his grip: the finale's introductory "darkness to dawn", for example, is here no interpolated episode, but an amassing of energies already in the air. The sound is full, deep and natural. Wand's is a traditionally unhurried unfolding of Schubert's *Unfinished*, and one which does not exploit its troubled lyrical expanses, bar by bar, for the utmost drama. Perceptible deviations from his well maintained pulse give heightened expressiveness to crucial moments in the 'symphonic' drama, such as the fearful start of the first movement's development section, and the second movement's haunting central transition. But the quality here that is most easy to recognize, and just as impossible to analyse, is its spirituality. The live origins may help to explain this, as they do a few trifling imprecisions in the playing.

Schumann Piano Quintet in E flat major, Op. 44[a]. Andante and Variations, Op. 46[b]. Piano Quartet in E flat major, Op. 47[c]. Fantasiestücke, Op. 73[d]. Adagio and Allegro in A flat major, Op. 70[e]. Märchenbilder, Op. 113[f]. Violin Sonata No. 2 in D minor, Op. 121[g].
[be]**Marie-Luise Neunecker** (hn); [acg]**Dora Schwarzberg**, [a]**Lucy Hall** (vns); [acf]**Nobuko Imai** (va); [bcd]**Natalia Gutman**, [ab]**Mischa Maisky** (vcs); [abdfg]**Martha Argerich**, [bce]**Alexandre Rabinovitch** (pfs). EMI Ⓕ CDS5 55484-2 (two discs: 146 minutes: DDD: 1/96). Recorded live in 1994.　　　Ⓖ

After "one memorable day of rehearsal", as the introductory note puts it, Martha Argerich and a group of friends recorded this generously long programme at a public concert in Holland "with the enthusiasm and intimate inspiration of a house-party". The rarity is the *Andante and Variations*, Op. 46, here brought up with all the spontaneous freshness of new discovery in a performance as enjoyable for its self-generating continuity as its diversity. Argerich and her fellow pianist, Rabinovitch divide keyboard responsibilities in the remainder of the programme. Her own major triumph comes in the Quintet (with truly inspirational help from Maisky's cello). Every note tingles with life and colour in an arrestingly imaginative reading of exemplary textural transparency. In none of the more familiar works in the concert is that little extra stimulus of live as opposed to studio recording combined with more finesse and finish than here. In the Quartet Rabinovitch is a little less successful in concealing Schumann's inclination to entrust too much to his own instrument, with some aggressive accentuation *en route*. The finale is breathlessly, albeit excitably, fast. Rabinovitch is joined by Marie-Luise Neunecker in a hearty performance on the second disc of the *Adagio and Allegro* for horn and piano. In the smaller pieces Argerich reaffirms herself as an artist of 'temperament', much given to the impulse of the moment. In place of clarinet, the Op. 73 *Fantasiestücke* are played here with cello (Natalia Gutman), one of Schumann's two sanctioned alternatives despite its low-lying voice. However, in the *Märchenbilder* she partners the prescribed viola (Nobuko Imai). The recording itself is pleasingly natural. And there is heartening audience applause, judiciously unprotracted, as a further reminder that we are in fact in the Concertgebouw at Nijmegen.

Additional recommendations ...

...Quartet, Op. 47[a]. Piano Quintet in E flat major, Op. 44[b]. **Beaux Arts Trio;** [b]**Dorf Bettelheim** (vn); [ab]**Samuel Rhodes** (va). Philips Ⓕ 420 791-2PH (58 minutes: ADD: 2/88).

...Piano Quintet. **Brahms** Piano Quintet in F minor, Op. 34. **Kodály Quartet; Jenö Jandó** (pf). Naxos Ⓢ 8 550406 (67 minutes: DDD: 2/91).

...Quartet, Op. 47[a]. Piano Quintet, Op. 44[b]. [a]**Jiří Panocha** (vn); [a]**Miroslav Sehnoutka** (va); [a]**Jaroslav Kulhan** (vc); **Jan Panenka** (pf); [b]**Smetana Quartet.** Supraphon Ⓕ 11 0367-2 (57 minutes: DDD: 10/91).

...Quartet, Op. 47. **Beethoven** Piano Quartet in E flat major, Op. 16. **Isaac Stern** (vn); **Jaime Laredo** (va); **Yo-Yo Ma** (vc); **Emanuel Ax** (pf). Sony Classical Ⓕ SK53339 (65 minutes: DDD: 10/94). *See review under Beethoven; refer to the Index.*　　　ⒼⒼ

...Piano Quintet. *Coupled with works by* **Brahms** Victor Aller (pf); **Hollywood Quartet.** Testament mono Ⓕ SBT3063* (three discs: 220 minutes: ADD: 1/95).

...Piano Quintet. Piano Quartet in E flat major, Op. 47. **Menahem Pressler** (pf); **Emerson Quartet.** DG Ⓕ 445 848-2GH (58 minutes: DDD: 1/96).

...Fantasiestücke[ab]. Märchenbilder[bc]. Märchenerzählungen, Op. 132[abc]. **Kurtág** Neun Stücke[a]. Jelek, Op. 5[a]. Hommage à R. Sch, Op. 15d[abc]. [c]**Eduard Brunner** (cl); [a]**Kim Kashkashian** (va); [b]**Robert Levin** (pf). ECM New Series Ⓕ 437 957-2 (76 minutes: DDD: 1/96).

...Piano Quintet. **Brahms** Piano Quintet in F minor, Op. 34. **Rudolf Serkin** (pf); **Busch Quartet.** Pearl mono Ⓜ GEMMCD9275* (65 minutes: ADD: 8/97).

...Adagio and Allegro in A flat major. **David Pyatt** (hn); **Martin Jones** (pf). *Coupled with works by various composers.* Erato Ⓕ 3984-21632-2 (66 minutes: DDD: 4/98). *See review in the Collections section; refer to the Index.*

Schumann Piano Trios – No. 2 in F major, Op. 80; No. 3 in G minor, Op. 110. **Fontenay Trio** (Michael Mücke, vn; Niklas Schmidt, vc; Wolf Harden, pf). Teldec Ⓕ 4509-90864-2 (54 minutes: DDD: 12/95). Recorded 1993.

For anyone seeking the complete Schumann in this genre, there is obviously strong competition from the Borodins and Beaux Arts, whose mellow two-disc sets both include Schumann's Op. 88 *Fantasiestücke*. But taken on its own merits, this Fontenay coupling of the Second and Third Trios has plenty to commend it in youthful verve and vividness of characterization, particularly welcome in No. 3 in G minor, where excessive repetition of initially arresting ideas can so easily sound merely patterned. Bigger tests come in the more personally motivated F major work, composed exactly ten years after Schumann's clandestine engagement to his beloved Clara, with the opening phrase of his 1840 love-song *Intermezzo* ("In the depths of my heart I keep a radiant image of you") as the secret underlying clue. Its introduction by the violin in the course of the first movement's development, though heartfelt, is just a little too backward. Also worrying is the almost aggressive accentuation of the pianist (a player certainly never backward in coming forward) in this movement's launching theme. All three artists respond warmly to the slow movement's *Mit innigem Ausdruck*, and they honour the third movement's slowish metronome marking rather than transforming it into a scherzo. Their relish of its quaint coda is particularly arresting. The recording is bright albeit a bit hard.

Additional recommendations ...

...Nos. 1-3. Fantasiestücke, Op. 88. **Borodin Trio.**
  Chandos Ⓕ CHAN8832/3 (two discs: 110 minutes: DDD: 11/90).
...Nos. 1-3. Fantasiestücke, Op. 88. **Beaux Arts Trio.**
  Philips Ⓕ 432 165-2PH2 (two discs: 110 minutes: DDD: 8/93).
...Nos. 1 and 2. **Grieg Trio.** Virgin Classics Ultraviolet Ⓜ CUV5 61313-2 (62 minutes: DDD: 2/97).

Schumann Violin Sonatas – No. 1 in A minor, Op. 105; No. 2 in D minor, Op. 121.
  Gidon Kremer (vn); **Martha Argerich** (pf). DG Ⓕ 419 235-2GH (49 minutes: DDD: 1/87). ⒼⒼ
Schumann Violin Sonatas – No. 1 in A minor, Op. 105; No. 2 in D minor, Op. 121; No. 3 in
  A minor – Intermezzo. **Ilya Kaler** (vn); **Boris Slutsky** (pf). Naxos Ⓢ 8 550870
  (51 minutes: DDD: 9/94). Recorded 1993.

Schumann's two violin sonatas are late works, dating from 1851, and both were written quickly, apparently in four and six days respectively. This rapidity of composition is nowhere evident except perhaps in the vigour and enthusiasm of the music. Argerich and Kremer, both mercurial and emotionally charged performers, subtly balance the ardent Florestan and dreamily melancholic Eusebius elements of Schumann's creativity. This is even more striking in the Second Sonata, a greater work than its twin, thematically vigorous with a richness and scope that make it at once a striking as well as ideally structured work. Kremer and Argerich have established a close and exciting duo partnership and this fine recording shows what like minds can achieve in music so profoundly expressive as this. The Naxos performances, powerfully recorded in Indiana by young Russian artists, are most enjoyable. The passion of their playing is perhaps not wholly Germanic, but every artist legitimately brings something of himself to the music he performs, and nothing here takes us out of touch with Schumann's world. Indeed, there is an impressive intensity to this playing, although refinement and tenderness are rightly also present. The single movement from the composite "FAE Sonata" dedicated to Joseph Joachim, in which Schumann collaborated with the young Brahms and Albert Dietrich, makes a useful bonus in a disc which would otherwise last under 50 minutes. The Naxos disc at super-bargain price represents fine value.

Additional recommendation ...

...Nos. 1-3. **Mark Kaplan** (vn); **Anton Kuerti** (pf). Arabesque Ⓕ Z6662 (69 minutes: DDD: 2/96).

Schumann Arabeske in C major, Op. 18. Davidsbündlertänze, Op. 6. Blumenstück in D flat major,
  Op. 19. Etudes symphoniques, Op. 13 (1852 version). **András Schiff** (pf). Teldec Ⓕ 4509-99176-2
  (76 minutes: DDD: 11/95). Recorded 1995.

Schumann was a great re-thinker, in Schiff's opinion not always for the better in later life – hence his choice of Schumann's original (1837) conception of the *Davidsbündlertänze* rather than its more usually heard 1851 revision. Except for a touch of mischief (subsequently removed) at the end of No. 9, textual differences are slight. But Schiff prefers the fewer repeat markings in the first edition, so that ideas never lose their freshness. More importantly, the exceptional immediacy and vividness of his characterization reminds us that initially Schumann signed nearly all of these 18 'bridal thoughts' with an F (the impetuous Florestan) or an E (the introspective, visionary Eusebius) – or sometimes both – as well as including literary inscriptions (and one or two more colourful expression marks) as a clue to the mood of the moment. Schiff laughs and teases, storms and yearns, as if the hopes and dreams of the youthful Robert, forbidden all contact with his distant beloved, were wholly his own – there and then. The impatient Florestan fares particularly well. For the much metamorphosed *Etudes symphoniques* Schiff chooses the generally used late version of 1852 (posthumously revised to restore two rejected earlier numbers) with its admirably tautened finale. Here, his bold, firmly contoured approach reaffirms it as the most magisterially 'classical' work the young Schumann ever wrote. Whereas Thibaudet, in his more fancifully brilliant recent recording, seeks its variety, Schiff emphasizes its continuity (partly by smoother tempo change *en route*) and unity as a whole. Even the five so-called supplementary variations emerge as more purposeful, less ruminative, than often heard. These Schiff wisely offers as a completely independent group at the end. The recital is completed by the *Arabeske* and *Blumenstück*, again played with a very strong sense of direction, even if Schiff is not yet Richter's equal in disguising the repetitiveness of the latter. Nothing but praise for the naturalness of the reproduction.

Additional recommendations ...

...Etudes symphoniques, Op. 13. Papillons, Op. 2. Arabeske in C major, Op. 18.
  Vladimir Ashkenazy (pf). Decca Ⓕ 414 474-2DH (DDD: 6/87).

...Etudes symphoniques, Opp. 13 and posth. Bunte Blätter, Op. 99. *Coupled with works by* **Chopin** and **Beethoven** Sviatoslav Richter (pf). Olympia Ⓕ OCD 338 and OCD339 (two discs, oas: 75 and 77 minutes: ADD: 4/94). *See review under Beethoven; refer to the Index.* ⒼⒼ
...Etudes symphoniques, Opp. 13 and posth. Theme and Variations on the name "Abegg", Op. 1. Widmung, Op. 25 No. 1 (arr. Liszt). *Coupled with works by* **Liszt** Evgeni Kissin (pf). Revelation Ⓜ RV10031 (66 minutes: ADD: 6/97).
...Arabeske, Op. 18. Presto passionato in G minor. Traumes Wirren, Op. 12 No. 7. Toccata in C major, Op. 7. *Coupled with works by various composers.* **Vladimir Horowitz** (pf). APR mono Ⓜ APR5517* (71 minutes: ADD: 5/98). *See review in the Collections section; refer to the Index.*

Schumann Fantasiestücke, Op. 12ᵃ – No. 1, Des Abends; No. 2, Aufschwung; No. 3, Warum?; No. 5, In der Nacht; No. 7, Traumes Wirren; No. 8, Ende von Lied. Etudes symphoniques, Opp. 13 and posth.ᵇ. Faschingsschwank aus Wien, Op. 26ᶜ. **Sviatoslav Richter** (pf). Revelation Ⓜ RV10012 (77 minutes: ADD: 1/97). Items marked ᵃ recorded live in1970, ᵇ1972, ᶜ1976.
Here are 77 minutes of delight from Russia's recently unearthed Aladdin's Cave beginning with Schumann's Op. 12 *Fantasiestücke*, recorded in May 1970. The *Etudes symphoniques* followed in January 1972. In what is perhaps the most pianistically rather than autobiographically inspired of all the major works of Schumann's twenties, Richter reminds us in no uncertain terms of his sleight of hand. The five supplementary variations (Op. posth.) he wisely inserts as a self-contained group of exquisite youthful dreams before returning to reality in the *con gran bravura* storms of No. 6. Finally, *Faschingsschwank aus Wien*, recorded in October 1976. It is difficult to recall a more plaintive account of the "Romanze" from anyone, achieved by simplicity within a questionably slow tempo. For the most part it is the work's teasing charm that he conveys with fingers of gossamer lightness and fleetness. Gallic rather than German Schumann, perhaps, but irresistible. Good tonal reproduction.

Schumann Fantasie in C major, Op. 17. March in G minor, Op. 76 No. 2. Concert Studies on Caprices by Paganini, Op. 10 – No. 4 in C minor; No. 5 in B minor; No. 6 in E minor. Novellette in F major, Op. 21 No. 1. Blumenstück in D flat major, Op. 19. Vier Nachtstücke, Op. 23.
Brahms Piano Sonatas – No. 1 in C major, Op. 1; No. 2 in F sharp minor, Op. 2. Variations on a Theme by Paganini, Op. 35. Capriccio in C major, Op. 76 No. 8. Intermezzo in E minor, Op. 116 No. 5. Ballade in G minor, Op. 118 No. 3. Rhapsody in E flat major, Op. 119 No. 4.
Sviatoslav Richter (pf). Philips Ⓕ 438 477-2PH3 (three discs: 184 minutes: DDD: 8/94). ⒼⒼ
Variable reproduction, coupled with this highly-strung artist's own unpredictability, inevitably results in ups and downs. But for the one-and-a-half discs of Schumann alone, this album can be cherished as a collector's piece. There is surely no one on the concert platform today more finely attuned to Schumann's secret inner world. The miniatures give particular pleasure and how keenly he responds to that element of "strangeness blended with the beautiful" (as romanticism was once defined) in the four *Nachtstücke* written with a supernatural premonition of his brother's death. All technical challenges are dissolved into the purest poetry in the three all-too-rarely heard *Concert Studies on Caprices by Paganini* and in the major work, the great Op. 17 *Fantasie*, his own emotional warmth is fortunately matched by some of the ripest sonority that we're given in this album. It's a performance which obviously comes from the deepest places of his heart. There are memorable things too in the two early Brahms sonatas, not least the strain of nostalgic lyricism so beautifully drawn from the first movement of No. 1 in C major. The two sets of *Paganini* Variations in their turn bring bewitchingly light and delicate prestidigitation and seductively sung melody. But in burlier bravura, and notably in both excitable homecomings, there are some gaucheries and inaccuracies that would certainly not have got through in a studio recording. Of the miniatures, the intimate, elusive E minor *Intermezzo* is exquisitely phrased and shaded.

Additional recommendations ...
...Fantasie. Fantasiestücke, Op. 12. **Alfred Brendel** (pf). Philips Ⓕ 411 049-2PH (ADD: 4/84).
...Kreisleriana. Piano Sonata No. 2. Novellette in F sharp minor, Op. 21 No. 8.
Vladimir Ashkenazy (pf). Decca Ⓕ 425 940-2DH (59 minutes: DDD: 4/92).
...Arabeske, Op. 18. Piano Sonata No. 2 in G minor, Op. 22. Vier Nachtstücke, Op. 23. Vier Klavierstücke, Op. 32. Toccata in C major, Op. 7. Presto passionato in G minor.
Bernd Glemser (pf). Naxos Ⓢ 8 550715 (68 minutes: DDD: 10/94).
...Fantasie. **Schubert** Piano Sonata No. 21 in B flat major, D960. **Sir Clifford Curzon** (pf). Orfeo D'Or Ⓜ C401951B (66 minutes: ADD: 4/96).
...Fantasie. **Schubert** Fantasy in C major, D760, "Wanderer". **Maurizio Pollini** (pf). DG The Originals Ⓜ 447 451-2GOR (52 minutes: ADD: 6/96). *See review under Schubert; refer to the Index.*
...Fantasie, Op. 131. **Brahms** Violin Concerto in D major, Op. 77. **Anne-Sophie Mutter** (vn); **New York Philharmonic Orchestra / Kurt Masur.** DG Ⓕ 457 075-2GH (54 minutes: DDD: 12/97).

Schumann Fantasiestücke, Op. 12ᵃ – No. 1, Des Abends; No. 2, Aufschwung; No. 3, Warum?; No. 5, In der Nacht; No. 7, Traumes Wirren; No. 8, Ende von Lied. Humoreske in B flat major, Op. 20ᵃ. Novelletten, Op. 21ᵇ – No. 1 in F major; No. 2 in D major; No. 8 in F sharp minor.
Sviatoslav Richter (pf). Melodiya mono Ⓜ 74321 29464-2* (71 minutes: ADD: 6/96). Items marked ᵃ recorded 1956, ᵇ1960.

The booklet contains an anecdote about Arthur Rubinstein hearing Richter for the first time, "It really wasn't anything out of the ordinary. Then at some point I noticed my eyes growing moist: tears began rolling down my cheeks ...". What produces such a reaction cannot be put into words, but it probably has to do with Richter's uncanny ability to convey a sense of inevitability. In Schumann, for instance, Richter takes characterization and virtuosity in his stride and aims at the emotional truth beyond. Impetuosity and fantasy are there, but at the structural level rather than in the detail. The simplicity of his *Humoreske* gets to the heart of the matter as unerringly as the *élan* of his *Fantasiestücke* and the tensed steel of his *Novelettes*. Decent mono sound.

Additional recommendation ...
...Fantasiestücke. **Harold Bauer** (pf). Biddulph mono Ⓜ LHW011* (75 minutes: ADD: 2/97).

Schumann Humoreske in B flat major, Op. 20. Kinderszenen, Op. 15. Kreisleriana, Op. 16.
   Radu Lupu (pf). Decca Ⓕ 440 496-2DH (75 minutes: DDD: 4/95). Recorded 1993.
   Gramophone Editor's record of the month.   ⒼⒼ
As piano playing this disc has an aristocratic distinction reminiscent of Lipatti. As music-making it is underpinned by a totally unselfconscious kind of intuition, making you feel you are discovering the truth of the matter for the first time. It is difficult to recall a more revealing performance of Schumann's *Humoreske*. Lupu captures all the unpredictability of its swift-changing moods while at the same time imparting a sense of inevitability to the sequence as a whole. Florestan's caprice is as piquant as Eusebius's tenderness is melting. Yet there is an underlying unity in the diversity from Lupu, enhanced by most beautifully timed and shaded 'links'. Goodness knows how long this work has been in his repertory. But here it emerges with the keen edge of new love. Next, *Kinderszenen*: simplicity is its keynote. To begin with (as notably in the opening "Von fremden Ländern und Menschen") you wonder if, in rejection of sentimentality, he might not be allowing himself enough time for wide-eyed wonderment. But you are soon won over by his limpid tonal palette and the sheer purity of his phrasing. Each piece tells its own magical little tale without the slightest trace of special pleading. Such pristine grace will never pall, however often heard. *Kreisleriana* in its turn offers rich contrasts of desperation, dedication and Hoffmannesque drollery. And except, perhaps, in the impetuous No. 7 (taken dangerously fast), it brings further reminders that we are in the presence of a master pianist – amongst so much else able to rejoice in this work's endless dialogues between left hand and right with his opulent bass and gleaming treble. Reproduction is totally faithful throughout.

Additional recommendations ...
...Kinderszenen. Kreisleriana. **Martha Argerich** (pf).
   DG Ⓕ 410 653-2GH (52 minutes: DDD: 5/84).   Ⓖ
...Kinderszenenᵃ. Faschingsschwank aus Wien, Op. 26ᵇ. Carnaval, Op. 9ᵇ. **Daniel Barenboim** (pf).
   DG Privilege Ⓑ 431 167-2GR (73 minutes: ADD: 8/91).
...Kreisleriana. Also includes other works by Schumann and Chopin.
   Vladimir Horowitz (pf). Sony Classical Ⓜ S2K53468 (two discs: 113 minutes: ADD: 7/94).
   Gramophone classical 100.   ⒼⒼⒼ
...Kreisleriana. Faschingsschwank aus Wien, Op. 26. **Pamela Ross** (pf).
   Connoisseur Society Ⓕ CD4185 (52 minutes: DDD: 9/94).
...Kinderszenen. *Coupled with works by* **Debussy** and **Tchaikovsky** Idil Biret (pf).
   Naxos Ⓢ 8 550885 (66 minutes: DDD: 10/94).
...Kreisleriana. Etudes symphoniques, Op. 13. **Franck** Prélude, Choral et Fugue.
   Shura Cherkassky (pf). Nimbus Ⓕ NI7705 (77 minutes: DDD: 3/95).   ⒼⒼ
...Kreisleriana. Carnaval, Op. 9. **Mitsuko Uchida** (pf).
   Philips Ⓕ 442 777-2PH (67 minutes: DDD: 5/95).
...Kinderszenen. Kreisleriana. Etudes symphoniques, Op. 13. Carnaval, Op. 9. Papillons, Op. 2. Davidsbündlertänze, Op. 6. Fantasiestücke, Op. 12 No. 1, Des Abends. Waldszenen, Op. 82 No. 7, Vogel als Prophet. **Alfred Cortot** (pf).
   Music & Arts mono Ⓕ CD858* (two discs: 131 minutes: ADD: 1/96).
...Kreisleriana. **Reubke** Piano Sonata in B flat minor. **Till Fellner** (pf).
   Erato Ⓕ 0630-12710-2 (63 minutes: DDD: 10/96). *See review under Reubke; refer to the Index.* Ⓖ
...Kinderszenen. Kreisleriana. Novelletten No. 1 in F major, Op. 21. **Vladimir Horowitz** (pf).
   DG Masters Ⓜ 445 599-2GMA (54 minutes: DDD: 7/97).
...Kreisleriana. Piano Sonata No. 1 in F sharp minor, Op. 11. **Murray Perahia** (pf).
   Sony Classical Ⓕ SK62786 (58 minutes: DDD: 1/98).

Schumann Piano Sonata No. 1 in F sharp minor, Op. 11. Fantasie in C major, Op. 17.
   Maurizio Pollini (pf). DG Ⓕ 423 134-2GH (63 minutes: ADD: 5/88). From 2530 379 (5/74). ⒼⒼ
Schumann Piano Sonata No. 1 in F sharp minor, Op. 11. Fantasie in C major, Op. 17.
   Leif Ove Andsnes (pf). EMI Ⓕ CDC5 56414-2 (64 minutes: DDD: 10/97). Recorded 1996.
   Gramophone Editor's choice.   Ⓖ
These works grew from Schumann's love and longing for his future wife Clara. Pollini's performances are superb, not least because they are so truthful to the letter of the score. By eschewing all unspecified rubato in the *Fantasie*, he reminds us that the young Schumann never wrote a more finely proportioned large-scale work; this feeling for structure, coupled with exceptional emotional intensity, confirms it as one of the greatest love-poems ever written for the piano. His richly characterized

account of the Sonata is refreshingly unmannered. Certainly the familiar charges of protracted patterning in the faster flanking movements are at once dispelled by his rhythmic *élan*, his crystalline texture and his ear for colour. The sound re-emerges with all its original clarity on CD.

The Norwegian, Leif Ove Andsnes never lets us forget that Schumann was a mere 25 when writing his First Piano Sonata. His recording, with its youthful lightness of heart, is most refreshing. With fastish tempo and delectably light, scintillating fingerwork he dances through the first movement's sometimes all-too-persistent fandango rhythm, and though adopting an unspecified slower tempo for the smoother second subject maintains an unbroken continuity of flow from first note to last. The Aria sings with a spring-like wonderment and grace. And even if the tongue-in-cheek pomposity at the start of the "Intermezzo" section is not fully relished, his lightness and clarity of texture and his rhythmic buoyancy win the day in the *Scherzo*, and yet again in the finale, which in heavier hands can so easily sound protracted. The *Fantasie* comes across with arrestingly impulsive immediacy. Andsnes's extreme contrasts of urgency and poetic musing in the first movement might be thought over-episodic, but the requested fantasy and passion are all there. The central movement is brilliantly excitable and his acute response to every passing innuendo makes the finale a truly moving human confession – albeit in a different world from Pollini's trance-like, superhuman inner calm. Apart from brief loss of refinement in the *Fantasie*'s moments of heightened fervour, the tone-quality of the recording matches the distinction of the playing.

Additional recommendations ...
...Piano Sonata No. 1. Waldszenen, Op. 82. Kinderszenen, Op. 15. **Vladimir Ashkenazy** (pf). Decca Ⓕ 421 290-2DH (74 minutes: DDD: 2/89).
...Fantasie. Fantasiestücke, Op. 12. **Brahms** Variations and Fugue on a Theme by Handel, Op. 24. **Benno Moiseiwitsch** (pf). Testament mono Ⓕ SBT1023* (78 minutes: ADD: 1/94).
...Piano Sonatas – No. 1; No. 3 in F minor, Op. 14. **Nikolai Demidenko** (pf). Hyperion Ⓕ CDA66864 (67 minutes: DDD: 1/97).

Schumann Piano Works. **Alfred Cortot** (pf). Music & Arts mono Ⓕ CD-858* (two discs: 131 minutes: ADD: 1/96).
Etudes symphoniques, Op. 13 (from HMV DB1325/7, 8/30). Carnaval, Op. 9 (DB1252/4, 7/29). Kreisleriana, Op. 16 (DB2608/11, 5/38). Papillons, Op. 2 (HMV DA1442/3, 5/37). Kinderszenen, Op. 15 (DB2581/2, 1/36). Davidsbündlertänze, Op. 6 (DB3263/5, 8/38). Fantasiestücke, Op. 12 No. 1, Des Abends (DB3338, 1/38). Waldszenen, Op. 82 No. 7, Vogel als Prophet (DA1901, 1/49).
It is good to have this Music & Arts sharply focused issue of Cortot's evergreen, ever-fresh performances on a well-presented two-CD set. These recordings have been reissued many times before. How many artists, today, one wonders, could hope to garner such tribute? So here, again, is that magically floated *cantabile* tugging at the heart-strings in "Des Abends" (how one longs for the rest of the cycle) yet maintained with the flawless line and impetus of a great singer. In the *Davidsbündlertänze*, one of Cortot's most poetically potent if battle-scarred recordings, his confusion in Florestan's *schneller* in No. 3 or in the vaulting leaps of No. 12 is, perhaps, not quite what the composer had in mind in his instruction, *Mit Humor*. Yet who can resist his *dolce cantando* in No. 14, the gem of his Schumann, alive with a rich polyphonic pianistic tradition that Alfred Brendel so sadly claims has virtually vanished from the music scene. In *Kinderszenen* the 'poet' of the epilogue is at once Schumann and Cortot, creator and re-creator, and in the *Etudes symphoniques* the gold-dust scattering of the posthumous studies throughout the main work is done with such passion and inwardness that only a Beckmesser could possibly object. Playing like this seems light years away from today's style or standard. But *pace* Cortot, his idiosyncrasy, his pell-mell virtuosity and poetic ecstasy may strike a foreign and even alien note in our more puritan times yet, as Yvonne Lefebure so eloquently put it, "even his wrong notes were those of a God".

Additional recommendations ...
...Etudes symphoniques. Arabeske in C major, Op. 18. **Brahms** Variations on a Theme by Paganini, Op. 35. **Jean-Yves Thibaudet** (pf). Decca Ⓕ 444 338-2DH (65 minutes: DDD: 10/95). *See review under Brahms; refer to the Index.*
...Carnaval, Op. 9. Faschingsschwank aus Wien, Op. 26. *Coupled with works by various composers.* **Arturo Benedetti Michelangeli** (pf). Testament mono Ⓕ SBT2088* (two discs: 130 minutes: ADD: 12/96). *See review in the Collections section; refer to the Index.*
...Papillons. **Murray Perahia** (pf). *Coupled with works by various composers.* Sony Classical Ⓜ SX4K63380 (four discs: 270 minutes: DDD/ADD: 4/98). *See review in the Collections section; refer to the Index.*

Schumann Theme and Variations on the name "Abegg", Op. 1. Fantasie in C major, Op. 17. Faschingsschwank aus Wien, Op. 26. **Vladimir Ashkenazy** (pf). Decca Ⓕ 443 322-2DH (58 minutes: DDD: 2/95). Recorded 1991.
The *Fantasie* in C is the centrepiece of this issue. Ashkenazy plays with a strong and consistently sustained sense of direction, as if trying to emphasize the continuity and coherence of the argument no less than the music's passion. It is an urgently committed, full-bodied performance and needless to say his command of the keyboard is superb, not least in the central march with its recklessly fast coda. It could well have been in response to Clara's plea for something less searching, something more brilliant and easily understood by the general public, that Schumann came up with the

Faschingsschwank aus Wien. Ashkenazy gives a spirited enough performance to justify his resort to a considerably swifter tempo than prescribed for the three fast movements. The Decca recording is pleasingly warm and true.

Additional recommendation ...

...Theme and Variations on the name "Abegg". *Coupled with works by various composers.*
  Sviatoslav Richter (pf). DG Double Ⓜ 447 355-2GDB2 (two discs: 150 minutes: ADD: 12/95).

Schumann Allegro in B minor, Op. 8. Novelletten, Op. 21. Drei Fantasiestücke, Op. 111. Gesänge der Frühe, Op. 133. **Ronald Brautigam** (pf). Olympia Ⓕ OCD436 (79 minutes: DDD: 6/94). Recorded 1993.   Ⓖ
The note reminds us that even the eight *Novelletten* chosen as the centrepiece here are not often heard in sequence as a set. Brautigam prefaces them with the early (1931-32) B minor *Allegro* originally intended as the first movement of a sonata. They are followed by the last two suites Schumann ever wrote for the piano – the *Gesänge der Frühe* only a year before his final breakdown. Most enjoyable is Brautigam's vitality – vitality of imagination no less than of fingers. You are immediately gripped by his plunge into the Op. 8 *Allegro*, with its arresting octave 'motto'. His mercurial fancy and ear for hidden melodic strands in the ensuing stream certainly makes nonsense of hasty dismissal of this work as mere old-style virtuoso note-spinning. Moreover, such is his unflagging impulse in the eight *Novelletten* that never for a moment are you tempted to accuse Schumann of over-repetitively patterned figuration. Potently characterized and contrasted as are the three *Fantasiestücke*, Op. 111 of 1851, Brautigam leaves you in no doubt as to their unity as a set – as he does again, still more subtly and movingly, in the more elusive spiritual world of the five *Gesänge der Frühe*. The bright, clear tonal reproduction is acceptable enough.

Additional recommendation ...

...Carnaval, Op. 9. Drei Fantasiestücke, Op. 111. Etudes symphoniques, Op. 13.
  Shura Cherkassky (pf). Decca Ⓕ 433 652-2DH (66 minutes: ADD: 1/95).   ⒼⒼ

Schumann Davidsbündlertänze, Op. 6. Waldszenen, Op. 82. Fantasiestücke, Op. 111.
  Andreas Haefliger (pf). Sony Classical Ⓕ SK48036 (65 minutes: DDD: 10/92). Recorded 1991. Ⓖ
Schumann Davidsbündlertänze, Op. 6. Fantasiestücke, Op. 12. **Benjamin Frith** (pf).
  Naxos Ⓢ 8 550493 (63 minutes: DDD: 3/93). Recorded 1991.
Although by 1851 Schumann had dropped overt references to that Laurel and Hardy of his creative imagination, Florestan and Eusebius (referring, more or less, to the *yin,* and *yang* – masculine and feminine, assertive and reflective – characters of individual pieces), frequent and telling changes of mood remained an essential ingredient of his mature style. *Davidsbündlertänze*, or "Dances of the League of David" exemplify this trend most vividly: two books, each containing nine separate pieces, alternating fast with slow, humorous with serious and invariably maintaining an element of surprise. There are two 'versions' of the *Davidsbündlertänze*, one from 1837, the other from 1851 and Andreas Haefliger achieves a felicitous musical balance by combining elements of both. His is an intelligent and thoughtful brand of pianism, sensitive to modulation and wonderfully warm in tone; one was was often reminded of the similarly perceptive art of our own much-loved (and much missed) master pianist, Solomon. What is most striking about the *Davidsbündlertänze* is the way Schumann plots key changes from one miniature to the next, effecting many magical contrasts, especially in the second book. Furthermore, the actual level of invention is always high, and the closing sequence utilizes some of Schumann's most bewitching invention: try, by way of example, the final pair – "Wie aus der Ferne" and "Nicht schnell" (tracks 17 and 18). *Waldszenen* is less a sweeping inspiration than a series of lonely vignettes; "The Prophet Bird" (track 25), a frequently performed 'encore' in its own right, is possibly the most atmospheric evocation of tree-top bird song pre-Messiaen, an eerie, questioning *morceau* that twists and turns with the unpredictability of its natural model. If *Waldszenen* takes us deep into the woods, the late *Fantasiestücke* take us further still; here loneliness transforms to disorientation (second movement), and youthful passion becomes defiant grandeur (third). Haefliger charts this bold and the disc's companion pieces with sure intuition, and he is beautifully recorded.
  The young prize-winning British pianist Benjamin Frith indulges the *Davidsbündlertänze*'s caprice, highlighting the contrasts between fast and slower pieces, and summoning his excellent technique for some exciting pianism. But then contrast lies at the very heart of Schumann's inspiration. Frith is quite unlike Haefliger in that he favours impulse over refinement, and isn't afraid to throw caution to the winds, if the mood dictates. His *Fantasiestücke*, too, are forthright and outspoken, although "Des Abends", "Warum" and "Ende vom Lied" each contain plenty of poetry. Naxos's recording is excellent. Certainly recommended, not only for the budget-conscious collector, but for those who enjoy youthful pianistic exuberance.

Additional recommendations ...

...Papillons, Op. 2. Davidsbündlertänze. Carnaval, Op. 9. Fantasie in C major, Op. 17.
  Etudes symphoniques, Op. 13. Kreisleriana, Op. 16. Kinderszenen, Op. 15. Piano Sonata No. 2
  in G minor, Op. 22. Arabeske, Op. 18. Bunte Blätter, Op. 99 – Novellette. Drei Romanzen, Op. 28.
  Humoreske, Op. 20. Waldszenen. Nachtstücke, Op. 23. **Wilhelm Kempff** (pf).
  DG Ⓑ 435 045-2GX4 (four discs: 297 minutes: ADD: 5/92).   ⒼⒼ
...Waldszenen. Arabeske in C major, Op. 18. Drei Romanzen, Op. 28. Faschingsschwank aus Wien,
  Op. 26. **Maria João Pires** (pf). DG Ⓕ 437 538-2GH (66 minutes: DDD: 6/95).

Schumann Drei Gedichte, Op. 30. Sechs Gedichte, Op. 36. Fünf Lieder, Op. 40. Romanzen und
Balladen, Opp. 45, 49 and 53. Belsatzar, Op. 57. Der Handschuh, Op. 87. **Olaf Bär** (bar);
Helmut Deutsch (pf). EMI Ⓔ CDC5 56199-2 (72 minutes: DDD: A/97). Texts and translations
included. Recorded 1996.   Ⓖ
"Die beiden Grenadiere" apart, Schumann's ballads crop up too rarely in recital and on disc. All the
more welcome, then, are Olaf Bär's bold and perceptive readings of some of the finest of them. In
Op. 45 he graphically realizes the *grand guignol* of "Der Schatzgräber" ("The treasure-seeker"), with
Helmut Deutsch relishing the onomatopoeic keyboard part. Equally compelling is the neglected
chivalric ballad, *Der Handschuh* ("The glove"): making vivid use, as ever, of his consonants, Bär slyly
mocks the pomposity of the royal retinue in the opening recitative, savours Schumann's lion and tiger
imitations (gleefully abetted by Deutsch) and catches to perfection the simpering, wheedling Lady
Kunigunde. Scarcely better known than these ballads are the three Geibel settings, Op. 30, and the six
songs, Op. 36 to homely, faded verses by Robert Reinick. Bär is virile and incisive in the alfresco
cheerfulness of "Der Knabe mit dem Wunderhorn" and the macho bravado of "Der Hidalgo", with
its swaggering bolero rhythms. Bär's freshness and unsentimental tenderness are very well suited to
the relatively modest songs of Op. 36. And he and Deutsch respond sharply to the character sketches
of Op. 40, from the shy delicacy of "Märzveilchen" ("March violets") through the sinister, twilit
"Muttertraum" to the aching intensity of "Der Soldat" and the desperation behind the wedding
merriment in "Der Spielmann". These days Bär's softer singing can sometimes be a shade breathy and
unfocused, with high notes not quite integrated into the line; nor is his legato always seamless.
Random comparison with Dietrich Fischer-Dieskau also finds the older baritone predictably
wider in his emotional and coloristic range, freer and more fluid in his phrasing and often more
subtle in his individual insights. But the more open, direct Bär is invariably a sympathetic singer
and an involving and, in the ballads, vividly dramatic interpreter. He and the ever-attentive
Deutsch certainly make a persuasive case for these less favoured products of Schumann's great song
year of 1840.

Additional recommendation ...
...**Dietrich Fischer-Dieskau** (bar); **Christoph Eschenbach** (pf).
DG Fischer-Dieskau Lieder Edition Ⓜ 445 660-2GX6
(six discs: 402 minutes: ADD: 11/77, 3/79, 11/79).   ⒼⒼⒼ

Schumann Frauenliebe und -leben, Op. 42. Gesänge, Op. 31 – No. 1, Die Löwenbraut; No. 2,
Die Kartenlegerin. Gedichte, Op. 35 – No. 1, Lust der Sturmnacht; No. 8, Stille Liebe. Rose,
Meer und Sonne, Op. 37 No. 9. Fünf Lieder, Op. 40. Der Schatzgräber, Op. 45 No. 1.
Volksliedchen, Op. 51 No. 2. Die Soldatenbraut, Op. 64 No. 1. Lieder-Album für die Jugend,
Op. 79 – No. 5, Vom Schlaraffenland; No. 22, Des Sennen Abscheid; No. 26, Schneeglöcken.
Mein schöner Stern!, Op. 101 No. 4. Abendlied, Op. 107 No. 6. Die Meerfee, Op. 125 No. 1.
Dein Angesicht, Op. 127 No. 2. **Anne Sofie von Otter** (mez); **Bengt Forsberg** (pf).
DG Ⓕ 445 881-2GH (79 minutes: DDD: 11/95). Texts and translations included.
Recorded 1993. *Gramophone Editor's choice.*   Ⓖ
This is one of those records where the promise of something exceptional in the first phrases is fully
borne out by all that follows. The *Frauenliebe* cycle is sung by a character, as vividly defined as any
Fiordiligi, Senta or Mimì in opera. Von Otter is one of those rare artists who can adapt the voice and
yet be true to its natural identity. In these songs of Schumann (not only in the *Frauenliebe*) she seems,
unselfconsciously, to find a new voice-personality for each and still to confine herself to what lies
naturally within her scope, forcing nothing and falsifying nothing. The woman of the 'life and love'
starts out as a girl. "Seit ich ihn gesehen" has a shy, private rapture which then grows bold for "Er, der
Herrlichste von allen", frank in its enthusiasm, buoyant in the spirit of its rhythm, radiant as the voice
rises to its highest notes. "Ich kann's nicht fassen, nicht glauben" is fully outgoing, an expression of
utter commitment, and the smile is always in the voice. The engagement-ring induces maturity, the girl
now a woman. The wedding-day preparations, confiding of motherhood, dandling the baby, and then
the emptiness of life at the husband's death: all are caught as in reality and in character. It is a
completely absorbed and absorbing performance.
   The generous selection of songs which follows works its spell partly by contrasts. The pastoral
sweetness of "Des Sennen Abschied" gives way to a grim, predatory ferocity of utterance in "Der
Schatzgräber", and the big Brahmsy sweep of "Lust der Sturmnacht" throws into relief the wistfully
tender mood of "Dein Angesicht". In these and in all else von Otter lights upon the right tone, and
the right shades of that tone. The programme is well planned, too, rounded off with "Rose, Meer und
Sonne", sketching the melodies of *Frauenliebe und -leben* with which the recital began. Occasionally
the piano is recorded too heavily or too prominently for the voice. But generally the sympathy and
unanimity of singer and pianist are all that could be desired – as is the recital *in toto*. No comparisons:
it doesn't matter how much of Schumann you already have on the shelves, this will still be a prized
addition.

Additional recommendation ...
...Fünf Lieder, Op. 40. *Coupled with works by various composers.* **Sir Peter Pears** (ten);
Murray Perahia (pf). Sony Classical Ⓜ SX4K63380 (four discs: 270 minutes: DDD/ADD: 4/98).
See review in the Collections section; refer to the Index.

Schumann Dichterliebe, Op. 48.
Mendelssohn Lieder, Op. 19*a* – No. 4, Neue Liebe; No. 5, Gruss. Lieder, Op. 34 – No. 2, Auf
Flügeln des Gesanges; No. 6, Reiselied. Morgengruss, Op. 47 No. 2. Allnächtlich im Träume,
Op. 86 No. 4.
Schubert Schwanengesang, D957 – Der Atlas; Ihr Bild; Das Fischermädchen; Die Stadt;
Am Meer; Der Doppelgänger. **Christoph Prégardien** (ten); **Andreas Staier** (fp).
Deutsche Harmonia Mundi Ⓕ 05472 77319-2 (57 minutes: DDD: 12/94). ✍
Texts and translations included. Recorded 1993.   Ⓠ
In their deeply poignant reading of *Dichterliebe,* these artists expose the wounded pain of the
protagonist, and the participation of a fortepiano gives the performance an intimacy that a grand
piano cannot match. The simple beauty of the singing in the early songs is rightly countermanded by
the darker, more dramatic tone and manner in "Im Rhein" and "Ich grolle nicht", with the top A on
"Herzen" piercing to the heart. These in turn give way to the plaintive sorrow of "Und wüssten's die
Blumen", the *Innigkeit* of "Hör ich das Liedchen", the delicately etched line and feeling of "Am
leuchtenden Sommermorgen", and the numbed emptiness, of "Ich hab im Traum geweinet". The
draining of all passion is summed up in the repeated final line of the penultimate song, "Zerfliesst wie
alte Schaum", with the fortepiano's afterthought so translucently played by Staier, whose postlude to
the whole cycle, restrained and understated though it is, speaks volumes of the sadness experienced
throughout. The truthfulness of the interpretation is seconded by the tenor's command of line and
phrase, the player's close rapport with his partner. This intelligently planned programme then offers
more Heine in the shape of settings by Mendelssohn and Schubert. The less demanding Mendelssohn
group allows an emotional respite between the soulful Schumann and the searing Schubert. From
Schwanengesang, that extraordinary pair of anguished songs, "Ihr Bild" and "Die Stadt", are given
their full measure of grief, with a gentle, rather fast "Das Fischermädchen" in between. Prégardien's
silver-voiced sorrowing and communing in "Am Meer" is just right, the verbal accents present but
never overdone. And so on to that Everest of a song, "Der Doppelgänger", a stark, nerve-tingling
interpretation that proves a fitting climax to a superb recital, faultlessly recorded.

Additional recommendations ...
...Liederkreis, Op. 24. Frauenliebe und -leben, Op. 42. Tragödie, Op. 64 No. 3. Abends am Strand,
    Op. 45 No. 3. Lehn' deine Wang, Op. 142 No. 2. Mein Wagen rollet langsam, Op. 142 No. 2.
    Brigitte Fassbaender (mez); **Irwin Gage** (pf). DG Ⓕ 415 519-2GH (57 minutes: DDD: 2/86).
...Dichterliebe, Op. 48. Liederkreis, Op. 39. **Olaf Bär** (bar); **Geoffrey Parsons** (pf).
    EMI Ⓕ CDC7 47397-2 (54 minutes: DDD: 9/86).
...Dichterliebe. Liederkreis, Op. 39. **Josef Protschka** (ten); **Helmut Deutsch** (pf).
    Capriccio Ⓕ 10 215 (62 minutes: DDD: 12/88).
...Myrthen, Op. 25 – No.1, Widmung; No. 3, Der Nussbaum; No. 7, Die Lotosblume; No. 9, Lied
    der Suleika; No. 11, Lied der Brait aus dem Liebesfrühling I; No. 12, Lied der Braut aus dem
    Liebesfrühling II; No. 15, Aus den hebräischen Gesängen; No. 21, Was will die einsame Träne?;
    No. 23, Im Westen. Sieben Gedichte, Op. 90. An den Sonnenschein, Op. 36 No. 4. Der Himmel
    hat ein Träne geweint, Op. 37 No. 1. Muttertraum, Op. 40 No. 2. Romanzen und Balladen,
    Op. 64 – No. 2, Das berlassne Mägdelein; No. 3, Tragödie. Melancholie, Op. 74 No. 6.
    Geisternähe, Op. 77 No. 3. Der Einsiedler, Op. 83 No. 3. **Mitsuko Shirai** (mez); **Hartmut Höll** (pf).
    Capriccio Ⓕ 10 445 (63 minutes: DDD: 11/93). *Gramophone Editor's choice.*
...Dichterliebe. *Coupled with works by* **Schubert** **Gérard Souzay** (bar); **Jacqueline Bonneau** (pf).
    Decca Historic Series mono Ⓜ 440 065-2DM* (71 minutes: ADD: 1/95).
...Dichterliebe. Liederkreis, Op. 24. Mein Wagen rollet langsam, Op. 142 No. 4. Es leuchtet meine
    Liebe, Op. 127 No. 3. Abends am Strand, Op. 45 No. 3. Myrthen, Op. 25 – No. 5, Lied aus dem
    Schenkenbuch im Divan I; No. 24, Du bist wie eine Blume. Der Kontrabandiste, Op. 74 No. 10.
    Erstes Grün, Op. 35 No. 4. Schöne Fremde, Op. 39 No. 6. **Dietrich Fischer-Dieskau** (bar);
    Hartmut Höll (pf). Erato Ⓕ 4509-98492-2 (69 minutes: DDD: 9/95).
...Myrthen, Op. 25 – No. 1, Widmung; No. 3, Der Nussbaum; No. 7, Die Lotosblume;
    No. 9, Lied der Suleika. Lieder-Album für die Jugend, Op. 79 – No. 10, Das Käuzlein; No. 12,
    Der Sandmann; No. 13, Marienwürmchen; No. 23, Er ist's; No. 26, Schneeglöckchen.
    Jasminenstrauch, Op. 27 No. 4. Die Blume der Ergebung, Op. 83 No. 2. Röselein, Op. 89 No. 6.
    Lieder und Gesänge, Op. 77 – No. 2, Mein Garten; No. 5, Aufträge. Gedichte. Op. 90 – No. 2,
    Meine Rose; No. 4, Die Sennin. Schmetterling, Op. 79 No. 2. Gedichte, Op. 35 – No. 4, Erstes
    Grün; No. 5, Sehnsucht nach der Waldgegend; No. 9, Frage. Die letzten Blumen starben, Op. 104
    No. 6. Die Meerfee, Op. 125 No. 1. Waldesgespräch, Op. 39 No. 3. Loreley, Op. 53 No. 2. Die
    Kartenlegerin, Op. 31 No. 2. Sehnsucht, Op. 51 No. 1. Mein schöner Stern!, Op. 101 No. 4.
    Coupled with works by various composers. **Elly Ameling** (sop); **Various soloists.**
    Deutsche Harmonia Mundi Ⓕ 74321 26617-2 (four discs: 239 minutes: ADD: 12/95).
    See review in the Collections section; refer to the Index.
...Dichterliebe. *Coupled with works by various composers.* **Aksel Schiøtz** (ten) with various artists.
    Danacord mono Ⓕ DACOCD453* (69 minutes: ADD: 4/97). *See review in the Collections
    section; refer to the Index.*
...Dichterliebe[a]. Liederkreis, Op. 24[a]. Frauenliebe und -leben, Op. 42[b]. [b]**Phyllis Bryn-Julson** (sop);
    [a]**John Shirley-Quirk** (bar); **Leon Fleisher** (pf). Arabesque Ⓕ Z6700 (73 minutes: DDD: 4/98).

Schumann Liederkreis, Op. 24. Dichterliebe, Op. 48. Belsatzar, Op. 57. Abends am Strand,
Op. 45 No. 3. Die beiden Grenadiere, Op. 49 No. 1. Lieder und Gesänge, Op. 127 – No. 2, Dein
Angesicht; No. 3, Es leuchtet meine Liebe. Vier Gesänge, Op. 142 – No. 2, Lehn deine Wang;
No. 4, Mein Wagen rollet langsam. **Ian Bostridge** (ten); **Julius Drake** (pf). EMI Ⓟ CDC5 56575-2
(69 minutes: DDD: 4/98). Texts and translations included. Recorded 1997.
Gramophone Editor's choice.   ⊖⊖⊖
This issue offers its manifold revelations concerning the setting of Heine's poetry by Schumann.
Bostridge makes one think anew about the music in hand, interpreting all these songs as much
through the mind of the poet as that of the composer and, being youthful himself, getting inside the
head of the vulnerable poet in his many moods. That, quite apart from his obvious gifts as a singer
and musician, is what raises Bostridge above most of his contemporaries who so often fail to live the
words they are singing. Every one of the magnificent Op. 24 songs has some moment of illumination,
whether it's the terror conveyed so immediately – and immediacy of reaction is of the essence all-
round here – in "Schöne Wiege", the breathtaking beauty and sorrow of "Anfang wollt ich" or the
breadth and intensity of "Mit Myrten und Rosen". In between the two cycles comes a group of the
1840 Leipzig settings that adumbrates every aspect of Bostridge's – and his equally perceptive
partner's – attributes. The vivid word-painting in *Belsatzar* brings the Old Testament scene arrestingly
before us. The inward fantasy of *Abends am Strand* is keenly evoked with an appropriately raw touch
on the word "Schrein" ("howl"). Then there's the unexpected heroic touch the tenor brings to *Die
beiden Grenadiere*, where Drake's imaginative contribution helps to paint the patriotic picture.
Perhaps best of all is the unjustly neglected *Es leuchtet meine Liebe*, a melodrama here perfectly
enacted by both performers. *Mein Wagen rollet langsam* forms a perfect introduction, in its lyrical
freedom, to *Dichterliebe*, an interpretation to rank with the best available in terms of the sheer beauty
of the singing and acute response to its sustained inspiration. Listen to the wonder brought to the
discovery of the flowers and angels in "Im Rhein", the contained anger of "Ich grolle nicht", the
sense of bereavement in "Hör ist das Liedchen" and you will judge this is an interpretation of
profundity and emotional identification, the whole cycle crowned by the sensitivity of Drake's playing
of the summarizing postlude. To complete one's pleasure EMI have provided an exemplary and
forward recording balance.
Additional recommendation...
...Dichterliebe. Liederkreis, Op. 24. Gesänge, Op. 142 – Lehn deine Wang; Mein Wagen rollet
langsam. Myrthen, Op. 25 – Die Lotosblume; Was will die einsame Tränen?; Du bist wie eine
Blume. Der arme Peter, Op. 53 No. 3. Tragödie, Op. 64 No. 3. **Wolfgang Holzmair** (bar); **Imogen
Cooper** (pf). Philips Ⓟ 446 086-2PH (67 minutes: DDD: 9/95). *Gramophone Editor's choice.*   ⊖

Schumann Liederkreis, Op. 24. Dichterliebe, Op. 48. **Matthias Goerne** (bar); **Vladimir Ashkenazy**
(pf). Decca Ⓟ 458 265-2DH (50 minutes: DDD: 5/98). Texts and translations included.
Recorded 1997. *Gramophone Editor's choice.*   ⊖⊖⊖
Matthias Goerne is with little doubt the most probing male Lieder singer to emerge from Germany
in recent years, an artist of extraordinary magnetism both in his live performances and on disc. With
his dark, velvet timbre, intense legato line and searching response to the fluctuating shades of Heine's
bittersweet verses, Goerne gives mesmeric readings of both *Dichterliebe* and the Op. 24 *Liederkreis*.
Partly because of the colour of his voice, partly because of some unusually broad tempos, both cycles
emerge as more sombre and haunted than in the comparably fine recordings by Wolfgang Holzmair
and Ian Bostridge. The fourth song of the *Liederkreis*, "Lieb Liebchen", seems suffused with genuine
death-weariness – barely a hint here of wryness or irony. In the following "Schöne Wiege meiner
Leiden", Goerne captures the feverishness of Heine's original which Schumann's lulling, nostalgic
melody tends to mitigate; later in the song the lover's tottering reason and death-longing are chillingly
realized. In the first two songs of *Dichterliebe* Goerne underlines the sense of sorrow and regret with
which Schumann shadows Heine's limpid love lyrics. And this sets the tone for a brooding, intensely
inward reading, flaring into self-lacerating bitterness in "Ich grolle nicht" and "Das ist ein Flöten und
Geigen", hardening into an iron stoicism in the closing song, before the overwhelming sense of
longing and loss in the last line. Throughout, Ashkenazy is a positive, sympathetic partner, though
here and there his sharply etched playing can be overassertive. If some may understandably prefer a
higher, lighter voice in these cycles, Goerne is the equal of both Holzmair and Bostridge in
interpretative insight and tonal beauty, and ventures a more daring range of expression than either.

Schumann Liederkreis, Op. 24. Myrthen, Op. 25 – No. 7, Die Lotosblume; No. 21, Was will die
einsame Träne?; No. 24, Du bist wie eine Blume. Romanzen und Balladen – Op. 45: No. 3,
Abends am Strand; Op. 49: No. 1, Die beiden Grenadiere; No. 2, Die feindlichen Brüder; Op. 53:
No. 3, Der arme Peter; Op. 64: No. 3, Tragödie[a]. Belsatzar, Op. 57. Lieder und Gesänge, Op. 127
– No. 2, Dein Angesicht; No. 3, Es leuchtet meine Liebe. Gesänge, Op. 142 – No. 2, Lehn deine
Wang; No. 4, Mein Wagen rollet langsam. **Stephan Genz** (bar); [a]**Christoph Genz** (ten);
Claar ter Horst (pf). Claves Ⓟ CD50-9708 (59 minutes: DDD: 5/98). Texts and translations
included. Recorded 1996-1997.
This is a recital of promise and fulfilment. Stephan Genz's voice and style are as wide-ranging as his
mode of expression. He lives every moment of Op. 24, entering into all aspects of Schumann's settings

and Heine's originals yet never overstepping the mark in his verbal painting. The other Heine settings receive no less than their due. The sensuous and plaintive qualities in Genz's tone are well suited to the three Heine poems in *Myrthen*. In contrast he rises to the histrionic challenges of *Die beiden Grenadiere*, *Belsatzar* and the rarely encountered *Die feindlichen Brüder*, performances that are felt as immediately as if at the moment of composition. In *Abends am Strand* the voice follows to the full the song's romantic import. In the third song of Op. 64, *Tragödie*, the baritone is joined by his talented tenor brother: their voices naturally blend well. Finally, Genz is inspired by that amazingly original song, *Mein Wagen rollet langsam*, to give of his absolute best. Here, as throughout, Claar ter Horst matches the perceptions of her partner, and both are caught in an amenable acoustic.

Additional recommendation ...
...Myrthen, Op. 25 – No. 1, Widmung; No. 24. *Coupled with works by various composers.*
Angela Gheorghiu (sop); **Malcolm Martineau** (pf). Decca Ⓕ 458 360-2DH
(75 minutes: DDD: 5/98). *See review in the Collections section; refer to the Index.*

Schumann Liederkreis, Op. 39. Frauenliebe und -leben, Op. 42. Myrthen, Op. 25 – No. 3, Der Nussbaum; No. 7, Die Lotosblume; No. 15, Aus den Hebräischen Gesängen. Der Soldat, Op. 40 No. 3. Lieder-Album für die Jugend, Op. 79 – No. 23, Er ist's; No. 28, Mignon. **Marjana Lipovšek** (mez); **Graham Johnson** (pf). Sony Classical Ⓕ SK57972 (65 minutes: DDD: 8/95). Texts and translations included. Recorded 1993.

It will be for the two cycles that most will be drawn to this disc. As each of these performances is so satisfying, striking a *via media*, perhaps under Johnson's influence, between reading too little or too much into the songs, and finding in every case the just tempo, they can be recommended wholeheartedly to anyone wanting the pair sung by a mezzo. The combination of romance and gothic mystery in the Op. 39 *Liederkreis* is captured unerringly by both artists, in technical and interpretive terms, though one might like a firmer line and a more hushed *piano* from the singer in "Mondnacht". Detailed analysis is hardly warranted as the cycle progresses in a wholly natural and acceptable way, line, tone, and particularly vibrato nicely judged, and certain phrases, such as the final one in "Auf einer Berg", given an added *frisson* of verbal emphasis. In *Frauenliebe*, the pair catch the sense of the girl's wonder, growing maturity, inner warmth, but any hont of sentimentality is firmly kept at bay. A sudden underlining of the word "mein" in "Helft mir, ihr Schwestern" evinces the woman's anti-feminist attitude of being at her master's command. "Weisst du nun die Tränen" in the sixth song is rightly the emotional core of the reading. The postlude is softly, hauntingly played by Johnson. The recording has presence and immediacy.

Schumann Liederkreis, Op. 39. Frauenliebe und -leben, Op. 42. **Soile Isokoski** (sop);
Marita Viitasalo (pf). Finlandia Ⓕ 0630-10924-2 (49 minutes: DDD: 3/96).
Texts and translations included. Recorded 1993-1995.

This interpretation from this young Finnish soprano can stand comparison with the best. In her wonderfully straightforward and musical performance, she marries a sincere spontaneity with a warming sense of line and phrase, a style well learnt yet put to her own, positive purpose. Before you is the rapturous bride-to-be in all her moods, then the young woman struck almost dumb by unexpected grief. Nothing in her portrayal is forced or in the least contrived yet everything, felt from the heart, goes to it. And the voice itself? Well, reminders of Flagstad's richness, Ameling's naturalness and Price's precision are here to be heard and enjoyed. She is just as imaginative in Op. 39 as in Op. 42, giving a very central, unaffected account of the *Liederkreis* encompassing all its varied moods and one that makes its points unobtrusively and, as with Op. 42, with the emphasis on long-breathed phrasing and rock-steady tone. The partnership with Viitasalo is obviously a fruitful one. The two artists think and 'breathe' alike though in Op. 42 he is just occasionally too prominent, at least as recorded.

Additional recommendations ...
...Liederkreis, Op. 39. 12 Gedichte, Op. 35. **Dame Margaret Price** (sop); **Graham Johnson** (pf). Hyperion Ⓕ CDA66596 (59 minutes: DDD).
...Liebeslied, Op. 51 No. 5. Nachtlied, Op. 96 No. 1. Lieder und Gesänge aus Wilhelm Meister, Op. 98a – No. 1, Mignon; No. 5, Heiss mich nicht reden; No. 7, Singet nicht in Trauertönen. *Coupled with works by various composers* **Dawn Upshaw** (sop); **Richard Goode** (pf). Elektra-Nonesuch Ⓕ 7559-79317-2 (53 minutes: DDD: 8/94). *See review in the Collections section; refer to the Index.*
...Myrthen, Op. 25a. Lieder und Gesänge, Op. 27. Die Löwenbraut, Op. 31 No. 1. a**Lynne Dawson** (sop); **Ian Partridge** (ten); **Julius Drake** (pf). Chandos Ⓕ CHAN9307 (72 minutes: DDD: 12/94).
...Liederkreis, Op. 39 – No. 1, In der Fremde; No. 3, Waldesgespräch; No. 4, Die Stille; No. 10, Zwielicht; No. 12, Frühlingsnacht. Frauenliebe und -leben, Op. 42. Myrthen, Op. 25 – No. 1, Widmung; No. 3, Der Nussbaum; No. 7, Die Lotosblume; No. 9, Lied der Suleika. Fünf Gedichte der Königen Maria Stuart, Op. 135. Dein Angesicht, Op. 127 No. 2. Meine Rose, Op. 90 No. 2. Aufträge, Op. 77 No. 5. Stille Tränen, Op. 35 No. 10. **Brahms** Deutsche Volkslieder, WoO33 – Da unten im Tale; Feinsliebchen; In stiller Nacht. Die Trauernde, Op. 7 No. 5. **Irmgard Seefried** (sop); **Erik Werba** (pf). Orfeo D'Or Salzburg Festspieldokumente mono Ⓕ C398951B* (77 minutes: ADD: 3/96).

Schumann Complete Lieder, Volume 1. Das verlassene Mägdlein, Op. 64 No. 2. Melancholie, Op. 74 No. 6. Aufträge, Op. 77 No. 5. Op. 79 – No. 7a, Zigeunerliedchen I; No. 7b, Zigeunerliedchen II; No. 23, Er ist's!. Die Blume der Ergebung, Op. 83 No. 2. Röslein, Röslein!, Op. 89 No. 6. Sechs Gedichte und Requiem, Op. 90. Op. 96 – No. 1, Nachtlied; No. 3 Ihre Stimme. Lieder und Gesänge aus Wilhelm Meister, Op. 98a – No. 1, Kennst du das Land?; No. 3, Nur wer die Sehnsucht kennt; No. 5, Heiss' mich nicht reden; No. 7, Singet nicht in Trauertönen; No. 9, So lasst mich scheinen. Sechs Gesänge, Op. 107. Warnung, Op. 119 No. 2. Die Meerfee, Op. 125 No. 1. Sängers Trost, Op. 127 No. 1. Mädchen-Schwermut, Op. 142 No. 3. **Christine Schäfer** (sop); **Graham Johnson** (pf). Hyperion Ⓟ CDJ33101 (75 minutes: DDD: 8/96). Texts and translations included. Recorded 1995.
Gramophone Award Winner 1997.   ⒼⒼ

This disc launches Hyperion's Schumann Lieder project as auspiciously as Dame Janet Baker's recital opened their Complete Schubert Edition. As ever, Graham Johnson shows an unerring gift for matching singer and song. These are almost all late pieces, written between 1849 and 1852 under the shadow of depression and sickness; and their intense chromaticism can all too easily seem tortuous. However, imaginatively supported by Johnson, Christine Schäfer illuminates each of these songs with her pure, lucent timbre, her grace and breadth of phrase and her unselfconscious feeling for verbal meaning and nuance. The voice is an expressive, flexible lyric-coloratura; she can spin a scrupulously even legato, integrates the high notes of, say, "Er ist's" perfectly within the melodic line, and has the breath control to sustain the long phrases of "Requiem" with apparent ease. Aided by Johnson's lucid textures and uncommonly subtle feel for rubato and harmonic direction, Schäfer avoids any hint of mawkishness in songs like "Meine Rose", Op. 90 No. 2, "Mädchen-Schwermut" and "Abendlied. Several songs here have been overshadowed or totally eclipsed by the settings by Schubert, Wolf or Brahms, and Schäfer and Johnson do much to rehabilitate them: in "Der Gärtner" (from Op. 107), for instance, the gardener's hopeless adoration inspires a new glow and fullness in the tone, with Johnson cunningly clarifying the intricate cross-rhythms.

Schäfer brings an exquisite wondering stillness to the Goethe "Nachtlied", more disturbed and earthbound than Schubert's sublime setting, but here, at least, scarcely less poignant. She also has the dramatic flair to bring off the difficult Mignon songs, especially the volatile, quasi-operatic "Heiss' mich nicht reden" and "Kennst du das Land", where the final verse, evoking Mignon's terrifying passage across the Alps, builds to a climax of desperate, almost demented yearning. At the other end of the emotional spectrum, Schäfer brings a guileful, knowing touch to the first of the *Zigeunerliedchen*; the Mendelssohnian "Die Meerfee" glistens and glances and "Aufträge" has a winning eagerness and charm, with a delicious sense of flirtation between voice and keyboard. In sum, a delectable, often revelatory recital. The recording is natural and well balanced, while Graham Johnson's typically searching commentaries complement the performances in presenting the most eloquent case possible for Schumann's much maligned and neglected late songs.

Additional recommendation ...

...Die Blume der Ergebung, Op. 83 No. 2. Mein Garten, Op. 77 No. 2. Jasminenstrauch, Op. 27 No. 4. Herzeleid, Op. 107 No. 1. Erstes Grün, Op. 35 No. 4. Volksliedchen, Op. 51 No. 2. *Coupled with works by various composers.* **Dame Felicity Lott** (sop); **Graham Johnson** (pf). Hyperion Ⓟ CDA66937 (65 minutes: DDD: 10/97). *See review in the Collections section; refer to the Index.*

Schumann Complete Lieder, Volume 2. Drei Gedichte, Op. 30. Die Löwenbraut, Op. 31 No. 1. 12 Gedichte, Op. 35. Lieder und Gesänge aus Wilhelm Meister, Op. 98a – No. 2, Ballade des Harfners; No. 4, Wer nie sein Brot mit Tränen ass; No. 6, Wer sich der Einsamkeit ergibt; No. 8, An die Türen will ich schleichen. Vier Husarenlieder, Op. 117. **Simon Keenlyside** (bar); **Graham Johnson** (pf). Hyperion Ⓟ CDJ33102 (70 minutes: DDD: 3/98). Texts and translations included. Recorded 1997. *Gramophone Editor's choice.*   ⒼⒼ

In his notes Graham Johnson says that what we have always lacked is a convincing way of performing late Schumann songs, often spare in texture and elusive in style. Well, he and Keenlyside seem to have found one here in their wholly admirable versions of the very different Opp. 98a and 117. The Op. 98a settings of the Harper's outpourings from *Wilhelm Meister* have always stood in the shade of those by Schubert and Wolf. This pair show incontrovertibly that there's much to be said for Schumann's versions, capturing the essence of the old man's sad musings, as set by the composer in a typically free and imaginative way, alert to every nuance in the texts. The extroverted Lenau *Husarenlieder* could hardly be more different. Keenlyside identifies in turn with the bravado of the first, the cynicism of the second, and the eerie, death-dominated mood of the fourth. The third, as Johnson avers, is a bit of a dud. Then it's back to the miracle year of 1840 for three seldom-heard Geibel *Knabenhorn* settings, Op. 30. The pair enter into the open-hearted mood called for by these songs, most of all in the irresistible "Der Hidalgo". Keenlyside is just as forthright in the ballad *Die Löwenbraut* and in those of Op. 35, the well-known Kerner settings, which display Schumann's Florestan side, and he brings impressive control to the Eusebius ones, not least the all-enveloping "Stille Tränen". The interpretation of this quasi-cycle is convincing and unerringly paced. The recording, Johnson's persuasive playing and his long and informative notes are of the exceptional standard we have come to expect from this source.

Schumann Genoveva. **Ruth Ziesak** (sop) Genoveva; **Deon van der Walt** (ten) Golo; **Rodney Gilfry** (bar) Hidulfus; **Oliver Widmer** (bar) Siegfried; **Marjana Lipovšek** (mez) Margaretha; **Thomas Quasthoff** (bar) Drago; **Hiroyuki Ijichi** (bass) Balthasar; **Josef Krenmair** (bar) Caspar; **Arnold Schoenberg Choir; Chamber Orchestra of Europe / Nikolaus Harnoncourt.**
Teldec Ⓕ 0630-13144-2 (two discs: 129 minutes: DDD: 1/98). Notes, text and translation included. Recorded live in 1996. ⒼⒼⒼ

For most listeners, Schumann's only opera is still a relatively unknown quantity but lovers of Schumann will celebrate a work that is at once intimate, thought-provoking and gloriously melodious. The libretto (by Schumann himself, after Tieck and Hebbel) deals with secret passion and suspected adultery, while the music mirrors emotional turmoil with great subtlety, and sometimes with astonishing imagination. Copious foretastes are provided in the familiar overture, and thereafter, discoveries abound. Sample, for example, the jagged counter-motif that shudders as Genoveva's husband Siegfried entreats Golo (his own *alter ego*) to guard his wife while he is away at war (disc 1, track 5, at 1'58"); or the off-stage forces representing drunken servants at 2'22" into track 9; or the almost Expressionist writing at 4'00" into track 10 where Golo responds – with seething hatred – to Genoveva's vengeance. You might also try track 2 on disc 2, at 3'37", where Golo brings Siegfried news of Genoveva's supposed adultery, music that is both pained and equivocal. The entreaties of Drago's ghost aren't too far removed from Siegmund's "Nothung!" in Act 1 of *Die Walküre* (track 4, at 6'10"), and Genoveva's singing from "a desolate, rocky place" (track 5, first minute or so), sounds fairly prophetic of Isolde (who was as yet unborn, so to speak). Harnoncourt suspects that Genoveva was a "counterblast" to Wagner, and although Wagner apparently thought the opera "bizarre", there remains a vague suspicion of sneaking regard, even a smidgen of influence. Teldec's balancing is mostly judicious and the musical direction suggestive of burning conviction. The worthy though relatively conventional Gerd Albrecht (in Orfeo's mellow 1992 recording) only serves to underline the leaner, more inflected and more urgently voiced profile of Harnoncourt's interpretation. As to the two sets of singers, most preferences rest with the latter's line-up. Stage effects are well handled and the sum effect is of a top-drawer Schumann set within an unexpected structural context.

Additional recommendation ...
...**Soloists; Hamburg State Opera Chorus; Hamburg Philharmonic Orchestra / Gerd Albrecht.**
Orfeo Ⓕ C289932H (two discs: 178 minutes: DDD: 1/94). Ⓖ

Schumann (arr. Beecham) Manfred – Incidental Music, Op. 115. **Gertrud Holt** (sop); **Claire Duchesneau** (mez); **Glyndwr Davies, Ian Billington** (tens); **Niven Miller** (bar); **Laidman Browne, Jill Balcon, Raf de la Torre, David Enders** (spkrs); **BBC Chorus; Royal Philharmonic Orchestra / Sir Thomas Beecham.** Sir Thomas Beecham Trust mono Ⓜ BEECHAM4*
(78 minutes: ADD: 9/91). From Fontana CFL1026/7 (2/59). Recorded 1954-1956. ⒼⒼ

Schumann was haunted by Byron's autobiographically-inspired dramatic poem, *Manfred*, from a very early age. When eventually writing his incidental music for it (15 numbers and an overture) in 1848-49 he confessed to never having devoted himself to any composition before "with such lavish love and power". No one in this country has ever done more for it than Sir Thomas Beecham, who even staged it at the Theatre Royal, Drury Lane, London, way back in 1918, some 36 years before reviving it for the BBC and at the Festival Hall in performances leading to this now legendary recording. Score-followers will at once note Beecham's appropriation and scoring of two of the composer's roughly contemporaneous keyboard miniatures as additional background music for the guilt-wracked, soliloquizing Manfred. But their choice and placing is so apt that even Schumann himself might have been grateful. By present-day standards Laidman Browne might be thought a shade too overtly emotional in the title-role. But speakers (including a splendidly awesome Witch of the Alps and rustic chamois-hunter), like singers, orchestra and the magnetic Sir Thomas himself, are all at one in vividness of atmospheric evocation. Splendid remastering also plays its part in making this medium-priced disc a collector's piece.

Additional recommendation ...
...**Soloists; Basle Madrigalists; Swiss Workshop Philharmonic Orchestra / Mario Venzago.**
MGB Musiques Suisses Ⓕ CD6122 (62 minutes: DDD: 10/95).

Schumann Der Rose Pilgerfahrt, Op. 112. **Inga Nielsen, Helle Hinz** (sops); **Annemarie Møller, Elizabeth Halling** (mezzos); **Deon van der Walt** (ten); **Guido Päevatalu** (bar); **Christian Christiansen** (bass); **Danish National Radio Choir and Symphony Orchestra / Gustav Kuhn.** Chandos Ⓕ CHAN9350 (62 minutes: DDD: 7/95). Text included. Recorded 1993.

Amidst today's great upsurgence of interest in Schumann's later choral undertakings, the work's long neglect is no doubt due to its all-too-naïve tale of a rose who, after an eagerly sought transformation into a maiden to experience human love, chooses to sacrifice herself for her baby. Schumann's own ready response to Moritz Horn's poem can best be explained by its underlying moral message together with a strain of German rusticity then equally close to the composer's heart. Having said that, how grateful Schumann lovers should be to Chandos for at last introducing the work to the English catalogue in so sympathetic yet discreet a performance from this predominantly Danish cast. All credit to the conductor, Gustav Kuhn, for revealing so much fancy in fairyland, so much brio in peasant merriment, and so much charm in more tender lyricism without ever making heavy weather of this essentially *gemütlich* little score. No praise can be too high for the Danish National Radio Choir: such immediacy of response leaves you in no doubt as to their professional status. Nor do the soloists or orchestra disappoint. Tonal reproduction is agreeably natural.

Schumann Szenen aus Goethes Faust. **Karita Mattila, Barbara Bonney, Brigitte Poschner-Klebel, Susan Graham** (sops); **Iris Vermillion** (mez); **Endrik Wottrich, Hans-Peter Blochwitz** (tens); **Bryn Terfel** (bass-bar); **Jan-Hendrik Rootering, Harry Peeters** (basses); **Tölz Boys' Choir; Swedish Radio Chorus; Berlin Philharmonic Orchestra / Claudio Abbado.**
Sony Classical Ⓟ S2K66308 (two discs: 115 minutes: DDD: 5/95). Notes, text and translation included. Recorded live in 1994.   ⒼⒼⒼ

No one before Schumann had ever attempted to set Goethe's mystical closing scene, which he finished in time for the Goethe centenary in 1849. What eventually emerged as his own Parts 1 and 2 (in turn portraits of Gretchen and the by now repentant Faust) followed later, after his move from a Mendelssohn-dominated Leipzig to a Wagner-ruled Dresden, hence the striking difference in style. Nothing Schumann ever wrote is more dramatic than Faust's blinding and death in the course of Part 2. The Berlin Philharmonic is very forwardly recorded – occasionally perhaps a little too much so for certain voices. But never in the case of Bryn Terfel in the title-role. Any advance fears that he might disappoint after the mature Fischer-Dieskau (for Klee) were immediately banished not only by the generosity and flow of his warm, round tone but also the total commitment and conviction of his characterization. Moreover as Dr Marianus in Part 3 he offers some wonderfully sustained *mezza* and *sotto voce*. Karita Mattila's Gretchen, less youthfully vulnerable than Elizabeth Harwood (for Britten) and certainly less excitably impressionable than Edith Mathis (Klee), is always sympathetically pure-toned, clean-lined and assured. As Ariel and Pater Ecstaticus Endrik Wottrich has more in common with the stylish, tighter-voiced Peter Pears (Britten) than the open-throated, uninhibited Nicolai Gedda (Klee). But like Jan-Hendrik Rootering's sinister Mephistopheles and Evil Spirit, and still more Harry Peeters's Pater Profundis, he at times, as positioned, seems outweighed by the orchestra.

No praise can be too high for the Four Grey Sisters (so tellingly contrasted in vocal colour) led by Barbara Bonney: their midnight encounter with Faust and his eventual blinding, is brilliantly done. And there is splendidly characterful choral singing throughout from both adult and youthful choirs. Both Klee and Britten are fortunate in having Dietrich Fischer-Dieskau at the head of their casts, and in both performances he tellingly changes his style from the quasi-operatic demands of the title-role to the smoother, suaver lyricism of Doctor Marianus in the holier Part 3. With Walter Berry (Mephistopheles, the Evil Spirit and Pater Seraphicus), Nicolai Gedda (Ariel and Pater Ecstaticus) and Edith Mathis (Gretchen and Una Poenitentium) in support, Klee's Düsseldorf recording offers the stronger soloists, though the English team under Britten lack nothing in sensitivity. In the more operatically conceived Parts 1 and 2 and the visionary Part 3, Abbado himself takes the music to heart just as closely and intensely as the spacious Britten and the more eagerly and urgently dramatic Klee, whose overall timing, incidentally is some five minutes shorter than Abbado's and almost eight minutes shorter than Britten's. And needless to say what Abbado draws from his orchestra (even if not matching the ECO and Britten's shattering outburst at the actual moment of Faust's death) makes nonesense of the charge that Schumann was an inept scorer. This is worth every penny of its full-price but should not cause regret if you already own one or other of its two splendid mid-price rivals.

Additional recommendations ...
...**Soloists; Wandsworth School Choir; Aldeburgh Festival Singers; English Chamber Orchestra / Benjamin Britten.** Decca Ⓜ 425 705-2DM2 (two discs: 118 minutes: ADD: 7/90).   ⒼⒼⒼ
...**Soloists; Tölz Boys' Choir; Düsseldorf Symphony Orchestra / Bernhard Klee.**
EMI Ⓜ CMS7 69450-2 (two discs: 110 minutes: DDD: 5/95).   Ⓖ

Further listening ...
...Konzertsatz in D minor (1839). *Coupled with works by various composers.*
English Chamber Orchestra / Sayard Stone. Koch International Classics 37197-2 (10/96).
See review under Mendelssohn; refer to the Index.
...String Quartets, Op. 41 – No. 1 in A minor; No. 3 in A major. **Lark Quartet.**
Arabesque Z6696 (A/97).
...String Quartet No. 3 in A major, Op. 41 No. 3. *Coupled with string quartets by* **Haydn** and
Shostakovich **Allegri Quartet.** Naim Audio NAIMCD016 (4/98). *See review under Haydn; refer to the Index.*
...Carnaval, Op. 9. *Coupled with works by various composers.* **Dame Myra Hess** (pf).
Biddulph mono LHW025* (3/96). *See review in the Collections section; refer to the Index.*   Ⓖ
...Träumerei, Op. 15 No. 7. *Coupled with works by various composers.* **Pavel Nersessian** (pf).
Bel Air Music BAM9725 (3/98). *See review in the Collections section; refer to the Index.*
...Spanische Liebeslieder, Op. 138. *Coupled with works by* **Brahms** **Barbara Bonney** (sop);
Anne Sofie von Otter (mez); **Kurt Streit** (ten); **Olaf Bär** (bar);
Bengt Forsberg, Helmut Deutsch (pf duet). EMI CDC5 55430-2 (10/95).
...Das Paradies und die Peri, Op. 50ᵃ. Overture, Scherzo and Finale, Op. 52.
[a]**Soloists;** [a]**Dresden State Opera Chorus; Staatskapelle Dresden / Giuseppe Sinopoli.**
DG 445 875-2GH2 (12/95).
...Das Paradies und die Peri, Op. 50. **Soloists; Leipzig Radio Chorus and Symphony Orchestra / Wolf-Dieter Hauschild.** Berlin Classics 0091 882BC (9/97).

Gerard Schurmann

Dutch/British 1929

Suggested listening ...
...The Gardens of Exile. *Coupled with* **Rózsa** Cello Concerto, Op. 32ª. [a]**Peter Rejto** (vc);
Pecs Hungarian Symphony Orchestra / Howard Williams.
Silva Classics SILKD6011 (9/96). *See review under Rózsa; refer to the Index.*

Heinrich Schütz

German 1585-1672

Schütz Symphoniae sacrae, SWV341-67. **Emma Kirkby, Suzie Le Blanc** (sops); **James Bowman**
(alto); **Nigel Rogers, Charles Daniels** (tens); **Stephen Varcoe** (bass); **Richard Wistreich** (bass);
Jeremy West, Nicholas Perry (cornets); **Purcell Quartet** (Catherine Mackintosh, Catherine Weiss,
vns; Richard Boothby, va da gamba; Robert Woolley, hpd). Chandos Chaconne Ⓕ CHAN0566/7
(two discs: 139 minutes: DDD: 4/95). Text and translation included. 🎵 Recorded 1993-1994.
Gramophone Editor's choice.   Ⓖ
These discs are in various ways revelatory. Schütz's collection is difficult to get through in one sitting,
but each item in the collection is a jewel, albeit not ostentatiously displayed. This is church music on
a small scale in terms of physical resources, but of enormous invention and beauty. Sometimes the
Purcell Quartet do not push the music along quite enough. In general, however, the instrumentalists
respond with enthusiasm and great understanding of the style of these rather recondite works. It takes
considerable sensitivity to bring out the rich textures of *Meine Seele erhebt den Herren* or *Der Herr
ist meine Stärke* without enjoying such moments at the expense of the vocal soloist. The relatively
well-known bass solo *Herr, nun lässest du deinen Diener* is another example of a perfect match
between voice and instruments. Emma Kirkby brings all her customary charm and precision to her
two solo arias. Both tenors are in their element, if sometimes a little understated, and Stephen Varcoe
and Richard Wistreich really understand and communicate the glowing black and gold colours of
Schütz's writing for the bass voice. Schütz's debt to Monteverdi is very much evident in *Der Herr ist
mein Licht* for two tenors and even more so in *Es steh Gott auf*, for the same scoring, but Schütz's
natural reluctance to "deck out my work with foreign plumage" means that his own voice as a
composer is always in evidence. It is difficult to be precise about this, especially when the second
volume of *Symphoniae sacrae* does undeniably show such a strong Italian influence as compared with
its predecessor. Yet this reconciliation of Italian *stile concertato* with Schütz's northern reticence is
one of the challenges in performing his music, and one to which this recording rises magnificently.

Additional recommendation ...
...Symphoniae sacrae. Vater Abraham, erbarme dich mein, SWV477.
La Capella Ducale; Musica Fiata / Roland Wilson (cornett/rec).
Sony Classical Vivarte Ⓕ S2K68261 (two discs: 147 minutes: DDD: 12/97).

Schütz Geistliche Chormusik, SWV369-97 – Herr, auf dich traue ich, SWV377ª; Die mit Tränen
säen, SWV378[b]; So fahr ich hin zu Jesu Christ, SWV379[c]; O lieber Herre Gott, SWV381; Ich bin
eine refende Stimme, SWV383; Die Himmel erzählen dei Ehre Gottes, SWV386; Herzlich lieb hab
ich dich, o Herr, SWV387; Das ist je gewisslich wahr, SWV388; Unser Wandel ist im Himmel,
SWV390; Selig sind die Toten, SWV391; Was mein Gott will, das gescheh allzeit, SWV392[bc].
Kleiner geistlichen Concerten, Erster Theil, SWV282-305 – Eile mich, Gott, zu erretten,
SWV282ª; O süsser, o freundlicher, SWV285[b]; Schaffe in mir, Gott, ein reines Herz, SWV291[ab].
Kleiner geistlichen Concerten, Anderer Theil, SWV306-37 – Ich liege und schlafe, SWV310[c];
Wann unsre Augen schlafen ein, SWV316[bc]. [a]**Agnes Mellon** (sop); [b]**Mark Padmore** (ten);
[c]**Peter Kooy** (bass); **Collegium Vocale / Philippe Herreweghe.** Harmonia Mundi Ⓕ HMC90 1534
(61 minutes: DDD: 5/96). 🎵 Texts and translations included.
This anthology shows both sides of Schütz's output: the solid *prima prattica* training which is evident
in his fine handling of counterpoint, and the Monteverdian lessons learned and shown off in the
Kleiner geistlichen Concerten. Common to both styles is an impressive economy of means, so that with
very small resources Schütz obtains an extraordinary variety of colour and responds with immediacy
to each text. To all this Collegium Vocale bring a brilliance of colour and a splendid choral blend
(particularly evident in *Herr, auf dich* and *Die mit Tränen*, to pick two random examples), and a vivid
response to Schütz's often difficult tempo changes. The speech-propelled writing in such motets as
O lieber Herre Gott or *Die Himmel erzählen* is far from easy to bring across convincingly, but both are
rendered here with impressive conviction and power. The *Concerte* are rather disappointing after such
magnificent concerted choral singing, their highly baroque word-setting seeming superficial, but they
are superbly sung, and it is especially good to hear Peter Kooy shown to such advantage.

Additional recommendation ...
...Geistliche Chormusik, SWV381-93. Ich weiss das mein Erlöser lebet, SWV457. **Emmanuel Music
Chorus / Craig Smith.** Koch International Classics Ⓕ 37174-2 (67 minutes: DDD: 11/93).

Schütz Ich hab mein Sach Gott heimgestellt, SWV305. Ich will dem Herren loben allezeit,
SWV306. Was hast du verwirket, SWV307. O Jesu, nomen dulce, SWV308. O misericordissime
Jesu, SWV309. Ich leige und schlafe, SWV310. Habe deine Lust an dem Herren, SWV311. Herr,

ich hoffe darauf, SWV312. Bone Jesu, verbum Patris, SWV313. Verbum caro factum est,
SWV314. Hodie Christus natus est, SWV315. Wann unsre Augen schlafen ein, SWV316. Meister,
wir haben die ganze Nacht gearbeitet, SWV317. Die Furcht des Herren, SWV318. Ich beuge
meine Knie, SWV319. Ich bin jung gewesen, SWV320. Herr, wann ich nur dich habe, SWV321.
Rorate coeli desuper, SWV322. Joseph, du Sohn David, SWV323. Ich bin die Auferstehung,
SWV324. **Tölz Boys' Choir / Gerhard Schmidt-Gaden** with **Roman Summereder** (org).
Capriccio Ⓔ 10 388 (77 minutes: DDD: 4/93). 🖋 Texts and translations included.
Recorded 1989-1990.

Getting music published evidently encountered economic difficulties during the Thirty Years' War, for
Heinrich Schütz had to issue his *Kleine Geistliche Konzerte* ("Little Sacred Concertos") – short motets
for vocal soloists and continuo – in two parts in, respectively, 1636 and 1639. No. 24 from Part 1 and
Nos. 1-19 from Part 2 comprise the programme for this second volume from soloists of the Tölz Boys'
Choir and although, at first sight, this may seem too regimented an approach to produce satisfying
listening for the whole disc, Schütz himself structured the items so that there is a progression
throughout the set, not only in increased numbers of soloists but also in intensity and intellectual
scope. The voices of the soloists here are typically very individual and characterful, and all are
remarkably adroit and stylish, so the personal witness that is so pronounced in the text is particularly
well portrayed. These are performers well used to the subtleties of baroque word setting and they
highlight all the ingenuity that Schütz lavished on these seemingly simple texts. There is an evident
delight in the way the composer deployed his limited resources, constantly ringing the changes on
traditional formulas to produce a richness of ideas that it took a Bach or Handel to emulate. The
rather close recording allows all these intricacies to emerge undiminished and although the resonance
of the acoustic seems restrained, this is no bad thing for music that, despite its title, has the feel of
chamber music.

Further listening ...

...Ach Herr, straf mich nicht, SWV24; Wohl dem, der nicht wandelt, SWV28; Wie lieblich sind
deine Wohnunge, SWV29; Singet dem Herrn ein neues Lied, SWV35; An den Wassern zu Babel,
SWV37; Lobe den Herren, meine Seele, SWV39. Das ist gewisslich wahr, SWV277. Erhöre mich,
wenn ich rufe, SWV289. Ich liege und schlafe, SWV310. Meine Seele erhebt den Herren,
SWV494. *Coupled with* **Schein** Suite XII – Pavan. Suite XVII – Pavan. [a]**Oxford Camerata /
Jeremy Summerly** with **Laurence Cummings** (org). Naxos 8 553044 (3/97).

...Saul, Saul, was verfolgst du mich, SWV415. Ich danke dem Herrn, SWV34. Magnificat anima
mia, SWV468. Stehe auf, meine Freundin, SWV499. *Coupled with works by various composers.*
Schütz Academy / Howard Arman. Capriccio 10 409 (5/93).

...Christmas Story, SWV435[a]. Cantiones sacrae – O bone, o dulcis, o benigne Jesu, SWV53;
Et ne despicias, SWV54; Spes mea, Christe Deus, SWV69; Cantate Domino canticum rovum,
SWV81. Psalmen Davids – Jauchzet dem Herren, alle Welt, SWV36. [a]**Anna Crookes** (sop);
[a]**Paul Agnew** (ten); [a]**Michael McCarthy** (bass); **Oxford Camerata / Jeremy Summerly.**
Naxos 8 553514 (4/97).

...Freue dich des Weibes deiner Jugend, SWV453 (with Frieder Lang, ten). Ist nicht Ephraim mein
teuer Sohn, SWV40. Saul, Saul, was verfolgst du mich, SWV415. Auf dem Gebirge, SWV396
(Ashley Stafford, Michael Chance, altos). Musicalische Exequien, SWV279-81 (Lang).
**Monteverdi Choir; English Baroque Soloists; His Majesties Sagbutts and Cornetts /
Sir John Eliot Gardiner.** Archiv Produktion 423 405-2AH (11/88). 🖋

...Psalmen Davids sampt etlichen Moteten und Concerten, SWV22-47. **Soloists;
Stuttgart Chamber Choir; Cologne Musica Fiata / Frieder Bernius.** Sony S2K48042.   Ⓖ

Cyril Scott   British 1879-1970

Suggested listening ...

...(arr. Kreisler) Lotus Land, Op. 47 No. 1. *Coupled with works by various composers.* **Kennedy** (vn);
John Lenehan (pf). EMI Ⓔ CDC5 56626-2 (75 minutes: ADD: 5/98). *See review in the Collections
section; refer to the Index.*

Alexander Scriabin   Russian 1872-1915

Scriabin Piano Concerto in F sharp minor, Op. 20.
Tchaikovsky Piano Concerto No. 1 in B flat minor, Op. 23. **Nikolai Demidenko** (pf); **BBC
Symphony Orchestra / Alexander Lazarev.** Hyperion Ⓔ CDA66680 (65 minutes: DDD: 10/94).
Recorded 1993.   Ⓖ

The chief attraction here is the unusual coupling which pairs two sharply opposed examples of
Russian romanticism, and although the reasons for the neglect of Scriabin's Piano Concerto are not
hard to fathom (its lyrical and decorative flights are essentially inward-looking), its haunting,
bittersweet beauty, particularly in the central *Andante* is hard to resist. Demidenko's own comments,
quoted in the accompanying booklet, are scarcely less intense and individual than his performance:
"in the ambience, phrasing and cadence of his music we meet with a world almost without skin, a

world of nerve-ends where the slightest contact can bring pain". His playing soars quickly to meet the music's early passion head on, and in the first *più mosso scherzando* he accelerates to produce a brilliant lightening of mood. His flashing *fortes* in the *Andante*'s second variation are as volatile as his *pianissimos* are starry and refined in the finale's period reminiscence, and although he might seem more tight-lipped, less expansive than Ashkenazy on Decca, he is arguably more dramatic and characterful. Demidenko's Tchaikovsky, too, finds him ferreting out and sifting through every texture, forever aiming at optimum clarity. While this is hardly among the greatest Tchaikovsky Firsts on record, it is often gripping and mesmeric. The orchestra respond admirably to their mercurial soloist and certainly come alight at key moments in both concertos. The recorded balance is not always ideal and the piano sound is sometimes uncomfortably taut.

Scriabin Piano Concerto in F sharp minor, Op. 20[a]. Prometheus, Op. 60, "Le poème du feu"[b].
Le poème de l'extase, Op. 54[c]. [ab]**Vladimir Ashkenazy** (pf); [b]**Ambrosian Singers;**
[ab]**London Philharmonic Orchestra;** [c]**Cleveland Orchestra / Lorin Maazel.** Decca Ⓕ 417 252-2DH
(66 minutes: ADD: 4/89). Items marked [a] and [b] from SXL6527 (1/72), recorded 1971,
[c]SXL6905 (9/79), recorded 1978.   ⒼⒼ
This CD gives us the essential Scriabin. The Piano Concerto has great pianistic refinement and melodic grace as well as a restraint not encountered in his later music. With *Le poème de l'extase* and *Prometheus* we are in the world of *art nouveau* and Scriabin in the grip of the mysticism (and megalomania) that consumed his later years. They are both single-movement symphonies for a huge orchestra: *Prometheus* ("The Poem of Fire") calls for quadruple wind, eight horns, five trumpets, strings, organ and chorus as well as an important part for solo piano in which Ashkenazy shines. The sensuous, luminous textures are beautifully conveyed in these performances by the LPO and the Decca engineers produce a most natural perspective and transparency of detail, as well as an appropriately overheated sound in the sensuous world of *Le poème de l'extase*.

Additional recommendations ...
...Piano Concerto[a]. Symphony No. 3. [a]**Roland Pöntinen** (pf); **Stockholm Philharmonic Orchestra /**
Leif Segerstam. BIS Ⓕ CD475 (77 minutes: DDD: 1/91).   Ⓖ
...Le poème de l'extase. Symphony No. 3. **Berlin Radio Symphony Orchestra / Vladimir Ashkenazy.**
Decca Ⓕ 430 843-2DH (70 minutes: DDD: 11/91).
...Le poème de l'extase. *Coupled with works by* **Bartók**
New York Philharmonic Orchestra / Pierre Boulez.
Sony Classical Boulez Edition Ⓜ SM2K64100 (two discs: 123 minutes: ADD: 9/95).

Scriabin Prometheus, Op. 60, "Le poème du feu"[a].
Stravinsky The Firebird. [a]**Alexander Toradze** (pf); **Kirov Opera** [a]**Chorus and Orchestra /**
Valery Gergiev. Philips Ⓕ 446 715-2PH (72 minutes: DDD: 7/98).
Gramophone Editor's choice.   ⒼⒼ
Stravinsky and the short-lived Scriabin were almost contemporaries (only ten years difference between them); of these two exactly contemporary works (1909-10), *Prometheus*, as Oliver Knussen has put it, is "so much more than a period piece; pregnant with possibilities for the future", whereas *The Firebird*, aside from its "Infernal Dance", rarely does anything more startling than pick up from where Rimsky-Korsakov left off – indeed, in certain sections, it shows that Stravinsky also knew his Scriabin rather well (for example, the *Firebird*'s "Dance of Supplication"). Gergiev's *Firebird* is certainly a startling performance. All manner of things contribute to the impression of distinction, among them the fact that this is that rare thing on record, an all-Russian complete *Firebird*. One has heard Western orchestras bring more grace to "The Dance of the Firebird", but never have Western strings openly sung the final moments of the Princesses' "Khovorod" quite like this. The music-making seems alive with a special presence: the orchestra is fairly close, though there is a real sense of the hall, never more so than when a heart-stopping crack is let loose from the drums on Kashchey's appearance. But the primary presence here (obvious enough, but it needs saying) is of a man of the theatre, maybe too audibly (for some) breathing life into the proceedings, moving from one section of the ballet to the next with the transitional mastery of a Furtwängler, and taking risks with tempo (do hear the end of the "Infernal Dance"). The darkness to light of the ballet's last few minutes is nothing less than mesmeric – we are in the presence of a happening. *Prometheus* is equally compelling. Toradze's solo contribution is slightly less the centre of the piece's universe than Argerich in the sensational Abbado recording, in terms of both imaginative daring and recorded scale, though it never lacks character. And the benefit is to even up the soloist and orchestra dynamic. The only reservation about the Abbado concerned the relatively fined down impression of Scriabin's huge orchestra. Yet with the more imposing-sounding Russian team, to take one example, when the five trumpets are let off the leash for their assertions near the end of the piece, you really know about it. Gergiev's is also a much broader view of the piece (some four minutes longer), but it never sounds overly languid, indeed it enables him and Toradze, unlike Argerich and Abbado, to achieve a dizzying *accelerando prestissimo* in the final bars that is faster than anything that has preceded it.

Additional recommendation ...
...Prometheus. *Coupled with works by various composers.* **Martha Argerich** (pf);
Berlin Singakademie. Sony Classical Ⓕ SK53978 (75 minutes: DDD: 1/95).
Gramophone Editor's choice. See review in the Collections section; refer to the Index.   ⒼⒼⒼ

Scriabin Symphonies – No. 1 in E major, Op. 26[a]; No. 2 in C minor, Op. 29; No. 3, Op. 43,
"Divine Poem"[b]. Le poème de l'extase, Op. 54. Piano Concerto in F sharp minor, Op. 20[c].
Prometheus, Op. 60. Rêverie, Op. 24. [a]**Tamara Siniawskaia** (sop); [a]**Alexander Fedin** (ten);
[b]**Vladimir Krainev**, [c]**Gerhard Oppitz** (pfs); [a]**Figuralchor; Frankfurt Radio Symphony Orchestra /
Dmitri Kitaienko.** RCA Victor Symphony Edition Ⓑ 74321 20297-2 (three discs: 225 minutes:
DDD: 12/95). Recorded 1991-1994.

These recordings are half the price of Muti's acclaimed Philadelphia set (listed below). What is more,
Kitaienko's survey, unlike Muti's, includes the Piano Concerto and the short *Rêverie*. It also includes
a chorus for the final bars of *Le Poème de l'extase* (a bizarre idea that has a dubious precedent in
Scriabin's use of it at the same point in *Prometheus*), and there are copious unmarked parts for
cymbals in the numbered symphonies, from a light dusting of metal to the occasional clash (there is
a dubious precedent here too, in that generations of conductors, particularly Russian ones, have felt
their use to be necessary). Kitaienko's textual deviations also include a fondness for silent pauses: they
may be useful signposts, breathing spaces or dramatic interpolations; they may also be felt to be
disruptive. So much for the extras. Is there anything missing? Most obviously, ample Philadelphia
string tone, and some of the most voluptuous string playing (with portamento) to have come from
that orchestra since Stokowski's days. Arguably Scriabin's music thrives on such things. Even the BBC
Symphony Orchestra strings manage greater warmth and variety of tone colour (and portamento) in
the opening minute of the central *Andante* from the Piano Concerto, and, staying with Scriabin's most
hauntingly beautiful tune, is there not an imbalance when the clarinet (which must have been
Scriabin's favourite orchestral instrument) takes over the tune?

In Frankfurt, it is the piano decorations of the tune which dominate. The piano moves back a few
metres for *Prometheus*, as it probably should, which is a way of saying that if you are used to the
famous Ashkenazy/Maazel, you might feel that the piano part lacks projection and character
(Alexeev is similarly distant for Muti), but then *everything* is much clearer and closer on that old
Decca recording. More generally, you may wish to know whether Scriabin's climaxes cause the earth
to move as often (and by as much) as it does in the Muti set. Not quite. Kitaienko risks greater
extremes of tempo than most. The ups and downs in *Le poème de l'extase* perhaps add to its allure.
Elsewhere, one or two tempo transitions and manoeuverings are a little awkward, for example, from
the slowest of all *Andantes* at the outset of the Second Symphony's slow movement to its necessarily
much faster *più vivo* sections (Kitaienko takes 15'44" in this movement; Muti 13'40" and Järvi 11'30").
The exception is the vast first movement of the Third Symphony, where Kitaienko keeps a cool
head and a long view, and untypically, Muti is all at sea. Swings and roundabouts then. If a
bargain acquisition of all Scriabin's work for orchestra appeals – this is it, apart from an early
symphonic poem.

Additional recommendation ...

...No. 1[a]; Nos. 2 and 3. Le poème de l'extase[b]. Prometheus[c]. [a]**Stefania Toczyska** (mez);
    [a]**Michael Myers** (ten); [b]**Frank Kaderabek** (tpt); [c]**Dmitri Alexeev** (pf); [a]**Westminster Choir;**
    [c]**Philadelphia Choral Arts Society; Philadelphia Orchestra / Riccardo Muti.**
    EMI Ⓕ CDS7 54251-2 (three discs: 188 minutes: DDD: 7/91).   Ⓠ

...No. 3. Le poème de l'extase, Op. 54. **Moscow Symphony Orchestra / Igor Golovschin.**
    Naxos Ⓢ 8 553582 (76 minutes: DDD: 1/98).

Scriabin Etude in C sharp minor, Op. 2 No. 1. 12 Etudes, Op. 8. Etudes, Op. 42.
    Etude in E flat major, Op. 49 No. 1. Etude, Op. 56 No. 4. Three Etudes, Op. 65. **Piers Lane** (pf).
    Hyperion Ⓕ CDA66607 (56 minutes: DDD: 12/92). Recorded 1992. *Selected by
    Sounds in Retrospect.*   ⒼⒼ

Although Scriabin's *études* do not fall into two neatly packaged sets in the same way as Chopin's
celebrated contributions, there is nevertheless a strong feeling of continuity and development running
throughout the 26 examples produced between the years 1887 and 1912. This is admirably
demonstrated in this excellent issue from Hyperion, which, far from being an indigestible anthology
proves to be an intriguing and pleasurable hour's worth of listening charting Scriabin's progression
from late-romantic adolescence, to harmonically advanced mystical poet. Indeed, although these
studies can be counted as amongst the most digitally taxing and hazardous of their kind, Scriabin
also saw them as important sketches and studies for his larger works, and as experiments in his
gradually evolving harmonic language and mystical vision. Piers Lane attains the perfect
balance between virtuoso display and poetic interpretation. Expressive detail and subtle nuance are
finely brought out, and he is more than receptive to Scriabin's sometimes highly idiosyncratic
sound world; rarely, for instance, has the famous "Mosquito" *Etude* (Op. 42 No. 3) been captured
with such delicate fragility as here, and in No. 1 of the three fiendishly difficult *Etudes,* Op. 65
(fifths, sevenths and ninths!) the tremulous, ghostly flutterings are tellingly delivered with a
gossamer-light touch and an appropriate sense of eerie mystery. The clear, spacious recording is
exemplary.

Additional recommendation ...

...Etudes – Op. 2 No. 1; D sharp minor, Op. 8 No. 12. *Coupled with works by various composers.*
    Pavel Nersessian (pf). Bel Air Music Ⓕ BAM9725 (65 minutes: DDD: 3/98). *See review in the
    Collections section; refer to the Index.*

Scriabin Etudes[a] – C sharp minor, Op. 2 No. 1; Op. 8: No. 5 in E major; No. 11 in B flat minor;
Op. 42: No. 2 in F sharp minor; No. 3 in F sharp major; No. 4 in F sharp major;
No. 5 in C sharp minor; No. 6 in D flat major; No. 8 in E flat major; Trois Etudes, Op. 65.
Piano Sonata No. 6 in G major, Op. 62[b].
Miaskovsky Piano Sonata No. 3 in C minor, Op. 19[c].
Prokofiev Piano Sonata No. 7 in B flat major, Op. 83[d]. **Sviatoslav Richter** (pf).
Melodiya mono Ⓜ 74321 29470-2* (68 minutes: ADD: 6/96). Items marked [a] recorded 1952,
[b]1955, [c]1953, [d]1958.

Richter's interpretations in the 1950s had an elemental power and unselfconscious abandon that was
refined and tempered in later life; the problem is the unreliable 1950s Soviet recording quality,
compounded, presumably, by some decay in the master-tapes over the years, and not entirely
redeemed by the NoNoise remastering technique. Nevertheless, here is an other-worldly Scriabin,
cataclysmic and elevated, culminating in a vaporous, explosive, ultimately clamorous account of the
Sixth Sonata. The Miaskovsky – formulaic Scriabin with an academic safety net – is probably better
heard on elsewhere; from the amount of background noise on Melodiya you might think a *babushka*
with her vacuum cleaner was competing for attention. Finally comes a muscular and emotionally
searing Prokofiev Seventh which presents the only serious alternative to Pollini.

Scriabin Complete Piano Sonatas – No. 1 in F minor, Op. 6; No. 2 in G sharp minor,
Op. 19, "Sonata-fantasy"; No. 3 in F sharp minor, Op. 23; No. 4 in F sharp, Op. 30; No. 5 in
F sharp major, Op. 53; No. 6 in G major, Op. 62; No. 7 in F sharp major, Op. 64, "White Mass";
No. 8 in A major, Op. 66; No. 9 in F major, Op. 68, "Black Mass"; No. 10 in C major, Op. 70.
Fantasie in B minor, Op. 28. Sonata-fantaisie in G sharp minor. **Marc-André Hamelin** (pf).
Hyperion Ⓕ CDA67131/2 (two discs: 146 minutes: DDD: 6/96).

Scriabin was an ambitious composer. A romantic alchemist, he saw his music as a transmuting agent.
Through its influence pain would become happiness and hate become love, culminating in a phoenix-
like rebirth of the universe. With Shakespearian agility he would change the world's dross into
"something rich and strange". Not surprisingly, given Scriabin's early prowess as a pianist, the ten
sonatas resonate with every exoticism, ranging through the First Sonata's cries of despair (complete
with magnificent Russian funeral march), to the Second Sonata's Baltic Sea inspiration, the Third
Sonata's "states of being", the "flight to a distant star" (No. 4) and "the emergence of mysterious
forces" (No. 5). Nos. 7 and 9 are *White* and *Black Mass* Sonatas respectively, and the final sonatas
blaze with trills symbolizing an extra-terrestrial joy and incandescence. Even less surprisingly such
music makes ferocious demands on the pianist's physical stamina and imaginative resource. However,
Marc-André Hamelin, a cool customer, takes everything in his stride.

Blessed with rapier reflexes he nonchalantly resolves even the most outlandish difficulties. He
launches the First Sonata's opening outcry like some gleaming trajectory and, throughout, his
whistle-stop virtuosity is seemingly infallible. You might, however, miss a greater sense of the music's
Slavonic intensity, its colour and character; a finer awareness, for example, of the delirious poetry at
the heart of the Second Sonata's whirling finale. Hamelin's sonority is most elegantly and precisely
gauged but time and again his fluency (admittedly breathtaking) erases too much of the work's
originality and regenerative force. However, he shows a greater sense of freedom in the Fifth Sonata,
and in the opalescent fantasy of the later sonatas, he responds with more evocative skill to subjective
terms, as well as to moments where Scriabin's brooding introspection is lit by sudden flashes of
summer lightning. Yet even here some collectors may miss Ashkenazy's romantic volatility in his set
of the sonatas, or Horowitz's cunning and diablerie (in Sonatas Nos. 3, 5 and 9). Hyperion's
recordings are a little tight and airless in the bass and middle register, but their two-disc set is
beautifully presented and includes a superb essay on Scriabin.

Additional recommendations ...

...Piano Sonatas Nos. 1-10. **Vladimir Ashkenazy** (pf).
Decca Ⓜ 425 579-2DM2 (two discs: 131 minutes: ADD/DDD: 1/90).
...Piano Sonatas Nos. 3 and 5. Preludes – Op. 11: Nos. 1, 3, 9, 13, 14 and 16; Op. 13 No. 6; Op. 15
No. 2; Op. 16 – Nos. 1 and 4; Op. 27 No. 1; A minor, Op. 51 No. 2; Op. 48 No. 3; Op. 67 No. 1;
Op. 59 No. 2. Etudes – Op. 8 No. 7; Op. 42: Nos. 5 and 12. **Vladimir Horowitz** (pf).
RCA Victor Gold Seal Ⓕ mono/stereo GD86215* (66 minutes: ADD: 1/90). Ⓖ
...Piano Sonatas Nos. 2 and 9. Etudes – Op. 8: Nos. 2, 4 and 5. Op. 42: Nos. 3, 4 and 7. Four Pieces,
Op. 51. Vers la flamme, Op. 72. **Prokofiev** Visions fugitives, Op. 22. **Nikolai Demidenko** (pf).
Conifer Classics Ⓕ CDCF204 (73 minutes: DDD: 8/91). ⒼⒼ
...Poème-nocturne. Two Danses. Vers la flamme. Fantasie in B minor, Op. 28.
Coupled with works by **Shostakovich** and **Prokofiev** Sviatoslav Richter (pf).
Philips Ⓕ 438 627-2PH2 (two discs: 152 minutes: DDD: 8/94). . ⒼⒼ
...Piano Sonata No. 3. Preludes – Op. 11 No. 1; Op. 39 No. 2; Op. 39 No. 3; Impromptu in B flat
minor, Op. 12 No. 2. Etudes – Op. 8 No. 7; Op. 42 No. 4; Op. 42 No. 6.
Coupled with works by **Rachmaninov** Vladimir Sofronitzki (pf).
Multisonic Russian Treasure Ⓜ 310181-2* (58 minutes: ADD: 5/94). Ⓖ
...Piano Sonatas Nos. 2 and 5. *Coupled with works by* **Chopin** Sviatoslav Richter (pf).
Praga mono/stereo Ⓑ CMX354007* (61 minutes: ADD: 6/96).

...Piano Sonata No. 6. Etudes – C sharp minor, Op. 2 No. 1; Op. 8: No. 5 in E major; No. 11 in
B flat minor; Op. 42: No. 2 in F sharp minor; No. 3 in F sharp major; No. 4 in F sharp major;
No. 5 in C sharp minor; No. 6 in D flat major; No. 8 in E flat major; Trois Etudes, Op. 65.
Coupled with works by **Miaskovsky** and **Prokofiev** **Sviatoslav Richter** (pf).
Melodiya mono Ⓜ 74321 29470-2* (68 minutes: ADD: 6/96).
...Piano Sonatas Nos. 2, 5, 6, 7 and 9. Fantasie in B minor, Op. 28. **Bernd Glemser** (pf).
Naxos Ⓢ 8 553158 (62 minutes: DDD: 8/96).
...Piano Sonata No. 2. *Coupled with works by* **Rachmaninov** and **Prokofiev**
Sergio Fiorentino (pf). APR Fiorentino Edition Ⓜ APR5552 (63 minutes: DDD: 9/96)
...Piano Sonatas Nos. 1 and 4. **Rachmaninov** Piano Sonata No. 1 in D minor, Op. 28.
Sergio Fiorentino (pf). APR Ⓜ APR5556 (72 minutes: DDD: 7/97). *See review under
Rachmaninov; refer to the Index.*

Scriabin Piano Sonatas – No. 3 in F sharp minor, Op. 23; No. 4 in F sharp, Op. 30; No. 5, Op. 53.
12 Etudes, Op. 8. **Yuki Matsuzawa** (pf). Pianissimo Ⓕ PP10394 (72 minutes: DDD: 6/94).
Gramophone Editor's choice.   ☺☺
Yuki Matsuzawa has an unassailably secure technical mastery, dealing with apparent ease and
panache with the formidable virtuosity required by, for example, the Ninth, Tenth and Twelfth Studies
of Op. 8 – and it is rare to find a pianist observing indications so absolutely exactly yet so seemingly
naturally, without a trace of being applied mechanically. As the first *Etude* reveals, she possesses that
almost teasing lightness that Pasternak (who knew Scriabin) tells us was typical of his playing; and in
lyrical passages such as the dreamy poetic *Andante* of the Third Sonata her tone is ravishingly
beautiful. She is meticulous about detail and she has a sensitive feeling for phrase and structure and
a proper appreciation of the expressive implications of key shifts (e.g. in Op. 8 No. 8). She brings off
the self-questioning of the Third Sonata, lingering over its initial subject, and the neurosis of the
Fourth, with its passing echoes of *Tristan*, the chromatic appoggiaturas which give the first
movement's harmonies a special character, and a truly fleeting *volando* in its second movement (which
contains that direction in an Italian that never was, *giobilosco*). In the Fifth Sonata, written when
Scriabin was making so great a change in his idiom, she is convincingly deft, if taking the *languido*
sections very freely. This is a brilliant recording début.

Scriabin 24 Preludes, Op. 11.
Shostakovich 24 Preludes, Op. 34. **Artur Pizarro** (pf). Collins Classics Ⓕ 1496-2
(68 minutes: DDD: 11/97). Recorded 1997. *Gramophone Editor's choice.*   ☺
In Scriabin's 24 Preludes, Op. 11, Artur Pizarro once again confirms his glittering array of first prizes
in performances of rare pianistic refinement, arguing the composer's volatility, his sudden calms and
squalls, with unfaltering conviction. Nothing is hectic or rushed, everything sings and flows with a
natural ease and impetus. The majority of Scriabin's aphorisms, with their affectionate memories of
Chopin, are romantically self-communing and in this enraptured dreamworld Pizarro could hardly
show a more consistent poise or subtlety. His rubato (in No. 4) is telling but never affected or
excessive, his pedalling both lavish and acute (in No. 11, with its insinuating lilt and sultry undertow).
In No. 16 his way of pushing each sinister phrase forward suggests the music's darkness, its emerging
and receding violence, and, throughout, his flexibility and warmth are almost tangible. Pizarro's easy
and immaculate technique, too, make light of Shostakovich's more quirky Op. 34 Preludes. Here, he
is equally at home in the vaudeville pranks of No. 6, or the stillness of No. 17, the *presto tarantella*
whirl of No. 9 or the dark ceremonial of No. 14. Collins's sound beautifully captures Pizarro's
unfailing tonal bloom.
Additional recommendation ...
...24 Preludes – No. 2 in A minor; No. 4 in E minor; No. 5 in D major; No. 6 in B minor;
No. 8 in F sharp minor; No. 9 in E major; No. 10 in C sharp minor; No. 11 in B major;
No. 12 in G flat minor; No. 13 in G flat major; No. 14 in E flat minor; No. 16 in B flat minor;
No. 18 in F minor; No. 20 in C minor; No. 22 in G minor; No. 24 in D minor.
Coupled with works by **Rachmaninov** **Andrei Gavrilov** (pf).
EMI Eminence Ⓜ CD-EMX2237 (72 minutes: DDD: 12/95).   ☺
Further listening ...
...Fantasy in A minor. *Coupled with works by* **Tchaikovsky** **Katia Labèque, Marielle Labèque** (pfs).
Philips 442 778-2PH (12/95).
...Mazurkas, Opp. 3, 25 and 40. **Artur Pizarro** (pf). Collins Classics 1394-2 (6/94).   ☺
...Deux poèmes, Op. 32. Prélude et Nocturne, Op. 9. *Coupled with works by various composers.*
Anatol Ugorski (pf). DG 447 105-2GH 3/96). *See review in the Collections section;
refer to the Index.*

Peter Sculthorpe   Australian 1929

Sculthorpe Port Essington. String Sonatas – No. 1; No. 2; No. 3. Lament for Strings. Irkanda IVª.
Australian Chamber Orchestra / Richard Tognetti (ªvn). ABC Classics Ⓕ 8 770042
(76 minutes: DDD: 10/97). Recorded 1996. *Selected by Soundings.*

This is a generously full collection of Peter Sculthorpe's music, excellently played by the Australia Chamber Orchestra. Sculthorpe's music impresses with its personable character and sense of local colour (which itself stems from the composer's rapt absorption in Australia's indigenous landscape and wildlife). Perhaps the most striking composition here is *Port Essington* (1977), whose genesis goes back to a score for a 1974 television film describing the Victorian settlers' attempt to establish a military base at Essington on the Cobourg Peninsula on the Northern coast of Australia (an undertaking scuppered by their refusal to adapt to the inhospitable surroundings). As Sculthorpe himself explains: "The music exists on two planes: the string orchestra represents the Bush; and a string trio, playing what appears to be nineteenth-century salon music, represents the Settlement". Based around an Aboriginal chant heard at the very outset, it is an imaginative, deeply rewarding creation and genuinely touching, too. Indeed, a similar duality between the New World and the Old informs the First Sonata for Strings. Based on Sculthorpe's Tenth Quartet of 1983, its two framing "Sun Song" movements and central "Interlude" utilize ideas and rhythms found in the songs of the native American Pueblo Indians and form a pleasing contrast to the reflective chorales which comprise the second and fourth movements. The Sonatas Nos. 2 and 3 (1988 and 1994 respectively) are likewise based on earlier quartet offerings, the Ninth from 1975 and the Eleventh from1990. Both are entirely characteristic of their creator and contain plenty to enchant and intrigue the listener (No. 3 brings with it echoes of Sculthorpe's exotic 1988 orchestral essay, *Kakadu*). Elsewhere, the deeply felt *Lament* (1976) seems to pick up where the threnodic *Irkanda IV* left off some 15 years previously.

Sculthorpe Little Nourlangie[a]. Music for Japan[b]. Piano Concerto[c]. The song of Tailitnama[d].
[d]**Kirsti Harms** (mez); [b]**Mark Atkins** (didjeridu); [c]**Tamara Anna Cislowska** (pf); [a]**David Drury** (org); **Sydney Symphony Orchestra / Edo de Waart.** ABC Classics Ⓟ 8 770030
(53 minutes: DDD: 12/97). Text included. Recorded 1996.
Little Nourlangie dates from 1990. It takes its name from a small outcrop of rocks in Australia's Kakadu National Park on which can be found the Aboriginal Blue Paintings, depicting fish, boats and ancestral figures and which inspired the composer. *Little Nourlangie* is a characteristically striking creation, scored with much imaginative flair. It shares its diatonic main theme with that of Sculthorpe's 1989 guitar concerto, *Nourlangie*, and comprises four-and-a-half minutes of "straightforward, joyful music" (to quote the composer). By contrast, *Music for Japan* exhibits a much more uncompromising demeanour. It was written in response to the Expo '70 exhibition in Osaka and according to annotator Graeme Skinner, is at once "his most abstract and modernist orchestral score". The work's title should be carefully heeded: the piece remains very much 'about' Australia, an impression doubly confirmed by the incorporation of a tape featuring a didjeridu played by Mark Atkins. Sculthorpe has long been preoccupied with the music from other countries situated in and around the Pacific – and Japanese music in particular, elements of which he has incorporated into other works such as the present Piano Concerto of 1983. It is a single-movement work divided into five sections. After the slumbering *Grave* first section (which eventually attains a satisfying thrust), textures lighten as first bassoon and then oboe intone a haunting new theme based on a Japanese melody. Dynamics and momentum build grandly in the central *Animato* section, after which the limpid quietude of the cadenza (marked *Come notturno*) and *Estatico* final section (wherein a solo cello raptly takes up the Japanese idea) are especially effective.
Sculthorpe's Piano Concerto is an imposing creation, less indigenous-sounding and 'pictorial' than many of his other compositions, including *The song of Tailitnama* (1974). Conceived for high voice, six cellos and percussion, this haunting piece was in fact written for a TV documentary entitled *Sun Music for Film*. Framed by a soprano vocalise utilizing the Japanese scale known as *hirajoshi*, the Aboriginal chant at its heart derives its text from songs collected in 1933 at the ritual site of Tailitnama in Central Australia. Edo de Waart presides over a set of performances that exhibit great commitment and exemplary finish. The recording and presentation are excellent too.
Further listening ...
...Earth Cry. Irkanda IV[a]. Small Town[b]. Kakadu. Mangrove. [a]**Donald Hazelwood** (vn); [b]**Guy Henderson** (ob); **Sydney Symphony Orchestra / Stuart Challender.** ABC Classics 8 77000-2 (11/95). *Gramophone Editor's choice.*   Ⓖ
...Nourlangie[a]. From Kakadu. Into the Dreaming. *Coupled with* **Westlake** Antarctica[b]. **John Williams** (gtr); [a]**Australian Chamber Orchestra / Richard Hickox;** [b]**London Symphony Orchestra / Paul Daniel.** Sony Classical SK53361 (5/95).
...Djilile. *Coupled with works by various composers.* **Fretwork.** Virgin Classics VC5 45217-2 (12/97). *See review in the Collections section; refer to the Index.*

Charles Seeger   American 1886-1979

Suggested listening ...
...John Hardy. *Coupled with works by Ruth Crawford.* **Lucy Shelton** (sop); **Schönberg Ensemble / Oliver Knussen.** DG 449 925-2GH (12/97). *See review under Crawford; refer to the Index.*

Andrés Segovia

Spanish 1893-1987

Suggested listening ...

...Canciónes populares de distintos paises. Estudio sin luz. La macarena. Prelude No. 14 in B minor. Estudio in E major. *Coupled with works by various composers.* **Elliot Fisk** (gtr). MusicMasters 67174-2 (4/97). *See review in the Collections section; refer to the Index.*

Ludwig Senfl

Swiss/German c1486-1542/3

Suggested listening ...

...Will niemand singen. Ein Maidlein zue dem Brunnen ging. Dort oben auf dem Berge. Nun wöllt ihr hören neue Mär. Ich soll und müess ein'n Büehlen haben. Oho, so geb' der Mann. Es wollt' ein Maidlein Wasser hol'n. Es wollt' ein Frau zuem Weine gahn. Lamentatio. Ich stuend an einem Morgen. Albrecht mirs schwer. Ich weiss nit was er ihr verheiss (two versions). *Coupled with works by various composers.* **Convivium Musicum; Villanella Ensemble / Sven Berger.** Naxos 8 553352 (1/96). *See review in the Collections section; refer to the Index.* Ⓔ

Déodat de Séverac

French 1873-1921

Suggested listening ...

...Tantum ergo. *Coupled with works by* **Fauré** and **Vierne** Oxford Schola Cantorum. Naxos 8 550765 (9/94). *See review under Fauré; refer to the Index.*

Rodion Shchedrin

USSR 1932

Shchedrin Symphony No. 2 (25 Preludes for Orchestra). Concerto for Orchestra No. 3, "Old Russian Circus Music". **BBC Philharmonic Orchestra / Vassily Sinaisky.** Chandos Ⓕ CHAN9552 (80 minutes: DDD: 9/97). Recorded 1996.

After a long period of suffering from relative obscurity, the music of Rodion Shchedrin is making new friends in the West and this recording of the Second Symphony is especially welcome. A key work of Russian-Soviet music, premièred in 1965 , it is a rare example of officially sanctioned experimentalism, reminding us that the composer occupied a paradoxical position as licensed modernist of the *ancien régime*. There have been attempts to reposition him politically in recent years but this should not be allowed to obscure the extraordinary dexterity of his music. While many of his earlier works clatter away amiably enough, consciously eschewing the profound, the Second Symphony is made of sterner stuff. It consists of 25 preludes that fall into five broad 'movements', the frequent recourse to radical musical languages presumably validated by the theme – Peace and War, Life and Death. Some sections draw upon the symphonic rhetoric of Shostakovich and Prokofiev, albeit without the tonal moorings, so don't expect that old diatonic tunefulness. There are earnest emotings and there are novelties – like the fantasy on the sound of an orchestra tuning up and the very 1960s deployment of House of Horror harpsichord. It is at the very least a fascinating document from an enormously skilful operator. While some of the high-lying string passages are taxing and sound it, the playing is remarkably good. The sound is clear, rich and wide-ranging.

Further listening ...

...The Carmen Ballet[a]. Anna Karenina[b]. [a]**Bolshoi Theatre Orchestra / Gennadi Rozhdestvensky;** [b]**USSR Symphony Orchestra / Evgeni Svetlanov.** Melodiya 74321 36908-2 (4/97).

...The Sealed Angel. **Alexander Golyschev** (fl); **Moscow Chamber Choir; USSR Russian Choir / Vladimir Minin.** Melodiya 74321 36905-2 (4/97).

...Sotto voce. *Coupled with* **Gagneux** Triptyque. **Mstislav Rostropovich** (vc); **London Symphony Orchestra / Seiji Ozawa.** Teldec 4509-94570-2 (6/96).

...Stihira. *Coupled with Violin Concertos by* **Glazunov** and **Prokofiev** **National Symphony Orchestra, Washington / Mstislav Rostropovich.** Erato 0630-17722-2 (9/97).

...25 Preludes. 24 Preludes and Fugues. **Rodion Shchedrin** (pf). Melodiya 74321 36906-2 (4/97).

...Dead Souls. **Soloists; Moscow Chamber Chorus; Chorus and Orchestra of the Bolshoi Theatre, Moscow / Yuri Temirkanov.** Melodiya 74321 29347-2 (12/96).

Richard Shephard

British 1949

Suggested listening ...

...Salisbury Service. *Coupled with works by various composers.* **Portsmouth Cathedral Choir / Adrian Lucas** with **David Thorne** (org). Priory PRCD527 (2/96). *See review in the Collections section; refer to the Index.*

John Sheppard
British c1515-1559/60

Sheppard The Lord's Prayer. The Second Service – Magnificat; Nunc dimittis. Gaude, gaude, gaude Maria. Filie Ierusalem. Reges Tharsis et insulae. Spiritus sanctus procedens. Laudem dicite Deo nostro. Hec dies. Impetum fecerunt unanimes. Libera nos, salva nos. **Choir of Christ Church Cathedral, Oxford / Stephen Darlington.** Nimbus Ⓕ NI5480 (67 minutes: DDD: 9/96). Texts and translations included. Recorded 1995.

This enjoyable recording opens with two works in English which were probably written within days of John Sheppard's early death, as Roger Bowers's introductory essay explains. The hypothesis is an intriguing one, for *The Lord's Prayer* and the Second Service largely lack the wayward dissonances that play an integral (and controversial) part in this composer's style. Whether the difference is due to the switch to the vernacular is a moot point, for the Latin Responds that make up most of the disc show off the older style more conspicuously. The most impressive of these is undoubtedly the elaborate *Gaude, gaude, gaude Maria*, but the piece that most clearly enunciates its composer's idiosyncrasies has to be the concluding *Libera nos* (Sheppard wrote two identically scored settings of this text, but neither the programme details nor Bowers's essay makes clear which one is given here). Bowers's involvement in this project serves notice that the Christ Church Cathedral Choir do things authentically or not at all. Sheppard's special predilection for high voices makes the participation of boy trebles here particularly appropriate. In such traditional choral establishments, unanimity of ensemble is crucial given the number of boys involved. From that standpoint this choir is difficult to fault, although towards the end of the recital a certain tiredness is just perceptible. If anything, the sound is a shade top-heavy at times (as in *Filie Ierusalem*), but a couple of the Responds dispense with trebles altogether (for practical reasons carefully explained by Bowers), providing a welcome contrast.

Additional recommendation ...
...Verbum caro factum est. Laudem dicite Deo. Reges Tharsis et insulae. In manus tuas I. Filiae Ierusalem venite. In pace in idipsum. Paschal Kyrie. Haec dies. Spiritus sanctus, procedens a throno. Justi in perpetuum vivent. Libera nos, salva nos I. Jesu salvator seculi, verbum. Deus tuorum militum II. Ave maris stella. Jesu salvator seculi, redemptis. Missa "Cantate". Salvator mundi Domine. **The Sixteen / Harry Christophers.**
Hyperion Dyad Ⓑ CDD22021 (two discs: 112 minutes: DDD: 4/97).

Sheppard Magnificat. O happy dames. Laudem dicite Deo. In manus tuas I-III. Spiritus sanctus procedens I.
Anonymous Inclita sancte. In diebus illis.
Davy Joan is sick and ill at ease. Ah mine heart, remember thee well.
Mason Vae nobis miseri. Quales sumus. **The Magdalen Collection / Harry Christophers.**
Collins Classics Ⓕ 1511-2 (74 minutes: DDD: 7/97). Texts and translations included. Recorded 1997.

For many years 'Music at Magdalen' was a phrase that could hardly be spoken without evoking the name of Bernard Rose, choirmaster (or *informator choristarum*) from 1957 to 1981. Here, 27 men, nine of each voice, form the gracefully named Magdalen Collection on this commemorative record, with Harry Christophers (at Magdalen 1973-7) conducting music by three *informatores* of the late-fifteenth or early-sixteenth century: Richard Davy, who moved from Oxford to Exeter in 1497, John Mason, *informator* in 1509 and John Sheppard, who had two spells at the College in the 1540s. The voices here are sonorous and fine (with just a slightly sandpapery surface somewhere among the tenors). Though brought together for the occasion, they sing as with a common feeling for style; in, for example, the three settings by Sheppard of *In manus tuas*, the long lines of music are well sustained, and in the particularly beautiful second setting the rise and fall are movingly caught. In the secular pieces, they bring a suitably light touch, with a confident responsiveness to rhythm and text.

Additional recommendation ...
...In manus tuas III. The Second Service: Magnificat; Nunc dimittis. Aeterne Rex altissime. Dum transisset Sabbatum II. Hostis Hérodes impie. Te Deum laudamus. Mass, "The Western Wynde". **The Sixteen / Harry Christophers.** Hyperion Ⓕ CDA66603 (63 minutes: DDD: 8/93).

Further listening ...
...In manus tuas Domine II. Gaude virgo Christiphera. Reges Tharsis et insulae. Libera nos, salva nos I. Libera nos, salva nos II. *Coupled with* **Tye** Missa Euge Bone. Peccavimus Patribus nostris. **Clerkes of Oxenford / David Wulstan.** Proud Sound PROUCD126 (5/90).
...Mass – "Be not afraide" (with plainsong Propers). Steven firste after Christ. Sancte Dei pretiose. Impetum fecerunt unanimes. Gaudete caelicole omnes. *Coupled with* **Sampson** Psallite felices. **The Cardinall's Musick / Andrew Carwood.** Meridian CDE84220 (12/92).

William Shield
British 1748-1829

Suggested listening ...
...String Quartet in C minor, Op. 3 No. 6. *Coupled with works various composers.* **Salomon Quartet.** Hyperion CDA66780 (3/96). *See review in the Collections section; refer to the Index.*

Dmitry Shostakovich

Shostakovich Cello Concertos – No. 1 in E flat major, Op. 107; No. 2 in G major, Op. 126.
Mischa Maisky (vc); **London Symphony Orchestra / Michael Tilson Thomas.** DG Ⓕ 445 821-2GH
(65 minutes: DDD: 4/95). Recorded 1993. *Gramophone Editor's choice.*   ⒼⒼ

Shostakovich Cello Concertos – No. 1 in E flat major, Op. 107; No. 2 in G major, Op. 126.
Truls Mørk (vc); **London Philharmonic Orchestra / Mariss Jansons.** Virgin Classics
Ⓕ VC5 45145-2 (66 minutes: DDD: 2/96). Recorded 1995. *Selected by Soundings.*   Ⓖ

The Second Cello Concerto is one of the major concertos of the post-war period – as potent a representative of the composer's later style as the last three symphonies, be it through irony (second movement), poetry (first and third) or anger (beginning of the third). Few cellists have tended the *p espressivo* of the *Largo*'s opening bars as lovingly as Mischa Maisky does, while the rapt quality of his soft playing and the expressive eloquence of his double-stopping wring the most from Shostakovich's extended soliloquy. Michael Tilson Thomas points and articulates with his usual skill. Only the opening of that movement (with its furious whoop horns) seems marginally underprojected, although the main climax later on is both immensely powerful and extraordinarily clear. The First Concerto harbours fewer mysteries than the Second and yet remains a pivotal work. Maisky phrases beautifully, while Tilson Thomas and the LSO again come up trumps, even though 1'33" into the finale the dramatic switch to 6/8 sounds less spontaneous than it does under, say, Maxim Shostakovich. In other respects, however, this is a forceful and fairly outgoing interpretation, beautifully recorded and a suitable coupling for the disc's star act – the finest available studio recording of the Second Concerto. In fact, this CD is now the prime recommendation for the two concertos coupled together. Although Truls Mørk and Mariss Jansons offer admirably strong, well-considered interpretations of both works, that recommendation stands. The Virgin release has the virtue of exceptional engineering; in fact, it's one of the best recordings to emerge from Abbey Road in recent years – a spacious, highly attentive production with a pin-sharp solo image and a consistently vivid orchestral backdrop. In that respect alone, Virgin score a definite point over their excellent DG rival. As to interpretation, Mørk is a less outwardly demonstrative player than Maisky and Jansons a rather less imaginative Shostakovich conductor than Michael Tilson Thomas.

Additional recommendations ...

...No. 1. **Barber** Cello Concerto, Op. 22. **Raphael Wallfisch** (vc); **English Chamber Orchestra / Geoffrey Simon.** Chandos Ⓕ CHAN8322 (59 minutes: DDD: 2/85).

...Nos. 1 and 2. **Heinrich Schiff** (vc); **Bavarian Radio Symphony Orchestra / Maxim Shostakovich.**
Philips Ⓕ 412 526-2PH (61 minutes: DDD: 10/85).   ⒼⒼ

...Nos. 1 and 2. **Natalia Gutman** (vc); **Royal Philharmonic Orchestra / Yuri Temirkanov.**
RCA Victor Red Seal Ⓕ RD87918 (66 minutes: DDD: 1/91).

...Nos. 1 and 2. **Torleif Thedéen** (vc); **Malmö Symphony Orchestra / James DePreist.**
BIS Ⓕ CD626 (65 minutes: DDD: 7/94).

...No. 2[a]. Symphony No. 5 in D minor, Op. 47[b]. [a]**Boston Symphony Orchestra / Seiji Ozawa;**
[b]**Washington National Symphony Orchestra / Mstislav Rostropovich** ([a]vc).
DG Classikon Ⓑ 439 481-2GCL (79 minutes: ADD/DDD: 9/95).

Shostakovich Piano Concertos – C minor for Piano, Trumpet and Strings, Op 35[ab]; No. 2 in
F major, Op. 102[b]. Three Fantastic Dances, Op. 5 (all from French Columbia FCX769, 10/61).
24 Preludes and Fugues, Op. 87 – No. 1 in C major; No. 4 in E minor; No. 5 in D major; No. 23
in F major (FCX771); No. 24 in D minor (Parlophone PMC1056, 7/58). **Dmitri Shostakovich**
(pf); [a]**Ludovic Vaillant** (tpt); [b]**French Radio National Orchestra / André Cluytens.** EMI Composers
in Person mono Ⓕ CDC7 54606-2* (76 minutes: ADD: 4/93). Recorded 1958-1959.   ⒼⒼ

Before devoting himself entirely to composition Shostakovich pursued a successful parallel career as a concert pianist, playing mostly romantic repertoire. These recordings were made at a time when he still played his own works in public, and they show him to have been a highly skilled player. His performances of both concertos are quite brilliant, and have a particularly vivacious, outgoing quality. In the First Concerto Ludovic Vaillant plays the trumpet part with character and great virtuosity, and the orchestral playing under Cluytens matches that of the composer in its joyous high spirits. The three little *Fantastic Dances* are wittily brought to life. A different, far more serious and academic world is evoked by Shostakovich in his Preludes and Fugues. Here the composer shapes his own long contrapuntal lines with great skill, and these are very compelling, highly concentrated performances. The mono recordings are all very acceptable, save that of the last Prelude and Fugue, where a certain rustiness creeps into the sound. All these items have obvious historical importance, but they also offer many rewards to the listener who is primarily interested in the music.

Additional recommendations ...

...Cello Sonata[a]. Concerto for Piano, Trumpet and Strings[b]. Piano Concerto No. 2[c].
[a]**Mstislav Rostropovich** (vc); **Dmitri Shostakovich** (pf); [b]**Moscow Radio Symphony Orchestra / Alexander Gauk;** [c]**Moscow Philharmonic Orchestra / Samuil Samosud.**
Russian Disc Ⓕ RDCD15005 (64 minutes: ADD: 2/95).

...Concerto for Piano, Trumpet and Strings. *Coupled with works by various composers.*
Eileen Joyce (pf); **Arthur Lockwood** (tpt); **Hallé Orchestra / Leslie Heward.**
Dutton Laboratories mono Ⓜ CDAX8010* (67 minutes: ADD: 2/95).

Shostakovich Piano Concertos – C minor for Piano, Trumpet and Strings, Op. 35[a]; No. 2 in
F major, Op. 102. The Unforgettable Year 1919, Op. 89 – The assault on beautiful Gorky.
Dmitri Alexeev (pf); [a]**Philip Jones** (tpt); **English Chamber Orchestra / Jerzy Maksymiuk.**
Classics for Pleasure ⑧ CD-CFP4547 (48 minutes: DDD: 1/89). From CFP414416-1 (11/83).
Shostakovich's Piano Concertos were written under very different circumstances, yet together they
contain some of the composer's most cheerful and enlivening music. The First, with its wealth of
perky, memorable tunes, has the addition of a brilliantly-conceived solo trumpet part (delightfully
done here by Philip Jones) that also contributes to the work's characteristic stamp. The Second
Concerto was written not long after Shostakovich had released a number of the intense works he had
concealed during the depths of the Stalin era. It came as a sharp contrast, reflecting as it did the
optimism and sense of freedom that followed the death of the Russian dictator. The beauty of the
slow movement is ideally balanced by the vigour of the first, and the madcap high spirits of the last.
The poignant movement for piano and orchestra from the Suite from the 1951 film *The Unforgettable
Year 1919*, "The assault on beautiful Gorky", provides an excellent addition to this disc of perceptive
and zestful performances by Alexeev. He is most capably supported by the ECO under Maksymiuk,
and the engineers have done them proud with a recording of great clarity and finesse. A joyous issue.
Additional recommendations ...
...Concerto for Piano, Trumpet and Strings[a]. Chamber Symphony in C minor, Op. 110a. Preludes,
Op. 34[b] – Nos. 5, 6, 10, 13, 14, 17 and 24. [ab]**Evgeni Kissin** (pf); [a]**Vassili Kan** (tpt); **Moscow
Virtuosi / Vladimir Spivakov.** RCA Victor Red Seal ⑮ RD87947 (58 minutes: DDD: 12/89).
...Concerto for Piano, Trumpet and Strings[a]. Piano Concerto No. 2 **Poulenc** Double Piano
Concerto in D minor[c]. [a]**André Previn**, [c]**Arthur Gold**, [c]**Robert Fizdale** (pfs);
[a]**William Vacchiano** (tpt); **New York Philharmonic Orchestra / Leonard Bernstein.**
Sony Classical Bernstein Royal Edition ⑯ SMK47618 (61 minutes: ADD: 6/94).
...Concerto for Piano, Trumpet and Strings[a]. **Haydn** Piano Concerto in D major, HobXVIII/11.
Martha Argerich (pf); [a]**Guy Touvron** (trpt); **Württemberg Chamber Orchestra / Jörg Faerber.**
DG ⑫ 439 864-2GH (42 minutes: DDD: 1/95).
...Concerto for Piano, Trumpet and Strings. **William Kapell** (pf); **Philadelphia Orchestra /
Eugene Ormandy.** Arbiter mono ⑫ ARBITER108* (71 minutes: ADD: 5/98).

Shostakovich Violin Concerto No. 1 in A minor, Op. 99.
Prokofiev Violin Concerto No. 1 in D major, Op. 19. **Maxim Vengerov** (vn);
London Symphony Orchestra / Mstislav Rostropovich. Teldec ⑫ 4509-92256-2
(62 minutes: DDD: 2/95). Recorded 1994. Includes bonus sampler disc.
Gramophone Award Winner 1995. Gramophone Editor's choice. ⓖⓖⓖ
Shostakovich Violin Concerto No. 1 in A minor, Op. 99.
Prokofiev Violin Concerto No. 2 in G minor, Op. 63. **Vadim Repin** (vn); **Hallé Orchestra /
Kent Nagano.** Erato ⑫ 0630-10696-2 (59 minutes: DDD: 1/96).
There is an astonishing emotional maturity in Vengerov's Shostakovich. He uses Heifetz's bow but it
is to David Oistrakh that he is often compared. His vibrato is wider, his manners less consistently
refined, and yet the comparison is well founded. Oistrakh made three commercial recordings of the
Shostakovich, one of which is listed below, and one can guess that Vengerov has been listening to
those earlier Oistrakh renditions as there is nothing radically novel about his interpretation. It is
possible that some will find Vengerov's impassioned climaxes a shade forced by comparison. Yet he
achieves a nobility and poise worlds away from the superficial accomplishment of most modern rivals.
He can fine down his tone to the barest whisper; nor is he afraid to make a scorching, ugly sound.
While his sometimes slashing quality of articulation is particularly appropriate to the faster
movements, the brooding, silver-grey *Nocturne* comes off superbly too, though it seems perverse that
the engineers mute the low tam-tam strokes. Rostropovich has the lower strings dig into the third
movement's passacaglia theme with his usual enthusiasm. Indeed the orchestral playing is very nearly
beyond reproach. Vengerov and Rostropovich take an unashamedly epic, wide-open-steppes view of
the Prokofiev concerto and it works well. Closely observed digital recording uncovers a wealth of
detail, most of it welcome, with the conductor's erstwhile clumsy tendency barely noticeable. Towards
the end of the first movement, the approach to the reprise of the opening melody on solo flute with
harp, muted strings and lightly running tracery from the soloist is very deliberately taken, and the
long-breathed finale builds to a passionate, proto-Soviet climax. The central scherzo is predictably
breathtaking in its virtuosity. Need one go on? If you're looking for a recording of the Shostakovich,
Vengerov's coupling may be less logical than Lydia Mordkovitch's (see below) but do not be deterred
from investigating this extraordinary disc. However committed you are to alternative interpretations,
these demand to be heard.
Vadim Repin's interpretation of the Shostakovich comes across as less quintessentially Russian in
its avoidance of rhetorical overkill. Without in any way underplaying the bravura passages (the
Scherzo is taken at an incredible speed), he stresses rather the chamber-like intimacy of Shostakovich's
score. Rather surprising, perhaps, is the flowing tempo for the slow third movement, but, thanks also
to Nagano and the Hallé, we do actually hear the music as a passacaglia. With Vengerov and
Rostropovich intent on heightening strong emotions rather than clarifying textures, the LSO's
contribution is comparatively impenetrable on Teldec. In the "Nocturne" the tam-tam, inaudible in

Abbey Road, is perfectly caught in Manchester. Given Repin's dazzling achievement in the Shostakovich concerto, his Prokofiev is a shade disappointing. The violin is less sweetly caught and Repin sometimes makes the kind of uningratiating noises which imply some impatience with the straightforward *Romeo and Juliet*-style lyricism of the work. The finale sounds spontaneous but the lovely slow movement could do with more space to indulge its sweetly singing lines. However, if the coupling appeals, Repin represents a clear first choice – and anyone who cares about the Shostakovich will want to hear Repin's disc.

Additional recommendations ...

...No. 1; No. 2 in C sharp minor, Op. 129. **David Oistrakh** (vn); **Czech Philharmonic Orchestra / Evgeny Mravinsky.** Praga PR250 052*.

...No. 1. **Glazunov** Violin Concerto in A minor, Op. 82. **Itzhak Perlman** (vn); **Israel Philharmonic Orchestra / Zubin Mehta.** EMI Ⓕ CDC7 49814-2 (55 minutes: DDD: 1/90).

...Nos. 1 and 2. **Lydia Mordkovitch** (vn); **Scottish National Orchestra / Neeme Järvi.** Chandos Ⓕ CHAN8820 (69 minutes: DDD: 4/90). *Gramophone Award Winner 1990.*   Ⓖ

...No. 1ª. Piano Concerto No. 2 in F major, Op. 102ᵇ. ªBoris Belkin (vn); ᵇCristina Ortiz (pf); Royal Philharmonic Orchestra / Vladimir Ashkenazy. Decca Ⓕ 425 793-2DH (60 minutes: DDD: 8/90).

...Nos. 1 and 2. **Dmitry Sitkovetsky** (vn); **BBC Symphony Orchestra / Andrew Davis.** Virgin Classics Ⓕ VC7 59601-2 (67 minutes: DDD: 9/90).   Ⓖ

...Nos. 1 and 2. **Ilya Kaler** (vn); **Polish National Radio Symphony Orchestra, Katowice / Antoni Wit.** Naxos Ⓢ 8 550814 (71 minutes: DDD: 10/97).

Shostakovich Violin Concerto No. 2 in C sharp minor, Op. 129.
Prokofiev Violin Concerto No. 2 in G minor, Op. 63. **Maxim Vengerov** (vn); **London Symphony Orchestra / Mstislav Rostropovich.** Teldec Ⓕ 0630-13150-2 (62 minutes: DDD: A/97). Recorded 1996.

This is an exceptionally fine peformance of the Shostakovich, the desperate bleakness perfectly realized. There has been no finer account since that of the dedicatee, David Oistrakh. With Rostropovich rather than Kondrashin on the podium, tempos are comparatively deliberate in the first two movements, but there is no lack of intensity in the solo playing and rather more in the way of light and shade. In the stratospheric, impossibilist writing of the *Adagio*, Vengerov is technically superb, while the all-pervading atmosphere of desolation has never been more potently conveyed. The finale is more extrovert than some will like, the fireworks irresistible, and yet you do not lose the disquieting sense of a composer at the end of his tether, seemingly contemptuous of his own material. The Prokofiev is rather less successful, however. The balance there is partly to blame – the orchestra a remote presence, the soloist rather too closely scrutinized – but also there is a lack of intimacy in the interpretation itself. Vengerov self-consciously scales down his tone for the first movement's exquisite second subject, but the second movement, very slow and grand, is plagued by Rostropovich's over-insistent nuancing. Even if the finale has its impressive passages, there isn't quite enough light-hearted Spanishry in a piece written not to Soviet order but for Robert Soëtans to play in Madrid. Vengerov is in a class of his own. His sometimes 'overwrought' manner fits this music like a glove.

Shostakovich Moscow-Cheryomushki, Op. 105 – concert suite (ed. Cornall). The Bolt – ballet suite, Op. 27*a* (1934 version). The Gadfly, Op. 97 – Overture; The cliff; Youth; Box on the ear; Barrel organ; Contredanse; Galop; At the market place; The rout; The passage of Montanelli; Finale; The Austrians; Gemma's room. **Philadelphia Orchestra / Riccardo Chailly.** Decca Ⓕ 452 597-2DH (73 minutes: DDD: 12/96). Recorded 1995. *Gramophone Editor's choice.*   Ⓠ

Although entitled "The Dance Album", interestingly only one of the items on this disc (*The Bolt*) is actually derived from music conceived specifically for dance. However, what the disc reveals is that Shostakovich's fondness for dance forms frequently found expression in his other theatrical/film projects. The world première recording of a suite of four episodes from the 1959 operetta *Moscow-Cheryomushki* will be of particular interest to Shostakovich devotees. Despite the somewhat mundane plot, the score produces some surprisingly attractive and entertaining numbers, most notably perhaps the invigorating "A spin through Moscow" and the "Waltz". For the suite from the ballet *The Bolt*, Chailly brings us the less frequently heard 1934 version in which the composer dropped two of the eight numbers and changed some of the titles in order to deflect from the story-line of the ballet. Lots of parody and plenty of Shostakovich with his tongue planted firmly in his cheek is what we get, and if this side of the composer's output appeals then you will certainly enjoy Chailly's and his players' spirited and colourfully buoyant performances of this energetic score. Less familiar light is also shed on the music from the film *The Gadfly* which is heard here in a version which brings together 13 of the score's episodes and preserves Shostakovich's original orchestration, as opposed to the suite prepared and re-orchestrated by Levin Atovmyan. All the performances on the disc are superbly delivered with panache and high spirits and the recorded sound is excellent.

Additional recommendations ...

...The Bolt. **Royal Stockholm Philharmonic Orchestra / Gennadi Rozhdestvensky.** Chandos Ⓕ CHAN9343/4 (two discs: 147 minutes: DDD: 6/95). Recorded 1994.   Ⓠ

...The Gadfly – film music. King Lear, Op. 58*a*. Hamlet, Op. 116*a* – Introduction; The ghost; In the Garden. **KBS Symphony Orchestra / Vakhtang Jordania.** Koch International Classics Ⓕ 37274-2 (79 minutes: DDD: 12/94).

...Suites – The Gadfly; Five Days, Five Nights, Op. 111*a*. **National Symphony Orchestra of Ukraine / Theodore Kuchar.** Naxos Ⓢ 8 553299 (77 minutes: DDD: 5/97).

Shostakovich The Golden Age. **Royal Stockholm Philharmonic Orchestra / Gennadi Rozhdestvensky.** Chandos Ⓕ CHAN9251/2 (two discs: 134 minutes: DDD: 5/94). Recorded 1993. *The Golden Age* (1930) is an industrial exhibition organized in a capitalist country, at which a group of Soviet sportsmen have been invited to compete. The general idea of Shostakovich's characterization is clearly to differentiate between goodies and baddies by assigning them respectively healthy-folk and decadent-bourgeois idioms. But then the trouble was, he couldn't stop himself enjoying being decadent. Not all of the 37 movements stand up independently of the stage-action. But the finales and the whole of Act 3 are top-notch stuff, at times surprisingly threatening in tone and symphonic in continuity; and there are several movements which could undoubtedly be promoted alongside the four in the familiar concert suite (the Tap Dance of Act 2 is especially appealing, for instance). Those who know their Shostakovich will be constantly intrigued by foretastes of *Lady Macbeth*, the Fourth Symphony and the *Hamlet* music, and by the appearance of Shostakovich's "Tea for Two" arrangement as an Interlude in Act 2. This first complete recording is a major coup for Chandos. Admittedly not even their flattering engineering can disguise a certain lack of confidence and idiomatic flair on the part of the Royal Stockholm Philharmonic Orchestra. But let that not deter anyone with the least interest in Shostakovich, or ballet music, or Soviet music, or indeed Soviet culture as a whole, from investigating this weird and intermittently wonderful score.

Shostakovich Symphonies. [a]**London Philharmonic Orchestra;** [b]**Concertgebouw Orchestra / Bernard Haitink.** Decca London Ⓜ 444 430-2LC11 (11 discs, oas: ADD/DDD: 11/93). Texts and translations included.
425 063-2DM[a] (65 minutes) – No. 1 in F minor, Op. 10 (from SXDL7515, 5/81); No. 3 in E flat major, Op. 20, "The first of May" (with the London Philharmonic Choir. SXDL7535, 7/82).
425 064-2DM[a] (76 minutes) – No. 2 in B major, Op. 14 (London Phil Ch. SXDL7535, 7/82); No. 10 in E minor, Op. 93 (SXL6838, 10/77). *425 065-2DM* (68 minutes) – No. 4 in C minor, Op. 43 (SXL6927, 11/79)[a]. *425 066-2DM* (76 minutes) – No. 5 in D minor, Op. 47 (SXDL7551, 12/82. **Gramophone** *Award Winner 1982-83*)[b]; No. 9 in E flat major, Op. 70 (SXDL7515, 5/81)[a].
425 067-2DM[b] (74 minutes) – No. 6 in B minor, Op. 54 (411 939-2DH2, 8/85. *Selected by Sounds in Retrospect*); No. 12 in D minor, Op. 112, "The year 1917" (SXDL7577, 6/83). *425 068-2DM* (79 minutes) – No. 7 in C major, Op. 60, "Leningrad" (D213D2, 11/80)[a]. *425 069-2DM* (73 minutes) – No. 15 in A major, Op. 141 (SXL6906, 3/79)[a]; From Jewish Folk Poetry, Op. 79 (Elisabeth Söderström, sop; Ortrun Wenkel, contr; Ryszard Karczykowski, ten. 417 261-2DH, 3/87)[b]. *425 071-2DM* (62 minutes) – No. 8 in C minor, Op. 65 (SXDL7621, 11/83)[b]. *425 072-2DM* (61 minutes) – No. 11 in G minor, Op. 103, "The year 1905" (411 939-2DH2, 8/85. *Selected by Sounds in Retrospect*)[b]. *425 073-2DM* (64 minutes) – No. 13 in B flat minor, Op. 113, "Babiy Yar". (Marius Rintzler, bass; Concertgebouw Choir. 417 261-2DH, 3/87)[b]. *425 074-2DM*[b] (72 minutes) – No. 14, Op. 135 (Julia Varady, sop; Dietrich Fischer-Dieskau, bar. SXDL7532, 1/82). Six Marina Tsvetaeva Poems, Op. 143 (Ortrun Wenkel. 417 261-2DH, 3/87). ⒼⒼ
This, the first complete Western cycle of the symphonies, that of Bernard Haitink, returns to the catalogue at mid-price, Decca having jettisoned a few minor works and decoupled several major ones. It is hard to argue with this presentation when it includes modern annotations and full recording data. Concerned for tradition, and with the need to challenge it, the young Shostakovich could be classical and modern, polemical and prankish by turns. Haitink, not entirely po-faced, turns in a thoroughly decent account of the First Symphony, missing just a little of the element of pastiche. The recoupling with the Third does strike sparks, the language of the later music variously foreshadowed in divergent contexts. In the Fourth Symphony, Haitink offers no stupendous revelations, content to bring out the dignity of the writing in a piece where we have come to expect something more sensational, less perfectly controlled. Even the hurtling *moto perpetuo* fugato passage for strings which triggers the main climax of the first movement seems just a little studied. His outer movements are helpfully split, by additional cues – but his literalness and sobriety fall short of the ideal, as, marginally, does the playing. Haitink's Fifth, deeply considered and almost indecently well upholstered, is not easy to assess. Originally greeted with extreme reverence in these pages – its release followed hard on the heels of the publication of *Testimony* which surely influenced the critical response – it is an earnest attempt to make structural sense of the music's grand symphonic aspirations. It is only because the orchestral playing is generally so immaculate that one registers the curious glitch 2'13" into the *Largo*. That movement is generally less affecting than it can be, yet the preceding *Allegretto* is triumphantly brought off as a heavy-footed Mahlerian *Ländler*. Then again, the first movement's long-limbed second subject chugs along reluctantly, dourly unphrased, with none of the easeful balm to be found in other interpretations.
     Haitink's Fifth is now generously paired with his solid, untrivial but scarcely earth-shattering Ninth. His Sixth and Twelfth is characterized by playing of predictable *gravitas* and tonal splendour. Indeed, this Twelfth could be seen as the 'best' modern version. The *Leningrad* is another matter. Rightly praised for its symphonic integrity and splendid sound, Haitink's *nobilmente* reappraisal is now a much cheaper option than Bernstein's two-disc epic on DG, though some will respond more favourably to the raw authenticity of Rozhdestvensky. Haitink's stoical view of the Eighth is highly

impressive, though not very varied in mood. Curiously, the finale is mis-cued. Kurt Sanderling's reading (listed under the review of No. 8) is also highly impressive. The Tenth has always seemed less dependent on a conductor steeped in the Russian tradition, and the only drawback of Haitink's well-played, well-recorded account is his unsubtle, over-confident tone in the enigmatic third movement *Allegretto*. There is real demonic abandon in the scherzo. Karajan's Tenth is very desirable but he offers no makeweight. Haitink offers a carefully prepared account of No. 2, where the choral contribution has the odd awkward moment but the overall effect is very arresting. His Eleventh too has such weight and precision that his customary detachment is mostly less noticeable than his phenomenal control.

Haitink's Thirteenth boasts another of Decca's huge, reverberant recordings, of such 'cinematic' brilliance and range that it threatens to dwarf the music-making. While chorus and orchestra are on terrific form, even this monolithic work ideally requires greater flexibility and plasticity than the conductor seems willing to provide. The soloist, Marius Rintzler, would seem to be at one with Haitink's brooding approach. Kondrashin's account (listed further on) makes a very recommendable alternative. As one of the first of Shostakovich's late scores to be taken seriously in the West, it is odd that the Fourteenth should have been so poorly represented in the CD catalogue. Haitink's polyglot reading (not quite that authorized by the composer, incidentally) does not really represent a viable solution – too much vital and specific tone colour is lost along with the original note-values. To make matters worse, Fischer-Dieskau is in hectoring mode and both soloists' proximity to the microphones makes for uncomfortable listening, though the orchestral contribution is excellent. Barshai (listed below) can lay claim to *absolute* authenticity. It is a fascinating document, as he and Vishnevskaya rage against the dying of the light in every song, slicing seconds (sometimes minutes) off the timings of the Western account. Reshetin is superb too, less inclined to histrionics. Generally speaking the sound is close and crude, by no means intolerable but sufficiently prone to distortion to inhibit a general recommendation. In its way, however, this disc is indispensable. Haitink's Fifteenth has always been highly regarded, despite some less than needle-sharp contributions from the percussion where it matters most.

At medium price, and with a rather high-level transfer of its coupling (whose historical significance is ably outlined in the insert-note), this merits a place at or near the top of anyone's list. To sum up: Haitink's set, superbly engineered, is nothing if not reliable. For those who prize technical finesse over raw passion, Haitink remains a plausible first choice. These are endlessly fascinating, endlessly equivocal works.

Additional recommendations ...

...Nos. 9[a] and 14[b]. [b]**Galina Vishnevskaya** (sop); [b]**Mark Reshetin** (bass); [b]**Moscow Chamber Orchestra / Rudolf Barshai;** [a]**USSR Symphony Orchestra / David Oistrakh.**
Russian Disc Ⓕ RDCD11192 (73 minutes: ADD: 1/94). *Gramophone Editor's choice.* ⒼⒼ

...No. 12. **Leningrad Philharmonic Orchestra / Evgeny Mravinsky.**
Erato Ⓜ 2292-45754-2 (39 minutes: DDD: 6/92). ⒼⒼⒼ

...No. 14[a]. King Lear, Op. 58[ab]. [a]**Makuara Kasrashubili** (sop); [b]**Nina Romanova** (mez); [a]**Anatoly Safiulin** (bass); [a]**USSR Ministry of Culture Symphony Orchestra / Gennadi Rozhdestvensky;** [b]**Leningrad Chamber Orchestra / Eduard Serov.** Olympia Ⓜ OCD182 (62 minutes: DDD: 12/88).

...Complete Symphonies. **Soloists; London Voices; Washington Choral Arts Society; Washington National Symphony Orchestra; London Symphony Orchestra; Moscow Academic Symphony Orchestra / Mstislav Rostropovich.**
Teldec Ⓜ 0630-17046-2 (12 discs: 703 minutes: ADD/DDD: 10/97).

Shostakovich Symphonies – No. 1 in F minor, Op. 10; No. 6 in B minor, Op. 54.
Scottish National Orchestra / Neeme Järvi. Chandos Ⓕ CHAN8411 (64 minutes: DDD: 6/86).
Recorded 1984-1985. Ⓖ
The First Symphony, the 19-year-old composer's graduation piece from the then Leningrad Conservatory in 1925, may be indebted to Stravinsky, Prokofiev, Tchaikovsky and even Scriabin. But it rarely sounds like anything other than pure Shostakovich. The sophisticated mask of its first movement is drawn aside for a slow movement of Slav melancholy and foreboding, and the finale brilliantly stage-manages a way out. The Sixth (1939) takes the familiar Shostakovichian extremes of explosive activity and uneasy contemplation (that the composer reconciles in the finale of the First) and separates them into individual movements. Two swift movements (a mercurial but menacing *Scherzo*, and a real knees-up of a finale) follow on from an opening *Largo* whose slow lyrical declamations eventually all but freeze into immobility. Järvi has a will (and Chandos, the engineering) to explore the extremes of pace, mood and dynamics of both symphonies; his account of the First Symphony convinces precisely because those extremes intensify as the work progresses. Some may crave a fuller, firmer string sound, but the passionate intensity of the playing (in all departments) is never in doubt.

Additional recommendations ...

...No. 6. **Rachmaninov** Symphony No. 3 in A minor, Op. 44. **London Symphony Orchestra / André Previn.** EMI Studio Ⓜ CDM7 69564-2 (75 minutes: ADD: 12/88).

...Nos. 1[a], 5[b] and 7[c]. Prelude in E flat minor, Op. 34[d] (orch. Stokowski).
[abd]**Philadelphia Orchestra;** [c]**NBC Symphony Orchestra / Leopold Stokowski.**
Pearl mono Ⓜ GEMMCD9044* (two discs: 156 minutes: ADD: 1/94). ⒼⒼ

...No. 6; No. 12 in D minor, Op. 112, "The year 1917". **Leningrad Philharmonic Orchestra /**
Evgeny Mravinsky. Praga Ⓕ PR254 017 (61 minutes: ADD: 8/94).
...No. 1. Concerto for Piano, Trumpet and Strings in C minor, Op. 35ª. ªMikhail Rudy (pf);
ªOle Edward Antonsen (tpt); Berlin Philharmonic Orchestra / Mariss Jansons.
EMI Ⓕ CDC5 55361-2 (55 minutes: DDD: 12/95).

Shostakovich Symphonies – No. 2 in B major, Op. 14, "To October"; No. 3 in E flat major,
"The first of May", Op. 20. **London Voices; London Symphony Orchestra / Mstislav Rostropovich.**
Teldec Ⓕ 4509-90853-2 (48 minutes: DDD: 10/94). Recorded 1993.　　　　　　Ⓖ
Rostropovich's disc is cut at a low level, which will make the dark opening pages of the Second
Symphony implausibly opaque unless you reset the controls. The string playing then emerges as
impressively polished, the wind aptly angular and spiky, more characterful than their rivals as the
music gains pace. Only the LSO's leader seems a trifle thin of tone (as recorded). Under Rostropovich,
uniquely among recent exponents of the score, the factory whistle is not doubled by brass. Thereafter
the churchy acoustic ensures that his London Voices sound at least as numerous rival recordings; and
the men at least are more comfortable with the idiom. The climax is both fervent and unusually secure
of pitch. Rostropovich's account of the Third is an outstanding achievement. Relishing the
opportunities for display, the LSO find their best form – crisper of ensemble than in previous outings
with this inspirational, if not always ideally lucid, conductor – and the recorded sound is surely the
best in Teldec's cycle. The opening clarinet theme is exquisitely done and, amid the corybantic tumult
of Revolution, the lyrical moments are empowered here with rare emotional clout. Already we hear
the authentic voice of the composer Rostropovich knew as friend and mentor, the disillusioned
chronicler of Soviet reality.
Additional recommendation ...
...Festival Overture. Ballet Suites – No. 1; No. 2; No. 3; No. 4; No. 5, Op. 27a.
Katerina Izmaylova – Suite. **Royal Scottish Orchestra / Neeme Järvi.**
Chandos Ⓜ CHAN7000/1 (two discs: 114 minutes: DDD: 5/95).

Shostakovich Symphony No. 4 in C minor, Op. 43.
Britten Russian Funeral. **City of Birmingham Symphony Orchestra / Sir Simon Rattle.**
EMI Ⓕ CDC5 55476-2 (68 minutes: DDD: 11/95). Recorded 1994.
This could just be the most important Western recording of the Fourth since the long-deleted
Ormandy and Previn versions. Naturally, it complements rather than replaces Kondrashin's reading,
taped shortly after the work's belated unveiling in December 1961: papery strings and lurid brass
cannot disguise that conductor's unique authority even when Shostakovich's colouristic effects are
muted by rudimentary Soviet sound engineering. In his recording, Rattle's approach is more
obviously calculated, supremely brilliant but just a little cold. A certain firmness and self-confidence
is obvious from the first. The restrained Hindemithian episode is relatively square, the first climax
superbly built. The second group unfolds seamlessly with the glorious *espressivo* of the strings not
much threatened by the not very mysterious intrusions of harp and bass clarinet. Tension builds
again, some way into the development, with the lacerating (Kondrashin-like) intensity of the strings'
moto perpetuo fugato passage. Six miraculously terraced discords herald the two-faced recapitulation.
Kondrashin and Järvi find more emotional inevitability in Shostakovich's destabilizing tactics
hereabouts. Rattle doesn't quite locate a compensating irony, although his closing bars are
convincingly icy, with nicely audible gong. Even in Rattle's experienced hands, the finale is not all
plain sailing. The initial quasi-Mahlerian march is underpinned by disappointingly fuzzy timpani
strokes which lose the point of their own lopsidedness. But then the section's mock-solemn climax is
simply tremendous (and tremendously loud). The incisive *Allegro* is launched with (deliberate?)
abruptness at an unbelievably fast tempo and, even if the music doesn't always make sense at this pace,
the results are breathtaking. The denouement is approached with real flair. A superbly characterized
trombone solo, hushed expectant strings and the most ambiguous of all Shostakovich perorations is
unleashed with devastating force. The coda is mightily impressive too, not as slow as it might be, but
with just the right dragging quality in the articulate and unanimous basses. After this, the Britten
encore risks seeming beside the point; this really is emotional play-acting. In sum, neither Kondrashin
or Järvi's more direct emotional involvement are easily passed over. On the other hand, Rattle does
give us a thrilling example of what a relatively objective, thoroughly 'modern' approach has to offer
in the 1990s. With its huge dynamic range and uncompromising, analytical style, EMI's recording
pulls no punches, and the awesome precision of the CBSO's playing makes for an unforgettable
experience.
Additional recommendations ...
...No. 4. **Scottish National Orchestra / Neeme Järvi.**
Chandos Ⓕ CHAN8640 (61 minutes: DDD: 12/89).　　　　　　　　　　　　Ⓖ
...No. 4. **National Symphony Orchestra / Mstislav Rostropovich.**
Teldec Ⓕ 9031 76261-2 (65 minutes: DDD: 11/92).
...No. 4. **Moscow Philharmonic Orchestra / Kyrill Kondrashin.**
Melodiya Ⓜ 74321 19840-2 (60 minutes: ADD: 11/94).
...Nos. 4 and 10. **Philadelphia Orchestra / Eugene Ormandy.**
Sony Classical Essential Classics Ⓑ SB2K62409 (two discs: 120 minutes: ADD: 1/97).

Shostakovich Symphony No. 5 in D minor, Op. 47. Ballet Suite No. 5, Op. 27a.
   Scottish National Orchestra / Neeme Järvi. Chandos Ⓕ CHAN8650 (76 minutes: DDD: 4/90).
   Recorded 1988.
There are more Shostakovich Fifths than you can shake a stick at in the CD catalogue at present, and several of them are very good. Järvi's makes perhaps the safest recommendation of them all: it has a generous coupling (which cannot be said of many of its rivals), it has no drawbacks (save, for some tastes, a slight touch of heart-on-sleeve in the slow movement) and a number of distinct advantages. A profound seriousness, for one thing, and an absolute sureness about the nature of the finale, which many conductors feel the need to exaggerate, either as brassy optimism or as bitter irony. Järvi takes it perfectly straight, denying neither option, and the progression from slow movement (the overtness of its emotion finely justified) to finale seems more natural, less of a jolt than usual. The SNO cannot rival the sheer massiveness of sound of some of the continental orchestras who have recorded this work, but while listening one hardly notices the lack, so urgent and polished is their playing. A very natural and wide-ranging recording, too, and the lengthy Suite (eight movements from Shostakovich's early ballet *The Bolt*, forming an exuberantly entertaining essay on the various modes that his sense of humour could take) makes much more than a mere fill-up.
Additional recommendations ...
...No. 5. Five Fragments, Op. 42. **Royal Philharmonic Orchestra / Vladimir Ashkenazy.**
   Decca Ⓕ 421 120-2DH (56 minutes: DDD: 6/88).
...Nos. 5 and 9. **Atlanta Symphony Orchestra / Yoel Levi.**
   Telarc Ⓕ CD80215 (78 minutes: DDD: 6/90).
...No. 5. Festival Overture, Op. 96. **London Symphony Orchestra / Maxim Shostakovich.**
   Collins Classics Ⓕ 1108-2 (59 minutes: DDD: 9/90).
...No. 5. **Leningrad Philharmonic Orchestra / Evgeny Mravinsky.**
   Erato Ⓜ 2292-45752-2 (44 minutes: ADD: 6/92).   ⒼⒼ
...No. 5. **New York Philharmonic Orchestra / Leonard Bernstein.**
   Sony Classical Bernstein Royal Edition Ⓜ SMK47615 (71 minutes: ADD: 6/94).
...No. 5. Cello Concerto No. 1 in E flat major, Op. 107[a]. [a]**Miloš Sadló** (vc); **Czech Philharmonic Orchestra / Karel Ančerl.** Supraphon Crystal Collection Ⓜ 11 0676-2 (72 minutes: ADD: 8/93).
...No. 5[a]. Festival Overture in A major, Op. 96[ab]. [a]**Russian Federation State Symphony Orchestra,** [b]**Bolshoi Theatre Brass Ensemble / Evgeni Svetlanov.**
   Canyon Classics Ⓕ EC3672-2 (53 minutes: DDD: 10/94).
...No. 5. Novorossisk Chimes, "The Fire of Eternal Glory". October, Op. 131. Overture on Russian and Kirghiz Folk Themes, Op. 115. **Royal Philharmonic Orchestra / Enrique Bátiz.**
   IMG RecordsⒻ IMGCD1609 (76 minutes: DDD: 2/95).
...No. 5. Festival Overture. **Royal Philharmonic Orchestra / Sir Charles Mackerras.**
   Tring International Royal Philharmonic Collection Ⓢ TRP032 (53 minutes: DDD: 9/95).
...Nos. 5 and 6. **Philadelphia Orchestra / Leopold Stokowski.**
   Dutton Laboratories mono Ⓜ CDAX8017* (79 minutes: ADD: 12/96).
...No. 5. Chamber Symphony, Op. 110a. **Vienna Philharmonic Orchestra / Mariss Jansons.**
   EMI Ⓕ CDC5 56442-2 (71 minutes: DDD: A/97).

Shostakovich Symphonies – No. 7 in C major, Op. 60, "Leningrad". No. 1 in F minor, Op. 10.
   Chicago Symphony Orchestra / Leonard Bernstein. DG Ⓕ 427 632-2GH2
   (two discs: 120 minutes: DDD: 1/90). Recorded live in 1988.   ⒼⒼ
The *Leningrad* Symphony was composed in haste as the Nazis sieged and bombarded the city (in 1941). It caused an immediate sensation, but posterity has been less enthusiastic. What business has the first movement's unrelated long central 'invasion' episode doing in a symphonic movement? Is the material of the finale really distinctive enough for its protracted treatment? Michael Oliver, in his original *Gramophone* review wrote that in this performance "the Symphony sounds most convincingly like a symphony, and one needing no programme to justify it". Added to which, and no disrespect is intended by this observation, the work's epic and cinematic manner has surely never been more powerfully realized. These are live recordings, with occasional noise from the audience (and the conductor), but the Chicago Orchestra has rarely sounded more polished or committed under any conditions. The strings are superb in the First Symphony, full and weightily present, and Bernstein's manner in this Symphony is comparably bold and theatrical of gesture. A word of caution: set your volume control carefully for the *Leningrad* Symphony's start; it is scored for six of both trumpets and trombones and no other recording has reproduced them so clearly, and to such devastating effect.
Additional recommendations ...
...No. 7. **Royal Scottish Orchestra / Neeme Järvi.** Chandos Ⓕ CHAN8623 (69 minutes: DDD: 8/88).
...No. 7. **BBC National Orchestra of Wales / Mark Wigglesworth.**
   BIS Ⓕ CD873 (79 minutes: DDD: 8/97).
...No. 7. **St Petersburg Philharmonic Orchestra / Vladimir Ashkenazy.** Decca Ⓕ 448 814-2DH
   (71 minutes: DDD: 10/97). *Includes introduction by composer, broadcast from Leningrad in 1941.*

Shostakovich Symphony No. 8 in C minor, Op. 65. **London Symphony Orchestra / André Previn.**
   EMI Matrix Ⓜ CDM5 65521-2 (61 minutes: ADD: 10/95). From HMV ASD2917 (10/73).

The Eighth Symphony, written in 1943, two years after the *Leningrad*, offers a wiser, more bitterly disillusioned Shostakovich. The heroic peroration of the Seventh's finale is here replaced by numbed whimsy and eventual uneasy calm. André Previn has since re-recorded the symphony but this youthful account serves to remind us that the music is the product of a young man's imagination. The remake has greater breadth in every sense and, note for note, the orchestral playing is often finer. However, many will prefer the urgency of this earlier version. At that time, Previn seemed content to add a patina of mid-Atlantic gloss, and a good deal of subtlety, to the raw expressivity of the earlier Soviet recordings; he had not yet adopted the self-consciously epic manner thought appropriate today. There are few who know how to bring off the symphony as a gloomy and spiritless *in memoriam*, but the lithe freshness of the Previn is a compelling alternative. EMI's transfer is punchy and focused.

Additional recommendations ...

...No. 8. **Washington National Symphony Orchestra / Mstislav Rostropovich.**
Teldec Ⓕ 9031-74719-2 (61 minutes: DDD: 10/92).

...No. 8. **London Symphony Orchestra / André Previn.**
DG Ⓕ 437 819-2GH (68 minutes: DDD: 3/95).

...No. 8. **Leningrad Philharmonic Orchestra / Evgeny Mravinsky.**
Russian Disc Ⓕ RDCD10917 (62 minutes: AAD: 2/97).

...No. 8 – Adagio. *Coupled with works by* **Prokofiev, Rachmaninov** and **Koussevitzky** Boston Symphony Orchestra / Serge Koussevitzky. Biddulph mono Ⓕ WHL045* (78 minutes: ADD: 2/97).

Shostakovich Symphonies – No. 9 in E flat major, Op. 70[a] ; No. 15 in A major, Op. 141[b].
Moscow Philharmonic Orchestra / Kyrill Kondrashin. Melodiya Ⓜ 74321 19846-2 (54 minutes: ADD: 11/94). Item marked [a] from HMV ASD2409 (1/69), [b]EX290387-3 (1974). ⒼⒼ

After Mravinsky's politically motivated refusal to undertake the première of the Thirteenth in 1962, Shostakovich found a stalwart interpreter in Kyrill Kondrashin. Shostakovich recordings don't come any more authentic than this. Objectively speaking, the playing of the Moscow Philharmonic is not uniformly distinguished. Kondrashin can be startlingly brisk, the panache and brilliance hardening into mannerism. The transfers are no more than serviceable and the badly translated accompanying notes are untrustworthy at best. That said, here is unbeatable music-making, and these are arguably among Kondrashin's greatest recordings. The classic Ninth (from 1965) is conveniently paired with a superbly vivid Fifteenth (from 1974), generally hard-driven *à la* Mravinsky but far more convincingly poised. The first movement goes at a frightening lick, deserting the toy shop for the asylum, the slow movement lacks only the very last ounce of desolation and the finale, always intelligently conceived, is suitably emotive at the close. The sound has immediacy and just enough depth. Though of earlier vintage, the Ninth enjoys a more generous acoustic, the tape a little prone to distortion at moments of stress (which for Kondrashin come more often than usual). Both interpretations have a tonal weight and sarcastic intent which cannot fail to shock the uninitiated . To sum up: he finds in these scores an unrivalled degree of dramatic tension, bringing to the surface raw emotions that more smoothly executed Western accounts play down. We may be impressed by the diligent literalness and sobriety of Haitink, but to what extent should we worry if he illuminates aspects of the music the composer himself thought unimportant? It isn't simply a matter of 'authentic' orchestral timbre. Kondrashin's versions document a very special kind of insight.

Additional recommendations ...

...Nos. 5 and 9. **St Peterburg Philharmonic Orchestra / Yuri Temirkanov.**
RCA Victor Red Seal Ⓕ 09026 68548-2 (71 minutes: DDD). Ⓖ

...No. 9. *Coupled with works by various composers.* **The Solti Orchestral Project, Carnegie Hall / Sir Georg Solti.** Decca Ⓕ 444 458-2DH (77 minutes: DDD: 12/94). Ⓖ

Shostakovich Symphony No. 10 in E minor, Op. 93.
Mussorgsky (orch. Shostakovich) Songs and Dances of Death[a]. [a]**Robert Lloyd** (bass); **Philadelphia Orchestra / Mariss Jansons.** EMI Ⓕ CDC5 55232-2 (72 minutes: DDD: 6/95).
Recorded 1994.

Stalin died on 5th March 1953, the same day as Prokofiev. In the summer of that year Shostakovich produced a symphony which can be taken as his own return to life after the dark night of dictatorship – the last two movements included, for the first time in his output, his personal DSCH signature (the notes D, E flat, C, B natural, in the German spelling). In the West the Tenth Symphony is now widely regarded as the finest of the cycle of 15, not just for its sheer depth of personal feeling, but because it finds the purest and subtlest musical representation of that feeling. Perhaps this is why it is less dependent than some of Shostakovich's major works on a conductor steeped in the Russian idiom. Anyone expecting a welter of hairpin *diminuendos* and expressive nudges will be disappointed by Jansons's Shostakovich – solid, sturdy and rhythmically taut rather than overly individualistic for the most part. Jansons's first movement is basically brisk with thrustful strings and conscientiously Soviet-style woodwind. It is a cogent enough view and yet the sense of underlying desolation is lacking, despite the conductor's vocal exhortations. The *Scherzo* is brilliantly articulated – even if the relatively leisurely pace robs the music of its potential to intimidate. The 'difficult' third movement is more convincing, though again unusually confident in tone. It would be churlish not to single out the superb horn playing. The main body of the finale (the introduction is separately tracked by the way) is launched with precise rhythmic clarity rather than irrepressible enthusiasm. In short, this is an excellent, sometimes dazzling choice among modern versions but it may strike seasoned listeners as slightly sterile, at once tightly controlled and spiritually disengaged. There is more passion in the coupling. Robert Lloyd is curiously under-represented on CD in the Russian repertoire that suits him so well. His admirers are bound to want this performance, which is very impressive as sheer singing. There is a gorgeously long-breathed "Serenade" and the more demonstrative songs are highly characterized without stooping to the coarse theatricality of some native singers. Throughout the disc, the close focus of the recording exposes a few instances of less than perfect synchronization but with playing so spectacularly accomplished, if not recognizably Philadelphian, this must be counted an outstanding achievement in its way.

Additional recommendation ...
...No. 10[a]. The Bolt – Suite, Op. 27*a*: Overture; The Bureaucrat; The Drayman's Dance; Intermezzo[b]. [a]**Leningrad Philharmonic Orchestra / Evgeny Mravinsky;** [b]**Czech Philharmonic Orchestra / Gennadi Rozhdestvensky.** Praga [a]mono/stereo Ⓔ PR250 053* (64 minutes: ADD: 9/95).

Shostakovich Symphony No. 11 in G minor, Op. 103, "The year 1905". **Leningrad Philharmonic Orchestra / Evgeny Mravinsky.** Praga Ⓕ PR254 018* (61 minutes: ADD: 8/94). Recorded live in 1967.   ⒼⒼ

Despite the rawness and occasional congestion of the sound this is a performance of extraordinary vehemence. There is an element in the work, of course, that is very close to agitprop; there are pages in the terrifying scherzo and in the finale that are not so much composed in primary colours as splashed on to a wall in broad strokes of dripping red and black. Many recent performances have refined this element with sheer orchestral virtuosity, but that is not Mravinsky's way: his brass players yell at the tops of their voices, his percussion threatens to overwhelm the rest of the orchestra, his violins come within an ace of breaking their strings with the sheer scorch of their bows' impact. It is valuable too for the unique sound of a Soviet orchestra during the Soviet period playing a profoundly Soviet work: you really do get the impression that every member of the orchestra knows and has complex reactions to all those quoted revolutionary or pre-revolutionary songs. The work is about a revolt against intolerable oppression. Such a revolt, suppressed like that in Leningrad in 1905, took place in Prague not long after this performance. It has such eloquence that you can almost persuade yourself that it played a part in that.

Additional recommendations ...
...No. 11. **Leningrad Philharmonic Orchestra / Evgeny Mravinsky.** Russian Disc Ⓕ RDCD11157 (56 minutes: ADD: 1/94).
...No. 11. **Leningrad Philharmonic Orchestra / Evgeny Mravinsky.** Revelation Ⓜ RV10091 (60 minutes: ADD: 3/98).

Shostakovich Symphony No. 11 in G minor, Op. 103, "The year 1905". **St Petersburg Philharmonic Orchestra / Vladimir Ashkenazy.** Decca Ⓕ 448 179-2DH (55 minutes: DDD: 5/96).

There are many felicitous touches here, rather less in the way of *gravitas*. For once, the motto theme is clearly audible from the start, just as, at the very end of the piece, the alternating major and minor thirds ring out cleanly against the orchestral clamour. Detail emerges vividly throughout, with the recording team favouring relatively close balances to convey the orchestra's distinctive sonority. The trumpets blaze through with the old fervour at key points in the second movement; the strings retain their characteristic huskiness even if they sound thinner than they used to. And yet to adopt generally brisk tempos without Mravinsky's insistent ferocity of address is to risk taming the beast. If the work is to be associated with big, universalized ideas of requiem and redemption – a (Brittenish?) search for eternal rest in the face of violence and death – it will require careful handling. Inbal has refashioned the ˙Eleventh as a sequence of glowing icons. Ashkenazy is a discreet interpreter in the best sense but, given his avoidance of the *self-consciously* profound, you may feel that Shostakovich's rhetoric is not always empowered with sufficient clout to banish the doubts. To sum up: this is a fresh, unaffected reading.

Shostakovich Symphony No. 13 in B flat minor, Op. 113, "Babi Yar". **Anatoly Kocherga** (bass); **National Male Choir of Estonia; Gothenburg Symphony Orchestra / Neeme Järvi.** DG Ⓕ Ⓞ 449 187-2GH (58 minutes: DDD: 6/97). Text and translation included. Recorded 1995.

This is the most entertaining modern recording of what is usually counted a forbidding work. You may even feel that the conductor's flexible tempos and extrovert manner represent a distraction from the real issues. That would be unfair, although the changes of pace in *Babi Yar* are undeniably abrupt and deprive the closing bars of their usual solidity and impact. The Estonian choir sound very confident and the bullish effect is enhanced by willing if not always refined playing from an orchestra that lacks great weight of string tone. The big, spacious recording helps of course but Anatoly Kocherga is the crucial player, not a deep bass perhaps but an authentic Boris with a range of expressive nuance and a ready responsiveness to text that some will find overstated. In the paradoxical finale, Yevtushenko's joke at the expense of the compliant Soviet writer Alexei Tolstoy is unusually well pointed, and the final pages are intensely poignant even if they no longer feel like the inevitable outcome of a symphonic journey as undertaken by Haitink. Järvi may lack his *gravitas* but his alternative could well appeal to those put off by the perceived severity of the piece. Transliterated Russian text and translations are provided.

Shostakovich Symphony No. 14, Op. 135[a]. Two Pieces for String Quartet (arr. Sikorski). [a]**Margareta Haverinen** (sop); [a]**Petteri Salomaa** (bass); **Tapiola Sinfonietta / Joseph Swensen.** Ondine Ⓕ ODE845-2 (59 minutes: DDD: 4/96). Text and translation included. Recorded 1994-1995.

The multilingual version of the Fourteenth Symphony was sanctioned by the composer but it remains something of a rarity on disc; some vital and specific tone colour is lost along with the original note values, and the 'three lilies' adorn the grave of "The Suicide" more elegantly in the Russian. Bernard Haitink may not agree. He elected to use the multilingual text in his 1980 recording and now Joseph Swensen presents this compelling alternative. We tend to take sonic excellence for granted these days but this is a true state-of-the-art recording with the soloists more naturally placed than in the rival Decca issue and an orchestral sound combining great clarity with just enough hall resonance. The performance has character too, if lacking the pervasive chill of the earliest Soviet accounts. The conductor secures excellent results from the Tapiola Sinfonietta. They are a lean and super-efficient group, yet without the loss of character this can sometimes imply. Of the soloists, the young bass-baritone Petteri Salomaa is particularly impressive: his is a voice of rare tonal beauty, a Billy Budd rather than a Boris. His pronunciation is a little odd at times – something more noticeable in a version which has the singers feigning familiarity with four languages – but you may not see this as a problem. Tempos are perceptibly more 'extreme' than Haitink's, with the opening "De profundis" dangerously slow in the modern manner and a strikingly well-characterized instrumental contribution to "A la Santé" ("In the Santé Prison"). The fillers, larger than life, brilliantly dispatched and curiously inappropriate, are based on original quartet pieces which only came to light in the mid-1980s. The first shares material with *Lady Macbeth of Mtsensk*; the second appears as the polka from *The Age of Gold*! This is nevertheless a more rewarding, more probingly conducted disc than most of the current Shostakovich crop.

Shostakovich (arr. Derevianko)[a] Symphony No. 15 in A major, Op. 141. **Schnittke** Praeludium in memoriam Dmitri Shostakovich. **Gidon Kremer** (vn); [a]**Clemens Hagen** (vc); [a]**Vadim Sakharov** (pf/celesta); [a]**Michael Gärtner,** [a]**Edgar Guggeis,** [a]**Peter Sadlo** (perc). DG Ⓕ 449 966-2GH (47 minutes: DDD: 6/97). Recorded 1995.

While the last of Shostakovich's symphonies has chamber-like qualities, it is also acutely imagined in terms of orchestral sonority, so much so that you may be somewhat taken aback. Viktor Derevianko's arrangement of the Fifteenth is by no means unsympathetic – it would appear to have had the blessing of the composer – but it cannot have been easy to find aural equivalents for the densely scored climaxes of the slow movement and finale. Certainly these passages no longer stand out from the rest as they do in the original work. Nor do the snatches of Wagner which open that finale have anything like their original emotive force: there's no getting away from the fact that quotations from *The Ring* sound incongruous on piano. On the other hand, Derevianko's skeleton exposes the nub of the argument in a way that may prove instructive for those who prize Shostakovich above all as a manipulator of symphonic form. And what a relief to encounter a properly articulated percussion pattern at the close. There are some implausibly tinny moments along the way, but much of the music-making is spellbinding, and one is struck again and again by the players' unerring sensitivity. There are few performances of the orchestral score that embody so many convincing interpretative decisions. The finale's massive non-peroration is evidently as taxing for Kremer as it is for an orchestral string section. Elsewhere, technical standards (whether of playing or recording) are beyond reproach. The Schnittke makeweight is equally well served; it is one of his more effective lamentations, concise as well as deeply felt. Notwithstanding the short measure, this package is recommended to adventurous spirits.

Shostakovich String Quartets. **Fitzwilliam Quartet** (Christopher Rowland, Jonathan Sparey, vns; Alan George, va; Ioan Davies, vc). Decca Ⓑ 455 776-2LC6 (six discs: 377 minutes: ADD: 6/92). Items marked [a] from L'Oiseau-Lyre DSLO31 (3/79); [b]DSLO28 (6/78), [c]DSLO23 (11/77), [d]DSLO29 (12/78), [e]DSLO11 (4/76), [f]DSLO30 (2/79), [g]DSLO9 (12/75). Recorded 1975-1977.
Gramophone classical 100.   ⒼⒼⒼ
No. 1 in C major, Op. 49[a]; No. 2 in A major, Op. 68[a]; No. 3 in F major, Op. 73[b]; No. 4 in D major, Op. 83[c] (*Gramophone Award Winner 1977*); No. 5 in B flat major, Op. 92[d]; No. 6 in G major, Op. 101[d]; No. 7 in F sharp minor, Op. 108[d]; No. 8 in C minor, Op. 110[e]; No. 9 in E flat major, Op. 117[f]; No. 10 in A flat major, Op. 118[f]; No. 11 in F minor, Op. 122[b]; No. 12 in D flat major, Op. 133[c] (*Gramophone Award Winner 1977*); No. 13 in B flat minor, Op 138[g]; No. 14 in F sharp minor, Op. 142[g]; No. 15 in E flat minor, Op. 144[e].

If Shostakovich's cycle of 15 symphonies can be said to represent a musical thread passing through the whole of the composer's public life, then it can be argued that his cycle of 15 string quartets represents the private persona of the man behind the mask, from the beginning of his personal anguish in the late-1930s, until his death in 1975. At the time of his First Quartet, composed in 1938, he was already an experienced and respected composer with five symphonies to his credit as well as much music for stage and film. Thenceforth his symphonic music inscrutably presented the emotions – albeit largely ironically – that the State expected from its leading composer, while the quartets provided an outlet for the emotions within and for his personal responses to the events taking place in the world around him. If the music is rich in irony, then the language that Shostakovich uses is remarkably straightforward with a defined tonality, simple melodies, uncluttered rhythms and clear textures. Yet, there is only one possible composer, so recognizably individual is the voice. At the same time, the music is full of allusions – the motif D-E flat-C-B based on his initials DSCH is now common knowledge, as are the autobiographical self-quotations in the Eighth Quartet. But there are other recurring fingerprints – melodic motifs, rhythmic patterns, harmonic progressions – the secrets of which are perhaps known only to a handful of Shostakovich's oldest and closest friends. If they were ever to be revealed, then we would have a much more complete picture of Shostakovich the man.

The Fitzwilliam Quartet recorded their cycle originally in the mid-1970s, shortly after a concentrated period of study with the composer. Despite being recorded in analogue, the sound quality is still remarkably good. They have a remarkable understanding of the idiom and of the music's underlying motivation. In the First Quartet they capture the uneasy mood (reminiscent of the contemporary Fifth Symphony) behind the seemingly placid surface. In the Fourth Quartet, they give the Jewish idioms – a metaphor for the oppressed artist and never far away in Shostakovich's music – a more deliberate, and thus more natural-sounding, tempo. Probably the best known of the quartets is No. 8, composed in Dresden in 1960 and dedicated to the victims of Fascism and of the War, and in view of the constant use of the DSCH motif and the quotations from several of his own pieces, there can be little doubt that Shostakovich considered himself among their number. It's a grim, often macabre, work and, once again they capture the loneliness of the composer. So often, his solo melodies, set against a stark and sombre accompaniment, sound like a voice crying in the wilderness. The quartets are well worth getting to know and the performances by the Fitzwilliam Quartet, despite being 23 years old, still seem to reach the heart of the composer's intentions.

Shostakovich String Quartets. **Shostakovich Quartet** (Andrei Shishlov, Sergei Pishchugin, vns; Alexander Galkovsky, va; Alexander Korchagin, vc). Olympia Ⓕ OCD531/5 (five discs, oas: 77, 78, 74, 78 and 73 minutes: ADD: 9/94). Recorded 1978-1985.
OCD531 – No. 1 in C major, Op. 49; No. 3 in F major, Op. 73; No. 4 in D major, Op. 83. Two Pieces for String Quartet (1931). *OCD532* – No. 2 in A major, Op. 68; No. 5 in B flat major, Op. 92; No. 7 in F sharp minor, Op. 108. *OCD533* – No. 6 in G major, Op. 101; No. 8 in C minor, Op. 110; No. 9 in E flat major, Op. 117. *OCD534* – No. 10 in A flat major, Op. 118; No. 11 in F minor; No. 15 in E flat minor. *OCD535* – No. 12 in D flat major; No. 13 in B flat minor;   Ⓖ No. 14 in F sharp major.

Any attempt to rank these players in relation to their more widely acclaimed opposite numbers in the Borodin Quartet seems pointless at this level of dedication; both teams have lived through this most extraordinary of twentieth-century quartet-cycles many times. If any general observation about the two can be made, it is that the Borodins find more corporate subtleties and passing shades in some of the earlier quartets, while the individual members of the Shostakovich Quartet make even stronger, more vibrant soloists. In the context of Shostakovich's many, very vocal solos and recitatives, it hardly seems invidious to single out the first violinist, Andrei Shishlov – dark, powerful and flawless of intonation throughout. Listen to his sleight-of-hand freedom in the unaccompanied melody of No. 6's finale: the Borodins' Mikhail Kopelman doesn't begin to touch imagination like that. These players also teach us to hold in equal awe the more classically contained quartets – No. 6 and the outer movements of No. 10 have a special grace – and all the slow movements are impressively unfolded with a steady fluency (notable in the passacaglias). As for the last rites of No. 15, not even the Borodins find such implicit human warmth in the still fugato of the Elegy. In tandem with the impassioned solos of the later movements, it's an impressive summing-up of this team's best intentions. Balances in the earlier recordings are less than kind to second fiddle and cellist and are uncomfortably boxy. You'll also have to adjust the volume-level for consecutive listening. If you seek only a single-disc token of the achievement, Vol. 4 (featuring Quartets Nos. 10, 11 and 15) is the one to have.

Additional recommendations ...
...Nos. 1-15. **Borodin Quartet.** Melodiya Ⓜ 74321 40711-2 (six discs: DDD).
...Nos. 4, 8 and 11. **Coull Quartet.** ASV Ⓕ CDDCA631 (64 minutes: DDD: 4/89).
...No. 8. *Coupled with works by various composers.* **Kronos Quartet.**
   Elektra Nonesuch Ⓕ 7559-79242-2 (62 minutes: DDD: 4/91).
   See review in the Collections section; refer to the Index.   ⒼⒼ
...Nos. 2 and 12. **Eder Quartet.** Naxos Ⓢ 8 550975 (61 minutes: DDD: 4/97).
...Nos. 3 and 5. **Eder Quartet.** Naxos Ⓢ 8 550974 (60 minutes: DDD: 4/97).
...No. 3. *Coupled with string quartets by* **Haydn** *and* **Schumann** Allegri Quartet. Naim Audio Ⓕ NAIMCD016 (73 minutes: DDD: 4/98). *See review under Haydn; refer to the Index.*
...No. 14. **Van Vlijmen** Trimurti, trittico per quartetto d'archi. **Schönberg Quartet.**
   Attacca Babel Ⓕ BABEL9786 (62 minutes: DDD: 5/98).

Shostakovich String Quartets – No. 1 in C major, Op. 49; No. 15 in E flat minor, Op. 144.
   Borodin Quartet (Mikhail Kopelman, Andrei Abramenkov, vns; Dmitri Shebalin, va; Valentin Berlinsky, vc). Teldec Ⓕ 4509-98417-2 (53 minutes: DDD: 2/97). Recorded 1995.
The point of coupling Shostakovich's first and last string quartets is obvious, and the contrast between what the composer himself called his "Springtime Quartet" and the unprecedented sequence

of six slow movements written months before his death could not be more poignant. The performances take full account of this contrast, not only in sheer amplitude of gesture (the single-note crescendos in the second movement of the Fifteenth Quartet are scorching) but also in command of scale: the desolation of the Fifteenth's opening movement, as long as all four of the First put together, is unrelieved, but it is never for one moment monotonous. There are big gestures even in the First Quartet, but these players have the tonal range to encompass an almost naïve sweetness in its second movement as well. The recordings are very fine.

Shostakovich String Quartets – No. 4 in D major, Op. 83; No. 11 in F minor, Op. 122; No. 14 in F sharp major, Op. 142. **Hagen Quartet** (Lukas Hagen, Rainer Schmidt, vns; Veronika Hagen, va; Clemens Hagen, vc). DG Ⓕ 445 864-2GH (71 minutes: DDD: 9/95). Recorded 1993-1994.

The Hagens have chosen a fascinating journey to the unusual at-one-with-the-world radiance that ends the Fourteenth. Already in this interpretation of the Fourth we hear those voices from beyond the grave that trouble the later quartets. The introspective shading of the *Andantino*'s earlier stages, climax included, sounds as if the mutes are already on. And when in fact the players do take them up – for the rest of the movement and the whole of the ensuing *Allegretto* – the sound becomes even more refined; note how first violin Lukas Hagen sings out his solo at fig. 29 (track 2, 3'31") with a frail, unearthly beauty which sounds as if it emanates from a viola d'amore. Corporate work is faultlessly and subtly in sympathy with the essence of the piece; the only individual weakness occurs when Shostakovich asks the cellist to come to the fore in the finale's build-up of tension – Clemens Hagen's tone doesn't really make itself felt here – though the collective *fortissimo* cry from the heart shortly afterwards makes amends with even more intensity than some of the Hagen's senior counterparts (including the Shostakovich Quartet on Olympia) have previously found there. Clemens does rather lack the presence to take the lead in Quartet No. 14, dedicated to the cellist of the Beethoven Quartet, and emphasizing his role accordingly; the sound can be lovely, but right at the start he has the misfortune to be echoed by his more characterful brother. Still, the F sharp major ending is as implicitly moving as it can be, and joint string power in crises comes very close to the genuine Russian article. Indeed, in the fifth-movement *Humoresque* of the Eleventh the limelighted second violin – Rainer Schmidt, the quartet's febrile and ever-impressive outside influence – brings so much forceful tone to the swelling of his two repeated notes that it sounds for all the world as if two violins are playing in unison, not just the one. Again, the joint approach to chants and combats, not to mention Lukas's extraordinary handling of the *glissandos* in the second movement, bring an urgently vocal quality to the work.

Shostakovich String Quartet No. 8 in C minor, Op. 110.
Schnittke String Quartet No. 2.
Tchaikovsky String Quartet No. 1 in D major, Op. 11. **Duke Quartet** (Louisa Fuller, Rick Koster, vns; John Metcalfe, va; Ivan McCready, vc). Collins Classics Ⓕ 1450-2 (70 minutes: DDD: 2/96). Recorded 1995.

Shostakovich has 15 String Quartet masterpieces to choose from, none of which is either 'early' or musically insubstantial; but because the Eighth has historical-political connotations – it does tell a story – it tends to be the most often recorded; the others tend to get ignored, at least outside of recorded or live cycles. The Duke Quartet 'go for the jugular', especially in the three *Largos*: the second in particular yields a handsome body of tone while the sudden ray of light at 3'44" has real pathos. The only minor reservation concerns the *Allegretto*, which sounds just a mite too cheerful for the ghostly, cynical statement that it is. Placing Schnittke's Second Quartet directly after Shostakovich's Eighth was a stroke of genius, especially as its opening harmonies seem to echo the D-S-C-H motif that closes the earlier work. Schnittke's piece incorporates a frenzied *Agitato* (with wild arpeggios to the fore), a prayer-like *Mesto* and an intense *Moderato* finale that retreats among ethereal harmonics. It is a very powerful piece; the programme ends with Tchaikovsky's classically proportioned First Quartet. Here the Duke Quartet's phrasing is somewhat fussy, especially in the first movement, and there are also some uncomfortable tempo relations. Still, the last two movements are sprightly enough, the recordings are good and the whole adds up to a programme that is certainly worth hearing – especially for the sake of the Shostakovich and the Schnittke.

Shostakovich Piano Quintet in G minor, Op. 57ᵃ. Piano Trio No. 2 in E minor, Op. 67.
Elisabeth Leonskaja (pf); **Borodin Quartet** (Mikhail Kopelman, ᵃAndrei Abramenkov, vns; ᵃDmitri Shebalin, va; Valentin Berlinsky, vc). Teldec Ⓕ 4509-98414-2 (63 minutes: DDD: 2/97). Recorded 1995.   Ⓖ

The Piano Quintet is almost symphonic in its proportions, lasting some 35 minutes and has been popular with audiences ever since its first performance in 1940. Much of its popularity stems from Shostakovich's highly memorable material, particularly in the boisterous and genial *Scherzo* and finale movements. Because of the presence of a piano and of the powerful emotions expressed in them the Quintet and Trio are commonly given very big performances indeed. Those on this recording are by no means small, but they are chamber music, and that seems to be the view of the pianist as well as the string players. The finale of the Piano Trio actually gains in power from this, the greatest weight of tone being reserved for the true climax, and half the intensity of the Quintet, in this reading, comes from a remarkably wide and masterfully controlled range of sonority and dynamic: note how very gradually the fugal second movement acquires warmth and how the poignant "Intermezzo" gains pathos from the delicate clashes of the piano line. Leonskaja is a superb partner in both works, and no mere visiting soloist but a born chamber player. The recordings are very fine, with the balance just right in both works.

Additional recommendations ...

...Piano Quintet. **Britten** String Quartet No. 1 in D major, Op. 25. [a]**Clifford Benson** (pf); **Alberni Quartet.** CRD Ⓕ CRD3351 (57 minutes: DDD: 3/89).

...Piano Quintet[a]. Piano Trio No. 2 in E minor, Op. 67. [a]**Eugene Drucker** (vn); [a]**Lawrence Dutton** (va); **Beaux Arts Trio** (Isidore Cohen, vn; Peter Wiley, vc; Menahem Pressler, pf). Philips Ⓕ 432 079-2PH (57 minutes: DDD: 8/91).

...Piano Quintet. **Franck** Piano Quintet in F minor. **Victor Aller** (pf); **Hollywood Quartet.** Testament mono Ⓕ SBT1077* (67 minutes: ADD: 5/96).

...Piano Trio No. 2. **Tchaikovsky** Piano Trio in A minor, Op. 50. **Vadim Repin** (vn); **Dmitry Yablonsky** (vc); **Boris Berezovsky** (pf). Erato Ⓕ 0630-17875-2 (67 minutes: DDD: 1/98).

Shostakovich plays Shostakovich Symphony No. 10 in E minor, Op. 93 (arr. pf duet)[a]. The Gadfly – Guitars (arr. cpsr). Preludes, Op. 34 (arr. Tsyganov)[b] – No. 10 in C sharp minor; No. 15 in D flat major; No. 16 in B flat minor; No. 24 in D minor. [b]**Leonid Kogan** (vn); **Dmitri Shostakovich,** [a]**Moishei Vainberg** (pfs). Revelation Ⓕ RV70002* (55 minutes: ADD: 2/98). Recorded 1954-1956. Ⓖ

Shostakovich plays Shostakovich Preludes and Fugues, Op. 87 – No. 16 in B flat minor[a]; No. 17 in A flat major[c]; No. 18 in F minor[c]; No. 20 in C minor[b]; No. 22 in G minor[b]; No. 23 in F major[a]; No. 24 in D minor[b]. Three Fantastic Dances, Op. 5[c]. **Dmitri Shostakovich** (pf). Revelation Ⓕ RV70003 (65 minutes: ADD: 2/98). Items marked [a] recorded live in 1951, [b]1952, [c]1956. Ⓖ

To all those Shostakovich collectors who missed the duet version of the Tenth Symphony in one of its previous incarnations, its reappearance will be self-recommending. The piano itself may be out of tune, the ensemble imperfect, the tempos prone to rush in the excitement of the moment, and the piece itself occasionally sounds threadbare without its orchestral garb. But there is something undeniably moving about hearing the composer and his friend (the latter only a few months after his release from prison) as though in your own room, introducing a brand new and as yet unapproved masterpiece. This impression is reinforced by the dry, close recording. There is an unmistakable single-minded intensity in the playing too. Passages such as the end of the first movement (with the two piccolos in Shostakovich's orchestration) have a hollowed-out soulfulness which has the ring of authenticity, while the *Scherzo* is faster than any on record except for Ančerl and the Czech Philharmonic on a long-unavailable LP. The remainder of this disc is negligible stuff although with some beautiful playing from Kogan.

The solo disc is anything but that. Shostakovich is on top pianistic form, with beauty of tone, subtlety of balance and (for the most part) patient phrasing, all in abundance. Compositionally these are exercises in concentration – in the sense not so much of economy as of sustained thought, probing the purest of musical ideas for their potential. Time and again you can sense the first movement of the Tenth Symphony waiting in the wings; in the C minor Prelude and Fugue it is the first movement of the Eleventh Symphony that beckons. This world of pure contrapuntal thought was one Shostakovich stepped into with as much relief, gratitude and awe as other composers found in religious composition. When the final page of the D minor fugue builds up through an ecstatic *accelerando* eventually to encompass the entire keyboard range it is like witnessing the exaltation of a man born again through music. There are some oddities. At 6'35" in the B flat minor Fugue, for instance, Shostakovich misreads the rhythm in the left hand, notices his mistake, and re-plays the beat correctly. As with the previous Revelation disc of Preludes and Fugues there is a slight fuzz around each note, presumably as a result of some noise elimination process.

Shostakovich Piano Sonatas – No. 1, Op. 12; No. 2 in B minor, Op. 61. Five Preludes. 24 Preludes, Op. 34. **Colin Stone** (pf). Olympia Ⓜ OCD574 (79 minutes: DDD: 6/96). Recorded 1995.

Shostakovich's Five Preludes from student days are not otherwise currently available, and Colin Stone is to be congratulated for including these gauche but attractive pieces rather than the ubiquitous *Fantastic Dances*. Indeed his playing is well prepared throughout and the recording quality is as clean as his playing; the piano itself sounds pretty well ideally regulated. What you won't find is the wildness of the First Sonata, where Stone has gone for clarity rather than the impossibly frenetic metronome marks. Nor do the Op. 34 Preludes rival Mustonen (listed below) for point and characterization; some listeners may actually prefer the steadier approach to the impulsive Finn's shock tactics. Colin Stone offers an admirably sane view, then, and the expense of buying anything better is considerable. There is certainly a lot more to this music than sanity, but this survey can still be confidently recommended to anyone looking for a single-disc supplement to the Preludes and Fugues.

Additional recommendations ...

...24 Preludes, Op. 34. **Alkan** 25 Préludes dans les tons majeurs et mineur, Op. 31. **Olli Mustonen** (pf). Decca Ⓕ 433 055-2DH (76 minutes: DDD: 10/91). *Gramophone Award Winner 1992. See review under Alkan; refer to the Index.*   ⒼⒼ

...24 Preludes, Op. 34. **Scriabin** 24 Preludes, Op. 11. **Artur Pizarro** (pf).
Collins Classics Ⓕ 1496-2 (68 minutes: DDD: 11/97). *Gramophone Editor's choice.*
See review under Scriabin; refer to the Index.

Shostakovich 24 Preludes and Fugues, Op. 87. **Tatyana Nikolaieva** (pf). Melodiya
Ⓕ 74321 19849-2 (three discs: 168 minutes: DDD: 2/95). Recorded 1987.　　　　ⒼⒼ
Tatyana Nikolaieva was in at the birth of Shostakovich's Preludes and Fugues, and she made them
one of the cornerstones of her repertoire. But you don't need to know those facts in order to sense
the authority and insight of her interpretations. She gives the three-hour cycle a wonderful over-
arching sense of unity, of an unbroken voyage of exploration. That may not have been the composer's
intention (he actually spoke out specifically against such a view of the work), but there are plenty of
indications in the structure and character of his music to justify Nikolaieva's approach. Her
recordings of the complete Preludes and Fugues are undoubtedly the finest monuments to a much
lamented artist. It is truly sad that her playing was not fully appreciated in the West until so late in
her career. Not that her performances on the Hyperion set are seriously flawed, but Hyperion's
recorded sound is seriously over-resonant and distantly balanced and this is music which lives or dies
by its clarity. By contrast the Melodiya acoustic is a fraction too close and dry, but still greatly
preferable. It gives space for the music to breathe rather than suffocating it with unwanted stage-mist;
and it enables many more of Nikolaieva's nuances to register. So the first choice is the Melodiya
version. Owners of the Hyperion set without unlimited budgets may nevertheless feel that the more
essential supplement is Richter's peerless accounts of six of them.
Additional recommendations ...
...**Tatyana Nikolaieva** (pf). Hyperion Ⓕ CDA66441/3 (three discs: 166 minutes: DDD: 3/91).
Gramophone Award Winner 1991.　　　　　　　　　　　　　　　　　　　　　　　Ⓖ
...24 Preludes and Fugues – No. 4 in E minor; No. 12 in G sharp minor; No. 14 in E flat major;
No. 15 in D flat major; No. 17 in A flat major; No. 23 in F major. *Coupled with work by*
Prokofiev and **Scriabin** Sviatoslav Richter (pf).
Philips Ⓕ 438 627-2PH2 (two discs: 152 minutes: DDD: 8/94).　　　　　　　　　ⒼⒼ
...24 Preludes and Fugues – No. 1 in C major; No. 5 in D major; No. 24 in D minor.
Coupled with works by **Chopin** and **Mozart** Emil Gilels (pf).
Testament mono Ⓕ SBT1089* (64 minutes: ADD: 5/97).

Shostakovich Preludes and Fugues, Op. 87 – No. 1 in C major; No. 2 in A minor; No. 3 in
G major; No. 4 in E minor; No. 5 in D major; No. 6 in B minor; No. 7 in A major; No. 8 in
F sharp minor; No. 12 in G sharp minor; No. 13 in F sharp major; No. 14 in E flat minor.
Dmitry Shostakovich (pf). Revelation mono Ⓜ RV70001* (61 minutes: ADD: 7/97).
Recorded 1952. *Gramophone Editor's choice.*　　　　　　　　　　　　　　　　ⒼⒼⒼ
Here is an inspiring collection, with more of Shostakovich's Prelude and Fugue performances than
have ever been brought together on one disc, in superbly remastered recordings. Shostakovich never
made any secret of his fallibility as a pianist, and the faster fugues in particular are scrambly, in a way
that suggests not legitimate impetuosity but straightforward pianistic anxiety. But the slips and spills
pale into insignificance beside the sheer authority and character of the playing. The C major Prelude
immediately takes us into the pure, sane world that betokens the composer's escape from
mundaneness into the higher reality of music, probably the purest he had ever composed (the opening
of the First String Quartet, also in C major, has something of the same feeling). The A minor Prelude
has a 'Rustle of Spring'-like impressionist character not even the redoubtable Nikolaieva could
emulate. And so it goes on. The slower pieces are especially wonderful – intensely sustained and
coloured with subtle, dark, emotional shadings unmatched by other pianists. The long sinking to rest
of the F sharp minor Fugue is nothing short of masterly, and its massive five-part major-mode
counterpart has an immensely moving, timeless *gravitas*. The stoical inwardness of the G sharp minor
Prelude is an object-lesson in how to perform a Shostakovich passacaglia – relevant to conductors as
well as pianists. A most important issue.

Shostakovich From Jewish Folk Poetry, Op. 79ª. The New Babylon – suite (arr. Rozhdestvensky).
ªTatyana Sharova (sop); ªLudmila Kuznetsova (mez); ªAlexei Martynov (ten); Russian State
Symphony Orchestra / Valéry Polyansky. Chandos Ⓕ CHAN9600 (70 minutes: DDD: 6/98).
Text and translation included. Recorded 1995 and ª1996.
This recording of Shostakovich's song-cycle *From Jewish Poetry* is first-rate. For a start Polyansky's
three vocal soloists are uncommonly well chosen: the light, youthful, slightly vulnerable soprano, the
rich, world-weary mezzo and the ardent but unheroic tenor are ideally suited to the texts Shostakovich
cunningly chose, to convey his solidarity with mass suffering. Polyansky sets spacious tempos which
allow every nuance of that suffering to register, and his orchestra are responsive and idiomatic in
colouring. The recording, by Russian engineers, feels almost too good to be true in its excessive
warmth; otherwise this version is easily preferable to the rival Rozhdestvensky on RCA. Polyansky's
choice of the first of Shostakovich's 35 or so film scores makes for a more than welcome coupling.
Polyansky offers an admirably idiomatic version of the Suite. He is especially adept at choosing
timbres to reflect mood and situation. Even if you don't know the story-line the music was designed
to accompany, this performance is so vividly characterized it can hardly fail to engage you.

Additional recommendation ...

...From Jewish Folk Poetry. **B. Fleischmann** Rothschild's Violin (orch. Shostakovich). **Soloists; Rotterdam Philharmonic Orchestra / Gennadi Rozhdestvensky.** RCA Victor Red Seal
Ⓕ 09026 68434-2 (66 minutes: DDD: 4/97). *See review under Fleischmann; refer to the Index.*

Shostakovich Six Romances on Japanese Poems, Op. 21[a]. Six Poems of Marina Tsvetayeva, Op. 143[b]. Suite on Verses of Michelangelo, Op. 145[c]. [b]**Elena Zaremba** (contr); [a]**Ilya Levinsky** (ten); [c]**Sergei Leiferkus** (bar); **Gothenburg Symphony Orchestra / Neeme Järvi.**
DG Ⓕ 447 085-2GH (71 minutes: DDD: 1/96). Texts and translations included. Recorded 1994.
Leiferkus has recorded nothing finer than this rightly daunting interpretation of the *Suite on Verses of Michelangelo*, Shostakovich's greatest, most monolithic song-cycle – equal first if you include the Fourteenth Symphony. One should never underestimate Leiferkus's sheer vocal beauty of line and sheen in the superb declamatory settings of "Dante" and its companion-piece hymn to the exiled poet (parallels with Solzhenitsyn were inescapable in 1974); nor is there that lack of a deeper understanding elsewhere in the cycle sometimes sensed in previous recordings by Leiferkus. As for the orchestral playing, the shadowy chords underpinning the earlier songs and punctuating the wonderful exchange of verses between Strozzi and Michelangelo on the sculptor's sleep in "Night" are carefully projected with all the infinite atmosphere one has come to expect from Järvi's rapport with his supremely resonant Gothenburg strings. The similar mood of the near-contemporary Tsvetayeva settings, no less profound in their reflection on creativity and the State, make a perfect coupling for the *Michelangelo* Suite. Zaremba, a true contralto, is another great Russian voice – very impressive indeed, like Leiferkus, in majestic declamation, but more distractingly loud (and her up-front role in the recording doesn't help) when she should be withdrawn. That is also true of the tenor, Ilya Levinsky in the *Romances on Japanese Poems*. A dark sidelight on *Lady Macbeth of the Mtsensk District*, the plangent aspect of the sequence is best served when Levinsky plays respectively the rejected and the unrequited lovers of the fourth and the fifth songs. Investigate the first two cycles to check the vocal progress of two fine young Russian singers; but don't miss Leiferkus's *Michelangelo* Suite.

Further listening ...

...Ballet Suites (arr. Atovmyan) – No. 1; No. 3. Jazz Suites – No. 1; No. 2. **Frankfurt Radio Symphony Orchestra / Dmitri Kitaienko.** RCA Victor Red Seal 09026 68304-2 (10/97).
...Hamlet, Op. 116*a*[b] – Introduction; Ball at the palace; The ghost; The poisoning; The players; Duel and death of Hamlet. *Coupled with works by* **Kabalevsky** and **Miaskovsky National Philharmonic Orchestra / Bernard Herrmann.** Unicorn-Kanchana Souvenir UKCD2066 (2/95). *See review under Kabalevsky; refer to the Index.*
...Incidental Music – Hamlet, Op. 32; King Lear, Op. 58*a*. **Louise Winter** (mez); **David Wilson-Johnson** (bar); **City of Birmingham Symphony Orchestra / Mark Elder.** Cala CACD1021 (1/96).
...Suites – New Babylon[a]; The Golden Hills[b]. [a]**Moscow Philharmonic Orchestra;** [b]**USSR Ministry of Culture Symphony Orchestra / Gennadi Rozhdestvensky.** Russian Disc RDCD11064 (5/95).
...Cello Sonata in D minor, Op. 40[a]. *Coupled with* **Rachmaninov** Cello Sonata in G minor, Op. 19[b]. **Daniil Shafran** (vc); [b]**Yakov Flier, Dmitri Shostakovich**[a] (pfs). Revelation mono RV10017* (10/96).
...Concertino, Op. 94. *Coupled with works by various composers.* **Duo Reine Elisabeth.** Koch International Classics DICD920150 (11/94).
...Viola Sonata, Op. 147[a]. *Coupled with works by* **Bartók** and **Stravinsky Raphael Hillyer** (va); [a]**Reinbert de Leeuw** (pf). Koch Schwann 311612 (5/95).
...Hypothetically Murdered, Op. 31*a* (reconstructed McBurney). Five Fragments, Op. 42. Suite No. 1 for Jazz Band. Four Songs, Op. 46[a] (No. 4 orch. McBurney). [a]**Dmitri Kharitonov** (bass); **City of Birmingham Symphony Orchestra / Mark Elder.** Cala United CACD1020 (1/94).
...The Gamblers (cptd. K. Meyer). **Soloists; North-West German Philharmonic Orchestra / Mikhail Yurovsky.** Capriccio 60 062-2 (6/95).
...Lady Macbeth of the Mtsensk District. **Soloists; Ambrosian Opera Chorus; London Philharmonic Orchestra / Mstislav Rostropovich.** EMI CDS7 49955-2 (5/90).   ⒼⒼ
...Moscow, Cheryomushki. **Soloists; Russian State Symphonic Cappella; The Hague Residentie Orchestra / Gennadi Rozhdestvensky.** Chandos CHAN9591 (4/98).

Jean Sibelius
Finnish 1865-1957

Sibelius Violin Concerto in D minor, Op. 47[a]. Serenade in G minor, Op. 69 No. 2[a]. En saga, Op. 9. [a]**Julian Rachlin** (vn); **Pittsburgh Symphony Orchestra / Lorin Maazel.** Sony Classical Ⓕ SK53272 (60 minutes: DDD: 6/94). Recorded 1992. *Gramophone Editor's choice.*   Ⓖ
Sibelius Violin Concerto in D minor, Op. 47.
Tchaikovsky Violin Concerto in D major, Op. 35. **Kyung-Wha Chung** (vn); **London Symphony Orchestra / André Previn.** Decca The Classic Sound Ⓜ 425 080-2DCS (66 minutes: ADD: 5/95). From SXL6493 (11/70). Recorded 1970.   Ⓖ
Julian Rachlin was only 18 when he made his recording and here he is in one of the most challenging of concertos, whose difficulties he takes easily in his stride. He has consistent beauty of tonal colour,

a pure silvery tone with intonation to match, and possesses the aristocratic quality this music calls for. He is technically flawless – stunning in fact – and his eloquence is unfailingly persuasive: for example, the beautifully articulate way in which he echoes the questioning phrase in the slow movement (track 2, 2'34"). The tiny mannerisms in which he indulges would not inhibit a placing alongside such classics as Oistrakh and Perlman. Certainly his artistry and sensitivity place him securely among the finest players of the day. The G minor *Serenade* is quintessential Sibelius. It has a poignant, wistful melancholy all its own, and there are few pieces which more keenly evoke the magic of the white nights of the Scandinavian summer. Rachlin, coming as he does from the Baltic, though he left Lithuania when he was six, would understand all that. Lorin Maazel's *En saga* is a straight, often very fast, but thoroughly atmospheric account of the score. The recording is splendidly balanced. Outstanding.

If the vital test for a recording is that a performance should establish itself as a genuine one, not a mere studio run-through, Chung's remains a disc where both works are made to leap out at you in concentration and vitality, not just through the soloist's weight and gravity, expressed as though spontaneously, but through the playing of the LSO under Previn at a vintage period. The great melodies of the first two movements of the Sibelius are given an inner heartfelt intensity rarely matched, and with the finale skirting danger with thrilling abandon. Chung's later Montreal version of the Tchaikovsky is rather fuller-toned with the tiny statutory cuts restored in the finale. Yet the very hint of vulnerability amid daring, a key element in Chung's magnetic, volatile personality, here adds an extra sense of spontaneity. This remains breathtaking playing, and the central slow movement, made to flow without a hint of sentimentality, has an extra poignancy. The Kingsway Hall sound, full and sharply focused, gives a sense of presence to match or outshine today's digital recordings.

Sibelius Violin Concerto in D minor, Op. 47. Two Serenades, Op. 69. Humoresque in D minor, Op. 87 No. 1. **Anne-Sophie Mutter** (vn); **Staatskapelle Dresden / André Previn.**
DG Ⓕ 447 895-2GH (49 minutes: DDD: 3/96). Recorded 1995. *Gramophone Editor's choice.* Ⓖ
The power and intensity of Mutter's performance of the concerto emerges immediately in the opening phrases. Where most violinists treat them as a deep meditation, Mutter with comparable intensity makes them tougher than usual, using momentarily a vibratoless tone, slightly steely, establishing this more clearly as an *Allegro moderato* first movement rather than a lyrical slow one. Even if one misses some of the raptness of Mullova or Chung, it is a very valid view, and the power of the reading is reinforced by the relatively close balance of the solo instrument. Not that her reading lacks inner qualities, for despite the close balance the opening of the slow movement finds Mutter playing in rapt meditation on a half-tone. In the middle of the movement she expands in romantic warmth before returning finally to the most intense *pianissimo*. Her timing for the finale is even faster than Perlman's, with power again the keynote, and as in the earlier movements Previn proves a most sympathetic, bitingly effective partner. The all-Sibelius coupling is apt if (at 49 minutes) hardly generous. On any count Mutter clearly establishes all three pieces as far more than just salon Sibelius, with Previn and the orchestra, beautifully recorded, relishing the atmospheric and original colourings.

Additional recommendations ...
...Violin Concerto. **Sinding** Suite for Violin and Orchestra, Op. 10, "In alten Stil". **Itzhak Perlman** (vn); **Pittsburgh Symphony Orchestra / André Previn.** EMI Ⓕ CDC7 47167-2 (ADD: 9/85).
...Violin Concerto. **Tchaikovsky** Violin Concerto in D major, Op. 35. **Viktoria Mullova** (vn); **Boston Symphony Orchestra / Seiji Ozawa.** Philips 416 821-2PH (67 minutes: DDD: 5/87).
...Violin Concerto[a]. **Brahms** Violin Concerto in D major, Op. 77[b]. **Ginette Neveu** (vn); **Philharmonia Orchestra /** [a]**Walter Susskind,** [b]**Issay Dobrowen.** EMI Références mono Ⓜ CDH7 61011-2* (70 minutes: ADD: 3/88). Ⓖ
...Violin Concerto (original 1903-04 version and final 1905 version). **Leonidas Kavakos** (vn); **Lahti Symphony Orchestra / Osmo Vänskä.** BIS Ⓕ CD500 (75 minutes: DDD: 4/91). *Gramophone Award Winner 1991. Selected by Sounds in Retrospect.*
...Violin Concerto. **Brahms** Violin Concerto. **Tasmin Little** (vn); **Royal Liverpool Philharmonic Orchestra / Vernon Handley.** EMI Eminence Ⓜ CD-EMX2203 (72 minutes: DDD: 2/93). *See review under Brahms; refer to the Index.* Ⓖ
...Violin Concerto. **Beethoven** Violin Concerto in D major, Op. 61. **David Oistrakh** (vn); **Stockholm Festival Orchestra / Sixten Ehrling.** Testament mono Ⓕ SBT1032* (75 minutes: ADD: 7/94). Ⓖ
...Violin Concerto. **Tchaikovsky** Violin Concerto in D major, Op. 35. **Vadim Repin** (vn); **London Symphony Orchestra / Emmanuel Krivine.** Erato Ⓕ 4509-98537-2 (67 minutes: DDD: 5/96).
...Violin Concerto[a]. Karelia Suite, Op. 11. Belshazzar's Feast – suite, Op. 51. [a]**Pekka Kuusisto** (vn); **Helsinki Philharmonic Orchestra / Leif Segerstam.** Ondine Ⓕ ODE878-2 (65 minutes: DDD: 5/96).
...Violin Concerto. **Nielsen** Violin Concerto, Op. 33. **Maxim Vengerov** (vn); **Chicago Symphony Orchestra / Daniel Barenboim.** Teldec Ⓕ 0630-13161-2 (70 minutes: DDD: 9/96).

Sibelius Finlandia, Op. 26. Karelia Suite, Op. 11. Tapiola, Op. 112. En Saga, Op. 9. **Philharmonia Orchestra / Vladimir Ashkenazy.** Decca Ovation Ⓜ 417 762-2DM (63 minutes: DDD: 12/88). Recorded 1980-1985.

More than 30 years separate *En Saga* and *Tapiola*, yet both works are quintessential Sibelius. The latter is often praised for the way Sibelius avoided 'exotic' instruments, preferring instead to draw new and inhuman sounds from the more standard ones; and the former is, in many ways, just as striking in the way Sibelius's orchestration evokes wind, strange lights, vast expanses and solitude. Both works suggest some dream-like journey: *En Saga* non-specific though derived from Nordic legend; *Tapiola* more of an airborne nightmare in, above and around the mighty giants of the Northern forests inhabited by the Green Man of the Kalevala, the forest god Tapio (the final amen of slow, bright major chords brings a blessed release!). Ashkenazy's judgement of long term pacing is very acute; the silences and shadows are as potent here as the wildest hurricane. And Decca's sound allows you to visualize both the wood and the trees: every detail of Sibelius's sound world is caught with uncanny presence, yet the overall orchestral image is coherent and natural. In addition, his *Finlandia* boasts some of the most vibrant and powerful brass sounds on disc.

Additional recommendations ...

...Finlandia. Pelleas and Melisande. *Coupled with works by* **Liszt** and **Smetana**
  Berlin Philharmonic Orchestra / Herbert von Karajan.
  DG Digital Masters Ⓜ 445 550-2GMA (70 minutes: DDD: 9/83).
...Karelia Suite. The maiden in the tower. **Soloists; Gothenburg Concert Hall Chorus and**
  Symphony Orchestra / Neeme Järvi. BIS Ⓕ CD250 (DDD: 3/85).
...Finlandia (arr. H. Fricker). *Coupled with works by various composers.* **Christopher Herrick** (org).
  Hyperion Ⓕ CDA66676 (75 minutes: DDD). *See review in the Collections section;*
  refer to the Index.
...Tapiola. Pohjola's Daughter, Op. 49. Rakastava, Op. 14. Andante lirico. **Gothenburg Symphony**
  Orchestra / Neeme Järvi. BIS Ⓕ CD312 (56 minutes: DDD: 6/87).
...Finlandia. Karelia Suite. En Saga. The Swan of Tuonela. Tapiola. Luonnotar, Op. 70ª.
  ªElisabeth Söderström (sop); **Philharmonia Orchestra / Vladimir Ashkenazy.**
  Decca Ovation Ⓜ 430 757-2DM (73 minutes: DDD: 7/93).
...Finlandia. Karelia Suite. Tapiola. Valse triste, Op. 44 No. 1. Legends, Op. 22 – No. 2, The Swan
  of Tuonela. Scènes historiques, Op. 25 – No. 3, Festivo. **Berlin Philharmonic Orchestra /**
  Hans Rosbaud. DG The Originals mono Ⓜ 447 453-2GOR* (62 minutes: ADD: 8/96).

Sibelius Six Humoresques, Opp. 87 and 89ª. Two Serenades, Op. 69ª. Two Pieces, Op. 77ª.
Overture in E major. Ballet scene. ªDong-Suk Kang (vn); **Gothenburg Symphony Orchestra /**
Neeme Järvi. BIS Ⓕ CD472 (62 minutes: DDD: 2/91). Recorded 1989.

The music for violin and orchestra here is marvellously rewarding and gloriously played. The six *Humoresques*, Opp. 87 and 89 come from the same period as the Fifth Symphony, at a time when Sibelius was toying with the idea of a second violin concerto, and some of the material of the *Humoresques* was possibly conceived with a concerto in mind. Sibelius wrote that these radiant pieces convey something of "the anguish of existence, fitfully lit up by the sun", and behind their outward elegance and charm, there is an all-pervasive sadness. This is even more intense in the *Serenades*, which are glorious pieces and quintessential Sibelius. Dong-Suk Kang is an outstanding player. His impeccable technique and natural musical instinct serve this repertoire well and he seems to have established an excellent rapport with Järvi and the Gothenburg orchestra. The two fill-ups are juvenilia and are only intermittently characteristic. The Overture is very much in his *Karelia* idiom, though they are of undoubted interest to all Sibelians. The recording up to BIS's usual high quality.

Sibelius Kullervo, Op. 7. **Marianne Rørholm** (contr); **Jorma Hynninen** (bar); **Helsinki University**
Chorus; Los Angeles Philharmonic Orchestra / Esa-Pekka Salonen. Sony Classical Ⓕ SK52563   Ⓖ
(70 minutes: DDD: 7/93). Text and translation included. Recorded 1992.
Sibelius Kullervo, Op. 7. **Monica Groop** (sop); **Jorma Hynninen** (bar); **Polytech Choir;**
Finnish Radio Symphony Orchestra / Jukka-Pekka Saraste. Finlandia Ⓕ 0630-14906-2
(69 minutes: DDD: 9/96). Text and translation included. Recorded 1996.

Sibelius's *Kullervo* was the symphonic poem-cum-symphony with which he made his breakthrough in Finland in 1892. Common to all recordings, including Salonen's, is the magisterial presence of Jorma Hynninen. Salonen keeps a firm grip on the proceedings and maintains a real sense of momentum throughout. Moreover, temptations to dwell on beauty of incident or to indulge in expressive emphasis are resisted, and this extraordinary piece is all the more telling as a result. The dramatic force of the central scena is vividly realized and both Marianne Rørholm and Jorma Hynninen are impressive – as indeed are the male voices of the Finnish chorus. An impressive performance, and the orchestral playing and recording are absolutely first class. On the Finlandia disc Hynninen's voice is still commanding though less youthful than previously. Monica Groop is on fine form and the choral singing is very good, though not as perfectly focused as the Estonian and Helsinki University Choirs are for Berglund on EMI. However, Saraste sets the right tempos and gets exactly the right spirit. This music unfolds with an inexorable forward movement and Saraste really sees to it that it does. In the fourth movement, "Kullervo goes to battle", he feels (and is) far faster and more characterful than Berglund, though the EMI recording is better ventilated with more space round the sound. The Finlandia does not have quite enough front-to-back perspective and is a bit bottom heavy. But never mind, it is still more than acceptable and the performance is so strongly communicative and its sense of commitment is so strong that it is worth the extra outlay.

Additional recommendations ...
...**Eeva-Liisa Saarinen** (mez); **Jorma Hynninen** (bar); **Estonian State Academic Male Choir; Helsinki University Male Choir; Helsinki Philharmonic Orchestra / Paavo Berglund.** EMI Matrix Ⓜ CDM5 65080-2 (72 minutes: DDD: 7/94).
...**Soile Isokoski** (sop); **Raimo Laukka** (bar); **Danish National Radio Choir and Symphony Orchestra / Leif Segerstam.** Chandos Ⓕ CHAN9393 (76 minutes: DDD: 3/96).

Sibelius Legends, Op. 22, "Lemminkäinen Suite". Tapiola, Op. 112. **Helsinki Philharmonic Orchestra / Leif Segerstam.** Ondine Ⓕ ODE852-2 (70 minutes: DDD: 7/96). Recorded 1995.
The four *Legends* first began to surface in Sibelius's mind in 1893, at the same time as he was working on his *Kalevala* opera, *The Building of the Boat*, the prelude to which became "The swan of Tuonela". (It is not the only thing from the opera that found its way into the *Legends*. The lovely A minor idea for muted strings in the middle section of "Lemminkäinen in Tuonela" is also among the sketches, where Sibelius scribbled over it the words, "the Maiden of Death". In the opera she would have rowed Väinämöinen across the river to Tuonela. In the tone-poem she symbolizes the very opposite, the loving mother whose ministrations return Lemminkäinen to life.) In 1954 Sibelius reversed the order of the inner movements so that "The swan" preceded "Lemminkäinen in Tuonela". Perversely Segerstam disregards the composer's wishes and places them in the old order. To be fair, there is a case for this order in that you otherwise have two highly dramatic pieces ("Lemminkäinen in Tuonela" and "Lemminkäinen's Homeward Journey") placed alongside each other, and in any event we can readily forgive him this liberty since most CD players enable the listener to play them as Sibelius proscribed. Segerstam gets very good results from the Helsinki orchestra who respond with a keen enthusiasm that is inspiriting. The performance is free from excessive mannerisms and his account of *Tapiola* is very impressive. He tellingly evokes the chilling terrors and the awesome majesty of the Nordic forest.

Sibelius Luonnotar, Op. 70[a]. Karelia Suite, Op. 11. Andante festivo. The Oceanides, Op. 73. King Christian II, Op. 27 – Suite. Finlandia, Op. 26. [a]**Soile Isokoski** (sop); **Gothenburg Symphony Orchestra / Neeme Järvi.** DG Ⓕ 447 760-2GH (72 minutes: DDD: 6/96). Text and translation included. Recorded 1992-1995.
This CD offers the *Karelia* and *King Christian II* suites, both from the 1890s, together with outstanding accounts of two of the strangest and most haunting masterpieces of Sibelius's maturity, *Luonnotar* and *The Oceanides*. Of special interest is *Luonnotar*, which tells of the creation of the world as related in Finnish mythology and was written for the legendary Aino Ackté. Not surprisingly, perhaps, it places cruel demands on the soloist both in terms of tessitura and dynamics. Soile Isokoski is magnificent and possesses an impressive accuracy both in intonation and dynamics above the stave. Järvi gets an excellent response from his fine Gothenburg players and tellingly conveys the atmosphere and mystery of this extraordinary score. James Hepokoski's excellent note speaks of it as "unlike anything else in the entire repertoire" – which indeed it is! What a wonderfully evocative score *The Oceanides* is, and what an atmospheric, and indeed magical account, we have here. The performances of the *Karelia* and *King Christian II* suites are not quite in this class but they are enjoyable, and the recording is quite exemplary.
Additional recommendation ...
...*Luonnotar*[a]. Legends, Op. 22. Nightride and Sunrise, Op. 55. [a]**Solveig Kringelborn** (sop); **Royal Stockholm Philharmonic Orchestra / Paavo Järvi.** Virgin Classics Ⓕ VC5 45213-2 (63 minutes: DDD: 12/96).

Sibelius Pelleas and Melisande – Incidental Music, Op. 46. Swanwhite, Op. 54 – The Harp; The Maiden with the Roses; The Prince Alone; Swanwhite and the Prince; Song of Praise. King Christian II – Incidental Music, Op. 27[a]. [a]**Sauli Tiilikainen** (bar); **Iceland Symphony Orchestra / Petri Sakari.** Chandos Ⓕ CHAN9158 (79 minutes: DDD: 7/93). Text and translation included. Recorded 1992. *Gramophone Editor's choice.* Ⓖ
These performances are natural and unaffected and radiate immense care and pleasure in music-making. The *King Christian II* music includes "The Fool's Song", complete with soloist, and very good he is too, and a short "Minuet". Petri Sakari's performance is totally unaffected, plain and full of enthusiasm; the players sound as if they are enjoying this score and communicate their pleasure. Phrasing is attentive, musical through and through but never fussy. The *Pelleas and Melisande* is a version many collectors would want to have. It is imaginative, totally musical, strong on atmosphere and observant of dynamic subtleties. There may be readers who might find some of the tempos on the slow side; they are unhurried, but in context they feel right. Unfortunately there is only room for five movements from the *Swanwhite* music. All are beautifully played; every detail is allowed to take its time and the phrasing, though attentive, is free of the slightest taint of narcissism. Let "Swanwhite and the Prince" serve as an example of how well thought out and natural in feeling the phrasing is! Added to this, the Chandos recording is beautifully transparent, warm and well detailed.

Sibelius The Tempest – Incidental Music, Op. 109 (from Philips ABR4045, 12/55)[a]. Scènes historiques: Op. 25 – No. 3, Festivo; Op. 66 (both from Columbia 33C1018, 11/53)[a]. Karelia Suite, Op. 11 – No. 1, Intermezzo; No. 3, Alla marcia (HMV DB6248. Recorded 1945)[b]. Finlandia, Op. 26 (Columbia LX704, 4/38)[c]. [a]**Royal Philharmonic Orchestra;** [b]**BBC Symphony**

Orchestra; [c]London Philharmonic Orchestra / Sir Thomas Beecham. EMI Beecham Edition mono Ⓜ CDM7 63397-2* (73 minutes: ADD: 7/90). Recorded 1938-1955. ❻❻❻

Sibelius Symphonies – No. 4 in A minor, Op. 63[a] (from HMV DB3351/5, 3/38); No. 6 in D minor, Op. 104[b] (DB6640/42, 6/50). The Tempest – Incidental Music, Op. 109: Prelude[a] (DB3894, 12/39). Legends, Op. 22 – Lemminkäinen's return[a] (DB3355/6, 3/38). The bard, Op. 64[a] (DB3891, 12/39). [a]London Philharmonic Orchestra; [b]Royal Philharmonic Orchestra / Sir Thomas Beecham. EMI Beecham Edition mono Ⓜ CDM7 64027-2* (79 minutes: ADD: 3/92). Recorded 1937-1947. ❻❻❻

One of the special things about Beecham's Sibelius was its sheer sonority: there was a fresh, vernal sheen on the strings quite different from the opulence of Koussevitzky or Karajan but with all their flexibility and plasticity of phrasing, and a magic that is easier to discern than define. Suffice it to say that his feeling for atmosphere in Sibelius was always matched by a strong grip on the architecture. His 1956 recording of the two suites from *The Tempest* enjoys legendary status and is pure magic. The 1952 performances of four of the *Scènes historiques* have that similar ring of authenticity that transcend any sonic limitations. Beecham's stark account of the Fourth Symphony carries special authority since it was done after a long correspondence with the composer; and the 1947 RPO performance of the Sixth enjoyed Sibelius's imprimatur. The Prelude to *The Tempest* is as chillingly realistic as *Lemminkäinen's return* is exciting.

Additional recommendations ...

...Legends. **Gothenburg Symphony Orchestra / Neeme Järvi.**
BIS Ⓕ CD294 (49 minutes: DDD: 6/86).

...Scènes historiques – Suite No. 1, Op. 25; Suite No. 2, Op. 66. **Gothenburg Symphony Orchestra / Neeme Järvi.** BIS Ⓕ CD295 (56 minutes: DDD: 1/87).

...Legends. Luonnotar, Op. 70[a]. The bard. [a]**Phyllis Bryn-Julson** (sop); **Scottish National Orchestra / Sir Alexander Gibson.** Chandos Collect Ⓜ CHAN6586 (62 minutes: ADD: 11/92).

...Rakastava. Scènes historiques, Opp. 25 and 66. Valse lyrique. **Scottish National Orchestra / Sir Alexander Gibson.** Chandos Collect Ⓜ CHAN6591 (54 minutes: ADD: 11/93).

Sibelius The Wood-Nymph, Op. 15. The Wood-Nymph (melodrama)[a]. A lonely ski-trail[a]. Swanwhite, Op. 54 – incidental music (original version). [a]**Lasse Pöysti** (narr); **Lahti Symphony Orchestra / Osmo Vänskä.** BIS Ⓕ CD815 (62 minutes: DDD: 6/96). Recorded 1996. *Selected by Soundings.*

Although most Sibelians will know of the tone-poem, *The Wood-Nymph*, they will not have heard it, as the score has remained in Helsinki University Library. It opens very much in *Karelia* mode, and as one might expect, inhabits much the same world as the *Lemminkäinen Legends*. Though it is less developed than the 1892 *En Saga*, let alone the *Legends* in their definitive form, it still bears the characteristic Sibelian hallmarks. The present disc gives us an opportunity to put it alongside the melodrama of the same name, scored for speaker, horn, strings and piano. This is a setting of the mainland-Swedish poet, Viktor Rydberg, best known in the Sibelius context for *Autumn Evening* ("Höstkväll"). The tone-poem which was given a month after the première of the melodrama follows much the same basic layout, though the chamber music-like texture offers numerous felicities. Not content with these interesting novelties, the CD also gives us two other works new to the catalogue, another short melodrama, *A lonely ski-trail* to words by Bertel Gripenberg, which in its piano form comes from 1925 and which Sibelius scored for harp and strings as late as 1948, a short, slight and atmospheric piece; and above all, the complete incidental music to Strindberg's *Swanwhite*. The score runs to some 30 minutes and is full of that special light and sense of space characteristic of *Pelléas et Mélisande*. The playing of the Lahti orchestra under Osmo Vänskä is excellent and the recording, too, is very fine: spacious, well detailed and refined. Obviously a self-recommending issue which no Sibelian should miss.

Sibelius Symphonies – No. 1 in E minor, Op. 39[a]; No. 7 in C major, Op. 105[b]. Karelia Overture, Op. 10[c]. **London Symphony Orchestra / Anthony Collins.** Beulah mono Ⓕ 1PD8* (62 minutes: ADD: 6/94). Item marked [a] from Decca LXT2694 (8/52), [b]LXT2940 (12/54), [c]LW5209 (3/56). Recorded 1952-1955. ❻

Sibelius Symphonies – No. 2 in D major, Op. 43[a]; No. 6 in D minor, Op. 104[b]. **London Symphony Orchestra / Anthony Collins.** Beulah mono Ⓕ 2PD8* (69 minutes: ADD: 6/94). Item marked [a] from Decca LXT2815 (10/53), [b]LXT5084 (11/55). Recorded 1953-1955. ❻

Sibelius Symphony No. 3 in C major, Op. 52[a]. Pohjola's Daughter, Op. 49[b]. Pelleas and Melisande[c] – No. 2, Melisande; No. 6, Pastorale; No. 7, At the spinning wheel; No. 8, Intermezzo; No. 9, Death of Melisande. Nightride and Sunrise, Op. 55[d].
London Symphony Orchestra / Anthony Collins. Beulah mono Ⓕ 3PD8* (68 minutes: ADD: 6/94). Item marked [a] from Decca LXT2960 (12/54), [b]LXT2962 (12/54), [c]LXT5084 (11/55), [d]LXT5083 (10/55). Recorded 1954-1955. ❻

The name Anthony Collins (1893-1963) probably doesn't mean a great deal to the majority of younger readers, but for quite a few serious Sibelius *aficionados* his 1950s Decca recordings hold cult status. In these transfers the original recordings are revealed for the fine achievements they were: beautifully balanced, clear and vivid, allowing us to hear these performances in intimate detail – which is how they deserve to be heard. Collins is a first-rate musical landscape-painter. He doesn't just give us the bold sweeping brush-strokes, important as they are; he shows how the landscapes team with minute life. Rustling string textures aren't blandly homogenized – tiny details catch the ear, and then vanish again. Woodwind bird calls or horn calls can be acutely expressive – some passages remind one of Sibelius's comments about quasi-human voices in the nature sounds around his forest-home. But exaggeration is alien to the Collins approach. Nothing is forced, almost everything is fresh and vital, and it isn't only in the symphonies that the Collins touch is refreshing. *Pohjola's Daughter* comes to life as effectively as the symphonies, and Vol. 3 contains a real rarity, an entirely satisfactory *Nightride and Sunrise*.

Additional recommendation ...
...Pohjola's Daughter. *Coupled with works by various composers.* **Boston Symphony Orchestra / Serge Koussevitzky.** Dutton Laboratories mono Ⓜ CDAX8015* (75 minutes: ADD: 1/97).

Sibelius Symphonies – No. 1 in E minor, Op. 39 (from 414 534-1DH, 5/86); No. 2 in D major, Op. 43 (SXDL7513, 11/80); No. 3 in C major, Op. 52 (414 267-1DH, 8/85); No. 4 in A minor, Op. 63 (SXDL7517, 5/81); No. 5 in E flat major, Op. 82 (SXDL7541, 1/82); No. 6 in D minor, Op. 104 (414 267-1DH, 2/85); No. 7 in C major, Op. 105 (SXDL7580, 8/83).
Philharmonia Orchestra / Vladimir Ashkenazy. Decca Ⓜ 421 069-2DM4 (four discs: 232 minutes: ADD/DDD: 12/87). Recorded 1980-1996.

Of all the cycles of Sibelius's symphonies recorded during recent years this is one of the most consistently successful. Ashkenazy so well understands the thought processes that lie behind Sibelius's symphonic composition just as he is aware, and makes us aware, of the development between the Second and Third Symphonies. His attention to tempo is particularly acute and invariably he strikes just the right balance between romantic languor and urgency. The Philharmonia play for all they are worth and possess a fine body of sound. The recordings are remarkably consistent in quality and effectively complement the composer's original sound-world.

Additional recommendations ...
...Nos. 1-3. Luonnotar, Op. 70[a]. Pohjola's Daughter, Op. 49. [a]**Phyllis Curtin** (sop);
New York Philharmonic Orchestra / Leonard Bernstein.
Sony Classical Bernstein Royal Edition Ⓜ SM2K47619 (two discs: 129 minutes: ADD).
...Nos. 4-7. **New York Philharmonic Orchestra / Leonard Bernstein.**
Sony Classical Bernstein Royal Edition Ⓜ SM2K47622 (two discs: 122 minutes: ADD).
...Nos. 4 and 5. **San Francisco Symphony Orchestra / Herbert Blomstedt.**
Decca Ⓕ 425 858-2DH(68 minutes: DDD: 7/91).   Ⓖ
...Nos. 1-7. The Oceanides. Kuolema – Scene with cranes. Nightride and Sunrise, Op. 55.
City of Birmingham Symphony Orchestra; Philharmonia Orchestra / Sir Simon Rattle.
EMI Ⓜ CMS7 64118-2 (four discs: 267 minutes: DDD: 2/92).   Ⓖ
...Nos. 1-7. **Vienna Philharmonic Orchestra / Lorin Maazel.**
Decca Ⓑ 430 778-2DC3 (three discs: 212 minutes: ADD: 2/92).   Ⓖ
...Nos. 4 and 6. **City of Birmingham Symphony Orchestra / Sir Simon Rattle.**
EMI Ⓜ CDM7 64121-2 (67 minutes: DDD: 2/92).   ⒼⒼ
...Nos. 4 and 6[a]. The Tempest: Prelude. Legends – Lemminkaïnen's return. The bard.
London Philharmonic Orchestra; [a]Royal Philharmonic Orchestra / Sir Thomas Beecham.
EMI mono Ⓜ CDM7 64027-2* (79 minutes: ADD: 3/92).   ⒼⒼ
...Nos. 1 and 3. **Philharmonia Orchestra / Paul Kletzki.**
Testament mono Ⓕ SBT1049* (63 minutes: ADD: 4/95).
...No. 7[a]. Pelleas and Melisande – No. 2, Melisande[a]; No. 4, Spring in the park[b]; No. 8, Intermezzo[b]; No. 9, Death of Melisande[b]. The Tempest – incidental music, Op. 109[b]: Prelude; The oak-tree; Humoresque; Caliban's Song; Berceuse; Prospero; Miranda. Scènes historiques, Op. 25 – Festivo[b]. In memoriam, Op. 59[b]. Legends, Op. 22 – Lemminkäinen's return[b].
[a]**New York Philharmonic Orchestra, [b]London Philharmonic Orchestra / Sir Thomas Beecham.**
Dutton Laboratories mono Ⓜ CDAX8013* (76 minutes: ADD: 7/95).
...Nos. 1-7. Karelia Overture. Pohjola's Daughter. Pelleas and Melisande – Melisande; Pastorale; At the spinning wheel; Intermezzo; Death of Melisande. Nightride and Sunrise.
London Symphony Orchestra / Anthony Collins.
Beulah mono Ⓜ 1-4PD8* (four discs: 258 minutes: ADD: 4/97).

Sibelius Symphony No. 1 in E minor, Op. 39. Karelia Suite, Op. 11. Finlandia, Op. 26.
Oslo Philharmonic Orchestra / Mariss Jansons. EMI Ⓕ CDC7 54273-2 (62 minutes: DDD: 1/92).
Recorded 1990.   Ⓖ

Jansons's account of the First Symphony is thrilling. It has excitement and brilliance without exaggerations. Tempos throughout are just right, the phrasing breathes naturally and the sonority is excellently focused. Jansons never presses on too quickly but allows each phrase, each musical sentence to register so that the listener feels borne along on a natural currrent. Moreover, excitement is not whipped up but arises naturally from the music's forward momentum. The Oslo Philharmonic are a highly responsive orchestra of no mean virtuosity and they play with a splendid intensity and fire not only in the symphony but also the *Karelia Suite* and *Finlandia* which sound very fresh. All the artistic decisions in this reading seem to be right and the orchestral playing further enhances the high renown this ensemble now enjoys. Very good recording too.

Additional recommendations ...

...No. 1. **Vienna Philharmonic Orchestra / Leonard Bernstein.**
DG 435 351-2GH (41 minutes: DDD: 4/92).
...Nos. 1 and 4. **Vienna Philharmonic Orchestra / Lorin Maazel.**
Belart Ⓑ 461 325-2 (69 minutes: ADD: 2/97).

Sibelius Symphonies – No. 1 in E minor, Op. 39; No. 4 in A minor, Op. 63. **London Symphony Orchestra / Sir Colin Davis.** RCA Victor Red Seal Ⓕ 09026 68183-2 (78 minutes: DDD: 1/97). Recorded 1994. *Gramophone Award Winner 1997.*   ⒼⒼ
Sir Colin Davis takes us completely inside the Fourth Symphony – we become part of it and feel we inhabit it. It is arguably the finest and most powerful reading of the work to have emerged since the days of Karajan. It was always one of the triumphs of his Boston survey on Philips. Along with the 1937 Beecham and the 1966 Berlin Philharmonic Karajan sets the Colin Davis was one of the most inward and searching readings committed to disc. We are not long – indeed barely a few bars – into the first movement before we realize that we are in a totally different world from most other interpretations. There is a far greater sense of breadth but it is in terms of imaginative insight that Davis scores. What is there to say of his First save that it, too, has an excitement, a sense of immediacy and authenticity of feeling that is equally convincing. This is Sibelius conducting of real stature and the LSO respond with total commitment. RCA provide a first-rate recording. .
Additional recommendation ...
...Nos. 1 and 4. **Lahti Symphony Orchestra / Osmo Vänskä.**
BIS Ⓕ CD861 (76 minutes: DDD: 9/97). *Selected by Soundings.*   Ⓖ

Sibelius Symphonies – No. 1 in E minor, Op. 39; No. 7 in C major, Op. 105. **San Francisco Symphony Orchestra / Herbert Blomstedt.** Decca Ⓕ 444 541-2DH (62 minutes: DDD: 5/96). Recorded 1993-1994.
This performance of the Seventh is magisterial and majestic Sibelius without a trace of interpretative egotism. It is built up with real feeling for balance and proportion and as a whole, the reading is powerful and marvellously controlled, with no want of dignity or nobility. The First Symphony is among the best to have appeared in recent years. We have not been short of good versions in recent years – Ashkenazy and the Philharmonia, Jansons and the Oslo Philharmonic and Bernstein and the Vienna Philharmonic to name only three. Blomstedt admits no concessions to the gallery; we are given this symphony with plenty of fire and no lack of virtuosity on the part of the San Francisco players. Here we get Sibelius straight and unadorned. The sound is faithful and well balanced.

Sibelius Symphonies – No. 2 in D major, Op. 43; No. 6 in D minor, Op. 104. **London Symphony Orchestra / Sir Colin Davis.** RCA Victor Red Seal Ⓕ 09026 68218-2 (73 minutes: DDD: 12/95). Recorded 1994.
The eloquent polyphony, purity of utterance and harmony of spirit give the Sixth Symphony a special place in the canon. Sibelius's mastery enables him to move with a freedom so complete that the musical events are dictated by their own inner necessity. And in Davis's hands this music unfolds with a freedom and naturalness that are totally convincing. As Sibelius said of the Fourth Symphony, this is music "with nothing of the circus about it", and in this reading there is no playing to the gallery. There is no playing to the gallery either in Sir Colin's account of the Second Symphony. He views the work as a whole and does not invest detail with undue expressive vehemence at its expense, but strikes just the right balance between the nationalist-romantic inheritance on the one side and the classical power of Sibelius's thinking on the other. The first movement has dignity and breadth, and as with Karajan, the pacing of climaxes is magisterial. The recording has splendid presence and space.
Additional recommendations ...
...No. 2. Romance in C major, Op. 42. **Gothenburg Symphony Orchestra / Neeme Järvi.**
BIS Ⓕ CD252 (48 minutes: DDD: 10/84).
...No. 6. Pelleas and Melisande. **Gothenburg Symphony Orchestra / Neeme Järvi.**
BIS Ⓕ CD237 (DDD: 10/84).
...No. 2. **Berlin Philharmonic Orchestra / Herbert von Karajan.**
EMI Studio Ⓜ CDM7 69243-2 (48 minutes: ADD: 4/88).
...Nos. 2, 5 and 7. Swanwhite – The Maidens with roses. Tapiola. Pohjola's Daughter.
Boston Symphony Orchestra; BBC Symphony Orchestra / Serge Koussevitzky.
Pearl mono Ⓕ GEMMCDS9408* (two discs: 125 minutes: AAD: 7/90).   Ⓖ
...No. 4. The Tempest – Suite No. 1. **Danish National Radio Symphony Orchestra / Leif Segerstam.**
Chandos Ⓕ CHAN8943 (65 minutes: DDD: 8/91).
...Nos. 2 and 3. **City of Birmingham Symphony Orchestra / Sir Simon Rattle.**
EMI Ⓜ CDM7 64120-2 (51 minutes: DDD: 2/92).
...No. 2. Finlandia. Karelia Suite. **Philharmonia Orchestra / Vladimir Ashkenazy.**
Decca Headline Ⓑ 430 737-2DM (72 minutes: DDD: 8/92).
...No. 2. Tapiola. Kuolema – Valse triste. **San Francisco Symphony Orchestra / Herbert Blomstedt.**
Decca Ⓕ 433 810-2DH (69 minutes: DDD: 3/93).   Ⓖ
...No. 2. The Swan of Tuonela. Kuolema – Valse triste. Andante festivo for Strings.
Oslo Philharmonic Orchestra / Mariss Jansons. EMI Ⓕ CDC7 54804-2 (61 minutes: DDD: 7/93).

...No. 2. Romance in C major, Op. 42. Kuolema – Valse triste. Finlandia. **Boston Symphony Orchestra / Vladimir Ashkenazy.** Decca Ⓕ 436 566-2DH(65 minutes: DDD: 10/93).
...No. 2. Finlandia, Op. 26. Valse triste, Op. 44 No. 1. The Swan of Tuonela. **Boston Symphony Orchestra / Sir Colin Davis.** Philips Solo Ⓜ 442 389-2PM (69 minutes: ADD: 9/94).
...Nos. 2 and 7. **Philadelphia Orchestra / Eugene Ormandy.** Sony Classical Ⓑ SBK53509* (66 minutes: ADD: 9/94).
...Nos. 2 and 3. **Lahti Symphony Orchestra / Osmo Vänskä.** BIS Ⓕ CD862 (76 minutes: DDD: A/97).

Sibelius Symphonies – No. 3 in C major, Op. 52; No. 5 in E flat major, Op. 82. **London Symphony Orchestra / Sir Colin Davis.** RCA Victor Red Seal Ⓕ 09026 61963-2 (61 minutes: DDD: 3/95). Recorded 1992. Ⓖ
Some 20 years have passed since Davis's last Sibelius cycle, with the Boston Symphony Orchestra for Philips. Generally speaking Sir Colin's version of the Third has greater breadth and sense of scale than his previous account or any other. His first movement has a majestic stride and great power; and he has the measure of the slow movement's pantheistic musings. The Fifth is more tautly held together than before; the first movement moves forward and onwards with a powerful feeling of inevitability and purpose. The transition in the first movement to the scherzo section is masterly. Listening to this disc, one wonders anew at the sheer originality of this piece, and that is, of course, the touchstone of a great performance. Sir Colin Davis understands Sibelius as do few others and senses the vital currents that flow through these symphonies, and the LSO know this and respond with playing of distinction. The recording is in every way first-class, vivid in detail and truthful in perspective.
Additional recommendations ...
...Nos. 4 and 5. **Philharmonia Orchestra / Vladimir Ashkenazy.** Decca 430 749-2DM (65 minutes: DDD).
...No. 3. King Christian II, Op. 27 – excerpts. **Gothenburg Symphony Orchestra / Neeme Järvi.** BIS Ⓕ CD228 (DDD: 10/84).
...Nos. 5 and 6. **Berlin Philharmonic Orchestra / Herbert von Karajan.** DG Galleria Ⓜ 439 982-2GGA (69 minutes: ADD: 1/95).
...Nos. 3 and 5. **Oslo Philharmonic Orchestra / Mariss Jansons.** EMI Ⓕ CDC5 55533-2 (58 minutes: DDD: 5/96).
...Nos. 3 and 6. **San Francisco Symphony Orchestra / Herbert Blomstedt.** Decca Ⓕ 448 817-2DH (60 minutes: DDD: 11/96).

Sibelius Symphonies – No. 3 in C major, Op. 52[a]; No. 5 in E flat major, Op. 82[b]. March of the Finnish Jaeger Battalion, Op. 91 No. 1[c]. [ab]**London Symphony Orchestra;** [b]**Helsinki Philharmonic Orchestra / Robert Kajanus.** Koch Historic mono Ⓜ 37133-2* (62 minutes: ADD: 2/94).
Item marked [a] from HMV DB1980/83 (1/34), [b]DB1739/42 (recorded 1932), [c]Danish HMV X2825 (1928). Recorded 1928-1933. *Gramophone classical 100.* ⒼⒼⒼ
Finlandia have already reissued all Kajanus's London recordings on a three-disc set. Their edition contains transfers made by Anthony Griffith for World Records, issued in the 1970s, and they still sound very good indeed. Griffith had the advantage of working from original masters: Koch's Mark Obert-Thorn has been obliged to use commercial pressings and while he has obtained good sound, there is inevitably more background noise and an unevenness in the quality which is not present in Finlandia's transfers. However, Koch have scored an important point by including Kajanus's only Sibelius recording with his own Helsinki orchestra. The piece itself is perhaps the composer's weakest, but the performance has great historical importance, for it is played by an orchestra with which Sibelius had close links, and under a conductor who was his chosen interpreter. We can hear clearly just why Sibelius admired Kajanus so much in the two symphonies here. At the age of 76 he was still able to generate a good deal of tension and energy in the LSO's playing, yet there is a particular sense of balanced, logical music-making, a seemingly natural authority in the phrasing and an apparent inevitability in the way he unfolds the composer's symphonic argument. Everything seems perfectly in place, and the music speaks to us in a very direct and compelling fashion.
Additional recommendation ...
...Nos. 1[a], 2[b], 3[c] and 5[d]. Belshazzar's Feast – suite, Op. 51[e]. Pohjola's Daughter, Op. 49[f]. Karelia Suite, Op. 11 – No. 1, Intermezzo[b]; No. 3, Alla marcia[a]. Tapiola, Op. 112[g]. [ab]**symphony orchestra,** [cdefg]**London Symphony Orchestra / Robert Kajanus.** Finlandia mono Ⓕ 4509-99963-2* (three discs: 186 minutes: ADD: 10/96).

Sibelius Symphonies – No. 4 in A minor, Op. 63[a]; No. 7 in C major, Op. 105[b]. Kuolema, Op. 44 No. 1 – Valse triste[c]. **Berlin Philharmonic Orchestra / Herbert von Karajan.** DG Galleria Ⓜ 439 527-2GGA (66 minutes: ADD: 5/94). Item marked [a] from SLPM138974 (6/66), [b]SLPM139032 (10/68), [c]SLPM139016 (3/68). Ⓖ
Karajan recorded the Fourth Symphony three times, once in the 1950s with the Philharmonia and twice with the Berlin Philharmonic. The work obviously meant a great deal to him. He insisted on its inclusion in his very first concert on his appointment at the Berlin Philharmonic in the early-1960s at a time when Sibelius's cause had few champions in Germany, so keen was he to stake its claim as one of the great symphonies of the day. Karajan's account has withstood the test of time as one of the

most searching, profound and concentrated performances of this masterpiece, and its reappearance at mid price was very welcome. The Seventh is finer than his earlier Philharmonia version but does not enjoy quite the same classic status. Karajan's *Valse triste* is wonderfully seductive. Indispensable!.
Additional recommendation ...
...No. 7. **Nielsen** Symphony No. 1 in G minor, FS16 **Copenhagen Philharmonic Orchestra / Okko Kamu.** Classico Ⓕ CLASSCD115 (52 minutes: DDD: 9/96).

Sibelius Symphony No. 5 in E flat major (original 1915 version). En Saga, Op. 9 (original 1892 version). **Lahti Symphony Orchestra / Osmo Vänskä.** BIS Ⓕ CD800 (58 minutes: DDD: 4/96). Recorded 1995. *Gramophone Editor's choice. Selected by Soundings.*
Gramophone Award Winner 1996.   ⒼⒼ
Every so often a CD appears which, by means of some interpretative insight, changes our view of a piece of music. This disc changes our whole perspective in a wholly different sense, for it gives us a glimpse of two familiar masterpieces in the making. Sibelius struggled with the Fifth Symphony for almost seven years from about 1912 until it reached its definitive form in 1919. Although the finished score of the first version does not survive, the orchestral material does, and thus it was not difficult to reconstruct the score. The 1915 score is now available to the public at large in dedicated performance. To study how the two scores differ is to learn something important about the creative process and it is this mystery that makes the disc imperative listening – and not just for Sibelians. The four-movement 1915 score has a more complex harmonic language than the final score and so it provides a missing link, as it were, between the Fourth Symphony and the definitive Fifth. The opening horn motive has yet to emerge, and the finale's coda has yet to acquire its original hammer-blow chords. And in between you will find that the various themes, some distinctly recognizable, others taking off in totally unexpected directions and charting unknown regions. Something of the cosmic feel of this music emerges in a letter Sibelius wrote in 1914, "God opens the door for a moment and his orchestra was playing the Fifth Symphony". Of course, Sibelius knew what he was doing, and in the 1919 version, he managed to keep the door open for rather longer! The version of *En Saga* with which we are familiar does not come between the *Kullervo* Symphony and the *Karelia* music but from 1901 between the First and Second Symphonies and was made for Busoni. The original offers fascinating material for comparison: there is a brief glimpse of Bruckner, whose work he had encountered in Vienna a year or two earlier, and the orchestral writing, though not always as polished as in the later version, still has flair. All praise to the Lahti orchestra and their fine conductor, and the excellent and natural balance.
Additional recommendations ...
...No. 5[a]. **Nielsen** Symphony No. 4, FS76, "The inextinguishable"[b]. Pan and Syrinx, FS87[b].
[a]**Philharmonia Orchestra;** [b]**City of Birmingham Symphony Orchestra / Sir Simon Rattle.** EMI Ⓜ CDM7 64737-2 (78 minutes: DDD: 11/93).   ⒼⒼ
...No. 5 (original and 1919 versions). **Lahti Symphony Orchestra / Osmo Vänskä.** BIS Ⓕ CD863 (68 minutes: DDD: 12/97).

Sibelius Symphony No. 7 in C major, Op. 105. Rakastava, Op. 14. En Saga, Op. 9. Kullervo, Op. 7[a]. [a]**Hillevi Martinpelto** (sop); [a]**Karl-Magnus Fredriksson** (bar); **London Symphony** [a]**Chorus and Orchestra / Sir Colin Davis.** RCA Victor Red Seal Ⓕ 09026 68312-2 (two discs: 138 minutes: DDD: 12/97). Text and translation included.   Ⓖ
Those who recall Sir Colin Davis's performance with the LSO of *Kullervo* at London's Barbican Centre in 1992 (subsequently televised) will not have forgotten its epic sweep and magisterial control. On record, Sir Colin's account brings us not only Sibelius's first essay in the form but also his last. The set also includes two other works conceived in the 1890s, *En Saga* and *Rakastava*. The latter is one of Sibelius's most affecting pieces. It is affectingly played, too, though Davis perhaps makes rather heavy weather of the last movement where the farewells seem to be overcharged and too protracted. In Sir Colin's hands the Seventh Symphony is by turns powerful, epic and serene, its climaxes expertly placed. But to turn to *Kullervo*: what works in the concert-hall may not make the same impression when heard in the intimacy of the home. First, let me say that the LSO play with refinement and spirit, and the London Symphony Chorus are responsive. They are excellent in the middle movement. The first movement is slower than than the Barbican performance yet after a few bars it seems exactly right. It is spacious and broad which underlines the Brucknerian feeling to the piece. The slow movement, "Kullervo's Youth", is splendidly characterized, as is the central "Kullervo and his Sister" movement. Karl-Magnus Fredriksson may not be quite as dark-toned as Hynninen (for Salonen), or the admirable Hillevi Martinpelto quite as authoritative as Isokowski (Segerstam) or Groop (Saraste), but they both acquit themselves well. The remaining two movements are paced with unerring judgement. Strangely enough, looking at the figures, Davis takes about ten minutes longer than such an *echt* Sibelian as Paavo Berglund and yet at no point does it feel it. It is puzzling that Sibelius should have entertained such strong doubts about *Kullervo* as to discourage performances during his lifetime. Sir Colin's excellently recorded performance reveals *Kullervo* as the great work it is.

Sibelius Kyllikki, Op. 41. Three Sonatinas, Op. 67. Two Rondinos, Op. 68. Piano Sonata in F major, Op. 12. Finlandia, Op. 26. **Marita Viitasalo** (pf). Finlandia Ⓕ 4509-98984-2 (69 minutes: DDD: 11/96). Recorded 1994.

This disc assembles some of the best of Sibelius's piano music – *Kyllikki* and the three *Sonatinas*, Op. 67. These pieces enjoyed the advocacy of Wilhelm Kempff and Glenn Gould among others, though Kempff never committed them to disc. Sibelius's countryman, the composer Selim Palmgren for whom the piano was a natural means of expression, wrote that "even in what for him were alien regions, [Sibelius] moves with an unfailing responsiveness to tone colour". It is false piety to include the transcription of *Finlandia*, made at a time when the piano arrangement served to disseminate music more widely, a function long since overtaken by the gramophone. Marita Viitasalo is an intelligent and sympathetic interpreter and the piano is very closely balanced.

Sibelius Five Pieces, Op. 81. Novelette, Op. 102. Five Danses champêtres, Op. 106. Four Pieces, Op. 115. Three Pieces, Op. 116. **Nils-Erik Sparf** (vn); **Bengt Forsberg** (pf). BIS Ⓕ CD625 (57 minutes: DDD: 5/95). Recorded 1993.

No one listening to this music would doubt that Sibelius had a special feeling for the violin. Whether he is composing lighter music such as the captivating "Rondino" from the Op. 81 set or the more substantial later pieces, such as the first of the *Danses champêtres*, which comes close to the world of *The Tempest*. Neither the Op. 115 nor the Op. 116 set contains great music but they are much finer than they have been given credit for. Both "On the heath" and the "Ballade", Nos. 1 and 2 of Op. 115 have an innocence that calls to mind the wonderful *Humoresques* for violin and orchestra. In particular "The Bells", Op. 115 No. 4 is a rather cryptic miniature and the "Scène de danse" of Op. 116, with its striking tonal juxtapositions, is a kind of Finnish equivalent of the Bartók *Romanian Dances*. Nils-Erik Sparf and Bengt Forsberg are dedicated and sensitive exponents who make the most of the opportunities this repertoire provides. The piano tone sounds a little thick at the bottom end of the spectrum, and the violin is by no means the dominant partner in the aural picture. This reservation is a small one and the performances are to be recommended with enthusiasm.

Sibelius King Christian II, Op. 27 – Fool's Song of the Spider. Five Christmas Songs, Op. 1. Eight Songs, Op. 57. Hymn to Thaïs. Six Songs, Op. 72 – No. 3, The kiss; No. 4, The echo nymph; No. 5, Der Wanderer und der Bach; No. 6, A hundred ways. Six Songs, Op. 86. The small girls. **Monica Groop** (mez); **Love Derwinger** (pf). BIS Ⓕ CD657 (66 minutes: DDD: 9/94). Texts and translations included. Recorded 1994.

Monica Groop, following her success in the Cardiff Singer of the World Competition, has had a busy career. Communication is her strength, and unevenness of line a relative weakness. Sibelius's songs are a rich and still undervalued part of the song repertoire. Still only four or five are really well known, and none of those is included here. Not all are of very special quality: the title is probably the best thing about the "Fool's Song of the Spider" (from *King Christian II*), and the *Hymn to Thaïs* gains interest through being Sibelius's only song in English rather than through intrinsic merit. Yet there are many delights here, including the closing waltz-song, *The small girls*. The acoustic is perhaps somewhat too reverberant but has plenty of presence.

Sibelius Songs, Volume 3. Seven Songs, Op. 13. Six Songs, Op. 50. Six Songs, Op. 90. The Wood Nymph. Belshazzar's Feast – The Jewish Girl's Song. Resemblance. A Song. Serenade. The Thought[a]. **Anne Sofie von Otter**, [a]**Monica Groop** (mezzos); **Bengt Forsberg** (pf). BIS Ⓕ CD757 (67 minutes: DDD: 4/96). Texts and translations included. *Gramophone Editor's choice.*   Ⓖ

The vast majority of Sibelius's songs are in Swedish, the language with which he grew up as a child, and here they are given by a distinguished native Swedish partnership. The *Seven Songs*, Op. 13, are all Runeberg settings and come from the composer's early years (1891-2). Best known, perhaps, are "Spring is flying" ("Våren flyktar hastigt") and "The dream" ("Drömmen"), but there are others, such as "The young hunter" ("Jägargossen"), that are no less delightful and characterful. The other Runeberg settings here, the *Six Songs*, Op. 90, come towards the end of Sibelius's career as a song composer (1917-18). "The north" ("Norden"), as in all the nature poetry of Runeberg, touches a very special vein of inspiration. Along with "Die stille Nacht" ("The silent city"), Op. 50 No. 5, which is equally affectingly given by these two artists – it is among his finest songs. Interest naturally focuses on the rarities. *The Wood Nymph* ("Skogsrået"), not to be confused with the melodrama or the tone-poem, is recorded here for the first time. As well as *A Song* ("En visa"), there are two other early Runeberg settings, the 1888 *Serenade*, and *Resemblance* ("Likhet"), both of them also première recordings. "The Jewish Girl's Song" ("Den judiska flickans sång") will be familiar from the incidental music to *Belshazzar's Feast*, and is affecting in this form – particularly sung as it is here. Given the artistry and insight of this splendid partnership, and the interest and beauty of the repertoire, this is a self-recommending issue.

Sibelius Arioso, Op. 3. Seven Songs, Op. 17. Row, row duck. Six Songs, Op. 36. Five Songs, Op. 37. Pelleas and Melisande, Op. 46 – The three blind sisters. Six Songs, Op. 88. Narcissus. **Anne Sofie von Otter** (mez); **Bengt Forsberg** (pf). BIS Ⓕ CD457 (57 minutes: DDD: 6/90). Texts and translations included.

In all, Sibelius composed about 100 songs, mostly to Swedish texts but his achievement in this field has, naturally enough, been overshadowed by the symphonies. Most music lovers know only a handful like "Black roses", Op. 36 No. 1, and "The Tryst" and the most popular are not always the best. Sibelius's output for the voice has much greater range, diversity and depth than many people suppose. For collectors used to hearing them sung by a baritone, the idea of a soprano will seem strange but a lot of them were written for the soprano Ida Ekman. Anne Sofie von Otter not only makes a beautiful sound and has a feeling for line, but also brings many interpretative insights to this repertoire. The very first song from the Op. 17 set is a marvellous Runeberg setting, "Since then I have questioned no further" and it was this that Ida Ekman sang for Brahms. Von Otter captures its mood perfectly and has the measure of its companions too. Her account of "Black roses" is particularly thrilling and she is very persuasive in the weaker Op. 88 set. She sings throughout with great feeling for character and her account of "Astray", Op. 17 No. 6, has great lightness of touch and charm. The Opp. 36 and 37 sets are among the finest lyrical collections in the whole of Sibelius's song output, and they completely engage this artist's sensibilties. These are performances of elegance and finesse; Bengt Forsberg proves an expert and stylish partner and both artists are well recorded.

Sibelius Incidental Music – Everyman, Op. 83[a]; Belshazzar's Feast, Op. 51[b]. The Countess's
  Portrait, Op. posth. [ab]**Lilli Paasikivi** (mez); [a]**Petri Lehto** (ten); [a]**Sauli Tiilikainen** (bar); [a]**Pauli
  Pietiläinen** (org); [a]**Leena Saarenpaä** (pf); [a]**Lahti Chamber Choir; Lahti Symphony Orchestra /
  Osmo Vänskä.** BIS Ⓕ CD735 (65 minutes: DDD: 5/96). Texts and translations included.
  Recorded 1995.

These are all first recordings and interest centres on the score Sibelius wrote for Hofmannsthal's morality play, *Jedermann* ("Everyman") in 1916. The final score comprises 16 numbers and runs to some 40 minutes. Some of the music is fragmentary and hardly makes sense out of context, though most of it is atmospheric and all of it is characteristic. The sustained *Largo* section for muted, divided strings (track 11), is among the most searching music Sibelius ever wrote for theatre and, artistically, is fit to keep company with *The Tempest* music. Overall the material does not lend itself to being turned into a suite in the same way as *Belshazzar's Feast* but this recording rescues from obscurity some strangely haunting and at times really inspired music – the last 25 minutes are very powerful. By all accounts Hjalmar Procopé's *Belshazzar's Feast* was a feeble play and when it first appeared, one newspaper cartoon showed the playwright being borne aloft in the composer's arms. There seems little doubt that his name would not be alive were it not for Sibelius's music. The latter certainly makes an expert job of creating an effective and (in the case of the "Notturno") a moving concert suite. The present issue gives us an additional six minutes or so of unfamiliar music; there are 11 numbers in all, though familiar passages from the suite are broken up. *The Countess's Portrait* (1906) is a wistful, pensive and charming piece for strings, which was only published two years ago. Obviously this is a self-recommending issue of exceptional interest.

Sibelius Incidental Music – Karelia[a]; Kuolema, Op. 44[b]. Valse triste, Op. 44 No. 1 (1904 versions).
  [a]**Heikki Laitinen,** [a]**Taito Hoffren** (sngrs); [b]**Kirsi Tiihonen** (sop); [ab]**Raimo Laukka** (bar);
  Lahti Symphony Orchestra / Osmo Vänskä. BIS Ⓕ CD915 (76 minutes: DDD: 4/98).
  Texts and translations included. Recorded 1997. *Selected by Soundings.*   Ⓖ

This is a disc which will be of great interest to Sibelians. The original score of the *Karelia* music was discovered in the conductor Kajanus's library after his death in 1933 and his widow returned it to Sibelius three years later. The music extended to eight tableaux which portrayed various episodes in Karelian history. In the 1940s Sibelius destroyed the score, about which he had had second thoughts since its première in 1893, sparing only the overture, the movements familiar from the suite and the first number, "A Karelian Home – News of War". Fortunately for posterity, a set of orchestral parts came to light, albeit incomplete, and were put into shape by Kalevi Kuoso. It was these that the composer Kalevi Aho used in preparing the edition on which this recording is based. In all there are some 40 minutes of music, over half of which is new. Those familiar with the "Ballade" from the Op. 11 Suite will no doubt be slightly disconcerted to hear the familiar cor anglais melody taken by a baritone and will find the piece too long in its original form. The opening of the fifth Tableau, "Pontus de la Gardie at the gates of Käkisalmi [Kexholm Castle] in 1580", is highly effective and leads into the famous "Alla marcia". It is fascinating to hear what the piece is like, and what Sibelius was prepared to lose. Listening to this reaffirms and illumines both the sureness of his artistic judgement and the vitality of his creative imagination. Sibelius's incidental music to *Kuolema*, the play by his brother-in-law, Arvid Järnefelt, dates from 1903. The most familiar music from it is the *Valse triste*, which Sibelius revised the following year, adding flute, clarinet, horns and timpani and making it altogether more sophisticated harmonically and melodically. Osmo Vänskä and his Lahti players prove reliable and responsive guides in this atmospheric music and it is hard to imagine their performances being improved on. Wide-ranging and expertly balanced recorded sound.

Sibelius The Tempest – Incidental Music, Op. 109. **Kirsi Tiihonen** (sop); **Lilli Paasikivi** (mez);
  Anssi Hirvonen, Paavo Kerola (tens); **Heikki Keinonen** (bar); **Lahti Opera Chorus and Symphony
  Orchestra / Osmo Vänskä.** BIS Ⓕ CD581 (68 minutes: DDD: 2/93). Text and translation
  included. Recorded 1992. *Selected by Sounds in Retrospect.*   Ⓖ

A first recording of the full score! Sibelius's music for *The Tempest,* his last and greatest work in its genre, was the result of a commission for a particularly lavish production at the Royal Theatre, Copenhagen in 1926. The score is far more extensive than the two suites and consists of 34 musical numbers for soloists, mixed choir, harmonium and large orchestra. Readers will be brought up with a start by the music for the "Berceuse", the second item, which uses a harmonium rather than the strings with which we are familiar from the two suites and although it is still more magical in the familiar orchestral suite, the original has an other-worldly quality all its own. The music is played in the order in which it was used in the 1927 production of the play and there are ample and excellent explanatory notes. The "Chorus of the Winds" is also different but no less magical in effect. Of course, taken out of the theatrical context, not everything comes off – but even if the invention is not consistent in quality, at its best it is quite wonderful. The singers and chorus all rise to the occasion and Osmo Vänskä succeeds in casting a powerful spell in the "Intermezzo", which opens Act 4. The recording is marvellously atmospheric though it needs to be played at a higher than usual level setting as it is a little recessed. For Sibelians this is a self-recommending issue.

Sibelius Complete Choral Songs. [a]**Tapiola Chamber Choir;** [b]**Friends of Sibelius / Hannu Norjanen;** [c]**Tapiola Choir / Kari Ala-Pöllänen** with [d]**Ilmo Ranta** (pf); **Johanna Torikka** ([e]org/[f]harm). Finlandia Ⓔ 0630-19054-2 (two discs: 147 minutes: DDD: 6/98). Texts and translations included. Recorded 1996-1997.
Partsongs, Op. 18[a] – No. 1, The Broken Voice; No. 3, The Boat Journey of Väinämöinen; No. 4, Fire on the Island; No. 6, The Song of my Heart. Busy as a Thrush[a]. Play, Beautiful Girl[a]. Rakastava, Op. 14[a]. The Thrush's Toiling[a]. Festive March[a]. Cantata for the Helsinki University Ceremonies of 1897, Op. 23[a]. To Thérèse Hahl[a]. Nostalgia[c]. Not with Grief[a]. Wonderful Gifts[c]. March of the Finnish Jaeger Battalion, Op. 91 No. 1[d]. Three Runeberg Songs[a]. Awaken![a]. Choir of the Winds[d]. Ballad[a]. The Son's Bride[d]. Men from Plain and Sea, Op. 65a[a]. Dreams[a]. Christmas Song[a]. Give Me No Splendour, Op. 1 No. 4[a]. Bell Melody of Berghaill Church, Op. 65b[a]. Three Introductory Antiphons, Op. 107b. Ode, Op. 113 No. 11[a]. Carminalia[bcdf]. Primary School Children's March[c]. In the Morning Mist[c]. Hail, O Princess[a]. The Landscape Breathes, Op. 30[a]. Three American School Songs[d]. The Way to School[a]. School Song[a]. March of the Labourers[a]. The World Song, Op. 91b[d]. Song of the Athenians, Op. 31 No. 3[bcd]. To the Fatherland[a]. Song for the People of Uusimaa[a]. Finlandia[a].

This survey of Sibelius's complete choral songs is important – and irresistible – not only for its consistently fine performances, but for the historical context it provides for a deeper understanding of both Sibelius and his later contemporaries. The two-disc set begins where – in the mythology of Finnish oral tradition – all music began: with the life-giving song of Väinämöinen from the *Kalevala*'s compilation of folk poetry; the verse which tuned Sibelius's ear to the musicality of the Finnish language (at a time when he and his social class still spoke Swedish) also inspired his first distinctive song settings. Here, excellent production most sensitively captures the division and shifting of the finely blended voices of the Tapiola Chamber Choir, as solo and ensemble voices trace the asymmetrical metres and modal cadences of works such as *The Boat Journey* ("Venematka") from Op. 18 and *The Lover* ("Rakastava"). References to the *Kalevala* return in the group of songs for ceremonies and festivities in which solo exhortations are pitted against shifting choral harmonies, as images of journey, hope and freedom are expressed in the supple melodies of ten songs for a university degree ceremony from 1897 (Op. 23). A fervent and optimistic tribute to Finland's great national romantic painter Albert Edelfelt sets works by Sibelius's beloved Swedish-language poet, Rüneberg: and his *Autumn Evening* ("Höstkvällen") could be an aural re-creation of one of the painter's own canvases. Sibelius's music pierces dark, close harmonies with high lines of anguish, presaging the imaginative virtuosity of later masterpieces such as *Men from Plain and Sea* and *Dreams* with their sense of the wandering and yearning of the human spirit. The second disc follows three simple Christmas carols with the composer's sacred and liturgical pieces. Among these early prentice works, the bells of Helsinki's great Kallio Church ring out: the peal which Sibelius wrote for the fine 1912 Nordic Jugendstil building still rings out twice a day, and here we are treated to the words as well. The songs for children range from distinctly uninspired English-language commissions for American schools, to a tiny and perfect setting of *The Landscape Breathes*, in which the girls' voices slowly and chromatically thaw from their unison freeze. Finland's and Sibelius's unique species of unjingoistic patriotism returns at the end with gently yet distinctively harmonized hymns to specific regions of the motherland and, finally and inevitably, with the great *Finlandia* hymn.

Further listening ...
...Scaramouche – Incidental Music, Op. 71. The Language of the Birds – Wedding March.
Gothenburg Symphony Orchestra / Neeme Järvi. BIS CD502 (4/92).
...Piano Quartet in C minor[a]. Violin Sonata in F major[b]. String Trio in G minor[c]. Suite for String Trio in A major[c]. [b]**Ernst Kovacic,** [c]**Jan Söderblom,** [a]**Massimo Quarta,** [a]**Ilaria Miori** (vns); [c]**Ilari Angervo** (va); [c]**Jan-Erik Gustafsson,** [a]**Martti Rousi** (vcs); [b]**Juhani Lagerspetz,** [a]**Viatcheslav Novikov** (pfs). Ondine ODE826-2 (6/95).
...Piano Quintet in G minor (1890)[a]. String Quartet in D minor, Op. 56, "Voces intimae".
Gabrieli Quartet; [a]**Anthony Goldstone** (pf). Chandos CHAN8742 (2/90).
...String Quartets – E flat major; A minor; B flat major, Op. 4; D minor, Op. 56, "Voces intimae".
Sibelius Academy Quartet. Finlandia 4509-95851-2 (8/92).
...String Quartet in D minor, Op. 56, "Voces intimae". *Coupled with works by* **Grieg** *and* **Wolf**
Budapest Quartet. Biddulph mono LAB098* (4/95).
...Piano Works, Volume 4. – Melody for the Bells of Berghäll Church, Op. 65. Five Pieces, Op. 75. 13 Pieces, Op. 76. Five Pieces, Op. 85. Six Pieces, Op. 94. Six Bagatelles, Op. 97. **Annette Servadei** (pf). Olympia OCD634 (12/95).

...Piano Works, Volume 5. – Valse lyrique, Op. 96*a*. Autrefois, Op. 96*b*. Valse chevaleresque, Op. 96*c*. Eight Pieces, Op. 99. Five Pieces, Op. 101. Five Pieces, Op. 103. Five Esquisses, Op. 114. Finlandia, Op. 26. **Annette Servadei** (pf). Olympia OCD635 (12/95).

Valentin Silvestrov

USSR/Ukrainian 1937

Silvestrov Symphony No. 5. Postludium[a]. [a]**Alexei Lubimov** (pf); **Deutsches Symphony Orchestra, Berlin / David Robertson.** Sony Classical Ⓕ SK66825 (65 minutes: DDD: 10/96). Recorded 1995. *Gramophone Editor's choice.*   ⒼⒼ
Silvestrov's Fifth is one of the best-kept secrets of the ex-Soviet symphonic repertoire. It was composed in 1980-82, and its 1988 Melodiya recording, never widely available in the West, became something of a cult hit with his fellow-Ukrainians and with Russian musicians and students. Like the *Postludium* with which it is coupled here, it is quite deliberately nostalgic – a symphony composed, as it were, after the death of the genre and consisting only of poignant memories. In musical terms those memories are of the melodic and accompanimental figures characteristic of nineteenth-century song; so the structure consists of quietly ecstatic extended melodies spaced by even more ecstatic efflorescences of piano-accompaniment-derived textures. Throughout the symphony's unbroken, slow-moving 47-minute span, Silvestrov's precise ear for harmony, his extreme sensitivity to orchestral texture, and his subtlety of large-scale control, are remarkable. Just as importantly, his visions of timeless beauty are set in the context of 'here-and-now' emotional pain (if you are sampling before buying, be sure to hear past the first three minutes where that context is set up). The way these contrasting phases foreshadow, overlap and echo one another has the feeling of genuine symphonic mastery. Find yourself a quiet hour and let this masterpiece cast its magic spell.
Additional recommendation ...
...No. 5[c]. Kitsch Music for Piano[a] – No. 1, Allegro vivace; No. 2, Moderato. String Quartet No. 1[b]. [a]**Irina Plotnikova** (pf); [b]**Lysenko Quartet**; [c]**Kiev Conservatoire Symphony Orchestra / Roman Kofman.** Melodiya Ⓜ 74321 49959-2 (72 minutes: ADD: 4/98).
Further listening ...
...Dedication[a]. Post scriptum[b]. **Gidon Kremer** (vn); [b]**Vadim Sacharov** (pf); [a]**Munich Philharmonic Orchestra / Roman Kofman.** Teldec 4509-99206-2 (12/96).

Robert Simpson

British 1921-1997

Simpson String Quartet No. 13. String Quintet No. 2[b]. Clarinet Quintet[a]. [a]**Thea King** (cl); [b]**Christopher van Kampen** (vc); **Delmé Quartet** (Galina Solodchin, John Trusler, vns; John Underwood, va; Jonathan Williams, vc). Hyperion Ⓕ CDA66905 (64 minutes: DDD: A/97). Recorded 1997.   ⒼⒼ
This invigorating and thought-provoking disc is part of Hyperion's invaluable Simpson cycle, the music as enjoyable as ever. In the Clarinet Quintet of 1968 the wind partner is treated as an equal of the strings, which makes the linear and contrapuntal inventiveness all the more remarkable and absorbing, though for some it may make the music seem no more than monochrome. Like late Beethoven, Simpson seems to begin by charting a realm just out of emotional reach yet somehow crucial to one's psychic well-being. The mental energy gained then spills over into actual fast music, even into an engaging jigginess. The Quintet feels as though it could go on much longer than its actual 31 minutes without the inventive resources drying up. The rarefied conclusion is all the more moving for its steadiness of gaze. The Thirteenth Quartet (1989) retains many familiar Simpson hallmarks. It opens with a sinewy, deceptively triadic theme which soon gives way to spidery, triplety counterpoint. It is all very ascetic and self-denying and the second and fourth movements go into an interior, attenuated world in which it is difficult to feel entirely at home. The even more recent String Quintet No. 2 keeps its cards just as close to its chest. Again the design alternates austere, lyrical music with a knotty *Allegro*, initially short-lived but gradually expanding, while the slower sections remain more or less constant in duration. The impression is less of conflict and resolution than of a stand-off between the two tempo-types, eyeing one another in mutual suspicion; the conclusion is bleak-Sibelian. The Delmé are longstanding Simpson advocates and they seem to have the ideal sound for him – crystalline, alert and focused, as though beyond obvious human expressiveness in a realm of higher wisdom. The same goes for their admirable partners, Thea King and Christopher van Kampen. This may be one of the less immediately accessible Simpson programmes, but it is still richly rewarding.
Further listening ...
...Music for Brass Band: Energy. The Four Temperaments. Introduction and Allegro on a Bass by Max Reger. Volcano. Vortex. **Desford Colliery Caterpillar Band / James Watson.** Hyperion CDA66449 (1/91).
...Symphonies Nos. 1 and 8. **Royal Philharmonic Orchestra / Vernon Handley.** Hyperion CDA66890 (2/97). *Gramophone Editor's choice.*   Ⓖ
...Symphonies Nos. 2 and 4. **Bournemouth Symphony Orchestra / Vernon Handley.** Hyperion CDA66505 (12/92). *Selected by Sounds in Retrospect.*

...Symphonies Nos. 3 and 5. **Royal Philharmonic Orchestra / Vernon Handley.**
Hyperion CDA66728 (2/95).　　　ⓖ
...Symphony No. 9. **Bournemouth Symphony Orchestra / Vernon Handley.**
Hyperion CDA66299 (12/88). *Gramophone Award Winner 1989.*　　　ⓖ
...Horn Trio. Horn Quartet[a]. **Richard Watkins** (hn); **Pauline Lowbury** (vn); [a]**Caroline Dearnley** (vc);
Christopher Green-Armytage (pf). Hyperion CDA66695 (12/94).
...String Quartets Nos. 3 and 6. String Trio (Prelude, Adagio and Fugue). **Delmé Quartet.**
Hyperion CDA66376 (7/90).
...String Quartets Nos. 7 and 8. **Delmé Quartet.** Hyperion CDA66117 (2/90).
...String Quartet No. 9. **Delmé Quartet.** Hyperion CDA66127 (2/90).
...String Quartet No. 12. String Quintet[a]. **Coull Quartet;** [a]**Roger Bigley** (va).
Hyperion CDA66503 (7/92).
...Piano Sonata. Variations and Finale on a Theme of Haydn. Michael Tippett, His Mystery.
Variations and Finale on a Theme by Beethoven. **Raymond Clarke** (pf).
Hyperion CDA66827 (5/96).
...Violin Sonata. Trio for Violin, Cello and Piano. **Lowbury Piano Trio.**
Hyperion CDA66737 (7/95).

Thomas Simpson

British 1582-probably after 1630

Suggested listening ...
...Ricercar, "Bonny Sweet Robin". Divisions. *Coupled with works by various composers.*
Richard Campbell (viol/bandora/gtr); **David Miller** (lte/theorbo/gtr/cittern); **The Dufay Collective.**
Chandos New Direction CHAN9446 (10/96). *See review in the Collections section; refer to the*
Index.

Emil Sjögren

Swedish 1853-1918

Suggested listening ...
...Lieder from Wolff's "Tannhäuser", Op. 12 – No. 4, Hab'ein Röslein dir gebrochen; No. 6,
Ich möchte schweben. Du schaust mich an mit stummen Fragen. *Coupled with works by various*
composers **Anne Sofie von Otter** (mez); **Bengt Forsberg** (pf). DG 449 189-2GH (5/96).
Gramophone Editor's choice. See review in the Collections section; refer to the Index.　　　ⓖⓖ

Nikos Skalkottas

Greek 1904-1949

Skalkottas Violin Concerto, AK22[a]. Largo Sinfonico, AK4a. Greek Dances, AK11 – Epirotikos;
Kretikos; Tsamikos; Thessalikos; Mariori mou-Mariori mou; Arkadikos; Kleftikos (arr. cpsr).
[a]**Georgios Demertzis** (vn); **Malmö Symphony Orchestra / Nikos Christodoulou.** BIS ⓕ CD904
(78 minutes: DDD: 6/98). Recorded 1997.
From Nikos Skalkottas's earliest works, a personal idiom was evident, combining European
modernism with the rhythmic dynamism of Greek traditional music, and characterized by a tensile
strength and translucency of sound. Like Bartók, Skalkottas wrote 'popular' music without
compromise. The *Greek Dances* are ideal encore pieces, not least in these suave arrangements for
strings. The Violin Concerto of 1937 is among his major works, with a solo part that is demanding
yet integral to the symphonic nature of the score – something that Georgios Demertzis's vital account
readily conveys. While Schoenberg's influence is apparent in the linear nature of the writing, a more
telling comparison is with the concerto by Gerhard, for the way in which note-rows are transformed
into melodic ideas of subtlety and flexibility. The close of the *Andante* has true lyrical repose, before
the finale provides fireworks as well as clinching the musical design. The *Largo Sinfonico* embodies
some of Skalkottas's most personal music; its 26-minute span is a seamless fusion of variation and
sonata forms, as satisfying formally as emotionally. Nikos Christodoulou's notes speak of a private
musical universe, yet the plangency of the cello theme and the remorseless tread of the central
climaxes betray an unease surely inseparable from the time of composition. The final bars, with the
thematic material recast as a series of unearthly chords, feel as much a stoic acceptance of reality as
they are a 'harmony of the spheres'. With the Malmö orchestra fully attuned to the idiom,
Christodoulou's powerfully shaped reading makes for a compelling experience

Richard Smert

British 15th century

Suggested listening ...
...Jesu fili Dei. *Coupled with works under* **Anonymous** Shirley Rumsey, Christopher Wilson (ltes);
Gothic Voices / Christopher Page (lte). Hyperion CDA66857 (2/97). *Gramophone Editor's choice.*
See review under Anonymous; refer to the Index.　　　ⓖ

Bedřich Smetana

Bohemian 1824-1884

Smetana Má vlast. **Czech Philharmonic Orchestra / Rafael Kubelík.** Supraphon Ⓕ 11 1208-2
(78 minutes: DDD: 9/91). Recorded live in 1990.   ⒼⒼ
Smetana Má vlast. **Concertgebouw Orchestra / Antál Dorati.** Philips Solo Ⓜ 442 641-2PM
(79 minutes: DDD: 6/95). Recorded 1987.

Smetana's great cycle of six tone-poems, *Má vlast*, celebrates the countryside and legendary heroes
and heroines of Bohemia. It is a work of immense national significance encapsulating many of the
ideals and hopes of that country. What a triumphant occasion it was when Rafael Kubelík returned
to his native Czechoslovakia and to his old orchestra after an absence of 42 years and conducted *Má
vlast* at the 1990 Prague Spring Festival. Supraphon's disc captures that live performance – not
perfectly, since the sound is efficient rather than opulent – but well enough to show off what is
arguably the finest performance on record since Talich's early LP set. You would never imagine that
Kubelík had emerged from five years of retirement and a recent serious illness, such is the power and
eloquence of his conducting. Typically he takes a lyrical rather than a dramatic view of the cycle, and
if there is strength enough in more heroic sections there is also a refreshing lack of bombast. Kubelík's
intimate knowledge of the score (this is his fifth recording of it) shows time and time again in the most
subtle touches. Even the weakest parts of the score are most artfully brought to life, and seem of much
greater stature than is usually the case. "Vltava" flows beautifully, with the most imaginative flecks of
detail, and in "From Bohemia's Woods and Fields" there are vivid visions of wide, open spaces. The
orchestra, no doubt inspired by the occasion, reward their former director with superlative playing.

The Concertgebouw Orchestra, vividly directed by Antál Dorati, give a strongly characterized
performance of this epic cycle. The romantic opening of "Vyšehrad" benefits from the glowing hall
ambience, while "Vltava" builds impressively from the gentle trickling streams to the river's powerful
course through the St John's rapids – and how beautifully the Concertgebouw strings sing the main
theme. "Šárka", for all its bloodthirsty scenario, never descends into melodrama, "From Bohemia's
woods and fields" is gloriously diverse, and the darkly sombre opening of "Tábor" contrasts with the
hammered forcefulness of "Blaník", which never becomes bombastic because of the crisply pointed
orchestral articulation, while the performance is enhanced by the lovely playing in its enchanting
pastoral interlude. Dorati's imaginative grip on this last, wayward 15-minute piece holds the listener
throughout all its episodes to the grandiloquent final peroration. The recording is out of Philips's top-
drawer.

Additional recommendations ...

...Má vlast. **Vienna Philharmonic Orchestra / Rafael Kubelík.** Belart Ⓑ 450 060-2 (ADD).
...Má vlast. **Bavarian Radio Symphony Orchestra / Rafael Kubelík.** Orfeo Ⓕ C115841A (DDD).
...Má vlast. **Vienna Philharmonic Orchestra / James Levine.** DG Ⓕ 431 652-2GH (76 minutes: DDD).
...Má vlast – Vltava. *Coupled with works by* **Dvořák** **Boston Symphony Orchestra / Rafael Kubelík.**
DG Double Ⓜ 439 663-2GX2 (two discs: 146 minutes: ADD).
...Má vlast. **Boston Symphony Orchestra / Rafael Kubelík.**
DG Galleria Ⓜ 429 183-2GGA (76 minutes: ADD: 4/90).
...Má vlast – Vltava. *Coupled with works by* **R. Strauss** **Vienna Philharmonic Orchestra /**
Wilhelm Furtwängler. EMI Références mono Ⓜ CDH5 65197-2* (73 minutes: ADD: 10/94).
...Má vlast – Vltava. The bartered bride – Overture; Polka; Furiant; Dance of the Comedians.
Coupled with works by various composers. **Royal Liverpool Philharmonic Orchestra / Libor Pešek.**
Virgin Classics Ⓕ VC7 59285-2 (76 minutes: DDD: 11/94).
...Má vlast. **Polish National Radio Symphony Orchestra / Antoni Wit.**
Naxos Ⓢ 8 550931 (80 minutes: DDD: 4/95). *Gramophone Editor's choice.*
...Má vlast. **London Classical Players / Sir Roger Norrington.**
Virgin Veritas Ⓕ VC5 45301-2 (77 minutes: DDD: 11/97). 🖊
...Má vlast. Our lasses, T49. **Czech Philharmonic Orchestra / Václav Talich.**
Biddulph mono Ⓜ WHL049* (76 minutes: ADD: 5/98).

Smetana Má vlast. **Czech Philharmonic Orchestra / Václav Talich.** Supraphon mono Ⓕ 11 1896-2*
(74 minutes: AAD: 1/94). From LPV247/8 (9/57). Recorded 1954.
Gramophone classical 100.   ⒼⒼⒼ

Sample at just under six minutes into "From Bohemia's Woods and Fields" and you reach the very
heart of this great performance. The CPO brass lunge towards the main melody with unconstrained
eagerness, their impact much aided by smiling *glissandos*. And as Talich and his players climb aboard
Smetana's home-spun melody, everything assumes a sunny glow: it's almost as if the entire work thus
far had prepared for that one magical moment. But there are of course countless additional
splendours: Vltava's luminous mobility, Sárka's grimness (so different here to the excitable Kubelík),
Tábor's sense of foreboding and the chest-swelling patriotism of Blaník. The strings retain more than
a hint of the portamentos that were such a distinctive feature of Talich's 1929 recording listed below,
but the woodwinds are notably superior and the basically excellent sound releases more of the music's
dynamism than was easily audible on 78s. The transfer makes a warmer case for the original tapes
than the old LPs did, and generally serves Talich well – except in one maddening respect. A couple of
bars have dropped from "Tábor", thus utterly ruining the contour of a major climax. The offending
cut was not present on the original recording. If you can write off the missing bars as 'historical wear

and tear', then expect a *Má vlast* that's way above average, an inspired affirmation of national pride by a wonderful people who had only recently escaped one form of tyranny, and would subsequently fall prey to another.
Additional recommendation ...
...Má vlast. **Czech Philharmonic Orchestra / Václav Talich.**
Koch International Legacy mono Ⓕ 37032-2* (79 minutes: ADD: 6/91). ❺❺❺

Smetana Piano Trio in G minor, B104.
Tchaikovsky Piano Trio in A minor, Op. 50. **Golub Kaplan Carr Trio** (Mark Kaplan, vn; Colin Carr, vc; David Golub, pf). Arabesque Ⓕ Z6661 (75 minutes: DDD: 3/96). Recorded 1994.
The Tchaikovsky trio is well represented on CD with some 17 listings as opposed to a mere half-dozen of the Smetana, but no other version offers them together. The Golub Kaplan Carr Trio give exemplary, well-shaped accounts of both works, which grip the listener with their musicality and unforced, natural eloquence. They perform the Tchaikovsky trio complete without any of the cuts that the composer sanctioned and play it without the slightest overstatement. All three are fine players but when one sees the discography of some cellists (no disrespect intended to any of them), it is puzzling that Colin Carr has not enjoyed greater exposure as a soloist. The recording has great presence and though it may be a bit too forward for some tastes it is still well balanced.

Smetana Má vlast – Vltava. The bartered bride – Overture; Polka[a]; Furiant; Dance of the Comedians. The Kiss – Overture. Libuše – Prelude. The two widows – Overture. [a]**Cleveland Orchestra Chorus; Cleveland Orchestra / Christoph von Dohnányi.** Decca Ⓕ 444 867-2DH (57 minutes: DDD: 2/96). Text and translation included. Recorded 1993-1994.
Pride of place must go to the magnificent Overture to *Libuše*, a work that was completed in 1872 but not actually premièred until 1881, two years before Dvořák composed his *Hussite* Overture along vaguely similar lines. The opening brass-and-timpani fanfare anticipates Janáček's *Sinfonietta*, although ensuing incident is more reminiscent of Smetana's own *Má vlast* and, especially, Wagner (note the beautiful, *Lohengrin*-style descending passage from 5'27"). Dohnányi effects ideal pacing and tapers a beautifully graded *diminuendo* away from the bold opening (from, say, 1'10"), but the strings are occasionally less than precise – especially at around 4'17". *The two widows* opens somewhat in the manner of late Verdi though the overall flavour is unmistakable, especially at 3'20" where Smetana launches a quietly mischievous fugue over a held bass pedal. Then there is the delightful "Polka" and the lively Overture to *The Kiss*, both prime-cut samplings of Smetana's mature style. *The bartered bride* suite is very nicely done, although synchronization falters momentarily just after 1'00" into the Overture, and don't expect Dohnányi's "Dance of the Comedians" to match Szell's Cleveland recording of 30 years earlier for precision, especially among the strings. In the "Polka", vivid stereophony lends considerable presence to the chorus, who make a vivid entrance: You may feel you have been gatecrashed by a crowd of unannounced guests! "Vltava" is equally effective, what with its stylishly phrased opening, sensitive transitions (especially into the "Peasant's Wedding" episode) and powerful current later on. The sound is resonant and full-bodied, except that important 'hunting' horns are virtually inaudible at 1'46" and some louder climaxes want for detail. Still, this remains an enjoyable programme
Additional recommendations ...
...The bartered bride – Overture; Polka; Furiant; Dance of the Comedians. *Coupled with works by various composers.* **Royal Philharmonic Orchestra/ Rudolf Kempe.**
EMI Profile Ⓑ CZS5 68736-2 (two discs: 156 minutes: ADD: 9/96).
...Má vlast – Vltava. *Coupled with works by* **Liszt** and **Sibelius** **Berlin Philharmonic Orchestra / Herbert von Karajan.** DG Digital Masters Ⓜ 445 550-2GMA (70 minutes: DDD: 9/83).

Smetana The bartered bride. **Gabriela Beňačková** (sop) Mařenka; **Peter Dvorský** (ten) Jeník; **Miroslav Kopp** (ten) Vašek; **Richard Novák** (bass) Kecal; **Jindřich Jindrák** (bar) Krušina; **Marie Mrázová** (contr) Háta; **Jaroslav Horáček** (bass) Mícha; **Marie Veselá** (sop) Ludmila; **Jana Jonášová** (sop) Esmeralda; **Alfréd Hampel** (ten) Circus master; **Karel Hanuš** (bass) Indian; **Czech Philharmonic Chorus and Orchestra / Zdeněk Košler.** Supraphon Ⓕ 10 3511-2 (three discs: 137 minutes: DDD: 10/91). Notes, text and translation included.
From 1116 3511 (7/82).
There is something special about a Czech performance of *The bartered bride* and this one is no exception. The hint of melancholy which runs through the work is wonderfully evoked, as well as its marvellous gaiety. Zdeněk Košler has the rhythm and lilt of the music in his bones, like any Czech conductor worth his salt. The Czech Philharmonic has long had one of the finest of all woodwind sections, and especially in this music they play with a sense of their instruments' folk background, with phrasing that springs from deep in Czech folk-music. This sets the musical scene for some moving performances. The warm, lyrical quality of Gabriela Beňačková's voice can lighten easily to encompass her character's tenderness in the first duet, "Věrné milováni", or "Faithful love", the considerable show of spirit she makes when Jeník appears to have gone off the rails. Her Act 1 lament is most beautifully song. Peter Dvorský as Jeník plays lightly with the score, as he should, or the character's maintaining of the deception can come to seem merely cruel. Even old Kecal comes to new life, not as the conventional village bumbler, but as a human character in his own right as Richard

Novák portrays him – quite put out, the old boy is, to find his plans gone astray. In fact, all of the soloists are excellent. The chorus enjoy themselves hugely, never more so than in the Beer chorus. Altogether a delightful, touching and warming performance.

Additional recommendations ...

...**Soloists; Prague Radio Chorus and Symphony Orchestra / Karel Ančerl.** Multisonic mono
Ⓜ 310185-2* (two discs: 120 minutes: ADD: 9/94).

...The bartered bride – Overture; Dance of the villagers; Polka; Furiant; Fanfare; Dance of the
comedians. String Quartet No. 1 in E minor, "From my life" (orch. G. Szell).
London Symphony Orchestra / Geoffrey Simon. Chandos Ⓕ CHAN8412 (DDD: 8/86).

...Overture.*Coupled with works by various composers.* **The Solti Orchestral Project, Carnegie Hall /
Sir Georg Solti.** Decca Ⓕ 444 458-2DH (77 minutes: DDD: 12/95). *See review in the Collections
section; refer to the Index.*   Ⓖ

...The bartered bride – Overture. *Coupled with works by* **Dvořák** Josef Suk (vn);
Czech Philharmonic Orchestra / Karel Ančerl.
Orfeo Festspiel Dokumente mono Ⓕ C395951B* (78 minutes: ADD: 4/96).

Smetana Libuše. **Gabriela Beňačková** (sop) Libuše; **Václav Zítek** (ten) Přemysl; **Antonín Svorc**
(bass) Chrudoš; **Leo Marian Vodička** (ten) Stáhlav; **Karel Průša** (bass) Lubtor; **René Tuček** (bar)
Radovan; **Eva Děpoltová** (sop) Krasava; **Věra Soukupová** (mez) Radmila; **Prague National
Theatre Chorus and Orchestra / Zdeněk Košler.** Supraphon Ⓕ 11 1276-2
(three discs: 166 minutes: DDD: 4/94). Notes, text and translation included. Recorded live in 1983.
Libuše is a patriotic pageant, static and celebratory, with such plot as there is concerning the mythical
founder of Prague, Libuše, and her marriage to the peasant Přemysl, founder of the first Czech
dynasty. Václav Zítek makes a fine, heroic Přemysl; but the triumphant performance comes, as it
must, from Gabriela Beňačková. The opera concludes with a series of tableaux in which Libuše
prophesies the future kings and heroes who will assure the stability and greatness of the nation. At
the end of a long performance her voice is undimmed in its ringing splendour; and earlier, as near the
very start, the beauty of her tone and line seeks out all the warmth, character and humanity which
she proves to be latent in Smetana's spacious but seemingly plain vocal writing. *Libuše* is scarcely
Smetana's greatest opera, as he liked to claim, but especially in so splendid a performance from
Beňačková, and under the grave but impassioned direction of Zdeněk Košler, it makes compelling
gramophone listening. The live recording includes some applause, but little other distraction.

Further listening ...

...Piano Trio in G minor, B104. *Coupled with* **Dvořák** Piano Trio No. 4 in E minor, B166,
"Dumky". **Rostislav Dubinsky** (vn); **Yuli Turovsky** (vc); **Luba Edlina** (pf).
Chandos CHAN8445 (7/87).

...String Quartets – No. 1 in E minor, "From my life"; No. 2 in D minor. **Lindsay Quartet.**
ASV CDDCA777.

...String Quartet No. 1 in E minor, "From my life". *Coupled with works by various composers.*
Hollywood Quartet. Testament mono/stereo SBT1072* (5/96).   Ⓖ

...14 Czech Dances, T112. Bagatelles and Impromptus, B40. **Radoslav Kvapil** (pf).
Unicorn-Kanchana DKPCD9139 10/93).   ⒼⒼ

...Czech Polkas and Dances, T112. *Coupled with works by* **Debussy** Rudolf Firkušný (pf).
EMI Firkušný Edition mono CDM5 66069-2*.

...Macbeth and the Witches. Six Rêves, T112. Trois Polkas de Salon, B94 (Op. 7). Trois Polkas
poétiques, B95 (Op. 8). Quatre Souvenirs de Bohème en forme de polka, B115-16
(Opp. 12 and 13). **Radoslav Kvapil** (pf). Unicorn-Kanchana DKPCD9152 (2/95).

...Three Choruses, T119.*Coupled with works by various composers.* **Prague Chamber Choir /
Josef Pancik.** Chandos CHAN9257 (12/95).

...The Brandenburgers in Bohemia. **Soloists; Prague National Theatre Chorus and Orchestra /
Jan Hus Tichý.** Supraphon 11 1804-2 (5/94).

...Dalibor. **Soloists; Prague National Theatre Chorus and Orchestra / Zdeněk Košler.**
Supraphon SU0077-2 (12/95).

...The Devil's Wall. **Soloists; Prague National Theatre Chorus and Orchestra / Zdeněk Chalabala.**
Supraphon 11 2201-2 (11/95).

...The Kiss. **Soloists; Brno Janáček Opera Chorus and Orchestra / František Vajnar.**
Supraphon 11 2180-2 (9/95).

...The Two Widows. **Soloists; Prague Radio Chorus and Symphony Orchestra / Jaroslav Krombholc.**
Praga PR250 022/3 (6/93).

Dame Ethel Smyth   British 1858-1944

Smyth String Quintet in E major, Op. 1[a]. String Quartet in E minor. [a]**Joachim Griesheimer** (vc);
Mannheim Quartet (Andreas Krecher, Claudia Hohorst, vns; Niklas Schwarz, va;
Armin Fromm, vc). CPO Ⓕ CPO999 352-2 (68 minutes: DDD: 11/96). Recorded 1994.
The Mannheim Quartet, reinforced in the early Quintet by the cellist Joachim Griesheimer, give
superb performances of keenly inventive works which belie the old idea that Smyth was influenced

above all in her chamber music by Brahms. As is pointed out in the note (poorly translated from the German), the delightfully fresh first movement of the Quintet, written in 1881 when Smyth was in her mid twenties, keeps reminding one of Dvořák, notably the Op. 96 Quartet and the *New World* Symphony. Yet those two works were written after this, not before, and one wonders just what the influence was. In the five-movement scheme the outer movements are by far the most substantial, with the three middle movements as contrasting interludes, a delicate *Andantino*, a jolly *Scherzo* and – most remarkably – a raptly lyrical *Adagio* which in a tantalizingly brief three-and-a-half minutes has the composer taking on the role of visionary, with a nod in the direction of the *Cavatina* from Beethoven's B flat Quartet, Op. 130. Delightful and refreshing as the Quintet is, it is the Quartet, begun in 1902 but not completed till ten years later, which demonstrates the composer's originality most clearly. It was bold of her, instead of starting with an *Allegro*, to have an easily lilting *Allegretto lirico* as a sonata-form first movement. It is the more remarkable when you realize that this predominantly gentle and sweet inspiration dates from the years when Smyth was most active in the suffragette cause, finally getting herself put in prison. The second movement is a jaunty scherzo with a hint of English folk music in the themes, and the lively finale, starting with a fugato, also has an English flavour. The beautiful, extended slow movement, like the brief *Adagio* of the Quintet, is peacefully lyrical, again belying the composer's often violent personality. These are outstanding performances, well recorded.

Additional recommendation ...

...Violin Sonata in A minor, Op. 7[a]. String Quintet[b]. Cello Sonata in A minor, Op. 5[c]. String Quartet[d]. [c]**Friedmann Kupsa** (vn); [bc]**Johanna Varner** (vc); [ac]**Céline Dutilly** (pf); [bd]**Fanny Mendelssohn Quartet.** Troubadisc Ⓕ TDCD03 (two discs: 114 minutes: ADD: 7/94).

Further listening ...

...Concerto for Violin, Horn and Orchestra[a]. Serenade in D major. [a]**Sophie Langdon** (vn); [a]**Richard Watkins** (hn); **BBC Philharmonic Orchestra / Odaline de la Martinez.** Chandos CHAN9449 (6/96).

...Entente cordiale – Interlude (Two interlinked French melodies). Fête galante – Minuet. *Coupled with works by* **Bliss** *and* **Vaughan Williams BBC Symphony Orchestra, Light Symphony Orchestra / Sir Adrian Boult.** Dutton Laboratories mono CDAX8016* (1/97).

...Piano Sonatas – No. 1 in C major; No. 2 in F sharp minor; No. 3 in D major. Four Four-Part Dances. Two Canons. Invention in D major. Suite in E major. To Youth!. Piece in E major. Variations on an Original Theme in D flat major. Prelude and Fugues – F sharp major; C major. **Liana Serbescu** (pf). CPO CPO999 327-2 (3/96).

...Violin Sonata in A minor, Op. 7. Cello Sonata in A minor, Op. 5. Piano Trio in D minor. **Chagall Trio.** Meridian CDE84286 (10/95).

...Four Songs (1907)[a]. Three Songs (1913)[b]. Horn Trio in A major[c]. **Various soloists.** Troubadisc TRO-CD01405 (6/94).

Solage

French *fl* 1370-90

Suggested listening ...

...Fumeux fume par fumee. *Coupled with works by various composers.* **Alla Francesca.** Opus 111 OPS30-173 (7/98). *See review in the Collections section; refer to the Index.* Ⓖ Ⓖ Ⓖ

Antonio Soler

Spanish 1729-1783

Soler Keyboard Sonatas – No. 36 in C minor; No. 72 in F minor; No. 88 in D flat major; No. 119 in B flat major. Fandango.

D. Scarlatti Keyboard Sonatas – Kk7; Kk84; Kk185; Kk187; Kk193; Kk208; Kk491; Kk492. **Virginia Black** (hpd). Cala United Ⓕ CACD88005-2 (58 minutes: DDD: 8/94). ⚡

This highly recommendable disc is particularly exhilarating, even among a multitude of Scarlatti recordings. Thought has been given to the order of the sonatas selected, so as to provide a smooth key-sequence as well as contrasts of mood and pace. Black starts off in fine style with the sturdy Kk491 Sonata, complete with trumpet tuckets: she shows that it is perfectly possible to maintain strict time without any danger of sounding mechanical. On the other hand, her slight flexibility for expressive purposes in Kk208 is judged to a nicety. There is joyousness in Kk492, with its quasi-guitar thrummings and rushing scales, and noisy high spirits in Kk187; the exuberant vivacity of Kk7 really needed to be seen – not to check that there was no cheating in the perversely lengthy cross-handed sections (for who could not trust Virginia Black), but to enjoy the left-hand leaps, as we do the sixths and thirds of Kk84. The chosen sonatas by Scarlatti's disciple Soler are equally pleasurable. The chattering repeated notes of No. 88 and the right-hand leaps of tenths in No. 119 are entirely in the tradition of his mentor: the modulations in the second half of No. 36 and No. 119 point to Soler's special interest in that subject. (By an unfortunate mis-reading, this latter is billed as *Allegro arioso* instead of *Allegro airoso*, which is a very different thing.) The only disappointment in the disc is the amazing and spectacular *Fandango* (which may or may not be by Soler, but is remarkable whoever wrote it): not only does Virginia Black make numerous cuts in this, but her small inflexions of pace undermine the relentlessly cumulative drive of the dance rhythm. No details are given of the harpsichord employed, but it is a fine instrument with a magnificently rich tone.

Additional recommendations ...

...No. 1 in A major; No. 3 in B flat major; No. 24 in D minor; No. 25 in D minor; No. 28 in C major; No. 29 in C major; No. 30 in G major; No. 31 in G major; No. 96 in E flat major; No. 118 in A minor. Prelude No. 1 in D minor. **Bob van Asperen** (hpd).
Auvidis Astrée Ⓕ E8768 (71 minutes: DDD: 7/92). 🎵

...No. 7 in C major; No. 8 in C major; No. 9 in C major; No. 20 in C sharp minor; No. 21 in C sharp minor; No. 34 in E major; No. 95 in A major. Prelude No. 3 in C major.
Bob van Asperen (hpd). Auvidis Astrée Ⓕ E8769 (68 minutes: DDD: 7/92). 🎵

...No. 10 in B minor; No. 11 in B major; No. 12 in G major, "de la Cordorniz"; No. 13 in G major; No. 14 in G major; No. 52 in E minor; No. 73 in D major; No. 74 in D major; No. 92 in D major, "Sonata de clarines"; No. 106 in E minor. Prelude No. 6 in G major. **Bob van Asperen** (hpd).
Auvidis Astrée Ⓕ E8780 (69 minutes: DDD: 7/92). 🎵

...No. 15 in D minor; No. 22 in D flat major; No. 23 in D flat major; No. 54 in D minor; No. 61 in C major; No. 75 in F major; No. 76 in F major; No. 80 in G minor; No. 81 in G minor; No. 84 in D major; No. 86 in D major. **Bob van Asperen** (hpd).
Auvidis Astrée Ⓕ E8772 (70 minutes: DDD: 7/92). 🎵

...No. 18 in C minor; No. 19 in C minor; No. 26 in E minor; No. 27 in E minor; No. 36 in C minor; No. 85 in F sharp minor; No. 90 in F sharp minor; No. 91 in C major. No. 94 in G major.
Bob van Asperen (hpd). Auvidis Astrée Ⓕ E8773 (75 minutes: DDD: 7/92). 🎵

...No. 37 in D major; No. 46 in C major; No. 56 in F major; No. 98 in B flat major; No. 100 in C minor; No. 103 in C minor; No. 108 in C major, "del Gallo"; No. 109 in F major; No. 112 in C major. Fandango. Prelude No. 5 in D major. **Bob van Asperen** (hpd).
Auvidis Astrée Ⓕ E8771 (77 minutes: DDD: 7/92). 🎵

Further listening ...

...Quintets – No. 3 in G major; No. 4 in A minor; No. 5 in D major. **Concerto Rococo.**
Pierre Verany PV792111 (4/94). 🎵 *Gramophone* Editor's choice.

...Canzonettas – La semplice; La volubile; La costanza; La mercede.
Coupled with works by various composers. **Marta Almajano** (sop); **José Miguel Moreno** (gtr).
Glossa GCD920202 (2/96). *See review in the Collections section; refer to the Index.*

Fernando Sor
Spanish 1778-1839

Sor Fantaisies – No. 12, Op. 58; No. 13, Op. 59, "Fantaisie élégiaque". Studies, Op. 60.
  Nicholas Goluses (gtr). Naxos Ⓢ 8 553342 (65 minutes: DDD: 8/96). Recorded 1994.
Sor Grand Sonatas – C major, Op. 22; C major, Op. 25. Divertissement, Op. 23.
  Eight Short Pieces, Op. 24. **Adam Holzman** (gtr). Naxos Ⓢ 8 553340 (75 minutes: DDD: 8/96).
  Recorded 1994.

Sor's guitar works is an *oeuvre* that is perhaps the most consistent in quality, and most manageable in quantity of any major guitar composer of the period. Whilst Sor was born and died later than Beethoven his language was closer to that of Mozart, barely on the edge of romanticism. He was a polished and elegant composer, whose works have more quiet emotional content and expressiveness than those of any of his contemporaries, and though he often calls for technical virtuosity he doesn't lean too heavily on it.

The *Fantaisie* Op. 58 is not one of Sor's more riveting works. Goluses plays it in a somewhat matter-of-fact way. The *Fantaisie élégiaque*, arguably Sor's finest single work, elicits a very different response, a deeply sensitive and dignified reading in which the moments of silent grief are given the breathing-space and time they call for. Sor devoted five opus numbers to his 97 studies, of which Op. 60 was the last. Each has a clear technical and/or musical purpose and even the simplest is lovingly crafted music – which is how Goluses treats it, with lots of care lavished on it. It should be remembered that the guitar of Sor's time differed from today's in construction, stringing and sound, and that Sor played without using the right-hand nails. Goluses uses a modern instrument and plays with nails, which inevitably leads to differences in sound and, to some extent, interpretation. Given and accepting the differences, Goluses sets a bench-mark for present-day guitarists.

The major works in Holzman's programme are the two sonatas, each with four movements. Of these Op. 25 is by far the finer – and the best work of its kind from the period; the last movement is a Minuet, a final lightening of the atmosphere that was not then uncommon. The *Divertissement*, Op. 23 contains ten pieces – *Valses*, *Allegrettos*, *Andantes*, a *Minuetto* and an *Allemande*. With a few exceptions they are, like the studies, more likely to be of interest to guitarists than to the general listener. Holzman plays very well, with a softer sound than Goluses, and in a tighter acoustic. At slower tempos he exercises a pleasing degree of rubato and commendable dynamic shading; one wishes he had done likewise in the quicker ones, which incline to the metronomic. These are two discs that should, both in their own right and at super-budget price, be irresistible to guitarists.

Additional recommendation ...

...Fantasia élégiaque, Op. 59. Introduction and Variations on a Theme by Mozart, Op. 9. Etudes –
  Op. 6 No. 11; Op. 31 No. 12; Op. 35 No. 22. *Coupled with works by* **Coste** Raphaëlla Smits (gtr).
  Accent Ⓕ ACC29182D (61 minutes: DDD: 8/93).

Sor Introduction and Variations on "Que ne suis-je la fougère!", Op. 26. Introduction and Variations on "Gentil Housard", Op. 27. Introduction and Variations on "Malbroug", Op. 28. 12 Studies, Op. 29. Fantaisie et Variations brillantes, Op. 30. **Jeffrey McFadden** (gtr). Naxos Ⓢ 8 553451 (62 minutes: DDD: 4/97). Recorded 1995.

This contribution to Naxos's integral archive of Sor's guitar music consists neatly of the last works he published with Meissonnier, before transferring to the more prestigious house of Pacini. Sets of variations, whether *per se* or framed in the *Fantaisie*, Op. 30, abound. The *12 Studies*, Op. 29 are described as "Book 2", those of Op. 6 being "Book 1", and are here given as Nos. 13-24, as they were in the original edition of 1827. Jeffrey McFadden, a Canadian, is a squeaky-clean and very musical player, with the clear and three-dimensional tone for which his fingers are admirably suited. No composer for the guitar of the time wrote studies that were more truly expressive than those of Sor; McFadden plays them, and everything else here, with humanity and respect, neither mechanically nor with any excess of romantic sweetness. This outstanding disc would be cheap at twice the price.

Further listening ...
...Minuet, Op. 11 No. 6. Studies, Op. 6 – No. 6 in A major; No. 9 in D minor; No. 11 in E major; No. 12 in A major. Etude in A major, Op. 31 No. 19. Etudes, Op. 35 – No. 13 in C major; No. 17 in D major; No. 22 in E minor. Minuetto, Op. 22. *Coupled with works by* **Aguado** and **Tárrega Norbert Kraft** (gtr). Naxos 8 553007 (1/95).
...Trois Pièces de Société, Op. 33. 24 Exercises, Op. 35. **Steven Novacek** (gtr). Naxos 8 553341 (1/98).
...Pieces – Op. 5: No. 3 in C major; No. 4 in C major. Op. 24: No. 6 in F major; No. 7 in F major; No. 8 in B flat major. Minuets, Op. 11 – No. 2 in G sharp minor; No. 3 in G major; No. 6 in A major; No. 7 in A minor; No. 8 in B flat major; No. 9 in E minor; No. 10 in F major. Studies – Op. 29: No. 21 in D major. Op. 31: No. 13 in C major; No. 18 in B minor. Op. 35: No. 5 in A minor; No. 11 in D minor; No. 12 in F major; No. 18 in B minor; No. 19 in C sharp major. Op. 60: No. 14 in E minor; No. 18 in A minor; No. 22 in E minor; No. 23 in B major. *Coupled with works by* **Marschner** and **Werthmüller**. **Tilman Hoppstock** (gtr). Signum SIGX75-00 (2/98). *See review in the Collections section; refer to the Index.*
...Le premier pas vers moi, Op. 53. Fantasia, Op. 54*b*. Trois Duos faciles et progressifs, Op. 55. Trois Petits Divertissements, Op. 61. Divertissement, Op. 62. Souvenir de Russie, Op. 63. **Robert Kubica, Wilma van Berkel** (gtrs). Naxos 8 553418 (12/97).
...Studies, Op. 31 – Mouvement de prière religieuse. Ariettas – Povero cor t'inganni; Lagrime; Io mentitor!; Perduta l'anima. Nel cor più non mi sento. Seguidillas – Muchacha, y los vergüenza; Si dices que mis ojos; Los canonigos, madre; Las mujeres y cuerdas; Mis descuidados ojos. *Coupled with works by various composers.* **Marta Almajano** (sop); **José Miguel Moreno** (gtr). Glossa GCD920202 (2/96). *See review in the Collections section; refer to the Index.*
...Thèmes variés et Douze Minuets, Op. 11 – Andante maestoso; Andante expressivo. Introduction and Variations on a theme by Mozart, Op. 9. *Coupled with works by various composers.* **José Miguel Moreno** (vihuela/gtr). Glossa GCD920103 (8/95). ✍

Leo Sowerby   American 1895-1968

Suggested listening ...
...Magnificat and Nunc dimittis in D major. *Coupled with works by various composers.* **St Thomas Church Choir, New York / Gerre Hancock** with **Patrick Allen** (org). Priory PRCD600 (1/98). *See review in the Collections section; refer to the Index.*

Louis Spohr   German 1784-1859

Spohr Violin Concertos – No. 1 in A major, Op. 1; No. 14 in A minor, Op. 110, "Sonst und Jetzt"; No. 15 in E minor, Op. 128. **Ulf Hoelscher** (vn); **Berlin Radio Symphony Orchestra / Christian Fröhlich**. CPO Ⓕ CPO999 403-2 (66 minutes: DDD: 11/97). Recorded 1995.

Hoelscher has the elegance and almost vocal quality with which Spohr's violin writing is associated, but he can also master the virtuosity which is needed for the oddest work here, entitled *Sonst und Jetzt*, or "Then and Now". There is something of an in-joke for violinists here. Irritated by the playing of the Norwegian virtuoso, Ole Bull, whom Schumann regarded as the equal of Paganini, Spohr wrote this piece contrasting the lyrical qualities of the violin (in an expansive re-creation of the minuet) with a hectic *Tarantella* embodying all he disliked in the showy 'modern' style. The idea falls flat as a piece of music criticism, simply because Spohr produces rather a good *Tarantella* and integrates it ingeniously and not contentiously with his more lyrical music. Hoelscher could have made the point by playing the two kinds of music in more extreme fashion; but, if it is true that nothing is colder than the ashes of dead controversies, the more musical course is to play the work as he does, warmly and without *parti-pris*. Concerto No. 15 is a rather more weary piece, in which Spohr goes through the motions expertly but without his full creative attention. Op. 1 is a juvenile work (he was 18), obviously close to his beloved Mozart in spirit but also heavily influenced by Kreutzer, Rode and especially Viotti. The best movement is the delightful *Siciliano*, which Spohr embellishes lovingly.

Spohr Nonet in F major, Op. 31. Octet in E major, Op. 32. Waltz in A major, Op. 89, "Erinnerung an Marienbad". **Academy of St Martin in the Fields Chamber Ensemble.** Philips Ⓕ 438 017-2PH (74 minutes: DDD: 11/95). Recorded 1992.

Spohr's two most popular chamber works go well together, here in performances that come closer to a lyrical, reflective, even sometimes wistful manner than the more extrovert style of the Nash Ensemble. Theirs was friendly chamber music playing in a comparatively light context; the Academy suggest greater depths, sometimes at the expense of the music's gaiety in the faster movements. The finale of the Octet can sound livelier than on this disc, and perhaps should, though there is at least consistency with all that has gone before; and the 'Harmonious Blacksmith' depicted in the variation movement is a more melancholy fellow than Handel surely intended. But the playing is thoughtful and well judged, not only in matters of living ensemble (something more than merely timing) but in exploring and bringing to life the music through a flexible and sensitive application of its form. So the first movements of both works come off well as sonata structures as powerful and supple as Spohr must have intended, which will doubtless give these performances lasting satisfaction. The sound is well balanced, with a proper attention to the rich middle registers. As a *bonne bouche*, there is the waltz which he wrote in salon manner for the typical spa ensemble of the day.

Additional recommendations ...

...Nonet. Octet. **Gaudier Ensemble.** Hyperion Ⓕ CDA66699 (61 minutes: DDD: 8/94).

...Nonet. Octet. **Nash Ensemble.** CRD Ⓕ CRD3354 (56 minutes: ADD: 3/89).

Spohr Piano Trios – No. 3 in A minor, Op. 124; No. 4 in B flat major, Op. 133. **Borodin Trio** (Rostislav Dubinsky, vn; Laszlo Varga, vc; Luba Edlina, pf). Chandos Ⓕ CHAN9372 (66 minutes: DDD: 10/95). Recorded 1994.

Spohr's late piano trios are virtuoso works, in every sense. They are ingeniously composed and are difficult to balance with true effect; above all they demand great technical dexterity, and the dexterity to allow many extremely difficult passages to play a secondary or supporting role. In particular No. 3 in A minor places demands on the players which need virtuosity of the kind which the Borodin Trio are well able to provide. Their skills need no recommendation by now; here, they also have a subtlety and quickness of response that come from a proper sympathy with Spohr's idiom. They rise to the occasion with, for instance, the racing piano fingerwork in the Variations of No. 3; they also respond with the flexibility of tempo the music needs for its full expressive effect. Moreover, in places where Spohr seems to have lost concentration for a moment or two – his capacity to meander down beguiling but distracting chromatic paths, his habit of striking a cliché chord like a dramatic attitude, his gear-changing modulations – the Borodin hold faith and make the music come off effectively. The A minor Trio is the more worthwhile piece, and deserves all this interpretative concentration; but the rather less well invented work in B flat, apparently here receiving a first recording, is worth having for some pleasant and recreational music. The recording team cannot always have had an easy task with balance; it all works excellently.

Additional recommendation ...

...Piano Trios – No. 3 in A minor, Op. 124; No. 5 in G minor, Op. 142. **Hartley Piano Trio.** Naxos Ⓢ 8 553164 (62 minutes: DDD: 1/96).

Further listening ...

...Clarinet Concerto No. 1 in C minor, Op. 26. *Coupled with works by* **Mozart** *and* **Weber**
Ernst Ottensamer (cl/ᵃbasset cl); **Vienna Philharmonic Orchestra / Sir Colin Davis.**
Philips 438 868-2PH (6/94). *See review under Mozart; refer to the Index.*

...Symphonies – No. 1 in E flat major, Op. 20; No. 5 in C minor, Op. 102. **Košice State Philharmonic Orchestra / Alfred Walter.** Marco Polo 8 223363.

...Double Quartet in D minor, Op. 65. String Sextet, Op. 140. String Quintet in G major, Op. 33 No. 2. **L'Archibudelli** and **Smithsonian Chamber Players.**
Sony Classical Vivarte SK53370 (4/94). 🗡

...Double Quartet No. 1 in D minor, Op. 65. *Coupled with works by* **Berwald** *and* **Weber**
Gervase de Peyer (cl); **Melos Ensemble.** EMI Matrix CDM5 65995-2 (12/96).

...Duos concertants, Op. 67 – No. 1 in A minor; No. 2 in D major; No. 3 in A minor.
Heinz Schunk, Ulrike Petersen (vns). CPO CPO999 343-2 (3/96).

...Septet in A minor, Op. 147ᵇ. *Coupled with* **Beethoven** Quintet for Piano and Wind in
E flat major, Op. 16ᵃ.
ᵇ**Chantal Juillet** (vn); ᵇ**Christopher van Kampen** (vc); **Pascal Rogé** (pf); **London Winds.**
Decca 443 892-2DH (4/96). *See review under Beethoven; refer to the Index.*   Ⓖ

...String Quintet in A minor, Op. 91. String Sextet in C major, Op. 140. Potpourri on themes of
Mozart in B flat major, Op. 22. **Academy of St Martin in the Fields Chamber Ensemble.**
Chandos CHAN9424 (4/96).

...Fantasia in C minor, Op. 35. *Coupled with works by various composers.* **Naoko Yoshino** (hp).
Philips 446 064-2PH (2/96). *See review in the Collections section; refer to the Index.*

...Sechs Lieder, Op. 103. Faust – Ich bin allein. Variations in B flat major on a Theme from
"Alruna". *Coupled with works by various composers.* **Elizabeth Ritchie** (sop); **Victoria Soames** (cl);
Anna Coleman (vn); **Matthew Souter** (va); **Alastair Blayden** (vc); **Jennifer Purvis** (pf).
Clarinet Classics CC0006 (3/94).

...Faust. **Soloists; Bielefeld Opera Chorus; Bielefeld Philharmonic Orchestra / Geoffrey Moull.**
CPO CPO999 247-2 (8/94).
...Faust. **Soloists; Stuttgart Radio Chorus; Kaiserslautern Radio Orchestra / Klaus Arp.**
Capriccio 60 049-2 (12/94).
...Jessonda. **Soloists; Hamburg State Opera Chorus; Hamburg Philharmonic Orchestra /
Gerd Albrecht.** Orfeo C240912H (11/91).

Sir John Stainer
British 1840-1901

Stainer The Crucifixion. **Martyn Hill** (ten); **Michael George** (bass); **BBC Singers;
Leith Hill Festival Singers / Brian Kay** with **Margaret Phillips** (org). Chandos Ⓟ CHAN9551
(71 minutes: DDD: A/97). Text included. Recorded 1997.
It is easy to dismiss Stainer's *Crucifixion* as the epitome of English musical disfunctionality in the
nineteenth century. Yet, over 100 years after its première at Marylebone Parish Church in 1887, this
work still has a following. Despite moments of questionable taste Stainer's formula strikes a chord for
a surprisingly broad audience. In its favour, it unfolds with a seamless ease, never jolting the listener
with gratuitous theatricality or the type of rhetorical intensity which the English find mildly
embarrassing. Emotional engagement here is about an unintrusive sobriety, affected by a glowing
sentimental identification with the Saviour's plight – all very Victorian but clearly a strong residue of
such a temperament still remains. One has to admire Stainer for writing a challenging work of sensible
length which, without an orchestra, is achievable and satisfying for a capable parish choir: Stainer's
Crucifixion is a celebration of amateurism, that cherished English virtue. Brian Kay has worked a
great deal with committed amateurs, in this case the Leith Hill Festival Singers, the festival of which
he is director. There is indeed an underlying freshness of expression here, of singers with eyes and ears
on stalks and a real sense of purpose to the performance. They are fortified by the excellent BBC
Singers. Margaret Phillips's imaginative and genial registrations, not to mention her skilful
accompaniment, provide notable support to the excellent contributions of Martyn Hill and Michael
George. An unselfregarding and genuine performance.

Carl Stamitz
German 1745-1801

Stamitz Symphonies – F major, Op. 24 No. 3; Op. 13 – No. 4 in G major; No. 5 in C major;
D major, "La chasse". **London Mozart Players / Matthias Bamert.** Chandos Ⓟ CHAN9358
(62 minutes: DDD: 5/95). Recorded 1994.
Besides showing Stamitz's flair for melody and effective use of contrast, the London Mozart Players
are responsive to the touches of genuine originality in these pieces. Try the first movement of the
C major Symphony, Op. 13 No. 5, where the slow introduction ingeniously returns as a coda, or the
textural variety in the G major Symphony, Op. 13 No. 4, where flutes replace oboes in the outer
movements, while the second movement, in which the LMP elegantly convey the music's spaciousness,
is scored for strings and continuo alone. Bamert's firm, sympathetic direction is also evident in the
F major Symphony, Op. 24 No. 3, where the second and third movements are particularly effective
for the subtlety with which the LMP defuse the slow movement's dramatic intensity, with delightfully
buoyant playing in the work's radiantly cheerful finale. *La chasse* is the highlight of the disc. The
declamatory character of the slow introduction gives way to operatic brilliance in the subsequent
Allegro, and the slow movement's graceful stateliness culminates in a vividly descriptive portrayal of
the hunt in the finale. The stylish performances make a strong case for this repertoire.
Further listening ...
...Viola Sonata in B flat major. *Coupled with works by various composers.*
Anna Barbara Duetschler (va); **Ursula Duetschler** (fp). Claves CD50-9502 (11/95). ✒

Jan Stamitz
Bohemian 1717-1757

Suggested listening ...
...Trumpet Concerto in D major (realized Boustead). *Coupled with works by various composers.*
Håkan Hardenberger (tpt); **Academy of St Martin in the Fields / Sir Neville Marriner.**
Philips 420 203-2PH (12/87). *See review in the Collections section; refer to the Index.*

Charles Villiers Stanford
Irish/British 1852-1924

Stanford Symphony No. 3 in F minor, Op. 28[a], "Irish".
Elgar Scenes from the Bavarian Highlands, Op. 27[b]. [b]**Bournemouth Symphony Chorus;
Bournemouth Sinfonietta / Norman Del Mar.** EMI British Composers Ⓜ CDM5 65129-2
(70 minutes: ADD: 7/95). Text included. Item marked [a] from HMV ASD4221 (8/82),
[b]ASD4061 (9/81). Recorded 1981-1982.

A valuable addition to the catalogue on its initial appearance, Norman Del Mar's characteristically enterprising 1982 recording of Stanford's *Irish* Symphony re-emerges in splendidly vital fashion on this beautifully presented release. Compared with Vernon Handley and the excellent Ulster Orchestra, Del Mar is perhaps just a touch lacking in charm and it is undoubtedly the former who more effectively minimizes the element of dutiful convention which occasionally afflicts both outer movements (Handley is nearly three minutes quicker in the opening *Allegro moderato*, yet there is no feeling of undue haste). However, Del Mar draws the threads together most satisfyingly for the symphony's ample peroration, and his Bournemouth band respond with commendable vigour throughout. Preceding the Stanford here is a rare outing for the orchestral version of Elgar's *Scenes from the Bavarian Highlands*. This six-movement choral suite shows Elgar at his most carefree and joyous, qualities savoured to the full in Del Mar's exuberant, nicely disciplined performance. A thoroughly enjoyable reissue.

Additional recommendation ...

...No. 3. Irish Rhapsody No. 5 in G minor, Op. 147. **Ulster Orchestra / Vernon Handley.** Chandos Ⓕ CHAN8545 (56 minutes: DDD: 1/88).

Stanford Requiem, Op. 63[a]. The Veiled Prophet of Khorassan[b]: Overture; Ballet music – No. 1; No. 2; There's a bower of roses[c]. [a]**Frances Lucey,** [c]**Virginia Kerr** (sops); [a]**Colette McGahon** (mez); [a]**Peter Kerr** (ten); [a]**Nigel Leeson-Williams** (bass); [a]**RTE Philharmonic Choir; National Symphony Orchestra of Ireland /** [a]**Adrian Leaper,** [b]**Colman Pearce.** Marco Polo Ⓕ 8 223580/1 (two discs: 104 minutes: DDD: 7/97). Texts and translations included. Recorded 1994.

It is most moving to hear this Requiem and to reflect that for the best part of a century a work so rich in feeling and craftsmanship has lain largely silent and unregarded. The opening *Requiem aeternam* ought of itself, one would think, to have ensured at least the occasional revival: a warm, lyrical composition, firmly structured and with something unmistakably personal about it, rather as with Dvořák. The *Kyrie* seems to express affection, though 'For what?' one wonders – perhaps for the sheer beauty of sound. The "Gradual" allows interest to slip, recaptured by the "Sequence", plentiful in ideas and rising to a generous climax in the "Lacrimosa". The "Offertorium" brings a touch of nineteenth-century Grand Manner, tightening up later in a robust, fugal "Quam olim Abrahae". The *Sanctus* ends vigorously with its "Pleni sunt caeli", and a sweet, well-sustained orchestral passage (perhaps with Beethoven in mind) leads into the "Benedictus". A Funeral March introduces the *Agnus Dei*, and the whole work, not all that much shorter than the Verdi Requiem, ends with a spacious, steadily developed "Lux aeterna". Soloists and chorus are used with relish for the capabilities of the human voice, and in listening one thinks quite as much of opera as of oratorio. As a fill-up on the second disc we are given further rarities, the Overture and other excerpts from *The Veiled Prophet of Khorassan*, the first of Stanford's operas. The Overture, more Brahms than Mendelssohn and with a genial suggestion of the Irish jig, is a thoroughly likeable piece, so once more we are left feeling that here is still another area of Stanford's output that might reward attention. The performances are able and enthusiastic. Recorded sound might be sharper, but at least it falls more kindly on the ears than do many of more vaunted origin. In any case, we are deeply in Marco Polo's debt for this revival.

Stanford Stabat mater, Op. 96[a]. Te Deum laudamus, Op. 10 No. 1[b]. Six Bible Songs, Op. 113[c]. [ab]**Ingrid Attrot** (sop); [ab]**Pamela Helen Stephen** (mez); [ab]**Nigel Robson** (ten); **Stephen Varcoe** (bar); [c]**Ian Watson** (org); [ab]**Leeds Philharmonic Chorus;** [ab]**BBC Philharmonic Orchestra / Richard Hickox.** Chandos Ⓕ CHAN9548 (74 minutes: DDD: 9/97). Texts and translations included. Recorded 1995.

Writing of his old teacher in 1952, Vaughan Williams foretold that his time would come round again: "With the next generation the inevitable reaction will set in and Stanford will come into his own". It has taken more than a generation, but at last it does begin to look as though he was right. This recording of a "symphonic cantata", the *Stabat mater*, strong in ideas, deeply felt and structurally assured, will certainly strengthen the steadily growing appreciation of his worth. The Prelude, impressive as it is, is almost *too* soundly constructed, and the first choral movement, rich in its Verdi-like foreground of soloists, signs off with a slightly self-conscious repetition of the opening words by the soprano. Stanford is never abashed by the prospect of melodic commitment, and the orchestral Intermezzo comes out boldly with what promises to be a good, old-fashioned Grand Tune; but then he seems to remember where he is, and the piece ends with murky explorations that seem not quite to find what they may be seeking. The work itself ends, as Lewis Foreman suggests in his useful notes, in Eternity: "we seem to reach the crest of a hill only to find the path stretching onward and upward to another". The performance carries conviction, with Hickox exercising that natural rightness of his so that in a work such as this, without predecessors on record, a listener will feel that this is how it should 'go'. Fine orchestral playing and choral singing give pleasure throughout. The solo quartet is led by Ingrid Attrot's colourful but none too evenly produced soprano, and in the *Bible Songs* Stephen Varcoe sings sensitively to the judiciously registered organ accompaniment of Ian Watson. The most tuneful of *Te Deums* follows, blithe and buoyant in its orchestrated version.

Additional recommendation ...

...Bible Songs[ac] – No. 4, A song of peace; No. 6, A song of wisdom. Hymns, Op. 113[bd] – No. 4, Pray that Jerusalem; No. 6, O for a closer walk with God. Evening Services[bd] – G major, Op. 81;

C major, Op. 115. For lo, I raise up, Op. 145[bd]. Three Motets, Op. 38[b]. Magnificat, Op. 164[bd]. The Lord is my shepherd[bd]. Postlude in D minor, Op. 105 No. 6[c]. [a]**John Mark Ainsley** (ten); [b]**Choir of King's College, Cambridge / Stephen Cleobury** ([c]org) with [d]**James Vivian** (org). EMI British Composers Ⓕ CDC5 55535-2 (75 minutes: DDD: 6/97).

Stanford Morning and Evening Services in B flat major, Op. 10[a]. Evening Services – A major, Op. 12[a]; F major, Op. 36[a]; E flat major[b]. Two Anthems, Op. 37[b]. Three Motets, Op. 38. Pater noster. The Lord is my Shepherd[a]. **Winchester Cathedral Choir / David Hill** with [a]**Stephen Farr,** [b]**Christopher Monks** (org). Hyperion Ⓕ CDA66964 (78 minutes: DDD: 2/98). Texts included. Recorded 1997.

Delius in an extremity of wonder and dismay is said to have remarked that Parry would have set the whole something Bible to music if he had had the something time. Stanford similarly must have been suspected of a purpose, under similar conditions, to set the Evening canticles in every key in the *Well-tempered Clavier*. A major, B flat major, C major, F major and G major are familiar to us already; here Hyperion comes up with E flat major; and this is but Vol. 1. The *Magnificat and Nunc dimittis* in E flat major dates back to 1873 and, according to the valuable notes by Dr Jeremy Dibble, is not with any certainty known even to have been performed. Perhaps this is because both settings are almost indecently tuneful. The 23-year-old Irishman comes out with an apocalyptic "scattered the proud", a broadly melodious "to be a light" and "Gloria"s as catchy as a comic opera. In these clap-happy days it might enjoy a new lease of life, except of course that it is far too good. As for the B flat major settings written six years later, these (both Morning and Evening services) have long owed their popularity to a melodic gift that is almost Schubertian and a correspondingly deft mastery of construction.

The A major and F major settings also lie within the scope of this first volume, leaving G major (with the treble solo) and C major (best of all) for another day. Winchester Cathedral Choir are surely one of the best in the UK. Under David Hill, the trebles have acquired something of the bright, distinctive tone of the Westminster Cathedral boys. The men are excellent, and all of them sound as though they are singing for the joy of it. Several of these works involve more than the customary four parts, and the eight-part *Pater noster*, recorded for the first time, has splendid richness, with the choir forming massive columns or pillars of sound in the powerful climax. Stanford's writing for the organ, endowing the accompaniment with an independent life, is also a delight and at times we might wish that the fine playing of both organists had been brought into sharper focus. The choir we hear with rare clarity, and to do so is an unmixed pleasure. The record is most welcome, as is the prospect of more to come.

Additional recommendations ...
...Morning and Evening Services – B flat major, Op. 10; C major, Op. 115. Benedictus and Agnus Dei in F major. **Durham Cathedral Choir / James Lancelot** with **Keith Wright** (org). Priory Ⓕ PRCD437 (80 minutes: DDD: 4/94). Ⓖ
...Six Short Preludes and Postludes – Set 2, Op. 105. Complete Organ Sonatas – No. 1 in F major, Op. 149; No. 2 in G minor, Op. 151, "Sonata Eroica"; No. 3 in D minor, Op. 152, "Britannia"; No. 4 in C minor, Op. 153, "Celtica"; No. 5 in A major, Op. 159, "Quasi una fantasia". **Desmond Hunter** (org). Priory Ⓕ PRCD445 (two discs: 129 minutes: 9/94).
...Evening Services – A major, Op. 12; G major, Op. 81. **Durham Cathedral Choir / James Lancelot** with **Keith Wright** (org). Priory Ⓕ PRCD514 (78 minutes: DDD: 6/95).
...Evening Service in A major, Op. 12[a]. *Coupled with works by various composers.* **Lichfield Cathedral Choir / Andrew Lumsden** with **Mark Shepherd.** Priory Ⓕ PRCD505 (56 minutes: DDD: 10/95). *See review in the Collections section; refer to the Index.*
...Three Motets, Op. 38[a]. The Lord is my shepherd[ab]. If ye then be risen with Christ[ab]. For lo, I raise up, Op. 145[ab]. Ye choirs of New Jerusalem, Op. 123[ab]. How beauteous are their feet[ab]. Three Motets, Op. 135[a] – No. 1, Ye holy angels bright; No. 3, Glorious and all-powerful God. Three Preludes and Fugues, Op. 193[c] – No. 2 in B minor; No. 3 in C major. [a]**Choir of New College, Oxford / Edward Higginbottom** with [b]**Paul Plummer,** [c]**Andrew Smith** (org). CRD Ⓕ CRD3497 (68 minutes: DDD: 6/97).
...Three Motets, Op. 38. *Coupled with works by various composers.* **Choir of St Mary's Cathedral, Edinburgh / Timothy Byram-Wigfield.** Priory Ⓕ PRCD557 (64 minutes: DDD: 10/97). *See review in the Collections section; refer to the Index.*

Further listening ...
...Clarinet Concerto in A minor, Op. 80. *Coupled with* **Finzi** Clarinet Concerto in C minor, Op. 31. **Thea King** (cl); **Philharmonia Orchestra / Alun Francis.** Hyperion CDA66001 (6/87).
...Piano Concerto No. 1 in G major, Op. 59. *Coupled with* **Parry** Piano Concerto in F sharp major. **Piers Lane** (pf); **BBC Scottish Symphony Orchestra / Martyn Brabbins.** Hyperion CDA66820 (2/96). *See review under Parry; refer to the Index.*
...Serenade (Nonet) in F major, Op. 95. *Coupled with* **Parry** Nonet in B flat major. **Capricorn.** Hyperion CDA66291 (9/89).
...Symphony No. 1 in B flat major. Irish Rhapsody No. 2 in F minor, Op. 84, "Lament for the son of Ossian". **Ulster Orchestra / Vernon Handley.** Chandos CHAN9049 (10/92).
...Piano Trio No. 2 in G minor, Op. 73. *Coupled with works by* **Holst** and **Bax Pirasti Trio.** ASV CDDCA925 (9/95). *See review under Bax; refer to the Index.*

...Violin Sonata in D major, Op. 11. *Coupled with works by* **Dunhill** and **Bantock**
Susanne Stanzeleit (vn); **Gusztáv Fenyö** (pf).
Cala United CACD88031 (7/96). *See review under Bantock; refer to the Index.*

...Fantasia and Toccata in D minor, Op. 57. *Coupled with works by various composers.*
Keith John (org). Priory PRCD370 (11/92). *Selected by Sounds in Retrospect.*
See review in the Collections Section; refer to the Index.   ⓐⓐⓐ

...(arr. Grainger) Four Irish Dances, Op. 89 – No. 1, A March-Jig; No. 4, A Reel. *Coupled with piano works by* **Grainger Marc-André Hamelin** (pf). Hyperion CDA66884 (1/97).
Gramophone Editor's choice. See review under Grainger, refer to the Index.   ⓐⓐ

...The bluebird. *Coupled with works by various composers.* **Oxford Camerata / Jeremy Summerly.**
Naxos 8 553088 (5/97).

...For lo, I raise up, Op. 145. *Coupled with works by various composers.*
St Paul's Cathedral Choir / John Scott with **Andrew Lucas** (org).
Hyperion CDA66826 (7/96). *See review in the Collections section; refer to the Index.*

...From the red rose. *Coupled with works by various composers.*
Dame Felicity Lott (sop); **Graham Johnson** (pf).
Hyperion CDA66937 (10/97). *See review in the Collections section; refer to the Index.*

...To the soul. *Coupled with works by various composers.* **Thomas Hampson** (bar); **Craig Rutenberg**
(pf). EMI CDM5 55028-2 (10/97). *See review in the Collections section; refer to the Index.* ⓐⓐⓐ

John Stanley   British 1712-1786

Suggested listening ...

...Trumpet Concerto in D major. *Coupled with works by various composers.*
Crispian Steele-Perkins (tpt); **Bournemouth Sinfonietta / Richard Studt** (vn).
Carlton Classics 30366 0038-2 (4/97). *See review in the Collections section; refer to the Index.*

...Voluntaries – A minor, Op. 6 No. 2; D minor, Op. 7 No. 4; G major, Op. 7 No. 9. *Coupled with works by various composers.* **Jennifer Bate** (org). Unicorn-Kanchana DKPCD9106 (11/91).
Selected by Sounds in Retrospect. See review in the Collections section; refer to the Index.   ⓐ

Stanley & Allen   British 19th/20th century

Suggested listening ...

...Cabbages, Cabeans and Carrots. *Coupled with works by various composers.*
Dame Felicity Lott (sop); **Graham Johnson** (pf). Hyperion CDA66937 (10/97).
See review in the Collections section; refer to the Index.

Agostino Steffani   Italian 1654-1728

Suggested listening ...

...Scherzo, Guardati. *Coupled with works by various composers.*
Ann Monoyios (sop); **Berlin Barock Compagney.**
Capriccio 10 459 (10/95). ✍ *See review in the Collections section; refer to the Index.*   ⓐ

Wilhelm Stenhammar   Swedish 1871-1927

Stenhammar Piano Concerto No. 1 in B flat minor, Op. 1[a]. Symphony No. 3 in C major –
fragment. [a]**Mats Widlund** (pf); **Stockholm Philharmonic Orchestra / Gennadi Rozhdestvensky.**
Chandos Ⓕ CHAN9074 (51 minutes: DDD: 10/92). Recorded 1992.

Stenhammar Piano Concerto No. 2 in D minor, Op. 23[a]. Serenade in F major, Op. 31[b]. Florez
och Blanzeflor, Op. 3[c]. [c]**Ingvár Wixell** (bar); [a]**Janos Solyom** (pf); [a]**Munich Philharmonic Orchestra;**
[bc]**Swedish Radio Symphony Orchestra / Stig Westerberg.** EMI Matrix Ⓜ CDM5 65081-2
(73 minutes: ADD: 5/94). Text and translation included. Items marked [a] from Swedish HMV
4E 063 34284 (8/81), [bc] Swedish HMV 4E 061 35148 (8/80). Recorded 1970-1974.

The First Piano Concerto comes from 1893, when Stenhammar was 22, and such was its success
during the 1890s that he was invited to play it with the Berlin Philharmonic under Richard Strauss.
In time, however, he grew tired of it and became careless as to its fate. Both the autograph and the
orchestral parts were destroyed when Breslau was bombed during the Second World War. But recently
a copy probably made for the American première came to light in the Library of Congress. Chandos
also offer a short fragment from the Symphony No. 3 in C major, on which Stenhammar embarked
in 1918-19. At not much under 50 minutes it is perhaps overlong, but still has much charm, and
Widlund and Rozhdestvensky make a most persuasive case for it. The recording has great depth and
warmth and the strings of the Stockholm Orchestra have great richness of sonority. The *Serenade* is
arguably Stenhammar's masterpiece. In its Overture the writing is vibrant and luminous, full of subtly

changing textures and colours, and like the finale is of symphonic proportions. Apparently Stenhammar toyed at one stage with the idea of adding the word *selvaggio* or "wild" to the title of the *Scherzo*, the mercurial centrepiece of the whole work, which is played with captivating spirit here. Stig Westerberg's 20-year-old recording comes up very fresh indeed. The playing throughout is ardent, sensitive and vital. This issue offers two additional pieces, most notably János Solyom's brilliant account of the Second Piano Concerto with the Munich Philharmonic, sounding as if it were recorded yesterday. It is strongly indebted to Saint-Saëns, and the *Scherzo* has a Mendelssohnian effervescence and delicacy. The early and endearing if Wagnerian *Florez och Blanzeflor*, finely sung by Ingvár Wixell, is the admirable makeweight.

Additional recommendation ...
...Piano Concerto No. 1[a]. Two Sentimental Romances, Op. 28[b]. Florez och Blanzeflor, Op. 3[c]. [a]**Love Derwinger** (pf); [b]**Ulf Wallin** (vn); [c]**Peter Mattei** (bar); **Malmö Symphony Orchestra / Paavo Järvi.**
BIS Ⓕ CD550 (68 minutes: DDD: 10/92). *Selected by Sounds in Retrospect.*

Stenhammar Symphonies – No. 1 in F major; No. 2 in G minor, Op. 34. Excelsior!, Op 13.
Serenade in F major, Op 31. **Gothenburg Symphony Orchestra / Neeme Järvi.**
DG Ⓕ 445 857-2GH2 (two discs: 139 minutes: DDD: 8/95). Recorded 1992-1993.
Gramophone Editor's choice.
This set offers the two symphonies, the *Serenade* in its finished form without the *Reverenza* movement, which Stenhammar eventually rejected and the early overture, *Excelsior!*. The first disc offers an exemplary performance of the brilliant overture, *Excelsior!* – full of youthful confidence and Wagnerian exuberance – as well as the First Symphony. The Swedish daily press, reviewing the première of the overture in 1897, commented that Stenhammar "speaks more German than Swedish". They might well have said the same of the First Symphony, which Stenhammar himself called "idyllic Bruckner", but there are Brahmsian touches too. It is a marvellous score, fertile in invention and generous in spirit. Järvi brings to the glorious *Serenade* an appropriate lightness of touch and in the *Notturno* he takes plenty of time over the piece; feelings are delicately touched upon and there is a great sense of wonder. The performance as a whole is very sympathetic and, as one would expect, idiomatic. There is splendid definition in the recording.

Additional recommendation ...
... No. 2. Excelsior!. **Royal Scottish National Orchestra / Petter Sundkvist.**
Naxos Ⓢ 8 553888 (58 minutes: DDD: 6/97).

Further listening ...
...String Quartets – No. 1 in C major, Op. 2[a]; No. 2 in C minor, Op. 14[b]. [a]**Fresk Quartet;**
[b]**Copenhagen Quartet.** Caprice CAP21337.
...String Quartets – No. 3 in F major, Op. 18; No. 4 in A minor, Op. 25. **Gotland Quartet.**
Caprice CAP21338.
...String Quartets – No. 5 in C major, Op. 29, "Serenade"[a]; No. 6 in D minor, Op. 35[b].
[a]**Fresk Quartet;** [b]**Copenhagen Quartet.** Caprice CAP21339.
...Piano Sonatas – No. 1 in C major; No. 2 in C minor; No. 3 in A flat major; No. 4 in G minor.
Fantasie in A minor. **Lucia Negro** (pf). BIS CD634 (3/96).
... Piano Sonata in A flat minor, Op. 12. Violin Sonata in A minor, Op. 19. Allegro ma non tanto in A major. Allegro brillante in E flat major. **Lucia Negro** (pf); **Tale Quartet.** BIS CD764 (8/97).
...Seven Poems from Thoughts of Solitude, Op. 7. Five Songs to texts by Johann Ludvig Runeberg, Op. 8. Four Swedish Songs, Op. 16. Five Songs of Bo Bergman, Op. 20. Songs and Moods, Op. 26. Late Harvest. **Peter Mattei** (bar); **Bengt-Ake Lundin** (pf). BIS CD654 (9/95).
...Songs and Moods, Op. 26 – No. 1, The Wanderer; No. 4, Miss Blonde and Miss Brunette; No. 5, A ship sails; No. 9, Coastal song. Songs, Op. 37 – No. 1, Jutta comes to the Volkungs; No. 2, In the maple's shade. *Coupled with works by various composers.* **Anne Sofie von Otter** (mez);
Bengt Forsberg (pf). DG 449 189-2GH (5/96). *Gramophone Editor's choice. See review in the Collections section; refer to the Index.*   ⒼⒼ

Bernard Stevens   British 1916-1983

Stevens Fantasia on "Giles Farnaby's Dreame". Piano Sonata in one movement, Op. 25. Aria.
Howells Gadabout. Three Pieces, Op. 14. Sonatina. **Jeremy Filsell** (pf). Guild Ⓕ GMCD7119
(70 minutes: DDD: 11/96). From Gamut GAMCD541.
This is an effective, but slightly odd coupling of composers, since all the Howells is available from Margaret Fingerhut and the best of his keyboard music is probably for the organ, with the notable exception of the outstanding clavichord works, all of which John McCabe has recorded on the piano (both listed under Howells). The earliest Howells here lacks his mature fingerprints, but the late *Sonatina* (1971) is pared down but recognizable, especially in the slow movement. Filsell approaches everything sympathetically, but "Procession" from Op. 14 is not sufficiently rhythmically regular to reflect its subject. The Stevens works, headed by the Sonata (1954), are not otherwise represented in the catalogue. The single movement is in the rhetorical tradition of the British piano sonata, in a rather grey, mainstream dialect less personal than Rawsthorne but not far from some of Hoddinott's or Mathias's works. The slow central section (based on the two-chord alternation from the finale of

Vaughan Williams's Symphony No. 6) starting at 6'30" is pleasantly lyrical, then it meanders until overtaken by a kind of jig (11'32") to finish. The *Aria* from the early 1960s is delightful – is this the core of Stevens, who was said to be always smiling? The *Farnaby* Variations are resourceful, a considered exploration of the virginal piece bridging the gap between the centuries, ending rather surprisingly with a diatonic fugue. All this is convincingly played, in a slightly metallic piano sound.

Further listening ...
...Cello Concerto, Op. 18[a]. A Symphony of Liberation. [a]**Alexander Baillie** (vc);
   BBC Philharmonic Orchestra / Sir Edward Downes. Meridian CDE84124 (3/87).
...Dance Suite, Op. 28. Piano Concerto, Op. 26[a]. Variations, Op. 36. [a]**Martin Roscoe** (pf);
   National Symphony Orchestra of Ireland / Adrian Leaper. Marco Polo 8 223480 (11/94).
...Violin Concerto, Op. 4[a]. Symphony No. 2, Op. 35. [a]**Ernst Kovacic** (vn);
   BBC Philharmonic Orchestra / Sir Edward Downes. Meridian CDE84174 (4/90).

Robert Strassburg   American 1915

Suggested listening ...
...Prayer of Columbus. *Coupled with works by various composers.*
   Thomas Hampson (bar); **Craig Rutenberg** (pf).
   EMI CDM5 55028-2 (10/97). *See review in the Collections section; refer to the Index.*

Franz Strauss   German 1822-1905

Suggested listening ...
...Nocturno, Op. 7. *Coupled with works by various composers.* **David Pyatt** (hn); **Martin Jones** (pf).
   Erato 3984-21632-2 (4/98). *See review in the Collections section; refer to the Index.*

Eduard Strauss   Austrian 1835-1916

Johann Strauss I   Austrian 1804-1849

Josef Strauss   Austrian 1827-1870

Johann Strauss II   Austrian 1825-1899

Ein Straussfest II [a]**Cincinnati Pops Chorale and Orchestra / Erich Kunzel.** Telarc Ⓟ CD80314
(68 minutes: DDD: 7/93). Recorded 1991-1992.
   E. Strauss Ohne Aufenthalt, Op. 112. **Josef Strauss** Plappermäulchen, Op. 245.
Sphärenklänge, Op. 235. Jockey, Op. 278. **J. Strauss I** Chinese Galop, Op. 20. **J. Strauss II**
Egyptischer Marsch, Op. 335[a]. Künstler-Quadrille, Op. 71. Kaiser-Walzer, Op. 437. Freikugeln,
Op. 326. Jubelfest-Marsch, Op. 396. Tritsch-Tratsch-Polka, Op. 214. Geisselhiebe, Op. 60[a]. Klipp
Klapp, Op. 466. Wein, Weib und Gesang, Op. 333. Perpetuum mobile, Op. 257.
This collection deliberately sets out to adorn popular Strauss pieces with sound effects to outdo anything one hears at a Vienna New Year Concert. It starts with a performance of Eduard Strauss's *Ohne Aufenthalt* that is accompanied throughout by steam railway effects, has bullets flying mercilessly in the *Freikugeln* Polka, and includes neighing nags and swishing whips in the *Jockey* Polka. The fun is increased by the inclusion of the *Künstler–Quadrille*, a sort of 1850s "Hooked on Classics" number that begins with Mendelssohn's 'Wedding March' and continues through the likes of Mozart's Symphony No. 40 and Chopin's 'Funeral March' Sonata to Beethoven's *Ruins of Athens* and *Kreutzer* Sonata. If the Viennese lilt is just a shade lacking in the waltzes, the playing is nevertheless excellent and lively throughout. The Strausses themselves would have approved.

Additional recommendation ...
...Tritsch-Tratsch-Polka, Op. 214. *Coupled with works by various composers.*
   New London Orchestra / Ronald Corp.
   Hyperion Ⓟ CDA66998 (3/98). *See review in the Collections section; refer to the Index.*

New Year's Day Concert, 1998 [a]**Vienna Boys' Choir; Vienna Philharmonic Orchestra /**
   Zubin Mehta. RCA Victor Red Seal Ⓜ 09026 63144-2 (two discs: 91 minutes: DDD: 4/98).
Recorded live in 1998.
   Hellmesberger I Kleiner Anzeiger. **E. Strauss** Bahn frei!, Op. 45. **J. Strauss I**
Marianka-Polka, Op. 173. Radetzky Marsch, Op. 228. **J. Strauss II** Annen-Polka, Op. 117[a].
Nachfalter, Op. 157. Tritsch-Tratsch, Op. 214[a]. Wiener Bonbons, Op. 307. An der schönen,
blauen Donau, Op. 314. Nur fort!, Op. 383. Rosen aus dem Süden, Op. 388. Nordseebilder,
Op. 390. Wo uns're Fahne weht, Op. 473. Prinz Methusalem – Overture. **Josef Strauss**
Die Schwebende, Op. 110. Jocus Polka, Op. 216. In der Heimat!, Op. 231. Plappermülchen,
Op. 245. Neue Melodien-Quadrille, Op. 254.

The Vienna Philharmonic on this recording is still the orchestra that seems to have the edge over all others in allying technical perfection to capturing the sparkle and lilt of the music. As with recent custom, this release contains the main concert on the first CD, with the encores on a short second disc. Applause is retained to create the live atmosphere. As ever, the concert mixes traditional items with others that are less well known. Alongside favourites such as *An der schönen, blauen Donau* and *Rosen aus dem Süden*, the *Plappermäulchen* and *Bahn frei!* polkas and the *Radetzky Marsch*, eight pieces are new to the concerts. Not that all their music will necessarily be unfamiliar. The overture to *Prinz Methusalem*, for instance, contains a theme that Marischka and Korngold filched for their adaptation of *Eine Nacht in Venedig*, while Josef Strauss's *Neue Melodien-Quadrille* provides opportunities to spot quotations from operas by Donizetti and Verdi. Very much in the unjustly neglected category are Johann Strauss II's elegant waltzes, *Nachfalter* and the picturesque *Nordseebilder*, while the younger Josef Hellmesberger's *Kleiner Anzeiger* galop means that he is represented in these concerts for the second year running. As a further novelty there is the appearance of the Vienna Boys' Choir to give variety to a couple of familiar polkas. This disc is fully up to the standard of its predecessors in choice of items, performance and recording quality.

Viennese Dance Music [a]Wolfgang Schulz (fl); [b]Ernst Ottensamer (cl); [c]Alois Posch (db); [d]Heinz Medjimorеč (pf); [e]Alfred Mitterhofer (harm); **Alban Berg Quartet** (Günter Pichler, Gerhard Schulz, vns; Thomas Kakuska, va; Valentin Erben, vc). EMI Ⓕ CDC7 54881-2 (62 minutes: DDD: 6/94). Recorded 1992.
J. Strauss I (arr. Weinmann) Wiener Gemüths, Op. 116[c]. Beliebte Annen, Op. 137[c]. Eisele und Beisele Sprünge, Op. 202[c]. **J. Strauss II** Schatz, Op. 418 (arr. Webern)[de]. Wein, Weib und Gesang, Op. 333 (arr. Berg)[de]. Kaiser-Walzer, Op. 437 (arr. Schoenberg)[abd]. **Lanner** (arr. Weinmann) Marien-Walzer, Op. 143[c]. Steyrische-Tänze, Op. 165[c]. Die Werber, Op. 103[c].

In the Alexander Weinmann arrangements of Lanner and the elder Johann Strauss, one is able to appreciate to the full the clear lyrical lines of works whose full orchestration is very much built upon the foundation of the string quartet. Likewise, in the large-scale waltzes of the younger Strauss one cannot but admire the skill and affection with which Webern, Berg and Schoenberg used the limited resources available to their Society for Private Musical Performances. Indeed, if string quartet, piano, flute and clarinet inevitably struggle to capture the full splendour of the march introduction to the *Kaiser–Walzer*, the imaginative way in which Schoenberg finds a chamber ensemble substitute for Strauss's full orchestral sound is perhaps the most impressive aspect of the various arrangements here. On its own terms, the collection is extremely impressive. The Alban Berg Quartet have made a fine selection of some of the most melodic works from over half a century of prodigious invention, and they play them with affection and relish. From Lanner's tender *Marien–Walzer*, through to Strauss junior's most magisterial waltz, the clarity and refinement of the playing is tempered with a sense of lightheartedness and fun. If you fancy a Viennese dance collection with a different slant, don't hesitate to go for this admirable release.

J. Strauss II Complete Edition, Volumes 34-36. [a]**Bratislava Radio Symphony Orchestra / Michael Dittrich; Košice State Philharmonic Orchestra /** [b]**Johannes Wildner,** [c]**Alfred Walter.** Marco Polo Ⓕ 8 223234/6 (three discs, oas: 69, 74 and 68 minutes: DDD: 7/94). Volumes marked [ab] recorded 1991, [c] 1989-1991.
8 223234[a] – Russischer Marsch, Op. 426. Slaven-Potpourri, Op. 39. Fünf Paragraphe, Op. 105. La favorite, Op. 217. Nikolai-Quadrille, Op. 65. Abschied von St Petersburg, Op. 210. Der Kobold, Op. 226. Im russischen Dorfe, Op. 355 (orch. Schönherr). Dolci pianti (with Jozef Sikora, vc). Niko-Polka, Op. 228. *8 223235*[b] – Zivio!, Op. 456 (orch. Fischer). Architecten-Ball-Tänze, Op. 36. Jäger, Op. 229. Accelerationen, Op. 234. Der Liebesbrunnen, Op. 10 (orch. Kulling). Die Zeitlose, Op. 302. Königslieder, Op. 334. Im Sturmschritt, Op. 348. Der Blitz, Op. 59 (orch. Babinski). Heut' ist heut', Op. 471 (orch. Babinski). Die Wahrsagerin, Op. 420. *8 223236*[c] – Matador-Marsch, Op. 406 (orch. Fischer). Kreuzfidel, Op. 301. D'Woaldbuama (Die Waldbuben), Op. 66 (orch. Babinski). Process, Op. 294. Elfen-Quadrille, Op. 16 (orch. Kulling). Mephistos Höllenrufe, Op. 101. Bitte schön!, Op. 372. Die Extravaganten, Op. 205. Fledermaus-Quadrille, Op. 363. Der Klügere gibt nach, Op. 401. Neu-Wien, Op. 342. Diplomaten-Polka, Op. 448.

Volume 34 offers a distinct Russian flavour. The most obviously familiar item is the opening *Russischer Marsch* while the waltz *Abschied von St Petersburg* will also be familiar to some. It's a fine swinging waltz, with an attractive cello solo in the introduction. *Dolci pianti*, one of three romances surviving from Strauss's Russian visits, provides further material for a cello soloist, while the piquant *Niko–Polka* offers as good an example as any of the delights to be found among the unfamiliar works of the Waltz King. Not the least attraction of Vol. 34 is the conductor Michael Dittrich and his alert, *echt-Wienerisch* performances here. On Vol. 35 Johannes Wildner's conducting shows up to much better effect than has often been the case. Marches have always been his strong point, and the collection thus gets off to a good start with *Zivio!* from the operetta *Jabuka*. There are other attractive pieces on offer, too, from the perpetual favourite *Accelerationen*, through the delicate polka–mazurka *Die Zeitlose* to the magisterial *Königslieder* (a waltz from Strauss's most successful period) and the polka–mazurka *Die Wahrsagerin* on melodies from *The Gipsy Baron*. Volume 36 offers perhaps the most attractive music of the three volumes. Again the performance of the haunting waltz *Mephistos*

Höllenrufe may not erase memories of some previous versions, but such pieces as the *Neu-Wien* waltz and the excellently played *Fledermaus–Quadrille* are among the composer's most agreeable creations. Perhaps the most pleasant surprise of all comes from the waltz *Die Extravaganten* which, with its endearing themes and richly inventive harmonic and orchestral touches, shows above all the merits of Marco Polo's voyage of Straussian rediscovery.

J. Strauss II Complete Edition, Volumes 43, 44 and 45. **Slovak State Philharmonic Orchestra, Košice / ^aChristian Pollack, ^bAlfred Walter.** Marco Polo Ⓕ 8 223243/5 (three discs, oas: 58, 56 and 59 minutes: DDD: 3/96).
8 223243^a – Reitermarsch, Op. 428. Walzer-Bouquet No. 1. Postillon d'amour, Op. 317. Simplicius-Quadrille, Op. 429. Wilde Rosen, Op. 42 (arr. Babinski/Kulling). Die Tauben von San Marco, Op. 414. Auf dem Tanzboden, Op. 454 (arr. Pollack). Des Teufels Antheil (arr. Pollack). Trifolien (with Josef and Eduard Strauss). Herrjemineh, Op. 464. *8 223244*^a – Maskenfest-Quadrille, Op. 92. Aschenbrödel-Walzer. Von der Börse, Op. 337. Monstre-Quadrille (with Josef Strauss). Autograph Waltzes (arr. Cohen). Auf freiem Fusse, Op. 345. Schützen-Quadrille (with Josef and Eduard Strauss). Altdeutscher Walzer (arr. Pollack). Nur nicht mucken, Op. 472 (arr. Peak). Hinter den Coulissen (with Josef Strauss). *8 223245*^b – Fest-Marsch, Op. 452. Zigeunerbaron-Quadrille, Op. 422. Ischler Walzer. Ritter Pasman – ballet music. Pasman-Quadrille (arr. Pollack). Eva-Walzer. Potpourri-Quadrille. Der Carneval in Rom – ballet music (arr. Schönherr).

As this Marco Polo series reaches its final stretches, it delves increasingly into the more remote corners of the Waltz King's output. Vols. 43 and 44 include as many as four collaborations between Johann and his two brothers, of which the *Trifolien* waltz and *Schützen-Quadrille* most engagingly permit a comparison of all three brothers' strengths. Both volumes also include a waltz from the composer's 1876 visit to the USA. The *Walzer-Bouquet* No. 1 (originally the *Manhattan Waltzes*) is a convincingly authentic Strauss arrangement of themes from his earlier waltzes, but it is difficult to feel as sure of the worth or authenticity of the *Autograph Waltzes*, which may merely comprise themes thrown off by Strauss and worked up by an eager US publisher. The other particular curiosities of these two volumes are *Auf dem Tanzboden*, a musical evocation of a painting, and the *Altdeutscher Walzer*, which is really no more than an *entr'acte* from the operetta, *Simplicius*. Of the more conventional items, the attractive early waltz *Wilde Rosen* is already known from a previous recording by the same orchestra on this label (Marco Polo, 2/94). It receives a compelling performance here from Christian Pollack, without the somewhat heavy beat he imparts to the *Walzer-Bouquet*. Generally Pollack seems better in the polkas and quadrilles, which he gives genuine 'lift' and sparkle, as here in several delightful polkas and the *Maskenfest-Quadrille*, which contains themes familiar to anyone who knows *Graduation Ball*. By contrast, Vol. 45 is relatively free of the polkas and polka-mazurkas that tend to sound somewhat leaden in the hands of Alfred Walter. Over half this CD is devoted to items from Strauss's only opera *Ritter Pasman* – not just the ballet music (played in a fuller version than on some occasions), but also the *Pasman-Quadrille* and *Eva-Walzer* arranged by other hands from the score. The posthumous *Ischler Walzer* proves a piece of genuine charm, and the *Potpourri-Quadrille* compiled by Strauss for his visit to London in 1867 provides fun value with its quotations from earlier Strauss quadrilles interspersed with a selection of Scottish airs. The inclusion of the *Carneval in Rom* ballet music in a modern arrangement seems unfortunate in a collection such as this with an accent on authenticity. As a whole, though, this proves one of the best of Walter's volumes, and all three CDs rank among the more interesting and enjoyable in this adventurous series.

J. Strauss I Radetzky March, Op. 228.
J. Strauss II Die Fledermaus – Overture. Perpetuum mobile, Op. 257. Accelerationen-Waltz, Op. 234. Unter Donner und Blitz-Polka, Op. 324. Morgenblätter-Waltz, Op. 279. Persischer Marsch, Op. 289. Explosionen-Polka, Op. 43. Wiener Blut-Waltz, Op. 354. Egyptischer Marsch, Op. 335. Künstlerleben-Waltz, Op. 316. Tritsch-Tratsch-Polka, Op. 214.
J. Strauss II/Josef Strauss Pizzicato Polka. **Vienna Philharmonic Orchestra / Willi Boskovsky** (vn). Decca Ovation Ⓜ 417 747-2DM* (65 minutes: ADD). Recorded 1958-1973.

There have been no finer recordings of Johann Strauss than those by Boskovsky and the Vienna Philharmonic. The velvety sheen and elegance of the orchestra's sound, combined with the unique lilt that comes so naturally to Viennese players, produced magical results. For this compilation Decca have sensibly mixed seven of the most famous waltzes and polkas from those sessions with other popular Strauss compositions in various rhythms, from the celebrated *Die Fledermaus* Overture, through popular polkas and novelty pieces (for *Perpetuum mobile* Boskovsky himself can be heard explaining that it has no ending) to the ever-popular *Radetzky March*. The recorded sound is not up to the most modern digital standards, but reprocessing has produced a remarkably homogeneous sound for recordings originating over a 15-year period.

Additional recommendation ...

...Radetzky March. *Coupled with works by various composers.* **London Symphony Orchestra / Sir Charles Mackerras.** Mercury Living Presence Ⓜ 434 352-2MM (75 minutes: ADD: 12/95).

J. Strauss II Die Fledermaus. **Dame Elisabeth Schwarzkopf** (sop) Rosalinde; **Rita Streich** (sop) Adele; **Nicolai Gedda** (ten) Eisenstein; **Helmut Krebs** (ten) Alfred; **Erich Kunz** (bar) Doctor Falke;

Rudolf Christ (ten) Orlovsky; **Karl Dönch** (bar) Frank; **Erich Majkut** (ten) Blind; **Luise Martini** (sop) Ida; **Franz Böheim** (bar) Frosch; **Philharmonia Chorus and Orchestra / Herbert von Karajan.** EMI ⓜ CHS7 69531-2* (two discs: 110 minutes: ADD: 11/88). From Columbia 33CX1309-10 (11/55). Recorded 1955.　　　　　　　　　　　　　　ⒼⒼ
This 1955 recording can readily be recommended to anyone less concerned with modernity of sound than with enjoying a well-proven, classic interpretation of Strauss's operetta masterpiece. Herbert von Karajan, whose preference for slow tempos and beauty of sound above all else was then still in the future, here directs with affection and *élan*. Amongst the principals Elisabeth Schwarzkopf leads the cast majestically and ravishingly. Notably in the *Csárdás*, her firm lower notes swell gloriously into a marvellously rich and individual register. As her maid, Adele, Rita Streich is an agile-voiced, utterly charming foil, launching her "Laughing Song" with deliciously credible indignation. Nicolai Gedda also enters into the fun with supreme effect. Throughout he sings with youthful ardour and freshness, but he also has a high old time impersonating the stammering Blind in the Act 3 trio. Erich Kunz's rich, characterful baritone is also heard here to good effect as Doctor Falke, the character who arranges the 'bat's revenge' which forms the story of *Die Fledermaus*. Unconventionally, the young Prince is played by a tenor rather than the mezzo-soprano for whom the role was written. Purists may object, but the result is dramatically convincing, and musically could hardly be bettered when the singer is the sweet-toned Rudolf Christ. Altogether this set can still rival any later one in theatrical effectiveness and EMI have done a good job in refurbishing it, with the disc-break sensibly placed between Acts 1 and 2.

Additional recommendations ...
...(with Gala Sequence). **Soloists; Vienna State Opera Chorus and Orchestra / Herbert von Karajan.** Decca Ⓕ 421 046-2DH2* (two discs: 143 minutes: ADD: 12/87).
...**Vienna State Opera Chorus; Vienna Philharmonic Orchestra / André Previn.** Philips Ⓕ 432 157-2PH2 (two discs: 112 minutes: DDD: 9/91).
...**Soloists; Netherlands Opera Chorus; Concertgebouw Orchestra / Nikolaus Harnoncourt.** Teldec ⓜ 4509-91974-2 (72 minutes: DDD: 7/93).
...**Soloists; Philharmonia Chorus; Philharmonia Orchestra / Otto Ackermann.** Classics for Pleasure Silver Doubles Ⓢ CD-CFPSD4793 (two discs: 113 minutes: ADD: 4/96).

J. Strauss II Die Fledermaus (sung in English). **Rosemarie Arthars** (sop) Rosalinde; **Adey Grummet** (sop) Adele; **David Fieldsend** (ten) Eisenstein; **Khosrow Mahsoori** (ten) Alfred; **Gordon Sandison** (bar) Falke; **Deborah Hawksley** (mez) Orlovsky; **Lynton Black** (bar) Frank; **Howard Ludlow** (ten) Blind; **Wendy Schoemann** (sop) Ida; **Paul Barnhill** (spkr) Frosch; **D'Oyly Carte Opera Chorus and Orchestra / John Owen Edwards.** Sony Classical Ⓕ S2K64573 (two discs: 111 minutes: DDD: 1/96). Notes and texts included.
Recordings of *Die Fledermaus* in English were common enough during the early days of LP. Since then the work has tended to be regarded as the province of international star opera casts, which makes the D'Oyle Carte release all the more welcome. Comparisons with those international, German-language versions are scarcely appropriate, though on any terms the present recording is a resounding success. It presents the score, extremely well played and sung (in Alistair Beaton's new translation), in a form that enables English-speaking listeners to keep unusually well apace of a notoriously complex plot. The tone of the performance is admirably set by the overture, in which symphonic pretensions are set aside in favour of a light and leisurely journey through the engaging material. John Owen Edwards never forces the tempo but allows the melodies to unfold naturally, and eases gently into the big waltz tunes. Musical standards remain uniformly high throughout the performance, which omits any ballet music but restores the two brief passages in Act 2 (in the opening chorus and the *csárdás*) that are usually cut. Without ever being sent up, the work once more becomes part of the international popular musical theatre tradition rather than part of an overblown operatic form. The cast is almost universally strong, with David Fieldsend (Eisenstein), Adey Grummet (Adele) and Gordon Sandison (Falke) each admirable in his or her way and Rosemarie Arthars a particular joy as she switches effortlessly between a testing singing part and dialogue that contributes so much to making this *Fledermaus* an integral experience.

J. Strauss II Der Zigeunerbaron. **Pamela Coburn** (sop) Saffi; **Herbert Lippert** (ten) Barinkay; **Wolfgang Holzmair** (bar) Homonay; **Rudolf Schasching** (ten) Zsupán; **Christiane Oelze** (sop) Arsena; **Júlia Hamari** (mez) Czipra; **Elisabeth von Magnus** (contr) Mirabella; **Jürgen Flimm** (bar) Carnero; **Robert Florianschutz** (bass) Pali; **Hans-Jürgen Lazar** (ten) Ottokar; **Arnold Schoenberg Choir; Vienna Symphony Orchestra / Nikolaus Harnoncourt.** Teldec Ⓕ 4509-94555-2 (two discs: 150 minutes: DDD: 6/95). Notes, text and translation included. Recorded live in 1994.
This set comes with a sticker proclaiming the inclusion of 40 minutes of unpublished music. Well, 14 perhaps – certainly no more than 15. False claims aside, though, this proves an uncommonly interesting and enjoyable release. The extra music comes because Nikolaus Harnoncourt and Johann Strauss specialist Norbert Linke have sought to restore *Der Zigeunerbaron* to the form it had before Strauss made various cuts. The real merits of the set lie elsewhere. Not least, Harnoncourt has stripped away generations of Viennese schmaltz and performing tradition. This is the very first recording to include every number of the published score, and for once the music is sung at its original pitch, without the usual downward transpositions for Zsupán and Homonay. Most particularly

Harnoncourt has completely rethought the style of the performance. *Der Zigeunerbaron* is a long work, described as "Komische Oper" rather than "Operette", and much of its music is unusually solid for Strauss. Harnoncourt gives the major numbers full weight, phrasing them beautifully, drawing refined singing from the soloists, among whom Herbert Lippert and Pamela Coburn combine beautifully in the duet "Wer uns getraut?", and Christiane Oelze is a delectably sweet Arsena. The necessary light relief comes not only from Zsupán (Rudolf Schasching in fine voice) but from usually omitted subsidiary numbers. Elisabeth von Magnus sings Mirabella's "Just sind es vierundzwanzig Jahren" with exhilarating comic zest, and joins with Jürgen Flimm (more actor than singer) to make the trio "Nur keusch und rein" an irresistible delight. The recording comes from a live concert performance, with some audience laughter and coughs but with applause suppressed. This deserves to win new admirers both for Harnoncourt and for Strauss's masterly score.

Further listening ...

...New Year's Day Concert, 1987 – Die Fledermaus – Overture. Annen-Polka, Op. 117. Vergnügungszug-Polka, Op. 281. Unter Donner und Blitz-Polka, Op. 324. Frühlingsstimmen-Waltz, Op. 410[a]. An die schönen blauen Donau-Waltz, Op. 314. *Coupled with* **J. Strauss I** Beliebte Annen-Polka, Op. 137. Radetzky March, Op. 228. **J. Strauss II/Josef Strauss** Pizzicato Polka. **Josef Strauss** Sphärenklänge-Waltz, Op. 235. Delirien-Waltz, Op. 212. Ohne Sorgen-Polka, Op. 271. **Kathleen Battle** (sop); **Vienna Philharmonic Orchestra / Herbert von Karajan.** DG 419 616-2GH (11/87).

...New Year's Day Concert, 1989 – Accelerationen-Waltz, Op. 234. Bauern-Polka, Op. 276. Die Fledermaus – Overture. Künstlerleben-Waltz, Op. 316. Eljen a Magyar!-Polka, Op. 322. Im Krapfenwald'l-Polka française, Op. 336. Frühlingsstimmen-Waltz, Op. 410. Ritter Pasman – Csárdás. An die schönen blauen Donau-Waltz, Op. 314. *Coupled with* **J. Strauss I** Radetzky March, Op. 228. **J. Strauss II/Josef Strauss** Pizzicato Polka. **Josef Strauss** Die Libelle-Polka Mazur, Op. 204. Moulinet-Polka française, Op. 57. Plappermäulchen-Polka schnell, Op. 245. Jockey-Polka schnell, Op. 278. **Vienna Philharmonic Orchestra / Carlos Kleiber.** Sony Classical SK45938 (2/91).

...New Year's Day Concert, 1995 – Reitermarsch, Op. 428. Morgenblätter, Op. 279. Process, Op. 294. Mephistos Höllenrufe, Op. 101. Perpetuum mobile, Op. 257. Russische Marsch – Phantasie, Op. 353. An der schönen, blauen Donau, Op. 314. Schützen. *Coupled with* **Lanner** Favorit-Polka, Op. 201. **E. Strauss** Electrisch. **J. Strauss I** Radetzky March, Op. 228. Alice, Op. 238. **Josef Strauss** Arm in Arm, Op. 215. Thalia, Op. 195. Mein Lebenslauf ist Lieb und Lust, Op. 263. Auf Ferienreisen, Op. 133.**Vienna Philharmonic Orchestra / Zubin Mehta.** Sony Classical SK66860 (5/95).   ⊙

...New Year's Day Concert, 1996 – Fest-Marsch, Op. 452. Blumenfest, Op. 111. Lagunen-Walzer, Op. 411. Waldmeister – Overture. Phönix-Schwingen, Op. 125. Die Göttin der Vernunft – Overture[a]. Sekunden-Polka, Op. 258. Kaiserwalzer, Op. 437. Furioso-Polka, Op. 260. An der schönen, blauen Donau, Op. 314. *Coupled with* **Ziehrer** Wiener Bürger, Op. 419. **Josef Strauss** Die Nasswalderin, Op. 267 (arr. Rot). Die Tanzende Muse, Op. 266. Jokey-Polka, Op. 278. **E. Strauss** Mit Vergnügen!, Op. 228. **J. Strauss I** Radetzky-Marsch, Op. 228. **Vienna Philharmonic Orchestra / Lorin Maazel** ([a]vn). RCA Victor Red Seal 09026 68421-2 (5/96).

...New Year's Day Concert, 1997 – Motoren, Op. 265. 'S gibt nur a Kaiserstadt! 's gibt nur a Wien!, Op. 291. Hofballtänze, Op. 298. Bluette, Op. 271. Die Bajadere, Op. 351. Freuet euch des Lebens, Op. 340. Patronessen-Polka, Op. 286. Neue Pizzicato-Polka, Op. 449. Fata Morgana, Op. 330. Russicher Marsch, Op. 426. An der schönen blauen Donau, Op. 314. *Coupled with* **Hellmesberger** Leichtfüssig. **J. Strauss I** Radetzky Marsch, Op. 228. **Josef Strauss** Carriere, Op. 200. Frauenherz, Op. 166. Dynamiden, Op. 173. Vortwärts!, Op. 127. Eingesendet, Op. 240. **Suppé** Leichte Kavallerie – Overture. **Vienna Philharmonic Orchestra / Riccardo Muti.** EMI CDC5 56336-2 (3/97). Also includes a bonus disc (36 minutes) containing the remainder of the concert.

...Complete Edition, Volume 37. Triumph-Marsch, Op. 69 (orch. Fischer). Jugend-Träume, Op. 12 (orch. Pollack). Das Komitat geht in die Höh!, Op. 457 (orch. Pollack). Die Königin von Leon-Quadrille, Op. 40 (orch. Pollack). Neue steirische Tänze, Op. 61 (orch. Pollack). Tanze mit dem Besenstiel!, Op. 458 (orch. Pollack). Spitzentuch-Quadrille, Op. 392. Schwungräder, Op. 223. Sonnenblume, Op. 459 (orch. Pollack). Romance No. 2 in G minor, Op. 255 (orch. Schönherr. With Regina Jauslin, vc). Traumbilder II, Op. posth. **Košice State Philharmonic Orchestra /** [a]**Christian Pollack,** [b]**Alfred Walter.** Marco Polo 8 223237 (9/95).

...(arr. Benatzky) Casanova – Nuns' Chorus and Laura's Song. *Coupled with works by various composers.* **Lesley Garrett** (sop); **Crouch End Festival Chorus; Royal Philharmonic Concert Orchestra / James Holmes.** Silva Screen Classics SILKTVCD1 (2/96). *See review in the Collections section; refer to the Index.*

...Die Fledermaus – Klänge der Heimat. *Coupled with works by various composers.* **Renée Fleming** (sop); **English Chamber Orchestra / Jeffrey Tate.** Decca 458 858-2DH (3/98). *See review in the Collections section; refer to the Index. Selected by Soundings.*

...Frühlingsstimmen, Op. 410. *Coupled with works by various composers.* **Inessa Galante** (sop); **Latvian National Symphony Orchestra / Imants Resnis.** Campion RRCD1344 (A/97). *See review in the Collections section; refer to the Index.*

Richard Strauss

R. Strauss Orchestral works, Volume 1 – Horn Concertos – No. 1 in E flat major, Op. 11[a]; No. 2 in E flat major, AV132[b]. Oboe Concerto, AV144[c]. Duet Concertino, AV147[d]. Burleske in D minor, AV85[c]. Parergon, Op. 73[f]. Panathenäenzug Symphonic Study in the form of a Passacaglia, Op. 74[g]. Till Eulenspiegels lustige Streiche, Op. 28[h]. Don Juan, Op. 20[i]. Ein Heldenleben, Op. 40[j]. [ab]**Peter Damm** (hn); [c]**Manfred Clement** (ob); [d]**Manfred Weise** (cl); [d]**Wolfgang Liebscher** (bn); [e]**Malcolm Frager** (pf); [fg]**Peter Rösel** (pf); **Dresden Staatskapelle / Rudolf Kempe**. EMI Ⓜ CMS7 64342-2 (three discs: 224 minutes: ADD: 12/92). Items marked [abcdefg] from HMV SLS5067 (10/76), [h]SLS894 (3/75), [i]SLS861 (10/73), [j]SLS880 (6/74). ⒼⒼ

R. Strauss Orchestral works, Volume 2 – Violin Concerto in D minor, Op. 8[a]. Symphonia domestica, Op. 53[b]. Also sprach Zarathustra, Op. 30[c]. Tod und Verklärung, Op. 24[d]. Der Rosenkavalier – Waltzes[e]. Salome – Dance of the Seven Veils[f]. Le bourgeois gentilhomme – Suite, Op. 60[g]. Schlagobers – Waltz[h]. Josephslegende – Suite[i]. [a]**Ulf Hoelscher** (vn); **Dresden Staatskapelle / Rudolf Kempe**. EMI Ⓜ CMS7 64346-2 (three discs: 222 minutes: ADD: 12/92). Items marked [a] from HMV SLS5067 (10/76), [bfi]SLS894 (3/75), [cgh]SLS861 (10/73), [de]SLS880 (6/74). ⒼⒼ

R. Strauss Orchestral works, Volume 3 – Metamorphosen for 23 Solo Strings, AV142[a]. Eine Alpensinfonie, Op. 64[b]. Aus Italien, Op. 16[c]. Macbeth, Op. 23[d]. Don Quixote, Op. 35[e]. Dance Suite on Keyboard Pieces by François Couperin, AV107[f]. [e]**Paul Tortelier** (vc); [e]**Max Rostal** (va); **Dresden Staatskapelle / Rudolf Kempe**. EMI Ⓜ CMS7 64350-2 (three discs: 208 minutes: ADD: 12/92). Items marked [abd] from HMV SLS861 (10/73), [c]SLS894 (3/75), [ef]SLS880 (6/74). *Gramophone classical 100.* ⒼⒼⒼ

"From the store of glorious memories of my artistic career, the tones of this master orchestra ever evoke feelings of deepest gratitude and admiration" (thus spoke Richard Strauss when greeting the Dresden orchestra in 1948 on its 400th Anniversary). You get the feeling that this orchestra is justifiably proud of its tones, and its Straussian associations; it takes only a few minutes of the wind concertos disc (the first CD in Volume 1), with the principals as soloists, to be aware of those tones, and to detect a special radiance that probably derives from that pride. Kempe, it seems, was the man to draw it out, and give it purpose; after his *Till Eulenspiegel*, for example, virtually all others either affect character, or are characterless. Some may find Kempe an occasionally circumspect Straussian, one who preferred decorum to decibels in the protracted cacophony that concludes the *Symphonia domestica*, and who ensures that the famous "2001" opening to *Also sprach Zarathustra* isn't so awesome that the rest of the piece is an anti-climax. Neither did he have at his disposal the saturated sonorities of the Berlin Philharmonic that supported Karajan's breadth and power. It is difficult, though, to think of many other Straussians with the imagination and understanding to bring these scores to life from within. To catalogue Kempe's Straussian credentials would take up more space than is available; suffice it to say that, like Fritz Reiner, clarity of texture and a natural flexibility of pacing were prerequisites for the characterful animation and interaction of orchestral soloists or instrumental groups, but never at the expense of the long-term direction of the music. His technique, too, ensured the kind of feats of ensemble and precision that you might have expected from the Chicago Symphony Orchestra under Reiner, but Kempe's orchestra, of course, retains its warmer and cherishably Old World tones.

There are many self-evidently great Strauss performances here. A lithe, demon-driven *Don Juan*; perhaps the most vital and communicative *Don Quixote* ever recorded (greatly ennobled by Tortelier's presence); and *Ein Heldenleben* whose hero is drawn with humanity, even vulnerability and self-doubt (the reaction to the critics is unbearably sad; the scene with the hero's wife, properly reactive) and the ideal choice for those who find the work's egotism unpalatable. EMI have mixed the familiar with the unfamiliar in each box, and dedicated Straussians will find the by-ways explored with comparable commitment and skill. The recordings, made between 1970 and 1975 (the year before Kempe's premature death), vary in perspective from an ideally distanced, natural layout (*Till* and *Aus Italien*), to the closer and slightly 'contained' (*Eine Alpensinfonie* and *Ein Heldenleben*), and the vividly present (*Le bourgeois gentilhomme* and *Metamorphosen*). Clear, light-toned timpani with very little bass resonance further enhance Kempe's precise rhythmic control (even though they sound like tom-toms at the start of *Also sprach Zarathustra*), and soloists are invariably up-front, but rarely at the expense of orchestral detail. The whole invaluable enterprise benefits from the warm acoustics of the Lukaskirche in Dresden.

Additional recommendations ...

...Don Juan. Till Eulenspiegels lustige Streiche. Also sprach Zarathustra. Ein Heldenleben. Le bourgeois gentilhomme – Suite. Tod und Verklärung. Symphonia domestica.
Vienna Philharmonic Orchestra / Richard Strauss.
Preiser mono Ⓕ 90216* (three discs: 206 minutes: AAD).

...Ein Heldenleben. Don Juan. **Berlin Philharmonic Orchestra / Herbert von Karajan.**
DG Galleria Ⓜ 429 717-2GGA* (ADD). Ⓖ

...Tod und Verklärung. Symphonia domestica, Op. 53. Salome, Op. 54 – Dance of the Seven Veils.
Philadelphia Orchestra / Eugene Ormandy. Sony Classical Ⓑ SBK53511* (75 minutes: ADD). ⒼⒼ

...Metamorphosen. Tod und Verklärung. **Berlin Philharmonic Orchestra / Herbert von Karajan.**
DG Ⓕ 410 892-2GH (52 minutes: DDD: 2/84). ⒼⒼ

...Horn Concertos. **Weber** Horn Concertino in E minor, J188. **Hermann Bauman** (hn);
Leipzig Gewandhaus Orchestra / Kurt Masur. Philips Ⓕ 412 237-2PH (DDD: 6/85).

...Horn Concertos[a]. **Hindemith** Horn Concerto[b]. **Dennis Brain** (hn); **Philharmonia Orchestra /**
[a]**Wolfgang Sawalllsch,** [b]**Paul Hindemith.** EMI Ⓕ CDC7 47834-2* (49 minutes: ADD: 10/87).

...Le bourgeois gentilhomme – Suite. Divertimento, Op. 86. **Chamber Orchestra of Europe /**
Erich Leinsdorf. ASV Ⓜ CDCOE809 (63 minutes: DDD: 11/88).

...Eine Alpensinfonie. **Vienna Philharmonic Orchestra / André Previn.**
Telarc Ⓕ CD80211 (48 minutes: DDD: 9/90).

...Aus Italien. Die Liebe der Danae, Op. 83 – Symphonic Fragment. Der Rosenkavalier,
Op. 59 – Waltz Sequences, Acts 2 and 3. **Slovak Philharmonic Orchestra / Zdeněk Košler.**
Naxos Ⓢ 8 550342 (59 minutes: DDD: 2/91).

...Don Juan. Don Quixote[a]. [a]**Franz Bartolomey** (vc); [a]**Heinrich Koll** (va);
Vienna Philharmonic Orchestra / André Previn. Telarc Ⓕ CD80262 (60 minutes: DDD: 10/91).

...Ein Heldenleben[a]. Don Juan, Op. 20[b]. Till Eulenspiegels lustige Streiche[b].
[a]**Philadelphia Orchestra / Eugene Ormandy;** [bc]**Cleveland Orchestra / George Szell.**
Sony Classical Essential Classics Ⓑ SBK48272 (75 minutes: ADD: 5/93).   Ⓖ

...Le bourgeois gentilhomme – Suite. Salome, Op. 54 – Dance of the Seven Veils. **Brahms**
Symphony No. 3 in F major, Op. 90. **Vienna Philharmonic Orchestra / Clemens Krauss.**
Koch Legacy mono 37129-2* (75 minutes: ADD: 5/93).

...Ein Heldenleben. Till Eulenspiegels lustige Streiche. **Cleveland Orchestra /**
Christoph von Dohnányi. Decca Ⓕ 436 444-2DH (61 minutes: DDD: 10/93).

...Metamorphosen. *Coupled with works by* **Honegger** and **Webern** Seattle Symphony Orchestra /
Gerard Schwarz. Delos Ⓕ DE3121 (71 minutes: DDD: 4/94).

...Ein Heldenleben[a]. Also sprach Zarathustra[b]. Don Juan[b]. Till Eulensiegels lustige Streiche[b].
Eine Alpensinfonie[c]. [a]**Vienna Philharmonic Orchestra;** [b]**Chicago Symphony Orchestra;**
[c]**Bavarian Radio Symphony Orchestra / Sir Georg Solti.**
Double Decca Ⓜ 440 618-2DF2 (two discs: 152 minutes: ADD: 5/94).

...Don Quixote[a]. Burleske[b]. [a]**Milton Preves** (va); [a]**Antonio Janigro** (vc); [b]**Byron Janis** (pf); **Chicago**
Symphony Orchestra / Fritz Reiner. RCA Victor Ⓜ 09026 61796-2 (63 minutes: ADD: 9/94).

...Don Juan, Op. 20[a]. Duett-Concertino, AV147[b]. Burleske in D minor, AV85[c]. Till Eulenspiegels
lustige Streiche[d]. [b]**Heinrich Geuser** (cl); [b]**Willi Fugmann** (bn); [c]**Margrit Weber** (pf);
[abc]**Berlin RIAS Orchestra;** [d]**Berlin Philharmonic Orchestra / Ferenc Fricsay.**
DG Dokumente mono Ⓜ 445 403-2GDO* (67 minutes: ADD: 11/94).

...Capriccio – Prelude. Metamorphosen (arr. Leopold)[a]. **Mozart** String Quintet
in C minor, K406/K516*b*. **Vienna String Sextet; Alois Posch** (db).
EMI Ⓕ CDC5 55108-2 (61 minutes: DDD: 2/95).

...Don Quixote[a]. Ein Heldenleben. Eine Alpensinfonie. Festmusik zur Feier des 2600 jährigen
Bestehens des Kaiserreichs Japan, Op. 84. Der Rosenkavalier – Waltz Sequence, Act 3.
[a]**Philipp Haass** (va); [a]**Oswald Uhl** (vc); **Bavarian State Orchestra / Richard Strauss.**
Preiser mono Ⓕ 90205* (two discs: 145 minutes: AAD: 8/95).

...Also sprach Zarathustra. Der Rosenkavalier – suite. Don Juan. **Bavarian Radio Symphony**
Orchestra / Lorin Maazel. RCA Victor Red Seal Ⓕ 09026 68225-2 (77 minutes: DDD: 10/95).

...Don Quixote[b]. **Lalo** Cello Concerto in D minor[a]. **Jacqueline du Pré** (vc); [b]**Herbert Downes** (va);
[a]**Cleveland Orchestra / Daniel Barenboim;** [b]**New Philharmonia Orchestra / Sir Adrian Boult.**
EMI Ⓕ CDC5 55528-2 (73 minutes: ADD: 11/95).

...Don Quixote. *Coupled with works by various composers.* **Leonard Rubens** (va);
Royal Philharmonic Orchestra / Sir Thomas Beecham.
EMI Références mono Ⓜ CDH5 65502-2* (78 minutes: ADD: 12/95).

...Don Juan. *Coupled with works by various composers.* **The Solti Orchestral Project, Carnegie Hall /**
Sir Georg Solti. Decca Ⓕ 444 458-2DH (77 minutes: DDD: 12/95). *See review in the Collections*
section; refer to the Index.   Ⓖ

...Burleske[a]. Der Rosenkavalier – suite. Salome – Dance of the seven veils. Festliches Präludium,
Op. 61[b]. [a]**Jeffrey Kahane** (pf); [b]**Michael Chertok** (org); **Cincinnati Symphony Orchestra /**
Jésus López-Cobos. Telarc Ⓕ CD80371 (65 minutes: DDD: 12/95).

...Till Eulenspiegels lustige Streiche. Don Quixote. *Coupled with works by various composers.*
Giusto Cappone (va); **Paul Tortelier** (vc); **Berlin Philharmonic Orchestra, / Rudolf Kempe.**
EMI Profile Ⓑ CZS5 68736-2* (two discs: 156 minutes: ADD: 9/96).

...Burleske. **Schumann** Piano Concerto in A minor, Op. 54. **Hélène Grimaud** (pf); **Deutsches**
Symphony Orchestra, Berlin / David Zinman. Erato Ⓕ 0630-11727-2 (52 minutes: DDD: 2/96).

...Symphonia domestica. Tod und Verklärung. **Bavarian Radio Symphony Orchestra / Lorin Maazel.**
RCA Victor Red Seal Ⓕ 09026 68221-2 (74 minutes: DDD: 11/96).

...Symphonia domestica. Parergon[a]. [a]**Gary Graffman** (pf); **Vienna Philharmonic Orchestra /**
André Previn. DG Ⓕ 449 188-2GH (64 minutes: DDD: 11/96).

...Die Liebe der Danae – Symphonic fragments (arr. Krauss). Der Rosenkavalier – Suite
(poss. arr. Rodzinski). *Coupled with works by various composers.* **Hallé Orchestra /**
Sir John Barbirolli. Dutton Laboratories mono Ⓜ CDSJB1004* (75 minutes: ADD: 11/96).

...Also sprach Zarathustra. *Coupled with works by various composers.* **Boston Symphony Orchestra /**
Serge Koussevitzky. Dutton Laboratories mono Ⓜ CDAX8015* (75 minutes: ADD: 1/97).

...Symphonia domestica. *Coupled with works by* **Wagner** Berlin Philharmonic Orchestra / **Herbert von Karajan.** EMI Karajan Edition Ⓜ CDM5 66107-2 (76 minutes: ADD: 3/97).
...Horn Concertos. **Britten** Serenade for Tenor, Horn and Strings, Op. 31[a]. [a]**Ian Bostridge** (ten); **Marie Luise Neunecker** (hn); **Bamberg Symphony Orchestra / Ingo Metzmacher.** EMI Ⓕ CDC5 56183-2 (57 minutes: DDD: 8/97). *See review under Britten; refer to the Index.*
...Also sprach Zarathustra. Don Juan. Burleske[a]. [a]**Emanuel Ax** (pf); **Philadelphia Orchestra / Wolfgang Sawallisch.** EMI Ⓕ CDC5 56364-2 (69 minutes: DDD: 9/97).
...Metamorphosen. *Coupled with works by* **Brahms** and **Mozart** Vienna Philharmonic Orchestra / **Herbert von Karajan.** EMI Karajan Edition mono Ⓜ CDM5 66390-2* (72 minutes: ADD: 9/97).
...Le bourgeois gentilhomme – Suite. **Wagner** Tannhäuser – Overture. Die Meistersinger von Nürnberg – Prelude, Act 1. Götterdämmerung – Siegfried's Rhine Journey; Siegfried's Funeral March. **Philharmonia Orchestra / Wolfgang Sawallisch.** Testament Ⓕ SBT1112* (76 minutes: ADD: A/97).
...Don Juan. Don Quixote[a]. Horn Concerto No. 1[b]. [b]**Myron Bloom** (hn); [a]**Rafael Druian** (vn); [a]**Abraham Skernick** (va); [a]**Pierre Fournier** (vc); **Cleveland Orchestra / George Szell.** Sony Classical Masterworks Heritage Ⓜ MHK63123 (71 minutes: ADD: 2/98).

R. Strauss Also sprach Zarathustra, Op. 30[a]. Ein Heldenleben, Op. 40[b]. **Chicago Symphony Orchestra / Fritz Reiner.** RCA Living Stereo Ⓜ 09026 61494-2* (76 minutes: ADD: 4/93). Item marked [a] from HMV ALP1214 (11/55), [b]ALP1209 (6/55). Recorded 1954. ⒼⒼⒼ
Gramophone classical 100.
It is astonishing to reflect that this recording of *Also sprach Zarathustra* was made on March 8th, 1954 in stereo when Toscanini was still (just) recording in low-fi in New York's Carnegie Hall. The sound may be tonally fierce by current standards (less so than many oft-praised Mercury reissues) but the balance is fully acceptable, with the first and second violins set close to the listener (and the microphones) on either side of the podium, and the basses hard left. Reiner's *Also sprach* is intense and extrovert. In his second year with the Chicago Symphony Orchestra, the conductor was already getting a thrilling response from the strings, although woodwind intonation could be a problem. Confident and well played as it is, the spectacular opening sunrise inevitably lacks the impact of modern recordings. What we have instead is a measure of raw passion and forward thrust unequalled on disc. In reflective passages, conductor and/or engineers display some reluctance to achieve a real *pianissimo*, but as the tempo builds Reiner invariably creates great excitement and the orchestral playing is marvellous. Reiner's reading of *Ein Heldenleben* has humanity as well as virtuosity – the touching closing section is memorable.

R. Strauss Don Quixote, Op. 35[a]. Don Juan, Op. 20[b]. [a]**Milton Preves** (va); [a]**Antonio Janigro** (vc); **Chicago Symphony Orchestra / Fritz Reiner.** RCA Victor Living Stereo Ⓜ 09026 68170-2 (59 minutes: ADD: 6/97). Item marked [a] from SB2099 (1/61), recorded 1959, [b]SB2128 (10/61), recorded 1954. ⒼⒼⒼ
Fritz Reiner's posthumous reputation is such that an enthusiastic recommendation for this well-packed reissue is probably superfluous. But even now there is a sense in which the disc brings together two sides of Reiner's music-making. The *Don Juan*, recorded as early as December 1954, is one of the most exciting of all time, racing panther-like from the opening gestures, lush and self-consciously *espressivo* in the sweeping string theme. The hushed playing is as exquisite as contemporary technology would permit (the opening is disfigured by noticeable wow). And yet one can see why earlier commentators were reluctant to endorse it without reservation. It is a self-consciously brilliant reading and just a shade heartless. No such reservations surround the *Don Quixote*, made in April 1959 during Antonio Janigro's American début, and recorded with astonishing fidelity using a different orchestral set-up (without divided violins). As so often in this revelatory series, the transfers have been carefully handled, drying out the sound just enough to maximize inner detail but retaining all the distinctive bloom of the venue. This is disciplined yet red-blooded music-making of a kind in short supply these days.

R. Strauss Horn Concertos[a] – No. 1 in E flat major, Op. 11, No. 2 in E flat major, AV132. Duett-Concertino, AV147[b]. Serenade, Op. 7. [a]**David Pyatt** (hn); [b]**Joy Farrall** (cl); [b]**Julie Andrews** (bn); **Britten Sinfonia / Nicholas Cleobury.** EMI Eminence Ⓜ CD-EMX2238 (66 minutes: DDD: 8/95). Recorded 1994. *Gramophone Award Winner 1996.* ⒼⒼⒼ
David Pyatt won the BBC's "Young Musician of the Year" Competition back in 1988. Since then the fledgling has well and truly flown. This is sensationally good horn playing. Primarily, there's his noble legato: the heart of the matter, a beautiful sound, full, even and unclouded. He is sparing with the brassy timbres, holding them in reserve for dramatic effect, for such times as the instrument's well-rounded jocularity must take on a brazen, huntsmen-like air, or rise to shining heroics – like the challenging motto theme of the First Concerto. His shaping of the big phrases rolls off the page with ease and authority, but equally, so much of his personality is conveyed in the rhythmic articulation: a dashing, Jack-be-nimble mischievousness (even a touch of impudence?) in Strauss's athletic *allegros*. Most of all, though – and this is rare – he loves to play quietly, really quietly. He is a master of those dreamy, far-away departures – twilit forest-murmurings: mysterious, unreal. The recording helps in this, too, with a beautifully integrated balance. The sound of the early *Serenade*, Op. 7 is particularly

fine with ripe, euphonious tuttis and room enough for individual personalities (and the Britten Sinfonia boasts several) to open up. And that is the most remarkable aspect of the piece, the utterly natural way it blends and contrasts across the whole spectrum of wind voices. Two of them take centre stage in the delightful *Duett-Concertino*. Joy Farrall's clarinet and Julie Andrews's bassoon are like Octavian and the Baron Ochs in this gentle but spirited opus. A spendid disc, then, sympathetically directed by Nicholas Cleobury.

R. Strauss Eine Alpensinfonie, Op. 64. Don Juan, Op. 20. **San Francisco Symphony Orchestra / Herbert Blomstedt.** Decca Ⓕ 421 815-2DH (70 minutes: DDD: 6/90). Recorded 1988. ⒼⒼ

The *Alpine* Symphony is the last of Richard Strauss's great tone-poems and is in many ways the most spectacular. The score is an evocation of the changing moods of an alpine landscape and the huge orchestral apparatus of over 150 players encompasses quadruple wind, 20 horns, organ, wind machine, cowbells, thunder machine, two harps and enhanced string forces. Its pictorialism may be all too graphic but what virtuosity and inspiration Strauss commands. Herbert Blomstedt's reading penetrates beyond the pictorialism into the work's deeper elements. It emerges as a gigantic hymn to nature on a Mahlerian scale. Tempos are slower, but these are justified by the noble expansiveness of the final pages, towards which the whole performance moves with impressive inevitability. The San Francisco Symphony's playing is magnificent, with subtle use of vibrato by the strings and superb performances, individual and corporate, by the wind sections. The recording is on a spacious scale to match the performance, the big climaxes really thrilling and the whole well balanced. The *Don Juan* performance is fine too.

Additional recommendations ...

...Eine Alpensinfonie. **Concertgebouw Orchestra / Bernard Haitink.**
Philips Ⓕ 416 156-2PH (50 minutes: DDD: 7/86). *Selected by Sounds in Retrospect.* Ⓖ
...Eine Alpensinfonie. Der Rosenkavalier – suite[a]. [a]**Tivoli Augmented Orchestra; Bavarian State Orchestra / Richard Strauss.** Koch Legacy mono Ⓜ 37132-2* (72 minutes: ADD: 1/93).

R. Strauss Serenade, Op. 7. Suite in B flat major, Op. 4. Sonatina No. 2 in E flat major, AV143, "Fröhliche Werkstatt". Wind soloists of the **Chamber Orchestra of Europe / Heinz Holliger.**
Philips Ⓕ 438 933-2PH (74 minutes: DDD: 9/95). Recorded 1993. Ⓖ

With the second of the composer's late *Sonatinas* (also known as the Symphony for Wind Instruments) the COE wind players have made sure that outer-movement lines have plenty of muscle, that the bigger harmonies bloom without ever sounding overblown and that the whole adds up to a rainbow of generous invention, effects and colours such as one would hardly have thought possible even given Strauss's extraordinary knowledge of the medium. With a sophisticated, easy-going team like the Netherlands Wind Ensemble, the Indian summer burble has an instant charm that palls rather quickly; but while not even the COE team can quite stop the mind from wandering in the very prolix finale, there is a dynamic and tonal rigour about the first movement which rivets attention. The line of easy invention between the teenage Strauss's first characteristically happy inspirations in the *Serenade* and the octogenarian's refuge in his 'happy workshop' is broken by the more uneven qualities of the Op. 4 *Suite*. The COE players do it the credit of taking it seriously, making the most of the characteristic swing from an assumed pale cast of thought into the character of a prototype *Till Eulenspiegel*. Again, the full chordings – closely but deliciously captured by the excellent recording – are a constant delight, and one assumes Holliger's shaping hand in the flexible vocalizing of the many *bel canto* lines (starting with the *Serenade*'s ineffable counter-melody). A winner.

Additional recommendations ...

...Suite, Op. 4. Sonatinas Nos. 1 and 2. Serenade. **London Winds / Michael Collins** (cl).
Hyperion Ⓕ CDA66731/2 (two discs: 105 minutes: DDD: 8/93).
...Serenade,[a]. Suite, Op. 4[b]. Sonatinas – No. 1 in F major, "Aus der Werkstatt eines Invaliden", AV135[b]; No. 2[a]. Oboe Concerto, AV144[c]. [c]**Heinz Holliger** (ob); [ab]**Netherlands Wind Ensemble;** [c]**New Philharmonia Orchestra / Edo de Waart.** Philips Ⓜ 438 733-2PM2 (two discs: 132 minutes: ADD: 7/94). Ⓖ

R. Strauss Feuersnot – Love scene. Salome – Dance of the Seven Veils. Die Frau ohne Schatten – Symphonic Fantasy.
Weber Der Freischütz – Overture. Oberon – Overture. **Staatskapelle Dresden / Giuseppe Sinopoli.**
DG Ⓕ 449 216-2GH (57 minutes: DDD: 3/97).

In his complete recording of *Salome* for DG, made in Berlin (reviewed further on), Sinopoli has already shown us how warmly sympathetic he is to Strauss's operatic music. With his Dresden orchestra the results are if anything even more sensuous, when ravishing string tone is perfectly married to Sinopoli's moulded and flexible style. The Love scene from Strauss's very first opera, *Feuersnot*, is drawn from the closing pages of the work, a delectable lollipop that ought to be much better known, in places looking forward to the later Strauss of *Der Rosenkavalier*. Salome's Dance is given a luscious performance with no holding back, and with each section of a piece that can seem bitty leading magnetically to the next. Much the longest piece on the disc is the Symphonic Fantasy from *Die Frau ohne Schatten*. Again Sinopoli's concentration and the gorgeous playing of the orchestra, sumptuously recorded, give cohesion to an obviously sectional piece. Inevitably, it is second best to the opera, with the symbolism eliminated, but thanks to Strauss's cunning it makes a welcome item for those with a sweet tooth. The link with the two popular Weber overtures is a tenuous one, presumably a reference to the association of each composer with Dresden. In Weber some may resist Sinopoli's moulded, warmly expressive style in the slow introductions, but with such superb playing and such keen concentration through to exhilarating *allegros*, it would take a curmudgeon not to be seduced.

Additional recommendation ...
...Feuersnot – Liebesszene. Guntram – Overture. Capriccio – Prelude. *Coupled with works by*
Pfitzner Orchestra of the Deutsche Oper, Berlin / Christian Thielemann.
DG Ⓕ 449 571-2GH (75 minutes: DDD: 3/97). *Gramophone Editor's choice.*
See review under Pfitzner, refer to the Index.   ◷◷

R. Strauss Gesänge, Op. 33 – No. 3, Hymnus; No. 4, Pilgers Morgenlied. Gesänge, Op. 51. Grössere Gesänge, Op. 44 – No. 1, Notturno.
Mahler (orch. Berio) Lieder und Gesänge – No. 1, Frühlingsmorgen; No. 3, Hans und Grethe; No. 6, Um schlimme Kinder artig zu machen; No. 7, Ich ging mit Lust durch einen grünen Wald; No. 10, Zu Strassburg auf der Schanz; No. 13, Nicht wiedersehen! **Andreas Schmidt** (bar); **Berlin Radio Symphony Orchestra / Cord Garben.** RCA Victor Red Seal Ⓕ 09026 61184-2 (62 minutes: DDD: 8/94). Texts and translations included. Recorded 1992.
The real discovery here is Strauss's 15-minute-long, wholly neglected "Notturno", a narrative with orchestra to a poem by Richard Dehmel. It tells of the vision of a dream of Death in the shape of a much-loved friend who appears in bright moonshine, in the depths of the night, playing a beseeching air on his violin. As Norman Del Mar says in Vol. 3 of his biography of the composer (London: 1972): "The title *Notturno* is Dehmel's own and the long poem is one of great emotional intensity". So is Strauss's extraordinarily hypnotic and original setting. The mood of the piece is hallucinatory and tormented, uncannily recalling that of Tristan's desperate outbursts in Act 3. Schmidt interprets it with a notable feeling for its haunting, eerie quality, in a recording of presence. Almost as neglected are the two songs that comprise Strauss's Op. 51. The Uhland setting, "Das Thal" is the most ambitious, describing someone who wants to get away from it all. Its sustained lyricism and atmospheric scoring are Strauss at his most compelling. Berio's orchestrations of some of Mahler's early settings don't sound entirely Mahlerian, but Schmidt sings them all so beautifully that criticism is silenced.

R. Strauss Deutsche Motette, Op. 62[a]. Gesänge, Op. 34. An den Baum Daphne (epilogue to "Daphne"), AV137[b]. Die Göttin im Putzzimmer, AV120. [a]**Tina Kiberg,** [b]**Marianne Lund** (sops); [b]**Christian Lisdorf** (treb); [a]**Randi Stene** (contr); [a]**Gert Henning-Jensen** (ten); [a]**Ulrik Cold** (bass); [b]**Copenhagen Boys' Choir; Danish National Radio Choir / Stefan Parkman.** Chandos Ⓕ CHAN9223 (57 minutes: DDD: 5/94). Texts and translations included. Recorded 1993.
Under Stefan Parkman the Danish National Radio Choir have established a reputation second to none. Parkman handles his singers as if they were a fully fledged symphony orchestra; which is not at all inappropriate in this programme by the supreme master of orchestral colour. From the heart of the 16 chorus parts of the *Deutsche Motette* a further seven are projected by solo voices emerging imperceptibly from the midst of a dense, luxuriant texture. The depth of colour and range of emotions are every bit as extensive in these works as in the great orchestral tone-poems; indeed few orchestral tone-poems evoke dusk and sunset so vividly as "Der Abend", the first of the 1897 *Zwei Gesänge*. There is a wonderfully luminous soundscape here; a combination of superb compositional skill, sensitive musical direction, superlative choral singing and a warm, full-bodied recording.

Additional recommendation ...
...An den Baum Daphne[a]. Zwei Gesänge, Op. 34. Drei Männerchöre, Op. 45. Die Göttin im Putzzimmer. Deutsche Motette, Op. 62. [a]**King's College Choristers, Cambridge; BBC Singers / Stephen Cleobury.** Collins Classics Ⓕ 1495-2 (71 minutes: DDD: 1/98).

R. Strauss Lieder – Op. 10: No. 2, Nichts; No. 9, Allerseelen; Winternacht, Op. 15 No. 2; Ständchen, Op. 17 No. 2; A11' mein Gedanken, Op. 21 No. 1; Op. 22: No. 3, Efeu; No. 4, Wasserrose; Op. 27: No. 2, Cäcilie; No. 3, Heimliche Aufforderung; Op. 29: No. 1, Traum durch die Dämmerung; No. 3, Nachtgang; Op. 32: No. 2, Sehnsucht; No. 3, Liebeshymnus; Der Rosenband, Op. 36 No. 1; Op. 37: No. 3, Meinem Kinde; No. 4, Mein Auge; No. 5, Herr Lenz; No. 6, Hochzeitlich Lied; Befreit, Op. 39 No. 4; Op. 49: No. 1, Waldseligkeit; No. 6, Junggesellenschwur; Weihnachtsgefühl, AV94. **Simon Keenlyside** (bar); **Malcolm Martineau** (pf). EMI Eminence Ⓜ CD-EMX2250 (64 minutes: DDD: 6/96). Texts and translations included. Recorded 1995.
Simon Keenlyside understands and respects both Strauss's sentiment and his sentimentality for what it is. With steady, thoughtfully considered word-placing, he relieves *Allerseelen* of its sicklier scents and keeps its movement light and fresh, bringing the song to a strong, firmly syllabic climax. This skill in estimating the expressive potential of verbal weight and measure also strengthens the contours of his *Sehnsucht*; and in *Ständchen* keeps the vocal focus clear and bright in the more fleet, high notes. Keenlyside exploits the heroic character of his baritone in the bold rhetorical questions of *Nichts*, and in *Liebeshymnus* where the voice rings out with fearless resilience in its top register. This sense of heroic address and acclamation tends to replace, for Keenlyside, the more tremulous, passionate

response some singers find in songs such as the *Hochzeitlich Lied* and *Heimliche Aufforderung*: the lip seldom trembles here, the voice yields little to Strauss's harmonic sidesteps and melodic melismas. Whether you miss that, or find it a relief, will be purely a matter of taste. With Malcolm Martineau delighting equally in the complexity and the simplicity of the piano writing displayed in this 20 years' worth of love songs, the recital should certainly take a significant place in any Strauss collection.

Additional recommendations ...

...Op. 10 – No. 1, Zueignung; No. 2, Nichts; No. 4, Die Georgine; No. 6, Die Verschwiegenen; No. 7, Die Zeitlose; No. 8, Allerseelen. Heimkehr, Op. 15 No. 5. Op. 21 – No. 2, Du meines Herzens Krönelein; No. 3, Ach Lieb, ich muss nun scheiden. Vier Mädchenblumen, Op. 22. O wärst du mein, Op. 26 No. 2. Morgen, Op. 27 No. 4. Traum durch die Dämmerung, Op. 29 No. 1. Ich trage meine Minne, Op. 32 No. 1. Befreit, Op. 39 No. 4. Gefunden, Op. 56 No. 1. Op. 66 – No. 2, Einst kam der Bock als Bote; No. 6, O lieber Künstler sei ermahnt; No. 9, Es war mal eine Wanze; No. 11, Die Händler und die Macher. Op. 67 – Wie erkenn' ich mein Treulieb; No. 2, Guten Morgen, 's ist Sankt Valentinstag; No. 3, Sie trugen ihn auf der Bahre bloss; No. 6, Wanderers Gemütsruhe. **Mitsuko Shirai** (mez); **Hartmut Höll** (pf). Capriccio Ⓕ 10 497 (72 minutes: DDD: 2/95). Texts included.

...Die Drossel, AV34. Der müde Wanderer, AV13. Lass ruh'n die Toten, AV35. Abend- und Morgenrot, AV42, Wiegenlied, AV41. Nebel, AV47. Weihnachtsgefühl, AV94. Weihnachtslied, AV2. Ein Röslein zog ich mir im Garten, AV49. Lieder aus Letzte Blätter, Op. 10 – No. 1, Zueignung; No. 3, Die Nacht; No. 8, Allerseelen. Wie sollten wir geheim sie halten, Op. 19 No. 4. Schlichte Weisen, Op. 21 – No. 1, All' mein Gedanken, mein Herz und mein Sinn; No. 2, Du meines Herzens Krönelein; No. 3, Ach Lieb, ich muss nun scheiden. Lieder, Op. 27 – No. 1, Ruhe, meine Seele; No. 4, Morgen!. Schlagende Herzen, Op. 29 No. 2. Leises Lied, Op. 39 No. 1. Lieder, Op. 49 – No. 2, In goldener Fülle; No. 3, Wiegenliedchen; No. 7, Wer lieben will, muss leiden; No. 8, Ach, was Kummer, Qual und Schmerzen. Gefunden, Op. 56 No. 1. Das Bächlein, Op. 88 No. 1. **Marie McLaughlin** (sop); **Graham Johnson** (pf). Hyperion Ⓕ CDA66659 (63 minutes: DDD: 8/95).

...Op. 49 No. 1, Waldseligkeit. Fünf kleine Lieder, Op. 69 – No. 1, Der Stern; No. 3, Einerlei; No. 5, Schlechtes Wetter. Befreit, Op. 39 No. 4. Hat gesagt – bleibt's nicht dabei, Op. 36 No. 3. *Coupled with works by various composers.* **Lisa della Casa** (sop); **Arpad Sándor** (pf). EMI Salzburg Festival Edition mono Ⓜ CDH5 66571-2 (64 minutes: ADD: 2/98). *See review in the Collections section; refer to the Index.*

R. Strauss Four Last Songs, AV150. Zueignung, Op. 10 No. 1. Morgen, Op. 27 No. 4.
Wagner Wesendonk Lieder. **Elisabeth Meyer-Topsøe** (sop); **Copenhagen Philharmonic Orchestra / Hans Norbert Bihlmaier.** Kontrapunkt Ⓕ 32156 (50 minutes: DDD: 1/94). Notes, texts and translations included. Recorded 1993. Ⓖ

R. Strauss Four Last Songs, AV150.
Wagner Wesendonk Lieder. Tristan und Isolde – Prelude and Liebestod. **Cheryl Studer** (sop); **Dresden Staatskapelle / Giuseppe Sinopoli.** DG Ⓕ 439 865-2GH (61 minutes: DDD: 7/94). Notes, texts and translations included. *Gramophone Editor's choice.* Ⓖ

Here is a discovery, perhaps the most promising *Jugendlich-Dramatische* soprano to burst on the scene since Cheryl Studer. With a full, glowing tone that soars easily above the stave without let or hindrance, an even line, and an innate feeling for a long phrase, Elisabeth Meyer-Topsøe has chosen repertory that shows off her gifts ideally. She sings the *Wesendonk Lieder* with a truly Wagnerian amplitude of phrase and a fair feeling for the text. You only have to hear the generosity of "Stehe still!", with vibrato used to enhance the expression (a lovely "Wesen in wesen", a refulgent close), or the passage starting "Wohl ich weiss es" in "Im Treibhaus" to hear these matters made manifest. Others have, of course, found deeper shades in the songs, but these will surely come to this young artist in time. Similarly the sense of valediction in the *Four Last Songs* can be more easily encompassed by maturer singing, but few have managed the long, tricky phrases of "Beim Schlafengehen" with such a long breath or such daring, exciting fullness. The Wagner is faithfully recorded. In the Strauss items, the voice sometimes seems to go out of focus and the orchestra is lacking real definition. The conducting and playing are always adequate but not quite of the calibre this aspiring artist deserves.

In the Strauss, Cheryl Studer's voice, lyrical yet with dramatic overtones, seems near-ideal for Strauss and for this work in particular, quite apart from the sheer beauty and technical accomplishment of her singing. In the first two songs there is the necessary ecstasy and longing in her singing as Strauss reviews, elegiacally, his musical credo. For example, one could cite the loving treatment in "September" of the phrases beginning "Langsam tut er", the singer's tone poised, the shading of the line perfectly natural. It is the seamless legato and lovely voice that again make "Beim Schlafengehen" so rewarding while, in the final song, Studer is suitably hushed and reflective. Sinopoli and the Staatskapelle Dresden provide ideal support for their singer with the playing in all these works as lyrically expressive as the singing above it, all tempos ideally judged. Similar praise can be given to the reading of the *Wesendonk Lieder*. Here, once again, one notes Studer's amazing combination of vocal mastery and interpretative insight. Every dynamic and expressive mark is scrupulously followed (listen to the *piano* at "Luft" and "Duft" in the second song) in the pursuit of seamless phrasing and a due attention to the text. The richness of her singing, the thorough mastery of German diction and phraseology, make this another special performance. Sinopoli's reading of the Prelude to *Tristan* is flowing, intense and spontaneous and the playing is predictably superb, all adding to the disc's worth. The recordings are for the most part happily spacious and well focused.

Additional recommendation ...

...Morgen. *Coupled with works by various composers.* Renée Fleming (sop); English Chamber Orchestra / Jeffrey Tate. Decca Ⓕ 458 858-2DH (70 minutes: DDD: 3/98). *See review in the Collections section; refer to the Index. Selected by Soundings.*

...Morgen. Liebeshymnus, Op. 32 No. 3. Der Rosenband, Op. 36 No. 1. Wiegenlied, Op. 41 No. 1. Das Bächlein, AV118. *Coupled with works by* Mozart Christine Schäfer (sop); [a]Maria João Pires (pf); Berlin Philharmonic Orchestra / Claudio Abbado. DG Ⓕ 457 582-2GH (65 minutes: DDD: 4/98). *Gramophone Editor's choice. See review under Mozart; refer to the Index.* Ⓠ

...Zueignung. *Coupled with works by various composers.* Lesley Garrett (sop); Britten Sinfonia / Ivor Bolton. Conifer Classics Ⓕ 75605 51329-2 (73 minutes: DDD: 12/97). *See review in the Collections section; refer to the Index.*

...Zueignung. *Coupled with works by various composers.* Angela Gheorghiu (sop); Malcolm Martineau (pf). Decca Ⓕ 458 360-2DH (75 minutes: DDD: 5/98). *See review in the Collections section; refer to the Index.*

R. Strauss Lieder and Arias. Lisa della Casa (sop); Vienna Philharmonic Orchestra / [a]Karl Böhm, [b]Rudolf Moralt, [c]Heinrich Hollreiser. Decca Historic mono Ⓜ 425 959-2DM* (67 minutes: ADD: 4/90). Texts and translations included. Recorded 1953-1954.
Four Last Songs, AV150 (from LW5056, 12/53)[a]. Arabella – Er ist der Richtige nicht (with Hilde Gueden, sop. LW5029, 10/53)[b]; Der Richtige so hab ich stets zu mir gesagt (Paul Schoeffler, bass-bar. LXT5017, 4/55)[c]; Das war sehr gut, Mandryka (Alfred Poell, bar. LW5029)[b]. Ariadne auf Naxos – Es gibt ein Reich[c]. Capriccio – Closing scene (Franz Bierbach, bass. Both LXT5017)[c].

R. Strauss Lieder and Arias. Dame Elisabeth Schwarzkopf (sop); Philharmonia Orchestra / [a]Otto Ackermann, [b]Lovro von Matačic. EMI Références mono Ⓜ CDH7 61001-2* (68 minutes: ADD: 4/88). Items marked [a] from Columbia 33CX1107 (1/54), [b]33CX1226 (3/55). Recorded 1953-1954. *Gramophone classical 100.* ⒼⒼⒼ
Four Last Songs, AV 150[a]. Capriccio – Morgen mittag um Elf[a]. Arabella[b] – Ich danke, Fräulein ... Aber der Richtige; Mein Elemer; Sie wollen mich heiraten; Das war sehr gut (all with Anny Felbermayer, sop; Josef Metternich, bar).

Strauss's *Four Last Songs* are a perfect summation of the composer's lifelong love-affair with the soprano voice deriving from the fact that he married a soprano, Pauline Ahna. They are also an appropriate and deeply moving farewell to his career as a composer and to the whole romantic tradition and they have inspired many glorious performances. In recent times there has been a tendency to linger unnecessarily over what are already eloquent enough pieces. Lisa della Casa, in her naturally and lovingly sung performance under Karl Böhm (the first-ever studio recording of the pieces back in 1953) makes no such mistake. In this incarnation this is a wonderful offering at medium price backed by other invaluable Strauss interpretations from the Swiss diva. Her particular gift is to sing the pieces in a natural, unforced manner with gloriously unfettered tone. Her and Böhm's tempos tend to be faster than those employed by most of her successors.

The Four Last Songs are sung with equal beauty by Elisabeth Schwarzkopf. She sings "Im Abendrot" even more beautifully than della Casa, and with an even more serene feeling of the coming of Death. Her interpretation is extraordinarily moving. The songs gain a great deal also, by being sung in the published order. It is good to have these outstanding performances on CD, especially as they also allow us to hear Schwarzkopf in two Strauss operatic roles she never sang on stage. The voice is at its best and there are moments of rare insight, such as the lovely *pp* "Du kennst mich wieder" in "Frühling". Also the Philharmonia of 1953 were something special and the excellent balance of the recording brings out Straussian subtleties galore. The *Capriccio* finale was recorded before Schwarzkopf made the complete recording. It is a more forceful, less lovable performance. The *Arabella extracts*, on the other hand, exacerbate regret that she didn't record the whole opera. She brings just the right mixture of hauteur and impulsiveness to the enigmatic heroine.

Additional recommendations ...

...Four Last Songs. Cäcilie, Op. 27 No. 2. Morgen, Op. 27 No. 4. Wiegenlied, Op. 41 No. 1. Ruhe meine Seele, Op. 27 No. 1. Meinem Kinde, Op. 37 No. 3. Zueignung, Op. 10 No. 1 (orch. Heger). Jessye Norman (sop); Leipzig Gewandhaus Orchestra / Kurt Masur. Philips Ⓕ 411 052-2PH (DDD: 2/84). Ⓠ

...Four Last Songs [a]. Muttertändelei, Op. 43 No. 2[a]. Waldseligkeit, Op. 49 No. 1[a]; Zueignung, Op. 10 No. 1[a]. Freundliche Vision, Op. 48 No. 1[a]. Die heiligen drei Könige, Op. 56 No. 6[b]. Ruhe, meine Seele, Op. 27 No. 1[b]. Meinem Kinde, Op. 37 No. 3[b]. Wiegenlied, Op. 41 No. 1[b]. Morgen, Op. 27 No. 4 (with Edith Peinemann, vn)[b]. Das Bächlein, Op. 88 No. 1[b]. Das Rosenband, Op. 36 No. 1[b]. Winterweihe, Op. 48 No. 4. Dame Elisabeth Schwarzkopf (sop); [a]Berlin Radio Symphony Orchestra; [b]London Symphony Orchestra / George Szell. EMI Ⓕ CDC7 47276-2 (64 minutes: ADD: 12/85). ⒼⒼⒼ

...Four Last Songs[a]. Metamorphosen for 23 Solo Strings. Oboe Concerto[b]. [a]**Gundula Janowitz** (sop); [b]**Lothar Koch** (ob); **Berlin Philharmonic Orchestra / Herbert von Karajan.**
DG Galleria Ⓜ 423 888-2GGA (75 minutes: ADD: 12/88).   ⓆⒼ
...Four Last Songs[a]. All' mein Gedanken, Op. 21 No. 1[b]. Allerseelen, Op. 10 No. 8[b]. Begegnung, AV72[b]. Cäcilie, Op. 27 No. 2[b]. Hat gesagt, Op. 36 No. 3[b]. Madrigal, Op. 15 No. 1[b]. Malven, Op. posth[b]. Morgen, Op. 27 No. 4[b]. Muttertändelei, Op. 43 No. 2[b]. Die Nacht, Op. 10 No. 3[b]. Schlechtes Wetter, Op. 69 No. 5[b]. Ständchen, Op. 17 No. 2[b]. Zueignung, Op. 10 No. 1[b].
Dame Kiri Te Kanawa (sop); [a]**Vienna Philharmonic Orchestra / Sir Georg Solti** ([b]pf).
Decca Ⓕ 430 511-2DH (50 minutes: DDD: 9/91).
...Four Last Songs.[a]. Capriccio – Morgen mittag um elf! ... Kein andres[b]. Tod und Verklärung, Op. 24[c]. [ab]**Gundula Janowitz** (sop); [a]**Berlin Philharmonic Orchestra / Herbert von Karajan;** [b]**Bavarian Radio Symphony Orchestra;** [c]**Dresden Staatskapelle / Karl Böhm.**
DG Classikon Ⓑ 439 467-2GCL (65 minutes: ADD: 4/95).
...Four Last Songs[a]. Cäcilie, Op. 27 No. 2[a]. Befreit, Op. 39 No. 4[a]. Wiegenlied, Op. 41 No. 1[a]. Muttertändelei, Op. 43 No. 2[a]. Waldseligkeit, Op. 49 No. 1[a]. Der Rosenkavalier – Suite.
[a]**Renée Fleming** (sop); **Houston Symphony Orchestra / Christoph Eschenbach.**
RCA Victor Red Seal Ⓕ 09026 68539-2 (69 minutes: DDD: 3/97).

R. Strauss Ariadne auf Naxos – Ein schones war; Es gibt ein Reich. Arabella – Mein Elemer!.
Wagner Die Walküre – Der Männer Sippe; Du bist der Lenz. Lohengrin – Einsam in trüben Tagen. Tannhäuser – Dich teure Halle; All-mächt'ge Jungfrau. Der fliegende Holländer – Joho hoe! ... Traft ihr das Schiff. Tristan und Isolde – Mild und leise. **Elisabeth Meyer-Topsøe** (sop); **Copenhagen Philharmonic Orchestra / Hans Norbert Bihlmaier.** Kontrapunkt Ⓕ 32249 (60 minutes: DDD: 4/97). Texts included.

There are few, if any, sopranos today who can sing this repertory more securely than Meyer-Topsøe. A pupil of Nilsson, she sings with her teacher's ringing confidence, tone and technique solid and unblemished. It is heartening to hear once more a Scandinavian interpreter of Wagner with such a thrilling sound, one for whom the challenge of Senta, Elsa, Elisabeth and Isolde are as nothing. All that said, there is as yet room in some items for more dramatic involvement. One might expect more sense of obsession in Senta's Ballad, more intensity of longing in Elsa's Dream, more interior ecstasy in "Du bist der Lenz". Studio restrictions and/or a somewhat careful conductor may not be a help in that respect. An exception to this stricture is the Liebestod where Meyer-Topsøe sounds a Nilsson-like touch of transfiguration. Her Straussian credentials are impeccable and are amply confirmed here in her Ariadne and Arabella. Here's evidence, most of all in a gloriously outgoing "Es gibt ein Reich", of identification with a given role. Her Arabella is hardly less engrossing as she ponders on her "Fremde Mann", the soprano's even, youthful timbre exactly right for the eager yet thoughtful girl. Bihlmaier seems happier in Strauss than in Wagner. The recording rightly has the singer centre-stage, the exciting voice caught in a natural acoustic. The fact that the accompanying notes contain German texts only, without translations, shouldn't prevent connoisseurs from acquiring this disc.

R. Strauss Der Rosenkavalier – Wie du warst! Wie du bist; Da geht er hin ... Ach, du bist wieder da! ... Die Zeit, die ist ein sonderbar Ding; Mir ist die Ehre; Mein Gott, es war nicht mehr ... Heut oder morgen ... Marie Theres'... Hab' mir's gelobt ... Ist ein Traum. **Régine Crespin, Elisabeth Söderström, Hilde Gueden** (sops); **Heinz Holecek** (bar); **Vienna State Opera Concert Choir; Vienna Philharmonic Orchestra / Silvio Varviso.** Decca Ⓑ 452 730-2DC (62 minutes: ADD: 10/97). From SXL6146 (3/65). Recorded 1964.

This, one of the most desirable discs in the whole recorded history of the opera, has led a Cinderella existence since it first appeared 33 years ago. Now invited to the ball it ought to be accorded status as a princess. Crespin, quite heart-rending as the Marschallin, is in pristine voice. She fills her music with silvery, sensuous tone and at the same time judges every note, every phrase to perfection, whether in the monologue, or the final scenes of Acts 1 and 3. These extracts benefit from having, as Strauss intended, a soprano Octavian – and what a soprano! Söderström's vibrant, impassioned singing is just what the role calls for. Together she and Crespin make the close of Act 1 a thing to savour. Then in the Silver Rose Presentation she is joined by Gueden still able in her late-forties to float Sophie's high-lying phrases as to the manner born, while in the last act Gueden finds just the right sense of embarrassment in the presence of the Marschallin. It is a thousand pities the opera was not recorded complete, not least because Varviso, as at those Covent Garden performances, is in his absolute element, elegant and ardent, finding an idiomatic Straussian ebb and flow with the VPO on rapturous form, all recorded with Decca's 1960s skill. Christopher Raeburn provides the notes, filling in the plot as best he can in the absence of texts and translations. This is a must for all Straussians.

R. Strauss Salome – Ach, du wolltest mich nicht deinen Mund küssen lassen.
Guntram – Fass'ich sie bang. Ariadne auf Naxos – Es gibt ein Reich. Arabella – Mein Elemer!.
Die Aegyptische Helena – Zweite Brautnacht!.
Mozart Lucio Silla – Ah, corri, vola ... Quest'improvviso tremito. Don Giovanni – Or sai chi l'onore; Crudele! Ah no, mo bene ... Non mi dir. Idomeneo – Idol mio, se ritroso; Oh smania! oh furie! ... D'Oreste, d'Aiace. **Jane Eaglen** (sop); **Israel Philharmonic Orchestra / Zubin Mehta.**
Sony Classical Ⓕ SK60042 (65 minutes: DDD: 6/98). Texts and translation included.

The partnership of Eaglen and the Israel Philharmonic under Zubin Mehta is at its strongest in the Richard Strauss tracks of this Mozart and Strauss compilation. The orchestra's superbly balanced wind soloists create dark shadows for *Guntram*'s Freihild, as she reflects within them, at first perplexed and then, in unflaggingly focused voice, thankful for her love for the Minnesinger – and for the glory of her top B. If Ariadne's distraction is captured rather less convincingly, then the sustained rapture of *Die Aegyptische Helena*'s "Zweite Brautnacht!" draws the full effulgence from Eaglen's golden soprano in what seems to be one breathless sentence. The five Mozart arias here remind us just what a formidable Mozartian Eaglen is; and one only wishes that Mehta were her equal in this respect – one longs for a livelier orchestral presence. Eaglen's own skills at pacing and charging with emotion Electra's passages of accompanied recitative make for real momentum, lit by a bright platinum gleam in the voice in "Oh smania! ... D'Oreste, d'Aiace"; and her instinctive phrasing gives eloquent voice to Electra's more demure moments in "Idol mio".

R. Strauss Die aegyptische Helena – excerpts[a]. Die Frau ohne Schatten – excerpts[b]. Daphne – excerpts[c]. [a]**Viorica Ursuleac**, [a]**Margit Bokor**, [b]**Hilde Konetzni**, [b]**Emmy Loose**, [b]**Else Schulz**, [c]**Maria Reining** (sops); [b]**Else Boettcher** (mez); [b]**Melanie Frutschnigg**, [b]**Elisabeth Höngen** (contrs); [a]**Franz Völker**, [a]**Helge Roswaenge**, [b]**Torsten Ralf**, [b]**Wenko Wenkoff**, [b]**William Wernigk**, [c]**Anton Dermota**, [c]**Alf Rauch** (tens); [a]**Alfred Jerger**, [b]**Josef Herrmann**, [b]**Alfred Poell**, [b]**Tomislav Neralic** (bars); [b]**Herbert Alsen**, [b]**Georg Monthy**, [b]**Marjan Rus**, [b]**Roland Neumann** (basses); **Vienna State Opera Chorus and Orchestra /** [a]**Clemens Krauss**, [b]**Karl Böhm**, [c]**Rudolf Moralt**. Koch Schwann mono Ⓜ 314552* (two discs: 145 minutes: ADD: 11/94).
Item marked [a] recorded live in 1933, [b]1943, [c]1942.

This enshrines valuable extracts from the original Viennese performances of *Helena* and *Daphne*, and some 90 minutes from what proves to be one of the most convincing readings ever of *Die Frau ohne Schatten*. The *Helena* provides the final proof that the somewhat maligned Ursuleac was, in the 1930s, a Strauss soprano *par excellence* and, supported by her husband Krauss's inspiriting direction, she fills the famous solo "Zweite Brautnacht" and other equally taxing passages with refulgent tone and soaring phraseology. For 1933 the sound is remarkable, and has the minimum amount of distortion. When *Die Frau* is sung and conducted as here at a 1943 revival, it does indeed sound like Strauss's outright masterpiece as many experts on the composer declare it to be. Böhm recognizes the virtues of sheerly beautiful sound (amply provided by his cast and the Vienna Philharmonic), textural clarity of a chamber-music kind and keeping the score on the move. Excellent as have been her successors as the Empress, Konetzni just about surpasses them all for the steadiness of her tone, her firm legato and her involvement. The first Daphne at the State Opera was Maria Reining. In her long opening solo, she is inclined to spoil her lovely singing by sliding into notes from below, but she reaches her glorious best in her duet with Apollo and from then on goes from strength to strength, making light of the extraordinary demands Strauss places on his soprano. Both Moralt and Böhm are ardent advocates of this vital but flawed score. Any Straussian must have this issue. Others who wish to find out just how to sing and conduct the composer's operas authentically may well like to sample it too.

R. Strauss Arabella. **Julia Varady** (sop) Arabella; **Helen Donath** (sop) Zdenka; **Dietrich Fischer-Dieskau** (bar) Mandryka; **Walter Berry** (bass) Waldner; **Helga Schmidt** (mez) Adelaide; **Elfriede Höbarth** (sop) Fiakermilli; **Adolf Dallapozza** (ten) Matteo; **Hermann Winkler** (ten) Elemer; **Klaus-Jürgen Küper** (bar) Dominik; **Hermann Becht** (bar) Lamoral; **Doris Soffel** (mez) Fortune Teller; **Arno Lemberg** (spkr) Welko; **Bavarian State Opera Chorus; Bavarian State Orchestra / Wolfgang Sawallisch**. Orfeo Ⓕ C169882H (two discs: 144 minutes: DDD: 1/89).
Notes, text and translation included. From EMI SLS5224 (10/81).

Complete except for a brief cut in Matteo's part in Act 3, Sawallisch's 1981 Orfeo recording of *Arabella* has been easily fitted on to two CDs. Sawallisch is the most experienced conductor of Strauss's operas alive today and at his best in this one, his tempos just right, his appreciation of its flavour (sometimes sentimental, at others gently ironic and detached) unequalled. Helen Donath's delightful Zdenka is a perfect foil for Varady's Arabella. Varady's singing of the title-role is characterful and intelligent. One should be left with ambivalent feelings about this heroine; is she lovable or a chilling opportunist? Or both? And while Fischer-Dieskau's singing of Mandryka has not the total security of his earlier DG recording of the role with Keilberth, he remains the best Mandryka heard since the war.

Additional recommendation ...
...**Soloists; Bavarian State Opera Chorus and Orchestra / Joseph Keilberth**.
DG Ⓜ 437 700-2GX3 (three discs: 159 minutes: ADD: 8/93).

R. Strauss Ariadne auf Naxos. **Gundula Janowitz** (sop) Ariadne; **Teresa Zylis-Gara** (sop) Composer; **Sylvia Geszty** (sop) Zerbinetta; **James King** (ten) Bacchus; **Theo Adam** (bass-bar) Music Master; **Hermann Prey** (bar) Harlequin; **Siegfried Vogel** (bass) Truffaldino; **Hans Joachim Rotzsch** (ten) Brighella; **Peter Schreier** (ten) Scaramuchio, Dancing Master; **Erika Wustmann** (sop) Naiad; **Annelies Burmeister** (mez) Dryad; **Adele Stolte** (sop) Echo; **Erich-Alexander Winds** (spkr) Major-Domo; **Dresden Staatskapelle / Rudolf Kempe**. EMI Opera Ⓜ CMS7 64159-2 (two discs: 118 minutes: ADD: 11/92). Notes, text and translation included.
From HMV SAN215/7 (11/68).   Ⓖ

At mid price this classic set cannot be recommended too highly. Nobody knew more about how to pace Strauss's operas than Kempe and he was at his best when working with the Dresden Staatskapelle, a group of players who have Strauss in their veins. This reading brings out all the sentiment and high spirits of this delightful work, and the results are beautifully recorded. Janowitz's golden tones were ideal for the title role, which she sings with poise and inner feeling, though she makes little of the text. Zylis-Gara is a suitably impetuous Composer in the engaging Prologue where 'he' meets and has a gently erotic encounter with the charming but flighty Zerbinetta, a role here taken with brilliant accomplishment by Sylvia Geszty, who made it her own in the 1960s. James King is a forthright though none too flexible Bacchus. The smaller parts are also well taken. The more recent Masur version, with the admirable Leipzig Gewandhaus, has Jessye Norman as a stately Ariadne, Julia Varady as a fiery Composer, Edita Gruberová as a bright-eyed, dexterous Zerbinetta, Paul Frey as an anonymous Bacchus. Masur, like Kempe, is steeped in the work's performing tradition and is the best of modern sets.

Additional recommendations ...
...**Soloists; Leipzig Gewandhaus Orchestra / Kurt Masur.**
Philips Ⓕ 422 084-2PH2 (two discs: 118 minutes: DDD: 11/88).
...**Soloists; London Philharmonic Orchestra / Sir Georg Solti.**
Decca Grand Opera Ⓜ 430 384-2DM2 (two discs: 121 minutes: ADD: 5/92).
Ariadne auf Naxos⁹. Wagner Die Meistersinger von Nürnberg – excerpts[b].
Soloists; Vienna State Opera [b]Chorus and Orchestra / Karl Böhm.
Koch Schwann mono Ⓜ 314732* (two discs: 156 minutes: ADD: 5/96).
...**(1912 version). Soloists; Orchestra of the Opéra National de Lyon / Kent Nagano.**
Virgin Classics Ⓕ VCD5 45111-2 (two discs: 136 minutes: DDD: 9/97).

R. Strauss Ariadne auf Naxos[a]. **Maria Reining** (sop) Ariadne; **Irmgard Seefried** (sop) Composer; **Alda Noni** (sop) Zerbinetta; **Max Lorenz** (ten) Bacchus; **Paul Schoeffler** (bass-bar) Music Master; **Erich Kunz** (bar) Harlekin; **Marjan Rus** (bass) Truffaldino; **Peter Klein** (ten) Brighella; **Richard Sallaba** (ten) Scaramuchio; **Emmy Loose** (sop) Naiad; **Melanie Frutschnigg** (contr) Dryad; **Elisabeth Rutgers** (sop) Echo; **Josef Witt** (ten) Dancing Master; **Alfred Muzzarelli** (spkr) Major-domo; **Hans Schweiger** (bar) Footman; **Friedrich Jelinek** (ten) Officer; **Hermann Baier** (bar) Wig-maker.
Wagner Die Meistersinger von Nürnberg – excerpts[b]. **Maria Reining** (sop); **Martha Rohs** (mez); **Max Lorenz, Peter Klein** (tens); **Josef Herrmann, Erich Kunz** (bars); **Vienna State Opera [b]Chorus and Orchestra / Karl Böhm.** Koch Schwann mono Ⓜ 314732 (two discs: 156 minutes: ADD: 5/96). Item marked [a] recorded live in 1944, [b]1943.

This opens with some desirable extracts from a 1943 *Die Meistersinger*, conducted by the sterling Böhm. It is adorned by Herrmann's lyrical, poetic Sachs, a reading based on firm tone, incisive diction and finely etched legato singing, the best example of this underrated baritone's art on record. The *Flieder* receives an inward, thoughtful interpretation, followed by an account of the duet with Maria Reining's radiant Eva that approaches an ideal. Then he leads into the Act 3 Quintet as poetically as any Sachs on disc, the ensemble itself led off by Reining's poised singing. Lorenz is his usual over-effusive self in the Prize song, and the final track has Herrmann somewhat tiring in Sachs's final solo. The sound is mostly excellent. So, these are further important mementoes of the unrivalled ensemble then resident in Vienna. The same can be said of the complete *Ariadne*, conducted by Böhm at the Opera for Strauss's eightieth birthday. This is also available from Preiser, where the transfer yields marginally superior results. But, of course, you have here a bonus in the Wagner, and so better value for money in terms of quantity of music. Either way the *Ariadne* is a 'must', arguably the most idiomatic recording the Strauss masterpiece has ever received.

Additional recommendation ...
...**Soloists; Vienna State Opera Orchestra / Karl Böhm.** Preiser mono Ⓕ 90217*
(two discs: 117 minutes: AAD: 11/94).

R. Strauss Elektra. **Birgit Nilsson** (sop) Elektra; **Regina Resnik** (mez) Klytemnestra; **Marie Collier** (sop) Chrysothemis; **Tom Krause** (bar) Orestes; **Gerhard Stolze** (ten) Aegisthus; **Pauline Tinsley** (sop) Overseer; **Helen Watts** (contr), **Maureen Lehane, Yvonne Minton** (mezzos), **Jane Cook, Felicia Weathers** (sops) First, Second, Third, Fourth and Fifth Maids; **Tugomir Franc** (Tutor); **Vienna Philharmonic Orchestra / Sir Georg Solti.** Decca Ⓕ 417 345-2DH2 (two discs: 108 minutes: ADD: 12/86). Notes, text and translation included. From SET354/5 (11/67). ⒼⒼ

Elektra is the most consistently inspired of all Strauss's operas and derives from Greek mythology, with the ghost of Agamemnon, so unerringly delineated in the opening bars, hovering over the whole work. The invention and the intensity of mood are sustained throughout the opera's one-act length, and the characterization is both subtle and pointed. It is a work peculiarly well suited to Solti's gifts and he has done nothing better in his long career in the studios. He successfully maintains the nervous tension throughout the unbroken drama and conveys all the power and tension in Strauss's enormously complex score which is, for once, given complete. The recording captures the excellent singers and the Vienna Philharmonic in a warm, spacious acoustic marred only by some questionable electronic effects. Notwithstanding the latter, this is undoubtedly one of the greatest performances on record and sounds even more terrifyingly realistic on this magnificent transfer.

Additional recommendations ...
...Soloists; **Bavarian Radio Chorus and Symphony Orchestra / Wolfgang Sawallisch.**
EMI Ⓕ CDS7 54067-2 (two discs: 102 minutes: DDD: 12/90).
...Soloists; **Berlin State Opera Chorus; Staatskapelle Berlin / Daniel Barenboim.**
Teldec Ⓕ 4509-99175-2 (two discs: 101 minutes: DDD: 7/96).

R. Strauss Die Frau ohne Schatten. **Julia Varady** (sop) Empress; **Plácido Domingo** (ten) Emperor; **Hildegard Behrens** (sop) Dyer's Wife; **José van Dam** (bar) Barak the Dyer; **Reinhild Runkel** (contr) Nurse; **Albert Dohmen** (bar) Spirit-Messenger; **Sumi Jo** (sop) Voice of the Falcon; **Robert Gambill** (ten) Apparition of a Young Man; **Elzbieta Ardam** (mez) Voice from above; **Eva Lind** (sop) Guardian of the Threshold; **Gottfried Hornik** (bar) One-eyed Brother; **Hans Franzen** (bass) One-armed Brother; **Wilfried Gahmlich** (ten) Hunchback Brother; **Vienna Boys' Choir; Vienna State Opera Chorus; Vienna Philharmonic Orchestra / Sir Georg Solti.**
Decca Ⓕ 436 243-2DHO3 (three discs: 195 minutes: DDD: 5/92). Notes, text and translation included. Recorded 1989-1991. *Gramophone Award Winner 1992.* ⓋⓋⓋ
This was the most ambitious project on which Strauss and his librettist Hugo von Hofmannthal collaborated. It is both fairy tale and allegory with a score that is Wagnerian in its scale and breadth. This Solti version presents the score absolutely complete in an opulent recording that encompasses every detail of the work's multi-faceted orchestration. Nothing escapes his keen eye and ear or that of the Decca engineers. The cast boasts splendid exponents of the two soprano roles. Behrens's vocal acting suggests complete identification with the unsatisfied plight of the Dyer's Wife and her singing has a depth of character to compensate for some tonal wear. Varady gives an intense, poignant account of the Empress's taxing music. The others, though never less than adequate, leave something to be desired. Domingo sings the Emperor with customary vigour and strength but evinces little sense of the music's idiom. José van Dam is likewise a vocally impeccable Barak but never penetrates the Dyer's soul. Runkel is a mean, malign Nurse as she should be though she could be a little more interesting in this part. It benefits from glorious, dedicated playing by the VPO.

Additional recommendations ...
...Soloists; **Tölz Boys' Choir; Bavarian Radio Chorus and Symphony Orchestra / Wolfgang Sawallisch.** EMI Ⓕ CDS7 49074-2 (three discs: 191 minutes: DDD: 9/88).
...Soloists; **Vienna State Opera Chorus; Vienna Philharmonic Orchestra / Sir Georg Solti.** Decca Grand Opera Ⓜ 430 387-2DM2 (two discs: 144 minutes: ADD: 5/92).

R. Strauss Friedenstag[a]. **Hans Hotter** (bass-bar) Commandant; **Viorica Ursuleac** (sop) Maria; **Herbert Alsen** (bass) Sergeant; **Josef Witt** (ten) Rifleman; **Hermann Wiedemann** (bass) Corporal; **Carl Bissuti** (bass) Musketeer; **Nikolaus Zec** (bass) Bugler; **Anton Dermota** (ten) A Piedmontese; **Hermann Gallos** (ten) Officer; **Georg Monthy** (bass) Front-line Officer; **Karl Kamann** (bass) Holsteiner; **Willy Franter** (ten) Burgomaster; **Viktor Madin** (bar) Prelate; **Mela Bugarinovic** (mez) Woman of the People.
Arabella – excerpts[b]. Ariadne auf Naxos – excerpts[c]. [b]**Margit Bokor,** [bc]**Adele Kern,** [c]**Dora Komarek,** [c]**Anny Konetzni,** [c]**Elisabeth Rutgers,** [c]**Else Schulz,** [b]**Viorica Ursuleac** (sops); [c]**Elena Nikolaidi,** [b]**Gertrud Rünger** (mezzos); [c]**Friedrich Jelinek,** [c]**Alexander Pichler,** [c]**Richard Sallaba,** [c]**Set Svanholm,** [c]**William Wernigk** (tens); [c]**Hermann Baier,** [c]**Alfred Poell** (bars); [bc]**Alfred Jerger** (bass-bar); [b]**Richard Mayr,** [c]**Alfred Vogel** (basses); [c]**Alfred Muzzarelli** (spkr); **Vienna State Opera** [ab]**Chorus and Orchestra /** [ab]**Clemens Krauss,** [c]**Rudolf Moralt.**
Koch Schwann mono Ⓜ 314652* (two discs: 143 minutes: ADD: 10/95).
Item marked [a] recorded live in 1939, [b]live in 1933, [c]1941.
This issue offers us a complete performance of Strauss's underrated and under-recorded *Friedenstag* given by its creators in 1939, shortly after its première in Munich. Here Krauss, Ursuleac and Hotter prove incontrovertibly that the work has a strength and validity not often accorded it by even the most dedicated of Straussians. You marvel at the immense conviction and energy Krauss brings to it. Then, his wife Ursuleac gives the performance of her life as Maria. She is fearless and tireless in tackling the high As, B flats and Bs in which the role abounds, singing with vibrant tone and in a possessed manner fitting an overwrought woman starved of the love of her husband (the Commandant) who has poured all his energies into war. Finally, she provides the necessary ecstasy when she wins him back and sees the war come to an end. As ever, Strauss glories in his writing for a *lirico-spinto*, and Ursuleac glories with him. The 30-year-old Hotter, in towering voice, gives to the Commandant's part the right sense of a man dedicated to his ideal of defending his Kaiser's cause and honour at whatever cost to his men or to his personal life. A team of Viennese stalwarts of the day fills the smaller roles satisfactorily, with the young Dermota notable as the Piedmontese youth musing on his beloved Italy and its girls: it's another role nicely etched in by the composer. The music is so different from most of what Strauss was writing at the time. Instead of harking back to romanticism, as in *Arabella* and *Daphne*, he composes here in a tougher style more in keeping with his own time, bringing into play Hindemithian, even Bergian ideas. The final paean to peace recalls the Mahler of the symphonies' choral sections. Mind you, the piece – as many have commented – is more dramatic oratorio than opera. The recorded sound, taken in this case off a broadcast, is good by the standard of these sets, but by no means anything special. However, the voices don't distort and much of the orchestral detail can be gleaned. *Friedenstag* is flanked by excerpts from two other works by Strauss. Those from a 1933 *Arabella*, also

a Viennese 'first', featuring the original singers of the two main roles, are not so desirable since Ursuleac and Jerger recorded the most important passages commercially (for Decca-Polydor in 1933). Nevertheless, it is good to hear Krauss conducting with such *élan*.

R. Strauss Der Rosenkavalier. **Dame Elisabeth Schwarzkopf** (sop) Die Feldmarschallin; **Christa Ludwig** (mez) Octavian; **Otto Edelmann** (bass) Baron Ochs; **Teresa Stich-Randall** (sop) Sophie; **Eberhard Waechter** (bar) Faninal; **Nicolai Gedda** (ten) Italian Tenor; **Kerstin Meyer** (contr) Annina; **Paul Kuen** (ten) Valzacchi; **Ljuba Welitsch** (sop) Duenna; **Anny Felbermayer** (sop) Milliner; **Harald Pröghlöf** (bar) Notary; **Franz Bierbach** (bass) Police Commissioner; **Erich Majkut** (ten) Marschallin's Majordomo; **Gerhard Unger** (ten) Faninal's Majordomo, Animal Seller; **Karl Friedrich** (ten) Landlord; **Loughton High School for Girls and Bancroft's School Choirs; Philharmonia Chorus and Orchestra / Herbert von Karajan.** EMI ℗ CDS7 49354-2 (three discs: 191 minutes: ADD: 1/88). Notes, text and translation included. From Columbia SAX2269/72 (11/59). Recorded 1956. *Gramophone classical 100. Gramophone Award Winner 1988.* ⊙⊙⊙

Der Rosenkavalier concerns the transferring of love of the young headstrong aristocrat Octavian from the older Marschallin (with whom he is having an affair) to the young Sophie, a girl of *nouveau riche* origins who is of his generation. The portrayal of the different levels of passion is masterly and the Marschallin's resigned surrender of her ardent young lover gives opera one of its most cherishable scenes. The comic side of the plot concerns the vulgar machinations of the rustic Baron Ochs and his attempts to seduce the disguised Octavian (girl playing boy playing girl!). The musical richness of the score is almost indescribable with stream after stream of endless melody, and the final trio which brings the three soprano roles together is the crowning glory of a masterpiece of our century. This magnificent 1956 recording, conducted with genius by Karajan and with a cast such as dreams are made of, has a status unparalleled and is unlikely to be challenged for many a year. The Philharmonia play like angels and Elisabeth Schwarzkopf as the Marschallin gives one of her greatest performances. The recording, lovingly remastered, is outstanding. In 1956 stereo recording was new to the commercial recording world and, unwilling to gamble everything on the new medium, producer Water Legge arranged for the sessions to be captured in both mono and stereo, using separate microphone layouts and separate balance engineers. The mono recording (listed below) has never before been issued on CD. One is, in fact, immediately struck by the mono recording's warmer, closer balance: Schwarzkopf, for example, a significantly more rounded, fuller and essentially dominant presence, never in danger of being overwhelmed by the orchestra. The detail and transparency of the overall canvas on the stereo recording is more naturally convincing but the mono will make a special appeal to those who prefer intimate access to these great singers. The dilemma is that each recording is impressive in its way and yet so very different. Students of the voice will almost certainly favour the mono recording; devotees of the opera itself may well prefer the stereo.

Additional recommendations ...

...**Soloists; Vienna State Opera Chorus; Vienna Philharmonic Orchestra / Sir Georg Solti.** Decca ℗ 417 493-2DH3 (three discs: 200 minutes: ADD: 3/87).

...**Soloists; Dresden Kreuzchor; Dresden State Opera Chorus; Dresden Staatskapelle / Bernard Haitink.** EMI ℗ CDS7 54259-2 (three discs: 223 minutes: DDD: 9/91).

...**(Abridged). Soloists; Vienna State Opera Chorus; Vienna Philharmonic Orchestra / Robert Heger.** Die Aegyptische Helena – Helen's awakening; Funeral march; Bei jener Nacht; Zweite Brautnacht, Zaubernacht!; **Rose Pauly** (sop); **Berlin State Opera Orchestra / Fritz Busch.** Breit über mein Haupt, Op. 19 No. 2. Morgen, Op. 27 No. 4. **Robert Hutt** (ten); **Richard Strauss** (pf). Pearl mono ℗ GEMMCDS9365* (two discs: 115 minutes: ADD: 3/90).

...**Soloists; Loughton High School for Girls and Bancroft's School Choirs; Philharmonia Chorus and Orchestra / Herbert von Karajan.** EMI mono ℗ CDS5 56113-2* (three discs: 191 minutes: ADD: 9/96). *Gramophone classical 100. Gramophone Award Winner 1988.* ⊙⊙⊙

R. Strauss Salome. **Cheryl Studer** (sop) Salome; **Bryn Terfel** (bar) Jokanaan; **Horst Hiestermann** (ten) Herod; **Leonie Rysanek** (sop) Herodias; **Clemens Bieber** (ten) Narraboth; **Marianne Rørholm** (contr) Page; **Friedrich Molsberger** (bass) First Nazarene; **Ralf Lukas** (bass) Second Nazarene; **William Murray** (bass) First Soldier; **Bengt Rundgren** (bass) Second Soldier; **Klaus Lang** (bar) Cappadocian; **Orchestra of the Deutsche Oper, Berlin / Giuseppe Sinopoli.** DG ℗ 431 810-2GH2 (two discs: 102 minutes: DDD: 9/91). Notes, text and translation included. Recorded 1990. ⊙⊙

R. Strauss Salome. **Birgit Nilsson** (sop) Salome; **Eberhard Waechter** (bar) Jokanaan; **Gerhard Stolze** (ten) Herod; **Grace Hoffman** (mez) Herodias; **Waldemar Kmentt** (ten) Narraboth; **Josephine Veasey** (mez) Page; **Tom Krause** (bar) First Nazarene; **Nigel Douglas** (ten) Second Nazarene; **Zenon Koznowski** (bass) First Soldier; **Heinz Holecek** (bass) Second Soldier; **Theodore Kirschbichler** (bass) Cappadocian; **Vienna Philharmonic Orchestra / Sir Georg Solti.** Decca ℗ 414 414-2DH2 (two discs: 99 minutes: ADD: 7/85). Notes, text and translation included. Recorded 1961. From SET228 (3/62). *Gramophone classical 100.* ⊙⊙⊙

Strauss's setting of a German translation of Oscar Wilde's play is original and erotically explicit. It caused a sensation in its day and even now stimulates controversy. Sinopoli's recording is a magnificent achievement, mainly because of Cheryl Studer's representation of the spoilt Princess who demands and eventually gets the head of Jokanaan (John the Baptist) on a platter as a reward for her striptease ("Dance of the Seven Veils"). Studer, her voice fresh, vibrant and sensuous, conveys exactly Salome's growing fascination, infatuation and eventual obsession with Jokanaan, ending in the arresting necrophilia of the final scene. She expresses Salome's wheedling, spoilt nature, strong will and ecstasy in tones apt for every aspect of the strenuous role. She is supported to the hilt by Sinopoli's incandescent conducting and by Bryn Terfel's convincing Jokanaan, unflaggingly delivered, by Hiestermann's neurotic Herod, who makes a suitably fevered, unhinged sound as the near-crazed Herod, and Rysanek's wilful Herodias. The playing is excellent and the recording has breadth and warmth. This is eminently recommendable. For a newcomer to the work, Studer's superb portrayal may just tip the balance in favour of Sinopoli, though Sir Georg Solti's famous version is in a class of its own, with a gloriously sung Salome and the ravishingly beautiful playing of the Vienna Philharmonia.

Sir Georg Solti's *Salome* was one of Decca's notable Sonic-stage successes and still beats most of its operatic competitors in terms of sound alone. There is a real sense here of a theatrical performance, as directed by John Culshaw, with an imaginative use of movement. Of course, the vivid, nervous energy of Strauss has always been Solti's territory and this is an overwhelming account of Strauss's sensual piece, sometimes a little too hard-hitting for its or our good: there are places where the tension might be relaxed just a shade, but throughout, the VPO answer Solti's extreme demands with their most aristocratic playing. With only a single break, the sense of mounting fever is all the more felt. Nilsson's account of the title-role remains another towering monument to her tireless singing. Here, more even than as Brünnhilde, one notices just how she could fine away her tone to a sweet and fully supported *pianissimo*, and her whole interpretation wants nothing of the erotic suggestiveness of sopranos more familiar with the role on stage. Stolze's Herod is properly wheedling, worried and, in the final resort, crazed, but there are times, particularly towards the end of his contribution, when exaggeration takes over from characterization. Other interpretations show how effects can be created without distortion of the vocal line. Waechter is an aggressive rather than a visionary Jokanaan. Grace Hoffman is a suitably gloating Herodias. Much better than any of these, Nilsson apart, is Kmentt's wonderfully ardent Narraboth. Hardly any of the rivals since 1961 has managed a true challenge to this outstanding set.

Additional recommendations ...

...Soloists; Staatskapelle Dresden / Seiji Ozawa.
Philips Ⓕ 432 153-2PH2 (two discs: 103 minutes: DDD: 10/94).

...Soloists; Vienna Philharmonic Orchestra / Christoph von Dohnányi.
Decca Ⓕ 444 178-2DHO2 (two discs: 100 minutes: DDD: 4/95).   Ⓖ

...Soloists; Staatskapelle Dresden / Otmar Suitner.
Berlin Classics Ⓜ 0091 012BC (two discs: 94 minutes: ADD: 4/96).

Further listening ...

...Intermezzo – symphonic interludes. *Coupled with* **Schmidt** Symphony No. 1 in E major.
Detroit Symphony Orchestra / Neeme Järvi. Chandos CHAN9357 (4/96).

...Symphonia domestica, Op. 53 (arr. Singer). *Coupled with works by* **Dukas** *and* **Ravel**
Martha Argerich, Alexandre Rabinovitch (pfs). Teldec 4509-96435-2 (7/96). *Gramophone Editor's choice. See review under Dukas; refer to the Index.*   ⒼⒼ

...Cello Sonata in F major, Op. 6. *Coupled with* **Thuillé** Cello Sonata, Op. 22. **Sophie Rolland** (vc);
Marc-André Hamelin (pf). ASV CDDCA913 (3/95).   Ⓖ

...Piano Sonata in B minor, Op. 5. Fünf Klavierstücke, Op. 3. Stimmungsbilder, Op. 9.
Oleg Marshev (pf). Danacord DACOCD440 (10/97).

...Drei Hymnen, Op. 71. *Coupled with works by various composers.* **Karita Mattila** (sop);
Chorus; Berlin Philharmonic Orchestra / Claudio Abbado. Sony Classical SK53975 (3/95).

...Stiller Gang, Op. 31 No. 4. *Coupled with works by various composers.* **Mitsuko Shirai** (mez);
Tabea Zimmermann (va); **Hartmut Höll** (pf).
Capriccio 10 462 (9/95). *See review in the Collections section; refer to the Index.*   Ⓖ

...Arabella – Das war sehr gut, Mandryka. Der Rosenkavalier – Da geht er hin; Die Zeit, die ist ein sonderbar Ding; Mein schöner Schatz ... Ich werd' jetzt in die Kirchen geh'n; Marie Theres'! ... Hab' mir's gelobt. *Coupled with works by various composers.* **Leonie Rysanek** (sop);
Various soloists and orchestras. EMI Références mono CDH5 65201-2* (2/95).

...Capriccio. **Soloists; Philharmonia Orchestra / Wolfgang Sawallisch.**
EMI mono CDS7 49014-8* (9/87).   ⒼⒼ

...Daphne[a]. Daphne – excerpts[b]. An den Baum Daphne, AV137[c]. **Soloists; [ac]Vienna State Opera Chorus; [a]Vienna Philharmonic Orchestra; [b]Dresden State Opera Orchestra / [ab]Karl Böhm, [c]Walter Hagen-Groll.** Preiser mono 90237* (11/95).

...Daphne – Ich komme, grünende Brüder. *Coupled with works by various composers.* **Renée Fleming** (sop); **London Symphony Orchestra / Sir Georg Solti.** Decca 455 760-2DH (10/97).
Gramophone Editor's choice. See review in the Collections section; refer to the Index.

...Daphne – Ich komme, grünende Brüder. Ariadne auf Naxos – Es gibt ein Reich.
Die Aegyptische Helena – Zweite Brautnacht!. *Coupled with works by various composers.*
Dame Kiri Te Kanawa (sop); **Philharmonia Orchestra / Julius Rudel.**
EMI CDC5 56417-2 (11/97). *See review in the Collections section; refer to the Index.*

...Salome – Ach, du wolltest mich nicht deinen Mund küssen lassen[a]. Feuersnot – Feuersnot! Minnegebot![b]. Der Rosenkavalier – Marie Theres'[c]. Daphne – Ich komme grünende Brüder[a].

Taillefer, Op. 52ᵈ. **Maria Cebotari, ᶜPaula Buchner, ᶜTiana Lemnitz** (sops); ᵈ**Walther Ludwig** (ten); ᵇ**Karl Schmitt-Walter** (bar); ᵈ**Hans Hotter** (bass-bar); ᵈ**Rudolf Lamy Singers; Berlin Radio Symphony Orchestra / Artur Rother.** Preiser mono 90222* (8/95).

Igor Stravinsky   Russian/French/American 1882-1971

The reviews which follow comprise part of "The Complete Edition" (Sony Classical Ⓜ S22K46290 22 CDs: ADD: 7/91). The items reviewed here were subsequently issued as separate sets.

Stravinsky The Complete Edition, Volume 1. **Various artists / Igor Stravinsky.**
Sony Classical Ⓜ SM3K46291* (three discs: 194 minutes: ADD: 8/92). Recorded 1959-1962.
Gramophone classical 100.   ❷❷❷
The Firebird (Columbia Symphony Orchestra. From CBS 72046, 9/62). Scherzo à la russe
(Columbia Symphony Orchestra). Scherzo fantastique (CBC Symphony Orchestra). Fireworks
(Columbia Symphony Orchestra. All from CBS GM31, 2/82). Petrushka (Columbia Symphony
Orchestra. Philips SABL175, 4/61). The Rite of Spring (Columbia Symphony Orchestra.
SABL174, 4/61). Les noces (Mildred Allen, sop; Regina Sarfaty, mez; Loren Driscoll, ten;
Richard Oliver, bass; Samuel Barber, Aaron Copland, Lukas Foss, Roger Sessions, pfs;
American Concert Choir; Columbia Percussion Ensemble). Renard (George Shirley,
Loren Driscoll, tens; William Murphy, bar; Donald Gramm, bass; Toni Koves, cimbalom;
Columbia Chamber Ensemble. Both from CBS SBRG72071, 12/62). L'histoire du soldat – Suite
(Columbia Chamber Ensemble. SBRG72007, 6/62).
Inspiration for this collection of mainly stage music came from Stravinsky's native folk-song, folk-dance, folk-tale and folk ritual; and the set contains virtually all the music from Stravinsky's 'Russian' period, including the three great ballets. It is fascinating to chart his development from the 1908 *Scherzo fantastique* with its orchestral colours scintillating in the best Rimsky-Korsakovian manner, to the wholly original language of *Les noces* with its almost exclusively metrical patterns and monochrome scoring (soloists, chorus, pianos and percussion) begun only six years later. The links are there: witness the Rimskian bumble-bee that flies through the *Scherzo* to find its winged counterpart two years on in *The Firebird*; and the primitive rhythmic force of Kastchei's "Infernal dance" in *The Firebird* finding its fullest expression, another three years later, in *The Rite of Spring*; and so on. Each work is a logical, if time-lapse progression from the previous one. The set concludes with the 15-minute long animal rites of the farmyard opera-cum-burlesque *Renard* (1916); and *L'histoire du soldat* (1918), a morality play designed for a small touring theatre company (the Suite included here omits the speaking roles); both, like *Les noces*, leaving behind the lavish orchestra of *The Rite* for small and unusual instrumental and vocal combinations.
   To have the composer at the helm, and a consistent approach to the way the music is recorded, ensures that those links are clearly established. And the orchestra that takes the lion's share of the task, the Columbia Symphony, was assembled by CBS to include many of the finest players in America. It is possible to criticize the recordings (made between 1959 and 1963) for close balances and spotlighting, but many modern contenders, more distantly recorded, will more often than not deprive you of adequate articulation of the music's linear and rhythmic ingenuity. The dynamic range and contours of *The Rite of Spring* do seem momentarily reduced and disturbed by the techniques, otherwise all these recordings reproduce with good tone, range, openness and presence. As to Stravinsky the conductor, only *Les noces* finds him at less than his usual rhythmically incisive self. This *Petrushka* is more representative: it pulsates with inner life and vitality – incidentally, Stravinsky uses his leaner, clearer 1947 revision, not the original 1911 score as the booklet claims.

Stravinsky The Complete Edition, Volume 2. **Various artists / Igor Stravinsky.** Sony Classical
Ⓜ SM3K46292 (three discs: 210 minutes: ADD: 8/92). *Gramophone classical 100.*   ❷❷❷
Apollo (Columbia Symphony Orchestra). From SBRG72355, (11/65). Agon (Los Angeles
Festival Symphony Orchestra. SBRG72438, 8/66). Jeu de cartes (Cleveland Orchestra). Scènes de
ballet (CBC Symphony Orchestra). Bluebird – Pas de deux (Columbia Symphony Orchestra.
All from SBRG72270, 5/65). Le baiser de la fée (Columbia Symphony Orchestra. SBRG72407,
5/66). Pulcinella (Irene Jordan, sop; George Shirley, ten; Donald Gramm, bass; Columbia
Symphony Orchestra. SBRG72452, 7/66). Orpheus (Chicago Symphony Orchestra. SBRG72355).
Volume 2 comprises ballets written between 1919 and 1957. *Pulcinella* was based on music originally thought to have been written by Pergolesi, but now known to be the work of various eighteenth-century composers. In 1919 Stravinsky had not long embraced neo-classical style, but here was a brilliant example of old wine in new bottles, with the melodies sounding as if they come from the pen of Stravinsky himself. The composer conducts a lively, sharply-accented account of the score. 1928 saw the production of two Stravinsky ballets. *Apollo*, a mainly quiet, contemplative score, written for string orchestra, has many passages of great beauty. Stravinsky the conductor does not linger over these, but allows the work's cool classical elegance to speak for itself. In *Le baiser de la fée* Stravinsky used themes by Tchaikovsky as the basis for his score. Once again, the music seems quite transformed, and the result is a most captivating work. Stravinsky's watchful, affectionate performance is perfectly proportioned. His arrangement of the "Pas de deux" from Tchaikovsky's *Sleeping Beauty* is no more

than a reduction for small pit orchestra, however, and a mere curiosity. In *Jeu de cartes*, which dates from 1936, Stravinsky used music by Rossini and others, but here the references are only fleeting, and merely enhance the humour of this robust, outgoing score. His performance brings out all the work's vigour and personality very effectively, but here and there rhythms become slightly unstuck, and a slightly hectic quality manifests itself.

Scènes de ballet was written in 1944, and possesses a slightly terse quality in the main, though there are some more lyrical passages. Stravinsky does nothing to soften the work's edges in his performance, and it emerges as a strong, highly impressive piece. *Orpheus* was completed in 1947, and shows Stravinsky's neo-classical style at its most highly developed. Much of the music is quiet, after the manner of *Apollo*, but then the orchestra suddenly erupts into a passage of quite savage violence. Stravinsky conducts this passage with amazing energy for a man in his eighties, and elsewhere his performance has characteristic clarity and a very direct means of expression typical of a composer performance. Finally *Agon*, written in 1957, attracts the listener with its colourful opening fanfares, and then pursues an increasingly complex serial path in such a brilliant and highly rhythmical fashion that one is hardly aware that the technique is being used. This work, brilliantly conducted by Stravinsky, is an ideal introduction to his late style, and to the serial technique itself. Remastering has been carried out with the greatest skill, and all the recordings in this set sound very well indeed for their age.

Stravinsky The Complete Edition, Volume 4. **Various artists / Igor Stravinsky.** Sony Classical
Ⓜ SM2K46294 (two discs: 143 minutes: ADD: 8/92). *Gramophone classical 100.*   ⒼⒼⒼ
Symphonies – No. 1 in E flat major (Columbia Symphony Orchestra SBRG72569, 11/67).
Stravinsky in rehearsal. Stravinsky in his own words (GM31). Symphony in Three Movements
(Columbia Symphony Orchestra. SBRG72038, 9/62). Symphony in C (CBC Symphony
Orchestra). Symphony of Psalms (Toronto Festival Singers, CBC Symphony Orchestra.
SBRG72181, 8/64).

The word 'symphony' appears in the title of each work on these two discs, but this term covers some very diverse material. Stravinsky was in his mid-twenties when he wrote his Symphony in E flat, and the score is very much in the style of his teacher Rimsky-Korsakov. It has genuine colour and flair, however, and the octogenarian conductor brings paternalistic affection and a good deal of vigour to his performance. The *Symphony in C* dates from 1940, when Stravinsky was in his neo-classical phase. The work has many beautiful pages, as well as much pungent wit. In this performance Stravinsky drives the music much harder than he did in his 1952 mono recording with the Cleveland Orchestra, and although there are some exciting moments the music does tend to lose its elements of grace and charm. The performance of the *Symphony in Three Movements* is also characterized by the use of fastish tempos. But this violent work, written in 1945, and inspired by events in World War Two, responds more readily to a strongly driven interpretation. Stravinsky wrote his *Symphony of Psalms* in 1930, and this composition reflects his deep religious convictions in varied settings from the Book of Psalms. His use of a chorus is interestingly combined with an orchestra which lacks upper strings. Stravinsky conducts a fervent, serious, beautifully balanced performance. All the 1960s recordings in this set sound very well in their CD transfers. In some quarters the elderly Stravinsky has been wrongly portrayed as a frail, inadequate figure who only took over performances when works had been thoroughly rehearsed for him. Nothing could prove more clearly that this was not true than the rehearsal excerpts in this set, which show a vigorous, alert octogenarian very much in control of proceedings, and rehearsing passages in some detail.

Additional recommendations ...
...The Firebird – Concert Suite. **Rimsky-Korsakov** Scheherazade, Op. 35.
Paris Opera-Bastille Orchestra / Myung-Whun Chung. DG Ⓕ 437 818-2GH (DDD).
...Le baiser de la fée. **Tchaikovsky** (arr. Stravinsky) The Sleeping Beauty – Bluebird pas de deux.
Scottish National Orchestra / Neeme Järvi. Chandos Ⓕ CHAN8360 (51 minutes: DDD: 7/85).
...The Firebird. Scherzo à la russe (versions for jazz ensemble and orchestra). Quatre études
(1952 version). **City of Birmingham Symphony Orchestra / Sir Simon Rattle.**
EMI Ⓕ CDC7 49178-2 (65 minutes: DDD: 4/89).   ⒼⒼ
...Symphonies of Wind Instruments. Concerto for Piano and Wind Instruments. Capriccio.
Movements for Piano and Orchestra. **Paul Crossley** (pf); **London Sinfonietta / Esa-Pekka Salonen.**
Sony Classical Ⓕ SK45797 (54 minutes: DDD: 10/90).
...The Firebird. Le chant de rossignol. Fireworks, Op. 4. Scherzo à la russe. Tango. **London
Symphony Orchestra / Antál Dorati.** Mercury Ⓜ 432 012-2MM (74 minutes: ADD: 11/91). ⒼⒼⒼ
...Orpheus. Jeu de cartes. **Royal Concertgebouw Orchestra / Neeme Järvi.**
Chandos Ⓕ CHAN9014 (53 minutes: DDD: 3/92).
...Symphony in C. Symphony in Three Movements. **Royal Scottish Orchestra /
Sir Alexander Gibson.** Chandos Collect Ⓜ CHAN6577 (51 minutes: DDD: 6/92).
...The Firebird. Le Chant de Rossignol. **Danish National Radio Symphony Orchestra /
Dmitri Kitaienko.** Chandos Ⓕ CHAN8967 (77 minutes: DDD: 9/92).
...The Firebird. Fireworks, Op. 4. Four Etudes. **Chicago Symphony Orchestra / Pierre Boulez.**
DG Ⓕ 437 850-2GH (60 minutes: DDD: 11/93). *Selected by Sounds in Retrospect.*
...Scherzo fantastique. **Rimsky-Korsakov** Scheherazade, Op. 35. **Royal Concertgebouw Orchestra /
Riccardo Chailly.** Decca Ⓕ 443 703-2DH (59 minutes: DDD: 10/94).

...Divertimento from "Le baiser de la fée". *Coupled with works by* **Prokofiev** and **Hovhaness**
Chicago Symphony Orchestra / Fritz Reiner. RCA Victor Living Stereo Ⓜ 09026 61957-2
(64 minutes: ADD: 9/95). *See review under Hovhaness; refer to the Index.*
...Le baiser de la fée. **Bartók** Two Pictures, Sz46. **La Scala Philharmonic Orchestra, Milan /**
Riccardo Muti. Sony Classical Ⓕ SK58949 (61 minutes: DDD: 9/95).
...The Firebird – Concert Suite. **Falla** El amor brujo[a]. El sombrero de tres picos – Dance of the
Miller's Wife; Neighbours' Dance; Miller's Dance; Final Dance. [a]**Grace Bumbry** (mez);
Berlin Radio Symphony Orchestra / Lorin Maazel.
DG The Originals Ⓜ 447 414-2GOR (65 minutes: ADD: 10/95).

Stravinsky Violin Concerto in D major[a].
Lutosławski Partita for Violin, Orchestra and Obbligato Solo Piano (1985)[b]. Chain 2 (1984)[c].
Anne-Sophie Mutter (vn); [b]**Phillip Moll** (pf); [a]**Philharmonia Orchestra / Paul Sacher;** [bc]**BBC**
Symphony Orchestra / Witold Lutosławski. DG Ⓕ 423 696-2GH (56 minutes: DDD: 2/89).   Ⓖ
This disc contains some spellbinding violin playing in a splendidly lifelike recording, and it's a bonus
that the music, while unquestionably 'modern', needs no special pleading: its appeal is instantaneous
and long-lasting. Mutter demonstrates that she can equal the best in a modern classic – the Stravinsky
Concerto – and also act as an ideal, committed advocate for newer works not previously recorded.
The Stravinsky is one of his liveliest neo-classical pieces, though to employ that label is, as usual, to
underline its rough-and-ready relevance to a style that uses Bach as a springboard for an entirely
individual and unambiguously modern idiom. Nor is it all 'sewing-machine' rhythms and pungently
orchestrated dissonances. There is lyricism, charm, and above all humour: and no change of mood is
too fleeting to escape the razor-sharp responses of this soloist and her alert accompanists,
authoritatively guided by the veteran Paul Sacher. Lutosławski's music has strongly individual
qualities that have made him perhaps one of the most approachable of all contemporary composers.
This enthralling collaboration between senior composer and youthful virtuoso is not to be missed.
Additional recommendations ...
...Violin Concerto. **Prokofiev** Violin Concertos – No. 1 in D major, Op. 19; No. 2 in G minor,
Op. 63. **Kyung-Wha Chung** (vn); **London Symphony Orchestra / André Previn.**
Decca Ⓜ 425 003-2DM (72 minutes: ADD: 7/90).   Ⓖ
...Violin Concerto. **Prokofiev** Violin Concertos – No. 1 in D major, Op. 19; No. 2 in G minor,
Op. 63. **Cho-Liang Lin** (vn); **Los Angeles Philharmonic Orchestra / Esa-Pekka Salonen.**
Sony Classical Ⓕ SK53969 (70 minutes: DDD: 3/95).   Ⓖ
...Violin Concerto[a]. **Ravel** Tzigane[b]. **Berg** Violin Concerto[a]. **Itzhak Perlman** (vn);
[a]**Boston Symphony Orchestra / Seiji Ozawa;** [b]**New York Philharmonic Orchestra / Zubin Mehta.**
DG The Originals Ⓜ 447 445-2GOR (57 minutes: [a]ADD/[b]DDD: 7/96).
...Violin Concerto. **Prokofiev** Violin Concerto No. 2 in G minor, Op. 63.
Itzhak Perlman (vn); **Chicago Symphony Orchestra / Daniel Barenboim.**
Teldec Ⓕ 4509-98255-2 (46 minutes: DDD: 7/97).
...Violin Concerto. **Bartók** Violin Concerto No. 2, Sz112. **Viktoria Mullova** (vn); **Los Angeles**
Philharmonic Orchestra / Esa-Pekka Salonen. Philips Ⓕ 456 542-2PH (57 minutes: DDD: 5/98).
See review under Bartók; refer to the Index.   ⒼⒼ

Stravinsky Apollon musagète (1947 version). The Firebird – Suite. Scherzo fantastique,
Op. 3[a]. **Royal Concertgebouw Orchestra / Riccardo Chailly.** Decca Ⓕ 458 142-2DH
(71 minutes: DDD: 1/98). Item marked [a] from 443 703-2DH (10/94). Recorded 1994-1995.
Gramophone Editor's choice. Selected by Soundings.
Illumination is everywhere here. The fact that Stravinsky's revision dispensed with "half the
woodwind, two of the three harps, glockenspiel and celesta from the original scoring" (to quote the
excellent insert-note) hardly constitutes the bleaching process that a less colour-sensitive performance
might have allowed. Part of the effect is due to a remarkably fine recording where clarity and tonal
bloom are complementary, but Chailly must take the credit for laying *all* Stravinsky's cards on the
table rather than holding this or that detail to his chest. Everything tells, much as it does in the *Scherzo*
fantastique – whether the euphonious winds and brass at 3'52", the motorized repeated notes later on
(at 8'31") or the ornamental swirlings that, in stylistic terms, dance us all the way from Rimsky's
Arabian Nights to the unmistakably Russian world of *The Firebird. Apollon musagète* is of course
something else again and Chailly takes the lyrical line, pointing without punching and allowing his
excellent strings their head. The coda is jaunty, the "Apothéose" suitably mysterious and "Variation
d'Apollon" features fine solo work from the orchestra's leader, Jaap van Zweden. Viable alternatives
include leaner, more ascetic readings but Chailly balances gracefulness with tonal substance and his
engineers provide glorious sound.

Stravinsky Apollon musagète[a]. Pulcinella – suite[a]. Capriccio[b]. [b]**John Ogdon** (pf); **Academy of**
St Martin in the Fields / Sir Neville Marriner. Decca The Classic Sound Ⓜ 443 577-2DCS
(70 minutes: ADD: 4/95). Items marked [a] from Argo ZRG575 (10/68), [b]ZRG674 (2/72).
Recorded 1967-1970.   ⒼⒼ
The Academy's 1968 coupling of the *Pulcinella* suite and *Apollo* was their first foray into twentieth-
century repertoire on disc and it now returns with *Capriccio* a substantial bonus. The transfers are

excellent. In *Pulcinella*, the unprecedented crispness of the Academy's ensemble may no longer inspire particular awe – we are accustomed to squeaky-clean Stravinsky nowadays – so it is the elegant, characterful solos and clear, warm (not quite plummy) Kingsway Hall ambience that places this account in a special category. *Apollo* sounds superb too, that final "Apotheosis" as blissful as ever, although, as its final chord dies, the improved clarity in the bass alerts us to the presence of an unwelcome intruder – the London Underground. *Capriccio*, not perhaps one of Stravinsky's more inspiring works, is well served by John Ogdon, less so by the over-resonant acoustic of The Maltings, Snape, which sometimes obscures instrumental detail. Notwithstanding these reservations, this is an outstanding collection.

Additional recommendations ...

...Symphony of Psalms[a]. Concerto for Piano and Wind Instruments[b]. Pulcinella – suite[c].
[b]Seymour Lipkin (pf); **[a]English Bach Festival Chorus; [a]London Symphony Orchestra; [bc]New York Philharmonic Orchestra / Leonard Bernstein.**
Sony Classical Bernstein Royal Edition Ⓜ SMK47628 (68 minutes: ADD: 11/94).

...Pulcinella – suite. Concerto in E flat major, "Dumbarton Oaks". Two Suites.
Chamber Orchestra of the Teatre Lliure, Barcelona / Josep Pons.
Harmonia Mundi Ⓕ HMC90 1609 (51 minutes: DDD: 3/97).

Stravinsky Le baiser de la fée. Faun and Shepherdess, Op. 2[a]. Ode. [a]**Lucy Shelton** (sop);
Cleveland Orchestra / Oliver Knussen. DG Ⓕ 449 205-2GH (64 minutes: DDD: 11/97).
Text and translation included. Recorded 1995-1996. *Gramophone Editor's choice.* ⒼⒼ
Oliver Knussen offers us the best-played, best-recorded and most sensitively interpreted account of *Le baiser de la fée* that we have had so far on CD, with meticulous attention to Stravinsky's dynamic markings and delicate instrumental pointing. Stravinsky's subtle Tchaikovsky orchestrations (the musical 'grid' of *Le baiser*) inspire a reading that exhibits delicate sensibilities and quick reflexes, and Knussen's fill-ups respond equally well to those same qualities. The mildly erotic *Faun and Shepherdess* is seductively played, with soprano Lucy Shelton sounding agile and vocally appealing. The tripartite *Ode* is a quietly eventful memorial for Natalie Koussevitzky. Even Stravinsky's own 1965 Columbia Symphony Orchestra recording, although full of lovely things and obviously of great historical interest, is outclassed by DG's superior recording.

Stravinsky Circus Polka. Ode. Scherzo à la Russe. Scènes de ballet. Concertino. Agon.
Greeting Prelude "Happy Birthday to you". Canon on a Russian popular tune.
Variations "Aldous Huxley in memoriam".
Stafford Smith/Key (arr. Stravinsky) The star-spangled banner. **London Symphony Orchestra / Michael Tilson Thomas.** RCA Victor Red Seal Ⓕ 09026 68865-2 (76 minutes: DDD: A/97).
Recorded 1996.
This CD has been absorbingly programmed to chart the progress from Stravinsky's early years in America, awkwardly coming to terms with a new language, a new and rather harsh economic climate and a musical public that welcomed him warmly enough but was at the same time welcoming scores of other refugee musicians. Acutely conscious of money and the absence of it, he attempted in vain to obtain film music commissions from Hollywood and tried to write pop songs and to make money in the relatively prosperous world of jazz. But the *Scherzo à la Russe*, originally for jazz band (played here in its orchestral version), sounds like a rejected movement from *Petrushka*. Rather more shrewdly he wrote the *Scènes de ballet* for a Broadway revue, and was rewarded with a respectable run of performances. The *Concertino*, written for string quartet long before Stravinsky's arrival in America, arranged there for a chamber orchestra of 12 instruments, is a neat demonstration of how much of his late style was already present in his earlier work. The proto-serial *Agon* and the super-serial *Variations* both represent Stravinsky's relief and sheer exuberance, not so much at finding serialism as at realizing that he had been writing quasi-serially all his life and that he could exploit its techniques while still remaining himself. What makes this a hugely entertaining as well as an instructive survey is the infectious zest of the performances. The enjoyable racket of the *Circus Polka*, the gorgeous trumpet tune in *Scènes de ballet*, the sheer delight in inventing entrancing new sonorities that is central to *Agon*, the more arcane but none the less obvious pleasure in the *Aldous Huxley* Variations of constructing perfect, crystalline mechanisms – all these are conveyed with exemplary precision. The recordings match the lucid brilliance of the performances.

Stravinsky Petrushka (1947 version)[a]. Symphony in Three Movements. [a]**Peter Donohoe** (pf);
City of Birmingham Symphony Orchestra / Sir Simon Rattle. EMI Ⓕ CDC7 49053-2
(57 minutes: DDD: 5/88). Ⓖ
Stravinsky's second great ballet score has been well served on disc from the earliest days of LP. He recorded it himself (rather indifferently) but there is in any event a good case for preferring the brilliance and clarity of digital sound in this of all works. Simon Rattle's performance is most notable for its fresh look at details of scoring and balance, with pianist Peter Donohoe making a strong impression. The results are robust and persuasive, though one sometimes has the impression that the characters are being left to fend for themselves. The atmospheric sound with its generous middle and bass is certainly very natural. The symphony too is eminently recommendable, sounding more grateful and high spirited than it sometimes has, with Rattle particularly relishing the jazzy bits.

Additional recommendations ...
...Petrushka. Firebird – Suite. Pastorale (arr. Stokowski). **Shostakovich** (arr. Stokowski).
Prelude in E minor, Op. 34 No. 14. **Philadelphia Orchestra / Leopold Stokowski.**
Dutton Laboratories mono Ⓜ CDAX8002* (60 minutes: ADD: 5/93).
...Orpheus. Petrushka. **Philharmonia Orchestra / Esa-Pekka Salonen.**
Sony Classical Ⓕ SK53274 (64 minutes: DDD: 2/94).
...Symphony in C. Symphony in Three Movements. Symphony of Psalms[a].
London Symphony [a]Chorus and Orchestra / Michael Tilson Thomas.
Sony Classical Ⓕ SK53275 (71 minutes: DDD: 7/94).
...Petrushka. *Coupled with works by various composers.* **Shura Cherkassky** (pf).
Decca Ⓕ 433 657-2DH (79 minutes: ADD: 2/96). Ⓖ
...Petrushka. *Coupled with works by* **Ravel** and **Petrov** Leningrad Symphony Orchestra /
Yuri Temirkanov. Melodiya Ⓜ 74321 32044-2 (69 minutes: ADD: 2/97).

Stravinsky Petrushka (1947 version). Pulcinella[a]. [a]Anna Caterina Antonacci (sop); [a]Pietro Ballo
(ten); [a]William Shimell (bar); **Royal Concertgebouw Orchestra / Riccardo Chailly.**
Decca Ⓕ 443 774-2DH (73 minutes: DDD: 6/95). Text and translation included.
Recorded 1993. *Gramophone Editor's choice.* ⒼⒼ
Stravinsky Pulcinella[a]. Renard[b]. Two Suites. Rag-Time. [a]Jennifer Larmore (mez); [b]John Aler,
[ab]Frank Kelly (tens); [ab]Jan Opalach, [b]John Cheek (basses); **Saint Paul Chamber Orchestra /
Hugh Wolff.** Teldec Ⓕ 4509-94548-2 (73 minutes: DDD: 5/96). Texts and translations included.
Recorded 1994.
In *Petrushka* Chailly has his players characterize even the smallest detail. Note the tongue-in-cheek
lead-in to the "Russian Dance" and the carefree 'squeeze-box' character of the dance itself (with
dynamic crossfire between wind and brass and some excellent piano playing). "Petrushka" (second
tableau) is played *con amore*, with much humanity and not entirely without malice: perhaps the anger
and frustration aren't as blatant as Bernstein's on DG; but the pain and humiliation certainly are. It's
a performance that breathes, that sings and neither rushes its fences nor loses sight of the score's very
specific rhythmic profile. As for the recording, given top-ranking engineers – who could rightly expect
anything less than exceptional? The coupling, too, is equally colourful: a pert, sweet-centred
Pulcinella, with an expressive *concertino* in the "Ouverture", winsome phrasing elsewhere and
extremely brilliant accounts of the two *Allegro assais* (tracks 23 and 35). Here there is an incisiveness,
attack and buoyancy to the rhythms. The singing is vividly characterized and, again, the recording is
spectacular, with a trombone "Vivo" that should serve the same 'demonstration' function as
Ansermet's and Marriner's did in the days of LP. Now, as then, Decca take a definite sonic lead in this
delightful music.
Hugh Wolff's *Pulcinella* is a witty, incisive alternative. Just try the *Vivo* with its frolicking trombone
and wilting double-bass solo and note how stylishly they phrase their closing duet. His singers are
generally above par, Jennifer Larmore especially. Wolff offers for couplings the best *Rag-Time* for 11
instruments on disc – gently swinging and without a hint of self-consciousness – plus keenly focused
accounts of the two Suites for small orchestra and an exceedingly enjoyable *Renard*. Here the singing
is again excellent and there's a novelty in that Wolff has tweaked the published translation and in so
doing has effected a more natural flow to the comedy. Again, there is a plethora of detail – subtle
underlinings, useful clarifications and felicitous turns of phrase – and the recording is excellent.
Additional recommendations ...
...Petrushka. The Rite of Spring. Firebird Suite (1919). Scènes de Ballet.
Symphony in Three Movements. **Israel Philharmonic Orchestra / Leonard Bernstein.**
DG Masters Series Ⓜ 445 538-2GMA2 (DDD).
...Pulcinella[a]. Jeu de cartes. [a]Teresa Berganza (mez); [a]Ryland Davies (ten);
[a]John Shirley-Quirk (bar); **London Symphony Orchestra / Claudio Abbado.**
DG Galleria Ⓜ 423 889-2GGA (62 minutes: ADD: 1/89).

Stravinsky The Rite of Spring. Apollon musagète. **City of Birmingham Symphony Orchestra /
Sir Simon Rattle.** EMI Ⓕ CDC7 49636-2 (65 minutes: DDD: 11/89). Ⓖ
Recordings of *The Rite of Spring* are legion, but it is rare to find Stravinsky's most explosive ballet
score coupled with *Apollon musagète*, his most serene. The result is a lesson in creative versatility,
confirming that Stravinsky could be equally convincing as expressionist and neoclassicist. Yet talk of
lessons might suggest that sheer enjoyment is of lesser importance, and it is perfectly possible to relish
this disc simply for that personal blend of the authoritative and the enlivening that Simon Rattle's
CBSO recordings for EMI so consistently achieve. Rattle never rushes things, and the apparent
deliberation of *The Rite*'s concluding "Sacrificial Dance" may initially surprise, but in this context it
proves an entirely appropriate, absolutely convincing conclusion. Rattle sees the work as a whole,
without striving for a spurious symphonic integration, and there is never for a moment any hint of a
routine reading of what is by now a classic of the modern orchestral repertoire. The account of *Apollo*
has comparable depth, with elegance transformed into eloquence and the CBSO strings confirming
that they have nothing to fear from comparison with the best in Europe or America. The recordings
are faithful to the intensity and expressiveness of Rattle's Stravinsky, interpretations fit to set beside
those of the composer himself.

Additional recommendations ...

...The Rite of Spring. Apollon musagète. **Berlin Philharmonic Orchestra / Herbert von Karajan.**
DG Ⓕ 415 979-2GH (66 minutes: ADD: 9/86).
...The Rite of Spring. Symphony in E flat major. Symphony in Three Movements. Symphony in C.
Symphony of Psalms[a]. [a]**Festival Singers, Toronto; Columbia Symphony Orchestra;**
[a]**CBC Symphony Orchestra / Igor Stravinsky.**
Sony Classical Ⓜ SM2K46294 (two discs: 142 minutes: ADD: 8/92).　　　　　ⒼⒼⒼ
...The Rite of Spring. **Mussorgsky** Pictures at an Exhibition. **Philadelphia Orchestra /**
Riccardo Muti. EMI Ⓜ CDM7 64516-2 (64 minutes: DDD: 11/92).
...Apollon musagète[a]. Petrushka[b]. The Firebird[b]. The Rite of Spring[b]. [a]**London Symphony**
Orchestra / Igor Markevitch; [b]**London Philharmonic Orchestra / Bernard Haitink.**
Philips Duo Ⓜ 438 350-2PM2 (two discs: 151 minutes: ADD: 1/94).　　　　　Ⓖ
...Apollon musagète[a]. Two Suites for Small Orchestra[a]. Four Norwegian Moods[a]. Circus Polka[a].
L'histoire du soldat[b]. Symphony of Psalms[c]. **Soloists;** [c]**Russian State Academic Choir and**
Orchestra; [a]**London Symphony Orchestra;** [b]**instrumental ensemble / Igor Markevitch.**
Philips The Early Years Ⓜ 438 973-2PM2 (two discs: 128 minutes: 2/95).
...Apollon musagète. The Rite of Spring. **London Symphony Orchestra / Robert Craft.**
Koch International Classics Ⓕ 37359-2 (59 minutes: DDD: 6/97).
...The Rite of Spring (two versions). **Philharmonia Orchestra / Igor Markevitch.**
Testament mono/stereo Ⓕ SBT1076* (67 minutes: ADD: 6/97).
...The Rite of Spring. The Firebird – Suite. **Royal Philharmonic Orchestra / Yuri Simonov.**
Tring International Royal Philharmonic Collection Ⓢ TRP109 (66 minutes: DDD: 12/97).
...The Firebird. **Scriabin** Prometheus, Op. 60, "Le poème de feu"[a]. [a]**Alexander Toradze** (pf);
Kirov Opera [a]**Chorus and Orchestra / Valery Gergiev.** Philips Ⓕ 446 715-2PH (72 minutes:
DDD: 7/98). *Gramophone Editor's choice. See review under Scriabin; refer to the Index.*　　　　ⒼⒼ

Stravinsky The Rite of Spring. Canticum sacrum[a]. Requiem canticles[b]. Choral Variations on
"Vom Himmel hoch"[c]. [b]**Irène Friedli** (mez); [a]**Frieder Lang** (ten); [ab]**Michel Brodard** (bar);
[a]**Lausanne Pro Arte Choir; Suisse Romande Chamber Choir and Orchestra / Neeme Järvi.**
Chandos Ⓕ CHAN9408 (75 minutes: DDD: 3/96). Texts and translations included.
Recorded 1994.
Järvi's is a weighty account of *The Rite* (it is scored, after all, for a very large orchestra; some
analytical readings almost disguise this) and it packs a massive punch. He does not opt for showily
fast tempos (save towards the end of the "Sacrificial Dance", where a combination of high speed and
rather heavy sonority garbles a little of the detail) and at times – in the "Mystical Circle", for instance
– he leans on the accents, diminishing the springiness of the rhythm. Elsewhere, though, the
articulation tingles appropriately, and the orchestral sound is often beautiful, often cleanly detailed.
One would not, even so, put it among the top half-dozen current recordings of *The Rite of Spring*
were it not for the quite splendid couplings, where the very qualities that are a slight disadvantage in
The Rite give urgency and eloquence to a couple of scores that are still regarded as among Stravinsky's
most difficult. "Both soloists are good, especially the elegantly lyrical tenor, and the chorus sing with
wonderfully jubilant confidence. A slight tendency to overmark dynamics, noticeable in *The Rite*, is
evident at the beginning of the *Requiem canticles*, where Stravinsky firmly instructs that the strings
are not to play loudly and Järvi just as firmly begs to differ. But he has obviously been moved by the
fervour of the piece, and he demonstrates that a sonorous, full-voiced account can be just as effective
as the more usual reading of the score as a quiet chamber ritual. After that there is no doubting how
much fun Stravinsky had in so industriously outdoing Bach's contrapuntal ingenuity in the *Choral*
Variations. Järvi obviously loves all those extra twiddly bits too, and is more successful than any other
conductor at demonstrating what a Christmassy work it is. Decent recordings throughout, little
lacking in resonance in the *Canticum sacrum* (its pauses very precisely tailored to the reverberation
time of St Mark's in Venice, after all) and the organ-blower motor of the Victoria Hall in Geneva
sounds as though it needs servicing. Otherwise a highly recommendable coupling, especially to those
who love *The Rite* but have hitherto found late Stravinsky off-puttingly austere.

Stravinsky Two Suites[d]. Four Etudes, Op. 7[b]. Four Norwegian Moods[d]. Concerto for
Two Solo Pianos[bc]. Ode[d]. Rag-time[d]. Piano-rag-music[b]. Renard[ad]. [a]**Thom Baker,**
[a]**Drew Martin** (tens); [a]**David Evitts,** [a]**Wilbur Pauley** (basses); [b]**Mark Wait,** [c]**Tom Schultz** (pfs);
[d]**St Luke's Orchestra / Robert Craft.** MusicMasters Ⓕ 67110-2 (76 minutes: DDD: 9/94).
Text and translation included.　　　　ⒼⒼ
This is Stravinsky on a relatively small scale – slick, light-textured and free-flowing, purged of
expressive exaggeration but by no means slavishly literal. Indeed, the opening number of the Suite
No. 1 is surprisingly romantic in feeling. More predictably, subsequent items find the musicians trying
to achieve the appropriate spikiness in what can seem a rather resonant performance space. The short
orchestral pieces are interleaved with an unpredictable assortment of keyboard works, the piano tone
generally a little shallow though perfectly acceptable. Craft's restraint points up the unchanging
aspects of Stravinsky's musical language. The effective English-text version of *Renard* uses a variant
of Stravinsky's own translation but on its own, more intimate, fairy-tale terms Craft's performance is
an undoubted success. The *Ode* will come as a delightful discovery to many. Its second movement

(very convincingly done here) is drawn from music originally composed for the hunting scene in the Hollywood film of *Jane Eyre* (starring Orson Welles); its third achieves real profundity in a three-minute span.

Additional recommendation ...

...Etudes, Op. 7. *Coupled with works by various composers.* **Erika Haase** (pf).
Tacet Ⓕ Tacet53 (74 minutes: DDD: 2/98).

Stravinsky Rag-time[bce]. Octet[be]. Three Pieces[b]. L'histoire du soldat – Suite[bcf]. Pastorale[be]. Concertino[bce]. Septet[be]. Epitaphium[abd]. [a]**Lorna McGhee** (fl); [b]**Dmitri Ashkenazy** (cl); [c]**Alan Brind** (vn); [d]**Cristina Bianchi** (hp); [e]**European Soloists Ensemble / Vladimir Ashkenazy** ([f]pf).
Decca Ⓕ 448 177-2DH (59 minutes: DDD: 8/96).
This is probably Ashkenazy's finest Stravinsky CD. The catchy but immensely clever Septet scores a double bulls-eye by employing formal ingenuity (the closing Gigue features four separate fugues on four versions of an eight-note row) without 'losing' the untutored listener. Written for violin, viola, cello, clarinet, horn, bassoon and piano, it is followed by the disc's closing selection, a 1'29" *Epitaphium* that offers brief confirmation of the older Stravinsky's serial leanings. The journey started with *Rag-time*, composed in 1918 and peppered with the metallic twang of a cimbalom. Ashkenazy's performance of this is very well played, as is the Octet, with its scampering variations and gentle, bossa-nova style final bars (did Stravinsky ever write anything more charming than this?). Again, the performance is confident and unfussy, while Dmitri Ashkenazy blows plenty of spirit into the *Three Pieces* for solo clarinet (the third especially) and Ashkenazy *père* joins him – together with violinist Alan Brind – for a no-nonsense account of a trio arrangement of *The Soldier's Tale* Suite. Here Brind favours light bowing and bland characterization, whereas the elegant *Pastorale* and lively *Concertino* are, by turns, colourful and punchy. Decca's recordings are uniformly good throughout; so is the standard of playing, and although one might maintain other preferences in this or that individual piece (with Stravinsky himself invariably leading the field), the programme is both stimulating and entertaining.

Stravinsky Piano-rag music. Circus Polka. Sonata. Serenade in A major. Tango. Four Studies, Op. 7. Scherzo. Sonata in F sharp minor. **Victor Sangiorgio** (pf). Collins Classics Ⓕ 1374-2 (71 minutes: DDD: 9/93). Recorded 1991.
Victor Sangiorgio launches his Stravinsky programme with a superbly colourful account of the *Piano-rag music*. He commands an excellent variety of attack and resonance, and this combines with his natural rhythmic *élan* and his fine ear for textural voicing to make the *Circus Polka* and the *Tango* especially effective. The *Studies* go well too, especially the Chaplinified Scriabin of No. 4. The short 1902 *Scherzo* is the only seriously flawed performance, marred as it is by a tendency towards spasmodic over-punctuation. But at least Sangiorgio pays this slight piece, and the anything-but-slight F sharp minor Sonata, the compliment of meticulous preparation. Third-hand Tchaikovsky the Sonata may be, but there is still something irresistible about the Russian gung-ho of its finale. The recording is very immediate in its impact, possessing both warmth and clarity.

Additional recommendations ...

...Petrushka. *Coupled with works by various composers.* **Duo Reine Elisabeth.**
Koch International Classics Ⓢ DICD920150 (66 minutes: DDD: 11/94).
See review in the Collections Section; refer to the Index.
...Petrushka – three movements. Valse pour les enfants. Ragtime. Piano-rag music.
Les cinq doigts. Sonata. Serenade in A major. Tango. Circus Polka. Three Easy Pieces[a].
Aleck Karis, [a]**Robert Lubin** (pfs). Bridge Ⓕ BCD9051 (73 minutes: DDD: 3/95).
...Petrushka – three movements. *Coupled with works by various composers.* **Maurizio Pollini** (pf).
DG The Originals Ⓜ 447 431-2GOR (68 minutes: ADD: 6/95). *See review in the Collections section; refer to the Index.*   ⒼⒼ
...Petrushka – Russian dance. *Coupled with works by various composers.* **Vladimir Horowitz** (pf).
APR mono Ⓜ APR5517* (71 minutes: ADD: 5/98). *See review in the Collections section; refer to the Index.*

Stravinsky Pastorale[a]. Deux poèmes de Paul Verlaine[d]. Two poems of Konstantin Bal'mont[a]. Three Japanese lyrics[a]. Three little songs, "Recollections of my childhood"[a]. Pribaoutki[d]. Cat's Cradle Songs[b]. Four Songs[a]. Mavra – Chanson de Paracha[a]. Three Songs from William Shakespeare[b]. In memoriam Dylan Thomas[c]. Elegy for J.F.K.[d]. Two Sacred Songs (after Wolf)[c]. [a]**Phyllis Bryn-Julson** (sop); [b]**Ann Murray** (mez); [c]**Robert Tear** (ten); [d]**John Shirley-Quirk** (bar); **Ensemble InterContemporain / Pierre Boulez.**
DG 20th Century Classics Ⓜ 431 751-2GC (58 minutes: ADD: 2/92). Texts and translations included. From 2531 377 (7/82). Recorded 1980.   Ⓖ
It may be true that this disc lacks the focus of a single major work, but it is also much more than a random compilation of unrelated miniatures. Principally, it offers an aurally fascinating contrast between two groups of pieces: Stravinsky's relatively early Russian settings, as he worked through his own brand of nationalism, reaching from the salon style of *Pastorale* to the folk-like vigour of a work like *Pribaoutki*; then the late serial compositions, written in America, which prove that the rhythmic vitality and melodic distinctiveness of the early works survived undimmed into his final years.

Stravinsky may have regarded texts as collections of sounds whose natural rhythms had no role to play in their musical setting, but the essential meaning still comes through unerringly, whether it is that of the plaintive Paracha's song from the opera *Mavra* or the sombre *Elegy for J.F.K.* (to an Auden text). The disc is rounded off by the very late Wolf arrangements, and whilst one might quibble here and there about Boulez's choice of tempo, or the balance of voice and instruments, the disc as a whole is immensely satisfying as a comprehensive survey of an important repertory.

Stravinsky L'histoire du soldat – Suite[a]. La Marseillaise[d]. Valse pour les enfants[e]. Sketches for a Sonata[e]. Pribaoutki[af]. Cats' Cradle Songs[af]. Monumentum pro Gesualdo di Venosa ad CD annum[abcef]. Mass[abcefg]. The dove descending breaks[abcefg]. Canticum sacrum ad honorem Sancti Marci nominis[abcefg]. [a]**Catherine Ciesinski** (mez); [b]**Jon Humphries** (ten); [c]**David Evitts** (bar); [d]**Rolf Schulte** (vn); [e]**Mark Wait** (pf); [g]**The Gregg Smith Singers**; [f]**Orchestra of St Luke's / Robert Craft.** MusicMasters Ⓟ 67152-2 (78 minutes: DDD: 10/95). Recorded 1992-1994.

Craft's 'hands-on' relationship with this music tells at virtually every juncture. *Canticum sacrum*, for example, sounds so much more confident than it does under the composer's own direction. Compare the two versions of the second movement ("Euntes in mundum") and Craft's extra urgency and superior blending immediately hold one's attention. Taken overall, the newer recording is notably faster than its predecessor, whereas the performance of the *Mass* seems to acknowledge Stravinsky's early music influences, especially in terms of a singing style which, in Stravinsky's own recording sounds – at least next to Craft – strangely unidiomatic. Craft was responsible for introducing Stravinsky to the work of Carlo Gesualdo, and the *Momentum pro Gesualdo di Venosa ad CD annum* – a wonderfully supple recomposition of three five-part madrigals for woodwinds, brass and strings – is in fact dedicated to him. Again, the playing is cleanly accomplished, while the *L'histoire du soldat* Suite is the only performance that rivals Stravinsky's third recording (included in Sony's 22-disc retrospective). Craft has taken great pains over the percussion parts, which are placed here as per the original score. The remaining items on this generously filled collection include a sensitive account of the *a cappella* anthem, *The dove descending*, the lively *Pribaoutki* (the first of which was particularly admired by Prokofiev), the *Cats' Cradle Songs* (admired by Webern) and three comparative rarities: the première on record of two gnomic piano pieces based on orchestral sketches (total timing: 44 seconds), a 50-second *Valse pour les enfants* and a highly palatable solo violin arrangement of *La Marseillaise* (composed on New Year's Day 1919, seven weeks after the Armistice), again presented for the first time on disc and extremely well played by Rolf Schulte. It would make a splendid recital 'encore'. An excellent disc, then. Craft balances scholarship and enthusiasm with perceptive musicianship, and his comprehensive annotations provide an invaluable listening aid.

Stravinsky Les noces[a]. Mass[b]. [a]**Anny Mory** (sop); [a]**Patricia Parker** (mez); [a]**John Mitchinson** (ten); [a]**Paul Hudson** (bass); **English Bach Festival Chorus**; [b]**Trinity Boys' Choir**; [a]**Martha Argerich**, [a]**Krystian Zimerman**, [a]**Cyprien Katsaris**, [a]**Homero Francesch** (pfs); [a]**English Bach Festival Percussion Ensemble**; [b]members of the **English Bach Festival Orchestra / Leonard Bernstein.** DG 20th Century Classics Ⓜ 423 251-2GC (44 minutes: ADD: 6/88). Texts and translations included. From 2530 880 (2/78). ⒼⒼ

Stravinsky Les noces.
Traditional Russian Village Wedding Songs Play, Skomoroshek. River. Trumpet. Cosmas and Demian. The drinker. Green forest. God bless, Jesus. My white peas. Steambath. Berry. Black beaver. In the house. Bunny with short legs. The bed. Birch tree. **Pokrovsky Ensemble / Dmitri Pokrovsky.** Nonesuch Ⓟ 7559-79335-2 (54 minutes: DDD: 9/94). English texts included. *Gramophone Editor's choice.* ⒼⒼ

Many readers will probably look askance at the timing here – could DG really not have done anything with the spare 30 minutes' capacity? However, never mind the width, feel the quality – these are top-drawer Bernstein performances, excellently recorded. *Les noces* sports an impressive array of pianists; but that need not be a decisive factor, since rhythmic precision and good balance are far more at a premium than individual flair or power – fortunately these individuals are equally fine ensemble players. It is even more important that the choir should be meticulously prepared (which they are), that the vocal soloists should be precise and full-blooded (which they are) and that the conductor should impart a sense of the profundity of the whole conception (which Bernstein emphatically does). The Mass is an ideal coupling for *Les noces*, not just because of the shared importance of the chorus, but because it too displays a fundamental ritual experience, in this case the sacrament of worship rather than marriage, with archetypal clarity. Bernstein's reading has all the calm devotion of the composer's own, even if the soloists are rather variable. A highly recommendable reissue.

For the Nonesuch recording Dmitri Pokrovsky and the singers in his ensemble travelled to southern and western Russia in search of melodies and texts related to *Les noces*; and they found rich pickings. True, the melodic similarities are not as tangible as the folk sources for *Petrushka* but the 15 songs, here recorded with immense flair and enjoyment to a variety of instrumental accompaniments, will be a revelation for non-specialists and specialists alike. Be prepared for some fairly acerbic sounds. Authentic Russian folk polyphony is an extraordinarily modern-sounding experience, as is authentic open-throated singing. The value of the disc is multiplied by the fact that the singers have carried over the style and expressive content of the folk-songs into their performance of *Les noces* itself, bringing it to life in a way that must surely be unprecedented and uniquely illuminating. Not only that, but Pokrovsky had the inspired idea of recreating the instrumental parts on an Apple Macintosh computer, thus continuing Stravinsky's search for the ideal mechanical realization.

Additional recommendations ...

...Symphony of Psalms[c]. Pater noster. Credo. Ave Maria. Mass[c]. Canticum sacrum. [a]**John Mark Ainsley** (ten); [b]**Stephen Roberts** (bar); **Westminster Cathedral Choir;** [c]**City of London Sinfonia / James O'Donnell.** Hyperion Ⓕ CDA66437 (68 minutes: DDD: 9/91).

...The Rite of Spring. Les noces[a]. [a]**Soloists;** [a]**Ernest Senff Chamber Chorus;** [a]members of **Piano Circus; Deutsches Symphony Orchestra, Berlin / Vladimir Ashkenazy.** Decca Ⓕ 444 542-2DH (58 minutes: DDD: 9/96).

Stravinsky The Flood[a]. Abraham and Isaac[b]. Variations "Aldous Huxley in memoriam"[c]. Requiem canticles[d].
Wuorinen A Reliquary for Igor Stravinsky[e]. [d]**Susan Bickley** (sop); [a]**Peter Hall** (ten/spkr); [abd]**David Wilson-Johnson** (bar); [a]**Stephen Richardson** (bass); [a]**Michael Berkeley,** [a]**Bernard Jacobson,** [a]**Lucy Shelton** (spkrs); [d]**New London Chamber Choir; London Sinfonietta / Oliver Knussen.** DG Ⓕ 447 068-2GH (70 minutes: DDD: 10/95). Texts and translations included.   Ⓖ

There is a confidence and spontaneity about the music-making on this disc that signal something special. Under Oliver Knussen's authoritative direction the performances leap from the speakers with a vividness that is the ideal complement to the music's rhythmic litheness and intensity of colour. Not all the Stravinsky works represent the composer at his best. *The Flood* (a 'musical play' for television) has marvellous episodes, not least the 'flood' music itself, but other passages, like the melodrama in which God gives Noah his instructions, are less inspired. All four works make strong impressions in these recordings, however, and the *Huxley* Variations and *Requiem canticles* are the crowning glory, with an excellent balance between sharpness of detail and shapely, expressive phrasing. In *The Flood* Michael Berkeley's narration is rather too matter of fact alongside Bernard Jacobson's more actorish Noah, and in the *Requiem canticles'* 'Tuba mirum' David Wilson-Johnson is not ideally focused in tone, but these are very minor cavils. In *Abraham and Isaac* Wilson-Johnson is exemplary in projecting the lyricism as well as the drama of one of Stravinsky's most complex pieces of vocal writing. Charles Wuorinen's *Reliquary* refers to material which Stravinsky was working on at the time of his death, but the last thing Wuorinen was aiming at was pious imitation of the master. There's an exuberant elaboration here that is almost Schoenbergian, at least until the understated coda, and this strong piece fully earns its place on the disc. All the recordings are crisply focused, the sound very immediate.

Stravinsky Oedipus Rex[a]. Symphony of Psalms[b]. **Ivo Zídek** (ten); Oedipus; **Věra Soukupová** (mez) Jocasta; **Karel Berman** (bass) Créon; **Eduard Haken** (bass); Tiresias; **Antonin Zlesák** (ten) Shepherd; **Zdeněk Kroupa** (bar) Messenger; **Jean Desailly** (narr); **Czech Philharmonic Chorus and Orchestra / Karel Ančerl.** Supraphon Historical Ⓕ 11 1947-2 (73 minutes: AAD: 3/93). Item marked [a] from SUAST50678 (1/68), [b]SUAST50778 (8/68). Recorded 1964-1966.   Ⓖ

Oedipus Rex is one of Stravinsky's most compelling theatre pieces, a powerful drama that re-enacts the full force of a glorious highspot in ancient culture. The text is by Jean Cocteau, who once said, pertaining to his work on *Oedipus*, that "any serious work, be it of poetry or music, of theatre or of film, demands a ceremonial, lengthy calculation, an architecture in which the slightest mistake would unbalance the pyramid" (quoted from *Diary of an Unknown,* pub. Paragon House). The fusion of words and music in *Oedipus,* indeed its very 'architecture' is masterly and arrests the attention consistently, from the animated severity of the opening narration, through the cunningly calculated tension of its musical argument, to the tragic restraint of its closing pages. Karel Ančerl was one of Stravinsky's most committed exponents. This particular recording of *Oedipus Rex* was taped in the Dvořák Hall of the House of Artists, Prague, and earned itself at least three major gramophone awards. Ančerl traces and intensifies salient points in the tragedy yet maintains a precise, sensitive touch; his vocal collaborators include the noble Karel Berman (Créon) who, like Ančerl himself, suffered considerably during the Nazi occupation of Czechoslovakia; then there's a fine Jocasta in Věra Soukupová and the convincing but occasionally unsteady Ivo Zídek singing the part of Oedipus. Both here and in the *Symphony of Psalms* – one of the most serenely perceptive performances of the work ever recorded – the Czech Philharmonic Chorus excel, while Supraphon's 1960s engineering (not, alas, the DDD suggested on the box) has an appealing brightness .

Additional recommendations ...

...Soloists; Swedish Radio Chorus; Eric Ericson Chamber Choir; Orphei Dranger; Swedish Radio Symphony Orchestra / Esa-Pekka Salonen. Sony Classical Ⓕ SK48057 (50 minutes: DDD: 7/92).

...Soloists; Shin-yu Kai Choir; Saito Kinen Orchestra / Seiji Ozawa. Philips Ⓕ 438 865-2PH (53 minutes: DDD: 3/94).

Stravinsky The Rake's Progress. **Jerry Hadley** (ten) Tom Rakewell; **Dawn Upshaw** (sop) Anne; **Samuel Ramey** (bass) Nick Shadow; **Grace Bumbry** (mez) Baba the Turk; **Steven Cole** (ten) Sellem; **Anne Collins** (contr) Mother Goose; **Robert Lloyd** (bass) Trulove; **Roderick Earle** (bass) Keeper; **Chorus and Orchestra of Opéra de Lyon / Kent Nagano.** Erato Ⓕ 0630-12715-2 (two discs: 138 minutes: DDD: 8/96).

Any number of the world's opera-houses would have given their eye teeth for the privilege of presenting the première of Stravinsky's only true opera, but he, intensely money-conscious though he was (and he had worked on the piece for three years without a commission fee), insisted on La Fenice in Venice. Because he was fond of the city, of course, but also because *The Rake's Progress* is a chamber opera. And this is a chamber performance of it, with a fairly small orchestra, much singing of almost *parlando* quality and crystal-clear words. It is also intimate, with a strong sense of the stage, of characters reacting to each other. With Nagano's on the whole brisk tempos, it gives the impression of a real performance, and a gripping one. Upshaw's is not the purest soprano voice to have attempted the role of Anne, and there have been more spectacular high Cs than hers, but she is movingly vulnerable, totally believable. So is Hadley, acting at times almost too vividly for the music's line: as he occasionally demonstrates he has a wonderfully beautiful head voice. He is not, therefore, quite the touchingly likeable "shuttle-headed lad" that Alexander Young portrayed so unforgettably in the composer's own recording, but no other Tom Rakewell surpasses him. Ramey's is a bigger voice than most of the others here – firm and superbly produced. Collins and Lloyd are both first-class as Mother Goose and Trulove, Cole an unusually light-voiced, confidingly conspiratorial Sellem. Bumbry is the disappointment of the cast, over-loud and baritonal almost throughout, but the French chorus sing nimbly and in admirable English. Stravinsky's own recording is still to be cherished, but of modern recordings of *The Rake's Progress* this is by some way the most enjoyable.

Additional recommendations ...
...**Soloists; Sadler's Wells Opera Chorus; Royal Philharmonic Orchestra / Igor Stravinsky.**
Sony Classical Ⓜ SM2K46299 (three discs: ADD: 8/92).
...**Soloists; Gregg Smith Singers; Orchestra of St Luke's / Robert Craft.**
MusicMasters Ⓕ 67131-2 (two discs: 128 minutes: DDD: 3/95).
...**Soloists; Tokyo Opera Singers; Saito Kinen Orchestra / Seiji Ozawa.**
Philips Ⓕ 454 431-2PH2 (two discs: 137 minutes: DDD: 6/97).

Further listening ...
...Concerto in D major. *Coupled with works by* **Berlin Philharmonic Orchestra / Herbert von Karajan.**
DG The Originals 447 435-2GOR (12/95). *See review under Honegger; refer to the Index.* ⒼⒼⒼ
...Fanfare for a New Theatre. *Coupled with works by various composers.* **Meridian Arts Ensemble.**
Channel Classics Channel Crossings CCS8195 (4/96). Ⓖ
...Chanson russe. Divertimento. Suite Italienne. Duo concertant. *Coupled with works by*
Rachmaninov and **Tchaikovsky** Itzhak Perlman (vn); Samuel Sanders, Bruno Canino (pfs).
EMI Perlman Edition CDM5 66061-2 (3/97).
...Three Pieces. *Coupled with works by* **Ravel** and **Debussy** **Lindsay Quartet.**
ASV CDDCA930 (12/95).
...Ave Maria. Credo. *Coupled with works by various composers.* **King's College Choir, Cambridge /**
Stephen Cleobury. EMI CDC5 56439-2 (10/97). *See review in the Collections section; refer to the Index. Selected by Soundings.*
...Pater noster. Ave Maria. *Coupled with works by various composers.* **The King's Singers.** RCA
Victor Red Seal 09026 68255-2 (8/96). *See review in the Collections section; refer to the Index.*
...Les noces (sung in English. Soloists; BBC Chorus; percussion ensemble / Igor Stravinsky). Octet
(Marcel Moyse, fl; Emile Godeau, cl; Gustave Dhérin, Marius Piard, bns; Eugène Foveau, Pierre
Vignal, tpts; André Lafosse, Raphaël Delbos, tbns / Stravinsky). Capriccio (Stravinsky, pf;
Walther Straram Concerts Orchestra / Ernest Ansermet). Symphony of Psalms (Alexis Vlassov
Choir; Straram Orchestra / Stravinsky). Pastorale (Louis Gromer, ob; Georges Durand, cor ang;
André Vacellier, cl; Gabriel Grandmaison, bn; Samuel Dushkin, vn / Stravinsky). Petrushka –
Danse russe. The Firebird – Scherzo; Berceuse. Le chant du rossignol – Airs du rossignol; Marche
chinoise (all with Dushkin, vn; Stravinsky, pf). Rag-time (Lucien Lavaillotte, fl; Godeau, cl;
Jean Devemy, hn; Foveau, tpt; Roger Tudesq, tbn; Roland Charmy, Henri Volant, vns; Etienne
Ginot, va; Louis Juste, db; Aladar Racz, cimbalom; Jean Morel, perc / Stravinsky). Piano-
rag-music (Stravinsky). Suite italienne – Serenata; Scherzino. Duo concertant (Dushkin;
Stravinsky). Serenade in A major (Stravinsky). Concerto for Two Pianos (Soulima and
Igor Stravinsky, pfs). **Various artists.** EMI Composers in Person mono CDS7 54607-2* (5/93).
Recorded 1928-1934.

Alessandro Striggio
Italian c1540-1592

Suggested listening ...
...Ecce beatam lucem. *Coupled with works by various composers.* **Huelgas Ensemble / Paul van Nevel.**
Sony Classical Vivarte SK66261 (4/96). *See review in the Collections section; refer to the Index.*

Barbara Strozzi
Italian 1619-1664 or later

Suggested listening ...
...Corrente terza. *Coupled with works by various composers.* **Rinaldo Alessandrini** (hpd).
Opus 111 OPS30-118 (4/95). 🖉 *See review in the Collections section; refer to the Index.* ⒼⒼ

Simon Stubley

British died 1754

Suggested listening ...

...Voluntary in C major. *Coupled with works by various composers.* **Jennifer Bate** (org).
Unicorn-Kanchana DKPCD9106 (11/91). *Selected by Sounds in Retrospect. See review in the Collections section; refer to the Index.*   Ⓖ

Josef Suk

Bohemian 1874-1935

Suk Asrael, Op. 27. **Bavarian Radio Symphony Orchestra / Rafael Kubelík.** Panton Ⓕ 81 1101-2
(64 minutes: ADD: 1/94). Recorded 1981.   ⒼⒼⒼ
To use large scale symphonic form for the purging of deep personal grief carries the danger that the result will seriously lack discipline. In 1904-05 Suk's world was shattered by two visits from *Asrael* (the Angel of Death in Muslim mythology): he lost his father-in-law (and revered teacher) Dvořák, and his beloved wife, Otylka. Forgivably, Suk does perhaps linger a little too long in the fourth movement's gentle, mainly lyrical portrait of Otylka, but elsewhere the progress is as satisfying psychologically as it is symphonically. Much of the music has a concentrated dream-like quality; at the extremes, spectral nightmare visions merge with compensatory surges of lyrical ardour. Set Kubelík's reading alongside any of the other modern versions and one is immediately aware of a wholly compelling imaginative intensity and interpretative flair that betoken a true poet of the rostrum. Kubelík's control throughout is awesome and he conjures up playing of enormous expressive subtlety from his fine Munich orchestra. No other recorded performance – not even Václav Talich's legendary 1952 Supraphon account – succeeds in conveying the intensely personal nature of this music with such devastating emotional candour. Technically, too, one need have no qualms about this Panton disc – the Bavarian Radio engineers secure most truthful results.
Additional recommendations ...
...Asrael. **Royal Liverpool Philharmonic Orchestra / Libor Pešek.**
Virgin Classics Ⓕ VC7 59638-2 (62 minutes: DDD: 9/91).   ⒼⒼ
...Asrael. *Czech Philharmonic Orchestra / Jiří Bělohlávek.*
Chandos Ⓕ CHAN9042 (59 minutes: DDD: 5/92).
...Asrael. *Dvořák* Stabat mater, B171. **Soloists; Czech Philharmonic Chorus and Orchestra / Václav Talich.** Supraphon Historical mono Ⓜ 11 1902-2* (two discs: 147 minutes: ADD: 12/93).   ⒼⒼ
...Asrael. **Russian State Symphony Orchestra / Evgeni Svetlanov.**
Russian Disc Ⓕ RDCD11011 (64 minutes: DDD: 1/94).   Ⓖ

Suk Ripening, Op. 34ª. Praga, Op. 26. **Royal Liverpool Philharmonic** ªChoir and Orchestra / **Libor Pešek.** Virgin Classics Ⓕ VC7 59318-2 (67 minutes: DDD: 1/94). Recorded 1992.
Gramophone Editor's choice.   Ⓖ
Completed in 1917, *Ripening* shows Suk at the height of his powers. This vast yet tightly organized tone-poem shares many of the autobiographical concerns of its large-scale orchestral predecessors (*Asrael* and *A Summer Tale*). Throughout, Suk handles his outsize forces with a truly Straussian confidence and virtuosity, nowhere more strikingly than in the extended Fugue which attains a climax of truly devastating proportions; the profound serenity of the ensuing coda (where a wordless female chorus is used to magical effect) could not have been harder won. The coupling, *Praga*, is an affectionate, enjoyably grandiloquent portrait-in-sound of that fair city dating from 1904. Pešek and the RLPO are accomplished and communicative. The engineering, too, is first-class.
Additional recommendation ...
...Praga. A Summer's Tale, Op. 29. **Czech Philharmonic Orchestra / Libor Pešek.**
Supraphon Ⓕ 11 1984-2 (76 minutes: DDD: 8/95).

Suk Chamber works, Volumes 1-3. ˡ**Jiří Válek** (fl); ᵉᵍʰⁱʲˡⁿᵒ**Josef Suk,** ᵍ**Jitka Nováková,** ᵒ**Ludmila Vybíralová,** ᵒ**Miroslav Kosina,** ᵒ**Jaroslav Krištůfek,** ᵒ**Zdeněk Mann** (vns); ᵉ**Jan Talich** (va); ᵉ**Michaela Fukačová,** ᵏ**Marek Jerie,** ⁿ**František Host,** ᵒ**Ivo Laniar** (vcs); ᵒ**Tomáš Josífko** (db); ⁿ**Renata Kodadová** (hp); **Josef Hála** (ʰˡpf/ᵐharm); ᵉⁱʲ**Jan Panenka,** ᶠ**Pavel Stěpán,** ᵏ**Iván Klánský** (pfs); ᵒ**Josef Fousek,** ᵒ**Libor Kubánek** (perc); ᶜᵈ**Suk Trio** (Josef Suk, vn; Josef Chuchro, vc; ᶜJosef Hála, ᵈJan Panenka, pfs); ᵃᵇᶠᵐⁿ**Suk Quartet** (ᵃᶠᵐAntonín Novák, ᵇⁿIvan Straus, Vojtěch Jouza, vns; Karel Rehák, va; Jan Stros, vc). Supraphon Ⓜ 11 1874-2 (three discs, aas: 71, 74 and 63 minutes: ADD/DDD: 2/94). Recorded 1966-92.
11 1531-2: String Quartets – No. 1 in B flat major, Op. 11ª (from 1111 2974, 10/82); No. 2, Op. 31ᵇ. Tempo di menuettoᵇ. Meditation on an old Czech hymn, Op. 35aᵇ (all from 1111 3370, recorded 1984). Quartet movement in B flat majorª (recorded 1978, new to UK).
11 1532-2: Piano Trio in C minor, Op. 2ᶜ. Elégie, Op. 23ᵈ (SUAST50863, 12/69). Piano Quartet in A minor, Op. 1ᵉ. Piano Quintet in G minor, Op. 8ᶠ (recorded 1978, new to UK).
11 1533-2: Mélodieᵍ. Minuetʰ. Balada in D minorⁱ (SUAST5077, 8/68). Four Pieces, Op. 17ʲ (SUAST5077). Ballade in D minor, Op. 3 No. 1ᵏ. Serenade in A major, Op. 3 No. 2ᵏ (both recorded 1983, new to UK). Bagatelle, "Carrying a bouquet"ˡ. Barcarolle in B flat majorᵐ. Balada in D minorᵐ (both recorded 1978, new to UK). Elégie, Op. 23ⁿ. Sousedskáᵒ.   ⒼⒼⒼ

A treasure-trove of heartfelt music performed with refinement and flair. Volume 1 concentrates on Suk's string quartet output (Suk himself was the second violinist in the great Czech Quartet for 40 years). If the First Quartet (1896) doesn't quite show the same freshness or entrancing melodic vein of the String Serenade of four years earlier, it remains a delightfully unassuming creation with the genial presence of Suk's teacher Dvořák looming large over the proceedings. It is followed by a rare hearing for the alternative finale Suk composed some 19 years later in 1915. By this time, of course, the composer had already found his own strongly personal voice. Both the resourceful Second Quartet of 1911 (an ambitious one-movement essay of nearly 28 minutes' duration and considerable emotional variety) and the deeply-felt *Meditation on an old Czech Hymn* (1914) are works of some substance well worth exploring, and these passionate accounts enjoy excellent sound. The remaining two volumes perhaps contain more to interest Suk *aficionados* than newcomers, though the adorable *Four Pieces* for violin and piano, Op. 17, have always remained great favourites.

Volume 2 features youthful offerings: the Piano Trio, the Piano Quartet, the likeable, if rather garrulous, Piano Quintet of 1893 and the touching *Elégie* for piano, violin and cello from 1902, written to celebrate the anniversary of the death of the poet and dramatist, Julius Zeyer. Apart from the *Four Pieces* already mentioned, the third and final volume also contains, amongst much else, the *Elégie* in its original guise for violin, cello, string quartet, harmonium and harp, no fewer than three different *Ballades* in D minor conceived for various instrumental combinations during Suk's days at the Conservatory, the "Barcarolle" slow movement of a very early String Quartet from 1888, as well as the composer's last completed piece from 1935, the engaging *Sousedská* for five violins, double bass, cymbals and triangle. Recording dates range from 1966 to 1992 (most of the material is designated as AAD), but the quality is consistently praiseworthy and the volumes are available either separately or gathered together within an attractive slipcase.

Suk Six Pieces, Op. 7. Spring, Op. 22a. Summer moods, Op. 22b. About Mother, Op. 28.
Radoslav Kvapil (pf). Unicorn-Kanchana Ⓕ DKPCD9159 (74 minutes: DDD: 2/96).
Recorded 1994.
Suk wrote some 60-odd short piano pieces, many of them collected into groups sharing an experience; about a third of them are here, in four collections. Three of these, the Six Picccs (Op. 7), and the connected *Spring* and *Summer moods* (Op. 22), antedate the dreadful double blow that befell him in 1904 and 1905; the sequence *About Mother* belongs to 1907, and is more backward-looking and reflective, marked by sorrow but not with the darkness that was shadowing his large-scale orchestral works in these years. The latter are pieces written for his son, touching domestic vignettes that avoid sentimentality, and are marked by foreboding in the last of them, when the irregularity of the rhythms reflects the frail beat of his wife's heart. The pieces make an excellent anthology of Suk's music, and Kvapil has their manner ideally. He can touch off a mood of gentleness or wit or, more rarely, something almost wry in its oblique, private feeling. Some of the pieces are very simple, and would buckle under playing of greater intensity; some need a little intelligent help in holding them together, or in making the most of Suk's handling of a single idea permeating the invention. Kvapil is unerringly sensitive to their mood, and makes this a most affecting recital.

Additional recommendation ...
...Summer moods. About Mother. Suite, Op. 21. Episodes. Humoreske. Album Leaf.
Niel Immelman (pf). Meridian Ⓕ CDE84317 (74 minutes: DDD: 1/97).

Further listening ...
...Serenade in E flat major, Op. 6. *Coupled with* **Dvořák** Symphony No. 6 in D major, B112.
Czech Philharmonic Orchestra / Václav Talich. Koch Legacy mono 37060-2* (1/92).   Ⓖ
...Serenade in E flat major, Op. 6. Fairy Tale, Op. 16. **Czech Philharmonic Orchestra /**
Jiří Bělohlávek. Chandos CHAN9063 (3/93).
...Serenade in E flat major, Op. 6. *Coupled with works by* **Grieg** and **Tchaikovsky**
Polish Radio Chamber Orchestra / Agnieszka Duczmal. ASV CDQS6094 (3/94).
...Serenade in E flat major, Op. 6. Meditation on an old Czech hymn, Op. 35a.
Coupled with **Janáček** Suite. **Virtuosi di Praga / Oldrich Vlcek.**
Koch International Classics DICD920234 (9/95).
...Serenade in E flat major, Op. 6. *Coupled with* **Dvořák** Serenade in E major, B52.
Prague Chamber Philharmonic Orchestra / Jiří Bělohlávek. Supraphon SU3157-2 (4/97).
...A Summer's Tale, Op. 29. **Royal Liverpool Philharmonic Orchestra / Libor Pešek.**
Virgin Classics VC5 45057-2 (8/95).
...Spring, Op. 22a. About Friendship, Op. 36. Things lived and dreamt, Op. 30. Pieces, Op. 7 –
No. 1, Love song; No. 2, Humoreske; No. 4, Two Idylls. **Niel Immelman** (pf).
Meridian CDE84269 (1/94).
...10 Songs, Op. 15. *Coupled with works by various composers.* **Prague Chamber Choir / Josef Pancik**
with **Marian Lapsansky, Daniel Buranovsky** (pf duet). Chandos CHAN9257 (12/95).

Sir Arthur Sullivan   British 1842-1900

Sullivan Cello Concerto in D major (reconstr. Mackerras and Mackie)[a]. Symphony in E major,
"Irish"[b]. Overture di ballo[b].

Elgar Romance, Op. 62 (arr. vc)[a]. [a]**Julian Lloyd Webber** (vc); [a]**London Symphony Orchestra /
Sir Charles Mackerras;** [b]**Royal Liverpool Philharmonic Orchestra / Sir Charles Groves.**
EMI British Composers Ⓜ CDM7 64726-2 (71 minutes: ADD/DDD: 4/94). Items marked
[a] from CDC7 47622-2 (2/87), recorded 1986; [b]HMV ASD2435 (2/69), recorded 1968.
Sir Charles Groves's sturdy yet affectionate reading of Arthur Sullivan's wholly charming *Irish
Symphony* was always one of the best of his EMI offerings with the RLPO and the 1968 recording
remains vivid. In the sparkling *Overture di ballo*, again, Groves conducts with plenty of character.
There are also first-rate performances of Sullivan's undemanding Cello Concerto from 1866 (in a fine
reconstruction by Sir Charles Mackerras – the manuscript was destroyed in Chappell's fire of 1964)
as well as Elgar's wistful little *Romance* (originally for bassoon). This is a thoroughly attractive mid-
price reissue.
Additional recommendation ...
...Symphony. Imperial March. Victoria and Merrie England – Suite No. 1. Overture in C major,
"In memoriam". **BBC Concert Orchestra / Owain Arwel Hughes.**
CPO Ⓕ CPO999 171-2 (72 minutes: DDD: 4/95).

Sullivan Victoria and Merrie England. **RTE Sinfonietta / Andrew Penny.** Marco Polo Ⓕ 8 223677
(78 minutes: DDD: 6/96).
Five years before Edward German's comic opera *Merrie England*, this Sullivan ballet score was staged
at the Alhambra Theatre as part of the celebrations of Queen Victoria's Diamond Jubilee. The
original full score appears not to have survived. However, a complete piano reduction was published,
along with an orchestral suite, and in addition Sullivan reused earlier material such as his *Imperial
March* and music from his early ballet *L'île enchantée*. From all these sources Roderick Spencer has
made this very convincing re-creation of the full score. And very worthwhile it proves too. As the
notes explain, British ballet in those days was not classical ballet as we know it today but mime-
drama. Spectacle was what it was all about, and Sullivan rose to the occasion admirably. There are
some most attractive passages – not only in the recycled material but also, for instance, the Solo
Variation for the May Queen and perhaps above all the Waltz of Wood Nymphs, which would well
repay taking over into the light music repertory. In addition Sullivan skilfully weaves in various
patriotic British melodies as well as traditional dances such as a morris dance and a sailors' hornpipe.
Such pastiche is the sort of thing that Sullivan did particularly well, and Andrew Penny and the RTE
Sinfonietta do the whole score proud. This is as rewarding as any of the CDs of Sullivan without
Gilbert that Marco Polo have issued.

Sullivan The Gondoliers. Overture di Ballo (1870 version). **Richard Suart** (bar) Duke of Plaza-
Toro; **Philip Creasey** (ten) Luiz; **John Rath** (bass) Don Alhambra; **David Fieldsend** (ten) Marco;
Alan Oke (bar) Giuseppe; **Tim Morgan** (bar) Antonio; **David Cavendish** (ten) Francesco;
Toby Barrett (bass) Giorgio; **Jill Pert** (contr) Duchess of Plaza-Toro; **Elizabeth Woollett** (sop)
Casilda; **Lesley Echo Ross** (sop) Gianetta; **Regina Hanley** (mez) Tessa; **Yvonne Patrick** (sop)
Fiametta; **Pamela Baxter** (mez) Vittoria; **Elizabeth Elliott** (sop) Giulia; **Claire Kelly** (contr) Inez;
D'Oyly Carte Opera Chorus and Orchestra / John Pryce-Jones. TER Ⓕ CDTER2 1187
(two discs: 109 minutes: DDD: 5/92). Recorded 1991.
This is one of a series of recordings by the new D'Oyly Carte Opera Company that offers a vastly
better quality of sound than any of its ageing competitors. Orchestral detail is the most immediate
beneficiary, and the overture serves to demonstrate John Pryce-Jones's lively tempos and lightness of
touch. Outstanding among the singers are perhaps John Rath, who gives Don Alhambra's "I stole the
prince" and "There lived a king" real presence, and Jill Pert, a formidable Duchess of Plaza-Toro.
Richard Suart not only provides the leading comedy roles with exceptionally clear articulation and
musicality, but also adds considerable character to his portrayals; his "I am a courtier grave and
serious" is a sure winner. David Fieldsend and Alan Oke provide attractive portrayals of the two
gondoliers, and Lesley Echo Ross and Regina Hanley are also most agreeable. Seasoned listeners may
note numerous changes of detail as a result of the purging of the performance material of changes
made to the parts around the time of the 1920s Savoy Theatre revivals. There is no dialogue, but
added value is provided by Sullivan's sunniest comic opera score being accompanied by the sparkling
Overture di Ballo, played in its original version with some traditional cuts opened up.
Additional recommendation ...
...Soloists; **D'Oyly Carte Opera Chorus; New Symphony Orchestra / Isidore Godfrey.**
Decca Ⓜ 425 177-2LM2 (two discs: 129 minutes: ADD: 1/90).

Sullivan HMS Pinafore. **Richard Suart** (bass) Sir Joseph Porter; **Felicity Palmer** (mez) Little
Buttercup; **Rebecca Evans** (sop) Josephine; **Thomas Allen** (bar) Captain Corcoran; **Michael
Schade** (ten) Ralph Rackstraw; **Donald Adams** (bass) Dick Deadeye; **Valerie Seymour** (sop) Hebe;
Richard Van Allan (bass) Bill Bobstay; **John King, Philip Lloyd-Evans** (bars) Bob Becket;
Welsh National Opera Chorus and Orchestra / Sir Charles Mackerras. Telarc Ⓕ CD80374
(74 minutes: DDD: 1/95). Notes and text included. Recorded 1994.
Gramophone Editor's choice.   Ⓖ
As always, Mackerras keeps the livelier numbers moving along comfortably without ever a hint of
rushing, whilst giving full weight to the tender moments and, above all, caressing all the details of

Sullivan's delicious orchestration. Right from the overture, with its beautifully shaped *Andante* section, this is music-making to perfection. Of the singers, Felicity Palmer's Buttercup truly oozes plumpness and pleasure, while Thomas Allen's Captain does not just the crew of the *Pinafore*, but all of us, proud. If Rebecca Evans's Josephine is a shade lacking in colour, Mackerras has found in Michael Schade's Ralph Rackstraw a most elegant addition to his G&S team. As for Richard Suart's Sir Joseph Porter, this is surely as stylish a demonstration of patter singing as one can find anywhere on disc, while Donald Adams's Dick Deadeye is no worse for his 40-odd years singing the role. Add orchestral playing of refinement, choral work whose perfection extends from the formal numbers to the varied inflexions of "What nevers?", plus a recording that brings out the instrumental detail to perfection, and one has a *Pinafore* that is unadulterated delight from first note to last.

Additional recommendation ...
...**Soloists; D'Oyly Carte Opera Chorus; New Symphony Orchestra / Isidore Godfrey.**
Decca London Ⓜ 414 283-2LM2 (98 minutes: ADD: 1/90).

Sullivan The Mikado[a]. **John Holmes** (bass) The Mikado; **John Wakefield** (ten) Nanki-Poo;
Clive Revill (bar) Ko-Ko; **Denis Dowling** (bar) Pooh-Bah; **John Heddle Nash** (bar) Pish-Tush;
Marion Studholme (sop) Yum-Yum; **Patricia Kern** (mez) Pitti-Sing; **Dorothy Nash** (sop)
Peep-Bo; **Jean Allister** (mez) Katisha.
Iolanthe[b] – excerpts. **Elizabeth Harwood, Elizabeth Robson, Cynthia Morey** (sops); **Heather Begg,**
Patricia Kern (mezzos); **Stanley Bevan** (ten); **Eric Shilling, Denis Dowling, Julian Moyle** (bars);
Leon Greene (bass); **Sadler's Wells Opera Chorus and Orchestra / Alexander Faris.**
Classics for Pleasure Ⓑ CD-CFPD4730 (two discs: 135 minutes: ADD: 4/94).
Item marked [a] from HMV CSD1458/9 (10/62), [b] CSD1434 (7/62). Recorded 1962.
At the core of these performances are some of the finest British singers of 30 years ago, all of whom were chosen not just for their singing but for their sense of the theatricality and humour of Gilbert and Sullivan. Just listen, for instance, to how John Heddle Nash gives full expression to every word of Pish-Tush's "Our great Mikado". Here, too, is Marion Studholme's delicious Yum-Yum and Elizabeth Harwood's joyous Phyllis. If one singles out Clive Revill for special mention, it is because his Ko-Ko is uniquely well judged and imaginative, combining superb comic timing, verbal clarity and vocal dexterity. His "little list" is hilarious, and one can almost feel one's hand gripped at the words "shake hands with you *like that*". At the helm in both works is Alexander Faris who knew supremely well how to capture the lightness and sparkle of operetta. The new Overture put together for *The Mikado* by Stephen Dodgson may come as a surprise, but it is apt and cleverly done. The sound is inevitably dated when compared to more recent recordings, but it scarcely mars the enjoyment.

Additional recommendations ...
...**Soloists; D'Oyly Carte Chorus; Royal Philharmonic Orchestra / Royston Nash.**
Decca Ⓜ 425 190-2LM2 (two discs: 90 minutes: ADD: 1/90).
...**Soloists; Welsh National Opera Chorus and Orchestra / Sir Charles Mackerras.**
Telarc Ⓕ CD80284 (79 minutes: DDD: 5/92).

Sullivan The Pirates of Penzance. **Eric Roberts** (bar) Major-General Stanley; **Malcolm Rivers** (bar)
Pirate King; **Gareth Jones** (bar) Samuel; **Philip Creasy** (ten) Frederic; **Simon Masterton-Smith**
(bass) Sargeant of Police; **Marilyn Hill Smith** (sop) Mabel; **Patricia Cameron** (sop) Edith; **Pauline**
Birchall (mez) Kate; **Susan Gorton** (contr) Ruth; **D'Oyly Carte Opera Chorus and Orchestra /**
John Pryce-Jones. TER Ⓕ CDTER2 1177 (two discs: 85 minutes: DDD: 9/90). Recorded 1990.
The revival of the D'Oyly Carte Opera Company produced the first digital recordings of complete Gilbert and Sullivan scores, and this TER set is a very happy example. Philip Creasy is an engaging and vocally secure Frederic, and Marilyn Hill Smith trips through "Poor wandering one" with a delectable display of vocal ability and agility. The couple's interplay with the chorus in "How beautifully blue the sky" is quite enchanting, and their exchanges in "Stay, Frederic, stay" splendidly convincing. Eric Roberts makes the Major-General a thoroughly engaging personality, and the dotty exchanges between Simon Masterton-Smith's Sargeant of Police and his police force are sheer joy. Even such details as the girls' screams at the appearance of the pirates in Act 1 have a rare effectiveness. John Pryce-Jones keeps the score dancing along. Those who want the dialogue as well as the music must look elsewhere, but this version is certainly to be recommended.

Additional recommendation ...
...**Soloists; D'Oyly Carte Opera Chorus; Royal Philharmonic Orchestra / Isidore Godfrey.**
Decca Ⓜ 425 196-2LM2 (1/90).

Sullivan The Yeomen of the Guard. **Peter Savidge** (bar) Sir Richard Cholmondeley; **Neill Archer**
(ten) Colonel Fairfax; **Donald Adams** (bass) Sergeant Meryll; **Peter Hoare** (ten) Leonard;
Richard Suart (bar) Jack Point; **Donald Maxwell** (bar) Shadbolt; **Alwyn Mellor** (sop) Elsie;
Pamela Helen Stephen (mez) Phoebe; **Felicity Palmer** (mez) Dame Carruthers; **Clare O'Neill** (sop)
Kate; **Ralph Mason** (ten) First Yeoman; **Peter Lloyd Evans** (bar) Second Yeoman.
Sullivan Trial by Jury. **Rebecca Evans** (sop) Plaintiff; **Barry Banks** (ten) Defendant; **Richard Suart**
(bar) Judge; **Peter Savidge** (bar) Counsel; **Donald Adams** (bass) Usher; **Gareth Rhys-Davies** (bar)
Foreman; **Welsh National Opera Chorus and Orchestra / Sir Charles Mackerras.** Telarc
Ⓕ CD80404 (two discs: 121 minutes: DDD: 2/96). Recorded 1995. Notes and texts included.

Between them, *The Yeomen of the Guard* and *Trial by Jury* contain all that is best in Sullivan's music for the theatre. In the former there is some of his more serious and ambitious writing, in the latter some of his most consistently light-hearted and engaging. All of this is brought out in the latest of Telarc's series of recordings with Welsh National Opera. As always, Sir Charles Mackerras paces the music impeccably, and he has assured contributions from such stalwarts as Donald Adams, Felicity Palmer and Richard Suart. The last-named may be a shade light-voiced compared with some of the more comic performers of Jack Point and the Learned Judge; but in *The Yeomen* it is surely his performance that stands out. His handling of the dialogue after "Here's a man of jollity" is masterly, and his "Oh, a private buffoon" is as winning as any, with impeccable clarity of diction and a perfectly judged French accent for "jests ... imported from France". Neill Archer and Alwyn Mellor are admirable as Fairfax and Elsie; but Pamela Helen Stephen could have displayed more of the minx in Phoebe Meryll's personality, while in *Trial by Jury* Barry Banks seems to have too small a voice to convince as the Defendant. If this set doesn't quite stand out in the same way as Mackerras's *Mikado* and *Pinafore* it would still be a clear recommendation from the versions of *The Yeomen of the Guard* listed below. Yet perhaps the major competition still comes from the 1964 D'Oyly Carte coupling of the same works, with Sargent conducting *Yeomen* in relaxed but winning fashion and Elizabeth Harwood still unmatched as Elsie Maynard.

Additional recommendations ...

...The Yeoman of the Guard. **Soloists; Glyndebourne Festival Chorus; Pro Arte Orchestra /
Sir Malcolm Sargent.** EMI Ⓜ CMS7 64415-2 (two discs: 93 minutes: ADD).

...The Yeoman of the Guard[a]. Trial by Jury[b]. **Soloists; D'Oyly Carte Opera Chorus,
[a]Royal Philharmonic Orchestra / Sir Malcolm Sargent; [b]Orchestra of the Royal Opera House,
Covent Garden / Isidore Godfrey.** Decca Ⓜ 417 358-2LM2 (two discs: 125 minutes: ADD: 1/90).

...The Yeoman of the Guard. **Soloists; D'Oyly Carte Opera Chorus and Orchestra /
John Owen Edwards.** TER Ⓕ CDTER2 1195 (two discs: 115 minutes: DDD: 4/93).
Gramophone Editor's choice.

Further listening ...

...Overtures – HMS Pinafore; The Pirates of Penzance; Patience; Iolanthe; Princess Ida;
The Mikado; The Gondoliers; The Yeoman of the Guard; Di ballo; Ruddigore.
**New Sadler's Wells Opera Orchestra; D'Oyly Carte Opera Orchestra / John Pryce-Jones,
Simon Phipps, John Owen Edwards.** TER CDVIR8316 (5/93).

...The Contrabandista – Only the night wind sighs alone. *Coupled with works by various composers.*
Lesley Garrett (sop); **Crouch End Festival Chorus; Royal Philharmonic Concert Orchestra /
James Holmes.** Silva Screen Classics SILKTVCD1 (2/96). *See review in the Collections section;
refer to the Index.*

...Guinevere and other Ballads – O mistress mine. She is not fair to outward view. Golden days. A
life that lives for you. Guinevere!. Thou art lost to me. Once again. County guy. Mary Morison.
If doughty deeds. Orpheus with his lute. Sigh no more, ladies. Sweet day, so cool. Ich möchte
hinaus es jauchzen. Arabian love song. Tears, idle tears. Oh! ma charmante. I would I were a
King. **Richard Conrad** (bar); **William Merrill** (pf). Pearl SHECD9636 (2/95).

...Iolanthe. **Glyndebourne Festival Chorus; Pro Arte Orchestra / Sir Malcolm Sargent.**
EMI CMS7 64400-2.

...Patience. **Soloists; D'Oyly Carte Opera Chorus; New Symphony Orchestra / Isidore Godfrey.**
Decca 425 193-2LM2 (1/90).

...Patience. Princess Ida. **Soloists; D'Oyly Carte Opera Chorus; symphony orchestra /
Sir Malcolm Sargent.** Happy Days mono 75605 52273-2* (2/97).

...Pineapple Poll – excerpts. *Coupled with* **Verdi** The Lady and the Fool.
London Philharmonic Orchestra / Sir Charles Mackerras. Classics for Pleasure CD-CFP4618.

...Ruddigore. The Pirates of Penzance. **Soloists; Glyndebourne Festival Chorus; Pro Arte Orchestra /
Sir Malcolm Sargent.** EMI CMS7 64412-2.

Lepo Sumera
Estonian 1950

Sumera Symphony No. 5. Music for Chamber Orchestra[a]. In memoriam. [a]**Håvard Lysebo** (fl);
Malmö Symphony Orchestra / Paavo Järvi. BIS Ⓕ CD770 (65 minutes: DDD: 5/97).
Recorded 1995.

Lepo Sumera's Fifth Symphony (1955) is a much more impressive symphonic edifice than any of its predecessors, which avoided the true synthesizing character that seems the essence of the form. The Fifth, though, is more integrated, if still sectional in construction; a work, unlike the Fourth, more than the sum of its parts, not less. Whether the higher degree of thematic fusion was the result of the single span or vice versa, the music has in places a sweep that is reminiscent of Rautavaara's Fifth. The other pieces are both quite early but no mere makeweights, and show from where Sumera's sound world derived. *Music for Chamber Orchestra* (1977) is a delightful score with some beautiful passages for the solo flute. Like the 1972 *In memoriam* (a tribute to Sumera's former teacher, Heino Eller) and the Third Symphony (1988) there is a jumble of styles – at the root a kind of polystylism-meets-New Simplicity – that is quite invigorating. Paavo Järvi directs three top-notch performances, recorded with the customary skill of the house.

Further listening ...
...Musica tenera. Piano Concerto[a]. Symphony No. 4, "Serena borealis". [a]Kalle Randalu (pf);
Malmö Symphony Orchestra / Paavo Järvi. BIS CD690 (9/95).
...Piano Concerto. *Coupled with works by* **Lemba** *and* **Tubin**. Lauri Väinmaa (pf);
Estonian National Symphony Orchestra / Arvo Volmer. Finlandia Ⓕ 3984-20684-2 (5/98).
See review under Lemba; refer to the Index.
...Symphonies Nos. 1-3. Malmö Symphony Orchestra / Paavo Järvi. BIS CD660 (12/94).

Herbert Sumsion
British 1899-1995

Suggested listening ...
...Introduction and Theme. *Coupled with works by various composers.* Christopher Herrick (org).
Hyperion CDA66778 (3/96). *See review in the Collections section; refer to the Index.*

Choi Young Sup

Suggested listening ...
...Guriwoon Guemgang San. *Coupled with works by various composers.*
Angela Gheorghiu (sop); Malcolm Martineau (pf).
Decca 458 360-2DH (5/98). *See review in the Collections section; refer to the Index.*

Franz von Suppé
Austrian 1819-1895

Suppé Overtures – Leichte Kavallerie; Tricoche und Cacolet; Boccaccio. Afrikareise – Titania
Waltz. Fatinitza. Humorous variations on the popular song, "What comes there from on high?"
Die Heimkehr von der Hochzeit. Herzenseintracht – polka. Franz Schubert. Triumph Overture.
Slovak State Philharmonic Orchestra, Košice / Alfred Walter. Marco Polo Ⓕ 8 223683
(62 minutes: DDD: 12/95). Recorded 1994.
This volume of Marco Polo's Suppé series offers another fascinating insight into the wider output of
a composer unjustly typecast through the brilliance of his rousing overtures. Here the familiar *Leichte
Kavallerie* and *Fatinitza* overtures serve to demonstrate the thoroughly reliable conducting and
playing of Alfred Walter and the Košice orchestra, without quite offering a challenge to the most
rousing interpretations available elsewhere. What are of interest are the rarities. Of the unfamiliar
overtures, that to *Tricoche und Cacolet*, a Viennese adaptation of a Meilhac and Halévy play, is
perceptibly in the French style of Offenbach, with some attractive themes and a marvellous passage
for bassoon, while the *Triumph Overture* has a typically exciting ending. The overture to *Die Heimkehr
von der Hochzeit* is perhaps less striking, while that to *Franz Schubert* (a one-act operetta portraying
the composer on stage) is mainly notable for its use of Schubertian themes – *Der Erlkönig*, *Der
Wanderer*, the German Dance No. 7 (also used later in *Lilac Time*), *Der Schäfer und der Reiter* and
Die Taubenpost. Among the other pieces, the *Afrikareise* waltz finds Suppé very much in Straussian
territory, while *Herzenseintracht* proves that he could also produce a polka with the best. Perhaps the
most intriguing item is Suppé's set of humorous variations on the *Fuchslied*, a popular Viennese
student song which we would recognize as *A-hunting we will go*. It all provides further enjoyable proof
that Suppé's entertaining writing extended way beyond his overtures.

Additional recommendations ...
...Overtures – Die schöne Galathee; Boccaccio; Dichter und Bauer; Leichte Kavallerie; Ein Morgen,
ein Mittag, ein Abend in Wien; Pique Dame. *Coupled with works by* **Auber Detroit Symphony
Orchestra / Paul Paray.** Mercury Living Presence Ⓜ 434 309-2MM (66 minutes: ADD). Ⓖ
...Overtures – Leichte Kavallerie; Tantalusqualen; Die Irrfahrt um's Glück; Die Frau Meisterin;
Ein Morgen, ein Mittag, ein Abend in Wien; Pique-Dame; Wiener Jubel; Dichter und Bauer.
Academy of St Martin in the Fields / Sir Neville Marriner.
EMI Ⓕ CDC7 54056-2 (61 minutes: DDD: 10/90).
...Overtures – Die schöne Galathee; Isabella; Das Modell; Tantalusqualen; Der Krämer und sein
Kommis; Paragraph drei; Boccaccio. Fatinitza – March. Donna Juanita. **Slovak Philharmonic
Orchestra, Košice / Alfred Walter.** Marco Polo Ⓕ 8 223648 (71 minutes: DDD: 6/95).
...Leichte Kavallerie – Overture. *Coupled with works by various composers.*
Vienna Philharmonic Orchestra / Riccardo Muti.
EMI Ⓕ CDC5 56336-2 (66 minutes: DDD: 3/97). Also includes a bonus disc.

Suppé Requiem in D minor. **Aleksandra Baranska** (sop); **Katarzyna Suska** (contr); **Jerzy Knetig**
(ten); **Andrzej Hiolski** (bass); **Cracow Philharmonic Chorus and Orchestra / Roland Bader.**
Koch Schwann Ⓕ 312482 (71 minutes: DDD: 11/96). Text and translation included.
Recorded 1989.
Suppé composed his Requiem in 1855 in memory of Franz Pokorny, the theatre manager to whom he
owed much of his early conducting and compositional experience. After a few performances it lay

forgotten. Then in 1988 it was performed at the Montpellier Festival and although recorded in 1989 we have had to wait some time for its appearance. The demands of a large-scale religious work held no terrors for Suppé, a thoroughly trained and proficient musician. The work is powerfully and imaginatively written, with much of the operatic flavour of Verdi's Requiem of 19 years later. The chorus have the major vocal contribution, with the bulk of the solo opportunities going to the two lower voices. Anyone wishing to sample the riches of the work should try the hauntingly beautiful "Hostias", with its eerie brass and woodwind and stirring bass solo, or the "Agnus Dei", with its plaintive funeral march developing into a typically expansive Suppé theme. This Koch release offers a spacious reading, notably in the "Dies irae" and the "Rex tremendae". This is an impressive and moving work that has much more to offer than mere curiosity value.

Conrad Susa   American 1935

Suggested listening ...
...Magnificat and Nunc dimittis (St Thomas Service). *Coupled with works by various composers.* **St Thomas Church Choir, New York / Gerre Hancock** with **Patrick Allen** (org). Priory PRCD600 (1/98). *See review in the Collections section; refer to the index of reviews.*

Tylman Susato   Flemish c1500-1561/4

Suggested listening ...
...Danserye – Les quatre Branles. *Coupled with works by various composers.* **Mhairi Lawson** (sop); **Circa 1500.** ASV Gaudeamus CDGAU163 (12/97). 🎵 *See review in the Collections section; refer to the Index.*

Johann Svendsen   Norwegian 1840-1911

Svendsen Symphony No. 2 in B flat major, Op. 15. Romance in G major, Op. 26[a]. Carnival in Paris, Op. 9. Norwegian Artists' Carnival, Op. 14. Norwegian Rhapsody No. 2, Op. 19.
[a]**Marianne Thorsen** (vn); **Stavanger Symphony Orchestra / Grant Llewellyn.** Chatsworth Ⓕ FCM1002 (70 minutes: DDD: 9/94). Recorded 1993.
Even though he and Grieg were good friends, Svendsen did not involve himself in the folk-song movement to anywhere near the same extent as his great countryman. His basic sympathies remained predominantly classical and he continued to work within the sonata-form discipline; yet there is a distinctive Norwegian feel to his melodic ideas. The Second Symphony was Svendsen's last large-scale work for, alas, the creative fires burnt themselves out prematurely, and after the popular *Romance* in G major, he virtually gave up composing. The Stavanger orchestra under the Welsh conductor Grant Llewellyn give a straightforward, enthusiastic account of the piece, not preferable to Järvi on BIS: the Stavanger orchestra is not the equal of Gothenburg. All the same, they acquit themselves well in the *Norwegian Rhapsody* No. 2 and the other orchestral pieces, as for that matter does the 21-year-old Marianne Thorsen, who plays with an unaffected simplicity and purity that is touching. Very clean, well-balanced sound with plenty of presence and body throughout.
Additional recommendations ...
...Symphonies – No. 1 in D major, Op. 4; No. 2. Two Swedish folk-melodies, Op. 27. **Gothenburg Symphony Orchestra / Neeme Järvi.** BIS Ⓕ CD347 (71 minutes: DDD: 11/87).
...Romance[a]. Octet in A major, Op. 3. **Nielsen** String Quintet in G major, FS5. [a]**Kenneth Sillito** (vn); **Academy of St Martin in the Fields Chamber Ensemble.** Chandos CHAN9258 (5/94).   Ⓖ
...Romance. *Coupled with works by various composers.* **Gil Shaham** (vn); **Orpheus Chamber Orchestra.** DG Ⓕ 449 923-2GH (58 minutes: DDD: 3/97).

Gyorgy Sviridov   Russian/USSR 1915-1998

Suggested listening ...
...Tsar Feodor Ioannovich – Prayer[a]; Sacred love; A verse of repentance. Songs of troubled times – Autumn; Bright fields; Spring and the sorcerer; The ikon[a]. *Coupled with works by various composers.* [a]**James Bowman** (alto); **Holst Singers / Stephen Layton.** Hyperion CDA66928 (8/97). *See review in the Collections section; refer to the Index.*

Jan Pieterszoon Sweelinck   Dutch 1562-1621

Sweelinck Toccata in C major. Balio del granduca. Ricercar. Malle Sijmen. Mein junges Leben hat ein End'. Aeolian Echo Fantasia. Onder een linde groen. Toccata in A minor I. Erbarm dich mein, o Herre Gott. Poolsche dans. **James David Christie** (org). Naxos Ⓢ 8 550904

(64 minutes: DDD: 2/95). Played on the C.B. Fisk Organ, Houghton Chapel, Wellesley College, USA. Recorded 1993.

James David Christie presents what is, in effect, a most satisfactory re-creation of one of Sweelinck's organ recitals, given daily between 1580 and 1621, for the burghers of Amsterdam. One hopes they were properly appreciative of the most consistently witty and generous-spirited keyboard music before the era of Buxtehude, Couperin and Bach. While Christie may not possess the lyricism of a Leonhardt, the humane warmth of a Piet Kee, or the mercurial whimsy of a Koopman, he is, in his own right, a bold, stylish, unhasty player, clearly thoroughly versed in early performance practice, with an incisive technique disclosing musical intelligence and common sense. He is particularly successful in the five major variation sets here, relishing the variety of decorative motifs but still conveying an impression of structural coherence and unity. Just occasionally his articulation might have worked better in a somewhat larger acoustic: at times a more obviously singing touch might have suggested greater tenderness in quieter moments and more ample majesty in louder ones. However, with appealing registrations, an almost ideal choice of programme, good notes and undistractingly natural recording, this disc merits general recommendation.

Further listening ...

...Fantasia. *Coupled with works by various composers.* **Glenn Gould** (pf).
Sony Classical mono SMK53474* (9/95).

...Psalm 140. *Coupled with works by various composers.* **Kristian Olesen** (org).
Priory PRCD444 (5/97).

...Or soit loué l'Etérnal. Mon Dieu, j'ay en toy esperance. Qui au conseil des malins. Vous tous qui la terr' habitez. Revenge moy, pren la querelle. Mon am'en Dieu taut seulement. Les cieux en chacun lieu. Du Seigneur les bontez. Ne sois fasché. Or sus serviteurs de Seigneur. Jamais ne cesseray. Vouloir m'est pris. Le Toutpuissant à mon Seigneur. D'ou vient, Seigneur. Vous tous les habitans. **Trinity College Choir, Cambridge / Richard Marlow.** Conifer Classics CDCF205 (8/92).

Franz Syberg

Danish 1904-1955

Suggested listening ...

...Prelude, Intermezzo and Fugato. *Coupled with works by various composers.* **Kevin Bowyer** (org).
Nimbus NI5468 (7/96). *See review in the Collections section; refer to the Index.*

András Szöllösy

Hungarian 1921

Suggested listening ...

...Paesaggio con morti. *Coupled with works by various composers.* **Peter Frankl** (pf).
ASV CDDCA860 (6/93). *See review in the Collections section; refer to the Index.* ⒼⒼⒼ

Karol Szymanowski

Polish 1882-1937

Szymanowski Violin Concertos[a] – No. 1, Op. 35; No. 2, Op. 61. Three Paganini Caprices, Op. 40[b]. Romance in D, Op. 23[b]. **Thomas Zehetmair** (vn); [b]**Silke Avenhaus** (pf); [a]**City of Birmingham Symphony Orchestra / Sir Simon Rattle.** EMI Ⓟ CDC5 55607-2 (65 minutes: DDD: 8/96). Recorded 1996. *Gramophone Award Winner 1997.* ⒼⒼ

They make an admirable coupling, the two Szymanowski violin concertos, but a demanding one for the soloist. They are both so beautiful that it must be tempting to embellish both with a similarly glowing tone. They inhabit quite different worlds (they were written 16 years apart) and Zehetmair shows how well they respond to quite different approaches. In the First, after a rapt solo entry, he uses for the most part a lovely but delicate tone, expanding to athletic incisiveness but not often to lushness. It fits very well with Rattle's handling of the orchestra: occasionally full and rich but mostly a sequence of exquisitely balanced chamber ensembles. Generous but finely controlled rubato from both soloist and conductor allows the concerto's improvisatory fantasy to flower; and the quiet close even has a touch of wit to it. Zehetmair's sound is immediately less ethereal, more robust, for the opening melody of the Second Concerto. This is the sort of tone, you suspect, that he would use in Bartók's Second Concerto, and it points up a vein of indeed Bartókian strength to this work's longer and firmer lines. Rattle, too, seeks out bolder and more dense colours. It is characteristic that even the more musing lyrical pages here are given a warmer colour than superficially similar moments in the First Concerto. The *Paganini Caprices* were equipped by Szymanowski not with deferential accompaniments but with independent and quite freely composed piano parts. They change Paganini, even where the violin part is unmodified (most of the time but not quite all), into a late romantic virtuoso, with a hint of Lisztian poetry alongside the expertly pointed-up fireworks of the Twenty-Fourth *Caprice*; even here Zehetmair is a listening violinist, not one to upstage his excellent pianist. The *Romance*, the warmest and most luscious piece here, is beautifully done but with a touch of restraint to prevent it cloying. A first-class coupling, and a recording that makes the most of the superb acoustic of Symphony Hall in Birmingham.

Additional recommendations ...

...Violin Concertos Nos. 1 and 2. *Coupled with works by* **Górecki** and **Baird**
Konstanty Kulka (vn); **Polish National Radio Symphony Orchestra / Jerzy Maksymiuk.**
EMI Matrix Ⓜ CDM5 65418-2 (73 minutes: ADD: 3/96).
...Violin Concertos Nos. 1 and 2. Concert Overture, Op. 12. **Lydia Mordkovitch** (vn); **BBC**
Philharmonic Orchestra / Vassily Sinaisky. Chandos Ⓕ CHAN9496 (59 minutes: DDD: 3/97).

Szymanowski Harnasie, Op. 46[a]. Symphony No. 4, Op. 60, "Symphonie concertante"[b].
Mazurkas, Op. 50[c] – No. 1 in C major; No. 2 in A major. Theme and Variations in B flat minor,
Op. 3[c]. [a]**Andrzej Bachleda** (ten); [a]**Wiesław Kwasny** (vn); [bc]**Felicja Blumental** (pf); [a]**Cracow Radio**
Chorus and Symphony Orchestra / Antoni Wit; [b]**Polish National Radio Symphony Orchestra /**
Jerzy Semkow. EMI Matrix Ⓜ CDM5 65307-2 (75 minutes: ADD: 4/95). Items marked
[ab] from HMV SLS5242 (9/82), [c]Unicorn RHS347 (6/78). Recorded 1974-1979.   Ⓖ
With the exception of the early and accomplishedly Brahmsian *Theme and Variations*, this is all late
Szymanowski, Szymanowski giving up just a little of the colour and opulence of his middle period to
respond with delight to the fresh and invigorating rawness of the folk music of the Tatra region. He
responds most obviously, of course, in the folk ballet *Harnasie*, with its frequent imitations of raucous
folk fiddling and the fervour of choral folk-song and its heartfelt evocations of Poland's mountain
country. But surely the wonderfully poised opening theme of the *Symphonie concertante* owes
something to this influence too (a theme so beautiful that Szymanowski cannot resist returning to it
as the true destination of all the previous beauties of his slow movement)? The last movement might
almost be a supplement to *Harnasie*, but the use throughout of wind and string solos sounds very
much like a 'refinement' of the peasant fiddle and trumpet in the ballet. Since the performances are
very good indeed, and the recordings clean and decent, the coupling is a very recommendable one.
All the more so since Western pianists still seem reluctant to programme the *Symphonie concertante*,
and *Harnasie*, which calls for tenor and violin soloists and a chorus as well as orchestra, is
unlikely ever to prove popular in the concert-hall. Both are full of delights. The *Theme and Variations*
and the two *Mazurkas* are well played; the latter will undoubtedly whet your appetite for the more
intimate and subtle aspects of 'late Szymanowski', and will send you off hunting for the other
18 *Mazurkas*.

Additional recommendations ...

...Harnasie[a]. Mandragora, Op. 43[b]. [a]**Jozef Stepién,** [b]**Paulos Raptis** (tens); **Polish National Opera**
Chorus; Polish National Opera Orchestra / Robert Satanowski. Koch Schwann 311064 (12/91).
...No. 2 in B flat major, Op. 19; No. 4[a]. [a]**Howard Shelley** (pf); **BBC Philharmonic Orchestra /**
Vassily Sinaisky. Chandos Ⓕ CHAN9478 (56 minutes: DDD: 10/96).

Szymanowski Métopes, Op. 29. 12 Etudes, Op. 33. Masques, Op. 34. Mazurkas, Op. 50 – No. 7,
Poco vivace; No. 13, Moderato; No. 15, Allegretto dolce. Two Mazurkas, Op. 62. **Mikhail Rudy**
(pf). EMI Ⓕ CDC5 55390-2 (72 minutes: DDD: 10/96). Recorded 1994.
'Big' and 'strong' are words that spring to mind quite often during these readings; not perhaps the first
adjectives one would choose to describe Szymanowski, yet they seem highly appropriate here. What
do the *Métopes* have in common? They are portraits of women (the Sirens, Calypso, Nausicaa) all of
whom at least threaten to be too strong for Odysseus. "Isle of the Sirens" is a big piece, for all its florid
voluptuousness; there is firm strength as well as impressionist colour to the portrait of Calypso;
Szymanowski's Nausicaa is an exotic enchantress as well as a seductive one. The *Masques*, of course,
respond still more to strong and purposeful virtuosity, and Rudy brings richness of colour as well as
bold pianism to "Shéhérazade", while in "Tantris le bouffon" he somehow suggests the humiliation
of Tristan, in this version of the legend forced to disguise himself as a jester to gain access to Isolde;
there is even something of frustration or of desperation beneath the ardour of his "Sérénade de Don
Juan". After all this, the *Mazurkas* come as a surely deliberate shock: a distilled, pared-down music
after all that richness and colour and, in the late *Mazurka*, Op. 62 No. 1, an outpouring of the purest
lyricism. All in all, enormously enjoyable, not least the ample acoustic which matches the scale of the
performances so well. If you want to convert someone to Szymanowski's piano music, start here.

Additional recommendations ...

...Four Etudes, Op. 4. Metopes, Op. 29. Fantasy. Masques, Op. 34. **Dennis Lee** (pf).
Hyperion Ⓕ CDA66409 (64 minutes: DDD: 7/91).
...Mazurkas, Op. 50 Nos. 1-4[a]. *Coupled with works by various composers.* **Artur Rubinstein** (pf).
RCA Victor Gold Seal Ⓜ 09026 61445-2 (64 minutes: ADD: 10/93). *See review in the Collections*
section; refer to the Index.   ⒼⒼⒼ
...Nine Preludes, Op. 1. Variations in B flat minor, Op. 3. Variations on a Polish folk theme, Op. 10.
Four Etudes, Op. 4. Piano Sonatas – No. 1 in C minor; No. 2 in A major, Op. 21. Fantasy,
Op. 14. Prelude and Fugue in C sharp minor. **Martin Jones** (pf).
Nimbus Ⓕ NI5405/06 (two discs: 135 minutes: DDD: 9/94).
...Mazurkas, Op. 50 Nos. 1-4. Metopes, Op. 29. Four Etudes, Op. 4.
Piano Sonata No. 2 in A major, Op. 21. **Martin Roscoe** (pf).
Naxos Ⓢ 8 553016 (67 minutes: DDD: 9/95). *Gramophone Editor's choice.*   Ⓖ
...Mazurkas, Op. 50 Nos. 5-12. Variations on a Polish folk theme, Op. 10. Masques, Op. 34.
Fantasy in C major, Op. 14. **Martin Roscoe** (pf). Naxos Ⓢ 8 553300 (72 minutes: DDD: 5/97).

Szymanowski 20 Mazurkas, Op. 50. Two Mazurkas, Op. 62. **Pawel Kamasa** (pf).
 Koch Schwann Ⓕ 310662 (57 minutes: AAD: 4/97). *Selected by Soundings.*
Kamasa himself adds a note to the accompanying booklet explaining why it was decided not to record these performances digitally. One can only report that the piano tone as reproduced here is very beautiful, very subtle of colour, indeed very responsive to Kamasa's poetic handling of this music. Another note, by the late Witold Lutosławski, praises his "tremendous understanding" of Szymanowski's harmonies and his "precise and purposeful" use of the pedal. Indeed he is a pianist of such exceptional gifts that this disc is recommended even to listeners who are not especially interested in Szymanowski. But they will surely soon become so under the influence of playing such as this, in which keyboard colour is so exquisitely clear, in which quite dense chords are never opaque. In them one can hear Szymanowski's excitement at discovering in the supposedly 'crude' folk music of the Tatra Mountains not only a harmonic asperity and a rhythmic boldness that excited him but a nobility of utterance that gives these brief pieces a quite disproportionate stature. They are indeed, as Kamasa says with a rueful apology for such seeming overstatement, 'symphonic', and his performances also have the urgency and fantasy to reveal what big pieces they are, despite their brevity.

Szymanowski Stabat mater, Op. 53[a]. Litany to the Virgin Mary, Op. 59[b]. Symphony No. 3, Op. 27, "The song of the night"[c]. [ab]**Elzbieta Szmytka** (sop); [a]**Florence Quivar** (contr); [c]**Jon Garrison** (ten); [a]**John Connell** (bass); **City of Birmingham Symphony Orchestra and Chorus / Sir Simon Rattle**. EMI Ⓕ CDC5 55121-2 (56 minutes: DDD: 8/94). Texts and translations included. Recorded 1994. *Gramophone Editor's choice.*
 Gramophone Award Winner 1995. ⒼⒶⒼ
The first impression here is that Rattle is relatively new to Szymanowski. There's a huge enthusiasm here, a missionary quality that bespeaks the recent convert. On the other hand the care over matters of balance, the knowledge of just those points where Szymanowski's complexity needs very careful handling if it's not simply to blur into opacity, suggest a conductor who has been there before and knows the dangers. You get the feeling that a conscious decision was made to delay recording this music until the circumstances were right. The CBSO Chorus not only sound thoroughly at home in the music but in the language too.The clincher on the decision to go ahead with this recording might well have been Rattle's realization that in Elzbieta Szmytka he had a soprano who might have been born to sing Szymanowski's pure, floated and very high-lying soprano lines (in the *Stabat mater* and the *Litany*; in the symphony he uses a tenor, which was Szymanowski's own first choice). The result is very fine indeed: one of the most beautiful Szymanowski recordings ever made. And yet 'beautiful Szymanowski' isn't all that hard if the orchestra's good enough and the conductor capable. Rattle's insistence that all of the music be heard, its bones and sinews as well as its flesh, its urgency and passion as well as its deliquescent loveliness, makes for uncommonly gripping Szymanowski as well. He reminds one of how much more there is to the Third Symphony than voluptuous yearning: solemnity, for one thing, and a fierce ardour that can indeed knock you sideways. The choice of soloists for the *Stabat mater* is interesting: alongside Szmytka's radiant purity are Quivar's throaty vibrancy and Connell's weighty darkness. Not a matching trio, but the contrast is appealing; it adds to the rich differentiation of sonority that Rattle draws from his chorus and orchestra. Garrison in the symphony is a touch hard and strenuous, less enraptured than one or two of the Polish tenors (and sopranos) who've recorded it, but he's a musicianly and likeable singer. The recording is outstanding: lucid, rich and spacious, with tremendous and perfectly focused climaxes.

Additional recommendation ...
...Stabat mater[a]. Symphony No. 3[b]. Three Fragments from poems by Jan Kasprowicz, Op. 5[c]. [ab]**Stefania Woytowicz** (sop); [ac]**Krystyna Szostek-Radkowa** (mez); [a]**Andrzej Hiolski** (bar); **Polish Radio and Television [ab]Choir and [b]Symphony Orchestra, Cracow; [ac]Polish Radio and Television Great Symphony Orchestra, Katowice / [a]Stanislaw Wislocki, [b]Tadeusz Strugala, [c]Jerzy Maksymiuk**. Koch Schwann Ⓕ 312652 (70 minutes: ADD: 4/94).

Further listening ...
...Symphonies – No. 2 in B flat major, Op. 19[b]; No. 3, Op. 27, "The song of the night"[a]. Concert Overture in E major, Op. 12[b]. [a]**Wieslaw Ochman** (ten); [a]**Cracow Polish Radio Chorus; Polish National Radio Symphony Orchestra / [a]Jerzy Semkow, [b]Jacek Kaspszyk**. EMI Matrix CDM5 65082-2 (7/94).
...Symphony No. 2 in B flat major, Op. 19. *Coupled with works by* **Bentzon** *and* **Shostakovich Copenhagen Philharmonic Orchestra / Okko Kamu**. Classico CLASSCD129 (10/96).
...String Quartets – No. 1 in C major, Op. 37; No. 2, Op. 56. *Coupled with works by* **Lutosławski** *and* **Penderecki Varsovia Quartet**. Olympia OCD328 (6/89).
...String Quartets – No. 1 in C major, Op. 37; No. 2, Op. 56. *Coupled with works by* **Bacewicz Maggini Quartet**. ASV CDDCA908 (2/95).
...Violin Sonata in D minor, Op. 9. Mythes, Op. 30. Nocturne and Tarantella, Op. 28. **Lydia Mordkovitch** (vn); **Marina Gusak-Grin** (pf). Chandos CHAN8747 (6/91).
...Violin Sonata in D minor, Op. 9. *Coupled with works by* **K. Khachaturian** *and* **Prokofiev David Oistrakh** (vn); **Vladimir Yampolsky** (pf). Testament mono* SBT1113* (2/98). *See review under Prokofiev; refer to the Index.* ⒼⒶⒼ

Germaine Tailleferre

French 1892-1983

Tailleferre Intermezzo. Larghetto. Jeux de plein air. Toccata. Suite Burlesque. Two Waltzes. Fandango. La nouvelle Cythère. Image. Sonata for two pianos. **Mark Clinton, Nicole Narboni** (pfs). Elan Ⓕ ELAN82278 (64 minutes: DDD: 11/97). Recorded 1996.
Gramophone Editor's choice.

Milhaud was responsible for introducing the young Germaine Tailleferre, who had been brilliantly carrying off prize after prize at the Conservatoire, to Satie, who on hearing her *Jeux de plein air* in 1917 declared her his "musical daughter" and brought her into contact with other young musicians who later were to be dubbed "Les Six". His enthusiasm was understandable, for the two traditional games depicted (the second being "Hunt the slipper") had drawn from her witty, light-hearted music (though with infinitely greater invention and technique than he had ever shown). *Gaminerie* also dominates the Poulenc-like *Toccata*, a perky piece played here with deliciously pointed staccato. At this time Tailleferre was also experimenting with polytonality, as can be heard in the initially meditative *Image*. Her background of Satie and Ravel (a friend of hers), however, emerges in the *Two Waltzes* of 1925, the first utterly charming but harmonically spiced, the second sprucely brilliant. All the pieces on this disc are unpretentious, concise and very brief: even the 1974 so-called Sonata, bubbling with Gallic gaiety, lasts a mere six minutes, and the *Suite Burlesque*, wonderfully frisky for an 87-year-old, consists of fragmentary chippings. The sparkling *Intermezzo* and the *Larghetto* are taken from her quite considerable film music; but her theatrical sense is best illustrated by the only work here of any length – *La nouvelle Cythère*, written in 1929 for Diaghilev's Ballets Russes but never performed because of his death. It is an attractive work, full of freshness, vitality and variety, and if only it were orchestrated would surely be welcomed by some ballet company today. No fewer than seven of the present ten works (six of which are still unpublished) here make their first appearance on disc. The Clinton-Narboni duo is absolutely first-rate, with an immensely engaging spirit, delicacy, variety of touch and subtle shadings, and the recording matches it in quality. An irresistibly joyous disc.

Further listening ...
...Romance. *Coupled with works by various composers.* **Marcelo Bratke** (pf).
Olympia Explorer OCD487 (12/96). *See review in the Collections section; refer to the Index.*

Toru Takemitsu

Japanese 1930-1996

Takemitsu To the Edge of Dream[c]. Folios – I, II and III. Toward the Sea III[a]. Here, There and Everywhere. What a Friend. Amours Perdues. Summertime. Vers, l'Arc-en-ciel, Palma[bc].
    John Williams (gtr); [a]**Sebastian Bell** (alto fl); [b]**Gareth Hulse** (ob d'amore); [c]**London Sinfonietta /
Esa-Pekka Salonen.** Sony Classical Ⓕ SK46720 (60 minutes: DDD: 1/92).   Ⓖ

Toru Takemitsu is an original, refined composer and something of a latter-day impressionist, as titles like *To the Edge of Dream* suggest. It may therefore come as a surprise to find him arranging songs by Lennon and McCartney, Gershwin and others, for solo guitar. Yet these prove to have attractive touches of the subtlety found in Takemitsu's own compositions, and they also provide useful contrast to the more substantial works on this beguiling disc. *Folios*, the earliest composition included, already reveal Takemitsu's musical catholicity in its reference to a Bach chorale. *Toward the Sea* and *Vers, l'Arc-en-ciel, Palma* are both more expansive mood pieces, the former (for guitar and alto flute) almost too reticent and hesitant beside the richer textures of the latter, which is enhanced by the additional solo role given to the oboe d'amore as well as its beautifully laid out orchestral accompaniment. *To the Edge of Dream* is in effect a guitar concerto, with a wider range of mood and an even more developed role for the orchestra than *Vers, l'Arc-en-ciel, Palma*. It provides a particularly satisfying focus for a sensitively performed and well recorded disc. Even if we hear rather more of the guitar relative to the orchestra than we would in the concert-hall, this is not unreasonably artificial.

Additional recommendation ...
...To the Edge of Dream. *Coupled with works by* **Arnold** *and* **Rodrigo** Julian Bream (gtr);
City of Birmingham Symphony Orchestra / Sir Simon Rattle.
EMI Ⓕ CDC7 54661-2 (58 minutes: DDD: 7/93).   Ⓖ

Further listening ...
...A Flock Descends into the Pentagonal Garden. Dreamtime. Star-Isle. Orion and Pleiades[a].
    [a]**Paul Watkins** (vc); **BBC National Orchestra of Wales / Tadaaki Otaka.** BIS CD760 (1/97).
...November Steps[a]. Eclipse[b]. Viola Concerto, "A String around Autumn"[c]. [ab]**Katsuya Yokoyama**
(shakuhachi); [ab]**Kinshi Tsuruta** (biwa); [c]**Nobuko Imai** (va); [ac]**Saito Kinen Orchestra / Seiji Ozawa.**
Philips 432 176-2PH (8/92).   Ⓖ
...Visions[b]. *Coupled with works by* **Carter** *and* **Berio** Chicago Symphony Orchestra /
Daniel Barenboim. Teldec 4509-99596-2 (8/95).
...A Way A Lone. *Coupled with works by* **Barber** *and* **Britten** Tokyo Quartet.
    RCA Victor Red Seal 09026 61387-2 (2/94). *See review under Barber; refer to the Index.*   ⒼⒼ
...Litany. Pause uninterrupted. Piano Distance. For away. Les yeux clos. Les yeux clos II. Rain tree sketch. Rain tree sketch II. **Noriko Ogawa** (pf). BIS Ⓕ CD805 (56 minutes: DDD: 3/97). *Selected by Soundings.*

...Paths (In Memoriam Witold Lutosławski). *Coupled with works by various composers.*
Håkan Hardenberger (tpt). Philips 446 065-2PH (11/96).
...Cherry Blossoms. Songs I – Small Sky; I Just Sing; In a Small Room; The Game of Love; Unseen
Child; Will Tomorrow, I Wonder, Be Cloudy or Clear? To the Island. All that the Man Left
Behind When He Died. A Song of Circles and Triangles. Sayonara. Wings. **Shin-yu Kai Choir /
Shin Sekiya.** Philips 438 135-2PH (8/94).
...Fantasma/Cantos. Water-Ways. Waves. Quatrain II. Soloists; [a]**BBC Welsh Symphony Orchestra /
Tadaaki Otaka.** RCA Victor Red Seal 09026 62537-2 (1/95).

Otar Taktakishvili
USSR 1924-1989

Suggested listening ...
...Flute Sonata. *Coupled with works by various composers.* **Leslie Newman** (fl); **Amanda Hurton** (pf).
Cala CACD88026 (6/96). *See review in the Collections section; refer to the Index.*

Thomas Tallis
British *c*1505-1585

Tallis Lamentations of Jeremiah. Motets – Absterge Domine; Derelinquat impius; Mihi autem
nimis; O sacrum convivium; In jejunio et fletu; O salutaris hostia; In manus tuas; O nata lux de
lumine. Salve intemerata virgo. **The Tallis Scholars / Peter Phillips.** Gimell Ⓟ 454 925-2PH
(68 minutes: DDD: 5/92). Texts and translations included.
This, the third volume of the survey by The Tallis Scholars of the music of the Tudor composer,
Thomas Tallis, contains the well-known *Lamentations*, eight motets, and the extended motet *Salve
intemerata virgo*. The *Lamentations* and motets are typical of the style of late Renaissance English
composers. The overall mood is one of considerable austerity and their simplicity is indicative of the
probability of their having been written for the private use of loyal Catholics rather than for formal
ritual. *Salve intemerata virgo,* on the other hand, looks back to the glories of the late fifteenth century.
In particular Tallis's use of the phrygian mode gives the work as a whole a strong sense of the
medieval. Despite this disparity of styles the Tallis Scholars acquit themselves, as always, with great
distinction. In the *Lamentations* and motets they achieve an appropriate sense of intimacy, while in
Salve intermerata virgo they rise fully to the challenges of one of the more extended and demanding
examples of Tudor choral composition. In addition the formidable challenges which this latter work
sets for the conductor, such as the sense of pace, variation of dynamics, and overall architecture of
the work, are all extremely well handled by Peter Phillips. The recording is very fine.
Additional recommendations ...
...Lamentations of Jeremiah. Salvator mundi II. O sacrum convivium. Mass a 4. Absterge Domine.
The Hilliard Ensemble / Paul Hillier. ECM New Series Ⓟ 833 308-2 (DDD: 4/88).
...Ave Dei patris filia. Ave rosa sine spinis. Salve intemerata virgo. Missa Salve intemerata.
Canterbury Cathedral Choir / David Flood. Metronome Ⓟ METCD1014 (71 minutes: DDD: 11/96).

Tallis Lamentations of Jeremiah[a]. Absterge Domine[b]. In jejunio et fletu[a]. If ye love me[a]. O sacrum
convivium[b]. Audivi vocem de caelo[a]. Derelinquat impius[a]. Salvator mundi, salva nos I[a]. Solfa-ing
Song a 5[b]. In Nomine a 4 No. 1[b]. Benedictus[a]. Fond youth is a bubble[b]. Psalm Tunes for
Archbishop Parker's Psalter[a] – No. 3, Why fum'th in sight; No. 8, Tallis's Canon. Like as the
doleful dove[b]. When shall my sorrowful sighing slake[b]. Te lucis ante terminum I[a]. [a]**Theatre of
Voices / Paul Hillier;** [b]**The King's Noyse / David Douglass.** Harmonia Mundi Ⓟ HMU90 7154
(71 minutes: DDD: 7/96).
This is imaginative programme planning – atmospheric renaissance music performed by choral and
instrumental forces in amiable juxtaposition rather than combination. The 16-strong Theatre of
Voices, who are based at the University of California at Davis, sing throughout with a dark-browed
gravitas and warmth of feeling that are thoroughly appropriate and give considerable pleasure. The
secular music plus (surprisingly perhaps, but interestingly) *Absterge Domine* and *O sacrum convivium*
are done by The King's Noyse, an expert renaissance violin consort, though they realize the sombre
harmonic undertow so characteristic of Tallis less successfully than the singers. It ends with the
tranquil evening office hymn, *Te lucis ante terminum* (complete with its alternating plainchant).
Unlike most English groups in this repertoire, the Theatre of Voices do not use falsettists (authenticity
may be on their side). Compared with The Tallis Scholars, the high-lying tenor parts here – often
assigned by other groups to male altos – are perhaps not always impeccably blended, and the female
voices sometimes have a slight flatward colouring. But, in compensation, this American group
certainly taps a rich vein of pathos in this affecting music while remaining stylistically convincing, and
Tallis's two most famous psalm-tunes are done with much relish. A distinctive, and on the whole,
commendable issue, warmly recorded, and with a sumptuously produced CD booklet.
Additional recommendation ...
...Lamentations of Jeremiah. Audivi vocem de caelo. **Byrd** Lamentations of Jeremiah.
Mass for Four Voices. **Clerks of New College Choir, Oxford / Edward Higginbottom.**
Collins Classics Ⓟ 1487-2 (66 minutes: DDD: 7/96).

Tallis Videte miraculum[b]. Homo quidam[b]. Audivi vocem[a]. Candidi facti sunt Nazarei[b]. Dum transisset Sabbatum[b]. Honor, virtus et potestas[b]. Hodie nobis[a]. Loquebantur variis linguis[b]. In pace, in idipsum[a]. Spem in alium (with Wim Becu, bass sackbut; Paul Nicholson, Alan Wilson, orgs)[ab]. [a]**Taverner Consort;** [b]**Taverner Choir / Andrew Parrott.** EMI Reflexe Ⓕ CDC7 49555-2 (62 minutes: DDD: 5/89). ✍ Texts and translations included. ❷❷

Tallis, one of the greatest composers of sacred music, has been sympathetically and generously acknowledged by Andrew Parrott and the Taverner Choir with this disc of Latin church music. It includes the masterly 40-part responsary *Spem in alium* written, it would seem, in reply to a similarly ambitious one by Tallis's Italian contemporary, Alessandro Striggio. The performances are characterized by translucent textures, a wonderful feeling for structure and a fluent understanding of the composer's contrapuntal ingenuity. Certainly there are occasional hints of vocal strain in the uppermost reaches of the part writing but they do little to spoil an affectionate, technically assured account of thrilling music. Parrott illuminates the music with his own deep understanding of it, but above all with the skilful deployment of vocal talent that he has at his command.

Additional recommendations ...

...Spem in alium. Salvator mundi I and II. Sancte Deus, sancte fortis. Gaude gloriosa Dei mater. Miserere nostri. Loquebantur variis linguis. **The Tallis Scholars / Peter Phillips.** Gimell Ⓕ 454 906-2PH (43 minutes: DDD: 3/86).

...Dum transisset Sabbatum. Gaude gloriosa Dei mater. Magnificat and Nunc dimittis. In jejunio et fletu. Derelinquat impius. Candidi facti sunt Nazarei. Salvator mundi II. Absterge Domine. **New College Choir, Oxford / Edward Higginbottom.** CRD Ⓕ CRD3429 (57 minutes: DDD: 4/87).

...O salutaris hostia. In jejunio et fletu. Salvator mundi I and II. In manuas tuas, Domine. Lamentations of Jeremiah. O sacrum convivium. O nata lux de lumine. Te lucis ante terminum. Spem in alium (with Winchester College Quiristers; Vocal Arts; Timothy Byram-Wigfield, org). **Winchester Cathedral Choir / David Hill.** Hyperion Ⓕ CDA66400 (59 minutes: DDD: 5/90). ❶

...Spem in alium. *Coupled with works by various composers.* ✍ **Huelgas Ensemble / Paul van Nevel.** Sony Classical Vivarte Ⓕ SK66261 (53 minutes: DDD: 4/96). *See review in the Collections section; refer to the Index.*

...Salvator mundi, salva nos I. O nata lux de lumine. In manus tuas. *Coupled with works by various composers.* **Soloists; Westminster Cathedral Choir / James O'Donnell.** Hyperion Ⓕ CDA66850 (72 minutes: DDD: 5/96). *See review in the Collections section; refer to the Index.*

...Jesu salvator saeculi[a]. Gloria tibi trinitas[b]. Iste confessor Domini sacratus[b]. Salvator mundi, salva nos I[a]. Jam lucis orto sidere[b]. Ex more docti mistico[b]. Videte miraculum[a]. Ecce tempus idoneum[b]. Jam Christus astra ascenderat[a]. Veni Redemptor gentium[b]. Quod chorus vatum[a]. Clarifica me pater[b]. O nata lux de lumine[a]. Poyncte for the Virginals[b]. Natus est nobis hodie[b]. Laudate Dominum[a]. [a]**St John's College Choir, Cambridge / Christopher Robinson** with [b]**Robert Woolley** (org). Chandos Chaconne Ⓕ CHAN0588 (52 minutes: DDD: 8/97).

Further listening ...

...Anthems – If ye love me; Hear the voice and prayer; A New commandment; O Lord, give thy Holy Spirit; Purge me, O Lord; Verily, verily say I unto you; Remember not, O Lord God; Out from the deep; O Lord, in Thee is all my trust; Christ rising again; Blessed are those that be undefiled. Psalm Tunes for Archbishop Parker's Psalter. **The Tallis Scholars / Peter Phillips.** Gimell 454 907-2PH (12/86).

...Jam lucis orto sidere. *Coupled with works by various composers.* **Mhairi Lawson** (sop); **Circa 1500.** ASV Gaudeamus CDGAU163 (12/97). ✍ *See review in the Collections section; refer to the Index.*

...Mass Puer natus est nobis. Suscipe quaeso Dominus. Salvator mundi Domine ... Adesto nunc proprius. *Coupled with works by* **White** The Clerkes of Oxenford / David Wulstan. Calliope Approche CAL6623 (11/95).

...Short Service, "Dorian Service". *Coupled with works by various composers.* **Ripon Cathedral Choir / Kerry Beaumont** with **Robert Marsh** (org). Priory Ⓕ PRCD555 (63 minutes: DDD: 1/97).

Tan Dun

Chinese/USA 1957

Tan Dun Symphony 1997. Yo-Yo Ma (vc); **Imperial Bells Ensemble of China; Yip's Children's Choir; Hong Kong Philharmonic Orchestra / Tan Dun.** Sony Classical Ⓕ SK63368 (72 minutes: DDD: 9/97). Text and translation included. Recorded 1997.

Writing history into music is nothing new. The reunification of Hong Kong with China has inspired numerous commissions of one sort or another, Dun's *Symphony 1997* being among them. However, few will have utilized musical instruments that date back 2,400 years. The bianzhong is a family of tuned bells that, collectively, spans a five-octave range. They were discovered in an ancient tomb that as excavated as recently as 1978 and Dun's symphony gives them pride of place. In "Heaven" (the symphony's first main episode), the bianzhong's grandeur "rises from the earth's grave", though their presence is scarcely less imposing elsewhere. *Symphony 1997* opens and closes with a simple, touching "Song of Peace". It is cast in three sections ("Heaven", "Earth" and "Mankind"), the solo cello taking the role of commentator through wordless song. "Water" (track 8) is a sub-division of "Earth" and includes a demonstrative solo cadenza reminiscent of the finale from Kodály's Op. 8 Solo Sonata, whereas the following track has the orchestra slowly re-enter like some huge, sonorous community. Needless to say, Yo-Yo Ma's playing has great panache and intensity. "Earth" represents Dun at his most characteristically inventive, but elsewhere dominant influences include Chinese popular music, various European late-romantics, Hindemith, Stravinsky and Varèse. There are also reminiscences of Beethoven (a quotation from "Ode to Joy") and Puccini (an old love-song used in *Turandot*). *Symphony 1997* is a highly theatrical, lavishly scored montage, frequently rhythmic, richly atmospheric and with merging styles that reflect both China and the neighbour that has once again become family.

Tan Dun Marco Polo. **Thomas Young** (ten) Polo; **Alexandra Montano** (mez) Marco; **Dong-Jian Gong** (bass) Kublai Khan; **Susan Botti** (sop) Water; **Shi-Zheng Chen** (sngr) Rustichello, Li Po; **Nina Warren** (sop) Sheherazada, Mahler, Queen; **Stephen Bryant** (bar) Dante, Shakespeare; **Cappella Amsterdam; Netherlands Radio Chamber Orchestra / Tan Dun.** Sony Classical Ⓕ S2K62912 (two discs: 100 minutes: DDD: 7/97). Notes and text included. Recorded live in 1996.

Mobility and re-creation are key concepts in Tan Dun's 'opera within an opera', although readers expecting gravy-train minimalism will be disappointed. Tan uses rhythm in the old-fashioned way, at key dramatic moments or in support of internal and external action. The 're-creative' element concerns opera directors and their potential responses "to different elements of these tales [concerning Marco Polo] in creating the dramatic world of the opera". The 'plot', which has been skilfully rendered verbal by Paul Griffiths (although words in this context have a strongly allusive function), concerns three journeys, one physical, the other two spiritual and musical, respectively. The components of the name 'Marco'/'Polo' are initially polarized to represent 'Marco the traveller' and 'Polo the memory' (their words are similarly divided), although the two do eventually join forces for a duet. Musically, *Marco Polo* is based on the interconnection of two very separate currents – Eastern operatic and instrumental traditions ("Opera 1"), and Western opera traditions with a blend of Eastern and Western instruments ("Opera 2"). The forceful opening (a recurring idea) is shared among Chinese percussion, whereas much of the string writing that follows curves in the style of Chinese popular music. The 'physical' aspect of the journey calls on medieval, Middle Eastern, Indian, Tibetan, Mongolian and Chinese influences. Mahler counts among the 'Western' components (Shakespeare and Dante are two others), quite literally on track 14 of the second disc where "Der Trunkene im Frühling" from *Das Lied von der Erde* makes a cameo appearance. Tan Dun's instrumentalists and vocal team give virtuoso performances, but special mention should be made of Susan Botti and Thomas Young, although the most astonishing vocal contribution of all comes from Shi-Zheng Chen, whose range and agility are remarkable. *Marco Polo*'s instrumentation includes a substantial battery of percussion, various national instruments (pipa, sitar, Tibetan bells and so on), 'optional' old instruments, plus woodwind, brass and strings. Documentation is intriguing, albeit occasionally cryptic, and the recording is excellent.

Further listening ...
...A Sinking Love. *Coupled with works by various composers.* **Michael Chance** (alto); **Fretwork.** Virgin Classics VC5 45217-2 (12/97). *See review in the Collections section; refer to the Index.*

Alexander Taneyev

Russian 1850-1918

A. Taneyev String Quartets – No. 1 in G major, Op. 25; No. 2 in C major, Op. 28; No. 3 in A major, Op. 30. **Talan Quartet** (Vladimir Talanov, Alexander Talanov, vns; Olga Bulakova, va; Alexei Steblov, vc). Olympia Ⓜ OCD543 (68 minutes: DDD: 10/95). Recorded 1994.

Alexander Taneyev was yet another of the amateurs who contributed so much to Russian music, scribbling away secretly under his desk at the Imperial Chancellery, and even managing to write a couple of operas as well as orchestral and chamber music. In his three string quartets, at any rate, he reveals a fluent charm that owes most to the Russian lyrical tradition upheld by his namesake, among many others, and glorified by Tchaikovsky, but also taking account of the long Viennese inheritance. His qualities show best in a melodic charm and an ability to produce music in various manners well suited to the medium; he was also professional enough to write a decent fugue. If he does not really sustain the forms of the movements well, and can occasionally seem to get a bit caught up in processes that do not have sufficient musical motivation, there are some lively *Scherzos* and some lyrical meditations in the *Larghetto* movements of, in particular, Nos. 2 and 3. Collectors of Russian music will no doubt want to add these rarities to their shelves, and may find themselves taking them down to play for relaxation quite often; they will also find sympathetic and well-turned performances from the Talan Quartet.

Further listening ...
...Symphony No. 4 in C minor, Op. 12. The Oresteia – Overture. **Philharmonia Orchestra / Neeme Järvi.** Chandos CHAN8953 (4/92).
...Piano Quintet in G minor, Op. 30. **Jerome Lowenthal** (pf); **Paul Rosenthal, Yukiko Kamei** (vns); **Marcus Thompson** (va); **Stephen Kates** (vc). Arabesque Z6539.
...Piano Trio in D major, Op. 22. **Borodin Trio.** Chandos CHAN8592 (2/89).

Giuseppe Tartini   Italian 1692-1770

Tartini Violin Concertos – C major, D12; D minor, D45; E major, D51; B flat major, D117. **Gordan Nikolitch** (vn); **Auvergne Orchestra / Arie van Beek.** Olympia Ⓜ OCD476 (59 minutes: DDD: 7/97). Recorded 1996.

Tartini's violin concertos come and go in a wide variety of performing styles; Nikolitch and the Auvergne Orchestra are not practitioners of period instruments but they are at one in their approach to the music, disciplined in matters of expression, mainly clean and lively in their ensemble and appreciative of qualities which make Tartini's concertos the distinctive and rewarding pieces that they undoubtedly are. The expressive focal point of many of the concertos is the slow middle movement. There are some lyrical examples in this programme including, in the case of the C major Concerto (D12), not one slow movement, but two. This was a distinctive Tartini hallmark, the provision of alternative slow movements providing a poetic motto mainly drawn from Metastasio and Tasso, to establish the basic mood of the piece in question. Both of the slow movements of the C major work contain mottoes from Metastasio's *Demofoonte*, while the single slow movement of the E major Concerto (D51) has an unidentified one concerning a turtle-dove. There is plenty that is rewarding in this programme. Nikolitch is an athletic player who, nevertheless, turns his back on any opportunity for vacuous showmanship. This conjunction of soloist and orchestra under the direction of Arie van Beek is an effective one. A slight acidity of tone in the ripieno section of the E major Concerto is not sufficient to dampen one's spirits.

Additional recommendation ...

...C major, D2; F major, D67; A major, D96; A minor, D115; B minor, D125. **Piero Toso** (vn); **I Solisti Veneti / Claudio Scimone.** Erato Ⓜ 0630-12988-2 (68 minutes: ADD: 9/96).

Tartini Violin Concertos – D major, D15; G major, D78; B flat major, D123; G major, D80; A minor, D115. **Gordan Nikolitch** (vn); **Auvergne Orchestra / Arie van Beek.** Olympia Explorer Series Ⓜ OCD475 (76 minutes: DDD: 2/97). Recorded 1996.

The Auvergne Orchestra are not a period instrument ensemble but they demonstrate a lively and playful rapport with late baroque music. The performances are full of vitality and caprice. Nikolitch is a sensitive player who is constantly aware of the underlying poetry in Tartini's music, above all in slow movements. In these Tartini sometimes appended poetic mottoes, often in secret code, mainly drawn from Tasso and Metastasio. These established the mood of the movement in question and, more and more, became the focal point of the work. Sometimes, too, Tartini would provide a concerto with an alternative slow movement, one of which he might regard as definitive. One such instance is included in this programme (in the G major Concerto, D80) where, happily, Nikolitch gives us both slow movements. The dance-like character of many of the outer movements is an attractive feature of Tartini's concertos. Only the finale of D15 is short on inspiration. Bright and clear recorded sound.

Tartini (arr. Manze) Violin Sonatas – G minor, "Devil's Trill", B:g5; A minor, B:a3. Variations on a Gavotte by Corelli, B:F11 – excerpts. Pastorale in A major, B:A16. **Andrew Manze** (vn). Harmonia Mundi Ⓔ HMU90 7213 (69 minutes: DDD: 5/98). 📀 Recorded 1997.

The romantic connotations of Tartini's Violin Sonata in G minor, the *Devil's Trill*, deriving from the composer's own account of an appearance by the devil in a dream, have contributed towards making it one of the great *morceaux favoris* of the nineteenth and twentieth centuries. It is, furthermore, just about the only remaining piece of baroque music where a piano accompaniment can still be countenanced without uniformly raised eyebrows. Some traditions do, indeed, die hard. But, of course, Tartini never intended anything of the kind; in fact, he probably never envisaged a keyboard continuo part at all, since none of his surviving autographs contains a figured bass for keyboard realization. They do, however, mostly include unfigured bass parts though, as Tartini himself remarked, he provided them, often as an afterthought, and more for reasons of convention than any other. Andrew Manze sees this as a justification for playing all the pieces in his programme without bass accompaniment. On the whole the experiment works well, since the expressive content and structural *puissance* of the music lies foremost in Tartini's melodic line. There are moments, however, where harmonic support from the bass is required, and at such times, above all in the *Devil's Trill* Sonata, Manze has had to introduce chords in the violin part to compensate for the absence of a cello. Manze's athletic technique, his musical sensibility and perhaps, too, his engaging sense of fun, ensure fascination and entertainment in equal measure. The 'diabolical' finale of the G minor Sonata has rhythmic poise, expressive delicacy and commendable virtuosity, and few admirers of this challenging piece will feel seriously compromised by the absence of a string bass. None will regret the passing of the piano in this context. A stimulating release, beautifully recorded, and rich in fantasy.

Additional recommendation ...

...Pastorale in A major. Violin Sonata, "Devil's Trill". Sonate e una pastorale – No. 2 in F major; No. 8 in C minor; No. 10 in G minor, "Didone abbandonata"; No. 12 in F major. **Locatelli Trio.** Hyperion Ⓔ CDA66430 (73 minutes: DDD: 4/92). 📀

Further listening ...

...Violin Sonatas – D major, BD19; B flat major, BB1; A major, BA4, "sopra lo stile che suona il Prette dalla Chitarra Portoghese"; B flat major, BB5 (Op. 5 No. 6). **Locatelli Trio.** Hyperion CDA66485 (11/92). 📀

Richard Tauber

Suggested listening ...
...Der singende Traum – Du bist die Welt für mich. *Coupled with works by various composers.*
Jerry Hadley (ten); **Munich Radio Orchestra / Richard Bonynge.**
RCA Victor Red Seal 09026 68258-2 (9/97). *Gramophone Editor's choice.*
See review in the Collections section; refer to the Index.

John Tavener

Tavener The Protecting Veil[a]. Thrinos.
Britten Solo Cello Suite No. 3, Op. 87. **Steven Isserlis** (vc); [a]**London Symphony Orchestra /**
Gennadi Rozhdestvensky. Virgin Classics Ⓕ VC7 59052-2 (74 minutes: DDD: 3/92).
Gramophone Award Winner 1992. ⒼⒼ
The Protecting Veil is one of the feasts of the Mother of God, according to the ritual of the Orthodox Church. John Tavener's ability to transfer such a concept into a concert work of wide appeal and proven impact is indeed remarkable, even if its success has more to do with the simple, direct emotionalism of the music than with its specific religious connotations. Direct emotionalism, certainly – but the music's predominantly slow pace and sustained lyricism, offset by occasional, striking dramatic gestures of sorrow and lamentation, make huge demands on the stamina and technique of the performers. Both Steven Isserlis and Gennadi Rozhdestvensky, not normally one of the more self-effacing of conductors, deserve high praise for the way they sink themselves into the music's contemplative but constantly illuminating ethos, and refugees from the battering of more complex contemporary music need look no further for solace and consolation. The brief lament of the unaccompanied cello piece *Thrinos* is no less affecting, while the Britten suite provides valuable contrast through music from which the intense and unshakeable religious faith of Tavener's work is conspicuous by its absence. The recording quality is outstandingly good.

Additional recommendations ...
...Eternal Memory. *Coupled with* **Bloch** From Jewish Life.
Steven Isserlis (vc); **Moscow Virtuosi / Vladimir Spivakov.**
RCA Victor Red Seal (special price) 09026 61966-2 (21 minutes: DDD: 4/94). Ⓖ
...The Protecting Veil[a]. Thrinos. Eternal Memory[a].
Raphael Wallfisch (vc); [a]**Royal Philharmonic Orchestra / Justin Brown.**
Tring International Royal Philharmonic Collection Ⓢ TRP048 (58 minutes: DDD: 1/96).

Tavener Akhmatova Requiem[a]. Six Russian Folksongs[b]. [a]**Phyllis Bryn-Julson,** [b]**Elise Ross** (sops);
[a]**John Shirley-Quirk** (bar); [b]**Nash Ensemble;** [a]**BBC Symphony Orchestra / Gennadi Rozhdestvensky.**
BBC Radio Classics Ⓑ 15656 9197-2 (69 minutes: ADD: 9/97). Text of Requiem included.
Item marked [a] recorded live in 1981, [b]1979.
The *Akhmatova Requiem* is one of John Tavener's darkest, most austere large-scale works and is a setting of a cycle of poems by the Russian poet Anna Akhmatova written as a testimony to the horrors of the Stalinist regime. "I have tried to convey the grim, numbing cold of the poetry" says Tavener, and it has to be said that the unremitting bleakness and sombre hues of this piece succeed in every respect. The *Requiem* is amongst Tavener's finest and important compositions. At times the bleak sound-world of Shostakovich is brought to mind, but there are unmistakably Tavenerisms too – whooping horn figurations, tolling bells, long, sustained string passages and the largely intoned, declamatory and uncompromising vocal writing. The recording on this disc was taken from its Prom performance in 1981 and is an incredibly intense, exceptionally fine rendition under the baton of Gennadi Rozhdestvensky. The *Six Russian Folksongs* make a very attractive, lightweight companion to the *Akhmatova Requiem* and are effectively delivered here by the soprano Elise Ross and the Nash Ensemble. The settings, which include the famous "Kalinka", are colourfully embellished with the sound of the domra – a Russian folk instrument similar in sound to the balalaika.

Tavener Innocence[a]. The Lamb. The Tiger. The Annunciation. Hymn to the Mother of God. Hymn for the Dormition of the Mother of God. Little Requiem for Father Malachy Lynch[b].
Song for Athene. [a]**Patricia Rozario** (sop); [a]**Leigh Nixon** (ten); [a]**Graham Titus** (bass); [a]**Alice Neary** (vc); [a]**Charles Fullbrook** (bells); [a]**Martin Baker** (org); **Westminster Abbey Choir;** [b]**English Chamber Orchestra / Martin Neary.** Sony Classical Ⓕ SK66613 (64 minutes: DDD: 12/95). Texts included.
Recorded 1994-1995.
This is recommended as a single disc to convince anyone of the mastery of John Tavener. As well as the superb new work, *Innocence*, specially written for Westminster Abbey – encapsulating in 25 minutes what many of his more expansive pieces have told us – we have a rich and rewarding selection of other shorter choral pieces. They include not just the established favourites like the two intense Blake settings, *The Lamb* and *The Tiger*, and the two hymns for the Mother of God – here more openly passionate than in previous recordings – but the bald and direct *Little Requiem for Father Malachy Lynch*, the sharply terraced *Annunciation* and the *Song for Athene* of two years ago, all among Tavener's most beautiful and touching inspirations. The theme of *Innocents* is Innocent

Victims, which prompted Tavener to compose a ritual built on texts from varied sources, Christian, Jewish, Islamic and Hindu. This involves a range of elements, set physically apart from each other. So the main choir, soprano (representing Holy Wisdom) and cello are at the centre, with the baritone soloist on one side intoning prayers for mercy in the language of the Orthodox church, and with the tenor soloist entering behind with Islamic prayers, and far away the pure sounds of a boys' choir. The result is both moving and atmospheric, with the climax introducing one element after another in rich crescendo, to provide a resolution very comparable to Britten's in the *War Requiem*. Neary draws intensely committed singing from his choir, with the principal soloists, Patricia Rozario and Graham Titus, both excellent, as well as the tenor, Leigh Nixon, with Alice Neary an expressive cellist. All the performances have a warmth of expressiveness which defies any idea of ecclesiastical detachment. The discs of shorter Tavener works from both The Sixteen (Collins, 6/94) and St George's Chapel Choir (Hyperion) offer excellent performances of the four shortest and best-known works, but they seem relatively cool next to Neary's, whose reading of the *Hymn to the Mother of God* is overwhelmingly powerful within its three-minute span. The recording vividly captures Westminster Abbey's acoustic with extreme dynamics used impressively to convey space and distance.

Additional recommendations ...

...Ikon of Light[a]. Funeral Ikos[b]. The Lamb[c]. Members of the **Chilingirian Quartet; The Tallis Scholars / [ab]Peter Phillips, [c]John Tavener.** Gimell Ⓕ 454 905-2PH (55 minutes: DDD: 6/91).

...Hymn for the Dormition of the Mother of God. Hymn to the Mother of God. Little Lamb, who made thee? (The Lamb)[b]. The Tiger. Ikon of Light[a]. Today the Virgin. Eonia. [a]**Duke Quartet; The Sixteen / Harry Christophers.** Collins Classics Ⓕ 1405-2 (67 minutes: DDD: 6/94).

...Angels[a]. The Annunciation. The Lament of the Mother of God[b]. Thunder entered Her[c]. Hymns of Paradise[d]. God is with us. [b]**Solveig Kringelborn** (sop); [c]**William Kendall** (ten); [d]**Donald Sweeney** (bass); [d]**violin ensemble;** [c]**Iain Simcock** (handbells); [ace]**David Dunnett** (org); **Winchester Cathedral Choir / David Hill.** Virgin Classics Ⓕ VC5 45035-2 (63 minutes: DDD: 8/94).

...The Annunciation. Ikon of the Nativity. The Lamb. A Nativity. Today the Virgin. The Lord's Prayer. Many Years. Wedding Prayer. He Hath Entered the Heven. The Acclamation. *Coupled with works by* **Górecki** *and* **Pärt** Magnificat. Summa. **Oxford Pro Musica Singers / Michael Smedley.** Proud Sound Ⓕ PROUCD136 (77 minutes: DDD: 12/94).

...The Lamb. Funeral Ikos. A Hymn to the Mother of God. Hymn for the Dormition of the Mother of God. Magnificat and Nunc dimittis. *Coupled with works by various composers.* **Vasari Singers / Jeremy Backhouse.** EMI Eminence Ⓜ CD-EMX2251 (74 minutes: DDD: 8/96). *See review in the Collections section; refer to the Index.*

...Funeral Ikos. The Lamb. *Coupled with works by various composers.* **The King's Singers.** RCA Victor Red Seal Ⓕ 09026 68255-2 (69 minutes: DDD: 8/96). *See review in the Collections section; refer to the Index.*

...The Lamb. *Coupled with works by various composers.* **New College Choir, Oxford; Capricorn / Edward Higginbottom.** Erato Ⓕ 0630-14634-2 (73 minutes: DDD: 1/97).

Tavener Svyati[d]. Eternal Memory[e]. Akhmatova Songs[ac]. The Hidden Treasure[bc]. Chant[ce]. [a]**Patricia Rozario** (sop); [b]**Daniel Phillips,** [b]**Krista Bennion Feeney** (vns); [b]**Todd Phillips** (va); [ce]**Steven Isserlis** (vc); [d]**Kiev Chamber Choir / Mykola Gobdych;** [e]**Moscow Virtuosi / Vladimir Spivakov.** RCA Victor Red Seal Ⓕ 09026 68761-2 (70 minutes: DDD: 6/97). Text included. Item marked [e] from 09026 61966-2 (9/94). Recorded 1995. *Gramophone Editor's choice.*

"O Holy One", or "Svyatiy", to quote its correct transliteration) sets a religious text as a backdrop to Isserlis's warm, soaring solo oration. *Eternal Memory* recalls the 1992 *Gramophone* Award-winning *The Protecting Veil*, albeit with its own very individual structure: it opens with a paradisiacal passage in the style of Byzantine chant (think of the *1812* Overture's first few minutes), then turns restless for a middle section that suggests Biber's "Drunken Revellers" (in *Battalia*) gate-crashing a Shostakovich string quartet. The revellers eventually hobble off, the Byzantine mood returns and "Paradise persists". And if proof were needed that not all Tavener sounds the same, then the six stark but startling *Akhmatova Songs* would surely provide it. All are utterly unalike, varying in style from the wailing declamations of "Dante", through the more comforting tones of "Pushkin and Lermontov" to the concise mini-drama of "The Muse". Soprano Patricia Rozario is a vivid vocal actress who commands an astonishingly wide range. *The Hidden Treasure* Quartet is, in a sense, a cello solo with string trio accompaniment. The work follows a sort of bridge from the Paradise "from which we have fallen" to the "Paradise which Christ promised to the repentant thief". The CD ends with palindromic *Chant* for unaccompanied cello, a four-minute encore from the eloquent soloist who more-or-less predominates throughout 70 arresting minutes. One hesitates to offer a blanket recommendation in an area where critical reaction is frequently polarized, but do at least try the *Akhmatova Songs*, music that could profitably sit alongside similarly compelling song-cycles by Mussorgsky and Shostakovich. RCA's sound quality is excellent throughout.

Further listening ...

...String Quartets – The Last Sleep of the Virgin; The Hidden Treasure. *Coupled with* **Pärt** String Quartets – Summa; Fratres. **Chilingirian Quartet.** Virgin Classics VC5 45023-2 (5/94).   Ⓖ

...To a child dancing in the wind[a]. Lamentation, Last Prayer and Exultation[b]. A Mini Song Cycle for Gina[c]. Melina. **Patricia Rozario** (sop); [a]**Kathryn Lukas** (fl); [a]**Stephen Tees** (va); [a]**Helen Tunstall** (hp); [b]**Iain Simcock** (handbells); [ac]**John Tavener** (pf). Collins Classics 1428-2 (2/95).

...We shall see Him as He is. **Soloists; Britten Singers; Chester Festival Chorus;
BBC Welsh Symphony Chorus and Orchestra / Richard Hickox.** Chandos CHAN9128 (1/93).
...Akathist of Thanksgiving. **James Bowman, Timothy Wilson** (altos); **Westminster Abbey Choir;
BBC Singers; BBC Symphony Orchestra / Martin Neary** (org). Arc of Light SK64446 (9/94).
...Mary of Egypt. **Soloists; Ely Cathedral Choristers; Britten-Pears Chamber Choir;
Aldeburgh Festival Ensemble / Lionel Friend.** Collins Classics 7023-2 (5/93).

John Taverner
British c1490-1545

Taverner Hodie nobis caelorum Rex. Mater Christi sanctissima. Magnificat sexti toni. Nesciens
mater. Quemadmodum a 6ª. Missa Mater Christi sanctissima. In nomine a 4ª. ªFretwork
(Wendy Gillespie, Richard Campbell, treble viols; Susanna Pell, Julia Hodgson,
Richard Boothby, bass viols; William Hunt, great bass viol); **The Sixteen / Harry Christophers.**
Hyperion Ⓕ CDA66639 (65 minutes: DDD: 3/94). ✍ Texts and translations included.
Recorded 1992.
The Sixteen offer an impressive account of the composer's five-part *Missa Mater Christi sanctissima*,
based on his votive anthem of the same name. It is a lively and vigorous work, beautifully crafted, and
this performance amply matches that craftsmanship. Harry Christophers attempts no liturgical
reconstruction, concentrating instead upon sheer musical quality. Three female sopranos replace the
boy trebles. The music is all pitched up a tone, which has the effect of adding brilliance to every
climax. He demonstrates the surprisingly good acoustic of St Jude's in Hampstead – an acoustic of
space and definition, ideal for the interweaving of the strands of early Tudor polyphony; indeed,
clarity and a sense of space are hallmarks of the recording. The supporting programme of the
Christmas responsory, *Hodie*, the votive anthem *Mater Christi* and a four-part *Magnificat* is
completed – unexpectedly, but most delightfully – by two pieces for viols.

Taverner Missa Gloria tibi Trinitasª. Kyrie, "Leroy"ª. Dum transisset Sabbatum Iª. Mass a 4,
"Western Wynde"ᵇ. **The Tallis Scholars / Peter Phillips.** Gimell Ⓕ 454 995-2PH
(79 minutes: DDD: 12/95). Texts and translations included. Items marked ª from CDGIM004
(7/86), ᵇCDGIM027 (9/93). Recorded 1984-1993.
This disc shows a striking panorama of The Tallis Scholars over the past ten years. Most of this
comes from a CD of 1986. But by adding their more recent recording of the *Western Wynde* Mass
they have created an anthology containing some of Taverner's most remarkable music: the two most
famous Masses alongside two of his loveliest smaller works. For the *Western Wynde* Mass The Tallis
Scholars present themselves at their most mandarin: everything beautifully in place, gentle, soothing,
immaculate. The marvellous range of inventive lines that Taverner weaves around this trite little
melody is given full scope to blossom and grow. Nothing is hurried or allowed to stand out too much.
This is in striking contrast to their much earlier approach to the Mass *Gloria tibi Trinitas*: here Peter
Phillips takes the music very much by the scruff of the neck, changing pace and textures to articulate
the massively complex six-voice textures. This is a tremendously exciting performance because it so
often throws caution to the winds. In other words, some listeners may find the *Western Wynde* a touch
bland and *Gloria tibi Trinitas* a touch rough, but it makes for an exciting and varied record. And
nobody could possibly resist the still beauty they give to the *Leroy Kyrie.*

Additional recommendations ...
...*"Western Wynde".* Mater Christi. *Coupled with works by* **Tallis New College Choir, Oxford /
Edward Higginbottom.** CRD Ⓕ CRD3372 (60 minutes: ADD: 4/89).
...*"Leroy".* "Western Wynde". Dum transisset Sabbatum I. Christe Jesu, pastor bone. Mater Christi
sanctissima. *Coupled with works by* **Byrd King's College Choir, Cambridge / Sir David Willcocks.**
Double Decca Ⓜ 452 170-2DF2 (two discs: 147 minutes: ADD: 2/97).

Taverner Missa Sancti Wilhelmi. Motets – O Wilhelme, pastor bone; Dum transisset Sabbatum;
Ex eius tumba. **The Sixteen / Harry Christophers.** Hyperion Ⓕ CDA66427
(52 minutes: DDD: 4/92). Texts and translations included.
The *Missa Sancti Wilhelmi* is not one of Taverner's best known works, but there is no reason why this
should be the case. Though it does not have the sometimes rather wild melodic beauty of the six-voice
Masses, it is nevertheless an impressive work in a more modern imitative style, in keeping with its
model *O Wilhelme, pastor bone.* The Sixteen perform with their customary clarity and precision, and
convey enthusiasm even in the somewhat syllabic *Gloria* and *Credo* movements of the Mass,
something which is not always easy to do. While both the 'Wilhelm' works and *Dum transisset
Sabbatum* are among Taverner's later works, there is no doubt at all that *Ex eius tumba* is one of the
earliest. It is firmly late medieval in style, and the intricate tracery of its construction, so well captured
here by The Sixteen, makes a thought-provoking contrast to the pieces in a more 'continental'
imitative style. At 15 minutes this is a substantial composition, and one can only be surprised that it
is so little-known: perhaps the large amount of chant which forms an integral part of the work has
discouraged performers. *Dum transisset Sabbatum* is, however, the high point of the disc, and if The
Sixteen do not quite attain the ecstatic heights achieved in the recording by The Tallis Scholars
(reviewed above), neither do they fail to rise to Taverner's inspiration.

Further listening ...
...Missa Mater Christi. O Wilhelme, pastor bone. Mater Christi sanctissima.
Christ Church Cathedral Choir, Oxford / Stephen Darlington. Nimbus NI5218 (4/90).
...Quemadmodum desiderat cervus. *Coupled with works by various composers.*
Choir of St Mary's Cathedral, Edinburgh / Timothy Byram-Wigfield.
Priory PRCD557 (10/97). *See review in the Collections section; refer to the Index.*

André Tchaikovsky
Polish/British 1935-1982

Suggested listening ...
...String Quartet No. 2 in C major, Op. 5. *Coupled with works by various composers.* **Lindsay Quartet.**
ASV CDDCA825 (1/93). *See review in the Collections section; refer to the Index.*

Pyotr Ill'yich Tchaikovsky
Russian 1840-1893

Tchaikovsky Piano Concerto No. 1 in B flat minor, Op. 23[a]. The Nutcracker – Suite, Op. 71*a*
(arr. Economou)[b]. **Martha Argerich,** [b]**Nicolas Economou** (pfs); [a]**Berlin Philharmonic Orchestra /
Claudio Abbado.** DG Ⓕ 449 816-2GH (53 minutes: DDD: 9/96). Item marked [a] recorded live in
1994, [b]410 616-2GH (8/87). *Gramophone Editor's choice.* ⒼⒼⒼ
Tchaikovsky's First Concerto has already appeared twice on disc from Martha Argerich in
complementary performances: live and helter-skelter on Philips with Kondrashin (reviewed under
Rachmaninov; refer to the Index), studio and magisterial with Dutoit on DG. Now, finely recorded,
here is a third, live recording with the Berlin Philharmonic and Claudio Abbado surpassing even
those earlier and legendary performances. Argerich has never sounded on better terms with the piano,
more virtuoso yet engagingly human. Lyrical and insinuating, to a degree her performance seems to
be made of the tumultuous elements themselves, of fire and ice, rain and sunshine. The Russians may
claim this concerto for themselves, but even they will surely listen in disbelief, awed and – dare one
say it – a trifle piqued. Listen to Argerich's *Allegro con spirito*, as the concerto gets under way, where
her darting *crescendos* and *diminuendos* make the triplet rhythm speak with the rarest vitality and
caprice. Her nervous reaching out towards further pianistic frays in the heart-easing second subject is
pure Argerich and so are the octave storms in both the first and third movements that will have
everyone, particularly her partners, tightening their seat belts. The cadenza is spun off with a hypnotic
brilliance, the central *Prestissimo* from the *Andantino* becomes a true "scherzo of fireflies", and the
finale seems to dance off the page; a far cry from more emphatic Ukranian point-making and
brutality. For encores DG have reissued Argerich's 1983 performance of *The Nutcracker* where she is
partnered by Nicolas Economou in his own arrangement, a marvel of scintillating pianistic prowess,
imagination and finesse.

Additional recommendations ...
...No. 1. **Grieg** Piano Concerto in A minor, Op. 16[a]. **Artur Rubinstein** (pf); **Boston Symphony
Orchestra / Erich Leinsdorf;** [a]**RCA Victor Symphony Orchestra / Alfred Wallenstein.**
RCA Victor Gold Seal Ⓜ 09026 61262-2 (63 minutes: ADD). Ⓖ
...No. 2 in G major, Op. 44; No. 3 in E flat major, Op. 75. **Peter Donohoe** (pf); **Bournemouth
Symphony Orchestra / Rudolf Barshai.** EMI Ⓕ CDC7 49940-2 (63 minutes: DDD). Ⓖ
...No. 1[a]. Prokofiev Piano Concerto No. 3 in C major, Op. 26[b]. **Martha Argerich** (pf);
[a]**Royal Philharmonic Orchestra / Charles Dutoit;** [b]**Berlin Philharmonic Orchestra /
Claudio Abbado.** DG Ⓕ 415 062-2GH (63 minutes: ADD: 5/85). ⒼⒼⒼ
...No 1. Concert Fantasia, Op. 56. **Mikhail Pletnev** (pf); **Philharmonia Orchestra /
Vladimir Fedoseyev.** Virgin Classics Ⓕ VC7 59612-2 (64 minutes: DDD: 4/91).
...No. 1[a]. Morceau, Op. 19 No. 6. *Coupled with works by* **Balakirev** and **Prokofiev**
Andrei Gavrilov (pf); [a]**Philharmonia Orchestra / Riccardo Muti.**
EMI Studio Plus Ⓜ CDM7 64329-2 (74 minutes: DDD: 11/92). Ⓖ
...No. 3[a]. Symphony No. 7 in E flat major (cptd. Bogatryryev). [a]**Geoffrey Tozer** (pf);
London Philharmonic Orchestra / Neeme Järvi.
Chandos Ⓕ CHAN9130 (57 minutes: DDD: 4/93).
...No. 1[a]. **Mussorgsky** Pictures at an Exhibition. **Vladimir Horowitz** (pf); [a]**NBC Symphony
Orchestra / Arturo Toscanini.** RCA Victor Gold Seal Ⓜ GD60321 (61 minutes: ADD: 9/93). ⒼⒼ
...Nos. 1-3. Concert Fantasia in G major, Op. 56. **Barry Douglas** (pf); **Philharmonia Orchestra /
Leonard Slatkin.** RCA Victor Ⓜ 09026 61631-2 (two discs: 124 minutes: DDD: 6/94).
...Nos. 2 and 3. **Victoria Postnikova** (pf); **Vienna Symphony Orchestra / Gennadi Rozhdestvensky.**
Decca Ovation Ⓜ 436 485-2DM (68 minutes: DDD: 6/94).
...No. 1[a]; No. 2[b]. [a]**Sviatoslav Richter,** [b]**Emil Gilels** (pfs); [a]**Leningrad Philharmonic Orchestra /
Evgeny Mravinsky;** [b]**USSR Symphony Orchestra / Evgeny Svetlanov.**
Melodiya mono Ⓜ 74321 17083-2* (73 minutes: ADD: 9/94).
...No. 1. **Scriabin** Piano Concerto in F sharp minor, Op. 20. **Nikolai Demidenko** (pf); **BBC
Symphony Orchestra / Alexander Lazarev.** Hyperion Ⓕ CDA66680 (65 minutes: DDD: 10/94).
See review under Scriabin; refer to the Index. Ⓖ

...No. 1[b]. **Rachmaninov** Piano Concerto No. 3 in D minor, Op. 30[a]. **Martha Argerich** (pf); [a]**Berlin Radio Symphony Orchestra / Riccardo Chailly;** [b]**Bavarian Radio Symphony Orchestra / Kyrill Kondrashin.** Philips Ⓕ 446 673-2PH (73 minutes: DDD: 8/95). *See review under Rachmaninov; refer to the Index.* ⒼⒼⒼ

...No. 1. *Coupled with works by* **Rachmaninov** Géza Anda (pf); **Philharmonia Orchestra / Alceo Galliera.** Testament mono Ⓕ SBT1064* (76 minutes: ADD: 10/95).

...No. 1[a]. The Seasons, Op. 37[b] – January; February; April; May; August; October; November; December. **Ronan O'Hora** (pf); [a]**Royal Philharmonic Orchestra / James Judd.** Tring International Royal Philharmonic Collection Ⓢ TRP023 (65 minutes: DDD: 10/95).

...No. 1[a]. Symphony No. 6 in B minor, Op. 74, "Pathétique". Manfred Symphony, Op. 58. The Voyevoda – Overture. The Tempest, Op. 18. [a]**Vladimir Horowitz** (pf); **NBC Symphony Orchestra / Arturo Toscanini.** Music & Arts mono Ⓕ CD956* (two discs: 147 minutes: AAD: 4/97). ⒼⒼ

...No. 2. Concert Fantasia in G major, Op. 56. **Bernd Glemser** (pf); **Polish National Radio Symphony Orchestra / Antoni Wit.** Naxos Ⓢ 8 550820 (76 minutes: DDD: 4/97).

...No. 1. **Rachmaninov** Piano Concerto No. 3 in D minor, Op. 30[a]. **Vladimir Horowitz** (pf); **New York Philharmonic Symphony Orchestra / Sir John Barbirolli.** APR mono Ⓕ APR5519* (66 minutes: ADD: 6/97). *See review under Rachmaninov; refer to the Index.* ⒼⒼⒼ

...No. 1[a]. Suite No. 4 in G major, Op. 61, "Mozartiana". [a]**Constantine Orbelian** (pf); **Philharmonia Orchestra / Neema Järvi.** Chandos Ⓕ CHAN8777 (63 minutes: DDD: 5/90).

Tchaikovsky Piano Concertos – No. 1 in B flat minor, Op. 23[a]; No. 2 in G major, Op. 44[b]; No. 3 in E flat major, Op. 75[a]. Violin Concerto in D major, Op. 35[c]. [c]**Kyung-Wha Chung** (vn); [ab]**Victoria Postnikova** (pf); [ab]**Vienna Symphony Orchestra / Gennadi Rozhdestvensky;** [c]**Montreal Symphony Orchestra / Charles Dutoit.** Double Decca Ⓜ 448 107-2DF2 (two discs: 142 minutes: DDD: 11/96). Items marked [a] from 410 112-1DH (5/84), [b]410 113-1DH (8/84), [c]SXDL7558 (12/82).

If your main priorities in Tchaikovsky concertos are visceral excitement, barnstorming virtuosity and nifty tempos, then this is probably not the set for you. Tempos here are generally broad, and although there is no lack of pianistic thunder – Victoria Postnikova commands a handsome tone – the interpretative accent falls securely beneath the music's surface. The First Concerto is revealing in the sense that dialogue between soloist and orchestra is particularly sensitive; listen, for example, to the delicately voiced woodwinds at 6'38" (in the first movement), to Postnikova's subsequent response and, most especially, to the pianist's free yet nimble handling of the second movement's treacherous *valse-prestissimo* (4'05"). As Tchaikovsky Firsts go, this is among the most searching, the most personal and certainly the most individual available, though one can already hear a loud opposition: "*too* slow, *too* mannered, *too* indulgent, *too* soft-grained, orchestrally". Again, in the Second and Third Concertos Postnikova plumbs the depths. Her handling of Tchaikovsky's epic cadenzas is second to none – starting at 1'55" into the Second Concerto's first movement, then (most notably) between 13'26" and 19'13", where the solo writing is so massive in scale that you temporarily forget the mute presence of an orchestra. Rozhdestvensky views Tchaikovsky's orchestral architecture with a fine sense of perspective. This is *real* interpretation and presents a powerful case for a much maligned work (torso though it is). True, there is still room for critical controversy (the Second Concerto's first movement is hardly *Allegro brillante*), but Postnikova and Rozhdestvensky have so much to say about the music. Decca also offer a poised and elegantly phrased account of the Tchaikovsky Violin Concerto, where a rather edgy-sounding Kyung-Wha Chung is offered blandly 'regular' support by the Montreal Symphony Orchestra under Dutoit. Not a world-beater by any means but a sensible makeweight, very well recorded. As indeed is the rest of the set, although the Vienna Symphony strings will strike some as rather thin in tone. An altogether riveting reissue and a genuine bargain as well.

Tchaikovsky Violin Concerto in D major, Op. 35[a].
Brahms (arr. Joachim) Hungarian Dances[b] – No. 1 in G minor; No. 2 in D minor; No. 4 in B minor; No. 7 in A major. **Sarah Chang** (vn); [b]**Jonathan Feldman** (pf); [a]**London Symphony Orchestra / Sir Colin Davis.** EMI Ⓕ CDC7 54753-2 (49 minutes: DDD: 12/93). Recorded 1992-1993.

Tchaikovsky Violin Concerto in D major, Op. 35.
Prokofiev Violin Concerto No. 1 in D major, Op. 19. **Julian Rachlin** (vn); **Moscow Radio Symphony Orchestra / Vladimir Fedoseyev.** Sony Classical Ⓕ SK66567 (58 minutes: DDD: 8/95). Recorded live in 1994.

The range of dynamic truthfulness conveyed in Sarah Chang's performance, helped by a clear, full, naturally-balanced recording, brings not just momentary delight in individual phrases but cumulative gain, in this reading which so strongly hangs together. Not only does Chang play with exceptionally pure tone, avoiding heavy coloration, but her individual artistry does not demand the wayward pulling-about often found in this work. In that she is enormously helped by the fresh, bright and dramatic accompaniment provided by the LSO under Sir Colin Davis. In the outer movements Chang conveys wit along with the power and poetry, and the intonation is immaculate. Brahms's *Hungarian Dances* are delectable, marked by the sort of naughty pointing of phrase and rhythm that tickles one's musical funny-bone just as the playing of Kreisler always did. Here is a young artist who really does live up to the claims of the publicists.

Julian Rachlin gives exceptionally characterful and distinctive readings of both these concertos, not because they are conventionally high-powered, but because of their thoughtfulness and hushed intensity. He is helped by a natural balance for the solo instrument in these live recordings made in the Moscow Conservatoire. Some may feel that the relatively backward balance and Rachlin's determination to observe every *pianissimo* marking detracts from the power of these readings: however, in the Tchaikovsky, by establishing at the start a rapt, meditative manner, instantly magnetic, he has you accepting and welcoming his own scale of dynamic values. In the big cadenza of the first movement, for example, he may not provide such dazzling fireworks as others do but with his intense concentration he makes it sound like spontaneous expression, volatile and mercurial, not just a display vehicle. The central "Canzonetta", taken at a flowing *Andante*, is a hushed meditation, with Rachlin adopting an extra degree of *pianissimo* for the second half of the main reprise. He uses such echo effects – not always marked in the score – in the lyrical episodes of the finale, notably the *Molto meno mosso* section, which he takes so slowly than no further *rallentando* is possible. In that movement too Rachlin, rather than thrusting on with sheer power, makes the music sparkle. The volatile quality of this live recording sets problems for the orchestra, which could be crisper. In the Prokofiev they have fewer problems, and here even more the yearning, hushed beauty of Rachlin's treatment of the great melodies is very moving. This is not only a poetic performance, with the outer movements both lighter and faster-flowing than usual, but one which consistently brings out the wit and fun in the writing.

Additional recommendations ...

...Violin Concerto. **Mendelssohn** Violin Concerto in E minor, Op. 64. **Takako Nishizaki** (vn); **Slovak Philharmonic Orchestra / Kenneth Jean.** Naxos Ⓢ 8 550153 (67 minutes: DDD).

...Violin Concerto. **Mendelssohn** Violin Concerto in E minor, Op. 64. **Nathan Milstein** (vn); **Vienna Philharmonic Orchestra / Claudio Abbado.** DG Galleria Ⓜ 419 067-2GGA (58 minutes: DDD: 8/87).

...Violin Concerto. Sérénade mélancolique in B minor, Op. 26. Souvenir d'un lieu cher, Op. 42 – No. 3, Mélodie (orch. Glazunov). Valse-scherzo in C major, Op. 34. **Xue-Wei** (vn); **Philharmonia Orchestra / Salvatore Accardo.** ASV Ⓕ CDDCA713 (54 minutes: DDD: 9/90).

...Violin Concerto[a]. String Quartet No. 1 in D major, Op. 11 – Andante (arr. Kreisler)[b]. *Coupled with works by various composers.* Itzhak Perlman (vn); [b]Janet Goodman Guggenheim (pf); [a]Israel Philharmonic Orchestra / Zubin Mehta. EMI Ⓕ CDC7 54108-2 (72 minutes: DDD: 2/91).

...Violin Concerto. **Brahms** Violin Concerto in D major, Op. 77. **Jascha Heifetz** (vn); **Chicago Symphony Orchestra / Fritz Reiner.** RCA Living Stereo Ⓜ 09026 61495-2* (64 minutes: ADD: 4/93). ⒼⒼⒼ

...Violin Concerto. **Sibelius** Violin Concerto in D minor, Op. 47. **Gil Shaham** (vn); **Philharmonia Orchestra / Giuseppe Sinopoli.** DG Ⓕ 437 540-2GH (67 minutes: DDD: 9/93).

...Violin Concerto[a]. **Brahms** Violin Concerto in D major, Op. 77[b]. **Ida Haendel** (vn); [b]London Symphony Orchestra / Sergiu Celibidache; [a]Royal Philharmonic Orchestra / Sir Eugene Goossens. Testament mono Ⓕ SBT1038* (76 minutes: ADD: 10/94).

...Violin Concerto. **Sibelius** Violin Concerto in D minor, Op. 47. **Kyung-Wha Chung** (vn); **London Symphony Orchestra / André Previn.** Decca The Classic Sound Ⓜ 425 080-2DCS (66 minutes: ADD: 5/95). *See review under Sibelius; refer to the Index.* Ⓖ

...Violin Concerto. *Coupled with works by various composers.* **David Oistrakh** (vn); **Dresden Staatskapelle / Franz Konwitschny.** DG The Originals mono Ⓜ 447 427-2GOR2* (two discs: 142 minutes: ADD: 6/95).

...Violin Concerto. **Glazunov** Violin Concerto in A minor, Op. 82. **Maxim Vengerov** (vn); **Berlin Philharmonic Orchestra / Claudio Abbado.** Teldec Ⓕ 4509-90881-2 (55 minutes: DDD: 11/95). *Gramophone Editor's choice. See review under Glazunov; refer to the Index.*

Tchaikovsky 1812 – Overture, Op. 49. Romeo and Juliet – Fantasy Overture. Marche slave, Op. 31. Francesca da Rimini, Op. 32. **Royal Liverpool Philharmonic Orchestra / Sian Edwards.** EMI Eminence Ⓜ CD-EMX2152 (66 minutes: DDD: 12/89).

It is an extraordinary achievement that the young British conductor, Sian Edwards, should have made her recording début with a Tchaikovsky programme of such distinction. She immediately achieves a splendid artistic partnership with the Royal Liverpool Philharmonic Orchestra, whose playing is so full of vitality, and whether in *1812* with its vigour and flair, its cluster of lyrical folk melodies, and a spectacular finale with thundering canon, or in *Marche slave*, resplendently patriotic, in a uniquely Russian way, together they bring the music tingling to life in every bar. *Romeo and Juliet*, on the other hand, needs a finely judged balance between the ardour and moonlight of the love music, the vibrant conflict of the battle, and the tragedy of the final denouement, which is uncannily well managed. Most intractable interpretatively is *Francesca da Rimini*, with its spectacularly horrifying picture of Dante's inferno which the composer uses to frame the central sequence depicting the lovers, Francesca and Paolo, and the doom-laden atmosphere which surrounds their intense mutual passion. Edwards's grip on this powerfully evocative sequence of events is unerringly sure, and she takes the orchestra through the narrative as only an instinctive Tchaikovskian could. The work opens with an unforgettable sense of nemesis and ends with a truly thrilling picture of the whirlwinds of Hell, into which the lovers are cast, still in their final passionate embrace. All in all this is one of the best Tchaikovsky discs in the mid-price catalogue. The recording is excellent.

Additional recommendations ...
...1812 – Overture, Op. 49. Capriccio italien, Op. 45. Mazeppa – Cossack Dance.
 Cincinnati Symphony Orchestra / Erich Kunzel. Telarc Ⓕ CD80041 (35 minutes: DDD: 12/83).
...Romeo and Juliet (1869 version). Hamlet – Incidental Music, Op. 67*a*[a]. Festival Overture on the
 Danish national hymn, Op. 15. Serenade for Nikolai Rubinstein's name day. Mazeppa – Battle of
 Poltava; Cossack Dance. [a]**Janis Kelly** (sop); [a]**Derek Hammond-Stroud** (bar); **London Symphony
 Orchestra / Geoffrey Simon.** Chandos Ⓕ CHAN8310/11 (two discs: 94 minutes: DDD: 7/84).   Ⓖ
...Marche slave. Suite No. 1, Op. 43 – Marche miniature. *Coupled with works by various composers.*
 Chicago Symphony Orchestra / Fritz Reiner. RCA Victor Living Stereo Ⓜ 09026 61958-2
 (71 minutes: ADD: 8/94). *See review in the Collections section; refer to the Index.*   ⒼⒼⒼ
...Capriccio italien, Op. 45. Marche slave. Eugene Onegin – Waltz; Polonaise. *Coupled with works
 by* **Liadov** *and* **Mussorgsky** **Kirov Theatre Chorus and Orchestra / Valery Gergiev.**
 Philips Ⓕ 442 775-2PH (54 minutes: DDD: 7/95). *See review under Liadov; refer to the Index.*
...Francesca da Rimini. *Coupled with works by* **Schubert** *and* **Debussy**
 New York Philharmonic Symphony Orchestra / Sir John Barbirolli.
 Dutton Laboratories Essential Archive mono Ⓑ CDEA5000* (69 minutes: ADD: 1/96).
...Francesca da Rimini. Suite No. 3 in G major, Op. 55. **Detroit Symphony Orchestra / Neeme Järvi.**
 Chandos Ⓕ CHAN9419 (69 minutes: DDD: 4/96).
...1812 (arr. Buketoff)[a]. The Sleeping Beauty – Suite, Op. 66*a* (arr. Litton). Voyevoda, Op. 78.
 Moscow[b]. [b]**Svetlana Furdui** (mez); [b]**Vassili Gerelo** (bar); **Dallas Symphony** [ab]**Chorus and
 Orchestra / Andrew Litton.** Delos Ⓕ DE3196 (78 minutes: DDD: 5/97).

Tchaikovsky Francesca da Rimini, Op. 32. Hamlet – Fantasy Overture, Op. 67.
 New York Stadium Orchestra / Leopold Stokowski. dell'Arte Ⓕ CDDA9006* (ADD: 4/88).
 From Everest SDBRD3011 (1/68). Recorded 1958. *Gramophone classical 100.*   ⒼⒼⒼ
A good record is always a good record, and this comment applies even more to a great record.
Stokowski's inspired performance of *Hamlet* is far, far superior to any other recorded version.
Francesca is nearly as fine and generates enormous tension at the sequence just before the lovers are
discovered where their passion is encompassed in polyphonic string textures of the greatest intensity.
Then, after the dramatic moment of their death, they are consigned to the whirlwinds of Dante's
Inferno, which rage frenziedly until the riveting final climax, where the gong is not allowed to drown
the nemesis of bold orchestral dissonances at the last few bars. Stokowski's reading is equally
memorable for the beguiling wind solos in the romantic middle section – depicting the idyll of the
lovers – shaped with characteristic magic. *Hamlet* is sensational. It is also even better recorded than
Francesca and the sonority of the lower strings is particularly telling at the electrifying opening, while
at the big climax the weight of the trombones and tuba is splendidly caught. But perhaps the most
spectacular moment is the forboding march-like sequence, dominated by the side-drum, which is
sinisterly dramatic each time it appears: this device anticipates Shostakovich at the climax of the first
movement of the Fifth Symphony and the emotional character of the playing is very Russian in its
fervour. The desolation of mood of the coda is intensely moving, with a power of melancholy to equal
that at the close of the *Pathétique* Symphony. *Hamlet* does not have a love theme to match *Romeo and
Juliet*, but its equivalent possesses a unique colour when it appears in the woodwind. Ophelia's melody
on the oboe is utterly poignant and when it returns there is a rustling in the strings which subtly
creates a sense of uneasiness. If you are wondering about the identity of the New York Stadium
Orchestra, Bert Whyte, the brilliant engineer of this recording, and also one of the founders of the
Everest label, has affirmed that it is the New York Philharmonic under a pseudonym. This was the
pre-Bernstein era and the ensemble isn't always immaculate, but the tremendous commitment of the
playing more than compensates. It is not clear whether Bryan Crimp's remastered version (which
dell'Arte issued on a 12-inch 45rpm disc) is used for the CD, but certainly the sound is cleaner than
originally, if perhaps a little drier. During the closing years of his life Stokowski said, "When I get to
Heaven I shall shake Tchaikovsky by the hand and thank him for all the wonderful music he has given
us". If that came about the composer might, in return, have expressed complete satisfaction with this
recording.

Tchaikovsky Manfred Symphony, Op. 58. The Tempest, Op. 18. **Russian National Orchestra /
 Mikhail Pletnev.** DG Ⓕ 439 891-2GH (76 minutes: DDD: 12/94).
 Gramophone Editor's choice.   ⒼⒼ
There are no cheap thrills in Pletnev's *Manfred*. Percussion and brass are very carefully modulated,
their brilliance and power reserved quite noticeably for what Pletnev sees as the few crucial climactic
passages in the outer movements. Timpani in particular provide support rather than make a show –
it is the lower strings that course through Manfred's outburst in the second movement (from 5'50"),
not the almost standard spurious timpani swells. It is the strong, dark woodwind, not the more usual
stuttering horns, that you initially hear in the first movement's concluding *Andante con duolo* (from
13'09"). The deep satisfaction to be had from this account comes from the superlative strings, and
from Pletnev's pacing which, more often than any of the listed additional recommendations takes
notice of Tchaikovsky's tempo indications, most obviously in the properly flowing third movement's
pastoral, and in the successful bonding of the finale's episodic structure (the magniloquent Muti's
Achilles' heel). More eccentric is Pletnev's drop in tempo for those rising unison scales on strings at

the start of the bacchanale (from 0'18"), but it is less troubling than Toscanini's and particularly Jansons's speeding up for those hammering chords before Astarte returns; and, mercifully, there are none of the cuts made by Toscanini. *The Tempest*, a generous coupling (Muti and Jansons, listed below, have none), brings much the same priorities and equal rewards – no more need be said, except to observe that the horns receive a better deal from the balance than in the symphony. As to the recording generally, timpani are probably less focused than Pletnev would have wanted; in all other respects, the sound does full justice to the riches of his orchestra and the seriousness of his intent.

Additional recommendations ...

...Manfred Symphony. **Oslo Philharmonic Orchestra / Mariss Jansons.** Chandos Ⓕ CHAN8535 (53 minutes: DDD: 5/88).

...Manfred Symphony. Romeo and Juliet – Fantasy Overture. **NBC Symphony Orchestra / Arturo Toscanini.** RCA Victor Gold Seal mono Ⓜ GD60298* (67 minutes: ADD: 6/92).

...Manfred Symphony. **Philharmonia Orchesta / Riccardo Muti.** EMI Studio Plus Ⓜ CDM7 64872-2 (59 minutes: DDD: 3/94).

...Manfred Symphony. Festival Overture on the Danish national hymn in D major, Op. 15[b]. **USSR Symphony Orchestra / Evgeni Svetlanov.** Melodiya Ⓜ 74321 17098-2 (70 minutes: ADD: 12/94).

...Manfred Symphony. **Borodin** Symphony No. 2 in B minor. **Philharmonia Orchestra / Paul Kletzki.** Testament mono Ⓕ SBT1048* (78 minutes: ADD: 3/95).

Tchaikovsky The Nutcracker. The Sleeping Beauty – Aurora's Wedding. **Montreal Symphony Orchestra / Charles Dutoit.** Decca Ⓕ 440 477-2DH2 (two discs: 135 minutes: DDD: 3/94). Recorded 1992.

Many of the favourite characteristic dances seem freshly minted, notably the "Dance of the Sugar-plum Fairy", with its deliciously liquid celesta, and the perky "Chinese Dance". The "Waltz of the Snowflakes" (Act 1) with the children's chorus also has great charm. The transparency of the recorded sound, which helps to make all this possible, is immediately noticeable in the delightful gossamer string textures of the "Miniature Overture". But the big Act 2 *Adagio*, too, is exceptionally satisfying, its histrionics conveyed with passionate flair, yet without hysterical rhetoric at the excitingly grand climax. The recording is extremely vivid: bright but without glare, and the balance between detail, weight and hall resonance seems exactly right. "Aurora's Wedding" is the very much truncated version of *The Sleeping Beauty* which Diaghilev adopted in repertory after his extravagant London production of the complete ballet in 1921 nearly bankrupted him. The music, after introducing both Carabosse and the Lilac Fairy, passes on to the christening, includes the hunting scene in Act 2, where the Prince has a vision of his sleeping princess, then moves on to the happy ending and the dances which form the highlight of the last act. Top choice for *The Nutcracker* can safely rest between Dutoit and Ashkenazy. Previn's mid-price 1972 LSO version also emerges very favourably against the competition.

Additional recommendations ...

...The Nutcracker[a]. Queen of Spades – Duet of Daphnis and Chloë[b]. [b]**Cathryn Pope** (sop); [b]**Sarah Walker** (mez); [a]**Tiffin Boys' School Choir; London Symphony Orchestra / Sir Charles Mackerras.** Telarc Ⓕ CD80137 (two discs: 88 minutes: DDD: 5/87).

...The Nutcracker[a]. **Glazunov** The Seasons, Op. 67. [a]**Finchley Children's Music Group; Royal Philharmonic Orchestra / Vladimir Ashkenazy.** Decca Ⓕ 433 000-2DH2 (two discs: 131 minutes: DDD: 4/92). *Selected by Sounds in Retrospect. See review under Glazunov; refer to the Index.*

...The Nutcracker. Serenade in C major, Op. 48[a]. **London Symphony Orchestra;** [a]**Philharmonia Hungarica / Antál Dorati.** Mercury Ⓜ 432 750-2MM2* (two discs: 109 minutes: ADD: 9/92). 🅖🅖

...The Nutcracker. **Ambrosian Singers; London Symphony Orchestra / André Previn.** Classics for Pleasure Ⓜ CD-CFPD4706 (two discs: 86 minutes: ADD: 3/93).

Tchaikovsky Serenade in C major, Op. 48. Souvenir de Florence, Op. 70. **Vienna Chamber Orchestra / Philippe Entremont.** Naxos Ⓢ 8 550404 (65 minutes: DDD: 10/91). Recorded 1990.

This is one of the many CDs now on the market that dispel the myth once and for all that only full-price recordings contain really outstanding performances. The Naxos label is just about as 'bargain' as you can get, and here they have given us superlative performances of two of Tchaikovsky's most endearing works. The Serenade in C contains a wealth of memorable and haunting music, beautifully and inventively scored and guaranteed to bring immense pleasure and delight to those dipping their toes in to the world of classical music for the first time. Philippe Entremont and the Vienna Chamber Orchestra give a marvellously polished and finely poised performance full of warmth, affection and high spirits, and the famous second movement Waltz in particular is played with much elegance and grace. The *Souvenir de Florence*, originally written for string sextet, makes a welcome appearance here in Tchaikovsky's own arrangement for string orchestra. This is a delightfully sunny performance, full of suavity, exuberance and romantic dash, but always alert to the many subtleties of Tchaikovsky's skilful and intricate part-writing. The *Adagio cantabile* is particularly notable for some extremely fine and poetic solo playing from the violin and cello principals of the VPO. The beautifully spacious recording does ample justice to the performances.

Additional recommendations ...

...Serenade. Suite No. 4 in G major, Op. 61, "Mozartiana". Elegy in G major in honour of Ivan Samarin. String Quartet No. 1 in D major, Op. 11 – Andante cantabile (orch. Serebrier).

The Sleeping Beauty (orch. Stravinsky) – Variations de la Fée de lilas; Entr'acte.
Scottish Chamber Orchestra / José Serebrier. ASV Ⓕ CDDCA719 (77 minutes: DDD: 3/91).
...Serenade in C major. *Coupled with works by* **Mozart Saito Kinen Orchestra / Seiji Ozawa.**
Philips Ⓕ 438 137-2PH (60 minutes: DDD: 9/94).
...Souvenir de Florence. Variations on a Rococo Theme in A major, Op. 33. Andante cantabile,
Op. 11. Nocturne in C sharp minor, Op. 19 No. 4. Eugene Onegin – Lensky's Aria (all arr. cpsr).
Mischa Maisky (vc); Orpheus Chamber Orchestra. DG Ⓕ 453 460-2GH (73 minutes: DDD: 6/97).

Tchaikovsky The Sleeping Beauty, Op. 66. **Kirov Theatre Orchestra / Valery Gergiev.**
Philips Ⓕ 434 922-2PH3 (three discs: 164 minutes: DDD: 7/93). Recorded 1992.
Many authorities regard this as Tchaikovsky's finest ballet score and, indeed, one of the greatest ballet
scores of all time. It contains many wonderful things: the Waltz from Act One includes some
wonderfully arching phrasing that soars with tremendous passion, while the "Panorama" of Act 2 is
one of the composer's finest melodic ideas. The "Pas de six" of Act 1 and the contrasted Fairy dances
of Act 3 bring the same almost Mozartian grace (combined with Tchaikovsky's own very special
feeling for orchestral colour) that he displays in the *Nutcracker* characteristic dances, which turn
simple ballet vignettes into great art. Valery Gergiev, the conductor of the Kirov Theatre Orchestra
of St Petersburg is at home in this score. He secures splendidly alive and sympathetic playing from his
orchestra and the Philips recording is full and sumptuous, with a rich theatrical atmosphere.
Tchaikovsky's big climaxes expand properly, the strings are full and natural and the woodwind colours
glow.
Additional recommendations ...
...The Sleeping Beauty. **Philharmonia Orchestra / George Weldon.**
Classics for Pleasure Ⓑ CD-CFPD4458 (two discs: 117 minutes: ADD: 1/89).   Ⓖ
...The Sleeping Beauty. **Royal Opera House Orchestra, Covent Garden / Mark Ermler.**
Royal Opera House Records Ⓕ ROH306/8 (three discs: 173 minutes: DDD: 5/90).
...The Sleeping Beauty – excerpts. **Royal Opera House Orchestra, Covent Garden / Mark Ermler.**
Royal Opera House Records Ⓕ ROH003 (72 minutes: DDD: 5/90).
...The Sleeping Beauty – excerpts (arr. Pletnev). **Mussorgsky** Pictures at an Exhibition.
Mikhail Pletnev (pf). Virgin Classics Ⓕ VC7 59611-2 (64 minutes: DDD: 4/91).
...The Sleeping Beauty. **Czecho-Slovak State Philharmonic Orchestra / Andrew Mogrelia.**
Naxos Ⓢ 8 550490/2 (three discs: 173 minutes: DDD: 4/93).

Tchaikovsky Suite No. 2, Op. 53. The Tempest, Op. 18. **Detroit Symphony Orchestra /
Neeme Järvi.** Chandos Ⓕ CHAN9454 (64 minutes: DDD: 8/96).
Tchaikovsky's elusive blend of instrumental precision and free-flowing thematic fantasy in the Second
Suite meets its match in the Detroit/Järvi partnership: the conductor's imagination works alongside
the lean, clean Detroit sound with interesting results. The strings are not always the ideal: the lush
chordings and central fugal energy of the opening movement, "Jeu de sons", cry out for a richer,
Russian tone. But the semiquaver patter is beautifully done, the lower lines clear and personable. Keen
articulation and driving force go hand-in-glove as Järvi prepares for the entry of the four accordions
in the virile "Rondo-Burlesque", sweeping on to the folk-song of the central section with
characteristic aplomb. And yes, the accordions are here: "the engagement of these instruments is not
indispensable ... but the composer believes that their sonority is apt to increase the effectiveness", it
says in the score. It is in the Schumannesque phrases and the subtly shifting moods of the most poetic
movement, "Rêves d'enfant", that Järvi really comes into his own; the short-lived, other-worldly
radiance at the heart of the movement seems more than ever like a preliminary study for the
transformation scenes of *The Nutcracker*, just as the woodwind choruses throughout the work look
forward to that and *Sleeping Beauty.* The magical haze surrounding Prospero's island in *The Tempest*
doesn't quite come off; here it's Pletnev (reviewed above) who surprises us with the true magician's
touch, but then his Russian horns, and later his trumpeter, cast their incantations more impressively.
Järvi is no more successful than any other conductor in stitching together Tchaikovsky's strong
impressions of the play, though a little more forward movement in the love-music might have helped.

Tchaikovsky Swan Lake, Op. 20. **Montreal Symphony Orchestra / Charles Dutoit.**
Decca Ⓕ 436 212-2DH2 (two discs: 154 minutes: DDD: 2/93). Recorded 1991.   ⒼⒼ
Tchaikovsky Swan Lake. Op. 20. **Philadelphia Orchestra / Wolfgang Sawallisch.**
EMI Ⓕ CDS5 55277-2 (two discs: 159 minutes: DDD: 1/95).   Ⓖ
No one wrote more beautiful and danceable ballet music than Tchaikovsky, and this account of *Swan
Lake* is a delight throughout. This is not only because of the quality of the music, which is here played
including additions the composer made after the première, but also thanks to the richly idiomatic
playing of Charles Dutoit and his Montreal orchestra in the superb and celebrated location of St
Eustache's Church in that city. Maybe some conductors have made the music even more earthily
Russian, but it is worth remembering that the Russian ballet tradition in Tchaikovsky's time was
chiefly French and that the most influential early production of this ballet, in 1895, was
choreographed by the Frenchman Marius Petipa. Indeed, the symbiosis of French and Russian
elements in this music (and story) is one of its great strengths, the refinement of the one being
superbly allied to the vigour of the other, notably in such music as the "Russian Dance" with its

expressive violin solo. This is a profoundly romantic reading of the score, and the great set pieces such as the Waltz in Act 1 and the marvellous scene of the swans on a moonlit lake that opens Act 2 are wonderfully evocative; yet they do not for that reason overshadow the other music, which supports and strengthens them as gentler hills and valleys might surround and enhance magnificent, awe-inspiring peaks, the one being indispensable to the other. You do not have to be a ballet *aficionado* to fall under the spell of this wonderful music, which here receives a performance that combines romantic passion with an aristocratic refinement and is glowingly recorded.

Full marks to EMI for capacity-filled discs with the minimum necessary missing (two short double bar line repeats in Act 3's early stages). Forest, lake, moonlight and melancholy; these are the scenes that find Sawallisch in his element. The superb solo oboe is free to float his sad song in the swan scene (end of Act 1 and beginning and end of Act 2; how marvellous to hear the slurred staccato so well taken); the tempo is broad, the perspective deep, and Sawallisch's control of dynamics and his fluid pace (different in all three scenes) is masterly. Also impressive is the ballet's storm-tossed finale, less elemental at the start than Dutoit, but the moment these strings ride that storm, you know you are in Philadelphia. At this point, Sawallisch loosens the reins on his elsewhere tightly controlled brass (Dutoit's use of the brass is more judiciously opportunist). In general, Sawallisch uses a narrow range of tempos: Tchaikovsky's slower dances, such as the "Intrada" to the Act 1 "Pas de trois", can initially seem surprisingly brisk, and the difference between the *Andante* and the *Allegro* in the second part of the succeeding "Pas de deux" is small. Arguably, this moderation of speed brings an appreciable continuity to the musical scheme of things, and is a welcome corrective to the short-term, maximum contrast approach. The symphonic aspirations of the ballet can be overstressed, and it is significant that Sawallisch is at his most convincing in the most obviously 'symphonic' section of the score—the whole of Act 4. Significant, too, is Sawallisch's complete avoidance of the familiar theatrical tricks of the trade, such as rhetorical slowings at the ends of numbers. EMI's sound, apart from an occasional hollow 'ring' to tuttis, is full, spacious and well balanced. Woodwind are more consistently featured than on the Dutoit set, and percussion is well controlled. The tracking is generous; the documentation, wide ranging; and the presentation, classy. All in all, a deeply considered, seriously intentioned *Swan Lake*; one to stir the mind, if not the limbs.

Additional recommendations ...

...Swan Lake. **Russian State Symphony Orchestra / Evgeni Svetlanov.**
  Melodiya Ⓜ 74321 17082-2 (three discs: 153 minutes: DDD).
...Swan Lake. **Royal Opera House Orchestra, Covent Garden / Mark Ermler.**
  Royal Opera House Records Ⓕ ROH301/03 (three discs: 153 minutes: DDD: 12/89).
...Swan Lake. **Philharmonia Orchestra / John Lanchbery.**
  Classics for Pleasure Ⓑ CD-CFPD4727 (two discs: 154 minutes: DDD: 9/89).   Ⓖ
...Swan Lake – excerpts. The Nutcracker – Ballet Suite. Romeo and Juliet. **Chicago Symphony Orchestra / Sir Georg Solti.** Decca Ovation Ⓜ 430 707-2DM (70 minutes: DDD: 8/91).
...Swan Lake. **Slovak Radio Symphony Orchestra, Bratislava / Ondrej Lenárd.**
  Naxos Ⓢ 8 550246/7 (two discs: 140 minutes: DDD: 12/91).
...Swan Lake – excerpts. *Coupled with works by various composers.* **London Symphony Orchestra / Pierre Monteux.** Philips The Early Years Ⓜ 442 544-2PM5 (five discs: 311 minutes: ADD: 12/94).
  See review in the Collections section; refer to the Index.   ⒼⒺⒼ
...Swan Lake – Neapolitan Dance. *Coupled by works by various composers.* Timofei Dokshitzer (tpt); **Bolshoi Theatre Orchestra / Gennadi Rozhdestvensky.**
  Melodiya Ⓜ 74321 32045-2 (70 minutes: ADD: 2/97).

Tchaikovsky Symphonies and Orchestral Works. **Concertgebouw Orchestra / Bernard Haitink.**
Philips Bernard Haitink Symphony Edition Ⓜ 442 061-2PB6 (six discs: 423 minutes: ADD: 10/94). Recorded 1961-1979.
Symphonies – No. 1 in G minor, "Winter Daydreams", Op. 13 (from 9500 777, 4/81); No. 2 in C minor, Op. 17, "Little Russian" (9500 444, 6/79); No. 3 in D major, Op. 29, "Polish" (6768 267, 9/81); No. 4 in F minor, Op. 36 (9500 622, 11/79); No. 5 in E minor, Op. 64 (6500 922, 2/76); No. 6 in B minor, Op. 74, "Pathétique" (9500 610, 4/80). Manfred Symphony, Op. 58 (9500 778, 6/81). Romeo and Juliet – fantasy overture. Capriccio italien, Op. 45 (both from SAL3462, 5/65). 1812 – Overture, Op. 49. Marche slave, Op. 31. Francesca da Rimini, Op. 32 (all from 6500 643, 2/74). The storm, Op. 76 (9500 444).
It is clear that Haitink is more at home with symphonic substance than the shorter colourful showpieces. This set documents his development as a conductor (and a Tchaikovskian) – the shorter pieces being recorded between 1961 and 1972, the symphonies between 1974 and 1979. The exception is the student Tchaikovsky's overture, *The storm*, recorded with the symphonies, and the performance of which is so masterful, colourful and exciting, that you might think it a more mature work (though exactly *whose* 'more mature' work it might be isn't always easy to say). As eighty per cent of the contents of this package comprise the symphonies, let us briefly deal with the rest. You might wonder if Haitink had ever heard an Italian singing an Italian song as anything less capricious or Italian would be hard to imagine. There are moments in the feud music of *Romeo and Juliet* that suggest Haitink's resolve, and his communication of that resolve, was not what it was shortly to become. From eight years later, we have the brilliantly realized (and recorded) letter of the score in *Francesca*, the *1812* Overture and *Marche slave*.

On to the symphonies: as a symphonic cycle, it remains temperate, considered and patient, living mostly at a fair distance from the edge, with rarely a hint of exaggeration or overemphasis – sterling qualities indeed. Haitink's grand and dignified manner is immensely stirring and satisfying. Throughout the symphonies, tempos and dynamics are chosen to guarantee impeccable articulation, beauty of tone production, flawless instrumental balances and a typical awareness of the important climactic moment. These recordings of the symphonies have all been available on CD before, with the exception of *Manfred* which was long overdue for reissue. Its pastoral and orgy (third and fourth movements) encapsulate what is both most frustrting and most formidable in Haitink's Tchaikovsky. Philips's Concertgebouw engineering broke new ground with the symphonies. The tuttis here reproduce with a clarity and epic splendour that have rarely, if ever, been bettered.

Additional recommendations ...
...Nos. 1-6. Capriccio italien, Op. 45. Manfred Symphony, Op. 58. **Oslo Philharmonic Orchestra /**
Mariss Jansons. Chandos Ⓜ CHAN8672/8 (seven discs: 319 minutes: DDD: 1/89). Ⓖ
...No. 1[a]; Nos. 2-6[b]. Romeo and Juliet – Fantasy Overture[b]. [a]**New Philharmonia Orchestra;**
[b]**Philharmonia Orchestra / Riccardo Muti.**
EMI Ⓜ CZS7 67314-2 (four discs: 272 minutes: ADD: 9/91). Ⓖ
...Nos. 1-6. Romeo and Juliet. **Vienna Philharmonic Orchestra / Lorin Maazel.**
Decca Ⓑ 430 787-2DC4 (four discs: 267 minutes: ADD: 4/92).
...Nos. 1-6. Francesca da Rimini, Op. 32. Marche slave, Op. 31. Fate, Op. 77. Romeo and Juliet.
Capriccio italien, Op. 45. Swan Lake – Suite. **Royal Philharmonic Orchestra / Yuri Temirkanov.**
RCA Victor Red Seal Ⓜ 09026 61821-2 (six discs: 391 minutes: DDD: 5/94).
...Nos. 1-6. Francesca da Rimini. Serenade in C major, Op. 48. Romeo and Juliet. Fate, Op. 77.
Capriccio italien. The Tempest, Op. 18. Voyevoda, Op. 78. Andante cantabile for Cello and
Strings, Op. 11. **USSR Symphony Orchestra / Evgeni Svetlanov.**
Melodiya Ⓑ 74321 17101-2 (six discs: 403 minutes: ADD/DDD: 12/94).
...No. 3. **Oslo Philharmonic Orchestra / Mariss Jansons.**
Chandos Ⓕ CHAN8463 (45 minutes: DDD: 7/86).
...No. 3. Capriccio italien. **Berlin Philharmonic Orchestra / Herbert von Karajan.**
DG Ⓕ 419 178-2GH (64 minutes: DDD: 12/86).
...No. 6. Romeo and Juliet[b]. **National Symphony Orchestra / Albert Coates.**
Beulah mono Ⓕ 1PD6* (66 minutes: ADD: 7/94).

Tchaikovsky Symphony No. 1 in G minor, Op. 13, "Winter Daydreams". **Oslo Philharmonic**
Orchestra / Mariss Jansons. Chandos Ⓕ CHAN8402 (44 minutes: DDD: 2/86). Ⓖ
Tchaikovsky Symphony No. 2 in C minor, Op. 17, "Little Russian". Capriccio italien, Op. 45.
Oslo Philharmonic Orchestra / Mariss Jansons. Chandos Ⓕ CHAN8460
(48 minutes: DDD: 11/87).
The composer himself gave the work the title *Winter Daydreams*, and also gave descriptive titles to the first two movements. The opening *Allegro tranquillo* he subtitled "Dreams of a winter journey", while the *Adagio* bears the inscription "Land of desolation, land of mists". A *Scherzo* and finale round off a conventional four-movement symphonic structure. In the slow movement Jansons inspires a performance of expressive warmth and tenderness, while the *Scherzo* is managed with great delicacy and sensitivity. Both the opening movement and the finale are invested with vigour and passion, and everywhere the orchestral playing is marvellously confident and disciplined. The recording has not only impact and immediacy but also warmth and refinement. Jansons also has the full measure of Tchaikovsky's Second Symphony. It is a direct performance – the first movement allegro is relatively steady, but never sounds too slow, because of crisp rhythmic pointing – and the second movement goes for charm and felicity of colour. The finale is properly exuberant, with the secondary theme full of character, and there is a fine surge of adrenalin at the end. The *Capriccio italien*, a holiday piece in which the composer set out to be entertaining, is also played with great flair and the hint of vulgarity in the Neapolitan tune is not shirked. Again the closing pages produce a sudden spurt of excitement which is particularly satisfying. The recording here is just short of Chandos's finest – the massed violins could be sweeter on top, but the hall resonance is right for this music and there is a proper feeling of spectacle.

Additional recommendation ...
...No. 1. Romeo and Juliet. **Prague Symphony Orchestra / Gaetano Delogu.**
Supraphon Ⓕ SU3256-2 (65 minutes: DDD: 6/97).

Tchaikovsky Symphonies – No. 4 in F minor, Op. 36[a]; No. 5 in E minor, Op. 64[b]; No. 6 in
B minor, Op. 74, "Pathétique"[c]. **Leningrad Philharmonic Orchestra / Evgeny Mravinsky.**
DG Ⓕ 419 745-2GH2 (two discs: 129 minutes: ADD: 8/87). Item marked [a] from
SLPM138657 (6/61), [b]SLPM138658 (10/61), [c](SLPM138659 (11/61). Recorded 1960.
Gramophone classical 100. ⒼⒼⒼ
These recordings are classics of the gramophone, landmarks not just of Tchaikovsky interpretation, but of recorded orchestral performances in general. The Leningrad Philharmonic play like a wild stallion, only just held in check by the willpower of its master. Every smallest movement is placed with fierce pride; at any moment it may break into such a frenzied gallop that you hardly know whether to feel exhilarated or terrified. The whipping up of excitement towards the fateful outbursts in

Symphony No. 4 is astonishing – not just for the discipline of the *stringendos* themselves, but for the pull of psychological forces within them. Symphony No. 5 is also mercilessly driven and pre-echoes of Shostakovichian hysteria are particularly strong in the coda's knife-edge of triumph and despair. No less powerfully evoked is the stricken tragedy of the *Pathétique*. Rarely, if ever, can the prodigious rhythmical inventiveness of these scores have been so brilliantly demonstrated. The fanatical discipline is not something one would want to see casually emulated – few orchestras would stand for it in any case – but it is applied in a way which sees far into the soul of the music and never violates its spirit. Strictly speaking there is no real comparison with Mariss Jansons's Chandos issues, despite the fact that Jansons had for long been Mravinsky's assistant in Leningrad. His approach is warmer, less detailed, more classical, and in its way very satisfying. Not surprisingly there are deeper perspectives in the Chandos recordings, but DG's refurbishing has been most successful, enhancing the immediacy of sound so appropriate to the lacerating intensity of the interpretations.

Tchaikovsky Symphony No. 4 in F minor, Op. 36. **Oslo Philharmonic Orchestra / Mariss Jansons.**
Chandos Ⓕ CHAN8361 (42 minutes: DDD: 9/86). From ABRD1124 (7/85).
Selected by Sounds in Retrospect.
A high emotional charge runs through Jansons's performance of the Fourth, yet this rarely seems to be an end in itself. There is always a balancing concern for the superb craftsmanship of Tchaikovsky's writing: the shapeliness of the phrasing; the superb orchestration, scintillating and subtle by turns; and most of all Tchaikovsky's marvellous sense of dramatic pace. Rarely has the first movement possessed such a strong sense of tragic inevitability, or the return of the 'fate' theme in the finale sounded so logical, so necessary. The playing of the Oslo Philharmonic Orchestra is first rate: there are some gorgeous woodwind solos and the brass manage to achieve a truly Tchaikovskian intensity. Recordings are excellent: at once spacious and clearly focused, with a wide though by no means implausible dynamic range.

Additional recommendations ...
...No. 4. Capriccio italien, Op. 45. **Berlin Philharmonic Orchestra / Herbert von Karajan.**
DG Galleria Ⓜ 419 872-2GGA (59 minutes: DDD).
...No. 4. Marche slave, Op. 31. **London Symphony Orchestra / Gennadi Rozhdestvensky.**
Carlton Ⓜ 30369 0043-2 (53 minutes: DDD: 12/87).
...No. 4. Francesca da Rimini, Op. 32. **New York Philharmonic Orchestra / Leonard Bernstein.**
DG Ⓕ 429 778-2GH (76 minutes: DDD: 4/91).
...Nos. 2ᵃ and 4ᵇ. ᵃ**New Philharmonia Orchestra,** ᵇ**Vienna Philharmonic Orchestra / Claudio Abbado.**
DG Galleria Ⓑ 429 527-2GR (75 minutes: ADD: 8/91).
...Nos. 2 and 4. **Polish National Radio Symphony Orchestra / Adrian Leaper.**
Naxos Ⓢ 8 550488 (79 minutes: DDD: 5/93).
...Nos. 4-6. **London Symphony Orchestra / Igor Markevitch.**
Philips Duo Ⓜ 438 335-2PM2 (two discs: 132 minutes: ADD: 2/94).   ⒼⒺⒼ

Tchaikovsky Symphonies – No. 4 in F minor, Op. 36ᵃ; No. 5 in E minor, Op. 64ᵇ; No. 6 in B minor, Op. 74, "Pathétique"ᶜ. Romeo and Juliet – Fantasy overtureᵈ. Serenade in C major, Op. 48 – Waltzᵉ. **Concertgebouw Orchestra / Willem Mengelberg.** Music and Arts mono Ⓕ CD809* (two discs: 149 minutes: AAD: 10/94). Item marked ᵃ from Columbia L2366/70 (2/30), ᵇL2176/82 (1/29), ᶜTelefunken SK2214/18 (recorded 1937), ᵈColumbia LX55/6 (10/30), ᵉL2182.   ⒼⒺ
Those readers who treat Tchaikovsky's written scores as sacrosanct will likely baulk at these provocative re-creations; but, be warned, those who risk sampling Mengelberg's realization of the music's emotional core could quite easily be mesmerized into forgetting the very existence of a printed source. So forget his dynamic adjustments, his re-harmonizing a crucial chord at the end of the Fifth Symphony, or the dazzling array of tempos that he inflicts on the Fourth's finale. That was his way, his manner of communication; yet the end products are nothing short of spellbinding, even on those occasions when we are prompted to shake our heads at the sheer nerve of it all. Mengelberg's charting of the Fourth Symphony's first movement is a masterpiece of interpretative rhetoric: the central development is angrily impatient, the final build-up a terrifying tread towards some unimaginable catastrophe. The *Andantino* is played with a degree of rubato that would tax even an accomplished soloist, while the *Romeo and Juliet* Fantasy Overture, the *1812* Overture and the first two movements of the Fifth Symphony rage, riot or relax as the spirit dictates. Under Mengelberg's inspired baton, the Fifth's first movement in particular is like a tightly-coiled spring that snaps loose whenever the temperature rises, and the equally charismatic *Pathétique* climaxes with a desperately weeping *Adagio lamentoso*. The Music and Arts transfers are remarkably quiet and detailed but the Fifth Symphony is split between two CDs.

Tchaikovsky Symphony No. 5 in E minor, Op. 64. **Oslo Philharmonic Orchestra / Mariss Jansons.**
Oslo Philharmonic Orchestra / Mariss Jansons. Chandos Ⓕ CHAN8351 (43 minutes: DDD: 3/85).
Recorded 1984. *Gramophone classical 100.*   ⒼⒺⒼ
With speeds fast but never breathless and with the most vivid recording imaginable, this is as exciting an account as we have had of this symphony. In no way does this performance suggest anything but a metropolitan orchestra, and Jansons keeps reminding one of his background in Leningrad in the

great years of Mravinsky and the Philharmonic. Nowhere does the link with Mravinsky emerge more clearly than in the finale, where he adopts a tempo very nearly as hectic as Mravinsky's on his classic DG recording. In the first movement he resists any temptation to linger, prefering to press the music on, and the result sounds totally idiomatic. In the slow movement Jansons again prefers a steady tempo, but treats the second theme with delicate rubato and builds the climaxes steadily, not rushing his fences, building the final one even bigger than the first. In the finale it is striking that he follows Tchaikovsky's notated slowings rather than allowing extra *rallentandos* – the bravura of the performance finds its natural culmination. The Oslo string ensemble is fresh and bright and superbly disciplined, while the wind soloists are generally excellent with an attractively furry-toned but not at all wobbly or whiny horn solo in the slow movement. The Chandos sound lives up to its reputation, very specific and well focused despite a warm reverberation, real-sounding and three-dimensional with more clarity in tuttis than the rivals provide. This was the first issue in Jansons's Tchaikovsky cycle and could hardly have been more promising.

Additional recommendations ...
...No. 5. Sérénade mélancolique[a]. [a]**Shizuka Ishikawa** (vn); **Czech Philharmonic Orchestra / Lovro von Matačic**, [a]**Zdenek Košler**. Supraphon Crystal Collection Ⓜ 11 0656-2 (52 minutes: ADD).
...No. 5. Eugene Onegin – Tatyana's letter scene[a]. [a]**Eilene Hannan** (sop); **London Philharmonic Orchestra / Sian Edwards**. EMI Eminence Ⓜ CD-EMX2187 (59 minutes: DDD: 1/92).
...No. 5. **Mozart** Symphony No. 40 in G minor, K550. **North German Radio Symphony Orchestra / Günter Wand**. RCA Victor Red Seal Ⓕ 09026 68032-2 (73 minutes: DDD: 6/95).   Ⓖ
...No. 5. 1812 – Overture. Again, as before, alone, Op. 73 No. 6 (orch. Stokowski). Chant sans paroles in A minor, Op. 40 No. 6 (orch. Stokowski). **Philadelphia Orchestra / Leopold Stokowski**. Biddulph mono Ⓜ WHL015* (69 minutes: ADD: 11/95).
...No. 5. 1812 – Overture, Op. 49. **Chicago Symphony Orchestra / Daniel Barenboim**. Teldec Ⓕ 0630-10904-2 (60 minutes: DDD: 8/96).

Tchaikovsky Symphony No. 5 in E minor, Op. 64.
Mussorgsky Songs and Dances of Death[a]. [a]**Anatoly Kotscherga** (bass); **Berlin Philharmonic Orchestra / Claudio Abbado**. Sony Classical Ⓕ SK66276 (65 minutes: DDD: 3/95).
Text and translation included. Recorded live in 1994.
Sony's booklet tells us that Shostakovich's orchestration was used for the Mussorgsky songs; "Shostakovich ed. Abbado" would be more accurate, though you will need a score to pick up most of Abbado's changes, mainly small additions and alterations to the string parts. These alterations tie in with an approach to all four songs that finds soloist and conductor generally avoiding the Grand Guignol tactics and timing that Hvorostovsky and Gergiev so obviously relish. Kotscherga has the richer, darker bass voice that seems ideal for these songs, and which he varies to great effect: ashen-voiced and gravelly for the opening of "Lullaby", turning to a silken whisper for its haunting refrain; and he judiciously coarsens tone and manner to mimic and menace the doomed drunkard in "Trepak". When Kotscherga 'opens up', the power and pitching are thrilling, not least in the "Ty maja!" ("You are mine!") at the end of "Serenade". With Abbado's alterations giving the strings a little more to do, and the Berlin strings at their expressive finest, their contribution to the success of the Mussorgsky songs is considerable. And so it is in the Tchaikovsky. Though they never appear to dominate the scene, as has often been the case in DG's Berlin recordings, such moments as their full-toned, impassioned song at the climax of the symphony's slow movement, and *feroce* and *marcatissimo* playing in the finale's main *Allegro*, duly astonish. This is Abbado's third recording of Tchaikovsky's Fifth and, as before, he allows himself a fair measure of freedom in pacing (considerably more than Jansons). On balance, Abbado finds more shadow in the score than the breezy Jansons, especially in the symphony's opening minutes and the finale is one of the most exciting on disc, with superb brass. The orchestra are present, but the Philharmonie's ambience adds just enough warmth and space to the proceedings. Those who prefer the more obviously spacious setting that Chandos gave to Jansons may find it a little dry.

Tchaikovsky Symphony No. 6 in B minor, Op. 74, "Pathétique". Marche slave, Op. 31.
Russian National Orchestra / Mikhail Pletnev. Virgin Classics Ⓕ VC7 59661-2
(53 minutes: DDD: 1/92). *Gramophone classical 100.*   ⒼⒼⒼ
There's no denying that Russian orchestras bring a special intensity to Tchaikovsky, and this Symphony in particular. But, in the past, we have had to contend with lethal, vibrato-laden brass, and variable Soviet engineering. Not any more. Pianist Mikhail Pletnev formed this orchestra in 1990 from the front ranks of the major Soviet orchestras, and the result here has all the makings of a classic. The brass still retain their penetrating power, and an extraordinary richness and solemnity before the Symphony's coda; the woodwind (soft, veiled flute tone, dark-hued bassoons) make a very melancholy choir; and the strings possess not only the agility to cope with Pletnev's aptly death-defying speed for the third movement march, but beauty of tone for Tchaikovsky's yearning cantabiles, and their lower voices add thunderous black density to the first movement's development's shattering intrusion. Pletnev exerts the same control over his players as he does over his fingers, to superb effect. The dynamic range is huge and is comfortably reproduced here with clarity, natural perspectives, a sense of instruments playing in a believable acoustic space, and a necessarily higher volume setting than usual. *Marche slave*'s final blaze of triumph, under the circumstances, seems apt.

Additional recommendations ...

...No. 6. **Oslo Philharmonic Orchestra / Mariss Jansons.**
Chandos Ⓕ CHAN8446 (44 minutes: DDD: 5/87).

...No. 6. Romeo and Juliet. **Philharmonia Orchestra / Giuseppe Sinopoli.**
DG Masters Ⓜ 445 601-2GMA (70 minutes: DDD: 7/97).

...No. 6 – Allegro molto vivace (arr. Feinberg). *Coupled with works by various composers.*
Arcadi Volodos (pf). Sony Classical Ⓕ SK62691 (61 minutes: DDD: 10/97). *Gramophone Editor's choice. Selected by Soundings. See review in the Collections section; refer to the Index.*   ⒼⒼ

Tchaikovsky String Quartets – No. 1 in D major, Op. 11; No. 2 in F major, Op. 22; No. 3 in E flat minor, Op. 30. Quartet Movement in B flat major. Souvenir de Florence, Op. 70ª.
ªYuri Yurov (va); ª**Mikhail Milman** (vc); **Borodin Quartet** (Mikhail Kopelman, Andrei Abramenkov, vns; Dmitri Shebalin, va; Valentin Berlinsky, vc). Teldec Ⓕ 4509-90422-2 (two discs: 151 minutes: DDD: 1/94). Recorded 1993. *Gramophone Award Winner 1994.*   ⒼⒼⒼ

Who could fail to recognize the highly characteristic urgency and thematic strength of the F major Quartet's first movement development section, or miss premonitions of later masterpieces in the Third Quartet's *Andante funèbre*. None of these works is 'late' (the last of them predates the Fourth Symphony by a couple of years), yet their rigorous arguments and sweeping melodies anticipate the orchestral masterpieces of Tchaikovsky's full maturity. So why the neglect – that is, of all but the First Quartet? The most likely reason is our habitual expectation of orchestral colour in Tchaikovsky, a situation that doesn't really affect our appreciation of the early, almost Schubertian D major Quartet (the one with the *Andante cantabile* that moved Tolstoy to tears). The Second and Third Quartets are noticeably more symphonic and particularly rich in the kinds of harmonic clashes and sequences that Tchaikovsky normally dressed for the orchestral arena. Even minor details, like the quick-fire exchanges near the beginning of No. 3's *Allegretto*, instantly suggest 'woodwinds' (you can almost hear oboes, flutes and clarinets jostle in play), while both finales could quite easily have been transposed among the pages of the early symphonies. But if these and other parallels are to register with any conviction, then performers need to locate them, and that's a challenge the Borodins meet with the ease of seasoned Tchaikovskians. Generally speaking, the earlier performances (listed below) have the more incisive attack (especially in the First Quartet); the newer ones are more 'natural' and spontaneous, most noticeably in the first movement of the exuberant *Souvenir de Florence* sextet, and in that wonderful passage from the Second Quartet's first movement where the lead violin calms from agitated virtuosity to a magical recapitulation of the principal theme – an unforgettable moment, superbly paced in the Teldec reading. We also get a bonus in the shape of a 15-minute B flat Quartet movement – an appealing torso imbued with the spirit of Russian folk-song – which is accommodated partially at the expense of the First Quartet's last movement repeat (included in the 1979 recording).

Additional recommendations ...

...Nos. 1-4. Quartet Movement in B flat major. Souvenir de Florence, Op. 70ª. ª**Genrikh Talalyan** (va); ª**Mstislav Rostropovich** (vc); **Borodin Quartet.** Melodiya Ⓕ 74321 18290-2 (two discs: 154 minutes: ADD: 10/94).

...No. 1. *Coupled with works by* **Borodin** *and* **Glazunov** **Hollywood Quartet.**
Testament mono Ⓕ SBT1061* (80 minutes: ADD: 8/95).

...No. 1. *Coupled with works by* **Schnittke** *and* **Shostakovich** **Duke Quartet.** Collins Classics Ⓕ 1450-2 (70 minutes: DDD: 2/96). *See review under Shostakovich; refer to the Index.*

Tchaikovsky Piano Trio in A minor, Op. 50.
Arensky Piano Trio No. 1 in D minor, Op. 32. **Cho-Liang Lin** (vn); **Gary Hoffman** (vc); **Yefim Bronfman** (pf). Sony Classical Ⓕ SK53269 (76 minutes: DDD: 9/94). Recorded 1992. *Gramophone Editor's choice.*   Ⓖ

This is a recording of Tchaikovsky's Trio to take its place in some very august company, and that in particular offers new insight into the nature and structure of the long, difficult opening movement. The work is dedicated "To the memory of a great artist" (Tchaikovsky's mentor Nikolay Rubinstein), and the movement is entitled *Pezzo elegiaco*. The players treat it with considerable flexibility of tempo, which works extremely well when their understanding of its unusual structure is so acute. This is the finest kind of chamber music-making. It is fresh, and it takes risks, as all performances do that deal in the making of music and not the execution of a plan of campaign. The ensuing variations are delightfully done, with a nimble scherzo, a tinkling musical clock, a waltz that has a charming, even witty lilt, and a fugue that proves the point of including it (Tchaikovsky nervously said it could be cut). They even bring off the rather noisy finale before the touching return of the opening elegy. Arensky's Trio, now a regular partner to Tchaikovsky's on record, is also given a fine performance, with a brilliant scherzo and grave, intense playing of the beautiful *Elegia*. The recording is particularly sensitive to the demands put upon everyone by Tchaikovsky, who wrote some notoriously thick chords for the piano. They need careful handling by the pianist, but much can be contributed by engineers sensitive to the problems. This is as fine a performance as any on record.

Additional recommendations ...

...Piano Trio. **Smetana** Piano Trio in G minor, B104. **Golub Kaplan Carr Trio.**
Arabesque Ⓕ Z6661 (75 minutes: DDD: 3/96). *See review under Smetana; refer to the Index.*

...Piano Trio. **Shostakovich** Piano Trio No. 2 in E minor, Op. 67. **Vadim Repin** (vn);
   Dmitry Yablonsky (vc); **Boris Berezovsky** (pf). Erato Ⓕ 0630-17875-2 (67 minutes: DDD: 1/98).

Tchaikovsky Capriccio italien, Op. 45. Swan Lake, Op. 20 (arr. Debussy). The Sleeping Beauty,
   Op. 66 (arr. Rachmaninov). Marche slave, Op. 31 (arr. Batalini).
Scriabin Fantasy in A minor. **Katia Labèque, Marielle Labèque** (pfs). Philips Ⓕ 442 778-2PH
   (56 minutes: DDD: 12/95).

This is a fascinating and, for the most part, brilliantly played collection. The 20-year-old Debussy's
arrangement of three dances from *Swan Lake* opens with a glittering flourish, and then presents the
music in totally pianistic terms: the "Danse russe" is most engaging and the "Danse napolitaine"
invites and receives scintillating brilliance at its close. Rachmaninov was just 18 when he arranged the
suite from *Sleeping Beauty* and Tchaikovsky was greatly displeased with the result. "It was a mistake
to entrust this work to a *boy*", said he angrily to Ziloti, who had arranged the commission. The latter
hastily re-edited Rachmaninov's work. But Rachmaninov deplored his failure and probably had a
hand in revising the final version, which is certainly pianistically effective. The Labèques obviously
enjoy the drama of the "Introduction", attacking it with relish and then putting in a splendid pianistic
'bang' at the climax of "La fée des lilas". The surprise here is that they entirely miss the rhythmic
point (and all the magic) of the famous "Panorama", playing it too fast, and failing to notice that it
should float gently above the (almost syncopated) bass, which here rocks prosaically. They are at
home in the "Waltz", however, which is played with fine sparkle, and they make the most of
Rachmaninov's extra decorations, though they are inclined to rush their fences a little here and there.
   Alexandra Batalini's transcription of the *Marche slave* ends the recital grandiloquently – the
orchestral detail is all there, particularly the effulgent twiddly bits in the treble, and it is made to sound
so commandingly pianistic that one does not miss the orchestra (and that's saying a good deal with a
composer like Tchaikovsky). The coda is quite splendid and this performance, with its thrilling
fireworks at the end, would deservedly bring the house down at a live recital, which is just what it
sounds like, with a very real and immediate piano recording. It is a pity the recital was programmed
to open with Tchaikovsky's own four-handed piano transcription of the *Capriccio italien*, for the
composer (although he admired his own efforts) showed no real skill at re-thinking a spectacular
orchestral show-piece for the piano. It opens with the famous bugle call played by one hand(!), and
as "the rest of the brass joins in", the extended fanfare is little short of tedious. Fortunately when the
Labèque sisters get to the echo theme they are able to invest it with their own effervescence, even if
they are a bit impetuous, and the "Tarantella" finale certainly tests their virtuosity, just as the
composer intended. The Scriabin *Fantasy* follows, opening nocturnally and later becoming
harmonically more complex.

Additional recommendation ...
...(arr. Pletnev) The Sleeping Beauty – Introduction; Dance of Maids of Honour and Pages;
   Variation d'Aurore; Danse des baronnes (Gavotte); Pas de caractère – Puss in Boots; Pas de
   quatre; Adagio; Sarabande; Finale. *Coupled with works by various composers.* **Pavel Nersessian**
   (pf). Bel Air Music BAM9725 (3/98). *See review in the Collections section; refer to the Index.*

Tchaikovsky The Seasons, Op. 37*b*. Six Morceaux composés sur un seul thème, Op. 21.
   Mikhail Pletnev (pf). Virgin Classics Ⓕ VC5 45042-2 (66 minutes: DDD: 12/94).
   Recorded 1994.   ⓆⒼ

Pletnev finds colours and depths in *The Seasons* that few others have found even intermittently.
Schumann is revealed as a major influence, not only on the outward features of the style, but on the
whole expressive mood and manner. The opening of "May" is straight from the contemplative
Schumann – his Eusebius persona – while the mercurial staccato-legato exchanges near the start of
"January" are intrusions from the lighter Florestan. That alternation of civilized soulfulness and
delicious, faintly wicked humour recurs again and again in this performance. Even the melancholy
song of "October" has its tiny touches of Pletnevian naughtiness, but how beautifully the tune itself
sings. And as a display of pianism the whole record is outstanding, all the more so because Pletnev's
brilliance isn't purely egoistic. Even when he does something unmarked – like attaching the hunting
fanfares of "September" to the final unison of "August" – he's so persuasive that you could believe
that this is somehow inherent, if not actually explicit, in the material. There's plenty of poetry, colour
and panache in Postnikova's interpretation (see above), but Pletnev has the edge – a touch more
brilliance here, more singing eloquence there, a slightly broader palette, and above all a unique ability
to surprise. Pletnev's coupling, the six *Morceaux*, Op. 21, emerge here as fascinating, richly enjoyable
works. This is all exceptional playing, and the recording – bright in the treble, but also warm in tone
– is ideally attuned to all its moods and colours.

Additional recommendations ...
...Album for the young (orig. piano version)[a]. Album for the young (for string quartet, arr.
   Dubinsky)[b]. [a]**Luba Edlina** (pf); [b]**Rostislav Dubinsky** (vn); [b]**Mimi Zweig** (vn); [b]**Jerry Horner** (va);
   [b]**Yuli Turovsky** (vc). Chandos Ⓕ CHAN8365 (59 minutes: DDD: 11/85).
...Album for the young, Op. 39. *Coupled with works by* **Debussy** and **Schumann** Idil Biret (pf).
   Naxos Ⓢ 8 550885 (66 minutes: DDD: 10/94).
...Piano Sonata in G major, Op. 37. **Mussorgsky** Pictures at an Exhibition. **Sviatoslav Richter** (pf).
   Melodiya mono Ⓜ 74321 29469-2* (61 minutes: ADD: 6/96).

Tchaikovsky Morceaux – Op. 10 (Nos. 1 and 2 from Eurodisc 205 455, 9/84;
remainder new to UK, recorded 1983); Op. 19 – No. 1, Rêverie du soir, No. 5, Capriccioso;
Op. 40 – No. 2, Chanson triste, No. 8, Valse; Op. 51 – No. 1, Valse de salon, No. 3, Menuetto
scherzoso, No. 5, Romance; Op. 72 – No. 5, Méditation, No. 12, L'espiègle, No. 15, Un poco di
Chopin. Romance in F minor, Op. 5. Valse-scherzo in A major, Op. 7 (all from 205 455).
The Seasons, Op. 37b – No. 1, January; No. 5, May; No. 6, June; No. 11, November
(Eurodisc 610 075, 10/84). **Sviatoslav Richter** (pf). Olympia Ⓟ OCD334
(80 minutes: DDD/ADD: 1/94). Recorded 1983.   ⊖⊖⊖
Richter elevates Tchaikovsky's miniatures far beyond the salon. No interpretative frills, just trenchant
fingerwork and perfectly sculpted sound, so that slight unbendings become immensely touching. The
effect is to convey not so much the surface melancholy of these pieces as their underlying strength of
character. A curious sense of permanence comes through, as though the music is being contemplated
rather than felt. Not for imitation, perhaps (and who could imitate such perfect harmonic and
structural weighting?), but this is breathtaking, inspiring artistry, and it sets its own terms.
Sound quality is on the dry side. But Richter's is the sort of playing which positively benefits from
close analytical scrutiny, and serious collectors of piano recordings should need no further
encouragement.

Tchaikovsky Liturgy of St John Chrysostom, Op. 41. Nine Sacred Pieces. An angel crying.
Corydon Singers / Matthew Best. Hyperion Ⓟ CDA66948 (75 minutes: DDD). Texts and
translations included. Recorded 1997.
Tchaikovsky's liturgical settings have never quite caught the popular imagination which has followed
Rachmaninov's (his All-Night Vigil, at any rate). They are generally more inward, less concerned with
the drama that marks Orthodox celebration than with the reflective centre which is another aspect.
Rachmaninov can invite worship with a blaze of delight, setting "Pridite"; Tchaikovsky approaches
the mystery more quietly. Yet there is a range of emotion which emerges vividly in this admirable
record of the Liturgy together with a group of the minor liturgical settings which he made at various
times in his life. His ear for timbre never fails him. It is at its most appealing, perhaps, in the lovely
"Da ispravitsya" for female trio and answering choir, beautifully sung here; he can also respond to the
Orthodox tradition of rapid vocalization, as in the Liturgy's Creed and in the final "Blagosloven
grady" (in the West, the Benedictus). Anyone who still supposes that irregular, rapidly shifting
rhythms were invented by Stravinsky should give an ear to his Russian sources, in folk poetry and
music but also in the music of the Church. Matthew Best's Corydon Singers are by now old hands at
Orthodox music, and they present these beautiful settings with a keen ear for their texture and their
'orchestration'. The recording was made in an (unnamed) ecclesiastical acoustic of suitable resonance,
and sounds well. Transliterated texts and translations are provided in a booklet that includes an
outstandingly good essay on the tradition and the music by Ivan Moody.
Additional recommendation ...
...Liturgy of St John Chrysostom – We hymn Thee; The cherubic hymn. Sacred pieces – No. 7,
Blessed are they. *Coupled with works by various composers.* **Holst Singers / Stephen Layton.**
Hyperion Ⓟ CDA66928 (79 minutes: DDD: 8/97). *See review in the Collections section;
refer to the Index.*

Tchaikovsky My genius, my angel, my friend. Take my heart away. Songs, Op. 6 – No. 1, Do not
believe, my friend; No. 2, Not a word, o my friend; No. 5, Why?; No. 6, None but the lonely
heart. Cradle song, Op. 16 No. 1. Reconciliation, Op. 25 No. 1. The fearful minute, Op. 28 No. 6.
It was in the early spring, Op. 38 No. 2. Songs, Op. 60 – No. 6, Frenzied nights; No. 7, Gipsy's
song; No. 12, The mild stars shone for us. Songs, Op. 63 – No. 4, The first meeting; No. 5, The
fires in the rooms were already out. Serenade, Op. 63 No. 1. Songs, Op. 73 – No. 2, Night; No. 4,
The sun has set; No. 6, Again, as before, alone. **Olga Borodina** (mez); **Larissa Gergieva** (pf).
Philips Ⓟ 442 013-2PH (60 minutes: DDD: 6/94). Translations included. Recorded 1993.
Gramophone Editor's choice.   ⊖⊖
Olga Borodina is among the most considered of Tchaikovsky interpreters on disc. In the "Cradle
song", one of Tchaikovsky's most haunting pieces, Joan Rodgers sounds carefree as she rocks her
baby to sleep, where Borodina is heavier, sensing dark threats all around. Larissa Gergieva adds to the
unsettling atmosphere of that song by stressing the chromatic tensions in the accompaniment. In
general, it might have been better to have had a pianist less amenable to slow speeds than Gergieva,
but Borodina has such a range of colour and expression in her voice that she can fill the time
profitably. One marvels at the beauty of the singing and admires its sustained intensity. In "Night" a
darkness descends over the voice from the opening lines, but in "Again, as before, alone" she tries
something even more daring, draining all the life and vibrancy from her tone in a way that is
quite unforgettable. One would hardly dare play the final track often (Hvorostovsky is matter-of-
fact by comparison). The booklet does not include Russian texts either in Cyrillic or transliteration,
but there is a free CD, "Presenting Olga Borodina" in three excerpts from existing Philips opera
sets. In fact, there is no need to persuade us that the young Russian mezzo is a star: Borodina is
one of the major singers of her generation and this recital demands that she be accepted on her own
terms.

...Songs – Op. 6: No. 4, A tear trembles; No. 6, None but the lonely heart. Op. 25: No. 1, Reconciliation. Op. 28: No. 6, The fearful minute. Op. 38: No. 1, Don Juan's Serenade. Op. 60: No. 4, The nightingale; No. 11, Exploit. Op. 63: No. 2, I opened the window. Op. 73: No. 6, Again, as before, alone. *Coupled with works by* **Rachmaninov Dmitri Hvorostovsky** (bar); **Oleg Boshniakovich** (pf). Philips Ⓕ 432 119-2PH (52 minutes: DDD: 10/91).
...Songs – Op. 6: No. 1, Do not believe, my friend; No. 2, Not a word, o my friend; No. 5, Why?; No. 6, None but the lonely heart. Cradle song, Op. 16 No. 1. The canary, Op. 25 No. 4. Op. 28: No. 3, Why did I dream of you?; No. 6, The fearful minute. Op. 38: No. 2, It was in the early spring; No. 3, At the ball. Op. 47: No. 1, If only I had known; No. 6, Does the day reign?; No. 7, Was I not a little blade of grass?. Op. 54: No. 8, The cuckoo; No. 9, Spring song; No. 10, Lullaby in a storm. Op. 60: No. 1, Last night; No. 4, The nightingale; No. 10, Behind the window in the shadow. Op. 63 – Serenade: O child beneath thy window. To forget so soon. **Joan Rodgers** (sop); **Roger Vignoles** (pf). Hyperion Ⓕ CDA66617 (65 minutes: DDD: 2/93).
...Songs, Op. 47 – No. 1, If only I had known; No. 6, Does the day reign?; No. 7, Was I not a little blade of grass? Zemfira's song. *Coupled with works by* **Mussorgsky** and **Rachmaninov Ewa Podles** (contr); **Graham Johnson** (pf). Forlane Ⓕ UCD16683 (70 minutes: DDD: 5/95). *See review in the Collections section; refer to the Index.*

Tchaikovsky Songs, Op. 6 – No. 1, Do not believe, my friend; No. 2, Not a word, o my friend; No. 4, A tear trembles; No. 5, Why?; No. 6, None but the lonely heart. Reconciliation, Op. 25 No. 1. No response, or word, or greeting, Op. 28 No. 5. Songs, Op. 38 – No. 1, Don Juan's Serenade; No. 2, It was in the early spring; No. 3, At the ball; No. 5, The love of a dead man. Songs, Op. 47 – No. 3, Dusk fell on the earth; No. 4, Sleep, poor friend; No. 5, I bless you, forests. Songs, Op. 57 – No. 2, On the golden cornfields; No. 5, Death. Frenzied nights, Op. 60 No. 6. I should like in a single word. My genius, my angel, my friend. **Sergei Leiferkus** (bar); **Semion Skigin** (pf). Conifer Classics Ⓕ 75605-51266-2 (62 minutes: DDD: 8/96). Texts and translations included.
This first volume in Leiferkus's collection of Tchaikovsky's songs with Semion Skigin contains a good number of favourites. He has the innate sympathy for the melodic lines to refresh even so well known, and often abused, a song as the one usually called in this country *None but the lonely heart*. This is beautifully sung, with a tinge of mournfulness in the tone and a long, carefully crafted shading of the melody. He can also turn to a hearty, even ruthless tone for the vehemence of *Don Juan's Serenade*, a fine partnership with Skigin as the piano hurtles forward mercilessly under the rollicking of the tune. Two songs of oblique love are among the best in the whole recital. *My genius, my angel, my friend* is tenderly phrased, as if all leading towards the long, held note that closes the song, on the cherished words "moy drug" – "my friend". There is also gentleness, and that sense of love never wholly grasped which haunted Tchaikovsky so bitterly, in *At the ball* – one of his most moving songs – as the singer cannot bear to let the vision glimpsed across the crowded dance floor vanish altogether. Leiferkus seems in a few of the songs to be placed a little far back for the best effect, but in general the balance is carefully arranged so as to keep voice and piano in proper focus with each other. Certainly this is necessary in songs where melodic lines can blend so skilfully. Here is a recital of the quality one would expect from so fine an artist.

Tchaikovsky Why did I dream of you?, Op. 28 No. 3. 16 Children's Songs, Op. 54. 12 Songs, Op. 60 – No. 1, Last night; No. 2, I'll tell you nothing; No. 3, O, if only you knew; No. 5, Simple words; No. 10, Behind the window in the shadow. **Ilya Levinsky** (ten); **Semion Skigin** (pf). Conifer Classics Ⓕ 75605 51268-2 (65 minutes: DDD: 1/97). Texts and translations included. Recorded 1995.
Ilya Levinsky's disc chiefly consists of the *16 Children's Songs*, the best of them delightful pieces in Tchaikovsky's most direct and well-crafted vein. They do, of course, need a comparable craft from the singer, and Levinsky very intelligently takes the words that touched Tchaikovsky as his own starting point. Though his tenor is light, poised and graceful – his singing of "Why did I dream of you?" suggests that he must be a good Lensky – it is not a voice of naturally great range, but he uses it so expressively and eloquently that each of his interpretations has real meaning. "Christ had a garden" (from Op. 54), rubbed almost smooth by countless soupy arrangements and soupier performances, is here sung with an attention that entirely refreshes it. Levinsky can also make a good comic turn out of "The Cuckoo" from the same set, as the wretched bird ends up by insisting interminably on the merits of its song. He is wittily accompanied here by Semion Skigin, whose perception and skill is a hallmark of this generally excellent series. A word, too, for David Brown's helpful notes and for excellent translations of the texts (printed in transliteration) by Joan Pemberton Smith.

Tchaikovsky The Snow Maiden. **Irina Mishura-Lekhtman** (mez); **Vladimir Grishko** (ten); **Michigan University Musical Society Choral Union; Detroit Symphony Orchestra / Neeme Järvi.** Chandos Ⓕ CHAN9324 (79 minutes: ADD: 3/95). Text and translation included. Recorded 1994.
Tchaikovsky wrote his incidental music for Ostrovsky's *Snow Maiden* in 1873, and though he accepted it was not the best of which he was capable, he retained an affection for it and was upset when Rimsky-Korsakov came along with his full-length opera on the subject. The tale of love frustrated had its appeal for Tchaikovsky, even though he was not to make as much as Rimsky was of the failed

marriage between Man and Nature. But though he did not normally interest himself much in descriptions of the natural world, there are charming numbers that any lover of Tchaikovsky's music will surely be delighted to encounter. A strong sense of a Russian folk celebration, and of the interaction of the natural and supernatural worlds, also comes through, especially in the earlier part of the work. There is a delightful dance and chorus for the birds, and a powerful monologue for Winter; this is vigorously but somewhat hectoringly sung by Alexander Arkhipov for Chistiakov (listed below), where Vladimir Grishko, placed further back, sounds more magical. Natalia Erassova (also for Chistiakov) gets round the rapid enunciation of Lel's second song without much difficulty, but does not quite bring the character to life; Irina Mishura-Lekhtman has a brighter sparkle. Chistiakov's Shrove Tuesday procession goes at a much steadier pace than Järvi's, and is thus the more celebratory and ritual where the other is a straightforward piece of merriment. Both performances have much to recommend them, and it is not by a great deal that Järvi's is preferable. The balance is further tilted by CdM providing only an English (and French) translation of the text unmatched to a Russian text or transliteration; Chandos provide transliteration and English translation.

Additional recommendation ...

...**Natalia Erassova** (sop); **Alexander Arkhipov** (ten); **Nikolai Vassiliev** (bar); **Russian State Choir; orchestra / Andrey Chistiakov.** CdM Russian Season Ⓕ LDC288 090 (73 minutes: DDD: 3/95).

Tchaikovsky Iolanta – Who can compare with my Mathilde[d]. Iolanta and Vaudémont duet[ac]. Oprichnik – Natalya's arioso[ac]. Mazeppa – The old man's gone, how my heart beats – Sleep my baby, my pretty[bc]. The Maid of Orleans – Farewell, Forests[a]. The Queen of Spades – Stay, I beg of you![c]. I love you beyond all measure[d]. Undina – Undina's song[b]. The Voyevoda – Bastryukov's aria[c]. Vakula the Smith – Oskana's aria[b]. Eugene Onegin – Let me perish, but first let me summon (Letter Scene)[a]. The Enchantress – Kuma's arioso[b]. [a]**Inessa Galante,** [b]**Marina Shaguch** (sops); [c]**Alexander Fedin** (ten); [d]**Sergei Leiferkus** (bar); **Royal Opera House Orchestra, Covent Garden / Neeme Järvi.** Royal Opera House Records Ⓕ 75605 55022-2 (79 minutes: DDD: A/97). Recorded 1997.

There can scarcely be a more beautiful or subtler account of the Letter Scene from *Eugene Onegin* than that given here by Inessa Galante. She makes us believe that these are the inner thoughts of an obsessed young girl as she moulds her phrases with a sense of spontaneous feeling: you can almost see Tatyana writing in her boudoir. The voice itself shows that it has blossomed into a warm, vibrant, evenly produced instrument and its owner uses it with unfailing musicality, aided by Järvi's sympathetic support. This is the glorious centrepiece of "The Tchaikovsky Experience", with excerpts from all his operas. Galante possibly even more moving as vulnerable Iolanta learning of her blindness from her admirer Vaudémont in the composer's last opera. This, one of the most touching duets in Tchaikovsky, perhaps in all opera, is compellingly sung here by Galante and the tenor Alexander Fedin. Marina Shaguch deserves almost as much praise. Her voice isn't as easily produced as Galante's but is more dramatic in character. She has some of the rarer material to interpret, such as the haunting solo from *Undina* and as poor, demented Maria at the end of *Mazeppa*, singing a lullaby to her sweetheart dying in her arms. Sergei Leiferkus sings with his customary conviction in Robert's soliloquy from *Iolanta*. Though his account of Yeletsky's solo from *The Queen of Spades* isn't as ingratiating as some, it is delivered with compensating intelligence. Järvi conducts all the music with command of idiom, drawing refined playing from the ROH Orchestra. Unfortunately texts and translations aren't included but you can write off for them. None the less this is an important disc, well recorded, and generously filled.

Tchaikovsky Eugene Onegin – Let me perish, but first let me summon. The Queen of Spades – What am I crying for, what is it?. The Enchantress – Where are you, beloved? ... Hurry to my side. Oprichnik – I heard voices and footsteps.
Verdi La forza del destino – Son giunta! ... Madre, pietosa Vergine[a]; Pace, pace, mio Dio. Otello – Mia madre aveva ... Piangea cantando ... Ave Maria. Aida – Qui Radames verra? ... O patria mia. Il trovatore – Tacea la notte placida ... Di tale amor. **Galina Gorchakova** (sop); [a]**Chorus and Orchestra of the Kirov Opera / Valery Gergiev.** Philips Ⓕ 446 405-2PH (60 minutes: DDD: 3/96). Texts and translations included. Recorded 1995. *Gramophone Editor's choice.*   Ⓖ

Gorchakova promises to be one of the vocal giants of her generation. This recital programme marks her first steps into the Italian repertoire on disc. For a star of the Kirov, Verdi's St Petersburg opera – *La forza del destino* – makes an apt choice. Arriving at the monastery gate, her Leonora immediately announces herself as a Verdi soprano of tragic stature, shaping "Madre, pietosa Vergine" with the dark colouring of a troubled soul. The Willow Song from *Otello* is predictably doom-laden, for Gorchakova is no simple, creamy, lyrical Desdemona. The Aida is less successful and sounds as if it is not yet fully in her voice. It might have been better to offer "Ritorna vincitor", as she seems uncomfortable with long, slow phrases around the top of the stave. The top C is very loud and the conclusion, broken off sharply in full voice, is not what Verdi asks for. After that, the *Trovatore* goes much better: the aria has splendid vocal depth and the cabaletta (one verse only) is surprisingly nimble, especially at Gergiev's brilliant pace. Elsewhere his conducting of the Verdi could do with more pace. As an interpreter of Tchaikovsky, Gorchakova has already won her laurels on the stage. Despite the size and dark colour of the voice, her soprano is still youthful enough for her to play a plausible Tatyana and the Letter Scene will be one of the major reasons for acquiring this disc. The heart of the scene is sung with the kind of *pianissimo* that one would use to carry to the back of the theatre, rather than an inward *pianissimo* intended for the microphone. The *Queen of Spades* aria (Lisa's short solo from Act 1, not her main aria) is so full of beautiful, soaring tone that one resents being cut off just at the point where Herman enters for their duet. The brief aria from *The Enchantress* includes an exciting high B. Elsewhere there is one worrying sign to be mentioned. That is a tendency to go flat when the music is soft and slow (both the *Otello* and the *Aida* suffer from passages of sinking pitch) and one has to hope that difficulties like this are not allowed to defeat her. Gorchakova is no highly polished automaton as a singer, as we know from a couple of problematical live appearances. Her artistry is about letting this voice out of its cage and harnessing its formidable energy. The Philips recording team have done well to capture it so truthfully in the studio. A vocal beast like this is not easily tamed.

Additional recommendation ...

...Eugene Onegin – I love you, Olga; Monsieur Triquet, favour us with a coupleta; Faint echo of my youth. Mazeppa – In bloody battle, on the field of honour ... Here days passed by in happy succession. Cherevichki – Does your heart, maiden, not hear. The Queen of Spades – I do not know her name; Forgive me, loveliest of creatures; What is our life? A game!. *Coupled with works by various composers.* **Sergei Larin** (ten); **Philharmonia Orchestra / Gennadi Rozhdestvensky.** Chandos Ⓕ CHAN9603 (75 minutes: DDD: 5/98). *See review in the Collections section; refer to the Index.*

Tchaikovsky Eugene Onegin. **Dmitri Hvorostovsky** (bar) Eugene Onegin; **Nuccia Focile** (sop) Tatyana; **Neil Shicoff** (ten) Lensky; **Olga Borodina** (mez) Olga; **Alexander Anisimov** (bass) Prince Gremin; **Sarah Walker** (mez) Larina; **Irina Arkhipova** (mez) Filipievna; **Francis Egerton** (ten) Triquet; **Hervé Hennequin** (bass-bar) Captain; **Sergei Zadvorny** (bass) Zaretsky; **St Petersburg Chamber Choir; Orchestre de Paris / Semyon Bychkov.** Philips Ⓕ 438 235-2PH2 (two discs: 141 minutes: DDD: 12/93). Notes, text and translation included. Recorded 1992. *Gramophone Editor's choice.* Ⓖ

Tchaikovsky Eugene Onegin. **Evgeny Belov** (bar) Eugene Onegin; **Galina Vishnevskaya** (sop) Tatyana; **Sergei Lemeshev** (ten) Lensky; **Larissa Adyeva** (mez) Olga; **Ivan Petrov** (bass) Prince Gremin; **Valentina Petrova** (sop) Larina; **Evgenya Verbitskaya** (mez) Filipyevna; **Andrei Sokolov** (ten) Triquet; **Igor Mikhailov** (bass) Zaretsky; **Georgi Pankov** (bass) Captain; **Bolshoi Theatre Chorus and Orchestra / Boris Khaikin.** Melodiya mono Ⓜ 74321 17090-2* (two discs: 140 minutes: ADD: 12/94). From Parlophone PMA1050/52 (7/59). Recorded 1955. Ⓖ

Entirely at the service of Tchaikovsky's marvellous invention, Semyon Bychkov illuminates every detail of the composer's wondrous scoring with pointed delicacy and draws playing of the utmost acuity and beauty from his own Paris orchestra – enhanced by the clear, open recording – and the St Petersburg Choir are superbly disciplined and alert with their words. Focile offers keen-edged yet warm tone and total immersion in Tatyana's character. Aware throughout of the part's dynamic demands, she phrases with complete confidence, eagerly catching the girl's dreamy vulnerability and heightened imagination in the Letter scene, which has that sense of awakened love so essential to it. Hvorostovsky is in his element. His singing has at once the warmth, elegance and refinement Tchaikovsky demands from his anti-hero. Together he, Focile and Bychkov make the finale the tragic climax it should be; indeed the reading of this passage is almost unbearably moving. Shicoff has refined and expanded his Lensky since he recorded it for Levine and Anisimov is a model Gremin, singing his aria with generous tone and phrasing while not making a meal of it. Olga Borodina is a perfect Olga, spirited, a touch sensual, wholly idiomatic with the text – as, of course, is the revered veteran Russian mezzo Arkhipova as Filipievna, an inspired piece of casting.

The classic Khaikin version, generally accepted as the most convincing and knowledgeable performance the work has yet received, wears its 44 years lightly: indeed, the recording of the voices and even the orchestra, albeit in mono, has a great deal to teach producers today in terms of a natural sound. The reading's virtues are, above all, Khaikin's unforced, unexaggerated, wholly integrated direction, with players and singers who know the score from the inside giving an entirely idiomatic reading (if you can forgive the watery horns). From the very first scene you feel the impetus of the performance and are drawn into its truly Russian ambience. Khaikin brings into perfect balance the dramatic and yearning aspects of the score in a lyrical, delicate reading. With his incisive but sympathetic beat, he clearly characterizes those many passages of intimate feeling without which any account of the piece crucially fails. The young Vishnevskaya is a near-ideal Tatyana, having exactly the right voice for the part and totally convincing us that she *is* Tatyana. She is incomparable. What a genuine, unsophisticated outpouring of passion the Letter scene becomes as she interprets it, and how superbly she sings it! Few tenors before or since Lemeshev have offered precisely the right tone and character for Lensky. From his first entry we hear a plaintive timbre and easy way with the language that proclaim a true poet. Belov's Onegin, though not quite in that class, is a resolute member of a real ensemble and rises to the challenge of the final scenes. All that disappoints is the presentation: numerous spelling mistakes and no libretto.

Additional recommendations ...

...**Soloists; John Alldis Choir; Orchestra of the Royal Opera House, Covent Garden / Sir Georg Solti.** Decca Ⓕ 417 413-2DH2 (two discs: 143 minutes: ADD: 8/87).

...Soloists; **Leipzig Radio Chorus; Dresden Staatskapelle / James Levine.**
DG Ⓕ 423 959-2GH2 (two discs: 149 minutes: DDD: 3/89).
...Soloists; **Sofia National Opera Chorus; Sofia Festival Orchestra / Emil Tchakarov.**
Sony Classical Ⓕ S2K45539 (two discs: 143 minutes: DDD: 3/91).

Tchaikovsky Iolanta. **Galina Gorchakova** (sop) Iolanta; **Gegam Grigorian** (ten) Vaudémont;
Dmitri Hvorostovsky (bar) Robert; **Sergei Alexashkin** (bass) King René; **Nikolai Putilin** (bar)
Ibn-Hakia; **Larissa Diadkova** (mez) Martha; **Nikolai Gassiev** (ten) Alméric; **Tatiana Kravtsova**
(sop) Brigitta; **Olga Korzhenskaya** (mez) Laura; **Gennadi Bezzubenkov** (bar) Bertrand;
Chorus and Orchestra of the Kirov Opera, St Petersburg / Valery Gergiev.
Philips Ⓕ 442 796-2PH2 (two discs: 96 minutes: DDD: 7/96). Notes, text and translation
included. Recorded 1994.

Iolanta, the touching little princess, blind and virginal, into whose darkness and isolation there
eventually shines the 'bright angel' of Duke Robert, is delightfully sung by Galina Gorchakova. There
is a freshness and sense of vulnerability here, especially in the opening scenes with Martha in the
garden as she sings wistfully of something that appears to be lacking in her life: the Arioso is done
charmingly and without sentimentality. Gegam Grigorian sometimes sounds pinched and under
strain, even in the Romance. He is also overshadowed by Dmitri Hvorostovsky who is here at his best:
warm and with a somewhat dusky tone, responding with great sensitivity to the often elusive melodic
lines which Tchaikovsky writes in this, his last opera. The King, Provence's 'bon roi René', is benignly
if a little throatily sung by Sergei Alexashkin, and he has at hand a sturdy-voiced Ibn-Hakia in
Nikolai Putilin. Valery Gergiev conducts a sensitive performance, responding constructively to the
unusual scoring (much disliked by the possibly jealous Rimsky-Korsakov), and not overplaying the
more demonstrative elements in a score that gains most through some understatement. The booklet
very sensibly prints in parallel columns a transliteration of the Russian, then English, German and
French; the text in the original Cyrillic is printed separately at the end.

Tchaikovsky Mazeppa. **Sergei Leiferkus** (bar) Mazeppa; **Galina Gorchakova** (sop) Mariya;
Anatoly Kotscherga (bass) Kochubey; **Larissa Dyadkova** (mez) Liubov; **Sergei Larin** (ten) Andrei;
Monte Pederson (bar) Orlik; **Richard Margison** (ten) Iskra; **Heinz Zednik** (ten) Drunken Cossack;
Stockholm Royal Opera Chorus; Gothenburg Symphony Orchestra / Neeme Järvi.
DG Ⓕ 439 906-2GH3 (three discs: 166 minutes: DDD: 11/94). Notes, text and translation
included. Recorded 1993.   Ⓖ

It was *Eugene Onegin* that turned Tchaikovsky into Russia's best-loved composer, not the more
calculated recipes for success of *The Maid of Orleans*, *Mazeppa* or *Charodeyka* ("The Enchantress").
Onegin works for us today because it is sincerely felt from start to finish; but the fascination of those
lesser-known operas lies in the way they move in and out of scenes and predicaments which clearly
touched the composer. Of the three, *Mazeppa* has the greatest share of first-rate music, extending our
appreciation of Tchaikovsky's blacker side as he attempts to reflect the cruelty inflicted by the anti-
hero. Gorchakova's response to Mazeppa's patriotic scheme in Act 2 gives us a fairer picture of the
Gorchakova phenomenon than ill-focused earlier stages of this semi-interpretation: shining strength
above the stave goes some way towards redeeming the placidity of the whole. It takes Larissa
Dyadkova's far more committed cut and thrust in the electrifying scene between Mariya and her
mother to spur Gorchakova to a more consistent sense of occasion. Anatoly Kotscherga would
clearly like to deliver more than his limited vocal resources permit him as the outraged father seethes
in Act 1 but he rises to his supreme challenge as Tchaikovsky plumbs the depths for Kochubey's
prison monologue: here, indeed, are the range of tone-colour and introspection missing from
Gorchakova's mad scenes. Leiferkus has less to deal with as the headstrong tyrant; even so, he strikes
firmly at the heart of darkness, and there could be no more free- and easy-sounding delivery of the
wonderful aria that Tchaikovsky gave his baritone at a late stage in the compositional process. In the
cases of both the victim's darkest hour and this, the conqueror's most sensitive one, Järvi reinforces
the orchestra's role as an equal partner in characterization – driving home the lower-instrument
gloom and terror of Kochubey's circumstances, underlining the light and lovely, woodwind-
dominated scoring of "O, Mariya!" as Mazeppa muses Gremin-like on the sincerity of his late-
flowering love. As a whole the set is a faithful testament to *Mazeppa*'s power to move and appal.

Tchaikovsky The Queen of Spades. **Gegam Grigorian** (ten) Herman; **Maria Gulegina** (sop) Lisa;
Irina Arkhipova (mez) Countess; **Nikolai Putilin** (bar) Count Tomsky; **Vladimir Chernov** (bar)
Prince Yeletsky; **Olga Borodina** (mez) Pauline; **Vladimir Solodovnikov** (ten) Chekalinsky; **Sergei
Alexashkin** (bass) Surin; **Evgeni Boitsov** (ten) Chaplitsky; **Nikolai Gassiev** (ten) Major-domo;
Gennadi Bezzubenkov (bass) Narumov; **Ludmila Filatova** (mez) Governess; **Tatiana Filimonova**
(sop) Masha; **Kirov Theatre Chorus and Orchestra / Valery Gergiev.** Philips Ⓕ 438 141-2PH3
(three discs: 166 minutes: DDD: 10/93). Notes, text and translation included. Recorded 1992.

There are major problems with all the current sets of *The Queen of Spades*, but Valery Gergiev, one
of the outstanding Tchaikovskians of the day, here coaxes from a thoroughly Western-sounding
Kirov Theatre Orchestra what is surely the most refined account of the score yet recorded, and one
that is never lacking energy or full-blooded attack. His is not so much a compromise approach as one
which stresses fatalism and underlying sadness. The recording was made in the Kirov Theatre itself,

and there is admittedly some constriction to the orchestral sound-picture; but for many the atmosphere of a real stage-venue will be a plus, and the all-important balance between voices and orchestra is just right. If the spine still fails to tingle as often as it should, that is mainly a reflection of the respectable but unexciting singing, though it would be folly to expect greater thrills from any of the three rival sets, and in many ways Gergiev's conducting elevates his above them all.

Additional recommendations ...

...Soloists; **Gouslarche Boys' Choir; Svetoslav Obretenov National Chorus; Sofia Festival Orchestra / Emil Tchakarov.** Sony Classical Ⓕ S3K45720 (three discs: 159 minutes: DDD: 12/90).

...Soloists; **American Boychoir; Tanglewood Festival Chorus; Boston Symphony Orchestra / Seiji Ozawa.** RCA Victor Red Seal Ⓕ 09026-60992-2 (three discs: 156 minutes: DDD: 11/92).

Further listening ...

...Méditation, Op. 42 No. 1 (arr. Glazunov). *Coupled with* **Khachaturian** Violin Concerto in D minor. **Itzhak Perlman** (vn); **Israel Philharmonic Orchestra / Zubin Mehta.** EMI CDC7 47087-2 (7/85). *See review under Khachaturian; refer to the Index.*

...Sérénade mélancolique. *Coupled with works by various composers.* **Gil Shaham** (vn); **Orpheus Chamber Orchestra.** DG 449 923-2GH (3/97).

...Suites – No. 3 in G major, Op. 55. No. 4. **USSR Symphony Orchestra / Evgeni Svetlanov.** Melodiya 74321 17100-2.

...Variations on a Rococo Theme in A major, Op. 33. Nocturne in D minor, Op. 19, No. 4. Pezzo capriccioso in B minor, Op. 62. Legend: Christ had a garden, Op. 54 No. 5. Was I not a little blade of grass. Andante cantabile for Cello and Strings, Op. 11. **Raphael Wallfisch** (vc); **English Chamber Orchestra / Geoffrey Simon.** Chandos CHAN8347 (2/85).

...Variations on a Rococo Theme in A minor, Op. 33. Nocturne in C sharp minor, Op. 19 No. 4. *Coupled with works by* **Miaskovsky** and **Shostakovich** Julian Lloyd Webber (vc); **London Symphony Orchestra / Maxim Shostakovich.** Philips 434 106-2PH (5/92).

...Variations on a Rococo Theme, Op. 33. *Coupled with* **Dvořák** Cello Concerto in B minor, B191. **Mstislav Rostropovich** (vc); **Berlin Philharmonic Orchestra / Herbert von Karajan.** DG The Originals 447 413-2GOR (5/95). *See review under Dvořák; refer to the Index.*
Gramophone classical 100.   ⓖⓖⓖ

...Valse-scherzo in C major, Op. 34. Souvenir d'un lieu cher, Op. 42 (orch. Glazunov). **Gil Shaham** (vn); **Russian National Orchestra / Mikhail Pletnev.** DG 457 064-2GH (3/98).

...Andante cantabile, Op. 11. *Coupled with works by* **Dvořák, Arensky** and **Davïdov** **Pieter Wispelwey** (vc); **Paul Giacometti** (harm). Channel Classics CCS8695 (6/96).

...String Quartet No. 1 in D major, Op. 11 – Andante cantabile. Souvenir de Hapsal, Op. 2 – No. 3, Chanson sans paroles. Souvenir d'un lieu cher, Op. 42 – Mélodie in E flat. *Coupled with works by* **Rachmaninov** and **Stravinsky** Itzhak Perlman (vn); **Samuel Sanders** (pf). EMI Perlman Edition CDM5 66061-2 (3/97).

...Eugene Onegin – Letter scene. *Coupled with works by various composers.* **Renée Fleming** (sop); **Larissa Diadkova** (mez); **London Symphony Orchestra / Sir Georg Solti.** Decca 455 760-2DH (10/97). *Gramophone* Editor's choice. *See review in the Collections section; refer to the Index.*

Alexander Tcherepnin   USSR/French/American 1899-1977

A. Tcherepnin Piano Concertos – No. 1, Op. 12; No. 4, Op. 78, "Fantaisie"; No. 5, Op. 96. **Murray McLachlan** (pf); **Chetham's Symphony Orchestra / Julian Clayton.** Olympia Ⓕ OCD440 (71 minutes: DDD: 12/95). Recorded 1995.

The Tcherepnin piano concertos are in their various ways cast in the same exuberant, heartfelt romantic manner. However, there is considerable variety within this general approach. The First, written in Paris in 1920, takes not the slightest interest in what was beginning to occupy French musicians and most other Parisian expatriates at the beginning of that exciting decade: it looks east, to a Georgia which Tcherepnin had known before exile, and north to an influence from, of all composers, Sibelius. The result is inventive but, predictably, less original than the later concertos. The Fourth, written in 1947, looks further east to China, a country which Tcherepnin had toured in the 1930s and where he met his future wife. It is more a set of three tone-poems, lightly accommodating Chinese musical gestures into the familiar romantic language, than a symphonic concerto. The Fifth belongs to 1963, and is a much more enigmatic work, and also by some way the most original of the entire set of six. Murray McLachlan is a fine advocate of this music, which is technically demanding and, in the Fifth Concerto, also demanding of a subtle understanding if the most is to be made of its laconic gestures and rather greyer lyricism. The Chetham's Symphony Orchestra reaffirm their ability to cope with technically testing scores and, guided by Julian Clayton, to make musical sense of them with the command of more experienced musicians.

Further listening ...

...Piano Concertos – No. 2, Op. 26; No. 3, Op. 48; No. 6, Op. 99. **Murray McLachlan** (pf); **Chetham's Symphony Orchestra / Julian Clayton.** Olympia OCD439 (11/94).

...Symphony No. 4, Op. 91. Suite, Op. 87. Russian Dances. Romantic Overture, Op. 67. **Košice State Philharmonic Orchestra / Win-Sie Yip.** Marco Polo 8 223380 (10/92).

Georg Philipp Telemann

Telemann Concerto for Three Horns, Violin and Orchestra in D major[a]. Overture-Suites –
C major, TWV55: C5, "La Bouffonne"; F major, TWV55: F11, "Alster Echo". Concerto in
G major, "Grillen-Symphonie". [a]**Anthony Halstead,** [a]**Christian Rutherford,** [a]**Raul Diaz** (hns);
Collegium Musicum 90 / Simon Standage (vn). Chandos Chaconne Ⓕ CHAN0547
(70 minutes: DDD: 7/94). ✍   Ⓖ

This release provides some very varied and exotic fare, in the form of an assorted programme of
orchestral music showing Telemann at his most irrepressibly good-humoured and imaginative. There's
a concerto for three rattling horns and a solo violin (a splendid sound, with the horns recorded at
what seems like the ideal distance), and an elegant suite for strings which sounds like Handel, Bach
and a few French composers all thrown in together. More striking, though, is the most substantial
piece on the disc, the *Alster Echo* Overture-Suite, a nine-movement work for strings, oboes and horns
full of tricks and surprises occasioned by a whole host of representative titles. Thus "Hamburg
Carillons" brings us horns imitating bells, "Concerto of Frogs and Crows" has some mischievously
scrunchy wrong notes, and in "Alster Echo" there's a complex network of echoes between oboes and
horns. But the show-stealer by a long way on this disc is the *Grillen-Symphonie* ("Cricket
Symphony"), which Telemann jokingly noted on the manuscript as being "in the Italian, English,
Scottish and Polish styles". What he meant by that is hardly the point; this is a work for the gloriously
silly scoring of piccolo, alto chalumeau, oboe, violins, viola, and two double-basses, a somewhat
Stravinskian combination that you're unlikely to encounter every day. But it's not just the
instrumentation that's irresistibly odd. There is a slow movement with curious, melancholy woodwind
interventions a little reminiscent of *Harold in Italy*, and a finale which is quite a hoot.

Telemann Concerto for Two Oboes, Three Trumpets, Timpani and Strings[a]. Overture-Suite in
G minor, TWV55: g 4. Musique de table – Overture-Suite in D major, TWV55: D 1.
Paul Goodwin, [a]**Lorraine Wood** (obs); [a]**Mark Bennett,** [a]**Michael Harrison,** [a]**Nicholas Thompson**
(tpts); **The English Concert / Trevor Pinnock.** Archiv Produktion Ⓕ 439 893-2AH
(59 minutes: DDD: 8/94). ✍   ⓊⒼ

This extensive D major work is well represented in the catalogue. In the circumstances, this piece for
solo oboe and trumpet with strings is a less desirable proposition than the richly endowed and little-
known gems which we have been introduced to by Pinnock so far. This disc contains only one such
work but it is a flawless G minor Suite displaying Telemann's brilliant and variegated ideas of
blending and offsetting three *concertante* oboes with strings. After the exquisitely balanced overture
the picturesque dances are executed with refined characterization, most notably in the robustly
Ramellian, "Les Irresoluts". If the inclusion of the Produktion II suite (from Musique de table) is
perhaps a missed opportunity for more *objets inconnus*, it is certainly not a waste of air time since it
rivals, if not improves upon Goebel's account with the trumpeter, Friedemann Immer (see below).
Pinnock's approach is about right in its bold gestures, with the forward placing of the trumpet and
oboe making for a persuasive dialogue, even if Mark Bennett's gleaming tone tends to predominate.
Bennett's virtuoso 'natural' trumpet playing is demanded again in a performance of one or two extant
concertos Telemann wrote for three trumpets. He and his colleagues are meticulously matched here in
a thrilling performance which simply has to be heard by those who relish baroque music at its
grandest and most rhetorical. Overall then, another fine achievement.
Additional recommendation ...
...Musique de table – Produktions I-III. **Cologne Musica Antiqua / Reinhard Goebel.**
Archiv Produktion Ⓕ 427 619-2AH4 (four discs: 254 minutes: DDD: 10/89). ✍

Telemann Concertos, Volumes 1 and 2. **Collegium Musicum 90 / Simon Standage** (vn).
Chandos Ⓕ CHAN0519 and CHAN0512 (two discs, oas: 63 and 64 minutes: DDD: 4/92). ✍
Recorded 1990-1991.
CHAN0519: Concertos – A minor for Violin; E minor for Flute and Violin (Rachel Brown, fl);
G major for Four Unaccompanied Violins; A major for Four Violins (Micaela Comberti,
Miles Golding, Andrew Manze, vns); E major for Violin. Orchestral Suite in G minor,
"La Changeante". *CHAN0512:* Concertos – G major for Violin; D major for Two Flutes, Violin
and Cello (Brown, Siu Peasgood, fls; Jane Coe, vc); F sharp minor for Violin; G major for
Two Violins (Comberti). Orchestral Suite in B flat major, "Ouverture burlesque".   Ⓖ

It is difficult to mention Telemann without referring to the prolific and eclectic nature of his output,
both of which are reflected in his very numerous concertos, and in these recordings the two works that
are *not* concertos – *La Changeante* and *Ouverture burlesque*, both of which evoke the spirit of the
commedia dell'arte. What changes in *La Changeante* is not only the moods of the movements but also
their keys; only the first and last of the eight are in the home key of G minor, the others are in a
variety of different ones, a most unusual feature at that time. The ouverture-suites are predominantly
French in style but the concertos represent Telemann's highly individual variant of Venetian models.
Whilst Vivaldi's concertos are predominantly in three movements (quick-slow-quick), Telemann's are
usually in four or five, with no set pattern of pace, and they take both *da chiesa* and *da camera* forms.
Telemann's muse seems rarely to have slept, likewise his acute sense of instrumental colour. When
Playford wrote of "Sprightly and cheerful musick" he was referring to that of the cittern; had he lived

a little longer he might have felt the same about that of Telemann, not least if he had heard it played so expertly by Collegium Musicum 90, who are brought into your home by most faithful recorded sound.

Additional recommendation ...

...Concertos – Three Oboes, Three Violins and Strings in B flat major; Concerto for Four Violins and Strings in G major; Concerto for Recorder, Bassoon and Strings in F major; Overture-Suite in F major. **Vienna Concentus Musicus / Nikolaus Harnoncourt.** Teldec Das Alte Werk Reference Ⓜ 0630-12320-2 (54 minutes: ADD: 8/96). 🗲

Telemann Overture-Suite in A minor[a]. Concerto in E minor for Recorder and Flute[b]. Viola Concerto No. 1 in G major[c]. Ouverture des Nations: anciens et modernes for Strings and Continuo, TWV55[d]. [b]**Franz Verster** (fl); [c]**Paul Doctor** (va); [a]**South-West German Chamber Orchestra / Friedrich Tilegant;** [bd]**Amsterdam Chamber Orchestra / André Rieu;** [c]**Concerto Amsterdam / Frans Brüggen** ([ab]rec). Teldec Das Alte Werk Ⓜ 9031-77620-2 (69 minutes: ADD: 7/93). 🗲 Items marked [abd] recorded 1967, [c]1968. ⒼⒼ

Four performances of the highest calibre, marvellously recorded in the 1960s and now sounding as fresh as the day they were made. Two of them feature the distinguished recorder player Frans Brüggen (who is now more often heard on disc as a conductor). He is at his inimitable finest, and this is very fine indeed, in the masterly Suite in A minor for recorder and strings (every bit as fine a work as the Bach B minor Suite for the same instrumentation) and the E minor Concerto for recorder, transverse flute and strings with its attractive interplay of solo texture. Here he is joined by Franz Verster. Brüggen then moves to the conductor's podium to direct the Concerto Amsterdam, joined by a superb viola player, Paul Doctor, in the justly famous G major Viola Concerto. The *Ouverture des Nations: anciens et modernes* is another suite (comprising nine movements), full of the composer's most felicitous invention. The music is played with great character and the CD transfer is exemplary.

Telemann Overture-Suite in C major, TWV55: C3, "Hamburger Ebb und Fluth". Overture-Suite in D major[a]. Concerto in A minor for Two Recorders, Two Oboes and Strings[b]. Concerto in E minor for Recorder, Flute and Strings[c]. [b]**Dominique Gauthier** (fl); [a]**Philippe Foulon** (va da gamba); **Orchestre Musica Antiqua / Christian Mendoze** ([bc]rec). Pierre Verany Ⓕ PV796022 (68 minutes: DDD: 7/96). 🗲

An attractive programme of suites and concertos – two of each – comes from the Orchestre Musica Antiqua under their director, Christian Mendoze. Musica Antiqua were founded some 15 years ago but their representation on disc, at least in the UK, has been infrequent. As we might expect, these musicians bring a markedly French atmosphere to Telemann's Suites. And why not? Telemann was drawn to French ouvertures and their appended suites of dances at an early age and his love of them never deserted him. In the Suite in C major, variously subtitled *Wassermusik* and *Hamburger Ebb und Fluth*, indigenous French gestures especially can be felt in rhythmic *inégalités* and in the ornamented resolution of several final cadences. This Suite is colourfully scored for pairs of recorders and oboes with bassoon and strings and it is the woodwind department of the Ensemble which gives the performance its lustre. That is not to imply any serious shortcoming in the string playing but rather that the recording balance favours the wind instruments. None of the four works, in fact, is well served by the acoustic, which is hollow in sound and reverberant in a way that only intermittently captures the character of the instruments; and the solo and *concertino* players are placed too close to the microphone. Whatever the shortcomings of the recording itself, however – and anyway this is purely a matter of personal preference – the spirited and mainly stylish playing of these musicians is hardly open to question. In the D major Suite the solo viola da gamba, to which Telemann gives pride of place throughout, is expressively played by Philippe Foulon. He is a gambist who proves his eloquence above all in the fine Sarabande of the work. The two concertos are for solo woodwind and strings. The A minor work is scored for pairs of recorders, oboes and violins with basso continuo, while that in E minor, the best-known piece in the programme, features an unusual partnership of recorder and flute, the old and the new, so to speak. The A minor Concerto is the slighter of the two and is the one work here which Telemann enthusiasts may not have in their library. It is an engaging piece with lively dialogue among the three instrumental groups; but it lacks the colourful invention of the E minor Concerto, with its tender slow movements and wild, swirling Polish dance finale. What the performances lack in finesse is generously compensated for in sheer interpretative *esprit*.

Additional recommendation ...

...Overture-Suite, "Hamburger Ebb und Fluth". **Handel** Water Music, HWV348-50. **The King's Consort / Robert King.** Hyperion Ⓕ CDA66967 (70 minutes: DDD: 10/97). 🗲

Telemann Overture-Suites – G minor, TWV55: g4; A minor, TWV55: a2[a]; C major, TWV55: C6; D major, TWV55: D15; D minor, TWV55: d3; F minor, TWV55: f1[a]. **Vienna Concentus Musicus / Nikolaus Harnoncourt.** Teldec Das Alte Werk Ⓜ 4509-93772-2 (two discs: 148 minutes: ADD: 12/94). 🗲 Items marked [a] from SAWT9507 (3/68), others recorded 1978. ⒼⒼ

Harnoncourt is nowhere more at home than in the aesthetic world of this music. The Overtures of the ravishing G minor Suite and the bolder C major work show him to be a master of noble gesture and purposeful articulation. Compared with Trevor Pinnock's accounts of these two works (see reviews elsewhere), the current performances are less even in terms of orchestral exactitude and pure luxuriance of texture but there is a robust, biting energy about Harnoncourt which is infectious; often, as in the Bourée *en trompette* of the C major work, one imagines that the exaggerated contrasts and deliberate accentuations would appear mannered if executed by anyone other than Harnoncourt. Throughout, he conjures up subtle rhythmic deviations, each paragraph flexibly shaped but still controlled and naturally breathed. If pliancy of this kind is an answer to making sense of baroque phrasing, then texture speaks volumes too: Telemann's oboe writing in particular, and its place within a string body is exceptionally skilled; his scoring of three oboes is especially effective and the oboists play with irresistible *esprit*. The D major Suite is full of instances where their performances brim with personality, contributing greatly to that fruity and ever so musty nose which characterizes Concentus Musicus on vintage form. The recorded sound is full of presence. To sum up: with Harnoncourt one can imagine few exponents better suited to this colourful repertoire. Pinnock's two recent recordings of suites are obligatory for baroque collectors generally but this release is full of many unique delights and it contains three works not otherwise available in the catalogue.

Additional recommendations ...
...A minor, TWV55: a2[a]. Concertos – F major; C major. Sinfonia in F major[a].
Peter Holtslag (rec); **The Parley of Instruments / Peter Holman,** [a]**Roy Goodman.**
Hyperion Ⓕ CDA66413 (66 minutes: DDD: 10/91). ✍
...C major, TWV55: C6; D major, TWV55: D19; B flat major, TTWV55: B10. **The English Concert /**
Trevor Pinnock. Archiv Produktion Ⓕ 437 558-2AH (77 minutes: DDD: 6/93). ✍   ⓆⓆ
...D major, TWV55: D6[b]; A minor, TWV55: A2[a]. Sinfonia in F major, TWV50: 3[ab]. Concerto for
Recorder, Viola da gamba and Strings in A minor[ab]. [a]**Marion Verbruggen** (rec);
[b]**Sarah Cunningham** (va da gamba); **Orchestra of the Age of Enlightenment / Monica Huggett.**
Harmonia Mundi Ⓕ HMU90 7093 (74 minutes: DDD: 1/94). ✍   Ⓠ

Telemann Overture-Suites – G major, TWV55:G4, "Des Nations anciens et modernes";
B flat major, "Völker-Overture". Concerto for Two Chalumeaux and Strings in D minor[a].
Sonata for Two Chalumeaux and Continuo in F major[a]. Viola Concerto in G major[b].
[a]**Colin Lawson,** [a]**Michael Harris** (chalumeaux); **Collegium Musicum 90 / Simon Standage** (vn/[b]va).
Chandos Chaconne Ⓕ CHAN0593 (77 minutes: DDD: 9/96). ✍ Recorded 1995.
Gramophone Editor's choice.

The seemingly endless supply of Telemann's orchestral music shows no sign of palling in this release from Collegium Musicum 90, which mixes two colourful overture-suites with works for that mellow forerunner of the clarinet, the chalumeau, and the Concerto for viola which is famous mainly for being, well, a concerto for viola. The last three works are somewhat conventional, it must be admitted, but all show how readily the adaptable Telemann was able to find distinctive and attractive qualities in individual instruments, however unusual; the concerto for two chalumeaux, especially, has a calming summer-night feel to it. All are expertly played by their respective soloists. Undoubtedly of more interest, though, are the two suites, both of which feature a sequence of movements depicting the peoples of different European nations. Telemann's allusions are sometimes a little obscure – it's not easy to work out what makes one movement Swedish and another Swiss – but the results are certainly fun; try "Les turcs", or the brief but extraordinary "Les moscovites", with its three-note bell ostinato not unlike Bizet's *L'Arlésienne*. The performances are clean, neatly characterized and brightly recorded, from an orchestra that is really beginning to settle into a character of its own these days. One can't listen to Telemann without warming to the man in the way one does to Haydn, but on the evidence of these pieces you would have to deduce that not only was he an affable companion but also unfailingly witty and probably an entertaining mimic as well. How his musicians must have loved him!

Telemann Essercizii Musici. **Cologne Camerata.** Deutsche Harmonia Mundi Ⓕ 05472 77361-2
(four discs: 236 minutes: DDD: 3/97). Recorded 1994-1995. ✍
Essercizii Musici consists of 12 trios, ten sonatas for melody instrument with basso continuo and two suites for solo harpsichord. The contents are satisfying on two levels since not only do they furnish the listener with unflagging entertainment but they also provide the performer with music written with unusual sympathy for the instruments in question. Telemann could turn his hand to almost anything and, it would seem, at the drop of a hat, did so. Here we have music both of intrinsically high calibre and of a cast which effortlessly explores the most alluring vocal range of each instrument. It is music which, in short, fulfils one of the composer's fervently declared aims, to give each instrument what suits it best, thus pleasing both player and audience. The members of Cologne Camerata, individually and corporately, enliven the music with stylistic and instrumental fluency. Telemann's distinctive expressive inflexions are not difficult to translate in performance yet their very ingenuousness, simplicity and lack of contrivance too often results in their being glossed over. These musicians revel in the melancholy suspensions, playful gymnastics and convivial instrumental dialogue with which these solos and trios abound. Certainly not all the pieces are of equal depth, but in trios such as that in C minor (No. 1), A major (No. 4), B flat (No. 8) and E flat (No. 12), Telemann reveals an extraordinary *puissance*, making a contribution to mid-eighteenth century chamber music that is both significant and inspired. In short, this is an important and delightful issue which should make instant appeal among lovers of eighteenth-century music. Fine recorded sound.

Additional recommendation ...
...Trios[a] – No. 4; No. 7 in F major, TWV42: F3; No. 8. Trio Sonatas[a] – F major, TWV42: F14; A minor, TWV42: a1; A minor,TWV42: a6. Fantaisies for Flute without Continuo, TWV40: 2-13 – No. 1 in A major; No. 5 in C major (played in F major). Der getreue Music-Meister – Sonata in C major, TWV41: C2[a]. **Sébastien Marq** (rec); [a]**Le Concert Français.** Auvidis Astrée Ⓔ E8554 (70 minutes: DDD: 2/96). ✍

Telemann Sonates Corellisantes – No. 1 in F major, TWV42: F2. Paris Quartets, "Nouveaux quatuors en Six Suites" – No. 6 in E minor, TWV43: e4. Essercizii Musici – Trio No. 8 in B flat major, TWV42: B4. Quartets – A minor, TWV43: a3; G minor, TWV43: g4. **Florilegium Ensemble.** Channel Classics Ⓔ CCS5093 (53 minutes: DDD: 10/93). ✍ Recorded 1992.   Ⓖ
The rarity here is the *Sonata Corellisante* for two violins and continuo in which Telemann pays tribute to Corelli. The remaining works are the sixth and perhaps finest of the 1738 *Nouveaux Quatuors* or *Paris Quartets* as they have become known, a little *Quartet* (or *Quadro*) in G minor, a B flat Trio from the *Essercizii Musici* collection (*c.*1739) and a fine Concerto da camera (Quartet) in A minor, very much along the lines of Vivaldi's pieces of the same kind in which each instrument other than the continuo has an obbligato role. The finest work here is the *Paris Quartet* which consists of a Prelude, a sequence of dance-orientated movements and an elegiac Chaconne that lingers long in the memory. The performance is full of vitality and probes beneath the music's superficialities. There is, throughout the programme, an intensity and a youthful spontaneity about this playing which has considerable appeal; and the continuo line, furthermore, is handled with boldness and imagination.

Additional recommendations ...
...Paris Quartets[a]. Suite in F major[b]. Overture-Suite in E flat major, TWV55: Es3[c].
[a]**Amsterdam Quartet;** [b]**Jaap Schroder** (vn); [bc]**Concerto Amsterdam / Frans Brüggen.**
Teldec 4509-92177-2. ✍   Ⓖ
...Musique de table – Quartet in E minor. Paris Quartets – No. 1 in D major, TWV43: D3; No. 2 in A minor, TWV43: a2. Six Concerts et Six Suites – Concert No. 3 in A major, TWV42: A3.
Hortus Musicus / Andres Mustonen (vn). Finlandia Ⓔ 4509-95578-2 (52 minutes: DDD: 9/95). ✍
...Paris Quartets (Quadri). **Christopher Krueger** (fl); **Boston Museum Trio.**
Centaur Ⓔ CRC2260 (72 minutes: DDD: 8/96).

Telemann Kleine Cammer-Music – Partita No. 2 in G major, TWV41:G2. Essercizii Musici – Solo No. 5 in B flat major, TWV41:B6; Solo No. 11 in E minor, TWV41:e6; Trio No. 12 in E flat major, TWV42:Es3. Der getreue Music-Meister – Sonata in A minor, TWV41:a3. Harmonischer Gottes-Dienst – No. 26, Am Sonntage Jubilate in C minor, TWV1:356[a]; No. 31, Am ersten Pfingstfeiertage in G major, TWV1:1732[a]. **Paul Goodwin** (ob); **Nigel North** (lte/theorbo); **Susan Sheppard;** [a]**Lynden Cranham** (vcs); **John Toll** (hpd). Harmonia Mundi Ⓔ HMU90 7152 (65 minutes: DDD: 1/97). ✍ Recorded 1995. *Gramophone Editor's choice.*   Ⓖ
Paul Goodwin is surely one of the finest baroque oboists of the moment, so when he turns his mind to such a master of agreeable and skilfully composed chamber music as Telemann, it must be worth our while listening in. Every piece has its own character and charms: here is a seven-movement Partita from the *Kleine Cammer-Music* of 1716, then a couple of Solos and a quirky Trio involving an obbligato harpsichord from the *Essercizii Musici* of 1739, while a Lesson from the giant 1720s part-work, *Der getreue Music-Meister*, sits alongside movements with oboe obbligato from the slightly earlier sacred cantata collection *Harmonischer Gottes-Dienst*. The variety of form and nomenclature is more than matched on this disc by that of accompaniments which, as so many of the best continuo teams do these days, make an indispensable creative contribution to the success of the performance as a whole. With the boisterous and inspired Romanesca pair of Nigel North and John Toll on board this is no surprise. A cello also takes the original vocal line in the cantata movements, though the identity of the player (Susan Sheppard) is not made clear in the booklet. As for Goodwin himself, his playing is bold and bright with solid, versatile technique and fluid phrasing, and his interpretations are detailed and intelligent while losing nothing in spontaneity. The recorded sound for all instruments is perhaps rather aggressive over the space of an hour's listening, but then these are performances which by their very refusal to be timid demand full attention.

Additional recommendation ...
...Kleine Cammer-Music – Partita No. 2 in G minor, TWV41:g2. Der getreue Music-Meister – Sonata for Oboe and Continuo in A minor, TWV41:a3; Sonata for Two Oboes and Continuo in C minor, TWV42:c4[a]. Musique de Table – Sonata for Oboe and Continuo in G minor. Concerto for Two Oboes, Trumpet and Continuo No. 2 in D[ab]. Essercizii Musici – Trio Sonata in E flat for Oboe, Harpsichord and Continuo, TWV42:Es3[c]. **Marcel Ponseele,** [a]**Taka Kitazako** (obs); [b]**Per-Olov Lindeke** (tpt); [c]**Fred Jacobs** (theorbo); **Richte van der Meer** (vc); **Pierre Hantaï** (hpd). Accent Ⓔ ACC95110D (65 minutes: DDD: 8/96). ✍

Telemann 12 Fantaisies for Violin without Continuo, TWV40: 14-25. Der Getreue Music-Meister – "Gulliver" Suite in D, TWV40:108[a]. **Andrew Manze,** [a]**Caroline Balding** (vns). ✍
Harmonia Mundi Ⓔ HMU90 7137 (78 minutes: DDD: 6/96). Recorded 1994.
Andrew Manze brings a very definite and distinctive angle to the 12 *Fantaisies*, one which we can hear from the outset delicately balances clarity of thought with the sense of restoring the lost art of

extemporization. We have learnt to take virtuosity for granted with Manze – his remarkable feats allow the most prejudiced to forget that he is playing a baroque fiddle. But without such an instrument he could barely create such a biting astringency in the more self-effacing and tortured moments (*Fantaisie* No. 6) or a cultivated assurance and definition in articulation to the recognizably regular sections, such as *Fantaisie* No. 10, where Telemann is working in established forms – particularly in the latter works in the set where dance forms predominate. If characterization is the key, Manze is arguably the most persuasive of all his rivals. He grows through phrases in the Gigue of the Fourth *Fantaisie* in a fashion which gives the work a peculiarly stoical strength, purrs through the contrapuntally conceived *Fantaisies* (Nos. 1-6 in particular) with nonchalant disdain for their often extreme technical demands and leaves sighs and pauses hanging with supreme eloquence. If Homburger brings some moments of keener grace and repose, then one must also recognize the robust integrity and humour of Sheppard's accounts. But for sheer lucidity, breadth of imagination and colour, one is drawn again and again to Manze's version; he most acutely captures the sense of a famous public figure ensconced in a private world against the backdrop of a musical world in a state of flux. To add spice to an already outstanding release, we have the short and delightful *Gulliver* Suite for two violins where Manze is joined by Caroline Balding – trust Telemann to be up-to-the-mark only a year or two after *Gulliver's Travels* was published!

Additional recommendations ...
...12 Fantaisies. **Betina Maag Santos** (vn). Gallo Ⓕ CD-718 (75 minutes: ADD: 8/94).   Ⓖ
...12 Fantaisies. **Maya Homburger** (vn).
Maya Recordings Ⓕ MCD9302 (72 minutes: DDD: 8/94). ✒   Ⓖ
...12 Fantaisies. **Peter Sheppard** (vn). Meridian Ⓕ CDE84266 (67 minutes: DDD: 8/94).
...12 Fantaisies. **Angèle Dubeau** (vn). Analekta fleurs de lys Ⓜ FL2 3048 (68 minutes: DDD: 11/97).

Telemann 12 Sonate metodiche. **Barthold Kuijken** (fl); **Wieland Kuijken** (va da gamba); **Robert Kohnen** (hpd). Accent Ⓕ ACC94104/5D (two discs: 140 minutes: DDD: 5/96). ✒ Recorded 1994.
No, the title is hardly an incentive to part with one's pocket-money. But with Telemann we should know better than to be taken in by such packaging details. These are, in fact, 12 skilfully written and entertaining sonatas, published in two sets of six and issued in 1728 and 1732. Telemann seems, right from the start, to have had two instruments in mind: flute or violin, and though Barthold Kuijken has elected to play all of them on a baroque flute, he does so with such technical mastery that there is little cause for regret. He savours the many playful ideas contained in the faster movements and realizes a touching sense of melancholy in several of the slow ones. Among the most impressive of the sonatas is that in B minor which Kuijken plays with sensitivity and technical panache. The interpretation is on a sufficiently elevated level to warrant unqualified praise. The recorded sound is first-rate.

Telemann Hamburger Admiralitätsmusik, TWV24:1[a]. Overture-Suite in C major, TWV55:C3, "Hamburger Ebb und Fluth". [a]**Mieke van der Sluis** (sop); [a]**Graham Pushee** (alto); [a]**Rufus Müller** (ten); [a]**Klaus Mertens, [a]David Thomas, [b]Michael Schopper** (basses); [a]**Alsfeld Vocal Ensemble; Bremen Baroque Orchestra / Wolfgang Helbich.** CPO Ⓕ CPO999 373-2 (two discs: 119 minutes: DDD: 2/97). ✒ Text and translation included. Recorded live in 1995.
Readers with an affection for Telemann will quickly recognize an old friend in the orchestral suite *Hamburger Ebb und Fluth*. The piece has been recorded many times over the past 35 years or so and is one of the most engaging examples from his pen of a form at which he excelled. The Bremen Baroque Orchestra give a lively and elegantly shaped performance of the work, introducing to its French overture a degree of *gravitas* appropriate to the occasion. Following the orchestral suite comes the *Admiralitätsmusik* serenade itself whose own introductory French overture's opening gestures call to mind the overture to Handel's *Music for the Royal Fireworks* written a quarter of a century later. Richey's poem is a paean to Hamburg, its institutions, its government and, not least, its prosperity. Each of the soloists assumes a role. Hamburg (Harmonia) is assigned to the soprano, judicial wisdom (Themis) to a countertenor, prosperity (Mercurius) to a tenor, the Elbe (Albis), North Sea (Neptunus) and republican liberty (Mars) to three basses. Recitatives and arias for these dramatis personae make up the greater part of Richey's text, lightly seasoned with occasional choruses for nymphs, tritons and the like. While it is more than likely that the audience in whose honour the serenade was written responded more readily to the topical and topographical allusions in Richey's text than to Telemann's music, quite the reverse applies today. Richey's platitudinous, at times flatulent sentiments are not likely to fire the imagination of late twentieth-century landlubbers. Yet Telemann's contribution, though uneven, is colourfully depictive and, as always, full of alluring charm. The solo team is a strong one, but the Alsfeld Vocal Ensemble do not always match them in tonal precision. The string playing is clean but would have better served the music if it had been more rhythmically incisive. In summary, this is a fascinating issue. Clear sound from a live recording made in Bremen.

Telemann Der Herr ist König, TWV8:6[a]. Die Donner-Ode, TWV6:3[b]. [a]**Ann Monoyios,** [b]**Barbara Schlick** (sops); [b]**Axel Köhler** (alto); **Wilfried Jochens** (ten); [a]**Harry van der Kamp,** [b]**Hans-Georg Wimmer, Stephan Schreckenberger** (basses); **Rheinische Kantorei; Das Kleine Konzert / Hermann Max.** Capriccio Ⓕ 10 556 (65 minutes: DDD: 11/95). Texts and translations included. Recorded 1990-1992.

The *Donner-Ode* was one of Telemann's biggest public successes during his lifetime and is a striking piece in its own right, a vivid reaction to the Lisbon earthquake of 1755. The shock caused to the international community by this dreadful event (in which some 60,000 people were killed) was enormous, and in Hamburg a special day of penitence was the occasion for this "Thunder Ode", though it does perhaps suggest a rather smug satisfaction that such a disaster didn't befall northern Germany. "The voice of God makes the proud mountains collapse", the text proclaims, "Give thanks to Him in His temple!". The music, too, both in its mood and in that extraordinarily up-to-date style of Telemann's later years, frequently conjures the benign, entertainingly song-like pictorial mood of a Haydn Mass or oratorio. Entertaining is the word, though, especially in this energetic performance under Hermann Max. He is more fleet-footed and buoyantly athletic than Richard Hickox, benefiting from what is becoming his customary excellent team of German soloists. Hickox's *Donner-Ode* is coupled with Telemann's charmingly Frenchified motet, *Deus judicium tuum*, but Max chooses another German work, the cheerful cantata *Der Herr ist König*, written much earlier in the composer's life and rather more Bach-like in character and form (though it is worth pointing out that since it survives partly in Bach's hand, we ought perhaps to conclude that Telemann was the one wielding the influence here). As in the *Ode*, choir, soloists and orchestra are bright, tight-knit and well recorded, making this release as a whole an enjoyable one.

Additional recommendation ...

...Die Donner-Ode[a]. Deus judicium tuum. **Patrizia Kwella** (sop); **Catherine Denley** (mez); **Mark Tucker** (ten); **Stephen Roberts** (bar); [a]**Michael George** (bass); **Collegium Musicum 90 Chorus; Collegium Musicum 90 / Richard Hickox.** Chandos Chaconne Ⓟ CHAN0548 (61 minutes: DDD: 8/94). ✔   Ⓖ

Telemann Die Hirten an der Krippe zu Bethlehem, TWV1: 797[a]. Siehe, uch verkündige Euch, TWV1:1334[b]. Der Herr hat offenbaret, TWV1:262[c]. [bc]**Constanze Backes** (sop); [ac]**Mechthild Georg** (contr); **Andreas Post** (ten); **Klaus Mertens** (bass); **Michaelstein Chamber Choir; Telemann Chamber Orchestra / Ludger Rémy.** CPO Ⓟ CPO999 419-2 (65 minutes: DDD: 12/97). ✔
Texts and translations included. Recorded 1996.

The tenderly expressive and ingenuous character of German Protestant Christmas music of the baroque seldom fails to exert its magic. Though the greatest achievements in this tradition greatly diminished after Bach, there were exceptions. One of them is Telemann's intimate and characteristically imaginative oratorio *Die Hirten an der Krippe zu Bethlehem* ("The Shepherds at the Crib in Bethlehem"). It belongs to the period of the composer's last creative outburst which began in the mid-1750s and lasted for almost exactly a decade. The text is by the Berlin poet, Ramler and though Ramler's taste for classical forms sometimes makes his work stiff and austere, nothing could be further removed from this than his intimate account and celebration of Christ's birth. Certainly, it touched a chord in Telemann who responded with music of expressive warmth and irresistible charm. This is not at all the world of Bach's *Christmas Oratorio*, indeed it is only approximately a sixth of the length of Bach's masterpiece. Telemann's concept is one rather of noble simplicity, a sought-after goal in post-Bach church music which, in this respect, at least, provided a perfect foil to Ramler's text. Every reader will recognize the melody of the opening number as belonging to the Latin carol *In dulci jubilo*. Telemann's harmonization of the sixteenth-century tune, straightforward but with an occasional harmonic piquancy, sets the scene concisely and intimately. Thereafter, follows one delight after another. Of outstanding beauty are the "Shepherd's Song" and the bass aria, "Hirten aus den goldnen Zeiten". This is an extremely pleasurable, well-filled, disc with a pervasive charm. The remaining two items are both Christmas cantatas, of 1761 and 1762 respectively and contain music of enormous appeal. Performances are excellent, with outstanding singing by Klaus Mertens and Mechthild Georg. Both choir and orchestra rise to the occasion under the sensitive and stylish direction of Ludger Rémy. Three hitherto unrecorded pieces in performances of such vitality make this comfortably a very strong issue.

Telemann Orpheus. **Roman Trekel** (bar) Orpheus; **Ruth Ziesak** (sop) Eurydice; **Dorothea Röschmann** (sop) Orasia; **Werner Güra** (ten) Eurimedes; **Maria Cristina Kiehr** (sop) Ismene; **Hanno Müller-Brachmann** (bar) Pluto; **Isabelle Poulenard** (sop) Cephisa, Priestess; **Axel Köhler** (alto) Ascalax; **RIAS Chamber Choir, Berlin; Academy for Ancient Music, Berlin / René Jacobs.** Harmonia Mundi Ⓟ HMC90 1618/9 (two discs: 159 minutes: DDD: 3/98). ⒼⒼ
Notes, text and translation included. Recorded 1996. *Gramophone Editor's choice.*

This is the first performance on disc of an opera that was recognized as being the product of Telemann's pen only some 20 years ago. The first performance of *Orpheus* took place in Hamburg, at the famous Gänsemarkt Opera in 1726. The original libretto was by a Frenchman, Michel du Boullay. Telemann himself seems to have adapted the text to suit Hamburg taste but though the libretto has survived virtually complete, a small part of the score is lost. For the edition used here, Peter Huth – who has also contributed a useful essay – Jakob Peters-Messer and René Jacobs, have filled the lacunae with music from other Telemann sources. Telemann's *Orpheus* has an additional dimension to the standard version of the legend in the person of Orasia, widowed Queen of Thrace. She occupies a key position in the drama first as murderess of Eurydice of whose love for Orpheus she is jealous, then of Orpheus himself, since he, understandably, rejects her advances. The plot develops effectively, contributing greatly to the dramatic coherence and overall satisfaction provided by text and music alike. In common with a great many operas for the Hamburg stage, *Orpheus* contains arias sung in languages other than the German vernacular. Italian was the usual alternative, but here there are airs in French, too, and Telemann, on these occasions, lends emphasis to the 'mixed style' aesthetic, in which he was an ardent believer, by retaining the distinctive stylistic character of each country. But the German arias are often both the most interesting and the most varied, since it is the Lied and the *arioso*, as developed in the Passion-Oratorio settings, that provide those additional ingredients which vitalize, refresh and give distinction to his music.

The cast is first-rate. Dorothea Röschmann projects a passionate and temperamental Orasia for whom Telemann has provided several strongly characterized arias. Orpheus is sung by Roman Trekel, Eurydice by Ruth Ziesak. Telemann adorns both roles with an affecting blend of lyricism and pathos. Eurydice's part in the drama is, perforce, relatively small but her music is often alluring and nowhere more so, perhaps, than when she welcomes the shades, who gather to prevent an opportunity for the lovers to look upon one another during the rescue scene. There are some forward-looking harmonies here which foreshadow later developments in opera. Orpheus's music is, appropriately, captivating more often than not; and it is strikingly varied in character. The other major beneficiary of Telemann's musical largesse is Orpheus's friend, Eurimedes, a tenor role expressively sung by Werner Güra. Pluto, a bass-baritone role sung with resonance and authority by Hanno Müller-Brachmann, appears in Act 1 only; but he has some splendid music". The remaining roles are small but, of these, Ismene, one of Orasia's ladies-in-waiting, deserves mention for the aria, "Bitter und süss sind Rachgier und Liebe". This double-edged piece is ravishingly sung by Maria Cristina Kiehr. And another, for Pluto's servant Ascalax, contains moments of vivid word-painting fluently if, perhaps, tamely handled by Axel Köhler. In choosing a soprano of the calibre of Isabelle Poulenard to sing the minor role of Cephisa, a nymph, Jacobs showed shrewd judgement, since Telemann wrote a virtuoso aria for her which Poulenard sings with brilliance and technical skill. Cephisa also shares some delightful music with a chorus of nymphs. There are several fine (though brief) choruses, lightly and articulately sung by the RIAS Chamber Choir and a handful of invigorating instrumental numbers. The instrumental movements are very well played by the Berlin Academy for Ancient Music. Jacobs and his musicians deserve congratulations, and so do Harmonia Mundi for their first-rate recording. This is an important and hugely enjoyable release.

Further listening ...

...Concerto for Two Oboes, Trumpet and Strings No. 1 in D major. *Coupled with works by various composers.* **Crispian Steele-Perkins** (tpt); **Neil Black, James Brown** (obs); **English Chamber Orchestra / Anthony Halstead.** Carlton Classics 30366 0066-2 (10/97). *See review in the Collections section; refer to the Index.*

...Concerto for Trumpet, Two Oboes and Strings in D major. *Coupled with works by various composers.* **Crispian Steele-Perkins,** [a]**John Thiessen** (tpts); **Tafelmusik / Jeanne Lamon** (vn). Sony Classical Vivarte SK53365 (4/95). 🎵

...Horn Concerto in D major. *Coupled with works by various composers.* **Barry Tuckwell** (hn); **Academy of St Martin in the Fields / Sir Neville Marriner.** EMI Forte CZS5 69395-2 (2/97). *See review in the Collections section; refer to the Index.*

...Ich weiss, dass mein Erlöser lebt. *Coupled with works by* **Bach** *and* **Hoffmann.** **C.P.E. Bach Chamber Orchestra / Peter Schreier** (ten). Philips 442 786-2PH (5/98). *See review under Bach; refer to the Index.*

...Sonata (Septett) in E minor. *Coupled with works by* **Gluck** *and* **Rebel** **Cologne Musica Antiqua / Reinhard Goebel.** Archiv Produktion 445 824-2AH (12/95). 🎵

...Trumpet Concerto in D major. *Coupled with works by various composers.* **Niklas Eklund** (baroque tpt); **Drottningholm Baroque Ensemble / Nils-Erik Sparf.** Naxos 8 553531 (11/96). 🎵 *See review in the Collections section; refer to the Index.*

...Trio Sonatas – G minor, TWV42:g9; A minor, TWV42:a4. *Coupled with works by various composers* **Palladian Ensemble.** Linn Records CKD050 (5/97). 🎵 *See review in the collections section; refer to the Index.*

...12 Fantaisies for Flute without Continuo, TWV40: 2-13. **Peter Holtslag** (rec). Globe GLO5117 (12/94). 🎵   Ⓖ

...Die Auferstehung und Himmelfahrt Jesu, TWV6:6. **Soloists; Rheinische Kantorei; Das Kleine Konzert / Hermann Max.** Capriccio 10 596 (7/96).

...Cantatas – Tirsis am Scheidewege; Nach Finsternis und Todesschatten; Meines Bleibens ist nicht hier. Das Frauenzimmer verstimmt sich immer. Vergiss dich selbst, mein schönster Engel. An der Schlaf. Die Einsamkeit. Concerto grosso in E minor – Adagio. **René Jacobs** (alto); **Berlin Academy for Ancient Music.** Capriccio 10 338 (11/92). 🎵

...Du aber Daniel, gehe hin – Mit sehnenden verlangen; Richt ihr müde Augen nieder. *Coupled with works by various composers.* **Elly Ameling** (sop); **Various soloists.** Deutsche Harmonia Mundi 74321 26617-2 (12/95). *See review in the Collections section; refer to the Index.*

...Missa brevis. Deus judicium tuum. Alles redet jetzt und singet. **Soloists; Rheinische Kantorei; Das Kleine Konzert / Hermann Max.** Capriccio 10 315 (11/91). 🎵

...Pimpinone. **John Ostendorf** (bass); **Julianne Baird** (sop); **St Luke's Baroque Orchestra / Rudolph Palmer.** Newport Classic NCD60117 (1/92). 🎵

...Schwanengesang, TWV4: 6 Herr, strafe mich nicht in Deinem Trinitatis, TWV1: 771.

Soloists; La Stagione / **Michael Schneider.** CPO CPO999 212-2 (7/94). ✒
...St Matthew Passion. **Soloists; Darmstadt Chorus and Chamber Orchestra / Wolfgang Seeliger.**
Christophorus CHR77149 (5/95).
...Don Quichotte auf der Hochzeit des Comacho. **Soloists; Bremen Vocal Ensemble
for Ancient Music; La Stagione / Michael Schneider.** CPO CPO999 210-2 (9/94). ✒ Ⓖ
...Der getreue Music-Meister. **Soloists; Würzburg Bach Choir; instrumental ensemble /
Josef Ulsamer.** Archiv Produktion 447 722-2AX4 (4/96). Ⓖ
...Der neumodische Liebhaber Damon oder Die Satyrn in Arkadien. **Soloists; La Stagione
Vocal Ensemble; La Stagione / Michael Schneider.** CPO CPO999 429-2 (A/97). ✒

Avet Terterian
Armenian 1929-1994

Terterian Symphonies – No. 3; No. 4. **Armenian Philharmonic Orchestra / Loris Tjeknavorian.**
ASV Ⓕ CDDCA986 (55 minutes: DDD: A/97). Recorded 1996.
When Avet Terterian came to London's Royal Festival Hall to hear his Seventh Symphony in
November 1994, it was the first time his music had been heard in the UK. We now have a fine
opportunity to discover on disc just how distinctive and provocative his voice was. Like so many of
his generation in Russia and its satellite republics, Terterian found that voice by a fusion of Polish
school 'sonoristics' and spiritual symbolism. In his case the catalyst was provided by the folk
instruments of his native Armenia. They helped unlock for him a world of philosophical and
psychological essences, far removed from the picture-postcard nationalism of a Khachaturian. He
developed an obsession with the mystique of the single sound, and this took him to paradoxical
thresholds – where profound meaning almost tips into absurdity, where hyper-expressivity almost tips
into pure noise. The Third Symphony begins with arresting thumps on the timpani, not heralding
anything else, just there as a kind of ritual incantation. Other ingredients in the first movement are
inscrutable bass-register grunts accompanied by fragile-sounding bells, and piercing bagpipe-like
noises with whooping horns and fearful grimaces on brass. Part of the fascination is that the large
orchestra (including 12 horns) spend so much of their time listening to the still, small voice of some
solo instrument. The second movement in particular is often only just above the threshold of
audibility, sounding extraordinarily disconsolate in its microtonal drifting. The finale returns to more
dramatically polarized forces, which persist to the very end. The Fourth Symphony is an unbroken 34-
minute span, featuring a taped Russian bell, a kind of cracked harpsichord chorale, and much queasy
undulating violin writing. At the 27'30" mark an apparently easy fade into oblivion is overturned by
force, as though violating a state of mourning. The end comes, characteristically, with muffled drum
and stifled bell. The dryish recordings do nothing to varnish the music's discomforting surfaces but
those surfaces conceal emotional depths which seem to be genuine and unique. This is impressive
music delivered with intensity in these performances.

Gaudencio Thiago de Mello
Brazilian 20th century

Suggested listening ...
...A Hug for Pixingha[a]. Chants for the Chief[ab] – No. 1, A Chamada dos ventos/Canção Nocturna;
No. 2, Uirapurú do Amazonas (both arr. cpsr). Lago de Janaucá[a]. A Hug for Tiberio. Cavaleiro
sem Armadura (arr. Wolff)[ab]. *Coupled with works by various composers.* **Sharon Isbin** (gtr) with
[a]**Gaudencio Thiago de Mello** (perc); [b]**Paul Winter** (sax). Teldec 0630-19899-2 (7/98).
Gramophone Editor's choice. See review in the Collections section; refer to the Index. ⒼⒼ

Thibault de Champagne
French 1201-1253

Suggested listening ...
...Amour me fait commencier. *Coupled with works by various composers.*
Anne Azéma (sop/spkr); **vocal and instrumental ensemble.**
Erato 0630-17072-2 (12/97). ✒ *See review in the Collections section; refer to the Index.*
...Aussi conme unicorne sui. Deus est ensi conme li pellicanz. Chançon ferai, que talenz
m'en est pris. *Coupled with works by various composers.*
Paul Hillier (voc); **Andrew Lawrence-King** (psaltery/hp/org).
Harmonia Mundi HMU90 7184 (4/97). *See review in the Collections section; refer to the Index.*

Michael Tilson Thomas
American 1944

Suggested listening ...
...We two boys together clinging. *Coupled with works by various composers.*
Thomas Hampson (bar); **Craig Rutenberg** (pf).
EMI CDM5 55028-2 (10/97). *See review in the Collections section; refer to the Index.* ⒼⒼⒼ

Johannes Tinctoris

Suggested listening ...
...Lamentationes Jeremie. *Coupled with works by various composers.* **Orlando Consort.**
Metronome METCD1015 (4/97). *See review in the Collections section; refer to the Index.*
...Missa sine nomine. *Coupled with works by various composers.* **Early Music Consort of London /**
David Munrow. Virgin Classics Veritas VED5 61334-2 (11/97). *See review in the Collections*
section; refer to the Index.

Sir Michael Tippett

Tippett Concerto for Double String Orchestra. Fantasia concertante on a Theme of Corelli.
The Midsummer Marriage – Ritual Dances[a]. **BBC Symphony [a]Chorus and Orchestra /**
Andrew Davis. Teldec British Line Ⓕ 4509-94542-2 (64 minutes: DDD: 10/96).
Text and translation included. Recorded 1993.
Andrew Davis's formidable Tippettian credentials shine through in every bar of this outstanding
anthology. Aided by realistic, firmly focused sound, the *Concerto for Double String Orchestra* sounds
glorious here. What's more, Davis directs a performance of enormous humanity, intelligence and
dedication – even Sir Neville Marriner's excellent EMI remake now seems a little matter-of-fact by
comparison. In the slow movement Davis secures a rapt response from his BBC strings (the exquisite
closing bars are drawn with ineffable tenderness), while the finale bounds along with irrepressible
vigour and fine rhythmic panache. Davis's *Fantasia concertante* is an even more remarkable
achievement. This is another inspirational display: sensitive and fervent, yet marvellously lucid and
concentrated too. Once again, the BBC strings are on radiant form, and the lyrical intensity of their
playing during the central climax has to be heard to be believed. Davis's identification with this
sublime music is total. Much the same applies, for that matter, to the present committed and incisive
account of the "Ritual Dances" from *The Midsummer Marriage*, a veritable *tour de force* to which the
BBC Symphony Chorus contribute thrillingly in the final dance.
Additional recommendations ...
...Concerto for Double String Orchestra[b]. Divertimento on Sellinger's Round[b]. Little Music for
Strings[b]. Sonata[a]. [a]**Michael Thompson Horn Quartet;** [b]**Academy of St Martin in the Fields /**
Sir Neville Marriner. EMI British Composers Ⓕ CDC5 55452-2 (66 minutes: DDD: 1/96).
...Concerto for Double String Orchestra. Fantasia concertante on a Theme of Corelli. Songs for
Dov[a]. [a]**Nigel Robson** (ten); **Scottish Chamber Orchestra / Sir Michael Tippett.**
Virgin Classics Ultraviolet Ⓜ CUV5 61326-2 (75 minutes: DDD: 2/97).

Tippett Divertimento on Sellinger's Round. Little Music for Strings. The Heart's Assurance
(orch. Bowen)[a]. Concerto for Double String Orchestra. [a]**John Mark Ainsley** (ten);
City of London Sinfonia / Richard Hickox. Chandos Ⓕ CHAN9409 (71 minutes: DDD: 3/96).
Text included. Recorded 1995.
Chandos have here secured the first recording of the orchestral version of Tippett's major song-cycle,
The Heart's Assurance. The *Concerto for Double String Orchestra* is Tippett's first masterwork, and
it's marvellous to have a recording that does justice to all those antiphonal textural subtleties. One
might wish for a touch more brio in the first movement, and a richer, stronger tone in places: for
example, the slow movement's sublime outer sections. But this is still a very satisfying performance,
not least because the finale comes across with such a winning blend of vitality and eloquence. Meirion
Bowen's orchestration of *The Heart's Assurance* has Tippett's approval, and it is undoubtedly a
resourceful piece of work. What makes the effect so different from the voice and piano original is that
the all-important doublings of voice and instrument seem so much more prominent when the
instrument in question can sustain the sound for as long as the voice itself. For this reason the original
may be preferable, and in addition, despite John Mark Ainsley's excellent contribution to this
recording, the final song doesn't build to its overwhelming climax as inexorably as it should. However,
this is a valuable Tippett issue from Chandos, and the recording is satisfyingly rich in detail.
Additional recommendation ...
...Little Music for Strings. *Coupled with works by* **Rubbra** *and* **Bliss** Soloists of Australia /
Ronald Thomas. Chandos Collect Ⓜ CHAN6576 (60 minutes: ADD/DDD: 6/92).

Tippett The Rose Lake[a]. The Vision of St Augustine[b]. [b]**John Shirley-Quirk** (bar);
London Symphony [b]Chorus and Orchestra / [a]Sir Colin Davis, [b]Sir Michael Tippett.
Conifer Classics Ⓕ 75605 51304-2 (68 minutes: [b]ADD/[a]DDD: 1/98). Text and translation
included. Item marked [a] recorded 1997, [b] from RCA SER5620 (4/72, recorded 1971).
Selected by Soundings.   ⓖⓖ
Although Tippett let it be known that *The Rose Lake* would be his last orchestral work, it does not
sound valedictory. It is based on the profound impression made on him, during a holiday in Senegal,
of a small lake which at midday was transformed from whitish green to translucent pink. Tippett
imagines the lake singing and frames the five verses of its song with glittering ostinatos and bright
toccatas, with much tuned percussion including three octaves of the rototoms of which he made such

effective use in *Byzantium*. It is a simple, rondo-like structure but a satisfying one, with the lake first awakening (calm, woodland horns), its song then echoing from the sky (woodwind and string counterpoint) and reaching 'full song' (a long, eloquent string line underpinned by drums) at the centre. The latter half of the work is not a literal mirror-image of the first but a series of poetic and ingenious 'doubles' of what went before, ending with magical horn calls recalling those in *The Midsummer Marriage*, a quiet rattle of xylophone and rototoms and, as a surprising coda, an abrupt sequence of staccato wind chords. It is a lovely and a moving piece, brimming with characteristically Tippettian melody. Almost as important, it is of just the right length to couple with the composer's own recording of one of his greatest but also one of his least often performed masterpieces. *The Vision of St Augustine* is hideously difficult to perform, but the choral singing here is quite heroic, and John Shirley-Quirk's account of the taxing solo part is nothing short of superb. It is truly visionary and profoundly moving. Sir Colin Davis's account of *The Rose Lake* is as urgently communicative as Tippett's own of the cantata, and the older recording is by no means put in the shade by the newer: both are excellent. This, in short, is an essential coupling for all admirers of Tippett's music.

Tippett Symphony No. 1. Piano Concerto[a]. [a]**Howard Shelley** (pf); **Bournemouth Symphony Orchestra / Richard Hickox.** Chandos Ⓕ CHAN9333 (72 minutes: DDD: 4/95).
Recorded 1994. *Selected by Sounds in Retrospect.*   Ⓖ

The riot of proliferating counterpoint that is Tippett's Symphony No. 1 presents enough problems of orchestral balance to give recording teams (not to mention conductors) nightmares. Chandos have managed highly creditable degrees of containment and clarity, without loss of realism, and the impact, when the last movement finally settles on to its long-prepared harmonic goal, is powerful and convincing. As with other Hickox performances in this Tippett series, doubts as to whether initial impetus is sufficient to keep the complex structures on course prove groundless. This is a fine account, well balanced between lively rhythmic articulation and broad melodic sweep. The performance of the Piano Concerto is no less notable for the inexorable way in which its mighty design unfolds. There may be too much decorum, too little passion, in certain episodes, yet Howard Shelley makes persuasive sense of the *con bravura* marking in the finale, and his shaping of the first movement's long, dreamingly decorative lines is as alert and sensitive as his control of the second movement's more dynamic discourse. This is a truly symphonic concerto, with a wealth of invention, remarkable textural ingenuity and a particularly imaginative use of the orchestra (especially the celesta) to complement the bright colours of the solo instrument. The recording is faultless.

Tippett Symphony No. 2. New Year – Suite. **Bournemouth Symphony Orchestra / Richard Hickox.** Chandos Ⓕ CHAN9299 (65 minutes: DDD: 10/94). Recorded 1994.
Gramophone Editor's choice.   Ⓖ

The balance Hickox achieves between attention to detail and large-scale symphonic sweep is exemplary, and especially impressive in the tricky finale, where he conveys the essential ambiguity of an ending which strives to recapture the optimistic *élan* of the work's opening without ever quite managing it. The Chandos recording, too, gives us much more of the symphony's contrapuntal detail. The first recording of music from Tippett's latest opera *New Year*, premièred in 1989, is thoroughly welcome. The music of this suite may seem over-emphatic to anyone who hasn't experienced the opera in the theatre, and the recording relishes the booming electric guitars and wailing saxophones, as well as the taped spaceship effects. Yet there are many imaginative moments, like the use of the 'paradise garden' sarabande borrowed from *The Mask of Time*, and the exotic arrangement of *Auld Lang Syne* near the end. This is Tippett firing on all cylinders, with a performance and recording to match.

Tippett Praeludium. Symphony No. 3[a]. [a]**Faye Robinson** (sop); **Bournemouth Symphony Orchestra / Richard Hickox.** Chandos Ⓕ CHAN9276 (64 minutes: DDD: 6/94). Text included.
Recorded 1993.

The Third Symphony, first heard in 1972, is one of Tippett's most complex and highly charged attempts to create a convincing structure from the collision between strongly contrasted musical characteristics. The work evolves from a purely orchestral drama – fast first movement, slow second movement, both large-scale, followed by a shorter scherzo – to a less extended but also tripartite sequence of blues settings, the whole capped by a huge, climactic coda in which the soprano voice finally yields the last word to the orchestra. The first two movements (Part 1, as Tippett calls it) remain a considerable technical challenge, especially to the strings, but this performance manages to sustain an appropriate level of tension without sounding merely effortful, and without skimping on the opportunities for eloquence of phrasing. It could well be that Tippett has over-indulged the percussion in the slow movement, but this vivid and well-balanced Chandos recording lets us hear ample detail without exaggerating the bright colours and hyper-resonant textures. The later stages have the advantage of a superbly characterful singer in Faye Robinson. She has the power, the edge, and also the radiance, to make Tippett's progression from idiosyncratic blues to Beethoven-quoting peroration utterly convincing. The work ends, famously, on a question-mark, dismissing the unrestrained affirmation of Beethoven's *Choral* finale in favour of the unresolved opposition of loud brass and soft strings. Will that "new compassionate power/To heal, to love" which the text "senses" actually be achieved? Twenty years on, the jury is still out on Tippett's great humanist challenge.

Meanwhile, there can be no questioning the achievement of this performance and recording, coupled strikingly with the highly characteristic *Praeludium* for brass, bells and percussion of 1962. Sir Colin Davis's account of the symphony (currently unavailable), will always be admired as a magnificent pioneering effort, but Chandos have given us the version for our time.

Tippett String Quartets – No. 1[a]; No. 2 in F major[a]; No. 3[a]; No. 4[b]; No. 5[c]. **Lindsay Quartet** (Peter Cropper, Ronald Birks, vns; [a]Roger Bigley, [bc]Robin Ireland, vas; Bernard Gregor-Smith, vc). ASV Ⓕ CDDCS231 (two discs: 123 minutes: ADD/DDD: 5/96). Items marked [a] from L'Oiseau-Lyre DSLO10 (12/75), [b]DCA608 (5/88), [c]CDDCA879 (1/94). Recorded 1975-1992.
Tippett coached the Lindsay Quartet for these recordings of his first three quartets, and the other two were written for them. In a note written for their twenty-fifth anniversary in 1992 he said that in these recordings they were "concerned to establish good precedents in matters of style, so that succeeding generations of interpreters start at an advantage". In fact one of the most enjoyable things about these readings is that they are so very characteristic of the Lindsay Quartet. Of course a number of the qualities that one might call 'characteristic' are uncommonly well suited to Tippett's earlier quartets: big tone, sheer vigour of attack and an infectious enjoyment of his lithe sprung rhythms. These performances are indeed excellent precedents for later interpreters. They do establish a style – big-scaled, urgently communicative – that is presumably 'authentic' and yet they challenge listeners as well as other performers to imagine how else they might be done. They also affirm the aching absence of a quartet between the Third and the Fourth (Tippett intended to write one in the late 1940s or early 1950s but got side-tracked by *The Midsummer Marriage* and did not write another for over 20 years) and make one wonder what the rejected two movements of the First Quartet might be like. It is wonderful, though, to hear the five as a sequence in such authoritative readings. The recordings sound very well, but have been transferred at an exceptionally high level.
Additional recommendations ...
...Nos. 1-4. **Britten Quartet.** Collins Classics Ⓕ 7006-2 (two discs: 97 minutes: DDD: 12/91).
...No. 4. **Britten** String Quartet No. 3, Op. 94. **Lindsay Quartet.**
ASV Ⓕ CDDCA608 (53 minutes: DDD: 5/88).
...Nos. 3 and 5. **Kreutzer Quartet.** Chandos Ⓕ CHAN9512 (61 minutes: DDD: 6/97).
...Nos. 1, 2 and 4. **Kreutzer Quartet.** Chandos Ⓕ CHAN9560 (70 minutes: DDD: 12/97).

Tippett String Quartet No. 5. **Lindsay Quartet** (Peter Cropper, Ronald Birks, vns; Robin Ireland, va; Bernard Gregor-Smith, vc). ASV Ⓕ CDDCA879 (76 minutes: DDD: 1/94).
Brown Fanfare to welcome Sir Michael Tippett. **Purcell** Fantasias – F major, Z737; E minor, Z741; G major, Z742. **Morris** Canzoni Ricertati – No. 1, Risoluto; No. 6, Lento sostenuto.
C. Wood: String Quartet in A minor.
This curious mixture of a programme is a precise re-creation of the concert at which Tippett's Fifth String Quartet had its first performance. Music by two of his teachers and one of his great inspirers is preceded by a greeting prelude that quotes both Purcell and Tippett himself. Tippett's Quartet is quite typical of him, both in its exquisitely singing lyricism and in the fact that it is by no means a mere looking back towards his earlier lyrical phases. Here intensification of expression is often achieved by distillation, towards such a simplicity of utterance that at crucial moments the music thins sometimes to one, often to no more than two, of the quartet's voices. R.O. Morris's *Canzoni Ricertati* subject faintly folk-like melodies to ingenious fugal and canonic treatment. In Charles Wood's quartet, the ingenious interplay of short motives in his scherzo is something that might have caught the young Tippett's ear, and his finale dresses up the Irish folk-song *The lark in the clear air* in its best Sunday clothes. The Purcell *Fantasias* point up Tippett's Purcell-ancestry rather touchingly as does Christopher Brown's miniature *Fanfare*. The Lindsay's beautiful performances are cleanly but not clinically recorded.

Tippett Piano Sonatas – No. 1; No. 2; No. 3. **Nicholas Unwin** (pf). Chandos Ⓕ CHAN9468 (55 minutes: DDD: 11/96). Recorded 1995.
These are very big performances indeed, giving a clear and infectious impression of how satisfying these sonatas must be when you have a technique as commanding as Nicholas Unwin's. The tireless toccata vein in Tippett's piano writing, the abrupt grandeur of some of his juxtapositions, what one might call the 'Beethoven-plus' element (angular dotted figures not far from the *Grosse Fuge*, a buoyant humour closely related to the late *Bagatelles*) – all these are finely conveyed. Possibly missing is the blithely springy lightness of touch that some other pianists have found, especially in the First Sonata. Unwin is capable of light, transparent textures, and of fluid lyricism, so he provides pretty well 90 per cent or more of what these sonatas require. No one has supplied more, though it might have been a different 90 per cent. Which is to say that these are works that can take a variety of interpretations and gain from them. How good that they are doing so. The recordings match the performances well, with a commandingly big piano sound, but there is no lack of more sober colour.
Additional recommendations ...
...Nos. 1-4. **Paul Crossley** (pf). CRD Ⓕ CRD3430/1 (two discs: 94 minutes: DDD: 6/92).
...No. 2. *Coupled with works by various composers.* **Steven Neugarten** (pf). Metier Ⓕ MSVCD92008 (53 minutes: DDD: 1/96). *See review in the Collections section; refer to the Index.*

...No. 1. *Coupled with works by various composers.* **Murray Perahia** (pf).
Sony Classical Ⓜ SX4K63380 (four discs: 270 minutes: DDD/ADD: 4/98). *See review in the Collections section; refer to the Index.*

Tippett The Windhover. The Source. Magnificat and Nunc dimittis, "Collegium Sancti Johannis Cantabrigiense"[a]. Lullaby. Four Songs from the British Isles. Dance, Clarion Air. A Child of Our Time – Five Negro Spirituals. Plebs angelica. The Weeping Babe. **Finzi Singers / Paul Spicer** with [a]**Andrew Lumsden** (org). Chandos Ⓕ CHAN9265 (55 minutes: DDD: 7/95). Texts included. Recorded 1994.
The Finzi Singers are eloquent in the Spirituals, and polished in the *British Songs* (especially the beguiling "Early One Morning"). However, it is especially good to have the works which represent early sightings of Tippett's later, less lusciously lyrical style – the *Lullaby* (with countertenor, reminding us that it was written for the Deller Consort) and the *Magnificat* and *Nunc dimittis*: here not only are the intonation and phrasing of the tricky lines supremely confident, but the accompanying organ is recorded with exemplary naturalness. The vocal sound throughout is generally no less successful. There may be almost too full and rich a texture for the linear intricacies of *Plebs angelica* and *The Weeping Babe* to make their maximum effect, but there is no lack of exuberance in *Dance, Clarion Air* and the other secular pieces.

Additional recommendations ...
...Dance, Clarion Air. The Weeping Babe. Plebs angelica. Bonny at Morn. Crown of the Year. Music. A Child of Our Time – Five Negro Spirituals. **Soloists; Christ Church Cathedral Choir / Stephen Darlington.** Nimbus Ⓕ NI5266 (51 minutes: DDD: 1/91).
...Plebs angelica. *Coupled with work by various composers.* **St Paul's Cathedral Choir / John Scott** with **Andrew Lucas** (org). Hyperion Ⓕ CDA66826 (7/96).
...Magnificat and Nunc dimittis. *Coupled with works by various composers.* **Rochester Cathedral Choir / Roger Sayer** with **William Whitehead** (org). Priory Ⓕ PRCD529 (72 minutes: DDD: 7/96).
...Five Negro Spirituals – By and By. *Coupled with works by various composers.* **Lesley Garrett** (sop); **chorus; Britten Sinfonia / Ivor Bolton.** Conifer Classics Ⓕ 75605 51329-2 (73 minutes: DDD: 12/97). *See review in the Collections section; refer to the Index.*

Tippett Songs and Purcell Realizations. **Martyn Hill** (ten); [a]**Craig Ogden** (gtr); [b]**Andrew Ball** (pf). Hyperion Ⓕ CDA66749 (70 minutes: DDD: 4/95). Texts included. Recorded 1994.
Gramophone Editor's choice.
Music[b]. Songs for Ariel[b]. Songs for Achilles[a]. Boyhood's End[b]. The Heart's Assurance[b].
Purcell If music be the food of love, Z379/2[b]. The Fairy Queen – Thrice happy lovers[b]. The Fatal hour comes on apace, Z421[a]. Bess of Bedlam, Z370[b]. Pausanias – Sweeter than roses[b].
The two longest works – the cantata *Boyhood's End* and song-cycle *The Heart's Assurance* – challenge the musicianship and sensitivity of singer and pianist alike. *Boyhood's End* (1943), a setting of prose that is never prosaic, shows the ecstasy of *Midsummer Marriage* to be already within the system, and the profusion of notes has to be mastered so that the dance shall seem as delicate and natural as graceful improvisation. In *The Heart's Assurance* (1951) the spirit is similar though the technical accomplishment of all concerned, composer and performers, is heightened. For the singer, in addition to fearsome difficulties of pitch and rhythm, there is likely to be some problem of tessitura, particularly in the third of the songs, "Compassion". For the pianist, concentration has to be divided between the virtuosic writing of his own part and responsiveness to the singer, his notes, words and expression. Martyn Hill and Andrew Ball are wonderfully at one in all this, and the balancing of voice and piano has been finely achieved. The *Songs for Achilles*, with guitar, also convey a sense of ardent improvisation, and the voice rings out freely. The *Songs for Ariel* here work their natural magic. Tippett's affinities with Purcell are felt at one time or another in most of these compositions, starting indeed with the opening of the programme, the setting of Shelley's *Sleep*. It is good also to have the Purcell 'realizations' included. The recording was issued to mark the composer's ninetieth birthday, a most touching and eloquent tribute.

Additional recommendation ...
...Songs for Ariel. *Coupled with works by various composers.* **Sir Peter Pears** (ten); **Benjamin Britten** (pf). Belart Ⓑ 461 550-2 (69 minutes: ADD: 12/97). *See review in the Collections section; refer to the Index.*

Tippett The Knot Garden[a]. A Child of Our Time[b]. [a]**Raimund Herincx** (bass) Faber; [a]**Yvonne Minton** (mez) Thea; [a]**Jill Gomez** (sop) Flora; [a]**Dame Josephine Barstow** (sop) Denise; [a]**Thomas Carey** (bar) Mel; [a]**Robert Tear** (ten) Dov; [a]**Thomas Hemsley** (bar) Mangus; [b]**Jessye Norman** (sop); [b]**Dame Janet Baker** (mez); [b]**Richard Cassilly** (ten); [b]**John Shirley-Quirk** (bar); [b]**BBC Singers;** [b]**BBC Choral Society;** [a]**Orchestra of the Royal Opera House, Covent Garden,** [b]**BBC Symphony Orchestra / Sir Colin Davis.** Philips Ⓕ 446 331-2PH2 (two discs: 145 minutes: ADD: 9/95). Notes and texts included. Item marked [a] from 6700 063 (4/74), recorded 1993, [b]6500 985 (11/75), recorded 1975.
The Knot Garden is a classic of its period and a central work in its composer's output. Some of the more enthusiastic reviews after the first performance of *The Knot Garden* were rather perplexed by its

structure: it is a short opera, but its three acts are divided into 23 scenes, often brief and abruptly juxtaposed. However, the form of the piece now seems to be admirably clear, musically strong and ideally appropriate to the subject. It is not so much a narrative as an examination of a set of relationships. The First Act introduces six of the seven characters, briefly demonstrates their problems and then introduces a catalyst in the person of Denise, the freedom-fighter disfigured by torture. She sings an updated version of an ancient operatic form – the virtuoso display aria, here brilliantly put to new purposes – which in turn prompts an ensemble-finale in the again updated form of a blues with a fast boogie-woogie middle section. As an opera about relationships it needs particularly sensitive handling by the singers, and the cast (that of the first performance) is outstanding. Tear gives his character ("a homosexual in pink socks!", sneered one reviewer) real charm and pathos as well as singing his uncommonly difficult lines with great flair. Barstow is even finer: an electric presence with a visionary intensity to her aria of remembered anguish. Minton and Herincx are both excellent, Gomez touchingly vulnerable, while Hemsley's immaculate diction and gentlemanly tones are perfect for Mangus, the psychiatrist Prospero who "puts them all to rights". Davis is as eloquently urgent in the opera as in the oratorio, *A Child of Our Time*, which, in a generally fine, rather opera-scaled reading, makes an ideal coupling: two complementary aspects of Tippett the maker of healing images.

Additional recommendations ...
...A Child of Our Time[a]. The Weeping Babe[b]. **Soloists; [a]Royal Liverpool Philharmonic Choir; [b]John Alldis Choir; [a]Royal Liverpool Philharmonic Orchestra / [a]Sir John Pritchard, [b]Sir Colin Davis.** Belart Ⓢ 461 123-2 (69 minutes: ADD).
...A Child of Our Time. **Soloists; City of Birmingham Symphony Chorus and Orchestra / Sir Michael Tippett.** Collins Classics Ⓕ 1339-2 (69 minutes: DDD: 9/92).
...A Child of Our Time. **Soloists; London Symphony Chorus and Orchestra / Richard Hickox.** Chandos Ⓕ CHAN9123 (73 minutes: DDD: 2/93).
...A Child of Our Time. **Soloists; Brighton Festival Chorus; Royal Philharmonic Orchestra / André Previn.** Carlton Classics Ⓑ 30367 0205-2 (67 minutes: DDD: 8/97).

Further listening ...
...Symphony No. 4[a]. Byzantium[b]. [b]**Faye Robinson** (sop); **Chicago Symphony Orchestra / Sir Georg Solti.** Decca 433 668-2DH (4/93).   Ⓖ
...Piano Sonata No. 4. *Coupled with works by various composers.* **Nicholas Unwin** (pf). Metier MSVCD92009 (1/96). *See review in the Collections section; refer to the Index.*
...The Mask of Time. **Soloists; BBC Singers; BBC Symphony Chorus and Orchestra / Andrew Davis.** EMI British Composers CMS7 64711-2 (10/93).
...King Priam. **Soloists; London Sinfonietta Chorus; London Sinfonietta / David Atherton.** Chandos CHAN9406/7 (2/96).
...The Midsummer Marriage. **Soloists; Chorus and Orchestra of the Royal Opera House, Covent Garden / Sir Colin Davis.** Lyrita SRCD2217 (1/96).

Jehan Titelouze   French 1562/3-1633

Suggested listening ...
...Le magnificat – Tone IV. *Coupled with works by various composers.* **St Thomas Church Choir, New York / Gerre Hancock** with **Patrick Allen** (org). Priory PRCD600 (1/98). *See review in the Collections section; refer to the Index.*

Loris Tjeknavorian   Iranian 1937

Suggested listening ...
...Danses fantastiques. *Coupled with works by* **Khachaturian Armenian Philharmonic Orchestra / Loris Tjeknavorian.** ASV CDDCA884 (3/94). *See review under Khachaturian; refer to the Index.* Ⓖ

Henri Tomasi   French 1901-1971

Suggested listening ...
...Trumpet Concerto. *Coupled with works by various composers.* **Sergei Nakariakov** (tpt); **Alexander Markovich** (pf); **Lausanne Chamber Orchestra / Jésus López-Cobos.** Teldec 4509-90846-2 (10/93). *See review in the Collections section; refer to the Index.*

Thomas Tomkins   British 1572-1656

Tomkins Prelude. Fancy. Three In Nomines. Voluntary[a]. Pavan and Galliard of Three Parts. Fancy (arr. cpsr). Toy, "Made at Poole Court"[a]. Pavan[a]. Robin Hood. Two Pavans. Ground. **Bernhard Klapprott** (hpd/[a]virg). Dabringhaus und Grimm Ⓕ Ⓓ MDG607 0704-2 (72 minutes: DDD: 10/97). Recorded 1995. ✍

Tomkins is perhaps best known as a later representative of the school of English madrigalists, and one of Byrd's most talented pupils; yet he composed in all the genres available to him, and left a substantial quantity of keyboard music. Indeed, he was a keen student of the works of other virginalists and, like Byrd, extended his activity in this area to the very last years of his life. Tomkins is at his best when unfettered by pre-ordained conceits, and while he cannot match his great mentor's grasp of form or his knack for writing instantly memorable tunes, the best pieces here are not without charm (the little *Toy*, for example). Bernhard Klapprott plays mostly on a harpsichord, and more rarely on a much softer virginal, which seems the more effective of the two instruments for conveying the music's unaffected delicacy. He strives to find the right expression for each piece; rubato is applied differently from one work to the next according to each piece's character, rather than exclusively by genre. Tempos could have been equally varied: they are uniformly on the slow side, even where greater agility would at least be warranted (as in the Galliard). The choice of instrument may have something to do with this: the virginal's softer sound encourages more rapid runs, whereas the harpsichord's seems to do the opposite. Still, a pleasing disc: Klapprott's advocacy of Tomkins reminds us how much of this first golden age of the keyboard remains unexplored.

Tomkins Third Service[a]. O Lord, let me know mine end[a]. O that the salvation were given[a]. Know you not[a]. In Nomine (1648). In Nomine (1652). Voluntaries – G major; C major; A minor.
[a]**New College Choir, Oxford / Edward Higginbottom** with **David Burchell** (org). CRD Ⓕ CRD3467 (62 minutes: DDD: 9/94). Texts included. Recorded 1990. *Gramophone Editor's choice.*

This is a well-balanced programme of sacred music by Thomas Tomkins. The four movements of the Third, or Great Service, together with the three anthems are spaced out among five organ pieces – two *In Nomines* and three voluntaries – chosen and arranged in such a way that the resulting key sequence has a satisfying natural flow. After an unassuming intonation, the truly royal *Te Deum* of the Great Service takes off with great verve and vigour, the rich ten-part texture of the full sections contrasting well with the lighter scoring of the verses. This energy and these contrasts are characteristic of the performances as a whole. There is some delightful solo singing in the verse anthems, in particular the alto solo in *O Lord, let me know mine end*. The two solo trebles are kept busy: they have a rather distinctive but complementary tone-quality, which makes up for a slight imbalance in volume. In general, however, the balance is good and the ensemble and dovetailing excellent. The trebles are a confident group with good articulation; they soar up to their top B flats with the utmost ease.

Additional recommendations ...

...Third Service – Magnificat and Nunc dimittis. Cathedral Music – O sing unto the Lord a new song. Then David mourned. My beloved spake unto me. Above the stars my saviour dwells. Glory be to God on high. Almighty God, the fountain of all wisdom. When David heard. My shepherd is the living Lord. Sing unto God. Behold, the hour cometh. O God, the proud are risen against me. **St George's Chapel Choir, Windsor / Christopher Robinson** with **Roger Judd** (org). Hyperion Ⓕ CDA66345 (63 minutes: DDD: 3/90).

...Third Service. Anthems – Almighty God, the fountain of all wisdom; Be strong and of good courage; O God, the proud are risen against me; O sing unto the Lord; Then David mourned; When David heard; Woe is me. **The Tallis Scholars / Peter Phillips.** Gimell Ⓕ 454 924-2PH (58 minutes: DDD: 3/92).

...Third Service, "Great Service". *Coupled with works by various composers.* **Ripon Cathedral Choir / Kerry Beaumont** with **Robert Marsh** (org). Priory Ⓕ PRCD555 (63 minutes: DDD: 1/97).

Further listening ...

...Barafostus' Dream. *Coupled with works by* **Gibbons, Byrd, Anonymous, Aston** and **J. Bull** In Nomine. **Sophie Yates** (virg). ✍ Chandos Chaconne CHAN0574 (12/95).

Ernest Tomlinson

British 1927

Suggested listening ...

...Little Serenade. *Coupled with works by various composers.* **Pro Arte Orchestra / George Weldon.** EMI British Composers CDM5 66537-2 (1/98). *See review in the Collections section; refer to the Index.*

Giuseppe Torelli

Italian 1658-1709

Suggested listening ...

...Concerto in E minor for Four Violins and Strings. *Coupled with works by various composers.* **Cologne Musica Antiqua / Reinhard Goebel.** Archiv Produktion 435 393-2AH (9/92). ✍ *See review in the Collections section; refer to the Index.*

...Sonata in G major, Op. 1 No. 1. Concerto a quattro in D minor, Op. 6 No. 10. *Coupled with works by various composers.* **Berlin Barock Compagney.** Capriccio 10 459 (10/95). ✍ *See review in the Collections section; refer to the Index.* Ⓖ

...Sonata a 5 con tromba, G7. *Coupled with works by various composers.* **Håkan Hardenberger** (tpt); **I Musici.** Philips 442 131-2PH (5/95). *See review in the Collections section; refer to the Index.* Ⓖ

...Trumpet Concerto No. 2 in D major. *Coupled with works by various composers.*
Crispian Steele-Perkins (tpt); **English Chamber Orchestra / Anthony Halstead.**
Carlton Classics 30366 0066-2 (10/97). *See review in the Collections section; refer to the Index.*
...Trumpet Sonata in D major. *Coupled with works by various composers.*
Niklas Eklund (baroque tpt); **Drottningholm Baroque Ensemble / Nils-Erik Sparf.**
Naxos 8 553531 (11/96). ✍ *See review in the Collections section; refer to the Index.*

Michael Torke

American 1961

Torke Javelin[a]. December[b]. Run[a]. Adjustable Wrench[cd]. Green[f]. Music on the Floor – second
movement[ce]. Bright Blue Music[f]. [a]**Atlanta Symphony Orchestra / Yoel Levi;** [b]**Philharmonia
Orchestra / Michael Torke;** [cde]**London Sinfonietta /** [d]**Kent Nagano,** [e]**Lothar Zagrosek;** [f]**Baltimore
Symphony Orchestra / David Zinman.** Argo Ⓕ 452 101-2ZH (63 minutes: DDD: 8/96).
Items marked [a] and [b] new to UK, [cd] from 430 209-2ZH (12/90), [ce]443 528-2ZH (1/95).
Gramophone Editor's choice.   ⒼⒼ
Under the collective title, "Javelin. The Music of Michael Torke", this excellent anthology contains
both new and previously unrecorded material. It also brings together on one disc some of the most
optimistic, joyful and thoroughly uplifting music to appear in recent years. Admittedly, Torke's music
may not be heavily laden with the socio-political messages of our time or deal with the darker corners
of man's psyche, but that certainly doesn't make it any less relevant. Of the new pieces presented here
the main attraction is *Javelin*, which was composed in 1994 and is the official commission of the 1996
Olympic Games. *Javelin* is lithe and sleek and very athletic and heroic in tone – its bright and breezy
countenance more than fulfilling its sporting brief. The work's classical reverberations place it
alongside pieces such as *Green* and *Bright Blue Music. December*, too, is very classical in tone. Scored
for strings the writing has a certain English quality about it, recalling at times Tippett. *Run*, which
dates from 1992, can be counted amongst Torke's process pieces, though the word 'process' should be
used with caution, as the result tends away from minimalism rather than towards it. Torke's own
description of the piece as "someone setting out on their morning run, taking in the ever-changing
panorama of the rising sun over a still-sleeping city" is very evocative; it's a high-energy, invigorating
work. The remaining pieces are taken from earlier Torke/Argo releases, and consist of the beautiful
central movement from *Music on the Floor*, the 'pop'-inspired chamber work *Adjustable Wrench*
(Torke's most frequently performed composition) and the two exhilarating roller-coaster-ride
orchestral pieces *Bright Blue Music* and *Green*. Performances and recordings of all the pieces on this
disc are superb, and if you are coming to Torke's music for the first time it cannot be recommended
too highly. Even if you already have the original recordings of some of these pieces the disc is worth
considering for the new items alone.
Additional recommendations ...
...Colour Music – Green; Purple; Ecstatic Orange; Ash; Bright Blue Music. **Baltimore Symphony
Orchestra / David Zinman.** Argo Ⓕ 433 071-2ZH (54 minutes: DDD: 2/92).   ⒼⒼⒼ
...The Yellow Pages[e]. Slate[abcd]. Adjustable Wrench[d]. Vanada[d]. Rust[e]. **Michael Torke** (pf);
[a]**Edmund Niemann, Nurit Tilles** (pf, four hands); [b]**James Pugliese** (xylophone); [c]**Gary Schall**
(marimba); **London Sinfonietta /** [d]**Kent Nagano,** [e]**David Miller.**
Argo Ⓕ 430 209-2ZH (55 minutes: DDD: 12/90).   Ⓖ

Torke Overnight Mail[a]. Telephone Book[b]. July[c]. Flint[d]. Change of Address[e]. [d]**Anton Lukoszevieze**
(vc); [d]**Mark Thistlewood** (db); [d]**Philip Bush** (pf); [cd]**Apollo Saxophone Quartet** (Tim Redpath,
Rob Buckland, Andrew Scott, Will Gregory, saxes); [b]**Present Music** (Marie Sander, fl;
Bill Helmer, cl; Eric Segnitz, vn; Paul Gmeinder, vc); [e]**Michael Torke Band / Michael Torke** ([bd]pf);
[a]**Orkest de Volharding / Jurjen Hempel.** Argo Ⓕ 455 684-2ZH (67 minutes: DDD: 3/98).
Recorded 1996-1997. *Gramophone Editor's choice.*
At his best, Torke manages to capture a feeling of glowing euphony and an effortless quality that is
rare in new music today. If the highlights of this disc are *Telephone Book* and *July*, a great deal of
credit is due to the performances which are superb. It is hard to imagine a more expressive and
beautifully timed rendition of *July* than the one given by the Apollo Saxophone Quartet, whose
approach manages to combine considerable refinement of tonal blending with the spontaneity almost
of a live performance. The first movement of *Telephone Book* is none other than *The Yellow Pages*,
which Torke has recorded before for Argo. The two versions are remarkably similar in approach but
this recording with Present Music is funkier, fuller in sound and shows greater insight into the work's
structure. The two movements, "The Blue Pages" and "The White Pages", which also feature the same
technique of 'static transposition', are also well characterized and sustained. However, the CD as a
whole lacks contrast and prospective listeners might be advised not to hear it all the way through but
to concentrate on individual works. "Priority", the first movement of *Overnight Mail*, is particularly
impressive, and both *Flint* and *Change of Address* have many striking ideas. This recording confirms
that Michael Torke is one of the foremost compositional talents in America today.
Further listening ...
...Black and White – Charcoal. *Coupled with works by various composers.* **Baltimore Symphony
Orchestra / David Zinman.** Argo 444 454-2ZH (7/95).

...Soprano Saxophone Concerto. *Coupled with works by* **R.R. Bennett** and **Myers John Harle**
  (sax); **Albany Symphony Orchestra / David Alan Miller.** Argo 443 529-2ZH (7/95).
...Soprano Saxophone Concerto. *Coupled with works by various composers.* **Gerard McChrystal**
  (sax); **London Musici / Mark Stephenson.** Silva Classics SILKD6010 (6/96). *See review in the*
  Collections section; refer to the Index.
...Four Proverbs[a]. Monday[b]. Music on the floor[b]. Tuesday[b]. [a]**Catherine Bott** (sop); [a]**Argo Band /**
  Michael Torke; [b]**London Sinfonietta / Lothar Zagrosek.** Argo 443 528-2ZH (1/95).   Ⓖ

Veljo Tormis   Estonian 1930

Tormis Estonian Calendar Songs – Martinmas Songs; St Catherine's Day Songs; Shrovetide Songs;
  Swing Songs; St John's Day Songs for Midsummer's Eve; Three Estonian Game Songs.
  Estonian Philharmonic Chamber Choir / Tõnu Kaljuste. Virgin Classics Ⓕ VC5 45185-2
  (52 minutes: DDD: 1/97). Texts and translations included. Recorded 1995.
  Gramophone Editor's choice.
Works by Veljo Tormis, particularly those for voices, seem altogether more natural than the better-
known output of Pärt which can strike you as artificial by comparison. The present collection of
songs, inspired by the rituals of the Estonian folk calendar, resonates in the mind long after actual
listening has ceased. Tormis has a predilection for cycles and sets – indeed sets of cycles; these 32
songs (all composed 1966-7) are grouped into six sets, ranging from simple triptychs (the *Shrovetide*
and *Game Songs* – the games all relating to Christmas) to fully fledged cycles for Martinmas (nine
songs) and St John's Day (seven). The *Martinmas Songs*, like most of its companions here but unlike
the *Forgotten Peoples* cycle (10/92), are tiny – none exceeds 100 seconds and six last under a minute.
The *St John's Day Songs*, however, are a different matter: bigger-boned if mostly brief ("Fire Spell",
with their insistent declamations, is electric), although the final "St John's Song", at over five-and-a-
half minutes, is more a small cantata or motet than a 'mere' song. The Estonian shoir under their
Chief Conductor, Tõnu Kaljuste, do themselves and the music proud in beautifully sung renditions.
Further listening ...
...Overture No. 2. *Coupled with works by various composers.* **Royal Scottish Orchestra / Neeme Järvi.**
  Chandos CHAN8656 (8/89).
...The Bishop and the Pagan. *Coupled with works by various composers.* **The King's Singers.**
  RCA Victor Red Seal 09026 68255-2 (8/96). *See review in the Collections section; refer to the*
  Index.
...Livonian Heritage. Votic Wedding Songs. Izhorian Epic. Ingrian Evenings. Vespian Paths.
  Karelian Destiny. **Estonian Philharmonic Chamber Choir / Tonu Kaljuste.**
  ECM New Series 434 275-2 (10/92).
...Kullervo's Message. *Coupled with works by various composers.* **The Hilliard Ensemble.**
  ECM New Series 453 259-2 (1/97). *See review in the Collections section; refer to the Index.*

José de Torres   Spanish 1670-1738

Suggested listening ...
...Más no puedo ser. Al clamor. *Coupled with works by various composers.* **Al Ayre Español /**
  Eduardo López Banzo. Deutsche Harmonia Mundi 05472 77325-2 (8/95). *See review in the*
  Collections section; refer to the Index. *Gramophone Editor's choice.*   Ⓖ
...Miserere. Lamentación segunda, del Jueves Santo. *Coupled with works by* **Durón** and **Navas**
  Al Ayre Español / Eduardo López Banzo. Deutsche Harmonia Mundi 05472 77376-2 (7/97). 🖋
  Gramophone Editor's choice. See review under Durón; refer to the Index.

Enrico Toselli   Italian 1883-1926

Suggested listening ...
...Serenade. *Coupled with works by various composers.*
  Inessa Galante (sop); **Latvian National Opera Orchestra / Alexander Vilumanis.**
  Campion RRCD1344 (A/97). *See review in the Collections section; refer to the Index.*

Charles Tournemire   French 1870-1939

Tournemire Symphonies – No. 5 in F minor, Op. 47; No. 8 in G minor, Op. 51, "Le triomphe
  de la mort". **Liège Philharmonic Orchestra / Pierre Bartholomée.** Auvidis Valois Ⓕ V4793
  (69 minutes: DDD: 3/98). Recorded 1997.
The Liège Philharmonic may not be a world-class orchestra, but they play with wholehearted
commitment and sensitive dynamics, and they are directed by a conductor who is clearly in sympathy
with the Franckian school, so that these performances offer a very satisfactory presentation of this

deeply felt, passionate music. Tournemire (one of Franck's successors at Ste Clotilde) could best be described as a romantic mystic: unlike some other enormously prolific composers, his ideas have quality and his treatment of them is both original and extremely effective. Those wishing to sample his style are recommended to start with the beatific *Pastorale* of the Fifth Symphony, a work written in 1913-14 and inspired by Alpine scenery which produced in him a poetic mood of exaltation. The Eighth Symphony of a decade later, which employs a gigantic orchestra in virtuoso and varied fashion and is somewhat bolder in harmonic idiom, is subtitled *Triumph over death* and was written on the death of the composer's dearly loved wife (to whom the Fifth had been dedicated). Both works are most unorthodox in form. The Fifth consists of a first movement in which a chorale appears three times, each time followed by an *Allegro* section: the second movement is the tender *Pastorale* that then leads into a joyous finale headed "Towards the light". The Eighth is still more unusual in that a single theme ingeniously runs throughout its two movements, the first a sorrowing *Lento* that is followed by a luminous more light-hearted section; the second continues for a while in similar vein but with more brilliant scoring, gives way to an intimate meditation and ends in a transport of radiance. A remarkably individual and gripping work that demands to be heard.

Tournemire Suite Evocatrice, Op. 74.
Vierne Symphony No. 3, Op. 28.
Widor Symphonie Gothique, Op. 70. **Jeremy Filsell** (org). Herald Ⓟ HAVPCD145 (71 minutes:
    DDD: 3/92). Played on the Harrison and Harrison organ of Ely Cathedral. Recorded 1991. ❽❽
Compared with, say, the symphonies of Tchaikovsky or Sibelius the organ symphonies of Widor and his pupil Vierne are not particularly long. But in terms of organ music they are among the longest single works in the repertory. Within their five-movement form the composers set out to exploit the full expressive range of the organ and it was no coincidence that the organ symphony developed in turn of the century France. The great French organ builder Aristide Cavaillé-Coll was then producing instruments capable of hitherto undreamt-of colour and expression. Both Widor (at St Sulpice) and Vierne (at Notre Dame) had at their disposal the finest instruments in Paris and they indulged themselves fully in their symphonies. The subtitle of Widor's Ninth (*Gothic*) says it all. The structure is vast, intricately detailed, and almost forbidding in its grandness. Vierne's Third also presents an awesome spectacle, full of complex music and technically demanding writing, while Tournemire's neo-classical Suite provides a moment almost of light relief in such heavyweight company. Jeremy Filsell is an outstanding virtuoso player with a gift for musical communication and, in the Ely Cathedral organ, an instrument which produces the range of the great French instruments, but within an altogether clearer acoustic. These are performances and recordings of exceptional quality.
Further listening ...
...Petite rapsodie improvisée. *Coupled with works by various composers.* **Judith Hancock** (org).
    Koch International Classics 37228-2 (9/96).

Marcel-Lucien Tournier

French 1879-1951

Suggested listening ...
...Jazz Band. *Coupled with works by various composers.* **Naoko Yoshino** (hp). Philips 446 064-2PH
    (2/96). *See review in the Collections section; refer to the Index.*

Giovanni Trabaci

Italian c1575-1647

Suggested listening ...
...Partite sopra "Rugiero". *Coupled with works by various composers.* **Rinaldo Alessandrini** (hpd).
    Opus 111 OPS30-118 (4/95). ☞ *See review in the Collections section; refer to the Index.* ❽❽

Eduard Tubin

Estonian/Swedish 1905-1982

Suggested listening ...
...Piano Concertino. *Coupled with works by* **Lemba** *and* **Sumera**.
    Lauri Väinmaa (pf); **Estonian National Symphony Orchestra / Arvo Volmer**.
    Finlandia 3984-20684-2 (5/98). *See review under Lemba; refer to the Index.*
...Symphony No. 7. Piano Concertino[a]. Sinfonietta on Estonian motifs. [a]**Roland Pöntinen** (pf);
    Gothenberg Symphony Orchestra / Neeme Järvi. BIS CD401 (1/89).

Edmund Turges

British c1450

Suggested listening ...
...Magnificat. *Coupled with works by* **Prentes** *and* **Cornysh** The Cardinall's Musick / Andrew
    Carwood. ASV Gaudeamus CDGAU164 (9/97). *See review under Cornysh; refer to the Index.*

Joaquín Turina
Spanish 1882-1949

Turina Danzas fantásticas, Op. 22. La procesión del Rocio, Op. 9. Sinfonía sevillana, Op. 23. Ritmos, Op. 43. **Bamberg Symphony Orchestra / Antonio de Almeida.** RCA Victor Red Seal Ⓕ RD60895 (63 minutes: DDD: 7/92).

Turina was a magnificent orchestrator and although he was – as Antonio de Almeida points out in his useful booklet annotations – a "quintessential Sevillian", he was also acutely aware of musical trends beyond his own locality. His style approximates the youthful opulence of early Debussy (whose sensuous *Printemps* frequently comes to mind), yet the piquant instrumentation that graces, say, "Exaltación" from the *Danzas fantásticas*, or the whole of *La procesión del Rocio* is refreshingly individual – beautifully aired and crafted, with the sum of its gleaming parts amounting to an appealing tonal blend. Were it not for the give-away nature of specifically Spanish melodies, Dvořák (of the *Slavonic Dances*) would as likely come to mind as Falla – particularly in the *Danzas*. *La procesión* (1912) predates the other pieces on the disc, while *Ritmos* was composed as late as 1928. It was premièred by Casals, but here more than anywhere else on the disc, one is reminded of Almeida's great mentor, Sir Thomas Beecham. Just listen to the way he points *Ritmos*'s atmospheric "Danza lenta", or sample the excitement he generates in the "Danza exótica" from the same work; then turn back to "Fiesta en San Juan de Aznalfarache" from *Sinfonía sevillana* – awash with colour from the first bar to the last – and witness how the Bamberg players exploit Turína's varied tonal palette. As for the recording (a co-production between BMG Classics and Bavarian Radio), it's truly demonstration-worthy; a fair sampling point is the "Valse trágico" from *Ritmos*, which features a spectacular mushrooming tam-tam. Turina's use of winds, brass and percussion, in particular, is as judicious as it is impressive, and he never overcrowds his orchestral climaxes. Unalloyed delight

---

Turina Piano Trios – No. 1, Op. 35; No. 2, Op. 76. Círculo, Op. 91
Granados Piano Trio, Op. 50. **Beaux Arts Trio** (Ida Kavafian, vn; Peter Wiley, vc; Menahem Pressler, pf). Philips Ⓕ 446 684-2PH (73 minutes: DDD: 4/97). Recorded 1995.

Of the youthful Granados Trio (dated by one commentator "*c*1900" though the first performance was given in 1895), which occupies a third of the disc, you will listen in vain for most of the influences quoted in the accompanying notes and find instead a pleasantly lyrical, if rather inconsequential and bland (except in the excitable finale) work whose only obvious Hispanicism is an isolated phrase at the end of the Trio to the elfin *Scherzetto*. Turina's works for trio, written over a quarter of a century later, are altogether more skilful, more subtle and rewarding, and considerably more nationalistic (though coloured by impressionist influences) – conspicuously in the First Trio's harmonically evocative theme followed by five variations in regional dance styles, including a *muñeira*, a *zortzico* and a *soleares*. The swaying rhythms in its finale too – which in the best Schola Cantorum tradition recapitulates earlier material – and of the more restrained Second Trio's initial movement and its sparkling second-movement *zortzico*, are idealized-Spanish in style. Turina's talent for romantically picturesque music is demonstrated in his *Círculo*, which depicts sunrise, midday and sunset, a programme that allows him again to utilize the cyclic form he had learnt from Vincent d'Indy. The present accomplished performances can, despite a rather often over-hefty piano, be recommended to all interested in this seldom heard area of Spanish music.

Further listening ...
...Rapsodia sinfónica, Op. 66. *Coupled with works by* **Albéniz** *and* **Falla**
  Alicia de Larrocha (pf); **London Philharmonic Orchestra / Rafael Frühbeck de Burgos.**
  Decca 410 289-2DH (10/84). *See review under Albéniz; refer to the Index.*   Ⓖ
...Rapsodia sinfónica, Op. 66. *Coupled with works by various composers.* **Dame Moura Lympany** (pf);
  Philharmonia Orchestra / Walter Susskind. Dutton Laboratories mono CDCLP4000* (1/97). *See review in the Collections section; refer to the Index.*
...La oración del torero, Op. 34. *Coupled with works by various composers.*
  Soloists; Hollywood Quartet; Concert Arts Strings / Felix Slatkin.
  Testament mono SBT1053* (3/95). *See review in the Collections section; refer to the Index.*   ⒼⒼ
...Cuentos de España, Book 2, Op. 47. Sanlúcar de Barrameda, Op. 24. Niñerias, Book 1, Op. 21.
  Mirian Conti (pf). Koch International Classics 37322-2 (10/96).
...Tres danzas andaluzas, Op. 8. Danza fantásticas, Op. 22. Jardín de Oriente – Danza. Dos danzas sobre temas populares españoles, Op. 41. Danzas gitanas, Op. 55; Op. 84. Concierto sin orquesta, Op. 88. **Albert Guinovart** (pf). Harmonia Mundi HMI98 7009 (10/96).
...Guitar Sonata, Op. 61. *Coupled with works by various composers.* **Pepe Romero** (gtr).
  Philips 442 150-2PH (4/95). Items marked ᵃ trans. P. Romero.
...Mujeres de Sevilla, Op. 89. Mujeres Españolas, Op. 17. Mujeres Españolas, Op. 73. Danzas Andaluzas, Op. 8. Bailete, Op. 79. **David Buechner** (pf). Connoisseur Society CD4186 (10/94).   Ⓖ

Mark-Anthony Turnage
British 1960

Turnage Blood on the Floor. **Martin Robertson** (sax/bass cl); **John Scofield** (elec gtr); **Peter Erskine** (drum kit); **Ensemble Modern / Peter Rundel.** Argo Ⓕ 455 292-2ZH (69 minutes: DDD: 5/98). Recorded live in 1996.   ⒼⒼ

Blood on the Floor is an impressive demonstration of the composer's ability to straddle the worlds of jazz, rock and art music without descending to the modish doodling of his crossover peers. The overall title comes from a painting by Francis Bacon, while the music ranges widely in its references and allusions. Understandably, the disc's packaging plays upon the theme of urban alienation and, of course, *Blood on the Floor* has its harrowing aspects. A younger brother of the composer died as a consequence of drug addiction and several of its nine movements could scarcely be more explicitly titled. At the same time, the punchy, amplified, vernacular element should not disguise the fact that this is also an elegantly crafted suite, ingeniously laid out for the 30-odd musicians of Ensemble Modern plus a solo trio of electric guitar, drum kit and saxophone. The participation of John Scofield puts flesh on the bones of Turnage's longstanding idiomatic involvement with Miles Davis, and the 'classical' influences include the usual culprits Stravinsky, Britten and, conceptually at least, Hans Werner Henze. Somehow, the contradictions don't jar as you'd expect. Operating in an age in which the acquisition of a unified and personal voice is no longer considered top priority, Turnage's eclecticism does not lead to the usual anonymity. His bluesy, shell-shocked lyricism is very much his own. The abrasive opening movement spews out key thematic material in a series of angry, violent climaxes, and yet this is not the dominant mood. "Junior Addict", inspired by a poem by Langston Hughes, is powerfully melodic with its bleak soprano saxophone solo weaving through woodwinds above a subterranean bass. Get this far and you should be hooked. Elsewhere the symphonic Turnage is in the ascendant, seeming to aim for the clinching quasi-Mahlerian expression of hope tempered by fatalism, dispelling the fears. The present recording is edited together from live performances given in a variety of venues and the immediate style of miking, pop-influenced track-listings and (trilingual) annotations will not be to everyone's taste. That said, the playing is undeniably superb and, for the moment, this feels like a major release whether it represents the last gasp of the Third Stream or a radical new beginning.

Further listening ...
...Drowned Out[a]. Kai[b]. Three Screaming Popes[c]. Momentum[a]. [b]**Ulrich Heinen** (vc); [b]**Birmingham Contemporary Music Group;** [ac]**City of Birmingham Symphony Orchestra / Sir Simon Rattle.** EMI CDC5 55091-2 (9/94). *Gramophone Editor's choice.*   🟢🟢
...**Your Rockaby**[a]. Night Dances[b]. Dispelling the Fears[c]. **Soloists;** [a]**BBC Symphony Orchestra / Andrew Davis;** [b]**London Sinfonietta / Oliver Knussen;** [c]**Philharmonia Orchestra / Daniel Harding.** Argo 452 598-2ZH (10/96). *Gramophone Editor's choice.*   🟢🟢
...On All Fours[a]. Lament for a Hanging Man[b]. Sarabande[c]. Release[d]. [bc]**Fiona Kimm** (mez); [abd]**Martin Robertson** (sax); [a]**Christopher Van Kampen** (vc); [cd]**Ian Brown** (pf); [abd]**Nash Ensemble / Oliver Knussen.** NMC NMCD024M (9/95).
...Greek. **Soloists; Greek Ensemble / Richard Bernas.** Argo 440 368-2ZHO (7/94).

Erkki-Sven Tüür   Estonia 1959

Tüür Architectonics VI. Passion. Illusion. Crystallisatio. Requiem[a]. [a]**Estonian Philharmonic Chamber Choir; Tallinn Chamber Orchestra / Tõnu Kaljuste.** ECM New Series Ⓕ 449 459-2 (64 minutes: DDD: 7/96). Text and translation included.
Architectonics VI sounds like one of those titles that are too good to resist, and it is to the credit of Erkki-Sven Tüür that he admits as much in the brief interview in the booklet to this beguiling disc (the sumptuous annotation in English is translated in reduced form in German and French). Tüür's piece – written in 1992 – isn't architectonic in construction (well, any more than the music of a hundred other composers), but it is well put together and effective on its own terms. *Passion* and *Illusion*, both for string orchestra and composed in 1993, are closer in spirit to the prevailing 'New Simplicity' of current East Baltic composition. *Passion*, indeed, is occasionally reminiscent of Tüür's better-known compatriot, Arvo Pärt, although the brief *Illusion* has a curiously English feel to it. The title track, *Crystallisatio* (1995), is scored for three flutes, bells, string orchestra and live electronics and is somewhat more demanding in scope. It is here that Tüür's synthesis of minimalism with serial techniques is heard most eloquently; not wholly achieved, perhaps, but fascinating in application. By far the biggest piece is the Requiem (1992-3; in memory of the conductor Peeter Lilje). It is a deeply felt, half-hour-long setting of the mass for the dead, and is of markedly different character to the other pieces here. This is a handsomely produced, thought-provoking release. Anyone wanting to hear up-to-the-minute new music that will not sear the ears off his (or her) head should try it.

Additional recommendation ...
...Architectonics – I; II; III, "Postmetaminimal Dream"; IV, "Per Cadenza ad Metasimplicity"; V; VI; VII. **NYYD Ensemble.** Finlandia Ⓕ 0630-14908-2 (63 minutes: DDD: 4/97).

Further listening ...
...Searching for Roots. Insula deserta. Zeit-raum. *Coupled with works by* **Pärt** *and* **Tubin** **Royal Stockholm Philharmonic Orchestra / Paavo Järvi.** Virgin Classics VC5 45212-2 (5/97).
...Conversio. **Gidon Kremer** (vn); **Vadim Sacharov** (pf). Teldec 0630-14654-2 (11/97). *Gramophone Editor's choice. See review in the Collections section; refer to the Index.*
...String Quartet. *Coupled with works by* **Pärt** *and* **Tubin** **Tallinn Quartet; Love Derwinger** (pf). BIS CD574 (1/94).
...String Quartet. *Coupled with works by* **Vasks** *and* **Pärt** **Duke Quartet.** Collins Classics 1475-2 (7/96).

Geirr Tveitt
Norwegian 1908-1981

Suggested listening ...
...50 Folk-tunes from Hardanger, Op. 150 – Welcome with honour; A-wooing; The most beautiful song on earth; Langeleik tune; Tears and laughter for a boat; The long, long winter night; The Father of the Child. *Coupled with works by various composers.* **Leif Ove Andsnes** (pf). EMI CDC5 56541-2 (6/98). *See review in the Collections section; refer to the Index.*

Christopher Tye
British c1505-1572

Suggested listening ...
...Rachell's weepinge. Farewell my good one forever. *Coupled with works by various composers.* **Kronos Quartet.** Nonesuch 7559-79457-2 (12/97). *Gramophone Editor's choice. See review in the Collections section; refer to the Index.*
...Sit fast. *Coupled with works by various composers.* **Fretwork.** Virgin Classics VC5 45217-2 (12/97). ☞ *See review in the Collections section; refer to the Index.*

Viktor Ullmann
Austro/Hungarian 1898-1944

Ullmann Die Weise von Liebe und Tod des Cornets Christoph Rilke[a]. Variationen und Doppelfuge über ein Theme von Arnold Schoenberg, Op. 3a[b].
Schoenberg Sechs Klavierstücke, Op. 19[c]. Ode to Napoleon, Op. 41[d]. [a]**Gert Westphal,** [d]**Roland Hermann** (spkrs); [d]**Tim Vogler,** [d]**Frank Reinecke** (vns); [d]**Stefan Fehlandt** (va); [d]**Michael Sanderling** (vc); [a]**Michael Allan,** [bc]**Günther Herzfeld,** [d]**Frank-Immo Zichner** (pfs). Edition Abseits
Ⓕ EDA008-2 (65 minutes: DDD: 11/95). Texts and translations included. Recorded 1994.
Coupling Ullmann and Schoenberg makes sense. Even in the desperate conditions of the concentration camp Theresienstadt, where his Rilke setting was composed, Ullmann followed a more recognizably German compositional path than his fellow internees. His teacher's work was the yardstick against which he would have gauged his own development. Listening to the *Variations* in conjunction with *Die Weise von Liebe und Tod des Cornets Christoph Rilke* one is aware of a simplification of technique and expression not solely attributable to the practical constraints of Ullmann's last years. But then he was never a slavish Schoenbergian: the *Variations* begin with an artfully academic inversion of the theme, extend its possibilities in a language that owes more to Berg and take a quasi-Hindemithian line in the rhetorical counterpoint of the fugue. Herzfeld gives what seems to be an accurate, often bravura performance, whereas his Schoenberg Op. 19 pieces (the source of Ullmann's theme) lack a certain tension, the sound itself rather too soft-grained. Competition in this repertoire is fierce.
Ullmann's setting of 12 extracts from Rilke's novella is a quirky but compelling assertion of self against insurmountable odds. The problem of integrating speech and music into a unified whole is not so much solved as avoided, in favour of a series of vignettes depicting stages in the protagonist's journey towards a mythical future. Simple leitmotivic fragments provide overall coherence, although the text's evocative qualities are inevitably cramped by the two-dimensional effect of the medium: Ullmann did not live to complete an orchestral version. When performed with this degree of conviction, *Die Weise von Liebe und Tod des Cornets Christoph Rilke* is more than a historical curiosity, even if Ullmann cannot match the ironic force that Schoenberg draws from Lord Byron's withering 'tribute'. The present performance of the *Ode to Napoleon* lacks the flexibility and *élan* one expects to hear in the English language original but Hermann makes a solid case for Schoenberg's own (unpublished) German translation. The players capture the intricacy, if not always the immediacy, of the instrumental commentary – the recording is spacious but could be better focused. An uneven disc then, but definitely one of the more interesting Ullmann offerings to date.

Further listening ...
...String Quartet No. 3, Op. 43. *Coupled with works by* **Klein** Hawthorne Quartet; Virginia Eskin (pf). Channel Classics CCS1691 (12/91). *See review under Klein; refer to the Index.*   ⒼⒼ
...Liebeslieder, Op. 18[a]. Lieder, Op. 17[a]. Three Sonnets from the Portuguese, Op. 29[a]. Six Sonnets, Op. 34[a]. Geistliche Lieder, Op. 20[a]. Liederbuch des Hafis, Op. 30[b]. Der Mensch und sein Tag, Op. 47[b]. Immer inmitten[c]. Chinese Songs – Wanderer erwacht in der Herberge; Der mude Soldat[b]. Drei Lieder (1942)[b]. Sonnen-untergang[a]. Der Frühling[a]. Abendphantasie[a].
[a]**Christine Schäfer** (sop); [c]**Liat Himmelheber** (mez); [b]**Yaron Windmüller** (bar); **Axel Bauni** (pf). Orfeo C380952 (5/96).
...Songs. **Petr Matuszek** (bar); **Pavel Eret** (vn); **Libor Kaňka** (va); **Vladan Kočí** (vc); **Aleš Kaňka** (pf). Supraphon SU3284-2 (1/98).
...Der Kaiser von Atlantis, oder Die Tod-Verweigerung. Hölderlin-Lieder – Abend-phantasie; Der Frühling; Wo bist du?. **Soloists; Leipzig Gewandhaus Orchestra / Lothar Zagrosek.** Decca Entartete Musik 440 854-2DH (12/94).   Ⓖ
...Der Sturz des Antichrist. **Soloists; Bielefeld Opera Chorus; Bielefeld Philharmonic Orchestra / Rainer Koch.** CPO CPO999 321-2 (10/96).

Craig Urquhart

American 1953

Suggested listening ...
...Among the multitude, 1980. *Coupled with works by various composers.*
Thomas Hampson (bar); **Craig Rutenberg** (pf).
EMI CDM5 55028-2 (10/97). *See review in the Collections section; refer to the Index.*

Johannes Urreda

Flemish/Spanish late 15th century

Suggested listening ...
...Nunca fué pena ma yor. *Coupled with works by various composers.* **The Hilliard Ensemble.**
Virgin Classics Veritas VED5 61394-2 (11/97). *See review in the Collections section; refer to the
Index.*

Galina Ustvol'skaya

USSR 1919

Ustvol'skaya Concerto for Piano, Strings and Timpani[a]. Octet[b]. Piano Sonata No. 3[c].
Grand Duet[d]. [b]**A. Kosoyan**, [b]**Kh. Chinakov** (obs); [b]**A. Stang**, [b]**A. Liskovich**, [b]**A. Dukor**, [b]**F. Soakov**
(vns); [d]**Oleg Stolpner** (vc); [b]**V. Znamensky** (timpani); [a]**Pavel Serebryakov**, [b]**M. Karandashova**,
[cd]**Oleg Malov** (pfs); [a]**Chamber Orchestra of the Leningrad State Philharmonic Society.**
Melodiya Ⓜ 74321 49956-2 (75 minutes: ADD: 6/98). Recorded [a]1970, [bc]1975, [d]1985.
Here's an excellent CD for anyone wanting to sample the music of Galina Ustvol'skaya. The
repertoire offers only a restricted chronological survey (up to 1959), but the performances have the
fanatical intensity which is a *sine qua non* for her peculiar mode of agonized communication. The
Concerto for piano, strings and timpani shows the roots of her style in Prokofiev and Shostakovich –
in 1946 Ustvol'skaya was still in Shostakovich's Leningrad composition class. Pavel Serebryakov gives
the instrument an appropriately hard time, knocking it out of tune fairly early in the proceedings, but
something of the *frisson* of playing previously banned music (the première was not until 1969)
certainly comes across. By 1950 Ustvol'skaya was writing the kind of stripped-bare textures which
Shostakovich recognized as an influence on him. The Octet (for two oboes, four violins, timpani and
piano!) is a case in point, and it climaxes in percussive blows of a quite fearsome insistence. Oleg
Malov, the one performer closest to Ustvol'skaya over the years, delves deep into the ascetic mysteries
of the Third Piano Sonata. Malov and Oleg Stolpner show what a massively impressive piece the
Grand Duet can be in the right hands. Once again the piano's treble register doesn't survive more than
a couple of minutes before becoming seriously detuned, though otherwise the recording quality is
fine. Rival performances pale by comparison. In sum, here is a chance to hear all the music on this
disc as it should be heard.
Additional recommendation ...
...Concerto for Piano, Strings and Timpani. *Coupled with works by various composers.*
Alexei Lubimov (pf); **Deutsche Kammerphilharmonie, Bremen / Heinrich Schiff.**
Erato Ⓕ 0630-12709-2 (64 minutes: DDD: 8/96).
...Grand (Bolshoi) Duet. *Coupled with works by* **Gubaidulina Maya Beiser** (vc);
Christopher Oldfather (pf). Koch International Classics 37258-2 (11/95).

Jehan Vaillant

French *fl* 1360-1390

Suggested listening ...
...Par maintes foys. *Coupled with works by various composers.* **Alla Francesca.**
Opus 111 OPS30-173 (7/98). *See review in the Collections section; refer to the Index.*

Moishei Vainberg

Polish 1919-1996

Vainberg String Quartets – No. 1, Op. 2/141; No. 10, Op. 85; No. 17, Op. 146. **Gothenburg Quartet**
(Ingrid Sjönnemo, Elin Anderberg, vns; Mia Wassenius, va; Anders Robertson, vc).
Olympia Ⓕ OCD628 (61 minutes: DDD: 5/98). Recorded 1997.
Vainberg's First Quartet, as recorded here, bears the odd opus number 2/141, and the date 1937-86.
The explanation is that Vainberg wrote it as his first essay in the form, when he was 18 and seemingly
impressed by both Berg and Schoenberg. The vicissitudes of his life (if one can use so light a term to
cover his and his family's sufferings at the hands of both Nazi and Communist anti-Semitism) caused
the work to be lost; and in 1985 he wrote it down again from memory. He is said to have been
possessed of a phenomenal memory but it is difficult to suppose that some element of revision or
recomposition all those years later was not involved. At any rate, the outcome is an odd work, well
written and individual in character. However, it lacks the distinctive nature of either the Tenth
Quartet of 1964 or still more the Seventeenth of 1987. It is a very interestingly written work, inserting

a slow movement in the course of a sonata movement rather in the manner of the so-called *Phantasy* once suggested to English composers by W.W. Cobbett and successfully achieved by, especially, Frank Bridge. Vainberg can have known nothing of this, but he reaches a comparable solution to a formal problem, and does so with real invention and structural good judgement. The Gothenburg Quartet play these three pieces with liveliness and perception, and anyone curious about this remarkable sequence of works would find a good sampler here.

Vainberg 24 Preludes, Op. 100. Solo Cello Sonata No. 1, Op. 72. **Yosif Feigelson** (vc).
Olympia ⓜ OCD594 (57 minutes: DDD: 11/97). Recorded 1996.
Vainberg composed the cycle of 24 Preludes for Rostropovich, but, for reasons which are not disclosed by Per Skans in his otherwise admirably informative insert-notes, the two men fell out, and the work, written in 1968, was not performed until 1996 by the present artist. It is a remarkably impressive and entertaining piece. The longest of the Preludes lasts only just over three minutes; most of the others last under two. The tonal design – a climb 12 degrees up the chromatic scale from C, followed by a similar descent – gives the music coherence, but what holds the forefront of the listener's attention is a virtuoso variety of invention, some of it witty, some of it grave and with baroque overtones, some of it allusive, with references to colleagues including Vainberg's friend and advocate Shostakovich (whose DSCH motif from his Cello Concerto marks No. 21). It is a pity that Rostropovich did not take the work up, as his reputation could have done much to make the music known and to have helped Vainberg when he needed all the help he could get. But the performances of the cycle, and of the rather less remarkable Solo Cello Sonata, are outstanding, and collectors who overcome an understandable reluctance to embark upon an hour's unaccompanied cello music by a still little-known composer are more than likely to find themselves wondering why he is not better known.
Further listening ...
...Symphonies – No. 14, Op. 117; No. 18, "War – there is no word more cruel", Op. 138[a].
[a]**Latvian State Academic Chorus; USSR Radio Symphony Orchestra / Vladimir Fedoseyev.**
Olympia OCD589 (12/96).
...Symphony No. 17, Op. 137, "Memory". The Banners of Peace, Op. 143.
USSR Radio Symphony Orchestra / Vladimir Fedoseyev. Olympia OCD590 (2/97).
...Symphony No. 19, Op. 142, "The Bright May". Chamber Symphony No. 3, Op. 151.
USSR Radio Symphony Orchestra / Vladimir Fedoseyev. Olympia OCD591 (5/97).
...Piano Quintet, Op. 18[a]. String Quartet No. 12, Op. 103[b]. [a]**Moishei Vainberg** (pf);
[a]**Borodin Quartet;** [b]**Yevgeni Smirnov,** [b]**Arnold Kobyhyansky** (vns); [b]**Vyatcheslav Trushin** (va);
[b]**Alla Vasilieva** (vc). Olympia OCD474 (4/95). ⓖ

Enriquez de Valderrábano
Spanish *c*1500-*c*1556

Suggested listening ...
...Contrapunto sobre el tenor del conde claros. *Coupled with works by various composers.*
Ensemble Clément Janequin / Dominique Visse (alto). Harmonia Mundi HMC90 1627 (4/98).
Gramophone Editor's choice. See review in the Collections section; refer to the Index. ⓖⓖ

Fartein Valen
Norwegian 1887-1952

Suggested listening ...
...Variations, Op. 23. *Coupled with works by various composers.* **Leif Ove Andsnes** (pf).
EMI CDC5 56541-2 (6/98). *See review in the Collections section; refer to the Index.*

Antonio Valente
Italian *c*1529-*c*1580

Suggested listening ...
...Tenore del passo e mezzo. *Coupled with works by various composers.* **Rinaldo Alessandrini** (hpd).
Opus 111 OPS30-118 (4/95). ✒ *See review in the Collections section; refer to the Index.* ⓖⓖ
...Tenore del passo e mezzo. *Coupled with works by various composers.* **Sophie Yates** (hpd).
Chandos Chaconne CHAN0601 (9/97). ✒ *See review in the Collections section; refer to the Index.*

Francisco Valls
Spanish 1665-1747

Suggested listening ...
...En un noble, sagrado firmamento. *Coupled with works by various composers.*
Al Ayre Español / Eduardo López Banzo. Deutsche Harmonia Mundi 05472 77325-2 (8/95). ✒
See review in the Collections section; refer to the Index. ⓖ

Jacob Van Eyck

Dutch 1589/90-1657

Suggested listening ...

...Crimson Velvet. Merry Cuckolds. Our Father which in Heaven art. *Coupled with works by various composers.* **Mhairi Lawson** (sop); **Circa 1500**. ASV Gaudeamus CDGAU163 (12/97). ✐
See review in the Collections section; refer to the Index.

Vanessa-Mae

Singapore 20th century

Suggested listening ...

...Violin Fantasy on Puccini's "Turandot"[b]. Happy Valley – The 1997 Re-Unification Overture, 1997[c]. *Coupled with* **Chen/Ho** Butterfly Lovers Concerto[a]. **Vanessa-Mae** (vn); [c]**Chinese Ladies' Choir;** [a]**London Philharmonic Orchestra / Viktor Fedotov;** [bc]**Royal Opera House Orchestra, Covent Garden /** [b]**Fedotov,** [c]**David Arch.**
EMI CDC5 56483-2 (2/98). *See review under Chen/Ho; refer to the Index.*

Edgar Varèse

French/American 1883-1965

Varèse Ionisation[ce]. Amériques[ce]. Arcana (All from CBS 76520, 6/78)[ce]. Density 21.5[b]. Offrandes[ade]. Octandre[de]. Intégrales (All from IM39053, 3/85)[de]. [a]**Rachel Yakar** (sop); [b]**Lawrence Beauregard** (fl); [c]**New York Philharmonic Orchestra;** [d]**Ensemble InterContemporain /** [e]**Pierre Boulez.** Sony Classical Ⓜ SMK45844 (77 minutes: ADD/DDD: 10/90).
Texts and translations included.   Ⓖ
The music of Varèse has been poorly represented on disc and in the concert-hall in recent years. Quite why so important a figure in twentieth-century music should be neglected like this is hard to say, and even more difficult to comprehend when one samples the quality of the music presented here. Varèse was a pioneer, a quester and above all a liberator. Music for him was a form of twentieth-century alchemy – the transmutation of the ordinary into the extraordinary, an alchemical wedding of intellectual thought with intuitive imagination. It was the writings of the fourteenth-century cosmologist and alchemist Paracelsus that formed the inspiration behind his orchestral work *Arcana*, a vast canvas of sound built entirely out of one melodic motive. Echoes of Stravinsky and others are discernible, but the totality of *Arcana* is pure Varèse. The same is true of *Amériques*, a title that Varèse emphasized was not to be taken as "purely geographical but as symbolic of discoveries – new worlds on earth, in the sky or in the minds of men". Here romanticism and modernism seem to coexist side by side, where allusions from works such as *La mer* and *The Firebird* seem like memories carried into his brave new world. The remaining items consist of smaller chamber works which display Varèse's most radical, though equally rewarding, styles. Boulez and his players give committed, virtuosic performances of these challenging and intriguing works. Well worth exploring.

Additional recommendation ...

...Intégrales[a]. Ionisation[a]. Ecuatorial[ab]. Densité 21.5[c]. Déserts[a]. Nocturnal[ad]. [d]**Phyllis Bryn-Julson** (sop); [b]**Nicholas Isherwood** (bass); [c]**Philippe Pierlot** (fl); [d]**French Radio Mens' Chorus;** [a]**French National Orchestra / Kent Nagano.** Erato Ⓕ 0630-14332-2 (69 minutes: DDD: 2/97).

Peteris Vasks

Latvian 1946-

Vasks Musica dolorosa. Cantabile. Lauda. Symphony for Strings, "Voices". **I Fiamminghi / Rudolf Werthen.** Telarc Ⓕ CD80457 (61 minutes: DDD: 2/98). Recorded 1996.
"Latvia has never had a Sibelius or a Grieg ... as its musical spokesperson," explains Richard Rodda in the booklet, "so it is of special significance that Peteris Vasks has begun to receive international recognition just at the time of the country's newly won independence." That begs a serious question: is Vasks's new-found fame entirely musical in origin, or at least partly the consequence of political necessity, and/or external curiosity about a hitherto largely overlooked country? The same could have been true at the start for Grieg and Sibelius, of course (Norway and Finland both achieved political freedom in their lifetimes), so only time will tell in the case of Vasks. Gut feeling suggests he is not of their stature (is it an accident that Vasks is the only Latvian composer to have emerged into wider view, whereas a gaggle of Lithuanians and especially Estonians – think just of Pärt, Tormis, Tüür – have appeared on disc?), though there is no denying his compositional skill, and the immediacy of appeal of works such as *Musica dolorosa* (1983) or the symphony *Stimmen* ("Voices", 1990-1991) which, allied to a not-too-radical musical idiom, probably explains the recording industry's sustained interest. If you have not encountered Vasks before, then I Fiamminghi's excellently played disc is a very good place to start. Rudolf Werthen, who has a tendency to adopt swifter tempos than other conductors, has the interpretative measure of the music.

Additional recommendations ...

...Symphony for Strings, "Voices". Cello Concerto[a]. [a]**David Geringas** (vc); **Riga Philharmonic Orchestra / Jonas Aleksa.** Conifer Classics Ⓕ 75605 51271-2 (62 minutes: DDD: 12/96).

...Musica dolorosa. **Gidon Kremer** (vn); **Deutsche Kammerphilharmonie.**
Teldec Ⓟ 0630-14654-2 (79 minutes: DDD: 11/97). *Gramophone Editor's choice.*
See review in the Collections section; refer to the Index.
Further listening ...
...Cantabile. Cor Anglais Concerto[a]. Message. Musica Dolorosa. Lauda. [a]**Normunds Schnee**
(cor ang); **Riga Philharmonic Orchestra / Kriss Rusmanis.** Conifer Classics CDCF236 (1/95).
...String Quartet No. 2, "Sommer Gesänger". *Coupled with* **Pärt** Fratres. **Tüür** String Quartet.
Duke Quartet. Collins Classics 1475-2 (7/96).

Juan Vásquez   Spanish c1510-c1560

Suggested listening ...
...A, hermosa, abrime cara de rosa. Con qué la lavaré. Torna, Mingo, a namorarte. Si no os uviera
mirado. En la fuente del rosel. Soledad tengo de tí. Buscad buen amor. O dulce contemplación.
De los álamos vengo. *Coupled with works by various composers.* **La Columbina Ensemble.**
Accent ACC95111D (11/96). *See review in the Collections section; refer to the Index.*
...Ojos morenos. Que yo, mi madre, yo. Mi mal de causa es. Gentil senora mia. Cavallero,
queraysme dexar. Agora que sé de amor. El que sin ti bivir, ya no querría. Lágrimas de mi
consuelo. *Coupled with works by various composers.* **Ensemble Clément Janequin / Dominique Visse**
(alto). Harmonia Mundi HMC90 1627 (4/98). *Gramophone Editor's choice. See review in the*
Collections section; refer to the Index.   ⓖⓖ
...Orphenica lyra – De los álamos vengo; Con qué la lavaré; Glosa sobre Tan que vivray;
De Antequera sale el moro. *Coupled with works by various composers.* **La Romanesca /**
José Miguel Moreno (vihuela). Glossa GCD920203 (5/96). 🗲 *Gramophone Editor's choice.*
See review in the Collections section; refer to the Index.   ⓖ

Ralph Vaughan Williams   British 1872-1958

Vaughan Williams Symphonies – No. 1, "A Sea Symphony"[a]; No. 2, "A London Symphony"[b];
No. 3, "A Pastoral Symphony"[c]; No. 4 in F minor[d]; No. 5 in D major[e]; No. 6 in E minor[g];
No. 7, "Sinfonia antartica"[h]; No. 8 in D minor[b]; No. 9 in E minor[g]. Flos campi[f]. Serenade to
Music[i]. [c]**Alison Barlow,** [h]**Alison Hargan,** [a]**Joan Rodgers** (sops); [a]**William Shimell** (bar);
[f]**Christopher Balmer** (va); [afh]**Liverpool Philharmonic Choir; Royal Liverpool Philharmonic**
Orchestra / Vernon Handley. EMI Eminence Ⓜ CDBOX-VW1 (six discs: 396 minutes:
DDD: 1/95). Items marked [a] from CD-EMX2142 (2/89), [b]CD-EMX2209 (8/93), [cd]CD-EMX2192
(11/92), [ef]CD-EMX9512 (3/88), [g]reviewed below, [hi]CD-EMX2173 (9/91). No. 2: *Gramophone*
Editor's choice. Nos. 2 and 8 *selected by Sounds in Retrospect.*   ⓖⓖ
Vaughan Williams Symphonies – No. 6 in E minor; No. 9 in E minor.
Royal Liverpool Philharmonic Orchestra / Vernon Handley. EMI Eminence Ⓜ CD-EMX2230
(67 minutes: DDD: 1/95). Recorded 1994. *Gramophone Editor's choice.*   ⓖⓖ
Handley's performances can withstand comparison with the very best. The first to appear was the
Fifth Symphony. Rightly acclaimed on its initial release, this remains a gloriously rapt, yet formidably
lucid realization. The coupling, a supremely dedicated rendering of the exquisite *Flos campi*, is just as
distinguished. Handley's masterly pacing is a compelling feature of both the *Sea Symphony* and
Sinfonia antartica, but, whilst it is difficult to fault either performance on artistic grounds, here more
than elsewhere one notes the limitations of the slightly cramped acoustic of Liverpool's Philharmonic
Hall. There are no technical shortcomings about the Third or Fourth. Handley's illuminatingly
intense *Pastoral* yields only to André Previn's sublime LSO account and his Fourth only (amongst
modern counterparts) to Slatkin's in terms of unbridled ferocity and orchestral virtuosity. The second
and Eighth bring outstandingly perceptive, marvellously communicative music-making, with both
scores emerging as fresh as the day they were conceived. Handley's interpretation of the Sixth
Symphony is a model of cogency and long-term control. Don't be deceived by the element of slight
reserve in the opening movement. It soon transpires that Handley already has his eyes firmly set on
the work's terrifying apex, namely the baleful climax of the succeeding *Moderato*. Handley's scherzo
teems with busy detail, its feverish contrapuntal workings laid out before us with maximum clarity
and force. So many performances have come to grief in the extraordinary finale; Handley's is a
triumphant exception. In this desolate, inconsolable landscape (with not an *espressivo* marking in
sight), Handley, even more than the admirable Andrew Davis, achieves a truly awesome hush and
concentration.
    And what of the Ninth, VW's other 'E minor'? Few interpreters on disc have probed much beneath
the surface of this elusive, craggy masterpiece. Though Handley's memorably responsive Liverpool
orchestra can't quite boast a string section as lustrous or refined as Slatkin's Philharmonia, he
captures more of the music's mordant wit, whilst allowing the listener to revel afresh in the
astonishing vitality and startlingly original sonorities of VW's ever-imaginative inspiration. The
overriding impression left by both performances is one of supreme sensitivity and utter dedication to
the cause. In the visionary finale, whose monumental, block-like structure gradually takes shape

before our eyes like Stonehenge itself, Handley's conception just has the edge in terms of elemental power and effortless inevitability. The recordings are admirably natural.

Additional recommendations ...

...Nos. 1-9. **Soloists; London Symphony Chorus and Orchestra / Bryden Thomson.**
Chandos Ⓕ CHAN9087/91 (five discs: 352 minutes: DDD).

...Nos. 1-9. Norfolk Rhapsody No. 1. Fantasia on a Theme by Thomas Tallis. Fantasia on "Greensleeves". Five Variants of "Dives and Lazarus". **Soloists; Philharmonia Chorus and Orchestra / Leonard Slatkin.** RCA Victor Ⓜ 09026 61460-2 (six discs: DDD).

...Nos. 3 and 5. **London Philharmonic Orchestra / Sir Adrian Boult.**
Belart Ⓢ 461 118-2 (72 minutes: ADD).

...No. 5. Flos campi[a]. [a]**Christopher Balmer** (va); [a]**Liverpool Philharmonic Choir; Royal Liverpool Philharmonic Orchestra / Vernon Handley.**
EMI Eminence Ⓜ CD-EMX9512 (62 minutes: DDD: 3/88).

...No. 2. Fantasia on a Theme by Thomas Tallis. **London Philharmonic Orchestra / Bernard Haitink.**
EMI Ⓕ CDC7 49394-2 (66 minutes: DDD: 7/88).   Ⓖ

...No. 3. Oboe Concerto in A minor[a]. **Yvonne Kenny** (sop); [a]**David Theodore** (ob); **London Symphony Orchestra / Bryden Thomson.** Chandos Ⓕ CHAN8594 (56 minutes: DDD: 8/88).

...No. 2. Concerto grosso. **London Symphony Orchestra / Bryden Thomson.**
Chandos Ⓕ CHAN8629 (65 minutes: DDD: 10/89).

...No. 2. Concerto Accademico[a]. The Wasps – Overture. [a]**James Oliver Buswell IV** (vn); **London Symphony Orchestra / André Previn.** RCA Gold Seal Ⓜ GD90501 (71 minutes: ADD: 3/91).   Ⓖ

...Nos. 3 and 4. **Heather Harper** (sop); **London Symphony Orchestra / André Previn.**
RCA Victor Gold Seal Ⓜ GD90503 (73 minutes: ADD: 3/91).

...Nos. 7[a] and 8. [a]**Heather Harper** (sop); [a]**Ambrosian Singers; London Symphony Orchestra / André Previn.** RCA Victor Gold Seal Ⓜ GD90510 (72 minutes: ADD: 3/91).

...No. 2. Fantasia on a Theme by Thomas Tallis. **London Philharmonic Orchestra / Sir Adrian Boult.**
EMI Ⓜ CDM7 64017-2 (60 minutes: ADD: 5/92).

...Nos. 3 and 4. [a]**Alison Barlow** (sop); **Royal Liverpool Philharmonic Orchestra / Vernon Handley.**
EMI Eminence Ⓜ CD-EMX2192 (67 minutes: DDD: 11/92).

...Nos. 2 and 8. **Royal Liverpool Philharmonic Orchestra / Vernon Handley.**
EMI Eminence Ⓜ CD-EMX2209 (72 minutes: DDD: 8/93). *Gramophone* Editor's choice.   ⒼⒼ

...No. 2. Fantasia on "Greensleeves". Serenade to Music. The Wasps – Overture.
Soloists; Queen's Hall Orchestra / Sir Henry Wood.
Dutton Laboratories mono Ⓜ CDAX8004* (63 minutes: ADD: 10/93).   Ⓖ

...Nos. 3[a] and 4. Fantasia on "Greensleeves". [a]**Linda Hohenfeld** (sop); **Philharmonia Orchestra / Leonard Slatkin.** RCA Victor Red Seal Ⓕ 09026 61194-2 (73 minutes: DDD: 11/93).
Gramophone Editor's choice.

...No. 2[a]. Partita for Double String Orchestra[b]. **London Philharmonic Orchestra / Sir Adrian Boult.**
Belart [a]mono/[b]stereo Ⓢ 461 008-2* (65 minutes: ADD: 12/94).

...Nos. 1-8. Partita for Double String Orchestra. **Soloists; London Philharmonic Choir; London Philharmonic Orchestra / Sir Adrian Boult.**
Belart mono/stereo Ⓢ 461 442-2* (five discs: 353 minutes: ADD: 6/97).

...Nos. 3 and 7. **Patricia Rozario** (sop); **BBC Symphony Chorus and Orchestra / Andrew Davis.**
Telarc Ⓕ 0630-13139-2 (77 minutes: DDD: 12/97). *Selected by Soundings.*

Vaughan Williams Symphony No. 1, "A Sea Symphony". **Dame Felicity Lott** (sop); **Jonathan Summers** (bar); **Cantilena; London Philharmonic Choir and Orchestra / Bernard Haitink.**
EMI Ⓕ CDC7 49911-2 (71 minutes: DDD: 1/90). Text included. Recorded 1989.   ⒼⒼ

A firm hand on the tiller is needed to steer a safe course through this, Vaughan Williams's first and most formally diffuse symphony, completed in 1909. Haitink is clearly an ideal choice of helmsman and he is helped by a remarkably lucid recording that resolves details that would rarely be revealed in live performance. What might be more unexpected here is the obvious affinity he shows for this music: whilst never transgressing the bounds of Vaughan Williams's characteristically English idiom, he manages to place the work in the European mainstream, revealing a whole range of resonances, from Bruckner and Mahler to the Impressionists. Not all the glory should go to the conductor, of course. Both soloists are particularly fine, the vulnerability behind the spine-tingling power of Felicity Lott's voice providing excellent contrast to the staunch solidity of Jonathan Summers. The LPO Chorus, aided by Cantilena, are on top form and the whole enterprise is underpinned by the LPO's total commitment and expertise. Here is the recording of this glorious work for which we have been waiting.

Additional recommendations ...

...**Joan Rodgers** (sop); **William Shimell** (bar); **Royal Liverpool Philharmonic Choir and Orchestra / Vernon Handley.** EMI Eminence Ⓜ CD-EMX2142 (70 minutes: DDD: 2/89).

...**Yvonne Kenny** (sop); **Brian Rayner Cook** (bar); **London Symphony Chorus and Orchestra / Bryden Thomson.** Chandos Ⓕ CHAN8764 (66 minutes: DDD: 2/90).

...**Heather Harper** (sop); **John Shirley-Quirk** (bar); **London Symphony Chorus and Orchestra / André Previn.** RCA Victor Gold Seal Ⓜ GD90500 (66 minutes: ADD: 3/91).

...**Dame Isobel Baillie** (sop); **John Cameron** (bar); **London Philharmonic Choir and Orchestra / Sir Adrian Boult.** Belart mono Ⓢ 450 144-2* (68 minutes: ADD: 7/94).   Ⓖ

Vaughan Williams Symphonies – No. 3, "A Pastoral Symphony"[a]; No. 4 in F minor.
[a]**Amanda Roocroft** (sop); **London Philharmonic Orchestra / Bernard Haitink.**
EMI Ⓕ CDC5 56564-2 (72 minutes: DDD: 5/98). Recorded 1996.
These are thought-provoking interpretations of great dedication and intelligence. If Haitink's deeply
felt conception of *A Pastoral Symphony* is the most daringly broad we've yet had on disc, its
concentration and abundant character grip from first measure to last. Aided by orchestral playing of
the highest quality, the opening movement unfolds with a luminous serenity, its climaxes unerringly
'placed', yet Haitink is also acutely aware of the ominous stirrings just beneath the surface. Most
distinctive of all is the *Moderato pesante* third movement which, as Haitink views it, is a
monumentally sombre, even intimidating affair. This is an interpretation of compelling individuality
and tragic intensity which all Vaugan Williams *aficionados* should investigate forthwith. The same
holds true for the Fourth. Again, Haitink presides over a performance of immense integrity and
perceptive long-term rigour. Speeds here are less controversial. By not driving the first movement too
hard, Haitink ensures that we can savour the full expressive eloquence of the strings' *appassionato
sostenuto* secondary idea. What's more, the scherzo possesses fine rhythmic point, and the transition
into the finale generates a tremendous expectancy. In this last movement Haitink keeps a firm hand
on the tiller and steadfastly refuses to whip up any artificial excitement, but its rugged symphonic
strength must surely command enormous respect.

Vaughan Williams Symphonies – No. 4 in F minor[a]; No. 5 in D major[b].
[a]**BBC Symphony Orchestra / Ralph Vaughan Williams;** [b]**Hallé Orchestra / Sir John Barbirolli.**
Dutton Laboratories mono Ⓜ CDAX8011* (66 minutes: ADD: 6/95). Item marked [a] from
HMV DB3367/70 (1/38), recorded 1937; [b]HMV C3388/92 (5/44), recorded 1944.   ⒼⒼ
No performance on record of Vaughan Williams's Fourth Symphony has ever quite matched this very
first one, recorded under the composer's baton in October 1937. As Michael Kennedy says in his
highly illuminating note for the Dutton Laboratories reissue, it is "taken at a daredevil pace", and
more importantly has a bite and energy beyond any rival. If early listeners to this violent work were
shocked by the composer's new boldness, here his conducting demonstrates the passionate emotion
behind the piece – paradoxically the most conventional of his symphonies in structure, as it is the
most radical in idiom. The remastered sound is so vivid and immediate, so full of presence, that in
places one almost has the illusion of stereo before its time. Sir John Barbirolli's première recording of
the Fifth Symphony, made in February 1944 eight months after the first performance, is hardly less
remarkable. This, too, has never quite been matched since for the stirring passion of the great climaxes
in the first and third movements, with Barbirolli in each carefully grading the intensity between
exposition and recapitulation. It is also a revelation to find him taking the triple-time of the
Passacaglia finale much faster than latter-day rivals, relating it far more closely than usual to the great
example of the finale of Brahms's Fourth Symphony, making it no pastoral amble but a searing
argument. Here again hiss – very high on the original wartime 78s, has been virtually eliminated, but
that has left the high violins sounding rather papery. Even so, there is no lack of weight or bite in the
big climaxes, with brass and wind atmospherically caught. An outstanding issue for all lovers of this
composer's music, not just those who specialize in historic recordings.

Additional recommendations ...
...No. 4. Violin Concerto in D minor, "Concerto Accademico"[a]. [a]**Kenneth Sillito** (vn); **London
Symphony Orchestra / Bryden Thomson.** Chandos Ⓕ CHAN8633 (50 minutes: DDD: 1/89).
...No. 5. The England of Elizabeth – excerpts. **London Symphony Orchestra / André Previn.**
RCA Victor Gold Seal Ⓜ GD90506 (59 minutes: ADD: 3/91).
...No. 4[a]. **Holst** The Planets, H125[b]. [a]**BBC Symphony Orchestra / Ralph Vaughan Williams;**
[b]**London Symphony Orchestra / Gustav Holst.**
Koch International Classics mono Ⓕ 37018-2* (69 minutes: ADD: 4/91).   Ⓖ
...Nos. 4 and 6. **New Philharmonia Orchestra / Sir Adrian Boult.**
EMI Ⓜ CDM7 64019-2 (69 minutes: ADD: 5/92).
...No. 5[a]. **Bax** Tintagel[b]. [a]**Philharmonia Orchestra;** [b]**London Symphony Orchestra /
Sir John Barbirolli.** EMI British Composers Ⓜ CDM5 65110-2 (54 minutes: ADD: 3/95).
...Nos. 4[a] and 6[b]. Fantasia on a Theme by Thomas Tallis[a]. **New York Philharmonic Symphony
Orchestra /** [a]**Dimitri Mitropoulos,** [b]**Leopold Stokowski.**
Sony Classical Essential Classics mono/stereo Ⓑ SBK62754* (73 minutes: ADD: 12/96).

Vaughan Williams Symphony No. 6 in E minor. Fantasia on a Theme by Thomas Tallis.
The Lark Ascending[a]. [a]**Tasmin Little** (vn); **BBC Symphony Orchestra / Andrew Davis.**
Teldec British Line Ⓕ 9031-73127-2 (62 minutes: DDD: 8/91). Recorded 1990.
Selected by Sounds in Retrospect.   Ⓖ
Andrew Davis has clearly thought long and hard before committing this enigmatic and tragic
symphony to disc, and the result is one of the most spontaneous and electrifying accounts of the Sixth
Symphony available. The urgency and vigour of the first and third movements is astonishing, leaving
one with the impression that the work might have been recorded in one take. His treatment of the
second subject's reprise in the closing pages of the first movement is more underplayed and remote
than the beautifully sheened approach of some recordings, but is arguably more nostalgic for being

so. The feverish, nightmare world of the *Scherzo* is a real *tour de force* in the hands of an inspired BBC Symphony Orchestra, and the desolate wasteland of the eerie final movement has rarely achieved such quiescence and nadir as here. Davis's searchingly intense *Tallis Fantasia* is finely poised with a beautifully spacious acoustic. The disc concludes on a quietly elevated note with Tasmin Little's serene and gently introspective reading of *The Lark Ascending*. The recording is excellent.

Additional recommendations ...

...Fantasia on a Theme by Thomas Tallis. Fantasia on Greensleeves.
  Coupled with works by **Elgar** **Sinfonia of London / Sir John Barbirolli.**
  EMI Ⓕ CDC7 47537-2* (58 minutes: ADD: 2/87).   ⒼⒼⒼ
...Fantasia on a Theme by Thomas Tallis. Norfolk Rhapsody No. 1. In the Fen Country.
  Five Variants of "Dives and Lazarus". **London Philharmonic Orchestra / Bryden Thomson.**
  Chandos Ⓕ CHAN8502 (59 minutes: DDD: 5/87).
...Nos. 6 and 9. **London Symphony Orchestra / André Previn.**
  RCA Victor Gold Seal Ⓜ GD90508 (73 minutes: ADD: 3/91).
...Fantasia on a Theme by Thomas Tallis. Partita for Double String Orchestra. Oboe Concerto[a].
  English Folk-Song Suite (orch. Jacob). Fantasia on "Greensleeves" (arr. Greaves).
  [a]**Jonathan Small** (ob); **Royal Liverpool Philharmonic Orchestra / Vernon Handley.**
  EMI Eminence Ⓜ CD-EMX2179 (68 minutes: DDD: 12/91).
...The Lark Ascending. *Coupled with works by various composers.* **David Wise** (vn);
  Liverpool Philharmonic Orchestra / Sir Malcolm Sargent.
  Dutton Laboratories mono Ⓜ CDAX8012* (75 minutes: ADD: 5/95).
...Fantasia on a Theme by Thomas Tallis. *Coupled with works by* **Holst** and **Walton**
  BBC Symphony Orchestra / Sir Adrian Boult. Beulah mono Ⓜ 2PD12* (70 minutes: ADD: 12/96).
...The Lark Ascending[a]. Fantasia on "Greensleeves". English Folk Song Suite. (trans. G. Jacob).
  Coupled with works by various composers. [a]**Iona Brown** (vn); **Academy of St Martin in the Fields /**
  Sir Neville Marriner. Decca Double Ⓑ 452 707-2DF2 (two discs: DDD: 8/97).
...The Lark Ascending. **Elgar** Violin Concerto in B minor, Op. 61. **Kennedy** (vn);
  City of Birmingham Symphony Orchestra / Sir Simon Rattle.
  EMI Ⓕ CDC5 56413-2 (72 minutes: ADD: 1/98). *See review under Elgar; refer to the Index.*

Vaughan Williams Symphony No. 7, "Sinfonia antartica". **Sheila Armstrong** (sop);
  London Philharmonic Choir and Orchestra / Bernard Haitink. EMI Ⓕ CDC7 47516-2
  (42 minutes: DDD: 1/87). From EL270318-1 (10/85). Recorded 1984.   Ⓖ
Scored for wordless soprano solo and chorus plus a large orchestra, this Seventh Symphony was based on the composer's music for the film *Scott of the Antarctic*. It comprises five movements; the Prelude, which conveys mankind's struggle in overcoming hostile natural forces; a *Scherzo*, which depicts the whales and penguins in their natural habitat; "Landscape", which portrays vast frozen wastes; Intermezzo, a reflection of the actions and thoughts of two members of the party; and "Epilogue", describing the final tragic assault on the South Pole. Bernard Haitink's conducting is highly imaginative, very concentrated and very committed and the LPO respond to him with some wonderfully atmospheric playing, full of personality and colour. Armstrong's eerie disembodied soprano voice and the remote chorus heighten the atmosphere, so that the score emerges as a powerful, coherent essay in symphonic form. The recording is magnificently sonorous and spacious.

Additional recommendations ...

...No. 7[a]. Toward the Unknown Region. [a]**Catherine Bott** (sop); **London Symphony Chorus and**
  Orchestra / Bryden Thomson. Chandos Ⓕ CHAN8796 (55 minutes: DDD: 4/90).
...No. 7[a]. Serenade to Music. [a]**Alison Hargan** (sop); **Royal Liverpool Choir and Orchestra /**
  Vernon Handley. EMI Eminence Ⓜ CD-EMX2173 (57 minutes: DDD: 9/91).
...No. 7[a]. **Walton** Cello Concerto[b]. [b]**Gregor Piatigorsky** (vc); [a]**Heather Harper** (sop); [a]**Ambrosian**
  Singers; [a]**London Symphony Orchestra / André Previn;** [b]**Boston Symphony Orchestra / Charles**
  Munch. RCA Victor Classical Navigator Ⓢ 74321 29248-2 (72 minutes: AAD/ADD: 6/96).

Vaughan Williams Symphony No. 9 in E minor. Piano Concerto in C major[a]. [a]**Howard Shelley**
  (pf); **London Symphony Orchestra / Bryden Thomson.** Chandos Ⓕ CHAN8941
  (57 minutes: DDD: 7/91). Recorded 1990. *Selected by Sounds in Retrospect.*   Ⓖ
Alongside the scorching account of the apocalyptic Fourth Symphony, this clear-headed, perceptive traversal of the enigmatic Ninth has fair claims to be regarded as the best thing in Bryden Thomson's underrated VW cycle for Chandos. Thomson's urgent conception of the opening *Moderato maestoso* in particular has a sweep and momentum one might not have previously associated with this movement, yet the gain in terms of sheer concentration and symphonic stature is irrefutable. Granted, some may find the outer sections of the succeeding *Andante sostenuto* just a little too lacking in evocative magic, but there's no gainsaying the effectiveness of gallumphing woodwind in the oafish scherzo; certainly, the LSO's saxophone trio seem to be enjoying their day out hugely. In the finale, too, Thomson's approach is more boldly assertive than usual – not the way one would always want to hear this music, perhaps, but a thoroughly valid and convincing performance all the same. The coupling, Howard Shelley's distinguished remake of the same composer's craggily elusive Piano Concerto, is both imaginative and desirable. All in all, a highly recommendable disc: the LSO are in fine fettle throughout, whilst Chandos's glowing sound come close to the ideal.

...Nos. 8 and 9. **London Philharmonic Orchestra / Sir Adrian Boult.**
EMI Ⓜ CDM7 64021-2 (64 minutes: ADD: 5/92).
...Piano Concerto. **Foulds** Dynamic Triptych, Op. 88. **Howard Shelley** (pf);
Royal Philharmonic Orchestra / Vernon Handley. Lyrita Ⓕ SRCD211 (57 minutes: DDD: 3/93). Ⓖ
...Nos. 8 and 9. Flourish for Glorious John (Barbirolli). **Philharmonia Orchestra / Leonard Slatkin.**
RCA Victor Red Seal Ⓕ 09026 61196-2 (63 minutes: DDD: 8/93). Ⓖ
...No. 9[a]. **Arnold** Symphony No. 3, Op. 63[b]. **London Philharmonic Orchestra / [a]Sir Adrian Boult,**
[b]**Sir Malcolm Arnold.** Everest Ⓕ EVC9001* (70 minutes: ADD: 4/95).
...Piano Concerto. *Coupled with works by* **Finzi** *and* **Delius** **Piers Lane** (pf);
Royal Liverpool Philharmonic Orchestra / Vernon Handley. EMI Eminence Ⓜ CD-EMX2239
(61 minutes: DDD: 11/95). *See review under Finzi; refer to the Index.*

Vaughan Williams Job – A masque for dancing[a]. The Wasps – Overture[b].
Arnold Four Scottish Dances, Op. 59[c]. **London Philharmonic Orchestra / [ab]Sir Adrian Boult,**
[c]**Sir Malcolm Arnold.** Everest Ⓕ EVC9006 (57 minutes: ADD: 5/95). Item marked [a] from
SDBR3019 (2/68), recorded 1958, [b]new to UK, [c]World Record Club ST99 (1/62). ⒼⒼⒼ
This is the third of Sir Adrian Boult's four recordings of *Job*, a work he conducted with peerless
authority for over 40 years (he was, of course, the score's dedicatee). The performance is one of
enormous dedication and considerable insight, achieving a rare serenity in Scene 3 ("Minuet of the
Sons of Job and their Wives"), Scene 5 ("Dance of the Three Messengers") and, above all, in the
Epilogue, which is more movingly realized than ever before or since. However, the chosen venue of
London's Royal Albert Hall evidently brought problems for the Everest recording team: it's an odd
sound, tightly miked and rather lacking in body, with brass balance closer than is ideal. Nor was the
London Philharmonic in the healthiest of shape at the time: string tone can be unreliable and
intonation occasionally suspect. Boult also directs a cherishable, delectably pointed rendering of *The
Wasps* Overture, whose glorious central melody really does seem to unfold with all the time in the
world here. Finally, Sir Malcolm Arnold conducts his own, irresistibly tuneful *Scottish Dances*. The
sound in both these items is impressively vivid for its late-1950s vintage. A very welcome reissue.
...Job. *Coupled with works by* **Bliss** *and* **Smyth** BBC Symphony Orchestra, [a]**Light Symphony**
Orchestra / Sir Adrian Boult. Dutton Laboratories mono Ⓜ CDAX8016* (76 minutes: ADD: 1/97).
...Job. **London Philharmonic Orchestra / Vernon Handley.**
Classics for Pleasure Ⓑ CD-CFP4603 (48 minutes: DDD: 3/93).
...Job. The Lark Ascending[a]. [a]**David Greed** (vn); **English Northern Philharmonia /**
David Lloyd-Jones. Naxos Ⓢ 8 553955 (61 minutes: DDD: 7/97). *Selected by Soundings.*
...The Wasps – Overture[a]. Fantasia on a Theme by Thomas Tallis[a]. Oboe Concerto[b].
Symphony No. 4 in F minor[c]. [b]**John Williams** (ob); [ab]**Bournemouth Symphony Orchestra;**
[c]**Royal Philharmonic Orchestra / [a]Constantin Silvestri, [bc]Paavo Berglund.**
EMI British Composers Ⓜ CDM5 66539-2 (75 minutes: ADD: 1/98).

Vaughan Williams Mass in G minor (1922)[b]. Te Deum in G major (1928)[c].
Howells Requiem (1936)[a]. Take him, earth, for cherishing (1963). [a]**Mary Seers** (sop);
[ab]**Michael Chance** (alto); [ab]**Philip Salmon** (ten); [ab]**Jonathan Best** (bass); **Corydon Singers /**
Matthew Best with [c]**Thomas Trotter** (org). Hyperion Ⓕ CDA66076 (60 minutes: ADD: 10/87).
Texts included. From A66076 (8/83). ⒼⒼ
Vaughan Williams's unaccompanied Mass in G minor manages to combine the common manner of
Elizabethan liturgical music with those elements of his own folk-music heritage that make his music
so distinctive, and in so doing arrives at something quite individual and new. The work falls into five
movements and its mood is one of heartfelt, if restrained, rejoicing. Howells's Requiem dates from
1936, a year after the death of his only son. The work was not released in his lifetime but was
reconstructed and published in 1980 from his manuscripts. It is a most hauntingly beautiful work of
an obviously intensely personal nature. *Take him, earth, for cherishing* was composed to
commemorate the assassination of J.F. Kennedy. The text is an English translation by Helen Waddell
of Prudentius's fourth-century poem, *Hymnus circa Exsequias Defuncti*. Again it demonstrates the
great strength of Howells's choral writing, with a clear outline and aptly affecting yet unimposing
harmonic twists. The Corydon Singers give marvellous performances and the sound is very fine.
...Mass in G minor. *Coupled with works by* **Bax** *and* **Finzi**
Soloists; King's College Choir, Cambridge / Sir David Willcocks.
EMI British Composers Ⓜ CDM5 65595-2 (73 minutes: [a]ADD/DDD: 1/97).

Vaughan Williams Dona nobis pacem[a]. Sancta civitas[b]. [a]**Yvonne Kenny** (sop); [b]**Philip Langridge**
(ten); **Bryn Terfel** (bass-bar); [b]**St Paul's Cathedral Choir; London Symphony Chorus and**
Orchestra / Richard Hickox. EMI British Composers Ⓕ CDC7 54788-2
(63 minutes: DDD: 12/93). Texts included. Recorded 1992. *Selected by Sounds in Retrospect.*
This is a generous and inspiring coupling of two of Vaughan Williams's most important choral
utterances. Hickox coaxes magnificent sounds from the LSO throughout: in *Dona nobis pacem*, for

example, the sense of orchestral spectacle during "Beat! Beat! drums!" is riveting in its physical impact. As ever, the contribution of the London Symphony Chorus combines full-throated discipline and sensitivity to nuance, and Hickox's trio of soloists are all excellent, with Bryn Terfel outstandingly eloquent. *Sancta civitas* is a work whose multi-layered scoring places great demands on both conductor and production team alike: suffice it to report, it is difficult to see Hickox's inspirational account of this still-underrated score (with its striking pre-echoes of *Job* and the Fourth Symphony) being surpassed for years to come. EMI's clean, wide-ranging sound is admirable.

Additional recommendation ...

...Dona nobis pacem[a]. Five Mystical Songs. [a]**Edith Wiens** (sop); **Brian Rayner Cook** (bar); **London Philharmonic Choir and Orchestra / Bryden Thomson.** Chandos Ⓕ CHAN8590 (57 minutes: DDD: 3/89).

Vaughan Williams Serenade to Music[a]. Flos campi[b]. Five mystical songs[c]. Fantasia on Christmas carols[d]. [a]**Elizabeth Connell,** [a]**Linda Kitchen,** [a]**Anne Dawson,** [a]**Amanda Roocroft** (sops); [a]**Sarah Walker,** [a]**Jean Rigby,** [a]**Diana Montague** (mezzos); [a]**Catherine Wyn-Rogers** (contr); [a]**John Mark Ainsley,** [a]**Martyn Hill,** [a]**Arthur Davies,** [a]**Maldwyn Davies** (tens); [acd]**Thomas Allen,** [a]**Alan Opie** (bars); [a]**Gwynne Howell,** [a]**John Connell** (basses); [b]**Nobuko Imai** (va); [bcd]**Corydon Singers; English Chamber Orchestra / Matthew Best.** Hyperion Ⓕ CDA66420 (68 minutes: DDD: 8/90). Texts included. Recorded 1990.

In 1938 Sir Henry Wood celebrated his 50 years as a professional conductor with a concert. Vaughan Williams composed a work for the occasion, the *Serenade to Music*, in which he set words by Shakespeare from Act 5 of *The Merchant of Venice*. Sixteen star vocalists of the age were gathered together for the performance and Vaughan Williams customized the vocal parts to show off the best qualities of the singers. The work turned out to be one of the composer's most sybaritic creations, turning each of its subsequent performances into a special event. Hyperion have gathered stars of our own age for this outstanding issue and Best has perceptively managed to give each their head whilst melding them into a cohesive ensemble. A mellow, spacious recording has allowed the work to emerge on disc with a veracity never achieved before. The coupled vocal pieces are given to equal effect and the disc is substantially completed by Nobuko Imai's tautly poignant account of *Flos campi*, in which the disturbing tension between solo viola and wordless chorus heighten the work's crypticism.

Additional recommendation ...

...Flos campi[a]. Viola Suite[b]. Two Hymn-Tune Preludes[c]. The Poisoned Kiss – Overture[c]. The Running Set[c]. [ab]**Frederick Riddle** (va); [a]**Bournemouth Sinfonietta Chorus; Bournemouth Sinfonietta / [ab]Norman Del Mar,** [c]**George Hurst.** Chandos Collect Ⓜ CHAN6545 (66 minutes: ADD: 11/92).

Vaughan Williams On Wenlock Edge[acd]. Five Mystical Songs[bc]. Four Hymns[af] – No. 1, Lord, come away; No. 3, Come Love, come Lord. Three Poems by Walt Whitman[bc] – No. 1, Nocturne; No. 3, Joy, shipmate, Joy!. Four Poems by Fredegond Shove[ac] – The water mill. Four Last Songs[bc] – No. 2, Tired. The House of Life[ac] – No. 2, Silent Noon. The Splendour falls[ac]. It was a lover and his lass[abc]. Dirge for Fidele[abc]. Two English Folksongs[abe]. [a]**Anthony Rolfe Johnson** (ten); [b]**Simon Keenlyside** (bar); [c]**Graham Johnson** (pf); [d]**Duke Quartet** ([e]Louisa Fuller, Rick Koster, vns; [f]John Metcalfe, va; Ivan McCready, vc). Collins Classics Ⓕ 1488-2 (78 minutes: DDD: 12/96). Texts included. Recorded 1996.

This makes an auspicious start to an ambitious series from Collins Classics devoted to English song. At its heart lies Keenlyside's sincere, unobtrusive account of the *Five Mystical Songs* in its version for voice and piano, one wholly in accord with these lovely Herbert settings. His warm, firm tone, smooth line and refined way with words combine to create an unforgettable impression. Keenlyside is no less impressive in the individual songs assigned to him, notably the late song "Tired", one of four poems the elderly composer wrote to texts by his wife, Ursula, in 1956, and in the two Whitman settings, the hypnotic "Nocturne" and the exuberant "Joy, Shipmate, Joy!", which Keenlyside delivers with appropriate brio. He brings his wry sense of humour to "The Lawyer", one of two folk-song settings with violin dating from 1925. The other, "Searching for Lambs" is one of Rolfe Johnson's sensitive contributions. The latter also delivers a typically sympathetic, subtly phrased, musing account of the famous "Silent Noon" from *The House of Life* cycle. Then he draws a wide range of emotion and colour from the familiar *On Wenlock Edge*. Once or twice these Housman settings reveal his tone under stress, as at the end of "Heron Hill"; till then that moving song receives an inward, deeply felt reading. The cycle is suitably supported by the intense, characterful playing of the Duke Quartet and Graham Johnson, though they don't quite banish memories of the well-loved 1970 reading on EMI by Ian Partridge and the Music Group of London. Johnson's contribution to the rest of a well-filled CD is as thoughtful as one would expect. The disc begins and ends with two little-known and pleasing Shakespeare duets where the singers' voices blend nicely. The recording is excellent.

Additional recommendations ...

...Four Hymns[a]. Merciless Beauty[a]. The Water Mill[b]. The New Ghost[c]. Ten Blake Songs[d]. On Wenlock Edge[e]. **Ian Partridge** (ten) [d]**Janet Craxton** (ob); [b]**Jennifer Partridge** (pf); [ace]**Music Group of London.** EMI British Composers Ⓜ CDM5 65589-2 (70 minutes: ADD: 11/96).

...Poems by Walt Whitman – No. 2, A clear midnight; No. 3. *Coupled with works by various composers.* **Thomas Hampson** (bar); **Craig Rutenberg** (pf). EMI Ⓜ CDM5 55028-2 (67 minutes: DDD: 10/97). *See review in the Collections section; refer to the Index.* Ⓖ Ⓖ Ⓖ

Vaughan Williams On Wenlock Edge[a]. Songs of Travel[b].
Butterworth Love blows as the wind blows[c].
Elgar Pleading, Op. 48 No. 1[c]. Song Cycle, Op. 59[c]. Two Songs, Op. 60[c]. [ac]**Robert Tear** (ten);
[b]**Thomas Allen** (bar); **City of Birmingham Symphony Orchestra / ** [ab]**Sir Simon Rattle,**
[c]**Vernon Handley.** EMI British Composers Ⓕ CDM7 64731-2 (69 minutes: DDD/ADD: 3/94).
Items marked [ab] from EL270059-2 (9/84), [c]HMV ASD3896 (9/80). Texts included.
Recorded 1979-1983.
Neither of Vaughan Williams's song cycles was originally written with orchestral accompaniment. *On
Wenlock Edge* was scored for accompaniment of piano and string quartet, while the *Songs of Travel*
were written with piano. Both lose a little when sung with orchestra but the gain seems to considerably
outweigh any loss, especially when three such superb artists are involved. Tear's singing is notable for
some wonderfully long phrases (as also is Allen's in the other cycle) together with the other Tear
qualities, of clarity of words and such matters. The CBSO play especially well for Rattle – all in all,
superb performances that do real justice to Vaughan Williams's imagination, his care for words and
his orchestration. The Tear/Handley Elgar and Butterworth items are rarities and were all première
recordings. Throughout, Tear sings with his customary sensitivity and the CBSO under Handley give
irreproachably alert imaginative support. The recording is vivid and beautifully balanced.
Additional recommendations ...
...Songs of Travel. *Coupled with works by various composers.* **Bryn Terfel** (bass-bar);
   Malcolm Martineau (pf). DG Ⓕ 445 946-2GH (77 minutes: DDD: 8/95). *Gramophone Editor's* ⒼⒼⒼ
   record of the month. See review under Butterworth; refer to the Index.
...Songs of Travel. Linden Lea. *Coupled with songs by* **Parry** Robert Tear (ten); **Philip Ledger** (pf).
   Belart Ⓑ 461 493-2 (77 minutes: ADD: A/97). *See review under Parry; refer to the Index.*

Vaughan Williams Five Tudor Portraits[a]. Five Variants of "Dives and Lazarus". [a]**Jean Rigby**
(mez); [a]**John Shirley-Quirk** (bar); **London Symphony** [a]**Chorus and Orchestra / Richard Hickox.**
Chandos Ⓕ CHAN9593 (55 minutes: DDD: 3/98). Text included. Recorded 1997.   Ⓖ
First heard at the 1936 Norwich Festival, Vaughan Williams's *Five Tudor Portraits* find the composer
at his most dazzlingly inventive, the resourceful and witty writing fitting Skelton's words like a glove.
Moreover, an irresistible humanity illuminates the most ambitious of the settings, "Jane Scroop (Her
Lament for Philip Sparrow)", which contains music as compassionate as Vaughan Williams ever
conceived. It is a life-enhancing creation and well deserving of this first-rate recording. Aided by
disciplined, ever-willing orchestral support, the London Symphony Chorus launch themselves in lusty
fashion into the ale-soaked narrative of "The Tunning of Elinor Rumming", though the resonant
acoustic rather precludes ideal clarity of diction. Hickox is exuberant in this sparkling tableau, while
Jean Rigby's characterful contribution should raise a smile. John Shirley-Quirk's is a touching
presence in "My Pretty Bess", and the mordant, black humour of "Epitaph of John Jayberd of Diss"
is effectively captured. Jane Scroop's lament in the fourth (and surely best) movement finds these fine
artists at their most perceptive. How ravishingly Hickox moulds his strings in the hushed passage
following "It was proper and prest!" where the music movingly anticipates the poignancy of the
closing section. Listen out, too, for the wealth of exquisitely observed woodwind detail in the
enchanting funeral processional. The concluding "Jolly Rutterkin" goes with a swing, though Shirley-
Quirk is a mite unsteady at the top of his range. The coupling is a heart-warming and lucid *Dives and
Lazarus*, with the LSO strings producing their most lustrous tone.

Vaughan Williams Riders to the Sea[a]. Merciless Beauty[b]. Epithalamion[c]. [a]**Norma Burrowes** (sop)
Nora; [a]**Dame Margaret Price** (sop) Cathleen; [a]**Helen Watts** (contr) Maurya; [a]**Benjamin Luxon**
(bar) Bartley; [a]**Pauline Stevens** (mez) Woman; [a]**Ambrosian Singers**; [a]**Orchestra Nova of London /**
Meredith Davies. [b]**Philip Langridge** (ten); [c]**Stephen Roberts** (bar); [c]**Jonathan Snowden** (fl);
[c]**Howard Shelley** (pf); [b]members of the **Endellion Quartet** (Andrew Watkinson, James Clark, vns;
David Waterman, vc); [c]**Bach Choir**; [c]**London Philharmonic Orchestra / Sir David Willcocks.**
EMI British Composers Ⓜ CDM7 64730-2 (75 minutes: ADD/DDD: 4/94). Item marked [a] from
HMV ASD2699 (9/71), recorded 1970; [bc]CDC7 47769-2 (3/88), recorded 1986. Texts included. Ⓖ
Vaughan Williams completed his masterly setting of J.M. Synge's one-act drama, *Riders to the Sea*,
in 1932. Although it has enjoyed the occasional revival, it remains one of the least-known and most
under-appreciated of Vaughan Williams's major works. Indeed, with scoring that is both economical
and intensely evocative, it can be a gripping experience, especially when presented as sympathetically
as here. The cast is a uniformly strong one, and Meredith Davies inspires everyone to give of their very
best. The 1970 sound has come up superbly, creating a rather more vivid impression, in fact, than its
modern partners from 1986. These are also both considerable rarities. *Epithalamion* is a large-scale
cantata from 1957 based on Edmund Spenser's love-poem of the same name: musically, it draws
extensively on material used in VW's 1938 masque, *The Bridal Day*, and its emotional centrepiece,
"The Lover's Song", boasts a viola solo of exquisite beauty. Finally, there is *Merciless Beauty*, three
pithy Chaucer settings for tenor and string trio dating from 1921. Performances are all one could wish.
Additional recommendation ...
...Riders to the Sea[a]. Household Music. Flos campi[b]. [a]**Soloists**; [b]**Philip Dukes** (va);
   [b]**Northern Sinfonia Chorus; Northern Sinfonia / Richard Hickox.** Chandos CHAN9392 (11/95).

Further listening ...

...Old King Cole – ballet. *Coupled with works by various composers.* **London Philharmonic Orchestra / Sir Adrian Boult.** Belart mono ⑬ 461 354-2* (60 minutes: ADD: 9/97).   ⑭

...49th Parallel – Prelude. The Story of a Flemish Farm – Suite.
Coastal Command – Suite. The England of Elizabeth – Explorer; Poet; Queen. **Radio Telefis Eire Concert Orchestra / Andrew Penny.** Marco Polo 8 223665 (10/95).

...Phantasy Quintet. Violin Sonata in A minor. String Quartet No. 2 in A minor. Six Studies in English folk song. **Music Group of London.** EMI British Composers CDM5 65100-2 (9/94).

...Six Studies in English folk song. *Coupled with works by various composers.* **Jonathan Cohler** (cl); **Judith Gordon** (pf). Crystal CD733 (5/95).

...Violin Sonata in A minor. *Coupled with works by* **Fricker** *and* **Rawsthorne** **Susanne Stanzeleit** (vn); **Julian Jacobson** (pf). Cala United CACD88036 (7/96). *See review under Fricker; refer to the Index.*

...A Bunyan Sequence. **Sir John Gielgud, Richard Pasco, Ursula Howells** (narrs); **Aiden Oliver** (treb); **Corydon Singers; City of London Sinfonia / Matthew Best.** Hyperion CDA66511 (8/91).

...Bushes and briars. Loch Lomond. John Dory. Greensleeves. Ward the Pirate. Ca' the Yowes. The unquiet grave. The Seeds of Love. Early in the spring. The Turtle Dove. An Acre of Land. Five English Folksongs. Bushes and briars. Wassail song. *Coupled with works by various composers.* **London Madrigal Singers / Christopher Bishop; Baccholian Singers of London; Philip Jones Brass Ensemble; English Chamber Orchestra / Ian Humphris.** EMI British Composers CMS5 65123-2 (2/96). *See review in the Collections section; refer to the Index.*

...The Old Hundredth Psalm Tune. Toward the Unknown Region. O taste and see. O clap your hands. Let us now praise famous men. Benedicite. *Coupled with works by* **Walton** Soloists; **Waynfelte Singers; Winchester Cathedral Choir; Bournemouth Symphony Orchestra / David Hill.** Argo 436 120-2ZH (5/93).

...Three Shakespeare Songs. *Coupled with works by various composers.* **Netherlands Chamber Choir / John Alldis.** Globe GLO5170 (2/98). *See review in the Collections section; refer to the Index.*

...A Song of Thanksgiving[a]. Three Choral Hymns[b]. Magnificat[c]. The Shepherds of the Delectable Mountains[d]. The Old Hundredth Psalm Tune[e]. [a]**Sir John Gielgud** (narr); [a]**Lynne Dawson,** [d]**Linda Kitchen** (sops); [c]**Catherine Wyn-Rogers** (contr); [d]**John Mark Ainsley,** [b]**John Bowen,** [d]**Adrian Thompson** (tens); [d]**Alan Opie** (bar); [d]**Bryn Terfel** (bass-bar); [d]**Jonathan Best** (bass); [a]**John Scott,** [bce]**Roger Judd** (orgs); [a]**London Oratory Junior Choir; Corydon Singers; City of London Sinfonia / Matthew Best.** Hyperion CDA66569 (8/92).

...Hugh the Drover. **Soloists; New London Children's Choir; Corydon Singers; Corydon Orchestra / Matthew Best.** Hyperion CDA66901/2 (10/94).

...Hugh the Drover. **Soloists; St Paul's Cathedral Choir; Ambrosian Opera Chorus; Royal Philharmonic Orchestra / Sir Charles Groves.** EMI British Composers CMS5 65224-2 (10/94).

...Mother I will have a husband. *Coupled with works by various composers.* **Oxford Camerata / Jeremy Summerly.** Naxos 8 553088 (5/97).

Pavel Vejvanovsky

Moravian ?c1633 or c1639-1693

Vejvanovsky Music for Trumpet and Strings. **Ars Antiqua Austria / Gunar Letzbor.** Symphonia ⑫ SY96151 (73 minutes: DDD: 2/98). 🎗

Enthusiasts for the music of Biber, Schmelzer and Co. will find plenty to admire in the compositions included here. The mid-seventeenth-century composer, Pavel Vejvanovsky, worked at the court of Kromeriz, where Heinrich Biber was briefly his colleague. He was employed as a trumpeter, and much of the buoyant and colourful pieces presented here includes opulent writing for that instrument. The string parts are equally demanding, and there are baroque contrasts, weird juxtapositions and mordant harmonic inflexions aplenty. As the booklet says, "imaginative, rich, ornate, full and airy" – and played with real panache. This is a real find: do try it.

Francesco Veracini

Italian 1690-1768

Veracini Sonate accademiche, Op. 2 – No. 7 in D minor; No. 8 in E minor; No. 9 in A major; No. 12 in D minor. Capriccio sesto con due soggetti in G minor. **Fabio Biondi** (vn); **Maurizio Naddeo** (vc); **Rinaldo Alessandrini** (hpd); **Pascal Monteilhet** (theorbo). Opus 111 ⑫ OPS30-138 (61 minutes: DDD: 9/95). Recorded 1995.

Despite the continuing rediscovery of so much of the Italian baroque, Veracini's music remains comparatively unknown both in the concert-hall and on record. This neglect is as unjustified as the traditional unfavourable comparison of his music with that of Vivaldi. He was a performer whose curious style was already noticed during his lifetime by the English writer Charles Burney, who once said that by travelling and playing all over Europe Veracini had formed a "style of playing peculiar to himself". The same might be said of his composing, which far from being simply an assimilation of contemporary modes, speaks with a sharply individual voice that constantly surprises with its freshness and originality. This almost kaleidoscopic shifting of moods and manners is fully evident in the *Sonate accademiche*, a collection of pieces published in 1744, but the fruits of a lifetime's experience playing in Dresden, London and Venice. As such they are shot through with virtuoso passagework, double-stopping and other technical features characteristic of Veracini's performances. These are here negotiated by Fabio Biondi with an easy brilliance that nevertheless does not sacrifice poetry for mere outward display. His approach is vigorous, with plenty of tone when required, and attractively alive. The overall sound is sharp and clean. Both he and the other performers use either period instruments or modern copies, and Rinaldo Alessandrini's informed and committed direction, and support, brings out all the delicacy of Veracini's rich and varied textures.

Further listening ...
...Overtures – No. 1 in B flat major; No. 2 in F major; No. 3 in B flat major; No. 4 in F major; No. 6 in B flat major. **Cologne Musica Antiqua / Reinhard Goebel.**
Archiv Produktion 439 937-2AH (12/94). 🎵   Ⓖ
...Overture No. 5 in B flat major. *Coupled with works by various composers.* **Cologne Musica Antiqua / Reinhard Goebel.** Archiv Produktion 447 644-2AH (1/96). 🎵   Ⓖ

Giuseppe Verdi
Italian 1813-1901

Verdi Overtures and Preludes – Nabucco; Ernani; I masnadieri; Macbeth; Il corsaro; La battaglia di Legnano; Luisa Miller; Rigoletto; La traviata; I vespri Siciliani; Un ballo in maschera; La forza del destino; Aida. **Berlin Philharmonic Orchestra / Herbert von Karajan.**
DG Ⓕ 419 622-2GH (73 minutes: ADD: 10/87). From 413 544-1GX2 (2/86). Recorded 1975.
Karajan was one of the most adaptable and sensitive of dramatic conductors. His repertoire in the theatre is extraordinarily wide being at home equally in Verdi, Wagner, Richard Strauss and Puccini. In this selection from his celebrated 1976 collection of all of Verdi's overtures, he gives us some fine insights into the composer's skill as an orchestrator, dramatist and poet. Though Karajan had only recorded *Aida* complete his dramatic instincts bring some fine performances of the lesser known preludes. The earliest, *Nabucco* from 1842 (the collection is arranged chronologically), already shows a mastercraftsman at work, with a slow introduction promising much. *La traviata* shows a quite different skill – the delcate creation of a sensitive poet working in filigree. The final four preludes are great works fully worthy of this individual presentation. Even the lesser known Preludes are enhanced by Karajan's dramatic instincts. Good recordings, though less than outstanding.

Additional recommendations ...
...La traviata – Preludes, Acts 1 and 3. *Coupled with works by various composers.*
Philharmonic Symphony Orchestra of New York / Arturo Toscanini.
Pearl mono Ⓕ GEMMCDS9373* (three discs: 230 minutes: ADD: 3/90).
Gramophone classical 100. *See review in the Collections section; refer to the Index.*   ⒼⒼⒼ
...I vespri siciliani – Overture. Luisa Miller – Oh! fede negar potessi ... Quando le sere al placido. *Coupled with works by various composers.* **Luciano Pavarotti; Harlem Boys' Choir; New York Philharmonic Orchestra / Leone Magiera.** Decca Ⓕ 444 450-2DH (77 minutes: DDD: 2/95).
...Overtures – Oberto, Conte di San Bonifac; Un giorno di regno; Nabucco; Giovanna d'Arco; Alzira; Attila; La battaglia di Legnano; Luisa Miller; I vespri Siciliani; Aroldo; La forza del destino. Preludes – Ernani; I masnadieri; Macbeth; Il corsaro; Rigoletto; La traviata; Un ballo in maschera; Aida. **Berlin Philharmonic Orchestra / Herbert von Karajan.**
DG Double Ⓜ 453 058-2GTA2 (two discs: 113 minutes: ADD: 7/97).

Verdi Overtures, Preludes and Ballet Music, Volume 1. Overtures – Oberto; Nabucco; Giovanna d'Arco; Alzira; La battaglia di Legnano. Preludes – Attila; I masnadieri; Il corsaro; Un giorno di regno; Ernani; I due Foscari; Macbeth; Ballet Music – Macbeth. **BBC Philharmonic Orchestra / Sir Edward Downes.** Chandos Ⓕ CHAN9510 (76 minutes: DDD: 9/97). Recorded 1996.
These performances from an experienced British operatic stalwart have dignity (witness the brass in *Nabucco*), panache, and splendidly colourful orchestral playing, including real string virtuosity, using the widest range of dynamic. The crescendo at the opening of *Giovanna d'Arco* is most compelling. Some of the shorter preludes are full of atmosphere. The brief *Macbeth* Prelude is particularly potent and the ballet music is both dramatic and rumbustious while *I masnadieri* closes with a swooning cello solo. *La battaglia di Legnano* which ends the programme has plenty of full-blooded brass at the opening and close. The recording is spectacular.

Verdi Messa da Requiem[a]. Quattro pezzi sacri[b]. [a]**Luba Orgonasova,** [b]**Donna Brown** (sops); [a]**Anne Sofie von Otter** (mez); [a]**Luca Canonici** (ten); [a]**Alastair Miles** (bass); **Monteverdi Choir; Orchestre Révolutionnaire et Romantique / Sir John Eliot Gardiner.** Philips Ⓕ 442 142-2PH2 (two discs: 120 minutes: DDD: 4/95). 🎵 Notes, texts and translations included. Recorded 1992.
Gramophone Editor's choice.   ⒼⒼ
Verdi Messa da Requiem[a]. Quattro pezzi sacri. Elena Filipova (sop); [a]Gloria Scalchi (mez); [a]César Hernández (ten); [a]Carlo Colombara (bass); **Hungarian State Opera Choir and Orchestra / Pier Giorgio Morandi.** Naxos Ⓢ 8 550944/5 (two discs: 126 minutes: DDD: 1/98).
Texts and translations included. Recorded 1996. *Gramophone Editor's choice.*   Ⓖ

Gardiner's Verdi Requiem is in a class of its own. His are readings that combine a positive view and interpretative integrity from start to finish, something possible only in the context of the superb professionalism of the (augmented) Monteverdi Choir, who sing with burnished, steady tone throughout and suggest, rightly, a corporate act of worship. Their contribution is beyond praise – and Verdi would surely have marvelled at that. He might also have been surprised and delighted to hear the soloists' contribution sung with such precision by such a finely integrated quartet, who perform the important unaccompanied passages with special grace and sensitivity. Instead of hearing the usual jostle of vibratos, here the four voices are firm and true. Individually they are also distinguished. Pride of place must go to Orgonasova who gives the performance of her life. The exactly placed high B in the "Quid sum miser" section of the *Dies irae*, the perfect blending with von Otter at "Dominum", the whole of the *Andante* section of the "Libera me", sung with ethereal tone and a long breath, make the heart stop in amazement. In "Oro supplex" Gardiner follows Verdi's tempo marking. More often he follows tradition, with slower speeds than those suggested, and he allows more licence than the score, or conductors like Toscanini. But as his liberties all seem so convincing in the context of the whole, who should complain? In the *Pezzi sacri*, Gardiner gives the most thrilling account yet to appear. The recording, made in Westminster Cathedral, has a huge range which may cause problems in confined spaces. You are liable to be overwhelmed by, for instance, the *Dies irae*.

Morandi brings to his interpretation a youthful, Italian energy and generosity of expression, exactly matching those qualities in the work itself. Given a judicious choice of young soloists, all up to their exigent tasks, an excellent chorus (a shattering *Dies irae*, an alert, not too drilled *Sanctus*, a disciplined "Libera me" fugue) and a well-fashioned recording, this set makes a compelling case for recommendation as an alternative to Gardiner's period-performance set. If you doubt that a super-budget account can be so good try track 7, the "Rex tremendae", where you can hear how Morandi builds a movement unerringly to an appropriately tremendous climax. The soloists show how involved they are in the work, form a good ensemble and individually exhibit the intelligence to sing quietly as needed. Elena Filipova and Scalchi combine into a rich-toned duo in "Liber scriptus", spoilt a little by moments of indeterminate pitch from the soprano (later the two contrast well in the *Agnus Dei*). Hernández, with his warm, baritonal, Spanish-style tenor, sings a sensitive "Ingemisco" (a touch of insecurity at the start excepted), succeeded by Colombara's truly magisterial conjuring of the flames of hell at "Confutatis maledictis". Filipova's floated entry at "huic ergo" in the succeeding trio and the sheer intensity of the whole "Lacrymosa" bring the *Dies irae* to a fitting close. The rest of the performance is on an equivalent level of achievement, Morandi always judging speeds to a nicety. The fill-up to this large-scale reading, costing less than all its competitors, is another fine performance of the *Quattro pezzi sacri*.

Additional recommendations ...

...Messa da Requiem. Quattro pezzi sacri. **Soloists; Philharmonia Chorus and Orchestra / Carlo Maria Giulini.** EMI Ⓔ CDS7 47257-8 (two discs: 129 minutes: ADD: 4/87).   ⒼⒼ

...Messa da Requiem[a]. Opera choruses – Don Carlos – Spuntato ecco il dì. Macbeth – Patria oppressa. Otello – Fuoco di gioia. Nabucco – Va, pensiero, sull'ali dorate. Aida – Gloria all'Egitto. [a]**Susan Dunn** (sop); [a]**Diane Curry** (mez); [a]**Jerry Hadley** (ten); [a]**Paul Plishka** (bass); **Atlanta Symphony Chorus and Orchestra / Robert Shaw.** Telarc Ⓕ CD80152 (two discs: 113 minutes: DDD: 3/88). *Gramophone Award Winner 1988. Selected by Sounds in Retrospect.*

...Messa da Requiem. Quattro pezzi sacri. **Soloists; Vienna State Opera Concert Chorus; Vienna Philharmonic Orchestra / Claudio Abbado.** DG Ⓕ 435 884-2GH2 (two discs: 127 minutes: DDD: 9/93).

...Messa da Requiem. **Soloists; Chicago Symphony Chorus and Orchestra / Sir Georg Solti.** RCA Victor Gold Seal Ⓜ 09026-61403-2 (two discs: 82 minutes: ADD: 9/93).

...Messa da Requiem. **Soloists; Chicago Symphony Chorus and Orchestra / Daniel Barenboim.** Erato Ⓕ 4509-96357-2 (two discs: 83 minutes: DDD: 11/94). *Selected by Sounds in Retrospect.*

...Messa da Requiem[a]. Quattro pezzi sacri – No. 4, Te Deum. [a]**Zinka Milanov** (sop); [a]**Bruna Castagna** (mez); [a]**Jussi Björling** (ten); [a]**Nicola Moscona** (bass); **Westminster Choir; NBC Symphony Orchestra / Arturo Toscanini.** Music and Arts mono Ⓜ CD240* (two discs: 99 minutes: AAD: 3/95).

...Messa da Requiem. **Soloists; Chorus and Orchestra of the Rome Opera / Tullio Serafin.** Dutton Laboratories mono Ⓑ CDLX7010* (73 minutes: ADD: 3/95).

...Messa da Requiem[a]. La traviata[b] – Preludes, Act 1 and 3. I vespri siciliani – Overture[b] . *Coupled with works by various composers.* [a]**Dame Elisabeth Schwarzkopf** (sop); [a]**Oralia Dominguez** (mez); [a]**Giuseppe di Stefano** (ten); [a]**Cesare Siepi** (bass); [a]**Chorus and Orchestra of La Scala, Milan,** [b]**Santa Cecilia Academy Orchestra, Rome / Victor de Sabata.** EMI Références mono Ⓜ CHS5 65506-2* (two discs: 148 minutes: ADD: 9/95).

...Messa da Requiem[b]. **Cherubini** Requiem Mass No. 1 in C minor[a]. **Soloists;** [a]**Ambrosian Singers;** [b]**Ambrosian Chorus; Philharmonia Orchestra / Riccardo Muti.** EMI Forte Ⓜ CZS5 68613-2 (two discs: 135 minutes: [a]ADD/[b]DDD: 7/96).

Verdi Opera choruses – Nabucco – Gli arredi festivi giù cadano infranti; Va, pensiero, sull'ali dorate. I Lombardi – Gerusalem!; O Signore, dal tetto natio. Macbeth – Tre volte miagola; Patria oppressa. I masnadieri – Le rube, gli stupri. Rigoletto – Zitti zitti. Il trovatore – Vedi! le fosche notturne spoglie; Squilli, echeggi la tromba guerriera. La traviata – Noi siamo zingarelle ... Di

Madride nio siam mattadori (with Marsha Waxman, mez; David Huneryager, Richard Cohn, basses). Un ballo in maschera – Posa in pace. Don Carlos – Spuntato ecco il dí. Aida – Gloria all'Egitto. Otello – Fuoco di gioia. Requiem – Sanctus. **Chicago Symphony Chorus and Orchestra / Sir Georg Solti.** Decca Ⓕ 430 226-2DH (70 minutes: DDD: 4/91). Texts and translations included. Recorded 1989.

Verdi's choruses occupy a special place in his operas. They are invariably red-blooded and usually make a simple dramatic statement with great impact. The arresting "Chorus of the Hebrew Slaves" ("Va, pensiero") from *Nabucco* is probably the best-known and most popular chorus in the entire operatic repertoire, immediately tugging at the heart-strings with its gentle opening cantilena, soon swelling out to a great climax. Solti shows just how to shape the noble melodic line which soars with firm control, yet retaining the urgency and electricity in every bar. He is equally good in "Gli arredi festivi", from the same opera, not only in the bold opening statement, shared between singers and the resplendent sonority of the Chicago brass, but also later when the mood lightens, and women's voices are heard floating over seductive harp roulades. The dramatic contrasts at the opening of "Gerusalem!" from *I Lombardi* are equally powerfully projected, and the brass again makes a riveting effect in "Patria oppressa" from *Macbeth*. But, of course, not all Verdi choruses offer blood and thunder: the volatile "Fire chorus" from *Otello* flickers with an almost visual fantasy, while the wicked robbers in *I Masnadieri* celebrate their excesses (plunder, rape, arson and murder) gleefully, and with such rhythmic jauntiness that one cannot quite take them seriously. The "Gipsies chorus" from *La traviata* has a nice touch of elegance, and the scherzo-like "Sanctus", from the *Requiem*, which ends the concert, is full of joy. But it is the impact of the dramatic moments which is most memorable, not least the big triumphal scene from *Aida*, complete with the ballet music, to provide a diverse interlude in the middle. The recording is in the demonstration class.

Additional recommendations ...

...Nabucco – Gli arredi festivi giù cadano infranti; Va, pensiero, sull'ali dorate. Macbeth – Patria oppressa. Il trovatore – Vedi! le fosche notturne spoglie; Ora co'dadi, ma fra poco. La traviata – Noi siamo zingarelle; Si ridesta in ciel (with Alena Cokova, mez; Stanislav Vrabel, bass). Don Carlos – Spuntato ecco il dì d'esultanza. Aida – Gloria all'Egitto. Otello – Fuoco di gioia. La Battaglia di Legnano – Deus meus, pone illos ut rotam (Eva Jenisova, sop; Cokova); Giuramento (L'udovit Ludha, ten). Ernani – Si rideste il Leon di Castiglia. La forza del destino – Rataplan! rataplan! (Ida Kirilová, mez). **Slovak Philharmonic Choir; Slovak Radio Symphony Orchestra / Oliver Dohnányi.** Naxos Ⓢ 8 550241 (56 minutes: DDD: 4/91).

Verdi Opera Arias: Nabucco – Ben io t'avenni ... Anch'io dischiuso un giorno. Il trovatore – Tacea la notte placida ... Di tale amor; Timor di me? ... D'amor sull'ali rosee. La traviata – E strano! ... Ah, fors'è lui ... Follie! Sempre libera[a]; Teneste la promessa ... Addio del passato. Un ballo in maschera – Ecco l'orrido campo ... Ma dall'arido stelo divulsa ... Morro, ma prima in grazia. La forza del destino – Pace, pace, mio Dio. **Julia Varady** (sop); [a]**Lothar Odinius** (ten); **Bavarian State Orchestra / Dietrich Fischer-Dieskau.** Orfeo Ⓕ C186951 (51 minutes: DDD: 1/96). Recorded 1995.

Varady endows these arias we have heard hundreds of times, and of which we all have our favourite memories and recordings, with renewed life through an art which is fully responsive, highly fastidious, lovely in the quality of its sound and individual in its timbre and inflexion. The beauty of tone is evident first of all in its well-preserved purity (and Varady, born in 1941, is of an age when normally allowances have to be made). Here is not a full-bodied, rich Ponselle-like voice, but she makes wonderfully effective use of her resources, which include a surprisingly strong lower register and an upward range that (as we hear) easily encompasses the high D flat and has an E flat available. She is dramatic in style yet also thoroughly accomplished in her scales, trills and other *fioriture*. Her first *Trovatore* aria, for instance, includes the cabaletta with its full complement of technical brilliances. The musical instinct seems almost infallible – a 'wrong' portamento or rubato always irritates and here everything seems right. A remarkable sensitivity is at work throughout. The orchestra is conducted by Fischer-Dieskau, Varady's husband, and here too is a fine example of a positive, non-routine collaboration, the pacing and shading of the orchestral parts so frequently having something specific to offer (for example, in the letter passage from *La traviata*). The recording is well balanced.

Additional recommendations ...

...Aida – Se quel guerrier io fossi! ... Celeste Aida. Un ballo in maschera – Forse la soglia attinse ... Ma se m'è forza perderti. Don Carlo – Fontainebleau! ... Io la vidi e al suo sorriso. Ernani – Mercè, diletti amici ... Come rugiada. La forza del destino – La vita è inferno ... Oh tu che in seno agli angeli. Luisa Miller – Oh! fede negr potessi ... Quando le sere al placido. Macbeth – O figli, figli miei! ... Ah, la paterna mano. Otello – Dio! mi potevi scagliar; Niun mi tema. Rigoletto – Questa o quella; La donna è mobile. Simon Boccanegra – O inferno! ... Sento avvampar nell'anima. La traviata – Lunge da lei ... De' miei bollenti spiriti. Il trovatore – Il presagio funesto ... Ah si, ben mio ... Di quella pira (with Ambrosian Singers). **Carlo Bergonzi** (ten); **New Philharmonia Orchestra / Nello Santi.** Philips Ⓜ 454 390-2PM (67 minutes: ADD: 4/97).

...La forza del destino – Son giunta! ... Madre, pietosa Vergine[a]; Pace, pace, mio Dio. Otello – Mia madre aveva ... Piangea cantando ... Ave Maria. Aida – Qui Radames verra? ... O patria mia. Il trovatore – Tacea la notte placida ... Di tale amor. *Coupled with works by* **Tchaikovsky** **Galina Gorchakova** (sop); [a]**Chorus and Orchestra of the Kirov Opera / Valery Gergiev.**

Philips Ⓕ 446 405-2PH (60 minutes: DDD: 3/96). *Gramophone Editor's choice. See review under Tchaikovsky; refer to the Index.*

...La traviata – Libiamo, ne' lieti calici[a]; Dite alla giovine[b]. *Coupled with works by various composers.* **Inessa Galante** (sop); [a]**Janis Sprogis** (ten); [b]**Samsons Izjumovs** (bar); **Latvian National Symphony Orchestra /** [a]**Paul Mägi,** [b]**Alexander Vilumanis.** Campion Ⓕ RRCD1344 (63 minutes: AAD/DDD: A/97). *See review in the Collections section; refer to the Index.*

...Otello – Era più calmo? ... Mia madre aveva ... Piangea cantando ... Ave Maria[a]. *Coupled with works by various composers.* **Renée Fleming** (sop); **London Symphony Orchestra / Sir Georg Solti.** Decca Ⓕ 455 760-2DH (72 minutes: DDD: 10/97). *Gramophone Editor's choice. See review in the Collections section; refer to the Index.*

...La forza del destino – La Vergine degli angeli. *Coupled with works by various composers.* **Lesley Garrett** (sop); **chorus; Britten Sinfonia / Ivor Bolton.** Conifer Classics Ⓕ 75605 51329-2 (73 minutes: DDD: 12/97). *See review in the Collections section; refer to the Index.*

Verdi Opera Arias. **Roberto Alagna** (ten); **Berlin Philharmonic Orchestra / Claudio Abbado.** EMI Ⓕ CDC5 56567-2 (64 minutes: DDD: 4/98). Texts and translations included. Recorded 1997. *Gramophone Editor's choice.*

Luisa Miller – Oh! fede negar potessi ... Quando le sere al placido. I lombardi alla prima crociata – La mia letizia infondere. Aida – Se quel guerrier ... Celeste Aida. Ernani – Mercè, dilette amici ... Come rugiada al cespite ... O tu che l'alma adora (with London Voices). Un ballo in maschera – Forse la soglia ... Ma se m'è forza perderti. Otello – Dio! mi potevi; Niun mi tema (with Andrew Busher, ten; James Bobby, bar; Richard Fallas, Noel Mann, basses). La forza del destino – Prelude, Act 3; La vita è inferno ... O, tu che in seno. Macbeth – O figli, o figli miei! ... Ah, la paterna mano. Jérusalem – L'ëmir auprès de lui ... Je veux encore entendre. Il trovatore – Ah! si, ben mio ... Di quella pira (with Angela Gheorghiu, sop; London Voices).

Alagna here shows, in the most demanding programme imaginable, that there is little if anything wrong with his technique and a great deal right with his sense of Verdian style. Indeed, he takes the score as his bible. That is evident, for instance, in his treatment of Otello. In the great Act 3 Monologue, besides thinking himself into the Moor's deep well of despondency at this juncture of the tragedy, evinced in a slightly juddering tone, he sings the opening passage as written, staying on the A flat and E flat, not going for unwanted melodrama. Then the cantilena is sung with the appropriate touch of pained nobility. In the Death scene he finds the right pent-up voice for "Come sei pallida" and the repeated "Desdemona", then sings "Or morendo" with a *pp* on the high G, as Verdi enjoins. So much else in the recital is just as thoughtfully interpreted. He solves the problem of the high B flat at the end of "Celeste Aida" by starting it *mezzo-forte* and shading it away affectingly in a well-executed *diminuendo*, having sung the whole aria in a suitably poetic manner. Alagna is the brigand to the life in Ernani's introductory aria. Riccardo's (or if you like Gustaf's) Act 3 aria is charged with emotion, the tone properly plaintive and darkened for the middle section. Then there's perhaps the most taxing aria for tenor in all Verdi: Alvaro's "O, tu che in seno" from *Forza*. Following the most eloquent playing by the Berlin Philharmonic's clarinet in the long introduction, Alagna catches the Inca's sense of longing in the recitative and then rises to the challenge of the aria's relentless tessitura with fine-grained, almost heroic tone. Nor does he shirk the high Cs in "Di quella pira". The rarity here is the item from *Jérusalem*, sung in Alagna's other tongue. The Berlin Philharmonic's contribution, under Abbado's distinguished direction, is as accomplished as you might expect. The recording allows us to hear the full bloom of Alagna's voice, but occasionally the sound of the voice appears to stray or float around the sound spectrum, a disconcerting effect, but that's not enough of a distraction to prevent a strong recommendation to all who fancy the tenor and/or his programme.

Verdi Aida. **Maria Callas** (sop) Aida; **Richard Tucker** (ten) Radames; **Fedora Barbieri** (mez) Amneris; **Tito Gobbi** (bar) Amonasro; **Giuseppe Modesti** (bass) Ramphis; **Nicola Zaccaria** (bass) King of Egypt; **Elvira Galassi** (sop) Priestess; **Franco Ricciardi** (ten) Messenger; **Chorus and Orchestra of La Scala, Milan / Tullio Serafin.** EMI Callas Edition mono Ⓕ CDS5 56316-2* (two discs: 144 minutes: ADD: 11/87). Notes, text and translation included. From Columbia 33CX1318/20 (1/56). Recorded 1955.   ⒼⒼ

Verdi Aida. **Montserrat Caballé** (sop) Aida; **Plácido Domingo** (ten) Radames; **Fiorenza Cossotto** (mez) Amneris; **Piero Cappuccilli** (bar) Amonasro; **Nicolai Ghiaurov** (bass) Ramphis; **Luigi Roni** (bass) King of Egypt; **Esther Casas** (sop) Priestess; **Nicola Martinucci** (ten) Messenger; **Chorus of the Royal Opera House, Covent Garden; New Philharmonia Orchestra; Trumpeters of the Royal Military School of Music, Kneller Hall / Riccardo Muti.** EMI Ⓕ CDS5 56246-2 (three discs: 148 minutes: ADD: 1/87). Notes, text and translation included. Recorded 1974. From HMV SLS977 (2/75). *Gramophone Classical 100.*   ⒼⒼⒼ

Aida, the daughter of the Ethiopian king, is a prisoner at the Egyptian court where she falls in love with Radames, an Egyptian captain of the guard; Amneris, the Egyptian princess, also loves him. The tensions between these characters are rivetingly portrayed and explored and the gradual build-up to Aida's and Radames's union in death is paced with the sureness of a master composer. Callas's Aida is an assumption of total understanding and conviction; the growth from a slave-girl torn between love for her homeland and Radames, to a woman whose feelings transcend life itself represents one of the greatest operatic undertakings ever committed to disc. Alongside her is Fedora Barbieri, an

Amneris palpable in her agonized mixture of love and jealousy – proud yet human. Tucker's Radames is powerful and Gobbi's Amonasro quite superb – a portrayal of comparable understanding to stand alongside Callas's Aida. Tullio Serafin is quite simply ideal and though the recording cannot compete with modern versions (it was never, in fact, a model of clarity), nowhere can it dim the brilliance of the creations conjured up by this classic cast.

Caballé for Muti gives what is generally considered her most successful Verdi performance on record, full of those vocal subtleties and beauties that inform her best singing, at its finest perhaps in the lovely floated passages , but no less effective when it comes to the power needed to fill Verdi's phrases generously. Moreover, the characterization, perhaps inspired by Muti, fulfils almost every aspect of the role's demands. In contrast to Caballé's delicacy and plangency, there is Cossotto's imperious, fiercely sung Amneris, just as electrifying when she is at the end of her tether in Act 4 as when she is baiting Aida in Act 2. Domingo sings an upright, musical Radames, Cappuccilli is a forthright, unsubtle Amonasro, Ghiaurov a properly merciless Ramphis. Muti gives an impassioned, subjective account of the score, sometimes indulging in sudden *accelerandos* and *crescendos* that are unwarranted by the score. The balance between this set and Claudio Abbado on DG is a fine one. Ricciarelli (Abbado), though not vocally anywhere near so reliable as Caballé, is still an Aida to be reckoned with because she understands the emotions of the part so well. But Domingo on the Abbado set offers the most heroic Radames on any available set, and one fashioned in long breaths and refined phrasing. Abbado himself is inclined to take a more measured view of the score than Muti and he is just as able as Muti to create the right atmosphere for a scene, by his attention to Verdi's illustrative detail. With Muti digitally remastered, the differences in recorded quality are even more marked. The EMI sound is bigger in scale, more reverberant and spacious, but in the indoor scenes, as it were, the Abbado often seems the more natural. Both choruses and orchestras are well caught, and distinguish themselves with splendidly vital contributions. By a hair's breadth Muti is preferable.

Additional recommendations ...

...**Soloists; Chorus and Orchestra of La Scala, Milan / Claudio Abbado.**
  DG Ⓕ 410 092-2GH3 (three discs: ADD: 12/83). 　　　　　　　　　　　　　　　 ⒼⒼ
...**Soloists; Rome Opera House Chorus and Orchestra / Sir Georg Solti.**
  Decca Ⓕ 417 416-2DH3 (three discs: 152 minutes: ADD: 9/87).
...**Soloists; Vienna State Opera Chorus; Vienna Philharmonic Orchestra / Herbert von Karajan.**
  EMI Ⓜ CMS7 69300-2 (three discs: 155 minutes: ADD: 4/88).
...**Soloists; Rome Opera House Chorus and Orchestra / Jonel Perlea.**
  RCA Victor mono Ⓜ GD86652* (three discs: 149 minutes: ADD: 8/88).
...**Soloists; Chorus of La Scala, Milan; Milan Symphony Orchestra / Lorenzo Molajoli.**
  VAI Audio mono Ⓕ VAIA1083* (two discs: 136 minutes: ADD: 4/96).

Verdi Un ballo in maschera. **Giuseppi di Stefano** (ten) Riccardo; **Tito Gobbi** (bar) Renato;
  Maria Callas (sop) Amelia; **Fedora Barbieri** (mez) Ulrica; **Eugenia Ratti** (sop) Oscar;
  Ezio Giordano (bass) Silvano; **Silvio Maionica** (bass) Samuel; **Nicola Zaccaria** (bass) Tom;
  Renato Ercolani (bar) Judge; **Chorus and Orchestra of La Scala, Milan / Antonino Votto.**
  EMI Callas Edition mono Ⓕ CDS5 56320-2* (two discs: 130 minutes: ADD: 9/87).
  Notes, text and translation included. From Columbia 33CX1472/4 (10/57). 　　　　　　 Ⓖ

Ballo manages to encompass a vein of lighthearted frivolity (represented by the page, Oscar) within the confines of a serious drama of love, infidelity, noble and ignoble sentiments. None of the more recent recordings has quite caught the opera's true spirit so truly as this one under Votto's unerring direction. Callas has not been surpassed in delineating Amelia's conflict of feelings and loyalties, nor has di Stefano been equalled in the sheer ardour of his singing as Riccardo. Add to that no less a singer than Tito Gobbi as Renato, at first eloquent in his friendship to his ruler, then implacable in his revenge when he thinks Riccardo has stolen his wife. Fedora Barbieri is full of character as the soothsayer Ulrica, Eugenia Ratti a sparky Oscar. It is an unbeatable line-up.

Additional recommendations ...

...**Soloists; Haberdashers' Aske's School Girls' Choir; Medici Quartet; Chorus of the
  Royal Opera House, Covent Garden; New Philharmonia Orchestra / Riccardo Muti.**
  EMI CMS5 66510-2 (two discs: 127 minutes: ADD).
...**Soloists; London Opera Chorus; Royal College of Music Junior Department Chorus; National
  Philharmonic Orchestra / Sir Georg Solti.** Decca Ⓕ 410 210-2DH2 (two discs: DDD: 9/85).
...**Soloists; Chorus and Orchestra of La Scala, Milan / Claudio Abbado.**
  DG Ⓜ 453 148-2GTA2 (two discs: 127 minutes: ADD: 9/86).
...**Soloists; RCA Italiana Opera Chorus and Orchestra / Erich Leinsdorf.**
  RCA VictorGold Seal Ⓜ GD86645 (two discs: 128 minutes: ADD: 11/88).
...**Soloists; Robert Shaw Chorale; NBC Symphony Orchestra / Arturo Toscanini.**
  RCA Victor Gold Seal mono Ⓜ GD60301* (two discs: 122 minutes: ADD: 7/91).
...**Soloists; Metropolitan Opera Chorus and Orchestra / Ettore Panizza.**
  Myto mono Ⓕ 2MCD90317* (two discs: 147 minutes: ADD: 2/94).
...**Excerpts. Aida[b] – excerpts. Falstaff[c] – excerpts. Soloists; Vienna State Opera Chorus
  and Orchestra / [a]Karl Böhm, [b]Vittorio Gui, [c]Clemens Krauss.**
  Koch Schwann mono Ⓜ 314582* (two discs: 149 minutes: ADD: 4/95).

...Soloists; **Vienna State Opera Concert Choir; Vienna Philharmonic Orchestra /
Herbert von Karajan.** DG Ⓜ 449 588-2GX2 (two discs: 135 minutes: DDD; 2/97).
...Soloists; **Chorus and Orchestra of the Royal Opera House, Covent Garden / Sir Colin Davis.**
Philips Duo Ⓜ 456 316-2PM2 (two discs: 130 minutes: ADD: 12/97).

Verdi Don Carlo. **Plácido Domingo** (ten) Don Carlos; **Montserrat Caballé** (sop) Elisabetta;
Shirley Verrett (mez) Princess Eboli; **Sherrill Milnes** (bar) Rodrigo; **Ruggero Raimondi** (bass)
Philip II; **Giovanni Foiani** (bass) Grand Inquisitor; **Delia Wallis** (mez) Thibault; **Ryland Davies**
(ten) Count of Lerma; **Simon Estes** (bass) A Monk; **John Noble** (bar) Herald;
Ambrosian Opera Chorus; Royal Opera House Orchestra, Covent Garden / Carlo Maria Giulini.
EMI Ⓔ CDS7 47701-8 (three discs: 208 minutes: ADD: 7/87). Notes, text and translation
included. From SLS956 (7/71).   Ⓖ

In no other Verdi opera, except perhaps *Aida*, are public and private matters so closely intermingled,
so searchingly described as in this large-scale, panoramic work, in which the political intrigues and
troubles of Philip II's Spain are counterpointed with his personal agony and the lives and loves of
those at his court. This vast canvas inspired Verdi to compose one of his most varied and glorious
scores. Giulini, more than any other conductor, searches out the inner soul of the piece and his cast
is admirable. The young Plácido Domingo makes a vivid and exciting Carlos, whilst Montserrat
Caballé spins glorious tone and phrases in encompassing Elisabeth's difficult music. Shirley Verrett is
a vital, suitably tense Eboli, Sherrill Milnes an upright, warm Rodrigo and Ruggero Raimondi a
sombre Philip. Throughout, the Covent Garden forces sing and play with fervour and understanding
for their distinguished conductor.
...Soloists; **Chorus and Orchestra of the Royal Opera House, Covent Garden / Bernard Haitink.**
Philips Ⓔ 454 463-2PH3 (three discs: 208 minutes: DDD: 12/97).

Verdi Don Carlos. **Roberto Alagna** (ten) Don Carlos; **Karita Mattila** (sop) Elisabeth;
Waltraud Meier (mez) Eboli; **Thomas Hampson** (bar) Rodrigue; **José van Dam** (bass-bar)
Philippe II; **Eric Halfvarson** (bass) Grand Inquisitor; **Csaba Airizer** (bass) Monk; **Anat Efraty**
(sop) Thibault; **Scot Weir** (ten) Comte de Lerme, Herald; **Donna Brown** (sop) Voice from Heaven;
Chorus of the Théâtre du Châtelet; Orchestre de Paris / Antonio Pappano. EMI Ⓔ CDS5 56152-2
(three discs: 206 minutes: DDD: 10/96). Notes, text and translation included.
Recorded live in 1996.

This is an eloquent and inspiriting performance of Verdi's singular music-drama depicting private
tragedy within public conflict, and a recording of the French version. For anyone wanting the original
French, which is, after all, the text Verdi adhered to throughout myriad versions, the only rival to this
set is the Abbado version listed below. Text-wise, Pappano excludes the opening scene for the chorus
at Fontainebleau, cut by the composer before the first night; he includes the important dress-changing
scene at the start of Act 3 (which explains Carlos's ardour towards the 'wrong' woman), a snippet of
the Elisabeth-Eboli duet in Act 4, and the whole of the Carlos/Philippe duet after Posa's death (the
theme of which was reused in the Requiem). Pappano also chooses some of the alternative settings,
notably in the Posa-Philippe duet in Act 2 and the farewell encounter of Elisabeth and Carlos in Act
5, amendments that Verdi made for the neglected 1872 Naples revision. Neither seems an
improvement: you can judge for yourself by listening to the Abbado which remains faithful to what
we usually hear – and what Verdi finally decided on his last revision. Indeed on the Abbado we hear
the 'orthodox' version throughout the main recording: alternatives are consigned to appendices which
you can then programme in at your own discretion. On practically all counts Pappano stands
comparison with his senior Italian colleague. His is a subtly shaped, superbly paced and vital
interpretation from start to finish. He is as able to encompass the delicacies of the Veil Song and the
succeeding exchanges as he is to purvey the grand, tragic passion of Elisabeth and Carlos in Act 2,
the intricacies and changes of feeling in the colloquy between Rodrigue and Philippe, the terrible
menace of the Grand Inquisitor. The Orchestre de Paris support him with playing of dedication and
sensitivity. Giulini's noble conducting of the Italian version (reviewed above) comes to mind when
listening to Pappano and his players. Praise cannot be higher.

By and large he has singers who can sustain his vision. Mattila sings a lovely Elisabeth. Her soft-
grained yet strong tone and exquisite phrasing in all her solos and duets is balm to the ear. Ricciarelli
(Abbado) is also affecting but not so secure and at times too moony. By Mattila's side Alagna offers
an equally involving Carlos. Without quite the fullness of voice or sheer vocal opulence offered by
Domingo (Abbado), Alagna presents a more vulnerable picture of the unbalanced infante. His is a
fully rounded portrayal that will please his many admirers, the difficult tessitura seldom troubling him
and his French, of course, is impeccable. As Rodrigue, Marquis de Posa, Hampson also has idiomatic
French. His mellifluous baritone well suits this French version and he provides many moments of
vocal beauty. Arguably, the death needs a more imposing voice but the added decibels can easily be
borne to appreciate Hampson's intelligence. By his side, Nucci (Abbado) sounds cool and
uninteresting. Van Dam nicely balances the exterior authority and interior agony of Philippe,
everywhere in command of line, language, phrase, much more incisive than Abbado's woolly
Raimondi. The recording catches the *frisson* of the theatrical experience. The positioning of the
singers on stage never causes problems; everything is clear and in its place, and the balance with the
pit sounds natural. The Abbado is a formidable achievement as a whole and a trail-blazer – but this

one catches more truly the surge and swell of emotional and dramatic tensions so vital in the work's interpretation. It is a landmark in the *Don Carlos* discography.

Additional recommendation ...
...(Includes appendix). **Soloists; Chorus and Orchestra of La Scala, Milan / Claudio Abbado.**
DG Ⓕ 415 316-2GH4 (four discs: DDD: 12/85).

Verdi Ernani. **Plácido Domingo** (ten) Ernani; **Mirella Freni** (sop) Elvira; **Renato Bruson** (bar) Don Carlos; **Nicolai Ghiaurov** (bass) Don Ruy, Gomez de Silva; **Jolanda Michieli** (sop) Giovanna; **Gianfranco Manganotti** (ten) Don Riccardo; **Alfredo Giacomotti** (bass) Iago; **Chorus and Orchestra of La Scala, Milan / Riccardo Muti.** EMI Ⓕ CDS7 47083-8 (three discs: 128 minutes: DDD: 12/85). Notes, text and translation included.
From HMV SLS143584-3 (1/84). Recorded live in 1982.

Renato Bruson's Don Carlo is an assumption that is as gripping dramatically as it is vocally. In his portrayal more than anywhere, the musical tension of *Ernani* becomes manifest and everywhere Bruson offers superb Verdi singing. Domingo's Ernani is hardly less impressive. Combining the correct style of Bergonzi for Schippers and the insolent pride exhibited by Lamberti for Gardelli, he benefits from being caught live on stage. His opening aria and cabaletta are full of delicate touches and obedience to the dynamic marks. In the last act, his recitative, "Tutto ora tace d'intorno" has great pathos, and his contributions to the final trio an overwhelming eloquence. Here, too, Freni achieves most, the etching in of "Il riso del tuo volto fa ch'io veda", a brief utterance of happiness, most affecting, and her desperate appeals to Silva for mercy sung with brio. In her opening aria and cabaletta, the famous "Ernani, Ernani", too much is asked of a voice not really meant by nature for this kind of heavy duty. Here she yields in sheer opulence of tone to Leontyne Price (Schippers), and the grace and magnetism in Sass's assumption, but somehow in the studio neither of these excellent sopranos quite matches the sorrow and heartbreak of Elvira's predicament that Freni manages in the theatre. Ghiaurov, rusty as his voice had become, creates a great impression of dignity and implacable strength, and many of those qualities are carried over into his singing. "Infelice" is delivered with mature nobility, "Ah, io l'amo" is intensely moving. Ghiaurov is denied Silva's probably spurious cabaletta. Otherwise the work is given complete. Muti conducts the score in exemplary manner. He has learnt when to allow his singers licence to phrase with meaning and when to press on. The La Scala chorus give us the genuine sound of Italian voices in full flight, sounding much more inside their various assumptions than their rivals. Ensemble isn't perfect at every point, but never far enough astray to be worrying on repeated hearings. Italian audiences are not renowned for their silences. Their movements are occasionally in evidence as are the on-stage effects, but the atmosphere of being in an opera-house and taking part, as it were, in a real occasion has all the advantages over the aseptic feeling of a studio. Nor is there anything to complain about in voice-orchestra balance.

Additional recommendations ...
...**Soloists; RCA Italian Opera Chorus and Orchestra / Thomas Schippers.**
RCA Victor Ⓜ GD86503 (two discs: 130 minutes: ADD: 8/88).
...**Soloists; Hungarian Army Chorus; Hungarian State Opera Chorus and Orchestra / Lamberto Gardelli.** Philips Ⓜ 446 669-2PM2 (two discs: 128 minutes: DDD: 8/96).

Verdi Falstaff. **Tito Gobbi** (bar) Falstaff; **Rolando Panerai** (bar) Ford; **Luigi Alva** (ten) Fenton; **Dame Elisabeth Schwarzkopf** (sop) Alice; **Anna Moffo** (sop) Nannetta; **Fedora Barbieri** (mez) Quickly; **Renato Ercolani** (ten) Bardolfo; **Nicola Zaccaria** (bass) Pistola; **Tomaso Spataro** (ten) Dr Caius; **Nan Merriman** (mez) Meg Page; **Philharmonia Chorus and Orchestra / Herbert von Karajan.** EMI Ⓕ CDS7 49668-2* (two discs: 120 minutes: ADD: 9/88). Notes, text and translation included. From SAX2254/6 (7/61). Recorded 1956.   ⒼⒼ

This *Falstaff* still stands (with Toscanini) peerless in the catalogue. At its centre stands Tito Gobbi, and his is a presence large enough to encompass both the lord and the jester, the sensuous and the sensual, and the deep seriousness as well as the deep absurdity of his vision. Few Falstaffs have such a measure of the simplicity of his first monosyllables in the bustle around him; few find the poise as well as the confusion within his music. Renato Bruson's hugely human Falstaff, solemn, vulnerable, yet properly volatile, will continue to make Giulini's 1982 DG recording irresistibly tempting. However, Karajan's recording is incomparable in its quartet of merry wives. Schwarzköpf's Alice radiates both the "gioia nell'aria" and the "gioia nel'cor" of Verdi's writing, Fedora Barbieri's redoubtable Mistress Quickly, with her stentorian cries of "Povera donna!", puts other readings in the shade; Anna Moffo's Nannetta, perfectly matched in timbre and agility with Luigi Alva's Fenton, is a constant delight. It is, above all, their corporate presence which works at such a distinctively higher level. Rolando Panerai is a magnificent Ford; his "E sogno? o realtà?" is a high point of the performance. This 1956 recording has been discreetly and skilfully doctored, but a little background hiss does remain. But one doesn't actually end up hearing it. This great recording is a-flutter with pungent solo detail, realizing, with Nannetta, that the world is "tutto deliro, sospiro e riso". The episodes of the opera, its exits and entrances, its subjects and counter-subjects, pass with the unique sensibility of Verdi's final great exuberant fugue of life.

Additional recommendations ...
...**Soloists; Los Angeles Master Chorale and Philharmonic Orchestra / Carlo Maria Giulini.**
DG Ⓕ 410 503-2GH2 (two discs: 123 minutes: ADD: 12/83).

...**Soloists; RCA Italiana Opera Chorus and Orchestra / Sir Georg Solti.**
Decca Grand Opera Ⓜ 417 168-2DM2 (two discs: 115 minutes: ADD: 3/90).
...**Soloists; Chorus and Orchestra of La Scala, Milan / Riccardo Muti.**
Sony Classical Ⓕ S2K58961 (two discs: 123 minutes: DDD: 11/94).

Verdi Falstaff. **Giuseppe Valdengo** (bar) Falstaff; **Frank Guarrera** (bar) Ford; **Antonio Madasi** (ten)
Fenton; **Herva Nelli** (sop) Alice; **Teresa Stich-Randall** (sop) Nannetta; **Cloe Elmo** (contr) Quickly;
John Carmen Rossi (ten) Bardolfo; **Norman Scott** (bass) Pistola; **Gabor Carelli** (ten) Dr Caius;
Nan Merriman (mez) Meg Page; **Robert Shaw Chorale; NBC Symphony Orchestra /**
Arturo Toscanini. RCA Gold Seal mono Ⓜ GD60251* (two discs: 117 minutes: ADD: 5/90).
Notes, text and translation included. Recorded 1950. *Gramophone Classical 100.*   ⒼⒼⒼ
This *Falstaff* remains, as it always has been, one of the half a dozen greatest opera sets ever recorded.
It is a miracle in every respect. How Toscanini loved Verdi and how he strained every sinew to fulfil
this amazing score's variety in line, feeling and colour. Whether it is the clarity and discipline of the
ensembles, the extraordinary care taken over orchestral detail or the alert control of dynamics,
Toscanini is supreme, yet nothing is done for effect's sake; everything seems natural, inevitable,
unforced, as though the score was being crated anew before us with chamber-music finesse – and the
atmosphere of a live performance adds to the feeling of immediacy. Nobody dares, or seems to want
to interrupt the magic being laid before them. Toscanini in his old age is matching the subtlety and
vitality of the composer's own Indian summer – or one might say spring, so delicate and effervescent
does the scoring sound. If, vocally, the main glory is the wonderful sense of ensemble gained through
hours of hard rehearsals, individual contributions are almost all rewarding. Indeed, Valdengo's
Falstaff, under Toscanini's tutelage, has not been surpassed on disc even by Gobbi. Flexibility, charm,
exactness, refinement inform his beautifully and wisely sung portrayal. He is no less pointed and
subtle in his encounter with Frank Guarrera's imposing Ford. Another great joy of the set is the
women's ensemble, their contribution the very epitome of smiling chatter. The Alice, Meg and
Nanetta (Stich-Randall – none better), all sound, as they were, fresh and youthful. Herva Nelli is a
lively and delightful Alice and Cloe Elmo's Quickly is as rich and ripe of voice and diction as any on
disc, though a trifle coarse at times. The Fenton is sweet and Italianate in tone, but not as stylish as
others. The smaller roles are all very much part of the team. This set should be a source of revelation
to a new generation of collectors who may have a wrong-headed view of what Toscanini was about.
The remastering gives it clearer, more immediate sound than ever heard before from the originals.

Verdi La forza del destino (1869 version). **Martina Arroyo** (sop) Leonora; **Carlo Bergonzi** (ten)
Don Alvaro; **Piero Cappuccilli** (bar) Don Carlos; **Ruggero Raimondo** (bass) Padre Guardiano;
Biancamaria Casoni (mez) Preziosilla; **Sir Geraint Evans** (bar) Melitone; **Antonio Zerbini** (bass)
Marchese; **Florindo Andreolli** (ten) Trabuco; **Mila Cova** (mez) Curra; **Virgilio Carbonari** (ten)
Mayor; **Derek Hammond-Stroud** (bar) Surgeon; **Ambrosian Opera Chorus; Royal Philharmonic**
Orchestra / Lamberto Gardelli. EMI Opera Ⓜ CMS7 64646-2* (three discs: 168 minutes:
ADD: 6/93). Notes, text and translation included. From HMV SLS948 (3/70). Recorded 1969.
Gramophone Editor's choice.
Verdi La forza del destino (1862 version). **Galina Gorchakova** (sop) Leonora; **Gegam Grigorian**
(ten) Don Alvaro; **Nikolai Putilin** (bar) Don Carlos; **Mikhail Kit** (bass) Padre Guardiano;
Olga Borodina (mez) Preziosilla; **Georgy Zastavny** (bar) Melitone; **Askar Abdrazakov** (bass)
Marchese; **Nikolai Gassiev** (ten) Trabuco; **Lia Shevtzova** (mez) Curra; **Gennadi Bezzubenkov** (bass)
Mayor; **Yuri Laptev** (ten) Surgeon; **Kirov Theatre Chorus and Orchestra / Valery Gergiev.**
Philips Ⓕ 446 951-2PH3 (three discs: 158 minutes: DDD: 4/97). Notes, text and translation
included. Recorded 1995.
This wonderfully multifarious opera demands an array of principal singers who need to be skilled in
an unusually wide range of vocal and dramatic skills. It is a 'chase' opera in which Carlos pursues
Alvaro and Leonora through two countries, through cloister and convent, through scenes popular
and martial, all treated on the most expansive scale. It is dominated by its series of magnificent duets
that are composed so that the music marches with the development of situation and character.
Gardelli's reissue is an excellent mid-price buy. It features Bergonzi, that prince among Verdi tenors,
as an exemplary and appealing Alvaro, and Piero Cappuccilli – like Bergonzi at the peak of his
powers when this set was made – as a full-blooded and Italianate Carlos. In the three all-important
duets, their voices blend ideally. Leonora was the most successful of Arroyo's recorded roles, and she
sings here with a feeling and urgency appropriate to Leonora's desperate situation. Casoni's vital
Preziosilla, Raimondi's grave but over-lugubrious Padre Guardiano and Sir Geraint's keenly
characterized Melitone complete a well-chosen cast. Over all presides Gardelli, a Verdi conductor
with an instinctive feeling for the ebb and flow of his music, always attending to the needs of the
music, never calling attention to himself. All of the versions listed below have much to commend
them. The Levine is more opulently but not so stylishly sung and perhaps a little too hectically
conducted. The *Gramophone* Award-winning Sinopoli is the stuff of which great music drama is
made, especially in the opera's closing pages. It is wonderfully enacted by Paata Burchuladze (Padre
Guardiano), Rosalind Plowright (Leonora) and José Carreras (Alvaro), with subtle changes of pace
and perspective from Sinopoli and glorious string playing. The Serafin boasts the irreplaceable Callas
and superb conducting but has some indifferent singing, significant excisions and a mono recording.

It is appropriate that the first recording of the first version of *Forza* should come from St Petersburg, where the work had its première in 1862. However, whilst the première was predominantly an Italian affair, Gergiev's set is given entirely by Russian artists. By and large, they fare splendidly, four of the five principals enjoying the weight of voice and command of the appropriate style to make their roles tell. Gorchakova evinces the weight of voice, also the broad sweep of tone and line, that her solos demand. Added to that there is a feeling for dramatic situation. "Pace, pace", for instance is suitably filled with foreboding, the lustrous, dark timbre recalling that of Ponselle – and there can be no higher praise. Just once or twice, at the top, the voice becomes a shade strident and ideally one wants more pointed articulation of the text – how familiar is that complaint today in opera singers' performances! – but it is an interpretation of formidable achievement. Grigorian is an exciting Alvaro; no other tenor today, and few in the past, could fulfil the exacting demands of the part as easily as he does: the confident *spinto* thrust in the voice is just right. He effortlessly rises to the generosity of phrase the role calls for and fills the many elegiac phrases with the feeling of melancholy they need. Only Bergonzi for Gardelli surpasses him by virtue of more idiomatic Italian and a finer line, but the superiority is slight and Bergonzi doesn't have to contend with the added music of 1862. Grigorian finds a worthy adversary in Putilin's Carlos. Putilin need fear no comparisons even with the admirable Cappuccilli for Gardelli. Although, like his predecessors and coevals in the role, he is shy of following Verdi's dynamic markings, in other respects his refulgent baritone is just the instrument for Carlos and he breathes the right fire in his implacable hatred of his imagined enemy Alvaro. Borodina easily encompasses the high-lying (for a mezzo) demands of Preziosilla and sounds the right seductive and martial notes for her role. The one disappointment is the singing of the veteran Kit, who sounds grey and woolly, with no real centre to his tone, not the voice to exert the dignity and authority of Padre Guardiano. As the humorous element in Verdi's mix, Zastavny seems at first a shade faceless but as his part progresses, one begins to admire the fact that it is being sung truly, not guyed, which makes his sermon seem a proper successor to the monologues of Rigoletto and Macbeth, albeit in a comic vein. The minor parts are well done and the excellent recording is in the best Philips tradition.

Additional recommendations ...

...Soloists; Ambrosian Opera Chorus; Philharmonia Orchestra / Giuseppe Sinopoli.
DG Ⓕ 419 203-2GH3 (three discs: 178 minutes: DDD: 5/87). *Gramophone Award Winner 1987.
Selected by Sounds in Retrospect.*
...Soloists; Chorus and Orchestra of La Scala, Milan / Riccardo Muti.
EMI Ⓕ CDS7 47485-8 (three discs: 164 minutes: DDD: 5/87).
...Soloists; Chorus and Orchestra of La Scala, Milan / Tullio Serafin.
EMI mono Ⓜ CDS5 56323-2* (three discs: 164 minutes: ADD: 10/87).
...Soloists; John Alldis Choir; London Symphony Orchestra / James Levine.
RCA Ⓕ RD81864 (three discs: 171 minutes: ADD: 10/87).

Verdi I Lombardi alla prima crociata. **June Anderson** (sop) Giselda; **Luciano Pavarotti** (ten) Oronte; **Samuel Ramey** (bass) Pagano; **Richard Leech** (ten) Arvino; **Ildebrando d'Arcangelo** (bass) Pirro; **Yanni Yannissis** (bass) Acciano; **Jane Shaulis** (mez) Sofia; **Anthony Dean Griffey** (ten) Prior; **Patricia Racette** (mez) Viclinda; **Chorus and Orchestra of the Metropolitan Opera, New York /** **James Levine.** Decca Ⓕ 455 287-2DHO2 (two discs: 129 minutes: DDD: 10/97). Notes, text and translation included. Recorded 1996.
Pavarotti appeared in the Metropolitan Opera production of *I Lombardi* in 1993 and this recording is the delayed result, following after a gap of three years. Little, if anything, seems to have been lost in the interim. He is in good voice and sings Oronte's aria with a fine sense of legato, binding the decorative turns of the cabaletta beautifully into the vocal line and throwing in a respectable top C to show us he still can. *I Lombardi* is a viscerally exciting opera. The first complete recording, conducted by Lamberto Gardelli, set a good benchmark in 1972, but that need not deter us from welcoming this lively newcomer. The Metropolitan Opera Orchestra plays with splendid precision and, as Turks and Crusaders, women of the harem and virgins, the Met Chorus has a high old time on both sides of *I Lombardi*'s war-zone. Levine himself has improved beyond recognition as a Verdian; this studio recording is well paced and has a good sense of theatre. Everything is swift and crisp on the surface, though the Philips set sometimes has a deeper sense of Italianate *rubato* that probes to the emotions below. The best role goes to the soprano Giselda, specially tailored for the delicate skills of Erminia Frezzolini. Among the current crop of Verdi sopranos, June Anderson is probably as plausible a modern Frezzolini as any. There is some lovely, pure-toned singing in her big scene at the end of the Second Act and her coloratura is shining bright, both in this cabaletta and later in "In fondo all'alma". Samuel Ramey makes a relatively lightweight Pagano, who alone decorates his second verses. In the second tenor role Richard Leech holds his own, though his voice does not take well to the microphone. Ildebrando d'Arcangelo proudly represents the younger generation of Italian singers in the small role of Pirro and Patricia Racette sings brightly as Viclinda. Gardelli's crusading first recording has a rough Italianate vigour that lovers of early Verdi will enjoy, but Levine and his forces more than hold their ground with pace and brilliance, and a bright, modern recording with on balance a better cast and the voices well forward.

Additional recommendation ...

...Soloists; Ambrosian Singers; Royal Philharmonic Orchestra / Lamberto Gardelli.
Philips Ⓜ 422 420-2PM2 (two discs: 135 minutes: ADD: 11/89).

Verdi Luisa Miller. **Montserrat Caballé** (sop) Luisa; **Luciano Pavarotti** (ten) Rodolfo;
Sherrill Milnes (bar) Miller; **Bonaldo Gaiotti** (bass) Count Walter; **Anna Reynolds** (mez) Federica;
Richard Van Allan (bass) Wurm; **Annette Céline** (mez) Laura; **Fernando Pavarotti** (ten) Peasant;
London Opera Chorus; National Philharmonic Orchestra / Peter Maag. Decca Ⓕ 417 420-2DH2
(two discs: 144 minutes: ADD: 10/88). Notes, text and translation included.
From SET606/08 (5/76).
This transitional work shows Verdi enhancing his skills and refining his musical style. The plot, based
on a Schiller drama, involves the tragedy and death of Luisa and her beloved Rodolfo brought about
by the evil Wurm, apt predecessor of Verdi's Iago. The title-role could not find a more appealing
interpreter than Caballé, who spins a fine line and is highly responsive to Luisa's sad situation. She is
partnered by Pavarotti at the height of his powers as Rodolfo. He excels in "Quando le sere al
polacido", the work's most famous aria. As Luisa's equivocal father, Miller, Milnes gives one of his
best performances on disc and Van Allan is a properly snarling Wurm. Maag, an underrated
conductor, directs a strong, well-proportioned performance. He gives the impression of being in love
with this opera and he goes right to the heart of the score, finding its seriousness as well as its fire.
The last act is specially fine, containing what are regarded as among the gramophone classics, the two
duets of Luisa, first with her father, then with Rodolfo. The production is unobtrusively effective in
creation of atmosphere and is spaciously recorded.
Additional recommendation ...
...**Soloists; Chorus and Orchestra of the Royal Opera House, Covent Garden / Lorin Maazel.**
DG Ⓕ 423 144-2GH2 (two discs: 133 minutes: ADD: 5/88).

Verdi Macbeth. **Piero Cappuccilli** (bar) Macbeth; **Shirley Verrett** (mez) Lady Macbeth;
Nicolai Ghiaurov (bass) Banquo; **Plácido Domingo** (ten) Macduff; **Antonio Savastano** (ten)
Malcolm; **Carlo Zardo** (bass) Doctor; **Giovanni Foiani** (bass) Servant; **Sergio Fontana** (bass)
Herald; **Alfredo Mariotti** (bass) Assassin; **Stefania Malagú** (mez) Lady-in-waiting;
Chorus and Orchestra of La Scala, Milan / Claudio Abbado. DG The Originals
Ⓜ 449 732-2GOR2 (two discs: 154 minutes: ADD: 3/97). Notes, text and translation included.
From 2709 062 (10/76). Recorded 1976.
Verdi's lifelong admiration for Shakespeare resulted in only two operas based on his plays. *Macbeth*,
the first, originally written in 1847, was extensively revised in 1865. Without losing the direct force of
the original, Verdi added greater depth to his first ideas. Once derided as being un-Shakespearian, it
is now recognized as a masterpiece for its psychological penetration as much as for its subtle melodic
inspiration. Abbado captures perfectly the atmosphere of dark deeds and personal ambition leading
to tragedy, projected by Verdi, and his reading holds the opera's disparate elements in the score under
firm control, catching its interior tensions. He is well supported by his Scala forces. Shirley Verrett
may not be ideally incisive or Italianate in accent as Lady Macbeth, but she peers into the character's
soul most convincingly. As ever, truly inspired by Abbado, Cappuccilli is a suitably haunted and
introverted Macbeth who sings a secure and unwavering legato. Domingo's upright Macduff and
Ghiaurov's doom-laden Banquo are both admirable in their respective roles.
Additional recommendations ...
...**Soloists; Berlin Deutsche Opera Chorus and Orchestra / Giuseppe Sinopoli.**
Philips Ⓕ 412 133-2PH3 (three discs: 135 minutes: DDD: 2/85).
...**Soloists; Metropolitan Opera Chorus and Orchestra / Erich Leinsdorf.**
RCA Victor Ⓜ GD84516 (two discs: 130 minutes: ADD: 9/88).
...**Soloists; Ambrosian Opera Chorus; New Philharmonia Orchestra / Riccardo Muti.**
EMI Ⓜ CMS7 64339-2 (two discs: ADD: 2/93).
...**Soloists; Chorus and Orchestra of La Scala, Milan / Victor de Sabata.**
EMI mono EMS7 64944-2* (two discs: 139 minutes: ADD: 1/94).

Verdi Otello. **Plácido Domingo** (ten) Otello; **Cheryl Studer** (sop) Desdemona; **Sergei Leiferkus** (bar)
Iago; **Ramon Vargas** (ten) Cassio; **Michael Schade** (ten) Roderigo; **Denyce Graves** (mez) Emilia;
Ildebrando d'Arcangelo (bass) Lodovico; **Giacomo Prestia** (bass) Montano; **Philippe Duminy**
(bass) Herald; **Hauts-de-Seine Maîtrise; Chorus and Orchestra of the Opéra-Bastille, Paris /**
Myung-Whun Chung. DG Ⓕ 439 805-2GH2 (two discs: 132 minutes: DDD: 12/94). Notes, text
and translation included. Recorded 1993. *Gramophone Editor's choice. Selected by Sounds in*
Retrospect.   ⒼⒼ
Just as *Othello* is a difficult play to bring off in the theatre, so *Otello* is a difficult opera to bring off
out of it. For some years now, Domingo has been, on stage, the greatest Otello of our age. On record,
though, he has had less success. Leiferkus and Domingo have worked closely together in the theatre;
and it shows in scene after scene – nowhere more so than in the crucial sequence in Act 2 where Otello
so rapidly ingests Iago's lethal poison. By bringing into the recording studio the feel and experience
of a stage performance – meticulous study subtly modified by the improvised charge of the moment
– both singers help defy the jinx that so often afflicts *Otello* on record. The skill of Leiferkus's
performance is rooted in voice and technique: clear diction, a disciplined rhythmic sense and a
mastery of all ornament down to the most mordant of mordents. Above all, he is always *there* (usually
stage right in this recording), steely-voiced, rabbiting on obsessively. We even hear his crucial

interventions in the great Act 3 *concertato*. Domingo is in superb voice; the sound seems golden as never before. Yet at the same time, it is a voice that is being more astutely deployed. To take that cruellest of all challenges to a studio-bound Otello, the great Act 3 soliloquy "Dio! mi potevi", Domingo's performance is now simpler, more inward, more intense. He has rethought the role for the microphone, much as a great actor might adapt his Othello for the radio, or a singer might shift from the broad brush-strokes of theatre performance to the keener disciplines of Lieder-singing. It helps, perhaps, that Domingo's voice has darkened, winning back some of its russet baritonal colourings. But in the end the genius of the performance lies in its ability to distil.

Chung's conducting is almost disarmingly vital. Verdi's scoring is more Gallic than Germanic. The score sounds very brilliant in the hands of the excellent Opéra-Bastille orchestra, and, in Act 4, very beautiful. Maybe Chung is wary of the emotional depths and, occasionally, the rhythmic infrastructure is muddled and unclear. And yet, the freshness is all gain. He is already a master of the big ensemble, and the line of an act. Tension rarely slackens. Where it does the mixing and matching of takes is probably to blame. Studer's is a carefully drawn portrait of a chaste and sober-suited lady. Perhaps Verdi had a sweeter-voiced singer in mind for this paragon of "goodness, resignation, and self-sacrifice" (Verdi's words, not Shakespeare's). Studer's oboe tones keep us at a certain distance. There is little of Rysanek's warmth and vulnerability (Serafin) and yet you will look in vain for a better Desdemona. What's more, Studer is a singer who can single-mindedly focus the drama afresh, as she does more than once in Act 3. DG's recording is clear and unfussy and satisfyingly varied; Studer, in particular, is much helped by the beautifully open acoustic the engineers provide for the closing act. This is undoubtedly the best *Otello* on record since the early 1960s. It also happens to be the first time on disc that a great Otello at the height of his powers has been successfully caught in the context of a recording that can itself be generally considered worthy of the event, musically and technically.

Verdi Otello. **Ramon Vinay** (ten) Otello; **Herva Nelli** (sop) Desdemona; **Giuseppe Valdengo** (bar) Iago; **Virginio Assandri** (ten) Cassio; **Leslie Chabay** (ten) Roderigo; **Nan Merriman** (mez) Emilia; **Nicola Moscona** (bass) Lodovico; **Arthur Newman** (bass) Montano; **NBC Chorus and Symphony Orchestra / Arturo Toscanini.** RCA Victor Gold Seal mono Ⓜ GD60302* (two discs: 125 minutes: ADD: 3/92). Recorded 1947. From HMV ALP1090/92 (12/53).
Gramophone classical 100.   ❸❸❸

One of the century's legendary achievements on record confirms its reputation on this well-managed reissue. Here Toscanini's blazing intensity, his full comprehension of every facet of the score are evident throughout. The attack and dedication of chorus and orchestra are apparent throughout; so is the discipline and textural clarity on all sides. The sound remains dry but somehow this very close, confined quality accords with the work's own claustrophobic quality – if only Otello had gone out into the open air and thought about the reality of the evidence before him, he might not have been so easily caught up in Iago's web of deceit. Valdengo's Iago continues to put Gobbi's for Serafin and Tibbett's for Panizza, in the shade. His light, almost elegant and seemingly cheerful tone, his mordant, sinister delivery of the *Credo*, his insinuating and perfectly accurate delivery of the imagined Dream all tell of his willingness to follow Toscanini's guidance, for he never sang so well for anyone else. This is a faultless performance. So, in terms of interpretation, is Vinay's Otello – the tormented, fearsomely commanding Moor to the life. Nelli's sincerity of purpose, her accuracy and her true tone compensate for a slightly pallid reading of Desdemona's thoughts and feelings. Certainly she makes more of the text than Dame Kiri Te Kanawa (Solti/Decca) and often sings with a finer line, while missing Rethberg's warmth on the Panizza version. The smaller roles are all worthily taken. Any incidental drawback should not prevent anyone hearing this overwhelming interpretation. Toscanini identifies so sympathetically with the human condition, as did Verdi himself – and it is from Verdi, at whose feet he sat, that Toscanini learnt his trade.

Additional recommendations ...

...**Soloists; Chorus and Orchestra of La Scala, Milan / Lorin Maazel.**
EMI Ⓕ CDS7 47450-8 (two discs: 142 minutes: DDD: 12/86).

...**Soloists; Rome Opera Chorus and Orchestra / Tullio Serafin.**
RCA Victor Gold Seal Ⓜ GD81969* (two discs: 144 minutes: ADD: 11/88).

...**Soloists; Metropolitan Opera Chorus and Orchestra / Ettore Panizza.**
Music & Arts mono Ⓕ CD645* (two discs: 139 minutes: AAD: 9/91).

...**Soloists; Metropolitan Opera Children's Chorus; Chicago Symphony Chorus and Orchestra / Sir Georg Solti.** Decca Ⓕ 433 669-2DH2 (two discs: 129 minutes: DDD: 11/91).

Verdi Otello. **Giuseppe Giacomini** (ten) Otello; **Dame Margaret Price** (sop) Desdemona; **Matteo Manuguerra** (bar) Iago; **Dino di Domenico** (ten) Cassio; **Alain Gabriel** (ten) Roderigo; **Martine Mahé** (mez) Emilia; **Luigi Roni** (bass) Lodovico; **Vincent le Texier** (bass-bar) Montano; **Anton Kúrňava** (bass) Herald; **Slovak Philharmonic Chorus; Les Petits Chanteurs de Bordeaux; Orchestre National de Bordeaux Aquitaine / Alain Lombard.** Forlane Ⓕ 216774 (two discs: 128 minutes: DDD: 3/98). Notes, text and translation included. Recorded live in 1991.

On the evidence of this *Otello*, and much else, Giacomini is more viscerally exciting than any of the famous Three. Certainly no tenor in this role since Del Monaco in his prime had the elemental, almost frightening power evinced by Giacomini's reading, but his talents go well beyond the possession of a real *tenore robusto*. His dark, louring tone and agonized delivery of the text exactly match the passion and jealousy of the Moor, alternately achingly sorrowful as he imagines his wife's infidelities, and fierily tormented as he rants and raves at her supposed wrongdoing. There is much to study in this searing interpretation, which is on a par with Vinay's for Toscanini and sung in the same dark-grained, tormented fashion. Giacomini's overwhelming portrayal is worthily supported. Dame Margaret Price provides rounded, cleanly produced tone, even if there are a few signs of wear, and her interpretation – in response to a real occasion – is emotionally compelling. In the Act 3 duet, she brings to the passage beginning "Mi guarda!" and the line "E son io l'innocente" the depth of Desdemona's heart-stricken soul as she tries to defend herself against Otello's accusations, and her Act 4 scene is shaped and executed with the expected sense of impending doom. Matteo Manuguerra, an experienced and sympathetic Verdian, was already in his mid-sixties when this performance took place and there are times when his voice has to be husbanded, but he shows much intelligence in portraying the subtlety of Iago's evil. The smaller roles are decently if not exceptionally cast. Alain Lombard keeps the performance consistently on the boil. He handles the public scenes, most notably the Act 3 ensemble (given uncut), with the urgency and large scale they call for. His chorus and orchestra, while not quite in the highest class, perform with keen awareness of the score's pithy quality. This set may not entirely challenge the hegemony of the 1947 Toscanini and Serafin sets, but it is histrionically exciting, largely because of the live ambience (the audience is remarkably quiet, clapping only at the end of acts) and there is a straightforward honesty about it that has eluded more glamorous recordings. Stage noise is seldom in evidence. The recording is at times over-resonant, but catches the excitement of the occasion. With Giacomini giving such an authentically vivid account of the title-role, most Verdians will want to own a set that goes so unerringly to the heart of the matter.

Verdi Rigoletto. **Tito Gobbi** (bar) Rigoletto; **Giuseppe di Stefano** (ten) Duke; **Maria Callas** (sop) Gilda; **Nicola Zaccaria** (bass) Sparafucile; **Adriana Lazzarini** (mez) Maddalena; **Giuse Gerbino** (mez) Giovanna; **Plinio Clabassi** (bass) Monterone; **William Dickie** (bar) Marullo; **Renato Ercolani** (ten) Borsa; **Carlo Forti** (bar) Count Ceprano; **Elvira Galassi** (sop) Countess Ceprano; **Chorus and Orchestra of La Scala, Milan / Tullio Serafin.**
EMI mono Ⓕ CDS5 56327-2* (two discs: 118 minutes: ADD: 2/87). Notes, text and translation included. From Columbia 33CXS1324, 33CX1325/6 (2/56). Recorded 1955.   **Ⓖ**
The story of the hunchbacked jester Rigoletto at the court of a licentious Duke who seduces the Fool's daughter Gilda by masquerading as a poor student, and the consequent attempts at revenge on the part of Rigoletto, produced from Verdi one of the most telling of his middle-period triumphs. His identification with each of the characters and the sheer energy and sensuous ardour of the score is quite remarkable. Nowhere else on record have these characterizations been delineated with such intelligence and commitment as by Gobbi, Callas and di Stefano on this 44-year-old set. Serafin presides over everything with an unerring grasp of Verdian timing.
Additional recommendations ...
...**Soloists; Vienna State Opera Chorus; Vienna Philharmonic Orchestra / Carlo Maria Giulini.**
DG Ⓕ 415 288-2GH2 (two discs: DDD: 11/85).
...**Soloists; RCA Italiana Opera Chorus and Orchestra / Sir Georg Solti.**
RCA Victor Gold Seal Ⓕ GD86506 (two discs: 113 minutes: ADD: 9/88).
...**Soloists; Chorus and Orchestra of La Scala, Milan / Riccardo Muti.**
EMI Ⓕ CDS7 49605-2 (two discs: 116 minutes: DDD: 11/89).
...**Soloists; Chorus and Orchestra of the Teatro Communale, Bologna / Riccardo Chailly.**
Decca Ⓕ 425 864-2DH2 (two discs: 107 minutes: DDD: 1/90).
...**Soloists; Slovak Philharmonic Chorus; Czecho-Slovak Radio Symphony Orchestra / Alexander Rahbari.** Naxos Ⓢ 8 660013/4 (two discs: 115 minutes: DDD: 3/92).
...**Soloists; Stockholm Royal Opera Chorus and Orchestra / Sixten Ehrling.**
BIS mono Ⓜ CD296* (116 minutes: ADD: 8/94).
...**Rigoletto, with additional items by Benedict, Bizet, Donizetti, Evans, Kaper, Lehár, Martin y Guerrero, Payán and Serrano sung by Lina Pagliughi** (sop) and **Tino Folgar** (ten). **Soloists; Chorus and Orchestra of La Scala, Milan / Carlo Sabajno.**
Pearl mono Ⓜ GEMMCDS9180* (two discs: 155 minutes: ADD: 6/96).
...**Soloists; Chorus and Orchestra of the Santa Cecilia Academy, Rome / Giuseppe Sinopoli.**
Philips Duo Ⓜ 462 158-2PM2 (two discs: 128 minutes: DDD: 6/98).

Verdi Rigoletto. **Renato Bruson** (bar) Rigoletto; **Andrea Rost** (sop) Gilda; **Roberto Alagna** (ten) Duke; **Dimitri Kavrakos** (bass) Sparafucile; **Mariana Pentcheva** (contr) Maddalena; **Giorgio Giuseppini** (bass) Monterone; **Antonella Trevisan** (mez) Giovanna; **Ernesto Gavazzi** (ten) Borsa; **Silvestro Sammaritano** (bass) Marullo; **Nicoletta Zanini** (mez) Countess Ceprano; **Antonio de Gobbi** (bass) Count Ceprano; **Marilena Laurenza** (sop) Page; **Ernesto Panariello** (bass) Usher; **Chorus and Orchestra of La Scala, Milan / Riccardo Muti.** Sony Classical Ⓕ S2K66314 (two discs: 121 minutes: DDD: 12/95). Recorded live in 1994.
Muti's previous recording of this opera is only six-and-a-half years old. That was made with the forces of La Scala in La Scala for EMI but not at a live performance, unlike this one. You immediately feel that added *frisson* of a 'real' occasion and that continues throughout a well-prepared and well-integrated performance, applause restricted to ends of acts, virtually no audience noise. As for Muti's

interpretation, it has changed very little during the intervening period. It remains rewardingly vital, rhythmically speaking. Every moment is acutely and alertly sprung with speeds tending to be on the brisk side. It is at the furthermost extreme from Giulini's grand, leisurely approach, more akin to Chailly's. It is a pleasure to hear how Muti, in both versions, observes the importance Verdi gives to oboe, clarinet and bassoon, how profitably he makes all his singers observe to the letter what Verdi wrote. Ah, Roberto Alagna! Many will want this set for his participation alone. Listen to the Duke's aria and cabaletta at the start of Act 3 and you will hear this young tenor's tone perfectly suited and his phrasing immaculately turned. Both in "La donna è mobile" and the opening of the Quartet one might like a shade more variation in dynamics and tonal colour, just the things provided by La Scola on the EMI version, but then Alagna has the more sappy, brilliant voice and, above all, the *slancio* the part demands, and his singing reflects the Duke's wilful, libidinous nature. His is a most attractive contribution to the set. At the end of the Duke-Gilda duet, Muti demands and gets the full cadenza written into the score. It is finely turned by Alagna, and by Rost, who offers an altogether lovely performance, ideal in almost every respect. With just the right weight of voice for the role, all her singing is full-toned and precisely articulated, and the tone itself is vibrant and tangy. She very much recalls Cotrubas on the Giulini set, but Rost has the firmer tone, and this Gilda dies heart-rendingly. Rost hasn't the specifically Italian sound of Muti's Dessì (EMI), who also makes a most affecting Gilda, but Rost is the more accomplished technician.

The years have been kind to Bruson's voice (he was 58 when this recording was made), but it has to be said that, especially in the first half of the opera, the vibrato is now disturbing when the tone comes under pressure. Perhaps because he is afraid he cannot sustain a line at a lower dynamic level, he seems unwilling to sing at less than *mezzo-forte*. His remains a considered, eloquent interpretation through which courses a father's concern and anguish. But turn to Muti's Zancanaro (EMI) and you hear the exact voice for the jester, more biting, stronger, more flexible and varied in tone than Bruson's, at least the equal of Cappuccilli's on the Giulini set. Only Gobbi for Serafin provides a range of colour and shades of meaning beyond all his rivals. Kavrakos is a suitably sturdy, dour Sparafucile. After a blowzy start Pentcheva proves a seductive-sounding Maddalena, but these and the smaller roles are as well if not better cast on EMI. So that set is by no means put out of court by this one; indeed the earlier Muti is probably the most overall recommendable one among modern versions, just about superior to the Decca/Chailly – unless that is you want Giulini's appealingly sung, deeply thought-through version. But this set does boast Alagna's superbly vital Duke and Rost's greatly appealing Gilda, which may well sway you in its favour. Had the recording more presence it would run the EMI close and in any case it certainly deserves to be up among the top versions. However, as engineered here – the action seems somewhat distanced, as though you are sitting in the balcony rather than the stalls. You need a very high volume setting to get a satisfactory level from the singers; then the orchestra sound too loud. Of course the Serafin will remain unrivalled for many, but its aged sound and the disfiguring cuts must be a serious drawback to anyone coming afresh to the work's discography.

Verdi Simon Boccanegra. **Piero Cappuccilli** (bar) Simon Boccanegra; **Mirella Freni** (sop) Amelia; **José Carreras** (ten) Gabriele; **Nicolai Ghiaurov** (bass) Fiesco; **José van Dam** (bass-bar) Paolo; **Giovanni Foiani** (bass) Pietro; **Antonio Savastano** (ten) Captain; **Maria Fausta Gallamini** (sop) Maid; **Chorus and Orchestra of La Scala, Milan / Claudio Abbado.** DG The Originals Ⓜ 449 752-2GOR2 (two discs: 136 minutes: ADD: 10/97). Notes, text and translation included. From 2709 017 (11/77). Recorded 1977.

This famous recording in its new guise, remastered, at mid price in The Originals series, must be a very strong contender for the preferred available version. It has become a gramophone classic, a performance in the studio after a series of performances at La Scala in the Strehler staging. The close, slightly claustrophobic recording exactly mirrors the mood of nefarious activities and intrigues following Boccanegra's rise to be Doge of Genoa, he and his lovely daughter victims of the dark deeds round them. In his plebeian being, clement exercise of authority and warm, fatherly love, Simon Boccanegra is made for Cappuccilli who, under Abbado's tutelage, sings it not only *con amore* but with exemplary, delicately tinted tone and unbelievably long-breathed phrasing. As his daughter Amelia, Freni was just entering her quasi-*spinto* phase, and expands her lyric voice easily into the greater demands of this more dramatic role. Similarly heavier duties had not yet tarnished the youthful ardour and sap in the tone of the 30-year-old Carreras. As implacable Fiesco, Ghiaurov exudes vengeful command and van Dam evil machinations as the villain Paolo. Over all presides Abbado in what remains one of his greatest recordings, alert to every facet of the wondrous score, timing every scene, in an opera tricky to pace, to near-perfection, and in sum bringing theatrical drama into the home. This set should now be an essential adornment to any reputable collection of Verdi.

Additional recommendation ...
...**Soloists; Chorus and Orchestra of the Rome Opera House / Gabriele Santini.** EMI mono Ⓜ CMS7 63513-2* (two discs: 119 minutes: ADD: 9/90).

Verdi Stiffelio. **José Carreras** (ten) Stiffelio; **Sylvia Sass** (sop) Lina; **Matteo Manuguerra** (bar) Stankar; **Wladimiro Ganzarolli** (bass) Jorg; **Ezio di Cesare** (ten) Raffaele; **Maria Venuti** (mez) Dorotea; **Thomas Moser** (ten) Federico; **Austrian Radio Chorus and Symphony Orchestra /**

Lamberto Gardelli. Philips Ⓜ 422 432-2PM2 (two discs: 109 minutes: ADD: 3/90). Notes, text and translation included. From 6769 039 (10/80). Recorded 1979.

This work is gradually gaining the reputation it deserves as companies and audiences realize its quality (it gains its first performance at Covent Garden in the 1992-23 season). It tells of Stiffelio, a Protestant clergyman, in a Catholic country, whose wife Linda has committed adultery and finds it in his heart, after her father has killed her lover, to forgive her. The work has elements that pre-echo *Otello* and is yet another example of Verdi finding the specific music for a specific predicament. This performance, firmly conducted by Gardelli, has an involved, involving assumption of the title-role by Carreras. This role is a gift for an accomplished tenor and he catches the moral fervour and uncertainties of the part with his open-hearted, spontaneous performance. Sylvia Sass also offers a rewarding, strongly emotional performance as Lina.

Verdi La traviata. **Tiziana Fabriccini** (sop) Violetta; **Roberto Alagna** (ten) Alfredo; **Paolo Coni** (bar) Germont; **Nicoletta Curiel** (mez) Flora; **Antonella Trevisan** (mez) Annina; **Enrico Cossutta** (ten) Gastone; **Orazio Mori** (bass) Baron; **Enzo Capuano** (bass) Marquis; **Francesco Musinu** (bass) Doctor; **Ernesto Gavazzi** (ten) Giuseppe; **Ernesto Panariello** (bass) Servant; **Silvestro Sammaritano** (bass) Messenger; **Chorus and Orchestra of La Scala, Milan / Riccardo Muti.**
Sony Classical Ⓕ S2K52486 (two discs: 136 minutes: DDD: 10/93). Notes, text and translation included. Recorded live in 1992. *Gramophone Editor's choice.*   ⒼⒼ

Verdi La traviata. **Angela Gheorghiu** (sop) Violetta; **Frank Lopardo** (ten) Alfredo; **Leo Nucci** (bar) Germont; **Leah-Marian Jones** (mez) Flora; **Gillian Knight** (mez) Annina; **Robin Leggate** (ten) Gaston; **Richard Van Allan** (bass) Baron; **Roderick Earle** (bass) Marquis; **Mark Beesley** (bar) Doctor; **Neil Griffiths** (ten) Giuseppe; **Bryan Secombe** (bass) Messenger; **Rodney Gibson** (ten) Servant; **Chorus and Orchestra of the Royal Opera House, Covent Garden / Sir Georg Solti.**
Decca Ⓕ 448 119-2DHO2 (two discs: 127 minutes: DDD: 8/95). Notes, text and translation included. Recorded live in 1994.   Ⓖ

An exciting and eloquent reading on all sides, this version must now be rated with the established frontrunners – but, as with some of those, most notably any of Callas's versions, it is not for the fainthearted, or for those who like their Violettas to have full, equally, produced voices. Fabriccini is evidently not an Act 1 Violetta. But even without assured coloratura and with problems at the *passagio*, she is one who is going to hold our attention and move us. In the Second Act so much bespeaks not only complete identification with Violetta's predicament but also vocal acumen of an exceptional kind, often based on the seemingly lost art of portamento. Because this is a live performance we are conscious that the singer's acting is part of the secret of the reading's success, that and the obvious youth of a soprano who is not yet a preening prima donna. The final tragedy is still better, very much modelled on Callas. The voice, more settled now than anywhere in the performance manages her role with long-breathed phrasing and pathetic accents, the result of a true understanding of Verdian style yet never self-conscious in its effect – this is undoubtedly great singing *and* interpretation. The death is deeply moving. Alagna, in the role that brought him to attention, is just the Alfredo for this Violetta; youthfully ardent; with keen-edged tone, finely attuned to the legato essential in Verdi. The recording is taken from four performances, given at La Scala, and is a theatrical view full of electricity, vitally executed by the forces of La Scala, as vital as any in the recorded history of the work. Don't miss it.

Turning to the Decca set, for Angela Gheorghiu, a young Romanian of great promise, Violetta was the right role at the right time. The whole drama is there in her voice, every expression in the eyes and beat of the heart reflected in the way she shapes and colours Verdi's vocal lines. Her quiet singing is particularly lovely, affording subtle variations of tenderness and inner anxiety. When she does choose to make a point with force, as in her sudden warmth of feeling towards Giorgio Germont at "Qual figlia m'abbracciate" or her chilling cry of "Morro!", accompanied by a loud thump on the table, her ideas always hit home. A few moments of vocal weakness are accentuated by the microphone, mainly a tendency to go sharp and some hardness at the top of the voice that was not troublesome in the theatre. Otherwise, she is the most complete and moving Violetta we have had since her compatriot, Ileana Cotrubas. These live performances were remarkably the first time that Sir Georg Solti, at the age of 82, had conducted a staged *La traviata* and he wanted two young singers who were coming fresh to the opera, as he was himself. What was so spellbinding in the theatre was the touching intimacy they brought to their scenes together. Instead of the duets for Violetta and Alfredo turning into standard Italian operatic bawling, they became lovers' whispers, each phrase floating like a kiss from one set of lips to the other. The effect comes across here in the cadenzas, where Gheorghiu and Frank Lopardo really seem to be listening to each other. Elsewhere, one is more aware than in the theatre that Lopardo's light tenor is far from being an idiomatic Italian voice. His idiosyncratic tone quality and un-Italian vowels can be problematical, as is some ungainly lifting up into notes.

Leo Nucci, Decca's resident Verdi baritone at the moment, makes a standard Giorgio Germont, not more, and apart from Leah-Marian Jones's energetic Flora, the smaller roles do not say a great deal for the Royal Opera's depth of casting, with its selection of gruff bass voices and prim Anglo-Saxon accents. Solti insisted that the opera be performed complete (more unusual in the theatre than it is on disc). But there is nothing studied about his conducting: the performance is fresh and alive from the first note to the last, the result of a lifetime's experience of how to pace a drama in the opera-house. With the increasing number of live opera sets, a recommendation for *La traviata* is likely to be based on whether one is prepared to accept noises-off or not. (Decca's recording is well balanced and vivid, dancing feet and banging doors included.) Levine on DG is a stronger contender, as he has an all-purpose theatricality and Pavarotti as his tenor, but Studer is a generalized and unmoving Violetta next to Gheorghiu. Among the live sets, Giulini and Callas at La Scala in 1955 must be *hors concours*, an unforgettable performance of the greatest inspiration, but in rather awful sound. Muti's more recent La Scala set, in which he has to wrestle with Tiziana Fabbricini's wayward talents as Violetta, is the nearest comparison.

Additional recommendations ...

...Soloists; **Rome Opera Chorus and Orchestra / Tullio Serafin.**
  Classics for Pleasure ⑧ CD-CFPD4450* (two discs: 119 minutes: ADD).
...Soloists; **Rome Opera Chorus and Orchestra / Fernando Previtali.**
  RCA Victor Gold Seal Ⓜ GD84144 (two discs: 113 minutes: ADD).
...Soloists; **Bavarian State Opera Chorus and Orchestra / Carlos Kleiber.**
  DG Ⓕ 415 132-2GH2 (two discs: DDD: 3/86).
...Soloists; **Ambrosian Opera Chorus; Band of HM Royal Marines; Philharmonia Orchestra /
  Riccardo Muti.** EMI Ⓕ CDS7 47538-8 (two discs: 129 minutes: DDD: 11/87).   Ⓖ
...Soloists; **Chorus and Orchestra of La Scala, Milan / Carlo Maria Giulini.**
  EMI mono Ⓜ CMS7 63628-2* (two discs: 124 minutes: ADD: 2/91).
...Soloists; **Metropolitan Opera Chorus and Orchestra / James Levine.**
  DG Ⓕ 435 797-2GH2 (two discs: 122 minutes: DDD: 11/92).
...Preludes, Acts 1 and 3. *Coupled with works by various composers.* **Hallé Orchestra /
  Sir John Barbirolli.** Dutton Laboratories mono Ⓜ CDSJB1004* (75 minutes: ADD: 11/96).

Verdi La traviata (sung in English). **Valerie Masterson** (sop) Violetta; **John Brecknock** (ten) Alfredo; **Christian du Plessis** (bar) Germont; **Della Jones** (mez) Flora; **Shelagh Squires** (mez) Annina; **Geoffrey Pogson** (ten) Gaston; **John Gibbs** (bar) Baron; **Denis Dowling** (bar) Marquis; **Roderick Earle** (bass) Doctor; **Edward Byles** (ten) Joseph; **Chorus and Orchestra of English National Opera / Sir Charles Mackerras.** Classics for Pleasure Silver Doubles ⑧ CD-CFPSD4799 (two discs: 119 minutes: ADD: 4/96). From HMV SLS5216 (10/81). Recorded 1980.
This recording was made after the end of Sir Charles Mackerras's reign at the London Coliseum, but still in time to capture the traditional values over which he presided at English National Opera. Above all, the set is a perfect example of what recording opera in English should be about. The translation is remarkably close to the Italian, always using words with the same linguistic origin where possible, and the singers take the text to heart. There is no libretto in the booklet and none is needed. John Brecknock, in particular, used to be renowned for the clarity of his words in the theatre. His Alfredo sounds a young man of good bearing, singing with an attractive English ardour even if he was slightly past his best by this time. Christian du Plessis makes a Giorgio Germont with enough voice, but limited imagination. Both artists get a single verse of their cabalettas, Brecknock ending his with a dutiful top C. Among the supporting cast Della Jones's spitfire Flora briefly snatches the spotlight, as she makes her consonants crackle with energy. All of them worked regularly with Mackerras at ENO and sing with a care for the details of the score that must emanate from him. There is not, however, much passion about the performance. So far the set's virtues may be ephemeral, but Valerie Masterson's delectable Violetta deserves her chance with posterity. There is a moment towards the end of "Un di felice" where Mackerras gives her a little extra time and she floats the high A with an intuitive freedom that seems to cradle the very spirit of the opera in the palm of her hand. As much as any international singer, Masterson knows where to find Violetta's heart in the music. She is not in equally good voice throughout (the recording was made over a period of three months) but at its best her soprano has a delicate, bone-china fragility that very nearly embodies the role. It is difficult to imagine anyone who wants *La traviata* in English being disappointed.

Verdi Il trovatore. **Plácido Domingo** (ten) Manrico; **Aprile Millo** (sop) Leonora; **Vladimir Chernov** (bar) Conte di Luna; **Dolora Zajick** (mez) Azucena; **James Morris** (bass) Ferrando; **Sondra Kelly** (contr) Ines; **Anthony Laciura** (ten) Ruiz; **Glenn Bater** (bass) Old Gipsy; **Tim Willson** (ten) Messenger; **New York Metropolitan Opera Chorus and Orchestra / James Levine.** Sony Classical Ⓕ S2K48070 (two discs: 129 minutes: DDD: 6/94). Notes, text and translation included.
Recorded 1991.   Ⓖ
This is the most recommendable among modern versions of *Trovatore*, with a reading all-round that finely balances the lyrical and melodramatic elements in the score. Once Leonora appears, the reading takes on true Verdian style. Millo floats "Come d'aurato" effortlessly on a fine line and throughout her part is replete with the right kind of Verdian *spinto* sound, the correct phraseology. This is a reading to please the ear and move the heart. Immediately this Leonora is confronted with Conte di Luna, we hear the firm, vibrant, implacable tones of Chernov. His voice is surely now in its absolute prime and he sings everything with the confident panache that suggests as much. Our upright hero is Domingo, aged a little since his earlier recordings of Manrico for Mehta and Giulini (listed overleaf). The artistry and management of the voice are as rewarding as of old and Domingo reserves his best for the last and greatest scene when both his sovereign phrasing – "Riposa, o madre" sung in a single breath – and his involvement take on the aura of active participation. Manrico's feelings of love for his mother, momentary contempt for Leonora and eventual tragic pathos are firmly targeted: we hear

once more the noble tenor we know and can listen to in sappier voice for Giulini. As Azucena, Zajick gives an effective and strong-willed performance, wanting only the last ounce of character: she is also at her best in the final act. The Met chorus is no more than adequate on this occasion, but as ever the house's orchestra plays with the virtuosity it reserves for its Musical Director. Levine's reading is well timed, properly earthy yet refined in the many delicate touches Verdi evinces in arias and duets. His is a more dramatically vital reading than Giulini's which is at times unconscionably slow (his version runs to three discs). Luciano Pavarotti's predominantly lyrical tenor (for Mehta on Decca) is not ideal for Manrico but he sings it with such unfailing musicality and sense of line that Pavarotti enthusiasts need not hesitate to acquire this version, confident that their hero's portrayal is set in suitable surroundings. However, the whole reading is not as well integrated as the Levine, and by a hair's breadth that is probably the better sung. Mehta's earlier, much-lauded recording for RCA remains very much in the frame.

Additional recommendations ...

...Soloists; Chorus and Orchestra of La Scala, Milan / Herbert von Karajan.
EMI CDS5 56333-2* (two discs: 129 minutes: ADD).   Ⓖ

...Soloists; Saint Cecilia Academy Chorus and Orchestra / Carlo Maria Giulini.
DG Ⓕ 423 858-2GH2 (two discs: 140 minutes: DDD: 2/85).

...Soloists; Ambrosian Opera Chorus; New Philharmonia Orchestra / Zubin Mehta.
RCA Victor Red Seal Ⓕ RD86194 (two discs: 137 minutes: ADD: 8/88).

...Soloists; Robert Shaw Chorale; RCA Victor Orchestra / Renato Cellini.
RCA Victor mono Ⓜ GD86643* (two discs: 117 minutes: ADD: 8/88).

...Il trovatore[a]. La forza del destino[b] – excerpts. [ab]Soloists; [a]Chorus of the Royal Opera House,
Covent Garden; [a]London Philharmonic Orchestra / Vittorio Gui;
[b]Chorus and Orchestra of RAI, Rome / Oliviero de Fabritiis.
Legato Classics mono Ⓜ LCD-173* (two discs: 158 minutes: ADD: 2/94).

...Soloists; Chorus and Orchestra of the Maggio Musicale Fiorentino / Zubin Mehta.
Decca Ⓕ 430 694-2DHO2 (two discs: 132 minutes: DDD: 7/95).

...Soloists; Chorus and Orchestra of La Scala, Milan / Tullio Serafin.
DG Double Ⓜ 445 451-2GX2 (two discs: 126 minutes: ADD: 1/96).

...Il trovatore. Soloists; Chorus and Orchestra of La Scala, Milan / Tullio Serafin.
DG Doubles Ⓜ 453 118-2GTA2 (two discs: 126 minutes: ADD: 3/98).

Further listening ...

...String Quartet in E minor. *Coupled with works by* **Puccini** and **Donizetti** Alberni Quartet.
CRD CRD3366 (5/89).

...Attila. Soloists; Chorus and Orchestra of La Scala, Milan / Riccardo Muti.
EMI CDS7 49952-2 (5/90).

...I due Foscari. Soloists; Austrian Radio Chorus and Symphony Orchestra / Lamberto Gardelli.
Philips 422 426-2PM2 (12/89).

...Oberto, Conte di San Bonifacio. Soloists; London Voices; Academy of St Martin in the Fields /
Sir Neville Marriner. Philips 454 472-2PH2 (8/97).

...I vespri Siciliani. Soloists; Chorus and Orchestra of La Scala, Milan / Riccardo Muti.
EMI CDS7 54043-2 (1/91).

Alfredo Vianna   Brazilian 1898-1975

Suggested listening ...

...Cochichando (arr. Barbosa-Lima). *Coupled with works by various composers.* **Sharon Isbin** (gtr)
with **Gaudencio Thiago de Mello** (perc). Teldec 0630-19899-2 (7/98). *Gramophone Editor's choice.*
See review in the Collections section; refer to the Index.   ⒼⒼ

Pauline Viardot-Garcia   French 1821-1910

Suggested listening ...

...Hai luli!. Havanaise. Les filles de Cadix. *Coupled with works by various composers.* **Cecilia Bartoli**
(mez); **Myung-Whun Chung** (pf). Decca Ⓕ 452 667-2DH (68 minutes: DDD: 12/96). *Gramophone
Editor's record of the month. See review in the Collections section; refer to the Index.*   ⒼⒼⒼ

Tomás Luis de Victoria   Spanish 1548-1611

Victoria Officium defunctorum (1605). **Gabrieli Consort / Paul McCreesh.** Archiv Produktion
Ⓕ 447 095-2AH (60 minutes: DDD: 12/95). Text and translation included. Recorded 1994.
Gramophone Editor's record of the month.   ⒼⒼⒼ
This is a remarkable recording. In some ways it is like a rediscovery, for here is an approach not too
far from Pro Cantione Antiqua at their best and yet that group never recorded the work. That sense
of rediscovery comes in fact as much from the difference between this and the versions by The Tallis

Scholars and Westminster Cathedral Choir (under David Hill): though the latter places the Matins lesson *Taedet animam meam* in a semi-liturgical reconstruction of Lauds, this Gabrieli Consort recording takes a different approach and adds chant to the Requiem Mass itself, thus creating even more of a context for Victoria's magisterial work. We have therefore the Epistle and preceding prayer, the Tract, Sequence, Gospel, Preface, Lord's Prayer and Postcommunion in addition to the polyphony; this also means, for example, that the *Kyrie* is sung nine-fold with alternating chant instead of simply three-fold only in polyphony. One may presume that the chant was taken from a suitable Spanish source by Luis Lozano Virumbrales, an expert in this field and author of the insert-notes together with Paul McCreesh. The performance itself is stately and imposing, with a tremendous homogeneity of sound: the use of an all-male choir, together with the added chant, lends it a tangibly monastic feel, though it would have been a fortunate monastery indeed that had falsettists of this quality. About the performance of the chant there are two points of interest: firstly, that it is doubled, like the polyphony, by a bajón, common Spanish practice at this period, and secondly, that McCreesh is not afraid to have the falsettists singing the chant too. The pace of the polyphony often seems to be unhurried, but it never feels slow. Indeed, in almost every case the polyphonic sections are taken slightly quicker than The Tallis Scholars, and Westminster Cathedral Choir are of course faced with the hugely reverberant acoustics of their home building. From the beginning the singing is involving and incarnate, but the real magic comes nearer the end: from the *Agnus Dei* onwards one feels that the Gabrieli Consort have really got the measure of the music and are allowing it to speak through them. The final great responsory, the "Libera me" is performed with heart stopping power and conviction. The Tallis Scholars approach the music as though it were a concert suite, with no added chant, and in many respects this pays dividends, since they are able to build it up in an almost architectural way, whereas the Westminster choir, though they also add no chant except for the opening Matins lesson, somehow concentrate more on each separate section of the Mass. Of course this works: Victoria's sublime music is indeed conceived architecturally. And yet this is not all; McCreesh's approach shows something else, shows how it would have fitted into and complemented the liturgical framework without ever losing its own internal power and drama (for that of course is what it was intended for). A revelatory disc.

Additional recommendations ...
...Officium defunctorum. **Lôbo** Versa est in luctum. **The Tallis Scholars / Peter Phillips.** Gimell Ⓕ 454 912-2PH (47 minutes: DDD: 9/87). Ⓖ
...Officium defunctorum. **Westminster Cathedral Choir / David Hill.** Hyperion Ⓕ CDA66250 (58 minutes: DDD: 9/87). Ⓖ
...Officium defunctorum. **Magnificat Choir / Philip Cave.** Linn Records Ⓕ CKD060 (52 minutes: DDD: 2/97).

Victoria Officium Hebdomadae Sanctae – Lamentations of Jeremiah. Vexilla Regis. Pange lingua gloriosi. **The Sixteen / Harry Christophers.** Collins Classics Ⓕ 1518-2 (76 minutes: DDD: 5/98). Texts and translations included. Recorded 1997. *Gramophone Editor's choice.*
This is what recording should be about: a project with a vision in which thoughtfully planned programming is allied to excellent performances and recorded sound to flesh out our knowledge of a repertory while at the same time giving great pleasure to the listener. Pleasure may seem an odd word to use in the context of a recording of *Lamentations* and hymns for Holy Week as there is absolutely no sense in which Victoria's music is anything other than emotionally harrowing, especially when sung with the appropriately fierce intensity brought to it by The Sixteen under the direction of Harry Christophers. Vocal scoring, balancing of chords and the sense of tension and release generated by carefully prepared suspensions become crucial components in these spare textures, and all are comprehended superbly well in this recording. The essentially homophonic idiom also inspires much more shaping of phrase and use of dynamic contrasts than is commonly encountered today in performances of sacred polyphony of a more contrapuntal kind. It is noticeable that in the two hymns inserted between the *Lamentations*, the greater contrapuntal complexity and comparatively florid melodic writing of the polyphonic verses results in less shaping, the overlapping movement of the voices having a continuous swell that tends to diffuse such arresting effects. The last two verses of the Passiontide hymn *Vexilla Regis* are, however, no less dramatic than the *Lamentations*: the sixth verse ("O crux ave, spes unica"), which would usually have been sung with the singers kneeling before the Crucifix, is strikingly sustained, while the last verse ("Te summa Deus Trinitas") has a triumphal quality that almost exuberantly communicates the central message of the Passion of Christ. The insert-notes are exemplary. Rush out and buy this beautiful and moving recording.

Victoria Veni Sancte Spiritus[a]. Dum complerentur. Missa Dum complerentur. Popule meus. Vexilla Regis. Veni Creator Spiritus. Pange lingua gloriosi. Lauda Sion[a]. **Westminster Cathedral Choir / James O'Donnell** with [a]**Joseph Cullen** (org). Hyperion Ⓕ CDA66886 (70 minutes: DDD: 9/97). Texts and translations included. Recorded 1996.
Westminster Cathedral Choir here make a special contribution to the music of Tomás Luis de Victoria. The *Missa Dum complerentur*, for Pentecost, is based on Victoria's own motet; he adds an extra voice in the parody Mass setting and draws much on the opening material of the motet as well as its distinctive "Alleluia" sections which ring out like a peal of bells – especially in this excellent performance. Indeed, the motet is finely conceived, with Victoria characteristically responding to the

imagery of the text with changes of texture and pacing within the essentially contrapuntal idiom: a true master. The choir, with its full-bodied sound and well-sustained vocal lines, has, over long years of tradition in singing this particular part of the repertory, achieved an almost intuitive feel for the flow of the music, which is perhaps as near as we'll ever get today to the authentic situation of professional church singers in Rome or the Spanish cathedrals in the sixteenth century. What we'll never know is whether the sonority – in particular the timbre of the boys' voices – resembles anything Victoria might have heard, that distinctive focus and intensity of tone well illustrated by the two Holy Week settings on the disc: the homophonic *Popule meus* and the hymn *Vexilla Regis*. This, and the two Pentecost hymns, are performed *in alternatim* with alternate verses in plainchant and polyphony. This is a superb and compelling disc that adds to our knowledge and appreciation of Victoria's art.

Further listening ...
...Et egressus est. Ecce vidimus eum. Amicus meus. Unus ex discipulis. Eram quasi agnus. Seniores populi. Benedictus Deus Dominus Israel. Vere languores nostros. *Coupled with works by various composers.* **La Colombina.** Accent ACC9394 (8/94).
...Missa O magnum mysterium. Missa Ascendens Christus in altum. Motets – O magnum mysterium. Ascendens Christus. **Westminster Cathedral Choir / David Hill.** Hyperion CDA66190 (9/87).
...Missa O quam gloriosum. Motet – O quam gloriosum. Missa Ave maris stella. **Westminster Cathedral Choir / David Hill.** Hyperion CDA66114 (6/86). ⓖⓖ
...Missa Trahe me post te. Trahe me post te. Alma redemptoris mater. Ave regina coelorum. Regina coeli. Salve regina. Magnificat primi toni. **Westminster Cathedral Choir / James O'Donnell.** Hyperion CDA66738 (68 minutes: DDD: 3/95). *Gramophone Editor's choice.*
...Responsories for Tenebrae. **Westminster Cathedral Choir / David Hill.** Hyperion CDA66304 (7/89).
...Salve regina. Alma Redemptoris mater. Ave Maria, gratia plena. Omnis pulchritudo Domini. *Coupled with* **Palestrina** Missa Ut re mi fa sol la. Ecce, nunc benedicite a 12. **Montreal Studio Ancienne Choir.** Analekta Fleurs de Lys FL2 3120 (4/98).

Johann Vierdanck
German 1605-1646

Suggested listening ...
...Sonata, "Als ich einmal Lust bekam". Sonata a 4. *Coupled with works by various composers.* **Majesties Sagbutts and Cornetts.** Hyperion CDA66847 (11/96). *See review in the Collections section; refer to the Index.*

Louis Vierne
French 1870-1937

Vierne Symphonies – No. 2, Op. 20; No. 3, Op. 28. **Colin Walsh** (org). Priory Ⓟ PRCD446 (72 minutes: DDD: 10/94). Played on the organ of Lincoln Cathedral. Recorded 1992. ⓖⓖⓖ
Here is something out of the ordinary. It's not just that Colin Walsh is an impassioned advocate of the French romantic school or that he possesses a technique which all but takes one's breath away. Neither is it the ravishing Lincoln instrument, glorious though it sounds here in one of Priory's most vivid recordings to date. It's the way Walsh brings the music itself into such sharp focus. Vierne's creation takes centre stage, unobscured either by a player's virtuosity or an organ's enticing allure: the latter something of a rare feat since organ buffs seem to prefer to listen to the instrument rather than what's being played on it. Walsh manages the instrument deftly enough – after all, he knows it as intimately as anyone (and certainly more intimately than Priory's typesetters who have missed out a whole division from the printed specification) – so we never really notice his subtle and skilful registrations, giving all the more impact to those great climactic moments. So often a Vierne symphony can sound like a well-ordered sequence of individual pieces, but here the essential interdependence of the movements is most powerfully demonstrated. The composer's marvellous sense of structure and ingenious architectural designs are shown for the great musical gifts they are.

Additional recommendations ...
...No. 3. *Coupled with works by* **Tournemire** and **Widor** Jeremy Filsell (org). Herald Ⓟ HAVPCD145 (71 minutes: DDD: 3/92). *See review under Tournemire; refer to the Index.* ⓖⓖ
...No. 1 in D minor, Op. 14; No. 3. **Michael Murray** (org). Telarc Ⓟ CD80329 (75 minutes: DDD: 5/94).
...No. 1 in D minor, Op. 14; Nos. 2 and 3; No. 4 in G minor, Op. 32; No. 5 in A minor, Op. 47; No. 6 in B minor, Op. 59. **Ben van Oosten** (org). Dabringhaus und Grimm Ⓜ MDG316 0732-2 (four discs: 230 minutes: DDD: A/97).

Further listening ...
...Les cloches de Hinckley, Op. 55 No. 6. *Coupled with works by various composers.* **Marie-Bernadette Dufourcet** (org). Priory PRCD422 (6/95).
...Pièces de fantaisie. Suite No. 1, Op. 51 – Andantino. *Coupled with works by* **Fauré** and **Séverac** Colm Carey (org). Naxos 8 550765 (9/94). *See review under Fauré; refer to the Index.*
...Triptyque, Op. 58. Pièces en style libre, Op. 31. **Colin Walsh** (org). Priory PRCD319 (3/92).

...Messe solennelle in C sharp minor, Op. 16. Tantum ergo. Ave Maria. *Coupled with works by* **Dupré** and **Widor** Joseph Cullen, Andrew Reid (orgs); **Hyperion Chorus of Baritones; Westminster Cathedral Choir / James O'Donnell.** Hyperion CDA66898 (4/97). 🅖🅖

René Vierne
French 1878-1918

Suggested listening ...
...Six pièces de différents caractères. *Coupled with works by various composers.* **Marie-Bernadette Dufourcet** (org). Priory PRCD422 (6/95). *See review in the Collections section; refer to the Index.*

Henry Vieuxtemps
Belgian 1820-1881

Vieuxtemps Violin Concertos – No. 2 in F sharp minor, Op. 19; No. 3 in A major, Op. 25. **Misha Keylin** (vn); **Janáček Philharmonic Orchestra / Dennis Burkh.** Naxos Ⓢ 8 554114 (57 minutes: DDD: 12/97). Recorded 1995.
By good fortune Naxos have chosen a splendid player to introduce us to Nos. 2 and 3. The Russian artist, Misha Keylin, emigrated to the USA at the age of nine and by 15 was already a soloist at Carnegie Hall. His timbre is rich, with a duskily subtle control of colour, his technique impeccable, and there is the kind of Slavonic flair that can bring these lightweight but masterly concertos fully to life. As the opening ritornello of the Second Concerto immediately demonstrates, Burkh's accompaniments with the leonine Janáček Philharmonic are extremely vivid and supportive, polished too. In the *Andante* Keylin phrases the melody most enticingly, in a heartfelt but never cloying manner and the finale is just as graceful, with the histrionics ever tasteful. The Third Concerto opens with a throbbing, spirited tutti; the solo entry, with its rhythmic snap, is arresting and has an exciting, Paganini-like progress and a dainty secondary theme. The *Adagio* is a darkly eloquent cantilena and the finale, marked *con delicatezza*, the soloist launches into a scintillating rondo, with attractive contrasting episodes. In short one cannot conceive that these two thoroughly diverting concertos could be given a more auspicious CD début. The Naxos recording is first-rate. A genuine bargain.

Further listening ...
...Violin Concerto No. 5 in A minor, Op. 37. *Coupled with works by* **Mendelssohn** and **Mozart** Jascha Heifetz (vn); **London Symphony Orchestra / Sir Malcolm Sargent.** EMI Références mono CDH5 65191-2* (10/94).
...Violin Concerto No. 5 in A minor, Op. 37ᵃ. *Coupled with* **Lalo** Symphonie espagnole, Op. 21ᵇ. **Sarah Chang** (vn); ᵃ**Philharmonia Orchestra,** ᵇ**Royal Concertgebouw Orchestra / Charles Dutoit.** EMI CDC5 55292-2 (5/96). *See review under Lalo; refer to the Index.* Ⓖ
...Fantasia appassionata, Op. 35. Ballade and Polonaise, Op. 38. Chant d'amour. Désespoir. Souvenir. Morceaux de salon – Op. 22: No. 3, Rêverie; No. 4, Tarantelle in A minor; Op. 32: No. 2, Rondino. Feuille d'album, Op. 40 – No. 1, Romance. Hommage à Paganini, Op. 9. Romances sans paroles, Op. 8 – No. 2, Innocence. Souvenir d'Amérique on "Yankee Doodle", Op. 17. **Ruggiero Ricci** (vn); **Marco Vincenzi** (pf). Dynamic CDS112 (1/97).

Heitor Villa-Lobos
Brazilian 1887-1959

Villa-Lobos Bachianas Brasileiras Nos. 2, 4 and 8. **Cincinnati Symphony Orchestra / Jesús López-Cobos.** Telarc Ⓕ CD80393 (70 minutes: DDD: 2/96). Recorded 1995.
Gramophone Editor's choice. Ⓖ
If any parallels existed between Bach and Brazilian idioms, they were largely in Villa-Lobos's mind – even the Fugue in No. 8 of these *Bachianas Brasileiras* is totally un-Bach-like; so anyone coming fresh to these exotically coloured, rather sprawling works should not be misled by false expectations. But fascinating, indeed haunting, in a highly individual way, they are; and the present performances are welcome, all the more since no other version of No. 8 is currently available. In view of the composer's sublime indifference to instrumental practicalities (as, for instance, the feasible length of a trombone *glissando*), his carelessness over detail in his scores, his Micawber-like trust that problems of balance he had created would be sorted out in performance, the chaotic state of the printed scores and orchestral parts of his music (littered as they are with wrong notes and questionable points), and numerous misreadings in past performances, the only half-way reliable yardstick for conductors or critics is the composer's own recordings, made in the 1950s and now preserved in a six-CD box on EMI. Compared to them, the present issue shows a number of differences. Chief of these is the warmer, more generalized sound, with less emphasis on clarity of detail. This works reasonably well in the Preludio of No. 8, where concentration on the melodic line and the adoption of a slower tempo aid the movement's lyricism (likewise the more sentimental approach to the Aria of No. 2); the Aria of No. 8 is unquestionably more poetic and the Dansa of No. 4 lighter; but in the most famous movement, the hilarious and ingenious "Little train of the Caipira" of No. 2, the rasps near the start and the clatter of wheels on the track (evoked by the fiendishly difficult piano part) are far too subdued in favour of the 'big tune'. López-Cobos deals persuasively with knotty questions of balance

such as in the middle section of No. 3's Toccata, and brings to the fore the bell-like araponga bird's cry in No. 4's Coral, but makes less of that movement's jungle screeches. He makes clear the thematic link between the sections of No. 4's Aria, and seeks to overcome the repetitious pattern of its Preludio by taking a faster speed rather than by the wealth of tonal nuance the composer himself introduced. Perhaps such detailed comparisons are superfluous: enjoy, enjoy!

Villa-Lobos Bachianas Brasileiras – No. 4; No. 5[a]; No. 7; No. 9. Chôros No. 10, "Rasga o coração"[b]. [a]**Renée Fleming** (sop); [b]**BBC Singers; New World Symphony / Michael Tilson Thomas.** RCA Victor Red Seal Ⓕ 09026 68538-2 (78 minutes: DDD: 3/97). Recorded 1996.

In his booklet-note, the commentator here calls *Chôros* No. 10 the masterpiece of that quintessentially Brazilian series. It is certainly the most ambitious, with very large orchestral and choral forces in a complex mélange of urban street song (a popular *schottisch* by Medeiros), chattering native Indian chants and bird-song twitterings, of mysterious jungle atmosphere, compulsive ostinato rhythms and virtuoso orchestral effects. The present performance is excellent. The couplings here are illuminating, consisting as they do of more Villa-Lobos – four of his highly individual tributes to Bach's influence. By far the best known of the *Bachianas Brasileiras* is, of course, No. 5, whose Aria demonstrates the composer's ability to spin a haunting long-flowing melody. Renée Fleming is the sweet-toned soloist with the cello section of this accomplished orchestra of young graduates from American conservatoires: warmly lyrical as she is, however, and brilliantly exact in the dartings of the Dansa, her words are not very distinct even in the slow-moving Aria. By his deeply expressive shaping of No. 4's Preludio Tilson Thomas avoids any satiety with its extreme monothematicism, and in the second movement secures coherent continuity despite the (rather loud) insistent interventions of the araponga bird's repeated note. He produces a beautifully poetic tranquillity in the brief Prelude of No. 9 and complete lucidity and rhythmic buoyancy in its Fugue. If that is the most Bachian of the series, the much more substantial No. 7 also has its moments of homage: its first movement has a fine breadth, and its finale is an impressive and serious-minded large-scale fugue that begins quietly and culminates in a grandiose blaze of sound; but the busy Toccata is characteristically and challengingly Brazilian, and the first part of its Giga (before it goes all Hollywood) is delightfully fresh in this invigorating performance.

Villa-Lobos Gênesis. Erosño (Origem do rio Amazonas). Amazonas. Dawn in a tropical forest. **Czecho-Slovak Radio Symphony Orchestra, Bratislava / Roberto Duarte.** Marco Polo Ⓕ 8 223357 (62 minutes: DDD: 3/92). Recorded 1990.

Do not be deterred by the thought of an Eastern European orchestra playing unfamiliar Villa-Lobos. The Czecho-Slovak Radio Orchestra is clearly a very skilled and flexible body, and the conductor Roberto Duarte, a Brazilian authority on Villa-Lobos, has instilled South American colour and rhythmic vitality into his players quite brilliantly. The best of the four works is probably the earliest, *Amazonas*, which was written in 1917. Here, at the age of 30, Villa-Lobos's imagination was extraordinarily fertile, and this early evocation of Brazilian folklore, with its use of unusual instruments and strange orchestral timbres, is remarkably advanced for its date. The short tone poem *Dawn in a tropical forest* is a late work dating from 1953, and this has a more lyrical, more classical style. The remaining two works also come from the last phase in Villa-Lobos's career, and have similar themes. *Gênesis*, written in 1954, is a large-scale symphonic poem and ballet which depicts its enormous subject with all the extravagant colour and use of complex rhythms which were the composer's trademark. *Erosño*, or *The origin of the Amazon*, composed in 1950, is another ambitiously complex work. All four items are captured in faithful, wide-ranging sound.

Additional recommendation ...

...Amazonas. Symphony No. 4, "Victoria". Cello Concerto No. 2[a].
[a]**Andrés Díaz** (vc); **Simón Bolívar Symphony Orchestra, Venezuela / Enrique Diemecke.** Dorian Ⓕ DOR90228 (66 minutes: DDD: 5/97).

Villa-Lobos Quinteto em forma de chôros[a]. Modinha[b]. Bachianas Brasileiras No. 6[c]. Distribuçiño de flôres[b]. Assobio a jato[d]. Chôros No. 2[e]. Canção do amor[b]. Trio for Oboe, Clarinet and Bassoon[f]. **William Bennett** (fl); [ae]**Neil Black** (ob); [a]**Janice Knight** (cor ang); [aef]**Thea King** (cl); [acf]**Robin O'Neill** (bn); [d]**Charles Tunnell** (vc); [b]**Simon Weinberg** (gtr). Hyperion Ⓕ CDA66295 (61 minutes: DDD: 9/89).

If there is one consistent feature in Villa-Lobos's enormous and diverse output, it is his unpredictability. His restless, supercharged mind never tired of experimenting with new sonorities, and he never felt inhibited, in the course of a work, from following unrelated new impulses. This has the effect of making his music at the same time attractive and disconcerting. The multi-sectional Quintet, the most significant item here, is highly complex but extremely entertaining in its quirky way; and it is played with marvellous neatness, finely judged tonal nuances and high spirits. The rarely heard Trio, the earliest work here, is a particularly spiky atonal piece, typical of its period (1921), depending almost entirely on exuberantly thrusting and counter-thrusting rhythm: it calls for virtuosity, and gets it. The sixth of the *Bachianas Brasileiras* (easily the best available recorded performance) is most sensitively shaped, and the second *Chôros*, which makes great demands on the two players both individually and in mutual responsiveness, is outstandingly polished. A disc of outstanding artistry.

Villa-Lobos Bachianas Brasileiras – No. 2: Toccata[a]; No. 4[b]; No. 5[c]. Miniaturas – No. 2, A Viola[d].
Modinhas e Canções, Series I – No. 3, Cantilena[d]. Momoprecoce[e]. Chôros No. 10,
"Rasga o coração"[f]. [c]**Victoria de los Angeles** (sop); [d]**Frederick Fuller** (bar); [e]**Magda Tagliaferro**
(pf); [f]**Chorale des Jeunesses Musicales de France;** [abcef]**French Radio National Orchestra /
Heitor Villa-Lobos** ([d]pf). EMI Composers in Person mono Ⓟ CDC5 55224-2*
(78 minutes: ADD: 6/95). Items marked [ac] from HMV ALP1603 (9/58, recorded 1956),
[b]Columbia 33CX1648 (6/59, recorded 1957), [d]HMV B9700 (12/48), [e]French Columbia FCX346
(1954), [f]FCX603 (1/63. 1957). ⒼⒼ
No one disc could fully illustrate the extent of Villa-Lobos's bewilderingly vast and unruly output's
stylistic diversity; but this one makes a very good attempt. For those encountering him for the first
time the simplest approach is via his purely lyrical side – the two songs so sympathetically sung by
Frederick Fuller, *A Viola* with its gently insistent rumba rhythm and *Cantilena* wending its way above
an unchanging pedal-note before repeating the melody wordlessly. The same wordless treatment is
adopted in the haunting first movement of the *Bachianas Brasileiras* No. 5 for soprano and eight
cellos (which has become Villa-Lobos's best-known piece, thanks partly to commercial exploitation):
the radiance of Victoria de los Angeles's voice more than compensates for the less than tidy ensemble
in places that the composer achieves as conductor. Moving to the non-vocal works, nobody could fail
to enjoy the Toccata from the Second *Bachianas Brasileiras*, a brilliantly vivid sound-picture of a little
country train determinedly and happily chuffing along – as inventive as Honegger's earlier *Pacific 231*
but more fun: the final exhausted long emission of steam cannot but make you laugh. The orchestral
virtuosity which that piece demands reappears in the complex rhythms of the finale of *Bachianas
Brasileiras* No. 4, whose much more straightforward first three movements, however, provide some
clue to the composer's avowed preoccupation with Bach. Villa-Lobos's lifelong interest in children is
illustrated by the noisily high-spirited fantasy *Momoprecoce* (derived from the piano suite *Children's
carnival*): its dedicatee, Magda Tagliaferro, brings to it all the requisite energy and boisterousness. The
newcomer to Villa-Lobos, having weathered its strikingly individual scoring and sometimes strident
dissonances, can now advance to the exotic atmosphere of the heartfelt cry for "Brazilian heart and
Brazilian earth" of the *Chôros* No. 10, which brings into play a chorus chanting against a hail of
staccato syllables: the overall effect is totally unique and immensely exciting. It should be added that
the quality of transfer throughout the disc is bright and clear.
Additional recommendations ...
...Bachianas Brasileiras No. 5[a]. **Canteloube** Chants d'Auvergne. **Dame Kiri Te Kanawa** (sop);
[a]**Lynn Harrell** (vc); **English Chamber Orchestra / Jeffrey Tate.** Double Decca Ⓜ 444 995-2DF2
(two discs: 111 minutes: DDD: 1/96). *See review under Canteloube; refer to the Index.* Ⓖ
...Bachianas Brasileiras No. 5. Modinha. *Coupled with works by various composers.* **Anna Noakes**
(fl); **Gillian Tingay** (hp). ASV White Line Ⓜ CDWHL2101 (76 minutes: DDD: 11/96).
See review in the Collections section; refer to the Index.

Villa-Lobos Missa São Sebastião. Bendita sabedoria. Praesepe (with Ansy Boothroyd, mez).
Cor dulce, cor amabile. Panis angelicus. Sub tuum praesidium. Ave Maria (a 5). Ave Maria (a 6).
Pater noster. Magnificat-alleluia (Elizabeth McCormack, mez)[a]. **Corydon Singers and** [a]**Orchestra /
Matthew Best.** Hyperion Ⓟ CDA66638 (77 minutes: DDD: 8/93). Texts and translations
included.
Any listener not informed in advance and asked to identify the composer of all these religious works
except the Mass (the earliest here) would be most unlikely to think of Villa-Lobos. That larger-than-
life exotic, that extravagantly experimental and boisterous figure, the composer of such chastely
restrained music, the sweetly gentle *Cor dulce*, the mellifluous imitative counterpoint of the first of the
Bendita sabedoria (six brief choral pieces on biblical texts), the controlled fervour of the *Pater noster*?
Even the impressive and grandiose *Magnificat-alleluia* (written in 1958 at the request of Pope Pius XII
to celebrate Lourdes Year) gives no hint of its country of origin. The one clue here might be that, of
the two *Ave Marias*, the (earlier) five-part setting is in Portuguese. It is only the Mass that reveals all.
Amid its austere style and purely diatonic, contrapuntal idiom the *Sanctus* suddenly seems to come
from a different background: then one remembers that Sebastian is the patron saint of Rio de Janeiro;
and looking into the score one finds that the liturgical heading of each movement is followed by a
local one, the final *Agnus Dei* bearing the subtitle "Sebastian, protector of Brazil". This programme,
all of unaccompanied music except for the *Magnificat-alleluia*, should not be listened to as a
continuity if some feeling of sameness is to be avoided: the Corydon Singers are most efficient in all
they do, even if their tone is not the most seductive, but the outstanding performance is of the Mass.
Further listening ...
...Dança frenética. Danças características africanas. Dança dos mosquitos. Rudepoema.
Bratislava Radio Symphony Orchestra / Roberto Duarte. Marco Polo 8 223552 (2/95).
...The Discovery of Brazil – Suites Nos. 1-4. **Slovak Philharmonic Chorus; Slovak Radio Symphony
Orchestra / Roberto Duarte.** Marco Polo 8 223551 (8/94). *Gramophone Editor's choice.* Ⓖ
...String Quartets Nos. 2 and 7. **Danubius Quartet.** Marco Polo 8 223394 (2/95). ⒼⒼ
...String Quartet No. 6. *Coupled with works by various composers.* **Arthur Gleghorn** (fl); **Mitchell
Lurie** (cl); **Ann Mason Stockton** (hp); **Hollywood Quartet; Concert Arts Strings / Felix Slatkin.**
Testament mono SBT1053* (3/95). *See review in the Collections section; refer to the Index.* ⒼⒼ

...String Quartets Nos. 7 and 15. **Latin American Quartet.** Dorian DOR90246 (1/98).
...Caixinha de música quebrada. Próle do bébé, Book 1. Cirandinhas. Carnaval das crianças.
Marcelo Bratke (pf). Olympia OCD455 (2/95).
...Próle do bébé, Book 1. *Coupled with works by various composers.* **Artur Rubinstein** (pf).
RCA Victor Gold Seal 09026 61445-2 (10/93). *See review in the Collections section;*
refer to the Index.   ⒼⒼⒼ
...Rudepoêma. Cirandas. **Alma Petchersky** (pf). ASV CDDCA959 (12/96).
...Forest of the Amazon. **Renée Fleming** (sop); **Moscow Institute Male-Voice Choir;**
Moscow Radio Symphony Orchestra / Alfred Heller. Consonance 810012 (5/96).

Pierre Villette
French 1926-1969

Suggested listening ...
...Attende Domine. Hymne à la Vierge. O magnum mysterium. O sacrum convivium. Salve regina.
Coupled with works by **Bax Rodolfus Choir / Ralph Allwood** with **Christopher Hughes** (org).
Herald HAVPCD176 (9/95). *See review under Bax; refer to the Index.*

Gilbert Vinter
British 1909-1969

Suggested listening ...
...Portuguese Party. *Coupled with works by various composers.* **Pro Arte Orchestra / George Weldon.**
EMI British Composers CDM5 66537-2 (1/98). *See review in the Collections section;*
refer to the Index.

Robert de Visée
French c1660-1725

Suggested listening ...
...Tombeau des Mesdemoiselles de Visée. *Coupled with works by various composers.*
Mauricio Buraglia (theorbo) Auvidis Astrée E8592 (12/96). ✍
Gramophone Editor's choice. See review under Lalande; refer to the Index.   Ⓖ

Antonio Vivaldi
Italian 1678-1741

Vivaldi Bassoon Concertos – C major, RV472; D minor, RV482; E minor, RV484; F major, RV491;
G major, RV494; G minor, RV495; A minor, RV499. **Klaus Thunemann** (bn); **I Musici.**
Philips Ⓕ 446 066-2PH (57 minutes: DDD: 2/96). Recorded 1994.
Vivaldi's distinctive individuality is in full flower in the rich invention which characterizes the tuttis of
the fast movements of his bassoon concertos; and in the slow movements, as so often elsewhere, he
proves himself a poet with the most delicate of sensibilities. In all of them, he seems to have been
inspired by the colour and range of the instrument itself, exploring almost every possibility available
to him in the bassoon of his day and, like Rameau in France, writing especially rewardingly for it in
the tenor register. Thunemann, of course, plays an instrument of present-day manufacture, in keeping
with the modern string instruments of I Musici; but he makes a very beautiful sound indeed,
capitalizing on the inherent virtues of up-to-date technology. To all but the most committed
Vivaldians only one of the seven concertos here may seem at all familiar. That is the atmospheric
Concerto in E minor (RV484) with its undulating first movement tuttis inspired, one might suspect,
by Venetian waters. Thunemann instils life into every bar of his interpretation, performing dazzling
feats of athleticism apparently with the utmost of ease, while at the same time giving thought to
ornamentation. Not a note is either out of tune or misplaced and, in slow movements, many of which
possess beguiling lyrical charm, Thunemann reveals himself as a musician of great sensitivity. The
Largo of the first concerto on the disc (RV491) is a striking example. Readers familiar with Vivaldi's
sacred vocal music will recognize its derivation in part from a passage to be found both in his
Magnificat(RV610) and his *Kyrie* (RV587). In the present context Vivaldi imbues an already arresting
harmonic pattern with a drowsy, almost dreamlike fantasy in which the bassoon writing, treated here
with an affecting improvisatory freedom, ranges widely with some striking intervals against sustained,
softly modulating strings. It's a brief moment of magic.

Vivaldi Bassoon Concertos – C major, RV474; F major, RV489; A minor, RV498. Chamber
Concertos – F major, RV571; G minor, RV576; G minor, RV577. **Danny Bond** (bn); **Academy
of Ancient Music / Christopher Hogwood.** L'Oiseau-Lyre Ⓕ 436 867-2OH
(58 minutes: DDD: 4/95). ✍ Recorded 1992.   Ⓖ
One of the mysteries surrounding Vivaldi's 37 complete bassoon concertos is that they are so difficult;
recordings tended to prove the point – they *are* tough nuts. But here Danny Bond surmounts every
obstacle with rounded tone, secure intonation, every note clearly played, with musicality to match that

of his colleagues – and on a period bassoon to boot. The other three works are *concerti grossi* (*"con molti strumenti"*) of which RV571, the most virtuosic, has no other listed recording. The Concertos, RV576 and 577 were, as their large wind band proclaims, written for the ample resources of the Dresden orchestra. All the soloists are on superb form, the ensemble is spirited and beautifully balanced – as is the recording thereof. A wholly delightful disc.

Vivaldi Cello Concertos – C minor, RV402; D minor, RV406; G major, RV414. Sonatas – A minor, RV44; E flat major, RV39; G minor, RV42. **Christophe Coin** (vc); **Academy of Ancient Music / Christopher Hogwood** (hpd). L'Oiseau-Lyre Ⓕ 433 052-2OH (67 minutes: DDD: 1/92). 🎹 Recorded 1990. 🅶🅶

Vivaldi wrote rewardingly for the cello as the music on this issue demonstrates. Christophe Coin's feeling for dance rhythms, his clear articulation and musical phrasing and his sharp ear for detail bring the concertos and sonatas alive in an infectious way. He is both firmly and imaginatively supported in the sonatas by a fine continuo group, and in the concertos by the strings of the Academy of Ancient Music. In the sonatas Christopher Hogwood varies the colour of the accompaniments by moving between harpsichord and organ while cello and baroque guitar add further variety and support. In the concertos, fast movements are characterized by vigorous, idiomatic passagework for the solo instrument punctuated by pulsating Vivaldian rhythms in the tuttis. In the slow movements, richly endowed with lyricism, the expressive intensity of the music is, on occasion, almost startling, revealing Vivaldi as a composer capable of far greater affective gestures than he is often given credit for. This music was intended to move the spirit, to appeal to the senses, and it seldom, if ever, fails to do so.

Additional recommendations ...

...Cello Concertos – C minor, RV402; D major, RV403; D minor, RV406; F major, RV412; G major, RV414; A minor, RV422; B minor, RV424. Ofra Harnoy (vc); **Toronto Chamber Orchestra / Paul Robinson**. RCA Victor Red Seal Ⓕ RD60155 (73 minutes: DDD: 4/90).

...Cello Concertos – D major, RV404; D minor, RV407; F major, RV411; G minor, RV417; A minor, RV420. Concerto for Violin, Cello and Strings in F major, "Il Proteo ò sia il mondo al rovescio", RV544[a]. **Ofra Harnoy** (vc); [a]**Igor Oistrakh** (vn); **Toronto Chamber Orchestra / Paul Robinson**. RCA Victor Red Seal Ⓕ 09026 61578-2 (59 minutes: DDD: 1/94).

...Cello Concertos, Volume 1 – C major, RV398; C major, RV399; RV404; D minor, RV406; F major, RV410; F major, RV412; A minor, RV419. **Raphael Wallfisch** (vc); **City of London Sinfonia / Nicholas Kraemer** (hpd/org). Naxos Ⓢ 8 550907 (57 minutes: DDD: 1/96).

...Cello Concertos, Volume 3 – RV402; D major, RV403; D minor, RV407; E minor, RV409; A minor, RV418; B flat major, RV423; B minor, RV424. **Raphael Wallfisch** (vc); **City of London Sinfonia / Nicholas Kraemer** (hpd/org). Naxos Ⓢ 8 550909 (54 minutes: DDD: 1/96).

...Cello Concertos, Volume 4 – D minor, RV405; RV411; G major, RV414; G minor, RV416; G minor, RV417; RV420; A minor, RV421. **Raphael Wallfisch** (vc); **City of London Sinfonia / Nicholas Kraemer** (hpd/org). Naxos Ⓢ 8 550910 (61 minutes: DDD: 1/96).

...Cello Concertos – A minor, RV418[b]; E flat major, RV408[b]; G minor, RV416[b]; A minor, RV419[b]; G major, RV413[b]. Concerto for Violin, Cello and Strings in B flat major, RV547[ac]. **Ofra Harnoy** (vc); [a]**Igor Oistrakh** (vn); **Toronto Chamber Orchestra /** [b]**Richard Stamp**, [c]**Paul Robinson**. RCA Victor Red Seal Ⓕ 09026 68228-2 (63 minutes: DDD: 12/97).

Vivaldi Cello Concerto in A minor, RV422[c]. Violin Concerto in D minor, Op. 4 No. 8[b]. String Concertos – C major, RV117; E minor, RV134; G major, RV151, "Alla rustica". Amor, hai vinto, RV683[a]. Cessate, omai cessate, RV684[a]. [a]**Sara Mingardo** (mez); [b]**Francesca Vicari** (vn); [c]**Luigi Piovano** (vc); **Concerto Italiano / Rinaldo Alessandrini** (hpd). Opus 111 Ⓕ OPS30-181 (60 minutes: DDD: 11/97). 🎹 Recorded 1996. Texts and translations included.
Gramophone Editor's choice.

This thoughtfully and attractively devised programme by Rinaldo Alessandrini and Concerto Italiano breaks up a sequence of five well contrasted concertos with two of Vivaldi's chamber cantatas. The two vocal pieces are both for alto with divided violins, viola and continuo; and their subject matter, dealt with in the customary pattern of two alternating recitatives and arias, concerns the efficacy of Cupid's arrows on those incredibly susceptible denizens of Arcadia. Sara Mingardo enlivens this music at every turn. Her voice is warm in tone, evenly projected and, in a pastoral setting where the cruel pangs of love are felt in almost every bar, appropriately anguished. The chamber cantatas are still among Vivaldi's better kept secrets and there is much that satisfies heart and mind alike. Of the five concertos three are *concerti a quattro*, or strings without soloist; in the solo concertos cellist Luigi Piovano and violinist Francesca Vicari, who also leads Concerto Italiano, are fluently stylish and technically assured. Like Alessandrini and his ensemble, they bring plenty of graceful gesture and effective articulation to the music. A most satisfying recital of Vivaldi's music, both on account of interpretation and for the window it opens on to the composer's widely ranging expressive vocabulary.

Vivaldi Chamber Concertos – D major, RV93. D major, RV94. F major, RV98, "La tempesta di mare". G minor, RV104, "La notte". G minor, RV107, A minor, RV108. F major, RV442. Trio Sonata in D minor, RV63. **Il Giardino Armonico Ensemble.** Teldec Ⓕ 4509-91852-2 (67 minutes: DDD: 7/94). 🎹 Recorded 1990-1992. 🅶

There are baroque groups that are frankly dull and there are others on whom stylistic felicity sits naturally and gracefully. Il Giardino Armonico, an 11-strong group of young Italians, is one of the best. Italy, the birthplace of the baroque, has been curiously slow in coming forward with a specialized unit such as this, but the wait has been worthwhile; Il Giardino Armonico are as Italian as the music itself – brightly coloured, individualistic, confident, stylish, arrestingly decorated, bubbling with enthusiasm and ... add your own adjectives. The only un-Italian thing about them is their collective unanimity! Set these performances against any others in the catalogue and, with no detriment to the others, the differences are likely to deal you a blow to the solar plexus. Any sneaking fear that such unbridled *élan* leads to a uniformly vigorous approach is unfounded; equally 'Italian' is their wide dynamic range, dramatically exploited in RV104 and RV63, and all calls for serenity are answered. The recording is as bright and clear as the music.

Additional recommendations ...
...Chamber Concertos – A minor, RV86; C major, RV88; F major, RV99; G minor, RV103; G minor, RV105; G minor, RV107. Sonata for Recorder, Bassoon and Continuo in A minor, RV86. **Philidor Ensemble.** Philips Ⓕ 434 995-2PH (53 minutes: DDD: 9/93).
...Trio Sonatas – G minor, RV85[a]; C major, RV82[b]. Double Concerto for Viola d'amore, Lute and Orchestra in D minor, RV540[c]. Chamber Concerto in D major, RV93[d]. **Rolf Lislevand** (lte); **Manfred Kraemer** ([abd]vn; [c]va d'amore); [cd]**Pablo Valetti**, [c]**Brigitte Täubl**, [c]**Eva Posvanecz** (vns); [c]**Laura Johnson** (va); [c]**Lorenz Duftschmid** (violone); [c]**Balázs Máté** (vc); **Béatrice Pornon**, [c]**Brian Feehan** (theorbos); **Eduardo Eguez** (gtr); **Guido Morini** (org). Auvidis Astrée Ⓕ E8587 (40 minutes: DDD: 4/97). ✍

Vivaldi Concertos for Two Violins and Strings – C major, RV505; D major, RV511; A minor, RV523 (Micaela Comberti, vn). Concerto for Two Cellos and Strings in G minor, RV531 (Jane Coe, David Watkin, vcs). Concerto for Two Oboes and Strings in D minor, RV535 (Anthony Robson, Catherine Latham, obs). Concerto for Two Violins, Oboe and Strings in C major, RV554. **Collegium Musicum 90 / Simon Standage** (vn). Chandos Chaconne Ⓕ CHAN0528 (65 minutes: DDD: 3/93). ✍ Recorded 1991.

It was natural, with so many talented young ladies available at the Pietà, that Vivaldi should have written a large number of concertos with two or more soloists. More than two dozen are for two violins and most remain unrecorded; RV505 and 511 are both mature works, the former leaning toward *galant* style and the latter 'unified' by elements that are common to its outer movements. RV554, originally a triple concerto for violin, oboe and organ, was rewritten by Vivaldi for oboe and two violins, in which latter form it is given in this recording. The Concerto for two oboes, RV535, is 'Corellian' in its four-movement *da chiesa* form and in its 'conversations' between the soloists and the *ripieno* strings – a Vivaldian rarity. If Vivaldi wrote a more eloquently pathetic melody than that of the *Largo* of the Double Cello Concerto, RV531, it is hard to bring it to mind; it is an early work – why did he never return to that most rewarding of media? Collegium Musicum 90 field a modest string band, which adds leanness of sound to their other virtues of stylishness and crispness of ensemble. Excellent oboe soloists contribute to the allure of this recording.

Vivaldi Concertos – G major, RV151, "Alla rustica"; B flat major for Violin and Oboe, RV548; G major for Two Violins, RV516; A minor for Oboe, RV461; G major for Two Mandolins, RV532; C major, RV558. **The English Concert / Trevor Pinnock.** Archiv Produktion Ⓕ 415 674-2AH (53 minutes: DDD: 9/86). ✍ Ⓖ

The *Concerto con molti stromenti*, RV558, calls for a plethora of exotic instruments and Vivaldi's inventiveness, everywhere apparent, seems to know no bounds. The vigorous melodies have splendid verve whilst the slow movements are no less exciting. The concertos which employ plucked instruments, are particularly entrancing to the ear – here is virtuosity indeed, with Pinnock sensibly opting for an organ continuo to emphasize the difference between the plucked strings and the bowed. The Double Mandolin Concerto, RV532, is beautifully played with a real build-up of tension in the tuttis. The playing of The English Concert is affectionate and rhythmically precise and the recording is good, with the gentler sounding instruments well brought out of the fuller textures.

Additional recommendation ...
...Concertos – C major, RV555[a]; C major, RV556 "per la Solennità di S Lorenzo". C major, RV558; C major, RV559; C major, RV560; B flat major, RV579, "Concerto funebre"[a]. **Ensemble Matheus / Jean-Christophe Spinosi** ([a]vn). Pierre Verany Ⓕ PV796023 (59 minutes: DDD: 7/96).

Vivaldi Concerto for Four Violins and Strings in D minor, RV549[abcf]. Cello Concertos[d] – G major, RV413; A minor, RV418. Concerto for Violin, Cello and Strings in B flat major, RV547[df]. Concerto for Two Violins, Two Cellos and Strings in G major, RV575[adef]. String Concertos – C major, RV117; E minor, RV134; F minor, RV143; A major, RV159. [a]**Stephen Marvin**, [b]**Chantal Rémillard**, [c]**Cynthia Roberts** (vns); [d]**Anner Bylsma**, [e]**Christina Mahler** (vcs); **Tafelmusik / Jeanne Lamon** ([f]vn). Sony Classical Vivarte Ⓕ SK48044 (66 minutes: DDD: 9/92). ✍ Recorded 1990. Ⓖ Ⓖ

The Canadian period-instrument group Tafelmusik has been building up an impressive discography of music ranging from Corelli to Mozart. Here the players address themselves to Vivaldi in a first-rate recording of concertos for various combinations of strings. Though Vivaldi himself was a violinist he wrote for almost every other instrument of his day with informed skill. One of those to benefit was the cello which features as a solo instrument to a greater or lesser extent in five of the concertos in this programme. The soloist is the Dutch virtuoso Anner Bylsma whose animated playing generates a feeling of excitement and spontaneity by no means easily captured on disc. If he has a fault then it is that he is too often attracted by breakneck tempos and it is that which detracts from the opening movement of the G major Concerto (RV413). Apart from that one minor criticism the disc is one to be treasured not only for the excellence of the playing but also for the judicious choice of repertory. The Concerto in G major for two violins, two cellos and strings (RV575) is a beautifully crafted work with notably expressive writing for the solo instruments. The four concertos for ripieno strings, in which Vivaldi foreshadows the early classical symphonists, provide a rewarding contrast with the remaining programme and are played here with accomplishment and affection.

Additional recommendations ...

...Concertos – RV575[f]; Strings in G minor, RV156; Oboe and Strings in C major, RW449[a]; Bassoon and Strings in F major, RV485[b]; Strings in B flat major, RV166; Violin, Two Recorders, Two Oboes and Strings in G minor, RV577[d], "per l'orchestra di Dresda"; Piccolo and Strings in C major, RV444[e] [de]**Peter Holtslag**, [d]**Catherine Latham** (recs); [ad]**Paul Goodwin**, [d]**Lorraine Wood** (obs); [b]**Alberto Grazzi** (bn); [df]**Peter Hanson**, [f]**Walter Reiter** (vns); [f]**Jane Coe**, [f]**David Watkin** (vcs); **The English Concert / Trevor Pinnock.**
Archiv Production Ⓟ 445 839-2AH (59 minutes: DDD: 10/95). ✍

...Cello Concertos, Volume 2 – C major, RV400; C minor, RV401; E flat major, RV408; RV413; A minor, RV422. Concerto for Two Cellos and Strings in G minor, RV531[a]. [a]**Keith Harvey, Raphael Wallfisch** (vcs); **City of London Sinfonia / Nicholas Kraemer** (hpd/org).
Naxos Ⓢ 8 550908 (57 minutes: DDD: 1/96).

...Concertos – RV575; RV577. Chamber Concerto in D major, RV95, "La Pastorella". String Concerto in C major, RV114. Flute Concertos, Op. 10 – No. 2 in G minor, RV439, "La notte". Concerto for Multiple Instruments, "per la Solennità di S Lorenzo" in C major, RV556. **Taverner Players / Andrew Parrott.** Virgin Classics Veritas Ⓜ VER5 61275-2 (58 minutes: DDD: 9/96). ✍

Vivaldi Double Concerto for Two Oboes and Strings in D minor, RV535. Concertos for Multiple Instruments – D major, RV562; A major, RV552, "per eco in lontano"; F major, RV568; F major, RV569; G minor, RV577, "per l'orchestra di Dresda". **Philharmonia Baroque Orchestra / Nicholas McGegan.** Reference Recordings Ⓟ RRCD77 (72 minutes: DDD: 9/97). ✍ Recorded 1996.
Here is Vivaldi-playing with a commendably light, athletic touch. It is so easy to make a meal out of his orchestral tuttis yet these performances inspire the music with expressive delicacy and rhythmic vitality. The programme is a colourful one of concertos for a variety of instruments, wind and strings, in various combinations. Apart from occasional instances of predictable passagework, present above all in some of the wind writing, this music is engaging on many different levels. Slow movements such as the wonderfully free violin fantasy of RV562 reveal the exhilarating flights of fancy of which Vivaldi was capable, while the profusion of alluring inflexions present in fast and slow movements alike, makes strong appeal to the senses. Vivaldi was no stranger to the art of parody and, in the opening movement of RV568, we find him introducing sensuous, sighing quaver motifs present in the finale of the *Concerto a due Cori per la Santissima Assenzione di Maria Vergine* (RV535). This kind of approach to Vivaldi's music greatly enlivens and refreshes its innate character. The disc is superbly recorded, allowing us to revel in every sonorous detail of solo and continuo playing alike.

Vivaldi Double and Triple Concertos – Two Cellos and Strings in G minor, RV531; Violin, Cello and Strings in F major, RV544, "Il Proteo ò sia il mondo rovescio"; Three Violins and Strings in F major, RV551; Violin and Strings in A major, RV552, "violine per eco in lontano"; Violin, Two Cellos and Strings in C major, RV561; Two Violins, Two Cellos and Strings in D major, RV564. **Christophe Coin** (vc); **Il Giardino Armonico Ensemble / Giovanni Antonini.** Teldec Das Alte Werk Ⓟ 4509-94552-2 (64 minutes: DDD: 8/95). Recorded 1994. Ⓖ
Gramophone Editor's choice. Gramophone Award Winner 1996.
This is a strong programme which almost unfailingly presents the Venetian composer in his most colourful clothing. Though Vivaldi often wrote imaginatively for pairs of wind instruments his musical ideas were of necessity confined by their technical limitations. With violins and cellos, on the other hand, he was better able to extend his creative faculties, which resulted in music of more sustained interest. This is certainly true of the two concertos which he wrote for two violins, two cellos and strings, one of them (RV564) included here. Making an even rarer appearance on disc is a Concerto in F major for violin and cello (RV544), the least well known of three such works from Vivaldi's pen. Two versions of this concerto exist, the other (RV572) containing additional parts for pairs of flutes and oboes. Both carry the engaging title *Il Proteo ò sia il mondo al rovescio*. Infrequently performed, too, is a C major piece for violin, two cellos and strings (RV561), though the characteristically Vivaldian ritornello of the opening movement may recall other contexts in the minds of listeners. The three remaining works are fairly mainstream Vivaldi: the G minor Concerto for two cellos (RV531), the F major Concerto for three violins (RV551) and the A major Concerto for two violins, one of them functioning as an echo, the *violine per eco in lontano* (RV552). From this, readers will infer a pleasing variety of texture and, within the limits of a purely string programme, colour. Il Giardino Armonico have thought carefully about the latter, ringing the changes in the

keyboard continuo between organ and harpsichord, and introducing a theorbo, too. But what makes this disc a real winner is the exhilarating character of the playing, both solo and ripieno. Playing of vitality and lyricism brings Vivaldi's music to life in a thrilling manner. Indeed, the integrity and musicianly character of these performances is in no small measure heightened by the presence of Christophe Coin. Fine music, fine playing and a fine recording. An outstanding issue.

Vivaldi L'estro armonico, Op. 3. **Academy of Ancient Music / Christopher Hogwood.**
L'Oiseau-Lyre Florilegium Ⓜ 414 554-2OH2 (two discs: 96 minutes: DDD: 1/86). ✍
From D245D2 (12/81).
This set of Concertos is arranged as a display of variety, and ordered in a kaleidoscopic way that would maintain interest were it to be played in its entirety. These works are often played with an inflated body of *ripieno* (orchestral) strings, but in this recording they are played as Vivaldi intended them; only four violins are used. The contrast does not come from antiphony or weight of numbers but is provided through the *tutti* versus episodic passages. One could not assemble a more distinguished 'cast' than that of the AAM in this recording, showing clearly just why this music is best played on period instruments, by specialists in baroque style, who are not afraid to add a little embellishment here and there. Performances and recording are splendid. This is required listening.
Additional recommendation ...
...**Roberto Michelucci** (vn); **I Musici.** Philips Ⓜ 426 932-2PM2 (two discs: ADD: 7/91). ✍

Vivaldi Six Flute Concertos, Op. 10. **Patrick Gallois** (fl); **Orpheus Chamber Orchestra.**
DG Ⓕ 437 839-2GH (49 minutes: DDD: 5/94). Recorded 1992. *Gramophone Editor's choice.* Ⓖ
Patrick Gallois is a player of agility and sensitivity, an intelligent artist who can make his metal flute speak with all the subtlety of varied articulation and tone colour that some of us had come to assume was only possible on the wooden baroque instrument. These are deliciously light performances, in the best sense of the word; plenty of air allowed in, sparing and thoughtful use of vibrato, and above all an infectious bounce to the music-making in general. Gallois's sunny approach is matched by the excellent string players of the Orpheus Chamber Orchestra, whose stunning unanimity of ensemble, crispness of attack and sheer concentration-level once again make it hard to believe that they operate without a conductor. And both soloist and orchestra are equally responsive, too, to the uniquely tranquil beauties of the Vivaldian slow movement.

Vivaldi Oboe Concertos – C major, RV447[b]; F major, RV457[a]; A minor, RV461[a]; A minor, RV463[b]; D minor, RV535[ab]. Concerto for Two Clarinets, Two Oboes and Strings in C major, RV559[abc].
[a]**Stephen Hammer,** [b]**Frank de Bruine** (obs); [c]**Eric Hoeprich,** [c]**Antony Pay** (cls); **Academy of Ancient Music / Christopher Hogwood.** L'Oiseau-Lyre Ⓕ 433 674-2OH
(60 minutes: DDD: 7/93). ✍ Recorded 1991.
This delightful miscellany of concertos by Vivaldi for one and two oboes – in a single instance, here, they are joined by a pair of clarinets – confirms Stephen Hammer as one of the very finest baroque oboe players around. He and Christopher Hogwood have achieved a happy partnership which realizes on the one hand the exuberant vitality of Vivaldi's rhythms, and on the other the rich seam of fantasy running through so much of his music. Few if any of Vivaldi's 18 or so surviving solo concertos for the instrument are disappointing. Stephen Hammer and Frank de Bruine have picked four of the best constructed and most alluring of them, taking two concertos each. They join forces in the D minor Concerto for two oboes, and are further joined by Eric Hoeprich and Antony Pay for one of Vivaldi's two concertos for two oboes and two clarinets. The latter piece is effectively written with the focus on the contrasting sonorities of the single and double reed families. Hammer negotiates the solo writing with consummate skill, athletic, precise in tuning and articulation and tasteful in his ornamentation and the remainder comes over with comparable panache. Both oboists unfailingly bring out the poetry in the music with sensibility and restraint. Fine recorded sound.

Vivaldi Oboe Concertos – C major, RV447; C major, RV450; D major, RV453; A minor, RV461; A minor, RV463. Concerto for Violin and Oboe in B flat major, RV548. **Douglas Boyd** (ob);
[a]**Marieke Blankestijn** (vn); **Chamber Orchestra of Europe.** DG Ⓕ 435 873-2GH
(59 minutes: DDD: 5/93). Recorded 1991. ⒼⒼ
As well as being an inspired composer for his own instrument – the violin – Vivaldi could equally turn his hand to concertos for a great many other instruments. One of the principal beneficiaries of his skill was the oboe, for which he wrote 17 solo concertos, three for two oboes and another for oboe and violin. In this virtuoso programme the oboist, Douglas Boyd, has chosen five of the solo oboe concertos together with the more modestly conceived but no less captivating Concerto in B flat for oboe and violin. The oboe concertos have been selected discerningly, not only for their musical interest but also, it would seem, with an eye to their rarity value on the concert platform. Boyd, playing a modern oboe, gives fluent, sensitively shaped performances and is supported in a lively manner by the strings of the Chamber Orchestra of Europe. Boyd is expressive in slow movements – they almost invariably possess considerable lyrical appeal – and athletic in faster ones; and he needs to be, for Vivaldi seldom showed mercy on his soloists. From among the many beautiful movements here the *Larghetto* of the Concerto in A minor (RV461) stands out and may be ranked among Vivaldi's happiest creations for the oboe. Fine recorded sound.

Vivaldi Sinfonia for Strings in G major, RV149. Concertos for Violin and Strings, Op. 8 – No. 5 in E flat major, RV253, "La tempesta di mare"; No. 6 in C major, RV108, "Il piacere". Double Concerto for Viola d'amore, Lute and Strings in D minor, RV540. Concertos for Multiple Instruments – A major, RV552, "per eco in lontano"; C major, RV558. **Academy of Ancient Music / Andrew Manze** (vn). Harmonia Mundi ℗ HMU90 7230 (65 minutes: DDD: 4/98). ✍ Recorded 1996.   ❷❸

In one respect or another all the pieces here are vintage Vivaldi and, taken together, they offer a fair conspectus of his expressive range, his feeling for instrumental colour and his originality. Three of the four works performed have become firm favourites among twentieth-century audiences: the Concertos for viola d'amore and lute (RV540), for violin, echo violins and strings (RV552) and *con molti istromenti* (RV558). The fourth item, a wonderfully spirited *Sinfonia* (RV149), Vivaldi wrote as an introduction to a serenata, now lost, by another composer. The performances are splendid. Manze has a pleasing awareness of the inherent poesy and fantasy in Vivaldi's music and has the technique to make the most of it. *La tempesta di mare* is particularly enjoyable and the tenderly expressive Concerto for viola d'amore and lute – the gently swung rhythm of the sublime *Largo* is as pleasing as Manze's ornamented repeats – but readers are unlikely to be disappointed by anything here. The orchestra are generally on good form, responsive to Vivaldi and Manze alike. These aspects can be savoured above all in the C major Concerto with its treble recorders, tenor chalumeaux, mandolins, theorbos, violins, cello and string tutti. Vivaldi was clearly intent on showing off the diverse, multicoloured musical talents of his pupils in this rhythmically infectious piece. In summary, this is a delightful, well-conceived programme, executed with refinement of taste and technique.

Vivaldi String Concertos – C major, RV117; C minor, RV118; D major, RV123; D minor, RV128; F major, RV136; F minor, RV143; G major, RV146; A major, RV159; A major, RV160; B flat major, RV163, "Conca". **I Musici.** Philips ℗ 438 876-2PH (55 minutes: DDD: 5/94). Recorded 1992.

Here is a generous and varied selection from among the concertos which Vivaldi wrote for strings without soloist. He composed over 40 such pieces of which ten are included here. Anyone who still thinks that one Vivaldi concerto sounds much the same as another should address himself to these vital, often forward-looking pieces. They are full of striking contrasts and ideas which point strongly in the direction of the early symphony and the tautly constructed fugues at the conclusion of the Concerto in D major (RV123) and the beginning of the Concerto in F minor (RV143) are but two reminders of how effective a contrapuntist Vivaldi could be if he so wished. I Musici give a lively view of these engaging concertos with tidy ensemble and good intonation and should disappoint only those who no longer find enjoyment in listening to baroque repertory played on modern instruments.

Additional recommendations ...
...C major, RV114; RV118; C minor, RV120; RV128; E minor, RV133; E minor, RV134; RV143; G major, RV151, "Alla rustica"; G minor, RV152; G minor, RV157; A major, RV158; "Conca"; B flat major, RV167. Sinfonias for Strings – C major, RV116; E major, RV132; F major, RV137; F major, RV140; G major, RV146; B minor, RV168. **I Solisti Veneti / Claudio Scimone.** Erato ℗ 4509-96382-2 (two discs: 127 minutes: ADD/DDD).   ❷❸

...C major, RV113; C major, RV114; D minor, RV127; F major, RV138; G major, RV151, "Alla rustica"; G minor, RV153; G minor, RV156; G minor, RV157; A minor, RV161; B flat major, RV167. **Accademia I Filarmonici / Alberto Martini** (vn). Naxos ⑤ 8 553742 (57 minutes: DDD: 8/97).

Vivaldi String Concertos – C minor, RV761; D minor, RV129, "Concerto madrigalesco"; G minor, RV517[a]; B flat major, RV547[b]; C minor, RV202; E flat major, RV130, "Sonata al santo sepolcro". Sinfonia in B minor, RV169, "Sinfonia al santo sepolcro". [a]**Adrian Chamorro** (vn); [b]**Maurizio Naddeo** (vc); **L'Europa Galante / Fabio Biondi** (vn). Opus 111 ℗ OPS30-9004 (52 minutes: DDD: 9/91). ✍ Recorded 1990.   ❷❸

This invigorating programme contains well-known and less well-known concertos by Vivaldi. The performances sparkle with life and possess an irresistible spontaneity. The Concertos for one and two violins (RV761 and RV202) are comparative rarities and are played with agility and insight by the soloist director Fabio Biondi and his alert and responsive ensemble. Biondi himself is capable of light and articulate bowing and has a natural feeling for graceful turns of phrase. Vivaldi's virtuoso writing occasionally finds chinks in his armour but with enlightened music-making of this order it matters little. Everywhere Vivaldi's infectious rhythms are tautly controlled and the music interpreted with character and conviction. Perhaps the highlight of the disc is the Concerto in B flat for violin and cello. Outer movements are crisply articulated and played with almost startling energy while the poignant lyricism of the *Andante* is touchingly captured. A refreshing and illuminating disc; the recorded sound is clear and ideally resonant.

Vivaldi Viola d'amore Concertos – D major, RV392; D minor, RV393; D minor, RV394; D minor, RV395; A major, RV396; A minor, RV397. **Orchestra of the Age of Enlightenment / Catherine Mackintosh** (va d'amore). Hyperion ℗ CDA66795 (67 minutes: DDD: 4/96). ✍ Recorded 1995.   ⓐ

John Evelyn (1620-1706) was beguiled and surprised by the sound of the viola d'amore, but he should hardly have been so by the fact that it was on that occasion "played ... by a *German*"; that was the nationality of most of the composers who wrote for it – Bach, Biber, Telemann and Mattheson. The instrument was distinguished by its wide compass, its use of sympathetic strings (not bowed but allowed to resonate), and the fact that it lent itself to playing "the lyra way" (as with the bass viola da gamba), facilitating the use of multiple stopping and contrapuntal textures. Vivaldi was obviously no less attracted by it; six concertos are a lot for such an unusual instrument, and it is fair to say that they represent some of the most beguiling music he wrote. Mackintosh, on top form, acts her role with the utmost virtuosity, lovely tone, unimpeachable intonation, and fine style – with some elegant embroidery. The OAE are admirable, making this splendidly engineered recording one to treasure.

Vivaldi Violin Concertos – D major, RV223; A major, RV349; D minor, RV248; D major, RV229; A major, RV343; F major, RV267. **Israel Chamber Orchestra / Shlomo Mintz** (vn).
MusicMasters ℗ 67120-2 (59 minutes: DDD: 10/94).   🟢🟢
Shlomo Mintz has hit on the charming idea of assembling six concertos which Vivaldi intended expressly at one time or another for his gifted pupil, Anna Maria at the Pietà in Venice. If the music is anything to go by then Signora Anna Maria must have been prodigiously talented; much of the music here is of a markedly virtuoso character and of enormous appeal, melodic and rhythmic. Mintz himself does considerable justice to the works, effortlessly surmounting the technical difficulties posed by Vivaldi's writing. Equally admirable is his spirited approach and the wholehearted enthusiasm with which he throws himself into the playful invention, often strikingly varied, of the outer movements. The only reservation, a small one, lies in the recorded sound which has a slight hollowness, especially noticeable in slow movements and in passages where the solo violin is accompanied solely by cello and keyboard continuo. A captivating issue.

Vivaldi Violin Concertos, Op. 8 – Nos. 1-4, "The Four Seasons"[a]; No. 8 in G minor[a]; No. 9 in D minor[b]. [a]**Enrico Onofri** (vn); [b]**Paolo Grazzi** (ob); **Il Giardino Armonico Ensemble.**
Teldec ℗ 4509-96158-2 (61 minutes: DDD: 1/95). 🎵 Recorded 1993.   🟢
Vivaldi Violin Concertos, Op. 8, "Il cimento dell'armonia e dell'inventione" – No. 5 in E flat major, RV253, "La tempesta di mare"; No. 6 in C major, RV180, "Il piacere"; No. 7 in D minor, RV242; No. 9 in D minor, RV236; No. 10 in B flat major, RV362, "La caccia"; No. 11 in D major, RV210; No. 12 in C major (two versions, RV178 and RV449[a]). **Enrico Onofri** (vn); [a]**Paolo Grazzi** (ob); **Il Giardino Armonico Ensemble / Giovanni Antonini.** Teldec Das Alte Werk ℗ 4509-94566-2 (74 minutes: DDD: 4/96). 🎵 Recorded 1994-1995.
Il Giardino Armonico don't do anything extraordinary; it is more a matter of their demonstration of what can be achieved with small forces – 5.1.2.1 plus soloist and continuo. Here, small is flexible and it highlights the differences in colour achieved by varying the continuo – bassoon, cello, organ, harpsichord and theorbo, unobscured by the *ripieno*, all have their moments. Numbers of 'chamber' dimensions also favour unanimity of attack and changes of dynamics and pace, all vividly accomplished by IGA. The dog barks harshly in "Spring" but without disturbing the shepherd's peaceful dreams, and the chill of "Autumn" in the *Adagio molto* is conveyed by the ethereal strings with the harpsichord firmly relegated to a supporting role. Onofri is as good a soloist as may be met in a long march, pitch-perfect, incisive but not 'edgy', and effortlessly alert to every nuance. All the foregoing good things are also to be found in the other two concertos from Op. 8, together with Grazzi's liquid-toned and agile oboe playing in that in D minor, attractively supported in the *Largo* by theorbo and bassoon. A tasty addition to any collection.

In the completion disc of Il Giardino Armonico's Op. 8, as two of the concertos exist in alternative forms, with oboe *vice* violin (RV236 = 454, RV178 = 449), they are given in both versions – with negligible differences in tempo. The virtues of Il Giardino Armonico are, if anything, even more vividly apparent in this recording. Onofri is once again spellbinding in his imaginative use of a varied continuo, here highlighted in the *Adagio* of RV362 (*La caccia*) played only by violin and theorbo. One complaint: if there is logic behind the order in which the concertos are presented, it is not apparent. The first volume has six concertos (61 minutes), Vol. 2 has eight (74 minutes), whereas to place Nos. 1-6 and RV454 on one disc, and Nos. 7-12 and RV449 on the other would have created no apparent problem. One would, however, need a far more compelling reason not to make a beeline for the nearest record store in search of these magical and finely recorded discs.

Additional recommendations ...
...Op. 8 Nos. 1-12. Flute Concerto in D major, RV429. Cello Concerto in B minor, RV424.
    Stephen Preston (fl); **Simon Standage** (vn); **Anthony Pleeth** (vc); **The English Concert /**
    Trevor Pinnock. CRD ℗ CRD3348/9 (two discs: 154 minutes: ADD: 8/88). 🎵
...Op. 8 Nos. 1-6. **European Community Chamber Orchestra / Marieke Blankestijn** (vn);
    Richard Lester (vc); **Harold Lester** (hpd). Teldec ℗ 4509-91683-2 (59 minutes: DDD: 6/94).
...Op. 8 Nos. 1-4. **Kreisler** Violin Concerto in C major, "in the style of Vivaldi". **Gil Shaham** (vn);
    Orpheus Chamber Orchestra. DG ℗ 439 933-2GH (50 minutes: DDD: 3/95).
...Op. 8 Nos. 1-6. **Freiburg Baroque Orchestra / Gottfried von der Goltz** (vn); **Harp Consort /**
    Andrew Lawrence-King (hpd/hp). Deutsche Harmonia Mundi ℗ 05472 77384-2
    (66 minutes: DDD: 1/98). *Gramophone Editor's choice.*

Vivaldi Violin Concertos, Op. 8 – Nos. 1-4, "The Four Seasons"ᵃ. Oboe Concertos, Op. 7ᵇ – No. 1
in B flat major, RV465; No. 5 in F major, RV285a. ᵃ**Andrew Manze** (vn); ᵇ**Marcel Ponseele** (ob);
Amsterdam Baroque Orchestra / Ton Koopman. Erato Ⓕ 4509-94811-2
(56 minutes: DDD: 8/96). ✍   ⓰⓰⓰
This is a splending set, valid for a lifetime of pleasure. Little differences in attention to detail soon
begin to show, first at 0'17" of the first movement of "Spring", where the chords that are usually hit
hard are here given a happy little squeeze. Amsterdam Baroque (consisting here of 13
instrumentalists) play with the unanimity of one mind and body, with extreme changes of volume that
never sound theatrically contrived, as concerned with the fate of every note as with the shaping of
each phrase. Manze's bow breathes vocal life into his strings; in the slow movements many notes
whisper their way into being, and his *fortissimo* whiplashes have rasp-free edges. There are many
delightful little personal touches – his slurred resolution of the sighing appoggiatura at 2'50" in the
third movement of "Spring", and the way he nudges his way up the ladder of trills in the first
movement of "Autumn" are just two. The remaining works come from Op. 7, in the first of which
(RV465) the oboe is the designated soloist; its transcribed role in No. 5 (RV285a) accords with
baroque practice. Both are charming works with a high level of inspiration, played with no less
affection than the *Seasons*.

Vivaldi Violin Concertos, Op. 8 – Nos. 1-4, "The Four Seasons"; No. 5 in E flat major,
"La tempesta di mare"; No. 6 in C major, "Il piacere". **Mariana Sirbu** (vn); **I Musici.**
Philips Ⓕ 446 699-2PH (60 minutes: DDD: 2/97). Recorded 1995.
Mariana Sirbu here joins the company of the many artists who have recorded *The Four Seasons*. Sirbu
is no less incisive than any of the others and, particularly in the slow movements which she plays with
little added adornment, her lines are fine and imaginatively nuanced. I Musici remain crisp and
responsive, and a novel touch is their addition of a lute to the continuo; it is from time to time audible,
providing the little fill-ins usually the prerogative of the harpsichord, as for example in the final *Presto*
of "Summer" and the *Adagio molto* of "Autumn", though in the latter its economical comments
perhaps lack the icy edge of the harpsichord. The inclusion of two other concertos from Op. 8 (*La
tempesta di mare* and *Il piacere*), no less compellingly played, suggests that Sirbu will complete her
recording of the whole of the set. This may be counted among the very best middle-of-the-road
versions of *The Four Seasons*, strongly recommended to first-time buyers. The well-balanced
recording has brightness and life.

Vivaldi Violin Concertos, Op. 12 – No. 1 in G minor, RV317; No. 2 in D minor, RV244; No. 3 in
D major, RV124; No. 4 in C major, RV173; No. 5 in B flat major, RV379; No. 6 in B flat major,
RV361. **Pavlo Beznosiuk** (vn); **Academy of Ancient Music / Christopher Hogwood.**
L'Oiseau-Lyre Ⓕ 443 556-2OH (53 minutes: DDD: 11/97). ✍ Recorded 1993.
Vivaldi's last two printed collections of concertos, Opp. 11 and 12 were issued in 1729. Each set
contained six works and each, to some extent, is representative of Vivaldi's mature concerto style.
Op. 12 can boast the composer's only published concerto for orchestral strings without solo violin; for
though he wrote some 40 such pieces all but this one remained unpublished until the present century.
RV124, the third concerto in the set, is an impressive example of how imaginative Vivaldi was in
writing *concerti ripieni*, further offering evidence, in its fugal *Allegro* finale, of his too often
overlooked skill in counterpoint. The remaining concertos for solo violin and strings are variable in
their appeal. The First and Second are of a somewhat stern, unbending aspect though Pavlo
Beznosiuk's lissom violin playing and his lightly bowed grace-notes in the first movement of the
Concerto No. 1 in G minor lend much charm to the music. Beznosiuk and the Academy of Ancient
Music, under Christopher Hogwood's sensitive and thoughtful direction, fully explore the sonority of
Vivaldi's string textures. But it is, above all, Beznosiuk's stylish, vital and incisive playing that brings
a sparkle to music which can otherwise sound arid and uninspired. In this he is strongly supported by
the crisp attack of the Academy strings, and the effectively varied colours of a stylish continuo group
which includes organ, harpsichord and archlute. The concluding three concertos are of a more
immediately benign disposition. The opening gestures of No. 4 might almost belong to the overture
to a comic intermezzo, but there is a carefree and airy spirit running throughout the movement. The
Fifth Concerto is a robust, vivacious work, plentifully endowed with distinctive hallmarks of the
composer's style. The solo violin writing is full of caprice to which Beznosiuk responds with vigour
and virtuosity. The Sixth Concerto is spirited in character, and in the bold theatrical gestures of the
finale, hardly less interesting than its predecessor. This playing, solo and ripieno, enlivens the music
at every turn, charming our senses with its recognition of Vivaldi's great poetic gift. A rewarding issue
of a neglected opus.

Vivaldi Violin Concertos – C minor, RV199, "Il sospetto"; D major, RV234, "L'inquietudine";
E major, RV270, "Il riposo"; E major, RV271, "L'amoroso"; E minor, RV277, "Il favorito";
C major, RV581. **Mariana Sirbu** (vn); **I Musici.** Philips Ⓕ 442 145-2PH (63 minutes: DDD: 7/95).
Recorded 1993.   ⓰⓰
All but one piece (RV581) in this attractive programme from I Musici were included in a 1958
recording by the same ensemble (no longer available). This newer issue is by and large more enjoyable,

with livelier, more sharply defined rhythms, clearer articulation and brisker tempos. The last-mentioned need not necessarily imply virtue but in this instance it is a decided plus, above all in *L'inquietudine* whose restless character was only partly realized in the earlier recording. While the solo work was spread among five players on the 1958 disc, it is allotted to just one on the newer issue – Mariana Sirbu. She is manifestly a fine violinist with a warm, even tone, a sharp ear for tonal and interpretative detail and a feeling for the various states of mind suggested in some of the subtitles. The expressive *Andante* of *Il favorito* is beautifully controlled and, in the hands of a soloist of this calibre, explains how the concerto, quite austere on first acquaintance, acquired its title. *L'amoroso* comes over well, too, with tenderly spoken phrases and a playful lyricism in the outer movements. Sirbu ornaments both tastefully and with admirable discretion. Only in *Il riposo* does one feel some disappointment. This delicately crafted piece is scored for muted strings throughout and at some stage in Vivaldi's life acquired Christmas connotations with an additional subtitle "per il Santissimo Natale". Sirbu and I Musici set too brisk a pace in the opening movement and the result is a shade perfunctory. Even so, the playing itself maintains the high level of excellence achieved throughout the remainder of the programme, with impressive virtuosity from Sirbu in the C major Concerto, RV581, recorded here in its version for solo violin and double orchestra. In short, a delightful issue, recommended for music and performances alike.

Additional recommendation ...
...RV199; RV234; D major, RV208; RV270; RV271; B flat major, RV363; RV553.
   Soloists; I Solisti Veneti / Claudio Scimone. Erato 4509-97415-2.

Vivaldi Cello Sonatas – E flat major, RV39; E minor, RV40; G minor, RV42; A minor, RV44; B flat major, RV45; B flat major, RV46. **Pieter Wispelwey** (vc); **Florilegium Ensemble** (Elizabeth Kenny, William Carter, ltes/theorboes/gtrs; Daniel Yeadon, vc; Neal Peres da Costa, hpd/org). Channel Classics Ⓕ CCS6294 (66 minutes: DDD: 11/94). ✒ Recorded 1994.
Vivaldi wrote with great imagination for the cello, and the sonatas like the concertos, of which three times as many exist, are plentifully endowed with affecting melodies – the third movement of the E minor Sonata is a superb example – and virtuoso gestures. It would seem, on the strength of these pieces, that Vivaldi possessed a rare sensibility to the expressive *cantabile* possibilities in writing for the cello. Certainly, few baroque composers other than Bach and perhaps Geminiani realized the instrument's solo potential better than he. Wispelwey is a sensitive player who draws a warm if at times under-assertive sound from his instrument. Fast movements are clearly articulated, slow ones lyrically played with some feeling for the poetry of the music. The performances are thoughtful and enlightened, with a continuo group that includes organ, harpsichord, cello, archlutes, theorboes and guitars in a variety of combinations. The recorded sound is fine. Well worth exploring though Anthony Pleeth's ASV recording of all nine sonatas (listed below) may ultimately prove the more satisfying of the two.

Additional recommendations ...
...RV40; F major, RV41; A minor, RV43; RV45; RV46; B flat major, RV47. **Christophe Coin** (vc); **Christopher Hogwood** (hpd). L'Oiseau-Lyre Florilegium Ⓕ 421 060-2OH (72 minutes: DDD: 4/89). ✒
...RV39; RV40; RV41; RV42; RV43; RV44; RV45, RV46, RV47. **Anthony Pleeth, Suki Towb** (vcs); **Robert Woolley** (hpd/org). ASV Gaudeamus Ⓕ CDGAD201 (two discs: 123 minutes: DDD: 11/91). ✒
...RV39, RV40; RV41; RV42, RV43; RV44, RV45; RV46; RV47. **David Watkin** (vc); **Helen Gough** (vc continuo); **David Miller** (lte/theorbo/gtr); **Robert King** (org/hpd). Hyperion Ⓕ CDA66881/2 (two discs: 116 minutes: DDD: 8/95). ✒

Vivaldi Trio Sonatas for Two Violins and Continuo, Op. 1 – No. 7 in E flat, RV65; No. 8 in D minor, RV64; No. 9 in A flat, RV75; No. 10 in B flat, RV78; No. 11 in B minor, RV79; No. 12 in D minor, "Variations on La Follia", RV63. **L'Arte dell'Arco / Christopher Hogwood** (hpd/org). Deutsche Harmonia Mundi Ⓕ 05472 77350-2 (54 minutes: DDD: 5/98). ✒ Recorded 1997.
The stronger works of Vivaldi's Op. 1 are concentrated within the second half of the set, recorded here. Among them is the best known of the Trios from the collection, the 20 variations on the theme of Spanish origin, *La Follia*. L'Arte dell'Arco was founded in 1994 and has so far focused its attention on Venetian music, both familiar and less familiar. The instruments are tuned fractionally higher than today's concert pitch, rather than the lower A=415, around which most current period-instrument groups prefer to hover. Recent research points to a Venetian tradition of a higher, therefore brighter, pitch in the seventeenth and eighteenth centuries. Another feature of the recording lies in the instruments themselves, which belong to the collection of the Ospedale della Pietà with which Vivaldi was associated, on and off, throughout his working life. The performances are extremely appealing: great consideration is given to instrumental sonority and interplay, and careful thought has gone into the punctuation and phrasing of the music. In this way the listener is at once engaged both in the gesture and oratory of these beautifully crafted pieces. Vivaldi's layout of movements, in all but the last sonata of the set, loosely conforms with that of a typical *sonata da camera* and, within his chosen schemes, he injects all the expressive contrasts and rhythmic vitality which characterize his concertos. L'Arte dell'Arco sensibly, and to some effect, ring the changes of colour and texture in the basso continuo; cello, theorbo, harpsichord and chamber organ are all called upon but, in one of the

sonatas, the two violins are supported by cello, without either keyboard or plucked string. With Christopher Hogwood's exemplary keyboard continuo realizations and tasteful judgement, the pleasure in this disc is complete.

Vivaldi 12 Violin Sonatas, "Manchester Sonatas" – No. 1 in C major, RV3. No. 2 in D minor, RV12. No. 3 in G minor, RV757. No. 4 in D major, RV755. No. 5 in B flat major, RV759. No. 6 in A major, RV758. No. 7 in C minor, RV6. No. 8 in G major, RV22. No. 9 in E minor, RV17*a*. No. 10 in B minor, RV760. No. 11 in E flat major, RV756. No. 12 in C major, RV754.
La Romanesca (Andrew Manze, vn; Nigel North, lte/theorbo/gtr; John Toll, hpd).
Harmonia Mundi Ⓕ HMU90 7089/90 (two discs: 145 minutes: DDD: 1/94). 🎯
Recorded 1992. *Gramophone Editor's choice.*

Vivaldi is so well known for his concertos that we are apt to overlook his admittedly much smaller output of sonatas. This set of 12 for violin and continuo was discovered in Manchester's Central Music Library during the 1970s though five of them exist in versions which have been known for much longer. It is probable that all of them date from the early- to mid-1720s when Vivaldi assembled them to present to Cardinal Ottoboni on the occasion of his visit to Venice, the city of his birth, in 1726. The violinist Andrew Manze has an appealing rapport with this music and is expressive in his shaping of phrases. He reveals sensibility towards Vivaldi's pleasing melodic contours. Indeed, this is a quality in which these sonatas abound, not only in the varied Preludes with which each Sonata begins but also in the brisker, sometimes very brisk allemandes and correntes. He ornaments the music with an effective blend of fantasy and good taste and he dispenses with bowed continuo instruments, preferring the lighter textures provided by harpsichord, archlute, theorbo or guitar. This is music of great beauty and vitality which will delight most if not all lovers of the late baroque; and it is sympathetically interpreted and warmly and intimately recorded.

Vivaldi Dixit Dominus in D major, RV595[ab]. Domine ad adiuvandum me in G major, RV593[a]. Credidi propter quod, RV605. Beatus vir in B flat major, RV598[ab]. Beatus vir in C major, RV597[abc]. [a]**Susan Gritton**, [b]**Catrin Wyn-Davies** (sops); [b]**Catherine Denley** (mez); [c]**Charles Daniels** (ten); [c]**Neal Davies** (bar); [c]**Michael George** (bass); **Choir of The King's Consort; The King's Consort / Robert King.** Hyperion Ⓕ CDA66789 (70 minutes: DDD: 8/97). 🎯
Texts and translations included. Recorded 1997.

Here are two of Vivaldi's most extended and impressive psalm settings. These are the single-choir *Dixit Dominus*, RV595 (Psalm 110), and double-choir *Beatus vir*, RV597 (Psalm 112). Vivaldi set both psalms more than once and King's programme also includes the single movement *Beatus vir*, RV598, as well as the response, *Domine ad adiuvandum me*, RV593, and the conservatively styled Vesper psalm, *Credidi propter quod*, RV605. One aspect of this music which ought to strike listeners is its sheer variety. Not just variety in colour but also of expressive nuance achieved, as so often by Vivaldi, by gently beguiling inflexions, and by a simple directness of communication. Both of the generously proportioned psalm settings on this disc provide ample evidence of his originality in the sphere of sacred vocal music. The King's Consort Choir, some 20 voices in all, make a lively and warm-textured contribution; the solo line-up is also quite strong; with Susan Gritton and Catrin Wyn-Davies providing an evenly matched, lightly articulated partnership in their two duets. Neal Davies and Michael George are splendidly robust in their vigorous "Potens in terra" duet from *Beatus vir* (RV597). Catherine Denley gives an appropriately strongly inflected account of "Judicabit in nationibus", but is intimate and tender in her beautiful "De torrente in via bibet" (from *Dixit*). The remaining soloist, Charles Daniels, delivers the virtuoso "Peccator videbit" (*Beatus vir*, RV597) with articulate lightness and comfortable agility. Though consisting of only three movements and of short duration, the G major *Domine ad adiuvandum me*, is easily on a level with the larger-scale pieces. Its expressive warmth is irresistible, its textual illustration effective and its structure taut, coherent and satisfying. A rewarding issue, well documented and spaciously recorded.

Vivaldi Domine ad adiuvandum me festiana, RV593. Beatus vir, RV597. Stabat mater, RV621. Magnificat, RV610*a*. **Ex Cathedra Chamber Choir and Baroque Orchestra / Jeffrey Skidmore.**
ASV Gaudeamus Ⓕ CDGAU137 (70 minutes: DDD: 12/92). 🎯 Texts and translations included. Recorded 1991. ⒼⒼ

This is an interesting and mainly successful attempt to place a handful of Vivaldi's sacred pieces in a liturgical context. The most well-known work here is the *Stabat mater* for alto voice and strings, but the others deserve to be heard more often than they are. Ex Cathedra Chamber Choir is a well-disciplined, youthful sounding ensemble whose contribution to the recording is first-rate. And it is from the choir that solo voices emerge as required, giving the performances a homogeneity of sound and intent. The instrumentalists, too, make a strong contribution and together with the voices project interpretations which are full of vitality. There are, of course, rival versions on disc of all the music sung here but, on the strength of the thoughtful way it has been presented by the director of Ex Cathedra, Geoffrey Skidmore, this is perhaps the most affecting of them. Few will be disappointed, for example, by the gently inflected, poignant account of the *Stabat mater* by the countertenor Nigel Short. Hardly a detail has been overlooked, even to the extent of allowing the listener to hear a distant bell during the opening Versicle. In short, only the painfully and unnecessarily small typeface of the accompanying texts fails to please.

Additional recommendations ...

...Magnificat. In turbato mare irato, RV627. Concertos – D minor, RV129, "Concerto madrigalesco"; G minor, RV157; G major, RV151, "Concerto alla rustica". Lungi dal vago volto, RV680. **Soloists; Tafelmusik Chamber Choir and Orchestra / Jean Lamon** (vn).
Hyperion Ⓕ CDA66247 (57 minutes: DDD: 12/87). ✍   Ⓖ

...Vestro Principi divino, RV633. Stabat mater. Filiae mestae, RV638. Nisi Dominus, RV608.
Gérard Lesne (alto); **Il Seminario Musicale Ensemble.**
Harmonic Ⓕ H/CD8720 (58 minutes: DDD: 3/91). ✍

...Laudate pueri Dominum, RV600[a]. Stabat mater[b]. Deus tuorum militum, RV612[c]. Sanctorum meritis, RV620[d]. [ad]**Margaret Marshall** (sop); [bc]**Jochen Kowalski** (alto); [ad]**Jacques Ogg** (org); **Concertgebouw Chamber Orchestra / Vittorio Negri.**
Philips Ⓕ 432 091-2PH (49 minutes: DDD: 2/92).

...Gloria in D major, RV589[a]. Magnificat[b]. Laetatus sum, RV607[c]. Laudate Dominum in D minor, RV606[c]. In exitu Israel in C major, RV064[c]. Sinfonia al Santo Sepolcro in B minor, RV169. Sonata al Santo Sepolcro in E flat major, RV130. (All using womens' voices only)
[ab]**Emily Van Evera,** [b]**Nancy Argenta** (sops); [ab]**Alison Place,** [b]**Catherine King** (mezzos); [ab]**Margaret Cable** (contr); [abc]**Taverner Choir; Taverner Players / Andrew Parrott.**
Virgin Classics Veritas Ⓕ VC7 59326-2 (68 minutes: DDD: 1/95). ✍

...Stabat mater[a]. Nisi Dominus in G minor, RV608[a]. Salve regina in C minor, RV616[a].
String Concerto in D minor, RV128. Sinfonia in B minor, RV169, "Sinfonia al Santo Sepolcro".
[a]**Michael Chance** (alto); **The English Concert / Trevor Pinnock** (org).
Archiv Produktion Ⓕ 453 428-2AH (64 minutes: DDD: 8/97).   Ⓖ

Vivaldi Gloria in D major, RV589[a]. Magnificat in G minor, RV611[a]. Concerto for Strings in D minor, RV243. Concerto for Oboe, Trumpet and Strings in D major, RV563[b]. [a]**Deborah York,** [a]**Patrizia Biccire** (sops); [a]**Sara Mingardo** (contr); [b]**Andrea Mioh** (ob); [b]**Gabriele Cassone** (tpt); [a]**Akademia; Concerto Italiano / Rinaldo Alessandrini.** Opus 111 Ⓕ OPS30 195 (60 minutes: DDD: 6/98). Texts and translations included. Recorded 1997.
Gramophone Editor's choice.

Once you recover from the shock of hearing the opening chorus of Vivaldi's *Gloria* sung at what initially strikes you as a breakneck tempo, you will quickly begin to enter into the vital spirit of Rinaldo Alessandrini's performance. In fact it is not only this introductory movement that is thought-provoking but also the carefully considered tempos of several other sections of the work, some of them much slower than we have become used to. Alessandrini lays far greater emphasis than many of his rivals on the meaning of the Latin text. The two supplicatory sections, "Domine Deus, Rex caelestis" and "Domini Deus, Agnus Dei", are both sensitively handled with affective dynamic shading; in the first of them Alessandrini avails himself of Vivaldi's option for a violin solo rather than the more customarily heard oboe. The piece is lyrically sung by Deborah York with a beautifully sustained and imaginatively ornamented violin accompaniment played by Francesca Vicari. The soloist in the second of these movements, Sara Mingardo, also makes a favourable impression. The other sacred vocal work in this release is the latest of several adaptations Vivaldi made of a *Magnificat* which he had originally written for the Pietà. One of the principal differences between this version and the earlier ones lies in five effectively contrasted arias for named singers among the *figlie di coro* of the Pietà. In this performance the solos are distributed among three rather than five artists, but it hardly matters since each is sung with distinctive character and accomplished technique. Two concertos of contrasting aspect and instrumentation complete this very attractive programme. Both have been recorded previously, though, in the case of RV563 (sometimes encountered under the catalogue number RV781), not quite in the way it is performed here, with a natural trumpet and oboe as playful protagonists in the outer movements. In the slow movement the trumpet is tacet, the oboe assuming a solo role with scalewise passages of a somewhat vacuous character. Never mind, this is a rewarding issue above all, perhaps, for the expressive performance of the *Magnificat*.

Additional recommendation ...

...Glorias – D major, RV588; D major RV589. **Soloists; St John's College Choir, Cambridge. Wren Orchestra. George Guest.** Decca Eclipse Ⓑ 448 223-2DEC (71 minutes: ADD: 2/96).

Vivaldi In furore gustissimae irae, RV626[a]. Longe mala, umbrae, terrores, RV629[b]. Clarae stellae, scintillate, RV625[c]. Canta in prato, ride in monte, RV623[a]. Filiae mestae Jerusalem in C minor, RV638[c]. Nulla in mundo pax, RV630[a]. [a]**Deborah York** (sop); [b]**Catherine Denley** (mez); [c]**James Bowman** (alto); **King's Consort / Robert King.** Hyperion Ⓕ CDA66779 (69 minutes: DDD: 7/96). ✍ Texts and translations included.   Ⓖ

The promising first volume of Robert King's exploration of Vivaldi's sacred music (reviewed above) gave us a selection of large-scale choral works; Vol. 2 offers five of his motets for solo voice and strings, together with RV623, one of the *Introduzioni* he composed to precede his liturgical choral pieces. As ever with Vivaldi, they are utterly beguiling pieces of music, impossible to dislike and easy to be beguiled by. Their Latin texts – which usually allow for two arias separated by a recitative and followed by an "Alleluia" – are about as profound as the sonnets which accompany *The Four Seasons*, but they inspire in Vivaldi just the same kind of charmingly uncomplicated reaction. Nightingales, scenes of general Arcadian bliss, the storms of God's wrath and the touching sorrow of the mournful daughters of Jerusalem before the Cross – all bring forth what you might be tempted to call stock responses were it not for the fact that the music is always so instantly recognizable as being by Vivaldi. Vivaldi's singers must have been good to judge from these pieces, which show a brand of virtuosity more at home in the instrumental concerto than the aria. James Bowman and Catherine Denley are both on good form (the latter having a particularly taxing number to sing), but the star of the disc is Deborah York, yet another of the many outstanding young sopranos to have arrived on the scene in recent years. Her *In furore iustissimae irae* is a *tour de force* of vocal power and agility with a teasing little top C at the end of the first aria; while the deceptive beauties of *Nulla in mundo pax sincera* are artfully conjured by sly little portamentos. The string accompaniments throughout are buoyant but beefy, aided by an excellent recorded sound, and the tempos seem well judged.

Additional recommendation ...
...Nulla in mundo pax – Nulla in mundo pax. *Coupled with works by various composers.*
Lesley Garrett (sop); **Britten Sinfonia / Ivor Bolton.** Conifer Classics Ⓕ 75605 51329-2 (73 minutes: DDD: 12/97). *See review in the Collections section; refer to the Index.*

Vivaldi Magnificat in G minor, RV610*a*[a]. Lauda Jerusalem in E minor, RV609[b]. Kyrie in G minor, RV587[c]. Credo in E minor, RV591[d]. Dixit Dominus in D major, RV594[e]. [abe]**Susan Gritton,** [abe]**Lisa Milne** (sops); [ae]**Catherine Denley** (mez); [ae]**Lynton Atkinson** (ten); [e]**David Wilson-Johnson** (bar); **King's Consort Choristers and Choir; King's Consort / Robert King.** Hyperion Ⓕ CDA66769 (63 minutes: DDD: 6/95). ☞ Texts and translations included. Recorded 1994.
Gramophone Editor's choice.   Ⓖ
King's 'super-group' featuring choristers drawn from seven English cathedral and collegiate choirs sound better than ever – technically reliable, with a good, full sound – and are a credit to King's vision in bringing them together. This volume has five typically uplifting works, three of which – *Lauda Jerusalem*, *Dixit Dominus* and the G minor *Kyrie* – offer the opulent sound of double choir and orchestra. *Dixit Dominus* is the most substantial, a colourful 23-minute sequence of varied solos and choruses, with trumpets, oboes and two organs all chipping in, most notably in an awe-inspiring depiction of the Day of Judgement. The other two are perhaps less striking, though *Lauda Jerusalem* is certainly charming in its two-soprano interchanges. Highlights of the single-chorus works include another exquisite soprano duet and a fiery "Fecit potentiam" in the *Magnificat*, and an extraordinary "Crucifixus" in the *Credo* which departs from the pain-wracked norm by seemingly depicting with lugubrious slow tread Christ's walk to Calvary. King manages very well in capturing the essence of Vivaldi's bold, sometimes disarmingly straightforward style. These tidy performances are driven with just the right amount of springy energy – neither too much nor too little – and are well recorded in the warm resonance of St Jude's Church, Hampstead in London.

Vivaldi Salve regina in C minor, RV616[a]. Introduzione al Miserere, RV641[a]. Introduzione al Gloria, RV637[a]. Salve regina in G minor, RV618[a]. Concerto for Violin and Strings in C major, RV581[b] ("per la Santissima Assenzione di Maria Vergine"). [a]**Gérard Lesne** (alto); [b]**Fabio Biondi** (vn); **Il Seminario Musicale.** Virgin Classics Veritas Ⓕ VC7 59232-2 (77 minutes: DDD: 6/93). ☞ Texts and translations included. Recorded 1991.
The principal works here are two settings of the Marian antiphon *Salve regina*, but the French countertenor Gérard Lesne follows this with an extended *Introduzione* to a *Miserere*, one of two by Vivaldi, and an *Introduzione* to a *Gloria*; and by way of making up a programme, he divides the four vocal pieces into two groups inserting a Violin Concerto between them. The main bias of this music is contemplative, often deeply so, as is the case with the darkly expressive, sorrowful introduction to the *Miserere non in pratis*. Lesne approaches the music with style. Indeed, a stronger advocate for these affecting compositions is hard to imagine since he is technically almost faultless. Then there is the Concerto in C major (*in due cori*), a splendid example of Vivaldi's skill in this medium, admirably played by the violinist Fabio Biondi with Lesne's own group Il Seminario Musicale. Vivaldi enthusiasts will require no further proof of this disc's merit, but readers in general should also find much to enjoy here, both in the singing and playing. The recorded sound is pleasantly resonant, serving the best interests of Lesne's voice and of the instruments too. A fine release.

Vivaldi Stabat mater in F minor, RV621[a]. Cessate, omai cessate, RV684[a]. Filiae mestae Jerusalem in C minor, RV638[a]. String Concertos – C major, RV114; E flat major, RV130, "Sonata al Santo Sepolcro". [a]**Andreas Scholl** (alto); **Ensemble 415 / Chiara Banchini** (vn). Harmonia Mundi Ⓕ HMC90 1571 (52 minutes: DDD: 4/96). Texts and translations included. Recorded 1995.
Gramophone Editor's choice. Selected by Soundings. Gramophone Award Winner 1996.   ⒼⒼⒼ
Here is a very attractively prepared menu whose main course is the *Stabat mater* for countertenor and strings. Hors-d'oeuvres and side-dishes consist of a ripieno concerto (RV114), a chamber cantata for countertenor and strings (RV684), a string sonata in E flat (RV130) and an introductory motet to a lost *Miserere* (RV638). Taken together, the pieces demonstrate something of Vivaldi's diverse style as a composer. The two instrumental works offer the strongest contrasts, the Concerto suggestive, above all in its opening movement, of an opera sinfonia, the Sonata redolent with poignant suspensions and darkly sonorous in its first movement, but yielding to a tautly constructed fugue in the second. The chamber cantata, if closely related to the two sacred vocal items on the disc in respect of tonal colour, differs from them in character. Conforming with the standard Italian cantata pattern at the time of

two pairs of alternating recitative and *da capo* aria Vivaldi enlivens his pastoral idyll with two particularly affecting arias, the first with a palpitating pizzicato violin, the second a virtuoso vocal *tour de force* illustrating the plight of the forsaken lover. Andreas Scholl brings the whole thing off superbly with only a moment's faulty intonation at the close of the first aria. Unlike settings of the *Stabat mater* by Pergolesi and others, Vivaldi used only the first ten of the 20 stanzas of the poem. His deeply expressive setting of the poem will be familiar to many readers but few will have heard such an affecting performance as Scholl achieves here. The lyrical prayer of human yearning for faith contained in the "Fac ut ardeat" movement is tenderly sung and here, as throughout the programme, sympathetically supported by Ensemble 415 under Chiara Banchini's experienced direction.

Vivaldi Juditha Triumphans, RV644. **Maria Cristina Kiehr** (sop); **Ann Murray, Susan Bickley, Sarah Connolly, Jean Rigby** (mezzos); **The King's Consort Choir; The King's Consort / Robert King.** Hyperion Ⓕ CDA67281/2 (two discs: 148 minutes: DDD: 5/98). Text and translation included. Recorded 1997.
All the solo roles in Vivaldi's only surviving oratorio, *Juditha Triumphans*, were written for the female voices of the Ospedale della Pietà in Venice, where Vivaldi was, at the time, acting choirmaster. The work, with its Latin libretto by Giacomo Cassetti, dates from 1716. In his introduction, Michael Talbot surmises that the oratorio would have been introduced by a sinfonia. That seems likely, but none has survived, so two movements from one of Vivaldi's colourfully scored concertos *con molto stromenti* (RV555) serve as a preface to Robert King's recording. The cast, with Ann Murray in the title-role, is a strong one, and the wonderfully diverse instrumental obbligatos are a constant delight; yet the sum of the parts does not always add up to an entirely rewarding whole. The powerful drama is understated. Anyone coming to this work for the first time will, of course, be unencumbered by comparisons with earlier recordings, and will probably be delighted by who and what they hear in this latest recording. That is as it should be since, overall, this is the most stylish if not always the most dramatically satisfying of the versions to have appeared on disc. Certainly, Maria Cristina Kiehr turns in a performance of constant pleasure as Holofernes's servant Vagaus and Sarah Connolly's fuller-textured voice, with its warmth of timbre, conveys a sympathetic picture of Abra, Judith's servant. There is more passion to the story of Judith and Holofernes and Vivaldi's setting of it than we are allowed to hear in this performance but that said, King's reading, more than any other, allows us to revel in the sheer beauty and kaleidoscopic brilliance of Vivaldi's score. His singers and players have served him well.

Vivaldi Opera Arias and Sinfonias: Griselda – Sinfonia; Ombre vane, ingiusti orrori; Agitata da due venti. Tito Manlio – Non ti lusinghi la crudeltade. Ottone in Villa – Sinfonia; Gelosia, tu già rendi l'alma mia; L'ombre, l'aure, e ancora il rio[a]. L'Atenaide – Ferma, Teodosio. Bajazet – Sinfonia. L'Incoronazione di Dario – Non mi lusinga vana speranza. Catone in Utica – Se mai senti spirarti sul volto; Se in campo armato. **Emma Kirkby, [a]Liliana Mazzarri** (sops); **The Brandenburg Consort / Roy Goodman.** Hyperion Ⓕ CDA66745 (75 minutes: DDD: 5/95). 🎵 Texts and translations included. Recorded 1994. 🅖🅖
This release of arias and sinfonias from Vivaldi's operas gives us a *bonne bouche* of what lies in store for artists and record companies inclined to explore this still somewhat overlooked aspect of Vivaldi's output. The programme is also an entertaining one in its own right and it is far from being a mere highlights disc. The arias have been chosen with discernment, thoughtfully grouped and effectively interspersed with three of Vivaldi's opera *sinfonias*. The formula proves so successful that it even occurs to you that this was maybe the happiest solution to reviving at least the more problematic of Vivaldi's operas. Emma Kirkby's voice is still maturing, filling out, and she is able to achieve an ever increasing variety of colour. Her "Ombre vane, ingiusti orrori", a ravishing piece from *Griselda* (1735), is beautifully and effortlessly controlled, delicately shaded and rhythmically vital; and her feeling for apposite embellishment comes across with pleasing spontaneity and stylistic assurance. The voice is supported and highlighted by the sympathetic partnership of The Brandenburg Consort conducted by Roy Goodman. This disc will delight Vivaldi enthusiasts. Excellent recorded sound.

Vivaldi Ottone in Villa. **Monica Groop** (mez) Ottone; **Nancy Argenta** (sop) Caio Silio; **Susan Gritton** (sop) Cleonilla; **Sophie Daneman** (sop) Tullia; **Mark Padmore** (ten) Decio; **Collegium Musicum 90 / Richard Hickox.** Chandos Chaconne Ⓕ CHAN0614 (two discs: 145 minutes: DDD: 5/98). 🎵 Notes, text and translation included. Recorded 1997. 🅖🅖
Vivaldi claimed to have written over 90 stage works, but he may have been exaggerating. What is undeniable is that, much as we may marvel at the profusion of his concertos, which certainly brought him fame, he was most successful in his day as an opera composer. This, his very first opera, premièred in Vicenza in 1713, was an instant hit, and Vivaldi himself thought well enough of it to employ the music of one aria no fewer than five more times. The work was produced very simply, without special scenery or effects, and with modest forces – only five singers (one a castrato) and a small orchestra of strings, a pair of very economically used oboes doubling recorders, and continuo. The story is a relatively uncomplicated one by the standards of baroque opera, of amatory pretences and misunderstandings: it has been admirably summarized by Eric Cross (who has edited the work) as a "light-weight, amoral entertainment in which the flirtatious Cleonilla consistently has the upper

hand, and gullible Emperor Ottone (a far from heroic figure) never discovers the truth about the way he has been deceived". The score proceeds in a succession of *secco* recitatives (with just a very occasional *accompagnato*) and *da capo* arias – which the present cast ornament very stylishly. There are no duets or ensembles except for a perfunctory final chorus in which the characters merely sing in unison; but there is an abundance of tuneful arias, and when Vivaldi can be bothered to write proper accompaniments to them – he often merely has violins doubling the voice, plus a bass-line– he can provide interesting imitative counterpoint. Several arias employ only the upper strings without cello and bass except in ritornellos. The small Vicenza theatre could not afford star singers, so only limited opportunities were provided for vocal virtuosity; but the present cast makes the most of its opportunities, both in display and in meditative mood. It is not always easy to tell the three sopranos apart, but Susan Gritton well suggests the scheming minx Cleonilla; Nancy Argenta with her bright voice has the castrato role that includes several fine arias, and displays a *messa di voce* in an echo aria; and Sophie Daneman, in a breeches role, produces a wide range of colour. Monica Groop slightly undercharacterizes Ottone except when roused to dismiss Rome's anxiety at his dalliance. It is quite a relief to hear one male voice, and Mark Padmore is excellent. Richard Hickox keeps a firm rhythmic hand on everything and delivers quite the best and neatest Vivaldi operatic recording yet.

Vivaldi Tito Manlio. **Giancarlo Luccardi** (bass) Tito Manlio; **Norma Lerer** (mez) Decio; **Margaret Marshall** (sop) Lucio; **Júlia Hamari** (mez) Servilia; **Rose Wagemann** (mez) Manlio; **Birgit Finnilä** (mez) Vitellia; **Domenico Trimarchi** (bar) Lindo; **Claes Hakon Ahnsjö** (ten) Geminio; **Berlin Radio Chorus; Berlin Chamber Orchestra / Vittorio Negri.**
Philips ⑩ 446 332-2PM4 (four discs: 238 minutes: ADD: 7/96). Notes, text and translation included. From 6769 004 (9/78).

Tito Manlio was produced for the Mantuan Carnival season in 1719 and, if we are to believe a note by Vivaldi himself at the head of the score, was written in the space of five days. This recording of the work was first issued on LP in 1978 but only now makes its début on CD. *Tito Manlio* certainly ranks among the most successful of all the ten Vivaldi operas so far commercially recorded. The libretto, by Matteo Noris, whom Vivaldi set on more than one occasion, centres round a dispute between the Romans and the Latins which has arisen because the Roman Senate, headed by Titus Manlius, has denied the Latins a consul of Latin birth. The Latins declare war on Rome but, since until now the opposing camps have been on friendly terms, Titus forbids his son Manlius to engage the enemy in single combat. Manlius disobeys him and is sentenced to death by his father. These events, together with drama provided by lovers separated by war, sustain the opera successfully by and large, through three substantial acts. All this takes place in about BC340, by the way. Vivaldi's melodic invention is alluring and, if the libretto is no masterpiece, at least it provides a wealth of opportunities for evocative image painting. The role of Lucio is stylishly sung by Margaret Marshall. Titus's daughter Vitellia, sung by Birgit Finnilä, is also allotted some engaging music. Then there is Titus's music, sung by Giancarlo Luccardi; he had a reputation as a stern consul and Vivaldi underlines this side of his character with some robust arias. Manlius, Titus's son, sung by Rose Wagemann, also has some strong arias – not surprisingly since his predicament seems hopeless on all fronts. In short, this is an opera which both in content and performance, albeit dated in some respects, goes some way towards rehabilitating Vivaldi in the minds of readers who, over the years, have encountered more than their fair share of indifferent recordings. The cast is mainly a strong one with the Berlin Chamber Orchestra (using modern instruments) providing solid support. If the overture to the work has survived it can no longer be identified. Negri, instead, has chosen three movements from three different concertos (RV562, 579 and 141). The solution is both apt in context and extremely effective. A welcome and stimulating reissue.

Further listening ...
...Concertos – Two Horns and Strings: F major, RV539[a]; F major, RV538[b]; Two Trumpets and Strings in C major, RV537[c]; Two Oboes and Two Clarinets in C major, RV560[d]; Oboe, Bassoon and Strings in G major, RV545[e]; Two Flutes and Strings in C major, RV533[f]. Sinfonia for Strings in D major, RV122[g]. [f]**Duke Dobing**, [f]**Deborah Davis** (fls); [deg]**Christopher Hooker**, [deg]**Helen McQueen** (obs); [d]**Ruth McDowall**, [d]**David Rix** (cls); [eg]**Joanna Graham** (bn); [c]**Crispian Steele-Perkins**, [c]**Michael Meeks** (tpts); [ab]**Stephen Stirling**, [ab]**Tim Caister** (hns); **City of London Sinfonia / Nicholas Kraemer** (hpd).
Naxos 8 553204 (1/96).
...Concerto for Two Trumpets and Strings in C major, RV537. *Coupled with works by various composers.* **Crispian Steele-Perkins, John Thiessen** (tpts); **Tafelmusik / Jeanne Lamon** (vn).
Sony Classical Vivarte SK53365 (4/95). 🎣
...Concerto for Two Trumpets and Strings in C major, RV537 (rev. Malipiero). *Coupled with works by various composers.* **Håkan Hardenberger, Reinhold Friedrich** (tpts); **I Musici.**
Philips 442 131-2PH (5/95). *See review in the Collections section; refer to the Index.* ⓖ
...Concerto for Two Trumpets and Strings in C major, RV537. *Coupled with works by various composers.* **Crispian Steele-Perkins** (tpt); **Bournemouth Sinfonietta / Richard Studt** (vn).
Carlton Classics 30366 0038-2 (4/97). *See review in the Collections section; refer to the Index.*
...Concerto grosso in A minor, RV522[ab]. *Coupled with works by various composers.* [a]**Harp Consort / Andrew Lawrence-King** ([b]double harp). Deutsche Harmonia Mundi 05472 77366-2 (4/98). 🖋
See review in the Collections section; refer to the Index.

...Dresden Concertos – C major, RV170; G major, RV314*a*; G minor, RV319; A major, RV341; B flat major, RV366, "Il Carbonelli"; B flat major, RV383. **Accademia I Filarmonici / Alberto Martini** (vn). Naxos 8 553792 (8/97). 🗲

...Dresden Concertos – C major, RV184; D minor, RV241; E major, RV267; F major, RV292; G minor, RV239; B flat major, RV363. **Roberto Baraldi** (vn); **Accademia I Filarmonici / Alberto Martini.** Naxos 8 553793 (11/97). 🗲

...12 Violin Concertos, Op. 4, "La stravaganza". **Soloists; Academy of St. Martin in the Fields / Sir Neville Marriner.** Decca 444 821-2DF2 (1/96).

...Violin Sonatas – C minor, RV5; D minor, RV15; G minor, RV26; G minor, RV28; B flat major, RV34; Saraband in C major (attrib). **Fabio Biondi** (vn); **Maurizio Naddeo** (vc); **Rinaldo Alessandrini** (hpd). Opus 111 OPS30-154 (12/96). 🗲

...Gloria in D major, RV588. *Coupled with* **A. Scarlatti** Dixit Dominus II. **Soloists; The English Concert Choir; The English Concert / Trevor Pinnock.** Archiv Produktion 423 386-2AH (5/88). 🗲

...Dorilla in Tempe. **Soloists; Nice Opera Chorus; Nice Baroque Ensemble / Gilbert Bezzina.** Pierre Verany PV794092 (2/95).   Ⓖ

Giovanni Viviani   Italian 1638-1692 or later

Suggested listening ...
...Capricci armonici – Sonata prima. *Coupled with works by various composers.* **Håkan Hardenberger** (tpt); **I Musici.** Philips 442 131-2PH (5/95). *See review in the Collections section; refer to the Index.*   Ⓖ

Kevin Volans   South African 1949

Volans This is How it is[a]. Walking Song. Leaping Dance[a]. Concerto for Piano and Wind Instruments[bc]. Untitled (In memoriam G.H.V.)[ad]. [c]**Peter Donohoe**, [d]**Kevin Volans** (pfs); **Netherlands Wind Ensemble /** [a]**Wim Steinmann,** [b]**Daniel Harding.** Chandos New Direction Ⓕ CHAN9563 (59 minutes: DDD: 1/98). Recorded 1995-6.

Often Volans will end a piece with new material in such a way that the listener is left hanging (as at the end of *Leaping Dance* and *Untitled*), waiting for a sense of closure that never comes; the vernacular African elements on this disc are presented almost raw, giving them a poignancy peculiar to Volans's music. At his best he can create a sound that is arrestingly beautiful and sustain interest in the way it is developed for the whole of the piece. For this reason *Walking Song, Leaping Dance* and *Untitled* are the pieces to listen to first, for they communicate their ideas with a rare combination of directness and sophistication. But it is surprising that *This is How it is* was placed at the start of the CD as it seems by far the weakest piece and, although the Concerto has many striking textures, it is doubtful whether it sustains them effectively throughout. Despite Peter Donohoe's remarkably sensitive performance, the Concerto's frequent references to the slow wind chords from Stravinsky's *Symphony of Wind Instruments* inevitably lead to a loss of musical tension. However, there is much to entrance the listener here, played with commitment and textural sensitivity by the Netherlands Wind Ensemble. Anyone who has fallen under the spell of *White Man Sleeps* should definitely consider buying this disc.

Further listening ...
...String Quartets – No. 2, "Hunting: Gathering"; No. 3, "The Songlines". **Balanescu Quartet.** Argo 440 687-2ZH (8/94).
...String Quartets – No. 4, "Ramanujan Notebooks"; No. 5, "Dancers on a Plane". Movement for String Quartet. **Duke Quartet.** Collins Classics 1417-2 (7/95).
...White man sleeps (1982[d] and 1986[a] versions). Mbira[b]. She who sleeps with a small blanket[c]. [bd]**Kevin Volans,** [b]**Deborah James,** [d]**Robert Hill** (hpds); [d]**Margriet Tindemans** (va da gamba); [bcd]**Robyn Schulkowsky** (perc); [a]**Smith Quartet.** Cala United CACD88034 (10/91).

Arcadi Volodos   USSR 1972

Suggested listening ...
...Concert Paraphrase on Mozart's "Turkish March". *Coupled with works by various composers.* **Arcadi Volodos** (pf). Sony Classical SK62691 (10/97). *Gramophone Editor's choice. Selected by Soundings. See review in the Collections section; refer to the Index.*   ⒼⒼ

Jan Voříšek   Bohemian 1791-1825

Voříšek 12 Rhapsodies, Op. 1. Le désir, Op. 3. Le plaisir, Op. 4. **Artur Pizarro** (pf). Collins Classics Ⓕ 1477-2 (75 minutes: DDD: 2/97). Recorded 1996. *Gramophone Editor's choice.*   Ⓖ

Voříšek's output was small: having already recorded the better known piano works, including the *Fantasia*, Op. 12 and the Sonata, Op. 20 (listed below), Artur Pizarro here virtually completes the solo piano music with the youthful *Rhapsodies* and two other early works. Commended by Beethoven, the 12 *Rhapsodies* are all similar in form (a basic ternary ABA), expression (fast and often virtuosic outer sections with a contrasting lyrical middle section), and style (strong rhythmic elements including frequent accents and syncopation, diminished chords, and rapid modulation). Pizarro's performances are exceptional in every respect: the spiritual bravura of his *perpetuum mobile* playing is matched by his complete control, crystalline clarity and rhythmic incisiveness. The articulation of the *Third Rhapsody* (similar in texture and profile to the second movement of the *Fantasia*), the softer focus of the delicate Sixth *Rhapsody*, and the rhythmic momentum of the Eleventh (a daring precursor to Alkan's fearsome "Comme le vent" from *Etudes dan les tons mineurs*) are by turns enchanting and astonishing. The remaining two works are played with equal stylishness, although ultimately they are not quite so involving. The recordings are suitably bright – a wonderful disc.

Further listening ...
...Symphony in D major, Op. 24. *Coupled with works by* **Arriaga** **Scottish Chamber Orchestra /**
Sir Charles Mackerras. Hyperion CDA66800 (11/95). *Gramophone Editor's choice.*   ⓖⓖ
...Fantasia in C major, Op. 12. Piano Sonata in B flat major, Op. 20. Variations in B flat major,
Op. 19. Six Impromptus, Op. 7. **Radoslav Kvapil** (pf). Unicorn-Kanchana. DKPCD9145 (6/94).
...Fantasia in C major, Op. 12. Piano Sonata in B flat major, Op. 20. Variations in B flat major,
Op. 19. Six Impromptus, Op. 7. **Artur Pizarro** (pf). Collins Classics 1458-2 (10/95).

Richard Wagner   German 1813-1883

Wagner Die Meistersinger von Nürnberg – Prelude, Act 1[a]; Da zu dir der Heiland kam[b];
Wach auf![b]; Morgenlich leuchtend[b]. Der fliegende Holländer – Overture[c].
Tannhäuser – Overture[d]; Entry of the Guests[e]. Lohengrin – Prelude, Act 3[f].
Götterdämmerung[g] – Hier sitz' ich zur Wacht; Hoiho! Ihr Gibichsmannen. [b]**Tiana Lemnitz** (sop);
[b]**Torsten Ralf** (ten); [g]**Herbert Janssen** (bar); [g]**Ludwig Weber** (bass); [bg]**Royal Opera House Chorus,**
Covent Garden; London Philharmonic Orchestra / Sir Thomas Beecham.
Dutton Laboratories mono Ⓑ CDLX7007* (69 minutes: ADD: 6/94). Item marked [a] from
Columbia LX557 (12/36), [b]LX645/6 (10/37, recorded live in the Royal Opera House, Covent
Garden in 1936), [c]LX732/3 (9/38), [d]LX768/9 (2/39), [e]LX733 (9/38), [f]LX482 (5/36), [g]LX636/7
(9/37. Royal Opera House, 1936).   ⓖⓖ
Beecham was a lifelong Wagnerian and these superlative performances make one regret all the more that he never recorded a Wagner opera complete in the studio. The greatest 'might have been' would be a complete Covent Garden *Die Meistersinger* of 1936, when a superb cast had been assembled: given that the recording facilities were there to make the sides included here, one wonders why the rest of the opera wasn't also committed to disc. A month after those excerpts were taken live Beecham went into the studio to record his masterly account of the Prelude to Act 1. Here the whole panoply of the score is set expectantly before us. The Royal Opera House Chorus sing well, though not exceptionally so. Ralf, a compact, musical tenor sings a pleasing, poetic Prize song, for which he duly receives the crown from Lemnitz's nonpareil of an Eva, perfect trill and all. Nine days after the *Meistersinger* extracts were made, EMI were back at Covent Garden for *Götterdämmerung*. All that officially resulted were two solos, in which we hear Weber as an implacable then fiendishly celebratory Hagen. The rest of the items demonstrate Beecham's ability to inject zestful conviction into pre-*Ring* Wagner without ever overblowing the sound, as so often happens today. These readings also confirm the virtuoso calibre of his pre-war LPO, who play with a precision and character that leap from the loudspeakers with amazing freshness and vitality in these faultless transfers, not a 78rpm surface to be heard, a tribute to Dutton Laboratories' skills in using the CEDAR system to best advantage.

Additional recommendations ...
...Lohengrin –Preludes, Acts 1 and 3. Gotterdämmerung – Dawn and Siegfried's Rhine Journey.
Coupled with works by various composers. **Philharmonic Symphony Orchestra of New York /**
Arturo Toscanini. Pearl mono Ⓑ GEMMCDS9373* (three discs: 230 minutes: ADD: 3/90).
Gramophone classical 100. See review in the Collections section; refer to the Index.   ⓖⓖⓖ
...Die Meistersinger von Nürnberg – Prelude, Act 1. *Coupled with works by various composers.*
The Solti Orchestral Project, Carnegie Hall / Sir Georg Solti. Decca Ⓕ 444 458-2DH
(77 minutes: DDD: 12/94). *See review in the Collections section; refer to the Index.*   ⓖ
...Die Meistersinger von Nürnberg – Prelude, Act 1. Die Walküre – Ride of the Valkyries.
Götterdämmerung – Siegfried's Funeral March; Dawn and Siegfried's Rhine Journey.
Tannhäuser – Overture; Venusberg Music. Lohengrin – Prelude, Act 3.
Royal Concertgebouw Orchestra / Riccardo Chailly.
Decca Ⓕ 448 155-2DH (64 minutes: DDD: 3/96).
...Die Walküre – Der Männer Sippe; Du bist der Lenz. Lohengrin – Einsam in trüben Tagen.
Tannhäuser – Dich teure Halle; All-mächt'ge Jungfrau. Der fliegende Holländer – Joho hoe! ...
Traft ihr das Schiff. Tristan und Isolde – Mild und leise. *Coupled with works by* **R. Strauss**
Elisabeth Meyer-Topsøe (sop); **Copenhagen Philharmonic Orchestra / Hans Norbert Bihlmaier.**
Kontrapunkt Ⓕ 32249 (60 minutes: DDD: 4/97). *See review under R. Strauss; refer to the Index.*

Wagner Rienzi – Overture. Tristan und Isolde – Prelude and Liebestod[a]. Die Meistersinger von Nürnberg – Prelude. Siegfried Idyll. Parsifal – Prelude. Lohengrin – Prelude. [a]**Jane Eaglen** (sop); **London Classical Players / Sir Roger Norrington.** EMI Ⓕ CDC5 55479-2 (64 minutes: DDD: 11/95). Recorded 1994.

The born-again New Queen's Hall Orchestra and Barry Wordsworth were first in the field with a whole disc of period instrument Wagner. The London Classical Players and Norrington have, of course, been playing together rather longer, and it shows nearly everywhere. How much of the extra polish and precision of the LCP's finished product is due to editing is not the issue. That Norrington is much more a man of the theatre is immediately apparent from the anticipatory hush of the first bars of *Rienzi*, and generally from the greater contrasts of tempo and dynamics (and the extra brass bite and brilliance). From Norrington's group, there are also more revelations of texture (apart from the tuba) and timbre. In matters of tempo, Norrington's disc, true to form, sets the cat among the pigeons. There's a *Meistersinger* Prelude almost two minutes shorter than the average. Perhaps its most startling feature (once you have adjusted to the slimline Masters) is a sudden increase in speed at 5'55" where, as Ernest Newman put it, "the Masters sweep the apprentices aside, [the Masters' theme] thundering out in trumpets and trombones". Norrington's way here would seem to propose that the Masters are simply joining in with the fun. Even more controversial will be the *Tristan* Prelude. For this 6/8, Norrington has two slow beats in the bar (all others, six moderate ones) and he ignores Felix Mottl's injunction to remain in tempo up to the climax. The *Parsifal* Prelude is a human, immediate and musical experience (look elsewhere for mystical refulgence and long-drawn reverence). And the *Siegfried Idyll* is a real charmer; less of the traditional fireside warmth (the cradle song almost dances), but considerably more than usual woodland magic (period woodwind coming into their own). In short, vintage Norrington.

Additional recommendations ...

...Götterdämmerung – Siegfried's Rhine Journey; Siegfried's Funeral March. Parsifal – Prelude, Act 1. Siegfried – Forest Murmurs. Tristan und Isolde – Prelude and Liebestod. Die Walküre – Ride of the Valkyries. **Philharmonia Orchestra / Yuri Simonov.** Collins Classics Ⓕ 1207-2 (68 minutes: DDD: 10/91).

...Overtures – Rienzi; Tannhäuser. Preludes – Lohengrin, Act 1; Tristan und Isolde, Act 3; Die Meistersinger von Nürnberg, Act 1; Parsifal, Act 1 and close of Act 3. **New Queen's Hall Orchestra / Barry Wordsworth.** Eye of the Storm (special price) EOS5001 (two discs: 144 minutes: DDD: 6/95). Set includes two performances of each work together with an illustrated talk on "The Instruments". ☞

...Der fliegende Holländer – Overture. Tannhäuser – Overture. Lohengrin – Prelude, Act 1; Prelude, Act 3. Die Meistersinger von Nürnberg – Prelude, Act 1. Tristan und Isolde – Prelude and Liebestod. **Chicago Symphony Orchestra / Daniel Barenboim.** Teldec Ⓕ 4509-99595-2 (63 minutes: DDD: 4/96). *Selected by Soundings.*

...Tannhäuser – Overture; Entry of the Guests (Grand March). Lohengrin – Prelude. Lohengrin – Prelude. Der fliegende Holländer – Overture. Rienzi – Overture. A faust Overture. **Cleveland Orchestra / George Szell; Philadelphia Orchestra / Eugene Ormandy.** Sony Classical Essential Classics Ⓑ SBK62403 (70 minutes: ADD: 1/97).

...Tristan und Isolde – Prelude and Liebestod (arr. Humperdinck). Lohengrin – Preludes, Acts 1 and 3. **R. Strauss** Symphonia domestica, Op. 53. **Berlin Philharmonic Orchestra / Herbert von Karajan.** EMI Karajan Edition Ⓜ CDM5 66107-2 (76 minutes: ADD: 3/97).

Wagner Der Ring des Nibelungen – spoken introduction with 193 musical examples. **Deryck Cooke** (narr); **various singers; Vienna Philharmonic Orchestra / Sir Georg Solti.** Decca The Classic Sound Ⓜ 443 581-2DCS2 (two discs: 141 minutes: ADD: 5/95). Booklet of musical illustrations included. From RING1/22 (12/68). Recorded 1967.   Ⓖ Ⓖ Ⓖ

Deryck Cooke died, prematurely, in 1976 before he completed his comprehensive study on *The Ring*. Fortunately, in 1967, Decca had had the foresight to invite him to record this introduction to the cycle. In this he developed at length his ideas on its leitmotifs using 193 examples, most of them taken from the Solti recording, and a few made specifically to illustrate a point Cooke was making. Wagner, as he avers, described the motifs as "melodic moments of feeling", not signposts or tags. He also adds that their psychological significance and development are of the essence in comprehending *The Ring*, and divides them into four groups – character, objects, events and emotions – which he then proceeds to describe, in simple, pungent language, how they are deployed throughout the work. His straightforward, unfussy method and delivery, so typical of a man quite without egotistical pretension, enhances one's understanding and, more important, enjoyment of this mighty work. It is an absorbing and essential adjunct to anybody's recording of the cycle.

Wagner Tannhäuser – Dich teure Halle. Die Walküre – Der Männer Sippe. Der fliegende Holländer – Joho hoe! Traft ihr das Schiff. Götterdämmerung – Höre mit Sinn; Starke Scheite. Lohengrin – Einsam in trüben Tagen. Parsifal – Grausamer! Fühlst du im Herzen. Tristan und Isolde – Wie lachend sie. **Waltraud Meier** (mez); **Bavarian Radio Symphony Orchestra / Lorin Maazel.** RCA Victor Red Seal Ⓕ 09026 68766-2 (72 minutes: DDD: 8/97). Texts and translations included. Recorded 1966-7. *Gramophone Editor's choice.*

This is without question the most thrilling Wagner disc to appear in years. Bleeding chunks have had a bad press, but when they are performed like this, with utter conviction, verbal acuity and vocal control, producing results at once inspiriting and deeply moving, criticism is silenced. Meier and Maazel have reached, instinctively or not, an ideal rapport: together they create a unanimity of outlook based on urgency in conveying the sense of each passage, so that each heroine comes before us newly minted, at speeds in every case faster than what has become the custom today. In Senta's Ballad, Meier and Maazel bring before us, so immediately, the distraught, possessed woman of Wagner's imagining. Then we hear an Elsa totally convinced of her saviour's arrival, as Meier, with her ever vivid word-painting, mentions "Ein golden Horn", a more positive girl than usual. Waltraute's Narration, benefiting from Maazel's forward-moving tempo and Meier's deeply felt utterance, coheres into a symbol of Wagner's late mastery. Kundry is portrayed as truly trying to win back Parsifal. Isolde's irony is felt in every bar of her Narration and Curse: it's the ability to imprint the smallest phrase on the mind that so distinguishes all these readings and makes them special. You hear that again in Sieglinde's compelling description of Wotan's appearance, even more in Brünnhilde's Immolation. Meier is reaching towards the pinnacle of Wagner singing represented by this latter role; here are the strength of will and the pathos called for by the great finale. The Bavarian Radio Symphony sound truly committed to Maazel, who faithfully follows the ebb and flow of Meier's singing, and the recording, sympathetic to the voice, offers worthy support.

Wagner Tannhäuser – Overture and Venusberg Music. Die Meistersinger von Nürnberg – Prelude, Act 3. Tristan und Isolde – Prelude and Liebestod. **Berlin Philharmonic Orchestra / Herbert von Karajan.** DG Karajan Gold Ⓟ 439 022-2GHS (50 minutes: DDD: 7/96). From 413 754-2GH (2/85). Recorded 1984.

What is so special about Karajan's digital recordings that they are reissued at full price and, ungenerously in this case, with only their original programme? The answer might be another question: when, in modern times, have you heard from Berlin (or anywhere else) such long-drawn, ripe, intense, characterful, perfectly formed and supremely controlled Wagner playing? Not from some other sources with the *Tannhäuser* Overture, whose Pilgrims are less solemn and grand and whose revellers produce less of Karajan's joyous *éclat*. Moving on a few minutes, and the passage where Karajan's Venus succeeds in quelling the riot finds Karajan effecting a spellbinding sudden *diminuendo* (from 4'41", track 2), leaving us with the enchanted eddying of the orchestra. It must surely qualify as one of Karajan's 'greatest moments', had not the seemingly unstoppable tidal wave that preceded it already done so. The true keeper of Berlin's 'Wagner on record' latterly has been Daniel Barenboim. His *Tristan* Prelude (from his complete recording, reviewed further on) is more conventionally paced (i.e. faster) than Karajan's, with the phrasing just as steeply raked, and the balance and control, in some respects, even more accomplished. But the breadth of Karajan's conception is matched by his concentration (it never feels too slow), the playing is achingly intense, the whole superbly built, and the reserves of tone he is able to draw on for the climax seem limitless (the tone is never forced).

Wagner Tannhäuser – Overture. Siegfried Idyll. Tristan und Isolde – Prelude and Liebestod[a]. [a]**Jessye Norman** (sop); **Vienna Philharmonic Orchestra / Herbert von Karajan.** DG Ⓟ 423 613-2GH (54 minutes: DDD: 8/88). Text and translation included. Recorded live in 1987. ⒼⒼ

For the Wagner specialist who has a complete *Tannhäuser* and *Tristan* on the shelves, this disc involves some duplication. Even so, it is not hard to make room for such performances as are heard here. For the non-specialist, the programme provides a good opportunity for a meeting halfway, the common ground between Master and general music-lover being the *Siegfried Idyll*. This offers 20 minutes of delight in the play of musical ideas, structured and yet impulsive, within a sustained mood of gentle affection. The orchestration is something of a miracle, and it can rarely have been heard to better advantage than in this recording, where the ever-changing textures are so clearly displayed and where from every section of the orchestra the sound is of such great loveliness. It comes as a welcome contrast to the *Tannhäuser* Overture, with its big tunes and *fortissimos*, the whole orchestra surging in a frank simulation of physical passion. A further contrast is to follow in the *Tristan* Prelude, where again Karajan and his players are at their best in their feeling for texture and their control of pulse. Jessye Norman, singing the *Liebestod* with tenderness and vibrant opulence of tone, brings the recital to an end. There is scarcely a single reminder that it was recorded live.

Wagner Tristan und Isolde – Love Music (arr. Stokowski). Die Walküre – Ride of the Valkyries; Wotan's Farewell and Magic Fire Music. Götterdämmerung – Siegfried's Death and Funeral March (both arr. Gerhardt). Siegfried Idyll. **National Philharmonic Orchestra / Charles Gerhardt.** Chesky Ⓟ CD161 (78 minutes: DDD: 2/98). Recorded 1985-1995.

Charles Gerhardt made a memorable series of recordings of film music for RCA, and he is equally at home in the flamboyant world of Wagner without voices. He opens with Stokowski's unashamedly indulgent synthesis of the themes from *Tristan und Isolde*, with the vocal parts seamlessly welded into the orchestration, beginning at the Introduction to Act 2, including the Love Music from the same act and the Liebestod. Gerhardt moves naturally from yearning and languishing to real passion, following Stokowski in using divided strings, employing 16 first violins, ten second violins, 12 violas and 12 double-basses. The off-stage six-part hunting-horn episode (at 1'35") sounds glorious with the expansion to ten horns weighted with a bass trombone, Wotan's infinitely touching Farewell to his daughter, Brünnhilde, in *Die Walküre*, and the following truly magical Fire Music. Even without the voices the tremendously committed string playing is very moving indeed, and the recording is superb. The *Siegfried Idyll* is also beautifully played and makes a flowing, gentle interlude. Gerhardt lets the tension slip a little in the middle but gathers the themes together magnetically in the involving closing section. He then begins Siegfried's Death and Funeral March earlier than Stokowski, at the moment when Hagen kills Siegfried. The result is very direct and powerful with fine brass playing. The Valkyries then ride, or rather gallop in at breakneck speed to finish the concert exuberantly. The recordings were made in Walthamstow (*Tristan*, 1985), All Saint's, Petersham (*Die Walküre*, 1994 – the best sound of all), Air Studios (*Siegfried Idyll*, 1995), *Götterdämmerung* (St John's, Smith Square, 1990), and the Valkyries bring another clear, bright studio offering (1995). This is a record for hi-fi buffs, and on really discerning equipment it is fascinating to compare the way the five different engineers have coped with the widely varying ambience effects, with their microphone placing.

Wagner Die Walküre – Ride of the Valkyries; Wotan's Farewell and Magic Fire Music. Siegfried – Forest murmurs. Götterdämmerung – Siegfried's Rhine Journey; Siegfried's funeral march and Immolation scene. Siegfried Idyll. **Staatskapelle Dresden / Donald Runnicles.** Teldec Ⓕ 0630-17109-2 (74 minutes: DDD: 5/98). Recorded live in 1996.   Ⓖ
These excerpts are taken not from opera performances, but from an orchestral concert in the Dresden Staatsoper – and what a magnificently expansive acoustic it has! At the opening of the programme the Valkyries ride in with tremendous weight and purpose; and if when following on, the tearingly poignant scene of "Wotan's Farewell" begins rather in mid-stream, from then onwards one has the sense of a firm and continuing narrative line. Runnicles paces with the experience of the opera-house and creates the most natural ebb and flow of tempo, conveying at first great tenderness, and then on through Wotan's very human grief to the passion of Loge's Fire music (glorious string playing throughout). The Forest murmurs acts as a central interlude, Wagner's tone-painting delightfully evoked, with flashes of urgency anticipating Siegfried's coming quest. In the great Immolation scene so powerful is that final conflagration of brass, with its overriding lyrical string apotheosis, that one is almost aware of the heat of the flames. Throughout, Runnicles generates maximum tension, and one never has the sense that these are just excerpts, purple patches; instead one is carried satisfyingly onwards to the gods' final nemesis and the destruction of Valhalla. The glorious *Siegfried Idyll* acts as a touchingly romantic epilogue. Again the orchestra play very beautifully indeed. Overall this is one of the finest and most moving single-disc summations of what Wagner's orchestral writing is all about, and in the *Ring* the orchestra tell us everything that is happening on stage.

Additional recommendations ...

...Opera Choruses – Der fliegende Holländer; Tannhauser; Lohengrin; Die Meistersinger von Nürnberg; Götterdämmerung; Parsifal. **Bayreuth Festival Chorus and Orchestra / Wilhelm Pitz.** DG Privilege Ⓑ 429 169-2GR* (53 minutes: ADD: 4/90).

...Rienzi – Overture. Tannhäuser – Overture; Venusberg Music. Die Meistersinger von Nürnberg – Prelude, Act 1. Lohengrin – Prelude Act 3. Der fliegende Holländer – Overture. **Orchestra of the Metropolitan Opera, New York / James Levine.** DG Ⓕ 435 874-2GH (60 minutes: DDD: 10/93).

...Tannhäuser – Overture[a]. Lohengrin – Prelude, Act 1. Die Walküre – Ride of the Valkyries[a]. Götterdämmerung – Prelude and Siegfried's Rhine Journey[a]; Siegfried's Funeral March; Immolation Scene[b]. Der fliegende Holländer – Overture[a]. Tristan und Isolde – Prelude and Liebestod[c]. Die Meistersinger von Nürnberg[a] – Preludes – Acts 1 and 3; Dance of the Apprentices. Parsifal – Prelude and Good Friday Music[c].
[b]**Kirsten Flagstadt** (sop); [a]**Vienna Philharmonic Orchestra;** [b]**Philharmonia Orchestra;** [c]**Berlin Philharmonic Orchestra / Wilhelm Furtwängler.**
EMI Références mono Ⓜ CHS7 64935-2* (two discs: 144 minutes: ADD: 4/94).

...Rienzi – Overture. Tannhäuser – Venusberg Music. Tristan und Isolde – Prelude and Liebestod. Die Meistersinger von Nürnberg – Prelude, Act 3; Dance of the Apprentices; Entry of the Masters. Siegfried Idyll. **New York Philharmonic Orchestra / Sir John Barbirolli.** Dutton Laboratories mono Ⓜ CDSJB1001* (76 minutes: ADD: 3/95).   ⒼⒼ

...Tannhäuser – Dich teure Halle; Allmächt'ge Jungfrau. Die Meistersinger von Nürnberg – O Sachs! Mein Freund!. Die Walküre – Du bist der Lenz. *Coupled with works by various composers.* **Dame Kiri Te Kanawa** (sop); **Philharmonia Orchestra / Julius Rudel.** EMI Ⓕ CDC5 56417-2 (57 minutes: DDD: 11/97). *See review in the Collections section; refer to the Index.*

...Tannhäuser – Overture. Die Meistersinger von Nürnberg – Prelude, Act 1. Götterdämmerung – Siegfried's Rhine Journey; Siegfried's Funeral March. **R. Strauss** Le bourgeois gentilhomme – Suite, Op. 60. **Philharmonia Orchestra / Wolfgang Sawallisch.** Testament Ⓕ SBT1112* (76 minutes: ADD: A/97).

Wagner Der fliegende Holländer. **Theo Adam** (bar) Holländer; **Anja Silja** (sop) Senta; **Martti Talvela** (bass) Daland; **Ernst Kozub** (ten) Erik; **Annelies Burmeister** (mez) Mary; **Gerhard Unger** (ten) Steuermann; **BBC Chorus; New Philharmonia Orchestra / Otto Klemperer.** EMI Ⓕ CDS5 55179-2 (three discs: 152 minutes: ADD). Notes, text and translation included. Recorded 1968.   ⒼⒼⒼ

Wagner Der fliegende Holländer. **Robert Hale** (bass-bar) Holländer; **Hildegard Behrens** (sop) Senta; **Kurt Rydl** (bass) Daland; **Josef Protschka** (ten) Erik; **Iris Vermillion** (mez) Mary; **Uwe Heilmann** (ten) Steuermann; **Vienna State Opera Concert Choir; Vienna Philharmonic Orchestra / Christoph von Dohnányi.** Decca Ⓕ 436 418-2DHO2 (two discs: 145 minutes: DDD: 4/94). Notes, text and translation included. Recorded 1991. *Gramophone Editor's choice.* Ⓖ

Klemperer's magisterial interpretation of this work was unavailable in any form for far too long so that its reissue was most welcome. In treating the work symphonically, it is something of a contrast with the 1985 Bayreuth/Philips version under Woldemar Nelsson which employs faster speeds and a more dynamic view of the score like the famous 1955 Keilberth set from Bayreuth. As ever, Klemperer by and large justifies some moderate tempos by the way in which he sustains line and emphasizes detail. Only once or twice – in the Spinning and Sailors choruses – do you sense a lack of propulsion. Otherwise there is throughout a blazing intensity to the reading that brooks no denial. The storm and sea music in the Overture and thereafter is given stunning power, and the Dutchman's torture and passion is evoked in the orchestra. Indeed, the playing of the New Philharmonia is a bonus throughout. Klemperer catches as convincingly as anyone the elemental feeling of the work – the sense of the sea, basic passions and the interplay of character unerringly adumbrated. There have been few baritones before or since Theo Adam who have sustained the line of the Dutchman so well and so intelligently reached the heart of the matter where the text is concerned. Silja's bright, sometimes piercing timbre isn't to everyone's taste, but hers is a most moving portrayal of trust and loyalty and love unto death, the interpretation of an outstanding singing-actress. Martti Talvela, singing magnificently and suggesting a formidable presence, is a bluff, burly Daland. Ernst Kozub's Erik has its clumsy moments but one admires the shining tone. Gerhard Unger offers an ardent, cleanly articulated Sailor. Annelies Burmeister is a ripe Mary. The BBC Chorus are very much in the picture. The overall sound is a shade on the dry side, but better that than the excessive reverberation on so many opera sets today.

Singers, conductor, chorus, orchestra and engineers combine to make Dohnányi's set the most successful modern recording of the work. With the Vienna Philharmonic responding to Dohnányi's precise and energizing beat from start to finish the sea does really seem to course through the score as Wagner intended. Dohnányi emphasizes the raw, even untutored sound of much of the orchestration, giving the wind and brass the prominence they deserve. Taut, springy rhythms abound from the Overture onwards. He opts for the three-act version and the full ending. Hale is an exemplary Dutchman and sings with great depth and understanding. This is evident throughout a masterly traversal of his long monologue, where the required torment in the tone is revealed to the full. Behrens captures Senta's single-minded passion and infatuation, singing the quieter passages with refined sensitivity, the forceful ones with fearless attack; and satisfaction extends to the lesser roles. The chorus are superb as sailors, ghost crew and townspeople, singing with firm tone and exact attack. Nothing here is left unconsidered yet, amazingly, for the most part a real sense of the theatre is achieved throughout. For that we have to thank the Decca team. Balance, depth, perspectives all seem blessedly natural; undoctored and inevitable, so that one is able to take the sound picture for granted.

Additional recommendations ...
...**Soloists; Chorus and Orchestra of the Royal Opera House, Covent Garden / Antál Dorati.** Decca Grand Opera Ⓜ 417 319-2DM2 (two discs: 145 minutes: ADD: 8/90).
...**Soloists; Bayreuth Festival Chorus and Orchestra / Woldemar Nelsson.** Philips Ⓜ 434 599-2PH2 (two discs: 134 minutes: DDD: 10/92).
...**Soloists; Bayreuth Festival Chorus and Orchestra / Karl Böhm.** DG Ⓜ 437 710-2GX2 (two discs: 134 minutes: ADD: 8/93).
...**Soloists; Austrian Radio Chorus and Symphony Orchestra / Pinchas Steinberg.** Naxos Ⓢ 8 660025/6 (two discs: 139 minutes: DDD: 9/93). *Gramophone Editor's choice.*
...**Soloists; Bayreuth Festival Chorus and Orchestra / Wolfgang Sawallisch.** Philips Ⓜ 442 103-2PM2 (two discs: 124 minutes: ADD: 9/94).
...**Soloists; Berlin Deutsche Oper Chorus and Orchestra / Franz Konwitschny.** Berlin Classics Ⓕ BC2097-2 (two discs: 141 minutes: ADD: 9/94).
...**Soloists; Bavarian State Opera Chorus and Orchestra / Clemens Krauss.** Preiser mono Ⓕ 90250* (two discs: 143 minutes: ADD: 6/96).
...Der fliegende Holländer[a]. Die Meistersinger von Nürnberg – Was duftet.Wahn! Wahn! Uberall Wahn![c]. **Soloists;** [a]**Bayreuth Festival Chorus and Orchestra / Richard Kraus;** [c]**Joel Berlund** (bar); [b]**Ludwig Hofmann** (bass); [b]**Berlin State Opera Orchestra / Franz Alfred Schmidt;** [c]**Royal Stockholm Orchestra / Nils Grevillius.** Preiser mono Ⓕ 90232* (two discs: 153 minutes: ADD: 6/96).
...**Soloists; Chorus and Orchestra of the Bayreuth Festival / Joseph Keilberth.** Teldec mono Ⓜ 4509-97491-2* (two discs: 139 minutes: ADD: 9/97).

Wagner Lohengrin. **Paul Frey** (ten) Lohengrin; **Cheryl Studer** (sop) Elsa of Brabant; **Gabriele Schnaut** (sop) Ortrud; **Ekkehard Wlaschiha** (bar) Telramund; **Manfred Schenk** (bass) King Henry; **Eike Wilm Schulte** (bar) Herald; **Bayreuth Festival Chorus and Orchestra / Peter Schneider.** Philips Ⓜ 434 602-2PH4 (four discs: 212 minutes: DDD: 10/92). Recorded 1990.
Wagner Lohengrin. **James King** (ten) Lohengrin; **Gundula Janowitz** (sop) Elsa; **Dame Gwyneth Jones** (sop) Ortrud; **Thomas Stewart** (bar) Telramund; **Karl Ridderbusch** (bass) King Henry;

Gerd Nienstedt (bass) Herald; **Bavarian Radio Chorus and Symphony Orchestra / Rafael Kubelík.**
DG Ⓜ 449 591-2GX3 (three discs: 222 minutes: ADD: 8/96). Notes, text and translation
included. From 2720 036 (12/71).

Schneider's is a splendidly absorbing performance of *Lohengrin*. This underrated conductor provides
a straightforward, no-nonsense reading in the best *Kapellmeister* tradition, avoiding the extremes of
tempo interpretation of some more highly-powered conductors. He obtains playing and singing of the
highest calibre from the Bayreuth orchestra and chorus, sustains the long and sometimes tedious-
seeming paragraphs of Acts 1 and 2 without ever allowing boredom to intervene, and brings
extraordinary tension to such forward-looking scenes as Lohengrin's arrival, the Ortrud-Telramund
dialogue and the psychologically intense duet for Elsa and Lohengrin in Act 3. Elsa was one of the
roles with which Studer made her name on the international scene; she sings it here once more with
refulgent tone, understanding of the text and comprehension of Elsa's dreamy then troubled
personality. Particularly affecting is her desperate appeal to Lohengrin at the end of Act 2. Paul Frey
is a sensitive, chivalrous Lohengrin, even if his voice hasn't quite the Heldentenor strength of some of
his predecessors. Evil is reasonably well represented. Wlaschiha is a vital and nasty Telramund, keenly
projecting the character's chip-on-the-shoulder malevolence of the words. Schnaut has an imposing,
powerful soprano although more could have been made of the words than she achieves. Schenk is a
well-routined King, Schulte a superb Herald. Incidentally, Schneider observes the traditional
(Wagner's) cut just before Lohengrin's Farewell, although the passage is printed in full in the booklet.
This set is well worth considering in a sparse recommendable field of available versions.

The attributes of Kubelík's *Lohengrin*, which appears for the first time on CD, have been
underestimated. It will hold your interest from first to last, not least thanks to Kubelík's masterly
overview. Not only does he successfully hold together all the disparate strands of the sprawling work,
he also imparts to them a sense of inner excitement through his close attention to the small notes and
phrases that so often delineate character in this score and through his vital control of the large
ensembles. He is helped inestimably by the Bavarian Radio forces – gloriously singing strings,
characterful winds, trenchant, involving chorus – of which he was, in 1971, a beloved chief. There's
never a dull moment in his vivid, theatrical *Lohengrin*. The recording imparts a suitably spacious
atmosphere to the piece but also places the principals up front where they should be except when
distancing is required – as at Lohengrin's first appearance and at the moment when Elsa appears on
the balcony to address the night breezes. Janowitz's Elsa is one of the set's major assets. Pure in tone,
imaginative in phrasing, she catches the ear from her first entry, very much suggesting Elsa's
vulnerability. Later she eloquently conveys her deep feelings in the love duet, followed by her voicing
of all the doubts that beset her character. King's Lohengrin is more ordinary; today we would be
grateful for such solid, musical and well-judged singing. Few if any Lohengrins can sing the passage
starting "Höchstes Vertraun" (third disc, track 5) with anything like King's true tone and powerful
conviction. Though not as detailed or subtle in his colouring of the text as some, Thomas Stewart
sings a sturdy Telramund, managing the high tessitura with consummate ease. He is horribly plausible
in his complaints against Elsa. This portrayal discloses him as a grossly undervalued singer. Dame
Gwyneth Jones's portrayal, taken all-round, is reasonably convincing despite turning a vibrato that
might flatteringly be called opulent into something more objectionable. Her Ortrud registers high on
the scale of vicious malevolence in the part. The difficulty, as it always has been with this intelligent
artist, is that the subtlety evinced in quiet passages is vitiated when the tone comes under pressure –
but some Ortruds today are far more guilty in that respect than Jones. As King Henry, Ridderbusch
offers a judicious blend of sympathy and authority dispensed in fluent, warm tone. Nienstedt makes
the Herald's pronouncements moments to savour. The chorus are nothing short of superb. So, this
makes an irresistible bid for recommendation. It is well recorded, sounding wholly resplendent and as
cogently conducted as any of its rivals.

Additional recommendations ...

...**Soloists; Vienna State Opera Chorus; Vienna Philharmonic Orchestra / Sir Georg Solti.**
Decca Ⓕ 421 053-2DH4 (four discs: 223 minutes: DDD: 10/87).

...**Soloists; Vienna State Opera Chorus; Vienna Philharmonic Orchestra / Rudolf Kempe.**
EMI Ⓕ CDS7 49017-8 (three discs: 219 minutes: ADD: 2/88).

...**Soloists; Bayreuth Festival Chorus and Orchestra / Joseph Keilberth.**
Teldec Historic Series mono Ⓜ 4509-93674-2* (four discs: 220 minutes: ADD: 10/94).

...**Soloists; Cologne Radio Chorus; North German Radio
Chorus and Symphony Orchestra / Wilhelm Schüchter.**
EMI Références mono Ⓜ CHS5 65517-2* (three discs: 197 minutes: ADD: 12/95).

Wagner Die Meistersinger von Nürnberg. **Bernd Weikl** (bar) Hans Sachs; **Ben Heppner** (ten)
Walther; **Cheryl Studer** (sop) Eva; **Kurt Moll** (bass) Pogner; **Siegfried Lorenz** (bar) Beckmesser;
Deon van der Walt (ten) David; **Cornelia Kallisch** (contr) Magdalene; **Hans-Joachim Ketelsen**
(bar) Kothner; **Michael Schade** (ten) Vogelgesang; **Hans Wilbrink** (bar) Nachtigall; **Ulrich Ress**
(ten) Zorn; **Hermann Sapell** (bar) Eisslinger; **Roland Wagenführer** (ten) Moser; **Rainer Büse** (bass)
Ortel; **Guido Götzen** (bass) Schwarz; **Friedmann Kunder** (bass) Foltz; **René Pape** (bass)
Nightwatchman; **Bavarian State Opera Chorus; Bavarian State Orchestra / Wolfgang Sawallisch.**
EMI Ⓕ CDS5 55142-2 (four discs: 257 minutes: DDD: 8/94). Notes, text and translation
included. Recorded 1993.

Sawallisch's *Meistersinger* is very much a version for today – profoundly musical, as it was bound to be under him, sung with a consistent beauty of sound, and recorded truthfully and spaciously. Anybody coming to the work for the first time, and wanting a version backed by modern sound, will find it a sensible choice, a performance for the most part measuring up to the score's many demands on its interpreters. Sawallisch obtains singing and playing on the highest level of achievement, observant of detail, rich in texture, sure in pacing and – very important in this score – anxious to move forward where there is any danger of the music seeming over-extended, as in the recital of the tones and the Act 2 episode of Beckmesser's courting. Sawallisch's reading also catches the warmth that pervades the whole opera, yet is also successful in deftly projecting its comedy. It must be said, however, that with Sawallisch the earth doesn't move, the spirit is seldom lifted as it should be – and can be, witness Karajan and Abendroth. On the other hand, nobody is better than Sawallisch at characterizing the disputes between the Masters in Act 1, or the pointed humour of the Act 2 Sachs/Beckmesser scene, and much else of that nature is unobtrusively right. Where the recording itself is concerned, great care has been taken over the placing of the singers in relation to one another and the correct distancing of the voices when called for. The balance in relation to the orchestra seems just about ideal. In the modern manner the chorus is placed a little too far back. Even so, Sawallisch takes an honoured place in the illustrious company listed below. His reading is full of thoughtful *apercus* and natural flow, and displays a sensible overview of the score. Vocally it will satisfy all but those with the most demanding tastes in, and/or, long experience in Wagnerian interpretation.

Additional recommendations ...
...Soloists; St Hedwig's Cathedral Choir, Berlin; Chorus of the Deutsche Oper, Berlin; Berlin State Opera Chorus; Berlin Philharmonic Orchestra / **Rudolf Kempe.**
EMI mono Ⓜ CMS7 64154-2* (four discs: 260 minutes: ADD: 2/93).　　　ⒼⒼ
...Soloists; Bayreuth Festival Chorus and Orchestra / **Hermann Abendroth.**
Preiser mono Ⓕ 90174* (four discs: 262 minutes: ADD: 2/94).
...Soloists; Vienna State Opera Chorus; Vienna Philharmonic Orchestra / **Hans Knappertsbusch.**
Decca Historic Series mono Ⓜ 440 057-2DMO4* (four discs: 266 minutes: ADD: 10/94).
...Soloists; Vienna State Opera Chorus; Vienna Philharmonic Orchestra / **Karl Böhm.**
Preiser mono Ⓕ 90234* (four discs: 266 minutes: AAD: 6/95).
...Soloists; Chicago Symphony Chorus and Orchestra / **Sir Georg Solti.**
Decca Ⓕ 452 606-2DHO4 (four discs: 259 minutes: DDD: 3/97).

Wagner Die Meistersinger von Nürnberg. **Otto Edelmann** (bass) Hans Sachs; **Hans Hopf** (ten) Walther; **Dame Elisabeth Schwarzkopf** (sop) Eva; **Friedrich Dalberg** (bass) Pogner; **Erich Kunz** (bar) Beckmesser; **Gerhard Unger** (ten) David; **Ira Malaniuk** (contr) Magdalene; **Heinrich Pflanzl** (bar) Kothner; **Erich Majkut** (ten) Vogelsang; **Hans Berg** (bass) Nachtigall; **Josef Janko** (ten) Zorn; **Krl Mikorey** (ten) Eisslinger; **Gerhard Stolze** (ten) Moser; **Heinz Tandler** (bass) Ortel; |**Heinz Borst** (bass) Schwarz; **Arnold van Mill** (bass) Foltz; **Werner Faulhaber** (bass) Nightwatchman; **Bayreuth Festival Chorus and Orchestra / Herbert von Karajan.**
EMI Références mono Ⓜ CHS7 63500-2* (four discs: 267 minutes: ADD: 9/90).
Notes and text included. From Columbia LX1465/98 (12/51). Recorded live in 1951.
Gramophone classical 100.　　　　　　　　　　　　　　　　　　　　Ⓖ ⒼⒼ
In his well-researched note to this reissue, Richard Osborne very properly writes that "the miracle of Karajan's conducting is that it marries fervour with lucidity in particular measure". That can be heard most tellingly in the work's most inspired section – the first four scenes of Act 3. The instrumental detail that characterizes and describes Beckmesser's movements as he steals into Sachs's study is delineated with a refined clarity that ideally brings out its humour. Then in the following scene Karajan is inspired to heights of intensity and concentration as Sachs and Eva play out their emotional entanglement culminating in "O Sachs, mein Freund" and the Quintet. It is here, too, that Schwarzköpf's Eva and Edelmann's Sachs add a further touch of eloquence to their already finely wrought performances. The underrated Edelmann gives the best sung Sachs in any complete recording. He has the prime virtues of perfect firmness, a true legato and a strong, full-bodied, unforced, totally likeable tone. You may not find the individuality of phrase here that other, older interpreters give us, but in his varied responses to the masters, Eva, Walther and Beckmesser, he is unfailingly true to Sachs as the poet-cobbler, and his voice proves virtually tireless. One might argue as to whether the youthful Schwarzkopf is quite as lovable and outgoing an Eva as Grümmer for Kempe (this set's closest mono rival), but in respect of radiant tone, musical phrasing, wit allied to beauty, she hasn't a peer. Nor has Gerhard Unger as David, who sings his role with the fresh tone and eager responses it calls for. With the rest of the singers, a few – but not many – reservations have to be made. This set won't be for those who mind occasional coughs – they're most troublesome in the Third Act Prelude, just when you want silence to admire Karajan's deeply moving interpretation – or who must have stereo and perfect voice/orchestra balance. But for anyone who appreciates a true-to-life, responsive and exceptionally intense experience this is a version to cherish.

Wagner Die Meistersinger von Nürnberg. **Thomas Stewart** (bar) Hans Sachs; **Sándor Kónya** (ten) Walther; **Gundula Janowitz** (sop) Eva; **Franz Crass** (bass) Pogner; **Thomas Hemsley** (bar) Beckmesser; **Gerhard Unger** (ten) David; **Brigitte Fassbaender** (mez) Magdalene; **Kieth Engen**

(bass) Kothner; **Horst Wilhelm** (ten) Vogelgesang; **Richard Kogel** (bass) Nachtigall;
Manfred Schmidt (ten) Zorn; **Friedrich Lenz** (ten) Eisslinger; **Peter Baille** (ten) Moser;
Anton Diakov (bass) Ortel; **Karl Christian Kohn** (bass) Schwartz; **Dieter Slembeck** (bass) Foltz;
Raimund Grumbach (bass) Nightwatchman; **Bavarian Radio Chorus and Symphony Orchestra /**
Rafael Kubelík. Calig Ⓕ CAL50971/4 (four discs: 272 minutes: ADD: 1/97). Recorded 1967.
There could be no more fitting memorial to Kubelík than the appearance of this, probably the most
all-round satisfying *Meistersinger* in the era of stereo. It was recorded in 1967 by Bavarian Radio to
mark the work's centenary the following year. Kubelík conducts an unforced, loving interpretation,
showing a gratifying grasp of overall structure. As a whole the reading has an unobtrusive cohesion
achieved within flexible tempos and dynamics. Everything proceeds at an even, well-judged pace with
just the right surge of emotion at the climaxes. All this is conveyed unerringly to his own Bavarian
Radio Symphony forces. Stewart's Sachs is certainly his most successful performance on disc. He
offers a finely moulded, deeply considered reading that relies on firm, evenly produced, mostly warm
tone to create a darkish, philosophical poet-cobbler. Kónya is simply the most winning Walther on
any set, superseding Sawallisch's excellent Heppner by virtue of a greater ardour in his delivery and
Kempe's admirable Schock because he has the more pleasing voice. Kónya pours out consistently
warm, clear tone, his tenor hovering ideally between the lyric and the heroic. Nor are there many
better Evas than the young Janowitz, certainly none with a lovelier voice. Schwarzkopf for Karajan
and Grümmer for Kempe may achieve a greater intensity of phrase (as at the start of the Quintet) but
Janowitz is very nearly their equal. Franz Crass, a less pompous Pogner than some, sings his part
effortlessly, with noble feeling. Hemsley, though singing his first Beckmesser, evinces a close affinity
with the Town Clerk's mean-mindedness, and his German is faultless. As in his previous assumptions
of the role (Karajan and Kempe), Unger is a paragon among Davids, so eager in his responses
and finding just the right timbre for the role. His Magdalene, again perfect casting, is the
young Fassbaender. With a characterful Kothner in Engen, the requirements for a near-ideal
Meistersinger ensemble are in place. As the recording doesn't betray its age this would undoubtedly
be the first choice among stereo versions, superseding even Karajan because Kubelík's cast
is superior.

Wagner Parsifal. **Jess Thomas** (ten) Parsifal; **George London** (bass-bar) Amfortas; **Hans Hotter**
(bass) Gurnemanz; **Irene Dalis** (mez) Kundry; **Gustav Neidlinger** (bass) Klingsor; **Martti Talvela**
(bass) Titurel; **Niels Möller** (ten) First Knight; **Gerd Neinstedt** (bass) Second Knight;
Sona Cervená (mez), **Ursula Boese** (contr), **Gerhard Stolze, Georg Paskuda** (tens) Squires;
Gundula Janowitz, Anja Silja, Else-Margrete Gardelli, Dorothea Siebert, Rita Bartos (sops),
Sona Cervená (mez) Flower Maidens; **Bayreuth Festival Chorus and Orchestra / Hans**
Knappertsbusch. Philips Ⓕ 416 390-2PH4 (four discs: 250 minutes: ADD: 6/86).
Notes, text and translation included. Recorded live in 1962. From SAL3475 (11/64).   ⒺⒼⒺ
There have been many fine recordings of this great Eastertide opera, but none have so magnificently
captured the power, the spiritual grandeur, the human frailty and the almost unbearable beauty of the
work as Hans Knappertsbusch. This live recording has a cast that has few equals. Hotter is superb,
fleshing out Gurnemanz with a depth of insight that has never been surpassed. London's Amfortas
captures the frightening sense of impotence and anguish with painful directness whilst Thomas's
Parsifal grows as the performance progresses and is no mean achievement. Dalis may lack that final
degree of sensuousness but gives a fine interpretation. Throughout Knappertsbusch exercises a quite
unequalled control over the proceedings; it is a fine testament to a great conductor. The Bayreuth
acoustic is well reproduced and all in all it is a profound and moving experience.

Wagner Parsifal. **Peter Hofmann** (ten) Parsifal; **José van Dam** (bass-bar) Amfortas; **Kurt Moll**
(bass) Gurnemanz; **Dunja Vejzovic** (mez) Kundry; **Siegmund Nimsgern** (bass) Klingsor;
Victor von Halem (bass) Titurel; **Claes Hakon Ahnsjö** (ten) First Knight; **Kurt Rydl** (bass) Second
Knight; **Marjon Lambriks, Anne Gjevang** (mezzos), **Heiner Hopfner** (ten), **Georg Tichy** (bass)
Squires; **Barbara Hendricks, Janet Perry, Inga Nielsen** (sops), **Audrey Michael** (mez), **Doris Soffel,**
Rohângiz Yachmi Caucig (contrs) Flower Maidens; **Hanna Schwarz** *mez* Voice from above
Berlin Deutsch Opera Chorus; Berlin Philharmonic Orchestra / Herbert von Karajan.
DG Ⓕ 413 347-2GH4 (four discs: 256 minutes: ADD: 10/84). Notes, text and translation
included. From 2741 002 (4/81). Recorded 1979-1980. *Gramophone Award Winner 1981.*   ⒺⒼ
Karajan's *Parsifal* seems to grow in stature as an interpretation on each rehearing; on its CD transfer
it appears to have acquired a new depth, in terms of sound, because of the greater range of the
recording and the greater presence of both singers and orchestra. As in practically all cases, CD offers
a more immediate experience. Karajan's reading, a trifle stodgy in Act 1, grows in intensity and feeling
with the work itself, reaching an almost terrifying force in the Prelude to Act 3 which is sustained to
the end of the opera. Moll's Gurnemanz is a deeply expressive, softly-moulded performance of
notable beauty. Vejzovic, carefully nurtured by Karajan, gives the performance of her life as Kundry.
Hoffmann's tone isn't at all times so steady as a Parsifal's should be, but he depicts the character's
anguish and eventual serenity in his sincere, inward interpretation. Van Dam is a trifle too placid as
Amfortas but his singing has admirable power and steadiness. Nimsgern is the epitome of malice as
Klingsor. The choral singing hasn't quite the confidence of the superb orchestral playing which has
both qualities of Keats's imagining of beauty and truth in abundance.

Additional recommendations ...
...Soloists; Welsh National Opera Chorus and Orchestra / Sir Reginald Goodall.
EMI Ⓜ CMS5 65665-2 (four discs: 295 minutes: DDD).
...Soloists; Berlin State Opera Chorus; Berlin Philharmonic Orchestra / Daniel Barenboim.
Teldec Ⓕ 9031-74448-2 (four discs: 256 minutes: DDD: 10/91).
...Soloists; Bayreuth Festival Chorus and Orchestra / Hans Knappertsbusch. Teldec Historic Series
mono Ⓜ 9031-76047-2* (four discs: 272 minutes: ADD: 8/93). *Gramophone Editor's choice.*

Wagner Das Rheingold. **John Tomlinson** (bass) Wotan; **Linda Finnie** (mez) Fricka; **Graham Clark**
(ten) Loge; **Helmut Pampuch** (ten) Mime; **Günter von Kannen** (bar) Alberich; **Eva Johansson** (sop)
Freia; **Kurt Schreibmayer** (ten) Froh; **Bodo Brinkmann** (bar) Donner; **Birgitta Svendén** (mez) Erda;
Matthias Hölle (bass) Fasolt; **Philip Kang** (bass) Fafner; **Hilde Leidland** (sop) Woglinde;
Annette Küttenbaum (mez) Wellgunde; **Jane Turner** (mez) Flosshilde; **Bayreuth Festival
Orchestra / Daniel Barenboim**. Teldec Ⓕ 4509-91185-2 (two discs: 149 minutes: DDD: 10/93).
Notes, text and translation included. Recorded live in 1991.
Wagner Die Walküre. **Poul Elming** (ten) Siegmund; **Nadine Secunde** (sop) Sieglinde;
Anne Evans (sop) Brünnhilde; **John Tomlinson** (bass) Wotan; **Linda Finnie** (mez) Fricka,
Siegrune; **Matthias Hölle** (bass) Hunding; **Eva Johansson** (sop) Gerhilde; **Eva-Maria Bundschuh**
(sop) Helmwige; **Ruth Floeren** (sop) Ortlinde; **Shirley Close** (mez) Waltraute; **Hebe Dijkstra** (mez)
Rossweisse; **Birgitta Svendén** (mez) Grimgerde; **Hitomi Katagiri** (mez) Schwertleite;
Bayreuth Festival Orchestra / Daniel Barenboim. Teldec Ⓕ 4509 91186-2
(four discs: 233 minutes: DDD: 10/93). Recorded live in 1992.
These are enthralling performances. Tomlinson's volatile Wotan is the most potent reading here. He
manages to sing every word with insistent meaning and forceful declamation while maintaining a firm
legato. His German is so idiomatic that he might have been speaking the language his whole life and
he brings breadth and distinction of phrase to his solos at the close of both operas. Anne Evans has
a single, important advantage over other recent Brunnhildes in that her voice is wholly free from
wobble and she never makes an ugly sound. Hers is a light, girlish, honest portrayal, sung with
unfailing musicality if not with the ultimate insights. Linda Finnie is an articulate, sharp-edged
Fricka, and Graham Clark a sparky, incisive Loge. Nadine Secunde's impassioned Sieglinde is
matched by the vital, exciting Siegmund of Poul Elming and Matthias Hölle as both Hunding and
Fasolt is another of those black basses of which Germany seems to have an inexhaustible supply. The
whole of *Das Rheingold* is magnificently conducted by Barenboim, a more expansive Wagnerian than
Böhm. By 1991 he had the full measure of its many facets, brought immense authority and power to
building its huge climaxes, yet finds all the lightness of touch for the mercurial and/or diaphanous
aspects of this amazing score. He has the inestimable advantage of a Bayreuth orchestra at the peak
of their form, surpassing – and this says much – even the Metropolitan orchestra for Levine, and
Barenboim's reading is more convincing as a whole than Levine's. Similar qualities inform his
interpretation of *Die Walküre*. Barenboim has now learnt how to match the epic stature of Wagner's
mature works, how to pace them with an overview of the whole and there is an incandescent,
metaphysical feeling of a Furwänglerian kind in his treatment of such passages as Wotan's anger and
the Valkyrie ride. Again, the orchestra are superb. They are backed by a recording of startling
presence and depth, amply capturing the Bayreuth acoustic.
Additional recommendations ...
...Das Rheingold. **Soloists; Vienna Philharmonic Orchestra / Sir Georg Solti.**
Decca Ⓕ 455 556-2DHO2 (two discs: ADD: 10/84).
...Das Rheingold. **Soloists; Bavarian Radio Symphony Orchestra / Bernard Haitink.**
EMI Ⓕ CDS7 49853-2 (two discs: 149 minutes: DDD: 12/89).
...Die Walküre. **Soloists; Bayreuth Festival Orchestra / Clemens Krauss.**
Foyer mono Ⓕ 4-CF2008* (four discs: 212 minutes: ADD: 6/88).
...Die Walküre – Act 1. **Soloists; Bayreuth Festival Orchestra / Karl Böhm.**
Philips Solo Ⓜ 442 640-2PM (62 minutes: ADD: 7/95).

Wagner Rienzi. **René Kollo** (ten) Cola Rienzi; **Siv Wennberg** (sop) Irene; **Janis Martin** (sop)
Adriano; **Theo Adam** (bass) Paolo Orsini; **Nikolaus Hillebrand** (bass) Steffano Colonna; **Siegfried
Vogel** (bass) Raimondo; **Peter Schreier** (ten) Baroncelli; **Günther Leib** (bass) Cecco del Vecchio;
Ingeborg Springer (sop) Messenger of Peace; **Leipzig Radio Chorus; Dresden State Opera Chorus;
Dresden Staatskapelle / Heinrich Hollreiser**. EMI Ⓜ CMS7 63980-2 (three discs: 225 minutes:
ADD: 2/92). Notes, text and translation included. From SLS990 (11/76). Recorded 1974-1976.
Rienzi is grand opera with a vengeance. Political imperatives count for more than mere human
feelings, and politics means ceremony as well as warfare: marches, ballet music and extended choruses
are much in evidence, while even the solo arias often have the rhetorical punch of political harangues.
It could all be an enormous bore. Yet the young Wagner, basing his work on Bulwer Lytton's story of
the tragic Roman tribune, did manage to move beyond mere tub-thumping into a degree of intensity
that – for those with ears to hear – prefigures the mature genius to come. In the end, Rienzi himself is
more than just a political animal, and the existential anguish of Tannhäuser, Tristan and even
Amfortas glimmers in the distance. It would be idle to pretend that this performance is ideal in every
respect, either musically, or as a recording. But its virtues outweigh its weaknesses by a considerable

margin. Siv Wennberg was not in best voice at the time, but the other principals, notably René Kollo and Janis Martin, bring commendable stamina and conviction to their demanding roles. Above all the conductor Heinrich Hollreiser prevents the more routine material from sounding merely mechanical, and ensures that the whole work has a truly Wagnerian sweep and fervour.

Additional recommendation ...

...**Soloists; Bavarian State Opera Chorus and Orchestra / Wolfgang Sawallisch.**
Orfeo d'Or Ⓕ C346953D (three discs: 195 minutes: ADD: 5/96).

Wagner Der Ring des Nibelungen.

Das Rheingold. **Theo Adam** (bass-bar) Wotan; **Annelies Burmeister** (mez) Fricka; **Wolfgang Windgassen** (ten) Loge; **Erwin Wohlfahrt** (ten) Mime; **Gustav Neidlinger** (bass) Alberich; **Anja Silja** (sop) Freia; **Hermin Esser** (ten) Froh; **Gerd Nienstedt** (bass) Donner; **Vera Soukupova** (mez) Erda; **Martti Talvela** (bass) Fasolt; **Kurt Boehme** (bass) Fafner; **Dorothea Siebert** (sop) Woglinde; **Helga Dernesch** (sop) Wellgunde; **Ruth Hesse** (mez) Flosshilde; **Bayreuth Festival Chorus and Orchestra / Karl Böhm.** Philips Ⓕ 412 475-2PH2 (two discs: 137 minutes: ADD: 7/85). Notes, text and translation included. Recorded at a performance in the Festspielhaus, Bayreuth in 1967. From 6747 037 (9/73). ⒼⒼⒼ

Die Walküre. **James King** (ten) Siegmund; **Leonie Rysanek** (sop) Sieglinde; **Birgit Nilsson** (sop) Brünnhilde; **Theo Adam** (bass) Wotan; **Annelies Burmeister** (mez) Fricka, Siegrune; **Gerd Nienstedt** (bass) Hunding; **Danica Mastilovic** (sop) Gerhilde; **Liane Synek** (sop) Helmwige; **Helga Dernesch** (sop) Ortlinde; **Gertraud Hopf** (mez) Waltraute; **Sona Cervená** (mez) Rossweisse; **Elisabeth Schärtel** (contr) Grimgerde; **Sieglinde Wagner** (contr) Schwertleite; **Bayreuth Festival Chorus and Orchestra / Karl Böhm.** Philips Ⓕ 412 478-2PH4 (four discs: 210 minutes: ADD: 2/85). Notes, text and translation included. Recorded live in 1967. From 6747 037 (9/73). ⒼⒼⒼ

Siegfried. **Wolfgang Windgassen** (ten) Siegfried; **Theo Adam** (bass) Wanderer; **Birgit Nilsson** (sop) Brünnhilde; **Erwin Wohlfahrt** (ten) Mime; **Gustav Neidlinger** (bass) Alberich; **Vera Soukupova** (mez) Erda; **Kurt Boehme** (bass) Fafner; **Erika Köth** (sop) Woodbird; **Bayreuth Festival Orchestra / Karl Böhm.** Philips Ⓕ 412 483-2PH4 (four discs: 223 minutes: ADD: 8/85). Notes, text and translation included. Recorded live in 1967. From 6747 037 (9/73). ⒼⒼⒼ

Götterdämmerung. **Birgit Nilsson** (sop) Brünnhilde; **Wolfgang Windgassen** (ten) Siegfried; **Josef Greindl** (bass) Hagen; **Gustav Neidlinger** (bass-bar) Alberich; **Thomas Stewart** (bar) Gunther; **Ludmila Dvořáková** (sop) Gutrune; **Martha Mödl** (mez) Waltraute; **Dorothea Siebert** (sop) Woglinde; **Helga Dernesch** (sop) Wellgunde; **Sieglinde Wagner** (contr) Flosshilde; **Marga Höffgen** (contr) First Norn; **Annelies Burmeister** (mez) Second Norn; **Anja Silja** (sop) Third Norn; **Bayreuth Festival Chorus and Orchestra / Karl Böhm.** Philips Ⓕ 412 488-2PH4 (four discs: 249 minutes: ADD: 5/85). Notes, text and translation included. Recorded live in 1967. From 6747 037 (9/73). ⒼⒼⒼ

Wagner's *Der Ring des Nibelungen* is the greatest music-drama ever penned. It deals with the eternal questions of power, love, personal responsibility and moral behaviour, and has always been open to numerous interpretations, both dramatic and musical. For every generation, it presents a new challenge, yet certain musical performances have undoubtedly stood the test of time. One would recommend the recording made at Bayreuth in 1967 because, above all others, it represents a true and living account of a huge work as it was performed in the opera house for which it was largely conceived. Every artist who appears at Bayreuth seems to find an extra dedication in their comportment there, and on this occasion many of the singers and the conductor surpassed what they achieved elsewhere. Böhm's reading is notable for its dramatic drive and inner tension. For the most part he also encompasses the metaphysical aspects of the score as well, and he procures playing of warmth and depth from the Bayreuth orchestra. Birgit Nilsson heads the cast as an unsurpassed Brünnhilde, wonderfully vivid in her characterization and enunciation, tireless and gleaming in voice. Wolfgang Windgassen is equally committed and alert as her Siegfried and Theo Adam is an experienced, worldly-wise Wotan. No *Ring* recording is perfect or could possibly tell the whole story but this faithfully recorded version conveys the strength and force of the epic's meaning.

Additional recommendations ...

...**Der Ring des Nibelungen. Vienna State Opera Chorus; Vienna Philharmonic Orchestra / Sir Georg Solti.** Decca Ⓑ 455 555-2DMO14* (14 discs: 876 minutes: ADD: 3/89).
Gramophone classical 100. ⒼⒼⒼ

...**Der Ring des Nibelungen. Soloists; Chorus and Orchestra of RAI, Rome / Wilhelm Furtwängler.**
EMI mono Ⓜ CZS7 67123-2* (13 discs: 902 minutes: ADD: 2/91). ⒼⒼⒼ

...**Der Ring des Nibelungen. Soloists; Bayreuth Festival Chorus and Orchestra / Karl Böhm.**
Philips Ⓑ 446 057-2PB14 (14 discs: 819 minutes: ADD: 10/94). *This is the same recording as the one reviewed above.* ⒼⒼⒼ

...**Der Ring des Nibelungen. Bavarian State Opera Chorus; Bavarian State Orchestra / Wolfgang Sawallisch.** EMI B CZS5 72731-2 (14 discs: 847 minutes: DDD: 8/98). ⒼⒼⒼ

...**Das Rheingold. Soloists; Bayreuth Festival Orchestra / Clemens Krauss.**
Foyer mono Ⓕ 3-CF2007* (three discs: 145 minutes: ADD: 6/88). ⒼⒼⒼ

...**Die Walküre. Soloists; Bayreuth Festival Orchestra / Clemens Krauss.**
Foyer mono Ⓕ 4-CF2008* (four discs: 212 minutes: ADD: 6/88). ⒼⒼⒼ

...Siegfried. **Soloists; Bayreuth Festival Orchestra / Clemens Krauss.**
Foyer mono Ⓕ 4-CF2009* (four discs: 237 minutes: ADD: 6/88).
...Siegfried (sung in English). **Soloists; Sadler's Wells Opera Orchestra / Sir Reginald Goodall.**
EMI Ⓜ CMS7 63595-2 (four discs: 278 minutes: ADD: 3/91).
...Götterdämmerung. **Soloists; Bayreuth Festival Orchestra / Clemens Krauss.**
Foyer mono Ⓕ 4-CF2010* (four discs: 260 minutes: ADD: 6/88).   ⒼⒼⒼ
...Götterdämmerung. **Soloists; Metropolitan Opera Chorus and Orchestra / James Levine.**
DG Ⓕ 429 385-2GH4 (four discs: 270 minutes: DDD: 8/91).
...Götterdämmerung (sung in English). **Soloists; English National Opera Chorus and Orchestra /
Sir Reginald Goodall.** EMI Ⓜ CMS7 64244-2 (five discs: ADD: 11/92).

Wagner Der Ring des Nibelungen. **Soloists; Mens' Voices of the Leipzig State Opera;
Dresden State Opera Chorus; Staatskapelle Dresden / Marek Janowski.** RCA Victor Red Seal
Ⓑ 74321 45417-2 (14 discs: 839 minutes: DDD: 12/97). Notes, texts and translations included.
Item marked [a] from Eurodisc 301 137 (11/81), [b]301 143 (5/84), [c]301 810 (5/84), [d]301 817 (5/84).
Recorded [a]1980, [b]1981, [c]1982 and [d]1983.
Das Rheingold[a]. **Theo Adam** (bass-bar) Wotan; **Yvonne Minton** (mez) Fricka; **Peter Schreier** (ten)
Loge; **Christian Vogel** (ten) Mime; **Siegmund Nimsgern** (bass-bar) Alberich; **Marita Napier** (sop)
Freia; **Eberhard Büchner** (ten) Froh; **Karl-Heinz Stryczek** (bass) Donner; **Ortrun Wenkel** (contr)
Erda; **Roland Bracht** (bass) Fasolt; **Matti Salminen** (bass) Fafner; **Lucia Popp** (sop) Woglinde;
Uta Priew (mez) Wellgunde; **Hanna Schwarz** (contr) Flosshild.
Die Walküre[b]. **Siegfried Jerusalem** (ten) Siegmund; **Jessye Norman** (sop) Sieglinde;
Jeannine Altmeyer (sop) Brünnhilde; **Theo Adam** (bass-bar) Wotan; **Yvonne Minton** (mez) Fricka;
Kurt Moll (bass) Hunding; **Eva-Maria Bundschuh** (sop) Gerhilde; **Ruth Falcon** (sop) Helmwige;
Cheryl Studer (sop) Ortlinde; **Ortrun Wenkel** (contr) Waltraute; **Uta Priew** (mez) Rossweisse;
Christel Borchers (mez) Siegrune; **Kathleen Kuhlmann** (contr) Grimgarde; **Anne Gjevang** (contr)
Schwertleite. Siegfried[c]. **René Kollo** (ten) Siegfried; **Theo Adam** (bass-bar) Wanderer;
Jeannine Altmeyer (sop) Brünnhilde; **Peter Schreier** (ten) Mime; **Siegmund Nimsgern** (bass-bar)
Alberich; **Ortrun Wenkel** (contr) Erda; **Norma Sharp** (sop) Woodbird.
Götterdämmerung[d]. **Jeannine Altmeyer** (sop) Brünnhilde; **René Kollo** (ten) Siegfried;
Matti Salminen (bass) Hagen; **Siegmund Nimsgern** (bass-bar) Alberich; **Hans Günter Nöcker** (bar)
Gunther; **Norma Sharp** (sop) Gutrune; **Ortrun Wenkel** (contr) Waltraute; **Uta Priew** (mez)
Wellgunde; **Lucia Popp** (sop) Woglinde; **Anne Gjevang** (contr) First Norn; **Daphne Evangelotos**
(mez) Second Norn; **Ruth Falcon** (sop) Third Norn.
Here's a true and desirable bargain. This, the first digitally recorded cycle to appear on CD, has always
had a great deal to commend it, and at the budget price it becomes even more attractive. One of its
most telling assets is the actual recording, still the most natural, clear and most sensitively balanced
available. Then it has the Dresden Staatskapelle playing with the utmost beauty from start to finish
and with lean power when that's called for. Voices and players are in an ideal relationship. Which is
not to say that such purple passages as the Magic Fire Music, Ride of the Valkyries, Rhine Journey
and Funeral March want anything in visceral excitement. Janowski conducts a direct, dramatic
interpretation, concerned throughout with forward movement. His clear-sighted conducting conveys
theatrical excitement from start to finish without fuss or attempts at portentous readings. All this
makes it an ideal introduction to the *Ring* for any young collector, who can later go on to more
philosophically inclined interpretations. The casts are by and large excellent. *Das Rheingold* is
dominated by three central performances – Nimsgern's vibrant, articulate Alberich, Schreier's
wonderfully vital, strikingly intelligent and articulate Loge and Adam's experienced Wotan. But
Fricka, Giants and Rhinemaidens are all well cast, and the whole performance grips one's attention
from start to finish as the kaleidoscopic drama unfolds. *Die Walküre* introduces us to Norman's
involving if not wholly idiomatic Sieglinde and, even better, the youthful Jerusalem's near-ideal
Siegmund, forthright and sincere, not forgetting Moll's granite Hunding. Adam is so authoritative, so
keen with the text, so inside his part that an occasional unsteadiness can be overlooked. With
Altmeyer's Brünnhilde we come to the one drawback of the set. Though in this and the succeeding
operas, we are thankful for such clear, clean and youthful tone, her reading is unformed and one-
dimensional, lacking the essential insights of a Varnay or Behrens. In the title-role in *Siegfried* Kollo
gives one of his most attractive portrayals on disc, full of thoughtful diction poised on clear-cut tone.
Schreier misses nothing in his interpretation of the dissembling, wily Mime, Adam is at his very best
as the wise, old Wanderer, and the smaller parts are well catered for. In *Götterdämmerung*, Salminen
is a commanding, often subtle Hagen, though inclined to bark in his call, Nöcker a splendid Gunther.
This set is particularly recommended to anyone wanting a reasonably priced introduction to the cycle.
Even at a higher level, it has much going for it in comparison with supposedly more prestigious
recordings.

Wagner Der Ring des Nibelungen – abridged. Pearl mono Ⓜ GEMMCDS9137*
(seven discs: 500 minutes: AAD: 4/95). From HMV D1080 (5/26), D1088 (6/26), D1092 (6/26),
D1319 (3/29), D1320/33 (12/27), D1530/35 (3/29), D1546 (3/29), D1572/87 (4/29), D1690/94
(4/30), D1836/7 (4/31), HMV C2237/8 (11/32), HMV DB963 (11/26), DB1578/83 (2/32),
DB1710/13 (12/32), DB1720/21 (6/33).

Sopranos – Florence Austral, Noel Eadie, Florence Easton, Tilly de Garmo, Nora Gruhn, Genia Guszalewicz, Frida Leider, Göta Ljüngberg, Elsie Suddaby, Louise Trenton. *Mezzos* – Evelyn Arden, Lydia Kindermann, Elfriede Marherr-Wagner, Maartje Offers, Maria Olczewska. *Contraltos* – Emmi Leisner, Gladys Palmer, Nellie Walker. *Tenors* – Waldemar Henke, Rudolf Laubenthal, Kennedy McKenna, Lauritz Melchior, Albert Reiss, Heinrich Tessmer, Walter Widdop. *Baritones* – Howard Fry, Emil Schipper, Deszö Zádor. *Bass-baritones* – Rudolf Bockelmann, Friedrich Schorr. *Basses* – Ivar Andrésen, Frederick Collier, Arthur Fear, Eduard Habich, Emanuel List. *Orchestras* – Berlin State Opera, London Symphony, Vienna State Opera. *Conductors* – Karl Alwin, Sir John Barbirolli, Leo Blech, Albert Coates, Lawrance Collingwood, Robert Heger, Karl Muck.   ⓖⓖⓖ

Here we have, in its entirety, what one might term the Old Testament of *The Ring* recordings, the discs made in the late 1920s and early 1930s in London and Berlin. The operas given the major share are *Die Walküre* and *Siegfried*. The four extracts from *Das Rheingold* are notable only for Friedrich Schorr's magisterial "Abendlich strahlt". *Götterdämmerung* suffers most from being reduced to brief extracts, although the passages have been well chosen to give a substantial flavour of the vast work. Coates and the slightly less admirable Blech share the conducting with a few incursions from Heger, the young Barbirolli and others. The playing, mostly by the LSO of the day and the Berlin State Opera Orchestra, is remarkable for its sweep, also for its care over detail, much of which has astonishing clarity considering the dates of the recordings. Coates is particularly successful in projecting the ardour of the *Walküre* love duet and the forging of the sword in *Siegfried*. His speeds are always on the swift side.

Of course, the singing is the most treasurable aspect of the whole enterprise. Encountering Leider again one realizes anew that few, if any, have equalled her combination of vocal security, close-knit line and phrasing, and that matching of feeling with a goddess's natural dignity. Her Brünnhilde is an assumption all aspiring heroic sopranos should closely study (but they don't!). Fledgling Heldentenors would be unwise to listen to Melchior for they might be inclined to suicide. The sheer *élan*, strength and verbal acuity of his singing are, and will surely remain, unique. For these reasons alone he is unsurpassable as Siegfried, a role that ideally suited his remarkable attributes. Schorr's Wotan is just as remarkable. Once again tone, technique and text are in perfect accord as his noble bass-baritone fills every passage grandly, movingly. The sound is vivid throughout these seven (for the price of five), generously filled CDs. The voices are recorded more successfully than in most modern versions of these works, and their relationship with the orchestra is more natural than that favoured in studios today. This is a set no enquiring Wagnerian, whatever complete version of *The Ring* he or she owns, should be without.

Wagner Tannhäuser (Paris version). **Plácido Domingo** (ten) Tannhäuser; **Cheryl Studer** (sop) Elisabeth; **Andreas Schmidt** (bar) Wolfram; **Agnes Baltsa** (mez) Venus; **Matti Salminen** (bass) Hermann; **William Pell** (ten) Walther; **Kurt Rydl** (bass) Biterolf; **Clemens Biber** (ten) Heinrich; **Oskar Hillebrandt** (bass) Reinmar; **Barbara Bonney** (sop) Shepherd Boy; **Chorus of the Royal Opera House, Covent Garden; Philharmonia Orchestra / Giuseppe Sinopoli.** DG Ⓕ 427 625-2GH3 (three discs: 176 minutes: DDD: 9/89). Notes, text and translation included.   ⓖ

Plácido Domingo's Tannhäuser is a success in almost every respect. He evokes the erotic passion of the Venusberg scene and brings to it just the right touch of nervous energy. This is boldly contrasted with the desperation and bitterness of the Rome Narration after the hero's fruitless visit to the Pope seeking forgiveness: Domingo's description of how Tannhäuser avoided every earthly delight on his pilgrimage is delivered with total conviction. In between he berates the slightly prissy attitude of his fellow knights on the Wartburg with the dangerous conceit of someone who knows a secret delight that they will never enjoy in their measured complacency. His tenor must be the steadiest and most resplendent ever to have tackled the part, although his German is far from idiomatic with several vowel sounds distorted. Baltsa also has some problems with her German, but she has the range and attack, particularly in the upper register, for an awkwardly lying part. Here comparisons have to be made with Christa Ludwig for Solti (listed below), in one of her most successful assumptions. She is not only more familiar with the role but also has the more voluptuous voice and is superbly seconded by Solti; which brings us to Sinopoli. It is obviously his concern throughout to bring out every last ounce of the drama in the piece, both in terms of orchestral detail, which receives very special attention from the Overture, given a big, full-blooded reading, onwards, but also in his awareness in this opera of the longer line, often sustained by the upper strings. The Philharmonia's violins respond with their most eloquent playing. The kind of *frisson* Sinopoli offers is evident in the anticipatory excitement at the start of Act 2 and the iron control he maintains in the big ensemble later in the same act. Cheryl Studer's secure, beautiful voice has no difficulty coping with Sinopoli's deliberate tempos. She takes her part with total conviction, both vocal and interpretative, phrasing with constant intelligence. Andreas Schmidt is a mellifluous, concerned Wolfram, Salminen a rugged, characterful Landgrave and Barbara Bonney an ideally fresh Shepherd Boy. As knights, ladies and pilgrims the Covent Garden Chorus sing with consistent beauty of sound, and have been sensibly balanced with the orchestra. As Sinopoli has chosen to conduct the Paris version, the Solti set is its main rival. It has always been one of Solti's most recommendable opera recordings, and in its CD format it remains a formidable achievement. Domingo and Studer, however, incline one towards this version, as does the wide range of the finely engineered recording, which makes the excellent Decca seem a bit dated.

Additional recommendations ...
...Soloists; Vienna Boys' Choir; Vienna State Opera Chorus; Vienna Philharmonic Orchestra / Sir Georg Solti. Decca Ⓕ 414 581-2DH3 (three discs: DDD: 2/86).
...Chorus and Orchestra of the Berlin State Opera / Franz Konwitschny. EMI Studio Ⓜ CMS7 63214-2 (three discs: 183 minutes: ADD: 10/90).

Wagner Tristan und Isolde. **Wolfgang Windgassen** (ten) Tristan; **Birgit Nilsson** (sop) Isolde; **Christa Ludwig** (mez) Brangäne; **Eberhard Waechter** (bar) Kurwenal; **Martti Talvela** (bass) King Marke; **Claude Heater** (ten) Melot; **Peter Schreier** (ten) Sailor; **Erwin Wohlfahrt** (ten) Shepherd; **Gerd Nienstedt** (bass) Helmsman; **Bayreuth Festival Chorus and Orchestra / Karl Böhm.** Philips Ⓜ 434 425-2PH3 (three discs: 219 minutes: ADD: 10/92). From DG 419 889-2GH3 (7/88). Notes, text and translation included. Recorded live in 1966. ⒼⒼⒼ

Wagner Tristan und Isolde. **Siegfried Jerusalem** (ten) Tristan; **Waltraud Meier** (mez) Isolde; **Marjana Lipovšek** (mez) Brangäne; **Matti Salminen** (bass) King Marke; **Falk Struckmann** (bar) Kurwenal; **Johan Botha** (ten) Melot; **Peter Maus** (ten) Shepherd; **Roman Trekel** (bar) Helmsman; **Uwe Heilmann** (ten) Sailor; **Berlin State Opera Chorus; Berlin Philharmonic Orchestra / Daniel Barenboim.** Teldec Ⓕ 4509-94568-2 (four discs: 235 minutes: DDD: 9/95). Notes, text and translation included.

Böhm's recording is a live Bayreuth performance of distinction, for on stage are the most admired Tristan and Isolde of their time, and in the pit the 72-year-old conductor directs a performance which is unflagging in its passion and energy. Böhm has a striking way in the Prelude and *Liebestod* of making the swell of passion seem like the movement of a great sea, sometimes with gentle motion, sometimes with the breaking of the mightiest of waves. Nilsson characterizes strongly and her voice with its marvellous cleaving-power can also soften quite beautifully. Windgassen's heroic performance in the Third Act is in some ways the crown of his achievements on record, even though the voice has dried and aged a little. Christa Ludwig is the ideal Brangäene, Waechter a suitably-forthright Kurwenal, and Talvela an expressive, noble-voiced Marke. Orchestra and chorus are at their finest.

Over several seasons of conducting the work at Bayreuth, Barenboim has by now thoroughly mastered the pacing and shaping of the score as a unified entity. Even more important he has peered into the depths of both its construction and meaning, emerging with answers that satisfy on almost all counts, most tellingly so in the melancholic adumbration of Isolde's thoughts during her narration, in the sadly eloquent counterpoint of bass clarinet, lower strings and cor anglais underpinning King Marke's lament, and in the searingly tense support to Tristan's second hallucination. These are but the most salient moments in a reading that thoughtfully and unerringly reveals the inner parts of this astounding score. The obverse of this caring manner is a certain want of spontaneity, and a tendency to become a shade self-regarding. You occasionally miss the overwhelming force of Furtwängler's metaphysical account or the immediacy and excitement of Böhm's famous live Bayreuth reading but the very mention of those conductors suggests that Barenboim can live in their world and survive the comparisons with his own perfectly valid interpretation. Besides, he has the most gloriously spacious yet well-focused recording so far of this opera and an orchestra not only familiar with his ways but ready to execute them in a disciplined and sensitive manner. The recording also takes account of spatial questions, in particular the placing of the horns offstage at the start of Act 2.

Salminen delivers a classic account of Marke's anguished reproaches to Tristan, his singing at once sonorous, dignified and reaching to the heart, a reading on a par with that of his fellow-countryman Talvela for Böhm. Meier's Isolde is a vitally wrought, verbally alert reading, which catches much of the venom of Act 1, the visceral excitement of Act 2, the lambent utterance of the Liebestod. Nothing she does is unmusical; everything is keenly intelligent, yet possibly her tone is too narrow for the role. Lipovšek's Brangäne tends to slide and swim in an ungainly fashion, sounding at times definitely overparted. Listening to Ludwig (Böhm) only serves to emphasize Lipovšek's deficiencies. Then it is often hard on the newer set to tell Isolde and Brangäne apart, so alike can be their timbre. As with his partner, Jerusalem sings his role with immaculate musicality; indeed he may be the most accurate Tristan on disc where note values are concerned, one also consistently attentive to dynamics and long-breathed phrasing. On the other hand, although he puts a deal of feeling into his interpretation, he hasn't quite the intensity of utterance of either Windgassen (Böhm), or, even more, Suthaus (Furtwängler). His actual timbre is dry and occasionally rasping: in vocal terms alone Suthaus is in a class of his own. Yet, even with reservations about the Isolde and Tristan, this is a version that will undoubtedly hold a high place in any survey of this work, for which one performance can never hope to tell the whole story.

Additional recommendations ...
...Soloists; Bavarian Radio Chorus and Symphony Orchestra / Leonard Bernstein. Philips Ⓕ 438 241-2PH4 (four discs: 266 minutes: DDD).
...Soloists; Leipzig Radio Chorus; Dresden Staatskapelle / Carlos Kleiber. DG Ⓕ 413 315-2GH4 (four discs: 235 minutes: DDD: 11/86).
...Soloists; Chorus of the Royal Opera House, Covent Garden; London Philharmonic Orchestra / Fritz Reiner, Sir Thomas Beecham. EMI Références mono Ⓜ CHS7 64037-2* (three discs: 212 minutes: ADD: 1/92).
...Soloists; Welsh National Opera Chorus and Orchestra / Sir Reginald Goodall. Decca Grand Opera Ⓜ 443 682-2DMO4 (four discs: 259 minutes: DDD: 5/95).

...excerpts. **Soloists; Vienna State Opera Chorus and Orchestra / Wilhelm Furtwängler.**
Koch Schwann mono Ⓜ 314612* (two discs: 140 minutes: ADD: 5/95).
...**Soloists; Bavarian State Opera Chorus; Bavarian State Orchestra / Hans Knappertsbusch.**
Orfeo mono Ⓕ C355943D (three discs: 232 minutes: ADD: 5/95).   ⒼⒼ
...**Soloists; Metropolitan Opera Chorus and Orchestra, New York / Erich Leinsdorf.**
Naxos Historical mono Ⓢ 8 110008/10* (three discs: 202 minutes: ADD: 5/98).

Wagner Tristan und Isolde. **Ludwig Suthaus** (ten) Tristan; **Kirsten Flagstad** (sop) Isolde;
Blanche Thebom (mez) Brangäne; **Josef Greindl** (bass) King Marke; **Dietrich Fischer-Dieskau**
(bar) Kurwenal; **Edgar Evans** (ten) Melot; **Rudolf Schock** (ten) Shepherd, Sailor;
Rhoderick Davies (ten) Helmsman; **Chorus of the Royal Opera House, Covent Garden;**
Philharmonia Orchestra / Wilhelm Furtwängler. EMI mono Ⓕ EMI CDS5 56254-2*
(four discs: 236 minutes: ADD: 5/86). Notes, text and translation included.
From HMV ALP1030/5 (3/53). Recorded 1952. *Gramophone Classical 100.*   ⒼⒼⒼ
Those of us who had worn out our original HMV pressings of this recording of *Tristan und Isolde*
were grateful to EMI for marking the Furtwängler centenary by reissuing this recording on CD. We
should now be doubly grateful. It was remastered again in 1997, achieving a marked improvement
over its 1985 transfer. At best, the sound is remarkable. At the start of Act 2, for instance, there is an
exceptional depth of perspective to the mono sound. Elsewhere, in the big climaxes, the sound does
become congested; though it never breaks up or distorts, there is some perceptible hardening of the
musical arteries. The digital remastering also makes studio noises more audible: for instance, the brief
rumpus at the end of Tristan's first phrase in "O sink hernieder". The performance, as is well known
by now, is memorable for the reach, beauty and re-creative power of Furtwängler's conducting and
Flagstad's authoritative, beautifully pointed account of Isolde's role. Though they lacked opera-house
experience, the Philharmonia Orchestra, in 1952, were probably the world's finest orchestra. It is
difficult to accept the view, sometimes stated, that Flagstad was unsuited at this time to the role of
Isolde. It would have been better caught younger; but that said, there were no contemporary Isoldes
to better Flagstad's. The young Dietrich Fischer-Dieskau is a superb Kurwenal; there could be tiny
reservations about other members of the cast: the hugely impressive but perhaps rather too formal
Tristan of Ludwig Suthaus, Josef Greindl's King Marke, and so on. A unique listening experience.

Wagner Die Walküre. **Poul Elming** (ten) Siegmund; **Alessandra Marc** (sop) Sieglinde;
Gabriele Schnaut (mez) Brünnhilde; **Robert Hale** (bass-bar) Wotan; **Anja Silja** (sop) Fricka;
Alfred Muff (bass) Hunding; **Michèle Crider** (sop) Gerhilde; **Ruth Falcon** (sop) Helmwige;
Susan Marie Pierson (sop) Ortlinde; **Karin Goltz** (mez) Waltraute; **Susan Shafer** (mez) Rossweisse;
Katherine Ciesinski (mez) Siegrune; **Sandra Walker** (mez) Grimgerde; **Penelope Walker** (mez)
Schwertleite; **Cleveland Orchestra / Christoph von Dohnányi.** Decca Ⓕ 440 371-2DHO4
(four discs: 225 minutes: DDD: 10/97). Notes, text and translation included. Recorded 1992.
Dohnányi conducts a well-paced, thought-through reading that at once creates dramatic excitement
and attends to the longer view. We sense the inner pleasures and anxieties of each character in turn:
Siegmund's extended defiance, Sieglinde's ecstasy in Act 1, even more her spiritual desperation in
Act 2 and final elevation when she knows she is pregnant, Wotan's misery, fury, love, Brünnhilde's
missionary zeal in Act 2, her remorse in Act 3. In brief the conductor persuades singers and players
alike to give us the essence of the work. One can hardly ask for more, apart from a level of excellence
in execution on both sides. Neither orchestra nor cast disappoints, the players responding with a fiery,
expertly played and vital performance. In Act 1 we encounter the warm, dark-grained Sieglinde of
Alessandra Marc, whose slightly covered, expressive tone and phrasing recall that of Rysanek in the
part. Poul Elming is an almost ideal Siegmund, his tone pleasing with that slightly metallic touch
common in Scandinavian singers, especially tenors, his reading sung eagerly off the words. His
antagonist, Hunding, is sung with astonishing immediacy and biting venom by Alfred Muff, every
syllable made to tell. In Act 2 we meet at once Gabriele Schnaut's very positive Brünnhilde. Bright
and forceful in her war cry, she shows suitable concern at her father's distress, and is wise and dignified
in her colloquy with Siegmund. In Act 3 her appeal to Wotan "War es so schmählich?" is lovingly
projected with more than a touch of Varnay in her voice, praise enough. Robert Hale's Wotan is a
more familiar quantity. With a voice properly poised for the part between baritone and bass, he has
no difficulty with either his high or low notes, can sing a true line and is fully conversant with every
facet of Wotan's dilemma. He is no less successful in trying to defy Fricka or in thundering against
his errant daughter. You may find the ultimate in psychological insight missing, but most of the
interior anguish of the part is there, impeccably delivered. As his Fricka, Anja Silja gives a typically
intelligent, keenly articulated performance. The recording, including a few unobtrusive sound effects,
is large in scale. A grand, satisfying performance on almost every count.
Further listening ...
...A Faust Overture. *Coupled with works by various composers.* **London Philharmonic Orchestra;**
Berlin Philharmonic Orchestra / Sir Thomas Beecham. Dutton Laboratories mono CDLX7009*
(10/94). *See review in the Collections section; refer to the Index.*
...Paraphrase on Isolden's Liebestod from "Tristan und Isolde", S447 (trans. Liszt).
Coupled with works by various composers. **Vladimir Horowitz** (pf).
Sony Classical SK45818 (8/90). *See review in the Collections section; refer to the Index.*   ⒼⒼⒼ

...Wesendonk Lieder. *Coupled with works by various composers.*
Dame Margaret Price (sop); **Graham Johnson** (pf).
Forlane UCD16728 (2/95). *See review in the Collections section; refer to the Index.*
...Die Feen. **Soloists; Bavarian Radio Chorus; Bavarian Radio Symphony Orchestra /**
Wolfgang Sawallisch. Orfeo C062833F.
...Der fliegende Holländer – Joho hoe! Traft ihr das Schiff; Wie aus der Ferne. *Coupled with works*
by various composers. **Leonie Rysanek** (sop); **Sigurd Björling** (bar); **Royal Opera House Chorus,**
Covent Garden / Wilhelm Schüchter. EMI Références mono CDH5 65201-2* (4/95).
...Tannhäuser – Dich teure Halle; Allmächt'ge Jungfrau. Lohengrin – Einsam in trüben Tagen;
Euch Lüften, die mein Klagen. Rienzi – Gerechter Gott. *Coupled with works by various*
composers. **Gundula Janowitz** (sop); **Irwin Gage** (pf); **Vienna Symphony Orchestra /**
Wilfried Boettcher; Orchestra of the Deutsche Staatsoper, Berlin / Ferdinand Leitner.
DG Double 447 352-2GDB2 (12/95).

Emile Waldteufel   French 1837-1915

Waldteufel, Flots de joie, Op. 145. Château en Espagne, Op. 225. Gaîté, Op. 164. Tout à vous,
Op. 142. Bella, Op. 113. Brune ou blonde, Op. 162. Acclamations, Op. 223. La Barcarolle,
Op. 178. Béobile. **Slovak State Philharmonic Orchestra, Košice / Alfred Walter.** Marco Polo
Ⓟ 8 223684 (66 minutes: DDD: 6/96). Recorded 1992-1995.

Alfred Walter's Waldteufel series is distinguished by his characteristic professionalism and the Slovak
orchestra at Košice play with warmth and considerable polish. This volume contains entirely
unfamiliar repertoire, and much of it deserves to be better known: *Gaîté, Brune ou blonde* and *La
Barcarolle* all have attractive ideas, the last-named nothing like Offenbach, but with a gently bouncing
lilt. Vol. 7 again brings several striking numbers: *Rêverie* and the nostalgic *Au revoir* are aptly named,
while *Trésor d'amour* uses flutes to usher in a tune of graceful delicacy. *Coquetterie*, too, has a
capricious, winningly scored introduction entirely in keeping with its title. The highlight of the disc is
Béobile, a pizzicato novelty of such verve that if better known it could be a great favourite. The
recording is excellent, with a nice ballroom resonance.

Further listening ...
...Les patineurs, Op. 183. *Coupled with works by various composers.* **New London Orchestra /**
Ronald Corp. Hyperion CDA66998 (3/98). *See review in the Collections section; refer to the Index.*

William Vincent Wallace   Irish 1812-1865

Wallace Maritana. **Majella Cullagh** (sop) Maritana; **Lynda Lee** (mez) Lazarello; **Paul Charles Clarke**
(ten) Don Caesar; **Ian Caddy** (bass) Don José; **Damien Smith** (bar) Captain; **Quentin Hayes** (bass)
King of Spain; **RTE Philharmonic Choir and Concert Orchestra / Prionnsías O'Duinn.** Marco Polo
Ⓟ 8 223406/7 (two discs: 198 minutes: DDD: 8/97). Notes and text included. Recorded 1995.

All the histories and encyclopaedias tell us that there were no 'successful' operas composed in Britain
between Purcell's *Dido and Aeneas* and Britten's *Peter Grimes.* We have become so used to hearing this
that it gets repeated without question. But London, Dublin and later Manchester all knew a vigorous
operatic life in the eighteenth and nineteenth centuries. As John Allen points out in his excellent
introduction to this recording of William Vincent Wallace's *Maritana*, there existed a "now largely
forgotten school of Romantic English opera". Wallace was born in the Pyrénées in 1812, of Irish
parents. His career took him from Dublin to Australia, New Zealand and South America. Coming to
London in 1845, he composed *Maritana* for Drury Lane, where it was an immediate success. Wallace's
music is clearly influenced by the operas of Rossini and Donizetti. The plot is based on D'Ennery's
and Dumanoir's play *Don César de Bazan* which was later used for Massenet's *Don César de Bazan*,
and the broad outline – condemned man marries a girl he has never met on the eve of his execution
– was parodied by Gilbert in *The Yeomen of the Guard*. In a way, *Maritana* is one of the first musicals.
Although Wallace takes the style of Donizetti as his starting-point, he departs from it sharply at key
moments to insert popular ballads, well known up and down the land in hundreds of arrangements.
Prionnsías O'Duinn leads a vigorous performance, even if the disparity of styles, half-Italian, half-
Victorian drawing-room, doesn't quite come off all the time. Majella Cullagh in the title-role, Lynda
Lee as the put-upon apprentice lad, Lazarello, Paul Charles Clarke as Don Caesar and Ian Caddy as
the evil Don José all sing with total conviction. It isn't at all difficult to understand *Maritana's*
popularity, nor with the ensuing snobbery of the twentieth century, why it fell out of favour.

William Wallace   Scottish 1860-1940

Wallace Creation Symphony in C sharp minor. Prelude to The Eumenides. Pelléas and Mélisande
Suite – The love of Pelléas for Mélisande; Spinning Song; The death of Mélisande. **BBC Scottish**
Symphony Orchestra / Martyn Brabbins. Hyperion Ⓟ CDA66987 (73 minutes: DDD: 2/98).
Recorded 1997. *Gramophone Editor's choice.*

The centrepiece here – and quite a 'find' it is too – comprises the mighty *Creation Symphony* upon which Wallace began work in 1896. Premièred three years later under the composer's own guidance at one of Sir Granville Bantock's New Brighton concerts, it is a hugely ambitious four-movement edifice of considerable organic and emotional scope. Each movement is prefaced with a quotation from the Book of Genesis. Thus an introductory *Adagio* ("In the beginning God created the heaven and the earth ...") conjures a mood of awesome mystery and expectancy, leading without break into the stirring main *Allegro* portion, wherein Wallace continues the process of satisfying thematic development. After a really well-made climax, a soothing *Moderato* brings a beautiful new idea representing light itself ("exemplified by very soft strains, as an influence that comes from above", in Wallace's description). At the outset of the ensuing *Andantino* ("And God made two great lights ..."), some magically delicate, luminous scoring perfectly evokes the cosmic wonder of the night sky. The third-movement *Allegro* ("And the Spirit of God moved upon the face of the waters ...") is perhaps more conventional – a scherzo in all but name – though it ends, like the preceding *Andantino*, by cleverly combining its main ideas. Imposing fanfares launch the *Allegro maestoso* finale ("So God created man in his own image ...") which Wallace intended as a celebration not only of the miracle of human creation but also of love itself. The disc begins with the Prelude to *The Eumenides*, a noble and exciting ten-and-a-half minute essay inspired by Aeschylus's drama, first heard in 1893 under August Manns. In addition, we get the final three numbers in the five-movement *Pelléas and Mélisande* Suite of 1900 (a sequence sanctioned by Wallace himself, so we are told). The perky "Spinning Song" could hardly form a greater contrast with Sibelius's anxious response of five years later, while "The death of Mélisande" is an impassioned threnody, its grief at once theatrical and courtly. Performances throughout are of a high standard, with Martyn Brabbins drawing consistently involving and nicely groomed playing from his admirable BBC band. The sound, too, is vivid, if occasionally a little raw.

Further listening ...

...Symphonic Poems – No. 1, The Passing of Beatrice; No. 3, Sister Helen; No. 5,
Sir William Wallace; No. 6, Villon. **BBC Scottish Symphony Orchestra / Martyn Brabbins.**
Hyperion CDA66848 (11/96). *Gramophone Editor's choice.*   Ⓖ

Sir William Walton

British 1902-1983

Walton Cello Concerto[a]. Symphony No. 1 in B flat minor. [a]**Robert Cohen** (vc);
Bournemouth Symphony Orchestra / Andrew Litton. Decca London Ⓕ 443 450-2LH
(74 minutes: DDD: 10/95). Recorded 1993.
Walton Scapino. Violin Concerto in B minor[a]. Symphony No. 2. [a]**Tasmin Little** (vn);
Bournemouth Symphony Orchestra / Andrew Litton. Decca London Ⓕ 444 114-2LH
(68 minutes: DDD: 10/95). Recorded 1994.
Walton Belshazzar's Feast[a]. Henry V. Crown Imperial. [a]**Bryn Terfel** (bass-bar); [a]**Waynflete Singers;**
[a]**L'Inviti;** [a]**Bournemouth Symphony Chorus and Orchestra / Andrew Litton.** Decca London
Ⓕ 448 134-2LH (60 minutes: DDD: 10/95). Text included. Recorded 1995.

More than anyone since Previn, Litton thrillingly conveys the element of wildness in Walton's finest inspirations, notably in the works of the pre-war period. It is partly a question of his treatment of the jazzy syncopations which are such a vital element in Walton. Litton is not alone in treating them with a degree of idiomatic freedom – the composer himself as interpreter set the pattern – but as with Previn Litton's affinity with the jazz element comes from inside, clearly reflecting his American background. Consistently he makes the music crackle with high voltage electricity, and again he echoes Previn in the way he can screw tension up to the limit and beyond, resolving grinding dissonances on heart-warming concords. That is particularly important in the First Symphony. The Rattle version is superb, but next to Litton's it seems almost too safe, too closely controlled, lacking the extremes of tension, the wildness. Litton even surpasses Previn in the climactic resolution of the finale. With him this movement in no way seems a let-down after the rest, as it easily can – reflecting the composer's problems over completing it. The climactic resolution on an outburst from multiple timpani and percussion is more shattering than ever before on disc, with the Decca recording team achieving wonders in the weight and brilliance of the sound. In general the transfer level is a degree lower than in most rival versions. In the Cello Concerto too the sound is a degree less immediate than in Rattle's version with Lynn Harrell, and that matches a broad contrast of interpretation. Where Harrell remains unrivalled in power and tonal resonance, Robert Cohen for Litton follows a deeper, more hushed, more meditative approach, even when as in the first movement he has a more flowing speed. Harrell is the more powerful, Cohen the more mercurial as well as the more tender. The way that Cohen makes the opening notes of the slow finale seem to emerge from afar is magical.

In all three discs the exceptionally full and vivid recording brings out the opulence as well as the sensuousness of Walton's orchestration, regularly enhancing Litton's expressive warmth as a Waltonian in the great romantic melodies. Not only that, the bitingly dramatic contrasts of brass and percussion have never been more vivid, with the Bournemouth orchestra playing magnificently, not just with brilliance but with passionate commitment. On the second disc Symphony No. 2 is given very sharp focus; it follows – as in a concert – the *Scapino* overture and the Violin Concerto. Tasmin Little as soloist gives the most tenderly beautiful performance, matching Litton in her control of Waltonian contrasts between tender lyricism and sparkling wit. Like Litton, too, Little is able to hold full tension through pauses, often daringly extending them as in a live performance, so that the cadenzas in the first and last movements have a rare intensity. This is a work which has inspired many outstanding performances, not least from women violinists, and Little in spontaneity and tenderness is unsurpassed.

Where the first two discs were recorded in the helpful acoustic of the Southampton Guildhall, *Belshazzar's Feast* was put into the grander setting of Winchester Cathedral. The problems for the engineers must have been daunting, for the reverberation time is formidably long, yet thanks to brilliant balancing there is ample detail and fine focus in exceptionally incisive choral and orchestral sound. The great benefit is that this emerges as a performance on a bigger scale than its rivals, with the contrasts between full chorus and semi-chorus the more sharply established. The vividly dramatic soloist is Bryn Terfel, spine-chilling in his narration describing the writing on the wall. In *Crown Imperial* a cathedral acoustic does bring some lack of clarity, but it is a stirring performance. Andrew Litton's years as Principal Conductor of the Bournemouth Symphony Orchestra could hardly have had a richer culmination on disc.

Additional recommendations ...

...Cello Concerto[a]. **Vaughan Williams** Symphony No. 7, "Sinfonia antartica"[b].
[a]**Gregor Piatigorsky** (vc); [b]**Heather Harper** (sop); [b]**Ambrosian Singers**; [a]**Boston Symphony Orchestra / Charles Munch**; [b]**London Symphony Orchestra / André Previn**.
RCA Victor Classical Navigator Ⓢ 74321 29248-2 (72 minutes: AAD/ADD: 6/96).

...Symphony No. 2. Partita. Variations on a Theme by Hindemith. **Cleveland Orchestra / George Szell.** Sony Classical Essential Classics Ⓑ SBK62753 (66 minutes: ADD: 12/96). ⒼⒼ

...Cello Concerto. **Britten** Cello Symphony, Op. 68. **Julian Lloyd Webber** (vc); **Academy of St Martin in the Fields / Sir Neville Marriner.**
Philips Ⓕ 454 442-2PH (71 minutes: DDD: 8/97). *Gramophone Editor's choice.*

Walton Viola Concerto in A minor[a]. Symphony No. 2. Johannesburg Festival Overture.
[a]**Lars Anders Tomter** (va); **English Northern Philharmonia / Paul Daniel.** Naxos Ⓢ 8 553402 (61 minutes: DDD: 5/96). Recorded 1995.

This disc opens with one of the wittiest, most exuberant performances of the *Johannesburg Festival Overture*: characteristically Daniel encourages the orchestra's virtuoso wind and brass soloists to point the jazz rhythms idiomatically, making the music sparkle. The Viola Concerto is just as delectably pointed, the whole performance instantly magnetic. Tomter's tone, with its rapid flicker-vibrato, lacks the warmth of Kennedy's (reviewed below), but the vibrato is only obtrusive in that upper-middle register and his intonation is immaculate, his attack consistently clean, to match the crisp ensemble of the orchestra. Although he adopts relatively measured speeds both for the scherzo and the jaunty opening theme of the finale, the rhythmic lift brings out the *scherzando* jollity of the latter all the more. Daniel's keen observance of dynamic markings is again brought out in the stuttering fanfare theme of the scherzo, with muted trumpets and trombones for once played *pianissimo* as marked. The close of the slow epilogue has never been recorded with such a profound hush as here, subsiding in darkness, and the recording team are to be complimented on getting such beautiful sound, clean with plenty of bloom. Paul Daniel adopts a relatively broad tempo in the Symphony's first movement, which makes less impact than in Andrew Litton's powerful Decca version (reviewed above), and the flowing tempo for the central slow movement makes for a lighter, less passionate result too. The finale, with its brassy first statement of the Passacaglia theme, brings fine dynamic contrasts, but again Litton and others produce a fatter, weightier sound, which on balance is preferable. Yet Daniel's view is a very valid one, to round off most convincingly an invaluable addition to the Walton discography.

Walton Violin Concerto. Viola Concerto. **Nigel Kennedy** (vn/va); **Royal Philharmonic Orchestra / André Previn.** EMI Ⓕ CDC7 49628-2 (57 minutes: DDD: 4/88). From EL749628-1 (1/88).
Selected by Sounds in Retrospect.   Ⓖ

These concertos are among the most beautiful written this century. Walton was in his late twenties when he composed the viola work and in it he achieved a depth of emotion, a range of ideas and a technical assurance beyond anything he had so far written. Lacking in the brilliance of the violin, the viola has an inherently contemplative tonal quality and Walton matches this to perfection in his score, complementing it rather than trying to compensate as other composers have done. There is a larger element of virtuosity in the Violin Concerto, but it is never allowed to dominate the musical argument. Nigel Kennedy gives wonderfully warm and characterful performances which are likely to stand unchallenged as a coupling for a long time. He produces a beautiful tone quality on both of his instruments, which penetrates to the heart of the aching melancholy of Walton's slow music, and he combines it with an innate, highly developed and spontaneous-sounding sense of rhythmic drive and bounce which propels the quick movements forward with great panache. Previn has long been a persuasive Waltonian and the RPO respond marvellously, with crisp and alert playing throughout. The recordings are very clear and naturally balanced with the solo instrument set in a believable perspective.

Additional recommendations ...

...Violin Concerto. Violin Sonata. Two Pieces. **Lydia Mordkovitch** (vn); **London Philharmonic Orchestra / Jan Latham-Koenig.** Chandos Ⓕ CHAN9073 (69 minutes: DDD: 10/92).

...Violin Concerto. *Coupled with works by* **Barber** and **Bloch** Joshua Bell (vn); **Baltimore Symphony Orchestra / David Zinman.** Decca Ⓕ 452 851-2DH (68 minutes: DDD: 7/97). *Gramophone Editor's choice. See review under Barber, refer to the Index.*

Walton Façade – Suites Nos. 1-3[a]. Siesta[b]. Sinfonia concertante[ca]. Portsmouth Point[a].
Arnold Popular Birthday[a]. [c]**Eric Parkin** (pf); **London Philharmonic Orchestra /** [a]**Jan Latham-König,** [b]**Bryden Thomson.** Chandos Ⓕ CHAN9148 (59 minutes: DDD: 1/94). Recorded 1990-1992.
The *Sinfonia concertante* (1926-27) with its sharply memorable ideas in each movement and characteristically high voltage, has never had the attention it deserves, and that is all the more regrettable when there is such a dearth of attractive British piano concertos. The soloist, Eric Parkin, is perfectly attuned to the idiom, warmly melodic as well as jazzily syncopated. He points rhythms infectiously and shapes melodies persuasively, though the recording sets the piano a little backwardly, no doubt to reflect the idea that this is not a full concerto. Jan Latham-König proves most understanding of the composer's 1920s idiom, giving the witty *Façade* movements just the degree of jazzy freedom they need. The Third Suite, devised and arranged by Christopher Palmer, draws on three apt movements from the *Façade* entertainment, ending riotously with the rag-music of "Something lies beyond the scene". That is a first recording, as is Constant Lambert's arrangement of the Overture, *Portsmouth Point. Siesta* is given an aptly cool performance under Thomson, and the *Popular Birthday* is Malcolm Arnold's fragmentary linking of *Happy Birthday to You* with the "Popular Song" from *Façade*, originally written for Walton's seventieth birthday. The impact of some of the pieces, notably in *Façade,* would have been even sharper, had the warmly atmospheric Chandos recording placed the orchestra a fraction closer.

Walton Overtures – Johannesburg Festival; Portsmouth Point; Scapino. Capriccio burlesco. The First Shoot (orch. Palmer). Granada Prelude. Prologo e Fantasia. Music for Children. Galop final (orch. Palmer). **London Philharmonic Orchestra / Bryden Thomson.** Chandos Ⓕ CHAN8968 (70 minutes: DDD: 11/91).
While enthusiasts for Walton's music may justifiably complain that there is not enough of it, they usually concede that what there is is readily available in good recorded performances. However, thanks to the dedicated and skilful work of Christopher Palmer, still more of it is now coming to light. How many people, one wonders, have ever heard *The First Shoot*, a miniature ballet written for a C.B. Cochran show in 1935, the *Granada Prelude* devised for that television company in the 1960s, or the *Prologo e Fantasia* which was the composer's last work, written for Rostropovich and his National Symphony Orchestra of Washington. Such fresh and welcome goodies as these appear along with familiar material such as the splendidly open-air, nautical overture *Portsmouth Point* that Walton wrote nearly 40 years earlier, at the very start of his career. The Cochran piece, as orchestrated by Palmer, has five little sections that are delightfully jazzy in a way that recalls *Façade* and one's only regret is that there's not more of it. All this music is in the excellent hands of Bryden Thomson and the LPO, and Palmer's booklet essay is a model of stylish, informative writing. The recording is richly toned in the successful Chandos style, which takes some edge off the composer's characteristically sharp scoring but is still most enjoyable.

Walton Symphony No. 1 in B flat minor[a].
Vaughan Williams The Wasps – Overture[b]. **London Symphony Orchestra / André Previn.**
RCA Victor Gold Seal Ⓜ GD87830 (52 minutes: ADD: 2/89). Item marked [a] from SB6691 (1/67, recorded 1966), [b]SB6856 (3/72, recorded 1971).*Gramophone classical 100.* ⒼⒼⒼ
André Previn's 1966 version of Walton's First Symphony with the LSO marked a breakthrough in his recording career, instantly establishing him as a major new figure, not least in interpreting British music and Walton above all. As a performance it has still not been surpassed or even matched on record, and this fine transfer issued at mid price simply confirms this opinion. Even now Previn has rarely made a record as bitingly intense as this. A slight emotional reticence in the slow movement and in the epilogue to the finale with its elegiac trumpet solo add rather than detract from its merits. Also, the flute solo at the start of the slow movement has rarely sounded so chill and bare as here, where other interpreters can seem too overtly emotional, too warm for this melancholy music. *The Wasps* Overture is a most enjoyable makeweight. There is a hint of rasp on the brass tone at times, betraying the age of the recording, but the precision of focus and balance on CD are all the more impressive, with plenty of body in the sound.

Walton Symphony No. 1 in B flat minor. Cello Concerto[a]. [a]**Lynn Harrell** (vc); **City of Birmingham Symphony Orchestra / Sir Simon Rattle.** EMI British Composers Ⓕ CDC7 54572-2 (74 minutes: DDD: 12/92). Recorded 1990-1991. Ⓖ
Simon Rattle's version of Walton's First Symphony is as intelligent and dynamic a traversal as one would expect from this talented figure. Texturally speaking, the inner workings of Walton's score are laid bare as never before, aided by what sounds like a meticulously prepared CBSO. Some may find a touch of contrivance about Rattle's control of dynamics in the scorching first movement, but there's absolutely no gainsaying the underlying tension or cumulative power of the whole. Under Rattle the *Scherzo* darts menacingly (the most convincing account of this music since the classic 1966 Previn account), whilst the slow movement is an unusually nervy, anxious affair. Certainly, the finale is

superbly athletic and lithe, though by now one is beginning to register that EMI's sound is, for all its transparency and natural perspective, perhaps a little lightweight for such enormously red-blooded inspiration. Overall, though, Rattle's is a very strong account – indisputably one of the finest we've had in recent years – and his disc's claims are enhanced by the coupling, a wholly admirable performance of the same composer's luxuriant Cello Concerto. Here Rattle and Lynn Harrell form an inspired partnership, totally dedicated and achieving utter concentration throughout – no mean feat in this of all works which demand so much from both performers and listeners.

Additional recommendations ...

...Nos. 1[a] and 2[b]. [a]**London Philharmonic Orchestra;** [b]**London Symphony Orchestra /** **Sir Charles Mackerras.** EMI Eminence Ⓜ CD-EMX2206 (74 minutes: DDD: 12/89). Ⓠ

...No. 1[a]. Viola Concerto[b]. Façade – excerpts[c]. [b]**Frederick Riddle** (va); [c]**Dora Stevens** (sop); [c]**Hubert Foss** (pf); **London Symphony Orchestra /** [a]**Hamilton Harty,** [b]**Sir William Walton.** Dutton Laboratories mono Ⓜ CDAX8003* (72 minutes: ADD: 12/93).

Walton Symphony No. 1 in B flat minor. Partita. **English Northern Philharmonia / Paul Daniel.** Naxos Ⓢ 8 553180 (64 minutes: DDD: 2/98). Recorded 1994. *Gramophone Editor's choice.*

Paul Daniel and the English Northern Philharmonia follow up the success of their first Walton disc for Naxos (reviewed above) with a second which is equally successful. If anything Daniel demonstrates even more clearly here his natural affinity with Walton's music. In the sustained paragraphs of the First Symphony he knows unerringly how to build up tension to breaking point, before resolving it, and then building again – a quality vital above all in the first and third movements. He is freer than many in his use of rubato too, again often a question of building and resolving tension, as well as in the degree of elbow-room he allows for jazzy syncopations, always idiomatic. This symphony, with its heavy orchestration, would certainly have benefited from rather drier sound, but well-judged microphone balance allows ample detail through. Only occasionally do you feel a slight lack of body in high violin tone, a tiny reservation. Daniel's reading of the *Partita*, originally written for Szell and the Cleveland Orchestra (his performance is listed above), brings out above all the work's joyfulness. It may not be quite as crisp in its ensemble as that of the dedicatees, but the degree of wildness, with dissonances underlined, proves a positive advantage in conveying enjoyment. In the slow movement Daniel at a relatively slow speed is markedly more expressive than those brilliant models, again a point which makes the performance more endearing, and if Daniel's speed for the finale is just a little cautious, the precision and rhythmic bounce readily justify his approach. Irrespective of price, this is a version of the much-recorded symphony that competes with the finest ever, and outshines most.

Walton Piano Quartet[a]. Violin Sonata[b]. Five Bagatelles[c]. [ab]**Janice Graham** (vn); [a]**Paul Silverthorne** (va); [a]**Moray Welsh** (vc); [c]**Tom Kerstens** (gtr); [a]**Israela Margalit,** [b]**John Alley** (pfs). EMI Anglo-American Chamber Music Ⓕ CDC5 55404-2 (69 minutes: DDD: 8/96).

This is a splendid addition to EMI's Anglo-American Chamber Music series, with superb string players from the LSO, and with Israela Margalit making a distinguished contribution. The two major works are also coupled on the Chandos disc, but here you get a bonus in an outstanding performance of the *Five Bagatelles* for guitar, originally written for Julian Bream. With Israela Margalit injecting fire, the performance of the Piano Quartet is also lighter and more volatile than in the Chandos set with Hamish Milne as pianist. That impression is enhanced by the EMI recording balance, with textures rather more open, letting the solo work stand out more. But where the first two movements in this performance have more sparkle and fantasy, the Chandos team gain increasingly in the slow movement and finale, which have extra weight and intensity. You could argue that the EMI team's treatment of the slow movement – lighter, more flowing yet still warm – is more apt for the work of a precocious 16-year-old composer, and though the finale is not quite as biting as in the Chandos performance, the vigour is hardly less, and the players more readily respond to the moments of repose, as in the pause before the final coda. Janice Graham is the brilliant, winningly expressive violinist in both works, again more fanciful, more volatile in the Violin Sonata than her opposite number, Kenneth Sillito, notably in the first movement. In the slow variations which form the second of the two movements Sillito grows ever warmer, conveying an extra weight and intensity, but both performances are outstanding, bringing warmth and purposefulness to what can easily seem one of the more wayward of Walton's major works. The sound is remarkably consistent, excellent in each.

Additional recommendations ...

...Piano Quartet[a]. Violin Sonata. **Kenneth Sillito** (vn); [a]**Robert Smissen** (va); [a]**Stephen Orton** (vc); **Hamish Milne** (pf). Chandos CHAN8999 (3/92).

...Violin Sonata. **Elgar** Violin Sonata in E minor, Op. 82. **Lorraine McAslan** (vn); **John Blakely** (pf). ASV Quicksilva Ⓢ CDQS6191 (50 minutes: DDD: 11/96).

Walton Anon in love[bc]. A Song for the Lord Mayor's Table[ad]. Façade – Long steel grass[bd]; Tango-pasodoble[bd]; Popular Song (all arr. Palmer)[bd]; Daphne[ad]; Through Gilded Trellises[ad]; Old Sir Faulk[ad]. Winds[bd]. Tritons[bd]. Christopher Columbus – Beatriz's Song[bd]. As You Like It – Under the Greenwood Tree[bd]. [a]**Dame Felicity Lott** (sop); [b]**Martyn Hill** (ten); [c]**Craig Ogden** (gtr); [d]**Graham Johnson** (pf). Collins Classics Ⓕ 1493-2 (52 minutes: DDD: 10/97). Texts included. Recorded 1996.

Walton was not the most prolific of composers, but he contributed a masterpiece to practically every genre in which he worked. Similarly, while we do not often think of him in association with the song or the song-cycle, his solo cantata, *A Song for the Lord Mayor's Table* is surely something special. So, you might say, is *Anon in love*, the sequence of Elizabethan lyrics originally set (as heard here) for tenor and guitar and premièred at Aldeburgh in 1960. The question of versions is of prime importance where this record is concerned. On the corresponding Chandos issue the songs are orchestrally accompanied. *Anon in love* was rescored for strings, harp and (very sparingly) percussion, the *Lord Mayor* for full orchestra, which, as Michael Kennedy notes in his introductory essay, Walton really had in mind from the first. The performances match their accompaniments. Dame Felicity Lott might well have characterized on a larger scale had she been singing with orchestra. In the songs from *Façade*, the difference is most marked in "Old Sir Faulk", where Lott sounds merely pretty and high-spirited by comparison with Gomez's lightly Americanized flamboyance. However "irksome" Walton found the labour, he wrote very well for the piano; so, at least, it seems when Graham Johnson is the pianist. Even *Façade* sounds pianistic in his hands, and in the second set (arranged by the late Christopher Palmer) the partnership works brilliantly. As a milk-white witness of Spanish night-life, Martyn Hill makes scary magic of "Long Steel Grass". The shorter pieces go well too, particularly the 16-year-old's turbulent accentuations in his setting of Swinburne's *Winds*. The recital is a valuable addition to Collins's English Song series.

Additional recommendations ...

...Christopher Columbus – suite from the radio production[a]. Façade – Long Steel Grass[b]. Three Songs[b]. Anon in Love[c]. A Song for the Lord Mayor's Table[d]. The Twelve[e]. [bd]**Jill Gomez**, [e]**Patricia Forbes** (sops); [a]**Linda Finnie**, [e]**Ruth Gleave** (mezzos); [c]**Simon Gay** (alto); [c]**Martyn Hill**, [a]**Arthur Davies**, [e]**James Oxley** (tens); [e]**Peter Harvey** (bar); [ae]**Westminster Singers; City of London Sinfonia / Richard Hickox**. Chandos Ⓕ CHAN8824 (65 minutes: DDD: 12/90).

...Anon in Love[ac]. Toccata in A minor[bd]. Ten duets for children[de]. Façade – Valse[d]. Two Pieces[bd]. Five Bagatelles[c]. The Winds[ad]. Tritons[ad]. [a]**John Mark Ainsley** (ten); [b]**Kenneth Sillito** (vn); [c]**Carlos Bonell** (gtr); [d]**Hamish Milne**, [e]**Gretel Dowdeswell** (pfs). Chandos Ⓕ CHAN9292 (67 minutes: DDD: 10/94).

Walton Belshazzar's Feast[a]. Coronation Te Deum. Gloria[b]. [b]**Ameral Gunson** (contr); [b]**Neil Mackie** (ten); [a]**Gwynne Howell**, [b]**Stephen Roberts** (bars); **Bach Choir; Philharmonia Orchestra / Sir David Willcocks**. Chandos Ⓕ CHAN8760 (62 minutes: DDD: 1/90). Texts included. Recorded 1989.

With Sir David Willcocks in charge of the choir which he has directed since 1960, one need have no fears that the composer's many near-impossible demands of the chorus in all three of these masterpieces will not be met with elegance and poise. There is as well, in *Belshazzar*, a predictably fine balance of the forces to ensure that as much detail as possible is heard from both chorus and orchestra, even when Walton is bombarding us from all corners of the universe with extra brass bands and all manner of clamorous percussion in praise of pagan gods. Such supremely musical concerns bring their own rewards in a work that can often seem vulgar. The revelation here is the sustained degree of dramatic thrust, exhilaration and what Herbert Howells called "animal joy" in the proceedings. How marvellous, too, to hear the work paced and scaled to avoid the impression of reduced voltage after the big moments. Gwynne Howell is the magnificently steady, firm and dark toned baritone. The *Gloria* and *Coronation Te Deum* are informed with the same concerns: accuracy and professional polish are rarely allowed to hinder these vital contributions to the British choral tradition. The recording's cathedral-like acoustic is as ideal for the *Te Deum*'s ethereal antiphonal effects, as it is for *Belshazzar*'s glorious spectacle; and Chandos match Willcocks's care for balance, bar by bar.

Walton Façade[a]. Overtures – Portsmouth Point; Scapino[b]. Siesta[b].
Arnold English Dances, Op. 33[c]. [a]**Dame Edith Sitwell**, [a]**Sir Peter Pears** (spkrs); [a]**English Opera Group Ensemble / Anthony Collins**; [bc]**London Philharmonic Orchestra / Sir Adrian Boult**. Decca London mono Ⓜ 425 661-2LM* (74 minutes: DDD). Items marked [a] from LXT2977 (11/54), [b]LXT5028 (6/55), [c]LW5166 (6/55). Ⓖ

This is the classic and authoritative reading of the fully approved selection of *Façade* settings. Dame Edith herself reads two-thirds of the numbers, Sir Peter the remaining third. The poetess herself reads them with such *joie de vivre*, such a natural feeling for her own verses and inflexions that nobody could be expected to rival her. Her timing is perfect, her delivery deliciously idiosyncratic, the intonations obviously what she and presumably Walton wanted. Sir Peter isn't far behind her in ability to relish the writing and the instrumental ensemble plays with refinement allied to virtuosity. The 1950s mono recording stands the test of time remarkably well.

Additional recommendations ...

...Façade[a]. **Sitwell** Poems: Two Kitchen Songs. Five Songs – Daphne; The Peach Tree; The Strawberry; The Greengage Tree; The Nectarine Tree. On the Vanity of Human Aspirations. Two Poems from "Façade" – The Drum; Clowns' Houses. The Wind's Bastinado. The Dark Song. Colonel Fantock. Most Lovely Shade. Heart and Mind. **Prunella Scales, Timothy West** (spkrs); [a]**members of London Mozart Players / Jane Glover**. ASV Ⓕ CDDCA679 (64 minutes: DDD/ADD: 4/90).

...Façade – Suites Nos. 1 and 2. *Coupled with works by* **Bliss** and **Lambert**
  English Northern Philharmonia / David Lloyd-Jones.
  Hyperion Ⓕ CDA66436 (74 minutes: DDD: 3/91). *Selected by Sounds in Retrospect.*   Ⓖ
...Façade. Façade 2. **Lynn Redgrave** (narr); **Chamber Music Society of Lincoln Center /**
  Joseph Silverstein. Arabesque Ⓕ Z6699 (65 minutes: DDD: 1/98).

Walton The Bear. **Della Jones** (mez) Madame Popova; **Alan Opie** (bar) Smirnov;
  John Shirley-Quirk (bar) Luka; **Northern Sinfonia / Richard Hickox.** Chandos Ⓕ CHAN9245
  (53 minutes: DDD: 1/94). Text included. Recorded 1993.
If Walton's sense of humour was firmly established from the start in *Façade*, his one-acter, *The Bear*,
among his later works brings out very clearly how strong that quality remained throughout his life. In
this Chekhov tale, Walton times the melodramatic moments marvellously – notably the climactic duel
between the mourning widow and her husband's creditor (the bear of the title) and Hickox brings that
out most effectively. Walton also deftly heightens the farcical element by introducing dozens of
parodies and tongue-in-cheek musical references, starting cheekily with echoes of Britten's
Midsummer Night's Dream. Hickox brings out the richness of the piece as well as its wit, helped by
the opulent Chandos recording which still allows words to be heard clearly. The casting of the three
characters is as near ideal as could be. Della Jones is commanding as the affronted widow, consistently
relishing the melodrama like a young Edith Evans. Alan Opie as Smirnov, 'the bear' is clean-cut and
incisive, powerfully bringing out the irate creditor's changing emotions, while John Shirley-Quirk, still
rich and resonant, is very well cast as the old retainer, Luka.

Walton Troilus and Cressida. **Judith Howarth** (sop) Cressida; **Arthur Davies** (ten) Troilus;
  Clive Bayley (bass) Calkas; **Nigel Robson** (ten) Pandarus; **Alan Opie** (bar) Diomede;
  James Thornton (bar) Antenor; **David Owen-Lewis** (bass) Horaste; **Yvonne Howard** (mez)
  Evadne; **Peter Bodenham** (ten) Priest; **Keith Mills** (ten) Soldier; **Bruce Budd** (bass) First
  Watchman; **Stephen Dowson** (bass) Second Watchman; **Brian Cookson** (ten) Third Watchman;
  Chorus of Opera North; English Northern Philharmonia / Richard Hickox. Chandos
  Ⓕ CHAN9370/1 (two discs: 133 minutes: DDD: 5/95). Notes and text included.
  Recorded 1995. *Gramophone Award Winner 1995.*   ⒼⒼⒼ
Troilus and Cressida is here powerfully presented as an opera for the central repertory, traditional in
its red-blooded treatment of a big classical subject. Few if any operas since Puccini's have such a rich
store of instantly memorable tunes as *Troilus and Cressida.* Walton wrote the piece in the wake of the
first great operatic success of his rival, Benjamin Britten. What more natural than for Walton, by this
time no longer an *enfant terrible* of British music but an Establishment figure, to turn his back on
operas devoted like Britten's to offbeat subjects, and to go back to an older operatic tradition using a
classical love story, based on Chaucer (not Shakespeare). Though he was much praised for this by
early critics in 1954, he was quickly attacked for being old-fashioned. Even when in the tautened
version of the score he offered for the 1976 Covent Garden revival – with the role of the heroine
adapted for the mezzo voice of Dame Janet Baker – the piece was described by one critic as a dodo.
Yet as Richard Hickox suggests, fashion after 40 years matters little, and the success of the Opera
North production in January 1995 indicated that at last the time had come for a big, warmly
romantic, sharply dramatic work to be appreciated on its own terms. This recording was made under
studio conditions during the run of the opera in Leeds in the UK. The discs amply confirm what the
live performances suggested, that Walton's tautening of the score, coupled with a restoration of the
original soprano register for Cressida, has proved entirely successful.
  Hickox conducts a performance that is magnetic from beginning to end. The scene is
atmospherically set in Act 1 by the chorus, initially off-stage, but then with the incisive Opera North
chorus snapping out thrilling cries of "We are accurs'd!". The libretto is unashamedly archaic in its
use of 'opera-speak' like that, with "thee"s and "thou"s and the occasional "perchance". Though the
text may put some off, it is plainly apt for a traditional 'well-made opera' on a classical subject. The
first soloist one hears in the High Priest, Calkas, Cressida's father, about to defect to the Greeks, and
the role is superbly taken by the firm, dark-toned Clive Bayley. Troilus's entry and his declaration of
love for Cressida bring Waltonian sensuousness and the first statements of the soaring Cressida
theme. Arthur Davies is not afraid of using his head voice for *pianissimos*, so contrasting the more
dramatically with the big outbursts and his ringing top notes. This is a younger-sounding hero, more
Italianate of tone than the very English-sounding Lewis on the Walton set. Similarly, Judith
Howarth's Cressida is much more girlish than either Dame Janet Baker in the Covent Garden set
conducted by Lawrence Foster or Dame Elisabeth Schwarzkopf on the Walton excerpts disc. More
than those great predecessors Judith Howarth brings out the vulnerability of the character along with
sweetness and warmth. After Calkas has defected to the Greeks, her cry of "He has deserted us and
Troy!" conveys genuine fear, with her will undermined. All told, although some fine music has been
cut, the tautened version is far more effective both musically and dramatically, with no *longueurs* at
all. The role of Diomede, Cressida's Greek suitor, can seem one-dimensional, but Alan Opie in one
of his finest performances on record sharpens the focus, making him a genuine threat, with the
element of nobility fully allowed. As Antenor, James Thornton sings strongly, but is less steady than
the others, while Yvonne Howard is superb in the mezzo role of Evadne, Cressida's treacherous
servant and confidante. Not just the chorus but the orchestra of Opera North, the English Northern

Philharmonia, respond with fervour. Naturally and idiomatically they observe the Waltonian rubato and the lifting of jazzily syncopated rhythms which Hickox as a dedicated Waltonian instils, echoing the composer's own example. As for the recorded sound, it brings a complete contrast with the dry Covent Garden acoustic on the old EMI complete set or even the close-up mono sound of the Walton extracts. The bloom of the acoustic enhances the score, helped by the wide dynamic range.

Additional recommendations ...

...Soloists; **Chorus and Orchestra of the Royal Opera House, Covent Garden / Lawrence Foster.**
EMI British Composers Ⓜ CMS5 65550-2 (two discs: 126 minutes: ADD: 7/95).

...Excerpts. **Soloists; Philharmonia Orchestra; Orchestra of the Royal Opera House,**
Covent Garden / Sir William Walton.
EMI British Composers mono Ⓜ CDM7 64199-2* (55 minutes: ADD: 1/94).

Further listening ...

...Crown Imperial. *Coupled with works by* **Vaughan Williams** and **Holst**
BBC Symphony Orchestra / Sir Adrian Boult. Beulah mono 2PD12* (12/96).

...Film Music, Volume 2 – Spitfire Prelude and Fugue. A Wartime Sketchbook (arr. Palmer).
Escape Me Never – Suite (arr. Palmer). The Three Sisters (ed. Palmer). The Battle of Britain –
Suite. **Academy of St Martin in the Fields / Sir Neville Marriner.** Chandos CHAN8870 (12/90).

...The Quest (ed. Palmer). The Wise Virgins – Ballet Suite. **London Philharmonic Orchestra /**
Bryden Thomson. Chandos CHAN8871 (4/91).

...The Wise Virgins. Siesta. Portsmouth Point. Scapino. *Coupled with works by* **Arnold** and **Elgar**
London Philharmonic Orchestra / Sir Adrian Boult. Belart mono 461 359-2* (9/97).

...String Quartets – No. 1; A minor. **Gabrieli Quartet.** Chandos CHAN8944 (10/91).

...String Quartet in A minor. *Coupled with works by* **Bridge** and **Elgar** Coull Quartet.
Hyperion CDA66718 (10/94).

...String Quartet in A minor. *Coupled with works by* **Hindemith** and **Prokofiev** Hollywood
Quartet. Testament mono SBT1052* (3/95). *See review under Hindemith; refer to the Index.* ⒼⒼ

...Chichester Service. *Coupled with works by various composers.* **Rochester Cathedral Choir /**
Roger Sayer with **William Whitehead** (org). Priory PRCD529 (7/96).

...Henry V – a Shakespeare scenario (arr. Palmer). **Christopher Plummer** (narr); **Westminster Abbey**
Choristers; Chorus and Academy of St Martin in the Fields / Sir Neville Marriner.
Chandos CHAN8892 (4/91).

...Magnificat and Nunc dimittis. Cantico del sole. Antiphon. Set me as a seal upon thine heart.
Missa brevis. Where does the uttered music go?. Jubilate Deo. A Litany. The Twelve. Carols – All
this time; What cheer?; King Herod and the Cock. Make we joy now in this fest.
Trinity College Choir, Cambridge / Richard Marlow. Conifer Classics CDCF164 (5/89).

...The twelve. *Coupled with works by various composers.* **Choir of St Mary's Cathedral, Edinburgh /**
Timothy Byram-Wigfield with **Peter Backhouse** (org). Priory PRCD557 (10/97). *See review in the*
Collections section; refer to the Index.

Peter Warlock
British 1894-1930

Warlock The Wind from the West. To the Memory of a Great Singer. Take, o take those lips away.
As ever I saw. The Bayly berith the bell away. There is a lady sweet and kind. Lullaby. Sweet
content. Late summer. The Singer. Rest, sweet nymphs. Sleep. A Sad Song. In an arbour green.
Autumn Twilight. I held love's head. Thou gav'st me leave to kiss. Yarmouth Fair. Pretty Ring
Time. A Prayer to St Anthony of Padua. The Sick Heart. Robin Goodfellow. Jillian of Berry.
Fair and True. Ha'nacker Mill. The Night. My Own Country. The First Mercy. The Lover's
Maze. Cradle Song. Sigh no more, ladies. Passing by. The Contented Lover. The Fox.
John Mark Ainsley (ten); **Roger Vignoles** (pf). Hyperion Ⓕ CDA66736 (69 minutes: DDD: 1/95).
Texts included. Recorded 1994. *Gramophone Editor's choice.*   Ⓖ

Philip Heseltine, so strangely renamed, did not facilitate either the singing or the playing of his songs.
For the voice they have a way of passing awkwardly between registers, and though the high notes are
not very high they tend to be uncomfortably placed. The pianist, caught for long in a pool of
chromatics, suddenly finds his hands flying in both directions. Yet for the singer with the control of
breath and command of voice that John Mark Ainsley so splendidly employs here, and for a pianist
with Roger Vignoles's sureness of touch and insight, they must be wonderfully satisfying to perform,
for there is such a love of song implicit in them and such a personal voice speaks through them. The
programme here is arranged chronologically, from 1911 to 1930. Early and Elizabethan poems are the
favourite source, and then the poems of contemporaries such as Belloc, Symons and Bruce Blunt.
Even the earliest of the songs, *The Wind from the West*, has the characteristic touch of a lyrical
impulse, directly responsive to words, and a fastidious avoidance of strophic or harmonic banality.
Often a private unease works within the chromaticism as in the *Cradle Song* ("Be still, my sweet
sweeting"), yet nothing could be more wholehearted in gaiety when he is in the mood for it (viz. *In an
arbour green, Robin Goodfellow, Jillian of Berry*). Ainsley sings with fine reserves of power as well as
softness; he phrases beautifully, and all the nuance that is so essential for these songs (in *Sleep*, for
instance) is most sensitively judged. Vignoles is entirely at one with singer and composer. There are
excellent notes by Fred Tomlinson, and a fine watercolour by Peter de Wint graces the booklet.

...I held love's head. Thou gav'st me leave to kiss. The Singer. Consider. A Sad Song. Rutterkin. *Coupled with works by various composers.* **Sarah Leonard** (sop); **Malcolm Martineau** (pf). Cala United Ⓕ CACD88016-2 (61 minutes: DDD: 3/95).
...The Curlew[a]. Sleep[a]. A Sad Song[a]. The Fairest May[a]. My lady is a pretty one[a]. Take, O take those lips away[a]. My little sweet darling[a]. Mourn no moe[a]. My gostly fader[a]. Chopcherry[a]. Capriol Suite. Serenade. [a]**John Mark Ainsley** (ten); **Nash Ensemble / Martyn Brabbins.** Hyperion Ⓕ CDA66938 (59 minutes: DDD: 12/97).

Further listening ...
...Capriol Suite. Serenade. The Curlew. Where riches is everlasting. The Shrouding of the Duchess of Malfi. The lady's birthday. Pretty Ring Time. Autumn Twilight. Captain Stratton's Fancy. Yarmouth Fair. *Coupled with* **Traditional** (arr./ed. Warlock) Bethlehem Down. Adam lay y-bounden. I saw a fair maiden. Balulalow. **Various artists.** EMI British Composers CDM5 65101-2 (9/94).
...Serenade. Capriol Suite. *Coupled with works by various composers.* **Academy of St Martin in the Fields / Sir Neville Marriner.** Decca Double 452 707-2DF2 (8/97).
...A Cornish Carol. I saw a fair maiden. Benedicamus Domino. The full heart. The rich cavalcade. Corpus Christi. All the flowers of the Spring. As dew in Aprylle. Bethlehem Down. A Cornish Christmas Carol. *Coupled with works by* **Moeran** Finzi Singers / Paul Spicer. Chandos CHAN9182 (10/93). *Gramophone Editor's choice. See review under Moeran; refer to the Index.* Ⓖ
...Piggesnie. Along the stream. *Coupled with works by various composers.* **Sir Peter Pears** (ten); **Viola Tunnard** (pf). Belart 461 550-2 (12/97). *See review in the Collections section; refer to the Index.*
...The Shrouding of the Duchess of Malfi. The lady's birthday. *Coupled with works by various composers.* **London Madrigal Singers / Christopher Bishop; Baccholian Singers of London; Philip Jones Brass Ensemble; English Chamber Orchestra / Ian Humphris.** EMI British Composers CMS5 65123-2 (2/96). *See review in the Collections section; refer to the Index.*

Elinor Warren
American 1900-1991

...We two. *Coupled with works by various composers.* **Thomas Hampson** (bar); **Craig Rutenberg** (pf). EMI CDM5 55028-2 (10/97). *See review in the Collections section; refer to the Index.* ⒼⒼⒼ

Raymond Warren
British 1928

...Bristol Service. *Coupled with works by various composers.* **Bristol Cathedral Choir / Christopher Brayne** with **Ian Ball** (org). Priory PRCD528 (8/96). *See review in the Collections section; refer to the Index.*

Stephen Watson
British 20th century

...O Captain! My Captain![a]. Autumn boughs. Symphonic Study. [a]**Jeremy Huw Williams** (bar); [a]**London Philharmonic Choir; London Philharmonic Orchestra / David Angus.** Herald HAVPCD198 (7/97).

Sydney Watson
British 1903

...Evening Service in E major. *Coupled with works by various composers.* **Lichfield Cathedral Choir / Andrew Lumsden** with **Nigel Potts** (orgs). Priory PRCD505 (10/95). *See review in the Collections section; refer to the Index.*

Franz Waxman
German/American 1906-1967

...Fantasy on Bizet's "Carmen". *Coupled with works by* **Korngold** and **Rózsa** Jascha Heifetz (vn); **RCA Victor Symphony Orchestra / Donald Voorhees.** RCA Victor Gold Seal mono/stereo GD87963* (4/89). *See review under Korngold; refer to the Index.* ⒼⒼⒼ

...Fantasy on Bizet's "Carmen". *Coupled with works by various composers.*
Sergei Nakariakov (tpt); **Alexander Markovich** (pf).
Teldec 4509-94554-2 (6/95). *See review in the Collections section; refer to the Index.* ⓖⓖ

Samuel Webbe II
British c1770-1843

Suggested listening ...
...Variations in A major on "Adeste Fideles". *Coupled with works by various composers.* **Salomon Quartet.** Hyperion CDA66780 (3/96). *See review in the Collections section; refer to the Index.*

Carl Maria von Weber
German 1786-1826

Weber Clarinet Concertos[a] – No. 1 in F minor, J114. No. 2 in E flat major, J118. Grand duo concertant, J204[b]. **Sharon Kam** (cl); [b]**Itamar Golan** (pf); [a]**Leipzig Gewandhaus Orchestra / Kurt Masur.** Teldec Ⓕ 0630-15428-2 (64 minutes: DDD: 3/97). Recorded 1996.
Gramophone Editor's choice.   ⓖ
Weber Clarinet Concertos[a] – No. 1 in F minor, J114; No. 2 in E flat major, J118. Clarinet Concertino in E flat major, J109[a]. Clarinet Quintet in B flat major, J182[b]. **Kari Kriikku** (cl); [b]**New Helsinki Quartet** (Jan Söderblom, Petri Aarnio, vns; Ilari Angervo, va; Jan-Erik Gustafsson, vc); [a]**Finnish Radio Symphony Orchestra / Sakari Oramo.** Ondine Ⓕ ODE895-2 (76 minutes: DDD: 9/97). Recorded 1996.   ⓖ
Teldec provide a good programme in having the two Weber clarinet concertos coupled with a work which is virtually another concerto but with piano accompaniment, the *Grand duo concertant.* Sharon Kam is a young Israeli whom Kurt Masur heard in her home country, immediately inviting her back to Leipzig to play concertos. She was contracted by Teldec in 1994, but this is the first disc entirely devoted to her playing, revealing her as a most imaginative and individual artist, using the widest tonal and dynamic range, and with a very sure technique, with every note cleanly in place. As the opening movement of the First Concerto demonstrates, she has the gift of magicking a phrase, and one mark of her magnetism and flair is the way she can hold tension over an exaggerated pause or *tenuto.* Most remarkable of all is the dark intensity of Kam's account of the slow minor-key *Romanza* of the Second Concerto, with the soloist clearly the one insisting on a very measured tempo, when Masur's preference is always towards flowing *Andantes.* She is similarly impressive in the *Grand duo concertant,* though there the piano tone of Itamar Golan is on the shallow side.
Kari Kriikku's are brilliant performances of works that more or less reinvented the clarinet as an instrument of brilliance, or at any rate in the hands and under the flashing fingers of Weber's friend Heinrich Baermann. The formidable difficulties hold no terrors for Kriikku; indeed, wonderfully fluent as his playing is in, for instance, the fireworks music that ends the Second Concerto and the Quintet, one almost wants there to be more sense of difficulties overcome as witness of the virtuoso as hero. But that would be to quibble, especially when Kriikku has such a wide range of expression and such an intelligent approach to the music. He plays the First Concerto as a slightly tense, witty work, giving the *Adagio* a long-breathed lyricism and the finale humour as well as wit. The only questionable element is his own over-long cadenza to the first movement. The Second Concerto is treated as a more lyrical and dramatic work, with an elegant *polacca* finale, and there is a beautiful length of phrasing in the *Andante,* as there is in the "Fantasia" movement of the Quintet. Kriikku neatly touches off the mock-sinister intervention in the Quintet's finale, refusing to take it seriously. He is well accompanied throughout.
Additional recommendations ...
...Grand duo concertant. *Coupled with works by various composers.* **Andrei Gavrilov** (pf).
EMI Forte Ⓜ CZS5 69334-2 (two discs: 151 minutes: ADD). *See review in the Collections section; refer to the Index.*   ⓖ
...Clarinet Concertino. *Coupled with works by various composers.*
Emma Johnson (cl); **English Chamber Orchestra / Sir Charles Groves.**
ASV Ⓕ CDDCA559 (55 minutes: DDD: 11/86).   ⓖⓖ
...Clarinet Quintet in B flat major, J182. *Coupled with works by* **Hummel** *and* **Reicha**
Charles Neidich (cl); **L'Archibudelli.** Sony Classical Ⓕ SK57968 (78 minutes: DDD: 9/95). 🎵
...Clarinet Quintet in B flat major, J182[a]. *Coupled with works by* **Spohr** *and* **Berwald**
Gervase de Peyer (cl); **Melos Ensemble.** EMI Matrix Ⓜ CDM5 65995-2 (69 minutes: ADD: 12/96).

Weber Symphonies – No. 1 in C major, J50; No. 2 in F minor, J51. Konzertstück in F minor, J282[a]. [a]**Melvyn Tan** (fp); **London Classical Players / Sir Roger Norrington.** EMI Ⓕ CDC5 55348-2 (60 minutes: DDD: 9/95). 🎵 Recorded 1994.   ⓖ
Weber's symphonies may not be conventional symphonies nor his *Konzertstück* a conventional piano concerto, but they are highly original pieces and the performer who does not start from that premise will get nowhere with them. Norrington plays both symphonies more as sequences of remarkable orchestral inventions, and does so with great wit and style. He has flexibility, a gift for a neat rhythmic swerve or a sly rubato, a sense of timing as he makes the most of the unexpected pauses or abrupt

explosions of sound; not least, he has a quick ear for the textures, and appreciates how the use of viola tone, or of hand-horns and their variously coloured notes, or of the contrast of solo woodwind instruments, is of the essence of the invention and not simply a colouring of it. These are delightfully fresh, enjoyable performances. Melvyn Tan's of the *Konzertstück* is in similar vein. The instrument he uses, a copy of an 1815 Streicher, is ideally suited to the light textures but can also produce enough weight to balance with the full orchestra; and he spares himself nothing with his hurtling tempos. A substantial element in this pioneering work is about virtuosity as a stimulus for invention, rather than difficulties for their own sake, and about how that can express itself in originality of form. Tan has the sense of relishing difficulties and fearlessly overcoming them, together with a vein of poetry in it all, which reminds one of accounts of Weber's own playng. The recording does full justice to all this artistry.

Additional recommendations ...

...Konzertstück, J282. Piano Concertos Nos. 1 and 2. **Nikolai Demidenko** (pf); **Scottish Chamber Orchestra / Sir Charles Mackerras.** Hyperion Ⓕ CDA66729 (57 minutes: DDD: 6/95).

...Symphonies Nos. 1 and 2. Turandot – Overture; Act 2 March; Act 5 Funeral March. Silvana – Tanz der Edelknaben; Fackel Tanz. Die drei Pintos – Entr'acte. **Queensland Philharmonic Orchestra / John Georgiadis.** Naxos Ⓢ 8 550928 (65 minutes: DDD: 2/95).

Weber Piano Sonatas – No. 1 in C major, J138; No. 2 in A flat major, J199. Rondo brillante in E flat major, J252, "La gaité". Invitation to the dance, J260. **Hamish Milne** (pf). CRD Ⓕ CRD3485 (76 minutes: DDD: 9/92). Recorded 1991.

Weber's piano music, once played by most pianists, has since suffered neglect and even the famous *Invitation to the dance* is now more often heard in its orchestral form. Since he was a renowned pianist as well as a major composer, the neglect seems odd, particularly when other pianist composers such as Chopin and Liszt are at the centre of the concert repertory; but part of the trouble may lie in the difficulty of the music, reflecting his own huge hands and his tendency to write what the booklet-essay calls "chords unplayable by others". Hamish Milnes makes out a real case for this music, and his playing of the two sonatas is idiomatic and resourceful, even if one cannot banish the feeling that Weber all too readily used the melodic and harmonic formulae of eighteenth-century *galanterie* and simply dressed them up in nineteenth-century salon virtuosity. From this point of view, a comparison with Chopin's mature sonatas or Liszt's magnificent single essay in the form reveals Webcr as a lightweight. A hearing of the first movement in the First Sonata will quickly tell you if this is how you may react, while in its *Presto* finale you may praise a Mendelssohnian lightness but also note a pomposity foreign to that composer. Leaving aside the musical quality of these sonatas, this is stylish playing which should win them friends. The *Rondo brillante* and *Invitation to the dance* make no claim to be other than scintillating salon music, and are captivating in Milne's shapely and skilful performances. The recording is truthful and satisfying.

Additional recommendations ...

...Nos. 1 and 2. **Martin Jones** (pf). Pianissimo Ⓕ PP20792 (58 minutes: DDD: 9/92).

...No. 1. Nine Variations on a Russian theme, "Schöne Minka", J179. Six Variations on an original theme, J7. Invitation to the dance, J260. **Alexander Paley** (pf). Naxos Ⓢ 8 550988 (66 minutes: DDD: 2/95).

...No. 2. Six Variations on Naga's air (from Vogler's opera "Samori"), J43. Seven Variations on a Gipsy song, J219. Grande polonaise, J59. **Alexander Paley** (pf). Naxos Ⓢ 8 550989 (61 minutes: DDD: 2/95).

Weber Meine Lieder, meine Sänge, J73. Klage, J63. Der Kleine Fritz an seine jungen Freunde, J74. Was zieht zu deinem Zauberkreise, J86. Ich sah ein Röschen am Wege stehn, J67. Er an Sie, J57. Meine Farben, J62. Liebe-Glühen, J140. Uber die Berge mit ungestüm, Op. 25 No. 2. Es stürmt auf der Flur, J161. Minnelied, J160. Reigen, J159. Sind es Schmerzen, J156. Mein Verlangen, J196. Wenn ich ein Vöglein war', J233. Mein Schatzerl is hübsch, J234. Liebesgruss aus der Ferne, J257. Herzchen, mein Schätzchen, J258. Das Veilchen im Thale, J217. Ich denkc dein, J48. Horch'!, Leise horch', Geliebte, J56. Elle était simple et gentilette, J292. **Dietrich Fischer-Dieskau** (bar); **Hartmut Höll** (pf). Claves Ⓕ CD50-9118 (52 minutes: DDD: 11/93). Texts and translations included. Recorded 1991. Ⓖ

"In my opinion the first and most sacred duty of a song-writer is to observe the maximum of fidelity to the prosody of the text that he is setting." Weber was writing in defence of a number he composed for an obscure play, but his words can stand as an apologia for his 90-odd songs. His contribution to German song has been underrated, for his ideas were different from those of his contemporaries. Fischer-Dieskau used to resist suggestions that he might take up Weber's songs, and it is good that he has now done so, even late in his career. Always sensitive to words, he now responds with the subtlety of understanding that comes from many years of closeness to German poetry. Only very occasionally is there the powerful emphasis on the single expressive word that sometimes used mar his interpretations, keeping them too near the surface of the poetry. He can still use individual colour marvellously: the tonal painting of 'blue', 'white' and 'brown' in *Meine Farben* is exquisitely done. But more remarkable, here and in other songs, is the manner in which he follows the novel melodic lines which Weber has contrived out of the poetry. *Ein steter Kampf* is a masterly example; so is *Was zieht zu deinem Zauberkreise*, one of the few songs in which Weber enters Schubertian territory; so are *Es stürmt auf der Flur* and *Liebesgruss aus der Ferne.* Not even Fischer-Dieskau can quite bring off the coy *Der Kleine Fritz* by slightly sending it up (the only hope), and there is something a bit hefty about *Reigen,* a very funny wedding song full of "Heissa, lustig!" and "Dudel, didel!", though Hartmut Höll does wonders with the clanking accompaniment. Höll varies his tone so much here from the warmth and depth of his touch elsewhere that one wonders if the engineers did not take a small hand: why not? These are charming, touching, witty, colourful verses, often by minor figures of Weber's circle, and they drew from him music that heightens their point. Fischer-Dieskau's intelligent artistry could not more eloquently support the praise for Weber from Wilhelm Müller, poet of *Die schöne Müllerin* and *Winterreise,* as "master of German song".

Weber Der Freischütz. **Peter Schreier** (ten) Max (Hans Jörn Weber); **Gundula Janowitz** (sop) Agathe (Regina Jeske); **Edith Mathis** (sop) Aennchen (Ingrid Hille); **Theo Adam** (bass) Caspar (Gerhard Paul); **Bernd Weikl** (bar) Ottokar (Otto Mellies); **Siegfried Vogel** (bass) Cuno (Gerd Biewer); **Franz Crass** (bass) Hermit; **Gerhard Paul** (spkr) Samiel; **Günther Leib** (bar) Kilian (Peter Hölzel); **Leipzig Radio Chorus; Dresden Staatskapelle / Carlos Kleiber.** DG Ⓕ 415 432-2GH2 (two discs: 130 minutes: ADD: 11/86). Notes, text and translation included. From 2720 071 (11/73). Recorded 1973.

Carlos Kleiber's fine set of *Der Freischütz* earns reissue on CD for a number of reasons. One is the excellence of the actual recorded sound with a score that profits greatly from such attention. Weber's famous attention to details of orchestration is lovingly explored by a conductor who has taken the trouble to go back to the score in manuscript and observe that there are differences between that and most of the published versions (this recording was made before Joachim Freyer's invaluable edition for Peters in 1976). So not only do we hear the eerie sound of low flute thirds and the subtle contrast of unmuted viola with four-part muted violins in Agathe's "Leise, leise", among much else, with a new freshness and point, but all the diabolical effects in the Wolf's Glen come up with a greater sense of depth, down to the grisliest detail. The beginning of the Overture, and the opening of the Wolf's Glen scene, steal upon us out of a primeval silence, as they should. All this would be of little point were the performance itself not of such interest. There is a good deal to argue about but this is because the performance is so interesting. Whatever one may feel about some of Kleiber's tempos, and one may feel some of them to be unwise in both directions, they spring beyond doubt from a careful, thoughtful and musical mind. The singing cast is excellent, with Gundula Janowitz an outstanding Agathe to a somewhat reflective Max from Peter Schreier, at his best when the hero is brought low by the devilish machinations; Edith Mathis is a pretty Aennchen, Theo Adam a fine, murky Caspar. The dialogue, spoken by actors, is slightly abbreviated and in one or two respects amended. Kubelik's performance is the more subtle and commanding, and also the more colourful. It is more traditional than Kleiber's, without any loss of freshness; Kleiber produces much new insight, however, often penetratingly. The magical old score can take both approaches.

Additional recommendations ...

...Soloists; Chorus of the Deutsche Oper, Berlin; Berlin Philharmonic Orchestra / **Joseph Keilberth.** EMI Ⓜ CMS7 69342-2* (two discs: 134 minutes: ADD: 9/89).

...Soloists; Berlin Radio Chorus and Symphony Orchestra / **Marek Janowski.** RCA Victor Red Seal Ⓕ 09026 62538-2 (two discs: 131 minutes: DDD: 1/95).

...Soloists; Berlin Deutsche Oper Chorus and Orchestra / **Lovro von Matačić.** RCA Victor Ⓜ 74321 25287-2 (two discs: 139 minutes: ADD: 6/95).

...Soloists; Bavarian Radio Chorus and Symphony Orchestra / **Rafael Kubelik.** Decca Ⓜ 443 672-2DMO2 (two discs: 134 minutes: ADD: 8/95).

...Overtures – Der Freischütz; Oberon. *Coupled with works by various composers.* **London Philharmonic Orchestra; Berlin Philharmonic Orchestra / Sir Thomas Beecham.** Dutton Laboratories mono Ⓑ CDLX7009* (75 minutes: ADD: 10/94). *See review in the Collections section; refer to the Index.*

...Excerpts – Wie nahte mir der Schlummer ... Leise, leise, fromme Weise; Und ob die Wolke. Oberon – Ozean du Ungeheuer! ... Wolkenlos strahlt denn die Sonne; Traure, mein Herz. *Coupled with works by various composers.* **Gundula Janowitz** (sop); **Irwin Gage** (pf); **Vienna Symphony Orchestra / Wilfried Boettcher; Orchestra of the Deutsche Staatsoper, Berlin / Ferdinand Leitner.** DG Double Ⓜ 447 352-2GDB2 (two discs: 152 minutes: ADD: 12/95).

...Overture. Euryanthe – Overture. *Coupled with works by various composers.* **Hallé Orchestra / Sir John Barbirolli.** Dutton Laboratories mono Ⓜ CDSJB1004* (11/96).

...Overture. Oberon – Overture. *Coupled with works by* **R. Strauss Staatskapelle Dresden / Giuseppe Sinopoli.** DG Ⓕ 449 216-2GH (57 minutes: DDD: 3/97). *See review under R. Strauss; refer to the Index.*

...Der Freischütz – Wie nahte mir der Schlummer ... Leise, leise, fromme Weise; Und ob die Wolke. *Coupled with works by various composers.* **Dame Kiri Te Kanawa** (sop); **Philharmonia Orchestra / Julius Rudel.** EMI Ⓕ CDC5 56417-2 (57 minutes: DDD: 11/97). *See review in the Collections section; refer to the Index.*

...Der Freischütz – Kommt ein schlanker Bursch. *Coupled with works by various composers.* **Inessa Galante** (sop); **Latvian National Symphony Orchestra / Imants Resnis.** Campion Ⓕ RRCD1344 (63 minutes: AAD/DDD: A/97). *See review in the Collections section; refer to the Index.*

Further listening ...
...Horn Concertino in E minor, J188. *Coupled with works by various composers.*
Barry Tuckwell (hn); **Academy of St Martin in the Fields / Sir Neville Marriner.**
EMI Forte CZS5 69395-2 (2/97). *See review in the Collections section; refer to the Index.*
...Invitation to the dance. Overtures – Der Beherrscher der Geister; Euryanthe; Oberon; Abu
Hassan; Der Freischütz; Peter Schmoll. **Berlin Philharmonic Orchestra / Herbert von Karajan.**
DG Galleria 419 070-2GGA (6/88).
...Piano Sonata No. 3 in D minor, J206. Eight Variations on an air from Vogler's ballet "Castore e
Polluce", J40. Seven Variations on Bianchi's air "Vien quà, Dorina bella", J53. Seven Variations
on an original theme, J55. Momento capriccioso in B flat major, J56. **Alexander Paley** (pf).
Naxos 8 550989 (2/95).
...Piano Sonata No. 4 in E minor, J287. Seven Variations on a theme from Méhul's opera "Joseph",
J141. Les adieux, 'Op. 81'. Rondo brillante in E flat major, "La gaité", J252. Polacca brillante,
"L'hilarité", J268. **Alexander Paley** (pf). Naxos 8 553006 (2/95).
...Abu Hassan[b]. **Humperdinck** Hänsel und Gretel[a]. Soloists; [a]**Mozart Chorus;** [a]women's voices of
the **Deutsche Oper Chorus, Berlin;** [b]**chorus; Berlin Radio Symphony Orchestra /** [a]**Artur Rother,**
[b]**Leopold Ludwig.** Preiser mono 90209* (3/96).
...Oberon. **Soloists; Bavarian Radio Chorus and Symphony Orchestra / Rafael Kubelík.**
DG 419 038-2GX2 (12/91).
...Oberon. **Soloists; Berlin Radio Chorus; Deutsches Symphony Orchestra, Berlin / Marek Janowski.**
RCA Victor Red Seal 09026 68505-2 (3/98).
...Peter Schmoll und seine Nachburn. **Soloists; Hagen Philharmonic Orchestra / Gerhard Markson.**
Marco Polo 8 223592/3 (4/94).

Frederick Weber

German 1766-1842

Suggested listening ...
...Variations in F major. *Coupled with works by various composers.* **John Wallace** (tpt); **John
Anderson** (ob d'amore); **Peter Thomas** (vn); **Philharmonia Orchestra / Christopher Warren-Green,
Simon Wright.** Nimbus NI7016 (2/95). *See review in the Collections section; refer to the Index.*

Anton Webern

Austrian 1883-1945

Webern Passacaglia, Op. 1. Six Pieces, Op. 6. Five Pieces, Op. 10. Variations, Op. 30.
Bach (arr. Webern) Musikalisches Opfer, BWV1079 – Ricercar a 6.
Schoenberg A Survivor from Warsaw, Op. 46[a]. [a]**Gottfried Hornik** (narr); [a]**Vienna State Opera
Chorus; Vienna Philharmonic Orchestra / Claudio Abbado.** DG Ⓕ 431 774-2GH
(50 minutes: DDD: 5/93). Text and translation included. Recorded 1989-1992.   Ⓠ

Claudio Abbado has recorded rather more in the way of progressive twentieth-century music over the
years than many other star conductors. It would be good to have much more. Meanwhile, we must be
grateful for these recordings of Webern, including a fine reading of the rarely-heard and forcefully
dramatic Variations, Op. 30. Abbado and the VPO are predictably responsive to the romantic
intensity of the early *Passacaglia*, with nothing routine in their performance, and the sets of
expressionist miniatures are even more convincing in their blend of delicacy and power. The fourth
piece from Op. 6, the closest Webern ever came to concentrating the essence of a Mahlerian funeral
march, and ending with an ear-splitting percussion crescendo, is all the more effective for Abbado's
refusal to set a self-indulgently slow tempo. Technically, these recordings outshine the competition,
though both Boulez and Karajan remain memorable as interpreters – Boulez especially in Op. 30,
Karajan most notably in Op. 6. Given the evident rapport between Webern and Abbado it seems odd
that the disc doesn't include more of Webern's music – for example, the Symphony, Op. 21. The Bach
arrangement is nevertheless an ear-opening exercise in passing baroque counterpoint through a
kaleidoscope of expressionist tone-colours, and Schoenberg's *A Survivor from Warsaw* retains its
special power to move and disturb.

Additional recommendations ...
...Passacaglia. Five Movements, Op. 5. Six Pieces, Op. 6. Symphony, Op. 21. **Berlin Philharmonic Orchestra
/ Herbert von Karajan.** DG 20th Century Classics Ⓜ 423 254-2GC (46 minutes: ADD: 7/88). ⒼⒻ

Webern Passacaglia, Op. 1. Five Pieces, Op. 5. Six Pieces, Op. 6. Im Sommerwind.
Bach (orch. Webern) Musikalisches Opfer, BWV1079 – Ricercar a 6.
Schubert (orch. Webern) Deutsche Tänze, D820. **Berlin Philharmonic Orchestra / Pierre Boulez.**
DG Ⓕ 447 099-2GH (67 minutes: DDD: 3/96). Recorded 1993-1994. *Selected by Soundings.*

With the exception of the Bach and Schubert arrangements this is all relatively early, pre-serial
Webern, yet Boulez devotes as much care and as much affection to the D minor *Passacaglia* and to
the undeniably immature but irresistibly luscious *Im Sommerwind* as to the far more characteristic Op.
5 and Op. 6 pieces. Indeed, if the *Passacaglia* is anything to go by, a Brahms symphony cycle from
Boulez would be a fascinating prospect, while his reading of the 'idyll for large orchestra' suggests that

his Delius might be no less interesting. Boulez does not imply that the mature Webern is present here in embryo; but he does perhaps make us ask how much of that later music is, like this, inspired by nature. To be reminded of Brahms by the *Passacaglia* is no less appropriate. This is a Janus of a piece, looking back not only to Brahms's Fourth Symphony but beyond (the presence of the Bach/Webern *Ricercar* points that up), and at the same time moving onwards from the delicate chamber passages in *Im Sommerwind* towards the 'orchestral chamber music' of Op. 5 and Op. 6. Boulez looks both ways too, with rich orchestral amplitude and expressive phrasing (very broad rubato) but he also notices Webern's already marked liking for transparent textures, quiet subtleties of string colour and the sound of the muted trumpet. And yes: heard in this context the shorter pieces are a logical progression. They are intensely expressive, with a wide range of emotion often within a very few bars; no wonder Boulez prefers the earlier, richer scoring of Op. 6. He obviously loves their Mahler-derived dissolution of the boundary between orchestral and chamber music, and encourages the Berlin Philharmonic to play with great tonal beauty, aware that a recurrent marking in mature Webern is "tenderly". Those qualities recur in the Bach and Schubert arrangements; the rubato in the Fourth Schubert Dance and the Viennese charm of the Fifth suggest that a Boulez *Fledermaus*, even, might be a gleam at the back of his mind. The recordings, very properly, are warm as well as clean.

Webern Complete works, Opp. 1-31. **Various artists.** Sony Classical Ⓜ SM3K45845 (three discs: 223 minutes: ADD: 6/91). Notes, texts and translations included. From 79204 (12/78). Recorded 1967-1972. *Gramophone classical 100.* *Gramophone Award Winner 1978.*   ❸❸❸
Passacaglia, Op. 1 (London Symphony Orchestra / Pierre Boulez). Entflieht auf leichten Kähnen, Op. 2 (John Alldis Choir / Boulez). Five Songs from "Der siebente Ring", Op. 3. Five Songs, Op. 4 (Heather Harper, sop; Charles Rosen, pf). Five Movements, Op. 5 (Juilliard Quartet). Six Pieces, Op. 6 (LSO / Boulez). Four Pieces, Op. 7 (Isaac Stern, vn; Rosen, pf). Two Songs, Op. 8 (Harper, sop; chamber ensemble / Boulez). Six Bagatelles, Op. 9 (Juilliard Qt). Five Pieces, Op. 10 (LSO / Boulez). Three Little Pieces, Op. 11 (Gregor Piatigorsky, vc; Rosen, pf). Four Songs, Op. 12 (Harper, sop; Rosen, pf). Four Songs, Op. 13. Six Songs, Op. 14 (Harper, sop; chbr ens / Boulez). Five Sacred Songs, Op. 15. Five Canons on Latin Texts, Op. 16 (Halina Lukomska, sop; chbr ens / Boulez). Three Songs, Op. 18 (Lukomska, sop; John Williams, gtr; Colin Bradbury, cl / Boulez). Two Songs, Op. 19 (John Alldis Ch, mbrs LSO / Boulez). String Trio, Op. 20 (mbrs Juilliard Qt). Symphony, Op. 21 (LSO / Boulez). Quartet, Op. 22 (Robert Marcellus, cl; Abraham Weinstein, sax; Daniel Majeske, vn; Rosen, pf / Boulez). Three Songs from "Viae inviae", Op. 23 (Lukomska, sop; Rosen, pf). Concerto, Op. 24 (mbrs LSO / Boulez). Three Songs, Op. 25 (Lukomska, sop; Rosen, pf). Das Augenlicht, Op. 26 (John Alldis Ch, LSO / Boulez). Piano Variations, Op. 27 (Rosen, pf). String Quartet, Op. 28 (Juilliard Qt). Cantata No. 1, Op. 29 (Lukomska, sop; John Alldis Ch; LSO / Boulez). Variations, Op. 30 (LSO / Boulez). Cantata No. 2, Op. 31 (Lukomska, sop; Barry McDaniel, bar; John Alldis Ch; LSO / Boulez). Five Movements, Op. 5 – orchestral version (LSO / Boulez). **Bach** (orch. Webern) Musikalischen Opfer, BWV1079 – Fuga (Ricercata) No. 2 (LSO / Boulez). **Schubert** (orch. Webern) Deutsche Tänze, D820 (Frankfurt Radio Orchestra / Anton Webern. Recorded live in 1932).   ❸❸❸
Webern is as 'classic' to Pierre Boulez as Mozart or Brahms are to most other conductors, and when he is able to persuade performers to share his view the results can be remarkable – lucid in texture, responsive in expression. Despite his well-nigh exclusive concern with miniature forms, there are many sides to Webern, and although this set is not equally successful in realizing all of them, it leaves the listener in no doubt about the music's sheer variety, as well as its emotional power, whether the piece in question is an ingenious canon-by-inversion or a simple, folk-like *Lied*. From a long list of performers one could single out Heather Harper and the Juilliard Quartet for special commendation; and the smooth confidence of the John Alldis Choir is also notable. The recordings were made over a five-year period and have the typical CBS dryness of that time. Even so, in the finest performances which Boulez himself directs – as indicated in the review above, the *Orchestral Variations*, Op. 30 is perhaps the high point – that remarkable radiance of spirit so special to Webern is vividly conveyed. It is a fascinating bonus to hear Webern himself conducting his Schubert arrangements – music from another world, yet with an economy and emotional poise that Webern in his own way sought to emulate.

Additional recommendations ...
...Movement. String Quartet (1905). Five Movements. Six Bagatelles. String Quartet, Op. 28. **Quartetto Italiano.** Philips Ⓕ 420 796-2PH (53 minutes: ADD: 4/88).   ❸❸
...Five Movements. Six Bagatelle. String Quartet, Op. 28. Trio. Movement (1925). String Quartet (1905). Slow Movement (1905). Rondo (c. 1906). **Arditti Quartet.** Auvidis Montaigne Ⓕ MO789008 (66 minutes: DDD; 12/91).   ❸❸
... Five Movements. Langsamer Satz. *Coupled with works by* **Schoenberg** *and* **Berg** **Brindisi Quartet.** Metronome Ⓕ METCD1007 (70 minutes: DDD: 6/95).
...Piano Variations, Op. 27. *Coupled with works by various composers.* **Maurizio Pollini** (pf). DG The Originals Ⓜ 447 431-2GOR (68 minutes: ADD: 6/95). *See review in the Collections section; refer to the Index.*   ❸❸
...Piano Variations, Op. 27. *Coupled with works by* **Schoenberg** *and* **Berg** **Glenn Gould** (pf). CBC Records Perspective Series mono Ⓕ PSCD2008* (65 minutes: ADD: 1/96).

...Two Pieces for Cello and Piano. Four Pieces, Op. 7. Three Little Pieces, Op. 11. Cello
Sonata. *Coupled with works by various composers.* **Sabine Meyer** (cl); **Gidon Kremer** (vn);
Veronika Hagen (va); **Clemens Hagen** (vc); **Oleg Maisenberg** (pf). DG Ⓕ 447 112-2GH
(76 minutes: DDD: 4/96). *See review in the Collections section; refer to the Index.*
...Concerto for Nine Instruments, Op. 24[ab]. Three Little Pieces, Op. 11[ab]. Four Pieces, Op. 7[ab].
Coupled with works by **Schoenberg** and **Berg** [a]Houston Symphony Chamber Players /
Christoph Eschenbach ([b]pf). Koch International Classics Ⓕ 37337-2 (74 minutes: DDD: 12/96).

Webern Symphony, Op. 21. Das Augenlicht, Op. 26[c]. Cantatas – No. 1, Op. 29[ac]; No. 2, Op. 31[abc].
Variations, Op. 30. Five Pieces, Op. posth. Drei Lieder[a]. [a]**Christiane Oelze** (sop); [b]**Gerald Finley**
(bar); [c]**BBC Singers; Berlin Philharmnonic Orchestra / Pierre Boulez.** DG Ⓕ 447 765-2GH
(59 minutes: DDD: 3/97). Texts and translations included. Recorded 1994.	ⒼⒼ
Pierre Boulez has been conducting this music for 40 years, and his interpretations have evolved from
the youthful Domaine Musical recordings, through the incisive CBS readings of 1967-72 (reviewed
above), to this present 'late' style. Boulez encourages the Berlin Philharmonic to play with great tonal
beauty, and the recordings are warm as well as clean. Tempos are generally broader than they were 30
years ago, and forms are outlined more expansively. There are moments of high drama – the sudden
outburst from the solo horn in the second movement of Op. 21, the representations of thunder and
lightning in the first movement of Op. 29 – but these are balanced by an eloquent spaciousness and
refinement, as with the glowing canonic lines in the first movement of Op. 21. Only in Boulez's
account of the *Variations*, Op. 30 do you feel that the emphasis on lyric inwardness risks an excess of
decorum, the raw contrasts of texture and mood so strong in the CBS version sacrificed to an overall
blend that deprives Webern of some of his power to shock. That power is explosively present in the
Five Pieces from 1913, especially in the astonishing No. 3, and also, less aggressively, in the whispered
Sprechgesang of the *Drei Lieder*. But the other side of Webern, the sheer tenderness of his lyrical
imagination, is conveyed here with particular distinction by the solo singing and the beautifully
integrated BBC Singers, superbly accurate in the cantatas and *Das Augenlicht*. A distinguished disc.

Webern Slow movement (Langsamer Satz). Five Movements, Op. 5. String Quartet (1905).
Six Bagatelles, Op. 9. Rondo. Movement (Sehr lebhaft), Op. posth. Three Little Movements[a].
String Trio, Op. 20. String Quartet, Op. 28. [a]**Mary Ann McCormick** (mez); **Emerson Quartet**
(Eugene Drucker, Philip Setzer, vns; Lawrence Dutton, va; David Finckel, vc).
DG Ⓕ 445 828-2GH (68 minutes: DDD: 5/95). Recorded 1992.	ⒼⒼ
Although almost half the playing time is occupied by late-romantic juvenilia, even the neo-
Schoenbergian exercises of the 1905 Quartet are not without interest, the main motive signalling its
serial potential until it gives way to a warm, well-upholstered tonality. Nor is there anything in the
least perfunctory in the Emerson's performances of these early efforts. Their command of the
multifarious techniques Webern calls for from Op. 5 onwards is complete, and they play with wholehearted freedom of expression in a well-balanced, rather closely focused recording. An attractive
flexibility in the already intense compression of Op. 5 is complemented by a special refinement, which
ensures that every note counts in the miniscule *Bagatelles*. It also pays dividends in the fiercely
coherent lines of the Trio and its gossamer-like satellite *Movement*. To end with, the Quartet, Op. 28
inhabits a different, more sober world, at least until the finale brings back some of the old
expressionistic turbulence to counter the rhythmic smoothness and motivic balance which dominate
the earlier movements. This admirable performance sets the seal on a most distinguished enterprise.

Webern Drei Gedichte (1899-1903). Acht frühe Lieder (1901-04). Fünf Lieder (1906-08).
Fünf Lieder aus "Der siebente Ring", Op. 3. Fünf Lieder, Op. 4. Vier Lieder nach Gedichten von
Stefan George (1908-09). Vier Lieder, Op. 12. Drei Lieder aus, Op. 23, "Viae inviae".
Drei Lieder, Op. 25. **Christiane Oelze** (sop); **Eric Schneider** (pf). DG Ⓕ 447 103-2GH
(76 minutes: DDD: 4/96). Texts and translations included. Recorded 1994.
Webern's songs are quiet and mostly brief (there are 40 of them here in the space of 76 minutes). They
are intimate, ethereal, more concerned with distilling subtle emotional states than with telling stories
or painting pictures. Christiane Oelze's voice and musicianship are well suited to them. Her voice is
not large, but by careful control of dynamics she can easily encompass those infrequent moments
where a big phrase or an ample gesture is required. The sound is pure and bright, her sense of line as
admirable as her intonation and her pianist is an artist of great intelligence, refinement and command
of colour. The recording balances them very well, not tempted by Oelze's confiding manner to come
too close. The first mature songs here are those with opus numbers, and these earlier sets an account
of how that maturity was achieved. In the two outer songs of the *Drei Gedichte* we already hear a
prediction of Webern's later manner, but the central setting of Richard Dehmel's "Nachtgebet der
Braut" might be by another composer, with its four verses of overheated Wagnerian passion. Real
urgency arrives with serialism and the last three sets of songs on this disc. With it arrives also fantasy,
wit and a feeling of being at ease with the past; now Webern can make subtle but unmistakable
allusions to (among others) Bachian aria and Viennese *Ländler* (this latter hint beautifully picked up
by Oelze and Schneider). And by now he is also choosing poems, either very simple or exaltedly
religious, that are ideally suited to his distilled, immaculate precision. Webern became a great
songwriter with Op. 12, but the path to that achievement is absorbingly charted on this disc.

Matthias Weckmann   German 1619 or earlier-1674

Suggested listening ...
...Toccata III. *Coupled with works by various composers.* **His Majesties Sagbutts and Cornetts.**
Hyperion CDA66847 (11/96). *See review in the Collections section; refer to the Index.*

Thomas Weelkes   British 1576-1623

Suggested listening ...
...Hosanna to the Son of David. *Coupled with works by various composers.*
St Paul's Cathedral Choir / John Scott. Hyperion CDA66994 (12/97).
See review in the Collections section; refer to the Index.

Kurt Weill   German/American 1900-1950

Weill Der Silbersee – Ich bin eine arme Verwandte (Fennimores-Lied); Rom war eine Stadt
(Cäsars Tod); Lied des Lotterieagenten. Die Dreigroschenoper – Die Moritat von Mackie Messer;
Salomon-Song; Die Ballade von der sexuellen Hörigkeit. Das Berliner Requiem – Zu Potsdam
unter den Eichen (arr. Hazell). Nannas-Lied. Aufstieg und Fall der Stadt Mahagonny – Alabama
Song; Wie man sich bettet. Je ne t'aime pas. One Touch of Venus – I'm a stranger here myself;
Westwind; Speak low. **Ute Lemper** (sop); **Berlin Radio Ensemble / John Mauceri.**
Decca New Line Ⓕ 425 204-2DNL (50 minutes: DDD: 3/89). Texts and translations included.
The songs in this collection are mostly from the major works Weill composed between 1928 and 1933,
but also included are one from his years in France and three items from the 1943 Broadway musical
One Touch of Venus. The collection introduces a most exciting talent in the person of Ute Lemper. By
comparison with the husky, growling delivery often accorded Weill's songs in the manner of his widow
Lotte Lenya, we here have a voice of appealing clarity and warmth. What distinguishes her singing,
though, is the way in which these attributes of vocal purity are allied to a quite irresistible dramatic
intensity. Her "Song of the Lottery Agent" is an absolute *tour de force,* apt to leave the listener
emotionally drained, and her *Je ne t'aime pas* is almost equally overwhelming. Not least in the three
numbers from *One Touch of Venus,* sung in perfect English, she displays a commanding musical
theatre presence. This is, one feels, how Weill's songs were meant to be heard.
Additional recommendations ...
...(arr. Berio. Sung in English) Der Dreigroschenoper – Die Ballade von der sexuellen Hörigkeit.
Marie Galante – Le grand Lustucru. Happy End – Surabaya-Johnny. **Berio** Recital I for Cathy[a].
11 Folk Songs[b]. **Cathy Berberian** (mez); [a]**London Sinfonietta;** [b]**Juilliard Ensemble / Luciano Berio.**
RCA Victor Gold Seal Ⓜ 09026 62540-2 (65 minutes: ADD: 7/95). *See review under Berio; refer
to the Index.*   ⊙⊙
...Zu Potsdam unter den Eichen. Divertimento, Op. 5 – Chorale-Fantasy: Herr Gott dein Zorn tu
von uns wenden. *Coupled with works by various composers.* **BBC Symphony Chorus /
Stephen Jackson; Poznan Opera Chorus; Poznan Philharmonic Orchestra / Andrzej Borejko.**
Largo Ⓕ Largo5130 (two discs; 117 minutes: DDD: 7/95).

Weill Lost in the Stars. **Gregory Hopkins** (ten) Leader; **Arthur Woodley** (bass-bar) Stephen Kumolo;
Reginald Pindell (bar) Absalom, John, Man, Villager; **Cynthia Clarey** (sop) Irina; **Carol Woods**
(sngr) Linda; **Jamal Howard** (treb) Alex; **Richard Vogt** (spkr) Stationmaster, Judge;
New York Concert Chorale; St Luke's Orchestra / Julius Rudel. MusicMasters Ⓕ 67100-2
(72 minutes: DDD: 11/93). Recorded 1992.
Lost in the Stars is subtitled "A Musical Tragedy" and was adapted by Maxwell Anderson from Alan
Paton's novel *Cry the Beloved Country.* Weill and Anderson's use of a chorus to comment on the
action and advance the story makes the play difficult to stage, and Anderson's sentimentalization of
the Paton original has made it one of the most dated of Weill's works. Julius Rudel conducted a
production of *Lost in the Stars* for the New York City Opera in 1959, and observes in the booklet that
he found these recording sessions "somewhat akin to a religious experience". This certainly
communicates itself, especially in the choral sequence "Cry the Beloved Country" which frames the
death-cell confrontation between father and son. Without much recorded dialogue, the condescending
sugariness of the Anderson contribution is reduced and Weill's experimentation with the choruses as
well as his usual high quota of great melodies make this one of the finest modern recordings of his
work. In the main role of the black preacher, Kumolo, Arthur Woodley sings with fervour and fine
diction and the Orchestra of St Luke's manage an accurate 1940s sound; a real achievement. This is
a major addition to the catalogue and essential to any collection of Weill's work – or of twentieth-
century opera.

Weill Die sieben Todsünden[a]. Symphony No. 2. [a]**Teresa Stratas,** [a]**Nora Kimball** (sops);
[a]**Frank Kelley,** [a]**Howard Haskin** (tens); [a]**Herbert Perry,** [a]**Peter Rose** (basses); [a]**Chorus and
Orchestra of the Opéra National de Lyon / Kent Nagano.** Erato Ⓕ ⊙ 0630-17068-2

(65 minutes: DDD: 9/97). Text and translation included. Item marked [a] recorded at a video
session in 1993. Symphony recorded 1996. *Gramophone Editor's choice*.   🄶🄶
Weill and Brecht's *Seven Deadly Sins*, written in haste just after their flight from Hitler's Germany,
was their last major collaboration. The question of its interpretation will always be bound up with the
memory of Lotte Lenya, who created the role of Anna I. This performance of *Sins* was recorded at
the same time that Stratas performed it for Peter Sellars's film of the work (available on video from
Decca). There is a certain amount of stage noise in this recording, especially in "Lust" – the heart of
the work. Stratas's singing isn't pretty, but then it's not meant to be; she uses all her declamatory
powers, and projects text and music in such a dramatic and heartfelt way that it puts this version
immediately in the front rank. Nagano's conducting begins with a very slow introduction, which may
sound off-putting to those familiar with the much sprightlier Rattle or Masur versions, which also
have soprano soloists. As the performance progresses though, Nagano's control of the drama seems
just right – this isn't a concert reading, but a full-scale theatrical event. The recorded sound of the
symphony is noticeably better than that of *Sins*. As Weill's only major orchestral work, it has never
really caught on, though the orchestral writing is as sophisticated as anything in his operas. With so
many versions of *Die sieben Todsünden*, preferences for voice and coupling are important.
Fassbaender and von Otter both have a selection of Weill songs and arias, Réaux with Masur has the
Lulu suite, Ross with Rattle, Stravinsky's *Pulcinella*. For first-time Weill buyers, we are inclined to
recommend this version over all the others; Stratas is terrific and the coupling is perfect.

Additional recommendations ...

...Die Sieben Todsünden. Mahagonny-Gesänge[a]. **Soloists; Berlin RIAS Sinfonietta / John Mauceri.**
Decca Ⓕ 430 168-2DH (66 minutes: DDD: 4/91).

...Die Sieben Todsünden[a]. **Stravinsky** Pulcinella[b]. **Soloists; [b]Northern Sinfonia;**
[a]**City of Birmingham Symphony Orchestra / Sir Simon Rattle.**
EMI Ⓜ CDM7 64739-2 (73 minutes: ADD/DDD: 12/93).

...Die Sieben Todsünden[a]. Songs[b] – Complainte de la Seine; Youkali; Nannas Lied,
"Meine Herren, mit Siebzehn Jahren"; Wie lange noch?; Es regnet; Berlin im Licht. **Brigitte**
Fassbaender (mez); [a]**Soloists;** [a]**Hanover Radio Philharmonic Orchestra / Cord Garben** ([b]pf).
Harmonia Mundi Ⓕ HMC90 1420 (55 minutes: DDD: 12/93). *Gramophone Editor's choice.*   🄶

...Die Sieben Todsünden[a]. **Berg** Lulu – Symphonie. **Angelina Réaux** (sop); [a]**Hudson Shad; New**
York Philharmonic Orchestra / Kurt Masur. Teldec Ⓕ 4509-95029-2 (68 minutes: DDD: 12/94).

...Die Sieben Todsünden[a]. Songs – Lady in the Dark – One life to live; My ship[c]. Propaganda
Songs – Schickelgruber; Buddy on the nightshift[b]. Nannas Lied[b]. Happy End – Bilbao Song;
Surabaya-Johnny; Das Lied von der harten Nuss[c]. Je ne t'aime pas[b]. Der Abschiedsbrief[b].
One Touch of Venus – I'm a stranger here myself; Foolish heart; Speak low[c]. **Anne Sofie von**
Otter (mez); [a]**Soloists;** [b]**Bengt Forsberg** (pf); [ac]**North German Radio Symphony Orchestra /**
Sir John Eliot Gardiner. DG Ⓕ 439 894-2GH (78 minutes: DDD: 12/94).

Weill Street Scene. **Kristine Ciesinski** (sop) Anna Maurrant; **Richard Van Allan** (bass)
Frank Maurrant; **Janis Kelly** (sop) Rose Maurrant; **Bonaventura Bottone** (ten) Sam Kaplan;
Terry Jenkins (ten) Abraham Kaplan; **Meriel Dickinson** (mez) Emma Jones; **Angela Hickey** (mez)
Olga Olsen; **Claire Daniels** (sop) Jennie Hildebrand; **Fiametta Doria** (sop) First Nursemaid;
Judith Douglas (mez) Second Nursemaid; **English National Opera Chorus and Orchestra /**
Carl Davis. TER Classics Ⓕ CDTER21185 (two discs: 146 minutes: DDD: 11/91). Recorded 1989.
Street Scene is the most ambitious product of Weill's American years. It's something of a *Porgy and
Bess* transferred from Catfish Row to the slum tenements of New York. Where *Porgy and Bess* is
through-composed with recitatives, though, *Street Scene* offers a mixture of set musical numbers,
straight dialogue, and dialogue over musical underscoring. The musical numbers themselves range
from operatic arias and ensembles to rousing 1940s dance numbers. It is consistently well sung,
particularly where style is concerned. Weill described the work as a "Broadway opera", and it
demands a vernacular rather than a classical operatic singing style. This it duly gets from Kristine
Ciesinski as Anna Maurrant, while Janis Kelly's beautifully clear but natural enunciation and her
sense of emotional involvement make daughter Rose's "What good would the moon be?" a
performance of real beauty. Praiseworthy too is Richard Van Allan as the murderous husband, his
"Let things be like they always was" creating a suitably sinister effect. Among the subsidiary
attractions is the appearance of Catherine Zeta Jones, performing the swinging dance number
"Moon-faced, starry-eyed".

Further listening ...

...Concerto for Violin and Wind Orchestra, Op. 12[a]. Kiddush[b]. Kleine Dreigroschenmusik.
[a]**Yuval Waldman** (vn); [b]**Grayson Hirst** (ten); [b]**Ray Pellerin** (org); [b]**Amor Artis Chamber Choir and**
Orchestra / Johannes Somary. Newport Classic NCD60098 (12/91).

...Concerto for Violin and Wind Orchestra, Op. 12. *Coupled with works by* **Hindemith** and **Toch**
Christian Tetzlaff (vn); **Deutsche Kammerphilharmonie.** Virgin Classics VC5 45056-2 (7/95).

...Concerto for Violin and Wind Orchestra, Op. 12. *Coupled with works by* **Korngold** and **Krenek**
Chantal Juillet (vn); **Berlin Radio Symphony Orchestra / John Mauceri.**
Decca Entartete Musik 452 481-2DH (4/97).

...Kleine Dreigroschenmusik. Symphonies Nos. 1 and 2. **Lisbon Gulbenkian Foundation Orchestra /**
Michel Swierczewski. Nimbus NI5283.

...Symphonies Nos. 1 and 2. *Coupled with works by* **Busoni** and **Schoenberg**
New Philharmonia Orchestra / Frederik Prausnitz; BBC Symphony Orchestra / Gary Bertini.
EMI Matrix CDM5 65869-2 (4/96).
...String Quartet. *Coupled with works by* **Schulhoff** and **Hindemith** Brandis Quartet.
Nimbus NI5410 (3/95). *See review under Schulhoff; refer to the Index.* ⒢
...Dirge for Two Veterans. *Coupled with works by various composers.* **Thomas Hampson** (bar);
Craig Rutenberg (pf). EMI CDM5 55028-2 (10/97). *See review in the Collections section;*
refer to the Index. ⒢⒢⒢
...One Touch of Venus – That's him. Lady in the Dark – The saga of Jenny; My ship. Lost in the
Stars – Stay well. *Coupled with works by various composers.* **Dawn Upshaw** (sop); **orchestra /**
Eric Stern. Nonesuch 7559-79345-2 (12/94). *Gramophone Award Winner 1995. See review in the*
Collections section; refer to the Index. ⒢⒢
...Die Dreigroschenoper. **Soloists; Berlin RIAS Chamber Choir and Sinfonietta / John Mauceri.**
Decca 430 075-2DH (3/90).
...Der Silbersee. **Soloists; Cologne Pro Musica; Cologne Radio Symphony Orchestra /**
Jan Latham-König. Capriccio 60 011-2 (8/90).

Jaŕomir Weinberger

Bohemian/American 1896-1967

Suggested listening ...
...Schwanda the Bagpiper – Polka. *Coupled with works by various composers.*
New London Orchestra / Ronald Corp.
Hyperion CDA66998 (3/98). *See review in the Collections section; refer to the Index.*

Leó Weiner

Hungarian 1885-1960

Weiner Serenade, Op. 3.
Bartók Cantata profana, Sz94[a].
Kodály Psalmus Hungaricus, Op. 13[b]. [ab]**Tamás Daróczy** (ten); [a]**Alexander Agache** (bar); **Hungarian**
Radio and Television [ab]**Chorus and** [b]**Children's Chorus;** [b]**Schola Cantorum Budapestiensis; Budapest**
Festival Orchestra / Sir Georg Solti. Decca Ⓕ 458 929-2DH (59 minutes: DDD: 6/98). Texts and
translations included. Recorded 1997. *Gramophone Editor's choice.*
It is apt, if ironic, that these very last recordings of Sir Georg Solti, product of sessions in Budapest
1977, three months before his death, should make up the perfect valedictory disc. Ironically too, these
were his very first recordings made in his native Hungary with Hungarian musicians. Solti's plan was
to pay tribute to his three great teachers at the Liszt Conservatoire in Budapest, not only in this
recording but in a concert of the same three representative works, designed to round off this year's
(1998) Budapest Spring Festival. In the event the concert went ahead as a memorial to Solti with most
of the same performers conducted by Iván Fischer. The rarity here is the Serenade of Leó Weiner, the
teacher closest to Solti in his student days, one who both challenged him and drew him out. The
amiability of this music, far less individual, less specifically Hungarian than that of Bartók or Kodály,
seems to reflect Weiner's character as Solti's mentor. Beautifully written in four cleanly constructed
movements, this is a delightful piece full of fresh, crisply conceived ideas, as in the easygoing sonata-
form first movement. The warmly responsive woodwind soloists of the Budapest Festival Orchestra
come into their own in the interlude of the third movement with its sequence of solos getting faster,
in turn for clarinet, bassoon, oboe and flute. Solti could never have conceived a more winning last
offering on disc. In his final reconciliation with his native land (which, as he always pointed out,
rejected him twice over, both under the Fascists and the Communists) Solti found extra warmth in
music he loved, while keeping the biting intensity which was always a hallmark of his conducting. As
he explains in the accompanying booklet, Solti came finally to feel that the story of Bartók's *Cantata*
profana – about nine sons turned by magic into stags, who finally return home – symbolized his own
life-story. The chorus sing superbly, with the Romanian baritone, Alexander Agache, a strong and
dark soloist, though the powerful and strenuous tenor, Tamás Daróczy, sings with too wide a vibrato
to give much pleasure on disc. His singing is the drawback in the Kodály too, a more serious one when
the tenor plays such a central part in this psalm sequence. None the less, what matters is the
incandescence of the whole performance. With glowing sound, reflecting the helpful acoustic of the
Italian Institute in Budapest, the piece receives here idiomatic singing and playing.
Further listening ...
...Three Hungarian Rural Dances. *Coupled with works by various composers.* **Peter Frankl** (pf).
ASV CDDCA860 (6/93). *See review in the Collections section; refer to the Index.* ⒢⒢⒢

Judith Weir

British 1954

Weir The Art of Touching the Keyboard[d]. I Broke off a Golden Branch[d]. El Rey de Francia[d].
The King of France[a]. Distance and Enchantment[ae]. The Bagpiper's String Trio[e]. Ardnamurchan

Point[bc]. [a]**Susan Tomes**, [b]**William Howard**, [c]**Petra Casén** (pfs); [d]**Schubert Ensemble of London**; [e]**Domus** (Krysia Osostowicz, vn; Timothy Boulton, va; Richard Lester, vc). Collins Classics Ⓕ 1453-2 (58 minutes: DDD: 12/95). Recorded 1995.

Judith Weir's music is not simplistic, nor does it ape any style from the past, and it is not in the least minimalist, but it has qualities that could appeal to a vastly wider audience than the 'contemporary music public'. Her music is bold, clean and uncluttered, with a strong melodic line and purposeful forward movement. Those qualities are present even when she is paying an overt homage to Schubert, as in the exquisitely lyrical opening of *I Broke off a Golden Branch* (written for the Schubert Ensemble of London, and for the forces of the *Trout* Quintet), all the more so since the other preoccupation of this fine work is to avow a debt: to the beautiful, ancient folk music of the region we used to call Yugoslavia. Anyone who can carry out both of these objectives – and the gesture to Schubert is as delightfully affectionate as the tribute to Croatia is eloquent – and still remain unmistakably herself is evidently a very considerable composer. Strong melody is a feature of all these pieces: long, eventful, often florid melody. Indeed, despite changes of mood, direction, tempo and texture you can hear each piece as a single long melody. Even *The Art of Touching the Keyboard*, an avowed study of types of keyboard attack, has a surprising unity, a feeling that the whole piece is in a single span. *Ardnamurchan Point*, despite being for two keyboards, is mostly a single line throughout, a sort of journey; as with the tortuous road that suggested the title, you know that there will be a grand view at the end of it. That this sort of line has its roots in folk music is acknowledged in *Distance and Enchantment*, a piano quartet based on two folk melodies about mysterious vanishings (an appendix, in fact, to Weir's opera *The Vanishing Bridegroom*) and in *The Bagpiper's String Trio*. Nearly all these pieces were written for close friends, in most cases the artists on this disc; Weir says that of all her works these (for that very reason?) are the ones she most enjoys listening to. That quality too, of the anticipation of shared pleasure, is clearly audible in the performances.

Further listening ...

...Ettrick Banks. *Coupled with works by various composers.* **John Scott** (org). Priory PRCD485 (8/96). *Selected by Soundings.*

...The Consolations of Scholarship – Chinese Yuan drama[a]. King Harald's Saga[b]. [a]**Linda Hirst** (sop); [b]**Jane Manning** (sop); [a]**Lontano / Odaline de la Martinez**. Cala United CACD88040 (3/90).

...Don't let that horse. *Coupled with works by various composers.* **Jane Manning** (sop); Jane's Minstrels. NMC Artists' Series NMCD025 (10/95). Ⓖ

...(arr. Finnissy) Songs from the Exotic (on the rocks). *Coupled with works by various composers.* **Tapestry**. British Music Label BML012 (12/95).

...Blond Eckbert. **Soloists; English National Opera Chorus and Orchestra / Sîan Edwards**. Collins Classics 1461-2 (7/95). Ⓖ

Silvius Weiss
German 1686-1750

Weiss Lute Sonatas, Volume 1 – No. 36 in D minor; No. 42 in A minor; No. 49 in B flat major. **Robert Barto** (lte). Naxos Ⓢ 8 553773 (72 minutes: DDD: A/97). 🎼 Recorded 1996.

Sylvius Weiss, the greatest lutenist of his age, was an almost exact contemporary of Bach, his most famous admirer. The style of lute music was dominated by French influence until the end of the seventeenth century, when the instrument's 'centre of gravity' moved to Eastern Europe, where Weiss was born in Breslau (now Wrocław) and spent much of his working life. The ornate *style précieux*, of which harpsichordists had learnt much from lutenists, gave way to a simpler *cantabile* one, a stepping-stone on the road to the *galant*. In many of Weiss's solo lute sonatas and suites the French influence survived in the *non mesuré* elements in the preludes and fantasias, and the appearance of various character pieces. Baroque lute music often sounds like an archbishop delivering a solemn sermon, but Weiss runs the gamut from profoundly solemn allemandes and sarabandes to light-footed *galanteries* and joyously prancing gigues. Everything, not least the harmonic adventurousness, bespeaks a composer who was no less renowned as an extemporizer. Weiss's music abounds in technical difficulty but Robert Barto has no apparent problem in concealing the fact. He is a supple and stylish performer, and this excellently recorded disc contains some of the finest playing of Weiss around.

Further listening ...

...Sonata in A minor, "L'infidèle". Prelude, Fantasia and Fugue in C major. Tombeau sur la mort de M. Comte de Logy. *Coupled with works by* **Bach** and **Vivaldi Nigel North** (lte). Linn Records CKD006 (12/92). 🎼

...L'Amant malheureux in A minor. Capriccio in D major. Plainte in B flat major. Prelude in D major. Prelude in E flat major. Suite I – B flat major; D minor; F major. Suite II in G minor. Suite in A major "L'esprit italien". **Lutz Kirchhof** (lte). Sony Classical S2K48391.

Franz Werthmüller
Austrian 1769-1841

Suggested listening ...

... Sonata in A major, Op. 17. *Coupled with works by* **Marschner** and **Sor Tilman Hoppstock** (gtr). Signum SIGX75-00 (2/98). *See review in the Collections section; refer to the Index.*

Samuel Wesley

British 1766-1837

S. Wesley In exitu Israel[a]. Ave regina caelorum[a]. Magnificat anima mea[a]. 12 Short Pieces with a Voluntary added[b] – A minor; Gavotte in F. Services in F[a] – Te Deum laudamus; Jubilate Deo. Ostende nobis Domine[a]. Ecce panis angelorum[a]. Domine salvam fac regem nostrum[a]. Omnia vanitas (Carmen funebre)[i]. Voluntary in D[b]. Tu es sacerdos[a]. Might I in Thy sight appear[a]. O Lord God most Holy[a]. Dixit Dominus[a]. [a]**Gonville and Caius College Choir, Cambridge / Geoffrey Webber** ([b]org). ASV Gaudeamus Ⓕ CDGAU157 (65 minutes: DDD: 6/96). Recorded 1995.
Samuel, the father, has been rather neglected in favour of Samuel Sebastian, the son. This disc opens with the eight-part motet, *In exitu Israel* which is probably his masterpiece. Notoriously difficult to sing without some smudging of the quavers, it also requires firm direction to stop it from 'running away'. Here the cleanness of line is impeccable as is the steadiness of tempo, and the clarity of the performance is both aided and tested by the unreverberant acoustic of Selwyn Chapel. The Gonville and Caius College Choir have a deservedly growing reputation, with voices of good, fresh quality, ears well attuned to each other, and admirable alertness in matters of phrasing and rhythm. The inner parts perhaps need strengthening, especially in relation to the robust bass-line, which one would not wish to hear 'tamed' at the expense of colour and character. The sopranos are as good treble-substitutes as any, and provide some very adequate soloists. Wesley's genius worked largely within the restraints of his period: essentially he was an eighteenth-century composer, his unostentatious style graceful and economical. He had an unfashionable enthusiasm for Bach, which brings a contrapuntal vigour into many of his best pieces. The bravura accompaniment to *Domine salvam fac* reminds us that he was also the leading British organist of his time, and an attractive feature of this recital is its inclusion of organ works that are not always so easy to play as they may look. Geoffrey Webber gives a tasteful account, playing (for instance) the Gavotte as a dance-movement, and not in the grandiose disguise of its frequent appearances at the end of Cathedral Evensong.
Further listening ...
...Violin Concerto No. 2 in D major. *Coupled with works by various composers.* **Elizabeth Wallfisch** (vn); **The Parley of Instruments / Peter Holman** (fp). Hyperion CDA66865 (11/96). 🎵
...Symphonies – No. 3 in A major; No. 4 in D major; No. 5 in E flat major; No. 6 in B flat major. **Milton Keynes Chamber Orchestra / Hilary Davan Wetton.** Unicorn-Kanchana DKPCD9098 (10/91).
...Voluntaries – E flat major, Op. 6 No. 7; B flat major. *Coupled with works by various composers.* **Jennifer Bate** (org). Unicorn-Kanchana DKPCD9106 (11/91). *Selected by Sounds in Retrospect. See review in the Collections section; refer to the Index.* Ⓖ

Christoph Weyse

German/Danish 1774-1842

Weyse Christmas Cantata No. 3. Easter Cantata No. 1. **Bodil Anderson** (sop); **Dorthe Elsebet Larsen** (sop); **Kirsten Dolberg** (alto); **Peter Grønlund** (ten); **Stephen Milling** (bass); **Tivoli Concert Choir; Tivoli SO / Michael Schønwandt.** Da Capo Ⓕ 8 224049 (52 minutes: DDD: 2/98). Recorded 1997.
Christoph Weyse was a Danish composer of German extraction. From 1789 he was based in Copenhagen, becoming distinguished as a pianist and church organist. He was the court composer from 1819, producing cantatas, songs, symphonies and much more. Among his important works are the innovatory *Allegri di bravura* for piano (1796), the fine if traditional ensembles in his sacred cantatas, and above all the songs, particularly the spiritual ones to texts by Ingemann (1837-38). This is a delightful disc. He may not have been a particularly original composer, but these two cantatas (from 1836 and 1821 respectively) are full of fresh vitality and some glorious melodies. The singers bring to them the conviction that the words are significant poetry, however naïve they may appear at first sight. Michael Schønwandt directs flawless performances, captured in vivid sound.
Further listening ...
...Angel of Light, go in splendour. In distant steeples. The Sleeping-Draught – Fair lady, open your window. *Coupled with works by various composers.* **Aksel Schiøtz** (ten) with various artists. Danacord mono DACOCD454* (5/97). *See review in the Collections section; refer to the Index.*

Gillian Whitehead

New Zealand 1941

Suggested listening
...Awa Herea. *Coupled with works by various composers.* **Tracey Chadwell** (sop); **Pamela Lidiard** (pf). British Music Society BMS420/1CD (3/98). *See review in the Collections section; refer to the Index.*

Percy Whitlock

British 1903-1946

Whitlock Dignity and Impudence (arr. Riley). Seven Sketches on Verses from the Psalms. Two Fantasie Chorals. Three Reflections. **Graham Barber** (org). Priory Ⓕ PRCD525 (72 minutes: DDD: 1/98). Played on the Willis organ of Hereford Cathedral. Recorded 1995.

Malcolm Riley has arranged *Dignity and Impudence* from the orchestral score Whitlock wrote in 1932, although the composer used to play it on the organ himself. Falling between the swashbuckling public manner of Elgar and Walton, it is well worth having and the orchestral originals belong to the tradition of British light music and should be revived. A landmark is the first complete recording of the *Seven Sketches on Verses from the Psalms*. Surprisingly Whitlock said he didn't care for the third one, "Plaint", although this piece seems a particularly personal statement where he moves away from his predictable Georgian cathedral idiom, occasionally spiced up with chromatics from Delius or impressionist chords from Debussy, to something closer to Frank Bridge. The slender beauties of the folk-like opening "Pastorale" are slightly rushed by Barber but he demonstrates a sympathetic command of the idiom, especially high spots such as the tuba rhetoric of the "Exultemus". The sonorities on Hereford's Willis, which Whitlock himself tried out, are ideal. In the two *Fantasie Chorals* Whitlock is more ambitious, following the model of Franck's masterpieces but coming closer to Bruckner's improvisatory meandering. The second one manages a strong peroration. At his best Whitlock is a kind of organist's Fauré, modal and subtle, and in Barber's performances he gets the strongest possible advocacy. The recording is sometimes light on bass and there are a few mechanical noises, but it's a resplendent sound, worthy of the Willis tradition at its finest.

Additional recommendation ...
...Three Reflections. Organ Sonata in C minor. Five Short Pieces. Wessex Suite – March: Rustic Cavalry. **Robert Gower** (org). ASV Ⓔ CDDCA957 (75 minutes: DDD: 7/96).

Whitlock Sing praise to God who reigns above[a]. Jesu, grant me this I pray. Solemn Te Deum[a]. · Three Introits[a]. The Saint whose praise today we sing. Communion Service in G[a]. Glorious in heaven. Magnificat and Nunc dimittis (1924)[a]. O gentle presence[a]. Come let us join our cheerful songs[a]. O gladsome light. Magnificat and Nunc dimittis (1930). **Rochester Cathedral Choir / Roger Sayer** with [a]**William Whitehead** (org). Priory Ⓕ PRCD583 (70 minutes: DDD: 6/97). Texts included. Recorded 1996.
A pupil of Vaughan Williams, Whitlock wrote a symphony and other full-scale orchestral works, but it is by some short organ pieces, anthems and other liturgical settings that he is remembered: a cheerful style, usually, practical and professional, not wasting his own notes or anybody else's time. A very fair selection is given here, ranging in chronology from a teenage composition (*O gladsome light*) to a hymn anthem (*Come let us join our cheerful songs*) published in the year of his death. His Communion Service of 1928 is typical of his effective, unpretentious workmanship. Unaccompanied anthems, such as *Jesu, grant me this I pray* and *The Saint whose praise today we sing*, are perhaps more personal: exercises in a loved and ancient tradition. One feels too that he *deserves* to be remembered: a shy, frail young man, and courageous as in middle age he faced the prospect of blindness armed with a magnifying glass and a memory he trained to learn the accompaniments of whole oratorios by heart.

Further listening ...
...Hymn Preludes – Darwall's 148th; Song 13. *Coupled with works by various composers.* **Gareth Green** (org). Naxos 8 550582 (3/93).
...Evening Service in D major. *Coupled with works by various composers.* **Rochester Cathedral Choir / Roger Sayer** with **William Whitehead** (org). Priory PRCD529 (7/96).

Charles Marie Widor   French 1844-1937

Suggested listening ...
...Organ Symphony No. 5 in F minor, Op. 42. *Coupled with works by* **Poulenc** and **Guilmant** Ian Tracey (org). Chandos CHAN9271 (11/94). *See review under Guilmant; refer to the Index.* ⒼⒼ
...Symphonie gothique. *Coupled with works by* **Vierne** and **Tournemire** Jeremy Filsell (org). Herald HAVPCD145 (3/92). *See review under Tournemire; refer to the Index.* ⒼⒼ

Henryk Wieniawski   Polish 1835-1880

Wieniawski Violin Concertos – No. 1 in F sharp minor, Op. 14; No. 2 in D minor, Op. 22. Fantaisie brillante on Themes from Gounod's "Faust", Op. 20. **Marat Bisengaliev** (vn); **Polish National Radio Symphony Orchestra / Antoni Wit.** Naxos Ⓢ 8 553517 (70 minutes: DDD: 4/97). Recorded 1995.
By the time Wieniawski wrote his Second Violin Concerto, ten years after the First (which he wrote when in his teens) his finesse as a composer was more developed, and it is the Second, with its haunting melodies, that has remained more consistently in the repertory. Even so, this coupling of the two is apt and welcome on this super-budget Naxos issue. Marat Bisengaliev quickly demonstrates Wieniawski's positive qualities. Though he is not as persuasive an interpreter as some of his rivals in this repertoire, rather less individual and imaginative in his phrasing, and less bold in bravura writing, the security of his technique is formidable, with a wide tonal range. His gentle half-tones in the slow movements of both works are strikingly beautiful, magically caught in this excellent Polish recording. Wit and the Polish National Radio Symphony Orchestra provide most sympathetic support. In the 20-minute *Fantaisie* on themes from *Faust* Wieniawski shuffles the melodies skilfully, with

Mephistopheles's Calf of Gold aria providing a brilliant display passage. It makes a charming showpiece, if not one that bears much repetition. An excellent bargain.

Additional recommendations ...

...No. 2. *Coupled with works by various composers.* **Jascha Heifetz** (vn); **London Philharmonic Orchestra / Sir John Barbirolli.** EMI Références mono Ⓜ CDH7 64251-2* (69 minutes: ADD: 5/92).

...No. 2. *Coupled with* **Saint-Saëns** Violin Concerto No. 3 in B minor, Op. 61. **Julian Rachlin** (vn); **Israel Philharmonic Orchestra / Zubin Mehta.** Sony Classical Ⓕ SK48373 (52 minutes: DDD: 12/92). *See review under Saint-Saëns; refer to the Index.*

Further listening ...

...Polonaise No. 1 in D major, Op. 4. Légende, Op. 17. *Coupled with works by various composers.* **Maxim Vengerov** (vn); **Itamar Golan** (pf). Teldec 9031-77351-2 (4/94). *See review in the Collections section; refer to the Index.*

Légende, Op. 17. Zigeunerweisen. *Coupled with works by various composers.* **Itzhak Perlman** (vn); **Abbey Road Ensemble / Lawrence Foster.** EMI CDC5 55475-2 (1/96).

Philip Wilby   British 1949

Suggested listening ...

...Echo Carol. *Coupled with works by various composers.* **St Paul's Cathedral Choir / John Scott** with **Andrew Lucas** (org). Hyperion CDA66994 (12/97). *See review in the Collections section; refer to the Index.*

Sir David Willcocks   British 1919

Suggested listening ...

...Variations on "Breslau". *Coupled with works by various composers.* **Jane Watts** (org). Priory PRCD389 (10/97). *See review in the Collections section; refer to the Index.*

William, Monk of Stratford   British *fl* 15th-16th centuries

Suggested listening ...

...Magnificat. *Coupled with works by various composers.* **The Sixteen / Harry Christophers.** Collins Classics 1462-2 (3/96). *See review in the Collections section; refer to the Index.*

Graham Williams   British 1940

Suggested listening ...

...The song within. *Coupled with works by various composers.* **Mühlfeld Ensemble.** Clarinet Classics CC0007 (10/94). *See review in the Collections section; refer to the Index.*

Malcolm Williamson   Australian 1931

Suggested listening ...

...Symphony No. 7 for Strings. *Coupled with works by various composers.* **Brunel Ensemble / Christopher Austin.** Cala The Edge CACD77005 (6/97). *See review in the Collections section; refer to the Index.*

...Two Epitaphs for Edith Sitwell. Vision of Christ-Phoenix. *Coupled with works by* **J. Harvey** and **Maxwell Davies Kevin Bowyer** (org). Nimbus NI5509 (7/97).

Ian Wilson   Irish 1964

Suggested listening ...

...I Sleep at Waking. *Coupled with works by various composers.* **Gerard McChrystal** (sax); **London Musici / Mark Stephenson.** Silva Classics SILKD6010 (6/96). *See review in the Collections section; refer to the Index.*

Dag Wirén   Swedish 1905-1986

Suggested listening ...

...String Quartet No. 3 in D minor, Op. 18. *Coupled with works by various composers.* **Lindsay Quartet.** ASV CDDCA825 (1/93). *See review in the Collections section; refer to the Index.*

Hugo Wolf

Wolf Eichendorff Lieder – Der Freund; Der Musikant; Verschwiegene Liebe; Das Ständchen; Der Soldat I; Der Soldat II; Nachtzauber; Der Schreckenberger; Der Glücksritter; Lieber Alles; Heimweh; Der Scholar; Der verzweifelte Liebhaber; Unfall; Liebesglück; Seemanns Abschied; Erwartung; Die Nacht. In der Fremde – I, UP87; II, UP88; VI, UP93. Rückkehr, UP90. Nachruf, UP81.
Korngold Einfache Lieder, Op. 9 – No. 1, Schneeglöckchen; No. 2, Nachtwander; No. 3, Ständchen. Der Kranke, Op. 38 No. 2. **Boje Skovhus** (bar); **Helmut Deutsch** (pf). Sony Classical Ⓕ SK57969 (62 minutes: DDD: 1/95). Texts and translations included. Recorded 1993.
Lovers of good Lieder singing will surely respond eagerly to Skovhus's bold and velvet-toned singing and welcome a disc of songs which are currently under-represented in the catalogue. Eichendorff and Wolf are here predominantly outside, walking or riding along, and Wolf is free of the cares marking the Mörike settings that went before in his opus. Skovhus is the Musician, Soldier, Sailor, Swashbuckler, Fortune-hunter and Scholar to the life. But he can also encompass a more thoughtful mood, as expressed in pieces such as *Die Nacht*, where his quiet singing is perfection. Deutsch's mastery of Wolf's intricate rhythms and harmonies is never less than masterly, and he is recorded as an equal partner with the singer. Four of Korngold's Eichendorff settings form a neat pendant to the Wolf. Although his version of *Ständchen* is more obviously sentimental than Wolf's, it has its own character. *Schneeglöckchen* is suffused in Debussian harmony (Op. 9 was composed in 1917), and the final song, written 30 years later, is peculiarly Korngoldian in its passing-note harmony and deliberately post-romantic idiom. The interpreters are just as subtle yet unexaggerated in their performing here as in the Wolf.

Wolf Goethe Lieder – Harfenspieler I-III; Der Rattenfänger; Coptisches Lied I; Frech und froh I and II: Epiphanias; Genialisch Treiben; Der Schäfer; Blumengruss; Frühling übers Jahr; Anakreons Grab; Phänomen; Ob der Koran von Ewigkeit sei?; Trunken müssen wir alle sein!; So lang man nüchtern ist; Sie haben wegen der Trunkenheit; Hätt' ich irgend wohl Bedenken; Komm, Liebchen, komm!; Wie sollt ich heiter bleiben; Wenn ich dein gedenke; Ganymed. **Wolfgang Holzmair** (bar); **Thomas Palm** (pf). Collins Classics Ⓕ 1402-2 (55 minutes: DDD: 9/93). Texts and translations included. Recorded live in 1988. *Gramophone Editor's choice.*
Holzmair is a refreshing and challenging singer. He follows no known school and quite avoids the influence of Fischer-Dieskau. His voice is individual and tangy; his interpretations here, as elsewhere, are apparently spontaneous (the live recording helps) and unmarked by convention. His tone doesn't please everyone; it has a quick vibrato of a kind more frequently encountered in the earlier decades of the century than in the later, and it can harden under pressure. That's part of the price of taking risks: like Wolf he isn't always well behaved – and he's all the more stimulating for his immediacy of manner. Nowhere is that more apparent than in *Ganymed* where the wonder of the poem and its setting is wholly conveyed in this soaring interpretation. At the other end of the emotional scale in the inexhaustible variety of the Goethe settings is the desolation of the *Harfenspieler* ones, in the first of which the line "Dann bin ich micht allein" carries all the inner torment of the mysterious old man. Nor at the end of the next verse is Holzmair averse to bursting out in operatic-like pain at "Mich Einsamen die Pein". The all-important piano parts are in the safe hands of Thomas Palm, a most sensitive player. He is placed a shade too far backward in relation to the voice but this probably reflects what you would have heard in the concert-hall. Too much applause is included and the length is short by today's standards on CD. But, as they say, the quality is what matters and here it is high.
Additional recommendations ...
...Goethe Lieder – Mignon I; Mignon II; Mignon III; Mignon ("Kennst du das Land?"); Blumengruss; Die Bekehrte; Frühling übers Jahr; Anakreons Grab. *Coupled with works by various composers.* **Irmgard Seefried** (sop); **Erik Werba** (pf). Orfeo D'Or mono Ⓕ C297921B* (71 minutes: ADD: 9/93). *See review in the Collections section; refer to the Index.* ⒼⒼ
...Wanderers Nachtlied. Der Rattenfänger. Coptisches Lied II. Genialisch Treiben. Frühling übers Jahr. Anakreons Grab. Phänomen. Ob der Koran von Ewigkeit sei?. *Coupled with works by various composers.* **Dietrich Fischer-Dieskau** (bar); **Karl Engel** (pf). Orfeo D'Or mono Ⓕ C389951B* (72 minutes: ADD: 2/96).

Wolf Italienisches Liederbuch. **Dawn Upshaw** (sop); **Olaf Bär** (bar); **Helmut Deutsch** (pf). EMI Ⓕ CDC5 55618-2 (78 minutes: DDD: 9/96). Texts and translations included. Recorded 1996. *Gramophone Editor's choice.* ⒼⒼ
Both these singers approach the songs with such a natural style of interpretation that it is as if they had just discovered the wonders contained within this ever-delightful book and are only too eager to convey them to their audience – absolutely nothing of artifice or over-refinement found on some noted versions. They also convey in their singing a consistency of thought that is matched to perfection by the playing of their superb pianist, Helmut Deutsch. Yet individually the singers' attributes are different: Upshaw's open sincerity is everywhere in evidence, ideally complementing Bär's greater sophistication and urbanity. You can hear their skills wonderfully adumbrated in five successive songs in the middle of the recital. First Upshaw catches all the sadness of "Mir ward gesagt" to be answered by the soft-grained, warm, impassioned outpouring of Bär in "Und willst du

deinen Liebsten sterben". Then comes the inward feeling of "Sterb' ich", so unerringly articulated by Bär, and the revelation of Upshaw's sense of humour in "Mein Liebster ist so klein". Finally, Bär's pure sense of legato in "Benedeit dir sel'ge Mutter" keenly contrasts with the right touch of irony in the middle section.

From that you will have noted that the duo don't sing this collection in the printed order but one of Bär's own devising that makes eminent sense. Thus, for example, the railing songs are grouped together, the singers vying with each other in projecting scorn and anger. Later Upshaw shows the variety of her skills by catching, quite without exaggeration, the pain of "Was soll der Zorn" and the cheeky teasing of "Nein, junger Herr", itself nicely answered by Bär's "Hoffartig seid Ihr". So much else needs remarking on but listeners will want to discover for themselves the many pleasures of this rewarding issue. Drawbacks? Upshaw's peculiarly clear, clean tone just occasionally jars the ear in a way Seefried's does not and Bär doesn't quite match the range of colour or the many aperçus of Fischer-Dieskau's unique art. But this is a new interpretation for a new generation and one surpassing the varied attributes of Bonney and Hagegård and Lott and Schreier (though the Hyperion is the only version available featuring a tenor, and what a tenor!). This EMI disc is its own best advocate, well supported by a finely achieved recording.

Additional recommendations ...

...**Dame Elisabeth Schwarzkopf** (sop); **Dietrich Fischer-Dieskau** (bar); **Gerald Moore** (pf). EMI Ⓜ CDM7 63732-2 (79 minutes: ADD: 12/90). Ⓖ

...**Barbara Bonney** (sop); **Håkan Hagegård** (bar); **Geoffrey Parsons** (pf). Teldec Ⓕ 9031-72301-2 (76 minutes: DDD: 7/94). *Gramophone Editor's choice.* Ⓖ

...**Felicity Lott** (sop); **Peter Schreier** (ten); **Graham Johnson** (pf). Hyperion Ⓕ CDA66760 (80 minutes: DDD: 9/94). Ⓖ

...**Italienisches Liederbuch**[a]. Eichendorff Lieder. Nachruf. In der Fremde – I, II and VI. Rückkehr. Drei Gedichte von Michelangelo. [a]**Christa Ludwig** (mez); **Dietrich Fischer-Dieskau** (bar); **Daniel Barenboim** (pf). DG Galleria Ⓜ 439 975-2GGA2 (two discs: 142 minutes: ADD: 4/95).

Wolf Liederstrauss. Sechs Reinick Lieder. An ***. Traurige Wege. Herbstentschluss. Ernst ist der Frühling. Spätherbstnebel. Wo ich bin, mich rings umdunkelt. Du bist wie eine Blume. In der Fremde IV. Rückkehr. Lieder aus letzte Blätter – Die Nacht. Eichendorff Lieder – Erwartung. Nachruf. **Nico van der Meel** (ten); **Dido Keuning** (pf). Globe Ⓕ GLO5149 (63 minutes: DDD: 1/97). Texts and translations included.

Wolf's early songs have been unduly neglected. Setting in turn Lenau, Heine, Eichendorff and Reinick, inspiration for so many Lieder composers, Wolf seems to have based his style, at this time, on Schumann and to a lesser extent Brahms. Apart from influences, almost all these songs are a delight in themselves, requiring no need for comparisons, odious or otherwise. Wolf is not yet the wholly original composer of his master-songs written from 1888 onwards, but his unerring ability to distil the core of the poems of the romantic writers he was setting is already there for all to hear; so too are his innate gift for lyrical melody, attractively fashioned piano parts and subtle harmony. These attributes inform almost all these pieces. "Meine Liebchen, wir sassen beisammen" from the *Liederstrauss* Heine settings, is typical with its rippling accompaniment and well-defined vocal line. Another song from the same group, "Es blasen die blau'n Husaren" looks forward in its march-like rhythm to later attempts in this manner.

The Eichendorff setting, *In der Fremde*, pre-echoes even more significantly mature Wolf, while the Eichendorff "Die Nacht" and the haunting *Nachruf* are songs to savour by any yardstick. Even so, it is the six Reinick settings of 1882-3 that bring the greatest rewards, every one a miniature to cherish and, to quote the insert-note, "revealing a charm and tenderness that shows us the kinder side of Wolf's personality". Among them "Nachtgruss" and "Frühlingsglocken" demand repeated hearing, particularly when sung in the light, plangent tenor of Nico van der Meel. His may be a slightly dry, monochrome voice but after a while the almost vulnerable sound of his tone becomes an asset in these sorts of pieces, to which he also brings high intelligence and a keen ear for verbal nuance. Dido Keuning, perfectly balanced with van der Meel in an excellent recording, completes pleasure in a disc that lovers of Lieder should not overlook.

Wolf Mörike Lieder – Im Frühling; Auf eine Christblume I; Lied vom Winde. Goethe Lieder – Philine; Mignon; Der Schäfer; Blumengruss; Frühling übers Jahr; Anakreons Grab; Phänomen; Ganymed. Spanisches Liederbuch – Mühvoll komm' ich und beladen; In dem Schatten meiner Locken; Bedeckt mich mit Blumen; Wer tat deinem Füsslein weh; Wehe der, die mir verstrickte. Italieniches Liederbuch – Nun lass uns Frieden schliessen. Sechs Lieder für eine Frauenstimme – Mausfallen-Sprüchlein. Sechs alte Weisen. **Dame Elisabeth Schwarzkopf** (sop); **Gerald Moore** (pf). EMI Festspieldokumente mono Ⓕ CDH7 64905-2* (71 minutes: ADD: 10/93). Texts included. Recorded live in 1958. *Gramophone Editor's choice.* ⓆⓆⓆ

"A blissful experience of the purest lied art" reported the *Salzburger Nachrichten* on Schwarzkopf's recital. The recording derives from the Austrian Broadcasting Corporation's archive. It gives a marvellous sense of presence, recalling most vividly what it was that made the memory of Schwarzkopf's song recitals precious. First, the quality of voice, caught here at its purest and most radiant; then the full concentration of a total sensibility, emotion and intellect fused, upon the songs: every one of them lived a special life on each separate occasion. The riches of this recital are beyond the scope of a short review. Every song here deserves a paragraph to itself, and the appreciation of Gerald Moore's work would have a large share in each. The disc, for one who cares for Wolf's songs and the art of their performance, is beyond price.

Additional recommendations ...
...Mörike Lieder – Er ist's; Der Gärtner. *Coupled with works by various composers.* **Lisa della Casa** (sop); **Arpad Sándor** (pf). EMI Salzburg Festival Edition mono Ⓜ CDH5 66571-2* (64 minutes: ADD: 2/98). *See review in the Collections section; refer to the Index.*
...Mörike Lieder – Er ist's; Im Frühling; Der Gärtner. Eichendorff Lieder – Nachtzauber. Goethe Lieder – Frühling übers Jahr; Anakreons Grab. *Coupled with works by various composers.* **Dame Felicity Lott** (sop); **Graham Johnson** (pf). Hyperion Ⓕ CDA66937 (65 minutes: DDD: 10/97). *See review in the Collections section; refer to the Index.*

Hugo Wolf Society Edition Mörike Lieder – excerpts. Spanisches Liederbuch – excerpts. Italienisches Liederbuch – excerpts. Eichendorff Lieder – excerpts. Goethe Lieder – excerpts. Drei Gedichte von Michelangelo. Gedichte von Scheffel, Mörike, Goethe und Kerner – excerpts. Gedichte von Richard Reinick – excerpt. Lieder für eine Frauenstimme – excerpts. Gedichte nach Heine, Shakespeare und Lord Byron – excerpts. **Marta Fuchs, Ria Ginster, Tiana Lemnitz, Elisabeth Rethberg, Alexandra Trianti** (sops); **Elena Gerhardt** (mez); **Karl Erb, John McCormack, Helge Roswaenge** (tens); **Herbert Janssen, Gerhard Hüsch** (bars), **Friedrich Schorr** (bass-bar); **Alexander Kipnis, Ludwig Weber** (basses) with various pianists. EMI mono Ⓜ CHS5 66640-2* (five discs: 375 minutes: ADD: 6/98). Texts and translations included. From HMV originals, recorded 1931-1938.
Whatever has since been achieved in Wolf interpretation, the old Hugo Wolf Society recordings hold their place not only as regards the distinction of the readings but as evidence of the pioneering work done by Ernest Newman and Walter Legge in the promulgation of the composer's highly original style. Six volumes were issued on 78rpm discs between 1931 and 1938, but a planned seventh was not released as a set (because of the war intervening) until the LP reissue came out in 1981. Here a further six titles have been unearthed from the EMI archives. The CD box has a suitably distinguished cover and texts and translations have been provided. This is a cornucopia of delights for the Lieder lover. Gerhardt had the whole of the first volume to herself, and launches the project with a typical honesty of approach. Her slightly grand voice and inimitable style may not be to modern tastes but persist and you'll surely respond to the generosity of her singing. The next volumes are dominated by the mellow tones and deeply felt performances of Hüsch, Janssen and Kipnis, to whom Legge assigned exactly the right pieces for their respective styles. All are deeply rewarding, but Hüsch in love-songs from the *Spanish Songbook* and Kipnis in the *Michelangelo* Songs and so much else make particularly memorable contributions. Among the women, the much underrated Greek soprano, Alexandra Trianti brings just the right lightness of touch to some of the teasing, airy pieces from the *Italian Songbook*. Ria Ginster is a fresh, pleasing soprano, but she slightly undercharacterizes her offerings. Not so Elisabeth Rethberg, who encompasses the grander passions of the *Italian Songbook* and is unsurpassed in the sorrowful abasement of "Mühvoll komm' ich und beladen" from the *Spanish Songbook*. Legge perceptively brought in Schorr for a defiant "Prometheus" (in Wolf's orchestral version) and McCormack for an elevating "Ganymed". In 1937, Roswaenge sings a hair-raising "Feuerreiter".
   Other singers in the later volumes who bring their special individuality of utterance to bear on specific areas of Wolf's output are Fuchs (touching as Mignon and so eager in the great love-song, "Geh, Geliebter, geh jetzt!"), the refined, sensitive Erb and the lovely Lemnitz, whose "In der Frühe, Schlafendes Jesuskind" and "Wiegenlied im Sommer" are unmissable. Janssen also returned in 1937 for deeply eloquent accounts of some of the most inspired pieces in the *Spanish Songbook*, including a "Schlafendes Jesuskind" almost as rewarding as Lemnitz's reading. The gem among the previously unpublished items is Kipnis's sensual, intimate "Verschwiegene Liebe". Then to round things off Gerhardt is heard again in a newly issued version of a rarely heard, grief-laden song, "Uber Nacht", on which she lavishes all her love for Wolf. The pianists from Bos to Moore are uniformly excellent, though not always as perceptive as their successors today. It is Wolf and the singers who make this one of the great enterprises of the pre-war gramophone and of far more than historic interest.

Wolf Spanisches Liederbuch. **Anne Sofie von Otter** (mez); **Olaf Bär** (bar); **Geoffrey Parsons** (pf). EMI Ⓕ CDS5 55325-2 (two discs: 109 minutes: DDD: 8/95). Texts and translations included. Recorded 1992-1994.
The songs are performed not in the published order but in one devised by Bär for several recitals of the set given by this trio, and now carried over into the recording studio. For the ten religious songs the reordering works well. In any case here the two singers show a deep and rewarding comprehension of the agony and ecstasy of poems and music. Listen, too, to von Otter's sense of smiling wonder in "Ach, des Knaben Augen" as the holy mother looks into her son's eyes. By contrast in "Mühvoll komm' ich und beladen" she changes to a searing, soul-searching manner that captures completely the woman's remorse, magnificently so at the climactic "Nimm mich an". Bär is as tense and inward in the great "Herr, was trägt der Boden hier", capturing the voices of penitent and Christ to perfection. Note, too, Parsons's deliberately heavy gait in "Die du Gott gebarst". There are problems, however, in the more numerous secular songs.

With von Otter, apart from downward transpositions that make the piano parts sound unduly dark and Parsons consequently a shade heavy-handed, there is little to quarrel with. She teases, flirts, falls in love with the best of them, alert with her words, but never overdoing the archness as Schwarzkopf sometimes does. Bär, though, is not only up against the perhaps more formidable challenge of Fischer-Dieskau but also against his own reordering. He does not have – how could he? – the immense tonal range and emotional charge of the older baritone. "Herz, verzage nicht geschwind" is broader, more biting in Fischer-Dieskau's reading, for instance, "Ach im Maien" that much more mellifluous, but you could say that Bär's more contained, but by no means reticent approach has its own, Wolfian justification. But it is entirely Bär's fault that songs Nos. 21 and 24, which should be sung as a group, lose some of their force when separated as here, thoughtfully as Bär sings each in its turn. However, the readings as a whole are worthy of the collection. In the modern manner there is more space around the voices than on the closer-miked DG set, where Fischer-Dieskau is very much a presence in the room with you: you listen to the newer pair in more of a recital ambience. This newer version doesn't replace the old, which also has the advantage of price, but those who want another, fresh, valid view of the *Spanisches Liederbuch* or just want to hear von Otter in her element will wish to acquire these two absorbing discs.

Additional recommendation ...

...Spanisches Liederbuch. **Dame Elisabeth Schwarzkopf** (sop); **Dietrich Fischer-Dieskau** (bar); **Gerald Moore** (pf). DG Galleria Ⓜ 423 934-2GGA2 (two discs: 102 minutes: ADD: 3/89).

Wolf Spanisches Liederbuch – Die ihr schwebet um diese Palmen; Ach, des Knaben Augen; Mühvoll komm' ich und beladen; In dem Schatten meiner Locken; Sagt, seid Ihr es, feiner Herr; Mögen alle bösen Zungen; Alle gingen, Herz, zur Ruh; Tief im Herzen trag' ich Pein; Komm, o Tod, von Nacht umgeben; Ob auch finstre Blicke glitten; Bedeckt mich mit Blumen; Sie blasen zum Abmarsch; Wer tat deinem Füsslein weh; Geh' Geliebter, geh' jetz. Mörike Lieder – Das verlassene Mägdlein; Nimmersatte Liebe; Verborgenheit; Im Frühling; Elfenlied; Auf ein altes Bild; Lied vom Winde. **Elly Ameling** (sop); **Rudolf Jansen** (pf). Hyperion Ⓕ CDA66788 (59 minutes: DDD: 10/95). Texts and translations included. Recorded 1991.

This is a gratifying distillation of Ameling as a Wolf interpreter, a late flowering of her art in which we are consoled for some loss in the quality and quantity of tone by the insights offered. Indeed, in so many of these readings, her performance represents Wolf singing of the most telling kind. The four central songs tell us all. To "Ob auch finstre Blicke glitten" she brings a depth of verbal accent and inner expression that places it among Wolf's highest achievements. There follow a properly weary, care-ridden account of "Alle gingen, Herz, zur Ruh", a languorous evocation of "Bedeckt mich mit Blumen" and a tragic entry into the abasing world of "Mühvoll komm' ich und beladen". The two sacred songs are hardly less impressive. Her choice ends with a reading of "Geh' Geliebter", in which Ameling sheds the years to give us all the ardent thoughts of the girl reluctant at dawn to leave her lover. If you have hesitated before buying the complete EMI set, you might prefer to try this rewarding and distinguished selection. Ameling shows equal discernment in her choice from the Mörike settings, catching – as the best Wolf interpreters can do – the specific mood of each. If there is a favourite here it has to be "Das verlassene Mägdlein", where the dreadful anguish of the abandoned girl, so unerringly caught by Wolf, is expressed in a mood of almost toneless lassitude – just right. As ever, Jansen is an ideal partner for this singer, nowhere more so than when he rightly underplays the rhythm of "Sie blasen zum Abmarsch".

Further listening ...

...Italian Serenade. *Coupled with works by* **Grieg** *and* **Sibelius** Budapest Quartet Biddulph mono LAB098* (4/95).

Julia Wolfe
American 1958

Suggested listening ...

...Lick. *Coupled with works by various composers.* **Bang on a Can All-Stars.** Sony Classical SK66483 (2/96). *See review in the Collections section; refer to the Index.*

Charles Wood
Irish 1866-1926

Suggested listening ...

...This joyful Eastertide. *Coupled with works by various composers.* **St Paul's Cathedral Choir / John Scott** with **Andrew Lucas** (org). Hyperion CDA66916 (A/97). *See review in the Collections section; refer to the Index.*

Haydn Wood
British 1882-1959

Haydn Wood A May-Day Overture. Soliloquy. Variations on a once popular humorous song. Paris Suite. Roses of Picardy (orchestral version). A Manx Rhapsody. Frescoes – Sea shanties;

The Bandstand, Hyde Park. An Evening Song. A Day in Fairyland – Dance of a whimsical elf.
London Landmarks – The Horse Guards, Whitehall. **Slovak Radio Symphony Orchestra,**
Bratislava / Ernest Tomlinson. Marco Polo British Light Music Ⓕ 8 223605
(73 minutes: DDD: 8/97). Recorded 1993.
This pleasing collection of music by Haydn Wood features veteran light music conductor Ernest
Tomlinson, who coaxes the best out of the Bratislava players. The familiarity of Wood's
"Montmartre" march must have left many longing to hear the rest of the *Paris Suite*, and it is unlikely
that anyone could be disappointed with the languorous waltz and dreamy meditation that form its
first two movements. Here, too, in Wood's own orchestral version, is that most beautiful of melodies,
Roses of Picardy and the stirring march "The Horse Guards, Whitehall", the signature tune of *Down*
Your Way. Less familiar items include another stirring march, "The Bandstand" – a sort of
"Montmartre" without the string of onions – and there are a couple of delightful miniatures in *An*
Evening Song and "Dance of a whimsical elf". The more ambitious pieces include reminders of
Wood's Manx upbringing, and there is a curiosity in the *Variations on a once popular humorous song*
(the song in question being *If you want to know the time, ask a policeman*), which has some enigmatic
Elgarian touches to it. Wood brought a classical resource to his stirring melodies, and this is a
thoroughly worthwhile release.
Additional recommendation ...
...Roses of Picardy. *Coupled with works by various composers.* **Dame Felicity Lott** (sop);
    Graham Johnson (pf). Hyperion Ⓕ CDA66937 (65 minutes: DDD: 10/97). *See review in the*
    Collections section; refer to the Index.
Further listening ...
...The Horse Guards, Whitehall. *Coupled with works by various composers.* **The New London**
    Orchestra / Ronald Corp. Hyperion CDA66968 (5/97). *Gramophone Editor's choice.*   Ⓖ
...Moods – Joyousness[a]. Paris – Montmartre[b]. *Coupled with works by various composers.* [a]**Pro Arte**
    Orchestra / George Weldon; [b]**Studio Two Concert Orchestra / Reginald Kilbey.** EMI British
    Composers CDM5 66537-2 (1/98). *See review in the Collections section; refer to the Index.*
...Sketch of a Dandy. Serenade to Youth. Mannin Veen. Three London Cameos – Suite.
    Mylecharane. Moods Suite No. 6, "Joyousness". A Brown Bird Singing. Apollo. The Seafarer.
    Bratislava Radio Symphony Orchestra / Adrian Leaper. Marco Polo 8 223402 (8/92).

Sir Henry Wood
British 1869-1944

Suggested listening ...
...Fantasia on British Sea Songs. *Coupled with works by various composers.*
    BBC Symphony Orchestra / James Loughran. BBC Radio Classics 15656 9191-2 (11/97).
    See review in the Collections section; refer to the Index.

Hugh Wood
British 1932

Hugh Wood String Quartets – No. 1; No. 2, Op. 13; No. 3, Op. 20; No. 4. **Chilingirian Quartet**
(Levon Chilingirian, Charles Stewart, vns; Simon Rowland, va; Philip de Groote, vc).
Conifer Classics Ⓕ 75605-51239-2 (78 minutes: DDD: 6/95). Recorded 1994.
Wood's style is evident in the First Quartet, where the angular gestures of the introduction propose
ideas for future discussion, thus prompting references back to the opening movement, while another
strategy gradually reveals ideas that become dominant in the finale. The result is a sketch, as yet
somewhat tentative, of a quartet whose four movements are unified, finale-directed rather than first-
movement dominated. The Second and Third Quartets, seemingly stepping aside from this path, in
fact investigate it further. The Second, in 39 very brief linked sections, some of them mildly aleatoric,
gradually builds a powerful sense of forward impetus from an opening in which each brief and
violently juxtaposed musical event seems to propose a different direction. The Third has fewer
sections and a longer span, but a still greater emotional range, from its chilly opening to the big,
confident gestures with which it ends. Here there is no hint of the aleatory nor of disjunct
juxtaposition, but a gradual growth of eloquence, of a hard-won long line. It was written after an
unproductive period, and towards the end there is a distinctly Beethovenian sense of 'feeling new
strength'. The recent Fourth Quartet is a superb demonstration of that strength at full stretch: an
expository prelude, a tense *Scherzo* (itself expository also), a noble *Adagio* whose long lines can easily
bridge silences and quite sharp angles, and a finale that is most satisfyingly the audible destination of
all that preceded it. It is a masterly piece, enhanced by being heard as the culmination of its predecessors.
Finely and cleanly recorded, the Chilingirian Quartet sound passionately involved with this music.
Additional recommendation ...
...No. 3. *Coupled with works by various composers.* **Lindsay Quartet.** ASV Ⓕ CDDCA825
    (77 minutes: ADD: 1/93). *See review in the Collections section; refer to the Index.*
Further listening ...
...Piano Concerto, Op. 31. **Joanna MacGregor** (pf); **BBC Symphony Orchestra / Andrew Davis.**
    Collins 20th Century Plus 2007-2 (6/93).

James Wood
British 1953

James Wood Two men meet, each presuming the other to be from a distant planet[a].
Phainomena[b]. Venancio Mbande talking with the trees[c]. [c]**Kuniko Kato** (marimba); [a]**Steven Schick**
(perc); [b]**New London Chamber Choir; Critical Band / James Wood.** NMC Ⓟ NMCD044
(66 minutes: DDD: 12/97). Recorded 1993, 1995 and 1997.
This disc offers a great opportunity to explore James Wood's challenging but never incoherent
compositions. If the mixture of elaborate titles and prominent percussion leads you to suspect a
degree of pretentiousness, the quality of thought and the sensitivity to design as well as texture should
reassure you that Wood is a real composer, as well as a fine performer, and the recordings could hardly
be better. In *Phainomena* a touch of the pretentious can be detected in the way the music diffuses its
strengths through over-insistence on ritualistic vocal writing and repetitive instrumental dance-
patterns. But the other works are more effective, and vindicate Wood's own personal brand of
modernism. The plan of *Two men meet*, to proceed from confrontation to reconciliation, could be
simplistically schematic, but the subtlety of the interactions between percussion soloist and orchestra
makes this a consistently absorbing and appealing score. In *Venacio Mbande talking with the trees*, the
blend of intricate thought and clear, purposeful structure is if anything even more satisfying, with a
poetic quality to the writing that lingers in the mind. Fans of Evelyn Glennie ought to try this disc,
simply to see how well other percussion specialists match up to her achievements.

Searle Wright
American 1918

Suggested listening ...
...Magnificat and Nunc dimittis in E minor. *Coupled with works by various composers.*
St Thomas Church Choir, New York / Gerre Hancock with **Patrick Allen** (org).
Priory PRCD600 (1/98). *See review in the Collections section; refer to the Index.*

Charles Wuorinen
American 1938

Wuorinen Time's Encomium[a]. Piano Sonata No. 1[b]. String Quartet No. 1[c]. [b]**Robert Miller** (pf);
[c]**Fine Arts Quartet** (Leonard Sorkin, Abram Loft, vns; Bernard Zaslav, va; George Sopkin, vc).
Music & Arts Ⓟ CD932 (75 minutes: ADD: 7/97). Item marked [a] from Nonesuch H71125 (4/70),
recorded 1968-1969, [b]new to UK (recorded 1970), [c]Turnabout TV34515S (9/74), recorded 1971.
The years 1968-1970, when these works were composed, were of particular significance in Wuorinen's
development. Then in his early thirties, he had become aware that he was losing patience with New
Music's "directionlessness". On this evidence he was still quite happy with New Music's inherent
complexity of utterance. But in Wuorinen's best compositions persistent density of texture is offset by
an expressive exuberance redolent of the laid-back New York culture of the time. The ability of
advanced and elaborate composition to project a strong vein of witty inventiveness is best shown here
in *Time's Encomium*. The subtitle – "for synthesised and processed synthesised sound" – makes the
piece appear forbidding in the extreme, but Wuorinen evidently relished the technical possibilities of
a medium that dispenses with live performers. As with Nancarrow's *Studies* for player piano, there's
an element of sending-up the routines of traditional 'live' composition which adds greatly to the fun.
Yet this is a substantial musical statement, not to be written off as incidental music for an unmade
Tom and Jerry cartoon. The other works are more demanding. The Piano Sonata shares some of
Time's Encomium's fantasy and volatility: nevertheless, both the Sonata and the String Quartet, with
their large-scale, intensely active forms, risk precisely that sense of directionlessness which the
composer was seeking to avoid. The Quartet, in particular, seems determined to shun the kind of
rhapsodic flow that makes the other works more appealing. Even so, there's no denying the power of
the musical mind at work here, and the performances – aided by excellent remastering – will keep you
listening.

Further listening ...
...Album Leaf (violin and cello). Fortune. Cello Variations II. Violin Variations. Tashi.
The Group for Contemporary Music. Koch International Classics 37242-2 (9/94).
...A Winter's Tale[a]. Album Leaf (piano). String Sextet. Twang[a]. New York Notes.
[a]**Phyllis Bryn-Julson** (sop); **Lincoln Center Chamber Music Society / Charles Wuorinen.**
Koch International Classics 37272-2 (2/95).
...Mass for the restoration of St Luke in the Fields[a]. A Solis Ortu[b]. Ave Christe: Josquin[c]. Genesis[d].
[a]**James E. Pugh, Joseph Alessi, David Taylor** (trombs); [a]**Curtis Macomber** (vn); [a]**Harold Chaney**
(org); [ab]**New York Virtuoso Singers / Charles Wuorinen** ([c]pf); [d]**Minnesota Chorale and Orchestra /
Edo de Waart.** Koch International Classics 37336-2 (7/96).
...A Reliquary for Igor Stravinsky. *Coupled with works by* **Stravinsky**
Soloists; New London Chamber Choir; London Sinfonietta / Oliver Knussen.
DG 447 068-2GH (10/95). *See review under Stravinsky; refer to the Index.*   Ⓖ
...Piano Sonata No. 3. Bagatelle. Capriccio. *Coupled with* **Feldman** Palais de Mari. **Alan Feinberg**
(pf). Koch International Classics 37308-2 (9/96). *See review under Feldman; refer to the Index.*

Iannis Xenakis
Greek/French 1922

Xenakis A Colone[a]. Nuits. Serment. Knephas. Medea[a]. **New London Chamber Choir;**
[a]**Critical Band / James Wood.** Hyperion Ⓕ CDA66980 (58 minutes: DDD).
Texts and translations included. Recorded 1997. Ⓖ
This enterprising Hyperion release is a great success, showing just how varied – and unintimidating –
Xenakis's music can be. The performances are nothing short of phenomenal in their technical
assurance and emotional power, and the recording is also something special, giving the singers just
the right degree of space and resonance to project the often complex textures with all the necessary
precision. The earliest works offer different angles on the composer's ultra-expressionist idiom, with
Nuits (1967) adopting a very direct way of representing its anguished lament for the martyrs of
Greece's struggle for freedom after 1945. *Medea* (also 1967) uses much more text, and its chant-like
style has affinities with Stravinsky's *Les noces*, but the overall effect is much harsher, with abrasive yet
imaginative instrumental writing. *A Colone* (1977) also has Stravinskian affinities, and the text
(Sophocles's description of the delights of Colonus) prompts music which is uninhibitedly exuberant,
even dance-like. This warmer, more celebratory side of Xenakis is carried over into *Serment* (1980), a
short setting of a text derived from the Hippocratic Oath and not, one suspects, an entirely serious
effort, though there is nothing trivial about it either. Finally, the superb *Knephas* ("Darkness") of
1990 begins in an appropriately unsparing manner, but ends with a hymnic apotheosis which recalls
Messiaen in its harmonic character and warmth of atmosphere. Here is one of the twentieth century's
most important musical voices, and this recording does that voice full justice.
Further listening ...
...Jalons[a]. Phlegra[b]. Thalleïn[b]. Keren[c]. Nomos Alpha[d]. [c]**Benny Sluchin** (tbn); [d]**Pierre Strauch** (vc);
 Ensemble InterContemporain / [a]Pierre Boulez, [b]Michel Tabachnik. Erato 2292-45770-2. Ⓖ
...Metastasis. Pithoprakta. Eonta[a]. **French Radio National Orchestra / François Le Roux;**
 [a]**Paris Contemporary Music Instrumental Ensemble / Konstantin Simonovic.**
 Le Chant du Monde LDC278 368.
...Orestia. **Strasbourg University Music Department; Colmar Women's Voices; Anjou Vocal Ensemble;**
 Basse-Normandie Ensemble / Dominique Debart. Salabert Actuels SCD8906 (9/90).
...Palimpsest. Dikhthas[a]. Epeï. Akanthos[b]. [a]**Irvine Arditti** (vn); [a]**Claude Helffer** (pf);
 [b]**Penelope Walmsley-Clark** (sop); **Spectrum / Guy Protheroe.** Wergo WER6178-2. Ⓖ

José Ximénez
Spanish 1601-1672

Suggested listening ...
...Batalla de octavo tono (arr. Roberts). *Coupled with works by various composers.*
 His Majestys Sagbutts and Cornetts.
 Hyperion CDA66847 (11/96). *See review in the Collections section; refer to the Index.*

Eugène Ysaÿe
Belgian 1858-1931

Ysaÿe Solo Violin Sonatas, Op. 27 – No. 1 in G minor; No. 2 in A minor; No. 3 in D minor,
 "Ballade"; No. 4 in E minor; No. 5 in G major; No. 6 in E major. Poème élégiaque, Op. 12[a].
 Rêve d'enfant, Op. 14[a]. **Philippe Graffin** (vn); [a]**Pascal Devoyon** (pf). Hyperion Ⓕ CDA66940
 (78 minutes: DDD: 7/97). Recorded 1996.
Philippe Graffin has one major advantage over his rivals: his pure intonation. Even the most
demanding of Ysaÿe's flights of virtuosic fancy sound beautiful. Graffin refuses to overplay the
music; tone and expression are always natural and unforced, and there are none of the harsh accents
that occasionally disfigure Mordkovitch's performances. Though he follows Ysaÿe's very detailed
instructions more exactly than most violinists, there's also a strong element of fantasy, the music
developing in a seemingly unconstrained and spontaneous way, the individual movements sharply
characterized. The stunning bowing variations and rubato of the *Presto* finale of the Fourth Sonata,
and the playful grace of the *Allegretto poco scherzoso* in the First Sonata are just two examples. You
may be bothered by one thing in Graffin's playing – occasional rhythmic weakness. In the First
Sonata's finale, the rubato gets out of hand, losing the underlying rhythmic impetus, and the opening
Allemande of Sonata No. 4 is similarly undermined by his unwillingness to dwell sufficiently on the
longer notes. In these places Shumsky shows the way – his freedoms are always related to a strong
underlying sense of pulse. Graffin's *Danse Rustique* in Sonata No. 5, on the other hand, is splendidly
poised and bouncy. The beautifully played additional items are a real bonus, as are the thoughtful and
illuminating notes by Graffin himself. Shumsky and Mordkovitch give the music more grandeur,
maybe, and Shumsky's daring bravura in the Sixth Sonata is unrivalled. Graffin, however, as a 'grand
pupil' of Ysaÿe shows himself well placed to carry on the tradition of Ysaÿe performance, inspired
by the great violinist's own recordings. The recording is excellent.
Additional recommendations ...
...Nos. 1-6. **Lydia Mordkovitch** (vn). Chandos Ⓕ CHAN8599 (DDD: 5/88).
...Nos. 1-6. **Oscar Shumsky** (vn). Nimbus Ⓕ NI7715 (62 minutes: DDD: 10/96).

...Nos. 3 and 4. *Coupled with works by other composers.* Leila Josefowicz (vn).
Philips Ⓕ 446 700-2PH (62 minutes: DDD: 2/97).
Further listening ...
...Caprice d'après l'etude en forme de valse de Saint-Saëns. *Coupled with works by various
composers.* Joshua Bell (vn); Royal Philharmonic Orchestra / Andrew Litton.
Decca 433 519-2DH (1/92). *See review in the Collections section; refer to the Index.*

Riccardo Zandonai
Italian 1883-1944

Suggested listening ...
...Francesca da Rimini. Soloists; Sofia Chamber Choir; Vienna Volksoper Chorus;
Vienna Symphony Orchestra / Fabio Luisi. Koch Schwann 31368-2 (A/97).
...Francesca da Rimini[a] – Act 2: E ancora sgombro il campo del comune? ... Date il segno, Paolo,
date ... Un'erba io m'avea, per sanare ... Onta et orrore sopra. Act 3: No, Smadragedi, no! ...
Paolo, datemi pace! ... Ah la parola chi i miei occhi incontrano. Act 4: Ora andate ... E così,
vada s'è pur mio destino. *Coupled with* **Giordano** Fedora[b].
Soloists; [b]Monte-Carlo Opera Chorus and [ab]Orchestra / [a]Nicola Rescigno, [b]Lamberto Gardelli.
Decca Grand Opera 433 033-2DM2 (3/92). *See review under Giordano; refer to the Index.*

Jan Dismas Zelenka
Bohemian 1679-1745

Zelenka Capriccios – No. 2 in G major; No. 3 in F major. Concerto a 8 in G major. Hipocondrie
a 7 in A major. **Das Neu-Eröffnete Orchestre / Jürgen Sonnentheil.** CPO Ⓕ CPO999 458-2
(61 minutes: DDD: 1/98). ✍ Recorded 1996. *Gramophone Editor's choice.*
This set (the first in a series which is to undertake a complete survey of Zelenka's orchestral pieces)
contains two of Zelenka's five *Capriccios*, a Concerto for eight instruments and the intriguingly titled
Hipocondrie, which occupies ground somewhere between suite and concerto. Zelenka was skilled in
the art of combining instruments of differing colours, ordering them about in a way that makes us
wonder if he had a grudge against players. The horn-writing in the *Capriccios* is merciless, with
uncommonly high parts often emerging in exposed moments in the texture. Zelenka's melodic facility,
rhythmic imagination and instinctive feeling for effective instrumental ranges and colours are
sufficient to sustain interest. There is an inventive freshness about his music which contains surprises
at almost every turn. Sometimes, however, as in the finale of the Concerto in eight parts, sequential
patterns are overworked, giving the movement a somewhat amorphous, unsatisfying shape. Initial
rather good ideas, almost always arresting, are less well sustained than, say, Telemann's, even if they
are sometimes bolder and more adventurous. Sonnentheil achieves spirited, amiable performances
from Das Neu-Eröffnete Orchestre, an able body of period-instrumentalists. The two horns are
excellent and, if oboes and strings sound a shade unrefined occasionally, it does little to spoil
enjoyment of an entertaining programme which is well worth exploring.
Additional recommendations ...
...Capriccios – No. 1 in D major; Nos. 2 and 3; No. 4 in A major; No. 5 in G major.
Concerto a 8. Sinfonia a 8 in A minor. Hipocondrie a 7 in A major. Overture a 7 in F major.
Berne Camerata / Alexander van Wijnkoop.
Archiv Produktion Ⓜ 423 703-2AX3 (three discs: 164 minutes: ADD: 1/89).   Ⓖ
...Concerto a 8. Hipocondrie a 7 in A major. Sinfonia a 8 in A minor.
Coupled with works by **Pisendel** Freiburg Baroque Orchestra / Gottfried von der Goltz.
Deutsche Harmonia Mundi Ⓕ 05472 77339-2 (64 minutes: DDD: 10/95). ✍

Zelenka Trio Sonatas, Volume 2 – No. 1 in F major; No. 3 in B flat major; No. 4 in G minor.
Ensemble Zefiro (Paolo Grazzi, Alfredo Bernardini, obs; Alberto Grazzi, bn; Manfred Kraemer,
vn; Lorenz Duftschmid, violone; Gian Carlo Rado, theorbo; Rinaldo Alessandrini, hpd/org).
Auvidis Astrée Ⓕ E8563 (52 minutes: DDD: 2/96). Recorded 1995.
Zelenka was one of a gifted group of composers associated with the Dresden court during the first
half of the eighteenth century. The court orchestra, one of the best around at that time, boasted a
particularly accomplished wind section, and it may have been for some of these players that Zelenka
wrote his six trios. The sources have not survived complete in all cases and the realization, for
example, of the bass parts in the First and Third Sonatas, both of them included here, must always
be conjectural. Ensemble Zefiro have thought carefully about this and have arrived at a solution which
is both idiomatic and, it seems, in keeping with the surviving material. The playing is spirited and
plentifully endowed with virtuosity. The oboists Paolo Grazzi and Alfredo Bernardini are technically
secure and tastefully imaginative in their ornamentation. Bassoonist Alberto Grazzi is also fluent and
furthermore a sensitive ensemble player. Keyboard continuo is stylishly provided by Rinaldo
Alessandrini, sometimes playing harpsichord, at other times organ; and additional continuo support
includes violone and theorbo. Readers so far unacquainted with these sonatas are in for a treat for
this is music rich in fantasy, exciting for its virtuosic content, unusually extended in the working out
of its ideas, and effectively constructed.

Additional recommendation ...

...Nos. 1-6. **Paul Dombrecht, Marcel Ponseele, Ku Ebbinge** (obs); **Danny Bond** (bn); **Chiara Banchini** (vn); **Richte van der Meer** (vc); **Robert Kohnen** (hpd). Accent Ⓕ ACC8848D (two discs: 109 minutes: DDD: 3/89). ⫽ Ⓖ

Zelenka Trio Sonatas – No. 2 in G minor, No. 5 in F major; No. 6 in C minor. **Ensemble Zefiro** (Paolo Grazzi, Alfredo Bernardini, obs; Alberto Grazzi, bn; Roberto Sensi, db; Rolf Lislevand, theorbo; Rinaldo Alessandrini, hpd/org). Auvidis Astrée Ⓕ E8511 (52 minutes: DDD: 6/94). ⫽ Recorded 1993. Ⓖ

For sheer *élan* and spirit the baroque instrumental players on this disc take some beating. Zelenka's six sonatas for two oboes, bassoon and continuo are among the most rewarding and at times most difficult pieces of baroque chamber music in the oboe repertory. Indeed, pieces demanding such virtuosity from these instruments were probably without precedent at the time (1715). We can only speculate as to the circumstances which led to their composition but the writing is often such as to make us wonder if they were destined for friends or enemies of the composer. Here, then, is splendidly invigorating playing of music which offers a great deal beyond face value. The sounds of the solo instruments themselves, together with an effective continuo group of double-bass, harpsichord/organ and theorbo are admirably captured in the recording.

Zelenka The Lamentations of Jeremiah. **Michael Chance** (alto); **John Mark Ainsley** (ten); **Michael George** (bass); **Chandos Baroque Players.** Hyperion Ⓕ CDA66426 (73 minutes: DDD: 7/91). ⫽ Texts and translations included. Recorded 1990.

Between the incomparable settings by Thomas Tallis and the extremely austere one by Stravinsky (which he called *Threni*) the "Lamentations of Jeremiah" have attracted surprisingly few composers. Perhaps the predominantly sombre tone, without even the dramatic opportunities presented by the *Dies irae* in a Requiem, is off-putting. Be that as it may, Zelenka showed remarkable resourcefulness in his 1722 setting for the electoral chapel at Dresden, where he was *Kapellmeister*. His musical language is in many ways similar to that of J.S. Bach but there are also daring turns of phrase which are entirely personal. The six *Lamentations* feature each singer twice; this performance is intimate, even mystical, slightly spacious in tempo and with a resonant acoustic.

Further listening ...

...Sinfonia a 8 in A minor. *Coupled with* **Bach** Brandenburg Concerto No. 2 in F major, BWV1047. VIolin Concerto, BWV1052 (arr. Linder-Dewan)[a]. [a]**Kerstin Linder-Dewan** (vn); **F iori Musicali / Penelope Rapson.** Metronome METCD1019 (3/98).

Alexander Zemlinsky

Austrian 1871-1942

Zemlinsky Sechs Gesänge, Op. 13.
Mahler Lieder eines fahrenden Gesellen. Rückert-Lieder. **Anne Sofie von Otter** (mez); **North German Radio Symphony Orchestra / Sir John Eliot Gardiner.** DG Ⓕ 439 928-2GH (56 minutes: DDD: 3/97). Texts and translations included. Recorded live in 1993.
Gramophone Editor's choice. Ⓖ

This is another absolute winner for both von Otter and Gardiner. The three works make an ideal programme, the two Mahler pieces forming a sensible frame for the central Zemlinsky. In all three offerings von Otter offers that peculiar gift of hers consisting of utter conviction allied to wonderful musicianship. In terms of tempo, phrasing, balance and sheer interpretative know-how, the pair take no false steps and very many fruitful ones. You will look hard to find a version of *Lieder eines fahrenden Gesellen* filled with such sense of emotions being felt and expressed so immediately. Von Otter and Gardiner make the work live here and now for our time, Gardiner rewardingly alert to every nuance and subtlety in Mahler's orchestral writing, which the clear recording admirably seconds. The Zemlinsky is the real revelation, though, far preferable to the piano version of these shadowy Maeterlinck settings. These songs of sexual liberation and *fin de siècle* decadence, which mirror precisely the world of *Jugendstil* as exemplified in Klimt's paintings – and are equally multi-mirrored, highly coloured and erotic – cry out for instrumental clothing. Gardiner revels in the dream-world orchestration while von Otter perfectly catches their hothouse atmosphere and underlines the texts' meaning without ever indulging in any overemphases. It's almost a relief to come up into the open air of Mahler's Rückert setting, "Ich atmet' einen linden Duft", where von Otter lightens her timbre, bringing a gentle smile into her tone. In these settings, she once more finds the right 'face' for each song – even expanding grandly into the affirmations at the end of "Um Mitternacht" – and then ends a compelling disc with just the other-worldly serenity predicated by "Ich bin der Welt". There's no need to seek out any other recording of these pieces: this is the one to have.

Zemlinsky Ein lyrische Symphonie, Op. 18[a]. Symphonische Gesänge, Op. 20[b]. [a]**Alessandra Marc** (sop); [a]**Håkan Hagegård** (bar); [b]**Willard White** (bass); **Royal Concertgebouw Orchestra / Riccardo Chailly.** Decca Entartete Musik Ⓕ 443 569-2DH (65 minutes: DDD: 12/94). Texts and translations included. Recorded 1993. *Gramophone Award Winner 1995.*
Gramophone Editor's choice. ⒼⒼ

With the Concertgebouw one has no fear that the sheer beauty of Zemlinsky's orchestral textures will be understated, but the urgency and strength beneath the surfaces are evident too, and it's quite an achievement for such an orchestra of Mahler specialists to get Zemlinsky's sound, so like Mahler and yet so very unlike, unerringly right. The soloists are simply superb: Marc is voluptuously caressing, not least in her sensuous use of portamento, but very intelligent in her use of words, her understanding of the dramatic gist of her three songs, and her extended lower register gives her both security at the bottom of the range and a beautiful shading of mezzo-ish warmth; Hagegård has nobility and strength as well as tenderness, and the Lieder singer's subtlety that the third and last songs need. Throughout, the orchestral playing is immaculately balanced. Was Willard White chosen for the *Symphonische Gesänge* because they are settings of black American poets? If so, he has the intelligence to realize that there is nothing especially 'ethnic' about them; to realize also, as does Chailly, that although only one opus number separates them from *Ein lyrische Symphonie* they inhabit a different world, harsher and more bitter. They require great vocal splendour but also a certain reserve. White and Chailly succeed admirably.

Additional recommendations...

...Ein lyrische Symphonie. *Coupled with works by* **Berg** Vlatka Orsanic (sop); James Johnson (bar); **South West German Radio Symphony Orchestra / Michael Gielen.** Arte Nova Classics Ⓢ 74321 27768-2 (67 minutes: DDD).

...Ein lyrische Symphonie. **Deborah Voigt** (sop); **Bryn Terfel** (bass-bar); **Vienna Philharmonic Orchestra / Giuseppe Sinopoli.** DG Ⓕ 449 179-2GH (49 minutes: DDD: 12/96).

...Ein lyrische Symphonie[ac]. Lieder, Op. 2: Book 2 – No. 4, Im Lenz[b]. Gesänge, Op. 5: Book 2 – No. 1, Unter blühenden Bäumen[b]. Gesänge, Op. 7 – No. 2, Entbietung[b]. Gesänge, Op. 10 – Selige Stunde[b]. Lieder auf Gedichte von Richard Dehmel – No. 1, Stromüber; No. 4, Letzte Bitte[b]. [a]**Luba Orgonasova** (sop); **Bo Skovhus** (bar); [b]**Helmut Deutsch** (pf); [c]**North German Radio Symphony Orchestra / Claus Peter Flor.** RCA Victor Red Seal Ⓕ 09026 68111-2 (64 minutes: DDD: 12/96).

...Ein lyrische Symphonie[b]. **Berg** Lyric Suite (arr. cpsr). Fünf Orchesterlieder nach Ansichtskartentexten von Peter Altenberg, Op. 4[a]. [ab]**Vlatka Orsanic** (sop); [b]**James Johnson** (bar); **South West German Radio Symphony Orchestra / Michael Gielen.** Arte Nova Ⓢ 74321 27768-2 (67 minutes: DDD: 10/97).

Zemlinsky Posthumous Songs – Sechs Lieder[a]. Zwei Lieder[b]. Zwei Preislieder[c]. Wandl' ich im Wald des Abends[d]. Vier Lieder[e]. Zwei Brettl-Lieder[f]. Drei Lieder[g]. Zwei Balladen[h]. Lieder auf Gedichte von Richard Dehmel – Ansturm; Vorspiel; Auf See[i]. Vier Lieder[j]. Und einmal gehst du[k]. [acej]**Ruth Ziesak** (sop); [abefg]**Iris Vermillion** (mez); [abegi]**Hans-Peter Blochwitz** (ten); [adhk]**Andreas Schmidt** (bar); **Cord Garben** (pf). Sony Classical Ⓕ SK57960 (70 minutes: DDD: 6/95). Texts and translations included. Recorded 1993.

These are the songs Zemlinsky didn't publish; why not? When sung as they are here in chronological order the reason for a while seems obvious: they have little individuality until about a third of the way through the collection. From then on things get much more interesting. The three settings of Richard Dehmel have a concentrated, poignant intensity so impressive that one is tempted to speculate about hidden reasons for Zemlinsky's reticence. "Jane Grey" (from *Zwei Balladen*), for example, was entered for a competition to which Schoenberg submitted a setting of exactly the same text. Is that why it almost out-Schoenbergs Schoenberg in its tenuous hold on tonality, its curiously gripping bare angularity? But in "Der verlorene Haufen" (*Zwei Balladen*), also set by Schoenberg for the same competition, Zemlinsky seems to be out-Mahlering Mahler in the fearsome march-toccata that accompanies this grim tale of a front-line regiment contemplating death each morning. The manner of the Dehmel songs is recaptured in a haunting group of settings of Hofmannsthal (*Vier Lieder*); there are also two curious comic ballads (the *Brettl-Lieder*, one quite funny, the other – about a man who eats so much that he bursts – rather disgusting), a most beautiful cradle-song over a dead child ("Uber eine Wiege", *Drei Lieder*) and a much later, nobly stoic contemplation of old age (*Und einmal gehst du*) that are in no way inferior to the best of Zemlinsky's published songs. Blochwitz, Schmidt and Garben splendid, Vermillion matches them admirably and Ziesak, if a little hard and bright at times, can fine her voice down to an effective intimacy. The recordings are excellent.

Zemlinsky Eine florentinische Tragödie. **Iris Vermillion** (mez) Bianca; **Heinz Kruse** (ten) Guido Bardi; **Albert Dohmen** (bar) Simone. **A. Mahler** (orch. Colin and David Matthews) Die stille Stadt. Laue Sommernacht. Bei dir ist es traut. Licht in der Nacht. Waldeinsamkeit. Erntelied. **Iris Vermillion** (mez); **Royal Concertgebouw Orchestra / Riccardo Chailly.** Decca Entartete Musik Ⓕ 455 112-2DH (71 minutes: DDD: 12/97). Notes, texts and translations included. Recorded 1996. *Gramophone Editor's choice.*

Zemlinsky's *Florentine Tragedy* is a disturbing, shocking piece, but to make its fullest impact it also needs to sound ravishingly beautiful. Zemlinsky's sumptuous scoring often demands an orchestra of the Royal Concertgebouw's stature, and in this reading they sound quite magnificent. But the score also needs a conductor of subtlety and shrewdness to point up the two passages of contrasting serene lyricism, one where Simone's wife Bianca assures Count Bardi of her eternal love and another when husband and wife rediscover their love for each other. Vermillion is very fine at both these points, her mezzo timbre adding warmth to her line. Kruse is admirable too, fining down his ringing tenor in that duet scene, and, as Simone, Dohmen is forceful and dangerous. But Chailly is the real star of the performance, pacing the opera so well that it seems over in no time, drawing richly complex but never muddy textures from his remarkable orchestra. On hearing the Alma Mahler songs one is struck by the benefits of their orchestration. But here again, exquisitely though Vermillion sings these songs, Chailly must take at least half the credit. Each song is taken faster than in most recordings with piano, and every one of them gains from it in impulsive urgency. In both Zemlinsky's opera and Alma Mahler's songs the recording leaves nothing to be desired: the colours are rich but beautifully clean.

Zemlinsky Der König Kandaules (cpted Beaumont). **James O'Neal** (ten) König Kandaules;
    Monte Pederson (bar) Gyges; **Nina Warren** (sop) Nyssia; **Klaus Häger** (bass) Phedros;
    Peter Galliard (ten) Syphax; **Mariusz Kwiecien** (bar) Nicomedes; **Kurt Gysen** (bass) Pharnaces;
    Simon Yang (bass) Philebos; **Ferdinand Seiler** (ten) Sebas; **Guido Jentjens** (bar) Archelaos;
    Hamburg State Philharmonic Orchestra / Gerd Albrecht. Capriccio Ⓔ 60 071/2
    (two discs: 128 minutes: DDD: 9/97). Notes, text and translation included.
King Candaules, based on a play by André Gide, is Zemlinsky's last opera, written during the Nazis' rise to power and complete in short score when he fled to America in 1938. He showed it to his pupil Artur Bodanzky, then a Principal Conductor at the Met, but Bodanzky seems to have warned him that the libretto would not be acceptable – in one scene Candaules tricks his wife into undressing in front of a fisherman he has recently befriended, then into sleeping with him. Zemlinsky never completed the orchestration of *Der König Kandaules* but left a large number of indications of scoring. Antony Beaumont's orchestration sounds perfectly convincing. When two excerpts from the score were performed and recorded in 1994 it already looked as though a major work by Zemlinsky was about to be revealed. And that indeed is the case: a marvellous and quite characteristic score, but in some ways a dismaying one. All the orchestral richness and the voluptuously singing lines that one expects are there, but wedded to a plot that seems all too accurately to reflect the disorder and disillusion of the times in which it was written. Nyssia, the wife so chaste and beautiful that until now no one but Candaules has seen her unveiled, is portrayed in music of quite sumptuous allure, but her reaction to his betrayal is more Salome-like than tragic: she orders the fisherman Gyges to kill her husband and take his place, in her bed as well as on the throne. Gyges, the poor but honest peasant (and his music has a touch of nobility to it), is a murderer himself: he killed his own wife because, as Candaules would have agreed, she was his property. And Candaules the seeming altruist, whose greatest pleasure is to share his wealth with others, is in fact simply boasting of his good fortune: even his wife's beauty is a sort of torment to him if other men are not jealous of it. And in Zemlinsky's musical portrayal the more his baseness becomes obvious the more glamorous and sympathetic he is. The performance is a fine one, O'Neal lacking only the last touch of heroic vocal stature for Candaules, Warren only a little stretched by the Ariadne-like role of Nyssia, Pederson first class (a moment or two of suspect intonation aside) as Gyges. Albrecht is perfectly at home in this sort of music, the orchestra's admirable richness of tone does not obscure detail, and the recording is atmospheric (stage business audible) but clear. Zemlinsky's reputation has been growing year by year recently. It can only be enhanced by this ravishing, richly complex, disturbing opera.

Further listening ...
...Die Seejungfrau. Sinfonietta, Op. 23. **Cologne Gürzenich Orchestra / James Conlon.**
    EMI CDC5 55515-2 (11/97).
...Humoreske. *Coupled with works by various composers.* **Aulos Wind Quintet.**
    Koch Schwann 310100.   Ⓖ
...Two Movements for String Quintet[a]. Two Movements for String Quartet. **Schoenberg**
    String Quartet in D major. String Trio, Op. 45[b]. [a]**Andrea Wennberg** (va); **Corda Quartet**
    ([b]**Olga Nodel,** Christine Plath, vns; [b]**Frauke Tometten-Molino,** va; [b]**Edith Salzmann,** vc).
    Stradivarius STR33438 (10/97). *See review under Schoenberg; refer to the Index.*
...Fünf Gesänge, Op. 7[abc]. **A. Mahler** Fünf Lieder[bc]. Vier Lieder[abc]. Fünf Lieder[ac].
    [a]**Ruth Ziesak** (sop); [b]**Iris Vermillion** (mez); [c]**Christian Elsner** (ten); **Cord Garben** (pf).
    CPO CPO999 455-2 (1/98). *See review under A. Mahler; refer to the Index.*
...Gesänge nach Maeterlinck, Op. 13[a]. *Coupled with* **Reger** Variations and Fugue on a Theme of
    J.A. Hiller. [a]**Hedwig Fassbender** (mez); **Czech Philharmonic Orchestra / Václav Neumann.**
    Supraphon 11 1811-2 (7/93).
...Der Kreiderkreis. **Soloists; Berlin Radio Symphony Orchestra / Stefan Soltesz.**
    Capriccio 60016-2 (1/92).
...Sarema. **Soloists; Trier Theatre Chorus; Trier City Orchestra / István Dénes.**
    Koch Classics 36467-2 (3/97).
...Der Zwerg. **Soloists; Frankfurter Kantorei; Cologne Gürzenich Orchestra / James Conlon.**
    EMI CMS5 66247-2 (6/97).

Bernd Alois Zimmermann   German 1918-1970

Zimmermann Concertos – Oboe and Small Orchestra[a]; Trumpet and Orchestra, "Nobody knows
    the trouble I see"[b]; Canto di speranza[c]; Cello and Orchestra, "en forme de pas de trois"[c].
    [a]**Heinz Holliger** (ob); [b]**Håkan Hardenberger** (tpt); [c]**Heinrich Schiff** (vc); **South-West German Radio**

Symphony Orchestra / Michael Gielen. Philips Ⓕ 434 114-2PH (71 minutes: DDD: 11/93). Recorded 1989-1992.

The Oboe Concerto (1952) vigorously confronts the central post-war challenge: if you want to embrace the new (serialism) alongside the old (neo-classicism), how do you keep your balance? The answer, for Zimmermann, was 'precariously'. In the Trumpet Concerto (1954) the absorption of a negro spiritual and elements of jazz serve to intensify the trauma of a search for stylistic equilibrium. Yet again the result is an impressive work of art strongly built and progressing inexorably to a bleak conclusion. *Canto di speranza* (1953-57) brings us still closer to the apocalyptic modernism of the opera *Die Soldaten* (begun in 1958) as models – notably Webern – become objects of mockery. The Cello Concerto *en forme de pas de trois*, written after the opera in 1965-66, completes the process of recreative rejection. It is a haunting fantasy, at once ballet score and concert work, a parody of nineteenth-century terpsichorean conventions which is as bitter in tone as it is beguiling in sound. Philips have assembled three star soloists for this well-recorded disc, and with sterling orchestral support they do the music proud.

Zimmermann Antiphonen[a]. Omnia tempus habent[b]. Présence[c]. [b]**Julie Moffat** (sop); [c]**Peter Rundel** (vn); [a]**Tabea Zimmermann** (va); [c]**Michael Stirling** (vc); [c]**Hermann Kretzschmar** (pf); [ab]**Ensemble Modern / Hans Zender.** RCA Victor Red Seal Ⓕ 09026 61181-2 (56 minutes: DDD: 2/97). Recorded 1992

Omnia tempus habent sets verses from Ecclesiastes for soprano and an instrumental ensemble which, with copious use of flute and vibraphone, echoes then-contemporary Boulez and Berio. Like those masters, Zimmermann could turn a highly fragmented style to strong expressive ends, with an elaborate vocal line that tests Julie Moffat in what is in any case an unflatteringly close recording. The other works fare better. *Antiphonen* is in effect a viola concerto, and, like many such compositions, it involves its gentle protagonist in an Orpheus-like attempt to tame the instrumental furies embodied by snarling brass and menacing percussion. The contest is nothing if not melodramatic, the end an uneasy, exhausted compromise rather than a victory for one side or the other. Zimmermann even includes a variety of texts to be declaimed by the instrumentalists: maddeningly, these are not set out in the booklet and, in any case, the device is of dubious value. Far more effective are the purely instrumental textures of *Présence*, where the need to work with just three instruments seems to have refined Zimmermann's thinking. The result is one of his finest works. *Présence* is a ballet score, and the composer shows great resource in allowing hints of conventionally patterned dance music to infiltrate the spiky, scary idiom of the remainder. Although the drama reflects *Antiphonen*'s alternation of aggressive and submissive moods, the music is absorbing on its own terms, and the piece is performed with great spirit by members of the Ensemble Modern.

Additional recommendation ...

...Présence[a]. Intercomunicazione. [a]**Karl-Rudolf Menke** (spkr); **Ensemble Recherche.** Wergo Ⓕ WER6605-2 (58 minutes: DDD: 11/97).

Further listening ...

...Enchiridion[b]. Cello Sonata[a]. Four Short Studies[a]. Intercommunicazione[ab]. [a]**Michael Bach** (vc); [b]**Bernhard Wambach** (pf). CPO CPO999 198-2 (8/94).

Collections

Orchestral

A la carte Itzhak Perlman (vn); **Abbey Road Ensemble / Lawrence Foster.** EMI Ⓕ CDC5 55475-2
(63 minutes: DDD: 1/96). Recorded 1995.
Massenet Thaïs – Méditation. **Glazunov** Mazurka-Oberek in D major. Meditation, Op. 32.
Rachmaninov Vocalise, Op. 34 No. 14. **Sarasate** Zigeunerweisen, Op. 20. Introduction and
Tarantella, Op. 43. **Rimsky-Korsakov** (arr. Kreisler) Fantasia on Two Russian Themes, Op. 33.
Tchaikovsky (orch. Glazunov) Scherzo in C minor, Op. 42 No. 2. **Wieniawski** Légende,
Op. 17. Zigeunerweisen. **Kreisler** The Old Refrain. Schön Rosmarin.
A most enjoyable programme. Perlman approximates the 'old school' with something of an actor's
skill: he feels the period, not as a first-hand witness (even at 50, he is far too young for that), but as a
respectful recipient of a great tradition. His "Méditation" is an elevated 'easy listen', sensitively
accompanied. The Glazunov *Mazurka-Oberek* should be at least as popular as Saint-Saëns's concert
pieces for violin and orchestra, and Perlman does it proud. The initial pages of Rachmaninov's
Vocalise are a little over-sweet (too many well-oiled slides), but its latter half achieves genuine
expressive eloquence. Glazunov's *Meditation* is suitably honeyed and the Kreisler-Rimsky *Fantasia*
(where Goldmark's A minor Concerto hovers around the main theme) is given a truly splendid
performance. Of the rest, the two Kreisler pieces are exceptional, *Schön Rosmarin* especially, while
Lawrence Foster's expert Abbey Road Ensemble provide a discreet but flavoursome orchestral base.

American Music Boston Symphony Orchestra / Serge Koussevitzky.
Pearl mono Ⓜ GEMMCD9492* (79 minutes: AAD: 12/91). Recorded 1934-40.　　　ⒼⒼⒼ
Foote Suite in E minor, Op. 63 (from RCA Victor 11-8571/2.). **McDonald** San Juan Capistrano
(RCA Victor 17729. 1939). **Copland** El salón México (HMV DB3812/3, 10/40).
Harris Symphonies – No. 1 (American Columbia 68183/6. 1934); No. 3 (DB6137/8, 12/42).
Music lovers with a romantic hankering for the American desert and the Great Outdoors may well
know Roy Harris's high, wide and handsome Third Symphony already, but the chances of having
heard Serge Koussevitzky's 1939 recording of it are somewhat more remote. If you can accept and
enjoy the soundtracks of classic Westerns, then you'll have no trouble with this CD: the playing of the
Boston Symphony burns through a veil of surface hiss with the ease and accuracy of a blow-torch,
and Koussevitzky's conducting tends to confirm the judgement of many, that this is indeed the
greatest American symphony. It's a tremendous experience, and although the work is barely 17
minutes long, it none the less constitutes an epic journey. Koussevitzky was a great musical pioneer,
and his recordings of Copland's saucy *El salón México* and Arthur Foote's delightful Suite (easily as
appealing as, say, Grieg's *Holberg Suite*) are rightly regarded as classics. Add Harris's First Symphony
– a poorer recording, but a fascinating prophecy of greater work to come – and Harl McDonald's
colourful essays, and you have the basis of an absorbing concert, one that is likely to give you a great
deal of enjoyment.

Géza Anda Columbia Recordings, 1953-56. Géza Anda (pf); [a]Philharmonia Orchestra /
Alceo Galliera. Testament mono Ⓕ SBT1064/7* (four discs, oas: 76, 79, 80 and 63 minutes:
ADD: 10/95). Recorded 1953-56.　　　Ⓖ
SBT1064 – **Rachmaninov** Piano Concerto No. 2 in C minor, Op. 18[a]. Preludes – G minor,
Op. 23 No. 5; G major, Op. 32 No. 5 (both from 33CX1143, 9/54). **Tchaikovsky** Piano
Concerto No. 1 in B flat minor, Op. 23[a] (from 33CX1156, 11/54). *SBT1065* – **Bartók** For
Children, Sz42 (33CX1176, 11/54 and 33CX1316, 5/56). *SBT1066* – **Chopin** Piano Concerto
No. 1 in E minor, Op. 11[a] (33C1057, 2/59). 12 Etudes, Op. 25. Ballade No. 1 in G minor, Op. 23
(33CX1459, 9/57). *SBT1067* – **Liszt** Piano Sonata in B minor, S178. Mephisto Waltz No. 1,
S514. Concert Study, S144 No. 3, "Un sospiro". Etudes d'exécution transcendante d'après
Paganini, S140 – No. 3, La campanella (all from 33CX1202, 6/55). **Bartók** Sonatina, Sz55
(33CX1176). **Delibes/Dohnányi** Coppélia – Valse lente Paraphrase (33CX1156).
Géza Anda was a pianist of contradictions, a fastidious technician prone to impulsive gestures and a
master of natural rubato whose imagination occasionally ran riot. He was unquestionably among the
greatest players of his generation and these are among his finest recordings. The Tchaikovsky
concerto opens with a vintage Philharmonia in full cry, while the ensuing dialogue is poised on a
nerve's edge, inspired but excitable (Anda courts extremes, both in terms of tempo and inflexion) and
with some ravishing solo work. In the Rachmaninov Second Concerto, the pianist's control of
sonority facilitates lightning switches between a richly voiced *bel canto* and bustling passagework.
Anda certainly knew how to subdue his tone to a murmur then rise to the fray with a swingeing
fortissimo. He glides through the *Adagio sostenuto*, and although his finale seems more decorative
than demonic, there is little suggestion of the theatrical overkill that mars his reading of
Tchaikovsky's finale. Furthermore, the actual recording reveals – via judicious balancing – more
detail, more internal interplay than many of its DDD successors. Bartók's music was, of course,
something of an Anda speciality. *For Children* is not so much designed 'for children' as for 'beginners
of all ages' (many of the pieces are in any case technically demanding), but Anda's approach suggests
more the world of Schumann's *Kinderszenen* than the tangy flavour of Hungarian and Slovakian

folk-music. He cajoles, distends, lingers, colours, teases – in fact, he does everything you would expect of a master colourist working within a sequence of 78 miniatures. Chopin, however, is a more frequent victim of phrasal distortion and it is here in particular that Anda's finesse pays high dividends. Furthermore, the First Concerto is granted a superb accompaniment under Galliera, whose keen response to the soloist is a constant source of pleasure. Anda approaches Chopin from a Mozartian axis, with clean fingerwork, agile phrasing and a singing line that frequently recalls the playing style of Alfred Cortot. The Liszt Sonata is a brave shot that just misses its target. Anda's view of the work was, as of 1954, reckless, frequently heart-rending and full of tender ideas; furthermore, he had the technical equipment to take risks and triumph. However, minute instances of imperfect timing rather spoil the effect. The other items are mostly notable and include mesmerizing accounts of the First *Mephisto Waltz* and Third *Consolation*, a glittering Liszt/Busoni *La campanella*, a rather glum Bartók *Sonatina* and a performance of Dohnányi's *Coppélia* "Valse lente" Paraphrase that, for sheer style and pianistic bravura, deserves a place beside Horowitz's *Carmen* Variations and Rosenthal's *Carnaval de Vienne*. A real feast then, and all the more absorbing for the odd spot of interpretative controversy. The transfers give a clean, rounded piano tone, only occasionally troubled by tape flutter.

The Art of the Baroque Trumpet, Volume 1. **Niklas Eklund** (tpt); **Drottningholm Baroque Ensemble / Nils-Erik Sparf.** Naxos Ⓢ 8 553531 (57 minutes: DDD: 11/96). 🎵 Recorded 1995.
Telemann Trumpet Concerto in D major. **Molter** Trumpet Concerto No. 1 in D major, MWV4:12. **Fasch** Trumpet Concerto in D major. **L. Mozart** Trumpet Concerto in D major. **Torelli** Sonata a 5 in D major, No. 1, TV1. **Purcell** Trumpet Sonata No. 2 in D major, Z850. **Handel** Suite in D major.

Niklas Eklund comes from a growing dynasty of distinguished Swedish trumpeters. Yet it is his success on the baroque trumpet (meaning 'the real thing' without valves, not a small piccolo trumpet) which has brought him most instant recognition and of which he is already a remarkable exponent. Only very few would volunteer to record the dangerously exposed *Adagio* to Telemann's Trumpet Concerto with its curling and languid lines, pinned at the end to the rafters as it soars to an incandescent close. For Eklund, the pain is not evident though the work is unfondly and posthumously entitled "the graveyard" by battle-weary trumpeters. He effortlessly strokes the phrases, often giving the melody a graceful and natural elasticity, as he also does in the opening movements of the works by Leopold Mozart and Torelli. Purists may baulk at the bright projected sound as well as an acutely modern intonation, allowed by the common practice of using holes to tamper with natural harmonics. Yet one can claim, equally, that this is virtuoso playing for modern audiences whose ears and tonal expectations are far removed from those of the eighteenth century. An ongoing debate indeed, but in the meantime let us rejoice at playing of rare technical ability and musical panache, which brings a distinctive angle to all these works. The Drottningholm Baroque Ensemble are less persuasive than Eklund, sounding at times as if they are 'painting by numbers'. However, the soloist's vocalized, nobly conceived and varied articulation would be enriching even at a much higher price.

Baroque Trumpet Concertos **Håkan Hardenberger** (tpt); **I Musici.** Philips Ⓕ 442 131-2PH (54 minutes: DDD: 5/95). Items marked [a] transcribed for trumpet. Recorded 1993.   Ⓠ
Vivaldi (rev. Malipiero) Concerto for Two Trumpets and Strings in C major, RV537 (with Reinhold Friedrich, tpt). **Corelli** Sonata for Trumpet and Strings in D major. **Albinoni** Concerto in B flat major, Op. 7 No. 3[a]. **Torelli** Sonata a 5 con tromba, G7. **A. Marcello** Concerto for Oboe and Strings in D minor[a]. **Viviani** Capricci armonici – Sonata prima. **Franceschini** Sonata for Two Trumpets, Strings and Continuo in D major (Friedrich). **Baldassare** Sonata for Cornett, Strings and Continuo in F major[a].

No trumpet player can make a career as a baroque player on a modern instrument without performing music originally written for other instruments; the domestic repertoire is simply not sustainable (it could be argued that the Torelli and Corelli works only sound truly colourful on a natural trumpet and tonally bland even with Hardenberger's modern playing). No complaints with transcriptions *per se*: a good one can leave the original looking to its laurels. Some disappointment must be registered, however, that Hardenberger has not investigated his own fare from the multifarious collections of fine eighteenth-century concertos. Most listeners will enjoy this highly exacting playing and his silky articulation and rhythmic discipline – the Vivaldi is as high-tech and effortless as you will ever hear. I Musici are a curious choice of accompanists. Still sporting their timelessly vigorous and yet unashamedly Mediterranean approach to baroque chamber playing, there is quite a temperamental polarity here, one would suspect, between their style and Hardenberger's Nordic and less overtly emotional playing. The result, however, is not as marked as you might expect, since Hardenberger vocalizes more in this recording than in the past (all slow movements are warmer and less 'worked out' than in previous discs of this nature) and he responds to I Musici's full-blooded playing in a similarly jaunty way. The Marcello D minor Concerto has some especially sweet moments.

Alexander Brailowsky The Berlin Recordings, Volumes 1 and 2. **Alexander Brailowsky** (pf); [a]**Berlin Philharmonic Orchestra / Julius Prüwer.** Danacord mono Ⓔ DACOCD336/7*, DACOCD338/9* (two two-disc sets, oas: 135 and 117 minutes: ADD: 11/95). From Polydor originals; recorded 1928-34.

DACOCD336/7 – **Chopin** Piano Concerto No. 1 in E minor, Op. 11[a]. Piano Sonata No. 2 in B flat minor, Op. 35. Also includes 23 short works by Chopin. *DACOCD338/9* – **Liszt** Piano Concerto No. 1 in E flat major, S124[a]. Also includes works by **Debussy, Falla, Liszt, Mendelssohn, D. Scarlatti, Schubert, Schumann, Scriabin** and **Weber**

It's difficult not to be bowled over by Brailowsky's charm, delicacy and vitality, quite apart from his technical brilliance. Fortunately the Polydor engineers produced recordings of remarkable fidelity which allow his finely graded nuances to be fully appreciated, and in the modern transfer process used here, noise from the old 78rpm surfaces is minimal: there is, however, considerable variation in recording levels and in pitch (the piano used in 1928 was tuned very flat, so that a juxtaposition here of two Chopin *Etudes* in F minor and major from 1928 and 1934 respectively is jarring) – and there is a horrid discrepancy of pitch between what were the two sides of Liszt's *Hungarian Rhapsody* No. 12. By and large, the Chopin set is the better of the two. What is striking in the concerto is Brailowsky's shaping of phrases, his sensitivity and his delicately sparkling passagework. In the sonata he employs quite a lot of *affettuoso* rubato but shows he can also be simple: its *Scherzo* is scintillating and the finale (taken *prestissimo*) breathtaking. There is much finesse and convincing moulding of phrases in the *Barcarolle* and poetically tender caressing tone in the E flat *Nocturne*; the G minor *Ballade* is dazzling; and five Op. 25 *Etudes* are especially treasurable. Just occasionally he is too free for modern tastes in his rhythm, as in the middle section of the *Fantaisie-impromptu* and the Op. 69 A flat *Waltz*; but only in a B flat *Mazurka* are his rhythmic distortions unacceptable. The Liszt Concerto starts rather less well, with the opening cadenza over-pedalled and the first movement excessively wayward in rhythm (as is *Liebestraum* later on); but the *Allegretto vivace* section is deliciously playful, and by the end of the work one is completely won over. Brailowsky declines to treat three *Hungarian Rhapsodies* merely as barnstorming razzle-dazzle but discovers in them veins of poetry that are too often ignored. He is impressive in Liszt's arrangement of the *Tannhäuser* Overture and coquettish in his *Valse impromptu*, wonderfully vivacious in Mendelssohn's E minor *Scherzo* and the Scarlatti/Tausig *Capriccio*, and displays his virtuosity in Weber's *Moto perpetuo* and the Debussy *Toccata*. Elsewhere one has to forgive some mannered readings of familiar pieces; but what stays in the mind is an exceptionally beautiful, tenderly hushed performance of Debussy's *Serenade for the doll*. Yes, undoubtedly one of the great pianists.

British Light Music [abc]**Pro Arte Orchestra / George Weldon;** [d]**Studio Two Concert Orchestra / Reginald Kilbey;** [e]**Light Music Society Orchestra / Sir Vivian Dunn;** [fgh]**orchestra / Eric Coates.** EMI British Composers ⓜ CDM5 66537-2* (76 minutes: ADD/mono/stereo: 1/98). Item marked [a] from HMV 7P323 (recorded 1963), [b]HMV CSD1503 (10/63), [c]HMV 7EG8879 (3/65), [d]Columbia TWO334 (4/71), [e]TWO297 (6/70), [f]HMV 45-POP386 (11/57), [g]45-POP418 (1/58), [h]Pye N15003 (11/55). Recorded 1955-70.

Coates Springtime[a] – Dance in the twilight: Valse. Impression of a Princess[f]. Wood nymphs[g]. The Dam Busters[h]. **Collins** Vanity fair[b]. **Curzon** Punchinello[b]. **Tomlinson** Little Serenade[b]. **Binge** Miss Melanie[c]. The Watermill[e]. Elizabethan Serenade[d]. **A. Langford** Waltz for strings[b]. **Bayco** Elizabethan masque[b]. **Vinter** Portuguese Party[b]. **Dexter** Siciliano[b]. **Haydn Wood** Moods – Joyousness[b]. Paris – Montmartre[d]. **L. Osborne** Lullaby for Penelope[d]. **Farnon** Portrait of a flirt[d]. **F. Hartley** Rouge et noir[d]. **Duncan** Little Suite – March[e]. **Curzon** The boulevardier[e]. **Docker** Tabarinage[e]. **Hope** The ring of Kerry – No. 1, Jaunting car[e].

How bewildering the ways of fashion! A few years back a collection such as this would, if it had appeared at all, have sold a few copies and disappeared. Now, thanks to the enterprise of Marco Polo and Hyperion, British Light Music seems all the rage. The recordings made in February 1963 under the baton of George Weldon provided a treasure-chest of this sort of music and have long been the touchstone for those who have always delighted in the genre. Weldon could certainly have made up an entire CD, and one can only hope that the fact that he shares this collection with other conductors means that EMI have a second volume in mind. As it is, this compendium can surely only delight all who try it, mixing sparkling performances of classic, brilliantly tuneful pieces by Coates, Wood, Curzon, Binge, Farnon and others with rarer pieces such as Frederic Bayco's *Elizabethan masque*, Alan Langford's *Waltz for strings* and Leslie Osborne's *Lullaby for Penelope*. The three rare Coates recordings under the conductor himself may obviously be termed definitive; but each of the other conductors represented here knew equally well how to get the very best out of these slight but superbly crafted pieces. For all that the recording dates range over a period of 15 years, they are blended together well. The music, of course, is sheer delight. Let's hope for that second volume!

Carnegie Hall Project The Solti Orchestral Project, Carnegie Hall / Sir Georg Solti.
Decca Ⓕ 444 458-2DH (77 minutes: DDD: 12/95). Recorded live in 1994.   ⓖ
Wagner Die Meistersinger von Nürnberg – Prelude. **Brahms** Variations on a Theme by Haydn, Op. 56a, "St Antoni Chorale". **Shostakovich** Symphony No. 9 in E flat major, Op. 70.
R. Strauss: Don Juan, Op. 20. **Smetana** The bartered bride – Overture.

Over a 16-day period in June 1994 Sir Georg Solti supervised a series of rehearsals and study-sessions with an orchestra unique in America. Two years earlier he had been approached by Carnegie Hall to conduct an orchestra made up of young musicians. The idea developed to include 15 musicians from five top American orchestras – to act not only as leading players but to coach their respective sections. These live recordings, made at the two concerts, crowned the whole project. As a revelation not just of the orchestra's superb quality but of Solti as interpreter the most remarkable performance here is of the Shostakovich symphony. It would be hard to imagine a happier, more genial account of this equivocal work, witty and pointed, with humour unforced and buoyant. It is remarkable, too, what natural flexibility marks the playing in such a work as the *Meistersinger* Prelude, with free rubato in the big melodies coupled with perfect ensemble. The syncopations in the Smetana work have an infectious freedom too, seemingly spontaneous, again achieved with total precision. As for the Brahms Variations, it would be hard to find a performance so sharply characterized, with each section beautifully contrasted. The clarity of texture allows some magical solo playing to be fully appreciated in all the works, notably from the principal oboe and horn. Hard-headed orchestral musicians, noting the ideal conditions set up for the project, might well comment that it is no surprise that the results are so fine.

Cello Concertos Pablo Casals (vc); [ab]London Symphony Orchestra / Sir Landon Ronald; [cd]BBC Symphony Orchestra / Sir Adrian Boult. Biddulph mono Ⓜ LAB144*
(79 minutes: ADD: 1/98). Item marked [a] from HMV DB3056/8 (3/37), [b]HMV DB3063/4 (6/37), both recorded 1936, [c]HMV DB6338/41S (11/46, recorded 1945), [d]previously unissued, recorded 1946.
Elgar Cello Concerto in E minor, Op. 85[c]. **Boccherini** (arr. Grützmacher) Cello Concerto in B flat major, G48[a]. **Bruch** Kol Nidrei, Op. 47[b]. **Haydn** (arr. Gevaërt) Cello Concerto No. 2 in D major, HobVII*b*/2[d] – Allegro moderato; Adagio.

The leonine growl that prefaces Elgar's most introspective orchestral masterpiece is played here with uncompromising defiance, whereas the weary solo ascent that follows can rarely – if ever – have conveyed a deeper sense of disorientation. Casals's handling of the solo line is wistful, sometimes wilful, profoundly personal and ideally accompanied by the ever-attentive Sir Adrian Boult. Just listen to the *Scherzo*'s cheeky banter (track 7, from 1'25"), to the pointing of wind phrases in particular – precise yet unforced and always musically responsive. The most affecting passage of all occurs at around 6'31" into the finale (track 9), at the moment where Elgar seems overwhelmed by feelings almost too painful to bear. No other performance is quite as successful in contrasting the 'brave front' of Elgar's bolder tuttis with the ineffable sadness of his solo writing. Occasional hiccups in the cello line (the odd spot of discoloration) go for nothing and Casals's distant groaning merely serves – like Glenn Gould's humming and Toscanini's singing – to compound an impression of total commitment. Biddulph's annotation relates how a changing critical climate gradually became sympathetic to Casals's account of the Elgar Concerto (initial reactions were fairly hostile), and how Britain's handling of the Franco situation in Spain deeply offended Casals. Projected sessions never materialized and the Haydn Concerto recording that is here issued for the first time (it was set down the day after the Elgar) remained incomplete. What we do have, however, is very well recorded, typically eloquent and full of interpretative incident, with sundry expressive subtleties and an especially memorable account of the *Adagio*. Of course purists will baulk at Gevaërt's arrangement, just as they will lament Grützmacher's handiwork in a famous – and equally characterful – account of the Boccherini B flat Concerto. *Kol Nidrei*, on the other hand, is given one of the slowest, purest and most deeply felt readings imaginable, perfectly reflecting the pain, resolution and quiet victory that mark the three stages of repentance (Kol Nidre is the pivotal evening prayer for the Jewish Day of Atonement). Transfers are, again, excellent (Ward Marston was at the control desk) and if you are in search of 'The Essential Casals' – no, 'The Quintessential Casals' – then you need look no further.

Classical Trumpet Concertos John Wallace (tpt); [c]John Anderson (ob d'amore); [c]Peter Thomas (vn); Philharmonia Orchestra / Christopher Warren-Green, [c]Simon Wright. Nimbus Ⓕ NI7016 (75 minutes: DDD: 2/95). Items marked [a] from NIM2141 (7/84), [b]NI5065, recorded 1986, [c]NI5121 (4/89).
Haydn Concerto in E flat major, HobVIIe/1[a]. **Neruda** Concerto in E flat major[b].
Hummel Concerto in E flat major[b]. **F. Weber** Variations in F major[b]. **Fasch** Concerto for Trumpet, Oboe d'amore, Violin and Strings in E major[c].

The famous Haydn Concerto sounds bright and forthright with trumpeter and orchestra freshly caught in the spacious Church of All Saints, Tooting. Wallace's technical strength and impish articulation are characterized by crisp tonguing and a strident (if at times fairly uncompromising) trumpet sound in the outer movements. Peace is restored in a beautifully judged slow movement in which Wallace floats rather than imposes. Less refined than some other recordings of this work (track 2 at 3'43" has an extraordinary blemish in the lower register of the strings), there is a natural freshness here which one rarely hears in this old war-horse. The Neruda Concerto, written originally for the corno da caccia, makes an attractive trumpet piece, flawed only by its unbalanced episodic structure. Hummel's Concerto is a persuasive work, by and large, and it is given a bold reading here by Wallace, full of incident, some examples of which trip out of the bell in a fairly conventional manner. Others are decidedly quirky, such as the mock antiquated tuning on the opening trill of the second movement. Rather more effective are the dazzling embellishments which look forward to the salon and the new virtuoso tradition of the nineteenth century which the trumpet inhabited once valves had been invented. Friedrich Dionysius Weber's Variations in F are typical of this musically slight but entertaining world in which the cornet/trumpet was beginning to thrive. Wallace is utterly at home in this idiom, bringing to the music the swagger and facility upon which its characterization depends. Finally we step back to the Indian summer of the trumpet, the early classical years and the stratospherically high trumpet range demanded by Carl Friedrich Christian Fasch. His Concerto for trumpet, oboe d'amore and violin is an exciting work, brilliantly played.

Concertos for Four Violins Cologne Musica Antiqua / **Reinhard Goebel.**
Archiv Produktion Ⓟ 435 393-2AH (66 minutes: DDD: 9/92). ⚡ Recorded 1991.
Torelli Concerto in E minor for Four Violins and Strings. **Mossi** Concertos, Op. 4 – No. 12 in
G minor. **Valentini** Concerti grossi, Op. 7 – No. 11 in A minor. **Locatelli** Introduttioni teatrali
and Concerti, Op. 4 – No. 12 in F major. **Leo** Concerto in D major for Four Violins and Strings.
Even the most assiduous collectors and discerning connoisseurs of baroque concertos are likely to find novelties in this 'off the beaten track' programme from Cologne Musica Antiqua. Mossi, Valentini and Locatelli belong to the Roman school, though the latter shows marked Venetian leanings, while the remaining two composers are products of Bologna (Torelli) and Naples (Leo). Whatever doubts there may be concerning the intrinsic merit of these works they nevertheless provide a fascinating and valuable glimpse of what composers other than Corelli (Rome) on the one hand or Vivaldi (Venice) on the other were up to. Reinhard Goebel who, alas, was unable to lead his group from the violin in his usual manner, following an injury to his arm, directs effectively. The textures in these concertos are rich and contrasting and the players draw subtle resonances from them. The opening *Largo* and ensuing fugue of the Valentini work affords striking examples of Musica Antiqua's skill in pointing up the variety of string sound inherent in this repertory. This is a fascinating programme performed with Musica Antiqua's customary *élan* and precision.

European Light Music Classics New London Orchestra / **Ronald Corp.**
Hyperion Ⓟ CDA66998 (74 minutes: DDD: 3/98). Recorded 1997.
Jessel Parade der Zinnsoldaten, Op. 123. **Lehár** Gold und Silber, Op. 79. **Pierné** Marche
des petits soldats de plomb. **J. Strauss II** Tritsch-Tratsch-Polka, Op. 214. **Lincke** Lysistrata –
Glühwürmchen-Idyll. **Alfvén** Swedish Polka. **Gounod** Marche funèbre d'une marionnette.
Waldteufel: Les patineurs, Op. 183. **Heykens** Serenade No. 1. **Padilla** El relicario.
Becucci Tesoro mio!. **Hellmesberger I** Ballszene. **Weinberger** Schwanda the Bagpiper –
Polka. **Fetrás** Mondnacht auf der Alster. **Halvorsen** Entry March of the Boyars.
Those who enjoy British light music, with its reminders of BBC Radio signature tunes, may get much the same sensation from this collection, since it opens with Léon Jessel's *Parade der Zinnsoldaten*, which will be familiar to those of a certain age as the signature tune of BBC Radio *Children's Hour*'s "Toytown" series. By no means all the pieces in the collection will have such specific associations, and indeed some, such as Becucci's *Tesoro mio!* and Hellmesberger's *Ballszene*, may be unfamiliar even to enthusiasts of light music. The latter is an especially engaging piece from the family whose music featured in both the 1997 and 1998 New Year Concerts from Vienna. Most of the items will surely rouse fairly wide recognition, whether lighter pieces by more accomplished composers or such standards of between-the-wars light orchestras as Jonny Heykens's Serenade No. 1, José Padilla's very Spanish *El relicario* or Paul Lincke's "Glühwürmchen-Idyll". All these are excellent and unassuming compositions that are far too seldom heard nowadays. Ronald Corp's generally rather relaxed style perhaps doesn't reveal the glitter and sparkle of Lehár's *Gold und Silber* but is otherwise well suited to bringing out the essential charm of the music. The Waldteufel and Fetrás waltzes both come off splendidly, as do the other pieces in their varied styles.

Favourite Overtures, Volume 2. London Philharmonic Orchestra; [a]Berlin Philharmonic
Orchestra / **Sir Thomas Beecham.** Dutton Laboratories mono Ⓜ CDLX7009*
(75 minutes: ADD: 10/94). Recorded 1933-40.
Mozart Le nozze di Figaro (from Columbia LX639, 10/37). Don Giovanni (LX893, 10/40).
Die Zauberflöte[a] (HMV DB3465, 7/38). **Weber** Oberon (LX746, 11/38). Der Freischütz
(LX601, 5/37). **Brahms** Tragic Overture, Op. 81 (LX638/9, 10/37). **Wagner** A Faust Overture
(LX481/2, 5/36). **Berlioz** Le carnaval romain, Op. 9 (LX570, 2/37). **Rossini** La scala di seta
(LX255, 7/33).
The *Zauberflöte* Overture is taken from Beecham's complete recording of the opera, and he shows a measured, profound response to Mozart's inspiration. All his characteristic elegance is still there, but the 43 players of the Berlin Philharmonic are made to play in a concentrated, highly characterful fashion. He provides a strong, arrestingly dramatic account of the *Don Giovanni* Overture, yet his *Nozze di Figaro* bubbles over with charm and wit. He finds plenty of drama in the Wagner, and the Brahms has an appropriate and highly impressive strength and profundity of feeling. A reading such as this effectively gives the lie to Beecham's reputation in some quarters as a lightweight interpreter. Perhaps the best performance of all is the overture by his beloved Berlioz, for energy and excitement are matched by playing of the most affecting delicacy and poetry in the piece's more reflective passages. All the engineering is outstanding.

Flute Concertos Michael Faust (fl); Cologne Radio Symphony Orchestra / [a]Alun Francis,
[b]Serge Baudo. Capriccio Ⓟ 10 495 (64 minutes: DDD: 12/94). Recorded 1991-92.
Martin (arr. Ansermet) Ballade[a]. **Nielsen** Flute Concerto, FS119[a]. **Bernstein** Halil[a].
Ibert Flute Concerto[b].

Here is a valuable juxtaposition of twentieth-century works written in four countries between 1926 and 1981, and Michael Faust, a splendid flautist and artist, has the range to illuminate them all. The Martin is a coolly elegant piece that begins quietly but then has a good deal of animation; although essentially non-tonal, it has a clear sense of direction and is distinctly harmonious. Indeed, after around 4'30", we are reintroduced to Debussy's *faune* in an irresistibly slinky and sexy mood. The Danish peasant quirkiness of Nielsen's Concerto also comes across well, goat-footed Pan's flute now serving a northern wit and wildness. The writing for the timpani and trombone in the second movement gives the soloist's orchestral colleagues individuality in a way that was new in Nielsen's time but, thanks to him, is something of a feature in much of today's music. Indeed, this work has an oddly modern and faintly irresponsible feeling. Bernstein's threnody in memory of a young Israeli flautist killed in battle in 1973 is a fine piece and eloquently moving. Finally, Ibert's Concerto of 1934, along with Gallic wit, again evokes Arcadia, although it is here (according to the booklet-essay) "unreal as through a frosted-glass window". A well-planned and deftly performed programme.

Flute Concertos of the Sans-Souci Patrick Gallois (fl); CPE Bach Chamber Orchestra / Peter Schreier. DG Ⓕ 439 895-2GH (77 minutes: DDD: 2/95). Recorded 1993.
C.P.E. Bach Flute Concerto in G major, H445. **F. Benda** Flute Concerto in E minor.
Frederick the Great Flute Concerto in C major. **Quantz** Flute Concerto in G major.
It is a nice peg on which to hang a programme – that of music by an employer (Frederick the Great of Prussia) and three of his employees, every item of which was first played by the King himself. Quantz was employed as Frederick's flute teacher from 1741; in 1752 he published a treatise on flute playing in which he described how a good concerto should be: a first movement with a "majestic" ritornello and "pleasing and intelligible melodies", a second movement whose "melody must be just as moving and expressive as one with accompanying words", and a finale that is "short, gay and fiery". The King is said to have disapproved of "mournful or sad" slow movements – saying that they should be "peaceful, contented or seductive". With the exception of the *Aria, mesto* of Quantz's own Concerto, all the works in this recording meet these regal requirements. We cannot know whether Frederick was as good a flautist as he was (flatteringly?) reported to be, but we do know that Gallois is a remarkable one; he cannot obliterate the differences between the baroque and modern flutes but, so soft-edged is his tone and so subtle his nuances, he reduces them to relative unimportance. One cannot speak too highly of the orchestral playing or of Schreier's direction of it, a model of stylish, on-the-toes alertness and sympathetic response. The rarely heard concertos by Frederick and Benda, together with the 'virtual reality' recording, help to make this a disc to brighten the dullest day.

French Baroque Harpsichord Works Sophie Yates (hpd). Chandos Chaconne Ⓕ CHAN0545 (71 minutes: DDD: 11/93). ✔ Recorded 1993.
D'Anglebert Pièces de Clavecin – Suite in G minor; Tombeau de M. de Chambonnières.
F. Couperin L'Art de toucher le clavecin – Prélude in D minor. Livre de clavecin, Deuxième ordre – Seconde Courante; Sarabande, "La Prude"; Les Idées heureuses; La Voluptueuse.
Forqueray La Rameau; La Boisson; La Sylva; Jupiter. **Rameau** L'enharmonique.
L'Egyptienne. La Dauphine.
Sophie Yates has a real understanding of the French style – so difficult to capture, with its special conventions and elaborate ornamentation. Her phrasing is subtle as well as musical; and she proves herself capable of the flexibility proper to this music without risk to the underlying pulse or to continuity. Her reading of *La Dauphine*, Rameau's last harpsichord piece, is justifiably free and improvisatory, since it is thought to be a transcription of Rameau's extemporization at the wedding of the Dauphin in 1747. She savours Rameau's bold enharmonics, too, shows drive and energy in his *L'Egyptienne*, impressive dignity in Forqueray's tribute to his great contemporary and in a d'Anglebert sarabande, expressiveness in Forqueray's *La Sylva* and a sense of enjoyment in the trenchant drama of the flashing thunderbolts of his *Jupiter*. Yates also has the advantage of admirable recording of a particularly beautiful and rich-sounding instrument (a copy of a Goujon).

French Orchestral Works [a]French Radio National Orchestra; [b]Royal Philharmonic Orchestra / Sir Thomas Beecham. EMI Beecham Edition Ⓜ CDM7 63379-2* (68 minutes: ADD: 7/90). Ⓖ Ⓖ
Bizet Carmen – Suite No. 1 (from HMV HQS1108, 12/67)[a]. **Fauré** Pavane, Op. 50
(HMV ASD518, 4/63)[a]. Dolly Suite, Op. 56 (orch. Rabaud. HQS1136, 5/68)[a]. **Debussy**
Prélude à l'après-midi d'un faune (ASD259, 6/59)[b]. **Saint-Saëns** Le rouet d'Omphale, Op. 31
(ASD259)[b]. **Delibes** Le Roi s'amuse – Ballet Music (HQS1136)[b].
Even to those who never heard him in the flesh there is no mistaking Beecham's relish in, and flair for, the French repertoire. His combination of mischievous high spirits, almost dandyish elegance, cool outer classicism masking passionate emotion, swagger, refined nuance and delicate charm was perhaps unique – not matched even by such committed Francophiles as Constant Lambert. *Elan* is at once in evidence here in the *Carmen* prelude, and subtle dynamic gradations in the entr'actes to Acts 2 and 4; there is lightness, vivacity and tenderness in Fauré's *Dolly Suite* and a true Gallic reserve in his *Pavane*; and he enters with prim finesse into Delibes's pastiche dances. Debussy's erotic study, on repeated hearings of this performance, becomes the more Grecian and effective for its conscious understatement; and only the Saint-Saëns symphonic poem, for all the RPO's delicacy, seems to hang fire. But four or five bull's-eyes out of six is a pretty good score, and at medium price not to be missed.

From My Home Gidon Kremer (vn); [a]Vadim Sacharov (pf); [b]Deutsche Kammerphilharmonie.
Teldec Ⓟ 0630-14654-2 (79 minutes: DDD: 11/97). Item marked [a] from 0630-13597-2 (7/97).
Recorded 1996. *Gramophone Editor's choice.*
Dvarionas Elegie[b]. **Pärt** Fratres[b]. **Barkauskas** Partita. **Vasks** Musica Dolorosa[b].
Pelécis Violin and Piano Concerto, "Nevertheless"[ab]. **Plakidis** Two Grasshopper Dances[a].
Tüür Conversio[a].

Modern-music missionaries couldn't possible hope for a better promotional tool than this delightful
CD. Even the least sophisticated listener would respond to Gidon Kremer's absorbing programme.
Pärt's *Fratres* is given one of its finest recordings ever, with tactile solo arpeggios, a bleached-white
bed of string chords and plenty of tonal incident later on. Erkki-Sven Tüür's *Conversio* for violin and
piano opens lightly and restlessly, shifting metre and accents with playful insistence very much *à la*
Reich (in *Counterpoint* mode) before intensifying, fragmenting and transforming into a bold species
of Messiaenic-style bird-song. Vytautas Barkauskas's brief, five-movement unaccompanied *Partita*
features a colourful, syncopated scherzo and some strikingly harmonized double-stopped passages.
Kremer's emotionally charged account of Vasks's *Musica Dolorosa* gives way to a highly palatable,
27-minute musical journey by Georges Pelécis where the route covers warming counterpoint,
Chopinesque cadences, folk-style melodies and telling silences. It is the most obvious 'crossover'
bridge in the programme, though the Dvarionas *Elegie* that opens the CD is somewhat shorter and
has even more catchy tunes – a sort of Baltic *salut d'amour*, with Tchaikovsky close to hand. Plakidis's
gnomic *Grasshopper Dances* are highly entertaining. A disc such as this virtually amounts to
composition in itself, and although responsive to piecemeal listening, works best if heard straight
through at a single sitting. A pretty absorbing way to spend an evening.

Clara Haskil: The Legacy Clara Haskil (pf); [a]Arthur Grumiaux (vn); **Vienna Symphony
Orchestra /** [b]**Paul Sacher;** [c]**Bernhard Paumgartner;** [d]**Lamoureux Concerts Orchestra /
Igor Markevitch;** [e]**The Hague Philharmonic Orchestra / Willem van Otterloo.**
Philips mono/stereo Ⓜ 442 685-2PM12* (12 discs: 809 minutes: ADD: 11/95). Also available in
three boxed sets, as detailed below.   Ⓖ
442 625-2PM5 (five discs) – **Beethoven** Violin Sonatas[a] – No. 1 in D major, Op. 12 No. 1
(from ABL3204, 5/58); No. 2 in A major, Op. 12 No. 2; No. 3 in E flat major, Op. 12 No. 3 (both
from ABL3199, 4/58); No. 4 in A minor, Op. 23; No. 5 in F major, Op. 24, "Spring" (ABL3204);
No. 6 in A major, Op. 30 No. 1 (ABL3226, 12/58); No. 7 in C minor, Op. 30 No. 2 (ABL3207,
6/58); No. 8 in G, Op. 30 No. 3 (ABL3199); No. 9 in A major, Op. 47, "Kreutzer" (ABL3226);
No. 10 in G major, Op. 96 (ABL3207). **Mozart** Piano and Violin Sonatas[a] – G major,
K301/K293a; E minor, K304/K300c; F major, K376/K374d; B flat major, K378/K317d (all from
A00432L, 10/60); B flat major, K454; A major, K526 (ABL3144, 10/57). *442 631-2PM4* (four
discs) – **Beethoven** Piano Concerto No. 3 in C minor, Op. 37[d] (SABL172, 1/61). **Mozart**
Piano Concertos – No. 9 in E flat major, K271[b] (ABL3143, 7/57); No. 20 in D minor, K466
(two versions: [c]ABL3129, 4/57 and [d]SABL212, 4/62); No. 23 in A major, K488[b] (ABL3129);
No. 24 in C minor, K491[d] (SABL212). Rondo in A major, K386 (ABL3143). **Schumann**
Piano Concerto in A minor, Op. 54[e] (ABR4080, 2/55). **Falla** Noches en los jardines de España[d].
Chopin Piano Concerto No. 2 in F minor, Op. 21[d] (SABL173, 8/61). *442 635-2PM3* (three discs)
– **Beethoven** Piano Sonatas – No. 17 in D minor, Op. 31 No. 2, "Tempest" (two versions: new
to UK, recorded 1955 and ABL3358, 3/61); No. 18 in E flat major, Op. 31 No. 3 (two versions:
new to UK, recorded 1955 and ABL3358). **Mozart** Nine Variations in D major on a minuet by
Duport, K573 (6768 366, 11/83. 1954). Piano Sonata in C major, K330/K300h (ABL3365, 9/61).
Schumann Bunte Blätter, Op. 99 (ABL3029, 2/55). Theme and Variations on the name
"Abegg", Op. 1 (A11213G. 1951). Kinderszenen, Op. 15 (1955). Waldszenen, Op. 82 (both
A00775R. 1954). **D. Scarlatti** Keyboard Sonatas – B minor, Kk87; E flat major, Kk193;
F minor, Kk386. **Ravel** Sonatine (all A00143L. 1951). **Schubert** Piano Sonata in B flat major,
D960 (ABL3029).

What a legacy this is, brimming over with musical zest yet drawing on an exalted delicacy and
inwardness from what was clearly a 'still centre', a well of endless resource and nourishment. Haskil
may have enjoyed a low profile until the autumn of her tragically short career, but her friends and
admirers included Lipatti, Enescu, Stokowski, Cortot, Giulini and Tatyana Nikolaieva among others.
Her range was exceptional. Before ill-health intervened her specialities included Brahms's Second and
Saint-Saëns's Fifth Concertos, while Brahms's *Paganini* Variations and Liszt's *Feux follets* featured in
her solo recitals. Later, such exuberance was not so much cautioned or restrained as channelled into
her superlative Beethoven, Schumann (has any one played the *Abegg* Variations with such dizzy
aplomb or captured the Prophet Bird's quizzical stare with such uncanny directness?) and, most of all,
her Mozart. Indeed, listening once again to Haskil's Mozart is like re-entering a musical Elysium.
Everything sounds so exactly 'right', so gently but firmly unarguable. Her sense of difference between
Mozart and Beethoven is finely but unmistakably drawn. For just as she locates the underlying storms
of Beethoven's more outgoing spirit, she finds no less exactly an equilibrium beneath even the clouded
surface of Mozart's E minor Sonata, K304. In the greater, more ambitious utterances of K454 and in
the *moto perpetuo* finale of K526 she miraculously makes every bar subtle and ambiguous without
recourse to anything approaching overt drama or idiosyncrasy. The concertos, too, find this heaven-

sent artist at her greatest. Here is no impersonal sheen or expertise, but a deeply committed poetry resolved in playing of the most crystalline perfection. Listen to her in the second movement cadenza of K271 and you may wonder when you last heard playing of such speculative beauty. Haskil was famous for lifting her partner's performances on to the highest level. Instantly aware of her quality Grumiaux rarely played better than he does here in the Beethoven sonatas, and you will have to go a long way to hear two artists in more perfect accord than in the great final G major Sonata's otherworldly musings.

Clearly, one could go on for ever celebrating this or that aspect of such life-enhancing artistry. You may demur at Haskil's Schubert (perhaps predictably it has a classical rather than romantic bias), Chopin, Ravel and Falla (an exotic departure from her principally German repertoire) yet all these performances are alive with passing felicities. Is the Schumann Concerto disappointingly non-committal, without, say, Dame Myra Hess's warmth and affection? Did Haskil's energy start to fail at the time of the second recording of Beethoven's Op. 31 Sonatas (those tell-tale pauses for breath in the headlong equestrian finale of No. 3)? Such questions may well be asked. Yet her Mozart – that litmus test of musical quality – surely defies criticism, is profoundly musical rather than decorous; totally devoid of what Dr Leavis, in one of his most trenchant phrases, called "the extant social world". The recordings vary but have been for the most part beautifully refurbished and no praise could be high enough for Philips's presentation. There are three superb accompanying essays and a beautiful selection of photographs.

Horn Concertos Barry Tuckwell (hn); [ac]**Academy of St Martin in the Fields / Sir Neville Marriner;** [b]**English Chamber Orchestra.** EMI Forte Ⓜ CZS5 69395-2 (two discs: 150 minutes: ADD: 2/97). Items marked [a] from HMV ASD2985 (8/74), [b]ASD4008 (6/81), [c]ASD3774 (10/79).
Telemann Horn Concerto in D major[a]. **Cherubini** Horn Sonata No. 2 in F major[a].
C. Förster Horn Concerto in E flat major[a]. **Weber** Horn Concertino in E minor, J188[a].
L. Mozart Horn Concerto in D major[a]. **M. Haydn** (arr. Sherman) Horn Concertino in D major[b]. **Punto** Horn Concertos[b] – No. 5 in F major; No. 6 in E flat major; No. 10 in F major; No. 11 in E major. **Haydn** Horn Concerto No. 1 in D major[c].

Barry Tuckwell's easy bravura is readily demonstrated in the first movement of the opening concerto here, by Telemann. Its catchy *moto perpetuo* is dispatched with aplomb; then comes a fine *Adagio* which often moves to the very top of the horn's upper range and creates a tension that is released in the buoyant finale. The Cherubini sonata opens with a melancholy *Largo*, then erupts into joyous high spirits, while the racing opening arpeggios of the concerto by Leopold Mozart and the tight trills in the finale (with harpsichord echoes) are managed with comparable exuberance. The Weber is an attractively diverse and extensive (17-minute) set of variations and includes a good example of horn 'chords', where the soloist plays one note and hums another; it also has an exceptionally joyful finale. One of the novelties is a delightful concerto by the virtually unknown Christoph Förster. The work has an amiable first movement, marked *Con discrezione*, a brief, disconsolate *Adagio* and a closing *Rondo* where, although the clouds clear away, the lyrical feeling remains. In some respects most striking of all is the collection of four concertos by the Bohemian musician, Giovanni Punto, a successful, highly cultivated composer and horn virtuoso whose music is enjoyably distinctive – a mixture of Mozartian influences and Hummelian *galant bonhomie*. The individual CD of these four works was first issued to celebrate Barry Tuckwell's fiftieth birthday and the performances show him at his finest, so their inclusion here is highly appropriate. With his Academy of St Martin in the Fields on top form, Marriner conducts elegant, polished accompaniments throughout, except in the works by Joseph and Michael Haydn where Tuckwell directs the ECO himself. The analogue recordings are first-rate – smooth, warm and vivid and beautifully balanced.

Hungarian Connections [a]**Laurence Kaptain** (cimb); **Chicago Symphony Orchestra / Sir Georg Solti.** Decca Ⓕ 443 444-2DH (72 minutes: DDD: 1/95). Recorded live in 1993.
Gramophone Editor's choice.   ⒺⒼ
Bartók Hungarian Sketches, Sz97. Romanian folkdances, Sz68. **Kodály** Háry János, Op. 15 – Suite[a]. **Liszt** Two Episodes from Lenau's Faust, S110 – Der Tanz in der Dorfschenke. Hungarian Rhapsody No. 2 in D minor (orch. Döppler). **L. Weiner** Csongor és Tünde, Op. 10*b* – Introduction; Scherzo.

This is a terrific programme. The sequence is imaginative, the material extremely attractive, and the standard of performance high. The *Mephisto Waltz* swirls in heady abandon, with strings as delicate as thistledown, and some snappy work from the Chicago brass. The once-ubiquitous Second *Hungarian Rhapsody* is wittily turned, although Döppler's sundry added counterpoint and rather tame orchestration tend to mute the rustic edge of Liszt's original. The performance, though, has plenty of life and the recording conjures up a realistic sense of aural perspective. Sir Georg's empathy for this idiom is everywhere in evidence, and never more so than in Bartók's *Romanian folkdances*, where lightness of touch and sensitive rubato recreate a crucial feeling of improvisation. The *Hungarian Sketches* are tellingly pointed, with fluid lines in "Evening in the Village" and "Melody", a hilarious *ff* trombone/tuba belch in "A Little Tipsy" and cleanly differentiated percussion in the "Bear Dance". Solti's version is now perhaps the current front-runner, and makes for a most entertaining musical diversion. Nice, too, to hear music by the much underrated Leó Weiner, his *Csongor és Tünde* ballet with its subtle reminiscences of Nicolai's *Merry Wives of Windsor* Overture and Liszt's *Dante* Symphony. The busy scherzo is the sort of thing Bartók might have composed had he not outgrown the worlds of Strauss and Dohnányi, while the Introduction is reminiscent of Kodály in pastoral vein. Kodály himself is represented by a genial, often brilliantly played account of the *Háry János* Suite, superbly recorded and with some distinctive solo work. And what a blessed relief to hear the cimbalom properly integrated into the orchestral texture.

Les introuvables de Jacqueline Du Pré Jacqueline du Pré (vc); [a]Gerald Moore, [b]Ernest Lush, [c]Stephen Kovacevich (pfs); [d]London Symphony Orchestra / Sir John Barbirolli; [e]Royal Philharmonic Orchestra / Sir Malcolm Sargent; [f]New Philharmonia Orchestra, [g]Chicago Symphony Orchestra, [h]English Chamber Orchestra / Daniel Barenboim ([i]pf).
EMI Ⓑ CZS5 68132-2 (six discs: 857 minutes: ADD: 8/94). 🔾🔾
Elgar Cello Concerto in E minor, Op. 85[d] (from HMV ASD655, 12/65). **Delius** Cello Concerto[e] (ASD644, 8/65). **Saint-Saëns** Cello Concerto No. 1 in A minor, Op. 33[f]. **Schumann** Cello Concerto in A minor, Op. 129[f] (both from ASD2498, 11/69). **Dvořák** Cello Concerto in B minor, B191[g]. Silent woods, B182[g] (ASD2751, 1/72). **Haydn** Cello Concertos – No. 1 in C major[h] (ASD2331, 10/67); No. 2 in D major[d]. **Monn** (arr. Schoenberg) Cello Concerto in G minor[d] (ASD2466, 4/69). **Chopin** Cello Sonata, Op. 65[i]. **Franck** Violin Sonata in A major[i] (arr. vc/pf. ASD2851, 2/73). **Fauré** Elégie, Op. 24[a] (HMV SAN255, 7/69). **Bruch** Kol Nidrei, Op. 47[a] (HMV CSD1499, 8/63). **Bach** Cello Suites – No. 1 in G major, BWV1007; No. 2 in D minor, BWV1008 (from broadcast performances in 1962. CDM7 63165-2, 9/89). **Handel** Oboe Concerto in G minor, HWV287[b] (arr. vc/pf Slatter. Broadcast, 1961. CDM7 63166-2, 9/89). **Beethoven** 12 Variations on Handel's "See the conqu'ring hero comes", Wo045[i]. Seven Variations in E flat major on Mozart's "Bei Männern, welche Liebe fühlen", Wo046[i]. 12 Variations in F major on "Ein Mädchen oder Weibchen", Op. 66[i] (recorded live in 1970. All from HMV SLS5042, 5/76). Cello Sonatas[c] – No. 3 in A major, Op. 69; No. 5 in D major, Op. 105 No. 2 (HMV HQS1029, 10/66).
As the title suggests, this fine six-disc retrospective of Jacqueline du Pré's recording career – a mere ten years long – was masterminded by French EMI. Aptly the English commentary by Jeremy Siepmann quotes Sir John Barbirolli's memorable remark in Christopher Nupen's television film, *Jacqueline*: "If you have no excesses in the full bloom of youth, what will there be to pare away on the long road to maturity?" The wonder was that Jacqueline du Pré was mature in her artistry from the start, and it is good that from the period even before the first official EMI sessions the collection includes three BBC recordings: Bach's Cello Suites Nos. 1 and 2 and a Handel sonata arranged from the Oboe Concerto in G minor. Those early BBC recordings are inevitably flawed, but the sheer scale of the artistry is never for a moment in doubt. Of the handful of items recorded by EMI in July 1962 with Gerald Moore accompanying, only Bruch's *Kol Nidrei* is included. The Delius was du Pré's first concerto recording, and she was not nearly as much at ease as she came to be later. The CD transfers do not minimize any of the flaws in the original recordings, notably the disappointing sound given to her Chicago recording of the Dvořák Concerto. Not only is the orchestral sound both coarse and thin with a high degree of background hiss, the cello is balanced far too close. Even with that balance one registers clearly the wide dynamic range of du Pré's playing, down to a whispered *pianissimo*. It was right to include it and also the cello sonata recordings of Chopin and Franck, the last recordings ever made by du Pré on December 10th and 11th, 1971. The tone may not have been quite so even as earlier, but the fire and warmth are undiminished. All the concerto recordings are welcome with the tear-laden quality in the slow movement of the Schumann matching that in the Elgar. It is good that the supreme Beethoven sonata recordings she made with Stephen Bishop (later Kovacevich) are included here, both sparkling and darkly intense. From the Beethoven series recorded at the 1970 Edinburgh Festival by the BBC only the three sets of variations are included, artistically fascinating but with sound curiously distanced and uninvolving. This is a treasure-house for anyone who was ever magnetized by du Pré's playing, and at bargain price as well.

Les introuvables de János Starker János Starker (vc); [a]Gerald Moore (pf); Philharmonia Orchestra / [b]Carlo Maria Giulini, [c]Walter Susskind. EMI mono/stereo Ⓜ CZS5 68485-2* (six discs: 398 minutes: ADD: 12/95). Recorded 1956-59.
Bach Solo Cello Suites, BWV1007-12 (from Columbia 33CX1515, 4/58; 33CX1656, 9/59 and 33CX1745, 6/61). **Kodály** Solo Cello Sonata, Op. 8. **Dohnányi** Konzertstück in D major, Op. 12[c] (both from 33CX1595, 11/58). **Boccherini** Cello Concerto in B flat major, G482[b]. **Haydn** Cello Concerto No. 2 in D major, HobVIIb/2[b] (33CX1665, 10/59). **Schumann** Cello Concerto in A minor, Op. 129[b]. **Saint-Saëns** Cello Concerto No. 1 in A minor, Op. 33[b] (33CX1579, 2/59). **Dvořák** Cello Concerto in B minor, B191[c]. **Fauré** Elégie, Op. 24[c] (Columbia SAX2263, 1/59). **Milhaud** Cello Concerto No. 1, Op. 136[c]. **Prokofiev** Cello Concerto in E minor, Op. 58[c] (33CX1425, 7/57). Also contains short items [a] by Bach, Chopin, Debussy, Kreisler, Mussorgsky, Paganini, Popper, Saint-Saëns, Schubert, Schumann and Tcherepnin (all from 33CX1700, 6/60).
A few seconds' worth of sampling is all that is needed to establish the tonal identity of János Starker, a supremely accomplished player whose tough, dry, vibrant sound was fuller in youth than in older age but whose every stroke of the bow suggests profound musicality, at once forthright and ardently expressive. In the Bach Cello Suites the approach is 'classical-romantic' rather than 'authentic

baroque', with propulsive Preludes, buoyant Bourrées, Gavottes and Gigues, and deeply introspective accounts of the slower movements. He has recorded the Kodály Sonata on other occasions, but it would be difficult to upstage the well-employed virtuosity of this 1957 performance, especially in the raging final *Allegro molto vivace*, a dazzling dance sequence and the nearest Kodály ever came to sounding like Bartók. Of the concerto's, the Dvořák, in particular, features a most touching account of the slow movement, but EMI slip up in their tracking of the individual movements of the Saint-Saëns Concerto (the *Allegretto con moto* actually starts during track 7, and not at the beginning of track 8). The Schumann Concerto is more full-bodied but less subtle than Starker's RCA recording (see review under Saint-Saëns; refer to the Index); Dohnányi's delightful *Konzertstück* receives smiling advocacy, Fauré's *Elégie* weeps inwardly, while both the Milhaud and Prokofiev concertos – the former with its Mahlerian resonances (try the *Grave* second movement for side-glances towards *Das Lied*), the latter, a restless precursor of a musically superior *Symphony Concerto* – are treated to typically lithe, finely honed playing. Boccherini (with cadenzas by Hutter) and Haydn (where the cellist provides his own cadenzas) both respond to Starkerian tonal tapering, and then there are the encores – wistful, lean and tastefully turned. The transfers are mostly excellent.

Italian Concerto [a]Harp Consort; [b]The Irish Band / Andrew Lawrence-King ([c]double harp/[d]hp/[e]hpd/[f]org). Deutsche Harmonia Mundi Ⓟ 05472 77366-2 (70 minutes: DDD: 4/98). ✗ Recorded 1996-97.
Bach Italian Concerto in F major, BWV971[ae]. Aria variata in A minor, BWV989[d] (both arr. Lawrence-King). **Handel** Organ Concertos, Op. 4 – No. 1 in G major, HWV289[af]; No. 6 in B flat major, HWV294[ac]. **O'Carolan** Carolan's Concerto[bd]. **Vivaldi** Concerto grosso in A minor, RV522[ac].
This is a celebration of two things: the Italian influence on baroque music elsewhere in Europe (as the 'motivator' is a harpist don't be surprised to find Ireland on the agenda), and the freedoms enjoyed by musicians at that time. The latter are also twofold: the licence to improvise, and the relaxed attitude toward the reworking of existing material – which dominates this programme. Lawrence-King deploys four different types of harp, uses an unusually varied battery of continuo instruments, and re-dresses familiar concertos in unfamiliar garb. In some cases the ripieno is changed, the soloist in the Vivaldi becomes a harpist, and BWV989 is appropriated by the double-strung *Davidsharfe*. Bach adapted 16 concertos by Italian composers for solo harpsichord, the instrument for which he wrote his own *Italian Concerto*; Lawrence-King reconstructs from that work The Original Concerto That Never Was, adding oboe and bassoon to form a concertino in which the harpsichord takes a back seat and is somewhat starved of decibels: Bach in reverse. There is a surprise around many corners and an abundance of magical sound, even when the musical result is a little less than convincing, and the performances by the star-studded cast are superb. How 'authentic' it all is depends on how open-minded you are (Lawrence-King presents the case for the defence in his annotation) but only the most straitlaced will let that spoil their enjoyment.

Let the Trumpet Sound Crispian Steele-Perkins (tpt); Bournemouth Sinfonietta / Richard Studt (vn). Carlton Classics Ⓜ 30366 0038-2 (76 minutes: DDD: 4/97). Recorded 1996.
J. James Trumpet Concerto in D major, "The Four Seasons". **Vivaldi:** Concerto for Two Trumpets and Strings in C major, RV537. **Stanley** Trumpet Concerto in D major.
J. Clarke Three Trumpet Ayres. **Handel** Airs from Vauxhall Gardens. **Purcell** Ayres for the Theatre (both arr. Steele-Perkins).
Anyone who has seen Crispian Steele-Perkins in recital will know how persuasively he communicates his art, often fortified by instructive and entertaining verbal interludes. The somewhat clichéd title of this disc belies an unusually satisfying blend of recognizable trumpet music and imaginative arrangements, all made by the soloist. From a technical point of view, there is a degree of hidden virtuosity in that the natural trumpet Steele-Perkins plays is keyed at a higher than normal pitch to accommodate the modern instruments of the Bournemouth Sinfonietta. This hybrid of old and new is, if not unique, certainly rare; the juxtaposition is particularly successful here because the strings are sympathetic (if not always quite as stylish as a period band) to the special tonal nuances of the natural trumpet. Moreover, Steele-Perkins makes the most of the brighter but no less full sound of his 'old' instrument: he wafts with a languid, vocalized elegance in the impressive Concerto by John James and demonstrates the expressive power of articulation and embellishment on such an instrument, especially in his suite of great Handel tunes and the resourceful *Ayres for the Theatre* by Purcell. Recorded in a resonant acoustic, this is a thoroughly entertaining, fresh and invigorating programme. If a touch unrefined in the strings, the eager-sounding ensemble more than makes up for it.

Dinu Lipatti Les Inédits. [a]Dinu Lipatti, [b]Madeleine Lipatti, [b]Béla Siki (pfs); [c]Suisse Romande Orchestra / Ernest Ansermet; [d]South-West German Radio Orchestra / Paul Sacher; [e]orchestra. Archiphon mono Ⓟ ARC112/13* (two discs: 139 minutes: ADD: 10/95). From private and test recordings and public performances; recorded 1936-51.
Liszt Piano Concerto No. 1 in E flat major, S124[c] (recorded at a performance in Geneva on June 6th, 1947). **Lipatti** Concertino en style classique, Op. 3[ae] (venue unknown, c1948). Three Romanian Dances[ac] (Geneva, October 10th, 1945). Symphonie concertante[bc] (Geneva, September 14th, 1951). Tziganes[c] (Geneva, c1951). Also includes works

(some with various artists) by Bach, Bartók[d], Brahms, Chopin, Enescu, Fauré, Liszt, Ravel, Rimsky-Korsakov, D. Scarlatti and Schumann. The originators of this full-price, two-disc anthology make no secret of their problems in transferring old, imperfect, predominately private recordings to CD, or of their awareness when the odds go against them. But never mind the 'surface noise' and all that. Surely no Lipatti lover will want to be without these previously commercially unobtainable precious memories. Solos on the first disc range from Lipatti's first Parisian recordings of 1936 to extracts from a Zurich concert given only ten months before he died. Even as a 19-year-old student, in the *Presto vivace* of an F sharp minor Sonata by his godfather, Enescu, you recognize the pinpoint clarity of articulation and the rhythmic alacrity and precision that were to remain hallmarks of his style for life. This disc's main discoveries are, nevertheless, the two concertos, notably Lipatti's only known recording of Liszt's in E flat (a lifelong favourite) with Ansermet and the Suisse Romande, embodying his maturer 'rethoughts' after hearing a recording by Liszt's pupil, Emil von Sauer. The expansive grandeur of his bolder gestures, the exquisitely intimate poetry of his lyricism, and the delicately tingling scintillation of his prestidigitation are unforgettable. So, too, are the intensity underpinning his purity and his fingertip atmospheric evocation in the central *Adagio religioso* of Bartók's Third Concerto (also a work very close to his heart) in a much cleaner and truer recording than the Liszt – superior enough, in fact, to make it hard to forgive the conductor, Paul Sacher, for forbidding the issue of this 1948 Baden-Baden performance in its entirety. The second disc, invaluable for its reminders of the lure of composition for the younger Lipatti, "reunites for the first time all his symphonic work", as the very generously informative and caring accompanying booklet puts it. The collector's piece (despite inferior reproduction) is surely the Geneva world première of his *Three Romanian Dances* with himself as customarily close-knit soloist with Ansermet and the Suisse Romande. Here, irrepressible love of his own country's folk heritage emerges with near Bartók-like voltage. No one did more to canalize Lipatti's overflowing romantic imagination than his Parisian mentor, Nadia Boulanger, as is clearly revealed here in his Bach-cum-Haydn-inspired *Concertino en style classique*, Op. 3 of 1936, with himself as an even more lithe and light-hearted soloist. The fuller impact of the then eclectic Paris, not forgetting Stravinsky, is nevertheless more potently revealed in his *Symphonie concertante* for two pianos and string orchestra (1938), here with his widow and Béla Siki alongside Ansermet in 1951. Its central *Molto adagio* has the same haunting nocturnal mystery of many of Bartók's slow movements. Nothing brings home our loss in December 1950 more than this, not only of a pianist over-blessed and over-loved by the gods, but of a potentially spellbinding post-impressionist Romanian composer.

The London Viola Sound Viola sections from **Academy of St Martin in the Fields, BBC Symphony Orchestra, London Philharmonic Orchestra, English National Opera Orchestra / Geoffrey Simon.** Cala (special price) CACD0106 (36 minutes: DDD: 9/95). Items marked [a] arranged Milone, [b]Runswick, [c]Balcombe. Recorded 1995.
Gershwin Porgy and Bess – It ain't necessarily so[a]. **Weill** Kiddush[a] (with Rivka Golani, va). **Shostakovich** Moscow, Cherymushki – Galop[a]. **Dvořák** Slavonic Dance in E minor, B147 No. 2[a]. **Grainger** Arrival Platform Humlet, RMTB1[c]. **Ravel** Pavane pour une infante défunte[a]. **Prokofiev** War and Peace – Waltz[a]. **Bacharach** This guy's in love with you[b]. **Strayhorn** Take the "A" Train[a].
Every one of these pieces is given a new dimension by its arrangement. "It ain't necessarily so" creeps in seductively, at an enticing, lazy gait, on 48 violas; while in Weill's *Kiddush*, Rivka Golani/viola acts as a cantor in the bluesy solo line. Her warm timbre is ultimately nearly as succulent as the ripieno, yet she manages somehow to keep something of the music's underlying traditional Jewish religious feeling. It is a haunting piece. However, the highlight of the programme is the Shostakovich "Galop" (from his 1959 operetta, *Cherymushki*), which is a kind of civilized *moto perpetuo* sabre dance. It sounds wonderfully spirited on these massed violas, while in the more familiar, warm and elegant Dvořák *Slavonic Dance* the violins are not missed one bit. Grainger actually wrote on his score that he intended the jaunty, folksy, at times dark-throated *Arrival Platform Humlet* for "massed-middle-fiddles". It was conceived on the platforms of London's Liverpool Street and Victoria stations and is, as its composer details, "the sort of thing one hums to oneself as an accompaniment to one's tramping feet as one happily, excitedly paces up and down the arrival platform ... awaiting the arrival of belated train bringing one's sweetheart from foreign parts; great fun!". Ravel's lovely *Pavane* and the bittersweet Prokofiev *Waltz* bring subtle differences of colour, the sound warmly orientated, yet never exaggeratedly so, thus allowing the music's character to remain. Burt Bacharach's *This guy's in love with you* is richly arranged by Daryl Runswick, but without ostentatious schmalz, and is given a light rhythmic touch by Geoffrey Simon. The recording is full-toned and spacious.

Moura Lympany in recital Dame Moura Lympany (pf); [ae]**Philharmonia Orchestra / **[a]**Herbert Menges,** [e]**Walter Susskind.** Dutton Laboratories mono Ⓕ CDCLP4000* (77 minutes: ADD: 1/97). Items marked [a] from HMV CLP1038 (4/55), [b]C4203 (1/53), [c]C4209 (4/53), [d]B10531 (9/53), [e]C3913 (10/49).
Mozart Piano Concertos[a] – No 12 in A major, K414/K385*p*; No. 21 in C major, K467. **Albéniz** (arr. Godowsky) Tango, Op. 165 No. 2[b]. **Chopin** Fantaisie-impromptu in C sharp minor, Op. 66[c]. **Granados** Goyescas – No. 4, Quejas o la maja y el ruiseñor[d]. **Turina** Rapsodia sinfónica, Op. 66[e].

Now that Dame Moura Lympany has ended her performing career, this recorded tribute comes as a special blessing. For long associated with the romantic virtuoso repertoire which she played with an unalloyed polish and graciousness, Dame Moura possessed the most catholic of tastes and her 1955 disc of Mozart's Concertos, K414 and K467, is surely among her finest offerings. Every change of mood, every subtlety of modulation is registered without fuss, narcissism or the sort of self-consciousness so often taken for an authentic style; her performances are of superfine quality and in impeccable taste. There are distinguished contributions from individual members of the Philharmonia and although the orchestra under Herbert Menges occasionally moves with a heavier tread than their soloist, they are none the less satisfyingly robust with no scaling down of drama or gesture. In Turina's picture-postcard charmer there is less heat and dazzle than in some other readings, yet you could say that both here and in Granados's "Maiden and the Nightingale" there is delicacy rather than lurid colouring. The recordings are adequate.

Marches and Overtures à la Française Detroit Symphony Orchestra / Paul Paray.

Mercury Living Presence Ⓜ 434 332-2MM (66 minutes: ADD: 11/93). Items marked [a] from AMS16077 (3/61), [b]AMS16121 (11/62), [c]SEX15050 (3/62), [d]SEX15024. Recorded 1959-60. ❸❸❸
Meyerbeer Coronation March[a]. **Gounod** Marche funèbre d'une marionnette[a].
Saint-Saëns Suite algérienne in C major, Op. 60 – March militaire française[a]. Marche héroïque in E flat major, Op. 34[a]. **Rouget de Lisle** La marseillaise[a]. **Adam** Si j'étais roi – Overture[b].
Boieldieu La dame blanche – Overture[b]. **Offenbach** La belle Hélène – Overture[c]. Orphée aux enfers – Overture[c]. Les contes d'Hoffmann – Prelude[c]. **Rossini** Guillaume Tell – Overture[d].

They don't make collections like this any more! Or so it seems. Yet can musical tastes really have changed so radically from the days when people would patiently turn over a 78rpm record for the second half of Boieldieu's *La dame blanche* Overture? Unlikely, and there must surely be a welcome for such a collection of charmingly melodious, unpretentious and yet well-crafted pieces as on this CD. Paul Paray (1886–1979) was a genuine son of Normandy who in his seventies could still bring out the Gallic warmth, excitement and sparkle of these pieces. The recording sounds just a shade raw with the violins at the top of their range, but generally the warmth and richness of sound make it quite unbelievable that these recordings are now 38-odd years old.

Meeting Point Gerard McChrystal (sax); [a]London Musici / Mark Stephenson.

Silva Classics Ⓕ SILKD6010 (55 minutes: DDD: 6/96). Recorded 1995.
D. Heath Soprano Saxophone Concerto, "The Celtic"[a]. **I. Wilson** I Sleep at Waking.
Torke Soprano Saxophone Concerto[a]. **McGlynn** From Nowhere to Nowhere.
Nyman Where the Bee Dances[a].

McChrystal has an enviably full and warm soprano saxophone tone, and his intonation is as secure as his gift for melodic phrasing is unfailing. This is of inestimable advantage in a work such as Heath's Concerto, where the solo instrument is entirely dominant. The solo piece by Ian Wilson finds McChrystal on alto saxophone, and here his tone is pellucid, while his control of alternating fingering is precise and affecting. The music itself is cryptic and melancholy. McGlynn's solo effort is a good deal more conventional, closer to its folk music source, and is accordingly somewhat less striking. The two major works here are the Nyman and Torke concertos. Nyman's typical rhythmic and melodic patterns are to be found in abundance in *Where the Bee Dances*, but there is also a more discernible willingness to allow the music sequential development and several chances to pause and reflect than one normally associates with this composer. The gem in this collection, however, is the Torke, a three-movement concerto revelling in constantly transmuting thematic shards, unravelling orchestral colours and timbres, and genuinely engaging rhythmic complexities, often hinting at Far-Eastern influences. The outer movements are full of brilliant light, generated by the predominantly percussive scoring, supported by woodwinds and strings. The slow second movement is that modern rarity – a warm and moving construction with a ravishing theme which avoids any hint of sentimentality. It is also brilliantly scored. Unfortunately, this is the least well executed piece on the entire disc, with the London Musici woodwinds falling short of the high standards set elsewhere.

Pierre Monteux Edition [a]San Francisco Symphony Orchestra; [b]Chicago Symphony Orchestra; [c]Boston Symphony Orchestra; [d]RCA Victor Symphony Orchestra / Pierre Monteux.

RCA Victor Pierre Monteux Edition mono/stereo Ⓜ 09026 61893-2*
(15 discs: 16 hours 55 minutes: ADD: 9/94).   ❸❸
Beethoven Die Ruinen von Athen – Overture[a] (Recorded 1949). Symphonies[a] – No. 4 in B flat major, Op. 60 (Victor LM1714. 1952); No. 8 in F major, Op. 93 (GL43357, 11/82. 1950).
Bach (orch. Respighi) Passacaglia and Fugue in C minor, BWV582[a] (HMV DB21053/4, 5/50).
Berlioz Symphonie fantastique, Op. 14[a] (DB6670/5. 1945). Benvenuto Cellini – Overture[a] (1952). Les troyens – Prélude, Act 3[a] (previously unpublished. 1945). La damnation de Faust, Op. 24 – Hungarian March[a] (Camden CDN1009, 5/59. 1951). **Brahms** Symphony No. 2 in D major, Op. 73[a] (Victor 11-9237/40. 1945). Schicksalslied, Op. 54[a] (Stanford University Chorus. Victor LM149. 1949). **Mahler** Kindertotenlieder[a] (Marian Anderson, contr. HMV ALP1138, 5/54).
Chausson Symphony in B flat major, Op. 20 (LM1081. 1950). Poème de l'amour et de la mer, Op. 19[d] (with Gladys Swarthout, mez. 12-0978. 1947). **Chabrier** Le roi malgré lui – Fête polonaise[a] (12-0978. 1947). **Debussy** Images[a] (LM1197. 1951). Images oubliées – Sarabande[a]

(orch. Ravel. 11-9684. 1946). Nocturnes[c] (Berkshire Festival Chorus. GL43366, 11/82. 1955). La mer[c] (GL43366. 1954). **Liszt** Les Préludes, S97[c]. **Scriabin** Le poème de l'extase, Op. 54[c] (both LM1775. 1952). **Saint-Saëns** Havanaise in E major, Op. 83[c] (Leonid Kogan, vn. VICS1153, 2/66). **Delibes** Coppélia – Suite[c]. Sylvia – Suite[c] (both ALP1475, 10/57. 1953. **Gounod** Faust – Ballet Music[a] (prev. unpub. 1947). **Franck** Symphony in D minor[b] (SB6631, 10/65. 1961). Pièce héroique in B minor[a] (orch. O'Connell. DB6135, 10/42). **d'Indy** Istar, Op. 42[a] (CDN1009. 1945). Symphonie sur un chant montagnard français in G major, Op. 25a (Maxim Shapiro, pf. 11-8367/9. 1941). Fervaal, Op. 40 – Prélude[a] (CDN1009. 1945). Symphony No. 2 in B flat major, Op. 57[a] (11-8441/5. 1942). **Ravel** Daphnis et Chloé – Suite No. 1[a] (11-9683/4. 1946). Valses nobles et sentimentales[a] (DB6676/7. 1946). Alborada del gracioso[a] (12-1107. 1947). La valse[a] (DB5964/5, 4/42). **Lalo** Le roi d'Ys – Overture[a] (11-8489. 1942). **Ibert** Escales[a] (11-9907/8. 1946). **Rimsky-Korsakov** Scheherazade, Op. 35[a] (11-8384/8. 1942). Sadko, Op. 5[a] (12-0501/2. 1945). Symphony No. 2, Op. 9, "Antar"[a] (DB6918/20. 1946). **R. Strauss** Ein Heldenleben, Op. 40[a] (prev. unpub. 1947). Tod und Verklärung, Op. 24[a] (new to UK. 1960). **Stravinsky** Petrushka[a] (VICS1297, 6/68. 1959). The Rite of Spring[a] (GL85239, 8/85. 1951). **Tchaikovsky** Symphonies[c] – No. 4 in F minor, Op. 36 (SB2093, 12/60); No. 5 in E minor, Op. 64 (SB2045, 10/59); No. 6 in B minor, Op. 74, "Pathétique" (SB2029, 5/59).

"Under-heralded, under-sung, under-appreciated except by those who knew" runs Leon Fleischer's tribute, one of many, in the booklet of this important box-set. Inevitably, as the majority of these RCA Victor recordings were made during Monteux's 17-year tenure in San Francisco, you may wonder how to interpret the claims of colleagues at the time that Monteux had achieved marvels there. Be not anxious: the only San Francisco recording here that reveals the orchestra as seriously less than world-class is the *Tod und Verklärung* which Monteux recorded in 1960 as a guest, eight years after his directorship there had ceased. For the rest, what this playing lacks in ultimate refinement of tone, it more than makes up for with unfailing responsiveness to its conductor's priorities; and as the conductor is Monteux, that means a lot. There is not one single routinely played or badly balanced bar of music, though tolerance may be needed for unexpected gremlins in the machinery (moments of distortion and congestion) in the pre-tape San Francisco recordings (i.e. about a third of the set).

As Monteux was the conductor of the most (in)famous première this century, Stravinsky's *Rite*, and its subsequent champion, you might expect these two restored recordings of the work (he recorded it four times) to shine more brightly than they do. Ensemble is generally tighter in Boston but there are moments of untypical laxity and coarseness. The less heavyweight Paris Conservatoire reading (in stereo) shares much with the 1960 Stravinsky: not as incisive but quite as revealing of the score's no less revolutionary intimate secrets, in other words, for the connoisseur, more rewarding than the endless list of modern recordings that turn the work into a percussion concerto. Throughout the stereo account of *Petrushka*'s Fair scenes, the characterization is earthy without ever being clumsy, and Petrushka himself is pathos in person. Again, if you are looking for the general whipcrack impact of many a modern version, you will be disappointed, though there are numerous instances where Monteux knows and shows how to articulate a difficult figure or a whole passage (for example, the final chase and death of Petrushka) with greater precision than in the average showpiece account. Stravinsky also praised Monteux's 1950 San Francisco Beethoven Eighth. No wonder. Here is the jester in the Age of Elegance; and Monteux has the measure of both.

His airborne 1952 Beethoven Fourth is strong without heaviness or overemphasis; and that, to oversimplify, is the secret of Monteux's success in the Austro-German repertoire; the repertoire he loved more than any other, but which the public, or to be more precise, those that chose what the public should receive, decided was not his forte. All credit to RCA for the courage to release this previously unissued 1947 San Francisco *Heldenleben*; as well as the wisdom to record it in the first place. Monteux recorded Brahms's Second Symphony four times, and the first two were made in San Francisco. The box includes his first (1945) recording and it has all the *joie de vivre* and superb string detailing that you would expect from a Monteux performance, but the extent of which always takes you by surprise. Another surprise is the tensely blazing first movement development. Don't be put off by the constricted sound, or the lack of a proper *sotto voce* at the start of the finale; most Brahms Seconds sound hopelessly retentive after this. His 1945 Berlioz *Symphonie fantastique* is a properly volatile reading: one that lives close to the edge. The playing in an excitable and sharp-featured Waltz (with superbly managed *rits.*) may perhaps strike you as often too loud, but Monteux will then suddenly surprise you with a brilliantly placed hush. This was a real Monteux speciality – establishing a mean of quiet that was practical for projecting clarity (especially for gramophone listeners) and to allow players to phrase properly, and then to select the right moment to drop from it. Was there ever a more accomplished architect of the climactic paragraph? The accomplishment is that you are rarely aware of the mechanics of the operation. To analyse how he does it would probably take a week-long conductors' symposium, so let us settle for shorthand and call it an inspired mix of planning and spontaneity.

The set contains all Monteux's d'Indy recordings. A good decision; d'Indy needs his champion's recordings returned to circulation as a new generation of French conductors take up the cause. If the record moguls and opera impresarios of the time were unwilling to allow Monteux to indulge his passion for Wagner, he undoubtedly found a ready outlet in d'Indy, Franck and Chausson (and Lalo's *Le roi d'Ys* Overture). His celebrated 1961 Chicago Franck Symphony must be in the collection of anyone who loves the work. Monteux's Delibes and Gounod ballet suites are stylish, but also vital and strong. Typically, tempos here and in his Rimsky-Korsakov, are swift but fluid. There are references in the accompanying booklets to his knack of finding *Le tempo juste*, and time and again a phrase of Christoph von Dohnányi's came to mind: "when the music is on its feet, it does the right thing". Music on its feet was, of course, the making of Monteux, but well before the Diaghilev connection, the teenage Monteux had played second violin in the Folies Bergères. Years later Gershwin complimented him on his marvellous rhythmic sense, and Monteux cited his Folies experience as the training for it. This rhythmic sense ... the spirit of the dance (call it what you will) permeated everything Monteux conducted, especially his Ravel. The Boston Debussy *La mer* and *Nocturnes* – 1954 and 1955 respectively, the latter in stereo – are among the finest on disc. Suffice it to say that Monteux understood that Debussy knew exactly what he wanted. This *La mer* is an all too rare case of the conductor working *with* the composer, not imagining he knows better. The discs are also available separately.

Pierre Monteux The Early Years. [a]**Concertgebouw Orchestra**; [b]**London Symphony Orchestra / Pierre Monteux.** Philips The Early Years Ⓜ 442 544-2PM5 (five discs: 311 minutes: ADD: 12/94). Recorded 1961-64.   ⒼⒼⒼ
Beethoven Symphony No. 3 in E flat major, Op. 55, "Eroica"[a] (from 835132AY, 2/63).
Schubert Symphony No. 8 in B minor, D759, "Unfinished"[a] (GL5788, 1/65). **Tchaikovsky** Swan Lake – excerpts[b] (835142AY, 3/63). **Brahms** Symphony No. 2 in D major, Op. 73[b]. Academic Festival Overture, Op. 80[b] (both from SAL3435, 11/63). Tragic Overture, Op. 81[b] (previously unpublished. Recorded 1962). **Ravel** Boléro[b]. La valse[b]. Ma mère l'oye[b] (all from SAL3500, 5/65). **Debussy** Images[b]. Le martyre de St Sébastien – symphonic fragments[b] (SAL3459, 12/64).

"The Early Years – Pierre Monteux" it says on the box. The early years are, of course, those of Philips, not Monteux. This mid-price set offers his very last stereo recordings, made between 1962 and 1964, when Monteux was in his late eighties – vintage years to be sure, for the conductor, the LSO and Philips engineering – on five discs for the price of four. The new CDs have been "digitalized by Bitstream", a process which has fractionally opened out and brightened up the treble. Compared with today's average offerings from London or Amsterdam, hall ambience is minimal (especially in the Brahms symphony), but the balances are flawless, and the benefits of Monteux's separated first and second violin sections are everywhere to be heard. Of Monteux's two *Eroica* recordings, this 1962 Amsterdam account is the one to have: "textures have a Stravinskyan bite and clarity ... the Concertgebouw are producing that fierce, bright, glistening tone which has always been a sure sign that their collective psyche is aflame", wrote *Gramophone*'s Richard Osborne in 1988. The first movement of Monteux's Amsterdam *Unfinished* (with repeat) is unusually fast, relaxing beautifully for the second subject (good, focused tone and phrasing here, not the common *pianissimo* thread).The LSO *Swan Lake* selection (with some numbers pruned, and a couple of concert endings) is well chosen for contrast, and the opening number sets the scene with some rapid string playing of effortless precision and point. Rarely, if ever, do you hear the swan theme (solo oboe) sung with such dignity and melancholy, the syncopations in the Act 1 *Pas de Deux* Waltz handled with such elegance, or the ballet's closing minutes played with such tragic grandeur. On occasions Tchaikovsky sounds like Delibes, but Tchaikovsky would undoubtedly have approved of that. In the last of Monteux's four recordings of the Brahms Second Symphony, subtleties of nuance and timing, and modifications of pacing, reflect a lifetime's love and experience of the work. Typically, it is light-toned and gentle in cast, almost symphonic chamber music. You would expect a Monteux *Academic Festival Overture* to raise the spirits, and you won't be disappointed. The *Tragic Overture* is articulated more powerfully than the symphony, always on its feet, and with heaven-sent, *pianissimo* muted violins preparing the way for the noble brass transformation of the opening theme. Monteux's LSO strings come into their own for the Debussy and Ravel items. There is a very good case for suggesting that, in the range of expression he was capable of encouraging from his string desks, Monteux (himself originally an orchestral violinist, and then a violist in a string quartet) had no peers.You will hear a great range of vibrato, very prominent, for example, in the gorgeous husky tone for the viola and violin gipsy song solos in the first two movements of "Ibéria" (it is worth mentioning that Monteux's ancestors were Spanish), or the more exalted moments from *Le martyre*. And if you are unable to succumb totally to the maximum vibrato and extraordinary textures as Monteux leads us through the "Fairy Garden" at the end of *Ma mère l'oye*, then you are a lost cause.

Orchestral works Cristina Ortiz (pf); **Royal Philharmonic Orchestra / Moshe Atzmon.** Decca Ⓕ 414 348-2DH (58 minutes: DDD: 9/86). From 414 348-1DH (5/86). Recorded 1984.   Ⓖ
Rachmaninov Piano Concerto No. 2 in C minor, Op. 18. **Addinsell** Warsaw Concerto.
Litolff Concerto Symphonique No. 4 in D minor, Op. 102 – Scherzo. **Gottschalk** (orch. Hazell) Grande fantaisie triomphale sur l'hymne national brésilien, RO108.
The C minor Concerto of Rachmaninov symbolizes romanticism at its ripest. Its combination of poetry and sensuous warmth with languorously memorable melodic lines balanced by exhilarating pianistic brilliance happily avoids any suggestion of sentimentality. The simple chordal introduction from the soloist ushers in one of the composer's most luscious tunes, yet the slow movement develops even greater ardour in its melodic contour, and the composer holds back a further haunting expressive idea to bring lyrical contrast to the scintillating finale. The couplings here are most apt. The genuinely

inspired pastiche *Warsaw Concerto* by Richard Addinsell has a principal theme worthy to stand alongside those of Rachmaninov and its layout shows satisfying craftsmanship. Ortiz plays this main theme with great affection and she is equally beguiling in the delicious Litolff *Scherzo*. The effect here is of elegance rather than extrovert brilliance: this is reserved for the Gottschalk *Grande fantaisie triomphale*, which is played with a splendid panache that almost covers its inherent vulgarity and certainly emphasizes its ingenuous charm. Throughout the recording balance is realistic and the reverberation adds the most attractive bloom.

Red leaves ªTeresa Cahill (sop); **Brunel Ensemble / Christopher Austin.**
   Cala The Edge Ⓕ CACD77005 (77 minutes: DDD: 6/97). Text and translation included.
   Lutyens Six Bagatelles. O saisons, o châteaux, Op. 13ª. **McCabe** Red leaves. **Saxton** Birthday Piece for Richard Rodney Bennett. Elijah's Violin. **Williamson** Symphony No. 7 for Strings.
Of contemporary composers neglected by record companies, no case is more surprising than that of Malcolm Williamson. Irrespective of his position as Master of the Queen's Music it is clear – if the Symphony No. 7 (1984) is a reliable guide – that the music is well made and immediately appealing, in a mainstream style recalling Lennox Berkeley, the earlier Tippett and even, a little further back, the more ebullient sides of Warlock and Grainger. There is nothing avant-garde here, but the music's lack of inhibition and strength of character makes its neglect incomprehensible. The disc also includes music by other composers who are less well represented in current catalogues than they deserve. *Red leaves*, a fairly recent piece by John McCabe, is a neatly turned exercise in a pastoral tradition that may summon up politically incorrect hunting horns but can also express much deeper feelings. Elizabeth Lutyens's cantata, *O saisons, o châteaux*, is a fine demonstration of how an atonal style can enhance a mood of romantic lyricism. By contrast, the late set of *Bagatelles* is far too dutiful, and quite without the sprightly humour that the title implies. The disc also contains one of Robert Saxton's most substantial scores from the late-1980s. *Elijah's Violin* is not a violin concerto, but a cogently argued symphony for chamber orchestra based on an old Jewish folk-tale. Its expansive melodic writing and euphonious harmony are fine demonstrations of this composer's particular strengths and, together with the short but surprisingly intense *Birthday Piece for Richard Rodney Bennett* (1986), should win new friends for Saxton's music. This is a demanding programme for the performers, and although signs of effort are occasionally evident in the playing, it is never less than competent. The recordings are rather clinical, with less bloom, particularly to the string sound in the Williamson, but not to the extent that interest or enjoyment are marred.

Rhapsody Montreal Symphony Orchestra / Charles Dutoit. Decca Ⓕ 452 482-2DH
   (70 minutes: DDD: 5/97).
   Liszt Hungarian Rhapsody No. 2 in C sharp minor, S244. **Dvořák** Slavonic Rhapsody No. 3 in A flat minor, B86. **Alfvén** Swedish Rhapsody No. 1, Op. 19, "Midsummer Vigil". **Enescu** Romanian Rhapsody in A major, Op. 11 No. 1. **Glazunov:** Oriental Rhapsody in G major, Op. 29.
Imagine a cross between the *Polovtsian Dances* and *Scheherazade*, with plentiful echoes of both, and you will have a fair idea of how Glazunov's very rare *Oriental Rhapsody* sounds, every bit as colourful and attractive as the better-known pieces. In five evocative, well-contrasted movements following a clearly defined programme, it was written in 1889, the year after Rimsky wrote *Scheherazade*, when Glazunov in his mid twenties had been spending much of his time completing Borodin's *Prince Igor*. It would be more welcome in programmes in preference to the much more protracted *Scheherazade*. At least here Dutoit and the Montreal orchestra give it sumptuous treatment, warmly expressive and brilliant. The richness of the sound, outstanding even by Decca's Montreal standards, wraps you round from the very start of the Liszt. As hackneyed a piece as he ever wrote, it is here made sparkling and fresh, played with all the panache you could want, defying any danger of vulgarity. It comes not in the usual arrangement but in the one by Muller-Berghaus used by Toscanini and Boskovsky among others. Rightly the clarinettist Robert Crowley is individually credited, warmly imaginative in his cadenza near the start. The Dvořák, much more refined, similarly combines warmth and energy, while it is good to have the Alfvén and Enescu in sequence, both full of marvellously memorable melody, heightened by brilliant scoring. What might have been just a routine offering here becomes a cherishable disc which will appeal to the widest range of collectors.

Russian Showpieces Chicago Symphony Orchestra / Fritz Reiner.
   RCA Victor Living Stereo Ⓜ 09026 61958-2* (71 minutes: ADD: 8/94). Items marked ª from SB2001 (10/58), ᵇVIC1068 (2/65). Recorded 1957-59.   ⒼⒼⒼ
   Mussorgsky (orch. Ravel) Pictures at an Exhibitionª. A Night on the Bare Mountainª.
   Tchaikovsky Suite No. 1, Op. 43 – Marche miniatureᵇ. Marche slave, Op. 31ᵇ. **Borodin** Prince Igor – Polovtsian Marchᵇ. **Kabalevsky** Colas Breugnon – Overtureᵇ. **Glinka** Ruslan and Ludmilla – Overtureᵇ.
Reiner's *Pictures at an Exhibition* was one of the glories of the early stereo LP catalogue offering orchestral playing of the highest calibre. The richness of the brass sounds is apparent in the very opening "Promenade" and "Bydlo" really does sound like a heavy ox wagon. Reiner pictures the "Tuileries" lightly but nostalgically and the "Unhatched chicks" daintily, while the image of "Samuel Goldenburg" is unctiously conveyed by the full-bodied lower strings, which makes Schmuyle's

bleating the more telling in consequence, "Market Place at Limoges" becomes a lightly articulated orchestral scherzo. The finale is predictably and grandly spacious. After Mussorgsky's sonorous climax dies away, Tchaikovsky's piquant little march sounds like a gnat after an elephant, and makes a charming diversion before the menacing brass growls of *Night on the Bare Mountain* (in Rimsky's version) and the robustly accented Borodin "Polovtsian March", which takes us back to the world of Slavonic orchestral spectacle. *Marche slave* is slow and sombre, but certainly makes a powerful climax. Then the mood lightens again for the last two items, the *Colas Breugnon*, with its exuberant cross sycopations, matched by the racy *Ruslan and Ludmilla* Overture. One can only marvel at the consistency of the recording, so resplendent in its opulent concert-hall ambience.

Stokowski Transcriptions Philadelphia Orchestra / Wolfgang Sawallisch.
EMI Ⓕ CDC5 55592-2 (66 minutes: DDD: 5/96). Recorded 1995.   ⓐ
Bach Cantatas: No. 208 – Schafe können sicher weiden; No. 140 – Wachet auf!; No. 80 – Ein' feste Burg. Toccata and Fugue in D minor, BWV565. **Boccherini** String Quintet in E major, G275 – Minuet. **Beethoven** Piano Sonata No. 14 in C sharp minor, Op. 27 No. 2, "Moonlight" – Adagio sostenuto. **Chopin** Prelude in E minor, Op. 28 No. 4. **Franck** Panis angelicus. **Tchaikovsky** String Quartet No. 1 in D major, Op. 11 – Andante cantabile. At the ball, Op. 38 No. 3 (with Marjana Lipovšek, mez). **Debussy** Suite bergamasque – Clair de lune. Préludes, Book 1 – No. 10, La cathédrale engloutie. **Rachmaninov** Prelude in C sharp minor, Op. 3 No. 2.

Quite apart from reissues of the Stokowski's own recordings, there are several other discs of these highly coloured arrangements. Though Stokowski's own recordings, even those he made in extreme old age, generally have a degree more flair and dramatic bite than any others, the contrasts are not always what you would expect. So it is surprising to find that the BBC Philharmonic strings are more ripely resonant than those of the Philadelphia Orchestra in Franck's *Panis angelicus*, though that is an exception, and possibly Sawallisch simply wanted to minimize the piece's bold vulgarity. One of the items common to these discs is the *Adagio* from Beethoven's *Moonlight* Sonata, and there Sawallisch brings out far more of the mystery of what becomes an evocative, atmospheric piece, making the Bamert disc seem clinical. This collection also gains in glamour from having Marjana Lipovšek as an appropriately Slavonic-sounding soloist in the orchestration of the Tchaikovsky song, *At the ball*. This EMI disc provides a generous programme together with richly rounded recording, well defined in the bass. Yet Bamert's even more generous selection of 15 encore pieces overlaps on only three items, and includes more in which Stokowski has the greatest fun tweaking the ear provocatively, such as Mozart's *Turkish Rondo*: the advice to anyone with a sweet tooth is to get both discs for maximum indulgence.

Arturo Toscanini Philharmonic Symphony Orchestra of New York / Arturo Toscanini.
Pearl mono Ⓕ GEMMCDS9373* (three discs: 230 minutes: ADD: 3/90).
Gramophone classical 100.   ⓐⓖⓐ
Beethoven Symphonies – No. 5 in C minor, Op. 67 (previously unpublished. Recorded at a concert in Carnegie Hall, New York on April 9th, 1933); No. 7 in A major, Op. 92 (from HMV DB2986/90, 12/36, recorded 1936). **Brahms** Variations on a Theme by Haydn, Op. 56a, "St Antoni Chorale" (DB3031/2, 1/37). **Dukas** L'apprenti sorcier (HMV D1689, 10/29). **Gluck** Orfeo ed Euridice – Dance of the Blessed Spirits (D1784, 7/30). **Haydn** Symphony No. 101 in D major, "Clock" (D1668/71, 9/29). **Mendelssohn** A Midsummer Night's Dream, Op. 61 – – Scherzo (two versions: Brunswick 50106, 1/28; D1671, 9/29); Nocturne (50106). **Mozart** Symphony No. 35 in D major, K385, "Haffner" (D1782/4, 7/30). **Rossini** Semiramide – Overture (DB3079/80, 3/37). L'italiana in Algeri – Overture (DB2943, 10/36). Il barbiere di Siviglia – Overture (D1835, 10/30). **Verdi** La traviata – Preludes, Acts 1 and 3 (D1672, 6/30). **Wagner** Gotterdämmerung – Dawn and Siegfried's Rhine Journey (DB2860/61, 7/36). Lohengrin –Preludes, Acts 1 and 3 (DB2904, 9/36, DB2861, 7/36). Siegfried Idyll (DB29201/21, 5/37).

Almost every non-vocal classical record collection in the 1930s included some of Toscanini's recordings with the Philharmonic Symphony Orchestra of New York. They were the classical orchestral records of their day, and were universally admired. Nearly 60 years on they still make an enormous impact. In general they have more freedom of spirit than his later recordings with the NBC SO. All the terrific tension and drive of a Toscanini performance is there, but tempered at this stage with a rare lyricism and beauty of phrase. Play the *Traviata* Preludes and hear how the New York strings speak with an extraordinary depth of feeling and richness of tone; Dukas's scherzo is taken at breakneck speed, but there is still room for the most finely sculpted turns of phrase and telling changes of pulse – even now, when superlative orchestral playing is commonplace, this performance seems a miracle of refined, flexible virtuosity, and how extraordinary it must have seemed 60 years ago. These recordings are part of the conductor's 1929 series for Victor. Three years earlier he had had a brief flirtation with the Brunswick company, making just the two Mendelssohn sides. These comparatively cautious performances do not really add to our knowledge of Toscanini and they are difficult to find in their original 78rpm form, but Pearl were right to include them as part of a complete survey of his New York recordings. The 1929 series did nothing to change the great conductor's aversion to making records, and it was not until 1936 that Victor persuaded him to record again. In the meantime efforts had been made to record him in live performance, and these he always rejected. But somehow test pressings of a Beethoven Fifth Symphony from 1933 have survived and are included here. It is an enormously powerful, direct performance, full of fire and passion. The plum of the 1936 Victor sessions is surely Beethoven's Seventh Symphony, a performance of miraculous clarity, expressive force and explosive, titanic rhythm. Many judges feel that this is the greatest ever recording of the symphony, and once heard it stays in the mind permanently as the yardstick for other and lesser interpretations. Pearl's transfer engineering isn't up to its usual high standard. At its best the sound is tonally very good and full-bodied, but there is evidence of computerized filtering throughout the set in a general coarseness and unevenness of the sound image, where continual sampling results in rapid changes in the nature of the signal. However, despite reservations about the sound, here is a treasure trove indeed.

The Toscanini Collection New York Philharmonic Orchestra / Arturo Toscanini.
RCA Victor Gold Seal mono Ⓜ GD60318* (64 minutes: ADD: 11/92). Recorded 1929-36.
Gluck Orfeo ed Euridice – Ballet in D minor (from HMV D1784, 7/30). **Rossini** Il barbiere di Siviglia – Overture (D1835, 10/30). L'italiana in Algeri – Overture (HMV DB2943, 10/36). Semiramide – Overture (DB3079/80, 3/37). **Verdi** La traviata – Preludes, Acts 1 and 3 (D1672, 6/30). **Wagner** Götterdämmerung – Dawn and Siegfried's Rhine Journey (DB2860/61, 7/36). Lohengrin – Preludes, Acts 1 (DB2904, 9/36) and 3 (DB2861).

RCA's Toscanini Collection contains many very desirable reissues, but this disc has a particular quality in that it shows very clearly several outstanding but differing aspects of the great conductor's genius. The recordings, made in 1929 and 1936, have been made to yield a quality of sound which most listeners will find perfectly acceptable, and they date from a period when, as chief conductor of the New York Philharmonic Orchestra, Toscanini was in his artistic prime. Those who still imagine him always to be a hard, relentless interpreter should hear the exquisitely poised Gluck ballet music, or the tender, extraordinarily eloquent *Traviata* preludes. The Rossini Overtures are certainly propelled with a good deal of energy, but there's plenty of air in the rhythms, and some elegant phrasing amid the virtuoso playing of the magnificent New York Philharmonic. Wagner was particularly near to Toscanini's heart: the *Lohengrin* Act 1 Prelude has a wonderfully luminous quality, and "Siegfried's Rhine Journey" is played with tremendous strength and majesty.

Trumpet Concertos Håkan Hardenberger (tpt); Academy of St Martin in the Fields /
Sir Neville Marriner. Philips Ⓕ 420 203-2PH (59 minutes: DDD: 12/87). Recorded 1986.
Hummel Trumpet Concerto in E flat major. **Hertel** Trumpet Concerto in D major.
J. Stamitz (realized Boustead) Trumpet Concerto in D major. **Haydn** Trumpet Concerto in E flat major, HobVIIe/1.

This recording made such a remarkable impression when it first appeared in 1987 that it created overnight a new star in the firmament of trumpeters. The two finest concertos for the trumpet are undoubtedly those of Haydn and Hummel and Hardenberger plays them here with a combination of sparkling bravura and stylish elegance that are altogether irresistible. Marriner and his Academy accompany with characteristic finesse and warmth, with the lilting dotted rhythms of the first movement of the Hummel, seductively jaunty. The lovely *Andante* of the Haydn is no less beguiling and both finales display a high spirited exuberance and an easy bravura which make the listener smile with pleasure. He is no less distinctive in the lesser concerto of Johann Hertel and the other D major work attributed to Johann Stamitz but probably written by someone with the unlikely name of J.B. Holzbogen. This takes the soloist up into the stratosphere of his range and provides him also with some awkward leaps. The Hertel work also taxes the soloist's technique to the extremities but Hardenberger essays all these difficulties with an enviably easy aplomb and remains fluently entertaining throughout. The recording gives him the most vivid realism and presence but it is a pity that the orchestral backcloth is so reverberant; otherwise the sound is very natural.

Trumpet Concertos Sergei Nakariakov (tpt); ªAlexander Markovich (pf); Lausanne Chamber Orchestra / Jésus López-Cobos. Teldec Ⓕ 4509-90846-2 (56 minutes: DDD: 10/93). Recorded 1993.
Jolivet Concertino for Trumpet, Piano and Stringsª. **Hummel** Trumpet Concerto in E flat major. **Tomasi** Trumpet Concerto. **Haydn** Trumpet Concerto in E flat major, HobVIIe/1.

The young Russian, Sergei Nakariakov is in his element in the opening Jolivet Double Concerto, standing well out in front of his partner, Alexander Markovich. The balance is less than ideal, with the piano set rather backwardly and the orchestra in a dryish acoustic. The piano emerges more strongly in the very florid finale, the bubbling animation of the playing reaching a frenzy of activity towards the end. The Tomasi (1901-71) is an even better piece and could hardly be better played. In the Haydn and Hummel, the Nakariakov/López-Cobos performances do not quite match the famous version (reviewed above) by Håkan Hardenberger, who has the inestimable advantage of wonderfully smiling accompaniments from Marriner and the ASMF. However, the lovely *Andante* of the Haydn is so gracefully phrased by Nakariakov, that the ear is ravished and the finale sparkles delectably, as does, for that matter, the finale of the Hummel. As a whole this CD is a distinctive compilation, and confirms Nakariakov's position as one of the world's leading trumpeters. The Teldec recording is truthful.

Trumpet Concertos Crispian Steele-Perkins (tpt); [a]Neil Black, [a]James Brown (obs);
English Chamber Orchestra / Anthony Halstead. Carlton Classics Ⓜ 30366 0066-2
(63 minutes: DDD: 10/97). From PCD821 (6/86). Recorded 1986.
Haydn Trumpet Concerto in E flat major, HobVII*e* No. 1. **M. Haydn** Trumpet Concerto in
C major, MH60. **Humphries** Trumpet Concerto in D major, Op. 2 No. 12. **Neruda** Trumpet
Concerto in E flat major (ed. Steele-Perkins). **Telemann** Concerto for Two Oboes, Trumpet and
Strings No. 1 in D major[a]. **Torelli** Trumpet Concerto No. 2 in D major.
This reissue from 1986 contains a pleasing mixture of the familiar and the rediscovered. Though
frequently recorded, there are surprisingly few versions of the Haydn Trumpet Concerto which one
would be happy to experience on a regular basis but this is certainly one of them. Steele-Perkins's
playing is concerned with shape and decorum, not just demonstrative virtuosity. To this end, he brings
a lively buoyancy to the fast movements with especially well-judged articulation; the little-known
Michael Haydn Concerto (just as stratospheric as the better-known work) is a case in point with its
lyrical vocalizing, disarmingly complemented by a shimmering texture of languid flutes. Steele-
Perkins brings his cultivated sense of line to this work and the Torelli, though the Telemann
Concerto for trumpet and two oboes – a rather pedestrian piece it has to be said – is altogether less
invigorating. The resonant acoustic is advantageous throughout, particularly in the Neruda, a work
where momentum, in less distinguished company, is inclined to sag. Anthony Halstead and the ECO
provide sensitive and tasteful accompaniments throughout.

Twentieth-Century Flute Concertos Jennifer Stinton (fl); [a]Geoffrey Browne
(cor ang); Scottish Chamber Orchestra / Steuart Bedford. Collins Classics Ⓕ 1210-2
(66 minutes: DDD: 8/91).
Honegger Concerto da camera[a]. **Ibert** Flute Concerto. **Nielsen** Flute Concerto, FS119.
Poulenc (orch. L. Berkeley) Flute Sonata.
Strictly speaking, two of the four works on this disc are not flute concertos at all: the Honegger, like
the Richard Strauss *Duet Concertino*, is a chamber concerto for two equal instruments and the
Poulenc is an orchestral transcription of the Flute Sonata, but let that pass! Here is an intelligently
planned and excellently recorded programme which forms a wonderful showcase for this highly
accomplished soloist. In the Nielsen, Steuart Bedford adopts a rather measured tempo for the first
movement. Jennifer Stinton plays with considerable dash and virtuosity (her first movement cadenza
is very fine indeed – even if it is not quite as breathtaking as Gallois). More perhaps could have been
made of the contrast in mood in the second movement and generally speaking, the impression
conveyed is that the orchestra is less inside the idiom than in the more straightforward Ibert and
Poulenc score. Honegger's own *Concerto da camera* comes from the late 1940s at much the same time
as the Fourth Symphony (*Deliciae basiliensis*), and inhabits much the same landscape. Indeed, part of
the slow movement could come from the Larghetto of the symphony. Stinton and Geoffrey Browne
play with great sympathy for the idiom and their performance will hopefully make more friends for
this civilized and rewarding score. There are good, thoroughly expert performances of the popular
Ibert Concerto and Sir Lennox Berkeley's transcription of the Poulenc. This is an enjoyable disc and
Stinton plays with artistry and charm – and the recording is first-class, both in respect to balance and
naturalness and presence.

Twentieth Century Plus [f]Andrew Marriner (cl); [ace]BBC Sympony Orchestra / [a]Peter Eötvös,
[c]Matthias Bamert, [e]Lothar Zagrosek; [b]BBC Philharmonic Orchestra / Sir Peter Maxwell Davies;
[f]London Symphony Orchestra / Michael Tilson Thomas; [d]English Chamber Orchestra / Steuart
Bedford. Collins Classics Ⓜ 2001/5-2 (five discs, oas: 37, 25, 30, 16 and 20 minutes: DDD: 3/92).
Items marked [a] and [b] recorded live in 1990. ⒼⒼ
2001-2: **Birtwistle** Earth Dances[a]. *2002-2:* **Maxwell Davies** Caroline Mathilde – Concert
Suite from Act 1[b]. *2003-2:* **Saxton** In the beginning[c]. Music to celebrate the resurrection of
Christ[d]. *2004-2:* **Mason** Lighthouses of England and Wales[e]. *2005-2:* **Tavener** The Repentant
Thief[f].
No, not a five-CD set, but five separately available CD singles, each featuring the music of a
contemporary British composer. At first sight the overall title "Twentieth Century Plus" may seem a
contradiction in terms (the longest CD has a duration of only 37 minutes) but when one considers
that the price of each CD is considerably less than that of a full-price issue and that both
performances and recordings are of exceptionally high quality then these are bargains indeed. The
most important (and long awaited) issue here is perhaps Birtwistle's large and impressive orchestral
work – *Earth Dances*. Though massively complex in its construction and organization of material,
Earth Dances can be a richly rewarding experience for the listener. Its title relates both to the
'geological' strata-like layers of the music, and often violent surface energy that almost makes the
earth dance. Tavener's *The Repentant Thief* for clarinet and orchestra is built around a rondo-like
structure made up of 10 segments – five "Refrains", three "Dances" and two "Laments", and its title
refers to the thief who was crucified with Jesus on Golgotha. It was composed shortly after Tavener
had finished work on two large-scale works (*Resurrection* and the opera *Mary of Egypt*) and is
described by the composer as "a shorter, simple and rather primitive piece". Its simplicity, clear-cut
formal scheme and tunefulness make it an immediately accessible and absorbing experience, and this

is all the more enhanced by a magical performance of the solo clarinet part by Andrew Marriner. Like the *Eight Songs for a Mad King* before it, the Concert Suite from Act 1 of the ballet *Caroline Mathilde* by Maxwell Davies explores the subject of madness – Caroline Mathilde was the wife of the unbalanced King Christian VII of Denmark. The ballet traces the King's gradual mental deterioration, and his wife's subsequent love affair with the King's physician (Dr Struensee) through a series of short tableaux that mix Maxwell Davies's musical parody style with his more acerbic and intricate methods of composing. The remaining discs feature music by the younger composers Benedict Mason and Robert Saxton. The highly original, if somewhat unusual *Lighthouses of England and Wales* reveals Mason to be a composer of a striking individuality, not to mention an extremely gifted orchestrator, and Saxton's richly colourful pieces – *In the beginning* and *Music to celebrate the resurrection of Christ* – continue the composer's interest in the religious theme of darkness into light.

Vienna Philharmonic on Holiday Vienna Philharmonic Orchestra / Rudolf Kempe.
Testament Ⓟ SBT1127 (78 minutes: ADD: 3/98). Items marked [a] from HMV ASD525 (8/63), [b]ASD494 (12/62), [c]ASD478 (9/62). Recorded 1961.
Mascagni Cavalleria rusticana – Intermezzo[a]. **Ponchielli** La Gioconda – Dance of the Hours[b].
Schmidt Notre Dame – Intermezzo[a]. **Gounod** Faust – Valse[a]. **Bayer** Die Puppenfee – Suite[a].
Offenbach Orphée aux enfers – Overture[a]. **Gotovac** Ero the Joker – Dance[b]. **Schubert**
Rosamunde, D797[c] – No. 1, Die Zauberharfe Overture, D644; No. 5, Entr'acte in B flat major;
No. 9, Ballet in G major. **Gluck** Orfeo ed Euridice – Dance of the Blessed Spirits[c].
If we generally think of Kempe as a great interpreter of the central Viennese classics and of German opera, Wagner in particular, we also have to remember that as Beecham's successor as Music Director of the RPO, chosen by the players, he also had this Beecham-esque gift of finding magic in undemanding music. The title of the disc implies a Viennese occasion, and though composers' nationalities are varied, that is fair enough when the waltz rhythms, for example, have such a delicious Viennese lilt. That is so not just in Viennese items such as the delightful Josef Bayer suite, *Die Puppenfee*, but in Gounod too, with Kempe bringing out the delicacy as well as the vigour. The Bayer, with its sequence of dance movements, is sensuous too as Kempe presents it, and so is the Mascagni interlude which opens the recital. Kempe's use of rubato is often extreme – arguably too much so in the Schubert *Rosamunde* music – but it never fails to be winning in a very Viennese way, as in the rare Franz Schmidt "Intermezzo". Even more clearly than the Schubert, the Gluck item may be counted too sweet, certainly by latter-day standards, but it is hard not to capitulate before such persuasive treatment, not just from the Viennese players as an ensemble, but specifically from the principal violin and cello in their solos. The Ponchielli, once so popular, now neglected, sparkles with uninhibited joy, as does the Offenbach, and it is good to have such a rarity as the dance by Jakob Gotovac, rhythmic and colourful in a sequence of contrasted sections. The recordings were all made in the Musikvereinsaal in Vienna, with the superb Testament transfers bringing out a warmth and depth of focus that many a later recording engineer working in that famed hall might envy.

Violin Concertos Elizabeth Wallfisch (vn); **Brandenburg Orchestra / Roy Goodman.**
Hyperion Ⓟ CDA66840 (79 minutes: DDD: 9/96). Recorded 1995.
Mysliveček Violin Concerto No. 4 in B flat major. **Schubert** Rondo for Violin and Strings in A major, D438. **Spohr** Violin Concerto No. 8 in A minor, Op. 47, "in modo di scena cantate".
Viotti Violin Concerto No. 22 in A minor, G97.
The revival in the popularity of the violin concerto during the latter part of the eighteenth century is winningly celebrated in this delightful, superbly recorded programme. Mysliveček's Fourth Concerto sets the tone with music of graceful charm, in which Wallfisch engagingly deploys her fluent virtuosity to reveal the music's full expressive potential. With sensitive accompaniment from the Brandenburg Orchestra, she presents a satisfying feeling of orderly balance in the first movement, poignantly expresses the *Larghetto*'s affecting melodiousness with incisive phrasing, and negotiates the athletic leaps in the finale with compelling vitality. Wallfisch and the Brandenburg go on to give a truly enchanting account of Viotti's A minor Violin Concerto (No. 22) that exploits the valuable insights offered by Ferdinand David's performing edition of the piece. Although Schubert never wrote a violin concerto, he did leave some impressive *concertante* violin music that attests to his own early training on the instrument. Finally, Spohr's A minor Concerto (No. 8) gives an intriguing theatrical element to the programme and Wallfisch and his forces vividly evoke the music's striking vocal character.

Works for Cello and Orchestra Han-Na Chang (vc); **London Symphony Orchestra /**
Mstislav Rostropovich. EMI Ⓟ CDC5 56126-2 (60 minutes: DDD: 11/96). Recorded 1995.
Gramophone Editor's choice. ⒼⒼ
Bruch Kol Nidrei, Op. 47. **Fauré** Elégie, Op. 24. **Saint-Saëns** Cello Concerto No. 1 in A minor, Op. 33. **Tchaikovsky** Variations on a Rococo Theme in A major, Op. 33.
This is a quite lovely performance of the Tchaikovsky *Rococo* Variations. The phenomenally gifted Korean-born cellist, Han-Na Chang, 13 years old when she made this recording, has the most ravishing tone and a wonderfully musical sense of line. Rostropovich has said, "I did not play as well as her at that age," and no wonder! It is he (or rather the first horn of the LSO) who sets the scene so elegantly for her first entry; and then Chang introduces Tchaikovsky's engaging theme with disarming

simplicity, with the first variation following with consummate ease and the third generating just the right degree of energy. But it is the fourth, *Andante grazioso*, introduced very gently, which is especially magical. It is a pity she didn't choose to record the original version, but then nor did Rostropovich himself and her performance is only slightly less sophisticated in detail and every bit as endearing. The lovely Fauré *Elégie* then follows and again the cello line is like a vocal aria, the shaping and use of light and shade unerring. Moreover she seems equally at home in the slightly more plangent atmosphere of Bruch's famous Hebrew melody and again her use of dynamic contrast seems instinctive. The Saint-Saëns Concerto is both passionate and light-hearted in its bravura: the busy, swirling opening full of energy, echoed spiritedly by the orchestra. The theme of the opening returns with joyous abandon, with the lyrical interludes turned into moments of autumnal nostalgia, and the piece ends in vigorous good humour. The mastery of this music-making recalls the young Menuhin, equally instinctive in the lyrical response to a melodic line. The recording is first-class in every way.

Works for Violin and Orchestra Joshua Bell (vn); Royal Philharmonic Orchestra / Andrew Litton. Decca Ⓕ 433 519-2DH (60 minutes: DDD: 1/92). Recorded 1991.
Saint-Saëns Introduction and Rondo capriccioso, Op. 28. **Massenet** Thaïs – Méditation. **Sarasate** Zigeunerweisen, Op. 20. **Chausson** Poème, Op. 25. **Ysaÿe** Caprice d'après l'étude en forme de valse de Saint-Saëns. **Ravel** Tzigane.

The Spaniard, Pablo de Sarasate, and the great Belgian virtuoso, Eugene Ysaÿe, both travelled to study in Paris during the second half of the last century, and although both were celebrated as distinguished exponents of violin technique, their collective influence upon the composers active in France at much the same time proved to be far more significant, as this brilliant selection of virtuoso showpieces will readily confirm. The young American violinist, Joshua Bell, himself a grand-pupil of Ysaÿe via his teacher, Joseph Gingold, is heard to superb advantage here in commanding performances of music which will captivate as much as it will astonish. Bell captures the heady bravura of Saint-Saëns *Introduction and Rondo capriccioso* with breathtaking ease, and his spiccato playing in the coda is little short of phenomenal. Sarasate's perennial favourite *Zigeunerweisen* will also astound, with Bell's mastery of the whole panoply of technical effects, including multiple-stopping and left hand pizzicato, contributing to an authentic gipsy-style performance. No recording of this kind would be complete without the celebrated "Méditation" from Massenet's *Thaïs*, made especially compelling here, in Bell's affectionately rich-toned account. The same tonal refinement and sensitivity characterize his elegiac reading of the *Poème* by Chausson, ably supported by the Royal Philharmonic Orchestra under Andrew Litton. Ysaÿe's *Caprice d'après l'etude* is another, although rather less familiar *tour de force*, affording every possibility for virtuosic display, although it does not challenge Ravel's devilish *Tzigane* in terms of pure technical difficulty. This truly hair-raising rendition of the *Tzigane* would bring any concert audience to its feet, and Bell is wholly at ease with its Bartókian gipsy style. This thrilling playing crowns a hugely enjoyable collection from this dazzling young virtuoso. The clear and incisive Decca sound ensures that the forces are balanced effectively, and the natural ambience of Watford Town Hall lends a realistic dramatic weight to full orchestral climaxes, without undue spotlighting of the soloist. An admirable and meticulous release, then, whose appeal will gain Joshua Bell many new admirers.

Works for Violin and Orchestra Gidon Kremer (vn); [c]Andrei Gavrilov (pf); [a]Berlin Philharmonic Orchestra / Herbert von Karajan; [b]Philharmonia Orchestra / Riccardo Muti. EMI Forte Ⓜ CZS5 69334-2 (two discs: 151 minutes: ADD). Item marked [a] from HMV ASD3261 (10/76), [b]ASD143519-1 (10/83), [c]new to UK. Ⓖ
Brahms Violin Concerto in D major, Op. 77[a]. **Sibelius** Violin Concerto in D minor, Op. 47[b]. **Schumann** Violin Concerto in D minor, Op. posth[b]. **Weber** Grand duo concertant, J204[c]. **Hindemith** Violin Sonata in E flat major, Op. 11[c]. **Schnittke** Quasi una Sonata[c].

It would be hard to imagine a finer showcase for Kremer's talent than this two-disc collection. At mid price in EMI's Forte series it makes an outstanding bargain. The Schumann has been a benchmark performance for some years, strong and purposeful in the outer movements, hushed and dedicated in the central slow movement. With Muti a challenging yet sympathetic partner, the Sibelius is also given a remarkable performance, notable not just for Kremer's expressive warmth, but for his inner intensity in the great opening melodies of the first two movements, each played as a hushed meditation, but with the first flowing freely, fanciful and poetic, not too slow for an *Allegro moderato*. The finale is then fast and volatile. This recoupling for the two-disc format is also valuable for offering Kremer's glowing account of the Brahms Concerto, his first collaboration with Karajan, one which plainly inspired them both. The spaciousness of the first movement brings total concentration, to justify Kremer's freedom of expression. The slow movement possesses poise and purity, leading to a beautifully sprung account of the finale, with dance rhythms brought out. The analogue recording is comparably spacious. In the three new items Gavrilov proves a comparably inspired partner, with the Weber so winningly characterized – fiery in the first movement, dedicated in the *Andante* and exuberant in the finale – that one almost forgets the original clarinet version, so satisfying is the transformation. The early Hindemith Sonata can rarely have been played with such warmth and intensity, and the Schnittke work, full of extended, pregnant pauses, is superbly held together by the concentrated interplay of the performers, an astonishing 20-minute tapestry full of striking, unexpected ideas.

Chamber

Amber Waves American Clarinet Music. **Richard Stoltzman** (cl); **Irma Vallecillo** (pf).
RCA Victor Red Seal Ⓟ 09026 62685-2 (66 minutes: DDD: 9/96). Recorded 1994.
Gershwin (arr. Gach) Three Preludes. **Bernstein** Clarinet Sonata. **McKinley** Clarinet Sonata.
C. Fisher Clarinet Sonatine. **Hyman** Clarinata. **Rowles** The Peacocks. **Traditional**
(arr. Stoltzman) Amazing Grace.
Richard Stoltzman could be claimed as the James Galway of the clarinet. He has developed the
personality of the instrument in new ways, often drawing on jazz effects, in what he regards as an
American tradition. And he has a considerable following. He has recorded major pieces like the
Corigliano Concerto, but in this collection he's simply relaxing. He starts with an ingenious
arrangement of Gershwin's piano pieces, the *Three Preludes*, where the few extra effects in both
clarinet and piano are completely idiomatic. Then there's Bernstein's early Sonata, another American
classic. W.T. McKinley makes his début in the British catalogue with a rather overblown, four-
movement Sonata and so does Clare Fisher with *Sonatine*. There's nothing very individual in either
work, but Stoltzman obviously enjoys playing them. The real gems come when he goes deeper into
jazz, especially Jimmy Rowles's *The Peacocks*, which was used in the soundtrack of *Round Midnight*.
This brings out everything in Stoltzman's unique style – bent notes and microtonal slides in near
vocal effects. Magical! Dick Hyman is another jazz pianist and composer. His *Clarinata* is a red-hot
encore with a soupy middle section. Finally Stoltzman plays his own arrangement of *Amazing Grace*,
starting unaccompanied, and very touching it is too. An attractive collection, well recorded.

The American Album Anne Akiko Meyers (vn); André-Michel Schub (pf).
RCA Victor Red Seal Ⓟ 09026 68114-2 (55 minutes: DDD: 8/96). Recorded 1994.
D. Baker Blues. **Copland** Violin Sonata. Nocturne. **Ives** Violin Sonata No. 4, "Children's Day
at the Camp Meeting". **Piston** Violin Sonatina.
Walter Piston's clean-cut, purposeful *Sonatina* (1945) evinces a polish and economy of utterance
entirely characteristic of its creator. The centrepiece, an *Adagio espressivo* of Bachian serenity and
concentration (marvellously conveyed on this occasion), acts as an ideal foil to the outer movements,
both of which have a fine, almost jazzy spring to their heels. The Copland Sonata dates from 1942-3.
Following its completion, the composer embarked on *Appalachian Spring*, a work whose spare-
textured strength and deceptively powerful purity are also very much in evidence here. Indeed, this
sonata is top-notch Copland, by turns exhilaratingly lithe and memorably chaste. The *Nocturne*
(1926), a slumbering blues of exquisite, twilit beauty, is another striking inspiration. By contrast,
David Baker's *Blues* (1966) inhabits an altogether less shadowy, complex world of expression. It is a
melodious, uncomplicated essay, described by the composer as "stylistically a marriage of the blues
and gospel music". Last, but not least, there is Ives's Fourth Sonata (1906-16). Bearing the legend
"Children's Day at the Camp Meeting", it offers the usual endearing mix of sepia-tinted nostalgia,
playful pranking, revivalist hymn-tunes and vernacular tunes. Performances are consistently stylish
and utterly sympathetic. The recording, too, is first-rate.

An American Cellobration ªRichard Slavich (vc); ᵇAlice Rybak (pf). Crystal Records Ⓟ CD639
(64 minutes: DDD: 5/98).
Bolcom Cello Sonataᵃᵇ. **Copland** Billy the Kid – Waltz; Celebrationᵃᵇ. **Harbison** Suite for
Solo Celloᵃ. **Rochberg** Ricordanzᵃᵇ. Rorem After Reading Shakespeareᵇ.
A readily approachable quintet of works, winningly essayed by cellist Richard Slavich and pianist
Alice Rybak (both of whom currently teach at the University of Denver). Especially compelling are
the nine varied impressions that make up Ned Rorem's thoughtful suite for solo cello, *After Reading
Shakespeare* (1979). Both John Harbison's baroque-inspired Suite (1994) and William Bolcom's 1989
Sonata evince considerable substance and craft, while George Rochberg's screne *Ricordanza* (1972) is
a poignant elegy in memory of the composer's nephew.

American Works for Wind Quintet Reykjavik Wind Quintet (Bernhardur Wilkinson, fl; Dadi
Kolbeinsson, ob; Einar Jóhannesson, cl; Joseph Ognibene, hn; Hafsteinn Gudmundsson, bn).
Chandos Ⓟ CHAN9174 (66 minutes: DDD: 11/93). Recorded 1991-2.
Barber Summer Music, Op. 31. **Beach** Pastorale. **Fine** Partita. **Harbison** Wind Quintet.
Villa-Lobos Quinteto em forma de chôros. **Schuller** Suite.
American music, Icelandic instrumentalists, British venue. Barber's *Summer Music* is delightfully
relaxed and playful here, helped by the familiar glow of The Maltings' acoustic. Schuller's little Suite,
his first published work, is a teenage *jeu d'esprit* which already shows him experimenting with aspects
of jazz in the central Blues movement. Harbison's Wind Quintet is certainly serious in intent, its
musical language not always as approachable as we expect from this composer though the outer
movements are immediately striking. While eminently lean, lucid and fluent, Beach's brief *Pastorale*
risks sounding old hat after this – its idiom would have been considered antiquated in 1942 – and the
programme ends on a slightly disconnected note with one of Villa-Lobos's less shapely utterances.
Even so, this is a thoroughly recommendable package.

Balanescu Quartet Balanescu Quartet (Alexander Balanescu, Clare Connors, vns; Bill Hawkes, va; Caroline Dale, vc). Argo Ⓕ 436 565-2ZH (52 minutes: DDD: 3/93). Recorded 1992.   ⓔ
Byrne High Life. **Moran** Music from the Towers of the Moon. **Lurie** Stranger than Paradise. **Torke** Chalk.

Heterodox these pieces might be, but together they make a recital that's surprisingly and delightfully integrated. All four of the American composers represented here write in easily approachable styles. Each work is excellently served by highly dedicated, expert performances from the Balanescu Quartet, and by a faithful, well-defined recording. David Byrne's extraordinary hybrid of a piece, *High Life*, is the shortest piece on the disc, and consists of syncopated, repeated patterns over which apparently random, free-floating ideas come into being and then dissolve away. Robert Moran's contribution uses material from his opera *From the Towers of the Moon* and is in four short sections. His style is readily enjoyable, with fresh and energetic ideas, and attractive melodic invention. John Lurie's *Stranger than Paradise* is based on music written for a film of the same name: six descriptive episodes form a pleasantly evocative work which is influenced by blues and minimalist styles. *Chalk* is Michael Torke's word for the resinous residue formed by the action of a bow drawn strongly across a stringed instrument. The basic pulse of his piece is constant, in the style of the minimalists, and indeed there is plenty of vigorous, even hectic writing for the four instruments. Torke's insert-notes indicate that he much admires the Balanescu players, and they certainly play their hearts out for him.

Beyond the Iron Curtain Leslie Newman (fl); Amanda Hurton (pf). Cala Ⓕ CACD88026 (76 minutes: DDD: 6/96). Recorded 1994.
Taktakishvili Flute Sonata. **Feld** Flute Sonata. **Gubaidulina** Allegro rustico. Sounds of the Forest. **Amirov** Six Pieces. **Martinů** Flute Sonata No. 1.

The familiar work here is the Martinů Sonata, an unobtrusive masterpiece which contains the quintessence of his gentle, sympathetic personality. Admittedly it is hardly 'Beyond the Iron Curtain', for it was composed in America in 1945, and the descent of the Iron Curtain a few years later was the precise reason why Martinů was never again to return to his homeland. But never mind. It is a lovely, warm performance, beautifully recorded. The same could be said of the recital as a whole. Well-written flute music has a way of sounding French, no matter where it was written. So it should be no surprise to find the Georgian Taktakishvili taking his cue from Fauré, or his Czech contemporary Feld embracing a garrulous neo-classicism that could easily pass for Milhaud, or the Azerbaijani Amirov, another near-contemporary, hitting on an attractive blend of Ravel and Khachaturian. But you may be more than a bit surprised to find Gubaidulina sounding like Dutilleux in her charming, tarantella-like *Allegro rustico*. Her *Sounds of the Forest* is closer to her familiar world of mystic rustlings, but this too is far more instantly appealing than the music for which she is best known.

Black Angels Kronos Quartet (David Harrington, John Sherba, vns; Hank Dutt, va; Joan Jeanrenaud, vc). Nonesuch Ⓕ 7559-79242-2 (62 minutes: DDD: 4/91).   ⓔⓔ
Crumb Black Angels. **Tallis** (arr. Kronos Qt) Spem in alium. **Marta** Doom. A sigh. **Ives** (arr. Kronos Qt/Geist) They are there! **Shostakovich** String Quartet No. 8 in C minor, Op. 110.

This is very much the sort of imaginative programming we've come to expect from this talented young American quartet. With an overall theme of war and persecution the disc opens with George Crumb's *Black Angels*, for electric string quartet. This work was inspired by the Vietnam War and bears two inscriptions to that effect – *in tempore belli* (in time of war) and "Finished on Friday the Thirteenth of March, 1970", and it's described by Crumb as "a kind of parable on our troubled contemporary world". The work is divided into three sections which represent the three stages of the voyage of the soul – fall from grace, spiritual annihilation and redemption. As with most of his works he calls on his instrumentalists to perform on a variety of instruments other than their own – here that ranges from gongs, maracas and crystal glasses to vocal sounds such as whistling, chanting and whispering. *Doom. A sigh* is the young Hungarian composer István Marta's disturbing portrait of a Roumanian village as they desperately fight to retain their sense of identity in the face of dictatorship and persecution. Marta's atmospheric blend of electronic sound, string quartet and recorded folk-songs leave one with a powerful and moving impression. At first sight Tallis's *Spem in alium* may seem oddly out of place considering the overall theme of this disc, but as the insert-notes point out the text was probably taken from the story of Judith, in which King Nebuchadnezzar's general Holofernes besieged the Jewish fortress of Bethulia. Kronos's own arrangement of this 40-part motet (involving some multi-tracking) certainly makes a fascinating alternative to the original. A particularly fine account of Shostakovich's Eighth String Quartet (dedicated to the victims of fascism and war) brings this thought-provoking and imaginative recital to a close. Performances throughout are outstanding, and the recording first-class.

Brass Quintets Center City Brass Quintet (Anthony DiLorenzo, Ryan Anthony, tpts; Richard King, hn; Mark Lawrence, [a]Steven Witser, tbns; Craig Knox, tuba). Collins Classics Ⓕ 1489-2 (66 minutes: DDD: 1/97). Recorded 1993.
Arnold Quintet, Op. 73. **Ewald** Quintet No. 1 in B flat minor. **Bozza** Sonatine. **Maurer** Three Pieces. **Dahl** Music for Brass Instruments[a]. **Calvert** Suite from the Monteregian Hills.

No one could write for a brass quintet more wittily than Sir Malcolm Arnold and his tail-chasing opening theme, with its contrasting chorale, superficially reminds one of Britten's fugue in his *Young Person's Guide*; but the dark, central "Chaconne" is all Arnold's own; the disrespectful finale then mixes influences from everywhere including jazz and, of course, produces a *tune*, worthy of its infectious surroundings. Ewald's Quintet is more conventional but it is agreeable and sonorously scored; again there is no lack of melodic interest. Bozza's *Sonatine* is agreeable occasional music, with the melancholy of the slow movement nicely offset by the roisterously uninhibited scherzo. The finale is a grotesque march which quotes from Shostakovich and Ravel. Maurer's *Three Pieces* are brief but characterful and richly harmonized. Dahl opens by spectacularly recalling a Bach chorale, and then in his emotionally plangent third movement dips into dissonance, ending with a closely interwoven fugato and a thrillingly assertive coda. The mood then lightens for Calvert's *Suite from the Monteregian Hills*, winningly based on French-Canadian folk-songs. The first movement is contagiously rhythmic, the scherzo offbeat, and an exuberantly jazzy finale finally celebrates a French Christmas carol. Not a single item here is dull or lacking freshness of ideas, and the players relish this attractive repertoire, playing with sparkling bravura and blending expertly. The recording is in the demonstration bracket.

Cello Song Julian Lloyd Webber (vc); John Lenehan (pf). Philips Ⓕ 434 917-2PH
(53 minutes: DDD: 10/93). Recorded 1992.
Villa-Lobos O Canto do capadócio. **Bach** Cantata No. 156, Ich steh mit einem Fuss im Grabe – Sinfonia. **Castelnuovo-Tedesco** Sea murmurs, Op. 24a. **Schumann** Funf Stücke im Volkston, Op. 102 – No. 2, Langsam. **Scriabin** Etudes in B flat minor, Op. 8 No. 11. **Rachmaninov** Romance in F minor. **Grieg** Lyric Pieces, Book 3, Op. 43 – To the Spring. **Delius** Hassan – Serenade. **Elgar** Romance, Op. 62. **Chopin** Cello Sonata in G minor, Op. 65 – Largo. **Brahms** Five Lieder, Op. 105 – Wie Melodien zieht es mir. **Dvořák** Seven Gipsy Melodies, B104 (Op. 55) – Songs my mother taught me. **Debussy** Beau soir. **Messiaen** Quatuor pour la fin du temps – Louange à l'Eternité de Jésus. **Traditional** The Star of the County Down.

As the title of this disc implies, all the pieces contained therein are rather in the same slowish-paced, lyric vein, but their sequence has been cleverly chosen so that there is still plenty of variety to keep the listener's attention. Some of the items are original cello and piano pieces, others are skilful arrangements, and there is a good mixture of well known and unusual offerings. Elgar's bassoon *Romance* translates particularly well to the cello, as do the Brahms, Debussy and Dvořák songs and only in the arrangement of Grieg's piano piece, *To the Spring* does one feel that a cello is a little out of place. The Messiaen excerpt is the longest and the most profound item, and it exists quite happily as an entity away from the rest of the *Quatuor*. Throughout the programme Julian Lloyd Webber plays with exceptional sensitivity, sympathy and tonal beauty – in fact it would be difficult to find better performances of this kind of repertoire anywhere on records of today or yesterday. John Lenehan gives good support, and Philips have provided a mellow, roomy recording.

Chamber Works [a]Arthur Gleghorn (fl); [a]Mitchell Lurie (cl); [ab]Ann Mason Stockton (hp); [acd]Hollywood Quartet (Felix Slatkin, Paul Shure, vns; Paul Robyn, va; Eleanor Aller, vc); [b]Concert Arts Strings / Felix Slatkin. Testament mono Ⓕ SBT1053* (73 minutes: ADD: 3/95). Items marked [ab] from Capitol CCL7509 (7/52), [c]Capitol CTL7063 (9/54), [d]CTL7004 (6/51). Recorded 1949-53.
Ravel Introduction and Allegro[a]. **Debussy** Danse sacrée et danse profane[b]. **Turina** La oración del torero, Op. 34[c]. **Villa-Lobos** String Quartet No. 6[d]. **Creston** String Quartet, Op. 8[c].

What a wonderful feeling for line these players had, what an incredible, perfectly matched and blended ensemble they produced – and how well these transfers sound! The Sixth Quartet of Villa-Lobos (1940) is slight but attractive and receives here a performance of the utmost brilliance and clarity. Paul Creston's String Quartet is slightly Gallic in feeling, and sweeter and more euphonious than those of Piston or William Schuman. The sound, as elsewhere in these recordings, is slightly on the dry side, save in the Ravel *Introduction and Allegro*, which also offers the additional attraction of Arthur Gleghorn's flute playing (though given the excellence of Mitchell Lurie and Ann Mason Stockton, it seems invidious to single him out). The Debussy *Danse sacrée et danse profane* sounds every bit as magical as it did 40 years ago.

Chamber Works [a]Nikita Cardinaux (bass cl); Swiss Wind Quintet (Michael Hartmann, fl; Tilmann Zahn, ob; Urs Brügger, cl; Tomasz Sosnowski, bn; Henryk Kalinski, hn). Koch Discover International Ⓑ DICD920395 (65 minutes: DDD: 8/97).
Hindemith Kleine Kammermusik, Op. 24 No. 2. **Janáček** Mládí[a]. **Ligeti** Six Bagatelles. **Nielsen** Wind Quintet, FS100.

These performances are all excellent, the Swiss players seeming to be a well-balanced group, though the fine Koch recording undoubtedly helped. Their earthiness of tone suits *Mládí* well, the Nielsen less so, though they get as close to the essence of this work as any of their rivals. What is particularly pleasing is the Swiss Quintet's natural choice of tempos, as for instance in Nielsen's first movement. They also clearly enjoyed themselves, relishing the gentle humour as well as the more raucous moments in the

Hindemith and Ligeti; the latter is given an electric account. If you do not already have these works start here; if you do these are more than viable alternatives.

A Choice Collection **Palladian Ensemble** (Pamela Thorby, rec; Rachel Podger, vn; Susanne Heinrich, va da gamba; William Carter, gtr/theorbo). Linn Records Ⓕ CKD041 (66 minutes: DDD: 5/96). Recorded 1995.

Locke Broken Consorts – D major; C major. **Matteis** Setts of Ayres – Book 2: No. 10, Preludio in ostinatione; No. 12, Andamento malincolico; Book 3: No. 7, Preludio-Prestissimo; No. 8, Sarabanda-Adagio; No. 9, Gavotta con divisioni; Book 4: No. 27, Bizzararrie sopra un basso malinconico; No. 28, Aria amorosa-Adagio. **Baltzar** John come kiss me now. **Weldon** Sett of Ayres in D major. **Blow** Ground in G minor. **Butler** Variations on Callino Casturame. **J. Banister** Divisions on a Ground. **Anonymous** Old Simon the King.

The "choice collection" of "music of Purcell's London" is of items such as might have been heard at the concerts of then contemporary music held on the premises of Thomas Britton, the "small coal man", surely one of the most unlikely patrons in the history of music. It is in effect complementary to the Palladian Ensemble's earlier disc ("An Excess of Pleasure", also on Linn Records, Ⓓ CKD010, 7/93), with another liberal helping of Matteis's various and sometimes agreeably bizarre *Ayres* and two more of Locke's *Broken Consorts*, which we find absorbing rather than confusing – as Charles II did. With this disc John Weldon and Henry Butler are newcomers to the catalogue, the former with what amounts to an irregularly ordered suite, the latter with splendid variations on *Callino Casturame* in which Susanne Heinrich plays most expressively – and proves that chords played on the viola da gamba do not have to sound like teeth being pulled. *Old Simon the King* could not have been heard in Purcell's own time in this anonymous setting from *The division flute* of 1706, though it might have featured in one of Britton's concerts, but the tune was printed as early as 1652. If you are not already aware of the high quality of the instrumental playing, stylish musicality and imaginative approach of the Palladian Ensemble this disc provides a good opportunity to find what you have been missing.

Composers in Person [a]**Maria Barrientos,** [b]**Ninon Vallin** (sops); [c]**Enrique Granados,** [d]**Federico Mompou,** [b]**Joaquin Nin** (pfs); **Manuel de Falla** ([a]pf/[e]hpd); [e]**instrumental ensemble.** EMI Composers in Person mono Ⓕ CDC7 54836-2* (78 minutes: ADD: 11/93). Texts and translations included. Recorded between 1912 and 1950.

Granados Danzas españolas, Op. 37[c] – No. 7, Valenciana; No. 10, Danza triste (both from Odeon 68649/50). Goyescas – No. 7, El pelele[c] (68651. All recorded *c*1912). **Falla** Siete canciones populares españolas[a] (French Columbia D11701 and PFX1/2. 1928-30). El amor brujo[a] – Canción del fuego fátuo. Soneto a Córdoba (PFX2. 1930). Harpsichord Concerto[e] (French Columbia LFX92/3. 1930). **Mompou**[d] Scènes d'enfants – No. 5, Jeunes filles au jardin. Suburbis – No. 1, El carrer, el guitarrista i el vell cavall. Cançons i dansas – No. 5 (all from French Columbia FCX184); No. 6 (previously unpublished); No. 8. Paisajes – No. 1, La fuente y la campana (FCX184. All 1950). **Nin**[b] Cantos populares españolas – No. 3, Tonada de la niña perdida; No. 4, Montañesa; No. 6, Malagueña; No. 7, Granadina; No. 19, Canto Andaluz; No. 20, Polo (Odeon 188693/5. 1929).

With few exceptions all Spain's leading composers in the early part of this century were excellent pianists. Granados is represented by some discs dating from 1912. Despite their surface noise (very heavy in an improvised ramble on "El pelele"), his qualities are evident, particularly in a light, airy and crisply rhythmic "Valenciana". The major part of the present disc is given over, reasonably enough, to Falla, an indisputably greater composer than the others and a conspicuously first-class keyboard player. His playing of the Harpsichord Concerto is masterly, especially of the *Lento* which, exemplifying his plea that it should be taken as slowly as humanly possible, is enormously atmospheric and evocative of great bells during the Corpus Christi procession. Falla is equally outstanding in the seven folk-songs accompanying Maria Barrientos. Ninon Vallin's bright, clear voice is artlessly attractive in the folk-song settings of Nin, a virtuoso pianist who is evidently enjoying himself in the "Malagueña". In a totally different style, far more introspective and subtle, is the playing of Mompou. He takes the dance of the fifth *Canço i dansa* slower than usual, gives a fine lift to the sixth (dedicated to Rubinstein), and is utterly seductive in the sentimental tune of "Jeunes filles au jardin", played very slowly and freely.

Concertos and Duets **Christopher Hogwood, Christophe Rousset** (hpds/clavs/fps). L'Oiseau-Lyre Ⓕ 440 649-2OH (65 minutes: DDD: 8/96). Recorded 1993.

J.S. Bach Double Harpsichord Concerto in C major, BWV1061*a*. The Art of Fugue, BWV1080 – Contrapunctus 13. **C.P.E. Bach:** Four Duets, H610-13. **W.F. Bach:** Double Keyboard Concerto in F major, F10. **J.C. Bach:** Duet in G major, Op. 15.

In a convincingly argued note Christopher Hogwood points out that the Bach household was exceptional in always having several keyboard instruments and members of the family to play them, singly or together, and that the generic term 'clavier', applied to various types, needs to be understood in the light of the individual works that were composed there. On this disc, then, the J.S. works are played on harpsichords, those of W.F. and C.P.E. on clavichords and J.C.'s Duet on two square pianos. The most familiar work here, Johann Sebastian's C major Concerto, is presented without the strings, which seem to have been added later: the fugal finale is given an exhilarating bounce. Contrapunctus

13, in both its *rectus* and *inversus* forms, comes over with splendid clarity. Ensemble throughout is neat, and the balance between the instruments well judged, the contrast between them underlined not only by differences of timbre but by being separated into left and right channels. Despite a warning not to alter the volume control for the clavichord works, you may feel some slight adjustment desirable in order fully to appreciate their interplay, particularly the delightful Friedemann Concerto, in whose finale the instruments are pitted against each other with dramatic emphasis. The C.P.E. Duets, mostly arrangements of wind pieces, are of slighter interest, though No. a4 is jolly (and played with gusto); that by Johann Christian, in purely *galant* style, is engagingly showy, and the performers' evident enjoyment in it communicates itself to the listener.

Début Sarah Chang (vn); **Sandra Rivers** (pf). EMI Ⓔ CDC7 54352-2 (51 minutes: DDD: 1/93). Recorded 1991.
   Sarasate Concert Fantasy on "Carmen", Op. 25. **Elgar** Salut d'amour, Op. 12. La Capricieuse, Op. 17. **Khachaturian** Gayaneh – Sabre Dance. **Kreisler** Tempo di Menuetto in the style of Pugnani. **Paganini** Caprices, Op. 1 – No. 1 in E major; No. 15 in E minor. **Chopin** (arr. Milstein) Nocturne in C sharp minor, Op. posth. **Shostakovich** (arr. Zyganow) Preludes, Op. 34 – No. 10 in C sharp minor; No. 15 in D major. **Gershwin** (trans. Heifetz) Porgy and Bess – It ain't necessarily so. **Liszt** (arr. Milstein) Consolations, S172 – Lento placido. **Tchaikovsky** Souvenir d'un lieu cher, Op. 42 – Mélodie in E flat major. **Prokofiev** (arr. Heifetz) The Love for Three Oranges – March.
This astonishing disc heralds the recording début of another much-vaunted violinistic phenomenon, the 11-year-old Sarah Chang. A student of the acclaimed pedagogue Dorothy DeLay, Chang actually made this recording at the age of nine, playing a quarter-sized violin. With an impressive catalogue of major orchestral engagements to her credit, she is now continuing her studies at the Juilliard School in New York. Her taxing programme opens with an impeccable account of Sarasate's *Carmen* Fantasy, in an edition prepared by Zino Francescatti; dazzling playing, even if that last *frisson* of excitement is held in check. The two Elgar favourites are charming, even if slightly mannered, but Chang's bristling performances of Khachaturian's "Sabre Dance" and the famous Heifetz transcription of the March from Prokofiev's *The Love for Three Oranges* are both sensational. Her Paganini, too, is electrifying – she despatches the First and Fifteenth *Caprices* with the confident *élan* of a seasoned virtuoso. The same technical assurance is evident in two Preludes by Shostakovich, but undemonstrative offerings are marginally less convincing perhaps, at this very early stage, with some inflexibility in the Tchaikovsky and Kreisler works. She is a shade unyielding in her approach to Nathan Milstein's winning Chopin and Liszt arrangements, but her natural spontaneity works to greater advantage in "It ain't necessarily so", from *Porgy and Bess*, in the famous Heifetz version. Her recording début will enthral and captivate in equal measure.

Jacqueline du Pré – Her Early BBC Recordings Jacqueline du Pré, [f]William Pleeth (vcs); [deg]Ernest Lush, [c]Stephen Kovacevich (pfs). EMI Studio mono Ⓜ CDM7 63165/6-2* (two discs: 112 minutes: ADD: 9/89). Recorded at broadcast performances on [a]January 7th, 1962, [b]January 26th, 1962, [c]February 25th, 1965, [dg]March 22nd, 1961, [e]September 3rd, 1962, [f]March 17th, 1963. ⒼⒼ
   CDM7 63165-2: **Bach** Solo Cello Suites – No. 1 in G major, BWV1007[a]; No. 2 in D minor, BWV1008[b]. **Britten** Cello Sonata in C major, Op. 65 – Scherzo and March[c]. **Falla** (arr. Maréchal) Suite populaire espagnole[d]. *CDM7 63166-2*: **Brahms** Cello Sonata No. 2 in F major, Op. 99[e]. **F. Couperin** Nouveaux Concerts – Treizième Concert[f]. **Handel** (arr. Slatter) Oboe Concerto in G minor, HWV287[g].
We owe the BBC and EMI a debt of gratitude for making these valuable recordings available on disc. The performances date from her mid- to late- teens, and reveal a maturity and passion that is rare in so young a performer. This, together with her wonderful gift of communication, make these performances very special indeed. The two Bach Cello Suites have a magical, intimate poetry that transfixes the attention from the very first note and her beautifully phrased and lyrical readings more than compensate for any slight imperfections of articulation. Sadly we have only the "Scherzo" and "March" movements from the Britten Cello Sonata, and judging by the quality of these, a complete performance would surely have been a recording to treasure. These are sparkling performances, full of wit and good humour, reflecting the obvious rapport between the two young artists. The recording of Falla's *Suite populaire espagnole* dates from 1961 when du Pré was only 16 but is no less assured or technically accomplished. The performance is full of life and rhythmic vitality, with some very tender and expressive playing, as in the cantabile melodies of the "Nana" and "Cancion" movements. The mono recordings are not of the highest quality (the Bach Suites are taken from transcription discs, so there are traces of surface noise and clicks) but this is of little relevance when we are presented with playing as beautiful and captivating as this.

Espana! Katia and Marielle Labèque (pfs). Philips Ⓕ 438 938-2PH (59 minutes: DDD: 9/94). Recorded 1993.
   Falla La vida breve – Danses espagnoles. El amor brujo – Ritual Fire Dance. **Lecuona** Malagueña. **Albéniz** Suite española, Op. 47 – Sevilla; Cádiz; Aragon; Castilla. Pavana capricho, Op. 12. Iberia – Triana. Navarra. **Infante** Danses Andalouses.

The Labèque sisters give us the right Iberian mixture of vigour, brilliance, shadows and languor, and seem to be thoroughly enjoying themselves in music that they know well. There is no more exciting keyboard performance of Falla's "Ritual Fire Dance". This is actually a transcription by Mario Bragiotti. Indeed, save for the *Danses Andalouses* by Manuel Infante, every piece here is a transcription and the Labèques themselves have had a hand in that of Lecuona's exquisitely sultry *Malagueña*, which includes quietly plucked strings at the two-minute mark. But no one would know that this music was not originally written for two pianos, for everything is idiomatic. Indeed, the transcription of Albéniz's *Suite española* and *Pavana capricho* is by the composer, while that of his "Triana" (music that beautifully blends vivacity and delicacy) is by his friend Granados. The recording is intimate yet atmospheric.

English Viola Music Paul Coletti (va); [a]Leslie Howard (pf). Hyperion Ⓟ CDA66687
(67 minutes: DDD: 10/94). Recorded 1993.   Ⓖ
    Britten Elegy. **Vaughan Williams** Romance[a]. **R. Clarke** Lullaby[a]. Morpheus[a]. Viola Sonata[a].
    Grainger Sussex Mummers' Christmas Carol, BFMS17[a]. Arrival Platform Humlet, RMTB1.
    Bax Legend for Viola and Piano[a]. **Bridge** Pensiero, H53a[a]. Allegro appassionato, H82[a].
The centre-piece to Scottish violist Paul Coletti's enterprising recorded début is the very fine Sonata by Rebecca Clarke (1886-1979). Displaying a most beguiling harmonic resource (the sound-world is distinctly Gallic with distant echoes of such English contemporaries as Bax and Ireland), idiomatic mastery (the viola was Clarke's own chosen instrument) and exquisite finish. That other English violist-composer of note, Frank Bridge, is represented by his *Pensiero* and *Allegro appassionato* (both from 1908, and surprisingly the only two pieces he wrote for his own instrument). Vaughan Williams's *Romance* turned up amongst the composer's papers after his death: although only 5'40" in length, it squeezes a wealth of incident and emotion into its compact frame. Percy Grainger's heart-warming *Sussex Mummers' Christmas Carol* finds these performers at their most touchingly eloquent, whilst Coletti audibly relishes the bracing sonorities of the unaccompanied *Arrival Platform Humlet* (a 'little hum', in case you were wondering). Bax's *Legend* dates from July 1929, a peak period between his Third Symphony and *Winter Legends*. It's a ten-minute essay of slumbering power and richly-stocked invention; indeed, as so often with this composer's instrumental output, the writing is almost orchestral in its emotional scope and remarkable range of colour. The performances throughout are past praise in their sensitivity and dedication and the engineering is impeccable.

Fantaisie for Flute and Harp Anna Noakes (fl); Gillian Tingay (hp).
ASV White Line Ⓜ CDWHL2101 (76 minutes: DDD: 11/96). Recorded 1996.
    Traditional El diablo suelto. La partida. Spanish Love Song (trans. Galway). Urpila. Bailecito de Procesión. **Villa-Lobos** Modinha. Bachianas Brasileiras No. 5. **Fauré** Fantaisie, Op. 79.
    Après un rêve, Op. 7 No. 1. Sicilienne, Op. 78. Pièce. **L. Boulanger** Nocturne. **Saint-Saëns**
    Romance, Op. 37. **Ravel** Pavane pour une infante défunte. **Caplet** Rêverie. **Piazzolla** Histoire du Tango.
Here is a lightweight but entertaining collection, which happily juxtaposes French insouciance with Latin American sparkle. The pair of South American folk-songs which opens the programme are real lollipops; then comes some lilting Villa-Lobos; first the sultry rhythmic *Modinha*, nudged with a nice rhythmic subtlety, and then the famous (soprano/cello) *Bachianas Brasileiras* No. 5, which sounds seductive enough on the flute. The disc includes flowing, coolly beautiful Fauré and a gentle, haunting *Nocturne* by Lili Boulanger (meltingly phrased by Anna Noakes), followed by a romantic *morceau* by Saint-Saëns. One of the most enticing later pieces is the chimerical *Rêverie* of André Caplet and the recital ends with a highly individual and immediately arresting suite of four strongly flavoured miniatures by Astor Piazzolla called *Histoire du Tango*, bewitching in their combination of Latin rhythmic inflexions with a smoky Parisian night-club atmosphere. They are presented with much *élan* and sparkle and given added lift by various uninhibited percussive thwacks from both players. The balance seems very pleasing, and though the harp sounds somewhat recessed, it always provides a glowing, supporting web of sound.

First and Foremost Apollo Saxophone Quartet (Tim Redpath, Rob Buckland, Andrew Scott, Jonathan Rebbeck, saxs); John Harle ([a]alto sax/[b]keybds); [c]Roy Powell (keybds); [d]Will Gregory (bar and bass saxes); [e]Mike Hamnett (perc). Argo Ⓟ 443 903-2ZH (52 minutes: DDD: 8/95). Recorded 1993.
    Corea (arr. Apollo Saxophone Quartet) Children's Songs – Nos. 2-4, 6, 7, 11, 16 and 18[be].
    Nyman Four Songs for Tony. **D. Bedford** Fridiof Kennings[e]. **W. Gregory** Hoe down[ade].
    R. Powell Bow out[c].
If you chance to be a saxophobe but have a friend who isn't, buy him or her a copy of this disc as a present, though after hearing it you may possibly regret parting with it. All the music was written or arranged (by the composer) for saxophone quartet, and it spans a variety of idioms from that of classical music to those of jazz, the hoe down, film music and the Icelandic saga. A saxophone quartet is in effect a 'whole consort', to be listened to (unless you are certifiably allergic to its sound) like any other – a recorder consort, a brass ensemble, or a string quartet. In their first recording, the Apollo Quartet prove to be musically sensitive, tight in ensemble and painless in intonation. Dear old Adolphe, who even proposed the erection of a giant 'muzak machine' overlooking Paris, could never

have visualized anything like this. Powell's comment on *Bow out* perhaps epitomizes the best approach to the programme as a whole: "neither 'jazz' nor 'classical' ... [it] occupies its own space". The recording is of high quality in all respects.

French Music for Violin and Piano Isabelle van Keulen (vn); Ronald Brautigam (pf).
Koch Classics Ⓕ 36416-2 (64 minutes: DDD: 5/97).
Messiaen Thème et Variations. **Milhaud** Violin Sonata No. 2, Op. 40. **Ravel** Violin Sonata in G major. **Saint-Saëns** Violin Sonata No. 1 in D minor, Op. 75.
Virtually half a century of French violin music – and what a gulf between the clean-cut classicism of Saint-Saëns's 1885 Sonata and the introspective fervour of the early (1932) Messiaen *Thème et Variations*! Yet some connecting threads can still be detected between the four works here – the polytonality in the Milhaud (1917) and the Ravel (1927); the *perpetuum mobile* finales of the Saint-Saëns and the Ravel and the madcap *Vif* of the Milhaud; the piano's deliciously exotic arpeggiated harmonies in the Milhaud and its rapturous chords at the end of the Messiaen. However, the gem of this disc is Milhaud's Second Sonata, more endearingly played in its seductive opening and its slow movement's lovely cantilena than ever before recorded, and its two quick movements full of a wild energy. Ravel's Sonata, less coolly treated than by some, is given affectionate violin tone. The Saint-Saëns Sonata is often played too strenuously: this team, though warm-hearted, capture its classical restraint. Van Keulen's purity of tone is attractive in the *Adagio* section (which elsewhere can become too sugary), and particularly striking is her delicate *spiccato* in the scherzo-like *Allegro moderato* and her dazzling precision of bow and finger in the finale: Brautigam is at ease in the spectacularly virtuosic piano part. A disc to be warmly welcomed.

Howl, USA [b]Ben Johnston (voc); **Kronos Quartet** (David Harrington, John Sherba, vns; Hank Dutt, va; Joan Jeanrenaud, vc). Nonesuch Ⓕ 7559-79372-2 (57 minutes: DDD: 11/96).
Texts included. Recorded 1995.
Daugherty Sing Sing: J. Edgar Hoover. **Partch** (arr. Johnston) Eight Hitchhikers' Inscriptions from a Highway Railing at Barstow, California[b]. **Johnson** How It Happens (The Voice of I.F. Stone) – Cold War Suite. **Hyla** Howl.
Michael Daugherty's acid collage on the words and work of J. Edgar Hoover recalls the heyday of a paranoid phase in the history of the FBI. Daugherty gives you Hoover's voice, the ringing telephone, gunshots, sirens (imitated by the strings of Kronos), *The Star-spangled Banner* and – in branding Hoover "an ass" – the relevant quotation from Saint-Saëns's *Carnival of the Animals*. It's a hoot, but it's also deadly serious. Daugherty's voice-samples, upbeat accompaniments and dramatic interludes contrast with the decidedly off-beam lyrics of the eight inscriptions by "transcontinental hobo" Harry Partch. Here, Ben Johnston employs his worse-for-wear voice in an original arrangement where the various inscriptions are interspersed with a glum pizzicato ritornello. Far more durable is Scott Johnson's ongoing work, *How It Happens*, based on the writings of radical journalist I. F. Stone. Johnson's aim is to convince his listeners by exploiting "a clear musicality in human speech, both in moments of persuasion and in public rhetoric". Stone's voice is soft, decisive and clear, while Johnson and Kronos mirror his words (which are often repeated) to powerful effect: the closing sequence – where, beyond hypothesizing a missile attack, Stone posits the question "Think what would have happened if ..." – uses speech and music to suggest a sense of hopelessness that words alone could never have conveyed. Quiet though it is, Stone/Johnson is infinitely more disturbing than Hoover/ Daugherty. *Howl*, from which the disc takes its title, grants a wild aural backdrop to a Whitmanesque epic that helped get the 'beat' generation on the rails. It's a sort of 'Chamber Symphony in three movements', the first a hectic catalogue of the times, the second a commentary of society's soullessness and the third a pledge of 'holy' affirmation. Listen hard and you'll soon realize that not much has changed, save that nowadays the voice of protest has lost its edge. *Howl* marks a triumphant conclusion to a programme that is as much 'performance art' as it is music.

Impressions d'enfance Gidon Kremer (vn); [a]Oleg Maisenberg (pf). Teldec Ⓕ 0630-13597-2
(63 minutes: DDD: 7/97). Recorded 1996. *Gramophone Editor's choice.*
Bartók Violin Sonata No. 2, Sz76[a]. **Enescu** Impressions d'enfance, Op. 28[a].
Schulhoff Violin Sonata No. 2[a]. **Plakidis** Two Grasshopper Dances.
This is a fabulous recital, the sort that suggests wet ink on the page and performances born more of impulse than of duty. The Enescu sequence is pure delight, from the gipsy-like cadences of the unaccompanied "Minstrel" that opens the suite, through the virtual-reality chirruping of "The bird in the cage and the cuckoo on the wall", to the ingenious 'linking' miniatures – half a minute apiece or less – that etch a cricket and "Wind in the chimney". *Impressions d'enfance* (1940) ends with an extraordinarily graphic "Sunrise". The idiom straddles late Debussy and mature Bartók, though Enescu's characteristic Romanian flavouring soon gives the game away. Kremer's performances are agile, lean and impetuous, with copious slides and numerous flushes of warmth. Furthermore, he carries the camp-fire element into the Bartók, rhapsodizing rapturously over the final climax and effecting a magical *diminuendo* towards the sonata's close. Maisenberg commands a multi-shaded tonal palette and it's a delight to encounter a work that can be – in unsympathetic hands – a listening trial transformed into a sort of cerebral Hungarian rhapsody. Again, agility is a keyword. Which leaves Ervín Schulhoff's outspoken Second Violin Sonata, a product of 1927, touched by Hindemith's

influence in the first movement, and by heated emotions in the second. Kremer and Maisenberg give it showcase treatment and the recording is, as elsewhere, first-rate. The encore is unaccompanied, a pair of folky, heavily double-stopped *Grasshopper Dances* by Peteris Plakidis.

Industry Bang on a Can All-Stars ([ae]Maya Beiser, vc; [abd]Evan Ziporyn, saxes; [abd]Mark Stewart, gtrs; [ad]Robert Black, db; [abd]Lisa Moore, kbds; [abcd]Steven Schick, perc); [d]Cees van Zeeland, [d]Gerard Bouwhuis (pfs); [d]Amy Knowles (congas); [d]Icebreaker (Katherine Pendry, James Poke, panpipes; Richard Craig, sax; Damian le Gassick, fender rhodes). Sony Classical Ⓕ SK66483 (61 minutes: DDD: 2/96). Recorded 1994.
Wolfe Lick[a]. **L. Andriessen** Hout[b]. Hoketus[d]. **D. Lang** The Anvil Chorus[c].
Gordon Industry[e].

The All-Stars come across here as a fiercely aggressive group, combining the power and punch of a rock band with the precision and clarity of a chamber ensemble. The individual pieces cover a considerable idiomatic range but share the minimalist fascination with repetitive, gradually evolving structures. Rhythm is constant and vital, melody and harmony either stunted or non-existent. The programme kicks off with Julia Wolfe's *Lick* – sensibly enough as it's the most approachable work on the disc. In a surprisingly affectionate tribute to the rock music of her youth, Wolfe toys with the expectations of the genre with considerable formal cunning; and no one could deny the extraordinary panache of the playing. The Andriessen compositions lack any comparable lightness of touch. This is not to deny that they matter. They articulate in purest form the seminal impulse behind the other music here, remaking the static, consonant sounds of Terry Riley, Steve Reich and the rest into a vehicle of protest – edgy, jarring and *Angst*-ridden. *Hout* and *Hoketus* are as severe in their canonic processes as any of Reich's early phase pieces, and their halting angular ideas evoke the back streets of some dark and impenetrable urban jungle (possibly best left unexplored). Is there another composer who would think of obtaining a monolithic sonority from panpipes and saxophones over acoustic and electric pianos with bass guitars and a conga rhythm? Like it or not, this disc makes an impressively cogent, individualistic statement. The music certainly isn't subtle: it's a bruising assault on the soothing, pseudo-spiritual escapism of the Holy Minimalists on the one hand and the excessive, barely-heard complexities of the Modernist Old Guard on the other. The results are technically outstanding but definitely not for the faint-hearted.

In the Name of Bach [b]Catherine Bott (sop); [a]Julian Podger, [a]Robert Evans (tens); [a]Michael McCarthy (bass); **Florilegium.** Channel Classics Ⓕ CCS9096 (75 minutes: DDD: 7/96). Notes and texts included. Recorded 1995.
G.C. Bach Siehe, wie fein und lieblich (Geburtstagkantate)[a]. **J.E. Bach** Violin Sonata in F minor. **W.F. Bach** Adagio and Fugue in D minor, F65. Duetto for Two Flutes in E minor, F54. **J.E. Bach** Sammlung auserlesener Fabeln I – Die ungleichen Freunde[b]; Die Unzufriedenheit[b]; Der Affe und die Schäferin[b]; Der Hund[b]. **J.C. Bach:** Sonata for Keyboard, Violin and Cello in G major, T313/1 (Op. 2 No. 2). **J.B. Bach:** Overture in D major – Passepieds Nos. 1 and 2; La Joye.

Here is a Bach family anthology featuring three members of the clan whose music seldom finds its way into record catalogues. The earliest representative is Georg Christoph, one of Sebastian Bach's uncles. He was, for a time, town Kantor at Schweinfurt in Franconia where in 1684 he received a visit on his birthday from his two brothers. Georg Christoph was so delighted that, shortly afterwards, he wrote a cantata to record the event, *Siehe, wie fein und lieblich* ("Behold, how good and how pleasant it is for brethren to dwell together in unity"). Tenors Julian Podger and Robert Evans, with bass Michael McCarthy, provide a well-focused and evenly balanced ensemble seemingly to savour the spirit in which the piece was written. Next in the family chronology comes Johann Bernhard Bach, a cousin of J.S.B. Not a great deal of his music survives but among that which does are four orchestral suites which may well have resulted from his exposure to those of Telemann who was already a fluent master of the form. It is a pity that Florilegium saw fit to include only three short dances from the Fourth Suite in D major. The music is well worth performing without omission. The highly gifted but emotionally complex Wilhelm Friedemann is represented by the long-admired, poignant and oft recorded *Adagio and Fugue* in D minor for two flutes and strings, and by one of his several *Duettos* for two flutes, this one in E minor. Florilegium, corporately and individually, play the music with heartfelt expression and a sensibility that mirrors the stylistic idiom.

It is the music of J.S. Bach's nephew and pupil, Johann Ernst which occupies the greater part of the programme. This member of the family seems wholeheartedly to have embraced the early classical idiom, further demonstrating, both in the Violin Sonata in F minor and in the four songs selected from his *Sammlung auserlesener Fabeln*, that he was a composer with a distinctive and affecting musical vocabulary at his disposal. Catherine Bott gives warmly expressive performances, savouring the considerable lyrical content of a little-known area of Bach family industry. The prodigious talent of this dynasty once again reaches a peak in Florilegium's programme with a Quartet in G major by Johann Christian, the 'London Bach'. Musically speaking, the expansive opening movement is especially engaging but the entire work is played with elegance and charm by these artists. In summary, this is varied and enjoyable entertainment, well off the beaten track. Although the absence of any translation from the German of the texts of the four songs is regrettable, it does not prevent a warm recommendation.

Journey to the Amazon Sharon Isbin (gtr) with [a]Gaudencio Thiago de Mello (perc); [b]Paul Winter (sax). Teldec Ⓕ 0630-19899-2 (55 minutes: DDD: 7/98). *Gramophone Editor's choice.* ⒼⒼ
L. Almeida Historia do Luar[a]. **Lauro** Seis por derecho. El marabino. Valses venezolanos – No. 3, Natalia. **Barrios** Waltz, Op. 8 No. 4. Julia Florida. **Thiago de Mello** A Hug for Pixingha. Chants for the Chief – No. 1, A Chamada dos ventos/Canção Nocturna; No. 2, Uirapurú do Amazonas (both arr. cpsr). Lago de Janaucá. A Hug for Tiberio. Cavaleiro sem Armadura (arr. Wolff). **Montaña** Porro. **Savio** Batucada. **Brouwer** Canción de cuna, "Berceuse" (arr. Grenet). **Canonico** Aire de Joropo (arr. Lauro/Diaz). **Vianna** Cochichando (arr. Barbosa-Lima).

No one is currently doing more to free the guitar from its rent-a-programme image than Sharon Isbin. She is not South American, nor does the Amazon flow through Cuba, Colombia, Venezuela or Paraguay, but none of this matters in the least. Others before her have hitched rides with specialists in particular areas and sounded like uncomfortable passengers, but Isbin has loved and felt this music for over a quarter of a century and in the company of Thiago de Mello and Paul Winter is entirely at home. One might fear the addition of assorted percussive sounds and 'rain-forest' noises to be intrusive, especially in the familiar items, but they are atmospherically enhancing, handled with great discretion (delightfully in Grenet's arrangement of Brouwer's *Canción de cuna*) and often rhythmically uplifting. Lauro's setting of the traditional *Seis por derecho* has never sounded more full of vitality. The guitar has a wide range of tone colour, which Isbin exploits with skill and taste in traversing the gamut from tenderness to joyously rhythmic energy. The excellent annotation resides in a concertina-form booklet, which is user-friendly in that respect, but whose printing in white on a 'rain-forest' background is not equally so. Recording is beautifully clear and well balanced. Waste no time in getting your hands on this disc.

Kennedy plays Kreisler Kennedy, [a]Katharine Gowers, [b]Rosemary Furniss (vns); [b]Bill Hawkes (va); [b]Caroline Dale (vc); [c]John Lenehan (pf). EMI Ⓕ CDC5 56626-2 (75 minutes: ADD: 5/98). All items marked [d] arr. Kreisler.
Kreisler Liebesleid[c]. Tambourin chinois, Op. 3[c]. Praeludium and Allegro in the style of Pugnani[c]. String Quartet in A minor[b]. **Falla** La vida breve – Danse espagnole No. 1[cd]. **Granados** Danzas españolas, Op. 37 – Andaluza, "Playera", Op. 37 No. 5[cd]. **Heuberger** Der Opernball – Midnight Bells[acd]. **Rimsky-Korsakov** The Golden Cockerel – Hymn to the Sun[cd]. **C. Scott** Lotus Land, Op. 47 No. 1[cd]. **Traditional** The Londonderry air[acd].

Before Kennedy gives us Jimi Hendrix he is venturing back among Fritz Kreisler's nostalgic, sepia-tinted *morceaux*, music rooted in the gentle manners of a more leisured age. His selection was recorded "real live – no cheating" (his words) and favours precisely the sort of dry, 'small room' acoustic that Kreisler and (in particular) Heifetz favoured for their adorable RCA recordings. The musical approach is sweet-centred and forceful – idiosyncratic, too, when, in the *Praeludium and Allegro* he chills the *Allegro* by playing selected passages *sul ponticello*. Falla's "Danse espagnole" features ricochet bowing and strong pizzicatos; *Liebesleid* has a wan, almost chaste, quality that suits it; *Tambourin chinois* is skittish and lilting; *Lotus Land* and *Hymn to the Sun* deliver plenty of passion and a nice, fat tone; "Danse espagnole" has a sensual allure, while the *Londonderry air* wafts in sweetly from days of yore and Katharine Gowers takes the bow for a gentle voicing of *Midnight Bells*. Above all, Kennedy *communicates* this music, and he is much aided by the consistently imaginative piano playing of John Lenehan. The studio-recorded String Quartet (1919) is something else again, a *fin de siècle* escapade among four, tender and lyrical, frequently reminiscent of Korngold and Strauss, maybe even of Bartók and with a playful, gipsy-style finale that sails the Danube from Vienna to Budapest. Kennedy's team-mates play with great spirit and no lack of feeling, though the 'tone at the top' is unmistakable. Again, the sound is pleasantly immediate.

Kremerata Musica [a]Sabine Meyer (cl); [b]Gidon Kremer (vn); [c]Veronika Hagen (va); [d]Clemens Hagen (vc); [e]Oleg Maisenberg (pf). DG Ⓕ 447 112-2GH (76 minutes: DDD: 4/96). Recorded 1994.
Mahler Quartet in A minor[bcde]. **Schoenberg** Piece in D minor[be]. String Trio, Op. 45[bcd]. Phantasy, Op. 47[be]. **Webern** Two Pieces for Cello and Piano[de]. Four Pieces, Op. 7[bc]. Three Little Pieces, Op. 11[de]. Cello Sonata[de]. **Berg** Four Pieces, Op. 5[ae]. Chamber Concerto – Adagio (arr. cpsr)[abe].

This is a Second Viennese School disc that revels in extremes: for example, there could hardly be a greater contrast than that between Schoenberg's very early, very anodyne piece for violin and piano (it could easily be mistaken for Schubert at his least poetic) and his last instrumental work, the forceful, economical *Phantasy*. Even so, the playing throughout is so refined and expressive that the later music's eroded but still potent links with the romantic tradition are unmistakable. The result is fascinating, and one of the best releases of its kind for some years. Mahler's honorary membership of the Schoenberg school – as early patron and model – is acknowledged in his own youthful movement for piano quartet, an evocative mixture of Brahmsian and Wagnerian elements that showed the way forward with exemplary clarity. As for Schoenberg's pupils, Webern's rapid progress from languid late romanticism (in the two cello pieces of 1899) to aphoristic expressionism is powerfully displayed, the close positioning of the cello in the Op. 11 Pieces adding to the larger-than-life impression of these performances. Sabine Meyer's clarinet is also closely recorded in the Berg pieces, but music so rich in striking incident can stand such immediacy, as can Berg's arrangement of the *Chamber Concerto*'s slow movement for clarinet, violin and piano. Nevertheless, the finest music-making of all is heard in Schoenberg's Trio, an account in which technical mastery and expressive fantasy combine to brilliant effect.

Kronos Quartet Released 1985-95. [a]**Dumisani Maraire** (ngoma/hosho); [b]**Astor Piazzolla** (bandoneon); [c]**Patty Manning**, [c]**John Taylor**, [c]**Larry Caballero** (vocs); [d]**Djivan Gasparian** (duduk). Kronos Quartet (David Harrington, John Sherba, vns; Hank Dutt, vn; Joan Jeanrenaud, vc). Nonesuch Ⓕ 7559-79394-2 (two discs: 101 minutes: DDD: 2/96). Recorded 1985-95.
Maraire Mai Nozipo (from 7559-79275-2, 11/92)[a]. **Piazzolla** Asleep (7559-79254-2)[b].
B. Johnston Amazing Grace (7559-79163-2, 11/87). **Reich** Different trains – America: before the war (7559-79176-2, 6/89). **Górecki** String Quartet No. 2 (Quasi una fantasia), Op. 64 – Arioso: Andante cantabile (7559-79319-2, 4/93). **Riley** Salome Dances for Peace – The Ecstasy: excerpt (7559-79217-2, 9/90). **Crumb** Black Angels: 13 Images from the Dark Lands (Images I) – God-music (7559-79242-2, 4/91). **Glass** String Quartet No. 5 – third movement (7559-79356-2).
Tahmizyan A Cool Wind is Blowing (7559-79346-2)[d]. **Barber** Adagio for Strings, Op. 11.
Pärt (arr. Hofer) Fratres (both from 7559-79181-2). **R. Scott** (arr. S. Mackay) Dinner Music for a Pack of Hungry Cannibals. **S. Johnson** How it Happens (The Voice of I.F. Stone) – It raged.
Daugherty Elvis everywhere[c]. **Hendrix** (arr. S. Rifkin and Kronos Qt) Purple Haze (all new to UK).

Kronos is a quality act. No quartet currently performing has done more to bridge the divide between popular and 'serious' music, and although others have served contemporary repertoire with equal dedication (the Arditti Quartet being among the most notable), Kronos take top laurels for imagination, presentation and an intuitive sense of what best 'connects' with a non-specialist music-loving audience. This superb retrospective is both representative and symbolic of their best work – representative in that the styles of voices are uncommonly wide; symbolic in that the planning of the disc, its telling juxtaposition of chosen material, actually reflects the compositional methods of certain composers programmed. "Released" opens with Dumisani Maraire's breezy *Mai Nozipo* and goes on to include Ben Johnston's prolix but engrossing variations for quartet on *Amazing Grace*, an appealing extract from Terry Riley's epic *Salome Dances for Peace*, Crumb's mysterious *God-music*, Pärt's ubiquitous *Fratres* (one of the work's earlier recordings), an eerie piece for *duduk* (a sort of Eastern-sounding saxophone) by Tigran Tahmizyan and then, to finish, a poignant return home to the familiar strains of Barber's *Adagio*. All are superbly performed and very well recorded. However, the real highlight of the set – at least for those of us who already own the albums from which "Released" has been compiled – is the relatively brief second disc "Unreleased", starting with the upbeat hilarity of Raymond Scott's *Dinner Music for a Pack of Hungry Cannibals*, then progressing to Scott Johnson's humbling "It raged" from *How it Happens* (urgent dialogue centring on I.F. Stone's reasoned arguments against the stupidity of 'Holy Wars'), Michael Daugherty's astonishing *Elvis everywhere* (three brilliant mimics, fragments of song and a tragicomic coda) and a raw-and-rowdy remake of Hendrix's *Purple Haze*. There are no proper insert-notes on the music but the chosen selections are so vivid, so powerfully communicative, that written explanations would serve little purpose.

Lament [a]**Wilhelmenia Fernandez** (sop); [b]**Elvis Costello** (sngr); **Brodsky Quartet** (Michael Thomas, Ian Belton, vns; Paul Cassidy, va; Jacqueline Thomas, vc); [c]**Susan Monks** (vc); [c]**Mary Scully** (db). Silva Classics Ⓕ SILKD6001 (71 minutes: DDD: 10/94). Recorded 1994.
Stravinsky Three Pieces for String Quartet. **J. Alvarez** Metro Chabacano. **Traditional** She moved through the fair[b]. **D. Matthews** Adagio. **Szymanski** Five Pieces. **Massenet** Elégie[a].
M. Thomas Harold In Islington. Variations on a theme of Banjo Patterson, "Waltzing Matilda". **Sculthorpe** Lament[c].

Whether you find this programme annoyingly bitty or profoundly stimulating will be very much a matter of personal taste. The music-making has real integrity. The sound is excellent too, bright and vivid without adopting a clinical 'pop' ambience. Only the Stravinsky pieces are at all familiar and they receive a hyper-brilliant, realization which allows them to sit happily with the knowing minimalism of Javier Alvarez. His *Metro Chabacano* is a real discovery – if a Latinized combination of early Tippett, Steve Reich and sophisticated pop is your idea of fun. The plangent simplicity of the original folk melody is not necessarily best served by the treatment accorded to *She moved through the fair* which features rock musician Elvis Costello on vocals, palpably sincere but quavery. Should you find the restrained English eloquence of David Matthews's *Adagio* a little too mainstream, the post-modern polystylism of Pawel Szymanski's *Five Pieces* may be more to your taste. The Massenet arrangement is sensitive and unobtrusive with *Diva* star Wilhelmenia Fernandez conveying an appealing mixture of seductiveness and melancholy. The most significant new(ish) music on the disc is Peter Sculthorpe's *Lament*, an arrangement of a piece originally scored for string orchestra in 1976. Coherently structured, stylistically consistent and beautifully reworked for string sextet, the second cello and double-bass lending a dark, oppressive sonority, its musical argument seems almost old-fashioned in its convincing continuity. The climax is genuinely moving. Recommended to those with a post-modernist sensibility.

The Lindsays: 25 Years Lindsay Quartet (Peter Cropper, Ronald Birks, vns; [a]Robin Ireland, [b]Roger Bigley, vas; Bernard Gregor-Smith, vc). ASV Ⓕ CDDCA825 (77 minutes: ADD: 1/93). Recorded 1978-88.
Wirén String Quartet No. 3 in D minor, Op. 18[a]. **A. Tchaikovsky** String Quartet No. 2 in C major, Op. 5[b]. **Hugh Wood** String Quartet No. 3, Op. 20[b]. **Barber** String Quartet, Op. 11[a].
As its title suggests, this issue celebrates the Lindsay String Quartet's twenty-fifth anniversary, with all but the present violist Robin Ireland chalking up over 20 years' membership. The quartet has played works ranging from the classics to the less familiar modern ones by André Tchaikovsky and Hugh Wood that feature here. Indeed, what we have here is in no way central twentieth-century repertory: no 'great' composer at all, some will say, and regret it. Furthermore, these are recordings of BBC concert performances from 1978-88, and inevitably there are a few rustles that would otherwise have been edited out and applause after all the works except the Tchaikovsky. However, such is the vitality of the playing that one can overlook these matters, and the overall quality of the sound is good. Dag Wirén is a Swedish composer known mainly for just one work, a *Serenade for Strings*, but his Third Quartet has plenty of personality although in a conservative idiom. André Tchaikovsky was Polish-born but spent much of his life in England before dying by his own hand at the age of 46; a fine pianist as well as a composer, he had a prickly personality that is strongly reflected in his Second Quartet, written for the Lindsays and first played by them in this BBC performance of January 1978. Hugh Wood's Third Quartet, which the Lindsays premièred, is also a tough piece, and relies heavily on Second Viennese School gesturings, but the Lindsays play it with commitment. Finally, Samuel Barber's Quartet is maybe the best music here. Its celebrated central *Adagio* sounds strikingly fresh played in context on four instruments instead of alone in the usual version for string orchestra. It is a pleasure to salute the Lindsays and to welcome this excellent tribute disc.

Made in America Yo-Yo Ma (vc); [c]Ronan Lefkowitz, [d]Lynn Chang (vns); [ab]Jeffrey Kahane, [c]Gilbert Kalish (pfs). Sony Classical Ⓕ SK53126 (65 minutes: DDD: 4/94). Recorded 1991-92. Ⓖ
Bernstein (trans. Ma) Clarinet Sonata[a]. **Gershwin** (arr. Heifetz, trans. Ma)[b] Three Preludes.
Ives Trio for Violin, Clarinet and Piano[c]. **Kirchner** Triptych[d].
In Ives's Trio you have the feeling that his only way of coping with his love for the 'old tunes' was to send them up; yet he did so with such aplomb, daring and imagination that one can't help but respond gratefully. Ives's Trio is the final work in Yo-Yo Ma's absorbing programme. The first, Bernstein's wartime Clarinet Sonata, was arranged with the composer's authorization and is pure delight from start to finish: mild, melodious and ultimately high-spirited. Which leaves Gershwin and Kirchner, the former represented by a sensuous re-working of Heifetz's famous *Prelude* transcriptions, the latter by an astonishingly outspoken *Triptych*. Scored, respectively, for "Cello Solo" and "Violin and Cello Obbligato" (the movement subtitles), *Triptych* ends with a vigorous *Presto*. The entire programme is superbly performed, the Ives being particularly adroit, the Gershwin smoochy and playful. This is the sort of recital that will have you reaching for *The Gramophone Classical Catalogue* in search of more of the same.

Música Armorial Quinteto da Paraíba (Yerko Pinto, Ronedilk Cavalcante, vns; Samuel Espinoza, va; Nicolò Amati, vc; Xisto Medeiros, db). Nimbus Ⓕ NI5483 (55 minutes: DDD: 10/96). Recorded 1995.
Pereira Three Northeastern pieces. Variations on a theme of Guerra Peixe. **Madureira** Toré. Aralume. Preguiça. O Guerreiro. Baque de Luanda. Toada e Dobrado da Cavalhada. **Capiba** Toada e desafio. **Maciel** A Pedra do Reino. **Almeida** Rasga do Nordeste. **Anonymous** (arr. Gnattali) Mulher rendeira.
The term 'armorial', coined by the writer Ariano Suassuna, originally related to the spirit behind the architecture and plastic arts of north-east Brazil, and was later extended to include popular poetry and (in the 1970s) music. Armorial music is, we are told, not an extension of the nationalist movement of which Villa-Lobos was a seminal figure; the latter was too 'Europeanized' in language and instrumentation. Instead, it comes closer to the Brazilian spirit, turns its back on "nineteenth-century functional harmony" (here it largely does) and introduces "the instruments and sounds heard in festivals and market places" (here via modern instruments). The Quinteto (string quartet plus double-bass) take their name from the tiny north-eastern state of Paraíba in which its members live, and the music was written or adapted for them by composers with whose names only that of Gnattali will be familiar to most Europeans. With an utterly fascinating collection of rhythms, melodies (often modal, with lowered seventh and/or fifth) and strange instrumental sounds, we are transported no less closely to the heart of Brazil than we are to that of Mexico by a traditional *mariachi* band, and with greater variety. Be prepared to forget about classical forms and development, and to enjoy music such as has not been heard before from a quintet of 'standard' string instruments, even in the hands of Villa-Lobos. There is more to Brazilian music than sambas, rumbas and *chôros*. This is 'another', more quintessentially Brazilian Brazil. Relax and let it wash over you; it's a bath you are likely to take many times.

Musiques d'Espagne Sequeira Costa, Artur Pizarro (pfs). Collins Classics Ⓕ 1466-2 (62 minutes: DDD: 10/96). Recorded 1996. *Gramophone Editor's choice.*   Ⓖ

Granados (arr. Longas) Goyescas – El pelele. **Infante** Trois Danses Andalouses. Musiques d'Espagne. **Cassadó** (arr. Berkovitz) Requie-bros. **Albéniz** (arr. Marshall) Navarra. **Falla** La vida breve – Danses espagnoles Nos. 1 and 2 (arr. Samazeuilh). El Amor Brujo – Pantomime (arr. Dougherty); Ritual Fire Dance (arr. Braggiotti).

This is a delightful disc which, admittedly, perpetuates the perception of Spanish music as being largely characterized by the spirit of Andalusia – only "El pelele", *Navarra* and the second ("Montagnarde") of Infante's *Musiques d'Espagne* depict other regions – but thanks to intelligent planning, there is no feeling of lack of variety. The two distinguished pianists here (not Spanish but Portuguese) constitute a team of the very top class: their playing has a marvellous clarity (aided by a splendidly natural-sounding and well-balanced recording that allows every detail to tell), great vivacity, the utmost precision and crisp attack, strong rhythmicality combined with sensitive flexibility, and above all the most subtle shadings of dynamics and colour throughout. Except for the brilliant Infante pieces, all the items here are arrangements, none more skilful than those by Longas, Samazeuilh and the legendary Frank Marshall (Granados's pupil and Larrocha's teacher).

Music from Charlottenburg Castle [a]Ann Monoyios (sop); Berlin Barock Compagney. Capriccio Ⓕ 10 459 (61 minutes: DDD: 10/95). ✒ Texts included. Recorded 1993.   Ⓖ
Corelli Sonata in G minor, WoO2. Trio Sonata in G major, Op. 2 No. 12. **Ariosti** La rosa[a].
Torelli Sonata in G major, Op. 1 No. 1. Concerto a quattro in D minor, Op. 6 No. 10.
Bononcini Polifemo – Respira, alma, respira ... Dove sei, dove t'ascondi; Non soffrirà, mai Circe ... Pensiero di vendetta[a]. Cefalo e Procride – Cintia, il tuo nome invoco ... Sacro dardo, in te confido; Numi del ciel pietosi ... Bella auretta[a]. **Steffani** Scherzo, Guardati[a].

In the history of arts patronage Sophie Charlotte, wife of the Elector of Brandenburg and later Queen of Prussia, holds an honoured place. Besides building a fine summer palace on the river Spree, as a keen music-lover (with a reputation herself as a harpsichordist) she was at pains to engage leading composers, singers and instrumentalists for her court. Among them was the great violinist Torelli (one of the earliest to publish *Concerti grossi*) and, after him, the opera composer Ariosti, who in 1702 engaged the Bononcini brothers (of whom Giovanni was to become Handel's rival in London). Corelli was outside her immediate circle, but she took a lively interest in his work, and he dedicated his famous Op 5 set of sonatas to her. He is represented here by two works, a sonata containing a *Grave* of arresting chromaticisms, and a *Ciacona* that could easily become a popular hit like the now omnipresent Pachelbel Canon. Of the two Torelli works, the G major Sonata is a delight, with a charmingly springy initial *Allegro* and a dancingly light finale. The playing of this well-balanced group of (period) solo strings plus chamber organ is splendidly neat and crisply rhythmic, and the leader's embellishments – lots of *tirades* – are animated and stylish. The little Ariosti cantata (published in London and dedicated to Charlotte's brother, King George I) is preceded by a brilliant instrumental prelude and consists of two arias, one reflective and one fast. The scherzo – a warning against the wiles of Cupid – by one of Charlotte's favourite composers, Agostino Steffani, is more substantial, and displays a notable variety of mood. Bononcini's appeal as an opera composer is well illustrated by extracts from two works of 1702 outstanding are a deeply expressive *siciliana* for the hapless Galatea and a florid vengeance aria for Circe from *Polifemo*. Ann Monoyios, the possessor of a fresh, youthful-sounding voice with pure intonation, invests the former with pathos and reveals real virtuosity in the second; and her ornamentation of *da capos* in all the works she sings betokens an accomplished mastery of period practice. Most enjoyable. It is a pity that the texts are printed with only a German translation, and that the accompanying note is amateurishly rendered into English.

Neapolitan Chamber Works Il Giardino Armonico Ensemble / Giovanni Antonini (rec). Teldec Das Alte Werk Ⓕ 4509-93157-2 (54 minutes: DDD: 11/94). ✒ Recorded 1993.   ⒼⒼ
Sarri Concerto for Recorder, Two Violins, Viola and Continuo in A minor. **D. Scarlatti** Sonata for Mandolin and Continuo in D minor, Kk90. **Durante** Concerto for two Violins, Viola and Continuo in G minor. **A. Scarlatti** Sonata for Recorder, two Violins and Continuo in A minor. **Mancini** Sonata for Recorder, Two Violins and Continuo in D minor.

The idea of a selection of music that might have been heard in early eighteenth-century Naples is not a new one but, in the area of chamber music, it has not been more vividly brought to life than on this disc. Domenico Scarlatti's Sonata is one of several believed to have been intended for a solo instrument with continuo, and here the soloist is as clean and quick-fingered a mandolinist as you could find, even if you hired a private detective (he is also the violist!) – a beguiling performance indeed. The remaining items lack any other recording, and all are to be welcomed. Sarri was a prolific composer of vocal music and the Concerto was his only instrumental work, with the recorder singing 'arias' that would tax any diva. There is something in each of the others to surprise and delight, such as the subtly tear-shedding chromatics of the opening *Affetuoso* of Durante's Concerto and the *Piano* of Alessandro Scarlatti's Sonata, a recorder/violin duo. Every item is illuminated by sensitivity to expressive nuance and dynamics, and the recording is close to perfection.

New English Clarinet Music Mühlfeld Ensemble (Victoria Soames, cls; Julia Vohralik, vc; Jonathan Higgins, pf). Clarinet Classics Ⓕ CC0007 (74 minutes: DDD: 10/94). Recorded 1993.
Powers Trio. **Lutyens** Trio, Op. 135. **LeFanu** Lullaby. Nocturne. **G. Williams** The song within. **R. Marsh** Ferry Music.

All the pieces in this collection were commissioned by the Mühlfeld Ensemble. Their seriousness of intention is indicated by the composers they have chosen: there is no easy-access minimalism or neo-romanticism here. What most of these composers have in common is something much more challenging for performers: an economy of utterance that makes every note and every interval count. Of this Elisabeth Lutyens's late Trio is a perfect example, a little masterpiece of refined and pared-down expressiveness, beautifully made and no less beautifully played, each member of the trio realizing the importance of every inflexion to the overall design. It has the spareness of Webern, but longer lines. Anthony Powers's piece (what an under-represented composer in the record catalogue he is!) is well described by his own phrase: "subdued drama". A gradual progress from a slow prelude through a continually arrested scherzo to an eventual flowering of melody and of unified trio writing in the finale, it needs very concentrated playing if its line is to be perceived and its discontinuities bridged. Played as well as this it's an absorbing piece. Nicola LeFanu's two linked duos require no less concentration, the first because of its constant changes of direction away from the 'islands' of very slow lyrical intensity that are eventually shown to be its centre, the latter because it is in effect an unbroken melody, or series of self-regenerating melodies, some seven minutes long. The secret of performing such pieces is that the end of each should sound like an end: they do, most satisfyingly. Graham Williams, as the title of his piece suggests, surrounds a darkly expressive slow 'song' (for bass clarinet) with spikier, faster music that is related to it by a readily audible unifying melodic cell. Roger Marsh's five epigrammatic miniatures use a similar device and obvious 'mirrorings' between movements to create a sort of bridge structure, peaking of course in the centre but leaving no doubt that the fifth movement is the destination. All five pieces are better than 'interesting' and one wants a better word than 'enterprising' (which so often means 'a good try, but ... ') for the Mühlfeld Ensemble's remarkable success-rate in their commissioning. The recording is first-class.

Paris French Flute Sonatas. **Emmanuel Pahud** (fl); **Eric Le Sage** (pf). EMI Ⓟ CDC5 56488-2 (66 minutes: DDD: 3/98). Recorded 1997. *Selected by Soundings.*
Dutilleux Sonatine. **Ibert** Jeux. Aria. **Jolivet** Chant de Linos. **Messiaen** Le merle noir.
Milhaud Sonatina for Flute and Piano, Op. 76. **Poulenc** Flute Sonata. **Sancan** Sonatine.
Examinations are usually viewed with aversion and some suspicion, but the Paris Conservatoire's custom of commissioning new works for its final examinations has valuably enriched the repertoire for wind instruments: three of the works on this disc – the *Sonatinas* (of 1943 and 1946 respectively) of the exact contemporaries Dutilleux and Sancan, and Messiaen's *Le merle noir* – owe their origin to these competitive exams. By their nature they lay stress on technical virtuosity, as indeed do nearly all the works here, which though differing widely in idiom share a certain Gallic style recognizable by its "clarity, refinement and lightness of touch", as the insert-note puts it. These qualities are also characteristic of the playing of the Swiss-born Emmanuel Pahud, Principal Flute of the Berlin Philharmonic, who has a lighter tone than some of his distinguished predecessors. All the items here have been recorded before, however, with excellent piano partnership by Eric Le Sage, Pahud's brilliant and sensitive performances are outstanding. Exhilaratingly skittish in the brief *scherzando* finale of the Sancan and that of the Poulenc, intense in the Jolivet, mysteriously atmospheric in the first movement of the Dutilleux (a work undervalued by its composer), tender in the Ibert *Aria* and powerfully athletic at the end of the Messiaen, this is a winner of a disc.

Pastoral Emma Johnson (cl); [b]Judith Howarth (sop); [a]Malcolm Martineau (pf).
ASV Ⓟ CDDCA891 (74 minutes: DDD: 7/94).
Ireland Fantasy-Sonata in E flat major[a]. **Vaughan Williams** Six Studies in English folk song[a].
Three Vocalises for Soprano Voice and Clarinet[b]. **Bax** Clarinet Sonata[a]. **Bliss** Pastoral (posth.)[a].
Two Nursery Rhymes[b]. **Stanford** Clarinet Sonata, Op. 129.
A lovely programme, radiantly performed and most judiciously chosen. Things get under way in fine style with John Ireland's marvellous *Fantasy-Sonata*: beautifully written, passionately argued and encompassing (for Ireland) a wide range of moods; it's certainly a work that shows this underrated figure at the height of his powers. The Clarinet Sonata by Ireland's teacher, Stanford, is one of that composer's most successful works: formally elegant and most idiomatically laid out, it boasts a central *Adagio* (entitled "Caoine" – an Irish lament) of considerable eloquence. Johnson is a gloriously mellifluous exponent in both Vaughan Williams's *Six Studies* and the Bax Sonata, and in the first movement of the latter she manages to convey a slumbering mystery that is somehow almost orchestral in its imaginative scope. Judith Howarth joins Johnson for the haunting *Three Vocalises* (one of Vaughan Williams's very last utterances from his final year) and makes an equally agile showing in Bliss's delightful *Two Nursery Rhymes* and touching *Pastoral*. A real pleasure, then, from start to finish and Malcolm Martineau proffers superb accompaniments.

Henry Purcell and his Time Scaramouche (Andrew Manze, Caroline Balding, vns; Jaap ter Linden, bass viol; Ulrike Wild, hpd/org); [a]Foskien Kooistra (vn); [b]Konrad Junghänel (theorbo). Channel Classics Ⓟ CCS4792 (60 minutes: DDD: 5/94). 🎶 Recorded 1992.
Locke The Broken Consort – Suites Nos. 3[b] and 4. **W. Lawes** Fantasia-Suite No. 7 in D minor.
Jenkins Fantasia in three parts. **C. Simpson** Prelude. Divisions on a Ground[b]. **Baltzar**
Divisions on "John Come Kiss me Now"[b]. **Purcell** Pavans – B flat major, Z750; G minor, Z752[a].
Fantasia upon a Ground, Z731[ab].

On this disc of English seventeenth-century chamber music, Scaramouche offer an homogeneous selection of music and instrumental combinations. (The disc advertises itself, by the way, as offering the music of "Henry Purcell and His Time", a claim whose level of accuracy – Lawes, for one, died over a decade before Purcell was born – is eloquently symbolized by a portrait of an unmistakably Elizabethan lady on the front of the box!) Here the innocent charm of other selections of this nature is largely replaced by the weightier, more sober pronouncements of Lawes, Locke and Purcell, but also by a bold interpretative vigour which makes it just as lively a listen in its own way. Jaap ter Linden's rendition of his Simpson piece is suitably poetic, while Andrew Manze's version of *John Come Kiss me Now* has a Turkey-in-the-Straw ending that will make you chuckle. This may be a less polished and fluent recording than some others maybe, but in the end, moments like these – as well as the fact that there is lastingly rewarding music to be heard here – will make you want to play it again and again.

Recital David Pyatt (hn); Martin Jones (pf). Erato Ⓕ 3984-21632-2 (66 minutes: DDD: 4/98). Recorded 1996.
  Beethoven Horn Sonata in F major, Op. 17. **F. Strauss** Nocturno, Op. 7. **Koechlin** Horn Sonata, Op. 70. **Damase** Pavane variée. Berceuse, Op. 19. **Hindemith** Horn Sonata.
  Abbott Alla caccia. **Schumann** Adagio and Allegro in A flat major, Op. 70.

Beethoven's Horn Sonata – in its day successfully premièred by the famous Bohemian virtuoso and composer, Punto – is nevertheless written rather clumsily for the horn (the composer suggested the cello as a viable alternative) and even Dennis Brain had problems with it. David Pyatt – *Gramophone's* Young Artist of the Year in 1996 – sails off into the work with aplomb and gives it one of the finest performances on or off record. He makes it seem to sit easily on the instrument and provides just the right kind of timbre and buoyant lyrical flow – indeed it sounds like a masterpiece, which it very nearly is. He is helped both by a first-rate partnership with Martin Jones and an excellently balanced recording, which does not let the horn overwhelm the piano. The second piece here is an attractive novelty by Franz Strauss, the father of Richard, and another famous player who advised Wagner on the format of Siegfried's horn call. Koechlin's Sonata, more fluent than Beethoven's, has a rather fine *Andante très tranquille*, and another Frenchman, Jean-Michel Damase, provides two short but memorable occasional pieces. The Hindemith Sonata is wayward: it never seems quite sure where it is progressing harmonically, but Pyatt and Jones are so naturally and spontaneously attuned to the work that it becomes readily assimilable. Allan Abbott's *Alla caccia* is an endearing lollipop while Schumann's *Adagio and Allegro* here emerges flowing almost as easily as if it had been written by Mozart – who knew just what a horn could manage without sounding effortful. Altogether this is a splendid recital, which will give much pleasure to any lover of this intractable but highly rewarding instrument.

Russian Music for Two Pianos Duo Reine Elisabeth (Wolfgang Manz, Rolf Plagge, pfs). Koch Discover International Ⓢ DICD920150 (66 minutes: DDD: 11/94). Recorded 1992.
  Stravinsky Petrushka. **Scriabin** Romance in A minor. **Shostakovich** Concertino, Op. 94.
  Rachmaninov Six Morceaux, Op. 11.

This is essentially a 'fun' disc. The opening of *Petrushka* is relatively easygoing; without hammered rhythms or self-conscious virtuosity the music's colour and charm immediately come over. Yet characterization is perceptive. The scene in Petrushka's cell is gentle and touching although it does not lack drama, and the Blackamoor is darkly introduced without overdoing the menace. The closing fairground sequence is richly hued, with an almost orchestral palette. The rest of the programme is well contrasted. The Scriabin *Romance*, an endearing early piece, is melodically rich and the Shostakovich *Concertino*, which opens with a dramatic echo of the slow movement of Beethoven's Fourth Piano Concerto, has audaciously witty, toccata-like writing which really makes one smile when the playing is so infectious. The six Rachmaninov *Morceaux* are played with much sympathy and a natural charm. Good recording, forward and not too reverberant. A worthwhile and very real bargain.

Smetana Quartet [b]Pavel Štěpán (pf); **Smetana Quartet** (Jiří Novák, Lubomir Kostecký, vns; Milan Skampa, va; Antonín Kohout, vc). Testament Ⓕ SBT1074/5 (two discs, oas: 79 and 77 minutes: ADD: 3/96). Items marked [ab] from HMV ASD2350 (2/68), [c]ASD2402 (6/69), [d]new to UK (recorded 1965). Recorded 1965-66.   Ⓖ Ⓖ
  SBT1074 – **Dvořák** String Quartet No. 12 in F major, B179, "American"[a]. Piano Quintet in A major, B155[b]. **Janáček** String Quartet No. 1, "The Kreutzer Sonata"[d]. *SBT1075* – **Dvořák** Terzetto in C major, B148[c]. String Quartet No. 14 in A flat major, B193[c]. **Janáček** String Quartet No. 2, "Intimate Letters"[d].

Listening to these discs tempts one to think that in the 1960s the Smetana were the Berlin Philharmonic of quartets – just as in the 1950s the Hollywoods might have been fancifully called the Philadelphia Orchestra of quartets. Much of the playing here is in a class of its own, only later equalled by the Borodin and Alban Berg Quartets in terms of finesse and ensemble. The Dvořák performances must be numbered among the very best now in the catalogue: their phrasing has none of the artificiality that marks some professional quartets (that is to say that a phrasing once rehearsed becomes, as it were, mechanically reproduced so that while the line rises and falls it doesn't genuinely breathe) and it is an enormous relief to hear genuine *pianissimo* tone and so natural and unforced an ensemble. There are numerous recordings of each of the Janáček Quartets but in terms of tonal finesse, perfection of ensemble and depth of feeling the present issues would be difficult to beat.

The String Quartet in Eighteenth-Century England Salomon Quartet (Simon Standage, Micaela Comberti, vns; Trevor Jones, va; Jennifer Ward-Clarke, vc). Hyperion Ⓕ CDA66780 (69 minutes: DDD: 3/96). ✏ Recorded 1995.
Abel String Quartet in A major, Op. 8 No. 5. **Shield** String Quartet in C minor, Op. 3 No. 6. **Marsh** Quartetto in B flat major in imitation of the Stile of Haydn's Opera Prima. **Webbe** Variations in A major on "Adeste Fideles". **S. Wesley** String Quartet in E flat major.

For various reasons connected with the patterns of its social life, the string quartet was slow to become established in England. The work that opens this CD, by the German-born Abel, comes from the first set of quartets to be published in London (in 1769); it is an amiable piece, graceful enough, harmonically rather static and texturally unenterprising. The few Englishmen who ventured into the string quartet genre did rather better. William Shield's work, the sixth of a set published in 1782, begins with a passionate C minor gesture and has some echoes of Haydn both in the ingenuity of its humour and in its seriousness, though not in his technique nor his sureness of taste; but the *Adagio* is very remarkable, quite individual in the tone of its expression and reaching an extraordinarily imaginative climax in each half with a sort of free-flying violin passage, in its way breathtaking. The finale too is sombre in quite an original way. John Marsh (a lawyer and a landowner, though music was his passion), wrote his quartet "in imitation of the Stile of Haydn's Opera Prima" in the 1780s: it is a very fluent, polished piece, close in manner to Haydn's Op. 1 No. 1, with a spirited 6/8 opening movement, two minuets (the second particularly delightful) with an appealing *Largo* of charm and warmth, between them, and a witty finale with some lively invention. Samuel Webbe, too, used Haydn as his model – the slow movement of the *Emperor* Quartet – for his variations on *Adeste Fideles*: it is a beautiful, highly ingenious piece, harmonically rich, exquisitely crafted. But the most unexpected work here is certainly the Samuel Wesley Quartet, usually supposed to date from the very beginning of the nineteenth century but surely more likely, as Peter Holman says in his note, to be 20 years later – the energetic, leaping lines, the complex figuration, the abrupt gestures, the free textures: all this speaks of a later, post-classical era. It is a substantial and powerful piece, wholly individual in tone. The Salomon bring a good deal of fire to this piece, and indeed, once past the Abel, they play this music with splendid conviction, as it amply merits. This CD is something of a revelation.

Joseph Szigeti The Recordings with Béla Bartók and Andor Foldes. **Joseph Szigeti** (vn); [a]**Andor Foldes**, [b]**Béla Bartók** (pfs). Biddulph mono Ⓜ LAB070/71* (two discs: 129 minutes: ADD: 7/94) . From American Columbia and New Music Quarterly originals; recorded 1940-41. ❻❻
Bartók Rhapsody No. 1, Sz86[b]. Contrasts, Sz111[b] (with Benny Goodman, cl). **Bloch** Baal Shem[a]. **Debussy** Violin Sonata in G minor[a]. **Ives** Violin Sonata No. 4, "Children's Day at the Camp Meeting"[a]. **Schubert** Violin Sonata in D major, D384[a]. Also includes works by Bach, Brahms, Corelli, Debussy, Dvořák, Falla, Hubay, Kodály, Lalo, Milhaud, Mussorgsky and Schubert.

Ever the thinker among conjurors, Joseph Szigeti didn't so much transcend pyrotechnics as harness them to expressive ends. Szigeti's technique was in good working order on this set and fully up to realizing the sensuality implicit in works like Debussy's Sonata and "Clair de lune" from the *Suite bergamasque* (heard here in Rölens's effective arrangement). *Baal Shem* is gripping in its confessional ardour, enshrining profoundly perceptive interpretations. It was also fascinating to encounter the rare Ives Fourth Sonata. It is difficult to imagine the tender, central *Largo cantabile* sounding with greater melancholy than it does here. It is a strangely alluring piece, full of stylistic contradictions and ending with an engagingly off-beam *Allegro*. The Milhaud and Falla items (the booklet prints them in reverse order) are delightfully adroit, but Szigeti's own transcription of the *Háry János* Intermezzo is rather discursive and heavy-handed. The Bartók *Rhapsody* is given with appropriate rustic gaiety, while *Contrasts* – heard here in its best CD transfer yet – has just the right feeling of improvised burlesque. The Bach, Corelli and Schubert items convey the very essence of Szigeti's violinistic personality, his warmth, elegance and superior intelligence. The Corelli *La folia* will stop you in your tracks, especially the closing cadenza with its felicitous chord-work, a remarkable piece of playing by any standards. The Schubert D major *Sonatina*'s opening *Allegro molto* displays acute sensitivity to line, while in the carefree *Rondo* (taken from the big D major Piano Sonata, D850) Szigeti's quick-wristed, capricious phrasing is reminiscent of Heifetz's. The Bach *Bourrée* is typically crisp, deliberate and rhythmically supple. Quite honestly, everything here is so rich in incident that no amount of listening will dull its appeal. Joseph Szigeti's art is truly inexhaustible!

Trios for 4 Palladian Ensemble (Pamela Thorby, recs; Rachel Podger, vn; Susanne Heinrich, va da gamba; William Carter, archlte/gtr). Linn Records Ⓕ CKD050 (63 minutes: DDD: 5/97). ✏
Handel Trio Sonatas, Op. 2 – No. 1 in B minor; No. 4 in F major. **Telemann** Trio Sonatas – G minor, TWV42:g9; A minor, TWV42:a4. **Leclair** Ouverture in G major, Op. 13 No. 1. **Quantz** Trio Sonata in C major.

The programme has been artfully chosen to demonstrate the diversity of styles current at more or less the same period of time. The Handel sonatas, the earliest works here though not published until 1730, are fundamentally Italianate; Leclair, despite this overture in the French style, also displays *goûts réunis*; Telemann, catholic in his tastes, is happy to include robust folk influences; and Quantz, less contrapuntal and more *galant* than the others, looks ahead to pre-classical style. The present performances exude a sense of enjoyment in the verve the artists bring to the second and last movements of the Handel F major and the delicious lightness of the initial *Allegro* of the Quantz; and in the Telemann A minor (from the *Essercizii musici*) Pamela Thorby and Rachel Podger exhibit virtuoso tonguing and bowing (though the finale is too rushed). Equally attractive, however, is the shaping of *affettuoso* movements, notably the *Grave* of the Telemann G minor. The *Largo* of Handel's Op. 2 No. 1 can often sound lumbering, but the ensemble's adoption of the *Andante* speed indicated in the C minor version is much more convincing and effective. The only reservations about this disc – and they are very slight indeed – concern some of William Carter's contributions: his accents in the finale of Telemann's G minor Trio are rather too rumbustious, and in the lively first *Allegro* of Handel's Op. 2 No. 1 the archlute continuo is too dry.

Violin and Piano Works Andrew Haveron (vn); Daniel Blumenthal (pf). Cyprès Ⓟ CYP9604 (78 minutes: DDD: 3/98). Recorded 1997.
R. Strauss Sonata in E flat major, Op. 18. **Stravinsky** Divertimento. **Tchaikovsky** Mélodie for Violin and Piano, Op. 42 No. 3. Valse-Scherzo for Violin and Piano, Op. 34. **Waxman** Love Music from Richard Wagner's "Tristan und Isolde". Carmen Fantasy.
A prize-winner at last year's prestigious Queen Elisabeth competition in Belgium, young British fiddler Andrew Haveron is clearly a performer of considerable talent and genuine promise. He and Blumenthal give an excitingly unmannered account of Strauss's early Sonata, full of interpretative flair and flashing temperament. Both the Tchaikovsky and Waxman confections are no less compulsive, while the Stravinsky *Divertimento* fairly crackles with character; indeed, Haveron's playing here possesses great poise, sensitivity and truly sparkling rhythmic *élan*.

Virtuoso Music for Trumpet Sergei Nakariakov (tpt); Alexander Markovich (pf).
Teldec Ⓕ 4509-94554-2 (59 minutes: DDD: 6/95). Items marked [a] arr. Markovich, [b]Nakariakov, [c]Dokshitzer. Recorded 1994.   ⒼⒼ
Waxman Carmen Fantasia[a]. **Arban** Variations on a theme from Bellini's "Norma"[a]. Variations on a Tyrolean Theme[a]. **Falla** La vida breve – Danse espagnole[b]. **Saint-Saëns** Le carnaval des animaux – The swan[b]. **Paganini** Caprice in E flat major, Op. 1 No. 17[b]. Moto perpetuo in C major, Op. 11[b]. **Tchaikovsky** Valse-scherzo in C major, Op. 34[b]. **Sarasate** Zigeunerweisen, Op. 20[c]. **Fauré** Le Réveil[b]. **W. Brandt** Concert Piece No. 2.
Sergei Nakariakov is an extraordinary talent. It is one thing to be able to play the violin at the age of 17 with the technical aplomb of one's elders but a brass instrument – on a purely physical level – requires a strength and maturity which can be accelerated only so fast. His prowess as a trumpeter lies not only in the sphere of technical wizardry, which he has in super-abundance, but in a security of tone and interpretational vision: the subtle tuning in this selection of mainly-transcribed violin pieces and the gipsyish portamentos are astute and accomplished. The Russian-ness of his playing is fascinating; he has that intensity of tone that Westerners find so hard to emulate without sounding corny or chastened. Nakariakov has a focused but fat, epic sound (though no doubt it will get even more wholesome with age) and a total security and command in all registers. His technique is particularly admirable in the lower reaches where he seems rarely to need the air at his disposal to progress through phrases. Nakariakov's slow playing is fluid, especially in Fauré's *Le Réveil*.

Virtuoso Works for Violin and Piano Maxim Vengerov (vn); Itamar Golan (pf).
Teldec Ⓕ 9031-77351-2 (67 minutes: DDD: 4/94). Recorded 1993.
Wieniawski Polonaise No. 1 in D major, Op. 4. Légende, Op. 17. **Paganini** I palpiti, Op. 13. **Kreisler** Schön Rosmarin. Tambourin chinois. Caprice viennois. **Bloch** Baal shem – Nigun. **Tchaikovsky** Souvenir d'un lieu cher, Op. 42 – No. 2, Scherzo in C minor; No. 3, Mélodie in E flat major. **Messiaen** Theme and Variations. **Sarasate** Caprice basque, Op. 24. **Bazzini** La Ronde des lutins, Op. 25.
Maxim Vengerov is such a masterful musician that everything he touches turns to gold. Firstly, his intonation is impeccable. The purity and steadiness of Paganini's *I palpiti* is such that one never has the impression of his being under any strain. The double-stopping episodes in Wieniawski's *Légende* appear to come as naturally to him as single notes. He captures the mawkish Slavonic melancholy with real intensity. In the Kreisler selection Vengerov is gentle and generous-spirited, charmingly pure in *Schön Rosmarin* and idiomatic for the tongue-in-cheek *Tambourin chinois*. The Bazzini has terrific attack, too, though it might have been more impish. The piece is undeniably inconsequential, but one is left gawping at the phenomenal accuracy and confidence of the left-hand pizzicato section at the end. In conclusion it must be said that rarely if ever does one hear the Tchaikovsky *Mélodie* played with more eloquence or refined tone colour.

Works for Clarinet and Piano Michael Collins (cl); Kathryn Stott (pf).
EMI Eminence Virtuosi Ⓜ CD-EMX2287 (67 minutes: DDD: 9/92). Recorded 1992.
Schumann Fantasiestücke, Op. 73. **Debussy** Première rapsodie. **Poulenc** Clarinet Sonata. **Lovreglio** Fantasia on Verdi's "La traviata", Op. 45. **Weber** Grand duo concertant, J204. **Messager** Solo de concours.

Works for Clarinet and Piano Victoria Soames (cl); **Julius Drake** (pf).
Clarinet Classics Ⓕ CC0001 (68 minutes: DDD: 9/92).
Copland Clarinet Sonata. **Tailleferre** Arabesque. Solo Clarinet Sonata. **Honegger** Sonatine.
Poulenc Clarinet Sonata. **Milhaud** Sonatine, Op. 100. Duo Concertant, Op. 351.
One wishes that more music existed for the clarinet as a solo instrument, and it seems unfair that an instrument loved by Mozart, Weber and Brahms (to name but three composers) has such a small solo repertory. But there it is, and besides music by the men just mentioned there are other works of importance such as Schumann's *Fantasiestücke,* Debussy's *Rapsodie* and the Poulenc Sonata which appears on both these British discs. Michael Collins is one of the finest clarinettists active today, and certainly earns the title of virtuoso with the performances on the EMI disc. Messager's "competition solo" demands and receives great agility and panache, and Debussy's later piece is no less well served by this artist's refinement and subtlety. Weber's *Grand duo concertant* is a sonata in all but name, with fine melodies in its central *Andante* and a theatrical finale, and here Kathryn Stott matches Collins in her handling of the challenging piano part. The recording is excellent. On the Clarinet Classics disc, Copland's Clarinet Sonata nominally dates from the very end of his life but proves to be an expert reworking of the Violin Sonata which he composed four decades earlier in 1943. This was a vintage period for him and he described the work as mainly lyrical, with little virtuosity. In fact there is an American purity of flavour here that is uniquely his and which we also find in other works of this time such as the ballet, *Appalachian Spring.* Victoria Soames and Julius Drake give this sonata due weight as well as quiet poetry, and they are no less good in Poulenc's, which has the same blend of energy and tenderness, although Collins and Stott bring even more brilliance to its finale. The music by four members of Les Six is not all of the same stature, and although Milhaud's two pieces (separated by some three decades) are good value in their quirky way, the Honegger is not so interesting until its vivid finale. But it is good to have all these works together and the performances by Soames and Drake are unfailingly stylish, while the recording is well balanced and faithful.

Instrumental

American Piano Sonatas, Volume 1. **Peter Lawson** (pf). Virgin Classics Ⓕ VC7 59008-2
(76 minutes: DDD: 5/91).   ⊕⊕
Copland Piano Sonata in E flat major, Op. 26. **Ives** (ed. Cowell) Three-page Sonata.
Carter Piano Sonata. **Barber** Piano Sonata, Op. 26.
This disc offers four relatively unfamiliar but highly characterful American piano works in authoritative performances by a British-born pianist who clearly has their idiom at his fingertips – as well as their pretty challenging notes. As played here, the Copland Piano Sonata of 1941 has softness as well as strength, and for all its powerful utterance there is a strangely compelling lyricism at work too; one can see why the young Leonard Bernstein adored the work. The recording matches the music, being on the close side but extremely lifelike as piano sound. Ives's *Three-page Sonata*, which at over seven minutes is longer than the miniature that its title suggests, is a gnomic utterance, but as always with this composer we feel that he has something to say that could be said in no other way. Carter's Piano Sonata is an early work of 1946, which the composer revised much later in 1982; its debt to Copland is evident, but there is also a personal voice and the scope and sweep of the music is deeply impressive. Barber's Sonata (1949), which was written for Horowitz, is less radical in idiom than the other works played and thus more immediately approachable if by no means conventional, being a work of considerable power and eloquence, very well written for the piano.

Martha Argerich Début Recital. **Martha Argerich** (pf). DG The Originals Ⓜ 447 430-2GOR
(71 minutes: ADD: 6/95). Items marked [a] from SLPM138672 (1/63), [b]2530 193 (6/72).
Recorded 1960-71. *Gramophone classical 100.*   ⊕⊕⊕
Chopin Scherzo No. 3 in C sharp minor, Op. 39[a]. Barcarolle in F sharp major, Op. 60[a].
Brahms Two Rhapsodies, Op. 79[a]. **Prokofiev** Toccata in D minor, Op. 11[a]. **Ravel** Jeux d'eau[a].
Liszt Hungarian Rhapsody No. 6 in D flat major[a]. Piano Sonata in B minor, S178[b].
Here, on this richly filled CD, is a positive cornucopia of musical genius. Martha Argerich's 1961 disc remains among the most spectacular of all recorded débuts, an impression reinforced by an outsize addition and encore: her 1972 Liszt Sonata. True, there are occasional reminders of her pianism at its most fraught and capricious (Chopin's *Barcarolle*) as well as tiny scatterings of inaccuracies, yet her playing always blazes with a unique incandescence and character. The Brahms *Rhapsodies* are as glowingly interior as they are fleet. No more mercurial Chopin *Scherzo* exists on record and if its savagery becomes flighty and skittish (with the chorale's decorations sounding like manic bursts of laughter), Argerich's fine-toned fluency will make other, lesser pianists weep with envy. Ravel's *Jeux d'eau* is gloriously indolent and scintillating and the Prokofiev *Toccata* (a supreme example of his early iconoclasm) is spun off in a manner that understandably provoked Horowitz's awe and enthusiasm. Liszt's Sixth *Hungarian Rhapsody* is a marvel of wit and daring and the B minor Sonata

is among the most dazzling ever perpetuated on disc. The recordings have worn remarkably well and the transfers have been expertly done.

The Bach Family Organ Works. **Marie-Claire Alain** (org). Erato Ⓕ 0630-17073-2
(60 minutes: DDD: A/97). ✏ Played on the Migendt-Marx organ of the church "Zur frohen Botschaft", Berlin-Friedrichshain. Recorded 1996.
    C.P.E. Bach Fantasia e fuga a 4 in C minor, H103. Adagio per il organo a 2 claviere e pedal in D minor, H352. Prelude in D major, H107. Fuga in D minor, H372. Fuga a 4 in E flat major, H102. Fuga sopra il nome de Bach, H373. **W.F. Bach** Eight Fugues, F31. Chorales – Nun komm der Heiden Heiland; Christe, der du bist Tag und Licht; Jesu, meine Freude; Wir, Christenleut. **J.C. Bach** Fugue on B-A-C-H, T348/4. **J.C.F. Bach:** Fughetta on the name H-C-F-B-B-A-C-H, HWXII/14.

This disc might seem of little more than curiosity value, yet Marie-Claire Alain has elevated Bach's four musical sons to a plateau on which they have rarely before been allowed to stand. Whether it's the dramatic gestures of C.P.E.'s stirring *Fantasia e fuga* and his magnificent Fugue in E flat, the innocent charm of W.F.'s Fugues, J.C.'s quasi-operatic *Fugue on B-A-C-H* (with its strikingly forward-looking tonal adventurousness) or J.C.F's humble little Fugue based on his full signature (Hans-Christoph-Friedrich-Bückenburger-B-A-C-H) Alain reveals the very essence of the music, registering it with impeccable taste and, through her innate musicianship, convincing us that these are pieces which deserve not only to be heard, but which can stand alongside the monumental edifices which were J. S.'s legacy. At least two of Bach's sons knew the delightful organ on which Alain plays. C.P.E. composed his six sonatas and W.F. his eight fugues for Princess Anna Amalia who used to play on this very organ before it was rehoused in Berlin. The recording is beautifully clear and intimate. But best of all is Alain's intuitive and wondrously communicative playing. An important and valuable addition to the catalogue, and a disc to treasure.

Caoine Michelle Makarski (vn). ECM New Series Ⓕ 449 957-2 (74 minutes: DDD: 7/97). Recorded 1995.
    Biber Mystery Sonatas – Passacaglia in G minor. **Hartke** Caoine. **Reger** Sonata in A minor, Op. 91 No. 7 – Chaconne. **Rochberg** Caprice Variations (excerpts). **Bach** Partita No. 1 in B minor, BWV1002.

Carefully chosen, 'themed' recitals are always welcome. Yet it's far from easy to get the packaging right. Michelle Makarski's outstandingly played solo violin programme, for instance, is entitled "Caoine" (an Irish lament) and comes with a cover-photo of what appears to be an Irish peat bog. Sadly, Stephen Hartke's eponymous work is not much more interesting than that. Yet it would be worth owning this disc just for Makarski's chaste and stylish Biber and Bach, in which she is intelligently aware of stylistic points, without ever making a fetish of them and without denaturing the modern instrument. As a piece, Reger's *Chaconne* never quite takes off, but it does at least taxi around quite impressively. George Rochberg's 51 *Caprice Variations*, of which we hear 11 movements, are full of fantasy and aural resourcefulness – memorable rehearings of Paganini, via Bartók and Crumb. Clean but atmospheric recording enhances the attraction of this intelligently conceived disc.

Danish Organ Works Kevin Bowyer (org). Nimbus Ⓕ NI5468 (70 minutes: DDD: 7/96). Recorded on the Marcussen organ of Odense Cathedral, Denmark. Recorded 1995.
    Gade Three Tone Pieces, Op. 22. **Syberg** Prelude, Intermezzo and Fugato. **Nørgård** Partita concertante, Op. 23. **Nielsen** Commotio, FS155.

This disc contains four large and little-known works, although with the exception of *Prelude, Intermezzo and Fugato* by Franz Syberg, all are currently represented in the catalogue. Gade's three pleasant but unexceptional pieces are decidedly Mendelssohnian, Per Nørgård presents a work crammed full of diverse stylistic allusions (including a remarkably Shostakovich-like slow movement which Bowyer clearly relishes), while Nielsen's powerful *Commotio*, undeniably one of the glories of twentieth-century organ music, rules itself out of most organists' portfolios by being long and difficult. Bowyer's declared purpose in putting this programme together is to celebrate the Danish town of Odense – only Gade had no direct connection with the place. Bowyer himself has spent a considerable part of this decade there – winning the Odense international organ competition in 1990 and subsequently making most of his recordings there. He hardly needs an excuse for using the Marcussen in Odense Cathedral, however – it makes a simply lovely sound and he is clearly very much at ease with it.

Beau Génie Pieces from the Bauyn Manuscript, Volume 1. **Jane Chapman** (hpd). Collins Classics Ⓕ 1420-2 (69 minutes: DDD: 3/95). ✏ Recorded 1994.
    Suites and pieces by Chambonnières, L. Couperin, Pinel, D'Anglebert, Mezangeot, Rossi and unidentified members of the Monnard, Gautier, Richard and La Barre families

This release presents an enterprising and well-balanced programme, and one, too, which reflects the sort of practical contact with music that your average wealthy seventeenth-century enthusiast might actually have enjoyed. It is the first of three devoted to a manuscript collection named after the family for which it was copied around 1670, and whose musical tastes it presumably reflects. Two of the greatest figures of the French harpsichord school are here: Louis Couperin (represented by his solemn

G minor Suite) and his teacher Chambonnières (a C major Suite which includes ornamented repeats by Couperin). The bulk of the disc, though, is given over to lesser figures; true, there is a fine Sarabande by D'Anglebert, but the rest consists of a mixture of transcriptions of lute pieces by composers such as Mezangeot and Gautier, and dances by unidentified members of minor composer dynasties such as the La Barres and the Richards. Jane Chapman uses Dartington Hall Trust's much rebuilt 1614 Flemish harpsichord rather than a more sonorous and resonant French model. And why not? What really matters is her command of the French style, which is fluent and tidy and shows good judgement in the use of generally lively tempos.

Divers styles dans l'Eloquence Pieces from the Bauyn Manuscript, Volume 2. **Jane Chapman** (hpd). Collins Classics Ⓕ 1421-2 (71 minutes: DDD: 4/95). ✍ Recorded 1994.
L. Couperin Suites – A minor; D minor; Prélude in C major. Pavanne in F sharp minor.
Froberger Toccatas in A minor and G major. Suite in A minor. Ricercare in C major.
Frescobaldi Capriccio in G major. Fantasia in E minor. **Anonymous** Four Pavannes.
Here are pieces by three of the undisputed keyboard masters of the early baroque. Louis Couperin provides the main substance of the programme, in the shape of two large-scale suites, a lengthy *Pavanne* in the unusual key of F sharp minor to open the disc, and a solemn *Prélude* to end. One of the advantages, however, of this type of release over the single-composer (or, for that matter, single-country) species is that new cross-connections can be illustrated, and it is fortunate the Bauyn collection contains both a Couperin *Prélude* explicitly "a l'imitation de Mr Froberger" and the Froberger *Toccata* which was its model. Chapman includes both, and then takes the opportunity to give us more of the German composer's attractive and influential music, including a three-movement suite to go with the *Toccata*. Two pieces by Froberger's teacher Frescobaldi complete the disc, along with four short *Pavannes* which are anonymous but by no means worthy of disownment. Chapman's grasp of the French idiom is secure, her application of it once again eloquent and attractive. If she is a shade more convincing in the dance movements than in the grander *Préludes* and *Toccatas*, then that could well be partly down to her instrument, a 1614 Ruckers from Dartington Hall which has its own beauties, for sure, but which doesn't quite have the resonance and sheer weighty presence of a French model. If that's the only drawback, though, it's not much of one; this is a thoroughly worthwhile and enjoyable release.

Carnegie Hall Highlights Artur Rubinstein (pf). RCA Victor Gold Seal Ⓜ 09026 61445-2 (64 minutes: ADD: 10/93). Items marked [a] from SB6504 (9/62), [b]RL13850 (7/81). Recorded live ·in 1961. ⒼⒼⒼ
Debussy Préludes – La cathédrale engloutie; Ondine[a]. Images – Hommage à Rameau; Poissons d'or[a]. **Szymanowski** Mazurkas, Op. 50 – Nos. 1-4[a]. **Prokofiev** Vision fugitives, Op. 22 – Nos. 1-3, 9-14 and 16[a]. **Villa-Lobos** Próle do bébé, Book 1[a]. **Schumann** Arabeske in C major, Op. 18[b]. **Albéniz** Navarra[a].
Artur Rubinstein had a unique flair for live musical communication and these concert performances have great spontaneity. In fact, the whole disc might have been billed as 'The Essential Rubinstein', thus providing one of the few occasions where the 'essential' epithet would have been fully justified. And it's certainly all here – the wistful reverie (*Arabeske*), the mastery of rhythm and exotic colours (Szymanowski *Mazurkas*, *Navarra*, *Próle do bébé*), acute sensitivity to miniature forms (*Visions fugitives*), unforced virtuosity employed to musical ends (*Próle*) and a natural inclination towards musical impressionism (Debussy). RCA are more active with their back catalogue than most of their rivals so we can only hope that more Rubinstein is waiting in the wings.

Alfred Cortot Piano works by Albéniz, Chopin, Debussy, Fauré, Liszt, Mendelssohn, Ravel, Saint-Saëns, Scriabin and Weber. **Alfred Cortot** (pf). Biddulph mono Ⓜ LHW014/15* (two discs: 133 minutes: ADD: 10/94). From Victor originals; recorded 1919-25. Ⓖ
Cortot was, arguably, the most vivacious of all keyboard sophisticates, one whose dazzling mind and fingers flashed with a happy disregard for mere accuracy or musical propriety. Like the heroine of Muriel Spark's novel, *The Prime of Miss Jean Brodie*, Cortot proclaimed that beauty and truth rather than safety always came first. With exemplary completeness Biddulph present in this invaluable two-disc set Cortot's complete acoustic recordings, admirably transferred by Ward Marston from records dating from 1919-25. Cortot's inimitable wit and seduction grace Albéniz's *Triana* as well as *Seguidilla* and *Malagueña*, and two Fauré items offer further enchantment. Elsewhere there is a reminder in Cortot's death-defying spin through Saint-Saëns's *Etude en forme de valse* of a brilliance and rapidity that aroused the awe and envy of Horowitz and, in Scriabin's D sharp minor *Etude*, of a blazing rhetoric and insinuation that suggest total sympathy for the Russian romantic idiom. Alas, there are savage cuts in several pieces (Chopin's Op. 22 *Grande Polonaise*, minus its introductory *Andante Spianato*, is butchered virtually beyond recognition, the price of early recording techniques. This would also explain a pell-mell rush in several other works (try the 1923 Chopin *Berceuse*). Cortot preferred to take risks rather than modify his mood of the moment for the sake of mere expediency.

Alfred Cortot Piano Works by Albéniz, Bach, Brahms, Chopin, Handel, Liszt, Purcell, Saint-Saëns and Schubert. **Alfred Cortot** (pf). Biddulph mono Ⓜ LHW020* (77 minutes: ADD: 5/95). From HMV and Victor originals; recorded 1925-39. ⒼⒼ

Biddulph have unearthed some astonishing gems. Cortot's whirl through Albéniz's *Malagueña* and joyous charge through the *Seguidillas* (a kind of Spanish *Chopsticks*) may be familiar, but what of *Sous la Palmier*? Here Cortot spins a tale beneath the palms that would seduce a saint. As the insert-note so nicely puts it, all these performances have "an almost tangible Iberian heat", a lilt and insinuation that can make even the redoubtable Alicia de Larrocha sound sober and lacking in *joie de vivre*. Schubert's *12 Ländler*, D681, too, seem to dance off the page, and in the *Arioso* from Bach's F minor Concerto (the pianist's own arrangement) Cortot shows himself an incomparable 'singer' of the keyboard. Even his finest partners in artistry (and they include Dame Maggie Teyte and Gérard Souzay) must have marvelled at that exquisitely floating *pianissimo* and his alternately full and delicate *cantabile*. Then there is Cortot's Purcell selection, all within style but with that instantly recognizable rhythmic spring and vivacity, yet another recording of Saint-Saëns's *Etude en forme de valse* (which made Horowitz pale with envy) and Chopin performances as sprightly and elemental as any on record. The *Berceuse's* figurations foam and race with a happy disregard for tranquillity yet the playing is as mesmeric as it is iridescent. And although the First *Ballade* and Second *Impromptu* are periodically invaded by inaccuracies like swarms of locusts, nothing can detract from Cortot's innate elegance, fire and poetry. Ward Marston's transfers are exemplary, beautifully transcending age and crackles to capture performances which make most contemporary piano playing seem as insignificant as chaff in the wind.

Shura Cherkassky Piano Works. **Shura Cherkassky** (pf); ^aPhilharmonia Orchestra / Anatole Fistoulari. Testament mono Ⓕ SBT1033* (62 minutes: ADD: 9/94). Recorded 1952-58. Ⓖ
Liszt Piano Concerto No. 1 in E flat major, S124^a (from HMV DB9763/4, 10/52). Liebestraum in A flat major, S541 No. 3 (HMV 7ER5113, 1/59). Réminiscences de Don Juan (Mozart), S418 (HMV ALP1154, 10/54). Hungarian Rhapsody No. 13 in A minor, S244. Faust (Gounod) – Waltz, S407. **Saint-Saëns** Le carnaval des animaux – Le cygne. **Liadov** A musical snuffbox, Op. 32 (all from ALP1527, 11/57).
Here, in excellent transfers of HMV recordings dating from the 1950s, is a vintage Cherkassky recital. Mercurial and hypnotic, his way with Liszt's E flat Concerto reminds us in every nook and cranny that he has always been able to enliven and transform even the most over-familiar score. True, there are moments – such as the start of the *Allegro vivace* – where he is less than ideally poised or balletic (one of those instances where his elfin caprice can seem close to uncertainty and where he leads Fistoulari and the Philharmonia a Puckish dance: now you hear me, now you don't), yet his sparkle and charm are inimitable. Again, in Var. 1 of the *Don Juan* Fantasy he is perhaps more flustered than *elegantamente*, but even when his virtuosity is less than watertight, his playing is infinitely more fascinating and imaginatively varied. Cherkassky can be garrulous or somnolent, his phrasing languorous or choppy, yet in the ecstatic, long-breathed descent just before the coda of the *Liebestraum* No. 3 and in all of the *Hungarian Rhapsody* No. 13 and the *Faust* Waltz, his mastery has seldom sounded more effortless or unalloyed. Finally, two encores of *friandises*: Godowsky's fine-spun elaboration of Saint-Saëns's "Le cygne",

---

French Organ Works Simon Lindley (org). Naxos Ⓢ 8 550581 (74 minutes: DDD: 3/93). Played on the organ of Leeds Parish Church. Recorded 1991.
Guilmant Grand Choeur in D major, "alla Handel". Cantilene pastorale, Op. 19.
Vierne 24 Pièces en stile libre, Op. 31 – Epitaphe; Berceuse. Stele pour un enfant défunte.
M-A. Charpentier Te Deum, H146 – Prelude. **Langlais** Trois méditations (1962). **Bonnet** Romance sans paroles. **de Maleingreau** Suite mariale. **Boëllmann** Suite gothique, Op. 25.
Widor Symphony No. 5 in F minor, Op. 42 No. 1 – Toccata.
Two of the most popular organ showpieces are here – Widor's Toccata and the Toccata which comes as the last movement of Boëllmann's *Suite gothique*. In addition there is the majestic *Te Deum* Prelude by Charpentier (familiar to a wide audience as the Eurovision signature tune) and the gentle *Berceuse* which Vierne wrote for his baby daughter. Alongside these evergreens, mainstays of any organ-lover's CD collection, are some more unusual but no less enjoyable pieces: Guilmant's glorious *Grand Choeur "alla Handel"*, Bonnet's delightful *Romance sans paroles* and Paul de Maleingreau's *Suite mariale*. In short, a real feast of some of the best French organ music. Simon Lindley, organist at the musically-renowned Leeds Parish Church, gives fine, no-nonsense performances which should appeal especially to those exploring this music for the first time. The organ makes a super noise, and the Naxos recording is highly commendable. It may not be an instrument of which the *cognoscenti* of French organ music would immediately approve, but there is enough sensitivity and interpretative insight in Lindley's performances to make this a worthwhile buy for casual listener and specialist alike.

From Stanley to Wesley, Volume 6. **Jennifer Bate** (org). Unicorn-Kanchana Ⓕ DKPCD9106 (65 minutes: DDD: 11/91). Played on the organs of Adlington Hall, Cheshire; The Dolmetsch Collection, Haslemere, Surrey; The Chapel of St Michael's Mount, Cornwall; The Iveagh Bequeast, Kenwood, London; Killerton House, Broadclyst, Exeter, Devon and The Chapel of Our Lady and St Everilda, Everingham, Yorkshire. Recorded 1989-91. *Selected by Sounds in Retrospect.*   Ⓖ
Boyce Voluntary in D major. **Handel** Fugue in G major. Voluntary in C major.
Heron Voluntary in G major. **Hook** Voluntary in C minor. **Russell** Voluntary in F major.

Stanley Voluntaries – A minor, Op. 6 No. 2; D minor, Op. 7 No. 4; G major, Op. 7 No. 9.
Stubley Voluntary in C major. **S. Wesley** Voluntaries – E flat major, Op. 6 No. 7; B flat major.
Whilst most people would regard Bach and his North German contemporaries as synonymous with all that is best in eighteenth-century organ music there was also a significant school of organist-composers thriving in England. Chief amongst these was John Stanley whose music was greatly admired at the time, in particular by a recent immigrant from Germany, one George Frederic Handel (two fine examples of his own organ music are to be found on this CD). But while the German composers were writing for their great, majestic organs, their English counterparts were faced with something far humbler in scope and more delicate and intimate in character. To hear this music played on such an instrument is to have its true beauty revealed: here it is played not just on one authentic contemporaneous instrument, but the Unicorn-Kanchana team have scoured the length and breadth of England, from Cornwall to Yorkshire, to unearth six classic, and virtually unaltered examples. Jennifer Bate's immense musical and technical powers and her innate, native sense of style, imbues this disc with compelling musical authority which, added to the captivating sound of these six delightful organs, makes it an intriguing historical document – real 'living history', if you like. This CD is the sixth in a series and while each is a valuable addition to the recorded legacy of English music, this one in particular gives the less specialist collector a representative and varied selection of this wonderful, yet woefully overlooked area of our musical heritage.

Grand Piano
The Polish Virtuoso [a]Josef Hofmann, [b]Ignaz Friedman, [c]Ignaz Jan Paderewski (pfs).
Nimbus Ⓜ NI8802* (71 minutes: DDD: 12/95). From piano rolls released between 1919 and 1932.
Hofmann Impressions for Piano – No. 3, The Sanctuary[a]. Kaleidoscope, Op. 40 No. 4[a].
Moszkowski La jongleuse, Op. 52 No. 4[a]. Etincelles, Op. 36 No. 6[a]. Serenata, Op. 15 No. 1[b].
Guitarre, Op. 45 No. 2[a]. Caprice espagnol, Op. 37[a]. **Friedman** Viennese Waltzes on Themes from Gärtner – Nos. 1-4[b]. Estampes, Op. 22 – Nos. 2 and 4[b]. Elle danse, Op. 10 No. 5[b].
Paderewski Humoresques de concert, Op. 14[c] – No. 1, Minuet; No. 3, Caprice; No. 6, Cracovienne fantastique. Miscellanea, Op. 16[c] – No. 1, Légende in A flat major; No. 4, Nocturne in B flat major. Mélodie, Op. 8 No. 3[c].
Chopin Piano Sonata No. 2 in B flat minor, Op. 35. Nocturnes – D flat major, Op. 27 No. 2; F minor, Op. 55 No. 1. Polonaises – A major, Op. 40 No. l; A flat major, Op. 53. Scherzos – No. 1 in B minor, Op. 20; No. 3 in C sharp minor, Op. 39. Waltz in A flat major, Op. 42. Berceuse in D flat major, Op. 57. **Josef Hofmann** (pf). Nimbus Ⓜ NI8803* (76 minutes: DDD: 12/95). From piano rolls released between 1920 and 1927.
These performances taken from Duo-Art rolls made between 1915 and 1930 are played, via a 'robot' created in 1973, on a modern concert Steinway under the supervision of Gerald Stonehill, a world authority on the Duo-Art catalogue. As a result, they sound as vivid and sparkling as if they had been given yesterday – indeed, so vivid is the piano tone that it emphasizes brightness at the expense of warmth. To some extent this may be due to the difference in tone-quality between the instruments on which the recordings were made and that used for the reproduction, but sneaking doubts remain about the matching of the robot's responses, resulting in some lack of really soft passages.

Doubts about realism are lessened by a performance of Chopin's 'funeral march' Sonata by Hofmann (Cherkassky's teacher), revered by contemporaries such as Rachmaninov. Though the dynamic range in the piece is not large (the limitations being at the *ff* end), it sounds a convincingly natural reading. But better still are the A flat *Polonaise*, which boasts a fine crisp *élan*, the B minor *Scherzo*, which employs a very full dynamic range and, like the C sharp minor *Scherzo*, illustrates the real meaning of *Presto con fuoco*, and a delicately pearly A flat *Waltz*. The *Berceuse*, coolly played, slightly suffers from a weakness also found elsewhere in the series – too obtrusive a middle register in relation to the melody above, whether due to the voicing of the piano or to a miscalculation in the adjustment of Duo-Art's two dynamic systems ('accompaniment' and 'theme').Hofmann is heard again, and at his stunning best, on the disc devoted to three Polish virtuosos. A group of five pieces by his teacher Moszkowski is notable for perfectly controlled staccato touch, vital rhythmicality, neat rapid repeated notes and some delectable lightness; and two works of his own show limpid arpeggios (*La jongleuse*) and breath-taking mercurial virtuosity (*Kaleidoscope*).

Ignaz Friedman is represented by Moszkowksi's once popular *Serenata* and by a handful of his own pieces in which he can display the superb technique for which he was famous. There is undeniably an air of exhibitionism about *Elle danse* and the elaborate fantasias on waltz themes by a singer friend (No. 3 particularly lavishly ornate); but with such coruscating playing who would want to complain? Paderewski did not have the natural facility of the others – he was a late starter – but attracted huge and adoring crowds everywhere and was the most highly paid. There is a sparkle about his lively "Caprice" in the style of Scarlatti and a quite attractive, if conventional, nationalist feeling in the "Cracovienne fantastique". The series is provided with first-class notes and Nimbus are to be applauded for their courageous enterprise.

Great European Organs, Volume 26. **Keith John** (org). Priory Ⓕ PRCD370
(73 minutes: DDD: 11/92). Played on the organ of Gloucester Cathedral, UK. Recorded 1991.
Selected by Sounds in Retrospect. ⒼⒶⒷ

Stanford Fantasia and Toccata in D minor, Op. 57. **Reger** Five Easy Preludes and Fugues, Op. 56 – No. 1 in E major. **Shostakovich** Lady Macbeth of the Mtsensk district – Passacaglia. **Schmidt** Chaconne in C sharp minor. **Ravanello** Theme and Variations in B minor.

On the face of it this CD might look as if its appeal is purely for those with a specialist taste in large-scale post-romantic organ music. Certainly Schmidt's gargantuan *Chaconne* represents a daunting prospect both to player and listener, while Shostakovich's only organ solo begins with the kind of chilling dissonance which would certainly scare off those of a delicate disposition. Similarly neither Stanford nor Reger usually attract a crowd when their organ music played – and who has ever heard of Ravanello? But if ever a recording was made to shatter preconceptions, this is it. For a start the Gloucester organ makes a wondrous sound and Priory's recording is in a class of its own; in terms of sound alone this surely ranks as one of the best ever CDs of organ music. Then Keith John quite literally pulls out all the stops to produce an unparalleled display of virtuosity and musicianship. His technical prowess turns the Schmidt into a thrilling *tour de force* while few could question, after hearing his performances, that the Stanford is one of the best works ever written by a British composer or that Ravanello's music doesn't deserve the neglect it currently suffers. An essential disc.

Great European Organs, Volume 36. **Marie-Bernadette Dufourcet** (org). Priory ℗ PRCD422 (67 minutes: DDD: 6/95). Played on the Cavaillé-Coll organ of Notre-Dame-des-Champs, Paris. Recorded 1992.
Barié Trois Pièces, Op. 7. **R. Vierne** Six pièces de différents caractères. **d'Indy** Prélude in E flat minor, Op. 66. **Roussel** Prelude and Fughetta, Op. 41. **Honegger** Fugue and Chorale. **Dupré** Scherzo, Op. 16. **Langlais** Prelude and Fugue, Op. 1. **L. Vierne** Pièces de fantaisie, Op. 55 – Les cloches de Hinckley.

Marie-Bernadette Dufourcet plays these pieces with tremendous verve and assurance, finding in this small 34-stop organ surprising tonal resources and a wonderfully opulent sound. This is an immensely rewarding programme concentrating on works written between 1911 and 1929 and finding, not least in the six pieces by René Vierne (Louis's brother), true gems of great charm and individuality which really deserve to be better known. It is good, too, to have such authoritative performances of Honegger's two dark, almost tragic contributions to the instrument's repertoire as well as Vincent d'Indy's once popular *Prélude* in E flat minor (*not* B minor as the booklet suggests). Augustin Barié's *Trois Pièces* is hardly one of the msot popular French organ works, yet hearing it played like this, its relative neglect is even harder to justify. The recording is first-rate, the performances infinitely satisfying but the booklet is inadequate.

Great European Organs, Volume 41. **Roger Sayer** (org). Priory ℗ PRCD495 (76 minutes: DDD: 4/96). Played on the Klais organ of the Hallgrímskirkja, Reykjavík. Recorded 1994.
Bach Prelude and Fugue in D major, BWV532. Clavier-Ubung III, BWV669-89 – Christe, aller Welt Trost, BWV670. **Bonnal** Paysages Euskariens. **Langlais** Triptyque. **B. Ferguson** South and West Suite. **Dupré** Evocation, Op. 37 – Allegro deciso. Recorded 1994.

Here is an organ which makes a truly dazzling sound. Its 32-foot pedal reeds and three ranks of *chamade* Trumpets certainly add pizzazz to Bach's D major Prelude and Fugue. Roger Sayer gives first-rate performances which are both musically perceptive and technically assured – no sense here of allowing the thrill of the instrument to subvert musical integrity. The French works, particularly Langlais's divine *Triptyque*, sound absolutely spectacular, as does a remarkably French-sounding Suite, ostensibly reflecting aspects of the very English county of Devon, by Sayer's predecessor at Rochester Cathedral, Barry Ferguson. The hefty sound of this instrument reflects its bulk – apparently it weighs 25 tons. A pointless statistic, maybe, but without it we would learn precious little about the instrument from the accompanying booklet and the minimalist notes on the music are pitiful. When the music, the playing and the recording quality are as outstanding as this, it seems a shame to mar the result with shabby accompanying documentation.

Great European Organs, Volume 44. **Jane Watts** (org). Priory ℗ PRCD389 (72 minutes: DDD: 10/97). Played on the organ of Rochester Cathedral. Recorded 1993.
Popplewell Organ Suite. Elegy. **Willcocks** Variations on "Breslau". **Preston** Vox Dicentis. **Hoddinott** Organ Sonata. **Mathias** Variations on a Hymn Tune, Op. 20. Canzonetta, Op. 78 No. 2. Jubilate, Op. 67 No. 2. Chorale. Toccata giocosa, Op. 36 No. 2.

Mathias's *Variations on a Hymn Tune* is one of his best organ works, with an ingenious adaptation of variation form, highly inventive musical language, exquisite use of organ colour, and a distinctly Welsh flavour. Jane Watts, Welsh through and through, finds that essential Welshness and, via her immaculate technique and vivacious musicianship, produces a stirring performance of the music. Her programme on the new and magnificent Mander organ in Rochester Cathedral has none of the local flavour found in other volumes of this Great European Organs series. Instead Jane Watts has chosen music in which she has some particular personal interest, be it Mathias with its characteristic Welshness, or Hoddinott's concise but finely wrought Sonata, or pieces by friends and colleagues such as Sir David Willcocks who, as conductor of the Bach Choir, appointed Watts its accompanist. His *Variations on "Breslau"* is quite a gem. Strongly reminiscent in places of Langlais it is splendidly written and, when heard in such a committed and affectionate performance as this, is revealed to be one of the more rewarding organ works written in recent years.

Great European Organs, Volume 48. **Gerard Brooks** (org). Priory ℗ PRCD558
(79 minutes: DDD: 4/98). Played on the Cavaillé-Coll organ in the Abbey Church of St Ouen,
Rouen. Recorded 1995.
Commette Scherzo. **Guilmant** Marche funèbre et chant séraphique, Op. 17 No. 3.
Ibert Trois Pièces. **Philip** Toccata and Fugue in A minor. **Dallier** Cinq Invocations.
Here we have a magnificent recording of one of the truly Great European Organs. In Gerard Brooks,
Priory have found a player as eager to reveal the glories and subtleties of one of Cavaillé-Coll's
greatest creations as his own impressive virtuosity. Widor's description of this as a "Michelangelo of
an organ" seems singularly apt in the light of a disc which displays the instrument so vividly.
  A simple reading of the track list might imply that such opulent resources are being squandered on
a collection of oddities drawn from the ample dark recesses of French organ literature. If Guilmant
is the only familiar name (so far as organists are concerned Ibert is an obscure figure – although on
the strength of his *Trois Pièces* alone he could stand as a significant figure in early twentieth-
century French music), the music of the others is as familiar as a new Andrew Lloyd Webber score –
we're sure we've heard it all before but can't quite remember where. Edouard Commette's *Scherzo* is
clearly first cousin to Henri Mulet's famous *Carillon sortie*, Achille Philip's Toccata comes from the
same stable as that from Boëllman's *Suite gothique*, while Henri Dallier's *Invocations* inspired by Latin
Marian texts could easily pass for Vierne, especially the glittering final Toccata. But if the idioms are
familiar and the ideas derivative, the musical quality in both intellectual and emotional terms is
undeniable. Simply put, this is a programme of immensely enjoyable music, all of which bears
repeated listening and certainly deserves a place both in the catalogues and on the shelves of lovers of
good organ music.

Great European Organs, Volume 51. **Peter King** (org). Priory ℗ PRCD618
(78 minutes: DDD: 7/98). Played on the Klais organ of Bath Abbey.
Bach Pastorale in F major, BWV590. **G. Böhm** Vater unser im Himmelreich, WK ii 138.
Buxtehude Prelude, Fugue and Chaconne in C major, BuxWV137. **Eben** Homage to Dietrich
Buxtehude. **Guridi** Triptico del Buen Pastor. **Liszt** (trans. Schaab) Orpheus, S98. **Saint-Saëns**
Fantaisie in D flat major, Op. 101.
This seems rather a peculiar programme with a focus on Buxtehude and the North German baroque
and with a few other disparate pieces thrown in to spice up the menu. Peculiar or not, it works
superbly. The new Bath Abbey instrument is adorable – a complete rejection of the argument often
propounded that, on purely musical terms, an organ built outside the British Isles is inappropriate for
a major English ecclesiastical building – and it makes everything here sound convincing and
impressive. This sumptuous instrument is well served by a beautifully proportioned recording. For
those interested in the music rather than the instrument, Peter King's performances range from the
solid (Buxtehude's *Praeludium* in G minor) to the near-inspired (Bach's *Pastorale*). Eben's *Homage* is
based on material from the two Buxtehude pieces on the disc and uses Buxtehudian structures and
figurations in a typically astute Eben manner. The inclusion of the Liszt and Saint-Saëns is obviously
inspired by King's deep fondness for these pieces – it shows in every bar of these lovingly nurtured
performances – while the Guridi has moments which allow us to hear the organ's more atmospheric
qualities. Not everybody will be immediately attracted to this disc by the music, but for the sheer
pleasure of hearing a truly wonderful, modern instrument, this release cannot be recommended too
highly.

Le Groupe des Six Marcelo Bratke (pf). Olympia Explorer Ⓜ OCD487
(62 minutes: DDD: 12/96). Recorded 1996.
Auric Adieu New York. **Durey** Trois Préludes à la mémoire de Juliette Méérowitch, Op. 26.
Honegger Sept Pièces brèves. **Milhaud** Printemps – Volume 1, Op. 25; Volume 2, Op. 66.
Poulenc Trois Mouvements perpétuels. Trois Pièces. **Tailleferre** Romance. **Les Six:** Album
des Six.
With his clean-cut technique, tonal sensitivity and verve, Marcelo Bratke confirms the very favourable
impression created by his previous discs in this present focus on composers in France around 1920,
the immediate post-First-World-War period of the Bright Young Things. Yet, contrary to the popular
image, few of these pieces by Les Six are nose-thumbingly facetious: the only real exception, clearly
intended to *épater les bourgeois*, is the much too long and rather bad foxtrot with 'wrong-note'
harmonies by Auric, the youngest of the six. The oldest was the now almost completely forgotten
Durey; the highly charged first, at least, of his sombre tributes to a friend, and his contribution to a
1920 album, suggest an original mind. Of the three composers born in 1892, the most traditionally
diatonic music comes from Tailleferre, with an entirely Fauré-esque *Romance*; Milhaud is represented
by a predominantly calm set of pastorals, polytonal in idiom but, except for the first, not altogether
free from a charge of note-spinning; and the most interesting is Honegger, who besides a thoughtfully
dreamy "Sarabande" in the collective album contributes seven varied, tersely packed miniatures that
experiment in polytonality and atonality. Born in 1899 were Auric and his senior by five weeks,
Poulenc, who of course became much the most popular. His familiar *Mouvements perpétuels* are,
however, trivia as compared with the *Trois Pièces*, the Scriabinesque harmonies and exotic arabesques
of whose "Pastorale" hint at mysterious depths, and whose improvisatory "Hymne" furnished several

ideas for the later *Concert champêtre*; the brittle final "Toccata", with its rapid-fire note-repetitions, provides a scintillating vehicle for Bratke's brilliance of articulation. The recording quality matches his excellence.

Guitar Recital Jason Vieaux (gtr). Naxos Ⓢ 8 553449 (64 minutes: DDD: 11/97). Recorded 1995.
Barrios Waltzes, Op. 8 – Nos. 3 and 4. Julia Florida – Barcarola. **Bustamente** (arr. Morel) Misionera. **Pujol** Preludios – Nos. 2, 3 and 5. **Krouse** Variations on a Moldavian Hora. **Merlin** Suite del recuerdo. **Morel** Chôro. Danza Brasileira. Danza in E minor. **Orbón** Preludio y Danza.

This is the début recording by an artist of great talent. His technical prowess is impressive to say the least, as near flawless as one may get, and his tone is as clear and expressive as his musical thinking. There are now many finger-perfect guitarists on tap but those of Vieaux's natural musicality are rare indeed; everything in the moulding of the phrases comes from within – you just can't *programme* sensitivity of this kind. The main thrust of the music is Latin-American, a nice juxtaposition of the well known (Morel, Barrios, Pujol and Bustamente) with some unfamiliar but substantial (of their kind) pieces by Merlin and Orbón. The apparent 'misfit' is the work by Krouse, far removed from Latin America, but why should music of this quality be excluded, for whatever reason? It is included for the best of reasons, because the performer loves it and is right to do so. The theme is Moldavian and the language of the imaginative and technically punishing variations convincingly matches it. Vieaux plays everything with chameleon-like felicity of style and feeling. Superb recording and excellent notes complete an issue of the greatest distinction, by a player of whom we shall undoubtedly hear many more good things.

Guitar Works Tilman Hoppstock (gtr). Signum Ⓕ SIGX75-00 (56 minutes: DDD: 2/98). Recorded 1995-96.
Marschner Bagatelles, Op. 4 – E major; A minor; A major; G major; A major; F major. **Sor** Pieces – Op. 5: No. 3 in C major; No. 4 in C major. Op. 24: No. 6 in F major; No. 7 in F major; No. 8 in B flat major. Minuets, Op. 11 – No. 2 in G sharp minor; No. 3 in G major; No. 6 in A major; No. 7 in A minor; No. 8 in B flat major; No. 9 in E minor; No. 10 in F major. Studies – Op. 29: No. 21 in D major. Op. 31: No. 13 in C major; No. 18 in B minor. Op. 35: No. 5 in A minor; No. 11 in D minor; No. 12 in F major; No. 18 in B minor; No. 19 in C sharp major. Op. 60: No. 14 in E minor; No. 18 in A minor; No. 22 in E minor; No. 23 in B major. **Werthmüller** Sonata in A major, Op. 17.

After a long voyage of rediscovery of nineteenth-century guitar repertory there are still worthwhile finds to be made. Marschner (1795-1861) is familiar as an important composer of romantic opera and the possessor of a fine voice; what is less well known is that his principal instrument was the guitar, with which he enjoyed a successful career as a self-accompanied singer. The six (of 12) *Bagatelles* indicate that he had considerable skill with the guitar and within their modest limits (only one lasts for more than two minutes) they have great charm. On the other hand we know of Franz Werthmüller – and his dates (1769-1841) – only by a manuscript copy containing the Sonata in A major and a few smaller pieces "set for guitar in memory of the composer by Pfeifer". This substantial Haydnesque Sonata is a real boon to the guitar's repertory. Sor is no newcomer and the works recorded here break no fresh ground, but never have they enjoyed finer performances on the modern guitar. Hoppstock is an exceptional player, with a fine sense of style and unfailing sensitivity, and a technician of the first water; his tone is refined and beautifully nuanced, his delivery is clean and sure even in the passages where the utmost dexterity is called for, and his command of varied articulation is admirable – the opening of the Study, Op. 31 No. 18 makes one of many such points. It is a recording that no guitar lover should be without, and the excellent sound comes as a bonus.

Myra Hess 1938-42 HMV Recordings. **Dame Myra Hess** (pf). Biddulph mono Ⓜ LHW025* (76 minutes: ADD: 3/96). Recorded 1938-42.   Ⓖ
Schumann Carnaval, Op. 9 (from C3008/10, 6/38). **Matthay** Elves, Op. 17. Stray Fancies, Op. 22 (both from B8758, 8/38). **Bach** (arr. Hess) Cantata No. 147, Herz und Mund und Tat und Leben – Jesu, bleibet meine Freude ("Jesu, joy of man's desiring"). **D. Scarlatti** Keyboard Sonata in G major, Kk14 (B9035, 4/40). **Brahms** Piano Pieces, Op. 76 – No. 2, Capriccio in B minor; No. 3, Intermezzo in A flat major (B9189, 8/41). Capriccio in D minor, Op. 116 No. 7. Intermezzo in E flat major, Op. 117 No. 1. Intermezzo in C major, Op. 119 No. 3 (all from C3226, 6/41). **Ferguson** Piano Sonata in F minor, Op. 8 (C3335/7, 5/43).

Those who, sadly, retain an image of Dame Myra Hess as either a sober-suited pianist inclined towards severity or a 'graciousness' that excluded the toughest, most durable virtues, are in for a surprise. For here, on this truly glorious record, she ranges effortlessly from sheer wit and style (Schumann's *Carnaval*) to a dancing rhythmic magic (Scarlatti), from a glowing poetic inwardness (all the Brahms, with perhaps Op. 76 No. 3 as the distantly shining star of the set) to a matchless eloquence (Howard Ferguson's tragic masterpiece, his 1938-40 Piano Sonata). Yet all such qualities are seamlessly joined. Nothing is forced and whether you consider her regal tonal resource (tirelessly celebrated by Stephen Kovacevich, her finest pupil), or a naturalness and candour easy to underestimate, everything is achieved with supreme authority; an illusion achieved by only the truest artists. What an object-lesson, then, for today's harassed young pianists, jostling for attention in an increasingly commercial market-place, a reminder of a poetic and speculative artistry beyond price. Finally, David Lennick's transfers are masterly and Wayne Kiley's notes refer movingly to the legendary wartime National Gallery concerts held in London, where Hess's performances created an "indelible image of hope and vision in adversity".

Vladimir Horowitz The solo European recordings, 1930-36, Volumes 1 and 2. **Vladimir Horowitz** (pf). APR mono Ⓜ APR5516/7* (two discs, oas: 69 and 71 minutes: ADD: 5/98).
APR5516: **Chopin** Etudes – C sharp minor, Op. 10 No. 4; G flat major, "Black Keys", Op. 10 No. 5 (both from HMV DB2788, 4/36); F major, Op. 10 No. 8 (HMV DA1305, 11/33); F major, Op. 25 No. 3 (DB2238. Recorded 1934). Mazurkas – F minor, Op. 7 No. 3 (DA1305); E minor, Op. 41 No. 2 (DA1353, 6/34); C sharp minor, Op. 50 No. 3 (DB2788). Scherzo No. 4 in E major, Op. 54 (DB3205, 7/37). Piano Sonata No. 2 in B flat minor, "Funeral March", Op. 35 – Grave ... doppio movimento (unpublished on 78s. 1936). **Liszt** Funérailles, S173 No. 7 (DB1848, 6/33). Piano Sonata in B minor, S178 (DB1855/7, 9/33). *APR5517:* **D. Scarlatti** Keyboard Sonatas – B minor, Kk87; G, Kk125 (both DB2847, 7/36). **Haydn** Keyboard Sonata in E flat major, HobXVI/52 (DB1837/8, 6/33). **Beethoven** 32 Variations on an Original Theme in C minor, WoO80 (DA1387/8, 3/35). **Bach/Busoni** Nun freut euch, lieben Christen gmein, BWV734 (DA1388). **Schumann** Presto passionato in G minor (DA1301. 1932). Arabeske in C major, Op. 18 (DA1381, 2/35). Traumes Wirren, Op. 12 No. 7 (DA1353). Toccata in C major, Op. 7 (DB2238. 1934). **Debussy** Etude No. 11 "Pour les arpèges composés" (DB2247, 3/35). **Poulenc** Pastourelle. **Rimsky-Korsakov/Rachmaninov** The tale of Tsar Saltan – Flight of the bumble-bee. **Stravinsky** Petrushka – Russian dance (all from DB1869. 1932). **Rachmaninov** Prelude in G minor, Op. 23 No. 5 (DB1490, 6/32). **Prokofiev** Toccata in D minor, Op. 11 (unpublished as 78. 1930).

Horowitz's 1930-36 European recordings are beyond price and so it is more than gratifying to have them permanently enshrined on APR rather than fleetingly available elsewhere. This is notably true of Horowitz's legendary, forever spine-tingling 1932 recording of the Liszt Sonata. Here, once more, is that uniquely teasing and heroic sorcery with octaves and passagework that blaze and skitter with a manic force and projection; an open defiance of all known musical and pianistic convention. Horowitz's virtuosity, particularly in his early days, remains a phenomenon, and hearing, for example, the *vivamente* elaboration of the principal theme or the octave uproar preceding the glassy, retrospective coda is to be reminded of qualities above and beyond the explicable. His way with the Chopin *Mazurkas* unites their outer dance elements and interior poetry with a mercurial brilliance and idiosyncrasy and who but Horowitz could use his transcendental pianism to conjure a *commedia dell'arte* vision of such wit and caprice in Debussy's *Etude, Pour les arpèges composés*? Schumann's *Traumes Wirren* is spun off with a delicacy and dancing magic and in the same composer's *Presto passionato* Horowitz's performance hints at the schizophrenic violence and darkness that finally engulfed Schumann. Of the previously unpublished recordings, the first movement from Chopin's Second Sonata is as macabre and tricky as ever, with a steady, oddly menacing tempo. Prokofiev's *Toccata*, on the other hand, is tossed off at a nail-biting speed and not even a small but irritating cut, a wild, approximate flailing at the end and an added chord by way of compensation, can qualify the impact of such wizardry. In Rachmaninov's G minor Prelude, however, Horowitz's volatility gets the better of him. If Horowitz, in common with virtually every other pianist, was not equally convincing in every composer and was even 'a master of distortion' for some, he was a Merlin figure of an indelible, necromantic brio for all others. Bryan Crimp explains the origin of the recordings at admirable length and if they, though expertly transferred, show their age, nothing can lessen the impact of Horowitz's early charisma.

Vladimir Horowitz Piano works. **Vladimir Horowitz** (pf).
RCA Victor Gold Seal mono/ᵃstereo Ⓜ GD60377* (65 minutes: ADD: 6/92). 　　　　ⒺⒸⒺ
Prokofiev Piano Sonata No. 7 in B flat major, Op. 83 (from RB6555, 12/63. Recorded 1945). Toccata, Op. 11. **Poulenc** Presto in B flat major (both from HMV DB6971, 1947). **Barber** Piano Sonata in E flat major, Op. 26 (RB6555. 1950). **Kabalevsky** Piano Sonata No. 3, Op. 46 (new to UK. 1947). **Fauré** Nocturne No. 13 in B minor, Op. 119ᵃ (RL12548, 2/78. 1977).

Even today, when there is a six-deep queue of virtuosos who, laid end to end, would stretch halfway round the world, Vladimir Horowitz's playing is something to make the listener gasp and sit up. He has been called, with justification, "the greatest pianist alive or dead". Horowitz was associated with all three of the sonatas on this disc from their very beginnings. Prokofiev wrote his Seventh Sonata in 1942, and Horowitz gave the first American performance less than two years later. He sent a copy of this 1945 recording to the composer, and Prokofiev sent him an autographed copy of the score in return, inscribed "to the miraculous pianist from the composer". The performance is indeed superlative, with playing of extraordinary virtuosity, and Horowitz responds with equal flair to the sonata's 'barbaric' and lyrical elements. Kabalevsky's Third Sonata dates from 1946, and Horowitz gave the American première in February 1948, two months after he made this recording. The work is of lesser stature than the Prokofiev, but its three well-contrasted movements make up an effective enough sonata. Again, Horowitz plays brilliantly and very sympathetically throughout the work. The world première of Barber's Piano Sonata was given by Horowitz in 1949. This piece is brilliantly written and technically extremely demanding to play – a perfect vehicle, in fact, for Horowitz the virtuoso. The great pianist brings great flair to the shorter Poulenc and Prokofiev items: the Fauré was recorded at a later stage of his career, and is played in a more deliberate, though perfectly idiomatic fashion. Four of the items have been transferred from 78s in good sound. The Barber and Fauré come from tape sources and sound well – the latter is even in stereo. This is a disc all pianists and piano enthusiasts should have – and it's mid price too!

Vladimir Horowitz The Last Recording. **Vladimir Horowitz** (pf). Sony Classical Ⓕ SK45818 (58 minutes: DDD: 8/90). Recorded 1989.   ⒼⒼⒼ
Haydn Piano Sonata in E flat major, HobXVI/49. **Chopin** Mazurka in C minor, Op. 56 No. 3. Nocturnes – E flat major, Op. 55 No. 2; B major, Op. 62 No. 1. Fantaisie-impromptu in C sharp minor, Op. 66. Etudes – A flat major, Op. 25 No. 1; E minor, Op. 25 No. 5. **Liszt** "Weinen, Klagen, Sorgen, Zagen", Präludium, S179. **Wagner/Liszt** Paraphrase on Isolde's Liebestod from "Tristan und Isolde", S447.

More than any other pianist of his generation, Vladimir Horowitz was a legend in his lifetime, not only for his staggering technique but also for the personality and authority of his playing. Other pianists such as Rubinstein and Arrau may have been finer all-rounders (there were gaps in his repertory even in the classical and romantic field), but none has left so many performances distinguished by a special individuality that is covered, though hardly explained, by the word magic. As Murray Perahia has written, from the point of view of a pianist over 40 years his junior, "he was a man who gave himself completely through his music and who confided his deepest emotions through his playing". The performances in this last of his recordings, made in New York in 1989 and with superlative piano sound, are wonderfully crystalline and beautifully articulated, yet there is warmth, too, in the Haydn sonata that begins his programme and nothing whatever to suggest that octogenarian fingers were feeling their age or that his fine ear had lost its judgement. The rest of the disc is devoted to Chopin and Liszt, two great romantic composers with whom he was always associated, the last piece being Liszt's mighty transcription of Wagner's *Liebestod*, in which the piano becomes a whole operatic orchestra topped by a soprano voice singing out her love for the last time. Apparently this was the last music Horowitz ever played, and no more suitable ending can be imagined for a great pianistic career informed by a consuming love of music that was expressed in playing of genius. A uniquely valuable record.

The Hungarian Anthology Peter Frankl (pf). ASV Ⓕ CDDCA860 (78 minutes: DDD: 6/93). Recorded 1992.   ⒼⒼⒼ
Liszt Csárdás macabre, S224. **Dohnányi** Gavotte and Musette. **Kodály** Seven Pieces, Op. 11. **Bartók** (trans. cpsr.) Dance Suite, Sz77. **Weiner** Three Hungarian Rural Dances. **Kurtág** Plays and Games for Piano, Book 3 – excerpts. **Szöllösy** Paesaggio con morti.

An important reminder, this, of how and where Hungarian piano music is progressing. The last piece of Peter Frankl's programme dates from 1988; the *Paesaggio con morti* by András Szöllösy, an impressive, 11-minute study in musical shades and textures. Working back from there, and tracing the general direction of Szöllösy's route, is a relatively simple task. Oddly, Kodály more than Bartók seems – in this case, at least – the overriding influence: his *Seven Pieces*, Op. 11 have never sounded more engaging than here, and the largest of them, "Epitaphe", is surely among the composer's most dramatic inspirations. With György Kurtág's *Plays and Games for Piano*, credits revert back to Bartók. Leó Weiner's spicy *Hungarian Rural Dances* include a "Ronde de Marosszek"; but here again, it's more Bartók than Kodály who springs to mind. Bartók's own *Dance Suite* is, of course, a pivotal creation in its use of Eastern European and Arabic modes, and the way they are so expertly welded on to the work's overall structure. And then to Dohnányi and Liszt, although the former's pleasant *Gavotte and Musette* seems more a side-long glance at Smetana than an extension of the bold, bald and audacious world of Liszt's menacing *Czárdás macabre*. Here we can locate the seeds of Bartók's mature style, sown not merely among the realms of local folklore (although this disturbing *Csárdás* is profoundly Hungarian in spirit), but deep within the furthest recesses of our collective musical unconscious. Performances and recording are sympathetic.

Les introuvables de Marcelle Meyer, Volume 2. **Marcelle Meyer** (pf). EMI mono Ⓜ CZS5 68092-2* (four discs: 275 minutes: ADD: 6/95). From Les Discophiles Françaises originals; recorded 1946-55.   ⒼⒼⒼ
Rameau Pièces de clavecin – Suites: A minor (1706); E minor (1724); D major (1724); A minor (c1729); G major (c1729). Quatre Pièces en concert. **F. Couperin** Livres de clavecin, Book 2 – Les Barricades Mistérieuses; Passacaille; Book 3 – Les Folies françoises, ou Les Dominos; Les Fauvétes Plaintives; Le Dodo, ou L'Amour en berceau; Le Tic-Toc-Choc, ou Les Maillotins; La Muse-Plantine; Book 4 – L'Arlequine; Les Ombres Errantes. **D. Scarlatti** 32 Keyboard Sonatas. **Rossini** Péchés de ma vieillesse, Book 5, "Album pour les enfants adolescents" – Ouf! les petits pois; Un sauté; Book 8, "Album de chatêau" – Un regret, un espoir; Prélude prétentieux; Book 9 – La savoie aimante.

Unlike her contemporary, Wanda Landowska, Marcelle Meyer had no mission to rehabilitate the harpsichord, but simply treasured its repertoire on its own merit and was indefatigable in her determination to bring it before as wide an audience as possible. Meyer's Rameau is full of poetic insight, illuminatingly expressive but devoid of any misplaced sentimentality. But inevitably, the more stylistically and technically advanced pieces of the 1724 and *c*1729 collections fare better on a modern piano than the miniatures of the 1706 anthology, which remains more firmly rooted in the harpsichordist's realm. The other chief beneficiary of this precious four-disc compilation is Domenico Scarlatti, 32 of whose sonatas Meyer recorded in the 1950s. Not a single disappointment awaits the listener here. Her athletic technique, her love of clearly defined articulation and her unfailingly lucid textures are but among the more obvious qualities in her playing; over and above that are her ability to capture and sustain a particular effect and her feeling for the underlying poetry of Scarlatti's music. There are delights, too, to be found among the Couperin pieces – Meyer carefully chose those which lend themselves to the piano – and a selection of five pieces from Rossini's *Péchés de ma vieillesse*. Meyer was an artist who was skilled in evoking a wide spectrum of moods but it was in the evocation of that quietly contemplative, melancholy spirit that she excelled. The discs have been carefully and effectively remastered and the warm, intimate sound of the piano is a constant pleasure.

Piet Kee at the Concertgebouw Piet Kee (org). Chandos Ⓔ CHAN9188
(72 minutes: DDD: 10/93). Recorded 1993.
Franck Fantaisie in A major. **Mendelssohn** Organ Sonata in C major/minor. **Schumann** Fugue on B-A-C-H, Op. 60 No. 3. **Andriessen** Sonata da chiesa. **Saint-Saëns** Fantaisie in C major, Op. 157. **Alain** Deuxième fantaisie. Le jardin suspendu. **Messiaen** Les corps glorieux – Joie et clarté des corps glorieux.

Kee has made an ingenious choice of pieces which all treat the organ orchestrally, while at the same time finding some of these composers' finest, yet less familiar, creations. Alain's *Deuxième fantaisie* ranks considerably higher in musical worth than almost anything else he wrote – and if you doubt this, listen to the stimulating performance here. It is good, too, to see the name of Hendrik Andriessen appear on record again. A couple of decades or so ago he seemed to be all the rage; now representation of his music in the catalogues is minimal, to say the least, and to have his *Sonata da chiesa* back again alone makes this an invaluable release. For the most part these are outstanding performances. Kee is a master in the art of organ colour and, coupled with his meticulous and scholarly approach, one can't seriously question either the authority or sincerity of anything here – from a disarmingly delicate *Jardin suspendu* to a magisterial reading of the Mendelssohn sonata.

Evgeni Kissin in Tokyo Evgeni Kissin (pf). Sony Classical Ⓔ SK45931
(73 minutes: DDD: 11/90). Recorded live in 1987. ⒼⒼ
Rachmaninov Lilacs, Op. 21 No. 5. Etudes tableaux, Op. 39 – No. 1 in C minor; No. 5 in E flat minor. **Prokofiev** Piano Sonata No. 6 in A major, Op. 82. **Liszt** Concert Studies, S144 – La leggierezza; Waldestrauschen. **Chopin** Nocturne in A flat major, Op. 32 No. 2. Polonaise in F sharp minor, Op. 44. **Scriabin** Mazurka in E minor, Op. 25 No. 3. Etude in C sharp minor, Op. 42 No. 5. **Anonymous** (arr. Saegusa) Natu – Wa Kinu. Todai – Mori. Usagi.

One reason for buying this CD is that it contains dazzling piano playing by a 15-year-old Russian set fair for a career of the highest distinction. A better reason is that the recital contains as full a revelation of the genius of Prokofiev as any recording ever made in any medium. The Sixth Sonata is the first of a trilogy which sums up the appalling sufferings of Russia under Stalin in a way only otherwise found in Shostakovich's 'middle' symphonies. Kissin plays it with all the colour and force of a full orchestra and all the drama and structural integrity of a symphony, plus a kind of daredevilry that even he may find difficult to recapture. As for the rest of the recital only the Rachmaninov pieces are as memorable as the Prokofiev, though everything else is immensely impressive (the Japanese encore-pieces are trivial in the extreme, however). Microphone placing is very close, presumably in order to minimize audience noise; but the playing can take it, indeed it may even be said to benefit from it.

Fritz Kreisler The Complete Victor Recordings. **Fritz Kreisler** (vn) with various artists. RCA Victor Gold Seal mono Ⓜ 09026 61649-2* (11 discs: 781 minutes: ADD). Recorded 1910-46. Ⓖ
Works by Albéniz, Bach, Balogh, Bass, Beethoven, Berlin, Bizet, Boccherini, Braga, Brahms, Böhm, Cadman, Chaminade, Chopin, Cottenet, De Curtis, Dawes, Debussy, Dohnányi, Drdla, Dvořák, Earl, Falla, Foster, Friedberg, Friml, Gärtner, Gluck, Godard, Godowsky, Gounod, Grainger, Granados, Grieg, Handel, Haydn, Herbert, Heuberger, Hirsch, Hubbell, Jacobi, Johnson, Korngold, Koschat, Koželuch, Krakauer, Kramer, Kreisler, Lalo, Lehár, Lemare, Leroux, Liliuokalani, Logan, Mascagni, Massenet, Mendelssohn, Meyer-Helmund, Moszkowski, Nevin, Offenbach, Openshaw, Owen, Paderewski, Paganini, Poldini, Rachmaninov, Raff, Rameau, Ravel, Rimsky-Korsakov, Romberg, Schubert, Schütt, Scott, Seitz, Smetana, Spencer, Tchaikovsky, Thomas, Tosti, Townsend, Valdez, White and Winternitz.

If Jascha Heifetz was the firebrand among virtuosos, Bronislaw Huberman the passionate intellectual and Joseph Szigeti the articulate thinker, Fritz Kreisler was the ultimate gentleman – an easygoing, genial and comforting old-world master whose large discography centres mainly on the many sweetmeats associated with his name. This neatly packaged and beautifully transferred collection of "The Complete Victor Recordings" is in many respects the ultimate tribute: over 200 tracks covering the period 1910-46 and tracing a subtle stylistic curve from the vibrant and quick-wristed performances of the teens to the wistful, elegant and slightly off-colour 1946 recording of Kreisler's

Straussian *Viennese Rhapsodic Fantasietta*. However, readers unable to stomach acoustic 78s are duly warned that primitive technology dominates the first six CDs, whereas the rest is made up of generally well-engineered electrical recordings. Still, such was Kreisler's sure projection and richness of tone that, like certain great singers of the period (McCormack being a fair case in point), he triumphed over inadequacies of sound. High points of his early discography include revealing 'one off' recordings of the "Canzonetta" from Tchaikovsky's Violin Concerto and the *Scherzando* from Lalo's *Symphonie espagnole* (both 'first commercial releases'), Kreisler's own arrangement of Chopin's A minor *Mazurka*, Op. 67 No. 4, a truncated Bach Double Concerto with Efrem Zimbalist and the various items with John McCormack.

Kreisler's electrical RCA recordings are dominated, at least in terms of repertoire, by the oft-reissued sonata performances with Rachmaninov, all of them combining violinistic poise with taut, muscular pianism. As to the rest, there are countless gems and a plethora of duplications: six of the *Thaïs* "Méditation", five each of *Caprice viennois*, *Liebesleid* and *Liebesfreud*, four of Dvořák's *Humoresque*, etc. – so many subtle varieties of a single basic conception, whether in terms of colour, rubato or phrasing. Some contrasts are fairly marked; one can think in particular of *Mighty Lak' a Rose*, where the electrical recording with pianist Carl Lamson is so much more stylish than Kreisler's acoustical duet with Geraldine Farrar. Then there are the previously unissued 1929 sessions with Lamson, recorded within weeks of the Wall Street crash (where Kreisler himself lost money): poignant, reflective performances, though technically somewhat stronger than the 1945 recordings with orchestra which coincided almost to the minute with the German surrender. Kreisler's RCA discography is, of course, deficient in one very significant respect: there are no full-length major concertos. Readers are therefore urged to supplement this invaluable set with one or other of Kreisler's Brahms, Beethoven or Mendelssohn concerto recordings (available on either Biddulph or Pearl). "The King of Violinists" (as he was sometimes known) was an undisputed master of musical aperitifs and desserts: taken in moderation, these recordings will give boundless pleasure.

The Last Recital for Israel Artur Rubinstein (pf). RCA Victor Red Seal Ⓔ 09026 61160-2 (75 minutes: ADD: 3/93). Recorded 1975.   ⒼⒼ
    Beethoven Piano Sonata No. 23 in F minor, Op. 57, "Appassionata". **Debussy** La plus que lente. Pour le Piano – Prélude. **Schumann** Fantasiestücke, Op. 12. **Chopin** Etudes – C sharp minor, Op. 10 No. 4; E minor, Op. 25 No. 5. Nocturne in F sharp major, Op. 15 No. 2. Polonaise in A flat major, Op. 53.

Ever a supporter of youth in music, Artur Rubinstein gave a special concert in January 1975 at Ambassador College (California) for the benefit of the International Cultural Centre for Youth in Jerusalem; it was merely days before his eighty-eighth birthday. The event was sponsored entirely by contributions, and Rubinstein played to a packed house, which of course was no great surprise. However, what does truly amaze is the vitality and concentration of the performances. It might seem something of a cliché to say that Rubinstein plays the *Appassionata* like a man half his age, but it also happens to be the truth: the sheer energy and panache of the first movement so far exceeds expectations that one finds oneself checking the recording date to make sure that this isn't a reissue of an earlier Rubinstein recording. And in truth, the recording – taken from a video soundtrack – tends, unlike the playing, to sound older than it is. In addition to barnstorming Beethoven and endearingly warm-hearted Schumann, Rubinstein plays two Chopin *Etudes* that, believe it or not, he never recorded commercially: Op. 25 No. 5 and Op. 10 No. 4. Both are remarkable, as is a battle-scarred but riveting A flat major *Polonaise* (a Rubinstein speciality). But best of all is the famous E flat *Nocturne*, Op. 15 No. 2 – an intimate, beautifully phrased performance, so typical of the man and the best possible way to remember him. A simultaneously-released RCA video contains the entire programme, but the best items are on this CD. A life-affirming experience.

Dinu Lipatti The Last Recital. **Dinu Lipatti** (pf). EMI Références mono Ⓜ CDH5 65166-2* (73 minutes: ADD: 12/94). Items marked [a] from Columbia 33CX1499 (2/58), [b]33CX1500 (2/58). Recorded live in 1950.   ⒼⒼⒼ
    Bach Partita in B flat major, BWV825[a]. **Mozart** Piano Sonata No. 8 in A minor, K310/K300*d*[a]. **Schubert** Impromptus, D899[a] – No. 2 in E flat major; No. 3 in G flat major. **Chopin** Waltzes[b] – Nos. 1 and 3-14.

Apart from the two Schubert *Impromptus*, the programme of Lipatti's last recital consisted of works he had recorded only some ten weeks earlier for EMI, in a Geneva studio, while enjoying a miraculous cortisone-wrought new lease of life. However, when honouring this Besançon Festival engagement on September 16th, 1950, very much against the advice of his doctors, leukaemia had once more gained the upper hand. Less than three months later he was dead, aged only 33. As those of us who have long cherished the original LPs already know, the only evidence of weakness was the omission of the last of the concluding Chopin *Waltzes* (in his own favoured sequence, that in A flat major, Op. 34 No. 2). For the rest, the recital stands as "one of the great musical and human statements, a testimony to his [Lipatti's] transcendental powers, an almost frightening assertion of mind over matter" as the sympathetic introductory note puts it in the insert-booklet. One has to marvel at the clarity of articulation and part-playing in the Bach Partita, at once so attentive to craftsmanly cunning yet so arrestingly unpedagogic and alive. For Mozart he finds a wonderfully translucent sound-world, rich in subtleties of colouring – not least in the slow movement's laden song. And as in the two Schubert

Impromptus, the musical message is all the more affecting for its totally selfless simplicity and purity of expression. Even if just one or two of the *Waltzes* might be thought too fast, with over-swift internal tempo changes for contrasting episodes, his gossamer lightness of touch and mercurial imaginative fancy explain why his way with them has now acquired legendary status. The only small regret is that this most excellently remastered medium-price CD deprives us of the endearingly spontaneous extended arpeggio with which Lipatti prefaced the opening Partita, as if in greeting to his instrument, and likewise the improvisatory modulation with which he carried his Besançon listeners from Bach's B flat major to Mozart's A minor.

The long, long winter night Leif Ove Andsnes (pf). EMI Ⓕ CDC5 56541-2
(68 minutes: DDD: 6/98). Recorded 1997.
Grieg Norwegian Folksongs, Op. 66 – Cattle call; Tomorrow you marry; Cradle Song; I wander deep in thought. Norwegian peasant dances, Op. 72 – Halling from the hills; Prillar from the church-play; Gangar; Knut Luråsens Halling I; The goblin's bridal procession. **Tveitt**
50 Folk-tunes from Hardanger, Op. 150 – Welcome with honour; A-wooing; The most beautiful song on earth; Langeleik tune; Tears and laughter for a boat; The long, long winter night; The Father of the Child. **Johansen** Portraits, Op. 5. **Valen** Variations, Op. 23. **Saeverud** Tunes and Dances from Siljustøl: Suite No. 2, Op. 22 – Ballad of revolt. Suite No. 3, Op. 24 – Winflowers twiddle the moonbeam fiddle; Thor the hammerer. Suite No. 4, Op. 25 – Tone's cradle-song.

Leif Ove Andsnes shows he can be a thoughtful and eager advocate of the music of his compatriots in this recital of little-known Norwegian piano pieces. The long, long winter night which so concentrates the Northern mind and imagination, and which gives this disc its name, is the title of one of the *50 Folk-tunes from Hardanger* (we hear seven of them here) by Geirr Tveitt, a true radical with roots, who was born the year after Grieg died. Seventy per cent of his music went up in flames when his wooden house burnt down; but Andsnes has long been a champion of what remains. His imagination close-focuses the music even when Tveitt is doing little more than toying with his material: his constantly shifting finger-weight exploits the colours of the harmonic waywardness of "A-wooing" and "The Father of the Child". There is more to tease the ear in the four *Portraits* by the writer, critic and pianist David Monrad Johansen (1888-1974), whose "Little Stone God" and "Reindeer", from 1918, reveal the imagination of a Nordic Debussy even before the composer began his travels to Paris. Andsnes then gives a vigorous, lucid performance of Fartein Valen's 12 Variations on a 12-tone theme. The recital, which begins with characteristically probing and concentrated performances of nine miniatures from Grieg's *Norwegian Folksongs* and *Peasant dances* (*Slåtter*), ends with a tribute to Norway's great eccentric and musical polyglot, Harald Saeverud. His maverick talent is perhaps best focused in his piano music. Andsnes pays him enthusiastic tribute in four of the *Tunes and Dances from Siljustøl*, and in a final extract from Saeverud's own *Peer Gynt* music.

Yves Nat Piano Works. **Yves Nat** (pf); [a]**Paris Conservatoire Orchestra / Gaston Poulet.**
EMI mono Ⓞ CZS5 69461-2* (two discs: 147 minutes: ADD: 1/98). All items new to UK.
From French Columbia and Discophil françaix originals; recorded 1929-55.
Schubert Six Moments musicaux, D780. **Chopin** Piano Sonata No. 2 in B flat minor, Op. 35.
Fantasie in F minor, Op. 49. Barcarolle in F sharp major, Op. 60. **Brahms** Two Rhapsodies,
Op. 79. 28 Variations on a Theme by Paganini, Op. 35. Intermezzo in B flat minor, Op. 117
No. 2. **Franck** Symphonic Variations[a]. **Liszt** Hungarian Rhapsody No. 2 in C sharp minor,
S244. **Chopin** Waltz in E minor, Op. posth. **Stravinsky** Petrushka – Russian dance.
Nat Pour un petit moujik.

Yves Nat specialized in Bach's *48* and in Beethoven's 32 sonatas. For him the human heart was the truest metronome and his students were encouraged to fight for romantic freedom, for depth of sonority, variety of colour, voicing and instrumentation. He achieves a true *parlando* in Schubert's *Moment musical* No. 2 and in No. 6 his disarming simplicity is a far cry from other pianists. Yet he is every inch the romantic in Chopin, playing the Second Sonata's first movement with a true sense of its equestrian, nightmare momentum and offering an undignified, if temporarily fashionable, alternative to Chopin's scrupulously marked dynamic scheme in the Funeral March. True, compared to a Rubinstein or Lipatti, he skims the surface of the *Barcarolle*'s most ecstatically charged pages yet he is never less than a free spirit and one essentially attuned to Chopin's elegance and volatility. His Brahms, too, is frisky and characterful in a style frowned on today yet his avoidance of all textural and poetic opacity is a refreshing change from so many 'serious' alternatives. His second performance of the *Intermezzo*, Op. 117 No. 2 has a near Fauréan evanescence and if his Stravinsky is headlong and chaotic his Liszt sparks with genuine daredevilry. The transfers of these recordings have been superbly managed. Above all, even the most avid follower of French pianism will be enticed and astonished by breadth rather than narrowness of vision, by a magical richness and variety.

Nocturnal Julian Bream (gtr). EMI Ⓕ CDC7 54901-2 (73 minutes: DDD: 4/94). Recorded 1992.
Martin Quatre Pièces Brèves. **Britten** Nocturnal after John Dowland, Op. 70. **Brouwer**
Guitar Sonata. **Takemitsu** All in Twilight. **Lutosławski** (trans. cpsr): 12 Folk Melodies.

No one can truly reach into the depths of Britten's *Nocturnal* until Life has taught them some hard lessons, nor, perhaps, can they perceive the *Innigkeit* of Martin's work. The veteran, Julian Bream, with his technical armoury totally at the service of his emotions, demonstrates the truth of this in performances of moving intensity. Age has not dimmed his enthusiasm for pastures new: Brouwer's strong, and in places wryly humorous, Sonata with its teasing references to the composers to whom its three movements pay tribute, and Takemitsu's introspective *All in Twilight*, were written at his behest and are communicated with wonderful clarity. What Gareth Walters, the annotator, aptly describes as the "simple charm" of Bream's arrangements of Polish folk-melody settings by Lutosławski brings the recital to a lighter conclusion. The temptation to say that Bream has rarely played (or been recorded) better than here is too strong to resist!

Organ Fireworks, Volume 3. **Christopher Herrick** (org). Hyperion Ⓟ CDA66457
(71 minutes: DDD: 9/91). Played on the organ of St Eustache, Paris. Recorded 1990.   ⓔⓔⓔ
Batiste Offertoire in D minor. **Bossi** Pièce héroïque in D minor, Op. 128. Scherzo in D minor, Op 49 No. 2. **Dubois** Grand Choeur in B flat major. **Dupré** Cortège et Litanie, Op. 19 No. 2. **Jolivet** Hymne à l'Univers. **Lefébure-Wély** Marche in F major, Op. 122 No. 4. **Lemare** Concert Fantasy on "Hanover", Op. 4. Marche héroïque in D major, Op. 74. **Saint-Saëns** Allegro giocoso in A minor, Op. 150 No. 7.

Here is something truly spectacular. The brand new organ in St Eustache's Church, Paris was designed by the organist Jean Guillou who made sure it was an instrument fit for the finest of players and the greatest of music. In addition to a large array of stops, manuals and pipes it also boasts such extravagances as two consoles and a playback facility which enables the organ to play unattended. For this disc Christopher Herrick took advantage of this latter facility so that performances made during the day could be recorded in the small hours when extraneous noise was at a minimum. But the organ itself makes such a tremendously powerful, not to say, awesome noise, that one would have thought such a precaution unnecessary. Hyperion's vivid recording of this magnificent instrument stands out as one of the best recordings of an organ currently available on CD. Herrick's programme shows off both the instrument and his own amazing virtuosity to brilliant effect. There is great fun to be had from these pieces, none of which can really be said to be well known. This is a disc of pure, unadulterated pleasure.

Organ Fireworks, Volume 5. **Christopher Herrick** (org). Hyperion Ⓟ CDA66676 (75 minutes: DDD: 8/94). Played on the Virtanen organ in Turku Cathedral, Finland. Recorded 1993.
Alain Litanies, Op. 79. **Sibelius** (arr. H. Fricker) Finlandia, Op. 26. **Sløgedal** Variations on a Norwegian Folk Tune. **Mulet** Carillon-sortie in D major. **Lindberg** Organ Sonata in G minor, Op. 23 – Alla Sarabanda; Allegro con brio. **Mozart** Orgelstück (Fantasia) für eine Uhr, K608. **Lefébure-Wély** Marche. **Nielsen** Commotio, FS155. **Elgar** Pomp and Circumstance March in G major, Op. 39 No. 4.

This disc mines a rich seam of repertoire ranging from the sublime (Mozart's *Fantasia*) to the ridiculous (Lefébure-Wély's *Marche*), from the obscure (Sløgedal's *Variations*) to the familiar (Elgar's *Pomp and Circumstance* March). All have in common a virtuosity, be it simple showiness or something of greater musical substance, which, articulated by such an able player as Christopher Herrick and on an organ the mere sound of which can send shivers down the spine, means that we are treated to a thoroughly satisfying, carefully balanced display of aural pyrotechnics. Breathtaking clarity and an almost electrically charged brilliance of tone are the hallmarks of this magnificent Finnish organ. Never has *Finlandia* sounded quite as thrilling as it does with these flashing trumpets; never has Mulet's evergreen *Carillon-sortie* crackled as it does in this cold, clear Northern atmosphere. It gives a wonderful radiance to those less overtly flashy pieces and, combined with Herrick's intuitive musicianship, we have here performances of the Mozart *Orgelstück*, and Nielsen's mammoth *Commotio*, of great stature. This is a truly spectacular disc.

Organ Fireworks, Volume 6. **Christopher Herrick** (org). Hyperion Ⓟ CDA66778
(76 minutes: DDD: 3/96). Played on the Norman and Beard organ in the Town Hall, Wellington, New Zealand. Recorded 1995.
Hollins A Trumpet Minuet. **Elgar** Organ Sonata No. 1 in G major, Op. 28. **Cocker** Tuba tune. **Sumsion** Introduction and Theme. **Spicer** Kiwi Fireworks – Variations on "God defend New Zealand". **C.S. Lang** Tuba tune. **Lemare** Concertstück in the form of a Polonaise, Op. 80. **Wagner** (trans. Lemare, arr. Westbrook and Herrick) Die Meistersinger von Nürnberg – Prelude, Act 1.

This series turned into something of a world tour for Christopher Herrick and the "Organ Fireworks" team, and here they travel to New Zealand. They have come up with one genuine piece of 'home-grown' music (although C.S. Lang left New Zealand for England almost before he could tell a nappy from a nazard) and a connection with Edwin Lemare; he played this organ three months after its completion in 1906. However, the starting-point for this programme is the tradition of civic organ concerts which was exported from the town halls of Edwardian England to such far-flung corners of the British Empire as Singapore, South Africa and, of course, New Zealand. The Wellington Town Hall organ is typical of a large turn-of-the-century English symphonic organ and while it might seem a little extravagant to go half-way round the world to find one, it is, following its 1985-86 restoration, rare in being substantially unaltered and in excellent working condition. Full organ is gloriously meaty, the flue tone beautifully blended and the solo reeds a joy to behold – a silvery Tromba perfect for Hollins's elegant Minuet; a gutsy Tuba ideal for both Cocker and Lang. As ever Herrick's performances have both musical integrity and great communicative flair: his is a matchless performance of the Elgar Sonata, in which the composer's strangely awkward use of the organ, in places treating it almost orchestrally, is immaculately managed.

Organ Fireworks, Volume 7. **Christopher Herrick** (org). Hyperion Ⓔ CDA66917 (70 minutes: DDD: 8/97). Recorded on the Klais organ of the Hallgrímskirkja, Reykjavík. Recorded 1996.
Johnson Trumpet Tune in F major. **Guilmant** Deuxième Offertoire sur des Noëls, Op. 33.
Litaize Variations sur un Noël angevin. **Bonnet** In Memoriam – Titanic, Op. 10 No. 1.
Karg-Elert Improvisation, Op. 81, "Nearer my God to Thee". **Reubke:** Sonata on the 94th Psalm in C minor. **Lefébure-Wély** Noël varié. **Pachelbel** Prelude, "Vom Himmel hoch".
Edmundson Toccata, "Vom Himmel hoch".
Iceland: Land of Volcanoes. What an appropriate place for Christopher Herrick to set off this batch of fireworks. But in keeping with the awesome, almost vengeful spectacle of an Icelandic volcano in full spate these are not all the cheerful, colourful sparklers of a British Guy Fawkes Day. Central to the disc is a stunning performance of Julius Reubke's massive Sonata on the 94th Psalm ("O God, to whom vengeance belongeth"). It must be said straight away that this performance surpasses any version yet to appear on CD. Herrick throws himself into the work with almost manic intensity, culminating in a breathtakingly virtuosic account of the fugue. Equally spectacular is this magnificent Klais; its *chamade* reeds punching into the air with primeval ferocity, its dark, full-throated chorus reeds seeping over the music like molten lava. And all this captured in a recording of exceptional clarity and presence. Maintaining the tradition of choosing music to match the recording's geographical location, Herrick has come up with two pieces (by Bonnet and Karg-Elert) linked in some respect to the sinking of the *Titanic*. (Of course, it actually sank off Greenland but, in the scale of things, Iceland isn't *that* far away!) The rest of the programme (with the exception of a harmless *Trumpet Tune* by David Johnson) has a Christmassy flavour; reflecting, one supposes, the preponderance of snow in Iceland. There are splendid *Noëls* by Guilmant, Lefébure-Wély and Litaize, and the disc ends with a sizzling account of Edmundson's *Toccata* on the chorale *Vom Himmel hoch*. The recording is magnificent.

Organ Showpieces from St Paul's Cathedral Andrew Lucas (org). Naxos Ⓢ 8 550955 (71 minutes: DDD: 11/94). Recorded 1994.
T. Dubois Toccata in G minor. **Franck** Chorale No. 3 in A minor. **Gigout** Scherzo. **Langlais** Poèmes évangéliques, Op. 2 – No. 2, La Nativité. Paraphrases grégoriennes, Op. 5 – Hymne d'actions de grâce. **Murrill** Carillon. **Peeters** Aria, Op. 51. **Reger** Pieces, Op. 59 – No. 5, Toccata in D minor; No. 6, Fugue in D major; No. 9, Benedictus. **Vierne** Pièces de fantaisie, Op. 54 – No. 6, Carillon de Westminster.
A populist programme: with the possible exception of Langlais's magical "La Nativité" these pieces will already be well represented in most organ buffs' collections. But the very absence of such stalwarts as Widor and Bach points to a programme designed to be, if not actually adventurous, at least different. We have relatively concise Reger unencumbered by a morass of seething chromaticisms, a selection of French toccatas and scherzos offering more than mere flamboyance, and it's good to have plenty of moments for peaceful reflection – most memorably a lovely account of Flor Peeters's *Aria*. Andrew Lucas isn't just interested in showing off his technical prowess, impressive though this is (although those tricky pedal solos in Murrill's *Carillon* would not bear close scrutiny in a less generous acoustic). He knows the organ, the building, the music and how to communicate to his invisible audience. Listen to the rare elegance he brings to the Dubois *Toccata*, the wonderfully seamless flow of the Franck *Chorale*. Naxos have done well to secure the services of Gary Cole, no stranger to the art of organ recording or to this venue. He has given them a superbly atmospheric, if slightly subdued recording that effectively balances instrument and building.

Murray Perahia 25th Anniversary Edition Murray Perahia (pf/ªdir).
Sony Classical Ⓜ SX4K63380 (four discs: 270 minutes: DDD/ᵇADD: 4/98). Recorded 1977-97.
D. Scarlatti Keyboard Sonatas – B minor, Kk27; A major, Kk212 (SK62785, 5/97).
Mozart Six German Dances, K509. Adagio in B minor, K540. **Schubert** Impromptu in A flat major, D899 No. 4 (SK37291, 4/85). **Schumann** Papillons, Op. 2 (CBS 76635, 4/78)ᵇ.
Chopin Ballade No. 1 in G minor, Op. 23 (SK64399, 12/94). Piano Concerto No. 2 in F minor, Op. 21 (Israel Philharmonic Orchestra / Zubin Mehta. Recorded live. SK44922, 6/90).
Liszt Two Concert Studies, S145 – No. 2, Gnomenreigen (SK47180, 10/91). **Rachmaninov** Etudes-tableaux, Op. 39 – No. 5 in E flat minor; No. 6 in A minor (SK46437, 4/91).
Bartók Suite, Sz62. Eight Improvisations on Hungarian Peasant Songs, Sz74. Out of doors, Sz81 (all from CBS 76650, 9/81)ᵇ. **Berg** Piano Sonata, Op. 1. **Tippett** Piano Sonata No. 1.
Beethoven Quintet for Piano and Wind in E flat major, Op. 16 (Neil Black, ob; Thea King, cl; Graham Sheen, bn; Anthony Halstead, hn. CBS 42099, 8/86). **Schumann** Fünf Lieder, Op. 40 (Sir Peter Pears, ten. CBS 76815, 2/80)ᵇ. **Brahms** Piano Quartet No. 1 in G minor, Op. 25 (Norbert Brainin, vn; Peter Schidlof, va; Martin Lovett, vc. CBS SK42361, 12/87. CBS 76815, 2/80). **Mozart** Piano Concerto No. 27 in B flat, K595 (Chamber Orchestra of Europe. SK46485, 8/91)ª.

1997 marked the 25th anniversary of Murray Perahia's association with CBS Masterworks/Sony Classical. This set of four CDs celebrates him as a concerto soloist and chamber music player as well as recitalist, and although Sony's wish to exploit their back catalogue was probably paramount in the selection of items rather than a concern to pick only Perahia's outstanding achievements, it's a compilation which leaves you in no doubt of his stature as one of the best artists of our day. The two discs of solo pieces may look like a little bit of this and a little bit of that: yet they make rewarding sequences of music which are all the more interesting for the inclusion of repertoire not recently associated with this pianist. The Berg Sonata, the Tippett First Sonata and two tracks of Mozart have not been issued in this country before. The freshness of style and sophistication of technique in Tippett's First Sonata generate a vitality that leaps out at you. Perahia makes it sound carefree, which is just right – and no mean feat when you consider that the gestures and figuration Tippett invents are without concern for what might lie conveniently for the pianist's fingers. His version of Berg's Sonata is not hewn from some post-Wagnerian rock but vocalized and glowing with beautiful piano playing; it is also naturally paced and even quite fleet, in contrast to the kind of performance that constantly tugs at the expression. These readings of Berg and Tippett are distinguished and should not have lain in the vaults for so long.

'Anniversary editions' recommend themselves, or not, according to their contents, but a good point about this one is that it brings back to the catalogue the three Bartók works and the Schumann songs with Sir Peter Pears and makes these available for the first time on CD. The shallower sound on some of the earlier recordings (of the Schumann *Papillons*, for instance, which dates from 1976) is to be noted but is not a problem; a more serious reservation concerns the balance of the Brahms G minor Piano Quartet with members of the Amadeus Quartet, which is not a success. Everything else is a feast, and the prospect, profoundly to be wished, of a further 20 years or more of Murray Perahia playing at this level makes for a feel-good factor.

Piano Transcriptions Arcadi Volodos (pf). Sony Classical Ⓕ SK62691 (61 minutes: DDD: 10/97). Recorded 1996. *Gramophone Editor's choice. Selected by Soundings.*   ⓖⓖ
Horowitz Variations on a Theme from Bizet's "Carmen". **Rachmaninov** (arr. Volodos) Morning, Op. 4 No. 2. Melody, Op. 21 No. 9. **Liszt** Hungarian Rhapsody No. 2 in C sharp minor, S244 (arr. Horowitz). Litanei, S562 No. 1. Schwanengesang, S560 – No. 3, Aufenthalt; No. 10, Liebesbotschaft. **Rimsky-Korsakov** (arr. Cziffra) The tale of Tsar Saltan – Flight of the bumble-bee. **Prokofiev** Pieces from Cinderella – Gavotte, Op. 95 No. 2; Oriental dance, Op. 97 No. 6; Grand waltz, Op. 107 No. 1. **Tchaikovsky** (arr. Feinberg) Symphony No. 6 in B minor, Op. 74, "Pathétique" – Allegro molto vivace. **Bach** (arr. Feinberg) Trio Sonata No. 5 in C major, BWV529 – Largo. **Volodos** Concert Paraphrase on Mozart's "Turkish March".
Arcadi Volodos, Russian-born but Spanish-based, here declares himself both as elegant lyricist and spectacular virtuoso; his playing is as tactful as it is audacious, the work, surely, of a romantic pianist for our times. His tributes to Horowitz (the ultimate Russian virtuoso icon) and Cziffra (the *ne plus ultra* of pianistic necromancy) are as coolly masterful as they are personally engaging and are wholly devoid of wilfulness or undue idiosyncrasy. Those anxious for Horowitz's splintering treble and thundering bass or for Cziffra's manic explosions and accelerations will listen in vain. Mercifully, Volodos remains his own man, tempering some heart-stopping octaves and *glissandos* at the close of Feinberg's transcription of the scherzo from Tchaikovsky's *Pathétique* Symphony with a touch of nonchalance, and in Feinberg's other arrangement, guiding Bach gently but firmly into the nineteenth century. Volodos is no less beguiling in his own Rachmaninov song transcriptions; here is that dreamed-of vocal 'line', luscious *cantabile* and aristocratic rather than ostentatious voicing and texturing. Last but far from least his elaboration of Mozart's "Turkish March" seasons the most decadent and epicurean taste with a teasing wit and insouciance. Sony's sound is superlative and this delectable recital makes one long for more substantial as well as glittering fare from a pianist who, as his producer puts it, "never loosens the reins of his guiding intellect".

Piano Works Arturo Benedetti Michelangeli (pf). Testament mono Ⓕ SBT2088* (two discs: 130 minutes: ADD: 12/96). Includes a half-hour rehearsal sequence. Recorded live in 1957. Previously unpublished.
Chopin Fantasie in F minor, Op. 49. Ballade No. 1 in G minor, Op. 23. Waltz in E flat major, Op. posth. **Debussy** Images – Reflets dans l'eau; Hommage à Rameau; Cloches à travers les feuilles; Et la lune descend sur le temple qui fût. **Schumann** Carnaval, Op. 9. Faschingsschwank aus Wien, Op. 26. **Mompou** Cançons i danses No. 6 – Canción.
Readers who are familiar with Michelangeli's 1971 DG recording of Debussy's *Images* (see review under Debussy; refer to the Index) will be astonished at this highly mobile 1957 concert performance of "Cloches à travers les feuilles", which is almost a full minute faster than its stereo successor; or "Reflets dans l'eau", which glides across the water's surface with such swiftness and ease that the more considered DG alternative – glorious though it is – sounds studied by comparison. "Hommage à Rameau" is shaped with the utmost finesse and "Et la lune descend sur le temple qui fût" coloured by exquisitely graded nuances. The performance of Schumann's *Carnaval* is a choice gallery of aural sculpture, whether in the minutely calculated responses of "Pierrot", the teasing rubato of "Coquette", the energy and attack of "Papillons", the effortless flow of "Chopin" or the ecstatic lingerings in "Aveu". Michelangeli's "Eusebius" is tender but unsentimental, whereas his "Florestan"

has enough 'reflective' ingredients to suggest that the two characters are closer in spirit than we often think. *Faschingsschwank aus Wien* contrasts muscular assertiveness (the opening *Allegro*) with the most amazing control (in the "Romanze"), while the "Intermezzo" promotes a virtually orchestral range of dynamics. Michelangeli's Chopin has a rare nobility, the *Fantasie* especially which, at a rather faster tempo than usual, holds together as a narrative entity. Then there is the imposing First *Ballade* and the encores – a sunny posthumous E flat *Waltz* (a regular extra on Michelangeli's concert programmes) and Mompou's sad but tender "Canción". This disc leaves you humbled by, and grateful for, some wonderful piano playing. Michelangeli's art is both rare and elusive, his expressive vocabulary finely distilled and unlikely to impress those who listen only for technical mastery. It's therefore ironic that those who criticize Michelangeli for 'coldness' or 'aloofness' are often the very commentators who are so dazzled by his virtuosity that they cannot hear beyond it. Testament's transfers are superb.

Piano Works Pavel Nersessian (pf). Bel Air Music Ⓕ BAM9725 (65 minutes: DDD: 3/98). Recorded 1997.
Tchaikovsky (arr. Pletnev) The Sleeping Beauty – Introduction; Dance of Maids of Honour and Pages; Variation d'Aurore; Danse des baronnes (Gavotte); Pas de caractère – Puss in Boots; Pas de quatre; Adagio; Sarabande; Finale. **Schubert** Moment musical No. 1 in C major D780. Impromptus, D899 – No. 2 in E flat major; No. 4 in A flat major. **D. Scarlatti** Keyboard Sonata in E major, Kk380. **Scriabin** Etudes – C sharp minor, Op. 2 No. 1; D sharp minor, Op. 8 No. 12. **Rachmaninov** Prelude in G major, Op. 32 No. 5. **Moszkowski** Etincelles, Op. 36 No. 6. **Schumann** Träumerei, Op. 15 No. 7.

Pavel Nersessian is the sort of free spirit who can set a stage alight with high-flying bravura, personal colour and imagination. In an age still inclined to admire a more impersonal, tautly disciplined expertise Nersessian's romantic freedom, his indifference to convention, will surely both delight and provoke. His Schubert has an almost Russian undertow, delectably light-fingered and vertiginous in the E flat *Impromptu*'s cascades and without even a hint of a desire for the sort of mechanical perfection that can kill the spirit of such scintillation in a trice. The ease and naturalness of it all are mesmerizing, though you may quibble over this or that detail, demanding a more crystalline focus here, a sharper control there. More specifically, the A flat *Impromptu*'s central trio is less urgently motivated than from the finest Schubertians (Brendel and Lupu, for example) and there are also moments in Nersessian's Scarlatti when he fails to suggest that the most glittering character and wit come from a razor-sharp balance between discipline and fantasy. However, in Moskowski's *Etincelles* he is witty and and on home ground he is superlative. His Scriabin is sultry and individual and in Mikhail Pletnev's dazzling realization of Tchaikovsky's *The Sleeping Beauty* his virtuosity is enthralling and acute. Never merely a question of flawless trills and octaves (though they are present in super-abundance) his charisma comes from a freedom to concentrate on every conceivable tint and character. Rarely has Tchaikovsky sounded so indelibly Russian, yet so individual. The recordings are often confined but they hardly inhibit one's sense of Nersessian's glamour and excitement.

Piano Works Maurizio Pollini (pf). DG The Originals Ⓜ 447 431-2GOR (68 minutes: ADD: 6/95). Items marked [a] from 2530 225 (6/72), [b]2530 803 (7/78). Recorded 1971-76.
Gramophone classical 100. ⒼⒼⒼ
Prokofiev Piano Sonata No. 7 in B flat major, Op. 83[a]. **Boulez** Piano Sonata No. 2[b]. **Stravinsky** Petrushka – three movements[a]. **Webern** Piano Variations, Op. 27[b].

Perfection needs to be pursued so that you can forget about it. Pollini's *Petrushka* movements are almost inhumanly accurate and fast; but what comes across is an exhilarating sense of abandon, plus an extraordinary cumulative excitement. The Prokofiev Seventh Sonata remains a benchmark recording not only for the athleticism of its outer movements but for the epic remorselessness of the central *Andante*. The Webern Variations are a magical fusion of intellectual passion and poetry, and the Boulez Sonata vividly reminds us why the European avant-garde was such a powerful force in the 1950s. These recordings are a monument to what it is possible for two hands to achieve on one musical instrument. The 'original-image bit-processing' has given a notch more brilliance and presence, just as claimed, and another definite gain is the retention of atmosphere between movements.

Piano Recital Nicholas Unwin (pf). Metier Ⓕ MSVCD92009 (63 minutes: DDD: 1/96). Recorded 1994.
Tippett Piano Sonata No. 4. **Saxton** Piano Sonata. **C. Matthews** 11 Studies in Velocity. **C. Lambert** Elegy.
Piano Recital Steven Neugarten (pf). Metier Ⓕ MSVCD92008 (53 minutes: DDD: 1/96). Recorded 1994.
Tippett Piano Sonata No. 2. **Sackman** Piano Sonata. **Saxton** Chacony. **Connolly** Sonatina in Five Studies, Op. 1.

There are audible debts here, acknowledged by Robert Saxton in an affectionate tribute to Sir Michael printed among the other notes, but also clearly perceptible in Nicholas Sackman's fine Sonata. Placing the Tippett sonatas in these contexts, to which they stand up very well, also points up what a very distinguished cycle they are. Not least, each disc is an admirable visiting card for a young pianist of real interpretative gifts. Unwin is the more immediately striking of the two, perhaps because he has the challenge and the attendant rewards of Tippett's Fourth Sonata: the characteristic sonorities, the spare lyricism and the formal ingenuities are spot on. Saxton's one-movement Sonata, seemingly much freer than the Tippett but in fact controlled through all its splendid pianistic gestures by a firm and quite perceptible thematic discipline, is also very perceptively played, and Unwin enjoys himself hugely in Colin Matthews's boldly virtuoso Studies. The brief and ambiguous Constant Lambert *Elegy*, darkly vehement but bleak, is no less shrewdly characterized: a distinguished début recording.

However, one should not underestimate Steven Neugarten. Although in Tippett's Second Sonata there is a slight lack of that heady, ecstatic lyricism to which this grand and on the whole percussive sonata occasionally turns, you are impressed by the power and the attack of his playing, and he gives a sympathetic reading of Justin Connolly's misleadingly numbered Op. 1 (it was written in 1962 but revised and expanded in 1983). This is a gripping piece, vividly visual and dramatic within its spare, angular style. Saxton's *Chacony* is a curious but attractive "fantasy on a scale", giving Neugarten plenty of opportunity for agreeable pianistic rhetoric. Sackman's Sonata, with a long *cantabile* at its centre radiating stillness and lyricism into the more mechanistic and virtuoso outer movements, also amply deserves a recording, and a performance as compelling as this one. Like Unwin's recital it is excellently recorded, cleanly but not clinically.

Popular Organ Music, Volume 2. Works by Alain, Bach, Cochereau, Dukas, Franck, Haydn and Tchaikovsky. **David Briggs** (org). Priory Ⓕ PRCD568 (76 minutes: DDD: 2/97). Played on the organ of Gloucester Cathedral. Recorded 1996.

Rhythmic Energy, Volume 1. Works by Kikta, John, Prokofiev and Tchaikovsky.
    Keith John (org). Priory Ⓕ PRCD532 (75 minutes: DDD: 2/97). Played on the organ of Hallgrímskirkja, Reykjavík.

What's in a title? Certainly not much so far as Priory are concerned. It is doubtful if anyone would correctly guess the contents of this disc entitled "Popular Organ Music". No Toccata and Fugue in D minor, no Widor; yes, some Bach – including the *St Anne* Prelude and Fugue – and Franck's *Pièce heroïque*, which is popular with organists. But who would ever have expected Alain's *Le jardin suspendu*? As for Pierre Cochereau's *Boléro sur un thème de Racquet* there can be very few who even know of its existence; it's actually an improvisation painstakingly transcribed by David Briggs. His labours have not been in vain. This is a riveting piece accompanied throughout its 12-minute crescendo, Ravel-like, by a side-drum. It displays the wonderful Gloucester organ to scintillating effect as does the arrangement of Dukas's *L'apprenti sorcier*.

Briggs's own transcription of movements from the *Nutcracker* is no match for that of the complete suite by Keith John on his disc. Tchaikovsky's clever scoring of the "Miniature Overture" – no instrument lower in pitch than the viola – has been ignored by Briggs, who clearly has a penchant for a 16-footer or two, while John lets it sparkle with twinkling 8, 4, 2 and 1 foot flutes. (Listen also how ingeniously John imitates the celesta in the "Dance of the sugar-plum fairy".) Less impressive is his transcription of four movements from another great Russian ballet score, *Romeo and Juliet*, although only with Prokofiev's music do we have anything that really lives up to the disc's title: apart, that is, from a movement called "Rhythmic Energy" which concludes John's own intense and unappealing suite, *Time and Motion*. Reservations apart, both discs provide a spectacular feast of virtuoso playing and stunning organ sound. We have here two of the very finest British organists playing two top-flight instruments on magnificently recorded discs, that from Gloucester being well into the demonstration-quality league.

Romantic Music for Harp Naoko Yoshino (hp). Philips Ⓕ 446 064-2PH (69 minutes: DDD: 2/96). Recorded 1994.
    Spohr Fantasia in C minor, Op. 35. **Rosetti** Piano Sonata No. 2 in E flat major. **Debussy** Suite bergamasque – Clair de lune. **Prokofiev** 10 Pieces, Op. 12 – Prelude. **Casella** Harp Sonata, Op. 68. **Damase** Sicilienne variée. **Renié** Contemplation. **Tournier** Jazz Band. **Fauré** Impromptu, Op. 86. Recorded 1994.

Naoko Yoshino's status as a cultured musician and a harpist of superb technical control is asserted in the opening track of this, her first solo recording. Her phrasing is finely moulded, her articulation splendidly varied and clear, her use of tone colour enhancing but not obtrusive, her sound happily free from mechanical noises. In short, one may listen to the message without being overly conscious of the medium. Recordings of romantic harp music often lean heavily on pleasant pieces by harpists, spiced with tricks of the instrument's trade, and arrangements; here, only the Debussy is arranged (the Prokofiev is marked "for piano or harp"), and the only tricksy moments are in Tournier's piece, more ragtime than jazz; gestural sweeps across the strings, and sound 'cumuli' are in thankfully short supply. Casella offers the most substantial fare in what is in fact a more than usually interesting programme of this instrumental genre. Suppress any hesitation you may feel when faced with a disc of solo-harp music; this one is highly recommended.

Russian Piano Works Boris Berezovsky (pf). Teldec Ⓕ 4509-96516-2 (61 minutes: DDD: 7/96). Recorded 1994.
    Mussorgsky (arr. Tchernov): A Night on the Bare Mountain. **Rachmaninov** Etudes-tableaux, Op. 39 – No. 3 in F sharp minor; No. 4 in B minor; No. 7 in C minor; No. 9 in D major. **Liadov** Preludes – C major, Op. 39 No. 4; F sharp minor, Op. 40 No. 2; D flat major, Op. 57 No. 1.

Medtner Four Fairy Tales, Op. 34 – No. 2 in E minor; No. 3 in A minor. Fairy Tale in B flat minor, Op. 20 No. 1. Fairy Tale in D minor, Op. 51 No. 1. Romantic Sketches for the Young, Op. 65 – Book 2: Tale. **Balakirev** Islamey.

In this most imaginative programme Boris Berezovsky displays a formidable technique and, for the greater part, the sort of emotional commitment that is second nature to the greatest Russian pianists. His selection from the Op. 39 *Etudes* confirms that he is among Rachmaninov's most powerful and eloquent interpreters. In No. 3 in F sharp minor Berezovsky's romantic freedom and richness of expression are several removes from other, more conventional, approaches. His rubato is pained and ecstatic and the music seems to move across an immense emotional and dynamic spectrum within its brief but intricate space. What drama he achieves too, in the great funeral elegy of No. 7, complementing a hair-raising advance to the dissonant and audacious climax with a rare finesse in the central triple *piano* and *legatissimo* reminder of the Russian liturgy. And it is this finesse which makes every bar of the Liadov *Preludes* memorable, whether in the ultra-Russian memory of Chopin in No. 1, or the octave storms of No. 3 (where the parallel with Scriabin's *Etude*, Op. 8 No. 9 is remarkably close). Medtner's dark-hued *Fairy Tales*, too, find a potent and ideal interpreter both in malignant antics (the "Wood goblin", Op. 34 No. 3) and subtle and elusive attributes (the *Romantic Sketch*: the perfect encore to keep an audience guessing). The recital is framed by two towering feats of virtuoso pianism. Mussorgsky's *Night on the Bare Mountain*, arranged by Konstantin Tchernov, is a pulverizing experience – *allegro feroce*, indeed! And Balakirev's *Islamey* is tossed off at breakneck speed, its sadistic, madcap difficulties resolved like so much child's play. In its stunningly imperious way this performance is unrivalled. The recordings are close and airless and regrettably the accompanying notes are inadequate, but no piano buff should miss an awe-inspiring addition to this young artist's rapidly expanding discography.

Segovia: Canciones populares Elliot Fisk (gtr). MusicMasters Ⓟ 67174-2 (76 minutes: DDD: 4/97).
De Narvaez La canción del Emperador. **C.P.E. Bach** March, H1. Keyboard Sonata in B minor, H73 – Siciliana. **Haydn** String Quartet in G major, Op. 76 No. 1 – Minuet. **Chopin** Prelude in A major, Op. 29 No. 7. **Schumann** Romanze. **Brahms** Waltz in B flat major, Op. 39 No. 8. **Ponce** Preludio, Balletto and Giga – Preludio. **Mussorgsky** Pictures at an Exhibition – The old castle. **Franck** L' Organiste, Volume 1 – Andantino poco allegretto. **Debussy** Préludes, Book 1 – La fille aux cheveux de lin. **Scriabin** Prelude in E flat minor, Op. 16 No. 4 (all arr. Segovia). **Tansman** Segovia. **Segovia** Canciónes populares de distintos paises. Estudio sin luz. La macarena. Prelude No. 14 in B minor. Estudio in E major. **Roussel** Segovia, Op. 29. **Milhaud** Segoviana, Op. 366. **Castelnuovo-Tedesco** Tonadilla, sur le nom de Andrés Segovia, Op. 170 No. 5.

Very many guitarists have paid tribute to Segovia's evangelistic work on behalf of the guitar in the twentieth century – his artistry, his establishing of a repertory that looked both backwards and forwards, his long concert career and, in some cases, his personal help. None has done so more faithfully and with greater affection than Elliot Fisk. Fisk wisely makes no attempt to ape the style and sounds of Segovia's performances – they were touched by genius but, as has been said of Landowska's, "we don't do it that way now". Time has in all respects moved on. Fisk has recorded many of the pieces that were arranged by or written for Segovia, and he does it in his own way – with a pulse that is firmer than Segovia's often was, and with moments of tonal sweetness that recall but do not mimic those of the maestro. Segovia wrote many charming and beautifully crafted vignettes, some of which Fisk has recorded (three of them for the first time), and has included 16 of Segovia's arrangements of folk-songs from various countries. The relationship between Segovia and Fisk was one of mutual respect and affection, and this magnificent recording pays ample tribute to it.

Short Stories Anatol Ugorski (pf). DG 447 105-2GH (62 minutes: DDD: 3/96). Recorded 1994.
Busoni An die Jugend – Giga, bolero e variazione (study after Mozart). **Liszt** Liebestraum in A flat major, S541 No. 3. **Debussy** Suite bergamasque – Clair de lune. **Mendelssohn** Capriccio in E minor, Op. 16 No. 2. **Schumann** Kinderszenen, Op. 15 – Träumerei. **Chopin** Fantaisie-impromptu in C sharp minor, Op. 66. **Scriabin** Deux poèmes, Op. 32. Prélude et Nocturne, Op. 9. **Rachmaninov** Prelude in C sharp minor, Op. 3 No. 2. **Weber** Piano Sonata No. 1 in C major, J138 – Rondo (Perpetuum mobile). Invitation to the Dance, J260.

Anatol Ugorski, described in some quarters as a genius, in others as a charlatan (though frankly, you would have to be as deaf as a post to make such a claim), is nothing if not versatile, and all these performances are touched with a special individuality and commitment. He starts with a sophisticated surprise, the Mozart/Busoni *Giga, bolero e variazione*. Here, Mozart's spare and near-Alkanesque *Gigue* is viewed from a witty angle or prism and is played with great vitality. Old favourites such as Liszt's Third *Liebestraum*, Debussy's *Clair de lune* and the Rachmaninov Prelude come up as fresh as paint, fascinatingly and responsibly reconsidered so that, remarkably, one seems to be hearing them for the first time. Chopin's *Fantaisie-impromptu*, too, is as inflammatory in its outer virtuosity as it is lost in wonder in its central reveries, and the Scriabin items emerge with a hypnotic potency and character. True, Ugorski's tempos for the *Prélude et Nocturne* for the left hand are dangerously slow yet he holds one's attention throughout. Again, he can be heavy-footed on Weber's ballroom floor and seems momentarily strenuous in the, ideally, nonchalant glitter of the composer's *Perpetuum mobile*. One may have heard more fleet and tonally iridescent performances of all these pieces (Moiseiwitsch comes to mind), yet Ugorski's mix of high seriousness and idiosyncrasy is unusual, intriguing and rarely less than engaging. The recordings are excellent.

Solomon in Berlin Piano works. **Solomon** (pf). APR mono Ⓜ APR7030*
(two discs: 92 minutes: ADD: 4/95). Recorded live in 1956. ⒼⒼ
Bach Concerto in the Italian style, BWV971. **Beethoven** Piano Sonatas – No. 3 in C major,
Op. 2 No. 3; No. 14 in C sharp minor, Op. 27 No. 2, "Moonlight". **Chopin** Fantasie in F minor,
Op. 49. Nocturne in B flat minor, Op. 9 No. 1. Scherzo No. 2 in B flat minor, Op. 31.
Brahms Intermezzos – E major, Op. 116 No. 4; E flat minor, Op. 118 No. 6.
Rhapsody in B minor, Op. 79 No. 1.
This invaluable issue brings together on two short CDs recitals given by Solomon in 1956 for Berlin Radio. This was the time of Solomon's greatest success when, as Bryan Crimp puts it in his excellent notes, he had acquired a Midas touch, at long last reaping the rewards his artistry deserved. The recordings are clean but airless, yet they do little to dim one's sense of Solomon's quality, his masterly but unobtrusive virtuosity, his unsullied honesty and musicianship. How typical is his robust, pacy opening *Allegro* in the Bach, how impeccable his unfolding of the central *Andante*; a truly seamless aria in such hands. His rhythmic zest in the finale, too, is hard to resist. In Beethoven Solomon is, not surprisingly, no less remarkable. By 1956 he had modified his celebrated slow tempo for the first movement of Op. 27 No. 2, yet the playing remains sculpted and marmoreal, a statement mixing abstraction and elegy and wholly devoid of impressionism or 'moonlit' overtones. Solomon's Brahms is no less lucid and classic, though his B minor *Rhapsody* has a truly *agitato* sweep and propulsion. Here Solomon's poise and *sang-froid* are only just on the right side of detachment. The same might be said of his Chopin *Fantasie*. Solomon was hardly a pianist to wear his heart on his sleeve, and although there have been other, more richly idiosyncratic *Fantasies* on record, there are few more masterly or refined. Finally, criticism falls silent when you listen to Solomon in the B flat minor *Nocturne*, where his magically 'contained' eloquence re-creates a pearl beyond price. Here, heart and mind work in faultless harmony and alliance.

Tchaikovsky and his Friends Margaret Fingerhut (pf). Chandos Ⓕ CHAN9218
(78 minutes: DDD: 4/94). Recorded 1992.
Arensky Intermezzo in F minor, Op. 36 No. 12. Le ruisseau dans la forêt. Romance, Op. 53
No. 5. **Glazunov** Etudes, Op. 31 – No. 2 in C minor; No. 3 in E minor. Prelude in D major,
Op. 25 No. 1. **Liadov** Two Bagatelles, Op. 17. Prelude in B minor, Op. 11 No. 1. Prelude in
F sharp minor, Op. 39 No. 4. **Rachmaninov** Canon in E minor. Morceaux de fantaisie, Op. 3 –
No. 1, Elégie in E flat minor; No. 3, Mélodie in E major; No. 4, Policinelle in F sharp minor.
Taneyev Scherzo in E flat minor. Andante semplice. **Tchaikovsky** Humoresque in E minor,
Op. 10 No. 2. Nocturne in C sharp minor, Op. 19 No. 4. Chant sans paroles in A minor, Op. 40
No. 7. Dumka, Op. 59.
The title is a reasonable one, for the younger five composers here were Tchaikovsky's musical friends as well as being known to him and greatly admiring of him. The Russian salon piano piece, owing a good deal to song and therefore to French example, was an immensely popular genre in Moscow and St Petersburg circles, and Tchaikovsky set examples both good and risky. The lively pieces, such as his wonderfully catchy Humoresque, not only put Russian folk idioms into currency, but could seize the sharpest of twentieth-century Russian ears, Stravinsky's, and go into *The Fairy's Kiss* with his own rhythmic bounce. The tender ones could veer in the direction of sentimentality, and sometimes lurch over the margins of good taste. A good variety is represented here. Margaret Fingerhut has chosen intelligently. She has not spared herself, for there are one or two occasions where her technique is fully stretched. However, she has a real understanding of the genre, and can knock off the rapid fancy (such as Taneyev's Scherzo) and the sudden, almost manic burst of energy (uncharacteristically in the indolent Liadov's F sharp minor Prelude), as well as the dreamy meditation (Liadov's first Op. 17 Bagatelle, "La douleur" or Tchaikovsky's own Nocturne or Rachmaninov's Mélodie) and a genre piece such as Arensky's pretty little picture of a brook running through a forest. Her greatest talent is for a flexibility of phrasing that always sings. These are in the best sense sympathetic performances, and should give pleasure.

Virtuoso Piano Transcriptions Earl Wild (pf). Sony Classical Ⓕ SK62036
(67 minutes: DDD: 12/95). Recorded 1995. Ⓖ
Saint-Saëns (trans. Wild) Le rouet d'Omphale in A major, Op. 31. **Handel** Keyboard Suite
No. 5 in E minor, HWV430 – Adagio and Variations, "The Harmonious Blacksmith".
Chopin (trans. Wild) Concerto for Piano and Orchestra No. 2 in F minor, Op. 21 – Largo.
Rachmaninov (trans. Wild) These summer nights, Op. 12 No. 5. **Pabst** Paraphrase on
"Sleeping Beauty" (Tchaikovsky). **Wild** Improvisation on "Après un rêve" (Fauré). Hommage à
Poulenc. Reminiscences of "Snow White and the Seven Dwarfs" (Churchill). **Mozart** (trans.
Backhaus) Don Giovanni – Deh! vieni alla finestra. **Tchaikovsky** (trans. Wild) At the ball,
Op. 38 No. 3. Swan Lake – Dance of the Swans. **Tausig** Man lebt nur einmal. **Kreisler**
(trans. Rachmaninov) Liebesleid.

A pianist with a sweet tooth blessed with an autocratic and crystalline technique, Wild resurrects some of his old favourites (Rachmaninov's *These summer nights* and the Kreisler/Rachmaninov *Liebeslied*, for example) but for the most part provides new and delectable offerings. Take the Wild *Hommage à Poulenc* for example, where the Sarabande from Bach's First *Partita* is held in a relentlessly 'blue' spotlight, enveloped in luscious night-club harmony; a naughty but affectionate tilt at 'the old wig' and also at all purists and Beckmessers. His arrangement of Saint-Saëns's *Le rouet d'Omphale*, deriving in style from the Wagner-Liszt Spinning Chorus from *Der fliegende Holländer*, is dazzlingly resourceful and Handel's *Harmonious Blacksmith* takes on a new lease of life, decked out with mischievous but stylish additions. The decadent commentary on the Rachmaninov song ends with comic abruptness while Tchaikovsky's *At the ball* concludes with a flight nimble enough to show how lightly Wild has worn his years. Lovers of easy sentiment will enjoy the effusive *Reminiscences of "Snow White"* though admirers of Fauré's chaste voluptuousness will react to Wild's way with *Après un rêve* with more than a raised eyebrow. The Dance of the Swans from *Swan Lake* is as ear-tickling as ever and so, all in all, the instantly recognizable sheen and sparkle of this recital reflect a great pianist's tireless relish and delight in all things pianistic and seductive. The recordings are superb.

Virtuoso Strauss Transcriptions Piers Lane (pf). Hyperion Ⓔ CDA66785
(74 minutes: DDD: 2/96). Recorded 1994.
Schulz-Evler An der schönen, blauen Donau. **Friedman** Frühlingsstimmen. **M. Rosenthal**
Carnaval de Vienne. Fantasia on themes by Johann Strauss II. **Tausig** Nouvelles soirées de
Vienne – Nachtfalter, Op. 157; Man lebt nur einmal, Op. 167; Wahlstimmen, Op. 250.
Godowsky Symphonic metamorphosis on "Die Fledermaus".
Here is a recital lovingly planned to tickle even the most jaded palette. Familiar and unfamiliar transcriptions jostle for attention and culminate in the grandest of grand finales, one where previously heard material resurfaces in a truly uproarious display. Schulz-Evler's introduction sends fabulous spangles of sound spinning through the air and Rosenthal's mock-canonic start to his *Carnaval de Vienne* evolves into a crazy course of events. All these works, including Friedman's much less well-known *Frühlingsstimmen* pose some near insuperable problems, even for those blessed with Piers Lane's enviable energy and facility. Somehow the pianist has to create an illusion of effortlessness, a nonchalant capacity to juggle four, five and six jewelled batons simultaneously. Then, and only then, is he free to explore with the most lavish variety of colour and nuance the evocative Viennese memories lingering beneath so much incessant surface activity. Fancifully speaking, Lane leaps rather than glides across the dance floor, revelling in the kaleidoscopic configurations of Friedman's *Frühlingsstimmen* and whirling Rosenthal's final fantasy into a virtuoso vortex; you can almost hear an audience's roar of approval at the end. One occasionally misses an elegance inseparable from such music, the sort of rhetoric or quality that came more easily to pianists of the past. But if Lane is sometimes happier in athleticism than lyricism his record will still grab virtuoso fanciers by the ears. The recordings are excellent.

Choral

Advent at St Paul's St Paul's Cathedral Choir / John Scott ([c]org) with [b]Andrew Lucas (org).
Hyperion Ⓔ CDA66994 (71 minutes: DDD: 12/97). Texts and translations included.
Recorded 1997.
Anonymous Laudes Regiae. Angelus ad Virginem (arr. Willcocks)[b]. O come, O come,
Emmanuel (arr. Carter)[b]. Rejoice in the Lord alway. **Palestrina** Matins Responsory. Vesper
Responsory. **Handl** Ecce concipies[c]. **Peerson** Blow out the trumpet[b]. **R. Lloyd** Drop down, ye
heavens[b]. **Byrd** Laetentur coeli. **Wilby** Echo Carol[b]. **Weelkes** Hosanna to the Son of David.
Britten A Hymn of St Columba[b]. **Gibbons** This is the record of John[b]. **Rutter** Hymn to the
Creator of Light. **Bruckner** Virga Jesse floruit. **Parsons** Ave Maria. **A. Carter** Toccata on
Veni Emmanuel[c].
As in the seasonal calendar a single window opens first, so in this Advent recital a solo voice sings in the distance; and by the end, all windows alight, the great Cathedral is filled with the organ's *fortissimo* from deepest pedal sub-bass to brightest trumpet and topmost piccolo. The programme begins with some plainsong dating back to the first millennium of the era. The end, more plainsong but not so plain now, has *O come, O come, Emmanuel* decked in twentieth-century garb, audaciously arranged, then to become the subject of an organ toccata with sufficient energy to propel the hymn, the Cathedral and all into the new age. In between comes a satisfying alternation of ancient and modern. Particularly splendid is Martin Peerson's *Blow out the trumpet*, a fun-anthem, strong in rhythm and colour. Robert Parsons's five-part *Ave Maria* is also a joy. The modern works include an interesting, deeply felt piece by John Rutter, *Hymn to the Creator of Light*, its first section less ingratiating (but not therefore less good) than is his more characteristic style and, followed by an angular refulgence of praise, preparing for a lovely effect as a chorale-melody is introduced and sung

quietly in octaves amid an affectionate interweave of gentle polyphony. The famous choir are on top form. Britten's *Hymn of St Columba* is especially well performed, probably making the strongest impression of all. Andrew Lucas is the remorselessly exercised organist in this, and John Scott takes over for the Toccata: both do excellent work.

Agnus Dei II New College Choir, Oxford; [a]**Capricorn / Edward Higginbottom.**
Erato Ⓕ 3984-21659-2 (66 minutes: DDD: 6/98). Recorded 1997. *Gramophone Editor's choice.*
Albinoni Adagio in G minor[a]. **Bizet** Agnus Dei. **Schubert** Psalm 23, D706
(all arr. Cameron)[a]. **Brahms** Geistliches Lied, Op. 30[a]. **Fauré** Ave verum, Op. 65 No. 1
(both arr. Higginbottom)[a]. Requiem, Op. 48[a] – Pie Jesu; Libera me. **Martin** Mass for Double
Choir – Agnus Dei. **Byrd** Ave verum corpus. **Lotti** Crucifixus a 8. **Monteverdi** Selva morale e
spirituale – Beatus vir[a]. **Bruckner** Christus factus est[a]. **Purcell** Hear my prayer, O Lord, Z15.
Bach St John Passion, BWV245 – Ruht wohl.

A wise man said you should not swim in the same river twice, and somebody is bound to add that it wouldn't be the same river anyway. "Agnus Dei I" was a winner. The camel's prospects with regard to the needle's eye are rosy compared to the likelihood of a genuinely good choral record getting into the charts; but this one made it. Now comes "Agnus Dei II", with a similar programme and, no doubt, hopes for a comparable success. On the first record it was Barber's *Adagio* for strings, in the composer's own arrangement as a choral setting for the *Agnus Dei*, that won so many hearers and hearts; this time it will presumably be the famous *Adagio* ascribed to Tomaso Albinoni courtesy of Remo Giazotti and set here by John Cameron to a text, in Latin, from the New Testament. The disc's subtitle is "music to soothe the soul", which tends to prefer the sweet melancholy of a nostalgic *adagio* to the brisk *allegro* of a bracing *Brandenburg*, even though this would be much better for it. It could be that Dr Higginbottom and his choir were aware of this and took preventative action. The programme certainly has its quota of soothers, but they are taken at rather faster speeds than usual. Lotti's *Crucifixus*, Schubert's 23rd Psalm and Martin's *Agnus Dei* from the Mass for Double Choir are examples, and all of them benefit, especially in this context. The choir itself has long been one of the best in its normal repertoire of church music, and these excursions have emboldened it in coloration and expressive scope. Purcell's *Hear my prayer*, for instance, is sung with exceptional intensity. Some of the arrangements may be questionable. Albinoni is fair game, but Brahms's lovely Op. 30 forfeits the spiritual quietness of church when deprived of its organ accompaniment, and Schubert is not really in need of strings and harp. It remains a delightful record, and not to be dismissed by 'serious' musicians on account of its wider appeal. The real danger of swimming in the same river twice is of course that everybody who cheered you on first time will take not a blind bit of notice the second: it would be a pity if that happened here.

Bach Family Motets. Trinity College Choir, Cambridge; [a]**Rickman Godlee** (vc); [b]**Martin Peck** (db);
[c]**Christopher Allsop**, [d]**Andrew Lamb** (orgs) / **Richard Marlow.** Conifer Classics Ⓕ 75605 51306-2
(76 minutes: DDD: 11/97). Texts and translations included. Recorded 1995.
J.H. Bach Sei nun wieder zufrieden, meine Seele[abc]. Unser Leben ist ein Schatten[bcd].
J. Christoph Bach Ich lasse dich nicht[ab]. Der Mensch, vom Weibe geboren[bd]. Lieber Herr
Gott, wecke uns auf[bd]. **J.M. Bach I** Nun hab'ich überwunden[ad]. Halt, was du hast[bd]. Fürchtet
euch nicht[abd]. Sei, lieber Tag, willkommen[abd]. **J. Ludwig Bach** Das ist meine Freude[ac]. Unsere
Trübsal[abc]. Es danken dir, Gott[abc]. **J.S. Bach** Jauchzet dem Herrn, alle Welt, BWVAnh160[ac].
J.C.F. Bach: Wachet auf, ruft uns die Stimme, HWXV/1[ac].

Several generations of Bachs have been gathered by Richard Marlow and the Choir of Trinity College, Cambridge for their programme of motets. There is no dull music here and two of the pieces, at least, are of outstanding expressive beauty. The earlier of these is Johann Bach's profoundly affecting *Unser Leben ist ein Schatten* ("Our life is but a shadow"). This member of the clan survived both the Black Death and the savage bombardment of Erfurt during the Thirty Years War. It is hardly fanciful to read into Johann Bach's poignant picture of the frailty of human life the terrifying circumstances that beset Germany in the first half of the seventeenth century. The other, *Ich lasse dich nicht* ("I will not let Thee go, except Thou bless me"), is by Johann Christoph, the most original composer from among J.S. Bach's forebears. Indeed, this eight-strand motet, divided into two antiphonal four-part groups was once thought to be by J.S.B. These two pieces are of exceptional merit, yet much else here hardly ranks beneath them. The single piece by which J. S. Bach is represented here is not quite what it seems. The Psalm motet, *Jauchzet dem Herrn, alle Welt*, was first ascribed to Bach by his pupil and son-in-law, Johann Christoph Altnickol, who also made the earliest copy of it. Yet the piece is clearly an arrangement, very possibly by Bach himself, of his own music derived from a Christmas Cantata No. 28 and music by Telemann. The performances are very good indeed, with notably well-sustained singing by the women's voices. Marlow's direction is sensitive to text and music alike, and the programme is a delight from beginning to end. A valuable addition to the catalogue.

Bushes and Briars [a]**London Madrigal Singers / Christopher Bishop;** [b]**Baccholian Singers of
London; Philip Jones Brass Ensemble; English Chamber Orchestra /** [c]**Ian Humphris.**
EMI British Composers Ⓜ CMS5 65123-2 (two discs: 149 minutes: ADD: 2/96). Texts included.
Recorded 1969-76.

Vaughan Williams Bushes and briars. Loch Lomond. John Dory. Greensleeves. Ward the Pirate. Ca' the Yowes. The unquiet grave. The Seeds of Love. Early in the spring. The Turtle Dove. An Acre of Land. Five English Folksongs (all from HMV HQS1215, 7/70[a]). Bushes and briars. Wassail song. **Elgar** Five Partsongs from the Greek Anthology, Op. 45. The Wanderer. Reveille, Op. 54. **Howells** A Dirge. **Bax** The Boar's Head. **Delius** Wanderer's Song. **Warlock** The Shrouding of the Duchess of Malfi. The lady's birthday. **Britten** The Ballad of Little Musgrave and Lady Barnard (HMV CSD3783, 2/78[b]). **Holst** The Homecoming, H120. Choral Hymns from the Rig Veda (Group 4), H100 – No. 3, Hymn to Manas. Canons, H187 – No. 3, The fields of sorrow; No. 4, David's lament for Jonathan; No. 6, Truth of all truth. Choral Folk Songs, H136 – No. 1, I sowed the seeds of love; No. 3, Matthew, Mark, Luke and John; No. 4, The song of the blacksmith; No. 5, I love my love; No. 6, Swansea Town. Male Choruses, H186 – No. 1, Intercession; No. 2, Good Friday; No. 3, Drinking song; No. 4, A love song; No. 6, Before sleep. A Dirge for Two Veterans, H121 (CSD3764, 7/75[bc]).

From soulful first to sociable last, these part-songs are a delight for listeners as for singers. All who have warbled their way "through bushes and through briars" or taken tuneful farewell of their "little turtle dove" will know what pleasures they can bring, though no doubt many will reflect that the pleasure might have been heightened if their own group had numbered among them a few singers half as expert as those who perform so musically and intelligently on these recordings. The groups have in common a fine discipline that feels like instinct, a care for homogeneity of tone and style, and a keen appreciation of the civilized use of words, music and human society that such things betoken. Christopher Bishop's madrigal singers in the Vaughan Williams folk-song arrangements need more pace and more passion. For the rest, these performances deserve only praise. The Baccholians are particularly good in their rhythmic alertness, catching perfectly the subdued excitement of the *Wassail song* and the tricky syncopations of *The song of the blacksmith*. And what fine, fresh, considered and considerate compositions they are! The Six *Choral Folk Songs* of Holst are rich in variety, while the Six *Choruses* with strings have an equally satisfying unity. The *Dirge for Two Veterans* is a masterpiece, and indeed much could be said about them all which will have to go unsaid. Fortunately, it is hearing rather than 'saying' that really matters, and hearing is highly recommended.

The Christmas Collection Christmas through the centuries. **The Sixteen Choir and Orchestra / Harry Christophers.** Collins Classics Ⓜ 7045-2 (three discs, aas: 215 minutes: DDD: 12/97). *1300-2*[a] – A Traditional Christmas Collection (12/91). *1492-2*[b] – An Early English Christmas Collection. *1270-2*[c] – A Twentieth-Century Christmas Collection. Item marked [a] recorded 1991, [b]1996, [c]1990.

This set is most likely to be used essentially as an anthology. Certainly it passes the test of a good anthology, for wherever you take it up it yields something enjoyable. The twentieth century, for example, has Britten, Howells, Leighton, Walton and Warlock, each adding a seasonal flavour of his own. At the centre of the programme is Sir Peter Maxwell Davies's *O magnum mysterium*, a sequence of carols and instrumental sonatas written for Cirencester Grammar School in 1960. A certain bleakness attends quite a lot of this programme; the note-writer, Nicholas Robertson, has a suggestive phrase when he refers to "that singular mix of nervous joy that characterizes Christmas and its music". In the twentieth century this is something of a presence in the early music too: the minor tonality means something explicitly inimical, and there is a hollow place in medieval harmony where the third of the scale should be. But this is all fine stuff, from the plainsong *Verbum caro* to the elaborate setting by John Sheppard, or from the now famously lusty *Gaudete* to the tender refinement of Byrd's *Lullaby*. On all three discs the standard of performance is consistently high, though very occasionally the balance might be improved. Nowhere is the tasteful musicianship of the choir and its Director more evident than in the 'traditional' collection. The arrangements and accompaniments are impeccably well judged.

Credo [a]**Paul Nicholson** (alto); [b]**Richard Eteson**, [c]**Edward Saklatvala** (cantors); **King's College Choir, Cambridge / Stephen Cleobury.** EMI Ⓔ CDC5 56439-2 (64 minutes: DDD: 10/97). Texts and translations included. Recorded 1997. *Selected by Soundings.*
Rachmaninov Vespers, Op. 37[a] – Bless the Lord, O my soul; Blessed is the man. Liturgy of St John Chrysostom, Op. 31 – Cherubic Hymn; The Lord's Prayer. **Penderecki** The Cherubic Hymn. Agnus Dei. **Stravinsky** Ave Maria. Credo. **Panufnik** Song to the Virgin Mary. **Plainchant** Stetit angelus (Offertory antiphon); Credo I[b]; Ave Maria (Offertory antiphon); Alleluia; Tota pulchra es, Maria (Alleluia with verse); Missa pro defunctis – Agnus Dei[bc]; Pater noster[b].

The logic of this programme, juxtaposing two very different responses to religious texts, is not entirely apparent. The twentieth-century works are not directly influenced by the plainchant of the Western Catholic church yet neither are they all rooted in the Eastern Orthodox tradition. It is the second (1949) version of Stravinsky's *Credo* that is performed here – setting the Catholic rather than the Orthodox text – while both Panufnik and Penderecki were practising Catholics. Indeed only Rachmaninov's gorgeous pieces give us the genuinely Orthodox view – and that from a man who was not himself a staunch follower of the faith. Frankly, though, with music as indescribably beautiful as this and performances which are of almost breathtaking artistry, who needs logic in programming? The climax of Penderecki's *Cherubic Hymn* is measured to absolute perfection, every last ounce of passion squeezed from the long-drawn-out build-up to this shattering moment: the chanted *Pater noster* has that timeless quality which seems to come from another world – enhanced, as is everything on this disc, by a deliciously atmospheric recording. If there is a niggling reservation it is in the lack of real bass resonance, especially in the Rachmaninov. By the very nature of its make-up an English collegiate choir will never possess men's voices with the kind of maturity you would hear in a Russian Orthodox choir. But with such committed, sensitive and musically perceptive singing, we have here one of the very finest discs to have come from King's during Stephen Cleobury's tenure as Director.

Early One Morning New College Choir, Oxford / Edward Higginbottom. Erato Ⓟ 0630-19065-2 (63 minutes: DDD: 3/98). Texts included. Recorded 1997.
Anonymous Sumer is icumen in. **Grainger** Brigg Fair, BFMS7 (with Philip Cave, ten).
A. C. Macleod (arr. Statham) Skye Boat Song. **Molloy** (arr. Rowley): Kerry dance.
Traditional Blow the wind southerly. My love is like a red, red rose (both arr. Cameron). The Londonderry air (arr. Grainger). To the war has gone the Minstrel Boy (arr. anon). The Salley Gardens. O waly waly. Early one morning (all arr. Higginbottom). Shenandoah (arr. Erb). Oh, no John (arr. Halsey). Steal away to Jesus (arr. Trant). The Ash Grove (arr. Jacob). Swing low, sweet chariot (arr. Burleigh and Page). The Oak and the Ash (arr. Bairstow). Linden Lea. Loch Lomond. Greensleeves (all arr. Vaughan Williams).
As Edward Higginbottom acknowledges in his introductory notes, the folk-song becomes a different thing when sung from a written text and musical score; different again when that score is written in choral parts with enrichments of harmony and counterpoint. This last matter probably warrants more discussion, for views may differ about the art of arranging. Should the words and melody be 'given straight', with no more adornment than in the harmonizing of a hymn tune? That is Gordon Jacobs's way with *The Ash Grove*. Or should they become the basis for what is essentially a new composition, as in John Cameron's version of *Blow the wind southerly*? Ample opportunity to think about it arises during the course of this recital. It is, of course, unusual to have a church choir in such a programme but the fine tone (with a likeable individuality in that of the trebles), the intelligent phrasing, clear enunciation and sensitive shading are all admirable. There are some good soloists too, outstanding among them being the tenor Philip Cave who sings so beautifully in *Brigg Fair*. Occasionally the notes are 'individualized' at the expense of the flow; sometimes the punctuation may be a degree too deliberate. Of the selection itself the only complaint is that a few more quick-tempo items would not have gone amiss. Recorded sound is fine – not at all churchy though in fact recorded in the Chapel – and the booklet is attractively produced.

English Choral Works Netherlands Chamber Choir / John Alldis with [a]Manja Smits (hp). Globe Ⓟ GLO5170 (59 minutes: DDD: 2/98). Texts included. Recorded 1996.
Vaughan Williams Three Shakespeare Songs. **Howells** Requiem. **Holst** Choral Hymns from the Rig Veda – Group 3, H99[a]. **Britten** Five Flower Songs, Op. 47. **Bedford** The Golden Wine is Drunk.
This superb Dutch group under their permanent guest conductor, John Alldis, offer high-class choral singing. The magical start of "Full fathom five" (the first of Vaughan Williams's *Three Shakespeare Songs* from 1951) immediately proclaims an exceptional degree of perception from all involved. These artists give a no less sympathetic rendering of Howells's Requiem, that haunting soul mate and precursor to *Hymnus Paradisi*. Holst's third group of *Rig Veda* hymns receive luminously beautiful treatment from the Netherlands choir with harpist Manja Smits. The collection concludes with David Bedford's *The Golden Wine is Drunk* (1974), a 13-minute setting of Ernest Dowson for two eight-part choirs, whose textural imagination, melismatic beauty and liberating dissonance cast quite a spell, especially in a performance as hypnotically controlled and utterly dedicated as here. Recorded sound is admirable.

Great Cathedral Anthems, Volume 8. Choir of St Mary's Cathedral, Edinburgh / Timothy Byram-Wigfield with [a]Peter Backhouse (org). Priory Ⓟ PRCD557 (64 minutes: DDD: 10/97). Recorded 1996.
Harwood O how glorious is the Kingdom[a]. **Byrd** Christe, qui lux es et dies. O Lord, make thy servant Elizabeth our Queen. **Taverner** Quemadmodum desiderat cervus. **Gibbons** O clap your hands. **Lotti** Crucifixus a 8. **Stanford** Three Motets, Op. 38. **Ley** Prayer of King Charles I. **Brahms** Ein deutsches Requiem, Op. 45 – Wie lieblich sind deine Wohnungen (sung in English)[a]. **Howells** Salve regina. **Walton** The twelve[a].
If there are some to whom the choir of Edinburgh's Episcopal Cathedral are introducing themselves in this recital, they are likely to be impressed and want to hear more. This is a choir that can sustain long phrases (fine ones in the marvellous motet by Taverner), lengthy and concentrated works too (as with Walton's *The twelve*), finding plentiful resources of energy in matters of attack and rhythm. The trebles (14 plus four girls) are bright-toned and sing some formidably challenging music with well-founded confidence. The choir also possess useful soloists, most notably the baritone who so effectively opens *The twelve*. The organist proves his merit from the start with an exciting performance of the virtuosic solo which introduces *O how glorious is the Kingdom*, and skilfully manages the accompaniment (not as easy as it may sound) to "How lovely are Thy dwellings". It is an enterprising programme, finding room for cherished old acquaintances such as Charles I's evening prayer in its

graceful setting by Henry Ley. The acoustic is helpful, neither dry nor excessively reverberant, and the balance between choir and organ is judiciously established.

Hail, Gladdening Light Cambridge Singers / John Rutter. Collegium Ⓕ COLCD113 (72 minutes: DDD: 4/92). Texts and translations included.
Anonymous Rejoice in the Lord. **Purcell** Remember not, Lord, our offences, Z50. **J. Amner** Come, let's rejoice. **Tomkins** When David heard. **Bairstow** I sat down under his shadow. **J. Goss** These are they that follow the lamb. **Taverner** Christe Jesu, pastor bone. **Philips** O beatum et sacrosanctum diem. **Howells** Nunc dimittis. **Vaughan Williams** O vos omnes. **Dering** Factum est silentium. **Stanford** Justorum animae, Op. 38 No. 1. **C. Wood** Hail, gladdening light. **Tavener** A hymn to the mother of God. Hymn for the dormition of the mother of God. **Elgar** They are at rest. **Walton** A litany. **Morley** Nolo mortem peccatoris. **Tallis** O nata lux. **Rutter** Loving shepherd of Thy sheep. **R. Stone** The Lord's Prayer. **J. Sheppard** In manus tuas. **W.H. Harris** Bring us, O Lord God.

This has the subtitle "Music of the English Church" and it is arranged under four main headings: anthems and introits (these count as one), Latin motets, settings of hymns and other poetry, and prayer-settings. Each of them is well represented in a programme that varies delightfully in period and style, and in performances which are remarkably consistent in quality. Some of the items will come as discoveries to most listeners: for example, the anthem *Come, let's rejoice*, a splendid, madrigal-like piece written by John Amner, organist from 1610 to 1641 at Ely Cathedral where these recordings were made. Others are equally impressive in their present performance: a deep quietness attends the opening of Richard Dering's *Factum est silentium*, which ends with rhythmic Alleluias set dancing with subdued excitement. Among the hymn-settings is one by a 16-year-old called William Walton. Included in the prayers is the choirmaster's own setting, characteristically made for pleasure, of *Loving shepherd of Thy sheep*. All are unaccompanied, and thus very exactingly test the choir's blend of voices, its precision, articulation and feeling for rhythm. In all respects they do exceptionally well; the tone is fresh, the attack unanimous, the expression clear and sensitive, the rhythm on its toes. These are young and gifted singers, formed with disciplined enthusiasm into a choir with a distinctive style – and, incidentally, recorded with admirable results by a family firm which operates from a studio built at the bottom of the garden.

Hear my Prayer [a]Jeremy Budd (treb); St Paul's Cathedral Choir / John Scott with [b]Andrew Lucas (org). Hyperion Ⓕ CDA66439 (76 minutes: DDD: 10/91). Texts and translations included. Recorded 1990.
Allegri Miserere mei (with Nicholas Thompson, treb; Wilfred Swansborough, alto; Timothy Jones, bass)[a]. **B. Rose** Feast Song for St Cecilia (Simon Hill, alto; Alan Green, ten)[a]. **Brahms** Ein deutsches Requiem – Ich hab nun Traurigkeit (sung in English)[ab]. **Britten** Festival Te Deum, Op. 32[ab]. **Harvey** Come, Holy Ghost (Andrew Burden, ten; Nigel Beaven, bass)[a]. **Mendelssohn** Hear my prayer[ab]. **Stanford** Evening Canticles in G major (Jones)[ab]. **Tavener** I will lift up mine eyes. **Wise** The ways of Zion do mourn (Charles Gibbs, bass)[ab].

The special distinction of this disc is the work of the treble soloist, Jeremy Budd. He sings in a programme which is very much the choirboy's equivalent of an operatic soprano's "Casta diva" and more of that sort (come to think of it, Master Budd could probably have sung a splendid "Casta diva" into the bargain). As it is, he crowns the Allegri *Miserere* with its five top Cs, spot-on, each of them (rather like Melba singing "Amor" at the end of Act 1 in *La bohème* five times over). He commands the breath, the long line and the purity of tone necessary for the solo in Brahms's Requiem and copes with the difficult modern idiom of Jonathan Harvey's *Come, Holy Ghost* with an apparent ease that to an older generation may well seem uncanny. Other modern works are included. John Tavener's *I will lift up mine eyes*, written for St Paul's in 1990, has its characteristic compound of richness and austerity; and in this, the words penetrate the mist of echoes more successfully than do those of the *Feast Song for St Cecilia*, written by Gregory Rose and set to some very beautiful music by his father Bernard. It is good, as ever, to hear Stanford's Evening Service in G, with its almost Fauré-like accompaniment finely played by the excellent Andrew Lucas; and for a morning canticle there is Britten's *Te Deum* with its effective build-up to "Lord God of Sabaoth" and its faint pre-echo of *The Turn of the Screw* at "O Lord, save Thy people". There is also a melancholy anthem by Michael Wise, whose fate it was to be knocked on the head and killed by the watchman to whom he was cheeky one night in 1687.

A Hilliard Songbook New music for voices. The Hilliard Ensemble (David James, alto; Rogers Covey-Crump, John Potter, tens; Gordon Jones, bar). ECM New Series Ⓕ 453 259-2 (two discs: 120 minutes: DDD: 1/97).
B. Guy Un coup de dés (with Barry Guy, db). **Feldman** Only. **I. Moody** Endechas y Canciones. Canticum Canticorum I. **P. Hellawell** The Hilliard Songbook. **P. Robinson** Incantation. **Tormis** Kullervo's Message. *Plainchant:* Adoro te devote. **MacMillan** ... here in hiding ... . **Pärt** And One of the Pharisees ... . Summa. **E. Liddle** Whale Rant. **J. Metcalf** Music for the Star of the Sea. **Finnissy** Stabat autem iuxta crucem. **Casken** Sharp Thorne.

The Hilliard Ensemble have always had an interest in commissioning and performing works by living composers, but apart from a few high profile, major projects, few of their ventures in the contemporary domain have found their way on to disc. Though not exhaustive in its representation, "A Hilliard Songbook" (named after a song-cycle by Piers Hellawell) includes most of the prominent figures with whom the ensemble have been associated over the years, along with younger or lesser-known composers whose works find committed advocates here. Of course, The Hilliards and their sound are usually associated with a very different repertory, so the pleasure in this collection is twofold: first the fascination of hearing a familiar 'instrument' in an unaccompanied setting and secondly, the extent to which these composers deal with the silent presence within that sound of nearly six centuries of early polyphony. That presence is at its remotest in Barry Guy's *Un coup de dés*, the first work in the collection – though at times the almost Joycean hubbub of the 'libretto' calls to mind the town-cry pieces of Janequin and Gibbons. But such a link – if intentional – is never overtly stated; thereafter, references to specific repertories are more explicit, ranging from plainsong and Spanish homophonic *canciones* (Ivan Moody), hints of Gesualdian chromaticism at the start of James MacMillan's *... here in hiding ...* , note-against-note organum in Finnissy (only one of whose *Seven Sacred Motets* is recorded here), to medieval passion-plays (Pärt) or standard modal cadential formulae (Paul Robinson). Most of these pieces tend towards the pure triadic sonorities and the respond forms associated with so much medieval and liturgical music – and much tonal music since that time. In Veljo Tormis's *Kullervo's Message*, the strophic structure and figurative gestures (galloping horsemen, whispering messengers of death *et al*) put one in mind of Schubert's *Erlkönig* – but then, nineteenth-century German part-songs also have a place in The Hilliard's discography. The performances are of a standard that few living composers can hope for, and the more demanding selections are dispatched with commendable relish, and little hint of strain. Those who admire the ensemble's inimitable sound can look forward to an issue of real interest.

Ikon [a]James Bowman (alto); **Holst Singers / Stephen Layton.** Hyperion Ⓟ CDA66928 (79 minutes: DDD: 8/97). Texts and translations included. Recorded 1996.
Sviridov Tsar Feodor Ioannovich – Prayer[a]; Sacred love; A verse of repentance. Songs of troubled times – Autumn; Bright fields; Spring and the sorcerer; The ikon[a]. **Grechaninov** Liturgy of St John Chrysostom, Op. 29 – The cherubic hymn; The Creed[a]; Our Father. **Victor Kalinnikov** Radiant light. **Tchaikovsky** Liturgy of St John Chrysostom, Op. 41 – We hymn Thee; The cherubic hymn. Sacred pieces – No. 7, Blessed are they. **Pärt** Magnificat. **Górecki** Totus tuus, Op. 60. **Nystedt/Bach** Immortal Bach.
The most interesting discovery to be made on this anthology is Sviridov's choral music, both sacred and profane. A Russian nineteenth-century ancestry is audible in his work, and he is clearly following in the footsteps of Rachmaninov, with a splendid sureness of technique. James Bowman's voice joins the Holst Singers in one of the Blok settings, but his real showcase here is the Grechaninov *Creed*. This piece is really not much more than chords – but *what* chords! The solo recitative depends entirely on the musical personality of the singer, and Bowman carries it off to perfection. Here, as throughout, the Holst Singers' pronunciation of Slavonic and Russian is excellent, but it is interesting that the indubitably English sound produced particularly by the female voices brings out what one might term the 'English' connections of this very Russian music: on hearing them sing Grechaninov and Tchaikovsky one might easily be reminded of Walton or Stanford. The other pieces by Grechaninov and the Kalinnikov *Svete tikhi* ("Radiant light") are also finely sung, but the Tchaikovsky works suffer from too strict an adherence to the beat. No such problems affect Pärt's *Magnificat* or Górecki's *Totus tuus*, however, both of which are given superlative readings of the utmost sensitivity and control. However, Nystedt's *Immortal Bach*, though beautifully performed, hardly serves as a conclusion for an otherwise well-thought-out collection.

Magnificat and Nunc Dimittis, Volume 3. **Lichfield Cathedral Choir / Andrew Lumsden** with [a]Mark Shepherd, [b]Nigel Potts (orgs). Priory Ⓟ PRCD505 (56 minutes: DDD: 10/95). Texts included. Recorded 1994.
Stanford Evening Service in A major, Op. 12[a]. **S. Watson** Evening Service in E major[b].
G. Ives Evening (Edington) Service[a]. **Gibbons** First (Short) Service[a]. **Leighton** Evening (Magdalen) Service[a]. **Howells** Evening Service in G major[a]. **Dyson** Evening Service in D major[a].
Why do keys have characters? Maybe it's the 'feel' of the keyboard and the 'look' of the key-signature – with A major those three spiky sharps suggest something quite different from the laid-back four flats of their neighbour. Anyway, Stanford has caught the very essence of A major at the start of his *Magnificat*; and this performance has caught the essence of Stanford. Crisp, clear-headed, purposeful and glad-to-be-alive that is the A majorish character of the opening bars, splendidly played by Mark Shepherd. The choir, too, are alert and responsive, a thorough credit to Andrew Lumsden, their Director. This is an excellent record. Each of the settings has its special character, and all in their different ways are skilful in craftsmanship, the joinery of the business. Sydney Watson, whose Service in E follows Stanford in A, has a fine economy of means, discreet in its more modern harmonic flavouring. Howells ("my son in music" as Stanford called him) wrote more adventurous and memorable settings than this one in G, yet its affectionate traditionalism impresses too, and as it opens out in the *Gloria* of the Magnificat it conveys that rush of ecstasy or apprehension of the sublime that is so characteristic. The Lichfield sound is refreshing, and the vitality of their performances remains a good, bracing pleasure throughout.

Magnificat and Nunc Dimittis, Volume 4. **Portsmouth Cathedral Choir / Adrian Lucas** with **David Thorne** (org). Priory Ⓟ PRCD527 (79 minutes: DDD: 2/96). Texts included. Recorded 1995.

Brewer Evening Service in E flat major. **Andrews** Evening Service in G major.
Howells Evening Service in E major. Evening Service in B minor. **Lassus** Magnificat quarto toni. **Victoria** Nunc dimittis. **Stanford** Evening Service in C major, Op. 115. **Weelkes** Evening Service for Trebles – Magnificat; Nunc dimittis. **Darke** Evening Service in F major.
R. Shephard Salisbury Service. **Bairstow** Evening Service in D major.

One good thing after another; it almost surprises that a succession of *Mags* and *Nuncs* can be so varied, satisfying and enjoyable. The programmes in this excellent series allow for a fair variety of styles and centuries, but in this instance a particularly generous share of the credit must go to the performances. Forthright and invigorating, they give rise to a distinct suspicion that the whole business may be a pleasure: that the choristers have some rhythm in their bones and at certain points might even have a smile on their faces. It is there right from the start, with Brewer in E flat (and how undeservedly stodgy that can sound in performance) bright with energy and encouraging a conviction that there genuinely is something in which to rejoice. This extends to Lassus, Victoria and Weelkes, where, instead of the more usual formal reading of notes, there is a common effort of understanding and imagination, lifting the notes off the page and sometimes, with a little judicious semi-staccato, setting them a-dance. Nor is there any lack of sensitive shading or of repose in the right places – a fine feeling for mood in the lovely and little-known B minor setting of Howells, for example. A splendid recital, with a fine choice of repertoire, and consistently admirable playing by the organist.

Magnificat and Nunc dimittis, Volume 5. **Bristol Cathedral Choir / Christopher Brayne** with **Ian Ball** (org). Priory Ⓟ PRCD528 (73 minutes: DDD: 8/96). Texts included. Recorded 1994.
Anonymous Magnificat and Nunc dimittis. **Harke** Magnificat and Nunc dimittis in A flat major. **Howells** Evening Service in G major. **Jackson** Evening Service in G major.
Leighton Second Service, Op. 62. **Moore** Canterbury Service. **Morley** First Evening Service.
Noble Evening Service, Op. 6. **Warren** Bristol Service.

This series has won consistently enthusiastic reviews, and the present volume may well be the best yet. It begins with Noble in B minor, most dramatic of all the established favourites (did he ever do anything quite so good again?). Then comes Francis Jackson in G, pastoral-modal and aspiring to ecstasy, Howells-fashion. The *Bristol Service* of Professor Raymond Warren has more of Tippett in it, especially in the organ part and in the "Gloria". Clifford Harker, who was organist at the Cathedral for over 30 years, does a neater job of construction and knows how to bring out a rich, generous choral sound. Kenneth Leighton's Second Service has perhaps the most distinctive originality, in moods that are hauntingly tricky to pin down, something uneasy even in joy, by no means traditional in style and yet as sure in feeling for voices and organ as if his other name were Stanford. Howells in G is relatively easygoing; Philip Moore's *Canterbury Service* for trebles likewise; and the inclusion of Thomas Morley provides a welcome change of idiom. The choir seem totally undaunted by the difficulties which these twentieth-century composers throw at them. The boys sing with unfailingly fine tone, though with a tendency to open vowels in words such as "soul" and "Lord". The men too are fine, just occasionally coarsening the sound a little. Imaginative registration of the organ parts, clear recording and an informative booklet are further assets.

Magnificat and Nunc dimittis, Volume 7. **Hereford Cathedral Choir / Roy Massey** with [a]**Huw Williams** (org). Priory Ⓟ PRCD535 (68 minutes: DDD: 7/96). Texts included. Recorded 1995.
Sumsion Evening Service in D major[a]. **Darke** Evening Service in A minor. **Lloyd** Hereford Service[a]. **Davies** Evening Service in G major (Festal)[a]. **Vann** Hereford Service[a]. **Dyson** Evening Service in F major[a]. **Harwood** Evening Service in A flat major[a]. **Shephard** Hereford Service[a]. **Stanford** Services in F major, Op. 36 – Evening Service[a].

We follow these reliable generations of church musicians (which is what most of them are, the presence of Walton and Tippett being exceptions), and recall that composing was a part-time occupation, almost a luxury, in the daily round that normally comprised taking choir practice and playing the organ, giving lessons and conducting the choral society. The variety of the settings here is a striking feature – Harold Darke's for unaccompanied choir, Dyson's quietness. Almost invariably the individual finds something of his own to add – for example, Richard Lloyd reintroducing "My soul doth magnify" at the end of his *Magnificat*. Hearing again the well-known favourites (Sumsion in D major, Harwood in A flat), one appreciates exactly why they have so established themselves, just as in Stanford in F major (not among his most familiar settings) we see the hand of the master. We also watch 'modernity' cautiously advancing – in Stanley Vann's fine Hereford Service, for instance. Hereford Cathedral Choir are admirable throughout, and benefit from the clear recorded sound.

Magnificat and Nunc dimittis, Volume 13. **St Thomas Church Choir, New York / Gerre Hancock** with **Patrick Allen** (org). Priory Ⓟ PRCD600 (79 minutes: DDD: 1/98). Recorded 1996.
Friedell Magnificat and Nunc dimittis in F major. **Susa** Magnificat and Nunc dimittis (St Thomas Service). **Searle Wright** Magnificat and Nunc dimittis in E minor. **Titelouze** Le magnificat – Tone IV. **Sowerby** Magnificat and Nunc dimittis in D major. **Schuller** Magnificat and Nunc dimittis (St Thomas Service). **Ossewaarde** Magnificat and Nunc dimittis in C major.

Evensong on Fifth Avenue is an attractive prospect, and certainly the Choir of St Thomas's, on this showing, would be good to hear. With strong, forthright trebles, distinctive (un-English) altos, pleasant tenors and (best) an excellent bass line, they display a well-disciplined unity of style and purpose and in this programme ably tackle some challenging music. All but one of the settings were written in the present century, the odd one out being the *Magnificat* by Jean Titelouze (1563-1633) which alternates plainsong with organ solos. This owes its place to the recent installation of a gallery organ, a tribute to Dr Hancock on his 25th year as organist and choirmaster: the instrument sounds well and is skilfully played by Patrick Allen. The six full choral settings of both evening canticles will probably be found more pleasing individually than in sequence. Their differences from one another are clear enough, but the likeness, when compared with representative English settings, is in their taste for a certain dramatic excitability. Most memorable is the *St Thomas Service* of Conrad Susa, the *Magnificat* aptly characterized in Denis Stevens's note as "dancy, radiant and forward-looking". Ossewaarde in C major is interesting and effective in its handling of the triple rhythms, and Friedell in F major is a bold, colourful festal setting, well worth investigating. Closer recording might have been preferable, but these remarks must end on a congratulatory note, for, as the makers point out in commendably bold type, this is their 500th recording since setting up shop in 1980. They have done splendid work, coming in where other companies have passed by, giving pleasure and much-needed encouragement. All power to the next 500.

Miserere and other choral works Trinity College Choir, Cambridge / Richard Marlow. Conifer Classics Ⓕ CDCF219 (79 minutes: DDD: 2/94). Recorded 1993.
Parry I was glad. Jerusalem. **Schubert** Deutsche Messe, D872 – Sanctus. Ave Maria, D839. **Barber** Agnus Dei, Op. 11. **Burgon** Nunc dimittis. **Bach** Cantata No. 129, Gelobet sei der Herr, mein Gott – Dem wir das Heilig itzt (sung in English). **Allegri** Miserere. **Mendelssohn** Hear my prayer. **Gardiner** Evening Hymn. **Walford Davies** God be in my head. **Berlioz** L'Enfance du Christ – Shepherds' Farewell. **Franck** Panis angelicus. **Purcell** Hear my prayer, O Lord, Z15. **C. Wood** Hail, gladdening light. **Mozart** Ave verum corpus in D, K618. **Gounod** Ave Maria. **Vaughan Williams** The Old Hundredth Psalm Tunes. O taste and see.

The choir is at its absolute best here in Barber's arrangement of his famous *Adagio* for strings as an *Agnus Dei* for unaccompanied voices. In texture and balance, as in the precision of attack and chording, they are really superb. *Jerusalem* is phrased with breadth and care for sense. Breadth, too, distinguishes the performance of *I was glad*, the choir's fine sustaining power serving them well. They are expert in making the most of their resources, so that the quiet "O pray for the peace of Jerusalem", like the solo choir in the Allegri *Miserere*, makes doubly effective the rich sonority to come. All the solo work is good, with a remarkably authentic treble tone supplied by Andrea Cockerton in Mendelssohn's *Hear my prayer*. Purcell's *Hear my prayer* is probably the gem of the whole programme, which is broadly popular in character, a generous mix of periods and styles, with the choir's own style helping to impose a unity and always guaranteeing performances that will be careful in preparation and scrupulous in beauty of tone.

Music Inspired by World War Two [b]Sarah Leonard (sop); [a]Cornelia Kallisch (contr); [b]Thomas Randle (ten); [c]Udo Samel (spkr); [c]men's voices of the Bamberg Symphony Chorus; Bamberg Symphony Orchestra / Ingo Metzmacher. EMI Ⓕ CDC5 55424-2 (59 minutes: DDD: 3/97). Texts and translations included.
Hartmann Symphony No. 1, "Versuch eines Requiem"[a]. **Martinů** Memorial to Lidice. **Nono** Canti di vita e d'amore[b]. **Schoenberg** A Survivor from Warsaw, Op. 46[c].

"Disgust at the terror and destruction of war unites the works on this CD", writes Andreas Jaschinski in the accompanying essay. True, all four pieces derive their baleful inspiration from events in the Second World War, but disgust is a term that falls a long way short of the intensity of response drawn from each composer: the tyranny of Hitler's Reich within Germany; the Nazis' razing of the Czech village of Lidice in 1942 and the massacre of its inhabitants; the atomic holocaust at Hiroshima; the oppression and slaughter of Polish Jewry in the Warsaw ghetto. Each composition contains moments of truly visceral impact – the horns' heart-stopping declamation of the opening of Beethoven's Fifth at the climax of *Memorial to Lidice* (1942; one of the very few pieces by Martinů that does not smile), the chorus's entry with the hymn *Shem'a Yisroel* at the end of *A Survivor from Warsaw* (1947), or the searing dissonances, like flesh being atomized from the bone, in the first of Nono's *Canti di vita e d'amore*. Few symphonies have so electrifying an opening as Hartmann's First, with rampaging timpani and brass chords like thunderbolts, counterpointed by the numbed desolation of disbelief that the events behind the music were actually happening. This CD does not make for comfortable listening, though it is a moot point whether this is due to the ghastly associations each work carries with it or the overwhelmingly powerful expression of the notes themselves. The performances are compelling, even where rivals have an edge, but the programme renders comparisons irrelevant.

Officium Jan Garbarek (sax); **Hilliard Ensemble** (David James, alto; Rogers Covey-Crump, John Potter, tens; Gordon Jones, bar). ECM New Series Ⓕ 445 369-2 (78 minutes: DDD: 10/94). Latin texts included. Including Plainchant, Notre Dame polyphony and motets by Dufay, de la Rue and Morales – with saxophone. Recorded 1993. Ⓖ

The play between ancient chant and structured jazz-style improvisation creates a sort of spiritual time warp where past and present happily co-exist on the basis of shared musical goals. For no matter how one views so-called crossover (such a silly term), or the relative lack of wisdom in sticking to rigid musical boundaries, the evidence remains conclusive: "Officium" successfully transcends any limitations imposed by time and style. If you have any doubts, then play either the opening or closing tracks, both of which find Jan Garbarek (a master of apposite extemporization) easing around Christóbal de Morales's polyphonic "Pace mihi domine" (from the *Officium defunctorum*) as if it were his own creation. The effect is enchanting and when, eight tracks later (or earlier, according to whether you're in 'forward' or 'reverse' mode), the same piece is presented *sans* Garbarek's saxophone, we somehow miss the commentary. If the probable success of this album prompts certain jazz fans and early music specialists to commiserate over their invaded territories, or cynics to align Garbarek and the Hilliards with Górecki and the Monks, then take heart: we're still listening to Respighi's ancient masters, Stravinsky's 'Pergolesi', Tchaikovsky's Mozart and Loussier's Bach, not to mention Ellington's Tchaikovsky. Stylistic cross-pollination makes for a healthy creative environment, and this CD is one of its happiest symptoms. Recordings, documentation and presentation are exemplary.

Passiontide at St Paul's A Sequence of Music for Lent, Passiontide and Easter.
St Paul's Cathedral Choir / John Scott with **Andrew Lucas** (org). Hyperion Ⓕ CDA66916 (71 minutes: DDD: A/97). Texts and translations included. Recorded 1996.
Anonymous A Lent Prose. **Farrant** Call to remembrance, O Lord. **Mendelssohn** Symphony No. 2 in B flat major, Op. 52, "Hymn of Praise" – Ich harrete des Herrn (sung in English).
Bairstow The Lamentation. Psalm 114, When Israel came out of Egypt. **Sanders** The Reproaches. **Chapple** Ecce lignum Crucis. **Bruckner** Christus factus est. **Gibbons** Drop, drop slow tears. **Lotti** Crucifixum. **Wood** This joyful Eastertide. **Philips** Ecce vicit Leo.
Britten Te Deum in C major.
Among the attractions of this recital is the singing of the four treble soloists, especially that of Connor Burrowes, who is heard twice in the Lenten section and then finally in Britten's *Te Deum* where the precision and clarity of his tone are ideal. In "I waited for the Lord" he is matched with uncanny exactness by Edmond Hill: altogether a delightful performance. The choir itself sing magnificently, not least in quite simple things such as Gibbons's hymn tune for *Drop, drop slow tears*. The ordering of the programme into three sections for Lent, Passiontide and Easter, becomes something of a liability because (in musical terms) it involves consecutive slow movements. In particular, John Sanders's *Reproaches* are slightly weakened by following on after Bairstow's *Lamentation*, and Brian Chapple's *Ecce lignum Crucis* has to contend with both. It is probably better, in playing the disc, to take those three works separately. On the other hand, after so much penitential music *This joyful Eastertide* comes with additional pleasure in the freshness, both of the tune itself and of Charles Wood's harmonies. Bairstow's through-composed chant for *In exitu Israel* is effective too, especially in its culminating *fortissimo*. In all of this the St Paul's echo is an inescapable presence, but to the credit of all concerned, it does not dull the clarity. In fact, with Britten's *Te Deum* we become aware, perhaps more sharply than ever, of the work's purposeful construction, its assured mastery marking the coming-of-age of the 21-year-old composer.

Prometheus [a]Ingrid Ade-Jesemann, [a]Monika Bair-Ivenz (sops); [a]Susanne Otto (contr); [a]Peter Hall (ten); [a]Ulrike Krumbiegel, [a]Mathias Schadock (spkrs); [a]Michael Hasel (bass fl); [a]Manfred Preis (bass cl); [a]Christhard Gössling (euph/tuba); [b]Martha Argerich (pf); [b]Berlin Singakademie; [a]Freiburg Soloists Choir; Berlin Philharmonic Orchestra / Claudio Abbado.
Sony Classical Ⓕ SK53978 (75 minutes: DDD: 1/95). Texts and translations included. Recorded live in 1993.54437 *Gramophone* Editor's choice.. Ⓖ Ⓖ Ⓖ
Beethoven Der Geschöpfe des Prometheus – excerpts. **Liszt** Prometheus, S99.
Scriabin Prometheus, "Le poème du feu", Op. 60[b]. **Nono** Promoteo – suite[a].
Prometheus's theft of fire from Zeus and the cruelty of his punishment are all but absent from Beethoven's ballet. Even Melpomene's outburst of violence sounds disarmingly Schubertian, while the ensuing dances and finale are among the most diverting in the whole of Beethoven's orchestral output. It would be difficult to imagine a more beautifully shaped performance than Abbado's, where relative tensions are artfully judged, instrumental solos given with real style and the whole is captured in a warm, luminous recording. Liszt's glowering outburst – one of his most daring symphonic poems – is more an informed commentary than a genuine 'performance': lean, sinewy and consistent, yes, but too cool-headed by far. The disc's real *tour de force*, both sonically and musically, is Scriabin's Promethean effusion, his *Poem of fire*. Abbado serves as master of ceremonies, Argerich as a crazed high priestess, her delirious, delicate and unpredictable solo weaving through the orchestra like a bubbling stream of consciousness. That is how it *should* sound – overwrought, overpowering, utterly unhinged and yet calculated even to the smallest detail. The stylistic leap from Scriabin's tantalizing chromatics to Nono's non-gravitational soundscape – with its solo voices, synthesized sounds and woodwind-blown choruses – is tantamount to leaving the earth's orbit, and one's earthly body with it. Here we meet Prometheus head-on, lynched on an aural anxiety-loop where vague distortions are as many ripples on a sickly sea of sound. In short, this is a hugely stimulating production.

Psalms from St Paul's, Volume 4. **St Paul's Cathedral Choir / John Scott** with **Andrew Lucas** (org). Hyperion Ⓕ CDP11004 (76 minutes: DDD: 7/96). Texts included.
Stainer Psalm 41, Blessed is he that considereth the poor and needy. **S. Wesley** Psalm 42, Like as the hart. Psalm 43, Give sentence with me, O God. **Barnby/Anonymous** Psalm 44, We have

heard with our ears, O God. **R. Cooke** Psalm 45, My heart is inditing of a good matter. **Luther** (adapted): Psalm 46, God is our hope and strength. **Davy** Psalm 47, O clap your hands. **Goss** Psalm 48, Great is the Lord and highly to be praised. **Walmisley** Psalm 49, O hear ye this, all ye people. **Thalben-Ball** Psalm 50, The Lord, even the most mighty God, hath spoken. **Bairstow** Psalm 51, Have mercy upon me, O Lord God. **Scaife** Psalm 52, Why boastest thou thyself, thy tyrant. **Attwood** Psalm 53, The foolish body hath said. **M. Wise** Psalm 54, Save me, O God, by Thy name. **Foster/Martin** Psalm 55, Hear my prayer, O God.

The English Anthem, Volume 6. **St Paul's Cathedral Choir / John Scott** with [a]**Andrew Lucas** (org). Hyperion Ⓕ CDA66826 (69 minutes: DDD: 7/96). Texts included. Recorded 1995.
     Bairstow If the Lord had not helped me[a]. **Dearnley** Let thy hand be strengthened[a].
     Elgar Ave verum corpus, Op. 2 No. 1[a]. **W.H. Harris** Strengthen ye the weak hands[a].
     J. Harvey Dum transisset Sabbatum. **Parry** Songs of Farewell – My soul, there is a country.
     Stanford For lo, I raise up, Op. 145[a]. **Tavener** Three Antiphons. **Tippett** Plebs angelica.
     Walmisley Remember, O Lord, what is come upon us[a]. **Wood** 'Tis the day of resurrection[a].

Both of these series deserve success on a grand scale, for grandeur is part of their character. St Paul's is the king of cathedral choirs, and the sound of their singing, with the majesty of the organ and the awesome reverberance of the great building to match, is as rich and noble as any sound on earth. The programme of the sixth volume in the anthem series is the first not to include anything out of the top ten (or the Cathedral Choir's equivalent), yet its selection maintains as high a standard as any in quality. The penitential anthem by Walmisley is a masterpiece; Harris's 'wilderness' anthem (not called that but using most of the same text) has a strength which grows from one moment to the next, and Tavener's *Three Antiphons* are strikingly effective. Harvey's *Dum transisset Sabbatum* is also strong in ideas and finely crafted to suit St Paul's where, in 1995, it had its first performance.

The Psalms, it might be thought, are a great deal more specialized, not to say doubtful, in their appeal. It cannot really be said that the chants (those used here, at any rate) have any particular musical merit, and of course one hears them over and over again. But there *is* appeal, which is partly technical (appreciation of a job well done), partly retrospective (memory involved, individual but also 'collective'), and (ultimately) spiritual. Here, the 'job well done' involves some careful shaping, clarifying the structure of each psalm, and also the extent to which they are separate and individual or part of a group (so that, for example, Wolsey's 42nd, *Like as the hart*, leads straight into the 43rd, *Give sentence with me, O God*, its continuity emphasized by use of the same chant, with the descanted refrain, "O put thy trust in God", carried over from one to the other).

In both discs the choir are on excellent form and well recorded. Andrew Lucas plays with his customary skills of technique and imagination. Among the soloists the treble Connor Burrowes deserves special mention. John Scott, being only the choirmaster and conductor, must be used by now to going unmentioned but can take it as a compliment, for if things did not go right he would be mentioned surely enough!

Requiem of Reconciliation Tobias Janzik (treb); Donna Brown, Julie Moffat (sops); Ingeborg Danz (mez); Thomas Randle (ten); Andreas Schmidt (bar); **Stuttgart Gächinger Kantorei; Cracow Chamber Choir; Israel Philharmonic Orchestra / Helmuth Rilling.** Hänssler Classic Ⓕ 98 931 (two discs: 107 minutes: DDD: 11/95). Notes, text and translations included. Recorded live in 1995.
     Berio Prolog. **Cerha** Introitus and Kyrie. **Dittrich** Dies irae. **Kopelent** Judex ergo.
     Harbison Juste judex. **Nordheim** Confutatis. **Rands** Interludium. **Dalbavie** Domine Jesu
     Christe, Rex Gloriae. **Weir** Sanctus. **Penderecki** Agnus Dei. **Rihm** Communio I.
     Schnittke/ Rozhdestvensky Communio II. **Yuasa** Responsorium. **Kurtág** Epilog.

It was a great event in Stuttgart on August 16th, 1995 when 14 very different composers each contributed a section to a setting of the Requiem liturgy. It was the idea of Helmuth Rilling to celebrate the fiftieth anniversary of the end of the Second World War. The wonder is that the results are so consistent, the reflection – so the composers themselves felt – of concentrating on the theme of suffering, as well, of course, as Rilling's shrewd choice of contributors. Reflecting the text, the first half – up to Arne Nordheim's *Confutatis* – is the darker and more taxing. Only towards the end of that sequence does John Harbison's fine setting of *Juste judex* lighten the mood and textures, with Nordheim then the first identifiably to use the secondary idea presented to the composers of linking the Requiem with Gregorian chant. Nordheim uses the notes of the chant vertically as well as horizontally, while in the second half the Frenchman, Marc-André Dalbavie, in his *Domine Jesu Christe* goes much further in direct Gregorian echoes. Bernard Rands's thoughtful introduction to the second half gives just one word to the chorus, "Deus!". Then, after the Dalbavie, comes the most incandescent of the pieces, Judith Weir's brilliant setting of the *Sanctus* with its brass commentaries. The Japanese, Joji Yuasa, as a Buddhist was initially doubtful about taking part, but in the event his atmospheric, finely terraced setting of the *Responsorium* and *Libera me* makes a fine culmination before the rather perfunctory, if striking, *Epilog* of György Kurtág. Only one of the 14 contributions is a disappointment, but that is a serious one, the *Dies irae* of the German composer, Paul-Heinz Dittrich. As to the singing generally, the soloists make an outstanding team, with the Canadian soprano, Donna Brown, particularly impressive, while choruses and orchestra consistently respond to Rilling's direction with thrilling attack. With the vast forces superbly balanced, there is a bite and immediacy which allows one to appreciate every detail.

Sermons and Devotions The King's Singers (David Hurley, Nigel Short, altos; Robert Chilcott, ten; Bruce Russell, Philip Lawson, bars; Stephen Connolly, bass). RCA Victor Red Seal Ⓔ 09026 68255-2 (69 minutes: DDD: 8/96). Texts and translations included. **Górecki** Totus tuus, Op. 60. **Tormis** The Bishop and the Pagan. **Stravinsky** Pater noster. Ave Maria. **Poole** Wymondham Chants. **Tavener** Funeral Ikos. The Lamb. **Bennett** Sermons and Devotions.

Richard Rodney Bennett is probably better acquainted with The King's Singers' sound than anyone else. It's telling, then, that of the three works on this disc written specially for them, Bennett's is the only one which relies solely on their conventional singing ability. *Sermons and Devotions* uses an austere, unequivocally modern idiom, yet sung with such consummate artistry and pure vocal skills as it is here it all becomes remarkably accessible. Veljo Tormis's contribution to their repertoire sets pagan fifths and peasantish gruntings against quasi-medieval chants – all rather blatant and unsubtle but utterly captivating none the less – while Geoffrey Poole's *Wymondham Chants* employs yet more pseudo-medieval music, with high-pitched chattering vocalizations in the kind of aural spectacular which The King's Singers have made their own. *Totus tuus* has, over the decade of its existence, become something of a choral classic. Its rich, eight-part harmonies have a singularly warming effect. So it comes as something of a surprise to hear it not only reduced to six parts with a single male voice on each but sung by a group who are more usually associated with light-hearted, humorous music. Yet after the initial shock, the singers' sublime musicianship wins the day and in the end Górecki's masterpiece loses none of its intensity and maybe has even gained an extra dimension. As, indeed, is the case of equally outstanding and emotionally charged accounts of music by Stravinsky and Tavener. It all serves to remind us that The King's Singers, shorn of their usual vocal acrobatics, are still a musical group of the very highest order.

Spanish Baroque, Volume 1. Al Ayre Español / Eduardo López Banzo. Deutsche Harmonia Mundi Ⓟ 05472 77325-2 (70 minutes: DDD: 8/95). 🏷 Texts and translations included. Recorded 1994. Ⓖ
Anonymous Canción a dos tiples. Two Pasacalles. **Literes** Ah del rustico pastor.
C. Galán Al espejo que retrata. Humano ardor. **J. de Torres** Más no puedo ser. Al clamor.
F. Valls En un noble, sagrado firmamento. **F. de Iribarren** Quién nos dira de una flor.
Viendo que Jil, hizo raya.

López Banzo could well be set to achieve for the Spanish baroque what William Christie and Les Arts Florissants have done for French music of the seventeenth and eighteenth centuries. There are many parallels between English and Spanish musical cultures in the baroque: French and Italian stylistic and structural elements are incorporated into a musical language that is nevertheless as clearly Spanish as the Purcell idiom is English. The melodiousness characteristic of the Spanish repertory and its distinctive rhythmic patterns are immediately apparent. The *villancicos* and *cantadas* by Torres, Literes, Iribarren and Valls are all sectional works that alternate recitative and arias in the manner of the Italian cantata, but they also introduce minuets, elegant slow movements, lively refrains and even Spanish dances of popular origin such as the *jácara*. Indeed, the disc ends with one of those characteristically foot-tapping pieces (performed in cathedrals and chapels on such joyous feasts as Christmas) by Iribarren who was chapelmaster at Malaga Cathedral. The performances are very fine. The instrumentalists seem to be completely at home with the style and point up the idiomatic syncopations with just the right degree of emphasis. Under the secure direction of López Banzo, they generally serve the music extremely well. The singers are Spanish which is probably essential, at least at this stage in our knowledge of the repertory. They, too, are consistently excellent. The soprano Marta Almajano's voice is agile and well focused with a hint of that dark, enriching quality – like velvet-clad steel – that seems to characterize the Spanish voice (think of Victoria de los Angeles or even Plácido Domingo). She is, as the music demands, expressive or virtuoso, lyrical or brilliant, and in everything she has a superb sense of line.

Steal Away Spirituals and Gospel Songs. [a]**Ruby Philogene** (sop); [b]**London Adventist Chorale /** Ken Burton ([c]pf); [d]**Julius Drake** (pf). EMI Debut Ⓑ CDZ5 69707-2 (54 minutes: DDD: 9/97). Recorded 1996.
Traditional Oh, what a beautiful city (arr. Boatner)[ad]. Sometimes I feel like a motherless chile[ad]. Nobody knows de trouble I've seen[ad]. Couldn't hear nobody pray[abd]. Steal away to Jesus[abd]. 'Tis me, O Lord[ad]. De Gospel train[ad]. Ride on, King Jesus[ad] (all arr. Burleigh). Good News[bc]. Walk with me[bc]. By and by[ab]. Let my people go[ab] (all arr. Burton). True religion (arr. Simpson)[b]. I wanna be ready (arr. Miller)[ab]. Honor! Honor! (arr. Hall Johnson)[ab]. **W. James** Dark water[b]. **Dett** Listen to the lambs[b].

The members of the London Adventist Chorale are taken from Seventh Day Adventist churches around London. These are actual church choirs and they believe in what they are singing: this message really comes across. Ruby Philogene is a real discovery. She has exactly the right emotional quality to suit all the moods of these eloquent songs and dares to take *Nobody knows* and *Steal away* very slowly indeed. Sometimes she embellishes the line, always in style, and director Ken Burton brings the chorus unobtrusively into the refrains of *Steal away* with magical effect. Alongside the high-quality arrangements by Burleigh, Hall Johnson and Dett are Burton's own, showing that the

London Adventist Chorale is part of a continuing tradition in spirituals and gospel. The Ladies Quartet has some fine voices and, with Burton fulsome at the piano, a swinging sense of rhythm. Well recorded here, although the piano is sometimes favoured in balance, this is the ideal group for this repertoire.

Twentieth-Century Choral Music [a]Andrew Angus (bass); [b]John Keys (org); Vasari Singers / Jeremy Backhouse. EMI Eminence Ⓜ CD-EMX2251 (74 minutes: DDD: 8/96). Texts and translations included. Recorded 1995.
Pärt Summa. The Beatitudes[b]. Seven Magnificat Antiphons. **Tavener** The Lamb. Funeral Ikos. A Hymn to the Mother of God. Hymn for the Dormition of the Mother of God. Magnificat and Nunc dimittis. **Ridout** Litany[a]. **Górecki** Totus tuus, Op. 60.
It is not immediately obvious from listening to this disc where Pärt finishes and Tavener or Górecki takes over, so similar are their musical language and idiom. That is not to say that these works lack individuality or originality. Each in its own right is an expression of unarguably sincere emotion and immense musical beauty, and it is these two facets which are most immediately apparent from these lovingly nurtured performances. The sound is pure, the soprano line often floating ethereally above immaculately measured harmonies, Andrew Angus's delivery of the Priest's words in Alan Ridout's *Litany* achieving an ideal mix of dispassionate intoning and operatic fervour, and the overall choral tone so perfectly blended and exquisitely balanced that it quite takes the breath away. The Vasari Singers bring something distinctive to the programme, and certainly no lover of these composers' music should be without their hypnotic performance of Pärt's *Beatitudes* with its continual alternation of two unrelated chords and ending with a shattering organ postlude – marvellously played by John Keys.

Opera and song recitals

Marta Almajano Las mujeres y cuerdas. [a]Marta Almajano (sop); José Miguel Moreno (gtr). Glossa Ⓕ GCD920202 (68 minutes: DDD: 2/96). Texts and translations included. Recorded 1994-95.
Soler Canzonettas – La semplice; La volubile; La costanza; La mercede[a]. **Carulli** Andante affetuoso, Op. 320. **Giuliani** Ariette, Op. 95 – Quando sarà quel di; Le dimore amore non ama; Ad altro laccio[a]. Cavatine, Op. 39 – Confuso, smarrito[a]. Amor, perché m'accendi[a]. Di tanti palpiti, Op. 79[a]. Andantino sostenuto, Op. 71 No. 3. **Sor** Studies, Op. 31 – Mouvement de prière religieuse. Ariettas – Povero cor t'inganni; Lagrime; Io mentitor!; Perduta l'anima[a]. Nel cor più non mi sento[a]. Seguidillas – Muchacha, y los vergüenza; Si dices que mis ojos; Los canonigos, madre; Las mujeres y cuerdas; Mis descuidados ojos[a]. **Mertz** Bardenklänge, Op. 13 – Lied ohne Worte.
The album title is that of the final song, Sor's *Las mujeres y cuerdas*, with its caveat that both women and strings need 'tuning' – but carefully. The cover is adorned with Madrazo's painting (1853) of the Countess of Vilches (seated in the luxurious surroundings appropriate to her rank), whose demeanour suggests that she may be dreaming of romantic love, or perhaps listening to musical expressions of it. The gentle guitar was at that time popular as an accompanying instrument in the home or salon, incapable of supporting anything vulgar or excessive; the publishing of guitar-accompanied songs was a flourishing trade. The song by Martin y Soler, a composer of *opera buffa*, was published with the option of guitar or keyboard; all the others were composed or arranged by guitarists. Giuliani, the darling of the Viennese salons, exercised his (Italian) gift of melody in responding generously to the market, whilst Sor worked as a singing teacher during his sojourn in London, from which time the songs in this recording (and many others) date. These graceful and sometimes coquettish songs of the joys, frustrations and pains of love are punctuated by suitably day-dreaming guitar solos. Marta Almajano sings them beguilingly though not without sacrificing consonants to beauty of tone, but the texts are printed in the substantial booklet, as are a number of charming reproductions of paintings. Moreno's contribution is excellent in all respects. This well-recorded and lavishly produced album should appeal to all who care to share the dreams of the Countess of Vilches, in whatever surroundings they may find themselves.

Elly Ameling The Early Recordings. Elly Ameling (sop); [a]Hans-Martin Linde (rec); [b]Hans Deinzer (cl); [c]Angelica May (vc); [d]Jörg Demus (pf); [e]Gustav Leonhardt (hpd); [f]Collegium Aureum / [g]Franzjosef Maier (vn), [h]Gerhard Schmidt-Gaden, [i]Rudolf Pohl.
Deutsche Harmonia Mundi Ⓕ 74321 26617-2 (four discs: 239 minutes: ADD: 12/95). Texts and translations included. Recorded 1964-68.
Bach Anna Magdalena Notenbuch – Bist du bei mir[e]. Cantata No. 82, Ich habe genug[e] – Ich habe genug!; Schlummert ein (from BASF BAC3054, 8/74). Cantata No. 202, Weichet nur, betrübte Schatten[fg]. Cantata No. 209, Non sa che sia dolore[fg]. Cantata No. 211, Schweigt stille,

plaudert nicht (Coffee Cantata) – Nun folge; Heute noch[fg]. Cantata No. 212, Mer hahn en neue
Oberkeet (Peasant Cantata) – Im Ernst ein Wort!; Kleinzschocher müsse[fg] (BASF BAC3052/3,
7/74). **C.P.E. Bach** Magnificat in D minor, H772 – Quia respexit[fh] (BASF BAS29368-9, 12/73).
Telemann Du aber Daniel, gehe hin – Mit sehnenden verlangen; Richt ihr müde Augen nieder[fi]
(1C 065 99751, 10/78). **Handel** Pensieri notturni di Filli, "Nel dolce dell'oblio", HWV134[af].
Ah, che troppo ineguali, HWV230[f] (BASF BAC3058/9, 1/75). **Brahms** Lieder, Op. 57 – No. 2,
Wenn du nur zuweilen lächelst; No. 3, Es träumte mir; No. 4, Ach, wende diesen Blick; No. 8,
Unbewegte laue Luft[d]. Deutsche Volkslieder, WoO33 – No. 12, Feinsliebchen, du sollst mir nicht
barfuss geh'n; No. 15, Schwesterlein, Schwesterlein; No. 33, Och Moder, ich well en Ding han!;
No. 41, Es steht ein' Lind'; No. 42, In stiller Nacht, zur ersten Wacht[d]. Lieder, Op. 107 – No. 3,
Das Mädchen spricht; No. 5, Mädchenlied[d]. Vergebliches Ständchen, Op. 84 No. 4[d]. Ständchen,
Op. 106 No. 1[d]. Am Sonntag Morgen, Op. 49 No. 1[d]. Trennung, Op. 97 No. 6[d]. Während des
Regens, Op. 58 No. 2[d]. O kühler Wald, Op. 72 No. 3[d]. Von ewiger Liebe, Op. 43 No. 1[d] (BASF
BAC3065, 1/75). **Schumann** Myrthen, Op. 25 – No. 1, Widmung; No. 3, Der Nussbaum; No. 7,
Die Lotosblume; No. 9, Lied der Suleika[d]. Lieder-Album für die Jugend, Op. 79 – No. 10, Das
Käuzlein; No. 12, Der Sandmann; No. 13, Marienwürmchen; No. 23, Er ist's; No. 26,
Schneeglöckchen[d] (1C 065 99631, 11/78). Jasminenstrauch, Op. 27 No. 4[d]. Die Blume der
Ergebung, Op. 83 No. 2[d]. Röselein, Op. 89 No. 6[d]. Lieder und Gesänge, Op. 77 – No. 2, Mein
Garten; No. 5, Aufträge[d]. Gedichte, Op. 90 – No. 2, Meine Rose; No. 4, Die Sennin.
Schmetterling, Op. 79 No. 2[d]. Gedichte, Op. 35 – No. 4, Erstes Grün; No. 5, Sehnsucht nach der
Waldgegend; No. 9, Frage[d]. Die letzten Blumen starben, Op. 104 No. 6[d]. Die Meerfee, Op. 125
No. 1[d]. Waldesgespräch, Op. 39 No. 3[d]. Loreley, Op. 53 No. 2[d]. Die Kartenlegerin, Op. 31 No. 2[d].
Sehnsucht, Op. 51 No. 1[d]. Mein schöner Stern!, Op. 101 No. 4[d] (1C 065 99631, 11/78).
Schubert Der Hirt auf dem Felsen, D965[bd]. Seligkeit, D433[d]. Gretchen am Spinnrade, D118[d].
Du liebst mich nicht, D756[d]. Heimliches Lieben, D922[d]. Im Frühling, D882[d]. Die Vögel, D691[d].
Der Jüngling an der Quelle, D300[d]. Der Musensohn, D764[d] (BASF SAC3088, 2/75).
If, for instance, you have had a little too much of voices under stress, whether in the quest for volume
to compete with orchestras and powerful colleagues or for expression in the emotional turmoils of big
operatic business, then here is the singer to bring calm and comfort. The young Elly Ameling had a
voice which was as clear as a bell, not a fleck of impurity in its consistency, not a scratch on the lovely
surface of a tone-quality which served the happy spirit of its owner to perfection. When the earliest
of these records was made, in 1964, she had been singing in public for some five or six years and was
already an artist of note, but the outstanding feature (along with an admirable technique and
scrupulous musicianship) is the freshness. She sings with a straightforward delight in the music of the
masters, seemingly content to impose upon it nothing of herself save the beauty of her voice and the
devotion of her study. For the most part, her repertoire is ideally chosen. Only one of the songs,
Brahms's *Von ewiger Liebe*, exceeds her vocal means, wanting greater resources of power and a more
opulent body of tone to match the grand swell of the melody and the generous amplitude of the
accompaniment. Her ability at that time as an expressive singer is more severely tested, and one
reflects that in later years she would discover more, both in the music and in her own inner store of
emotion and understanding. *Gretchen am Spinnrade* is an obvious example. These are still exceptions,
however. Mostly the songs are of happiness, youth and spring, with only the occasional
overshadowing, as in the wistful mood of Brahms's *Es träumte mir* or the middle section of Schubert's
Der Hirt auf dem Felsen. In the booklet which comes with the boxed set (which needs careful
handling or it will fall apart), Ameling recalls the Deutsche Harmonia Mundi sessions at Schloss
Fugger in Kircheim unter Teck. "I was only 31," she says, "still wet behind the ears." She
acknowledges the helpfulness of her producer, and of Jörg Demus. The performances certainly
convey the feeling of a sympathetic collaboration, the playing being often of exquisite quality, with a
refreshing tendency to bring out the Schubertian side of Brahms. Unfortunately, the acoustics of the
castle were less amenable, and some of the sessions (Schubert and Schumann particularly) catch far
too much echo. This is so with some of the orchestrally accompanied pieces as well, such as the
otherwise captivating aria by Telemann. Still, the collection stands as a fine tribute to a greatly loved
singer. Her art was to develop, so that the recordings here might be considered as the equivalent of an
author's juvenilia. But we all know how unexpectedly moving that can be.

The Art of Arleen Auger Arleen Auger (sop); [a]members of the **Saint Paul Chamber Orchestra**
and the **Minnesota Orchestra / Joel Revzen** ([bc]pf). Koch International Classics Ⓟ 37248-2
(55 minutes: DDD: 4/94). Texts and translations included. Recorded 1986-91.
Larsen Six Sonnets from the Portuguese[a]. **Purcell** (ed. Britten) If music be the food of love,
Z379 No. 3. The Libertine – Nymphs and shepherds[b]. Pausanias – Sweeter than roses.
Schumann Myrthen, Op. 25 – No. 1, Widmung; No. 3, Der Nussbaum; No. 11, Lied der Braut
I; No. 12, Lied der Braut II. Romanzen und Balladen, Op. 64 – No. 1, Die Soldatenbraut.
Mozart Das Veilchen, K476. Dans un bois solitaire, K308/K295*b*. Das Lied der Trennung,
K519. Als Luise die Briefe, K520[c]. Abendempfindung, K523.
Here is a record to cherish, and with it, of course, a memory. The late Arleen Auger was loved for her
voice, her art and herself. All items here are taken from live performances, and the recorded balance
favours the accompaniment, but a great and very special beauty remains. Libby Larsen's settings of
six of Elizabeth Barrett-Browning's sonnets were written for the singer, and they suit her to perfection.

The idiom is lyrical, the writing for voice full of understanding about what should and should not be asked of a singer. Auger sings unerringly, with great beauty of tone and feeling for words. This, the Purcell songs, and the Mozart (Schumann on the whole suits her less well) are a lovely memorial: the fine legato (in Mozart), the even runs (in Purcell) and the gentle beauty of tone throughout. At the end of the programme comes Mozart's *Abendempfindung* with its quiet presentiment of death and its modest wish for remembrance, a wish that this record aptly helps to fulfil.

Janet Baker Song Recital. **Dame Janet Baker** (mez); **Gerald Moore** (pf). EMI Ⓜ CDM5 65009-2 (75 minutes: ADD: 11/94). Items marked ᵃ from HMV ASD2590 (9/70), ᵇASD2431 (1/69), ᶜHMV HQS1091 (7/67). Recorded 1967-69.
Fauréᵃ Automne, Op. 18 No. 3. Prison, Op. 83 No. 1. Soir, Op. 83 No. 2. Fleur jetée, Op. 39 No. 2. En sourdine, Op. 58 No. 2. Notre amour, Op. 23 No. 2. Mai, Op. 1 No. 2, La chanson du pêcheur, Op. 4 No. 1. Clair de lune, Op. 46 No. 2. **Schubert**ᵇ Am Grabe Anselmos, D504. Abendstern, D806. Die Vögel, D691. Die Götter Griechenlands, D677. Gondelfahrer, D808. Auflösung, D807. **R. Strauss**ᵇ Morgen, Op. 27 No. 4. Befreit, Op. 39 No. 4. Stanford**ᶜ La Belle Dame sans merci. **Parry**ᶜ Proud Maisie. O mistres mine. **Busch**ᶜ Rest. **Warlock**ᶜ Pretty ringtime. **Vaughan Williams**ᶜ Linden Lea. **Gurney**ᶜ: The fields are full. **Britten**ᶜ Corpus Christi carol. **Ireland**ᶜ The Salley Gardens. **Quilter**ᶜ Love's philosophy, Op. 3 No. 1.
This CD is a timely reminder, a generous one too, of Baker in her prime. At the peak of her career at the end of the 1960s, the tone is at its most beautiful, the singing as secure as it is intelligent. One realizes anew that here is one of the great singers of the century and one comfortable in so many idioms. It may be that some native singers of Fauré and Schubert capture the soul of these songs more unerringly, but few actually sing them so glowingly, so intensely. The typical Schubertian sadness brings out the very best in her. Nobody has sung *Am Grabe Anselmos* with so much sincere and deep feeling, nor have the lamenting echoes of *Die Götter Griechenlands* ever sounded more haunting. Technically the performances are also without fault. In her own language, Dame Janet is at home in every sense. The gems here are the Stanford ballad, the tensions of the tale sustained throughout by both artists, the tender sorrow of Britten's *Corpus Christi*, the fervent outpouring of Quilter's *Love's philosophy*. Everywhere Moore is at one with his partner, always supportive, perceptive, with that soft and inimitable touch of his. The recordings, for their dates, are exemplary in balance and presence.

Olaf Bär Lieder by German Opera Composers. **Olaf Bär** (bar); **Helmut Deutsch** (pf). EMI Ⓔ CDC5 55393-2 (67 minutes: DDD: 1/96). Texts and translations included. Recorded 1994.
Kreutzer Frühlingsglaube. Die Post. Die Kapelle, Op. 64 No. 1. Nachtreise. Entschluss, Op. 64 No. 2. Nähe des Geliebten. **Nicolai** Scarco d'affanni. Herbstlied, Op. 37. Il mistero, Op. 24 No. 2. **Goetz** Lieder, Op. 12 – No. 1, Geheimnis; No. 2, Schliesse mir die Augen beide; No. 3, Wandervöglein. Lieder, Op. 19 – No. 1, Ein Frühlingstraum; No. 2, Der Frühling kommt!; No. 3, Wandrers Nachtlied, "Der du von dem Himmel bist". **Humperdinck** Romanze. Blauveilchen. Entsagung. Oft sinn ich hin und wieder. Das Lied von Glück. Sonntagsruhe. **Marschner** Rheinromanzen, Op. 128 – No. 1, Die sieben Freier. Gesänge und Balladen, Op. 160 – No. 1, Der König von Thule; No. 2, Die Rache. Das Flämmchen auf der Heide, Op. 80 No. 12. Die Monduhr, Op. 102 No. 2. Das Lied von alten König, Op. 82 No. 2. Der betrogene Teufel, Op. 87 No. 1.
For all but the most knowledgeable in Lieder this will be a real and fascinating voyage of discovery. Each of the composers represented is known, if at all, by one or two operas, but all wrote liberally as song composers. Kreutzer's setting of *Die Post*, written before Schubert's, is worthy to stand beside it. *Die Kapelle* is even better, a funeral piece in the minor of much more than passing interest in its acute setting of an Uhland text, changes of key worthy of Schubert and intense repeats of the single word "Hirtenknabe". The three songs by Nicolai are pleasing but slight. Goetz, who died all too young, was admired by Brahms and one can hear why in the very Brahmsian *Schliesse mir die Augen beide*, a setting of an admirable poem by Ludwig Sturm. Goethe's other Lieder here are not so remarkable. Humperdinck also proves something of a disappointment except in the Wagnerian *Sonntagsruhe*. The remainder do not evince sufficiently individual personality. Marschner is quite another matter. Each song here is at least to be spoken of in the same breath as those by his contemporary, Loewe, whom he much resembles in style. *Die sieben Freier* is another of those Lorelei-inspired poems so beloved of the German romantics. This one deserves to stand alongside the best. Even better is the Gothic horror of both *Die Rache*, with its ostinato imitation of hoofbeats, and *Die Monduhr*, imbued throughout with a constantly varied motif in thirds. Perhaps these pieces aren't so unexpected from the composer of *Der Vampyr*. *Der betrogene Teufel* is a nice essay in the ribald, which is delivered by Bär in an appropriately biting timbre. But then throughout he is back on his most convincing form, relishing every word and note and singing with restored freedom. Deutsch, who also contributes the bookletnotes, proves a worthy partner. The recording is forward and well balanced.

Cecilia Bartoli Arie Antiche. **Cecilia Bartoli** (mez); **György Fischer** (pf). Decca Ⓔ 436 267-2DH (66 minutes: DDD: 12/92). Texts and translations included. Recorded 1990-91.
A. Scarlatti Già il sole dal Gange. Son tutta duolo. Se Florindo è fedele. O cessate di piagarmi. Spesso vibra per suo gioco. **Giordani** Caro mio ben. **Lotti** Pur dicesti, o bocca bella. **Cesti** Intorno all'idol mio. **Paisiello** Nel cor più non mi sento. Il mio ben quando

verrà. Chi vuol la zingarella. **Anonymous** O leggiadri occhi belli. **Marcello** Quella fiamma che m'accende. **Caldara** Selve amiche. Sebben, crudele. **Caccini** Tu ch'hai le penne, amore. Amarilli. **Parisotti** Se tu m'ami. **Cavalli** Delizie contente. **Vivaldi** Sposa son disprezzata. **Carissimi** Vittoria, vittoria!

With Scarlatti and Vivaldi among the composers, these *arie antiche* are not necessarily very old. Italian singers have long been accustomed to lumping together all songs earlier than Mozart (or perhaps Haydn) under this heading, piously including them at the start of a recital so as to establish a classical tone and give them time to try out their voices before entering on the more strenuous and popular part of their programme. Bartoli here devotes a whole disc to them, as things delightful in themselves, varied in mood and style, and calling in turn on almost all the essential arts of a good singer. No one can come away with a feeling of having been short-changed at the end of this. Her voice is ideal, both silken and chaste, finely controlled, cleanly produced. With a simple, direct song such as the famous *Caro mio ben* she will never fuss or show off; with Vivaldi's *Sposa son disprezzata* she exploits the most deliciously languishing tone and sometimes one more frankly passionate and 'operatic'. Most of the items are gems, and to all of them György Fischer brings the touch of the expert jeweller, knowing exactly how best to set off the beauties of voice and melody.

Cecilia Bartoli Chant d'amour. **Cecilia Bartoli** (mez); **Myung-Whun Chung** (pf).
Decca Ⓕ 452 667-2DH (68 minutes: DDD: 12/96). Texts and translations included.
Recorded 1996. *Gramophone Editor's record of the month.*   ⓆⒼⓆ
Bizet Chant d'amour. Ouvre ton coeur. Adieux de l'hôtesse arabe. Tarantelle. La Coccinelle.
Delibes Les filles de Cadix. **Viardot-Garcia** Hai luli!. Les filles de Cadix.
Berlioz Tristia, Op. 18 – La mort d'Ophélie. Zaïde, Op. 19 No. 1. **Ravel** Chants populaires – Chanson française; Chanson espagnole; Chanson italienne; Chanson hébraïque. Vocalise en forme de Habanera. Deux mélodies hébraïques. Tripatos.

Cecilia Bartoli goes from strength to strength. Taking on the French repertory in this delightful disc, she also gives us some great rarities. The opening Bizet group includes two of his best-known songs, *Ouvre ton coeur* and *Adieux de l'hôtesse arabe*. In the first, one perhaps might ask for more of a smile in the voice. Predictably, in the pessimistic Hugo poem about the Arab girl bidding farewell to the handsome traveller, Bartoli relishes the muezzin-like vocalise on "Hélas, adieu, souviens-toi". This is one of the best performances of this mini-drama since Conchita Supervia's orchestral-accompanied version. In this, and the succeeding *Tarantelle*, "tra-la-la"s and froth, one is prompted to wonder if there will one day be a Bartoli *Carmen*. La Coccinelle ("The ladybird") is a little salon gem, with a fast waltz motif. Bartoli uses a croaky little voice to act out the Ladybird. This song alone is worth the price of the CD.

Delibes's *Les filles de Cadix*, all trills and sunshine, is contrasted with an equally demanding setting of the same poem by Pauline Viardot. *Hai luli!* with words by Xavier de Maistre is a sad second-cousin to the Willow Song from Rossini's *Otello*. Havanaise is a real curiosity: the first and last stanzas, sung in Spanish, frame a middle section in French which breaks into a Rossinian flight of coloratura before returning to the swaying movements of the dance. Evenings *chez* Viardot must have been enlivened considerably by such songs. The narration of Ophelia's death, words by Ernest Legouvé, vaguely based on Shakespeare, ends with a wordless melody which Bartoli sings in a hushed, beautiful tone. In *Zaïde* she plays the castanets with skill; if this song is less interesting than the evocations of Spain by Bizet, Delibes and Viardot, that's Berlioz's fault, not Bartoli's. In the concluding Ravel group, an interesting contrast can be made between Viardot's *Havanaise* of the 1840s and Ravel's *Habanera* of 1907. In the four popular songs, Bartoli is especially effective in the Hebrew number as well as the two other *Mélodies hébraïques*, "Kaddish" and "L'énigme éternelle". All these Ravel songs have often been recorded, so one cannot help wishing that Bartoli and Chung had stayed with the nineteenth-century French salon repertory to uncover more rarities. Still, this is one of the most satisfying recitals by one of the great singers of our time. First-rate recording and sensitive accompaniment throughout.

Cecilia Bartoli An Italian Songbook. **Cecilia Bartoli** (mez); **James Levine** (pf).
Decca Ⓕ 455 513-2DH (67 minutes: DDD: 11/97). Texts and translations included.
Recorded 1996. *Gramophone Editor's choice.*
Rossini Péchés de vieillesse: Book 3 – L'esule; Book 11 – A ma belle mère; Aragonese. La passeggiata. Mi lagnerò tacendo – Boléro. Soirées musicales – La danza. **Bellini** Vaga luna che inargenti. L'abbandono. Malinconia, ninfa gentile. Il fervido desiderio. Torna, vezzosa Fillide. Vanne, o rosa fortunata. Dolente imagine di figlia mia. La farfalletta. Per pietà, bell'idol mio. **Donizetti** Il barcaiolo. Ah, rammenta, o bella Irene. Amore e morte. La conocchia. Me voglio fa'na casa.

The transforming power of imagination is rarely shown so clearly. On record and in recital these songs and their like have so often appeared as tepid little exercises, cautious investigations of the voice, the acoustic, the audience. But now, behold, they burgeon. Life abundant lies within the vocal line, and even the silly old accompaniments sound well. Such is the effect of the Bartoli-Levine combination. From the very first bars it feels that something special among Bartoli's many fine recordings have come into being here with these two distinguished artists in association. These are thoughtful, passionate and colourful performances, which outshine all previous versions of the more familiar songs. Among the less familiar items, Bellini's *Torna, vezzosa Fillide* may come as the most engaging discovery. Rossini's miniature Requiem for his mother-in-law seems not to be a joke, whereas the *Aragonese* (a setting in the style of Aragon of *Mi lagnerò tacendo*) surely must be. There might have been something to say here and now about intrusive 'h's and that other intrusion, a breathy quality sometimes cultivated in the interests of expression or intimacy, but they are not gross or prohibitive features of the singing here, and the lovely voice and lively art make ample amends.

Cecilia Bartoli Italian Songs. **Cecilia Bartoli** (mez); **András Schiff** (pf). Decca Ⓕ 440 297-2DH (68 minutes: DDD: 11/93). Texts and translations included. Recorded 1992.
Gramophone Editor's choice.   Ⓖ
Beethoven La Partenza, WoO124. Four Ariettas, Op. 82. In questa tomba oscura, WoO133.
Mozart Ridente la calma, K152/K210a. **Schubert** Didone abbandonata, D510. Im Haine, D738. An die Leier, D737. La Pastorella al Prato, D528. Vier Canzonen, D688. Pensa, che questo istante, D76. Willkommen und Abschied, D767. **Haydn** Arianna a Naxos, HobXXVI*b*/2.
It is good to be reminded of these composers' responses to the Italian muse in this particularly well-cast recital. Central Europe, in the person of András Schiff, meets Italy, in Cecilia Bartoli, to delightful, often revelatory effect. The simple form and undemanding vocal line of Beethoven's little *La Partenza* makes for a truthfulness of expression which Bartoli's clear, light-filled enunciation recreates to the full. With her warm breath gently supporting the voice's lively, supple inflexion, she reveals Beethoven's own skill in word-setting both here and in two fascinatingly contrasted settings of "L'amante impaziente" in the *Ariettas*, Op. 82. Schubert's ten *Canzone* selected here show a wide range of treatment, from the compressed lyric drama of Dido's lament "Vedi quanto adoro", in which Bartoli's lives intensely from second to second, to the honeyed Goldoni *pastorella* and the thrumming, pulsating serenade of "Guarda, che bianca luna", D688 No. 2. A gently, fragrantly shaped Mozart *Ridente la calma*, and a Haydn *Arianna a Naxos* of movingly immediate and youthful response complete this unexpectedly and unusually satisfying recital.

Barbara Bonney American Songs. **Barbara Bonney** (sop); [a]**Sato Knudsen** (vc); **André Previn** (pf). Decca Ⓕ 455 511-2DH (76 minutes: DDD: 2/98). Texts included. Recorded 1996.
Selected by Soundings.   ⒼⒼ
Previn Sallie Chisum remembers Billy the Kid. Vocalise[a]. **Copland** 12 Poems of Emily Dickinson. **Argento** Six Elizabethan Songs. **Barber** Ten Hermit Songs, Op. 29.
Barbara Bonney is allegedly related to Billy the Kid. Allegedly. She herself is convinced, or rather was convinced, when she first saw the pictures. The resemblance to her own father was "terrifying": the big searching eyes, the ears that stick out – the look. And then an American friend in London gave her a copy of *The Collected Works of Billy the Kid*, and that's where André Previn came in. *Sallie Chisum remembers Billy the Kid* – the spur of this all-American programme – takes its cues from Wild West history – or is that mythology? Sallie Chisum was a prostitute who went to bed with both Billy and Pat Garrett, and her words are starry-eyed. Previn sets them as she will have remembered them, touches of sweet sentiment in the voice played off against the dusty and gritty realities of the keyboard. There's more than a hint of the bar-room piano in that. And then up soars the voice recalling the "flower in his lapel" and the fragrance of it lends a touch of naïvety. The Argento was a shrewd choice, not just on account of its rarity value (this is the world première recording), but because Bonney and Previn both have ties with England which adds something to our perception of the cycle's Anglo/American cross-breeding. Both are brilliantly articulate and quick of reflex, the mix of ancient and modern, the ornate and the reflective – indeed the somnambulant – is beautifully judged. The Copland and Barber sets are splendid, too. In Copland's Emily Dickinson, Bonney of course has the wholesome, homespun qualities – the pure and simple gifts – this music demands. We know how raptly she will sustain "Heart, we will forget him!", and she does. There is ecstasy and truth in this voice. But she can be feisty, too, deploying a determined and surprisingly resilient low register for "There came a wind like a bugle" and the awesome plunge to "East of eternity" in "Sleep is supposed to be". And where Dickinson is the playful child – as in "Why do they shut me out of Heaven?" and "Going to Heaven!" – there is a knowing coyness. In all this, Previn's contribution, his partnership, is invaluable. Listen to him sign off "Going to Heaven!" Not so much the exclamation mark, more the wink. And listen to him, too, lending weight and masculinity to the bolder illuminations of Barber's *Hermit Songs*. His resoluteness undoubtedly helps Bonney darken and intensify her response to these songs. "The Monk and his Cat" sounds all the more cosy and incongruous in consequence. We may have each other, it seems to say, but in the end we have only ourselves. To that end, the closing song – "The Desire for Hermitage" – is marvellous. A very real sense of isolation permeates the final stanza. Bonney and Previn may be two, but for the time being they are one.

Olga Borodina and Dmitri Hvorostovsky Opera Arias and Duets [a]**Olga Borodina** (mez); [b]**Dmitri Hvorostovsky** (bar); **English Chamber Orchestra / Patrick Summers**. Philips Ⓕ 454 439-2PH (66 minutes: DDD: 6/98). Texts and translations included. Recorded 1997.
Rossini Il barbiere di Siviglia – Largo al factotum[b]; Una voce poco fa ... Io son docile[a]; Dunque io son?. **Donizetti** La favorita – Ma de' malvagi invan ... Vien, Leonord, a' piedi tuoi ... De' nemici tuoi[b]; Ebben, così si narra! ... Quando le soglie paterne ... In questo suol a lusingar;

Fia dunque vero? ... O mio Fernando[a]. **Rimsky-Korsakov** The Tsar's Bride – Thoughts of the beautiful girl[b]; What do you want? ... It seems that you no longer love your Lyubasha; This is what life has come to[a]. **Saint-Saëns** Samson et Dalila – J'ai gravi la montagne ... La victoire facile.

Exciting as was the prospect of a joint-recital, it did raise the question of the programme: duets for mezzo and baritone do not swarm to mind, especially considering that the nationality of the two artists would suggest the inclusion of something Russian. In fact, *The Tsar's Bride* provides what is probably the most cherishable part of the programme. The three passages given here impress as the work of a composer writing in intensely characteristic vein, and the solos find both singers at their best. In hers, Borodina shows just the imaginative sensitivity that seemed lacking in the duet, where Lyubasha's pleading so cries out for the caress of portamento and other enticements that were once familiar enough to singers of the Russian school. Still, these two are fine and often thrilling representatives of the modern generation. In the *Barbiere* group, Hvorostovsky brings many an original touch, as well as magnificence of voice and vitality to the "Largo al factotum", and in the duet responds to Rosina's wiles with lively appreciation. Borodina's "Una voce poco fa" is another brilliant piece of work, marred only by the jerky novelty of her "Io sono docile" which is the kind of thing that should be tried out at rehearsal and benignly dismissed. Special moments in the *Favorita* solos include the quiet beginnings of both arias, Borodina's launching of her cabaletta and Hvorostovsky's modulation of tone from the severity of the recitative to the plaintive "Vien, Leonora". The duet carries dramatic conviction and is graced by a sometimes flawless legato. Fine operatic grandeur is also achieved in the scene between Dalilah and the High Priest, Hvorostovsky singing the bass-baritone part with good dark colouring and fine resonance. The ECO play well and the voices are finely caught and balanced in the recording. The booklet must have been designed for some purpose other than reading: its small white print against an orange background will deter all but the most resolute seeker after knowledge.

Maria Callas Rarities. Maria Callas (sop); [a]Paris Conservatoire Orchestra / Nicola Rescigno; [b]Maggio Musicale Fiorentino Orchestra / Tullio Serafin; [c]Rome RAI Orchestra / Alfredo Simonetto; [d]Philharmonia Orchestra / Antonio Tonini; [e]Paris Opera Orchestra / Georges Prêtre. EMI Ⓔ CDC7 54437-2* (78 minutes: ADD: 2/93). Texts and translations included. Items marked [c] recorded live in 1954.
Beethoven Ah! perfido, Op. 65[a] (from Columbia SAX2540, 8/64). **Mozart** Don Giovanni – Non mi dir[b] (CMS7 63570-2, 11/91. Recorded in 1953). Die Entführung aus dem Serail – Martern aller Arten[c] (sung in Italian. New to UK). **Weber** Oberon – Ozean du Ungeheuer![d] (English. Previously unpublished. 1962). **Rossini** Armida – D'amore al dolce impero[c] (EX769741-1, 4/89). **Donizetti** Lucrezia Borgia – Tranquillo ei posa ... Com'è bello![d] (1961). **Verdi** Don Carlos – O don fatale[d] (1961). I vespri siciliani – Arrigo! ah, parli[d] (1960). Il trovatore – Vanne ... lasciami ... D'amor sull'ali rosee[a]. I lombardi – Te, Vergin santa[a] (all previously unpublished. Both recorded in 1964/5). Aida – Pur' ti riveggo ... Fuggiam gli ardor[e] (with Franco Corelli, ten. New to UK. 1964).

'Rarity' is one of those tricky words which, being really only quantitative, seems to imply something about quality as well. So the reader may well look doubtfully at the title: the "Callas Rarities" may indeed be rarities for the best of reasons, that of inferiority to versions and recordings that are less rare. In this instance, though, they are genuinely well worth having. For example, here is the Nile Duet from *Aida* with Franco Corelli, sole survivor of a projected album of duets to be recorded in 1964. Corelli provides the vocal thrills, sometimes even responding in kind to the dramatic intensity which characterizes Callas's performance from the start. Her voice is sometimes raw, and the soft B flat on "fuggiam" only just arrives and stays put. But always there is something distinctive: here it is the nostalgia, "Là tra foreste" being sung as a wistful, private vision of the homeland. Then there are the two incredibly brilliant solos from a concert at San Remo in 1954 ("Martern aller Arten" and "D'amore al dolce impero"); also previously unpublished versions, not alternative 'takes' but different performances, products of a different session. Usually one can see why they were not issued at the time, but here it is easier to see why they deserve to see the light of this later day.

Lisa della Casa at the Salzburg Festival, 1957 Lisa della Casa (sop); Arpad Sándor (pf). EMI Salzburg Festival Edition mono Ⓜ CDH5 66571-2* (64 minutes: ADD: 2/98). Recorded live in 1957.
Brahms Wie Melodien zieht es mir, Op. 105 No. 1. Feldeinsamkeit, Op. 86 No. 2. Von ewiger Liebe, Op. 43 No. 1. Meine Liebe ist grün, Op. 63. **Ravel** Chants populaires – Chanson espagnole; Chanson française; Chanson italienne. **Schoeck** Sieh' mich, Heil'ger, wie ich bin. Mit einem gemalten Bande. **Schubert** Lachen und Weinen, D777. Im Frühling, D882. Du bist die Ruh, D776. Gretchen am Spinnrade, D118. **R. Strauss** Fünf kleine Lieder, Op. 69 – No. 1, Der Stern; No. 3, Einerlei; No. 5, Schlechtes Wetter. Waldseligkeit, Op. 49 No. 1. Befreit, Op. 39 No. 4. Hat gesagt – bleibt's nicht dabei, Op. 36 No. 3. **Wolf** Mörike Lieder – Er ist's; Der Gärtner.

Probably because Schwarzkopf and Seefried were always in attendance at Salzburg, della Casa made only a sole appearance in Lieder; this is here rescued from oblivion through the efforts of Gottfried Kraus. Apparently someone at Austrian Radio with a mania for tidiness had cut up the tapes into their individual items and filed them as such. They have now been scrupulously reassembled in the original order. The work has been more than worthwhile. Della Casa sings with all the keen, pure tone and unaffected style for which she is famed. The sheer beauty of her singing is immediately apparent in her Schubert group, and in the final song, *Gretchen am Spinnrade*, she begins to evince a deep understanding of the importance of textual emphasis – as at "vergehen sollt" – in achieving creative tension: this is as desperate a portrayal of Marguerite's longing as one is likely to encounter. In Brahms's serene *Feldeinsamkeit* the underlining of the third syllable of "Himmelsblaue" and the hushed treatment of "Mir ist, als ob ich längst gestorben bin" (one of the most heartstopping moments in all his Lieder) shows an ideal understanding of interpretation. She changed course altogether for three of Ravel's *Chants populaires*, accenting her French idiomatically and with subtle meaning, especially in the sorrowful "Chanson italienne", where the last "mon amour" is searing. Her Strauss readings are of course famous and she recorded the songs given here elsewhere, but on a live occasion there's that extra *frisson* of feeling, most notably in *Befreit*, a song she made very much her own. *Hat gesagt* and *Schlechtes Wetter* are superior to Schwarzkopf's recordings simply because della Casa is just as amusing without resort to arch tones. The two Wolf encores are a delight. Sándor is a most sympathetic partner, though too backwardly placed. Although the recording of the voice is close, leading to a few moments of discomfort on loud notes, this is a recital not to be missed.

Tracey Chadwell's Song Book Tracey Chadwell (sop); [a]Pamela Lidiard (pf); [b]John Turner (recs). British Music Society Ⓕ BMS420/1CD (two discs: 141 minutes: ADD: 3/98). Texts included. Recorded 1988-94.
    Maconchy Sun, Moon and Stars[a]. Three Songs[a]. **Lefanu** I am Bread[a]. A Penny for a Song[a]. **Whitehead** Awa Herea[a]. **Cresswell** Words for Music[a]. **Lumsdaine** A Norfolk Songbook[b]. **Lilburn** Three Songs[a]. **Farquhar** Six Songs of Women[a]. **Joubert** The Turning Wheel, Op. 95[a]. **R. R. Bennett** A Garland for Marjory Fleming[a].
Tracey Chadwell, a soprano of exceptional gifts and intelligence, died in her mid-thirties early in 1996 after a long and courageous battle with leukaemia. Nicola Lefanu, who contributes an affectionate note to this anthology of recordings from the BBC archives, was at her last concert, three weeks before her death, and says that "she looked and sounded ravishing". She always did, and apart from its value as a memorial to a much loved and deeply missed artist and as a collection of fine songs (many of them written for her), this pair of discs could stand as a model to other singers in the expert management of a voice, in fearless vocal resource and joyful adventurousness in choice of repertory.

    She had admirable taste: there is no music here that needs special pleading, and her advocacy of all of it is compelling. Most of it is unfamiliar, much of it not recorded before, so it is probably helpful to single out a few particular pleasures that you might care to sample: Lefanu's haunting, intimate and subtle *I am Bread* easily sustaining its seven-minute duration, not least because of Chadwell's care over line and florid detail; the elegant talent of David Farquhar, making a simple but memorable thing of Sir Philip Sidney's "My true love hath my heart and I have his"; the strong drama and toughly strong melody of Gillian Whitehead's *Awe Herea*, using texts in Maori and English, and making huge demands of the singer's technique as well as her imagination; Richard Rodney Bennett's beautiful settings of the poems of a child who died at eight years old (Chadwell's tender line in "Sweet Isabell" is deeply moving here); the big, striking gestures of John Joubert's fine short cycle. She brings a wonderfully pure tone and limpid line to Elizabeth Maconchy's Thomas Traherne settings. She was an adorable singer, and these records should be widely heard. Pamela Lidiard, her regular accompanist, is an ideally sensitive partner and the recordings are excellent.

Régine Crespin Vocal Recital. Régine Crespin (sop); [b]John Wustman (pf); [a]Suisse Romande Orchestra / Ernest Ansermet. Decca Ⓕ 417 813-2DH (68 minutes: ADD: 11/88). Texts and translations included. Items marked [a] from SXL6081 (3/64), [b]SXL6333 (6/68). Recorded 1963-67.
    Berlioz Les nuits d'été. **Ravel** Shéhérazade[a]. **Debussy** Trois chansons de Bilitis[b]. **Poulenc** Banalités[b] – Chansons d'Orkenise; Hôtel. La courte paille[b] – Le carafon; La reine de coeur. Chansons villageoises[b] – Les gars qui vont à la fête. Deux poèmes de Louis Aragon[b].
Some recordings withstand the test of time and become acknowledged classics. This is one of them. Régine Crespin's voluptuous tone, her naturally accented French and her feeling for the inner meaning of the songs in the Berlioz and Ravel cycles are everywhere evident. Better than most single interpreters of the Berlioz, she manages to fulfil the demands of the very different songs, always alive to verbal nuances. In the Ravel, she is gorgeously sensuous, not to say sensual, with the right timbre for Ravel's enigmatic writing. The Debussy and Poulenc songs on this disc enhance its worth. Crespin offers an extremely evocative, perfumed account of the Debussy pieces and is ideally suited to her choice of Poulenc, of which her interpretation of "Hôtel" is a classic. Ansermet and his orchestra, though not quite note perfect, are – like the singer – right in timbre and colour for both these rewarding cycles. The sound is reasonable given the age of the recording. This is a most desirable acquisition.

Renée Fleming The Beautiful Voice. Renée Fleming (sop); English Chamber Orchestra / Jeffrey Tate. Decca Ⓕ 458 858-2DH (70 minutes: DDD: 3/98). Texts and translations included. Recorded 1997.
    Charpentier Louise – Depuis le jour. **Gounod** Faust – O Dieu! que de bijoux! ... Ah! je ris. **Massenet** Manon – Obéissons quand leur voix appelle. **Dvořák** Songs my mother taught me,

B104 No. 4. **Flotow** Martha – 'Tis the last rose of summer. **Puccini** La rondine – Chi il bel sogno di Doretta. **Korngold** Die tote Stadt – Glück, das mir verblieb. **Orff** Carmina Burana – In trutina. **R. Strauss** Morgen, Op. 27 No. 4. **Rachmaninov** (arr. Braden) Vocalise, Op. 34 No. 14. **J. Strauss II** Die Fledermaus – Klänge der Heimat. **Lehár** Die lustige Witwe – Es lebt eine Vilja. **Cano** Luna – Epilogo. **Canteloube** Chants d'Auvergne – Baïlèro.

Sweet tooth, prepare for action. What does Lamb say in his *Chapter on Ears*? Something about piling honey upon sugar and sugar upon honey. The programme capitulates in stages. It begins well, sharpening the palate with Marguerite's Jewel Song after Louise's erotic musings. Soon we are swaying dreamily with the "Viljalied" and then reclining in the drowsy sunshine and languid trickle of Canteloube's "Baïlèro". Louise, in this performance, cares for words and feelings as well as tone, Marguerite relishes her new role of 'coquette', and Manon plays lovingly with the consciousness of her own beauty. Throughout, the singing provides pleasures that are *not* simply those of "the beautiful voice", as the title has it. Occasionally, it is true, one wishes for a more athletic style (the creamy Caballé-Te Kanawa associations spiced with a dash of Ninon Vallin perhaps). But this *is* "the beautiful voice", no doubt about that, exercised with skill and heard in what will appeal widely as a programme of captivatingly beautiful music. Jeffrey Tate provides lively support.

Renée Fleming Great Opera Scenes. Renée Fleming (sop); [a]**Larissa Diadkova** (mez); [b]**Jonathan Summers** (bar); **London Symphony Orchestra / Sir Georg Solti.** Decca Ⓕ 455 760-2DH (72 minutes: DDD: 10/97). Texts and translations included. Recorded 1996.
Gramophone Editor's choice.

Mozart Le nozze di Figaro – Porgi, amor; E Susanna non vien! ... Dove sono. **Tchaikovsky** Eugene Onegin – Letter scene[a]. **Dvořák** Rusalka – O silver moon. **Verdi** Otello – Era più calmo? ... Mia madre aveva ... Piangea cantando ... Ave Maria[a]. **Britten** Peter Grimes – Embroidery in childhood[b]. **R. Strauss** Daphne – Ich komme, grünende Brüder.

Here's a singer who has reached complete maturity as an artist, revelling in her vocal and interpretative powers. To the warm and vibrant voice is added an imagination that places Fleming in the first rank among today's lyric sopranos. The eclectic, ambitious choice of programme allows us to hear every aspect of her art. She is exactly the impulsive Tatyana, the girl's unreasoned ardour pouring out here in a stream of richly varied tone and feeling. Desdemona's Willow song is full of foreboding, also full of lovely singing, the repeated "Cantiamo" voiced with precision of tone and timing, notes fined away with the utmost sensitivity. Ellen Orford's Embroidery aria is sung beautifully, the high B flat and A flat on "Now" taken perfectly *pianissimo* after the *forte* A. These scenes benefit enormously from being placed in context, allowing Fleming to fit into the relevant situation. Diadkova is an idiomatic, responsive Filipyevna, and she makes the most of Emilia's few phrases. Summers is a wise and experienced Balstrode. All in all, Fleming lays claim here to Te Kanawa territory, and proves a worthy successor. More than Dame Kiri, she identifies with each character and moulds her voice to the woman in question. For Sir Georg this is obviously a labour of love, nowhere more so than in the postlude to *Daphne*, most sensuously done; he and the LSO provide worthy support for their superb soloist. The recording is faultless, capturing voice and orchestra in ideal balance.

Inessa Galante Encore. Inessa Galante (sop); [b]**Janis Sprogis** (ten); [ce]**Samsons Izjumovs** (bar); [abc]**Latvian National Symphony Orchestra,** [de]**Latvian National Opera Orchestra / [a]Imants Resnis,** [b]**Paul Mägi,** [cde]**Alexander Vilumanis.** Campion Ⓕ RRCD1344 (63 minutes: AAD/DDD: A/97). Translations of some tracks included.

J. Strauss II Frühlingsstimmen, Op. 410[a]. **Weber** Der Freischütz – Kommt ein schlanker Bursch[a]. **Verdi** La traviata – Libiamo, ne' lieti calici[b]; Dite alla giovine[c]. **Toselli** Serenade[d]. **Offenbach** Les contes d'Hoffmann – Les oiseaux dans la charmille[d]. **Rossini** Il viaggio a Reims – Arpa gentil[d]. **Rimsky-Korsakov** Snow Maiden – Love duet[e]. **Rachmaninov** Vocalise, Op. 34 No. 14[d]. **Puccini** La bohème – Quando m'en vo' soletta[d]. **Donizetti** L'elisir d'amore – Chiedi all'aura lusinghiera[b]. Lucia di Lammermoor – Regnava nel silenzio ... Quando rapito in estasi[d]; Soffriva nel pianto[e]. **Puccini** Tosca – Vissi d'arte[d].

The lovely voice still shines with untarnished purity. Judged by repertoire, it would seem to be a light one, and yet there is nothing tweety about it; the timbre is that of a lyric soprano, an Agathe rather than an Aennchen. Yet here Aennchen is her role in the excerpt from *Der Freischütz*; she also sings Adina in *L'elisir d'amore* and the Snow Maiden; and probably quite rightly. Singing "Vissi d'arte" does not make her a Tosca, but on the other hand it does not find her overparted. She commands the seriousness if not quite the tragic intensity, and she rises to an effective climax without forcing the tone. In the coloratura repertoire, in as far as we sample it here, she demonstrates many of the required skills (neat staccato work, for instance) yet her progressions are not always fluent and she is certainly not overgenerous in the provision of notes *in alt*. Essentially she is (one would think) a lyric soprano but a well-equipped one. She would not, presumably, find any troublesome vocal dichotomy in the role of Violetta. Whether she has the emotional strength and the dramatic imagination for that great role is another matter. Pleasant as it is to have such a miscellany where all sorts of surprises lie in store, it would now be fairer to the artist if we could hear her in something complete. Still, there are some charmers here: Toselli's *Serenade*, the Rachmaninov *Vocalise* and most especially the improvising poetess's song with harp from *Il viaggio a Reims*. Just why the particular excerpts were chosen is sometimes hard to fathom, but none is unwelcome, and (apart from the *Tosca*) the complete opera containing the excerpt would be more welcome still.

Lesley Garrett A Soprano Inspired. **Lesley Garrett** (sop); [a]**chorus; Britten Sinfonia / Ivor Bolton.** Conifer Classics Ⓕ 75605 51329-2 (73 minutes: DDD: 12/97). Recorded 1997.
Mozart Exsultate, jubilate, K165/K158a – Alleluia. Vesperae solennes de confessore in C major, K339– Laudate Dominum. Mass No. 18 in C minor, "Great Mass" – Laudamus te. **Caccini** (arr. Ingham) Ave Maria. **Malotte** The Lord's Prayer. **Brahe** Bless this house. **Verdi** La forza del destino – La Vergine degli angeli[a]. **Vivaldi** Nulla in mundo pax, RV630 – Nulla in mundo pax. **R. Strauss** Zueignung, Op. 10 No. 1. **Handel** Messiah – I know that my Redeemer liveth. **Schubert** Ave Maria, D839. **Tippett** Five Negro Spirituals – By and By[a]. **Rodgers** The Sound of Music – Climb ev'ry mountain[a]. **Fauré** Requiem, Op. 48 – Pie Jesu. **Franck** Panis angelicus. **S. Adams** The Holy City. **Humperdinck** Hänsel und Gretel – Abends will ich schlafen gehn (sung in English). **d'Hardelot** Because. **Mascagni** Cavalleria rusticana – Regina coeli … Inneggiamo, il Signor.
Lesley Garrett is such a 'conviction' singer. She has always caught the imagination by the way she sings every word as if she meant it – as here in *The Holy City*, turning dross almost into gold. The programme for this CD is typically eclectic, drawn from the baroque to the Broadway musical. She sings Vivaldi, Handel (a nicely decorated "I know that my Redeemer liveth") and Mozart (the "Laudamus te" from the C minor Mass and a joyous "Alleluia" at the start) with straightforward vigour. In her opera selection, she phrases Leonora's Prayer from *Forza* with a fine feeling for Verdian line, follows the somewhat dubious tradition started by Elisabeth Schumann of singing the "Abendgesang" from *Hänsel und Gretel* with herself, and gives the Easter Hymn, though she couldn't undertake Santuzza on stage, with the passion appropriate to its context. The two Lieder, an open-hearted *Zueignung* is preferable to a rather sentimental *Ave Maria*. The "Pie Jesu" from Fauré's Requiem and Franck's *Panis angelicus*, both sung with the simple sincerity that is Garrett's hallmark, confirm that she has lost little or none of that fresh, forward, no-nonsense sound that is so appealing to her large audience. The unexpected choice of the Tippett item and the revival of d'Hardelot's *Because*, delivered with the security of technique that marks all these readings, is welcome. It is hard to resist her glorious account of "Climb ev'ry mountain". Ivor Bolton switches easily between idioms, though is obviously most at home in the baroque. The recording is brightly lit but not offensively so.

Lesley Garrett Soprano in Red. **Lesley Garrett** (sop); [a]**Crouch End Festival Chorus; Royal Philharmonic Concert Orchestra / James Holmes.** Silva Screen Classics Ⓕ SILKTVCD1 (60 minutes: DDD: 2/96). All items sung in English. Recorded 1995. *Gramophone Award Winner 1996.*
Romberg The New Moon – Softly, as in a morning sunrise; Lover, come back to me.
J. Strauss II (arr. Benatzky) Casanova – Nuns' Chorus and Laura's Song[a]. **Offenbach** La belle Hélène – On me nomme Hélène la Blonde. Orphée aux enfers – J'ai vu le Dieu Bacchus[a]; Ce bal est original[a]. **Novello** Perchance to dream – We'll gather lilacs. The Dancing Years – Waltz of my heart. **Lehár** Zigeunerliebe – Hör' ich Cymbalklänge. Friederike – Warum hast du mich wachgeküsst? Die lustige Witwe – Es lebt eine Vilja, ein Waldmägdelein[a]. **Coward** Bitter Sweet – If love were all. **Chabrier** L'étoile – O petite étoile; Je suis Lazuli!. **Heuberger** Der Opernball – Im chambre séparée. **Sullivan** The Contrabandista – Only the night wind sighs alone.
Lesley Garrett has won herself a huge following of those who respond to her straightforward, unaffected vocalizing, to the clarity and brightness of her voice and its ringing top notes. What also appeals about Garrett's recordings is the attention paid to less familiar material and the quest for authenticity of period style. Both facets are fully evident in this collection of operetta numbers from Paris, Vienna, Berlin, London and New York, ranging in time from classical Offenbach through to Coward, Novello and Romberg. The eager entreaties of Laura's Song from *Casanova*, the bright expressiveness of "If love were all" and the sheer joyfulness of "Waltz of my heart" (complete with piano contribution) are highlights. Especially gratifying, though, are the rarities. In the pedlar Lazuli's two numbers from Chabrier's *L'étoile*, Garrett's clarity of diction shows off Jeremy Sams's lyrics to fine effect and she should certainly win over the Sullivan faction with the first ever recording of an engaging little number from the pre-Gilbert operetta *The Contrabandista*. The aria from *La belle Hélène* is performed to Michael Frayn's text for the ENO adaptation of the work as *La belle Vivette*, while in Novello's "We'll gather lilacs" double tracking permits Garrett to duet with herself. Ensemble and momentum go curiously adrift at the choral entries in Offenbach's "Hymn to Bacchus", but this detracts only a little from another delightful Garrett collection.

Angela Gheorghiu – My World Angela Gheorghiu (sop); Malcolm Martineau (pf).
Decca Ⓕ 458 360-2DH (75 minutes: DDD: 5/98). Texts and translations included.
Recorded 1997. *Gramophone Editor's choice.*
J. Martini Plaisir d'amour. **Parisotti** Se tu m'ami, C xxii, 68. **Respighi** Nebbie.
Leoncavallo Mattinata. **Falla** El paño moruno. **Montsalvatge** Canto negro. **Satie** Je te veux. **Delibes** Les filles de Cadix. **Poulenc** Les chemins de l'amour. **Grieg** Solveig's Song.
Schumann Myrthen, Op. 25 – No. 1, Widmung; No. 24, Du bist wie eine Blume.
Schubert Ständchen, D957 No. 4. **R. Strauss** Zueignung, Op. 10 No. 1.

Brediceanu Mult mă'ntreabă inima. **Mezzetti** Cântec se sirenă. **Cavadia** Umbra.
Dvořák Songs my mother taught me, B104 No. 4. **Liszt** Oh! quand je dors, S282.
Hadjidakis Pai efiye to treno. **Traditional** (arr. Behar): Durme, kerido hijico. **Sup** Guriwoon
Guemgang San. **Mitake** Kawa no Nagare no yô ni. **Ovalle** Azulão. **Brodszky** Be my love.
This eclectic programme makes a welcome change from recorded recitals devoted to one composer,
one genre. Gheorghiu avers, in a disarmingly frank note, that she thrives on change, loves to be in
different countries and experience different idioms so she "wanted to create a unique recital
programme that would reflect all these aspects of my interests". She certainly has done that: her
generous choice boxes the compass from classical through German, Spanish, Italian and French song
to ethnic pieces. She also points out that many of the items exploit the warm qualities of her lower
voice: the haunting pieces, semi-popular, from the far east, for instance; even more the Greek popular
song. Still better, not surprisingly, are the three songs from her native Romania, especially the
seductive Siren's song and the glorious *Umbra*, a late-nineteenth-century romance. Then there's
Ovalle's insinuating *Azulão*, chosen apparently at the suggestion of Martineau, the singer's creative
partner, and sung in that soft-grained manner peculiar to Gheorghiu. She ends with a bravura
account of the Lanza favourite *Be my love*, the slight accent in the English almost an advantage.
Similarly her indeterminate German makes her three Lieder sound unidiomatic, but each of these
love-songs is given with such conviction that the customary criteria for judgement can for once be set
aside. Her French is much better; in any case the erotic charge of the Satie and Poulenc pieces is amply
felt. There's much else to commend: the elegiac quality in Respighi's infinitely sad *Nebbie* contrasting
with the earthy high spirits of Montsalvatge's *Canto negro* and the Delibes song, and the wistful touch
in the famous Dvořák. With an admirably faithful recording as a bonus, this ought to be a runaway
success.

Angela Gheorghiu Opera Arias. Angela Gheorghiu (sop); **Orchestra and** [a]**Chorus of Teatro Regio,
Turin / John Mauceri.** Decca Ⓕ 452 417-2DH (57 minutes: DDD: 6/96). Texts and translations
included. Recorded 1995.   Ⓖ
Verdi Falstaff – Ninfe! Elfi! Silfi!; Sul fil d'un soffio etesio[a]. **Massenet** Chérubin – Aubade:
Vive amour qui rêve, embrase et fuit[a]. Hérodiade – Celui dont la parole ... Il est doux, il est bon.
Catalani La Wally – Ebben? Ne andrò lontana. **Bellini** I Capuleti e i Montecchi – Eccomi in
lieta vesta ... Oh! quante volte. **Puccini** La bohème – Sì. Mi chiamano Mimì; Donde lieta uscì.
Boito Mefistofele – L'altra notte. **Gounod** Faust – O Dieu! que de bijoux! ... Ah! je ris.
Donizetti Don Pasquale – Quel guardo il cavaliere ... So anch'io la virtù magica.
Grigoriu Valurile Dunării – Muzica.
Here is a recital that begins in enchantment and ends in something a little less. If any two items are
individually responsible they are the arias from *Mefistofele* and *La Wally*. Perhaps Gheorghiu is
telling us to refine our ideas of these things: that the chesty Italian manner of Burzio and Muzio,
Callas and Scotto, should have 'gone out' with the actresses of the silent screen. Even so, what she
gives us in its place is surely incomplete. So it is that the most satisfying performances here are those
of a less overtly passionate nature. That does not include the Jewel song from *Faust*, where the rather
lazy tempo and lack of excitement in the style fail to catch the passionate impulses of laughter,
coquettishness, desire and even vanity in this naturally modest and simple girl. Massenet's Salomé and
Bellini's Giulietta are better suited; the Aubade from *Chérubin* is delightful; and we are back to the
beginning with Nannetta in Windsor Forest which is utter enchantment. The voice of course is a feast
in itself, the loveliest lyric soprano heard since Dame Kiri first came to us in the 1970s. The reticence,
which can be a limitation, has its positive side, and repeatedly one has to admire the way in which
fullness of volume and emotion is held in reserve for effective use at a climax.

Angela Gheorghiu and Roberto Alagna Opera Arias and Duets. [a]Angela Gheorghiu (sop);
[b]Roberto Alagna (ten); Orchestra of the Royal Opera House, Covent Garden / Richard Armstrong.
EMI Ⓕ CDC5 56117-2 (61 minutes: DDD: 6/96). Texts and translations included.   ⒼⒼ
Gramophone Editor's record of the month.
Mascagni L'amico Fritz – Suzel, buon di ... Tutto tace[ab]. **Massenet** Manon – Je suis seul! ...
Ah! fuyez, douce image[b]; Toi! Vous! ... N'est-ce plus ma main[ab]. **Donizetti** Anna Bolena – Al
dolce guidami[a]. Don Pasquale – Tornami a dir[ab]. **Offenbach** La belle Hélène – Au mont Ida[b].
Bernstein West Side Story – Only You ... Tonight, it all began tonight[ab]. **Gounod** Faust – Il se
fait tard! ... O nuit d'amour[ab]. **G. Charpentier** Louise – Depuis le jour[a]. **Berlioz** Les troyens –
Nuit d'ivresse![ab]. **Puccini** La bohème – O soave fanciulla[ab].
Ideally matched, the two young lyric artists of our day who have most taken the hearts and hopes of
public and critics sing here in a programme that is both aptly and imaginatively selected. It ranges
quite widely over the French and Italian repertoires, always combining instant satisfaction with a wish
for more. The Cherry duet from *L'amico Fritz* comes first, and the voices have just the right freshness
for it, the soprano warm-toned, the tenor elegant and cleanly defined; the style too is charming,
natural and mutually responsive. Then with the excerpts from *Manon* they are not only well suited but
show already a real dramatic impulse in their duet, again with its developments so well felt and
understood. The Garden scene works unusual magic. The solos provide welcome opportunities:
Gheorghiu, delightful in "Depuis le jour", is even more so in the aria from *Anna Bolena*, exquisitely
phrased and shaded as though it were the slow movement of a sonata by Mozart. "Ah! fuyez, douce

image" opens with the softness associated from long ago with Smirnov and Muratore; Alagna never forgets what he is singing about, is thrilling on his high B flats and finely controlled in the concluding *diminuendo*. His Mount Ida song from *La belle Hélène* has panache and humour, a deliciously promising *pianissimo* start to the last verse and a good robust C thrown in before he finishes. And then, inspiration on somebody's part, there is *West Side Story*. "Tonight" has never been better sung, and it also brings us to the other element in this recital – the playing of the Covent Garden orchestra under Richard Armstrong. In this, they make us realize afresh how distinctively flavoured (in harmony and orchestration) is Bernstein's marvellous score: the duet is intensely moving, yet the rhythm is kept strong and there is no sugar-coating or melting into slush. Repeatedly, in Gounod and Bernstein as in Mascagni and Puccini, one reacts with an 'I'd never noticed that before' or simply a smile or sigh of pleasure in the sound.

Jill Gomez Cabaret Classics. Jill Gomez (sop); **John Constable** (pf). Unicorn Kanchana
Ⓕ DKPCD9055 (57 minutes: DDD: 6/88). Texts and translations included.
  Weill Marie Galante – Les filles de Bordeaux; Le grand Lustucru; Le Roi d'Aquitaine; J'attends un navire. Lady in the Dark – My ship. Street Scene – Lonely house. Knickerbocker Holiday – It never was you. **Zemlinsky** Songs, Op. 27 – Harlem Tänzerin; Elend; Afrikanischer Tanz.
  Schoenberg Arie aus dem Spiegel von Arcadien. Gigerlette. Der genügsame Liebhaber. Mahnung. **Satie** La diva de l'Empire. Allons-y, Chochotte. Je te veux.
Schoenberg writing cabaret songs with a popular touch? Yes, and quite catchy ones too, as can be heard particularly in *Gigerlette* – prompting the intriguing speculation of what might have been had he not concentrated on *Gurrelieder*. On the other hand, his *Der genügsame Liebhaber* and Zemlinsky's three songs would have been most unlikely to go down well with cabaret audiences, however intellectual. At the other end of the spectrum are Satie's café-concert songs (the sentimental waltz *Je te veux* is languidly attractive) and the Weill items, which were not written for cabaret but are drawn from a 1934 Paris play and post-war Broadway musicals. That all these songs do not require a gin-sodden voice or raucous delivery is demonstrated with the utmost artistry by Jill Gomez, in turn seductive, pathetic, sly, sweet, swaggering, passionate, salacious – or simply singing beautifully. Her performance of Weill's *Lonely house* (one of his best) remains hauntingly in the mind.

Jerry Hadley Vienna. Jerry Hadley (ten); **Munich Radio Orchestra / Richard Bonynge.**
RCA Victor Red Seal Ⓕ 09026 68258-2 (61 minutes: DDD: 9/97). Texts and translations included. Recorded 1995. *Gramophone Editor's choice.*
  Eysler Bruder Straubinger – Küssen ist keine Sünd. Der lachende Ehemann – Weinlied.
  Fall Die Rose von Stambul – Ein Walzer muss es sein; O Rose von Stambul.
  Kálmán Die Csárdásfürstin – Tanzen möcht'ich; Ganz ohne Weiber geht die Chose nicht.
  Lehár Friederike – O Mädchen, mein Mädchen. Das Land des Lächelns – Immer nur lächeln; Von Apfelblüten einen Kranz; Dein ist meines ganzes Herz. Paganini – Gern hab'ich die Frau'n geküsst. Schön ist die Welt – Schön ist die Welt. Der Zarewitsch – Wolgalied.
  Tauber Der singende Traum – Du bist die Welt für mich.
Jerry Hadley's self-professed love of Viennese operetta shines through this fine collection, which winningly mixes the obvious tenor hits of twentieth-century Viennese operetta with some less obvious items. The obvious, of course, include no fewer than nine of the Franz Lehár songs that became associated with Richard Tauber. Hadley delivers these in less dramatic form than Tauber, but with no less compelling lyricism and with some typically Tauberian *pianissimo*. The less obvious items include yet another 'Tauber-Lied' in one that Tauber himself composed for his 1934 operetta, *Der singende Traum*. We are also treated to a couple of waltz numbers by the wickedly underrated Leo Fall; even rarer, and thus perhaps most welcome of all, are the charming numbers by Edmund Eysler, composer of homely Viennese operettas neglected since the days when they provided rewarding material for the likes of Julius Patzak. Beautifully recorded, this really is a model Viennese operetta recital.

Thomas Hampson German Opera Arias. Thomas Hampson (bar); [a]Pestalozzi Gymnasium
Children's Choir; Munich Radio Orchestra / Fabio Luisi. EMI Ⓕ CDC5 55233-2
(79 minutes: DDD: 9/95). Texts and translations included. Recorded 1994.
  Korngold Die tote Stadt – Mein Sehnen, mein Wähnen. **Lortzing** Zar und Zimmermann – Verraten! ... Die Macht des Zepters. Der Wildschütz – Wie freundlich strahlt ... Heiterkeit und Fröhlichkeit. **Marschner** Hans Heiling – An jenam Tag. Der Vampyr – Ha! Noch einen ganzen Tag. **Weber** Euryanthe – Wo berg' ich mich? ... So weih' ich mich dem Rachgewalten.
  Spohr Faust – Der Hölle selbst will ich...Liebe ist die zarte Blüthe. **Kreutzer** Das Nachtlager in Granada – Die Nacht ist schön. **Schreker** Der ferne Klang – In einem Lande ein bleicher König. **Humperdinck** Die Königskinder – Verdorben! Gestorben![a]. **Wagner** Tannhäuser – Wie Todesahnung ... O du mein holder Abendstern. Die Walküre – Winterstürme wichen dem Wonnemond.
In addition to being a singer of outstanding gifts and versatility, Hampson is also scholarly in his approach. He himself, with Jens Mete Fischer, contributes an essay on "the baritone in German opera", making it clear that he is aware of the tradition in which he sings. It is not surprising, then, that voices from the past should come to mind and stay there quite contentedly during the course of this recital. Schlusnus (in *Hans Heiling*), Hüsch (in *Königskinder*), Janssen (*Tannhäuser*), and for just

one phrase ("sie bringet Wünsche mancher Art mir dar" in *Der Wildschütz*) Fischer-Dieskau: a formidable array, and assuredly not assembled in order to bar the young American from entry to their ranks. His voice is uncommonly beautiful, he is scrupulous in his musicianship, and like the best Germans he knows the value of the Italian connection. If there is a limitation to his success in the chosen programme, it is simply the price that often has to be paid by a singer whose voice is an unmixed pleasure to the ear. For the villain of *Euryanthe* and the maniac of *Der Vampyr*, his voice-character is simply too good: goodness, not villainy, is its element. At times, too, there is need for more depth and body in the lower range (Spohr's Faust and Schreker's Count in *Der ferne Klang* are examples). Otherwise the singing is delightful, the *Zar und Zimmermann*, *Tannhäuser* and *Die tote Stadt* solos especially. In including Siegmund's "Winterstürme" from *Die Walküre*, Hampson was probably providing a talking-point as much as anything, and it is certainly interesting to hear how he will occasionally 'tenorize' while usually keeping to his normal baritone production, perhaps giving his admirers a moment's concern as he opens the voice for the F of "vereint" in the last phrase. The programme itself contains several rarities. The imaginative use of the solo violin in *Das Nachtlager in Granada* and the rich orchestration of *Der ferne Klang* are additional pleasures in a recital that is well accompanied, well recorded and informatively presented.

Thomas Hampson To the Soul – Songs to the Poetry of Walt Whitman. **Thomas Hampson** (bar);
  Craig Rutenberg (pf). EMI Ⓜ CDM5 55028-2 (67 minutes: DDD: 10/97). Texts included.
  Recorded 1993-94. Also includes readings by Thomas Hampson of "One's self I sing",
  "The mystic trumpeter", "I hear it was charged against me" and "Song of myself". ❻❻❻
  Rorem As Adam early in the morning. Look down fair moon. Sometimes with one I love. That
  shadow, my likeness. **Bridge** The last invocation, H136. **Stanford** To the soul, Op. 97 No. 4.
  Vaughan Williams Poems by Walt Whitman – No. 2, A clear midnight; No. 3, Joy, shipmate,
  joy!. **Strassburg** Prayer of Columbus. **Bacon** One thought ever at the fire. **Dalmas** As I
  watch'd the ploughman ploughing. **Hindemith** Memories of Lincoln – Sing on there in the
  Swamp. **Naginski** Look down fair moon. **Neidlinger** Memories of Lincoln. **H.T. Burleigh**
  Ethiopia saluting the colours. **Weill** Dirge for Two Veterans. **Ives** Walt Whitman. **G. Busby**
  Behold this swarthy face. **E.R. Warren** We two. **Urquhart** Among the multitude, 1980.
  Tilson Thomas We two boys together clinging. **Bernstein** Songfest – To what you said.
For a song recital to be devoted to settings of a single poet he must preferably be capable of inspiring music of widely differing types. This splendidly planned collection certainly demonstrates that to be true of Whitman: apparently Hampson has traced no fewer than 400 Whitman settings for voice and piano, and all his choices are at least interesting; some are real discoveries. Henry Thacker Burleigh was the first African-American to receive professional training as a composer (Dvořák was Burleigh's first teacher), and his use of jazzy syncopation (in 1915!) and Ives-like quotation of Civil War melodies in *Ethiopia saluting the colours* is vividly original. Elsewhere Stanford demonstrates that Whitman is accessible to Brahmsian gravity and eloquence while Ernst Bacon, with moving simplicity, sets three lines on human brotherhood to a melody like a chapel hymn. Kurt Weill effectively treats the *Dirge for Two Veterans* in his Broadway manner and in "Sing on there in the Swamp" Hindemith beautifully evokes the falling star of *Memories of Lincoln* with two coolly shining chords that generate a lyrical counterpoint to the vocal line. Ned Rorem, surely the most consistently fine contemporary composer of concert songs, is represented by four, all characteristically subtle and refined. There is not a weak song here; the performances throughout are exceptionally fine, intimately and subtly expressive but opening out nobly to expressions of passionate idealism. Hampson's readings are just that: they are pleasingly unhistrionic, not in the least bit acted, but they effectively frame the songs with his obvious commitment to Whitman. A most enterprising, absorbing and magnificently sung recital.

Ben Heppner Great Tenor Arias. **Ben Heppner** (ten); ᵃ**Bavarian Radio Chorus; Munich Radio
  Orchestra / Roberto Abbado**. RCA Victor Red Seal Ⓔ 09026 62504-2 (61 minutes: DDD: 11/95).
  Texts and translations included. Recorded 1993-4.
  Leoncavallo La bohème – Musette ! o gioia della mia dimora; Testa adorata. **Verdi** Luisa
  Miller – Oh! fede negar potessi; Quando le sere al placido. La forza del destino – La vita è
  inferno; Oh, tu che in seno. Aida – Se quel guerrier; Celeste Aida. Il trovatore – Ah! sì, ben mio;
  Di quella piraᵃ. **Puccini** Manon Lescaut – Donna non vidi mai. Turandot – Nessun dorma!ᵃ.
  La fanciulla del West – Ch'ella mi creda libero. **Bizet** Carmen – La fleur que tu m'avais jetée.
  Meyerbeer L'Africaine – Pays merveilleux; O Paradis. **Massenet** Hérodiade – Ne pouvant
  réprimer les élans de foi; Adieu donc, vains objets. Le cid – Ah! tout est bien fini; O souverain,
  ô juge, ô père. **Giordano** Andrea Chenier – Colpito qui m'avete; Un di all'azzurro spazio;
  Come un bel dì di maggio.
The name that immediately comes to mind in listening to this collection is that of Heppner's older contemporary, Domingo. Their timbre is similar, as is their vocal manner – consistently firm, plush tone brought to bear in a musically faultless approach to the piece in hand, with a fair understanding of the style required. A further likeness comes in Heppner's willingness to tackle Italian, French and German repertory with equal aplomb. Heppner immediately wins approval by beginning with Marcello's seldom-heard aria from Leoncavallo's *Bohème*, into which he pours forth generosity of tone and heart. Each of the Verdi items benefits from long-breathed phrasing, a sensitive attention to

dynamic levels and excellent Italian. The Puccini arias are, if anything, even better. The *Manon Lescaut* and *Fanciulla* arias bear comparison with either Björling or Domingo in this music. Heppner is less confident and idiomatic in French, which may account for a fluently sung but matter-of-fact Flower Song and for a want of sheer flair in "O Paradis", where the big phrase doesn't open out as it should: here any comparison with Caruso is inadvisable. The Massenet pieces are better. John the Baptist's sorrowful aria from *Hérodiade* brings the most plangent performance of all, not least at "Je ne regrette rien", itself pre-echoing Piaf. The *Cid* Prayer begins, as it should, with an inward recitative and, as in all Heppner's performances, he manages to think himself into character and situation: this is no machismo tenor, but Rodrigue himself before us. As a whole this is a most rewarding recital, well accompanied and warmly recorded.

Ying Huang Opera Arias. **Ying Huang** (sop); **London Symphony Orchestra / James Conlon.** Sony Classical Ⓕ SK62687 (68 minutes: DDD: 1/97). Texts and translations included.
Bellini La sonnambula – Oh! se una volta sola rivederlo ... Ah! non credea mirarti ... Ah! non giunge. **Donizetti** Don Pasquale – Quel guardo il cavaliere ... So anch'io la virtù magica. Lucia di Lammermoor – Regnava nel silenzio ... Quando rapito in estasi. **Puccini** La bohème – Quando m'en vò' soletta. Gianni Schicchi – O mio babbino caro. La rondine – Che il bel sogno di Doretta; Ore dolce e divine. Turandot – Signore, ascolta. **Rossini** Il barbiere di Siviglia – Una voca poco fà. Semiramide – Bel raggio lushingier. **Verdi** Un ballo in maschera – Volta la terrea fronte. Rigoletto – Gualtier Maldè! ... Caro nome. **Traditional** (arr. Constant) A little path; I live at the source of the Yangtze River.

In this recital we can sample the young Chinese soprano Ying Huang in what used to be regarded as the 'old' Italian repertoire (Rossini, Bellini and Donizetti). In Verdi she very properly confines herself to the lyric-leggiero roles. In Puccini, just a mite too mannerly for Musetta and too maidenly for Magda, she is an ideal Lauretta and Liù. Here, her voice sounds pure, young and slender, quite lovely in quality, aristocratic in timbre and usage. Fluent in passagework, she moves easily throughout the range, with a fresh bloom upon the top notes and no want of firmness or colour in the lower register. Her Italian seems good, and (for example) in "Una voce poco fà" she shows a lively appreciation of mood and humour. Two Chinese songs round off the programme, very charmingly if with a suspicion that they may have been pretty thoroughly westernized in their orchestral arrangements. James Conlon conducts, and the LSO play, with sympathy and without undue reticence. The recording gives no impression of trying to pass the voice off as bigger than it is. In the booklet, texts and translations are sensibly introduced with a brief synopsis.

Dmitri Hvorostovsky Songs and Dances of Death. **Dmitri Hvorostovsky** (bar); **Kirov Theatre Orchestra / Valery Gergiev.** Philips Ⓕ 438 872-2PH (62 minutes: DDD: 5/94). Texts and translations included. Recorded 1993.
Rimsky-Korsakov Sadko – The paragon of cities; Beautiful city! Kashchey the Immortal – In this, night's darkest hour. Snow Maiden (second version) – Under the warm blue sea. The Tsar's Bride – Still the beauty haunts my mind. **Borodin** Prince Igor – No sleep, no rest. **Rubinstein** The Demon – Do not weep, my child; On the airy ocean; I am he whom you called. Nero – Vindex's Epithalamium: I sing to you, Hymen divine! **Rachmaninov** Aleko – Aleko's cavatina. **Mussorgsky** Songs and Dances of Death.

In the scenes from Rubinstein's *The Demon* Hvorostovsky, superbly supported by Valery Gergiev and his Kirov orchestra recorded in their own theatre, has done nothing better than his impersonation of the devil; in the scenes from the third he projects the gloating demon to the life. This is splendid stuff. So is Vindex's rollicking Epithalamium from the same composer's *Nero*, sung with wonderful breadth and confidence. Then he changes character again to bring before us the emotional torment of Rachmaninov's Aleko as he recalls the love Zemfira once had for him. The best of the Rimsky items as regards music and interpretation are Nizgir's aria from the *Snow Maiden* and Gryaznoy's musing on past triumphs in the field of love from *The Tsar's Bride*. Here Hvorostovsky varies his tone more successfully than in the other Rimsky items. Mussorgsky's *Songs and Dances of Death* really need an imposing bass rather than a lyric baritone to make their true mark, yet these are more than acceptable performances, immeasurably helped by the excellent recording. This is a fascinating disc.

Sumi Jo Carnaval! **Sumi Jo** (sop); **English Chamber Orchestra / Richard Bonynge.** Decca Ⓕ 440 679-2DH (68 minutes: DDD: 9/94). Texts and translations included. Recorded 1993.
Adam Les Pantins de Violette – Le chanson du canari. Si j'étais roi – De vos nobles aïeux. **Balfe** Les puits d'amour – Rêves d'amour, rêves de gloire. **Boïeldieu** La fête du village voisin – Profitez de la view (Boléro). **F. David** La perle du Brésil – Couplets du Mysoli. **Delibes** Le roi l'a dit – Portons toujours des robes sombres. **Grétry** Les fausses apparences ou L'amant jalous – Je romps la chaîne qui m'engage. **Hérold** Le pré aux clercs – Jours de mon enfance. **Massenet** Don César de Bazan – Sevillana. **Massé** La reine Topaze – Ninette est jeune et belle ("Carnaval de Venise"). **Messager** Madame Chrysanthème – Le jour sous le soleil béni. **Offenbach** Un mari à la porte – J'entends, ma belle ("Valse tyrolienne"). **A. Thomas** Le songe d'une nuit d'été – Malgré l'éclat qui m'environne.

Sumi Jo is fortunate to have Bonynge as conductor and researcher to come up with a sequence of really rare and fascinating music although the selection is a little like being confronted with a *pâtissier*'s window display. Sumi Jo's coloratura is accurate and apparently effortless. Although her diction is not completely unintelligible, a lot of it is rather approximate. She is very affecting in the Messager aria and in another bird-song, from Adam's *Les Pantins de Violette*. In general she seems to be on firmer ground in the early nineteenth-century repertory – David, Adam and Hérold – than with the *fin de siècle* style where once or twice the demands of the long lines seem to encourage her to stray slightly off pitch. The Ambroise Thomas *Midsummer Night's Dream* is not an adaptation of the Shakespeare play, but a fantasy set at the court of Queen Elizabeth I, whose aria is heard here; very silly it all seems too. All in all, amongst these show-pieces there are valuable glimpses of the extraordinary richness of the seldom-heard *opéra-comique* repertory.

Sumi Jo Virtuoso Arias. Sumi Jo (sop); [a]**Monte-Carlo Philharmonic Orchestra / Paolo Olmi;** [b]**Paris Orchestral Ensemble / Armin Jordan.** Erato Ⓟ 4509-97239-2 (74 minutes: DDD: 6/95). Texts included. Items marked [a] new to UK, [b]from 2292-45469-2 (5/90). Recorded 1994.
Rossini Il barbiere di Siviglia – Una voce poco fa ... Io son docile[a]. **Bellini** La sonnambula – Ah! non credea mirarti ... Ah! non giunge[a]. **Delibes** Lakmé – Ou va la jeune indoue ... La-bas dans la forêt plus sombre[a]. **Verdi** Rigoletto – Gualtier Maldè ... Caro nome[a]. **Meyerbeer** Dinorah – Ombre légère[a]. **Donizetti** Lucia di Lammermoor – Mad scene[a]. **R. Strauss** Ariadne auf Naxos – Noch glaub' ich dem einen ganz ... So war es mit Pagliazzo ... Als ein Gott kam jeder gegangen[a]. **Bernstein** Candide – Glitter and be gay[a]. **Mozart** Die Zauberflöte – Der Hölle Rache[b]. **Yoon** (arr. Constant) Barley Field[a].
Many listeners, well disposed towards most kinds of vocal recital, still tend to approach a new 'coloratura' programme with misgivings – all of which would seem to be obviated here. The emotional range of the music goes well beyond mere prettiness, whether of girlish glee or wilting pathos. The florid passages (commonly tagged 'display') are assumed by the singer to have an expressive purpose, which she then seeks out and fulfils. Her tone is bright but not piercing, her style clean but not cold; she understands perfectly well that, though these arias are famous for their high notes, far more of the singer's time is spent in the middle register, where a scrawny or breathy tone and flawed legato will not be excused on account of a few brilliances *in alt*. Intelligence is clearly at work from the start, in the enunciation of the words. "Una voce poco fa qui nel cuor mi risuono": the "qui" ("here") is the 'gesture-word', the one that makes it actual and individual. "La vincerò" is determined, but not doubly-underlined or given that arch, over-confident touch which may gain a point but, in doing so, forfeits likeableness. In *La sonnambula* sympathy is actually *strengthened* by the cleaning-up of all those downward portamentos that have threatened to become inseparable from the music since Callas and Sutherland introduced them. Similarly, the Mad scene from *Lucia di Lammermoor* is enacted as a genuinely dramatic piece but with a fresh realization, rather than from a mind loaded with memories of those illustrious predecessors. The only way in which Jo appears at a disadvantage is in the relative hardness of some high notes. Zerbinetta's aria, for instance, is a shade uncomfortable (clearly written with more of the German *Kopfstimme* in mind), while the Korean song, *Barley Field*, is entirely lovely in sound and does not rise above an A flat.

Vesselina Kasarova A Portrait. Vesselina Kasarova (mez); [a]**Bavarian Radio Chorus; Munich Radio Orchestra / Friedrich Haider.** RCA Victor Red Seal Ⓟ 09026 68522-2 (64 minutes: DDD: 2/97). Texts and translations included. *Gramophone Editor's record of the month.* 🅖🅖
Handel Rinaldo – Or la tromba in suon festante. **Gluck** Orfeo ed Euridice – Che farò senza Euridice?. **Mozart** Le nozze di Figaro – Voi che sapete. Don Giovanni – Batti, batti, o bel Masetto. **Rossini** La Cenerentola – Nacqui all'affano[a] (with Isolde Mitternacht-Geissendörfer, sop; Barbara Müller, contr; Dankwart Siegele, ten; Tim Hennis, bass). Il barbiere di Siviglia – Una voce poco fa. L'italiana in Algeri – Pronti abbiamo e ferri e mani ... Amici in ogni evento ... Pensa alla patria[a]. **Donizetti** Anna Bolena – Sposa a Percy ... Per questa fiamma indomita ... Ah! pensate che rivolti[a] (Andreas Schulist, ten; Leonid Savitzky, bass). La favorita – Fia dunque vero ... O mio Fernando!. **Bellini** I Capuleti e i Montecchi – Se Romeo t'uccise un figlio ... La tremenda ultrice spada[a] (Schulist; Savitzky).
This is the stuff of legends: it is difficult to imagine a début opera recital that could give so much pleasure. The vibrant richness of Kasarova's tone allied to her totally uninhibited manner before the microphone allow her to bring to astonishing life each of the characters portrayed within. She begins as she continues, with tremendous panache as Rinaldo invokes trumpets to great deeds and Kasarova proves the warrior-lover to the life, Handel's complex coloratura used as an engine to express youthful fire. Then immediately she becomes the tender, lamenting Orpheus, real grieving in the plush, well-controlled tone. The two Mozart pieces disclose different timbres in the voice – bright and palpitating as befits Cherubino, soft-grained and sensuous as suits Zerlina. Kasarova is a fabulous Rossinian. In the three pieces here she combines vitality, verbal acuity and dispatch of *fioriture*. It's wonderful how she starts in mild, forgiving manner, caressing the start of "Non più mesta", then lets fly in viscerally exciting manner for the roulades. Even the well-trodden path of "Una voce" sounds newly-minted as you seem to hear Rosina's varied thoughts passing through her mind, the text freshly inflected. As Isabella inspires her followers in "Pensa all patria", one notes the subtle accents on "il tenero amor" and "Caro, ti parli in petto", evincing all Isabella's inner feelings for her beloved Lindoro. Then it's off on another invigorating display at "Fra pochi istanti". From here Kasarova moves on to so-called *bel canto* territory. With "O mio Fernando!" it's again the judgement of tonal colour, here sensual,

heartstopping, while Jane Seymour's resistance to Henry VIII (weakly impersonated here) shows yet another 'face', dignified and noble. But in both Leonora's and Romeo's cabaletta, "La tremenda ultrice spada", a little less might mean so much more: there is too much emphasis, too many breaths. But that is part of the style of a singer who is making no concessions to the studio, rather living out every moment of the given dramas, admirably supported by Haider and his orchestra.

Sergei Larin Russian Arias, Volume 1. **Sergei Larin** (ten); [a]**Ambrosian Opera Chorus**; **Philharmonia Orchestra / Gennadi Rozhdestvensky.** Chandos Ⓕ CHAN9603 (75 minutes: DDD: 5/98). Texts and translations included.
    Tchaikovsky Eugene Onegin – I love you, Olga; Monsieur Triquet, favour us with a coupleta; Faint echo of my youth. Mazeppa – In bloody battle, on the field of honour ... Here days passed by in happy succession. Cherevichki – Does your heart, maiden, not hear. The Queen of Spades – I do not know her name; Forgive me, loveliest of creatures; What is our life? A game!.
    Rimsky-Korsakov May Night – Hey there! Boys!a; How calm, how cool it is here. Sadko – Song of the Indian guest. **Rachmaninov** Boris Godunov – One last story. **Dargomïzhsky** Rusalka – Some unknown power. **Glinka** Ruslan and Lyudmila – There is a desert country. **Borodin** Prince Igor – Daylight is fading.
Since he has started making recital discs with Chandos Sergei Larin has come into focus as a recording artist much more clearly than when his name tended to get lost among many others in the cast-list of Russian operas. His art has certainly deepened now, with more fully expressive delineation of phrases and, perhaps with Rozhdestvensky to help, a more complete responsiveness to mood and structure. But perhaps he has outgrown Lensky, the impetuous, ill-fated young poet in *Eugene Onegin*. The love-song in Act 1 hasn't the youthful ardour and impulse, and the great aria of the Duel scene is a fine piece of singing rather than the elegiac and then impassioned utterance of doomed youth. Larin now is much closer (vocally) to Hermann in *The Queen of Spades* than to Lenski, and the fire burns bright in Hermann's "What is our life?". The programme is full of plums: there's the Hindu Guest with his famous song, Vladimir of *Prince Igor* with that lovely nocturnal invocation, and Levko with his lullaby in *May Night*. Less expected presences are Monsieur Triquet from *Eugene Onegin* and Pimen, the old monk in *Boris Godunov*. At first one thinks that that must be a crazy misprint; but no, it is a setting by Rachmaninov, an imaginatively orchestrated piece of student-work. The orchestra here make a notable contribution to the recital's success, and it is a further sign of grace that the chorus are brought in for the Cossacks' "Go get the Mayor" spree in *May Night*.

Sergei Larin Songs by The Mighty Handful. **Sergei Larin** (ten); **Eleonora Bekova** (pf). Chandos Ⓕ CHAN9547 (67 minutes: DDD: 6/97). Texts and translations included.
    Rimsky-Korsakov Op. 43 – No. 1, The lark sings louder; No. 2, Not the wind, blowing from the heights. The octave, Op. 45 No. 3. The nymph, Op. 56 No. 1. The clouds begin to scatter, Op. 42 No. 3. On the hills of Georgia, Op. 3 No. 4. Of what I dream in the quiet sky, Op. 40 No. 3. Enslaved by the rose, the nightingale, Op. 2 No. 2. Silence descends on the golden cornfields, Op. 39 No. 3. Withered flower, Op. 51 No. 3. **Cui** A Statue at Tsarskoye Selo. The burnt letter, Op. 33 No. 4. **Borodin** The pretty girl no longer loves me (with Alfia Bekova, vc). For the shores of thy far native land. **Balakirev** Thou art so captivating. Barcarolle. Look, my friend. **Mussorgsky** Songs and Dances of Death.
Based on the evidence here, there can be little doubt that the 'Might' would be located in just one of the Five, for Mussorgsky stands out like a thumb, sore, maybe, but massive. Balakirev is the weakest member as represented here, his three songs so nearly commonplace, raised above that level by performances of unusual sensitivity. Cui's two are likeable, Borodin's impressive, and the larger group by Rimsky-Korsakov have a strong emotional and melodic appeal though perhaps a certain sameness. With these poetic passions and melancholy romances Mussorgsky's *Songs and Dances of Death* have about as much in common as Goya's *Old Man among Phantoms* with Renoir's *Girl in a Hat*. Larin sings the *Songs and Dances* with the utmost beauty of tone and purity of lyricism. In return, they seem to take it as a compliment, which in a way it is: they are so strong as to need no histrionics of any kind but, rather, to sharpen their acrid flavour against the sheer beauty of the singer's voice. Death's serenade goes at a ringing *forte*, the mother pleads woefully for her sick child, the Field Marshal enjoys an uproarious triumph. But these are the *songs* of Death, and they are well and truly sung. We have done well enough with Russian baritones, but tenors have been less forthcoming in all this repertoire; and they are needed, for so many are love songs for which the tenor is best suited, and of course he may have a much wider expressive range than that. Larin's tenor is beautifully pure, firm and even; it does not thin out in the lower register, and can rise with a powerful ring or a well-integrated head-voice. Eleonora Bekova plays in a style that admirably matches his, and if many of the songs have a delicacy one may think of as feminine, the last of Mussorgsky's four presents a harder and harsher challenge, which she meets with ample resource.

Jennifer Larmore My Native Land. **Jennifer Larmore** (mez); **Antoine Palloc** (pf). Teldec Ⓕ 0630-16069-2 (75 minutes: DDD: 12/97). Selected texts included. Recorded 1996.
    Heggie He's gone away. The leather-winged bat. Barb'ry Allen. To say before going to sleep. White in the moon. **Copland** Old American Songs, Set 2 – The little horses; Zion's walls; At the river; Ching-a-ring. **J. Duke** In the fields. Twentieth century. Heart! We will forget him!.

Barber Bessie Bobtail, Op. 2 No. 3. Songs, Op. 10 – No. 1, Rain has fallen; No. 2, Sleep now; No. 3, I hear an army. Sure on this shining night, Op. 13 No. 3. **Hoiby** Winter Song. A letter. **Hundley** The astronomers. **Aborn** 'Tis Winter now. Shall I compare thee to a Summer's day. Make me an instrument of Thy peace. **Niles** Black is the color of my true love's hair. Fee Simple. **Abramson** Soldier, Soldier. **Naginski** Richard Cory. **Ives** My native land. The things our fathers loved. Memories.

Jennifer Larmore has chosen this programme with care: it feels like a personal choice, sung with personal concern. Whether it's recast traditional, homegrown original or something altogether loftier, she seems to know where it's coming from. American song is nothing if not outspoken and this is a full, ripe, outspoken voice. *Black is the color of my true love's hair* gives you the measure of it – a handsome song, handsomely recast, the low-lying phrases of its glorious melody just as dark as dark can be. Occasionally the characterization slips into the Bryn Terfel school of the overstated. But then again you wouldn't want to be without the broadness of her Southern Belle in Robert Abramson's setting of *Soldier, Soldier*. For the rest, the unfamilar are among the richest pickings. The directness of Jake Heggie's setting of the traditional text *He's gone away* is at once disarming. It's impossible to date and yet there is something long-standing and venerable about it. Four other Heggie songs are offered, and in each case it's amazing how he assumes the identity of his texts. Lee Hoiby's work is most appealing, not least his impassioned Wilfred Owen setting, *Winter Song* and Emily Dickinson's *A letter* which is as shy, sly and wry as its deliciously knowing text. But ultimately, there is Samuel Barber. His two James Joyce settings, *I hear an army* and *Rain has fallen* are stunning, the former vivid, vehement, the latter defined by an inconsolable and very particular melancholy, culminating in a furious piano cadenza that says more about frustration and despair than even Joyce's text. Antoine Palloc plays it here with an awareness and strength of purpose that mark out his contributions throughout the disc. And, of course, there is *Sure on this shining night* – as fine a song about wonder and the infinite as any. James Agee's text is one of nine reproduced in the beautifully illustrated booklet. It is a pity all the texts have not been included. Good as Larmore's diction is, they are needed.

Dame Felicity Lott My Garden. **Dame Felicity Lott** (sop); **Graham Johnson** (pf). Hyperion Ⓕ CDA66937 (65 minutes: DDD: 10/97). Texts and translations included. Recorded 1996.
Schumann Mein Garten, Op. 77 No. 2. Jasminenstrauch, Op. 27 No. 4. Herzeleid, Op. 107 No. 1. Die Blume der Ergebung, Op. 83 No. 2. Erstes Grün, Op. 35 No. 4. Volksliedchen, Op. 51 No. 2. **Wolf** Mörike Lieder – Er ist's; Im Frühling; Der Gärtner. Eichendorff Lieder – Nachtzauber. Goethe Lieder – Frühling übers Jahr; Anakreons Grab. **Franck** Le mariage des roses. **Chausson** Le temps des lilas. **Fauré** Green, Op. 58 No. 3. Les roses d'Ispahan, Op. 39 No. 4. **Chabrier** Lied. Toutes les fleurs. **Stanford** From the red rose. **Haydn Wood** Roses of Picardy. **Musto** Triolet. The Rose Family. **Barab** One Perfect Rose. **Berners** Red Roses and Red Noses. **Stanley & Allen** Cabbages, Cabeans and Carrots.

The green-fingered accompanist has cultivated another fine display. Graham Johnson's garden of song is a splendid place for finding not only the usual hardy annuals from Germany, but also rare flowerings of the repertoire from France, England and the United States. The first half of this disc is devoted to Schumann and Wolf in about equal measure. There are some unusual items among the Schumann, such as the opening "Mein Garten" and Ophelia's "Herzeleid"; for the Wolf selection, Johnson extends the frontiers of his garden rather drastically, so as to take in the green hill of "Im Frühling" and the graveyard of "Anakreons Grab". No doubt he wanted to include a few major songs, but it is in these that Dame Felicity is most likely to be found wanting. Compared with the best rival performances, neither "Im Frühling" nor "Nachtzauber" reveals its hidden depths though her warm and affectionate singing of "Anakreons Grab" is on a higher level. The lighter Wolf songs, by contrast, are nicely turned. Once into the French and English half, there is no looking back, not least because the singer is twice as communicative in these languages as she is in German. The opening line of Chausson's *Le temps des lilas* is as idiomatic as one could wish, floating elegantly and sensuously over the long opening sentence and knowing just where to place the crucial change in vocal colour. The English-language group finds her lavishing a sensuality on Stanford's music that would probably have made the composer blush. There are two fine pithy songs by the American John Musto and another sarcastic one by Seymour Barab; then, in another rapid change of costume, she reappears in Eliza Doolittle's rags to end the disc with a delightfully upper-class fake Cockney rendering of *Cabbages, Cabeans and Carrots*. In the best Graham Johnson style, the disc is instructive and fun at the same time.

Dame Felicity Lott and Ann Murray On Wings of Song – Songs and Duets.
[a]**Dame Felicity Lott** (sop); [b]**Ann Murray** (mez); **Graham Johnson** (pf). EMI Ⓕ CDC7 54411-2 (76 minutes: DDD: 7/92). Texts and translations included. Recorded 1991.
Purcell (arr. Britten) Come ye sons of art, away, Z323 – Sound the trumpet[ab]. The Indian Queen – I attempt from love's sickness[b]. Lost is my quiet for ever, Z502[ab]. King Arthur – Fairest isle[a]. What can we poor females do, Z518[ab]. **Mendelssohn** Wasserfahrt[ab]. Duets, Op. 63[ab] – No. 5, Volkslied; No. 6, Maiglöckchen und die Blümelein. Auf Flügeln des Gesanges, Op. 34 No. 2[b]. Neue Liebe, Op. 19a No. 4[ab]. Abendlied[ab]. **Rossini** Soirées musicales – No. 1, La promessa[a]; No. 10, La pesca[ab]. Péchés de vieillesse, Book 1 – Anzoletta co passa la regata[b]. Duetto buffo di due gatti[ab]. **Gounod** La siesta[ab]. **Delibes** Les trois oiseaux[ab]. **Massenet** Rêvons, c'est

l'heure[ab]. Joie![ab]. **Paladilhe** Au bord de l'eau[ab]. **Aubert** Cache-cache[ab]. **Balfe** Trust her not[ab].
Sullivan Coming home[ab]. **Quilter** It was a lover and his lass, Op. 23 No. 3[ab]. **Britten** Mother
comfort[ab]. Underneath the abject willow[ab].

These expert duettists (fellow contributors to the Songmakers's Almanac and Marschallin and
Octavian in many a *Rosenkavalier*) have already one highly successfully disc ("Sweet Power of Song"
– reviewed further on) to their joint credit, and now achieve what often proves the more difficult task
of providing an equally good sequel. But of course this is not really a double-act but a trio, and
Graham Johnson is, as ever, more than accompanist. When he arranges a programme, delight follows
as sure as night follows day. Here the delight lies partly in discovery (for instance, there is a charmer
of Gounod's, in Spanish style, the voices in dreamy thirds, the ending softly delicate). Then there is
the range of mood, from Purcell's assured, outward-going "Sound the trumpet" at the start to the
desolation that burrows within Britten's haunting *Mother comfort* near the end. Solos are deftly
chosen to bring out the best in each singer, as in the clean style and unostentatious manner of Felicity
Lott's "Fairest isle" and Ann Murray's finely phrased, evenly sustained *Auf Flügeln des Gesanges*.
Then there are the charming oddities: Sullivan's "Coming home" turns out to be a duet from *Cox and
Box* (but with different words), and 'Rossini's' cat-duet is now attributed to that singularly
unpredictable minor genius, Robert Pearsall. The recording is exemplary.

Dame Felicity Lott and Ann Murray Sweet Power of Song. **Dame Felicity Lott** (sop);
Ann Murray (mez); **Graham Johnson** (pf) with [a]**Galina Solodchin** (vn) and [a]**Jonathan Williams**
(va). EMI Ⓔ CDC7 49930-2 (62 minutes: DDD: 11/90). Texts and translations included.
Recorded 1989.
Beethoven[a] 25 Irish Songs, WoO152 – Sweet power of song; English Bulls. 12 Irish Songs,
WoO154 – The Elfin Fairies; Oh! would I were but that sweet linnet. **Berlioz** Pleure, pauvre
Colette. Le trébuchet, Op. 13 No. 3. **Brahms** Vier Duette, Op. 61. **Chausson** Two duos, Op. 11.
Fauré Pleurs d'or, Op. 72. Tarantelle, Op. 10 No. 2. **Gounod** D'un coeur qui t'aime.
L'Arithmétique. **Saint-Saëns** Pastorale. El desdichado. **Schumann** Liederalbum für die
Jugend, Op. 79 – No. 15, Das Glück; No. 19, Frühlings Ankunft; No. 23, Er ist's; No. 26,
Schneeglöckchen.

This is a delightful presentation of an entertaining programme. The singers' careers have run
concurrently with growing success on the international scene yet they remain faithful to Graham
Johnson as founding members of the Songmakers' Almanac. Here they recall many evenings of
happy duetting at that group's recitals. They sing together with an instinctive rapport that is most
gratifying. Johnson has devised a programme for them that provides an ingenious variety of mood
and style. Beethoven's Irish Songs may not be great music but they are given vivid advocacy here. So
are the attractive and more profoun duets by Schumann and Brahms. The Berlioz pieces, nicely
contrasted, are well done; so are the Gounod, Fauré and Chausson items, even if a shade more
accenting of words would have been welcome here. The real winner among the French items – surely
a collector's item of the future – is Gounod's *L'Arithmétique*, an amusing lesson in Victorian thrift
delivered in both French and English. Johnson supplies appropriate accompaniments and interesting
notes. The recording naturally balances voices and piano.

Opera Gala [a]**Ruth Ann Swenson** (sop); [b]**Plácido Domingo** (ten); [c]**Thomas Hampson** (bar);
Philharmonia [d]**Chorus and Orchestra / Eugene Kohn**. EMI Ⓔ CDC5 55554-2
(61 minutes: DDD: 12/96). Texts and translations included. Recorded 1995.
Bellini I Puritani – Or dove fuggo ... Ah! per sempre[bc]. **Bizet** Les pêcheurs de perles – C'est toi!
... Au fond du temple saint[bc]; Ton coeur n'a pas compris[ab]. **Donizetti** Don Pasquale – Pronto io
son[ab]. **Rossini** Il barbiere di Siviglia – Zitti, zitti[bc]. Guillaume Tell – Mon fils! ... Sois
immobile[c]. **A. Thomas** Mignon – Elle ne croyait pas[b]; Adieu, Mignon![b]. **Verdi** Alzira – Amici!
... Ah! per sempre[bcd].

Instead of cherry-picking the usual highlights, this recital gives us arias and duets in the context of
complete scenes, which affords the added novelty of the stars taking on supporting roles they would
never usually sing. It is not often one hears a Domingo or a Hampson playing the part of 'an official'
or 'an Indian warrior', but that is what happens here. Hampson sings with a natural fluency and
beauty of tone in the Bellini. Domingo is magnificently authoritative in the Verdi, delivering aria and
both verses of the cabaletta with splendid breadth and ringing tone. I doubt this music has ever been
sung better. Anybody wanting to investigate operas just off the beaten track in this celebrated
company should find it an attractive programme. Of the three singers, Domingo gets the most to do;
he also takes part in both duets from *Les pêcheurs de perles*, blending sumptuously with Hampson in
the favourite "Au fond du temple saint" and partnering a delicate Ruth Ann Swenson in the love duet,
both extracts again nicely set in context. Hampson has a second solo aria in "Sois immobile" from
Guillaume Tell, and then proves a characterful Malatesta to Swenson's lively Norina in the *Don
Pasquale* duet. Eugene Kohn accompanies with a generalized feel for the theatre. To close, the three
singers come together for a brisk rendition of the "Zitti, zitti" trio from *Il barbiere di Siviglia*.

Anne Sofie von Otter Wings in the night – Swedish Songs. **Anne Sofie von Otter** (mez);
Bengt Forsberg (pf). DG Ⓔ 449 189-2GH (74 minutes: DDD: 5/96). Texts and translations
included. Recorded 1995. *Gramophone Editor's choice.*   ⒢Ⓖ

Peterson-Berger Nothing is like the time of waiting. Swedish folk ballads, Op. 5 – No. 1, When I go myself in the dark forest; No. 3, Like stars in the heavens. Three Marit's Songs, Op. 12. Böljeby Waltz. Return. Aspåkers Polka. **Sigurd von Koch** Exotic Songs – No. 1, In the month of Tjaitra; No. 3, Of lotus scent and moonlight. The wild swans – Spring night's rain; Mankind's lot; The wild swans. **Stenhammar** Songs and Moods, Op. 26 – No. 1, The Wanderer; No. 4, Miss Blonde and Miss Brunette; No. 5, A ship sails; No. 9, Coastal song. Songs, Op. 37 – No. 1, Jutta comes to the Volkungs; No. 2, In the maple's shade. **Rangström** Poems by Bo Bergman – No. 1, Wings in the night; No. 3, Melody. The Dark Flower – No. 2, Prayer to the night; No. 4, Farewell. Pan. Old Swedish. **Alfvén** Songs, Op. 28 – No. 3, I kiss your hand; No. 6, The forest sleeps. **Sjögren** Lieder from Wolff's "Tannhäuser", Op. 12 – No. 4, Hab'ein Röslein dir gebrochen; No. 6, Ich möchte schweben. Du schaust mich an mit stummen Fragen.

If von Otter's and Forsberg's intention in compiling this recital was to provide an introduction to the riches of Swedish song so compelling that purchasers of it will hunger for more, they have succeeded. There are very few songs here that could not be programmed without apology or fear of comparison alongside the best German Lieder of the same period (the 40 years between 1884 and 1924). They contain considerable variety of mood and musical style, and the recital has been cleverly programmed to demonstrate in particular the range and the development of the two finest song composers here, Wilhelm Peterson-Berger and Wilhelm Stenhammar. Both were greatly gifted melodists, Peterson-Berger holding to an almost folk-like vein of simple lyricism, while Stenhammar reached further and touched darker moods, and the other composers here are by no means cast into the shade by these two masters. The performances are superb, quiet shadings of colour and subtle phrasings under immaculate control, a mere thread of voice often used to draw you into the heart of a song quite magically. Forsberg is an ideally imaginative and positive partner. You will probably find yourself playing several of these songs over and over again (for von Otter's exquisite little flourish of coloratura at the end of von Koch's *Of lotus scent*, for example, or for her delightful touch of humour and affection describing little chicks "who can hardly walk" stumbling into the first warm sun of summer in the first of Peterson-Berger's *Marit's Songs*).

Ian Partridge and Stephen Roberts Songs by Finzi and his Friends. [a]**Ian Partridge** (ten); [b]**Stephen Roberts** (bar); **Clifford Benson** (pf). Hyperion Ⓕ CDA66015 (51 minutes: ADD: 9/91). Texts included. From A66015 (9/81). Recorded 1981.
Finzi To a Poet, Op. 13a[b]. Oh fair to see, Op. 13b[a]. **Milford**[a] If it's ever spring again. The colour. So sweet love seemed. **Farrar** O mistress mine![a]. **Gurney**[b] Sleep. Down by the salley gardens. Hawk and Buckle. **Gill** In Memoriam[b].
This is a record that drew from its original reviewer, Trevor Harvey, high and unstinting praise when it appeared in 1981 as part of the commemoration of Finzi 25 years after his death. Finzi was never an avant-garde composer and during his lifetime received quiet and grateful acknowledgement from kindred spirits rather than anything more spectacular. In the last 20 years or so, appreciation has deepened and become more widespread. His songs, in particular, have a depth of feeling that is not always apparent at first hearing, and their idiom is that of a writer to whom overstatement or any other kind of cheapening would have been abhorrent. In this selection most of the chosen poems are affectionate and gentle, but F.L. Lucas's *June on Castle Hill* contains "whispers of wars to come", and George Barker's "Ode on the Rejection of St Cecilia" is a strong and sombre utterance that evokes an uncommonly hard-hitting style in the composer. His friend, Robin Milford, sets Hardy and Bridges with comparable sensitivity, and Ernest Farrar (killed in 1918) is remembered by his charmingly nonchalant *O mistress mine!*. Stephen Roberts is an admirable singer of the songs by Ivor Gurney, and Ian Partridge gives a lovely account of Finzi's Op. 13b *Oh fair to see*. Clifford Benson is the excellent accompanist throughout and recording and presentation are first-rate.

Pavarotti Plus Sixtieth Birthday Album. [a]**Luciano Pavarotti** (ten); [b]**Nathalie Dessay**, [c]**Kallen Esperian**, [d]**Nuccia Focile** (sops); [e]**Dolora Zajick**, [f]**Leah-Marian Jones** (mezzos); [g]**Giuseppe Sabbatini** (ten); [h]**Dwayne Croft**, [i]**Leo Nucci**, [j]**Piero Cappuccilli** (bars); [k]**Francesco Ellero D'Artegna** (bass); [l]**Philharmonia Chorus and Orchestra / James Levine**; [m]**Royal Philharmonic Orchestra / Leone Magiera**. Decca Ⓕ 448 701-2DH2 (two discs: 131 minutes: DDD: 2/96).
All items except *Inno delle Nazioni* recorded live in 1995. All items in which Pavarotti sings are also available on 448 700-2DH (71 minutes: DDD). Recorded 1995.
Verdi Inno delle Nazioni[al]. Il trovatore – Madre, non dormi? ... Ai nostri monti[aem]. La traviata – Libiamo, ne' lieti calici[a-k,m]; O mia Violetta ... Parigi, o cara[adm]. Aida – Fù la sorte dell'armi ... Amore, amore[cem]. La forza del destino – Invano Alvaro[aim]. Macbeth – O figli, o figli miei! ... Ah, la paterna mano[am]. Otello – Dio ti giocondi[acm]. Rigoletto – Giovanna, ho dei rimorsi ... E il sol dell'anima[bfgm]. I Lombardi – L'acque sante del Giordano ... Qual voluttà[ackm]. **Puccini** Tosca – Recondita armonia[am]. La bohème – Dunque, è proprio finita! ... Addio dolce svegliare[cdghm]; In un coupé? ... O Mimì, tu più non torni[ahm]. Manon Lescaut – Tra voi, belle[am]. **Leoncavallo** Pagliacci – Nedda! Silvio! a quest'ora[chm]. **Gounod** Faust – Alerte! alerte! ... Anges purs[dgkm]. **Thomas** Hamlet – Ophélie ... Doute de la lumière[bhm]. **Tchaikovsky** Eugene Onegin – Onegin, I was younger then[dhm]. **Donizetti** L'elisir d'amore – Venti scudi[gim].
Although the event probably lives in the memory as the Pavarotti Sixtieth Birthday Party, it was actually a gala to celebrate the 125th anniversary of the Red Cross, and its most memorable feature,

amongst all this exuberant sound, was probably a two-minute silence. The two CDs, well filled as they are, do not include everything in the programme, but, while the aria of Des Grieux in *Manon Lescaut* is out, the shorter, opening solo, "Tra voi, belle", is in, and a most delightfully humorous, idiosyncratic performance it receives, Pavarotti probably endearing himself more in that brief pleasantry than in the desperations of *Macbeth* and *La forza del destino*, or in the bitter ironies (which he does not quite catch) of Otello. With him are singers, mostly from the younger generation, each of whom is given a generous share of the evening's opportunities. Most interest centres on Giuseppe Sabbatini as the only other tenor and a possible 'successor'. His voice rings out well, with a full-bodied timbre and an ample fund of high notes; stylishness, however, is not an element notable in his performances, nor indeed in those of the others. Indeed, though the title is "Pavarotti Plus", the real 'plus' is still Pavarotti. In his sixtieth year he preserves, pre-eminently in this company, the two qualities that contribute most to the pleasure which lies in the sound of a singing voice: purity of timbre (no surface-scratch or breathiness) and evenness of emission. In essentials it is still a young voice. As he confronts the heroic demands of Verdi's *Hymn to the Nations*, we can only marvel at the stamina, and be grateful that in such a performance this most popular, and so most influential, of living opera singers sets so wholesome an example.

Sir Peter Pears The Land of Lost Content. **Sir Peter Pears** (ten); [ab]**Benjamin Britten**, [c]**Alan Bush**, [d]**Viola Tunnard** (pfs). Belart Ⓑ 461 550-2 (69 minutes: ADD: 12/97). Items marked [a] from Argo ZRG5418 (11/64), [bcd]ZRG5439 (9/65). Recorded 1963-64.
Ireland The Land of Lost Content[a]. The trellis[a]. **Bridge** 'Tis but a week, H146[a]. Goldenhair, H165[a]. When you are old and gray, H142[a]. So perverse, H61[a]. Journey's End, H167[a]. **Tippett** Songs for Ariel[b]. **A. Bush** Voices of the Prophets, Op. 41[c]. **Delius** To Daffodils[d]. **Moeran** The merry month of May[d]. **Dieren** Dream pedlary[d]. Take, o take those lips away[d]. **Warlock** Piggesnie[d]. Along the stream[d]. **Grainger** Bold William Taylor, BFMS43[d]. **Busch** The echoing Green[d]. The shepherd[d]. If thou wilt ease thine heart[d]. Come, o come, my life's delight[d].
Though Ireland's settings of Housman come first and give the disc its title, the group by Frank Bridge is stronger and more immediately impressive, with his particularly lovely setting of Yeats's *When you are old and gray and full of sleep* and the jaunty, catchy *So perverse*. The cycle by Alan Bush, *Voices of the Prophets*, gives the recital a firm centre, with its strongly committed treatment of politically correct passages from Isaiah, Milton, Blake and Peter Blackman. Warlock's *Piggesnie* is a delightful encore-song, Grainger's *Bold William Taylor* another, the one having Pears charmingly managing each verse in a single breath, the other a fine example of his vividness in narrative and dialogue. Three excellent pianists accompany him.

Ewa Podles Russian Songs. **Ewa Podles** (contr); **Graham Johnson** (pf). Forlane Ⓔ UCD16683 (70 minutes: DDD: 5/95). Translations included.
Rachmaninov Op. 4 – No. 2, Morning; No. 3, In the silence of the secret night. Op. 14 – No. 1, I wait for thee; No. 8, Oh, do not grieve; No. 9, She is as lovely as the moon; No. 11, Spring waters. Op. 26 No. 6, Christ is risen. **Mussorgsky** The Nursery. Songs and Dances of Death. **Tchaikovsky** Op. 47 – No. 1, If only I had known; No. 6, Does the day reign?; No. 7, Was I not a little blade of grass? Zemfira's song.
Podles is a welcome throwback to a more idiosyncratic style of singing. Taking risks in her interpretations, she earns her rewards. The voice itself is a vibrant, almost fruity contralto, far from the more refined, genteel kind we have become used to of late. In the two Mussorgsky cycles Podles comes into competition with Leiferkus, whose readings leave such a profound impression (see review under Mussorgsky; refer to the Index). Without quite the vocal acuity of her Russian counterpart, the Polish-born Podles makes her own mark. Her inveigling, impulsive child in *The Nursery* cycle is a delight. She and Johnson capture all the charming innocence of the cycle without ever becoming whimsical or cute. They achieve even greater success in the more formidable demands of *Songs and Dances of Death* (usually a man's task). In the first song, a kind of Russian *Erlkönig*, Podles is insinuating; in the second, a sinister barcarolle, she is deliberately sensual; in the third, appropriately fantastic (Johnson is superb here); while in the finale, the mood of heroic pessimism is exactly caught. This reading is just as valid as Leiferkus's more incisive, extrovert approach. Podles takes a big-scale, romantic view of Rachmaninov and Tchaikovsky. In Rachmaninov's Op. 14 No. 8, she uses a huge range of dynamics from an almost crooning start to an operatic *forte* at the song's climax, while *Christ is risen* is properly visionary. The recording is excellent in balance and perspective.

Lucia Popp Opera Arias – Gianni Schicchi, Die lustige Witwe and Rusalka; songs by Brahms, Dvořák, Kodály, Mahler, Mozart, Prokofiev and Rachmaninov. **Lucia Popp** (sop); **Geoffrey Parsons** (pf). Orfeo Ⓔ C363941B (69 minutes: ADD: 6/95). Recorded live in 1981. ⒼⒼ
The soprano is in most lovely voice, singing with warmth and delicacy, exercising a completely unostentatious mastery of perhaps a dozen facets of a singer's art. Her accompanist is what he always was, the superb professional; but, more than that, he works in complete sympathy with the singer and seems incapable of touching the simplest phrase without discovering its musical interest. At one point you can *see* him: it is in the last encore, the "Viljalied", where the piano introduction is pure Parsons. The encores are probably what everybody present would remember years afterwards. They are finely

graded – a Mozart song, happy and carefree after the subdued mood of Brahms's *In stiller Nacht* which ended the official programme: then there comes a little more concession to a romantic taste in Rachmaninov's *Lilacs*, and then, in order, Puccini, Dvořák and Lehár, all performed with taste and refinement, all yielding bigger returns with the drumming of feet and the shouting of bravos. Before this, the audience had enjoyed a recital with folk-song as its theme. The command of languages (Russian, Hungarian, Czech and German) is remarkable enough, and with it goes a musical expressiveness that can (at least to some extent) break the language barrier but texts would have been welcome. Recorded sound is excellent, and the disc a treasure.

Leontyne Price A Program of Song. **Leontyne Price** (sop); **David Garvey** (pf).
RCA Victor Living Stereo Ⓜ 09026 61499-2 (40 minutes: ADD: 5/93). Texts and translations included. Recorded 1959. New to UK.
Fauré Clair de lune, Op. 46 No. 2. Notre amour, Op. 23 No. 2. Au cimetière, Op. 51 No. 2. Au bord de l'eau, Op. 8 No. 1. Mandoline, Op. 58 No. 1. **Poulenc** Main dominée par le coeur. Miroirs brûlants. Ce doux petit visage. **R. Strauss** Allerseelen, Op. 10 No. 8. Schlagende Herzen, Op. 29 No. 2. Freundliche Vision, Op. 48 No. 1. Wie sollten wir geheim, Op. 19 No. 4. **Wolf** Mörike Lieder – Der Gärtner; Lebe wohl. Lieder für eine Frauen-stimme – Morgentau. Spanisches Liederbuch – Geh' Geliebter, geh' jetz.

There can be few recordings which so vividly resemble the sound of singer and pianist performing live in one's own home. This forward, warts-and-all 1959 RCA recording has a disconcerting immediacy, but it's not just the recorded sound which creates this sense of close intimacy. Leontyne Price sings with a captivating directness which belongs more to a domestic setting than the concert-hall – or even the opera house, for it was here that her reputation was made, becoming revered as one of the foremost Verdi sopranos. Her recorded legacy encompasses major roles from Mozart through Berlioz and Puccini to Gershwin and Samuel Barber, but this CD is special. This was her recording début made in the Town Hall, New York City, and shows her in repertoire with which she has not generally been associated. Yet she sings it with an intuition and sensitivity which would be the envy of singers whose lifetimes' work has been in Lieder and *chanson*. The French and German accents have an unmistakable American twang, but it's not the words which matter so much as the sense of involvement she brings to each and every one of these beautiful and memorable songs. A CD of great historic and artistic value.

Dame Margaret Price The Romantic Lied. **Dame Margaret Price** (sop); **Graham Johnson** (pf).
Forlane Ⓕ UCD16728 (71 minutes: DDD: 2/95). Texts and translations included. Recorded 1993.
Wolf Mörike Lieder – Er ist's; Begegnung; Der Gärtner; In der Frühe; Lebe wohl; Heimweh; Gesang Weylas; Bei einer Trauung. **Cornelius** Trauer und Trost, Op. 3. **Liszt** Freudvoll und leidvoll, S280. Uber allen Gipfeln ist Ruh, S306. Mignons Lied, S275. Der du von dem Himmel bist, S279. **Wagner** Wesendonk Lieder.

Price and Johnson have done it again. He has chosen a programme for her that exactly suits her talents and style, and she (with his inestimable help) has executed it with commitment and understanding. The programme in itself is fascinating, comparing and contrasting composers of roughly the same generation and period. The cross-fertilization of musical ideas is apparent, yet each emerges as an artist with something highly individual to say. Wolf isn't a composer with whom Price has been very much associated until now, but in a group of the Mörike settings, she proves herself at one with the poems and their music, catching in particular the restless ardour of *Begegnung*, the timeless mystery of *Gesang Weylas*, and the peculiarly Wolfian charm of the lighter pieces. Liszt is even more to her liking. She and Johnson choose the later, longer version of *Freudvoll und leidvoll* and make a grand romantic statement of it that is just right. The interpretation of the *Wesendonk Lieder* is the crowning glory of this wonderful recital. A virtually faultless reading, speeds (no unwanted lingering), phrasing, line and tone ideally adapted to the words and music. Johnson places the piano part in perfect relationship with the voice, helped by the exemplary recording of both.

Samuel Ramey Ev'ry time we say goodbye – American Songs. **Samuel Ramey** (bar); **Warren Jones** (pf). Sony Classical Ⓕ SK68339 (71 minutes: DDD: 2/97). Texts included. Recorded live in 1995.
Barber Hermit Songs, Op. 29 – No. 6, Sea-snatch. I hear an army, Op. 10 No. 3. Sure on this shining night, Op. 13 No. 3. Bessie Bobtail, Op. 2 No. 3. **Foster** If you've only got a moustache. Gentle Annie. Don't bet your money at the Shanghai. **Griffes** Evening song. An old song re-sung. The lament of Ian the Proud. Song of the dagger. **Gershwin** Nice work if you can get it. They all laughed. Embraceable you. Just another rhumba. **Bowles** They cannot stop death. Blue Mountain Ballads. **Porter** Blow, Gabriel, blow. Begin the Beguine. Ev'ry time we say goodbye. The tale of the oyster.

The opening Barber group kicks off with the short "Sea-snatch" (one of the *Hermit Songs*, composed for soprano); this, like the James Agee setting, *Sure on this shining night*, is sung by Cheryl Studer on the complete Barber songs set (see review under Barber; refer to the Index), where Thomas Hampson sings the baritone songs. Ramey's darker-hued voice lends a more wintry feel to the James Joyce poem, *I hear an army* as well as to the sad story of mad *Bessie Bobtail*. It's quite a leap to the three Stephen Foster ballads. *If you've only got a moustache* must have brought a touch of vaudeville into the parlours of pre-Civil War America. This, and the rather nasty cock-fighting song, *Don't bet your money at the Shanghai*, frame a more typical Foster song, *Gentle Annie*, a near cousin to the more celebrated *Jeannie*. Charles Griffes's songs have been recorded by Hampson, but he stuck to his settings of German poetry. Ramey here climaxes with the bloodthirsty *Song of the dagger*, projecting such lines as "My tears and thy blood shall flow together" with all the operatic fervour at his command. The groups of show tunes by Gershwin and Porter come either side of the five Paul Bowles songs. Of these the rarest is *They cannot stop death* to a text by Joe Massey. In the four *Blue Mountain Ballads* (words by Tennessee Williams) Ramey sounds quite straight. In the Gershwin group, "Embraceable you" sounds very surprising so low down; when Ramey sings "you alone bring out the gipsy in me" the effect is very different from what one imagines was achieved by Ginger Rogers when she first sang this in *Girl Crazy*. His version of "Just another rhumba" is notable for the agility he manages in the fast-moving refrain, prompting a built-in encore with the final verse. "The tale of the oyster", written by Porter for *Fifty Million Frenchmen*, was dropped after the opening, considered too *risqué*. Ramey does it with charm and diction that would have pleased the composer. Warren Jones provides a few words to help "Blow, Gabriel, blow" get going. This is a serious, and at the same time amusing, ride around a century of American song.

Anthony Rolfe Johnson A Shropshire Lad. **Anthony Rolfe Johnson** (ten); **Graham Johnson** (pf). Hyperion Ⓔ CDA66471/2 (two discs: 124 minutes: DDD: 8/95). Includes various poems from Housman's "A Shrophire Lad" read by Alan Bates. Texts included. Recorded 1994.
Barber With rue my heart is laden. **L. Berkeley** Because I liked you better. He would not stay for me. **Butterworth** Bredon Hill. When the lad for longing sighs. On the idle hill of summer. A Shropshire Lad – complete. **Horder** White in the moon. **Ireland** Hawthorn time. The heart's desire. The lent lily. Goal and wicket. The vain desire. The encounter. Epilogue. **Moeran** Far in a western brookland. **C.W. Orr** When I watch the living meet. Hughley steeple. Into my heart. O see how thick the goldcup flowers. The Isle of Portland. This time of year.

There should be a Hyperion 'Book of Essays'. Graham Johnson's introductions would probably make quite a handsome volume on their own, and there would certainly be room for Andrew Green's notes on this Housman anthology. If indeed (as he says) there has long been argument about the whys and wherefores of Housman's popularity among composers, with Ernest Newman claiming (where?) that *A Shropshire Lad* "cried out for music", then these discs should further the discussion, suggesting some very good reasons by simple juxtaposition of the speaking and the singing voice – or rather, of the sound of the text alone compared with the musical expression of feelings it evokes. The poems are presented in their printed order, all 63 of them (with two added from other volumes), 28 in musical settings, the rest recited. Alan Bates employs what may seem restricted means: he reads without any of the throb of poetry, the voice rarely extended in range or volume, the manner reflective yet dispassionate, almost dry. So may Housman himself have read, and one's first thought is that this probably accounts for it as a 'policy'. A little tentative experimentation (growing bolder) convinces that it is the right way, perhaps the only way; which is one reason why the poems, in Newman's words, cry out for music. The music lies within the lines as they pass, lovingly, through the mind, but the actual sound of the words, for all the prevalence of rhyme and rhythm, is curiously tight-lipped, prosaic, factual. Among the song-writers here, George Butterworth has an almost invariable rightness of note-catching. Others miss the sharpness, the more sardonic tone. The performances are sensitive to nuance, of both words and notes. Graham Johnson's touch is often uncannily suggestive, letting the melisma of the opening phrases of "Loveliest of trees" trickle deliciously through his fingers. Rolfe Johnson sings with all his customary gifts and skill, producing a rare (and right) effect of chilling uncertainty at the end of "Is my team ploughing?".

Leonie Rysanek Opera Arias. **Leonie Rysanek** (sop); [c]**Jon Vickers** (ten); [d]**Harold Steinberg** (bass); orchestra / **Arturo Basile**; [b]**Orchestra of the Metropolitan Opera, New York** / **Erich Leinsdorf**; [c]**Rome Opera Orchestra** / **Tullio Serafin**. RCA Classics Ⓜ 74321 37719-2* (78 minutes: ADD: 11/96). Items marked [a] from RB16148 (6/59), [b]SER4505/7 (6/60), [c]LDS6155 (11/61).
Verdi La forza del destino – Pace, pace, mio Dio![a]. Aida[a] – Ritorna vincitor; O patria mia. Macbeth – Nel di della vittoria ... Vieni t'affretta[bd]; La luce langue[b]. Otello – Già nella notte densa[c]; Mia madre aveva ... Piangea cantando[a]; Ave Maria[a]. Un ballo in maschera – Ma dall'arido stelo divulsa; Morrò, ma prima in grazia (previously unpublished, recorded 1958).
Puccini Tosca – Vissi d'arte[a]. Turandot – In questa reggia[a]. **Giordano** Andrea Chénier – La mamma morta[a]. **Mascagni** Cavalleria Rusticana – Voi lo sapete[a].

In 1996 Rysanek made her emotional farewell to the opera house (as Klytemnestra in *Elektra*) at the Salzburg Festival after virtually 50 years on stage, a remarkable if not unique record. Though she has been long recognized as an exceptional interpreter of Leonore and of many roles in the operas of Wagner and Richard Strauss, her extraordinary skills in the Italian *spinto* repertory have not been so fully recognized, at least in Britain. In all the wide-ranging arias she chooses she proves herself one of the most exciting and exacting interpreters of the respective roles on disc. She provided a kind of ideal marriage between the styles of her coevals, Callas, Tebaldi and Leontyne Price, with the interpretative insights of the one, the vocal opulence of the others, confirmed in her *Aida* solos. In every piece she has thought herself into the heart of the role and in every case she substantially obeys what is written in the score as regards phrasing and dynamics, most notably perhaps in "O patria mia" and "In questa reggia". Tosca was one of her few Covent Garden roles and "Vissi d'arte" shows her as the sensual heroine of Puccini's opera *par excellence*. The *Otello* love duet with Vickers comes from the admired complete set, a wonderfully balanced, eloquent rendering on both sides, Rysanek here as elsewhere providing ravishing *piano* singing to recall that of Milanov. The *Macbeth* items come from the complete RCA set and prove why the diva caused such a stir when she replaced Callas in the part at the Met in 1959. On the recital items Basile is a vital accompanist. The recordings sound much more vivid than on LP, marred by only fleeting moments showing tape degradation. No lover of Italianate singing at its best should be without this invaluable issue.

Dame Elisabeth Schwarzkopf Lieder Recital. **Dame Elisabeth Schwarzkopf** (sop); Gerald Moore (pf). EMI Festspieldokumente mono Ⓜ CDH5 66084-2* (70 minutes: ADD: 12/96). Texts included. Recorded live in 1956.
Bach Bist du bei mir. **Parisotti** Se tu m'ami. **Handel** Atalanta – Care selve. **Gluck** La rencontre imprévue – C'est un torrent (sung in German). **Beethoven** Wonne der Wehmut, Op. 83 No. 1. **Schubert** An Silvia, D891. Rosamunde, D797 – Der Vollmond strahlt. Die Vögel, D691. Der Einsame, D800. Didone abbandonata, D510. Die schöne Müllerin, D795 – Ungeduld. **Wolf** Goethe Lieder – Philine; Kennst du das Land?. Eichendorff Lieder – Die Zigeunerin; Nachtzauber. **R. Strauss** Ruhe, meine Seele, Op. 27 No. 1. Hat's gesagt, Op. 36 No. 3. Wiegenlied, Op. 49 No. 1. Schlechtes Wetter, Op. 69 No. 5. **Mozart** Warnung, K433. **Schumann** Der Nussbaum, Op. 25 No. 3.

Although this Salzburg recital is new to disc, its programme is made up of typical Schwarzkopf favourites, so there is little here that the assiduous collector will not have in some performance by the singer elsewhere. However, with Gerald Moore at his eloquent best, and with a better original recording quality, this is the one to have. Schwarzkopf herself also sounds in easier voice, shaping the opening lines of Wolf's *Kennst du das Land?* more fluently and generally responding to Moore's lighter touch. Inevitably, there are songs which some listeners will find over-interpreted (Wolf's *Philine* and *Die Zigeunerin* are both helped along with a nudge and a wink too many) but there is much to enjoy. The mixed opening group is full of variety. Schubert's *An Silvia* is delightfully playful, Schumann's *Der Nussbaum* almost unbearably tender. Enough: recommended.

Dame Elisabeth Schwarzkopf Songbook Dame Elisabeth Schwarzkopf (sop); [a]Gerald Moore, [b]Geoffrey Parsons, [c]Nicolas Medtner, [d]Cyril Szalkiewicz (pfs). EMI mono/stereo Ⓜ CHS5 65860-2* (three discs: 230 minutes: ADD: 4/96). Texts and translations included. Recorded 1947-74. Ⓖ
Mozart Warnung, K433[a] (from Columbia LB73, 11/48). Der Zauberer, K472 (two versions; LB118[a], 2/52 and HMV ASD2844[b], 8/73). Das Veilchen, K476[b] (ASD2404, 12/68). **Schubert** Die schöne Müllerin, D795 – Ungeduld[a] (Columbia 33CX1044, 9/54). Claudine von Villa Bella – Liebe schwärmt auf allen Wegen[a] (Columbia SAX5268, 10/66). **Mendelssohn** Auf Flügeln des Gesanges, Op. 34 No. 2[a] (SAX2265, 3/59). **Schumann** Liederkreis, Op. 39[b] – In der Fremde; Intermezzo; Waldesgespräch; Die Stille; In der Fremde II; Im Walde (all from ASD3037, 1/75). Aufträge, Op. 77 No. 5[a] (LB122, 3/52). Widmung, Op. 25 No. 1[a] (SAX5268). **Liszt** Die drei Zigeuner, S320[b] (ASD2634, 3/71). **Brahms** Vergebliches Ständchen, Op. 84 No. 4[a] (33CX1044). Liebestreu, Op. 3 No. 1[b]. Vergebliches Ständchen, Op. 84 No. 4[b]. Der Jäger, Op. 95 No. 4[b]. Wie Melodien zieht es mir, Op. 105 No. 1[b]. Immer leiser wird mein Schlummer, Op. 105 No. 2[b]. Ständchen, Op. 106 No. 1[b] (ASD2844). **Jensen** Murmelndes Lüftchen, Op. 21 No. 4[a] (SAX2265). **Mahler** Lob des hohen Verstandes[b]. **R. Strauss** Wer lieben will, Op. 49 No. 7[b]. Ach, was Kummer, Op. 49 No. 8[b] (ASD2404). Drei Lieder der Ophelia, Op. 67[b] (previously unpublished. From a BBC broadcast performance on December 2nd, 1968). **Wolf** Italienisches Liederbuch – 25 Lieder[a] (SAX2366, 12/61). Goethe Lieder[a] – Blumengruss; Epiphanias; Gleich und Gleich; Frühling übers Jahr (SAX2333, mono 3/60); Hoch beglückt in deiner Liebe; Als ich auf dem Euphrat schiffte; Nimmer will ich dich verlieren!; Der Schäfer (SAX2589, 2/66). Mörike Lieder[b] – Verborgenheit; Lebe wohl (ASD2404); Auf einem Christblume I (ASD2844); Auftrag. Kleine gleicht von allen Schönen[a] (ASD3124, 3/76). Wiegenlied im Sommer[a]. Mausfallen-Sprüchlein[a] (33CX1044). Spanisches Liederbuch – In dem Schatten meiner Locken[a]. **Grieg** Farmyard Song, Op. 61 No. 3[a] (SAX2265). I love but thee, Op. 5 No. 3[b]. With a waterlily, Op. 25 No. 4[b]. Last Spring, Op. 33 No. 2[b] (ASD2634). The first meeting, Op. 21 No. 1[b]. The way of the world, Op. 48 No. 3[b]. The time of roses, Op. 48 No. 5[b]. With a primrose, Op. 26 No. 4[b] (ASD2844). **Dvořák** Songs my mother taught me, B104 No. 4[a]. **Tchaikovsky** None but the lonely heart, Op. 6 No. 6[a] (SAX2265). **Mussorgsky** Gathering mushrooms[b] (ASD2404). **Medtner**[c] The muse, Op. 29 No. 1 (Columbia LX1425, 10/51). The rose, Op. 29 No. 6 (LX1423, 10/51). The waltz, Op. 32 No. 5 (LX1425). Kaum welken hier die Rosen, Op. 36 No. 3. Elfenliedchen, Op. 6 No. 3. Im Vorübergehen, Op. 6 No. 4 (LX1423). Songs, Op. 15 – Selbstbetrug, Op. 15 No. 3 (LX1424, 10/51). Aus "Lila", Op. 15 No. 5 (LX1425). Meeresstille, Op. 15 No. 7. Glückliche Fahrt, Op. 15 No. 8 (LX1424). Einsamkeit, Op. 18 No. 3. Songs, Op. 46 – No. 1, Praeludium; No. 5, Winter Night (LX1426, 10/51); No. 6, The Fountain (LX1424). **Sibelius**[d] Songs, Op. 72 – No. 3, The kiss; No. 4, The echo nymph; No. 6, A hundred ways. The north, Op. 90 No. 1. Songs, Op. 36 – No. 1, Black roses; No. 4, Sigh, sedges, sigh. Songs, Op. 37 – No. 1, The first kiss; No. 4, Was it a dream? (prev. unpublished. Finnish broadcast performance, June 11th, 1955).

"For me, the supreme Lieder singer of our time": the writer, careful to present his judgement as personal as well as fully deliberate (he has Fischer-Dieskau in view and makes a close comparison to substantiate the point a little later on), was Eric Sams, and there can be no one whose opinion on Lieder and the performance of Lieder is more worth having. All three discs have their treasures. The first includes, rather unexpectedly, Mendelssohn's *Auf Flügeln des Gesanges*, gracefully combining an unspoilt legato line with an intelligent attention to meaning. Six songs from Schumann's Eichendorff *Liederkreis* are salvaged from the complete recording. Among the Brahms songs is *Immer leiser wird mein Schlummer*, one of the few performances of that song to go on the assumption that the poem means what it says. The three *Ophelia* Songs of Strauss are new: recorded live at the Ernest Newman Commemoration Concert in 1968, and affording a welcome alternative to the version with Glenn Gould on Sony (3/93). The second disc is entirely devoted to Wolf, and has a particularly lovely early (1954) recording of the *Wiegenlied im Sommer*. Then on the final disc, called "Rarities", we are given a delightful selection of Grieg, starting with the *Farmyard Song* in English, a complete run of the Medtner recordings made with the composer in 1950, and, most valuably, a Sibelius group, taken from a Finnish Radio concert of 1955 and here released for the first time. These capture the voice at its most radiant and the spirit at its most impassioned: deeply felt performances and a genuine enrichment of the archive. The transfers have the great modern virtue of clarity, and also the modern vice of achieving it at the expense of the warmth and the absence of hardness which were characteristic of the voice we knew 'in the flesh'. Adjusted to suit taste, they can still give great pleasure.

Mitsuko Shirai Hölderlin Songs. **Mitsuko Shirai** (mez); **Hartmut Höll** (pf). Capriccio Ⓕ 10 534 (69 minutes: DDD: 12/94). Texts and translations included. Recorded 1986-93.
   Ullmann Abendphantasie. Der Frühling. **Eisler** Sechs Hölderlin-Fragmente.
   Komma Fünf Hölderlin Fragmente. **Reutter** Drei Hölderlin Lieder, Op. 67.
   Fröhlich Rückkehr in die Heimat. **Cornelius** Sonnenuntergang. **Jarnach** An eine Rose.
   Hauer Ehmals und jetzt. **Pfitzner** Abbitte, Op. 29 No. 1. **Fortner** Geh unter, schöne Sonne.
   Britten Hölderlin Fragments, Op. 61 – No. 5, Hälfte des Lebens.

Hölderlin evoked a unique world in those composers who have felt able to approach him, and this ingeniously compiled and finely performed recital amply and absorbingly bears that out. He was mad, of course, but in the midst of his mental whirlwind often achieved a lucid stillness that is profoundly sane. Viktor Ullmann, setting his verse in the Terezin concentration camp, matches this strange serenity very precisely with pure line and long curves that are tonally scarcely tethered. Hanns Eisler, setting him as an exile in California not long before Ullmann was killed, casts a quiet spell with sparely accompanied, atonal but graceful melodies, but is drawn into fierce vehemence and back to tonality by Hölderlin's and his own nostalgia for a Germany before chaos broke upon her. Karl Michael Komma, the only living composer here and in any case better known as a musicologist, is less interesting: his fragmentary but intense vocal lines reflect Hölderlin more precisely than his ungratefully clumpy keyboard writing. Fröhlich and Cornelius, contemporaries of Schubert and Brahms respectively, find the idiom more elusive, though Fröhlich at least hints at what a Hölderlin setting by Schubert might have been like. But in Hermann Reutter's three songs you can almost see him escaping from the almost salon style of No. 1 to find in No. 3 a vehemently bold vocal line that very aptly reflects Hölderlin's imagery of a hidden straight line underlying the crooked paths of fate. Pfitzner, too, gets very close both to the pain of *Abbitte* (a plea for forgiveness for troubling God with complaints) and to the wonderful serenity of the poem's end. Wolfgang Fortner's tolling ostinatos and beautiful melismatic lines suggest a song-writer of real distinction. Mitsuko Shirai's clear high mezzo and her subtle way with words make such a beautiful thing of a single song from Britten's Hölderlin cycle that one wishes she had recorded the whole set. The performances are consistently fine, though Hartmut Höll's piano is done no favours by a close, dry recording.

Mitsuko Shirai Songs with Viola. **Mitsuko Shirai** (mez); **Tabea Zimmermann** (va); **Hartmut Höll** (pf). Capriccio Ⓕ 10 462 (66 minutes: DDD: 9/95). Texts and translations included. Recorded 1993-94.   Ⓖ
   R. Strauss Stiller Gang, Op. 31 No. 4. **Brahms** Zwei Lieder, Op. 91. **A. Busch** Nun die
   Schatten dunkeln. Wonne der Wehmut. Aus den Himmelsaugen. **Loeffler** Quatre poèmes, Op. 5.
   Dargomïzhsky Elegy, "She is coming". **Marx** Durch Einsamkeiten. **Reutter** Fünf antike
   Oden, Op. 57. **Gounod** Evening song.

Voice and viola, we think, form a soothing combination: the sound of the words suggests as much, and memories of Brahms's Op. 91 (which is what we are likely to think of first and probably last) confirm it. The Brahms songs come second in this present programme, and on either side are compositions by Richard Strauss and Adolf Busch that are very much in keeping, the mood generally peaceful, the style essentially lyrical. Then come the *Quatre poèmes* of Charles Martin Loeffler (1861-1935). These, like the songs by Busch and, later, Hermann Reutter, are recorded now for the first time and they form a welcome addition to the small catalogue of Loeffler's works on record. In this programme, they, together with Reutter's "Sappho", provide a contrast, a more bracing and varied use of the combination: a relief from the soothing. Mitsuko Shirai, now mezzo-soprano, sings with almost consistently firm and beautiful tone. She lightens the voice skilfully, as in Brahms's "Gestillte Sehnsucht", and produces some beautifully sustained singing, as in the third of the Loeffler *Poèmes*, "Le son du cor". There is also an assured authority in this deeper voice with no less of the familiar charm. With fine playing by Tabea Zimmermann, especially in the Reutter cycle where the instrument is most imaginatively exploited, and with Hartmut Höll as sensitivel as ever, this is a desirable disc.

Dame Joan Sutherland The Art of the Prima Donna. Opera Arias – Artaxerxes, Die Entführung aus dem Serail, Faust, Hamlet, Les Huguenots, Lakmé, Norma[a], Otello, I puritani, Rigoletto[a], Roméo et Juliette, Samson, Semiramide[a], La sonnambula and La traviata.
Dame Joan Sutherland (sop); [a]**Chorus and Orchestra of the Royal Opera House, Covent Garden / Francesco Molinari-Pradelli.** Decca The Classic Sound Ⓜ 452 298-2DCS2
(two discs: 109 minutes: ADD: 5/97). Texts and translations included. From SXL2256/7 (12/60).
The occasion of Dame Joan Sutherland's seventieth birthday in November 1996 prompted Decca to reissue numerous opera sets from the 1960s. The two-disc recital, "The Art of the Prima Donna" has hardly ever been out of the catalogue since 1960 – now it's remastered for Classic Sound. There cannot be many admirers who haven't already got this, so for newcomers to Sutherland on disc one can only say – listen and wonder. Her voice, even throughout its range right up to the high E, always keeping its natural quality, is heard at its early fullness. Perhaps the best tracks of all are the first two on the first disc, "The soldier tir'd" from *Artaxerxes* and "Let the bright seraphim" from *Samson*, but every track is beautiful. "Casta Diva" – her earliest attempt at it – is certainly her most limpid recording of this prayer, "Bel raggio" from *Semiramide* has sparkling decorations, quite different from the ones she sang on the complete recording six years later, and the whole thing ends with the Jewel Song from *Faust*. It was a big voice and sounded at its best in larger theatres; listening to "O beau pays" from *Les Huguenots*, one can see Sutherland in one's mind's eye, in pale blue silk, as Marguerite de Valois at the Royal Albert Hall in 1968. It is diffifcult to imagine anyone, coming to it for the first time, being disappointed.

Dame Kiri Te Kanawa German Opera Arias. **Dame Kiri Te Kanawa** (sop);
Philharmonia Orchestra / Julius Rudel. EMI Ⓕ CDC5 56417-2 (57 minutes: DDD: 11/97).
Texts and translations included. Recorded 1996.
Weber Der Freischütz – Wie nahte mir der Schlummer ... Leise, leise, fromme Weise; Und ob die Wolke. **Mozart** Die Zauberflöte – Ach, ich fühl's. **Wagner** Tannhäuser – Dich teure Halle; Allmächt'ge Jungfrau. Die Meistersinger von Nürnberg – O Sachs! Mein Freund!. Die Walküre – Du bist der Lenz. **R. Strauss** Daphne – Ich komme ... Ich komme, grünende Brüder. Ariadne auf Naxos – Es gibt ein Reich. Die Aegyptische Helena – Zweite Brautnacht!.
Korngold Die tote Stadt – Glück, das mir verblieb.
This makes such a lovely beginning that one is doubly loath to report occasional disappointment. The arias from *Der Freischütz* are sung in the fine Lemnitz tradition of gently rounded tone, beautifully sustained phrases and unspoilt line. In the cavatina the mood is serenely set, and the quickened impulse of the middle section is sensitively reflected. The great solo in Act 2 has a delightful freshness of response: when she exclaims about the brightness of the stars it is as though she has just this minute looked up and noticed them. The 'grand tune' from the Overture, so awkwardly written for the voice, is clearly articulated without smudges or intrusive changes of register. Pamina's aria, too, is sung with all due beauty of voice and expression, the unaccompanied falling notes at the end touchingly lonesome and disconsolate. It may not be until the fifth track, Elisabeth's greeting in *Tannhäuser*, that Time "that takes survey of all the world" has to be acknowledged. This most lovely voice retains a good deal of its quality but it is not untouched. The vibrations are not as tight, the upper notes not as pure and the middle register has not acquired power and fullness to compensate. This is the most important factor in determining the success of much that follows. Sieglinde's "Du bist der Lenz" wants power and colour in just that part of the voice where they are least available. In *Daphne* and *Die Aegyptische Helena* one is too often aware of a tinkle on the surface of notes which a few years earlier would have been glorious to hear. Even in Marietta's song from *Die tote Stadt* the expectation of full-bodied sound freely released is thwarted as she opts instead for a more delicate style and produces this rather small, rather undernourished tone with a dreamy, inward expression in place of the rapt exultancy we remember from Lotte Lehmann. The orchestral playing provides pleasure throughout, especially in the lengthy passage in *Daphne* before the wordless voice is heard from off-stage. Recorded sound is fine.

Renata Tebaldi The Concert at Lewisohn Stadium, 1966. **Renata Tebaldi** (sop); **orchestra / Lamberto Gardelli.** VAI Audio mono Ⓕ VAIA1148 (54 minutes: AAD: 2/98). Recorded live in 1966.
Here's real treasure, a souvenir of Tebaldi singing live at Lewisohn Stadium in 1966. Always better heard live than from the studio she is on wonderful form, singing various arias, of which "L'altra notte" and "Voi, lo sapete" are superbly voiced and movingly interpreted. The mementoes of her Desdemona and Aida are almost as rewarding and she has to repeat the Rodgers and Hammerstein "If I love you", so heart-warming is the performance. Poor sound quality is worth tolerating for such splendid singing.

Bryn Terfel Opera Arias. **Bryn Terfel** (bass-bar); **Orchestra of the Metropolitan Opera, New York / James Levine.** DG Ⓕ 445 866-2GH (71 minutes: DDD: 6/96). Texts and translations included.
Gramophone Editor's choice. ⒼⒼ

Mozart Le nozze di Figaro – Non più andrai. Don Giovanni – Madamina, il catalogo è questo; Deh! vieni alla finestra. Così fan tutte – Rivolgete a lui lo sguardo. Die Zauberflöte – Der Vogelfänger bin ich ja. **Wagner** Tannhäuser – Wie Todesahnung ... O du mein holder Abendstern. Der fliegende Holländer – Die Frist ist um. **Offenbach** Les contes d'Hoffmann – Allez! ... Pour te livrer combat ... Scintille, diamant. **Gounod** Faust – Vous qui faites l'endormie. **Borodin** Prince Igor – No sleep, no rest. **Donizetti** Don Pasquale – Bella siccome un angelo. **Rossini** La Cenerentola – Miei rampolli femminini. **Verdi** Macbeth – Perfidi! All'angelo caontra me v'unite! ... Pietà, rispetto, amore. Falstaff – Ehi! paggio! ... L'Onore! Ladri!.

In a careless moment we might describe Bryn Terfel as a very physical singer, and it would be true up to a point. His physical presence is much in evidence when he sings, or for that matter when he talks or just breathes. Having seen him 'in the flesh', one seems to see him while hearing the sound of his voice on records. But the crowning distinction of Terfel's art (granted the voice, the technique and, the general musicianship) is its intelligence. As with words, so with characters: each is a specific, sharp-minded creation, and none is a stereotype. This Leporello exhibits his master's catalogue with pride; it is the book of life and not to be taken lightly. This Don Magnifico recounts his dream in all good faith (he doesn't *know* that he's a complete idiot, and doesn't deliberately set himself up to sound like one). No less impressive, as an aspect of intelligence, is the linguistic command, and still more so the use he makes of it: the sheer mental concentration of his Dutchman carries intense conviction and an ever-specific understanding. In short, a magnificent recital with fine recorded sound fine.

The Three Tenors in Concert, 1994 [a]José Carreras, [b]Plácido Domingo, [c]Luciano Pavarotti (tens); [d]Los Angeles Music Center Opera Chorus; Los Angeles Philharmonic Orchestra / **Zubin Mehta.** Teldec Ⓕ 4509-96200-2 (74 minutes: DDD: 12/94). Texts and translations included. Recorded live in 1994.

Massenet Le Cid – O souverain, ô juge, ô pere[a]. Werther – Pourquoi me réveiller?[c]. **Moreno Torroba** Maravilla – Amor, vida de mi vida[b]. **Rodgers** Spring Is Here – With a song in my heart[a]. **Lara** Granada[b]. **De Curtis** Non ti scordar di me[c]. Tu, ca nun chiagne![a]. **Leoncavallo** Pagliacci – Vesti la giubba[b]. **Puccini** Turandot – Nessun dorma![c]. **Verdi** Rigoletto – La donna è mobile[abcd]. La traviata – Libiamo, ne'lieti calci[abcd]. **Various** (arr. and orch. Schifrin) A Tribute to Hollywood[abcd]. Around the World[abcd].

Domingo sings the first phrase of "Vesti la giubba" quite beautifully and sustains the broad climax well. With richness of tone, well-covered 'passage' notes, an exciting ring and, in the middle section, non-disruptive emphasis, he gives an exemplary demonstration of how to sing a popular song in his first solo, "Amor, vida de mi vida". In *Granada* he exercises the traditional charm of a good stylist at the point of leading back into the melody. Pavarotti still thrills with the clarity and resonance of his voice in the long line of high As in "Nessun dorma". The medleys include some pleasant quiet moments in "Santa Lucia lontana" and some unabashed big brassy ones in "Brazil". If one were to engage upon a balanced critical account it would have to start with the opening number, Carreras uneven and over-emphatic in the Prayer from *Le Cid*, and then continue with Pavarotti's Werther sung in *l'accent du Sud*. But it is not the sort of occasion, or the sort of record, for such commentary. Perhaps one might raise a quibble about the representation, in the *Around the World* medley, of Britain with "All I ask of you", and about the frequent returns in this geographically-guided selection, to Italy. For the rest, it's true there is a kind of pleasure in the lush, glitzy chorus swirling around in "With a song in my heart", and in The Three Tenors "Singing in the Rain" in unison like the football crowd of a dream.

Dawn Upshaw Goethe Lieder. **Dawn Upshaw** (sop); **Richard Goode** (pf). Nonesuch Ⓕ 7559-79317-2 (53 minutes: DDD: 8/94). Texts and translations included. Recorded 1993. *Gramophone Editor's record of the month.*   Ⓖ

Schubert Rastlose Liebe, D138. Gretchen am Spinnrade, D118. Mignons Gesang, D877 No. 4. Suleika I, D720. Versunken, D715. Wanderers Nachtlied II, D768. Ganymed, D544. An den Mond, D296. **Schumann** Liebeslied, Op. 51 No. 5. Nachtlied, Op. 96 No. 1. Lieder und Gesänge aus Wilhelm Meister, Op. 98*a* – No. 1, Mignon; No. 5, Heiss mich nicht reden; No. 7, Singet nicht in Trauertönen. **Wolf** Blumengruss. Die Bekehrte. Die Spröde. Frühling übers Jahr. **Mozart** Das Veilchen, K476.

Upshaw and Goode are a musical marriage made in heaven, each a highly individual, probing and sincere artist prepared to challenge received views on a song. Thus their *Gretchen am Spinnrade* in this programme of all-Goethe settings is an outburst of a desperate and infinitely perturbed woman breaking conventional bonds. To emphasize the point Upshaw leans into the first syllable of "nimmer" at each repetition with added feeling and times the climax of the great song at the word "Kuss" in an overwhelming way, only such a similarly involving (although very different) interpreter as Lotte Lehmann could. Goode's playing simply underlines and reinforces the singer's intense utterance. The Schumann settings are filled with just as much spontaneous emotion and direct imagination. The pair make as strong a case as is possible for Schumann's setting of Mignon's *Kennst du das Land* being superior even to Wolf's, the repeated "Kennst du das wohl?" carrying an extraordinary charge. The singer's voice is also ideally fitted for Wolf's teasingly sensual *Die Spröde* and *Die Bekehrte* and the pair bring the lightest touch to *Blumengruss*. Finally they give Mozart's *Das Veilchen* a deeper meaning than almost any interpreters from the past. An ideally balanced, forward yet spacious recording enhances the pleasure to be derived from this deeply satisfying disc.

Dawn Upshaw I wish it so. **Dawn Upshaw** (sop); **orchestra / Eric Stern.** Nonesuch Ⓕ 7559-79345-2 (45 minutes: DDD: 12/94). Texts included. Recorded 1993. *Gramophone Award winner 1995.* 🔂🔂
Blitzstein Juno – I wish it so. No for an Answer – In the clear. Reuben, Reuben – Never get lost. **Sondheim** Anyone Can Whistle – There won't be trumpets. Saturday Night – What more do I need? The Girls of Summer – The Girls of Summer. Merrily We Roll Along – Like it was. Evening Primrose – Take me to the world. **Weill** One Touch of Venus – That's him. Lady in the Dark – The saga of Jenny; My ship. Lost in the Stars – Stay well. **Bernstein** West Side Story – I feel pretty. Candide – Glitter and be gay. The Madwoman of Central Park West – My new friends.

Bernstein, Blitzstein, Sondheim and Weill are a good quartet to explore in a recital and Dawn Upshaw's clear soprano is well suited to nearly all these songs. The Blitzstein numbers will only be familiar to specialists. "I wish it so" from Blitzstein's adaptation of O'Casey's *Juno* seems to herald the mood of the whole disc, songs of longing, some optimistic, some resigned. "In the clear" is one of the songs from *No for an Answer*, Blitzstein's follow-up to *The Cradle Will Rock*; it was first given in 1940, the same week that saw the first night of Weill's *Lady in the Dark*. In the Blitzstein, Eric Stern's arrangement with a solo cello part played by Matthias Niegele turns the song into a melancholy lullaby. This and a brilliant performance of "Glitter and be gay" from *Candide* show off Dawn Upshaw's impressive range – from the coloratura of the Bernstein to mezzo-ish moodiness for the Blitzstein. Of the Weill songs, "Stay well" from *Lost in the Stars* is especially successful, and "That's him" from *One Touch of Venus* is playful. The two numbers from *Lady in the Dark* are given the most extensive overhaul, the melody of "The saga of Jenny" such as it is disappears beneath Larry Wilcox's rearrangement and although Upshaw sings "My ship" quite beautifully, again Daniel Troob has made an arrangement that pulls it about rather. All in all, this is a very attractive foray into the Broadway territory.

Historic vocal

Victoria de los Angeles Songs and Arias – Brahms, Falla, Fusté, Granados, Guridi, Handel, Nin, Respighi, Schumann, Toldrá, Turina, Valverde and Vives. **Victoria de los Angeles** (sop) with various artists. Testament mono Ⓕ SBT1087* (75 minutes: ADD: 8/96). From HMV and privately recorded originals; recorded 1942-53.
The two Respighi songs are magical performances – *Stornellatrice*, with the golden voice at its richest and *E se un giorno tornasse*, a study in subtle shading of tone, a dialogue between a mother and her dying, jilted daughter. For those two brief items alone, superbly transferred, this collection is an essential for all admirers of this singer, but there is so much more. Having Handel's "O had I Jubal's lyre" in German rather than English may be odd, but the performance sparkles and among the Lieder it is good to have not just "Der Nussbaum" – the Schumann song which was always special to her – but two previously unpublished, "Widmung" from the Myrthe songs and "Ich grolle nicht" from *Dichterliebe*. Through the whole collection the superb transfers capture the full-throated glory of los Angeles's voice at the beginning of her career. The 1942 recordings of two Hungarian folk-songs, previously unpublished, may be rough and limited – made when the singer was only 18 – but they amply demonstrate that already the voice was fully developed in its beauty. No fewer than 18 of the 27 items are of Spanish songs, and though in one or two instances los Angeles was destined to make even more idiomatic readings later with a Spanish accompanist, these ones with Gerald Moore as her partner have a freshness and brilliance that has rarely been matched in this repertory. In particular it is good to have her first recording of the encore number which she made her own, *Clavelitos*.

Dame Isobel Baillie and Kathleen Ferrier To Music – Songs, Arias and Duets by [a]Arne, [ab]Brahms, [b]Elgar, [b]Gluck, [b]Greene, [a]Grieg, [b]Handel, [ab]Mendelssohn, [ab]Purcell, [a]Schubert and [a]Scott. [a]**Dame Isobel Baillie** (sop); [b]**Kathleen Ferrier** (contr); **Gerald Moore** (pf). APR mono Ⓜ APR5544* (69 minutes: ADD: 9/97). From Columbia originals and HMV test recordings; recorded 1941-45. All items sung in English.
This is a delightful disc, with a happily chosen programme and well-matched contributions from both singers. Even so, it has to be admitted that the first thought concerns date. The piano arrangements of Purcell duets and Handel arias are definitely of the period; nothing could be more remote from the modern style which was even then coming into vogue. But 'dated' in a much better way is the quality of the singing itself. Would you today find the runs in Purcell and Handel sung with at once such clear articulation and such smoothness? Dame Isobel is sometimes a little pipey but for the most part charming. Ferrier is royal. The transfers are excellent.

Lucrezia Bori Opera Arias – Acis y Galatea, Amantes chasqueaos, L'amour mouillé, La bohème, Les contes d'Hoffmann, Don Giovanni, Don Quijote de la mancha, Louise, Madama Butterfly, Manon, Mignon, Le nozze di Figaro, La rondine, Il segreto di Susanna, La traviata and La vida breve; songs by Arditi, Falla, Glazunov, Goetz, Götze, Joves, Nin, Pagans, Pestalozzi, Rumbold, Schumann, J. Strauss II, A. G. Thomas and Valverde. **Lucrezia Bori** (sop) with various artists. Romophone mono Ⓔ 81017-2* (two discs: 147 minutes: ADD: 7/96). From Victor originals; recorded 1925-37.

Until Romophone brought out the complete run of her Victor recordings, Bori looked like becoming the forgotten prima donna. Volume 1 (81016-2, 3/96) was welcomed in *Gramophone* as reintroducing "one of the most adorable and fascinating of singers on records", and its successor now follows her from the heyday of her career to the time of her last recordings, some 18 months after her official retirement at the age of 50. The originals were often issued on noisy shellac, and at 78rpm most played above the correct pitch. In these conditions the voice could sound thin, and the 'image' (if that overused word be permitted) suffered accordingly. The repertoire of songs may not have helped: perhaps in its time *Ciribiribin* and so forth were welcomed as a form of 'crossover', but even now, at this distance in time, from behind the sweetly tweet-a-tweeting singer, Groucho has only to lift an eyebrow or Harpo to turn down his nether lip, and the bird-song takes a perilously farcical flight. Fortunately we are just sufficiently far away to detach the records from impediments of this kind. The complete edition, which the two volumes comprise, returns the singer to us as new. Among the recordings said to be previously unpublished, best are two songs by Nin, dating from the singer's last session, at the end of 1937. There are also some alternative takes (all good), and the two 1925 duets with McCormack. A great pleasure lies in the discovery (or maybe confirmation) that the 1937 recordings show only slight deterioration of voice and have such vividness of character. Best remain well-known things such as Mimì's narrative, Musetta's waltz-song (sung as though it were Mimì's also), the *Mignon* solos and some of the Spanish songs such as the *Malagueña* by Don Pagans. The most commonplace, trivial or exasperatingly 'pretty' banalities endear themselves if they provide an additional opportunity to hear this exquisite, highly individual, totally lovable artist.

Caruso in Opera, Volume 2. Arias – L'africaine, Andrea Chenier, La bohème (Leoncavallo and Puccini), Carmen, Cavalleria Rusticana, Don Pasquale, Eugene Onegin, La favorita, Les huguenots, Macbeth, Martha, Nero, La reine de Saba, Rigoletto, Tosca and Il trovatore. **Enrico Caruso** (ten) with various artists. Nimbus Prima Voce mono Ⓜ NI7866* (79 minutes: ADD: 7/95). From Victor originals; recorded 1905-20.

The 1906 recording of "M'apparì" from *Martha* comes first, and it introduces an aspect of Caruso's singing that rarely finds a place in the critical commentaries: his subtlety. Partly, it's rhythmic. The move-on and pull-back seems such an instinctive process that we hardly notice it (though no doubt a modern conductor would – and check it immediately). It makes all the difference to the emotional life of the piece, the feeling of involvement and spontaneous development. Then there is the phrasing, marvellously achieved at the melody's reprise. The play of louder and softer tones, too, has every delicacy of fine graduation; and just as masterly is the more technical (though still expressive) covering and (rare) opening of notes at the *passaggio*. An edition of the score which brought out all these features of Caruso's singing would be a densely annotated document. It would, even so, be a simplification, for accompanying all this is the dramatic and musical feeling, which defies analysis – and, of course, the voice. That voice! You may feel you know all these records and hardly need to play them, yet there is scarcely an occasion when the beauty of it does not thrill with a sensation both old and new (the first 'Ah!' is one of recognition, the second of fresh wonder). So it is with nearly all of the items here: all, in fact, save the *Eugene Onegin* aria, which remains external, and the late *L'africaine* recording with its saddening evidence of deterioration. The transfers are excellent.

Boris Christoff Opera Arias – Don Carlo, Don Giovanni, Ernani, La forza del destino, Iphigénie en Aulide, Mefistofele, Nabucco, Norma, Simon Boccanegra, La sonnambula and I vespri siciliani. **Boris Christoff** (bass) with various artists. EMI Références mono Ⓜ CDH5 65500-2* (80 minutes: ADD: 3/96). From HMV originals; recorded 1949-55.

The grieving king, the patriarchal priest, the smirking demon: these are all expected presences in Christoff's gallery of vivid characters, and one might well extend the list mentally by a dozen or so more before thinking of Leporello. Christoff sang very little Mozart but the Catalogue aria in *Don Giovanni* featured in his concert programmes. It is a marvellous performance, and alone provides a very good reason for buying this disc. Almost as unlooked for may be the Count's aria in *La sonnambula*, sung with affection and a nearly perfect legato. Warmth of tone perhaps is wanting, in both that and the "Infelice" (*Ernani*), but there is certainly no lack of emotional warmth in the fine solos from *I vespri siciliani* and *Simon Boccanegra*. Philip's great aria in *Don Carlo* ends with a too overt and prolonged tearfulness (avoided in later versions) but this recording is still among the supremely impressive mementos of its era. It comes from one of Christoff's first sessions in the studios, and is strikingly natural and lifelike, as are all the 78s heard here. In the 1955 recordings one is more aware of the microphone: for example, in his most authoritative vein, Christoff is splendidly represented by the Gluck aria (*Iphigénie en Aulide*) made in 1951, whereas the same magnificence is present in the excerpts from *Nabucco* (1955) but just slightly diminished by seeming to be made larger than life. When all is over, however, the first item demands a replay: that Catalogue song of Leporello's. John Hughes's admirable notes concede that the performance "may lack the necessary touch of humour" – but it surely does not! Gaiety, rhythm, even a chuckle, a swelling grandeur in the portrayal of the "maiestosa", a daintiness in "la piccina": it is all there, and with it a certain suavity of style, and, rarer still, the elegant phrases of "Nella bionda" sung with scrupulous legato. This disc goes into the 'Essential Christoff Collection' forthwith.

Covent Garden on Record, Volumes 1-4. **143 singers with various accompaniments.** Pearl mono
Ⓜ GEMMCDS9923/6* (four three-disc sets, oas: 215, 227 and 222 minutes: AAD: 7/92).
Gramophone Award Winner 1992. ⓐⓖⓖ
An Aladdin's cave, where whatever the torch lights upon is treasure. At the entrance: Adelina Patti, well past her prime to be sure, but in that *Ah, non credea mirarti* what heartfelt pathos when she comes to the lines "Mi ravivar l'amore il pianto mio non puèo", what delicacy in the soft tones and the trill, and, after all, what a miracle that we should be able to hear as clearly as this, from the 63-year-old woman in retirement at her Welsh castle in 1906, the beauty remaining to the most world-renowned voice of her century. Further in among the treasures, the first Otello, the first Falstaff; near to them, a baritone, one Mario Ancona of 1904, almost forgotten today but truly superb in his Donizetti, as, by his side, is the bass Marcel Journet, sonorous and with a funny old chorus to support him in a passage from that epitome of nineteenth-century grand opera, *Les Huguenots*. Into the next chamber, and a voice arises celebrating the fickleness of womankind – the voice of the god of tenors, Caruso. His Irish friend McCormack, his business-partner Melba, his Neapolitan *amico* Scotti: all are there. Deeper in, and we have come through the First World War, to where British singers – Walter Widdop, Heddle Nash and Joan Cross among them – mingle freely and quite rightly with tip-top company such as Lotte Lehmann, Elisabeth Rethberg and Friedrich Schorr. At the end of the journey we reach the ominous date 1939: for the chambers of this Aladdin's cave of records have also been the years of the Covent Garden Opera House, with singers heard there, in the present theatre, as early as 1871, up to the end of the international seasons and the outbreak of World War Two. The singers are heard in the roles they sang, and are sometimes recorded 'live' from the stage, as with Chaliapin in 1928 and Gigli in 1939. Many of the recordings are of extreme rarity, and thanks to the expertise of Keith Hardwick, who compiled the programme and effected the transfers, a sizeable proportion of them are heard to greater advantage than ever before on CD or LP. Not everything is perfect, either in the singers themselves (they don't always do what we want them to), or the selections (nothing of some famous Covent Garden roles such as Caruso's Canio and Turner's Turandot) or even the transfers (a certain harshness in some of the later recordings). But the four albums, three CDs to a volume and each volume available separately, comprise one of the best of anthologies. They also document a fascinating period in the history of a great opera house: an extraordinary concentration of enterprise, historical time, musical talent and in some instances genius, all within the compass of these 12 discs.

Giuseppe De Luca Opera Arias – Un ballo in maschera, Il barbiere di Siviglia, La damnation de Faust, Dinorah, Don Giovanni, Don Pasquale, Ernani, La Gioconda, Hamlet, Hérodiade, Linda di Chamounix, Le nozze di Figaro, The Queen of Spades, Rigoletto, Le roi de Lahore, La traviata, Il trovatore and Zazà; songs by De Leva, Fasolo and Morlacchi. **Giuseppe De Luca** (bar) with various artists. Preiser Lebendige Vergangenheit mono Ⓕ 89135* (76 minutes: AAD: 5/97). From Fonotipia originals; recorded 1905-07.
With a voice like De Luca's, would we really reproduce it more like life today? And, as it happens, even the pianist doesn't fare too badly: at any rate, better than the orchestra that was just beginning to supplant him in the studios, but which is mercifully excluded throughout these sessions. De Luca himself is a sturdy survivor, totally meriting his 90-year preservation, a continual reference-point whenever the art of the baritone in general is under discussion. Try him, for a start, in Malatesta's "Bella siccome un angelo" from *Don Pasquale*, or the *Ernani* aria, or any of the three songs which end the recital. But all, even the Mozart, even something like the cynical "O monumento" (*La Gioconda*) for which he hasn't the temperament, bring their rewards. Here is quite simply one of the best sequences of baritone recordings to be found anywhere, or from any time. The transfers are blessed with a warmth and natural beauty of tone such as by all accounts De Luca so eminently possessed.

Giuseppe Di Stefano Opera Arias – L'amico Fritz, L'arlesiana, L'elisir d'amore, La fanciulla del West, La forza del destino, Gianni Schicchi, Manon, Mignon, Tosca, Turandot; songs by Bixio, Tagliaferri; Sicilian folk-songs. **Giuseppe Di Stefano** (ten) with various artists. Testament mono Ⓕ SBT1096* (79 minutes: ADD: 1/98). From Columbia, HMV and RCA originals; recorded 1944-56.
Very moving it is to hear this voice again in its absolute prime. It is hardly possible to hear those Swiss recordings of 1944, with piano, and be untouched by the thought, as well as the sound, of this 22-year-old, singing his heart out, with so much voice and, already, with so much art. The "Una furtiva lagrima" is perhaps not the fully polished article, but what Forster called the Italian "instinct for beauty" is there, with lovely shading and phrasing. It is good to have the two Bixio songs (*Se vuoi goder la vita* and *Mamma*), previously unpublished, heartfelt, open-throated performances in the national tradition that used to get mocked and is now so missed. Indeed, thinking of that sequence of recordings, one could well wish this disc had given priority to reproducing them all: there is an amazingly good "Pourquoi me réveiller?", for instance, and (till the end) a beautifully restrained *Musica proibita*. Still, what we have here fulfils exactly the promise of the label's name: it is a testament, and a testament of youth. The later operatic recordings, from 1955, find the tenor with some signs of wear and with a recklessly open way of taking his high As and B flats, but there is real

passion, and imagination with it. In the latest recording, a commonplace song called *Passione* from 1956, one almost looks up at the speakers to see the face there: it seems so very clear and lifelike. Some of the sound (recording or transfer) seems overbright – the second *Manon* solo is a prime example – but it is always vivid and compelling. In the booklet-listing a translation of the song-titles would have been welcome. It would also have been useful if Peter Hutchinson's notes had related the excerpts to Di Stefano's career (did he for instance ever sing Dick Johnson, Rinuccio and Calaf on stage?). Mr Hutchinson is quite right, though, in the simple, irrefutable advice given towards the end: "Just try him".

Zara Dolukhanova Opera Arias – Il barbiere di Siviglia, Don Carlo, Les huguenots, Kashchey the Immortal, Khovanshchina, The Maid of Orleans, Le nozze di Figaro, Samson et Dalila and Semiramide; Concert Arias by Prokofiev, Tchaikovsky and Verdi. **Zara Dolukhanova** (mez); **Moscow Philharmonic Orchestra / Grigory Stolarov.** Russian Disc mono ⓜ RDCD15023* (66 minutes: AAD: 3/96). Recorded live in Moscow in 1954.

Zara Dolukhanova is all but forgotten in the West. She certainly doesn't deserve to be. Her voice was a faultlessly produced mezzo of great beauty, extending upwards well into the soprano range, downward far enough to make a formidably sultry Dalila, yet without any of that ugly barking which some mezzos use instead of low notes. Her range of character was even wider, from a really charming and stylish Cherubino ("Non so più cosa son" in Russian) to a full-voiced, devout and thoroughly Verdian account (in Italian) of the first of the *Four Sacred Pieces*. Her coloratura was accomplished, so her Rossini comes off well in both languages (in a Russian "Una voce poco fa" she is a smiling, rather than a vixenish Rosina). The Russian items give an excellent idea of her vocal range: generous and eloquent amplitude of voice in Joan's farewell from Tchaikovsky's *The Maid of Orleans* (a soprano role modified for a mezzo, but still needing soprano brightness), dark gravity and urgency in Marfa's soothsaying from *Khovanshchina* and, in a particularly Wagner-influenced Rimsky-Korsakov monologue (*Kashchey*) the sort of dramatic declamation that makes you wonder whether she ever dipped a toe into the Wagnerian repertory. The recordings were made at a public concert during, judging from the sound of the coughing, a damp Moscow January. The orchestral playing is at times a little unkempt, and the voice is placed well forward. Yet with such a voice, who's complaining? Only the extracts from Russian operas are provided with texts, and the insert-notes are effusive rubbish ("wearing a simple white dress which fitted her perfect body"), but when they speak of her "most beautiful voice, which is simultaneously so powerful and exquisitely graceful, dense and succulent as a peach", they do not exaggerate.

Karl Erb Lieder by Adam, Bach, Beethoven, Brahms, Liszt, Loewe, Schoeck, Schubert, Schumann, Wolf and Zilcher. **Karl Erb** (ten); **Bruno Seidler-Winkler** (pf).
Preiser Lebendige Vergangenheit mono ⒠ 89208* (two discs: 149 minutes: AAD: 6/94).
From HMV and Electrola originals; recorded 1934-39.   ⓐⓖⓐ

Erb's career, voice and style closely resemble those of Peter Schreier today; their voices are uncannily similar in timbre, for they possess a tone of strange, plangent beauty that can on the other hand sound a shade piercing and uncomfortable. Almost all of the first CD is devoted to Erb's Schubert, covering a wide range of the better-known songs. Few, except perhaps for Schreier himself, have come closer to conveying the inner desolation and/or loneliness of such pieces as *Wanderers Nachtlied II, Dass sie hier gewesen* and "Der Wegweiser" and "Das Wirtshaus" from *Winterreise*. The piercing, sad quality of tone, the acute accentuation of words are here wholly appropriate. Yet Erb can lighten his voice and manner for such charmers as *An Sylvia* and *Liebesbotschaft*. The second disc in the main comprises Erb's Beethoven, Schumann, Brahms and Wolf. Some of his Schumann is beyond praise. His intimate, spontaneous readings of such favourites as *Meine Rose, Mondnacht* and *Der Nussbaum* sound newly minted. The same can be said of Brahms's glorious *O wüsst' ich doch den Weg zurück*. Again, his reading of Wolf's religious (Mörike and Ocana) settings are held on a thread of perfectly sustained legato. The transfers are excellent.

Geraldine Farrar in French Opera Opera Arias and Duets – Carmen, Les contes d'Hoffmann, Manon, Mignon, Roméo et Juliette and Thaïs. **Geraldine Farrar** (sop) with various artists.
Nimbus Prima Voce mono ⓜ NI7872* (79 minutes: ADD: 1/96). From Victor originals; recorded 1908-21.

This is a lovely addition to the Prima Voce series. Farrar's Carmen appears as a model of effectiveness within the restraints of good musical and dramatic behaviour. The "Séguedille" is sheer enchantment (irresistible promise in that breathed "je l'aimerai" and the dreamily provocative reprise of "Près des remparts"), while in the "Chanson bohème" we catch the energy of her personality as well as the carrying power of her by no means robust lyric soprano. These are all cherishable records, of the kind that on some pleasant desultory evening with the gramophone one will feel a prompting to take down from the shelves. Seasoned collectors should not necessarily assume that they already have everything on the disc: there is, for instance, the unpublished "Je veux vivre" (*Roméo et Juliette*) from 1911, a performance of surprising delicacy and charm. The Prelude to Act 4 is there, too, in a recording from 1921 said to be by the orchestra of La Scala conducted by Toscanini, one of those legendary sessions which put him off the gramophone for a decade. If he had heard the results as cleanly defined as they are here, he might have thought again.

Povla Frijsh Songs by Chausson, Clarke, Cui, Debussy, Duparc, Dupont, Dvořák, Fauré, Février, Fosse, Georges, Grieg, Grøndahl, Hahn, Henriques, Jordan, Koechlin, Křička, Milhaud, Mozart, Naginski, Poulenc, Ravel, Roussel, Schubert, Schumann, Sinding, Staub, Tchaikovsky, Thompson and Torelli; opera aria from Gluck's La Semiramide riconosciuta. **Povla Frijsh** (sop) with various artists. Pearl mono Ⓜ GEMMCDS9095* (two discs: 146 minutes: AAD: 4/95). From HMV, Victor and Nordisk Polyphon originals and broadcast performances; recorded 1926-42. Also includes part of an broadcast interview, recorded in 1953.

Frijsh's sound and manner may be described as an amalgam of Gerhardt, Lehmann (Lotte) and Teyte, the vocal style of the first, the total commitment of the second and the stylistic control in *mélodies* of the third. Or perhaps they could be characterized as the vocal equivalent of Garbo, with the same power to mesmerize. As an interpreter, she is the sort of free spirit rarely encountered in this day of uniformity (the recently retired Fassbaender is in the same category), one who takes liberties in the cause of conveying the full sense of a song, one who is a mistress of the lost art of portamento, particularly its downward variety, as a means of expression and of enhancing the line. She is no authenticist. If it suits her she will sing Scandinavian and German songs in the original; if it does not, she prefers translations, singing her Russian repertory in French. She is an explorer, tackling pieces well outside the regular repertory, at least as it is now conceived. Nothing here is more enthralling than Milhaud's *Chant de nourice*, the lullaby of a Jewish nurse telling her charge to be aware of its race, and that race's vicissitudes and pride. The inflexions at "O mon chéri" and "Dors ma fleur" rend the heart.

A totally different but equally riveting singer seems to be in our presence in Grøndahl's *You meet me in the dance*, the very essence of seductive power. In *L'heure silencieuse* by one Victor Staub, the mystery of the twilight hour is perfectly conveyed. So is the miniature drama of Février's *L'intruse* and the wintry mystery of Koechlin's *L'hiver*. But she is no less remarkable in better-known pieces. The languorous description of Ravel's "Le paon" (from *Histoires naturelles*), the gentle melancholy of Hahn's *L'infidelité*, the haunting memory of Tchaikovsky's *At the ball*, these linger in the mind. Most of the performances were recorded by HMV (1932-3) or Victor (1939-42) when the artist was between 50 and 60. Obviously the tone isn't that of a young woman, and in Lieder that is a distinct disadvantage. Yet the triumph over a declining voice, and what she could achieve with it, is just as remarkable in the majority of the pieces here. The transfers are faultless.

Lucien Fugère Opera Arias and Songs. **Lucien Fugère** (bar) with various artists. Symposium mono Ⓕ 1125* (78 minutes: AAD: 6/93). From French Columbia originals; recorded 1928-30. La basoche, Le jongleur de Notre-Dame, L'ombre, Die Zauberflöte, Don Giovanni, Le roi malgré lui, Dinorah, Le val d'Andorre, Louise, Les saisons, Le medecin malgré lui, La rencontre imprévue, Le maître de chapelle; songs by Chaminade, Couperin, Henrion, Levadé and Widor.

Dates to keep in mind: 1848, 1928, 1930, 1933 and 1935. On the first, Lucien Fugère was born, on the second he made the first of the records heard here, on the third he made the last; in 1933 he gave his last operatic performance, and two years later he died. A little mental arithmetic establishes that he was 80 when he recorded (for example) the solos from Massenet's *Le jongleur de Notre-Dame*; having listened to them, one has to do the sum again, this time counting up on one's fingers to make sure, for otherwise his age would be scarcely credible. Actually, the recordings made at 80 are not the best; 81 was better, 82 best of all. The year 1930 brought the 'Grand Air' from Paër's *Le maître de chapelle*, which is Fugère's masterpiece. This enacts in brief a miniature opera on the subject of Cleopatra, and vocally it uses every trick in the book: an exercise of brilliant resource, performed with wit, elegance, technical skill and the infinite variety of Cleopatra herself. And the voice does sound even younger, even more assured here than in the first sessions, the acoustic being less boxy and allowing more room for expansion. The transfers are clear and natural.

Amelita Galli-Curci Opera Arias and Songs. **Amelita Galli-Curci** (sop) with various artists. Conifer Happy Days mono Ⓜ CDHD201* (70 minutes: ADD: 3/94). From Victor originals; recorded 1917-29. Arias from Don Pasquale, The Golden Cockerel, Lucia di Lammermoor, Rigoletto, Semiramide, La sonnambula, La traviata and Il trovatore; songs by Bishop, A. Scarlatti and Yradier. **Amelita Galli-Curci** Opera Arias and Songs. **Amelita Galli-Curci** (sop) with various artists. Romophone mono Ⓕ 81003-2* (two discs: 159 minutes: ADD: 3/94). From Victor originals; recorded 1916-20. ⒼⒼⒼ Arias from Il barbiere di Siviglia, Dinorah, Don Pasquale, Lakmé, Lucia di Lammermoor, Manon Lescaut (Auber), Martha, Le nozze di Figaro, I puritani, Rigoletto, Roméo et Juliette, La sonnambula and La traviata; songs by Alvarez, Benedict, Bishop, Buzzi-Peccia, David, Delibes, Giordani, Grieg, Massenet, Proch, Samuels and Seppilli.

These two issues complement each other very happily, the Romophone going up to 1920, the Conifer concentrating on later recordings, with an overlap of only three items. In *Gramophone* in 1923 the Editor wrote: "One of the most solid grounds I have for facing the coming of old age with equanimity is the reasonable hope that I shall spend it listening to as many records of *la diva* Galli-Curci's voice as there are of Caruso's". The purity of her voice was certainly a delight; it was at that time firm and even throughout its wide compass; and her fluency in scalework, precision in staccato, and ability to swell and diminish on a long-held high note were exceptional. She was an artist who could phrase and nuance exquisitely and who, within the boundaries of a more or less pretty joy and sadness, could be quite poignantly expressive. In the years of her greatest fame and success, roughly the decade from 1916 to 1926, her operatic repertoire was the standard one for the 'coloratura' soprano, and it is well represented by her records. What they also have, making them treasurable beyond anything that such a summary might suggest, is a personal flavour, a caress, a way of making words sound like water purling gently on a summer's afternoon, a dreaminess that can awaken to fun and affection though she could also flatten rather sadly in pitch. For completeness and also for the fine quality of the transfers many will want the Romophone. The Conifer selection is certainly a good one, including rarities such as the Scarlatti cantata (*Solitudini amene, apriche collinetti*), "Bel raggio" and "Ah, non giunge". On the whole, the early records have been transferred on this CD more enjoyably than the electricals.

Les introuvables de Nicolai Gedda Opera Arias – Alceste, Aleko, Un ballo in maschera,
Benvenuto Cellini, La clemenza di Tito, Così fan tutte, Die Entführung aus dem Serail,
Eugene Onegin, The fair at Sorochintsï, Iphigénie en Tauride, A Life for the Tsar, Manon,
Manon Lescaut, May Night, Mignon, Mireille, The Queen of Spades, Rosalinda, Sadko and
Tosca; arias and songs – Alfvén, Bach, Beethoven, Debussy, Fauré, Glinka, Grieg, Hahn,
Mozart, Mussorgsky, Peterson-Berger, Poulenc, Rachmaninov, Respighi, Sibelius, Sjöberg,
R. Strauss, Tchaikovsky, Telemann and Turina. **Nicolai Gedda** (ten) with various artists.
EMI mono/stereo Ⓜ CMS5 65685-2* (four discs: 305 minutes: ADD: 10/96). Recorded 1957-71.
Gedda's discography is vast, covering 40 years or more and embracing almost every corner of the
tenor repertory. As a linguist he is phenomenal: on these four CDs he sings in German, French,
Russian, Norwegian, Swedish, Italian and Spanish. The selection comes mostly from recital discs
made in the 1960s, several of which were not available in the UK. To begin with Gedda the recitalist,
go to the third CD. He opens with three songs by Glinka, *Doubt, O thou dear, darling little girl* and
Souvenir. His tone is light but amazingly strong, a voice of gleaming white gold. Three songs by
Mussorgsky, *The little star* outstandingly beautiful, then irony in *By the Don* and *The billy goat* – this
last one about the beautiful girl who marries the hairy old man – lead to a classic Tchaikovsky group,
songs which Gedda made very much his own – *O moonlit night, At the ball, Legend* and *Don Juan's
Serenade*. The French recital which begins the second CD, with Aldo Ciccolini, has never been
available in Britain before. Although the words are clear, his way of pronouncing some of the French
texts is rather Italianate, rolling the 'r's and giving the endings of words a stronger 'e' than is really
necessary. Gedda is predictably at home with the Poulenc settings of Jean Moréas (*Air champêtre* and
Air grave) and two songs from the Apollinaire group *Banalités* ("Voyage à Paris" and "Hotel" with its
languorous ending, "Je veux fumer").
From an all-Beethoven recital comes *Adelaïde* and *An die ferne Geliebte*: a **Gramophone** review of
the original issue complained of a "lack of glow" in Gedda's voice. Different people hear different
things, of course, but glow is exactly what Gedda produces in the rapturous opening of Strauss's
Heimliche Aufforderung; this must be one of the best recordings of any Strauss song. His half-
laughing delivery of the line "veracht sie nicht zu sehr", and the wonderful feeling of expectancy and
intimacy between the lovers, who are caught in a crowd and long to be alone, would have satisfied
Lotte Lehmann, who in her lectures on Lieder demanded for this song "a mood overflowingly happy
and carefree". *Ständchen, Die Nacht*, a really tremendous performance of the ghostly *Befreit* and then
the brief, ecstatic *Liebeshymnus* bring this CD to a most satisfying conclusion. The operatic arias are
taken from four recitals. The earliest is a Mozart group conducted by Cluytens and the real gem is the
concert aria, K420, *Per pietà, non ricercate*. Gedda's voice here, when he was just 32, has a resonance
in the lower register and a fluidity which isn't present in the later recordings of popular Italian arias
under Patanè. French arias with Prêtre and Russian arias with the Belgrade Orchestra under Gika
Zdravkovich complete the picture, the whole sequence ending with Gedda's incomparable "Faint echo
of my youth" from *Eugene Onegin*: many people will remember him as Lensky above all his other
roles. Sadly, EMI don't supply texts or synopses but one is left with renewed wonder for Gedda's art.

Beniamino Gigli Opera Arias and Songs. **Beniamino Gigli** (ten) with various artists.
Memoir Classics mono Ⓕ CDMOIR417* (65 minutes: AAD: 6/93). From HMV originals.
Recorded 1921-39.
Arias from – L'Africaine, Andrea Chenier, La bohème, Cavalleria Rusticana, L'elisir d'amore,
La forza del destino, Martha, Mefistofele, Les pêcheurs de perles and Rigoletto. Songs by Bixio,
Cottrau, De Curtis, Denza, Di Chiara and Toselli.
Of all the famous Italian tenors, Gigli was the one whose voice seemed most to embody the sweets of
nature – the sunshine, the fruit filled "with ripeness to the core" and so forth. He sang as though for
the love of it, though of course collecting a substantial fee too (and in fact rather than submit to the
indignity of a reduction in salary he quit the Metropolitan in their financial crisis of 1932). The
records included here come from the years either side of that date and show him in his magnificent
prime, the leading lyric-dramatic tenor of the world. The programme begins with his "Che gelida
manina" of 1931, one of the top best-sellers in the HMV catalogues for many a year. His appeal lies
not only in the sweetness, the easy power and ring of his well-rounded voice, but also in a personality
that is almost winsomely human: a chubby chuckle, a boyish pleading, lightens up the 'face' of his

singing. There is fervour in his *Andrea Chenier*, good humour in his "La donna è mobile", and appropriate bad temper in his *Cavalleria Rusticana* duet with the formidable Dusolina Giannini. Then, in a selection of shamelessly tuneful Italian songs, he woos beguilingly, sometimes in the honeyed half-voice, ultimately with the thrilling vibrancy of his *fortissimo*. Two of the items (from *Mefistofele* and *La forza del destino*) are reproduced a semitone too high, but in general the quality of transfers is fine and the selection excellent. A superb performance.

Alma Gluck Opera Arias and Duets – Atalanta, La bohème, Carmen, Hänsel und Gretel, Hippolyte et Aricie, The kiss, Louise, Natoma, Pagliacci, Samson et Dalila, Semele, Snow maiden, La sonnambula, Theodora, La traviata, The Tsar's bride and Zemire und Azor; songs by Arditi, Cadman, Coleridge Taylor, Cornelius, Cottenet, Greene, Hahn, Hildach, Horsman, Lang, Leroux, Loewe, MacDowell, Moore, Ravel, Rimsky-Korsakov, Saint-Saëns, Sánchez de Fuentes, Sinding, Spross and Tosti. **Alma Gluck** (sop) with various artists. Marston mono Ⓕ 52001-2* (two discs: 151 minutes: ADD: A/97). From Victor originals; recorded 1911-18.
The "celestial purity" of Alma Gluck's voice (to quote Compton Mackenzie) is the first characteristic that impresses itself in this lovely selection of her recordings, and it does so immediately with the very first phrase of Handel's "Come, my beloved" ("Care selve"), a version to put side by side with John McCormack's. In "O sleep, why does thou leave me?", which follows, she hasn't his breadth of phrasing, yet the long run, divided into three, is gracefully done, and it is good to find, as in "Angels ever bright and fair", that she sings her Handel cleanly but with warmth, without rigidity of tempo yet neither wilful nor indulgent. Her "Rossignols amoureux" was a prize rarity in its day, and the song *Have you seen but a whyte lillie grow* was a special favourite of Sir Compton's. Included are some duets with Louise Horner, one of them, bearing the ominous title *Passage-birds' Farewell*, being a surprisingly robust piece of music and splendidly sung. Ward Marston, who has been responsible for many of the best transfers in recent years, is here credited with 'Audio Conservation', the producer and supplier of original copies being Lawrence F. Holdridge. We are deeply indebted to both of them.

Great Singers at the Maryinsky Theatre Opera Arias with various accompaniments. Nimbus Prima Voce mono Ⓜ NI7865* (78 minutes: ADD: 3/95). Notes and some synopses included. From HMV originals; recorded 1908-13.
Sopranos – **Olimpia Boronat** (Les Huguenots), **Eugenia Bronskaya** (Hamlet, A life for the Tsar), **Elena Katulskaya** (Mireille, Thaïs), **Maria Kovalenko** (The Queen of Spades), **Lydia Lipkowska** (The Snow Maiden), **Antonina Nezhdanova** (Fra Diavolo, Lakmé, La traviata, Die Zauberflöte). *Mezzo-soprano* – **Evgenia Popello-Davidova** (Lakmé). *Contralto* – **Evgenia Zbrueva** (The Queen of Spades). *Tenors* – **David Juzhin** (La Gioconda), **Andrei Labinsky** (Halka), **Dmitri Smirnov** (Mefistofele, La traviata), **Leonid Sobinov** (The demon), **Eugene Vitting** (The Queen of Spades). *Baritone* – **Mikhail Karakash** (The Queen of Spades). *Basses* – **Vladimir Kastorsky** (Eugene Onegin), **Lev Sibiriakov** (Judith, Thaïs, Requiem – Verdi).
Here is a superb collection, "courtesy [we are told] of the Director of Staff of the St Petersburg State Museum of Theatre and Music". All of the originals are rare, and some must be practically unique. Among the soprano solos, particularly exciting is Boronat's account of the Queen's cabaletta in *Les Huguenots*, queenly indeed as far as the letter of the score is concerned but brilliant in technique and often exquisite in shading. Nezhdanova in both *Lakmé* excerpts (the Bell song and now even more famous 'flower' duet) sings with lovely purity and easy command. Lipkowska's *Snow Maiden* is an utter charmer, and also delightfully youthful in tone is Katulskaya's Mireille. Of the tenors, Labinsky's *Halka* solo has exemplary evenness of line, as has the baritone Karakash in Yeletsky's aria. Kastorsky's Gremin and Sibiriakov's admonition of the Israelites in *Judith* are among the finest of all; and how skilfully Sibiriakov subdues his mighty bass in the *Thaïs* duet with Katulskaya. The original copies used are all in pristine condition.

Greatest Voices of Bolshoi Opera Arias. Various artists. Melodiya mono/stereo Ⓜ 74321 39505-2* (two discs: 149 minutes: ADD: 12/96). From HMV and Melodiya originals. Recorded 1910-80.
Sopranos – **Valeria Barsova** (Snow Maiden), **Xenia Derzhinskaya** (The Queen of Spades), **Vera Firssova** (Christmas Eve), **Tamara Milash-kina** (The Enchantress), **Antonina Nezhdanova** (A Life for the Tsar), **Bella Rudenko** (Lakmé), **Natalia Spieller** (Iolanta), **Galina Vishnevskaya** (La forza del destino). *Mezzo-sopranos* – **Irina Arkhipova** (Samson et Dalila), **Elena Obraztsova** (Boris Godunov), **Nadezhda Obukhova** (Prince Igor). *Tenors* – **Zurab Andzhaparidze** (The Queen of Spades), **Vladimir Atlantov** (Prince Igor), **Ivan Kozlovsky** (Boris Godunov, Snow Maiden), **Sergei Lemeshev** (Eugene Onegin, Sadko), **Georgi Nelepp** (Askold's Grave), **Leonid Sobinov** (Lohengrin). *Baritones* – **Pavel Lisitsian** (The Queen of Spades), **Yuri Mazurok** (Mazeppa), **Grigori Pirogov** (Askold's Grave). *Basses* – **Feodor Chaliapin** (Don Quichotte), **Maxim Mikhailov** (Prince Igor), **Evgeny Nesterenko** (A Life for the Tsar), **Ivan Petrov** (Iolanta), **Alexander Pirogov** (Prince Igor), **Mark Reizen** (Boris Godunov).
Here's a selection. From Glinka onwards, standards were set for Russian singing which we can, for the great nineteenth-century artists, only deduce from their music but which we may fairly suppose founded the great tradition we can hear upheld on record for much of the twentieth. What did Osip Petrov, the bass who dominated Russian opera for half a century from 1826, really sound like?

Probably less like Chaliapin – though the great dramatic bass is represented here in lyrical vein by his beautiful performance of Don Quichotte's death scene in 1927 (Massenet) – than his namesake Ivan Petrov as King René (1952), or than the powerful Maxim Mikhailov, superb in Khan Konchak's aria (1953), or than the cultivated Mark Reizen, whose début was as Pimen in 1921, singing wonderfully here in 1951 and who made his final appearance as Gremin in 1985, on his ninetieth birthday, to a devoted Bolshoi cast and audience. Alexander Pirogov's fine delivery of Galitsky's aria (1951) and Evgeny Nesterenko's of Susanin's farewell (1979) seem but younger branches of this great oak planted by Petrov.

The tenor tradition lies closer to French style than to anything more intrinsically Russian, let alone Italian. Here is the superlative Leonid Sobinov, in fine voice as Lohengrin (1910); but why not some of his Lensky, who here goes to the elegant Sergei Lemeshev (1953)? Here too is Ivan Kozlovsky, unforgettable as the Simpleton in *Boris* in 1927 and still in full command as Tsar Berendey in 1957. On the other hand, the powerful Slavonic line of dominating mezzos and contraltos has made a mark upon opera that has at times led to tradition becoming something of a prison. Nadezhda Obukhova exhibits some of these risks in the very strength of her singing of Konchakovna (1941); however, here are Elena Obraztsova (part of Marina's aria in 1968) and Irina Arkhipova (Dalila's "Mon coeur" in 1980) showing how rich and diverse it can be.

The sopranos are the most varied group. Some exhibit the powerful vibrato which has been such a cause of complaint in the West, though Valeria Barsova (1951) shows how it can be lightly and expressively applied to the Snow Maiden. Bella Rudenko's chirpy coloratura sparkles in Lakmé's Bell Song (1967). Antonina Nezhdanova exhibits a warmer, stronger manner in Antonida's Romance (1914) that suggests her as a mother figure to Galina Vishnevskaya, at the height of her powers as Verdi's *Forza* Leonora in 1959. Much more could be mentioned, and Grigori Pirogov's remarkable baritone as the Unknown in *Askold's Grave* (1910) should certainly not be overlooked. The transfers are fine.

Maria Ivogün Opera Arias and Songs. **Maria Ivogün** (sop); [a]**Michael Raucheisen** (pf); [b]**orchestra;** [c]**Berlin State Opera Orchestra / Leo Blech.** Nimbus Prima Voce Ⓜ NI7832* (78 minutes: ADD: 8/92).
Bishop Lo, here the gentle lark[b] (from Brunswick 10174, 11/25). **Handel** L'allegro, il penseroso ed il moderato, HWV55 – Sweet bird[b] (Polydor 85313, recorded 1925). **Donizetti** Don Pasquale – Ah! un foco insolito[b] (85302, recorded 1924). Lucia di Lammermoor – Ardon gl'incensi[b] (Odeon 76977, recorded 1917). **Rossini** Il barbiere di Siviglia – Una voce poco fa[b] (85309, recorded 1925). **Verdi** La traviata – E strano ... Ah, fors'è lui ... Sempre libera[b] (sung in German. 76982/3, recorded 1916). **Chopin** Nocturne in E flat major, Op. 9 No. 2[b] (arr. sop/orch. 76975). **Meyerbeer** Les Huguenots – Une dame noble et sage[b] (German. 76997). **Nicolai** Die Lustigen Weiber von Windsor – Nun eilt herbei[b] (76811. All recorded 1917). **Schubert** Ständchen (Horch! Horch! die Lerch), D899[b]. Winterreise, D911 – Die Post[b] (both from Brunswick 15075, 9/24). **J. Strauss II** Frühlingsstimmen, Op. 410[b] (85313, recorded 1924). G'schichten aus dem Wienerwald, Op. 325[b] (10174). An die schönen, blauen Donau, Op. 314[c]. Die Fledermaus – Klänge der Heimat[c] (HMV DB4412, 6/34). **Kreisler** Liebesfreud[b] (Brunswick 50050, 12/24). **Anonymous** O du liebs Angeli[a]. Z'Lauterbach han i'mein Strumpf verlor'n[a]. Gsätzli. Maria auf dem Berge[a] (all from HMV DA4402, 6/33).
Somewhere or other, after much searching of the memory, ransacking of the catalogues and phoning around among connoisseurs, it might be possible to discover a more delightful example of the coloratura's art than that of Maria Ivogün as displayed in her recording of Kreisler's *Liebesfreud*, made in 1924: if so, one such does not spring to mind now. With the most pure and delicate of tones, nothing shrill or piercing about them, she sings way above a normal mortal's reach, ease and accuracy in the purely technical feats going along with a lilt and feeling for the idiomatic give-and-take of waltz rhythm that are a joy musically. Turn to Handel, with the solo from *Il penseroso*, and the same art is put to lovely use in a different idiom. Her *Traviata* aria has warmth and spontaneity; her Frau Fluth in *Die lustigen Weiber von Windsor* is a woman of charm and energy; and the 1934 recording of the Czardas in *Die Fledermaus* shines as bright in spirit as in clarity of timbre. From the same period comes the set of four songs, Swiss and German, that show most touchingly her command of the art to be simple. This is an admirable introduction to a most lovely singer, and it represents the Prima Voce series at its best.

Hilde Konetzni Opera Arias – The bartered bride, Don Giovanni, Fidelio, Der Freischütz, Madama Butterfly, Der Rosenkavalier, Tannhäuser and Tosca; songs by R. Strauss.
Hilde Konetzni (sop) with various artists. Preiser mono Ⓕ 90078* (74 minutes: AAD: 1/95).
From Nixa, Telefunken, Columbia and German Radio originals; recorded 1937-50.
Look no further than this disc to hear a near ideal tone and technique. A lovely singer suggesting the very essence of natural, sincere, open-faced interpretation, Hilde Konetzni, leading soprano at the Vienna State Opera from the late 1930s to the early 1950s, projects the varying emotions of Leonore, Agathe, Elisabeth, Butterfly (albeit in German) and Mařenka (again in German) with an eager sincerity that at once silences criticism and puts her in the class of her coevals in similar repertory – the Marias Reining and Müller and Tiana Lemnitz (what a wealth of talent to draw on!). None of these attempted Leonore, and Konetzni's "Abscheulicher!" is a totally convincing interpretation – and

marvellously sung. Here is the vulnerable, heroic wife to the life, pouring out her feelings in steady, even, unfettered tones, negotiating the awkward intervals and the difficult tessitura as if they were no problem at all. That performance comes from the series of Telefunken discs that Konetzni made in 1937, with the admirable support of Schmidt-Isserstedt as conductor. They include versions of Agathe's "Wie nahte mir der Schlummer" and Elisabeth's arias that would be hard to better, so radiant and unencumbered is the delivery. Konetzni must also have been a touching Butterfly: her version of Cio-Cio-San's entrance and the Flower duet with Marie Luise Schilp as a warm Suzuki touch the heart. The mind is dazzled by the exquisite refinement evinced at the end of "Vissi d'arte" – or rather "Nur der Schönheit" as it is here. Ten years later Konetzni made a few treasured 78s for Columbia with Karajan at the helm. Her account of Mařenka's "Endlich allein" from *The bartered bride* shows no diminution of the singer's skills, only a deepening of the tone that also allowed her to convey all the Marschallin's sadness in that character's Act 1 Monologue. Also included here are four Richard Strauss songs made with the composer at the piano, in 1943. They are a trifle disappointing: in terms of colour and inflexion they are penny-plain. Nevertheless, do get this disc if you want to hear some truly heartfelt and wonderfully sung readings of these opera excerpts.

Erich Kunz Opera Arias – Don Giovanni, Der lustige Krieg, Eine Nacht in Venedig, Le nozze di Figaro, Der Vogelhändler, Der Waffenschmied, Der Wildschütz, Zar und Zimmermann, Die Zauberflöte and Der Zigeunerbaron; Viennese songs by various composers. **Erich Kunz** (bar) with various artists. Testament mono ⓕ SBT1059* (79 minutes: ADD: 9/95). From Columbia originals; recorded 1947-53.

Here is Kunz in his absolute prime, moving his agreeable voice around Figaro's, Leporello's and Papageno's music with the confidence derived from experience in the roles in Vienna, but without the slightest sense of routine. It should not be forgotten that he was one of the first German-speaking singers to learn his Da Ponte roles in Italian: his diction and accent in them, as we find here, are virtually perfect. Under Karajan, in Figaro's "Non più andrai" he is disciplined by a fast tempo, while Ackermann is more yielding in Leporello's "Madamina". Karajan also conducts the Giovanni/Zerlina duet (with the incomparable Seefried). It is a wonderful souvenir of two artists, their voices blending ideally, who sang so often together in that notable ensemble in Vienna. Kunz was also loved in his home city for his assumption of *buffo* parts in Lortzing's operas, and he brings to their arias, again with Ackermann in sympathetic support, a rich vein of comic characterization without ever resorting to caricature – Kunz was, above all, a sensitive musician. The second half of this issue is devoted to operetta items and Viennese songs. In the former it may be complained that he was often adopting, and transposing down, music written originally for a tenor: four songs from *Ein Nacht in Venedig*, in the Korngold rescension, rather suffer in that respect, yet Kunz's wholly idiomatic approach almost makes us forget the anomaly. In what are mostly Heurigen songs, he is absolutely in his element; only his older, tenor colleague, Julius Patzak was his peer in these. The accompanying Schrammel Ensemble are wholly authentic. Try, if you can, *Da draussen in der Wachau*, so beguiling in tone and style, and you will not be able to resist the rest.

Legendary Baritones Opera Arias and Songs with various accompaniments. Nimbus Prima Voce mono Ⓜ NI7867* (77 minutes: ADD: 10/95). From Columbia, Fonotipia, HMV, Victor, Polydor and German Odeon originals; recorded 1905-41.
Lucien Fugère (Le jongleur de Notre Dame); **Victor Maurel** (Tosti: Au temps du grand roi); **Antonio Magini-Coletti** (Falstaff); **Mattia Battistini** (La traviata); **Mario Ancona** (Un ballo in maschera); **Maurice Renaud** (Le roi de Lahore); **Eugenio Giraldoni** (Otello); **Riccardo Stracciari** (Tosca); **Giuseppe de Luca** (Ernani); **Titta Ruffo** (Falstaff); **Pasquale Amato** (I due Foscari); **Joseph Schwarz** (Tannhäuser); **Heinrich Schlusnus** (Hans Heiling); **Renato Zanelli** (Zazà); **Carlo Galeffi** (Rigoletto); **John Charles Thomas** (Andrea Chenier); **Lawrence Tibbett** (Il barbiere di Siviglia); **Gerhard Hüsch** (Der Wildschütz); **Igor Gorin** (Attila).

Prizes for all here, except possibly John Charles Thomas. *Andrea Chenier* is not the subtlest of operas, and "Nemico della patria" does not call for the fine nuance of a Fischer-Dieskau, but it does want more than the mouthing of words and *tutta forza* for the notes. The voice is magnificent, but in this 'legendary' company we look also for taste. And in its various guises we find it: in the 80-year-old Fugère with his immaculate definition and unmawkish tenderness; in Maurel with a charm of old-world manners in his courtly song to Madame la Marquise; Magini-Coletti with his humorous but gentlemanly Falstaff; Battistini wearing his elegant paternal suit, and Ancona bestowing upon the outraged husband the dignity of more-in-sorrow-than-in-anger. After that comes Maurice Renaud, about whom one might raise a complaint concerning emotional expression achieved at the expense of the vocal line; yet there is stylistic refinement too, and a richly imaginative care for the Massenet aria, phrase by phrase. With Stracciari one might wonder about the voice production, so free one moment, throat-laden in another; then there is Amato with his rapid vibrancy, Galeffi with his weakness for the emotional quiver. Yet all are artists, and their work will repay study. The Germans are a distinguished trio too, and the Russian-born Igor Gorin is superb in his *Attila* aria. Ruffo, rich in vocal colours, de Luca gracious in the exercise of traditional virtues ... But there it is: a prize-giving here would have something for (almost) everybody, including those responsible for the transfers and booklet, for the choice of singers and their matching up with arias.

Lotte Lehmann Songs – Balogh, Beethoven, Brahms, Cimara, Franz, Gounod, Grechaninov, Hahn, Jensen, Marx, Mozart, Pfitzner, Sadero, Schubert, Schumann, Sjöberg, Wolf and Worth. **Lotte Lehmann** (sop) with various artists. Romophone mono Ⓕ 81013-2* (two discs: 157 minutes: ADD: 5/96). From Victor originals; recorded 1935-40.

Lotte Lehmann was at the height of her powers as a song interpreter in the late 1930s: the bloom of youth is still in the tone, now enhanced by the experience of many years of stage interpretation. Thus, her characters *in extremis* become something of a talisman of suffering women. Her impassioned Gretchen in Schubert's great song is sister to, and inhabits the same world as, Lehmann's Leonore and Sieglinde. The searing intensity of "Was hör ich alte Laute?" in Schumann's *Alte Laute* goes through you, becomes etched in the mind, just as do certain phrases in her operatic portrayals. Yet while the passions are felt on a large scale throughout these songs, the intimate mould of Lieder singing is never breached. The readings are generous and free, never dull, careful or limited, or by another token overladen with detailed word-painting in the Schwarzkopf manner. Unlike many of her contemporaries Lehmann ranged wide in her choice of repertory. She digs out Jensen's *Lehn' diene Wang' an meine Wange* and makes you believe that this little sentimental song is a masterpiece. However, it is for the Schubert (including 12 songs from *Winterreise*, so immediate in effect, no holds barred), Schumann, Brahms and Wolf, that the myriad admirers of this artist will want these two lavishly filled CDs. The transfers are clean and clear, but at times impart a slight glare to Lehmann's tone. This offering is an essential addition to the Lehmann discography.

Giovanni Martinelli Opera Arias and Duets. **Giovanni Martinelli** (ten); [a]**Metropolitan Opera Chorus and Orchestra / Giulio Setti,** [b]**Josef Pasternack,** [c]**Rosario Bourdon.** Preiser Lebendige Vergangenheit mono Ⓕ 89062* (68 minutes: AAD: 3/93). Recorded 1926-27. ⓖⓖⓖ **Verdi** Rigoletto – La donna è mobile. Il trovatore – Quale d'armi fragor ... Di quella pira[a] (with Grace Anthony, sop). La forza del destino – Oh, tu che in seno; Invano Alvaro ... Le minacciei fieri accenti (with Giuseppe de Luca, bar). Aida – Se quel guerrier io fossi ... Celeste Aida[b]; Nume, custode e vindici (with Ezio Pinza, bass). **Giordano** Andrea Chenier – Un dì all'azzurro spazio[b]; Come un bel dì di maggio[c]. Fedora[b] – Amor ti vieta; Mia madre, la mia vecchia madre. **Mascagni** Cavalleria Rusticana[c] – O Lola; Mamma, quel vino è generoso. **Leoncavallo** Pagliacci – Recitar! ... Vesti la giubba[c]; Per la morte! smettiamo ... No, Pagliaccio non son[a] (with Grace Anthony). Zazà – E un riso gentil[c]. **Puccini** La bohème – Che gelida manina[b]. Tosca – E lucevan le stelle[b].

Here is one of the most fascinating of singers. He can also be one of the most thrilling, his voice having at its best a beauty unlike any other, his art noble in breadth of phrase and concentration of tone. It also has to be said that his records hardly make easy or restful listening, but what at first may even repel soon becomes compulsive, the intensity of expression and individuality of timbre impressing themselves upon the memory with extraordinary vividness. Martinelli's career was centred on the Metropolitan, New York, where he sang first at the height of the Caruso era, inheriting Caruso's more dramatic roles in 1921. This selection makes an unrepresentative start with "La donna è mobile", but the excerpts from *Il trovatore* and *La forza del destino* have the very essence of the man, masterly in his shaping and shading of recitative, or in the long curves of his melodic line and the tension of his utterance. There are also superb performances of solos from *Andrea Chénier* and *Pagliacci*, the involvement of his "No, Pagliaccio non son" unequalled before or since. These are recordings from 1926 and 1927, the period in which his vocal and artistic qualities were probably best matched. The transfers are fine apart from the song from Leoncavallo's *Zazà* which plays below pitch.

John McCormack Opera and Operetta Arias – Il barbiere di Siviglia, Barry of Ballymore, La bohème, Carmen, L'elisir d'amore, Faust, La fille du régiment, La Gioconda, In a Persian garden, Lakmé, Lucia di Lammermoor, Naughty Marietta, Les pêcheurs de perles, Rigoletto and La traviata; songs by Balfe, Barker, Blumenthal, Cherry, Claribel, Crouch, MacMurrough, Marshall, Parelli, Rossini and Traditional. **John McCormack** (ten) with various artists. Romophone mono Ⓕ 82006-2* (two discs: 155 minutes: ADD: 4/96). From Victor and HMV originals; recorded 1910-11.

You think, at the start of this journey through the recordings of two years, that here is McCormack at his absolute best, in the first of the *Lucia di Lammermoor* solos; but no, for the second one ("Tu che a Dio spiegasti l'ali"), made two months later, is better still, a perfection of lyrical singing, the music lying ideally within his voice as it was at that time, and with the heart and imagination more evidently involved. A little later comes "Una furtiva lagrima", where the modulation into D flat major ("m'ama") brings surely some of the most beautiful, most unflawed tenor singing ever recorded. This album, from 1910 and 1911, presents him in finest voice. He was only 25 at the outset: in the first flush of his operatic success and already the partner of Melba (heard with him in the *Rigoletto* Quartet and *Faust* Trio) and Tetrazzini. His favourite baritone partner was Mario Sammarco, who turns up as a blustery Figaro in his elegant Almaviva, retiring to a more discreet distance behind the recording horn in the duet from *Les Pêcheurs de perles* (the deservedly rare version included here along with the more familiar ten inch). They also join in the *gondolieri*-like harmonies of Rossini's *Li marinari* (splendid high Bs from McCormack) and give each other a run for their money in a full-bodied, exciting account of the duet from *La Gioconda*. McCormack, it is true, had still to develop eloquence as a singer of songs, but his eventual mastery is clearly foretold in the old Irish song, *She is far from the land*, a haunting and heartfelt piece of tender nostalgia. The transfers are excellent.

The Artistry of Fernando de la Mora Fernando de la Mora (ten); **Welsh National Opera Orchestra / Sir Charles Mackerras.** Telarc Ⓕ CD80411 (64 minutes: DDD: 1/96).
Gounod Roméo et Juliette – Ah! lève-toi, soleil. Faust – Salut! demeure chaste et pure.
Verdi La traviata – De' miei bollenti spiriti; O mio romorso! Rigoletto – Ella mi fu rapita!; Parmi veder le lagrime; La donna è mobile. **Puccini** La bohème – Che gelida manina. Tosca – Recondita armonia; E lucevan le stelle. **Cilea** L'arlesiana – E la solita storia. **Bizet** Carmen – La fleur que tu m'avais jetée. Les pêcheurs de perles – Je crois entendre encore.
Donizetti La fille du régiment – Ah! mes amis. **Ponchielli** La Gioconda – Cielo e mar!
Massenet Werther – Pourquoi me réveiller? **Giordano** Fedora – Amor ti vieta.
The title draws attention to "the artistry" of this tenor, and very justifiably too; but what we want to know about first is the voice. In his opening phrases the sound is tender and sweet, and we soon realize that Fernando de la Mora is a name to be noted and remembered. This is in Roméo's cavatina: this Mexican tenor sings with perhaps not such clean French definition but with rather more honey in the voice, perhaps more imaginatively too. But then in *La traviata* the production seems not quite so easy and secure, while a tendency to come up to a note from below (though no more than several eminent predecessors have done) compromises the style a little and a slightly nasalized quality intrudes in certain vowel-sounds. With "Che gelida manina", however, we are back with the charmer, the lyric tenor assured in his command of range and expression, the voice of the young lover and the reason why all the world loves a good young Italianate tenor. And so it goes on. Every item has it attractions, and many are very good indeed. In the now famous *Fille du régiment* solo he duly warms to his nine top Cs, and in the Flower song from *Carmen* he takes the high B flat softly but not falsetto. "Cielo e mar" is graced with a carefully preserved legato, though perhaps the tone is a bit limited in resources for this. "Salut! demeure" is sung gently and sensitively till it comes to the high C, a fine ringing note but isolated by the quietness of its context and by the prefatory breath taken before "la présence". Mackerras conducts, and the Welsh National Opera Orchestra play, with all due sympathy.

Claudia Muzio Opera Arias – Aida, Un ballo in maschera, La bohème, Carmen, Cavalleria Rusticana, Les contes d'Hoffmann, Ernani, La forza del destino, Gianni Schicchi, La Gioconda, Guillaume Tell, Louise, Madama Butterfly, Madame Sans-Gêne, Manon, Manon Lescaut, Mefistofele, Mignon, Otello, Pagliacci, Il segreto di Susanna, Suor Angelica, Tosca, La traviata, Il trovatore, I vespri siciliani and La Wally; songs by Braga, Burleigh, Buzzi-Peccia, Delibes, Donaudy, Giordano, Mascheroni, Olivieri, Roxas and Sanderson. **Claudia Muzio** (sop) with various artists. Romophone mono Ⓕ 81010-2* (two discs: 140 minutes: ADD: 1/95).
From Pathé and Edison originals; recorded 1917-25.   ⒼⒼⒼ
Romophone have put us in their debt by issuing the 1917-25 Pathés and adding four unpublished and fascinating Edison titles. Inevitably there is some overlapping with the first set (reviewed further on) but it is surprising how many titles were not remade by the soprano. Here we have, on the first disc, an impassioned and nicely shaded "Suicidio!" in a reading that is amazingly accomplished when you realize Muzio was just 28 at the time. "O patria mia" and "Un bel dì", neither repeated by her, adumbrate the sheer beauty of the voice of the young *spinto*: strength is there, but also refinement and feeling, although the technical command, as often with this singer, isn't always faultless. Above all, we catch an echo over the years of what Muzio must have been like: deeply affecting, in these roles, confirming contemporary comment. The songs are, as ever with this singer, irresistible. Buzzi-Peccia's *Baciarmi* is poised sensuously on a skein of gossamer tone. In another song, Burleigh's *Jean*, we can delight in Muzio's excellent and clear English and also in the better sound. Then come the four 'new' Edisons, which include Donaudy's *O del mio amato ben*, later repeated in 1935 for Columbia: the performance here is just as plangent. Even more tenderly accented is a little-known and unattributed song, *Torna amore*, and the even more evocative traditional *Mon jardin*. Yes, a great singer indeed.

Claudia Muzio Opera Arias and Duets – Adriana Lecouvreur, Andrea Chénier, L'Arlesiana, La bohème, Cavalleria Rusticana, Cecilia, La forza del destino, Mefistofele, Norma, Otello, La sonnambula, Tosca, La traviata and Il trovatore; songs by Buzzi-Peccia, Debussy, Delibes, Donaudy, Parisotti, Refice and Reger. **Claudia Muzio** (sop) with various artists. Romophone mono Ⓕ 81015-2* (two discs: 155 minutes: ADD: 6/96). From Columbia and Italian Columbia originals; recorded 1934-35. Also contains part of Act 1 of Puccini's *Tosca*, recorded live in 1932.   Ⓖ
This set completes Romophone's comprehensive survey of all Muzio's records, masterminded by Ward Marston. Since their first release, Muzio's Columbias of 1934-5 have always been her most accessible discs, but they have never, even on previous CD reissues, sounded so present and clear as they do here. This most eloquent of divas seems to be in the room with us and the music in hand is delivered with such sincere passion, such total conviction that tears are brought to the eyes. All those anonymous-sounding sopranos with their dull recitals today should sit down and listen to the individuality Muzio brings to every track here. Not for a moment can one be anything but enthralled by these readings. Since there is not enough material to fill two CDs, Romophone have added a

substantial extract from Act 1 of a 1932 San Francisco *Tosca*, primitively recorded and so far known only to a few Muzio fanatics. However, as a whole this is an essential issue for anyone wanting to know about the art of one of the century's most lovable and vital interpreters.

Claudia Muzio Opera Arias and Songs – Adriana Lecouvreur, L'Africaine, L'amico Fritz,
Andrea Chénier, Bianca e Fernando, La bohème, Carmen, Les contes d'Hoffmann, Eugene
Onegin, La forza del destino, Hérodiade, I Lombardi, Loreley, Madame Sans-Gêne, Mefistofele,
Pagliacci, Paride e Elena, Rinaldo, Salvator Rosa, La traviata, Il trovatore, I vespri siciliani,
La Wally and Zazà; songs by Bachelet, Buzzi-Peccia, Chopin, Guagni-Benvenuti, Herbert,
Mascheroni, Monahan, Pergolesi, Rossini and Sodero. **Claudia Muzio** (sop) with various artists.
Romophone mono Ⓔ 81005-2* (two discs: 153 minutes: ADD: 1/94). From HMV and Edison
originals; recorded 1911-25.   ⒼⒼⒼ

The crackles and surface noise that usually afflict Edison reproduction have all but been eliminated, so that we can hear Muzio's voice in its absolute prime without, as it were, the effort of listening through a sea of interference. The sheer beauty of the soprano's voice and her wonderful intensity of expression can now be experienced with astonishing immediacy. All the Muzio gifts, including that of refined, exquisite phrasing combined with that peculiarly heart-rending intensity that was hers alone, are heard in that enchanting song by Bachelet, *Chère nuit* (first disc, track 8). If your dealer will let you hear that, even if you are sceptical about singers of the past, you are sure to make off home with this set, eager to hear the rest. A feast of captivating interpretations from one of the century's three or four greatest singing-actresses.

The Incomparable Heddle Nash
Puccini La bohème – Act 4ᵃ. **Lisa Perli** (sop) Mimì; **Heddle Nash** (ten) Rodolfo; **Stella Andreva**
(sop) Musetta; **John Brownlee** (bar) Marcello; **Robert Alva** (bass) Schaunard; **Robert Easton**
(bass) Colline; **London Philharmonic Orchestra / Sir Thomas Beecham.**
Dutton Laboratories mono Ⓜ CDLX7012* (69 minutes: ADD: 2/95). Item marked ᵃ from
Columbia LX523/6 (10/36); remainder from HMV and Columbia originals; recorded 1929-35. Ⓖ
Opera Arias and Duets – Il barbiere di Siviglia, Così fan tutte, Don Giovanni, Die Fledermaus,
La jolie fille de Perth and Rigoletto. **Heddle Nash** (ten) with various artists.

When he made this recording of Act 4 of *La bohème* in 1935 Nash was at the height of his powers and sings a spontaneous, quite Italianate Rodolfo. Perli makes a simple, heartfelt Mimì. The rest of the cast falls far short of the principals, but Beecham is at his most alert, and sensitive too. Nash's Mozart is most elegantly represented by the well-nigh faultless versions of Ottavio's arias, made at the time of his sensational Covent Garden début in 1929 in *Don Giovanni*. The phrasing is refined, the breath long, the big run in "Il mio tesoro" encompassed in a single span. The Duke of Mantua's three arias tell us just why this was one of Nash's favourite roles early in his career. He makes the most of the execrable translation by singing it with total conviction, and his lyric tenor rings out with just the right *élan*, matched by subtle colourings. The Serenade from *La jolie fille de Perth* is justly renowned because it displays to perfection the elegiac, minstrel-like quality of Nash's tone and his impassioned delivery – and yet he is said to have had a cold on the day it was made! The transfers (including the solo items) are superior to any previous issues, bringing the voices into one's room without let or hindrance.

Heddle Nash Opera Arias and Ensembles – La bohème, Carmen, Cavalleria Rusticana, Faust,
Die Fledermaus, Friederike, La jolie fille de Perth, Les pêcheurs de perles, Rigoletto and Il
trovatore; songs by Ascher, Delius, MacMurrough, Rossini and R. Strauss. **Heddle Nash** (ten)
with various artists. Pearl mono Ⓜ GEMMCD9175* (72 minutes: AAD: 11/95).
From HMV and Columbia originals; recorded 1928-44.

At last some of Nash's HMV titles are out of copyright and Pearl have swiftly taken advantage of the fact to give us his fluid, impassioned, graciously phrased account of the *Carmen* Flower song and Faust's *Cavatine*. Better still, indeed something of a collector's piece, is his version of Nadir's "Je crois entendre" from *Les pêcheurs de perles*, sung in a dreamy *mezza voce*. Also from these 1944 sessions (though the date is wrongly given here as 1939) comes Richard Strauss's *Ständchen*, a rarity in its original form, and sung so beguilingly as to charm any girl out of her eyrie, not forgetting Gerald Moore's light-fingered playing. No British tenor today sings so effortlessly off the words. From the Columbias of the early 1930s we have a nice contrast between Nash's buoyant account of Rossini's *La danza*, sung in the original, and his ardent, plaintive *Macushla* (MacMurrough). Most welcome, too, is the reappearance of his account of the two Shelley settings (*To the Queen of my Heart* and *Love's Philosophy*) always among the most desirable of his discs. "Wayside Rose" from Lehár's *Friederika* is a souvenir of his appearance in that operetta; but is it not transferred a semitone or so too high? As the Duke of Mantua, Nash launches the *Rigoletto* Quartet with spontaneous *élan* and sounds suitably tormented in the *Trovatore* "Miserere", Licette a notable partner in both. There are reservations about the transfers. With the example of the Dutton Laboratories' "Incomparable Nash" (reviewed above), these occasionally hazy Pearl transfers from 78s are questionable. In his otherwise informative note Charles Haynes again gives the tenor's birthday as 1896, when it has now been conclusively proved to have been 1894. In spite of these drawbacks, do not miss the many vocal delights enshrined here.

Tancredi Pasero Opera Arias – Aida, Il barbiere di Siviglia, La bohème, Don Carlo, Ernani,
Faust, La favorita, La Gioconda, Mefistofele, Norma, I puritani, Simon Boccanegra,
La sonnambula, Il trovatore and I vespri siciliani. **Tancredi Pasero** (bass) with various artists.
Preiser Lebendige Vergangenheit mono Ⓕ 89114* (77 minutes: AAD: 2/97). From Fonotipia,
Columbia and Cetra originals. Recorded 1927-36.

When you listen to this superb CD you cannot help but warm to the individuality of Pasero's timbre,
once heard always recognizable from the crowd – but then there has never been a crowd of *bassos
cantante* of this quality in Italy or anywhere else. Recording companies of the day realized Pasero's
pre-eminence, yet not very many of his discs penetrated into the English-speaking market which
makes these reissues the more welcome. Here we have his earliest recordings, the 1927 Fonos, ten of
them, four Italian Columbias of 1927-8, and five Cetras of 1936. Throughout all of them one hears
the welcome consistency of Pasero's finely produced tone and of his line and diction. His is the classic
way to sing the solos of Verdi's bass characters, six of them represented here, Philip II twice, the 1936
account of the Act 3 solo a classic of singing and interpretation, superior to the foreshortened 1927
version. His Ramfis was formidable: here we have the duet of dedication which is adorned by the
heroic contribution of Francesco Merli. Another La Scala colleague of the bass, the young Ebe
Stignani, joins him in the duet of Alvise and Laura from *La Gioconda*, where Pasero's taunting of his
mezzo wife for her infidelity is managed with notable character. How splendid Ponchielli's music
sounds when delivered like this! Pasero was almost as successful in Bellini and Donizetti – the rousing
duet from *Puritani* with the virtually forgotten Gino Vanelli is further evidence of the high standards
among Italian singers then prevailing. Where are their like today? The 1927 and 1936 "La Calunnias",
virtually indistinguishable, show off the lighter side of this splendid bass's art. The truthfulness of the
transfers completes one's pleasure in a highly recommendable issue.

Adelina Patti Opera Arias and Songs. **Adelina Patti** (sop) with various artists. Nimbus
Prima Voce mono Ⓜ NI7840/1* (two discs: 120 minutes: ADD: 7/93). Recorded 1902-28.
Mario Ancona, Mattia Battistini, Emma Calvé, Fernando De Lucia, Edouard de Reszke,
Emma Eames, Lucien Fugère, Wilhelm Hesch, Lilli Lehmann, Félia Litvinne, Francesco
Marconi, Victor Maurel, Dame Nellie Melba, Lillian Nordica, Adelina Patti, Pol Plançon,
Maurice Renaud, Sir Charlles Santley, Marcella Sembrich, Francesco Tamagno and
Francesco Viñas.

This is a 'historical' issue for straightforward enjoyment. Although the originals were made in the very
earliest years of recording, they are reproduced here with a vividness that calls for very little in the
way of 'creative listening', making allowances and so forth. It starts in party mood with the first
Falstaff of all, Victor Maurel, singing to a bunch of cronies in the studio of 1907 the "Quand'ero
paggio" which he sang at La Scala in the première of 1893. They cheer and call for an encore, which
he gives them, then again (and best of all) this time in French. The record has been transferred many
times to LP and CD, but never has it been so easy for the listener to 'see' it and feel part of it. The
magnificent bass Pol Plançon follows with King Philip's solo from *Don Carlos*, beautifully even in
production and deeply absorbed in the character and his emotions. The hauntingly pure, well-
rounded soprano of Emma Eames in Tosti's *Dopo* (a real passion there despite its restraint), and then
the miraculously spry and elegant 80-year-old Lucien Fugère lead to the first of the Patti records: the
one her husband thought unladylike and asked to be withdrawn from the catalogue, *La calesera*, and
the most joyous she ever made. Tamagno, Melba, Nordica, Renaud: they are all here, and on
thrillingly good form. The copies of these rarities have been selected with great care, and, while other
transfers have, technically, got more "off" the record, none has captured the beauty of the voices more
convincingly.

Alfred Piccaver Opera Arias – L'africaine, Aida, Andrea Chenier, La bohème, Cavalleria
Rusticana, La fanciulla del West, Faust, Fedora, Fidelio, La forza del destino, La Gioconda,
Lohengrin, Madama Butterfly, Manon, Martha, Die Meistersinger von Nürnberg, Pagliacci,
Requiem (Verdi), Tosca, Il trovatore, Turandot and Werther; songs by De Curtis, Geehl,
Leoncavallo, Nevin, Tirindelli, Tosti and Woodforde-Finden. **Alfred Piccaver** (ten) with various
artists. Preiser Lebendige Vergangenheit mono Ⓕ 89217* (two discs: 148 minutes: AAD: 4/96).
From Polydor originals; recorded 1928-30. Recorded 1928-30.

What a prize British opera missed, when Alfred Piccaver's parents moved to the USA. As a child,
Piccaver heard Caruso at the Metropolitan and it was his example that fired him to study singing,
initially in New York and then after his first season in Prague in 1907, moving on to Milan. His career,
however, was almost entirely devoted to Vienna, where from 1913 until 1937 he was the idol of the
Viennese public, singing opposite Lehmann and Jeritza. The soprano, Margit Angerer, who joins him
in six duets on these Polydor records (made between 1928 and 1930), while obviously a talented singer,
does not impress with much character. No such accusation could be levelled at Piccaver. His is one of
those outgoing, all-embracing personalities, with a voice of apparently inexhaustible warmth and
power. Piccaver phrases in a splendidly healthy way – listen to the opening of "E lucevan le stelle":
even an aria as well known as this jumps out afresh when given such an relaxed outpouring of sound,
and unbroken legato. It's quite easy to imagine the thrill in the theatre. "The caressing velvet of his
voice was so unbelievably beautiful," wrote Lotte Lehmann. He certainly can act with the voice: the

farewell to the swan in the passage from Act 1 of *Lohengrin*, Florestan's aria (*Fidelio*), and the absolutely glorious account of Vasco da Gama's "O Paradis" from Meyerbeer's *L'africaine* (in Italian) all suggest a singer of such strength and presence that it is a wonder that Piccaver's name is not better known. It is a tribute to his singing that one can listen to both these CDs in a single sitting without tiring of his voice.

Ezio Pinza Opera Arias – Aida, Attila, La bohème, Le caïd, Don Carlo, Don Giovanni, Faust, La juive, Lucia di Lammermoor, Mignon, Norma, I puritani, Robert le diable, Il trovatore, I vespri siciliani and Die Zauberflöte. **Ezio Pinza** (bass) with various artists. Nimbus Prima Voce mono Ⓜ NI7875* (73 minutes: ADD: 6/96). From HMV and RCA Victor originals; recorded 1923-30.

There can surely be few dissenting voices where the quality of Pinza's singing is concerned. Play a record of his to a hardened old collector or a green newcomer and they will undoubtedly join in praising his golden, vibrant tone, seamless legato, the evenness of his vocal emission through a couple of octaves. It has been said that he seldom sings below *forte*: that is wholly negated here by a performance of the lullaby from Thomas's *Mignon*, sung almost entirely *mezza voce*, a lulling and soft-grained song that would send any child into blissful slumber. Another French item, the famous Tambour-major air from Thomas's lesser-known *Le caïd*, not only confirms Pinza's excellence in French enunciation, but also shows quite another side of his personality: jocular, a smile in the tone, exuberance in the delivery. The RCA Victors of Italian opera are well known, yet one marvels anew at the easy command of Pinza's Oroveso, Procida, King Philip and Ramphis, the character of each nicely etched in, even in extract. To complement these there is his grave Sarastro, his warmly sighing Colline. All the phrases where other basses either exaggerate or lose focus in reaching a high or low note are done quite effortlessly. His Giovanni suggests a formidable personality, and we end with him in the distinguished company of Rethberg and Gigli for their glorious account of the *Attila* trio. All the electrics are transferred carefully from RCA Victors in good condition. Where the six 1923-4 HMV acoustics are concerned you hear Nimbus's much-discussed additional resonance, room or otherwise, come into play. It is an acceptable procedure if you understand that you are not hearing exactly what the original sound is like. The most persuasive title here is "Cinta di fiori" from *Il puritani*, where the *cantabile* rolls out with fabulous ease.

Ezio Pinza Opera Recital. **Ezio Pinza** (bass) with various artists. Pearl mono Ⓜ GEMMCD9306* (76 minutes: AAD: 2/89).   ⒼⒼ

Verdi Aida – Mortal diletto ai Numi (Metropolitan Opera Orchestra, New York / Giulio Setti); Nume custode vindici (Giovanni Martinelli, ten; Metropolitan Opera Chorus and Orchestra. Both from Victor 8111). Ernani – Che mai vegg'io ... Infelice! (orchestra / Rosario Bourdon. HMV DB1750). Don Carlos – Dormiro sol nel manto mio regal (orchestra / Bourdon. DB1087, 3/28). I vespri siciliani – O patria ... O tu Palermo (orchestra / Bourdon. DB1087). Messa da Requiem – Confutatis maledictis (orchestra / Bourdon. HMV AGSB103). Simon Boccanegra – A te l'estremo addio ... Il lacerato spirito (chorus and orchestra / Carlo Sabajno. DB699, 6/24). Il trovatore – Di due figli ... Abbietta zingara (chorus and orchestra / Sabajno. DB828). **Mozart** Don Giovanni – Finch'han dal vino; Deh vieni alla finestra (orchestra / Bourdon. HMV DA1134, 10/31). Die Zauberflöte – O Isis und Osiris (sung in Italian. Orchestra / Bourdon. DB1088, 3/28). **Meyerbeer** Robert le Diable – Nonnes, qui reposez (sung in Italian. orchestra / Bourdon. DB1088). **Thomas** Le Caid – Enfant chéri ... Le tambour-major (orchestra / Bourdon. DB1086, 3/28). **Gounod** Faust – Le veau d'or (Metropolitan Opera Chorus and Orchestra / Setti. DA1108, 9/38). **Bellini** Norma – Ah del tebro (Chorus and orchestra / Sabajno. DA566, 5/25). I Puritani – Cinta de fiori (Orchestra / Sabajno. HMV VB70, 6/52). **Donizetti** La favorita – Splendon più belle (orchestra. DA708). Lucia di Lammermoor – Dalle stanze (chorus and orchestra / Sabajno. VB70). **Boito** Mefistofele – Ave Signor (orchestra. DB829); Son lo spirito (orchestra / Sabajno. DA567). **Halévy** La Juive – Si la rigeur (sung in Italian. Orchestra / Sabajno. DB698, 11/24); Vous qui du Dieu vivant (sung in Italian. Orchestra. DB829).

The first half of the century brought forth three fine Italian basses: Nazzareno de Angelis, Tancredi Pasero and Ezio Pinza. Of these it was Pinza who gained the greatest international fame, partly through the beauty of his voice and partly through the strength and vividness of his personality. Eventually it was the musical *South Pacific* that made him a household name, but his success here owed much in turn to the fact that he came to the Broadway show from the Metropolitan Opera House where he was leading bass from his house début in 1926 until 1948. Before coming to America he had sung at La Scala under Toscanini, his repertoire then ranging from the role of Pimen in *Boris Godunov* (he was later to sing Boris himself) to King Mark in *Tristan und Isolde*. At the Metropolitan he sang mostly in the Italian and French operas, with an increasing interest in Mozart, whose Don Giovanni became his most famous role, which he sang also at Salzburg and Covent Garden. This is represented in the present selection (called "The Golden Years") by two short solos, which may well be found to be the least satisfying of the performances. Sarastro's "O Isis und Osiris", on the other hand, sung in Italian as "Possenti numi" is magnificent in the sonority of tone and dignity of style. There is also some superb Verdi, above all the aria from *Ernani*, sung with deep feeling and subtlety of shading, and the "Confutatis" from the Requiem, ideally smooth, resonant and authoritative. In these and the earlier pre-electrical recordings Pinza shows clearly why he is so widely regarded as having been the supreme *basso cantate* of the century.

Pol Plançon Opera Arias – Le caïd, Le chalet, La damnation de Faust, Dinorah, Don Carlo, L'étoile du nord, Faust, Die Jahreszeiten, Martha, Mignon, Philémon et Baucis, Robert le diable, Roméo et Juliette, La Sonnambula, Stabat mater (Rossini) and Die Zauberflöte; songs by Adam, Bemberg, Faure, Ferrari, Flégier, Georges, Godard, Gounod, Massenet, Niedermeyer and Schumann. **Pol Plançon** (bass) with various artists. Romophone mono Ⓕ 82001-2 (two discs: 142 minutes: ADD: 12/94). From Victor originals; recorded 1903-08.

The new, inquiring collector will find copious writings on the merits of Plançon's unique voice and art. Perhaps Lord Harewood summed it all up when he commented on the bass's recording of Philip II's monologue: "He sings in French with a fullness and beauty of sound, a nobility of style, a smoothness of execution that have to be heard to be believed", to which one might add his plangency of tone – and these commendations apply to every single record he made, even if some are more amazing than others. So what is there new to say? That very few singers have seemed to *enjoy* performing on record as much as he, or evinced so much character; Gigli, Tauber, Supervia, and perhaps Bartoli, today. The smile and/or saturnine glee he brought to the music of Gounod's, Meyerbeer's and Berlioz's devils incarnate is superb: if you hear nothing else, listen to his insinuating "Voici des roses" from *La damnation de Faust* (the second disc, track 16). Then his *pièce de résistance* – "L'air du tambour-major" from Thomas's *Le caïd* – is unsurpassed for flexibility and lightness, and the treatment of grace notes, echoes of a lost art. But he is no less remarkable in 'serious' music such as "Pro peccatis" from Rossini's *Stabat mater*, where the tone rolls out in an effortless stream. Nor have his versions of the Porter's song from *Martha* and "O jours heureux" from *L'étoile du nord* been surpassed. Like most singers of his age, Plançon sang a deal of dross, but even these items are worth listening to for the pleasure of hearing a voice so immaculately produced throughout its range. Drawbacks? Well, to some modern ears his tone may be found lacking in resonance and vibrations. Plançon made many of his recordings twice, sometimes thrice. By and large the versions with orchestra of 1906-08 (on the second disc) are preferable to their predecessors with piano (the first disc): increasing familiarity with the recording horn seems to have allowed the bass to become ever more relaxed before it. As we have come to expect from this source, the transfers are virtually perfect – and prove quite conclusively that nothing has to be added to the sound to make old recordings thoroughly acceptable to today's collectors. Don't pass up this chance to hear one of the phenomenons of his – or any – day.

Pol Plançon and Emma Eames Opera Arias and Duets. **Emma Eames** (sop); **Pol Plançon** (bass) with various artists. Nimbus Prima Voce mono Ⓜ NI7860* (71 minutes: ADD: 1/95). From Victor originals; recorded 1903-11.
   Emma Eames – Carmen, Don Giovanni, Faust, Lohengrin, Le nozze di Figaro, Roméo et Juliette and Die Zauberflöte; song by Schubert. **Pol Plançon** – Le caïd, La damnation de Faust, Dinorah, L'étoile du nord, Faust, Robert le diable, Roméo et Juliette, La Sonnambula, Stabat mater (Rossini) and Die Zauberflöte.

Here, in the first place, is a marvellous sense of period. The world of 'the real record collectors of old', and of their authorities P.G. Hurst and Herman Klein, the sense, too, of a calendar in which the digits had changed from 18 to 19, while the great opera houses for just a few years longer the world stayed reassuringly the same: all of this is present. And we look at the photographs, with Eames's plaited tresses resting on the broad bosom without a hint of cleavage, and Plançon's suit, buttonhole and whiskers immaculately in place like the notes of his flawlessly even scale. Then the music itself, the programme opening (how appropriately) with Meyerbeer and ending with such essential nineteenth-century classics as *La Sonnambula* and Rossini's *Stabat mater*. Both of those are sung by Plançon, who has the slightly larger share. His was also the easier voice to record in those days, and the one which requires less adjustment of modern ears in listening. The incomparable mastery of style and technique, the beauty and resourcefulness of his voice, the life and variety of his characterizations, are all newly impressive. With the soprano, one sometimes wishes for a brighter tone; she is also no Susanna and in "Là ci darem" does some indefensible things with the time. Yet there are beauties here too, and, problematic as it may be for modern expectations to accept this, much can be gained from a study of her *Gretchen am Spinnrade*. The selection of recordings by both singers has been well made. The amount of hall-resonance in these Nimbus transfers is likely to be unacceptable only to people who have already made up their mind that they don't want any at all, and the horn-resonance points, troublesome in some of the earlier issues in the series, seem to have been virtually eliminated.

Maria Reining Opera and Operetta Arias – Andrea Chénier, La bohème, Eva, Friederike, Madama Butterfly, Manon Lescaut, Le nozze di Figaro, Tannhäuser and Die toten Augen; songs by R. Strauss. **Maria Reining** (sop) with various artists. Preiser Lebendige Vergangenheit mono Ⓕ 89065* (67 minutes: AAD: 9/94). From Electrola originals, including seven previously unpublished items and a 1943 radio broadcast; recorded 1942-43.

This is an important – and quite captivating – disc. It includes all Reining's Electrola discs, plus seven unpublished titles (presumably withheld at the time because of wartime restrictions). They are pure treasure. The three 'new' operatic titles, all cut in 1942, are "In quelle trine morbide" (*Manon Lescaut*), "Che tua madre" from *Madama Butterfly* (both sung in German) and "Psyche wandelt" (*Die toten Augen*). They show incontestably why Reining was considered the true successor to Lotte Lehmann in Vienna. The sheer beauty of her singing allied to its complete sincerity make all three moving experiences. Then there are four Strauss songs previously unpublished, also recorded in 1942, *Cäcilie* gloriously soaring as befits the ardent text, *Wiegenlied* and *Meinem Kinde* intimate and entrancing. Of the previously issued items, all display Reining's smiling tone, her judicious use of portamento. Any collector as yet unaware of Reining's virtues, so similar to those of Elisabeth Grümmer, her equally wonderful successor, should hurry to investigate this issue.

Elisabeth Rethberg Opera Arias – Aida, Andrea Chenier, La bohème, Der Freischütz, Lohengrin, Madama Butterfly, Le nozze di Figaro, Otello, Serse, Sosarme, Tannhäuser, Tosca and Die Zauberflöte; songs by Bishop, Braga, Cadman, Densmore, Flies, Gounod, Grieg, Griffes, Hildach, Jensen, Korschat, Lassen, Loewe, Massenet, Mendelssohn, Rubinstein, Schubert, Schumann, Taubert and Tchaikovsky. **Elisabeth Rethberg** (sop) with various artists. Romophone mono Ⓟ 81012-2* (two discs: 158 minutes: ADD: 2/95). From Brunswick originals; recorded 1924-29.   ⒼⒼⒼ

They're very collectable, these Romophone complete editions. Up they go on the shelves, and you know that there is another small but quite important area in the history of singing on records properly covered, ready for reference at any time, and reference that will be a pleasure because the standard of transfer is so reliable. In this instance it is the Rethberg Brunswicks: records which capture the voice in its lovely prime. Purely as a singer, Rethberg was surely the most gifted and accomplished lyric soprano of her age. The essential gift was a voice of exquisite quality, and her upbringing contributed to the purity of intonation and a feeling for musical style. Her production was even and fluent; on all these records there is scarcely a note or a phrase that is not delightful purely as singing. Some of the later records show it also as a voice capable of considerable expansion in volume. In Aida's "O patria mia" Rethberg is celestial, ample in volume, sensitive in feeling, phrasing beautifully, taking the C softly and in a broad single sweep. Equally lovely is her Mimì, and then in the *Andrea Chenier* aria there is such an unpressured beauty of utterance that it almost becomes a different composition. A previously unpublished delight is a blissful performance of Eugen Hildach's *Der Spielmann*, and among the less familiar songs is a charmer by Carl Taubert, *Es steht ein Baum in jenem Tal*.

Elisabeth Rethberg Opera Arias and Duets – L'Africaine, Andrea Chenier, The bartered bride, La bohème, Carmen, Madama Butterfly, Le nozze di Figaro, Tosca, Die Zauberflöte and Der Zigeunerbaron; songs by Bizet, Mozart, Pataky and R. Strauss.. **Elisabeth Rethberg** (sop) with various artists. Preiser Lebendige Vergangenheit mono Ⓟ 89051* (71 minutes: AAD: 7/94). From Odeon and Brunswick originals; recorded 1920-25.   ⒼⒼ

Elisabeth Rethberg died in 1976, when little notice was taken of the passing of a singer once voted the world's most perfect. The year 1994 was the centenary of her birth, so this fine selection of her early recordings was well timed. The earliest catch her at the charming age of 26 (the voice settled, but still that of a young woman), and the last of them, made in 1925, find her just into her thirties, mature in timbre, feeling and artistry. It is doubtful whether a judicious listener would at any point cry "Ah, it's an Aida voice!", but Aida was the part for which she became most famous. In Countess Almaviva's first aria, her legato is the next thing to perfection; in Pamina's "Ach, ich fühl's" the head tones are beautifully in place, the portamentos finely judged, emotion always implicit in the singing. The duets with Richard Tauber include the music of Micaëla and Don José sung with unrivalled grace and intimacy, Rethberg shading off the end of her solo most elegantly, Tauber softening in his so as to welcome and not overwhelm the soprano's entry. The songs are equally delightful.

Elisabeth Rethberg Opera Arias and Ensembles – L'Africaine, Aida, Attila, Un ballo in maschera, Boccaccio, Carmen, Cavalleria Rusticana, Don Giovanni, Faust, Die Fledermaus, Der fliegende Holländer, Lohengrin, I lombardi, Madama Butterfly, Die Meistersinger von Nürnberg, Le nozze di Figaro, Otello, Il rè pastore, Tannhäuser and Der Zigeunerbaron; songs by Brahms, Mendelssohn and Wolf. **Elisabeth Rethberg** (sop) with various artists. Romophone mono Ⓟ 81014-2* (two discs: 155 minutes: ADD: 10/95). From HMV, Parlophone and Bell Telephone originals; recorded 1927-34.

To the older collector of vocal recordings it is to be feared that not many of these records will come as new. Attention can be directed, however, to the last three. These were made in 1932 in the Bell Telephone Laboratories as part of an experiment in improved recording methods. They were recorded at 33rpm, and they achieved startling results. The quality of the voice is captured to perfection, but most impressive is the freedom of emission, no longer confined within the studio but able to ring and expand, the contrasts of loud and soft tones being effective and often as exquisite as they would have been in the flesh. Most revealing is Elisabeth's Greeting from *Tannhäuser*, sung with piano accompaniment but with a dramatic conviction and enthusiasm far more vivid than that of the earlier orchestral version (reviewed above). Other new items are unpublished takes of the two Verdi trios with Gigli and Pinza, differing slightly in balance, but very little in style. The six electric Parlophones include the tender Micaëla's aria and the solo from *L'Africaine* with its haunting unaccompanied introduction. Supreme among the Victors is the second *Un ballo in maschera* aria, the *Meistersinger* duet with Schorr running it close. It is also good to have the complete Nile scene from *Aida*, with Lauri-Volpi in his prime, de Luca a bit past his. Transfers are of the usual high standard, and with the first volume, this is clearly the primary source of a comprehensive Rethberg collection on disc.

Bidù Sayão Opera Arias – Faust, Manon and Roméo et Juliette; songs by Braga, Debussy, Duparc, Hahn, Koechlin, Moret, Ravel and Villa-Lobos. **Bidu Sayão** (sop) with various artists. Sony Classical Masterworks Heritage mono Ⓟ MHK62355* (73 minutes: ADD: 5/97).

Beauty, charm, exquisite voice, brilliant technique, personality, Bidu Sayão had – has – them all. This recital opens with her most famous recording, *Bachianas Brasileiras* No. 5 by Villa-Lobos, with the composer conducting. She recognized the opportunity for her particular soprano in the violin part that Villa-Lobos had written for this work and persuaded him to adapt it for soprano. Their famous recording was achieved in just one experimental take. In that her voice is used in a purely instrumental way, when she enters on the next track as Gounod's Juliette, one is struck by the presence the use of words adds to the voice. In the Jewel song from *Faust* she conveys a sense of joyous laughter to the "Ah" in "Ah, je ris de me voir belle", without any sense of vulgarity, or playing to the (armchair) gallery. Massenet's *Manon* was the role of her Met début in 1937 and again her vocal acting immediately sketches in Manon's playful character in the Act 1 aria about the "premier Voyage". How can a voice suggest a pout? One would have to ask Brigitte Bardot, but Sayão can do it, when she starts to sing about the "couvent" she's being sent to. Sayão's voice had none of the acid nasal quality of the typical French light soprano, so she can manage to do all sorts of little things with the language without making it sound harsh. Sayão studied with Jean de Reszke; she is the youngest of his pupils on disc, and perhaps the only one still around today, at least the only one who had a great career. The presentation is superb: there are splendid photographs and reproductions of the original LP sleeves.

Bidù Sayão Opera Arias – La bohème, Don Giovanni, Gianni Schicchi, Madama Butterfly, Le nozze di Figaro, Pagliacci, La sonnambula and La traviata. **Debussy** La damoiselle élue. **Bidù Sayão** (sop) with various artists. Sony Classical Masterworks Heritage mono Ⓜ MHK63221 (73 minutes: ADD: 4/98). From American Columbia originals; recorded 1941-50.

Charm is an elusive thing Singers guilty of laying it on too thick might listen to Sayão and try to hear what she does, and just as important, what she doesn't do. Take the contrast between Violetta and Mimì. In the Act 1 aria from *La traviata*, there is no smile in the voice. It's all beautiful, limpid singing, but when she reaches that crucial "Follie!" recitative, there is no joy in the cries of "gioir!" but, as is surely correct, desperation. Then comes Mimì and the tone is at once warmer, full of the reticent hopefulness that is typical of the personality; when she gets to the climactic "Ma quando ven lo sgelo" she really lets it all glow. Strange that these two Parisian coughers are so often bracketed together – in fact their basic characters are quite different and in the subtlest way Sayão shows how a singer can differentiate without resorting to any distortion or method-acting tricks. The revelation in this recital was Sayão's Cherubino. Lord Harewood in his notes says that she probably never sang it on the stage, but she makes of the two overfamiliar arias something totally delicious and new. Her Susanna was well known and one of her favourite parts (with Pinza as her Figaro), but although she has no difficulty in singing the Countess's aria, somehow one knows that the part isn't quite right for her. Both the Zerlina arias are done with just the right mixture of coquetry and toughness. Sayão sang Debussy's *La damoiselle élue* in New York with Toscanini, the year before her Met début in 1937. This recording, made in 1947 with Ormandy and the Philadelphia Orchestra, is a remarkable instance of her ability to invest words and vocal line with character. In a recent interview, Sayão related how much she had wanted to sing Madam Butterfly but, although she felt she could have acted it, the orchestration was too heavy for her voice, and so she never dared take on the role. Her recording of "Un bel dì" shows how she would have tackled it. Surprisingly, she did sing Nedda in *Pagliacci*, in her final season at San Francisco and she must have made an unusually sympathetic impression.

With its companion volume this CD restores much of Sayão's recorded legacy to the catalogue. She is one of the most consistently fascinating singers of this era at the Met, in the two decades surrounding the Second World War. The booklet, as with all these beautifully produced Masterworks reissues, has colour reproductions of early record sleeves and nostalgic photographs, including two of Sayão modelling a hat fashioned from a copy of her first LP.

Aksel Schiøtz The Complete Recordings 1933-46, Volume 1. **Aksel Schiøtz** (ten) with various artists. Danacord mono Ⓟ DACOCD451* (75 minutes: ADD: 2/97). From Danish HMV originals. Recorded between 1933 and 1946.

Opera and Oratorio Arias – Così fan tutte, Die Entführung aus dem Serail, Eugene Onegin, Don Giovanni, Faust and Die Zauberflöte; Acis and Galatea, Christmas Oratorio, Messiah, St Matthew Passion, Die Schöpfung and Solomon; songs by Dowland and Was mich auf dieser Welt betrübt (Buxtehude).

Schiøtz's singing was always the very epitome of silvery elegance. His attributes in Handel, Haydn and Mozart are amply confirmed in this, the first disc of Danacord's comprehensive ten-disc survey of all his recorded output. Sadly his career was cut short by a brain tumour in 1946, but for the ten years of his prime, he was rightly fêted for his beautiful singing and masterly sense of style. Long before period-instrument performances were current, Schiøtz and Wöldike were seeking an authentic style of performing Handel and Bach as exemplified here in the poised, unaffected account of the opening solos from *Messiah*, and arias from the *St Matthew Passion* and *Christmas Oratorio*. "Frohe Hirten" from the latter and the lovely aria by Buxtehude sound even better now that they have been released from the scratch on the originals, the transfers expertly done by EMI's Andrew Walter. Also in the oratorio field the aria from *Die Schöpfung* demonstrates perfectly the singer's delicately etched line and pure tone. There are few more fine-grained versions of Tamino's 'Portrait' aria, Ottavio's arias nor of Pedrillo's Serenade, but "Un aur'amorosa" suffers from an uncomfortably fast speed. Schiøtz is also among the most elegiac of Lenskys in that character's lament (slightly cut), the most sweet-toned of Fausts, the top C taken in the head as is the case with other tenors of his ilk. It seems hardly to matter that these pieces are sung in Danish. The Dowland, like the Handel, is given authentically, though a guitar rather than a lute is used for the accompaniments. As a bonus there are rehearsal performances of Acis's "Love sounds the alarm", minus *da capo*, and "Sacred raptures" from *Solomon*, the former impeccable, the latter showing an unaccustomed fallibility in the runs. The booklet is full of interesting photos and articles.

Aksel Schiøtz The Complete Recordings, 1933-46, Volume 2. **Aksel Schiøtz** (ten); [a]**Gerald Moore,**[bc]**Folmer Jensen** (pfs). Danacord mono Ⓔ DACOCD452* (75 minutes: ADD: 4/97). Texts and translations included. Item marked [a] from HMV DB6252/9 (6-9/47), [b]Danish HMV X6924, [c]Z729.

Schubert Die schöne Müllerin, D795[a]. **Grieg** Melodies of the Heart, Op. 5[b] – No. 1, Two brown eyes; No. 3, I love but thee. Songs, Op. 33 – No. 2, Last Spring[b]; No. 9, At Rondane[c]. Songs and Ballads, Op. 9 – No. 4, Outward Bound[c].

Aksel Schiøtz The Complete Recordings, 1933-46, Volume 3. **Aksel Schiøtz** (ten) with various artists. Danacord mono Ⓔ DACOCD453* (69 minutes: ADD: 4/97). Texts and translations included. Item marked [a] from HMV DB6270/2 (4/46), remainder from Danish HMV originals, recorded 1946.

Schumann Dichterliebe, Op. 48[a]. **Brahms** Die Mainacht, Op. 43 No. 2. Sonntag, Op. 47 No. 3. Ständchen, Op. 106 No. 1. **Grieg** Songs, Op. 49 – No. 3, Kind greetings, fair ladies; No. 6, Spring showers. The Poet's farewell, Op. 18 No. 3. **Bellman** Fredman's Epistles – Dearest brothers, sisters and friends; Old age is with me; Sit down around the spring here. Fredman's Songs – Hear bells give out a frightful boom; So tipsy we are taking leave; Joachim lived in Babylon. **Buxtehude** Aperite mihi portas justitiae, BuxWV7.

The years 1945-46 were particularly fruitful ones for Schiøtz in relation to recording. With Walter Legge's eager support the Danish tenor could at last come to London to resume his recording career with *Die schöne Müllerin*, which takes up the lion's share of Vol. 2. The Danacord transfer of this sensitive reading is now the one to go for: not only is the sound marginally superior to Preiser's earlier transfer (9/96) but added to it are five wonderful readings of Grieg songs, these actually recorded for the composer's centenary in 1943. In particular the popular *I love but thee* and the gloriously ardent *Last Spring* find in Schiøtz an ideal interpreter, a singer whose style so effortlessly and unassumingly goes to the heart of the matter. He is just as convincing in the three lesser-known songs by Grieg in Vol. 3, devoted to six months of recording activity at the start of 1946. Yet another facet of his art is revealed in the Bellman songs, aptly recorded in Sweden, Schiøtz disclosing his sense of humour in the bawdy songs of the eighteenth-century, pleasure-loving Bellman. In *So tipsy we are taking leave*, he captures to perfection the devil-may-care, bawdy mood and in all these attractive pieces finds a willing partner in Ulrik Neumann's guitar. But this third volume is most valuable for giving us Schiøtz's marvellous *Dichterliebe*, perhaps his finest achievement of all on disc. Then come three Brahms songs, never issued on 78s, that are also near ideal, especially the delicately floated line of *Die Mainacht*. Gerald Moore, as ever, fits his playing intuitively to the singer he's partnering. Then, after the Grieg and Bellman, comes more evidence of the tenor's and Wöldike's championship of Buxtehude, then a neglected figure, which again benefits from Schiøtz's innate sense of the right style for the music in hand. It also allows us to hear a pleasing mezzo (Elsa Sigfuss) and bass (Holger Nørgaard). Andrew Walter's remastering of all this disparate material at Abbey Road is faultless.

Aksel Schiøtz The Complete Recordings, 1933-46, Volume 4. **Aksel Schiøtz** (ten) with various artists. Danacord mono Ⓔ DACOCD454* (72 minutes: ADD: 5/97). From Scandinavian HMV originals; recorded 1938-41. Texts and translations included.

Schubert Die schöne Müllerin, D795 – No. 1, Das Wandern; No. 6, Der Neugierige; No. 7, Ungeduld; No. 8, Morgengruss; No. 10, Tränenregen; No. 11, Mein; No. 15, Eifersucht und Stolz; No. 17, Die böse Farbe; No. 19, Der Müller und der Bach; No. 20, Des Baches Wiegenlied. **Mozart** Per pietà, non ricercate, K420. **Weyse** Angel of Light, go in splendour. In distant steeples. The Sleeping-Draught – Fair lady, open your window. **Hartmann** Tell me, star of night, Op. 63. Little Christine – Sverkel's romance. **Lange-Müller** Once upon a time – Serenade; Midsummer Song. **Riisager** Mother Denmark. **Schubert/Berté** Das Dreimäderlhaus – excerpts.

"Hidden Treasure" is the appropriate subtitle for this volume of the complete Schiøtz recordings. It begins with the ten songs from what ought to have been a complete *Schöne Müllerin*, two songs recorded in London in 1939, eight with Hermann D. Koppel, who took over from Moore, in Denmark in 1939-40. The cycle was never finished, because – it seems – Koppel as a Jew had to flee his country when the Nazis occupied it. Schiøtz's voice, when he was 33, was even fresher, his reading even more spontaneous in suggesting the vulnerable youth's love and its loss, most poignant in an account of "Der Müller und der Bach" that surpasses in forlorn expression other famed tenor interpreters such as Patzak, Pears, Schreier and Bostridge but the whole sequence is a pleasure to hear for the plangency of Schiøtz's singing. There follows part of the Mozart aria *Per pietà* that the tenor sang as test for EMI in 1938, interesting as a rarity but not special. By contrast all the Danish items are desirable, among them the two Hartmann offerings: *Tell me, star of night*, a haunting song, is given ideal voicing by Schiøtz as is "Sverkel's romance" from a romantic work, *Little Christine*, based on an Andersen fable. The two items by Lange-Müller, written as incidental music for a play called *Once upon a time*, are even better, in particular the magical "Midsummer Song". The note-writer tells how wonderful was Schiøtz's singing of this item in an open-air performance in 1941. His recordings had made Schiøtz famous and he also appeared the same year playing the role of Schubert in *Lilac Time* of which we hear an amusing pot-pourri (a photo in the booklet shows him in the part). That Schiøtz was not averse to popular items is confirmed by Riisager's *Mother Denmark*, which he brought to London for that first session in May 1939. It is a song written for a *diseuse* about the delights of the homeland and Schiøtz delivers it with the intimacy it calls for. Again, the transfers are faultless and this example of Anglo-Danish co-operation is highly recommendable.

Tito Schipa Neapolitan Songs – Barthélemy, Benelli, Buzzi-Peccia, Califona, Costa, De Curtis, Di Capua, Falvo, Gambardella, Mario, Nutile, Sadero, Tagliaferri and Valente. **Tito Schipa** (ten) with various artists. Nimbus Prima Voce mono Ⓜ NI7887* (67 minutes: ADD: 11/97). From HMV originals; recorded 1925-38.
Now here, sure enough, is the Schipa magic. He begins with the tune that our music-halls, with a keen ear for a winner, appropriated for the refrain of *Two lovely black eyes*. Caruso sang it too, and with prodigious voice; but, set his *forza* against Schipa's *grazia* and, well, there's a time for everything, but you'd give Schipa six days of the week and reserve just a singer's sonorous sabbath for Caruso. Schipa lightens so that even in the first phrase he wins a smile. Buzzi-Peccia's *Mal d'amore* is a thoroughly charming essay in Neapolitan melancholy. *Guapparia* by Falvo, another master of the genre, brings the gaiety: "Come all you shady characters and hear me serenade Margarita" is an invitation not to be declined. Other delights include *Pesca d'amore* by Richard Barthélemy, Caruso's accompanist for some years, with its tenuous line of melody stretched as it were from branch to branch on a seemingly endless supply of breath. *Mandulinata a Napule* is the essence of all: again perfect, unmatchable. The Nimbus transfers are sympathetic and the synopses of these songs are useful.

Lotte Schöne Opera Arias – Der arme Jonathan, Un ballo in maschera, La bohème, Cagliostro in Wien, Così fan tutte, Don Pasquale, The Geisha, Don Giovanni, Die Fledermaus, Les huguenots, Indigo, Der lustige Krieg, Die lustigen Weiber von Windsor, Madama Butterfly, Manon, Le nozze di Figaro, Der Obersteiger, Rigoletto, Die schöne Galathee, Turandot, Der Vogelhändler and Die Zauberflöte; songs by Rossini, Rubinstein, Schubert, Joseph Strauss and Johann Strauss II. **Lotte Schöne** (sop) with various artists. Preiser Lebendige Vergangenheit mono Ⓕ 89224* (two discs: 154 minutes: AAD: 1/97). From Odeon, Vox, Electrola and HMV originals; recorded 1922-31.
This delightful soprano is one of the few for whom an average modern listener does not have to make some kind of 'historical' adjustment. She sings with unflawed beauty of tone, technical mastery and sureness of taste. Mozart is usually the great tester in this respect, but to this day there is no lovelier account of Pamina's aria in *Die Zauberflöte* and no Despina with more infectious gaiety and feeling for rhythm than Lotte Schöne's in these recordings from 1928. As for the glimpses we have of her Gilda and Mimì, her Manon, Butterfly and Liù, there is no touch which makes us cry "Dated!" or indeed which makes us think anything other than how fortunate we would count ourselves if she were still with us and singing like that today. It was as Liù, the slave-girl, that she won the immediate admiration of London audiences. This was at the British première of *Turandot* in 1927, when out of that cast she was everybody's favourite singer. The recordings assembled here are all taken from her best years, the first disc comprising records from the late pre-electrical era and the second having the complete run of HMV recordings from 1927 to 1931. The early items include two that were unpublished in their time, *The Blue Danube* and *Valse caprice*, both beautifully sung, and the gems are two solos from operettas, one a kind of gipsy song from *Cagliostro in Wien*, the other from Millöcker's *Der arme Jonathan* with the implausible title "Ach, wir armen Primadonnen". The real treasures are found on the second disc. The whole sequence is a blissful one, ending with the solos from *Turandot*, which show exactly why the Covent Garden audience held their breath in amazement in 1927.

Irmgard Seefried Goethe Lieder. **Irmgard Seefried** (sop); **Erik Werba** (pf). Orfeo D'Or mono Ⓕ C297921B* (71 minutes: ADD: 9/93). Recorded live in 1957. *Gramophone Editor's choice.* ⒼⒼ
Mozart Das Veilchen, K476. Das Kinderspiel, K598. **Beethoven** Egmont – Incidental Music, Op. 84: Die Trommel gerühret!; Freudvoll und leidvoll. Wonne der Wehmut, Op. 83 No. 1.
Schubert Suleika I, D720. Suleika II, D717. Heidenröslein, D257 (includes a false start). Der König in Thule, D367. Ganymed, D544. Gretchen am Spinnrade, D118. Im Frühling, D882. Ave Maria, D839. **Schumann** Myrthen, Op. 25 – No. 9, Lied der Suleika. **Wolf** Mignon I; Mignon II; Mignon III; Mignon ("Kennst du das Land?"); Blumengruss; Die Bekehrte; Frühling übers Jahr; Anakreons Grab.
All the performances on this disc are taken live from a single recital (devoted entirely to Goethe settings), a singer caught at the peak of her powers at a Salzburg recital of 1957. Listen to just four examples of her art and you will know all; the repeat of "Trocknet nicht" in Beethoven's *Wonne der Wehmut*, the first line of Schumann's ineffably beautiful and touching *Lied der Suleika* or the erotic

close to Schubert's "Was bedeutet die Bewegung" (Suleika I) or the start of Wolf's "So lass mich scheinen" (Mignon III). Here caught on the wing is the kind of sincere, innig singing that can't be learnt: it is instinctive. But, of course, that is not the end of it. Seefried knew as well as anyone that essential in Lieder performance: how to shape a song from start to finish in speeds that never ever drag, evident throughout this arresting recital, but most particularly in Wolf's *Mignon*, "Kennst du das Land?" (the intensity evinced here not equalled even by Schwarzkopf herself – how searing are the repeated cries of "Kennst du es wohl?") and *Gretchen am Spinnrade*, which – probably because this is a real event and not a studio invention – has a cumulative, riveting effect seldom if ever heard matched; eternal longing expressed in simple yet overwhelmingly poignant diction and expression – slight signs of strain at the top here wholly appropriate. We are given the recital unedited except for the excision of some applause. Thus endearingly we hear a Heidenröslein where the singer 'dries', makes an amusing apology and starts again. Erik Werba was the perfect pianist for this singer. An unforgettable recital, worth every penny even at full price. Don't miss it.

Irmgard Seefried Lieder by Brahms, Flies, Mozart, Schubert and Wolf. **Irmgard Seefried** (sop) with various artists. Testament mono Ⓕ SBT1026* (74 minutes: ADD: 9/93). From Columbia originals; recorded 1946-53.

Another 'must' for anyone who loves Seefried. In these wonderfully immediate and faithful transfers of performances made between 1946 and 1953 in Vienna and London, Seefried is heard at the peak of her powers, when her voice was at its freshest and easiest. In the Mozart whether the mood is happy, reflective or tragic, Seefried goes unerringly to the core of the matter. Here we have the archness of *Die kleine Spinnerin*, the naughty exuberance of *Warnung*, the deep emotion of *Abendempfindung* and *Unglückliche Liebe*. We are offered five Schubert songs, including an unsurpassed *Auf dem Wasser zu singen*, so airy and natural; a pure, elevated *Du bist die Ruh* and a poised, ravishing *Nacht und Träume*. The lullabies of Flies, Schubert and Brahms are all vintage Seefried. The Wolf items are a real treasure trove: a sorrowful, plangent account of *Das verlassene Mägdelein* (perhaps the most compelling interpretation of all here; unutterably moving), an enchanting, spontaneous *Elfenlied* (with Gerald Moore marvellously delicate here). For the most part, Moore is in attendance to complete one's pleasure in an irresistible and generously filled disc.

Singers of Imperial Russia, Volumes 1-4. **35 singers with various accompaniments.** Pearl mono Ⓜ GEMMCDS9997/9*, GEMMCDS9001/03*, GEMMCDS9004/06* and GEMMCDS9007/09* (four three-disc sets, oas: 207, 209, 222 and 221 minutes: AAD: 6/93). *Gramophone Award Winner 1993.*   Ⓖ Ⓖ Ⓖ
GEMMCDS9997/9: recorded 1900-11: *Soprano* – Medea Mei-Figner. *Tenors* – Ivan Ershov, Nikolai Figner and Leonid Sobinov. *Baritone* – Ioakim Tartakov. *Basses* – Adamo Didur and Vasili Sharonov.
GEMMCDS9001/03: 1901-11: *Sopranos* – Natalia Ermolenko-Juzhina and Maria Michailova. *Mezzo-soprano* – Antonina Panina. *Tenors* – David Juzhin, Andrei Labinsky and Gavril Morskoi. *Baritones* – Oskar Kamionsky and Polikarp Orlov. *Basses* – Dmitri Bukhtoyarov, Vladimir Kastorsky, Vasili Sharonov and Lev Sibiriakov.
GEMMCDS9004/06: 1901-24: *Sopranos* – Irena Bohuss, Anna El-Tour, Janina Korolewicz-Wayda, Maria Kuznetsova, Lydia Lipkowska and Nadezhda Zabela-Vrubel. *Contralto* – Evgenia Zbrueva. *Tenors* – Dmitri Smirnov and Eugene Witting. *Bass* – K. E. Kaidanov.
GEMMCDS9007/09: 1901-14: *Sopranos* – Maria Michailova and Antonia Nezhdanova. *Mezzo-soprano* – Galina Nikitina. *Contralto* – Evgenia Zbrueva. *Tenors* – Alexandr Alexandrovich, Alexandr Bogdanovich, Alexandr Davidov, Andrei Labinsky and Eugene Witting. *Baritone* – Nikolai Shevelev. *Basses* – Vladimir Kastorsky and Lev Sibiriakov.
This is the equivalent, in terms of gramophone history, of one of those exhibitions for which queues form long and deep and daily outside the Tate Gallery or the Royal Academy: in fact, if a similar exhibition of paintings, furniture and porcelain from the Tsar's palaces were mounted in London it would surely be a sell-out. Quite simply, there has never been a published collection to match this, both in the quality of the items and in its extensiveness. Of the singers of Imperial Russia, the world came to know Chaliapin, who eclipsed the rest. He is not among the artists presented here, but we have, among the basses, two who at least for vocal splendour are his equal: Adamo Didur, the Pole who was New York's first Boris Godunov (preceding Chaliapin there), and Lev Sibiriakov, another giant of a man with a magnificently produced voice to match. The tenors include Smirnov and Sobinov, a kind of collector's Tweedledum and Tweedledee, though in fact very unlike indeed. New to most listeners will be Ivan Ershov, heard in Siegfried's Forging Song from St Petersburg, 1903, with piano and anvil accompaniment: an astonishing voice and most accomplished in technique. Evgenia Zbrueva the contralto, sopranos Nezhdanova, Ermolenko-Jushina, Mei-Figner and the superbly recorded Korolewicz-Wayda are also plentifully represented. Most amazing of all, perhaps, is the vividness of sound. These are some of the world's rarest recordings and, almost without exception, they are in pristine condition.

Stars of English Oratorio, Volume 1. Opera and oratorio arias with various orchestras and conductors. Dutton Laboratories mono Ⓜ CDLX7025 (77 minutes: ADD: 2/98).

From Columbia, Decca, HMV and Parlophone originals; recorded 1928-49.
Sopranos – **Florence Austral** (The Golden Legend, Rossini Stabat mater), **Dame Isobel Baillie** (The Creation, Judas Maccabaeus, The Kingdom, Solomon), **Gwen Catley** (Joshua).
Contralto – **Kathleen Ferrier** (Elijah). *Tenor* – **Webster Booth** (The Creation), **Heddle Nash** (Judas Maccabaeus, Messiah). *Basses* – **Sir Keith Falkner** (Paulus), **Oscar Natzke** (Samson).
Heddle Nash's 1945 *Messiah* recordings were made in Kingsway Hall: the acoustical wonders of that legendary venue can be heard so clearly on Mike Dutton's transfers that the disc sounds as if it were new-minted. As Lyndon Jenkins comments in his note, this was the first recording with a soloist made by Legge's newly formed Philharmonia, as yet only the Philharmonia Chamber Orchestra. Just as fine are Nash's two *Judas Maccabaeus* solos made a year or so later. Dame Isobel Baillie, so often beside Nash at oratorio performances, is hardly less impressive, heard in four items, her Handel singing as clear and pure as Emma Kirkby's; but most welcome back in circulation, as Jenkins suggests, is Baillie's unsurpassed account of "The sun goeth down" from Elgar's *The Kingdom*, Sargent on the podium. In Handel's "Oh! had I Jubal's lyre", Catley matches Baillie in pure, unfettered singing: a lovely performance. Finally, in Handel, comes Natzke in a version of "Honour and Arms". Other classics refurbished by Dutton include Ferrier's involving account of the contralto's *Elijah* arias, Falkner's highly sympathetic solo from Mendelssohn's *Paulus*, and Austral's sensational "Inflammatus" from Rossini's *Stabat mater*, Barbirolli conducting. Its coupling, the solo from Sullivan's *The Golden Legend*, a fine piece, is much less familiar in transfers and thus doubly welcome. These, like everything here, sound – where the voice is concerned – as though they were recorded yesterday.

Stars of English Opera, Volume 1. Opera Arias with various orchestras and conductors.
Dutton Laboratories mono Ⓜ CDLX7018* (75 minutes: ADD: 4/96). From HMV and Columbia originals; recorded 1939-49. All items sung in English. Recorded 1938-49.
Sopranos – **Gwen Catley** (Rigoletto), **Joan Cross** (Così fan tutte), **Dame Joan Hammond** (Gianni Schicchi, Tosca); *Mezzos* – **Janet Howe** (Samson et Dalila), **Gladys Ripley** (Don Carlo), **Marjorie Thomas** (Alcina); *Tenors* – **Webster Booth** (Esmeralda), **James Johnston** (The bartered bride), **David Lloyd** (Don Giovanni, Die Zauberflöte), **Heddle Nash** (La favorita, Les pêcheurs de perles); *Baritones* – **John Hargreaves** (Rigoletto), **Redvers Llewellyn** (Falstaff), **Dennis Noble** (Il barbiere di Siviglia); *Bass* – **Oscar Natzke** (Die lustigen Weiber von Windsor).
The discs chosen come from that fruitful period in British singing in the years before, during and just after the war, when Columbia and HMV were busy recording a crop of native singers performing so eloquently in their native tongue. The group of tenors alone is a distinguished one, headed by Heddle Nash, whose dreamy, poised *mezza voce* is heard to perfection in Nadir's Romance from *Les pêcheurs de perles*, one of his most beguiling records. His ardent, refined singing of "Spirit so fair" from *La favorita*, made during the same 1944 Liverpool session, is equally desirable. So is James Johnston's account of Jeník's aria from *The bartered bride*. Most welcome of all are Don Ottavio's second aria and Tamino's Portrait solo as sung by David Lloyd, whose forthright, mellifluous tone and persuasive performances offer Mozart singing of the highest calibre. Joan Cross's account of Fiordiligi's Act 2 aria, is another fine piece of Mozart singing – and isn't that Dennis Brain playing the horn solos? Marjorie Thomas's refined art is recalled in her pure Handelian legato while Llewellyn offers character but a rather attenuated tone in Ford's aria, Hargreaves much feeling but stilted diction as Rigoletto. If these two baritones were limited in appeal, Noble was one of great distinction regarding tone, line and diction. His 1939 HMV "I'm the factotum" launches this disc in the most engaging way. Transfers, as usual from this source, are exemplary, surface noise wholly eliminated, voices clean and forward.

Stars of English Opera, Volume 2. Opera Arias and Ensembles with various orchestras and conductors. Dutton Laboratories mono Ⓜ CDLX7020* (77 minutes: ADD: 12/96). From HMV, Columbia and Decca originals; recorded 1928-49. All items except those marked [a] sung in English.
Sopranos – **Gwen Catley** (Don Giovanni, Die Zauberflöte), **Joan Cross** (Sadko, Il trovatore), **Noel Eadie** (Rigoletto), **Dame Joan Hammond** (Oberon), **Victoria Sladen** (Tosca), **Dame Eva Turner** (Turandot[a]); *Mezzo* – **Edith Coates** (Carmen, Rigoletto); *Contralto* – **Kathleen Ferrier** (Orfeo ed Euridice, Rodelinda); *Tenors* – **Webster Booth** (Rigoletto, Il trovatore), **Richard Lewis** (Manon[a], Les pêcheurs de perles[a]), **Heddle Nash** (Carmen); *Baritones* – **John Hargreaves** (Prince Igor), **Dennis Noble** (Don Giovanni, Le nozze di Figaro, Die Zauberflöte); *Bass* – **Arnold Matters** (Rigoletto).
These transfers are revelatory. The old favourites leap out of the speakers with amazing presence, beginning with Eva Turner's famous "In questa reggia", the 1928 version, which has never sounded quite as thrilling. Nor has Joan Hammond, heard in her vivid account of Rezia's scena, ever seemed quite as lifelike or Joan Cross's clean, clear singing been transferred so faithfully as here in the *Miserere*. Praise too for the intelligent reclamation of several neglected, worthwhile items. Cross's account of the Indian Guest's Song from *Sadko*, strictly a tenor piece, catches her plangent tones at their most compelling. On another rare Decca 78, Richard Lewis's smooth, youthfully mellifluous tone is ideal for Des Grieux's Dream Song and Nadir's Romance, although emotionally he sounds a shade detached, especially when compared with Nash's impassioned account of another French aria,

José's Flower Song, also distinguished by Nash's typically memorable use of the vernacular. Another piece of singing worthy of revival is John Hargreaves's heartfelt account of Prince Igor's homesick aria, surely the baritone's most desirable recording. Noble as a nimble Figaro and Papageno, Catley as a fiery Queen of Night, Coates as a haughty Carmen, Sladen as an affecting Tosca, and of course Ferrier in her best-selling "What is life?", show the strengths of British singing in the 1940s. The version of the *Rigoletto* Quartet headed by Booth's too-polite Duke might have been replaced by an earlier, Columbia version led by an exuberant Nash (with Noble as Rigoletto). This CD is a delight.

Stars of English Opera, Volume 3. Opera Arias and Ensembles with various orchestras and conductors. Dutton Laboratories mono Ⓜ CDLX7024 (77 minutes: ADD: 2/98). From HMV and Columbia originals and a private recording; recorded 1927-50.
Sopranos: **Dame Isobel Baillie** (Alessandro), **Joyce Gartside** (Simon Boccanegra), **Dame Joan Hammond** (Faust), **Dora Labbette** (La bohème), **Miriam Licette** (Le nozze di Figaro), **Dame Maggie Teyte** (The Maid of Orleans); *Contraltos:* **Kathleen Ferrier** (Orfeo ed Euridice), **Jean Watson** (Un ballo in maschera); *Tenors:* **Gerald Davies** (La bohème), **Tano Ferendinos** (L'arlesiana, Werther), **James Johnston** (Simon Boccanegra), **Heddle Nash** (L'elisir d'amore, Faust); *Baritones:* **Arnold Matters** (Simon Boccanegra), **Frederick Sharp** (Simon Boccanegra); *Basses:* **Norman Allin** (La reine de Saba), **Owen Brannigan** (Faust), **Howell Glynne** (Simon Boccanegra).

Norman Allin is perhaps the most striking revelation: sturdy and firm as a rock but by no means as hard-hearted, individual and memorable, but no joke, and (making a quick mental survey) nothing to be found quite like him today. Somewhat like him a generation after was Howell Glynne, who is heard here in Fiesco's aria from *Simon Boccanegra*, one of the best of the old Sadlers Wells singers and later a very good Baron Ochs at Covent Garden. It is good also to hear Jean Watson: Canadian-born, she came to us after the war and sang a stunning Azucena. Her Ulrica solo is scrupulous but not very dramatic. 'Scrupulous' is the word for all these, including the Melboid sopranos, Licette, (Labbette) Perli and Teyte. If there is a disappointment it is with Arnold Matters's dull-toned Boccanegra, balanced, however, by the pleasure of hearing Joyce Gartside and James Johnston as the lovers. And shedding her light over all is Kathleen Ferrier, whose test-pressing of "What is life?" suggests not so much a star of the British opera as a nearly full moon in the international firmament. It is a delightful collection, the sound vivid and compelling as ever.

Elsie Suddaby Songs and Arias by M. Arne, T. Arne, Bach, Besly, Carey, Denza, Ford, German, Handel, Haydn, Jackson, MacCunn, Mendelssohn, Morley, Mozart, Purcell, Schubert, Somervell, Stanford and Warlock. **Elsie Suddaby** (sop) with various artists. Amphion mono Ⓜ PHICD134* (80 minutes: ADD: 4/96). From HMV and Decca originals; Recorded 1924-52.
Elsie Suddaby (1893-1980) was a close contemporary of Isobel Baillie and Dora Labbette and in many ways she evinces the strongest personality of the three, and has a distinctive timbre very much her own. That can be heard in the first item, Michael Arne's *The lass with the delicate air*, a piece she virtually appropriated as her signature tune. She sings it with such variety of tone and, yes, such delicacy of accent, that one capitulates at once to so graceful an artist. In Dido's Lament, the singular quality of being able, simply and naturally, to move the listener is there: adding appoggiaturas to the recitative and discreetly employing portamento in the Lament itself she goes to the heart of the matter. There is also the joyfully affirmative side of her art, shown in a fresh account of "Rejoice greatly" from *Messiah* and "Endless pleasure", Semele wallowing in her conquest of Jupiter. Better still is a version of "Let the bright Seraphim" (*Samson*) that rings the rafters with its zealous delivery. Runs in all these Handel pieces are keenly accomplished though not quite with Baillie's assurance. These HMV recordings catch Suddaby in her prime, when she was in her thirties, yet on a Decca ten-inch of 1941 of Thomas Arne's *Where the bee sucks* and Morley's *It was a lover and his lass*, there is no diminution of her powers, and even the Warlock songs and Mozart's *Agnus Dei*, when Suddaby was in her late fifties, find the tone almost as fresh as ever and wholly free of wobble. The CD is a generous offering, the transfers are mostly well done and the booklet is obviously a labour of love.

Richard Tauber Opera Arias and Duets – Aida, Il barbiere di Siviglia, The bartered bride, La bohème, Carmen, Don Giovanni, Eugene Onegin, Der Evangelimann, La forza del destino, Fra Diavolo, I gioielli della Madonna, Der Kuhreigen, Madama Butterfly, Martha, Mignon, Der Rosenkavalier, Tosca, Die tote Stadt, La traviata, Il trovatore, Die Walküre and Die Zauberflöte. **Richard Tauber** (ten) with various artists. Preiser Lebendige Vergangenheit mono Ⓕ 89219* (two discs: 143 minutes: AAD: 10/96). From Odeon originals; recorded 1919-26.
Richard Tauber Das Deutsche Volkslied. Opera Arias – Don Giovanni and Die tote Stadt; songs by Heymann and R. Strauss. **Richard Tauber** (ten) with various artists. Claremont mono Ⓜ CDGSE78-50-64* (67 minutes: ADD: 10/96). From Parlophone and Odeon originals; recorded 1924-39.
These two issues present a neatly complementary view of Tauber's career. The Preiser set gives us a picture of the young tenor in his days almost exclusively as an opera artist in German-speaking lands singing his repertory in the vernacular. It evinces the golden, sappy, honeyed tone of Tauber in his prime. The style at this stage is wholly disciplined but already we hear that outgoing, spontaneous

exuberance that was soon to bring him world-wide fame in operetta. Few if any tenors have sung Mozart quite so beautifully as Tauber at this point in his career: the 1922 Bildnis aria is a model of its kind, preferable to his later version, and an object-lesson in phrasing for any aspiring tenor. His interpretations of Lensky's aria, the famous piece from *Der Evangelimann*, José's Flower Song, Jenik's aria (a glorious 1919 version) and Wilhelm Meister's farewell to Mignon show the plangent, almost melancholic timbre with which Tauber could invest such repertory. Then for pure singing his readings of the Italian Tenor's aria, Siegmund's Spring Song, Alfredo's aria and Pinkerton's outpouring of remorse are hard to beat. Add to this the many duets he never repeated in electric versions and you have a most desirable issue. In the company of regular colleagues of that time, such as Rethberg, Bettendorf, Sabine Kalter and, best of all perhaps, Lotte Lehmann (*Die tote Stadt* duets), his contributions reveal his generosity of both voice and manner. This is free-ranging, rich-hued singing marred only by most of the music being sung in the 'wrong' language. There are a few downward transpositions in the solos, but that was common practice at the time. Otherwise there's little to criticize here in the performances and none in the excellent transfers.

The more intimate side of Tauber's art comes in the series of *Volkslieder* he recorded for Parlophone in 1926, nicely transferred by Claremont. Here one admires the very personal way in which he caresses these charmingly unassuming pieces. Four Strauss songs from 1932 sessions follow, notable for the passion in the tone. What a pity the CD wasn't completed with more Lieder rather than operatic items already available in numerous transfers, including the less-than-satisfactory Ottavio arias of 1939. But at the end there's a gem: "Kennst du das kleine Haus am Michigansee?" where Tauber lavishes on a trifle all the magic of his incredible technique and heady tone, including those *pianissimos* conjured from nowhere. The transfers are excellent.

Luisa Tetrazzini Opera Arias – Un ballo in maschera, Il barbiere di Siviglia, Carmen, Dinorah, La forza del destino, Las hijas del Zebedeo, Lakmé, Linda di Chamounix, Lucia di Lammermoor, Mignon, La perle du Brésil, Rigoletto, Roméo et Juliette, Rosalinda, La sonnambula, La traviata, Il trovatore, I vespri siciliani and Die Zauberflöte; songs by Benedict, Brahms, Cowen, De Koven, Eckert, Gilbert, Grieg, Moore, Pergolesi, Proch and Venzano.
Luisa Tetrazzini (sop) with various artists. Romophone mono Ⓟ 81025-2*
(two discs: 150 minutes: ADD: 9/97). From Victor and Zonophone originals; recorded 1904-20.
Though Tetrazzini was one of the most prized and assiduously collected of recording artists in her time, her career on record was not really very satisfactory. As was true of several others she repeated the same items in several versions, whereas, especially in those days of such restricted recording-time, an extension to the repertoire would have been so much more welcome. The repertoire itself relied heavily on the familiar *chevaux de bataille*, the Mad scenes, Bell song, Shadow song and so forth, and often when something out of the way comes along, either, like the "Pastorale" from Veracini's *Rosalinda*, it is not well suited, or, as with Proch's vapid variations, it was not worth doing in the first place. There must also have been difficulties in successfully catching a voice which combined such brilliance and power with what could all too often emerge on record as a colourless and even infantile quality. Of the Victors reproduced here the best and most essential Tetrazzini is the 1911 "Ah, non giunge" (*La sonnambula*). The cabaletta, "Di tale amor", following "Tacea la notte" (*Il trovatore*) is also a joy. The *Lucia di Lammermoor* sextet and *Rigoletto* quartet with Caruso, Amato and others are also prime attractions, fine performances in many (not all) ways and remarkably clear and lifelike as recorded sound. The five Zonophones are interesting collector's pieces, not the write-off five that are sometimes said to be, but a mixed pleasure, with Tetrazzini cheerfully distributing pearls while her brother-in-law, Cleofonte Campanini, administers a remorselessly clonking piano accompaniment.

Maggie Teyte Songs by Berlioz, Chausson, Debussy, Duparc, Fauré, Hahn, Massenet and Ravel.
Dame Maggie Teyte (sop); **Gerald Moore** (pf) with various artists.
EMI Références mono Ⓜ CHS5 65198-2* (two discs: 157 minutes: ADD: 10/94). From HMV, Rimington Van Wyck, British Institute of Recorded Sound and Gramophone Shop of New York originals; recorded 1940-48.
"Je rapporte une rare émotion", the line from "Le martin-pêcheur", one of Ravel's *Histoires naturelles*, as Dame Maggie sings it, seems to signal the mood into which one is cast, listening to these famous recordings. The opening songs on the first CD, "Le spectre de la rose" and "Absence" from Berlioz's *Les nuits d'été* reveal at once all her positive virtues. The firmness of tone, the beauty of her high soft notes – like clear mountain spring water – which is not to say that there is anything watery about her interpretations; then the surprising sensuality of much of her phrasing and pronunciation – surprising because of the unmistakably British quality of her voice. She excelled above all in the *mélodie*, but her voice had none of the acid shrillness associated with French sopranos. Teyte's diction was excellent, but is not what one thinks of now as idiomatic French. "On ne chante pas comme on parle" she used to insist, and what one can hear is the Parisian fashion in the 1900s for affecting a slight English accent. That this came naturally to her must have added to her allure for audiences of the time. (Proust mentions her in his letters.) All the songs by Chausson are very fine. In *Le colibri* she demonstrates the richness of her low notes, and although the sound in *Poème de l'amour et de la mer* is somewhat restricted, this, too, is heady stuff. Chausson's *Chanson perpetuelle*, in which she is accompanied by Gerald Moore and the Blech String Quartet, has never been reissued before. This is one of Teyte's greatest records: the weight of sadness she brings to the poem by Charles Cros, with its

tragic "Il est devenu mon amant", is reason enough to buy this compilation. The Duparc songs are superbly dramatic – Teyte wrote that "the deeper shades of pastel" were not enough for song recitals and that a singer needed to use as much power and expression as for opera. Her deep understanding of Ravel's *Shéhérazade* makes hers a fascinating version, even if at first those brought up on later, more expansive recordings may find it a little cool. All the items on the second CD are accompanied by Gerald Moore. In her autobiography she lamented the passing of "the lost art of the musicale". What she meant was the chance of intimate contact between artist and audience in a drawing-room – something she achieves immediately in the opening *Elégie* of Massenet. Then flow 13 songs by Fauré; *Soir* was a special favourite of Dame Maggie's – she had once sung it with Fauré as her accompanist – "Bravo, ma petite!" he exclaimed afterwards. There is not a single piece on this set that does not merit attention, and each song reveals something of Teyte's art. There are no texts or translations.

Maggie Teyte Chansons – Berlioz, Debussy, Duparc and Fauré. **Dame Maggie Teyte** (sop) with various artists. Pearl mono Ⓜ GEMMCD9134* (74 minutes: ADD: 11/95). From HMV and Rimington van Wyck originals; recorded 1936-41.   Ⓖ

There was some sort of magic in the air at the EMI Abbey Road Studios in London on March 12th and 13th, 1936. Maggie Teyte, just short of her forty-eighth birthday, and Alfred Cortot, both of whom had been well acquainted with Claude Debussy, recorded 14 of his *mélodies*. This is no studio-bound recital but a performance, the passion and beauty of tone matched stroke for stroke by pianist and singer. These records, and the later ones Teyte made with Gerald Moore, are among the jewels of Debussy singing and playing. No one with an interest in French song should hesitate to acquire them, for they provide a lesson, not just in pronunciation of the French language (though like her contemporary and supposed rival, Mary Garden, Teyte sang with a pronounced English accent – something which entranced the French in the *belle époque*, when all things English were *à la mode*). The beauty of Teyte's tone, the freshness and girlish quality of her high notes – something which never deserted her, and she continued to sing for another 20 years – are constantly astonishing. So is the passion she puts into phrases such as "Qu'il était bleu, le ciel, et grand l'espoir!" in "Colloque sentimental" from the second book of *Fêtes galantes*, or the dark-hued "Il me dit: 'Les satyres sont morts,'" in "Le tombeau des Naïdes" from *Chansons de Bilitis*. Those who already have some of the other reissues of Teyte's Debussy recordings will find that this Pearl disc has a rather higher surface noise, perhaps the price one has to pay for getting the voice more forward. One wonders why Pearl have called the disc "Chansons", the correct term for these settings is *Mélodies* – or there is the good old English word 'song'.

Vienna State Opera Live Recordings, Volume 6. **Vienna State Opera Chorus and Orchestra / Wilhelm Furtwängler, Leopold Reichwein, Hans Knappertsbusch, Leopold Ludwig and Clemens Krauss.** Koch Schwann mono Ⓜ 314562 (two discs: 143 minutes: ADD: 1/95). Recorded 1933-42. *Sopranos* – **Helena Braun** (Parsifal; 1942), **Daniza Ilitsch** (Aida; 1942), **Anny Konetzni** (Siegfried; 1936. Die Walküre; 1937. Tristan und Isolde; 1941), **Viorica Ursuleac** (Die Meistersinger; 1933). *Mezzo-sopranos* – **Margarete Klose** (Tristan und Isolde; 1941), **Elena Nicolai** (Aida; 1942). *Contralto* – **Bella Paalen** (Die Meistersinger; 1933). *Tenors* – **Anton Arnold, Hermann Gallos** (both Die Meistersinger; 1933), **Josef Kalenberg** (Siegfried; 1936), **Max Lorenz** (Die Meistersinger; 1933. Tristan und Isolde; 1941. Parsifal, Götterdämmerung and Aida; all 1942), **William Wernigk, Herr Wolken, Erich Zimmermann** (all Die Meistersinger; 1933). *Baritones* – **Mathieu Ahlersmeyer** (Aida; 1942), **Hans Duhan, Alfred Jerger, Viktor Madin** (Die Meistersinger; 1933). *Bass-baritone* – **Paul Schoeffler** (Parsifal and Götterdämmerung; 1942). *Basses* – **Herbert Alsen** (Aida; 1942), **Karl Ettl** (Die Meistersinger; 1933), **Ludwig Hofmann** (Die Walküre; 1937), **Josef von Manowarda** (Götterdämmerung; 1942), **Alfred Muzzarelli, Hermann Reich** (Die Meistersinger; 1933), **Sigmund Roth, Adolf Vogel** (Parsifal; 1942), **Hermann Wiedemann, Nikolaus Zec** (Die Meistersinger; 1933).

This set is devoted largely to the appreciable art of Anny Konetzni as Isolde and Brünnhilde, and Max Lorenz as Siegfried, Parsifal, Walther and Radames. Don't let anyone ever tell you that sopranos shouldn't tackle Wagner until they are 40. Providing they have the voice and their technique is secure (admittedly two big provisos), they should be in no trouble. Here is Konetzni, in her early thirties, offering a fully formed portrayal of Brünnhilde, sung in a steady, rounded, warm tone throughout a wide register that no Hochdramatische could rival today. Kalenberg (her Siegfried) is an ordinary tenor but Lorenz is her equally secure and sensitive Tristan. Elsewhere Lorenz proves maddening. Here is undoubtedly one of *the* Heldentenor voices of the century, but one that is sometimes crudely used. In the 1933 *Die Meistersinger* extracts he has not yet acquired bad habits, so his Walther comes forth in pristine state in both the Trial and Prize songs, which means they have seldom sounded better. By the time of the 1942 *Parsifal*, *Götterdämmerung* and *Aida* he had started to gulp and over-emote in a manner that exaggerates the passion of the moment to an extent that it becomes uncouth. Yet there is still no denying the sheer excitement of the sound, and its shining strength above the stave. He still (on occasion) sings fastidiously, as in the *Aida* finale, where he gives us a Radames full of remorse and sadness. But then he is partnering the revelation of this issue, the Aida of the Yugoslav soprano, Ilitsch who sings quite ravishingly here, in German, of course. The beauty and sensuousness of her singing is quite remarkable and most ingratiating. In the other operas, Helena Braun proves a strong, involving Kundry, one of the best on disc, and the brief example ("Nun zäume dein Ross" from *Die Walküre*) of Hofmann's Wotan leaves one wanting more; so, of course, do Konetzni's following "Hojotoho"s. In *Die Meistersinger*, Ursuleac's reputation is further restored by her readings of "O Sachs, mein Freund" and the start of the Quintet, so warm and outgoing, even if occasionally unfocused. The three famous conductors leading most of the performances confirm their justified reputations as Wagnerians, and Ludwig does well in *Aida*.

Vienna State Opera Live Recordings, Volumes 22 and 24. **Vienna State Opera Chorus and Orchestra / Anton Paulik, Rudolf Moralt, Hans Knappertsbusch, Leopold Reichwein, Clemens Krauss.** Koch Schwann mono Ⓜ 314722* and 314742* (two two-disc sets, oas: 146 and 136 minutes: ADD: 5/96). Recorded at performances in the Vienna State Opera and at Salzburg in the years given.
314722 – Sopranos: **Irma Beilke** (Le nozze di Figaro; 1942), **Helena Braun** (Der fliegende Holländer; 1940. Le nozze di Figaro, Die Walküre and Götterdämmerung; all 1942), **Daga Söderqvist** (Götterdämmerung; 1942), **Gerda Sommerschuh** (Le nozze di Figaro; 1942), **Liane Timm** (Le nozze di Figaro; 1942). *Mezzo:* **Mela Bugarinovic** (Siegfried; 1941). *Contralto:* **Res Fischer** (Le nozze di Figaro; 1942). *Tenors:* **Joachim Sattler** (Siegfried; 1941), **William Wernigk** (Siegfried; 1941. Le nozze di Figaro; 1942), **Josef Witt** (Le nozze di Figaro; 1942). *Baritone:* **Erich Kunz** (Le nozze di Figaro; 1942). *Bass-baritones:* **Hans Hotter** (Der fliegende Holländer; 1940. Siegfried; 1941. Le nozze di Figaro, Parsifal and Die Walküre; 1942. Pagliacci; 1943), **Gustav Neidlinger** (Le nozze di Figaro; 1942). *Basses:* **Josef von Manowarda** (Der fliegende Holländer; 1940. Götterdämmerung; 1942), **Franz Normann** (Le nozze di Figaro; 1942). *314742 – Sopranos:* **Wanda Achsel** (Götterdämmerung; 1937), **Helena Braun** (Die Walküre; 1943), **Luise Helletsgruber** (Götterdämmerung; 1937), **Daniza Ilitsch** (Die Walküre; 1943), **Anny Konetzni** (Götterdämmerung; 1937), **Hilde Konetzni** (Die Walküre; 1943), **Olga Levko-Antosch** (Die Walküre; 1943), **Anne Michalsky** (Götterdämmerung; 1937), **Else Schulz** (Die Walküre; 1943), **Daga Söderqvist** (Die Walküre; 1943), **Adele Kern** (Siegfried; 1941), **Elisabeth Schumann** (Siegfried; 1937). *Mezzos:* **Mela Bugarinovic** (Siegfried; 1941), **Elena Nikolaidi** (Die Walküre; 1943), **Else Schürhoff** (Die Walküre; 1943), **Enid Szánthó** (Siegfried; 1936. Das Rheingold and Götterdämmerung; 1937), **Dora With** (Götterdämmerung; 1937. Die Walküre; 1943). *Contraltos:* **Rosette Anday** (Götterdämmerung; 1937), **Melanie Frutschnigg** (Die Walküre; 1943), **Bella Paalen** (Götterdämmerung; 1937). *Tenors:* **Josef Kalenberg** (Siegfried; 1936), **Max Lorenz** (Siegfried and Götterdämmerung; 1937. Die Walküre; 1943), **Set Svanholm** (Siegfried; 1941), **Erich Zimmermann** (Siegfried; 1936). *Baritones:* **Fred Destal** (Götterdämmerung; 1937), **Jaro Prohaska** (Götterdämmerung; 1937), **Emil Schipper** (Siegfried; 1936). *Bass-baritones:* **Hans Hotter** (Die Walküre; 1943), **Paul Schoeffler** (Siegfried; 1941). *Basses:* **Ludwig Hofmann** (Das Rheingold; 1937), **Nikolaus Zec** (Siegfried; 1937), **Alexander Kipnis** (Götterdämmerung; 1937).
This documents Hotter at the height of his powers as a young Heldenbariton in Vienna, giving us early glimpses of his Dutchman, Wotan/Wanderer and Amfortas. The voice at this stage of his career was lighter than it was to become. The top is not only produced more easily but has a brassy, focused quality less evident in later years. As an interpreter he seems more indulgent with his feelings: the readings have not yet become 'fixed' and in consequence they are deeply felt in a way that is different from the later versions. Most important perhaps are the extracts from Act 3 of *Die Walküre* and Acts 1 and 3 of *Siegfried*, since we have no substantial souvenirs of him, except of the Farewell, in these acts elsewhere at this stage of his career. Even in 1942, Hotter was supreme as the Wotan of *Die Walküre* Act 3, pouring out his anger and hurt to his erring daughter, then capitulating to her urgent demands for forgiveness. Hotter's tone seems to come forth as a stream of impassioned feeling, the phrasing eloquent in all respects, also firm in tone and long-breathed. The sheer authority of Hotter's singing would be hard to surpass, phrase after phrase filled with special meaning. Moralt and Knappertsbusch are respectively the yielding yet forward-moving conductors. His Amfortas must have been shattering, the character's long solos, even with passages missing, carrying the weight of the torture and agony in the injured and disturbed man's mind and heart: they have never been better done. The sound in all the above passages is very reasonable. That for the 1940 *Holländer*, however, is poor. Here he is partnered with Helena Braun's radiant Senta. Braun returns for Brünnhilde's Immolation. She sounds rather effortful at the end of a long evening and isn't helped by Reichwein's lacklustre conducting, but there's still much to admire in her thoughtful treatment of the text, always one of her strengths. Hotter reappears in Vol. 24 in another Act 3 of *Die Walküre* and another Farewell, distinguished not only by his presence, but also by Knappertsbusch in the pit. Indeed, he conducts all the extracts from *The Ring* in this, the final offering in this series, and it is perhaps the most persuasive reason for listening to them as he stamps his authority on everything. Schoeffler's Wanderer is lyrically sung but lacks Hotter's emotional charge. The 1936-7 extracts are lamed by indifferent sound. Fleetingly heard to good effect are Schumann as the Woodbird, Szánthó as Erda, Lorenz as Siegfried and, above all, Anni Konetzni, who again proves she was one of the great Brünnhildes, although heard all too briefly here.

A Portrait of Norman Walker Opera and Oratorio Arias – Acis and Galatea, The Children of Don, The Creation, The Dream of Gerontius, Dylan, Die Entführung aus dem Serail, Faust,

Judas Maccabaeus, Messiah, La morte d'Orfeo, La quattro stagioni (B. Marcello), Die Zauberflöte; songs by Capel, Haynes, Lane Wilson, Purcell and Storace. **Norman Walker** (bass) with various artists. Dutton Laboratories mono Ⓜ CDLX7021* (71 minutes: ADD: 12/96). From Columbia, HMV and Decca originals; recorded 1928-54.

Norman Walker was one of our leading basses for some 17 years from 1937 when he sang as the Commendatore and the Speaker at Glyndebourne and King Mark (with Dame Eva Turner as Isolde) at Covent Garden. From then on he balanced his career nicely between the stage and the concert-hall. After the war, he shared the role of Collatinus with Brannigan in the early performances of *The Rape of Lucretia* at Glyndebourne and was principal bass for six years with the Covent Garden company from 1948. At the same time he appeared up and down the country in countless oratorio performances, a much-loved soloist. This welcome reissue opens resplendently with Walker singing Handel and Haydn in the classic manner: steady, burnished tone, every run in its place and diction exemplary. Then comes Walker's unsurpassed account of the Angel of the Agony's solo from *Gerontius*, so urgent, so sympathetic, here allowed to run on to let us hear Heddle Nash sing "I go before my judge" so movingly. Of Walker's opera repertory we hear a student account of "O Isis und Osiris", which gives some evidence of what was to follow, and a test made in 1944 for Walter Legge of Osmin's aria, which suggests he might have been a good interpreter of that role. The extracts indicate Walker's dramatic prowess (though his Italian is far from idiomatic) – as does his brief contribution to the closing trio from *Faust*, with Joan Cross a suitably distraught Marguérite. More valuable than these, however, because they display so unerringly Walker's gifts as a conviction-singer, are the four British songs made at one session in 1952 with Gerald Moore. They are exemplified in the bass's confident tone, unobtrusive word-painting and subtle use of rubato. Indeed the singer, in these faultless transfers, seems in the room with us. Malcolm Walker provides a warm, personal cameo of his father in his notes.

The Harold Wayne Collection, Volume 8. **Suzanne Adams, Emma Calvé** (sops)); **Antonio Scotti, Maurice Renaud** (bars); **Anton van Rooy** (bass-bar); **Pol Plançon** (bass); **Sir Landon Ronald** (pf). Symposium mono Ⓔ 1100* (79 minutes: AAD: 3/93). From G&T originals. Recorded in 1902 with piano accompaniment.

Suzanne Adams – excerpts from Faust and Roméo et Juliette; songs by Stern, Vidal and Bishop. **Emma Calvé** – Carmen and Cavalleria Rusticana. **Scotti** – Méssaline, Don Giovanni, Faust, Carmen and Falstaff; songs by Rotoli and Tosti. **Maurice Renaud** – Tannhäuser; song by Holmès. **Anton Van Rooy** – Die Walküre, Die Meistersinger von Nürnberg, Tannhäuser and Das Rheingold. **Pol Plançon** – Philémon et Baucis, Roméo et Juliette, Le caïd and Les Huguenots; songs by J-B. Faure and Godard.

Though this is the eighth volume of a remarkable series, it is probably the first that can be recommended with assurance to a wider public than those listeners who have a specialized interest in the singers recorded during the early years of the gramophone. Those on the present disc were all made in London in 1902: they were the 'London Reds', beloved of collectors and now worth a small fortune. The first likely surprise for a newcomer is how vividly the voices come through. The great French bass Pol Plançon is heard in the opening tracks, and the immediacy and naturalness of reproduction are often astonishing. So too is the singing, with sonority and refinement, superb fluency of scales and triplets, a brilliantly articulated trill, the well-bound evenness of cello tone, and a lively sense of fun. Not all are as satisfyingly caught as Plançon: the famous Carmen of the time, Emma Calvé, proves more elusive, though her little asides and exclamations are entertaining. Harold Wayne is the owner of one of the world's finest private collections, and his generosity has allowed these rarities to become public property. It is an opportunity to gain a privileged glimpse of another age and of singers who are far too special, both as voices and artists, to be merely forgotten.

The Harold Wayne Collection, Volume 15. **Félia Litvinne** (sop); **Léon Escalaïs** (ten); **Victor Maurel** (bar) with various accompaniments. Symposium mono Ⓔ 1128* (80 minutes: AAD: 12/94). From Fonotipia and French Odéon originals; recorded 1900s.

Litvinne – L'africaine, Aida, Carmen, Cavalleria Rusticana, Le Cid, La favorita, Lohengrin, Samson et Dalila and Il trovatore. **Escalaïs** – Falstaff, Hérodiade, Mefistofele, Otello, Polyeucte and Il trovatore. **Maurel** – Don Giovanni, Falstaff and Otello; songs by De Lara, d'Hardelot, Paladilhe and Tosti.

The Harold Wayne Collection, Volume 21. **Ada Adini, Georgette Bréjean-Silver, Rose Caron** (sops); **Marie De Reszke** (mez); **Victor Capoul, Léon David, Ernest van Dyck** (tens); **Pericles Aramis** (bar); **Jean-François Delmas** (bass-bar); **Pedro Gailhard** (bass) with various accompaniments. Symposium mono Ⓔ 1172* (79 minutes: ADD). From Fonotipia originals; recorded 1904-05.

Adini – Hérodiade; song by Braga. **Bréjan-Silver** – La traviata. **Caron** – Sigurd; song by Gounod. **De Reszke** – song by Gounod. **Capoul** – Jocelyn. **David** – Carmen and Mignon; song by Bourgeois. **Van Dyck** – Die Walküre and Werther; songs by Nicolai and Schumann. **Aramis** – songs by De Lara, Massenet and Tosti. **Delmas** – La damnation de Faust, Les Huguenots, Patrie and Die Walküre; songs by Gounod and Schumann. **Gailhard** – L'Africaine and Faust; song by Yradier.

Mezzo-soprano quality is much in evidence here, but rather remarkably it also serves as a foil for the high notes, which are almost always as beautiful in their 'placing' as in the purity of tone. A fine example is the aria "Sur mes genoux" from *L'Africaine*, which she recorded twice. The high A naturals seem so easily taken and are admirably clear and firm. The two *Il trovatore* arias are also, if not quite technically perfect, then at least the work of an artist who knows what perfection might be, and who combines that vision with a fully human warmth of feeling. Best of all is "Pleurez, mes yeux" from *Le Cid*, one of Massenet's loveliest arias and performed here with rare strength and sensitivity. With Litvinne in this fifteenth volume are the heroic tenor Léon Escalaïs and the famous Maurel, 'creator' of Iago and Falstaff, both of those characters having solos included here. Maurel is heard in the complete run of Fonotipias (1904 and 1907), including an unedifying version of Don Giovanni's Serenade and a song in English, *A year ago* by Guy d'Hardelot which, feeble as the music may be, goes far to make amends.

These are all rare enough, but for a concentration of super-rarities Vol. 21 must take the prize. Here, for instance, is Rose Caron, prima donna of the Paris Opéra in the 1880s and 1890s, years rich in important premières in many of which the great bass Jean-François Delmas would also take part, and perhaps the tenor van Dyck (the original Werther) too. Of these three, Delmas is superb, Caron distinctive in the warm middle register, van Dyck (in euphemistic usage) interesting. Pedro Gailhard sings Yradier's *La paloma*, which was written for him; Victor Capoul (b.1839) sings the famous lullaby from *Jocelyn*, which he also sang at the première of the work in 1888. Then there is the extraordinary survival of a single record, a unique copy, by Marie De Reszke accompanied by her husband Jean. She sings Gounod's *Au rossignol*, and most beautifully, but the record was never issued, for Jean, dissatisfied with his own vocal recordings, ordered the whole lot to be destroyed, which the 'man from the company' hadn't quite the heart to do. When it came to copy No. 11 of this song he desisted and put it secretly by. Eventually it came to Dr Wayne and hence, thanks once more to his generosity and the enterprise of Symposium, to us.

The Harold Wayne Collection, Volume 20. **Giuseppe Anselmi** (ten) with various artists.
Symposium mono Ⓟ 1170* (79 minutes: ADD: 7/95). From Fonotipia originals; recorded 1907-10.
Opera Arias – Cavalleria Rusticana, Don Pasquale, Il Duca d'Alba, Fedora, Iris, Luisa Miller, Manon, Manru, Mignon, Pagliacci, Les pêcheurs de perles, Serse, La traviata and Werther; songs by Alagna, Mendelssohn, Mugnone, Scarlatti, R. Strauss and Tosti.

It is surely one of the most lovely tenor voices ever heard: that is the first reaction and the most regularly recurrent. Then there are the special moments, individual notes or phrases, where one listens without breathing. For much of the time Anselmi moves with the utmost grace, his notes and the passage between them are managed so easily and evenly that he could be mistaken for a singer of faultless style and impeccable technique. But a mistake that would sadly be. So, for example, take the recitative and aria "Sogno soave" from *Don Pasquale*, which opens the programme and was the first record he made. The sheer immediacy of the voice in its recorded sound is gratifying, his emotional involvement draws one towards him, and his caress of the aria's first phrases is utterly winning. He has that lovely way, now lost, of 'holding' a moment in the melody and very lightly embellishing it; and all of this with a voice of such mellow warmth that the occasional aspirate and hint of 'frog' can be more or less ignored. There follows a most eloquent sadness in the aria from *Il Duca d'Alba*, and after that a treasurable, perhaps supreme, performance of "Quando le sere" from *Luisa Miller*. But the *Traviata* brings a multi-aspirated "tutto passato", and *Mignon* sees the temporary return of the 'frog'. There are also stylistic paradoxes, as he begins "Vesti la giubba" with an exquisite privacy of grief and yet gives vent to laughs and sobs without restraint. Surprising inclusions in the programme are songs by Mendelssohn and Strauss, whose *Morgen!* is beautifully sung (in Italian) and then, as John Freestone remarks in his notes, has its effect ruined by a totally misguided rewriting of the ending. Never mind. This is not a disc to miss.

Early music

Plainchant

Gregorian Chant The complete 1930 HMV Recordings. **Solesmes Abbey Choir /**
Dom Joseph Gajard. Pearl mono Ⓜ GEMMCDS9152* (two discs: 96 minutes: ADD: 6/95).
From HMV D1971/82 (4/31).   ⒼⒼ

When in 1930 Solesmes, under Dom Gajard, produced their album of 12 records of Gregorian chant, it was a historic moment. They were making the first major contribution to the documentation of an art having its roots well back in the first millennium, an art underlying much of the subsequent development of Western music. The remarkable unity and flow of the chant was surely due to the fact that they were all singing this music day in, day out, and an occasional portamento, or lack of ensemble was a normal, understandable part of the package. This is a sound of youthful vigour, with all the hallmarks of the familiar Solesmes style already there, well in place: the soaring phrases with their softened peaks and quiet final syllables; the firm enunciation of first syllables; the lifted accents on short notes; the quaint interpretation of the salicus; but over it all, its own special, innate quality, which combines unmistakable spirituality with robust everyday living. That quality, and a certain quiet confidence, are present in this singing to a degree rarely attained by any other monastic choir. The remastering, naturally, has not succeeded in eliminating all the needle hiss. One hardly notices this, by the way, such is the selective power of the human ear! This collection is really Everyman's basic anthology of Gregorian chant. It ranges from well-known hymns and pieces of the Ordinary, through gems from the Temporale and the Common of Saints, to some of the greatest masterpieces of the repertoire, including the Good Friday responsory *Tenebrae factae sunt* and the splendid first mode offertory *Jubilate Deo* for the second Sunday after Epiphany. It also contains some items one rarely hears nowadays, such as the powerfully moving *Media vita* – "In the midst of life we are in death".

Gregorian Chant Mass for the Feast of St Thomas of Canterbury. The Office of Matins for St Thomas of Canterbury. St Dunstan's Kyrie. **Lay Clerks of Canterbury Cathedral Choir / David Flood.** Metronome Ⓕ METCD1003 (74 minutes: DDD: 2/95). Texts and translations included. Recorded 1994.

A recording of music for the Feast of St Thomas à Becket by the Lay Clerks of Canterbury Cathedral is a delightful idea. The music for this feast in the Salisbury rite is rich and memorable, particularly that for the Offices. In this case the selection from Matins includes five magnificent responsories and two antiphons, as well as the hymn *Martyr Dei* and the Invitatory, *Assunt Thomas Martyris*. This last item is particularly valuable, since though the Invitatory has generally not found much favour in recordings and concerts (either as chant or set polyphonically), the cumulative effect of the form is extraordinary. This anthology also includes the Mass for the Feast of St Thomas (in which the Sequence, *Solemne canticum*, is especially impressive) and the *Kyrie, Rex Splendens*, attributed to St Dunstan. The singing is restrained and sober and somewhat lacking in colour. The problem seems to be that there is little response to the words on the part of the singers: the chant somehow does not sound 'organic', as though it were sung liturgically. This is a difficult problem to solve, but there is no doubt that the quality of the singing itself is very high. Certainly no one with an interest in Western chant should hesitate to buy this very worthwhile recording.

Holy Week and Easter at Benevento Cathedral Ensemble Organum / Marcel Pérès. Harmonia Mundi Ⓕ HMC90 1476 (73 minutes: DDD: 12/94). Texts and translations included. Recorded 1993.

Beneventan Chant Adoration of the Cross. Paschal Vigil. Easter Sunday Mass of the Day.

This is a recording of exceptional interest. Beneventan chant represents an area of early liturgical music about which, until recently, little has been generally known, and which has been almost entirely overshadowed by Gregorian chant. To a large extent, in past centuries, Benevento and its surrounds were geographically cut off from both Roman and Carolingian influence. Many Greek monastic communities had previously taken refuge and settled in Southern Italy. It was normal that the inhabitants of Benevento should have contacts with these communities and that they should establish cultural and political links with Greece itself. It is hardly surprising to find that the Latin rite of the Cathedral of Benevento contains substantial traces of Greek influence and numerous bilingual texts. The liturgy of Holy Week is a case in point, in particular the *Adoration of the Cross*: each antiphon is heard first in Greek and then in Latin, followed by Latin psalmody to slight variations of the more familiar Gregorian psalm tones. Some of this music, of purely Beneventan origin, is of quite extraordinary beauty. The responsory *Amicus meus* (sung by Josep Benet and Marcel Pérès) is one such piece, and for which alone one would wish to possess this recording. Ensemble Organum's normal recourse to a style of singing inspired by Greek Orthodoxy really comes into its own here: the choice seems entirely fitting for a repertoire such as this. The singers are to be congratulated on such a splendid result, the fruit of their study with Lycourcos Angelopoulos. The ornamentation is sounding more natural, the *ison* well controlled. Professor Thomas Kelly's concise and informative notes are an excellent introduction to the music.

Melchite Sacred Chant Hymns to the Blessed Virgin. **Sister Marie Keyrouz** (sop); **L'Ensemble de la Paix.** Harmonia Mundi Ⓕ HMC90 1497 (63 minutes: DDD: 9/94). Recorded 1993.

With very little hint of nasality or of singing from the throat, Sister Marie Keyrouz accomplishes the most florid ululations with the greatest of ease, the voice continuously and impressively set in relief by a reverberant acoustic and a drone bass provided by a small choir of male voices. The area touched on by this extremely rare repertory is a fascinating one, not much illuminated by the brief, at times almost impenetrable notes provided. The Melchite churches of the Near East in the fourth and fifth centuries AD were those that remained, in a period of frequent schism, faithful to Byzantium ('Melchite' derives from a Syriac word meaning 'Emperor'). The liturgy of these churches was very influential: many of the most famous hymns of the Orthodox church, for example, were composed in the sixth century by Romanos the Melodist in Syriac style; like Sister Marie, Romanos was born in what is now the Lebanon. So some of these melodies, if authentic, may be part of a repertory more ancient than any other surviving Christian chant. For the earlier part of their history, of course, they would have had to rely on oral transmission for their survival. How far they were changed in that process, how far they were affected by an Islamic tradition growing up around them and by translation of their texts from Greek and Syriac into Arabic, only a specialist could say; certainly the notes accompanying this collection do not. This would be only a quibble were not three of the longer chants attributed to Sister Marie herself, described either as "in improvised style" or as "written improvisation"; one of these is a setting of part of Romanos's most celebrated text, the Akathistos. The main difference between these and most of those whose origin is unattributed is their greater virtuosity: in them Sister Marie uses a wider vocal range, a rather more dramatic, declamatory utterance and still more florid melismata. It makes fascinating listening: a border territory between Christian and Islamic chant, at times revealing a modal simplicity beneath the flexible ornament, at others well-nigh hiding it in ecstatic, microtonal wailings.

Cantiques de l'Orient Soeur Marie Keyrouz (sop); L'Ensemble de la Paix.
Harmonia Mundi Ⓟ HMC90 1577 (73 minutes: DDD: 7/96). Texts and translations included. *Gramophone* *Editor's choice.*   ⒼⒼ
Soeur Marie Keyrouz belongs to a rare breed of musicians: a fully trained female cantor of talent, she has already achieved international fame through her recordings of oriental Christian chants, in particular those of her own branch of Christianity, the Maronite Church. In this recording she reveals herself as a composer and a mystic poet as well as a brilliant performer. The seven sacred songs include the *Magnificat* and a psalm (*Like as the hart*): the five others are original poems on major Christian themes. Soeur Marie's special contributions are her musical settings of the *Magnificat* and of the last text, which deals with the soul's progress from darkness to light; and also her poem *La berceuse des saints*, a lullaby for the infant Jesus, which contains a depth of meaning well beyond the run-of-the-mill Christmas carol. The musical style of all the songs is modelled on that of the traditional liturgy: it exists within the framework of an established modality and exploits such favoured oriental delights as the augmented second. As regards performance, we have here yet another example of this chantress's imaginative excellence and control, combined with her usual quite extraordinary fluency.

Divine liturgy for the Feast of St Peter and St Paul Russian Patriarchate Choir /
Anatoly Grindenko. Opus 111 Ⓟ OPS30-161 (80 minutes: DDD: 1/97). Translations included.
This is another splendid recording of highly demanding repertoire, a worthy successor to the Russian Patriarchate Choir's previous recordings of early Russian chant and polyphony. In this case the repertoire in question is *znamenny* chant-based polyphony in three parts – *strochnoie* singing, the sources of which date from the sixteenth and seventeenth centuries. The transcription and reconstruction necessary to make this repertory performable included extensive rehearsal, as detailed in the insert-notes, and finally liturgical performance in Moscow once a week over three years! Such dedication, and the experience of singing this music as part of a liturgical celebration, pays tremendous dividends. Here the Liturgy is recorded with propers for the Feast of St Peter and St Paul. It is not only the larger musical items such as the incandescent Cherubic Hymn and almost exuberant setting of the Creed that impress: extraordinary control of breath and timbre is needed to sing such sustained music as that of *Tebe poem*, and since even the litanies offer no respite from the curious, unpredictable harmonies so characteristic of the style, when they are sung with such naturalness as this, one could well believe that the choir have been singing this music every week for 30 years rather than three. A magnificent achievement.

A Star in the East Medieval Hungarian Christmas Music. **Anonymous 4** (Ruth Cunningham, Marsha Genensky, Susan Hellauer, Johanna Rose, sngrs). Harmonia Mundi Ⓟ HMU90 7139 (68 minutes: ADD: 12/96). Texts and translations included. *Gramophone* *Editor's choice.*   ⒼⒼ
This disc is a selection of liturgical and paraliturgical Christmas pieces, taken from medieval Hungarian sources. Most are monophonic, but there is a modest sprinkling of simple polyphonic pieces for two, three and four voices. The charm of the performance lies in its unpretentious, almost childlike simplicity – suggested, maybe, by the delightful extracts from the Christmas story as quoted in the notes. The classic liturgical pieces, which include the Introit *Dum medium silentium*, the splendid Gradual *Speciosa forma*, and others, are heard in a version which tends to use the pentatonic scale, thus avoiding both B natural and B flat. The sung readings are impressive with their polyphonic settings. The rich Genealogy (*Liber generationis*) with its beautifully constructed melody are most enjoyable. Some of the vernacular pieces, as well as the Latin song for New Year's Day, have a regular ternary rhythm. The Hungarian *Te Deum* offers an interesting alternative for the concluding verses: it simply transposes the original theme up a fourth. The 110-page booklet is a marvel.

Medieval-Renaissance   12th-15th centuries

Eya Mater Gregorian Chant and Polyphony for the Blessed Virgin Mary, Elizabeth and Rachel.
Discantus / Brigitte Lesne. Opus 111 Ⓟ OPS30-143 (72 minutes: DDD: 5/96). Texts and translations included. Recorded 1995.   Ⓖ

Ave Eva Twelfth and Thirteenth Century Songs of Womanhood. **Brigitte Lesne** ([a]mez/[b]hp/[c]perc).
Opus 111 ℗ OPS30-134 (61 minutes: DDD: 5/96). Texts and translations included.
   Gautier de Coincy Entendez tuit ensemble[ac]. **Codax** Ondas de mar de vigo[b]. Mandad' ei
comigo[ab]. Quantas sabedes amar amigo[ac]. **Alfonso el Sabio** Razon an os diabos de fugir
(Cantiga de Santa Maria)[c]. Entre Av'e Eva[a]. **Robert de Reims** Qui bien vuet amors
descrivre[ac]. **Beatriz de Dia** A chantar m'er de çò qu'eu no volria[ab]. **Adam de la Halle**
Je muir, je muir d'amourettes[b]. **Anonymous** L'autrier m'en aloie[ab]. Li solaus luist et clers et
bians (lai Y'Yseult)[ac]. Noches buenas[a]. Mes cuers est emprisonnés[b]. Nonne sui, nonne, laissiés,
m'aler[ab]. Or piangiamo che piange Maria[a]. Onques n'amai tant con je fui amé[b]. Avant hier en un
vert prea[c]. Nani, nani[a]. Se vos non pesar ende (Cantiga de amigo)[ac]. Ir me quieria yo[ac].
"Eya Mater" highlights two major features of eleventh- to twelfth-century liturgical development: the
elaboration through troping of the long-established repertoire and its enrichment through
experimentation with the recently discovered dimension of polyphony. Whoever devised the
programme managed, deftly, to draw together its various strands by concentrating on a unifying
theme well suited to an all-female ensemble: the theme of motherhood. Three mothers figure in the
programme – Mary, the Virgin Mother of Christ; Elizabeth, the mother of John the Baptist; and
Rachel, whose lamentation for her slaughtered offspring foreshadows the grieving of those mothers
of the Holy Innocents slain, by order of Herod, during the infancy of the Christ Child. The skilful
planning of the programme is fully matched by the ease and excellence of the performances. In the
few pieces with neither tropes nor polyphony, the interpretation of the early neume notation is quietly
convincing, with ornament dissolving into the basic melodic structure with a fluidity few other vocal
groups seem able or willing to achieve.

Brigitte Lesne's solo recital, "Ave Eva", enters the world of the medieval woman from another angle,
one more of flesh and blood. She extends her time-range to the thirteenth century and even beyond.
Her starting-point is the somewhat rarefied theme of courtly love, but she comes down to earth with
such delightfully homely subjects as a Jewish mother singing her baby to sleep (*Nani, nani*), or the
portrait of the restless nun in her cell, longing for release (*Nonne sui, nonne, laissiés, m'aler*). Perhaps
surprisingly, the singer's characteristic timbre, far from sounding monotonous or wearisome on the
ear when sustaining such a full programme, has more of a mesmeric effect, and actually enhances the
illusion that one is penetrating a new, enthralling and relatively unexplored world of human
experience.

Dame de Flors Ecole Notre-Dame de Paris. **Discantus** (Anne Guidet, Claire Jéquier,
Lucie Jolivet, Brigitte Le Baron, Brigitte Lesne, Anne Quentin, Catherine Schroeder,
Catherine Sergent) **/ Brigitte Lesne.** Opus 111 ℗ OPS30-175 (59 minutes: DDD: A/97).
Texts and translations included. Recorded 1996.
One is struck by the overwhelming majority of pieces in honour of the Virgin Mary in the extant
sources of the School of Notre-Dame. Indeed, the rich and many-faceted devotion to Our Lady,
which characterized the Middle Ages and reached its peak in the twelfth and thirteenth centuries, was
itself paralleled by the secular devotion to the ideal Lady of chivalry sung by troubadour and trouvère
alike. Such devotion may well have contributed in no small measure to the development of the art of
music, in particular of the *ars antiqua* with its musical forms: organum, conductus and motet. This is
a gentle, unaffected programme of such pieces, some of them of almost childlike simplicity, others of
ingenious complexity. The theme that unites them is Mary, seen as Star, Fountain, Maidservant, but
above all, as Lady of Flowers, herself the mystical Flower watered by celestial dew, Rose, Lily,
Blossom without a thorn. Discantus present her with imagination and sensitivity. An all-female
ensemble of eight singers – might that not be a recipe for a bland 'sameness' in an hour-long Marian
programme? However, Discantus achieve an amazing degree of variety by the simplest of means: by
opposing vocal registers, by alternating solo and tutti, by varying the tempos and by delicate phrasing.
The mood of each piece is carefully studied. Despite one slight imperfection of pitch, the listener's ear
is absolutely captivated by the sheer beauty and purity of the music.

Mystery of Notre Dame [a]Orlando Consort (Robert Harre-Jones, alto; Charles Daniels,
Angus Smith, tens; Donald Greig, bar) with [b]Simon Berridge (ten); **Westminster Cathedral Choir.**
Archiv Produktion ℗ 453 487-2AH (76 minutes: DDD: 2/98). Texts and translations included.
Recorded 1996. *Gramophone Editor's choice.*
   Léonin[a] Et valde mane una sabbatorum; Alleluya – Assumpta est Maria; Alleluya – Video celos
apertos. **Pérotin**[b] Sederunt principes. **School of Pérotin**[a] Cristus resurgens – Dicant nunc;
Benedicta – Virgo, Dei genitrix. **Plainchant** Pascha nostrum immolatus; Victimae paschali
laudes; Beata es, virgo Maria; Eternim sederunt principes; Video celos apertos.
Anyone who has followed the work of the Orlando Consort has been waiting for them to record
Notre Dame music ever since they were formed ten years ago. As we may expect from their earlier
records, they use here the best and newest editions, namely the grand new set currently being produced
by L'Oiseau-Lyre. As we may also expect, they present the music with remarkable lyricism and
sweetness. In the two-voice organa of the *Magnus liber*, generally thought the work of Léonin, they
sing with such refined intonation that the music is irresistible. For the three-voice organa of the
"School of Pérotin" they magnificently succeed in the most important task, which is to make the
lilting triple rhythms fluid, whereas they can so easily sound joggy and meaningless. But their finest

achievement is in what must count as the grandest and most difficult piece in this entire repertory, the enormous four-voice *Sederunt principes* of Pérotin. The work is quite exceptionally minimalist in its restraint, its gentle onward flow, its almost obsessive concentration on a very small number of chords, its glorious canvases generated from so little material. Here the suave approach of the Orlandos brings the very best results, and it makes the recording required listening for anybody who loves this music. The intervening monophonic sections, and the separate chants, are performed by men and boys from the Westminster Cathedral Choir in an extreme equalist manner – that is, not just giving every note absolutely equal length but also making each note equally important. They actively resist any temptation to make the melodies flow or take on any subjective shape. Some listeners may find this extreme position fascinating, though it is not easy to understand how anybody could gain any aesthetic satisfaction from it. But the wonders of the CD are such that these are easily skipped in favour of the glorious singing of the Orlando in the polyphony.

Campus Stellae Twelfth-Century Pilgrims' Songs. **Discantus / Brigitte Lesne.**
Opus 111 Ⓕ OPS30-102 (69 minutes: DDD: 7/95). Recorded 1994.
Tropes of "Benedicamus domino" – Ad superni regis decus; Dies ista celebris; Congaudeant catholici; Dies ista gaudium; Gregis pastor; Mira dies oritur. Conductus motets – Plebs domini; Flore vernans gratie. Prosae – Alleluia ... Gratulemur et letemur; Res est admirabilis; Quam dilecta tabernacula; Clemens servulorum gemitus tuorum. Versi – Uterus hodie virginis floruit; Lilium floruit. Kyrie tropes – Rex immense; Cunctipotens genitor Deus. Judicii signum.
All-female ensembles have hitherto been rather thin on the ground, but following on from Anonymous 4 and the high-voice section of Sequentia, here is Discantus, a ten-member group of sopranos and contraltos, dedicated to breathing new life into the performance of sacred monody and early polyphony. This is an attractive and varied selection of pieces illustrating different aspects of twelfth-century French music, the main sources being two manuscripts from the school of St Martial de Limoges and the *Codex Calixtinus*, or *Liber Sancti Jacobi*, compiled in Burgundy, but relating to the famous pilgrimage to the shrine of St James of Compostela. The work which remains in the memory, after listening with delight to the whole of this absorbing programme, is undoubtedly a piece (from a rather later source) based on the Sibylline Oracles, *Judicii signum*, with its ominous, low-voiced announcement of the Last Judgement. Indeed, the alternation from piece to piece of high and low voices, of solo and choir, of monody and polyphony is adroitly and effectively managed throughout the recital, so that the musical interest of a well-balanced and well-planned programme is sustained. Brigitte Lesne and her singers have learnt how to make repercussion sound discreetly convincing. The cadential ornamentation, sometimes involving a kind of double polyphonic shake, might perhaps have gained from being allowed a little more panache. The vocal timbre is clear and fresh and the whole performance moves along with cheerful confidence.

The Pilgrimage to Santiago New London Consort / Philip Pickett.
L'Oiseau-Lyre Ⓕ 433 148-2OH2 (two discs: 126 minutes: DDD: 7/92). 🎵
Texts and translations included. *Selected by Sounds in Retrospect.*
Including Cantigas de Santa María (collected/composed by Alfonso el Sabio), the seven Cantigas de Amigo by Martin Codax and other medieval vocal and instrumental works from the Codices Las Huelgas and Calixtinus.
In recent years a far higher standard of performance together with more rigorous scholarship has come to be expected from those who choose to perform this kind of repertoire. Philip Pickett has been in the forefront of this impressive rise in confidence (as much about what is not known as is definitely known) as this two-disc set amply demonstrates. What may perhaps be surprising to some is the quality of the music itself. The *Cantigas* remain some of the most enticing melodies ever written, and the New London Consort do them full justice with an array of instrumentalists and singers who are, however, used with discretion. Similarly the moving *Cantigas de Amigo* of Martin Codax are beautifully sung with a restraint that pays expressive dividends, though they do not have quite the transcendent quality of Mara Kiek's recording with Sinfonye ("Bella Domna"; reviewed further on). The polyphonic music from the Las Huelgas and Calixtinus manuscripts completes, with a flourish, the survey tied together by the Santiago label. If there is early polyphony that sounds fresher than the four-part *Belial vocatur*, for example, it has yet to be recorded. In addition to polyphonic works of various genres, Pickett has also chosen to record the four *planctus* settings from the Las Huelgas Codex: moving in themselves, they are valuable pieces also for their historical associations.

Vox Iberica I Sons of Thunder. **Sequentia / Benjamin Bagby, Barbara Thornton.**
Deutsche Harmonia Mundi Ⓕ RD77199 (74 minutes: DDD: 12/92). Texts and translations included. Recorded 1989.
Codex Calixtinus Ad superni regis decus. Alleluia: Vocavit Ihesus Iacobum. Annua gaudia, Iacobe debita. Benedicamus Domino. Congaudeant catholici. Cum vidissent autem. Cunctipotens genitor deus. Dum pater familias. Dum esset. Exultet celi curia. Gratulantes celebremus festum. Huic Iacobo. Iacobe sancte tuum repettio. Iacobi virginei. In hac die laudes cum gaudio. Jocundetur et letetur. Misit Herodes. Nostra phalans. O adiutor. Regi perhennis glorie. Rex immense, pater pie. Vox nostra resonet.

Vox Iberica II Codex Las Huelgas. **Sequentia / Benjamin Bagby, Barbara Thornton.** Deutsche Harmonia Mundi Ⓕ 05472-77238-2 (75 minutes: DDD: 12/92). Texts and translations included. Recorded 1989.
Codex Las Huelgas Audi, pontus. Ave Maria, gracia plena. Benedicamus Domino cum cantico. Benedicamus: Hic est enim precursor. Benedicamus virgini matri. Casta catholica. Catholicorum concio. Ex illustri. Fa fa mi fa/ut re mi ut. In hoc festo gratissimo. Maria, virgo virginum. Mater patris et filia. Mundi dolens de iactura. O gloriosa Dei genitrix. O, plangant nostri prelati. O plena gracia. Psallat chorus in novo carmina. Qui nos fecit ex nichilo. Resurgentis Domini. Salve regina glorie. Stabat iuxta Christi crucem. Verbum patris hodie. Virgo sidus aureum. Four Planctus – Plange Castella misera; Quis dabit meo aquam; Rex obiit et labitur Castelle gloria; O monialis concio Burgensis.

Vox Iberica III Cantigas de Santa Maria. **Sequentia / Benjamin Bagby, Barbara Thornton.** Deutsche Harmonia Mundi Ⓕ 05472-77173-2 (78 minutes: DDD: 12/92). Texts and translations included. Recorded 1989.
Alfonso el Sabio Por nos, Virgen Madre. Como o nome da Virgen. Sobelos fondos do mar. Nenbre-sse-e, Madre de. Dized', ai trobadores. Maldito seja quen non loara. Quantos me creveren loaran. Quen bõa dona querrá. Pero que seja a gente. Santa Maria, strela do dia. Pois que Deus quis da Virgen. Macar poucos cantares acabei e con son. En todo logar á poder. **Riquier** Humils, forfaitz, repres e penedens. **Anonymous Thirteenth Century** Kharajas – Que faray, mamma?; Meu sidi Ibrahim; Gar si yes devina; Gardi vos ay yermanellas.

These three generously-filled discs provide a fascinating insight into Spain between the twelfth and fourteenth centuries. The country's history and culture as encompassed in the texts and music of the three repertories recorded is brought to life by Sequentia with all the immediacy of an illuminated miniature in a mediaeval manuscript. The music comes from three famous Spanish mediaeval manuscripts – the Las Huelgas manuscript, the Codex Calixtinus, and the collection of Cantigas de Santa María compiled at the court of King Alfonso "El Sabio" of Castile. What strikes one immediately is the freshness and imagination of virtually every piece here recorded. Sequentia's performances are commensurate with these qualities – listen, for example, to the magical textures of the women's choir singing *Sobelos fondos do mar* from the Cantigas collection, or the robust, steely harmony projected by the men in the organa from the Calixtinus manuscript. Surely one of the most remarkable pieces of the Middle Ages is the enormous *Virgo sidus aureum*, a prosa *"de Sancta Maria"* lasting over 14 minutes, whose text is a radiant mystical contemplation of the Mother of God. Liturgico-poetic parallels for it may well be sought in the East rather than the West – the Greek *Akathist* hymn from several centuries earlier, for example – but if Hildegard of Bingen, the "feather on the breath of God" is brought to mind, that would also be no surprise. It must be said that the poetic quality of all three of these collections is so high that the music could hardly fail to be of the same level of inspiration. This astonishing piece is given a splendid, coherent rendition (no easy task with a monophonic work of this length) by two soloists, female choir and symphonia, and one only has to listen to it after one of the rather shorter three-part conductus, such as *Mundi dolens de iactura*, or one of the powerful *organa* for St James, the "Son of Thunder", from the Calixtinus collection, to gain some idea of the impact and the extent of the variety to be found on these discs. The Cantigas collection convincingly conveys the accomplishments of the court of the king who "while he was pondering the heavens and looking at the stars...lost the earth and his kingdom", and places the Cantiga repertory in the context not only of the troubadours (in particular Guirault Riquier) but also the Mozarabic *kharjas* (or *jarchas*), whose music has been reconstructed, with some success, by Bagby. This testament to the richness of musical life in medieval Spain should not be missed.

Love's Illusion Motets from the Montpellier Codex. **Anonymous 4** (Ruth Cunningham, Marsha Genensky, Susan Hellauer, Johanna Rose, sngrs). Harmonia Mundi Ⓕ HMU90 7109 (64 minutes: DDD: 12/94). Texts and translations included. Recorded 1992-93.
One could easily imagine that a programme such as this, of 29 thirteenth-century motets, all composed around the same theme of *fin amours* and all sung unaccompanied by an all-female vocal ensemble, might end by becoming wearisome on the ear. Anonymous 4 have proved conclusively in this recording that this need not be so, that, in any case, there is already an infinite variety of mood and style among the songs and that it is possible further to vary them in performance, using no other means than the voices themselves. The directness of the group's approach is always refreshing: their tone is unaffected, their pitch secure. The songs are presented with simplicity in a clear acoustic. There is a total absence of any improvised doodling on reconstructed medieval instruments, which is rather a relief. One gets a sense of quiet satisfaction and enjoyment from the singers themselves, also the feeling that the singers are trying to teach us something about the music, the mechanics of the motet and how it works, almost as if they were demonstrating to a class of music students. They sometimes go out of their way to sing a single part and then to repeat it with another part added, and then finally to give us a polished rendering of the whole motet, complete with all its parts. Occasionally they add a drone – once with a doubling at the fifth above. The insert-notes are clear and informative.

The Spirits of England and France, Volume 1. **Gothic Voices) / Christopher Page;** [a]**Pavlo Beznosiuk** (medieval fiddle). Hyperion Ⓕ CDA66739 (63 minutes: DDD: 2/95). Texts and translations included. Recorded 1994.

The fourteenth and fifteenth centuries – **Anonymous** Quant la douce jouvencelle. En cest mois de May. Laus detur multipharia. Credo. La uitime estampie real^a. **J. Cooke** Gloria. **M. da Perugia** Belle sans per. **Machaut** Ay mi! dame de valour. **Pykini** Plaisance, or tost. *The twelfth and thirteenth centuries* – **Anonymous** Deduc, Syon, uberrimas. Je ne puis/Par un matin/Le premier jor/Iustus. Beata nobis gaudia. Virgo plena gratie/Virgo plena gratie/Virgo. Crucifigat omnes. Flos in monte cernitur. In Rama sonat gemitus. Ave Maria. La septime estampie real^a. La quarte estampie real^a. **Pérotin** (attrib.) Presul nostri temporis.
From the beautifully swift and unsentimental reading of the opening song, *Quant la douce jouvencelle*, through to the magically perfumed close with what Page calls the "irredeemably English style" of *Ave Maria*, each piece has its own musical excellence. In the works of around 1400 it is usually Rogers Covey-Crump who leads the singing, with a skilled and nuanced grasp of the style that seems to grow with each recording: long may his career continue. For the earlier works the spoils are divided between Paul Agnew, Julian Podger, Andrew Tusa and Leigh Nixon, all tenors with spirit and individuality. Finally, as an innovation in Gothic Voices recordings, Pavlo Beznosiuk plays three *estampes* on the medieval fiddle, without percussion and without any embellishment or deviation from the notes of their single surviving manuscript. While not everybody will be happy about this literal attitude to the problem of early instrumental music, Beznosiuk's playing is so rhythmically alive and so irresistible as to justify the approach. Once again, then, a superb recording from Gothic Voices; one that raises questions, that stimulates, that charms.

Worcester Fragments English Sacred Music of the Late Middle Ages. **Orlando Consort** (Robert Harre-Jones, alto; Charles Daniels, Angus Smith, tens; Donald Grieg, bar). Amon Ra Ⓔ CD-SAR59 (58 minutes: DDD: 8/93). Texts and translations included. Recorded 1992.
In this recording the Orlando Consort provide the listener with the chance to gain an overall impression of how music developed in England during the thirteenth and early fourteenth centuries – a development distinguished by its intriguing variety, creativity and undoubted beauty, its peculiar sweetness being marked by the constant harmonic use of the interval of a third. The Orlando Consort manage to achieve a balance between the type of buzzing vocal timbre, believed to have been that of the Middle Ages with its roughness of approach, and their own good solid modern standards of professional musicianship. The Consort also attempt to reproduce what scholars now believe to have been the way in which ecclesiastical Latin was pronounced in medieval England.

Bella Domna The Medieval Woman: Lover, Poet, Patroness and Saint. **Sinfonye** (Mara Kiek, voc; Andrew Lawrence-King, medieval hp; Jim Denley, perc) / **Stevie Wishart** (medieval fiddle, symphony). Hyperion Ⓔ CDA66283 (60 minutes: DDD: 6/88). 🗲 Texts and translations included.
    Martin Codax Cantigas de Amigo. **Anonymous Thirteenth Century** Domna, pos vos ay chausida. Estampies Royals – No. 3; No. 4; No. 6. Danse Royale. **de Fournival** Onques n'amai tant que jou fui amee. **La Comtesse de Die** A chantar m'er de so qu'ieu non volria.
    Anonymous Fourteenth Century Lasse, pour quoi refusai.   Ⓖ
This intriguing CD collection of medieval songs joined together by the themes of woman as lover, poet, patroness and saint was originally released in 1988 and represented the début of Stevie Wishart's group Sinfonye. The performances of this elusive music have all the freshness and excitement of first encounter. The musical centre stage is held predominantly by the extraordinary vocalist Mara Kiek, whose plaintive as well as idiosyncratic tone ideally matches the distance of the music between its composition and the present day: this is genuinely music from another time and place, with hardly any relationship to the twentieth century at all. Stevie Wishart's playing of the medieval fiddle, used predominantly as a drone instrument and the symphony, a kind of hurdy-gurdy, well matches in its freedom and espressivity Kiek's singing, as does the supportive percussion playing of Jim Denley on two types of medieval drum. The fourth and final member of the group is the harpist Andrew Lawrence-King, whose playing adds tremendous colour to these intriguing recreations of the medieval woman's expression of emotions such as betrayal and violation. The harshness as well as vigour of the medieval era is powerfully recreated in these performances. Hyperion's recording is appropriately neutral, catching at times some of the claustrophobia of the emotions expressed in the music. An extremely interesting recital of music unlikely to be encountered elsewhere.

Music for the Lion-Hearted King Gothic Voices / Christopher Page. Hyperion Ⓔ CDA66336 (60 minutes: DDD: 10/89). Texts and translations included.
    Anonymous Twelfth Century Mundus vergens. Novus miles sequitur. Sol sub nube latuit. Hac in anni ianua. Anglia, planctus itera. Etras auri reditur. Vetus abit littera. In occasu sideris. Purgator criminum. Pange melos lacrimosum. Ver pacis apperit. Latex silice. **Gace Brulé** A la doucour de la bele seson. **Blondel de Nesle** L'amours dont sui espris. Ma joie me semont.
    Gui IV, "Li chastelain de Couci" Li nouviaz tanz.
Christopher Page has a remarkable gift for creating enthralling programmes of early music bound together by a brilliantly-chosen central theme, or appellation. This collection is no less distinguished and every bit as fascinating, musically and historically. Whether or not Richard himself ever actually listened to any of these pieces is beside the point: they are all representative of the period of his lifetime and are gathered together here in his name for the 800th anniversary of his coronation (1189).

Two types of twelfth-century vocal music are represented: the *conductus* – which can be written for one, two, three or even four voices and the *chanson*, or noble, courtly love song. The singers cannot be applauded too highly for performances marked by an extraordinary insight into how this music should be tackled, that is, with a fair degree of restraint as well as know-how, given the sort of audience it might have had in Richard's day: the royal court or the household of some high-ranking ecclesiastical figure.

Le Jeu d'Amour The Game of Love in Medieval France. **Anne Azéma** (sop/spkr); **vocal and instrumental ensemble** (Noël Bisson, Catherine Jousselin, Ellen Santaniello, sngrs; Shira Kammen, rebec/vielle/hp; Margriet Tindemans, vielle/cittern/hp; Robert Mealy, vielle/hp; John Fleagle, ten/bagpipes/hp; Jesse Lepkoff, rec/fl). Erato Ⓕ 0630-17072-2 (60 minutes: DDD: 12/97).
  ✍ Texts and translations included. Recorded 1996.
  Moniot d'Arras Ce fu en mai, au dous tens gai. **Thibault de Champagne** Amour me fait commencier. **Jehannot de l'Escurel** Bien se lace. **Adam de la Halle** Je muir d'amourete. **Guillaume d'Amiens** Je mais ne serai saous. Prendés i garde. **Guillaume le Vinier** Pastourelle: Valuru, valuraine. **Muset** En mai, quant li rossignolet. **Anonymous** L'on dit qu'amors est dolce chose. Lai del Kievrefuel. Caroles on "La verte olive" – La jus desous la verte olive; C'est desoz l'olive; C'est la jus par dessous l'olive. Prennés i garde. Margot, Margot grief sunt li mau d'amer. Trois serors sor rive mer. En un vergier. Tuit cil qui sunt enamourat.
  Jean de Flagy Et tous les gens. **Guillaume de Dole** Main à main.
This recital of courtly songs and dances is drawn from the repertoire of the trouvères of Northern France, with named composers such as Colin Muset, Thibault de Champagne and Adam de la Halle, but also a host of other musicians of whom we can only catch glimpses through their music. Anne Azéma is herself responsible for the research, the selection, the transcriptions and their interpretation. She is also the prime performer, singing and declaiming with her customary verve and spirited delivery. Her pronunciation of the courtly French in the spoken items is quite delightful and her vocal timbre, with its lively edge, is always appealing. She sings of the courtly game of love, with its rules and sophistication, but also of the more unruly pastoral delights of May Day celebrations, the "caroles" and "rondels". One of the most stunning pieces is the fully developed *Lai del Kievrefuel* – the *Lay of the Honeysuckle*, traditionally the love-song composed by Tristan for Isolde and so-called because no plant in the woodland is sweeter or more fragrant. It begins with a long instrumental introduction, followed by fiery, passionate singing and one section comes across as hoarse semi-speech. Instruments – fiddles, rebec, flute, recorder, harp – play a large part, both independently, as introductions or interludes, and as discreet accompaniments, to complement the voice. But there are also a number of unaccompanied songs, and this variety is refreshing. The sound quality is excellent. Delightfully entertaining and instructive.

Chansons de Trouvères **Paul Hillier** (voc); **Andrew Lawrence-King** ([a]psaltery/[b]hp/[c]org).
  Harmonia Mundi Ⓕ HMU90 7184 (70 minutes: DDD: 4/97). Texts and translations included. Recorded 1996.
  Thibaut de Champagne Aussi conme unicorne sui[b]. Deus est ensi conme li pellicanz. Chançon ferai, que talenz m'en est pris[b]. **Gace Brulé** Les oxelés de mon païx[b]. A la douçor de la bele seson[a]. **Moniot d'Arras** Ce fu en mai[a]. **Colin Muset** En mai, quant li rossignolez[c]. **Anonymous** Volez vous que je vous chant[a]. Quant voi la flor nouvele[a].
The repertoire of *trouvère* songs is one "we are only now beginning to explore" writes Margaret Switten. Here we have an enlightened and well-chosen selection, sensitively presented and delightfully sung by Paul Hillier with insight and feeling. The main object of the poets' attention is *fin'amor*, but other themes, including the return of spring (*Volez vous que je vous chant* and *En mai, quant li rossignolez*), make their joyful appearance, and there is one piece in a completely different vein, a serious piece of religious polemics: *Deus est ensi conme li pellicanz*. The melodies, simple and stanzaic, are of great beauty. Outstanding in this respect is Gace Brulé's *A la douçor de la bele seson*. Many are modal (Dorian) and a few share a well-known opening phrase with a Gregorian *melodie-type* that Andrew Lawrence-King has made much use of in his accompaniments. His own contribution is momentous: if the manner in which these songs were originally performed still remains a mystery for the singer, it is even more of an enigma for the accompanist. But Andrew Lawrence-King has taken the word *trouvère* to heart: he is a true 'finder'. His empathy with text, music and singer is total: he 'invents' with a sure touch, and it is not going too far to say it is a touch of genius.

The Courts of Love Music from the time of Eleanor of Aquitaine. **Sinfonye** (Mara Kiek, voc; Andrew Lawrence-King, medieval hp; Jim Denley, perc) / **Stevie Wishart**.
  Hyperion Ⓕ CDA66367 (64 minutes: DDD: 8/90). ✍ Texts and translations included.
  Gui d'Ussel Si be'm partetz, mala domna, de vos. **Raimbaut de Vaqeiras** Calenda maya (vocal and instrumental versions). **Anonymous Twelfth Century** L'on qui dit q'amors est dolce chose. **Bernart de Ventadorn** Ara'm conseillatz seignor. Conartz, ara sai au be. Quan vei la lauzeta mover. **Cadenet** S'anc fuy belha ni prezada (vocal and instrumental versions). **Giraut de Bornelh** S'ie'us queir conseil, bel' amig' Alamanda. **Gace Brulé** Quant je voi la noif remise. Quant voi le tens bel et cler. Quant flours et glais et verdues s'esloigne. Quant li tens reverdoie.

This recital consists of songs and instrumental pieces dating from the end of the twelfth century and derived from the "courts of love" of Aquitaine, Champagne, Flanders and elsewhere. These courts, created around aristocratic figures such as Marie of Champagne and Eleanor of Aquitaine, were essentially a charade of the medieval law courts, to which lovers could bring their complaints. Thus the texts of the songs are concerned with the dilemmas of infidelity, betrayal and unrequited love. All that survives of this music is melodies for singing: these have been sensitively arranged by Stevie Wishart for a small selection of medieval instruments, including the symphony, a sort of hurdy-gurdy, medieval fiddles, lutes and percussion. All the players of Sinfonye are both expert and relaxed, projecting the music with great character. Six of the pieces are sung by Mara Kiek with considerable feeling: her unusual voice production and tone help to give a sense of 'distance' to the performances, and throughout strike a suitably plaintive note. Hyperion's recording catches all the vocal and instrumental inflexions with great fidelity and a most natural sense of balance. All in all, a fascinating glimpse of music and manners from a remote if influential corner of medieval civilization.

L'Unicorne Medieval French Songs. [a]**Anne Azema** (sop); [b]**Jesse Lepkoff** (fl); [c]**Cheryl Ann Fulton** (hp); [d]**Shira Kammen** (vielle/rebec/hp). Erato Ⓕ 4509-94830-2 (57 minutes: DDD: 11/94). 🎵 Texts and translations included. Recorded 1993.
Philippe de Thaon Serena en mer hante[acd]. Monosceros[ad]. **Anonymous** En mai au douz tens nouvel[abc]. Ensement com la panthere[abc]. Au renouvel[bcd]. Bele Doette[ab]. **Marie de France** Issi avint qu'un cers[ad]. D'un gupil[ad]. La danse de gupil[d]. **Thibault de Champagne** Aussi come unicorne sui[ad]. **Gauthier de Coincy** Le Cycle de Sainte Leochade[abcd]. **Moniot de Paris** Je chevauchoie l'autrier[acd].

Anne Azema always seems to bring a breath of fresh air to whatever she does, whether reading or singing. Here she is singing of springtime and love, of beasts and miracles, of a woman's grief but also of her joy. The melodies, often unforgettable in their simplicity, are interpreted with tenderness and quiet understanding. Many are ravishingly beautiful, in particular those describing the panther and the unicorn and also several of the songs from the *Cycle de Sainte Leocadie* in Gauthier de Coincy's *Miracles of Our Lady*. One of the finest songs in the programme is the thirteenth-century *Bele Doette*, a saga of grief experienced by a noble lady on hearing the news of her beloved's untimely death during the jousting. Azema's control of the slow rhythm and deepening emotion is total, and she matches this with perfection, as the story unfolds, in her singing of the short sad refrain that ends each strophe. The occasional instrumental interludes, for example *D'un gupil* ("The fox's dance") or *Au renouvel* provide graceful linkage between songs and readings; the accompaniments are generally discreet and understated, though the flute comes into its own in one song – *En mai au douz tens nouvel* – with its charming imitations of birdsong.

Canticum Canticorum The sacred symbol of love in the medieval musical tradition.
Ensemble Cantilena Antiqua / Stefano Albarello (alto). Symphonia Ⓕ SY95135 (72 minutes: DDD: 2/98).
This intriguing collection of music on the Song of Solomon includes not only twelfth- and thirteenth-century Western monody and polyphony, but also Hebrew, Sephardic and Maronite melodies. The performances blend voices and instruments in a manner much favoured by Italian ensembles today; there is some fine singing, that of the countertenor Stefano Albarello being particularly striking. Text and documentation are intelligently and stylishly presented.

The Spirits of England and France, Volume 2. **Gothic Voices** (Emma Kirkby, sop; Margaret Philpot, mez; Rogers Covey-Crump, Leigh Nixon, tens; Henry Wickham, bar) / **Christopher Page** (medieval lte) with **Robert White** (bagpipes); **Nick Bicat** (perc); **Pavlo Beznosiuk** (fiddle). Hyperion Ⓕ CDA66773 (62 minutes: DDD: 8/95). Texts and translations included. Ⓖ
Songs of the Trouvères – **Richart de Semilli** Je chevauchai. **Gace Brulé** Desconfortez, plains de dolor. Quant define fueille et flor. De bien amer grant joie atent. Cil qui d'amours. **Gontier de Soignies** Dolerousement commence. **Guibert Kaukesel** Un chant novel. Fins cuers enamourés. **Gautier de Dargies** La doce pensee. **Adam de la Halle** Assenés chi, Grievilier. **Ernoul li Vielle** Por conforter mon corage. **Audefroi le Bastart** Au novel tens pascor. **Anonymous** Domna pos vos ay chausida. Quant voi la fleur nouvele. Amors m'art con fuoc am flamma. Trois Estampies.
This is a disc devoted to monophonic song and one of startling power and originality. Essentially it explores two repertories: the serious *grand chant*, particularly in the work of Gace Brulé, whose four songs here are presented with tremendous conviction and in wonderfully spacious readings; and the lighter dance songs, where Page often includes instruments, played with robust good humour. As regards the rhythmic approach, this is neatly varied to match the needs of particular songs: sometimes an equalist interpretation, sometimes syllabic, and sometimes in strict metre roughly derived from the principles of modal rhythm. That seems a thoroughly judicious and musical solution, and it gives the disc considerable variety of pace. Margaret Philpot shows her astonishing stylistic range in the five songs she sings, from Richart de Semilli's jovial *Je chevauchai* via Gace Brulé's wonderful *De bien amer* and concluding with *Au novel tens pascor*, the late *chanson de toile* by Audefroi le Bastart. Emma Kirkby makes a welcome return to Gothic Voices with two glorious performances: her success in later

music has been so great over the last few years that it has been too easy to forget quite how expressive she can be in early monophony, especially with Page's rattling folk-style lute playing in *Domna pos vos ay chausida*. Beyond these it is particularly good that the disc includes a *descort* – that fascinating but undervalued genre – and a *jeu-parti*. Once again Gothic Voices have produced a record that sets new standards.

The Marriage of Heaven and Hell Thirteenth-Century French Motets and Songs. **Gothic Voices / Christopher Page.** Hyperion Ⓟ CDA66423 (46 minutes: DDD: 12/90). Texts and translations included.

Anonymous Je ne chant pas. Talens m'est pris. Trois sereurs/Trois sereurs/Trois sereurs. Plus bele que flors/Quant revient/L'autrier jouer. Par un martinet/Hé, sire!/Hé, bergier! De la virge Katerine/Quant froidure/Agmina milicie. Ave parens/Ad gratie. Super te Jerusalem/Sed fulsit virginitas. A vous douce debonnaire. Mout souvent/Mout ai esté en doulour. Quant voi l'aloete/Dieux! je ne m'en partiré ja. En non Dieu/Quant voi la rose. Je m'en vois/Tels a mout. Festa januaria. **Blondel de Nesle** En tous tans que vente bise. **Colin Muset** Trop volontiers chanteroie. **Bernart de Ventadorn** Can vei la lauzeta mover. **Gautier de Dargies** Autre que je ne seuill fas.

The reasons for the dazzling success of Gothic Voices both in the recording studio and in the concert-hall are once again evident in this collection. It is both an entertaining and well-planned recital and, if one chooses to take it that way, reading Christopher Page's insert-notes while listening, a detailed lecture-recital. The music, all French and dating from the thirteenth century, is that seemingly impenetrable repertoire of polytextual motets, unexpectedly compared and contrasted with monophonic trouvère songs. The comparison is illuminating, and the performances of both genres of music are up to Gothic Voices' usual high standards: intonation is perfect, textures are finely balanced, the performances are always conceived just as much melodically as harmonically, and the greatest respect is always paid to the words (even when there are three texts at the same time, as is often the case here!). The clever juxtaposition of the trouvère Bernart de Ventadorn's *Can vei la lauzeta mover* with the triple-texted motet *Quant voi l'aloete/Dieux! je ne m'en partiré ja/NEUMA* encapsulates the thinking behind this recording: a compelling musical experience and a provocative intellectual one.

The Study of Love French Songs and Motets of the Fourteenth Century. **Gothic Voices / Christopher Page.** Hyperion Ⓟ CDA66619 (60 minutes: DDD: 6/93). Texts and translations included. Recorded 1992. Ⓖ

Machaut Dame, je suis cilz/Fins cuer. Trop plus/Biauté paree/Je ne suis. Tres bonne et belle. Se mesdisans. Dame, je vueil endurer. **Pycard** Gloria. **Solage** Le basile. **Anonymous** Pour vous servir. Puis que l'aloe ne fine. Jour a jour la vie. Combien que j'aye (two versions). Marticius qui fu. Renouveler me feïst. Fist on dame. Il me convient guerpir. Le ior. En la maison Dedalus. La grant biaute. En esperent. Ay las! quant je pans.

The title of the disc speaks of the ways in which the discourses of love (and 'love') in the late Middle Ages are partly, perhaps largely, derived from books – the Bible, classical poetry and myths, the earlier medieval literary tradition – rather than some expression of unmediated personal feeling. But music was a powerful means for the late medieval artist to attempt to transcend the bookish intertextualities of the literary texts. Rarely have Gothic Voices, both as individuals and as a group, sounded more alive and present. The accord of vowel colour between the singers in some of the fully texted pieces is marvellous, a feature pointed up the more by juxtaposition with those works in which Page continues his experiments with lower-voice vocalization. Where some slight untidiness creeps in, the impression often (though not invariably) given is the positive one of risk being happily taken in the recording sessions, the very absence of which has so often been the downfall of lesser groups (and not just in medieval music). A wonderful addition to the catalogue, and the recorded sound is superlative.

Lancaster and Valois French and English Music, 1350-1420. **Gothic Voices** (Margaret Philpot, contr. Rogers Covey-Crump, Andrew Tusa, Charles Daniels, Leigh Nixon, tens; Stephen Charlesworth, Donald Grieg, bars; Andrew Lawrence-King, hp) / **Christopher Page** (lte). Hyperion Ⓟ CDA66588 (59 minutes: DDD: 9/92). Texts and translations included. Recorded 1991.

Machaut Donnez, signeurs. Quand je ne voy ma dame. Riches d'amour et mendians. Pas de tor en thies pais. **Solage** Tres gentil cuer. **Cesaris** Se vous scaviez, ma tres douce maistresse. Mon seul voloir/Certes m'amour. **Cordier** Ce jur de l'an. **Pycard** Credo. **Sturgeon** Salve mater domini/Salve templum domini. **Fonteyns** Regali ex progenie. **Anonymous** Puis qu'autrement ne puis avoir. Soit tart, tempre, main ou soir. Le ior. Avrai je ja de ma dame confort? Sanctus. Je vueil vivre au plaisir d'amours.

This is the tenth recording to come from Christopher Page's Gothic Voices and, the considerable success of their previous recordings notwithstanding, this is perhaps their best yet. In the space of 11 years, Page and his group have reinvented performance practice in medieval and fifteenth century music, as powerful and popularizing an influence as David Munrow and his Early Music Consort of London in the 1970s. "Lancaster and Valois" takes its name from the chosen repertoire: French secular songs of the late fourteenth and early fifteenth centuries juxtaposed with sacred English pieces from around 1400. Much thought has been given to the ordering of the pieces and the grouping of the voices, resulting in the greatest possible diversity. In *Tres gentil cuer* by Solage, Page sets an ideally lilting tempo, with the text finely enunciated by Margaret Philpot, the tenors (in this instance Charles Daniels and Leigh Nixon) adding definition but never threatening to engulf. This is followed by a *Credo* by the English composer Pycard, the longest and most stately piece on the disc, exploiting the richer timbres of tenors and baritones. With excellent sound and entertaining and scholarly notes by Christopher Page (the like of which also regularly inform his spoken interjections in concerts), this is an irresistible disc.

Balades a III chans Ferrara Ensemble / Crawford Young. Arcana Ⓟ A32
(59 minutes: DDD: 1/96). 🎵 Texts and translations included. Recorded 1994.   Ⓖ
Trebor Helas pitié envers moy dort si fort. Si Alexandre et Hector fussent en vie. **Cordier** Tout par compas suy composés. **Matteo da Perugia** Rondeau-refrain. Pres du soloil deduissant s'esbanoye. **Antonius de Civitate** Io vegio per stasone. **Grimace** Se Zephirus, Phebus et leur lignie. **Anonymous** Adieu vous di, tres doulce compaynie. Lamech Judith et Rachel de plourer. Le mont Aon de Thrace.
The *ballade*, that noblest form (in every sense) of fourteenth century secular music, was meant to honour the dukes and counts who did so much to foster the fine arts while war, famine and plague raged round them. Their musical protégés were by all accounts a slightly surreal bunch, dedicated seekers-out of weirdness, addicted to the bottle – possibly even to hashish. Small wonder that so much of their music seems hopelessly capricious on the page. Crawford Young's special achievement is to demonstrate what many enthusiasts of *Ars subtilior* have felt all along. In performance, that wilful strangeness can suddenly come across with astonishing naturalness: all it takes is the right singers, and here they are. Or perhaps that last sentence should read: "here she is". It is no slight on the other members of the Ferrara Ensemble to say that the mezzo-soprano, Lena Susanne Norin, steals the show. Her singing can only be described as luscious. True, the quality of these performances is partly a matter of direction. Tempo is of the first importance because it determines the specific gravity of the dissonances. Pitched too slow, the phrases are weighed down by them; too fast, and the dissonances are trivialized. Beyond that, however, the sensitivity to these details is down to Norin herself. This fierce-looking music, once tamed, becomes almost unbelievably sensuous. The tone of the accompanying string instruments is perfectly judged, the sound-recording outstanding – warm and glowing. The presentation of *ballades* is a tricky business: to perform all three stanzas can take well over ten minutes. In the past, singers have tended to confine themselves to just one or two stanzas. That has the advantage of fitting more music into a recital, but aesthetically it makes about as much sense as trimming the tail of a peacock. Young gives all three stanzas of the poem wherever possible, and in so doing he restores the *ballade*'s length, weight, complexity, in a word, the *heroic* intent that is the form's very *raison d'être*. A glorious recital.

Il Solazzo The Newberry Consort / Mary Springfels. Harmonia Mundi Ⓟ HMU90 7038
(62 minutes: DDD: 7/93). 🎵 Texts and translation included. Recorded 1990.   ⒼⒼ
Gramophone Editor's choice.
Anonymous Fourteenth Century Italian La Badessa. Bel fiore danza. Nova stella. Cominciamento di gioia. Trotto. Principe di virtu. **Jacopo da Bologna** Non al suo amante. **Landini** La bionda treccia. Dolce signorie. Donna, s'i, t'o fallito. El gran disio. **Ciconia** O rosa bella. Ligiadra donna. **Zacharo de Teramo** Rosetta. Un fior gentil. **Bartolino da Padova** Alba columba.
If medieval Italian music pales somewhat in comparison to the glories of opera from the nineteenth century onwards, there are still riches to be discovered in this collection of *trecento* vocal and instrumental works. The Chicago-based ensemble, The Newberry Consort, use a mere five performers to provide over an hour of entertainment. This was the era of writers such as Dante, Petrarch, Boccaccio, but also of Simone Prodenzani – the author of a cycle of sonnets entitled *Il Solazzo*, many of which were later set to music. Whilst some of the *Solazzo* texts are presented here in musical form (the scurrilous *La Badessa* is one), Italian ballata from leading composers of the time are also represented – Ciconia's *O rosa bella* and Landini's *La bionda treccia*, for example. The vocal numbers are all taken by mezzo Judith Malafronte and countertenor Drew Minter who clear the hurdles of tricky pronunciation and flamboyantly complex vocal lines to give a thoroughly communicative performance of this wonderful music. Mary Springfels provides elegant and musical direction as well as that essential ingredient to a disc such as this – the informative booklet. If the prospect of an hour of early Italian song sounds daunting, fear not, for the instrumental dances on the disc (especially the anonymous *Cominciamento di gioia*) are played with a vitality that will make you want to jump up and join in! Explorers of the riches from Italian times long gone by need have no qualms when sampling from this lively, superbly performed disc.

Svso in Italia Bella Music from the Courts and Cloisters of Northern Italy. La Reverdie
(Claudia Caffagni, Livia Caffagni, Elisabetta de' Mircovich, Ella de' Mircovich, Doron David Sherwin, Mauro Morini, Claudia Pasetto, sngrs and various instruments).
Arcana Ⓟ A38 (74 minutes: DDD: 9/96). Texts and translations included.

The members of the Italian ensemble La Reverdie all sing and play from a great variety of instruments (lute, harp, vielle, rebec, recorder, *cornetto muto*, percussion) and the repertory covered is similarly broad, ranging from the tenth century to the fifteenth. Most groups (especially Anglo-Saxon ones) tend to concentrate each programme on one period or genre, and from that standpoint La Reverdie could almost be accused of profligacy; on the other hand, the range of approaches is matched by their dexterity in handling them. Purely instrumental items are dispatched with relish, two- or three-voice madrigals are finely poised between lyricism and sprightliness, even the odd four-voice Latin motet doesn't feel out of place. The singing has an unselfconscious spontaneity about it, straight, agile and light. That probably accounts for the hint of diffidence in handling extreme registers, but in any case Italian musicians aren't and never have been interested in the sort of 24-carat polish of Anglo-Saxon groups. It is the range of achievement that is impressive here, and while some tracks are bound to set the purists' teeth on edge, those who associate medieval repertories with 'monk music' or wall-to-wall polyphony will find a welcome antidote here. The recording enhances the lightness and variety of scoring. All in all, a disc like one of those well-made light and sparkling wines from Northern Italy. Cheers!

Red Iris Instrumental music from fourteenth-century Italy – Istampite – Trotto; Tre Fontane; Principio di virtu; La manfredina and la rotta; Chominciamento di gioa; Palamento; Two Salterellos; Belicha. **Sinfonye** (Stevie Wishart, medieval fiddle/hurdy-gurdy/dir; Jim Denley, Pedro Estevan, perc). Glossa ℗ GCD920701 (53 minutes: DDD: 12/97). 🖉 Interactive CD. Recorded 1996.

Many people have recorded the fourteenth-century instrumental dances that appear only in a single manuscript now in London. Apart from some pieces apparently for keyboard, they are almost the only known early works for a solo melody instrument. The nine pieces (out of a total of 15) presented here offer no repertorial novelty. What is new is the way Stevie Wishart plays them. She views the shorter pieces as dances, to be performed with percussion accompaniment. This is common enough, though they are done extremely well, with Jim Denley and Pedro Estevan producing a stunning range of sounds from their various percussion instruments. But the longer ones are treated as elaborate and weaving instrumental solos, without any accompaniment. Stevie Wishart plays them on the vielle and, in one case, on the hurdy-gurdy, never rushing, never tempted to gloss over the many unexpected details in the lines. This kind of approach seems extremely productive: it stresses the sheer quality and inventiveness of the melodies, and it perhaps aligns them with their true historical context, the repertory of long monophonic *lais* from the fourteenth century. That in its turn somehow makes the pieces considerably more than virtuoso showpieces. But it says much for the power of Stevie Wishart's playing that she keeps the music constantly interesting (one of the pieces lasts over ten minutes) and is invariably persuasive. The disc comes with a CD-ROM track that portrays, among other things, frescoes of the time, the instruments and the manuscript. But even without that this is a superbly convincing performance, recorded with a nice full sound and giving relatively familiar music an added intellectual depth.

Music from a Prague Manuscript, c1500 Codex Speciálník – excerpts. **Hilliard Ensemble** (David James, alto; Rogers Covey-Crump, John Potter, tens; Gordon Jones, bass). ECM New Series ℗ 447 807-2 (77 minutes: DDD: 9/95). Texts and translations included. Recorded 1993.
The Hilliard Ensemble have been developing a knack for innovative programming. The idea behind their previous release, "Officium" (also on ECM) was unquestionably odd, whatever one thinks of the finished product. For this offering, the Hilliard go back to what they do best, the singing of early polyphony. A few years ago they devoted an entire CD to music from a single source, the Old Hall Manuscript. In terms of renown, the Codex Speciálník isn't a patch on Old Hall, but among musicologists it is notorious as one of the most unusual polyphonic sources in existence. Speciálník was copied in Prague c1500. Between its covers are some of the strangest bedfellows in medieval music: early-fifteenth-century local Czech composers rub shoulders with those of the Old Hall period (c1420) and others later still, including the generation active when the manuscript was copied. If this bizarre jumble reflects the musical tastes of the Prague congregation, then they were possessed of a rare degree of eclecticism. Nowadays, we jump from Perotin to Parry without a second thought, but even so, the differences in style are striking. There is something very touching about the Czech pieces in the collection, rough-hewn and jagged as they often are (they seem old-fashioned even by fourteenth-century standards); and some of the slightly later pieces (such as the jolly *In natali Domini*) have an unmistakably local, almost folksy flavour. A really fascinating collection, then, and one that should please all the constituents of the Hilliard's multifarious following. Although not always exempt from the criticism of uniformity that has sometimes been levelled at this ensemble, the best of these performances must count among their finest.

The Spirits of England and France, Volume 3. **Gothic Voices / Christopher Page.** Hyperion ℗ CDA66783 (67 minutes: DDD: 1/96). Texts and translations included. Recorded 1995.
Anonymous Abide, I hope it be the best. Exultavit cor in Domino. **Binchois** Qui veut mesdire si mesdie. Amoureux suy et me vient toute joye. Adieu mon amoureuse joye. Ay douloureux disant helas. Magnificat secundi toni. Se la belle n'a le voloir. **Bittering** En Katerina

solennia/Virginalis concio/Sponsus amat sponsum. **Cardot** Pour une fois et pour toute.
Dunstable Beata Dei genitrix. **Fontaine** J'ayme bien celui. **Johannes de Lymburga**
Descendi in ortum meum. **Legrant** Se liesse. **Machaut** Il m'est avis qu'il n'est. **Power** Gloria.
Velut Lassies ester vostres chans de liesse. Un petit oyselet chantant.

Gothic Voices continue their long-term exploration of early English and French polyphony with an offering devoted to the work of Binchois and his musical forebears of both 'nationalities'. Consistent with the ensemble's usual approach to this repertoire, voices and instruments are not mixed; instead, Christopher Page is joined by the lutenists Christopher Wilson and Shirley Rumsey in energetic renderings of several of the songs: light, and delightful, relief. The songs of Binchois are relatively late territory for Gothic Voices. It has been 12 years or so – in "The Castle of Fair Welcome" (on Hyperion) – since they covered this repertoire in any depth (who can forget the chilly pathos of *Dueil angoisseus*?), and comparison with the present disc is instructive. Over the years there have been more, and deeper, men's voices; the hard-edged, polished chrome patina has perhaps mellowed and burnished with time. Perhaps, too, the almost obsessive concern with clarity and intonation has been allowed to ease a little, in favour of a heightened sensitivity to the affective projection of both text and music. Perhaps, but only just. The hard edge creeps back in when the programme strays from Binchois back on to earlier repertory, such as Power's marvellous five-voice *Gloria* – here portrayed as an exercise in risk-taking for composer and singers alike. Its brashness, though glorious to listen to, leads to an inevitable query, for there seem to be not one but two programmes here. Binchois's songs, characterized by their restraint and understatement, seem uneasy in the company of so many of his exuberant contemporaries and immediate predecessors (and the not-so-immediate – what is Machaut doing here?). The singers do their utmost to reflect the difference in tone, but that only makes the discrepancy more telling. This is a pity, for the Binchois pieces are finely pitched, and deserved to have more space to themselves – more space also for the singers to acclimatize themselves to Binchois's languorous melancholy. Page knows a show-stopper when he hears one, and the haunted *Ay, douloureux*, clocking in at nearly nine minutes, stands out from other items in the collection like a hothouse plant. That is not meant to belittle the rest, but to suggest that, as a programme, this particular collection is perhaps not as well rounded as so many of its predecessors: the sum of its parts. And yet there is so much that is deeply moving and magical that anything less than a warm recommendation would be positively Scrooge-like.

Virtue and Vice German Secular Songs and Instrumental music from the time of Luther.
Convivium Musicum; Villanella Ensemble / Sven Berger. Naxos Ⓢ 8 553352 (70 minutes: DDD: 1/96). ☞ Texts and translations included. Recorded 1994. *Gramophone Editor's choice.* Ⓖ
Isaac Carmen. In meinem Sinn (three versions). Greiner, zancker, schnöpffitzer. Mein Freud allein. Ich stund an einem Morgen. La mi la sol. Las rauschen. **Obrecht** Tsat een meskin.
Senfl Will niemand singen. Ein Maidlein zue dem Brunnen ging. Dort oben auf dem Berge.
Nun wöllt ihr hören neue Mär. Ich soll und müess ein'n Büehlen haben. Oho, so geb' der Mann.
Es wollt' ein Maidlein Wasser hol'n. Es wollt' ein Frau zuem Weine gahn. Lamentatio. Ich stuend an einem Morgen. Albrecht mirs schwer. Ich weiss nit was er ihr verheiss (two versions).
Hofhaimer Erst weis ich was die Liebe ist. Greyner, Zanner. Mein eynigs A (two versions).
Zucht eer und lob. **Anonymous** Zenner greyner. **Heinrich Finck** Greiner Zanner. Gloria laus.
Ammerbach Die Megdlein sind von Flandern. **A. Bruck** So trinken wir alle. Es ging ein Landsknecht. **Küffer** Heth sold ein meisken garn om win. **G. Meyer** Bicinium germanicum.
Rhau Ich stuend an einem Morgen.

The programme here is very generous, yet it consists of works lasting no more than three minutes apiece. That it manages in spite of this to be both coherent and immediately appealing speaks volumes for its virtues. In Sven Berger's selection, the Franco-Flemish mainstream is chiefly represented by Heinrich Isaac and his pupil Ludwig Senfl, though both are clearly writing in a Germanic vein. That vein appears not to share the Italian concern with instrumental virtuosity: most of the non-vocal pieces are obviously designed for dancing. Nor are there any of the lovelorn texts familiar from the neighbouring Latin cultures. It is all country bumpkins and buxom wenches, yet the coarser obscenities found in French *chansons* are scrupulously avoided. One song simply declaims a list of herbs whose specific properties are left to the listener's sagacity. A variety of instrumental approaches is on offer, including a solo clavichord, a mixed consort of flutes and fiddles, or quartets of high instruments drawn from shawms, crumhorns, sackbuts, dulcians and curtal (a primitive bassoon). Barring the odd fluff, these wind instruments are played with tremendous verve and careful intonation. The players of Convivium Musicum occasionally lend their voices to the proceedings, but the vocal palm goes to the singers of the Villanella Ensemble. Purists may wish to query the use of a modern guitar on what is obviously a period instrument disc, but the combination of that instrument with two women's voices and a recorder will come as a revelation. A super-bargain in every way.

The Art of the Netherlands Early Music Consort of London / **David Munrow.** Virgin Classics Veritas Ⓜ VED5 61334-2 (two discs: 132 minutes: ADD: 11/97). Texts and translations included. From HMV SLS5049 (11/76). Recorded 1975.
Josquin Desprez Scaramella va alla guerra. Allégez moy, doulce plaisant brunette. Allégez moy, doulce plaisant brunette (anonymous arrangement for two lutes). El grillo è buon cantore. De profundis clamavi a 5. Benedicta es, caelorum regina. Credo "De tous biens playne".

Guillaume se va chauffeur. Adieu mes amours. Adieu mes amours (sixteenth-century anonymous arrangement for organ). Inviolata, integra et casta es, Maria. **Isaac** Donna di dentro dalla tua casa. Missa "La bassadanza". **Hayne Van Ghizeghem** De tous biens plaine. De tous biens plaine (arr. Josquin). **A. Agricola** De tous biens plaine (two versions). Fortuna desparata. **Brumel** Du tout plongiet/Fors seulement. Missa "Et ecce terrae motus". **Ghiselin** Ghy syt die wertste boven al. **Barbireau** Een wrolick wesen. **Hofhaimer** Ein fröhlich wesen. **Obrecht** Ein fröhlich wesen. Haec Deum caeli. Laudemus nunc Dominum. **Ockeghem** Prenez sur moi vostre exemple. Ma bouche rit. Intemerata Dei mater. **Busnois** Fortuna disperata. **Anonymous** Fortuna desparata. Mijn morken gaf mij een jonck wijff. **Tinctoris** Missa sine nomine. **La Rue** Missa "Ave sanctissima Maria". Ave sanctissima Maria. **Compère** O bone Jesu. **Mouton** Nesciens mater virgo virum.

This is arguably Munrow's most consistent and most polished collection, devoted to the sacred and secular polyphony of the mid- to late-fifteenth century. These recordings remain marvellously fresh and vital – even in the case of pieces that have since had more polished or more clearly recorded interpretations. That is especially true of the sacred music, recorded entirely vocally and (in most cases) one to a part. It would be a challenge to name a more tempestuous reading of Brumel's "Earthquake Mass", a more sombre, self-absorbed *Intemerata Dei mater* (this is still the only recording at super-low pitch), or more luminously clear canons (in *Ave sanctissima Maria* and *Nesciens mater*). In the recordings of secular music, the passage of time is rather more obvious. But idiosyncratic though it may now appear, the choice of instruments always combines flair and verve. In the songs, tempos are rather more languorous than one is now used to, but Munrow's finest inspirations still strike very deep. The phrase "essential listening" is often used (perhaps too often), but it surely applies to "The Art of the Netherlands". A word of warning: the contents of the three original LPs are not reproduced exactly. The entire instrumental portion, some 20 minutes of music, is cut. It is good, however, to have available again one of the most influential recordings of early music ever made.

Passion Orlando Consort (Robert Harre Jones, alto; Charles Daniels, Angus Smith, tens; Donald Greig, Robert Macdonald, basses). Metronome Ⓕ METCD1015 (62 minutes: DDD: 4/97). Texts and translations included. Recorded 1996.
Tinctoris Lamentations Jeremie. **Dufay** Victimae paschali laudes. Vexilla regis prodeunt. **Josquin Desprez** Victimae paschali laudes. **Isaac** Easter Mass Proper. **Compère** Crux triumphans. **Obrecht** Salve crux.

This is an attractive programme of Holy Week and Easter pieces, some by unlikely composers such as Tinctoris, the fifteenth-century musical theorist. It is centred around Isaac's four-part *Easter Mass*, with its polytextual structure. Isaac sets all the pieces of the Proper, with the exception of the Offertory, and he interweaves three popular Easter tunes. The end product is a wonderfully joyful and festive Mass, the nearest modern equivalent that comes to mind being Honegger's Christmas cantata with its carol sequence. Isaac's Mass is flanked by Tinctoris's moving *Lamentation*, two settings of the *Victimae paschali laudes*, and three fine pieces honouring the Cross. The Orlando Consort do full justice to this splendid programme. Their reedy vocal quality has come to be accepted as that of the late medieval and early renaissance period. The singing is superb, the individual parts easily identifiable yet marvellously blended. Listeners may be slightly foxed by the pronunciation of the Latin, particularly by the nasal French vowels. Much care has gone into this search for authenticity.

Sweet love, sweet hope Hilliard Ensemble (David James, alto; John Potter, Rogers Covey-Crump, tens; Gordon Jones, bass). Isis Ⓕ CD030 (71 minutes: DDD: 7/97). Texts and translations included. Recorded 1996.
Dufay J'atendray tant qu'il vous. Quel fronte signorille. Ce moys de may. Je me complains pitieusement. Ma belle dame souveraine. Navré je suis d'un dart penetratif. Entre vous, gentils amoureux. Belle, veuilles moy retenir. Je veux chanter de cuer joyeux. Ce jour l'an. Par droit je puis bien complaindre. **Rezon** Il est temps que je me retraye. **Hasprois** Ma doulce amour. **Brollo** Nulx ne pourroit ymaginer. **Paullet** J'aim. Qui?. **Malbecque** Adieu vous di, mes seigneurs et amis. Quant de la belle me parti. Dieu vous doinst bon jour. **Brixiensis** O spirito gentil, tu m'ay percosso. **Anonymous** Douce speranche my conforte tous jours. Or sus, mon cuer, vers ma dame t'encline.

This is an exciting disc, for a number of reasons. The so-called Canonici manuscript in the Bodleian Library was first noticed just over a century ago, and since then it has engaged the attention of countless scholars. With over 300 items, it is one of the most wide-ranging witnesses to the music of the early fifteenth century; as such, it is one of those sources that deserves a CD all to itself. It says much for its importance that without it, Dufay's extant secular output would be cut virtually in half, and Binchois would be similarly affected. As the best-represented composer in the manuscript, Dufay gets the lion's share in this programme as well (though sadly, Binchois goes unrepresented despite running a strong second). Naturally, the Hilliard Ensemble can present only a tiny fraction of what is on offer, but their choice of pieces is admirable. Admirable, too, is the Hilliards' flexibility: the four-voice pieces (*Par droit* and *Je me complains*, both by Dufay) entail extremes of range for all four singers, negotiated with consummate ease; and the exquisite ballata *O spirito gentil* (by the ineffably named Prepositus Brixiensis) exemplifies all that is best here. Elsewhere, one can point to a few rough edges, the odd fluffed note; but for the most part the Hilliards' accustomed dexterity is equal to just about everything. The Hilliards follow current fashion (and their own exigencies) in presenting the music with voices alone, but the decision to text all the voices all the time may strike you as odd. It seems perfectly natural to do so in syllabic pieces like the opening *J'atendray tant*; but others call just as clearly for wordless vocalization. The alternatives (splitting up notes to accommodate text or cutting out words or syllables altogether) seem counter-intuitive, and clutter the texture unnecessarily. In matters of detail, too, the use of the unrevised Besseler edition of Dufay's songs introduces solecisms that could easily have been avoided. Nevertheless, this is one of the most ambitious recitals of the repertory to appear in quite some time. The informative notes complement the programme sympathetically.

Beauté Parfaite The Autumn of the Middle Ages. **Alla Francesca.** Opus 111 Ⓟ OPS30-173 (68 minutes: DDD: 7/98). Texts and translations included. Recorded 1996. 🔒🔒🔒
Anonymous Pour vous servir. Or sus, mon cuer, vers ma dame t'encline. Tousjours servir je veuil. Tant qu'en mon cuer/Sur l'erbette. Or sus, vous dormes trop. Cheulz qui volent retourner. La belle et la gente rose. Quant la douce jouvencelle. Instrumental Piece. **Anthonello de Caserta** Beauté parfaite. **Binchois** Adieu, jusques je vous revoye. Ay douloureux disant helas. **Dufay** J'ay mis mon cuer. Je vous pri/Ma tres douce amie/Tant que mon argent. **Fontaine** Pastourelle en un vergier. **Grenon** La plus belle. **Legrant** Entre vous, nouviaux mariés. **Libert** Se je me plains. **Paullet** J'aim. Qui?. **Raulin de Vaux** Savés pour quoy suy sy gay. **Solage** Fumeux fume par fumee. **Vaillant** Par maintes foys.
This is probably the most rounded and successfully varied anthology of late-fourteenth- and early-fifteenth-century songs available. There have been several fine recordings of secular music from this period – a relief to those who feel that this area has suffered relative neglect in comparison to sacred genres. This collection spans a range of styles – from Solage at his weirdest (the famous *Fumeux fume*, sung here at a very slow tempo that is surprisingly effective) to Binchois at his most melancholy (*Ay douloureux*) and Dufay in his sprightly, May Day mode – and includes a number of light pastoral or genre pieces, jocose or slightly scurrilous: *Pastourelle en un vergier* is an example of the ballade form at its liveliest and most direct. As a cross-section of expressive registers and attitudes, it is a very astute and intelligent piece of programming. Equally impressive is the variety of interpretative approaches, and the polish with which each is carried off. There is great discrimination in the use of instruments. The astonishing artistry of the flautist and recorder player, Pierre Hamon is notable (*Par maintes foys*), but the individual singers are also given greater chance to shine individually and (most importantly) the two agendas no longer compete with each other. This is the place to mention Brigitte Lesne, whose distinctive but perfectly controlled vibrato is a singing-lesson in itself; and the scarcely less individual timbre of Emmanuel Bonnardot, restrained yet intense. Both are heard in *Adieu, jusques je vous revoye*. Even as straightforward a piece as *Pastourelle en un vergier* is fastidiously shaped, yet without the least bit of fuss. This awareness of the importance of detail is evident in the treatment of the texts. In all cases, they are responded to imaginatively, with a clear understanding of the intention, and the structural integrity of the poetic form (both literary and musical) is respected. Thus, it is easier to engage with the music on the many levels present both between and within pieces. Yet nearly every piece is approached in a different way: no mean feat with 22 works on offer. The disc closes with the magical *Je vous pri*, on paper a slight enough piece, but here deeply intelligent and compellingly expressive – adjectives that apply to these interpretations as well.

Missa Alleluia Music at the Burgundian Court. Works include: **La Rue** Missa Alleluia. **Obrecht** Salve regina. **Josquin Desprez** Huc me sydereo. **Capilla Flamenca.** Eufoda Ⓟ 1232 (60 minutes: DDD: 1/98).
Here is classically full-throated, rich Flemish singing. The motets are hardly new to the catalogue, but these readings more than hold their own. Worth noting is the use of choirboys, notably in Obrecht's six-voice *Salve regina*, and Josquin's *Huc me sydereo*, here in its six-voice version. But the centrepiece here is unquestionably the Mass by Pierre de la Rue. The singing is mostly very stylish, with a sound image to wallow in. Strongly recommended.

The Voice in the Garden Spanish Songs and Motets, 1480-1550. **Gothic Voices /** **Christopher Page** with **Christopher Wilson** (vihuela) and **Andrew Lawrence-King** (hp). Hyperion Ⓟ CDA66653 (52 minutes: DDD: 2/94). 📀 Texts and translations included. Recorded 1993. *Gramophone Editor's choice.* 🔒
Encina Mi libertad en sosiego. Los sospiros no sosiegan. **Peñalosa** Por las sierras de Madrid. Ne reminiscaris, Domine. Precor te, Domine. Sancta Maria. **Mena** Yo creo que n'os dió Dios. La bella malmaridada. **Enrique** Mi querer tanto vos quiere. **Anonymous** Pase el agoa, ma Julieta. Harto de tanta porfía. Dindirín, dindirín. Ave, Virgo, gratia plena. Dentro en el vergel. Entra Mayo y sale Abril. Instrumental works – **Narváez** Fantasía II tono; Fantasía III tono. Paseávase el rey moro. **Fernández Palero** Paseávase el rey moro. **Milán** Fantasías 10, 12 and 18. **Segni** Tiento. **Anonymous** A la villa voy.
As usual with Gothic Voices, there is a mixture of all-vocal and solo-instrument performances, never the twain meeting and a mixture of what used to be called sacred and secular: motets by Peñalosa sit cheek by jowl with love songs and instrumental fantasies, giving an unusual and intriguing picture of

the repertory. In general the record has all the qualities that make anything by Gothic Voices a required purchase for collections that aim at serious coverage of early centuries; and the resourceful selection of music makes it an important contribution to the understanding of Spanish culture. A note of special praise for Christopher Wilson's performances of the vihuela solos which have a control and eloquence that are truly impressive. Andrew Lawrence-King characteristically throws new light on some of this repertory with his immaculate range of colours and textures on the harp.

Canciones, Romances and Sonetos La Columbina Ensemble (Mariá Cristina Kiehr, sop; Claudio Cavina, alto; Josep Benet, ten; Josep Cabré, bass). Accent Ⓕ ACC95111D (56 minutes: DDD: 11/96). Texts and translations included. Recorded 1995.
Encina Triste España sin ventura! Antonilla es desposada. Tan buen ganadico. Mi libertad en sosiego. Pues que tú, Reina del cielo. Cucú, cucú, cucú. **Vásquez** A, hermosa, abrime cara de rosa. Con qué la lavaré. Torna, Mingo, a namorarte. Si no os uviera mirado. En la fuente del rosel. Soledad tengo de tí. Buscad buen amor. O dulce contemplación. De los álamos vengo. **Guerrero** Niño Dios, d'amor herido. Prado verde y florido. Huyd, huyd. Si tu penas no pruevo. Todo quanto pudo dar. **Romero** A quién contaré mis quejas. En Belén están mis amores. Como suele el blanco zisne. Soberana María. Las voces del fuego.

In this survey of Spanish song in the sixteenth and seventeenth centuries the pieces chosen admirably reflect the consistency of idiom and quality during the period. Distinctive to the repertory is the blend of popular and *culto* elements, in both text and music. Madrigalian elements gradually infiltrate the simple, homophonic idiom cultivated by Encina and are thoroughly mastered by Juan Vásquez, the genius of Spanish song of the first half of the sixteenth century, and subsequently by Francisco Guerrero. All these developments are further consolidated by Romero, a near contemporary of Monteverdi, the two- and three-part songs selected here reflecting the sixteenth-century continuum that dominates the early Spanish baroque. Apart from some *stile concitato* effects in the battle-cry refrains to *En Belén están mis amores* and *Las voces del fuego*, these technically highly accomplished but effective pieces are still predominantly in the renaissance polyphonic idiom. None of the songs is more than about four minutes long, and most last around two, so that La Colombina's carefully chosen groupings of works by the same composer make a larger structure, and they very successfully juxtapose the more familiar (Guerrero's *Prado verde y florido* or Vásquez's *De los álamos vengo*) with the less well known while giving a good insight into the range of the repertory. Their interpretations are always expressive and sensitive to the imagery of the text, and the blend and accuracy of ensemble are exemplary. These are utterly convincing performances without any need whatsoever for the 'orchestrated' approach so familiar from, say, Hespèrion XX. Here the madrigalian writing so apparent within Spanish forms such as the *villancico*, *romance* and *soneto* finally comes into its own for about the first time on CD.

El Cançoner del Duc de Calabria La Capella Reial de Catalunya / Jordi Savall. Auvidis Astrée Ⓕ E8582 (68 minutes: DDD: 9/96). Texts and translations included. Recorded 1995. *Gramophone Editor's choice.*   ⒼⒼ
Almodar Ah, Pelayo que desmayo! **Morales** Si n'os hubiera mirado. **Carceres** Soleta so jo ací. **Flecha** Que farem del pobre Joan! Teresica hermana. **Anonymous** Ay luna que reluzes. Dizen a mi que los amores he. Gózate, Virgen sagrada. Si de vos mi bien. Un niño nos es nacido. Con qué la lavaré. Ojos garços ha la niña. Si la noche haze escura (attrib. F. Guerrero). Estas noches à tan largas. Vella, de vós som amorós (attrib. M. Flechaa). Yo me soy la morenica. Falai, meus olhos.

This is vintage Capella Reial. The singing and playing are superb (as always), and the repertory – melodious and dancey by turn – of the Cançoner del Duc de Calabria is right up their alley. Amazingly, this is the first commercial recording dedicated to this songbook from the Valencian court of the Duke of Calabria – surprising because of the accessibility and quality of the music. Several items from the book have become well known (notably the ubiquitous *Riu, riu, chiu*, which, thankfully, is not included here), but up till now it has been difficult to gain an appreciation of the collection as a whole. Published in Venice in 1556, it records an earlier repertory, dating from the first decade of the sixteenth century through the 1530s and, possibly, 1540s. The Valencian court was one of the major cultural centres of the Iberian peninsula at this period, and the court culture was heavily influenced by the latest humanistic trends from Italy. In musical terms, the repertory of the *Cançoner* reflects this mix of imported and indigenous elements; most of the songs conform to the fixed-form *villancico* of the later fifteenth century, but within the essential refrain-and-verse structure much of the writing reveals a more madrigalian idiom. Indeed, popular-style refrains are often succeeded by madrigalian verses, and Capella Reial reinforce this through the scoring adopted; popular songs and refrains attract full-blown 'orchestrations' (the tutti ensemble of viols, winds, plucked instruments and percussion so characteristic of the Capellaensemble), or at least varied combinations of instruments, while the more imitative sections blend voices, viols and harp or vihuela. The songs are well chosen and nicely varied in poetic content and interpretation; it is particularly good to have the relatively few Catalan items from the songbook, which when sung by Jordi Savall's excellent team of native singers, are lent a distinctly dark flavour – thanks to the covered vowel sounds of the language. In short, this is an outstanding disc which brings to light another unjustly neglected corner of the repertory in performances that reveal Capella Reial at their very best: a must for any collection.

Canciones y Ensaladas Ensemble Clément Janequin / Dominique Visse (alto).
Harmonia Mundi ℗ HMC90 1627 (58 minutes: DDD: 4/98). ✏ Texts and translations
included. Recorded 1997. *Gramophone Editor's choice.* 🅖🅖
Brudieu En los mon pus sou dotada del set goigs. **Flecha** La bomba. La guerra. **Mudarra**
Fantasias – primer tono; quarto tono; quinto tono. **Valderrábano** Contrapunto sobre el tenor
del conde claros. **Vásquez** Ojos morenos. Que yo, mi madre, yo. Mi mal de causa es. Gentil
senora mia. Cavallero, queraysme dexar. Agora que sé de amor. El que sin ti bivir, ya no querria.
Lágrimas de mi consuelo.
It is a real pleasure to hear some more of Vásquez's excellent songs on disc: usually it is the *villancicos*
in popular vein that are featured, but here we have some of the more serious, madrigalian pieces. Try
Lágrimas de mi consuelo, one of his most extended settings in which he comes closest to the motet
style of the period, and savour those mournful suspensions. Mostly the songs are considerably
shorter, lasting only two or three minutes, but Vásquez is a masterful songster and perfectly
encapsulates the mood of each text. Brudieu's strophic setting, in Catalan, of the Seven Joys of the
Virgin calls for sustained singing, around which the instrumentalists here weave increasingly elaborate
extemporized divisions. All the songs, and also the *ensaladas*, are performed with one voice to a part
and slightly varying combinations of organ, viol and plucked strings (lute, vihuela, guitar). Each
member of the Ensemble Clément Janequin is closely miked, but the overall blend is superb, and the
rich, translucent sonority achieved is utterly compelling. What distinguishes this CD above all is the
liveliness of the musical response to the words that are being sung: the pronunciation is not 100 per
cent consistent, but every word is crystal-clear and the level of vocal energy and focus is always spot
on, all of which is especially noticeable in the *ensaladas*. Here the interpretation is just right: theatrical
and colourful, often funny, but never camp or ludicrously over the top, all this stemming from Visse's
own instinctive and secure sense of the theatrical. Even if Flecha had not considered this plausible
combination of voices and instruments when he composed the *ensaladas*, surely he would have
appreciated these versions of *La bomba* and *La guerra* for their sensitivity to the rhetoric of the texts
and the real flair at the heart of the performance.

Al alva venid Spanish Secular Music of the Fifteenth and Sixteenth Centuries. **La Romanesca**
(Marta Almajano, sop; Paolo Pandolfo, va da gamba; Juan Carlos de Mulder, vihuela/gtr; Pedro
Estevan, perc) / **José Miguel Moreno** (vihuela). Glossa ℗ GCD920203 (60 minutes: DDD: 5/96).
✏ Texts and translations included. Recorded 1995. *Gramophone Editor's choice.* 🅖
Anonymous Al alva venid. L'amor, dona, ch'io te porto. Rodrigo Martines. A los maitines era.
Nina y vina. **Narváez** Paseavase el rey moro. Lós Seys libros del delphin – Diferencias de
Guardame las vacas. **Encina** Más vale trocar. Si abrá en este baldrés! Qu'es de ti, desconsolado?
Hoy comamos y bevamos. **D. Ortiz** Trattado de glosas – Recercada segunda sobre el
passamezzo moderno; Recercada tercera para viola de gamba sola; Recercada quarta sobre la
folia; Recercada quinta sobre el passamezzo antiguo; Recercada settima sobre la Romanesca.
Pisador Libro de música – En la fuente del rosel; La manana de Sant Juan. **Vásquez**
Orphenica lyra – De los álamos vengo; Con qué la lavaré; Glosa sobre Tan que vivray; De
Antequera sale el moro. **Mudarra** Tres libros de musica – Si me Ilaman a mi; Ysabel, perdiste la
tu faxa; Guárdame las vacas.
Many of these pieces – songs and vihuela music from sixteenth-century Spain – have been recorded
at least once, if not dozens of times before, but this CD takes pride of place in this repertory. La
Romanesca perform with true *fantasía* but without any of the mannerisms – the excesses and the
understatements – of many of their predecessors and rivals: they seem to hit it just right. They have
mostly selected songs with a strong popular flavour – precisely those songs that have attracted most
attention because they are simply so attractive – but their realizations are restrained in terms of
instrumental accompaniment (plucked strings, viol and a smattering of percussion), but full of
musical vitality – in other words, the emphasis is, justly, on the music and not the 'orchestrated'
arrangement of it. The players, led by José Miguel Moreno, are brilliant, and the singer, Marta
Almajano shines in this repertory. She brings out perfectly the lyricism inherent in the popular-
inspired court song tradition – take, for example, Vásquez's lovely *De los álamos vengo*: these songs
demand an elusive blend of sophistication and simplicity. The instrumentalists make the most of the
virtuoso element already making itself felt in the works of the vihuelists and Ortiz's *recercadas*. It's
good to have a 'straight' version of Encina's *Más vale trocar*, which is often treated in an upbeat
manner at odds with the text. The same applies to Vásquez's *Con qué la lavaré* although this is,
arguably, just a touch too slow. Overall, and above all, it is purely a pleasurable experience to listen to
this disc. Take it with you wherever you go, and especially to that desert island.

Spain and the New World The Hilliard Ensemble (David James, Ashley Stafford, altos;
Rogers Covey-Crump, John Potter, Mark Padmore, tens; Gordon Jones, bar).
Virgin Classics Veritas ⑱ VED5 61394-2 (two discs: 126 minutes: DDD: 11/97).
From EMI CDS7 54341-2 (4/92). Texts and translations included. Recorded 1990-91.
Mondéjar Ave rex noster. **Peñalosa** Inter vestibulum et altare. Magnificat quarti toni.
Anonymous Tierra içielos se quexavan. Di, por que mueres en cruz. Dindirin, dindirin. Si la
noche haze escura. **Rivafrecha** Vox dilecti mei. **Escobar** Clamabat autem mulier. Pásame por

Dios barquero. Salve regina. **Alba** Stabat mater. **Encina** Triste España sin ventura!. Cucú, cucú, cucú cú. Hoy comamos y be bamos. Mas vale trocar. **Franco** In ilhuicac cihuapille (attrib.). Memento mei, Deus. Dios itlazo nantzine (attrib.). **Lienas** Salve regina. **Morales** Pater noster. Parce mihi, Domine. Magnificat a 6. **Lobo** O quam suavis est, Domine. **Guerrero** Ave Virgo sanctissima. **Padilla** Transfige, dulcissime Domine. **Luchas** A la caça, sus, a caça. **Urreda** Nunca fué pena ma yor. **Millán** O dulce y triste memoria. **Alonso** La tricotea.
Originally released in late-1991, this two-CD set was The Hilliard Ensemble's contribution to the Columbus commemorations of the following year. It was also their first recording after Paul Hillier's departure from the group. In keeping with the Columbus theme, the collection includes music composed both in the Old World and in the New. Unsurprisingly, the languages used are Latin for the sacred music and Spanish for the secular – but in addition there are two small pieces in Nahuatl, the tongue of the Aztecs. With well over two hours of music, there is time for The Hilliards to dwell on many composers and genres, most of whom have but a small representation on disc. Spanish polyphony has a marked tendency to asperity in its treatment of dissonance, and generally eschews the more complex forms of polyphony adopted by Franco-Flemish composers: that makes for sobriety in its sacred music, and directness in the secular. This is best heard in the music of Encina and Peñalosa in the early-sixteenth century; the closest Spain comes to a home-grown exponent of the international style is Morales, one of whose splendid *Magnificat*s stands out as a high point in the collection. All in all it is clear that The Hilliards are more at ease with sacred music than with secular pieces. Those in the latter category come across either as forced, or as insufficiently defined – humour is an elusive attribute. The collection as a whole, however, is a distinctive one, and offers a convincing picture of a country whose polyphonic tradition has often passed for a poor relation of the mainstream continental idiom.

The Rose and the Ostrich Feather Music from the Eton Choirbook, Volume 1. **The Sixteen /
Harry Christophers.** Collins Classics Ⓕ 1314-2 (63 minutes: DDD: 4/92). Notes and texts included. *Gramophone Award Winner 1992*. Recorded 1990.   Ⓖ
Fayrfax Magnificat ("Regale"). **Hygons** Salve regina. **Turges** From stormy wyndis.   Ⓖ
Stabat iuxta Christi crucem. **Anonymous** This day day dawes. **Cornysh** Salve regina.
The sacred music of early Tudor England (the end of the fifteenth century) has been unjustly neglected on CD and the welcome extended to this Collins release is further enhanced by the fact that Harry Christophers and his ensemble have since added four further volumes to this series dedicated to music from the Eton Choirbook (including the three). The destruction of great swathes of manuscript in the sixteenth century has left us with only isolated jewels such as this to remind us in sound what the eye can behold in the Perpendicular style of the architecture of the cathedrals of Canterbury, Worcester, Winchester and the Minster at York. Both architecture and music present soaring vaulted vistas and an attention to florid and ornate tracery. The Rose and the Ostrich Feather? These were both potent symbolic emblems of members of the royal house of Tudor and the words are incorporated into the two secular songs with English texts. The white rose was also an image closely associated with the Virgin Mary and most of the scores in the Choirbook are dedicated to her. Sadly, the disc is without translations of the Latin works but there is a fascinating essay by John Milsom. This music finds The Sixteen at their best, especially attentive to the severe tuning demands placed on the singers, for whom there is no instrumental accompaniment. Particularly notable is the control that Christophers exerts over the sound of his performers in this very taxing music (four of the performances on the disc last for over ten minutes). The recorded sound expertly captures and balances the expressive singing. Whether used as an aural accompaniment to a great architectural style or enjoyed purely for its sharply-defined reflection of one of the greatest periods of English music (existing within the choral tradition which continues to this day), this disc is altogether outstanding and should not be missed.

The Pillars of Eternity Music from the Eton Choirbook, Volume 3. **The Sixteen /
Harry Christophers.** Collins Classics Ⓕ 1342-2 (61 minutes: DDD: 7/93). Texts and translations included. Recorded 1992.
Cornysh Ave Maria, mater Dei. **Davy** O Domine caeli terraeque. A myn hart remembir the well. A blessid Jhesu. **Lambe** Stella caeli. **Wilkinson** Credo in Deum/Jesus autem. Salve regina.
This disc opens with Richard Davy's *O Domine caeli*, a vast and complex work lasting just over a quarter of an hour in performance, but apparently composed within a single day at Magdalen College, Oxford. It goes on and on in the most exalted, but perhaps inconsequential manner until its final resounding "Amen". What should a choir do with it except sing it as well as possible in terms of ensemble and intonation, as The Sixteen certainly do, and let the glorious sounds wash over the dumbfounded listener? Still more perplexing is Robert Wilkinson's *Credo in Deum/Jesus autem*, a 13-voice canon in which the individual voice parts represent Jesus and the 12 disciples. The net effect has been aptly described as "harmonious chaos", which it surely is, although, in common with all multi-voiced works of this period, it is harmonically static in a way that should delight minimalist fans. Symbolism is also the key to the structure of Wilkinson's setting of the *Salve regina* – the nine voice parts each representing a designated rank in the nine-fold hierarchy of angels. This is vintage Eton Choirbook, the composer pitting the full and sonorous directness of the tutti acclamations against the flights of fantasy in the solo sections. A very desirable disc.

The Flower of all Virginity Music from the Eton Choirbook, Volume 4. **The Sixteen /**
Harry Christophers. Collins Classics Ⓕ 1395-2 (63 minutes: DDD: 2/94). Texts and translations
included. Recorded 1993.
Kellyk Gaude flore virginali. **Nesbet** Magnificat. **Fayrfax** Most clere of colour. **Browne**
O Maria Salvatoris mater. Salve regina. **Anonymous** Ah, my dear son. Afraid, alas.
We know a good deal about the context for which the Marian music in the Eton Choirbook was
composed: each evening members of the College Choir were to gather before an image of the Virgin
and sing an antiphon in her honour (the College was itself dedicated to Mary). During Lent they were
to perform the *Salve regina*, and throughout the rest of the year 'an antiphon of the Blessed Virgin'
is all that is stipulated in the College statutes. This is the repertory represented on this disc, together
with a Magnificat and three songs with texts that can be loosely described as Marian. It is magnificent
music: the sheer scale of the two Marian motets and the monumental approach of their composers
Kellyk and Browne, is quite staggering. It is not difficult to imagine these works being sung on a
major Marian feast with the chapel singers before the lectern in a supreme act of Marian piety. The
Sixteen, of course, are now well sung in this repertory and they perform it wonderfully, with an
instinctive feel for the contrasts of sonority that so often define its structure.

The Voices of Angels Music from the Eton Choirbook, Volume 5. **The Sixteen /**
Harry Christophers. Collins Classics Ⓕ 1462-2 (62 minutes: DDD: 3/96). Texts and translations
included. Recorded 1995.
Davy Salve regina. In honore summae matris. **Lambe** Salve regina. **Plummer** Tota pulchra es.
Anna mater matris Christi. **William, Monk of Stratford** Magnificat.
These are vibrant performances, suitably varied in colour, nicely paced, and recorded with superb
clarity. That is to say that The Sixteen continue to explore the astonishing riches of the Eton
Choirbook with undiminished enthusiasm and imagination. The special spice in this particular issue
is in the two works by John Plummer, that strangely individual composer who treated harmonic
stillness more boldly than any other of his generation. His music makes a nice contrast and contains
a few hints of the kinds of floridity you get elsewhere in the Eton repertory; moreover it has a direct
expressive mood that comes across very effectively in these well-judged performances. Walter Lambe's
Salve regina seems to be among the earlier works in the Eton Choirbook; it has a neatly wayward
fantasy in its lovely textures. The truly fascinating works here are those of Richard Davy. You could
think that his enormous *In honore summae matris* occasionally rambles, at over 15 minutes; and there
are moments when even the patent virtuosity of The Sixteen seems challenged by the intricate
floridity of the passages entirely for lower voices; but there seems to be no limit to the range of ideas
and textures that Davy has at his disposal. His are unquestionably pieces that grow in stature on
repeated listening. Nobody is likely to be disappointed by this recording.

French Chansons The Scholars of London. Naxos Ⓢ 8 550880 (60 minutes: DDD: 2/95).
Texts and translations included. Recorded 1993.
Arcadelt En ce mois délicieux; Margot, labourez les vignes; De temps que j'estois amoureux;
Sa grand beauté. **Bertrand** De nuit, le bien. **Clemens Non Papa** Prière devant le repas;
Action des Graces. **Costeley** Arrête un peu mon coeur. **Gombert** Aime qui vouldra; Quand je
suis aupres. **Janequin** Le chant des oiseaux. Or vien ça, vien, m'amye. **Josquin Desprez**
Faulte d'argent. Mille regretz. **Lassus** Beau le cristal. Bon jour mon coeur. Un jeune moine.
La nuict froide et sombre. Si je suis brun. **Le Jeune** Ce n'est que fiel. **Passereau** Il est bel et
bon. **Sandrin** Je ne le croy. **Sermisy** Tant que vivray en eage florissant. Venez, regrets. La, la
Maistre Pierre. **Tabourot** Belle qui tiens ma vie. **Vassal** Vray Dieu.
Listening to this carefully crafted selection, one is struck by the flexibility of a style that
accommodates so many distinctive temperaments – the verve of Janequin, the suavity of Sermisy, the
gravity of Gombert. It is a democratic genre in the truest sense, appealing to the great (Josquin and
Lassus) while permitting lesser figures to shine as well. The term 'democratic' also describes the
chanson's appeal, then as now: here are some of the most beguiling tunes of any period. To call these
performances unobtrusive is to do them no injustice. The Scholars of London capture the wistful
elegance of the courtier pieces – for example, Le Jeune's *Ce n'est que fiel*. In some of the more
scurrilous songs (such as Josquin's *Faulte d'argent*) there is a Gallic rambunctiousness but at times the
tempos are a shade too brisk for comfort, and the choice of pitch-standard in Janequin's famous
Chant des oiseaux (sung here in its through-composed version) sets a strain on the singers' accustomed
agility. But such details merely affect the odd piece. This is a disc that gives great pleasure: like
ephemera trapped in amber, the music in this collection bears modest yet touching testimony to a
period that produced much 'great' music. Its smaller creations are no less admirable.

Forgotten Provence Martin Best Consort. Nimbus Ⓕ NI5445 (64 minutes: DDD: 3/96). 🎵
Recorded 1994.
Anonymous Ne l'oseray-je/Voulez-vous que je vous dire?. Dessus la rive. Vecy le May. Ma
charmante cadet. Alleluia justus ut palma. A l'entrada del temps clar. Li gelos. Air de cheval-
Jupon. Ara Lauzatz. Laude jocunda. Pucelete/Je languis. Alle, psallite cum luya. Rossignolet du
bois (two versions). Lo Sodard. Epiphanium Domino. **Beatriz de Dia** A chanter m'er de so

qu'eu no volria. **Giraut de Bornelh** Reis glorios. **Petrus de Cruce** Aucun ont trouve/Lonc tans. **Rudel de Blaye** Lanquan li jorn son lonc en may.

Here is a generous offering of the warm south: four centuries of song from herb-scented Provence, songs of love, songs of spring, songs and dances of the troubadours, traditional songs, motets and sequences – a profusion of wonderful melodies, well matched by the diversity of range and timbre of the performers. There are tenor and soprano soloists, groupings of altos, and tenors, by themselves or in alternation; and finally, some imaginative instrumentalists. There is a diversity of moods as well, ranging from the sprightly and boisterous to the languid. Martin Best displays his customary ease and wit, with those gliding ornaments that disappear discreetly into the fabric of the vocal line. Then there is Libby Crabtree with her clear, precise, yet glowing soprano voice. The highlights are surely *A chanter m'er*, by the twelfth-century troubadour Beatriz, Countess of Dia, sung by Crabtree; and its idealized counterpart *Lanquan li jorn*, composed by Jaufre Rudel de Blaye, a contemporary of Beatriz, and movingly performed by Best to a quiet accompaniment of psaltery and fidele. There are also some rollicking jollities, such as *Ara Lauzatz* and the traditional *Lo Sodard*. Three sequences complete these sketches of life in Provence between the twelfth and the sixteenth centuries, two with organum, the third, *Epiphanium Domino*, sung gently with the rhythmic interpretation suggested by Handschin in the old *Oxford History of Music*. Concise, illuminating insert-notes are offered, with translations but, sadly, no original texts.

Late Renaissance-Early Baroque   16th-17th centuries

Songs on Poems by Pierre de Ronsard Clément Janequin Ensemble / Dominique Visse (alto). Harmonia Mundi Ⓟ HMC90 1491 (59 minutes: DDD: 2/95). Texts included. Recorded 1993. **Regnard** Ni nuit ne jour. Dedans ce bois. Contre mon gré. Mon triste coeur. Heureux ennui. Las, toi qui es de moi. Bois Janin à moi. **Boni** Rossignol mon mignon. Las! sans espoir. Quand je dors. Ha, bel accueil. Comment au départir. **J. de Castro** Je suis tellement langoureux. Quand tu tournes tes yeux. De peu de bien. **Monte** Quand de ta lèvre. Si trop souvent. Le premier jour du mois de mai. **Rippe** Fantasie II.

It has been far too easy in the past to see French chanson composers in the second half of the sixteenth century as lesser figures – too restrained in their mode of expression, faint epigones of their predecessors (particularly Claudin de Sermisy and Clément Janequin), less inventive and resourceful than the great Italian madrigalists who were their contemporaries. But in fact they just needed to be performed with the kind of skill and refinement we now hear from the Clément Janequin Ensemble. It is not just that everything is perfectly in place, that many years of experience have blended them into an ensemble of wonderful flexibility. It is also that they manage to find the mood of each piece with miraculous precision. Certainly the music is a little restrained – though 'refined' would be the better description. On the page, these pieces can look remarkably similar. But every time the Janequin Ensemble put their finger on the songs' individuality. Just once they let everything rip, in Regnard's *Bois Janin à moi*; but otherwise within a fairly restricted palette they ring all the changes with massive skill. Not that there is anything effete about their singing. They have an outward and vibrant sound, sometimes helped by the assertive lute playing of Eric Bellocq. That directness may be part of their success in bringing this little-heard music to vivid and irresistible fruition.

Exultate Deo Masterpieces of Sacred Polyphony. [a]**Alexander Semprini**, [a]**Francis Faux**, [a]**Raymond Winterflood** (trebs); [a]**Adrian Peacock** (bass); **Westminster Cathedral Choir / James O'Donnell** with [b]**Joseph Cullen** (org). Hyperion Ⓟ CDA66850 (72 minutes: DDD: 5/96). Texts and translations included. Recorded 1995. **Palestrina** Exsultate Deo. Sicut cervus desi-derat. **Byrd** Ave verum corpus. Civitas sancti tui. Haec dies. **Parsons** Ave Maria. **Viadana** Exultate justi[b]. **Tallis** Salvator mundi, salva nos I. O nata lux de lumine. In manus tuas. **Philips** Ascendit Deus. Ave verum corpus Christi. **Allegri** Miserere mei[a]. **G. Gabrieli** Jubilate Deo I[b]. **Lotti** Crucifixus[b]. **Tye** Omnes gentes, plaudite. **Victoria** O quam gloriosum. **Monteverdi** Cantate Domino[b].

This anthology lives up to its billing: even those with only a nodding acquaintance with renaissance polyphony will probably have heard a fair proportion of these pieces. Most of them are mainstays, not just of the Catholic liturgical repertory, but of most major Anglican choral establishments. The selection of pieces here is wide-ranging and varied. More importantly, where pieces are especially famous, the standard of performance gives the competition a fair run for its money. There *is* the thrill in Allegri's *Miserere* of a boy treble (here, Alexander Semprini) hitting that high C – and no quibbles about the phrasing of the adjoining notes, either. The choir as a whole sound very well focused, and the unanimity of the trebles is admirable (though at times a slightly more veiled tone might have better suited the text). Where required, they sound very bright and forward (at the end of Tye's *Omnes gentes*, for example), despite a recording that could have been a bit withdrawn with a more timid choir.

Utopia Triumphans Huelgas Ensemble / **Paul van Nevel**. Sony Classical Vivarte Ⓟ SK66261 (53 minutes: DDD: 4/96). Texts and translations included. Recorded 1994.

Tallis Spem in alium. **Porta** Missa Ducalis – Sanctus; Agnus Dei. **Josquin Desprez** (attrib.) Qui habitat in adjutorio Altissimi. **Ockeghem** (attrib.) Deo gratias. **Manchicourt** Laudate Dominum. **G. Gabrieli** Symphoniae sacrae – Exaudi me Domine. **Striggio** Ecce beatam lucem.

Paul van Nevel describes this disc as a gallery of the renaissance's utopian visions, the musical counterparts of the seemingly miraculous discoveries and inventions that marked the period. Certainly these pieces stake out new realms of musical space, culminating in the two rival compositions for 40 voices by Striggio and Tallis. The most unexpected discovery here is the Mass by Costanzo Porta for a maximum of 14 voices. Porta (d.1601) was one of the last composers outside the Iberian peninsula to write in the purest Palestrinian idiom. The style is familiar enough, but the sheer opulence of the sound cannot fail to impress: one would like to have had more of it. By contrast, the 36-voice *Deo gratias* and the 24-voice *Qui habitat* (attributed to Ockeghem and Josquin respectively) are far less convincing. Both attributions have been called into question: the *Deo gratias* has no more than 18 voices sounding at any given time – could a composer of Ockeghem's reach have contented himself with such a sleight of hand? It seems unlikely. On a more positive note, the inclusion of Gabrieli's 16-voice motet brings a welcome hint of mannerism to this otherwise classical programme, and brings out the best in van Nevel's characteristic quirkiness. The Huelgas Ensemble are no strangers to such polyphonic behemoths. Their usual trademarks are in evidence here – a very Flemish depth and throatiness of timbre, captured in a warm acoustic – and if one disregards the odd fluffs, the balance between overall effect and attention to detail is finely judged. Even in the Tallis, where there is fierce competition, the Huelgas more than hold their own. One may prefer The Tallis Scholars for their more balanced casting, but this *Spem* presents the familiar work in the unfamiliar context of a distinctly un-English sound.

A Venetian Coronation, 1595 Gabrieli [a]Consort and Players / **Paul McCreesh.**
Virgin Classics Veritas Ⓕ VC7 59006-2 (71 minutes: DDD: 5/90). ✐ Texts and translations included. *Gramophone* Award Winner 1990. 🄖🄖

G. Gabrieli Intonazioni – ottavo tono; terzo e quarto toni; quinto tono alla quarta bassa (James O'Donnell, org solo). Canzonas – XIII a 12; XVI a 15; IX a 10. Sonata VI a 8 pian e forte. Deus qui beatum Marcum a 10[a]. Omnes gentes a 16[a]. **A. Gabrieli** Intonazioni – primo tono (O'Donnell); settimo tono (Timothy Roberts, org). Mass Movements[a] – Kyrie a 5-12; Gloria a 16; Sanctus a 12; Benedictus a 12. O sacrum convivium a 5[a]. Benedictus Dominus Deus sabbaoth (arr. Roberts. O'Donnell, Roberts). **Bendinelli** Sonata CCC-XXXIII. Sarasinetta.
M. Thomsen Toccata I.

The coronation of a new Doge of Venice was always a special occasion, and never more so than when Marino Grimani (1532-1605) was elected to that office. We do not know what music was played then, but the whole ceremony is notionally and credibly reconstructed in this recording by Paul McCreesh and his cohorts. The recording was made in Brinkburn Priory, a church whose acoustic (aided by some deft manipulation of the recording controls) is spacious enough to evoke that of the Basilica of St Mark, the site of the original event. Space *per se* is vital to the music of the Gabrielis, who excelled in using it by placing instrumental and vocal groups in different parts of the building – which thereby became an integral part of the music. A fine selection of music that *could* have been played then is enhanced by the opening tolling of a bell, a crescendo marking the leisurely approach of the ducal procession, and the impression of architectural space created by changing stereo focus. It would be difficult to speak too highly of the performances, supplemented by first-class annotation, in this memorable recording. A trip to Venice would cost a lot more than this disc but, though you could visit the real St Mark's, it would not buy you this superb musical experience.

The Feast of San Rocco, Venice, 1608 [a]La Capella Ducale; Cologne Musica Fiata /
Roland Wilson with **Christoph Lehmann** (org). Sony Classical Ⓕ S2K66254
(two discs: 126 minutes: DDD: 6/96). ✐ Texts and translations included. Recorded 1994. 🄖

G. Gabrieli Toccata. Symphoniae sacrae, liber secundus – Benedictus es, Dominus[a]; Cantate Domino[a]; In ecclesiis[a]; Jubilate Deo[a]; Misericordia tua Domine. Canzoni et Sonate – Canzon V, a 7; Canzon X, a 8; Canzon XVII, a 12; Sonata XIX, a 15; Sonata per tre violini. Dulcis Jesu patris imago[a]. Sacrae symphoniae – Canzon primi toni, a 10; Canzon in echo duodecimi toni, a 12. Buccinate in neomenia tuba a 19. Timor et tremor[a]. Toccata primi toni. Magnificat[a]. **Grandi** Motets, Book 2 – Cantemus Domino[a]; Heu mihi[a]. O quam tu pulchra es[a]. Motets with sinfonie – Salvum me fac, Deus[a]. **Monteverdi** Salve, o Regina[a]. **Cima** Concerti ecclesiastici – Sonata per il violino, cornetto e violone; Sonata per il violino e violone. **Barbarino** Motets, Book 1, "Il Primo libro de motetti" – O sacrum convivium[a]. **Castaldi** Capricci a 2 stromenti – Capriccio detto svegliatoio[a].

Wilson's starting-point is the famous description of the festivities that took place on the patronal feast-day in the Scuola di San Rocco, the most luxurious of the six Venetian *scuole grandi*, written by the English eccentric and traveller Thomas Coryate. Frustratingly, although Coryate provides a well-observed and detailed account of the various instrumental and vocal groupings used, the names of neither performers nor composers are revealed. To this extent "The Feast of San Rocco" is something of a fiction; nevertheless, it is an intelligent one, a thoughtful and well-researched attempt to put flesh and blood on the bare bones of Coryate's anecdote. Three main repertories are drawn upon: Gabrieli's large-scale motets; canzonas and other purely instrumental works also mostly by him; and smaller-scale solo motets mostly by Alessandro Grandi. The latter are especially welcome. Evidence of Monteverdi's influence is everywhere in his music, but that doesn't detract from its freshness and charm. There are darker moments, too, as in the extraordinary four-voice dialogue *Heu mihi*, an essay in the affective, chromatic manner. More typical of Grandi's work is the exquisite *O quam tu pulchra es*, an atmospherically erotic text from the Song of Songs, delivered here with urgent rhetorical force by David Cordier and underpinned by the lightest of continuo accompaniments. And one of the most virtuosic of all Grandi's motets, *Salvum me fac, Deus*, with its range of more than two octaves, is expertly negotiated by Harry van der Kamp in an engaged yet controlled performance. s regards the interpretation of the larger-scale festive pieces, Wilson has adopted the Praetorius approach to the thorny problem of instrumentation and voice distribution. Just occasionally the solo voices are overwhelmed by the instrumental forces, in the sense that vocal strain is evident and the words disappear; both *Buccinate in neomenia tuba* and *Dulcis Jesu patris imago* suffer from such moments. But at its best, as with *In ecclesiis*, this recording is as compelling as any comparative version on offer.

Sacred Music from Venice and Rome The Sixteen / Harry Christophers with [a]**Laurence Cummings** (org). Collins Classics Ⓟ 1360-2 (57 minutes: DDD: 10/93). Texts and translations included. Recorded 1992.
Caldara Crucifixus. **A. Gabrieli** De profundis clamavi. **Frescobaldi** Fiori musicali, Op. 12 – Toccata cromatica per l'Elevatione; Toccata per l'Elevationea. **Cavalli** Salve regina. **Monteverdi** Domine, ne in furore. **G. Gabrieli** Hodie completi sunt. **Lassus** Tui sunt coeli. Missa Bell'Amfitrit altera.

Clearly the starting-point was the colour and richness of the Venetian tradition from the Gabrieli to Caldara, and it is certainly good to have available works such as Andrea's *De profundis* and Giovanni's *Hodie completi sunt*, comparatively little-known motets that are not otherwise currently available in the catalogue. But the Lassus Mass, which takes up more than a third of the record, fits rather awkwardly into this scheme despite its eight-voice texture and characteristic manipulation of sonority and texture. However, it is the performances themselves that matter, and here The Sixteen produce a sequence of finely-turned and thoughtful interpretations. Their approach is uniformly sturdy and muscular, with plenty of controlled power in the lower voices and an attractively clear brightness in the upper ones. Harry Christophers, guided by an unerring sense of mobility and contrast, encourages his singers in readings which never fail to extract every last nuance of the text. The dialogue exchanges in Cavalli's well-known *Salve regina* are beautifully executed, and the vivid sense of drama in that performance is carried through to particularly good effect in the Monteverdi which follows it. This is one of the best records of these repertories to appear for some time.

Venetian Vespers Gabrieli Consort and Players / Paul McCreesh with [a]**Timothy Roberts** (org). Archiv Produktion Ⓟ 437 552-2AH2 (two discs: 96 minutes: DDD: 4/93). ✍ Texts and translations included. Recorded 1990. *Gramophone Award Winner 1993.* Ⓖ
Sacristy bell. **Gabrieli** (ed. Roberts) Intonazione[a]. Versicle and response: Deus in adiutorium; Domine ad adiuvandum. **Rigatti** Dixit Dominus. **Grandi** O intemerata. Antiphon: Beata es Maria. **Monteverdi** Laudate pueri. **Banchieri** Suonata prima[a]. Antiphon: Beatam me dicent. **Monteverdi** Laetatus sum. **Finetti** O Maria, quae rapis corda hominum. Antiphon: Haec est quae nescavit. **Rigatti** Nisi Dominus. **Banchieri** Dialogo secondo[a]. Antiphon: Ante thronum. **Cavalli** Lauda Jerusalem. **Grandi** O quam tu pulchra es. **Anonymous** Praeambulum[a]. Chapter: Ecce virgo. **Monteverdi** Deus qui mundum crimine iacentem. Versicle and response. Ave maria; Dominus tecum. Antiphon. Spiritus Sanctus. **Rigatti** Magnificat. **Marini** Sonata con tre violini in eco. Collect: Dominus vobiscum – Deus, qui de beatae Mariae. Dismissal: Dominus vobiscum – Benedicamus Domino. **Monteverdi** Laudate Dominum. **Fasolo** (ed. Roberts) Intonazione – excerpts[a]. **Rigatti** Salve regina.

Paul McCreesh's sense of adventure made quite an impact with his reconstruction of Doge Grimani's Coronation in 1595. This follow-up recording takes as its starting point a Vespers service "as it might have been celebrated in St Mark's, Venice 1643", and it is no less striking a speculation. McCreesh is wisely not attempting to re-create a historical event but to provide a rejuvenating context for some more wonderful Venetian church music. There can be little doubt that listening to psalm settings within a liturgical framework illuminates the theatricality and significance of the works in a unique way, barely possible in an ordinary format where one work simply follows another. Yet the quality of the music is what really counts and this is where McCreesh deserves the greatest praise. He has skilfully blended a range of diverse concerted works with equally innovative and expressive solo motets, each one offset by ornate organ interludes and home-spun plainchant. Monteverdi is well represented, as one would expect, but by introducing resident composers (who were regularly employed by the great basilica) a strong Venetian sensibility prevails in all these works despite the many contrasting styles of the new baroque age. The little-known Rigatti is arguably the sensation of this release with his highly dramatic and richly extravagant sonorities. The settings of *Dixit Dominus* and *Magnificat* are almost operatic at times though they maintain the spatial elements inspired by St Mark's. The Gabrieli Consort and Players are a group with an extraordinary homogeneity of sound and focused energy: Monteverdi's *Laetatus sum* is one of the many examples where they reach new heights in early seventeenth-century performance. The solo performances are deliciously executed too, particularly those involving the falsettists. This two-disc set is an achievement of the highest order.

Sacred Choral Works [a]Vienna Hofburgkapella Schola; [b]Concerto Palatino; Gradus ad Parnassum / Konrad Junghänel. Deutsche Harmonia Mundi Ⓔ 05472 77326-2 (74 minutes: DDD: 7/95). ✒
Texts and translations included. Recorded 1994.
Biber Missa alleluja[ab]. **Schmelzer** Vesperae sollennes[ab]. Sonata per Chiesa et Camera. Sacro-Profanus Concentus Musicus – Sonata XII. **Palestrina** Coelestis urbs Jerusalem. **Froberger** Fantasia II in A minor. **Anonymous** Gregorian Chant for the Dedication of a Church – Mass Propers[a]. Gregorian Chant for Vespers[a].
What this record achieves above all else is to confirm the suspicion that Austrian choral music of the seventeenth century is not confined to a couple of Requiem settings by Biber and a few other works of little or no musical interest. The spatial and textural intricacy of Biber's 36-part setting of the Mass is a wonder in itself and the product of a composer who 'worked' the galleries of Salzburg Cathedral to his advantage. A degree of this multi-antiphonal style is Venetian in flavour but only superficially; the quicker harmonic rhythm and sophisticated groupings, as well as other colourful central European quirks, reveal a composer whose manipulation of singers and instrumentalists has more to offer than abstract sonic resplendence; Biber is admirably sensitive to the text he is setting. The performances are equally sensitive. Junghänel never allows his singers or players to overblow as can be the temptation with polychoral repertoire. Obtaining the right balance between wafting, majestic sonorities and clearly defined solo contributions takes direction of a high order and one is left in no doubt that Biber's detailed but solemn score is being taken with the utmost seriousness. There are a few moments where articulation is under-explored and the strings can sound a little too diffident. Schmelzer's *Vespers* are finely constructed, too, with an imaginative range of scorings which Junghänel and his musicians execute with tenderness and great nobility throughout. A fine and illuminating release.

Music from Renaissance Portugal Cambridge Taverner Choir / Owen Rees.
Herald Ⓔ HAVPCD155 (69 minutes: DDD: 1/94). Texts and translations included.
Recorded 1992. *Gramophone Editor's choice.* Ⓖ
P. de Cristo Magnificat. Ave Maria. Sanctissimi quinque mar tires. De profundis. Lachrimans sitivit anima mea. Ave Regina caelorum. **D. Lôbo** Missa pro defunctis. **Anonymous** Si pie Domine. **A. Fernandez** Libera me Domine. Alma redemptoris mater. **Carreira** Stabat mater.
This is one of those rare examples of scholarship and musicianship combining to result in performances that are both impressive and immediately attractive to the listener in excellent music, totally neglected until now. There is a wonderful glow about this recording that reflects the skilful engineering on the part of Herald as well as the imagination of the sonority on Rees's part. The striking feature of his approach is the emphasis on the meaning of the words. This choir sing of the Day of Judgement or the rejoicing due to the Virgin as if they really mean it: Rees is not afraid to shape phrases, to use dynamics, to vary the intensity of the sound in the service of the words which, though even more familiar to the monks and chapel singers who originally performed these pieces at the monastery of Santa Cruz in Colmbra, would have had an immediacy and a reality for them that it is hard to recapture today. How graphic those texts, in fact, are, and how well this choir bring them to life.

Musica Mediterranea Kithara (Shirley Rumsey, [a]mez/lte/gtr/cittern; William Lyons, fl/rec; Jan Walters, hp; Christopher Wilson, lte/gtr; David Miller, theorbo/lte; Susanna Pell, bass viol). Chandos Chaconne Ⓔ CHAN0562 (62 minutes: DDD: 3/95). Texts and translations included. Recorded 1993.
Willaert A quand'haveva[a]. O bene mio[a]. **Nola** Cingari simo venit'a giocare. **D. Ortiz** La spagna. La gamba. O felici occhi miei. **Mudarra** Si me llaman a mi. **Barberiis** Madonna qual certezza. **Valderrábano** Discantar sobre un punto. **A. Valente** Tenore del passo e mezzo. **Molinaro** Ballo detto il Conte Orlando. **Picchi** Ballo e Saltarello ongaro. **Piccinini** Chiacconna. **Bottegari** Non se vedde giamai[a]. **Bassano** Vestiva i colli. **Rossi** Passacaglia. **Arañés** Un sarao de la Chacona[a]. **Anonymous** Riu, riu, chiu[a]. Recercar. Donna vagh'e leggiadra[a]. Folias.
This recording of music from renaissance Spain and Italy by the solo vocal and instrumental ensemble Kithara is a delight. The music, by Willaert, Ortiz, Mudarra, Valente, Picchi *et al.*, is charming and expressive by turn and the performances are above reproach, both at ensemble and solo level. Susanna Pell's excellent account of Ortiz's *La spagna* catches just the right slightly mournful feel with her rich-toned gamba-playing; William Lyons's divisions on the renaissance flute (which, quite exceptionally, he makes sound like a real musical instrument capable of varied timbres and expressive phrasing) in Bassano's *Vestiva i colli* are superbly executed; and the plucked string accompaniments and solo items, led by Christopher Wilson on a variety of instruments, are gossamer fine and rhythmically strong as and when required. Shirley Rumsey both sings and contributes to this colourful plucked string section. Her voice has a darker quality that is in many ways suitably Mediterranean. Dinko Fabris, in his accompanying notes, emphasizes "the true sensibility of the northern European travellers of that time" in Kithara's interpretations of this colourful music. He's right in that in many ways the group sound very 'English', given the excellent teamwork and high level of musicality that fights a little shy of anything too extrovert. A very enjoyable disc nevertheless.

Italian Harpsichord Works, 1550-1700 Rinaldo Alessandrini (hpd). Opus 111 Ⓟ OPS30-118 (77 minutes: DDD: 4/95). 🎵 Recorded 1994. ⓖⓖ
A. Valente Tenore del passo e mezzo. **Facoli** Pass'e mezzo moderno. **Giovanni de Maque** Due Gagliarde. Seconde Stravaganze. **A. Mayone** Partite sopra "Fidele". **Trabaci** Partite sopra "Rugiero". **Picchi** Balli – Ballo ongaro; Ballo alla polacha; Ballo ditto il Picchi. **Buono** Sonata quinta. **Frescobaldi** Toccata. **Lambardi** Gagliarda. Partite sopra "Fidele". **Merula** Capriccio cromatico. Toccata del secondo tono. **M. Rossi** Toccata settima. **Salvatore** Toccata prima. Canzon Francese terza. Due Correnti. **B. Storace** Toccata e Canzon. **B. Strozzi** Corrente terza. **Stradella** Toccata. **A. Scarlatti** Toccata per il cembalo.

Rinaldo Alessandrini has made a special study of sixteenth- and seventeenth-century Italian music, and here presents (with the co-operation of the West German Radio) two dozen pieces that illustrate changes of style there between 1576 (the year of Antonio Valente's pioneering harpsichord collection) and around 1700, and, to some extent, differences between the more austere northern school and the more extrovert southern one. It may perhaps not be generally realized that the keyboard virtuosity demanded by our own brilliant John Bull is matched by his Italian contemporaries: Alessandrini's rhythmically vital, stylish and engaged performances leave us in no doubt of that. He gives us a well-chosen range of forms. There are variations on the *passamezzo* ground, in the minor mode and in the major variant ("moderno") – both examples here of considerable elaboration: and there are other variations (*partite*) on the harmonic bass variously known as "Ruggiero" or "Fedele". Dance forms are represented by two examples of the *gagliarda* (both chordal in treatment), two of the *corrente* (that by Salvatore full of chromaticisms), and 'exotic' dances from Poland and Hungary. Of particular interest in several items is their composers' fascination with chromaticism (which produces some curious intonation in the unidentified tuning system of the 1678 Italian harpsichord used here): a *stravaganza* by de Macque (who was Flemish by birth but spent his life in Naples, where he taught Mayone and Trabaci) contains several bold surprises; a Merula *capriccio*, a contrapuntal Salvatore *canzona*, a Buono 'sonata' and a Rossi *toccata* with a truly astonishing ending likewise feature chromaticism. The seven in this programme – mostly rhapsodic and improvisatory-sounding – include a splendid example by Frescobaldi and a sombrely declamatory one by Merula; but the eventual falling-off of this keyboard style is signalled by Stradella' toccata, which is too reliant on formulas.

Romanesca Italian Harpsichord Works. **Sophie Yates** (hpd). Chandos Chaconne Ⓟ CHAN0601 (64 minutes: DDD: 9/97). 🎵 Recorded 1996.
Picchi Toccata. Intavolatura di Balli d'Arpicordo – Ballo ongaro; Ballo alla polacha; Todesca; Ballo ditto il Picchi. **Macque** Seconde stravaganze. **Frescobaldi** Partite – XIV, sopra l'aria della Romanesca; VI, sopra l'aria di Follia; Cento Partite, sopra Passacagli. Toccata in A minor. **Rossi** Toccata settima. **Gesualdo** Canzon francese del Principe. **Valente** Tenore del passo e mezzo con sei mutanze. **Merulo** Susanne un jour.

Fleetness of finger, on which these early Italians set much store, is a requisite for performing this repertoire; and in this Sophie Yates is eminently accomplished. Another requisite is to convey a sense that the music is being improvised on the spur of the moment. This is especially so in toccatas but it also applies to some extent in the outwardly stricter form of *partite* or variations, the commonest structural basis for keyboard music of the time. Yates provides a firm framework for Frescobaldi's variations on the *Follia* ground bass, but while neatly pointing its rhythmic quirks allows herself greater freedom in the set on the *Romanesca*; and she clearly relishes the harmonic twists in the variations on *Passacagli*. Valente's variations on the *Passamezzo antico* are different in kind, more overtly dance-like and lively, with a strongly marked rhythmic accompaniment. There are two *canzone* – keyboard versions of songs – here: a highly elaborate working by Merulo of Lasso's famous *Susanne un jour*, and an extraordinary piece by Gesualdo which contains some weird and wonderful chromatic trills. The most developed of the toccatas here is that by Frescobaldi, which inserts a formal contrapuntal section into its otherwise free style. Not the least of the pleasures on this disc is Yates's vigorous playing of four tuneful dances by Frescobaldi's contemporary, Picchi, of whom little more is known other than that he was an organist in Venice: how this dazzling Toccata of his found its way into the Fitzwilliam Virginal Book is a minor mystery.

Consonanze stravaganti Neapolitan music for organ, harpsichord and chromatic harpsichord. **Christopher Stembridge** (hpd/org). Ars Musici Ⓟ AM1207-2 (68 minutes: DDD: 1/98). 🎵
This magnificent recital charts a relatively unexplored corner of Italian music, played on rare and beautiful Italian instruments (including exotic plucked keyboards with 'split' chromatic keys). The opening *Capriccio* by Giovanni de Macque is alone worth the price of admission. Christopher Stembridge draws more than other interpreters from this weird and wonderful repertory.

English Folksongs and Lute Songs [a]**Andreas Scholl** (alto); **Andreas Martin** (lte).
Harmonia Mundi Ⓟ HMC90 1603 (69 minutes: DDD: 9/96). Texts included. Recorded 1996.
Gramophone Editor's choice. ⓖ
Dowland The First Booke of Songs or Ayres – Can she excuse my wrongs?[a]; All ye, whom love or fortune[a]. The Second Booke of Songs or Ayres – I saw my Lady weepe[a]; Flow my teares fall from your springs[a]; Sorrow sorrow stay, lend true repentant tears[a]. The Third and Last Booke of

Songs or Ayres – Behold a wonder heere[a]; Me, me and none but me[a]; Say, loue, if euer thou did'st find[a]. The Lady Russell's pavan. Go from my window. **Campion** I care not for these ladies[a]. My love hath vow'd[a]. My sweetest Lesbia[a]. **Traditional** The three ravens[a]. O waly, waly[a]. I will give my love an apple[a]. Barbara Allen[a]. Lord Rendall[a]. **Anonymous** King Henry[a]. Kemp's jig. Go from my window[a].

'Interval' is not a word that has ever been inserted into a song recital on CD, but it would be quite a good idea if it were. In this instance the stopping-point hardly needs to be marked, as it is so natural and obvious; and that is one of the many attractions of this well-designed programme. A group of songs by Dowland, followed by a piece for lute, makes a substantial first section; then come two folk-songs, another couple by 'Anon.' and a lively, well-contrasted selection of songs by Campion. The second half starts with more Dowland, a satisfyingly representative sequence constituting the heart of the programme, with more folk-songs to conclude. The mixture is a charming one and delightfully well ordered. The performances are equally pleasing. Perhaps it is inevitable that an English listener should still think of Alfred Deller in this repertoire, but here the name comes to mind also because of a distinct similarity of timbre. At the resonant centre of Andreas Scholl's voice is a passage of lower middle notes (perhaps D to G) where the vibrancy is strong and rich in a way very comparable to Deller's. Stylistically, on the other hand, Scholl has developed an art that is quite independent of his great original: his manner is more forthright, less responsive to the spiritual intensity of *Sorrow sorrow stay*, though still capable of introducing that 'poisoned' intonation which Deller and his successors would bring to *All ye, whom love or fortune hath betrayed*. As regards balance, the lute is placed as the accompanying instrument rather than as one of an equal, intimate partnership; still, all is clear, and the lute solos are played with fine technical skill and sensitive feeling for the essential rhythmic flexibility.

The dark is my delight Brian Asawa (alto); David Tayler (lte). RCA Victor Red Seal
Ⓟ 09026 68818-2 (74 minutes: DDD: 12/97). Texts included. Recorded 1997.
Anonymous This merry pleasant spring. There were three ravens. The dark is my delight. Willow Song. Miserere my Maker. Where the bee sucks. O death, rock me asleep. **Campion** How hath Flora robb'd her bower. Ayres – Come let us sound with melodie the praises; Turne backe you wanton flier. Author of light, revive my dying spright. Oft have I sigh'd for him that heares me not. **Dowland** The First Book of Songs or Ayres – Can she excuse my wrongs with vertues cloake; Now, O now I needs must part; Go, Cristall teares; Come againe: sweet loue doth now enuite; His goulden locks time hath to siluer turnd; Awaie with these selfe louing lads. The Second Booke of Songs or Ayres – Flow my teares fall from your springs; Sorrow sorrow stay, lend true repentant teares; A Sheperd in a shade his plaining made. The Third and Last Book of Songs or Aires – Time stands still; It was a time when silly Bees could speake.
The singing here is most distinctive at a clear, forthright *forte*, most pleasing at a gentle *piano*. The impression is of a bright voice, unusually high-toned, quite unlike (say) Deller and Bowman. The programme is most welcome. Campion's melodic grace after Dowland's more complex utterance earns its place, and both find a happy follow-up in the mixed anonymous group. Asawa's mellower tones give pleasure in *Time stands still* and *Go, Cristall teares*. He measures up to many of the challenges in *Sorrow sorrow stay* and is sensitive to the modulations in Campion's *Oft have I sigh'd*. In the first of the 'popular' songs, *This merry pleasant Spring*, he introduces an admirable trill. David Tayler accompanies tastefull. It is regretable that the recording is marred by little bumps and bulges and that the voice and lute have an unequal share in the balance.

Alfred Deller Songs and Airs – Anonymous, Bedyngham, Campion, Ciconia, Dowland, R. Joynson, Morley, Purcell, Rosseter and J. Wilson. **Alfred Deller** (alto) with various artists. EMI Références mono Ⓜ CDH5 65501-2* (77 minutes: ADD: 5/96). From HMV originals; recorded 1949-54.
All but two of the pieces here are by English composers of the late sixteenth and seventeenth centuries; the odd ones out are Johannes Ciconia's *O rosa bella* and John Bedyngham's setting of the same text, which belong to the fourteenth and fifteenth centuries, respectively. Curiously, some of these recordings reveal Deller on rather less than top form. Dowland's *Slow my tears*, for instance, is marred by a persistent huskiness while certain others display a marked expressive restraint. But, almost needless to say, there is also plenty of vintage Deller here, in which category Morley's Shakespeare settings, *It was a lover and a lass* and *O Mistress mine*, certainly belong. Comparably affecting are Robert Johnson's *Full fathom five* and the celebrated anonymous setting of Desdemona's *Sing, willow, willow, willow*. Most touching of all, though, is the anonymous *Caleno custure me!* from *Henry V*, which Deller sings with exquisite sensibility. That and the popular *Greensleeves* would be quite sufficient on their own to make you go at once in search of this disc. Sadly, the Purcell songs seem rather dated, not so much for Deller's singing of them as for the archaic sound of the harpsichord, the tuning, and the playing of them, sometimes technically insecure and often with quaintly realized continuo lines. Notwithstanding these reservations, the anthology is a precious one, with moments of real magic. The transfers to CD have been remastered skilfully with virtually no background noise at all.

A High-Priz'd Noise Violin Music for Charles I. **Parley of Instruments Renaissance Violin Band /**
Peter Holman. Hyperion Ⓟ CDA66806 (67 minutes: DDD: 6/96). 🎷 Recorded 1995.   Ⓖ

R. Johnson II The Prince's Alman and Coranto. Air in G minor. The Temporiser a 4. The Witty Wanton. Fantasia in G minor. **A. Ferrabosco II** Pavan and Alman. **Webster** Four Consort pieces. **Nau** Suite in F major. Ballet in F major. Pavan and Galliard in D minor. **Notari** Variations on the "Ruggiero". **W. Lawes** Alman in D major "for the Violins of Two Trebles". Airs for consort.

This recording is less concerned with musical monuments, such as Lawes's large consorts, than in rejuvenating a repertoire which might have accompanied the King's recreation, or been the actual means for it. Most of the works are written in dance forms, though we can be reasonably certain that the majority would not have been conceived for accompanying dance. The violin's specific association with active dance music – except of a more base and popular kind – goes only so far, as the seventeenth century progresses. Of the courtly violin bands it is the more expansive one in the Presence Chamber (performing for public rather than private space at court) which has the most instantly appealing repertory – the opening set of works by Robert Johnson and the wonderful *Pavan and Alman* by Alphonso Ferrabosco II; the latter composition, although timeless in its exquisite part-writing, is given new life with a period violin band. Both pieces gleam with an engaging transparency, a compelling sound for those who have yet to hear this ensemble. The *Pavan* is magically forthcoming in its gracious lines with just a hint of melancholy, a poignant fragility which gives way to the noble rapture of the *Alman*. The Parley's 14-strong group of four violins, six violas and four bass violins is marshalled with a degree of characterization that gleefully extricates this music from dusty library shelves. A high-priz'd noise indeed, with further insights into our rich instrumental heritage, performed here with fragrance and deep affection.

The Masque of Oberon (reconstructed by Peter Holman and Peter Downley). Music by Augustine and Jerome Bassano, Ferrabosco II, Holborne, Holman, Johnson, Lübeck, Nelham and Thomsen. **Musicians of the Globe / Philip Pickett.** Philips Ⓟ 446 217-2PH (50 minutes: DDD: 10/97). Texts and translations included. Also contains a bonus promotional CD introducing the Musicians of the Globe and Philip Pickett. Recorded 1994.

Shakespeare's Musick Music by Byrd, Dowland, Farnaby, Johnson, Jones, Morley and Wilson. **Musicians of the Globe / Philip Pickett.** Philips Ⓟ 446 687-2PH (68 minutes: DDD: 10/97). Texts included. Contains the same bonus CD as mentioned above. Recorded 1995.

That the 'house musicians' to the Globe Theatre should be such an eminent band of specialists in sixteenth- and seventeenth-century performance is tantalizing in itself to theatre-goers. Of still greater musical significance are the projects which Philip Pickett, Artistic Director of the Musicians of the Globe, has put together for an exciting series of recordings for Philips. "The Masque of Oberon" is an ominous début, judging by its spirited instrumental playing and fragrant vocal contributions; this is a skilfully concocted 'reconstruction' by Peter Holman. The occasion celebrated here is New Year's Day, 1611, where Ben Jonson's *Masque of Prince Henries* was performed at the Banqueting House. The Prince Henry in question is, of course, James I's eldest son whose young life ended only a year later. This Masque is anything but prescient of approaching sadness, rather an excuse for an uplifting and eclectic celebration of dance. Although we know that Alphonso Ferrabosco II and Robert Johnson – both court musicians – wrote music for *Oberon*, most of the music has had to be patiently stitched together from contemporary sources. A curmudgeon would point out that there is no evidence that the majority of songs and dances were heard on this particular occasion. Such a view, however, limits the imaginative process of reaching beyond the fragmentary nature of masque sources and rediscovering something of the distinctive features of a celebrated indigenous genre. Through fine performances (Paul Agnew, amongst the soloists, stands out) and a thoroughly satisfying choice of instrumental music for the revels, Pickett and Holman have contributed something especially valuable to English recorded music. The Musicians of the Globe's second programme, "Shakespeare's Musick", is equally adventurous. Few original song settings survive though it is hard to imagine that a good proportion of dance music in 'neutral' sources would not have had theatrical connections. This is a sensitively devised programme with artistic merit well beyond its contextual *modus operandi*, and one which alerts us to the elusive and multi-faceted role of music in and around contemporary Shakespearean theatre.

Johnny, Cock thy Beaver [a]John Potter (sngr); [b]Richard Campbell (viol/bandora/gtr); [c]David Miller (lte/theorbo/gtr/cittern); **The Dufay Collective.** Chandos New Direction Ⓟ CHAN9446 (74 minutes: DDD). Texts and translations included. Recorded 1995.

Playford The English Dancing Master: Part 1 – Halfe Hannikin; Goddesses. Part 2 – Aye me; Saturday night and Sunday morn; Pauls Wharfe. Appendix – The Indian Queen; On the cold ground; Of noble race was Shinkin; A Morisco; Jamaica; The Waits; Ham House; Pell Mell; Kettledrum; Johnny, Cock thy Beaver. **Dowland** Settings of Ballads and Other Popular Tunes – My Lord Willoughby's Welcome Home, P66a[c]. **T. Simpson** Ricercar, "Bonny Sweet Robin"[bc]. Divisions[bc]. **Farnaby** Mal Sims. Muscadin. A Maske. The Old Spagnioletta. **T. Ravenscroft** There were three ravens[abc]. New oysters. Jolly Shepherd[a]. A wooing song of a Yeoman of Kents Sonne[ab]. Come follow me[a]. Of all the birds that I ever see[a]. **Anonymous** Daphne[ac]. Fortune my foe[bc]. Bonny Sweet Robin. Jamaica[abc]. The Clothiers Song[abc].

This kaleidoscopic programme gives an overview of popular music in Jacobean and Carolean England. It defines two levels of popularity – with the upper-middle classes and with the common people. The former centres mainly on the material of domestic music-making, the modest songs they would have sung, and the instrumental solo or consort music with which, in the absence of radio or television, the household might have entertained themselves (and maybe guests) in their leisure time. Amateurs and professionals may have rubbed shoulders in the more virtuoso consort music. The latter, the common people's music, embraces "dance tunes and ballads sold and learnt on the street or in the tavern". To the efforts of the unschooled man in the street were added those of municipal waits and itinerant players. The album's title, that of the last song, refers to the cap-raising of buskers when approaching potential 'clients'. The Dufay Collective have assembled a rich and varied collection of 25 items, played and sung with patent enthusiasm and considerable skill; the bowed-string sound sometimes has rough edges and a few notes are not quite centred, which, even if not regarded as a touch of 'authenticity', does not diminish the pleasure given by this splendid disc. The variety of the music and of the sounds made possible by the battery of instruments used, prevents the ear from settling into any kind of rut. This disc, then, is a gust of refreshing air.

A Handefull of Pleasant Delites Circa 1500 (Mhairi Lawson, sop; Nancy Hadden, fls; Erin Headley, va da gamba/lyra viol/vn; Vanessa Coode, va da gamba; Steven Player, gtr/lte; Jacob Heringman, lte/cittern/va da gamba; Lucy Carolan, hpd). ASV Gaudeamus Ⓔ CDGAU163 (65 minutes: DDD: 12/97). 🗡 Texts included. Recorded 1996.
Anonymous In a Garden so Grene. All in a Garden Green. Grein Greus ye Rasses. What Mightie Motion. Fortune my Foe. Lyke as the Lark. Turkeyloney-Lyke as the Dumb Solsequiem. Kypascie. I smile to see how you devise. Tom of Bedlam. Taladh Chriosta. Lancashire Pipes. Maid will you marrie?. **Dowland** Frogg galliard, P90 (arr. van Eyck). **Van Eyck** Crimson Velvet. Merry Cuckolds. Our Father which in Heaven art. **Pavlett** A Toye. **Alison:** Our Father which in Heaven art (two versions). **Collard** A Ground. **Tallis** Jam lucis orto sidere. **Susato** Danserye – Les quatre Branles. **Various** Improvisation: Passymeasures/The Lady Greensleeves.
The album title is that of a sixteenth-century collection of ballad poems and tunes, but those recorded here are taken from a wide variety of other sources. In such collections secular and sacred sat randomly side by side. Most ballad poems were sung to more than one tune, and many tunes appeared in instrumental versions, either as dances, sets of variations, or as ground basses. Circa 1500's disc reflects these diversities and this in itself is sufficient justification for the kaleidoscopic character of the programme. Mhairi Lawson has a clear voice and she sings without the cultivated artifice that might strain belief in her as a singer of ballads; her few archaic pronunciations are of archaic words but as the texts are printed these should not cause any head-scratching. A most enjoyable and informatively annotated recording.

Grand Tour Music from Sixteenth- and Seventeenth-Century Italy, Spain and Germany.
His Majestys Sagbutts and Cornetts (Jeremy West, cornett; David Staff, cornett/tpt; Susan Addison, Peter Bassano, Paul Nieman, Stephen Saunders, sackbuts; Timothy Roberts, org/hpd). Hyperion Ⓔ CDA66847 (69 minutes: DDD: 11/96). Recorded 1993-95.
Buonamente Sonata a 6. Canzona a 6. **Marini** Sinfonia grave: La Zorzi. Sonata a quattro. Sonata a 6. **Merula** Chiacona. **Macque** Seconde Stravaganze. **Bassano** Vestiva i colli. **Castello** Sonate concertate in still moderno – Sonata duodecima. **Peñalosa** O Domina sanctissima. **Correa de Arauxo** Tiento de segundo tono. **Ximénez** (arr. Roberts) Batalla de octavo tono. **Anonymous** (arr. Roberts) Canciones de clarines. **Weckmann** Toccata III. **Schein** Padoana in D minor. **Vierdanck** Sonata, "Als ich einmal Lust bekam". Sonata a 4. **Scheidt** Canzona super Cantionem Gallicam. Galliard battaglia a 5.
HMSC reads like an arcane government department but over the years this distinguished group has become deservedly recognized by its acronym for being consistently approachable. This skilfully constructed 'tour' of European consort activity in the sixteenth and seventeenth centuries is a case in point: whilst 14 largely unknown composers, performed on primitive instruments, can appear a mite unpromising for all but the *cognoscenti*, one only has to experience the variety of timbre, articulation and expressive nuance to realize that HMSC are, first and foremost, fine and imaginative chamber musicians. As Italy, the first port of call, reveals, in the right hands these instruments can resonate nobly with palpably rich textures in sonatas by the likes of Buonamente, tickle and tease in the modern monodic world of Marini, and dart about with easy and virtuosic precision in Bassano's sophisticated *Vestiva i colli*. Here and elsewhere the cornettists Jeremy West and David Staff exhibit a lucid and collected understanding of what makes good musical sense. Such a lead is deftly followed by the sackbuts – Susan Addison's in particular – whose lyrical side is heard to great effect in the Castello (the recorded sound differs from neighbouring numbers, a consequence, no doubt, of sessions spread out over two years). It is the easy dialogue of the ensemble, elasticity of phrasing and the capacity to shape the lines with colour and interest which repeatedly captivates; the Spanish selection contains an anonymous *Canciones* where Staff's natural trumpet gives an added spice to proceedings. The only misgiving is that the perspective of the ensemble is often a touch too sweet and refined in an idiom which would have needed a more rasping and redoubtable demeanour to be heard outside – where a good deal of this music would have been performed. Much of the success of HMSC is down to Timothy Roberts's sensitive arrangements, both preconceived and spontaneously at the keyboard; his realizations and contrapuntal reductions are always a joy, not to mention his solos which break up a well-paced programme.

Chansons et Danceries Piffaro (**Eric Anderson,** sackbuts/rec/crumhorn/perc; **Adam Gilbert,** shawm/recs/bagpipes; **Grant Herreid,** ltes/gtr/rec/perc; **Joan Kimball,** shawms/recs/crumhorn/ bagpipes; **Gwyn Roberts,** shawms/recs/fl/crumhorn; **Robert Wiemken,** shawms/dulcian/recs/ crumhorn/hurdy-gurdy/perc; **Tom Zajac,** sackbut/recs/bagpipes/tabor/hurdy-gurdy). Archiv Produktion ℗ 447 107-2AH (63 minutes: DDD). ✍ Recorded 1994.
Josquin Desprez Adieu mes amours. Se j'ay perdu mon amy. Baisez moy, ma doulce amye. **Gombert** Musae Jovis. Quant je suis au prez de mamye. **Gervaise** Allemandes. Pavane "Delles-tarpe" et Basse Dance. **Crecquillon** Pis ne me peult venir. Content desir. **P. Wilder** Amour partes. Une nonnain refaite. **Du Tertre** Premiere suytte de Bransles d'Escos. **Willaert** Ricercare. **Maillard** Regina coeli. **Sermisy** Languir me fais. Content desir. **Buus** Content desir. **Anonymous** Bransles de village. Bransles de chevaux. Content desir. A Suite of Dances.
Piffaro's handling of a plethora of wind instruments (supported on occasion by plucked strings, hurdy-gurdy and percussion) reflects the advances made in technical skill in the playing of these early instruments during the last two decades. Wind instruments were divided into 'loud' and 'soft' categories (for outdoor or indoor use) and varieties of both types of consort inhabit this recording. The focus here is on French music of vocal and instrumental origin, drawn from various sixteenth-century sources. There is convincing evidence that both loud and soft consorts played at the French court into the seventeenth century, and echoes of the simpler forms of this music are still to be heard in rural Brittany. All this, presented with consummate skill and stylishness, ensures that interest never flags for a moment in this very collectable disc.

Sit Fast, Volume 1. [a]**Michael Chance** (alto); [b]**Paul Agnew** (ten), **Fretwork** (Wendy Gillespie, Richard Campbell, Williams Hunt, Julia Hodgson, Susanna Pell, Richard Boothby, viols). Virgin Classics ℗ VC5 45217-2 (76 minutes: DDD: 12/97). ✍ Texts included. Recorded 1996.
B. Guy Buzz. **Isaac** O decus ecclesiae. **Ruders** Second Set of Changes. **Tan Dun** A Sinking Love[a]. **Tye** Sit fast. **Bainbridge** Henry's Mobile. **Beamish** in dreaming[b]. **A. Ferrabosco I** Hexachord fantasy. **Sculthorpe** Djilile. **Ockeghem** Ut heremita solus. **Bryars** In nomine. **Costello** Put away forbidden playthings.
Early Music Kronos Quartet (David Harrington, John Sherba, vns; Hank Dutt, va; Joan Jeanrenaud, vc); [a]**Marja Mutru** (harmonium); [b]**David Lamb** (bagpipes); [c]**Wu Man** (dzhong ruan/da ruan); [d]**Olov Johansson** (nyckelharpa); [e]**Judith Sherman** (drum); [f]**Huun-Huur Tu** (Kaigal-ool Khovalyg, vocals/igil; Anatoly Kuular, vocals/byzaanchi; Kongar-ool Ondar, vocals/ toschpuluur). Nonesuch ℗ 7559-79457-2 (69 minutes: DDD: 12/97). *Gramophone Editor's choice.* Recorded 1993-7.
Machaut Kyries I-III[a] (arr. Kronos). **Tye** Rachell's weepinge. Farewell my good one forever. **D. Lamb** Långdans efter Byfåns Mats[b]. **Dowland** Lachrimae Antiquae[c]. **Pärt** Psalom. **Partch** Two Studies on Ancient Greek Scales (arr. Johnson). **Body:** Long-Ge. **Cage:** Totem Ancestor (arr. Salzman). Quodlibet. **Kassia** Using the apostate tyrant as his tool (arr. Touliatos). **Hardin** Synchrony No. 2[e]. **Pérotin** Viderunt omnes (arr. Kronos). **Purcell** Fantasia in B flat major, Z736. **Hildegard of Bingen** O virtus sapientae (arr. Pfau). **Schnittke** Collected songs where every verse is filled with grief (arr. Kronos). **Traditional** Brudmarsch frå Osta[d] (arr. Marin). Uleg-Khem[f] (arr. Mackey). *Bells:* Tolling of the knell (St Peter's of Solesmes).
Guy and Ruders are united with six others in Fretwork's programme, which alternates the old with the new and introduces, along the way, such moreish miniatures as Peter Sculthorpe's hypnotic *Djilile* (Whistling-duck on a bilabong) – which swaps Purcellian cadences for an Aboriginal prompting – and Sally Beamish's highly imaginative *in dreaming,* based on words from Act 3 of Shakespeare's *The Tempest.* Gavin Bryars conjures the expected homogeneity for his 9'25" *In nomine* (after Purcell's six-part composition of the same name and the longest piece on the disc); Tan Dun breathes fire into the words of T'ang Dynasty poet, Li Po; Simon Bainbridge hints at (though never reveals) a fragment of one of Purcell's *fantasias* and Elvis Costello has countertenor Michael Chance sing us out with a text that "laments the interrupted access to the musical possibilities of the music of Purcell's time". Clever stuff, all of it; quietly compelling too, even occasionally abrasive. "Sit Fast" approximates a garlanded bridge across the centuries; it is superbly engineered and surely strong enough to sustain repeated journeys. While Fretwork take Henry Purcell as their starting point, Kronos's "Early Music" is subtitled *Lachrimae Antiquae* (after John Dowland) and is scarcely less absorbing. The Kronos Quartet adapt their playing style to suit whichever period is to hand – or at least that appears to be the general rule. Pérotin's multi-paragraph *Viderunt omnes* is delivered without vibrato and with the kind of phrasal emphases that any conscientious early music vocal group might employ, but Hildegard of Bingen's *O virtus sapientae* – which is an even earlier piece than the Pérotin – shimmers to expressive vibrato and great warmth of tone. The chordal clashes in Guillaume de Machaut (which serve throughout the disc as a sort of ritornello) emerge out of Cage, converge with Swedish folk music or transport us to one of Purcell's greatest *fantazias* (No. 2), while Christopher Tye prefaces Schnittke's searingly intense *Collected songs where every verse is filled with grief* and Schnittke himself fades to silence and the eventual *Tolling of the knell* The sequence is its own story, and the story itself will vary according to each listener's individual sensibilities or imagination. Both discs balance profundity and daring with a touch of flippancy, always with style and interpretative finesse but never merely for the sake of novelty.

Information

Manufacturers and Distributors

Entries are listed as follows: **Manufacturer** or **Label**—UK Distributor

ABC Classics Select
Accent Complete Record Co.
Albany Select
Almaviva Discovery Records
Altamira Altamira Records
Altarus Kingdom
Amon Ra (Saydisc) Harmonia Mundi
Amphion Recordings Priory
Analekta Koch International
APR Harmonia Mundi
Arabesque Seaford Music
Arbiter Complete Record Co.
Arcana One for You
Archiphon TradeLink Music Distribution
Archive Documents Complete
Record Co. /Michael G Thomas
Archiv Produktion PolyGram Record
Operations
Arc of Light Sony Music Entertainment
Argo PolyGram Record Operations
Aria Music Discovery Records
Arion Discovery Records
Ars Musici Carlton Home Entertainment
Arte Nova Classics BMG Conifer
Arts Music Complete Record Co.
ASV Select
Athene Priory
Attacca Babel Impetus
Auvidis Harmonia Mundi
Avid Masters Avid Records/BMG UK
Bayer TradeLink Music Distribution
Beecham Trust Sir Thomas Beecham Trust
Belart PolyGram Record Operations
Berlin Classics Complete Record Co.
Beulah Priory
Biddulph Complete Record Co.
BIS Select
Bongiovanni Kingdom
Bridge Koch International
British Music Society Priory/British Music
Society
Cala Complete Record Co.
Calig Priory
Calliope Harmonia Mundi
Campion Records DI Music
Capriccio Target
Carlton Classics Carlton Home
Entertainment
Catalyst BMG Conifer
CBC Records Kingdom
CBS Sony Music Entertainment
CdM Russian Season (Le Chant du Monde)
Harmonia Mundi
Celestial Harmonies Select
Centaur Complete Record Co.
Chandos Chandos
Channel Classics Koch International
Le Chant du Monde Harmonia Mundi
Chesky Discovery Records
Christophorus Discovery Records
Claremont Complete Record Co.
Clarinet Classics Select

Classical Collector (EPM) Discovery Record
Classic fM BMG Conifer
Classico DI Music
Classics for Pleasure EMI
Claves Complete Record Co.
Collegium Select
Collins Classics Complete Record Co.
Conifer Classics BMG Conifer
Continuum Select
CPO Select
CRD Complete Record Co.
Crystal Impetus
Cyprès Discovery Records
Dabringhaus und Grimm (MDG) Chandos
Danacord Discovery Records
Da Capo (Marco Polo) Select
Decca PolyGram Record Operations
Delos Nimbus
Denon Complete Record Co.
Deutsche Harmonia Mundi BMG Conifer
DG PolyGram Record Operations
Dinemec Classics Koch International
Dorian Priory
Doyen Recordings BMG Conifer
Dutton Laboratories Complete Record Co.
Dynamic Priory
Earthsounds Earthsounds
ECM New Series New Note
Edition Abseits DI Music
Elan Discovery Records
Elektra Nonesuch Warner Classics
EMI Eminence EMI
EMI EMI
L'Empreinte Digitale Harmonia Mundi
Erato Warner Classics
Etcetera Koch International
Everest Complete Record Co.
Finlandia Warner Classics
Forlane Target
Four Hands Music Discovery Records
René Gailly One for You
GIB Classics Koch International
Gimell PolyGram Record Operations
Globe Complete Record Co.
Glossa Harmonia Mundi
Guild Priory
Hänssler Classic Select
Happy Days BMG Conifer
Harmonia Mundi Harmonia Mundi
Hat-Hut Harmonia Mundi
Herald Select
Hungaroton Target
Hyperion Select
IMP Classics Carlton Home Entertainment
IMP Masters Carlton Home Entertainment
Isis Records Priory
Jade BMG UK
Jecklin Vanderbeek and Imrie
Kingdom Records Kingdom
Koch Classics Koch International
Koch Discover International Koch
International

Koch International Classics Koch International
Koch Schwann Koch International
Kontrapunkt Discovery Records
LaserLight (Capriccio) Target
Legato Classics Parsifal Distribution
Linn Records PolyGram Record Operations
L'Oiseau-Lyre PolyGram Record Operations
London PolyGram Record Operations
Lorelt (Lontano) Discovery Records
Lyrita Nimbus
Marco Polo Select
John Marks Records TradeLink Music Distribution
Marston Complete Record Co.
Melodiya BMG Conifer
Memoir Classics Target
Mercury PolyGram Record Operations
Meridian Nimbus
Metier Priory
Metronome Complete Record Co.
MGB Musiques Suisses Complete Record Co.
Milan BMG UK
Millenium Classics New Note/BMG UK
Mode Harmonia Mundi
Motette Priory
Multisonic Priory
Music and Arts Harmonia Mundi
Musica Oscura Complete Record Co.
Musica Sveciae Complete Record Co.
MusicMasters Nimbus
Myto Parsifal Distribution
Naim Audio Koch International
Naxos Select
New Albion Harmonia Mundi
New World Harmonia Mundi
Newport Classic DI Music
Nightingale Classics Koch International
Nimbus Nimbus
NMC Complete Record Co.
Nonesuch Warner Classics
Ode Discovery Records
Olympia Priory
Ondine Complete Record Co.
Onyx DI Music
Opera Rara Select
Opus 111 Select
Orfeo Chandos
Ottavo Priory
Pavane Kingdom
Pearl (Pavilion) Harmonia Mundi
Philips PolyGram Record Operations
Phono Suecia Impetus
Pianissimo Pianissimo
Pierre Verany Discovery Records
Point Music PolyGram Record Operations
Praga Harmonia Mundi
Preiser Harmonia Mundi
Priory Priory
ProudSound Abacus
RCA BMG Conifer
Redcliffe Recordings Complete Record Co.
Reference Recordings May Audio Marketing
Revelation Records Warner Classics
Ricercar Discovery Records
Romophone Complete Record Co.
Royal Opera House Records BMG Conifer

Royal Over-Seas League Royal Over-Seas League
RPO Records Carlton Home Entertainment
Russian Disc Koch International
Sain Sain
Signum Priory
Silva Screen Koch International
Simax Chandos
Somm Recordings Priory
Sony Classical Sony Music Entertainment
Stafford J. Martin Stafford
Stradivarius Priory
Supraphon Koch International
Symposium Records Symposium Records
Tahra Records Priory
Telarc BMG Conifer
Teldec Warner Classics
TER Classics Complete Record Co./MCI Presents
Testament Complete Record Co.
Tremula Symposium Records
Tring International Tring International/Priory
Unicorn-Kanchana Harmonia Mundi
Upbeat Classics Target
Usk Recordings Complete Record Co.
VAI Audio Parsifal Distribution
Vanguard Classics Complete Record Co.
Varèse Sarabande Pinnacle
Vintage Music Co. Target
Virgin Classics EMI
Wergo Harmonia Mundi
Winter & Winter Harmonia Mundi
3D Classics Discovery Records

For additional information on Manufacturers and Distributors, refer to the Label Distribution Directory published in *Gramophone*.

Record Company Names and Addresses

Unless otherwise indicated all the Companies listed below are based in the UK; addresses for
Record Companies from outside the UK are given, where available (telephone and fax numbers
should be prefixed with the appropriate international dialing code).

Abacus Exchequer Gate, Lincoln LN2 1PZ.
Telephone 01522 576647 fax 01522 560550

Accent Records Eikstraat 31, 1673 Beert,
BELGIUM.
Telephone 32 2 356 1878 fax 32 2 360 2718

Albany Records PO Box 12, Carnforth,
Lancashire LA5 9PD.
Telephone 01524 735873 fax 01524 736448

Almaviva Ximenez de Enciso 35, 41004 Sevilla,
SPAIN.
Telephone 34 5 421 0004 fax 34 5 421 8720

Altamira 40 Hewitt Road, Hornsey,
London N8 0BL.
Telephone 0181-340 1639 fax 0181-347 5075

Altarus Records *UK* Easton Dene, Bailbrook
Lane, Bath BA1 7AA.
Telephone 01225 852323 fax 01225 852523
USA 31 Conant Road, Ridgefield, CT 06877.
Telephone 1 203 438 8342

Amphion Recordings Norton Lodge, 109
Beverley Road, Norton-on-Derwent, Malton,
North Yorkshire YO17 9PH.
Telephone 01653 698372

Analekta 364 Rue Guy, Montreal, Quebec H3J
1S6 *CANADA.*
Telephone 1 514 939 0559 fax 1 514 939 0232

Appian Publications and Recordings (APR)
PO Box 1, Wark, Hexham, Northumberland
NE48 3EW.
Telephone 01434 220627 fax 01434 220628

Arabesque Recordings 32 West 39th Street,
11th Floor, New York, NY 10018, *USA.*
Telephone 1 212 730 5000 fax 1 212 730 8316

Arbiter PO Box 541336, Linden Hill Station,
New York, NY 11354-0104, *USA.*
Telephone 1 718 939 6971

Arcana 7 Rue de Valmy, 44000 Nantes,
FRANCE.
Telephone 33 2 5188 2337 fax 33 2 5188 2339

Archiv Produktion 22 St Peter's Square,
London W6 9NW.
Telephone 0181-910 5000 fax 0181-910 3132

Argo 22 St Peter's Square, London W6 9NW.
Telephone 0181-910 5000 fax 0181-910 3132

Disques Arion 36, Avenue Hoche, 75008
Paris, *FRANCE.*
Telephone 33 1 4563 7670 fax 33 1 4563 7954

Arte Nova Bedford House, 69-79 Fulham High
Street, London SW6 3JW.
Telephone 0171-384 7500 fax 0171-384 7922

ASV 1 Beaumont Avenue, London W14 9LP.
Telephone 0171-381 8747 fax 0171-385 2653

Athene (D&J Recording) 7 Felden Street,
London SW6 5AE.
Telephone 0171-736 9485 fax 0171-371 7087

Auvidis *FRANCE* 47 Avenue Paul Vaillant
Couturier, 94250 Gentilly.
Telephone 33 1 4615 8800 fax 33 1 4740 3685
UK 19-21 Nile Street, London N1 7LL.
Telephone 0171-253 0865 fax 0171-253 3237

Avid Records Unit 2, Boeing Way, Brent
Road, Southall, Middlesex UB2 5LD.
Telephone 0181-893 5767 fax 0181-893 5955

Bayer AG Ku-Mipine-Makrolon (Dept),
51368 Leverkusen, *GERMANY.*
Telephone 49 214 30 8507

Sir Thomas Beecham Trust The West Wing,
Denton House, Denton, Harleston, Norfolk
IP20 0AA. Telephone 01986 788780

Belart 22 St Peter's Square, London
W6 9NW.
Telephone 0181-910 5000 fax 0181-910 3132

Berlin Classics Edel Records,
Wichmannstraße 4, 22607 Hamburg,
GERMANY.
Telephone 49 40 890 850 fax 49 40 896 521

Biddulph Recordings 34 St George Street,
London W1R 0ND.
Telephone 0171-408 2458 fax 0171-495 6501

Grammofon AB BIS Bragevägen 2,
18264 Djursholm, *SWEDEN.*
Telephone 46 8 755 4100 fax 46 8 755 7676

BMG Conifer UK Bedford House,
69-79 Fulham High Street, London
SW6 3JW.
Telephone 0171-384 7500 fax 0171-384 7922

BMG UK Lyng Lane, West Bromwich,
West Midlands B70 7ST.
Telephone 0121-500 5678 fax 0121-553 6880

Bongiovanni Via Rizzoli 28/e, 40125
Bologna, *ITALY.*
Telephone 39 51 225 722 fax 39 51 226 128

Bridge Records GPO Box 1864, New York,
NY 10116, *USA.*
Telephone 1 914 654 9270 fax 1 914 636 1383

British Music Society 7 Tudor Gardens,
Upminster, Essex RM14 3DE.
Telephone 01708 224795

Cala Records 17 Shakespeare Gardens,
London N2 9LJ.
Telephone 0181-883 7306 fax 0181-365 3388

Calig Musik und Video Steinerne Furt 68-7
Augsburg 86167, *GERMANY.*
Telephone 49 821 7004 787 fax 49 821 7004 785

Calliope 14 Rue de la Justice, BP 40 433, 60;
Compiègne Cedex, *FRANCE.*
Telephone 33 3 4423 2765 fax 33 3 4486 8278

Campion Records 13 Bank Square, Wilmslc
Cheshire SK9 1AN.
Telephone 01625 527844 fax 01625 536101

Capriccio Delta Music, Sailerbachstraße 16,
83115 Neubeuern, *GERMANY.*
Telephone 49 8035 1047 fax 49 8035 1049

Caprice Records Box 1225, 111 82
Stockholm, *SWEDEN.*
Telephone 46 8 791 4600 fax 46 8 10 9992

Carlton Home Entertainment
The Waterfront, Elstree Road, Elstree,
Hertfordshire WD6 3BS.
Telephone 0181-207 6207 fax 0181-207 5789

Catalyst Bedford House, 69-79 Fulham High Street, London SW6 3JW.
Telephone 0171-384 7500 fax 0171-384 7922

CBC Records PO Box 500, Station A, Toronto, Ontario M5W 1E6, *CANADA*.
Telephone 1 416 205 3498 fax 1 416 205 2376

CBS Records *see* SONY MUSIC ENTERTAINMENT

Celestial Harmonies PO Box 30122, Tuscon, Arizona 85751, *USA*.
Telephone 1 602 326 4400 fax 1 602 326 3333

Centaur Records 8867 Highland Road, Suite 206, Baton Rouge, LA 70808, *USA*.
Telephone 1 504 336 4877 fax 1 504 336 9678

Chandos Records Chandos House, Commerce Way, Colchester, Essex CO2 8HQ.
Telephone 01206 225200 fax 01206 225201

Channel Classics Records Waaldijk 76, 4171 CG Herwijnen, *THE NETHERLANDS*.
Telephone 31 41858 1800 fax 31 41858 1782

Le Chant du Monde 31 Rue Vandrezanne, 75013 Paris, *FRANCE*.
Telephone 33 1 5380 0222 fax 33 1 5380 0225

Chesky Records 355 West 52nd Street, 6th Floor, New York, NY 10019-6239, *USA*.
Telephone 1 212 586 7799 fax 1 212 262 0814

Christophorus Heuauerweg 21, 69124 Heidelberg, *GERMANY*.
Telephone 49 6221 785011 fax 49 6221 783422

Claremont GSE Claremont Records, PO Box 250, Newlands 7725, *SOUTH AFRICA*.
Telephone 27 21 686 6915 fax 27 21 686 6043

Clarinet Classics 77 St Albans Avenue, London E6 4HH. Telephone/fax 0181-472 2057

Classic fM Bedford House, 69-79 Fulham High Street, London SW6 3JW.
Telephone 0171-384 7500 fax 0171-384 7922

Classico Sankt Knudsvej 8, 1903 Frederiksberg C, *DENMARK*.
Telephone 45 3123 4540 fax 45 3131 1497

Classics for Pleasure EMI House, Brook Green, London W6 7EF.
Telephone 0171-605 5000 fax 0171-605 5050

Claves Records Trüelweg 14, 3600 Thun, *SWITZERLAND*.
Telephone 41 33 223 1637 fax 41 33 222 8003

Collegium Records PO Box 172, Whittlesford, Cambridge CB2 4QZ.
Telephone 01223 832474 fax 01223 836723

Collins Classics Premier House, 10 Greycoat Place, London SW1P 1SB.
Telephone 0171-222 1921 fax 0171-222 1926

The Complete Record Co. 12 Pepys Court, 84 The Chase, London SW4 0NF.
Telephone 0171-498 9666 fax 0171-498 1828

Connoisseur Society In Sync Laboratories, 2211 Broadway, Suite 10E, New York, NY 10024, *USA*.
Telephone 1 212 873 6769 fax 1 212 787 9747

Continuum 20 Lochiel Road, Remuera, Auckland 5, *NEW ZEALAND*.
Telephone/fax 64 9 520 7499

CPO Lübeckerstraße 9, 49124 Georgsmarienhütte, *GERMANY*.
Telephone 49 5401 8510 fax 49 5401 851 299

CRD PO Box 26, Stanmore, Middlesex HA7 4XB.
Telephone 0181-958 7695 fax 0181-958 1415

Crystal Records 28818 NE Hancock Road, Camas, WA 98607, *USA*.
Telephone 1 360 834 7022 fax 1 360 834 9680

Dabringhaus und Grimm Bachstraße 35, 32756 Detmold, *GERMANY*.
Telephone 49 5231 24001 fax 49 5231 26186

Da Capo (Marco Polo) Christianshavns Torv 2, 1410 Copenhagen K, *DENMARK*.
Telephone 45 32 960 602 fax 45 32 962 602

Danacord Records Norregade 22, 1165 Copenhagen, *DENMARK*.
Telephone 45 33 151 716 fax 45 33 12 1514

Decca Classics 22 St Peter's Square, London W6 9NW.
Telephone 0181-910 5000 fax 0181-810 3132

Dell'Arte Records PO Box 26, Hampton, Middlesex TW12 2NL. Telephone 0181-979 2479

Delos International Hollywood and Vine Plaza, 1645 North Vine Street, Suite 340, Hollywood, California CA 90028, *USA*.
Telephone 1 213 962 2626 fax 1 213 962 2636

Denon/Nippon Columbia 14-14, Akasaka 4-Chome, Minatu-Ku, Tokyo 107-11, *JAPAN*.
Telephone 81 3 3584 8271 fax 81 3 3584 8135

Deutsche Grammophon 22 St Peter's Square, London W6 9NW.
Telephone 0181-910 5000 fax 0181-810 3132

Deutsche Harmonia Mundi BMG Classics Music, Kastenbauerstraße 2, 81677 München, *GERMANY*.
Telephone 49 89 41360 fax 49 89 4136160

DI Music 13 Bank Square, Wilmslow, Cheshire SK9 1AN.
Telephone 01625 527844 fax 01625 536101

Dinemec Classics 17 Boulevard Helvetique, PO Box 3704, Geneva 3, *SWITZERLAND*.
Telephone 41 22 349 2225 fax 41 22 349 8377

Discovery Records The Old Church Mission Room, King's Corner, Pewsey, Wiltshire SN9 5BS.
Telephone 01672 563931 fax 01672 563934

Dorian Recordings 8 Brunswick Road, Troy, NY 12180, *USA*.
Telephone 1 518 274 5475 fax 1 518 274 4276

Doyen Recordings Doyen House, 17 Coupland Close, Moorside, Oldham, Lancashire OL4 2TQ.
Telephone/fax 0161-628 3799

Dutton Laboratories PO Box 576, Harrow, Middlesex HA3 6YW.
Telephone 0181-421 1117 fax 0181-421 2998

Dynamic Via Mura Delle Chiappe 39, 16136 Genoa, *ITALY*.
Telephone 39 10 27 22884 fax 39 10 2139 37

Earthsounds PO Box 1, Richmond, North Yorkshire DL10 5GB.
Telephone 01748 825959 fax 01748 850218

ECM Postfach 600331, 81203 München, *GERMANY*.
Telephone 49 89 851048 fax 49 89 854 5652

Elan PO Box 101, Riverdale, Maryland 20738, *USA*.
Telephone 1 301 864 0499 fax 1 301 209 8573

EMI Records Customer Services Dept, 64 Baker Street, London W1M 1DJ.
Telephone 0171-467 2000 fax 0171-467 2243

EMI Sales & Distribution Centre, Hermes Close, Tachbrook Park, Leamington Spa, Warwickshire CV34 6RP. Telephone 01926 888888

L'Empreinte Digitale Domaine de la Garde, 13510 Eguilles, *FRANCE.* Telephone 33 4 4233 3324 fax 33 4 4233 3324

Erato *FRANCE* 50 Rue des Tournelles, 75003 Paris. Telephone 33 1 4027 7000 fax 33 1 4804 9543; *UK* The Warner Building, 28 Kensington Church Street, London W8 4EP. Telephone 0171-938 0167 fax 0171-938 3986

Etcetera Voorstraat 5, 2964 AH Groot-Amners, *THE NETHERLANDS.* Telephone 31 184 662 799 fax 31 184 662 040

Forlane 15 Rue de l'Ancienne Mairie, 92100 Boulogne Billancourt, *FRANCE.* Telephone 33 1 4825 0217 fax 33 1 4603 2547

Four Hands Music 15 Birchmead Close, St Albans, Herts AL3 6BS. Telephone/fax 01727 858485

René Gailly 12 Rue O Maesschalck, 1083 Brussels, *BELGIUM.* Telephone 32 2 2465 9870 fax 32 2 2465 6955

Gimell Records 22 St Peter's Square, London W6 9NW. Telephone 0181 910 5000 fax 0181 910 3132

Globe Tapuit 4, 1902 KP Castricum, *THE NETHERLANDS.* Telephone 31 2518 55584 fax 31 2516 59511

Glossa Timoteo Paradós 31, 28200 San Lorenzo de El Escorial, *SPAIN.* Telephone 34 1 896 1480 fax 34 1 896 1961

Guild Music *UK* PO Box 1425, Piermont House, 33-35 Pier Road, St Helier, Jersey JE4 8QZ. *SWITZERLAND* Wiesholzerstraße 42b, 8262 Ramsen. Telephone 41 52 743 1600 fax 41 52 743 1553

Hänssler Classic Postfach 12 20, 73762 Neuhausen, *GERMANY.* Telephone 49 7158 1770 fax 49 7158 177119

Harmonia Mundi: *UK* 19-21 Nile Street, London N1 7LL. Telephone 0171-253 0865 fax 0171-253 3237; *FRANCE* Mas de Vert, 13200 Arles. Telephone 33 4 9049 9049 fax 33 4 9049 9614; *USA* 2037 Granville Avenue, Los Angeles, CA 90025-6103. Telephone 1 310 478 1311 fax 1 310 996 1389

Hat-Hut Box 461, 4106 Therwil, *SWITZERLAND.* Telephone/fax 41 61 721 6655

Herald Audiovisual Publications The Studio, 29 Alfred Road, Farnham, Surrey GU9 8ND. Telephone 01252 725349 fax 01252 735567

Hungaroton Fotex Plaza, 1126 Budapest XII, *HUNGARY.* Telephone 36 1 201 5390 fax 36 1 202 3794

Hyperion Records PO Box 25, Eltham, London SE9 1AX. Telephone 0181-294 1166 fax 0181-294 1161

Impetus Distribution 10 High Street, Skigersta, Ness, Isle of Lewis, Outer Hebrides HS2 0TS. Telephone 01851 810808 fax 01851 810809

Isis Records 52 Argyle Street, Oxford, OX4 1SS. Telephone/fax 01865 726553

Editions Jade *UK* Bedford House, 69-79 Fulham High Street, London SW6 3JW. Telephone 0171-384 7500 fax 0171-384 7922; *FRANCE* 4 Rue Marivaux, 75002. Telephone 33 1 4488 7309 fax 33 1 4488 7316

Jecklin and Co Rämistraße 42, 8024 Zürich, *SWITZERLAND.* Telephone 41 1 261 7733 fax 41 1 251 4102

Kingdom Records 61 Collier Street, London N1 9BE. Telephone 0171-713 7788 fax 0171-713 0099

Koch Discover International 1 Grange House, 229 Stoke Newington Church Street, London N16 9HL. Telephone/fax 0171-241 6459

Koch International: *UK* Charlotte House, 87 Little Ealing Lane, London W5 4EH. Telephone 0181-832 1818 fax 0181-832 1808; *USA* 2 Tri-Harbor Court, Port Washington, New York, 11050-4617. Telephone 1 516 484 1000 fax 516 484 4746

Koch Schwann Lochhamerstraße 9, 82152 München-Martinsried, *GERMANY.* Telephone 49 89 857 950 fax 49 89 857 95100

Kontrapunkt PO Box 35, Slottsalleen 16, 2930 Klampenborg, *DENMARK.* Telephone 45 3964 4244 fax 45 31 3964 5044

K617 15 Avenue du Général de Gaulle, 57050 Ban St-Martin, *FRANCE.* Telephone 33 3 8732 4386 fax 33 3 8732 4389

Largo Records Hohenstaufenring 43-45, 50674 Köln, *GERMANY.* Telephone 49 221 240 2234 fax 49 221 240 2310

LaserLight Delta Music, Sailerbachstraße 16, 83115 Neubeuern, *GERMANY.* Telephone 49 8035 1047 fax 49 8035 1049

Legato Classics Lyric Distribution, 9 Albertson Avenue, New York, NY 11057, *USA.* Telephone 1 516 484 5100 fax 1 516 484 6561

Linn Records 257 Drakemire Drive, Castlemilk, Glasgow G45 9SZ. Telephone 0141-303 5189 fax 0141-631 1485

L'Oiseau-Lyre 22 St Peter's Square, London W6 9NW. Telephone 0181-910 5000 fax 0181-910 3132

London 22 St Peter's Square, London W6 9NW. Telephone 0181-910 5000 fax 0181-910 3132

Lontano Toynbee Studios, 28 Commercial Street, London E1 6LS. Telephone 0171-247 2950 fax 0171-247 2956

Lyrita 99 Green Lane, Burnham, Slough, Bucks SL1 8EG. Telephone 01628 604208

Marston 412 N. Chester Road, Swarthmore, PA 19081, *USA.* Telephone 1 610 690 1703 fax 1 610 328 6355

May Audio Marketing Aireside Mills, Cononley, Keighley, West Yorkshire BD20 8LW. Telephone 01535 632700 fax 01535 632887

MCI Presents 76 Dean Street, London W1V 5HA. Telephone 0171-396 8899 fax 0171-396 8903

Memoir Classics PO Box 66, Pinner, Middlesex HA5 2SA. Fax only 0181-866 7804

Mercury 22 St Peter's Square, London W6 9NW. Telephone 0181-910 5000 fax 0181-910 3132

Meridian Records PO Box 317, Eltham, London SE9 4SF. Telephone 0181-857 3213 fax 0181-857 0731

Metier Sound and Vision PO Box 270, Preston, Lancashire PR2 3LZ. Telephone 01772 866178

Metronome Productions Carrick Business Centre, Beacon House, Commercial Road, Penryn TR10 8AR. Telephone 01326 37738 fax 01326 378643

MGB Musiques Suisses Postfach 266, 8031 Zürich, *SWITZERLAND.* Telephone 41 1 277 2071 fax 41 1 277 2335

Editions Milan Music *UK* Bedford House, 69-79 Fulham High Street, London SW6 3JW. Telephone 0171-384 7500 fax 0171-384 7922; *FRANCE* 4 Rue Marivaux, 75002. Telephone 33 1 4488 7309 fax 33 1 4488 7316

Mode PO Box 375, Kew Gardens, New York, NY 11415, *USA.* Telephone 1 212 595 6089

Motette-Ursina Neusser Weg 63a, 40474 Düsseldorf, *GERMANY.* Telephone 49 211 434864

Multisonic Zirovnická 2389, 10632 Praha 10 *CZECH REPUBLIC.* Telephone 420 2 6718 2112 fax 420 2 74 9295

Music and Arts Programs of America PO Box 771, Berkeley, California CA 94701, *USA.* Telephone 1 510 525 4583 fax 1 510 524 5111

Musica Oscura 47 Leamington Road Villas, London W11 1HT. Telephone 0171-229 5142

Musica Sveciae Blasieholmstorg 8, 11148 Stockholm, *SWEDEN.* Telephone 46 8 611 0397 fax 46 8 611 8718

MusicMasters 1710 Highway 35, Ocean, NJ 07712-9885, *USA.* Telephone 1 908 531 3375 fax 1 908 531 1505

Naim Audio Southampton Road, Salisbury, Wiltshire SP1 2LN. Telephone 01722 33226 fax 01722 412034

New Albion Records 584 Castro Street, Suite 515, San Francisco, CA 94114, *USA.* Telephone 1 415 621 5757 fax 1 415621 4711

New Note Electron House, Cray Avenue, St Mary Cray, Orpington, Kent BR5 3RJ. Telephone 016898 77884 fax 016898 77891

New World Records 701 Seventh Avenue, 7th Floor, New York, NY 10036, *USA.* Telephone 1 212 302 0460 fax 1 212 944 1922

Newport Classic 106 Putnam Street, Providence, Rhode Island, RI 02909, *USA.* Telephone 1 401 421 8143 fax 1 401 421 8154

Nightingale Classics Nussdorferstraße 38, 1090 Wien, *AUSTRIA.* Telephone 43 1 310 4017 fax 43 1 310 4967

Nimbus Records Wyastone Leys, Monmouth, Gwent NP5 3SR. Telephone 01600 890682 fax 01600 890779

NMC Francis House, Francis Street, London SW1P 1DE. Telephone/fax 0171-828 3432

Nonesuch: *USA* 75 Rockefeller Plaza, New York NY 10019. Telephone 1 212 484 7200; *UK* The Warner Building, 28 Kensington Church Street, London W8 4EP. Telephone 0171-938 0167 fax 0171-938 3986

Ode Record Co 2 York Street, Parnell, Auckland, *NEW ZEALAND.* Telephone 64 9 358 5491 fax 64 9 309 5132

Olympia Compact Discs 31 Warple Way, London W3 0RX. Telephone 0181-743 6767 fax 0181-749 1300

Ondine Fredrikinkatu 77 A 2, 00100 Helsinki, *FINLAND.* Telephone 358 9 492 348 fax 358 9 493 956

One for You 56 Vincent Road, Norwich, Norfolk NR1 4HH. Telephone/fax 01603 701167

Opera Rara 134-146 Curtain Road, London EC2A 3AR. Telephone 0171-613 2358 fax 0171-613 2261

Opus 111 37 Rue Blomet, 75015 Paris, *FRANCE.* Telephone 33 1 4567 3344 fax 33 1 4567 3388

Opus 3 Firma Ljundinspelning Harpungränd 54, 17547 Järfälla, *SWEDEN.* Telephone 46 8 580 18686 fax 46 8 580 17420

Orfeo International Music Augustenstraße 79, 8000 München 2, *GERMANY.* Telephone 49 89 522031 fax 49 89 529190

Ottavo Recordings Westeinde 10, 2512HD Den Haag, *THE NETHERLANDS.* Telephone 31 70 346 9494 fax 31 70 346 9684

Parsifal Distribution 21-27 Seagrave Road, London SW6 1RP. Telephone 0171-381 1170 fax 0171-381 1172

Pavane Records 17 Rue Ravenstein, 1000 Bruxelles, *BELGIUM.* Telephone 32 2 513 0965 fax 32 2 514 2194

Pavilion Records Sparrows Green, Wadhurst, East Sussex TN5 6SJ. Telephone 01892 783591 fax 01892 784156

Philips Classics 22 St Peter's Square, London W6 9NW. Telephone 0181-910 5000 fax 0181-910 3132

Phono Suecia Box 27327, 10254 Stockholm, *SWEDEN.* Telephone 46 8 783 8800 fax 46 8 783 9510

Pianissimo Ridgeway Road, Pyrford, Woking, Surrey GU22 8PR. Telephone 01932 345371

Pinnacle Electron House, Cray Avenue, St Mary Cray, Orpington, Kent BR5 3RJ. Telephone 016898 70622 fax 01698 78269

PolyGram Classics and Jazz 22 St Peter's Square, London W6 9NW. Telephone 0181-910 5000 fax 0181-910 3132

PolyGram Record Operations PO Box 36, Clyde Works, Grove Road, Romford, Essex RM6 4QR. Telephone 0181-910 1799 fax 0181-910 1675

Preiser Fischerstiege 9, 1010 Wien, *AUSTRIA.* Telephone 43 1 553 6228 fax 43 1 553 4405

Priory Records Unit 9b, Upper Wingbury Courtyard, Wingrave, Nr. Aylesbury, Bucks HP22 4LW. Telephone 01296 682255 fax 01296 682275

ProudSound 61 Iffley Road, Oxford OX4 1EB. Telephone/fax 01865 723764

RCA Bedford House, 69-79 Fulham High Street, London SW6 3JW. Telephone 0171-384 7500 fax 0171-384 7922

Redcliffe Recordings 68 Barrowgate Road, London W4 4QU. Telephone 0181-995 1223

Reference Recordings Box 7725X,
San Francisco, California, CA 94107, *USA.*
Telephone 1 415 355 1892 fax 1 415 355 1949
Revelation Records 22 Tideway Yard,
125 Mortlake High Street, London
SW14 8SN.
Telephone 0181-878 1144 fax 0181-878 7667
Ricercar Disques Burnaumont 73 6890
Anloy-Libin, *BELGIUM.*
Telephone 32 61 656144 fax 32 61 656246
Romophone PO Box 717, Oxford OX2 7YU.
Telephone 01865 515353 fax 01865 515335
Royal Opera House Records *see* BMG Conifer
Royal Over-Seas League Over-Seas House,
Park Place, St James's Street, London
SW1A 1LR.
Telephone 0171-408 0214 fax 0171-499 6738
Russian Disc 577 Brown Brook Road,
Southbury, CT 06488, *USA.*
Telephone 1 203 264 4073 fax 1 203 264 4185
Sain Llandwrog, Caernarfon, Gwynedd
LL54 5TG.
Telephone 01286 831111 fax 01286 831497
Saydisc Chipping Manor, The Chipping,
Wotton-under-Edge, Gloucestershire
GL12 7AD.
Telephone 01453 845036 fax 01453 521056
Seaford Music 24 Pevensey Road, Eastbourne,
East Sussex BN21 3HP.
Telephone 01323 732553 fax 01323 417455
Select Music and Video Distributors
34a Holmethorpe Avenue, Holmethorpe
Estate, Redhill, Surrey RH1 2NN.
Telephone 01737 760020 fax 01737 766316
Silva Screen 3 Prowse Place, London
NW1 9PH.
Telephone 0171-428 5500 fax 0171-482 2385
Simax Akersgten 7, 0158 Oslo, *NORWAY.*
Telephone 47 2241 2400 fax 47 2241 5552
Somm Recordings 13 Riversdale Road,
Thames Ditton, Surrey KT7 0QL.
Telephone 0181-398 1586 fax 0181-339 0981
Sony Music Entertainment 10 Great
Marlborough Street, London W1V 2LP.
Telephone 0171-911 8200 fax 0171-911 8600
Sony Music Operations Rabans Lane,
Aylesbury, Buckinghamshire HP19 3RT.
Telephone 01296 395151 fax 01296 395551
J. Martin Stafford 298 Blossomfield Road,
Solihull, West Midlands B91 1TH.
Telephone 0121-711 1975
Stradivarius Via G Fantoli 7, 20138 Milano,
ITALY.
Telephone 39 2 55400 332 fax 39 2 55400 385
Supraphon Palackého 1, 11299 Praha 1,
CZECH REPUBLIC.
Telephone 420 2 24 225831 fax 420 2 24 228043
Symposium Records 36 Paul's Lane,
Overstrand, Cromer, North Norfolk
NR27 0PF. Telephone/fax 01263 579715
Tahra 1 Allée Georges Bizet, 95870 Bezons,
FRANCE.
Telephone 33 1 3961 2690 fax 33 1 3961 1908

Target Records 222 Cray Avenue, Orpington,
Kent BR5 3PZ.
Telephone 01689 888888 fax 01689 888800
Telarc International 23307 Commerce Park
Road, Cleveland, Ohio OH 44122, *USA.*
Telephone 1 216 464 2313 fax 1 216 464 4108
Teldec Classics The Warner Building, 28
Kensington Church Street, London W8 4EP.
Telephone 0171-938 0167 fax 0171-938 3986
TER Classics 107 Kentish Town Road,
London NW1 8PD.
Telephone 0171-485 9593 fax 0171-485 2282
Testament 14 Tootswood Road, Bromley,
Kent BR2 0PD.
Telephone 0181-464 5947 fax 0181-464 5352
Michael G. Thomas 5a Norfolk Place,
London W2 1QN. Telephone 0171-723 4935
Tremula 63 Sandringham Road, Maidenhead,
Berkshire SL6 7PL. Telephone 01628 29142
TradeLink Music Distribution 3 Regal Lane,
Soham, Ely, Cambridgeshire CB7 5BA.
Telephone 01353 722223 fax 01353 723733
Tring International Triangle Business Park,
Wendover Road, Aylesbury, Buckinghamshire
HP22 5BL.
Telephone 01296 615800 fax 01296 614250
Unicorn-Kanchana Records PO Box 339,
London W8 7TJ.
Telephone 0171-727 3881 fax 0171-243 1701
Upbeat Recordings Sutton Business Centre,
Restmor Way, Wallington, Surrey SM6 7AH.
Telephone 0181-773 1223 fax 0181-669 6752
Usk Recordings 26 Caterham Road, London
SE13 5AR. Telephone/fax 0181-318 2031
Vanderbeek and Imrie 15 Marvig, Lochs,
Isle of Lewis PA86 9QP.
Telephone/fax 01851 880216
VAI Audio Video Artists International,
109 Wheeler Avenue, Pleasantville, NY 10570,
USA.
Telephone 1 914 769 3691 fax 1 914 769 5407
Vanguard Classics Groningenhaven 18,
PO Box 1308, 3430 BH Nieuwegein,
THE NETHERLANDS.
Telephone 31 3402 88400 fax 31 3 402 88 452
Varèse Sarabande 11846 Ventura Boulevard,
Suite 130, Studio City, California CA 91604,
USA.
Telephone 1 818 753 4143 fax 1 818 753 7596
Disques Pierre Verany 36, Avenue Hoche,
75008 Paris, *FRANCE.*
Telephone 33 1 4563 7670 fax 33 1 4563 7954
Vintage Music Co. 372 St John Street,
London EC1V 4NN. Telephone 0171-837 7748
Virgin Classics 64 Baker Street, London
W1M 1DJ.
Telephone 0171-467 2000 fax 0171-467 2243
Warner Classics (UK) The Warner Building,
28 Kensington Church Street, London W8 4EP.
Telephone 0171-938 0167 fax 0171-938 3986
Wergo Postfach 3640, 55026 Mainz,
GERMANY.
Telephone 49 6131 246891 fax 49 6131 246212

Mudarra, Alonso

Muldowney, Dominic

Mulet, Henri

Murrill, Herbert

Muset, Colin

Mussorgsky, Modest